CHRYSLER CORPORATION—Continued

FORD MOTOR COMPANY—TAB 2

Page No.

R/CH

MOTOR
AUTO REPAIR MANUAL

CHRYSLER CORPORATION & FORD MOTOR COMPANY

58th Edition, Volume 2

First Printing

John R. Lypen, SAE
Editor

Marian A. Maasshoff, SAE
Managing Editor

Warren Schildknecht, SAE
Senior Editor

Richard G. Glover, SAE
Assistant Editor

Donald R. Cobb
Assistant Editor

Kirk D. Lashbrook
Electronic Data Manager

Brad A. Harris
Assistant Editor

Debra L. Bibb
Assistant Editor

Lynda Slater
Production Assistant

Daniel Reynolds
Assistant Editor

Thomas H. Nash
Assistant Editor

Richard F. Cahoon
Product Support Specialist

Michele L. Hawley
Assistant Editor

Scott E. Mason
Assistant Editor

Kristen Parsons
Graphic Development Specialist

James M. Pirkola
Assistant Editor

Donald J. Schall
Assistant Editor

Published by

MOTOR

A Division of Hearst Business Publishing, Inc.

5600 Crooks Road, Troy, MI 48098

Printed in the U.S.A.

VEHICLE IDENTIFICATION

INDEX

CHRYSLER DOMESTIC
V.I.N. DEFINED

1st POSITION
COUNTRY
1 = United States
2 = Canada
3 = Mexico
4 = United States

2nd POSITION
MAKE
B = Dodge
C = Chrysler
E = Eagle
P = Plymouth

3rd POSITION
VEHICLE TYPE
3 = Passenger Car
4 = Multipurpose Vehicle
7 = Truck

4th POSITION
RESTRAINT/G.V.W.R.
RESTRAINT
A = Dual Air Bags
A = Air Bag
A = Auto Belts & Driver Air Bag
B = Automatic Belts
B = Manual Belts
C = Automatic Belts
C = Manual Belts
E = Active, Passenger Air Bag
E = Manual Belts & Dual Air Bags
F = Manual Belts (Mexico)
H = HYBRID Air Bag
X = Air Bag, Passenger Manual
Y = Air Bag, Passenger Automatic
G.V.W.R.
D = 1-3000 LB
E = 3001-4000 LB
F = 4001-5000 LB
G = 5001-6000 LB

5th POSITION
CARLINE
A = LeBaron LE/Landau
A = Spirit/Spirit LE
A = Acclaim
C = New Yorker
C = Chrysler "LHS"
C = New Yorker Salon
C = Dynasty/Dynasty LE
D = Concorde
D = Intrepid
D = Vision
D = New Yorker
D = Chrysler "LHS"
F = Laser/Talon (FWD)
G = Laser/Talon (AWD)
H = Voyager/Grand Voyager (FWD)
H = Caravan/Grand Caravan (FWD)
H = Caravan CV (FWD)
H = Town & Country (FWD)
J = Stratus/Cirrus LXi
K = Voyager/Grand Voyager (AWD)
K = Caravan/Grand Caravan (AWD)
K = Caravan CV (AWD)
K = Town & Country (AWD)
K = Talon (FWD)

5th POSITION (CONTINUED)
L = Concorde
L = Talon (AWD)
M = LeBaron
P = Shadow/Shadow ES
P = Sundance/Duster
R = Viper
S = Laser/Talon (FWD)
S = Neon
T = Laser/Talon (AWD)
U = LeBaron/LeBaron LS
U = LeBaron GTC/Convertible
U = Sebring/Avenger
V = Imperial
V = New Yorker Fifth Ave
W = Daytona/Daytona ES
W = Daytona IROC
W = Daytona IROC R/T

6th POSITION
SERIES
1 = Economy (E)
2 = Low Line (L)
3 = Medium Line (M)
4 = High Line (H)
4 = Talon ESI
4 = Avenger
5 = Premium (P)
5 = Talon TSI (FWD)
5 = Sebring LXI
6 = Special/Sport (S)
6 = Sebring LX
7 = Performance/Image (X)
8 = Talon TSI (AWD)
8 = Avenger ES

7th POSITION
BODY STYLE
PASSENGER CAR
1 = 2 Door Coupe/Sedan
2 = 2 Door Pillared H.T.
4 = 2 Door Hatchback
4 = 3 Door Hatchback
5 = 2 Door Convertible
6 = 4 Door Sedan
7 = 4 Door Pillared H.T.
8 = 4 Door Hatchback
9 = 4 Door Wagon
TRUCK
1 = Van
4 = Extended Wagon/Van
5 = Wagon

8th POSITION
ENGINE CODE
A = 2.2-L4, 16V Turbo III
B = 2.5-L4, TBI
B = 1.8-L4, MFI
C = 2.0-L4, SFI
C = 2.2-L4, Turbo
D = 2.2-L4, TBI
E = 8.0-V10, MPI
E = 2.0-L4, MFI
E = 2.0-L4, MPI Turbo
F = 3.5-V6, 24V MPI
F = 2.0-L4, MFI Turbo
G = 2.4-V6, MPI
H = 2.5-L4, SPI
H = 2.5-V6, SFI

8th POSITION (CONTINUED)
J = 2.5-L4, Turbo
J = 3.3-V6, CNG
K = 2.5-L4, TBI
L = 3.8-V6, MPI
L = 3.8-V6, SFI
M = 2.5-L4, Eurostar Diesel
N = 2.0-L4, SFI-SOHC
P = 2.5-L4, SFI Turbo II
R = 3.3-V6, MPI
R = 2.0-L4, MPI
T = 1.8-L4, MPI
T = 3.3-V6, MPI
U = 2.0-L4, MPI Turbo
U = 3.3-V6, Flex Fuel MPI
V = 2.5-L4, Flex Fuel TBI
W = 2.5-L4, TBI
X = 2.4-L4, SFI
Y = 2.0-L4, SFI-DOHC
Y = 2.0-L4, MPI
2 = 2.5-L4, SFI Turbo
3 = 3.0-V6, MPI
9 = 54-KW, Electric

9th POSITION
CHECK DIGIT

10th POSITION
MODEL YEAR
N = 1992
P = 1993
R = 1994
S = 1995

11th POSITION
ASSEMBLY PLANT
A = CTC Preproduction Pilot
A = Outer Drive
D = Belvidere
E = Bloomington (DSM)
F = Newark
G = St. Louis-1
H = Bramalea
N = Sterling Heights
R = Windsor
T = Toluca
U = Eurostar
V = New Mack
X = St. Louis-2

12th Thru 17th POSITION
PRODUCTION SEQUENCE NUMBER

CHRYSLER IMPORTS
V.I.N. DEFINED

1st POSITION
COUNTRY
- J = Japan
- M = Thailand
- 4 = USA (Diamond Star Motors)

2nd POSITION
MAKE
- B = Dodge
- C = Chrysler
- E = Eagle
- J = Chrysler
- L = Dodge, Thailand
- N = Eagle, Thailand
- P = Plymouth

3rd POSITION
VEHICLE TYPE
- 3 = Passenger Car
- 4 = MPV
- 7 = Truck

4th POSITION
G.V.W.R. & RESTRAINT SYSTEM
PASSENGER CAR
- A = Air Bag
- A = Dual Air Bags
- B = Manual Belts
- B = Manual Belts (Driver Air Bag)
- C = Passive Belts
- D = Manual Belts
- E = Passive Belts (Driver Air Bag)
- X = Driver Air Bag

TRUCK or MPV
- D = 1-3000 LB
- E = 3001-4000 LB
- F = 4001-5000 LB
- G = 5001-6000 LB
- J = 1-3000 LB
- K = 3001-4000 LB
- L = 4001-5000 LB
- M = 5001-6000 LB

5th POSITION
LINE
PASSENGER CAR
- A = Summit DL & ESI
- A = Summit LX
- A = Colt E, Colt DL
- A = Colt Premier/Summit
- A = Colt 100/Vista (Canada)
- B = Colt Vista/Summit, FWD
- B = Summit DL & LX
- C = Conquest TSI
- C = Colt Vista/Summit, AWD
- C = Summit Wagon
- D = Stealth, Stealth ES & R/T
- E = Stealth R/T Turbo, AWD
- G = Colt Vista, 2WD
- H = Colt Vista, 4WD
- H = 2000 GTX
- M = Stealth & Stealth R/T, FWD
- N = Stealth & Stealth R/T, AWD
- R = 2000 GTX
- U = Colt, Colt E
- U = Colt 200 (Canada)
- U = Colt GT, Summit
- U = Colt GL

5th POSITION (CONTINUED)
- U = Summit DL & LX
- U = Summit ES
- V = Colt DL Wagon, 2WD
- V = Summit Wagon, 2WD
- V = Colt Vista (2WD), Summit
- W = Colt DL Wagon, AWD
- W = Summit Wagon, AWD
- W = Colt Vista, AWD
- X = 2000 GTX, AWD

TRUCK
- J = Raider
- L = Ram 50, Custom & SE
- L = Ram 50 Sport
- L = Power Ram 50 SE & LE
- M = Power Ram 50
- M = Power Ram 50 SE & LE
- M = Power Ram 50 Custom
- M = Power Ram 50 Sport

6th POSITION
SERIES
- 1 = (E) Economy (S)
- 1 = Colt, Summit (E)
- 2 = Low (Base) (L)
- 2 = Colt GL, Summit ES (L)
- 3 = Medium (M)
- 3 = Colt Vista, 2WD (H)
- 3 = Colt Vista, 4WD (M)
- 3 = Summit DL (H)
- 3 = Summit, AWD (M)
- 4 = High (H)
- 4 = Stealth, Summit LX (H)
- 4 = Colt Vista SE (L)
- 5 = Premium (P)
- 5 = Sports (S)
- 5 = Stealth ES (T)
- 6 = Special/Sport (S)
- 6 = Stealth R/T (R)
- 7 = Performance/Image (X)
- 7 = Ultimate (U)
- 7 = Stealth R/T Turbo (U)
- 8 = Sports Line (T)

7th POSITION
BODY STYLE
PASSENGER CAR
- 0 = 4 Door Wagon
- 1 = 2 Door Sedan
- 1 = 2 Door Coupe
- 4 = 2 Door Hatchback
- 4 = 3 Door Hatchback
- 4 = Colt, Colt GL, Summit
- 4 = 2 Door Pillard H.T.
- 6 = 4 Door Sedan
- 6 = Summit, Summit ES
- 9 = 4 Door Wagon
- 9 = 5 Door Wagon

TRUCK
- 3 = Van
- 4 = Conventional Cab-Short
- 5 = Club Cab
- 5 = Extended Cab-Long
- 9 = Conventional Cab-Long

MPV
- 1 = 4 Door Wagon
- 1 = 5 Door Wagon
- 3 = 3 Door Metal Top
- 4 = 4 Door Wagon

8th POSITION
ENGINE CODE
- A = 1.5L, 3 Valve MPI
- B = 1.8L, MPI
- B = 2.0L, DOHC MPI
- B = 3.0L, DOHC MPI
- C = 1.8L, MPI
- C = 3.0L, DOHC Turbo
- D = 2.0L, Gas
- D = 1.8L, MPI
- E = 2.0L, MPI
- E = 2.6L, Gas
- F = 1.6L, Turbo
- F = 2.0L, MPI Turbo
- G = 2.4L, MPI
- H = 2.6L, Turbo
- H = 3.0L
- J = 3.0L, DOHC-MPI
- K = 1.5L, Gas
- K = 3.0L, DOHC-MPI-Turbo
- L = 2.4L, DOHC
- M = 3.5L, DOHC
- N = 2.6L, Turbo-Intercooler
- P = 1.5L, MPI
- R = 2.0L, DOHC MPI
- S = 3.0L, MPI-18 Valve
- T = 1.8L, MPI
- U = 2.0L, DOHC-MPI-Turbo
- V = 2.0L, MPI
- W = 2.4L, MPI
- X = 1.5L, MPI
- Y = 1.6L, DOHC MPI
- Z = 1.6L, DOHC Turbo

9th POSITION
CHECK DIGIT

10th POSITION
MODEL YEAR
- H = 1987
- J = 1988
- K = 1989
- L = 1990
- M = 1991
- N = 1992
- P = 1993
- R = 1994
- S = 1995

11th POSITION
ASSEMBLY PLANT
- A = Misushima-2
- E = Bloomington (DSM), USA
- G = Thailand
- J = Nagoya-3
- O = Thailand
- P = Nagoya-2
- U = Mizushima-1
- Y = Nagoya-1
- Z = Okazaki

12th Thru 17th POSITION
PRODUCTION SEQUENCE NUMBER

1992–94 FORD MOTOR CO.
V.I.N. DEFINED

1st POSITION
COUNTRY
- 1 = United States
- 2 = Canada
- 3 = South America
- 3 = Mexico
- 4 = United States
- 6 = Australia
- 9 = Brazil
- J = Japan
- K = Korea
- L = Taiwan
- W = Germany

2nd POSITION
MAKE
- B = Ford
- C = Ford
- C = Imported Truck
- F = Ford
- F = Mazda
- F = Mercury
- L = Lincoln
- M = Mercury
- N = Continental
- N = Ford
- Z = Ford

3rd POSITION
TYPE
- A = Passenger Car
- A = Imported Mercury Tracer
- B = Bus
- B = Passenger Car
- C = Truck, Stripped Chassis
- C = Basic, Stripped Chassis
- D = Incomplete Vehicle
- E = Passenger Car
- F = Equiped Without Power Train
- F = Imported, Incomplete Truck
- H = Incomplete Vehicle
- I = Passenger Car
- J = Incomplete Vehicle
- J = Passenger Car
- J = Imported Car, Festiva
- M = Multi Purpose Vehicle
- N = Passenger Car
- P = Passenger Car, Imported
- R = Passenger Car
- T = Truck, Complete
- V = Passenger Car
- 0 = Imported - Fiesta
- 1 = Imported - Merker/Scorpio
- 1 = Passenger Car, Imported
- 2 = Courier - Complete
- 2 = Multi Purpose Vehicle
- 3 = Incomplete Vehicle
- 4 = Multi Purpose Vehicle
- 4 = Courier - Incomplete
- 4 = Truck, Complete
- 6 = Imported - Festiva

4th POSITION
RESTRAINT SYSTEM
- B = Active Belts
- C = Air Bags & Active Belts
- D = Active Belts
- L = Air Bags & Active Belts
- P = Passive & Active Belts

5th POSITION
IDENTIFICATION
- M = Lincoln/Mercury Make
- P = Passenger Car (82-89)
- P = Ford Make (90-94)
- T = Imported & Non-Ford Built

6th & 7th POSITION
BODY SERIES NUMBER
See The Following Three Pages

8th POSITION
ENGINE CODE
- A = 2.3-L4, EFI/OHC
- A = 2.0-L4, MFI, Mazda (93-94)
- B = 3.3-V6, 1 Barrel
- B = 2.5-V6, MFI, Mazda (93-94)
- C = 2.2-L4, EFI (89-92)
- C = 3.8-V6, 2 Barrel (84-86)
- C = 3.8-V6, EFI (87-90)
- C = 3.8-V6, Supercharged (90)
- D = 2.3-L4, EFI/Turbo (83)
- D = 2.5-L4, CFI (86-90)
- D = 5.0-V8, MFI (93-94)
- E = 5.0-V8, EFI/HO
- E = 5.0-V8, MFI/HO (93)
- F = 5.0-V8, CFI/EFI
- G = 5.8-V8, 2 Barrel
- H = 1.3-L4, EFI, Mazda
- H = 1.3-L4, MFI, Mazda (93-94)
- H = 2.0-L4, Diesel
- J = 1.9-L4, CVH SEFI (93-94)
- J = 1.9-L4, SFI
- K = 1.3-L4, 2-V, Mazda
- K = 1.9-L4, HO-CVH-SEFI (94)
- L = 2.4-V6, Diesel/Turbo (84-85)
- L = 2.2-L4, EFI/TC (89-92)
- L = 2.2-L4, MFI/TC (93)
- M = 5.0-V8, CFI or EFI/High Output
- M = 2.3-L4, EFI (91-92)
- M = 2.3-L4, MFI (93)
- N = 2.5-L4, EFI
- N = 3.2-V6, DOHC (93)
- P = 2.3-L4, EFI/TC
- P = 3.2-V6, SHO DOHC (93-94)
- R = 2.3-L4, HSC (83-85)
- R = 2.2-L4, EFI/Turbo (89-90)
- R = 3.8-V6, OHV
- S = 2.3-L4, HSC/CFI/High Output/EFI
- T = 2.3-L4, EFI/Turbo/IC
- T = 5.0-V8, EFI (91-92)
- T = 5.0-V8, MFI (93-94)
- U = 3.0-V6, EFI
- U = 3.0-V6, MFI (93-94)
- V = 2.9-V6, Fuel Injected
- V = 4.6-V8, MFI (93-94)
- W = 2.3-L4, EFI/Turbo
- W = 4.6-V8, EFI (91-92)
- W = 4.6-V8, MFI (93-94)
- X = 3.3-V6, Fuel Injected
- X = 2.3-L4, HSC/CFI/EFI
- X = 2.3-L4, MFI (93-94)
- Y = 3.0-V6, SHO/EFI
- Y = 3.0-V6, MFI (93-94)
- Z = 1.6-L4, EFI/Mazda (91-92)
- Z = 1.6-L4, MFI (93-94)
- 1 = 1.3-L4, Fuel Injected
- 1 = 3.0-V6, MFI Flex Fuel (93-94)
- 2 = 1.6-L4, Fuel Injected
- 3 = 3.8-V6, CFI

8th POSITION (CONT'D)
- 3 = 3.8-V6, 2 Barrel (Canada)
- 4 = 1.6-L4, FI/High Output (83-85)
- 4 = 3.8-V6, EFI/SEFI (87-92)
- 4 = 3.8-V6, MFI (93-94)
- 5 = 1.6-L4, EFI/Mazda
- 6 = 1.6-L4, EFI/Turbo
- 6 = 2.3-L4, Propane
- 6 = 1.6-L4, EFI/TC/Mazda (91-92)
- 6 = 1.6-L4, MFI/TC/Mazda (93-94)
- 7 = 1.6-L4, Methanol/High Output
- 8 = 1.6-L4, EFI/Turbo
- 8 = 1.8-L4, EFI/Mazda
- 8 = 1.8-L4, MFI/Mazda (93-94)
- 9 = 1.9-L4, CFI

9th POSITION
CHECK DIGIT

10th POSITION
MODEL YEAR
- C = 1982
- D = 1983
- E = 1984
- F = 1985
- G = 1986
- H = 1987
- J = 1988
- K = 1989
- L = 1990
- M = 1991
- N = 1992
- P = 1993
- R = 1994

11th POSITION
ASSEMBLY PLANT
- A = Atlanta, GA
- B = Oakville, Ontario, Canada
- D = Avon Lake, OH
- E = Mahwah
- E = Niehl, West Germany
- F = Dearborn, MI
- G = Chicago, IL
- H = Lorain, OH
- J = Los Angeles, CA
- J = Monterrey
- K = Kansas City, MO
- M = West Germany
- N = Norfolk, VA
- P = Twin Cities, MN
- R = Hermosillo, Mexico
- R = San Jose, CA
- S = Allen Park, MI
- T = Metuchen, WI
- T = Edison
- U = Louisville, KY
- W = Wayne, MI
- X = St. Thomas, Canada
- Y = Wixom, MI
- Z = St. Louis, MO
- 2 = Taiwan
- 5 = Flat Rock, MI
- 6 = Kia, Korea
- 8 = Broadmeadows, Australia

12th Thru 17th POSITION
PRODUCTION SEQUENCE NUMBER

VEHICLE IDENTIFICATION

1995 FORD MOTOR CO.
V.I.N. DEFINED

1st POSITION
COUNTRY
- 1 = United States
- 2 = Canada
- 3 = Mexico
- 4 = United States
- 9 = Brazil
- J = Japan
- K = Korea
- L = Taiwan

2nd POSITION
MAKE
- B = Ford
- C = Ford
- F = Ford
- F = Mazda
- F = Mercury
- L = Lincoln
- M = Mercury
- N = Continental
- N = Ford
- N = Nissan
- Z = Ford

3rd POSITION
TYPE
- A = Passenger Car
- A = Imported Mercury Tracer
- B = Bus
- C = Basic, Stripped Chassis
- D = Incomplete Vehicle
- E = Passenger Car
- F = Equiped Without Power Train
- F = Imported, Incomplete Truck
- H = Incomplete Vehicle
- I = Passenger Car
- J = Incomplete Vehicle
- J = Passenger Car
- J = Imported Car, Aspire
- M = Multi Purpose Vehicle
- N = Passenger Car
- P = Passenger Car, Imported
- T = Basic, Complete
- T = Truck, Complete
- V = Passenger Car
- 2 = Multi Purpose Vehicle
- 3 = Incomplete Vehicle
- 4 = Truck, Complete

4th POSITION
RESTRAINT SYSTEM
- A = Active Driver, Passive Passenger
- A = Active Rear & Driver Air Bag
- B = Active Belts
- C = Air Bags & Active Belts
- D = Active Belts
- L = Air Bags & Active Belts
- P = Passive & Active Belts
- R = Passive, Active & Driver Air Bag
- S = Passive, Active & Dual Air Bags

5th POSITION
IDENTIFICATION
- M = Lincoln/Mercury Make
- P = Ford Make
- T = Imported & Non-Ford Built

6th & 7th POSITION
BODY SERIES NUMBER
See The Body Series Pages

8th POSITION
ENGINE CODE
- A = 2.0-L4, MFI, Mazda
- B = 2.5-V6, MFI, Mazda
- D = 5.0-V8, MFI
- H = 1.3-L4, MFI, Mazda
- J = 1.9-L4, CVH SEFI
- K = 1.9-L4, HO-CVH-SEFI
- L = 2.5-V6, MFI
- P = 3.2-V6, SHO DOHC
- R = 3.8-V6, OHV
- T = 5.0-V8, MFI
- U = 3.0-V6, MFI
- V = 4.6-V8, MFI
- W = 4.6-V8, MFI
- X = 2.3-L4, MFI
- Y = 3.0-V6, MFI, Yamaha
- Z = 1.6-L4, MFI, Mazda
- 1 = 3.0-V6, MFI Flex Fuel
- 3 = 2.0-L4, MFI-ZETA
- 4 = 3.8-V6, MFI-SEFI
- 6 = 1.6-L4, MFI/TC, Mazda
- 8 = 1.8-L4, MFI, Mazda
- 9 = 4.6-V8, Natural Gas

9th POSITION
CHECK DIGIT

10th POSITION
MODEL YEAR
- S = 1995

11th POSITION
ASSEMBLY PLANT
- A = Atlanta, GA
- F = Dearborn, MI
- G = Chicago, IL
- H = Lorain, OH
- K = Kansas City, MO
- M = Cuautitlan
- R = Hermosillo, Mexico
- S = Allen Park, MI
- W = Wayne, MI
- X = St. Thomas, Canada
- Y = Wixom, MI
- 5 = Flat Rock, MI
- 6 = Kia, Korea
- 8 = Broadmeadows, Australia

12th Thru 17th POSITION
PRODUCTION SEQUENCE NUMBER

AIR BAG SYSTEM PRECAUTIONS

TABLE OF CONTENTS

Chrysler Corporation

INDEX

AIR BAG SYSTEM DISARMING

It may be necessary to access and record all diagnostic trouble codes prior to disarming the Supplemental Restraint System (SRS).

1. Place ignition switch in lock position.
2. Disconnect and tape battery ground cable connector.
3. **Wait at least 2 minutes after dis-** connecting battery ground cable before doing any further work on vehicle. The SRS system is designed to retain enough voltage to deploy air bag for a short time even after battery has been disconnected.

AIR BAG SYSTEM ARMING

1. Connect battery ground cable.
2. From passenger side of vehicle, turn ignition switch to On position.
3. SRS warning light should illuminate for 6 to 8 seconds, then remain off for at least 45 seconds to indicate SRS system is functioning correctly.
4. If SRS indicator does not perform as described, refer to "Passive Restraints" section of this manual.

Ford Motor Company

INDEX

AIR BAG SYSTEM DISARMING

On models with passenger side air bag, both air bag modules must be disconnected to properly disarm system.

CAPRI

1992

1. Disconnect battery ground cable and battery back-up power supply.
2. Remove four nut and washer assemblies securing air bag to steering wheel.
3. Carefully disconnect air bag connector from clockspring.
4. **On models with passenger side air bag,** open glove compartment and rotate completely down past stops. Carefully disconnect passenger air bag connector.
5. **On all models,** attach a jumper wire to the air bag terminals on driver air bag clockspring, **Fig. 1.**
6. **On models with passenger side air bag,** install a jumper wire between the air bag terminals on wiring harness side of passenger air bag connector.
7. **On all models,** connect battery ground cable and back-up power supply.

1993
Early Production

1. Disconnect positive battery cable and back-up power supply.
2. Remove four nut and washer assemblies retaining air bag module to steering wheel.
3. Disconnect air bag connector.
4. Connect Rotunda air bag simulator tool No. 105-00008 or equivalent, to clockspring connector in base of steering wheel.
5. Connect positive battery cable and back-up power supply.

Late Production

1. Disconnect battery ground cable.
2. Wait one minute for back-up power supply to deplete stored energy.
3. Remove four bolts retaining air bag module to steering wheel.
4. Disconnect air bag connector.
5. Connect Rotunda air bag simulator tool No. 105-00008 or equivalent, to vehicle harness at top of steering column.
6. Connect battery ground cable.

1994

Refer to "Escort & Tracer" in this section for air bag disarming procedures.

MARK VII

1. Disconnect battery positive cable.

2. Remove four nut and washer assemblies retaining driver air bag module to steering wheel.
3. Carefully disconnect air bag module connector.
4. Attach Rotunda air bag simulator tool No. 105-00008 or equivalent, on clockspring to simulate air bag.
5. Connect battery positive cable.

MARK VIII

1. **On 1993 models,** disconnect battery positive cable.
2. **On 1994 models,** disconnect battery ground cable, then the battery positive cable.
3. **On 1995 models,** disconnect battery ground cable.
4. **On all models,** wait one minute for back-up power supply to discharge.
5. Remove two screw and washer assemblies retaining driver air bag module to the steering wheel.
6. Disconnect driver air bag module connector.
7. Connect Rotunda air bag simulator tool No. 105-00010 or equivalent to vehicle harness at top of steering column.
8. Remove passenger air bag as follows:
   a. Remove righthand and lefthand finish panels.
   b. Open glove compartment, press sides inward and lower glove compartment to floor.
   c. Working through glove compartment opening, remove two lower air bag module retaining bolts.
   d. Remove three remaining air bag module retaining screws from side of air bag cover.
   e. Disconnect electrical connector attached to lefthand side of air bag while removing air bag module.
9. Install Rotunda air bag simulator tool No. 105-00010 or equivalent on vehicle air bag harness connector in place of air bag.
10. **On 1993 models,** connect battery positive cable.
11. **On 1994 models,** connect battery positive cable, then the battery ground cable.
12. **On 1995 models,** connect battery ground cable.

CONTINENTAL

1. Disconnect battery positive cable
2. Wait one minute for back-up power supply to deplete.
3. Remove four nut and washer assemblies retaining driver air bag module to the steering wheel.
4. Disconnect driver air bag module connector.
5. Open glove compartment and rotate completely past stops. Disconnect passenger air bag connector.
6. On 1992 models, attach Rotunda air bag simulator tool No. 105-00008 or equivalent to air bag terminals on clockspring assembly to simulate air bag.
7. On 1993-95 models, attach Rotunda air bag simulator tool No. 105-00010 or equivalent to air bag terminals on clockspring assembly to simulate air

Fig. 1   Air bag jumper wire connections

bag.
8. **On 1992 models,** attach Rotunda air bag simulator tool No. 105-00008 or equivalent to air bag terminals on wiring harness side of passenger air bag module connector.
9. **On 1993-95 models,** attach Rotunda air bag simulator tool No. 105-00010 or equivalent to air bag terminals on wiring harness side of passenger air bag module connector.
10. **On all models,** connect positive battery cable.

CONTOUR & MYSTIQUE

1. Disconnect battery ground cable, then disconnect battery positive cable and allow at least one minute for back-up power supply to deplete.
2. Remove five retaining screws and steering column shrouds from column tube, then rotate steering wheel as necessary to access and remove air bag retaining bolts.
3. Disconnect driver side air bag module connector, then carefully remove module from vehicle. **To prevent injury by accidental deployment, place module on a bench with trim cover facing upward.**
4. Connect Rotunda air bag simulator tool No. 105-00010 or equivalent to air bag sliding contact connector at top of steering column.
5. Open glove compartment, then lower compartment to floor by pressing inward on sides.
6. Remove four screws, then disconnect glove compartment lamp and remove compartment upper cover.
7. Remove A/C evaporator register duct, then remove two retaining nuts from passenger side air bag module.
8. Remove two bolts from passenger side air bag module, then disconnect electrical connector and carefully remove module from vehicle. **To prevent injury from accidental deployment, place module on a bench with trim cover facing upward.**
9. Connect a second air bag simulator tool (Rotunda tool No. 105-00010 or equivalent) to passenger side air bag module wiring harness.
10. Reconnect positive battery cable, then the ground cable.

COUGAR & THUNDERBIRD

1. Disconnect battery ground cable, then the battery positive cable.
2. Wait approximately one minute for back-up power supply to discharge.

3. Remove two bolt and washer assemblies retaining driver side air bag assembly to steering wheel.
4. Disconnect driver side air bag connector, then remove air bag from steering wheel. Position air bag module on work bench with trim cover facing upward.
5. Connect Rotunda air bag simulator tool No. 105-00010 or equivalent to vehicle air bag wiring harness at top of steering column.
6. Remove passenger side air bag module as follows:
   a. Using a small screwdriver, detach dampening rod from righthand side of glove compartment.
   b. Pull lefthand side of glove compartment inward and allow glove compartment to drop downward.
   c. Remove air duct attaching screws, then the air duct.
   d. Remove two vertically positioned bolts from each side of air bag module.
   e. Remove the two remaining air bag module attaching bolts.
   f. Push air bag module outward from instrument panel. Do not handle air bag module by deployment doors.
   g. Disconnect electrical connector, then remove air bag module. Position air bag module on work bench with trim cover facing upward.
7. Connect Rotunda air bag simulator tool No. 105-00010 or equivalent to vehicle air bag wiring harness in place of the passenger side air bag module.
8. Reconnect battery positive cable, then the ground cable.

CROWN VICTORIA & GRAND MARQUIS

1. **On 1992-93 models,** disconnect battery positive cable.
2. **On 1994 models,** disconnect battery ground cable, then the battery positive cable.
3. **On 1995 models,** disconnect battery ground cable.
4. **On all models,** wait one minute for back-up power supply to discharge.
5. Remove four nut and washer assemblies retaining driver air bag module to the steering wheel.
6. Disconnect driver air bag module connector.
7. **On 1992 models,** connect Rotunda air bag simulator tool No. 105-00008 or equivalent to vehicle harness at top of steering column.
8. **On 1993-95 models,** connect Rotunda air bag simulator tool No. 105-00010 or equivalent to vehicle harness at top of steering column.
9. **On models with passenger side air bag,** remove passenger air bag as follows:
   a. **On 1993-94 models,** remove righthand instrument panel lower molding.
   b. **On 1993-94 Crown Victoria,** remove righthand instrument cluster finish panel retaining screws, then the panel.

c. **On 1993-94 Grand Marquis,** remove righthand register applique retaining screws, then the applique.

d. **On 1993-94 models,** remove cluster finish panel retaining screws, then the panel.

e. **On 1995 models,** remove instrument panel upper molding by disengaging snap-in tabs.

f. **On all models,** open glove compartment, press sides inward and lower glove compartment to floor.

g. Working through glove compartment opening, remove two front air bag module retaining screws.

h. Remove two rear air bag module retaining screws, then disconnect electrical connector and remove air bag module.

10. **On 1992 models,** install Rotunda air bag simulator tool No. 105-00008 or equivalent on vehicle air bag harness connector.

11. **On 1993-95 models,** install Rotunda air bag simulator tool No. 105-00010 or equivalent on vehicle air bag harness connector.

12. **On all models,** connect both battery cables.

TEMPO & TOPAZ

1. **On 1992-93 models,** disconnect battery positive cable.

2. **On 1994 models, disconnect battery ground cable, then the battery positive cable.**

3. **On all models,** wait one minute for back-up power supply to deplete stored energy.

4. Remove four nut and washer assemblies retaining driver air bag module to steering wheel.

5. Disconnect air bag module connector.

6. **On 1992 models,** attach Rotunda air bag simulator tool No. 105-00008 or equivalent to vehicle harness at top of steering wheel.

7. **On 1993-94 models,** attach Rotunda air bag simulator tool No. 105-00010 or equivalent, to vehicle harness at top of steering wheel.

8. **On 1992-93 models,** connect battery positive cable.

9. **On 1994 models, connect battery positive cable, then the battery ground cable.**

MUSTANG

1992–93

Refer to "Tempo & Topaz" for air bag disarming procedures.

1994–95

1. Disconnect battery ground cable.

2. **On 1994 models, disconnect battery positive cable.**

3. **On all models,** allow at least one minute for back-up power supply to deplete, then remove two rear cover plugs from steering wheel in order to access driver side air bag module screws.

4. Remove driver side air bag module

---

screws and washers, then disconnect electrical connector and carefully remove module from vehicle. **To avoid injury by accidental deployment, place module on a bench with trim cover facing up.**

5. Connect Rotunda air bag simulator tool No. 105-00010 or equivalent to air bag harness at top of steering column.

6. Open glove compartment door and push inward on sides of compartment to release it from instrument panel, then lower compartment assembly to floor.

7. Remove righthand A/C duct, then remove passenger side air bag retaining bolts from instrument panel steel reinforcement.

8. Disconnect electrical connector at lower lefthand corner of passenger side air bag module, then remove connector from instrument panel reinforcement.

9. Pull gently upon each corner of air bag cover to disengage from instrument panel, then push air bag module out from behind instrument panel. **To avoid injury by accidental deployment, place module on a bench with trim cover facing up.**

10. Install a second air bag simulator tool (Rotunda tool No. 105-00010 or equivalent) upon passenger side air bag harness, then connect battery ground cable.

SABLE & TAURUS

1. **On 1992-93 models,** disconnect battery positive cable.

2. **On 1994 models, disconnect battery ground cable, then the battery positive cable.**

3. **On 1995 models,** disconnect battery ground cable.

4. **On all models,** wait one minute for back-up power supply to discharge.

5. Remove four nut and washer assemblies retaining driver air bag module to the steering wheel.

6. Disconnect driver air bag module connector.

7. Connect Rotunda air bag simulator tool No. 105-00010 or equivalent to clockspring to simulate air bag.

8. **On models with passenger side air bag,** remove passenger air bag as follows:

a. Remove righthand and lefthand finish panel.

b. Remove instrument panel finish panel retaining spear clips.

c. open glove compartment, press sides inward and lower glove compartment to floor.

d. Working through glove compartment opening, remove two lower air bag module retaining bolts.

e. Remove four remaining air bag module retaining screws from side of air bag cover, then disconnect electrical connector attached to lefthand side of air bag and remove air bag module.

---

9. Connect Rotunda air bag simulator tool No. 105-00010 or equivalent to wiring harness.

10. **On 1992-93 models,** connect battery positive cable.

11. **On 1994 models, connect battery positive cable, then the battery ground cable.**

12. **On 1995 models,** connect battery ground cable.

TOWN CAR

1. **On 1992-93 models,** disconnect battery positive cable.

2. **On 1994 models, disconnect battery ground cable, then the battery positive cable.**

3. **On 1995 models,** disconnect battery ground cable.

4. **On all models,** wait one minute for back-up power supply to discharge.

5. Remove four nut and washer assemblies retaining driver air bag module to the steering wheel.

6. Disconnect driver air bag module connector.

7. **On 1992 models,** attach Rotunda air bag simulator tool No. 105-00008 or equivalent to vehicle harness at top of steering column.

8. **On 1993-95 models,** attach Rotunda air bag simulator tool No. 105-00010 or equivalent to vehicle harness at top of steering column.

9. **On all models,** remove instrument panel moldings, instrument panel finish panel retaining screws, then the panel.

10. Open glove compartment, press sides inward and lower glove compartment to floor.

11. Working through glove compartment opening, remove two lower air bag module retaining bolts.

12. Remove four remaining air bag module retaining screws, then disconnect electrical connector and remove air bag module.

13. **On 1992 models,** install Rotunda air bag simulator tool No. 105-00008 or equivalent on vehicle passenger side air bag harness connector.

14. **On 1993-95 models,** install Rotunda air bag simulator tool No. 105-00010 or equivalent on vehicle passenger side air bag harness connector.

15. **On 1992-93 models,** connect battery positive cable.

16. **On 1994 models, connect battery positive cable, then the battery ground cable.**

17. **On 1995 models,** connect battery ground cable.

PROBE

1. Disconnect battery ground cable.

2. Wait one minute for back-up power supply to deplete stored energy.

3. Remove four bolts retaining air bag module to steering wheel.

4. Disconnect air bag connector.

5. Connect Rotunda air bag simulator tool No. 105-00009 or equivalent to vehicle harness at top of steering column.

6. **On 1995 models,** proceed as fol-

lows:

a. Disconnect two passenger air bag diagnostic module connectors under lefthand instrument panel pad.
b. Open glove compartment door, then press in compartment sides to disengage retainers and lower compartment from instrument panel, then remove screws and glove compartment from vehicle.
c. Remove screws from glove compartment upper cover, then remove upper cover and disconnect passenger side air bag module electrical connectors.
d. Remove passenger side air bag module bolts, then remove module from vehicle by pressing outward from inside instrument panel. **Do not pull on wiring during removal or handling of air bag module. Place module on a bench with trim cover facing up to avoid injury by accidental deployment.**
e. Connect a second Rotunda air bag simulator tool No. 105-00009 or equivalent to passenger side air bag harness.
7. **On all models,** connect battery ground cable.

ASPIRE

1. Disconnect battery ground cable.
2. Wait one minute for back-up power supply to deplete stored energy.
3. Remove four bolts retaining air bag module to steering wheel.
4. Disconnect driver side air bag connector.
5. Connect air bag simulator to vehicle harness above glove compartment.
6. Remove passenger side air bag module.
7. Connect Rotunda air bag simulator tool No. 105-00009 or equivalent to passenger side air bag vehicle harness.
8. Connect battery ground cable.

ESCORT & TRACER

1. Disconnect battery positive cable.
2. Wait one minute for back-up power supply to deplete stored energy.
3. Remove bolts retaining air bag module to steering wheel.
4. Disconnect air bag connector.
5. Connect Rotunda air bag simulator tool No. 105-00010 or equivalent to vehicle harness at top of steering column.
6. **On 1995 models,** proceed as follows:
   a. Remove glove compartment, then the two passenger side air bag module bolts.
   b. Pull passenger side air bag module from instrument panel, then disconnect electrical connector. **To avoid injury by accidental deployment, place module on a bench with trim cover facing up. Do not pull on wires during removal or handling.**
7. **On all models,** connect battery positive cable.

AIR BAG SYSTEM ARMING

CAPRI

1992

1. Disconnect battery ground cable and back-up power supply.
2. Remove jumper wire from air bag terminals on clockspring assembly.
3. Connect driver side air bag connector.
4. Position air bag on steering wheel and secure with four nut and washer assemblies. **Torque** to 17-26 inch lbs.
5. **On models with passenger air bag,** remove jumper wire from air bag terminals on passenger air bag wiring connector in harness, then connect passenger air bag connector and close glove compartment door.
6. **On all models,** connect back-up power supply and battery ground cable.
7. Place ignition switch in Run position and note air bag warning lamp operation. Indicator lamp should illuminate for approximately 6 seconds, then turn off. If warning lamp does not illuminate, remains illuminated continuously or flashes, refer to "Passive Restraints" section of this manual.

1993

Early Production

1. Disconnect positive battery cable and back-up power supply.
2. Remove air bag simulator from clockspring connector at base of steering wheel.
3. Connect air bag connector.
4. Position air bag on steering wheel and secure with four nut and washer assemblies. **Torque** to 17-26 ft. lbs.
5. Connect positive battery cable and back-up power supply.
6. Place ignition switch in Run position and note air bag warning lamp operation. Indicator lamp should illuminate for approximately 6 seconds, then turn off. If warning lamp does not illuminate or remains illuminated continuously or flashes, refer to "Passive Restraints" section of this manual.

Late Production

1. Disconnect battery ground cable.
2. Wait one minute for back-up power supply to deplete stored energy.
3. Remove air bag simulator from vehicle harness at top of steering column.
4. Connect air bag connector.
5. Position air bag on steering wheel and secure with four bolts. **Torque** to 17-26 ft. lbs.
6. Connect battery ground cable.
7. Place ignition switch in Run position and note air bag warning lamp operation. Indicator lamp should illuminate for approximately 6 seconds, then turn off. If warning lamp does not illuminate or remains illuminated continuously or flashes, refer to "Passive Restraints" section of this manual.

1994

Refer to "Escort & Tracer" in this section for air bag arming procedures.

MARK VII

1. Disconnect battery positive cable.
2. Remove air bag simulator from air bag terminals on clockspring assembly.
3. Connect air bag module connector.
4. Position air bag assembly on steering wheel and secure with four nut and washer assemblies. **Torque** to 36-49 inch lbs.
5. Connect battery positive cable.
6. Place ignition switch in Run position and note air bag warning lamp operation. Indicator lamp should illuminate for approximately 6 seconds, then turn off. If warning lamp does not illuminate or remains illuminated continuously or flashes, refer to "Passive Restraints" section of this manual.

MARK VIII

1. **On 1993 models,** disconnect battery positive cable.
2. **On 1994 models, disconnect battery ground cable, then the battery positive cable.**
3. **On 1995 models,** disconnect battery ground cable.
4. **On all models,** wait one minute for back-up power supply to deplete stored energy.
5. Remove air bag simulator from clockspring connector at top of steering column.
6. Connect driver air bag connector.
7. Position driver air bag on steering wheel and secure with two screw and washer assemblies. **Torque** to 8-10 ft. lbs.
8. Remove air bag simulator from passenger harness connector.
9. Install passenger air bag as follows:
   a. Connect electrical connector to air bag module and position module in instrument panel.
   b. Install three upper retaining screws and **torque** to 9-18 inch lbs.
   c. Install lower module retaining bolts and **torque** to 62-97 inch lbs.
   d. Return glove compartment to correct position, then install instrument panel finish panel.
10. **On 1993 models,** connect battery positive cable.
11. **On 1994 models, connect battery positive cable, then the battery ground cable.**
12. **On 1995 models, connect battery ground cable.**
13. **On all models,** place ignition switch in Run position and note air bag warning lamp operation. Indicator lamp should illuminate for approximately 6 seconds, then turn off. If warning lamp does not illuminate or remains illuminated continuously or flashes, refer to "Passive Restraints" section of this manual.

CONTINENTAL

1. Disconnect battery positive cable.
2. Wait one minute for back-up power supply to discharge.
3. Remove air bag simulator from vehicle harness connector at top of steering column.
4. Connect driver air bag connector.
5. Position air bag assembly on steering wheel and secure with four nut and washer assemblies. **Torque** to 35-50 ft. lbs.
6. Remove air bag simulator from vehicle harness connector at passenger air bag.
7. Connect passenger air bag connector.
8. Connect battery positive cable.
9. Place ignition switch in Run position and note air bag warning lamp operation. Indicator lamp should illuminate for approximately 6 seconds, then turn off. If warning lamp does not illuminate or remains illuminated continuously or flashes, refer to "Passive Restraints" section of this manual.

CONTOUR & MYSTIQUE

1. Disconnect battery ground cable, then the battery positive cable.
2. Allow at least one minute for back-up power supply to deplete, then remove air bag simulator tool from driver side air bag sliding contact connector on steering column.
3. Connect driver side air bag electrical connector to air bag sliding contact connector, then position driver side air bag module in steering wheel and **torque** bolts to 35-50 inch lbs.
4. Remove air bag simulator tool from passenger side air bag wiring harness, then position passenger side air bag module in instrument panel.
5. Install retaining bolts and nuts and **torque** to 11-17 ft. lbs.
6. Install A/C evaporator register duct and glove compartment upper cover, then connect glove compartment lamp and install screws.
7. Install glove compartment assembly in instrument panel.
8. Connect battery ground cable, then the battery positive cable.
9. Place ignition switch in Run position and note air bag warning lamp operation. Indicator lamp should illuminate for approximately 6 seconds, then turn off. If warning lamp does not illuminate, remains illuminated continuously or flashes, refer to "Passive Restraints" section of this manual.

COUGAR & THUNDERBIRD

1. Disconnect battery ground cable, then the battery positive cable.
2. Wait approximately one minute for back-up power supply to discharge.
3. Disconnect Rotunda air bag simulator 105-00010 or equivalent from vehicle air bag wiring harness at top of steering column.
4. Connect driver side air bag electrical connector to air bag module.
5. Position driver side air bag module to steering wheel, then install attaching bolts and washers. **Torque** attaching screws to 90 to 122 inch lbs.
6. Disconnect Rotunda air bag simulator tool No. 105-00010 or equivalent from vehicle passenger side harness.
7. Connect electrical connector to passenger side air bag module.
8. Install passenger side air bag module as described in "Passive Restraints" section of unit repair.
9. Connect battery positive cable, then the negative cable.
10. Place ignition switch in the Run position and note air bag warning lamp operation. Indicator lamp should illuminate for approximately 6 seconds, then turn off. If warning lamp does not illuminate or remains illuminated continuously or flashes, refer to "Passive Restraints" section of this manual.

CROWN VICTORIA & GRAND MARQUIS

1. **On 1992-93 models,** disconnect battery positive cable.
2. **On 1994 models,** disconnect battery ground cable, then the battery positive cable.
3. **On 1995 models,** disconnect battery ground cable.
4. **On all models,** wait one minute for back-up power supply to deplete stored energy.
5. Remove air bag simulator from vehicle harness at top of steering column.
6. Connect driver air bag connector.
7. Position driver air bag on steering wheel and secure with four nut and washer assemblies. **Torque** to 24-33 inch lbs.
8. **On models with passenger side air bag,** remove air bag simulator from vehicle harness connector.
9. Install passenger air bag as follows:
   a. Connect electrical connector to air bag module and position module in instrument panel.
   b. **On 1993-94 models,** install two rear retaining screws and **torque** to 24-33 inch lbs.
   c. Install two front retaining screws and **torque** to 67-92 inch lbs.
   d. **On 1995 models,** install front retaining screws and **torque** to 19-25 inch lbs., then install lower retaining screws and **torque** to 6-8 ft. lbs.
   e. **On all models,** return glove compartment to correct position, then install instrument cluster finish panel.
   f. **On 1993-94 Grand Marquis,** install righthand register applique and **torque** retaining screws to 17-27 inch lbs.
   g. **On 1993-94 models,** install instrument panel lower molding.
   h. **On 1995 models,** snap instrument panel upper molding into place.
10. **On 1992-93 models,** connect battery positive cable.
11. **On 1994 models,** connect battery positive cable, then the battery ground cable.
12. **On 1995 models,** connect battery ground cable.

13. **On all models,** place ignition switch in Run position and note air bag warning lamp operation. Indicator lamp should illuminate for approximately 6 seconds, then turn off. If warning lamp does not illuminate or remains illuminated continuously or flashes, refer to "Passive Restraints" section of this manual.

TEMPO & TOPAZ

1. **On 1992-93 models,** disconnect battery positive cable.
2. **On 1994 models,** disconnect battery ground cable, then the battery positive cable.
3. **On all models,** wait one minute for back-up power supply to deplete stored energy.
4. Remove air bag simulator from vehicle harness connector at top of steering column.
5. Connect driver air bag connector.
6. Position driver air bag on steering wheel and secure with four nut and washer assemblies. **Torque** to 35-50 inch lbs.
7. **On 1992-93 models,** connect battery positive cable.
8. **On 1994 models,** connect battery positive cable, then the battery ground cable.
9. **On all models,** place ignition switch in Run position and note air bag warning lamp operation. Indicator lamp should illuminate for approximately 6 seconds, then turn off. If warning lamp does not illuminate, remains illuminated continuously or flashes, refer to "Passive Restraints" section of this manual.

MUSTANG

1992-93

Refer to "Tempo & Topaz" for air bag arming procedures.

1994-95

1. Disconnect battery ground cable.
2. **On 1994 models,** disconnect battery positive cable.
3. **On all models,** allow at least one minute for back-up power supply to deplete, then remove air bag simulator tool from harness connector at top of steering column.
4. Connect driver side air bag module, then position module in steering wheel and install screws and washers. **Torque** screws to 8-10 ft. lbs.
5. Remove air bag simulator tool from passenger side air bag module harness, then position module in instrument panel.
6. Attach connector to instrument panel reinforcement, then connect to wiring harness.
7. Install passenger air bag module retaining bolts and **torque** to 62-97 inch lbs.
8. Press gently upon air bag module corners to engage with instrument panel trim, then install righthand A/C duct.
9. Press sides of glove compartment assembly together and lift into position

in instrument panel, then close glove compartment door.

10. **On 1994 models,** connect battery positive cable.
11. **On all models,** connect battery ground cable.
12. Place ignition switch in Run position and note air bag warning lamp operation. Indicator lamp should illuminate for approximately 6 seconds, then turn off. If warning lamp does not illuminate, remains illuminated continuously or flashes, refer to "Passive Restraints" section of this manual.

SABLE & TAURUS

1. **On 1992-93 models,** disconnect battery positive cable.
2. **On 1994 models,** disconnect battery ground cable, then the battery positive cable.
3. **On 1995 models,** disconnect battery ground cable.
4. **On all models,** wait one minute for back-up power supply to deplete stored energy.
5. Remove air bag simulator from clockspring connector.
6. Connect driver air bag connector.
7. Position driver air bag on steering wheel and secure with four nut and washer assemblies. **Torque** to 35-50 inch lbs.
8. **On models with passenger side air bag,** remove air bag simulator tool from vehicle harness connector.
9. Install passenger air bag as follows:
   a. Connect electrical connector to air bag module and position module in instrument panel.
   b. Install four upper retaining screws and **torque** to 11-16 inch lbs.
   c. Install lower module retaining bolts and **torque** to 62-97 inch lbs.
   d. Return glove compartment to correct position.
   e. Install instrument panel finish panel locator pin into air bag bushing locator, then align spear clips and press finish panel into place.
10. **On 1992-93 models,** connect battery positive cable.
11. **On 1994 models,** connect battery positive cable, then the battery ground cable.
12. **On 1995 models,** connect battery ground cable.
13. **On all models,** place ignition switch in Run position and note air bag warning lamp operation. Indicator lamp should illuminate for approximately 6 seconds, then turn off. If warning lamp does not illuminate or remains illuminated continuously or flashes, refer to "Passive Restraints" section of this manual.

TOWN CAR

1. **On 1992-93 models,** disconnect battery positive cable.
2. **On 1994 models,** disconnect battery ground cable, then the battery positive cable.

3. **On 1995 models,** disconnect battery ground cable.
4. **On all models,** wait one minute for back-up power supply to deplete stored energy.
5. Remove air bag Simulator from vehicle harness at top of steering column.
6. Connect driver air bag connector.
7. Position driver air bag on steering wheel and secure with four nut and washer assemblies. **Torque** to 35-50 inch lbs.
8. Remove air bag Simulator from passenger harness connector.
9. Install passenger air bag as follows:
   a. Connect electrical connector to air bag module and position module in instrument panel.
   b. Install four upper retaining screws and **torque** to 24-35 inch lbs.
   c. Install lower module retaining bolts and **torque** to 4-8 ft. lbs.
   d. Return glove compartment to correct position, then install instrument panel finish panel.
   e. Install instrument panel moldings.
10. **On 1992-93 models,** connect battery positive cable.
11. **On 1994 models,** connect battery positive cable, then the battery ground cable.
12. **On 1995 models,** disconnect battery ground cable.
13. **On all models,** place ignition switch in Run position and note air bag warning lamp operation. Indicator lamp should illuminate for approximately 6 seconds, then turn off. If warning lamp does not illuminate or remains illuminated continuously or flashes, refer to "Passive Restraints" section of this manual.

PROBE

1. Disconnect battery ground cable.
2. Wait one minute for back-up power supply to deplete stored energy.
3. Remove air bag simulator from vehicle harness at top of steering column.
4. Connect air bag connector.
5. Position air bag on steering wheel and secure with four bolts. **Torque** to 61-86 inch lbs.
6. **On 1995 models,** disconnect air bag simulator tool from passenger side air bag harness, then install passenger side air bag module as follows:
   a. Insert air bag module into instrument panel, aligning guide pins with guide holes, then engage module tab with instrument panel clip. **Ensure wiring is not pinched between air bag module and instrument panel pad.**
   b. Install air bag module bolts and **torque** to 23-33 inch lbs., then connect air bag module electrical connectors securely.
   c. Insert connector pin into hole on rear of air bag module, then install glove compartment upper cover and glove compartment.
   d. Connect two diagnostic module connectors.

7. **On all models,** connect battery ground cable.
8. Place ignition switch in Run position and note air bag warning lamp operation. Indicator lamp should illuminate for approximately 6 seconds, then turn off. If warning lamp does not illuminate or remains illuminated continuously or flashes, refer to "Passive Restraints" section of this manual. Verify system operation.

ASPIRE

1. Disconnect battery ground cable.
2. Wait one minute for back-up power supply to deplete stored energy.
3. Remove air bag simulator from vehicle harness at top of steering column.
4. Connect driver side air bag connector.
5. Position driver side air bag on steering wheel and secure with four bolts. **Torque** to 80-115 inch lbs.
6. Remove air bag simulator from vehicle harness above glove compartment.
7. Install passenger side air bag module.
8. Connect battery ground cable.
9. Place ignition switch in Run position and note air bag warning lamp operation. Indicator lamp should illuminate for approximately 6 seconds, then turn off. If warning lamp does not illuminate or remains illuminated continuously or flashes, refer to "Passive Restraints" section of this manual. Verify system operation.

ESCORT & TRACER

1. Disconnect battery positive cable.
2. Wait one minute for back-up power supply to deplete stored energy.
3. Remove air bag simulator from vehicle harness at top of steering column.
4. Connect air bag connector.
5. Position air bag on steering wheel and secure with two bolts. **Torque** to 35-53 inch lbs.
6. **On 1995 models,** install passenger side air bag module as follows:
   a. Press air bag module mounting tabs in instrument panel down slightly, then connect module electrical connector and position module in instrument panel.
   b. Install two air bag module bolts and **torque** to 61-79 inch lbs.
   c. Install glove compartment in instrument panel and **torque** glove compartment door hinge to instrument panel screws to 69-104 inch lbs.
7. **On all models,** connect battery positive cable.
8. Place ignition switch in Run position and note air bag warning lamp operation. Indicator lamp should illuminate for approximately 6 seconds, then turn off. If warning lamp does not illuminate, remains illuminated continuously or flashes, refer to "Passive Restraints" section of this manual.

SERVICE REMINDER & WARNING LAMP RESET PROCEDURES

TABLE OF CONTENTS

Chrysler Corp./Eagle/AMC

ANTI-LOCK WARNING LAMP

This lamp will be illuminated when the ignition switch is placed in the ON position. The lamp maybe illuminated for as long as 30 seconds as a bulb and system check. If lamp remains illuminated or comes on while operating the vehicle, a problem in the anti-lock brake system is indicated. When lamp is illuminated, place ignition switch in OFF position, then restart engine. If lamp still remains illuminated, the anti-lock brake system should be serviced. The brake system will remain functional, but without the anti-lock function. After servicing the anti-lock brake system the lamp will automatically reset when the ignition switch is cycled to the OFF position.

AIR BAG SYSTEM WARNING LAMP

On models equipped with an air bag system, if the air bag warning lamp illuminates and stays on, diagnosis and repair of the air bag system will be necessary to reset the lamp.

BRAKE PAD WEAR WARNING LAMP

EAGLE MEDALLION

When this message is displayed, the disc brake pads should be inspected and replaced as necessary. After completing service, the message will be reset automatically.

EGR WARNING LAMP

1985–87 DODGE & PLYMOUTH COLT VISTA

This lamp will be illuminated every 50,000 miles to indicate interval for EGR system service. After performing EGR system service, the lamp can be reset by moving the reset switch lever located at the rear of the instrument cluster, **Fig. 1.**

CHECK ENGINE LAMP

CHRYSLER, DODGE & PLYMOUTH

The Check Engine lamp will be illuminated for approximately 3 seconds after the ignition switch has been placed in the ON position as a bulb check. If incorrect or no signals are received by the Single Board Engine Controller (SBEC) or Powertrain Control Module (PCM) from various sensors, the Check Engine lamp will illuminate. After diagnosing and servicing the fuel injection system or emission related systems, the SBEC/PCM memory will be cleared after approximately 50 to 100 ignition key on-off cycles.

EAGLE MEDALLION

This lamp will be illuminated during engine starting as a bulb check. Once the engine has started, the lamp should go off. If lamp remains illuminated, the fuel injection and emission control system diagnosis should be performed using tester M.S. 1700. During the diagnosis and repair procedure with tester M.S. 1700, the check engine lamp will be reset.

DODGE MONACO & EAGLE PREMIER

This lamp will be illuminated during engine starting as a bulb check. Once the engine has started, the lamp should go off. If lamp remains illuminated, the fuel injection and emission control system diagnosis should be performed using tester DRB II. During the diagnosis and repair procedure with tester DRB II, the check engine lamp will be reset.

CHECK ENGINE OR MALFUNCTION INDICATOR LAMP

DODGE & PLYMOUTH COLT & EAGLE SUMMIT

This lamp is used to monitor fuel injection and emission control system components for malfunctions. When the ignition switch is placed in the ON position, the lamp will illuminate for 2 to 3 seconds as a bulb check. If a problem is detected, the Powertrain Control Module (PCM) sends a message over the CCD bus to the Body Control Module (BCM). The BCM interprets this message and sends a signal to the instrument cluster to illuminate the lamp. The PCM memory is cleared by disconnecting the battery ground cable for approximately 10 seconds.

ELECTRONIC MONITOR

1988–89 CHRYSLER LEBARON

This system is an electronic monitor system with sensors, which displays messages on an instrument panel mounted console. If no messages are stored, the message "Monitored Systems OK" will be displayed approximately 6 seconds after ignition switch has been placed in th ON position. The system is actuated by depressing the check button located on the front of the message display. When this button is depressed, the system will sound a tone and cycle through the messages and then return to normal operation. If the monitor detects a fault, the component will be noted on the display. The fault messages are as follows:

BRAKE FLUID LOW—When this message is displayed, bring brake to proper level. The message will be reset after the ignition switch has been cycled to the OFF position.

COOLANT LEVEL LOW—When this message is displayed, bring coolant to proper level. The message will be reset after the ignition switch has been cycled to the OFF position.

DISC BRAKE PADS WORN—When this message is displayed, the disc brake pads should be inspected and replaced as necessary. After completing service, the message will be reset after the ignition switch has been cycled to the OFF position.

DRIVER, PASSENGER OR HATCH AJAR—Close door or hatch indicated to cancel message.

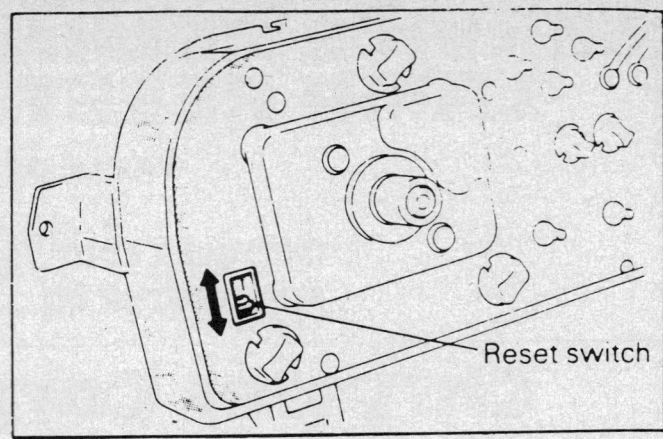

Fig. 1 EGR or Maintenance Required Lamp reset switch location. 1985–91 Dodge & Plymouth Colt Vista

ENGINE TEMPERATURE HIGH—This message will be indicated when an engine overheating condition is encountered. After repairing cause of engine overheating condition or when engine speed is less than 300 RPM, the message will be automatically cancelled.

EXTERIOR LAMPS ON—This message will appear when the ignition switch is in OFF, LOCK or ACC positions, the driver's door is open and the light switch is in the ON position. This message will be cancelled when light switch is placed in the OFF position or the door is closed.

HEADLAMP, BRAKE OR TAIL LAMP OUT—The display will be illuminated when brake is applied or light switch is in the ON position and a burned out lamp bulb is present. To reset message, replace burned out bulb, then actuate lamp circuit.

KEY IN IGNITION—This message will appear when the ignition switch is in the OFF, LOCK or ACC position and the driver's door is open. This message will be cancelled when the keys are removed or the door is closed.

LOW FUEL LEVEL—When this message is displayed, add fuel to vehicle to reset message.

LOW OIL PRESSURE—This message will be displayed when a low engine oil pressure condition exist. If message is encountered with vehicle operating at idle speed, increase engine RPM. If message remains or if message is encountered while operating vehicle, the engine lubricating system should be checked and service immediately. After engine lubricating system has been serviced, the message will be automatically cancelled.

LOW TRANS PRESSURE—When this message is displayed, a problem in the automatic transaxle is present. After completing automatic transaxle service, the message will be reset after the ignition switch has been cycled to the OFF position.

VOLTAGE LOW—When this message is displayed, a problem in the charging or electrical system exist. After servicing, the message will be reset after the ignition switch has been cycled to the OFF position.

WASHER FLUID LOW—When this message is displayed, bring washer fluid to proper level to reset message.

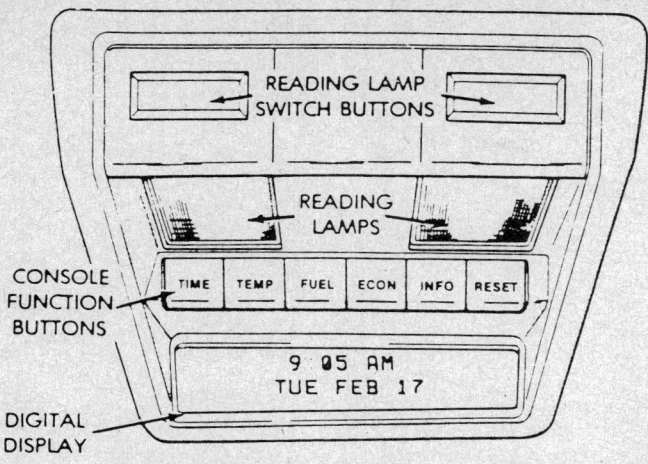

Fig. 2 Electronic Vehicle Information Center display console. 1988–89 Chrysler New Yorker & Dodge Dynasty

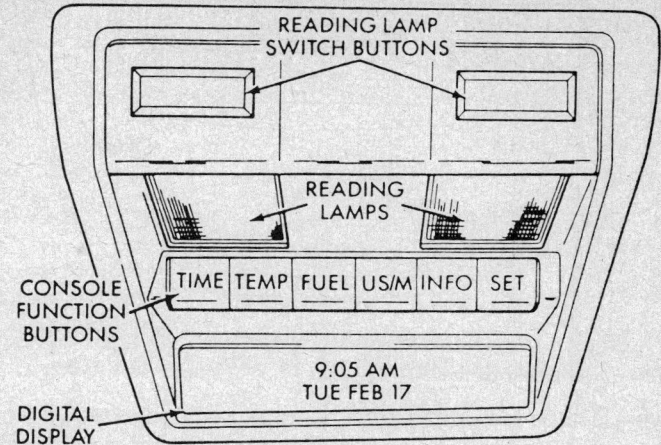

Fig. 3 Electronic Vehicle Information Center display console. 1990–92 Chrysler New Yorker, Fifth Avenue, Imperial & Dodge Dynasty

ELECTRONIC VEHICLE INFORMATION CENTER

1988–92 CHRYSLER NEW YORKER & NEW YORKER LANDAU & DODGE DYNASTY, 1990–92 CHRYSLER FIFTH AVENUE & IMPERIAL

On 1988-89 models, this system is a computer controlled monitor system, which displays messages on an overhead console, **Fig. 2.** When the vehicle is started and no faults are present, the display will indicate "MONITORED SYSTEMS OK." If the monitor detects a fault, a tone will be sounded and component will be noted on the display.

On 1990-92 models, the Electronic Vehicle Information Center is a computer controlled warning system which monitors various sensors used on the vehicle. The system supplements the warning indicators in the instrument cluster. When a warning message has been activated, a tone will sound to attract the driver's attention. The warning message will then be displayed on the overhead console, **Fig. 3,** until the condition has been corrected or a new display function is called up. A tone will announce each new warning condition. The warning messages are as follows:

CHECK ENGINE OIL LEVEL—When this message is displayed, check engine oil and adjust to proper level. The message will be reset after the ignition switch has been cycled to the OFF position.

CHECK TRANS—When this message is displayed, a problem in the automatic transaxle is present. After completing automatic transaxle service, the message will be reset after the ignition switch has been cycled to the OFF position.

COOLANT LEVEL LOW—When this message is displayed, bring coolant to proper level. The message will be reset after the ignition switch has been cycled to the OFF position.

DISC BRAKE PADS WORN—When this message is displayed, the disc brake pads should be inspected and replaced

as necessary. After completing service, the message will be reset after the ignition switch has been cycled to the OFF position.

DRIVER, PASSENGER, LEFT REAR, RIGHT REAR DOOR OR TRUNK AJAR—Close door to cancel message.

ENGINE TEMPERATURE CRITICAL—This message will be indicated when an engine overheating condition is encountered. After repairing cause of engine overheating condition, the message will be automatically cancelled.

EXTERIOR LAMPS ON—This message will appear when the ignition switch is in OFF, LOCK or ACC, the driver's door is open and the light switch is in the ON position. This message will be cancelled when light switch is placed in the OFF position or the door is closed.

HEADLAMP, BRAKE OR TAIL LAMP OUT—The display will be illuminated when brake is applied or light switch is in the ON position and a burned out lamp bulb is present. To reset message, replace burned out bulb, then actuate lamp circuit.

KEY IN IGNITION—This message will appear when the ignition switch is in the OFF, LOCK or ACC position and the driver's door is open. This message will be cancelled when the keys are removed or the door is closed.

LOW BRAKE FLUID—When this message is displayed, bring brake to proper level. The message will be reset after the ignition switch has been cycled to the OFF position.

LOW FUEL LEVEL—When this message is displayed, add fuel to vehicle. The message will be reset after the ignition switch has been cycled to the OFF position.

LOW OIL PRESSURE—This message will be displayed when a low engine oil pressure condition exist. If message is encountered with vehicle operating at idle speed, increase engine RPM. If message remains or if message is encountered while operating vehicle, the engine lubricating system should be checked and service immediately. After engine lubricating system has been serviced, the message will be automatically cancelled.

SERVICE REMINDER—This message will be indicated at 7,500 mile or 12 month intervals to indicate that required ser-

Fig. 4 Overhead Travel Information System (OTIS). Concord, Intrepid, LHS, New Yorker & Vision

vice is to be performed. After performing the required service, with the Service Reminder message displayed, depress the Vehicle Electronic Information Center Reset button.

TURN SIGNAL ON—This message will be indicated when the turn is on and vehicle has traveled a distance over 1/2 mile at a speed above 15 MPH. The message will be reset when the turn signal has been placed in the OFF position.

VOLTAGE IMPROPER—When this message is displayed, a problem in the charging or electrical system exist. After servicing, the message will be reset after the ignition switch has been cycled to the OFF position.

WASHER FLUID LOW—When this message is displayed, bring washer fluid to proper level. The message will be reset after the ignition switch has been cycled to the OFF position.

OVERHEAD TRAVEL INFORMATION SYSTEM (OTIS)

CONCORD, INTREPID, LHS, NEW YORKER & VISION

Overhead Travel Information System (OTIS) is a module with six informational displays and four buttons, **Fig. 4.** When the ignition switch is turned On, OTIS blanks the display for a half second, then illuminates all segment of the display for one second, then returns to the display active when the vehicle was last turned Off.

The six informational displays on the OTIS are as follows:
1. Compass/Temperature.
2. Average fuel economy.
3. Distance to empty.
4. Instantaneous fuel economy.
5. Trip odometer.
6. Elapsed time.

The four buttons on the OTIS are as follows:
1. Step—Depress this button to select display modes except Compass/Temperature.
2. C/T—Depress this button to display compass (vehicle direction) and temperature.
3. US/M—Switches display information between English and Metric readings.
4. RESET—Depress this button to reset the current display (for displays that can be reset).

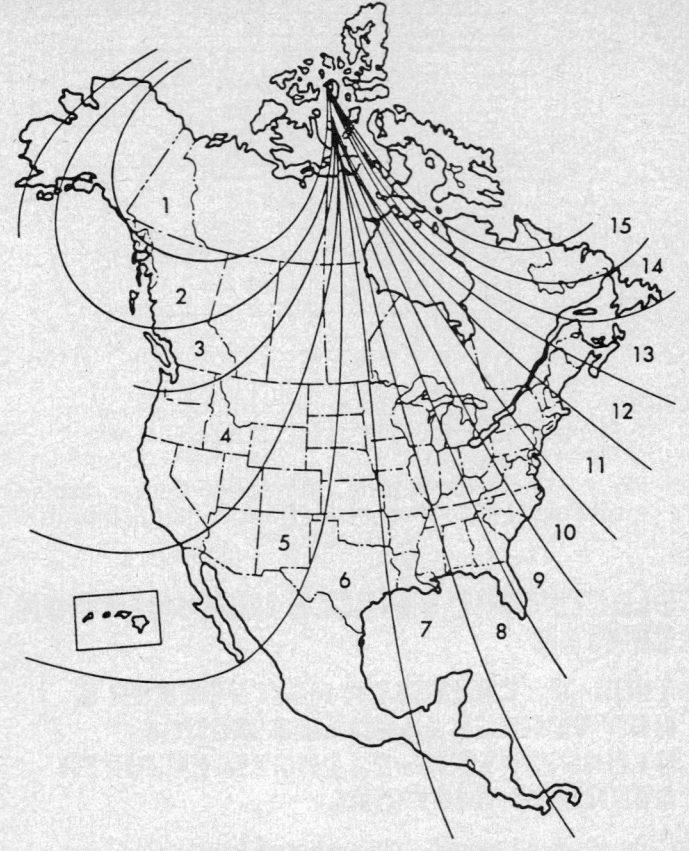

Fig. 5 Variance zone map

Compass Calibration

Do not attempt to set compass calibration near large metal objects such as other vehicles, buildings or bridges.
1. Remove all magnetic devices from roof panel.
2. Turn key to On position.
3. Press C/T button to select compass/temperature display.
4. Depress and hold RESET button for about 5 seconds. The VAR symbol will light during this time.
5. Continue to hold RESET button for about 10 seconds until CAL symbol illuminates.
6. Drive vehicle through 3 complete 360° turns in no less than 48 seconds. The compass will be calibrated when CAL symbol is extinguished.
7. Reset compass variance as follows:
   a. Press and hold reset button for about five seconds until VAR symbol is lit.
   b. The OTIS will display variance zone and VAR.
   c. Press STEP button to select desired zone, **Fig. 5.**
   d. Press RESET button to set new variance zone and resume normal operation.

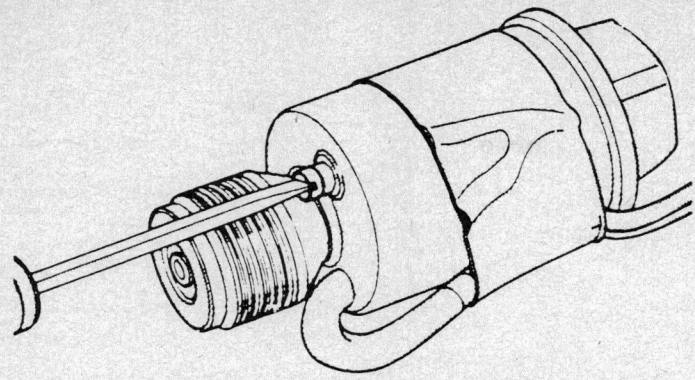

Fig. 6   Resetting emission or oxygen sensor maintenance reminder switch. 1980 Chrysler, Dodge & Plymouth (mechanical type) & 1980–81 AMC models

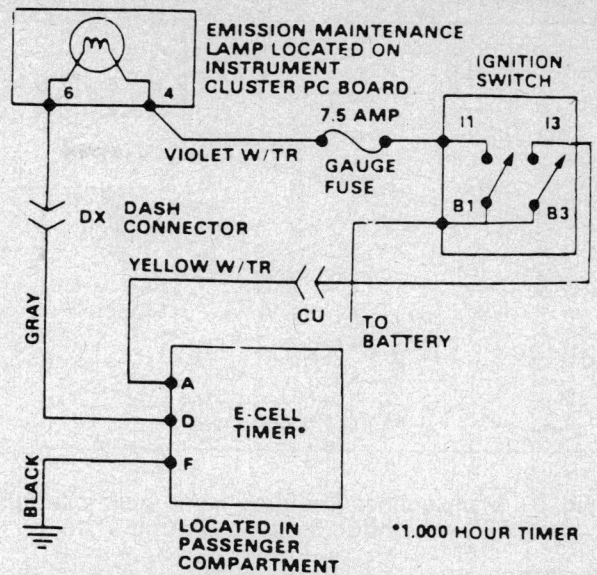

Fig. 7   Emission maintenance reminder indicator wiring schematic. 1982–83 AMC Concord & Spirit & 1982–87 Eagle

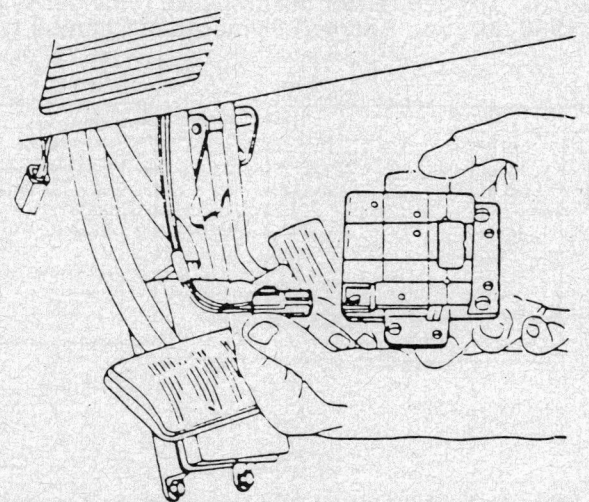

Fig. 8   Emission maintenance timer replacement. 1988 Eagle except Medallion & Premier

EMISSION MAINTENANCE REMINDER INDICATOR

1980–81 AMC CONCORD, EAGLE, PACER & SPIRIT

On 1980-81 models, at 30,000 miles intervals, a warning lamp will be illuminated on the instrument panel to indicate oxygen sensor replacement. After performing the required service, the reminder lamp switch must be reset. The switch is located between the upper and lower speedometer cables in the engine compartment on the lefthand side of the dash panel. Rotate the reset screw located on the switch ¼ turn counterclockwise, **Fig. 6.**

1982–83 AMC CONCORD & SPIRIT & 1982–87 EAGLE

The emission maintenance lamp will, **Fig. 7,** illuminate after 1000 hours of engine operation to indicate that the oxygen sensor must be replaced. After performing the required service, the emission maintenance E-Cell timer must be replaced for the next 1000 hour interval.

This timer is located in the passenger compartment, attached to the wiring harness leading to the MCU. To replace timer, remove printed circuit board, then remove timer from its enclosure and insert replacement timer.

1988 EAGLE EXCEPT MEDALLION & PREMIER

The emission maintenance timer will illuminate an indicator lamp on the instrument cluster when vehicle mileage has reached 82,500 miles. At this time, the oxygen sensor and PCV valve should be replaced, in addition to the other required emission maintenance scheduled for this mileage.

If the timer should fail before vehicle has accumulated 82,500 miles, the timer and oxygen sensor should both be replaced to maintain a proper sensor replacement interval.

After performing the required service, replace the emission maintenance timer as follows:
1. Remove emission maintenance timer to dash bracket attaching screws. The timer is located on the dash panel to the right of the steering column.
2. Remove timer from bracket, then disconnect electrical connector and remove timer from vehicle, **Fig. 8.**
3. Connect electrical connector to replacement timer, then position timer to mounting bracket and install and tighten attaching screws.

LOW COOLANT WARNING LAMP

1990–92 PLYMOUTH LASER & EAGLE TALON

The Low Coolant Warning Lamp will be illuminated whenever coolant level in the coolant reservoir is below a pre-determined level. Add coolant to bring reservoir to proper level to turn lamp off.

Fig. 9 Maintenance Required Lamp bulb location. 1988–91 Dodge & Plymouth Colt Vista

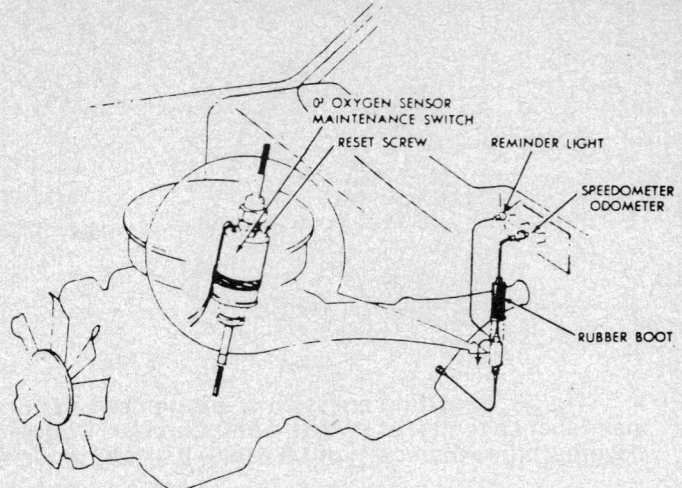

Fig. 10 Oxygen sensor maintenance reminder system. 1980 Chrysler, Dodge & Plymouth mechanical type

MAINTENANCE REQUIRED LAMP

1988–91 DODGE & PLYMOUTH COLT VISTA

This lamp will be illuminated at 50,000, 80,000, 100,000 and 150,000 miles to indicate interval for emission control system inspection. After performing emission control system inspection at the 50,000, 80,000 or 100,00 mile interval, the lamp can be reset by moving the reset switch lever located at the rear of the instrument cluster, **Fig. 1**. At the 150,000 mile interval, after performing inspection, remove bulb from lamp socket, **Fig. 9**.

OXYGEN SENSOR MAINTENANCE REMINDER LAMP

1980 CHRYSLER, DODGE & PLYMOUTH

At 30,000 miles intervals, a warning lamp will be illuminated on the instrument panel to indicate oxygen sensor replacement. The reminder can either be mechanical, **Fig. 10**, or electronic, **Fig. 11**. After performing the required service, the reminder lamp must be reset.

On the mechanical system, rotate the reset screw located on the switch counterclockwise until it stops, **Fig. 6**.

On the electronic system, remove 9 volt battery from module, which is located under the lefthand side of the instrument panel. Insert a suitable rod into hole on module case to reset switch. After resetting switch, install a replacement 9 volt battery.

POWER LOSS/LIMIT LAMP

CHRYSLER, DODGE & PLYMOUTH

The Power Loss/Limit lamp will be illuminated for approximately 3 seconds after the ignition switch has been placed in the ON position as a bulb check. If incorrect or no signals are received by the logic module from various sensors, the logic module will illuminate the Power Loss/Limit lamp. After diagnosing and servicing the fuel injection system or EGR system

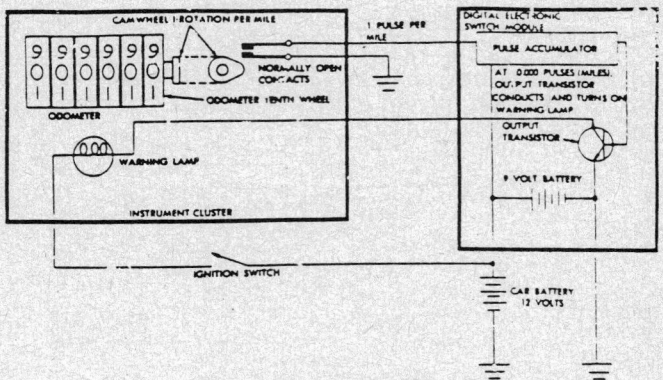

Fig. 11 Oxygen sensor maintenance reminder system. 1980 Chrysler, Dodge & Plymouth electronic type

(California models with EGR sensor), the logic module memory can be cleared by disconnecting and reconnecting the battery quick disconnect.

VEHICLE MAINTENANCE MONITOR (VMM) SYSTEM

DODGE MONACO & EAGLE PREMIER

This system, **Fig. 12,** monitors regular service and maintenance intervals, engine oil level, engine coolant level, windshield washer fluid level, brake and tail lamps, door ajar, transaxle (models w/4-150 engine) and oil, coolant and washer sensors.

When the vehicle is started and no faults are present, the display will indicate "MONITOR." If the monitor detects a fault, it will be noted on the display. If more than one fault is noted, the fault of the highest priority will be displayed first. The display will then note all existing faults and return to the fault of highest priority. The VMM fault messages are as follows:

DOOR—Door Ajar—Close door indicated on vehicle outline display to reset monitor.

LAMP—Brake Or Tail Lamp Outage—The display will be illu-

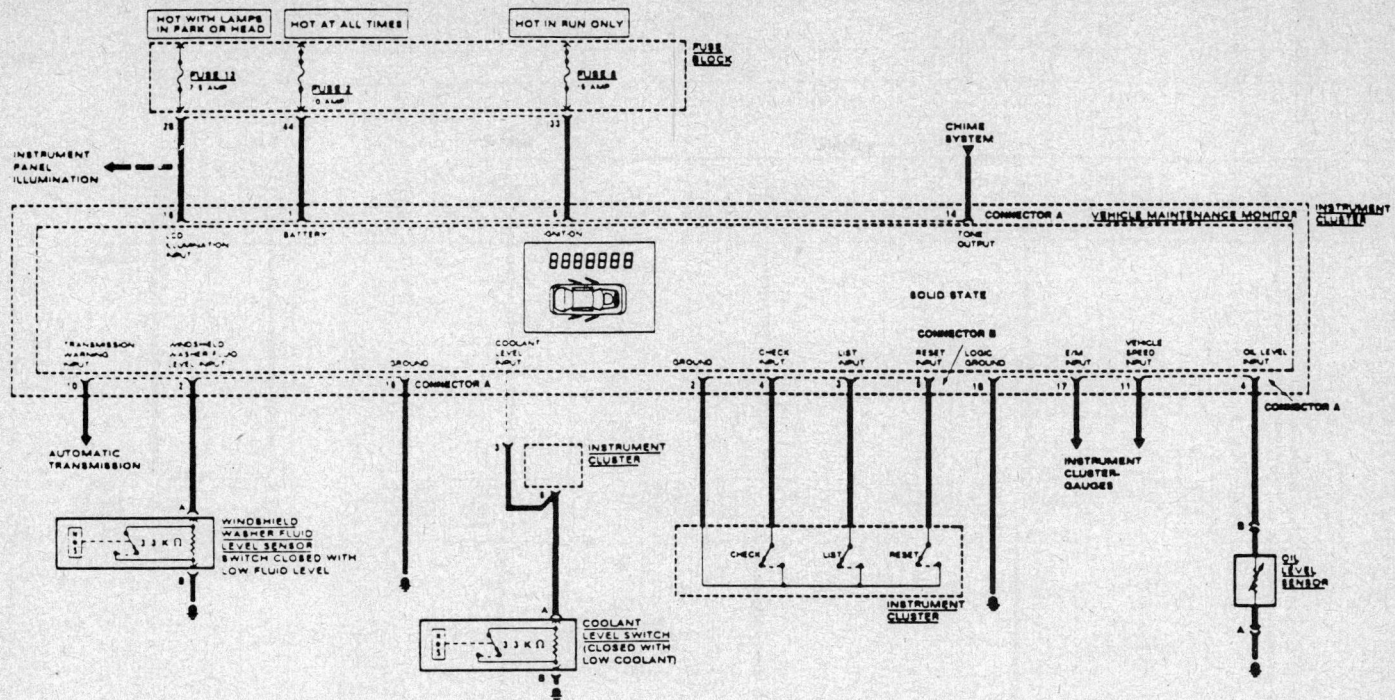

Fig. 12 Vehicle Maintenance Monitor (VMM) System wiring schematic (Part 1 of 2). Dodge Monaco & Eagle Premier

minated when brake is applied or light switch is in the ON position and a burned out lamp bulb is present. To reset monitor, replace burned out lamp bulb.

COOLANT—Low Engine Coolant Level—Bringing coolant to proper level will reset monitor.

OIL—Low Engine Oil Level—The system will check engine oil level approximately 12 minutes after the ignition switch has been placed in the OFF position. A low oil level condition must be indicated three consecutive times before the monitor will display "Oil." To reset monitor, add oil to bring to proper level, then while display is indicating the "Oil" message, depress Reset select switch until a beep is noted. Even if Reset select switch is not depressed, the system will automatically reset monitor after three proper oil level readings have been obtained.

WASHER—Low Washer Fluid Level—Bringing washer fluid to proper level will reset monitor.

TRANS—Service Transaxle (Models w/4-150 Engine)—Indicates defect in automatic transaxle.

SERVICE—Perform Required Service and Maintenance—This message will be indicated at 7,500 mile intervals to indicate that required service is to be performed. After performing the required service, depress Reset select switch until a beep is noted.

SENSOR—This message will be indicated when a defect in the oil, coolant or washer sensor circuit is noted. Refer to "Self-Diagnosis."

MILES (KMS)—Miles to next scheduled service interval.

Self-Diagnosis

To diagnosis, depress and hold the Check and List select switches, then place ignition switch in ON position. With the

instrument cluster switch in the English mode, all diagnosis will be performed automatically in sequence. With the instrument cluster in the Metric mode, the Check select switch will have to be depressed to proceed to the next test. The display will indicate which components are defective or satisfactory, refer to **Fig. 13**. After completing diagnosis, depress Check and List select switches to exit diagnosis mode.

Troubleshooting

1. If a condition of no display or incorrect information exist, start engine and check the following:
   a. On models less passive restraint check fuses 8 and 19 in fuse panel. On models with passive restraint, check fuses 2 and 8 in fuse panel. Replace any blown fuses.
   b. Using a suitable voltmeter, check terminal Nos. 1 and 5 of connector A, **Fig. 12**. Voltmeter should indicate battery voltage, if not check for open circuit to fuse panel.
   c. Connect a suitable ohmmeter between terminal Nos. 15 and 18 of connector A, **Fig. 12**. Ohmmeter should indicate zero ohms. If a no display condition is present, replace monitor. If a incorrect information condition is present, refer to "Self-Diagnosis." If reading is other than zero ohms, check for open circuit to ground.
   d. With all doors closed, connect an ohmmeter between terminal Nos. 6, 7, 8 and 9 of connector A, **Fig. 12**. Ohmmeter should indicate an infinite reading. If reading is other than infinite, check for short circuit to ground.
2. If monitor fails to change modes, disconnect electrical

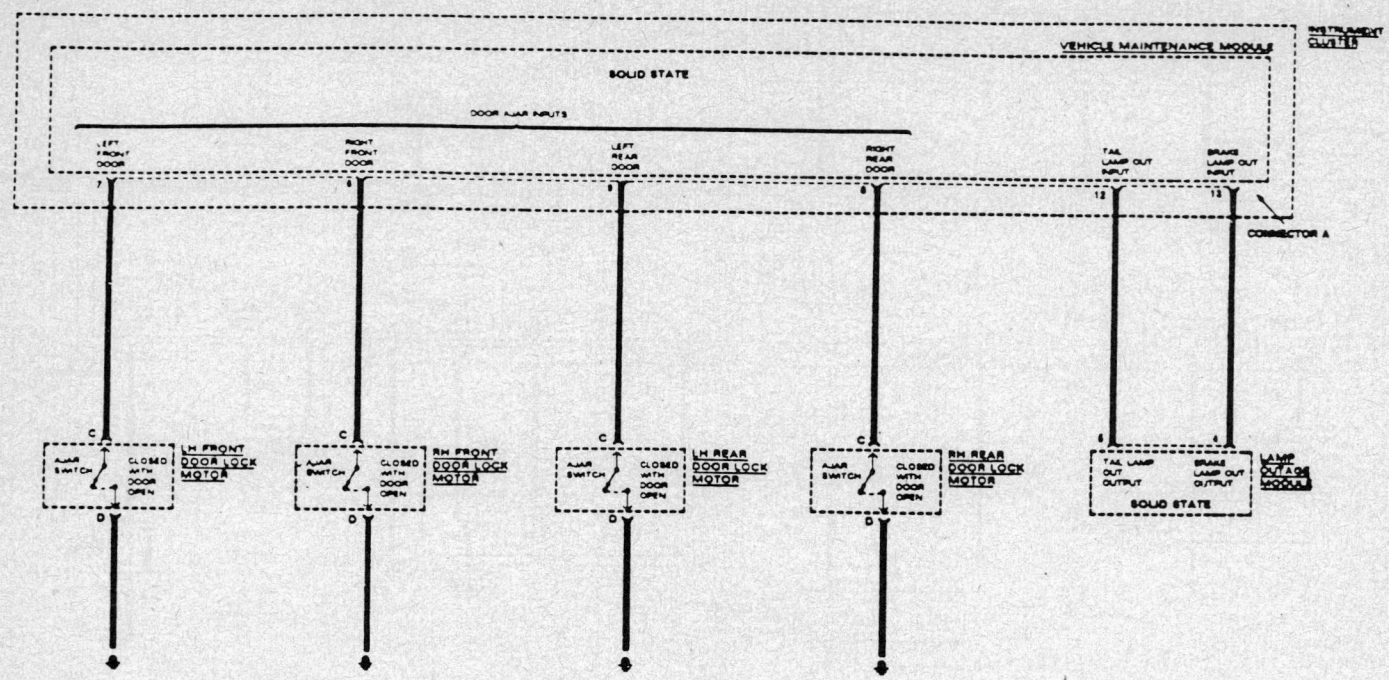

Fig. 12   Vehicle Maintenance Monitor (VMM) System wiring schematic (Part 2 of 2). Dodge Monaco & Eagle Premier

connector B, **Fig. 12,** and proceed as follows:

a. With Check select switch depressed, connect ohmmeter between terminal Nos. 2 and 4 of connector B. If ohmmeter reading is zero ohms, proceed to step b. If ohmmeter reading is other than zero ohms, replace mode select switches.

b. With List select switch depressed, connect ohmmeter between terminal Nos. 2 and 3 of connector B. If ohmmeter reading is zero ohms, proceed to step c. If ohmmeter reading is other than zero ohms, replace mode select switches.

c. With Reset select switch depressed, connect ohmmeter between terminal Nos. 2 and 5 of connector B. Ohmmeter reading should be zero ohms. If ohmmeter reading is other than zero ohms, replace mode select switches.

TEST 1 Initially, a number will be displayed on the monitor's screen. This number indicates the version of the maintenance module installed in the vehicle.

TEST 2

In Display	Meaning
"CAL 0"	Monitor Bad
"CAL 1-7"	Monitor OK
"CAL F"	Monitor Bad

TEST 3 The module internal memory is tested.

In Display	Meaning
"RAM P"	Monitor OK
"RAM F"	Monitor Bad

TEST 4 The module program is tested.

In Display	Meaning
"ROM P"	Monitor OK
"ROM F"	Monitor Bad

TEST 5 The monitor's clocks are tested.

In Display	Meaning
"TIME P"	Monitor OK
"TIME F"	Monitor Bad

TEST 6 The monitor's storage capability is tested.

In Display	Meaning
"NVM P"	Monitor OK
"NVM F"	Monitor Bad

TEST 7 The monitor's internal synchronization is tested.

In Display	Meaning
"PAR 0"	Monitor OK
"PAR N"	Monitor Bad

TEST 8 The monitor's display screen is tested.

In Display	Meaning
All Segments ON	Monitor OK
All Segments OFF	Monitor OK
"0"	Monitor OK
"1"	Monitor OK
"10"	Monitor OK
"100"	Monitor OK
"1000"	Monitor OK
"10000"	Monitor OK
"100000"	Monitor OK
"111111"	Monitor OK
"122222"	Monitor OK
"133333"	Monitor OK
"144444"	Monitor OK
"155555"	Monitor OK
"166666"	Monitor OK
"177777"	Monitor OK
"188888"	Monitor OK
"199999"	Monitor OK

The graphic segments will light one at a time in the following order: the engine symbol, the car outline, right front door, right rear door, rear tail lamps, left rear door, and left front door. Any deviation from the above patterns signifies a bad monitor. Should any of the segments fail to light, the monitor is bad.

TEST 9 This test can only be performed while the test program is in the manual mode. OIL will flash. Release CHECK button and press and hold LIST button until OIL flashes three times, then release LIST button and OIL will stop flashing. There will be a 30-45 second delay while system is testing. Oil level faults are displayed at this time. The engine oil level is tested.

In Display	Meaning
"OIL H"	Monitor OK, Oil Level Normal
"OIL L"	Monitor OK, but Oil Level Is Low
"OIL O"	Monitor OK, but Oil Level Sensor Is Open
"OIL S"	Monitor OK, but Oil Level Sensor Is Shorted

TEST 10 The oil level probe is tested. The intermittent fault can be cleared in diagnostic program by pressing RESET switch while message is displayed.

In Display	Meaning
"OIL IF"	Intermittent Fault With Oil Sensor
NO MESSAGE	Monitor OK, Sensor OK

TEST 11 The washer fluid level is tested.

In Display	Meaning
"WASH H"	Washer Fluid Level Normal
"WASH L"	Washer Fluid Level Low
"WASH O"	Washer Fluid Level Probe Open

TEST 12 The washer level sensor is tested. The intermittent fault can be cleared in diagnostic program by pressing RESET switch while message is displayed.

In Display	Meaning
"WASHER IF"	Intermittent Fault With Washer Fluid Sensor
NO MESSAGE	Monitor OK, Sensor OK

TEST 13 The coolant fluid level is tested.

In Display	Meaning
"COOL H"	Coolant Fluid Level Is Normal
"COOL L"	Coolant Fluid Level Is Low
"COOL O"	Coolant Fluid Level Probe Is Open

TEST 14 The coolant fluid level sensor is tested. The intermittent fault can be cleared in diagnostic program by pressing RESET switch while message is displayed.

In Display	Meaning
"COOL IF"	Intermittent Fault With the Coolant Level Sensor
NO MESSAGE	Monitor OK, Sensor OK

TEST 15 The tail lamp circuit is tested.

In Display	Meaning
"TLO P"	Tail Lamp Circuit OK
"TLO F"	Tail Lamp Circuit Open

TEST 16 The brake lamp circuit is tested.

In Display	Meaning
"BLO P"	Brake Lamp Circuit OK
"BLO F"	Brake Lamp Circuit Open

TEST 17 The status of the transmission diagnostic module is tested.

In Display	Meaning
"TRANS P"	Transmission Module OK
"TRANS F"	Transmission Module Fault

TEST 18 The frequency of the road speed sensor is displayed. When in manual mode, continuous monitoring is possible.

In Display	Meaning
"SPD XXX"	Frequency of Vehicle Speed Sensor

*Note: XXX will vary from 0 and increase as vehicle speed increases.

Fig. 13 Vehicle Maintenance Monitor (VMM) System self diagnosis test chart. Dodge Monaco & Eagle Premier

Ford Motor Co.

INDEX

ANTI-LOCK WARNING LAMP

This lamp will be illuminated when the ignition switch is placed in the ON position. The lamp maybe illuminated for as long as 30 seconds as a bulb and system check. If lamp remains illuminated or comes on while operating the vehicle, a problem in the anti-lock brake system is indicated. When lamp is illuminated, place ignition switch in OFF position, then restart engine. If lamp still remains illuminated, the anti-lock brake system should be serviced. The brake system will remain functional, but without the anti-lock function. After servicing the anti-lock brake system, the lamp will automatically be reset when vehicle is operated at a speed over 25 MPH.

AIR BAG SYSTEM WARNING LAMP

On models equipped with an air bag system, if the air bag warning lamp illuminates and stays on, diagnosis and repair of the air bag system will be necessary to reset the lamp.

AUXILIARY WARNING INDICATOR & GRAPHIC DISPLAY MODULE

MERKUR

This system monitors engine oil level, engine coolant level, windshield washer fluid level, brake pad wear, fuel level, seat belt usage, headlamp, brake and tail lamps, door ajar, liftgate ajar and ambient temperature.

When ignition switch is placed in the ON position, the graphic display module and all warning indicators will illuminate for 5 seconds. After 5 seconds, all warning lamps should go off and graphic display should indicate outline of vehicle and the two brake lights. The two brake light indications should go out once the brake pedal is depressed. If warning lamps remain illuminated or graphic display indicates a fault, check the following:

The low engine oil warning lamp is used to indicate when engine oil level is 12 mm or more below the specified level. The lamp will be illuminated during engine starting. If oil level is sufficient, the lamp will go off when engine is operating. If oil level is low the lamp will remain on until engine oil is added

and the ignition switch is placed in the OFF position. The module will take approximately 3 minutes to reset. If the engine is started during this period, the last recorded reading will be displayed.

The Low Coolant Warning Lamp will be illuminated whenever coolant level in the coolant recovery bottle is below the specified mark. Raise coolant level in recovery bottle to turn lamp off.

The low fuel warning lamp will be illuminated whenever fuel level drops below 1.4 gals. Add fuel to vehicle to turn lamp off.

The Washer Fluid Warning Lamp will be illuminated whenever fluid drops below the specified reservoir level. Raise washer fluid level in reservoir to turn lamp off.

The brake pad wear warning lamp will be illuminated when disc brake pads wear down to 1.5 mm. At 1.5 mm a wire loop in the brake pad is exposed and severed, which in turn illuminates the brake pad warning lamp. To turn lamp off, replace brake pads.

Air temperature is monitored by a sensor located on the righthand side of the vehicle behind the front bumper. The signal from the sensor is evaluated by the control assembly, which controls the low air temperature (ICE) indication on the graphic display. When air temperature is approximately 39°F, the ICE indication will be illuminated in yellow. When temperature drops to 32°F the triangle located around the ICE indication will be illuminated in red. If a short circuit in wiring between sensor and control assembly is present, the ICE indication on the graphic will flash. If an open circuit between the sensor and control assembly exist, the triangle will flash.

The graphic display will indicate when doors and liftgate are closed (green) and when doors and liftgate are ajar (red). To cancel door or liftgate ajar indication, close door or liftgate indicated.

The graphic will also indicate lamp bulb outage. Replacement of lamp bulb indicated will turn off graphic display indicator. A lamp out indication will also be present if an open or circuit in lamp wiring is present.

CHECK ENGINE LIGHT (WITH JUMPER WIRE)

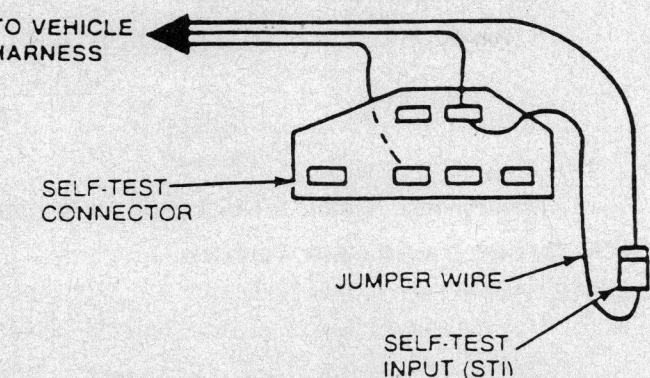

Fig. 1 Jumper wire connections for resetting Check Engine Lamp

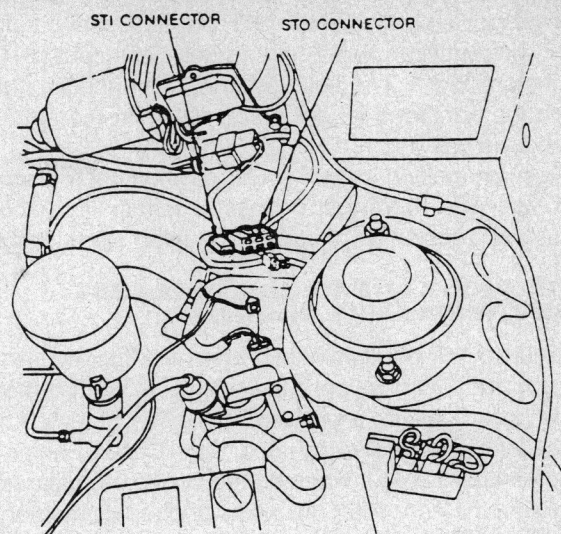

Fig. 2 STI connector location. 1988–90 Festiva

CHECK ENGINE LAMP

1987–93 MODELS w/EEC-IV

Except Capri, Festiva, Merkur, Probe w/2.2L Engine & Escort/Tracer w/1.8L Engine

This lamp will be illuminated when the ignition switch is placed in the ON position. After engine is started the lamp should go off, unless a problem has been detected by the EEC-IV system. Following diagnosis and repair, the Check Engine/MIL lamp will automatically reset when stored codes are cleared from the EEC-IV system memory. After diagnosis and repair, EEC-IV memory may be cleared of stored codes as follows:

1. With ignition switch in the OFF position, connect a jumper wire between Self Test and Self Test Input (STI) connectors, **Fig. 1.** On Ford Crown Victoria, Mercury Grand Marquis and Lincoln Town Car models, the Self Test and STI connectors are gray in color and are located on the front of lefthand fender apron, near the Electronic Engine Control (EEC) relay. On Ford Mustang models, the Self Test and STI connectors are gray in color and are located on the lefthand fender apron. On Ford Tempo, Topaz, 1987-90 Escort and Mercury Lynx, the Self Test connector is gray in color and the STI connector is black in color and they are both located on the righthand fender apron near the front of the strut tower. On Ford Taurus and Mercury Sable, the Self Test and STI connectors are gray in color and are located on the righthand fender apron near the front of the engine in the area of the AIR pump and alternator. On 1987-88 Ford Thunderbird and Mercury Cougar, the Self Test and STI connectors are gray in color and are located on the lefthand fender apron near the strut tower. On 1989-93 Ford Thunderbird and Mercury Cougar, the Self Test and STI connectors are gray in color and are located on the righthand fender apron near the strut tower. On 1987 Lincoln Mark VII & 1987-89 Continental, the Self Test and STI connectors are gray in color and are located on the righthand side of fender apron

near the ignition coil. On 1988-91 Lincoln Continental, the Self Test and STI connectors are attached to the Electronic Control Assembly, which is located in the engine compartment at the center of the firewall below the TFI ignition module.

2. Position ignition switch in ON position, then disconnect jumper wire from test connector terminals. Disconnect jumper as soon as check engine lamp starts flashing.

Festiva

The Check Engine Indicator lamp will be illuminated when the ignition switch in in the RUN position with engine not operating. When the engine is started, the Check Engine lamp should go off. If lamp remains on, a service code has been stored in the EEC-IV self test system memory. After diagnosis and repair, the self test memory may be cleared of stored codes as follows:

1. With ignition switch in the OFF position, connect a jumper wire between Self Test Input (STI) connector terminal and ground. The STI connector is located in the engine compartment at the rear lefthand side, **Fig. 2.**
2. Position ignition switch in ON position, then disconnect and reconnect jumper wire connected between STI connector and ground.
3. Disconnect jumper from STI connector as soon as check engine lamp stops flashing.
4. Disconnect battery ground cable and depress brake pedal for approximately 5 to 10 seconds.
5. Reconnect battery ground cable.

Merkur

This lamp will be illuminated when the ignition switch is placed in the ON position. After engine is started the lamp should go off, unless a problem has been detected by the EEC-IV system. After diagnosis and repair, the Check Engine lamp will automatically reset when stored codes are cleared from the EEC-IV system memory. After diagnosis and repair, EEC-IV memory may be cleared of stored codes as follows:

1. With ignition switch in the OFF position, connect a jumper wire between Self Test and Self Test Input (STI) connectors, **Fig. 1.** The Self Test and STI connectors located on the righthand fender apron between the strut tower and the battery.

2. Position ignition switch in ON position, then disconnect jumper wire from test connector terminals. Disconnect jumper as soon as check engine lamp starts flashing.

Capri, Probe w/2.2L Engine & 1991 Escort/Tracer w/1.8L Engine

This lamp will be illuminated when the ignition switch is placed in the ON position. After engine is started the lamp should go off, unless a problem has been detected by the system. After diagnosis and repair, the Check Engine lamp will automatically reset when stored codes are cleared from the system memory. After diagnosis and repair, memory may be cleared of stored codes as follows:

1. Disconnect battery ground cable, then depress brake pedal for approximately 5 to 10 seconds.
2. Reconnect battery ground cable.

1994–95 MODELS w/EEC-IV

This lamp will be illuminated when the ignition switch is placed in the ON position. After engine is started the lamp should go off, unless a problem has been detected by the EEC-IV system an diagnostic trouble codes are stored in the Powertrain Control Module (PCM). Following diagnosis and repair, the Check Engine/MIL lamp will automatically reset when stored diagnostic trouble codes are cleared from PCM memory. After diagnosis and repair, PCM memory may be cleared of stored codes as follows:

1. Connect electronic self-tester to LINK connector of NGS and Data Link Connector (DLC) and Self-Test Input (STI) connector on vehicle.
2. Using tester, retrieve diagnostic trouble codes (DTCs) from PCM.
3. When DTCs begin to be displayed, deactivate tester as follows:
   a. With Super Star II tester, unlatch center button (up position). With other scan tool, press STOP button.
   b. Except Super Star II tester/scan tool, remove jumper wire from between Self-Test Input (STI) connector and Signal Return Pin of DLC.
4. Continuous memory will be erased in the PCM.
5. To clear Keep Alive Memory (KAM), disconnect battery ground cable for at least five minutes.

1994–95 MODELS w/EEC-V

This lamp will be illuminated when the ignition switch is placed in the ON position. After engine is started the lamp should go off, unless a problem has been detected by the EEC-V system an diagnostic trouble codes are stored in the Powertrain Control Module (PCM). Following diagnosis and repair, the Check Engine/MIL lamp will automatically reset when stored diagnostic trouble codes are cleared from PCM memory. The PCM reset allows the scan tool to command the PCM to clear all diagnostic trouble codes.

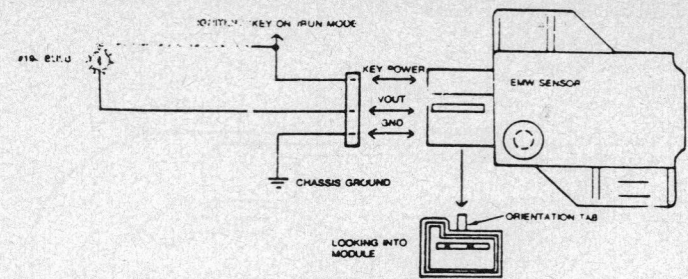

Fig. 3   Maintenance Reminder Lamp wiring schematic

PCM Reset Using Star Tester

1. Turn ignition Off.
2. Perform necessary vehicle preparation and visual inspection.
3. Connect Start Tester, then select vehicle model and year.
4. Follow operating instructions on tester screen. Select Generic OBD II Functions.
5. Press CONT button if all OBD II monitors are not complete.
6. Turn ignition switch to On position.
7. Select Clear Diagnostic Codes and press Start key.

PCM Reset Using Generic Scan Tool

1. Turn ignition Off.
2. Connect scan tool to DLC.
3. Turn ignition switch to On position.
4. Perform scan tool reset, then turn ignition switch to Off position.

Keep Alive Memory (KAM) Reset & PCM Reset Less Electronic Tester

To clear Keep Alive Memory (KAM), disconnect battery ground cable for at least five minutes. This will also result in PCM reset.

LOW COOLANT WARNING SYSTEM

The Low Coolant Warning Lamp will be illuminated whenever coolant level in the coolant recovery bottle is significantly below the cold full mark. Raise coolant level in recovery bottle to the cold full mark to turn lamp off.

CHECK OIL/LOW OIL LEVEL WARNING INDICATOR

This system is used to indicate when engine oil level is 1½ quarts or more below the specified level. The lamp will be illuminated during engine starting. If oil level is sufficient, the lamp will go off when engine is operating. If oil level is low the lamp will remain on until engine oil is added and the ignition switch is placed in the OFF position. The module will take approximately 5 minutes to reset. If the engine is started during this period, the last recorded reading will be displayed.

MAINTENANCE REMINDER INDICATOR

This lamp, **Fig. 3**, is used on some not equipped with electronic engine controls. The lamp will be illuminated after approximately 2000 engine starts (60,000 miles of vehicle operation). After performing the required emission control service, the lamp maybe reset as follows:

1. Turn ignition switch to OFF position.
2. Install a suitable screwdriver through the .2 inch hole labeled Reset, then lightly press down and hold.
3. While pressing screwdriver down, turn ignition switch to RUN position. The advisory lamp will then come on. Hold screwdriver down for approximately 5 seconds.
4. Remove screwdriver and note advisory lamp. Lamp should go out within 2 to 10 seconds indicating that a reset has occurred. If lamp does not go out, repeat procedure. Turn ignition switch to OFF position.
5. Turn ignition switch to RUN position. The advisory lamp should light for approximately 2 to 10 seconds indicating that a proper reset has been accomplished.

MALFUNCTION INDICATOR LAMP (MIL)

EXCEPT 1988–89 TRACER

Refer to "Check Engine Lamp" for lamp reset procedure.

1988–89 TRACER

The malfunction indicator lamp is used only on EFI models. This lamp indicates a malfunction in the Electronic Engine Control system. If a malfunction occurs, the lamp will illuminate. The malfunction detected may or may not be a noticeable driveability problem. The lamp will be automatically reset during diagnosis and repair of the system.

This indicator system monitors the following:
1. Air Temperature sensor (ACT).
2. Barometric Pressure (BP) sensor.
3. Clutch switch, manual transaxle.
4. Engine coolant temperature (ECT) sensor.
5. Engine coolant temperature (ECT) switch.
6. Exhaust gas oxygen (EGO) sensor.
7. Ignition coil ($-$) terminal.

MESSAGE CENTER

CROWN VICTORIA, GRAND MARQUIS & TOWN CAR

The Message Center is located to the right of the instrument cluster. It consists of three buttons: Select, E/M and Reset. The E/M button switches the display between English and Metric. The Reset button sets data to zero or instantaneous information. The Select button cycles the message display through the following selections:
1. Average speed.
2. Fuel remaining.
3. Average fuel economy and instantaneous fuel economy.
4. Distance to empty.
5. Trip distance.

MARK VIII
Air Ride Switch Off

This warning message is displayed when the air suspension service switch, located in the luggage compartment on the lefthand side, is off.

Check Air Ride System

This warning message is displayed when an air suspension system diagnostic trouble code has been detected by the air suspension/EVO control module.

Check Charging System

This warning message is displayed when the electrical system is not maintaining a proper voltage at the message center.

Check Engine Temp

This warning message is displayed when the coolant is overheating.

Low Engine Coolant

This warning message is displayed when the engine coolant level is below the cold line of the coolant recovery reservoir.

Check Exterior Lamps

This warning message is displayed when one of the following lamps is turned on and at least one of them is burned out: a stop lamp, rear parking lamp, or low beam headlamp.

Change Oil Soon Or Oil Change Required

The oil life functions include oil life, change oil soon and oil change required. The oil life is determined by three functions: Smart Tach pulses, miles driven and time elapsed.

When the oil life drops down to the range of 1-5 , the "Change Oil Soon " message will appear. When oil life is 0 , the "Oil Change Required" message will appear.

Depressing the oil change reset button will reset the oil life to 100 .

MULTIPLE FUNCTION WARNING INDICATOR

1987–89 MUSTANG GT

This system monitors engine oil, cooling system, fuel and washer reservoir levels for low fluid level conditions. During engine starting the lamps will be illuminated for approximately 3 seconds as a bulb check out. After approximately 3 seconds, when the bulb check is completed, low fluid level conditions will be verified, if present.

The low engine oil warning lamp is used to indicate when engine oil level is 1½ quarts or more below the specified level. The lamp will be illuminated during engine starting. If oil level is sufficient, the lamp will go off when engine is operating. If oil level is low the lamp will remain on until engine oil is added and the ignition switch is placed in the OFF position. The module will take approximately 90 to 150 seconds to reset. If the engine is started during this period, the last recorded reading will be displayed.

The Low Coolant Warning Lamp will be illuminated whenever coolant level in the coolant recovery bottle is below the cold full mark. Raise coolant level in recovery bottle to the cold full mark to turn lamp off.

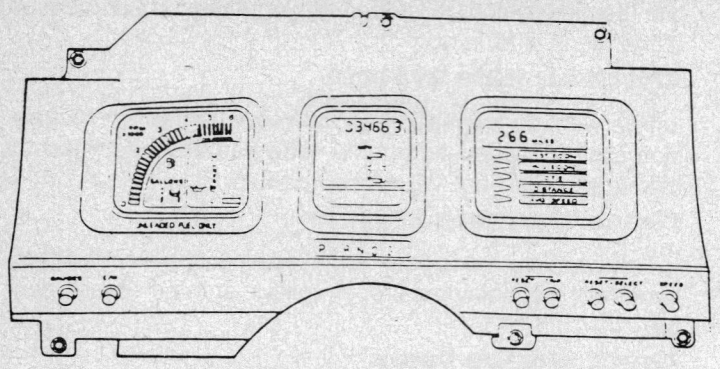

Fig. 4 Trip & reset button locations. 1985–88 Cougar & Thunderbird

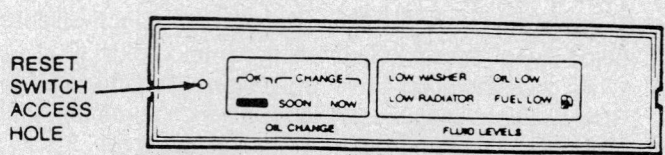

Fig. 5 Oil change interval indicator reset switch access hole location. 1989–93 Cougar & Thunderbird

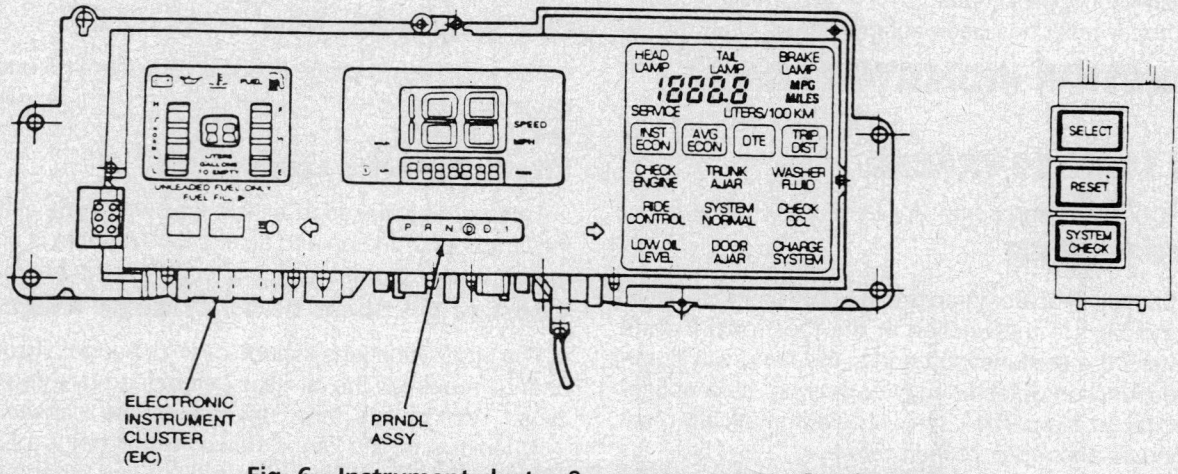

Fig. 6 Instrument cluster & message center. Continental

The low fuel warning lamp will be illuminated whenever fuel level is 1/8 tank capacity or less. Add fuel to vehicle to turn lamp off.

The Washer Fluid Warning Lamp will be illuminated whenever reservoir level is below 1/3 capacity. Raise washer fluid level in reservoir to turn lamp off.

SERVICE INTERVAL REMINDER

1985–88 COUGAR & THUNDERBIRD

At approximately 5,000 or 7,500 miles, depending on engine installation, the word SERVICE will appear on the display for approximately 1½ miles to indicate time for service interval. After completing the required service, reset service interval reminder by depressing and holding the Trip and Trip Reset buttons until three beeps are heard, Fig. 4.

1989–93 COUGAR & THUNDERBIRD

At approximately 7,500 miles, for models less super charged engine, the engine oil change indicator on the Vehicle Maintenance Monitor will indicate an oil change is needed. On models with super charged engine, the need for engine oil change will be indicated at 5,000 miles. After completing the required service, the oil change indicate can be reset by depressing the reset switch, Fig. 5. The reset switch is accessed through a switch access hole located to the left of the oil change indicator on the monitor display.

LINCOLN CONTINENTAL

After performing the require interval service, the service interval reminder mileage display on the instrument cluster can be reset as follows:
1. Depress System Check button on instrument panel, service interval reminder mileage should be displayed on fuel computer display, Fig. 6.
2. Depress Reset button, the service interval reminder mileage should start flashing.
3. Depress Reset and System Check buttons at the same time to reset mileage.

PROBE
Electronic Instrument Cluster

At 7,500 mile intervals, a Service Check message will be displayed under the System Scanner nomenclature on the instrument cluster for three minutes after engine start, Fig. 7. After performing the required interval service, reset the service interval by depressing and holding the Service reset button, located on the speed alarm keyboard, until three tones have sounded, Fig. 8.

Vehicle Maintenance Monitor

On models with Vehicle Maintenance Monitor, at 7,500 mile intervals a Service lamp, located on the overhead map lamp

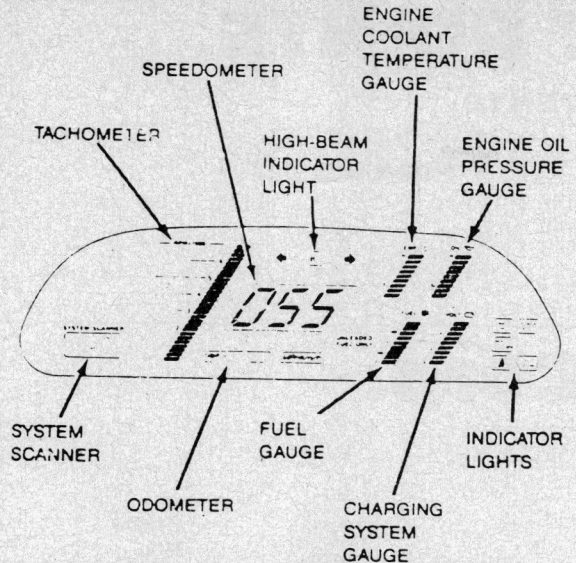

Fig. 7 Electronic instrument cluster. Probe

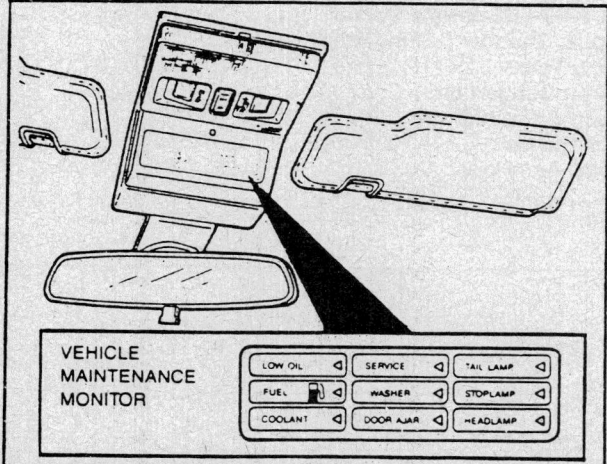

Fig. 9 Vehicle maintenance monitor. Probe

console, will be illuminated for 3 minutes after engine start, **Fig. 9.** After performing the required interval service, reset the service interval. On models with speed alarm keypad, depress and hold the Service reset button, until three tones have sounded. On models less speed alarm keypad, locate

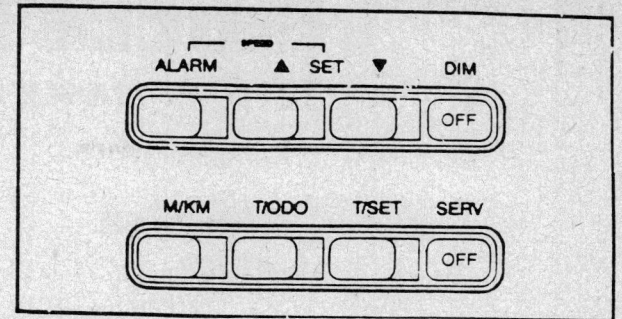

Fig. 8 Speed alarm keyboard. Probe

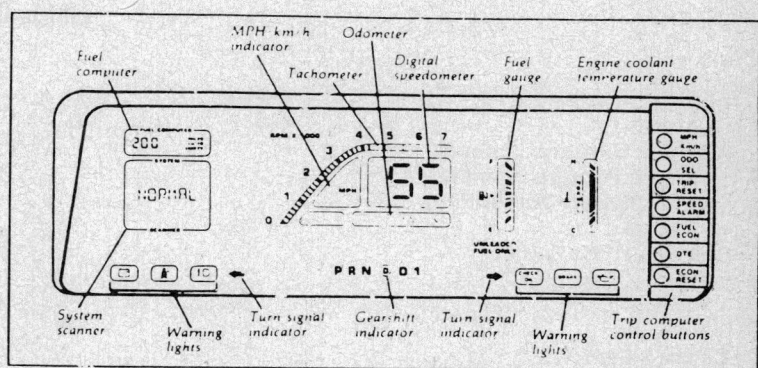

Fig. 10 Instrument cluster & trip control buttons. 1986–89 Sable & Taurus

reset hole in overhead console, then using a suitable tool depress the reset button located behind the hole.

1986–89 SABLE & TAURUS W/ELECTRONIC INSTRUMENT CLUSTER

At 7,200 mile intervals, a Service message will be displayed under the System Scanner nomenclature on the instrument cluster for 30 seconds after engine start, **Fig. 10.** After performing the required interval service, reset the service interval by simultaneously depressing the ODO Sel and Trip Reset buttons located on the instrument panel. The word service will disappear from the display and three tones will sound to indicate the service interval has been reset.

VEHICLE LIFT POINTS
TABLE OF CONTENTS

Chrysler Corp.
INDEX

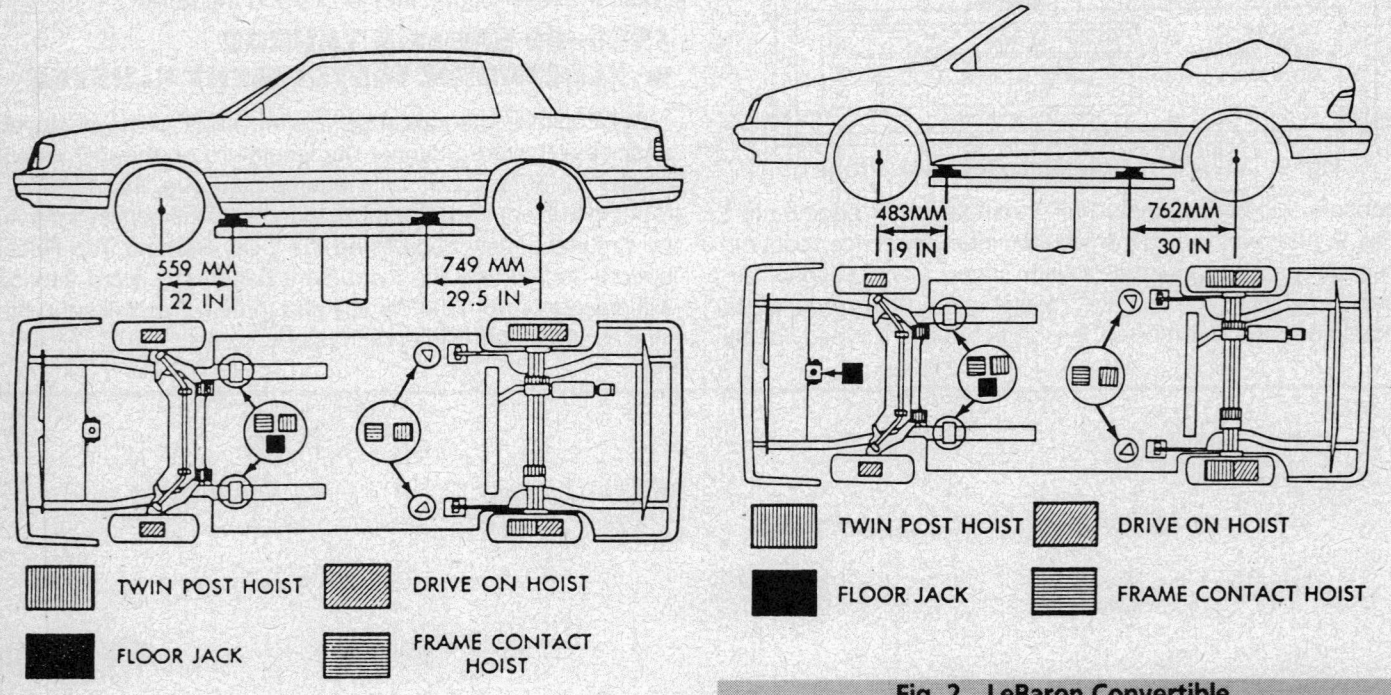

559 MM / 22 IN   749 MM / 29.5 IN

483MM / 19 IN   762MM / 30 IN

TWIN POST HOIST   DRIVE ON HOIST

FLOOR JACK   FRAME CONTACT HOIST

TWIN POST HOIST   DRIVE ON HOIST

FLOOR JACK   FRAME CONTACT HOIST

Fig. 2   LeBaron Convertible

Fig. 1   Acclaim, Dynasty, Imperial, Spirit, 1992–93 New Yorker Fifth Avenue & LeBaron Coupe

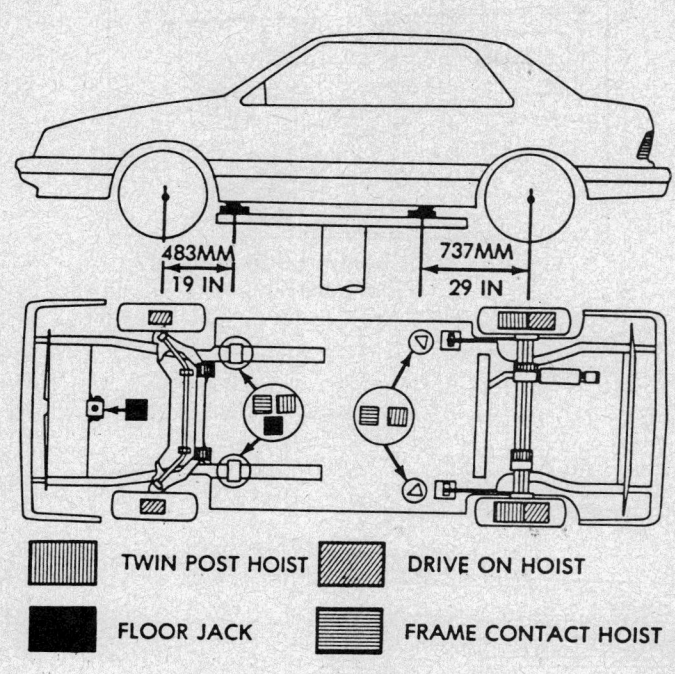

TWIN POST HOIST

DRIVE ON HOIST

FLOOR JACK

FRAME CONTACT HOIST

Fig. 3   Daytona, Shadow & Sundance

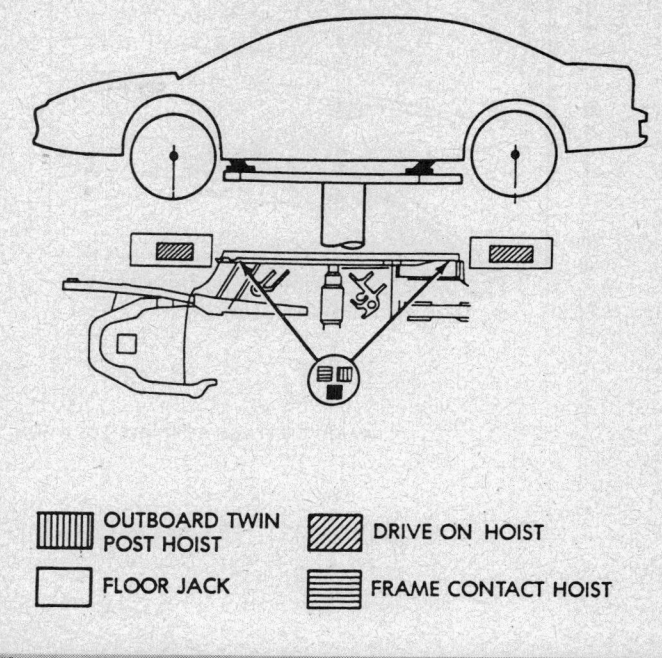

OUTBOARD TWIN POST HOIST

DRIVE ON HOIST

FLOOR JACK

FRAME CONTACT HOIST

Fig. 4   Concorde, Intrepid, Vision, 1994–95 LHS & New Yorker

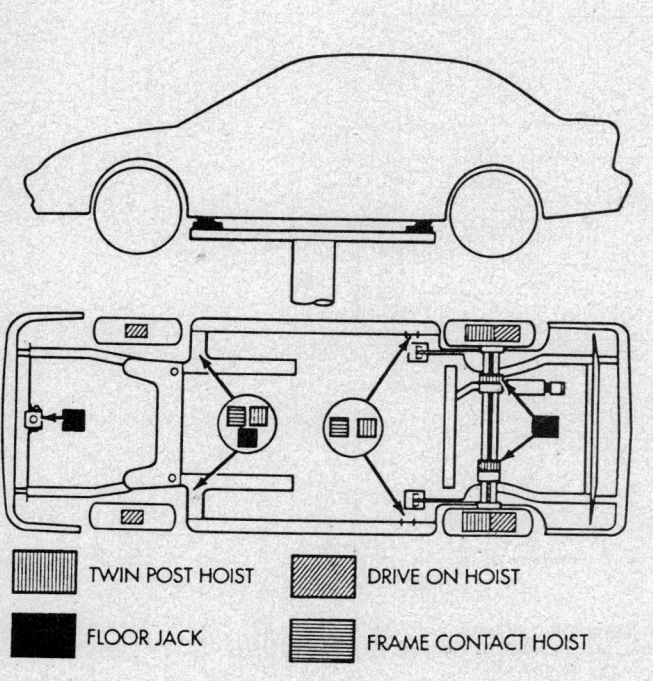

TWIN POST HOIST

DRIVE ON HOIST

FLOOR JACK

FRAME CONTACT HOIST

Fig. 5   Neon

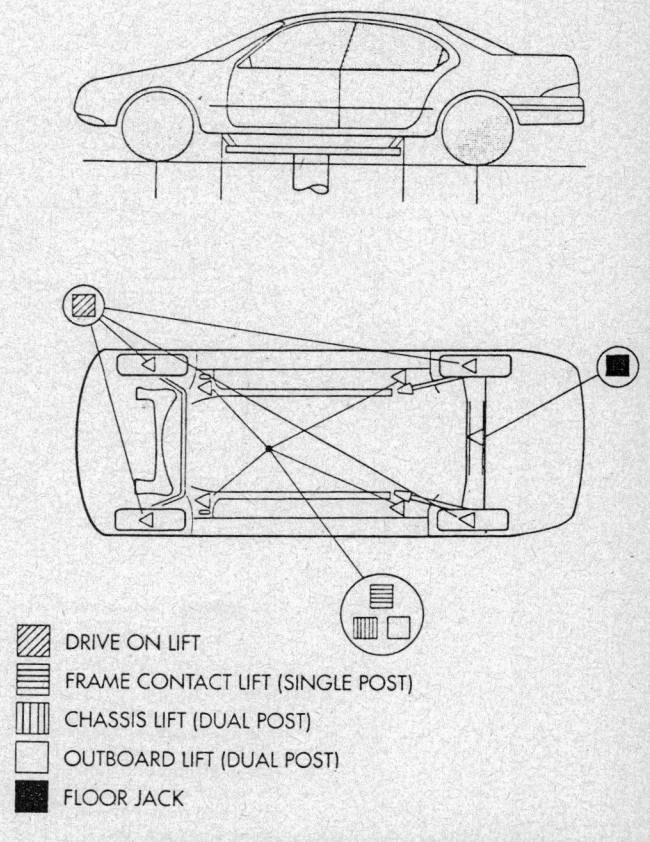

DRIVE ON LIFT

FRAME CONTACT LIFT (SINGLE POST)

CHASSIS LIFT (DUAL POST)

OUTBOARD LIFT (DUAL POST)

FLOOR JACK

Fig. 6   Cirrus & Stratus

Fig. 7   Colt & Summit Sedan (Front, Floor Jack)

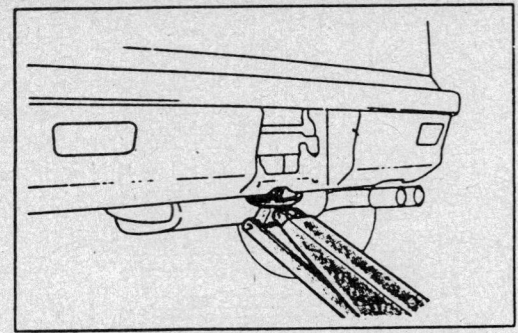

Fig. 8   Colt & Summit Sedan (Rear, Floor Jack)

FRAME CONTACT SUPPORT LOCATION

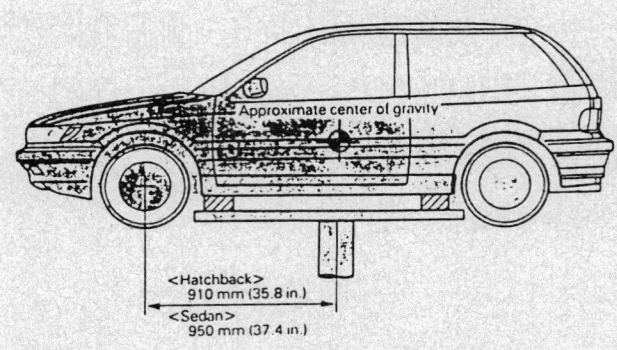

Approximate center of gravity

<Hatchback>
910 mm (35.8 in.)

<Sedan>
950 mm (37.4 in.)

LIFTING, JACKING SUPPORT LOCATION

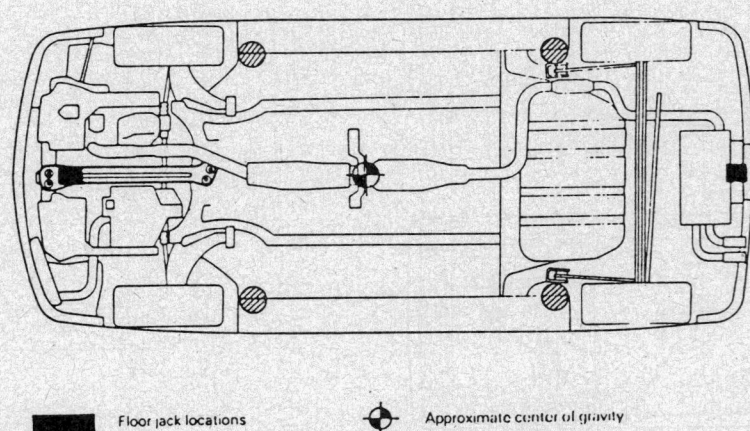

▬ Floor jack locations

⊕ Approximate center of gravity

▨ Frame contact hoist, twin post hoist or scissors jack (emergency) locations

Caution
* Never use a jack at the lateral rod or rear suspension assembly.
* In order to prevent scarring the center member, place a piece of cloth on the jack's contact surface (to prevent corrosion caused by damage to the coating).
* Never attempt to position a floor jack on any part of the vehicle underbody.
* Do not attempt to raise one entire side of the vehicle by placing a jack midway between the front and rear wheels. To do so could result in permanent damage to the body.

Fig. 9   Colt & Summit Sedan (Hoist)

LIFTING, JACKING SUPPORT LOCATION

2WD

4WD

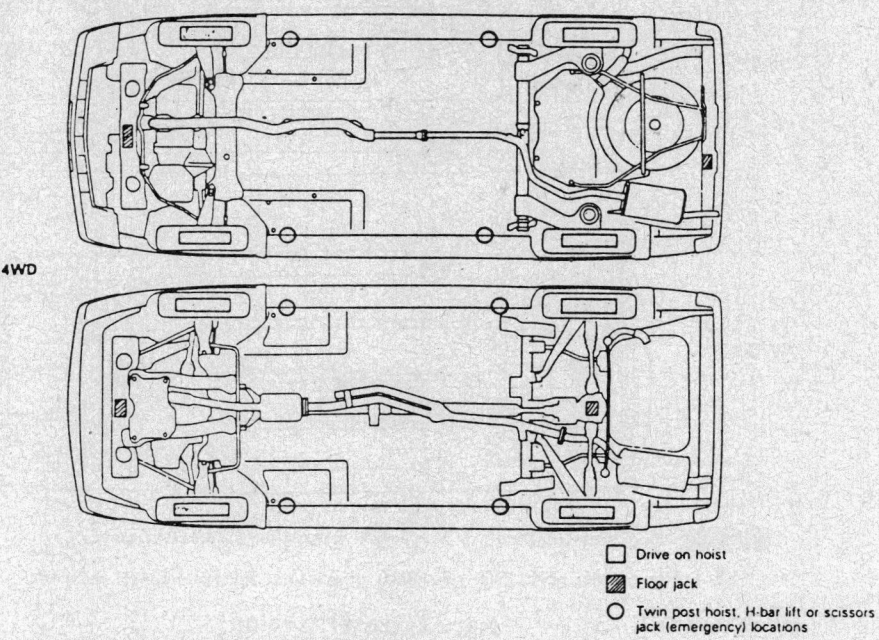

☐ Drive on hoist

▨ Floor jack

◯ Twin post hoist, H-bar lift or scissors
   jack (emergency) locations

Fig. 10 Colt Vista & Eagle Summit Wagon

FRAME CONTACT SUPPORT LOCATION

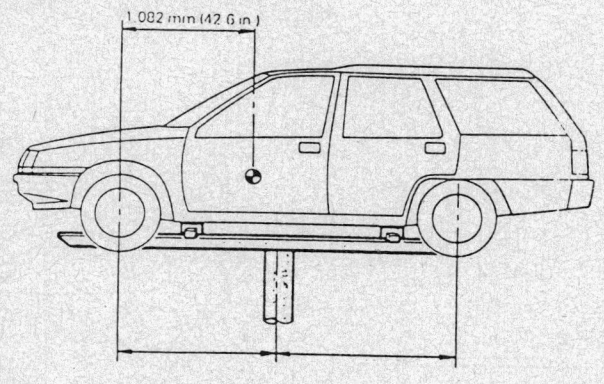

LIFTING, JACKING SUPPORT LOCATION

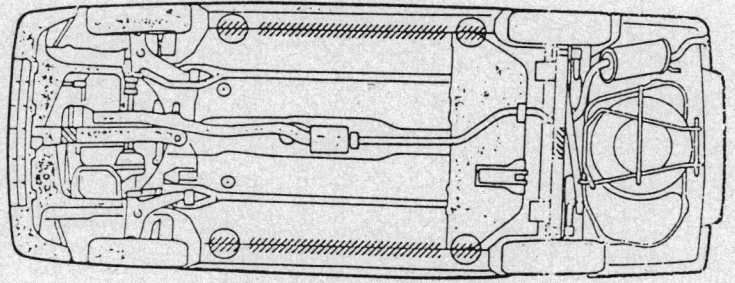

NOTE
Do not support car at locations
other than specified support point
Failure to do this will cause
damage etc

▨ Frame contact hoist

◩ Floor jack

◯ Twin post hoist or scissors jack (emergency) location

Fig. 11 Colt Wagon

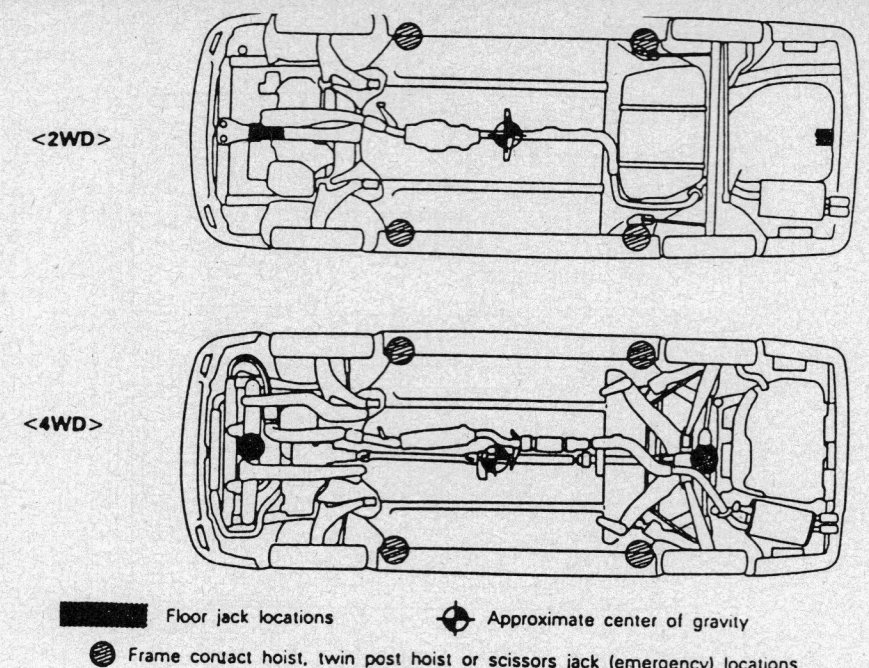

<2WD>

<4WD>

▬▬▬ Floor jack locations   ⊕ Approximate center of gravity

⊚ Frame contact hoist, twin post hoist or scissors jack (emergency) locations

Fig. 12   Laser & Talon

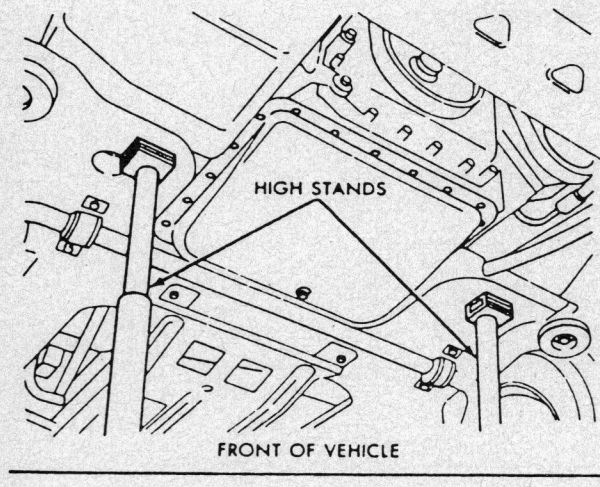

HIGH STANDS

FRONT OF VEHICLE

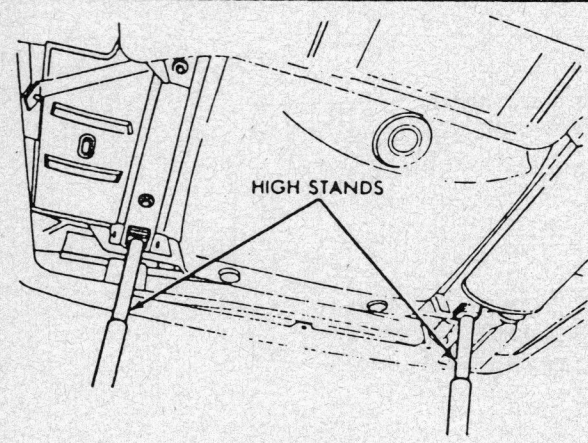

HIGH STANDS

REAR OF VEHICLE

Fig. 13   Monaco & Premier (High Stands)

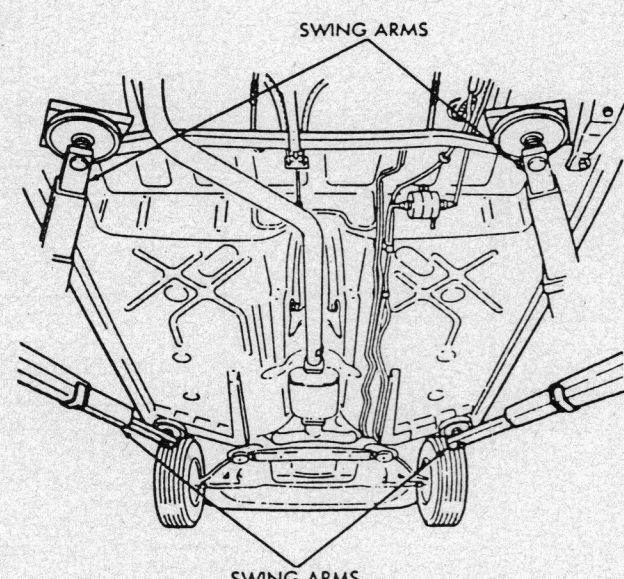

SWING ARMS

SWING ARMS

Fig. 14   Monaco & Premier (Swing Arm Hoist)

       CHRYSLER CORP.

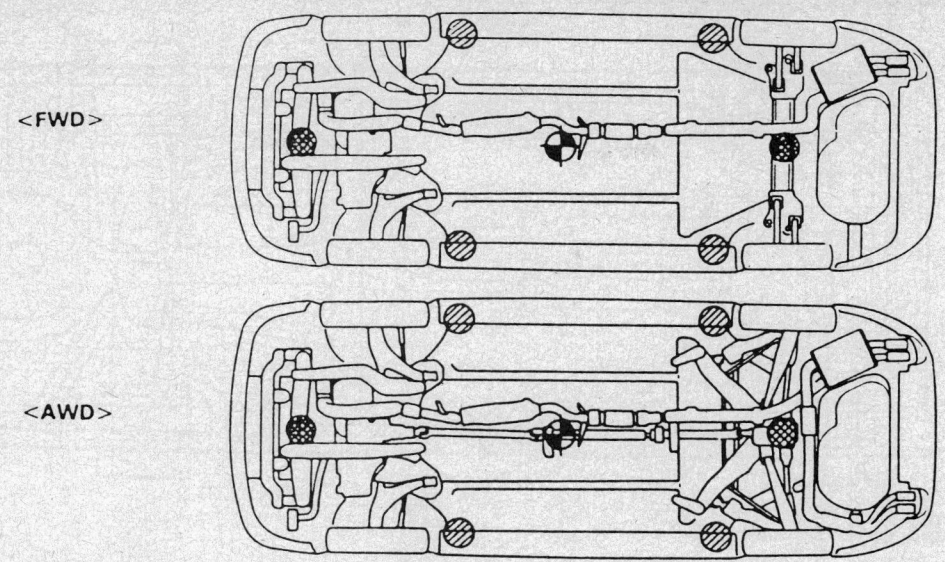

<FWD>

<AWD>

Fig. 15   Stealth

Ford Motor Co.
INDEX

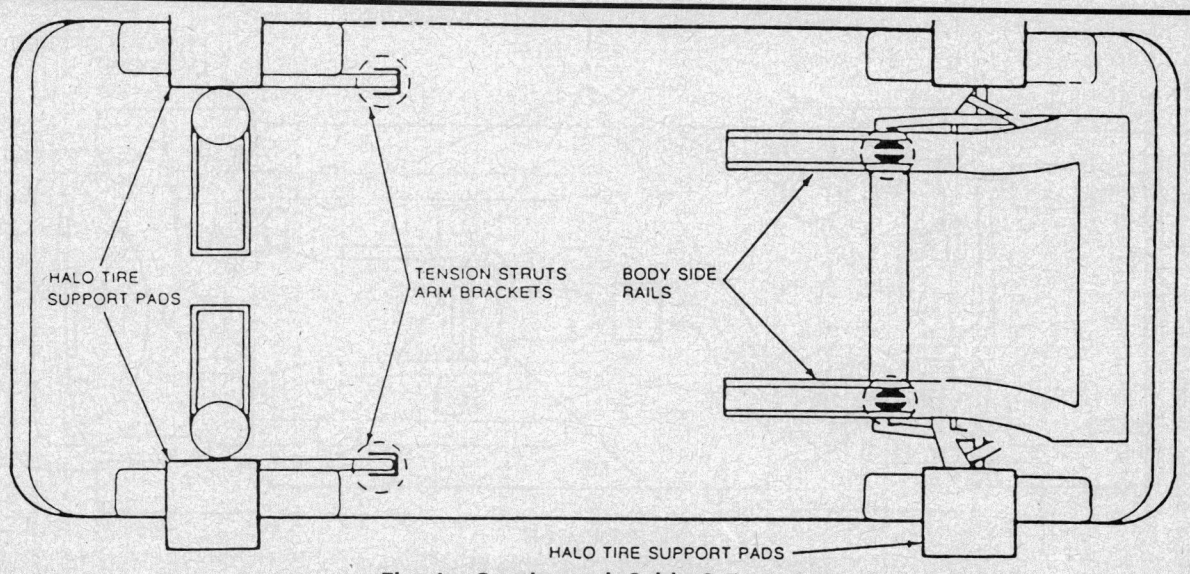

HALO TIRE SUPPORT PADS

TENSION STRUTS ARM BRACKETS

BODY SIDE RAILS

HALO TIRE SUPPORT PADS

Fig. 1   Continental, Sable & Taurus

VEHICLE LIFT POINTS

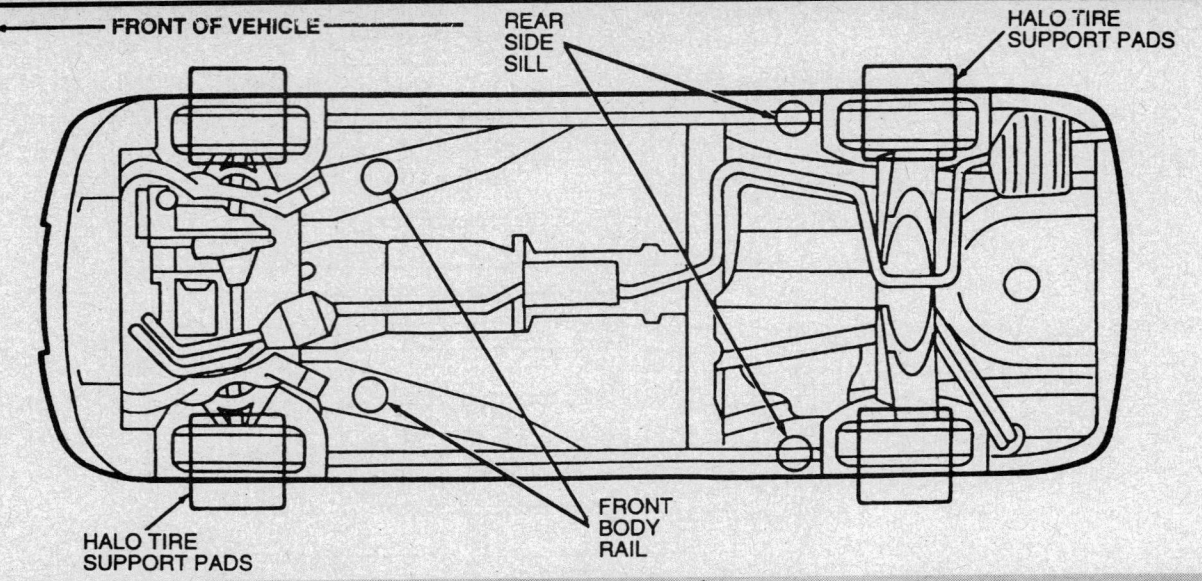

FRONT OF VEHICLE

REAR
SIDE
SILL

HALO TIRE
SUPPORT PADS

HALO TIRE
SUPPORT PADS

FRONT
BODY
RAIL

Fig. 2   Contour & Mystique

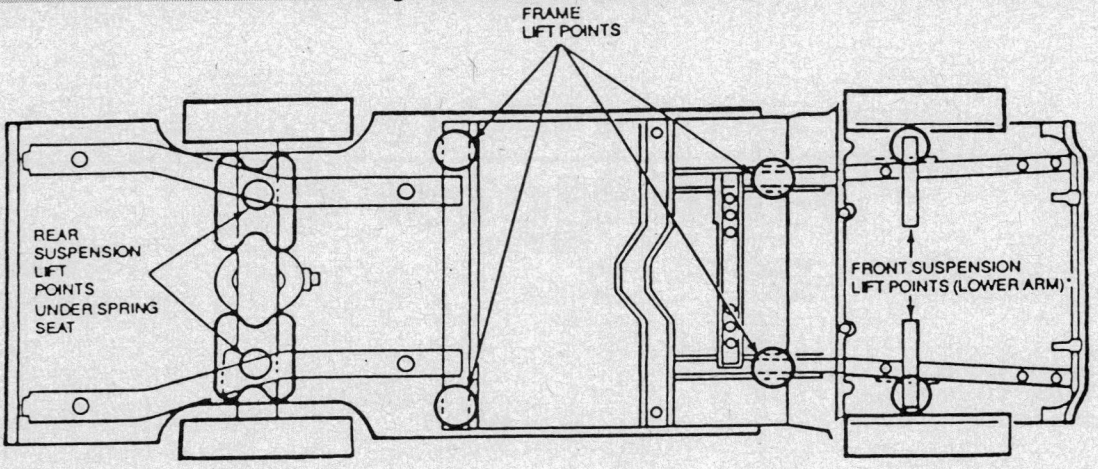

FRAME
LIFT POINTS

REAR
SUSPENSION
LIFT
POINTS
UNDER SPRING
SEAT

FRONT SUSPENSION
LIFT POINTS (LOWER ARM)*

* WHEN LIFTING BY LOWER ARM, USE CAUTION
NOT TO DAMAGE TENSION STRUT OR SHOCK CLEVIS

Fig. 3   1992–93 Cougar & Thunderbird

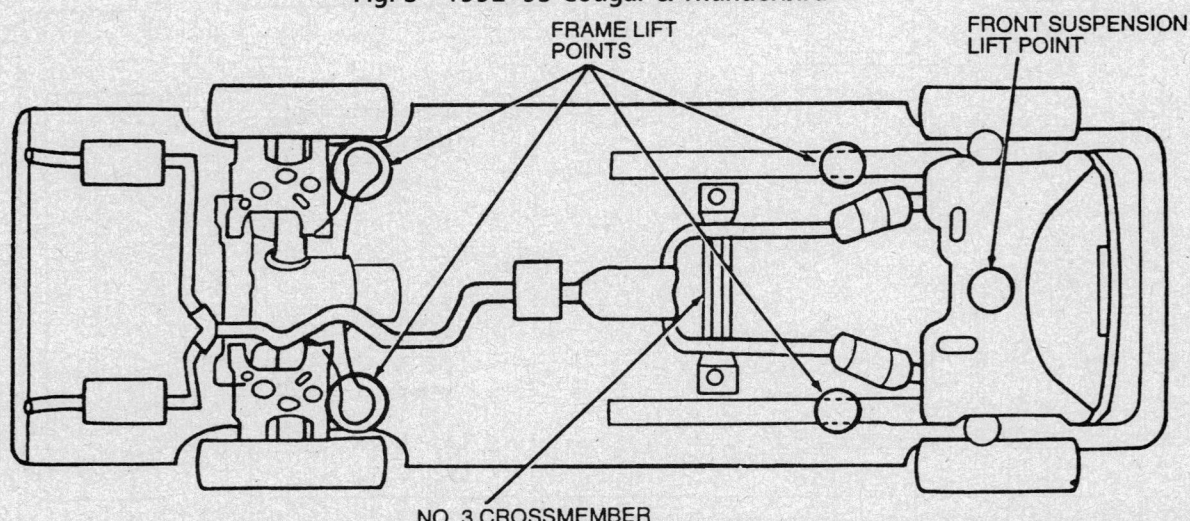

FRAME LIFT
POINTS

FRONT SUSPENSION
LIFT POINT

NO. 3 CROSSMEMBER

Fig. 4   1994–95 Cougar & Thunderbird

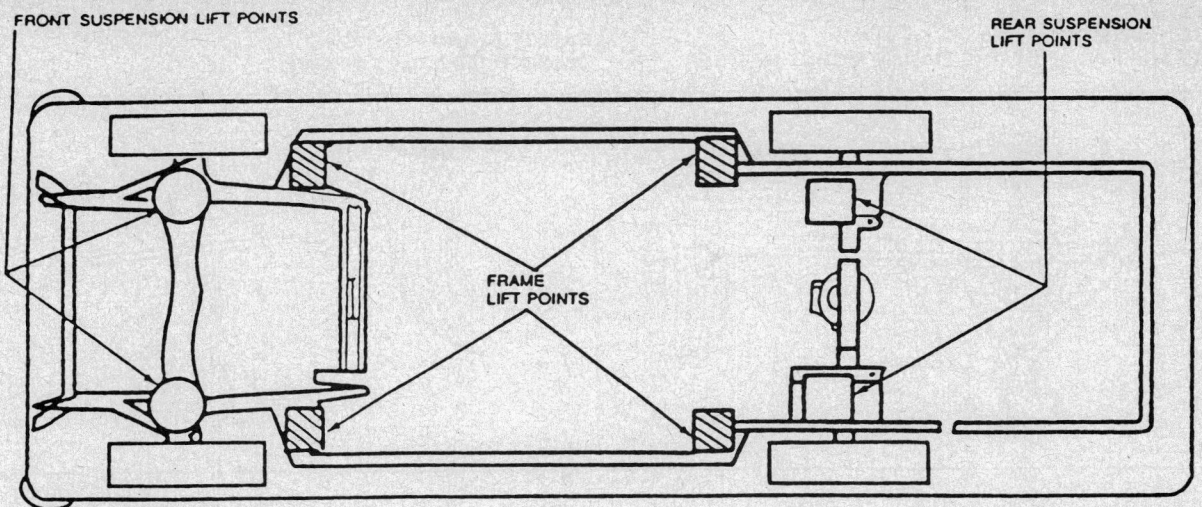

FRONT SUSPENSION LIFT POINTS

REAR SUSPENSION LIFT POINTS

FRAME LIFT POINTS

Fig. 5   Crown Victoria, Grand Marquis & Town Car

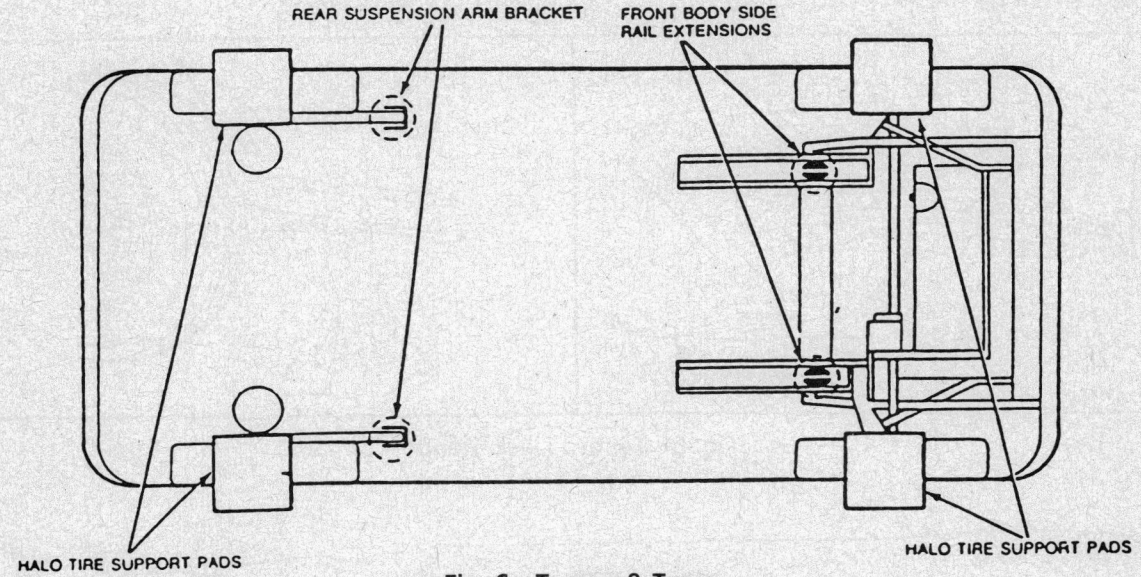

REAR SUSPENSION ARM BRACKET

FRONT BODY SIDE RAIL EXTENSIONS

HALO TIRE SUPPORT PADS

HALO TIRE SUPPORT PADS

Fig. 6   Tempo & Topaz

FRONT
On both side sills

REAR
On both side sills

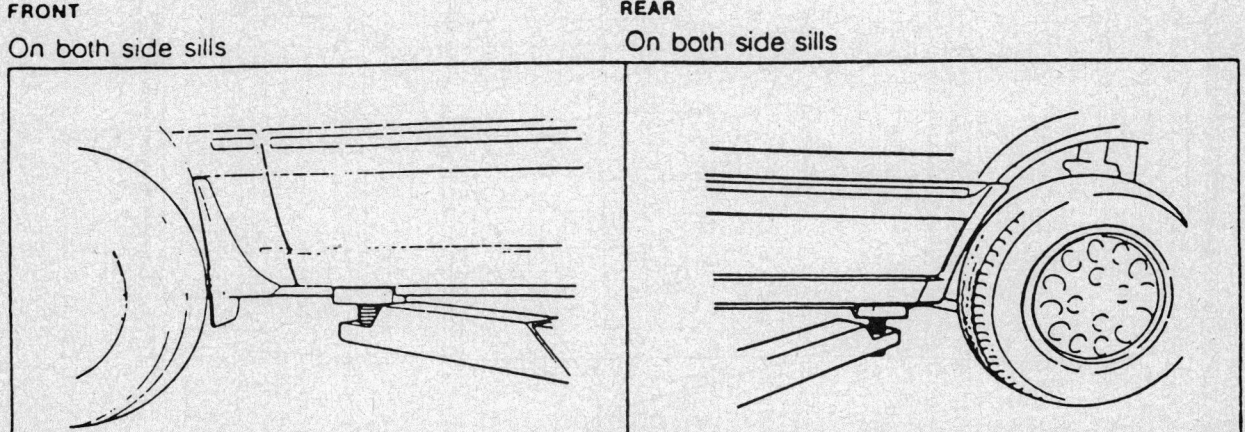

Fig. 7   Festiva (Hoist)

VEHICLE LIFT POINTS

FRONT
JACK POSITION:
AT THE FRONT OF THE ENGINE MOUNT MEMBER

SAFETY STAND POSITIONS:
ON BOTH SIDE SILLS (FRONT)

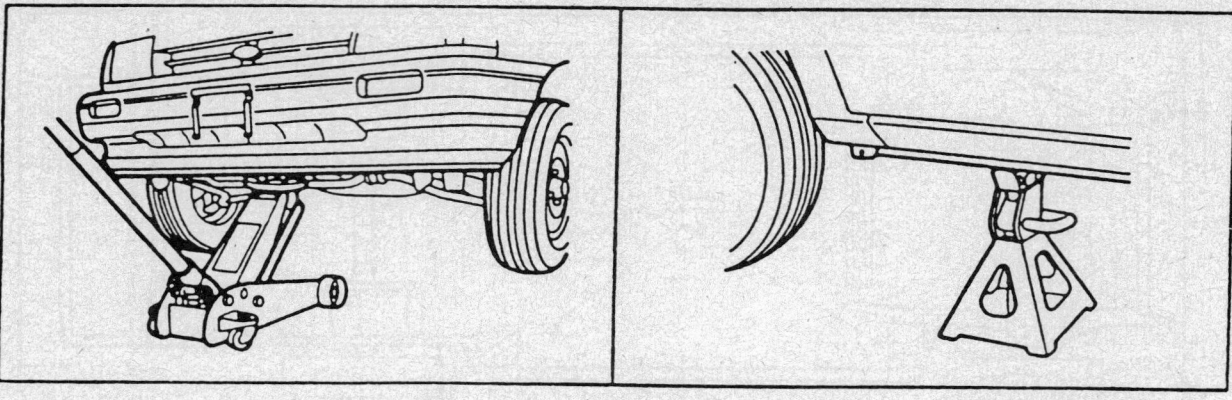

REAR
JACK POSITION:
AT THE CENTER OF THE REAR CROSSMEMBER

SAFETY STAND POSITIONS:
ON BOTH SIDE SILLS (REAR)

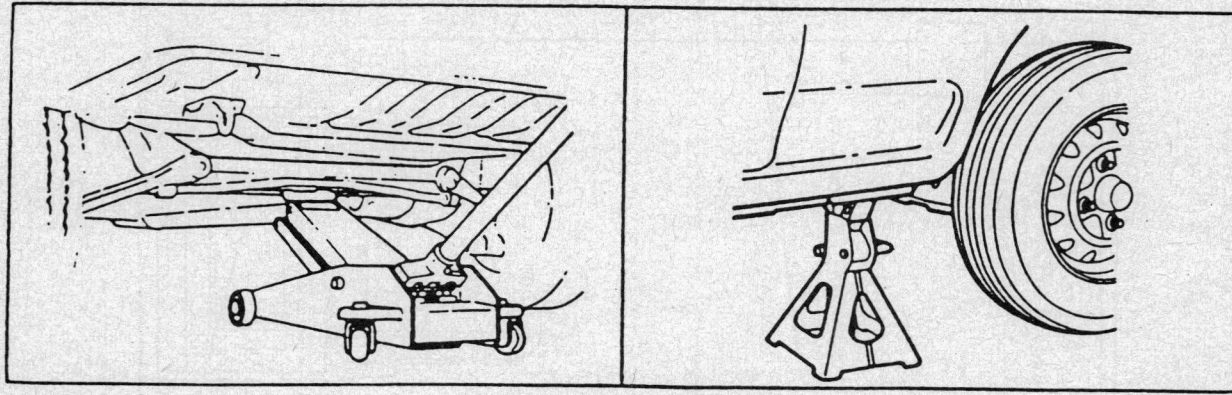

Fig. 8   Festiva (Jack Stand)

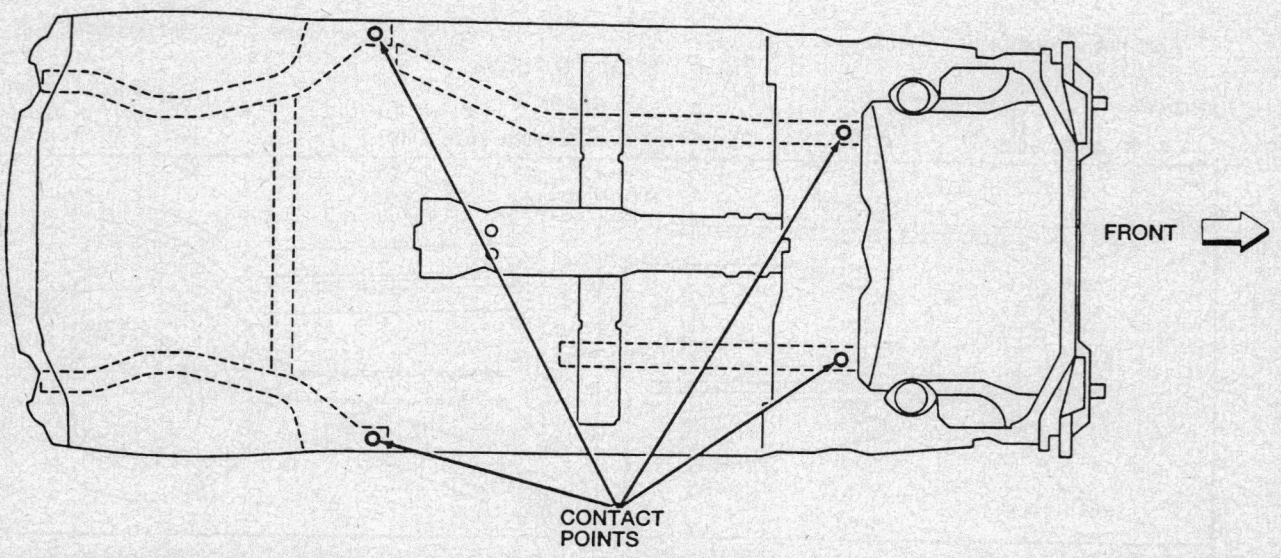

FRONT ⇨

CONTACT
POINTS

Fig. 9   Aspire

FORD MOTOR CO.

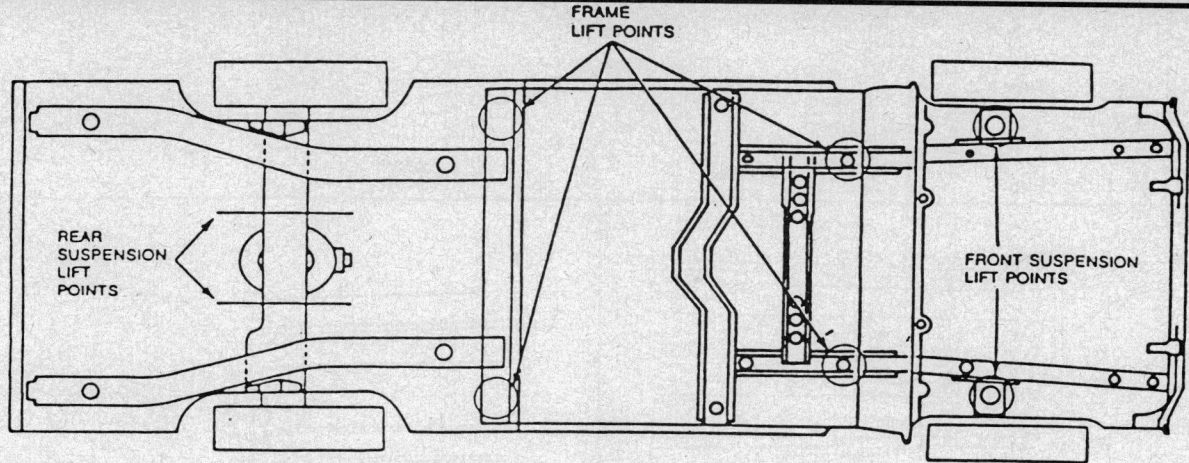

FRAME LIFT POINTS

REAR SUSPENSION LIFT POINTS

FRONT SUSPENSION LIFT POINTS

Fig. 10 Mark VII & Mustang

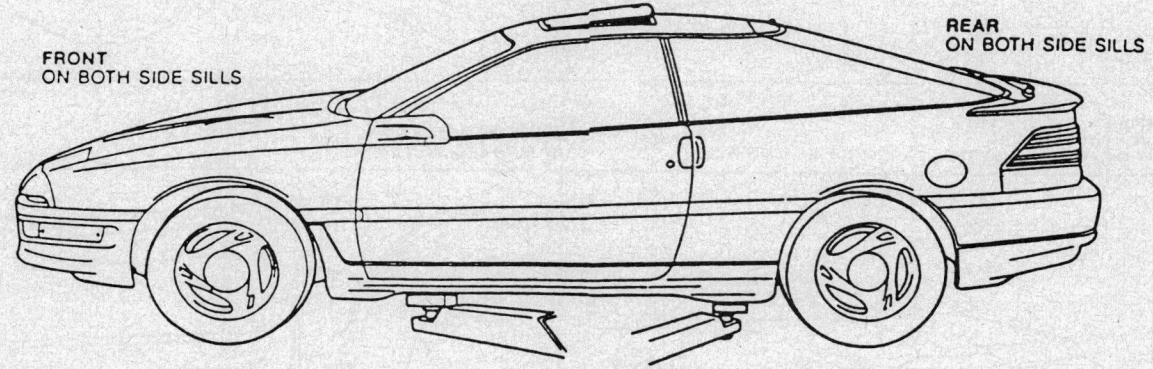

FRONT ON BOTH SIDE SILLS

REAR ON BOTH SIDE SILLS

Fig. 11 Probe (Hoist)

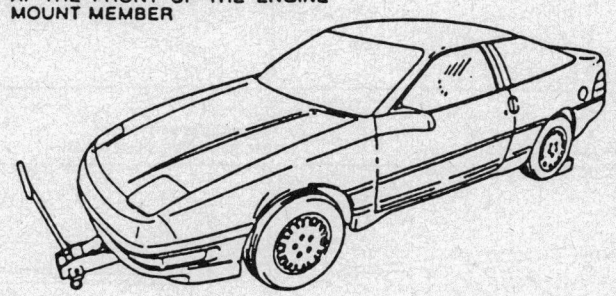

FRONT

JACK POSITION: AT THE FRONT OF THE ENGINE MOUNT MEMBER

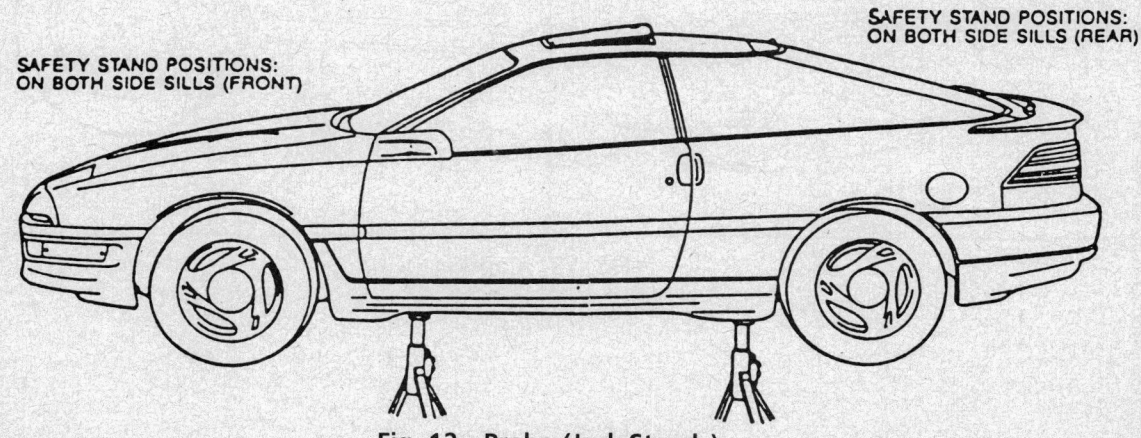

SAFETY STAND POSITIONS: ON BOTH SIDE SILLS (FRONT)

SAFETY STAND POSITIONS: ON BOTH SIDE SILLS (REAR)

Fig. 12 Probe (Jack Stands)

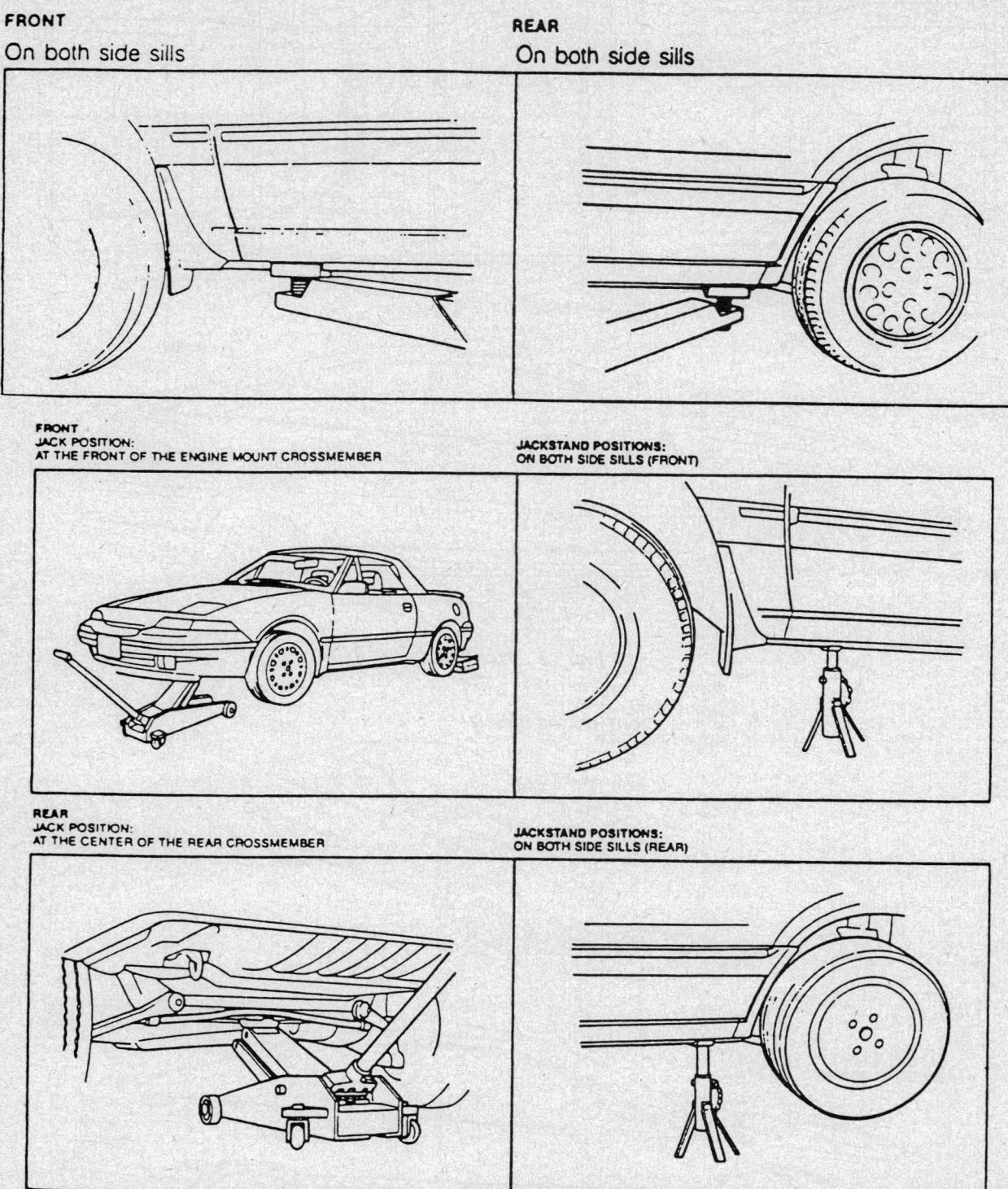

FRONT
On both side sills

REAR
On both side sills

FRONT
JACK POSITION:
AT THE FRONT OF THE ENGINE MOUNT CROSSMEMBER

JACKSTAND POSITIONS:
ON BOTH SIDE SILLS (FRONT)

REAR
JACK POSITION:
AT THE CENTER OF THE REAR CROSSMEMBER

JACKSTAND POSITIONS:
ON BOTH SIDE SILLS (REAR)

Fig. 13 Capri

Lifting

When lifting a vehicle, always position the hoist lifting pads so that they are in contact with the side sills.

CAUTION: Never allow the vehicle to be lifted by the trailing links.

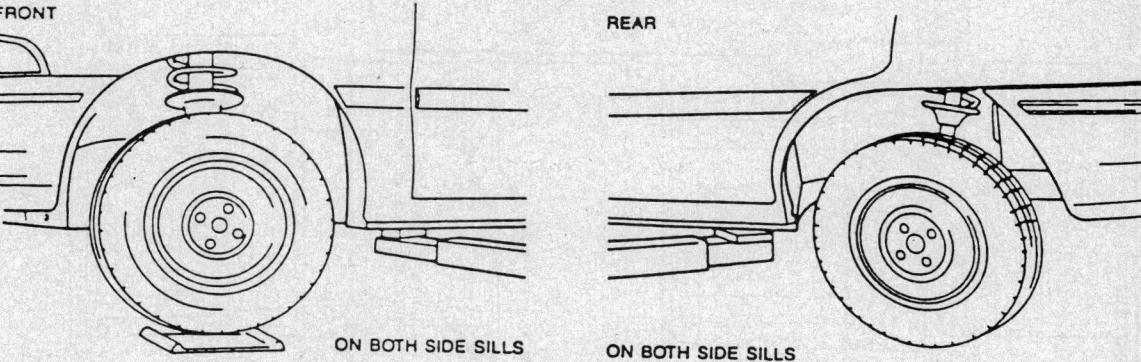

FRONT   REAR

ON BOTH SIDE SILLS   ON BOTH SIDE SILLS

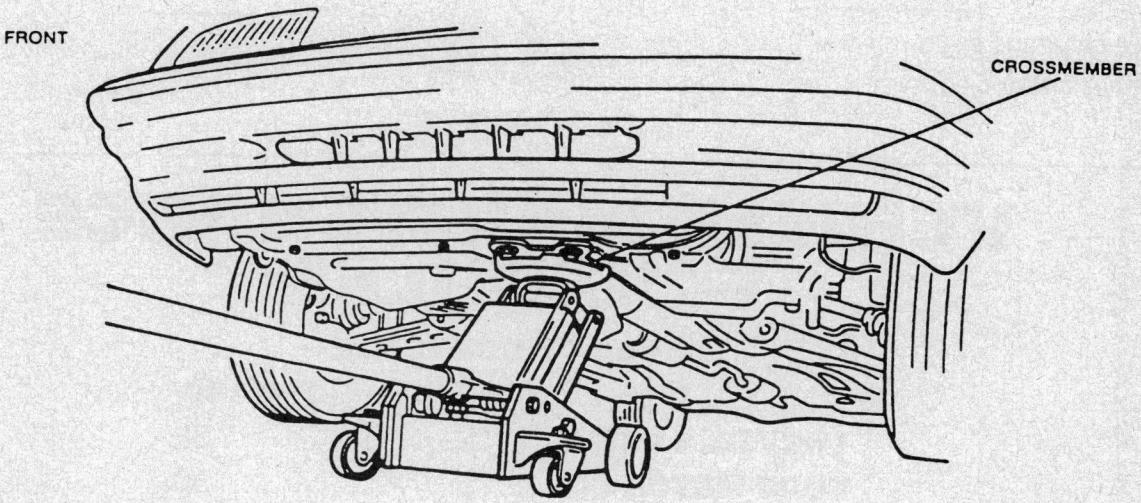

FRONT   CROSSMEMBER

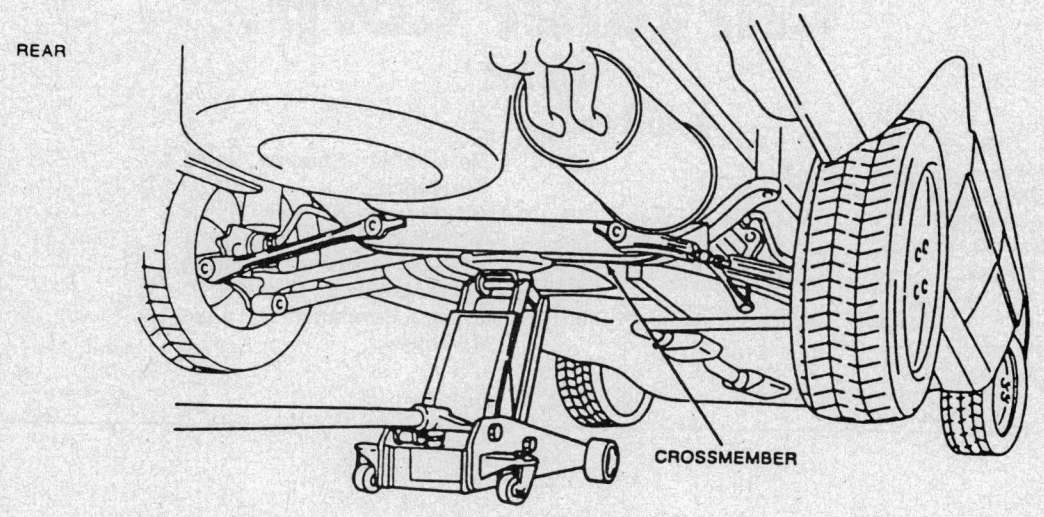

REAR

CROSSMEMBER

Fig. 14   Escort & Tracer

CAUTION: All four contact points must contact the adapters.

On frame contact hoists, adapters are necessary to lift the vehicle. The adapters must be placed at four contact points. Position the adapters so they are centered on the adapter contact area.

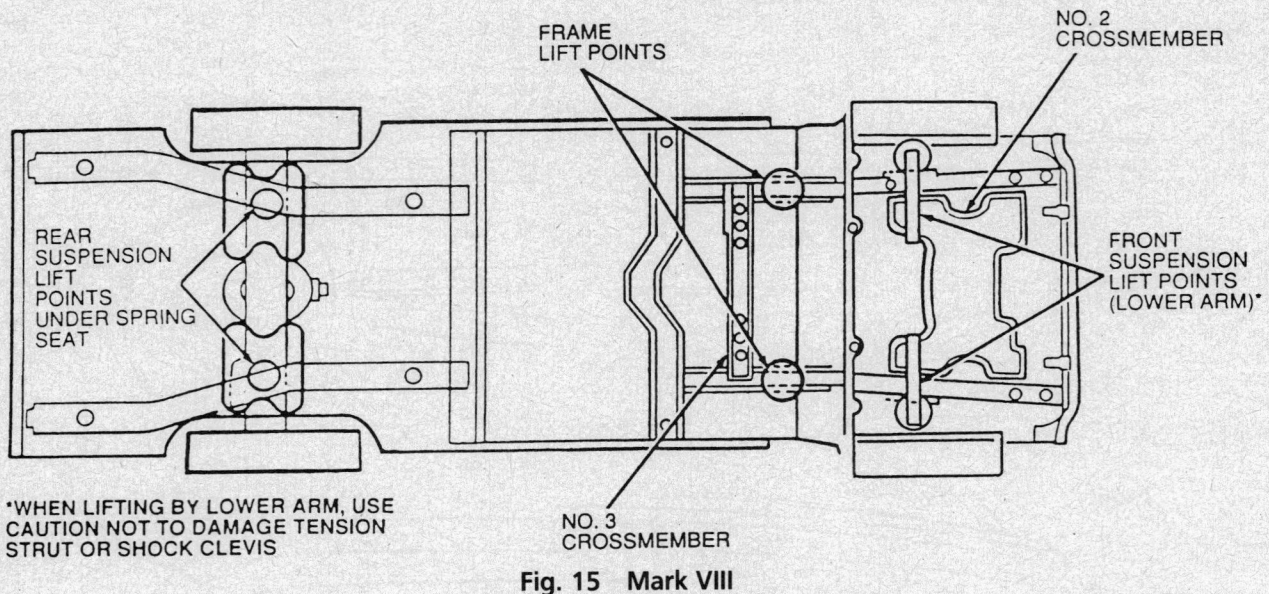

FRAME LIFT POINTS

NO. 2 CROSSMEMBER

REAR SUSPENSION LIFT POINTS UNDER SPRING SEAT

FRONT SUSPENSION LIFT POINTS (LOWER ARM)*

*WHEN LIFTING BY LOWER ARM, USE CAUTION NOT TO DAMAGE TENSION STRUT OR SHOCK CLEVIS

NO. 3 CROSSMEMBER

Fig. 15   Mark VIII

VEHICLE MAINTENANCE SCHEDULES

TABLE OF CONTENTS

Chrysler Corp.

INDEX

COLT & SUMMIT SEDAN

SCHEDULED MAINTENANCE FOR EMISSION CONTROL & PROPER VEHICLE PERFORMANCE

EMISSION CONTROL SYSTEM MAINTENANCE	SERVICE INTERVALS	MILEAGE IN THOUSANDS	7.5	15	22.5	30	37.5	45
		KILOMETERS IN THOUSANDS	12	24	36	48	60	72
ENGINE OIL (EXCEPT TURBO) CHANGE EVERY 12 MONTHS	OR		X	X	X	X	X	X
ENGINE OIL (TURBO) CHANGE EVERY 6 MONTHS	OR		X	X	X	X	X	X
ENGINE OIL FILTER REPLACE AT EVERY SECOND OIL CHANGE (1)	OR			X		X		X
REPLACE SPARK PLUGS	AT						X	
INSPECT AND ADJUST TENSION ON DRIVE BELTS, REPLACE AS NECESSARY	AT			X		X		X

(1) Note: If mileage is less than 7,500 miles each 12 months, replace oil filter at each oil change.

SEVERE SERVICE MAINTENANCE

Maintenance Item	Service to be Performed	Mileage Intervals Kilometers in Thousands (Miles in Thousands)									Severe Usage Conditions						
		12 (7.5)	24 (15)	36 (22.5)	48 (30)	60 (37.5)	72 (45)	80 (50)	84 (52.5)	96 (60)	A	B	C	D	E	F	G
Air Cleaner Element	Replace	More Frequently									X				X		
Spark Plugs	Replace		X		X		X			X		X	X				
Engine Oil	Change Every 3 Months or	Every 4,800 Km (3,000 Miles)									X	X	X	X			X
Engine Oil Filter	Replace Every 6 Months or	Every 9,600 Km (6,000 Miles)									X	X	X	X			X
Disc Brake Pads	Inspect for Wear	More Frequently									X					X	
Rear Drum Brake Linings and Rear Wheel Cylinders	Inspect for Wear and Leaks	More Frequently									X					X	

Severe usage conditions

A – Driving in dusty conditions
B – Trailer towing or police, taxi, or commercial type operation
C – Extensive idling
D – Short-trip operation at freezing temperatures (engine not thoroughly warmed up)

E – Driving in sandy areas
F – Driving in salty areas
G – More than 50% operation in heavy city traffic during hot weather above 32°C (90°F)

GENERAL MAINTENANCE SERVICE FOR PROPER VEHICLE PERFORMANCE

General Maintenance		Service Intervals		Kilometers in Thousands → 24	48	72	80	96
				Mileage in Thousands → 15	30	45	50	60
Timing Belt		Replace	at					X
Drive Belt (for Water Pump and Alternator)		Replace	at		X			X
Engine Oil	<N/A>	Change Every Year	or	Every 12,000 km (7,500 miles)				
	<T/C>	Change Every 6 Months	or	Every 8,000 km (5,000 miles)				
Engine Oil Filter	<N/A>	Change Every Year	or	X	X	X		X
	<T/C>	Change Every Year	or	Every 16,000 km (10,000 miles)				
Manual Transaxle Oil		Inspect Oil Level	at		X			X
Automatic Transaxle Oil		Inspect Oil Level Every Year	or	X	X	X		X
		Change Oil			X			X
Engine Coolant		Replace Every 2 Years	or		X			X
Disc Brake Pads		Inspect for Wear Every Year	or	X	X	X		X
Drum Brake Linings and Rear Wheel Cylinders		Inspect for Wear and Leaks Every 2 Years	or		X			X
Brake Hoses		Check for Deterioration or Leaks Every Year	or	X	X	X		X
Ball Joint and Steering Linkage Seals		Inspect for Grease Leaks and Damage Every 2 Years	or		X			X
Drive Shaft Boots		Inspect for Grease Leaks and Damage Every Year	or	X	X	X		X
Rear Wheel Bearings		Lubricate Grease Every 2 Years	or		X			X
Exhaust System (Connection Portion of Muffler, Pipings and Converter Heat Shields)		Check and Service as Required Every 2 Years	or		X			X

COLT VISTA & SUMMIT WAGON

2WD

Emission Control System Maintenance	Service Intervals	Kilometers in Thousands → 24	48	72	80	96
		Mileage in Thousands → 15	30	45	50	60
Check Fuel System (Tank, Line and Connections and Fuel filler Cap) for Leaks Every 5 Years	or				X	
Replace Fuel Hoses and Vapor Hoses Every 5 Years	or				X	
Replace Air Cleaner Element	at		X			X
Replace Spark Plugs	at		X			X

4WD

Emission Control System Maintenance	Service Intervals	Kilometers in Thousands → 12	24	36	48	60	72	80	84	96	108	120	128	132	144	156	160	168	180	192
		Mileage in Thousands → 7.5	15	22.5	30	37.5	45	50	52.5	60	67.5	75	80	82.5	90	97.5	100	105	112.5	120
Check Fuel System (Tank, Line and Connections and Fuel Filler Cap) for Leaks Every 5 Years	or							X									X			
Replace Vacuum Hoses, Secondary Air Hoses, Crankcase Ventilation Hoses and Water Hoses Every 5 Years	or										X									X
Replace Fuel Hoses and Vapor Hoses Every 5 Years	or								X									X		
Replace Air Cleaner Element	at				X					X					X					X
Clean Crankcase Emission-control System (PCV Valve)*	at											X								
Check Evaporative Emission-control System (except Canister)* for Leaks and Clogging Every 5 Years	or									X										X
Replace Canister*	at																X			
Replace Spark Plugs	at				X					X					X					X
Replace Ignition Cables* Every 5 Years	or									X										X
Replace EGR Valve*	at							X									X			
Replace Oxygen Sensor*	at												X							

NOTE
* Except for California

CHRYSLER CORP.

GENERAL MAINTENANCE SERVICE FOR PROPER VEHICLE PERFORMANCE

General Maintenance	Service Interval	Kilometers in Thousands		12	24	36	48	60	72	84	96
		Mileage in Thousands		7.5	15	22.5	30	37.5	45	52.5	60
Timing Belt (Including the Balancer Belt)	Replace		at								×
Drive Belt (for Water Pump and Alternator)	Replace		at				×				×
Engine Oil	Change Every Year		or	×	×	×	×	×	×	×	×
Engine Oil Filter	Change Every Year		or		×		×		×		×
Manual Transaxle Oil	Check Oil Level		at				×				×
Transfer Case*	Check Oil Level		at				×				×
Automatic Transaxle Fluid	Inspect Fluid Level Every Year		or		×		×		×		×
	Change Fluid		at				×				×
Engine Coolant	Replace Every 2 Years		or				×				×
Front Disc Brake Pads	Inspect for Wear Every Year		or		×		×		×		×
Drum Brake Linings and Rear Wheel Cylinders	Inspect for Wear and Leaks Every 2 years		or				×				×
Brake Hoses	Check for Deterioration or Leaks Every Year		or		×		×		×		×
Ball Joint and Steering Linkage Seals	Inspect for Grease Leaks and Damage Every 2 Years		or				×				×
Drive Shaft Boots	Inspect for Grease Leaks and Damage Every Years		or		×		×		×		×
Rear Axle*	With LSD	Change Oil	at				×				×
	Without LSD	Inspect Oil Level	at				×				×
Rear Wheel Bearings	Lubricate Grease Every 2 Years		or				×				×
Propeller Shaft Joint*	Lubricate Grease Every 2 Years		or				×				×
Exhaust System (Connection Portion of Muffler, Pipings and Converter Heat Shields)	Check and Service as Required Every Years		or				×				×

NOTE
LSD Limited-slip Differential
* 4WD

SEVERE SERVICE MAINTENANCE

Maintenance Item	Service to be Performed	Mileage Intervals Kilometers in Thousands (Miles in Thousands)				Severe Usage Conditions							
		24 (15)	48 (30)	72 (45)	96 (60)	A	B	C	D	E	F	G	H
Engine Oil	Change Every 3 Months or	Every 4,800 km (3,000 miles)				×	×	×	×			×	
Engine Oil Filter	Replace Every 6 Months or	Every 9,600 km (6,000 miles)				×	×	×	×			×	
Air Cleaner Element	Replace	More Frequently				×				×			
Crankcase Emission-control System*	Check and Clean as Required	More Frequently				×							
Spark Plugs	Replace at	×	×	×	×					×	×		
Front Disc Brake Pads	Inspect for Wear	More Frequently				×					×		
Rear Drum Brake Linings and Rear Wheel Cylinders	Inspect for Wear and Leaks	More Frequently				×					×		
Manual Transaxle and Transfer Case*	Change Oil at		×		×			×				×	×

NOTE
* 4WD

Severe usage conditions

A – Driving in dusty conditions
B – Trailer towing, or police, taxi, or commercial type operation
C – Extensive idling
D – Short-trip operation at freezing temperatures
  (engine not thoroughly warmed up)
E – Driving in sandy areas
F – Driving in salty areas
G – More than 50% operation in heavy city traffic during hot
  weather above 32°C (90°F)
H – Driving on off-road

1992-94 LASER & TALON
SCHEDULED MAINTENANCE FOR EMISSION CONTROL & PROPER VEHICLE PERFORMANCE

No.	Emission Control System Maintenance	Service Intervals	Kilometers in Thousands	24	48	72	80	96
			Mileage in Thousands	15	30	45	50	60
1	Check Fuel System (Tank, Line and Connections and Fuel Filler Cap) for Leaks Every 5 Years	or					X	
2	Replace Fuel Hoses and Vapor Hoses Every 5 Years	or					X	
3	Replace Air Cleaner Element	at			X			X
4	Replace Spark Plugs	at			X			X

GENERAL MAINTENANCE SERVICE FOR PROPER VEHICLE PERFORMANCE

No.	General Maintenance		Service Intervals		Kilometers in Thousands	24	48	72	80	96
					Mileage in Thousands	15	30	45	50	60
5	Timing Belt (Including the Balancer Belt)		Replace	at						X
6	Drive Belt (for Water Pump and Alternator)		Replace	at			X			X
7	Engine Oil	Non-Turbo	Change Every Year	or	Every 12,000 km (7,500 miles)					
		Turbo	Change Every 6 Months		Every 8,000 km (5,000 miles)					
8	Engine Oil Filter	Non-Turbo	Change Every Year	or		X	X	X		X
		Turbo	Change Every Year		Every 16,000 km (10,000 miles)					
9	Manual Transaxle Oil		Inspect Oil Level	at			X			X
10	Automatic Transaxle Fluid		Inspect Fluid Level Every Year	or		X	X	X		X
			Change Fluid	at			X			X
11	Engine Coolant		Replace Every 2 Years	or			X			X
12	Disc Brake Pads		Inspect for Wear Every Year	or		X	X	X		X
13	Brake Hoses		Check for Deterioration or Leaks Every Year	or		X	X	X		X
14	Ball Joint and Steering Linkage Seals		Inspect for Grease Leaks and Damage Every 2 Years	or			X			X
15	Drive Shaft Boots		Inspect for Grease Leaks and Damage Every Year	or		X	X	X		X
16	Rear Axle <4WD>	With LSD	Change Oil				X			X
		Without LSD	Inspect Oil Level				X			X
17	Exhaust System (Connection Portion of Muffler, Pipings and Converter Heat Shields)		Check and Service as Required Every 2 Years	or			X			X

NOTE
LSD: Limited-slip differential

SEVERE SERVICE MAINTENANCE

Maintenance Item	Service to be Performed	Mileage Intervals Kilometers in Thousands (Miles in Thousands)									Severe Usage Conditions						
		12 (7.5)	24 (15)	36 (22.5)	48 (30)	60 (37.5)	72 (45)	80 (50)	84 (52.5)	96 (60)	A	B	C	D	E	F	G
Air Cleaner Element	Replace	More Frequently									X				X		
Spark Plugs	Replace		X		X		X			X	X		X				
Engine Oil	Change Every 3 Months or	Every 4,800 km (3,000 miles)									X	X	X	X			X
Engine Oil Filter	Replace Every 6 Months or	Every 9,600 km (6,000 miles)									X	X	X	X			X
Disc Brake Pads	Inspect for Wear	More Frequently									X					X	

Severe usage conditions
A—Driving in dusty conditions
B—Trailer towing or police, taxi, or commercial type operation
C—Extensive idling
D—Short trip operation at freezing temperatures (engine not thoroughly warmed up)
E—Driving in sandy areas
F—Driving in salty areas
G—More than 50% operation in heavy city traffic during hot weather above 32°C (90°F)

CHRYSLER CORP.

1995 TALON

GENERAL MAINTENANCE SERVICE FOR PROPER VEHICLE PERFORMANCE

No.	General maintenance		Service to be performed		Kilometers in thousands	24	48	72	96	120	144	168
					Mileage in thousands	15	30	45	60	75	90	105
7	Timing belts		Replace	at					x*1		160,000 km*2 (100,000 miles)	
8	Drive belt (for generator, water pump, power steering pump)		Check condition	at			x		x		x	
9	Engine oil	Non-turbo	Change Every 6 months	or		Every 12,000 km (7,500 miles)						
			Change Every year	or								
		Turbo	Change Every 6 months	or		Every 8,000 km (5,000 miles)						
10	Engine oil filter	Non-turbo	Replace Every Year*3	or		x	x	x	x	x	x	x
		Turbo	Replace Every Year	or		Every 16,000 km (10,000 miles)						
11	Manual transaxle oil (including transfer)		Inspect oil level	at			x		x		x	
12	Automatic transaxle fluid		Inspect fluid level Every year	or		x	x	x	x	x	x	x
			Change fluid*4	at			x		x		x	
13	Engine coolant		Change Every 2 years	or			x		x		x	
14	Disc brake pads		Inspect for wear Every year	or		x	x	x	x	x	x	x
15	Brake hoses		Check for deterioration or leaks Every year	or		x	x	x	x	x	x	x
16	Ball joint and steering linkage seals		Inspect for grease leaks and damage Every 2 years	or			x		x		x	
17	Drive shaft boots		Inspect for grease leaks and damage Every year	or		x	x	x	x	x	x	x
18	Rear axle oil		Inspect oil level	at			x		x		x	
19	SRS*5 system		Inspect system			At 10 years						
20	Exhaust system (connection portion of muffler, pipings and converter heat shields)		Check and service as required Every 2 years	or			x		x		x	

NOTES
*1: For California, this maintenance is recommended but not required
*2: Not required if belt was previously changed.
*3: If the mileage is less than 12,000 km (7,500 miles) each year, the oil filter should be replaced at every oil change.
*4: Vehicles with turbocharger
*5: Supplemental Restraint system

SEVERE SERVICE MAINTENANCE

No.	Maintenance item	Service to be performed		Kilometers in thousands	24	48	72	96	120	144	168	Severe usage conditions							
				Mileage in Thousands	15	30	45	60	75	90	105	A	B	C	D	E	F	G	H
3	Air cleaner element	Replace			x	x	x	x	x	x	x	x				x			
5	Spark plugs	Replace			x	x	x	x	x	x	x		x		x				
9	Engine oil	Change Every 3 months	or	Every 4,800 km (3,000 miles)								x	x	x	x		x		
10	Engine oil filter	Replace Every 6 months	or	Every 9,600 km (6,000 miles)								x	x	x	x		x		
12	Automatic transaxle fluid	Change fluid*1			x	x	x	x	x	x	x	x		x				x	x
14	Disc brake pads	Inspect for wear Every 6 months	or					x				x				x			
22	Manual transaxle oil (Include transfer)	Change oil*2				x		x		x		x		x				x	x

*1: Vehicles without turbocharger.
*2: Vehicles with turbocharger.

MONACO & PREMIER

SCHEDULED MAINTENANCE FOR EMISSION CONTROL AND VEHICLE PERFORMANCE. Inspection and service should be performed when malfunction is suspected.

SERVICE – Kilometers x 1000	12	24	36	48	60	72
– Miles x 1000	7.5	15	22.5	30	37.5	45
CHANGE ENGINE OIL 12 Months or	X	X	X	X	X	X
REPLACE ENGINE OIL FILTER	X	X	X	X	X	X
INSPECT ENGINE AIR FILTER		X		X		X
REPLACE SPARK PLUGS (mileage only)					X	
INSPECT DRIVE BELTS (service as required)		X		X		X

GENERAL MAINTENANCE

	12	24	36	48	60	72
INSPECT BRAKE LININGS All wheels - service as required				X		X
GREASE TIE ROD ENDS at 3 years or					X	
GREASE BALL JOINTS AT 3 years or					X	
INSPECT DRIVE SHAFT BOOTS for leaks	X	X	X	X	X	X
INSPECT BRAKE HOSES at every oil change and whenever brakes are serviced						
INSPECT COOLING SYSTEM every 12 months						
FLUSH AND WINTERIZE COOLING SYSTEM every 30 months or 48,000 km (30,000 miles)						
INSPECT AND LUBRICATE REAR WHEEL BEARINGS				X		X

SEVERE SERVICE MAINTENANCE driving in stop/go conditions, long idling periods, frequent short trips, operating at sustained high speeds in temperatures above 32°C (90°F).

Kilometers x 1000	4.8	9.6	14	19	24	29	34	38	43	48	53	58	62	67	72	77
Mileage x 1000	3	6	9	12	15	18	21	24	27	30	33	36	39	42	45	48
CHANGE OIL[1] 6 months	X	X	X	X	X	X	X	X	X	X	X	X	X	X	X	X
REPLACE OIL FILTER	X		X		X		X		X		X		X		X	
REPLACE AIR FILTER Inspect and replace if required					X					X					X	
INSPECT BALL JOINTS	X	X	X	X	X	X	X	X	X	X	X	X	X	X	X	X
INSPECT CV JOINTS	X	X	X	X	X	X	X	X	X	X	X	X	X	X	X	X
CHANGE TRANS FLUID Adjust bands at time of fluid and filter change					X					X					X	
LUBRICATE TIE ROD ENDS Every 18 months or mileage specified					X					X					X	
INSPECT BRAKE LININGS All wheels - replace as necessary		X			X			X			X			X		

[1]Three months if SG service engine oil is used.

STEALTH
SCHEDULED MAINTENANCE FOR EMISSION CONTROL
& PROPER VEHICLE PERFORMANCE

Inspection and services should be performed any time a malfunction is observed or suspected. Retain receipts for all vehicle emission services to protect your emission warranty.

No	Emission Control System Maintenance	Service Intervals	Kilometers in Thousands	24	48	72	80	96
			Mileage in Thousands	15	30	45	50	60
1	Check Fuel System (Tank, Line and Connections and Fuel Filler Cap) for Leaks Every 5 Years	or					X	
2	Check Fuel Hoses for Leaks or Damage Every 2 Years	or			X			X
3	Replace Air Cleaner Element	at			X			X
4	Replace Spark Plugs at	SOHC			X			X
		DOHC						X

GENERAL MAINTENANCE SERVICE FOR PROPER VEHICLE PERFORMANCE

No.	General Maintenance		Service Intervals	Kilometers in Thousands	24	48	72	80	96
				Mileage in Thousands	15	30	45	50	60
5	Timing Belt		Replace	at					X
6	Drive Belt (for Alternator)		Inspect for Tension	at		X			X
7	Engine Oil	Non-Turbo	Change Every Year	or	Every 12,000 km (7,500 miles)				
		Turbo	Change Every 6 Months		Every 8,000 km (5,000 miles)				
8	Engine Oil Filter	Non-Turbo	Change Every Year	or	X	X	X		X
		Turbo	Change Every Year		Every 16,000 km (10,000 miles)				
9	Manual Transaxle Oil		Inspect Oil Level	at		X			X
10	Automatic Transaxle Fluid		Inspect Fluid Level Every Year	or	X	X	X		X
			Change Fluid	at		X			X
11	Engine Coolant		Replace Every 2 Years	or		X			X
12	Disc Brake Pads		Inspect for Wear Every Year	or	X	X	X		X
13	Brake Hoses		Check for Deterioration or Leaks Every Year	or	X	X	X		X
14	Ball Joint and Steering Linkage Seals		Inspect for Grease Leaks and Damage Every 2 Years	or		X			X
15	Drive Shaft Boots		Inspect for Grease Leaks and Damage Every Year	or	X				X
16	Rear Axle <AWD>	With LSD	Change Oil			X			X
		Without LSD	Inspect Oil Level			X			X
17	Exhaust System (Connection Portion of Muffler, Pipings and Converter Heat Shields)		Check and Service as Required Every 2 Years	or		X			X

NOTE
LSD: Limited-slip differential

SEVERE SERVICE MAINTENANCE

The maintenance items should be performed according to the following table:

Maintenance Item	Service to be Performed	Mileage Intervals Kilometers in Thousands (Miles in Thousands)									Severe Usage Conditions						
		12 (7.5)	24 (15)	36 (22.5)	48 (30)	60 (37.5)	72 (45)	80 (50)	84 (52.5)	96 (60)	A	B	C	D	E	F	G
Air Cleaner Element	Replace	More Frequently									X				X		
Spark Plugs	Replace		X		X		X			X		X	X				
Engine Oil	Change Every 3 Months or	Every 4,800 Km (3,000 Miles)									X	X	X	X			X
Engine Oil Filter	Replace Every 6 Months or	Every 9,600 Km (6,000 Miles)									X	X	X	X			X
Disc Brake Pads	Inspect for Wear	More Frequently									X					X	

Severe usage conditions

A Driving in dusty conditions
B Police, taxi, or commercial type operation
C Extensive idling
D Short trip operation at freezing temperatures (engine not thoroughly warmed up)
E Driving in sandy areas
F Driving in salty areas
G More than 50% operation in heavy city traffic during hot weather above 32°C (90°F)

1992 ACCLAIM, DAYTONA, DYNASTY, LEBARON, NEW YORKER, SHADOW, SPIRIT & SUNDANCE

SCHEDULED MAINTENANCE FOR EMISSION CONTROL AND VEHICLE PERFORMANCE. Inspection and service should be performed when malfunction is suspected.

SERVICE – km x 100	12	24	36	48	60	72
~ Miles x 1000	7.5	15	22.5	30	37.5	45
CHANGE ENGINE OIL Every 6 Months*	X	X	X	X	X	X
REPLACE ENGINE OIL FILTER**	X		X		X	
INSPECT ENGINE AIR FILTER		X		X		X
REPLACE SPARK PLUGS, Mileage Only				X		
INSPECT DRIVE BELTS, Service As Required			X		X	X
DRIVER SUPPLEMENTAL AIRBAG SYSTEM — INSPECT EVERY 3 YEARS OR 48,000 km (30,000 MILES). CORRECT AS NECESSARY: • SYSTEM COMPONENTS FOR DAMAGE OR DETERIORATION • DIAGNOSTIC UNIT FOR STORED MALFUNCTION MESSAGES • READINESS INDICATOR (AIRBAG) LAMP) FUNCTION				X		

* 4,800 km (3,000 miles) or 3 months if SG service engine oil is used in a turbocharged engine.
**If mileage is less than 12,000 km (7,500 miles), change filter at every oil change.

GENERAL MAINTENANCE

INSPECT BRAKE LININGS of All Wheels; Service as Required				X		X
GREASE TIE ROD ENDS at 3 Years or					X	
GREASE BALL JOINTS at 3 Years or					X	
INSPECT DRIVE SHAFT BOOTS for Leaks	X	X	X	X	X	X
INSPECT BRAKE HOSES at Every Oil Change and Whenever Brakes are Serviced						
INSPECT COOLING SYSTEM Every 12 Months						
FLUSH AND WINTERIZE COOLING SYSTEM Every 36 Months or 83,000 km (52,000 miles)						
INSPECT AND LUBRICATE REAR WHEEL BEARINGS				X		X
TIRE ROTATION at	X	24,000 km (15,000 miles) Thereafter				

SEVERE SERVICE MAINTENANCE: Driving in Stop/Go Conditions, Long Idling Periods, Frequent Short Trips, Operating at Sustained High Speeds in Temperatures Above 32°C (90°F).

km x 1000	4.8	9.6	14	19	24	29	34	38	43	48	53	58	62	67	72	77
Miles x 1000	3	6	9	12	15	18	21	24	27	30	33	36	39	42	45	48
CHANGE OIL***-6 Months	X	X	X	X	X	X	X	X	X	X	X	X	X	X	X	X
REPLACE OIL FILTER	X		X		X		X		X		X		X		X	
REPLACE AIR FILTER: Inspect and Replace if Required					X					X					X	
INSPECT BALL JOINTS	X	X	X	X	X	X	X	X	X	X	X	X	X	X	X	X
INSPECT CV JOINTS	X	X	X	X	X	X	X	X	X	X	X	X	X	X	X	X
CHANGE TRANSMISSION FLUID, Adjust Bands at Time of Fluid and Filter Change					X					X					X	
LUBRICATE TIE ROD ENDS Every 18 Months or Mileage Specified					X					X					X	
INSPECT BRAKE LININGS of All Wheels; Replace as Required			X				X			X			X		X	

***3 months if SG service engine oil is used

1993 DYNASTY, NEW YORKER, 1993–94 ACCLAIM, DAYTONA, LEBARON, SHADOW, SPIRIT & SUNDANCE

ALL VEHICLES EXCEPT CALIFORNIA 2.5 L & 3.0 L ENGINE WITH AUTO TRANSAXLE

EMISSION RELATED COMPONENT MAINTENANCE

Where time and mileage are shown, follow interval listed first.	miles X 1000	7.5	15	22.5	30	37.5	45	52.5	60	67.5	75	82.5	90	97.5
	kilometers X 1000	12	24	36	48	60	72	84	96	108	120	132	144	156
Air Cleaner Air Filter—Replace	AT				X				X				X	
Ignition Cables—Replace	AT								X					
PCV Valve—Check and Replace if Necessary	AT								X					
Spark Plugs—Replace	AT								X				O#	
Timing Belt 2.2-2.5 L Engine—Replace	AT												X	

NON-EMISSION RELATED COMPONENT MAINTENANCE

Where time and mileage are shown, follow interval listed first.	miles X 1000	7.5	15	22.5	30	37.5	45	52.5	60	67.5	75	82.5	90	97.5
	kilometers X 1000	12	24	36	48	60	72	84	96	108	120	132	144	156
Engine Coolant Flush and Replace at 36 Months**	OR							X**						
Engine Coolant Level, Hoses and Clamps—Inspect	AT	X	X	X	X	X	X	X	X	X	X	X	X	X
Engine Oil—Change Every 6 Months (4)	OR	X	X	X	X	X	X	X	X	X	X	X	X	X
Engine Oil Filter—Replace Every Second Oil Change	*		X		X		X		X		X		X	
Crankcase Filter (if equipped)—Replace	AT				X				X				X	
Accessory Drive Belts—Adjust Tension · Replace	AT	X	X		X		X				X		X	
Accessory Drive Belts—Auto Tension, Inspect***	AT								X					
Exhaust System—Inspect Every		X	X	X	X	X	X	X	X	X#	X	X#	X	X
Tire Rotation	AT	X	X	X	X	X	X	X	X	X	X	X	X	X

SEVERE SERVICE MAINTENANCE

Severe service is defined as: Stop-and-go driving in dusty conditions, extensive idling, frequent short trips, operating at sustained high speeds during hot weather above +90°F (+32°C), police, taxi, limousine, commercial type operation, or trailer towing. Including California 2.5 L & 3.0 L Engines with Auto Transaxle.

Where time and mileage are shown, follow interval listed first.		miles X 1000	3	6	9	12	15	18	21	24	27	30	33	36	39	42	45	48
		kilometers X 1000	5	10	15	20	24	29	34	39	43	48	53	58	62	67	72	77
Engine Oil	Refer to engine oil paragraph		X	X	X	X	X	X	X	X	X	X	X	X	X	X	X	X
Engine Oil Filter	Replace every second oil change			X		X		X		X		X		X		X		X
Brake Linings—Front and Rear	Inspect every				X			X			X			X			X	
CV Joint & Front Suspension Ball Joints	Inspect every oil change		X	X	X	X	X	X	X	X	X	X	X	X	X	X	X	X
Tie Rod Ends & Steering Linkage	Lubricate every 18 months OR					X					X					X		
Air Cleaner Air Filter	Replace if required every					X					X					X		
Automatic Transaxle	Change filter and fluid every					X					X					X		
PCV Valve	Replace if required every					X					X					X		

O = Recommended maintenance for proper performance.
X = Scheduled maintenance.
# = Not required if previously replaced.
* = If accumulated mileage is less than 7,500 miles for 12 months, replace oil filter at each oil change.
** = Flush and replace engine coolant every 24 months or 30,000 miles thereafter.
*** = Replace if required.
(4) = Flexible Fuel Vehicles — Change engine oil every 6 months or 8 000 km (5,000 miles).

CALIFORNIA VEHICLES W/2.5 & 3.0 L ENGINES & AUTO TRANSAXLE

EMISSION RELATED COMPONENT MAINTENANCE

Where time and mileage are shown, follow interval listed first.	miles X 1000	7.5	15	22.5	30	37.5	45	52.5	60	67.5	75	82.5	90	97.5
	kilometers X 1000	12	24	36	48	60	72	84	96	108	120	132	144	156
Air Cleaner Air Filter—Replace	AT				X				X				X	
Ignition Cables—Replace	AT								X					
PCV Valve—Check and Replace if Necessary	AT								O(3)					
Spark Plugs—Replace	AT				X				X				X	
Timing Belt 2.5 L Engine, Replace if Required	AT												O(3)	
Timing Belt 3.0 L Engine, Replace if Required	AT								O(3)				O(3)#	

NON-EMISSION RELATED COMPONENT MAINTENANCE

Where time and mileage are shown, follow interval listed first.	miles X 1000	7.5	15	22.5	30	37.5	45	52.5	60	67.5	75	82.5	90	97.5
	kilometers X 1000	12	24	36	48	60	72	84	96	108	120	132	144	156
Engine Coolant Flush and Replace at 36 Months**	OR							X**						
Engine Coolant Level, Hoses and Clamps—Inspect	AT	X	X	X	X	X	X	X	X	X	X	X	X	
Engine Oil—Change Every 6 Months	OR	X	X	X	X	X	X	X	X	X	X	X	X	X
Engine Oil Filter—Replace Every Second Oil Change	*		X		X		X		X		X		X	
Crankcase Filter (if equipped)—Replace	AT				X				X				X	
Accessory Drive Belts—Adjust Tension Replace	AT		X		X		X				X		X	
	AT								X					
Accessory Drive Belts—Auto Tension, Inspect***	AT								X					
Exhaust System—Inspect Every		X	X	X	X	X	X	X	X	X#	X	X#	X	
Tire Rotation	AT	X	X	X	X	X	X	X	X	X	X	X	X	

O = Recommended maintenance for proper performance.
X = Scheduled maintenance.
# = Not required if previously replaced.
* = If accumulated mileage is less than 7,500 miles for 12 months, replace oil filter at each oil change.
** = Flush and replace engine coolant every 24 months or 30,000 miles thereafter.
*** = Replace if required.
(3) = Recommended by Chrysler but not required to maintain warranty on drive belts and PCV valve.

CONCORDE, INTREPID, LHS, VISION & 1994–95 NEW YORKER

EMISSION RELATED COMPONENT MAINTENANCE

Where time and mileage are shown, follow interval listed first.	miles X 1000	7.5	15	22.5	30	37.5	45	52.5	60	67.5	75	82.5	90	97.5
	kilometers X 1000	12	24	36	48	60	72	84	96	108	120	132	144	156
Air Cleaner Air Filter-Replace	AT				X				X				X	
Ignition Cables-Replace	AT								X					
PCV Valve-Check and Replace if Necessary	AT								X			0#		
Spark Plugs-Replace	AT				X				X				X	

NON-EMISSION RELATED COMPONENT MAINTENANCE

Where time and mileage are shown, follow interval listed first.	miles X 1000	7.5	15	22.5	30	37.5	45	52.5	60	67.5	75	82.5	90	97.5
	kilometers X 1000	12	24	36	48	60	72	84	96	108	120	132	144	156
Engine Coolant Flush and Replace at 36 Months **	OR							X**						
Engine Coolant Level, Hoses and Clamps-Inspect	AT	X	X	X	X	X	X	X	X	X	X	X	X	X
Engine Oil-Change Every 6 Months	OR	X	X	X	X	X	X	X	X	X	X	X	X	X
Engine Oil Filter-Replace Every Second Oil Change	*		X		X		X		X		X		X	
Crankcase Filter (if equipped)-Replace	AT				X				X				X	
Accessory Drive Belts-Adjust Tension	AT		X		X		X							
Replace	AT								X					
Exhaust System-Inspect Every		X	X	X	X	X	X	X	X	X	X	X	X	X
Tire Rotation	AT	X	X	X	X	X	X	X	X	X	X	X	X	X

SEVERE SERVICE MAINTENANCE

Severe service is defined as: Stop-and-go driving in dusty conditions, extensive idling, frequent short trips, operating at sustained high speeds during hot weather above +90°F (+32°C), police, taxi, limousine, commercial type operation, or trailer towing.

Where time and mileage are shown, follow interval listed first.		miles X 1000	3	6	9	12	15	18	21	24	27	30	33	36	39	42	45	48
		kilometers X 1000	5	10	15	20	24	29	34	39	43	48	53	58	62	67	72	77
Engine Oil	Refer to engine oil paragraph		X	X	X	X	X	X	X	X	X	X	X	X	X	X	X	X
Engine Oil Filter	Replace every second oil change			X		X		X		X		X		X		X		X
Brake Linings-Front and Rear	Inspect every				X			X			X			X			X	
CV Joint & Front Suspension Ball Joints	Inspect every oil change		X	X	X	X	X	X	X	X	X	X	X	X	X	X	X	X
Tie Rod Ends & Steering Linkage	Lubricate every 18 months OR						X					X					X	
Air Cleaner Air Filter	Replace if required every						X					X					X	
Automatic Transaxle	Change filter and fluid every						X					X					X	
PCV Valve	Replace if required every											X						

0 = Recommended maintenance for proper performance.
X = Scheduled maintenance for LH vehicles.
# = Not required if previously replaced.
* = If accumulated mileage is less than 7,500 miles for 12 months, replace oil filter at each oil change.
** = Flush and replace engine coolant every 24 months or 30,000 miles thereafter.

CIRRUS, NEON & STRATUS

No.	Emission control system maintenance	Service to be performed		Kilometers in thousands	24	48	72	96	120	144	168
				Mileage in thousands	15	30	45	60	75	90	105
1	Fuel system (Tank, pipe line and connection, and fuel tank filler tube cap)	Check for leaks Every 5 years	or					×			
2	Fuel hoses	Check condition Every 2 years	or			×		×		×	
3	Air cleaner element	Replace	at			×		×		×	
4	Evaporative emission control system (except evaporative emission canister)	Check for leaks and clogging Every 5 years	or					×			
5	Spark plugs	Replace	at			×		×		×	
6	Ignition cables	Replace Every 5 years	or					×			

CHRYSLER CORP.

CIRRUS, NEON & STRATUS

GENERAL MAINTENANCE SERVICE FOR PROPER VEHICLE PERFORMANCE

Miles	Months	Recomended Maintenance
3,000	—	Change Engine Oil
7,500	6	Change Engine Oil
15,000	12	Change Engine Oil
		Replace Oil Filter
		Adjust Drive Belt Tension
22,500	18	Change Engine Oil
		Inspect Front Brake Pads And Rear Brake Linings
30,000	24	Change Engine Oil
		Replace Air Cleaner Element
		Replace Spark Plugs
37,500	30	Change Engine Oil
45,000	36	Change Engine Oil
		Replace Oil Filter
		Adjust Drive Belt Tension
		Flush And Fill Engine Coolant
52,500	42	Change Engine Oil
60,000	48	Change Engine Oil
		Replace Oil Filter
		Inspect & Replace PCV Valve, If Necessary
		Lubricate Front & Rear Suspension Ball Joints
		Replace Drive Belts
		Replace Air Cleaner Element
		Replace Spark Plugs
		Replace Ignition Cables

Miles	Months	Recomended Maintenance
67,500	54	Change Engine Oil
		Inspect Front Brake Pads & Rear Brake Pad Linings
75,000	60	Change Engine Oil
		Replace Oil Filter
		Adjust Drive Belt Tension
		Flush & Fill Engine Coolant If It Has Been 30,000 Miles Or 24 Months Since Last Changed
82,500	66	Change Engine Oil
		Flush & Fill Engine Coolant If It Has Been 30,000 Miles Or 24 Months Since Last Changed
90,000	72	Change Engine Oil
		Replace Oil Filter
		Inspect & Replace PCV Valve, If Necessary
		Lubricate Front & Rear Suspension Ball Joints
		Adjust Drive Belt Tension
		Replace Air Cleaner Element
97,500	78	Change Engine Oil
105,000	84	Change Engine Oil
		Replace Oil Filter
		Replace Engine Timing Belt

SEVERE SERVICE MAINTENANCE

Miles	Recomended Maintenance
3,000	Change Engine Oil
6,000	Change Engine Oil
	Replace Oil Filter
9,000	Change Engine Oil
12,000	Change Engine Oil
	Replace Oil Filter
	Inspect Front Brake Pads & Rear Brake Linings
15,000	Change Engine Oil
	Adjust Drive Belt Tension
	Inspect & Replace Air Cleaner Element, If Necessary
	Change Automatic Transaxle Fluid & Filter
	Adjust Transaxle Bands, If Equipped
18,000	Change Engine Oil
	Replace Oil Filter
21,000	Change Engine Oil
24,000	Change Engine Oil
	Replace Oil Filter
	Inspect Front Brake Pads And Rear Brake Linings
27,000	Change Engine Oil

Miles	Recomended Maintenance
30,000	Change Engine Oil
	Replace Oil Filter
	Inspect & Replace PCV Valve, If Necessary
	Lubricate Front & Rear Suspension Ball Joints
	Adjust Drive Belt Tension
	Replace Air Cleaner Element
	Replace Spark Plugs
	Change Automatic Transaxle Fluid & Filter
	Adjust Transaxle Bands, If Equipped
33,000	Change Engine Oil
36,000	Change Engine Oil
	Replace Oil Filter
	Flush & Fill Engine Coolant
	Inspect Front Brake Pads & Rear Brake Linings
39,000	Change Engine Oil
42,000	Change Engine Oil
	Replace Oil Filter
45,000	Change Engine Oil
	Inspect & Repalce Air Cleaner Element, If Necessary

Continued

SEVERE SERVICE MAINTENANCE

Miles	Recomended Maintenance
45,000 (cont.)	Adjust Drive Belt Tension
	Change Automatic Transaxle Fluid & Filter
	Adjust Transaxle Bands, If Equipped
48,000	Change Engine Oil
	Replace Oil Filter
	Inspect Front Brake Pads & Rear Brake Linings
51,000	Change Engine Oil
	Flush & Fill Engine Coolant
54,000	Change Engine Oil
	Replace Oil Filter
57,000	Change Engine Oil
60,000	Change Engine Oil
	Replace Oil Filter
	Inspect & Replace PCV Valve, If Necessary
	Lubricate Front & Rear Suspension Ball Joints
	Replace Drive Belts
	Replace Air Cleaner Element
	Replace Spark Plugs
	Replace Ignition Cables
	Change Automatic Transaxle Fluid & Filter
	Adjust Transaxle Bands, If Equipped
	Inspect Front Brake Pads & Rear Brake Linings
63,000	Change Engine Oil
66,000	Change Engine Oil
	Replace Oil Filter
69,000	Change Engine Oil
72,000	Change Engine Oil
	Replace Oil Filter
	Inspect Front Brake Pads & Rear Brake Linings
75,000	Change Engine Oil
	Adjust Drive Belt Tension

Miles	Recomended Maintenance
75,000 (cont.)	Inspect & Replace Air Cleaner Element, If Necessary
	Change Automatic Transaxle Fluid & Filter
	Adjust Transaxle Bands, If Equipped
78,000	Change Engine Oil
	Replace Oil Filter
81,000	Change Engine Oil
	Flush & Fill Engine Coolant
84,000	Change Engine Oil
	Replace Oil Filter
	Inspect Front Brake Pads & Rear Brake Linings
87,000	Change Engine Oil
90,000	Change Engine Oil
	Replace Oil Filter
	Inspect & Replace PCV Valve, If Necessary
	Lubricate Front & Rear Suspension Ball Joints
	Adjust Drive Belt Tension
	Replace Air Cleaner Element
	Replace Spark Plugs
	Change Automatic Transaxle Fluid & Filter
	Adjust Transaxle Bands, If Equipped
93,000	Change Engine Oil
96,000	Change Engine Oil
	Replace Oil Filter
	Inspect Front Brake Pads & Rear Brake Linings
99,000	Change Engine Oil
100,000	Replace Spark Plugs
102,000	Change Engine Oil
	Replace Oil Filter
	Replace Engine Timing Belt

Ford Motor Co.

INDEX

TEMPO & TOPAZ
NORMAL SERVICE MAINTENANCE

SERVICE INTERVAL Perform at the months or distances shown, whichever comes first.	Miles x 1000	3	6	9	12	15	18	21	24	27	30	33	36	39	42	45	48	51	54	57	60
	Kilometers x 1000	4.8	9.6	14.4	19.2	24	28.8	33.6	38.4	43.2	48	52.8	57.6	62.4	67.2	72	76.8	81.6	86.4	91.2	96
EMISSION CONTROL SERVICE																					
Change Engine Oil and Oil Filter (every 3 months) or		X	X	X	X	X	X	X	X	X	X	X	X	X	X	X	X	X	X	X	X
Spark Plugs: Replace											X										
Inspect Accessory Drive Belt(s)											X										
Replace Air Cleaner Filter①											X										X
Replace Crankcase Emission Filter①											X										X
Replace Engine Coolant, (every 36 months) or											X										X
Check Engine Coolant Protection, Hoses and Clamps									ANNUALLY												
GENERAL MAINTENANCE																					
Inspect Exhaust Heat Shields											X										X
Change Automatic Transaxle Fluid②											X										X
Inspect Disc Brake Pads and Rotors (Front)③											X										X
Inspect Brake Linings and Drums (Rear)③											X										X
Inspect and Repack Rear Wheel Bearings④											X										X

① If operating in severe dust, more frequent intervals may be required — consult your dealer.

② Change automatic transaxle fluid if your driving habits frequently include one or more of the following conditions:
- Operation during HOT WEATHER (above 32°C (90°F)).
- Towing a trailer or using a car top carrier.
- Police, taxi or door-to-door delivery service.

③ If your driving includes continuous stop and go driving or driving in mountainous areas, more frequent intervals may be required.

④ Replace rear wheel bearings at 100,000 miles (160,930 km).

SEVERE SERVICE MAINTENANCE

SERVICE INTERVALS Perform at the months or distances shown, whichever comes first.	Miles x 1000	7.5	15	22.5	30	37.5	45	52.5	60
	Kilometers x 1000	12	24	36	48	60	72	84	96
EMISSIONS CONTROL SERVICE									
Change Engine Oil and Oil Filter (Every 6 Months) or 7500 miles whichever occurs first		X	X	X	X	X	X	X	X
Replace Spark Plugs					X				X
Change crankcase emission filter					X				X
Inspect Accessory Drive Belt(s)					X				X
Replace Air Cleaner Filter①					X①				X①
Change Engine Coolant Every 36 Months or					X				X
Check Engine Coolant Protection, Hoses and Clamps					ANNUALLY				
GENERAL MAINTENANCE									
Check Exhaust Heat Shields					X				X
Inspect Disc Brake Pads and Rotors (Front)②					X②				X②
Inspect Brake Linings and Drums (Rear)②					X②				X②
Inspect and Repack Rear Wheel Bearing③					X③				X③

① If operating in severe dust, more frequent intervals may be required. Consult your dealer.
② If your driving includes continuous stop-and-go driving or driving in mountainous areas, more frequent intervals may be required.
③ Replace rear wheel bearings at 100,000 miles (160,930 km).

CONTINENTAL
NORMAL SERVICE MAINTENANCE

SERVICE INTERVALS Perform at the months or distances shown, whichever comes first.	Miles x 1000	7.5	15	22.5	30	37.5	45	52.5	60
	Kilometers x 1000	12	24	36	48	60	72	84	96
EMISSIONS CONTROL SERVICE									
Replace Engine Oil and Oil Filter Every 6 Months OR		X	X	X	X	X	X	X	X
Replace Spark Plugs					X				X
Replace Crankcase Filter①					X				X
Inspect Accessory Drive Belt(s)					X				X
Replace Air Cleaner Filter①					X				X
Replace Engine Coolant Every 36 Months OR					X				X
Check Engine Coolant Protection, Hoses and Clamps					ANNUALLY				
GENERAL MAINTENANCE									
Check Exhaust Heat Shields					X				X
Inspect Disc Brake Pads and Rotors (Front and Rear)					X②				X②
Inspect and Repack Rear Wheel Bearing					X				X
Rotate Tires		X		X		X		X	

① If operating in severe dust, more frequent intervals may be required. Consult your dealer.

② If your driving includes continuous stop-and-go driving or driving in mountainous areas, more frequent intervals may be required.

X All items designated by an X must be performed in all states.

VEHICLE MAINTENANCE SCHEDULES

SEVERE SERVICE MAINTENANCE

SERVICE INTERVAL Perform at the months or distances shown, whichever comes first.	Miles x 1000	3	6	9	12	15	18	21	24	27	30	33	36	39	42	45	48	51	54	57	60
	Kilometers x 1000	4.8	9.6	14.4	19.2	24	28.8	33.6	38.4	43.2	48	52.8	57.6	62.4	67.2	72	76.8	81.6	86.4	91.2	96
EMISSION CONTROL SERVICE																					
Replace Engine Oil and Oil Filter Every 3 months OR		X	X	X	X	X	X	X	X	X	X	X	X	X	X	X	X	X	X	X	X
Replace Spark Plugs											X										X
Inspect Accessory Drive Belt(s)											X										X
Replace Air Cleaner Filter ①											X										X
Replace Crankcase Filter ①											X										X
Replace Engine Coolant Every 36 Months OR											X										X
Check Engine Coolant Protection, Hoses and Clamps		ANNUALLY																			
GENERAL MAINTENANCE																					
Inspect Exhaust Heat Shields											X										X
Change Automatic Transaxle Fluid ②											②										②
Inspect Disc Brake Pads and Rotors Front and Rear											X③										X③
Inspect and Repack Rear Wheel Bearings											X										X
Rotate Tires			X					X					X				X				

① If operating in severe dust, more frequent intervals may be required — consult your dealer.

② Change automatic transaxle fluid if your driving habits frequently include one or more of the following conditions:
- Operation during HOT WEATHER (above 32°C (90°F)).
- Towing a trailer or using a car top carrier.
- Police, taxi or door-to-door delivery service.

③ If your driving includes continuous stop and go driving or driving in mountainous areas, more frequent intervals may be required.

X All items designated by an X must be performed in all states.

1992–94 COUGAR & THUNDERBIRD
NORMAL SERVICE MAINTENANCE

SERVICE INTERVALS Perform at the months or distances shown, whichever comes first.	Miles x 1000	7.5	15	22.5	30	37.5	45	52.5	60
	Kilometers x 1000	12	24	36	48	60	72	84	96
EMISSIONS CONTROL SERVICE									
Supercharged Engines — Change Oil and Filter	As Indicated by the Vehicle Maintenance Monitor, But Not Beyond Every 5,000 Miles (8 000 km) or 6 Months, Whichever Comes First								
Replace Engine Oil and Oil Filter As Indicated by the Vehicle Maintenance Monitor (if equipped), But Not Beyond Every 6 Months or 7,500 Miles Whichever Occurs First — Except Supercharged		X	X	X	X	X	X	X	X
Replace Spark Plugs — Except Supercharged						X			X
Replace Spark Plugs — Platinum Type Supercharged									X
Check Supercharger Lubricant						X			X
Replace Crankcase Emission Filter ①						X			X
Inspect Accessory Drive Belt(s)						X			X
Replace Air Cleaner Filter ①						X			X
Replace Engine Coolant Every 36 Months OR						X			X
Check Engine Coolant Protection, Hoses and Clamps		ANNUALLY							
GENERAL MAINTENANCE									
Check Exhaust Heat Shields						X			X
Inspect Disc Brake Pads and Rotors (Front and Rear Super Coupe/XR7) ②						X			X
Inspect Brake Linings and Drums (Rear) ②						X			X
Rotate Tires		X		X			X	X	

① If operating in severe dust, more frequent intervals may be required. Consult your dealer.

② If your driving includes continuous stop-and-go driving or driving in mountainous areas, more frequent intervals may be required.

FORD MOTOR CO.

SEVERE SERVICE MAINTENANCE

SERVICE INTERVAL Perform at the months or distances shown, whichever comes first.	Miles × 1000	3	6	9	12	15	18	21	24	27	30	33	36	39	42	45	48	51	54	57	60
	Kilometers × 1000	4.8	9.6	14.4	19.2	24	28.8	33.6	38.4	43.2	48	52.8	57.6	62.4	67.2	72	76.8	81.6	86.4	91.2	96
EMISSION CONTROL SERVICE																					
Replace Engine Oil and Oil Filter Every 3 Months OR		X	X	X	X	X	X	X	X	X	X	X	X	X	X	X	X	X	X	X	X
Replace Spark Plugs											X										X
Replace Spark Plugs (Supercharged use Platinum Type)																					X
Check Supercharger Lubricant											X										X
Inspect Accessory Drive Belt(s)											X										X
Replace Air Cleaner Filter①											X										X
Replace Engine Coolant, EVERY 36 Months OR											X										X
Check Engine Coolant Protection, Hoses and Clamps		ANNUALLY																			
GENERAL MAINTENANCE																					
Inspect Exhaust Heat Shields											X										X
Change Automatic Transmission Fluid②											X										X
Inspect Brake Pads and Rotors (front)③ (Front and Rear — Super Coupe/XR7③)											X										X
Inspect Brake Linings and Drums (Rear)③											X										X
Rotate Tires			X					X				X				X					

① If operating in severe dust, more frequent intervals may be required. Consult your dealer.
② Change automatic transmission fluid if your driving habits frequently include one or more of the following conditions:
   • Operation during hot weather (above 32°C (90°F)) carrying heavy loads and in hilly terrain.
   • Towing a trailer or using a car top carrier.
   • Police, taxi or door-to-door delivery service.
   • Vehicle accumulates 5,000 miles (8 000 km) or more per month or is used in CONTINUOUS stop-and-go service.
③ If your driving includes continuous stop-and-go driving or driving in mountainous areas, more frequent intervals may be required.
X All items designated by an X must be performed in all states.

CROWN VICTORIA, GRAND MARQUIS & TOWN CAR

NORMAL SERVICE MAINTENANCE

SERVICE INTERVALS Perform at the months or distances shown, whichever comes first.	Miles x 1000	7.5	15	22.5	30	37.5	45	52.5	60
	Kilometers x 1000	12	24	36	48	60	72	84	96
EMISSIONS CONTROL SERVICE									
Replace Engine Oil and Filter (Every 6 Months) OR 7,500 Miles Whichever Occurs First		X	X	X	X	X	X	X	X
Replace Spark Plugs					X				X
Replace Crankcase Emission Filter①					X				X
Inspect Accessory Drive Belt(s)					X				X
Replace Air Cleaner Filter①					X				X
Replace PCV Valve and Crankcase Emission Filter — 5.0L Engine			(X)		(X)		(X)		X
Check/Clean Choke Linkage (5.8L only)					X				X
Change Engine Coolant Every 36 Months OR					X				X
Check Engine Coolant Protection, Hoses and Clamps					ANNUALLY				
GENERAL MAINTENANCE									
Check Exhaust Heat Shields					X				X
Lube Suspension (Lincoln)				X③	X		X③		X
Lubricate Steering Linkage (Lincoln)			X		X		X		X
Inspect Disc Brake Pads and Rotors (Front)②					X				X
Inspect Brake Linings and Drums (Rear)②					X				X
Inspect and Repack Front Wheel Bearings					X				X
Rotate Tires		X		X		X		X	

① If operating in severe dust, more frequent intervals may be required. Consult your dealer.
② If your driving includes continuous stop-and-go driving or driving in mountainous areas, more frequent intervals may be required.
③ All vehicles except Lincoln Town Car.
X All items designated by an X must be performed in all states.
(X) This item not required to be performed, however, Ford recommends that you also perform maintenance on items designated by an (X) in order to achieve best vehicle operation. Failure to perform this recommended maintenance will not invalidate the vehicle emissions warranty or manufacturer recall liability.

VEHICLE MAINTENANCE SCHEDULES

SEVERE SERVICE MAINTENANCE

SERVICE INTERVAL Perform at the months or distances shown, whichever comes first. Miles × 1000	3	6	9	12	15	18	21	24	27	30	33	36	39	42	45	48	51	54	57	60
Kilometers × 1000	4.8	9.6	14.4	19.2	24	28.8	33.6	38.4	43.2	48	52.8	57.6	62.4	67.2	72	76.8	81.6	86.4	91.2	96
EMISSION CONTROL SERVICE																				
Replace Engine Oil and Oil Filter Every 3 Months OR	X	X	X	X	X	X	X	X	X	X	X	X	X	X	X	X	X	X	X	X
Replace Spark Plugs										X										X
Inspect Accessory Drive Belt(s)										X										X
Replace PCV Valve and Crankcase Emission Filter (5.0L Engine)					(X)					(X)					(X)					
Replace Air Cleaner Filter(1)										X										X
Replace Crankcase Emission Filter(1) (5.8L Engine)										X										X
Check/Clean Choke Linkage (5.8L Engine)										X										X
Replace Engine Coolant, EVERY 36 Months OR										X										X
Check Engine Coolant Protection, Hoses and Clamps	ANNUALLY																			
GENERAL MAINTENANCE																				
Inspect Exhaust Heat Shields										X										X
Change Automatic Transmission Fluid(2)										X										X
Lubricate Suspension (Lincoln)										X										X
Lubricate Steering Linkage (Lincoln)					X					X				X						X
Inspect Disc Brake Pads and Rotors(3)										X										X
Inspect Brake Linings and Drums (Rear) (Lincoln)(3)										X										X
Inspect and Repack Front Wheel Bearings										X										X
Rotate Tires		X					X				X						X			

1. If operating in severe dust, more frequent intervals may be required. Consult your dealer.
2. Change automatic transmission fluid if your driving habits frequently include one or more of the following conditions:
   - Operation during hot weather (above 32°C (90°F)) carrying heavy loads and in hilly terrain.
   - Towing a trailer or using a car top carrrier.
   - Police, taxi or door to door delivery service.
3. If your driving includes continuous stop-and-go driving or driving in mountainous areas, more frequent intervals may be required.
X All items designated by an X must be performed in all states.
(X) This item not required to be performed, however, Ford recommends that you also perform maintenance on items designated by an (X) in order to achieve best vehicle operation. Failure to perform this recommended maintenance will not invalidate the vehicle emissions warranty or manufacturer recall liability

ASPIRE & FESTIVA
NORMAL SERVICE MAINTENANCE

MILES × (1000)	7.5	15.0	22.5	30.0	37.5	45.0	52.5	60.0
KILOMETERS × (1000)	12	24	36	48	60	72	84	96
EMISSION CONTROL SERVICE								
Change Engine Oil (whichever occurs first) Every 6 Months or	X	X	X	X	X	X	X	X
Change Engine Oil Filter (whichever occurs first) Every 6 Months or	X	X	X	X	X	X	X	X
Spark Plugs Inspect/Clean		(2)				(2)		
Replace				X				X
Check Idle Speed		X		X		X		X
Inspect Cooling System Every 12 Months or		X		X		X		X
Replace Engine Coolant Every 36 Months or				X				X
Check Accessory Drive Belts				X				X
Replace Air Cleaner Element				(1)				(1)
Replace Fuel Filter				X				X
Replace Engine Timing Belt								X
GENERAL MAINTENANCE								
Inspect Brake Lines and Connections				X		X		X
Inspect Clutch Pedal				X		X		X
Inspect Front Disc Brakes				X		X		X
Inspect Drum Brakes				X				X
Inspect Safety Belts, Buckles, Retractors, & Anchors				X		X		X
Inspect Steering Linkage, Rack Guides & Tie Rod Ends				X		X		X
Tighten Bolts & Nuts on Chassis & Body				X		X		
Inspect Steering Operations & Gear Housing				X				X
Inspect Rack Seal Boots				X				X
Inspect Front Suspension Ball Joints				X				X
Inspect Drive Shaft Dust Boots				X				X
Inspect Exhaust System Heat Shield				X				X
Inspect Fuel Lines				(2)				X
Inspect Transaxle, Change Rod Boots						X		
Lubricate Front and Rear Wheel Bearings								X

(1) If operating in severe dusty conditions, ask your dealer for proper replacement interval.
(2) Recommended, but not required

FORD MOTOR CO.

SEVERE SERVICE MAINTENANCE

MILES × (1000)	3	6	9	12	15	18	21	24	27	30	33	36	39	42	45	48	51	54	57	60
KILOMETERS × (1000)	4.8	9.6	14.	19.	24.	28.	33.	38.	43.	48.	52.	57.	62.	67.	72.	76.	81.	86.	91.	96.
EMISSION CONTROL SERVICE																				
Change Engine Oil (whichever occurs first) Every 3 Months or	X	X	X	X	X	X	X	X	X	X	X	X	X	X	X	X	X	X	X	X
Change Engine Oil Filter (whichever occurs first) Every 3 Months or	X	X	X	X	X	X	X	X	X	X	X	X	X	X	X	X	X	X	X	X
Spark Plugs. Inspect/Clean		X		X		X		X				X		X		X		X		
Replace										X										X
Check Idle Speed					X					X										X
Inspect Cooling System Every 12 Months or					X					X					X					X
Replace Engine Coolant Every 36 Months or										X					X					X
Check Accessory Drive Belts										X										X
Replace Air Cleaner Element										(1)										(1)
Replace Fuel Filter										X										X
Replace Engine Timing Belt																				X

GENERAL MAINTENANCE																				
Inspect Brake Lines. Connections & Hoses					X					X					X					X
Inspect, Adjust Clutch Pedal					X					X					X					X
Inspect Front Disc Brakes					X					X					X					X
Inspect Rear Drum Brakes										X										X
Inspect Safety Belts, Buckles, Retractors & Anchors					X					X					X					
Inspect Steering Linkage, Rack Guides, & Tie Rod Ends					X					X					X					X
Tighten Bolts & Nuts on Chassis & Body					X										X					
Inspect Steering Operations and Gear Housing										X					X					X
Inspect Rack Seal Boots										X										X
Inspect Front Suspension Ball Joints										X										X
Inspect Drive Shaft Dust Boots										X										X
Inspect Exhaust System Heat Shield										X										X
Inspect Fuel Lines										(2)										X
Inspect Transaxle, Change Rod Boots															X					
Lubricate Front and Rear Wheel Bearings																				X

(1) If operating in severe dusty conditions, ask your dealer for proper replacement interval.
(2) Recommended, but not required.

MUSTANG
NORMAL SERVICE MAINTENANCE

SERVICE INTERVALS Perform at the months or distances shown, whichever comes first.	Miles x 1000	7.5	15	22.5	30	37.5	45	52.5	60
	Kilometers x 1000	12	24	36	48	60	72	84	96
EMISSIONS CONTROL SERVICE									
Replace Engine Oil and Filter Every 6 Months OR 7,500 Miles Whichever Occurs First		X	X	X	X	X	X	X	X
Replace Spark Plugs					X				X
Replace Crankcase Emission Filter①					X				X
Inspect Accessory Drive Belt(s)					X				X
Replace Air Cleaner Filter①					X				X
Replace PCV Valve and Crankcase Emission Filter — 5.0L			(X)		(X)		(X)		X
Replace Engine Coolant Every 36 Months OR					X				X
Check Engine Coolant Protection, Hoses and Clamps		ANNUALLY							
GENERAL MAINTENANCE									
Check Exhaust Heat Shields					X				X
Lube Tie Rods		X③			X		X③		X
Inspect Disc Brake Pads and Rotors②					X				X
Inspect Brake Linings and Drums (Rear)②					X②				X②
Inspect and Repack Front Wheel Bearings					X				X
Rotate Tires		X		X		X		X	

① If operating in severe dust, more frequent intervals may be required. Consult your dealer.
② If your driving includes continuous stop-and-go driving or driving in mountainous areas, more frequent intervals may be required.
③ All vehicles.
X All items designated by an X must be performed in all states.
(X) This item not required to be performed, however, Ford recommends that you also perform maintenance on items designated by an (X) in order to achieve best vehicle operation. Failure to perform this recommended maintenance will not invalidate the vehicle emissions warranty or manufacturer recall liability.

SEVERE SERVICE MAINTENANCE

SERVICE INTERVAL Perform at the months or distances shown, whichever comes first.	Miles × 1000	3	6	9	12	15	18	21	24	27	30	33	36	39	42	45	48	51	54	57	60
	Kilometers × 1000	4.8	9.6	14.4	19.2	24	28.8	33.6	38.4	43.2	48	52.8	57.6	62.4	67.2	72	76.8	81.6	86.4	91.2	96
EMISSION CONTROL SERVICE																					
Replace Engine Oil and Oil Filter Every 3 Months OR		X	X	X	X	X	X	X	X	X	X	X	X	X	X	X	X	X	X	X	X
Replace Spark Plugs											X										X
Inspect Accessory Drive Belt(s)											X										X
Replace PCV Valve and Crankcase Emission Filter — 5.0L						(X)					(X)					(X)					X
Replace Air Cleaner Filter①											X										X
Replace Engine Coolant, EVERY 36 Months OR											X										X
Check Engine Coolant Protection, Hoses and Clamps		ANNUALLY																			
GENERAL MAINTENANCE																					
Inspect Exhaust Heat Shields											X										X
Change Automatic Transmission Fluid②											X										X
Lubricate Tie Rods											X										X
Inspect Disc Brake Pads and Rotors②											X										X
Inspect Brake Linings and Drums (Rear)③											X										X
Inspect and Repack Front Wheel Bearings											X										X
Rotate Tires			X				X				X					X					

1. If operating in severe dust, more frequent intervals may be required. Consult your dealer.
2. Change automatic transmission fluid if your driving habits frequently include one or more of the following conditions:
   • Operation during hot weather (above 32°C (90°F)) carrying heavy loads and in hilly terrain.
   • Towing a trailer or using a car top carrier.
   • Police, taxi or door to door delivery service.
3. If your driving includes continuous stop-and-go driving or driving in mountainous areas, more frequent intervals may be required.
X All items designated by an X must be performed in all states.
(X) This item not required to be performed, however, Ford recommends that you also perform maintenance on items designated by an (X) in order to achieve best vehicle operation. Failure to perform this recommended maintenance will not invalidate the vehicle emissions warranty or manufacturer recall liability.

FORD MOTOR CO.

1992 PROBE

NORMAL SERVICE MAINTENANCE

	7.5	15	22.5	30.0	37.5	45.0	52.5	60.0
MILES X (000)	7.5	15	22.5	30.0	37.5	45.0	52.5	60.0
KILOMETERS X (000)	12	24	36	48	60	72	84	96
EMISSION CONTROL SERVICE								
Non-Turbocharged Change Engine Oil & Oil Filter	X	X	X	X	X	X	X	X
Turbocharged Replace Engine Oil & Oil Filter	EVERY 5,000 MILES (8,000 km) OR 6 MONTHS, WHICHEVER OCCURS FIRST							
Replace Spark Plugs: Turbocharged		(3)		X		(3)		X
Non-Turbocharged				X				X
Inspect Cooling System Every 12 Months or		X		X		X		X
Replace Engine Coolant Every 36 Months or				X				X
Inspect Accessory Drive Belts				X				X
Replace Air Cleaner Element (2)				X				X
Replace Fuel Filter								X
Replace Engine Timing Belt (1)								(1)
GENERAL MAINTENANCE								
Inspect Brake Lines and Connections		X		X		X		X
Inspect Front Disc Brakes		X		X		X		X
Inspect Drum Brakes				X				X
Tighten Bolts & Nuts on Chassis & Body		X				X		
Inspect Steering Operation & Gear Linkage				X				X
Inspect Front Suspension Ball Joints				X				X
Inspect Driveshaft Dust Boots				X				X
Inspect Exhaust System Heat Shield				X				X
Inspect Fuel Lines				(3)				X

(1) Replacement of the timing belt is required at every 60,000 miles (96,000 km). Failure to replace the timing belt may result in damage to the engine.

(2) If operating in severe dust, more frequent intervals may be required. Consult your dealer.

(3) This item not required to be performed, however, Ford recommends that you perform maintenance on this item in order to achieve best vehicle operation. Failure to perform this recommended maintenance will not invalidate the vehicle emissions warranty or manufacturer recall liability.

SEVERE SERVICE MAINTENANCE

MILES X (000)	3	6	9	12	15	18	21	24	27	30	33	36	39	42	45	48	51	54	57	60
KILOMETERS X (000)	4.8	9.6	14.	19.	24.	28.	33.	38.	43.	48.	52.	57.	62.	67.	72.	76.	81.	86.	91.	96.
EMISSION CONTROL SERVICE																				
Change Engine Oil & Oil Filter (whichever occurs first) Every 3 Months or	X	X	X	X	X	X	X	X	X	X	X	X	X	X	X	X	X	X	X	X
Replace Spark Plugs Turbocharged				(3)						X					(3)					X
Non-turbocharged										X										X
Inspect Cooling System Every 12 Months or					X					X					X					X
Replace Engine Coolant Every 36 Months or										X										X
Inspect Accessory Drive Belts										X										X
Air Cleaner Element: Inspect/Clean					(3)										(3)					
Replace (2)										X										X
Replace Fuel Filter																				X
Replace Engine Timing Belt (1)																				X
GENERAL MAINTENANCE																				
Inspect Brake Lines, Connections & Hoses					X					X					X					X
Inspect Front Disc Brakes					X					X					X					X
Inspect Rear Drum Brakes										X										X
Tighten Bolts & Nuts on Chassis & Body					X										X					
Inspect Steering Operations and Linkage										X										X
Inspect Front Suspension Ball Joints										X										X
Inspect Drive Shaft Dust Boots										X										X
Inspect Exhaust System Heat Shield										X										X
Inspect Fuel Lines										(3)										X
Change automatic transaxle fluid										(4)										(4)

(1) Replacement of the timing belt is required at every 60,000 miles (96,000 km). Failure to replace the timing belt may result in damage to the engine.

(2) If operating in severe dust, more frequent intervals may be required. Consult your dealer.

(3) This item not required to be performed, however, Ford recommends that you perform maintenance on this item in order to achieve best vehicle operation. Failure to perform this recommended maintenance will not invalidate the vehicle emissions warranty or manufacturer recall liability.

(4) Change automatic transaxle fluid if your driving habits frequently include one or more of the following conditions:
- Operation during hot weather (above 90ºF, 32ºC) carrying heavy loads and in hilly terrain.
- Towing a trailer or using a car top carrier.
- Police, taxi or door-to-door delivery service.

FORD MOTOR CO.

1993–95 PROBE

NORMAL SERVICE MAINTENANCE

Perform at the Months or Distances Shown, Whichever Occurs First								
Miles x 1000	67.5	75	77.5	90	97.5	105	112.5	120
Kilometers x 1000	108.5	120.5	125.5	144.5	156.5	168.5	181	193
Emission Control Service								
• Change engine oil and oil filter every 6 months OR 7,500 miles, (12 000 kilometers)	x	x	x	x	x	x	x	x
• Replace spark plugs				x				x
• Replace crankcase ventilation filter (1)				x				x
• Inspect accessory drive belt(s)				x				x
• Replace air cleaner filter (1)				x				x
• Replace engine coolant (every 36 months) OR				x				x
• Check engine coolant system, coolant, hoses and clamps				ANNUALLY				
• Inspect cooling system components every 36 months OR				- x				x
• Replace engine timing belt (3)								x
• Inspect idle speed (4)				x				x
• Inspect fuel lines (2)				x				x
• Replace fuel filter								x

	67.5	75	77.5	90	97.5	105	112.5	120
Miles x 1000	67.5	75	77.5	90	97.5	105	112.5	120
Kilometers x 1000	108.5	120.5	125.5	144.5	156.5	168.5	181	193
General Maintenance								
• Inspect exhaust heat shields				x				x
• Inspect front and/or rear disc brakes				x				x
• Inspect drum brakes				x				x
• Rotate tires	x	x	x	x	x		x	
• Inspect halfshaft dust boots				x				x
• Inspect steering operation and linkage				x				x
• Inspect front suspension ball joints				x				x
• Inspect brake lines, hoses and connections				x				x
• Inspect bolts and nuts on chassis and body				x				x
• Inspect clutch pedal operation (if equipped)				x				x

(1) If operating in severe dust, more frequent intervals may be required. Consult your dealer.

(2) This item not required to be performed, however, Ford recommends that you perform maintenance on this item in order to achieve best vehicle operation. Failure to perform this recommended maintenance will not invalidate the emissions warranty or manufacturer recall liability.

(3) Replacement of the timing belt is required at every 60,000 miles (96 000 km). Failure to replace the timing belt may result in damage to the engine.

(4) Recommended, but not required. Adjustment should be made if fault is found.

SEVERE SERVICE MAINTENANCE

Perform at the Months or Distances Shown, Whichever Occurs First

Miles x 1000	3	6	9	12	15	18	21	24	27	30	33	36	39	42	45	48	51	54	57	60
Kilometers x 1000	4.8	9.6	14.4	19.2	24	28.8	33.6	38.4	43.2	48	52.8	57.6	62.4	67.2	72	76.8	81.6	86.4	91.2	96
Emission Control Service																				
• Change engine oil and oil filter every 3,000 miles (4 800 kilometers) or 3 months	x	x	x	x	x	x	x	x	x	x	x	x	x	x	x	x	x	x	x	x
• Replace spark plugs										x										x
• Inspect accessory drive belt(s)										x										x
• Inspect/clean air cleaner filter (2)					x										x					
• Replace air cleaner filter (1)										x										x
• Inspect fuel lines (2)										x										x
• Replace engine coolant every 36 months OR										x										x
• Check cooling system, coolant, hoses and clamps	ANNUALLY																			
• Inspect cooling system components every 36 months OR										x										x
• Replace engine timing belt (4)																				x
• Inspect idle speed (5)										x										x
• Replace fuel filter																				x

Miles x 1000	3	6	9	12	15	18	21	24	27	30	33	36	39	42	45	48	51	54	57	60
Kilometers x 1000	4.8	9.6	14.4	19.2	24	28.8	33.6	38.4	43.2	48	52.8	57.6	62.4	67.2	72	76.8	81.6	86.4	91.2	96
General Maintenance																				
• Inspect exhaust heat shields										x										x
• Change automatic transaxle fluid (3)										x										x
• Inspect front and/or rear disc brakes					x					x					x					x
• Inspect rear drum brakes (3)										x										x
• Rotate tires		x				x					x					x				
• Inspect clutch pedal operation (if equipped)										x										x
• Inspect halfshaft dust boots										x										x
• Inspect brake line, hoses and connections										x										x
• Inspect front suspension ball joints										x										x
• Inspect bolts and nuts on chassis and body					x					x					x					x
• Inspect steering operation and linkage										x										x

(1) If operating in severe dust, more frequent intervals may be required. Consult your dealer.

(2) This item not required to be performed, however, Ford recommends that you also perform maintenance on these items in order to achieve best vehicle operation. Failure to perform this recommended maintenance will not invalidate the emissions warranty or manufacturer recall liability.

(3) Change automatic transaxle fluid if your driving habits frequently include one or more of the following conditions:
   • Operation during hot weather (above 90°F, 32°C), carrying heavy loads and in hilly terrain.
   • Police, taxi or door-to-door delivery service.

(4) Replacement of the timing belt is required every 60,000 miles (96 000 km). Failure to replace the timing belt may result in damage to the engine.

(5) Recommended but not required. Adjustment should be made if any fault is found.

FORD MOTOR CO.

SABLE & TAURUS
NORMAL SERVICE MAINTENANCE

SERVICE INTERVALS Perform at the months or distances shown, whichever comes first.	Miles x 1000	7.5	15	22.5	30	37.5	45	52.5	60
	Kilometers x 1000	12	24	36	48	60	72	84	96
EMISSIONS CONTROL SERVICE									
Replace Engine Oil and Oil Filter Every 6 Months OR		X	X	X	X	X	X	X	X
Replace Spark Plugs 2.5L, 3.8L					X				X
3.0L, SHO Platinum Plugs									X
Replace Cam Belt and Adjust Valve Lash — SHO									X
Replace Crankcase Filter — Four Cylinder Engine Only									X
Inspect Accessory Drive Belt(s)					X				X
Replace Air Cleaner Filter ①					X				X
Replace Engine Coolant Every 36 Months OR					X				X
Check Engine Coolant Protection, Hoses and Clamps		ANNUALLY							
GENERAL MAINTENANCE									
Inspect Battery Fluid Level (SHO only) ③				X			X		
Check Exhaust Heat Shields					X				
Inspect Disc Brake Pads and Rotors (Front) (Front and Rear — SHO) ②					X②				X②
Inspect Brake Linings and Drums (Rear) ②					X②				X②
Rotate Tires		X		X		X		X	

① If operating in severe dust, more frequent intervals may be required. Consult your dealer.

② If your driving includes continuous stop-and-go driving or driving in mountainous areas, more frequent intervals may be required.

X All items designated with an "X" must be performed in all states.

③ If operating in temperatures above 32°C (90°F) check more often.

SEVERE SERVICE MAINTENANCE

SERVICE INTERVAL Perform at the months or distances shown, whichever comes first.	Miles x 1000	3	6	9	12	15	18	21	24	27	30	33	36	39	42	45	48	51	54	57	60
	Kilometers x 1000	4.8	9.6	14.4	19.2	24	28.8	33.6	38.4	43.2	48	52.8	57.6	62.4	67.2	72	76.8	81.6	86.4	91.2	96
EMISSION CONTROL SERVICE																					
Replace Engine Oil and Oil Filter Every 3 Months OR		X	X	X	X	X	X	X	X	X	X	X	X	X	X	X	X	X	X	X	X
Spark Plugs SHO Platinum Plugs																					X
											X										X
Inspect Accessory Drive Belt(s)											X										X
Replace Air Cleaner Filter ①											X										X
Replace Crankcase Filter Four Cylinder Engines Only ①											X										X
Replace Cam Belt and Adjust Valve Lash — SHO																					X
Replace Engine Coolant Every 36 Months OR											X										X
Check Engine Coolant Protection, Hoses and Clamps									ANNUALLY												
GENERAL MAINTENANCE																					
Inspect Exhaust Heat Shields											X										X
Change Automatic Transaxle Fluid ②											X										X
Inspect Disc Brake Pads and Rotors (Front) ③ (Front and Rear — SHO)											X										X
Inspect Brake Linings and Drums ③											X										X
Inspect Battery Fluid Level (SHO only) ④					X											X					
Rotate Tires			X					X						X					X			

① If operating in severe dust, more frequent intervals may be required — consult your dealer.

② Change automatic transaxle fluid if your driving habits frequently include one or more of the following conditions:
- Operation during HOT WEATHER (above 32°C (90°F)).
- Towing a trailer or using a car top carrier.
- Police, taxi or door-to-door delivery service.

③ If your driving includes continuous stop and go driving or driving in mountainous areas, more frequent intervals may be required.

X All items designated with an "X" must be performed in all states.

④ If operating in temperatures above 32°C (90°F) check more often.

CAPRI
NORMAL SERVICE MAINTENANCE

CUSTOMER MAINTENANCE SCHEDULE A

Follow this Schedule if your driving habits MAINLY include one or more of the following conditions:

- Short trips of less than 10 miles (16 km) when outside temperatures remain below freezing.
- Operating in severe dust conditions.
- Operating during hot weather, in stop-and-go "rush hour" traffic.
- Extensive idling, such as police, taxi or door-to-door delivery service.

SERVICE INTERVAL Perform at the months or distances shown, whichever comes first.	Miles x 1000	3	6	9	12	15	18	21	24	27	30	33	36	39	42	45	48	51	54	57	60
	Kilometers x 1000	4.8	9.6	14	19	24	28	33	38	43	48	52	57	62	67	72	76	81	86	91	96
EMISSION CONTROL SERVICE																					
Change Engine Oil and Oil Filter (whichever occurs first) Every 3 Months or		X	X	X	X	X	X	X	X	X	X	X	X	X	X	X	X	X	X	X	X
Replace Spark Plugs: Turbocharged						④					X					④					X
Non-Turbocharged											X										X
Check Engine Coolant Protection, Hoses and Clamps		ANNUALLY																			
Replace Engine Coolant Every 36 Months or											X										X
Check Accessory Drive Belts											X										X
Inspect Air Cleaner Filter						X(5)										X(5)					
Replace Air Cleaner Element											X(1)										X(1)
Replace Fuel Filter																					X
Replace Engine Timing Belt		EVERY 60,000 MILES (96,000 km)																			
Check Engine Idle Speed											X(4)										X(4)
GENERAL MAINTENANCE																					
Rotate Tires			X				X						X					X			
Inspect Brake Lines, Connections & Hoses											X										X
Inspect Clutch Pedal Operation											X										X
Inspect Front and Rear Disc Brakes						X					X					X					X
Inspect Safety Belts, Buckles, Retractors & Anchors											X										X
Inspect Steering Linkage, Rack Guides & Tie Rod Ends											X										X
Tighten Bolts & Nuts on Chassis & Body											X										X
Inspect Steering Operations, Gear Housing and Rack Seal Boots											X					X					X
Inspect Front Suspension Ball Joints											X										X
Inspect Half Shaft Dust Boots											X										X
Inspect Exhaust System Heat Shield											X										X
Inspect Fuel Lines											2										
Lubricate Rear Wheel Bearings											X										X
Change Automatic Transaxle Fluid											3										3

1 If operating in severe dusty conditions, consult dealer for proper replacement interval.

2 Recommended, but not required.

3 Change automatic transaxle fluid if your driving habits frequently include one or more of the following conditions:
- Operation during hot weather (above 90°F, 32°C), carrying heavy loads and in hilly terrain.
- Police, taxi or door-to-door delivery service

4 This item not required to be performed, however, Ford recommends that you perform maintenance on this item in order to achieve best vehicle operation. Failure to perform this recommended maintenance will not invalidate the vehicle emissions warranty or manufacturer recall liability.

This maintenance is required in all states except California. However, we recommend that it also be performed on California vehicles.

SEVERE SERVICE MAINTENANCE

CUSTOMER MAINTENANCE SCHEDULE B

Follow maintenance Schedule B if, generally, you drive your vehicle on a daily basis for more than 10 miles (16 km) and NONE OF THE UNIQUE DRIVING CONDITIONS SHOWN IN SCHEDULE A APPLY TO YOUR DRIVING HABITS.

SERVICE INTERVAL Perform at the months or distances shown, whichever comes first.	Miles x 1000	7.5	15	22.5	30	37.5	45	52.5	60
	Kilometers x 1000	12	24	36	48	60	72	84	96
EMISSION CONTROL SERVICE									
Change Engine Oil & Filter (whichever occurs first) Every 6 Months or		X	X	X	X	X	X	X	X
Turbocharged Vehicles Replace Engine Oil & Filter		EVERY 5,000 MILES (8,000 KM) OR 6 MONTHS WHICHEVER OCCURS FIRST							
Replace Spark Plugs: Turbocharged			③		X		③		X
Non-Turbocharged					X				X
Check Engine Coolant Protection, Hoses and Clamps					ANNUALLY				
Replace Engine Coolant Every 36 Months or					X				X
Check Accessory Drive Belts					X				X
Replace Air Cleaner Element					X①				X①
Replace Fuel Filter									X
Replace Engine Timing Belt				REPLACE EVERY 60,000 MILES (96,000 km)					
Check Engine Idle Speed					X③				X③
GENERAL MAINTENANCE									
Inspect Brake Lines and Connections					X				X
Inspect Clutch Pedal Operation					X				X
Inspect Front and Rear Disc Brakes			X		X		X		X
Inspect Safety Belts, Buckles, Retractors & Anchors					X				X
Inspect Steering Linkage, Rack Guides & Tie Rod Ends					X				X
Tighten Bolts & Nuts on Chassis & Body					X				X
Inspect Steering Operations, Gear Housing and Rack Seal Boots					X				X
Inspect Front Suspension Ball Joints					X				X
Inspect Half Shaft Dust Boots					X				X
Inspect Exhaust System Heat Shield					X				X
Inspect Fuel Lines					②				X
Lubricate Rear Wheel Bearings					X				X
Rotate Tires		X		X		X		X	

① If operating in severe dust, more frequent intervals may be required. Consult your dealer.
② Recommended, but not required.
③ This item not required to be performed, however, Ford recommends that you perform maintenance on this item in order to achieve best vehicle operation. Failure to perform this recommended maintenance will not invalidate the vehicle emissions warranty or manufacturer recall liability.

VEHICLE MAINTENANCE SCHEDULES

ESCORT & TRACER
NORMAL SERVICE MAINTENANCE

Follow maintenance [Schedule A] if your driving habits **MAINLY** include one or more of the following conditions:
- Short trips of less than 10 miles (16 km) when outside temperatures remain below freezing.
- Towing a trailer, or using a car-top carrier.
- Operating in severe dust conditions.
- Operating during hot weather in stop-and-go "rush hour" traffic.
- Extensive idling, such as police, taxi or door-to-door delivery service.

PERFORM AT THE MONTHS OR DISTANCES SHOWN, WHICHEVER OCCURS FIRST

MILES x 1000	3	6	9	12	15	18	21	24	27	30	33	36	39	42	45	48	51	54	57	60
KILOMETERS x 1000	4.8	9.6	14.4	19.2	24	28.8	33.6	38.4	43.2	48	52.8	57.6	62.4	67.2	72	76.8	81.6	86.4	91.2	96
EMISSION CONTROL SERVICE																				
Change engine oil and oil filter (every 3 months) OR 3,000 miles whichever occurs first	x	x	x	x	x	x	x	x	x	x	x	x	x	x	x	x	x	x	x	x
Replace spark plugs										x										x
Inspect accessory drive belt(s)										x										x
Inspect air cleaner filter (1.8L only)				x(4)										x(4)						
Replace air cleaner filter (all engines) (1)										x(1)										x(1)
Replace crankcase ventilation filter (1) (1.9L only)										x(1)										x(1)
Replace engine coolant EVERY 36 months OR										x										
Check engine coolant protection, hoses and clamps	ANNUALLY																			
Engine timing belt (1.8L only)	REPLACE EVERY 60,000 MILES (96 000 Km)																			x

MILES x 1000	3	6	9	12	15	18	21	24	27	30	33	36	39	42	45	48	51	54	57	60
KILOMETERS x 1000	4.8	9.6	14.4	19.2	24	28.8	33.6	38.4	43.2	48	52.8	57.6	62.4	67.2	72	76.8	81.6	86.4	91.2	96
GENERAL MAINTENANCE																				
Inspect exhaust heat shields										x										x
Change automatic transaxle fluid										(2)										(2)
Inspect disc brake pads and rotors (3)										x(3)										x(3)
Inspect brake linings and drums (3)										x(3)										x(3)
Inspect and repack rear wheel bearings										x										
Rotate tires		x				x						x					x			
Inspect clutch pedal operation										x										x
Inspect halfshaft dust boots										x										x
Inspect brake line hoses and connections										x										x
Inspect front suspension ball joints										x										x
Inspect bolts and nuts on chassis and body										x										x
Inspect steering operation and linkage										x										x

(1) If operating in severe dust, more frequent intervals may be required, consult your dealer.

(2) Change automatic transmission fluid if your driving habits frequently include one or more of the following conditions:
- Operation during hot weather (above 90°F, 32°C), carrying heavy loads and in hilly terrain.
- Towing a trailer or using a car-top carrier.
- Police, taxi or door-to-door delivery service.

(3) If your driving includes continuous stop-and-go driving or driving in mountainous areas, more frequent intervals may be required.

(4) This maintenance is required in all states except California. However, we recommend that it also be performed on California vehicles.

SEVERE SERVICE MAINTENANCE

Follow maintenance [Schedule B] if, generally, you drive your vehicle on a daily basis for more than 10 miles (16 km) and NONE OF THE DRIVING CONDITIONS SHOWN IN SCHEDULE A APPLY TO YOUR DRIVING HABITS.

PERFORM AT THE MONTHS OR DISTANCES SHOWN, WHICHEVER OCCURS FIRST

MILES x 1000	7.5	15	22.5	30	37.5	45	52.5	60
KILOMETERS x 1000	12	24	36	48	60	72	84	96
EMISSION CONTROL SERVICE								
Change engine oil and oil filter — every 6 months OR 7,500 miles, whichever occurs first	x	x	x	x	x	x	x	x
Replace spark plugs				x				x
Change crankcase ventilation filter (1) (1.9L only)				x(1)				x(1)
Inspect accessory drive belt(s)				x				x
Replace air cleaner filter (1)				x(1)				x(1)
Replace engine coolant (every 36 months) OR				x				x
Check engine coolant protection, hoses and clamps	ANNUALLY							
Engine timing belt (1.8L only)	REPLACE EVERY 60,000 MILES (96 000 Km)							x

MILES x 1000	7.5	15	22.5	30	37.5	45	52.5	60
KILOMETERS x 1000	12	24	36	48	60	72	84	96
GENERAL MAINTENANCE								
Check exhaust heat shields				x				x
Inspect disc brake pads and rotors (2)				x(2)				x(2)
Inspect brake linings and drums (2)				x(2)				x(2)
Inspect and repack rear wheel bearings				x				x
Rotate tires	x		x		x		x	
Inspect halfshaft dust boots				x				x
Inspect steering operation and linkage				x				x
Inspect front suspension ball joints				x				x
Inspect brake line hoses and connections				x				x
Inspect bolts and nuts on chassis and body				x				x
Inspect clutch pedal operation (if equipped)				x				x

(1) If operating in severe dust, more frequent intervals may be required. Consult your dealer.

(2) If your driving includes continuous stop-and-go driving or driving in mountainous areas, more frequent intervals may be required.

FORD MOTOR CO.

Miles	Recommended Maintenance
5,000	Change Engine Oil
	Rotate Tires & Adjust Air Pressure
10,000	Change Engine Oil
15,000	Change Engine Oil
	Inspect Engine Cooling System, Hoses & Clamps
	Rotate Tires & Adjust Air Pressure
	Lubricate Steering Linkage
20,000	Change Engine Oil
25,000	Change Engine Oil
	Rotate Tires & Adjust Air Pressure
30,000	Change Engine Oil
	Inspect Engine Cooling System, Hoses & Clamps
	Replace Spark Plugs (Except 3.8L Supercharged Engine)
	Change Automatic Transmission Fluid
	Replace Air Cleaner Element
	Inspect Exhaust Heat Shields
	Lubricate Steering Linkage
	Check Clutch Hydraulic Fluid Level (3.8L Supercharged Engine Only)
	Inspect Front & Rear Brake Shoes And Linings
	Inspect Front & Rear Disc Brake Rotors, If Equipped
	Inspect Rear Brake Shoes, Linings & Brake Drums, If Equipped
35,000	Change Engine Oil
	Rotate Tires & Adjust Air Pressure
40,000	Change Engine Oil
45,000	Change Engine Oil
	Inspect Engine Cooling System, Hoses & Clamps
	Rotate Tires & Adjust Air Pressure
	Lubricate Steering Linkage
50,000	Change Engine Oil
	Change Engine Coolant Every 50,000 Miles Or 48 Months
55,000	Change Engine Oil
60,000	Change Engine Oil
	Change Automatic Transmission Fluid
	Inspect Engine Cooling System, Hoses & Clamps
	Replace Spark Plugs (Except 3.8L Supercharged Engine)
	Replace Air Cleaner Element
	Replace PCV Valve
	Inspect Exhaust Heat Shields
	Inspect Accessory Drive Belts
	Lubricate Steering Linkage
	Check Clutch Hydraulic Fluid Level (3.8L Supercharged Engine Only)
	Inspect Front & Rear Brake Shoes And Linings
	Inspect Front & Rear Disc Brake Rotors, If Equipped
	Inspect Rear Brake Shoes, Linings & Brake Drums, If Equipped
65,000	Change Engine Oil
	Rotate Tires & Adjust Air Pressure
70,000	Change Engine Oil

Miles	Recommended Maintenance
75,000	Change Engine Oil
	Rotate Tires & Adjust Air Pressure
	Inspect Engine Cooling System, Hoses & Clamps
	Lubricate Steering Linkage
80,000	Change Engine Oil
85,000	Change Engine Oil
	Rotate Tires & Adjust Air Pressure
90,000	Change Engine Oil
	Change Automatic Transmission Fluid
	Inspect Engine Cooling System, Hoses & Clamps
	Replace Spark Plugs (Except 3.8L Supercharged Engine)
	Replace Air Cleaner Element
	Inspect Exhaust Heat Shields
	Inspect Accessory Drive Belts
	Lubricate Steering Linkage
	Check Clutch Hydraulic Fluid Level (3.8L Supercharged Engine Only)
	Inspect Front & Rear Brake Shoes And Linings
	Inspect Front & Rear Disc Brake Rotors, If Equipped
	Inspect Rear Brake Shoes, Linings & Brake Drums, If Equipped
95,000	Change Engine Oil
	Rotate Tires & Adjust Air Pressure
100,000	Change Engine Oil
	Replace Rear Axle Lubricant
105,000	Change Engine Oil
	Rotate Tires & Adjust Air Pressure
	Lubricate Steering Linkage
	Inspect Engine Cooling System, Hoses & Clamps
110,000	Change Engine Oil
	Change Engine Coolant Every 30,000 Miles Or 36 Months
115,000	Change Engine Oil
	Rotate Tires & Adjust Air Pressure
120,000	Change Engine Oil
	Change Automatic Transmission Fluid
	Inspect Engine Cooling System, Hoses & Clamps
	Replace Spark Plugs
	Replace Air Cleaner Element
	Inspect Exhaust Heat Shields
	Inspect Accessory Drive Belts
	Change Engine Coolant Every 30,000 Miles Or 36 Months
	Lubricate Steering Linkage
	Check Supercharger Fluid Level (3.8L SC Only)
	Check Clutch Hydraulic Fluid Level (3.8L SC Only)
	Inspect Front & Rear Brake Shoes And Linings
	Inspect Front & Rear Disc Brake Rotors, If Equipped
	Inspect Rear Brake Shoes, Linings & Brake Drums, If Equipped

SEVERE SERVICE MAINTENANCE

Miles	Recommended Maintenance
3,000	Change Engine Oil & Filter
6,000	Change Engine Oil & Filter
	Rotate Tires & Adjust Air Pressure
9,000	Change Engine Oil & Filter
12,000	Change Engine Oil & Filter
15,000	Change Engine Oil & Filter
	Inspect Engine Cooling System, Hoses & Clamps
	Rotate Tires & Adjust Air Pressure
	Lubricate Steering Linkage
18,000	Change Engine Oil & Filter
21,000	Change Engine Oil & Filter
	Change Automatic Transmission Fluid
24,000	Change Engine Oil & Filter
	Rotate Tires And Adjust Air Pressure
27,000	Change Engine Oil & Filter
30,000	Change Engine Oil & Filter
	Replace Engine Coolant
	Replace Spark Plugs (Except 3.8L Supercharged Engine)
	Replace Air Cleaner Element
	Inspect Engine Cooling System, Hoses & Clamps
	Inspect Exhaust Heat Shields
	Lubricate Steering Linkage
	Check Clutch Hydraulic Fluid Level (3.8L Supercharged Engine Only)
	Inspect Front & Rear Brake Shoes And Linings
	Inspect Front & Rear Disc Brake Rotors, If Equipped
	Inspect Rear Brake Shoes, Linings & Brake Drums, If Equipped
33,000	Change Engine Oil & Filter
36,000	Change Engine Oil & Filter
42,000	Change Engine Oil & Filter
	Rotate Tires And Adjust Air Pressure
	Change Automatic Transmission Fluid
45,000	Change Engine Oil & Filter
	Inspect Engine Cooling System, Hoses & Clamps
	Lubricate Steering Linkage
48,000	Change Engine Oil & Filter
	Change Engine Coolant Every 30,000 Miles Or 36 Months
51,000	Change Engine Oil & Filter
	Rotate Tires And Adjust Air Pressure
54,000	Change Engine Oil & Filter
57,000	Change Engine Oil & Filter
60,000	Change Engine Oil & Filter
	Change Engine Coolant Every 30,000 Miles Or 36 Months
	Replace PCV Valve
	Check Supercharger Fluid Level (3.8L SC)
	Check Clutch Hydraulic Fluid Level (3.8L SC)
	Replace Spark Plugs
	Inspect Accessory Drive Belts
	Inspect Engine Cooling System, Hoses & Clamps
	Replace Air Cleaner Element
	Inspect Exhaust Heat Shields

Miles	Recommended Maintenance
	Inspect Front & Rear Disc Brake Rotors, If Equipped
	Inspect Rear Brake Shoes, Linings & Brake Drums, If Equipped
	Lubricate Steering Linkage
	Rotate Tires And Adjust Air Pressure
63,000	Change Engine Oil & Filter
	Change Automatic Transmission Fluid
66,000	Change Engine Oil & Filter
69,000	Change Engine Oil & Filter
	Rotate Tires And Adjust Air Pressure
72,000	Change Engine Oil & Filter
75,000	Change Engine Oil & Filter
	Inspect Engine Cooling System, Hoses & Clamps
	Lubricate Steering Linkage
78,000	Change Engine Oil & Filter
	Change Engine Coolant Every 30,000 Miles Or 36 Months
	Rotate Tires And Adjust Air Pressure
81,000	Change Engine Oil & Filter
84,000	Change Engine Oil & Filter
	Change Automatic Transmission Fluid
87,000	Change Engine Oil
	Rotate Tires And Adjust Air Pressure
90,000	Change Engine Oil
	Inspect Engine Cooling System, Hoses & Clamps
	Inspect Accessory Drive Belts
	Replace Air Cleaner Element
	Inspect Exhaust Heat Shields
	Lubricate Steering Linkage
	Replace Spark Plugs (3.8L SC)
	Check Clutch Hydraulic Fluid Level (3.8L)
	Inspect Front & Rear Disc Brake Rotors, If Equipped
	Inspect Rear Brake Shoes, Linings & Brake Drums, If Equipped
93,000	Change Engine Oil
96,000	Change Engine Oil
	Rotate Tires And Adjust Air Pressure
99,000	Change Engine Oil
100,000	Replace Rear Axle Lubricant
	Change Engine Coolant Every 100,000 Miles Or Every 12 Months
102,000	Change Engine Oil
105,000	Change Engine Oil
	Inspect Engine Cooling System, Hoses & Clamps
	Lubricate Steering Linkage
	Rotate Tires And Adjust Air Pressure
	Change Automatic Transmission Fluid
108,000	Change Engine Oil
	Change Engine Coolant Every 30,000 Miles Or 36 Months

SEVERE SERVICE MAINTENANCE

Miles	Recomended Maintenance
111,000	Change Engine Oil
114,000	Change Engine Oil
	Rotate Tires And Adjust Air Pressure
117,000	Change Engine Oil
120,000	Change Engine Oil
	Change Engine Coolant Every 30,000 Miles Or 36 Months
	Replace PCV Valve
	Check Supercharger Fluid Level (3.8L SC)

Miles	Recomended Maintenance
120,000 (cont.)	Check Clutch Hydraulic Fluid Level (3.8L SC)
	Inspect Engine Cooling System, Hoses & Clamps
	Lubricate Steering Linkage
	Inspect Exhaust Heat Shields
	Replace Air Cleaner Element
	Inspect Accessory Drive Belts
	Replace Spark Plugs
	Inspect Front & Rear Disc Brake Rotors, If Equipped
	Inspect Rear Brake Shoes, Linings & Brake Drums, If Equipped

ELECTRICAL SYMBOL & WIRE COLOR CODE IDENTIFICATION

TABLE OF CONTENTS

Electrical Symbol Identification

INDEX

ELECTRICAL SYMBOL IDENTIFICATION

	LEGEND OF SYMBOLS USED ON WIRING DIAGRAMS			
+	POSITIVE		CONNECTOR
−	NEGATIVE		MALE CONNECTOR
	GROUND		FEMALE CONNECTOR
	FUSE		DENOTES WIRE CONTINUES ELSEWHERE
	GANG FUSES WITH BUSS BAR		DENOTES WIRE GOES TO ONE OF TWO CIRCUITS
	CIRCUIT BREAKER		SPLICE
	CAPACITOR	J2 2	SPLICE IDENTIFICATION
Ω	OHMS		THERMAL ELEMENT
	RESISTOR	TIMER	TIMER
	VARIABLE RESISTOR		MULTIPLE CONNECTOR
	SERIES RESISTOR		OPTIONAL — WIRING WITH / WIRING WITHOUT
	COIL		"Y" WINDINGS
	STEP UP COIL	88:88	DIGITAL READOUT
	OPEN CONTACT		SINGLE FILAMENT LAMP
	CLOSED CONTACT		DUAL FILAMENT LAMP
	CLOSED SWITCH		L.E.D. — LIGHT EMITTING DIODE
	OPEN SWITCH		THERMISTOR
	CLOSED GANGED SWITCH		GAUGE
	OPEN GANGED SWITCH		SENSOR
	TWO POLE SINGLE THROW SWITCH		FUEL INJECTOR
	PRESSURE SWITCH	●36	DENOTES WIRE GOES THROUGH BULKHEAD DISCONNECT
	SOLENOID SWITCH	●19 STRG COLUMN	DENOTES WIRE GOES THROUGH STEERING COLUMN CONNECTOR
	MERCURY SWITCH	INST PANEL ●14	DENOTES WIRE GOES THROUGH INSTRUMENT PANEL CONNECTOR
	DIODE OR RECTIFIER	ENG ●7	DENOTES WIRE GOES THROUGH GROMMET TO ENGINE COMPARTMENT
	BY-DIRECTIONAL ZENER DIODE		DENOTES WIRE GOES THROUGH GROMMET
	MOTOR		HEATED GRID ELEMENTS
	ARMATURE AND BRUSHES		

Fig. 1 Chrysler Domestic

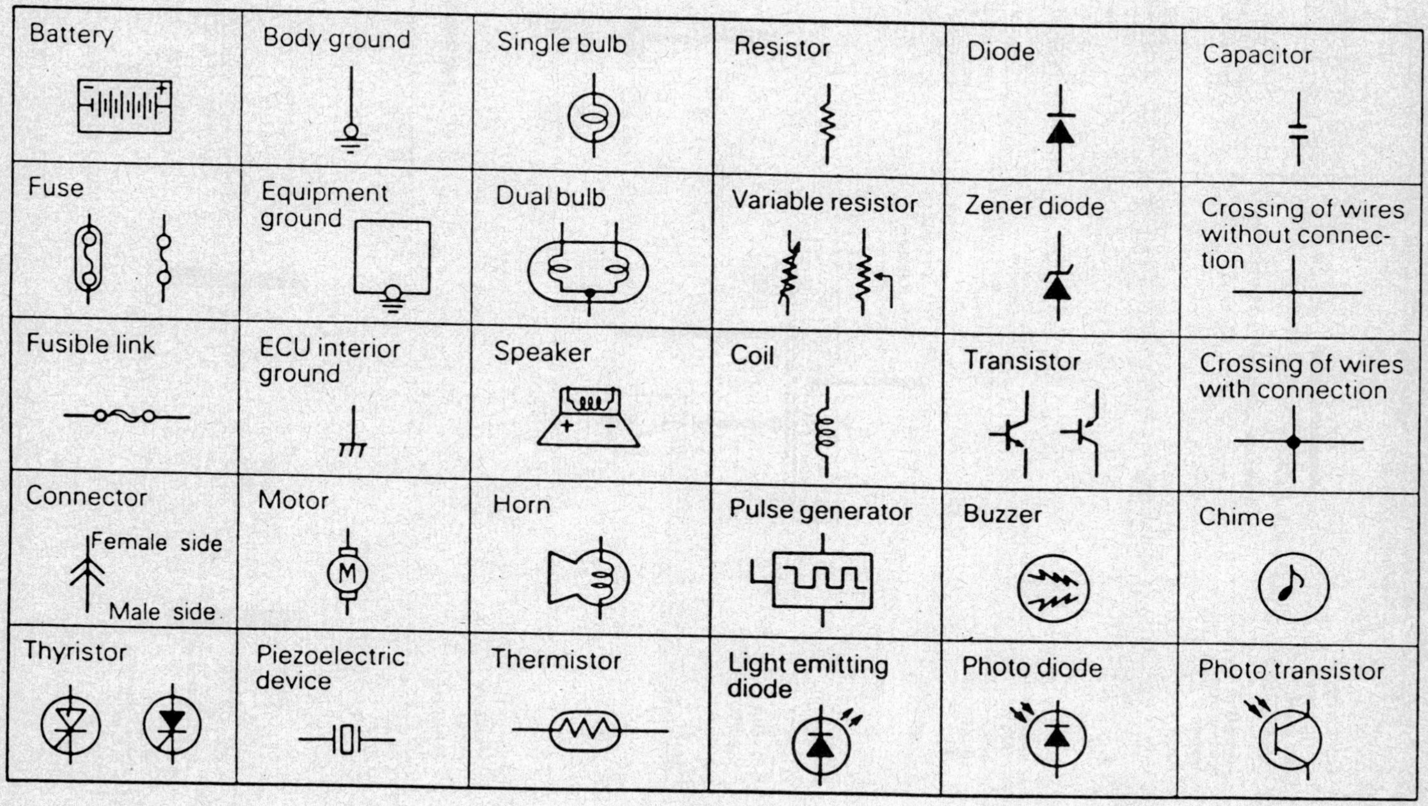

Battery	Body ground	Single bulb	Resistor	Diode	Capacitor
Fuse	Equipment ground	Dual bulb	Variable resistor	Zener diode	Crossing of wires without connection
Fusible link	ECU interior ground	Speaker	Coil	Transistor	Crossing of wires with connection
Connector Female side Male side	Motor	Horn	Pulse generator	Buzzer	Chime
Thyristor	Piezoelectric device	Thermistor	Light emitting diode	Photo diode	Photo transistor

Fig. 2   Chrysler Imports

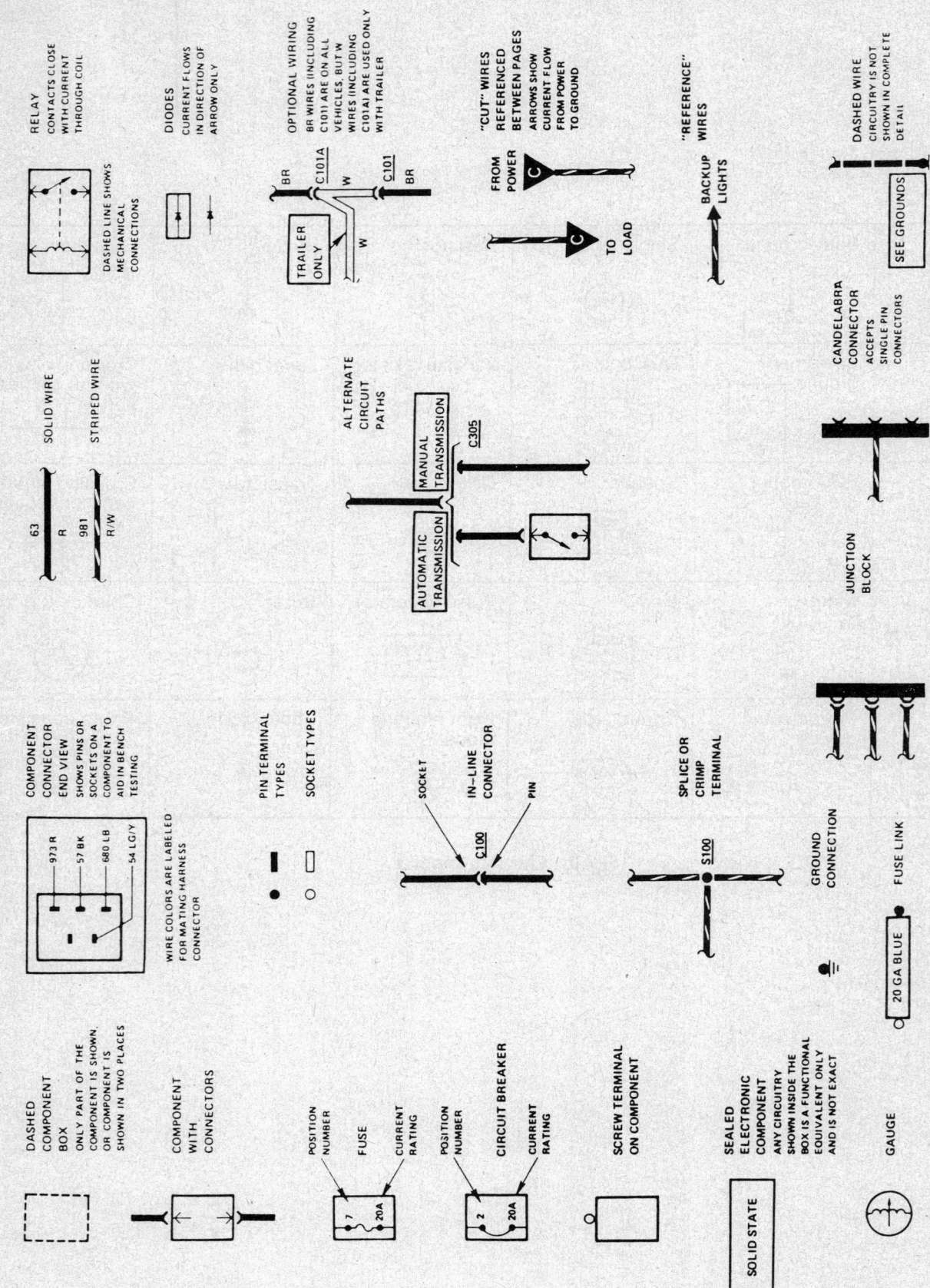

RELAY
CONTACTS CLOSE WITH CURRENT THROUGH COIL
DASHED LINE SHOWS MECHANICAL CONNECTIONS

DIODES
CURRENT FLOWS IN DIRECTION OF ARROW ONLY

OPTIONAL WIRING
BR WIRES INCLUDING C101 ARE ON ALL VEHICLES, BUT W WIRES INCLUDING C101A ARE USED ONLY WITH TRAILER

BR   C101A   W   C101   BR
TRAILER ONLY   W

"CUT" WIRES REFERENCED BETWEEN PAGES
ARROWS SHOW CURRENT FLOW FROM POWER TO GROUND

FROM POWER   C
C   TO LOAD

"REFERENCE" WIRES
BACKUP LIGHTS

DASHED WIRE
CIRCUITRY IS NOT SHOWN IN COMPLETE DETAIL
SEE GROUNDS

SOLID WIRE   STRIPED WIRE
63   981
R   R/W

ALTERNATE CIRCUIT PATHS
MANUAL TRANSMISSION   C305
AUTOMATIC TRANSMISSION

CANDELABRA CONNECTOR
ACCEPTS SINGLE PIN CONNECTORS

JUNCTION BLOCK

Fig. 3 1992 Ford (Part 2 of 2)

COMPONENT CONNECTOR END VIEW
SHOWS PINS OR SOCKETS ON A COMPONENT TO AID IN BENCH TESTING

973 R   57 BK   680 LB   54 LG/Y
WIRE COLORS ARE LABELLED FOR MATING HARNESS CONNECTOR

PIN TERMINAL TYPES
SOCKET TYPES

SOCKET   IN-LINE CONNECTOR   PIN
C100

SPLICE OR CRIMP TERMINAL
S100

GROUND CONNECTION

FUSE LINK
20 GA BLUE

DASHED COMPONENT BOX
ONLY PART OF THE COMPONENT IS SHOWN, OR COMPONENT IS SHOWN IN TWO PLACES

COMPONENT WITH CONNECTORS

POSITION NUMBER   FUSE   CURRENT RATING
7   20A

POSITION NUMBER   CIRCUIT BREAKER   CURRENT RATING
2   20A

SCREW TERMINAL ON COMPONENT

SEALED ELECTRONIC COMPONENT
ANY CIRCUITRY SHOWN INSIDE THE BOX IS A FUNCTIONAL EQUIVALENT ONLY AND IS NOT EXACT
SOLID STATE

GAUGE

Fig. 3 1992 Ford (Part 1 of 2)

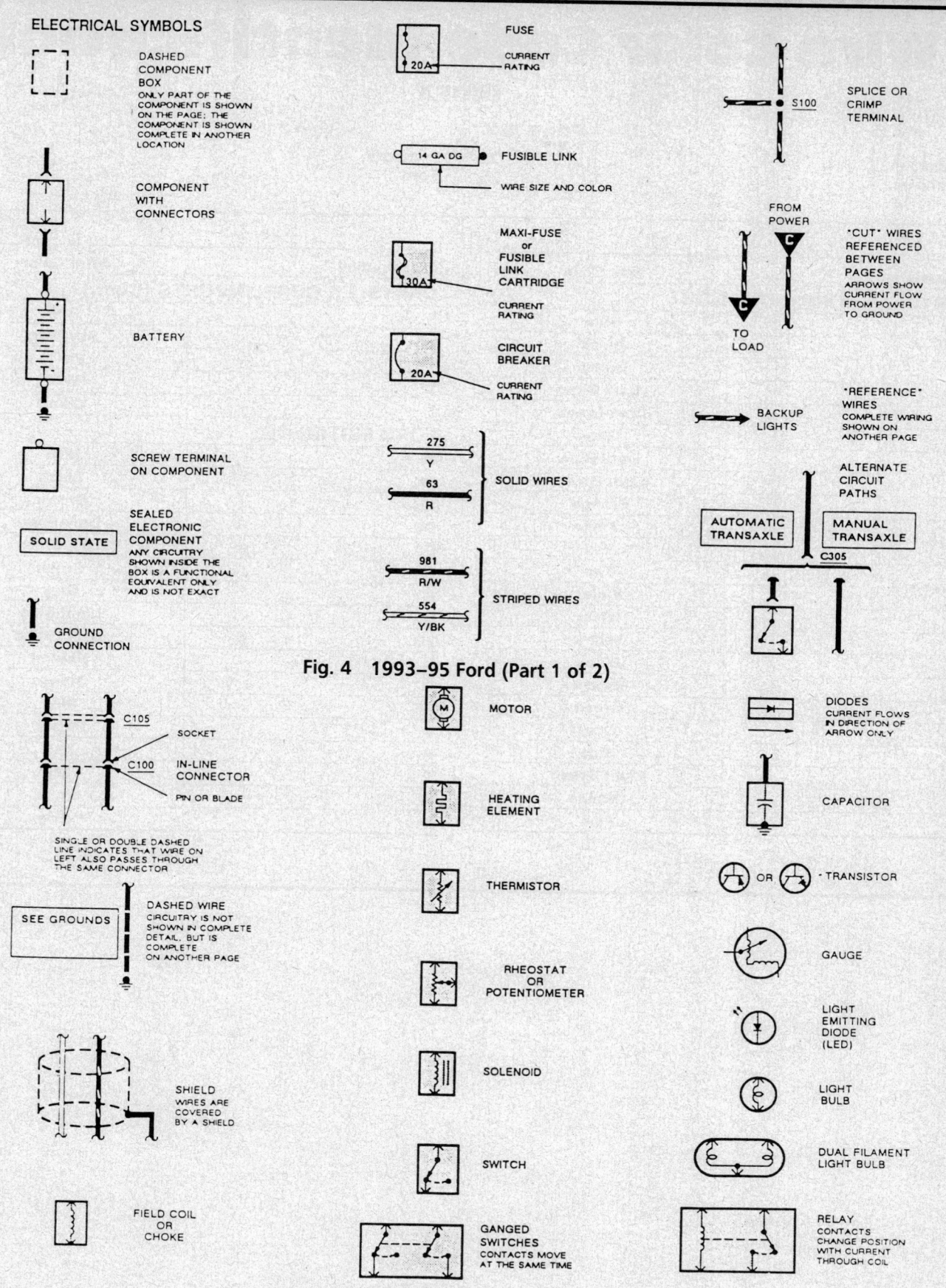

ELECTRICAL SYMBOLS

DASHED COMPONENT BOX
ONLY PART OF THE COMPONENT IS SHOWN ON THE PAGE; THE COMPONENT IS SHOWN COMPLETE IN ANOTHER LOCATION

COMPONENT WITH CONNECTORS

BATTERY

SCREW TERMINAL ON COMPONENT

SOLID STATE
SEALED ELECTRONIC COMPONENT
ANY CIRCUITRY SHOWN INSIDE THE BOX IS A FUNCTIONAL EQUIVALENT ONLY AND IS NOT EXACT

GROUND CONNECTION

C105 SOCKET
C100 IN-LINE CONNECTOR
PIN OR BLADE
SINGLE OR DOUBLE DASHED LINE INDICATES THAT WIRE ON LEFT ALSO PASSES THROUGH THE SAME CONNECTOR

SEE GROUNDS
DASHED WIRE
CIRCUITRY IS NOT SHOWN IN COMPLETE DETAIL, BUT IS COMPLETE ON ANOTHER PAGE

SHIELD
WIRES ARE COVERED BY A SHIELD

FIELD COIL OR CHOKE

FUSE
20A
CURRENT RATING

14 GA DG FUSIBLE LINK
WIRE SIZE AND COLOR

30A MAXI-FUSE or FUSIBLE LINK CARTRIDGE
CURRENT RATING

20A CIRCUIT BREAKER
CURRENT RATING

275 Y
63 R
SOLID WIRES

981 R/W
554 Y/BK
STRIPED WIRES

Fig. 4   1993–95 Ford (Part 1 of 2)

MOTOR

HEATING ELEMENT

THERMISTOR

RHEOSTAT OR POTENTIOMETER

SOLENOID

SWITCH

GANGED SWITCHES
CONTACTS MOVE AT THE SAME TIME

S100 SPLICE OR CRIMP TERMINAL

FROM POWER
C
TO LOAD
"CUT" WIRES REFERENCED BETWEEN PAGES
ARROWS SHOW CURRENT FLOW FROM POWER TO GROUND

BACKUP LIGHTS
"REFERENCE" WIRES
COMPLETE WIRING SHOWN ON ANOTHER PAGE

ALTERNATE CIRCUIT PATHS
AUTOMATIC TRANSAXLE | MANUAL TRANSAXLE
C305

DIODES
CURRENT FLOWS IN DIRECTION OF ARROW ONLY

CAPACITOR

OR TRANSISTOR

GAUGE

LIGHT EMITTING DIODE (LED)

LIGHT BULB

DUAL FILAMENT LIGHT BULB

RELAY
CONTACTS CHANGE POSITION WITH CURRENT THROUGH COIL

Fig. 4   1993–95 Ford (Part 2 of 2)

Wire Color Code Identification

INDEX

Page No.

Abbreviation	Wire Color
CHRYSLER CORP. DOMESTIC	
BL	Blue
BK	Black
BR	Brown
DB	Dark Blue
DG	Dark Green
GY	Gray
LB	Light Blue
LG	Light Green
OR	Orange
PK	Pink
RD	Red
TN	Tan
VT	Violet
WT	White
YL	Yellow
B	Black
BR	Brown
G	Green
GR	Gray
L	Blue
LG	Light Green
O	Orange
P	Pink

Abbreviation	Wire Color
CHRYSLER CORP. IMPORTS (Cont.)	
R	Red
SB	Sky Blue
V	Violet
W	White
Y	Yellow
FORD MOTOR CO.	
BL	Blue
BK	Black
BR	Brown
DB	Dark Blue
DG	Dark Green
GN	Green
GY	Gray
LB	Light Blue
LG	Light Green
N	Natural
O	Orange
PK	Pink
P	Purple
R	Red
T	Tan
W	White
Y	Yellow

CHRYSLER CORPORATION

CHRYSLER CORPORATION

ACCLAIM/SPIRIT, DAYTONA, DYNASTY/IMPERIAL, LEBARON, SHADOW/SUNDANCE & 1992-93 NEW YORKER

NOTE: The Following Models Are Covered In This Chapter: CHRYSLER— Imperial (VIN Y), LeBaron (VIN J), LeBaron Landau (VIN A), New Yorker Fifth Avenue (VIN Y), New Yorker (VIN C), DODGE— Daytona (VIN G), Dynasty (VIN C), Shadow (VIN P), Spirit (VIN A) PLYMOUTH— Acclaim (VIN A), Sundance (VIN P).

NOTE: Refer To Rear Of This Manual For Vehicle Manufacturer's Special Service Tool Suppliers.

INDEX OF SERVICE OPERATIONS

NOTE: For Service Operations Not Listed Below, Refer To The Table Of Contents In The Front Of This Manual.

INDEX OF SERVICE OPERATIONS—CONTINUED

Specifications
GENERAL ENGINE SPECIFICATIONS

Year	Engine Liter/CID	VIN Code ②	Fuel System	Bore and Stroke Inch (Millimeters)	Compression Ratio	Net HP @ RPM ③	Maximum Torque Ft. Lbs. @ RPM	Normal Oil Pressure psi @ 3000 RPM
1992	2.2L/4-135	D	TBI	3.44 x 3.62 (87.5 x 92)	9.5	93 @ 4800	122 @ 3200	25–80
	2.2L/4-135 ①	A	MPI	3.44 x 3.62 (87.5 x 92)	8.1	174 @ 5200	211 @ 2800	25–80
	2.5L/4-153	K	TBI	3.44 x 4.09 (87.5 x 104)	8.9	100 @ 4800	135 @ 2000	25–80
	2.5L/4-153 ①	J	MPI	3.44 x 4.09 (87.5 x 104)	7.8	150 @ 4800	180 @ 2000	25–80
	3.0L/V6-181	3	EFI	3.59 x 2.99 (91 x 76)	8.85	141 @ 5000	170 @ 2800	25–80
	3.3L/V6-202	R	EFI	3.66 x 3.19 (93 x 81)	8.9	147 @ 4800	185 @ 3600	30–80
	3.8L/V6-231	L	EFI	3.78 x 3.43 (96 x 87)	8.9	151 @ 4400	204 @ 3200	30–80
1993	2.2L/4-135	D	TBI	3.44 x 3.62 (87.5 x 92)	9.5	93 @ 4800	122 @ 3200	25–80
	2.2L/4-135 ①	A	MPI	3.44 x 3.62 (87.5 x 92)	8.1	174 @ 5200	217 @ 2800	25–80
	2.5L/4-153	K	TBI	3.44 x 4.09 (87.5 x 104)	8.9	100 @ 4800	135 @ 2000	25–80
	2.5L/4-153	B	TBI	3.44 x 4.09 (87.5 x 104)	7.8	150 @ 4800	180 @ 2000	25–80
	3.0L/V6-181	3	MPI	3.59 x 2.99 (91 x 76)	8.85	141 @ 5000	170 @ 2800	35–75
	3.3L/V6-202	R	MPI	3.66 x 3.19 (93 x 81)	8.9	147 @ 4800	183 @ 3600	30–80
	3.8L/V6-231	L	MPI	3.78 x 3.43 (96 x 87)	8.9	151 @ 4400	204 @ 3200	30–80
1994-95	2.2L/4-135	D	TBI	3.44 x 3.62 (87.5 x 92)	9.5	93 @ 4800	122 @ 3200	25–80
	2.5L/4-153	K,V	TBI	3.44 x 4.09 (87.5 x 104)	8.9	100 @ 4800	135 @ 2000	25–80
	3.0L/V6-181	3	MPI	3.59 x 2.99 (91 x 76)	8.85	141 @ 5000	170 @ 2800	35–75

CID-Cubic Inch Displacement.
EFI—Electronic Fuel Injection.
MPI—Multi-Port Injection.
TBI—Throttle Body Injection.
①—Turbocharged engine.
②—The 8th digit of the VIN denotes engine code.
③—Ratings are net-as installed in vehicle.

TUNE UP SPECIFICATIONS

Year & Engine/ V.I.N. Code [1]	Spark Plug Gap	Firing Order Fig. [2]	Ignition Timing BTDC		Mark Fig.	Curb Idle Speed [3]		Fast Idle Speed		Fuel Pump Pressure psi
			Man. Trans.	Auto. Trans.		Man. Trans.	Auto Trans.	Man. Trans.	Auto. Trans.	
1992										
2.2L/4-135 (D)	.035	C	12[9]	12[9]	D	850	850N	[6]	[6]	39[7]
2.2L/4-135 Turbo III (A)	.035	B[4]	[5]	[5]	[10]	750	750N	[6]	[6]	53–57[7]
2.5L/4-153 (K)	.035	C	12[9]	12[9]	D	850	850N	[6]	[6]	55[7]
2.5L/4-153 Turbo I (J)	.035	C	12[9]	12[9]	D	900	900N	[6]	[6]	48[7]
3.0L/V6-181 (3)	.041	F	12[9]	12[9]	E	700	700N	[6]	[6]	48[7]
3.3L/V6-202 (R)	.050	A[4]	[5]	[5]	[10]	—	750N	—	[6]	48[7]
3.8L/V6-231 (L)	.050	A[4]	[5]	[5]	[10]	—	750N	—	[6]	48[7]
1993										
2.2L/4-135 (D)	.035	C	12[9]	12[9]	D	850	850N	[8]	[8]	39[7]
2.2L/4-135 Turbo III (A)	.035	B[4]	[5]	[5]	[10]	750	750N	[8]	[8]	53–57[7]
2.5L/4-153 (K)	.035	C	12[9]	12[9]	D	850	850N	[8]	[8]	39[7]
2.5L/4-153 (B)	.035	C	12[9]	12[9]	D	900	900N	[8]	[8]	48[7]
3.0L/V6-181 (3)	.041	F	12[9]	12[9]	E	700	700N	[8]	[8]	48[7]
3.3L/V6-202 (R)	.050	A[4]	[5]	[5]	[10]	—	750N	[8]	[8]	48[7]
3.8L/V6-231 (L)	.050	A[4]	[5]	[5]	[10]	—	750N	[8]	[8]	48[7]
1994-95										
2.2L/4-135 (D)	.035	C	12[9]	12[9]	D	850	850N	[8]	[8]	39[7]
2.5L/4-153 (K, V)	.035	C	12[9]	12[9]	D	850	850N	[8]	[8]	39[7]
3.0L/V6-181 (3)	.041	F	12[9]	12[9]	E	700	700N	[8]	[8]	48[7]

BTDC-Before top dead center

[1]—The eighth digit of the Vehicle Identification Number (V.I.N.) denotes engine code.

[2]—Before removing wires from distributor cap, determine location of No. 1 wire in cap, as distributor position may have been altered from that shown at the end of this chart.

[3]—N: Neutral.

[4]—Direct Ignition System (DIS).

[5]—Direct Ignition System (DIS), not adjustable.

[6]—Idle speeds are controlled by the Automatic Idle Speed (AIS) motor.

[7]—Loosen gas cap to release pressure in tank. Ground one terminal of any injector with a jumper wire. connect remaining terminal of injector to the battery positive post using a jumper for no longer that 10 seconds, this will release fuel system pressure.

Remove cover from service valve on fuel rail. Connect a suitable fuel pressure tester to service valve. Check fuel pressure with engine running.

[8]—Controlled by Powertrain Control Module (PCM).

[9]—Check ignition timing with coolant sensor wire disconnected.

[10]—Equipped w/crankshaft position sensor.

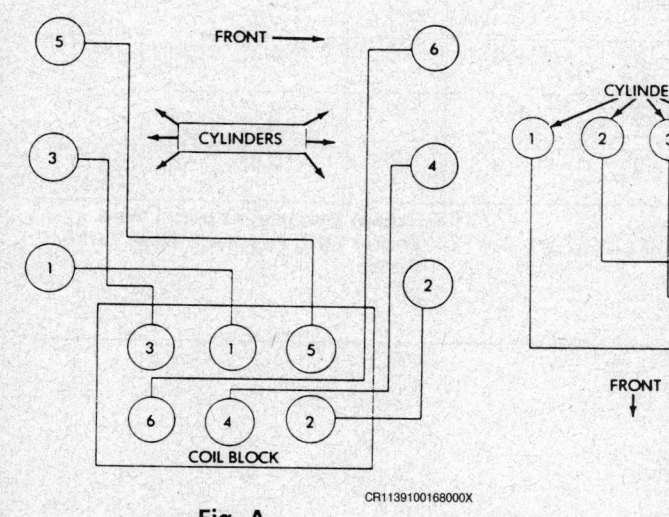

Fig. A

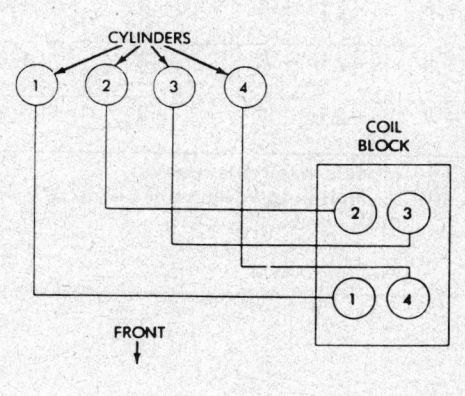

Fig. B

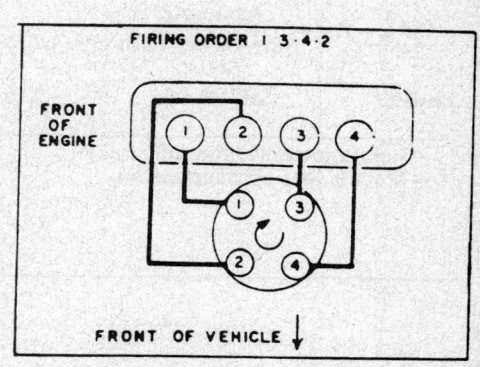

Fig. C

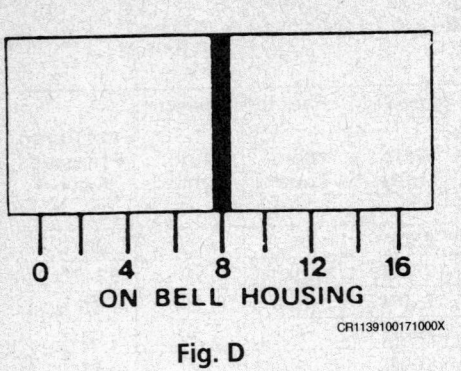

0   4   8   12   16
ON BELL HOUSING

CR1139100171000X

Fig. D

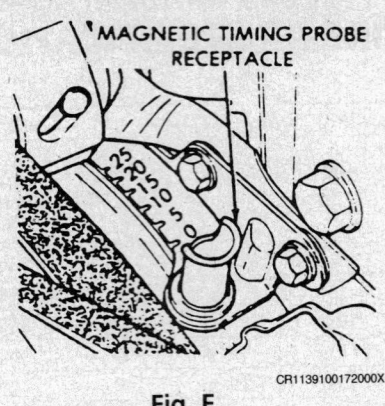

MAGNETIC TIMING PROBE RECEPTACLE

CR1139100172000X

Fig. E

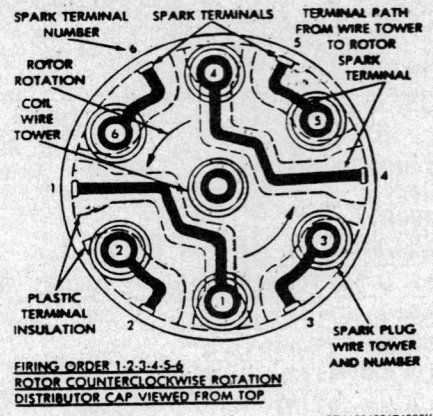

FIRING ORDER 1-2-3-4-5-6
ROTOR COUNTERCLOCKWISE ROTATION
DISTRIBUTOR CAP VIEWED FROM TOP

CR1139100174000X

Fig. F

FRONT WHEEL ALIGNMENT SPECIFICATIONS

| Year | Model | Camber Angle, Degrees | | | | Toe In Inch | Caster ① | Thrust Angle, Degrees |
| | | Limits | | Desired | | | | |
		Left	Right	Left	Right			
1992	All Models ⑤	-.2 to +.8	-.2 to +.8	+.3	+.3	④	2.8°	—
	Dynasty	-.2 to +.8	-.2 to +.8	+.3	+.3	④	2.7°	—
	Imperial ②	-.2 to +.8	-.2 to +.8	+.3	+.3	④	2.7°	—
	Imperial ③	-.2 to +.8	-.2 to +.8	+.3	+.3	④	3.0°	—
	New Yorker Fifth Avenue ②	-.2 to +.8	-.2 to +.8	+.3	+.3	④	2.7°	—
	New Yorker Fifth Avenue ③	-.2 to +.8	-.2 to +.8	+.3	+.3	④	3.0°	—
	New Yorker Fifth Sedan	-.2 to +.8	-.2 to +.8	+.3	+.3	④	2.7°	—
1993	All Models ⑤	-.2 to +.8	-.2 to +.8	+.3	+.3	④	2.8°	—
	Dynasty	-.2 to +.8	-.2 to +.8	+.3	+.3	④	2.7°	—
	Imperial ②	-.2 to +.8	-.2 to +.8	+.3	+.3	④	3.0°	—
	Imperial ③	-.2 to +.8	-.2 to +.8	+.3	+.3	④	3.0°	—
	New Yorker Fifth Avenue ②	-.2 to +.8	-.2 to +.8	+.3	+.3	④	2.7°	—
	New Yorker Fifth Avenue ③	-.2 to +.8	-.2 to +.8	+.3	+.3	④	3.0°	—
	New Yorker Fifth Sedan	-.2 to +.8	-.2 to +.8	+.3	+.3	④	2.7°	—
1994-95	All Models	-.2 to +.8	-.2 to +.8	+.3	+.3	④	2.8°	-0.4 to +0.4°

①—Reference only, non adjustable.
②—Models less air suspension.
③—Models w/air suspension.
④—7/32 inch in to 1/8 inch out (.4° to .2° out).
⑤—Except Dynasty, Imperial, New Yorker Fifth Avenue & New Yorker Sedan.

REAR WHEEL ALIGNMENT SPECIFICATIONS

| Year | Model | Camber Angle, Degrees | | | | Toe In Inch | Caster② | Thrust Angle, Degrees |
| | | Limits | | Desired | | | | |
		Left	Right	Left	Right			
1992	All Models	-1.3 to +.2	-1.3 to +.2	-.5	-.5	①	—	-.4 to +.4
1993–95	All Models	-1.3 to +.2	-1.3 to +.2	-.5	-.5	①	—	-.4 to +.4

① —5/16 inch out to 5/16 inch in (.6° out to .6° in).
② —Reference only, non adjustable.

COOLING SYSTEM & CAPACITY DATA

| Year | Model or Engine (VIN) ① | Coolant Capacity | | Radiator Cap Relief Pressure, Lbs. | Thermo. Opening Temp. Deg. F | Fuel Tank Gals. | Engine Oil Refill Qts. | Transaxle Oil | |
		Less A/C Qts.	With A/C Qts.					4 & 5 Speed Pts.	Auto. Trans. Qts. ②
1992	2.2L/4-135 (A,D)	9	9	16	195	14	4④	4.8	⑤
	2.5L/4-153 (J,K)	9	9	16	195	③	4④	4.8	⑤
	3.0L/V6-181 (3)	9.5	9.5	16	195	③	4④	4.8	⑤
	3.3L/V6-201 (R)	9.5	9.5	16	195	16	4④	—	⑤
	3.8L/V6-231 (L)	9.5	9.5	16	195	16	4④	—	⑤
1993	2.2L/4-135 (A,D)	9	9	16	195	14	4④	4.8	⑤
	2.5L/4-153 (J,K)	9	9	16	195	③	4④	4.8	⑤
	3.0L/V6-181 (3)	9.5	10	16	195	③	4④	4.8	⑤
	3.3L/V6-201 (R)	10	10	16	195	16	4④	—	⑤
	3.8L/V6-231 (L)	10	10	16	195	16	4④	—	⑤
1994-95	2.2L/4-135 (D)	9	9	16	195	14	4④	4.8	⑤
	2.5L/4-153 (K,V)	9	9	16	195	③	4④	4.8	⑤
	3.0L/V6-181 (3)	9.5	10	16	195	③	4④	4.8	⑤

① —The eighth digit of Vehicle Identification Number (VIN) denotes engine code.
② —Approximate. Make final check with dipstick.
③ —Except Acclaim, Dynasty & Spirit, 14 gals.; Acclaim, Dynasty & Spirit, 16 gals.
④ —Add ½ qt. w/filter change.
⑤ —Approximate refill capacity, 4 qts.

Total capacity, A413 auto. transaxle, except fleet less lock up, 8.9 qts.; fleet, 9.2 qts.; lock up, 8.5 qts. A604 auto. transaxle, 9.1 qts.

LUBRICANT DATA

| Year | Model | Lubricant Type | | | |
| | | Transaxle | | Power Steering | Brake System |
		Manual	Automatic		
1992–95	All	SG-SG/CD SAE 5W-30	①	②	DOT 3

① —Mopar ATF Type 71760 or Dexron II/Mercon.
② —Mopar PN 4549617, or equivalent.

Electrical

NOTE: On Air Bag Equipped Models, Refer To "Air Bag System Precautions" Located In The Front Of This Manual For System Disarming & Arming Procedures.

INDEX

PRECAUTIONS

AIR BAG SYSTEMS

Refer to "Air Bag System Precautions" in the front of this manual for system disarming and arming procedures.

FUSE PANEL & FLASHER LOCATION

The fuse panel is located under the instrument panel to the left of the steering column.

On Dynasty, Imperial, New Yorker and New Yorker Fifth Avenue, the hazard and turn signal flashers are located on the relay module.

On Shadow and Sundance, the hazard flasher is located on the relay module and the turn signal flasher is attached to the center A/C duct.

On Acclaim, LeBaron Landau and Spirit, the hazard flasher is located on the relay module and the turn signal flasher is attached to the left side A/C duct.

On Daytona and LeBaron coupe/convertible, the combo flasher is clipped to the A/C duct right of steering column. The turn signal relays are located on the relay bank clipped under the LH side of the I/P.

RELAY CENTER LOCATION

The relay center is located in the engine compartment, near the left strut tower.

STARTER
REPLACE

2.2L/4-135 & 2.5L/4-153 ENGINES

1. Disconnect battery ground cable.
2. Remove starter to flywheel housing and rear bracket to engine or transaxle attaching bolts.
3. **On models equipped with 2.2L/4-135 engine,** loosen air pump tube at exhaust manifold, then position tube bracket away from starter motor.
4. **On all models,** remove heat shield clamp and heat shield, if equipped.
5. Disconnect starter cable at starter motor and solenoid leads at solenoid, then remove starter motor.
6. Reverse procedure to install.

3.0L/V6-181, 3.3L/V6-202 & 3.8L/V6-231 ENGINES

1. Disconnect battery ground cable.

2. Remove three starter motor attaching bolts from transaxle bellhousing.
3. Remove two wire connector terminal nuts from starter, then disconnect wire connector and remove starter.
4. Reverse procedure to install.

DISTRIBUTOR
REPLACE

REMOVAL

1. Disconnect distributor lead wires from electrical connector.
2. Loosen distributor cap retaining screws, then remove distributor cap.
3. Rotate crankshaft until rotor is pointing in the direction of the engine block, then scribe a line on block for assembly reference.
4. Remove distributor hold-down bolt, then carefully lift distributor from engine.

INSTALLATION

1. Position distributor into engine with gasket installed on base of distributor.
2. Engage distributor drive gear with camshaft drive gear so distributor rotor aligns with scribe mark made during removal.
3. If engine was cranked while distribu-

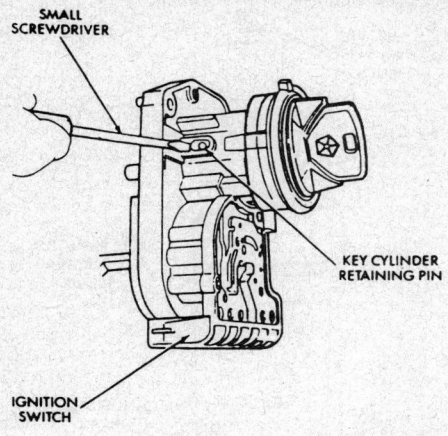

Fig. 1 Ignition lock cylinder retaining pin release

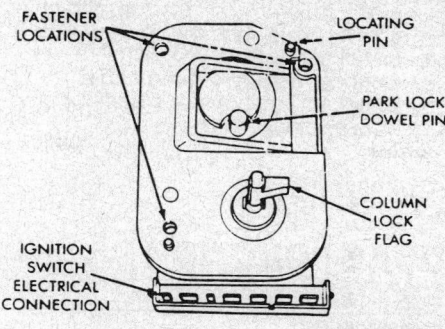

Fig. 2 Ignition switch, rear view

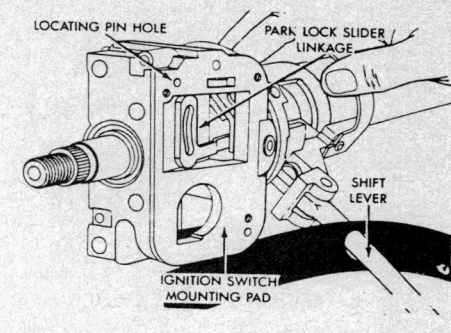

Fig. 3 Ignition switch mounting pad

tor was removed, proceed as follows:
a. Rotate crankshaft until No. 1 piston is at top dead center of compression stroke.
b. Rotate distributor rotor to No. 1 distributor cap terminal position.
c. Install distributor into engine, engaging distributor drive gear with camshaft. The rotor should be properly positioned under distributor cap No. 1 terminal.
4. Install distributor cap, then distributor hold-down.
5. Connect distributor lead wires to electrical connector.
6. Adjust ignition timing to specifications.

IGNITION LOCK
REPLACE

The ignition lock and ignition switch are removed as an assembly.
1. Disarm air bag as outlined under "Precautions."
2. Disconnect battery ground cable.
3. Remove tilt lever.
4. Remove three Torx column cover attaching screws, then the upper and lower column covers.
5. Using tamper proof Torx bit tool No. 440-TX20H or equivalent, remove three ignition switch mounting screws.
6. Carefully pull switch away from column. Release two connector locks on seven terminal wiring connector, then disconnect from ignition switch.
7. Release connector lock on four terminal connector, then disconnect from ignition switch.
8. Remove ignition lock from ignition switch as follows:
   a. With key inserted and switch in Lock position, use a small screwdriver to depress ignition lock re-

taining pin flush with lock cylinder surface, **Fig. 1.**
b. Rotate key clockwise to Off position. Ignition lock should now be unseated from ignition switch assembly. **Do not attempt to remove ignition lock at this time.**
c. With ignition lock in unseated position (lock bezel approximately 1/8 inch above halo light ring), rotate key counterclockwise to Lock position, then remove key.
d. Remove ignition lock from ignition switch.
9. Reverse procedure to install, noting the following:
   a. Connect two wiring connectors to ignition switch. Ensure switch locking tabs are fully seated in connectors.
   b. Install ignition switch on steering column.
   c. **On column shift models,** shift lever must be in P position and park lock dowel pin on ignition switch assembly must engage with column park lock slider linkage, **Figs. 2 and 3.**
   d. **On all models,** verify ignition switch is in Lock position (flag parallel with ignition switch terminals).
   e. Apply a dab of suitable grease to flag and pin, then position park lock link and slider to mid-travel.
   f. Position ignition switch against lock housing face. Ensure pin is inserted into park link contour slot.
   g. Install ignition switch retaining screws and **torque** to 12-22 inch lbs.
   h. With ignition lock and switch in Lock position, insert ignition lock into ignition switch until it bottoms.
   i. Insert key, then while carefully pushing ignition lock toward ignition switch, turn key clockwise to Run position.
   j. Check for proper operation on ignition switch in all positions.

IGNITION SWITCH
REPLACE

On these models, the ignition lock and ignition switch are removed as an assembly. Refer to procedure outlined under "Ignition Lock, Replace."

HEADLAMP SWITCH
REPLACE

EXCEPT DAYTONA & LEBARON COUPE/CONVERTIBLE

1. Disconnect battery ground cable.
2. Remove left trim bezel as follows:
   a. Pull bezel rearward until retaining clips disengage.
3. Remove three headlight switch attaching screws.
4. Pull switch assembly and wiring away from instrument panel, then disconnect wiring connector.
5. Disconnect escutcheon from mounting plate.
6. Unscrew bracket retainer nut attaching switch to bracket, then remove switch.
7. Reverse procedure to install.

DAYTONA & LEBARON COUPE/CONVERTIBLE

1. Disconnect battery ground cable.
2. Remove switch pod assembly. Refer to procedure outlined under "Instrument Cluster, Replace."
3. Remove turn signal lever by pulling straight out of pod.
4. Remove five pod inner panel attaching screws, then the inner panel.
5. Remove turn signal switch to gain access to headlight switch. Refer to procedure outlined under "Turn Signal Switch, Replace."

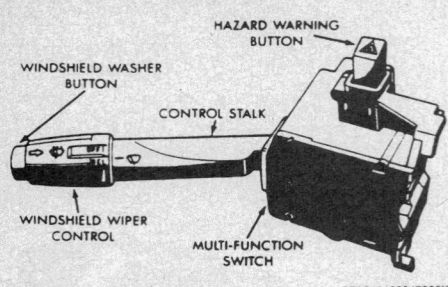

Fig. 4   Multi-function switch

7. Disconnect headlight switch linkage from buttons.
8. Remove switch mounting screws, then the switch.
9. Reverse procedure to install, noting the following:
   a. Latch switch linkage in up position.
   b. Insert dimmer shaft into dimmer knob while aligning switch in switch pod.
   c. Unlatch linkage and connect to push buttons.
   d. Check all switch modes for proper operation.

MULTI-FUNCTION SWITCH
REPLACE

EXCEPT DAYTONA & LEBARON COUPE/CONVERTIBLE
Removal

The multi-function switch contains electrical circuitry for turn signal, cornering lamps, hazard warning, headlamp dimmer, windshield wiper, pulse wipe and windshield washer switching. This switch is mounted to the lefthand side of the steering column. Should any function of the switch fail, the entire switch assembly, **Fig. 4**, must be replaced.

1. Disconnect battery ground cable.
2. Remove tilt lever, then upper and lower steering column covers.
3. Remove multi-function switch tamper proof attaching screws.
4. Carefully pull switch away from steering column. Loosen electrical connector screw. Screw will remain in connector.
5. Disconnect electrical connector from multi-function switch, then remove switch.

Installation

1. Install electrical connector to switch and **torque** retaining screw to 17 inch lbs.
2. Mount multi-function switch on column and **torque** attaching screws to 17 inch lbs.
3. Install upper and lower steering col-

umn covers and **torque** attaching screws to 17 inch lbs.
4. Install tilt lever.
5. Connect battery ground cable.
6. Check all functions of switch for proper operation.

DUAL-FUNCTION SWITCH
REPLACE

DAYTONA & LEBARON COUPE/CONVERTIBLE

On these models, the dual-function switch, **Fig. 5**, contains circuits for hazard warning switching and turn signal cancellation. The switch is mounted on the left-hand side of the steering column.

Removal

1. Disconnect battery ground cable.
2. **On models with tilt column,** remove tilt lever.
3. **On all models,** remove upper and lower steering column covers.
4. Remove tamper proof screws attaching switch to steering column.
5. Carefully pull switch away from column. Release connector lock on wiring connector, remove connector from switch, then remove the switch.

Installation

1. Install wiring connector to switch. Ensure switch locking tab is fully seated in wiring connector.
2. Mount switch on column and **torque** attaching screws to 17 inch lbs.
3. Install upper and lower steering column covers and **torque** attaching screws to 17 inch lbs.
4. **On models with tilt column,** install tilt lever.
5. **On all models,** connect battery ground cable.
6. Check all functions of switch for proper operation.

TURN SIGNAL SWITCH
REPLACE

For models not covered in this section refer to "Multi-Function Switch, Replace" or "Dual Function Switch, Replace" for replacement procedures.

DAYTONA & LEBARON COUPE/CONVERTIBLE

1. Disconnect battery ground cable.
2. Remove two screws from bottom of switch pod that hold turn signal switch.
3. Disconnect turn signal pigtail wire from headlamp switch at 8-way connector.
4. Reverse procedure to install.

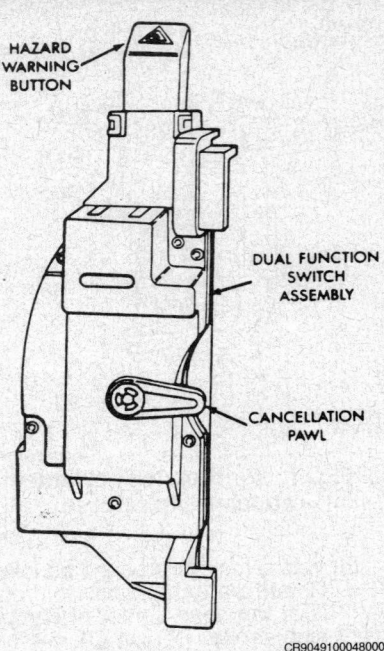

**Fig. 5   Dual-function switch.
Daytona & LeBaron
Coupe/Convertible**

DIMMER SWITCH
REPLACE

EXCEPT DAYTONA & LEBARON COUPE/CONVERTIBLE

On these models, the dimmer switch is contained within the multi-function switch. Refer to procedure outlined under "Multi-Function Switch, Replace."

DAYTONA & LEBARON COUPE/CONVERTIBLE

On these models, the dimmer switch is contained within the turn signal switch. Refer to procedure outlined under "Turn Signal Switch, Replace."

STEERING WHEEL
REPLACE

MODELS w/AIR BAG

Removal and installation of steering wheel requires use of DRB II readout tool for air bag system check. Perform system check before connecting battery ground cable.

Removal

1. Disconnect battery ground cable.
2. Ensure wheels are in straight ahead position and column is locked in place.

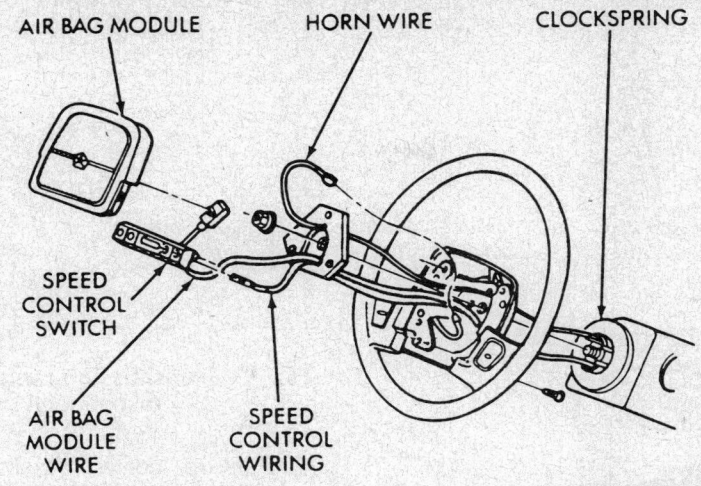

Fig. 6 Steering wheel components. Models w/air bag

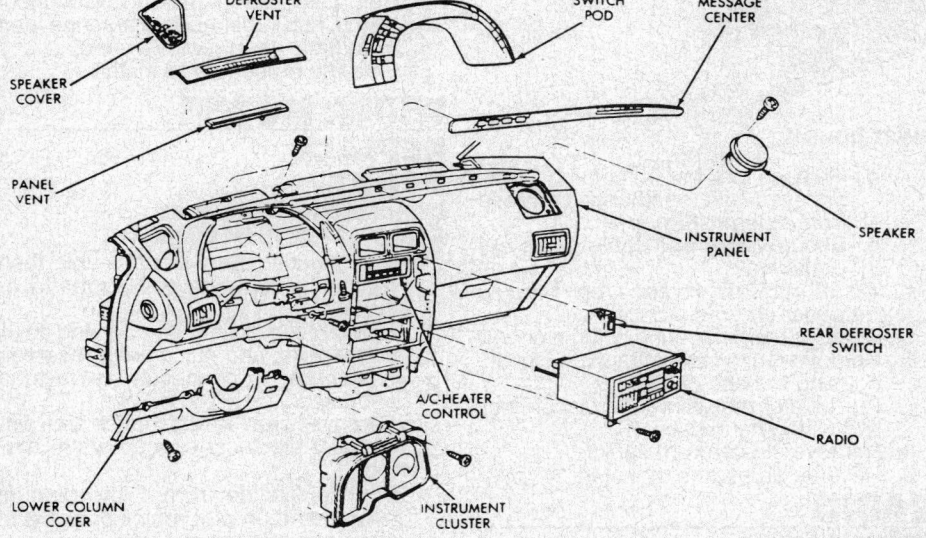

Fig. 7 Instrument panel components. Daytona & LeBaron

3. Using a 10 mm thin wall socket, remove four nuts attaching air bag module from back side of steering wheel, **Fig. 6.**
4. Lift air bag module, then disconnect electrical connector by spreading apart external latching arms and prying up on connector.
5. Remove speed control switch, if equipped.
6. If equipped, remove clockspring setscrew from storage location on steering wheel, then install screw in clockspring to maintain clockspring position. Screw is on a plastic tether. **There are two types of clocksprings used. One with a setscrew and one with an automatic lock, which engages when steering wheel is removed. Automatic locking clocksprings can be identified by lack of setscrew and tether strap.**
7. Remove steering wheel retaining nut.

8. Remove damper assembly, if equipped.
9. Remove steering wheel using puller tool No. C3428B or equivalent.

Installation

Removal and installation of steering wheel requires use of DRB II readout tool for air bag system check. Perform system check before connecting battery ground cable.
1. Ensure clockspring is properly positioned.
2. Install steering wheel and damper, if equipped.
3. Pull air bag and speed control wiring through the lower, larger hole in steering wheel; and horn wire through smaller hole at top of steering wheel, **Fig. 6. Use caution not to pinch wires.**
4. Install steering wheel retaining nut and **torque** to 45 ft. lbs.
5. Move clockspring setscrew to steer-

ing wheel storage location, if equipped.
6. Install speed control switch, if equipped.
7. Connect clockspring wiring connector to air bag module. **To ensure complete connection, latching arms must be visibly on top of connector housing.**
8. Install four air bag module attaching nuts and **torque** to 80-100 inch. lbs.
9. **Before connecting battery ground cable, perform air bag system check as follows:**
   a. Connect DRB II readout tool to air bag system diagnostic module (ASDM) diagnostic 6-way connector, located at right side of console.
   b. From passenger side of vehicle, turn ignition key to On position. Exit vehicle with DRB II.
   c. Ensure no one is inside vehicle, then connect negative battery cable.
   d. Using DRB II, read and record active fault data.
   e. Read and record any stored faults.
   f. If any faults are present, refer to procedure outlined under "Passive Restraint System" section.
   g. Erase stored faults if no active fault codes are present.
   h. With ignition key in On position ensure no one is inside vehicle.
   i. From passenger side of vehicle, turn ignition key to Off then On position and observe instrument panel air bag warning light. Light should go out after six to eight seconds, indicating system is operating correctly. **If air bag warning light does not illuminate, or goes on and stays on, there is a system malfunction. Refer to procedure outlined under "Passive Restraint System" section.**

MODELS LESS AIR BAG

1. Disconnect battery ground cable.
2. Remove horn pad assembly, then the steering wheel retaining nut.
3. Remove steering wheel using puller tool No. C-3428B or equivalent.
4. Reverse procedure to install, noting the following:
   a. Position steering wheel master serration over missing tooth on steering shaft.
   b. **Torque** steering wheel retaining nut to 45 ft. lbs.

INSTRUMENT CLUSTER
REPLACE

DAYTONA & LEBARON COUPE/CONVERTIBLE

1. Disconnect battery ground cable.
2. Remove switch pod assembly as follows:
   a. Pry up edge of panel vent grille, using a straightedge to disengage retaining clips, then remove grille, **Fig. 7.**

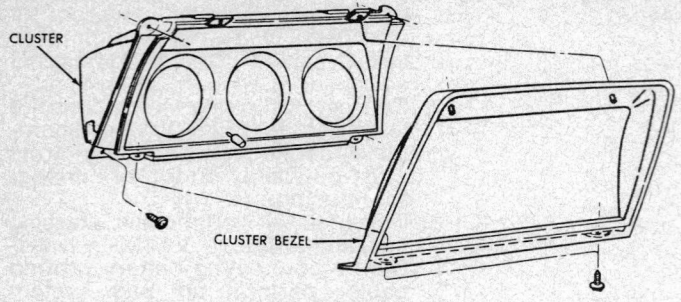

CR9099100056000X

Fig. 8   Instrument panel components. Except Daytona & LeBaron

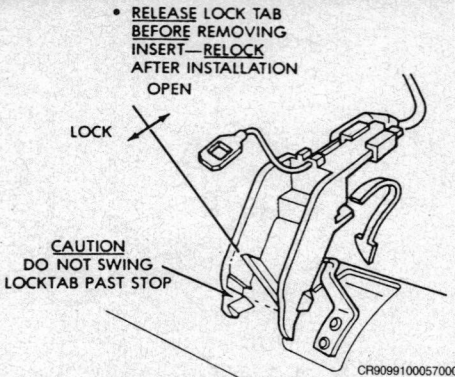

- RELEASE LOCK TAB **BEFORE** REMOVING INSERT—**RELOCK** AFTER INSTALLATION OPEN

LOCK

CAUTION
DO NOT SWING
LOCKTAB PAST STOP

CR9099100057000X

Fig. 9   Transmission range selector disconnect

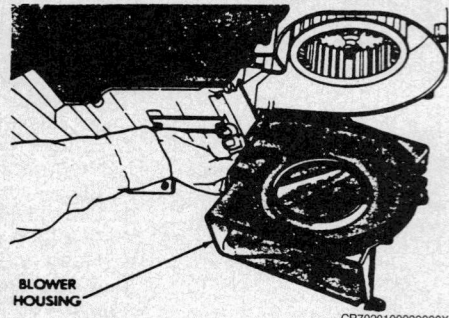

BLOWER HOUSING

CR7029100039000X

Fig. 10   Blower housing

b. Remove two attaching screws located under panel vent grille.
c. Remove two outboard attaching screws located under switch pod assembly.
d. Pull switch pod rearward to remove and simultaneously disconnect all wiring connections.
e. Remove switch pod assembly.
3. **On models with tilt column,** remove tilt lever.
4. **On all models,** remove upper and lower steering column covers.
5. Remove cluster trim bezel by pulling rearward to disengage retaining clips.
6. Remove four cluster attaching screws and pull cluster rearward.
7. Tilt cluster to disconnect all wiring connectors and turbo gauge hose, if equipped, then remove cluster assembly.
8. Reverse procedure to install.

EXCEPT DAYTONA & LEBARON COUPE/CONVERTIBLE

1. Disconnect battery ground cable.
2. Remove cluster bezel as follows:
   a. **On column shift models,** place shift lever in N position.
   b. **On models with tilt column,** adjust tilt to lowest position.
   c. **On all models,** pull cluster bezel rearward to disengage 11 retaining clips, then remove cluster bezel, **Fig. 8.**
3. **On column shift models,** proceed as follows:
   a. Remove lower steering column cover.
   b. Place gear selector in neutral or park position.
   c. Remove guide tube from behind fuse block and disconnect cable eyelet from column attaching arm.

d. Release lock bar on column insert, squeeze legs together and remove from column, **Fig. 9.**
e. Secure insert and cable guide out of the way.
4. **On all models,** remove rear window defogger and radio bezel.
5. Remove upper steering column cover.
6. Remove four screws attaching cluster housing to base panel.
7. Pull cluster rearward then disconnect two wiring harnesses.
8. Remove cluster from vehicle.
9. Reverse procedure to install.

RADIO

REPLACE
DYNASTY, IMPERIAL, NEW YORKER & NEW YORKER FIFTH AVENUE

1. Disconnect battery ground cable.
2. Remove cluster bezel attaching screws, then the cluster bezel.
3. Remove radio attaching screws, then pull radio away from dash panel.
4. Disconnect electrical connectors, antenna lead and ground strap.
5. Remove radio from vehicle.
6. Reverse procedure to install.

SHADOW & SUNDANCE

1. Remove center module bezel.
2. Remove lower center module cover if equipped with base console. Remove right console sidewall if equipped with full console.
3. Remove mounting screws and the radio from instrument panel. Disconnect wiring and remove ground straps.
4. Reverse procedure to install.

ACCLAIM, DAYTONA, LEBARON & SPIRIT

1. Disconnect battery ground cable.

2. Remove center bezel by pulling straight back to disengage from the five retaining clips.
3. Remove radio attaching screws.
4. Pull radio from panel and disconnect wiring, ground strap and antenna lead from radio, then remove radio.
5. Reverse procedure to install.

WIPER MOTOR

REPLACE
FRONT
Daytona, LeBaron Coupe/Convertible

1. Disconnect battery ground cable, then remove wiper arms and pivot attaching nuts.
2. Remove plastic screen covering cowl, if equipped, and disconnect reservoir hose from "T" connector on Daytona and Laser.
3. Remove wiper motor cover and disconnect electrical connectors to motor.
4. Push pivots downward into plenum chamber, then pull motor outward to clear mounting stud. Move wiper motor toward driver's side of vehicle as far as possible and pull righthand pivot and link assembly through opening, then move motor toward passenger side of vehicle and remove wiper motor, and lefthand pivot and link assembly.
5. Remove nut from end of motor shaft, then the motor crank.
6. Reverse procedure to install.

Except Daytona & LeBaron Coupe/Convertible

1. Disconnect battery ground cable.
2. Remove wiper arms, then the plastic cowl cover.
3. Remove pivot mounting stud retaining nuts and disconnect wiper motor wiring connector.
4. Remove motor mounting bracket retaining bolts, then the motor assembly from cowl plenum.
5. Reverse procedure to install.

REAR
Daytona

1. Disconnect battery ground cable.
2. Raise wiper arm, release latch and remove arm assembly.

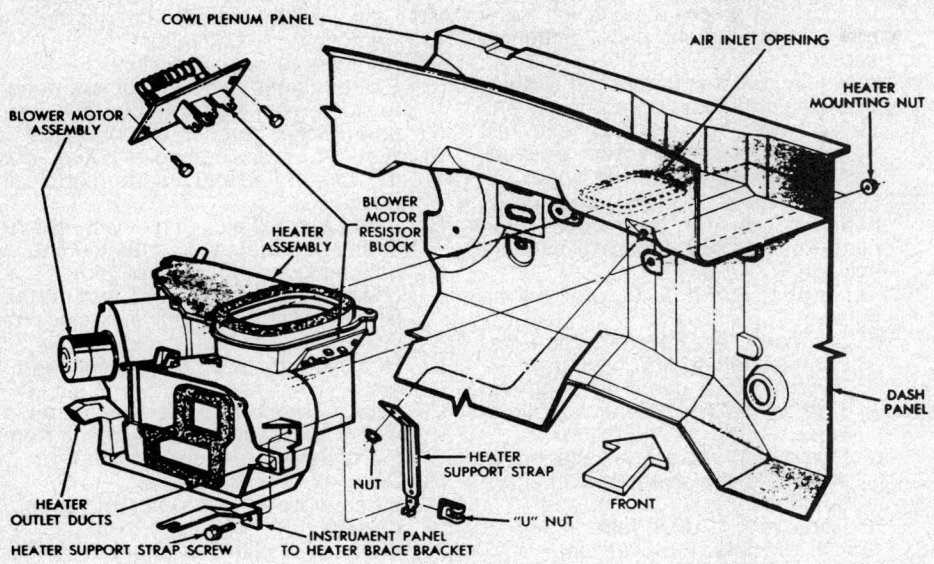

Fig. 11 Heater assembly

CR7029100040000X

3. Remove inner trim panel and disconnect electrical connector to motor.
4. Remove grommet from liftgate glass.
5. Remove 2 screws securing motor and the motor.
6. Reverse procedure to install.

WIPER SWITCH
REPLACE

On models equipped with a multi-function switch refer to "Multi-Function Switch, Replace."

BLOWER MOTOR
REPLACE

1. Disconnect battery ground cable.
2. Remove glove compartment.
3. **On models with A/C,** disconnect two vacuum lines from recirculating air door actuator.
4. **On all models,** disconnect blower lead wire connector.
5. Remove two screws from top of blower motor, attaching it to the heater A/C unit cover.
6. Remove five screws from around blower housing, then separate blower housing from heater A/C unit, **Fig. 10.**
7. Remove three screws attaching blower motor and wheel to unit housing, then separate blower assembly from unit housing.
8. Reverse procedure to install.

HEATER CORE
REPLACE

DYNASTY, IMPERIAL, NEW YORKER, NEW YORKER FIFTH AVENUE, SHADOW & SUNDANCE

1. Disconnect battery ground cable.

2. **On models with A/C,** discharge A/C system, then disconnect refrigerant lines from heater A/C unit housing.
3. **On all models,** drain cooling system, then disconnect heater hoses from heater core. Tape heater core tubes to prevent leakage during removal.
4. **On models with A/C,** remove A/C drain hose.
5. **On all models,** disconnect vacuum lines.
6. **On Dynasty and New Yorker models,** remove righthand upper and lower underpanel silencers.
7. **On Dynasty, New Yorker, Shadow and Sundance models,** remove steering column cover.
8. **On Dynasty and New Yorker models,** remove lefthand underpanel silencer.
9. **On all models,** position front seat or right front seat as far back as possible.
10. **On Shadow and Sundance models,** remove right A-pillar trim and right cowl side trim.
11. **On all models,** remove glove box.
12. **On Dynasty and New Yorker models,** remove right instrument panel reinforcement.
13. **On Shadow and Sundance models,** proceed as follows:
    a. Remove right instrument panel roll up screw.
    b. Remove center bezel.
    c. Remove lower center module cover.
    d. Remove floor console.
    e. Remove instrument panel support brace (from steering column opening to right cowl side at bottom of instrument panel).
    f. Remove instrument panel to support bracket (below glove box opening).
    g. Remove ash receiver.
    h. Remove radio. Refer to procedure

outlined under "Radio, Replace."
    i. Remove instrument panel top cover.
    j. Remove three right side instrument panel to fence attaching screws (below windshield).
14. **On Dynasty and New Yorker models,** remove ash receiver.
15. **On Shadow and Sundance models,** pull right lower side of instrument panel rearward.
16. **On all models,** remove center distribution and defroster adapter ducts.
17. **On Dynasty, New Yorker, Shadow and Sundance models,** disconnect relay module.
18. **On Shadow and Sundance models,** proceed as follows:
    a. Remove instrument panel to heater A/C unit housing bracket.
    b. Remove lower air distribution duct.
19. **On all models,** disconnect blower motor wire connector.
20. Disconnect demister hoses from top of heater A/C unit housing.
21. **On models less automatic temperature control (ATC),** proceed as follows:
    a. Disconnect temperature control flag from bottom of heater A/C unit, then disconnect cable from left side of heat distribution duct. Position cable aside to the left.
    b. Disconnect vacuum lines from heater A/C unit housing.
22. **On models with ATC,** disconnect instrument panel wiring from rear face of ATC unit.
23. **On Dynasty and New Yorker models,** disconnect righthand 25-way connector and fuse block from instrument panel.
24. **On all models except Dynasty and New Yorker,** fold right side floor carpet back.
25. **On all models,** remove four heater A/C unit housing attaching screws from inside engine compartment.
26. Remove heater A/C unit housing strap lower screw and position strap aside.
27. Move heater A/C unit housing rearward until clear of mounting studs, then lower the unit.
28. **On Shadow and Sundance models,** remove demister adapter from top of heater A/C unit.
29. **On all models,** pull lower right side of instrument panel rearward.
30. **On all models except Shadow and Sundance,** rotate heater A/C unit while pulling from instrument panel.
31. **On Shadow and Sundance models,** slide heater A/C unit from under instrument panel.
32. **On all models,** remove heater A/C unit top cover, **Fig. 11.**
33. Remove heater core to dash panel seal from core tubes, then remove heater core.
34. Reverse procedure to install.

ACCLAIM, LEBARON LANDAU & SPIRIT

1. Disconnect battery ground cable.
2. Remove glove compartment.
3. **On models with A/C,** disconnect two vacuum lines from recirculating air door actuator.
4. **On all models,** disconnect blower lead wire connector.
5. Remove two screws from top of blower motor, attaching it to the heater A/C unit cover.
6. Remove five screws from around blower housing, then separate blower housing from heater A/C unit, **Fig. 10.**
7. Remove three screws attaching blower motor and wheel to unit housing, then separate blower assembly from unit housing.
8. Remove relay panel above glove box opening.
9. Through glove compartment opening, disconnect A/C vacuum line and radio noise capacitor connectors, as equipped.
10. Remove left windshield pillar trim cover.
11. Remove left lower side cowl trim panel.
12. Remove hood release handle assembly attaching screws.
13. Remove steering column trim covers.
14. Disconnect parking brake release mechanism connecting rod (gain access through fuse panel opening).
15. Remove lower left instrument panel silencer.
16. Remove lower left instrument panel reinforcement.
17. Remove instrument panel center (radio) bezel.
18. Remove front floor console, if equipped.
19. Remove radio. Refer to procedure outlined under "Radio, Replace."
20. Remove heater A/C control.
21. Remove cigar lighter.
22. Remove message center/trip computer, if equipped.
23. Disconnect side window demister tubes from top of heater A/C unit.
24. Remove steering column upper attaching bolts and allow steering column to rest on drivers seat.
25. Remove upper instrument panel (defroster outlet) cover.
26. Remove upper instrument panel attaching screws from below windshield opening.

27. Loosen, but do not remove, left lower cowl to instrument panel attaching screw.
28. Carefully pull instrument panel away from dash panel on right side of vehicle and allow instrument panel to rest on passenger seat. **Protect passenger seat using a suitable cover.**
29. Drain cooling system, disconnect heater hoses from heater core, then plug heater core tubes to prevent spillage.
30. **On models with A/C,** proceed as follows:
    a. Discharge A/C system, then disconnect refrigerant lines from H-valve at dash panel on righthand side of vehicle. Seal refrigerant lines.
    b. Remove H-valve from evaporator plate. Seal H-valve to prevent contamination.
    c. Remove A/C drain tube.
31. **On all models,** remove heater A/C unit to dash panel attaching nuts.
32. From inside of vehicle, pull heater A/C unit housing rearward to clear dash panel silencer, then remove from vehicle.
33. Remove heater A/C unit top cover, **Fig. 11.**
34. Remove heater core to dash panel seal from core tubes, then remove heater core.
35. Reverse procedure to install.

DAYTONA & LEBARON COUPE/CONVERTIBLE

1. Disconnect battery ground cable.
2. **On models with A/C,** discharge A/C system.
3. **On all models,** drain cooling system.
4. **On models with A/C,** remove H-valve.
5. **On all models,** disconnect heater hoses from heater core. Plug heater core tubes to prevent spillage.
6. **On models with A/C,** remove A/C drain tube.
7. **On all models,** disconnect vacuum lines from water valve and vacuum supply nipple.
8. Remove heater A/C unit housing to dash panel attaching nuts.
9. Remove right front seat.

10. Remove right side cowl trim panel.
11. Remove body computer.
12. Remove glove box module.
13. Remove right lower instrument panel reinforcement bracket, then the support bracket from left end of brace.
14. Remove radio capacitor, lamp-out module and security alarm module, if equipped.
15. Using a suitable cutting device, cut instrument panel along indented line in padded cover to right of glove box opening. **Cut only plastic, not metal.** Remove reinforcement and piece of instrument panel attached to it.
16. Remove both side under panel silencers.
17. Reach through glove box opening and disconnect demister hoses from top of heater A/C unit housing.
18. Disconnect antenna cable.
19. Disconnect blower motor wiring connectors.
20. Disconnect blend air door control cable from unit housing and position aside.
21. Roll floor carpet back from under unit housing far enough to avoid interference with unit housing removal.
22. Remove lower steering column cover and reinforcement.
23. Remove lower reinforcement support bracket from the side of steering column opening to the left of radio.
24. Remove air distribution duct and defroster adapter through opening at left side of instrument panel.
25. Remove hanger strap from unit housing and position aside to the left.
26. Remove unit housing from under right side of instrument panel.
27. Remove heater A/C unit top cover, **Fig. 11.**
28. Remove heater core to dash panel seal from core tubes, then remove heater core.
29. Reverse procedure to install.

EVAPORATOR CORE REPLACE

1. Remove heater A/C housing as outlined under "Heater Core, Replace."
2. Remove evaporator core from housing.
3. Reverse procedure to install.

2.2L/4-135 & 2.5L/4-153 Engines

NOTE: On Air Bag Equipped Models, Refer To "Air Bag System Precautions" Located In The Front Of This Manual For System Disarming & Arming Procedures.

INDEX

PRECAUTIONS
AIR BAG SYSTEMS

Refer to "Air Bag System Precautions" in the front of this manual for system disarming and arming procedures.

FUEL SYSTEM PRESSURE RELEASE

Before servicing the fuel pump, fuel lines, fuel filter, throttle body or fuel injectors, the fuel system pressure must be released as follows:

1. Loosen fuel filler cap to release fuel tank pressure.
2. Disconnect injector wiring harness from engine harness.
3. Connect a jumper wire to ground terminal No. 1 of the injector harness to engine ground, **Fig. 1.**
4. Connect a jumper wire to the positive terminal No. 2 of the injector harness and touch the battery positive post for no longer then 5 seconds. This releases system pressure.
5. Remove jumper wires and continue fuel system service.

ENGINE MOUNT
REPLACE

The engine mounts incorporate slotted bolt holes to permit side to side positioning of the engine thereby affecting the length of the driveshaft. Failure to properly position engine may result in extensive damage to the engine or driveshafts.

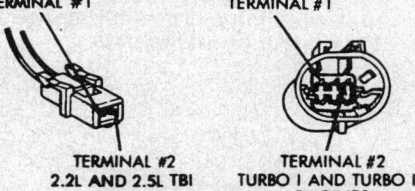

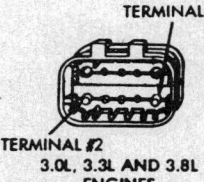

CR1069100225000X

Fig. 1   Injector harness connectors

RIGHT SIDE MOUNT

1. Remove right engine mount insulator vertical fasteners from frame rail, **Fig. 2.**
2. Remove load on engine mount by supporting engine and transmission assembly with a floor jack.
3. Remove through bolt from insulator assembly then the insulator.
4. Reverse procedure to install, noting the following:
  a. Tighten bolts to specification.
  b. Adjust engine mount insulator as necessary.

LEFT SIDE MOUNT

1. Raise and support vehicle and remove inner splash shield.
2. Support transaxle with a transmission jack.
3. Remove insulator through bolt then the transaxle mount bolts and mount, **Fig. 2.**
4. Reverse procedure to install, noting the following:
  a. Ensure slide tube is seated into rail bracket guides.
  b. Tighten bolts to specifications.
  c. Adjust engine mount insulator as necessary.

FRONT MOUNT

1. Support engine and transaxle assembly so engine will not rotate.
2. Remove insulator through bolt, **Fig. 2.**
3. Remove front engine mount bracket to crossmember screws and nuts then the insulator.
4. Reverse procedure to install, noting the following:
  a. Tighten bolts to specifications.
  b. Adjust engine mount insulator as necessary.

ENGINE MOUNT INSULATOR ADJUSTMENT

Insulator location on frame rail (right side) and transaxle bracket (left side) are adjustable in relation to driveshaft assembly length. Check and reposition right engine mount insulator (left insulator is a self adjusting floating type), under the following conditions:

1. Driveshaft distress.
2. Any front end structural damage.
3. Insulator replacement.
4. Engine removal.

When positioning the engine, check driveshaft length as outlined in the "Front Wheel Drive Axle" unit repair section under "Driveshaft Length, Adjust." Failure to properly position engine may result in extensive damage to the engine or driveshafts.

ENGINE
REPLACE

1. Release fuel system pressure then disconnect battery ground cable.
2. Scribe alignment marks on hood and hood hinge, then remove hood.
3. Drain cooling system, then disconnect radiator hoses from radiator and engine.
4. Remove air cleaner, radiator and fan assembly.
5. Remove A/C compressor from mounting bracket and position aside with hoses attached, if equipped.
6. Remove power steering pump from mounting bracket and position aside with hoses attached, if equipped.
7. Drain crankcase and remove oil filter.
8. Disconnect wire connectors at alternator, carburetor and engine.
9. Disconnect fuel line, heater hose and accelerator cable.
10. Remove alternator from mounting bracket and position aside.
11. **On models equipped with manual transaxle**, disconnect clutch cable, then remove transaxle lower cover.
12. **On all models**, disconnect exhaust pipe from exhaust manifold, then remove starter motor.
13. **On models equipped with automatic transaxle**, remove transaxle case lower cover and place alignment marks on flex plate and torque converter. Remove converter to flex plate attaching screws. Attach a C-clamp to front lower portion of converter housing to retain torque converter in housing when engine is being removed.
14. **On all models**, install a suitable transmission holding fixture and attach a suitable engine lifting device.
15. Remove righthand inner splash shield and disconnect ground strap.
16. Remove long bolt through yoke bracket and insulator. **If insulator screws are to be removed, mark position on side rail for exact reinstallation.**
17. Remove transaxle case to cylinder block mounting screws.
18. Remove front engine mount screw and nut.
19. **On models with manual transaxle,** remove anti-roll strut or damper.
20. **On models with manual transaxle,**

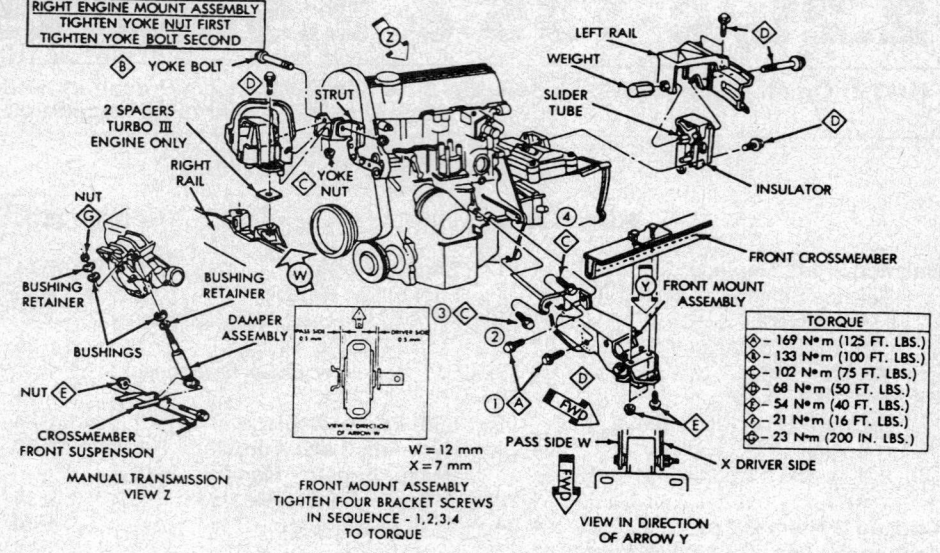

Fig. 2 Engine mount replacement

remove insulator through bolt from inside wheel house, or insulator bracket to transaxle screws.
21. **On all models,** carefully lift engine from vehicle.
22. Reverse procedure to install. When positioning the engine, check driveshaft length as outlined in the "Front Wheel Drive Axles" section. **Failure to properly position engine may result in extensive damage to the engine or driveshafts.**

INTAKE, EXHAUST MANIFOLD & TURBOCHARGER
REPLACE

EXCEPT TURBO

Before servicing the fuel pump, fuel lines, fuel filter, throttle body or fuel injectors, the fuel system pressure must be released as outlined under "Precautions."

1. Disconnect battery ground cable and drain coolant system.
2. Remove air cleaner and disconnect all vacuum and fuel lines and electrical connectors from carburetor or throttle body.
3. Disconnect throttle linkage, then remove power steering pump drive belt.
4. Disconnect power brake vacuum hose from manifold, if equipped.
5. Disconnect hoses from water crossover, then raise and support vehicle and disconnect exhaust pipe from exhaust manifold.
6. Remove power steering pump and position aside. Remove intake manifold support bracket.

7. Remove EGR tube and the intake manifold retaining screws.
8. Lower vehicle and remove intake manifold.
9. Remove exhaust manifold retaining nuts and exhaust manifold.
10. Reverse procedure to install.

TURBO

Except 2.2L/4-135 Turbo III Engine

1. Disconnect battery ground cable.
2. Remove air cleaner and throttle cable.
3. Disconnect automatic idle speed (AIS) motor and throttle position sensor (TPS) connectors.
4. Disconnect vacuum hoses from throttle body.
5. Disconnect detonation sensor, fuel injector and charge temperature sensor connectors.
6. Loosen tube nut on fuel pressure regulator. **Wrap shop towels around hoses to catch any gasoline spillage.**
7. Open fuel tube clip and remove fuel tube.
8. Disconnect vacuum hoses from fuel pressure regulator, then remove fuel pressure regulator attaching nuts and regulator.
9. Remove PCV, brake booster and vacuum vapor harness from intake manifold.
10. Disconnect knock sensor connector, then remove fuel rail to intake manifold attaching screws.
11. Remove fuel rail and injector assembly by pulling rail so injectors come straight out of their ports.
12. Remove front engine mount through bolt and rotate engine forward away from cowl.
13. Remove coolant and oil lines from turbocharger, then remove wastegate rod to gate retaining clip.
14. Remove turbo retaining nuts, then dis-

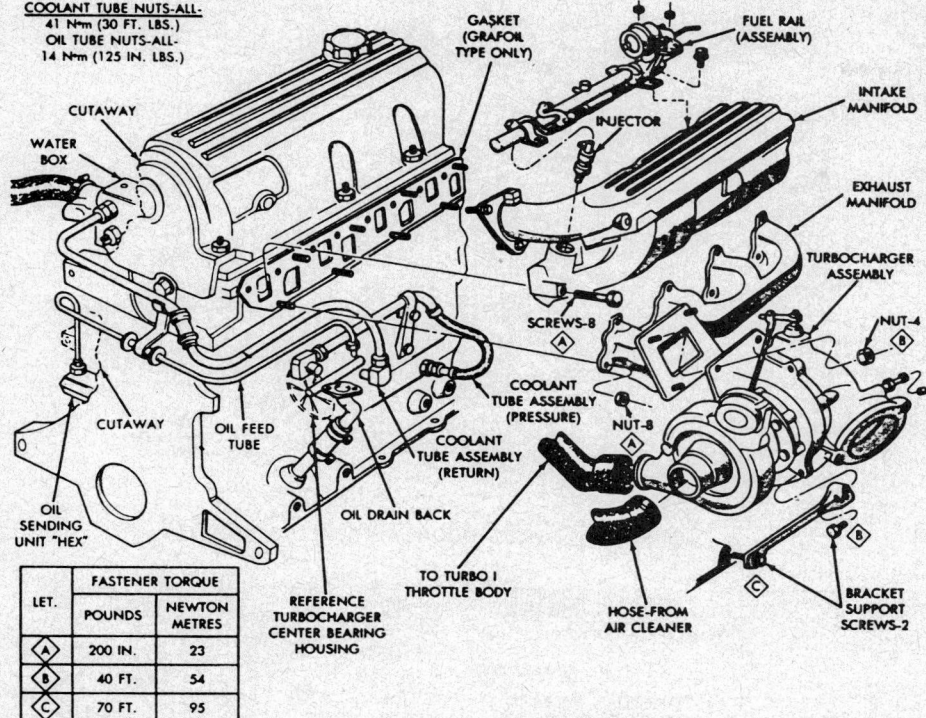

COOLANT TUBE NUTS-ALL-
41 N•m (30 FT. LBS.)
OIL TUBE NUTS-ALL-
14 N•m (125 IN. LBS.)

FASTENER TORQUE		
LET.	POUNDS	NEWTON METRES
A	200 IN.	23
B	40 FT.	54
C	70 FT.	95

Fig. 3 Exploded view of exhaust manifold and related components. Turbocharged engine

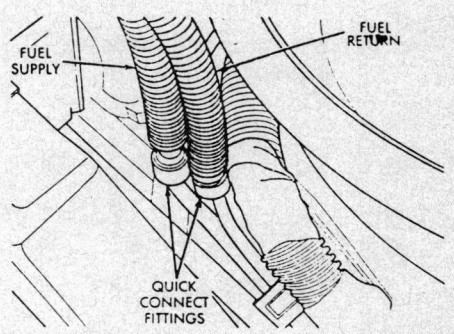

Fig. 4 Direct Ignition System (DIS) coil location

Fig. 5 Fuel supply & return hose connections

connect oxygen sensor electrical connector and vacuum lines.

15. Raise and support vehicle, then remove the right front wheel and tire assembly.
16. Remove turbo to block support bracket, then the driveshaft assembly **Fig. 3.**
17. Separate oil drain back tube from turbo housing and remove fitting.
18. Disconnect exhaust pipe from turbo, then remove remaining turbo to manifold retaining nut.
19. Remove lower coolant line and inlet fitting, then remove turbocharger.
20. Remove eight intake manifold screws and washers, then the intake manifold.
21. Remove eight exhaust manifold retaining nuts, then the exhaust manifold.
22. Reverse procedure to install, noting the following:
   a. Use new manifold gaskets.
   b. Use anti-seize compound on all threads.
   c. Tighten bolts and nuts to proper specifications, **Fig. 3.**

2.2L/4-135 Turbo III Engine (VIN A)
Intake Manifold

1. Release fuel system pressure as outlined under "Precautions."
2. Disconnect battery ground cable and drain cooling system.
3. Remove fresh air duct from air filter housing and inlet hose from intercooler.
4. Remove radiator hose to cylinder head, **Fig. 3.**

5. Remove Direct Ignition System (DIS) coils from intake manifold, **Fig. 4.**
6. Remove throttle and speed control cables.
7. Disconnect intercooler to throttle body outlet hose.
8. Disconnect vacuum hoses from throttle body and remove harness.
9. Disconnect automatic idle speed (AIS) motor and throttle position sensor connectors.
10. Remove PCV breather/separator box and vacuum harness, brake booster, vacuum vapor harness and fuel pressure regulator harness from intake manifold.
11. Disconnect fuel injector and charge temperature wiring connector.
12. Remove fuel supply and return hose quick connect at fuel tube assembly, **Fig. 5. Wrap shop towels around hoses to catch any gasoline spillage.**
13. Remove intake manifold bolts then the intake manifold.
14. Reverse procedure to install, noting the following:
   a. Use new manifold gaskets.
   b. Use anti-seize compound on all threads.
   c. Tighten bolts and nuts to specifications, **Fig. 3.**

Turbocharger

The turbocharger is removed from below the vehicle.
1. Release fuel system pressure as outlined under "Precautions."
2. Disconnect battery ground cable and drain cooling system.

3. Remove front engine mount through bolt and rotate engine forward away from cowl.
4. Remove air cleaner support.
5. Disconnect heated oxygen sensor and vacuum leads.
6. Remove coolant return line from water box and turbocharger housing and disconnect coolant inlet line.
7. Disconnect oil lines from turbocharger.
8. Remove two upper and one lower turbocharger retaining nuts.
9. Raise and support vehicle, then remove the right front wheel and tire assembly.
10. Remove air deflector and right driveshaft assembly **Fig. 3.**
11. Separate oil drain back tube from turbo housing and remove fitting.
12. Remove turbocharger to block support bracket.
13. Remove remaining turbocharger nut.
14. Disconnect exhaust pipe from turbo.
15. Remove lower coolant line and inlet fitting, then remove turbocharger.
16. Reverse procedure to install, noting the following:
   a. Use new manifold gaskets.
   b. Use anti-seize compound on all threads.
   c. Tighten bolts and nuts to specifications, **Fig. 3.**

Exhaust Manifold

1. Remove turbocharger
2. Remove eight exhaust manifold retaining nuts, then the exhaust manifold.

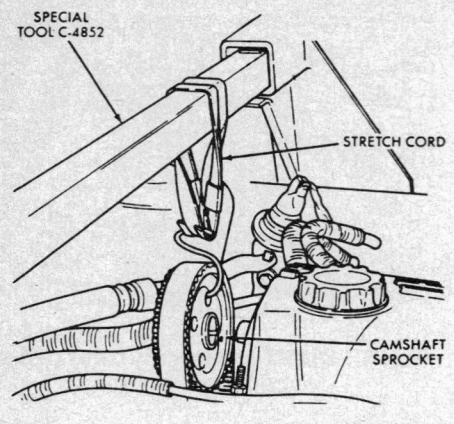

Fig. 6 Camshaft sprocket suspended position

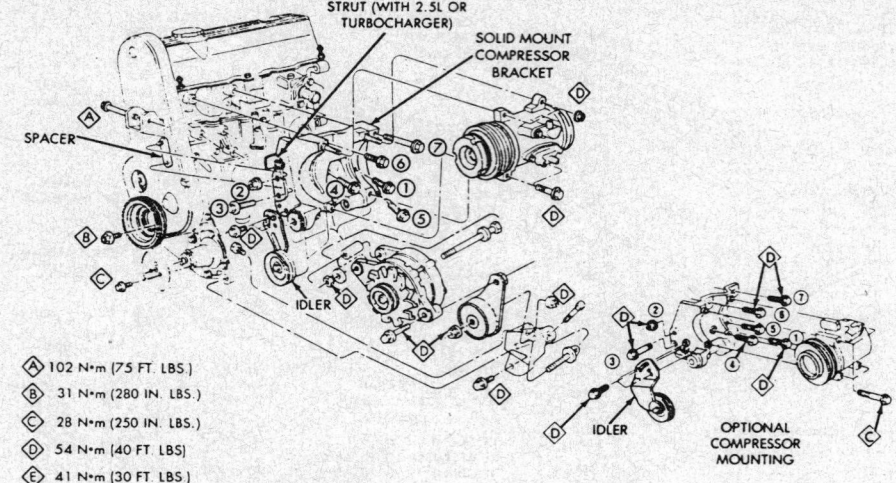

(A) 102 N·m (75 FT. LBS.)
(B) 31 N·m (280 IN. LBS.)
(C) 28 N·m (250 IN. LBS.)
(D) 54 N·m (40 FT. LBS)
(E) 41 N·m (30 FT. LBS.)

Fig. 7 Accessory & solid mount compressor bracket

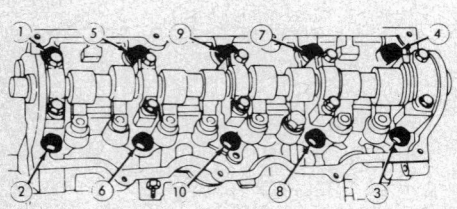

Fig. 8 Cylinder head bolt removal sequence

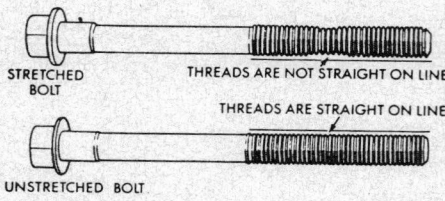

Fig. 9 Cylinder head bolt inspection

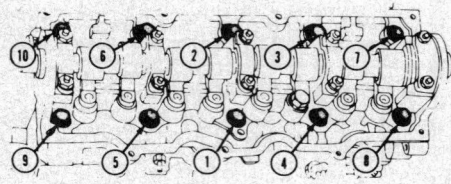

Fig. 10 Cylinder head bolt tightening sequence. Except 2.2L/4-135 Turbo III engine (VIN A)

3. Reverse procedure to install, noting the following:
   a. Use new manifold gaskets.
   b. Use anti-seize compound on all threads.
   c. Tighten bolts and nuts to specifications, **Fig. 3.**

CYLINDER HEAD
REPLACE

EXCEPT 2.2L/4-135 TURBO III ENGINE

Before servicing the fuel pump, fuel lines, fuel filter, throttle body or fuel injectors, the fuel system pressure must be released as outlined under "Precautions."

Removal and installation of cylinder head requires separation of camshaft sprocket from camshaft. In order to maintain camshaft, intermediate shaft and crankshaft timing, the timing belt is left indexed on the camshaft sprocket while the assembly is suspended under light tension, **Fig. 6.**

When removing camshaft sprocket from camshaft, adequate tension on sprocket and belt assembly must be maintained to prevent the timing belt from disengaging from the intermediate or crankshaft timing sprockets. **Failure to maintain adequate tension on timing belt may result in incorrect engine timing.**

Refer to "Timing Belt, Sprockets & Oil Seals," for camshaft sprocket removal.

Removal

1. Release fuel system pressure.

2. Disconnect battery ground cable, then drain cooling system.
3. Remove air cleaner and disconnect all vacuum lines, electrical wiring and fuel lines from throttle body.
4. Disconnect throttle linkage.
5. **On models with power steering,** loosen power steering pump, then remove power steering belt.
6. **On all models,** disconnect power brake vacuum hose from intake manifold.
7. Disconnect water hoses from water crossover.
8. Raise and support vehicle, then disconnect exhaust pipe from exhaust manifold.
9. Lower vehicle, remove power steering pump assembly and position aside.
10. Disconnect dipstick tube from thermostat housing, then rotate bracket from stud. **Do not bend bracket.**
11. Remove solid mount compressor bracket as shown, **Fig. 7.**
12. Remove cylinder head cover attaching bolts, then the cover.
13. Remove cylinder head bolts in sequence shown in **Fig. 8,** then the cylinder head assembly.

Inspection

1. Ensure cylinder head is flat within .004 inch (0.1 mm).
2. Inspect camshaft journals for scoring.

Installation

Always use the specific head gasket for the engine's year and displacement since they are not interchangeable.

Ensure proper head bolts are used. This bolt can be identified by an "11" stamped on bolt head. These bolts are used on all engines. Do not intermix 10 and 11 mm head bolts, as stripping of threads or cracking of the block may result. Inspect bolts to determine if they are stretched, **Fig. 9.** If all bolt threads are not straight on line, replace bolt.

1. Position cylinder head on block.
2. Refer to tightening sequence, **Fig. 10,** and tighten cylinder head bolts in four steps as follows:
   a. **Torque** all bolts 45 ft. lbs.
   b. **Torque** all bolts to 65 ft. lbs.
   c. **Torque** all bolts again to 65 ft. lbs.
   d. Tighten each bolt an additional 1/4 turn (90°), noting bolt torque. **If bolt torque is not over 90 ft. lbs. after tightening an additional 1/4 turn, bolt should be replaced.**
3. Reverse remaining removal steps to complete installation.

2.2L/4-135 TURBO III ENGINE (VIN A)
Removal

1. Release fuel system pressure as outlined under "Precautions."
2. Disconnect battery ground cable.
3. Drain cooling system.
4. Remove intake and exhaust manifold

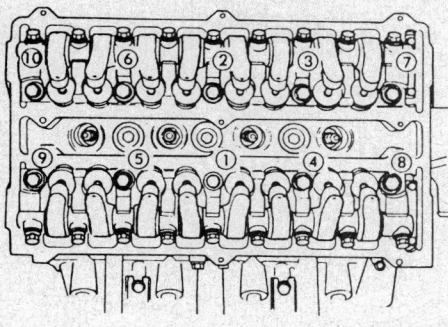

Fig. 11 Cylinder head bolt tightening sequence. 2.2L/4-135 Turbo III engine (VIN A)

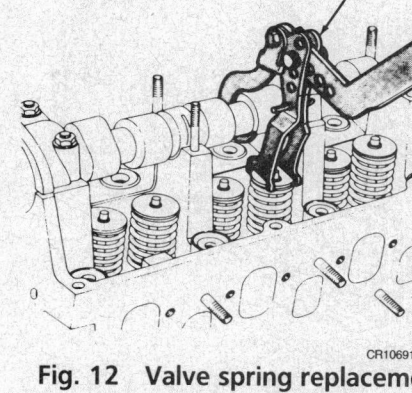

Fig. 12 Valve spring replacement

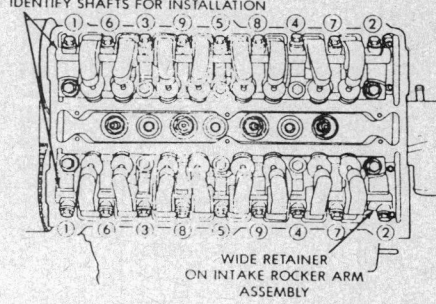

Fig. 13 Rocker arm shaft loosening sequence. 2.2L/4-135 Turbo III engine (VIN A)

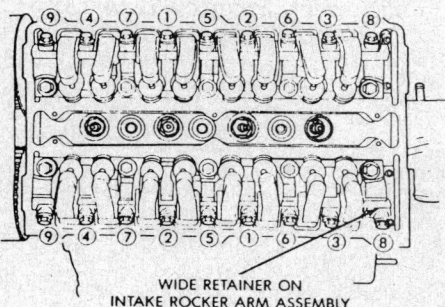

Fig. 14 Rocker arm shaft tightening sequence. 2.2L/4-135 Turbo III engine (VIN A).

and outlined under "Intake & Exhaust Manifold, Replace."

5. Remove timing belt as outlined under "Timing Belt, Sprockets & Oil Seals."
6. Remove solid mount compressor bracket as shown, **Fig. 7.**
7. Remove cylinder head bolts then the cylinder head.

Inspection

1. Ensure cylinder head is flat within .004 inch (0.1 mm).
2. Inspect camshaft journals for scoring.

Installation

The 2.2L/4-135 Turbo III head gasket is not interchangeable with the gasket used on the 2.5L/4-153 turbo engine.

Head bolt diameter is 11mm. These bolts are unique to this engine application and are not interchangeable with other engines. Cylinder head bolts should be examined before use. If the threads are necked down the bolts should be replaced, **Fig. 9.**

1. Position cylinder head on block.
2. Refer to tightening sequence, **Fig. 11**, and tighten cylinder head bolts in four steps as follows:
   a. **Torque** all bolts 45 ft. lbs.
   b. **Torque** all bolts to 65 ft. lbs.
   c. **Torque** all bolts again to 65 ft. lbs.
   d. Tighten each bolt an additional 1/4 turn (90°), noting bolt torque. If **bolt torque is not over 90 ft. lbs. after tightening an additional 1/4 turn, bolt should be replaced.**

3. Reverse remaining removal steps to complete installation.

VALVE SPRINGS
REPLACE
EXCEPT 2.2L/4-135 TURBO III ENGINE

1. **On models with cylinder head removed,** use valve spring compressor tool No. 4682 or equivalent, to compress valve spring enough to remove and install valve bead locks, **Fig. 12.**
2. **On models with cylinder head installed,** proceed as follows:
   a. Rotate crankshaft until piston is at TDC on compression stroke.
   b. Apply 90-100 psi of compressed air into spark plug hole of valve being removed.
   c. Using valve spring compressor tool No. 4683 or equivalent tool, compress valve spring enough to remove valve stem locks.
   d. Remove valve spring and spring seat.
   e. Remove valve seal.
3. **On all models,** reverse procedure to install.

2.2L/4-135 TURBO III ENGINE (VIN A)

1. Remove cylinder head as outlined under "Cylinder Head, Replace."
2. Compress valve springs using valve spring compressor tool No. C-3422-B and adapter Nos. 6537 and 6537 or equivalents.
3. Remove valve retaining locks, valve spring retainers, valve stem seals and valve springs.
4. Reverse procedure to install.

VALVE LIFTERS

Engine	Year	Lift, Inch
2.2L/4-135 ①	1992-95	.430
2.2L/4-135 ②	1992-95	.250

①—Except Turbo III engine (VIN A).
②—Turbo III engine (VIN A).

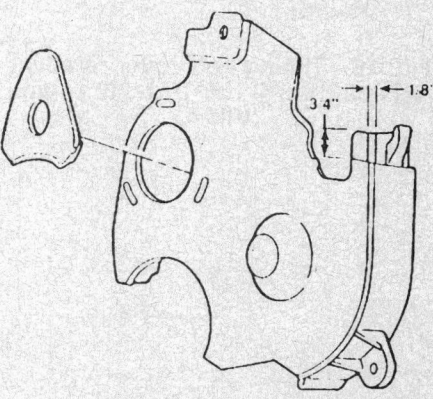

Fig. 15 Lower timing belt cover trimming

VALVE ADJUSTMENT

Hydraulic valve lifters are used; no adjustment is necessary.

ROCKER ARMS
REPLACE
EXCEPT 2.2L/4-135 TURBO III ENGINE

1. Remove valve cover.
2. Rotate cam until base circle is in contact with rocker arm. Depress valve spring using tool No. 4682 or equivalent and slide rocker arm out. Keep rocker arms in order for assembly.
3. Remove hydraulic lash adjuster.
4. Reverse procedure to install.

2.2L/4-135 TURBO III ENGINE (VIN A)

1. Remove ignition cable and valve covers.
2. Remove rocker arm shaft bolts in sequence shown in **Fig. 13.**
3. Slide rocker off shaft, keeping arms in order for assembly.
4. Remove hydraulic lash adjusters.
5. Reverse procedure to install using tightening sequence shown in **Fig. 14.**

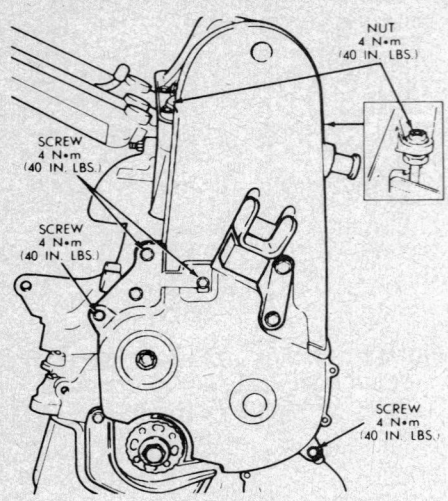

Fig. 16 Timing belt cover removal.
Except 2.2L/4-135 Turbo III engine
(VIN A)

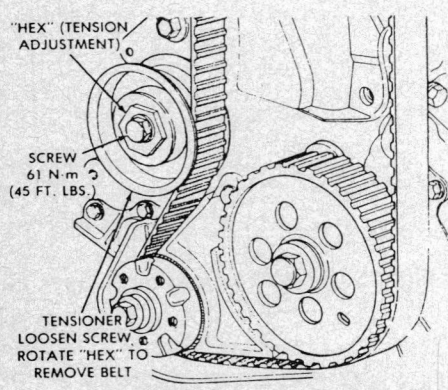

Fig. 19 Timing Belt Tensioner.
Except Turbo III Engine (VIN A)

TIMING BELT
REPLACE

EXCEPT 2.2L/4-135 TURBO III ENGINE
Removal

1. Remove upper and lower timing belt covers, then trim lower timing belt cover as shown in **Fig. 15. Do not trim more than amount illustrated;** removal of an excessive amount of material will result in unwanted exposure of timing belt.
2. Raise and support vehicle, then remove right inner splash shield.
3. Remove engine drive belts, then the crankshaft pulley and water pump pulley retaining bolts.
4. Remove crankshaft and water pump pulleys.
5. Lower vehicle, then remove nuts securing cover to cylinder head and cylinder block, **Fig. 16.**
6. Position a suitable jack under engine,

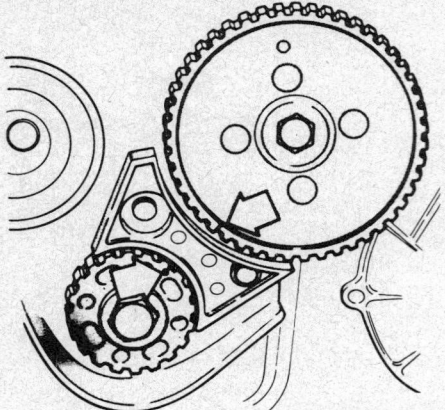

Fig. 17 Crankshaft & intermediate shaft timing mark alignment

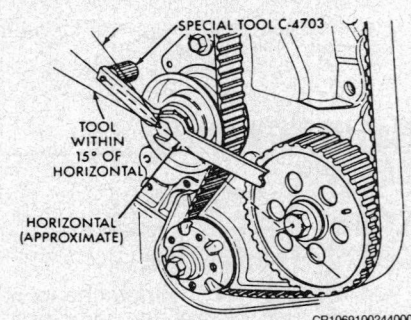

Fig. 20 Timing belt tension adjustment

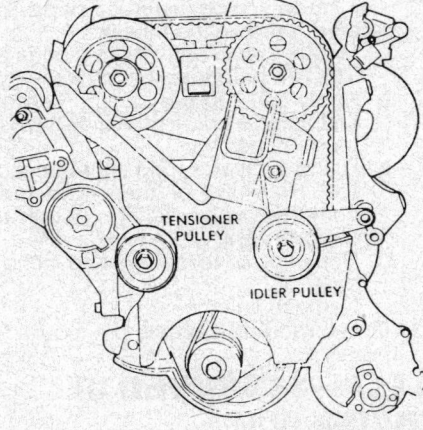

Fig. 22 Timing belt cover & tensioner. 2.2L/4-135 Turbo III engine (VIN A).

then remove right hand engine mount bolt and raise engine slightly.
7. Rotate crankshaft to align timing marks as shown in **Figs. 17 and 18.**
8. Loosen timing belt tensioner, then remove timing belt, **Fig. 19.**
9. If necessary, remove crankshaft sprocket using special tools shown in **Fig. 20** and refer to **Fig. 21** for removal and installation of camshaft and intermediate shaft sprockets.
10. Refer to **Fig. 22** for removal of crankshaft, intermediate shaft or camshaft seals.

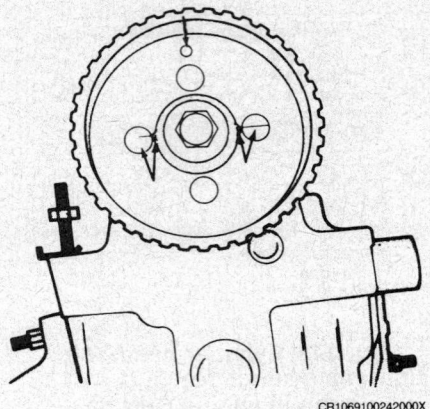

Fig. 18 Camshaft timing mark alignment. Except 2.2L/4-135 Turbo III engine (VIN A)

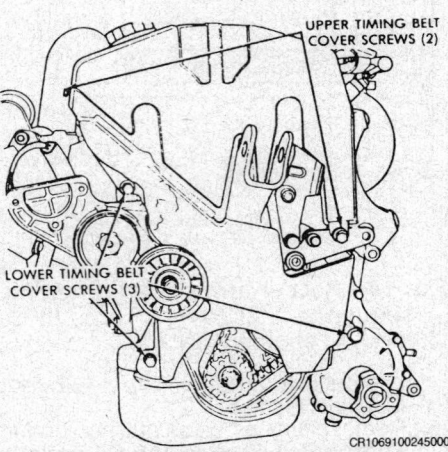

Fig. 21 Timing belt cover removal. 2.2L/4-135 Turbo III engine (VIN A).

Installation

1. Rotate crankshaft and intermediate shaft until markings on sprockets are aligned, **Fig. 17.**
2. Rotate camshaft until arrows on hub are aligned with No. 1 camshaft cap to cylinder head line, **Fig. 18.** Small hole must be located along vertical center line.
3. Install timing belt.
4. Remove spark plugs, then ensure crankshaft is at TDC position.
5. Loosen tensioner locknut using belt tensioner tool No. C-4703 or equivalent, **Fig. 23.**
6. Reset belt tension so that belt tensioning tool axis is within 15° of horizontal.
7. Rotate crankshaft two revolutions in clockwise direction and position at TDC, then tighten tensioner locknut.
8. Rotate crankshaft two full revolutions and recheck timing. **Do not allow oil or solvents to contact timing belt since they will deteriorate the rubber and cause tooth slippage.**
9. Reverse remaining removal steps to complete installation. Refer to **Fig. 24** for crankshaft, intermediate shaft and camshaft oil seal installation.

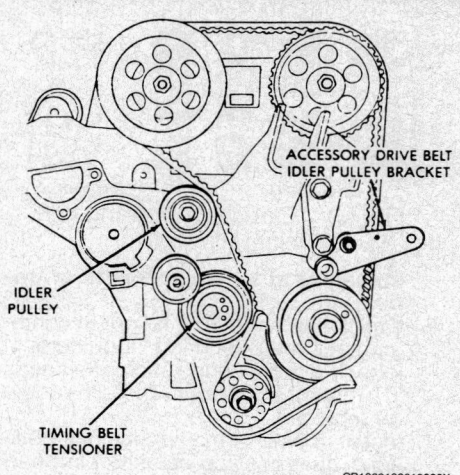

Fig. 23   Timing belt removal.
2.2L/4-135 Turbo III engine (VIN A).

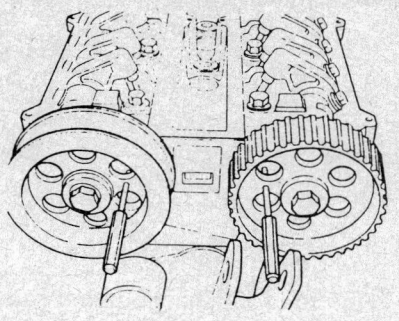

Fig. 24   Camshafts pinned into position. 2.2L/4-135 Turbo III engine (VIN A).

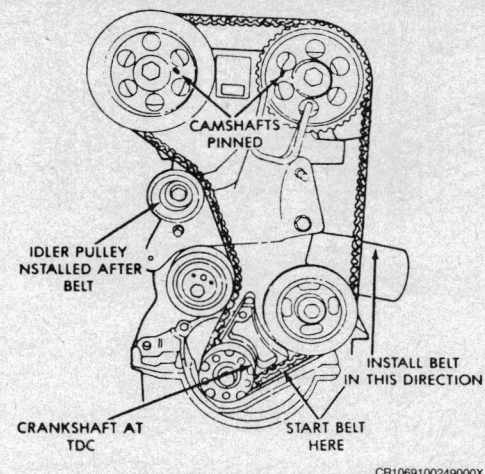

Fig. 25   Camshaft and crankshaft timing mark alignment. 2.2L/4-135 Turbo III engine (VIN A).

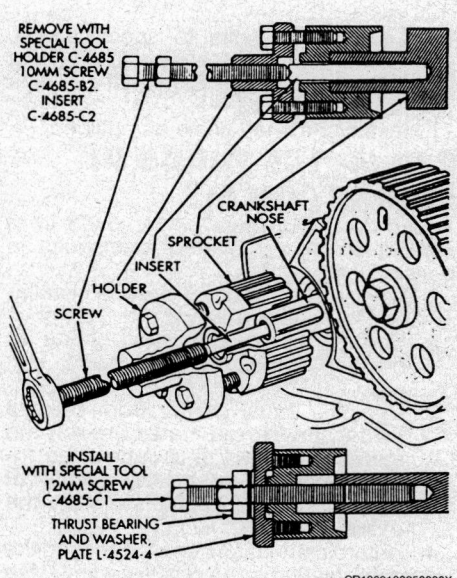

Fig. 26   Crankshaft sprocket replacement

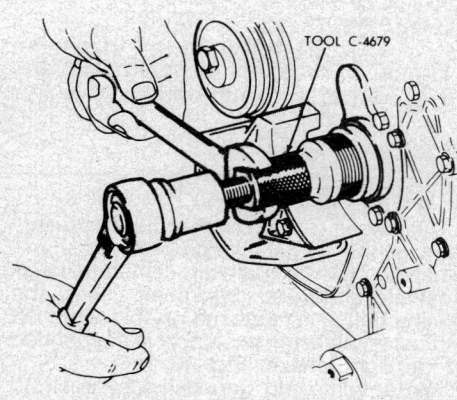

Fig. 27   Crankshaft, intermediate shaft & camshaft oil seal removal

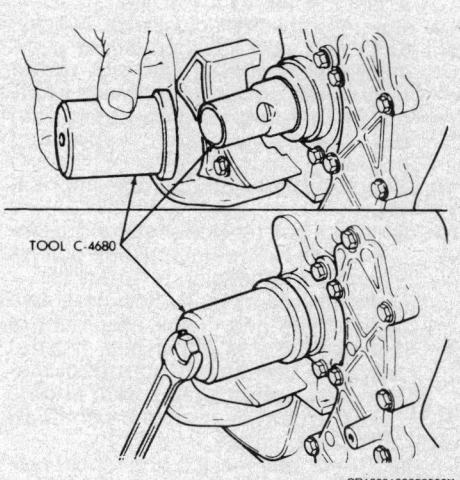

Fig. 28   Crankshaft, intermediate shaft & camshaft oil seal installation

2.2L/4–135 TURBO III ENGINE (VIN A)
Removal

1. Remove PCV tube, upper timing belt cover screws and cover, **Fig. 25.**
2. Remove accessory drive belt.
3. Raise and support vehicle and remove righthand wheel and inner splash shield.
4. Remove water pump and crankshaft pulleys.
5. Remove lower accessory drive belt idler and tensioner pulley, **Fig. 26.**
6. Remove lower timing belt cover screws and cover.
7. Lower vehicle.
8. Lift engine with engine support tool No. 4852 or equivalent and separate right engine mount.
9. Raise and support vehicle. Remove lower accessory drive belt idler pulley bracket assembly, **Fig. 27.**
10. Loosen timing belt tensioner, remove timing belt and idler pulley.
11. If necessary, remove crankshaft sprocket using special tools shown in **Fig. 20** and refer to **Fig. 21** for removal and installation of camshaft and intermediate shaft sprockets.
12. Refer to **Fig. 22** for removal of crankshaft, intermediate shaft or camshaft seals.

Installation

1. Remove air cleaner duct and the ignition cable cover.
2. Remove valve covers and loosen rocker arm assemblies about three turns, **Fig. 13.**
3. Align and pin both intake and exhaust cam sprockets with 3/16 drill bits or pin punches, **Fig. 28. Accessory shaft does not need to be timed.**
4. Install a dial indicator in No. 1 spark plug hole.
5. Rotate crankshaft until No. 1 cylinder is at top dead center. Mark the engine block for TDC reference.

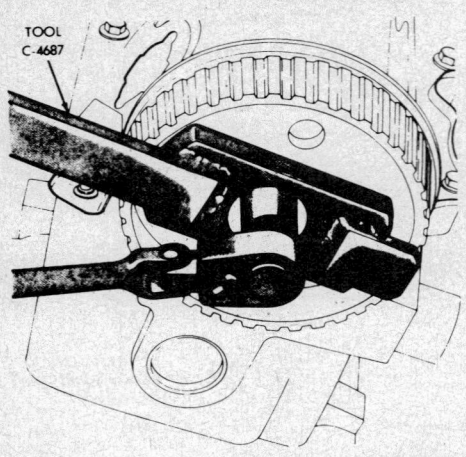

Fig. 29   Camshaft & intermediate shaft sprocket replacement

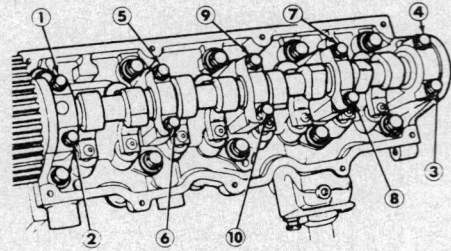

Fig. 30   Camshaft bearing cap removal

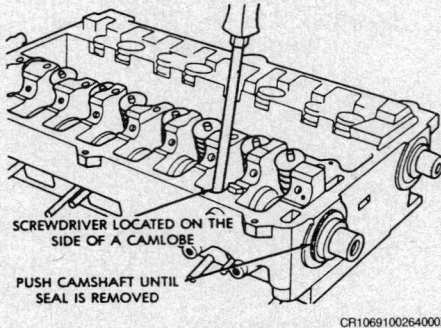

SCREWDRIVER LOCATED ON THE SIDE OF A CAMLOBE

PUSH CAMSHAFT UNTIL SEAL IS REMOVED

Fig. 32   Camshaft oil seal removal. 2.2L/4-135 Turbo III engine (VIN A).

Fig. 31   Camshaft bearing cap installation

6. Install timing belt and idler pulley in sequence shown in **Fig. 29**.
7. Remove dial indicator and drill bits or pins from camshaft sprockets.
8. Install belt tensioner gauge on timing belt between camshaft pulleys and adjust tension to 110 ft. lbs.
9. Rotate crankshaft clockwise two full turns and check alignment of camshaft and crankshaft. **Do not rotate crankshaft counterclockwise or attempt to rotate engine using cam or accessory shaft attaching screw.**
10. Check belt tension and adjust as follows:
    a. Install belt tensioner gauge on timing belt between camshaft pulleys and adjust tension to 110 ft. lbs.
    b. Rotate crankshaft clockwise two full turns and check alignment of camshaft and crankshaft. **Do not rotate crankshaft counterclockwise or attempt to rotate engine using cam or accessory shaft attaching screw.**
    c. Check belt tension and repeat procedure if necessary.
11. Tighten rocker arm shafts in sequence shown to specifications, **Fig. 14.**
12. Install valve covers, spark plug, ignition cable and ignition cable covers.
13. Reverse remaining removal steps to complete installation. Refer to **Fig. 24** for crankshaft, intermediate shaft and camshaft oil seal installation.

HYDRAULIC LASH ADJUSTERS
REPLACE

Refer to "Rocker Arms, Replace" for hydraulic lash adjuster replacement procedure.

CAMSHAFT
REPLACE

Camshaft replacement requires separation of the camshaft sprocket and camshaft. In order to maintain camshaft, intermediate shaft and crankshaft timing, the timing belt is left indexed on the camshaft sprocket while the assembly is suspended under light tension, **Fig. 30**.

When removing camshaft sprocket from camshaft, adequate tension on sprocket and belt assembly must be maintained to prevent the timing belt from disengaging from the intermediate or crankshaft timing sprockets. **Failure to maintain adequate tension on timing belt may result in incorrect engine timing.**

EXCEPT 2.2L/4-135 TURBO III ENGINE

1. Mark rocker arms to ensure installation in original position.
2. Evenly loosen camshaft bearing bolts in sequence shown in **Fig. 30** until all bolts have been loosened 3-4 turns.
3. Tap rear of camshaft with suitable mallet to break caps free.
4. Continue loosening bearing cap bolts, ensuring camshaft does not cock, then remove bearing caps and camshaft. **Loosen bearing cap bolts evenly. If camshaft cocks in bearing bores, bearing surfaces may be damaged.**
5. With caps removed from engine, check oil holes for obstructions. **Some engines may be equipped with oversize camshaft bearings. Engines with oversize camshaft bearings can be identified by green markings on cylinder head and**

camshaft at AIR pump side of engine.
6. Check camshaft lobe height in center (contact area) and on shoulders of lobe. If difference in reading exceeds .010 inch (.25 mm), camshaft should be replaced.
7. Install rocker arms in original positions, then position camshaft in bearing saddles of cylinder head.
8. Apply suitable sealant to No. 1 and No. 5 bearing cap.
9. Align caps in proper sequence, with No. 1 cap at timing belt end and No. 5 cap at flywheel end of engine, and ensure arrow on caps 1, 2, 3 and 4 point toward timing belt, **Fig. 31**. **Install caps before installing camshaft seals.**
10. Tighten cap bolts to specifications. Tighten cap bolts evenly in crossing pattern to ensure camshaft remains properly aligned.
11. Install camshaft seals as outlined.

2.2L/4-135 TURBO III ENGINE (VIN A)

Cylinder head must be removed from vehicle before removal of camshafts is possible.
1. Mark rocker arms to ensure installation in original position.
2. Remove rocker arms and shafts as outlined under "Rocker Arms, Replace."
3. Remove thrust plates from rear of camshafts. **Thrust plates are not the same thickness and cannot be interchanged. The intake camshaft uses a wider thrust plate than the exhaust.**
4. Before camshafts can be removed the cam seal must be removed first. **Use care not to damage seal surface of the camshaft.**
5. Using a screwdriver placed against the side of the cam lobe, push the cam out of the head, **Fig. 32**. The cam seal will be pushed out by the cam.
6. Slide the camshaft out of cylinder head using care not to scratch bearing surfaces in the head.
7. Check camshaft lobe height in center (contact area) and on shoulders of lobe. If difference in reading exceeds .010 inch (.25 mm), camshaft should be replaced.
8. Reverse procedure to install, noting the following:
    a. Lubricate camshaft journals with clean engine oil and carefully install camshaft into head.
    b. Install thrust plates and tighten to specifications.
    c. Install new cam seals.

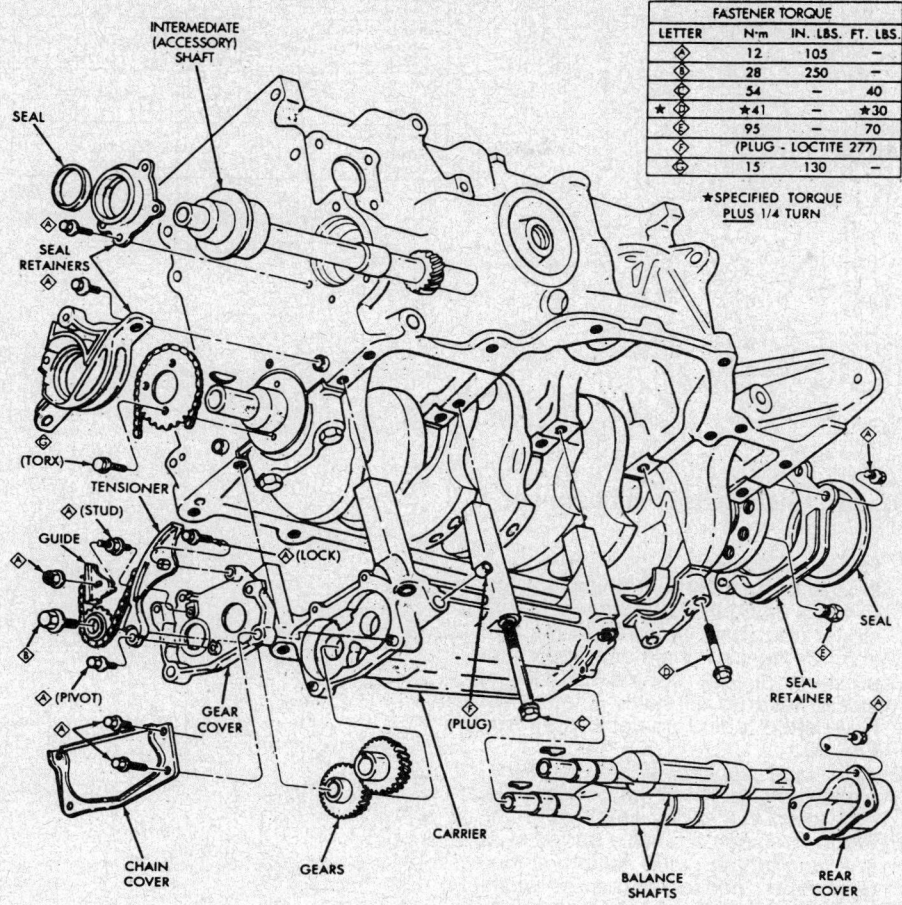

FASTENER TORQUE			
LETTER	N·m	IN. LBS.	FT. LBS.
◇	12	105	—
◇	28	250	—
◇	54	—	40
★ ◇	★41	—	★30
◇	95	—	70
◇	(PLUG - LOCTITE 277)		
◇	15	130	

★SPECIFIED TORQUE
PLUS 1/4 TURN

Fig. 33 Crankshaft, intermediate & balance shaft assemblies.

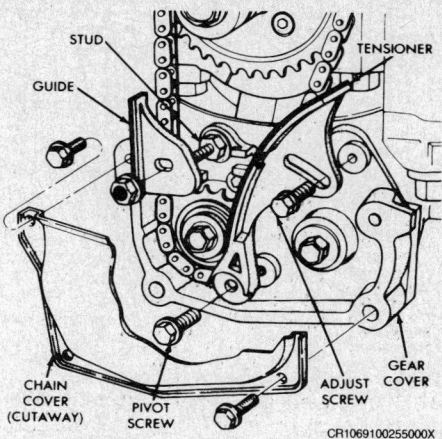

Fig. 34 Chain cover, guide & tensioner removal

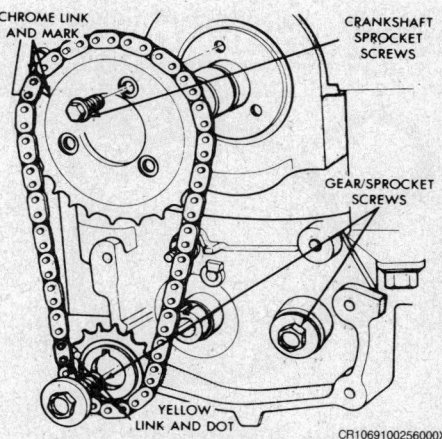

Fig. 35 Drive chain & sprocket removal

BALANCE SHAFT
REPLACE

Some 2.2L/4-135 and 2.5L/4-153 engines are equipped with two balance shafts installed in a carrier attached to the lower crankcase, **Fig. 33**.

The shafts are interconnected through gears to rotate in opposite directions. These gears are driven by a short chain from the crankshaft and rotate at two times crankshaft speed. This counterbalances certain engine reciprocating masses.

1. Replace shaft as follows:
   a. Remove oil pan, oil pickup, timing belt cover, belt, crankshaft belt sprocket and front crankshaft oil seal retainer.
   b. Remove chain cover, guide and tensioner, **Fig. 34**.
   c. Remove balance shaft gear and chain sprocket retaining screws and crankshaft chain sprocket Torx screws, then the chain and sprocket assembly, **Fig. 35**.
   d. Remove double-ended gear cover retaining stud, then the cover and balance shaft gears.
   e. Remove carrier rear cover and balance shafts.
   f. Remove six carrier to crankshaft attaching bolts to separate carrier.

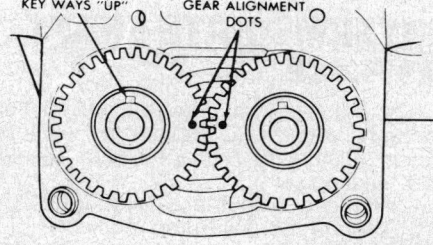

Fig. 36 Gear timing set

   g. Reverse procedure to install, then adjust crankshaft to balance shaft gear timing as described under "Balance Shaft Gear Timing Adjustment" and adjust chain tension as described under "Chain Tension Adjustment" in this section.

2. It is possible to replace carrier assembly with gear cover, gears, balance shafts and rear cover intact. Replace carrier assembly as follows:
   a. Remove chain cover and driven balance shaft chain sprocket screw.
   b. Loosen tensioner pivot and adjusting screws, then move driven balance shaft inboard (through) driven chain sprocket. Sprocket will hang in lower chain loop, **Fig. 33**.
   c. Remove carrier to crankshaft at-

taching bolts and carrier.
   d. Reverse procedure to install, then adjust crankshaft to balance shaft timing as described under "Balance Shaft Gear Timing Adjustment" and adjust chain tension as described under "Chain Tension Adjustment" in this section.

BALANCE SHAFT GEAR TIMING ADJUSTMENT

1. With balance shafts installed in carrier, position carrier on crankshaft and install six attaching bolts, tightening to specifications.
2. Rotate balance shafts until both shaft keyways are parallel to vertical centerline of engine, then install short hub drive gear on sprocket driven shaft. After installation, gear and balance shaft keyways must face up with gear timing marks meshed as shown, **Fig. 36**.
3. Install gear cover and tighten double ended stud/washer fastener to specifications.
4. Install crankshaft sprocket and tighten socket head Torx screws to specifications.
5. Rotate crankshaft until number one cylinder is at top dead center (TDC). The timing marks on chain sprocket

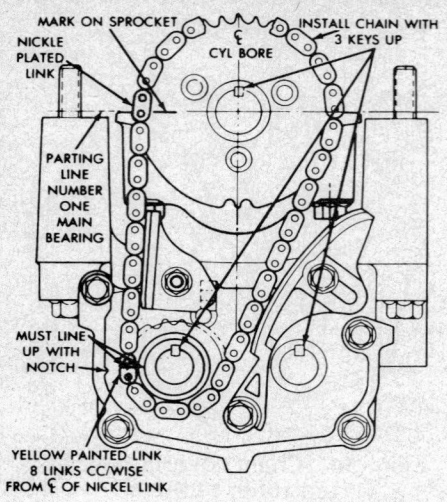

Fig. 37 Balance shaft timing set

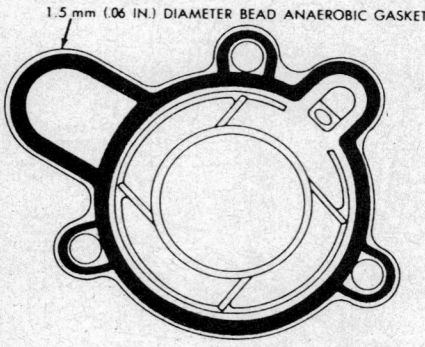

Fig. 40 Intermediate shaft retainer seal

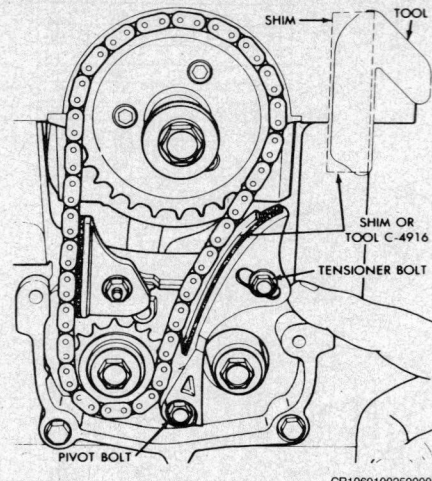

Fig. 38 Chain tension adjustment

Intermediate Shaft Journal and Bushing Sizes		
Intermediate Shaft		
Large Journal	42.670-42.703 mm (1.679-1.681 in.)	
Small Journal	19.670-19.703 mm (.774-.776 in.)	
Bushing Bore Diameter		
Large Bushing	42.720-42.750 mm (1.682-1.683 in.)	
Small Bushing	19.720-19.750 mm (.776-.777 in.)	
Clearance Allowed		
Large	.017/.080 mm (.0006-.003 in.)	
Small	.017-.080 mm (.0006-.003 in.)	

Fig. 39 Intermediate shaft journal specifications.

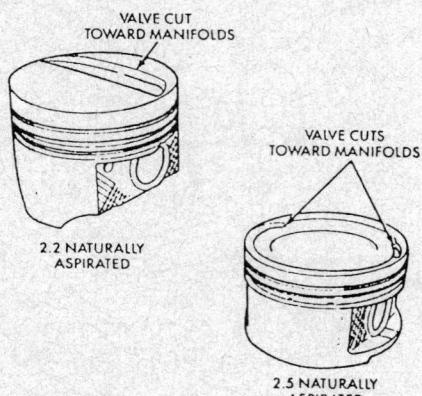

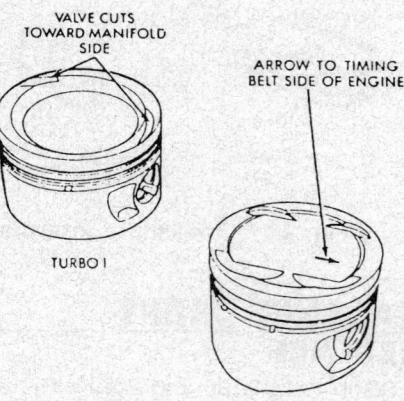

Fig. 41 Piston & connecting rod assembly

should line up with parting line on left side of number one main bearing cap, **Fig. 37.**

6. Place chain over crankshaft sprocket so that nickel plated link of chain is over timing mark on crankshaft sprocket, **Fig. 37.**
7. Place balance shaft sprocket into timing chain so that timing mark on sprocket (yellow dot) mates with yellow painted or nickel plated link on chain.
8. With balance shaft keyways at 12 o'clock, slide balance shaft sprocket onto nose of balance shaft. Balance shaft may have to be pushed in slightly to allow for clearance. **Balance shaft timing is correct if the timing mark on sprocket, painted link and arrow on side of gear cover are aligned.**
9. If sprockets are timed correctly, install balance shaft bolts, tightening to specifications. A wood block placed between crankcase and crankshaft counterbalance will prevent gear rotation.

CHAIN TENSION ADJUSTMENT

1. Install chain tensioner loosely assembled.

2. Place a .039 inch thick by 2.75 inch long shim (adjustment shim tool No. C-4916 or equivalent) between tensioner and chain, push tensioner and shim up against chain and apply firm pressure directly behind adjustment slot to take up all slack. Chain must have shoe radius contact as shown, **Fig. 38.**
3. With load applied, tighten top tensioner bolt first, then the bottom pivot bolt, to specifications. Remove shim.
4. Position guide on double ended stud, ensuring tab on guide fits into slot on gear cover, then install nut and washer assembly and tighten to specifications.
5. Install carrier covers and tighten screws to specifications.

INTERMEDIATE SHAFT REPLACE

On models with conventional ignition systems, remove distributor as outlined under "Distributor, Replace" in the "Electrical" section.
1. Remove oil pump assembly as outlined under "Oil Pump, Replace."
2. Remove intermediate shaft sprocket and seal as outlined under "Timing Belt, Replace."
3. Remove retainer plate attaching screws.
4. Remove retainer.
5. Remove intermediate shaft.
6. Remove intermediate shaft front bushing using tool No. C-4697-2 or equivalent.
7. Remove intermediate shaft rear bushing using tool No. C-4686-2 or equivalent.
8. Measure intermediate shaft. If not within specifications shown in **Fig. 39,** replace parts as needed.
9. Reverse procedure to install, noting the following:
   a. Install rear intermediate shaft bushing using tool No. C-4686-1 or equivalent until tool is flush with block.
   b. Install front intermediate shaft

bushing using tool No. C-4697-1 or equivalent until tool is flush with block.
   c. Lubricate distributor drive gear when installing.
   d. Apply Form-In-Place gasket material as shown in **Fig. 40** and install intermediate shaft retainer.
   e. Refer to "Timing Belt, Replace" for timing of intermediate shaft.

PISTON & ROD ASSEMBLY

When installing piston and rod assembly, valve cut must face toward manifold side of engine, **Fig. 41.** Turbocharged engine pistons will have an arrow or dimple toward front of engine. Oil hole on connecting rod must face timing belt side of engine.

Connecting rod side clearance should be .005-.013 inch.

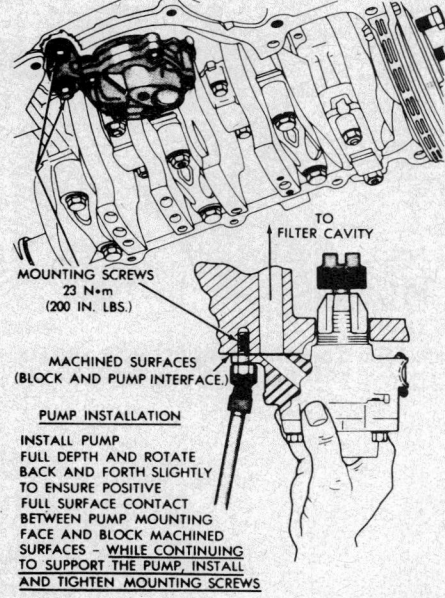

MOUNTING SCREWS
23 N·m
(200 IN. LBS.)

TO FILTER CAVITY

MACHINED SURFACES
(BLOCK AND PUMP INTERFACE.)

PUMP INSTALLATION

INSTALL PUMP FULL DEPTH AND ROTATE BACK AND FORTH SLIGHTLY TO ENSURE POSITIVE FULL SURFACE CONTACT BETWEEN PUMP MOUNTING FACE AND BLOCK MACHINED SURFACES – WHILE CONTINUING TO SUPPORT THE PUMP, INSTALL AND TIGHTEN MOUNTING SCREWS

Fig. 42   Oil pump replacement

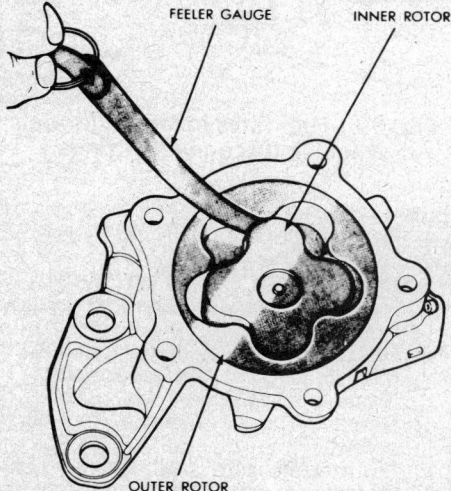

FEELER GAUGE

INNER ROTOR

OUTER ROTOR

Fig. 45   Oil pump rotor clearance check

CRANKSHAFT REAR OIL SEAL

REPLACE

1. Remove transaxle assembly.
2. Remove flywheel or flex plate from rear of crankshaft.
3. Pry out rear seal with a suitable tool. Use care not to nick or damage crankshaft flange seal surface or retainer bore.
4. Reverse procedure to install, noting the following:
   a. Use seal pilot tool C-4681 when installing seal.
   b. Lightly coat seal outside dimension with Loctite Stud N' Bearing Mount or equivalent.

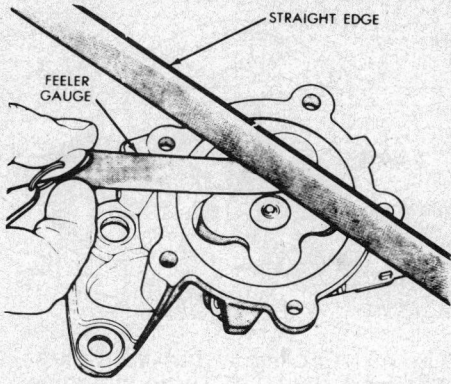

STRAIGHT EDGE

FEELER GAUGE

Fig. 43   Oil pump endplay measurement

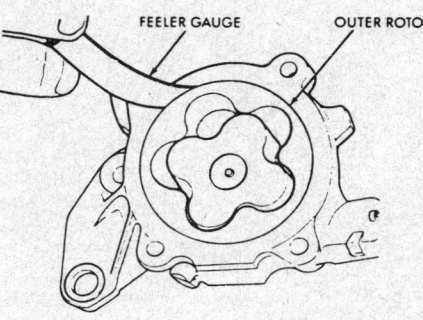

FEELER GAUGE

OUTER ROTOR

Fig. 46   Oil pump outer rotor clearance check

OIL PUMP

REPLACE

1. Remove oil pan.
2. Remove screw on pump cover retaining pick-up tube on oil pump then the pick-up tube.
3. Remove two screws securing oil pump to cylinder block assembly then the pump, **Fig. 42.**
4. Apply suitable sealant to pump to block interface.
5. Lubricate oil pump rotor and shaft and the drive gear.
6. Turn crankshaft and intermediate shaft until markings on sprockets line up, **Fig. 17. Slot in oil pump shaft must be parallel to center line of crankshaft when intermediate shaft and crankshaft are properly timed.**
7. Install pump full depth and rotate back and forth slightly to ensure proper positioning and alignment through full surface contact of pump and block machined interface surfaces. **Pump must be held in fully seated position while installing screws.**
8. Tighten attaching screws to specifications.

OIL PUMP SERVICE

1. Measure the following oil pump clearances:
   a. Endplay, **Fig. 43**, should be .0010–.0035 inch.

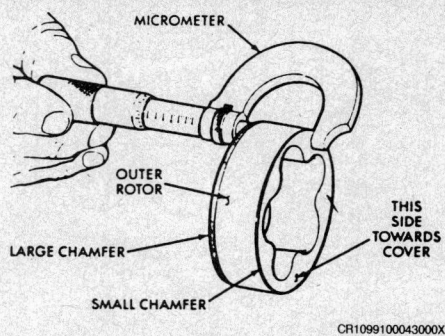

MICROMETER

OUTER ROTOR

LARGE CHAMFER

THIS SIDE TOWARDS COVER

SMALL CHAMFER

Fig. 44   Oil pump outer rotor thickness measurement

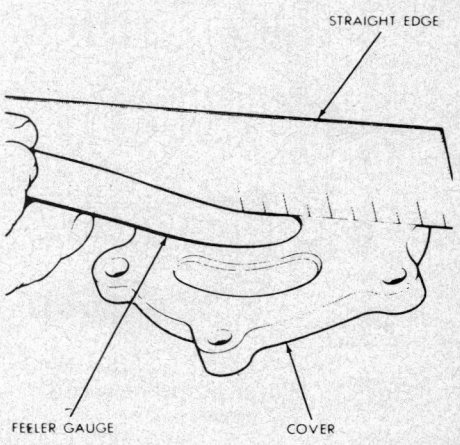

STRAIGHT EDGE

FEELER GAUGE

COVER

Fig. 47   Oil pump cover clearance check

b. Outer rotor specifications, **Fig. 44.** Thickness should be .9435 inch minimum and 2.469 inches minimum diameter. Install outer rotor with chamfered edge in pump body.
c. Clearance between rotors, **Fig. 45**, should be .008 inch maximum.
d. Outer rotor clearance, **Fig. 46**, should be .014 inch maximum.
e. Oil pump cover, **Fig. 47**, clearance should be .003 inch maximum.
f. Oil pressure relief valve spring free length should be 1.95 inches.

BELT TENSION DATA

Belt	New Lbs.	Used Lbs.
1992①		
Air Cond.	125	80
Alternator	130	80
Power Steer.	105	80
1993-95①		
Air Cond.	135	80
Alternator	135	80
Power Steer.	105	80

① —Except 2.2L/4-135 Turbo III engine (VIN A).

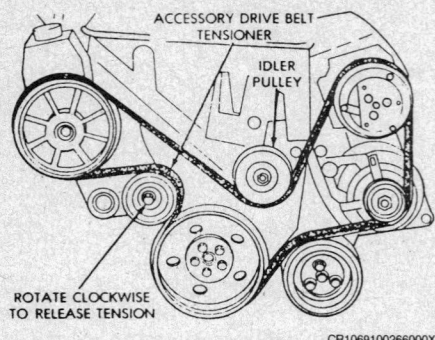

Fig. 48 Accessory drive belt routing. 2.2L/4-135 Turbo III engine (VIN A)

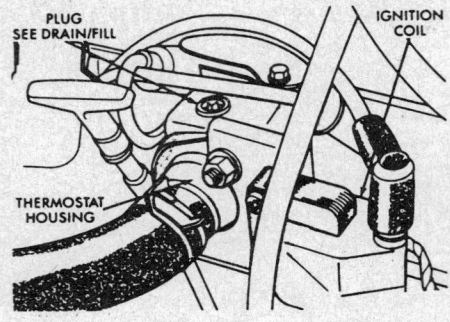

Fig. 49 Cooling system vent plug. Except 2.2L/4-135 Turbo III engine (VIN A)

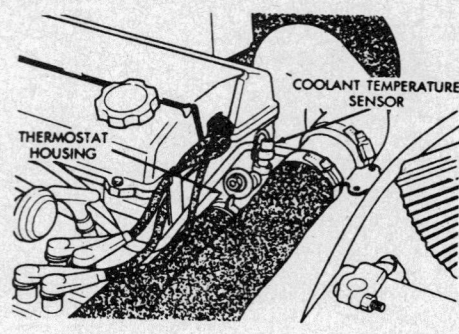

Fig. 50 Coolant temperature sensor. 2.2L/4-135 Turbo III engine (VIN A)

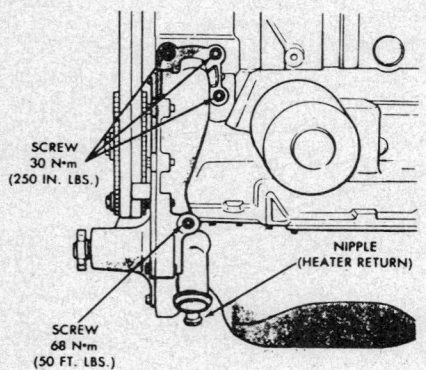

Fig. 51 Water pump installed view

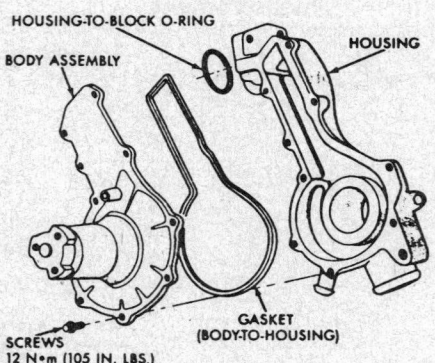

Fig. 52 Water pump components

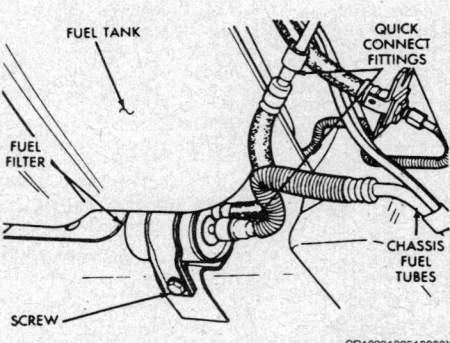

Fig. 53 Fuel filter location. Models w/quick disconnect fittings

SERPENTINE DRIVE BELT

BELT REPLACEMENT

2.2L/4-135 Turbo III Engine (VIN A)

1. Raise vehicle on hoist.
2. Remove right front splash shield.
3. Release tension by rotating tensioner clockwise, **Fig. 48.**
4. Reverse procedure to install.

BELT ROUTING

2.2L/4-135 Turbo III Engine (VIN A)

Refer to **Fig. 48** for serpentine drive belt routing.

COOLING SYSTEM BLEED

The cooling system on except Turbo III engines requires venting by removal of the plug on top of the water box, **Fig. 49.** On the Turbo III engines, venting requires removing the coolant temperature sensor on top of the thermostat housing, **Fig. 50.**

Fill the system with the recommended 50 percent mixture of antifreeze and water until mixture reaches the vent holes, then tighten the vent plug, on except Turbo III engines, or coolant temperature sensor, on Turbo III engines, to specifications. Continue to fill cooling system until full.

THERMOSTAT
REPLACE

1. Drain coolant system down to thermostat level.
2. Remove thermostat housing bolts and housing.
3. Remove thermostat, discard gasket and clean both gasket sealing surfaces.
4. Reverse procedure to install. Dip new gasket in water and ensure to center thermostat in water box on gasket.

WATER PUMP
REPLACE

1. Disconnect battery ground cable.
2. Drain cooling system, and remove upper radiator hose.
3. Remove A/C compressor from mounting brackets and position aside with refrigerant lines attached, if equipped.
4. Remove alternator.
5. Disconnect lower radiator hose, bypass hose. Remove four water pump to engine attaching screws and water pump, **Figs. 51 and 52.**
6. Reverse procedure to install.

RADIATOR
REPLACE

Do not attempt to remove radiator cap or service cooling system while engine is hot.

1. Disconnect battery ground cables.
2. Drain cooling system.
3. Remove hose clamps and hoses.
4. Remove coolant reserve system tank to filler neck tube.
5. Disconnect fan electrical connector, then remove fan and fan support.
6. Remove fan shroud, if equipped.
7. Remove upper radiator mounting screws.
8. **On models with A/C,** remove condenser mounting screws at top of radiator
9. **On all models,** Carefully lift radiator out, to avoid damage to cooling fins or water tubes.
10. Reverse procedure to install, refilling cooling system with suitable coolant.

FUEL PUMP
REPLACE

1. Relieve fuel pump pressure, refer to "Precautions" for proper procedure, then disconnect battery ground cable.
2. Remove fuel tank filler cap, then fuel filler tube to quarter panel attaching screws.
3. Raise and support vehicle, then remove draft tube cap on sending unit and siphon fuel from tank.
4. Disconnect all fuel lines and electrical connections to fuel tank.
5. Place suitable jack under fuel tank, then loosen retaining strap attaching bolts and lower tank from vehicle.
6. Loosen lock ring attaching fuel pump

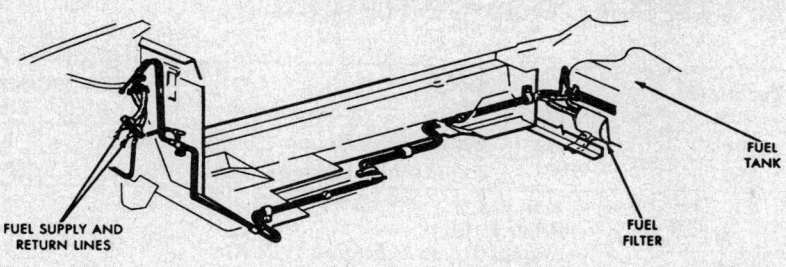

FUEL SUPPLY AND RETURN LINES

FUEL TANK

FUEL FILTER

CR1029102519000X

Fig. 54 Fuel filter location. Models less quick disconnect fittings

using brass drift and hammer by gently tapping lock ring sideways, then remove fuel pump and O-ring from tank.

7. Reverse procedure to install. Do not overtighten O-ring. **Torque** fuel strap nuts to 21 ft. lbs.

FUEL FILTER
REPLACE
MODELS w/QUICK DISCONNECT FITTINGS

1. Release fuel system pressure as outlined under "Precautions."
2. Remove fuel filter retaining screw and remove filter assembly from mounting plate, **Fig. 53**.
3. Wrap a shop tower around hoses fittings to absorb excess fuel.
4. Remove quick disconnect fittings at filter and supply tube.
5. Remove filter and discard clamps.
6. Reverse procedure to install, testing system for leaks.

MODELS LESS QUICK DISCONNECT FITTINGS

1. Release fuel system pressure as outlined under "Precautions."
2. Remove fuel filter retaining screw and remove filter assembly from mounting plate, **Fig. 54**.
3. Loosen outlet hose clamp on filter and inlet hose clamp on rear fuel tube.
4. Wrap a shop tower around hoses to absorb excess fuel.
5. Remove filter and discard clamps.
6. Reverse procedure to install, testing system for leaks.

VALVE TIMING

Engine Liter/CID	Year	Degrees ①			
		Intake		Exhaust	
		Opens	Closes ⑤	Opens ④	Closes ③
2.2L/4-135	1992-95	0 ②	56	44	8
2.2L/4-135 Turbo III	1992-93	25 ③	35	16	7.5
2.5L/4-153	1992-95	4 ②	60	40	12
2.5L/4-153 Turbo	1992	8 ③	56	40	8

①—Valve opening specification.
②—Before Top Dead Center.
③—After Top Dead Center.
④—Before Bottom Dead Center.
⑤—After Bottom Dead Center.

TIGHTENING SPECIFICATIONS

Year	Component	Torque/Ft. Lbs.
1992–95 —Cont'd	Balance Shaft Carrier To Block Bolt	40
	Balance Shaft Chain Snubber Nut	105 ①
	Balance Shaft Chain Snubber Stud & Washer	105 ①
	Balance Shaft Chain Tensioner Adjustment Screw	105 ①
	Balance Shaft Chain Tensioner Screw	105 ①
	Balance Shaft Front Chain Cover Screw	105 ①
	Balance Shaft Gear & Sprocket	250 ①
	Balance Shaft Gear Cover Screw	105 ①
	Balance Shaft Rear Cover Screw	105 ①
	Balance Shaft Sprocket To Crankshaft Torx Drive Cap Screw	130 ①
	Camshaft Bearing Cap Bolt	215 ①
	Camshaft Bearing Cap Nut ③	165 ①
	Camshaft Sprocket Bolt ③	65
	Camshaft Sprocket Bolt ⑦	47
	Camshaft Thrust Plate Retaining Nut ⑦	72 ①
	Connecting Rod Bearing Cap Nut ④	40 ④
	Connecting Rod Bearing Cap Nut ⑦	50
	Crankshaft Sprocket Bolt ③	90
	Crankshaft Sprocket Bolt ⑦	80
	Cylinder Head Bolt	②

Year	Component	Torque/Ft. Lbs.
1992–95	Cylinder Head Cover Bolt	105 ①
	Exhaust Manifold Nut ③	200 ①
	Exhaust Manifold Studs ⑦	210 ①
	Front Crankshaft Oil Seal Retainer Screw	105 ①
	Intake Manifold Bolt	200 ①
	Intermediate Shaft Retainer Screw	105 ①
	Intermediate Shaft Sprocket Bolt ⑦	53
	Intermediate Shaft Sprocket Bolt ③	65
	Lower Timing Belt Cover Screw ③	40 ①
	Lower Timing Belt Cover ⑦	72 ①
	Main Bearing Cap Bolt	30 ④
	Oil Pan Drain Plug	240 ①
	Oil Pan Screw ③	⑤
	Oil Pan Bolts ⑦	⑥
	Oil Pump Cover Screw	105 ①
	Oil Pump Mounting Screw	200 ①
	Oil Pump Strainer To Cover Screw	250 ①
	Oil Pump Strainer To Main Cap Screw	105 ①
	Rear Crankshaft Oil Seal Retainer Screw	105 ①
	Spark Plugs ③	26
	Spark Plugs ⑦	220 ①
	Rocker Arm Shaft Retaining Bolts ⑦	210 ①

Continued

TIGHTENING SPECIFICATIONS-Continued

Year	Component	Torque/Ft. Lbs.
1992-95 —Cont'd	Rocker Cover Bolts ⑦	115 ①
	Thermostat Housing Screw ③	250 ①
	Thermostat Housing Bolts ⑦	210 ①
	Timing Belt Idler Pulley Bolt ⑦	39
	Timing Belt Tensioner Pulley Bolt ⑦	39
	Upper Timing Belt Cover Screw	40 ①

Year	Component	Torque/Ft. Lbs.
1992-95 —Cont'd	Water Pump Housing Screw (Lower)	40
	Water Pump Housing Screw (Upper)	250 ①

① —Inch lbs.
② —Refer to text.
③ —Except Turbo III Engine (VIN A).
④ —After reaching specified torque, turn an additional ¼ turn.
⑤ —M6 screws, 105 inch lbs.; M8 screws, 200 inch lbs.
⑥ —M6 screws, 220 inch lbs.; M8 screws, 260 inch lbs.
⑦ —2.2L/4-135 Turbo III Engine (VIN A).

3.0L/V6-181 Engine

NOTE: On Air Bag Equipped Models, Refer To "Air Bag System Precautions" Located In The Front Of This Manual For System Disarming & Arming Procedures.

INDEX

PRECAUTIONS

AIR BAG SYSTEMS

Refer to "Air Bag System Precautions" in the front of this manual for system disarming and arming procedures.

FUEL SYSTEM PRESSURE RELEASE

1. Loosen fuel tank filler cap.
2. Disconnect injector wiring harness and connect a suitable jumper wire between ground terminal No. 1 and a suitable ground.
3. Connect a second jumper wire between terminal No. 2 of injector harness and battery positive for no longer than five seconds.
4. Remove jumper wires.

ENGINE MOUNT

REPLACE

The engine mounts incorporate slotted bolt holes to permit side to side positioning of the engine thereby affecting the length of the driveshaft. Failure to properly position engine may result in extensive damage to the engine or driveshafts.

RIGHT

1. Remove right engine mount insulator vertical fasteners from frame rail, **Fig. 1.**
2. Remove load on engine mount by supporting engine and transmission assembly with a floor jack.
3. Remove through bolt from insulator assembly then the insulator.
4. Reverse procedure to install, noting the following:
   a. Tighten bolts to specification.
   b. Adjust engine mount insulator as outlined under "Engine Mount Insulator Adjust."

LEFT

1. Raise and support vehicle and remove inner splash shield.
2. Support transaxle with a transmission jack.
3. Remove insulator through bolt then the transaxle mount bolts and mount, **Fig. 1.**
4. Reverse procedure to install, noting the following:
   a. Ensure slide tube is seated into rail bracket guides.
   b. Tighten bolts to specifications.
   c. Adjust engine mount as outlined under "Engine Mount Insulator Ad-

just."

FRONT

1. Support engine and transaxle assembly so engine will not rotate.
2. Remove insulator through bolt, **Fig. 1.**
3. Remove front engine mount bracket to crossmember screws and nuts then the insulator.
4. Reverse procedure to install, noting the following:
   a. Tighten bolts to specifications.
   b. Adjust engine mount as outlined under "Engine Mount Insulator Adjust."

ENGINE MOUNT INSULATOR

ADJUST

Insulator location on frame rail (right side) and transaxle bracket (left side) are adjustable in relation to driveshaft assembly length. Check and reposition right engine mount insulator (left insulator is a self adjusting floating type), under the following conditions:
1. Driveshaft distress.
2. Any front end structural damage.
3. Insulator replacement.
4. Engine removal.

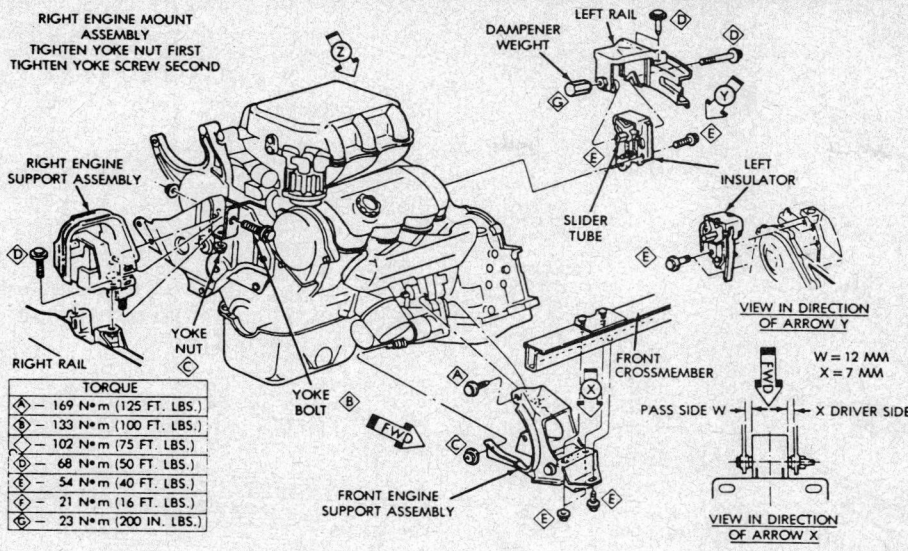

Fig. 1   Engine mount replacement

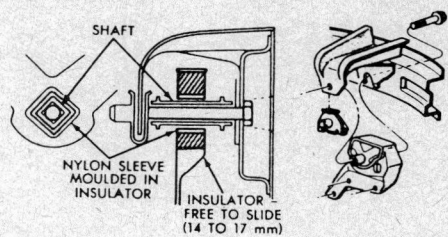

Fig. 2   Throttle cable

When positioning the engine, check driveshaft length as outlined in the "Front Wheel Drive Axle" unit repair section under "Driveshaft Length, Adjust." Failure to properly position engine may result in extensive damage to the engine or driveshafts.

16. Mark position of right engine mount insulator on right rail supports, then remove insulator to rails screws.
17. Remove front engine mount through bolt and nut.
18. Remove left engine mount insulator through bolt or insulator bracket to transaxle screws.
19. Carefully remove engine from vehicle.
20. Reverse procedure to install. Tighten flex plate and axle to block bolts to specifications.

ENGINE
REPLACE

1. Release fuel system pressure as outlined under "Precautions."
2. Disconnect battery ground cable.
3. Mark hood hinge locations and remove hood.
4. Drain cooling system, then disconnect all electrical connections.
5. Remove coolant hoses, radiator and fan assembly.
6. Disconnect fuel lines, then unhook the accelerator cable.
7. Remove air cleaner assembly, then raise and support vehicle.
8. Drain engine oil.
9. Remove air conditioning compressor mounting bolts and position compressor aside.
10. Disconnect exhaust pipe from manifold, then remove transaxle inspection cover and mark position of flex plate to torque converter.
11. Remove flex plate to torque converter attaching screws and clamp bottom of converter housing to prevent converter from moving.
12. Remove power steering attaching bolts and position pump aside.
13. Remove two lower transaxle to block screws, then the starter. Lower vehicle to ground.
14. Install suitable transmission holding fixture, then install engine lifting hoist and support engine.
15. Remove upper transaxle case to

block bolts.

INTAKE MANIFOLD
REPLACE

The air intake plenum is removed as an assembly with the intake manifold.
1. Disconnect battery negative cable, then relieve fuel system pressure as outlined under "Precautions."
2. Drain cooling system, then remove air cleaner to throttle body hose.
3. Remove throttle cable and transaxle kickdown linkage, Fig. 2, then remove all wiring connectors and vacuum hoses from throttle body.
4. Remove PCV and brake booster hoses, and EGR tube flange from air intake plenum.
5. Mark and remove all necessary wiring and vacuum connectors.
6. Remove fuel hoses from fuel rail.
7. Remove eight intake plenum to intake manifold hold-down bolts and remove plenum.
8. Disconnect fuel injector wiring harness, then remove fuel pressure regulator and fuel rail attaching bolts and lift assembly from vehicle.
9. Separate radiator hose from thermostat housing, then heater hose from heater pipe.
10. Remove eight nuts and washers and remove intake manifold, Fig. 3.

11. Reverse procedure to install, noting the following:
   a. Tighten intake manifold in several steps to specifications in sequence shown in Fig. 4.
   b. Ensure injector holes are clean and lubricate injector O-rings with a drop of clean oil before installation.
   c. Tighten fuel rail retaining bolts and fuel regulator retaining bolts to specifications.
   d. Tighten intake plenum bolts to specifications according to sequence shown in Fig. 5.

EXHAUST MANIFOLD
REPLACE

1. Release fuel system pressure as outlined under "Precautions."
2. Raise and support vehicle, then disconnect exhaust pipe from rear exhaust manifold.
3. Disconnect EGR tube from rear manifold, then the oxygen sensor lead wire.
4. Disconnect exhaust crossover pipe from manifolds, Fig. 6, then remove rear manifold to cylinder head retaining bolts and the manifold.
5. Lower vehicle, then remove heat shield from front manifold.
6. Remove crossover pipe to front exhaust manifold bolts, then the front exhaust manifold retaining nuts and manifold.
7. Reverse procedure to install, noting the following:
   a. Tighten rear exhaust manifold, exhaust pipe, crossover pipe and front exhaust manifold to specifications.

CYLINDER HEAD
REPLACE

1. Release fuel system pressure as outlined under "Precautions."
2. Remove camshaft as outlined under "Camshaft, Replace."
3. Remove rocker arm assemblies as outlined under "Rocker Arms, Replace."
4. Remove intake manifold, exhaust manifold and intake plenum as outlined under "Intake Manifold, Replace" and "Exhaust Manifold, Replace."
5. Disconnect and remove distributor as outlined under "Distributor, Replace" in the "Electrical" section.
6. Disconnect crossover pipe.
7. Remove cylinder head bolts in se-

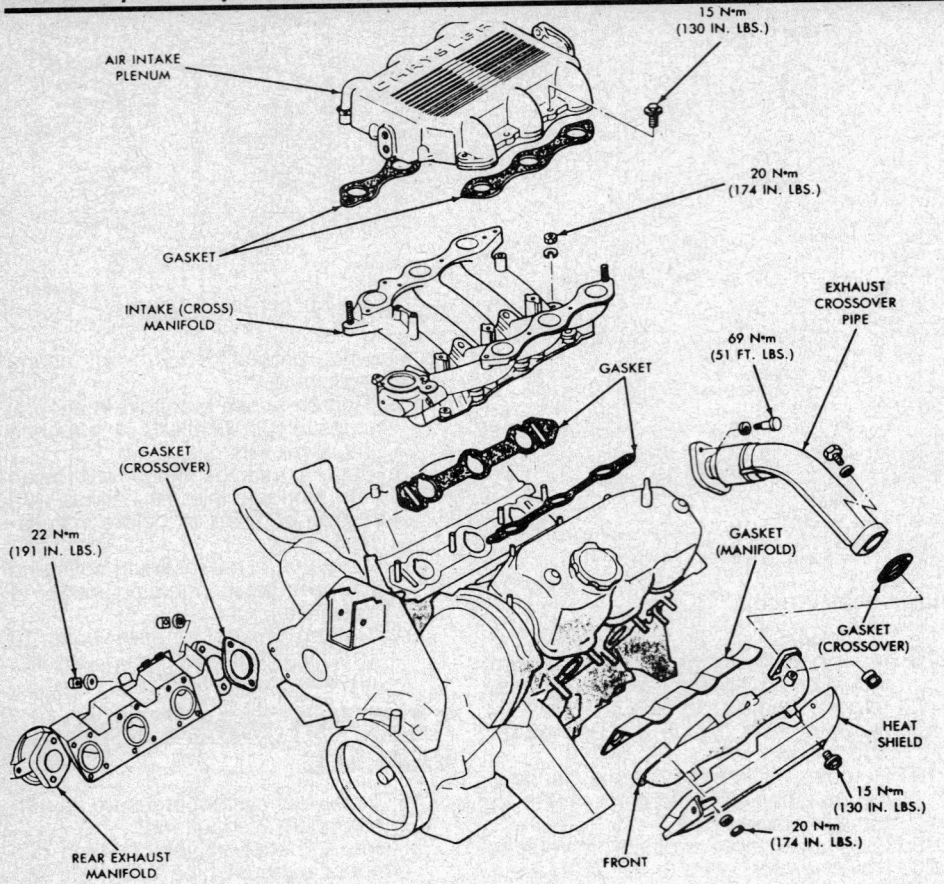

Fig. 3   Intake & exhaust manifolds

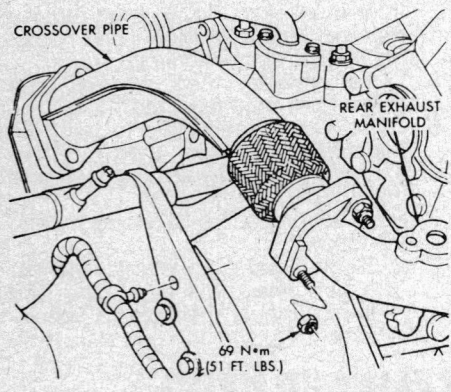

Fig. 6   Crossover pipe

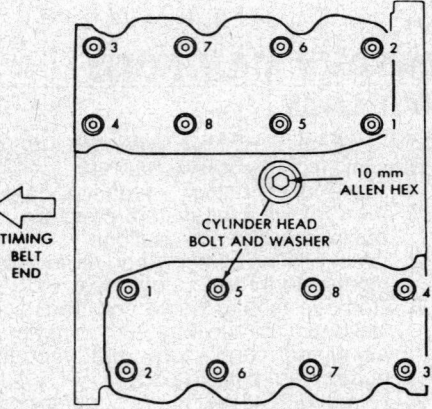

Fig. 7   Cylinder head bolt removal sequence

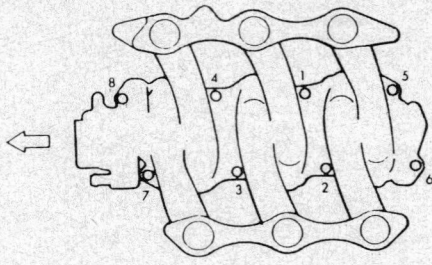

Fig. 4   Intake manifold nut torque sequence

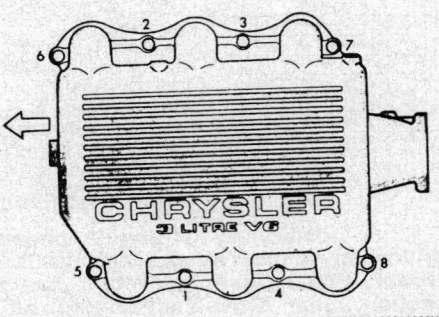

Fig. 5   Intake plenum torque sequence

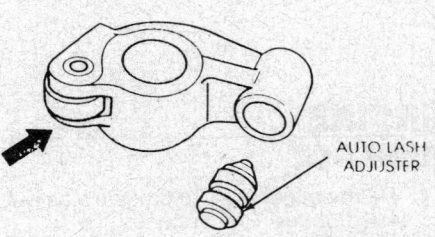

Fig. 8   Auto lash adjuster

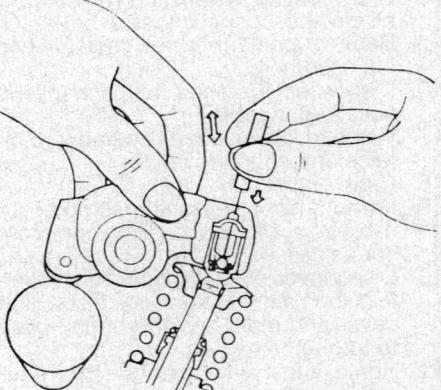

Fig. 9   Auto lash adjuster check

quence shown in **Fig. 7**, then remove cylinder head.

8. Inspect cylinder head before installing. Cylinder head must be flat within .002 inch.

9. Inspect auto lash adjuster, **Fig. 8**, as follows:
   a. Insert a small wire through the air bleed hole in the rocker arm, **Fig. 9**, and very lightly push the auto adjuster ball check down.
   b. While lightly holding check ball down, move rocker up and down to check for freeplay.
   c. If no freeplay is present, replace

adjuster. **Do not disassemble the auto lash adjuster.**

10. If valve spring replacement is necessary, use a suitable valve spring compressor tool to compress valve spring and remove spring retainer locks, retainer, valve spring, spring seat and valve stem seal.

11. Reverse procedure to install. Tighten head bolts to specifications in two or three steps in sequence shown in **Fig. 10**.

ROCKER ARMS
REPLACE

1. Remove rocker arm shaft as outlined under "Camshaft, Replace."
2. Inspect rocker arm mounting portion of shafts for wear or damage.

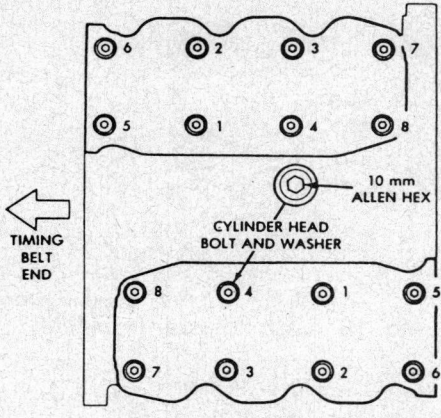

Fig. 10   Cylinder head bolt tightening sequence

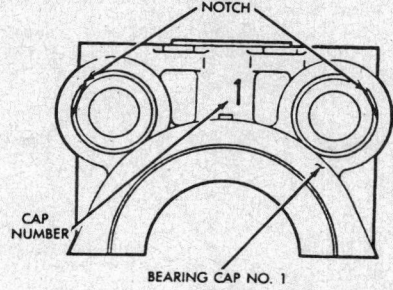

Fig. 11   No. 1 camshaft bearing cap

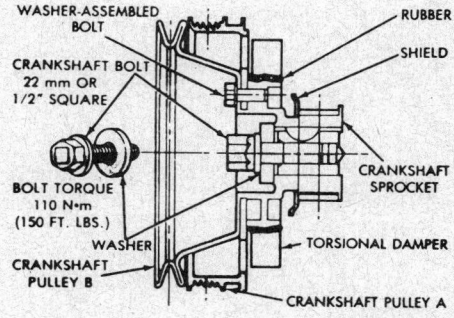

Fig. 14   Crankshaft pulley assembly

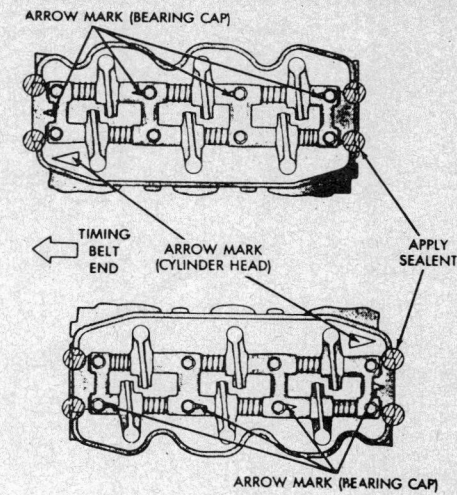

Fig. 12   Camshaft bearing cap installation

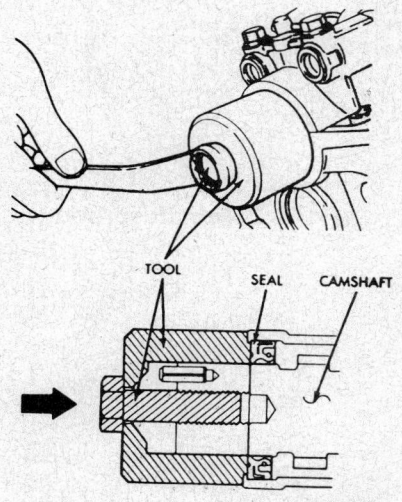

Fig. 13   Camshaft oil seal

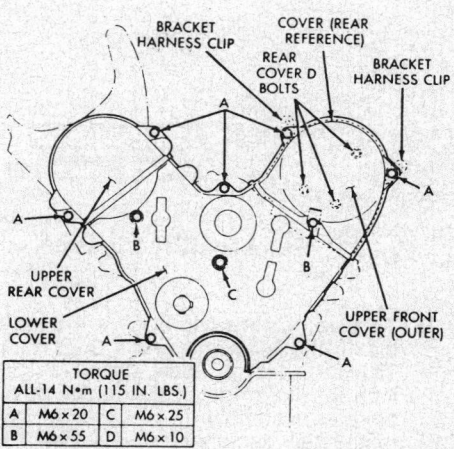

Fig. 16   Timing belt cover

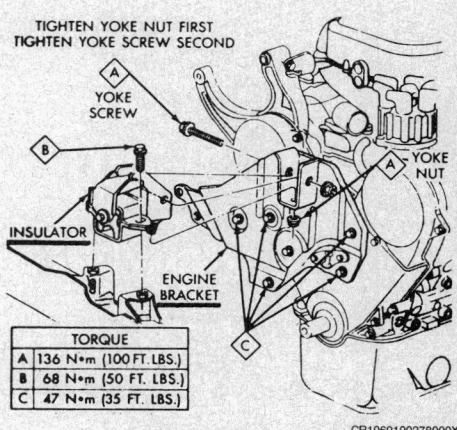

Fig. 15   Right engine mount & bracket

3. Check oil holes for clogging.
4. Install rocker shafts into No. 1 bearing cap with notches positioned as shown in **Fig. 11,** then install bolts to retain shafts.
5. Install rocker arms, bearing caps and springs, in order removed, onto shafts.
6. Install bolts in No. 4 bearing cap to retain assembly.
7. Lubricate camshaft journals and cams with engine oil before installation, then apply sealant as shown in **Fig. 12.**
8. Install rocker assemblies with arrow mark on bearing cap and mark on cylinder head pointing in the same direction, **Fig. 12.**
9. **Torque** bearing cap bolts to 85 inch lbs. in the following order; 3, 2, 1, 4.
10. Repeat step 9 and **torque** to 180 inch lbs., then install distributor drive adapter assembly.
11. Install new camshaft oil seal, **Fig. 13,** then a new end plug with tool No. MB998306 or equivalent.

TIMING BELT
REPLACE

1. Remove crankshaft drive pulleys and torsional damper, **Fig. 14.**
2. Place a jack under engine to support and slightly raise, then remove engine mount bracket, **Fig. 15.**
3. Remove timing belt cover, **Fig. 16,** then mark belt running direction for re-installation.
4. Loosen timing belt tensioner, then remove belt and crankshaft sprocket flange shield.
5. Place timing belt on crankshaft sprocket first. Keep belt tight on tension side and install belt on radiator side of camshaft sprocket.

6. Install belt on water pump pulley and then on rear camshaft sprocket and timing belt tensioner.
7. Rotate engine at the front camshaft sprocket, turning in opposite direction to tension the tension side of belt, then check that all timing marks line up, **Fig. 17.**
8. Install crankshaft sprocket flange, loosen tensioner bolt and turn crankshaft two full turns in clockwise direction.
9. Recheck timing marks, then tighten tensioner lock bolt to specifications.
10. Reassemble belt cover, brackets and pulleys in reverse order of removal.

CAMSHAFT
REPLACE

1. Release fuel system pressure as outlined under "Precautions."
2. Install auto lash adjuster retainer tool No. MD998443 or equivalent, **Fig. 18.**
3. Remove distributor extension, then loosen camshaft bearing caps without removing bolts from caps.
4. Remove rocker arm, rocker shafts and bearing cap as an assembly.

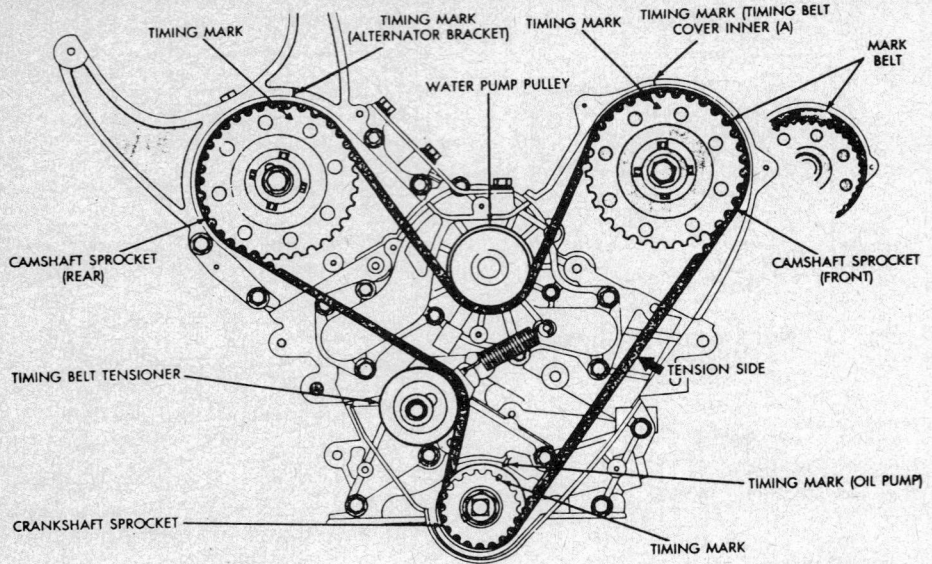

Fig. 17   Timing belt & pulleys

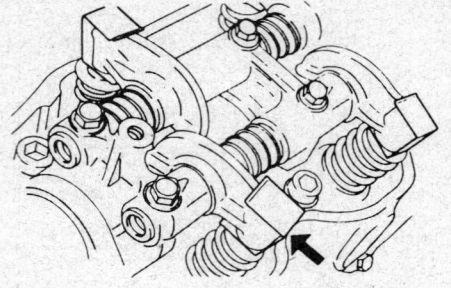

Fig. 18   Lash adjuster retainers

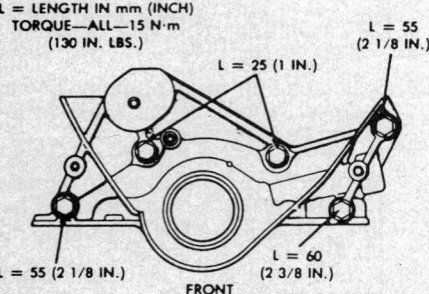

Fig. 20   Piston & rod assembly

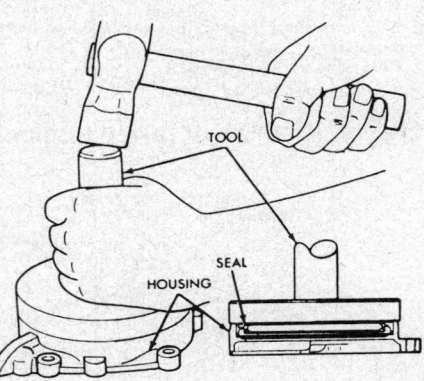

Fig. 21   Crankshaft rear oil seal

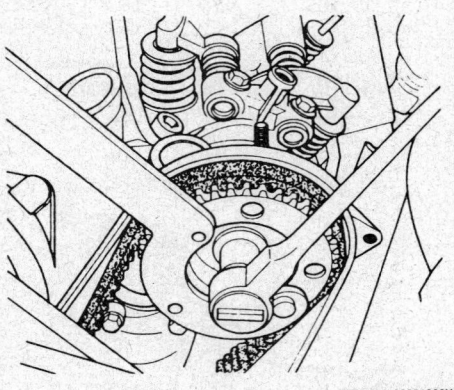

Fig. 19   Camshaft sprocket

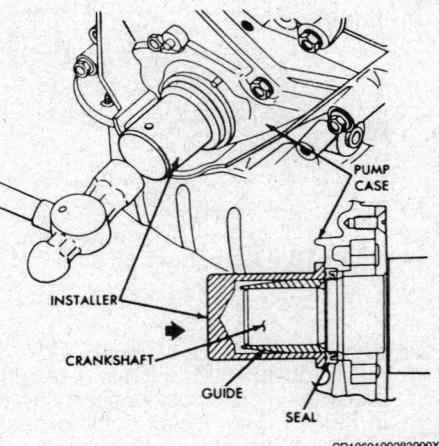

Fig. 22   Crankshaft front oil seal

Fig. 23   Oil pump assembly

5. If camshaft sprocket removal is necessary, hold camshaft with sprocket holding tool No. MB990775 or equivalent, **Fig. 19**, and remove sprocket bolt.
6. Inspect camshaft for scored journals, or any abnormal wear. Cam lobe height should be 1.604-1.624 inch.
7. Lubricate camshaft journals and cams with engine oil before installation, then install bearing cap ends with sealant applied as shown in **Fig. 12**.
8. Install rocker arm shaft assemblies with arrow mark on bearing cap and mark on cylinder head pointing in the same direction, **Fig. 12**.

9. **Torque** bearing cap bolts to 85 inch lbs. in the following order: 3, 2, 1, 4. **Torque** again in same order to 180 inch lbs., then install distributor drive adapter assembly.
10. Install new camshaft oil seal, **Fig. 13**, then a new end plug with tool No. MB998306 or equivalent.

PISTON & ROD ASSEMBLY

When installing piston and rod assemblies, cylinders 1, 3 and 5 should have the "R" facing forward, and cylinders 2, 4 and 6 should have the "L" facing forward. The connecting rod must always have the "72" mark facing forward, **Fig. 20**.

Connecting rod bearing clearance should be .001-.003 inch and rod side clearance should be .004-.010 inch.

CRANKSHAFT SEAL
REPLACE

Refer to **Figs. 21 and 22** for seal removal and installation.

OIL PUMP
REPLACE

1. Remove accessory drive belt as outlined under "Serpentine Drive Belt."
2. Remove timing belt as outlined under "Timing Belt, Replace," then the crankshaft pulley.
3. Remove five retaining bolts holding oil pump to block, **Fig. 23**.
4. Reverse procedure to install, noting the following:
   a. Install pump with proper length bolts in correct position.
   b. Tighten bolts to specifications, **Fig. 23**.

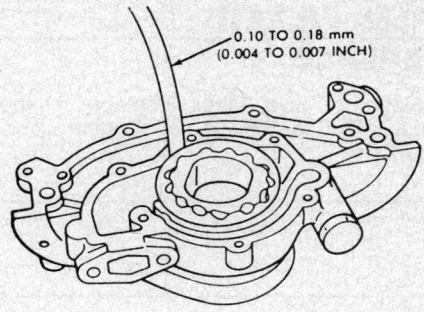

Fig. 24 Oil pump rotor to case clearance

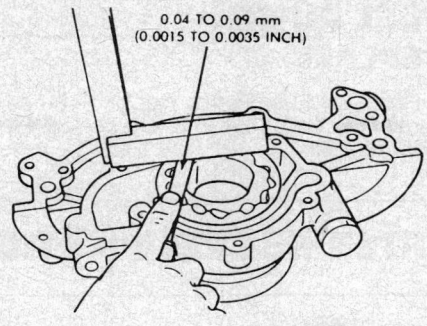

Fig. 25 Oil pump side clearance

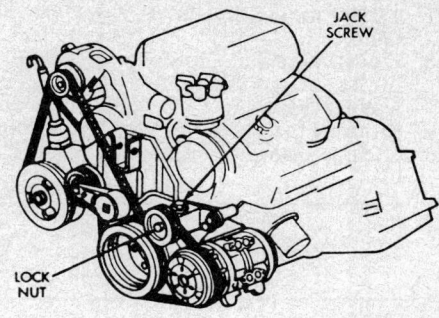

Fig. 26 A/C belt routing

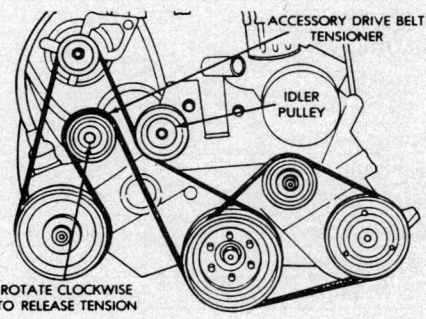

Fig. 27 Alternator & power steering belt routing

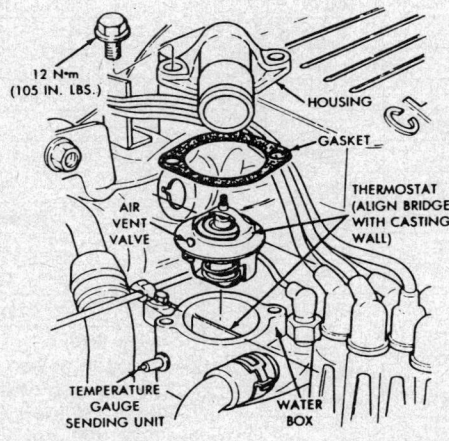

Fig. 28 Thermostat assembly

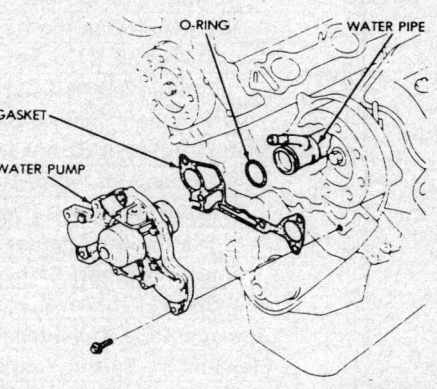

Fig. 29 Water pump replacement

OIL PUMP SERVICE

Check pump condition and perform checks according to **Figs. 24 and 25.**

SERPENTINE DRIVE BELT

BELT ROUTING

Refer to **Figs. 26 and 27** for drive belt routing.

BELT REPLACEMENT

Air Conditioning

1. Loosen adjusting locknut, then turn jack-screw, **Fig. 26,** counterclockwise to reduce belt tension and remove belt.
2. When reinstalling belt, adjust belt tension to 5/16 inch deflection between pulleys.

Alternator & Power Steering

1. **On 1992-93 models,** rotate tensioner counterclockwise to release tensioner pressure to remove or install belt, **Fig. 27.**

COOLING SYSTEM BLEED

These engines do not require a specified bleed procedure. After filling cooling system, run engine to operating temperature with radiator/pressure cap off. Air will then be automatically bled through cap opening.

THERMOSTAT
REPLACE

1. Drain coolant system down to thermostat level.
2. Remove thermostat housing bolts and housing.
3. Remove thermostat, discard gasket and clean both gasket sealing surfaces.
4. Reverse procedure to install, noting the following:
   a. Center thermostat in water box pocket.
   b. Ensure flange is seated correctly in the countersunk portion of intake manifold water box, **Fig. 28.**
   c. Install new gasket and housing.

WATER PUMP
REPLACE

The 3.0L/V6-181 engine water pump bolts directly to the engine block, using a gasket for pump to block sealing, **Fig. 29.** The water pump is driven by the timing belt and is serviced as a unit.

1. Disconnect battery ground cable.
2. Remove crankshaft drive pulleys and torsional damper, **Fig. 14.**
3. Place a jack under engine to support and slightly raise engine, then remove engine mount bracket, **Fig. 15.**
4. Remove timing belt cover, **Fig. 16,** then mark belt running direction for reinstallation.

5. Loosen timing belt tensioner, then remove belt and crankshaft sprocket flange shield.
6. Drain cooling system.
7. Remove water pump mounting bolts.
8. Separate water pump from water inlet pipe, **Fig. 29,** then remove water pump.
9. Reverse procedure to install, noting the following:
   a. Use a new O-ring on water inlet pipe.
   b. Tighten water pump mounting bolts to specifications.
   c. Refer to procedure outlined under "Timing Belt, Replace" for timing belt installation and tensioning procedure.

RADIATOR
REPLACE

Do not attempt to remove radiator cap or service cooling system while engine is hot.
1. Disconnect battery ground cable.
2. Drain cooling system.
3. Remove hose clamps and hoses.
4. Remove coolant reserve system tank to filler neck tube.
5. Disconnect fan electrical connector, then remove fan and fan support.
6. Remove fan shroud, if equipped.
7. Remove upper radiator mounting screws.
8. **On models with A/C,** remove con-

denser mounting screws at top of radiator

9. **On all models,** Carefully lift radiator out, to avoid damage to cooling fins or water tubes.
10. Reverse procedure to install, refilling cooling system with suitable coolant.

FUEL PUMP
REPLACE

Refer to "Fuel Pump, Replace" procedure in the "2.2L/4-135 & 2.5L/4-153 Engine" chapter.

FUEL FILTER
REPLACE

Refer to "Fuel Filter, Replace" in the "2.2L/4-135 & 2.5L/4-153 Engine" section.

TIGHTENING SPECIFICATIONS

Year	Component	Torque/Ft. Lbs.	Year	Component	Torque/Ft. Lbs.
1992–95	Alternator Bracket	250①	1992–95	Fuel Rail Bolts	115①
	Camshaft Bearing Cap	180① ②		Intake Manifold Nuts	174① ②
	Camshaft Sprocket	70		Intake Plenum Screws	130① ②
	Connecting Rod Cap	38		Oil Drain Plug	30
	Crankshaft Bearing Cap	60		Oil Pan	50①
	Crankshaft Pulley A (Crankshaft Bolt)	110		Oil Pickup	④
	Crankshaft Pulley B	250①		Oil Pump Assembly	③
	Cylinder Head Bolt (Cold)	80②		Oil Seal Rear Housing	95①
	Distributor Adapter	120①		Rear Exhaust Manifold Nuts	175①
	Engine Support Bracket	35		Rocker Cover	88①
	Exhaust Crossover Pipe	51		Timing Belt Tensioner	250①
	Exhaust Pipe Shoulder Bolts	250①		Transaxle To Engine Block	75
	Flex Plat To Torque Convertor	55			
	Front Exhaust Manifold Bolts	130①			
	Fuel Pressure Regulator Bolts	95①			

① —Inch lbs.
② —Tighten in two or three steps. Refer to text for tightening sequence.
③ —1992, 120 inch lbs.; 1993–95, 130 inch. lbs.
④ —1992, 160 inch lbs.; 1993–95, 191 inch. lbs.

3.3L/V6-202 & 3.8L/V6-231 Engines

NOTE: On Air Bag Equipped Models, Refer To "Air Bag System Precautions" Located In The Front Of This Manual For System Disarming & Arming Procedures.

INDEX

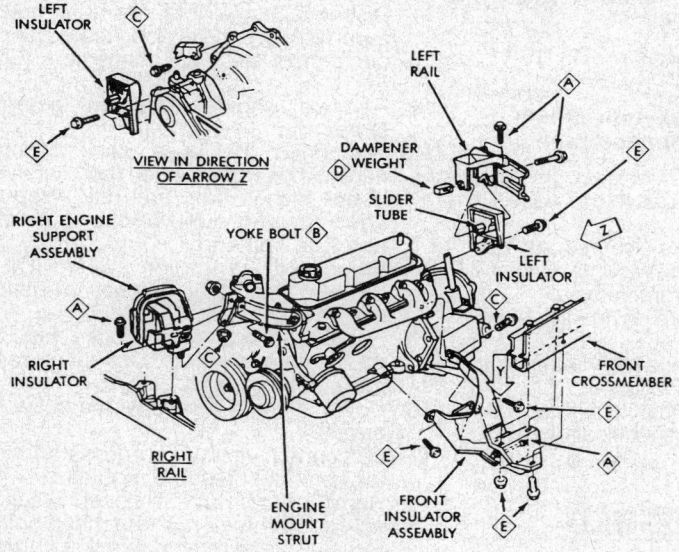

TORQUE	
A	68 N•m (50 FT. LBS.)
B	149 N•m (110 FT. LBS.)
C	102 N•m (75 FT. LBS.)
D	23 N•m (200 IN. LBS.)
E	54 N•m (40 FT. LBS.)

Fig. 1 Engine mounts

CR1069100289000X

PRECAUTIONS

AIR BAG SYSTEMS

Refer to "Air Bag System Precautions" in the front of this manual for system disarming and arming procedures.

FUEL SYSTEM PRESSURE RELEASE

1. Loosen fuel tank filler cap.
2. Disconnect injector wiring harness and connect a suitable jumper wire between ground terminal No. 1 and a suitable ground.
3. Connect a second jumper wire between terminal No. 2 of injector harness and battery positive for no longer than five seconds.
4. Remove jumper wires.

ENGINE MOUNT

REPLACE

The engine mounts incorporate slotted bolt holes to permit side to side positioning of the engine thereby affecting the length of the driveshaft. Failure to properly position engine may result in extensive damage to the engine or driveshafts.

RIGHT SIDE MOUNT

1. Remove right engine mount insulator vertical fasteners from frame rail, **Fig. 1**.
2. Remove load on engine mount by supporting engine and transmission assembly with a floor jack.
3. Remove insulator assembly through bolt, then the insulator.
4. Reverse procedure to install, noting the following:
   a. Tighten bolts to specifications.
   b. Adjust engine mount insulator as necessary.

LEFT SIDE MOUNT

1. Raise and support vehicle and remove inner splash shield.
2. Support transaxle with a transmission jack.
3. Remove insulator through bolt then the transaxle mount bolts and mount, **Fig. 1**.
4. Reverse procedure to install, noting the following:
   a. Ensure slide tube is seated into rail bracket guides.
   b. Tighten bolts to specifications.
   c. Adjust engine mount insulator as necessary.

FRONT MOUNT

1. Support engine and transaxle assembly so engine will not rotate.
2. Remove insulator through bolt, **Fig. 1**.
3. Remove front engine mount bracket to crossmember screws and nuts then the insulator.
4. Reverse procedure to install, noting

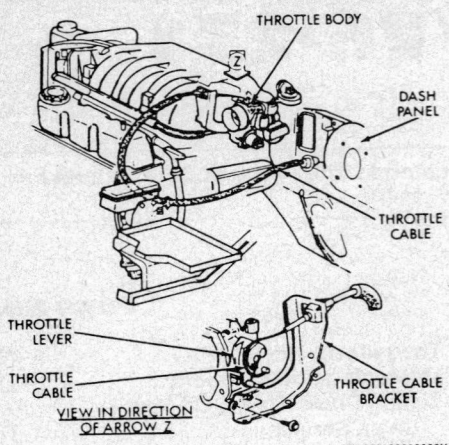

Fig. 2   Throttle cable

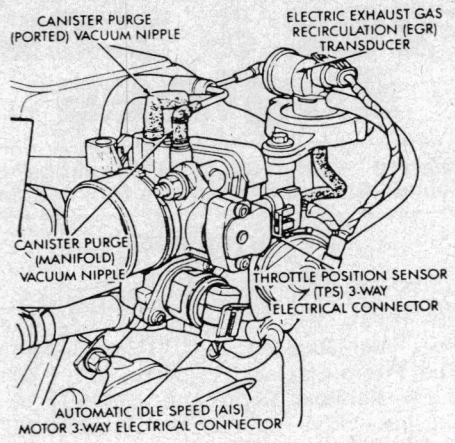

Fig. 3   Throttle body electrical & vacuum connections

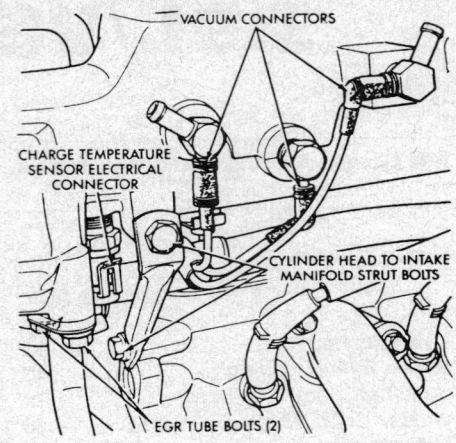

Fig. 4   Air intake plenum electrical & vacuum connections

the following:
a. Tighten bolts to specifications.
b. Adjust engine mount insulator as necessary.

ENGINE
REPLACE

1. Release fuel system pressure as outlined under "Precautions."
2. Disconnect battery ground cable.
3. Mark hood hinge locations and remove hood.
4. Drain cooling system, then disconnect all electrical connections.
5. Remove coolant hoses, radiator and fan assembly.
6. Relieve fuel pressure as follows:
   a. Loosen fuel tank filler cap.
   b. Disconnect injector wiring harness and connect a suitable jumper wire between ground terminal No. 1 and a suitable ground.
   c. Connect a second jumper wire between terminal No. 2 of injector harness and battery positive for no longer than five seconds.
   d. Remove jumper wires.
7. Disconnect fuel lines, then unhook the accelerator cable.
8. Remove air cleaner assembly, then raise and support vehicle.
9. Drain engine oil.
10. Remove air conditioning compressor mounting bolts and position compressor aside.
11. Disconnect exhaust pipe from manifold, then remove transaxle inspection cover and mark position of flex plate to torque converter.
12. Remove flex plate to torque converter attaching screws and clamp bottom of converter housing to prevent converter from moving.
13. Remove power steering attaching bolts and position pump aside.
14. Remove two lower transaxle to block screws, then the starter. Lower vehicle to ground.
15. Disconnect vacuum lines and ground strap.
16. Install suitable transmission holding fixture, then install engine lifting hoist and support engine.

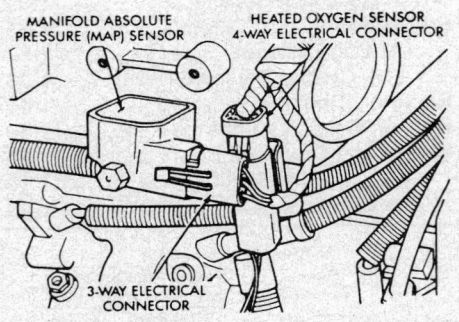

Fig. 5   MAP & oxygen sensor electrical connectors

17. Remove upper transaxle case to block bolts.
18. Disconnect engine mounts as outlined under "Engine Mounts, Replace."
19. Remove engine from vehicle.
20. Reverse procedure to install, noting the following:
   a. Tighten transaxle to cylinder block bolts to specification.
   b. Tighten flex plate to tighten converter bolts to specification.

INTAKE MANIFOLD
REPLACE
REMOVAL

1. Release fuel system pressure as outlined under "Precautions."
2. Disconnect battery ground cable.
3. Drain cooling system, then remove air cleaner and throttle body hose assembly.
4. Disconnect throttle cable from throttle body, Fig. 2, then disconnect wiring harness from throttle cable bracket.
5. Disconnect automatic idle speed (AIS) motor and throttle position sensor (TPS) wiring connectors from throttle body, Fig. 3.
6. Disconnect vacuum harness from throttle body, Fig. 3.

7. Disconnect PCV and brake booster hoses from air intake plenum, Fig. 4.
8. Disconnect EGR tube flange from intake plenum, Fig. 4.
9. Disconnect charge temperature sensor (CTS) electrical connector, then the vacuum harness connectors from intake plenum, Fig. 4.
10. Remove cylinder head to intake plenum strut, Fig. 4.
11. Disconnect manifold absolute pressure (MAP) sensor and heated oxygen sensor electrical connectors, Fig. 5.
12. Remove engine mounted ground strap.
13. Disconnect fuel hose quick disconnect fittings from fuel rail then carefully pull fittings from fuel rail. **Wrap a shop towel around hoses to catch any fuel spillage,**
14. Remove direct ignition system (DIS) coil and alternator bracket to intake manifold bolt, Fig. 6.
15. Remove intake plenum bolts, Fig. 7, then rotate plenum back over rear valve cover.
16. Cover intake manifold with a suitable cover.
17. Disconnect vacuum harness connector from fuel pressure regulator.
18. Remove fuel tube retainer bracket screw and fuel rail attaching bolts, Fig. 8. Spread retainer bracket to provide fuel tube removal clearance.
19. Disconnect fuel rail injector wiring clip from alternator bracket.
20. Disconnect cam sensor, coolant temperature sensor and engine temperature sensor connectors.
21. Disconnect fuel injector wiring clip from intake manifold water tube.
22. Remove fuel rail. Use caution not to damage injector O-rings when removing from ports, Fig. 9.
23. Remove upper radiator hose, bypass hose and rear intake manifold hose.
24. Remove intake manifold bolts, then the intake manifold.
25. Remove intake manifold seal retainers, Fig. 10, then the intake manifold gasket.

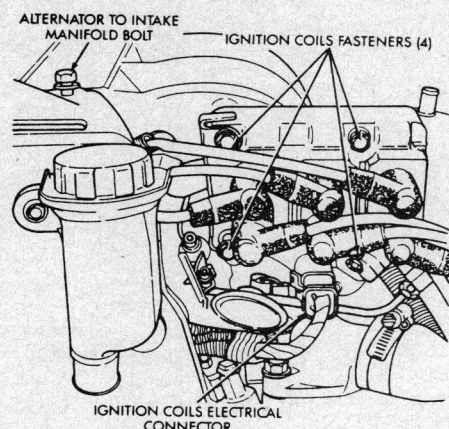

Fig. 6   DIS ignition coil

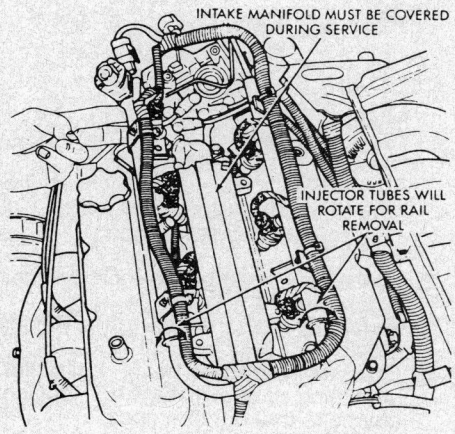

Fig. 9   Fuel rail removal

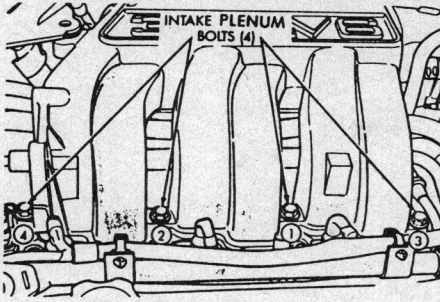

Fig. 7   Intake plenum bolt removal & tightening sequence

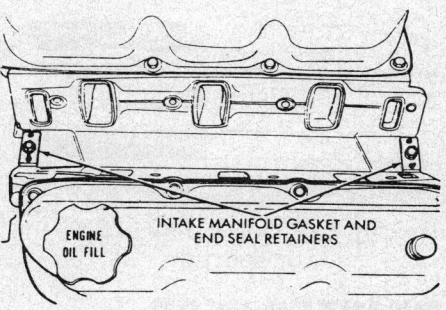

Fig. 10   Intake manifold end seal retainers

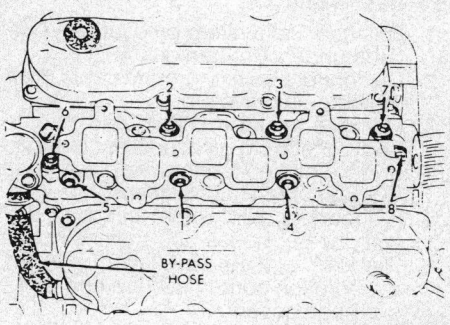

Fig. 12   Intake manifold bolt tightening sequence

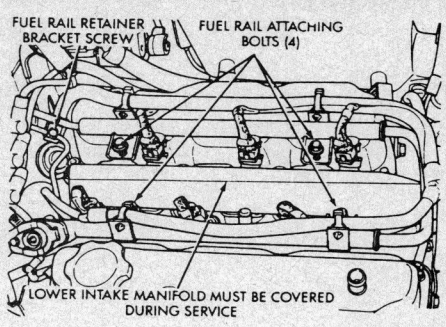

Fig. 8   Fuel rail attaching bolts

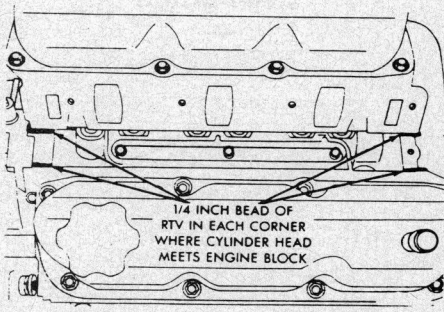

Fig. 11   Intake manifold gasket sealant application

INSTALLATION

1. Clean all surfaces of cylinder block and cylinder heads.
2. Apply a drop approximately 1/4 inch in diameter of rubber sealer, part No. 4318025 or equivalent, on each of the four manifold to cylinder head gasket corners, **Fig. 11.**
3. Carefully install intake manifold gasket and end seal retainers, **Fig. 10.** Tighten end seal retainer screws to specifications. **Intake manifold gasket is made of very thin metal and may cause personal injury, handle with care.**
4. Install intake manifold and retaining bolts and **torque** to 10 inch lbs. Tighten to specifications in sequence shown in **Fig. 12**, then tighten again to specifications. **After intake manifold is in place, inspect to ensure seals are in place.**
5. Ensure injector holes are clean and all plugs are removed.
6. Lube injector O-rings with clean engine oil to ease installation.
7. Position the tip of each injector into ports. Push assembly into place until injectors are fully seated in ports, **Fig. 9.**
8. Install four fuel rail attaching bolts and tighten to specifications.
9. Install fuel tube retaining bracket screw and tighten to specifications, **Fig. 8.**
10. Connect cam sensor, coolant temperature sensor and engine temperature sensor connectors.
11. Install fuel injector harness wiring clips on alternator bracket and intake manifold water tube.
12. Connect fuel pressure regulator vacuum line.
13. Remove covering from intake manifold and clean surface.
14. Install a new plenum gasket on intake manifold, position plenum on intake manifold and install bolts finger tight.
15. Install alternator bracket to intake manifold bolt, then the cylinder head to intake manifold strut bolts. **Do not torque.**
16. Tighten plenum bolts to specifications in sequence shown in **Fig. 7.**
17. Tighten alternator bracket to intake manifold bolt to specifications.
18. Tighten cylinder head to intake manifold strut bolt to specifications.
19. Connect engine ground strap, MAP and heated oxygen sensor electrical connectors, **Fig. 5.**
20. Connect CTS electrical connector, then the vacuum harness to intake plenum, **Fig. 4.**
21. Using a new gasket, connect EGR tube flange to intake manifold and tighten to specifications.
22. Attach wiring harness to hole in throttle cable bracket.
23. Connect AIS and TPS wiring connectors, **Fig. 3.**
24. Connect vacuum harness to throttle body, **Fig. 3.**
25. Install DIS coils. Tighten fasteners to specifications, **Fig. 6.**
26. Install fuel hose quick connector fittings to fuel rail. Push fittings onto rail until they click into place. Fuel supply fitting is 5/16 inch and fuel return fitting is 1/4 inch, **Fig. 5.**
27. Install throttle cable, **Fig. 2.**
28. Install air cleaner and hose assembly, then connect battery ground cable and fill cooling system.

EXHAUST MANIFOLD
REPLACE

REMOVAL

1. Disconnect battery ground cable.
2. Raise and support vehicle, then dis-

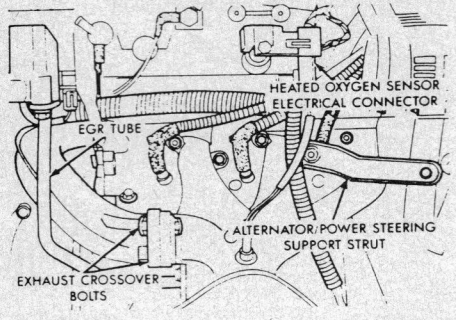

Fig. 13 EGR tube, oxygen sensor connector & alternator/power steering strut

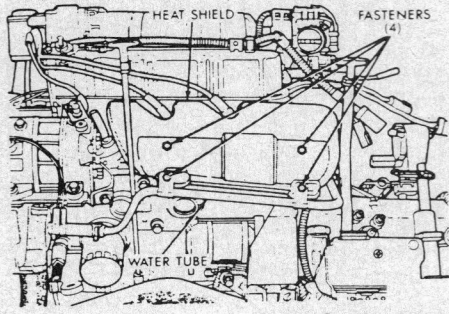

Fig. 14 Front exhaust manifold heat shield

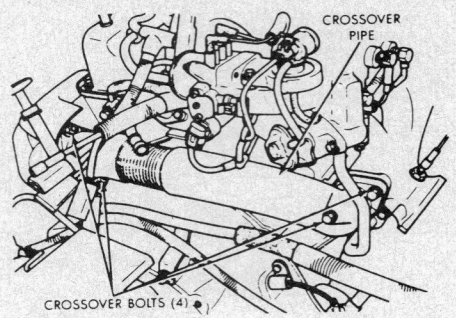

Fig. 15 Crossover pipe & bolts

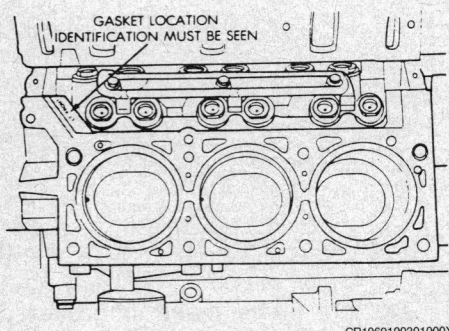

Fig. 16 Head gasket installation

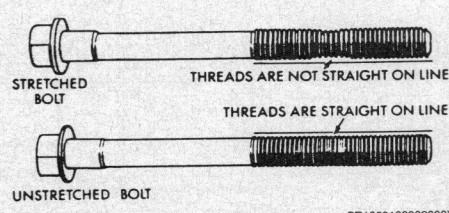

Fig. 17 Cylinder head bolt inspection

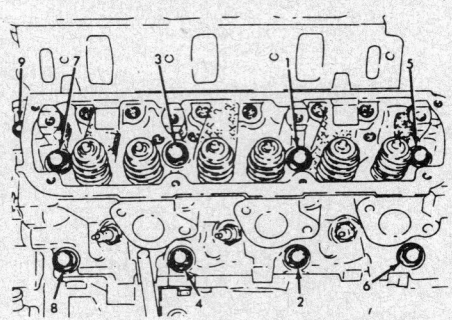

Fig. 18 Cylinder head bolt tightening sequence

connect exhaust pipe from rear (cowl side) exhaust pipe at articulated joint.

3. Separate EGR tube from rear manifold, then disconnect heated oxygen sensor connector, **Fig. 13.**
4. Remove alternator/power steering support strut, **Fig. 13.**
5. Remove bolts attaching crossover pipe to exhaust manifold, **Fig. 13.**
6. Remove bolts attaching rear manifold to cylinder head, then the manifold.
7. Lower vehicle, then remove screws attaching heat shield to front manifold, **Fig. 14.**
8. Remove bolts attaching crossover pipe to front exhaust manifold, **Fig. 15,** then the nuts attaching manifold to cylinder head. Remove front exhaust manifold assembly.

INSTALLATION

1. Install rear exhaust manifold and tighten attaching bolts to specifications.
2. Connect exhaust pipe to rear exhaust manifold and tighten shoulder bolt to specifications.
3. Connect crossover pipe to rear exhaust manifold and tighten bolt to specifications, then connect oxygen sensor electrical connector, **Fig. 13.**
4. Install EGR tube and alternator/power steering strut, **Fig. 13.**
5. Install front exhaust manifold and connect exhaust crossover, **Fig. 15.**
6. Install front exhaust manifold heat shield and tighten attaching screws to specifications.
7. Connect battery ground cable.

CYLINDER HEAD
REPLACE

REMOVAL

1. Release fuel system pressure as outlined under "Precautions."
2. Disconnect battery ground cable, then drain cooling system.
3. Remove intake manifold and throttle body. Refer to procedures outlined under "Intake Manifold, Replace" and "Exhaust Manifold, Replace."
4. Disconnect coil wires, sending unit wire, heater hoses and bypass hose.
5. Remove closed ventilation system, evaporation control system and cylinder head covers.
6. Remove exhaust manifolds. Refer to procedures outlined under "Intake Manifold, Replace" and "Exhaust Manifold, Replace."
7. Remove rocker arm and shaft assemblies. Remove pushrods noting position for installation in their original locations.
8. Remove nine bolts attaching each cylinder head, then the cylinder head assemblies.

INSPECTION

Inspect all surfaces with a straightedge if there is any reason to suspect leakage. If out of flatness exceeds .00075 inch (.019 mm) times the span length in inches in any direction, replace the head.

As an example, if a 12 inch span is .004 inch (.019 mm) out of flat, allowable is 12 x .00075 inch (.019 mm) equals .009 inch (.22 mm). This amount of out of flat is acceptable.

INSTALLATION

1. Clean all surfaces of cylinder heads and cylinder block.

2. Install new head gaskets on cylinder block, **Fig. 16.**
3. Install cylinder heads on cylinder block.
4. Examine cylinder head bolts for stretching as shown, **Fig. 17.** Replace any bolts that are stretched.
5. Tighten cylinder head bolts in sequence shown in **Fig. 18,** as follows:
   a. **Torque** all bolts to 45 ft. lbs.
   b. **Torque** all bolts to 65 ft. lbs.
   c. **Torque** all bolts again to 65 ft. lbs.
   d. Turn each bolt an additional ¼ turn, noting bolt torque. **If bolt torque is not over 90 ft. lbs. after tightening an additional ¼ turn, bolt should be replaced.**
6. Install pushrods, rocker arm and shaft assemblies with stamped steel retainers positioned as shown, **Fig. 19.** Tighten to specifications. **Rocker arm shaft should be tightened down slowly, starting with the center most bolts. Allow 20 minutes tappet bleed down time after installation of rocker shafts before engine operation.**
7. Install new cylinder head cover gaskets, then install cylinder head covers. Tighten to specifications.
8. Reverse remaining removal steps to complete installation.

VALVE LIFTERS

Engine	Year	Lift, Inch
3.3L/V6-201	1992-93	.400
3.8L/V6-231	1992-93	.400

VALVE ADJUSTMENT

Because automatic lash adjusters are used, no adjustment is necessary.

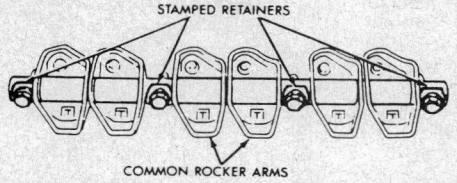

Fig. 19 Rocker arm shaft retainers

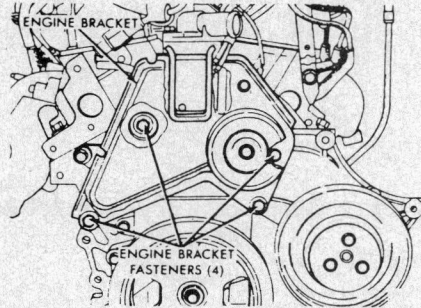

Fig. 22 Engine bracket

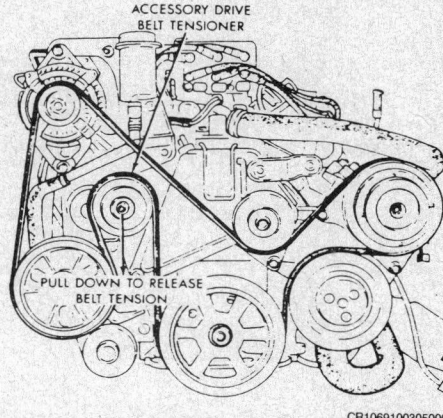

Fig. 20 Accessory drive belt routing

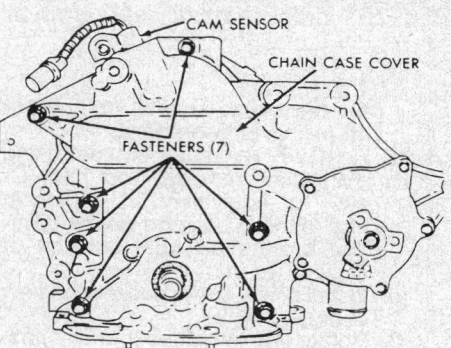

Fig. 23 Timing case cover

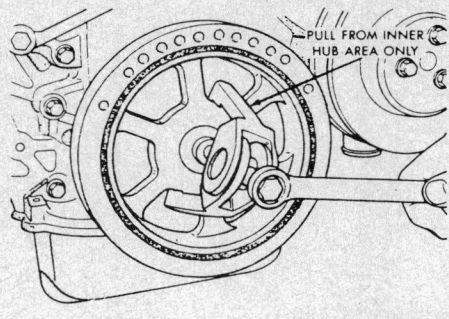

Fig. 21 Crankshaft pulley removal

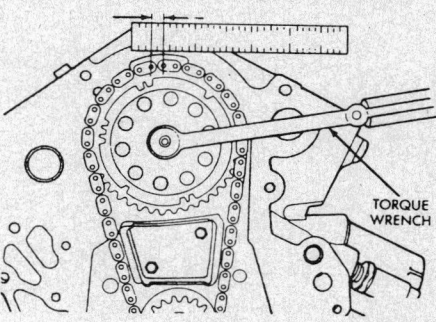

Fig. 24 Timing chain movement measurement

VALVE TIMING

1. Remove front valve cover and all six spark plugs.
2. Rotate engine until the No. 2 piston is at top dead center (TDC) of compression stroke.
3. Install a degree wheel on the crankshaft pulley.
4. Using proper adapter, install a dial into No. 2 spark plug hole. Using the indicator to find TDC on compression stroke.
5. Position degree wheel to zero.
6. Remove dial indicator from spark plug hole.
7. Place a .200 inch (5.08 mm) spacer between the valve stem tip of No. 2 intake valve and rocker arm pad. Allow tappet to bleed down to give a solid tappet effect.
8. Install a dial indicator so plunger contacts the No. 2 intake valve spring retainer as nearly perpendicular as possible. Zero the indicator.
9. Rotate engine clockwise until intake valve has lifted .010 inch (.254 mm). **Do not turn crankshaft any further clockwise as intake valve may bottom and result in serious damage.**
10. Degree wheel should read 3° before top dead center (BTDC) to 4° after top dead center (ATDC).

ROCKER ARMS
REPLACE

1. Remove intake manifold as outlined under "Intake & Exhaust Manifolds, Replace."
2. Disconnect spark plug wires, closed ventilation system and evaporation control system from head cover.
3. Remove cylinder head cover and gasket.
4. Remove four rocker arm shaft bolts and retainers.

5. Remove rocker arm and shaft assembly.
6. If rocker arm assemblies are disassembled for service or cleaning, assemble rocker arms in there original position.
7. Reverse procedure to install.

VALVE SPRINGS
REPLACE

1. Remove cylinder heads as outlined under "Cylinder Head, Replace."
2. Remove rocker arm shafts and camshafts as outlined under "Rocker Arm, Service."
3. Using a suitable valve spring compressor tool, compress valve spring and remove spring retainer locks, retainer, valve spring, spring seat and valve stem seal.
4. Reverse procedure to install.

TIMING CHAIN
REPLACE

1. Remove timing chain cover as follows:
   a. Disconnect battery ground cable.
   b. Drain cooling system.
   c. Support engine, then remove right engine mount.
   d. Raise and support vehicle, then drain engine oil.
   e. Remove oil pan and oil pump pick up. **It may be necessary to re-**

move transaxle inspection cover.
   f. Remove accessory drive belt as follows:
   g. Remove right front wheel and tire assembly, then the inner splash shield.
   h. Release belt tension by rotating the tensioner clockwise, **Fig. 20**, then remove accessory drive belt.
   i. Remove A/C compressor and position aside.
   j. Remove A/C compressor mounting bracket.
   k. Using a suitable puller, remove crankshaft pulley as shown, **Fig. 21. Pull from inner hub area only.**
   l. Remove idler pulley from engine bracket, then the engine bracket, **Fig. 22.**
   m. Remove cam sensor from chain case cover, then the chain case cover, **Fig. 23.**
2. Remove camshaft sprocket attaching cup washer, then remove timing chain with crankshaft and camshaft sprockets.
3. If timing chain is to be reinstalled, inspect as follows:
   a. Place a scale next to timing chain so that chain movement can be measured.
   b. Install a torque wrench and socket over camshaft sprocket, then apply torque in direction of crankshaft rotation to take up chain slack. Apply 30 ft. lbs. of torque with cylinder heads installed or 15 ft. lbs. of torque with cylinder heads removed. **With torque applied to**

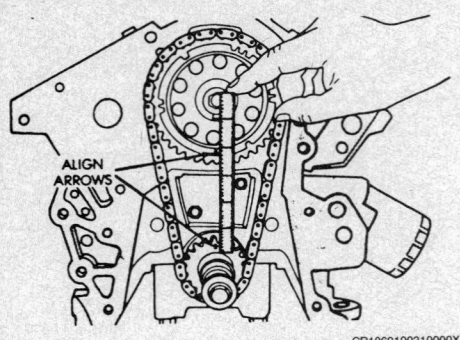

Fig. 25 Timing mark alignment

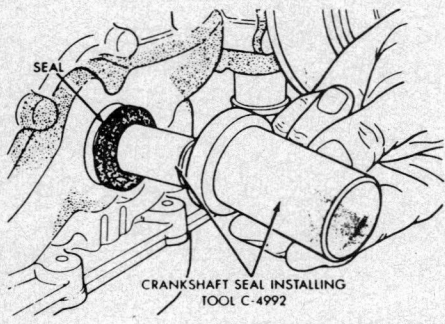

Fig. 28 Crankcase oil seal installation

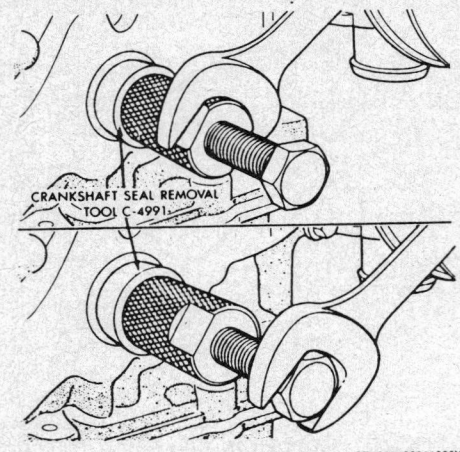

Fig. 26 Crankshaft oil seal removal

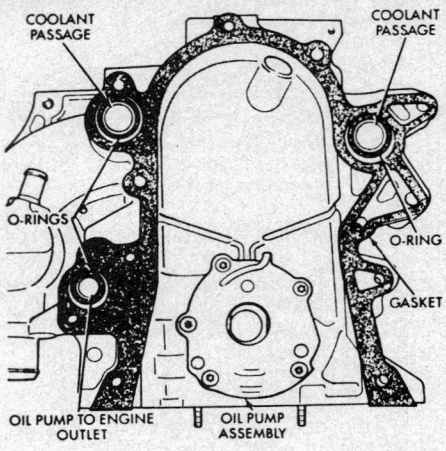

Fig. 27 Timing case cover gasket & O-rings

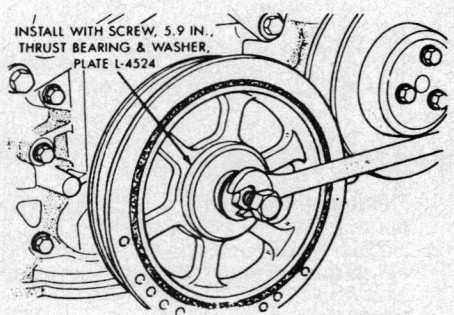

Fig. 29 Crankshaft pulley installation

camshaft sprocket bolt, crankshaft should not be allowed to move. It may be necessary to block crankshaft to prevent rotation.

c. Holding a scale with dimension reading even with edge of a chain link, apply the specified torque in the reverse direction and note amount of chain movement, **Fig. 24.**

d. If timing chain movement exceeds 1/8 inch (3.175 mm), chain must be replaced.

4. Install timing chain around both sprockets.

5. Turn crankshaft and camshaft to align keyway locations in both sprockets.

6. Lift sprocket and chain, keeping sprockets tight against chain in position described.

7. Slide both sprockets with chain evenly over their respective shafts, then use a straightedge to check alignment of timing marks, **Fig. 25.**

8. Install cup washer and camshaft sprocket bolt. Tighten bolt to specifications.

9. Check camshaft endplay. Endplay should measure .002-.006 inch (.051-.0152 mm) with a new thrust plate or up to .005-.012 inches on 1992-93 engines. If camshaft endplay is not as specified, replace thrust plate.

10. Install timing chain snubber.

11. Install timing chain cover and replace crankshaft oil seal as follows:

a. Ensure mating surfaces of chain case cover are clean and free of burrs. **Crankshaft oil seal must**

be removed to ensure correct oil pump engagement.

b. Remove crankshaft oil seal using crankshaft removal tool No. C-4991 or equivalent, as shown in **Fig. 26. Use caution not to damage crankshaft seal surface of cover.**

c. Install a new cover gasket and new O-rings, **Fig. 27.**

d. Rotate crankshaft so that oil pump drive flats are vertical.

e. Position oil pump inner rotor so that mating flats are in the same position as crankshaft drive flats, **Fig. 27.**

f. Install cover onto crankshaft. **Ensure oil pump is correctly engaged on crankshaft or severe damage may result.**

g. Install chain case cover screws and tighten to specifications.

h. Install crankshaft oil seal as follows:

i. Position seal into opening with seal spring towards inside of engine.

j. Install seal until flush with cover using seal crankshaft seal installing tool No. C-4992 or equivalent, **Fig. 28.**

k. Install crankshaft pulley using thrust bearing/washer plate tool No. L-4524 or equivalent and a 5.9 inch screw, **Fig. 29.** Tighten crankshaft pulley bolt to specifications.

l. Install engine bracket, **Fig. 22** and **torque** attaching screws to 40 ft. lbs.

m. Install idler pulley on engine bracket.

n. Install cam sensor.

o. Install A/C compressor mounting bracket, then the A/C compressor.

p. Install accessory drive belt, **Fig. 20.**

q. Install right front inner splash shield, then the wheel and tire assembly.

r. Install oil pump pickup, oil pan and transaxle inspection cover, if removed.

s. Install engine mount.

t. Fill crankcase with oil to proper level.

u. Fill cooling system.

v. Connect battery ground cable.

CAMSHAFT REPLACE

Before servicing the fuel pump, fuel lines, fuel filter, throttle body or fuel injectors, the fuel system pressure must be released as outlined under "Precautions."

1. Remove intake manifold as outlined under "Intake & Exhaust Manifold, Replace."

2. Remove cylinder heads as outlined under "Cylinder Head, Replace."

3. Remove timing chain cover and timing chain as outlined under "Timing Chain, Replace."

4. Remove rocker arm and shaft assemblies, pushrods and tappets. Identify each component so component will be replaced in its original location.

5. Remove camshaft thrust plate.

6. Install a long bolt into front of camshaft to aid in camshaft removal.

7. Remove the camshaft, using care not to damage cam bearing.

8. Reverse procedure to install, tightening all attaching bolts to specifications.

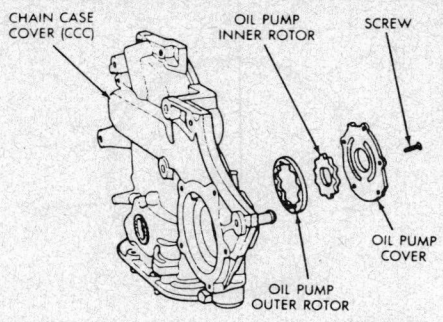

Fig. 30   Oil pump components

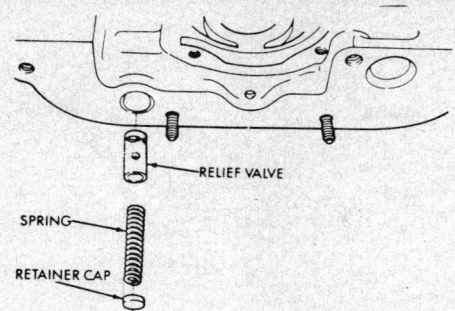

Fig. 31   Oil pressure relief valve components

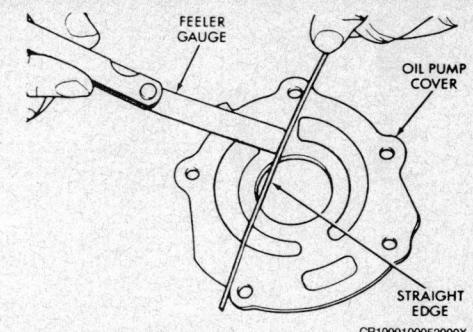

Fig. 32   Oil pump cover flatness check

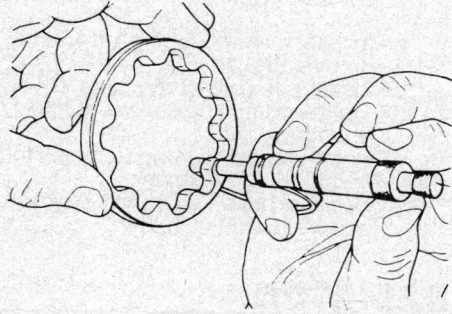

Fig. 33   Outer rotor thickness measurement

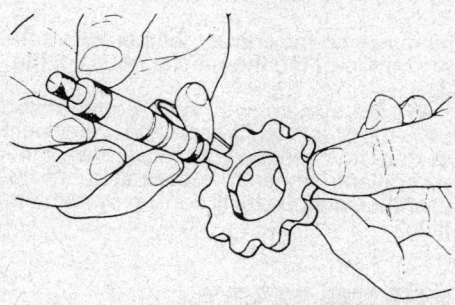

Fig. 34   Inner rotor thickness measurement

b. Lightly coat seal outside dimension with Loctite Stud N' Bearing Mount or equivalent.

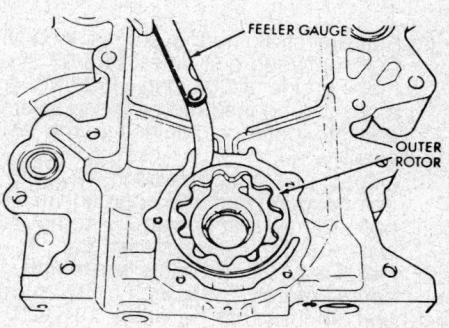

Fig. 35   Outer rotor clearance in case measurement

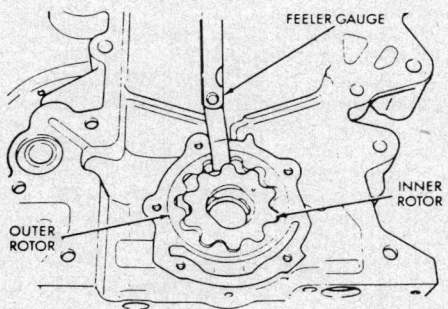

Fig. 36   Rotor clearance measurement

CRANKSHAFT SEAL
REPLACE

Refer to "Timing Belt, Replace" for seal replacement procedure.

CRANKSHAFT REAR OIL SEAL
REPLACE

1. Remove transaxle assembly.
2. Remove flywheel or flex plate from rear of crankshaft.
3. Pry out rear seal with a suitable tool. Use care not to nick or damage crankshaft flange seal surface or retainer bore.
4. Reverse procedure to install, noting the following:
   a. Use seal pilot tool No. C-4681 or equivalent when installing seal.

OIL PUMP SERVICE

It is necessary to remove the oil pan, oil pickup and chain case cover (CCC) to service oil pump rotors, **Fig. 30**. The oil pump relief valve can be serviced by removing the oil pan and oil pickup tube. Refer to procedure outlined under "Timing Chain, Replace" to remove timing chain case cover.

DISASSEMBLY

1. Remove relief valve as follows:
   a. Drill a 1/8 inch (3.175 mm) hole into the relief valve retainer cap, **Fig. 31**, then insert a self-threading sheet metal screw into cap.
   b. Clamp screw in a vise, then while supporting chain case cover (CCC), remove cap by tapping CCC with a soft hammer.
   c. Discard retainer cap, then remove relief spring and relief valve, **Fig. 31**.
2. Remove oil pump cover screws, then lift off cover, **Fig. 30**.
3. Remove pump rotors, **Fig. 30**.
4. Wash all parts in a suitable solvent and inspect for damage or wear.

INSPECTION & REPAIR

1. Clean all parts thoroughly. Mating surfaces of CCC should be smooth. Replace pump cover if scratched or grooved.
2. Lay a straightedge across pump cover surface, **Fig. 32**. If a .003 inch (.076 mm) feeler gauge can be inserted be-

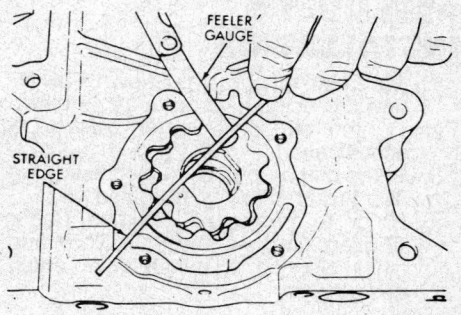

Fig. 37   Rotor & case clearance measurement

tween cover and straightedge, cover should be replaced.
3. Measure thickness and diameter of outer rotor, **Fig. 33**. If outer rotor thickness measures .3005 inch (7.36 mm) or less, or if the diameter is 3.141 inches (79.78 mm) or less, replace outer rotor.
4. If inner rotor thickness, **Fig. 34**, measures .301 inch (7.64 mm) or less, replace inner rotor and shaft assembly.
5. Install outer rotor into CCC, press one side with fingers and measure clearance between outer rotor and CCC, **Fig. 35**. If measurement is .022 inch (56 mm) or more, replace CCC only if outer rotor is within specifications.
6. Install inner rotor into CCC, then measure clearance between inner and outer rotors, **Fig. 36**. If clearance measured between rotors is .008 inch (.203 mm) or more, replace both rotors.

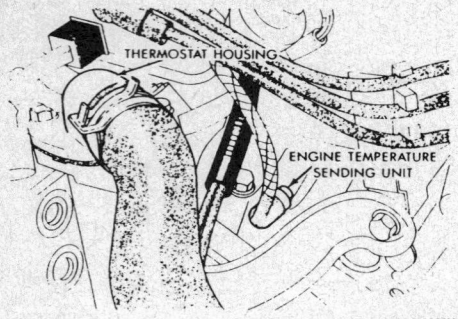

Fig. 38 Coolant temperature sensor location

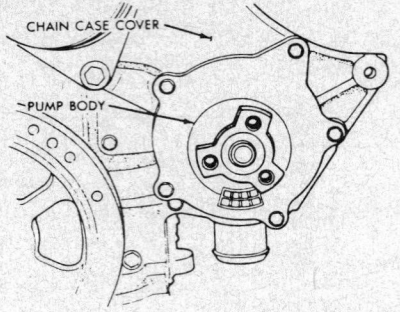

Fig. 39 Water pump installed view

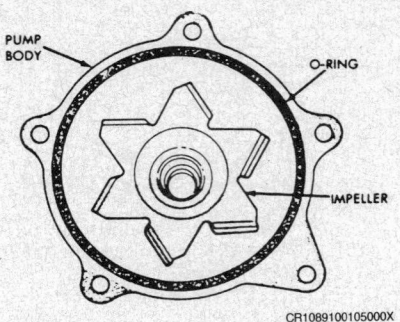

Fig. 40 Water pump body

7. Place a straightedge across face of CCC between bolt holes, **Fig. 37.** If a feeler gauge of .004 inch (.102 mm) or more can be inserted between rotors and straightedge, replace pump assembly.
8. Inspect oil pressure relief valve plunger for scoring and free operation in it's bore. Small marks can be removed with 400 grit wet or dry sand paper.
9. Relief valve spring has a free length of approximately 1.95 inch (49.5 mm) and should test between 19.5-20.5 pounds when compressed to $1^{1}/_{32}$ inch (34 mm). Replace spring that does not meet specifications.

ASSEMBLY & INSTALLATION

1. Assemble oil pump as shown, **Fig. 30 and 31,** using new parts as required.
2. Tighten oil pump cover screws to specifications.
3. Prime oil pump prior to installation by filling rotor cavity with engine oil.
4. Refer to procedure outlined under "Timing Chain Cover, Oil Seal and Chain Service" to install timing chain case cover.

SERPENTINE DRIVE BELT

BELT ROUTING

Refer to **Fig. 20** for serpentine drive belt routing.

BELT REPLACEMENT

1. Raise vehicle on hoist.
2. Remove right front splash shield.
3. Release tension by rotating tensioner clockwise, **Fig. 20.**
4. Reverse procedure to install.

COOLING SYSTEM BLEED

The cooling system on the 3.3L/V6-201 and 3.8L/V6-231 engines requires venting

by removing the coolant temperature sensor on top of the thermostat housing, **Fig. 38.**

Fill the system with the recommended 50% mixture of antifreeze and water until mixture reaches the vent holes, then tighten coolant temperature sensor to specifications. Continue to fill cooling system until full.

THERMOSTAT
REPLACE

1. Drain coolant system down to thermostat level.
2. Remove thermostat housing bolts and housing.
3. Remove thermostat, discard gasket and clean both gasket sealing surfaces.
4. Reverse procedure to install. Dip new gasket in water and ensure to center thermostat in recess.

WATER PUMP
REPLACE

1. Disconnect battery ground cable.
2. Remove accessory drive belt as follows:
   a. Remove right front wheel and tire assembly, then the inner splash shield.
   b. Release belt tension by rotating the tensioner clockwise, **Fig. 20,** then remove accessory drive belt.
3. Drain cooling system.
4. Remove three pump pulley bolts, then the pulley.
5. Remove five pump mounting screws, **Fig. 39,** then the pump assembly.
6. Remove and discard O-ring.
7. Reverse procedure to install, noting the following:
   a. Clean O-ring groove and O-ring surfaces on pump and chain case cover. Use caution not to scratch or gouge sealing surfaces.

b. Install a new O-ring in O-ring groove, **Fig. 40.**
c. Install pump to chain case cover. Tighten mounting screws to specifications.
d. Rotate pump by hand to check for freedom of movement.
e. Position pulley on pump. **Torque** screws to 250 inch lbs.

RADIATOR
REPLACE

Do not attempt to remove radiator cap or service cooling system while engine is hot.
1. Disconnect battery ground cable.
2. Drain cooling system.
3. Remove hose clamps and hoses.
4. Remove coolant reserve system tank to filler neck tube.
5. Disconnect fan electrical connector, then remove fan and fan support.
6. Remove fan shroud, if equipped.
7. Remove upper radiator mounting screws.
8. **On models with A/C,** remove condenser mounting screws at top of radiator
9. **On all models,** Carefully lift radiator out, to avoid damage to cooling fins or water tubes.
10. Reverse procedure to install, refilling cooling system with suitable coolant.

FUEL PUMP
REPLACE

Refer to "Fuel Pump, Replace" procedure in the 2.2L/4-135 & 2.5L/4-153 engine section.

FUEL FILTER
REPLACE

Refer to "Fuel Filter, Replace" procedure in the 2.2L/4-135 & 2.5L/4-153 engine section.

TIGHTENING SPECIFICATIONS

Year	Component	Torque/Ft. Lbs.
1992–95	A/C Compressor Bracket To Water Pump Bolt	30
	A/C Compressor Support Bolts	30
	A/C Compressor To Bracket Bolt	50
	Alternator Adjusting Strap Bolt	200①
	Alternator Adjusting Strap Mounting Bolt	30
	Alternator Bracket Bolt	30
	Alternator Mounting Pivot Nut	30
	Camshaft Sprocket Lockbolt	40
	Camshaft Thrust Plate	105①
	Chain Case Cover Bolt	②
	Connecting Rod Nut	40③
	Crankshaft Bolt (Vibration Damper)	40
	Crankshaft Pulley Screw To Crankshaft	40
	Cylinder Head Bolt	④
	Cylinder Head Cover Bolts	105①
	Cylinder Head To Intake Manifold Bolts	40
	DIS Coil Fasteners	105①
	EGR Tube Flange	200①
	Exhaust Crossover Pipe Flange Nut/Bolt	25
	Exhaust Manifold Screw	200①
	Exhaust Pipe Shoulder Bolts	250①
	Front Exhaust Manifold Heat Shield Screws	200①
	Flexplate	55

Year	Component	Torque/Ft. Lbs.
1992–95 —Cont'd	Fuel Rail Bolts	200①
	Fuel Rail Tube Bracket Bolts	35
	Intake Manifold Plenum Bolt	250①
	Intake Manifold Bolt	200① ④
	Intake Manifold Gasket Retaining Screw	105①
	Main Bearing Cap Bolt	30③
	Oil Filter Attaching Stud	30
	Oil Level Sensor Plug	20
	Oil Pan Drain Plug	20
	Oil Pan Screw	105①
	Oil Pressure Gauge Sending Unit	60①
	Oil Pump Cover Bolt T-30	105①
	Oil Pump Pick-Up Tube Screw	250①
	Rocker Shaft Bracket Bolt	250①
	Spark Plug	20
	Starter Mounting Bolt	50
	Tappet Retainer Yoke Screw	105①
	Temperature Gauge Sending Unit	60①
	Timing Chain Snubber Screw	105①
	Transaxle To Block Bolts	75
	Water Pump To Chain Case Cover Bolt	105①

① —Inch lbs.
② —M8 bolts, 20 ft. lbs.; M10 bolts, 40 ft. lbs.
③ —Turn an additional ¼ turn after reaching specified torque.
④ —Refer to text.

Clutch & Manual Transaxle

INDEX

ADJUSTMENTS

CLUTCH PEDAL

The clutch release cable, **Fig. 1,** cannot be adjusted. When the cable is properly routed, the spring between clutch pedal and positioner adjuster will hold clutch cable in proper position. An adjuster pivot is used to hold release cable in place to ensure complete clutch release when clutch pedal is depressed.

GEARSHIFT LINKAGE

Rod Linkage

1. Remove lockpin from transaxle selector shaft housing, **Fig. 2.**
2. Reverse lockpin so long end is facing downward, and insert pin into same threaded hole while pushing selector shaft into selector housing.
3. Raise and support vehicle then loosen clamp bolt that secures gearshift tube to gearshift rod.
4. Check that gearshift connector slides and rotates freely in gearshift tube.
5. Position shifter mechanism connector assembly so that isolator is contacting upstanding flange, while rib on isolator is aligned fore and aft with hole in blocker bracket. Hold connector isolator in this position and tighten clamp bolt on gearshift tube to specification. No significant force should be placed on linkage during this procedure, **Fig. 3.**
6. Lower vehicle, remove lockpin from selector shaft housing and reinstall lockpin in reversed position. Tighten pin to specification.
7. Check for proper operation.

Cable Linkage

Before replacing the gearshift selector or crossover cable for a hard shifting condition, disconnect both cables from the transaxle. Then, from inside of vehicle, manually operate the gearshift lever through all gear ranges. If the gearshift lever moves smoothly, the cable(s) should not be replaced.

Selector cable is not adjustable.

1. Remove lockpin from transaxle selector shaft housing, **Figs. 2 and 4.**
2. Reverse lockpin so long end is down and insert pin into same threaded

hole. A hole in selector shaft will align with lockpin, allowing lockpin to be screwed into housing. This locks selector shaft in 3-4 neutral position.

3. Remove gearshift knob and gearshift boot, **Fig. 4.**
4. Remove console, if equipped.
5. Adjust crossover cable and tighten adjusting screw to specification, **Fig. 5. Crossover cable adjusting screw must be properly tightened. Ensure crossover bellcrank does not move when tightening adjusting screw.**
6. Remove lockpin from selector shaft housing and reinstall lockpin so long end is up in selector shaft housing, **Fig. 2.** Tighten lockpin to specification.
7. Check for proper operation in first and reverse. Ensure reverse lockout operates properly. Gearshift mechanism and cables are now properly adjusted.
8. Install console, if equipped, gearshift boot and knob.

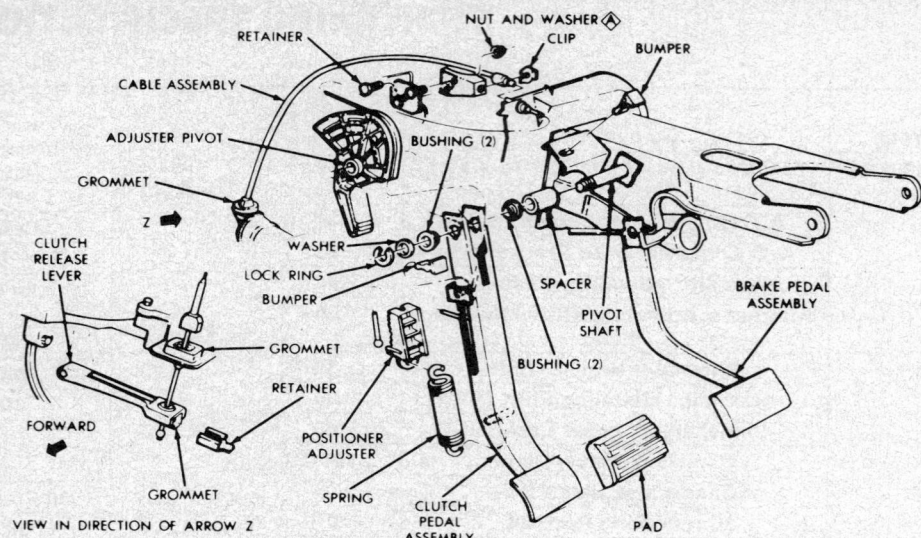

Fig. 1   Clutch cable routing

CLUTCH
REPLACE

1. Remove transaxle as outlined under "Transaxle, Replace" procedure.
2. Mark relationship between clutch cover and flywheel for reference during reassembly, then insert suitable clutch disc aligning tool through clutch disc hub.
3. Gradually loosen clutch cover attaching bolts, then remove pressure plate and cover assembly and disc from flywheel.
4. Remove clutch release shaft and slide release bearing assembly off input shaft seal retainer. Remove fork from release bearing thrust plate.
5. Reverse procedure to install. Align reference marks made during disassembly, then using a clutch disc alignment tool, install disc, plate and cover to flywheel. Refer to **Fig. 6** for tightening specifications.

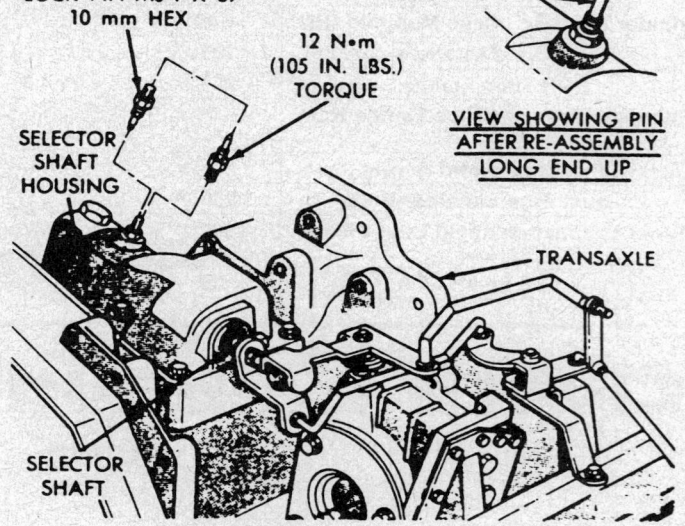

Fig. 2   Lockpin replacement

TRANSAXLE
REPLACE

1. Disconnect battery ground cable.
2. Install engine support fixture tool No. C-4852 or equivalent.
3. Raise and support vehicle.
4. Disconnect gearshift linkage, clutch cable and speedometer cable from transaxle.
5. Remove front wheel and tire assemblies.
6. Remove left front splash shield, then the impact bracket from transaxle, if equipped.

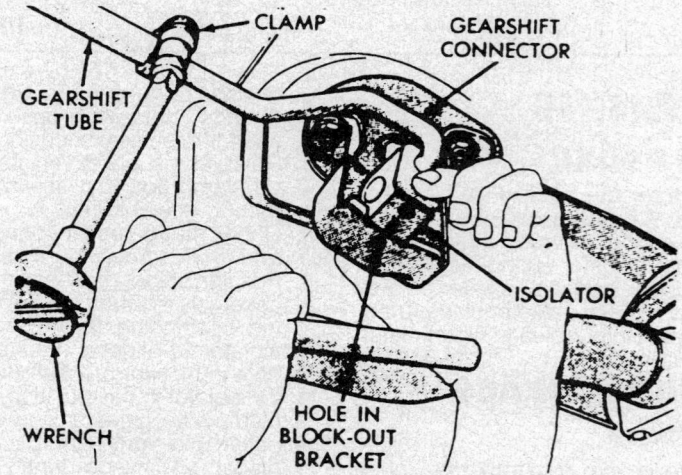

Fig. 3   Rod-type gearshift linkage adjustment

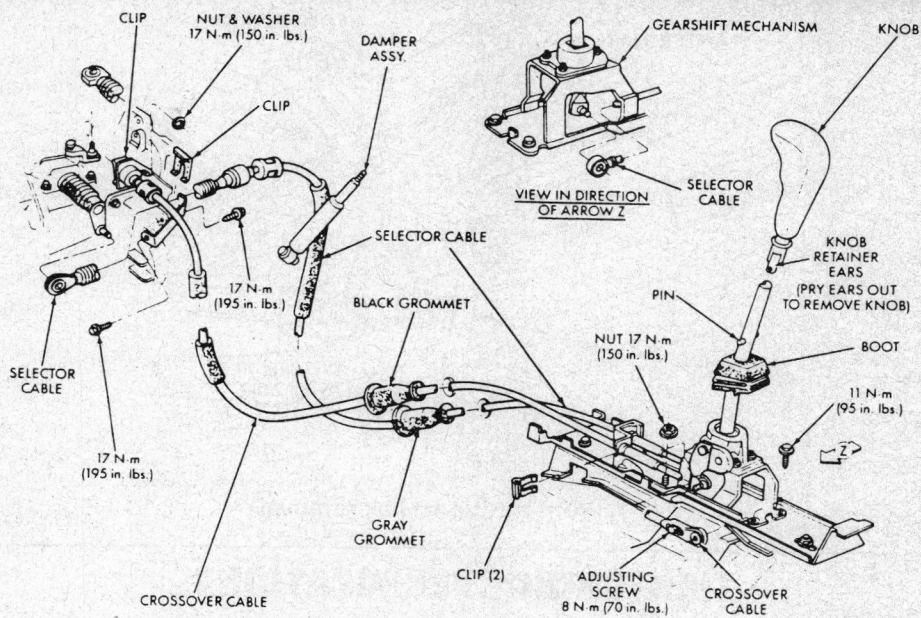

Fig. 4 Cable operated gearshift linkage

CR5049100060000X

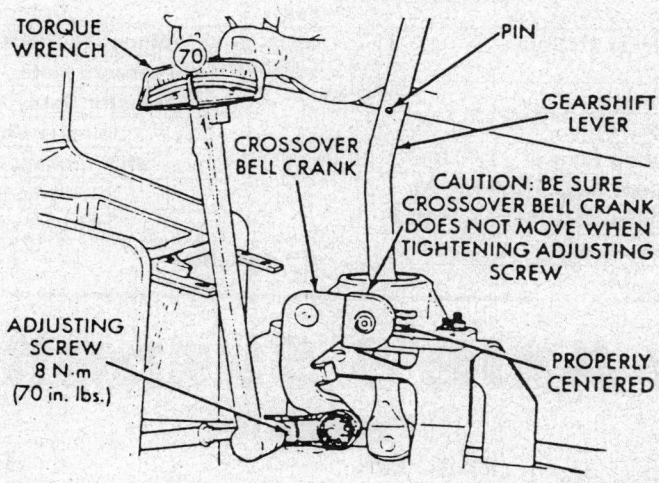

Fig. 5 Crossover cable adjustment

CR5049100061000X

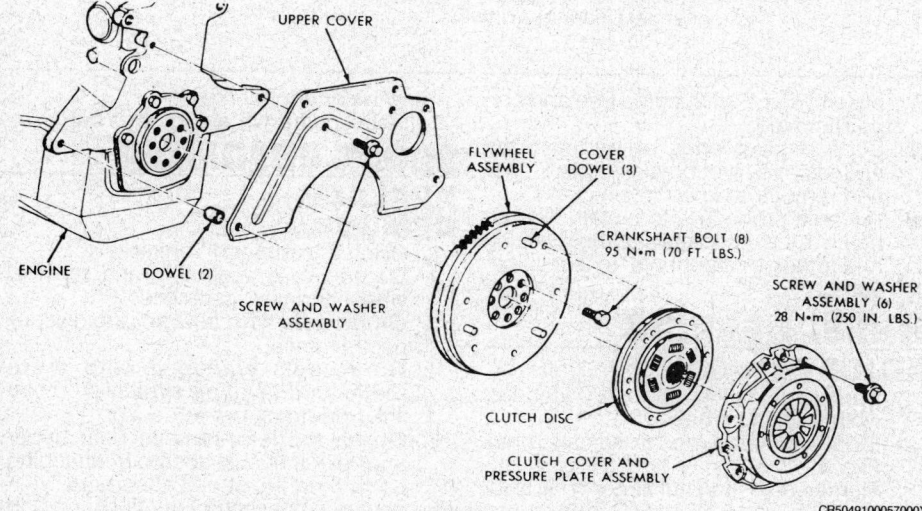

Fig. 6 Clutch assembly.

CR5049100057000X

7. Disconnect driveshafts.
8. Support transaxle and remove upper clutch housing bolts.
9. Remove left engine mount from transaxle noting location of bolts.
10. Remove anti-rotational link, **Fig. 7. Do not remove bracket from transaxle.**
11. Remove transaxle to engine attaching bolts.
12. Move engine and transaxle toward left side of vehicle until mainshaft clears clutch and lower and remove transaxle.
13. Reverse procedure to install. When installing left engine mount, refer to "Engine Mount, Replace" in appropriate engine section.

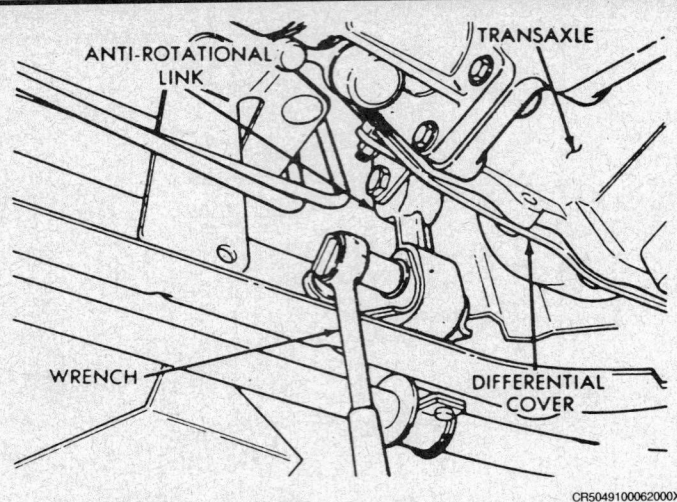

Fig. 7   Anti-rotational link removal

TIGHTENING SPECIFICATIONS

Year	Component	Torque/Ft. Lbs.
1992–95	Anti-Rotational Strut Bracket To Stud Nut	17
	Back-Up Lamp Switch	20
	Case To Engine Block Bolt	70
	Crossover Cable Adjusting Screw	70①
	Flywheel To Crankshaft Bolt	70
	Gearshift Housing To Case Bolt	21
	Gearshift Tube Clamp Bolt	170①

Year	Component	Torque/Ft. Lbs.
1992–95 —Cont'd	Mount To Block And Case Bolt	70
	Pressure Plate To Flywheel Bolt	21
	Selector Cable Adjusting Screw	70①
	Selector Shaft Lockpin	105①
	Shift Linkage Adjusting Pin	9
	Strut To Block Bolt	70
	Strut To Case Bolt	70

①—Inch lbs.

Rear Axle & Suspension

INDEX

REAR AXLE
REPLACE

1. Raise and support vehicle, then support rear axle and remove rear wheels.
2. Disconnect parking brake cable at connector and cable housing at floor pan bracket, **Fig. 1.**
3. Disconnect brake tube assembly from brake line on trailing arm support bracket and remove lock.
4. **On models equipped with automatic load leveling system,** disconnect link from sensor to track bar.
5. **On all models,** disconnect shock absorbers and track bar at rear axle. Support track bar end.
6. Lower axle until spring and isolator

assemblies, **Fig. 2,** come free and can be removed.
7. Support pivot ends of trailing arms and remove pivot bracket bolts. Lower and remove axle from vehicle.
8. Reverse procedure to install. Tighten brake tube assembly to hose fitting and other components to specifications.

WHEEL BEARING
ADJUST

1. **Torque** adjusting nut to 270 inch lbs. while rotating wheel.
2. Stop wheel and loosen adjusting nut, **Fig. 3.**
3. Tighten adjusting nut finger tight. End-play should be .001-.003 inch.
4. Install castle lock with slots aligned

with cotter pin hole.
5. Install cotter pin and grease cap.

SHOCK ABSORBER
REPLACE
REMOVAL

1. Raise and support vehicle.
2. Support axle assembly and remove wheel and tire assemblies.
3. **On models with air shocks,** disconnect air lines.
4. **On models equipped with automatic load leveling system,** remove link from track bar to sensor.
5. **On all models,** remove both upper and lower shock absorber attaching bolts, then the shock absorbers.
6. Lower axle assembly until spring and spring upper isolator can be removed,

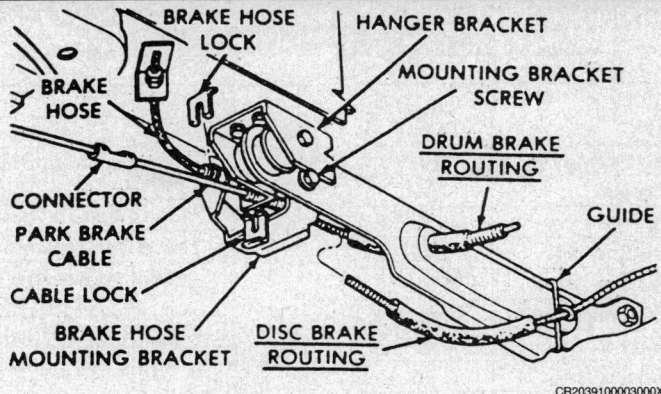

Fig. 1 Parking brake cable & brake tube assemblies

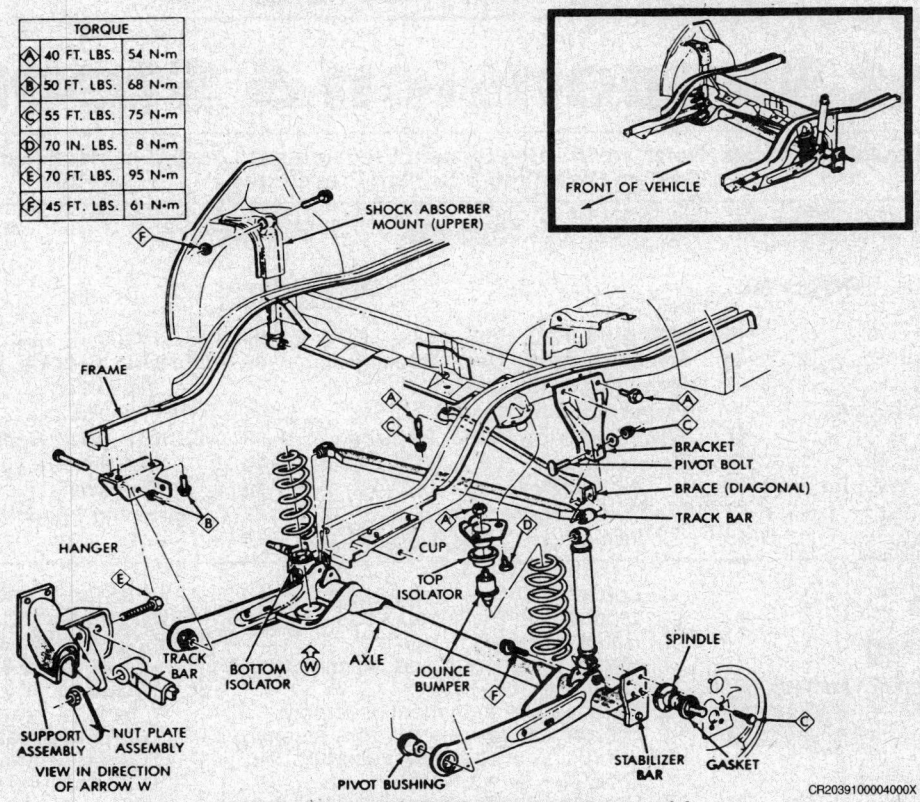

Fig. 2 Rear axle & suspension assembly

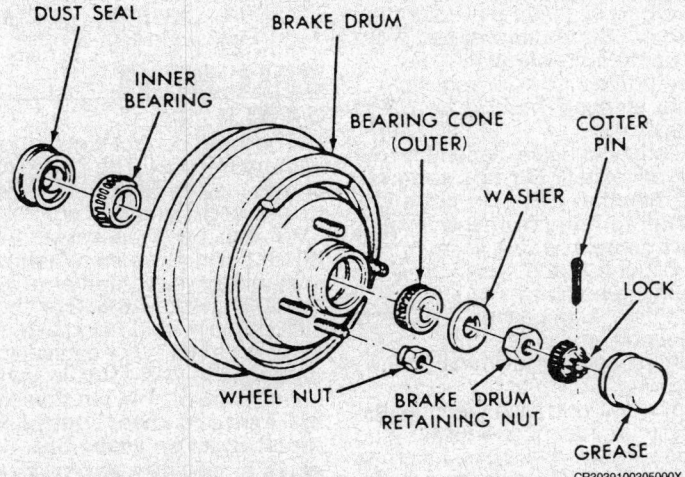

Fig. 3 Wheel bearing assembly

Fig. 2.
INSTALLATION

1. Position jounce bumper to rail, install and **torque** attaching screws to 70 inch lbs.
2. Install isolator over jounce bumper and install spring.
3. Raise axle and install shock absorbers. Loosely assemble lower shock absorber attaching bolts and tighten upper attaching bolts to specifications. On models with load leveling system, attach link to track bar.
4. With suspension supporting vehicle, tighten shock absorber lower attaching screws to specifications.

COIL SPRING
REPLACE

Refer to "Shock Absorber, Replace" for procedure.

TIGHTENING SPECIFICATIONS

Year	Component	Torque/Ft. Lbs.	Year	Component	Torque/Ft. Lbs.
1992–95	Brake Tube To Hose Fitting	140②	1992–95 —Cont'd	Track Bar Mounting Bracket To Rail Bolts	40
	Isolator Cup Screws	70②		Track Bar To Axle Attaching Bolts	70
	Spindle Mounting Bolts	55		Track Bar To Mounting Bracket Bolt	55
	Shock Absorber Mounting Nut	45		Trailing Arm To Hanger Bracket Mounting Bracket Bolts	40
	Strut Damper To Knuckle Leg	75②		Wheel Nuts	95
	Sway Bar Bushing And Cushion Bolt	40			
	Track Bar Brace/Body Stud	40			
	Track Bar Brace To Stud Nut	55			

①—After reaching specified torque, turn an additional 90°.
②—Inch lbs.

Front Suspension & Steering

NOTE: On Air Bag Equipped Models, Refer To "Air Bag System Precautions" Located In The Front Of This Manual For System Disarming & Arming Procedures.

INDEX

PRECAUTIONS

AIR BAG SYSTEMS

Refer to "Air Bag System Precautions" in the front of this manual for system disarming and arming procedures.

DESCRIPTION

These models use a MacPherson type front suspension with vertical shock absorber struts attached to the upper fender reinforcement and steering knuckle, **Fig. 1.** The lower control arms are attached inboard to a crossmember and outboard to the steering knuckle through a ball joint to provide lower steering knuckle position. During steering maneuvers, the strut and steering knuckle rotate as an assembly.

The driveshafts are attached inboard to the transaxle output drive flanges and outboard to the driven wheel hub.

HUB & BEARING

REPLACE

Replacement of the front drive hub and bearing can be done without having to remove the steering knuckle from the vehicle.

1. Remove cotter pin, hub nut and spring washer from end of driveshaft.

2. Loosen hub nut while vehicle is on ground with brakes applied.
3. Raise and support vehicle.
4. Remove hub nut and washer from stub axle.
5. Remove tire and wheel assembly.
6. Disconnect tie rod end from steering arm using suspension puller tool No. C-3894-A or equivalent.
7. Remove clamp nut securing ball joint stud into steering knuckle.
8. Remove caliper guide pin bolts then the caliper. **Suspend caliper from frame using suitable wire.**
9. Remove brake disc from vehicle.
10. Separate steering knuckle from ball joint stud.
11. Pull steering knuckle assembly out and off driveshaft. **Do not separate inner driveshaft joint. Do not allow driveshaft to hang from inner joint, support using suitable wire.**
12. Remove four hub and bearing assembly mounting bolts.
13. Remove hub and bearing assembly from steering knuckle.
14. Reverse procedure to install, noting the following:
    a. Install new hub and bearing assembly in steering knuckle and tighten screws in a cross pattern to specification. **Knuckle and bearing mounting surfaces must be**

smooth and free of foreign material and nicks.
    b. Install new seal using seal installer tool No. C-4698 or equivalent.
    c. **During any service procedures where knuckle and driveshaft are separated, clean seal and wear sleeve, then lubricate both parts.** Lubricate full circumference of seal and wear sleeve with Mopar Multi-Purpose Lubricant, part No. 4318063 or equivalent, as shown in **Fig. 2.**

BALL JOINT

REPLACE

The lower control arm ball joints operate with no freeplay. The ball joint is pressed into the lower control arm. Ball joints can be pressed from lower control arm using a 1¹/₁₆ inch deep socket and tool No. C-4699-2 or equivalent. When pressing ball joint into lower control arm, use tool Nos. C-4699-1 and C-4699-2 or equivalents. Install ball joint seal using a 1¹/₂ socket and tool No. C-4699-2 or equivalent. **On some models the ball joint is welded to the lower control arm. On these models the ball joint and lower control arm must be replaced as an assembly.**

BALL JOINT INSPECTION

With weight of vehicle resting on wheel

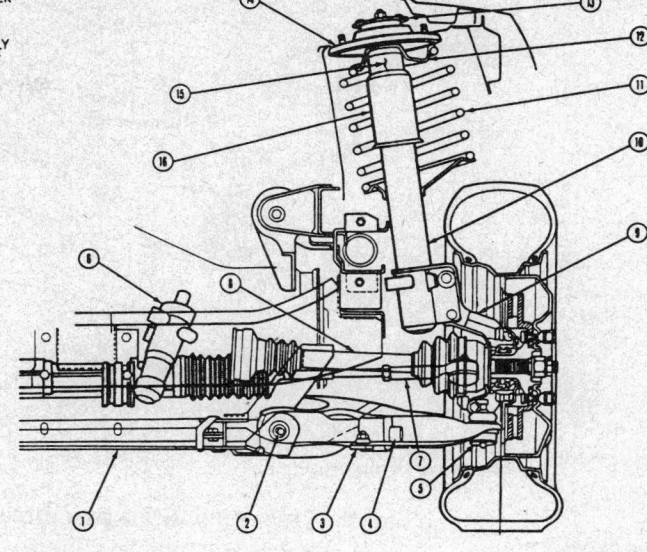

1. FRONT SUSPENSION CROSSMEMBER
2. FRONT PIVOT BOLT
3. LOWER CONTROL ARM
4. SWAY ELIMINATOR SHAFT ASSEMBLY
5. LOWER ARM BALL JOINT ASSEMBLY
6. STEERING GEAR
7. TIE ROD ASSEMBLY
8. DRIVESHAFT
9. STEERING KNUCKLE
10. STRUT DAMPER ASSEMBLY
11. COIL SPRING
12. UPPER SPRING SEAT
13. REBOUND STOP
14. UPPER MOUNT ASSEMBLY
15. JOUNCE BUMPER
16. DUST SHIELD

Fig. 1   Front suspension

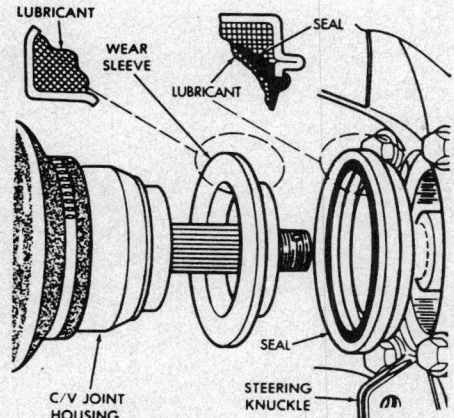

Fig. 2   Seal & wear sleeve lubrication

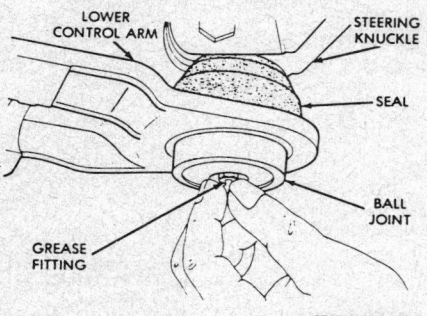

Fig. 3   Ball joint wear inspection

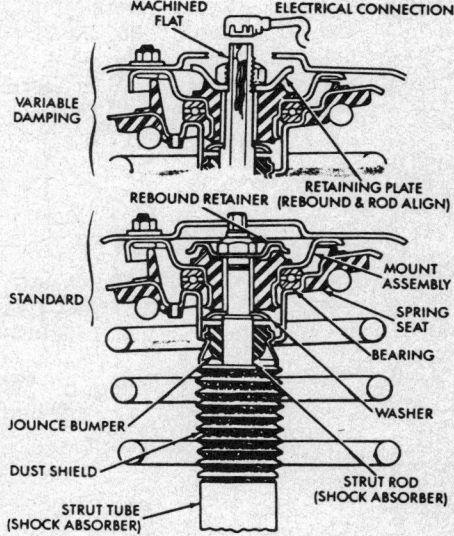

Fig. 4   Strut damper assembly

and tire assembly, attempt to move grease fitting with fingers, **Fig. 3.** Do not use a tool or added force to attempt to move grease fitting. If grease fitting moves freely, then ball joint is worn and should be replaced.

COIL SPRING
REPLACE

MODELS LESS AUTOMATIC LEVEL CONTROL

1. Remove strut damper assembly as outlined under "Strut Damper Assembly, Replace."
2. Using tool spring compression tool No. 4838 or equivalent, compress coil spring.
3. **On models with variable damping,** remove strut rod nut while holding strut rod to prevent rotation.
4. **On all models,** remove mount assembly, **Fig. 4.**
5. Remove coil spring from strut damper.
6. Inspect mount assembly for deterioration of rubber isolator, retainers for

cracks and distortion and bearings for binding.
7. Install bumper dust shield assembly.
8. Install spring and seat, upper spring retainer, bearing and spacer, mount assembly, rebound bumper and retainer and rod nut. Position spring upper retainer tab or notch correctly with respect to bottom bracket.
9. Tighten strut rod nut to specification on models less variable damping. On models with variable damping, hold retaining plate and strut rod with tool No. 6340 or equivalent and tighten strut rod nut to specifications. **Do not release spring compression before torquing nut.**
10. Remove spring compressor tool.

CONTROL ARM
REPLACE

The lower control arm is serviced as a complete assembly with pivot bushings and ball joint.

REMOVAL

1. Raise and support vehicle.
2. Remove front and rear inner pivot through bolt and ball joint to steering knuckle clamp bolt.
3. Separate ball joint from steering knuckle. **Pulling on steering knuck-**

le after releasing from ball joint can separate inner C/V joint.
4. Remove sway bar to control arm end bushing retainer nuts and rotate control arm over sway bar. Remove stub strut retainer. Inspect lower control arm for distortion and check bushings for deterioration.

INSTALLATION

1. Position control arm over sway bar, then install pivot bolts and loosely assemble nuts.
2. Install ball joint stud into steering knuckle, then install clamp bolt. Tighten bolt to specifications.
3. Install sway bar end bushing to control arm, then install retainer bolts. Tighten to specifications.
4. Lower vehicle so that the suspension is supporting the vehicle, then tighten pivot bolts to specifications.

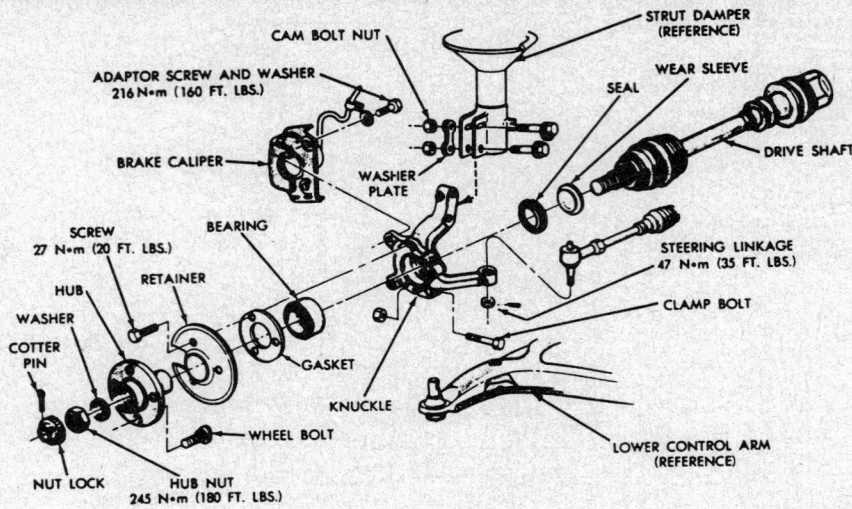

Fig. 5   Steering knuckle assembly

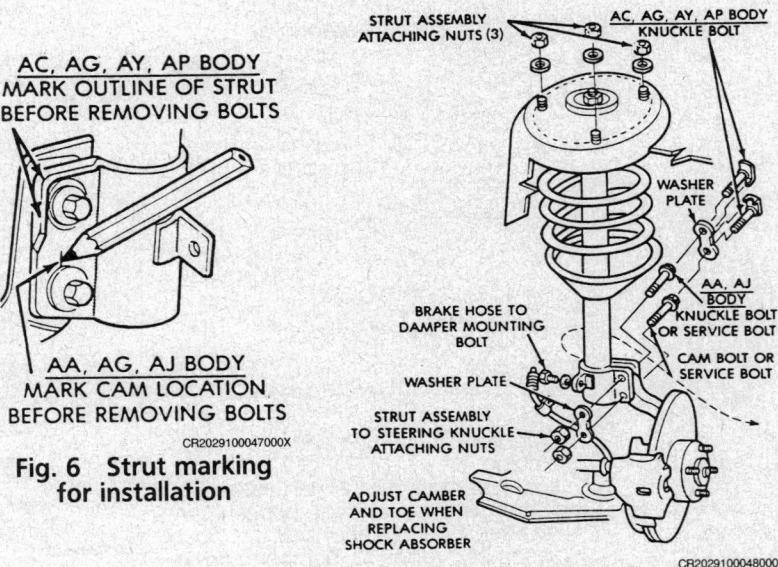

Fig. 6   Strut marking for installation

Fig. 7   Strut damper replacement

STEERING KNUCKLE
REPLACE
REMOVAL

1. Remove wheel hub cotter pin, locknut and spring washer.
2. Loosen hub nut with brakes applied, **Fig. 5. The hub and driveshaft are splined together through the knuckle and retained by hub nut.**
3. Raise and support vehicle.
4. Remove front wheel and the hub nut. Ensure that splined driveshaft is free to separate from spline in hub during knuckle removal. **A pulling force on the shaft can separate the inner C/V joint.** Tap lightly with a brass drift, if required.
5. Disconnect tie rod end from steering arm with puller tool No. C-3894-A or equivalent.
6. Disconnect brake hose retainer from strut damper.
7. Remove clamp bolt securing ball joint stud into steering knuckle and brake caliper adapter screw and washer assemblies.
8. Support caliper with a piece of wire. **Do not allow to hang by brake hose.**
9. Remove rotor.
10. Separate ball joint stud from knuckle assembly, then pull knuckle out and away from driveshaft. **Do not permit driveshaft to hang after separating steering knuckle from vehicle.**

INSTALLATION

1. Place steering knuckle on lower ball joint stud and driveshaft through hub.
2. Install and tighten ball joint to steering knuckle clamp bolt to specifications.
3. Install tie rod end into steering arm and tighten nut to specifications. Install cotter pin.
4. Install rotor.
5. Install caliper over rotor and position adapter to steering knuckle. Install adapter to knuckle bolts and **torque to 160 ft. lbs.**
6. Attach brake hose retainer to strut damper and tighten screw to specifications.
7. Install washer and hub nut, then with brakes applied, tighten hub nut to specifications.
8. Install spring washer, locknut and new cotter pin.

STABILIZER BAR
REPLACE
REMOVAL

1. Raise and support front of vehicle.
2. Remove nuts, bolts and retainers.
3. Remove stabilizer bar.

INSTALLATION

1. Position crossmember bushings on bar with curved surface up and split to front of vehicle. Set upper clamps onto crossmember bushings, lift bar

assembly into crossmember and install lower clamps and bolts.

2. Position retainers at control arms, then insert bolts and install nuts.
3. With lower control arms raised to design height, tighten bolts to specifications.

STRUT DAMPER
REPLACE

REMOVAL

1. Raise and support vehicle, then remove front wheels.
2. **On Acclaim, LeBaron Coupe/Convertible and Spirit,** mark position of camber adjusting cam for proper alignment during installation, **Fig. 6.**
3. **On all models except Acclaim, LeBaron Coupe/Convertible and Spirit,** mark outline of strut on knuckle for proper alignment during installation, **Fig. 6.**
4. **On all models,** remove cam bolt, knuckle bolt or bolts, washer plate or plates and brake hose to damper bracket attaching screw, **Fig. 7.**
5. **On models with active suspension,** disconnect all electrical and air connections.
6. **On all models,** remove strut damper to fender shield attaching nut and washer assemblies.
7. Remove strut damper from vehicle.

INSTALLATION

1. Position strut assembly into fender reinforcement, then install retaining nuts and washers and tighten to specification.
2. Position steering knuckle and washer plate to strut, then install cam and through bolts.

3. Install brake hose retainer on damper, then index alignment marks made during removal.
4. Position a four inch or larger C-clamp on steering knuckle and strut, then tighten clamp just enough to eliminate any looseness between strut and knuckle. Check alignment of marks made during removal. Tighten cam bolt nuts to specifications, then advance nuts an additional 1/4 turn.
5. Remove C-clamp, then install wheel and tire assembly. Tighten wheel lug nuts to specifications.
6. **On models with active suspension,** connect all electrical and air connections.

POWER STEERING PUMP
REPLACE

1. Disconnect vapor separator hose from carburetor or throttle body, then the two wires from A/C clutch cycling switch, if equipped.
2. Remove power steering pump drive belt adjusting bolt and nut, then the nut attaching pump end hose bracket, if equipped.
3. Raise and support vehicle, then remove nut attaching pump pressure hose bracket to crossmember.
4. Disconnect pressure hose from steering gear and allow fluid to drain into a suitable container.
5. Remove drive belt splash shield, then disconnect both pressure and return hoses at power steering pump. Cap hoses and fittings to prevent entry of dirt.
6. Remove lower stud nut and pivot bolt from power steering pump, then lower the vehicle.
7. Remove belt from pump, then move pump rearward to clear mounting bracket and remove adjusting bracket.

8. Rotate pump so pulley faces rear of vehicle, then lift pump assembly from vehicle.
9. Reverse procedure to install.

MANUAL STEERING GEAR
REPLACE

1. Raise and support vehicle, then remove front wheels.
2. Remove tie rod ends with a suitable puller.
3. Disconnect engine damper strut from crossmember, if equipped.
4. Remove front suspension crossmember attaching bolts, then lower the crossmember using a transmission jack, so that steering gear can be disconnected from steering column.
5. Disconnect lower stub shaft from steering gear coupling. **Do not remove roll pin.**
6. **On models with power steering,** disconnect hoses from steering gear.
7. **On all models,** remove bolts attaching steering gear to crossmember, then remove steering gear from crossmember.
8. Reverse procedure to install, noting the following:
   a. Using an assistant, from inside of vehicle, guide steering column coupling onto steering gear. **On models with manual steering, ensure master serrations are aligned.**
   b. **Right rear crossmember bolt is a pilot bolt that correctly locates crossmember. Tighten this bolt first then torque** all crossmember attaching bolts to 90 ft. lbs.
   c. Tighten bolts attaching steering gear to crossmember to specifications.
   d. Check for oil leaks.
   e. Adjust toe as outlined under "Wheel Alignment."

TIGHTENING SPECIFICATIONS

Year	Component	Torque/Ft. Lbs.
1992–95	Brake Hose To Damper Screw	10
	Cam Bolt Nuts	75 ⑥
	Control Arm Clamp Bolt	105
	Control Arm Pivot Bolts	125
	Crossmember Bolts	90 ⑦
	Hub & Bearing Retaining Screws	45 ⑤
	Hub Nut	180
	Manual Steering Gear Clamp And Housing Pad Bolts	17-25
	Manual Steering Gear Tie Rod End Locknut	45-65
	Manual Steering Gear Tie Rod End Nut	25-50
	Power Steering Gear Inner Tie Rod	70
	Power Steering Gear Tie Rod End Locknut	55
	Power Steering Gear Tie Rod End Nut	38
	Power Steering Gear To Crossmember Bolts	50
	Power Steering Pressure Hose Locating Bracket	9
	Power Steering Pressure Hose Tube Nuts	25
	Power Steering Pump Bracket Mounting Fasteners	①
	Power Steering Pump Discharge Fitting	②

Year	Component	Torque/Ft. Lbs.
1992–95 –Cont'd	Power Steering Pump Relief Valve Ball Seat	4 ③
	Power Steering Return Tube Locating Bracket	21
	Power Steering Return Tube Nut	25
	Stabilizer Bar Bushing And Cushion Bolt	50
	Steering Column Clamp Bolt	105 ④
	Steering Column Clamp Stud Nut	20 ④
	Steering Column Clamp Stud	105 ④
	Steering Gear To Crossmember Bolts	50
	Steering Wheel To Steering Shaft Nut	45
	Strut Damper To Knuckle Leg	75 ⑥
	Strut Retaining Nuts	20
	Strut Rod Bolts ⑧	55
	Strut Rod Bolts ⑨	75
	Wheel Lug Nuts	95

①—M8 bolts, 21 ft. lbs.; M10 bolts and nuts, 30 ft. lbs.; M10 stud, 35 ft. lbs.
②—Saginaw pump, 40 ft. lbs.; ZF pump, 37 ft. lbs.
③—Saginaw pump.
④—Inch lbs.
⑤—Torque screws in a cross pattern.
⑥—Turn an additional ¼ turn after reaching specified torque.
⑦—Refer to text.
⑧—Except variable damping.
⑨—Variable damping.

Wheel Alignment

INDEX

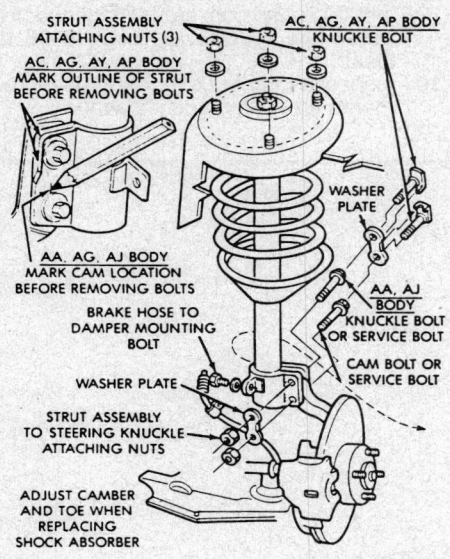

Fig. 1 Camber adjustment

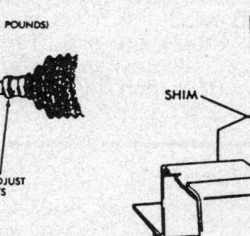

Fig. 2 Toe-in adjustment

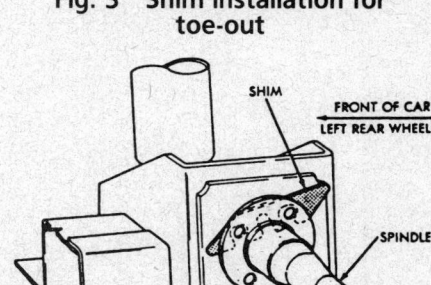

Fig. 3 Shim installation for toe-out

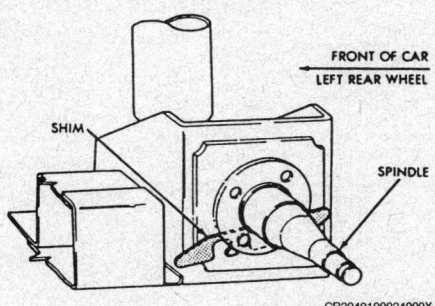

Fig. 5 Shim installation for negative camber

Fig. 6 Shim installation for positive camber

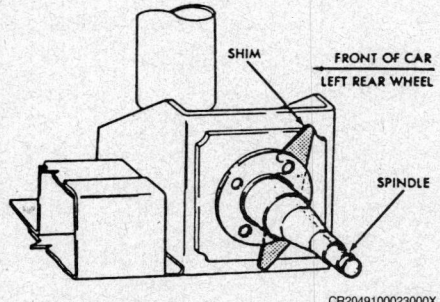

Fig. 4 Shim installation for toe-in

PRELIMINARY INSPECTION

Prior to any wheel alignment check or correction, check the following items:
1. Ensure tires are at recommended pressure.
2. Ensure tires are of equal size and have approximately the same wear pattern.
3. Check front wheel and tire assembly for radial runout.
4. Inspect lower ball joints and steering linkage for looseness.
5. Check front and rear springs for sagging or damage.

Front suspension inspections should be performed on a level floor or alignment rack with fuel tank at capacity and vehicle free of luggage and passenger compartment load. The vehicle should be bounced an equal number of times from the center of the bumper alternately, first from the rear, then the front, releasing at bottom of down cycle.

FRONT WHEEL ALIGNMENT

CASTER

The caster angle on these models cannot be adjusted.

CAMBER

Except Dynasty, Imperial, New Yorker, New Yorker Fifth Avenue, Sundance, Shadow & 1993 Daytona

1. Perform preliminary inspection procedures outlined under "Preliminary Inspection."
2. Loosen cam and knuckle bolts.
3. Rotate cam bolt to move top of wheels in or out to specified camber.
4. **Torque** cam bolts to 75 ft. lbs. plus an additional 1/4 turn.

Dynasty, Imperial, Sundance, Shadow, New Yorker, Fifth Avenue & 1993 Daytona

1. Perform preliminary inspection procedures outlined under "Preliminary Inspection."
2. Position vehicle on alignment equipment and read camber.
3. Remove strut assembly to steering knuckle bolts and replace them with bolts provided in alignment cam and bolt service package.
4. Rotate adjusting cam bolt, **Fig. 1**, to obtain specified camber setting.
5. Carefully reach around tire and tighten knuckle bolts to retain camber setting then **torque** knuckle bolts to 75 ft. lbs. plus an additional 1/4 turn.

TOE-IN

1. Perform preliminary inspection procedures outlined under "Preliminary Inspection."
2. Center steering wheel and hold in position with a suitable tool.
3. Loosen tie rod locknuts and rotate the rod, **Fig. 2**.

4. Adjust toe-in to specifications. **Use care not to twist steering gear rubber boots.**

5. **Torque** tie rod locknuts to 55 ft. lbs. Adjust position of steering gear rubber boots. Remove steering wheel holding tool.

REAR WHEEL ALIGNMENT

Due to the design of the rear suspension and the incorporation of stub axles or wheel spindles, it is possible to adjust the camber and toe of the rear wheels on these models. Adjustment is controlled by adding shims approximately .010 inch thick between the spindle mounting surface and spindle mounting plate. The amount of adjustment is approximately .3° per shim. Proceed as follows:

1. Remove wheel and tire assembly.
2. Pry off grease cap, then remove cotter pin and castle lock.
3. Remove adjusting nut, then remove brake drum.
4. Loosen, but do not remove brake assembly and spindle mounting bolts enough to allow clearance for shim installation, **Fig. 2.**
5. Refer to **Figs. 3 through 6** for proper placement of shims.
6. Tighten the four brake support plate and spindle to axle mounting bolts until snug, then **torque** bolts on all models except Imperial and Dynasty to ft. lbs. and to 80 ft. lbs. on Dynasty and Imperial.
7. Install brake drum, then install washer and nut. **Torque** adjusting nut to 20-25 ft. lbs. while rotating wheel, then back off adjusting nut with wrench to completely release bearing preload. Finger tighten adjusting nut.
8. Position locknut with one pair of slots inline with cotter pin hole, then install cotter pin. Endplay should be 0.001-0.003 inch.
9. Install grease cap, then wheel and tire assembly. **Torque** lug nuts to 95 ft. lbs.
10. Inspect alignment to ensure measurements are within specifications.

DODGE & PLYMOUTH NEON

NOTE: Refer To Rear Of This Manual For Vehicle Manufacturer's Special Service Tool Suppliers.

INDEX OF SERVICE OPERATIONS

NOTE: For Service Operations Not Listed Below, Refer To The Table Of Contents In The Front Of This Manual.

Specifications

GENERAL ENGINE SPECIFICATIONS

Year	Engine Liter/CID ①	VIN Code ②	Fuel System	Bore and Stroke Inch (Millimeters)	Compression Ratio	Net HP @ RPM	Maximum Torque Ft. Lbs @ R.P.M.	Normal Oil Pressure psi. @ 3000 RPM
1995	2.0L/4-122	S	MPI ③	87.50 x 83.0	9.8	132 @ 6000	129 @ 5000	25-80 ④

① —CID-cubic inch displacement.
② —8th digit of VIN denotes engine code.
③ —Sequential Multi-Port Fuel Injection.
④ —At curb idle, 4 psi.

TUNE UP SPECIFICATIONS

Liter/CID	Spark Plug Gap	Firing Order	Ignition Timing @ BTDC		Curb Idle Speed	Fuel Pump Pressure psi.
			Man. Trans.	Auto. Trans.		
1995						
2.0L/4 122	.035 In.	1-3-4-2	①	①	③	48 ②

①—Direct Ignition System (DIS), not adjustable.
②—Without vacuum applied to pressure regulator.
③—Below 1000 miles, 550–1300 RPM. Above 1000 miles, 600–1300 RPM.
④—Refer to Fig. A.

FRONT WHEEL ALIGNMENT SPECIFICATIONS

Year	Camber, Degrees ①		Caster, Degrees ①		Toe In, Degrees	
	Limits	Desired	Limits	Desired	Limits	Desired
1995	-0.4 to +0.4	0	+1.8 to +3.8 ②	+2.8	-0.1 to +0.3	+0.1

①—Reference angle only, non adjustable.
②—Side to side differential not to exceed .1°.

REAR WHEEL ALIGNMENT SPECIFICATIONS

Year	Camber Angle, Degree ①		Total Toe, Degrees ①		Thrust Angle, Degree ①
	Limits	Desired	Limits	Desired	
1995	-0.75 to +0.25	-0.25	-0.1 to +0.3	+0.1	-.1 to +.1

①—Reference angle only, non adjustable.

COOLING SYSTEM & CAPACITY DATA

Year	Engine Liter/ CID (VIN) ①	Coolant Capacity		Radiator Cap Relief Pressure, Lbs.	Thermo. Opening Temp. Deg. F	Fuel Tank Gals.	Engine Oil Refill Qts. ③	Auto. Transaxle Oil Qts. ②	Man. Transaxle Pts.
		Less A/C Qts.	With A/C Qts.						
1995	2.0L/4 122 (C)	7.4	7.4	15	195	11	4.5	④	4.0-4.6

①—The eighth digit of Vehicle Identification Number (VIN) denotes engine code.
②—Approximate, make final inspection with dipstick.
③—Includes oil filter.
④—After overhaul, 8.8 qts. Oil pan only, 4.0 qts.

LUBRICANT DATA

Year	Transaxle Lubricant Type		Power Steering	Brake System
	Automatic	Manual		
1995	Mopar ATF Type 7176	Mopar Type 9417	4318055 ①	DOT 3

①—Chrysler Corp. part No.

NOTE: Refer to Air Bag System Precautions Located In Front Of This Manual For System Disarming & Arming Procedures.

INDEX

PRECAUTIONS

AIR BAG SYSTEMS

Refer to "Air Bag System Precautions" in the front of this manual for system disarming and arming procedures.

FUSE PANEL LOCATION

The fuse panel is located behind the left side of the instrument panel, left of the steering column.

RELAY CENTER LOCATION

The relay center is located on the right-hand side of the engine compartment, next to the battery.

STARTER
REPLACE

1. Disconnect battery ground cable.
2. Raise and support vehicle.
3. **On models equipped with A/C,** proceed as follows:
   a. Using a floor jack or jackstand, support engine and transaxle so it will not rotate.
   b. Remove front engine mount through bolt from insulator and front crossmember mounting bracket.
   c. Lower engine to rotate assembly forward for access to starter.
4. **On all models,** remove starter to transaxle housing attaching bolts.
5. Remove starter from transaxle to gain access to electrical connectors.
6. Remove positive battery cable and alternator output wires from starter.
7. Remove ignition wire from starter solenoid.
8. Position starter vertically with flange pointed downward.
9. Lower starter from engine compartment while repositioning A/C lines for clearance.
10. Reverse procedure to install, noting

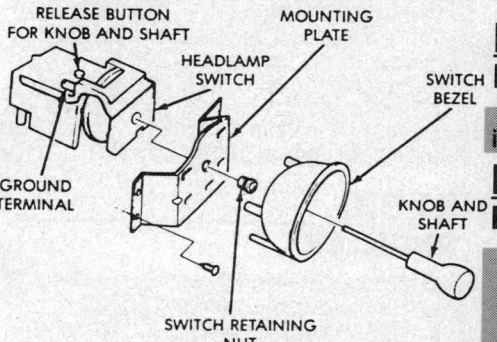

Fig. 1 Headlamp switch replacement

the following:
   a. **Torque** starter mounting bolts to 40 ft. lbs.
   b. **Torque** front engine mount through bolt to 40 ft. lbs.

ALTERNATOR
REPLACE

1. Disconnect battery ground cable.
2. Loosen alternator adjustment nut.
3. Turn front wheels fully to right, then raise and support vehicle.
4. Remove lower splash shield.
5. Disconnect alternator wiring.
6. Loosen alternator pivot bolt.
7. Remove alternator drive belt.
8. Remove three bolts from pivot bracket.
9. Remove pivot nut from T-bolt while supporting alternator.
10. Lower alternator and remove through wheelwell.
11. Reverse procedure to install, noting the following:
    a. **Torque** alternator mounting bolts to 40 ft. lbs.
    b. **Torque** alternator feed terminal nut to 75 in. lbs.

IGNITION LOCK
REPLACE

Refer to "Ignition Switch, Replace" for ignition lock replacement procedure.

IGNITION SWITCH
REPLACE

1. Disconnect battery ground cable.
2. Turn ignition switch to Run position.
3. Using suitable tool, depress lock cylinder retaining tab through hole in lower shroud and remove lock cylinder.
4. Disconnect ignition switch electrical connectors.
5. Remove ignition switch mounting screw.
6. Depress retaining tabs and pull ignition switch from steering column.
7. Reverse procedure to install, ensuring ignition switch is in Run position and actuator rod in lock housing is in Run position.

CLUTCH START SWITCH
REPLACE

1. Disconnect battery ground cable.
2. Disconnect electrical connector from switch.
3. Depress tabs on switch and push through mounting bracket.
4. Reverse procedure to install.

HEADLAMP SWITCH
REPLACE

1. Disconnect battery ground cable.
2. Remove steering column cover and liner.
3. Remove three screws securing headlamp switch mounting plate to instrument panel.
4. Pull headlamp switch assembly rearward from instrument panel opening.
5. Disconnect two electrical connectors from switch.
6. Depress button on bottom of switch,

then pull control knob out of switch, **Fig. 1.**
7. Unsnap headlamp switch bezel from mounting plate for access to retaining nut.
8. Remove retaining nut and mounting plate from switch.
9. Reverse procedure to install.

STOP LIGHT SWITCH
REPLACE

1. Disconnect battery ground cable.
2. Depress brake pedal and rotate switch counterclockwise approximately thirty degrees.
3. Pull switch rearward and remove from mounting bracket.
4. Disconnect wire connector from switch.
5. Pull switch plunger head out until ratchet sound stops.
6. Reverse procedure to install.

COMBINATION SWITCH
REPLACE

1. Disconnect battery ground cable.
2. Remove upper and lower steering column shrouds.
3. Remove combination switch mounting screws.
4. Reverse procedure to install.

TURN SIGNAL SWITCH
REPLACE

Refer to "Combination Switch, Replace" for procedure

DIMMER SWITCH
REPLACE

Refer to "Combination Switch, Replace" for procedure

STEERING WHEEL
REPLACE

1. Disconnect battery ground cable.
2. Place front wheels straight forward.
3. Rotate steering wheel 180 degrees clockwise.
4. Lock steering with column lock cylinder.
5. Remove speed control switch and connector.
6. Remove air bag module attaching bolts from rear of steering wheel.
7. Lift module and disconnect wiring.
8. Remove steering wheel retaining nut and vibration damper if equipped.
9. With appropriate tool, remove steering wheel while avoiding damage to clockspring wiring.
10. Reverse procedure to install, noting the following:
    a. Install steering wheel ensuring flats on hub align with clockspring.
    b. **Torque** steering wheel mounting nut to 45 ft. lbs.

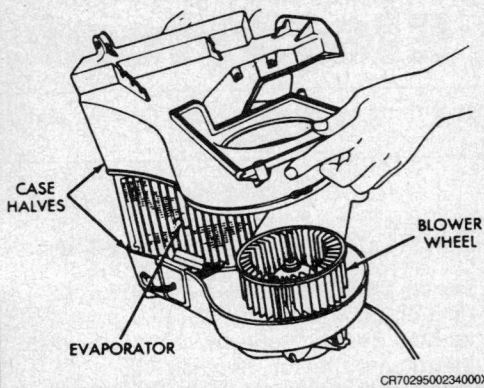

CASE HALVES

EVAPORATOR

BLOWER WHEEL

CR7029500234000X

Fig. 2 Evaporator case separation

INSTRUMENT CLUSTER
REPLACE

1. Disconnect battery ground cable.
2. Remove instrument panel top cover and cluster bezel.
3. Remove four screws attaching cluster housing to base panel.
4. Pull cluster rearward to disconnect from base panel.
5. Remove cluster assembly.
6. Reverse procedure to install.

RADIO
REPLACE

1. Disconnect battery ground cable.
2. Remove center module bezel
3. Remove two mounting screws on radio to remove from instrument panel.
4. Disconnect wiring and antenna lead from radio.
5. Reverse procedure to install.

WIPER MOTOR
REPLACE

1. Disconnect battery ground cable.
2. Remove wiper arms and blades.
3. Remove rear hood seal and cowl screen.
4. Remove electrical connector at wiper motor.
5. Remove mounting screws from wiper assembly.
6. Disconnect wiper linkage from ballcrank on wiper motor.
7. Reverse procedure to install.

WIPER SWITCH
REPLACE

1. Disconnect battery ground cable.
2. Remove three screws from steering column shroud and remove upper half of shroud.
3. Remove mounting screws on switch and remove switch.
4. Disconnect electrical connector from switch.
5. Reverse procedure to install.

BLOWER MOTOR
REPLACE

1. **On models less A/C,** disconnect blower motor electrical connector, then remove blower motor by turning motor counterclockwise while pulling down locking tab.
2. **On models with A/C,** remove right-side scuff plate, then pull back carpet.
3. Cut wheel housing silencer in line with blower motor wiring.
4. Disconnect blower motor wiring connector.
5. Remove blower motor retaining screws, then lower blower motor assembly from unit housing.
6. Reverse procedure to install, taping silencer in position.

HEATER CORE
REPLACE

1. Remove instrument panel .
2. Drain cooling system and disconnect heater hoses at dash panel.
3. Plug heater core outlets to prevent coolant spillage during housing removal.
4. **On models equipped with A/C,** evacuate and recover A/C refrigerant.
5. Remove suction line at expansion valve. Plug refrigerant lines to prevent contamination of system.
6. Remove expansion valve from evaporator.
7. Remove drain hose from evaporator case.
8. Remove three retaining nuts on firewall in engine compartment.
9. Remove right retaining screw from heater case.
10. Disconnect blue five-way connector from plenum.
11. Remove heater case assembly.
12. Reverse procedure to install.

EVAPORATOR CORE
REPLACE

1. Refer to "Heater Core, Replace" for unit removal.
2. Remove clips and screws to separate evaporator/blower case.
3. Remove evaporator case foam seal.
4. Remove four retaining screws from air duct and remove air duct with recirculation door assembly.
5. Disconnect fin sensing switch from harness.
6. Remove upper and lower clips and screws and separate case halves, **Fig. 2.**
7. Remove evaporator from case.
8. Reverse procedure to install.

2.0L/4–122 Engine

NOTE: Refer To 2.0L/4-122 Engine In The "Cirrus & Stratus" Section Of This Manual For Any Procedure Not Covered In This Section.

NOTE: Refer To "Air Bag System Precautions" Located In The Front Of This Manual For System Disarming & Arming Procedures.

INDEX

PRECAUTIONS

AIR BAG SYSTEMS

Refer to "Air Bag System Precautions" in the front of this manual for system disarming and arming procedures.

FUEL PRESSURE RELIEF

1. Disconnect ground cable from auxiliary jumper terminal.
2. Remove fuel filler cap.
3. Remove protective cap from fuel pressure test port on fuel rail.
4. Place open end of fuel pressure release hose, tool No. C-4799-1 or equivalent, into a suitable gasoline container, then connect other hose end to fuel pressure test port. Fuel pressure should bleed off through hose into container.

ENGINE MOUNT

REPLACE

FRONT

1. Support engine and transaxle with suitable floor jack.
2. Remove front engine mount through bolt from insulator and crossmember mounting bracket.
3. Remove mass damper, front mount nuts and insulator assembly.
4. Remove front mounting bracket.
5. Reverse procedure to install.

LEFT

1. Raise and support vehicle, then remove left front tire wheel assembly.
2. Remove power distribution center and place aside.
3. Support transaxle with suitable jack, then remove the insulator through bolt from mount.
4. Remove transaxle mount fasteners, then the mount.
5. Reverse procedure to install.

RIGHT

1. Remove purge duty solenoid from engine mount bracket.
2. Remove right engine mount insulator vertical fasteners from frame rail.
3. Carefully support engine/transaxle assembly to relieve pressure on mount.
4. Remove through bolt from insulator, then the insulator.
5. Reverse procedure to install.

ENGINE

REPLACE

1. Relieve fuel system pressure as outlined under "Precautions."
2. Disconnect and remove battery and tray, then disconnect the Power Control Module (PCM) electrical connector and position aside.
3. Drain cooling system.
4. Remove upper radiator hose and radiator fan module.
5. Remove lower radiator hose.
6. **On models with automatic transaxle,** disconnect oil cooler lines.
7. **On models with manual transaxle,** disconnect clutch cable, transaxle and throttle body linkage.
8. **On all models,** disconnect engine wiring harness electrical connectors.
9. Disconnect heater hoses.
10. Discharge and recover A/C refrigerant following procedure as outlined under "Air Conditioning."
11. Raise and support vehicle, then remove the right inner splash shield.
12. Remove accessory drive belts.
13. Remove axle shafts.
14. Disconnect exhaust pipe from manifold.
15. Remove front and rear engine mount bracket from the body.
16. Lower vehicle, then remove the air cleaner assembly.
17. Remove power steering pump and reservoir.
18. Remove A/C compressor.
19. Remove ground straps to body.
20. Raise and support vehicle to install engine dolly and cradle tool Nos. 6135, 6710 and 6810, or equivalents.
21. Loosen cradle engine mounts, to position engine locating holes to bedplate, then lower the vehicle until engine rests on cradle mounts, tighten mounts to cradle frame to prevent mount movement.
22. Lower vehicle so weight of engine and transmission is only on cradle.
23. Remove engine and transmission mount attaching bolts.
24. Slowly raise and support vehicle, move engine and transmission assembly on cradle to allow for removal around body flanges as required.
25. Reverse procedure to install. Refer to "Tightening Specifications" for fastener torque values.

RADIATOR

REPLACE

1. Disconnect battery ground cable.
2. Drain cooling system, then remove hose clamps from radiator.
3. Disconnect automatic transmission hoses from cooler and plug off.
4. Remove radiator to battery strut, then fan module assembly by disconnecting fan motor electrical connector.
5. Remove fan shroud retaining screws located on top of shroud.
6. Lift shroud up and out of bottom shroud attachment clips separating shroud from radiator.
7. **On models equipped with dual cooling fans,** the left fan module may be removed first, then the right side module.
8. **On all models,** remove upper radiator isolator bracket mounting screws, then engine block heater, if equipped.
9. Remove air conditioning condenser attaching screws located at front of radiator, if equipped. Do not discharge air conditioning system.
10. Remove radiator from engine compartment by lifting upward.
11. Reverse procedure to install.

TIGHTENING SPECIFICATIONS

Year	Component	Torque/Ft. Lbs.
1995	Camshaft Sprocket Bolt	85
	Connecting Rods Cap Bolts	20 ①
	Crankshaft Damper Bolt	105
	Crankshaft Main Bearing Bolts	25
	Cylinder Head Cover Bolts	9
	Engine Mount Bracket Attaching Bolts	30
	Exhaust Manifold Bolts	17
	Intake Manifold Bolts	9
	Oil Drain Plug	25
	Oil Pan Bolts	9
	Radiator Isolator Mounting Bracket	6
	Spark Plugs	20
	Thermostat Housing Bolts	17
	Timing Belt Tensioner	23
	Water Pump To Engine Block	9

① —Plus ¼ turn.

Clutch & Manual Transaxle

NOTE: Refer To "Air Bag System Precautions" Located In The Front Of This Manual For System Disarming & Arming Procedures.

INDEX

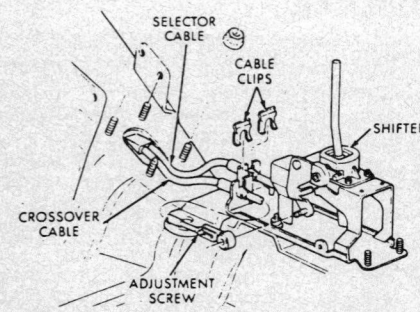

Fig. 1 Gearshift crossover cable adjustment

CR5019500430000X

ADJUSTMENTS

CLUTCH

The clutch cable used on these vehicles incorporates a self adjusting mechanism within the cable outer housing at the pedal end of the cable. A preload spring is used to take up slack in the cable and to keep the release bearing tensional against the fingers of the clutch pressure plate.

GEARSHIFT

The gearshift selector cable is not adjustable. If adjustment is required, only the crossover cable may be adjusted.

1. Remove gearshift console from vehicle.
2. Loosen crossover cable adjustment screw, Fig. 1.
3. Using a ¼ drill bit or equivalent, pin crossover cable lever to transmission, **Fig. 2**. Ensure drill bit engages through crossover lever into transaxle case at least one half inch.
4. Ensure shift lever is in the spring loaded neutral position. If necessary, move lever forward and back then allow lever to fall into it's natural neutral position.
5. Without allowing movement in either cable or lever, hand tighten crossover cable adjustment screw, then **torque** screw to 70 inch lbs.
6. Remove pin from transaxle crossover lever, then check transaxle shift functions.
7. Install gearshift console.

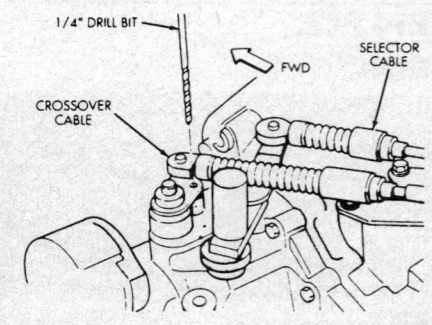

Fig. 2 Crossover lever pin procedure

CR5019500431000X

CLUTCH
REPLACE

1. Remove transaxle as outlined under "Transaxle Replace."
2. Mark clutch cover for possible later installation.
3. Support clutch disc with clutch pilot tool No. 6724 or equivalent during removal to prevent damage.
4. Loosen clutch cover bolts in a cross pattern about two turns at a time to

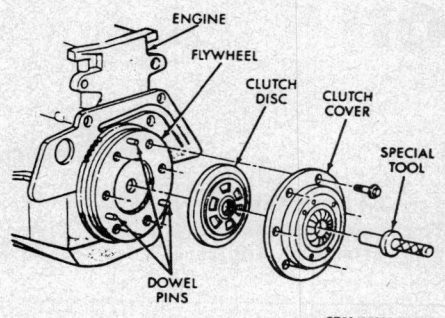

Fig. 3   Clutch assembly

CR5049500085000X

prevent clutch cover damage.
5. Remove clutch cover and clutch plate from flywheel , **Fig. 3**.
6. Reverse procedure to install, noting the following:
   a. The flywheel is manufactured with a slightly tapered surface and the clutch cover may have a concave taper of .000–.0039 inch.
   b. All surfaces must be clean and free of oil or corrosion.
   c. Align clutch disk to flywheel using clutch pilot tool No. 6724 or equivalent.
   d. Tighten clutch cover bolts in a cross pattern about two turns at a time to prevent clutch cover damage.
   e. **Torque** clutch cover bolts to 250 inch lbs.

TRANSAXLE
REPLACE

The transaxle may be removed from the vehicle without removing the engine.

1. Disconnect battery negative and positive cables, then pull power distribution center up and out of its holding bracket and position aside.
2. Remove battery heat shield, battery and battery tray from vehicle.
3. **On models with cruise control**, disconnect cruise control
4. **On all model**, disconnect back-up light switch and speed sensor wiring connectors from transaxle.
5. Using two suitable pry bars and applying equal pressure to each side of shift cable end and crossover cable end, pry cable ends from transaxle shift levers, **Fig. 4**.
6. Remove clutch housing cap to expose clutch cable and release lever, then pull back on clutch cable outer housing to unseat cable from transaxle and then disconnect cable from release lever.
7. Remove shift cable mounting bracket from transaxle housing, then the intake manifold support bracket and upper starter bolt.
8. Remove upper bellhousing bolts.
9. Install a suitable engine support bridge fixture, then adjust support bridge to relieve tension from engine and transaxle mounts.
10. Raise and support vehicle, then remove front wheels.
11. Drain transaxle oil into a suitable container.
12. Remove both front drive axles as outlined under" Driveshaft Replace" in the "Front Wheel Drive Axles" section of this manual.
13. Remove engine damper and bracket.
14. Disconnect starter wiring, then remove lower starter bolt and remove starter.

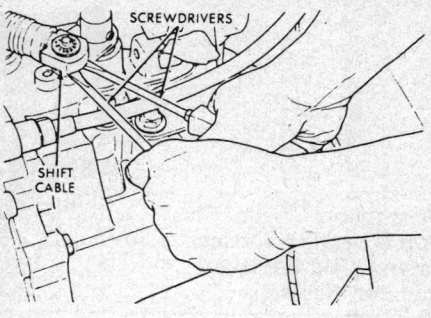

Fig. 4   Disconnecting shift cables

CR5039500504000X

15. Remove engine to transaxle braces, then remove lower bellhousing dust shield bolts.
16. Support transaxle with a suitable jack.
17. Remove front motor mount through bolt, then the front motor mount bolts from engine and transaxle.
18. Remove left transaxle mount to frame through bolt, then the mount from transaxle.
19. Lower transaxle and remove from vehicle.
20. Reverse procedure to install, noting the following:
    a. Tighten bolts to specifications.
    b. With transaxle level, refill to bottom of filler plug hole with Mopar Type M.S.9417 Manual Transaxle Fluid or equivalent.
    c. When installing front drive axles, always use new driveshaft retaining clips.

TIGHTENING SPECIFICATIONS

Year	Component	Torque/ ft. lbs.
1995	Bell Housing Cover Bolts	105 ②
	Front Motor Mount Bolt	40
	Left Motor Mount Bolt	40
	Lower Bell Housing Cover Screw	30
	Starter to Transaxle Bolts	40
	Transaxle To Engine Bolt	70
	Wheel Nuts	①

① —Tighten in a cross pattern in two steps. First step 50 ft. lbs., second step 100 ft. lbs.
② —Inch lbs.

Rear Suspension

INDEX

DESCRIPTION

The rear suspension is a fully independent MacPherson strut type **Fig. 1**. A forged spindle knuckle is bolted to the strut assembly. Lateral links and tension struts are used to control position and movement of the rear suspension.

Due to the construction of this type of suspension, only frame contact or wheel lift type hoisting equipment should be used to raise vehicle.

Rear suspension components which become damaged must be replaced. No attempt should be made to repair these components.

HUB & BEARING SERVICE

The rear hub and bearing are serviced as an assembly.
1. Raise and support vehicle, then remove wheel.
2. **On models with disc brakes,** remove caliper and disc as outlined under "Rotor Replace" in the "Disc Brakes" chapter of this manual.
3. **On models with drum brakes,** remove drum as outlined in the "Drum Brakes" chapter of this manual.
4. **On all models,** remove the hub retaining nut, then the the hub and bearing assembly.
5. Reverse procedure to install. Tighten nuts and bolts to specifications.

WHEEL BEARING
ADJUST

The wheel rear bearings on this vehicle are not adjustable. Tighten hub and bearing retainer nut to specifications.

SPINDLE KNUCKLE
REPLACE

1. Remove rear hub and bearing as outlined under "Hub & Bearing Service".
2. **On models with ABS,** remove the retaining bolt, then the speed sensor, **Figs. 2 and 3.** If speed sensor is seized, **do not use pliers to remove.** Gently tap on mounting ear with a suitable punch and hammer to loosen sensor.
3. **On models with drum brakes,** remove brake support plate mounting bolts, then without disconnecting brake fluid hose, position and support assembly aside. **Do not allow as-**

sembly to hang from the brake fluid hose.
4. **On models with disc brakes,** remove disc brake adapter plate mounting bolts, then without disconnecting brake fluid hose, position and support assembly aside. **Do not allow assembly to hang from the brake fluid hose.**
5. **On all models,** loosen but do not remove spindle knuckle to strut clevis nuts. **The spindle knuckle to strut clevis bolts are serrated for a tight fit into the knuckle. Do not turn bolt when loosening. Turn nut only, or damage to knuckle or bolt will occur.**
6. Remove lateral link to knuckle bolt, then using a suitable adjustable wrench to prevent tension strut from turning, remove tension strut nut, washer and bushing **Fig. 4.**
7. Remove spindle knuckle to strut clevis bolts that were previously loosened, then pull spindle knuckle straight out of strut and rotate off tension strut.
8. Reverse procedure to install, noting the following:
   a. Tighten bolts and nuts to specifications.
   b. When tightening spindle knuckle to strut clevis bolts, **do not turn bolts.** Tighten by turning nuts only.
   c. **The lateral link to spindle knuckle bolt must be installed with head of bolt towards front of vehicle.**
   d. Lateral link bolts must be tightened to specification with suspension supporting vehicle weight.
   e. Refer to **Fig. 5** when installing tension strut retainer washers and bushings.
   f. Check and adjust rear wheel alignment as outlined under the "Wheel Alignment" section of this chapter.

STRUT
REPLACE

1. Raise and support vehicle, then remove wheel.
2. Remove brake fluid hose support bracket from strut.
3. **On models with ABS,** remove speed sensor cable and routing clip from strut.
4. **On all models,** loosen but do not remove spindle knuckle to strut clevis bolts. **The spindle knuckle to strut clevis bolts are serrated for a tight fit into the knuckle. Do not turn bolt**

when loosening. Turn nut only, or damage to knuckle or bolt will occur.
5. Lower vehicle, then access four upper strut to strut tower mounting nuts. Removing carpeting and dust shield as necessary.
6. Loosen but do not remove upper strut to tower mounting nuts.
7. Using a suitable device, support suspension. **Do not allow suspension components to hang after removing strut. Do not place support under lateral links or tension strut as they may bend.**
8. Remove previously loosened upper strut mounting nuts and strut to spindle knuckle bolts.
9. Slide strut straight back off spindle knuckle, then lower strut from vehicle.
10. Reverse procedure to install, noting the following:
    a. Tighten bolts and nuts to specifications.
    b. When tightening spindle knuckle to strut clevis bolts, **do not turn bolts,** tighten by turning nuts only.
    c. Check and adjust rear wheel alignment as outlined under the "Wheel Alignment" section of this chapter.

STRUT SERVICE

Coil springs on this vehicle are available in different load rates. Spring rates may be different on each side of the vehicle depending on how the vehicle is equipped. Ensure correct spring rates are chosen during assembly.

The gas-charged strut damper is not rebuildable and is serviced as a unit.
1. Remove strut assembly as outlined under "Strut, Replace".
2. Using a suitable marker or paint, place match marks on components of strut assembly to aid in assembly alignment.
3. Place strut assembly into a suitable vise **Fig. 6. Do not clamp body of strut into vise.**
4. Using coil spring compressor tool No. C-4838 or equivalent, compress spring until tension is removed from upper strut mount assembly.
5. Using strut nut wrench tool No. L-4558A or equivalent, **Fig. 7** and a 10mm socket and breaker bar to hold strut shaft, remove strut shaft nut.
6. Remove outer washer, upper strut mount, coil spring, inner washer, dust shield, jounce bumper and spring isolator from strut **Fig. 1.**

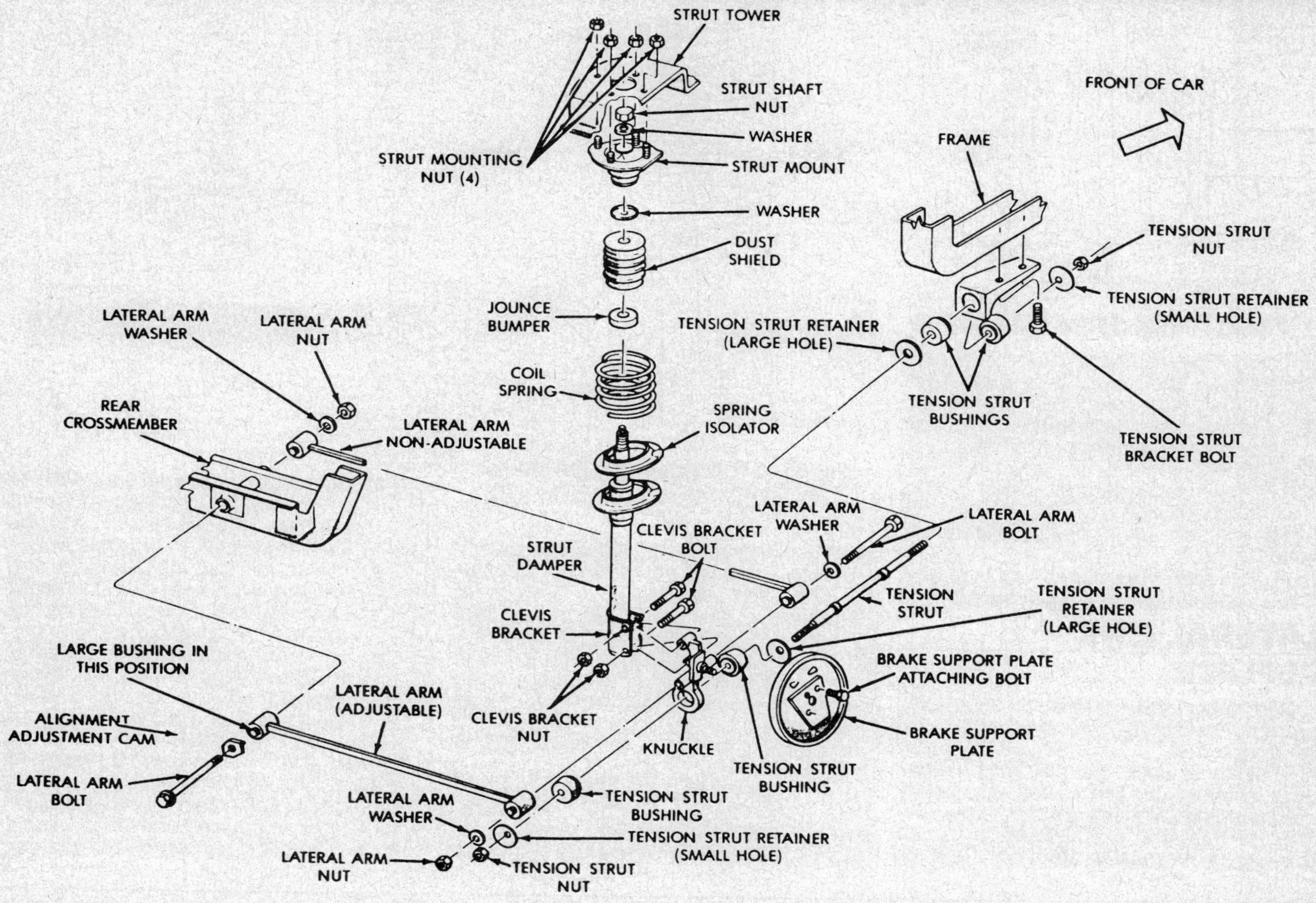

Fig. 1 Exploded view of rear suspension

CR2039500060000X

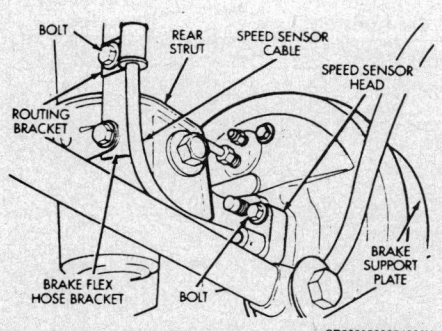

Fig. 2 ABS speed sensor location. Models w/drum brakes

CR2039500054000X

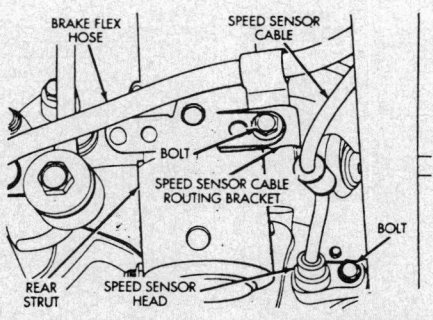

Fig. 3 ABS speed sensor location. Models w/disc brakes

CR2039500055000X

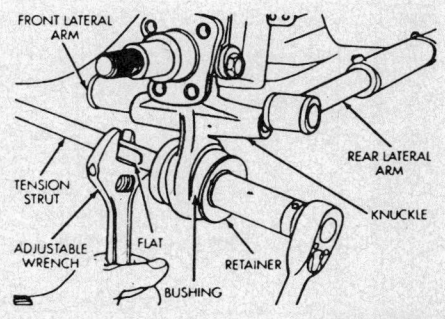

Fig. 4 Tension strut removal

CR2039500056000X

7. Reverse procedure to install, noting the following:
   a. Tighten nuts to specifications.
   b. Install inner strut shaft washer with raised edge up and outer strut shaft washer with raised edge down.
   c. Transfer alignment marks to any replaced component. Ensure alignment of all components during assembly.

TENSION STRUT
REPLACE

1. Using a suitable wrench to prevent tension strut from turning, remove nuts from both ends of tension strut.
2. Remove bushings and washers from tension strut, then remove tension strut.
3. Reverse procedure to install, noting the following:

   a. Tighten nuts to specifications.
   b. Refer to **Fig. 5** when installing tension strut bushings and washers.
   c. Check and adjust rear wheel alignment as outlined under the "Wheel Alignment" section of this chapter.

ROLL BAR
REPLACE

1. Raise and support vehicle, then remove both rear wheels.

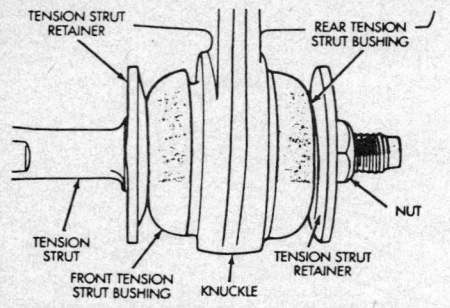

Fig. 5   Tension strut bushings

2. Disconnect roll bar from attaching links at each side, then swing bar down to clear links.
3. Remove bolts from roll bar attaching brackets, then remove roll bar from vehicle.
4. Reverse procedure to install, noting the following:
   a. Tighten nuts and bolts to specifications.
   b. Ensure slit in roll bar bushings face rear of vehicle when installed.

LATERAL LINK
REPLACE

Rear suspension lateral link bushings are not replaceable. Lateral links are serviced as a unit.

The lateral links are not interchangeable. The forward link is non adjustable, both bushings sleeves are the same size. The rearward link is adjustable, the small bushing sleeve must be placed at the spin-

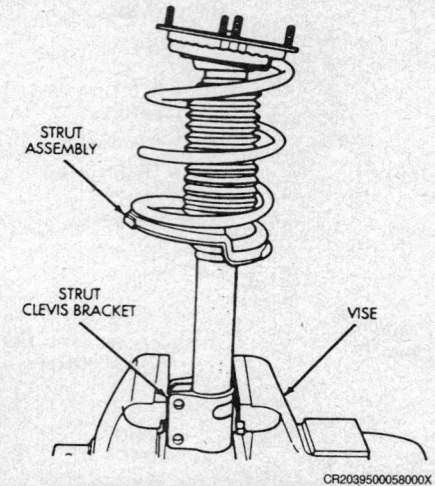

Fig. 6   Strut assembly mounted in vise

dle knuckle to allow toe adjustments.
1. Raise and support vehicle, then remove rear wheels.
2. Remove lateral link attachment bolt and washers at the spindle knuckle.
3. Remove lateral link attachment bolt, washers and adjustment cams at the cross member, then remove lateral links.
4. Reverse procedure to install, noting the following:
   a. Tighten nuts and bolts to specifications.
   b. Forward lateral links have same size bushing sleeves at each end.

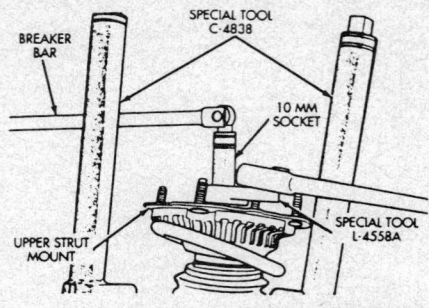

Fig. 7   Strut shaft nut. Removal & installation

   c. Rearward lateral links have two different size bushing sleeves, **small bushing sleeve must be installed at spindle knuckle end.**
   d. The short mounting bolt is used at the spindle knuckle end, **and must be installed with head of bolt towards front of vehicle.**
   e. The long mounting bolt is used at the crossmember end, **and must be installed with head of bolt towards rear of vehicle.**
   f. Lateral link bolts must be tightened to specification with suspension supporting vehicle weight.
   g. Check and adjust rear wheel alignment as outlined under the "Wheel Alignment" section of this chapter.

TIGHTENING SPECIFICATIONS

Year	Component	Torque/Ft lbs.
1995	Brake Caliper To Disc Brake Adapter, Bolt	16
	Brake Hose Mounting, Bolt	35
	Brake Hose Bracket Mounting, Bolt	17
	Disc Brake Adapter To Spindle Knuckle Mounting, Bolt	50
	Drum Or Disc Brake Plate To Spindle Knuckle, Bolt	50
	Hub And Bearing To Spindle Knuckle, Nut	124
	Lateral Link, Nut	70

Year	Component	Torque/Ft lbs.
	Strut Assembly Shaft, Nut	55
	Strut Assembly To Spindle Knuckle Clevis, Nut	70
	Strut Assembly To Tower, Nuts	300①
	Roll Bar Isolator Bracket To Frame, Bolt	300①
	Roll Bar To Rear Strut Link, Nut	300①
	Tension Strut Shaft, Nut	70
	Tension Strut to Body Attaching Bracket, Bolt	70
	Wheel Nuts	95

①—Inch lbs.

Front Suspension & Steering

INDEX

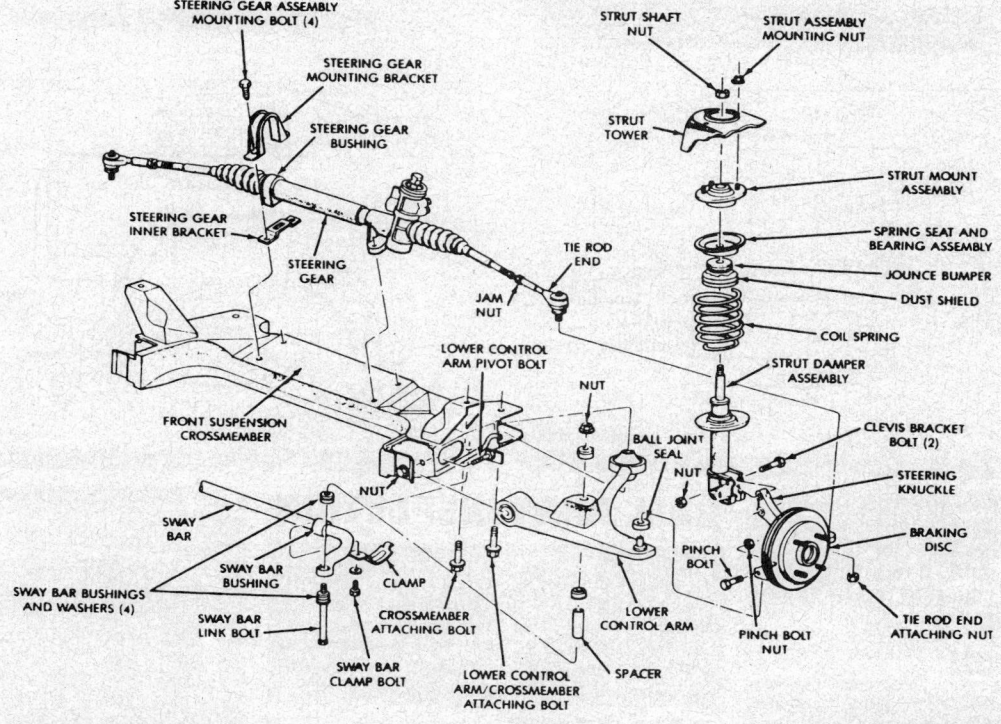

Fig. 1 Exploded view of front suspension system

DESCRIPTION

This suspension is a gas pressurized MacPherson strut system used in place of front suspension upper ball joint and upper control arm. The bottom of the strut is attached directly to the steering knuckle using two attaching bolts and nuts going through the clevis bracket and steering knuckle, **Fig. 1.**

A cast lower arm assembly is attached to the front suspension crossmember using two rubber isolator bushings and to the steering knuckle by means of a ball joint.

A sealed for life front hub and bearing assembly is attached to the front steering knuckle. The outer CV joint assembly is splined to the front hub and bearing assembly.

HUB & BEARING SERVICE
REMOVAL

1. Remove cotter pin, castle nut and hub

nut while vehicle is still on floor with brakes applied.
2. Raise and support vehicle, then remove front tire and wheel assembly.
3. Remove front disc brake caliper and place aside. **Do not let caliper assembly hang by hose.**
4. Remove front disc brake, then disconnect tie rod from steering knuckle using removal tool No. MB-990635, or equivalent.
5. Separate ball joint stud from steering knuckle by prying down on lower control arm. **Ensure ball joint seal is not damage.**
6. Pull steering knuckle assembly out and away from outer CV joint of driveshaft assembly.
7. Remove two steering knuckle to strut damper attaching bolts, then the steering knuckle and hub/bearing assembly from vehicle.

DISASSEMBLY

All steps of the hub bearing removal

from steering knuckle must be done using a hydraulic arbor press
1. Install bearing splitter tool No. P334, or equivalent, on steering knuckle and hub/bearing assembly to support steering knuckle when pressing out bearing.
2. Position steering knuckle and hub/bearing assembly in vise, **Fig. 2,** support by splitter tool No. P334, or equivalent.
3. Position driver tool No. 6644-2, or equivalent on small end of hub, then press hub from bearing. The one bearing race may come out with hub when hub is removed from bearing.
4. Remove bearing splitter from steering knuckle, then place steering knuckle is press supported by press blocks, **Fig. 3.**
5. Place bearing driver tool No. MB-990799, or equivalent, on outer race of hub bearing, then press hub bearing completely out of steering knuckle.
6. Install bearing splitter tool No. P334 on hub so it is between flange of hub

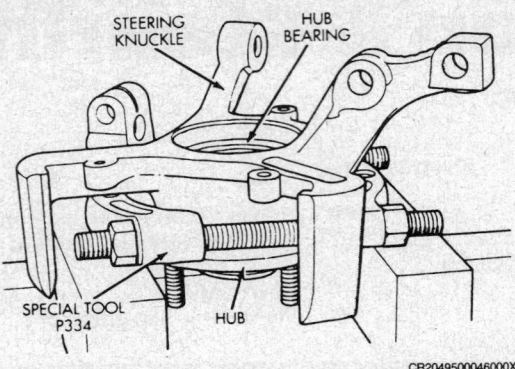

Fig. 2 Hub, bearing & steering knuckle supported for removal of hub

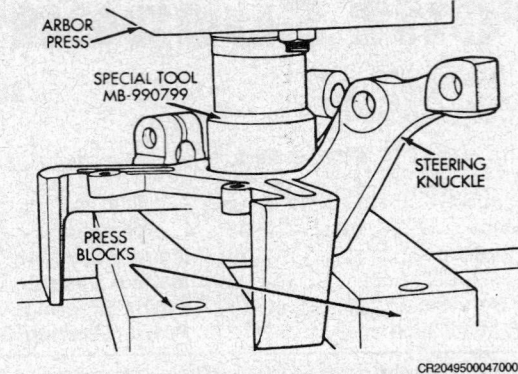

Fig. 3 Hub bearing removal

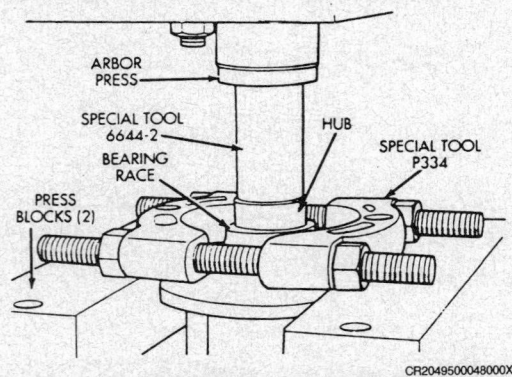

Fig. 4 Hub bearing race removal

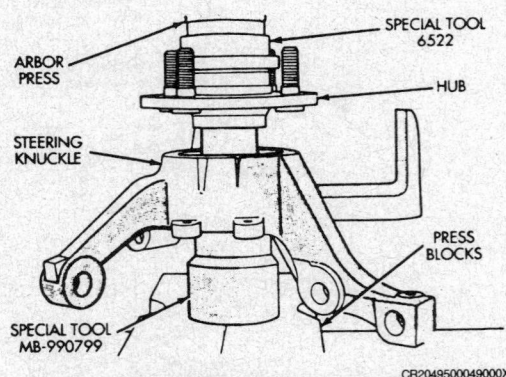

Fig. 5 Hub bearing installation

and bearing race remaining on hub.
7. Install assembly into press, then install place driver tool No. 6644-2, or equivalent on end of hub and press hub out of hub bearing race, **Fig. 4.**

ASSEMBLY & INSTALLATION

1. Install new bearing into bore of steering knuckle so it is square with bore, then place steering knuckle in press with receiver tool No. C-4698-2, or equivalent, supporting steering knuckle.
2. Place driver tool No. 5052, or equivalent on outer race of hub, then press hub bearing into steering knuckle until it is fully bottom in bearing bore of steering knuckle.
3. Install hub bearing retaining snap ring into groove in hub bearing bore of steering knuckle. **Ensure snap ring is fully seated.**
4. Place steering knuckle with hub bearing installed in press with receiver tool No. MB-990799, or equivalent, supporting inner race of hub bearing, **Fig. 5.**
5. Place hub into hub bearing ensuring it is square with bearing.
6. Place driver tool No. 6522, or equivalent on front face of hub, then press hub into bearing until it bottoms in hub bearing.
7. Reverse remaining steps to install new steering knuckle ball joint stud, clamp bolt and nut. Torque **clamp bolt to 70 ft. lbs.**

BALL JOINT INSPECTION

With weight of vehicle resting on wheel, grasp grease fitting and with no mechanical assistance or added force, attempt to move grease fitting, **Fig. 6.**
If the ball joint is worn the grease fitting will move easily. If movement is noted, replacement of ball joint is recommended.

BALL JOINT
REPLACE

1. Remove lower control arm following procedure outlined under "Control Arm, Replace."
2. Using screwdriver or other suitable tool, pry ball joint seal boot off ball joint assembly.
3. Position receiving cup tool No. 6758, or equivalent, to support lower control arm while receiving ball joint assembly.
4. Install receiver/Installer tool No. 6804, or equivalent, in top of ball joint assembly.
5. Using suitable press, press ball joint assembly completely out of control arm.
6. Reverse procedure to install.

STRUT
REPLACE

1. Loosen wheel lug nuts, then raise and support vehicle.
2. Remove wheel and tire assembly, then disconnect the hydraulic brake

hose routing bracket from strut bracket.
3. **On models with ABS,** speed sensor is combined with hydraulic hose routing bracket.
4. **On all models,** Remove two strut assembly clevis bracket to steering knuckle attaching bolts.
5. Remove three nuts attaching strut assembly upper mount to shock tower, then the strut.
6. Reverse procedure to install.

STRUT SERVICE

Refer to **Fig. 1** during following procedure.
1. Clamp strut assembly by the clevis bracket into suitable vise.
2. Scribe coil spring and strut assembly right or left, then using compressor tool No. C-4838, or equivalent, compress coil spring, **Fig. 7.**
3. Install socket strut nut tool No. L4558A, or equivalent on strut shaft retaining nut.
4. Install 10mm socket on hex head of strut shaft and remove nut while holding strut to keep from rotating.
5. Remove upper spring seat, pivot bearing and dust shield as an assembly.
6. Remove coil spring.
7. Reverse procedure to install.

CONTROL ARM
REPLACE

Refer to **Fig. 8** during following procedure.

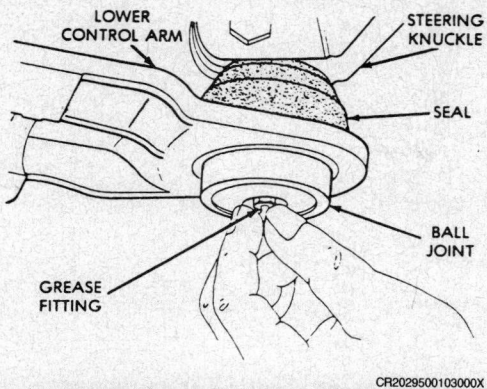

Fig. 6   Ball joint wear inspection

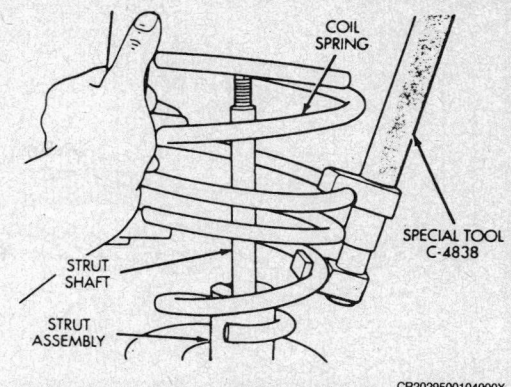

Fig. 7   Coil spring removal

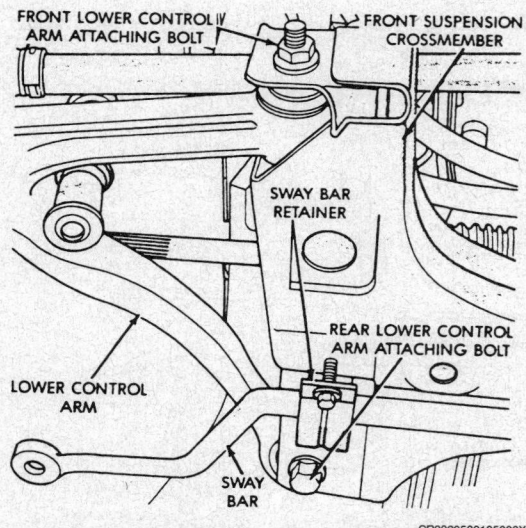

Fig. 8   Lower control arm removal

8. Scribe a line marking the location of where front suspension crossmember is mounted against body.
9. Position a transaxle jack beneath the center of the front suspension crossmember, then remove two bolts attaching front suspension crossmember to frame rails of vehicle.
10. Loosen both rear bolts and lower control arm to body of vehicle.
11. Using transaxle jack lower front suspension crossmember enough to allow steering gear to be removed.
12. Remove four bolts attaching steering gear assembly to front suspension crossmember, then the steering gear assembly.
13. Reverse procedure to install.

POWER STEERING PUMP
REPLACE

1. Disconnect battery ground cable, then the power steering pressure hose from power steering pump.
2. Remove power steering fluid supply hose to power steering suction fitting, then the power steering fluid supply hose.
3. Remove two power steering pump to cast bracket mounting and adjusting bolts.
4. Loosen bolt attaching front power steering pump mounting bracket to front engine mount only far enough to slide bracket from behind bolt.
5. Remove drive belt, then the power steering pump and bracket as an assembly.
6. Reverse procedure to install.

1. Raise and support vehicle, then remove wheel and tire assembly.
2. Remove steering knuckle ball joint ball stud, clamping nut and bolt.
3. Remove attaching links connecting sway bar to lower control arm, then loosen but do not remove, bolts attaching sway bar retainers to front suspension crossmember. Rotate sway bar away from lower control arm.
4. Using a pry bar, separate steering knuckle from ball joint stud, then remove front lower control arm bushing to crossmember attaching nut and bolt.
5. Remove rear lower control arm to crossmember and frame attaching bolt, then the lower control arm.
6. Reverse procedure to install.

STEERING KNUCKLE
REPLACE

Refer to "Hub & Bearing, Replace" for procedure.

POWER STEERING GEAR
REPLACE

This procedure applies to both power steering and manual steering gear assemblies. Refer to **Fig. 9** for power steering gear assembly.
1. Disconnect steering gear coupler from steering column shaft coupler.
2. Raise and support vehicle, then remove both front wheel and tire assemblies.
3. Remove engine/transaxle dampener on vehicles so equipped.
4. Remove attaching nuts from both tie rod ends.
5. Remove both tie rod end studs from steering knuckle using remover tool No. MB-990635, or equivalent, then disconnect wiring harness connector from power steering fluid pressure switch.
6. Remove power steering pressure and return hose routing bracket from front suspension crossmember.
7. Remove power steering fluid, pressure and return hoses from power steering gear assembly.

MANUAL STEERING GEAR
REPLACE

Refer to procedure outlined under "Power Steering Gear, Replace" and **Fig. 10** for service.

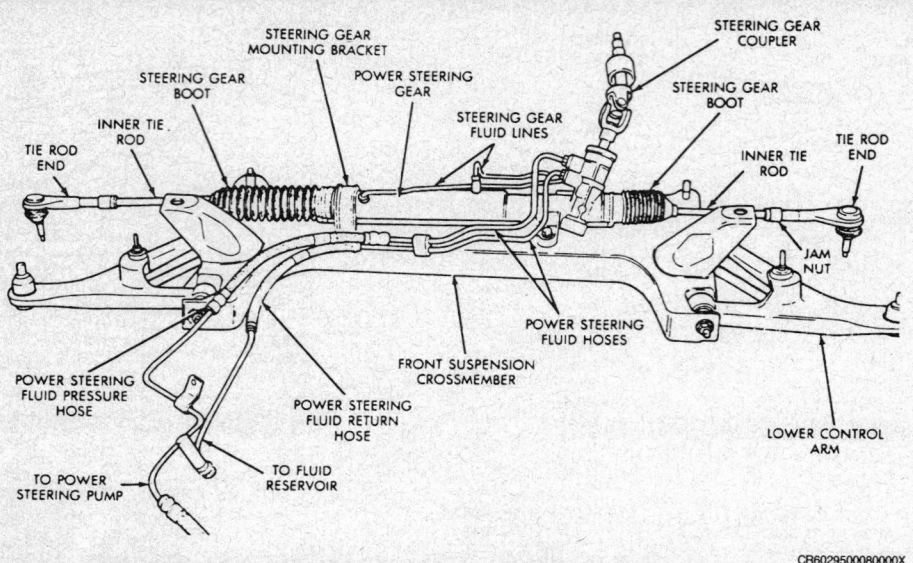

Fig. 9   Power steering gear assembly

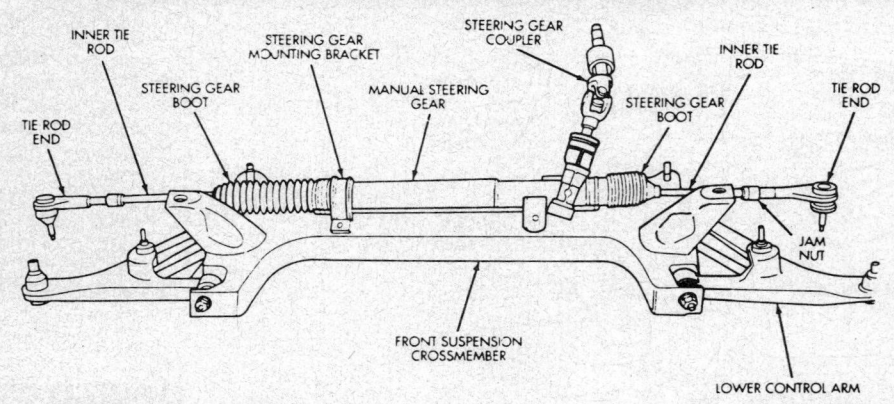

Fig. 10   Manual steering gear assembly

TIGHTENING SPECIFICATIONS

Year	Component	Torque Ft. Lbs.	Year	Component	Torque Ft. Lbs.
1995	Lower Control Arm To Crossmember	120		Stabilizer Bar To Crossmember	21
	Outer Tie Rod To Inner Tie Rod Lock Nut	45		Steering Gear To Crossmember Bolts	50
	Power Steering Pressure Hose Banjo Fitting	25		Strut Assembly To Shock Tower Mounting Bolts	25
	Power Steering Pressure & Return Hose Tube Nuts	23		Strut Assembly Shaft Nut	55
	Power Steering Pump To Rear Bracket Mounting Bolts	40		Tie Rod To Steering Knuckle	45
				Tie Rod End To Steering Knuckle Nut	45
				Wheel Lug Nuts	95

Wheel Alignment

INDEX

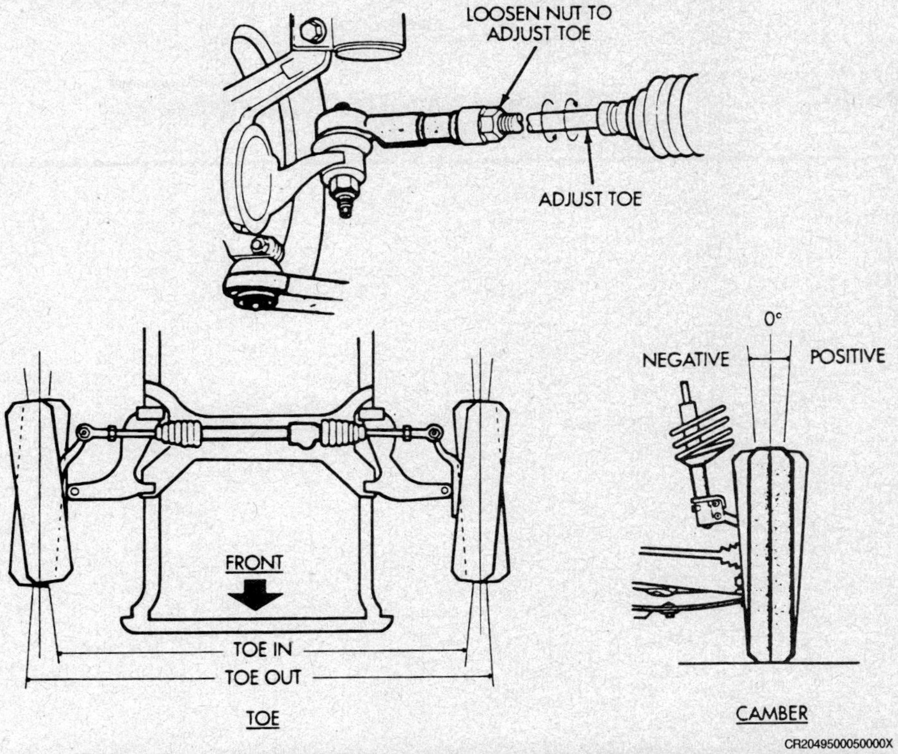

Fig. 1 Camber & toe alignment

PRECAUTIONS

AIR BAG SYSTEMS

Refer to "Air Bag System Precautions" in the front of this manual for system disarming and arming procedures.

PRELIMINARY INSPECTION

Ensure vehicle has a full tank of gas when wheel alignment specifications are checked or adjusted. One full tank of gas is approximately 75 lbs. If tank is not full, this change in weight will affect curb height of vehicle and alignment specifications. Check and adjust tire pressure. Ensure all tires are the same size. Inspect all suspension components for looseness or damage. Components showing signs of wear or damage should be replaced before alignment.

WHEEL ALIGNMENT

Front and rear caster and camber set-
tings are determined at the time vehicle is designed by location of vehicle's suspension components, **Fig. 1**. This should result in no required adjustment of caster and camber after vehicle is built or when servicing suspension components. Caster and camber are not normally considered an adjustable specification when performing an alignment on this vehicle.

If caster is not within specifications, check for damaged suspension components or body damage causing component locations to change. No adjustment is possible for caster.

CAMBER

1. Correctly position vehicle on alignment rack and install all required equipment, per alignment equipment specifications.
2. Center steering wheel and lock in place using steering wheel clamp.
3. Jounce vehicle and read front and rear alignment settings and compare to specifications.
4. If front and rear camber readings obtained are not within specifications, a "Mopar Service Kit" will be required.

5. Raise and support vehicle, then remove original upper bolt attaching front or rear strut clevis bracket to steering knuckle or rear knuckle.
6. Loosen lower bolt attaching strut clevis bracket to steering knuckle or rear knuckle only enough to allow knuckle to move in clevis bracket.
7. Install bolt from service kit into upper strut clevis bracket to steering knuckle or rear knuckle mounting hole.
8. Install nut provided by service kit on replacement bolt.
9. Tighten upper bolt and nut from service kit until snug, but still allowing movement between strut clevis bracket and knuckle.
10. Remove original lower bolt and install bolt from service kit into lower strut clevis bracket hole. Install nut and tighten until snug.
11. Lower vehicle until full weight is supported by suspension, then jounce front and rear of vehicle.
12. Adjust camber to preferred setting by pushing or pulling top of tire.
13. Tighten upper and lower strut clevis bracket bolts.
14. Jounce vehicle an equal number of times and verify rear camber setting. When vehicle is at correct setting, **torque** both front strut clevis brackets to 40 ft. lbs., plus an additional ¼ turn.

TOE

Refer to **Fig. 1** during this procedure.
1. Center steering wheel and lock in place using a steering wheel clamp. **When performing toe setting procedure, set rear wheel toe to specification first, then front wheel toe.**
2. Loosen nuts on attaching bolts for left and right lateral links to rear crossmember, **Fig. 2**.
3. Rotate lateral link adjustment cams, **Fig. 3**, until preferred rear toe specification is obtained.
4. While holding toe adjustment cams from turning, tighten right and left lateral links to rear crossmember attaching bolt nuts. This will securely hold adjustment cams in position.
5. Hold lateral link attaching bolt and adjustment cam from turning and **torque** lateral link attaching bolt to 70 ft. lbs.
6. Loosen front inner tie rod end jam nuts, then grasp inner tie rods at serration.
7. Rotate inner tie rods of steering gear and set front toe specification.
8. **Torque** tie rod lock nuts to 45 ft. lbs.

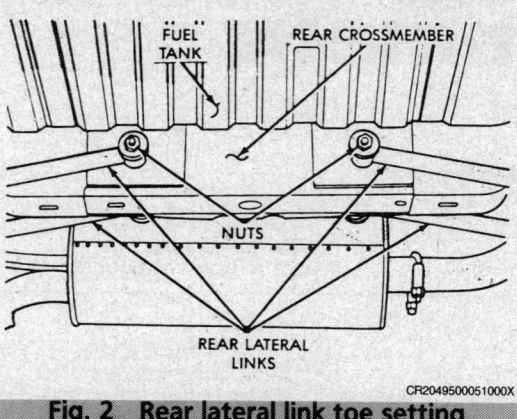

Fig. 2   Rear lateral link toe setting

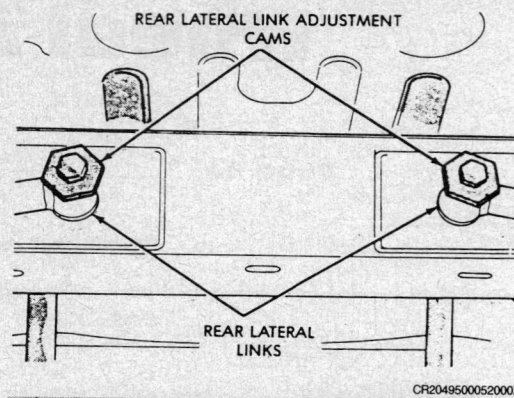

Fig. 3   Rear wheel toe adjustment cams

CHRYSLER
CIRRUS & DODGE STRATUS

NOTE: Refer To Rear Of This Manual For Vehicle Manufacturer's Special Service Tool Suppliers.

INDEX OF SERVICE OPERATIONS

NOTE: For Service Operations Not Listed Below, Refer To The Table Of Contents In The Front Of This Manual.

Specifications

GENERAL ENGINE SPECIFICATIONS

Year	Engine Liter/CID	Engine VIN Code [1]	Fuel System	Bore and Stroke Inch (Millimeters)	Compression Ratio	Net HP @ RPM [2]	Maximum Torque Ft. Lbs @ RPM	Normal Oil Pressure psi @ 3000 RPM
1995	2.0L/4-122	C	SMPI	3.44 x 3.27 (87.5 x 83)	9.8	132 @ 6000	129 @ 5000	25–80
	2.4L/4-148	X	SMPI	3.44 x 3.98 (87.5 x 101)	9.4	138 @ 5200	156 @ 4000	25–80
	2.5L/V6-152	H	SMPI	3.29 x 2.99 (83.5 x 76)	9.4	162 @ 6000	165 @ 4800	35–75

CID-Cubic Inch Displacement.
SMPI—Sequential Multi-Port Injection.

[1]—The 8th digit of the VIN denotes engine code.

[2]—Ratings are net-as installed in vehicle.

TUNE UP SPECIFICATIONS

Year & Engine/ VIN Code [1]	Spark Plug Gap	Ignition Timing BTDC Firing order	Ignition Timing BTDC Firing Order Fig.	Ignition Timing BTDC Man. Trans.	Ignition Timing BTDC Auto. Trans.	Minimum Air Flow Idle RPM [2]	Fuel Pump Pressure psi
1995							
2.0L/4-122/C	.035	1-3-4-2	A	[3]	[3]	600-1300	47-51
2.4L/4-148/X	.051	1-3-4-2	A	—	[3]	600-1300	47-51
2.5L/V6-152/H	.041	1-2-3-4-5-6	B	—	[3]	500-1100	47-51

BTDC-Before top dead center
[1]—The eighth digit of the Vehicle Identification Number (VIN) denotes engine code.

[2]—Engine idle is controlled by the PCM & is not adjustable.

[3]—Ignition timing is controlled by the PCM & is not adjustable.

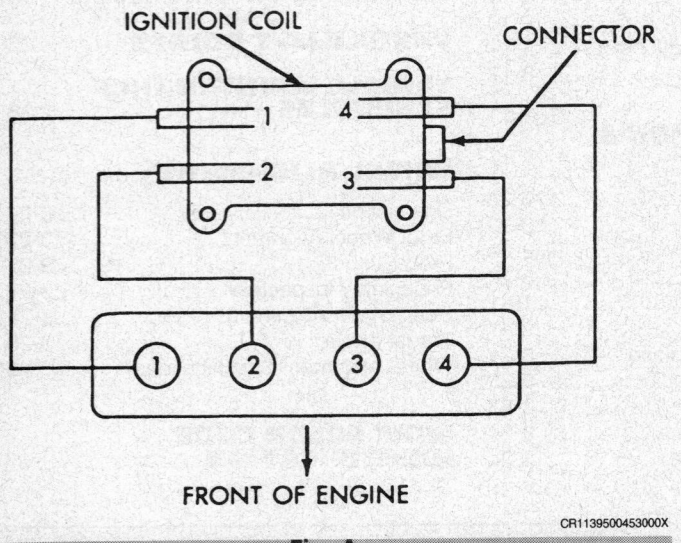

IGNITION COIL   CONNECTOR

1   4
2   3

1   2   3   4

FRONT OF ENGINE

Fig. A

CR1139500453000X

1   3   5

4 5
2   3
6 1

2   4   6

FRONT OF VEHICLE

FIRING ORDER
1 - 2 - 3 - 4 - 5 - 6

Fig. B

CR1139500454000X

FRONT WHEEL ALIGNMENT SPECIFICATIONS

| Year | Model | Camber Angle, Deg. [1] | | | | Total Toe Deg. | Caster, Deg. [1] |
| | | Limits | | Desired | | | |
		Left	Right	Left	Right		
1995	All	-0.3 to +0.9	-0.3 to +0.9	+0.3	+0.3	+.05	+2.3 to +4.3

[1]—Not adjustable, inspect to ensure within specifications.

REAR WHEEL ALIGNMENT SPECIFICATIONS

| Year | Model | Camber Angle, Deg. | | | | Total Toe Deg. [1] | Thrust Angle, Deg. |
| | | Limits | | Desired | | | |
		Left	Right	Left	Right		
1995	All	-0.6 to +0.2	-0.6 to +0.2	+0.2	+0.2	+.1	-.15 to +.15

[1]—On two wheel alignment rack, toe-out, four wheel alignment rack, toe-in.

COOLING SYSTEM & CAPACITY DATA

| Year | Engine/VIN Code [1] | Coolant Capacity Qts. [2] | Radiator Cap Relief Pressure, Lbs. | Thermo. Opening Temp. °F | Fuel Tank Gals. | Engine Oil Refill Qts. | Transaxle Oil | |
							5 Speed Qts.	Auto. Trans. Pts.
1995	2.0L/4-122/C	8.5	14-18	192	16	[3]	2.0-2.3	[4]
	2.4L/4-148/X	9.0	14-18	192	16	[3]	—	[4]
	2.5L/V6-152/H	10.5	14-18	192	16	[3]	—	[4]

[1]—The eighth digit of Vehicle Identification Number (VIN) denotes engine code.
[2]—Capacity includes heater & coolant reservoir.
[3]—With oil filter change 4.5 qts.; less oil filter change 4.0 qts.
[4]—After overhaul, 9.1 qts.; oil pan only, 4 qts.

LUBRICANT DATA

| Year | Model | Lubricant Type | | | |
| | | Transaxle | | Power Steering | Brake System |
		Manual	Automatic		
1995	All	Mopar Type M.S.9417	Mopar ATF Type 7176	Chrysler Part No. 4549617	DOT 3

[1]—Use Mopar type lubricants as specified or equivalents.

NOTE: Refer To "Air Bag System Precautions" Located In The Front Of This Manual For System Disarming & Arming Procedures.

INDEX

PRECAUTIONS

AIR BAG SYSTEM DISARMING

Refer to Air Bag System Precautions in the front of this manual for system disarming and arming procedures.

FUSE PANEL LOCATION

The interior accessory fuse panel is located between the instrument panel and the drivers side door. The door must be open to access the fuse panel. The fuse panel contains the headlamp relay, horn relay, rear window defogger relay, circuit breakers, and several fuses.

RELAY CENTER LOCATION

The engine compartment relays are located in the Power Distribution Center (PDC) next to the battery. The PDC contains the starter relay, radiator fan relay, A/C compressor clutch relay, auto shutdown relay, wiper relay, back-up lamp relay, transmission control relay, fuel pump relay and several fuses.

STARTER

REPLACE

The 2.0L/4-122, 2.4L/4-148 and 2.5L/V6-152 engines have three different starters made by Bosch, Nippondenso and Melco, respectively. The Bosch and Melco are permanent magnet starter motors. The Nippondenso is a reduction gear-field coil starter motor.

2.0L/4-122

1. Disconnect battery ground cable from remote ground terminal on shock tower.
2. Remove air cleaner resonator.
3. Remove battery positive cable nut from starter, then remove the battery positive cable and alternator output wire from starter.
4. Disconnect push on solenoid connector.
5. Remove two bolts attaching starter to transmission housing and remove starter from vehicle.
6. Reverse procedure to install, noting to clean corrosion from wire terminals before installation.

2.4L/4-148

1. Disconnect battery ground cable from remote ground terminal on shock tower.
2. Remove air cleaner resonator.
3. Remove three Transmission Control Module (TCM) mounting screws. Move TCM to provide access to top starter mounting bolt. **Do not disconnect TCM wiring.**
4. Remove bolt attaching starter to transmission housing and remove starter from vehicle.
5. Raise vehicle.
6. Remove battery cable nut from starter and remove cable.
7. Disconnect push on solenoid connector.
8. Remove top bolt attaching starter to transmission housing.
9. Reverse procedure to install, noting the following:
   a. **Torque** starter mounting bolts to 40 ft. lbs.
   b. Clean corrosion from wire terminals before installing wiring to solenoid.

2.5L/V6-152

1. Disconnect battery ground cable from remote ground terminal on shock tower.
2. Raise vehicle.
3. Remove oil filter.
4. Remove battery positive cable nut from starter and remove cable.
5. Disconnect push-on solenoid connector.
6. Remove three bolts attaching starter to transmission housing and remove starter from vehicle.
7. Reverse procedure to install. Clean corrosion from wire terminals before installation.

ALTERNATOR

REPLACE

2.0L/4-122 & 2.4L/4-148

1. Disconnect battery ground cable from remote ground terminal on shock tower.
2. Unplug field circuit from alternator.
3. Remove B+ terminal cover by spreading the cover with a small flat blade tool.
4. Remove B+ terminal nut and wire.
5. Loosen adjusting T-bolt, but do not remove.
6. Loosen pivot bolt, but do not remove.
7. Loosen adjusting bolt to allow removal of the alternator drive belt.
8. Remove adjusting T-bolt.
9. Remove pivot bolt, do not drop spacer.
10. **On models equipped with 2.0L/4-122 engine,** proceed as follows:
   a. release alternator from mounting bracket and move it toward passenger headlamp bucket.
   b. Remove alternator from head lamp bucket area.
11. **On models equipped with 2.4L/4-148 engine,** proceed as follows:
   a. remove ABS braking unit by removing the two lower plate mounting bolts.
   b. Remove coolant overflow bottle.
   c. Remove by sliding alternator under air conditioning lines towards passenger side of vehicle.

12. **On all models,** reverse procedure to install. Tighten all fasteners to specifications.

2.5L/V6–152

1. Disconnect battery ground cable from remote ground terminal on shock tower.
2. Unplug field circuit from alternator.
3. Remove B + terminal nut and wire.
4. Loosen top mounting ear bolt.
5. Loosen pivot bolt, but do not remove.
6. Loosen adjusting bolt on idler to allow removal of alternator drive belt.
7. Remove pivot bolt, do not drop spacer.
8. Remove top mounting ear bolt.
9. Remove upper alternator bracket, then the alternator.
10. Reverse procedure to install. Tighten all fasteners to specifications.

DISTRIBUTOR
REPLACE

2.5L/V6–152
Removal

1. Remove bolt holding air inlet resonator to intake manifold.
2. Loosen clamps holding air cleaner cover to air cleaner housing.
3. Remove PVC make-up air hose from air inlet tube.
4. Loosen hose clamp at throttle body.
5. Remove air inlet tube, resonator and air cleaner cover.
6. Remove EGR tube.
7. Remove spark plug cables from distributor cap.
8. Loosen distributor cap hold-down screws and remove cap.
9. Mark the rotor position and remove rotor. The mark indicates where to position the rotor when reinstalling the distributor.
10. Remove two harness connectors from distributor.
11. Remove two sets of distributor hold-down nuts and washers from studs.
12. Remove bolt and spark plug cable mounting bracket from top of distributor housing.
13. Remove bolt and transmission dip-stick tube.
14. Carefully remove distributor from engine.

Installation

1. Install rotor on shaft.
2. Position distributor in engine. Make certain that O-ring is properly seated on distributor. If O-ring is cracked or nicked replace with new one.
3. Carefully engage distributor drive with slotted end of camshaft. When the distributor is installed properly, the rotor will be in line with previously marked line on air intake plenum.
4. If engine was cranked while distributor was removed, establish proper relationship between distributor shaft and No. 1 piston position as follows:
   a. Rotate crankshaft until number one piston is at top of compression stroke.
   b. Rotate rotor to No. 1 rotor terminal.
   c. Lower distributor into opening, engaging distributor drive with drive on camshaft. With distributor fully seated on engine, rotor should be under No. 1 terminal.
5. Install distributor hold-down washers and nuts. **Torque** to 9 ft. lbs.
6. Install spark plug cable bracket.
7. Install two harness connectors to distributor.
8. Install distributor cap.
9. Install spark plug cables onto distributor cap. The cap is numbered as well as the cables. Ensure all high tension wires are firmly inserted in cap towers.
10. Install transmission dip stick tube.
11. Install EGR tube to intake manifold. **Torque** bolts to 95 inch lbs.

IGNITION LOCK
REPLACE

1. Remove upper steering column shroud.
2. Pull lower shroud down far enough to access lock cylinder retaining tab.
3. Place key cylinder in Run position. Depress retaining tab and remove key cylinder.
4. Reverse procedure to install.

IGNITION SWITCH
REPLACE

1. Disconnect battery ground cable.
2. Remove fuse panel cover from left end of instrument panel. Remove screw holding end of instrument panel top cover.
3. Pull center bezel off.
4. Remove screws holding instrument panel top cover to center of instrument panel.
5. Pull instrument panel top cover up enough to gain access to knee bolster screws.
6. Remove lower knee bolster screws and knee bolster.
7. Remove screws from lower steering column shroud.
8. Pull lower shroud to clear ignition cylinder and key release, if equipped.
9. Hold tilt wheel lever down and slide lower shroud forward to remove it from column.
10. Tilt wheel to full down position and remove upper steering column shroud.
11. Remove screws holding muti-function switch to lock housing.
12. Place key cylinder in Run position. Depress lock cylinder retaining tab and remove key cylinder.
13. Disconnect electrical connectors from ignition switch.
14. Remove ignition switch mounting screw with a No. 10 Torx tamper proof bit.
15. Depress retaining tabs and pull ignition switch from steering column.
16. Reverse procedure to install.

MULTI-FUNCTION SWITCH
REPLACE

1. Disconnect battery ground cable.
2. Remove upper steering column cover.
3. Remove muti-function switch mounting screws.
4. Disconnect wire connectors. Lift the switch straight up to remove.
5. Reverse procedure to install noting the following:
   a. **Torque** multi-function switch retaining screws to 20 inch lbs.
   b. **Torque** steering column cover retaining screws to 17 inch lbs.

STEERING WHEEL
REPLACE

1. Place the front road wheels in straight ahead position.
2. Remove the driver air bag module attaching T30 Torx bolts from back side of steering wheel. Lift module and disconnect wire by:
   a. Lift secondary latch.
   b. Disconnect connector from module using finger grips. Use care not to pull on wires. Never use metallic tool to pry on connector.
3. Remove speed control switch screws from back of steering wheel. Pull switch pods out and disconnect wires.
4. Disconnect horn wire from the air bag module mounting bracket. Remove speed control wires from under the bracket and from wire guides.
5. Remove steering wheel retaining nut.
6. Remove steering wheel with wheel puller tool. Feed all wires through steering wheel armature to avoid damaging wires.
7. Reverse procedure to install, noting the following:
   a. **Torque** steering wheel retaining nut to 45 ft. lbs.
   b. **Torque** speed control switch bolts to 10-20 inch lbs.
   c. **Torque** air bag module bolts to 80-90 inch lbs.

INSTRUMENT CLUSTER
REPLACE

1. Disconnect battery ground cable.
2. Remove instrument panel left end cap.
3. Tilt steering column down to its lowest position.
4. Remove instrument panel center bezel by disengaging four clips.
5. Remove instrument cluster hood by doing the following:
   a. Remove two screws adjacent radio.
   b. Remove screw below HVAC control in center.
   c. Remove screw at left end of panel.
   d. Pull on hood to disengage eight clips.
6. Remove instrument cluster from panel. Pull cluster rearward to disconnect wire connectors from base panel.
7. Reverse procedure to install.

CHRYSLER CIRRUS & STRATUS

RADIO
REPLACE

1. Disconnect battery ground cable.
2. Remove center bezel and two radio retaining screws, then the radio.
3. Pull radio straight out and disconnect both electrical connectors, antenna cable, radio ground strap, then remove the radio.
4. Reverse procedure to install.

WIPER MOTOR
REPLACE

1. Disconnect battery ground cable.
2. Remove wiper arms and blades.
3. Remove cowl screen.
4. Remove wiper motor assembly.
5. Disconnect drive linkage from motor output crank. Using a boll joint/tie rod separator, separate the ball cap from the ball.
6. Remove motor mounting nuts and motor.
7. Reverse procedure to install. **Torque** mounting screws to 89-106 inch lbs, and motor screws to 15-18 ft. lbs.

BLOWER MOTOR
REPLACE

1. Disconnect battery ground cable.
2. Remove lower right under panel silencer duct.
3. Remove blower motor connector from resistor block.
4. Remove blower motor retaining screws.
5. Lower blower motor from housing.
6. Reverse procedure to install.

HEATER CORE
REPLACE

1. Remove radio and climate control bezel.
2. Remove right instrument panel side trim.
3. Remove two screws at lower right side support beam.
4. Remove bolt for instrument panel support at A-pillar.
5. Remove left instrument panel side trim.

6. Remove upper instrument panel bezel.
7. Remove lower knee bolster.
8. Remove console screws at instrument panel.
9. Remove gearshift knob and shifter bezel.
10. Remove console screws at rear, then the rear half of console.
11. Remove front console screws, then the front half of console.
12. Remove right side instrument panel support strut.
13. Drain coolant.
14. Remove heater hoses at cowl.
15. Remove heater core cover screws and cover.
16. Remove heater core.
17. Reverse procedure to install.

EVAPORATOR CASE
REPLACE

1. Using an A/C recovery unit, discharge refrigerant from A/C system.
2. Remove air cleaner hose and air distribution duct from the engine.
3. Drain engine cooling system.
4. Disconnect heater hoses at dash panel, then plug the heater core inlet and outlet tubes.
5. Remove both A/C lines from expansion valve using special disconnect tool No. 7193 or equivalent, to disconnect connectors on A/C lines.
6. Cap expansion valve openings and the A/C hose openings to prevent dirt or moisture from entering refrigerant system during servicing.
7. Remove trim bezel around radio and climate control module.
8. Remove cluster hood bezel retaining screws in the trim bezel opening.
9. Pry up cluster hood bezel a few inches to expose the cubby bin bezel and wiring.
10. Remove cubby bin bezel and wiring.
11. Remove control module retaining screws.
12. Drop the A/C control module into cubby bin bezel opening, then disconnect the wiring on rear of control module.
13. Release cable clips from top of control module. Retain clips for future use.
14. Disconnect temperature control and recirculation control cables.
15. Remove control module.
16. Remove upper instrument panel bezel.

17. Remove right and left instrument panel end caps.
18. Remove left lower knee bolster. Disconnect mode door motor wiring.
19. Remove right and left interior door post kick panel.
20. Remove front and rear halves of floor console.
21. Remove radio.
22. Remove right side lower silencer/duct.
23. Remove glove box assembly.
24. Remove right side vertical support strut brace.
25. Remove left side vertical support strut brace.
26. Remove center lower distribution housing.
27. Remove bolts securing heater-A/C housing to metal I/P frame.
28. Remove upper instrument panel cowl trim cover.
29. Disconnect steering column from instrument panel. Lower steering column.
30. Remove instrument panel bolts at cowl fence.
31. Remove bolts at lower A-posts.
32. Remove instrument frame and wiring.
33. Remove bolts securing Heater-A/C housing to cowl.
34. Reverse procedure to install. Verify cables are properly adjusted and control module is seated properly.

EVAPORATOR CORE
REPLACE

1. Remove evaporator case as described under "Evaporator Case, Replace."
2. Remove recirculation door inlet cover.
3. Remove evaporator temperature probe.
4. Remove clips retaining evaporator housing to heater/distribution housing.
5. Separate evaporator housing from heater/distribution housing.
6. Remove seal around evaporator tube inlet.
7. Remove evaporator housing upper cover.
8. Lift evaporator out of lower housing.
9. Remove styrofoam seal around evaporator.
10. Transfer evaporator sensor. Place the evaporator sensor in the same location as on the previous evaporator.
11. Reverse procedure to install.

NOTE: Refer To "Air Bag System Precautions" Located In The Front Of This Manual For System Disarming & Arming Procedures.

INDEX

PRECAUTIONS

AIR BAG SYSTEMS

Refer to "Air Bag System Precautions" in the front of this manual for system disarming and arming procedures.

FUEL PRESSURE RELIEF

2.0L/4-122 & 2.4L/4-148 Engines

1. Disconnect ground cable from auxiliary jumper terminal.
2. Remove fuel filler cap.
3. Remove protective cap from fuel pressure test port on fuel rail Fig. 1.
4. Place open end of fuel pressure release hose, tool No. C-4799-1 or equivalent, into a suitable gasoline container, then connect other hose end to fuel pressure test port. Fuel pressure should bleed off through hose into container.

2.5L/V6-152 Engine

1. Disconnect fuel rail electrical harness from engine harness.
2. Connect suitable jumper wire between fuel rail harness connector terminal A142 and 12 volt power source.
3. Connect another suitable jumper wire to ground source, then momentarily ground one injector harness connector terminal, to release fuel system pressure.
4. Repeat procedure for 2 to 3 injectors.

ENGINE MOUNT
REPLACE

RIGHT SIDE

1. Raise and support vehicle, then remove the inner splash.
2. Remove right engine support assembly attaching bolts from frame rail, Figs. 2 and 3.
3. Lower vehicle and support engine assembly with floor jack to remove pressure on motor mounts.
4. Remove three engine support to engine bracket attaching bolts.
5. Reverse procedure to install. Tighten attaching nuts and bolts to specifications, Figs. 2 and 3.

ENGINE SUPPORT

1. Raise and support vehicle. Support engine and transmission assembly with jack.
2. Remove front and rear insulator attaching through bolts, referring to Fig. 4 for 2.0L/4-122 and 2.4L/4-148 en-

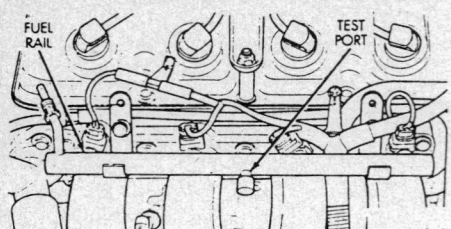

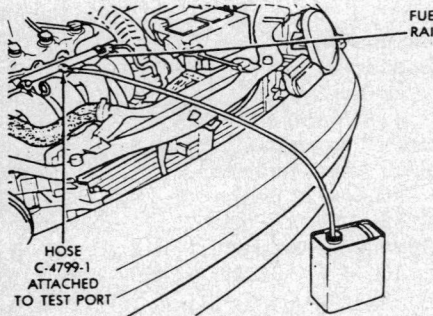

Fig. 1 Fuel system test port & fuel pressure release

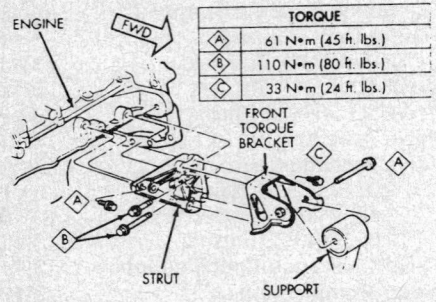

TORQUE	
A	61 N•m (45 ft. lbs.)
B	110 N•m (80 ft. lbs.)
C	33 N•m (24 ft. lbs.)

Fig. 4 Engine support module replacement. 2.0L/4–122 & 2.4L/4–148 engines

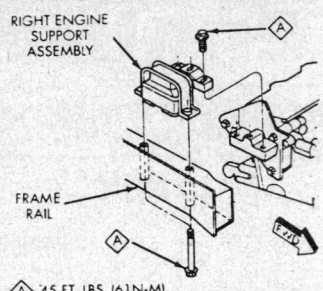

(A) 45 FT. LBS. (61 N•M)

Fig. 2 Right side engine mount replacement. 2.0L/4–122 & 2.4L/4–148 engines

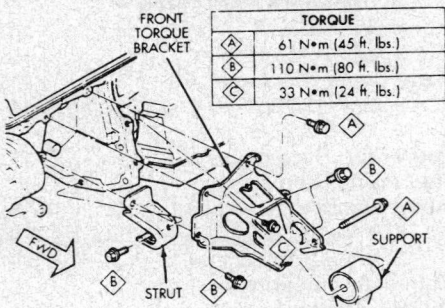

TORQUE	
A	61 N•m (45 ft. lbs.)
B	110 N•m (80 ft. lbs.)
C	33 N•m (24 ft. lbs.)

Fig. 5 Engine support module replacement. 2.5L/V6-152 engine

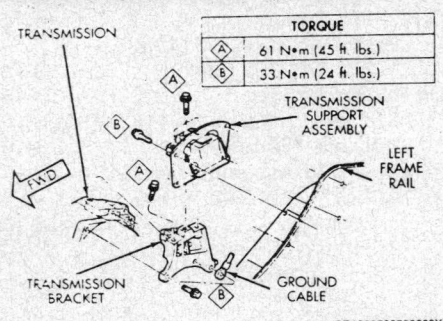

TORQUE	
A	61 N•m (45 ft. lbs.)
B	33 N•m (24 ft. lbs.)

Fig. 7 Left engine mount replacement. 2.4L/4–148 & 2.5L/V6-152 engines

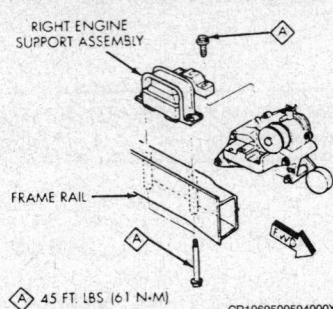

(A) 45 FT. LBS (61 N·M)

Fig. 3 Right side engine mount replacement. 2.5L/V6-152 engine

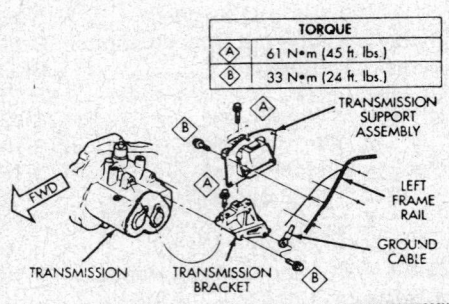

TORQUE	
A	61 N•m (45 ft. lbs.)
B	33 N•m (24 ft. lbs.)

Fig. 6 Left engine mount replacement. 2.0L/4–122 engine

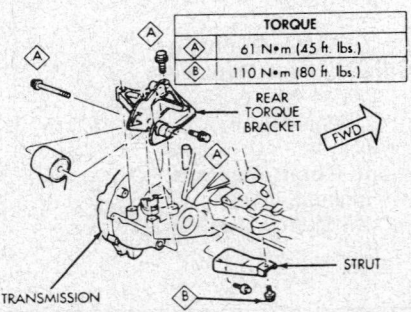

TORQUE	
A	61 N•m (45 ft. lbs.)
B	110 N•m (80 ft. lbs.)

Fig. 8 Rear engine mount replacement. 2.0L/4–122 engine

gines and **Fig. 5** for 2.5L/V6-152 engine.

3. Remove engine support module attaching bolts and module between lower radiator support and crossmember.
4. Reverse procedure to install. Tighten attaching nuts and bolts to specifications.

LEFT SIDE

1. Support transmission with jack.
2. Remove three mount to transmission attaching bolts, referring to **Fig. 6** for 2.0L/4-122 engine and **Fig. 7** for 2.4L/4-148 and 2.5 L/V6-152 engines.
3. Remove transmission mount attaching bolts and mount.
4. Reverse procedure to install, noting the following:
   a. Tighten attaching nuts and bolts to specifications.
   b. Adjust engine support assembly if necessary.

REAR

1. Raise and support vehicle, then re-

move left front wheel.
2. Support transmission with transmission jack.
3. Remove mount and rear suspension crossmember insulator attaching bolt, **Figs. 8 and 9.**
4. Remove four transmission mount attaching bolts and the mount.
5. Reverse procedure to install. Tighten attaching nuts and bolts to specifications, **Figs. 8 and 9.**

ENGINE
REPLACE

1. Relieve fuel system pressure as outlined under "Precautions."
2. Disconnect and remove battery and tray, then disconnect the Power Con-

trol Module (PCM) electrical connector and position aside.
3. Drain cooling system.
4. Remove upper radiator hose and radiator fan module.
5. Remove lower radiator hose.
6. **On models with 2.0L/4-122 engine,** disconnect clutch cable.
7. **On models with 2.4L/4-148 and 2.5L/V6-152 engines,** disconnect automatic transaxle cooler line and plug, if equipped.
8. **On all models,** disconnect transaxle and throttle body linkage.
9. Disconnect engine wiring harness electrical connectors.
10. Disconnect heater hoses.
11. Discharge and recover A/C refrigerant as outlined in "Air Conditioning" section.
12. Raise and support vehicle, then remove the right inner splash shield.
13. Remove accessory drive belts.

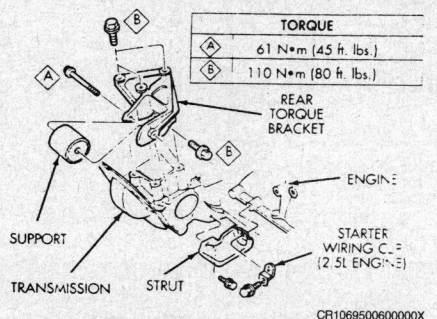

Fig. 9 Rear engine mount replacement. 2.4L/4-148 & 2.5 L/V6–152 engines

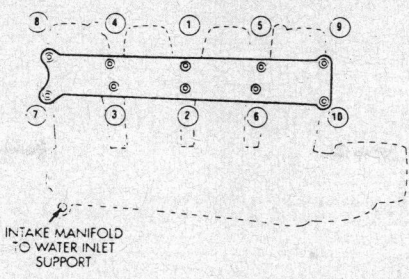

Fig. 10 Intake manifold tightening sequence. 2.0L/4-122 engine

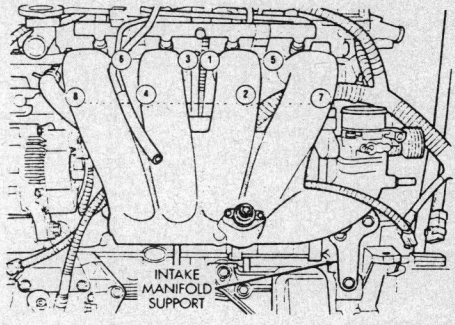

Fig. 11 Intake manifold tightening sequence. 2.4L/4-148 engine

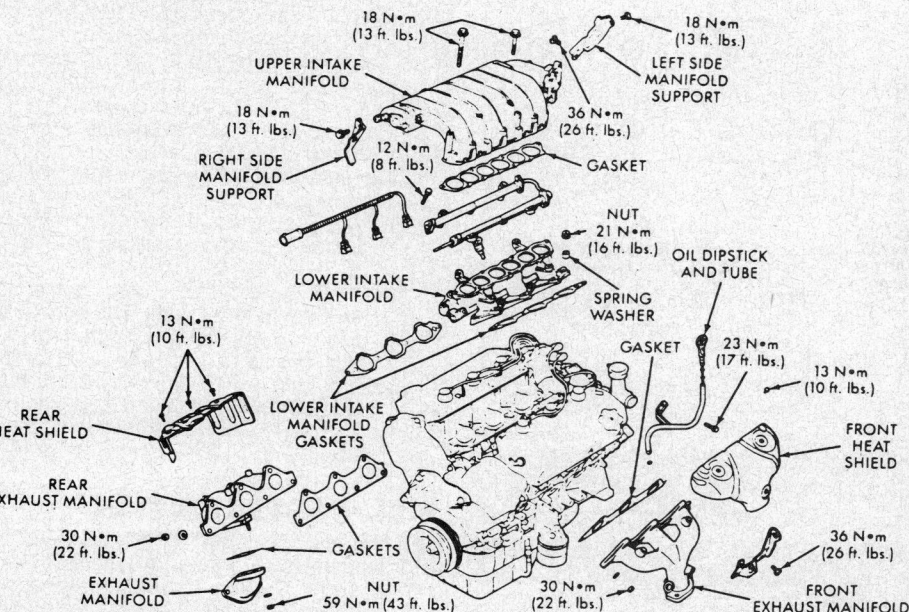

Fig. 12 Exploded view of intake & exhaust manifolds

14. Remove axle shafts.
15. Disconnect exhaust pipe from manifold.
16. Remove front and rear engine mount bracket from the body.
17. Lower vehicle, then remove the air cleaner assembly.
18. Remove power steering pump and reservoir.
19. Remove A/C compressor.
20. Remove ground straps to body.
21. Raise and support vehicle to install engine dolly and cradle tool Nos. 6135, 6710 and 6810 or equivalents.
22. Loosen cradle engine mounts, to position engine locating holes to bedplate, then lower the vehicle until engine rests on cradle mounts, tighten mounts to cradle frame to prevent mount movement.
23. Lower vehicle so weight of engine and transmission is only on cradle.
24. Remove engine and transmission mount attaching bolts.
25. Slowly raise and support vehicle, move engine and transmission assembly on cradle to allow for removal around body flanges as required.
26. Reverse procedure to install. Refer to

INTAKE MANIFOLD
REPLACE

2.0L/4–122 & 2.4L/4–148 Engines

1. Relieve fuel system pressure as outlined under "Precautions."
2. Remove air inlet resonator.
3. Disconnect fuel supply line quick connect from fuel tube assembly.
4. Remove fuel rail assembly attaching screws, then the fuel rail assembly cover injector holes.
5. Remove accelerator, kickdown and speed control cables from throttle lever and bracket.
6. Disconnect Idle Air Control (IAC) motor and Throttle Position Sensor (TPS) electrical connectors.
7. Disconnect vacuum hoses from throttle body.
8. Disconnect Manifold Absolute Pressure (MAP) intake air temperature electrical connectors.

9. Disconnect vapor and brake booster hoses.
10. Disconnect knock sensor electrical connector and harness from tab located on intake manifold .
11. Remove transmission to throttle body support bracket bolts at throttle body and loosen bolt at transmission.
12. Remove EGR tube attaching bolts, then the tube.
13. Remove intake manifold to inlet water tube support bolt and manifold support bracket, if required.
14. Remove ten intake manifold attaching bolts and washers, then the intake manifold.
15. Reverse procedure to install, noting the following:
    a. Clean all mating surfaces, then check for cracked or distorted manifold and torn or missing O-rings.
    b. **On models equipped with 2.0L/4-122 engine**, replace all seals, bolts and washers.
    c. **On all models**, tighten intake manifold attaching bolts in sequence **Figs. 10 and 11** to specifications.
    d. Tighten attaching nuts and bolts to specifications.

2.5L/V6–152 Engine

1. Relieve fuel system pressure as outlined under "Precautions".
2. Disconnect fuel supply tube from rail, using a towel to catch any gasoline spillage.
3. Disconnect MAP and intake air temperature sensors electrical connectors.
4. Remove plenum support bracket bolt located rearward of MAP sensor **Fig. 12**.
5. Remove air inlet resonator to intake manifold bolt.
6. Loosen throttle body air inlet hose clamp, release snaps holding air cleaner housing cover to housing, then remove the air cleaner cover and inlet hoses.
7. Disconnect TPS and IAC motor electrical connectors.
8. Depress throttle cable retainer tab and pull cable rearward out of bracket, then repeat for speed control cable, if equipped.

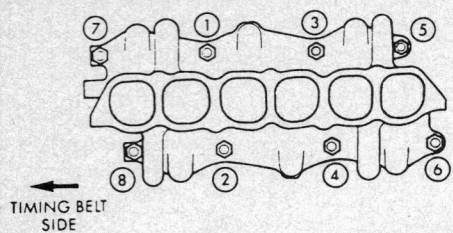

Fig. 13 Intake manifold tightening sequence. 2.5L/V6-152 engine

TIMING BELT SIDE

CR1059500099000X

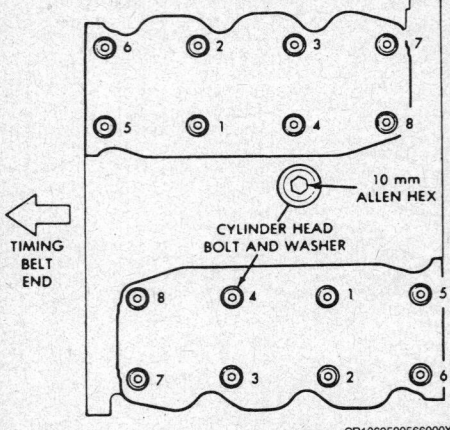

CR1069500564000X

Fig. 14 Cylinder head tightening sequence. 2.0L/4-122 engine

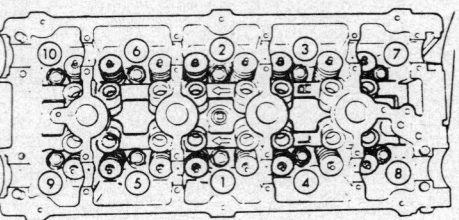

Fig. 15 Cylinder head tightening sequence. 2.4L/4-148 engine

CR1069500565000X

9. Remove EGR tube from intake manifold.
10. Remove plenum support bracket bolt, rearward of EGR tube.
11. Remove upper intake plenum attaching bolts, then the plenum.
12. Disconnect fuel injector electrical connectors.
13. Remove four fuel rail attaching bolts and spacers, then the fuel rail.
14. Remove lower intake manifold attaching bolts, then the intake manifold.
15. Reverse procedure to install, noting the following:
   a. Clean all mating surfaces, then inspect for cracked or distorted manifold and torn or missing O-rings.
   b. Install intake manifold with new gaskets and install intake manifold onto cylinder head tightening to specifications in sequence shown in **Fig. 13.**
   c. Tighten attaching nuts and bolts to specifications.

EXHAUST MANIFOLD
REPLACE

2.0L/4-122 & 2.4L/4-148 Engines

1. Raise and support vehicle.
2. Remove exhaust pipe from manifold. It may be necessary to remove entire exhaust system.
3. Remove exhaust manifold heat shield attaching bolts and heat shield.
4. Remove eight exhaust manifold attaching bolts and exhaust manifold.
5. Reverse procedure to install, noting the following:
   a. Install new manifold gasket.
   b. Tighten exhaust manifold and exhaust pipe attaching bolts to specifications.

2.5L/V6-152 Engine

1. Raise and support vehicle.
2. Disconnect exhaust pipe from rear exhaust manifold at flex joint. It may be necessary to remove entire exhaust system.
3. Remove cross-over pipe to manifold attaching bolts, then remove assembly.
4. Disconnect oxygen sensor lead wire at rear exhaust manifold.
5. Remove power steering pump bracket.

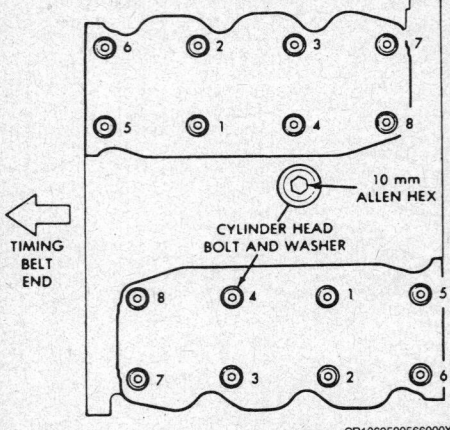

10 mm ALLEN HEX

CYLINDER HEAD BOLT AND WASHER

TIMING BELT END

CR1069500566000X

Fig. 16 Cylinder head bolt tightening sequence. 2.5L/V6-152 engine

6. Remove rear manifold to cylinder head attaching nuts, then the manifold.
7. Lower vehicle and disconnect front heated oxygen sensor.
8. Remove front heat shield to manifold attaching screws.
9. Remove front manifold attaching nuts and manifold.
10. Reverse procedure to install, noting the following:
   a. Install new manifold gaskets.
   b. Tighten all attaching bolts and nuts to specifications.

CYLINDER HEAD
REPLACE

2.0L/4-122 & 2.4L/4-148 ENGINES

1. Relieve fuel system pressure as outlined under "Precautions."
2. Drain cooling system.
3. Remove air cleaner and disconnect all vacuum lines, electrical harnesses and fuel lines from throttle body.
4. Remove throttle linkage.
5. Remove accessory drive belts.
6. Remove intake manifold power brake vacuum connection.
7. Raise and support vehicle, then remove exhaust pipe from manifold.
8. Remove and set aside power steering pump assembly.

9. Disconnect coil pack electrical connector and remove coil pack and bracket.
10. Remove cam sensor and fuel injector electrical connectors.
11. Remove timing belt and camshaft sprocket.
12. Remove cylinder head cover.
13. Remove rocker arm shaft assemblies.
14. Remove cylinder head bolts.
15. Reverse procedure to install, noting the following:
   a. Apply oil to bolts before installing. Install four short bolts in positions 7, 8, 9 and 10.
   b. Tighten cylinder head bolts in steps and in sequence as shown in **Figs. 14 and 15** by applying an initial **torque** of 25 ft. lbs. to all bolts, followed by a **torque** of 50 ft. lbs. Loosen bolts and repeat tightening procedure, then tighten bolts an additional 1/4 turn.

2.5L/V6-152 ENGINE

1. Remove camshaft sprockets. Refer to Timing Belt, Replace" for disassembly and removal of camshaft sprockets.
2. Remove rocker arms. Refer to " Rocker Arms, Replace" for disassembly and removal of rocker arms.
3. Remove upper intake manifold assembly. Refer to" Intake Manifold, Replace" for disassembly and removal of intake manifold.
4. Remove distributor.
5. Remove exhaust manifolds and crossover
6. Remove cylinder head bolts and cylinder head.
7. Reverse procedure to install. **Torque** bolts in sequence shown in **Fig. 16** to 80 ft. lbs.

VALVE ARRANGEMENT

2.0L/4-122 ENGINE

Intake valves are located on intake manifold side of engine and exhaust valves are located on exhaust manifold side of engine.

2.4L/4-148 ENGINE

Intake valves are located on intake manifold side of engine and exhaust valves are located on exhaust manifold side of engine.

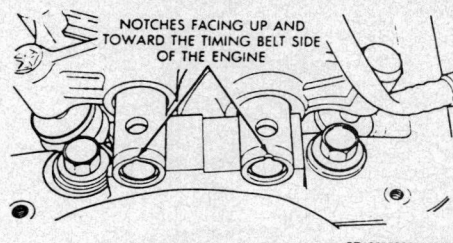

Fig. 17 Rocker arm shaft notch alignment

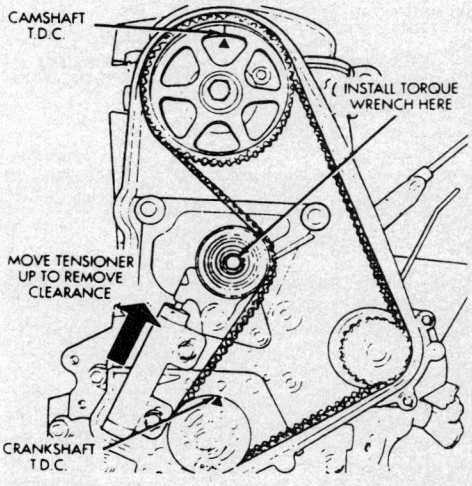

Fig. 20 Crankshaft & camshaft timing mark alignment. 2.0L/4-122 engine

2.5L/V6-152 ENGINE

Intake valves are located on upper side of right and left cylinder heads and exhaust valves are on lower side of cylinder heads.

CAMSHAFT LOBE LIFT SPECIFICATIONS

Engine	Intake Lift, Inch	Exhaust Lift, Inch
2.0L/4-122	.307	.277
2.4L/4-148	.324	.256
2.5L/V6-152	-	-

VALVE CLEARANCE SPECIFICATIONS

Engine	Intake Valve, Inch	Exhaust Valve, Inch
2.0L/4-122	.0018-.0030①	.0029-.0040①
2.4L/4-148	.0018-.0100①	.0029-.0100①
2.5L/V6-152	.0008-.0040①	.0016-.0060①

①—Equipped w/hydraulic valve lash adjusters.

VALVE ADJUSTMENT

On these engines, the intake and exhaust valves are equipped with hydraulic lash adjusters; there is no provision for adjustment.

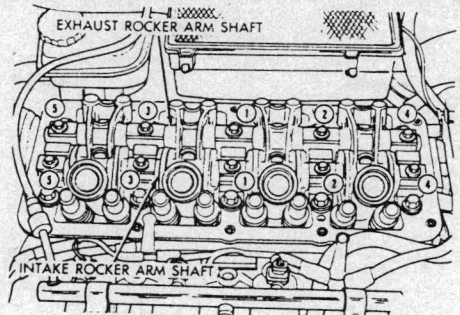

Fig. 18 Rocker arm shaft tightening sequence. 2.0L/4-122 engine

ROCKER ARMS
REPLACE

2.0L/4-122 ENGINE

1. Remove all electrical connections, brackets and components attached to valve cover.
2. Remove valve cover bolts, then the valve cover.
3. Identify rocker are shaft assemblies, then remove attaching bolts and rocker arm shaft assemblies.
4. Reverse procedure to install, noting the following:
   a. Install rocker arm and shaft assemblies with notches on shafts facing up and toward the timing belt side of engine Fig. 17.
   b. Tighten bolts to specifications in sequence shown Fig. 18.

2.5L/V6-152 ENGINE

1. Remove valve covers.
2. Identify rocker arm shaft assemblies before removal.
3. Install auto lash adjuster retainer tool No. MD998443 or equivalent. These retainers hold lash adjuster into position when rocker arms are serviced.
4. Remove rocker arm bolts and shaft assemblies.
5. Reverse procedure to install, noting the following:
   a. Install rocker arm and shaft assemblies with flat spot in rocker arm shafts facing toward timing belt side of engine for right cylinder head. For left cylinder head, install rocker arm and shaft assemblies with flat spot in rocker arm shafts facing toward transmission side of engine. Install retainers and spring clips in their original positions on exhaust and intake shafts
   b. Tighten bolts to specifications in sequence shown Fig. 19.
   c. Remove lash adjuster retainers from rocker arms.

FRONT COVER
REPLACE

2.0L/4-122 & 2.4L/4-148 ENGINES

1. Remove accessory drive belts.
2. Raise and support vehicle on a hoist

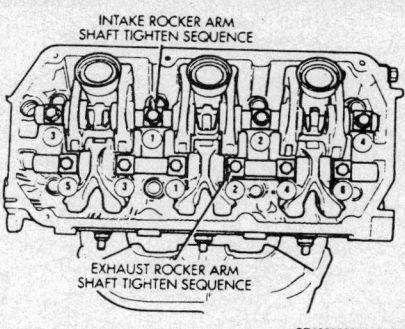

Fig. 19 Rocker arm shaft tightening sequence. 2.5L/V6-152 engine

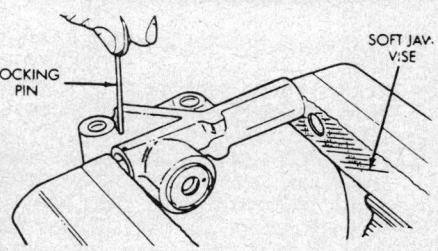

Fig. 21 Timing belt tensioner locking pin installation

and remove right inner splash shield.
3. **On models with 2.0L/4-122 engine,** remove crankshaft damper bolt. Remove damper using puller tool No. 1023 and insert tool No. C-4685-C2 or equivalents.
4. **On models with 2.4L/4-148 engine,** remove crankshaft damper bolt. Remove damper using puller tool No. 1026 and insert tool No. 6827 or equivalents.
5. **On all models,** lower vehicle and place jack under engine.
6. Remove right engine mount and bracket.
7. Remove front half of timing belt cover.
8. Reverse procedure to install.

2.5L/V6-152 ENGINE

1. Drain cooling system and remove radiator.
2. Remove right inner splash shield.
3. Remove accessory drive belts.
4. Remove right engine mount.
5. Remove crankshaft damper.
6. Remove engine mount bracket.
7. Remove timing belt upper left cover, upper right cover and lower cover in order.
8. Reverse procedure to install.

TIMING BELT
REPLACE

2.0L/4-122 ENGINE

1. Remove timing belt front cover as described under "Front Cover, Replace."
2. Align crankshaft and camshaft sprocket marks, Fig. 20, then loosen timing belt tensioner attaching bolts.
3. Remove timing belt and tensioner. If belt is to be reused, mark running di-

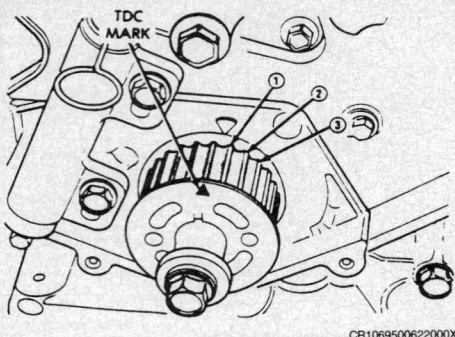

Fig. 22 Crankshaft sprocket & oil pump housing alignment marks. 2.0L/4-122 engine

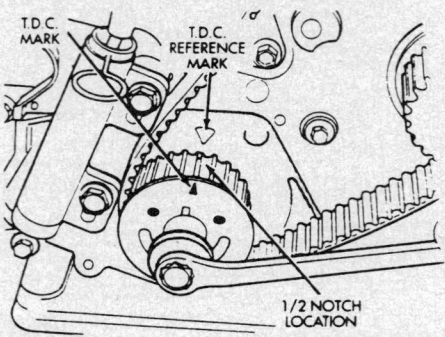

Fig. 23 Crankshaft sprocket ¹/₂ tooth rotation. 2.0L/4-122 & 2.4L/4-148 engines

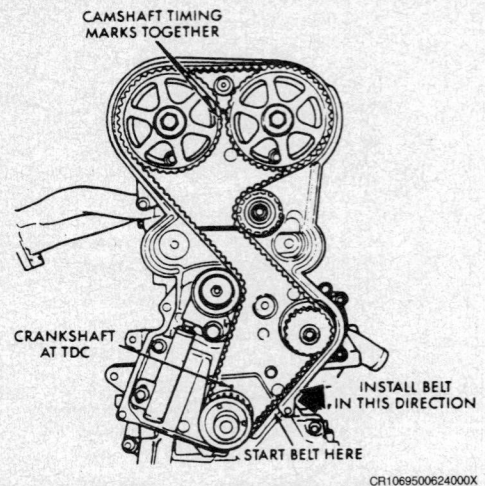

Fig. 24 Crankshaft & camshaft sprocket timing mark alignment. 2.4L/4-148 engine

rection on belt for installation reference.

4. Inspect timing belt for cracks, missing teeth, rubber hardening and abnormal wear and replace as necessary.

5. Position timing belt tensioner in a soft jawed vise, then slowly compress tensioner plunger into tensioner body.

6. With tensioner plunger compressed into body, insert a ⁵/₆₄ inch Allen wrench or other suitable locking pin through holes in tensioner body, **Fig. 21.** This will hold plunger in position until after tensioner has been installed on engine.

7. Align mark on crankshaft sprocket with arrow mark on oil pump housing, then back off to 3 sprocket teeth before Top Dead Center (TDC), **Fig. 22.**

8. Align camshaft sprocket mark with arrow mark on timing belt rear cover, **Fig. 20.**

9. Position crankshaft sprocket at ¹/₂ tooth before TDC, **Fig. 23.**

10. Position timing belt over crankshaft sprocket, around water pump sprocket, over camshaft sprocket, then around tensioner pulley.

11. Place crankshaft sprocket in TDC position to take up slack in timing belt.

12. Position timing belt tensioner on engine block, then loosely install attaching bolts.

13. Using a suitable torque wrench, apply a **torque** of 250 inch lbs. to timing belt tensioner pulley, **Fig. 20.**

14. While applying tension on tensioner pulley, move timing belt tensioner up against tensioner pulley bracket, then **torque** tensioner attaching bolts to 275 inch lbs.

15. Remove Allen wrench or locking pin retaining tensioner plunger in body. Timing belt pretension is correct when Allen wrench or pin can be freely removed from and installed in tensioner body holes.

16. Rotate crankshaft 2 revolutions in normal direction of rotation, then check crankshaft and camshaft sprocket timing mark alignment, **Fig. 20.** If timing marks are not properly aligned, repeat procedure.

17. Install front cover as described under "Front Cover, Replace."

18. After completing installation, perform relearn camshaft and crankshaft

alignment procedure using DRBII scan tool and attendant instructions.

19. Inspect valve timing as follows:
   a. Remove No. 1 spark plug from cylinder head.
   b. Using a suitable dial indicator, set No. 1 cylinder at TDC on its compression stroke.
   c. Remove access plug from timing belt front cover.
   d. Timing mark on camshaft sprocket should be aligned with arrow mark on timing belt rear cover, **Fig. 20.**

2.4L/4-148 ENGINE

1. Remove timing belt front cover as described under "Front Cover, Replace."

2. Align crankshaft and camshaft sprocket marks, **Fig. 24,** then loosen timing belt tensioner attaching bolts.

3. Remove timing belt and tensioner. If timing belt is to be reused, mark running direction on belt for installation reference.

4. Inspect timing belt for cracks, missing teeth, hardened rubber and abnormal wear.

5. Position belt tensioner in a soft jawed vise, then slowly compress tensioner plunger into tensioner body.

6. With tensioner plunger compressed into body, insert a suitable locking pin, **Fig. 21.** This will hold plunger in position until after tensioner has been installed on engine.

7. Align mark on crankshaft sprocket with arrow mark on oil pump housing, **Fig. 24.**

8. Align notches on camshaft sprockets, **Fig. 24.**

9. Place crankshaft sprocket ¹/₂ tooth counterclockwise from Top Dead Center (TDC) position, **Fig. 23.**

10. Position timing belt over crankshaft sprocket, then around water pump sprocket, idler pulley, camshaft sprockets and tensioner pulley, **Fig. 24.**

11. Place crankshaft sprocket at TDC position to take up slack in timing belt.

12. Position timing belt tensioner on engine block, then loosely install attaching bolts.

13. Using a suitable torque wrench, apply a **torque** of 250 inch lbs. to timing belt tensioner pulley.

14. While applying tension on tensioner pulley, move timing belt tensioner up against tensioner pulley bracket, then **torque** tensioner attaching bolts to 275 inch lbs.

15. Remove locking pin retaining tensioner plunger in tensioner body. Timing belt pretension is correct when locking pin can be freely removed from or installed through tensioner body holes.

16. Rotate crankshaft through 2 revolutions in direction of normal rotation, then check crankshaft and camshaft sprocket timing mark alignment, **Fig. 24.** If timing marks are not properly aligned, repeat procedure.

17. Install front cover as described under "Front Cover, Replace."

18. After completing installation, perform relearn camshaft and crankshaft alignment procedure using DRBII scan tool and attendant instructions.

19. Inspect valve timing as follows:
   a. Remove No. 1 spark plug from cylinder head.
   b. Using a suitable dial indicator, set No. 1 cylinder at TDC on its compression stroke.
   c. Remove access plug from timing belt front cover.
   d. Timing marks on camshaft sprockets should be aligned with each other, **Fig. 24.**

2.5L/V6-152 ENGINE

1. Remove timing belt front cover as described under "Front Cover, Replace."

2. Align crankshaft and camshaft sprocket marks, **Fig. 25,** then loosen timing belt tensioner attaching bolts.

3. Remove timing belt and tensioner. If timing belt is to be reused, mark running direction for installation reference.

4. Inspect timing belt for cracks, missing teeth, hardened rubber and abnormal wear.

5. Position timing belt tensioner in a soft jawed vise, then slowly compress tensioner plunger into tensioner body.

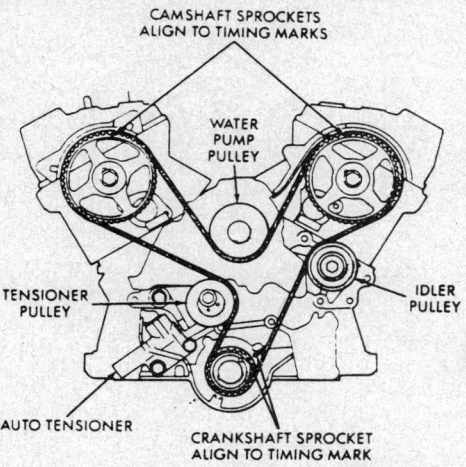

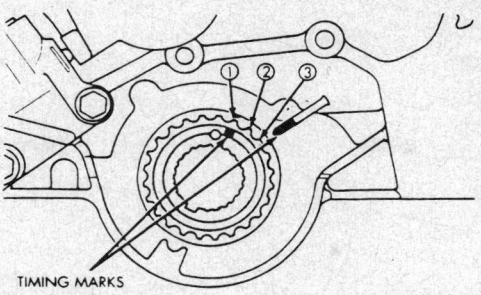

Fig. 26 Crankshaft sprocket teeth & mark location. 2.5L/V6-152 engine

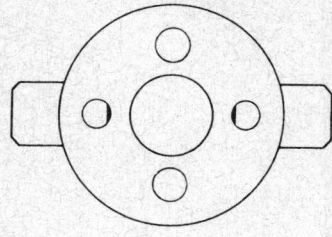

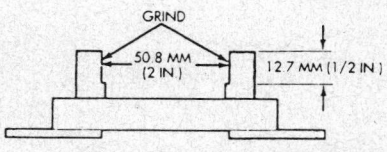

Fig. 27 Special tool modification

Fig. 25 Crankshaft & camshaft sprocket mark alignment. 2.5L/V6-152 engine

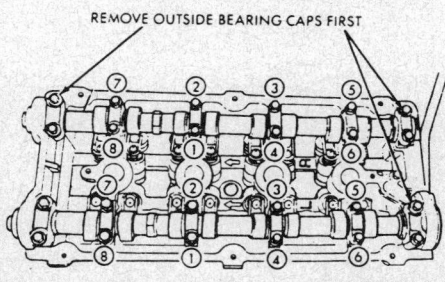

Fig. 28 Camshaft bearing cap removal

6. With tensioner plunger compressed into body, insert a suitable locking pin through holes in tensioner body, **Fig. 21**. This will hold plunger in position until after tensioner has been installed on engine.
7. Align mark on crankshaft sprocket with arrow mark on oil pump housing, then back off to 3 sprocket teeth before Top Dead Center (TDC), **Fig. 26**.
8. Align camshaft sprocket marks with marks on valve covers, **Fig. 25**.
9. Install timing belt as follows:
   a. Position timing belt over rear camshaft sprocket. Use a binder clip to secure timing belt to camshaft sprocket.
   b. With timing belt held taut, install belt under water pump pulley, then over front camshaft sprocket. Use a binder clip to secure timing belt to camshaft sprocket.
   c. Align crankshaft sprocket TDC mark with mark on oil pump cover, **Fig. 25**.
   d. Install timing belt over idler pulley, crankshaft sprocket and tensioner pulley.
10. Apply rotating force in clockwise direction to crankshaft sprocket to remove timing belt slack. Ensure timing marks are aligned, **Fig. 25**.
11. Using a suitable torque wrench and torque wrench tool No. MD998767 or equivalent, apply a **torque** of 39 inch lbs. to timing belt tensioner pulley, then **torque** tensioner pulley bolt to 35 ft. lbs.
12. With force still upon tensioner pulley, install timing belt tensioner to tensioner pulley bracket. **Torque** attaching bolts to 275 inch lbs.
13. Remove locking pin retaining tensioner plunger in body.
14. Rotate crankshaft 2 revolutions in clockwise direction, then check camshaft and crankshaft sprocket mark alignment, **Fig. 25**, and ensure locking pin slides freely through tensioner body holes. If camshaft and crankshaft sprocket marks are not properly

aligned and/or locking pin cannot slide freely through tensioner holes, repeat procedure.
15. Install front cover as described under "Front Cover, Replace."

CAMSHAFT
REPLACE

2.0L/4-122 ENGINE
1. Refer to "Timing Belt, Replace" to remove timing cover and belt.
2. Remove camshaft sprocket bolt.
3. Remove sprocket from camshaft with modified tool No. C-4687-1 or equivalent **Fig. 27**. Hold camshaft sprocket with modified tool while removing bolt.
4. Remove camshaft seal using camshaft seal remover tool No. C-4679 or equivalent.
5. Remove camshaft.
6. Reverse procedure to install, noting the following:
   a. Install new camshaft seal with seal insertion tool No. 998306 or equivalent.
   b. Install camshaft sprocket retaining bolt. Hold camshaft sprocket with tool No. C-4687 along with adapter tool No. C-4687-1 or equivalents and tighten to specifications.

2.4L/4-148 ENGINE
1. Remove valve cover.
2. Remove timing belt, sprockets and covers.
3. Bearing caps are identified for location. Remove outside bearing caps L1, R1, L6 and R6 first.
4. Loosen camshaft bearing cap attaching bolts in sequence, **Fig. 28**, one camshaft at a time.

5. Identify camshafts before removing from head. Camshafts are not interchangeable.
6. Reverse procedure to install.

2.5L/V6-152 ENGINE
1. Remove timing belt, sprockets and covers.
2. Remove cylinder head covers.
3. Attach auto lash adjuster retainers tool No. MD998443 or equivalent.
4. Mark rocker arm shaft assemblies for installation.
5. Remove rocker arm shaft bolts.
6. Remove cylinder head retaining bolts and cylinder head.
7. Remove thrust case from left head assembly and camshaft from rear of head.
8. Remove distributor from right head assembly and camshaft from rear of head.
9. Reverse procedure to install, noting the following:
   a. Tighten thrust case and camshaft sprocket to specifications.
   b. Tighten rocker arm assemblies in sequence shown in **Fig. 19** to specifications.

BALANCE SHAFT
REPLACE

2.4L/4-148 ENGINE
1. Remove timing belt cover, crankshaft damper and all other necessary components to allow access to balance shafts.
2. Remove gear cover double ended retaining stud, gear cover, and gears **Fig. 29**.
3. Remove balance shaft gear and chain sprocket retaining bolts and crankshaft chain sprocket. To remove chain and sprocket assembly, use two pry bars to work sprocket back and forth.
4. Remove carrier rear cover and balance shafts.
5. Remove four carrier to crankcase attaching bolts to separate carrier.
6. Reverse procedure to install, noting the following:
   a. Dot marks on balance shaft gears

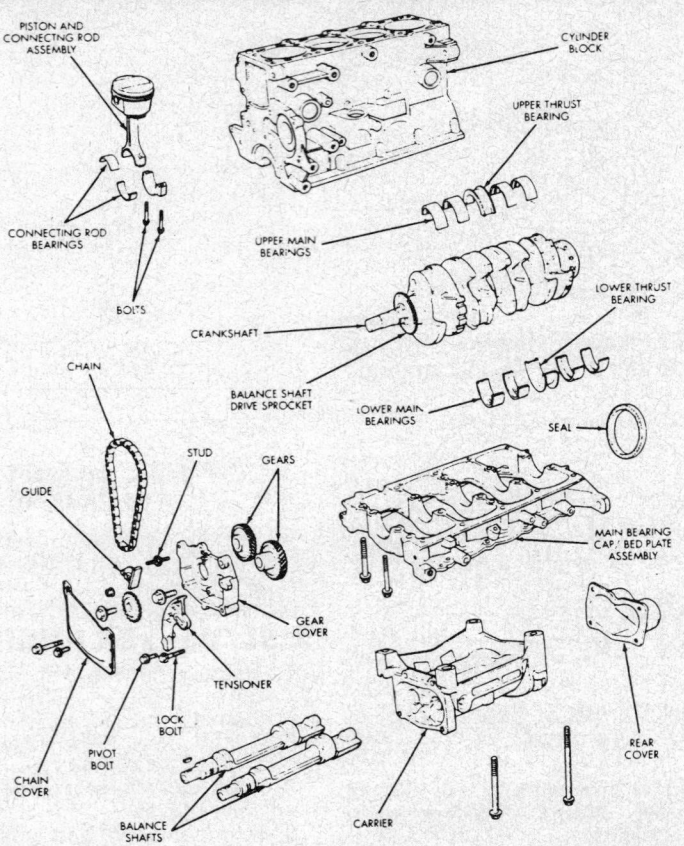

Fig. 29 Exploded view of cylinder block, balance shafts, crankshaft, piston & connecting rod assembly. 2.4L/4–148 engine

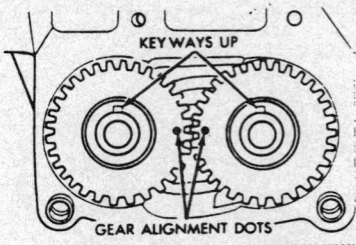

Fig. 30 Balance shaft gear alignment. 2.4L/4-148 engine

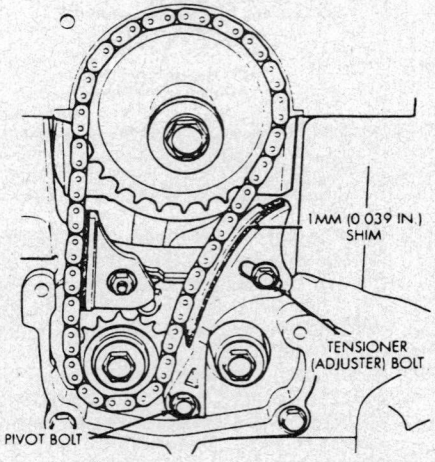

Fig. 31 Balance shaft timing chain & gears. 2.4L/4-148 engine

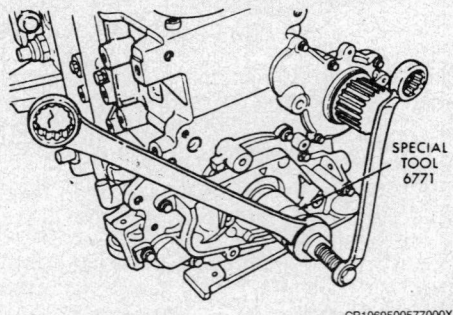

Fig. 34 Front crankshaft oil seal removal

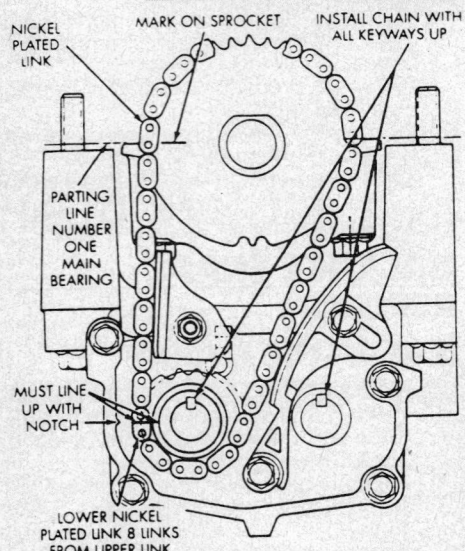

Fig. 32 Balance shaft timing chain tension adjustment. 2.4L/4-148 engine

must be aligned and balance shaft keys must face upward, **Fig. 30.**

b. Balance shaft timing chain and gear timing marks must be aligned as shown in **Fig. 31.**

c. When adjusting balance shaft tim-

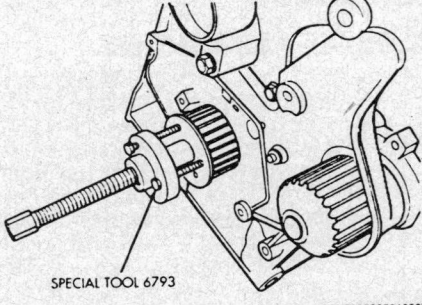

Fig. 33 Crankshaft sprocket removal

ing chain tension, position a shim .039 inch thick by 2.75 inches long between tensioner and chain. Push tensioner and shim against timing chain with a force of 5.5-6.6 lbs., **Fig. 32.** With force applied to timing chain, **torque** top tensioner bolt, then bottom tensioner bolt to 105 inch lbs.

PISTON & ROD ASSEMBLY

2.0L/4–122 & 2.4L/4–148 ENGINE

The L or H stamping on the front portion of the piston must face toward the front of the engine. The connecting rod and cap are stamped on the side with a cylinder number identification. The numbered side of the connecting rod cap must be installed on the same side as the numbered side of the rod.

2.5L/V6–152 ENGINE

The pistons are stamped with a letter and an arrow. Pistons stamped "R" are installed in cylinders 1, 3 and 5; pistons stamped "L" are installed in cylinders 2, 4 and 6. When a piston is installed in the engine, its arrow mark must face the front of the engine. The connecting rod and cap are stamped on the side with a cylinder number identification. The numbered side of the connecting rod cap must be installed on the same side as the numbered side of the rod.

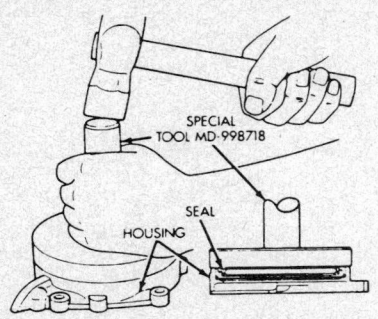

Fig. 35   Rear oil seal installation. 2.5L/V6-152 engine

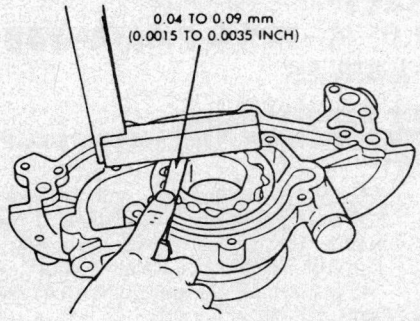

Fig. 38   Rotor end clearance check

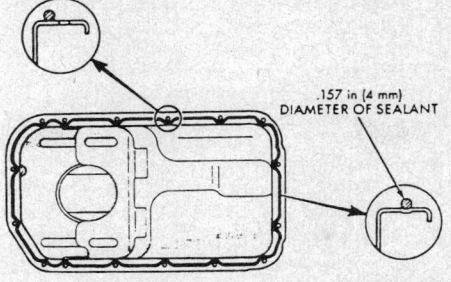

Fig. 36   Oil pan sealing. 2.5L/V6-152

ACCESSORY DRIVE BELT		GAUGE
2.0/2.4L ENGINE		
AIR CONDITIONING COMPRESSOR/GENERATOR	NEW	150 LB.
	USED	80 LB.
POWER STEERING PUMP	NEW	130 LB.
	USED	80 LB.
2.5L ENGINE		
AIR CONDITIONING COMPRESSOR/GENERATOR	NEW	150 LB.
	USED	80 LB.
POWER STEERING PUMP	NEW	130 LB.
	USED	80 LB.

Fig. 39   Belt tension chart

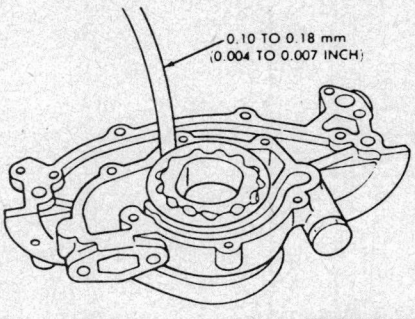

Fig. 37   Outer rotor & case clearance check

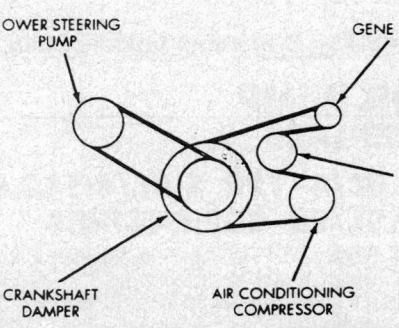

Fig. 40   Serpentine drive belt routing

PISTONS, PINS & RINGS

On **2.0L/4-122 engine**, pistons and rings are available in the standard size. The piston and pin are serviced as an assembly.

On **2.5L/V6-152 engine**, pistons and rings are available in the standard size and in oversizes of .50mm and 1.00mm. The piston and pin are serviced as an assembly.

MAIN & ROD BEARINGS

On **2.0L/4-122 engine**, main and rod bearings are available in the standard size and in undersizes of .025mm and .250mm.

On **2.4L/4-148 engine**, main and rod bearings are available in the standard size and in undersizes of .001, .002, .010, .011 and .012 inch.

CRANKSHAFT SEAL

REPLACE

2.0L/4-122 & 2.4L/4-148 ENGINES

1. Refer to "Timing Belt, Replace" procedure until crankshaft sprocket is accessible.
2. Remove crankshaft sprocket using sprocket remover tool No. 6793 and insert tool No. C-4685-C2 or equivalents, **Fig. 33.**
3. Remove seal using oil seal remover tool No. 6771 or equivalent to remove front crankshaft oil seal, **Fig. 34.**
4. Reverse procedure to install, noting

the following:
  a. Install new seal using seal installation tool No. 6780-1 or equivalent.
  b. Install crankshaft sprocket using tool No. 6792 or equivalent.

2.5L/V6-152 ENGINE

1. Refer to "Timing Belt, Replace" until front crankshaft oil pump is accessible.
2. Remove oil pump bolts and oil pump case.
3. Remove oil seal from oil pump case.
4. Reverse procedure to install, noting the following:
  a. Install new oil pump gasket.
  b. Install oil seal with crankshaft oil seal installer tool No. MB998306 or equivalent, into pump.

CRANKSHAFT REAR OIL SEAL

REPLACE

2.0L/4-122 & 2.4L/4-148 ENGINES

1. Pry out rear seal with screwdriver being careful not to nick or damage crankshaft flange seal surface or retainer bore.
2. Inspect shaft seal surface for nicks or dirt. Polish with 400 grit sandpaper if necessary.
3. Reverse procedure to install, after tapping new seal into place with plastic hammer.

2.5L/V6-152 ENGINE

1. After removal of crankshaft rear oil seal housing, install rear crankshaft oil seal in housing with seal installation tool No. MD998718 or equivalent, **Fig. 35.**

2. Apply Mopar silicon rubber adhesive sealant or equivalent to oil seal housing.
3. Apply light coating of engine oil to entire circumference of oil seal lip.
4. Install seal assembly on cylinder block and **torque bolts to 8-9 ft. lbs.**

OILPAN

REPLACE

2.0L/4-122 & 2.4L/4-148 ENGINES

1. Drain engine oil, then remove the oil pan attaching bolts and pan.
2. Clean oil pan and all gasket surfaces.
3. Reverse procedure to install, noting the following:
  a. Apply Mopar silicone rubber adhesive sealant or equivalent at oil pump to engine block parting line and on oil pan gasket to hold gasket in place.
  b. Tighten pan bolts to specifications.

2.5L/V6-152 ENGINE

1. Drain engine oil, then remove the oil pan attaching bolts and pan.
2. Clean oil pan and all gasket surfaces.
3. Reverse procedure to install, noting the following:
  a. Apply Mopar silicone rubber adhesive sealant or equivalent form in place gasket material. Apply as shown **Fig. 36**
  b. Tighten pan attaching bolts to specifications.

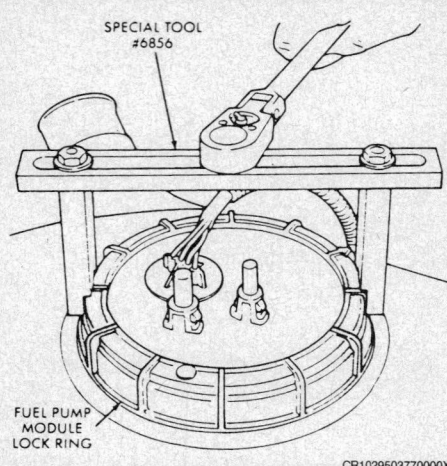

Fig. 41   Fuel pump module locknut

OIL PUMP
REPLACE

2.0L/4–122, 2.4L/4-148 & 2.5L/V6–152 ENGINES

1. Refer to "Timing Belt, Replace" until oil pump is accessible.
2. Remove oil pump attaching bolts and pump.
3. Reverse procedure to install. Tighten attaching bolts to specifications.

OIL PUMP SERVICE

2.0L/4–122 & 2.4L/4–148 ENGINE
Disassembly

1. Remove relief valve plug and gasket, then the spring and relief valve.
2. Remove oil pump attaching bolts and cover.
3. Remove pump rotors.

Inspection & Repair

1. Clean all parts thoroughly in a suitable solvent. Mating surface of oil pump should be smooth. Replace pump cover if scratched or grooved.
2. Lay a straightedge across pump cover surface. If .003 inch feeler gauge can be inserted between cover and straightedge, replace cover.
3. Measure thickness and diameter of outer rotor. I outer rotor thickness measures .301 inch or less, or if diameter is 3.148 inches or less, replace outer rotor.
4. If inner rotor measures .301 inch or less, replace inner rotor.
5. Place outer rotor into pump housing and press to one side. Measure clearance between rotor and housing. If measurement is .015 inch or more, replace housing.
6. Install inner rotor into pump housing. If clearance between inner and outer rotors is .008 or more, replace rotors.
7. Place a straightedge across face of pump housing, between bolt holes. If a feeler gauge of .004 inch or more

can be inserted between rotors and straightedge, replace pump assembly, only if rotors are in specification.
8. Inspect oil pressure relief valve plunger for scoring and free operation in its bore. Small marks may be removed with 400-grit wet or dry sand paper.
9. Oil pump relief valve spring is approximately 2.39 inches in length and should be test between 18-19 pounds when compressed to 1.6 inches. Replace spring that fails to meet specification.

Installation

1. Assemble pump using new parts as required. Install inner rotor with chamfer facing cast iron oil pump cover.
2. Apply Mopar gasket maker lightly to cover mounting surface on pump body. Attach cover and tighten to specifications.
3. Install relief valve, spring, gasket and cap and tighten to specifications.
4. Prime oil pump before installation by filling rotor cavity with clean engine oil.
5. Apply Mopar gasket maker to oil pump. Install oil-ring into counter bore on oil pump body discharge passage.
6. Install oil pump slowly onto crankshaft until seated to engine block. Tighten attaching bolts to specifications.

2.5L/V6–152 ENGINE
Removal

1. Remove accessory drive system.
2. Remove five attaching bolts and oil pump from engine block.

Inspection

1. Inspect oil pump case for damage and remove rear cover.
2. Remove pump rotors and inspect case for excessive wear.
3. Insert rotor into oil pump case and measure clearance, Figs. 37 and 38.
4. Replace if out of specifications.

Assembly & Installation

1. Clean block and pump surfaces.
2. Assemble pump using new parts as required; lubricate with clean oil. Align marks on inner and outer rotors when assembling.
3. Install cover and tighten to specifications.
4. Install relief valve, spring, gasket and cap and tighten to specification.
5. Prime oil pump before installation by filling rotor cavity with clean engine oil.
6. Apply Mopar gasket maker to oil pump. Install oil-ring into counter bore on oil pump body discharge passage.
7. Install oil pump slowly onto crankshaft until seated to engine block. Tighten attaching bolts to specifications.

BELT TENSION DATA

2.0L/4–122, 2.4L/4–148, & 2.5L/V6–152 ENGINES

Refer to **Fig. 39** for belt tension data.

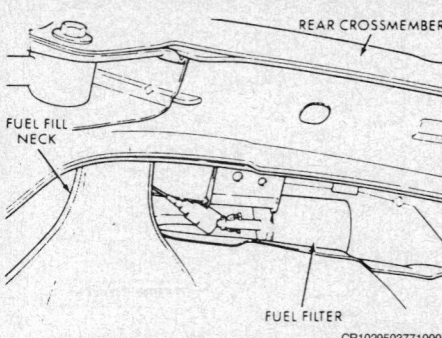

Fig. 42   Fuel filter location

SERPENTINE DRIVE BELT
2.0L/4–122 & 2.4L/4–148 ENGINES

Air Conditioning, Compressor And Generator Belt

1. Loosen T-Bolt locking nut and pivot bolt to remove and install Poly V belt and/or adjust belt tension, **Fig. 40**.
2. Tighten adjusting bolt to adjust belt tension to specification shown in belt tension chart, **Fig. 39**.
3. Torque T-Bolt locking nut and pivot bolt to 40 ft. lbs.

2.5L/V6–152 ENGINE

1. To remove or install air conditioning compressor and generator drive belt, loosen idler pulley lock bolt, then turn adjusting screw to move idler pulley, **Fig. 40**.
2. To adjust air conditioning and generator drive belt, loosen idler pulley bolt and adjust belt tension by tightening adjusting bolt. **Torque** pulley bolt to 40 ft. lbs. after adjustment.

COOLING SYSTEM BLEED
2.0L/4–122 & 2.4L/4–148 ENGINES

The air bleed valve is located on the front of the engine in the thermostat housing to engine outlet connector. There is a relief in the cylinder head for locating the air bleed. To bleed, open valve while engine is running until all has bled from cooling system.

2.5L/V6–152 ENGINE

The air bleed valve is located in the thermostat flange which is located below the throttle body. To bleed, open valve while engine is running until all has bled from cooling system.

THERMOSTAT
REPLACE
2.0L/4–122, 2.4L/4–148 & 2.5L/V6–152 ENGINES

1. Drain cooling system to thermostat level or below.

2. On **2.0L/4-122 and 2.4L/4-148 engines**, remove coolant recovery system hose and thermostat to engine outlet connector bolts.
3. On **2.5L/V6-152 engine**, remove inlet hose and coolant elbow from thermostat housing.
4. **On all engines**, remove thermostat assembly, and clean sealing surfaces.
5. Reverse procedure to install, noting the following:
   a. **On 2.0L/4-122 and 2.4L/4-148 engines**, torque engine outlet connector to cylinder head attaching bolts to 9 ft. lbs.
   b. **On 2.5L/V6-152 engine**, torque coolant inlet elbow attaching bolts to 8-9 ft. lbs.
   c. Fill cooling system.

WATER PUMP
REPLACE

2.0L/4-122 & 2.4L/4-148 ENGINES

1. Raise and support vehicle and remove right inner splash shield.
2. Remove accessory drive belts and power steering pump.
3. Drain cooling system.
4. Support engine from bottom and remove right engine mount.
5. Remove power steering pump bracket attaching bolts and set pump and bracket assembly aside. Power steering lines do not need to be disconnected.
6. Remove right engine mount bracket.
7. Remove timing belt.
8. Remove inner timing belt cover.
9. Remove water pump attaching bolts and the water pump.
10. Reverse procedure to install noting the following:
    a. Install new O-ring gasket in water pump body O-ring groove.
    b. **Torque** water pump attaching bolts to 9 ft. lbs.
    c. Fill cooling system.

2.5L/V6-152 ENGINE

1. Remove timing belt. Refer to "Timing Belt, Replace."
2. Drain cooling system.
3. Remove mounting bolts.
4. Separate pump from water inlet pipe and remove water pump.
5. Reverse procedure to install, noting the following:
   a. Inspect pump for cracks or leaks and replace if necessary.
   b. Install new water pipe O-ring and pump gasket.
   c. **Torque** pump attaching bolts to 20 ft. lbs.
   d. Fill cooling system.

RADIATOR
REPLACE

1. Remove air inlet resonator.
2. Drain cooling system.
3. Remove upper radiator crossmember.
4. Remove hose clamps and hoses from radiator.
5. Disconnect engine block heater electrical wire, if equipped.
6. Disconnect automatic transmission hoses from cooler and plug off.
7. Disconnect fan electrical connector.
8. Remove air conditioning condenser attaching screws located at front of radiator, if equipped. Do not discharge air conditioning system.
9. Remove radiator from engine compartment by lifting upward.
10. Reverse procedure to install.

FUEL PUMP
REPLACE

The electric fuel pump is not serviceable. If the fuel pump needs replacement, the complete fuel pump module must be replaced.

1. Remove fuel filler cap to release pressure.
2. Disconnect negative ground cable.
3. Remove fuel tank after draining.
4. Disconnect fuel filter lines from fuel pump module.
5. Clean top of tank to remove dirt and debris.

6. Remove locknut securing pump module with fuel pump module ring spanner tool No. 6856 or equivalent **Fig. 41**.
7. Remove fuel pump module and O-ring from tank, then discard O-ring.
8. Reverse procedure to install, noting the following:
   a. Install new pump module O-ring.
   b. **Torque** lock ring to 40 ft. lbs. using removal tool.

FUEL FILTER
REPLACE

1. Release fuel system pressure.
2. From inside trunk, disconnect fuel pump module wiring jumper from main body harness. The 4-pin connector is located under trunk map under on left side of trunk near base of shock tower. Locate body grommet for jumper near base of rear seat and push grommet out and feed jumper through hole in body.
3. Remove fuel cap to release tank pressure.
4. Raise and support vehicle and drain fuel from fuel tank.
5. Position a suitable fuel container with a capacity of at least 16 gallons, under drain plug located on bottom left edge of tank.
6. Remove drain plug and allow fuel to drain.
7. When tank stops draining install drain plug and **torque** to 32 inch lbs.
8. Remove driver's side fuel tank strap and loosen, do not remove, passenger side fuel tank strap allowing fuel tank fill neck to touch rear suspension crossmember.
9. Disconnect fuel lines from fuel pump module. These are quick connect fittings located on top of gas tank.
10. Disconnect fuel supply line from fuel brake module.
11. Remove fuel filter **Fig. 42**.
12. Reverse procedure to install. **Torque** fuel tank straps to 17-19 ft. lbs.

TIGHTENING SPECIFICATIONS
2.0L/4-122 & 2.4L/4-148 ENGINES

Year	Component	Torque/Ft. Lbs.
1995	Band Clamp	60
	Body Heat Shield	3-4
	Camshaft Sprocket Bolt ⑤	85
	Camshaft Sprocket Bolt ⑥	75
	Connecting Rod Cap Bolt	②
	Crankshaft Damper Bolt ⑤	105
	Crankshaft Pulley Bolt ⑥	100
	Cylinder Head	①
	Cylinder Head Cover Bolts	105 ③
	EGR Tube	7-8
	Engine Mount Bracket Bolts	30
	Exhaust Flange	20-21
	Exhaust Manifold Heat Shield	105 ③
	Exhaust Manifold To Cylinder Head	200 ③
	Fuel Rail To Intake Manifold	16-17
	Intake Manifold ⑤	105 ③
	Intake Manifold ⑥	20
	Main Bearing Cap Bolts	④
	Oil Filter	15

Year	Component	Torque/Ft. Lbs.
	Oil Filter Adapter To Engine	40
	Oil Pan Drain Plug	25
	Oil Pan To Engine Block	105 ③
	Oil Pump Cover	105 ③
	Oil Pump Mounting Bolts	20
	Oil Pump Pickup Tube Screw	20
	Oil Pump Relief Valve Retaining Cap ⑤	30
	Oil Pump Relief Valve Retaining Cap ⑥	40
	Rocker Arm And Shaft Assembly ⑤	250 ③
	Spark Plugs	20
	Thermostat Housing Bolts	200 ③
	Throttle Body To Intake	15-16
	Throttle Body Support Bracket	8-9
	Timing Belt Tensioner ⑤	275 ③
	Timing Belt Tensioner ⑥	20
	Timing Belt Tensioner Pulley ⑥	30
	Water Pump To Engine Block	105 ③

①—Refer to text.
②—Torque to 20 ft. lbs., then tighten an additional ¼ turn.
③—Inch lbs.
④—2.0L/4-122 engine: M8 bolts, 25 ft. lbs.; M11 bolts, 60 ft. lbs. 2.4L/4-148 engine: M8 bolts, 250 inch lbs.; M11 bolts, 30 ft. lbs. plus an additional ¼ turn.
⑤—2.0L/4-122 engine.
⑥—2.4L/4-143 engine.

2.5L/V6-152 ENGINE

Year	Component	Torque/Ft. Lbs.
1995	Air Intake Plenum	12-13
	Auto Tensioner Bolt	17
	Band Clamp	60
	Body Heat Shield	3-4
	Camshaft Sprocket	65
	Connecting Rod Cap Nut	37
	Crankshaft Bolt	134
	Crossover	22
	Cylinder Head Cover	2.5
	Cylinder Head	①
	Engine Support Bracket	33
	Exhaust Manifold	22
	Heater Pipe Assembly	13
	Idler Pulley Bolt	33
	Intake Manifold	16
	Main Bearing Cap Bolts	69

Year	Component	Torque/Ft. Lbs.
	Oil Filter	10
	Oil Pan	4
	Oil Pan Drain Plug	25
	Oil Pump Cover	7
	Oil Pump Relief Valve Cap	30
	Oil Pump To Engine Block	17-19
	Oil Screen	13
	Rocker Arm And Shaft Assembly	16-17
	Spark Plugs	18
	Tensioner Arm Assembly	33
	Tensioner Pulley Bolt	35
	Thermostat Housing	13
	Thrust Case	85
	Water Inlet Pipe	10
	Water Pump	17

①—Refer to text.

Clutch & Manual Transaxle

INDEX

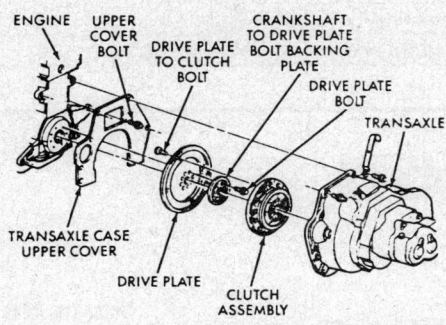

Fig. 1 Exploded view of clutch assembly

CR5049500082000X

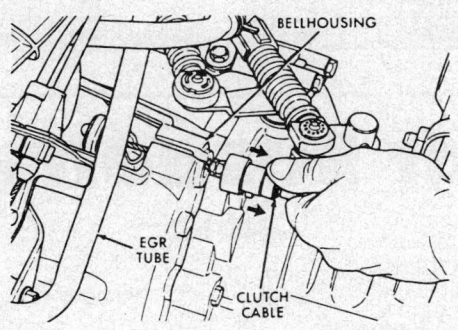

Fig. 2 Clutch cable removal

CR5049500083000X

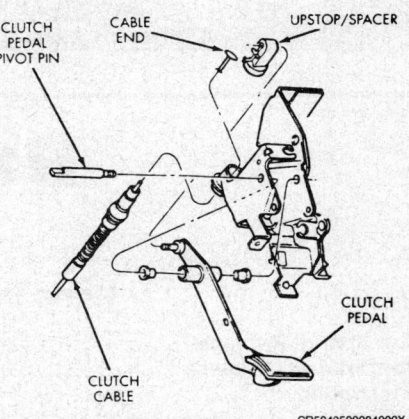

CR5049500084000X

Fig. 3 Clutch cable end at pedal assembly removal

ADJUSTMENTS

The clutch cable has a self-adjusting mechanism built into the cable which compensates for clutch disc wear. The cable requires no maintenance or lubrication. The cable assembly may not be adjusted.

CLUTCH
REPLACE

The modular clutch assembly used in these models consists of a single dry-type clutch disc and a diaphragm style clutch cover. The clutch assembly is serviced as a unit and cannot be disassembled.
1. Disconnect battery ground cable, then raise and support vehicle.
2. Remove starter wiring, then the starter assembly.
3. Remove transaxle as outlined under "Transaxle, Replace."
4. Remove modular clutch assembly from transaxle input shaft, **Fig. 1.** **Handle carefully to avoid contaminating friction surfaces.**
5. Reverse procedure to install, noting the following:
   a. Install drive plate mounting bolts in a crisscross pattern until all bolt are seat.
   b. Tighten bolts to specification using same crisscross pattern.

SHIFT CABLE
REPLACE

1. Remove air cleaner assembly, then the clutch cable inspection cover.

2. Pull back on clutch cable housing and disengage cable from housing, **Fig. 2.**
3. Disconnect clutch cable up-stop/spacer with cable strand, **Fig. 3.** Depressing the clutch pedal provides access to clutch cable strand.
4. Disconnect cable up-stop/spacer from pedal pivot by wedging a suitable flat blade pry tool between pin and retaining tab.
5. Hold tab slightly separate from pin, then pull the upstop/spacer off pedal.
6. Remove cable end from up-stop/spacer.
7. Reverse procedure to install.

TRANSAXLE
REPLACE

1. Disconnect battery ground cable, then remove the air cleaner at throttle body inlet.
2. Remove clutch housing vent cap, exposing clutch cable end and release lever, then disconnect clutch cable at transaxle.
3. Remove selector cable lever at transaxle.
4. Remove crossover lever cable, then the shift cable mounting bracket.
5. Disconnect accelerator cables ends and bracket from throttle body.
6. Remove upper starter bolt and upper bellhousing stud nut, then the throttle body support bracket.
7. Remove upper transaxle mounting bolts, then the upper bellhousing bolts.

8. Remove vehicle speed sensor (VSS), then the back-up lamp wiring at transaxle.
9. Install suitable engine bridge fixture and support engine.
10. Raise and support vehicle, then remove front wheels.
11. Drain transaxle fluid.
12. Remove both front driveshafts following procedure under "Axle Shaft, Replace."
13. Remove left lower splash shield/battery cover.
14. Remove left transaxle mount lower bracket bolts.
15. Remove engine lower crossbar retaining bolts.
16. Remove front engine steel mount bracket, then the bolts on front engine aluminum mount bracket.
17. Remove lower starter bolt, then the rear transaxle mount bracket.
18. Remove transaxle to rear lateral bending strut from engine and transaxle.
19. Remove lower dust shield screw.
20. Using suitable transaxle support jack, support transaxle.
21. Rotate engine crankshaft clockwise to gain access to driveplate clutch bolts, then remove driveplate clutch bolts.
22. Remove lower transaxle to engine bellhousing bolts, then the transaxle.
23. Reverse procedure to install.

TIGHTENING SPECIFICATIONS

Year	Component	Torque/ Ft. Lbs.
1995	Back-up Lamp Switch	18
	Clutch Pedal Pivot Shaft Nut	30
	Drive Plate To Modular Clutch Bolts	55
	Drive Plate To Crankshaft Bolts	70
	End Plate Cover Bolts	21
	Front Engine Mount To Transaxle	80
	Front Transaxle Mount Thru Bolt	45

Year	Component	Torque/ Ft. Lbs.
	Front Transaxle Mount To Engine Bolt	40
	Lateral Bending Strut To Engine	40
	Lateral Bending Strut To Transaxle	40
	Left Transaxle Mount Thru Bolt	80
	Transaxle To Engine Bolts	70
	Transaxle to Engine Intake Bracket Stud	70

Rear Suspension

INDEX

DESCRIPTION

The rear suspension, is a fully independent short and long arm style suspension, **Fig. 1**. An upper control arm bolts to the top of each rear cast knuckle to the rear suspension crossmember. The movement of the rear knuckle is controlled laterally by two lower lateral links going from the front and rear of the knuckle to the rear crossmember and upper control arm. Fore and aft movement of the knuckle is controlled by a trailing arm.

HUB & BEARING
REPLACE

All models are equipped with permanently-lubricated and sealed-for-life wheel bearings. There is no periodic lubrication or maintenance recommended for these units. If servicing is required, proceed as follows:

1. Raise and support vehicle, then remove rear wheel and tire assembly.
2. **On vehicles equipped with drum brakes,** remove brake drum.
3. **On vehicles equipped with disc brakes,** remove brake caliper from brake disc adapter, then the brake disc.
4. **On all models,** remove dust cap from hub/bearing assembly to spindle retaining nut.
5. Remove hub/bearing retainer assembly from spindle by pulling straight on spindle by hand.
6. Reverse procedure to install. Tighten hub/bearing assembly to spindle retaining nut to specifications.

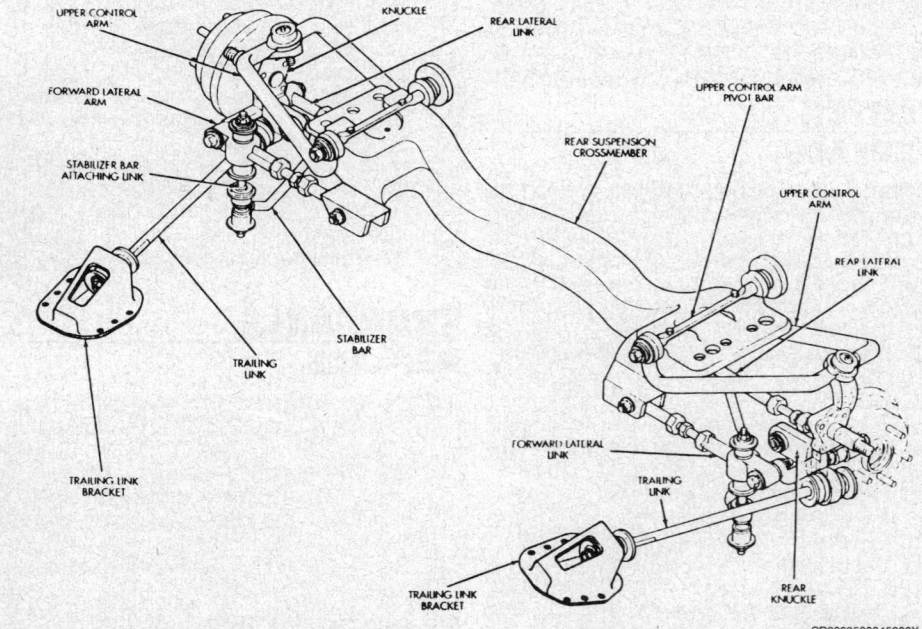

Fig. 1   Rear suspension components

SHOCK ABSORBER
REPLACE

1. Roll back carpeting on top of rear shock tower to access shock mounting bolts, then remove shock tower cover.
2. Remove two attaching nuts.
3. Raise and support vehicle.
4. Remove rear wheel and tire assembly, then the bolt attaching clevis bracket on shock to knuckle, **Fig. 2.**
5. Remove shock absorber clevis bracket from knuckle by pushing down on suspension.
6. Move shock absorber downward and tilt top of shock outward.
7. Remove shock from vehicle through top of wheelwell opening.
8. Reverse procedure to install.

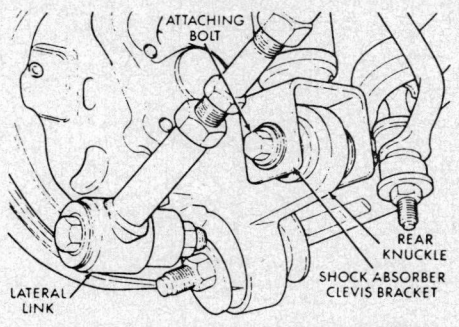

Fig. 2   Shock & knuckle location

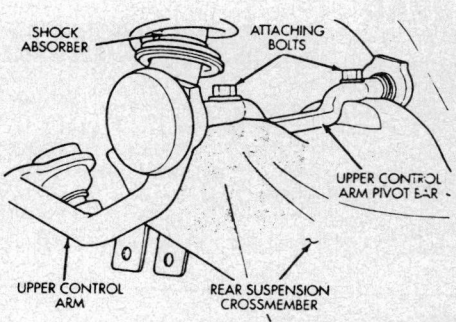

Fig. 5   Upper control arm & crossmember

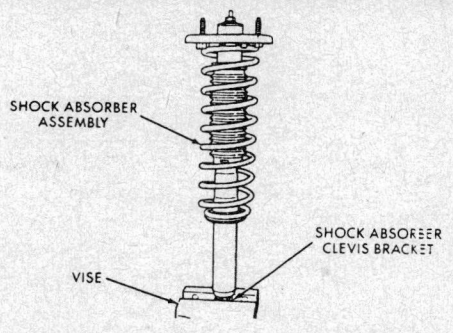

Fig. 3   Coil spring removal

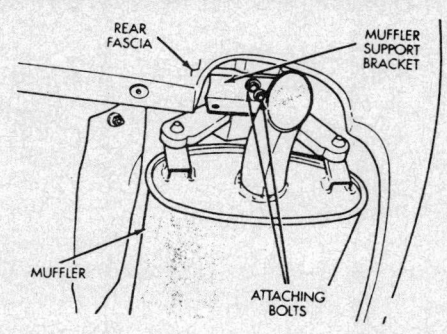

Fig. 4   Muffler support bracket

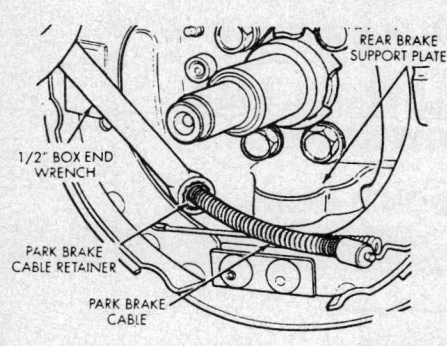

Fig. 6   Parking brake cable removal

COIL SPRING
REPLACE

1. Remove shock absorber as outlined under "Shock Absorber, Replace."
2. Position shock assembly in a vise, **Fig. 3**, clamping by clevis bracket at bottom of shock.
3. Mark coil spring and strut assembly right or left as needed.
4. Using coil spring compressor tool No. GP-2020-S2.5, or equivalent, compress coil spring.
5. Using a suitable tool, keep shock shaft rod from turning and remove shock shaft nut.
6. Remove washer, shock mounting bracket, washer on top of dust shield, then the dust shield.
7. Remove coil spring and spring compressor as an assembly.
8. Reverse procedure to install. Tighten mounting nuts to specifications.

CONTROL ARM
REPLACE

1. Raise and support vehicle, then remove both rear wheel and tire assemblies.
2. Remove shock absorber clevis bracket as outlined under "Shock Absorber, Replace" on both sides of vehicle.
3. Remove muffler support bracket from rear frame, **Fig. 4.**
4. Remove rear exhaust pipe hanger bracket from rear suspension crossmember and move exhaust down far as possible.

5. Remove cotter pin and castle nut from ball joint.
6. On side of vehicle requiring control arm removal, separate control arm ball joint from rear knuckle using puller tool No. CT-1106, or equivalent. **Reinstall castle nut on ball joint stud to protect threads.**
7. Position a suitable floor jack and block of wood under center of rear suspension crossmember to support and lower crossmember during removal. **Do not put strain on brake flex hoses or damage may occur.**
8. **On models equipped with ABS,** remove routing clips for wheel speed sensor cable from brackets on both upper control arms.
9. **On all models,** remove 4 bolts attaching rear suspension crossmember to rear frame rails.
10. Lower rear suspension crossmember far enough to access upper control arm pivot bar to crossmember attaching bolts, then the two bolts attaching upper control arm to crossmember, **Fig. 5.**
11. Remove control arm from vehicle.
12. Reverse procedure to install, noting the following:
    a. Align upper control arm pivot bar with mounting holes in rear suspension crossmember.
    b. Install the two pivot bar nuts to crossmember attaching bolts. Tighten to specifications.
    c. Using suitable jackstand, raise rear suspension crossmember up to frame rails and loosely install the four attaching nuts.
    d. Position appropriate size drift into position hole in each side of rear suspension crossmember and crossmember locating holes in frame rails, then tighten frame rail attaching bolts to specifications.
    e. Install upper ball joint stud in knuckle, then the ball join castle nut and tighten to specifications.

KNUCKLE
REPLACE

1. Raise and support vehicle, then remove rear wheel and tire assembly.
2. Remove brake drum or disc brake.
3. **On models equipped with ABS,** remove rear wheel speed sensor.
4. **On all models,** remove parking brake cable from brake actuator lever.

5. Remove parking brake cable as follows:
    a. Position a 1/2 inch box end wrench over cable retainer, **Fig. 6** to collapse retaining tabs.
    b. Pull brake cable from brake support plate.
6. Remove rear hub/bearing assembly retaining nut, then the washer and hub/bearing assembly from knuckle.
7. Remove four attaching bolts from rear support plate and knuckle.
8. Remove brake support plate, brake shoes and wheel cylinder as an assembly from knuckle.
9. Remove attaching nuts and bolts holding forward and rear lateral links to knuckle.
10. Disconnect ball joint stud from knuckle following procedure outlined under, "Control Arm Replace."
11. Remove knuckle.
12. Reverse procedure to install. Tighten all nuts and bolts to specifications.

STABILIZER BAR
REPLACE

1. Raise and support vehicle, then remove both rear wheel and tire assemblies.
2. Using a suitable wrench to keep stabilizer links from rotating, remove nuts attaching stabilizer link isolator bushings to stabilizer links.
3. Remove four bolts attaching stabilizer bar bushing clamps to rear suspension crossmember, **Fig. 7.**
4. Remove rear stabilizer bar to crossmember bushing clamps and bushings from stabilizer bar.

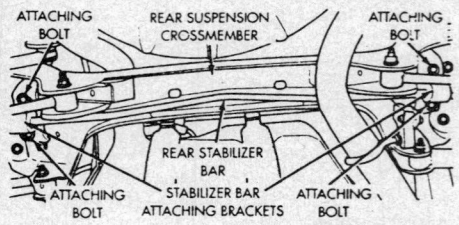

Fig. 7 Rear stabilizer bar components

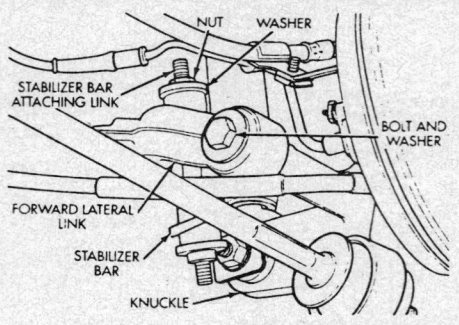

Fig. 8 Forward lateral link

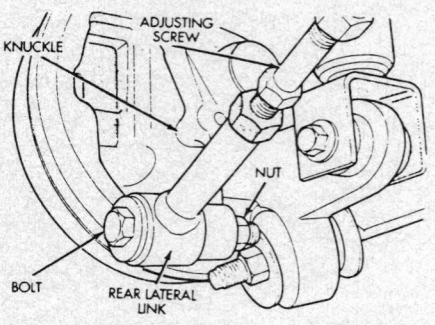

Fig. 9 Rear lateral link

5. Remove stabilizer bar between exhaust pipe and rear suspension crossmember.
6. Reverse procedure to install.

LATERAL LINK
REPLACE

FORWARD

1. Raise and support vehicle, then remove rear wheel and tire assembly from side of car being serviced.
2. Remove rear stabilizer bar attaching link from forward lateral link to knuckle, **Fig. 8.**
3. Remove nut, bolt and washer attaching lateral link to knuckle.
4. Remove nut and bolt attaching lateral link to rear suspension crossmember, then the lateral link.
5. Reverse procedure to install. Tighten all bolts and nuts to specifications.

REAR

1. Raise and support vehicle, then remove rear wheel and tire assembly from side of car being serviced.
2. Remove nut, bolt and washer attaching lateral link to knuckle, **Fig. 9.**
3. Remove nut and bolt attaching lateral link to rear suspension crossmember, then the lateral link.
4. Reverse procedure to install. Tighten all bolts and nuts to specifications.

TIGHTENING SPECIFICATIONS

Year	Component	Torque/Ft. Lbs.
1995	Brake Support Plate To Knuckle Mounting Bolts	45
	Hub & Bearing Assembly To Knuckle	184
	Lateral Link Attaching Nut	70
	Shock Assembly Clevis Bracket To Knuckle	70
	Shock Assembly Shaft Nut	55
	Shock Assembly To Body	25

Year	Component	Torque/Ft. Lbs.
	Sway Bar Isolator Bushing Retainer To Crossmember Bolt	20
	Sway Bar To Forward Lateral Link Attaching Link Nut	40
	Upper Ball Joint To Knuckle Castle Nut	63
	Upper Control Arm Pivot Bar To Crossmember	79
	Wheel Lug Nuts	80-110

Front Suspension & Steering

NOTE: Refer To "Air Bag System Precautions" Located In The Front Of This Manual For System Disarming & Arming Procedures.

INDEX

WHEEL BEARING
ADJUST

These models are equipped with permanently-sealed front wheel bearings. There is no periodic lubrication or maintenance recommended.

HUB & BEARING
REPLACE

Replacement of front hub bearing assembly must be done with steering knuckle removed.
1. Raise and support vehicle.

2. Remove cotter pin, lock nut and spring washer from front stub axle.
3. Lower vehicle, then loosen hub nut while vehicle is on the ground and brakes are applied.
4. Raise and support vehicle, then remove from wheel and tire assembly.
5. Remove front disc brake caliper and

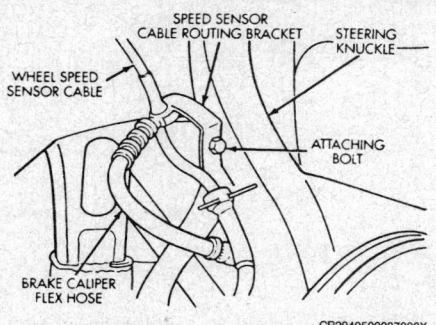

Fig. 1   Speed sensor routing cable bracket

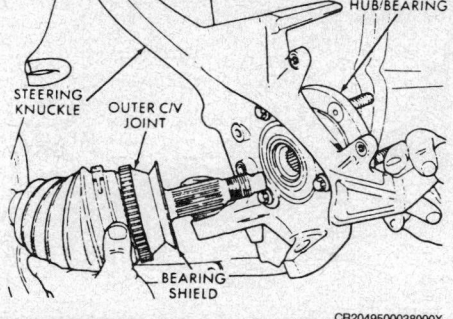

Fig. 2   Steering knuckle & outer CV joint

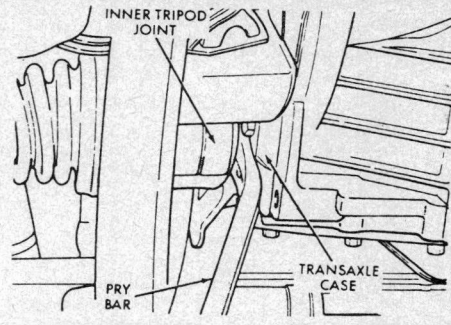

Fig. 3   Inner tripod joint removal

brake disc assembly and support aside from steering knuckle.

6. **On models equipped with 15 inch wheels,** remove lower ball joint heat shield from lower control arm.
7. **On all models,** remove attaching outer tie rod end to steering knuckle.
8. Using remover tool No. MB-991113, or equivalent, remove tie rod end from steering knuckle.
9. **On models with ABS,** remove speed sensor cable routing bracket, **Fig. 1.**
10. **On all models,** remove cotter pin and castle nut from stud of lower ball joint at steering knuckle.
11. Turn steering knuckle so front of steering knuckle is facing as far outboard in wheelwell as possible. Lightly tap boss on steering knuckle to separate from stud of lower ball joint. **Do not hit lower control arm or ball joint grease seal.**
12. Lift up on steering knuckle and separate from ball joint stud. **Support driveshaft so it does not hang by inner CV joint.**
13. Separate steering knuckle from outer CV joint by pulling away, **Fig. 2.**
14. Remove cotter pin and nut from upper ball joint to steering knuckle attachment.
15. Remove upper ball joint stud using puller tool No. C3894-A, or equivalent, then the steering knuckle.
16. Mount steering knuckle securely in a vise, then remove three bolts attaching hub/bearing assembly to steering knuckle.
17. Remove hub/bearing assembly from steering knuckle. **If bearing does not come out, tap lightly using a rubber mallet.**
18. Before installing hub/bearing assembly, clean all mounting surfaces thoroughly.
19. Install hub/bearing assembly in steering knuckle aligning bolts in bearing flange with hole in steering knuckle.
20. Reverse remaining procedure to install. Tighten all nuts and bolts to specifications.

DRIVESHAFT
REPLACE

Driveshaft on both lefthand side and righthand side of vehicle use a tuned rubber damper weight. The damper weight

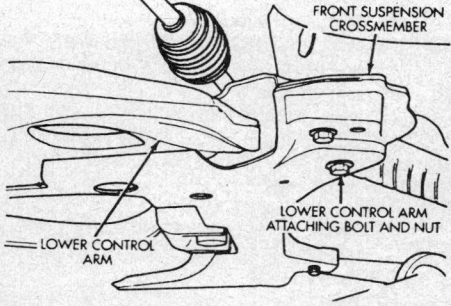

Fig. 4   Lower control arm removal

applications vary by which side of vehicle is used and engine application. On models equipped with ABS, the outer CV joint has a tone wheel which is used to determine vehicle speed for ABS operation.

1. Loosen, but do not remove, stub axle to hub/bearing retaining nut while vehicle is on floor and brakes applied, then raise and support vehicle and remove front wheel and tire assembly.
2. Remove brake caliper and support aside, then the brake disc.
3. Remove tie rod end attaching nut, then the tie rod end stud from steering knuckle using remover tool No. MB-991113, or equivalent.
4. **On models with ABS,** remove vehicle speed sensor cable routing bracket.
5. **On all models,** remove cotter pin and castle nut from stud of lower ball joint at steering knuckle.
6. Turn steering knuckle so front of knuckle is facing as far outboard in wheelwell as possible. Lightly tap boss on steering knuckle to separate from stud of lower ball joint.
7. Pull steering knuckle assembly out and away from outer CV joint
8. Support outer end of driveshaft assembly, then insert a pry bar between tripod joint and transaxle case, **Fig. 3,** side gear as far as possible by hand.
9. Hold inner tripod joint and interconnecting shaft of driveshaft assembly.
10. Remove inner tripod joint from transaxle by pulling it straight out of transaxle side gear.
11. Reverse procedure to install. Tighten all nuts and bolts to specifications.

BALL JOINT
REPLACE

The ball joints are not a replaceable component of the control arms and if determined to be defective will require replacement of affected control arm. Refer to "Control Arm, Replace," for procedure.

SHOCK ABSORBER
REPLACE

1. Raise and support vehicle, then remove the front wheel and tire assembly.
2. **On models equipped with ABS,** remove vehicle speed sensor cable routing bracket.
3. **On all models,** remove cotter pin and castle nut from upper ball joint stud to steering knuckle attachment.
4. Remove upper ball joint stud from steering knuckle using pull tool No. C-3894-A, or equivalent, then position steering outward toward rear of wheelwell.
5. Remove pinch bolt attaching shock clevis to shock.
6. Remove thru-bolt attaching shock to lower control arm.
7. Remove clevis from shock by carefully tapping clevis with soft brass drift off shock fluid reservoir.
8. Remove four bolts attaching shock/upper control arm mounting bracket to shock tower.
9. Remove shock and upper control arm mounting bracket as an assembly through front area of wheelwell.
10. Reverse procedure to install. Tighten all nuts and bolt to specifications.

CONTROL ARM
REPLACE
LOWER

1. Raise and support vehicle, then remove the front wheel and tire assembly.
2. **On models equipped with 15 inch wheels,** remove lower ball joint heat shield.
3. **On all models,** remove disc brake caliper and support aside, then the brake disc.
4. Disconnect ball joint from steering

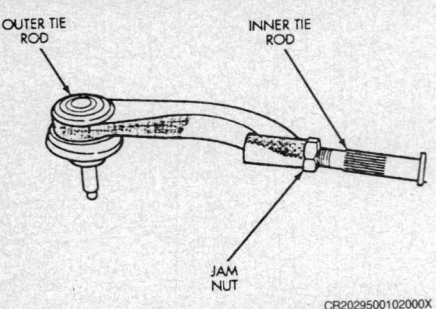

Fig. 5   Tie rod replacement

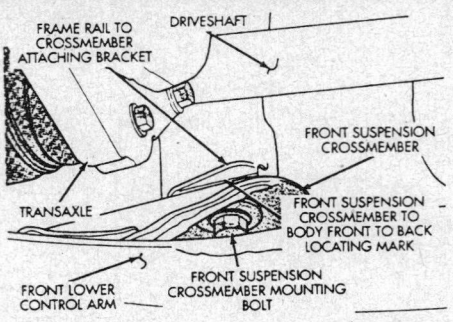

Fig. 6   Front suspension crossmember front to back locating mark (Part 1 of 2)

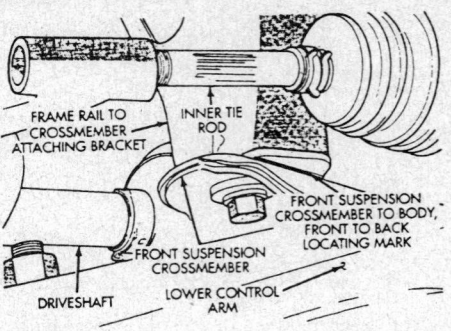

Fig. 6   Front suspension crossmember front to back locating mark (Part 2 of 2)

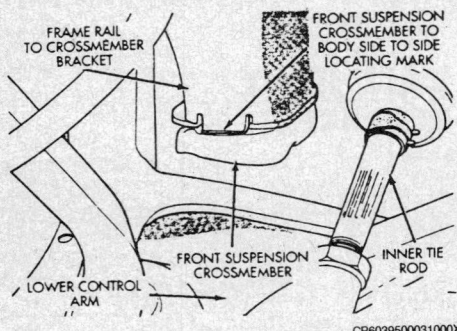

Fig. 7   Front suspension crossmember side to side locating mark

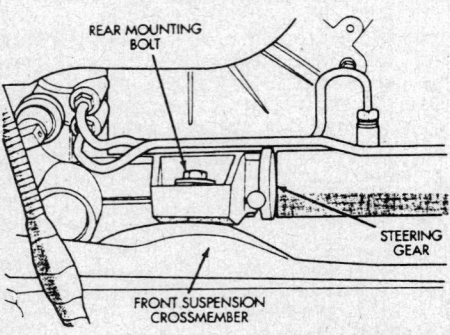

Fig. 8   Steering gear rear mounting isolator bolts

---

knuckle, then turn steering knuckle so front of knuckle is facing as far outboard as possible.

5. Separate steering knuckle from lower ball joint by lightly tapping with a rubber mallet.
6. Remove shock absorber clevis from lower control.
7. Using an Allen wrench to prevent stabilizer bar link from rotating, remove nut attaching stabilizer bar link assembly to lower control arm.
8. Remove attaching bolts of stabilizer bar bushing to front suspension crossmember and body of vehicle.
9. Lower one side of stabilizer bar away from lower control arm.
10. Remove nut and bolt attaching rear isolator bushing of lower control arm, **Fig. 4** then the nut and bolt attaching front isolator bushing of lower control arm.
11. Remove front isolator bushing of lower control arm to front suspension crossmember.
12. To remove lower control arm, proceed as follows:
    a. Remove front of lower control arm from front suspension crossmember first.
    b. Remove rear of lower control arm from between the top and bottom half of front suspension crossmember, keeping lower control arm as level as possible.
13. Reverse procedure to install.

UPPER

1. Raise and support vehicle, then remove the front wheel and tire assembly.

---

2. **On models equipped with ABS,** remove vehicle speed sensor cable routing bracket.
3. **On all models,** remove cotter pin and castle nut from upper ball joint stud to steering knuckle attachment.
4. Remove upper ball joint stud from steering knuckle using pull tool No. C-3894-A, or equivalent, then position the steering outward toward rear of wheelwell.
5. Remove pinch bolt attaching shock clevis to shock.
6. Remove thru-bolt attaching shock to lower control arm.
7. Remove clevis from shock by carefully tapping clevis with soft brass drift off shock fluid reservoir.
8. Remove four bolts attaching upper control arm/shock absorber mounting bracket to shock tower.
9. Remove shock absorber and upper control arm mounting bracket as an assembly.
10. Reverse procedure to install. Tighten all nuts and bolts to specifications.

STEERING KNUCKLE
REPLACE

Refer to procedure outlined under "Hub & Bearing, Replace."

STABILIZER BAR
REPLACE

1. Using an Allen wrench to prevent stabilizer bar link from rotating, remove nut attaching stabilizer bar link assembly to lower control arm.
2. Remove attaching bolts of stabilizer bar bushing to front suspension crossmember and body of vehicle.
3. Remove bushings, bushing retainers, and attaching links, then the stabilizer bar.
4. Reverse procedure to install. Tighten nuts and bolts to specifications.

TIE ROD
REPLACE

1. Raise and support vehicle, then remove the front wheel and tire assembly.
2. Remove nuts attaching both outer tie rod ends to steering knuckle.
3. Using remover tool No. MB-991113,

---

or equivalent, remove both tie rod end studs from steering knuckles.
4. Loosen inner to outer tie rod jam nut, **Fig. 5,** then remove the outer tie rod from inner tie rod.
5. Remove jam nut, then using pliers, expand tie rod boot, to inner tie rod clamp and remove from steering gear.
6. Reverse procedure to install. Tighten all nuts and bolts to specifications.

POWER STEERING GEAR
REPLACE

1. Disconnect battery ground cable, then siphon power steering fluid from remote power steering reservoir
2. From interior of vehicle, remove retaining pin from intermediate shaft coupler pinch bolt, then the pinch bolt from intermediate shaft coupler.
3. Separate intermediate shaft coupler from gear shaft.
4. Raise and support vehicle, then remove both front wheel and tire assemblies.
5. Remove nuts attaching both outer tie rod ends to steering knuckles.
6. Using remover tool No. MB-991113 or equivalent, remove both tie rod end studs from steering knuckles.
7. Using an awl, scribe a line on body, **Fig. 6,** marking the front to back installed location where front suspension crossmember is mounted on each side of vehicle.
8. Using an awl, scribe a line on front suspension crossmember, **Fig. 7,**

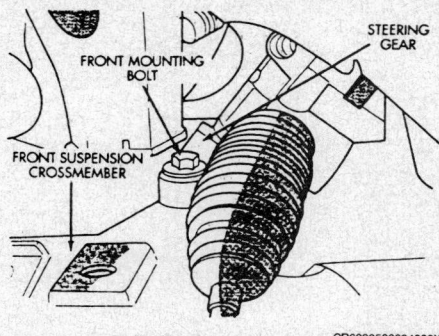

Fig. 9   Steering gear front mounting isolator bolts

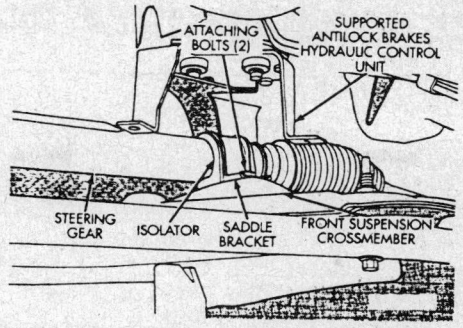

Fig. 10   Steering gear saddle bracket mounting bolts

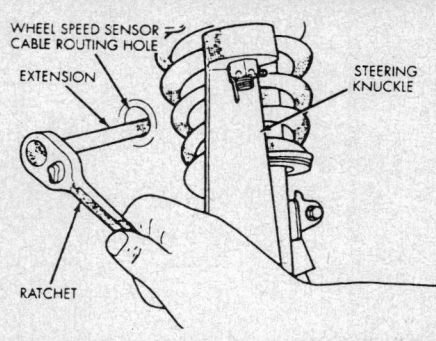

Fig. 11   Top bolt for power steering pump mounting bracket

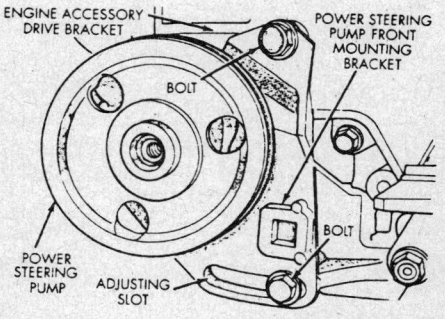

Fig. 12   Power steering pump front bracket

marking side to side installed location where front suspension crossmember is mounted against body on both sides of vehicle.

9. Remove stabilizer bar bushing clamp to body attaching bolts only.
10. **On models equipped with ABS,** remove three bolts, then secure the ABS hydraulic control unit to body for suspension crossmember removal. **Do not let unit hang by brake tubes.**
11. **On all models,** remove bolts attaching shock absorber clevis to lefthand and righthand lower control arms.
12. Remove two bolt attaching engine support bracket to front suspension crossmember.
13. Position a suitable jackstand under center of front suspension crossmember.
14. Remove from both sides of vehicle front two bolts attaching front suspension crossmember to frame rail of vehicle, then the rear attaching bolts.
15. Using jackstand, lower front suspension crossmember enough to allow steering gear to be removed from crossmember. **Ensure crossmember is supported by jackstand to avoid damage.**
16. Drain power steering fluid, pressure and return hoses from power steering gear assembly.
17. Disconnect power steering harness connector from fluid reservoir switch.
18. Remove two bolts at isolators, **Figs. 8 and 9,** attaching steering gear assembly to front suspension crossmember, then the two bolts attaching steering gear saddle bracket to front suspension crossmember, **Fig. 10.**
19. Remove steering gear assembly.
20. Reverse procedure to install. Tighten all nuts and bolts to specifications.

POWER STEERING PUMP
REPLACE

2.0L/4–122 & 2.4L/4–148 ENGINES

1. Disconnect battery ground cable, then siphon power steering fluid out of remote power steering fluid reservoir.
2. Raise and support vehicle, then remove righthand wheel and tire assembly.
3. Remove accessory drive splash shield from righthand front wheelwell.
4. Disconnect power steering fluid pressure hose from pressure fitting on power steering pump, then drain remaining power steering fluid.
5. Remove attaching hose clamp from power steering suction fitting, then the power steering supply hose.
6. Remove power steering pump adjusting nut, then the bolt attaching power steering pump to aluminum mounting bracket.
7. **On models with ABS,** remove ABS hydraulic control unit heat shield.

8. Remove speed sensor cable sealing grommet from inner fender, then disconnect the wheel speed sensor cable from wiring harness and secure aside. Pull through hole in inner fender and unclip wiring harness trough from frame rail.
9. **On all models,** Remove ABS sealing plug from hole in firewall.
10. Remove bolt attaching top of power steering pump front bracket to mounting bracket, **Fig. 11.**
11. Remove power steering pump drive belt.
12. Remove power steering pump and bracket as an assembly.
13. Reverse procedure to install. Tighten all fittings to specifications.

2.5L/V6–152 ENGINE

1. Disconnect battery ground cable, then siphon power steering fluid out of remote power steering fluid reservoir.
2. Raise and support vehicle, then remove the righthand wheel and tire assembly.
3. Remove accessory drive splash shield from righthand front wheelwell.
4. Disconnect power steering fluid pressure hose from pressure fitting on power steering pump, then drain remaining power steering fluid.
5. Remove power steering pressure hose from fitting on pump.
6. **On models with ABS,** remove ABS hydraulic control unit heat shield.
7. **On all models,** remove adjusting bolt in accessory drive mounting bracket.
8. Remove bolt at adjusting slot, **Fig. 12,** then the bolt from at top of power steering pump front mounting brackets.
9. Remove power steering drive belt.
10. Remove power steering pump.
11. Reverse procedure to install. Tighten all fittings to specifications.

TIGHTENING SPECIFICATIONS

Year	Component	Torque/ Ft. Lbs.
1995	Ball Joint Stud To Shock Tower Attaching Bolts	23
	Ball Joint Stud To Steering Gear Castle Nut	70
	Disc Brake Caliper Assembly To Steering Knuckle Bolts	16
	Front Crossmember Assembly To Body Mounting Nuts	120
	Front Stub Axle To Hub/Bearing Assembly	180
	Lower Control Arm To Crossmember Pivot Bolt	120
	Outer Tie Rod To Inner Tie Rod Lock Nut	55
	Power Steering Bracket To Engine Mounting Bolt	40
	Power Steering Pump Mounting To Front Bracket	40
	Power Steering & Return Hose	23
	Pressure Hose To Return Hose (2.0L/4-122 & 2.4L/4-148 Engines)	7
	Pressure Hose To Return Hose (2.5L/V6-152)	40
	Steering Gear To Crossmember Attaching Bolts	45
	Shock Absorber Shaft Nut	55
	Shock Assembly Clevis Bracket To Lower Control Arm Nut	120
	Stabilizer Bar Bushing Retainer To Crossmember Bolts	21
	Stabilizer Bar To Control Arm Attaching Link Nut	55
	Steering Gear To Crossmember Bolts	50
	Tie Rod End To Steering Knuckle Attaching Nut	45
	Wheel Lug Nuts	80-110

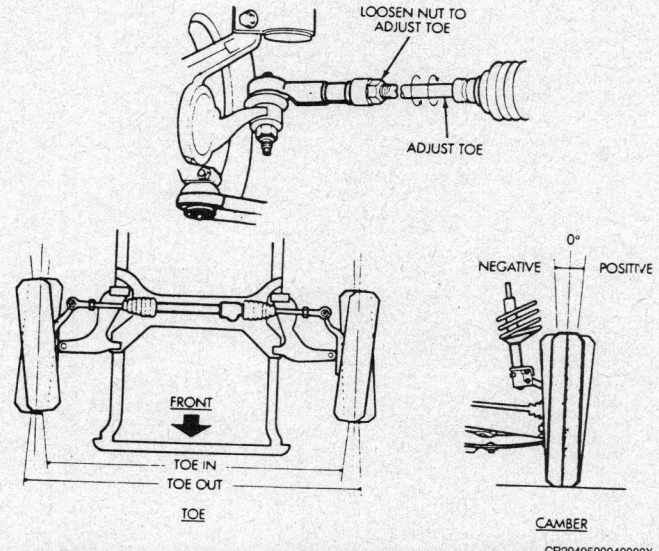

Fig. 1   Toe & thrust angle adjustment

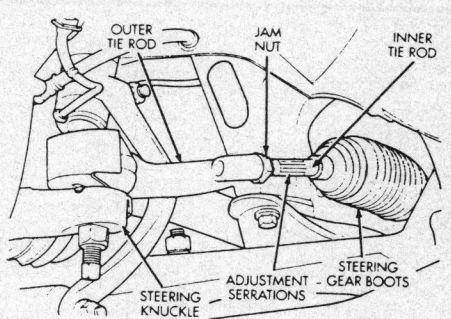

Fig. 2   Inner & outer tie rod adjustment

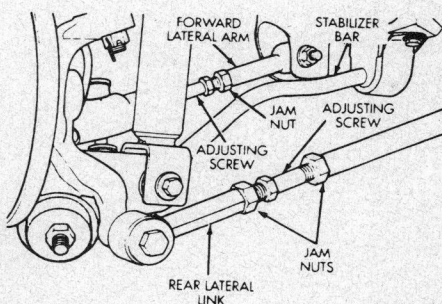

Fig. 3   Rear lateral arm adjustment

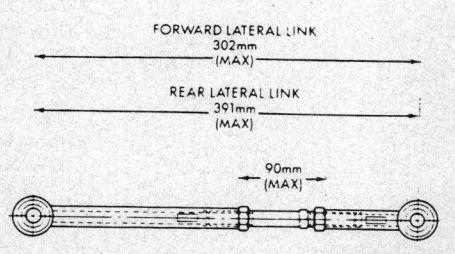

Fig. 4   Lateral link maximum length

Though not adjustable, front caster and camber must be checked and components replaced when outside of vehicle specification. Inspect all components for damage or signs of bending and replace as required.

Prior to checking or adjusting front or rear suspension alignment, inspect suspension components and wheel bearings for damage or excessive wear and replace as needed. Ensure tire pressure is properly adjusted, then raise and release front or rear bumper several times to allow vehicle to assume ride height.

Toe, measured in degrees or inches, is the amount of difference in distance between the front and rear tire edges, Fig. 1.

Thrust angle is the average of the toe setting on each rear wheel, Fig. 1.

PRELIMINARY INSPECTION
1. Ensure gas tank is full.
2. Check and inflate tires to specification. Check tires for same size and tread.
3. Check front wheel and tires for radial runout.
4. Check all suspension fasteners for proper torque.
5. Check ball joints and steering linkage for wear, looseness or damage.
6. Check all suspension component rubber bushings for wear or deterioration.

PRECAUTIONS
Vehicle hoisting equipment used must be frame contact type only. Use of equipment designed to lift vehicles by the rear axle cannot be used, as damage to rear suspension components will occur. Do not attempt to modify any suspension or steering components by heating or bending of the component.

DESCRIPTION
This vehicle is equipped with a non-adjustable front caster and camber suspension. Front caster and camber settings are determined at the time of design and require no adjustment during alignment.

FRONT WHEEL ALIGNMENT
Prior to performing front alignment, check rear alignment.
1. **Perform rear wheel alignment as outlined under "Rear Wheel Alignment".**
2. Loosen front inner and outer tie rod jam nuts and rotate inner tie rod end, **Fig. 2**, at steering gear to set front toe.

REAR WHEEL ALIGNMENT
1. Center steering wheel and lock using steering wheel clamp
2. Loosen adjusting screw jam nuts on four of the lateral arms and adjusting screws. Note each adjusting screw has one right-handed and one left-handed nut, **Fig. 3**. When setting rear camber and toe, the maximum lateral link lengths, **Fig. 4**, must not be exceeded. If exceeded, inadequate retention of adjustment link to inner and outer link may result.

3. Adjust rear lateral link adjusting screw, **Fig. 3**, to obtain approximate rear camber setting, then adjust forward lateral link adjusting screw in combination with rear lateral link for preferred rear camber specification as outlined under "Rear Wheel Alignment Specifications".

4. Adjust forward lateral link adjusting screw, **Fig. 3**, to set preferred rear toe specification

5. **Toe adjustment will cause a slight change in the camber setting. Should camber setting change during toe adjustment, continue to adjust camber and toe until both are at preferred specifications.**

6. Using crow foot and torque wrench, tighten all lateral link adjusting screw jam nuts **torque** 48 ft. lbs., while holding adjustment screws from turning.

THRUST ANGLE

The thrust angle is the average of the toe settings on each rear wheel. If measurement is not within specifications, readjust rear wheel toe to provide each wheel with 1/2 of the total toe measurement. When readjusting, do not exceed the total toe specification.

DODGE MONACO & EAGLE PREMIER

NOTE: Refer To Rear Of This Manual For Vehicle Manufacturer's Special Service Tool Suppliers.

INDEX OF SERVICE OPERATIONS

NOTE: For Service Operations Not Listed Below, Refer To The Table Of Contents In The Front Of This Manual.

Specifications

GENERAL ENGINE SPECIFICATIONS

Year	Engine Liter/CID ①	Engine VIN Code ②	Fuel System	Bore and Stroke Inch (Millimeters)	Compression Ratio	Net HP @ RPM ③	Maximum Torque Ft. Lbs @ R.P.M.	Normal Oil Pressure, psi
1992	3.0L/V6-180	U	TBI ④	3.660 x 2.870 (93 x 73)	9.3	150 @ 5000	171 @ 3750	60 ⑤

①—CID-cubic inch displacement.
②—8th digit of the VIN denotes engine code.
③—Ratings are net-as installed in vehicle.
④—Throttle body injection.
⑤—4000 RPM.

TUNE UP SPECIFICATIONS

| Year & Engine/ VIN Code ① | Spark Plug Gap | Ignition Timing BTDC | | | Curb Idle Speed Auto. Trans. | Fast Idle Speed Auto. Trans. | Fuel Pump Pressure, psi |
		Firing Order Fig.	Auto. Trans.	Mark Fig.			
1992							
3.0L/V6-182(U) ⑥	.035	A	④	③	⑤	④	43 ②

① —Eighth digit of the Vehicle Identification Number (VIN) denotes engine code.

② —Remove filler cap from fuel tank. Position shop towel around tube & fitting, then using a suitable tool disconnect black fuel supply line from fuel rail. Connect a suitable fuel pressure test gauge between tube & fuel rail. Start engine & check fuel pressure.

③ —Equipped w/crankshaft position sensor.

④ —Non-adjustable

⑤ —With transaxle in Neutral, 625–725N RPM; with transaxle in Drive, 565–665 RPM.

⑥ — Direct Ignition System.

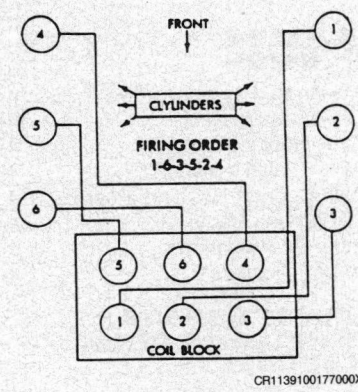

Fig. A

FRONT WHEEL ALIGNMENT SPECIFICATIONS

| Year | Model | Caster Angle, Degrees | | Camber Angle, Degrees | | | | Toe-Out Per Wheel, Inch |
| | | | | Limits | | Desired | | |
		Limits	Desired	Left	Right	Left	Right	
1992	All	+1.5 to +2.5	+2	-.17 to +.83	-.17 to +.83	+.33	+.33	0

① —Toe-out per wheel, 1/16 inch.

REAR WHEEL ALIGNMENT SPECIFICATIONS

| Year | Model | Camber Angle, Degrees | | | | Toe-In, Inch |
| | | Limits | | Desired | | |
		Left	Right	Left	Right	
1992	All	-1 to 0	-1 to 0	-.5	-.5	0

① —1/32 to 1/4 inch toe-in.

COOLING SYSTEM & CAPACITY DATA

Year	Model or Engine (VIN) ①	Coolant Capacity Less A/C Qts.	With A/C Qts.	Radiator Cap Relief Pressure, Lbs.	Thermo. Opening Temp. Deg. F	Fuel Tank Gas	Engine Oil Refill Qts.	Transaxle Oil Auto. Trans. Qts. ②
1992	3.0L/V6-182(U)	8.6	8.6	16-18	187	17	6③	④

①—The eighth digit of Vehicle identification number (VIN) denotes engine code.
②—Approximate. Make final check with dipstick.
③—Includes filter.
④—Fluid change only, 4 qts.; total capacity, 7.6 qts., use Mercon Type fluid. Differential, .75 qts., use 75W-140 hypoid gear lubricant.

LUBRICANT DATA

Year	Model	Lubricant Type Transaxle Transaxle	Differential	Power Steering	Brake System
1992	All	Mercon	75W-140②	①	DOT 3

①—Use Chrysler/Eagle Part No. 82200946 or equivalent power steering fluid.

Electrical

INDEX

FUSE PANEL & FLASHER LOCATION

The fuse panel is located under the LH side of the instrument panel.

The flasher is integral with headlamp/turn signal module in the relay/power distribution center.

RELAY CENTER LOCATION

The relay/power distribution center is located in the engine compartment, on the left inner fenderwell, near the LH strut tower.

STARTER
REPLACE

1. Disconnect battery ground cable.
2. Disconnect two wires from starter solenoid.

3. Remove starter attaching bolts, then the starter motor and mounting plate.
4. Reverse procedure to install.

IGNITION LOCK
REPLACE

1. Remove steering wheel, refer to "Steering Wheel Replace."
2. Remove turn signal canceler cam by unhooking tabs and sliding canceler off steering column. If vehicle is equipped with tilt wheel, remove tilt wheel control arm.
3. Remove upper and lower headlight pod retaining screws. There are two small retaining clips on the headlight and A/C-heater pods that may fall off when pod is removed.
4. Remove A/C-heater housing pod retaining screws, then carefully remove pod back.
5. Carefully remove headlight and A/C-heater pod.

6. Remove ignition switch trim ring by prying it away from pod housing, Fig. 1.
7. Remove retaining screws and the headlight pod back.
8. Remove screws from housing, then pass pods through openings in pod housing and remove housing, Fig. 2.
9. Place key in unmarked position lining up key with groove in lock cylinder housing, Fig. 3.
10. Press locking tab from underneath as shown, Fig. 3, then remove lock cylinder.
11. Reverse procedure to install, ensuring steering wheel is aligned with reference mark on steering shaft. Torque steering wheel nut to 52 ft. lbs.

IGNITION SWITCH
REPLACE

1. Disconnect battery ground cable.
2. Remove screws and instrument panel lower cover.

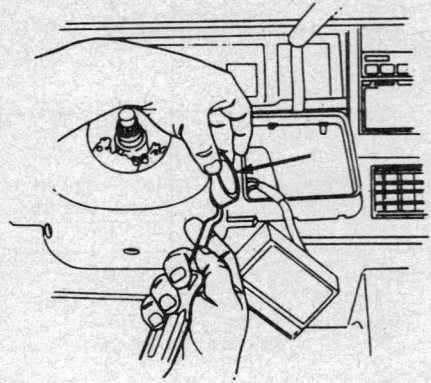

CR9049100049000X

Fig. 1   Ignition switch trim ring removal

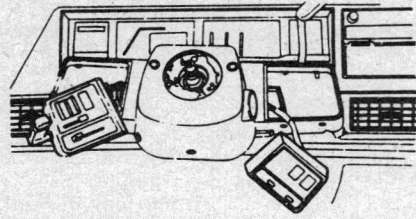

CR9049100050000X

Fig. 2   Headlight & A/C-heater pods removal

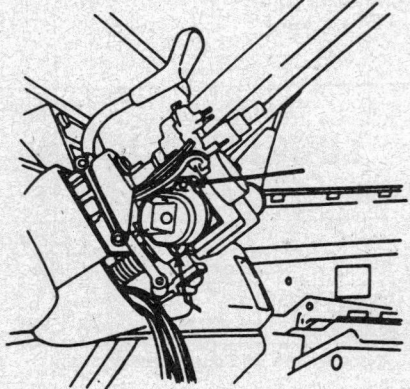

CR9049100051000X

Fig. 4   Ignition switch retaining screws

CR9129100007000X

Fig. 3   Key lock cylinder removal

3. Unfasten horn button and disconnect wires to remove.
4. Noting position of reference mark on the end of the steering shaft, remove steering wheel nut and slide steering wheel off shaft.
5. Disconnect electrical connector and remove steering wheel.
6. Remove turn signal canceler cam by unhooking tabs and sliding canceler off steering column. **If vehicle is equipped with tilt wheel, remove tilt wheel control arm.**
7. Remove upper and lower headlight pod retaining screws. **There are two small retaining clips on the headlight and A/C-heater pods that may fall off when pod is removed.**
8. Remove A/C-heater housing pod retaining screws, then carefully remove pod back.
9. Carefully remove headlight and A/C-heater pod.
10. Remove ignition switch trim ring by prying it away from pod housing, **Fig. 1.**
11. Remove retaining screws and the headlight pod back.
12. Remove screws from housing, then pass pods through openings in pod housing and remove housing, **Fig. 2.**
13. Remove screw, then separate and remove lower column shroud.
14. Remove upper column shroud attaching screws and the shroud.
15. Remove ignition switch retaining screws and separate ignition switch from lock cylinder housing, **Fig. 4.**
16. Cut tie straps, then remove screw and wire harness anchor.
17. Loosen hold-down nut in center of steering column connector.
18. Separate pod connectors from steering column connector by placing a flat blade screwdriver between the connectors to disengage locking tab.
19. Push on the wire side of headlight pod connector and slide the connector out of channels of steering column connector.
20. Remove ignition switch and harness.
21. Reverse procedure to install, ensuring steering wheel is aligned with reference mark on steering shaft. **Torque** steering wheel nut to 52 ft. lbs.

NEUTRAL SAFETY SWITCH
REPLACE

1. Disconnect neutral switch harness connector in engine compartment.
2. Raise and support vehicle, then remove splash shield.
3. Remove bolt attaching switch bracket to transaxle case, then the switch from case.
4. Remove neutral switch and harness from vehicle.
5. Reverse procedure to install, **torquing** switch bracket to 90 inch lbs.

HEADLAMP SWITCH
REPLACE

1. Disconnect battery ground cable.
2. Remove screws and instrument panel lower cover.
3. Remove screws and support bar, then pull air duct out of the way, **Fig. 5.**
4. Remove tie straps, loosen hold-down nut in center of steering column connector, and separate steering column connector, **Fig. 6.**
5. Separate headlight pod connector from steering column connector by placing a flat blade screwdriver between the connectors to disengage locking tab.
6. Push on wire side of headlight pod connector and slide connector out of channels of steering column connector.
7. Remove upper and lower retaining screws from pod.

8. Gently pull pod wires out through housing enough to expose the two screws and remove screws, **Fig. 7.**
9. Remove rear of pod housing, then gently pull pod forward and pull harness out through housing to remove pod.
10. Reverse procedure to install.

STOP LIGHT SWITCH
REPLACE

LESS CRUISE CONTROL

1. Disconnect switch electrical connectors.
2. Unseat switch retainer, then remove stop light switch.
3. Reverse procedure to install, noting the following:
   a. Ensure tabs on switch and retainer are aligned.
   b. Depress brake pedal and push in switch until housing is fully seated against switch bracket, release pedal and lightly pull up against internal master cylinder stop.

TURN SIGNAL SWITCH
REPLACE

The turn signal switch is located in the headlight pod on the steering column. The turn signal and pod are serviced as an assembly. Refer to "Headlamp Switch, Replace."

TURN SIGNAL CANCELING SWITCH REPLACE

1. Disconnect battery ground cable.
2. Remove screws and instrument panel lower cover.
3. Unfasten horn button and disconnect wires to remove.
4. Noting position of reference mark on the end of the steering shaft, remove steering wheel nut and slide steering wheel off shaft.
5. Disconnect electrical connector and remove steering wheel.
6. Remove turn signal canceler cam by unhooking tabs and sliding canceler off steering column. **If vehicle is equipped with tilt wheel remove tilt wheel control arm.**
7. Remove upper and lower headlight pod retaining screws. **There are two**

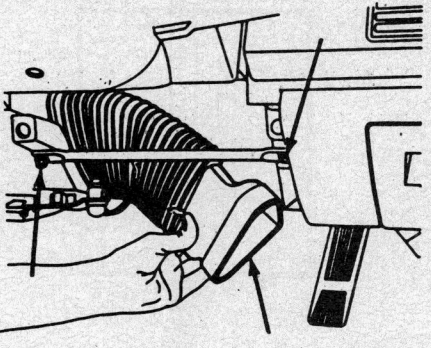

Fig. 5   Air duct & support bar

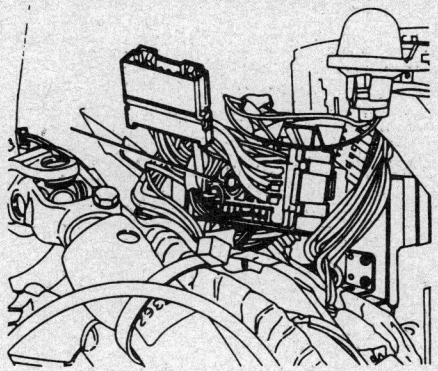

Fig. 6   Hold-down nut for steering column connector

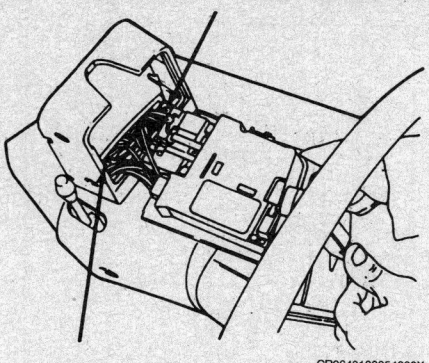

Fig. 7   Headlight switch back

Fig. 8   Turn signal canceling switch

small retaining clips on the headlight and A/C-heater pods that may fall off when pod is removed.

8. Remove A/C-heater housing pod retaining screws, then carefully remove pod back.
9. Carefully remove headlight and A/C-heater pod.
10. Remove ignition switch trim ring by prying it away from pod housing, **Fig. 1.**
11. Remove retaining screws and the headlight pod back.
12. Remove screws from housing, then pass pods through openings in pod housing and remove housing, **Fig. 2.**
13. Remove screw, then separate and remove lower column shroud.
14. Remove upper column shroud retaining screws and the shroud.
15. Remove screws to free turn signal canceling switch, then disconnect canceling switch connector and remove switch, **Fig. 8.**
16. Reverse procedure to install, ensuring steering wheel is aligned with reference mark on the steering shaft. **Torque** steering wheel nut to 52 ft. lbs.

DIMMER SWITCH
REPLACE

The dimmer switch is located in the headlight pod on the steering column. The dimmer switch and pod are serviced as an assembly. Refer to "Headlamp Switch, Replace."

STEERING WHEEL
REPLACE

1. Disconnect battery ground cable.
2. Remove horn pad and disconnect horn button.
3. Disconnect two wires and remove horn button.
4. Noting position of reference mark on the end of the steering shaft, remove steering wheel nut and slide steering wheel off shaft.
5. Disconnect cruise control electrical connector if equipped, then remove steering wheel.
6. Reverse procedure to install.

INSTRUMENT CLUSTER
REPLACE
REMOVAL

1. Disconnect battery ground cable.
2. Loosen screw that holds shift indicator anchor bracket in place.
3. Remove shift indicator cable anchor by sliding to keyhole position, **Fig. 9.**
4. Remove wire from rear of gearshift lever pulley.
5. Remove instrument cluster bezel retaining screws and the bezel, then remove cluster retaining screws.
6. Move gearshift lever to "1" position, then tilt cluster forward and disconnect electrical connectors.
7. Remove screws and instrument panel lower cover, then remove cluster.

INSTALLATION

1. Guide shift indicator wire into instrument panel and down to shift linkage.
2. Connect electrical connectors and install cluster with screws.
3. Loop shift indicator wire over pulley and install shift cable anchor onto screw, **Fig. 10.**
4. Move gearshift lever to neutral position and check position of shift indicator. If pointer is not aligned with N on display, slide anchor until indicator is correct. Tighten screw and check for proper positioning of indicator in all positions, **Fig. 10.**
5. Install bezel and instrument panel lower trim cover.

Fig. 9   Shift indicator cable anchor

RADIO
REPLACE

1. Disconnect battery ground cable.
2. Remove instrument cluster bezel.
3. Remove screws and pull radio forward and out of instrument panel.
4. Disconnect electrical connector, ground wire and antenna wire, then remove radio.
5. Reverse procedure to install.

WIPER MOTOR
REPLACE

1. Lift up on drivers side wiper arm, then bend retainer tab fully from wiper arm.
2. Remove drivers wiper arm assembly from arm shaft, then disconnect center and drivers washer hoses.
3. Lift up on passengers side wiper arm, then bend retainer tab fully from wiper arm.
4. Remove passengers wiper arm assembly from arm shaft.
5. Remove cowl screen hold-down bolts, then turn cowl screen locking screws 1/4 turn.
6. Remove left screen by sliding toward rear of car.
7. Using suitable fork, remove ball end of link by lifting upward.
8. Move linkage to maximum right position.
9. Hold motor crank arm, then remove center shaft locknut and spacer.

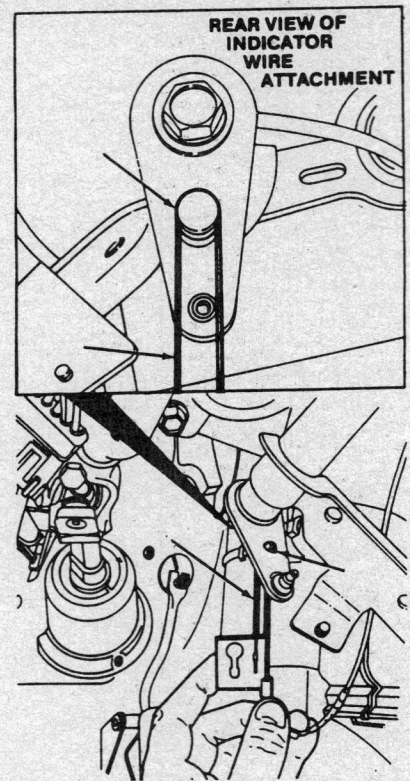

Fig. 10 Wire from gearshift lever pulley removal

CR9049100057000X

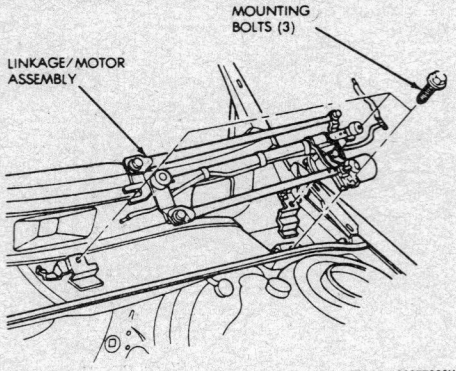

Fig. 11 Wiper assembly replacement

CR9029100077000X

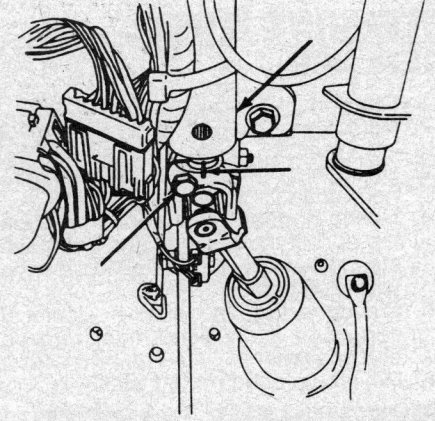

Fig. 13 Steering column shaft & intermediate shaft

CR7029100041000X

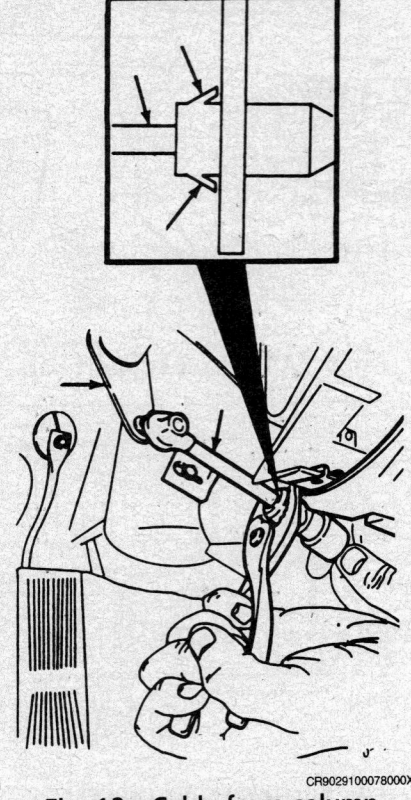

Fig. 12 Cable from column mounting bracket removal

CR9029100078000X

10. Remove motor crank arm from shaft, then the depressed park linkage.
11. Remove three wiper motor mounting bolts, then disconnect motor electrical connectors.
12. Disconnect washer hose at base of center tee fitting.
13. Remove wiper motor and linkage assembly, **Fig. 11.**
14. Reverse procedure to install, noting the following:
    a. **Torque** crank arm to motor shaft to 16 ft. lbs.
    b. Install center wiper arm onto shaft so that tip of blade is 0-2.5 inches.
    c. Install left wiper arm onto shaft so that tip of blade is 1.5-3.75 inches above grille.
    d. Cycle wipers once allowing them to park. Ensure wipers rest in park position.

WIPER SWITCH
REPLACE

The wiper switch is located in the headlight pod on the steering column. The wiper switch and pod are serviced as an assembly. Refer to "Headlight Pod, Replace."

BLOWER MOTOR
REPLACE

1. Disconnect coolant level switch electrical connector.
2. Remove coolant reservoir retaining

strap and move reservoir aside.
3. Remove coolant reservoir mounting bracket bolts and the bracket.
4. Pry off retaining clip and disconnect wires from blower motor.
5. Remove blower motor mounting screws and the blower motor.
6. Reverse procedure to install.

HEATER CORE
REPLACE
REMOVAL

1. Disconnect battery ground cable.
2. Remove instrument panel lower trim cover retaining screws and the cover.
3. Remove instrument panel support rod retaining screws and the rod.
4. Remove steering column wiring harness bulkhead connector retaining screw.
5. Disconnect automatic transaxle shift cable from lever with a screwdriver.
6. Compress cable retainer tangs with pliers and slide cable out of column mounting bracket, **Fig. 12.**
7. Loosen screw securing anchoring bracket in place, then move bracket to key hole position and remove it from its mounting bracket.
8. Lift indicator wire off of pulley.
9. Pull sleeve down to expose steering column universal joint.

10. Make a reference mark on steering column shaft and intermediate shaft and remove bolt from intermediate shaft, **Fig. 13.**
11. Remove bolts and nuts that hold steering column to instrument panel/brake sled.
12. Carefully lower steering column assembly to vehicle floor, then separate steering column shaft from intermediate shaft and remove column assembly from vehicle.
13. Remove defroster grille and remove bolts under grille.
14. Loosen but do not remove nut located near the parking brake release handle and nut which is located on the side kick panel.
15. Remove lower parking brake release handle retaining screws and the handle.
16. Remove ashtray, then disconnect cigarette lighter connectors and remove screw from ashtray cavity.
17. Remove bolt from brake sled and disconnect all electrical connections, **Fig. 14.**
18. Remove instrument panel to floor bracket attaching bolts.
19. Disconnect interior temperature sensor by pressing tabs together and pushing air temperature sensor hose rearward.
20. Carefully lift up and rearward to disengage and remove instrument panel, then remove floor duct extension.
21. Drain cooling system and discharge A/C system.

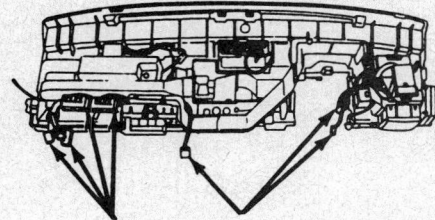

Fig. 14 Electrical connections for dash panel

22. Squeeze and slide heater core hose clamps off of heater core tubes towards engine and carefully pry heater hoses off of heater core tubes. **Heater core tubes are made of plastic and may break if too much pressure is applied.**
23. Disconnect coolant level switch connector, then remove coolant reservoir retaining strap and move reservoir aside.
24. Disconnect blower motor electrical connector and vacuum hose.
25. Disconnect refrigerant lines from dash panel using appropriate tools from tool kit No. MS-1979 or equivalent.
26. Remove nuts holding A/C-heater housing to firewall.
27. From inside vehicle, remove nuts holding A/C-heater housing, **Fig. 15.**
28. Carefully pull A/C-heater housing rearward and remove from vehicle.
29. Release plastic tabs and remove heater core.

INSTALLATION

1. Install heater core by gently pushing until core snaps into place.
2. Position A/C-heater housing to dash panel. Ensure drain tube extends through its opening in upper floor and blower motor connector and vacuum line extends through dash panel, **Fig. 16.**
3. Ensure ECU connectors are to right of drain tube and install nuts on inside of vehicle.
4. Install floor duct extension.
5. Install new O-rings on refrigerant lines and lubricate with a suitable refrigerant oil, then press each line into its connector until it snaps into place.
6. Connect vacuum hose and blower motor connector.
7. Install coolant reservoir mounting bracket and install reservoir using retaining strap.
8. Connect coolant level switch connector and carefully slide heater hoses onto heater core tubes.
9. Squeeze and slide heater core hose clamps to secure hoses.
10. Position instrument panel. Ensure panel mounting brackets engage studs on kick panels and wire harness is behind center mounting bracket.
11. While mating instrument panel to vehicle, connect all electrical connections and interior temperature sensor.
12. Install bolt to brake sled and screw into ashtray cavity.

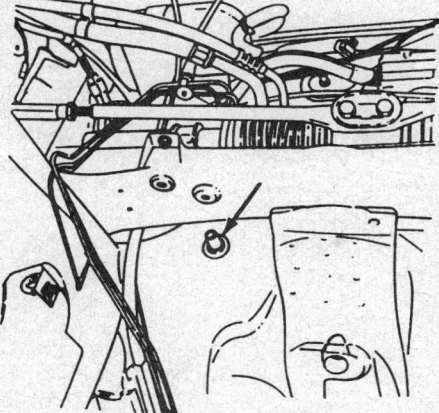

Fig. 15 A/C-heater housing

13. Install bolts to center support bracket, connect cigarette lighter connectors and install ashtray.
14. Tighten nut located near parking brake release handle and nut which is located on passenger side kick panel.
15. Install parking brake release handle.
16. Install bolts and the defroster grille.
17. Position and install steering column shaft in intermediate steering shaft U-joint. Align two shafts using reference marks made during removal.
18. Install, but do not tighten, U-joint bolt.
19. Lift steering column into position and install nuts and bolts that attach column to instrument panel. **Torque bolts to 35 ft. lbs.**
20. Tighten bolt in intermediate steering shaft U-joint.
21. Move plastic sleeve back into position and snap shift cable into mounting bracket.
22. Snap shift cable head onto mounting ball in shift arm.
23. Loop the shift indicator wire over the pulley and position anchoring bracket over screw.
24. Move gearshift lever to neutral position and check position of shift indicator. If pointer is not aligned with N on display, slide anchor until indicator is correct. Tighten screw and check for proper positioning of indicator in all positions, **Fig. 10.**
25. Install bulkhead connector and connector attaching screw and connect column connector.
26. Install instrument panel support rod, tighten rod attaching screws and install instrument panel lower trim cover.
27. Connect battery ground cable.
28. Fill cooling system and charge A/C system.

EVAPORATOR CORE
REPLACE

1. **On models equipped with knee bolster,** remove ash tray, then ash tray receiver retaining screw.
2. Disconnect cigar lighter electrical connector.

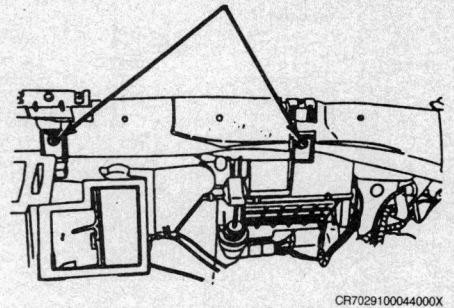

Fig. 16 Drain tube position A/C-heater housing

3. Remove two front console to bracket retaining screws.
4. Remove three armrest assembly to console retaining screws, then the armrest.
5. Remove two rear of console to bracket retaining screws.
6. Remove seat belt guide from inside console.
7. Remove console.
8. Remove two pivot bracket to knee bolster retaining bolts.
9. Loosen two pivot bracket retaining screws. **Do not remove retaining screws.**
10. Remove one screw and two Torx bolts retaining forward console bracket to floor.
11. Slide forward console bracket rearward.
12. Remove two knee bolster to instrument panel retaining screws from center of knee bolster.
13. Remove one knee bolster retaining screw located to left of steering column.
14. Remove one air duct to knee bolster retaining screw.
15. Remove garnish molding retaining screw located at bottom of instrument panel.
16. Remove four retaining nuts at ends of knee bolster.
17. Move knee bolster toward rear of vehicle enough to gain access to the two parking brake release handle retaining screws.
18. Remove brake handle retaining screws, then the knee bolster.
19. Remove heater core, refer to "Heater Core Replace."
20. Remove vacuum and electrical connectors from A/C control module, **Fig. 17.**
21. Remove A/C module retaining screws, then the module.
22. Unlock retaining tab and remove motor arm from door pivot arm.
23. Remove spring and clear vacuum line from motor.
24. Release heater core retaining tabs, then remove core, **Fig. 17.**
25. Remove foam gaskets, then disconnect blower motor electrical connector.
26. Remove blower motor.
27. Remove upper to lower housing attaching screws and clips.

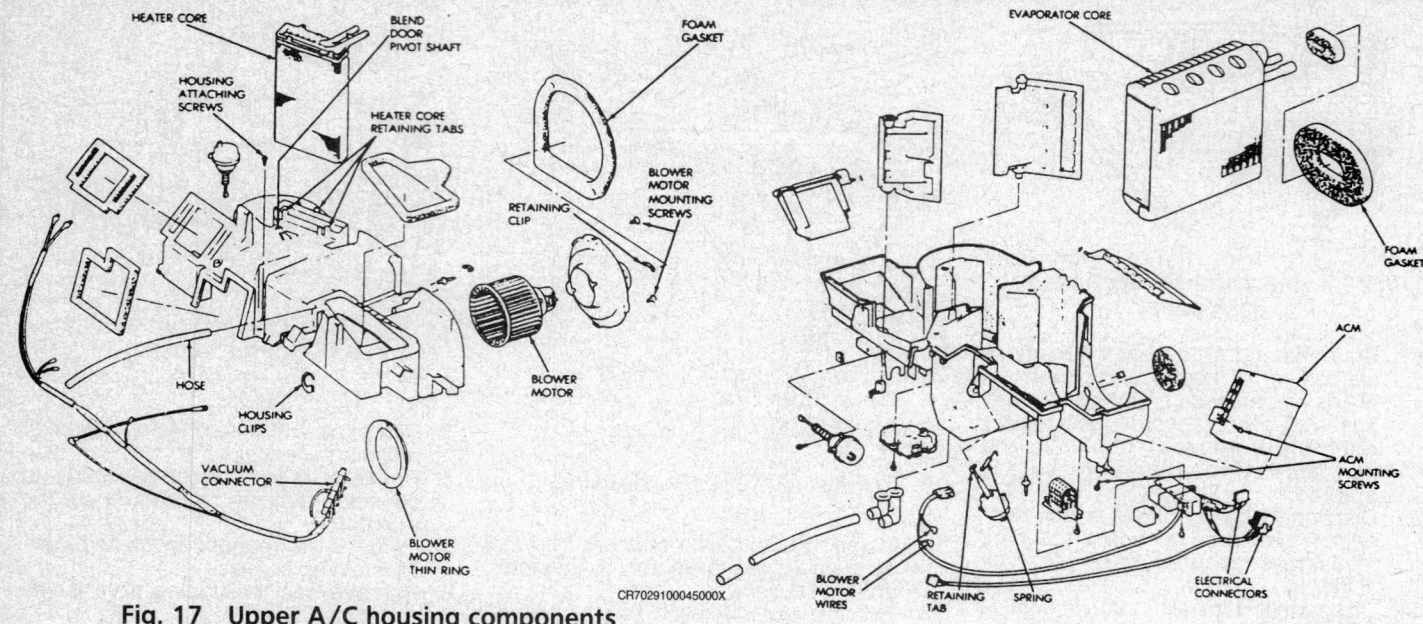

Fig. 17 Upper A/C housing components

Fig. 18 Lower A/C housing components

28. Separate upper and lower housing halves.

29. Remove evaporator core, **Fig. 18.**
30. Reverse procedure to install. **Add** **three ounces of refrigerant oil if evaporator core is replaced.**

3.0L/V6-180 Engine

INDEX

ENGINE MOUNT
REPLACE

FRONT

1. Disconnect battery ground cable.
2. Loosen stud locknuts.
3. Install suitable engine lifting equipment.
4. Raise engine slightly, then engine mount attaching nut and mount, **Fig. 1.**
5. Reverse procedure to install.

REAR

1. Disconnect battery ground cable.
2. Raise and support vehicle.
3. Remove underbody splash shield.
4. Using suitable jack stand, support transaxle assembly.
5. Remove crossmember to engine cradle attaching bolts.
6. Remove rear mount to support bracket attaching nut and bolt.
7. Remove exhaust down pipe.
8. Remove crossmember and rear cushion.
9. Remove bracket attaching bolts, then bracket.
10. Reverse procedure to install.

ENGINE
REPLACE

The engine and transaxle are removed as an assembly. This procedure must be performed on a side mount hoist.

1. Disconnect negative then positive battery cables, then drain cooling system.

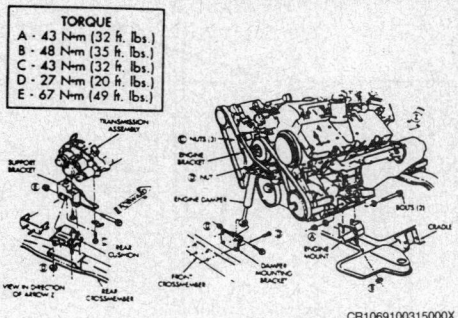

Fig. 1 Engine mounts

2. Remove throttle body plenum attaching screws, then remove hose from idle speed regulator.
3. Loosen hose clamp and remove throttle body plenum.
4. Disconnect crankcase ventilation hose and evaporative emissions canister hose from air cleaner.
5. Remove air sensor vacuum hose from air cleaner, then disconnect distributor coil wire and position aside.
6. Disconnect cruise control and accelerator cables from throttle arm, **Fig. 2.** Do not use tools to disconnect connectors.
7. Apply pressure to tabs on accelerator and cruise control cables and push them through attaching bracket. Set cable unit to side of engine compartment.
8. Disconnect hot air tube from air cleaner.
9. Disconnect air cleaner attaching clips and remove air cleaner.
10. Remove battery hold-down clamp and the battery.
11. Remove fuel tank filler cap to relieve pressure, then reinstall cap.
12. Disconnect black fuel supply tube from fuel rail and gray fuel return tube from fuel pressure regulator by applying pressure to retaining tabs and pulling apart.
13. Disconnect vacuum hoses from EGR solenoid.
14. Disconnect MAP sensor vacuum line and Hevac vacuum reservoir hose.
15. Remove bulkhead attaching screw and disconnect bulkhead connector. Position connector on top of engine.
16. Disconnect electrical connector from dash panel and remove vacuum booster hose from brake vacuum booster.
17. Disconnect coolant lines from dash panel and coolant bottle.
18. Disconnect radiator hoses from water pump and position aside.
19. Disconnect front engine shock absorber from engine bracket. Push shock up against cooling fan.
20. Open driver's door and remove bottom instrument panel section under steering wheel.
21. Disconnect shifter cable from arm on steering column.
22. Apply pressure to tabs on side cable housing and pull cable through holding bracket.

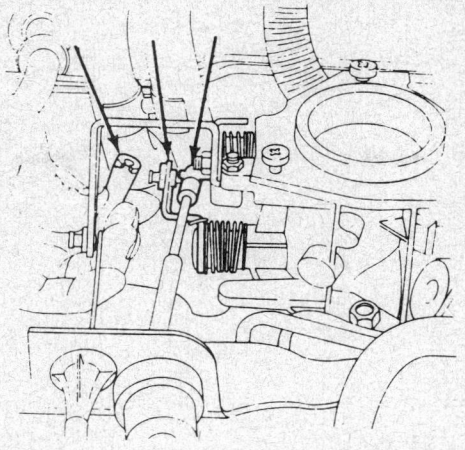

Fig. 2 Cable disconnection from throttle arm

23. Raise and support vehicle, then remove splash shield below alternator.
24. Disconnect knock sensor, oil level sensor, oil pressure sender and alternator electrical connectors.
25. Disconnect alternator output wire from back of alternator.
26. Disconnect wire harness clip from back of alternator and position aside.
27. Loosen accessory drive belt pivot bolt, locking bolt and adjusting bolt to loosen drive belt.
28. Remove power steering pump and pump reservoir mounting bolts.
29. Lower vehicle.
30. Unfasten A/C compressor and position aside, leaving refrigerant lines attached.
31. Raise and support vehicle, then remove front tires.
32. Unfasten brake calipers and position aside. Use suitable wire to hang calipers in spring strut. **Do not allow calipers to hang by hydraulic hose.**
33. Hold wheel hub in place using a suitable tool, then loosen wheel hub nut on both sides.
34. Remove steering knuckle to strut attaching bolt nuts on both sides of vehicle. **Use a brass drift to tap steering knuckle bolts out. Caution must be taken when removing steering knuckle bolts as these bolts are splined into the knuckle and should not be turned. On both sides of vehicle, remove the top steering knuckle bolt first.**
35. Pull strut out, pivoting steering knuckle on lower bolt. Remove the lower bolt and separate steering knuckle from strut.
36. Disconnect battery negative cable and solenoid wire from starter.
37. Remove middle starter attaching bolt and disconnect ground cable.
38. Remove sub-frame shield attaching bolts, and the shield.
39. Disconnect oxygen sensor electrical connector and catalytic converter from Y-pipe.
40. Pull shifter cable grommet down, then grasp cable and pull it through hole in body.

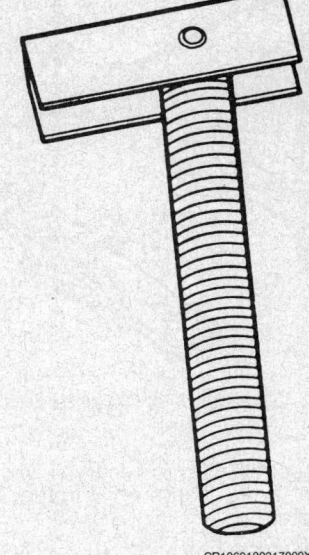

Fig. 3 Engine cradle-to dolly bolt

41. Install Mot. 1040.99 sub-frame dolly or equivalent to engine cradle. Install attaching bolts into cradle, **Fig. 3.** Push large end of channel iron up. Insert bolt into holes in cradle. Adjust bolt until channel iron lays flat in hole. Adjust remaining bolts in same manner.
42. Install engine dolly to cradle with dolly wheels toward rear of vehicle. Ensure arms at front of dolly are pointing up toward cradle. Install dolly to cradle by lifting dolly up and lining up holes in dolly with bolts just installed in cradle. Tighten attaching nuts.
43. Lower hoist until dolly rests on floor, then remove cradle mounting bolts.
44. Ensure all hoses, vacuum lines and wire harnesses are positioned so as not to snag or catch when vehicle is lifted off engine.
45. Slowly raise vehicle off engine.
46. Draw outline of dolly legs and center line of wheels on floor. Once dolly is repositioned under vehicle, it can be correctly positioned so that it aligns with vehicle at installation.
47. Reverse procedure to install.

INTAKE MANIFOLD
REPLACE

1. Disconnect battery ground cable.
2. Remove throttle body plenum.
3. Disconnect transmission kickdown cable from throttle body.
4. Disconnect accelerator cable and cruise control cable connector. **Do not use tools to disconnect cable or connectors.**
5. Disconnect brake vacuum booster hose.
6. Disconnect vacuum connection from throttle body adapter.
7. Disconnect Throttle Position Sensor (TPS) connector.
8. Disconnect idle air bypass hose from throttle body adapter.

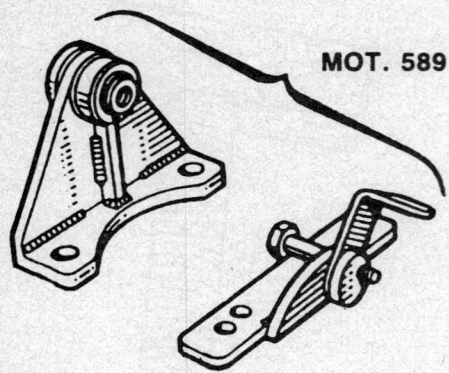

Fig. 4 Camshaft sprocket removal tool

CR1069100318000X

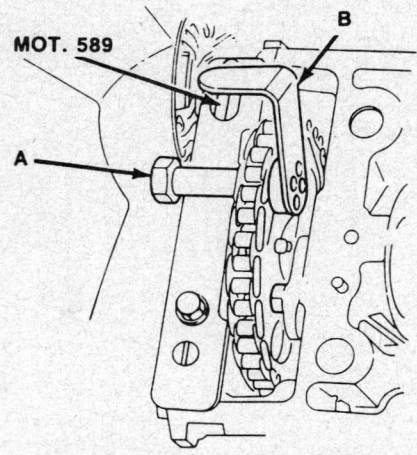

Fig. 5 Camshaft sprocket removal

CR1069100319000X

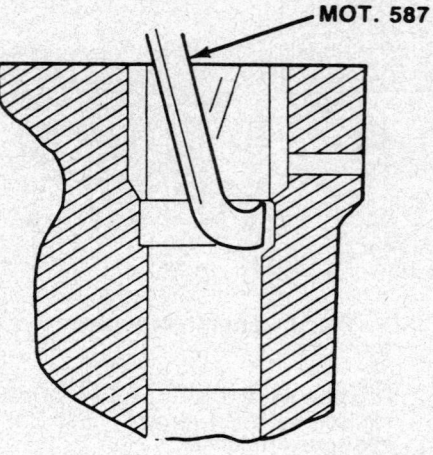

Fig. 6 Cylinder head locating dowel removal

CR1069100320000X

9. Disconnect Hevac reservoir vacuum hose from fitting on throttle body adapter.
10. Disconnect EGR tube.
11. Disconnect EGR valve transducer vacuum hose.
12. Disconnect air temperature sensor wire connector, located behind idle air bypass hose.
13. Tag each fuel injector connector with number of corresponding injector, then disconnect fuel injector wire harness from injectors and position aside.
14. Disconnect CCV vacuum hose from fitting between Nos. 2 and 3 runners.
15. Remove fuel tank filler cap to relieve fuel tank pressure, then install fuel tank filler cap.
16. Place shop towels under fuel tubes. Disconnect fuel supply tube from fuel rail and fuel return tube from fuel pressure regulator using M.S. 1999 fuel line disconnect tool, or equivalent. Slide tool onto nipple and push forward into quick-connector until handle stops on connector casing. Remove fuel tubes and position aside.
17. Remove intake manifold attaching bolts and the intake manifold.
18. Remove and discard O-rings in cylinder heads.
19. Reverse procedure to install.

EXHAUST MANIFOLD
REPLACE

1. Disconnect battery ground cable.
2. Disconnect EGR tube from right side exhaust manifold.
3. Raise and support vehicle.
4. Disconnect catalytic converter from Y-pipe by removing attaching nuts. Remove converter by pulling back and out of hanger.
5. Disconnect oxygen sensor electrical connector.
6. Remove attaching nuts securing Y-pipe to transmission crossmember.
7. Remove attaching nuts securing Y-pipe to exhaust manifolds. Position Y-pipe back and away from exhaust manifolds.
8. If right side manifold is to be removed, proceed as follows:
   a. Remove dipstick tube attaching

nut from exhaust manifold.
   b. Remove dipstick tube.
   c. Remove remaining exhaust manifold attaching nuts.
   d. Remove manifold and gasket.
9. If left side manifold is to be removed, proceed as follows:
   a. Remove hot air tube heat stove.
   b. Disconnect starter wires and ground cable.
   c. Remove lower exhaust manifold attaching nuts and the starter heat shield.
   d. Remove remaining exhaust manifold attaching nuts.
   e. Remove manifold and gasket.
10. Reverse procedure to install, noting the following:
   a. Exhaust manifold gaskets have a ring on one side. Install gaskets with ring toward cylinder head and tabs toward oil pan.
   b. Tighten attaching nuts and bolts to specifications.

CYLINDER HEAD
REPLACE

Cylinder head must be cool prior to removal to avoid cylinder head distortion.

RIGHT SIDE
Removal

1. Disconnect battery ground cable and drain cooling system.
2. Remove intake and exhaust manifolds from cylinder head as previously described.
3. Remove valve cover as described under "Valve Cover, Replace."
4. Remove spark plug wires from cylinder head.
5. Remove top alternator mounting bracket.
6. Remove timing case attaching bolts in cylinder head and inline bolts directly below. **Timing chain and sprocket must be held in place. If chain and sprocket slip, timing case must be removed and chain tensioners re-**

leased.
7. Turn engine over until camshaft sprocket dowel is straight up.
8. Attach tool No. Mot. 589 or 7317 or equivalent, to timing case cover, **Fig. 4.** Secure with two short cylinder head cover bolts.
9. Position adjusting lever (B) behind camshaft sprocket. Thread bolt (A) through front of tool, sprocket and into lever. Push lever up as far as possible and tighten bolt, **Fig. 5.**
10. Remove plug in front of timing case cover to gain access to camshaft sprocket bolt, then remove cylinder head attaching bolts.
11. Remove rocker arm shaft assembly. Install one head bolt in center and tighten two turns. Remove camshaft cover and gasket from rear of cylinder head.
12. Loosen camshaft thrust plate screw. Pull plate up and tighten screw to allow camshaft to move back as sprocket bolt is removed.
13. Loosen camshaft sprocket bolt and pull camshaft back until bolt is out of camshaft, then slide camshaft back away from sprocket.
14. Insert a drift punch into front and rear cylinder head bolt holes on exhaust manifold side of head. Tap dowels down below head gasket. **Do not lift or pry cylinder head straight up as this will cause cylinder liners to come up and out of block.**
15. Position a piece of wood against rear intake manifold side of cylinder head and strike with a hammer. Repeat procedure for front exhaust manifold.
16. Remove cylinder head bolts, cylinder head and cylinder head gasket.
17. Install tool No. 7315 or Mot. 588 or equivalent liner clamps, between cylinder liners to hold them in place.
18. Use tool No. 7314 or Mot. 587 or equivalent to remove cylinder head locating dowels, **Fig. 6.**
19. Place lint free shop towels in tops of cylinder bores.
20. Remove tool No. 7315 or Mot. 588 or equivalent liner hold-down clamps, to

clean cylinder block, then reinstall liner clamps.

21. Clean cylinder block and cylinder head mating surfaces.
22. Check liner protrusion.
23. Liner should protrude between .002 and .005 inch.

Installation

1. Trim timing case cover gasket flush with cylinder head surface.
2. Cut sections from new gaskets and attach them to the timing case cover. Apply a suitable weather strip adhesive and allow to dry.
3. Install .118 inch (3 mm) pin punches into holes in block below locating dowel bolt holes. Push dowels in holes until they contact pin punches.
4. Remove shop towels from cylinder bores.
5. Install new cylinder head gasket over alignment dowels.
6. Apply a thin coat of gasket sealer to cylinder head mating surface.
7. Install cylinder head.
8. Install timing case cover to cylinder head attaching bolts and tighten finger tight.
9. Position camshaft into sprocket. Align dowel with slot in camshaft. Install sprocket bolt and tighten finger tight.
10. Remove support bracket assembly.
11. Loosen camshaft thrust plate bolt and slide plate into groove in cylinder head. Tighten to specifications.
12. Remove pin punches.
13. Install rocker shaft assembly and cylinder head bolts.
14. Tighten cylinder head bolts as follows:
    a. **Torque** cylinder head bolts in sequence shown in **Fig. 7**, to 44 ft. lbs.
    b. Loosen bolt No. 1 completely, then **torque** bolt to 30 ft. lbs.
    c. Place graduated disc tool No. 7321 or equivalent, between socket and torque wrench. Turn graduated disc clockwise until locking stem rests against a solid object which will prevent disc from turning.
    d. Angle torque bolt No. 1 to 160-200°.
    e. Repeat procedure for remaining bolts in sequence.
15. Tighten timing case cover attaching bolts to specifications.
16. Tighten camshaft sprocket bolt to specifications.
17. Install valve covers, as described under "Valve Covers, Replace."
18. Install intake and exhaust manifolds, as previously described.
19. Apply Loctite to threads of timing case cover plug and install plug in timing case cover.
20. Install spark plug wires.
21. Connect alternator bracket.
22. Fill and bleed cooling system.
23. Install accessory drive belt.
24. Connect battery ground cable.
25. Turn engine off and allow to cool, then angle tighten all cylinder head bolts an additional 45° in tightening sequence.

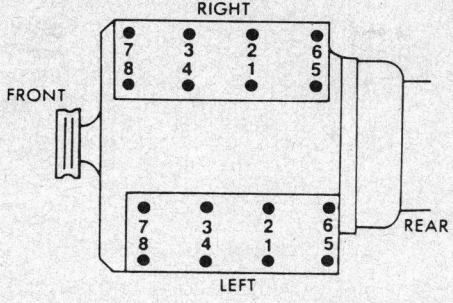

Fig. 7 Cylinder head bolt tightening sequence

26. Use a torque wrench to verify that each bolt has at least 52 ft. lbs. of **torque**.

LEFT SIDE

Removal

1. Disconnect battery ground cable and drain cooling system.
2. Remove intake and exhaust manifolds from cylinder head as previously described.
3. Remove valve head cover as described under "Valve Head Cover, Replace."
4. Remove spark plug wires from spark plugs.
5. Remove distributor cap, rotor and dust shield.
6. Turn engine over until camshaft sprocket dowel is straight up. **Timing chain and sprocket must be held in place. If chain and sprocket slip, timing case must be removed and chain tensioners released.**
7. Attach tool No. Mot. 589 or 7317 or equivalent, to support camshaft sprocket and chain while removing cylinder head cover. Remove bolt and adjusting lever from tool bracket and position aside. Secure with two short cylinder head cover bolts.
8. Thread bolt through bracket, sprocket and into adjusting lever. Pull lever up and tighten bolt.
9. Loosen camshaft thrust plate attaching bolt. Pull thrust plate up and away from camshaft. Tighten bolt.
10. Remove timing case cover from cylinder head attaching bolts.
11. Place a wrench on crankshaft pulley nut to prevent engine from turning over.
12. Position suitable tool into camshaft sprocket bolt and remove bolt.
13. Remove cylinder head attaching bolts.
14. Remove rocker shaft assembly.
15. Install one cylinder head bolt into middle bolt hole and tighten two full turns.
16. Insert a drift punch into front and rear cylinder head bolt holes on exhaust manifold side of head. Tap dowels down below head gasket. **Do not lift or pry cylinder head straight up as this will cause cylinder liners to come up and out of block.**
17. Position a piece of wood against rear intake manifold side of cylinder head

and strike with a hammer. Repeat procedure on all sides of cylinder head until head is loose.
18. Remove cylinder head bolt, cylinder head and cylinder head gasket.
19. Use tool No. 7314 or Mot. 587 or equivalent, to remove cylinder head locating dowels.
20. Place lint free shop towels in tops of cylinder bores.
21. Install tool No. 7315 or Mot. 588 or equivalent liner clamps between cylinder liners to hold them in place.
22. Clean cylinder block and cylinder head mating surfaces.
23. Check liner protrusion.
24. Liner should protrude between .002 and .005 inch.

Installation

1. Trim timing case cover gasket flush with cylinder head surface.
2. Cut sections from new gaskets and attach to timing case cover. Apply a suitable weather strip adhesive and allow to dry.
3. Install .118 inch (3 mm) pin punches into holes in block below locating dowel bolt holes. Push dowels in holes until they contact pin punches.
4. Remove shop towels from cylinder bores.
5. Install new cylinder head gasket over alignment dowels.
6. Apply a thin coat of gasket sealer to cylinder head mating surface.
7. Install cylinder head.
8. Install timing case cover to cylinder head attaching bolts and tighten finger tight.
9. Position camshaft into sprocket. Align dowel with slot in camshaft. Install sprocket bolt and tighten finger tight.
10. Remove support bracket assembly.
11. Loosen camshaft thrust plate bolt and slide plate into groove in cylinder head. Retighten camshaft thrust plate bolt to specifications.
12. Remove pin punches.
13. Install rocker shaft assembly and cylinder head bolts.
14. Tighten cylinder head bolts as follows:
    a. **Torque** cylinder head bolts in sequence shown, **Fig. 7**, to 44 ft. lbs.
    b. Loosen bolt No. 1 completely, then **torque** bolt to 30 ft. lbs.
    c. Place graduated disc Mot. 591.03 between socket and torque wrench. Turn graduated disc clockwise until locking stem rests against a solid object which will prevent disc from turning.
    d. Angle torque bolt No. 1 to 160° to 180°.
    e. Repeat procedure for remaining bolts in sequence.
15. Tighten timing case cover attaching bolts to specifications.
16. Tighten camshaft sprocket bolt to specifications.
17. Install valve covers, as described under "Valve Covers, Replace."
18. Install intake and exhaust manifolds as previously described.
19. Install distributor cap, rotor and dust shield.

20. Install spark plug wires.
21. Fill and bleed cooling system.
22. Connect battery ground cable.
23. Turn engine off and allow to cool, then angle tighten all cylinder head bolts an additional 45° in tightening sequence.
24. Use a torque wrench to verify that each bolt has at least 52 ft. lbs. of torque.

VALVE COVER
REPLACE
RIGHT SIDE
Removal

1. Disconnect battery ground cable.
2. Loosen accessory drive belt.
3. Remove spark plug wire holder.
4. Unfasten A/C compressor and position aside, leaving refrigerant lines attached.
5. Remove valve cover attaching bolts.
6. Remove cover and old gasket.

Installation

1. Clean cylinder head and valve head mating surfaces.
2. Apply a light coating of gasket sealer to cylinder head mating surfaces.
3. Install valve head cover with new gasket.
4. Install spark plug holder.
5. Install valve cover attaching bolts and tighten to specifications.
6. Install A/C compressor.
7. Install accessory drive belt.
8. Connect battery ground cable.

LEFT SIDE
Removal

1. Disconnect battery ground cable.
2. Disconnect throttle body plenum/air inlet hose assembly from throttle body and air cleaner.
3. Remove vacuum brake booster hose from throttle body.
4. Disconnect Crankcase Ventilation (CCV) fresh air hose from valve head cover.
5. Disconnect CCV vacuum hose from valve head cover.
6. Disconnect and remove air cleaner.
7. Remove power steering reservoir attaching bolts and position reservoir aside.
8. Disconnect accelerator cable from throttle body retainer bracket and position aside.
9. Remove idle speed regulator bracket attaching bolts from rear of valve cover.
10. Remove spark plug wire holder.
11. Remove valve head cover attaching bolts.
12. Remove cover and old gasket.

Installation

1. Clean cylinder head and valve head cover mating surfaces.
2. Apply a light coating of gasket sealer to cylinder head mating surfaces.

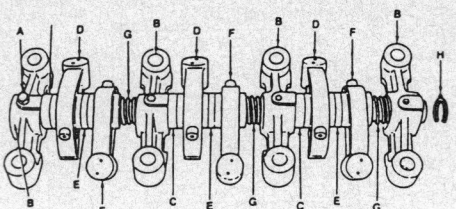

CR1069100322000X

Fig. 8 Rocker arm assembly

3. Install valve head cover and new gasket.
4. Install valve cover attaching bolts and tighten to specifications.
5. Install spark plug wire holder.
6. Install idle speed regulator bracket to rear of valve head cover.
7. Connect accelerator cable and cruise control cable to retainer bracket and throttle body.
8. Install power steering pump reservoir.
9. Install air cleaner.
10. Install CCV fresh air hose and vacuum hose.
11. Connect vacuum brake booster hose.
12. Connect throttle body plenum/air inlet hose assembly to air cleaner and throttle body.
13. Connect battery ground cable.

VALVE ADJUSTMENT

These engines are equipped with hydraulic valve lifters. There are no provisions for adjustment.

ROCKER ARMS
REPLACE

Left and right rocker shaft assemblies are identical and can be installed on either cylinder head, however, when reusing these assemblies always install shaft on original cylinder head.

Oil galley plugs in ends of rocker shafts are pressed in and are not replaceable. When disassembling shaft, position parts aside in order of removal.

1. Remove lock screw (A), pedestal (B) and thick spacer (C), **Fig. 8**.
2. Remove rocker arm with automatic lash adjuster on right (D).
3. Remove thin spacer (E).
4. Remove rocker arm with automatic lash adjuster on left (F).
5. Remove spring (G), then the circlip from end of rocker shaft (H).
6. Reverse procedure to assemble and install. Tighten attaching screw to specifications.

CRANKSHAFT DAMPER
REPLACE

1. Disconnect battery ground cable.
2. Remove damper bracket attaching locknut and bolt.
3. Remove front engine bracket attaching nut and bolt, then remove damper.
4. Reverse procedure to install.

FRONT COVER
REPLACE

1. Remove valve covers as described under,"Valve Cover, Replace."
2. Hold camshaft sprocket in place and remove distributor drive/camshaft sprocket bolt.
3. Pull distributor drive forward and off of camshaft sprocket.
4. Remove timing cover attaching bolt.
5. Place a pry bar between cylinder block and boss on front cover and carefully remove cover.
6. Remove gaskets.
7. Reverse procedure to install.

TIMING CHAIN
REPLACE
INSPECTION

Check timing chain and sprocket for wear. If either side has excessive wear, replace timing chains, sprockets, guide shoes and tensions for both sides.

1. Remove valve head cover as described under,"Valve Head Cover, Replace."
2. Pull up on top of timing chain. This produces a gap between the bottom of the timing chain and the bottom area between two sprocket teeth. A maximum clearance of .067 inch must be maintained. A gap of .067 inch corresponds to a travel of .866 inch by the timing chain tensioner plunger.
3. Insert the solid end of a number 51 drill bit (.067 inch diameter) to gauge size of gap. If drill bit does not fit into gap, wear is not excessive and components can be reused. If drill bit fits into gap between timing chain and sprocket teeth the following components must be replaced: timing chain shoes, tensioners, guides, sprockets and tensioner shoes.

REPLACEMENT
Removal

It may be necessary to remove engine before replacement of timing chain.

When removing timing chains, tensioners, guides, sprockets, and tensioner shoes, keep left and right sides separated. Components must be returned to their original positions.

1. Remove bolt attaching right side camshaft sprocket to camshaft.
2. Remove right side timing chain tensioner and let tensioner shoe hang down.
3. Remove right side timing chain, then the camshaft sprocket and timing chain guide.
4. Remove right side tensioner shoe.
5. Remove left side timing chain tensioner and timing chain.
6. Remove left side camshaft sprocket, then the timing chain guide and tensioner.
7. Remove tensioner filters.

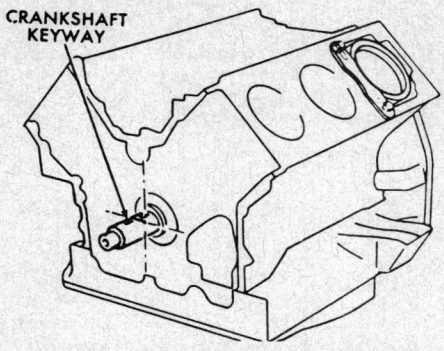

Fig. 9 Crankshaft keyway position

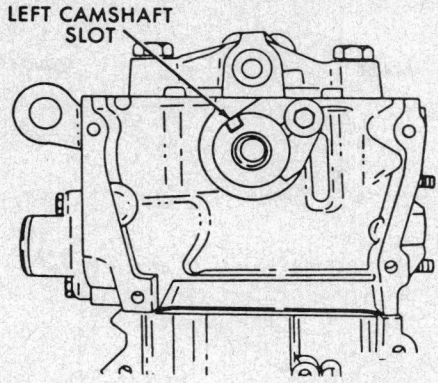

Fig. 10 Lefthand camshaft position

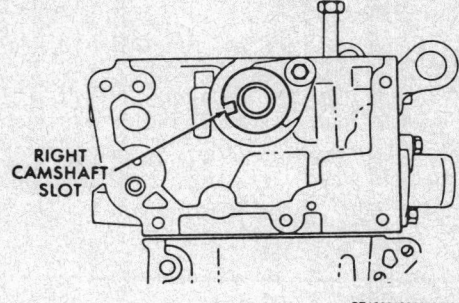

Fig. 11 Righthand camshaft position

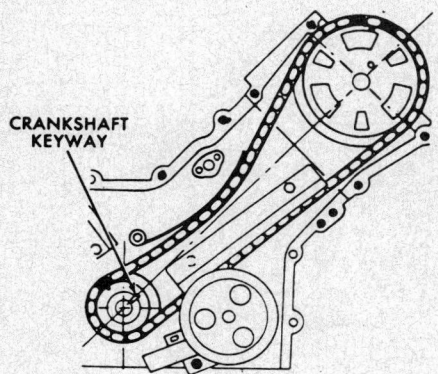

Fig. 12 Crankshaft keyway alignment of left cylinder bank

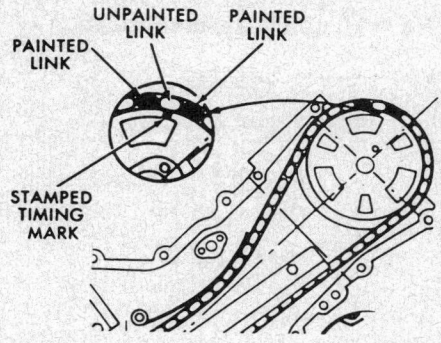

Fig. 13 Left camshaft sprocket to timing chain alignment

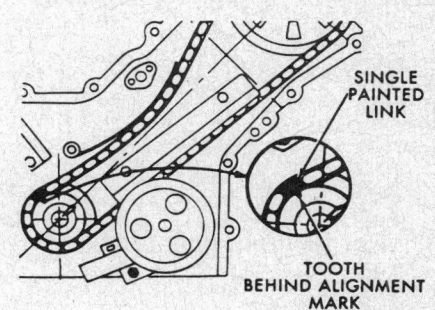

Fig. 14 Crankshaft sprocket to left chain alignment

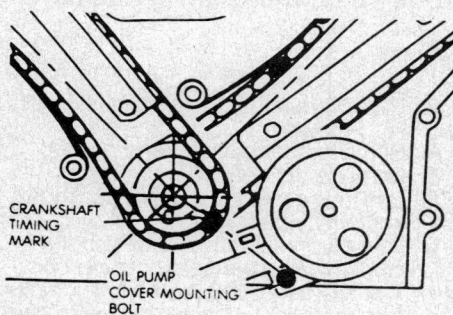

Fig. 15 Crankshaft middle sprocket alignment w/lower oil pump cover mounting bolt

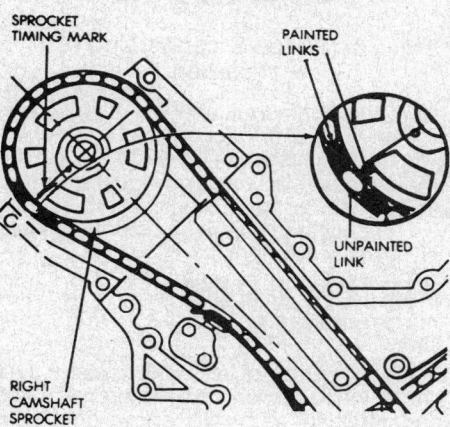

Fig. 16 Right camshaft sprocket to timing chain alignment

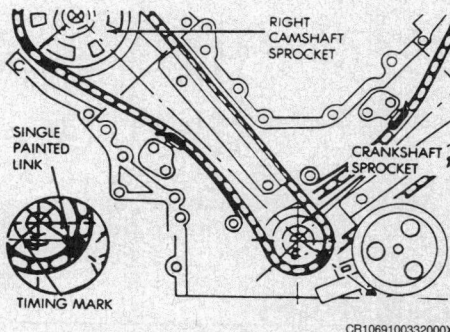

Fig. 17 Crankshaft to right timing chain alignment

Installation

Camshaft sprockets are not the same. The right sprocket has a spacer attached to it, and the left sprocket does not have a spacer. When installing chain tensioner, shoe and guides, they must be installed on the side they were removed from.

1. Install chain guides and tensioner shoes, then tighten to specifications.
2. Turn crankshaft until keyway points straight up, **Fig. 9**.
3. Turn right and left side camshafts until they are positioned as shown in **Fig. 10 and 11**.
4. Install cleaned tension filter, then turn crankshaft in a clockwise direction until crankshaft keyway is aligned with centerline of left cylinder bank, **Fig. 12**.
5. Install left timing chain so that unpainted link between the two painted links aligns with stamped timing mark on left camshaft sprocket, **Fig. 13**. Install left timing chain by positioning single painted link of left timing chain onto tooth of rear sprocket of crankshaft that is directly behind the tooth of middle sprocket that has the timing mark, **Fig. 14**.
6. Install left chain tensioner using a thin bladed screwdriver to turn ratchet counterclockwise, then push tensioner arm in. Position tensioner over filter and tensioner shoe into arm, then tighten to specification.
7. Rotate crankshaft approximately 150° until timing mark on crankshaft middle sprocket is aligned with lower oil pump cover mounting bolt, **Fig. 15**.
8. Install right timing chain so that unpainted link between the two painted links is aligned with stamped timing mark on right camshaft sprocket, **Fig. 16**.
9. Ensure single painted link on bottom of timing chain is aligned with timing mark on middle sprocket, **Fig. 17**.
10. Install right chain tensioner using a thin bladed screwdriver to turn ratchet counterclockwise, then push tensioner arm in. Position tensioner over filter and tensioner shoe into arm, then tighten to specification.
11. Install right camshaft sprocket bolt and tighten to specifications.
12. Push both tensioner shoes in to release the ratchet of tensioner from locked position and then let shoes out, **Fig. 18**.

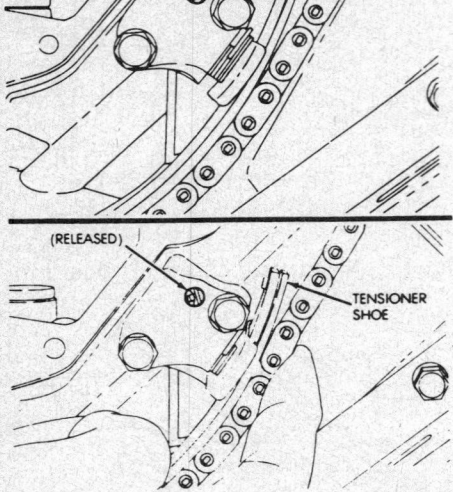

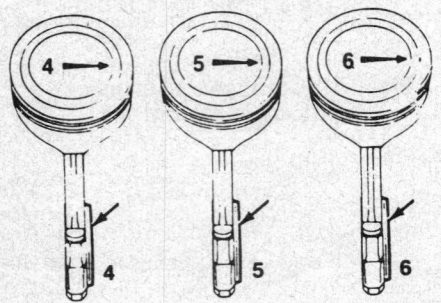

Fig. 18   Tensioner ratchet

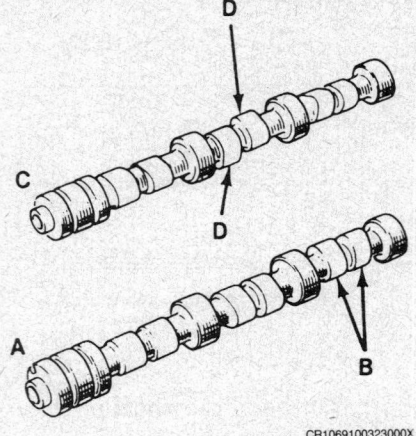

Fig. 19   Camshaft identification

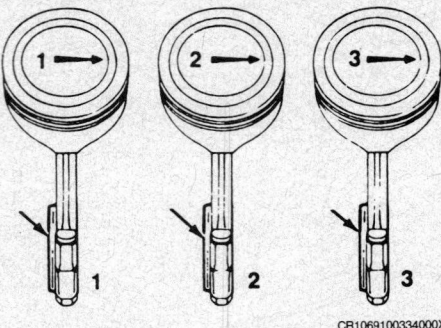

Fig. 20   Piston & connecting rod assembly. Left side

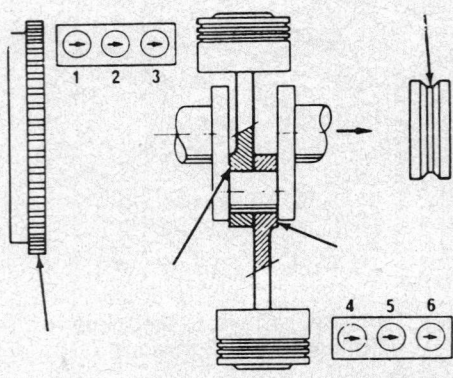

Fig. 22   Piston & connecting rod installation

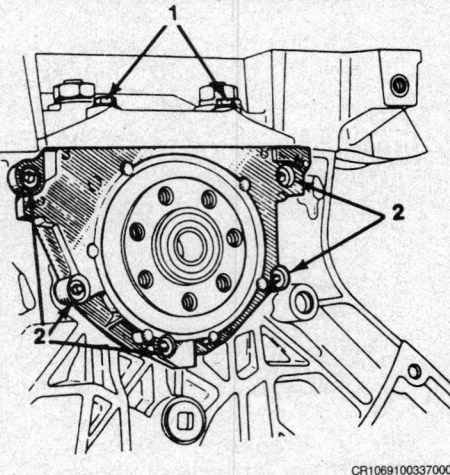

Fig. 23   Rear crankshaft seal removal

Fig. 21   Piston & connecting rod assembly. Right side

CAMSHAFT
REPLACE

The engine is equipped with dual camshafts. The right and left camshafts are not the same and cannot be interchanged. The camshafts can be identified by the location of the lobes, **Fig. 19.** On lefthand camshaft (A) both lobes (B) for each cylinder are on the same side. On righthand camshaft (C) the lobes (D) for each cylinder are on opposite sides. The camshafts are removed and installed from the rear of the cylinder heads.

REMOVAL
1. Remove camshaft cover from rear of cylinder head.
2. Loosen camshaft retainer attaching bolt and slide retainer up and out of the groove in camshaft. Tighten bolt.
3. Carefully slide camshaft out rear of cylinder head.

INSTALLATION
1. Lubricate and install camshaft from rear of cylinder head.
2. Loosen bolt and slide retainer into groove at front of camshaft. Tighten to specifications.

3. Check camshaft endplay using a feeler gauge or dial indicator. Endplay must measure .0030-.0055 inch.
4. Install cover with a new gasket at rear of cylinder head. Apply a light coating of Loctite to attaching bolt and tighten to specifications.

PISTON & ROD ASSEMBLY

When installing left bank pistons 1, 2 and 3, shoulder on connecting rod large end must be opposite arrow on piston crown, **Fig. 20.** On right bank pistons 4, 5 and 6, shoulder must be on same side as arrow on piston crown, **Fig. 21.**

Install left bank connecting rod/piston assemblies 1, 2 and 3 with arrow on crown of piston pointing toward crankshaft pulley end and shoulder of connecting rod pointing to flywheel end of engine. Install right bank connecting rod/piston assemblies 4, 5 and 6 with arrows on crown of piston and shoulder of connecting rod facing crankshaft pulley end of engine, **Fig. 22.**

CRANKSHAFT REAR OIL SEAL
REPLACE
1. Remove two attaching bolts from lower casing (1), **Fig. 23.**

2. Remove seal housing attaching bolts (2), **Fig. 23.**
3. Remove seal housing and gasket.
4. Remove old seal from housing.
5. Use new gasket and install seal housing to cylinder block.
6. Loosely install all attaching bolts including casing to seal housing bolts.
7. Tighten seal housing to block bolts first, then tighten lower casing to seal housing bolts.
8. Tighten attaching bolts to specifications.
9. Lightly oil inner and outer edges of new seal.
10. Place new seal on tool No. 6482 or equivalent seal installer.
11. Install new seal by gently tapping end of tool No. 6482 or equivalent until tool stops.
12. Remove tool No. 6482 or equivalent, turning tool while pulling out.

OIL PAN
REPLACE
1. Drain engine oil.
2. Remove oil pan attaching screws, then the oil pan and gasket.
3. Clean pan and gasket surfaces.
4. Install new gasket and reinstall pan.
5. Install oil pan attaching screws and tighten to specifications.
6. Refill engine oil.

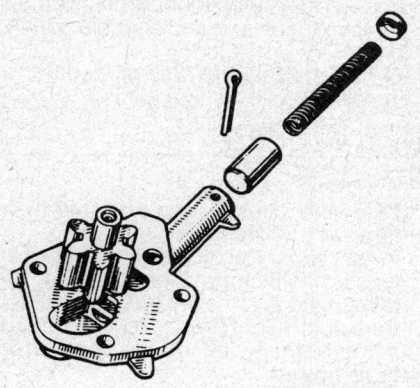

Fig. 24 Oil pump removal

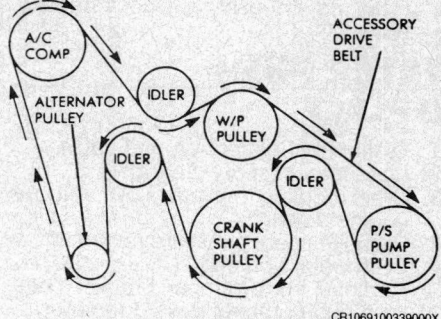

Fig. 25 Serpentine drive belt installation. Less A/C

Fig. 26 Serpentine drive belt installation. With A/C

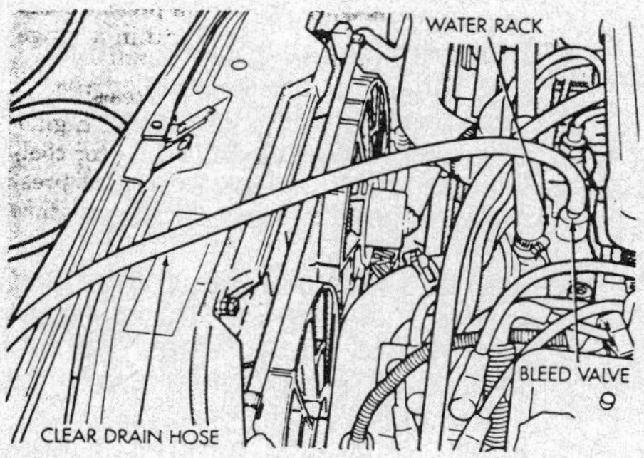

OIL PUMP
REPLACE
REMOVAL

1. Remove timing cover and rotate crankshaft until key is pointing up.
2. Remove oil pump sprocket attaching bolts.
3. Clean thread lock from attaching bolts.
4. Remove chain sprocket and chain.
5. Remove oil pump cover attaching bolts and then the cover.
6. Remove split key from oil pump cover and remove retainer, spring and relief valve, **Fig. 24.** Check condition of all parts. If any part shows excessive wear, the complete oil pump must be replaced.

INSTALLATION

1. Apply clean engine oil and install relief valve, spring and retainer into oil pump cover. When installing relief valve, open end must face spring.
2. Install split key.
3. Lubricate driven gear idler shaft with clean engine oil and install gear over idler shaft.
4. Install pump cover and pump cover retaining screws and tighten screws to specifications.
5. Prime oil pump by squirting oil through hole below oil filter connector.
6. Fill oil filter with clean engine oil and install on engine.
7. After timing chains have been installed, install oil pump sprocket and chain. Apply Loctite to threads of sprocket attaching bolts and tighten to specifications.

BELT TENSION DATA

Belt	New	Used
Accessory	180–200	140–160

Lbs.

SERPENTINE DRIVE BELT

BELT ROUTING

The serpentine drive belt must be installed as shown to ensure correct water

Fig. 27 Thermostat housing air bleed valve

pump rotation, **Fig. 25 and 26.** Incorrect routing of drive belt can cause engine to overheat. When a new accessory drive belt is installed, it must be tensioned after 7500 miles of use.

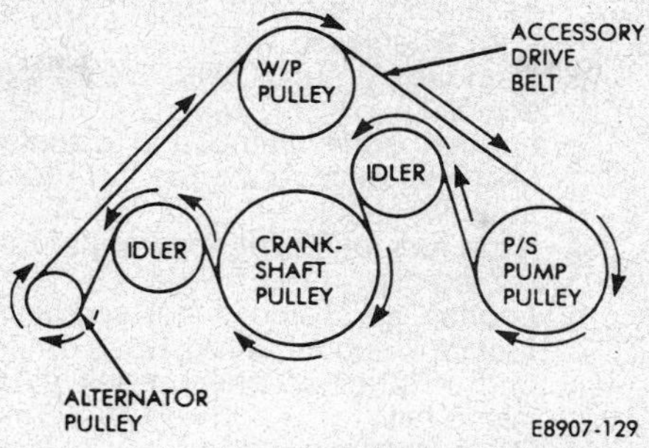

BELT, REPLACE

1. Disconnect battery ground cable.
2. Raise and support vehicle.
3. Remove splash shield below alternator.
4. Loosen alternator pivot bolt.
5. Loosen locking bolt.
6. Loosen adjusting bolt until belt can be removed from alternator pulley.
7. Lower vehicle.
8. Remove engine damper mounting bracket attaching locknuts, then push bracket toward engine.
9. Remove accessory drive belt.
10. Reverse procedure to install.

COOLING SYSTEM BLEED

1. Attach a .250 inch ID hose approximately 48 inches long to the bleed valve on the thermostat housing, **Fig. 27.** Route hose away from accessory drive belt and pulleys.
2. Place other end of hose into a clean container. **The hose will prevent coolant from contacting the accessory drive belt and drive pulleys.**
3. Open bleed valve, then slowly fill coolant pressure bottle until a steady stream of coolant flows from hose at-

tached to bleed valve.
4. Close bleed valve and continue filling to the Full mark of the coolant pressure bottle.
5. Install cap tightly on coolant pressure bottle, then remove hose from bleed valve.
6. Start and run engine until upper radiator hose is warm.
7. Turn engine off, then reattach drain hose to bleed valve on thermostat housing.
8. Open bleed valve until a steady stream of coolant flows from hose.
9. Close bleed valve and remove hose.
10. Ensure coolant level in coolant pressure bottle is at or slightly above the Full mark. **The Full mark on the coolant pressure bottle is the correct coolant level for a cold engine. A hot engine will normally have a coolant level higher than the full mark.**

THERMOSTAT
REPLACE

REMOVAL

Do not remove pressure cap while engine is hot or under pressure. Ensure coolant does not drip onto accessory drive belt or drive pulley. If it does, flush with clean water.

1. Drain coolant into a clean container for reuse. Drain until level is below the thermostat housing.
2. Disconnect coolant temperature sensor wire from sensor.
3. Remove spark plug wire holder from top of thermostat housing and place a shop towel over belts and pulleys.
4. Leave upper radiator hose connected. Remove two retaining bolts, housing, gasket and thermostat.
5. Clean mating surfaces, ensuring that thermostat well is clear of blockage.

INSTALLATION

1. Install thermostat with air bleed valve to rear of well and flat disk to bottom of thermostat well.
2. Install new gasket, then housing. Install retaining bolts and tighten to specifications.
3. Close radiator drain, then fill and bleed cooling system. Start engine, running until warm.
4. Check for leaks, then recheck level.

Refill as necessary. Check reserve bottle.

WATER PUMP
REPLACE

1. Disconnect battery ground cable.
2. Loosen accessory drive belt.
3. Drain cooling system, then remove engine cover.
4. Remove spark plug wire retainer from thermostat housing.
5. Remove front damper bracket bolts, then push bracket toward radiator.
6. Remove radiator hose from water rack and thermostat, then bypass hose from water rack.
7. Remove water pump lower attaching bolts.
8. Pull water pump outward and upward to remove.
9. Reverse procedure to install.

FUEL PUMP
REPLACE

1. The fuel pump/sender unit is located in the fuel tank. Remove fuel tank as follows:
   a. Disconnect battery ground cable.
   b. Remove fuel tank filler cap to relieve fuel tank pressure, then install fuel tank filler cap.
   c. Raise and support vehicle.
   d. Remove right rear wheel and tire assembly, then the splash shield from wheelwell.
   e. Remove ground wire retaining screw.
   f. Loosen hose clamp and disconnect fuel tank vent hose from fuel tank filler neck.
   g. Slide fuel tank vent hose out of retaining clip.
   h. Loosen and remove nut securing fuel tank support strap. Push other end of strap up and out left side frame rail.
   i. Place transmission jack under fuel tank to support it while removing tank.
   j. Disconnect quick-connect fittings from fuel filler inlet nipple tube, then wrap in suitable shop towel, then apply pressure to retainer tabs and pulling fitting back. Note that retainer stays on nipple.
   k. Pull black hose toward fuel tank and through hole in body.
   l. Disconnect fuel pump/sending unit electrical connector.
   m. Disconnect fuel tank to evaporator canister vapor tube at hose and gray hose.
   n. Remove fuel tank attaching bolts. Lower fuel tank on transmission jack two to three inches. Tip fuel tank down on jack while lowering it out of vehicle.
   o. Lower tank and remove it from transmission jack.
2. Loosen fuel pump module clamp, then remove fuel pump and sender assembly.
3. **On all models,** reverse procedure to install.

FUEL FILTER
REPLACE

1. Disconnect battery ground cable, then remove fuel filler cap.
2. Wrap shop towel around quick release connectors, then depress retainer tabs and slowly pull connectors from fuel filter. **Pressure will bleed off system when quick connector is removed.**
3. Remove fuel filter attaching screw, then fuel filter.
4. Remove retainers from nipples on fuel filter using a thin blade screwdriver. Push retainers back into fuel line quick connectors, ensure locking ears and shoulder on fuel tube are visible in windows on side of quick connect fitting.
5. Reverse procedure to install, noting the following:
   a. Fuel filters are marked with a IN and OUT. The side marked IN is connected to the fuel line coming from fuel tank.
   b. Mount new filter, lubricate fuel tube end with clean 30 weight oil, then connect fuel line quick connect fittings to fuel filter nipples.

TIGHTENING SPECIFICATIONS

*Torque Specifications Are For Clean And Lightly Lubricated Threads Only. Dry Or Dirty Threads Produce Increased Friction Which Prevents Accurate Measurement Of Tightness.

Year	Component	Torque/ Ft. Lbs.
1992	A/C Compressor Mounting Bolt	20
	Air Cleaner Hose Clamp	30①
	Alternator Locking Bolt	20
	Alternator Pivot Bolt	37
	Camshaft Sprocket Bolt	59
	Camshaft Thrust Plate Mounting Bolt	9
	Connecting Rod Nut	35
	Crankshaft Pulley Nut	133
	Crankshaft Rear Seal Housing Bolt	9
	Cylinder Head Bolt	②
	Cylinder Head Cover Bolt	9
	Cylinder Head Rear Cover Bolt	53①
	Differential Cover Bolt	20
	Distributor Cap Mounting Bolt	80①
	Distributor Rotor Mounting Bolt	26①
	Engine Cradle Bolt	92
	Engine Damper Bottom Locknut	20
	Engine Damper Top Nut	32
	Engine Mount Nut	48
	Engine Mount Stud Locknut	48
	Fuel Tank	12
	Halfshaft To Brake Hub Nut	181
	Idle Pulley To Timing Cover Bolt	30
	Oil Baffle Bearing Mounting Bolt	13

Year	Component	Torque/ Ft. Lbs.
1992	Oil Baffle Mounting Bolt	9
	Oil Pan Drain Plug	22
	Oil Pan Mounting Bolt	9
	Oil Pump Cover Bolt	9
	Oil Pump Sprocket Bolt	53①
	Oil Pump Sump To Block Bolt	9
	Power Steering Pump Front Bracket/Rear Bracket Nut	30
	Power Steering Pump Front Bracket/Timing Case Bolt	20
	Power Steering Pump Rear Mounting Bracket Stud Bolt	30
	Power Steering Pump Rear Mounting Bolt	20
	Rear Cushion To Support Bracket	49
	Rear Cushion To Exhaust Bracket	23
	Rocker Shaft Locknut	53①
	Splash Shield (Underbody)	21
	Starter Motor Mounting Bolt	31
	Thermostat Housing	9
	Timing Belt Tensioner	53①
	Timing Case Cover	9
	Timing Chain Guide	53①
	Timing Chain Tensioner Bolt	53①
	Timing Chain Tensioner Shoe Bolt	9
	Torque Converter To Driveplate	24
	Transaxle Mounting & Alignment Stud	48
	Transaxle Support Bracket Stud	30
	Water Pump	13

① —Inch lbs.
② —Refer to text for procedure.

Rear Axle & Suspension

INDEX

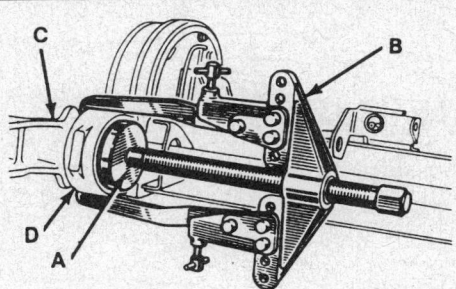

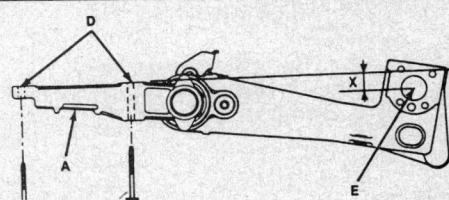

Fig. 3   Axle support bracket

Fig. 1   Axle shaft bolt torque sequence

Fig. 2   Rear axle bushing removal

REAR AXLE
REPLACE

1. Raise and support vehicle.
2. Remove rear wheel and tire assemblies.
3. Disconnect shock absorbers from axle.
4. Loosen adjustment nuts to allow balls on end of parking brake cables to pass through access holes. Remove cables from body support.
5. Disconnect brake hoses from metal brake lines and axle.
6. Position supporting jack under axle assembly and remove attaching bolts.
7. Remove axle assembly by lowering support jack.
8. Reverse procedure to install.

REAR AXLE SHAFT
REPLACE

1. Raise and support vehicle.
2. Remove rear wheel and tire assembly.
3. Remove and discard safety nuts securing brake drum to axle shaft hub.
4. Remove plastic hub cover using suitable screwdriver.
5. Remove brake drum from axle shaft hub.
6. Remove and discard axle shaft hub locknut.
7. Remove axle shaft hub from axle shaft using a suitable puller if necessary.

8. Remove axle shaft to rear axle attaching bolts.
9. Remove brake backing plate to axle shaft attaching bolt.
10. Remove axle shaft from trailing arm.
11. Reverse procedure to install, noting the following:
    a. Tighten axle shaft to rear axle attaching bolts in sequence shown, **Fig. 1**, to specifications.
    b. Tighten brake backing plate to axle shaft attaching bolt to specifications.
    c. Install and tighten new axle shaft hub locknut, then tighten to specifications.
    d. Install brake drum and new safety nuts to axle shaft hub.

REAR AXLE SUPPORT BUSHING
REPLACE

REMOVAL

1. Remove rear axle assembly as previously described.
2. Remove torsion bars from axle as described under, "Torsion Bar, Replace."
3. Install component (A) from T.Ar.1056, bushing remover set, or equivalent, and a two jaw extractor (B) on axle, **Fig. 2.**
4. Drive support bracket and bushing from rear axle.
5. To remove bushing from support bracket, weld a 1.02 inch nut to inside of bushing. This nut is used as a backup to drive bushing from support bracket.
6. Using a suitable hydraulic press and bearing splitter tool, drive bushing from support bracket with a suitable socket. Do not reuse bushing after removal.

INSTALLATION

1. Position new bushing into rear axle.
2. Using suitable driver tool and bushing receiving cup from T.Ar.1056, or equivalent, draw bushing into axle until flush with outside edge of axle.
3. Position support bracket to axle for proper bushing preload, **Fig. 3.** Before pressing support bracket (A) to axle bushing, it must be properly positioned. Adjust support bracket so that dimension "X" measures $^{27}/_{32}$–$^{29}/_{32}$ inch.
4. Position straightedge along top of support bracket where it attaches to body at points (D), **Fig. 3.**
5. After support bracket is positioned to axle, press support bracket to rear axle using T.Ar.1056, or equivalent.
6. Press support bracket until left and right support brackets are at a distance of 51.87–51.98 inch. This measurement is taken between left and right support bracket bolt holes.
7. Install torsion bars to axle as described under, "Torsion Bar, Replace."
8. Install rear axle assembly into vehicle as previously described.

HUB & BEARING
REPLACE

This installation procedure has been revised by a Technical Service Bulletin.

If wheel bearing must be replaced, the hub and bearing assembly must be replaced as a unit.

1. Raise and support vehicle.
2. Remove rear wheel and tire assembly.
3. Remove safety nuts securing brake drum to axle shaft hub.
4. Remove plastic hub cover using suitable screwdriver.
5. Remove brake drum from axle shaft hub.
6. Remove axle shaft hub locknut.

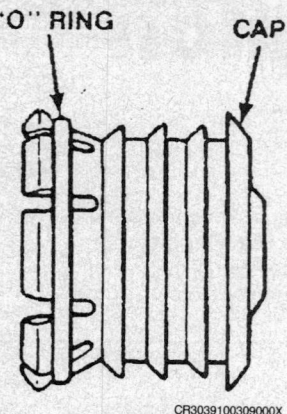

Fig. 4   Hub & bearing O-ring installation

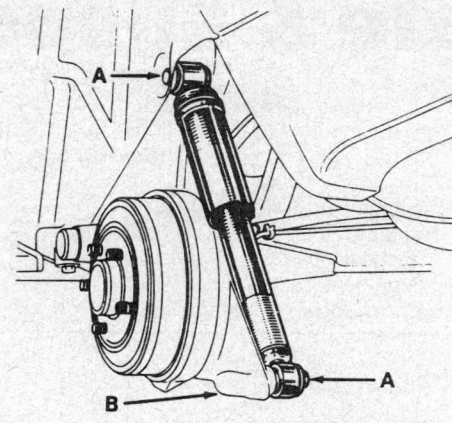

Fig. 5   Shock absorber bolt location

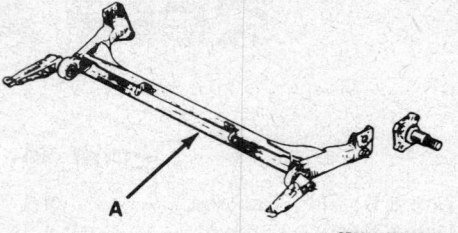

Fig. 6   Hydraulic jack positioning point

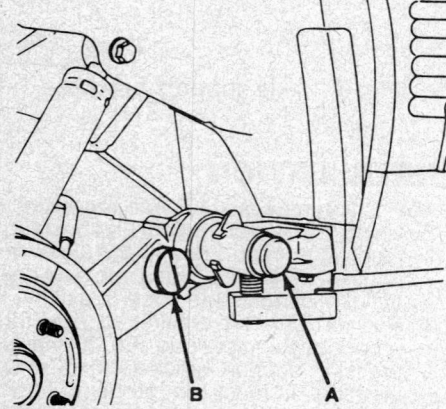

Fig. 7   Anti-sway bar protective end caps

7. Remove wheel hub and bearing assembly from vehicle.
8. Reverse procedure to install noting the following:
   a. Tighten new hub nut to specifications.
   b. Install O-ring, (PN 454339) or equivalent, to hub and bearing cap to eliminate water or dust entering rear wheel bearing, **Fig. 4.**
   c. Install brake drum to hub using new safety nuts.

HUB & BEARING SERVICE

INSPECTION

1. Raise and support vehicle.
2. Remove rear wheel and tire assembly.
3. Remove plastic cap from brake drum.
4. Bolt dial indicator to rear brake drum using dial indicator adapter ROU541, or equivalent.
5. Measure axial play at end of axle shaft. Axial play should not exceed .001 inch. If play exceeds this measurement, replace hub & bearing assembly.

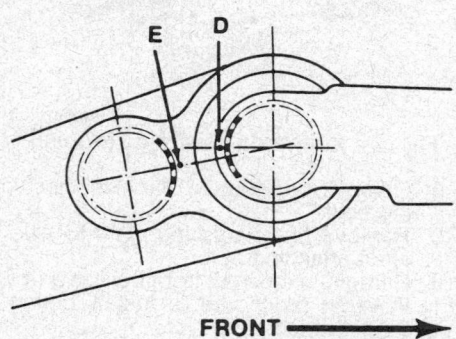

Fig. 8   Lower control arm reference marks

SHOCK ABSORBER
REPLACE

1. Raise and support vehicle. **Do not support vehicle weight under V-shaped channel on axle.**
2. Raise and support control arm at point B, **Fig. 5,** to relieve tension from shock absorber.
3. Remove shock absorber attaching bolts, then lower shock absorber from vehicle.
4. Reverse procedure to install. Tighten upper and lower attaching bolt.

TORSION BAR
REPLACE

REMOVAL

1. Raise and support vehicle. **Do not support vehicle weight under V-shaped channel on axle. Axle weight must be supported at point A, Fig. 6, using a suitable jack.**
2. Remove both rear wheel and tire assemblies.
3. Remove rear shock absorbers as previously described.
4. Remove protective caps (A) and (B), **Fig. 7,** from both sides of vehicle.
5. Remove clips from ends of suspension and anti-sway bars using a suit-

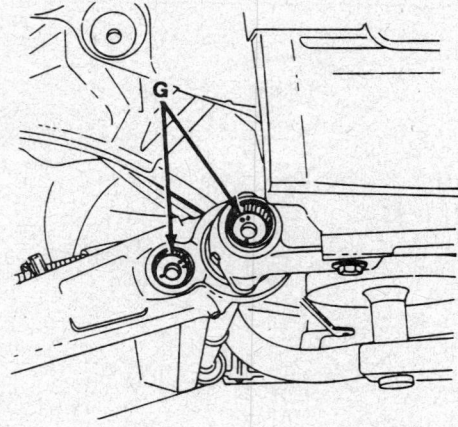

Fig. 9   Torsion bar reference & location marks

able screwdriver.
6. Note alignment mark D, **Fig. 8,** on suspension bar mount and make a reference mark (position E) on lower control arm as shown.
7. Note and record positions of marks G, **Fig. 9,** on all four torsion bars relative to marks D and E. Location of marks on torsion bars (position G) will vary depending on application.
8. Lower rear axle, then pull suspension bars using a suitable slide hammer until splines disengage.
9. Pull anti-sway bars out using a suitable slide hammer. **The rear axle assembly will be damaged if a load is applied to jack supporting the axle.**
10. Support axle at point L, **Fig. 10,** then loosen bolts (M) approximately four turns and bolts (N) approximately ten turns.
11. Lower jack until axle has dropped approximately one inch.
12. Remove suspension bars, then the torsion bar connecting link from vehicle.

INSTALLATION

1. Install torsion bars into rear axle. **Do not engage splines at this time. Ensure torsion bars are installed in original position.**
2. Raise axle and tighten rear axle mounting bolts to specifications.
3. Position rear trailing arms as follows:
   a. Adjust dimension X, **Fig. 11,** on each of two tools Sus.Lm.02 to $17^{15}/_{16}$ inches.
   b. Loosely install bolt (C) and spacer

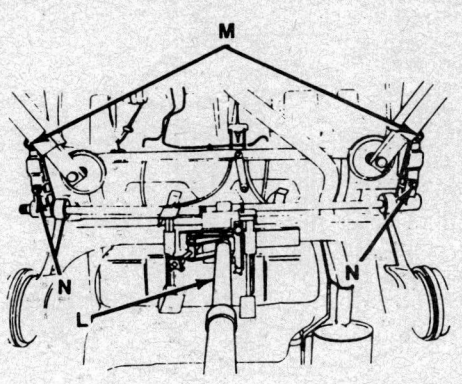

Fig. 10   Axle attaching bolt locations

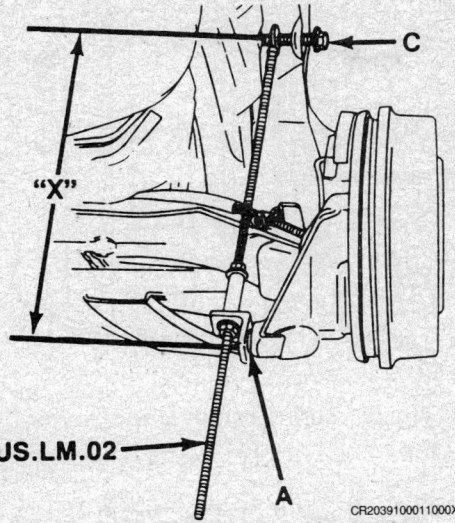

SUS.LM.02

Fig. 11   Axle spacing tool position

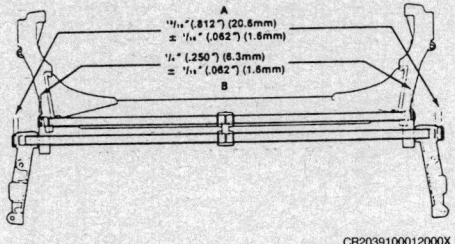

Fig. 12   Torsion bar spline dimensions

(A) from tool set No. T.Ar. 1056, or equivalent, into rear lower shock absorber mounting hole.

4. Apply a suitable lubricant to torsion bar splines and install torsion bars in original position. Ensure recorded marks G, D, and E are properly aligned to avoid added stress to bars.
5. Use recorded marks to position anti-sway bar G into mounting.
6. Install connecting link to splines of anti-sway bar G. Ensure connecting link is centered in V-shaped channel in axle.
7. Install anti-sway bar D in outer mounting and secure in connecting link.
8. Install both suspension bars through outer mounting and secure in connecting link. **Ensure all torsion bars are installed in original position. If splines are difficult to engage, slightly twist link as necessary using suitable pliers on the connecting link.**
9. Remove threaded rod tools from vehi-cle, then install shock absorbers.
10. Install clips and protective caps on end of torsion bars.
11. Center torsion bars in mountings as follows:
   a. Tap ends of suspension bars until outer end of bar protrudes 3/4-7/8 inch from outer edge of mount on both sides, **Fig. 12, using a large brass drift. Do not hammer directly on torsion bar splines.**
   b. Tap ends of anti-sway bars until outer end of bar protrudes 3/16-5/16 inch from outer edge of mount on both sides, **Fig. 12. Do not hammer directly on torsion bar splines.**
12. Install wheel and tire assemblies.

TIGHTENING SPECIFICATIONS

Year	Component	Torque/ Ft. Lbs.
1992	Axle Shaft Hub Locknut	123
	Axle Shaft-To-Rear Axle Attaching Bolts	47
	Brake Backing Plate-To-Axle Shaft Attaching Bolt	12
	Hub Nut	123
	Lower Shock Absorber Bolt	85
	Rear Axle Mounting Bolts	68
	Upper Shock Absorber Attaching Bolt	60
	Wheel Lug Nut	①

①—Steel wheel; 54-72 ft. lbs., aluminum wheel; 80-100 ft. lbs.

Front Suspension & Steering
INDEX

HUB & BEARING SERVICE

Hub and bearing are serviced separate-ly. The hub can be replaced without re-moving bearing from steering knuckle. In order to replace bearing from steering knuckle, the wheel hub must be removed as an assembly. If bearing components are worn or damaged, replace complete as-sembly.

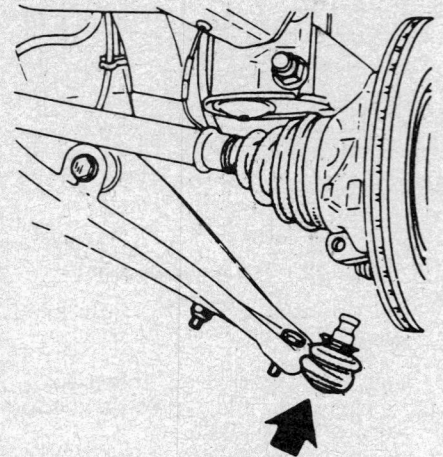

Fig. 1   Lower ball joint removal

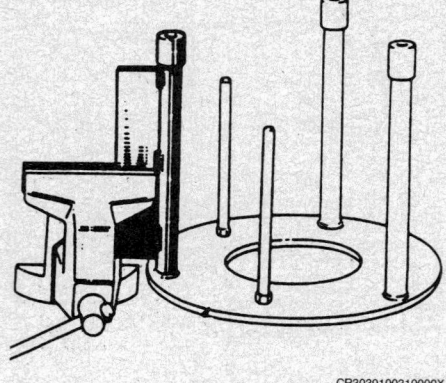

Fig. 2   Spring removal tool lower plate

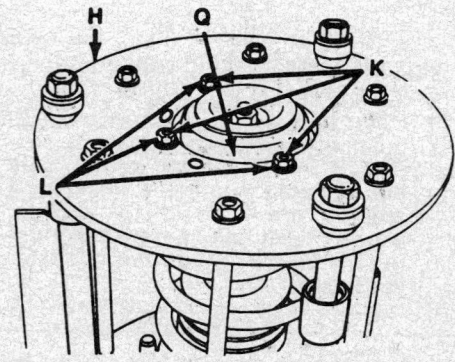

Fig. 4   Top adapter plate installation

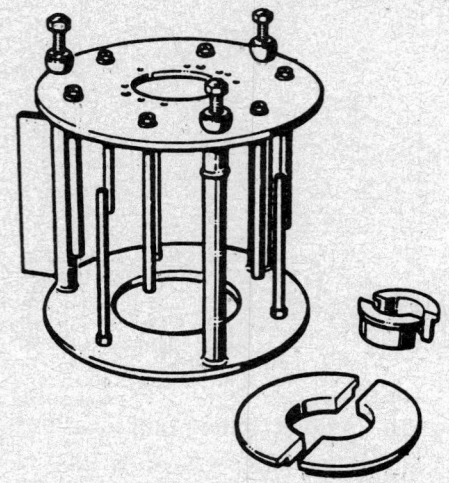

Fig. 3   Lower adapter plate removal

HUB, REPLACE
Removal

1. Raise and support vehicle.
2. Remove wheel and tire assembly, then unfasten brake caliper and position aside.
3. Remove hub nut and the hub using a suitable tool.
4. If replacing hub, remove bearing race using a suitable tool.

Installation

1. If necessary, install new bearing race in hub using a suitable press.
2. Lubricate bearing surface of hub with suitable chassis grease.
3. Insert hub on end of driveshaft and tap with a brass hammer so driveshaft extends past hub.
4. Install driveshaft nut and tighten to specifications.
5. Install brake rotor and caliper, then the wheel and tire assembly.

BEARING, REPLACE
Removal

1. Remove hub as described under "Front Wheel Hub, Replace."
2. Remove bearing assembly to steering knuckle attaching bolts, then the bearing assembly.
3. If necessary, remove bearing outer race using a suitable press and puller. **Bearing race and bearing should be replaced as a set.**

Installation

1. Pack new bearing with suitable grease.
2. Install bearing race in bearing.
3. Press other bearing race into front wheel hub.
4. Place bearing assembly in steering knuckle, then tighten attaching bolt to specifications.
5. Install front wheel hub.

BALL JOINT
REPLACE
LOWER
Removal

1. Raise and support vehicle.

2. Remove wheel and tire assembly, then protect driveshaft boot with shop towel.
3. Loosen stabilizer bar inner bracket bolts and remove outer mounting brackets.
4. Remove lower ball joint keybolt, then loosen lower control arm bolts.
5. Lower stabilizer bar, then with brass or plastic mallet, tap out ball joint in direction of arrow, Fig. 1.

Installation

1. Install new ball joint in lower control arm and finger tighten bolts.
2. Insert ball stud in steering knuckle. Tighten ball joint keybolt and nut to specifications.
3. Finger tighten stabilizer bar outer mounting brackets.
4. With vehicle weight supported by wheels, tighten inner and outer stabilizer bar mounting brackets to specifications.

COIL SPRING & STRUT SERVICE
REMOVAL

1. Raise and support vehicle. **Ensure vehicle weight is not supported under front lower control arms.**
2. Remove front tire and wheel assemblies.
3. Remove outer tie rod end securing nut, then the tie rod using suitable tool.

4. Remove three strut to body attaching nuts.
5. Remove securing nuts from bottom of shock absorber.
6. Remove lower shock absorber mounting bolts.
7. To prevent damage, wrap boot then press down on lower control arm and guide assembly out.

DISASSEMBLY

Suspension Tool Kit No. 1052.99 is supplied with various adapter plates for different models. Premier models use adapter plates stamped R-21.

1. Place lower plate from spring removal tool into a vise, Fig. 2.
2. Place lower adapter plates into lower plate, Fig. 3.
3. Place smaller adapter plates around lower part of strut assembly and properly seat into lower plate that is secured in the vise.
4. Install top adapter plate (H), Fig. 4, onto strut assembly and rotate strut to align with holes on plate. Install three $5/16$ inch by 1.5 inch bolts (L & K) in length through top plate and tighten to cushion (Q).
5. Threading rods into mounts, slowly compress coil spring to approximately $13/32$ inch.
6. Relieve spring tension evenly by loosening threaded bolts and remove spring.

STRUT CARTRIDGE REPLACEMENT

To avoid damage to strut assembly, mount strut in strut clamping vise No. YA-457 or equivalent.

1. Align tab (R) with opening (S) on jounce bumper, then remove jounce bumper and dust boot, Fig. 5.
2. Remove pressed-on cap. Use care to avoid damaging threads.
3. Remove $7/16$ to $31/64$ from top of strut body using a suitable cutting tool.
4. Remove and discard strut cartridge, then pour residual oil from strut body.
5. Remove excess metal from inside of

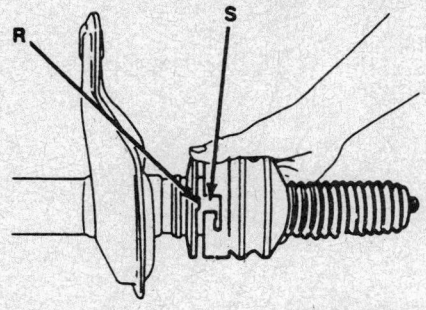

Fig. 5 Jounce bumper & dust boot removal

strut tube caused by cutting operation.

6. Install new cartridge and threaded cap. Tighten threaded cap to specifications.

ASSEMBLY

1. Install dust boot over strut body, **Fig. 6.**
2. Inspect rubber isolator tubes for any wear and replace if necessary.
3. Rotate spring on strut assembly so it bottoms into stop. Spring should be separated by isolator tubes.
4. Place spring retainer on top of spring so it bottoms on end of spring.
5. Install pivot bearing on top of spring retainer.
6. Place strut cushion on top of pivot bearing.
7. Place lower adapter plates (G) into lower plate, **Fig. 3.**
8. Place smaller adapter plates (F) around lower part of strut assembly and properly seat into lower plate that is secured in the vise.
9. Install top adapter plate (H), **Fig. 4,** onto strut assembly and rotate strut to align with holes on plate, install three $5/16$ inch by 1.5 inch bolts (L) in length through top plate and tighten down.
10. Threading rods (M) into mounts (N) slowly compress adapter plate evenly until strut shaft appears through upper plate.
11. Install rebound cup and tighten to specifications.
12. Remove from tool and install in vehicle.

INSTALLATION

1. Position spring/strut assembly on vehicle and finger tighten strut to body nuts.
2. Install lower mounting bolts and nuts, tightening nuts to specifications. **Bolts are splined and must not be tightened.**
3. Install upper mounting bolts and tighten to specifications.
4. Install tie rod end to strut nut and tighten to specifications.
5. Install wheel and tire assembly, lower vehicle.

CONTROL ARM
REPLACE
LOWER

1. Raise and support vehicle.

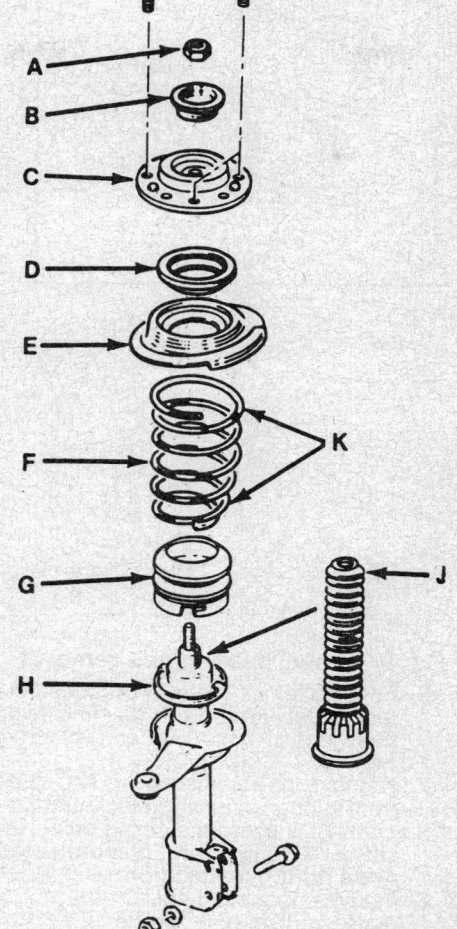

A-Locknut
B-Rebound Cup
C-Strut Cushion
D-Pivot Bearing
E-Spring Seat
F-Coil Spring
G-Jounce Bumper
H-Shock Absorber
J-Dust Boot
K-Rubber Spring Isolator Tubes

Fig. 6 Exploded view of spring strut assembly

2. Remove wheel and tire assembly, then protect driveshaft boot with shop towel.
3. Loosen stabilizer bar inboard bracket bolts (B), **Fig. 7.**
4. Remove stabilizer bar outboard mounting brackets.
5. Remove keybolt from lower ball joint.
6. Remove control arm to engine cradle attaching bolts, then the control arm.
7. Inspect lower control arm bushings for damage or excessive wear and replace if necessary.
8. Reverse procedure to install. Tighten ball joint keybolt nut and control arm to engine cradle bolt to specifications.

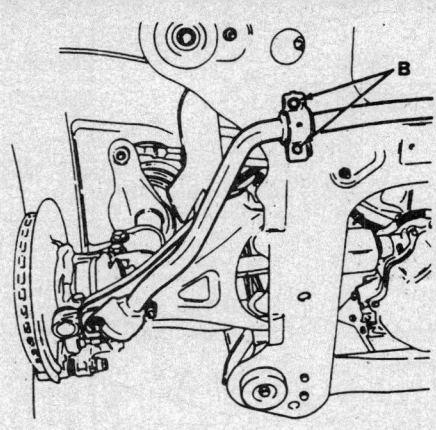

Fig. 7 Stabilizer bar inboard bracket bolts

CONTROL ARM BUSHING
REPLACE
LOWER

1. Remove lower control arm as described under "Lower Control Arm, Replace."
2. Remove bushings using a suitable press and socket.
3. Install new bushings using same tools used for removal. **Bushings must be installed equally in small increments until dimension E, Fig. 8, measures 7.461–7.499 and dimension F is the same at both bushings within .197 inch.**

STEERING KNUCKLE
REPLACE

When removing steering knuckle, the front wheel hub and wheel bearing assembly can be removed as an assembly.

REMOVAL

1. Raise and support vehicle.
2. Remove wheel and tire assembly, then protect driveshaft boot with shop towel.
3. Unfasten brake caliper and position aside, leaving hydraulic lines attached.
4. Remove driveshaft center nut and the rotor.
5. Remove wheel bearing to steering knuckle attaching bolts (L) through access hole (J) in front hub, **Fig. 9.**
6. Remove front hub and wheel bearing assembly using a suitable tool.
7. Remove ball joint keybolt and separate ball joint from knuckle.
8. Remove steering knuckle to strut attaching bolts, then the steering knuckle assembly.

INSTALLATION

1. Position ball joint in steering knuckle, then install ball joint keybolt and nut.
2. Install steering knuckle to strut attaching bolts.
3. Place front hub and wheel bearing assembly over driveshaft. Using access

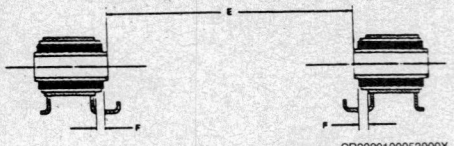

Fig. 8 Control arm bushing installation

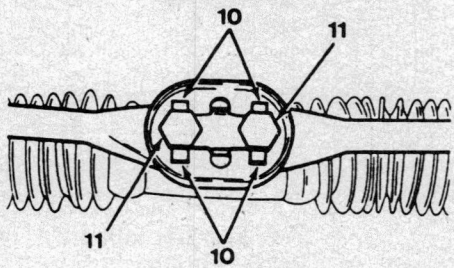

Fig. 10 Tie rod attaching bolt lock tabs

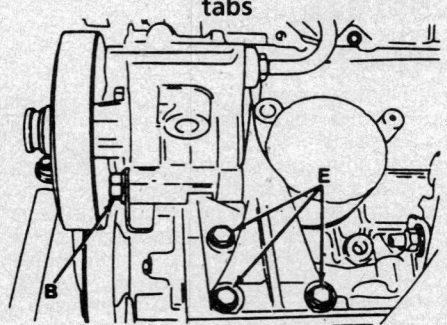

Fig. 11 Power steering bracket bolts (Part 2 of 3)

hole in wheel hub, attach wheel bearing to steering knuckle and tighten to specifications.
4. Tighten driveshaft nut to specifications.
5. Install brake rotor and caliper.

STABILIZER BAR
REPLACE
1. Remove anti-sway bar clamp bolts and nuts, then the anti-sway bar.
2. Temporarily install one nut to retain lower ball joint.
3. Check anti-sway bar bushings for damage or excessive wear and replace if necessary.
4. Reverse procedure to install. Tighten inner and outer anti-sway bar clamp to specifications.

POWER STEERING GEAR
REPLACE
REMOVAL
1. Remove instrument panel lower cover.
2. Unfasten steering shaft boot flange and slide upward for access of U-joint.
3. Mark intermediate shaft and steering shaft for installation reference.
4. Remove shaft through bolt.
5. In engine compartment, pry out splash shield clips using a suitable screwdriver.

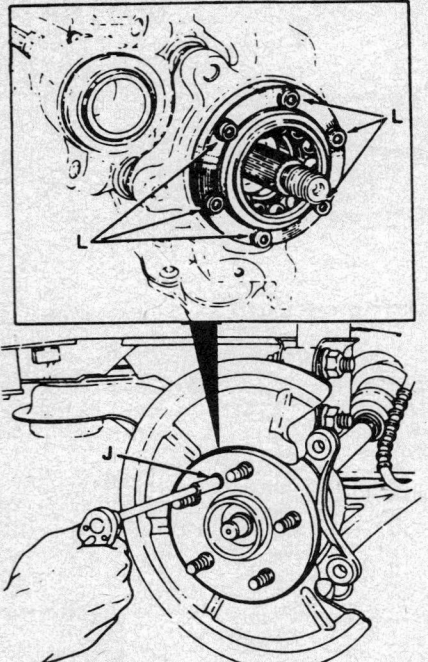

Fig. 9 Wheel bearing bolt removal

6. Fold back lock tab (10) on bolts (11) that attach tie rods to steering rack, then loosen bolts one or two turns, **Fig. 10.**
7. Remove power steering pump lines from rubber mounting block and disconnect lines from steering gear. **Replace O-rings on disconnected lines during installation.**
8. Remove mounting nut.
9. Raise and support vehicle.
10. Remove left front wheel and tire assembly, then disconnect tie rod ends from steering knuckles using a suitable tool.
11. Remove three bolts attaching steering gear to vehicle body and slide steering gear assembly through access opening in left fender panel.

INSTALLATION
1. Attach tie rods to steering gear. Do not tighten completely at this time.
2. Install gear assembly through access opening in left fender panel and install gear to body mounting bolts and nuts.
3. Connect tie rod ends to steering knuckle, tighten retaining nut to specifications.
4. Connect fluid lines with new O-rings to steering gear.
5. Install fluid lines into rubber mounting block.
6. Tighten tie rod to steering gear attaching bolts to specifications, then bend lock tabs over tie rod bolt heads.
7. Align and connect intermediate shaft and steering gear shaft with reference marks made during removal.
8. Install and tighten intermediate shaft coupling bolt to specifications.
9. Install steering shaft boot.
10. Fill power steering system to proper level.

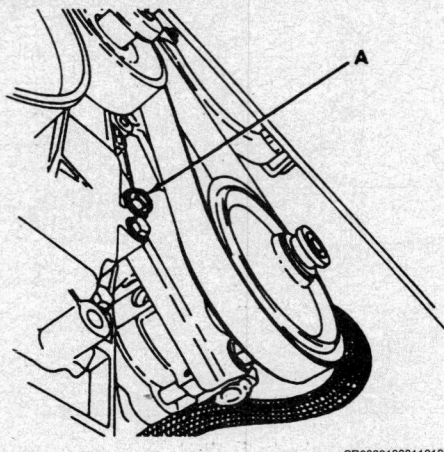

Fig. 11 Power steering bracket bolts (Part 1 of 3)

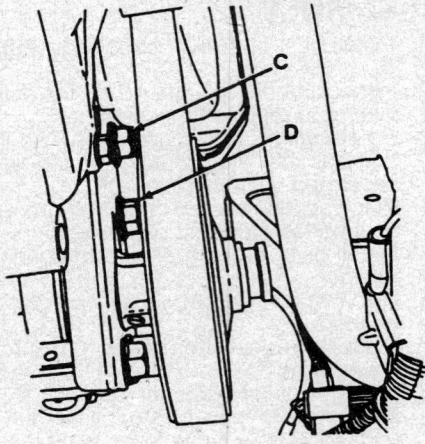

Fig. 11 Power steering bracket bolts (Part 3 of 3)

POWER STEERING PUMP
REPLACE
REMOVAL
1. Raise and support vehicle.
2. Remove underbody splash pan, then loosen drive belt.
3. Disconnect high pressure hose from pump.
4. Remove all pump bracket bolts, then the pump and bracket as an assembly.

INSTALLATION
1. Install pump assembly on engine.
2. Tighten pump bracket bolts and nuts A through E, **Fig. 11.** in alphabetical order. **Torque** rear bracket to reservoir bolt to 20 ft. lbs., front bracket to rear bracket stud to 15 ft. lbs. and all other nuts and bolts to 30 ft. lbs.
3. Connect return hose and pressure hose to pump.
4. Install and adjust drive belt.
5. Install underbody splash shield.
6. Lower vehicle and fill pump to proper level.

TIGHTENING SPECIFICATIONS

Year	Component	Torque/ Ft. Lbs.
1992	Ball Joint Keybolt And Nut	77
	Ball Joint Keybolt Nut	77
	Bearing Assembly Attaching Bolts	11
	Control Arm To Engine Cradle Bolts	103
	Driveshaft Nut	181
	Inner Anti-Sway Bar Clamps	21
	Inner Stabilizer Bar Mounting Brackets	21
	Intermediate Shaft Coupling Bolt	25
	Lower Mounting Bolts	123
	Outer Anti-Sway Bar Clamps	60
	Outer Stabilizer Bar Mounting Brackets	60
	Power Steering Bracket To Bracket Lower Nut/Stud	30
	Power Steering Bracket To Bracket Upper Nut	30
	Power Steering Bracket To Upper Stud	15
	Power Steering Front Bracket To Rear Bracket	30
	Power Steering Front Bracket To Timing Cover	20
	Power Steering Rear Bracket To Sump	30
	Rebound Cup Locknut	59
	Strut Rebound Cup	73
	Tie Rod End-To-Strut Nut	27
	Tie Rod Ends To Steering Knuckle Nuts	35
	Tie Rod-To-Steering Gear Attaching Bolts	55
	Upper Mounting Nuts	17
	Wheel Bearing To Steering Knuckle Bolts	11
	Wheel Lug Nut	①

① —Steel wheel; 54-72 ft. lbs., aluminum wheel; 80-100 ft. lbs.

Wheel Alignment

INDEX

PRELIMINARY INSPECTION

Prior to front end alignment, check vehicle for proper tire size and inflation. Also check wheel and tire radial lateral runout. Steering and suspension components should be inspected for damage and replaced if necessary. Wheel bearing end-play and brake operation should be corrected if necessary. Center steering gear as follows:

1. Support vehicle on alignment rack.
2. Turn steering wheel completely to the left, then completely to the right and count number of turns to the stop.
3. Turn steering wheel to the left one-half the number of turns counted.
4. If steering wheel needs to be centered, adjust after toe adjustment. Refer to "Steering Wheel Alignment."

FRONT WHEEL ALIGNMENT

CASTER & CAMBER

Caster and camber built-in angles are not adjustable. A difference of more than one degree between left and right caster or camber angles may result in pulling to one side, or tire wear. Inspection and replacement of damaged suspension and steering parts should be performed to correct alignment angles. Brake drag or an under inflated tire, can also cause the vehicle to pull.

Bounce vehicle several times and check alignment angles of caster and camber then. Repair or replace vehicle suspension parts if alignment is out of specifications.

TOE-OUT

Front wheel toe-out is adjusted only after the steering gear has been centered. Excessive toe-out will wear the inner edge of tires. Insufficient toe-out will wear outer edge of tires. To adjust toe-out, turn tie rods in or out.

1. Loosen tie rod locknut (A - righthand threads), then (B - lefthand threads), Fig. 1.
2. Turn adjusting sleeve (C) to required length, ensuring both tie rod ends have an equal amount of threads showing.
3. Torque locknuts and to 26 ft. lbs.

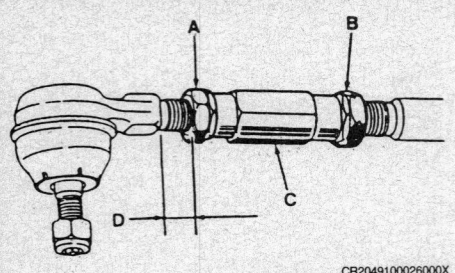

Fig. 1   Toe-out adjustment

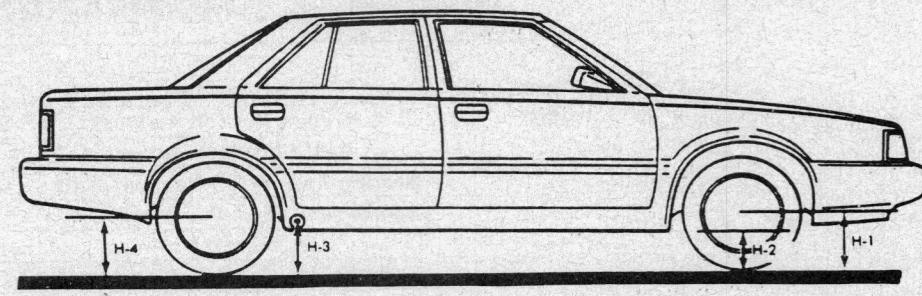

Fig. 2   Measuring vehicle height (Part 1 of 2)

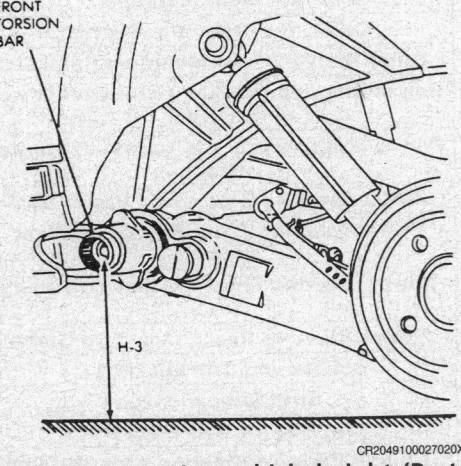

Fig. 2   Measuring vehicle height (Part 2 of 2)

VEHICLE RIDE HEIGHT

1. Measure height H-1 and H-4 from wheel hub horizontal centerline to surface on right and left sides of vehicle, **Fig. 2.**
2. Measure height H-2 from engine cradle at wheel hub vertical centerline to surface.
3. Measure height H-3 from front torsion bar horizontal centerline to surface, **Fig. 2.**
4. Compare height measurements from each side of vehicle, as follows:
   a. Subtract H-2 from H-1, measurement should be 3.36 to 3.98 inches.
   b. Subtract H-3 from H-4, measurement should be 1.25 to 1.87 inches.

EAGLE TALON & PLYMOUTH LASER

NOTE: Refer To Rear Of This Manual For Vehicle Manufacturer's Special Service Tool Suppliers.

INDEX OF SERVICE OPERATIONS

NOTE: For Service Operations Not Listed Below, Refer To The Table Of Contents In The Front Of This Manual.

Specifications
GENERAL ENGINE SPECIFICATIONS

Year	Engine Liter/CID	VIN②	Fuel System	Bore and Stroke, Inch	Compression Ratio	Net HP @ RPM ③	Maximum Torque, Ft. Lbs. @ RPM	Minimum Oil Pressure, psi @ RPM
1992	1.8L/4-107	T	MPI④	3.17 x 3.39	9.0	92 @ 5000	105 @ 3500	11.4 @ 700
	2.0L/4-122⑤	R	MPI④	3.35 x 3.46	9.0	135 @ 6000	125 @ 5000	11.4 @ 750
	2.0L/4-122⑥	U	MPI④	3.35 x 3.46	7.8	190 @ 6000	203 @ 3000	11.4 @ 750

Continued

GENERAL ENGINE SPECIFICATIONS-Continued

Year	Engine Liter/CID	Engine VIN②	Fuel System	Bore and Stroke, Inch	Compression Ratio	Net HP @ RPM ③	Maximum Torque, Ft. Lbs. @ RPM	Minimum Oil Pressure, psi @ RPM
1993-94	1.8L/4-107	B	MPI④	3.17 x 3.39	9.0	92 @ 5000	105 @ 3500	11.4 @ 700
	2.0L/4-122⑤	E	MPI④	3.35 x 3.46	9.0	135 @ 6000	125 @ 5000	11.4 @ 750
	2.0L/4-122⑥	F	MPI④	3.35 x 3.46	7.8	190 @ 6000⑦	203 @ 3000⑧	11.4 @ 750
1995	2.0L/4-122⑤	Y	MFI⑨	3.45 x 3.27	9.6	140 @ 6000	130 @ 4800	4.0 @ 700
	2.0L/4-122⑥	F	MFI⑨	3.35 x 3. 46	8.5	210 @ 6000①	214 @ 3000	11.4 @ 750

CID-cubic inch displacement.
①—205 @ 6000 w/automatic transmission.
②—Eighth digit of VIN denotes engine code.

③—Ratings are net as installed in vehicle.
④—Multi-point injection.
⑤—Except turbocharged.
⑥—Turbocharged.

⑦—180 @ 6000 w/automatic transmission.
⑧—195 @ 3000 w/automatic transmission.
⑨—Multiport Fuel Injection.

TUNE UP SPECIFICATIONS

Year	Liter/CID	VIN②	Spark Plug Gap, Inch	Firing Order	Firing Order Fig.	Ignition Timing,°BTDC Man. Trans.	Ignition Timing,°BTDC Auto. Trans.	Mark Fig.	Curb Idle Speed, RPM Man. Trans.	Curb Idle Speed, RPM Auto. Trans.	Fuel Pump Pressure, psi
1992	1.8L/4-107	T	.039-.043	1-3-4-2	A	5④⑦	5④	B	600-800	600-800	38.0④
	2.0L/4-122③	R	.039-.043	1-3-4-2	C	5⑤⑦	5⑤⑦	B	650-850	650-850	36.0-38.0⑤
	2.0L/4-122⑥	U	.028-.031	1-3-4-2	C	5⑤⑦	5⑤⑦	B	650-850	650-850	27.0⑤
1993-94	1.8L/4-107	B	.039-.043	1-3-4-2	A	5④⑦	5④	B	600-800	600-800	47.6④
	2.0L/4-122③	E	.039-.043	1-3-4-2	C	5⑤⑦	5⑤⑦	B	650-850	650-850	①
	2.0L/4-122⑥	F	.028-.031	1-3-4-2	C	5⑤⑦	5⑤⑦	B	650-850	650-850	①
1995	2.0L/4-122③	Y	.048-.053	1-3-4-2	G	5④⑦	5③④	C	600-800	600-800	47.0-50.0④
	2.0L/4-122⑥	F	.028-.031	1-3-4-2	H	5⑤⑦	5⑤⑦	C	650-850	650-850	42.0-44.8⑤

BTDC-Before top dead center.
CID-Cubic inch displacement.
①—Non turbo, 47-50 psi; turbo models w/manual transaxle, 36-38 psi; turbo models w/automatic transaxle, 41-46 psi at curb idle.

②—Eighth digit of VIN denotes engine code.
③—Electronically controlled.
④—At 700 RPM.
⑤—At 750 RPM.
⑥—Turbo.

⑦—With jumper wire connected between ignition timing adjustment connector and ground. Refer to Fig. D for 1.8L engines, Fig. E for 1992-94 2.0L/4-122 engines and Fig. Ffor 1995 2.0L/4-122 engine.

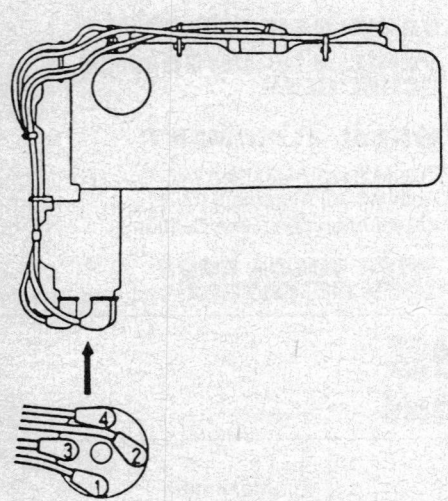

Fig. A

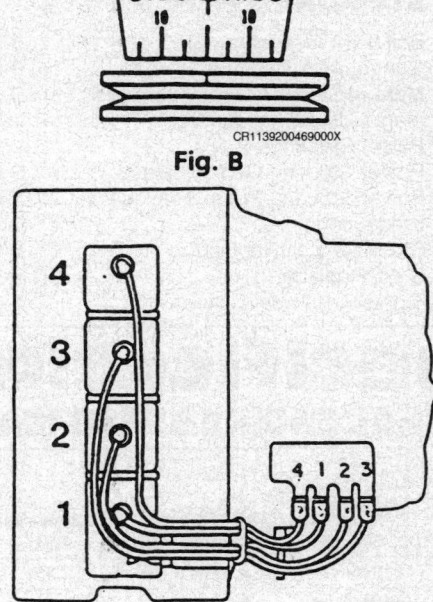

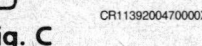

Fig. C

BTDC ↑ ATDC
10   10

CR1139200469000X

Fig. B

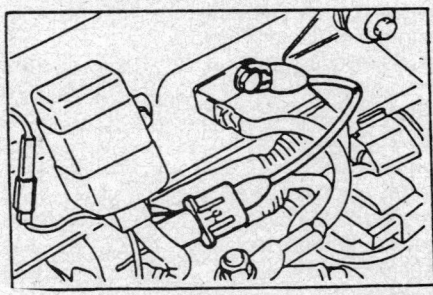

Fig. D   CR1139100181000X

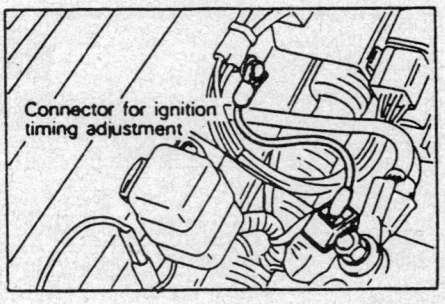

Connector for ignition timing adjustment

CR1139100182000X

Fig. E

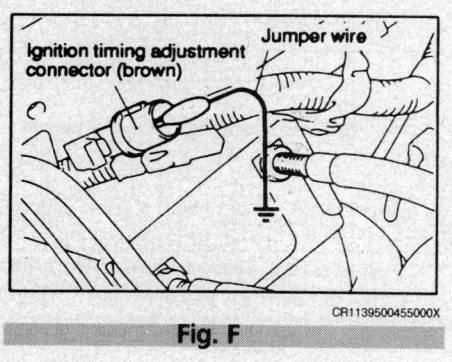

Fig. F

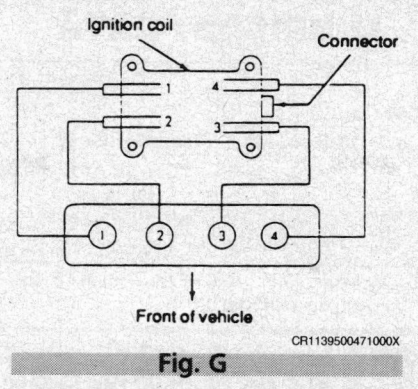

Fig. G

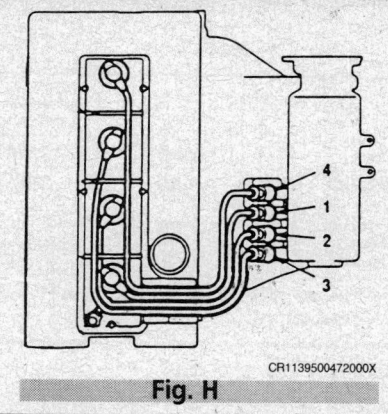

Fig. H

FRONT WHEEL ALIGNMENT SPECIFICATIONS

Year	Model	Camber Angle, Degrees		Caster Angle, Degrees		Toe In Inch
		Limits	Desired	Limits	Desired	
1992–94	①	$-4/15$ to $+11/15$	$+7/30$	$+15/6$ to $+25/6$	$+21/3$	0④
	②	$-5/12$ to $+7/12$	$+1/12$	$+11/10$ to $+29/20$	$+23/10$	0④
	③	$-1/3$ to $+2/3$	$+1/6$	$+11/5$ to $+24/5$	$+23/10$	0④
1995	⑤	$-5/12$ to $+7/12$	$+1/12$	$+31/6$ to $61/6$	$+42/3$	0④
	⑥	$-1/6$ to $5/6$	$+1/3$	$+31/6$ to $61/6$	$+42/3$	0④

①—FWD models w/1.8L engine.
②—FWD models w/2.0L engine.
③—AWD models.
④—Plus or minus .12 inch.
⑤—ESI model w/FWD and TSI model w/AWD.
⑥—TSI model w/FWD.

REAR WHEEL ALIGNMENT SPECIFICATIONS

Year	Model	Camber Angle, Degrees		Toe In, Inch
		Limits	Desired	
1992–94	②	$-11/4$ to $-1/4$	$-3/4$	0③
	①	$-21/20$ to $-11/20$	$-111/20$	.14③
1995	④	$-5/6$ to $51/8$	$-1/3$	.12③
	⑤	$-11/6$ to $-1/6$	$-2/3$	.12③

①—AWD models.
②—FWD models.
③—Plus or minus .118 inch.
④—FWD models w/ 14 inch wheels & AWD models w/Automatic transaxle.
⑤—FWD models w/ 16 inch wheels & AWD models w/ Manual transaxle.

COOLING SYSTEM & CAPACITY DATA

Year	Liter/CID	VIN Code	Coolant Capacity		Radiator Cap Relief Pressure, Lbs.	Thermo. Opening Temp., °F	Fuel Tank, Gals.	Engine Oil Refill, Qts.	Transaxle Oil		Rear Axle, Pts.
			Less A/C, Qts.	With A/C, Qts.					5 Speed, Qts.	Auto. Trans., Qts.	
1992	1.8L/4-107	T	6.6	6.6	11-15	190	15.9	4.1②	1.9	④	—
	2.0L/4-122	R,U	7.6	7.6	11-15	190	15.9	①	③	④⑦	.74
1993–94	1.8L/4-107	B	6.6	6.6	11-15	190	15.9	4.1②	1.9	④	—
	2.0L/4-122	E,F	7.6	7.6	11-15	190	15.9	①	③	④⑦	.74
1995	2.0L/4-122⑤	Y	7.4	7.4	14-18	195	15.9	4.5	2.1	9.1	—
	2.0L/4-122⑥	F	7.4	7.4	11-15	180	15.9	5.5	2.3	7.1⑧	.90

CID-Cubic inch displacement.
①—Non-turbocharged models, 4.6 Qts.; Turbocharged models, 4.8 Qts. Includes filter.
②—Includes filter.
③—Except turbo, 1.9 pints; turbo w/FWD, 2.3 pints; turbo w/AWD, 2.4 pints.
④—F4A22 transaxle, 6.4 qts.; F4A33 and W4A33 transaxles, 7.4 qts.
⑤—Less turbo.
⑥—With turbo.
⑦—Transfer, .63 qts.
⑧—Transfer, .59 qts.

LUBRICANT DATA

Year	Model	Lubricant Type					
		Transaxle		Transfer Case	Rear Axle	Power Steering	Brake System
		Manual	Automatic				
1992-94	All	API GL-4	①	75W-90 API GL-4	80W-90 API GL-5	②	DOT 3 or 4
1995	All	③	①	80W-90 API GL-4	80W-90 API GL-5	②	DOT 3 or 4

① —Mopar ATF type 7176, Dia. ATF SP or equivalent.
② —Mopar ATF type 7176, Dia. ATF SP, Dexron or Dexron II.
③ —Non-turbo, Mopar MS9417 MTX fluid or equivalent; turbo, 75W-90 GL-4.

Electrical

NOTE: On Air Bag Equipped Models, Refer To "Air Bag System Precautions" Located In The Front Of This Manual For System Disarming & Arming Procedures.

INDEX

PRECAUTIONS

AIR BAG SYSTEMS

Refer to "Air Bag System Precautions" in the front of this manual for system disarming and arming procedures.

FUSE PANEL & FLASHER LOCATION

1992-94

The fuse panel is located under the driver's side instrument panel.

The hazard and turn signal flasher is located behind the center console.

1995

The multi-purpose fuse panel and dedicated fuse panel are located under the driver's side instrument panel.

The hazard and turn signal flasher are located behind the center console.

On non-turbo models, the dedicated fuse panel/power distribution block is located in the front lefthand side of the engine compartment.

On turbo models, the dedicated fuse panel/power distribution block is located in the righthand side of the engine compartment.

STARTER

REPLACE

1992-94

1. Remove battery and battery tray.
2. Raise and properly support vehicle.
3. Disconnect speedometer cable from transaxle.
4. **On 1.8L engine models,** remove manifold bracket.
5. **On all models,** disconnect electrical connectors.
6. Remove starter attaching bolts, then the starter.
7. Reverse procedure to install.

1995

1. Disconnect battery ground cable, thn raise and support vehicle.
2. **On models less turbo with manual transmission,** remove aspirator assembly.

3. **On models with turbo,** remove air hose.
4. **On all models,** remove starter terminal and connector.
5. Remove starter.
6. Reverse procedure to install.

DISTRIBUTOR

REPLACE

1.8L/4-107 ENGINE

1. Disconnect battery ground cable.
2. Remove spark plug cables from distributor, **keep plug wires in order for installation.**
3. Remove distributor hold-down bolt, then the distributor.
4. Reverse procedure to install noting the following:
   a. Turn the crankshaft so that the No. 1 cylinder is at top dead center.
   b. Align distributor housing and gear mating marks, **Fig. 1.**
   c. Install distributor to engine while aligning fine cut groove of distributor installation flange with center of distributor installation stud.

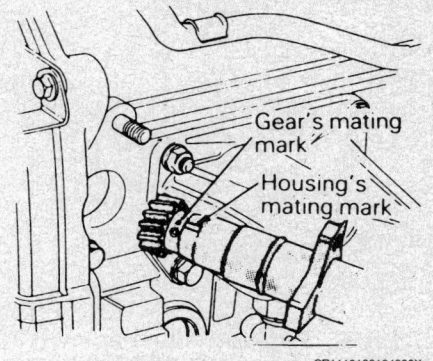

Fig. 1   Distributor alignment. 1.8L/4-107 engine

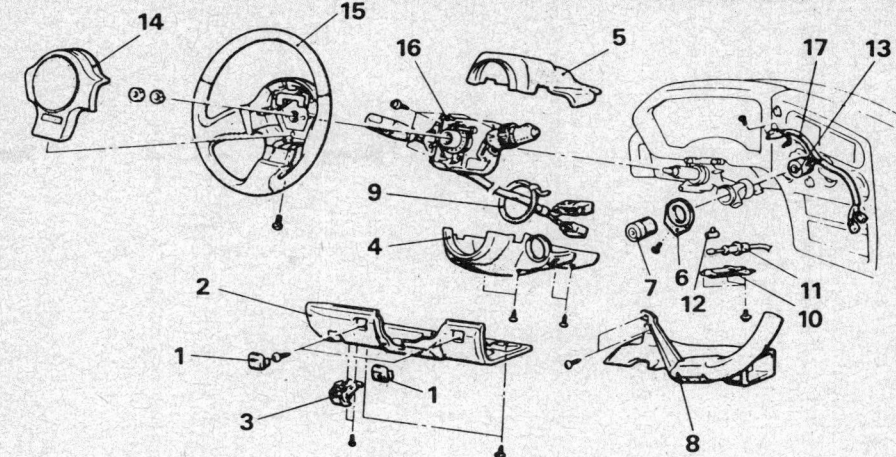

1. Plug
2. Knee protector
3. Hood lock release handle
4. Column cover lower
5. Column cover upper
6. Ignition key illumination light
7. Steering lock cylinder
8. Lap cooler duct and shower duct
9. Cable band
10. Cover*
11. Key interlock cable*
12. Slide lever*
13. Ignition switch segment

14. Horn pad
15. Steering wheel
16. Column switch
17. Key reminder switch segment

NOTE
* indicates vehicles with A/T safety-lock system.

Fig. 3   Ignition switch removal. 1992–94

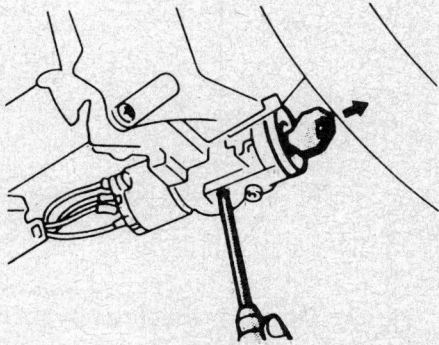

Fig. 2   Ignition lock release

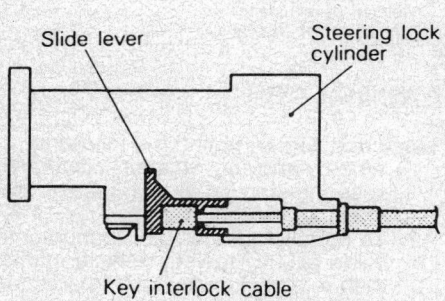

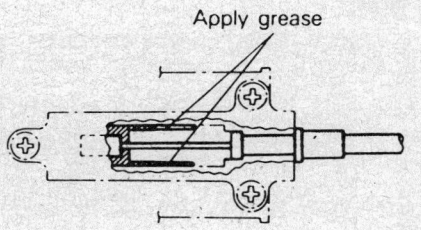

Fig. 4   Slide lever installation. 1992–94

IGNITION LOCK
REPLACE

1. Remove upper and lower steering column covers.
2. Insert key in steering lock cylinder, turn to Accessory position.
3. Using Phillips screwdriver, push lock-pin, Fig. 2, of steering lock cylinder inward and pull lock cylinder out of housing.
4. Reverse procedure to install.

IGNITION SWITCH
REPLACE

1992–94

Remove ignition switch in numbered sequence, Fig. 3, noting the following:
1. With key removed, install slide lever to steering lock cylinder.
2. Connect key interlock cable to slide lever and steering lock cylinder as shown, Fig. 4.
3. Apply coating of multi-purpose grease where shown, Fig. 4.
4. Remove horn pad attaching screw, then the horn pad by pressing upward.
5. Remove steering wheel using suitable wheel puller. **Do not use hammer as this may damage collapsible mechanism.**
6. Reverse procedure to install.

1995

1. Remove instrument panel undercover, Fig. 5.
2. Remove upper and lower column covers.
3. Disconnect ignition switch wiring connector.
4. Remove ignition switch.
5. Reverse procedure to install.

HEADLAMP SWITCH
REPLACE

Refer to "Combination Switch, Replace" for procedure.

COMBINATION SWITCH
REPLACE

1992–94

Remove column switch in numbered sequence, **Fig. 3**, noting the following:
1. Remove horn pad attaching screw, then the horn pad by pressing upward.
2. Remove steering wheel using wheel puller. **Do not use hammer as this may damage collapsible mechanism.**
3. Reverse procedure to install.

1995

1. Remove air bag module as described under "Air Bag System".
2. Remove steering wheel as described under "Steering Wheel, Replace".
3. Remove column switch in numbered sequence, **Fig. 5**.
4. Reverse procedure to install.

DIMMER SWITCH
REPLACE

1992–94

Remove pop-up, fog lamp and dimmer switches in numbered sequence, **Fig. 6**. Reverse procedure to install.

1995

Refer to "Combination Switch, Replace" for proper procedure.

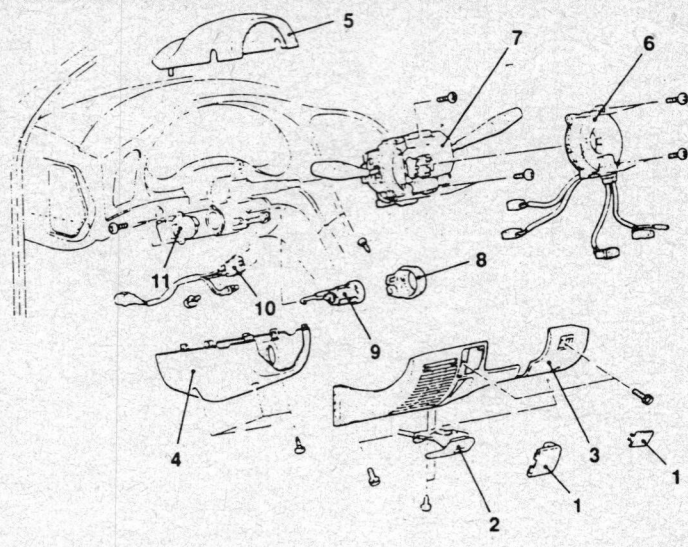

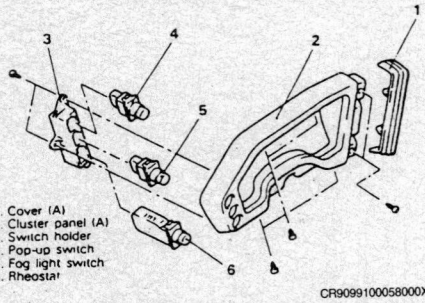

Fig. 6   Pop-up & dimmer switch replacement. 1992–94

1. Cover (A)
2. Cluster panel (A)
3. Switch holder
4. Pop-up switch
5. Fog light switch
6. Rheostat

CR9099100058000X

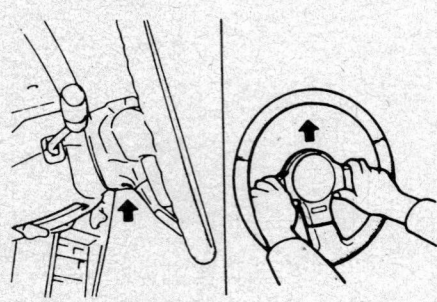

Fig. 7   Steering wheel removal. 1992–94

CR6049100091000X

Steering lock cylinder removal steps

• Steering wheel

1. Plug
2. Hood lock release handle
3. Instrument under cover
4. Column cover lower
5. Column cover upper
6. Clock spring
7. Column switch
8. Ignition key illumination ring or ring cover
9. Steering lock cylinder

Key reminder switch segment or key hole illumination light removal steps

4. Column cover lower
5. Column cover upper
10. Key reminder switch segment or key hole illumination light

Ignition switch segment removal steps

4. Column cover lower
5. Column cover upper
11. Ignition switch segment

CR9049500067000X

Fig. 5   Ignition switch removal. 1995

STEERING WHEEL
REPLACE

1992–94

1. Remove horn pad attaching screw, then the horn pad by pressing upward, **Fig. 7.**
2. Remove steering wheel attaching bolt.
3. Remove steering wheel using suitable wheel puller. **Do not use hammer as this may damage the collapsible mechanism.**
4. Reverse procedure to install.

1995

1. Remove air bag module as described under" Air Bag System".
2. Remove steering wheel attaching bolt, **Fig. 8.**
3. Remove steering wheel using suitable wheel puller. **Do not use hammer as this may damage the collapsible mechanism.**
4. Reverse procedure to install.

INSTRUMENT CLUSTER
REPLACE

1992–94

Remove instrument cluster in numbered sequence, **Fig. 9,** noting the following:
1. When removing adapter, disconnect speedometer cable at transaxle end of cable.
2. To remove adapter, pull speedometer cable slightly toward vehicle interior, then release lock by turning adapter.
3. Reverse procedure to install.

1995

1. Remove instrument cluster bezel.
2. Remove screws holding cluster to dash.
3. Gently pull cluster outward enough to remove connectors and clips from rear of cluster, allowing it to be removed.
4. Reverse procedure to install.

RADIO
REPLACE

1992–94

Remove radio in numbered sequence, **Fig. 10,** noting the following:
1. Use plastic trim tool to pry lower part of radio panel out of console.
2. Remove side cover of console box, then remove amplifier.
3. Reverse procedure to install.

1995

1. Use plastic trim tool to pry lower part of radio panel out of console.
2. Remove floor console assembly.
3. Remove radio bracket.
4. Gently pull outward on radio assembly enough to remove connectors from rear of unit.
5. Reverse procedure to install.

WIPER MOTOR
REPLACE

1992–94

Front

Remove front windshield wiper motor and transmission in numbered sequence, **Fig. 11,** noting the following:
1. Mark position of wiper arms before removal.
2. When mounting wiper arms check identification marks. Dr indicates driver side, As indicates passenger side.
3. Install wiper arm to pivot shaft so when in stop position wiper blades will be 1 inch from deck garnish.
4. Reverse procedure to install.

Rear

Remove rear windshield wiper motor and transmission in numbered sequence, **Fig. 12,** noting the following:
1. Using plastic trim tool, remove clip mounting areas on back of liftgate, then remove trim.
2. Install grommet with arrow positioned up.
3. Install wiper arm to pivot shaft so that

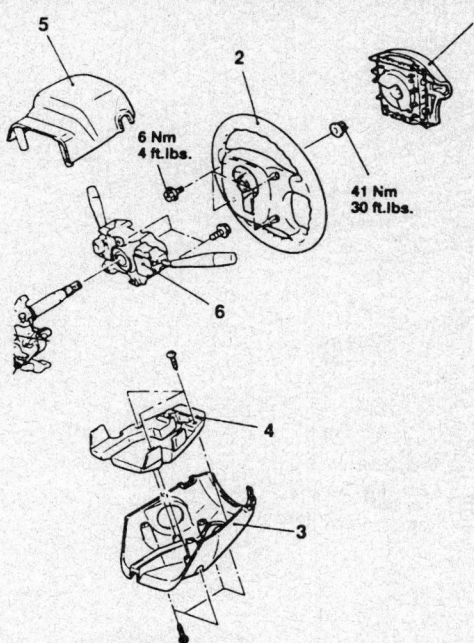

Removal steps

1. Air bag module
2. Steering wheel
3. Lower column cover
4. Column pad
5. Upper column cover
6. Clock spring and column switch assembly

Fig. 8 Steering wheel removal. 1995

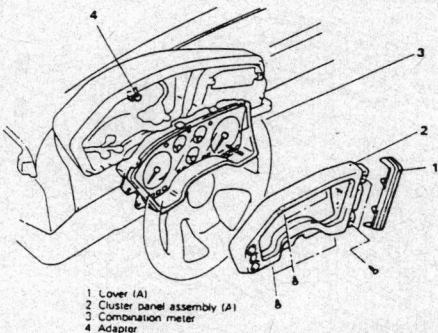

1. Cover (A)
2. Cluster panel assembly (A)
3. Combination meter
4. Adapter

Fig. 9 Instrument cluster replacement. 1992–94

blade will stop 1 inch from end liftgate glass.

4. Reverse procedure to install.

1995

Front

Remove front windshield wiper motor and transmission in numbered sequence, **Fig. 13**, noting the following:

1. Mark position of wiper arms before removal.
2. Reverse procedure to install

Rear

Remove rear windshield wiper motor and transmission in numbered sequence, **Fig. 14**, noting the following:

1. Mark position of wiper arm before removal.
2. Reverse procedure to install.

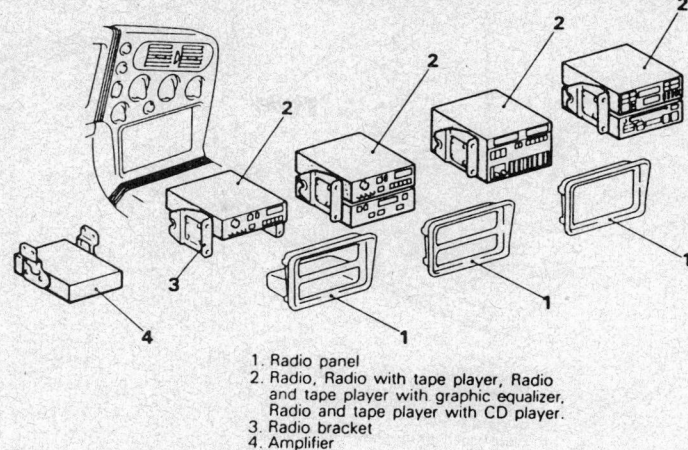

1. Radio panel
2. Radio, Radio with tape player, Radio and tape player with graphic equalizer, Radio and tape player with CD player.
3. Radio bracket
4. Amplifier

Fig. 10 Radio replacement. 1992–94

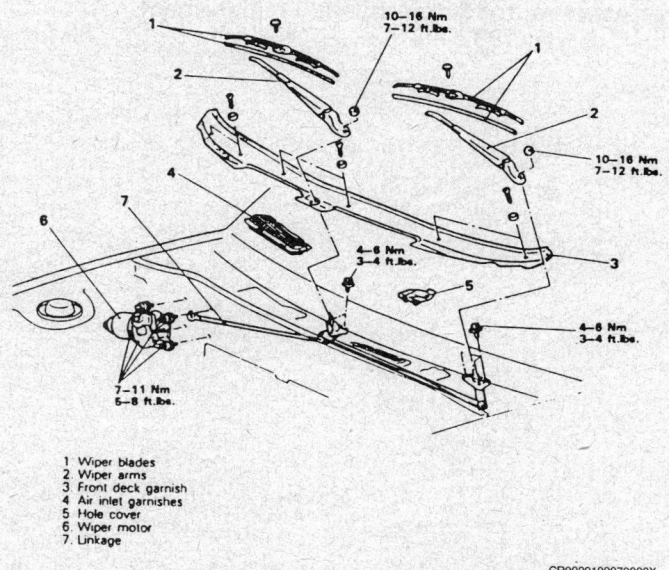

1. Wiper blades
2. Wiper arms
3. Front deck garnish
4. Air inlet garnishes
5. Hole cover
6. Wiper motor
7. Linkage

Fig. 11 Front wiper motor & transmission replacement. 1992–94

WIPER TRANSMISSION
REPLACE

Refer to "Wiper Motor, Replace" for procedure.

BLOWER MOTOR
REPLACE

1992–94

Remove blower motor in numbered sequence, **Fig. 15**, noting the following:

1. Clean blower case before installation.
2. Replace packing if cracked.
3. Reverse procedure to install.

1995

Remove blower motor in numbered sequence, **Fig. 16**, noting the following:

1. Clean blower case before installation.
2. Reverse procedure to install.

HEATER CORE
REPLACE

1992–94

Remove heater unit in numbered sequence, **Fig. 17**, noting the following:

1. Drain engine coolant.
2. Remove floor console as shown in **Fig. 18**.
3. Remove instrument panel as outlined under the "Dash Panel Service" section.
4. Remove evaporator assembly as outlined under "Evaporator Core, Replace."
5. To prevent bolts from falling into blower assembly, set air selection damper to outside air introduction.
6. Remove plate on heater unit, **Fig. 19**.
7. Pull heater core from heater unit. **Do not damage fin or pad part of heater core.**
8. Reverse procedure to install.

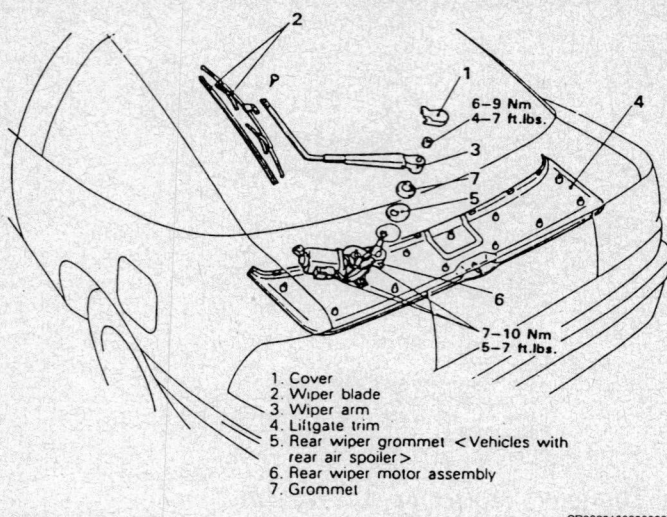

Fig. 12 Rear wiper motor & transmission replacement.
1992–94

1. Cover
2. Wiper blade
3. Wiper arm
4. Liftgate trim
5. Rear wiper grommet <Vehicles with rear air spoiler>
6. Rear wiper motor assembly
7. Grommet

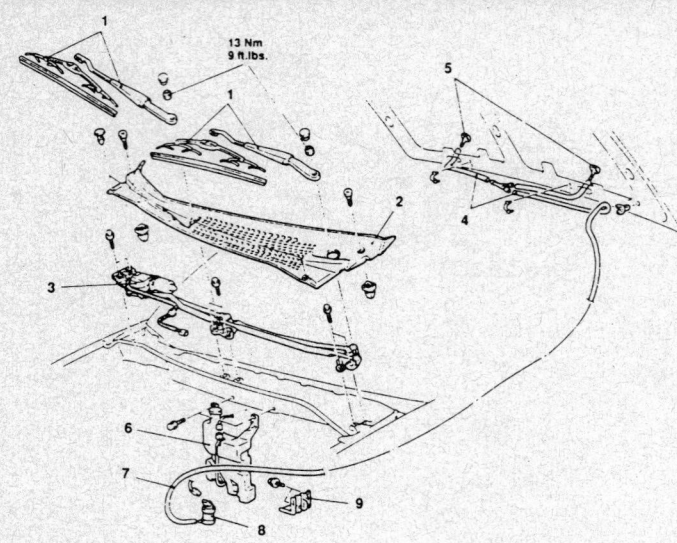

6–9 Nm
4–7 ft.lbs.

7–10 Nm
5–7 ft.lbs.

13 Nm
9 ft.lbs.

Motor and link assembly removal steps
1. Wiper arm and blade assembly
2. Front deck garnish
3. Motor and link assembly

Washer nozzle removal steps
4. Washer hose connection
5. Washer nozzle

Washer tank removal steps
6. Windshield washer tank
7. Washer hose
8. Washer motor
9. Washer tank bracket

Fig. 13 Front wiper motor & transmission replacement. 1995

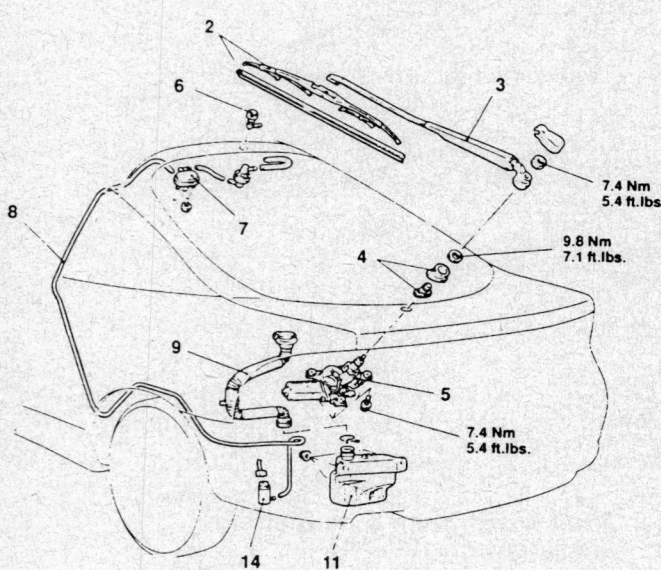

7.4 Nm
5.4 ft.lbs.

9.8 Nm
7.1 ft.lbs.

7.4 Nm
5.4 ft.lbs.

Rear wiper motor removal steps

2. Wiper blade
3. Wiper arm
4. Spacer assembly
• Liftgate lower trim

5. Rear wiper motor

Rear washer tank and hose removal steps
• Quarter upper trim (LH)
• Quarter lower trim (LH)

• Rear end trim
• Rear side trim
• Liftgate upper trim
6. Washer nozzle
7. Joint assembly
8. Tube assembly
9. Hose assembly
11. Rear washer tank
14. Rear washer motor

Fig. 14 Rear wiper motor & transmission replacement.
1995

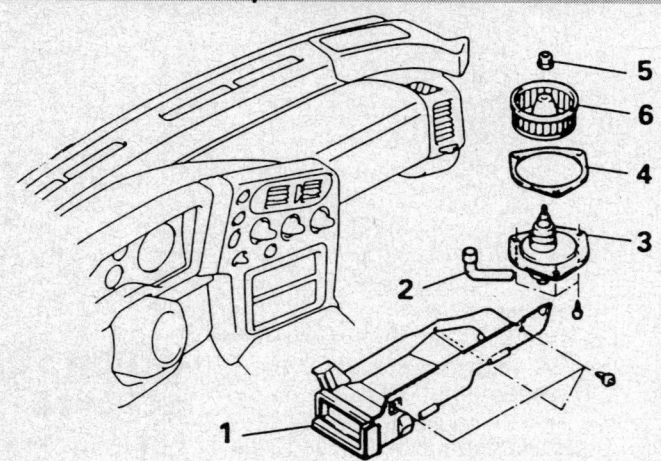

1. Shower duct R.H. <if so equipped>
2. Hose
3. Blower motor assembly
4. Packing
5. Fan installation nut
6. Fan

Fig. 15 Blower motor replacement. 1992–94

1995

Remove heater unit in numbered sequence, **Fig. 20**, noting the following:
1. Drain engine coolant.
2. Remove instrument panel as outlined in the "Dash Panel Service" section.
3. Reverse procedure to install. Refill engine coolant.

EVAPORATOR CORE
REPLACE

1992–94

Remove evaporator unit in numbered sequence, **Fig. 21**, noting the following:

1. Properly discharge refrigerant from A/C system as described under "Air Conditioning" section.
2. Remove floor console as shown in **Fig. 18**.
3. Remove instrument panel as outlined under the "Dash Panel Service" section.

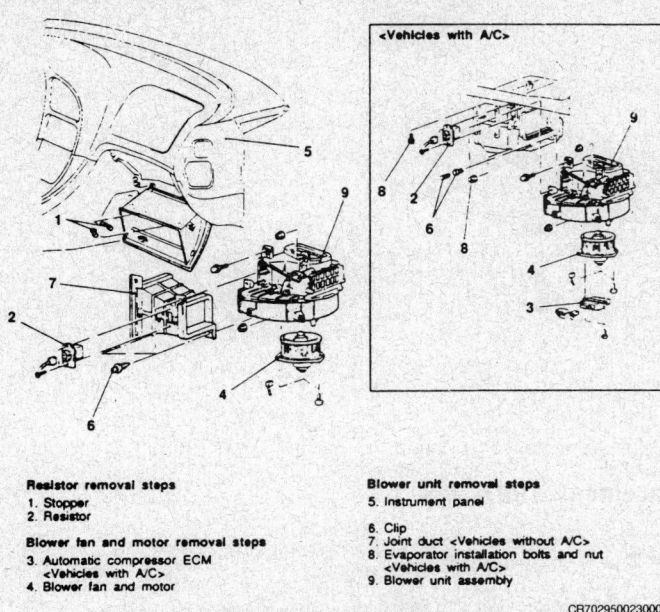

Resistor removal steps
1. Stopper
2. Resistor

Blower fan and motor removal steps
3. Automatic compressor ECM
   <Vehicles with A/C>
4. Blower fan and motor

Blower unit removal steps
5. Instrument panel
6. Clip
7. Joint duct <Vehicles without A/C>
8. Evaporator installation bolts and nut
   <Vehicles with A/C>
9. Blower unit assembly

CR7029500230000X

Fig. 16 Blower motor replacement. 1995

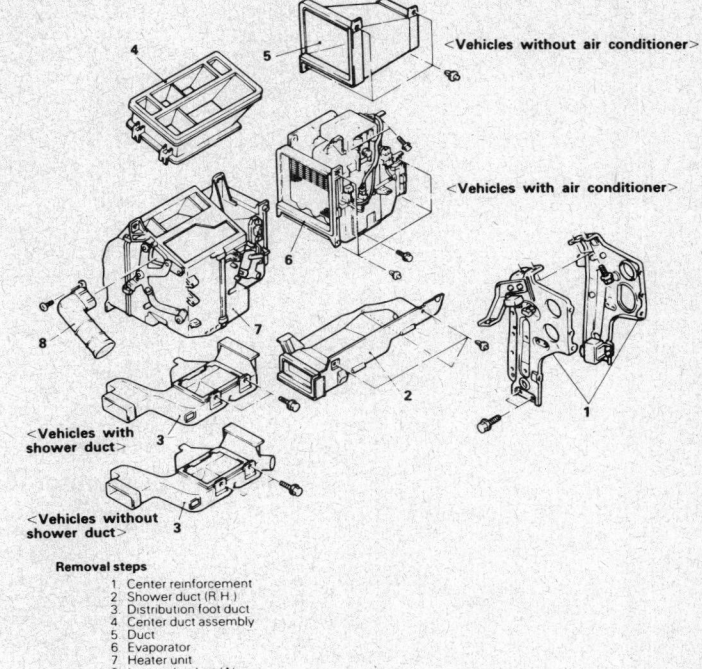

Removal steps
1. Center reinforcement
2. Shower duct (R.H.)
3. Distribution foot duct
4. Center duct assembly
5. Duct
6. Evaporator
7. Heater unit
8. Lap cooler duct (A)

CR7029100048000X

Fig. 17 Exploded view of heater unit. 1992–94

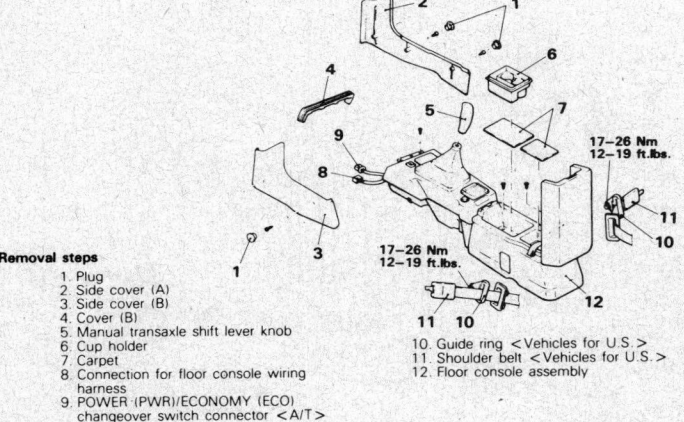

Removal steps
1. Plug
2. Side cover (A)
3. Side cover (B)
4. Cover (B)
5. Manual transaxle shift lever knob
6. Cup holder
7. Carpet
8. Connection for floor console wiring harness
9. POWER (PWR)/ECONOMY (ECO) changeover switch connector <A/T>

10. Guide ring <Vehicles for U.S.>
11. Shoulder belt <Vehicles for U.S.>
12. Floor console assembly

17–26 Nm
12–19 ft.lbs.

CR7029100049000X

Fig. 18 Floor console removal. 1992–94

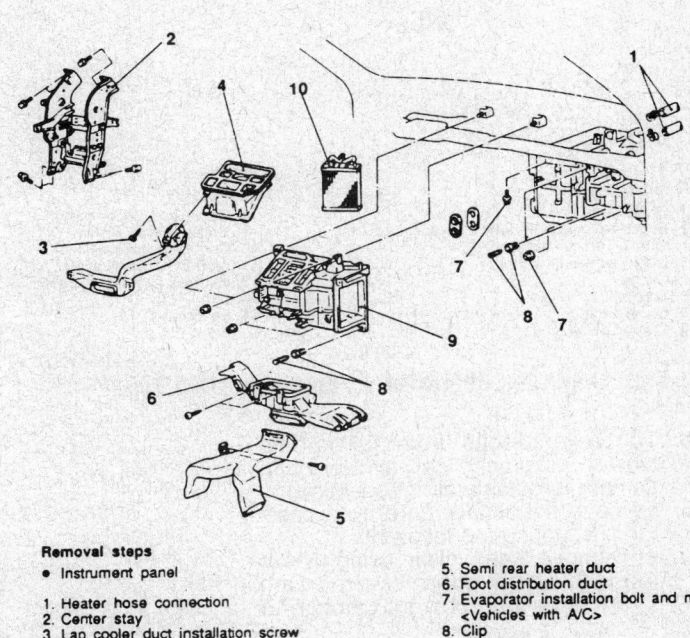

Removal steps
● Instrument panel

1. Heater hose connection
2. Center stay
3. Lap cooler duct installation screw
4. Center duct

5. Semi rear heater duct
6. Foot distribution duct
7. Evaporator installation bolt and nut
   <Vehicles with A/C>
8. Clip
9. Heater unit
10. Heater core

CR7029500231000X

Fig. 20 Exploded view of heater unit. 1995

Plate

CR7029100050000X

Fig. 19 Heater core plate removal. 1992–94

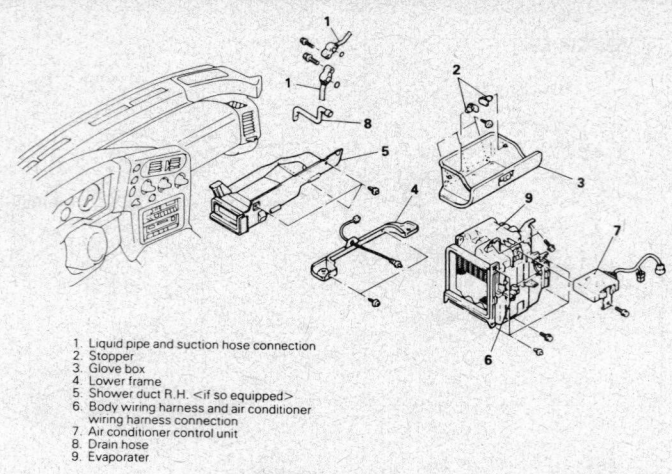

1. Liquid pipe and suction hose connection
2. Stopper
3. Glove box
4. Lower frame
5. Shower duct R.H. <if so equipped>
6. Body wiring harness and air conditioner wiring harness connection
7. Air conditioner control unit
8. Drain hose
9. Evaporator

CR7029100051000X

Fig. 21 Evaporator replacement. 1992–94

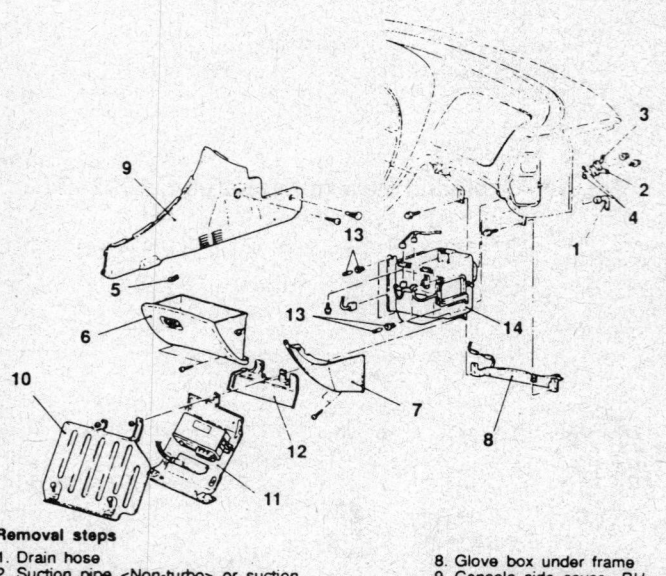

Removal steps

1. Drain hose
2. Suction pipe <Non-turbo> or suction hose <Turbo> connection
3. Liquid pipe connection
4. O-ring
5. Stopper
6. Glove box
7. Corner panel
8. Glove box under frame
9. Console side cover <RH>
10. Control unit cover
11. ABS-ECU bracket
12. Harness protector <Turbo>
13. Clip
14. Evaporator

CR7029500232000X

Fig. 23 Evaporator replacement. 1995

4. To prevent bolts from falling into blower assembly, set air selection damper to outside air introduction.
5. Remove evaporator core from case, **Fig. 22,** noting the following:
   a. Remove case clips using a flat blade screw driver covered with shop towel to prevent damage to case.
   b. Remove expansion valve by using two wrenches, one inlet side, one outlet side.
6. Pull evaporator core from evaporator case. **Do not damage fin or pad part of evaporator core.**
7. Reverse procedure to install, ensuring to properly recharge A/C system as described under "Air Conditioning" section.

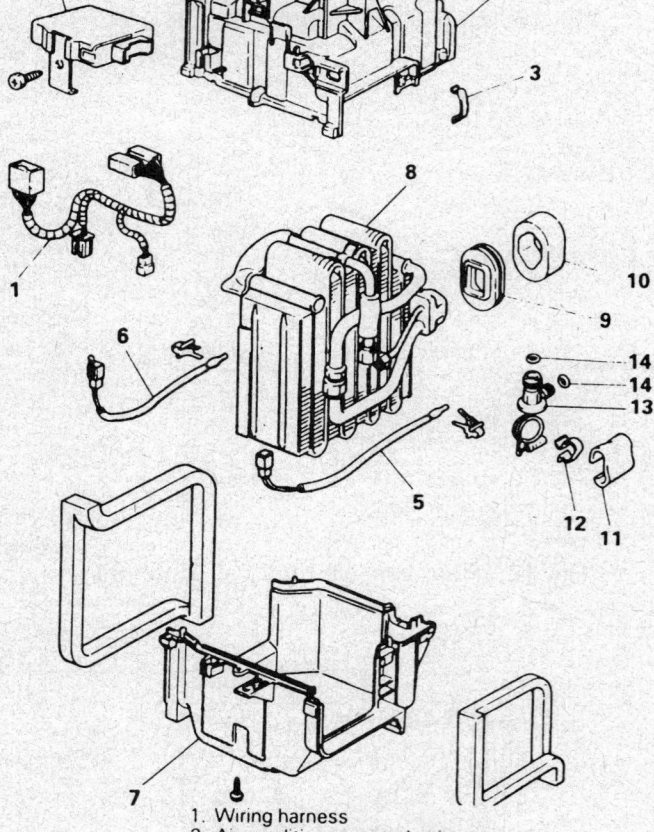

1. Wiring harness
2. Air conditioner control unit
3. Clips
4. Evaporater case (upper)
5. Air inlet sensor
6. Air thermo sensor
7. Evaporater case (lower)
8. Evaporater assembly
9. Grommet
10. Insulator
11. Rubber insulator
12. Clip
13. Expansion valve
14. O-ring

CR7029100052000X

Fig. 22 Exploded view of evaporator unit. 1992–94

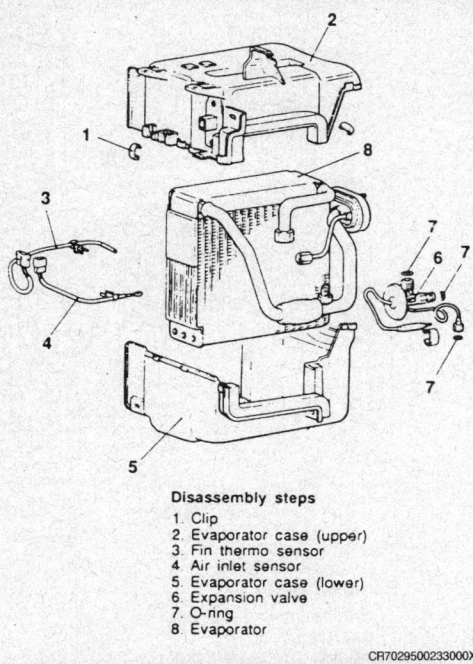

Disassembly steps
1. Clip
2. Evaporator case (upper)
3. Fin thermo sensor
4. Air inlet sensor
5. Evaporator case (lower)
6. Expansion valve
7. O-ring
8. Evaporator

CR7029500233000X

Fig. 24 Exploded view of evaporator unit. 1995

1995

Remove evaporator unit in numbered sequence, **Figs. 23 and 24**, noting the following:
1. Properly discharge refrigerant from A/C system as described in the "Air Conditioning" section.
2. Plug refrigerant lines to prevent air from mixing when disconnecting them.
3. **On models less turbo**, refill evaporator with 1.35 fl. oz. ND-OIL 8 compressor oil, or equivalent, before replacing evaporator.
4. **On models with turbo**, refill evaporator with 2.03 fl. oz. SUN PAG 56 compressor oil, or equivalent, before replacing evaporator.
5. Reverse procedure to install, ensuring to properly recharge A/C system as described in the "Air Conditioning" section.

Engines

NOTE: On Air Bag Equipped Models, Refer To "Air Bag System Precautions" Located In The Front Of This Manual For System Disarming & Arming Procedures.

INDEX

PRECAUTIONS

AIR BAG SYSTEMS

Refer to "Air Bag System Precautions" in the front of this manual for system disarming and arming procedures.

FUEL SYSTEM PRESSURE RELIEF

1. Disconnect fuel pump harness connector at fuel tank.
2. Start engine and let it run until it stalls, then turn ignition switch to off.
3. Reconnect fuel pump harness connector.

ENGINE MOUNT

REPLACE

EXCEPT ENGINE ROLL STOPPER
1992-94

Remove engine mount in numbered se-

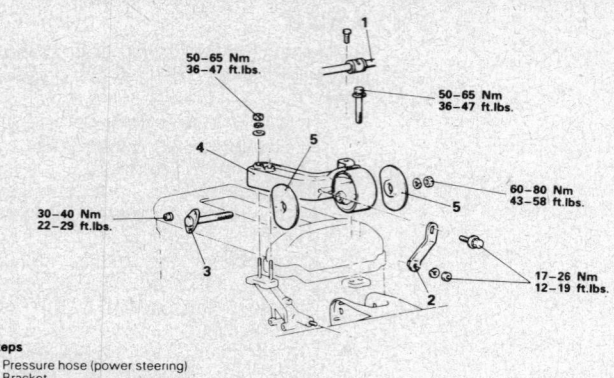

50–65 Nm
36–47 ft.lbs.

50–65 Nm
36–47 ft.lbs.

60–80 Nm
43–58 ft.lbs.

30–40 Nm
22–29 ft.lbs.

17–26 Nm
12–19 ft.lbs.

Removal steps
1. Pressure hose (power steering)
2. Bracket
3. Engine mount bracket and body connection bolt
4. Engine mount bracket
5. Mounting stopper

CR1069100340000X

Fig. 1 Engine mount assembly. 1992–94

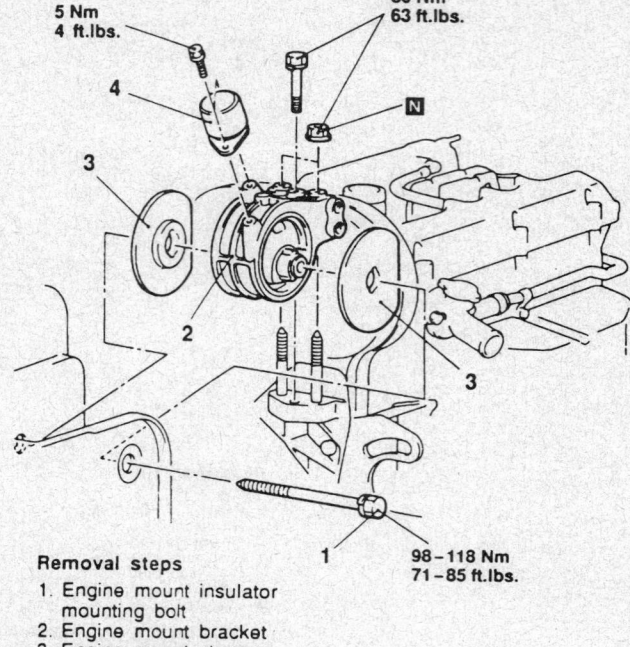

5 Nm
4 ft.lbs.

86 Nm
63 ft.lbs.

98–118 Nm
71–85 ft.lbs.

Removal steps
1. Engine mount insulator mounting bolt
2. Engine mount bracket
3. Engine mount stopper
4. Dynamic damper

CR1069500602000X

Fig. 2 Engine mount assembly. 1995

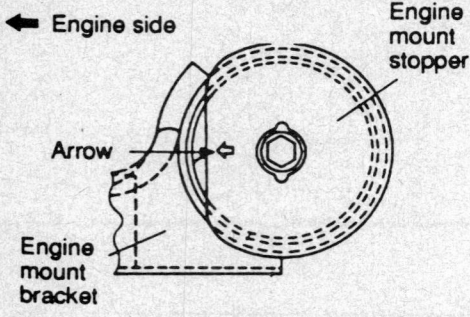

← Engine side

Engine mount stopper

Arrow

Engine mount bracket

CR1069500603000X

Fig. 3 Engine mount stopper installation. 1995

quence, **Fig. 1**, noting the following:
1. Slightly raise and support engine, removing weight of engine from mount.
2. **On 1.8L/4-107 engines,** bracket (2) is not used.
3. **On all engines,** inspect insulators for damage or cracks and replace as necessary.
4. Check brackets and replace if deformed or damaged.
5. When installing mounting stoppers, ensure arrow on stopper faces center of engine.
6. Reverse procedure to install.

1995

Remove engine mount in numbered sequence, **Fig. 2** noting the following:
1. Slightly raise and support engine, removing weight of engine from mount.
2. Inspect insulators for damage or cracks and replace as necessary.
3. Check brackets and replace if deformed or damaged.
4. When installing mounting stoppers, ensure arrow on stopper faces center of engine, **Fig. 3.**
5. Reverse procedure to install. Tighten to specifications.

ENGINE ROLL STOPPER

1992–94

Remove engine roll stoppers in numbered sequence, **Fig. 4**, noting the following:
1. Slightly raise and support engine, re-

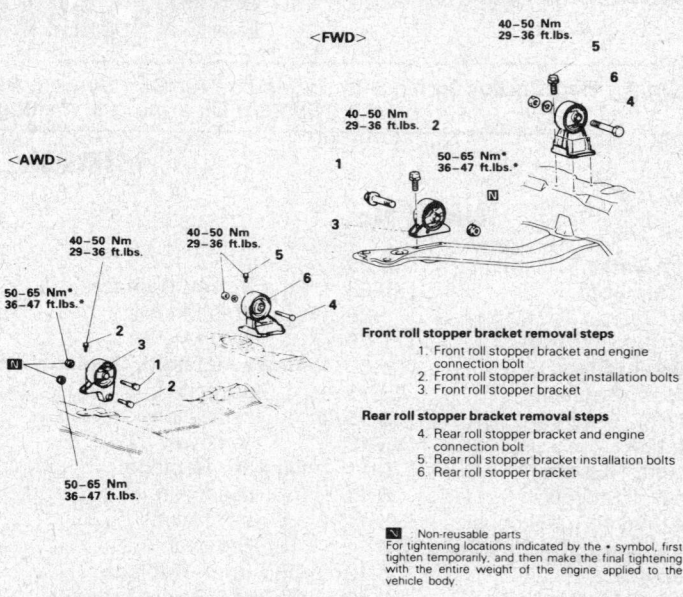

<FWD>

40–50 Nm
29–36 ft.lbs.

40–50 Nm
29–36 ft.lbs.

50–65 Nm*
36–47 ft.lbs.*

<AWD>

40–50 Nm
29–36 ft.lbs.

40–50 Nm
29–36 ft.lbs.

50–65 Nm*
36–47 ft.lbs.*

50–65 Nm
36–47 ft.lbs.

Front roll stopper bracket removal steps
1. Front roll stopper bracket and engine connection bolt
2. Front roll stopper bracket installation bolts
3. Front roll stopper bracket

Rear roll stopper bracket removal steps
4. Rear roll stopper bracket and engine connection bolt
5. Rear roll stopper bracket installation bolts
6. Rear roll stopper bracket

Ⓝ : Non-reusable parts
For tightening locations indicated by the * symbol, first tighten temporarily, and then make the final tightening with the entire weight of the engine applied to the vehicle body.

CR1069100341000X

Fig. 4 Engine roll stopper assemblies. 1992–94

moving weight of engine from mount.
2. Inspect insulators for damage or cracks and replace as necessary.
3. Inspect brackets and replace if deformed or damaged.
4. Discard and replace front roll stopper bracket installation nuts. When installing new nuts, first snug nuts to bolts, then lower engine and tighten to specifications once weight of engine is applied to mount.
5. When installing rear roll stopper bracket on models with automatic transmission, ensure distance between center hole and lower edge of

bracket is as shown in **Fig. 5.**
6. Install front roll stopper bracket with hole positioned as shown in **Fig. 6.**
7. When installing front roll stopper bracket, ensure distance between center hole of insulator and lower edge of bracket is as shown, **Fig. 7.**
8. Reverse procedure to install.

1995

Remove engine roll stoppers in numbered sequence, **Fig. 8**, noting the following:
1. Slightly raise and support engine, removing weight of engine from mount.

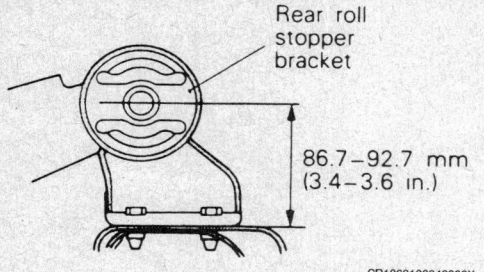

Fig. 5 Rear roll stopper bracket clearance. 1992–94

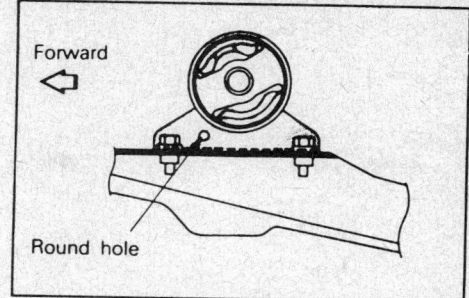

Fig. 6 Front roll stopper bracket installation. 1992–94

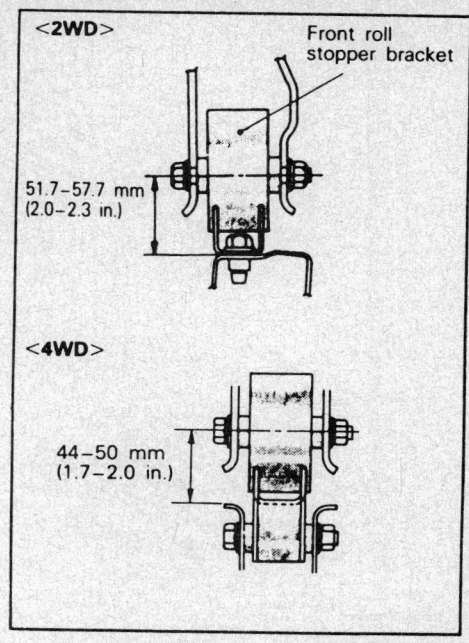

Fig. 7 Front roll stopper bracket insulator clearance check. 1992–94

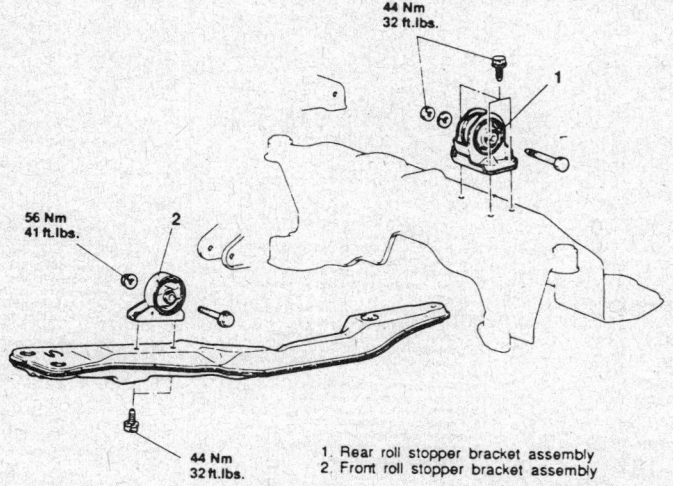

1. Rear roll stopper bracket assembly
2. Front roll stopper bracket assembly

Fig. 8 Engine roll stopper assemblies. 1995

2. Inspect insulators for damage or cracks and replace as necessary.
3. Inspect brackets and replace if deformed or damaged.
4. Inspect front roll stopper bracket assembly. If the dimension shown in **Fig. 9** is not 1.57-1.81 inches when the weight of the engine is on the body, replace the front roll stopper assembly.
5. When installing mounting stoppers, ensure arrow on stopper faces center of engine, **Fig. 3**.
6. Reverse procedure to install. Tighten to specifications.

ENGINE
REPLACE

1. Relieve fuel pressure as outlined under "Precautions."
2. Remove hood.
3. Drain coolant as follows:
   a. Place instrument panel temperature control lever in Hot position.
   b. Carefully remove radiator cap.
   c. Remove radiator drain plug.
4. Remove transaxle assembly.
5. Remove radiator as outlined uner "Radiator, Replace."
6. Remove engine in numbered sequence, **Figs. 10 through 12**, noting the following:
   a. Remove power steering pump

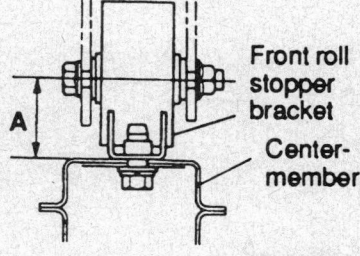

Fig. 9 Front roll stopper clearance. 1995

from bracket with hoses attached, then secure pump out of the way with a piece of wire.
   b. Remove air conditioner compressor from bracket with hoses attached, then secure compressor out of the way with a piece of wire.
   c. Using a suitable engine hoist, slightly raise engine, then remove engine mount bracket.
7. Reverse procedure to install.

INTAKE MANIFOLD
REPLACE

REMOVAL

Remove intake manifold in numbered sequence, **Figs. 13 and 14**, noting the following:

1. Drain coolant as follows:
   a. Place instrument panel temperature control lever in Hot position.
   b. Carefully remove radiator cap.
   c. Remove radiator drain plug.
2. **On 1.8L/4-107 engines,** when removing upper radiator hose, mark hose clamp in relation to hose for assembly reference.
3. **On all models,** before disconnecting high pressure fuel line, release fuel pressure as outlined under "Precautions."
4. Remove delivery pipe, fuel injector and regulator as an assembly.

INSPECTION

Inspect intake manifold and air intake plenum (if equipped) as follows:
1. Check for damage, cracks or defects.
2. Ensure coolant and jet air passages are clear.
3. Check installation surfaces with a straightedge. Replace if deflection exceeds .012 inch.

INSTALLATION

Reverse removal procedure to install. On 2.0L/4-122 engines, when installing throttle body, refer to bolt length chart, **Fig. 15**.

EXHAUST MANIFOLD
REPLACE

Remove exhaust manifold in numbered sequence, referring to **Fig. 16** on 1.8L/4-107 engines, **Fig. 17** on non-turbocharged 2.0L/4-122 engines and **Fig. 18** on turbocharged 2.0L/4-122 engines, noting the following:
1. **On 2.0L/4-122 turbocharged engine,** drain engine oil and coolant prior to removing exhaust manifold. To

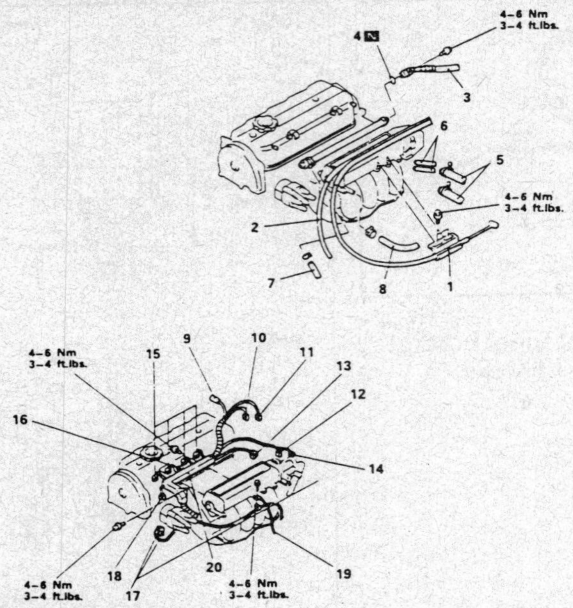

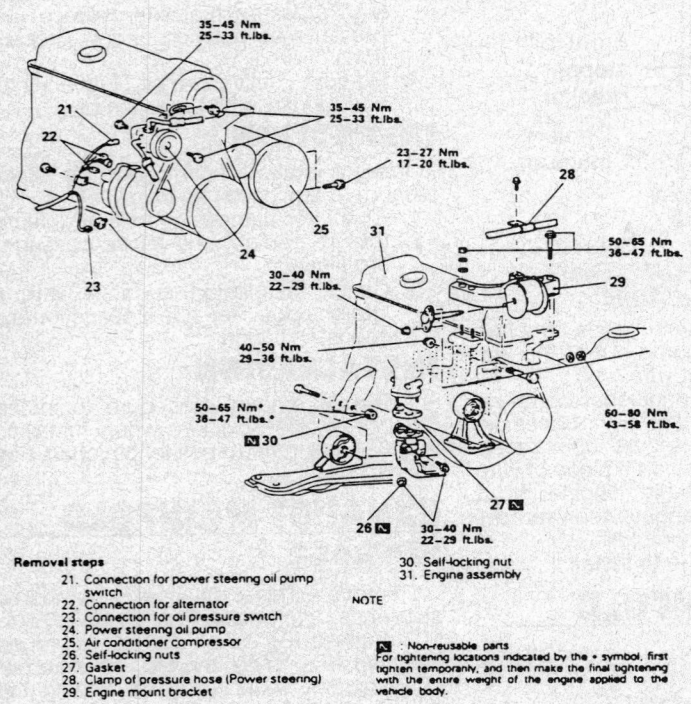

Removal steps

1. Connection for accelerator cable or throttle cable
2. Connection for accelerator cable (Auto-cruise control)
3. Connection for fuel high pressure hose
4. O-ring
5. Connection for heater hoses
6. Connection for vacuum hoses
7. Connection for fuel return hose
8. Connection for brake booster vacuum hose
9. Connection for oxygen sensor
10. Connection for engine coolant temperature gauge unit
11. Connection for engine coolant temperature sensor
12. Connection for ISC
13. Connection for TPS
14. Connection for MPS
15. Connection for fuel injectors
16. Connection for EGR temperature sensor
17. Connection for distributor
18. Connection for CRC filter
19. Connection for ground cable
20. Control wiring harness

N : Non-reusable parts

CR1069100346010X

Fig. 10   Engine assembly (Part 1 of 2). 1.8L/4-107 engine

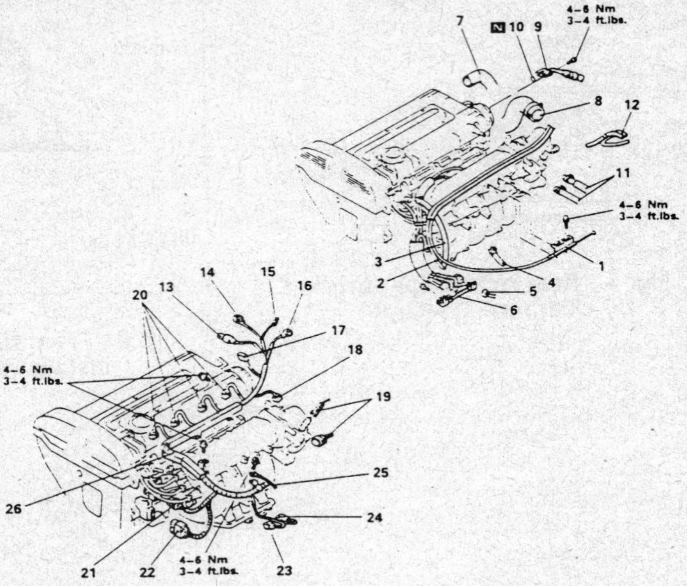

Removal steps

21. Connection for power steering oil pump switch
22. Connection for alternator
23. Connection for oil pressure switch
24. Power steering oil pump
25. Air conditioner compressor
26. Self-locking nuts
27. Gasket
28. Clamp of pressure hose (Power steering)
29. Engine mount bracket
30. Self-locking nut
31. Engine assembly

NOTE

N : Non-reusable parts
For tightening locations indicated by the • symbol, first tighten temporarily, and then make the final tightening with the entire weight of the engine applied to the vehicle body.

CR1069100346020X

Fig. 10   Engine assembly (Part 2 of 2). 1.8L/4-107 engine

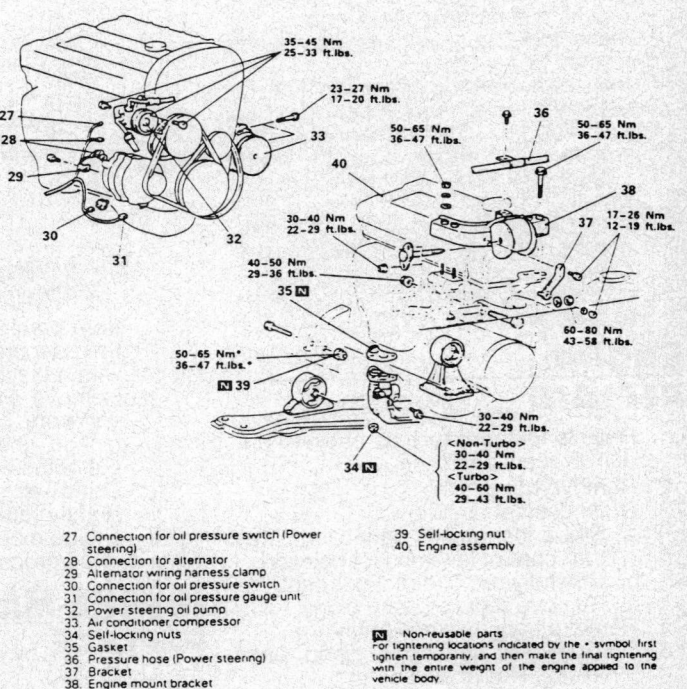

Removal steps

1. Connection for accelerator cable or throttle cable
2. Connection for accelerator cable (Auto-cruise control)
3. Connection for fuel return hose
4. Connection for brake booster vacuum hose
5. Connection for solenoid valve (Turbo)
6. Solenoid valve bracket (Turbo)
7. Connection for air hose A (Turbo)
8. Connection for air hose C (Turbo)
9. Connection for fuel high pressure hose
10. O-ring
11. Connection for heater hoses
12. Connection for vacuum hoses
13. Connection for oxygen sensor
14. Connection for engine coolant temperature sensor
15. Connection for engine coolant temperature gauge unit
16. Connection for engine coolant temperature switch (Air conditioner)
17. Connection for crank angle sensor
18. Connection for TPS
19. Connection for ISC and idle switch
20. Connection for fuel injectors
21. Connection for ignition coil
22. Connection for power transistor
23. Connection for knock sensor (Turbo)
24. Connection for EGR temperature sensor (California vehicles only)
25. Connection for ground cable
26. Control wiring harness

N : Non-reusable parts

CR1069100347010X

Fig. 11   Engine assembly (Part 1 of 2). 2.0L/4-122 non-turbo engine

27. Connection for oil pressure switch (Power steering)
28. Connection for alternator
29. Alternator wiring harness clamp
30. Connection for oil pressure switch
31. Connection for oil pressure gauge unit
32. Power steering oil pump
33. Air conditioner compressor
34. Self-locking nuts
35. Gasket
36. Pressure hose (Power steering)
37. Bracket
38. Engine mount bracket
39. Self-locking nut
40. Engine assembly

N : Non-reusable parts
For tightening locations indicated by the • symbol, first tighten temporarily, and then make the final tightening with the entire weight of the engine applied to the vehicle body.

CR1069100347020X

Fig. 11   Engine assembly (Part 2 of 2). 2.0L/4-122 non-turbo engine

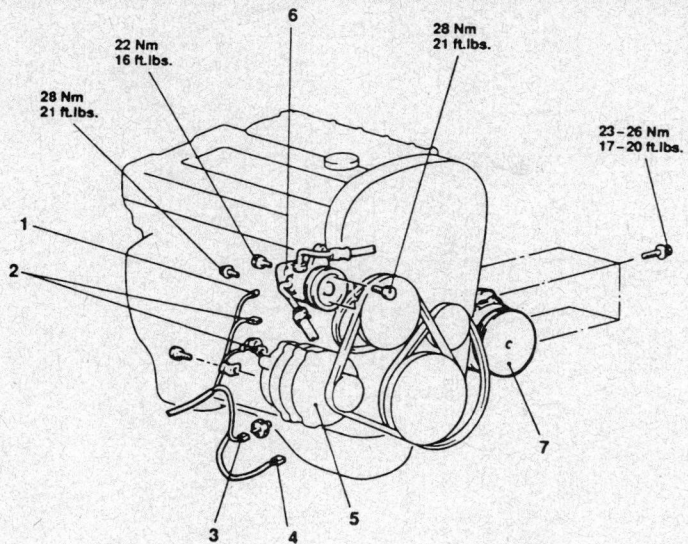

Removal steps

1. Power steering pressure switch connector
2. Generator connectors
3. Oil pressure switch connector
4. Oil pressure gauge unit connector
5. Generator
6. Power steering pump connection
7. A/C compressor connection

CR1069500606010X

Fig. 12 Engine assembly (Part 1 of 2). 2.0L/4-122 turbo engine

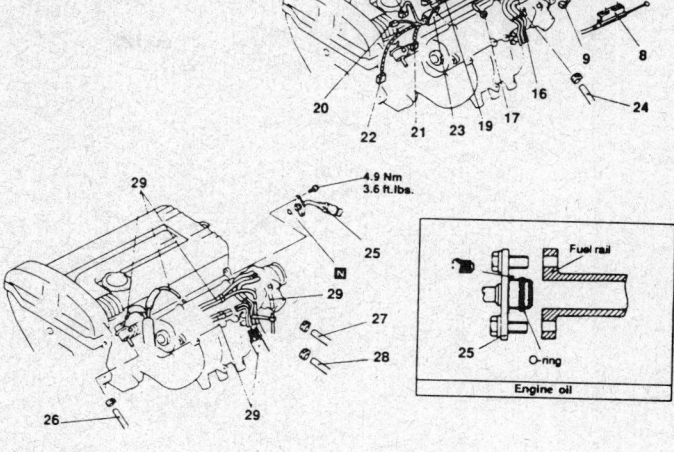

8. Accelerator cable connection
9. Idle air control motor connector
10. Knock sensor connector
11. Heated oxygen sensor connector
12. Engine coolant temperature gauge unit connector
13. Engine coolant temperature sensor connector
14. Ignition power transistor connector
15. Throttle position sensor connector
16. Condenser connector
17. Manifold differential pressure sensor connector

18. Injector connectors
19. Ignition coil connector
20. Camshaft position sensor connector
21. Crankshaft position sensor connector
22. Air conditioning compressor connector
23. Control wiring harness
24. Brake booster vacuum hose connection
25. High-pressure fuel hose connection
26. Fuel return hose connection
27. Water hose A connection
28. Water hose B connection
29. Vacuum hoses connection

CR1069500606020X

Fig. 12 Engine assembly (Part 2 of 2). 2.0L/4-122 turbo engine

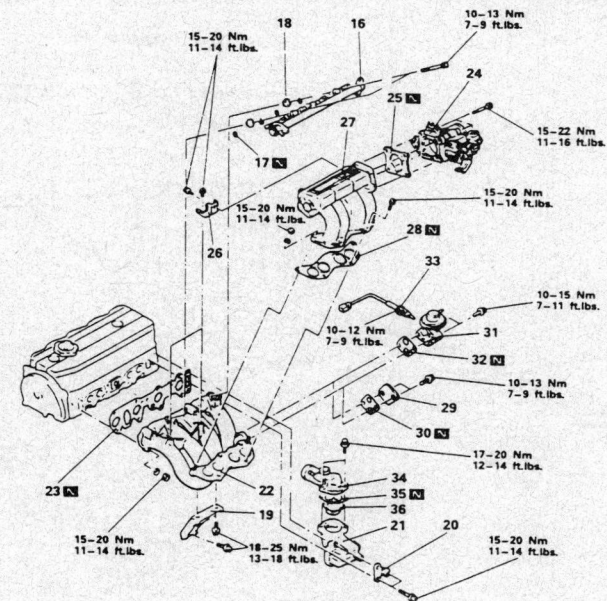

Removal steps

16. Delivery pipe, fuel injector and pressure regulator
17. Insulator
18. Insulator
19. Intake manifold stay
20. Engine hanger
21. Thermostat housing
22. Intake manifold
23. Intake manifold gasket
24. Throttle body assembly
25. Gasket
26. Air intake plenum stay
27. Air intake plenum
28. Air intake plenum gasket

29. Cover <Vehicles for Federal and Canada>
30. Gasket <Vehicles for Federal>
31. EGR valve <Vehicles for California>
32. EGR gasket <Vehicles for California>
33. EGR temperature sensor <Vehicles for California>
34. Water outlet fitting
35. Gasket
36. Thermostat

N Non-reusable parts

CR1059100060010X

Fig. 13 Intake manifold assembly (Part 1 of 2). 1.8L/4-107 engine

drain coolant, proceed as follows:
- a. Place instrument panel temperature control lever in Hot position.
- b. Carefully remove radiator cap.
- c. Remove radiator drain plug.

2. **On all models**, use oxygen sensor socket No. MD998703 or equivalent to remove oxygen sensor.

3. **On 2.0L/4-122 turbocharged engine**, leave power steering hoses attached when disconnecting power steering pump. Position pump out of the way and secure with a piece of wire.

4. **On all models**, reverse procedure to install. On 2.0L/4-122 turbocharged engine, apply machine oil to inner surface pipe flare prior to installing water pipe (18), **Fig. 18.**

CYLINDER HEAD
REPLACE

1.8L/4-107
Removal

Remove cylinder head in numbered sequence, **Fig. 19**, noting the following:

1. Before disconnecting high pressure fuel line, release fuel pressure as outlined under "Precautions."

2. Before removing upper radiator hose, mark hose clamp in relation to hose for assembly reference, then drain coolant as follows:
- a. Place instrument panel temperature control lever in Hot position.

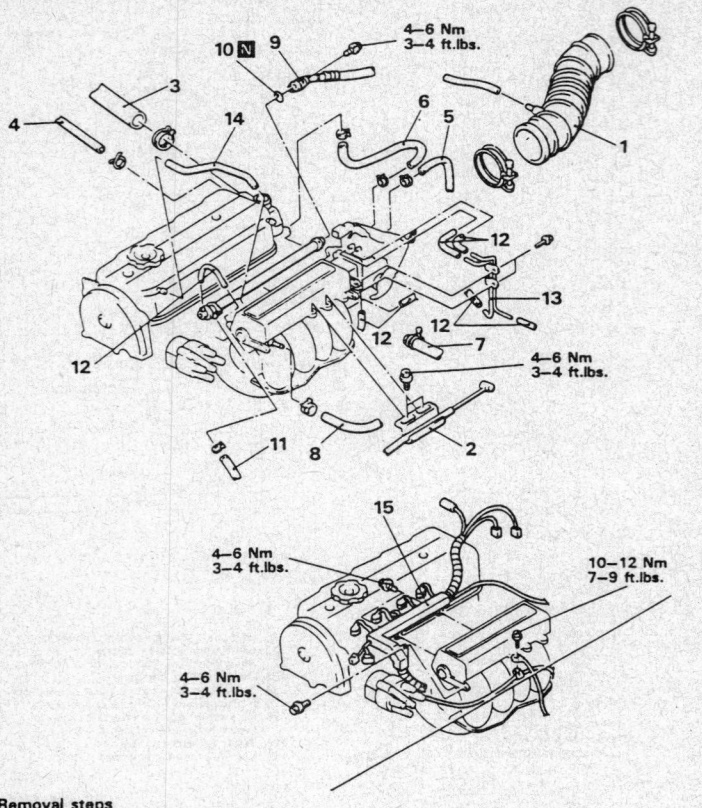

Removal steps
1. Air intake hose
2. Connection for accelerator cable
3. Connection for radiator upper hose
4. Connection for overflow tube
5. Connection for water by-pass hose
6. Water hose
7. Connection for heater hose
8. Connection for brake booster vacuum hose
9. Connection for fuel high pressure hose
10. O-ring
11. Connection for fuel return hose
12. Connection for vacuum hoses
13. Vacuum pipe
14. PCV hose
15. Connection for control harness

N : Non-reusable parts

CR1059100060020X

**Fig. 13   Intake manifold assembly (Part 2 of 2).
1.8L/4-107 engine**

b. Carefully remove radiator cap.
c. Remove radiator drain plug.
3. To remove engine mount bracket, slightly raise and support engine, removing weight of engine from mount.
4. Remove camshaft sprocket as follows:
   a. Turn crankshaft clockwise and align timing marks, **Fig. 20. Do not turn crankshaft counterclockwise.**
   b. Remove camshaft sprocket with timing belt attached, then lay sprocket and belt on timing belt front lower cover. **Do not rotate crankshaft once camshaft sprocket is removed.**
5. Using cylinder head bolt wrench No. TW-10B or equivalent, remove cylinder head bolts in sequence as shown in **Fig. 21.**

Installation

Reverse removal procedure to install, noting the following:

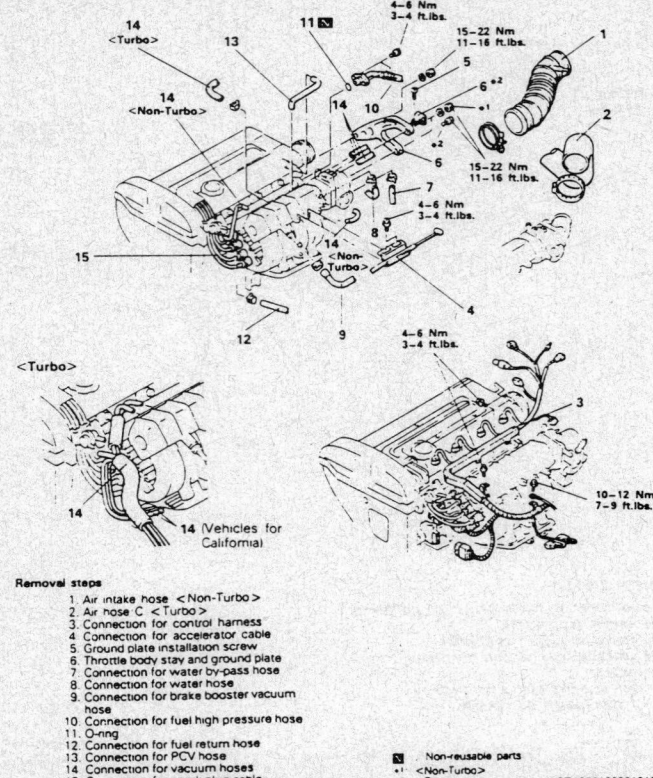

Removal steps
1. Air intake hose <Non-Turbo>
2. Air hose C <Turbo>
3. Connection for control harness
4. Connection for accelerator cable
5. Ground plate installation screw
6. Throttle body stay and ground plate
7. Connection for water by-pass hose
8. Connection for water hose
9. Connection for brake booster vacuum hose
10. Connection for fuel high pressure hose
11. O-ring
12. Connection for fuel return hose
13. Connection for PCV hose
14. Connection for vacuum hoses
15. Connection for spark plug cable

N : Non-reusable parts
*1 <Non-Turbo>
*2 <Turbo>

CR1059100061010X

**Fig. 14   Intake manifold assembly (Part 1 of 2).
2.0L/4-122 engine**

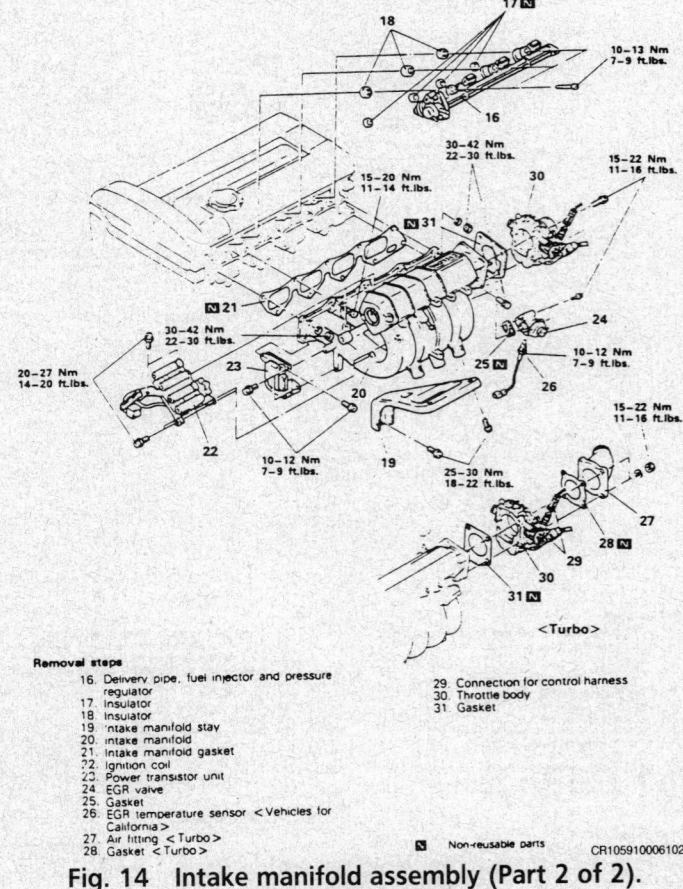

Removal steps
16. Delivery pipe, fuel injector and pressure regulator
17. Insulator
18. Insulator
19. Intake manifold stay
20. Intake manifold
21. Intake manifold gasket
22. Ignition coil
23. Power transistor unit
24. EGR valve
25. Gasket
26. EGR temperature sensor <Vehicles for California>
27. Air fitting <Turbo>
28. Gasket <Turbo>
29. Connection for control harness
30. Throttle body
31. Gasket

N : Non-reusable parts

CR1059100061020X

**Fig. 14   Intake manifold assembly (Part 2 of 2).
2.0L/4-122 engine**

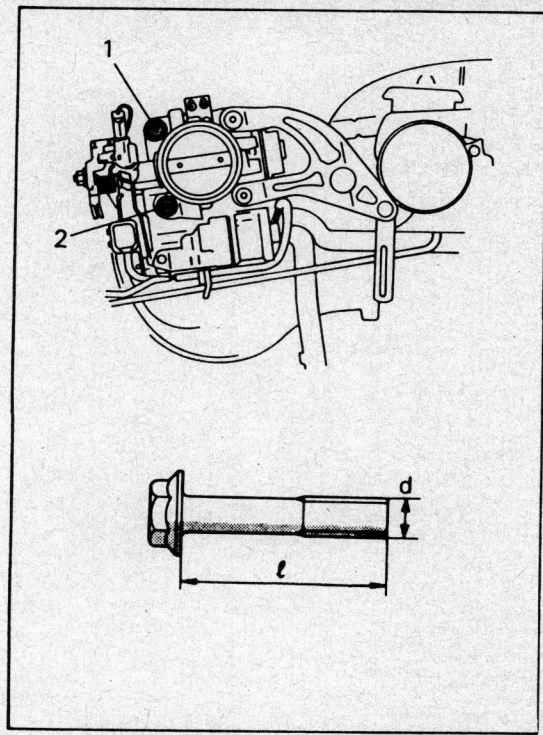

No.	d × ℓ mm (in.)
1	8 × 30 (.31 × 1.18)
2	8 × 55 (.31 × 2.16)

CR1059100062000X

Fig. 15 Throttle body attaching bolts. 2.0L/4-122 engine

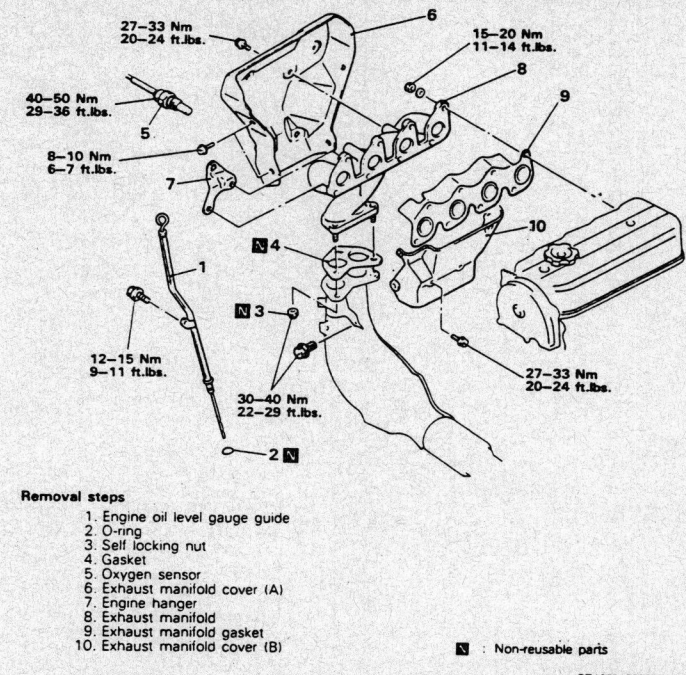

Removal steps

1. Engine oil level gauge guide
2. O-ring
3. Self locking nut
4. Gasket
5. Oxygen sensor
6. Exhaust manifold cover (A)
7. Engine hanger
8. Exhaust manifold
9. Exhaust manifold gasket
10. Exhaust manifold cover (B)

Ⓝ : Non-reusable parts

CR1079100006000X

Fig. 16 Exhaust manifold removal. 1.8L/4-107 engine

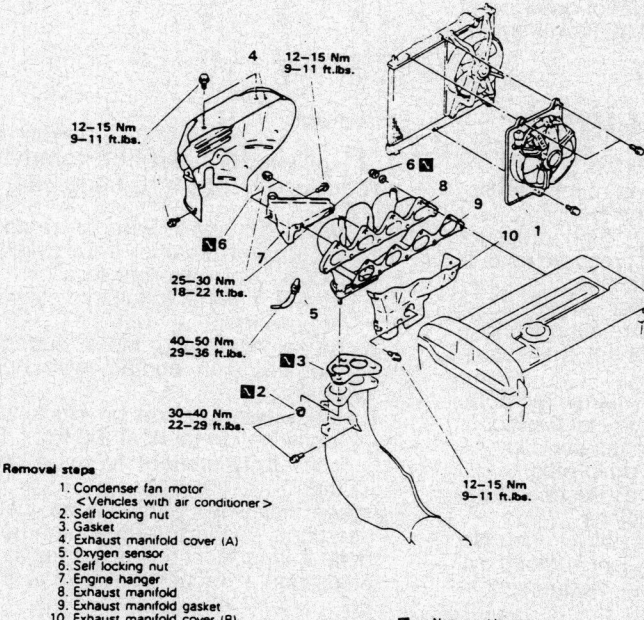

Removal steps

1. Condenser fan motor
   <Vehicles with air conditioner>
2. Self locking nut
3. Gasket
4. Exhaust manifold cover (A)
5. Oxygen sensor
6. Self locking nut
7. Engine hanger
8. Exhaust manifold
9. Exhaust manifold gasket
10. Exhaust manifold cover (B)

Ⓝ : Non-reusable parts

CR1079100007000X

Fig. 17 Exhaust manifold removal. 2.0L/4-122 non-turbo engine

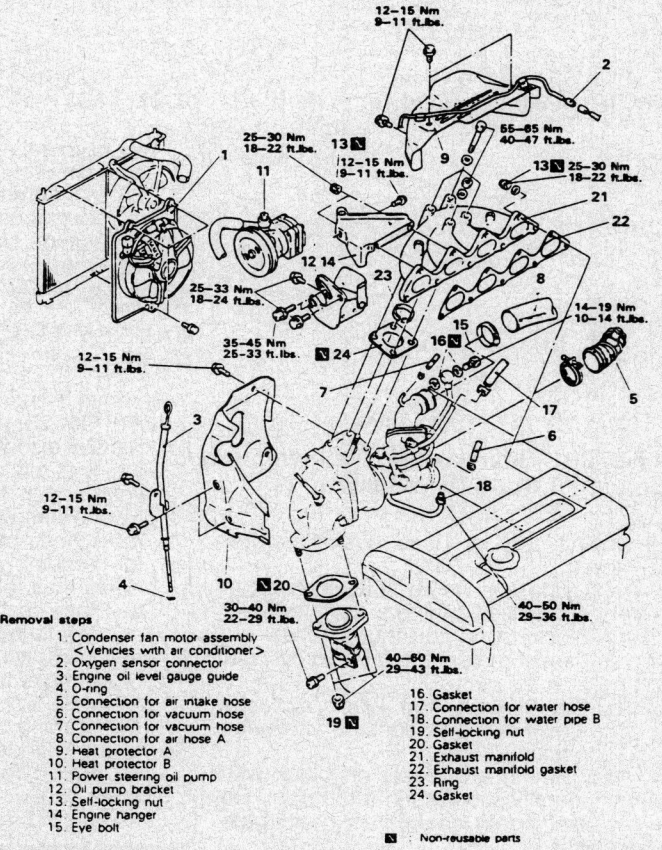

Removal steps

1. Condenser fan motor assembly
   <Vehicles with air conditioner>
2. Oxygen sensor connector
3. Engine oil level gauge guide
4. O-ring
5. Connection for air intake hose
6. Connection for vacuum hose
7. Connection for vacuum hose
8. Connection for air hose A
9. Heat protector A
10. Heat protector B
11. Power steering oil pump
12. Oil pump bracket
13. Self-locking nut
14. Engine hanger
15. Eye bolt
16. Gasket
17. Connection for water hose
18. Connection for water pipe B
19. Self-locking nut
20. Gasket
21. Exhaust manifold
22. Exhaust manifold gasket
23. Ring
24. Gasket

Ⓝ : Non-reusable parts

CR1079100008000X

Fig. 18 Exhaust manifold removal. 2.0L/4-122 turbo engine

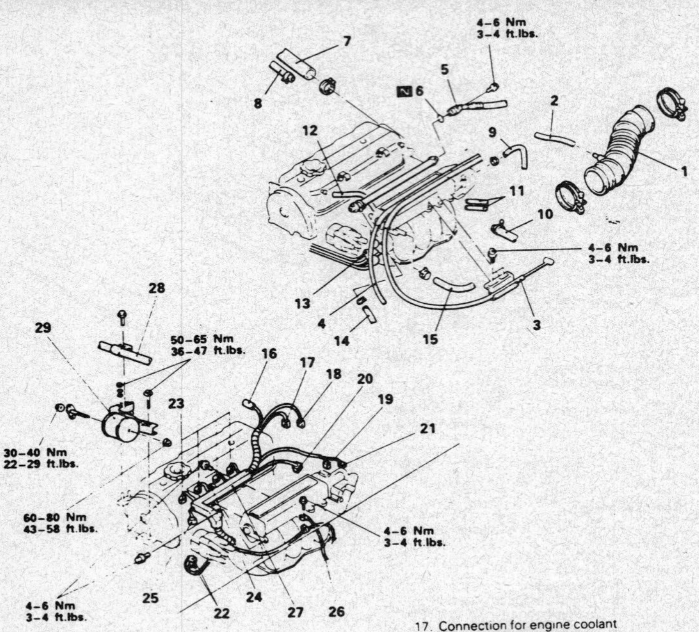

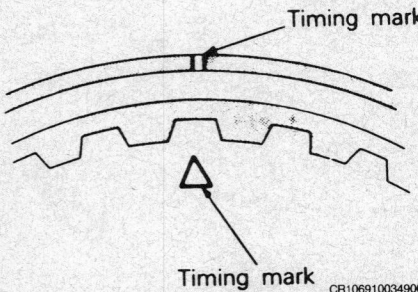

Fig. 19   Cylinder head removal (Part 1 of 2). 1.8L/4-107 engine

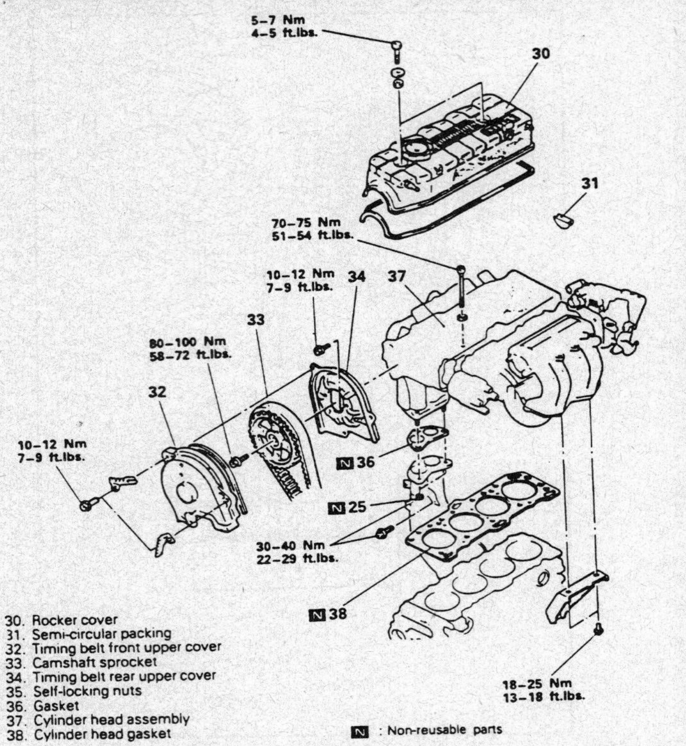

Removal steps

1. Air intake hose
2. Connection for breather hose
3. Connection for accelerator cable or throttle cable
4. Connection for accelerator cable (Auto-cruise control)
5. Connection for fuel high pressure hose
6. O-ring
7. Connection for radiator upper hose
8. Connection for water hose
9. Connection for water by-pass hose
10. Connection for heater hose
11. Connection for vacuum hose
12. Connection for PCV hose
13. Connection for spark plug cable
14. Connection for fuel return hose
15. Connection for brake booster vacuum hose
16. Connection for oxygen sensor
17. Connection for engine coolant temperature gauge unit
18. Connection for engine coolant temperature sensor
19. Connection for ISC
20. Connection for TPS
21. Connection for MPS
22. Connection for distributor
23. Connection for injector
24. Connection for EGR temperature sensor (California vehicles only)
25. Connection for CRC filter
26. Connection for ground cable
27. Control wiring harness
28. Clamp for pressure hose (Power steering)
29. Engine mounting bracket

CR1069100348010X

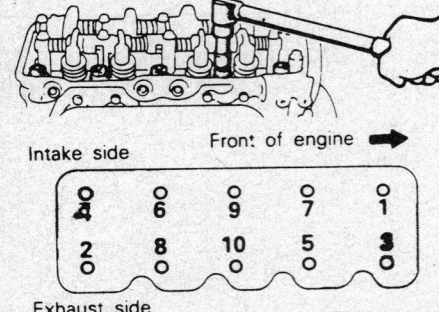

N : Non-reusable parts

Fig. 19   Cylinder head removal (Part 2 of 2). 1.8L/4-107 engine

30. Rocker cover
31. Semi-circular packing
32. Timing belt front upper cover
33. Camshaft sprocket
34. Timing belt rear upper cover
35. Self-locking nuts
36. Gasket
37. Cylinder head assembly
38. Cylinder head gasket

CR1069100348020X

Timing mark

Fig. 20   Timing mark alignment. 1.8L/4-107 engine

CR1069100349000X

1. Install cylinder head gasket as follows:
   a. Using a suitable scraper, remove old gasket material from cylinder block, using care not to allow old gasket material to fall into cylinder or passages.
   b. Clean head and block surfaces which come in contact with head gasket.
   c. Place head gasket on block with identification mark at top front. **Do not apply sealant to head gasket.**
2. When installing cylinder head, tighten head bolts to specifications in two or three steps and in order as shown in **Fig. 22.**
3. When installing semi-circular packing,

apply liberal amount of gasket sealant onto circumference of packing.
4. When installing high pressure fuel line (5), apply small amount of gasoline to hose union. Use care to avoid damaging O-ring.

2.0L/4-122
EXCEPT 1995 NON-TURBO
Removal

Remove cylinder head in numbered sequence, Fig. 23, noting the following:
1. Before disconnecting high pressure fuel line, release fuel pressure as outlined under "Precautions."
2. Before removing upper radiator hose, mark hose clamp in relation to hose for assembly reference, then drain coolant as follows:
   a. Place instrument panel temperature control lever in Hot position.
   b. Carefully remove radiator cap.
   c. Remove radiator drain plug.
3. Remove timing belt as described under "Timing Belt, Replace."
4. Using cylinder head bolt wrench No. MD998051 or equivalent, remove cylinder head bolts in sequence as shown in **Fig. 24.**

Installation

Reverse removal procedure to install, noting the following:
1. Install cylinder head gasket as follows:

Fig. 21   Cylinder head bolt removal sequence. 1.8L/4-107 engine

CR1069100350000X

a. Using a suitable scraper, remove old gasket material from cylinder block, using care not to allow old gasket material to fall into cylinder or passages.
b. Clean head and block surfaces that come in contact with head gasket.
c. Place head gasket on block with identification mark at top front. **Do not apply sealant to head gasket.**
2. When installing cylinder head, install head bolt washers, then tighten head bolts to specifications in two or three steps and in order as shown in **Fig. 25.**
3. When installing semi-circular packing, apply liberal amount of gasket sealant onto circumference of packing.
4. When installing rocker cover, apply gasket sealant to area as shown in **Fig. 26.**

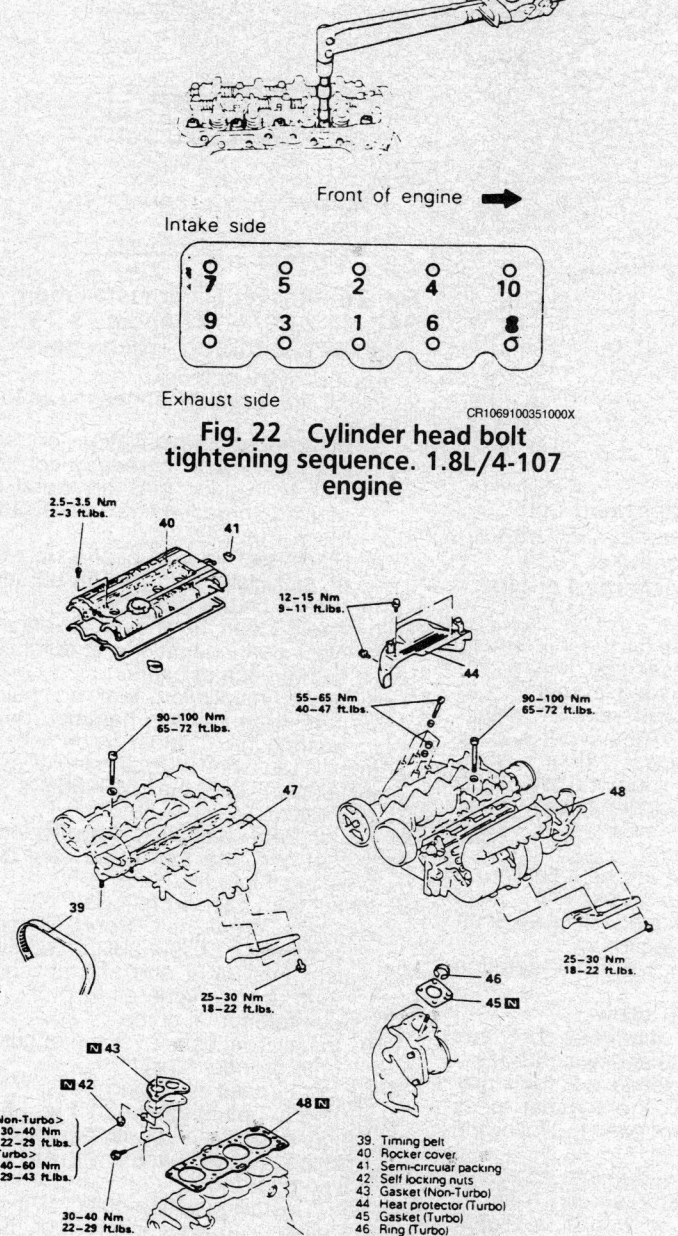

Front of engine →

Intake side

7	5	2	4	10
9	3	1	6	8

Exhaust side

CR1069100351000X

Fig. 22 Cylinder head bolt tightening sequence. 1.8L/4-107 engine

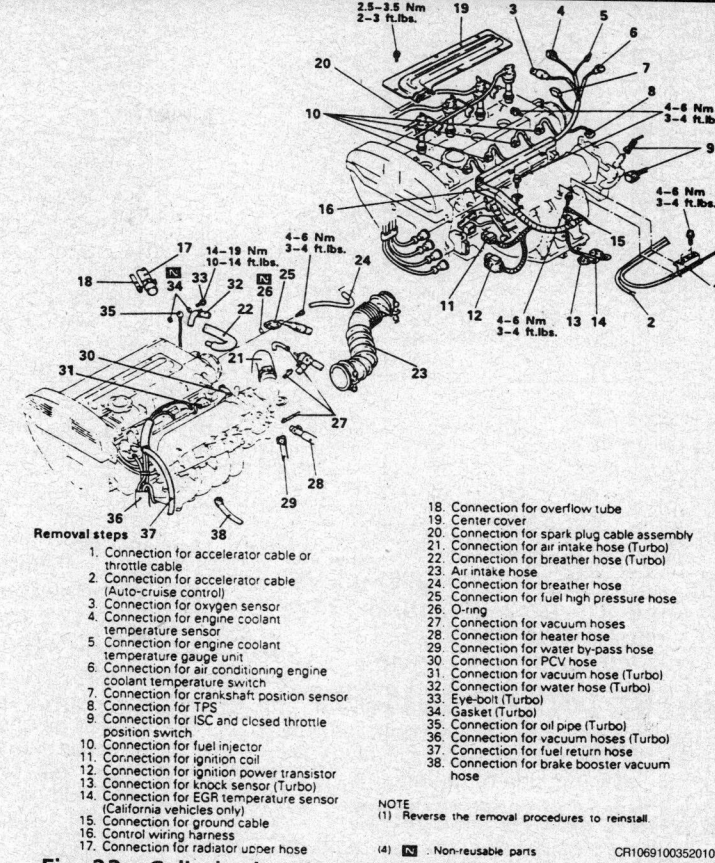

2.5–3.5 Nm 2–3 ft.lbs.
4–6 Nm 3–4 ft.lbs.
14–19 Nm 10–14 ft.lbs.
4–6 Nm 3–4 ft.lbs.
4–6 Nm 3–4 ft.lbs.

Removal steps

Removal steps
1. Connection for accelerator cable or throttle cable
2. Connection for accelerator cable (Auto-cruise control)
3. Connection for oxygen sensor
4. Connection for engine coolant temperature sensor
5. Connection for engine coolant temperature gauge unit
6. Connection for air conditioning engine coolant temperature switch
7. Connection for crankshaft position sensor
8. Connection for TPS
9. Connection for ISC and closed throttle position switch
10. Connection for fuel injector
11. Connection for ignition coil
12. Connection for ignition power transistor
13. Connection for knock sensor (Turbo)
14. Connection for EGR temperature sensor (California vehicles only)
15. Connection for ground cable
16. Control wiring harness
17. Connection for radiator upper hose
18. Connection for overflow tube
19. Center cover
20. Connection for spark plug cable assembly
21. Connection for air intake hose (Turbo)
22. Connection for breather hose (Turbo)
23. Air intake hose
24. Connection for breather hose
25. Connection for fuel high pressure hose
26. O-ring
27. Connection for vacuum hoses
28. Connection for heater hose
29. Connection for water by-pass hose
30. Connection for PCV hose
31. Connection for vacuum hose (Turbo)
32. Connection for water hose (Turbo)
33. Eye-bolt (Turbo)
34. Gasket (Turbo)
35. Connection for oil pipe (Turbo)
36. Connection for vacuum hoses (Turbo)
37. Connection for fuel return hose
38. Connection for brake booster vacuum hose

NOTE
(1) Reverse the removal procedures to reinstall.

(4) N : Non-reusable parts   CR1069100352010X

Fig. 23 Cylinder head removal sequence (Part 1 of 2). 2.0L/4-122 engine

2.5–3.5 Nm 2–3 ft.lbs.
12–15 Nm 9–11 ft.lbs.
55–65 Nm 40–47 ft.lbs.
90–100 Nm 65–72 ft.lbs.
90–100 Nm 65–72 ft.lbs.
25–30 Nm 18–22 ft.lbs.
25–30 Nm 18–22 ft.lbs.
N 43
N 42
<Non-Turbo> 30–40 Nm 22–29 ft.lbs.
<Turbo> 40–60 Nm 29–43 ft.lbs.
30–40 Nm 22–29 ft.lbs.
48 N

39. Timing belt
40. Rocker cover
41. Semi-circular packing
42. Self locking nuts
43. Gasket (Non-Turbo)
44. Heat protector (Turbo)
45. Gasket (Turbo)
46. Ring (Turbo)
47. Cylinder head assembly
48. Cylinder head gasket

N : Non-reusable parts   CR1069100352020X

Fig. 23 Cylinder head removal sequence (Part 2 of 2). 2.0L/4-122 engine

5. Install timing belt as described under "Timing Belt, Replace."
6. When installing high pressure fuel line (5), apply small amount of gasoline to hose union. Use care to avoid damaging O-ring.

1995 NON-TURBO
1. Disconnect battery ground cable.
2. Relieve fuel system pressure as described under "Precautions."
3. Drain engine coolant, then drain crankcase.
4. Disconnect electrical connectors from A/C compressor clutch, power steer-

ing pump switch, oxygen sensor, engine coolant temperature switch and sensor, MAP sensor and intake air temperature sensor.
5. Disconnect accelerator cable.
6. Disconnect TPS, IAC motor and injector harness electrical connectors.
7. Disconnect ignition coil, camshaft position sensor and EGR solenoid electrical connectors.
8. Disconnect heater hose, upper radiator hose, overflow tube and water hose connection. **Mark relationship between radiator hose and clamp for installation reference.**

9. Disconnect fuel high pressure and return hoses.
10. Disconnect purge air hose.
11. Disconnect power brake booster vacuum hose connection.
12. Remove intake manifold stay.
13. Remove intake and exhaust camshafts as described under "Camshaft, Replace."
14. Disconnect exhaust pipe from exhaust manifold.
15. Remove cylinder head attaching bolts, then remove cylinder head and gasket. After cylinder head removal, remove intake and exhaust manifold as necessary.
16. Reverse procedure to install, noting the following:
   a. Prior to installation, inspect cylinder head bolts for stretching by placing a straightedge against bolt threads. If all threads do not contact straightedge, replace bolt.
   b. Clean bolt threads and lubricate with clean engine oil.
   c. Tighten cylinder head bolts in sequence shown in Fig. 27. **Torque** bolts 1 through 6 to 25 ft. lbs. and bolts 7 through 10 to 20 ft. lbs., then **torque** bolts 1 through 6 to 50 ft. lbs. Again **torque** bolts 1 through 6 to 50 ft. lbs. and bolts 7 through 10 to 20 ft. lbs., then tighten all bolts an additional 90°.
   d. When installing radiator hoses, align marks on clamps and respective hoses.

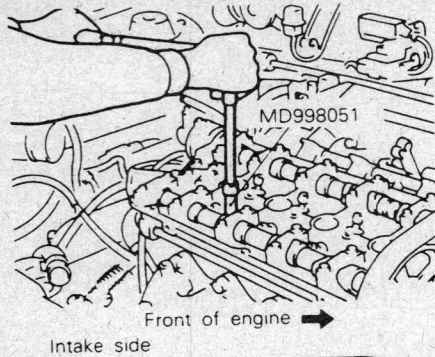

Fig. 24 Cylinder head bolt removal sequence. 1992-94 2.0L/4-122 engine & 1995 2.0L/4-122 turbocharged engine

VALVE ARRANGEMENT

Intake valves are on the righthand side of the engine and the exhaust valves are on the left hand side of the engine.

VALVE ADJUSTMENT

Hydraulic lash adjusters are used; no adjustment is necessary.

ROCKER ARMS
1.8L/4-107

Refer to "Camshaft, Replace" for rocker arm and rocker arm shaft replacement preocedures.

FRONT CASE & SILENT SHAFT SERVICE
1.8L/4-107

Disassemble

Disassemble front case, oil pump and silent shaft in numbered sequence, **Fig. 28**, noting the following:

1. Use oil pressure switch socket No. MD998054 or equivalent to remove oil pressure switch.
2. Remove oil pan as outlined under "Oil Pan, Replace."
3. When removing oil pump driven gear flange bolt, insert a Phillips screwdriver into plug hole on left side of cylinder block, **Fig. 29**, to block the silent shaft.
4. If front case will not come loose from block once all attaching bolts are removed, insert a flat screwdriver into slot as shown in **Fig. 30**, and pry case away from block. **Do not pry in any other location on case.**
5. Using silent shaft bearing puller MD998282 or equivalent, remove silent shaft front bearings as shown, **Fig. 31**.
6. Using silent shaft bearing puller MD998283 or equivalent, remove silent shaft rear bearings as shown, **Fig. 32**.

Fig. 25 Cylinder head bolt tightening sequence. 1992-94 2.0L/4-122 engine & 1995 2.0L/4-122 turbocharged engine

Inspection

1. Inspect silent shaft for the following:
   a. Clogged oil passages.
   b. Seized or damaged journal.
   c. Ensure oil clearance is within specifications. Clearance should be as follows: right front, .0012-.0024 inch; right rear, .0020-.0036 inch; left front, .0008-.0021 inch; left rear, .0020-.0036 inch.
2. Inspect front case for the following:
   a. Clogged oil passages.
   b. Damaged or seized left silent shaft front bearing section.
   c. Cracks or other signs of damage on case.
3. Test oil switch as follows:
   a. Connect an ohmmeter between switch terminal and switch body.
   b. If ohmmeter reads no continuity, replace switch. If ohmmeter reads continuity, proceed to following step.
   c. Insert a fine wedge into oil switch hole. Ohmmeter should read no continuity when wedge is slightly pressed into hole, If ohmmeter reads continuity, replace switch.
4. Inspect oil pump as follows:
   a. Install oil pump gears in front case and check tip clearance in location shown, **Fig. 33**.
   b. Check side clearance of gears.
   c. Check for ridge wear on surface of oil pump cover.
5. Inspect oil relief plunger. Ensure plunger slides smoothly and spring is functional.

Assemble

Reverse removal procedure to install, noting the following:

1. When installing silent shaft rear bearing, apply clean engine oil to engine block bearing hole and to outer circumference of bearing. Using bearing installation tool No. MD998286 or equivalent and a hammer, drive bear-

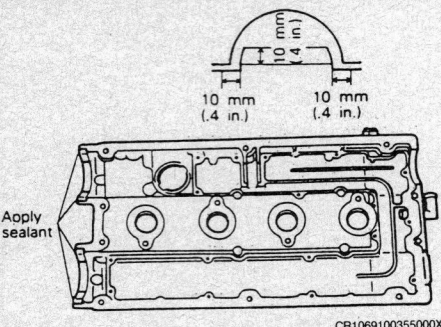

Fig. 26 Rocker cover installation. 1992-94 2.0L/4-122 engine & 1995 2.0L/4-122 turbocharged engine

ing into cylinder block.
2. Install silent shaft front bearing as follows:
   a. Using bearing installation tool set No. MD998280 or equivalent, install two guide pins (included in set) into threaded holes of cylinder block, **Fig. 34**,
   b. Place bearing onto bearing installer, locking ratchet ball of tool into hole in bearing, **Fig. 34**.
   c. Apply clean engine oil to engine block bearing hole and to outer circumference of bearing.
   d. Place installation tool on guide pins, then using a hammer, drive bearing into cylinder block.
3. Install crankshaft oil seal using oil seal installation tool No. MD998304 or equivalent.
4. Install silent shaft oil seal by placing a socket over the top of the seal and pressing it into the case.
5. Install front case as follows:
   a. Place crankshaft front oil seal guide NO. MD998285 or equivalent over front end of crankshaft, then apply engine oil to outer circumference of guide.
   b. Install front case over top of guide, onto cylinder block.
   c. Install case attaching bolts, referring to bolt length chart, **Fig. 35**.
6. When installing oil pump gears, align mark on drive gear notch with mark on driven gear tooth.
7. When installing flange bolt (14), insert a Phillips screwdriver into plug hole on left side of cylinder block, **Fig. 29**, to block the silent shaft. Tighten flange bolt and remove screwdriver.
8. When installing oil pump cover gasket, ensure round side of gasket faces oil pump cover.
9. Install oil pan as outlined under "Oil Pan, Replace."
10. When installing oil pressure switch, coat threads of switch with gasket adhesive. **Do not allow hole in end of switch to be covered with adhesive.** Install switch using oil pressure switch socket No. MD998054 or equivalent.

2.0L/4-122
Disassemble

Disassemble front case, oil pump and silent shaft in numbered sequence, **Fig. 36**, noting the following:

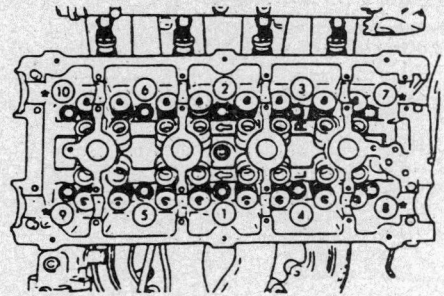

*Location of 110 mm (4.330 in.) short bolts.

CR1069500631000X

Fig. 27   Cylinder head bolt tightening sequence. 1995 2.0L/4-122 non-turbocharged engine

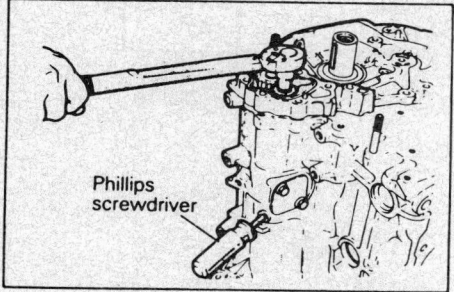

Phillips screwdriver

CR1069100361000X

Fig. 29   Flange bolt removal. 1.8L/4-107 engine

Slot for screwdriver

CR1069100362000X

Fig. 30   Front case removal. 1.8L/4-107 engine

1. Use oil pressure switch socket No. MD998054 or equivalent to remove oil pressure switch.
2. Remove oil pan as outlined under "Oil Pan & Oil Screen, Replace."
3. Use plug cap socket No. MD998162 or equivalent to remove front case plug cap (17).
4. When removing oil pump driven gear bolt, insert a Phillips screwdriver into plug hole, **Fig. 37**, to block the silent shaft.
5. Using silent shaft bearing puller No. MD998371 or equivalent, remove silent shaft front bearing as shown, **Fig. 31**.
6. Using silent shaft bearing puller No. MD998372 or equivalent, remove right silent shaft rear bearing as shown, **Fig. 32**.

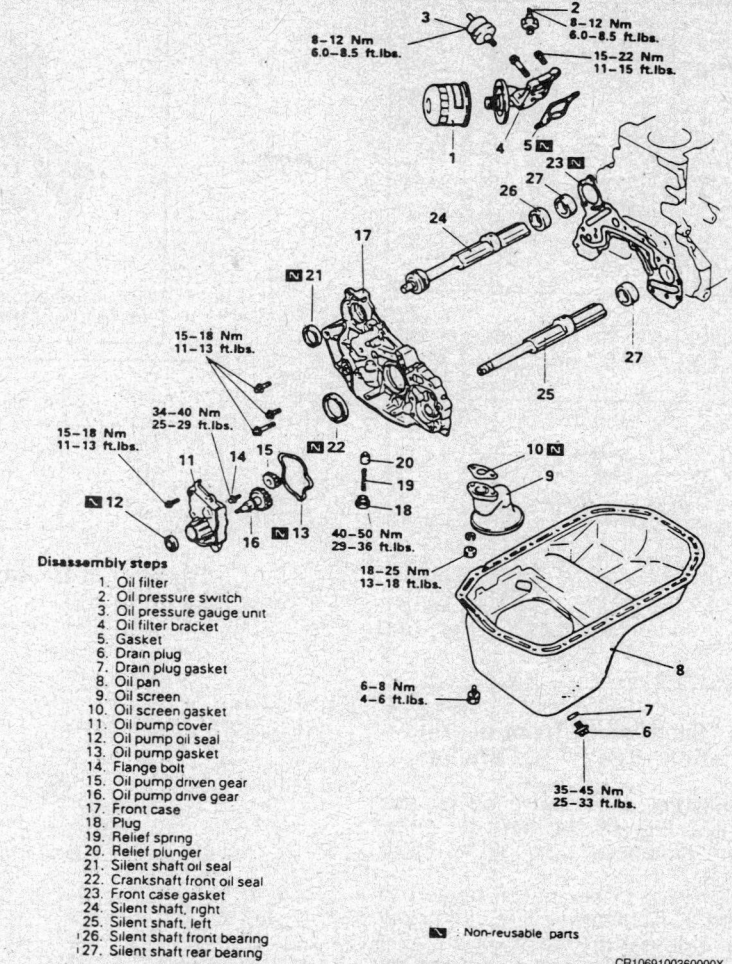

Disassembly steps
1. Oil filter
2. Oil pressure switch
3. Oil pressure gauge unit
4. Oil filter bracket
5. Gasket
6. Drain plug
7. Drain plug gasket
8. Oil pan
9. Oil screen
10. Oil screen gasket
11. Oil pump cover
12. Oil pump oil seal
13. Oil pump gasket
14. Flange bolt
15. Oil pump driven gear
16. Oil pump drive gear
17. Front case
18. Plug
19. Relief spring
20. Relief plunger
21. Silent shaft oil seal
22. Crankshaft front oil seal
23. Front case gasket
24. Silent shaft, right
25. Silent shaft, left
26. Silent shaft front bearing
27. Silent shaft rear bearing

Non-reusable parts

8–12 Nm 6.0–8.5 ft.lbs.
8–12 Nm 6.0–8.5 ft.lbs.
15–22 Nm 11–15 ft.lbs.
15–18 Nm 11–13 ft.lbs.
34–40 Nm 25–29 ft.lbs.
15–18 Nm 11–13 ft.lbs.
40–50 Nm 29–36 ft.lbs.
18–25 Nm 13–18 ft.lbs.
6–8 Nm 4–6 ft.lbs.
35–45 Nm 25–33 ft.lbs.

CR1069100360000X

Fig. 28   Front case, oil pump & silent shaft assembly. 1.8L/4-107 engine

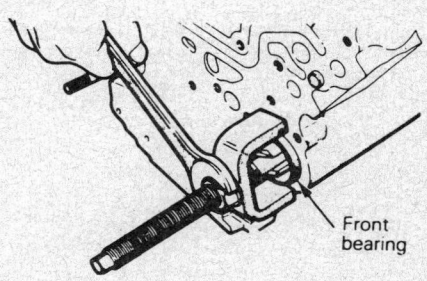

Front bearing

CR1069100363000X

Fig. 31   Silent shaft front bearing removal. 1.8L/4-107 engine

7. Using silent shaft bearing puller No. MD998374 or equivalent, remove left silent shaft rear bearing as shown, **Fig. 38**.

Inspection

1. Inspect front case for the following:
   a. Clogged oil passages.
   b. Damaged or seized left silent shaft front bearing section.
   c. Cracks or other signs of damage on case.
2. Inspect oil seal lip for wear or damage, replacing as necessary.
3. Test oil switch as follows:

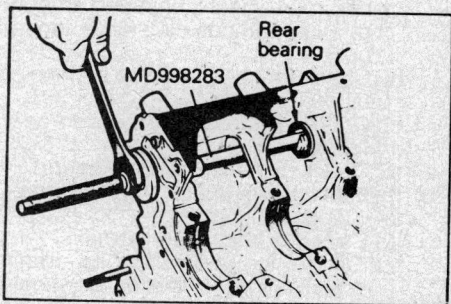

Rear bearing

MD998283

CR1069100364000X

Fig. 32   Silent shaft rear bearing removal. 1.8L/4-107 engine

a. Connect an ohmmeter between switch terminal and switch body.
b. If ohmmeter reads no continuity, replace switch. If ohmmeter reads continuity, proceed to following step.
c. Insert a fine wedge into oil switch hole. Ohmmeter should read no continuity when wedge is slightly pressed into hole. If ohmmeter reads continuity, replace switch.
4. **On models with turbocharged engine**, inspect oil cooler bypass valve as follows:
   a. Ensure valves move smoothly.

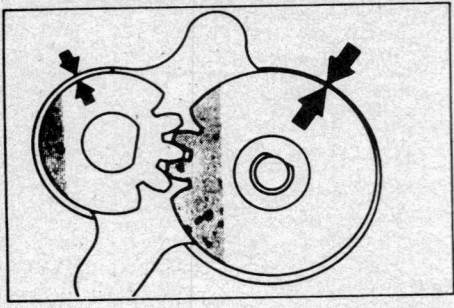

Fig. 33 Oil pump tip clearance check. 1.8L/4-107 engine

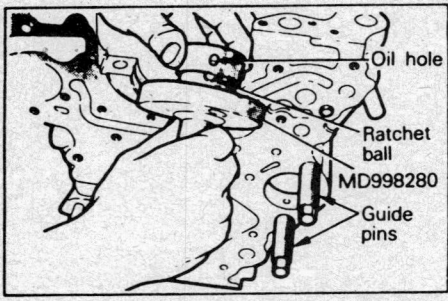

Fig. 34 Silent shaft front bearing installation. 1.8L/4-107 engine

b. Measure dimension L on bypass valve, **Fig. 39.** At room temperature, dimension L should be 1.358 inch.

c. Dip valve in engine oil heated to 212°F. Dimension L should now be at least 1.570 inch.

5. **On all models,** inspect oil pump as follows:
   a. Install oil pump gears in front case and rotate gears, ensuring smooth rotation without excessive looseness.
   b. Check for ridge wear on surface of oil pump cover.
   c. Check drive gear and driven gear tip clearance.
   d. Check side clearance of gears.
6. Inspect silent shaft for the following:
   a. Clogged oil passages.
   b. Seized or damaged journal.
   c. Ensure oil clearance is within specifications. Clearance should be as follows: right front, .0008-.0024 inch; right rear, .0008-.0021 inch; left front, .0002-.0036 inch; left rear, .0017-.0033 inch.
7. Inspect oil jet and check valve for clogging or damage.

Assemble

Reverse removal procedure to install, noting the following:
1. When installing oil jet, ensure nozzle is installed toward the piston.
2. When installing left silent shaft rear bearing, apply clean engine oil to engine block bearing hole and to outer circumference of bearing. Using bearing installation tool No. MD998374 or equivalent, **Fig. 40,** install bearing into

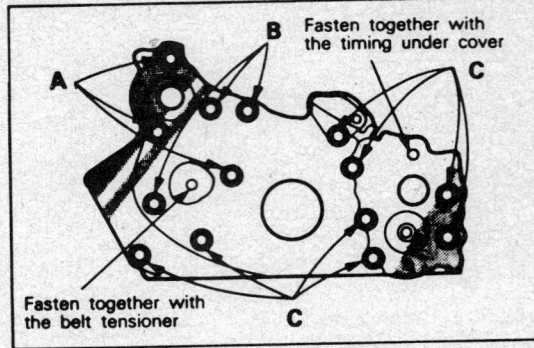

Code	Bolt size (diameter x length) mm (in.)	Head mark
A	8 x 20 (.32 x .79)	"4"
B	8 x 25 (.32 x .98)	"4"
C	8 x 40 (.32 x 1.57)	"4"

Fig. 35 Front case attaching bolts. 1.8L/4-107 engine

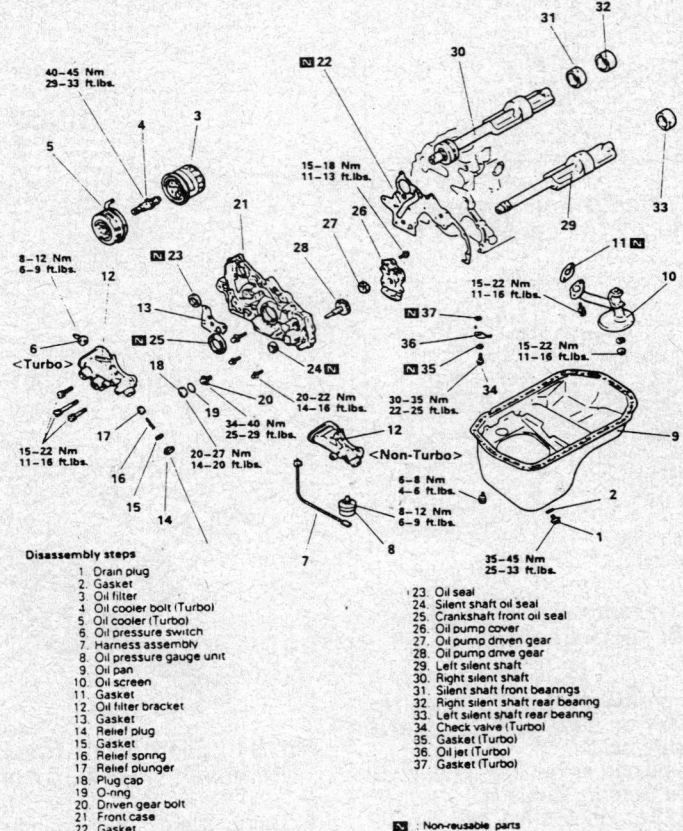

Disassembly steps
1. Drain plug
2. Gasket
3. Oil filter
4. Oil cooler bolt (Turbo)
5. Oil cooler (Turbo)
6. Oil pressure switch
7. Harness assembly
8. Oil pressure gauge unit
9. Oil pan
10. Oil screen
11. Gasket
12. Oil filter bracket
13. Gasket
14. Relief plug
15. Gasket
16. Relief spring
17. Relief plunger
18. Plug cap
19. O-ring
20. Driven gear bolt
21. Front case
22. Gasket
23. Oil seal
24. Silent shaft oil seal
25. Crankshaft front oil seal
26. Oil pump cover
27. Oil pump driven gear
28. Oil pump drive gear
29. Left silent shaft
30. Right silent shaft
31. Silent shaft front bearings
32. Right silent shaft rear bearing
33. Left silent shaft rear bearing
34. Check valve (Turbo)
35. Gasket (Turbo)
36. Oil jet (Turbo)
37. Gasket (Turbo)

N Non-reusable parts

Fig. 36 Front case, oil pump & silent shaft assembly. 2.0L/4-122 engine

cylinder block.

3. When installing right silent shaft rear bearing, apply clean engine oil to engine block bearing hole and to outer circumference of bearing. Using bearing installation tool No. MD998373 or equivalent, **Fig. 41,** install bearing into cylinder block. **Ensure oil hole in bearing is aligned with oil hole in cylinder block.**

4. When installing silent shaft front bearing, apply clean engine oil to engine block bearing hole and to outer circumference of bearing. Using bearing installation tool No. MD998373 or equivalent, **Fig. 42,** install bearing into cylinder block. **Ensure oil hole in bearing is aligned with oil hole in cylinder block.**

5. When installing oil pump gears, coat

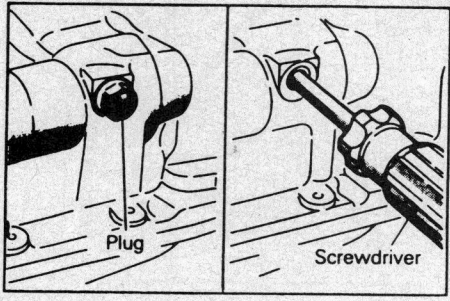

Fig. 37 Blocking silent shaft for oil pump sprocket removal

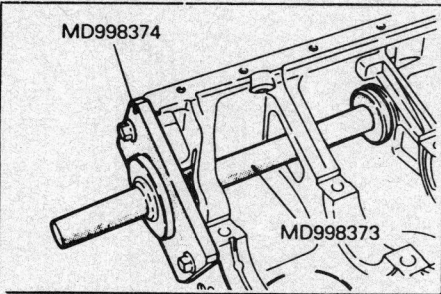

Fig. 40 Left silent shaft rear bearing installation. 2.0L/4-122 engine

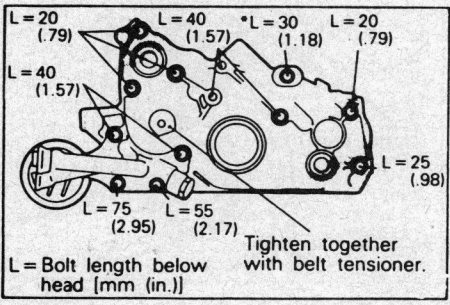

Fig. 43 Front case attaching bolts. 2.0L/4-122 engine

gears with clean engine oil, then align mark on drive gear notch with mark on driven gear tooth.

6. Install crankshaft oil seal using oil seal installation tool No. MD998375 or equivalent.
7. Install oil seal (22) and silent shaft oil seal (23) by placing a socket over the top of the seal and pressing it into the case.
8. Install front case as follows:
   a. Place crankshaft front oil seal guide No. MD998285 or equivalent over front end of crankshaft, then apply engine oil to outer circumference of guide.
   b. Install front case over top of guide, onto cylinder block. Temporarily tighten all bolts except the filter bracket attaching bolts, referring to bolt length chart, **Fig. 43.**
   c. Install oil filter bracket and the four attaching bolts.
   d. Tighten all bolts to specifications.

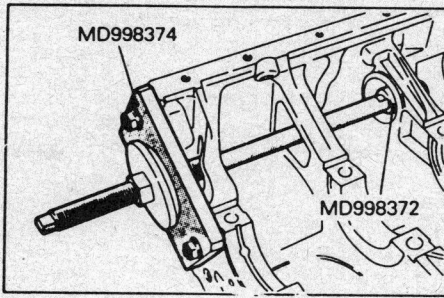

Fig. 38 Left silent shaft rear bearing removal. 2.0L/4-122 engine

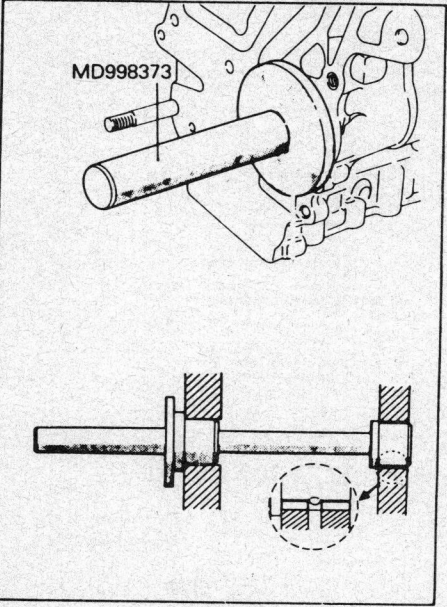

Fig. 41 Right silent shaft rear bearing installation. 2.0L/4-122 engine

9. When installing driven gear bolt (19), insert a Phillips screwdriver into plug hole on left side of cylinder block, **Fig. 37**, to block the silent shaft.
10. When installing plug cap, place a new O-ring into groove of case, then use plug cap socket No. MD998162 or equivalent to tighten cap.
11. Install oil pan as outlined under "Oil Pan, Replace."
12. When installing oil pressure switch, coat threads of switch with gasket adhesive. **Do not allow hole in end of switch to be covered with adhesive.** Install switch using oil pressure switch socket No. MD998054 or equivalent.

TIMING BELT
REPLACE

1.8L/4-107
Removal

Remove timing belt in numbered sequence as shown in **Fig. 44**, noting the following:

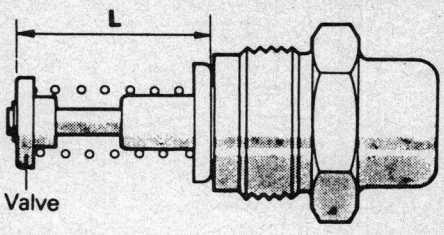

Fig. 39 Oil cooler bypass valve. 2.0L/4-122 engine

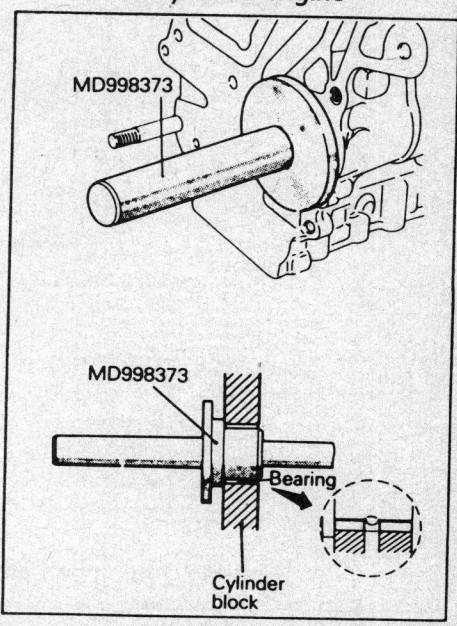

Fig. 42 Silent shaft front bearing installation. 2.0L/4-122 engine

1. To remove engine mounting bracket, slightly raise and support engine, removing weight of engine from mount.
2. Before removing timing belt (19), proceed as follows:
   a. Turn crankshaft clockwise and align timing marks, **Fig. 20. Do not turn crankshaft counterclockwise.**
   b. Mark timing belt to indicate direction of rotation for assembly reference.
   c. Loosen bolt and spacer nut on timing belt tensioner, move tensioner towards water pump as shown in **Fig. 45**, then hand tighten tensioner in this position.
3. Remove oil pump sprocket as follows:
   a. Remove plug on side of cylinder block, then insert Phillips screwdriver into hole to block left silent shaft, **Fig. 37.**
   b. Remove oil pump sprocket nut, then the sprocket.
4. Before removing timing belt B (28), mark back of belt to indicate direction of rotation for assembly reference.

Inspection

Inspect timing belts and replace if any of the following conditions exist:
1. Hardened or cracked back surface.
2. Cracked or separated canvas.

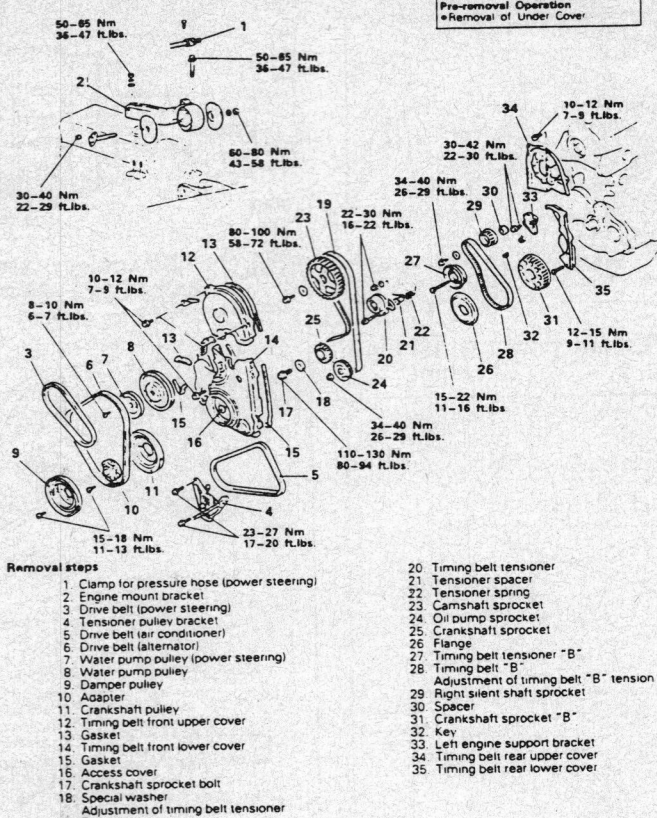

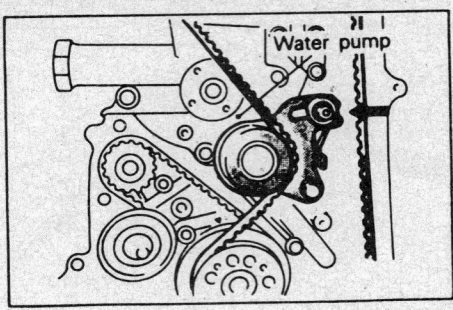

Fig. 45 Timing belt tensioner. 1.8L/4-107 engine

Removal steps

1. Clamp for pressure hose (power steering)
2. Engine mount bracket
3. Drive belt (power steering)
4. Tensioner pulley bracket
5. Drive belt (air conditioner)
6. Drive belt (alternator)
7. Water pump pulley (power steering)
8. Water pump pulley
9. Damper pulley
10. Adapter
11. Crankshaft pulley
12. Timing belt front upper cover
13. Gasket
14. Timing belt front lower cover
15. Gasket
16. Access cover
17. Crankshaft sprocket bolt
18. Special washer
   Adjustment of timing belt tensioner
19. Timing belt
20. Timing belt tensioner
21. Tensioner spacer
22. Tensioner spring
23. Camshaft sprocket
24. Oil pump sprocket
25. Crankshaft sprocket
26. Flange
27. Timing belt tensioner "B"
28. Timing belt "B"
   Adjustment of timing belt "B" tension
29. Right silent shaft sprocket
30. Spacer
31. Crankshaft sprocket "B"
32. Key
33. Left engine support bracket
34. Timing belt rear upper cover
35. Timing belt rear lower cover

Fig. 44 Timing belt assembly. 1.8L/4-107 engine

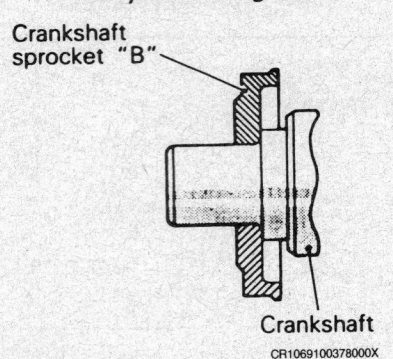

Fig. 46 Crankshaft sprocket installation

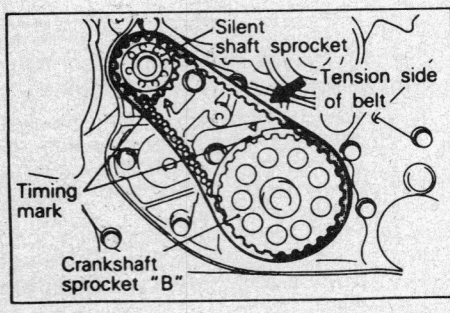

Fig. 47 Crankshaft sprocket B and silent shaft sprocket timing mark alignment. 1.8L/4-107 engine

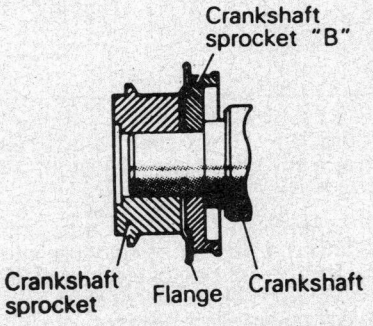

Fig. 48 Crankshaft sprocket flange installation

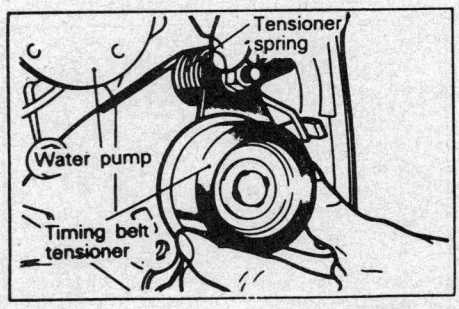

Fig. 49 Timing belt tensioner & spring. 1.8L/4-107 engine installation

3. Cracked tooth bottom.
4. Cracked side.
5. Abnormal wear.
6. Missing teeth.

Installation

Reverse removal procedure to install, noting the following:

1. Install crankshaft sprocket B (31) as shown in **Fig. 46.**
2. When installing spacer (30), apply a thin coating of engine oil to outside of spacer, then install spacer with chamfered end facing oil seal. **Failure to install chamfered end toward oil seal may result in oil leakage.**
3. Before installing timing belt B, ensure mark on crankshaft sprocket and mark on silent shaft sprocket are

aligned as shown in **Fig. 47.** Install belt and adjust tension as follows:

a. Temporarily install timing belt B tensioner with the flange toward the front of the engine and the center of the tensioner pulley to the left and above center of the attaching bolt.
b. While holding the tensioner in your hand, apply pressure on the timing belt until the tension side of the belt is taut, then tighten tensioner bolt.
c. To check tension, depress the tension side of the belt with your finger. Belt deflection should be .20–.28 inch.
4. Install flange (26) in direction as shown in **Fig. 48.**

5. Install the tensioner spring, tensioner spacer, timing belt tensioner and timing belt as follows:

a. Install tensioner spring, tensioner spacer and timing belt tensioner.
b. Place upper end of tensioner spring against water pump body, **Fig. 49,** then move tensioner fully toward water pump and temporarily secure.
c. Ensure timing marks on camshaft sprocket, crankshaft sprocket and oil pump sprocket are aligned as shown in **Fig. 50.** When aligning timing mark on oil pump sprocket, remove plug in cylinder block, **Fig. 37,** and insert Phillips screwdriver into plug hole. Ensure screwdriver shaft can be inserted at least 2.4 inches. If screwdriver can only be inserted .80–1.00 inch, turn sprocket one rotation and realign timing marks. Reinsert screwdriver and

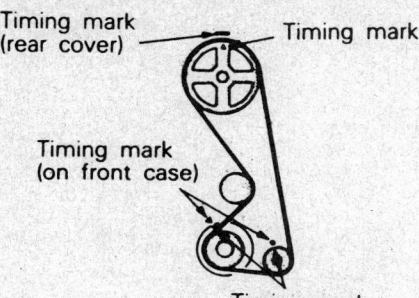

Fig. 50 Camshaft sprocket, crankshaft sprocket and oil pump sprocket timing mark alignment. 1.8L/4-107 engine

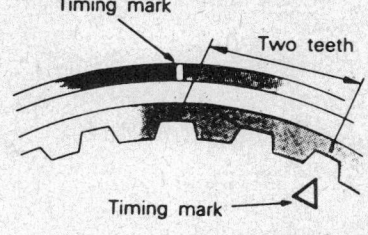

Fig. 51 Timing belt tension adjustment. 1.8L/4-107 engine

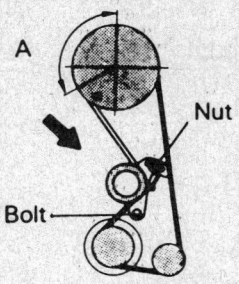

Fig. 52 Tensioner tightening. 1.8L/4-107 engine

leave it in hole until timing belt is completely installed.

6. Adjust timing belt tension as follows:
   a. Loosen tensioner mounting nut. This will apply tension to timing belt.
   b. Ensure each sprocket is still aligned with timing marks.
   c. Turn crankshaft clockwise distance of two teeth on camshaft sprocket, **Fig. 51. Do not rotate crankshaft counterclockwise.**
   d. Apply enough force on tensioner in direction of arrow so that no portion of belt raises out above pulley in area A, **Fig. 52.**
   e. Tighten tensioner installation bolt, then the tensioner spacer nut. **Do not tighten nut first, as belt will be thrown out of adjustment.**
   f. Check clearance between outside of belt and cover by pulling outward on belt between camshaft sprocket and oil pump sprocket. Deflection should be .40 inch.

7. When installing timing belt front lower and front upper covers, note location and size of attaching bolts as shown in **Fig. 53.**

2.0L/4-122

EXCEPT 1995 NON-TURBO

Removal

Remove timing belt in numbered sequence as shown in **Fig. 54**, noting the following:

1. To remove engine mount bracket, slightly raise and support engine, removing weight of engine from mount.
2. Before removing alternator drive belt, loosen water pump pulley mounting bolts.
3. Remove auto tensioner as follows:
   a. Turn crankshaft clockwise and align timing marks as shown in **Fig. 55.**
   b. Remove auto tensioner.
4. Prior to removal, mark timing belt to indicate direction of rotation for assembly reference.
5. To remove camshaft sprockets, proceed as follows:
   a. While holding camshaft in position with a crescent wrench at hexagon

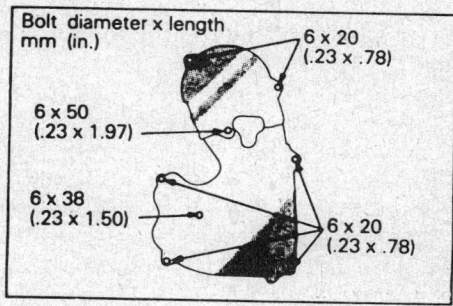

Fig. 53 Timing belt cover attaching bolts. 1.8L/4-107 engine

between No. 2 and No. 3 journals, remove camshaft sprocket bolt.
   b. Remove camshaft sprockets.
6. Remove oil pump sprocket as follows:
   a. Remove plug on side of cylinder block, then insert Phillips screwdriver into hole to block left silent shaft, **Fig. 37.**
   b. Remove oil pump sprocket nut, then the sprocket.

Inspection

Inspect timing belts and replace if any of the following conditions exist:
1. Hardened or cracked back surface.
2. Cracked or separated canvas.
3. Cracked tooth bottom.
4. Cracked side.
5. Abnormal wear.
6. Missing teeth.

Inspect tensioner pulley and idler pulley. Replace pulleys if binding, excessive play, abnormal noise or grease leakage occurs while turning.

Inspect auto tensioner for weak tension, leakage and rod end wear or damage. Check rod protrusion, **Fig. 56.** If protrusion exceeds .47 inch, replace auto tensioner.

Installation

Reverse removal procedure to install, noting the following:
1. Install crankshaft sprocket B (36) as shown in **Fig. 46.**
2. When installing spacer (35), apply a thin coating of engine oil to outside of spacer, then install spacer with chamfered end facing oil seal. **Failure to install chamfered end toward oil seal may result in oil leakage.**
3. Before installing timing belt B, ensure mark on crankshaft sprocket B and mark on silent shaft sprocket are aligned as shown in **Fig. 57.** Install

belt and adjust tension as follows:
   a. Temporarily install timing belt B tensioner with the flange toward the front of the engine and the center of the tensioner pulley to the left and above center of the attaching bolt.
   b. While holding the tensioner in your hand, apply pressure on the timing belt until the tension side of the belt is taut, then tighten tensioner bolt.
   c. To check tension, depress the tension side of the belt with your finger. Belt deflection should be .20-.28 inch.
4. Install flange (31) and crankshaft sprocket (30) in direction as shown in **Fig. 48.**
5. When installing oil pump sprocket, install a Phillips screwdriver into plug hole, **Fig. 37**, to block the left silent shaft, then install oil pump sprocket and attaching bolt.
6. To install camshaft sprockets, hold camshaft in position with a crescent wrench at hexagon between No. 2 and No. 3 journals, remove camshaft sprocket bolt, then install sprocket and attaching bolt.
7. When installing auto tensioner, if rod is in fully extended position, reset as follows:
   a. Using a soft-jawed vise, clamp the auto tensioner in a level position. **If plug protrudes from bottom of tensioner, place a flat washer around it to prevent damage from vise.**
   b. Slowly close vise until set hole (A) in tensioner rod is aligned with set hole (B) in tensioner cylinder, **Fig. 58.**
   c. Insert a piece of wire through the set holes, then install auto tensioner. **Leave wire installed in tensioner.**
8. Install the tensioner pulley with pinhole in pulley shaft to left of center bolt, **Fig. 59.** Hand tighten center bolt.
9. Install timing belt as follows:
   a. Turn camshaft sprockets so dowel pins are on top, then align timing marks so they face each other, parallel with the top surface of the cylinder head, **Fig. 60.**
   b. Align crankshaft sprocket timing mark, then the oil pump sprocket timing mark as shown in **Fig. 61.**

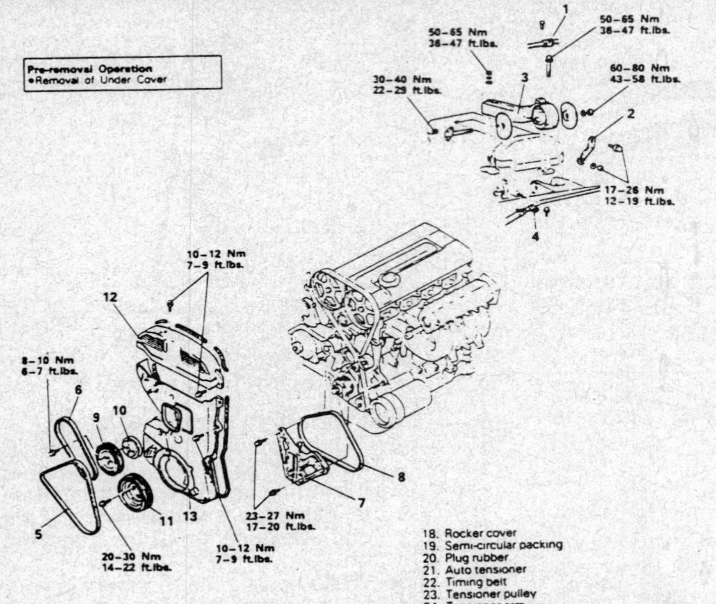

Pre-removal Operation
•Removal of Under Cover
50-65 Nm
36-47 ft.lbs.
50-65 Nm
36-47 ft.lbs.
30-40 Nm
22-29 ft.lbs.
60-80 Nm
43-58 ft.lbs.
17-26 Nm
12-19 ft.lbs.
10-12 Nm
7-9 ft.lbs.
8-10 Nm
6-7 ft.lbs.
23-27 Nm
17-20 ft.lbs.
20-30 Nm
14-22 ft.lbs.
10-12 Nm
7-9 ft.lbs.

Removal steps

1. Clamp for pressure hose (power steering)
2. Bracket
3. Engine mount bracket
4. Clamp of return pipe (power steering)
5. Drive belt (alternator)
6. Drive belt (power steering)
7. Tensioner pulley bracket
8. Drive belt (air conditioner)
9. Water pump pulley
10. Water pump pulley (power steering)
11. Crankshaft pulley
12. Timing belt front upper cover
13. Timing belt front lower cover
14. Center cover
15. Breather hose
16. PCV hose
17. Connection for spark plug cables
18. Rocker cover
19. Semi-circular packing
20. Plug rubber
21. Auto tensioner
22. Timing belt
23. Tensioner pulley
24. Tensioner arm
25. Idle pulley
26. Camshaft sprocket
27. Oil pump sprocket
28. Crankshaft sprocket bolt
29. Special washer
30. Crankshaft sprocket
31. Flange
32. Tensioner "B"
33. Timing belt "B"
34. Silent shaft sprocket
35. Spacer
36. Crankshaft sprocket "B"
37. Left engine support bracket
38. Timing belt rear right cover
39. Timing belt rear left cover (upper)
40. Timing belt rear left cover (lower)

CR1069100386010X

Fig. 54 Timing belt assembly (Part 1 of 2). 2.0L/4-122 except 1995 non-turbo

2.5-3.5 Nm
2-3 ft.lbs.
10-12 Nm
7-9 ft.lbs.
43-49 Nm
31-35 ft.lbs.
80-100 Nm
58-72 ft.lbs.
43-55 Nm
31-40 ft.lbs.
34-42 Nm
25-30 ft.lbs.
30-42 Nm
22-30 ft.lbs.
15-22 Nm
11-16 ft.lbs.
20-27 Nm
14-20 ft.lbs.
110-130 Nm
80-94 ft.lbs.
50-60 Nm
36-43 ft.lbs.

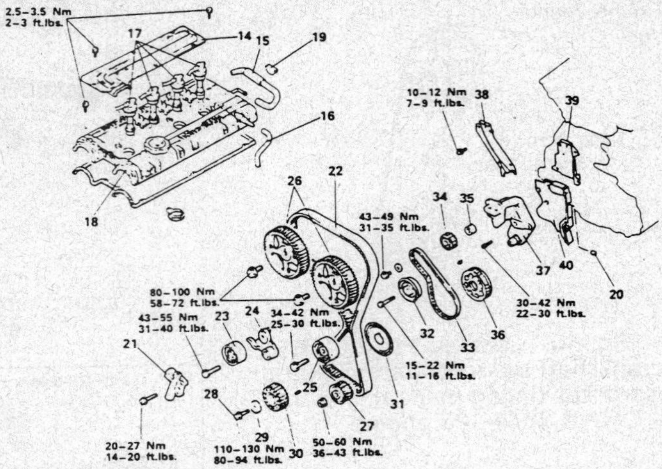

Installation steps

40. Timing belt rear left cover (lower)
39. Timing belt rear left cover (upper)
38. Timing belt rear right cover
37. Left engine support bracket
36. Crankshaft sprocket "B"
35. Spacer
34. Silent shaft sprocket
33. Timing belt "B"
Adjustment of timing belt "B" tension
32. Tensioner "B"
31. Flange
30. Crankshaft sprocket
29. Special washer
28. Crankshaft sprocket bolt
27. Oil pump sprocket
26. Camshaft sprocket
25. Idle pulley
21. Auto tensioner
24. Tensioner arm
23. Tensioner pulley
22. Timing belt
Adjustment of timing belt tension
20. Plug rubber
19. Semi-circular packing
18. Rocker cover
17. Connection for spark plug cables
16. PCV hose
15. Breather hose
14. Center cover
13. Timing belt front lower cover
12. Timing belt front upper cover
11. Crankshaft pulley
10. Water pump pulley (power steering)
9. Water pump pulley
8. Drive belt (air conditioner)
7. Tensioner pulley bracket
6. Drive belt (power steering)
5. Drive belt (alternator)
4. Return pipe clamp bolt (power steering)
3. Engine mount bracket
2. Bracket
1. Clamp for pressure hose (power steering)

CR1069100386020X

Fig. 54 Timing belt assembly (Part 2 of 2). 2.0L/4-122 except 1995 non-turbo

Exhaust cam shaft sprocket
Dowel pin
Intake cam-shaft sprocket
Cylinder head upper side
Timing mark
Timing mark
Timing mark
Crankshaft sproket
Oil pump sprockek

CR1069100387000X

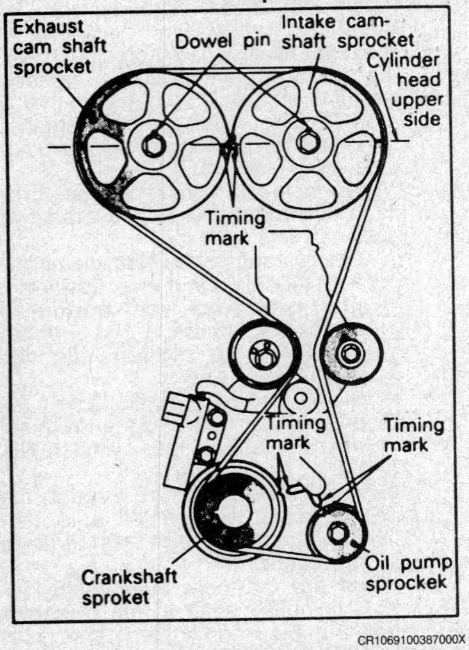

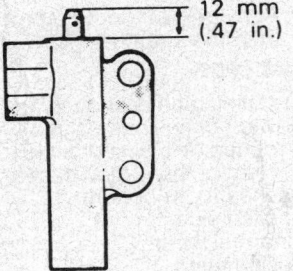

Fig. 55 Timing mark alignment. 2.0L/4-122 except 1995 non-turbo

Ensure oil pump sprocket is installed correctly by removing plug in cylinder block, **Fig. 37,** then inserting a Phillips screwdriver into plug hole. Ensure screwdriver shaft can be inserted at least 2.4

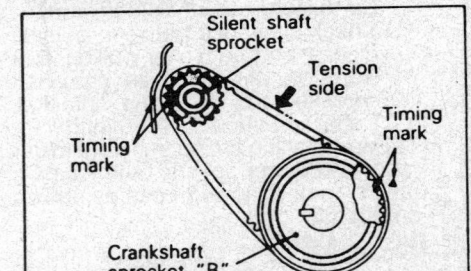

12 mm
(.47 in.)

CR1069100388000X

Fig. 56 Auto tensioner rod protrusion measurement. 2.0L/4-122 except 1995 non-turbo

inches. If screwdriver can only be inserted .80-1.00 inch, turn sprocket one rotation and realign timing marks. Reinsert screwdriver and leave it in the hole.

c. Thread timing belt over intake-side camshaft sprocket and clip belt onto sprocket as shown, **Fig. 62.** Using two wrenches, feed timing belt over exhaust-side sprocket, **Fig. 63,** then clip belt onto exhaust-side sprocket.
d. Thread timing belt over idler pulley, oil pump pulley sprocket, crankshaft pulley sprocket and tensioner pulley, then remove clips.
e. Lift tensioner pulley toward top and

Silent shaft sprocket
Tension side
Timing mark
Timing mark
Crankshaft sprocket "B"

CR1069100389000X

Fig. 57 Crankshaft sprocket B & silent shaft sprocket timing mark alignment. 2.0L/4-122 except 1995 non-turbo

Ⓐ
Ⓑ

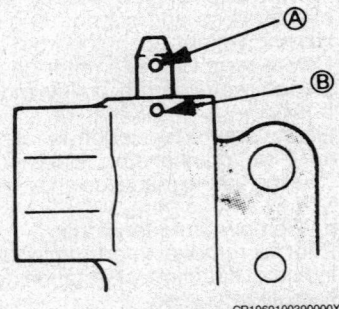

CR1069100390000X

Fig. 58 Auto tensioner rod retraction. 2.0L/4-122 except 1995 non-turbo

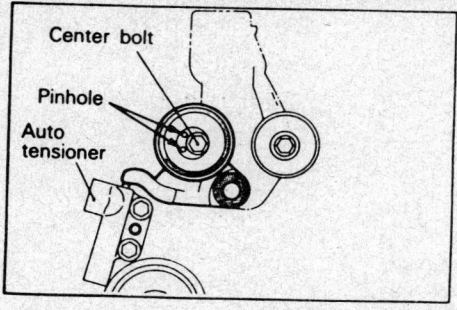

Fig. 59 Tensioner pulley installation. 2.0L/4-122 except 1995 non-turbo

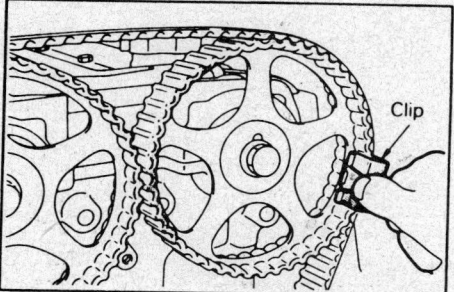

Fig. 62 Timing belt retaining to intake camshaft sprocket. 2.0L/4-122 except 1995 non-turbo

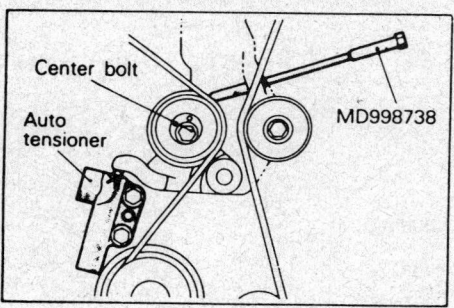

Fig. 65 Auto tensioner tool installation. 2.0L/4-122 except 1995 non-turbo

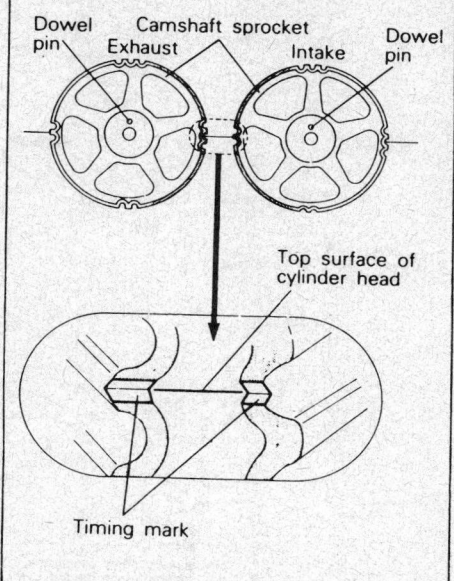

Fig. 60 Exhaust & intake camshaft sprocket timing mark alignment. 2.0L/4-122 except 1995 non-turbo

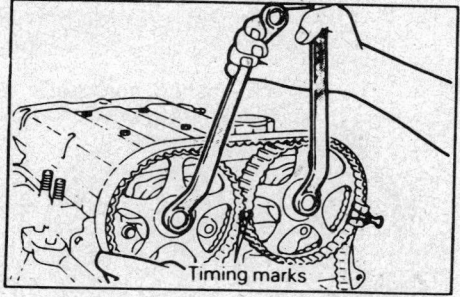

Fig. 63 Timing belt installation. 2.0L/4-122 except 1995 non-turbo

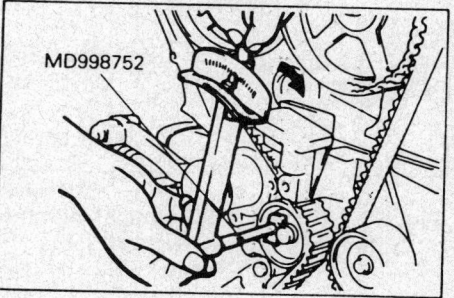

Fig. 61 Crankshaft sprocket & oil pump sprocket timing mark alignment. 2.0L/4-122 except 1995 non-turbo

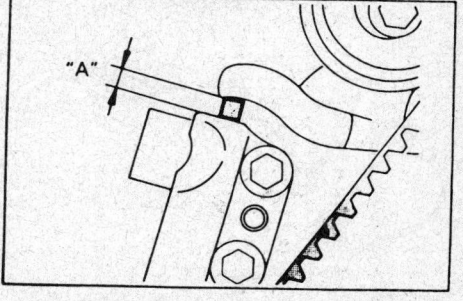

Fig. 64 Timing belt tension adjustment. 2.0L/4-122 except 1995 non-turbo

Fig. 66 Auto tensioner protrusion check. 2.0L/4-122 except 1995 non-turbo

center of engine, then tighten center bolt.

f. Ensure all timing marks are aligned, then remove screwdriver inserted into plug hole.

g. Turn crankshaft ¼ turn counterclockwise, then turn clockwise until marks are realigned.

10. Adjust timing belt tension as follows:

a. **It may be necessary to slightly raise and support engine to provide adequate body clearance during this step.** Loosen auto tensioner center bolt and install auto tensioner installation tool No. MD998752 or equivalent and a torque wrench as shown in **Fig. 64.** Apply 22.2-24.6 inch lbs. torque, then while holding tensioner pulley with installation tool, tighten center bolt.

b. Screw auto tensioner installation tool MD998738 or equivalent into

left engine support bracket until it contacts tensioner arm, **Fig. 65.** Screw tool in slightly more, then remove piece of wire installed into auto tensioner. Remove installation tool.

c. Rotate crankshaft clockwise two complete turns, then let tensioner set for 15 minutes. After time has expired, measure distance between tensioner arm and tensioner body (A), **Fig. 66.** Clearance should be .15-.18 inch. If clearance is not as specified, repeat steps 10A, 10B and 10C until clearance is within specifications.

d. If clearance does not exist between tensioner arm and body, reinstall installation tool MD998738 or equivalent, screwing tool in until it contacts tensioner arm. Once the tool contacts tensioner arm, screw in further (2.5-3 turns) until tensioner pushrod is moved back and tensioner arm contacts tensioner body. Remove installation tool.

e. Install rubber plug into timing belt rear cover.

11. When installing semi-circular packing,

apply liberal amount of gasket sealant onto circumference of packing.

12. When installing rocker cover, apply gasket sealant to area as shown in **Fig. 26.**

13. Refer to **Fig. 67** when installing timing belt upper and lower cover attaching bolts.

1995 NON-TURBO

Removal

Remove timing belt in numbered sequence as shown in **Fig. 68,** noting the following:

1. Remove crankshaft pulley as shown in **Fig. 69.**

2. Remove power steering pump from the bracket with hose attached and secure out of the way.

3. Place a suitable jack and wood block beneath engine and slightly raise engine to remove engine mount bracket.

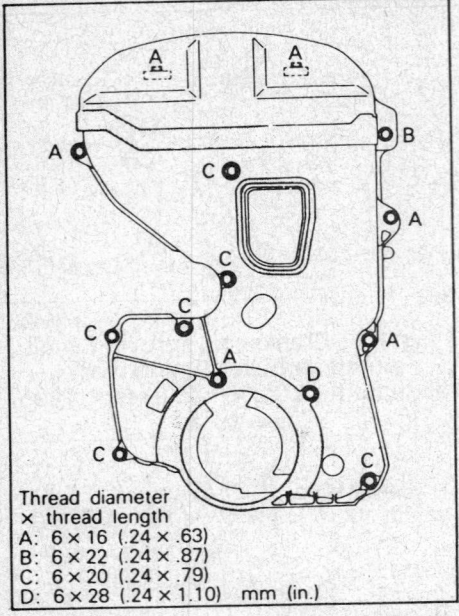

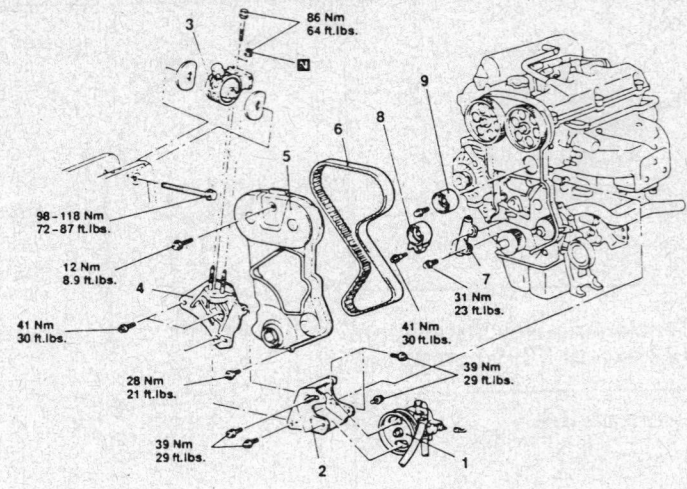

Fig. 67 Timing belt cover attaching bolts. 2.0L/4-122 except 1995 non-turbo

Thread diameter
× thread length
A: 6 × 16 (.24 × .63)
B: 6 × 22 (.24 × .87)
C: 6 × 20 (.24 × .79)
D: 6 × 28 (.24 × 1.10) mm (in.)

CR1069100399000X

Removal steps
1. Power steering pump connection
2. Power steering pump bracket
3. Engine mount bracket assembly
4. Engine mount bracket
5. Front timing belt cover
6. Timing belt
7. Timing belt tensioner
8. Tensioner pulley
9. Idle pulley

CR1069500607000X

Fig. 68 Timing belt assembly. 1995 2.0L/4-122 non-turbo

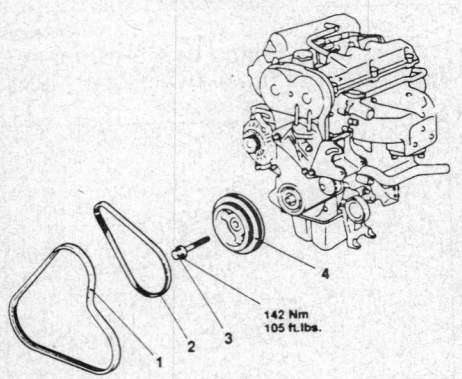

Removal steps
1. Drive belt (Power steering and A/C)
2. Drive belt (Generator)
3. Crankshaft bolt
4. Crankshaft pulley

142 Nm
105 ft.lbs.

CR1069500608000X

Fig. 69 Crankshaft pulley removal. 1995 2.0L/4-122 non-turbo

4. Align timing marks on camshaft intake and exhaust sprockets before loosening belt tensioner to remove timing belt, **Fig. 70.** Ensure camshaft and crankshaft are not rotated after belt is removed.
5. When belt tensioner is removed, it is necessary to compress the plunger into the tensioner body:
   a. Place tensioner in a suitable vise and slowly compress the plunger, **Fig. 71.**
   b. Index the tensioner in the vise the same way it is installed on the engine to ensure proper pin orientation when installed on engine.
   c. When plunger is compressed into tensioner body, install a pin through the body and plunger to retain plunger in place until tensioner is installed.

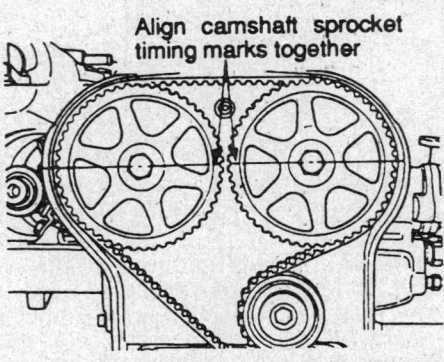

Align camshaft sprocket timing marks together

CR1069500609000X

Fig. 70 Camshaft sprocket timing alignment. 1995 2.0L/4-122 non-turbo

Installation

Reverse removal procedure to install noting:
1. Set the crankshaft sprocket to TDC by aligning the sprocket with the arrow on the oil pump housing, **Fig. 72.**
2. Using a suitable wrench, move crankshaft to ½ notch before TDC.
3. Set the camshaft timing marks by aligning the notches on sprockets, **Fig. 70.**
4. Install timing belt, starting at crankshaft, around water pump sprocket, idler pulley, camshaft pulleys and tensioner pulley, **Fig. 73.**
5. Move crankshaft sprocket to TDC to take up belt slack.
6. Install belt tensioner to engine block but do not tighten fasteners.
7. Using a suitable torque wrench on the tensioner pulley, **torque** to 28 ft. lbs.

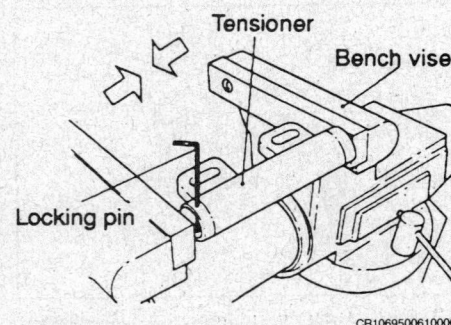

Tensioner

Bench vise

Locking pin

CR1069500610000X

Fig. 71 Timing belt tensioner compression. 1995 2.0L/4-122 non-turbo

8. With torque being applied to the tensioner pulley, **Fig. 74** move the tensioner up against the tensioner pulley bracket and **torque** fasteners to 23 ft. lbs.
9. Pull the tensioner plunger pin. Pretension is correct when pin can be easily removed or installed.
10. Rotate crankshaft two revolutions and check alignment of timing marks. If not correct, repeat procedure.

CAMSHAFT
REPLACE
1.8L/4-107
Removal

Remove rocker arms, rocker arm shafts and camshaft in numbered sequence, **Fig. 75**, noting the following:

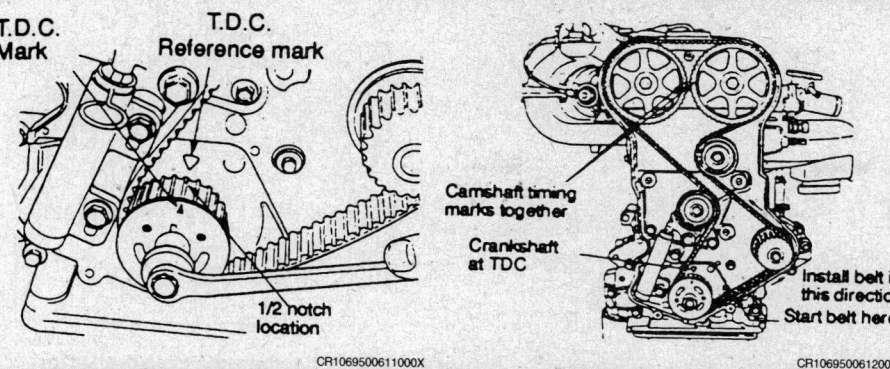

Fig. 72 Crankshaft sprocket alignment. 1995 2.0L/4-122 non-turbo

Fig. 73 Timing belt installation. 1995 2.0L/4-122 non-turbo

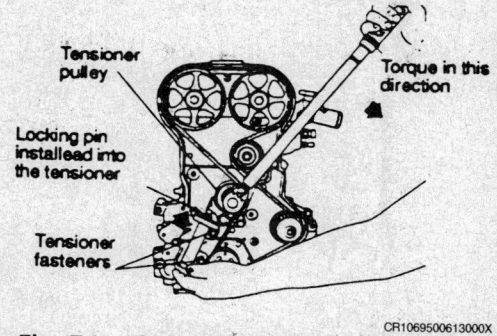

Fig. 74 Timing belt adjustment. 1995 2.0L/4-122 non-turbo

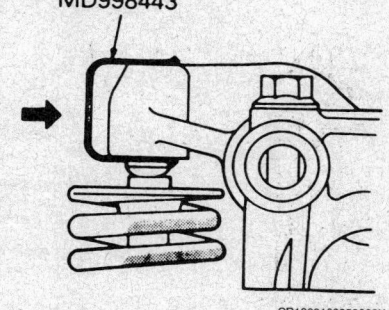

Fig. 76 Lash adjuster holder installation. 1.8L/4-107 engine

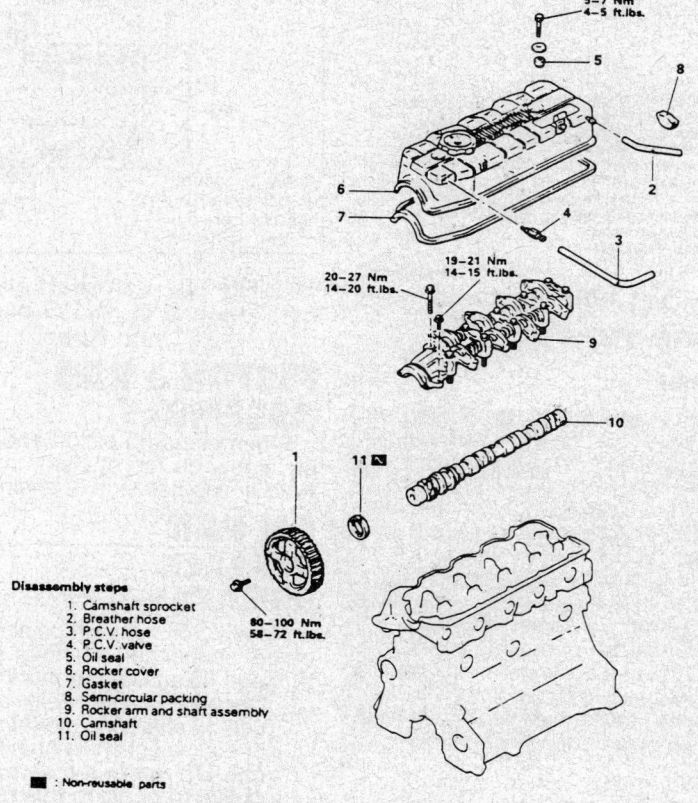

Disassembly steps
1. Camshaft sprocket
2. Breather hose
3. P.C.V. hose
4. P.C.V. valve
5. Oil seal
6. Rocker cover
7. Gasket
8. Semi-circular packing
9. Rocker arm and shaft assembly
10. Camshaft
11. Oil seal

■ : Non-reusable parts

Fig. 75 Rocker arms, rocker arm shafts & camshaft assembly. 1.8L/4-107 engine

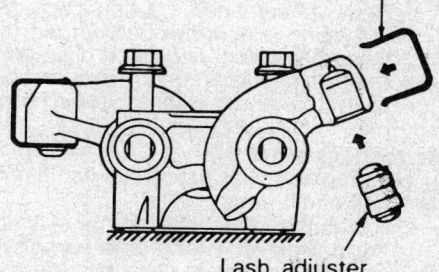

Fig. 77 Lash adjuster installation. 1.8L/4-107 engine

1. Before removing rocker arm and shaft assembly, install lash adjuster holder tool No. MD998443, or equivalent, **Fig. 76.** Tag rocker arms and lash adjusters according to cylinder number for assembly reference.

Inspection

1. Inspect camshaft journal surfaces for damage or seizure, replacing as necessary. If journal is seized, check cylinder head for possible damage.
2. Check camshaft cams for wear or damage, replacing as necessary. Ensure lobe height is within specifications.

Installation

Reverse removal procedure to install, noting the following:
1. Install oil seal (11) as follows:
   a. Apply engine oil to oil seal lip.
   b. Using seal installation tool No. MD998364 or equivalent, drive oil seal into cylinder head.
2. Install rocker arm and shaft assembly as follows:
   a. Install lash adjuster as shown, **Fig. 77**, using care not to spill oil which is inside it.
   b. Install lash adjuster holder No. MD998443 or equivalent to hold adjuster in place while installing rocker arm and shaft assembly.

   c. Install rocker arm and shaft assembly on cylinder head, then tighten bearing cap bolt.
   d. Remove lash adjuster holder tool.
3. When installing semi-circular packing, apply liberal amount of gasket sealant onto circumference of packing.

2.0L/4-122
EXCEPT 1995 NON-TURBO
Removal

Remove camshaft in numbered sequence, **Fig. 78**, noting the following:
1. Remove timing belt as outlined under "Timing Belt, Replace."
2. Remove camshaft sprockets as follows:
   a. While holding camshaft in position with a crescent wrench at hexagon between No. 2 and No. 3 journals, remove camshaft sprocket bolt.
   b. Remove camshaft sprockets.

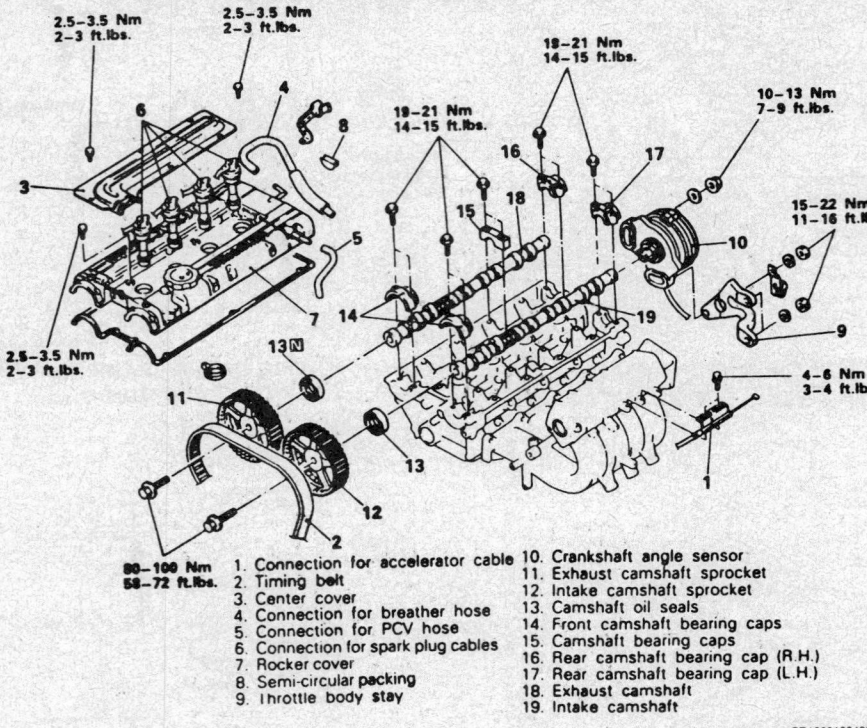

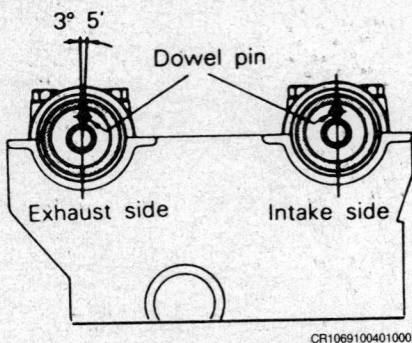

Fig. 79 Camshaft installation. 2.0L/4-122 except 1995 non-turbo

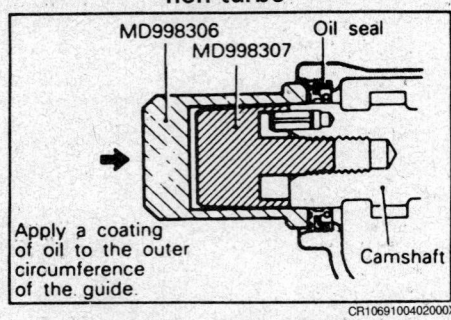

Fig. 80 Camshaft oil seal installation. 2.0L/4-122 except 1995 non-turbo

Fig. 78 Camshaft assembly. 2.0L/4-122 except 1995 non-turbo

1. Connection for accelerator cable
2. Timing belt
3. Center cover
4. Connection for breather hose
5. Connection for PCV hose
6. Connection for spark plug cables
7. Rocker cover
8. Semi-circular packing
9. Throttle body stay
10. Crankshaft angle sensor
11. Exhaust camshaft sprocket
12. Intake camshaft sprocket
13. Camshaft oil seals
14. Front camshaft bearing caps
15. Camshaft bearing caps
16. Rear camshaft bearing cap (R.H.)
17. Rear camshaft bearing cap (L.H.)
18. Exhaust camshaft
19. Intake camshaft

3. Remove camshaft oil seals using a suitable screwdriver.
4. Remove camshaft bearing caps by loosening installation bolts in two or three steps. If bearing cap is difficult to remove, gently tap on the rear portion of the camshaft with a plastic hammer.

Installation

Reverse removal procedure to install, noting the following:
1. Install the camshafts on the cylinder head. **Ensure intake side camshaft is installed on intake side and exhaust side camshaft is installed on exhaust side.** Intake side camshaft has a slot machined in the back end to drive the crank angle sensor. Once installed, the camshaft dowel pins should be in the positions as shown in **Fig. 79.**
2. When installing camshaft bearing caps, tighten evenly, in two or three steps.
3. When installing camshaft oil seal, use oil seal guide tool No. MD998307 and oil seal installation tool No. MD998306 or equivalents as shown, **Fig. 80.**
4. Install crank angle sensor as follows:
   a. Ensure mating mark on housing of crank angle sensor is aligned with notch in plate.
   b. Ensure crank angle sensor does not move when tightening attaching nut.
5. When installing semi-circular packing, apply liberal amount of gasket sealant onto circumference of packing.
6. When installing rocker cover, apply gasket sealant to area as shown in **Fig. 26.**

1995 NON-TURBO

Removal

Remove camshaft in numbered sequence, **Fig. 81**, noting the following:
1. Use camshaft sprocket holder and adapter tools No. C-4687 and C-4687-1, or equivalent, to ensure camshaft sprockets do not turn during removal.
2. Mark and identify intake camshaft and exhaust camshaft before removal as they are not interchangeable.
3. Loosen camshaft bearing cap attaching bolts in sequence shown in **Fig. 82**, one camshaft at a time.
4. Remove camshaft oil seals using suitable screwdriver to pry seal out.

Installation

1. Install new camshaft oil seals using special oil seal seating tools No. MB991554 and MB998713, or equivalents, **Fig. 83.**
2. Install camshaft bearing cap attaching bolts in sequence shown in **Fig. 82**, one camshaft at a time. Tighten to specifications.
3. Use camshaft sprocket holder and adapter tools No. C-4687 and C-4687-1, or equivalent, to ensure camshaft sprockets do not turn during installation.
4. Install cylinder head cover assembly to head and tighten in sequence shown in **Fig. 84.** Torque in three steps; first to 3.3 ft. lbs., then to 6.6 ft. lbs., finally to 8.9 ft. lbs.

PISTON & ROD ASSEMBLY

When installing piston and rod assembly, arrow on top of piston must face toward timing belt side of engine, **Fig. 85.**

OIL PAN
REPLACE
REMOVAL

Remove oil pan and oil screen in numbered sequence, referring to **Figs. 86 through 89**, noting the following:
1. Once all oil pan bolts are removed, use oil pan separator No. MD998727 or equivalent and a hammer to loosen pan. **Do not use a screwdriver or a chisel to perform this task, as damage to oil pan flange may result.**
2. Remove pan by placing a brass bar at corner of separator tool and striking it with a hammer.

INSPECTION

Replace the oil pan if damaged or cracked. Ensure screen is not clogged, cracked or damage.

INSTALLATION

Reverse removal procedure to install. When installing oil pan, ensure mating surfaces are clean, then apply gasket adhesive into groove in oil pan flange. Do not allow adhesive to cover bolt holes.

OIL PUMP
REPLACE

Refer to "Front Case & Silent Shaft Service" for procedure.

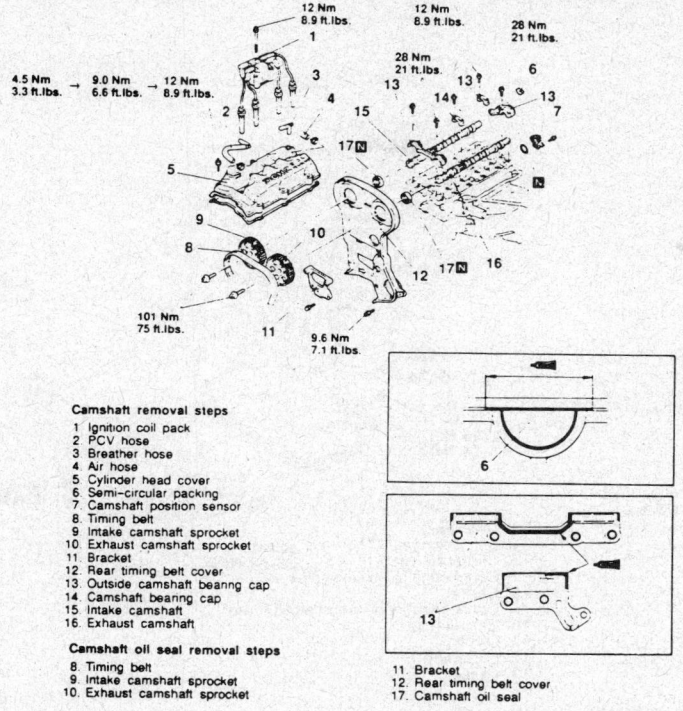

Camshaft removal steps
1 Ignition coil pack
2 PCV hose
3 Breather hose
4 Air hose
5 Cylinder head cover
6 Semi-circular packing
7 Camshaft position sensor
8 Timing belt
9 Intake camshaft sprocket
10 Exhaust camshaft sprocket
11 Bracket
12 Rear timing belt cover
13 Outside camshaft bearing cap
14 Camshaft bearing cap
15 Intake camshaft
16 Exhaust camshaft

Camshaft oil seal removal steps
8 Timing belt
9 Intake camshaft sprocket
10 Exhaust camshaft sprocket

11 Bracket
12 Rear timing belt cover
17 Camshaft oil seal

CR1069500614000X

Fig. 81   Camshaft assembly. 1995 2.0L/4-122 non-turbo

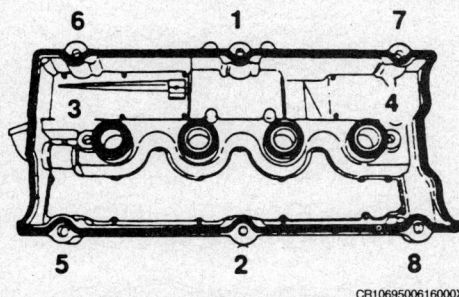

CR1069500616000X

Fig. 84   Cylinder head cover installation. 1995 2.0L/4-122 non-turbo

BELT TENSION DATA

Refer to **90** for belt tension data.

COOLING SYSTEM BLEED

These engines do not require a specified bleed procedure. After filling cooling system, run engine to operating temperature with radiator/pressure cap off. Air will then be automatically bled through cap opening.

THERMOSTAT
REPLACE

1992–94
Removal

Do not remove pressure cap while engine is hot or under pressure.

1. Drain coolant to below level of thermostat housing.
2. Remove radiator upper hose from engine.
3. Remove two retaining bolts, water outlet fitting, gasket and thermostat.
4. Clean mating surfaces.

Installation

1. Reverse removal procedures to install.
2. Install thermostat so that the flange seats in recess of intake manifold and thermostat case, **Fig. 91.**
3. Install retaining bolts. **Torque** to 12–14 ft. lbs.
4. Ensure drain is closed, then refill coolant. Replace cap, start engine until warm. Check for leaks, then recheck coolant and fill if necessary.

1995

Do not remove pressure cap while engine is hot or under pressure.
Remove thermostat in numbered sequence, **Fig. 92,** noting the following:
1. Drain coolant to below level of thermostat housing.
2. Mark and note the position of the hose clamps before removal.
3. Clean mating surfaces.
4. Reverse procedure to install, noting the following:
   a. Install retaining bolts and tighten to specification
   b. Align hose clamps in position as marked.
   c. Ensure drain is closed, then refill coolant. Replace cap, start engine until warm. Check for leaks, then recheck coolant and fill if necessary.

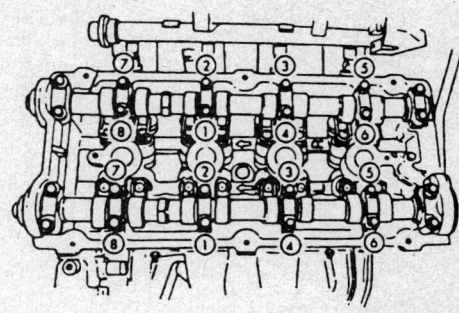

CR1069500615000X

Fig. 82   Camshaft bearing caps. 1995 2.0L/4-122 non-turbo

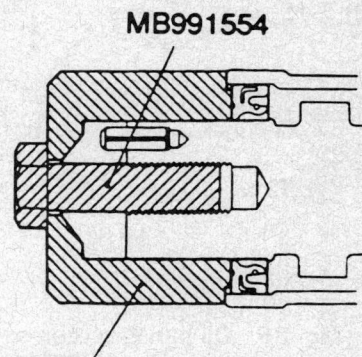

CR1069500617000X

Fig. 83   Camshaft oil seal installation. 1995 2.0L/4-122 non-turbo

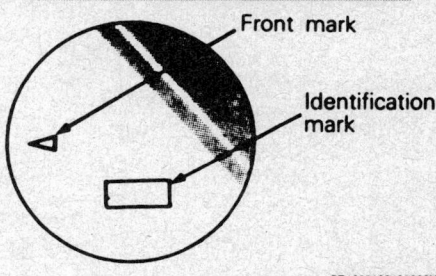

CR1069100403000X

Fig. 85   Top view of piston

WATER PUMP
REPLACE

1.8L/4-107
Removal

Remove water pump in numbered sequence, **Fig. 93,** noting the following:
1. Remove lower engine compartment cover.
2. Drain engine coolant as follows:
   a. Place instrument panel temperature control lever in Hot position.
   b. Carefully remove radiator cap.
   c. Remove radiator drain plug.
3. To remove engine mount bracket, slightly raise and support engine, removing weight of engine from mount.
4. Before removing water pump drive belt, loosen water pump pulley installation bolt.

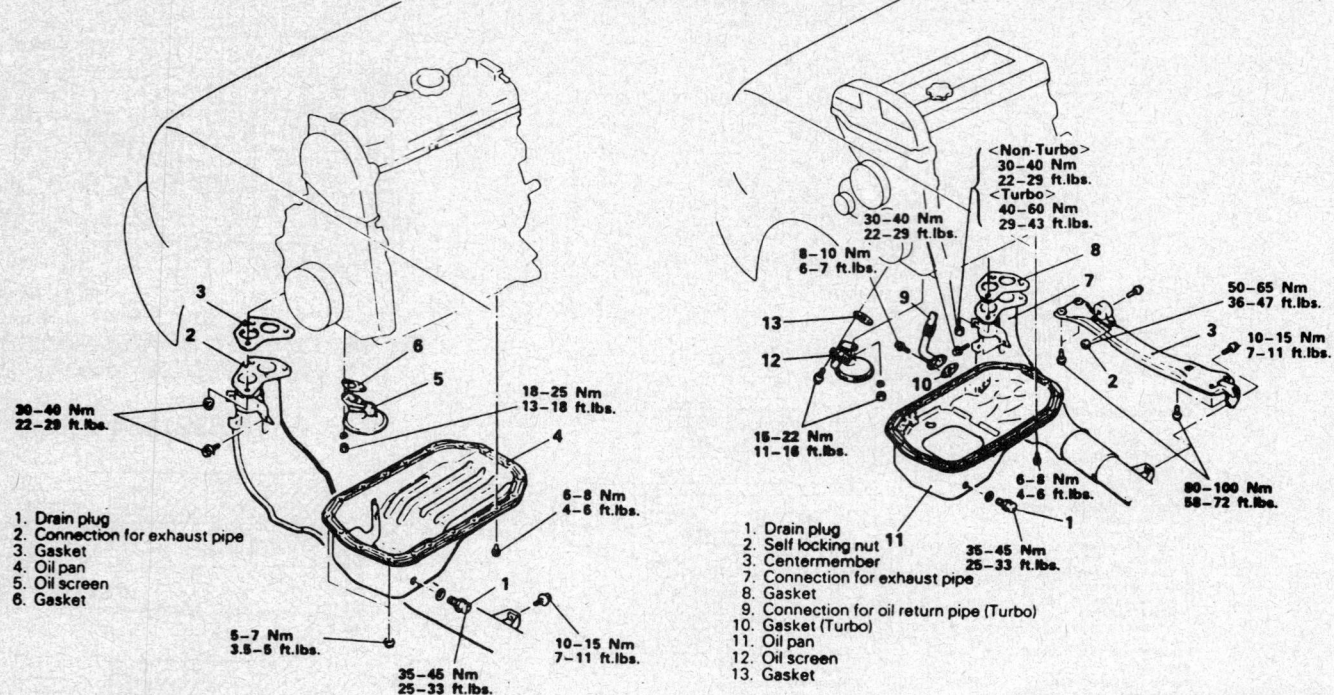

Fig. 86 Oil pan & screen assembly. 1.8L/4-107 engine

1. Drain plug
2. Connection for exhaust pipe
3. Gasket
4. Oil pan
5. Oil screen
6. Gasket

Fig. 87 Oil pan & screen assembly. 2.0L/4-122 FWD models, except 1995 non-turbo

1. Drain plug
2. Self locking nut
3. Centermember
7. Connection for exhaust pipe
8. Gasket
9. Connection for oil return pipe (Turbo)
10. Gasket (Turbo)
11. Oil pan
12. Oil screen
13. Gasket

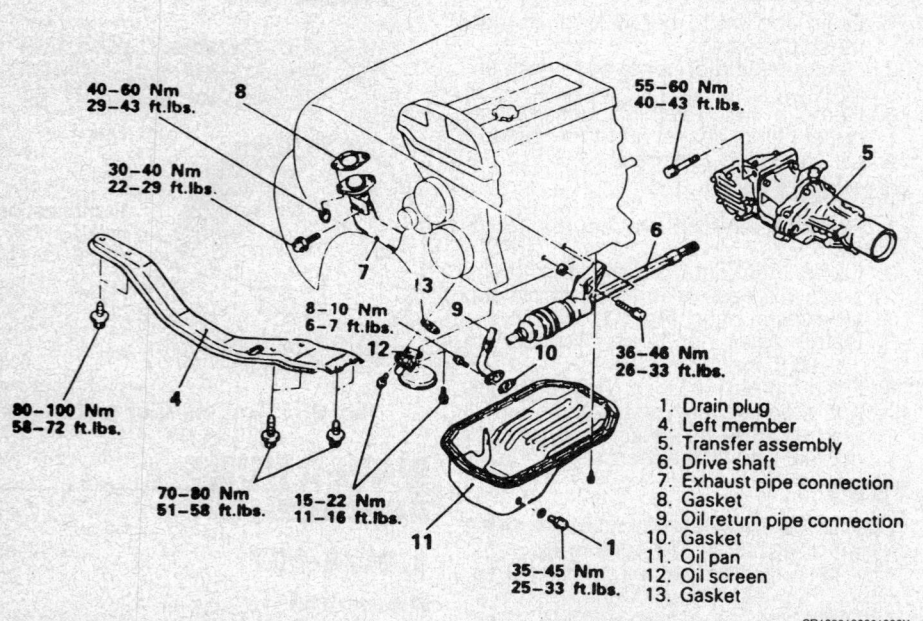

Fig. 88 Oil pan & screen assembly. 2.0L/4-122 AWD models, except 1995 non-turbo

1. Drain plug
4. Left member
5. Transfer assembly
6. Drive shaft
7. Exhaust pipe connection
8. Gasket
9. Oil return pipe connection
10. Gasket
11. Oil pan
12. Oil screen
13. Gasket

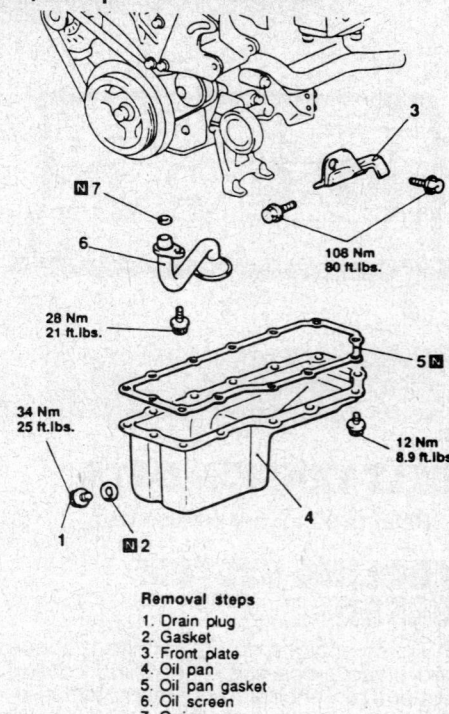

Removal steps
1. Drain plug
2. Gasket
3. Front plate
4. Oil pan
5. Oil pan gasket
6. Oil screen
7. O-ring

Fig. 89 Oil pan & screen assembly. 1995 2.0L/4-122 non-turbo

5. Remove rocker cover, timing belt covers, timing belt and timing belt B as outlined under "Timing Belt, Replace."

Installation

Reverse removal procedure to install, noting the following:
1. Coat the O-ring (26) with water to ease installation.
2. Refer to bolt length chart, **Fig. 94,** when installing water pump attaching bolts.

2.0L/4-122
1992—94

Removal

Remove water pump in numbered sequence, **Fig. 95,** noting the following:
1. Remove lower engine compartment cover.
2. Drain engine coolant as follows:
   a. Place instrument panel temperature control lever in Hot position.

b. Carefully remove radiator cap.
c. Remove radiator drain plug.
3. To remove engine mount bracket, slightly raise and support engine, removing weight of engine from mount.
4. Remove automatic tensioner, timing belt and timing belt B as outlined under "Timing Belt, Replace."

Year	Engine	Belt	New Lbs.	Used Lbs.
1992-94	All	A/C	104-126	71-88
		Alt.	110-154	88
1995	Non-Turbo	A/C	137-159	93-115
		Alt.	110-160	90-110
		Power Steering	137-159	93-115
1995	Turbo	A/C	86-99	57-75
		Alt.	110-154	88
		Power Steering	110-154	77-99

Fig. 90   Belt tension data

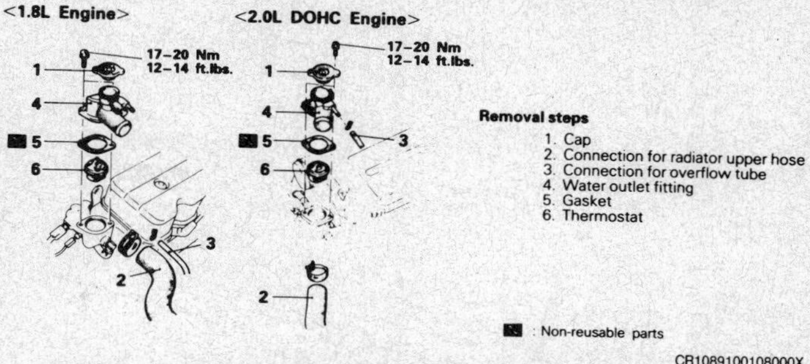

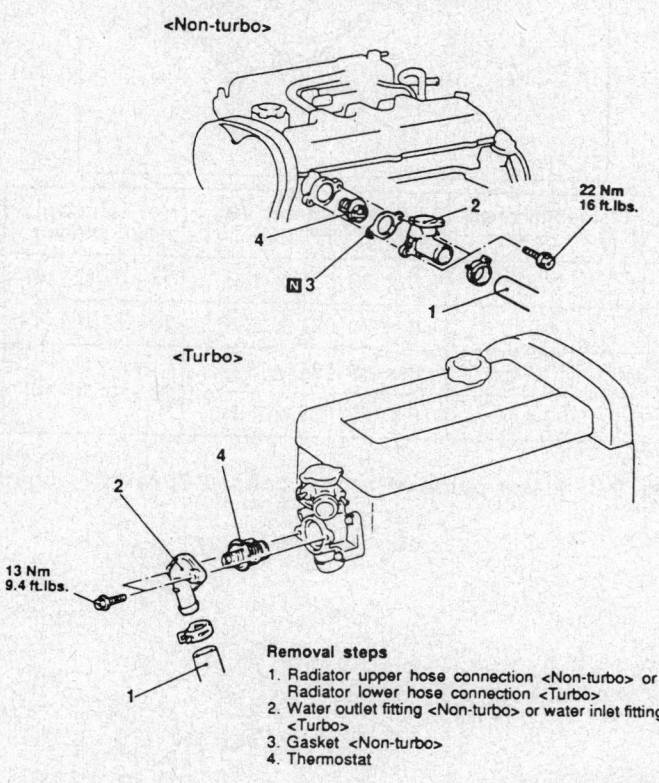

Fig. 91   Thermostat replacement. 1992–94

CR1089100108000X

Fig. 92   Thermostat replacement. 1995

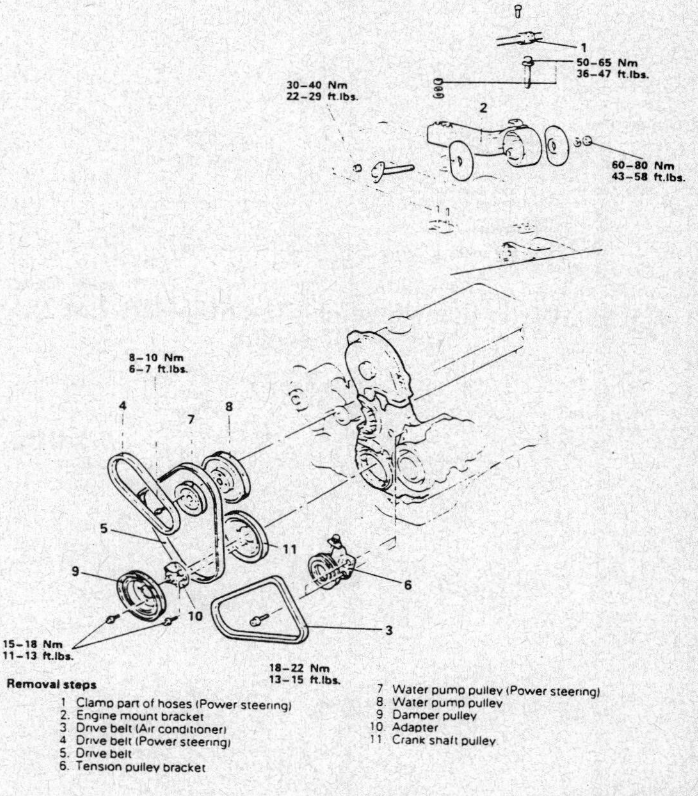

CR1089500145000X

Fig. 93   Water pump assembly removal (Part 1 of 2). 1.8L/4-107 engine

CR1089100109010X

Installation

Reverse removal procedure to install, noting the following:

1. Coat the O-ring (26) with water to ease installation.
2. Refer to bolt length chart, **Fig. 96**, when installing water pump attaching bolts.

1995

Non-Turbo

Remove water pump in numbered sequence, **Fig. 97**, noting the following:

1. Drain engine coolant as follows:
   a. Place instrument panel temperature control lever in Hot position.
   b. Carefully remove radiator cap.
   c. Remove radiator drain plug.
2. Remove timing belt rear cover as described under "Timing Belt, Replace."

3. Reverse procedure to install. Coat O-ring with water or coolant to ease installation.

Turbo

Remove water pump in numbered sequence, **Fig. 98**, noting the following:

1. Drain engine coolant as follows:
   a. Place instrument panel temperature control lever in Hot position.
   b. Carefully remove radiator cap.
   c. Remove radiator drain plug.
2. Remove timing belt rear cover as described under "Timing Belt, Replace."
3. Reverse procedure to install, noting the following:
   a. Coat O-ring with water or coolant to ease installation.
   b. Refer to bolt inset, **Fig. 98**, when installing water pump attaching bolts.

RADIATOR

REPLACE

1992–94

Remove radiator in numbered sequence, **Fig. 99**, noting the following:

1. Drain engine coolant as follows:
   a. Place instrument panel temperature control lever in Hot position.
   b. Carefully remove radiator cap.
   c. Remove radiator drain plug.
2. Mark and note the position of the hose clamps before removal.
3. **On models with turbo,** remove air cleaner bracket.
4. **On models with automatic transaxle,** plug or cover nipples and hoses for cooling lines to ensure dust, dirt or other contaminants do not enter lines.
5. **On all models,** reverse procedure to install, noting the following

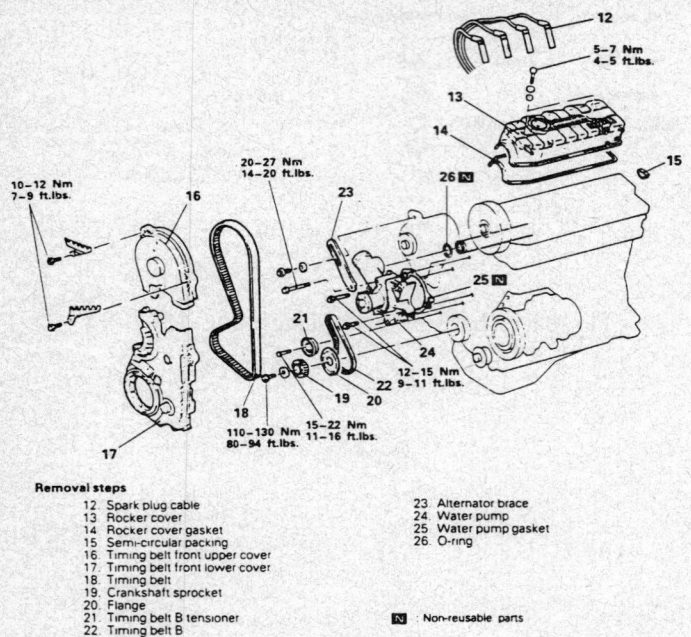

Removal steps

12. Spark plug cable
13. Rocker cover
14. Rocker cover gasket
15. Semi-circular packing
16. Timing belt front upper cover
17. Timing belt front lower cover
18. Timing belt
19. Crankshaft sprocket
20. Flange
21. Timing belt B tensioner
22. Timing belt B

23. Alternator brace
24. Water pump
25. Water pump gasket
26. O-ring

N : Non-reusable parts

Fig. 93 Water pump assembly removal (Part 2 of 2). 1.8L/4-107 engine

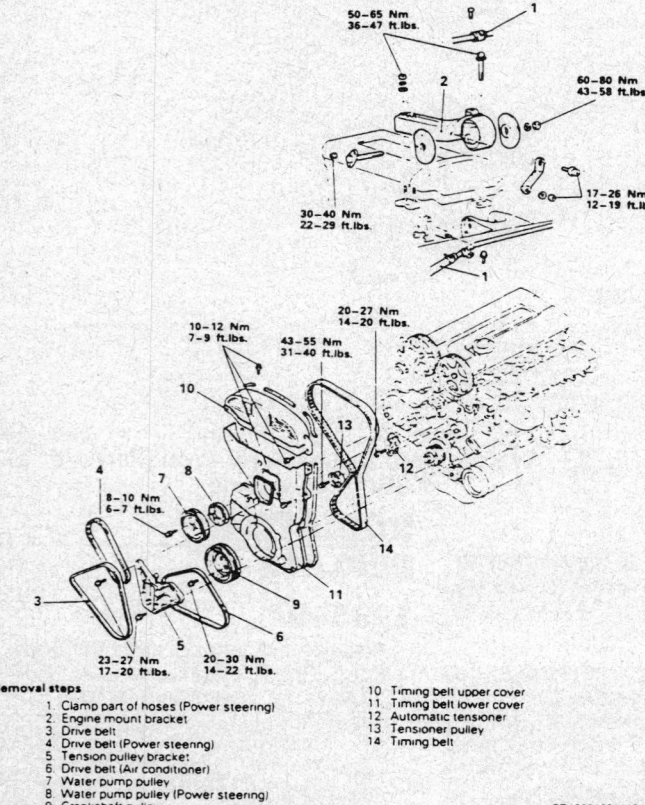

Removal steps

1. Clamp part of hoses (Power steering)
2. Engine mount bracket
3. Drive belt
4. Drive belt (Power steering)
5. Tension pulley bracket
6. Drive belt (Air conditioner)
7. Water pump pulley
8. Water pump pulley (Power steering)
9. Crankshaft pulley

10. Timing belt upper cover
11. Timing belt lower cover
12. Automatic tensioner
13. Tensioner pulley
14. Timing belt

Fig. 95 Water pump assembly removal (Part 1 of 2). 1992–94 2.0L/4-122 engine

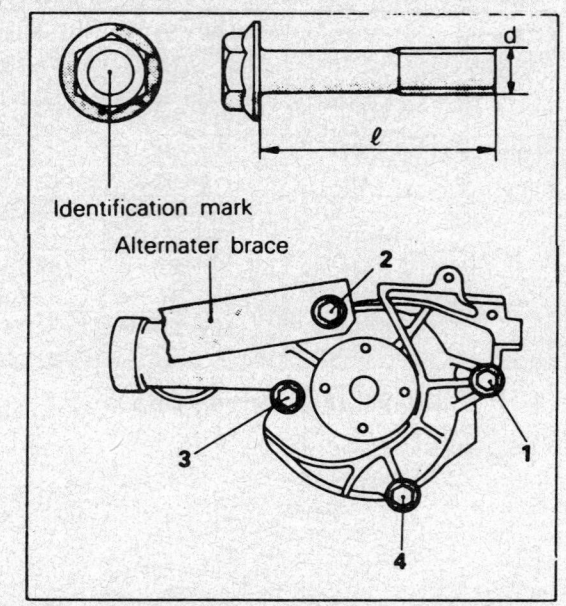

Identification mark

Alternater brace

No.	Identification mark	Bolt diameter (d) x length (ℓ) mm (in.)	Torque Nm (ft.lbs.)
1	4	8 x 28 (.31 x 1.1)	12–15 (9–10)
2	7	8 x 70 (.31 x 2.76)	20–27 (15–19)
3	4	8 x 55 (.31 x 2.17)	12–15 (9–10)
4	4	8 x 28 (.31 x 1.1)	

Fig. 94 Water pump attaching bolts. 1.8L/4-107 engine

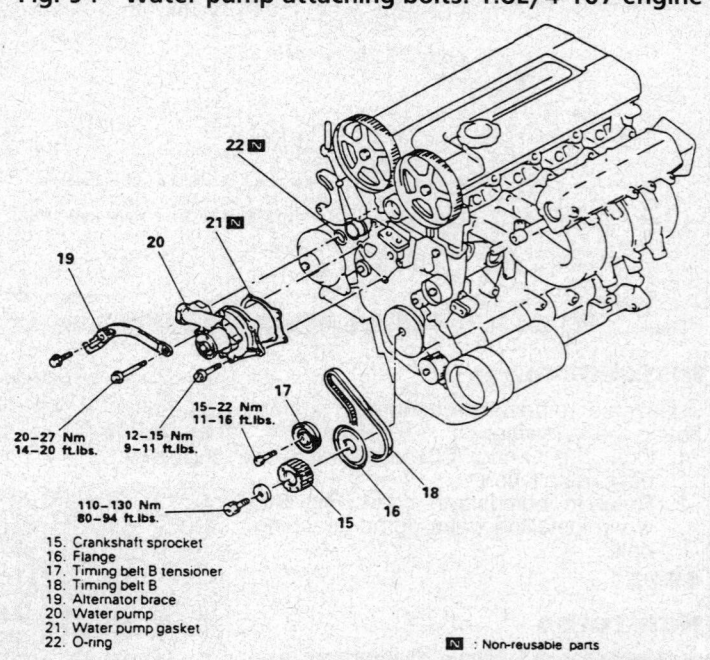

15. Crankshaft sprocket
16. Flange
17. Timing belt B tensioner
18. Timing belt B
19. Alternator brace
20. Water pump
21. Water pump gasket
22. O-ring

N : Non-reusable parts

Fig. 95 Water pump assembly removal (Part 2 of 2). 1992–94 2.0L/4-122 engine

a. Align hose clamps in position as marked.
b. **On models with turbo,** install air cleaner bracket
c. **On models with automatic transaxle,** install cooling lines.
d. **On all models,** ensure drain is

closed, then refill coolant. Replace cap, start engine until warm. Check for leaks, then recheck coolant and fill if necessary.

1995

Remove radiator in numbered sequence, **Figs. 100 and 101,** noting the following:

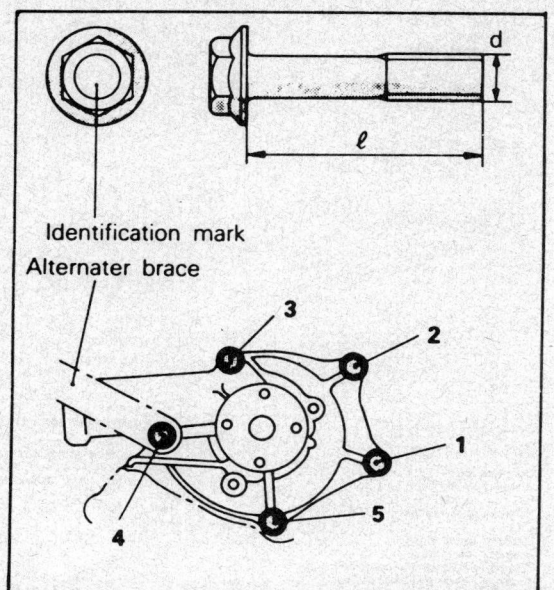

Identification mark
Alternater brace

No.	Identification mark	Bolt diameter (d) x length (ℓ) mm (in.)	Torque Nm (ft.lbs.)
1	4	8 x 14 (.31 x .55)	
2	4	8 x 22 (.31 x .87)	12–15 (9–10)
3	4	8 x 30 (.31 x 1.18)	
4	7	8 x 65 (.31 x 2.56)	20–27 (15–19)
5	4	8 x 28 (.31 x 1.10)	12–15 (9–10)

CR1089100112000X

Fig. 96 Water pump attaching bolts. 1992–94 2.0L/4-122 engine

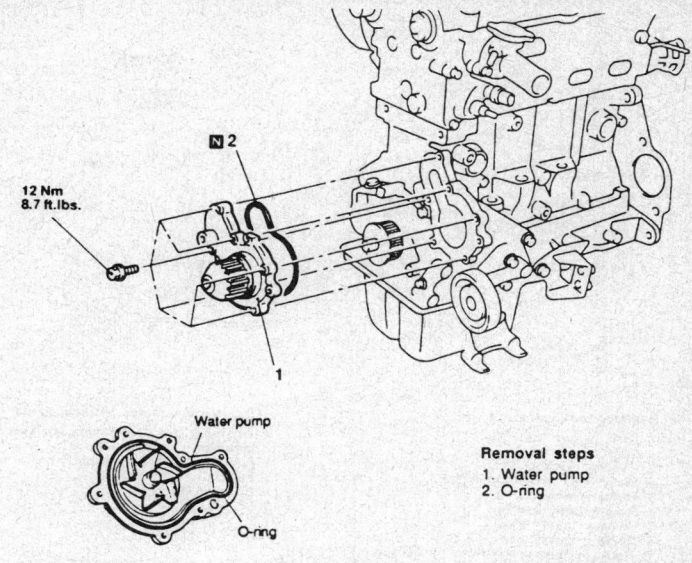

12 Nm
8.7 ft.lbs.

Water pump

O-ring

Removal steps
1. Water pump
2. O-ring

CR1089500146000X

Fig. 97 Water pump assembly removal. 1995 non-turbo

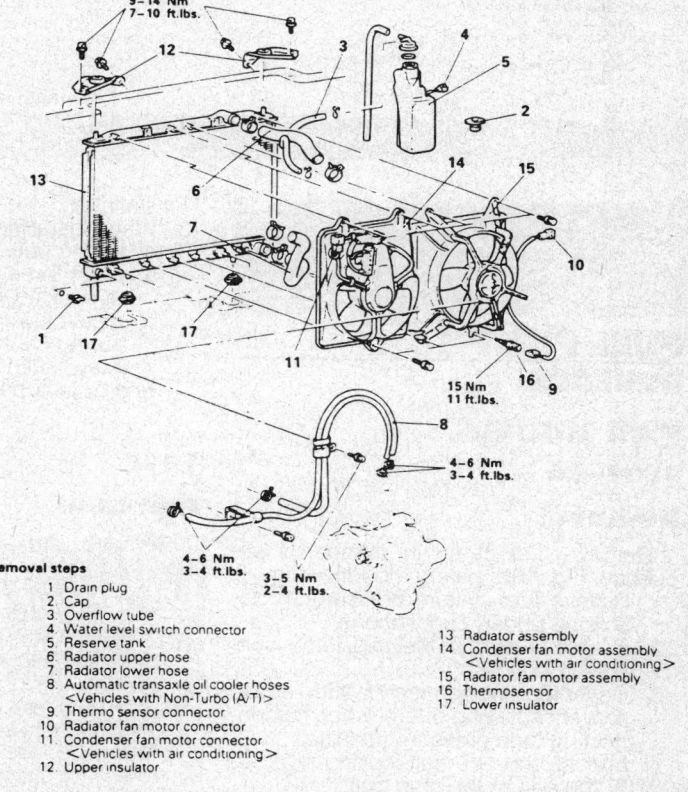

9–14 Nm
7–10 ft.lbs.

15 Nm
11 ft.lbs.

8

4–6 Nm
3–4 ft.lbs.

4–6 Nm
3–4 ft.lbs.

3–5 Nm
2–4 ft.lbs.

Removal steps
1. Drain plug
2. Cap
3. Overflow tube
4. Water level switch connector
5. Reserve tank
6. Radiator upper hose
7. Radiator lower hose
8. Automatic transaxle oil cooler hoses <Vehicles with Non-Turbo (A/T)>
9. Thermo sensor connector
10. Radiator fan motor connector
11. Condenser fan motor connector <Vehicles with air conditioning>
12. Upper insulator
13. Radiator assembly
14. Condenser fan motor assembly <Vehicles with air conditioning>
15. Radiator fan motor assembly
16. Thermosensor
17. Lower insulator

CR1089400148000X

Fig. 99 Radiator assembly. 1992-94

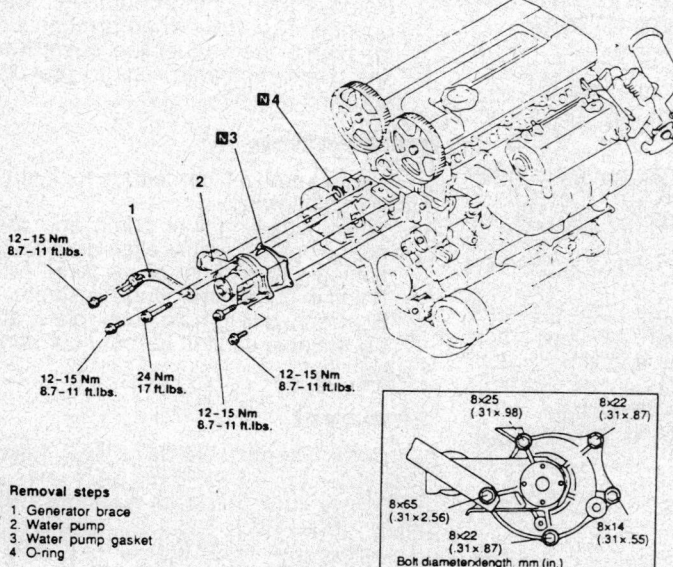

12–15 Nm
8.7–11 ft.lbs.

12–15 Nm
8.7–11 ft.lbs.

24 Nm
17 ft.lbs.

12–15 Nm
8.7–11 ft.lbs.

12–15 Nm
8.7–11 ft.lbs.

8×25
(.31×.98)

8×22
(.31×.87)

8×65
(.31×2.56)

8×22
(.31×.87)

8×14
(.31×.55)

Bolt diameter×length. mm (in.)

CR1089500147000X

Removal steps
1. Generator brace
2. Water pump
3. Water pump gasket
4. O-ring

Fig. 98 Water pump assembly removal. 1995 turbo

1. Drain engine coolant as follows:
   a. Place instrument panel temperature control lever in Hot position.
   b. Carefully remove radiator cap.
   c. Remove radiator drain plug.
2. Mark and note the position of the hose clamps before removal.
3. **On models with turbo,** remove air cleaner bracket.
4. **On models with automatic transax-** le, plug or cover nipples and hoses for cooling lines to ensure dust, dirt or other contaminants do not enter lines.
5. **On all models,** reverse procedure to install, noting the following:
   a. Align hose clamps in position as marked.
   b. **On models with turbo,** install air cleaner bracket.
   c. **On models with automatic transaxle,** install cooling lines.

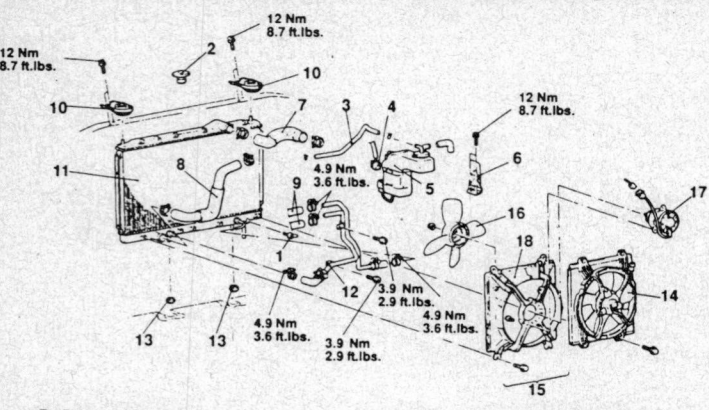

Radiator removal steps
1. Drain plug
2. Cap
3. Overflow tube
4. Water level switch connector
5. Reserve tank
6. Reserve tank bracket
7. Radiator upper hose
8. Radiator lower hose
9. Transaxle fluid cooler hose connection <Vehicles with A/T>
10. Upper insulator
11. Radiator assembly
12. Transaxle fluid cooler hose and pipe assembly <Vehicles with A/T>
13. Lower insulator
14. Condenser fan motor assembly <Vehicles with A/C>
15. Radiator fan motor assembly
16. Fan
17. Radiator fan motor
18. Shroud

Radiator fan motor removal steps
12. Transaxle fluid cooler hose and pipe assembly <Vehicles with A/T>
15. Radiator fan motor assembly
16. Fan
17. Radiator fan motor
18. Shroud

Fig. 100   Radiator assembly. 1995 2.0L/4-122 non-turbocharged engine

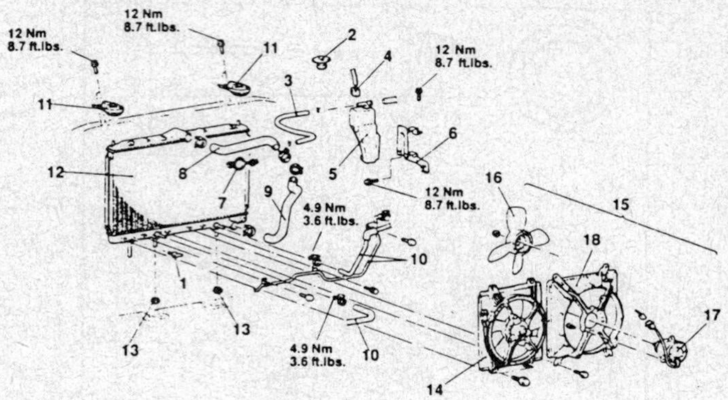

Radiator removal steps
1. Drain plug
2. Cap
3. Overflow tube
4. Water level switch connector
5. Reserve tank
7. Clip
8. Radiator upper hose
9. Radiator lower hose
10. Transaxle fluid cooler hose and pipe assembly <Vehicles with A/T>
11. Upper insulator
12. Radiator assembly
13. Lower insulator
14. Condenser fan motor assembly <Vehicles with A/C>
15. Radiator fan motor assembly
16. Fan
17. Radiator fan motor
18. Shroud

Radiator fan motor removal steps
5. Reserve tank
10. Transaxle fluid cooler hose and pipe assembly <Vehicles with A/T>
15. Radiator fan motor assembly
16. Fan
17. Radiator fan motor
18. Shroud

Fig. 101   Radiator assembly. 1995 2.0L/4-122 turbocharged engine

d. **On all models**, ensure drain is closed, then refill coolant. Replace cap, start engine until warm. Check for leaks, then recheck coolant and fill if necessary.

FUEL PUMP
REPLACE
FWD MODELS
1992-94
Removal

Remove fuel pump in numbered sequence, **Fig. 102**, noting the following:
1. Relieve fuel system pressure as described under "Precautions."
2. Remove fuel from fuel tank into a suitable container.
3. Cover fuel line connection with rags to prevent spraying of fuel when disconnecting high pressure fuel line.
4. Loosen the two self-locking nuts (3) to the end of the stud bolt.
5. After disconnecting the lateral rod and body (5), lower the lateral rod and suspend from axle beam using a piece of wire.

Installation

Reverse removal procedure to install, noting the following:
1. Install overfill limiter in the direction as shown, **Fig. 103**.
2. When installing fuel gauge unit, align the two positioning projections as shown, **Fig. 104**. Ensure bend in float assembly is pointed to left during in-

stallation.
3. When installing fuel pump, O-ring and attaching bolt, proceed as follows:
   a. Align three positioning projections of packing with holes in fuel pump.
   b. Install lowest holding bolt first, ensuring O-ring is not pinched.
4. Tighten self-locking nuts until rear end of tank band contacts body.

1995
Removal

Remove fuel pump in numbered sequence, **Fig. 105**.
1. Relieve fuel pressure as outlined under "Precautions."
2. Remove fuel from fuel tank into a suitable container.
3. When disconnecting high pressure fuel line, cover fuel line connection with rags to prevent spraying of fuel.
4. Remove rear seat cushion and floor plate for access to fuel pump.
5. Disconnect hoses and connectors to remove fuel pump

Installation

Reverse removal procedure to install, noting the following:
1. Align packing position projections with holes in fuel pump assembly.
2. Ensure fuel pump assembly and hoses are not leaking.
3. Before installing hole cover plate, apply suitable sealant to rear floor pan.

AWD MODELS
1992-94
Removal

1. Relieve fuel pressure as outlined under "Precautions."
2. Remove fuel pump in numbered sequence, **Fig. 106**. When disconnecting high pressure fuel line, cover fuel line connection with rags to prevent spraying of fuel.

Installation

Reverse removal procedure to install, noting the following:
1. When installing fuel pump and fuel gauge unit assembly, align three positioning projections of packing with holes in pump and gauge assembly.
2. Before installing hole cover plate, apply suitable sealant to rear floor pan.

1995
Removal

Relieve fuel pressure as outlined under "Precautions."
Remove fuel pump in numbered sequence, **Fig. 107**.
1. Remove fuel from fuel tank into a suitable container.
2. When disconnecting high pressure fuel line, cover fuel line connection with rags to prevent spraying of fuel.
3. Remove rear seat cushion and floor plate for access to fuel pump.
4. Disconnect hoses and connectors to remove fuel pump

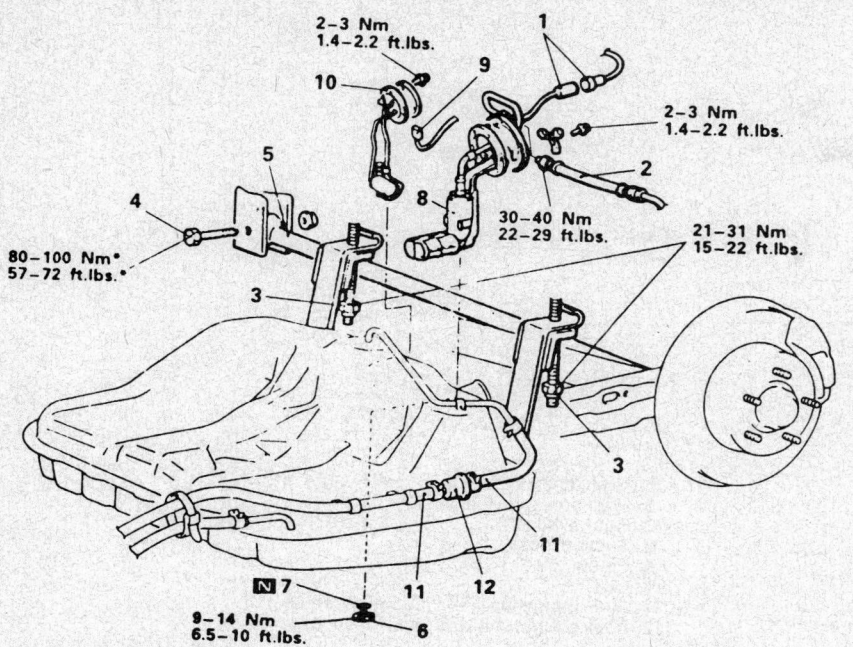

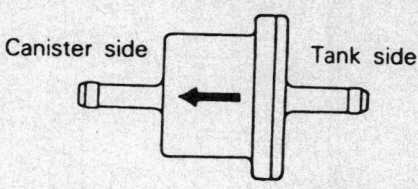

Fig. 103 Fuel tank overfill limiter. 1992–94 FWD models

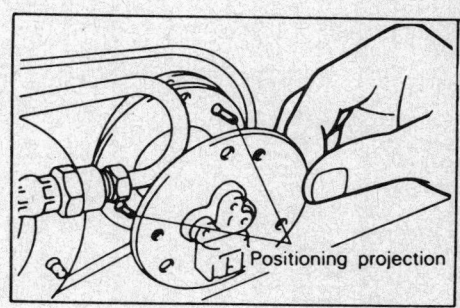

Fig. 104 Fuel gauge unit installation. 1992–94 FWD models

Fuel pump removal steps
1. Connection for fuel pump connector
2. High pressure fuel hose
3. Self locking nut
4. Lateral rod attaching bolt
5. Lateral rod and body connection
6. Bolt
7. O-ring
8. Electric fuel pump

Fuel gauge unit removal steps
3. Self locking nut
4. Lateral rod attaching bolt
5. Lateral rod and body connection
9. Connection for fuel gauge unit connector
10. Fuel gauge unit

Overfill limiter removal steps
11. Connection for vapor hose
12. Overfill limiter (Two-way valve)

Fig. 102 Fuel pump assembly removal. 1992–94 FWD models

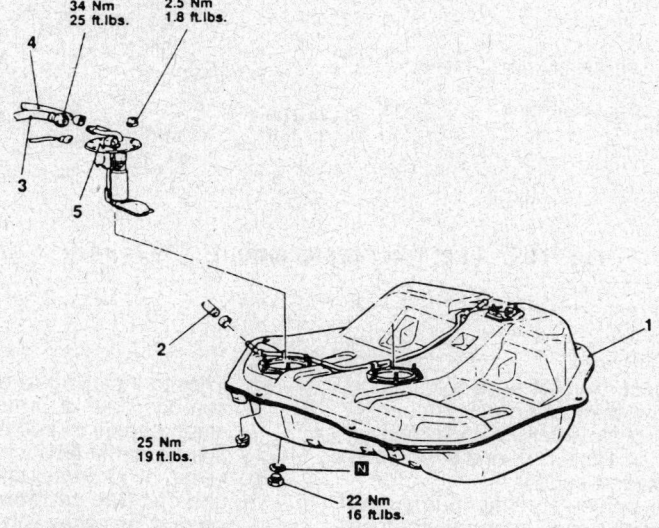

Removal steps
1. Fuel tank
2. Vapor hose
3. High-pressure fuel hose
4. Return hose
5. Fuel pump assembly

Fig. 105 Fuel pump assembly removal. 1995 FWD models

Installation

Reverse removal procedure to install, noting the following:
1. Ensure packing seal is not damaged or deformed.
2. Apply soapy water to fuel tank threads, then install fuel pump and cap.
3. Using special cap tightening tool No. MB991480, **Fig. 108**, or equivalent, **torque** cap to 36 ft. lbs.
4. Ensure fuel pump assembly and hoses are not leaking.

FUEL FILTER
REPLACE

1992–94

When replacing fuel filter refer to **Fig. 109** for removal and installation procedure.
Relieve fuel pressure as outlined under "Precautions."

1995

When replacing fuel filter, refer to **Fig. 110** for removal and installation procedure.
1. Relieve fuel pressure as outlined under "Precautions."
2. Remove battery and air intake hose to access fuel filter.
3. Reverse procedure to install.

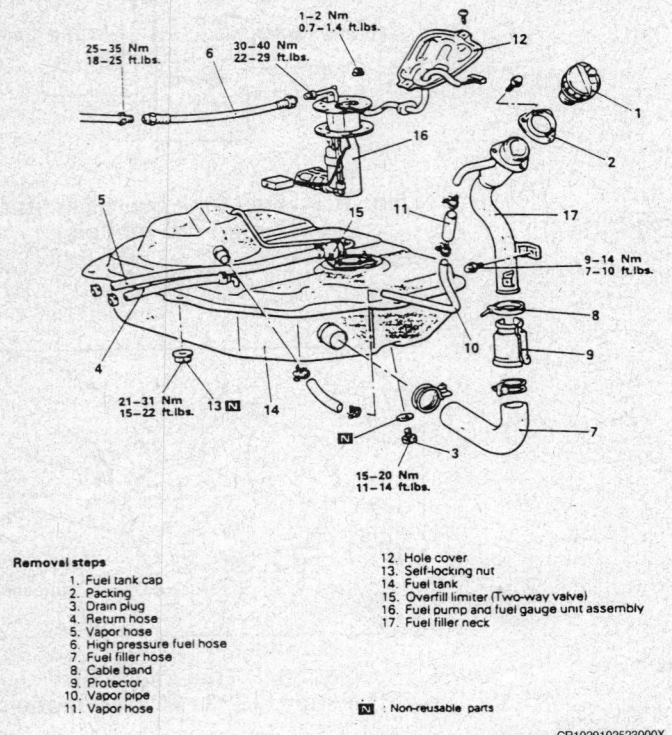

Removal steps

1. Fuel tank cap
2. Packing
3. Drain plug
4. Return hose
5. Vapor hose
6. High pressure fuel hose
7. Fuel filler hose
8. Cable band
9. Protector
10. Vapor pipe
11. Vapor hose
12. Hole cover
13. Self-locking nut
14. Fuel tank
15. Overfill limiter (Two-way valve)
16. Fuel pump and fuel gauge unit assembly
17. Fuel filler neck

: Non-reusable parts

CR1029102523000X

Fig. 106 Fuel pump assembly removal. 1992–94 AWD models

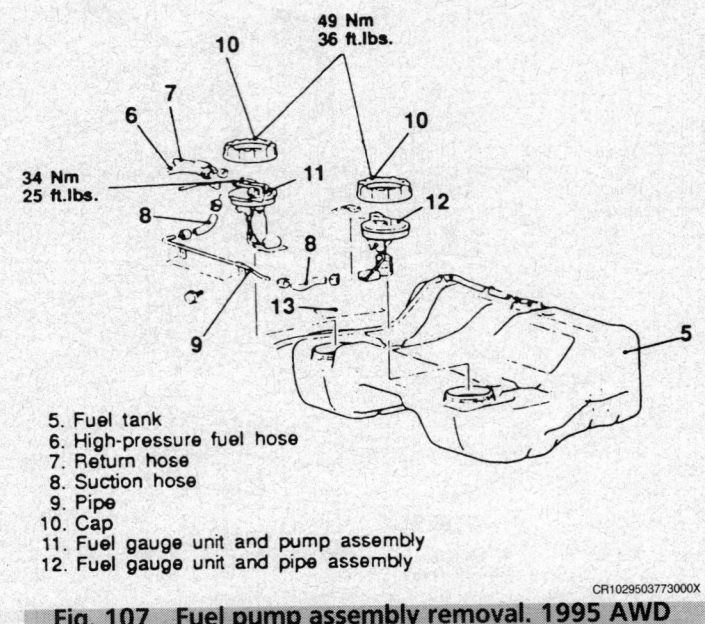

5. Fuel tank
6. High-pressure fuel hose
7. Return hose
8. Suction hose
9. Pipe
10. Cap
11. Fuel gauge unit and pump assembly
12. Fuel gauge unit and pipe assembly

CR1029503773000X

Fig. 107 Fuel pump assembly removal. 1995 AWD models

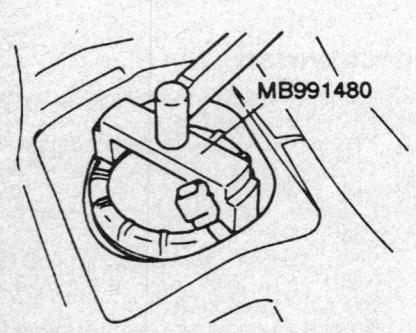

MB991480

CR1029503774000X

Fig. 108 Fuel pump cap installation. 1995 AWD models

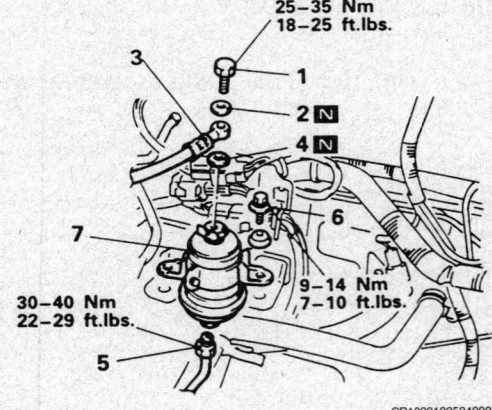

1. Eye bolt
2. Gasket
3. Connection for Fuel high-pressure hose
4. Gasket
5. Connection for Fuel main pipe
6. Mounting bolt
7. Fuel filter

Fig. 109 Fuel filter replacement. 1992–94

CR1029102524000X

TURBOCHARGER
REPLACE

Remove turbocharger in numbered sequence, **Fig. 111**, noting the following.
1. Disconnect battery ground cable.
2. Drain engine cooling system as follows:
   a. Place temperature control lever in hot position.
   b. Carefully remove radiator cap.
   c. Remove radiator drain plug.
3. Drain engine oil.

4. Disconnect oxygen sensor electrical connector, then using oxygen sensor socket tool No. MD998748 or equivalent and an offset box-end wrench, remove oxygen sensor.
5. Remove power steering pump from bracket with hoses attached, then secure pump aside with a piece of wire.
6. Remove turbocharger assembly with water pipes A and B and oil pipe attached. **After disconnecting oil pipe, ensure foreign material does not enter oil passage hole of turbocharger.**
7. Reverse procedure to install, noting the following:

a. Prior to installing turbocharger assembly, pour a small quantity of clean engine oil into oil supply pipe fitting hole in turbocharger.
b. Clean alignment surfaces of turbocharger. **Use caution not to allow gasket or other foreign material to enter oil passage hole.**
c. Use new gaskets, locknuts and O-rings.
d. Install oxygen sensor using oxygen sensor socket tool No. MD998748 or equivalent and an offset box-end wrench, then connect oxygen sensor electrical connector.

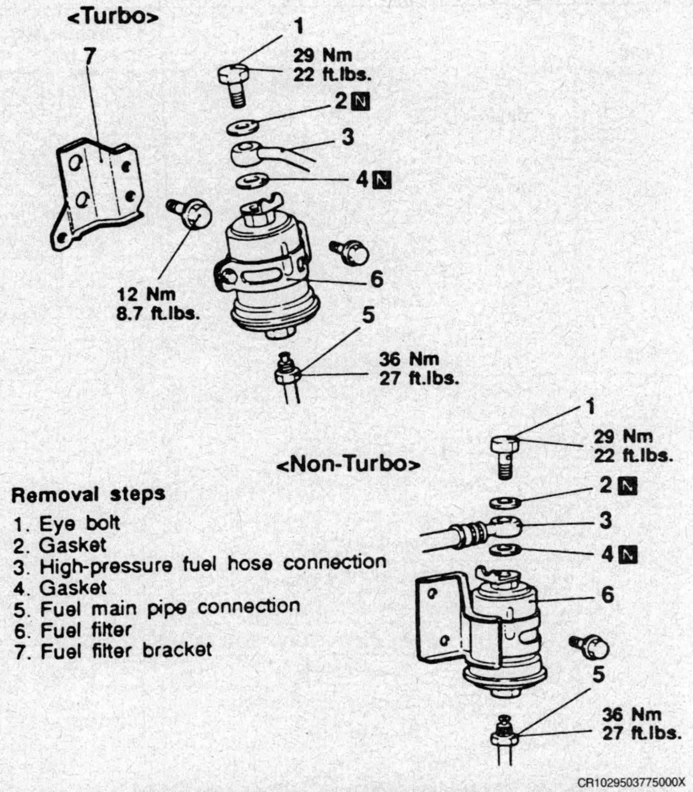

<Turbo>

7

1

29 Nm
22 ft.lbs.

2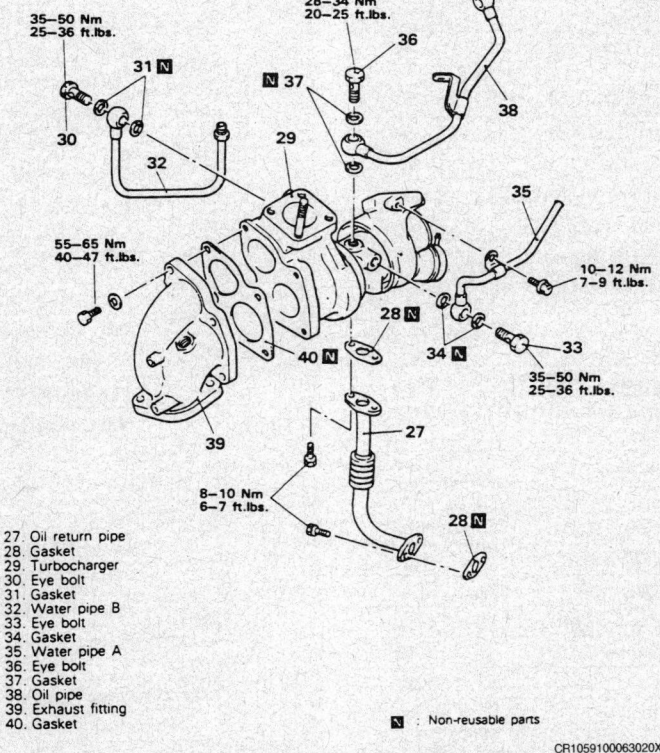

3

4

12 Nm
8.7 ft.lbs.

6

5

36 Nm
27 ft.lbs.

<Non-Turbo>

1

29 Nm
22 ft.lbs.

2

3

4

6

5

36 Nm
27 ft.lbs.

Removal steps

1. Eye bolt
2. Gasket
3. High-pressure fuel hose connection
4. Gasket
5. Fuel main pipe connection
6. Fuel filter
7. Fuel filter bracket

CR1029503775000X

Fig. 110 Fuel filter replacement. 1995

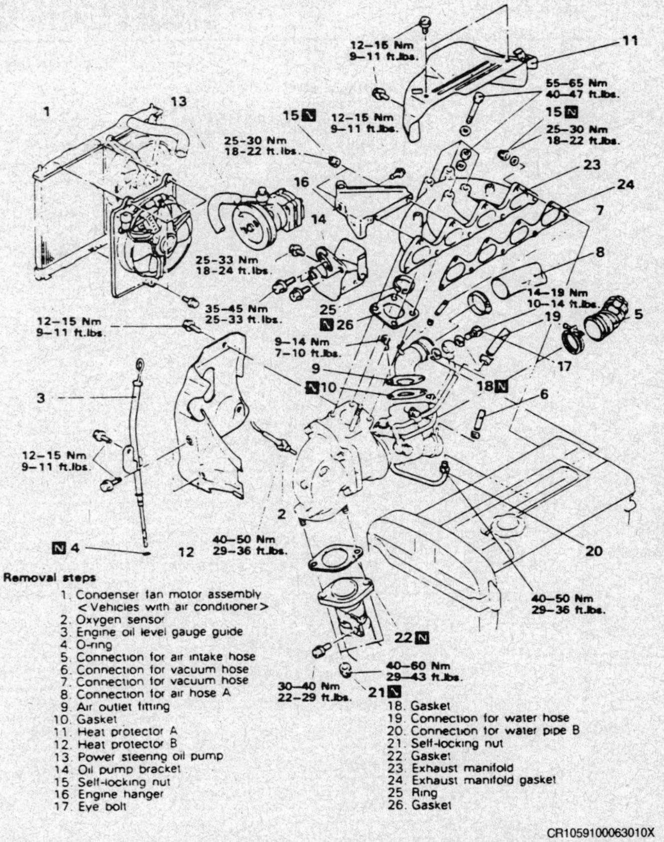

12–15 Nm
9–11 ft.lbs.

11

55–65 Nm
40–47 ft.lbs.

12–15 Nm
9–11 ft.lbs.

15

25–30 Nm
18–22 ft.lbs.

13

1

15

25–30 Nm
18–22 ft.lbs.

16

14

23

24

7

8

25–33 Nm
18–24 ft.lbs.

25

26

14–19 Nm
10–14 ft.lbs.

19

5

35–45 Nm
25–33 ft.lbs.

9–14 Nm
7–10 ft.lbs.

17

12–15 Nm
9–11 ft.lbs.

3

9

10

18

6

12–15 Nm
9–11 ft.lbs.

40–50 Nm
29–36 ft.lbs.

20

4

12

2

40–50 Nm
29–36 ft.lbs.

30–40 Nm
22–29 ft.lbs.

22

21

40–60 Nm
29–43 ft.lbs.

Removal steps

1. Condenser fan motor assembly
   <Vehicles with air conditioner>
2. Oxygen sensor
3. Engine oil level gauge guide
4. O-ring
5. Connection for air intake hose
6. Connection for vacuum hose
7. Connection for vacuum hose
8. Connection for air hose A
9. Air outlet fitting
10. Gasket
11. Heat protector A
12. Heat protector B
13. Power steering oil pump
14. Oil pump bracket
15. Self-locking nut
16. Engine hanger
17. Eye bolt
18. Gasket
19. Connection for water hose
20. Connection for water pipe B
21. Self-locking nut
22. Gasket
23. Exhaust manifold
24. Exhaust manifold gasket
25. Ring
26. Gasket

CR1059100063010X

Fig. 111 Turbocharger assembly removal (Part 1 of 2). 2.0L/4-122 engine

35–50 Nm
25–36 ft.lbs.

31

30

28–34 Nm
20–25 ft.lbs.

36

37

38

29

32

35

10–12 Nm
7–9 ft.lbs.

55–65 Nm
40–47 ft.lbs.

28

34

33

35–50 Nm
25–36 ft.lbs.

40

39

27

8–10 Nm
6–7 ft.lbs.

28

27. Oil return pipe
28. Gasket
29. Turbocharger
30. Eye bolt
31. Gasket
32. Water pipe B
33. Eye bolt
34. Gasket
35. Water pipe A
36. Eye bolt
37. Gasket
38. Oil pipe
39. Exhaust fitting
40. Gasket

N : Non-reusable parts

CR1059100063020X

Fig. 111 Turbocharger assembly removal (Part 2 of 2). 2.0L/4-122 engine

TIGHTENING SPECIFICATIONS

Year	Component	Torque/Ft. Lbs.	Year	Component	Torque/Ft. Lbs.
1992 –94	A/C Compressor Bracket	17-20		Oil Level Gauge Mounting Bolt	9-11
	Air Cleaner Resonator	7-9		Oil Pan (Bolts)	4-6
	Air Cleaner-to-Body	6-7		Oil Pan (Nuts)	3.5-5
	Auto Tensioner	14-20		Oil Pan Drain Plug	25-33
	Camshaft Bearing Cap Bolt (Long) ①	14-15		Oil Pipe-to-Engine (Turbo) ⑪	10-14
	Camshaft Bearing Cap Bolt (Short) ①	14-20		Oil Pressure Gauge Unit	6-9
	Camshaft Sprocket	58-72		Oil Pressure Switch	6-9
	Center Cover ⑪	2-3		Oil Pump Cover	29-36
	Centermember Bolt ⑪	58-72		Oil Pump Driven Gear	25-29
	Connecting Rod Bearing Cap ①	24-25		Oil Pump Sprocket	⑦
	Crankshaft Bearing Cap ①	37-39		Oil Return Pipe-to-Oil Pan (Turbo) ⑪	6-7
	Crankshaft Pulley	②		Oil Screen	11-16
	Crankshaft Sprocket	80-94		Oxygen Sensor ⑪	29-36
	Cylinder Head Bolts	③ ④		Power Steering Bracket	25-33
	Distributor ①	7-9		Radiator Upper Insulator	7-10
	Driveplate	94-101		Relief Plug	11-13
	EGR Valve	⑤		Rocker Cover	2-3
	Electric Fuel Pump (Bolt)	6.5-10		Silent Shaft Sprocket	⑧
	Electric Fuel Pump (Screws)	1.4-2.2		Tensioner Pulley Bracket	17-20
	Engine Coolant Temperature Sensor ⑪	15-29		Thermo Valve ①	14-28
	Engine Cooler Pipe-to-Front Case ⑪	29-33		Thermo Sensor To Radiator	2-3
	Engine Mount Bracket Nut	36-47		Throttle Body	⑨
	Engine Mount Bracket-to-Body	36-51		Throttle Position Sensor	1.1-1.8
	Engine Mount Insulator Nut (Large)	43-58		Timing Belt B Tensioner Bolt	11-16
	Engine Mount Insulator Nut (Small)	22-29		Timing Belt Front Cover	7-9
	Engine Oil Cooler Mounting Nut ⑪	6-9		Timing Belt Idle Pulley	25-30
	Engine Oil Hose Mounting Nut ⑪	2-4		Timing Belt Rear Cover	7-9
	Exhaust Manifold-to-Engine	18-22		Timing Belt Tensioner Pulley	⑩
	Exhaust Manifold-to-Turbocharger (Turbo) ⑪	40-47		Transaxle Mount Insulator Nut	43-58
	Exhaust Pipe Clamp Bolt	22-29		Transaxle Mount To Body	29-36
	Exhaust Pipe Support Bracket	22-30		Wastegate Actuator ⑪	7-9
	Exhaust Pipe-to-Hanger	7-11		Water Outlet ⑪	12-14
	Exhaust Pipe-to-Manifold (Non-Turbo)	22-29		Water Pipe To Engine ⑪	10-14
	Exhaust Pipe-to-Manifold (Turbo) ⑪	29-43		Water Pipe To Turbocharger ⑪	25-36
	Eye Bolt (Engine Oil Cooler Side) ⑪	22-25		Water Pump Bolt (4T)	9-11
	Eye Bolt (Oil Filter Bracket Side) ⑪	29-33		Water Pump Bolt (7T)	14-20
	Flywheel	94-101		Water Pump Pulley	6-7
	Front Case	14-16	1995	A/C Compressor Bracket	17-20
	Front Roll Stopper Bracket-to-Body	40-54		Air Cleaner-to-Body	6-7
	Front Roll Stopper Bracket-to-Centermember	29-36		Auto Tensioner (Non-Turbo)	23
	Front Roll Stopper Insulator Nut	36-47		Auto Tensioner (Turbo)	17
	Fuel Gauge Unit	1.4-2.2		Camshaft Bearing Cap Bolt (Non-Turbo)	⑫
	Fuel Tank Self-Locking Nut	57-72		Camshaft Bearing Cap Bolt (Turbo)	14-15
	Heat Shield-to-Exhaust Manifold ⑪	9-11		Camshaft Sprocket (Non-Turbo)	75
	Intake Manifold Stay Bolt	⑥		Camshaft Sprocket (Turbo)	65
	Intake Manifold To Engine (M8)	11-14		Center Cover (Turbo)	2.2
	Intake Manifold To Engine (M10)	22-30		Connecting Rod Bearing Caps (Turbo)	16
	Intercooler Air Bypass Valve ⑪	11-16		Connecting Rod Bearing Caps (Non-Turbo)	⑮
	Intercooler Air Pipe B ⑪	9-11			
	Intercooler-to-Body ⑪	9-11		Crankshaft Bearing Caps (Non-Turbo)	⑭
	Left Engine Support Bracket	22-30		Crankshaft Bearing Cap (Turbo)	⑬
	Oil Filter Bracket	11-16		Crankshaft Pulley (Non-Turbo)	105
				Crankshaft Pulley (Turbo)	18
				Crankshaft Sprocket (Turbo)	80-94

TIGHTENING SPECIFICATIONS

Year	Component	Torque/Ft. Lbs.
	Cylinder Head Bolt (Non-Turbo)	④ ⑰
	Cylinder Head Bolt (Turbo)	④ ⑱
	EGR Valve	16
	Electric Fuel Pump (Bolt)	1.8
	Engine Coolant Temperature Sensor	5
	Engine Oil Cooler Mounting Bolt (Turbo)	29-33
	Exhaust Manifold To Engine (Non-Turbo)	17
	Exhaust Manifold To Engine (Turbo)	22
	Exhaust Manifold To Turbocharger (Turbo)	44-47
	Exhaust Pipe Clamp Bolt	9.4
	Exhaust Pipe To Hanger	9.4
	Exhaust Pipe To Manifold (Non-Turbo)	33
	Exhaust Pipe To Manifold (Turbo)	33-36
	Flywheel	94-101
	Fuel Gauge Unit (FWD)	1.8
	Fuel Gauge Unit (AWD)	36
	Heat Shield To Exhaust Manifold (Turbo)	9-11
	Intake Manifold To Engine (Non-Turbo)	17
	Intake Manifold To Engine (Turbo)	14
	Oil Filter Bracket (Turbo)	11-16
	Oil Pan (Non-Turbo)	8.9
	Oil Pan (Turbo)	5.1
	Oil Pan Drain Plug (Non-Turbo)	25
	Oil Pan Drain Plug (Turbo)	29
	Oil Pressure Gauge Unit (Turbo)	7
	Oil Pressure Switch (Turbo)	7
	Oil Pump Cover (Non-Turbo)	17
	Oil Pump Cover (Turbo)	9-12
	Oil Pump Driven Gear (Turbo)	7
	Oil Return Pipe To Oil Pan (Turbo)	6.5
	Oil Screen (Non-Turbo)	21
	Oil Screen (Turbo)	14
	Oxygen Sensor	22
	Tensioner Pulley Bracket (Turbo)	17-20
	Throttle Body	11-16

Year	Component	Torque/Ft. Lbs.
	Timing Belt Tensioner Bolt (Turbo)	17-20
	Timing Belt B Tensioner (Turbo)	14
	Timing Belt Front Cover, Top (Non-Turbo)	8.9
	Timing Belt Front Cover, Bottom (Non-Turbo)	21
	Timing Belt Front Cover (Turbo)	7.2-8.7
	Timing Belt Tensioner Pulley (Non-Turbo)	30
	Water Pump (Non-Turbo)	8.7
	Water Pump (Turbo)	8.7-11

① —1.8L/4-107 Engine.
② —1.8L/4-107 Engine, 11–13 ft. lbs.; 2.0L/4-122, 14–22 ft. lbs.
③ —1.8L/4-107 Engine, 51–54 ft. lbs.; 2.0L/4-122, 65–72 ft. lbs.
④ —Tighten in two or three steps. Refer to text for bolt tightening sequence.
⑤ —1.8L/4-107 Engine, 7–11 ft. lbs.; 2.0L/4-122, 11–16 ft. lbs.
⑥ —1.8L/4-107 Engine, 13–18 ft. lbs.; 2.0L/4-122, 18–22 ft. lbs.
⑦ —1.8L/4-107 Engine, 26–29 ft. lbs.; 2.0L/4-122, 36–43 ft. lbs.
⑧ —1.8L/4-107 Engine, 25–29 ft. lbs.; 2.0L/4-122, 31–35 ft. lbs.
⑨ —1.8L/4-107 Engine, 7–9 ft. lbs.; 2.0L/4-122, 11–16 ft. lbs.
⑩ —1.8L/4-107 Engine, 16–22 ft. lbs.; 2.0L/4-122, 31–40 ft. lbs.
⑪ —2.0L/4-122 Engine.
⑫ —Main camshaft bearing caps, 21 ft. lbs.; small camshaft bearing caps, 8.9 ft. lbs.
⑬ —18 ft. lbs., then tighten an additional 90–100°.
⑭ —Inner crankshaft bearing caps, 55 ft. lbs.; outer crankshaft bearing caps, 20 ft. lbs.
⑮ —20 ft. lbs., then tighten an additional 90°.
⑯ —14.5 ft. lbs., then tighten an additional 90–100°.
⑰ —Refer to text.
⑱ —Torque to 58 ft. lbs., then fully loosen all bolts. Torque bolts to 15 ft. lbs., then tighten each bolt an additional 180° in 90° increments.

Clutch & Manual Transaxle

NOTE: On Air Bag Equipped Models, Refer To "Air Bag System Precautions" Located In The Front Of This Manual For System Disarming & Arming Procedures.

INDEX

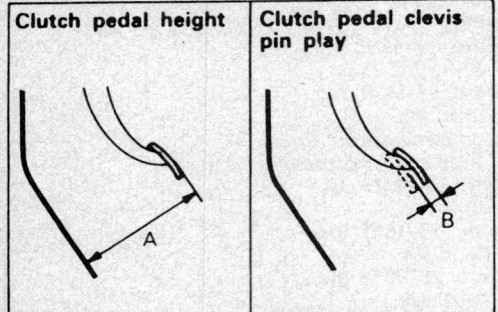

Fig. 1   Clutch pedal inspection

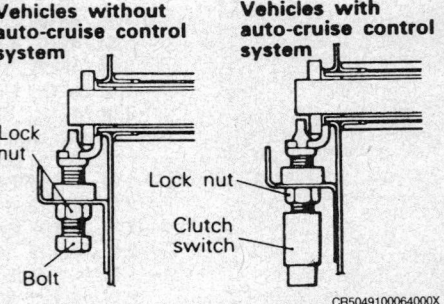

Fig. 2   Clutch pedal adjustment. 1992-94

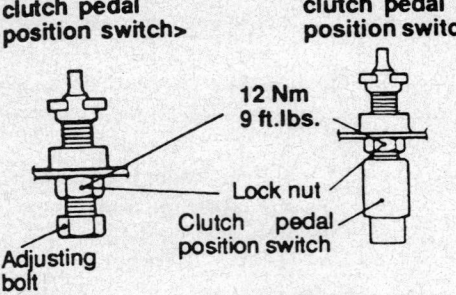

Fig. 3   Clutch pedal adjustment. 1995

Fig. 4   Pushrod adjustment

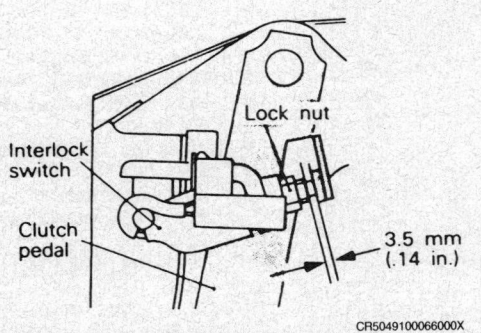

Fig. 5   Interlock switch adjustment

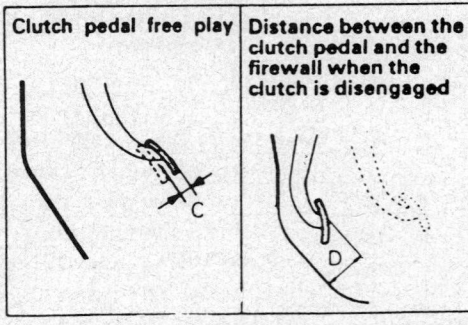

Fig. 6   Clutch pedal operation inspection

PRECAUTIONS

AIR BAG SYSTEMS

Refer to "Air Bag System Precautions" in the front of this manual for system disarming and arming procedures.

ADJUSTMENTS

CLUTCH PEDAL

1. Measure clutch pedal height or clevis pin play as shown, **Fig. 1.**
2. If height is higher than 6.93-7.13 inches, proceed as follows:
   a. **On 1992-94 models less auto-cruise system,** adjust bolt until pedal height is correct, **Fig. 2,** then secure by tightening locknut.
   b. **On 1992-94 models with auto-cruise,** disconnect clutch switch connector. Turn switch until pedal height is correct, **Fig. 2,** then secure by tightening locknut.
   c. **On 1995 models,** refer to **Fig. 3** for adjustment.
3. **On all models,** if pedal height is lower than 6.93-7.13 inches, proceed as follows:
   a. Loosen bolt or clutch switch and turn pushrod until pedal height is correct, **Fig. 4. Do not move pushrod toward master cylinder.**
   b. After adjustment, tighten bolt or clutch switch to reach pedal stopper, then lock with locknut.
4. If clevis pin play is not .04-.12 inch, turn pushrod until clevis pin play is correct.

5. Ensure interlock switch is as shown, **Fig. 5,** when clutch pedal is fully depressed, and if necessary, adjust.
6. Confirm clutch pedal freeplay, **Fig. 6,** is .24 to .51 inches.
7. Confirm distance between clutch pedal and firewall, when clutch is disengaged, **Fig. 6,** is 2.2 inches or more. If distance is not as specified, problem may be the result of air in hydraulic system or faulty master cylinder or clutch.

HYDRAULIC SYSTEM SERVICE

HYDRAULIC CLUTCH SYSTEM BLEEDING

Whenever the any component of the hy-

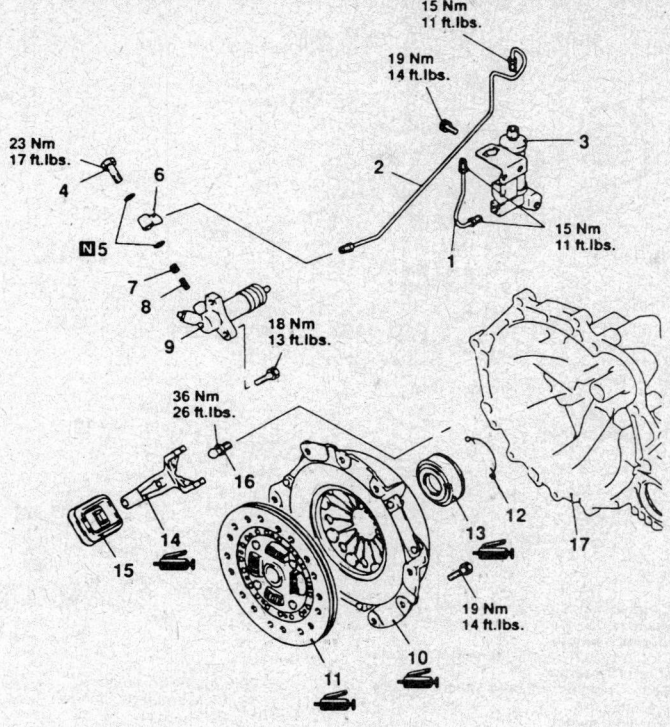

Fig. 7   Clutch assembly. 1995

Disassembly steps

1. Clutch oil tube (A)
2. Clutch oil tube
3. Clutch oil fluid chamber
4. Union bolt
5. Gasket
6. Union
7. Valve plate
8. Valve plate spring
9. Clutch release cylinder
10. Clutch cover
11. Clutch disc
12. Return clip
13. Clutch release bearing
14. Release fork
15. Release fork boot
16. Fulcrum
17. Transaxle

CR5049500087000X

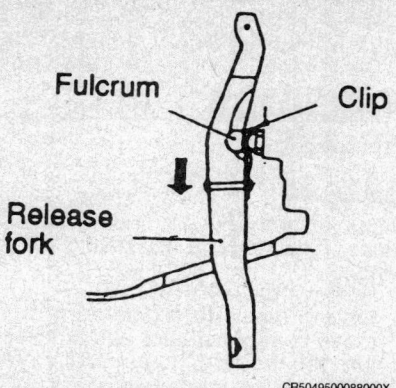

Fig. 8   Release fork removal. 1995

CR5049500088000X

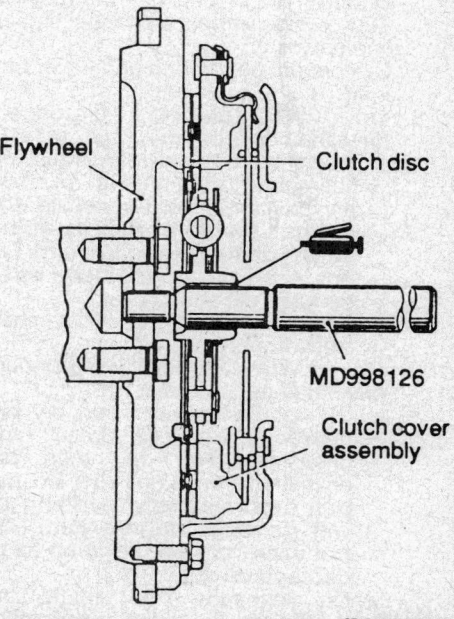

Fig. 9   Clutch disc installation. 1995

CR5049500089000X

draulic clutch system has been removed, bleeding must be performed.

Ensure clutch hydraulic cylinder is full, have helper depress clutch pedal and hold, open bleeder screw on hydraulic cylinder, then close bleeder screw. Repeat procedure until all air is bled from system.

CLUTCH SLAVE CYLINDER, REPLACE

1. Drain clutch fluid into a suitable container.
2. Disconnect clutch slave cylinder tube connections.
3. Remove slave cylinder retaining bolts then the slave cylinder.
4. Reverse procedure to install, noting the following:
   a. Apply multi-purpose grease to slave cylinder pushrod where it contacts the release fork.
   b. Bleed hydraulic clutch system as outlined under "Hydraulic Clutch System Bleeding."

CLUTCH
REPLACE
1992–94

1. Remove transaxle as outlined under "Transaxle, Replace."

2. Diagonally loosen clutch cover bolts in two or three steps.
3. Support clutch cover and remove cover bolts, lowering clutch and clutch cover.
4. Remove clutch bearing return clip, bearing, release fork, fulcrum and release fork boot from transaxle.
5. Reverse procedure to install.

1995

Replace clutch in numbered sequence **Fig. 7**, noting the following:
1. Remove transaxle as outlined under "Transaxle, Replace."
2. Diagonally loosen clutch cover bolts in two or three steps.
3. Support clutch cover and remove cover bolts, lowering clutch and clutch cover.
4. Slide release fork in direction of arrow as shown in **Fig. 8** and disengage fulcrum from clip to release fork. **Do not push the release fork in direction other than arrow or remove with force as clip may be damaged.**
5. Reverse procedure to install. Use special clutch positioning tool No. MD998126, or equivalents, to install clutch disc on flywheel, **Fig. 9**.

CLUTCH PEDAL
REPLACE
1992–94

Remove clutch pedal in numbered sequence, **Fig. 10**, noting the following:
1. Remove lap cooler duct, shower duct, and knee protector. Refer to the "Dash Panel" section for procedures.
2. Remove steering column assembly as outlined under "Steering Column, Replace" in the "Steering Column" section.
3. Remove relay box.
4. Reverse procedure to install, ensuring to apply lubricant to the clutch pedal bushings, clevis pin and washer and, on turbo models, bushing No. 8.

1995

Remove clutch pedal in numbered sequence, **Fig. 11** noting the following:
1. Remove junction box installation bolt.
2. Reverse procedure to install, ensuring to apply lubricant to the clutch pedal

bushings, clevis pin and washer and, on turbo models, rod B and bushing No. 10.

TRANSAXLE
REPLACE

1992-94

Remove transaxle in numbered sequence, **Figs. 12 and 13**, noting the following:

1. Remove battery.
2. **On models with cruise control,** remove control actuator and bracket.
3. **On all models,** remove air intake hose.
4. Raise and support vehicle.
5. Drain transaxle oil.
6. Remove clutch release cylinder and clutch oil line bracket bolt, then secure at body side without disconnecting oil line coupling.
7. Disconnect tie rod end and lower ball joint.
8. **On FWD models,** disconnect driveshaft as follows:
   a. Insert pry bar between transaxle case and driveshaft, **Fig. 14,** then pry driveshaft from transaxle. **Do not pull on driveshaft, as doing so will damage inboard joint. Do not insert pry bar so deep as to damage oil seal.**
   b. Secure removed end of driveshaft away from transaxle.
9. **On AWD models,** disconnect driveshaft as follows:
   a. On righthand side, insert pry bar between transaxle case and driveshaft, **Fig. 14,** then pry driveshaft from transaxle. **Do not pull on driveshaft, as doing so will damage inboard joint. Do not insert pry bar so deep as to damage oil seal.**
   b. On lefthand side, lightly tap driveshaft T.J. case with plastic hammer. **Remove driveshaft with hub and knuckle as an assembly.**
   c. Secure removed end of driveshaft away from transaxle.
10. Remove transfer case in numbered sequence, **Fig. 15,** noting the following:
    a. Move transfer case to left and lower from front side of vehicle, then remove propeller shaft.
11. **On all models,** support transaxle assembly using jack, after moving transaxle to right lower away from vehicle.
12. Reverse procedure to install noting:
    a. When installing driveshaft ensure inboard joint is straight relative to transaxle.
    b. Align serration, then securely insert driveshaft into transaxle.

1995

Remove transaxle in numbered sequence, **Fig. 16** for non-turbo models, **Fig. 17** for turbo models with Front Wheel Drive (FWD), and **Fig. 18** for turbo models with All Wheel Drive (AWD), noting the following:

1. Remove battery.

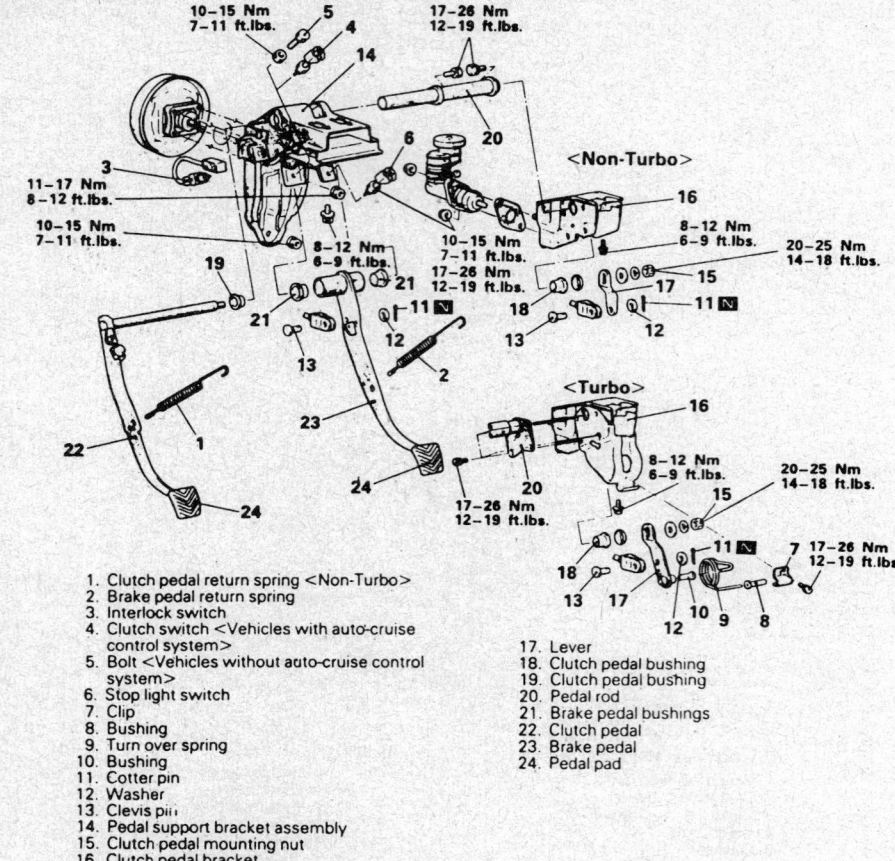

1. Clutch pedal return spring <Non-Turbo>
2. Brake pedal return spring
3. Interlock switch
4. Clutch switch <Vehicles with auto-cruise control system>
5. Bolt <Vehicles without auto-cruise control system>
6. Stop light switch
7. Clip
8. Bushing
9. Turn over spring
10. Bushing
11. Cotter pin
12. Washer
13. Clevis pin
14. Pedal support bracket assembly
15. Clutch pedal mounting nut
16. Clutch pedal bracket
17. Lever
18. Clutch pedal bushing
19. Clutch pedal bushing
20. Pedal rod
21. Brake pedal bushings
22. Clutch pedal
23. Brake pedal
24. Pedal pad

Fig. 10   Clutch pedal removal. 1992-94

2. Raise and support vehicle.
3. Drain transaxle oil.
4. Remove undercover.
5. **On AWD models,** remove transfer case.
6. **On all models,** using a suitable jack, slightly raise transaxle, then remove mounting bracket nuts. **Do not tilt transaxle assembly.**
7. Use special engine support No. MZ203827, or equivalent, to support engine assembly, **Fig. 19**.
8. Using special tool No. MB991113, or equivalent, remove tie rod ends, lateral lower arms, and compression lower arms, **Figs. 20 through 22**. **Loosen but do not remove nuts. Suspend special tool by cord to hold in place.**
9. **On AWD models,** remove drive shaft nut using special tool No. MB990767, or equivalent, **Fig. 23**.
10. **On all models,** disconnect driveshaft as follows:
    a. Insert pry bar between transaxle case and driveshaft, **Fig. 14,** then pry driveshaft from transaxle. **Do not pull on driveshaft, as doing so will damage inboard joint. Do not insert pry bar so deep as to damage oil seal.** Suspend drive shaft with suitable wire.

11. **On AWD models,** lightly tap center bearing bracket using a suitable plastic hammer to remove inner shaft from transaxle, **Fig. 24**.
12. **On all models,** remove clutch release cylinder without disconnecting oil line and suspend it nearby with suitable wire.
13. **On FWD models,** remove flexplate connecting bolts and transaxle assembly mounting bolts, ensuring:
    a. Transaxle must be solidly supported by suitable jack.
    b. Chalk mating marks on the flex plate and clutch pressure plate for easier installation, **Fig. 25**.
    c. Press clutch pressure plate into the transaxle for easier removal.
14. Reverse procedure to install noting;
    a. Inspect front roll stopper. If dimension shown in **Fig. 26** is not 1.57-1.81 inches, replace roll stopper bracket assembly.
    b. Ensure serrated part of drive shaft does not damage oil seal lip.
    c. **On AWD models,** install driveshaft nut washer as shown in **Fig. 27**. Using special tool No. MB990767, or equivalent, tighten driveshaft nut as specified in **Fig. 27**, ensuring there is no load on wheel bearings.

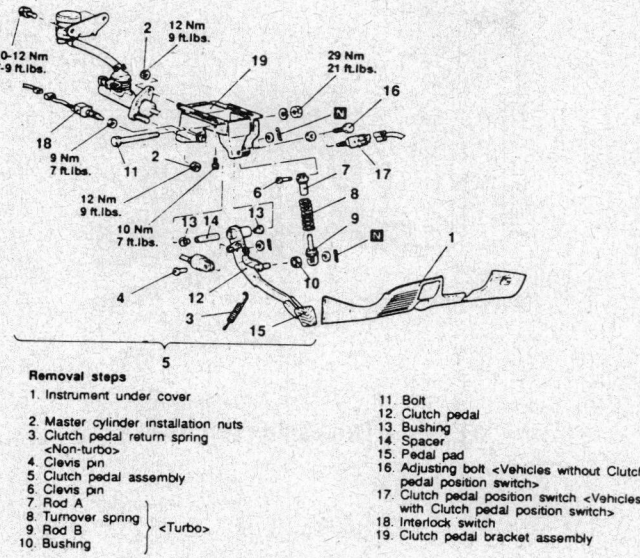

Fig. 11 Clutch pedal removal. 1995

CR5049500090000X

Removal steps
1. Instrument under cover
2. Master cylinder installation nuts
3. Clutch pedal return spring <Non-turbo>
4. Clevis pin
5. Clutch pedal assembly
6. Clevis pin
7. Rod A
8. Turnover spring   <Turbo>
9. Rod B
10. Bushing

11. Bolt
12. Clutch pedal
13. Bushing
14. Spacer
15. Pedal pad
16. Adjusting bolt <Vehicles without Clutch pedal position switch>
17. Clutch pedal position switch <Vehicles with Clutch pedal position switch>
18. Interlock switch
19. Clutch pedal bracket assembly

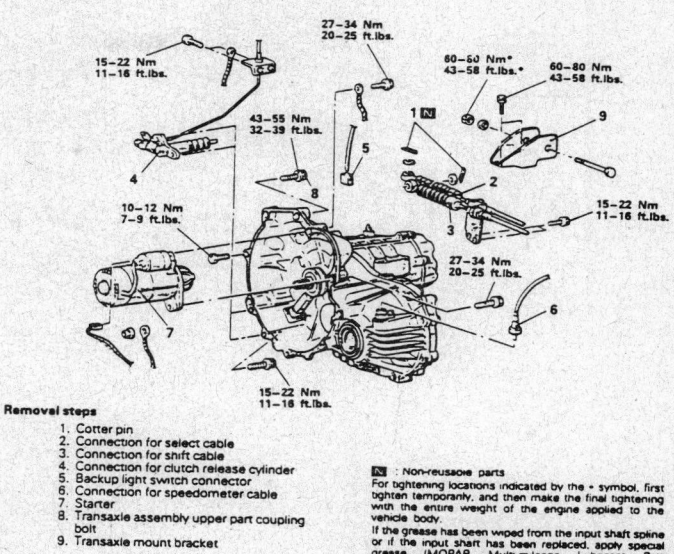

Fig. 12 Transaxle removal (Part 1 of 2). 1992–94 FWD models

CR5039100914010X

Removal steps
1. Cotter pin
2. Connection for select cable
3. Connection for shift cable
4. Connection for clutch release cylinder
5. Backup light switch connector
6. Connection for speedometer cable
7. Starter
8. Transaxle assembly upper part coupling bolt
9. Transaxle mount bracket

Ⓝ : Non-reusable parts

For tightening locations indicated by the • symbol, first tighten temporarily, and then make the final tightening with the entire weight of the engine applied to the vehicle body.
If the grease has been wiped from the input shaft spline or if the input shaft has been replaced, apply special grease (MOPAR Multi-mileage Lubricant Part No. 2525035 or equivalent) to the input shaft spline.

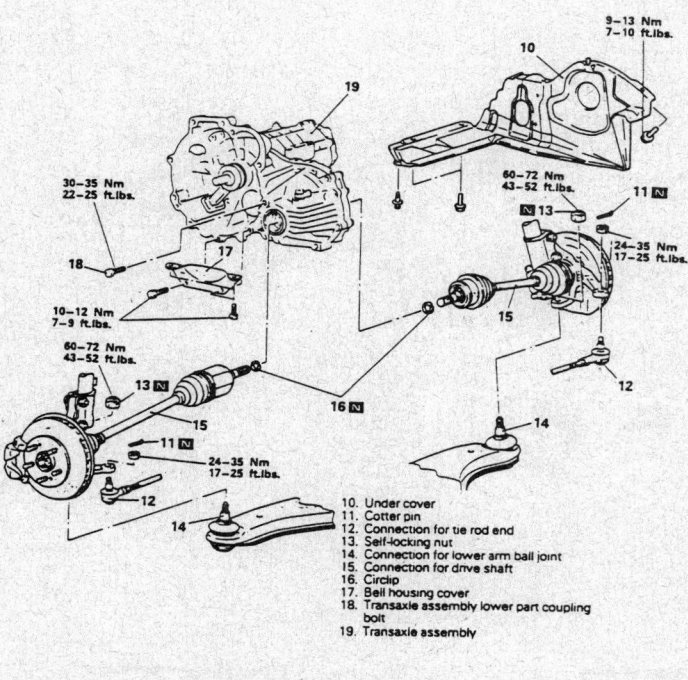

10. Under cover
11. Cotter pin
12. Connection for tie rod end
13. Self-locking nut
14. Connection for lower arm ball joint
15. Connection for drive shaft
16. Circlip
17. Bell housing cover
18. Transaxle assembly lower part coupling bolt
19. Transaxle assembly

Ⓝ : Non-reusable parts

CR5039100914020X

Fig. 12 Transaxle removal (Part 2 of 2). 1992–94 FWD models

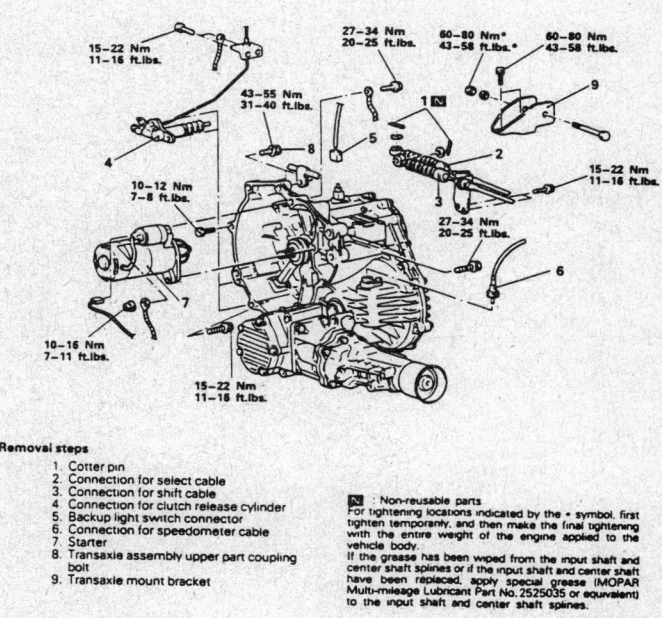

Fig. 13 Transaxle removal (Part 1 of 2). 1992–94 AWD models

CR5039100915010X

Removal steps
1. Cotter pin
2. Connection for select cable
3. Connection for shift cable
4. Connection for clutch release cylinder
5. Backup light switch connector
6. Connection for speedometer cable
7. Starter
8. Transaxle assembly upper part coupling bolt
9. Transaxle mount bracket

Ⓝ : Non-reusable parts

For tightening locations indicated by the • symbol, first tighten temporarily, and then make the final tightening with the entire weight of the engine applied to the vehicle body.
If the grease has been wiped from the input shaft and center shaft splines or if the input shaft and center shaft have been replaced, apply special grease (MOPAR Multi-mileage Lubricant Part No. 2525035 or equivalent) to the input shaft and center shaft splines.

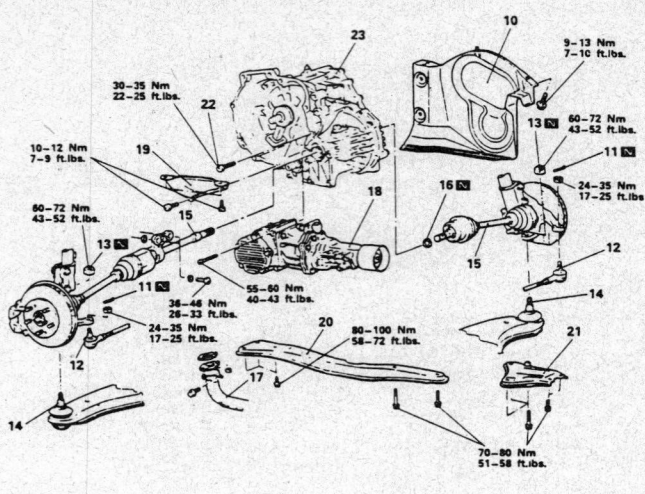

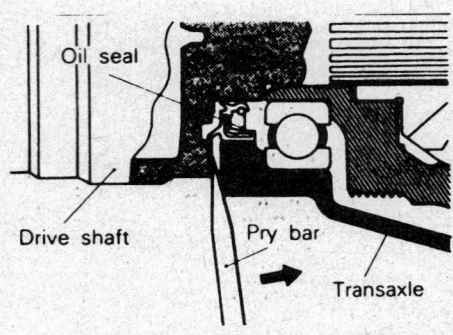

Fig. 14 Driveshaft removal.

10. Under cover
11. Cotter pin
12. Connection for tie rod end
13. Self-locking nut
14. Connection for lower arm ball joint
15. Connection for drive shaft
16. Circlip
17. Front exhaust pipe
18. Transfer assembly
19. Bell housing cover
20. Right member
21. Gusset
22. Transaxle assembly lower part coupling bolt
23. Transaxle assembly

N : Non-reusable parts

Fig. 13 Transaxle removal (Part 2 of 2). 1992–94 AWD models

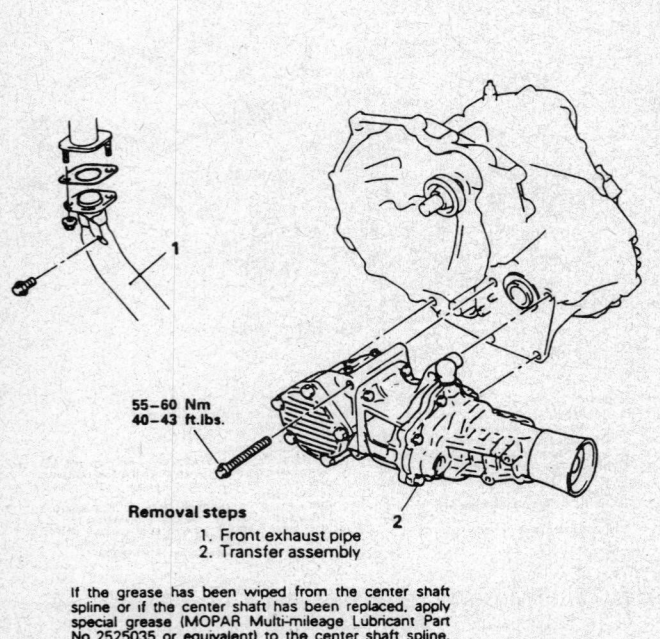

Removal steps
1. Front exhaust pipe
2. Transfer assembly

If the grease has been wiped from the center shaft spline or if the center shaft has been replaced, apply special grease (MOPAR Multi-mileage Lubricant Part No. 2525035 or equivalent) to the center shaft spline.

Fig. 15 Transfer case assembly removal. 1992–94

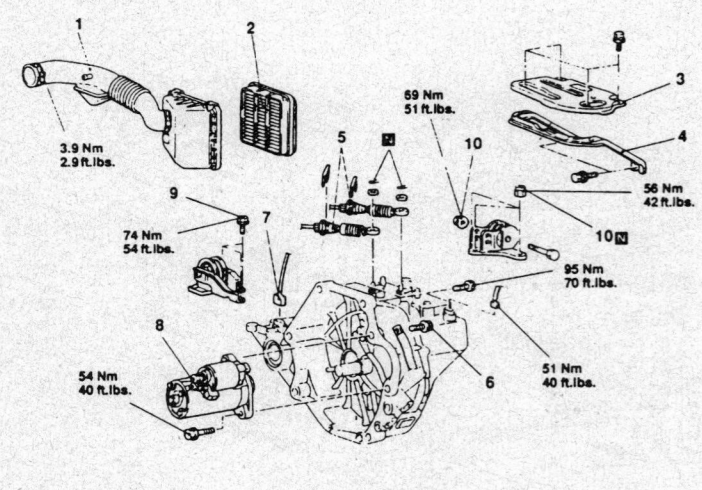

Removal steps
1. Air cleaner cover and air intake hose assembly
2. Air cleaner element
3. Battery tray
4. Battery tray stay
5. Shift cable and select cable connection
6. Backup light switch connector
7. Vehicle speed sensor connector
8. Starter motor
9. Rear roll stopper bracket mounting bolts
10. Transaxle mounting bracket mounting nuts

Fig. 16 Transaxle removal (Part 1 of 2). 1995 non-turbo

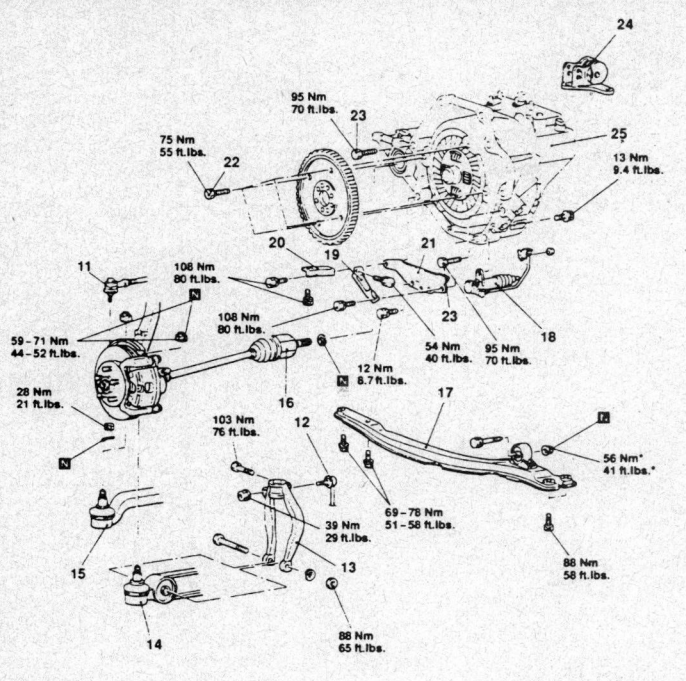

Lifting up of the vehicle

11. Tie rod end connection
12. Stabilizer link connection
13. Damper fork
14. Lateral lower arm connection
15. Compression lower arm connection
16. Drive shaft connection
17. Center member assembly
18. Clutch release cylinder connection
19. Front plate
20. Rear plate

21. Transaxle case lower cover
22. Flex plate connecting bolts
23. Transaxle assembly mounting bolts
24. Transaxle mounting
25. Transaxle assembly

Caution
*: Indicates parts which should be temporarily tightened, and then fully tightened with the vehicle on the ground in the unladen condition.

Fig. 16 Transaxle removal (Part 2 of 2). 1995 non-turbo

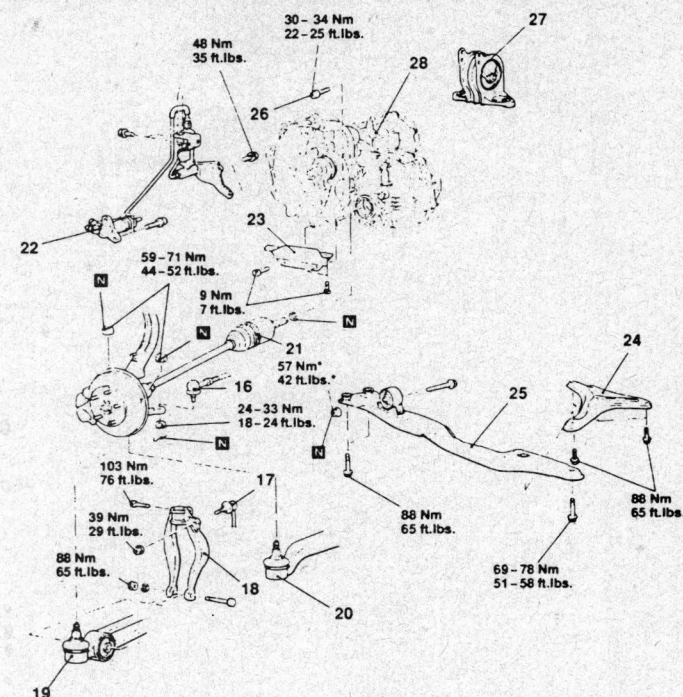

Lifting up of the vehicle

16. Tie rod end connection
17. Stabilizer link connection
18. Damper fork
19. Lateral lower arm connection
20. Compression lower arm connection
21. Drive shaft connection
22. Clutch release cylinder connection
23. Bell housing cover

24. Stay (R.H.)
25. Center member assembly
26. Transaxle assembly mounting bolt
27. Transaxle mounting
28. Transaxle assembly

Caution
*: Indicates parts which should be temporarily tightened, and then fully tightened with the vehicle on the ground in the unladen condition.

Fig. 17 Transaxle removal (Part 2 of 2). 1995 turbo FWD models

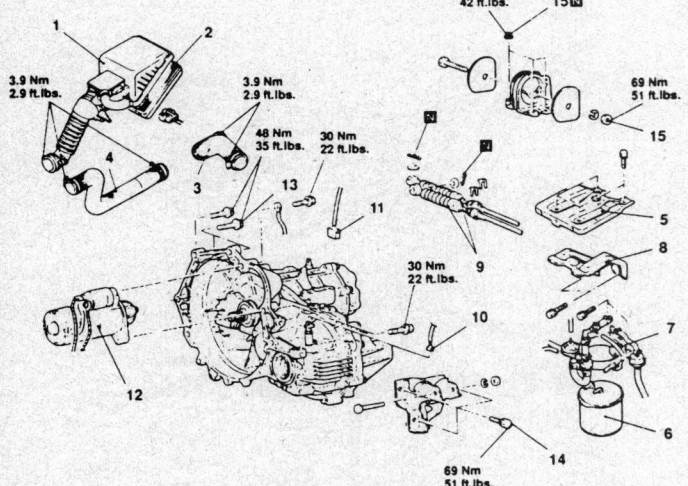

Removal steps

1. Air cleaner cover and air intake hose assembly
2. Air cleaner element
3. Air hose C
4. Air hose A
5. Battery tray
6. Evaporative emission canister
7. Evaporative emission canister holder
8. Battery tray stay

9. Shift cable and select cable connection
10. Backup light switch connector
11. Vehicle speed sensor connector
12. Starter motor
13. Transaxle assembly mounting bolts
14. Rear roll stopper bracket mounting bolts
15. Transaxle mounting bracket mounting nuts

Fig. 17 Transaxle removal (Part 1 of 2). 1995 turbo FWD models

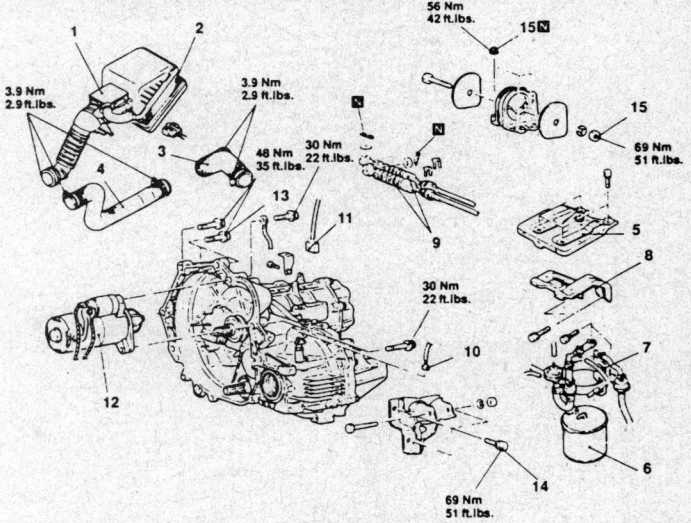

Removal steps

1. Air cleaner cover and air intake hose assembly
2. Air cleaner element
3. Air hose C
4. Air hose A
5. Battery tray
6. Evaporative emission canister
7. Evaporative emission canister holder
8. Battery tray stay

9. Shift cable and select cable connection
10. Backup light switch connector
11. Vehicle speed sensor connector
12. Starter motor
13. Transaxle assembly mounting bolts
14. Rear roll stopper bracket mounting bolts
15. Transaxle mounting bracket mounting nuts

Fig. 18 Transaxle removal (Part 1 of 2). 1995 turbo AWD models

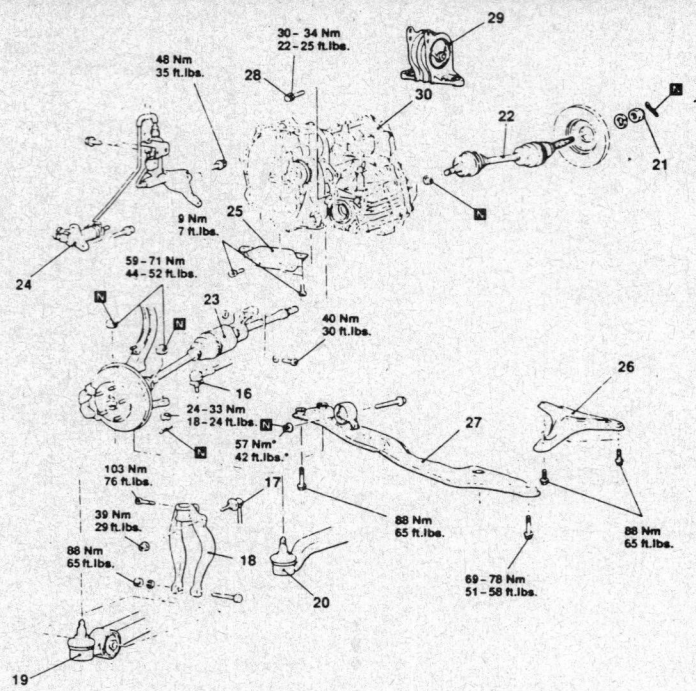

Lifting up of the vehicle

16. Tie rod end connection
17. Stabilizer link connection
18. Damper fork
19. Lateral lower arm connection
20. Compression lower arm connection
21. Drive shaft nut
22. Drive shaft
23. Drive shaft connection
24. Clutch release cylinder connection
25. Bell housing cover

26. Stay (R.H.)
27. Center member assembly
28. Transaxle assembly mounting bolt
29. Transaxle mounting
30. Transaxle assembly

Caution
*: Indicates parts which should be temporarily tightened, and then fully tightened with the vehicle on the ground in the unladen condition.

CR5039500927020X

Fig. 18   Transaxle removal (Part 2 of 2). 1995 turbo AWD models

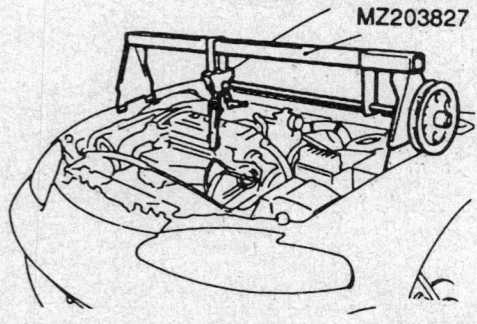

MZ203827

CR5039500928000X

Fig. 19   Engine assembly support. 1995

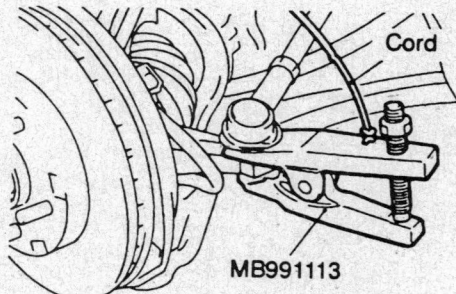

Cord

MB991113

CR5039500929000X

Fig. 20   Tie rod end removal. 1995

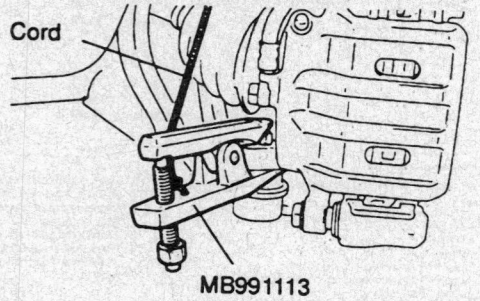

Cord

MB991113

CR5039500930000X

Fig. 21   Lateral lower arm removal. 1995

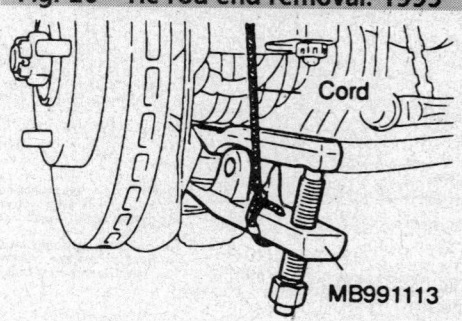

Cord

MB991113

CR5039500931000X

Fig. 22   Compression lower arm removal. 1995

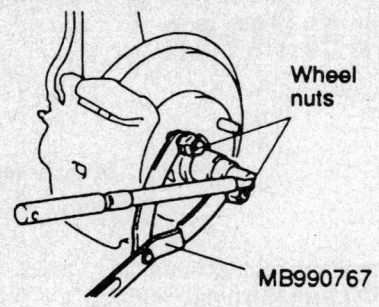

Fig. 23 Driveshaft nut removal. 1995 AWD models

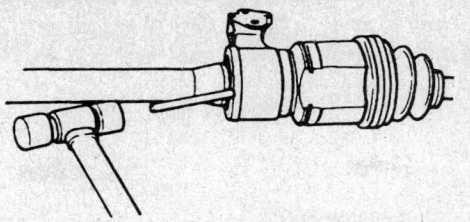

Fig. 24 Inner shaft removal. 1995 AWD models

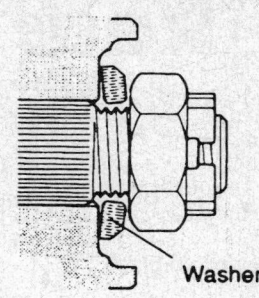

Washer

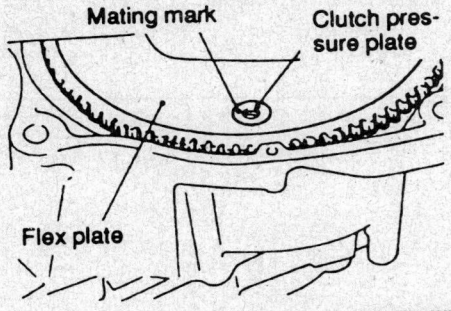

Fig. 25 Flex plate mating marks. 1995

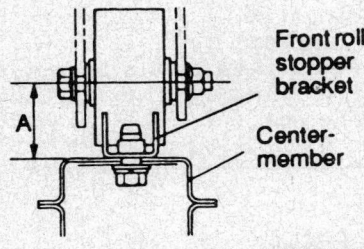

Fig. 26 Front roll stopper inspection. 1995

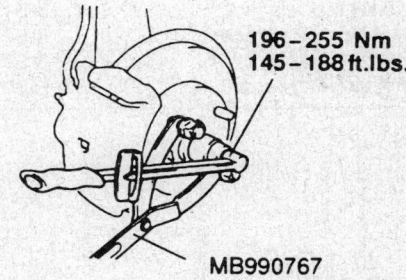

Fig. 27 Driveshaft nut installation. 1995 w/AWD

TIGHTENING SPECIFICATIONS

Year	Component	Torque/Ft. Lbs.
1992–94	Back-up Lamp Switch	22-25
	Bearing Retainer Bolt	11-15
	Bellhousing Cover	7-9
	Bleeder Plug	7-9
	Brake Booster Installation Nut	7-11
	Clutch Cover Assembly	11-16
	Clutch Pedal Bracket	6-9
	Clutch Pedal Support Bracket	6-9
	Clutch Pedal To Support Bracket	14-18
	Clutch Release Cylinder	11-16
	Clutch Tube Flare Nut	9-12
	Drain Plug	22-25
	Flywheel Bolts	94-191
	Fulcrum	25-30
	Input Shaft Locknut	102-115
	Lower Arm Ball Joint To Knuckle	43-52
	Poppet Plug	43-52
	Rear Housing Cover Bolt	11-15
	Restrict Ball Assembly	11-15
	Shift And Select Cable To Transaxle	11-16
	Speedometer Sleeve Bolt	20-25
	Starter Motor Mounting Bolt	20-25
	Stop Lamp Switch	7-11
	Stopper Bracket Bolt	11-15
	Tie Rod End To Knuckle	17-25
	Transaxle Bracket	43-58

Year	Component	Torque/Ft. Lbs.
1992–94 —Cont'd	Transaxle Case Tightening Bolt	26-30
	Transaxle Mounting Bolt (.47 inch)	32-39
	Transaxle Mounting Bolt (.40 inch)	22-25
	Transaxle Mounting Bolt (.31 inch)	7-9
	Transfer Assembly Mounting Bolt	40-43
1995	Back-up Lamp Switch	22
	Bearing Retainer Bolt	14
	Clutch Cover Assembly	11-16
	Clutch Pedal Bracket	6-9
	Clutch Pedal Support Bracket	6-9
	Clutch Pedal To Support Bracket	14-18
	Clutch Release Cylinder	11-16
	Compression Lower Arm	44-52
	Flywheel Bolts	55
	Lower Arm Ball Joint To Knuckle	44-52
	Poppet Plug	27
	Rear Housing Cover Bolt	14
	Rear Roll Stopper Bracket	51
	Restrict Ball Assembly	24
	Shift And Select Cable To Transaxle	11-16
	Speedometer Sleeve Bolt	3
	Starter Motor Mounting Bolt	40
	Stop Lamp Switch	24
	Tie Rod End To Knuckle	18-24
	Transaxle Case Tightening Bolt	29
	Transaxle Mounting Bolt	35
	Transfer Assembly Mounting Bolt	40-44

INDEX

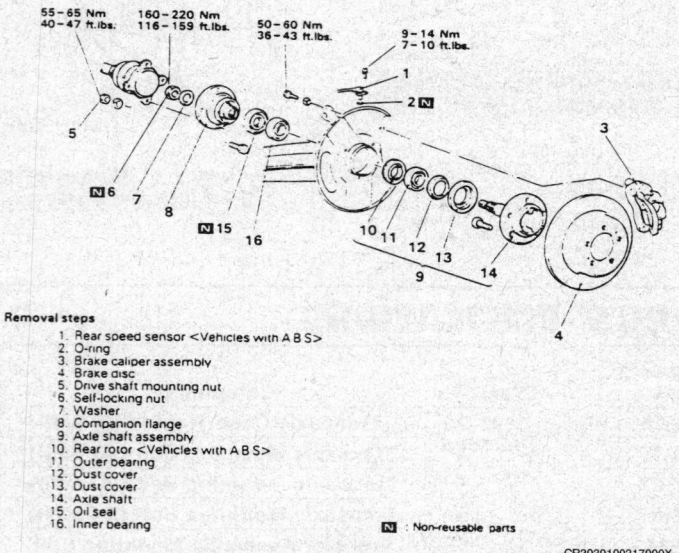

Removal steps
1. Rear speed sensor <Vehicles with A B S>
2. O-ring
3. Brake caliper assembly
4. Brake disc
5. Drive shaft mounting nut
6. Self-locking nut
7. Washer
8. Companion flange
9. Axle shaft assembly
10. Rear rotor <Vehicles with A B S>
11. Outer bearing
12. Dust cover
13. Dust cover
14. Axle shaft
15. Oil seal
16. Inner bearing

N : Non-reusable parts

CR3039100317000X

Fig. 1 Axle shaft replacement. 1992-94

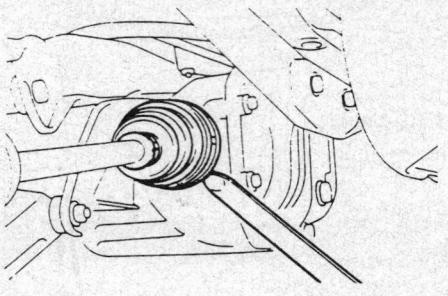

CR3039100315000X

Fig. 2 Driveshaft assembly removal. 1992-94

REAR AXLE
REPLACE
AWD MODELS
1992-94

Remove rear axle hub in numbered sequence, **Fig. 1,** noting the following:
1. Remove rear speed sensor as follows:
   a. Remove rear toothed rotor, then the clip.
   b. Remove cable band, then the connection to speed sensor.
   c. Remove rear speed sensor and bracket.
2. Suspend caliper assembly with a piece of wire. **Do not hang caliper by brake hose.**
3. Press off bearing using suitable press.
4. Reverse procedure to install.

REAR AXLE SHAFT
REPLACE
1992-94

1. Remove companion flange to driveshaft bolts.
2. Remove driveshaft from differential carrier using a suitable pry bar, **Fig. 2.**
3. Remove circlip from end of driveshaft.
4. Remove oil seal using a suitable oil seal remover tool.
5. Reverse procedure to install, noting the following:
   a. Install oil seal using suitable oil seal installer tool.
   b. When installing driveshaft, ensure not to damage oil seal by the driveshaft splines.
   c. Install driveshaft with the two part serration on right hand differential side. driveshaft can be identified by the color of the BJ boot band, yellow for left and orange for right.

1995

Remove rear driveshaft in numbered sequence, **Fig. 3** noting the following:
1. Remove drive shaft nut using removal tool No. MB990767, or equivalent.
2. Remove driveshaft by pushing the lower part of the knuckle to the outside of the vehicle, then separate the driveshaft from the differential carrier. At this time, use a suitable tire lever or similar tool to separate the driveshaft connection.
3. Reverse procedure to install noting the following:
   a. Ensure proper driveshaft placement. The right driveshaft has an orange boot band, while the left driveshaft has a green boot band.
   b. Ensure differential carrier oil seal is not damaged by driveshaft spline.
   c. Using special tool No. MB990767, or equivalent, tighten driveshaft nut to specifications, ensuring there is no load on wheel bearings.

DIFFERENTIAL CARRIER
REPLACE
1992-94

Replace differential carrier in numbered sequence shown in **Fig. 4,** noting the following:
1. Remove rear axle shaft as described under "Rear Axle Shafts, Replace"
2. Mark then disconnect propeller shaft assembly.

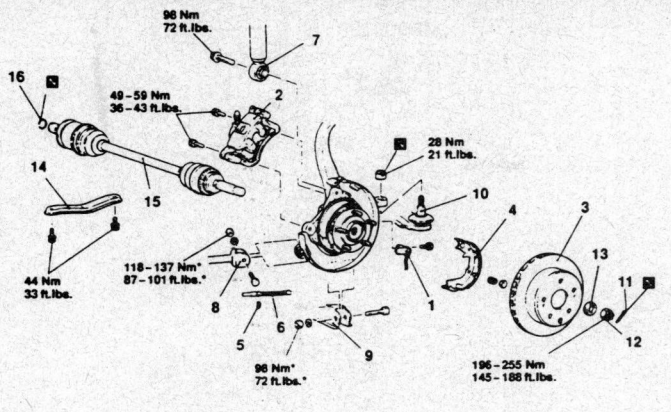

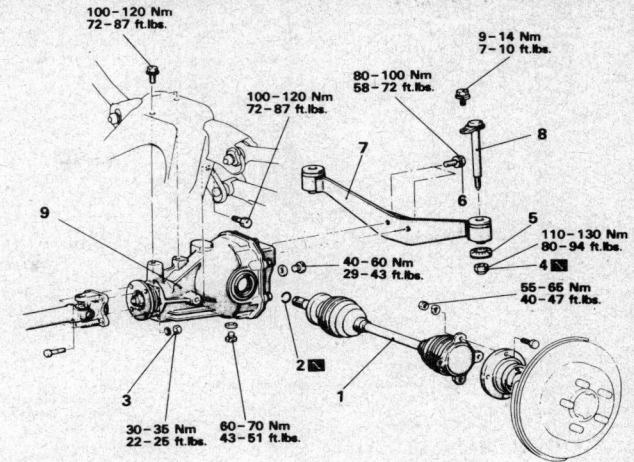

Removal steps

1. Rear speed sensor <Vehicles with ABS>
2. Caliper assembly
3. Brake disc
4. Shoe and lining assembly
5. Clip
6. Parking brake cable
7. Shock absorber connection
8. Trailing arm connection
9. Lower arm connection
10. Toe control arm connection
11. Cotter pin
12. Drive shaft nut
13. Washer
14. Differential mount support
15. Drive shaft
16. Circlip

Caution
1. For vehicles with ABS, be careful not to damage the drive shaft rotor.
2. *: Indicates parts which should be temporarily tightened, and then fully tightened with the vehicle on the ground in the unladen condition.

CR3039500356000X

Fig. 3 Driveshaft replacement. 1995

Removal steps

1. Drive shaft
2. Circlip
3. Propeller shaft connection
4. Differential support member installation nut
5. Stopper (lower)
6. Differential support member installation bolts
7. Differential support member
8. Differential support member installation bolts
9. Differential carrier

◪ : Non-reusable parts.

CR3039100314000X

Fig. 4 Differential carrier assembly. 1992–94

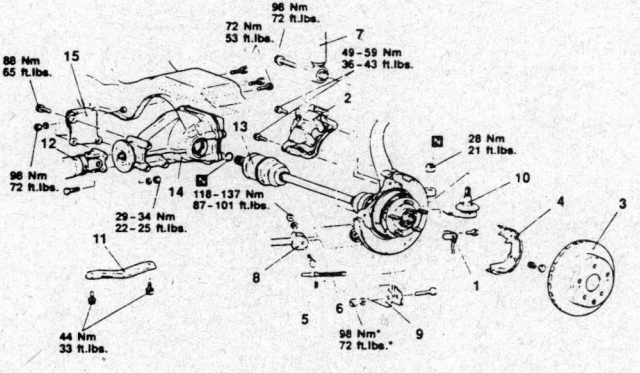

Removal steps

1. Rear speed sensor <Vehicles with ABS>
2. Caliper assembly
3. Brake disc
4. Shoe and lining assembly
5. Clip
6. Parking brake cable
7. Shock absorber connection
8. Trailing arm connection
9. Lower arm connection
10. Toe control arm connection
11. Differential mount support
12. Propeller shaft connection
13. Drive shaft connection
14. Differential carrier
15. Differential mount bracket assembly

Caution
*: Indicates parts which should be temporarily tightened, and then fully tightened with the vehicle on the ground in the unladen condition.

CR3039500357000X

Fig. 5 Differential carrier assembly. 1995

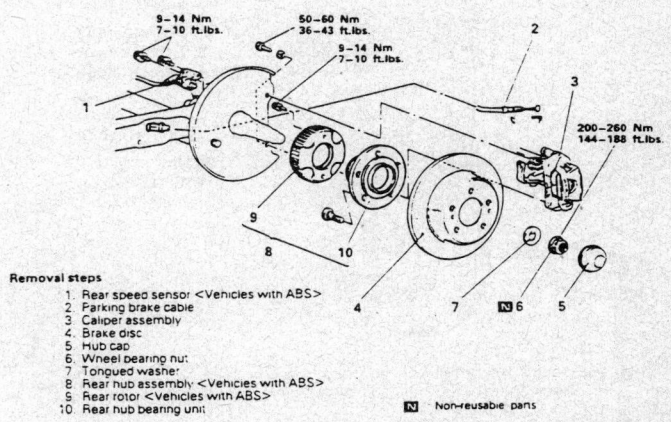

Removal steps

1. Rear speed sensor <Vehicles with ABS>
2. Parking brake cable
3. Caliper assembly
4. Brake disc
5. Hub cap
6. Wheel bearing nut
7. Tongued washer
8. Rear hub assembly <Vehicles with ABS>
9. Rear rotor <Vehicles with ABS>
10. Rear hub bearing unit

◪ : Non-reusable parts.

CR3039100316000X

Fig. 6 Rear axle hub replacement. 1992–94

HUB & BEARING
REPLACE
FWD MODELS
1992–94

Remove rear axle hub in numbered sequence, **Fig. 6**, noting the following:
1. Remove rear speed sensor as follows:
   a. Remove rear toothed rotor, then the clip.
   b. Remove cable band, then the connection to speed sensor.
   c. Remove rear speed sensor and bracket.
2. Suspend caliper assembly with a

3. Support differential carrier with suitable jack for removal.
4. Reverse procedure to install.

1995

Replace differential carrier in numbered sequence shown in **Fig. 5** noting the following:
1. Remove rear axle shaft as described under "Rear Axle Shafts, Replace."
2. Mark with mating marks, then disconnect propeller shaft assembly.
3. Suspend propeller shaft out of the way.
4. Support differential carrier with suitable jack for removal.
5. Reverse procedure to install.
6.

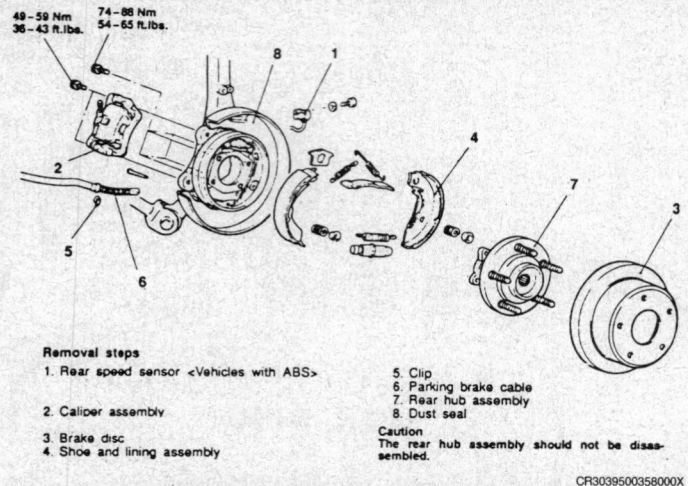

Removal steps

1. Rear speed sensor <Vehicles with ABS>
2. Caliper assembly
3. Brake disc
4. Shoe and lining assembly

5. Clip
6. Parking brake cable
7. Rear hub assembly
8. Dust seal

Caution
The rear hub assembly should not be disassembled.

CR3039500358000X

Fig. 7 Rear axle hub replacement. 1995

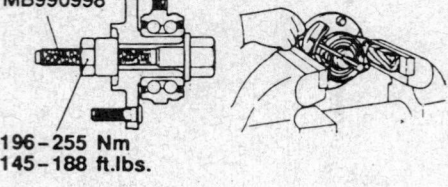

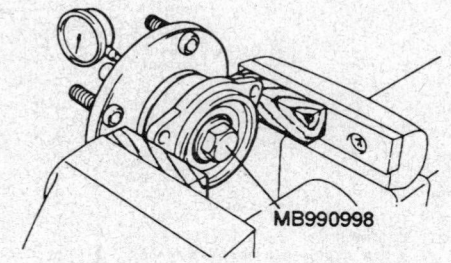

CR3039500359000X

Fig. 8 Hub endplay adjustment. 1995

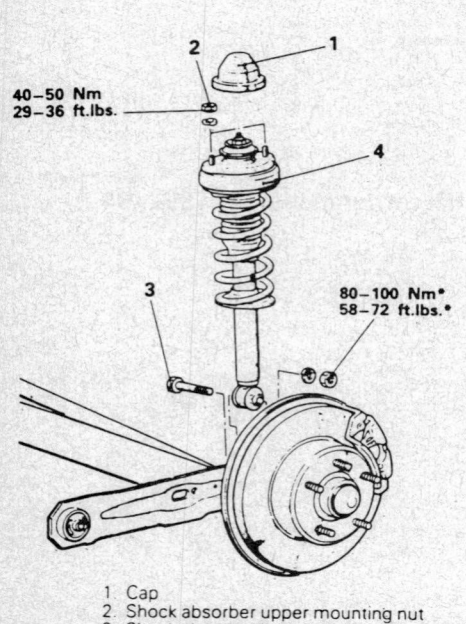

1. Cap
2. Shock absorber upper mounting nut
3. Shock absorber lower mounting bolt
4. Shock absorber

CR2039100013000X

Fig. 9 Strut assembly removal. 1992–94 FWD models

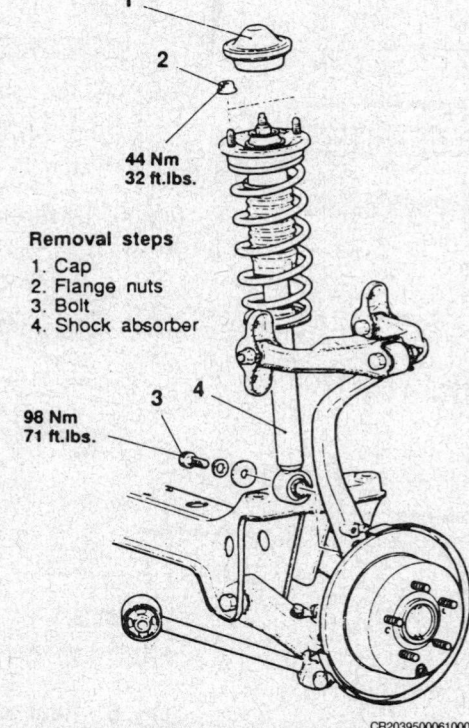

Removal steps
1. Cap
2. Flange nuts
3. Bolt
4. Shock absorber

CR2039500061000X

Fig. 10 Strut assembly removal. 1995

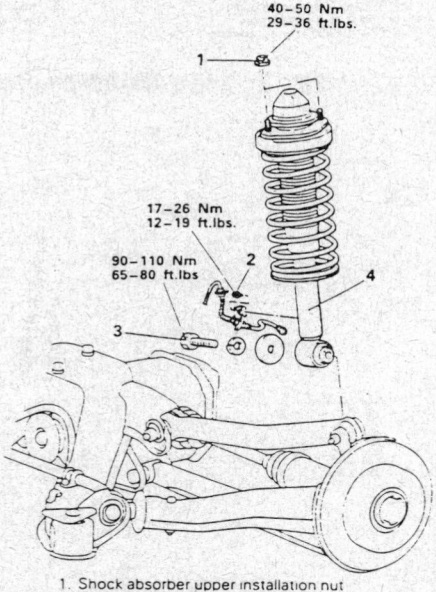

1. Shock absorber upper installation nut
2. Brake tube bracket installation bolt
3. Shock absorber lower installation bolt
4. Shock absorber assembly

CR2039100014000X

Fig. 11 Strut assembly removal. 1992–94 AWD models

piece of wire. **Do not hang caliper by brake hose.**

3. Rear hub bearing cannot be disassembled.
4. Press inner race until it contacts with spindle end.
5. Align wheel bearing nut with spindle indentation and crimp.
6. Reverse procedure to install.

1995

Remove rear axle hub in numbered sequence, **Fig. 7** noting the following:
1. Remove rear speed sensor.
2. Remove and suspend caliper assembly with a piece of wire. **Do not hang caliper by brake hose.**
3. Reverse procedure to install.

WHEEL BEARING
ADJUST

1992–94

1. To check bearing endplay, proceed as follows:
   a. Place dial gauge against hub surface, then move hub in axial direction.
   b. If endplay exceeds .004 inch, locknut should be tightened.
   c. Tighten locknut to specifications.
2. Replace hub bearing unit if adjustment cannot be made to within limit.

1995

1. To check bearing endplay, proceed as follows:
   a. Place hub in suitable vise, protected by wood blocks, **Fig. 8.**
   b. Place dial gauge against hub surface, then move hub in axial direction.
   c. If endplay exceeds .002 inch, use special wheel bearing installer tool No. MB990998, or equivalent, to tighten bearing. **Torque** special tool to 145–188 ft. lbs.
2. Replace hub bearing unit if adjustment cannot be made to within limit.

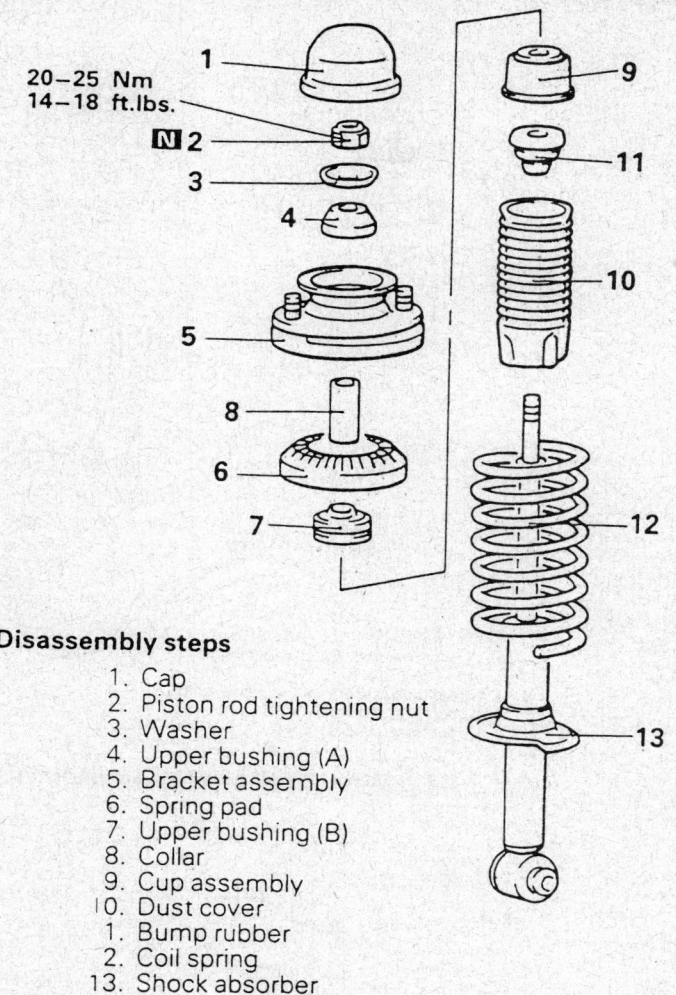

20–25 Nm
14–18 ft.lbs.

Disassembly steps
1. Cap
2. Piston rod tightening nut
3. Washer
4. Upper bushing (A)
5. Bracket assembly
6. Spring pad
7. Upper bushing (B)
8. Collar
9. Cup assembly
10. Dust cover
11. Bump rubber
12. Coil spring
13. Shock absorber

CR2039100015000X

Fig. 12 Exploded view of strut assembly. 1992–94

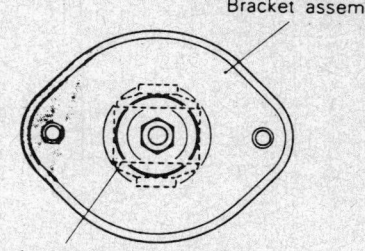

CR2039100016000X

Fig. 13 Upper spring mount installation. 1992–94

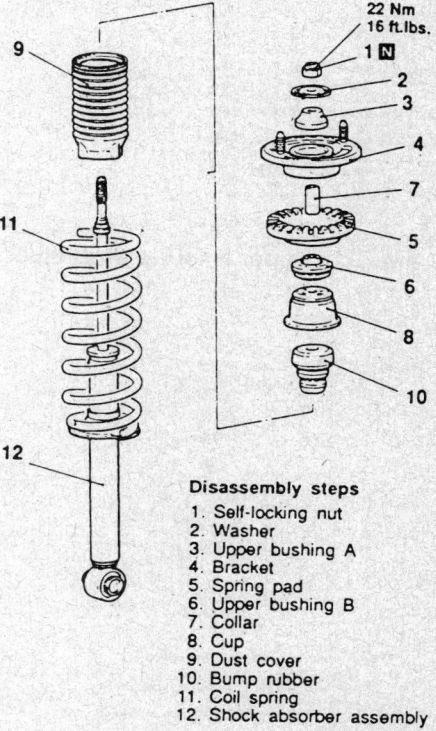

22 Nm
16 ft.lbs.

Disassembly steps
1. Self-locking nut
2. Washer
3. Upper bushing A
4. Bracket
5. Spring pad
6. Upper bushing B
7. Collar
8. Cup
9. Dust cover
10. Bump rubber
11. Coil spring
12. Shock absorber assembly

CR2039500062000X

Fig. 14 Exploded view of strut assembly. 1995

STRUT
REPLACE

FWD MODELS
1992–94

Remove strut assembly in numbered sequence, **Fig. 9**, noting the following:
1. Jack up torsion axle and arm assembly in order to release tension. Place jack at center of axle beam, ensuring jack does not contact lateral rod
2. Reverse procedure to install.

1995

Remove strut assembly in numbered sequence, **Fig. 10** noting the following:
1. Jack up torsion axle and arm assembly in order to release tension. Place jack at center of axle beam, ensuring jack does not contact lateral rod
2. Reverse procedure to install.

AWD MODELS
1992–94

Remove strut assembly in numbered sequence, **Fig. 11**. Reverse procedure to install.

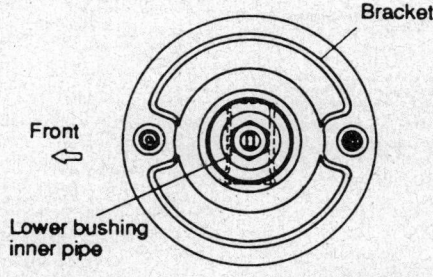

Bracket

Front

Lower bushing inner pipe

CR2039500063000X

Fig. 15 Upper spring mount installation. 1995

1995

Remove shock absorber assembly in numbered sequence, **Fig. 10**, noting the following:
1. Jack up torsion axle and arm assembly in order to release tension. Place jack at center of axle beam, ensuring jack does not contact lateral rod
2. Reverse procedure to install.

STRUT SERVICE
1992–94

Disassemble strut assembly in num-
bered sequence shown in **Fig. 12**, noting the following:
1. Ensure spring is properly seated in upper and lower spring seat when installing.
2. Install strut upper bracket as shown in **Fig. 13**, then tighten strut rod nut to specifications.

1995

Disassemble strut assembly in numbered sequence shown in **Fig. 14** noting the following:
1. Compress spring using spring compression tools No. MB991237 and MB991239, or equivalents, to ease in disassembly and assembly.
2. Ensure spring is properly seated in upper and lower spring seat when installing.
3. Install strut upper bracket as shown in **Fig. 15** then tighten strut rod nut to specifications.

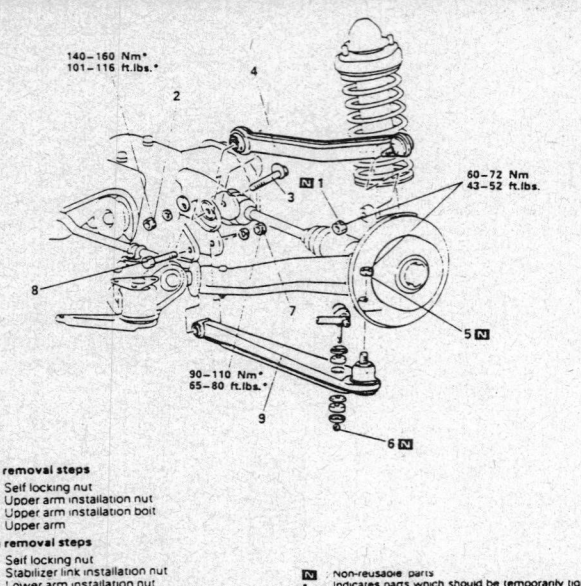

Upper arm removal steps
1. Self locking nut
2. Upper arm installation nut
3. Upper arm installation bolt
4. Upper arm

Lower arm removal steps
5. Self locking nut
6. Stabilizer link installation nut
7. Lower arm installation nut
8. Lower arm installation bolt
9. Lower arm

Ⓝ Non-reusable parts
Indicates parts which should be temporarily tightened, and then fully tightened with the vehicle in the unladen condition.

CR2039100017000X

Fig. 16   Upper & lower arm replacement. 1992–94

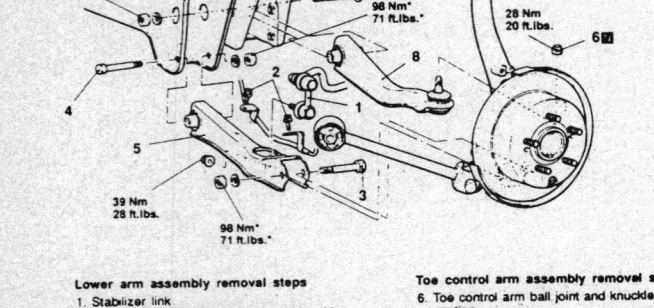

Lower arm assembly removal steps
1. Stabilizer link
2. ABS wheel-speed sensor clamp bolts <Vehicles with ABS>
3. Lower arm assembly and knuckle connecting bolt
4. Lower arm assembly mounting bolt
5. Lower arm assembly

Toe control arm assembly removal steps
6. Toe control arm ball joint and knuckle connection
7. Toe control arm assembly mounting bolt
8. Toe control arm assembly

Caution
*: indicates parts which should be temporarily tightened, and then fully tightened with the vehicles on the ground in the unladen condition.

CR2039500065000X

Fig. 18   Lower arm replacement. 1995

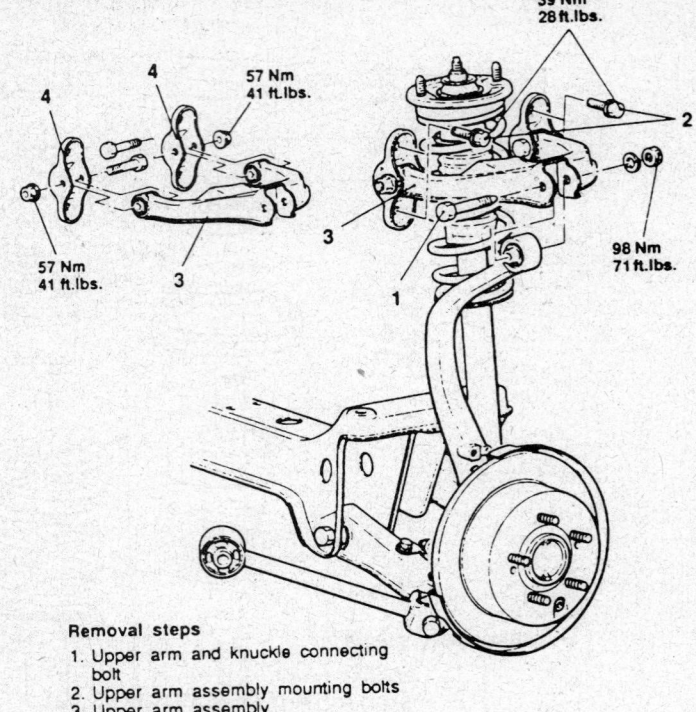

Removal steps
1. Upper arm and knuckle connecting bolt
2. Upper arm assembly mounting bolts
3. Upper arm assembly
4. Upper arm bracket

CR2039500064000X

Fig. 17   Upper arm replacement. 1995

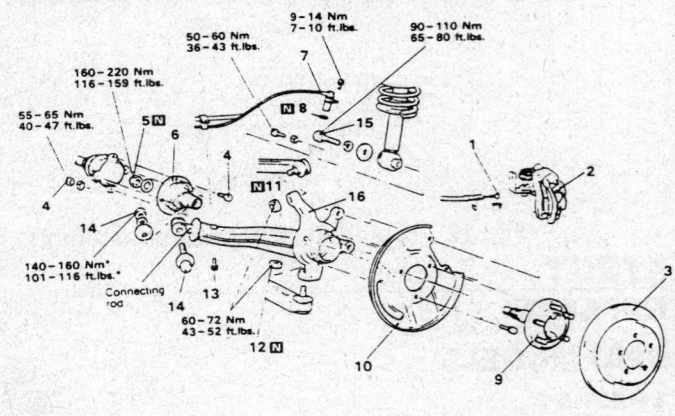

Removal steps
1. Parking cable end
2. Rear brake assembly
3. Rear brake disc
4. Drive shaft and companion flange installation bolt, nut
5. Self locking nut
6. Companion flange
7. Rear speed sensor <Vehicles with ABS>
8. O-ring
9. Rear axle shaft
10. Dust shield
11. Self locking nut (upper arm)
12. Self locking nut (lower arm)
13. Parking brake cable and rear speed sensor installation bolt
14. Trailing arm installation bolt, nut
15. Rear shock absorber installation bolt
16. Trailing arm

Ⓝ Non-reusable parts
Indicates parts which should be temporarily tightened, and then fully tightened with the vehicle in the unladen condition.

CR2039100020000X

Fig. 19   Trailing arm replacement. 1992–94

CONTROL ARM
REPLACE
AWD MODELS
1992–94

Remove upper and lower arm in numbered sequence, **Fig. 16**, noting the following:

1. Loosen, but do not remove self-locking nut.
2. Press fit lower arm bushing until outer edge is flush with lower arm edge.
3. Reverse procedure to install.

1995

Remove upper and lower arm in numbered sequences, **Figs. 17 and 18** noting the following:

1. Loosen, but do not remove self-locking nut.
2. Inspect all bushings and bolts for wear and damage.
3. Reverse procedures to install.

TRAILING ARM
REPLACE
AWD MODELS
1992–94

Remove trailing arm in numbered sequence, **Fig. 19**, noting the following:

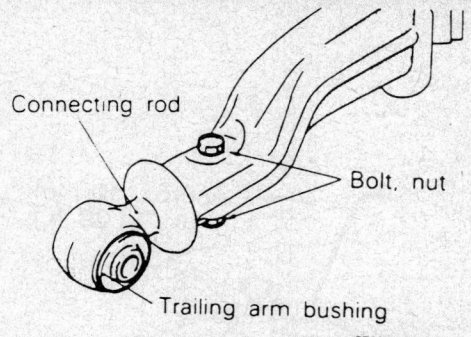

Connecting rod

Bolt, nut

Trailing arm bushing

CR2039100021000X

Fig. 20   Connecting rod removal. 1992–94

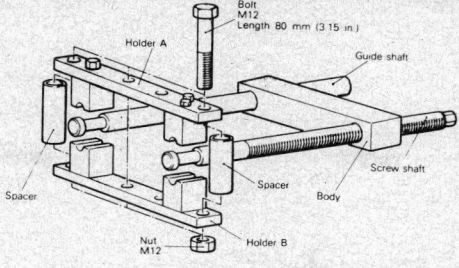

Bolt M12 Length 80 mm (3.15 in.)

Holder A

Guide shaft

Spacer

Spacer

Screw shaft

Body

Nut M12

Holder B

CR2039100022000X

Fig. 21   Rod remover tool No. MB991254 or equivalent. 1992–94

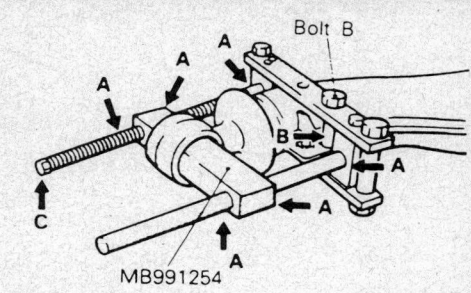

Bolt B

A A A

B

A

A

C

MB991254

CR2039100023000X

Fig. 22   Lubrication points. 1992–94

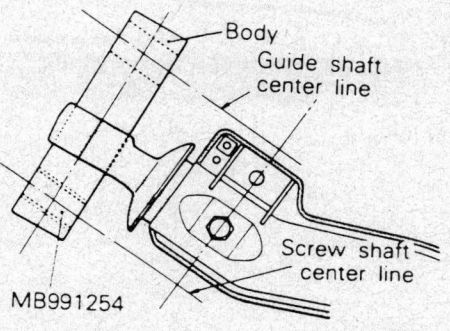

Body

Guide shaft center line

Screw shaft center line

MB991254

CR2039100024000X

Fig. 23   Rod remover tool No. MB991254, or equivalent installation. 1992–94

1. Suspend caliper assembly with a piece of wire. **Do not hang caliper by brake hose.**
2. Secure rear axle shaft, then remove self locking nut.
3. Using puller, remove rear axle shaft.
4. On upper and lower arms, loosen, but do not remove self locking nut.
5. Replace connecting rod as follows:
   a. Remove trailing arm bushing, then bolt and nut, **Fig. 20.**
   b. Using rod remover tool No. MB991254 or equivalent, **Fig. 21,** set onto trailing arm as shown in **Fig. 22.**
   c. Apply lubricant to sliding portion of tool (A), then install bolt (B) in trailing arm, **Fig. 22,**
   d. Using suitable wrench, turn portion as marked (C), **Fig. 22,** to remove connection rod.
   e. Installation of body should be performed with screw shaft and guide shaft center lines aligned as shown in **Fig. 23.**
   f. Apply soapy water to rubber portion of connection rod.
   g. Reverse procedure to press fit, tightening bolt to specifications.
6. Temporarily assemble rear axle shaft to trailing arm.
7. Install companion flange to rear axle shaft, then install locking nut.
8. Ensure rear axle shaft does not turn when tightening locknut.
9. Reverse procedure to install.

1995

Remove trailing arm in numbered se-

Removal steps

1. Knuckle and trailing arm assembly connecting bolt
2. Grommet
3. Trailing arm assembly mounting bolt
4. Stopper
5. Trailing arm assembly

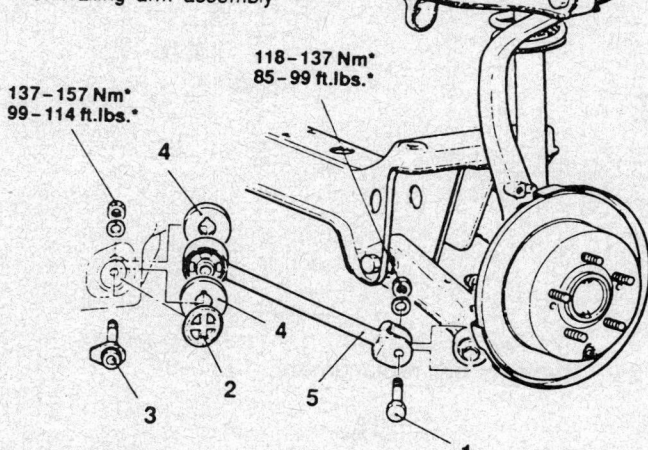

137–157 Nm*
99–114 ft.lbs.*

118–137 Nm*
85–99 ft.lbs.*

4

4

3

2

5

1

Caution
* : Indicates parts which should be temporarily tightened, and then fully tightened with the vehicles on the ground in the unladen condition.

CR2039500066000X

Fig. 24   Trailing arm assembly. 1995

quence, **Fig. 24** noting the following:
1. Inspect bushings and bolts for wear or damage.
2. Inspect trailing arm for bends or damage.
3. Reverse procedure to install.

STABILIZER BAR
REPLACE

AWD MODELS
1992–94

Remove stabilizer bar in numbered sequence, **Fig. 25,** noting the following:
1. Support rear suspension assembly with transaxle jack.
2. Remove crossmember brackets.
3. Lower transaxle jack slightly, maintaining gap between rear suspension and body.
4. Ensure stabilizer link ball joint starting **torque** is 15-28 inch lbs. If starting torque exceeds upper limit, replace link.

5. Reverse procedure to install.

1995

Remove stabilizer bar in numbered sequence, **Fig. 26** noting the following:
1. Reverse procedure to install ensuring to set the stabilizer bar so that the identification mark is at the left. Install the bushing, ensuring the dimension is as shown in **Fig. 27.**

TORSION ARM BUSHING
REPLACE

FWD MODELS
1992–94

Remove torsion axle and arm in numbered sequence, **Fig. 28,** noting the following:
1. Remove rear speed sensor as follows:
   a. Remove rear toothed rotor, then the clip.
   b. Remove cable band, then the con-

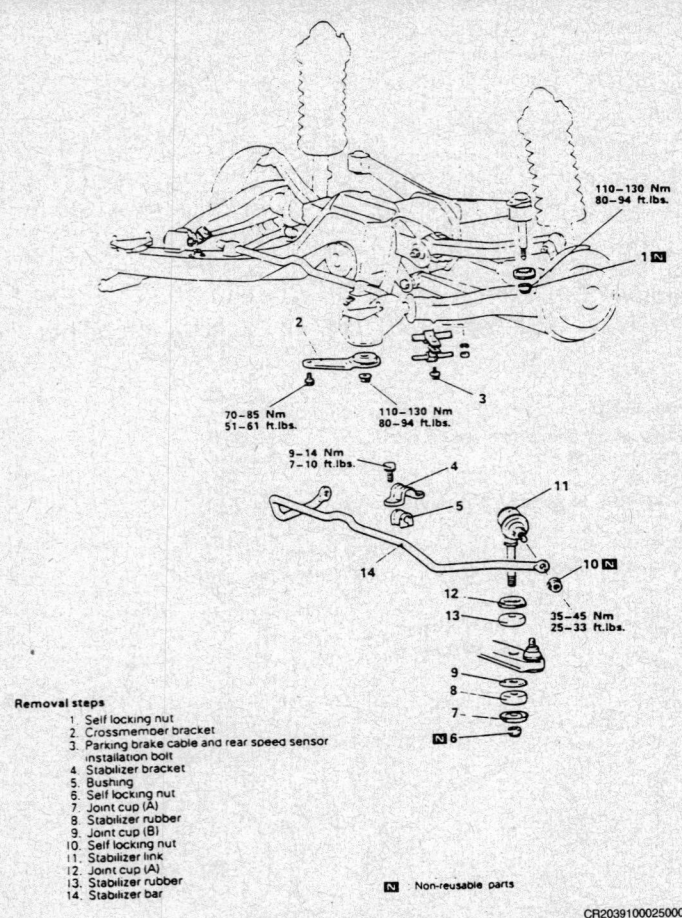

Fig. 27 Stabilizer bar bushing alignment. 1995

Approx. 10 mm (.39 in.)

CR2039500068000X

Removal steps
1. Self locking nut
2. Crossmember bracket
3. Parking brake cable and rear speed sensor installation bolt
4. Stabilizer bracket
5. Bushing
6. Self locking nut
7. Joint cup (A)
8. Stabilizer rubber
9. Joint cup (B)
10. Self locking nut
11. Stabilizer link
12. Joint cup (A)
13. Stabilizer rubber
14. Stabilizer bar

N Non-reusable parts

CR2039100025000X

Fig. 25 Stabilizer bar replacement. 1992–94

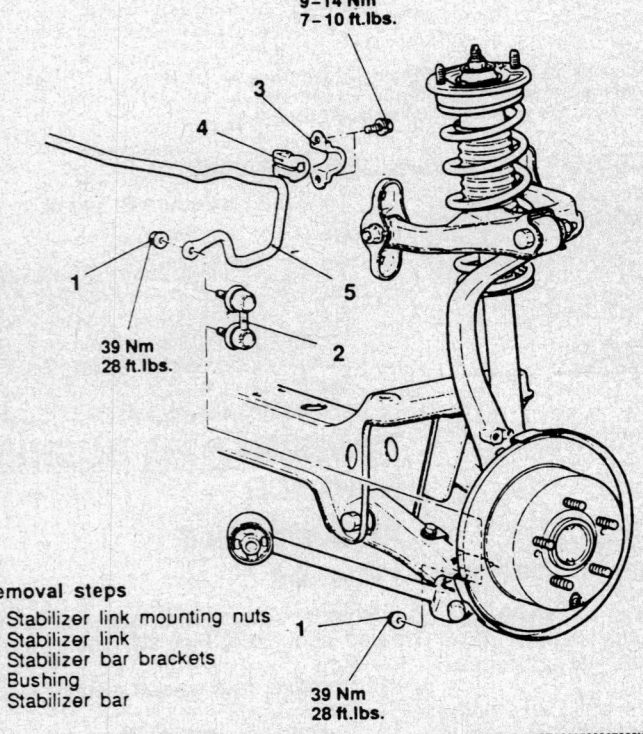

Removal steps
1. Stabilizer link mounting nuts
2. Stabilizer link
3. Stabilizer bar brackets
4. Bushing
5. Stabilizer bar

CR2039500067000X

Fig. 26 Stabilizer bar replacement. 1995

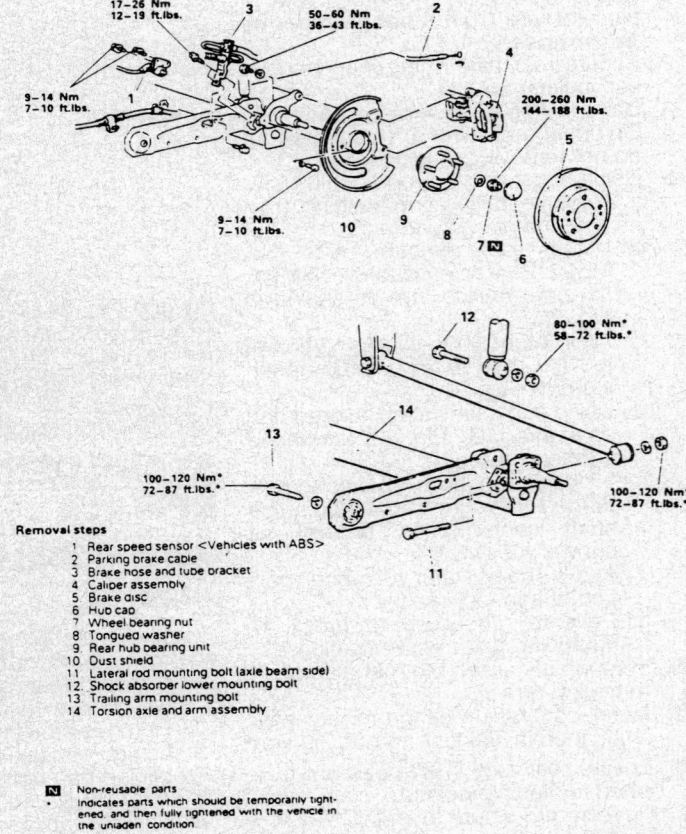

Removal steps
1. Rear speed sensor <Vehicles with ABS>
2. Parking brake cable
3. Brake hose and tube bracket
4. Caliper assembly
5. Brake disc
6. Hub cap
7. Wheel bearing nut
8. Tongued washer
9. Rear hub bearing unit
10. Dust shield
11. Lateral rod mounting bolt (axle beam side)
12. Shock absorber lower mounting bolt
13. Trailing arm mounting bolt
14. Torsion axle and arm assembly

N Non-reusable parts
* Indicates parts which should be temporarily tightened, and then fully tightened with the vehicle in the unladen condition.

CR2039100019000X

Fig. 28 Torsion axle & arm assembly replacement

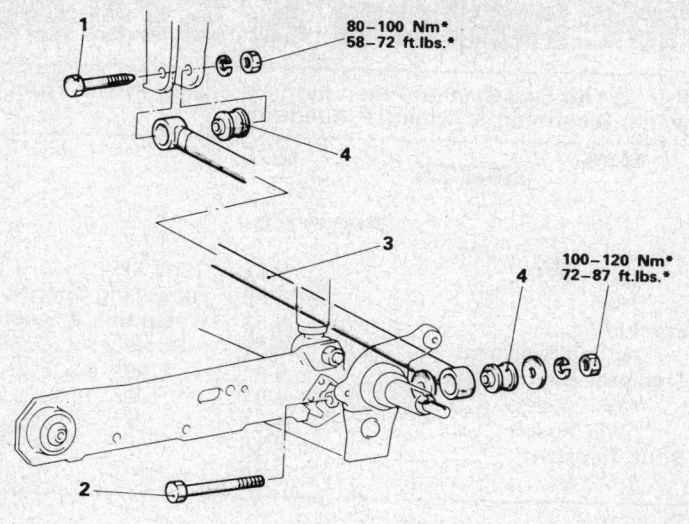

80–100 Nm*
58–72 ft.lbs.*

100–120 Nm*
72–87 ft.lbs.*

Removal steps
1. Lateral rod mounting bolt (body side)
2. Lateral rod mounting bolt (axle beam side)
3. Lateral rod
4. Lateral rod bushing

* : Indicates parts which should be temporarily tightened, and then fully tightened with the vehicle in the unladen condition.

CR2039100018000X

Fig. 29   Lateral rod replacement

c. Remove rear speed sensor and bracket.
   d. Reverse procedure to install.
2. Suspend caliper assembly with a piece of wire. **Do not hang caliper by brake hose.**
3. Rear hub bearing cannot be disassembled.
4. Remove shock absorber as previously described.
5. Adjust parking brake as described under "Parking Brake Adjust."
6. Install lateral rod mounting bolt as previously described.
7. Install hub unit until inner race contacts with spindle end.
8. Install wheel bearing and adjust as described under "Wheel Bearing, Adjust."
9. Reverse procedure to install.

LATERAL ROD
REPLACE
FWD MODELS
1992–94

Remove lateral rod in numbered sequence, **Fig. 29**, noting the following:
1. Install lateral rod mounting bolt from top of axle beam with nut on bottom of lateral rod.
2. Reverse procedure to install.

TIGHTENING SPECIFICATIONS

Year	Component	Torque/Ft. Lbs.
1992–94	Brake Tube Bracket To Rear Shock Absorber	12-19
	Center Exhaust Pipe To Front Exhaust Pipe Installation Nut	22-29
	Center Exhaust Pipe To Main Muffler Installation Bolt	29-36
	Companion Flange To Driveshaft	40-47
	Companion Flange To Rear Axle Shaft	116-159
	Crossmember Bracket To Body	51-61
	Crossmember Bracket To Crossmember	80-94
	Differential Carrier To Differential Support Member	58-72
	Differential Carrier To Propeller Shaft	22-25
	Differential Support Member To Body	80-94
	Hanger Installation Bolt	7-11
	Hook Installation Bolt	7-11
	Lateral Rod Mounting Nut (Body Side)	58-72
	Lateral Rod Mounting Nut (Axle Beam Side)	72-87
	Lower Arm To Knuckle	43-52
	Lower Arm To Crossmember	65-80
	Piston Rod Nut	14-18
	Rear Brake Assembly Installation Bolt	36-43
	Rear Speed Sensor Installation Bolt	7-10
	Shock Absorber Upper Mounting Nut	29-36
	Shock Absorber Lower Mounting Nut	58-72
	Stabilizer Link To Stabilizer Bar	25-33
	Trailing Arm Mounting Bolt	72-87

Year	Component	Torque/Ft. Lbs.
1992–94	Trailing Arm To Crossmember	101-116
	Upper Arm To Crossmember	101-116
	Upper Arm To Knuckle	43-52
	Wheel Bearing Nut	144-188
	Wheel Lug Nuts	87-101
1995	Crossmember Self-Locking	64
	Differential Carrier To Differential Support Member	72
	Driveshaft Nut	145-188
	Lower Arm Assembly Mounting	71
	Lower Arm To Knuckle	71
	Piston Rod Nut	16
	Propeller Shaft To Differential	22-25
	Rear Brake Assembly Installation Bolt	64
	Shock Absorber Upper Mounting Nut	32
	Shock Absorber Lower Mounting Nut	71
	Stabilizer Bar Bracket	7-10
	Stabilizer Link Mounting	28
	Stabilizer Link To Stabilizer Bar	28
	Toe Control Arm Assembly Mounting	50-56
	Toe Control Arm Ball Joint to Knuckle	20
	Trailing Arm Mounting Bolt	99-114
	Trailing Arm To Knuckle	85-99
	Upper Arm Assembly	71
	Upper Arm Bracket	41
	Upper Arm Mounting	28
	Wheel Lug Nuts	65-80

NOTE: On Air Bag Equipped Models, Refer To "Air Bag System Precautions" Located In The Front Of This Manual For System Disarming & Arming Procedures.

INDEX

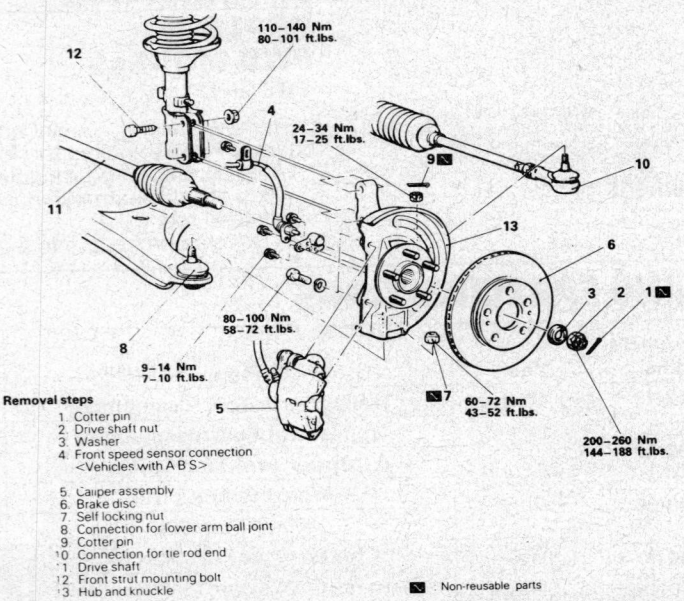

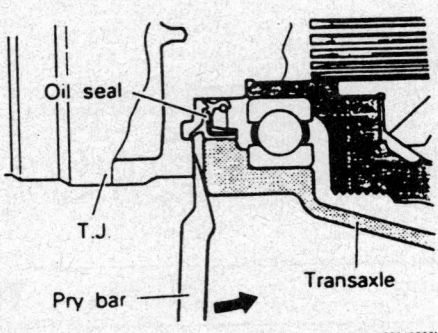

Fig. 2 Driveshaft removal. 1992-94

Removal steps

1. Cotter pin
2. Drive shaft nut
3. Washer
4. Front speed sensor connection <Vehicles with A B S>
5. Caliper assembly
6. Brake disc
7. Self locking nut
8. Connection for lower arm ball joint
9. Cotter pin
10. Connection for tie rod end
11. Drive shaft
12. Front strut mounting bolt
13. Hub and knuckle

■ Non-reusable parts

Fig. 1 Hub & knuckle assembly removal. 1992-94

PRECAUTIONS

AIR BAG SYSTEMS

Refer to "Air Bag System Precautions" in the front of this manual for system disarming and arming procedures.

WHEEL HUB & STEERING KNUCKLE

REPLACE

1992-94

Removal

Remove knuckle and hub assembly in numbered sequence, **Fig. 1**, noting the following:

1. Loosen driveshaft nut with vehicle on floor and brakes applied.
2. Remove speed sensor mounting bolts, then the sensor. **Use care not**

to damage pole piece at tip of speed sensor and the toothed edge of the rotor.

3. Remove and suspend caliper assembly using a piece of wire.
4. Insert pry bar between transaxle case and driveshaft, **Fig. 2**, then pry driveshaft from transaxle. **Do not pull on driveshaft.**

Disassemble & Assemble

Disassemble knuckle and hub assembly in numbered sequence, **Fig. 3**, noting the following:

1. Use knuckle arm bridge tool No. MB991001 or equivalent, to separate hub from knuckle. **Do not strike with hammer, as bearing damage could occur.**
2. Remove oil seal from knuckle.
3. Using puller, remove wheel bearing inner race from front hub. It may be necessary to crush oil seal so puller will catch inner race.
4. Remove snap ring from knuckle.

5. Remove bearings from knuckle.
6. Fill wheel bearings with grease, applying thin coating of grease to knuckle and bearing surfaces.
7. With wheel bearing inner race removed, press in bearing using oil seal installer tool No. MB990985 or equivalent.
8. Install wheel bearing inner race to wheel bearing.
9. Drive hub side of oil seal into knuckle until flush with knuckle end surface.
10. Mount hub assembly to knuckle and tighten to specifications.
11. Rotate hub assembly to seat bearing.
12. Measure wheel bearing starting torque; **torque** should be 16 inch lbs.
13. Measure endplay of hub; Endplay should be .008 inch.
14. If starting torque and hub endplay are not within specification, it is possible that assembly has not been installed correctly. Repeat disassembly and assembly procedure.

Installation

Reverse removal procedure to install, noting the following:

1. Install washer and wheel bearing nut in direction shown, **Fig. 4**.
2. After installing wheel, lower vehicle to ground, then final tighten wheel bearing nut.
3. If cotter pin holes do not match, **torque** nut up to 188 ft. lbs.

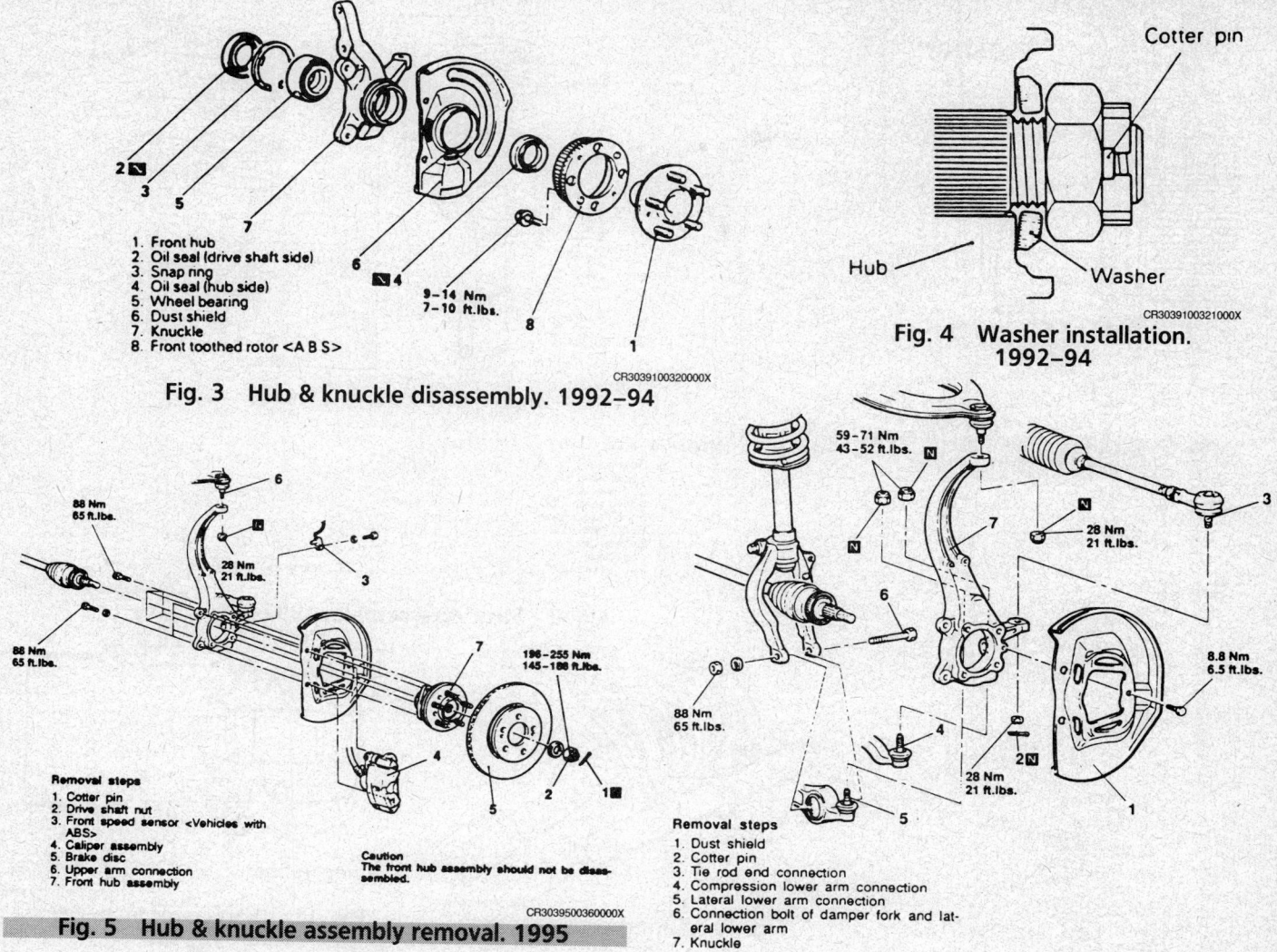

1. Front hub
2. Oil seal (drive shaft side)
3. Snap ring
4. Oil seal (hub side)
5. Wheel bearing
6. Dust shield
7. Knuckle
8. Front toothed rotor <A B S>

9–14 Nm
7–10 ft.lbs.

Fig. 3 Hub & knuckle disassembly. 1992–94

Fig. 4 Washer installation. 1992–94

Cotter pin

Hub

Washer

88 Nm
65 ft.lbs.

28 Nm
21 ft.lbs.

88 Nm
65 ft.lbs.

196–255 Nm
145–188 ft.lbs.

Removal steps
1. Cotter pin
2. Drive shaft nut
3. Front speed sensor <Vehicles with ABS>
4. Caliper assembly
5. Brake disc
6. Upper arm connection
7. Front hub assembly

Caution
The front hub assembly should not be disassembled.

Fig. 5 Hub & knuckle assembly removal. 1995

59–71 Nm
43–52 ft.lbs.

28 Nm
21 ft.lbs.

88 Nm
65 ft.lbs.

28 Nm
21 ft.lbs.

8.8 Nm
6.5 ft.lbs.

Removal steps
1. Dust shield
2. Cotter pin
3. Tie rod end connection
4. Compression lower arm connection
5. Lateral lower arm connection
6. Connection bolt of damper fork and lateral lower arm
7. Knuckle

Fig. 6 Knuckle assembly. 1995

1995
Removal

Remove knuckle and hub assembly in numbered sequence, **Fig. 5** noting the following:
1. Loosen driveshaft nut with vehicle on floor and brakes applied.
2. Loosen, but do not remove tie rod end nut.
3. Remove and suspend caliper assembly out of the way using a piece of wire.
4. Shift the knuckle to the outside in order to maintain the clearance between the front hub assembly mounting bolts and the driveshaft. **Do not damage the ball joint boot.**
5. **On models with ABS,** ensure to not damage rotor.

Disassemble & Assemble

The front hub assembly should not be disassembled. If required by damage or wear, it should be replaced.

Disassemble knuckle assembly in numbered sequence, **Fig. 6** noting the following:

1. Loosen, but do not remove tie rod end nut.
2. Loosen, but do not remove compression lower arm nut.
3. Loosen, but do not remove lateral lower arm nut.

Installation

Reverse removal procedure to install, noting the following:
1. Ensure to install driveshaft washer as shown, **Fig. 7.**
2. After installing wheel, lower vehicle to ground, then final tighten driveshaft nut.
3. If cotter pin holes do not match, **torque nut up to 188 ft. lbs.**

BALL JOINT INSPECTION

1992–94

Check ball joint for correct starting torque as follows:
1. Move ball joint stud from side to side several times.

2. Mount two nuts on ball joint, then using a suitable torque wrench measure starting torque. Starting torque should be within 26–87 inch lbs.
3. If starting torque exceeds upper limit, replace lower arm assembly.
4. If starting torque is below lower limit, the ball joint may still be reused unless it has drag or excessive play.

STRUT
REPLACE

1992–94
Removal

Remove strut assembly in numbered sequence, **Fig. 8,** noting the following:
1. Do not pry brake hose and line away from strut.

Disassemble & Assemble

Disassemble strut in numbered sequence, **Fig. 9,** noting the following:

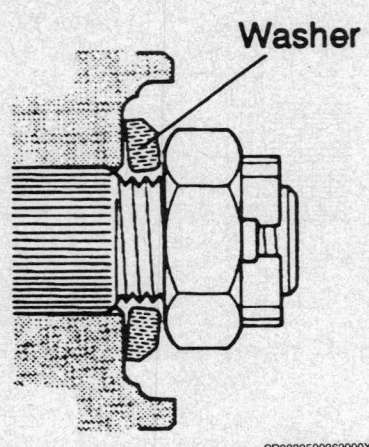

Washer

Fig. 7 Driveshaft washer installation. 1995

CR3039500362000X

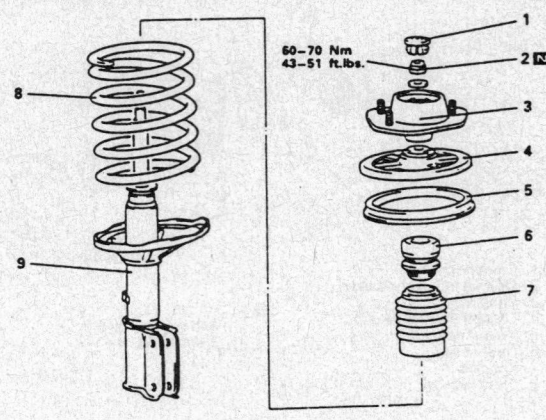

60—70 Nm
43—51 ft.lbs.

```
Disassembly steps
1. Dust cover
2. Self-locking nut
3. Strut insulator
4. Spring seat, upper
5. Spring pad, upper
6. Bump rubber
7. Dust cover
8. Coil spring
9. Strut assembly
```

Ⓝ : Non-reusable parts

CR2029100058000X

Fig. 9 Strut disassemble. 1992—94

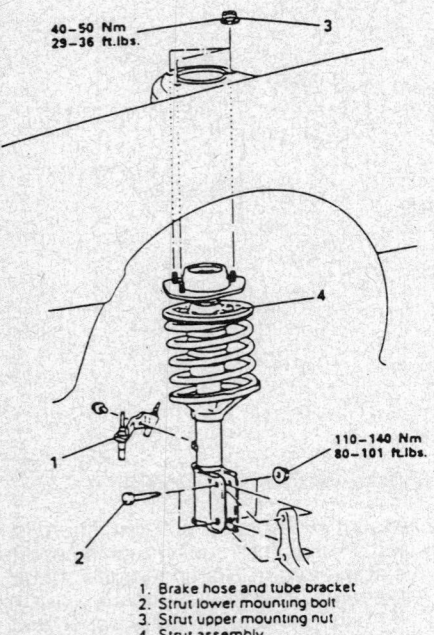

40—50 Nm
29—36 ft.lbs.

110—140 Nm
80—101 ft.lbs.

1. Brake hose and tube bracket
2. Strut lower mounting bolt
3. Strut upper mounting nut
4. Strut assembly

CR2029100057000X

Fig. 8 Strut assembly removal. 1992—94

1. Compress coil spring, **Fig. 10**, then remove locknut.
2. Join dust cover and bump rubber, **Fig. 11**.
3. Line up holes in spring upper and lower seats.

Installation

Reverse removal procedure to install, noting the following:
1. Install strut assembly insulator as shown, **Fig. 12**.

1995

Removal

Remove strut assembly in numbered sequence, **Fig. 13**.

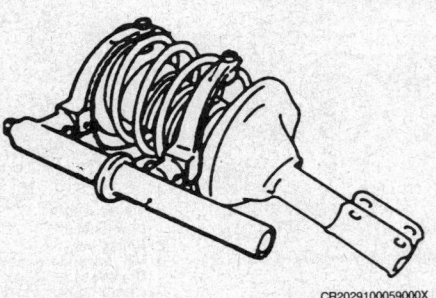

CR2029100059000X

Fig. 10 Spring compression. 1992—94

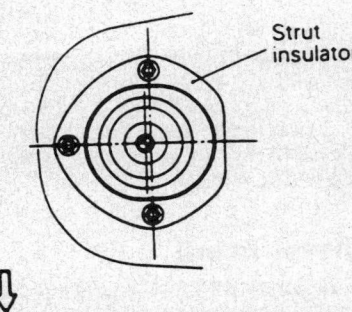

Strut insulator

Front ⇩

CR2029100061000X

Fig. 12 Insulator position. 1992—94

Disassemble & Assemble

Disassemble strut in numbered sequence, **Fig. 14** noting the following:
1. Compress spring using spring compression tools No. MB991237 and MB991239, or equivalents, to ease in disassembly and assembly.

Installation

Reverse removal procedure to install, noting the following:
1. Ensure spring is properly seated in

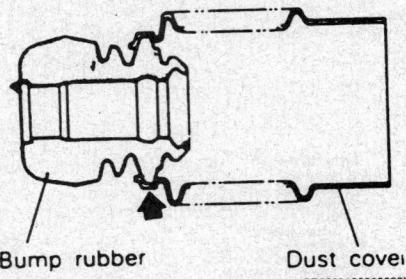

Bump rubber   Dust cover

CR2029100060000X

Fig. 11 Dust cover installation. 1992—94

upper and lower spring seat when installing.
2. Install strut upper bracket as shown in **Fig. 15**, then tighten strut rod nut to specifications.

CONTROL ARM
REPLACE

LOWER
1992—94

Remove lower control arm in numbered sequence, **Figs. 16 and 17**, noting the following:
1. Check ball joint starting torque. Torque should be 26—87 inch lbs. If reading exceeds specified amount, replace lower arm assembly.
2. Reverse procedure to install.

1995

Remove compression and lateral lower control arms in numbered sequence, **Fig. 18**, noting the following:
1. Loosen but do not remove compression lower arm ball joint.
2. Check compression lower arm ball

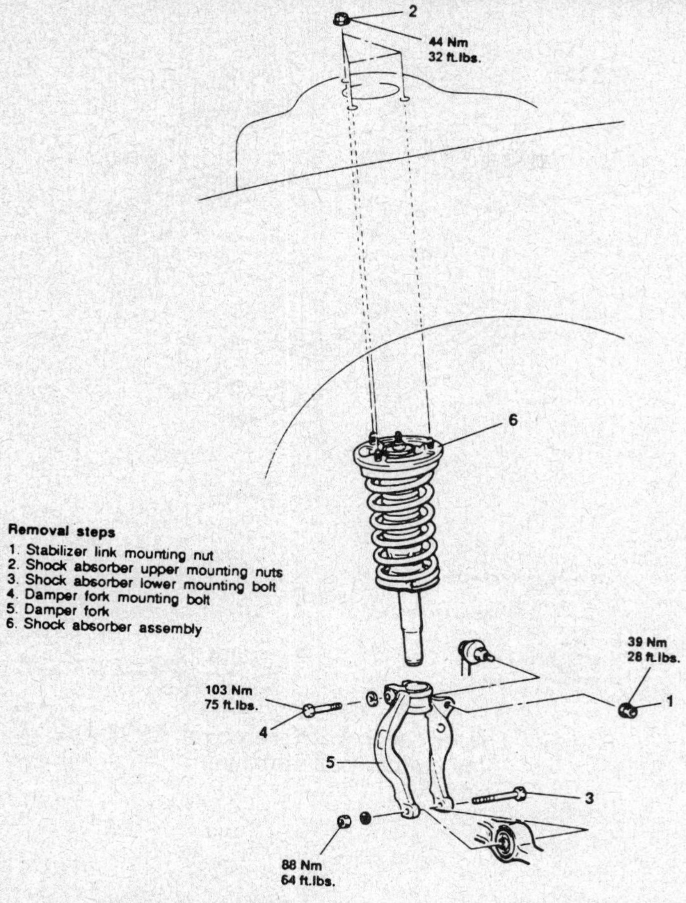

Removal steps
1. Stabilizer link mounting nut
2. Shock absorber upper mounting nuts
3. Shock absorber lower mounting bolt
4. Damper fork mounting bolt
5. Damper fork
6. Shock absorber assembly

44 Nm
32 ft.lbs.

2

6

39 Nm
28 ft.lbs.

103 Nm
75 ft.lbs.

4

5

1

3

88 Nm
64 ft.lbs.

CR2029500106000X

Fig. 13   Strut assembly removal. 1995

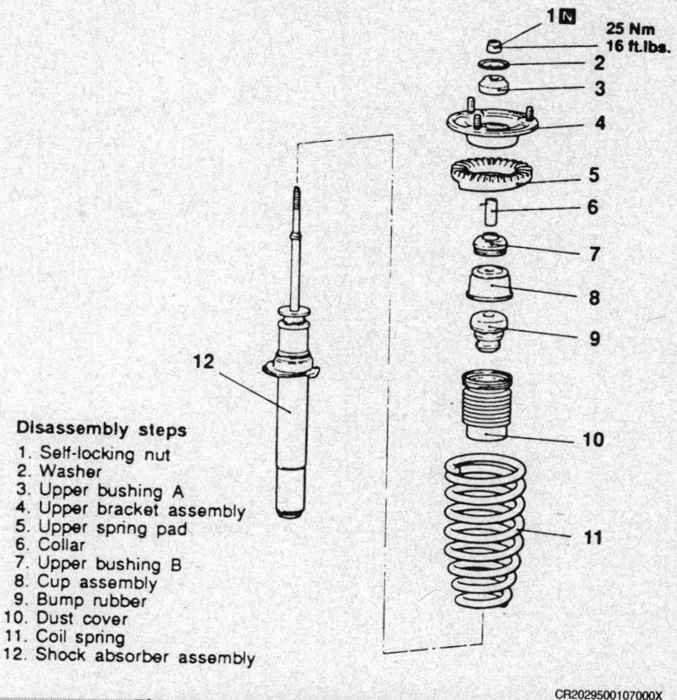

Disassembly steps
1. Self-locking nut
2. Washer
3. Upper bushing A
4. Upper bracket assembly
5. Upper spring pad
6. Collar
7. Upper bushing B
8. Cup assembly
9. Bump rubber
10. Dust cover
11. Coil spring
12. Shock absorber assembly

25 Nm
16 ft.lbs.

1
2
3
4
5
6
7
8
9
10
11
12

CR2029500107000X

Fig. 14   Strut disassemble. 1995

joint breakaway torque. Torque should be 4–22 inch lbs. If reading exceeds specified amount, replace lower arm assembly.
3. Loosen but do not remove knuckle/lateral lower arm ball joint.
4. Check lateral lower arm ball joint breakaway torque. Torque should be 9–30 inch lbs. If reading exceeds specified amount, replace lower arm assembly.

STABILIZER BAR
REPLACE
FWD MODELS
1992–94

Remove stabilizer bar in numbered sequence, **Figs. 19 and 20**, noting the following:
1. Front exhaust pipe must be removed.
2. Pull both ends of stabilizer bar to rear of driveshaft.
3. Move right side of bar until it clears lower arm.
4. Pull stabilizer bar out right side.
5. Check stabilizer bar ball joint starting torque; **torque** should be 15–28 inch lbs. If starting torque exceeds specified torque, replace stabilizer link.
6. Reverse procedure to install.

Inside of the body

Damper fork installation bolt

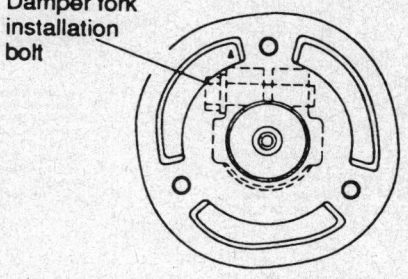

CR2029500108000X

Fig. 15   Upper bracket installation. 1995

1995

Remove stabilizer bar in numbered sequence, **Fig. 21** noting the following:
1. Reverse procedure to install ensuring to set the stabilizer bar so that the identification mark is at the left. Install the bushing, ensuring the dimension is as shown in **Fig. 22**.

AWD MODELS
1992–94

Remove stabilizer bar in numbered sequence, **Fig. 23**, noting the following:
1. Disconnect coupling of knuckle and lower arm on right side.
2. Pull sides of bar between driveshaft and lower arm.
3. Reverse procedure to install.

1995

1. Remove stabilizer bar in numbered sequence, **Fig. 21**.
2. Reverse procedure to install. Ensure stabilizer bar is set so identification mark is at the left. Install bushing, ensuring the dimension is as shown in **Fig. 22**.

POWER STEERING GEAR
REPLACE

Remove rack & pinion in numbered sequence, **Fig. 24**, noting the following:
1. Turn rack completely to right, the disconnect gearbox from crossmember.
2. While tilting gearbox downward, remove from left side.
3. Reverse procedure to install.

POWER STEERING PUMP
REPLACE
1992–94

Remove steering pump in numbered sequence, **Fig. 25** noting the following:
1. Remove reservoir cap and disconnect return hose to drain fluid.
2. Raise and support vehicle.
3. Disconnect high tension cable, then turn crank engine to drain fluid from gearbox.
4. Cover alternator (located under oil pump) if any hoses are removed.
5. Reverse procedure to install. When connecting pressure hose, ensure slit contacts oil pump guide bracket.

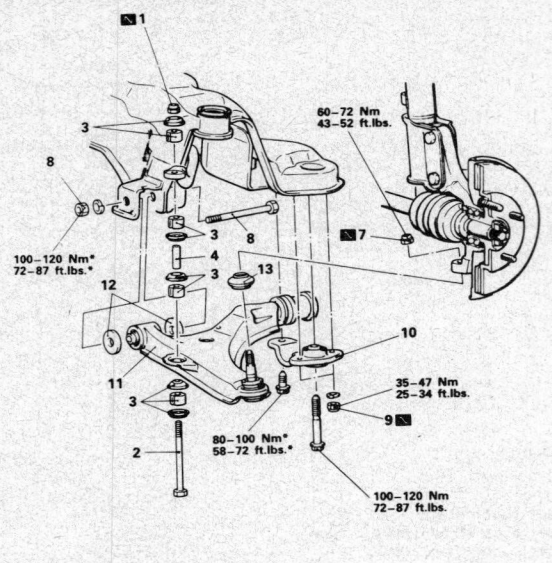

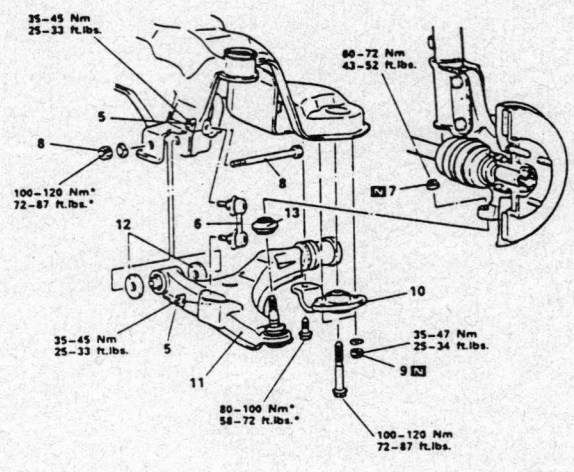

1. Stabilizer bar mounting nut
2. Stabilizer bar mounting bolt
3. Joint cups and bushing
4. Collar
7. Self-locking nut
8. Lower arm mounting nut and bolt
9. Self-locking nut.
10. Clamp
11. Lower arm
12. Stopper
13. Ball joint dust cover

⊠ : Non-reusable parts
* : Indicates parts which should be temporarily tightened, and then fully tightened with the vehicle in the unladen condition.

CR2029100065000X

Fig. 16 Lower control arm removal. 1992–94 w/rubber bushing stabilizer

Removal step

5. Stabilizer link mounting nut
6. Stabilizer link
7. Self-locking nut
8. Lower arm mounting nut and bolt
9. Self-locking nut
10. Clamp
11. Lower arm
12. Stopper
13. Ball joint dust cover

⊠ : Non-reusable parts
* : Indicates parts which should be temporarily tightened, and then fully tightened with the vehicle in the unladen condition.

CR2029100066000X

Fig. 17 Lower control arm removal. 1992–94 w/pillow-ball stabilizer

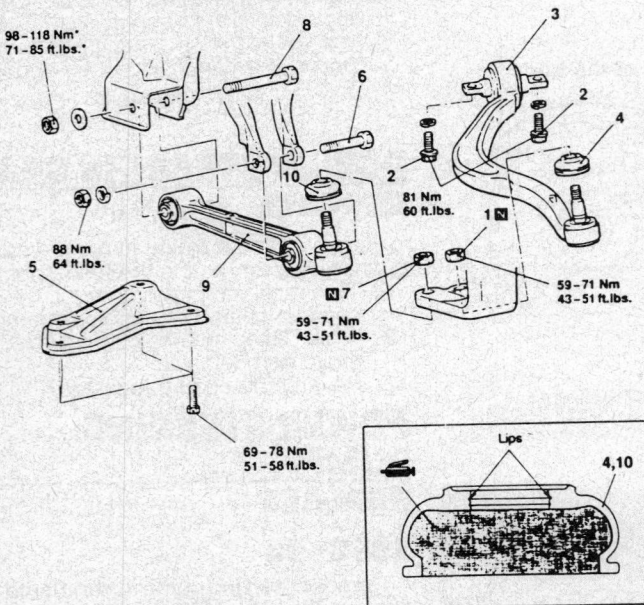

Compression lower arm assembly removal steps

1. Compression lower arm ball joint and knuckle connection
2. Compression lower arm mounting bolts
3. Compression lower arm assembly
4. Dust cover

Lateral lower arm assembly removal steps

5. Stay
6. Shock absorber lower mounting bolt
7. Lateral lower arm ball joint and knuckle connection
8. Lateral lower arm mounting bolt
9. Lateral lower arm assembly
10. Dust cover

Caution
* : Indicates parts which should be temporarily tightened, and then fully tightened with the vehicle on the ground in the unladen condition.

CR2029500109000X

Fig. 18   Compression & lateral lower arm assemblies. 1995

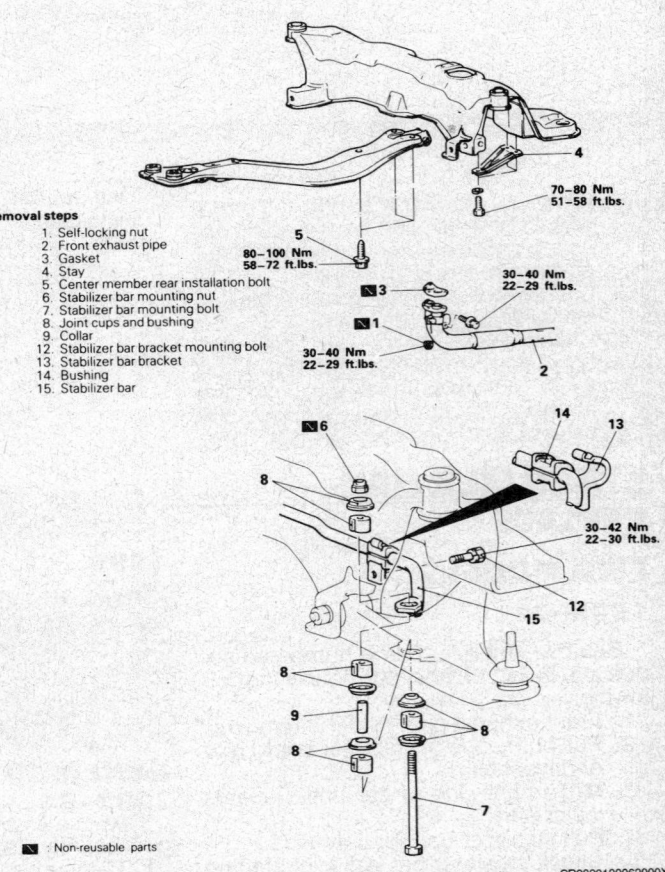

Removal steps

1. Self-locking nut
2. Front exhaust pipe
3. Gasket
4. Stay
5. Center member rear installation bolt
6. Stabilizer bar mounting nut
7. Stabilizer bar mounting bolt
8. Joint cups and bushing
9. Collar
10. Stabilizer bar bracket mounting bolt
11. (not visible)
12. Stabilizer bar bracket
13. Stabilizer bar bracket
14. Bushing
15. Stabilizer bar

⊠ : Non-reusable parts

CR2029100062000X

Fig. 19   Stabilizer bar removal. 1992–94 FWD w/rubber bushing stabilizer

FRONT SUSPENSION & STEERING

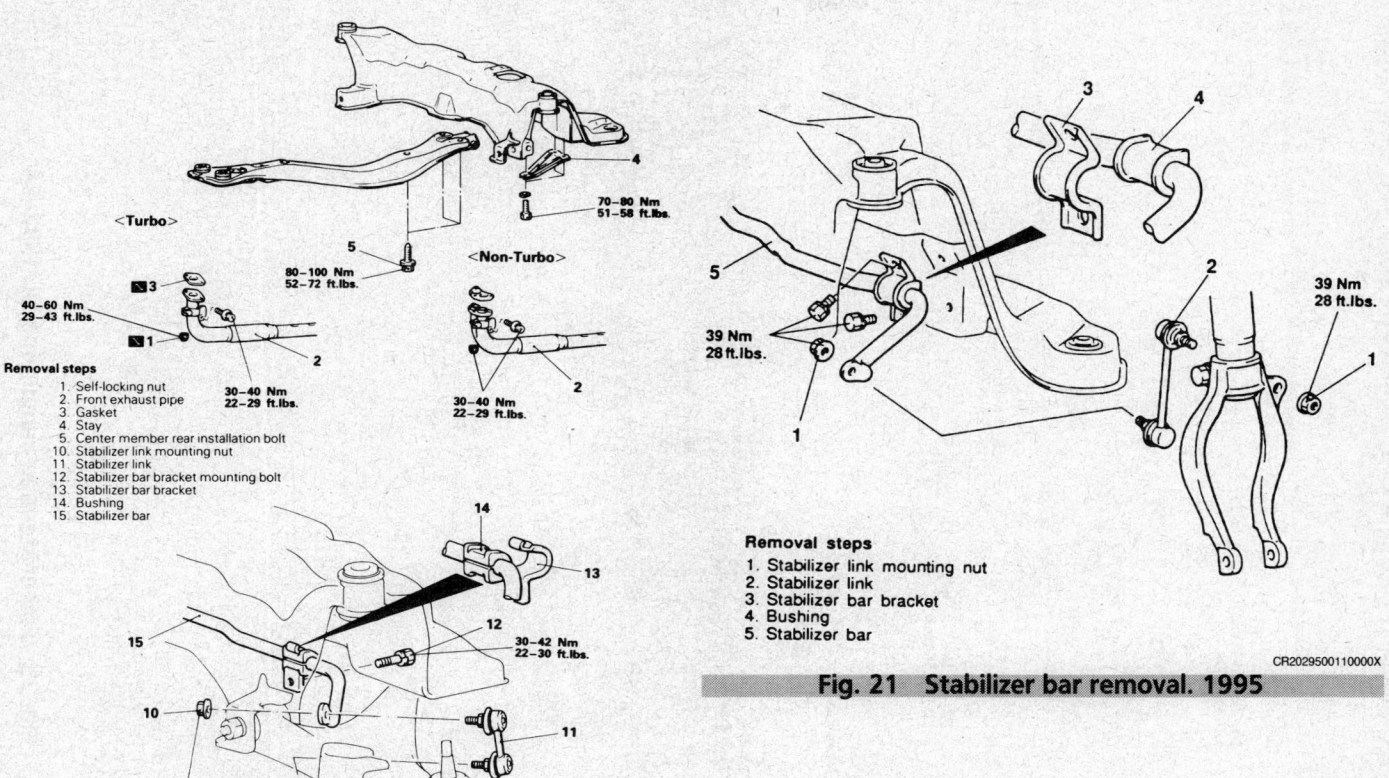

Removal steps
1. Self-locking nut
2. Front exhaust pipe
3. Gasket
4. Stay
5. Center member rear installation bolt
10. Stabilizer link mounting nut
11. Stabilizer link
12. Stabilizer bar bracket mounting bolt
13. Stabilizer bar bracket
14. Bushing
15. Stabilizer bar

40–60 Nm
29–43 ft.lbs.

80–100 Nm
52–72 ft.lbs.

70–80 Nm
51–58 ft.lbs.

30–40 Nm
22–29 ft.lbs.

30–40 Nm
22–29 ft.lbs.

30–42 Nm
22–30 ft.lbs.

35–45 Nm
25–33 ft.lbs.

<Turbo>

<Non-Turbo>

Removal steps
1. Stabilizer link mounting nut
2. Stabilizer link
3. Stabilizer bar bracket
4. Bushing
5. Stabilizer bar

39 Nm
28 ft.lbs.

39 Nm
28 ft.lbs.

CR2029500110000X

Fig. 21   Stabilizer bar removal. 1995

☒ Non-reusable parts

CR2029100063000X

**Fig. 20   Stabilizer bar removal. 1992–94 FWD
w/pillow-ball stabilizer**

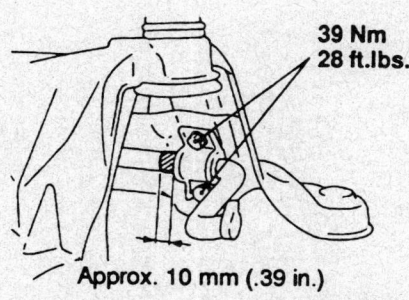

39 Nm
28 ft.lbs.

Approx. 10 mm (.39 in.)

CR2029500111000X

**Fig. 22   Stabilizer bar bushing
alignment. 1995**

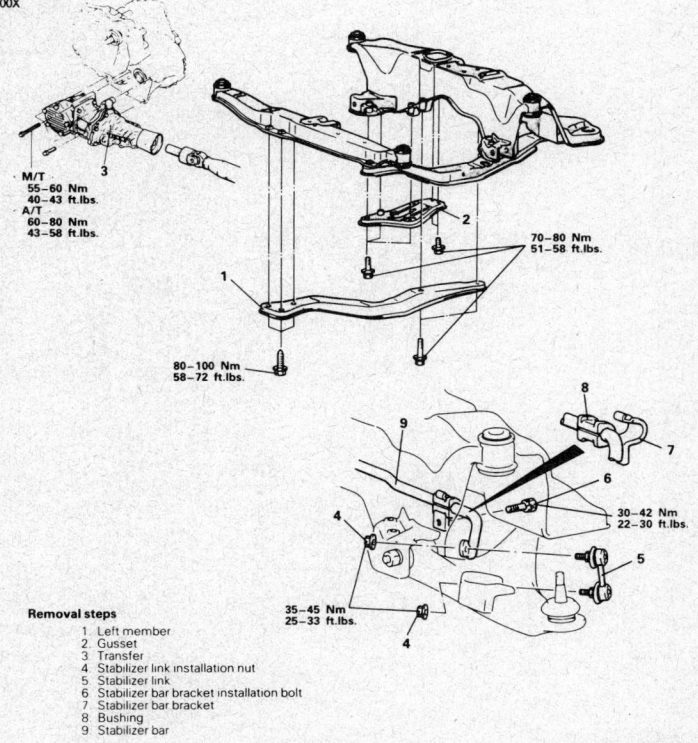

M/T
55–60 Nm
40–43 ft.lbs.
A/T
60–80 Nm
43–58 ft.lbs.

70–80 Nm
51–58 ft.lbs.

80–100 Nm
58–72 ft.lbs.

30–42 Nm
22–30 ft.lbs.

35–45 Nm
25–33 ft.lbs.

Removal steps
1. Left member
2. Gusset
3. Transfer
4. Stabilizer link installation nut
5. Stabilizer link
6. Stabilizer bar bracket installation bolt
7. Stabilizer bar bracket
8. Bushing
9. Stabilizer bar

CR2029100064000X

Fig. 23   Stabilizer bar removal. 1992–94 AWD models

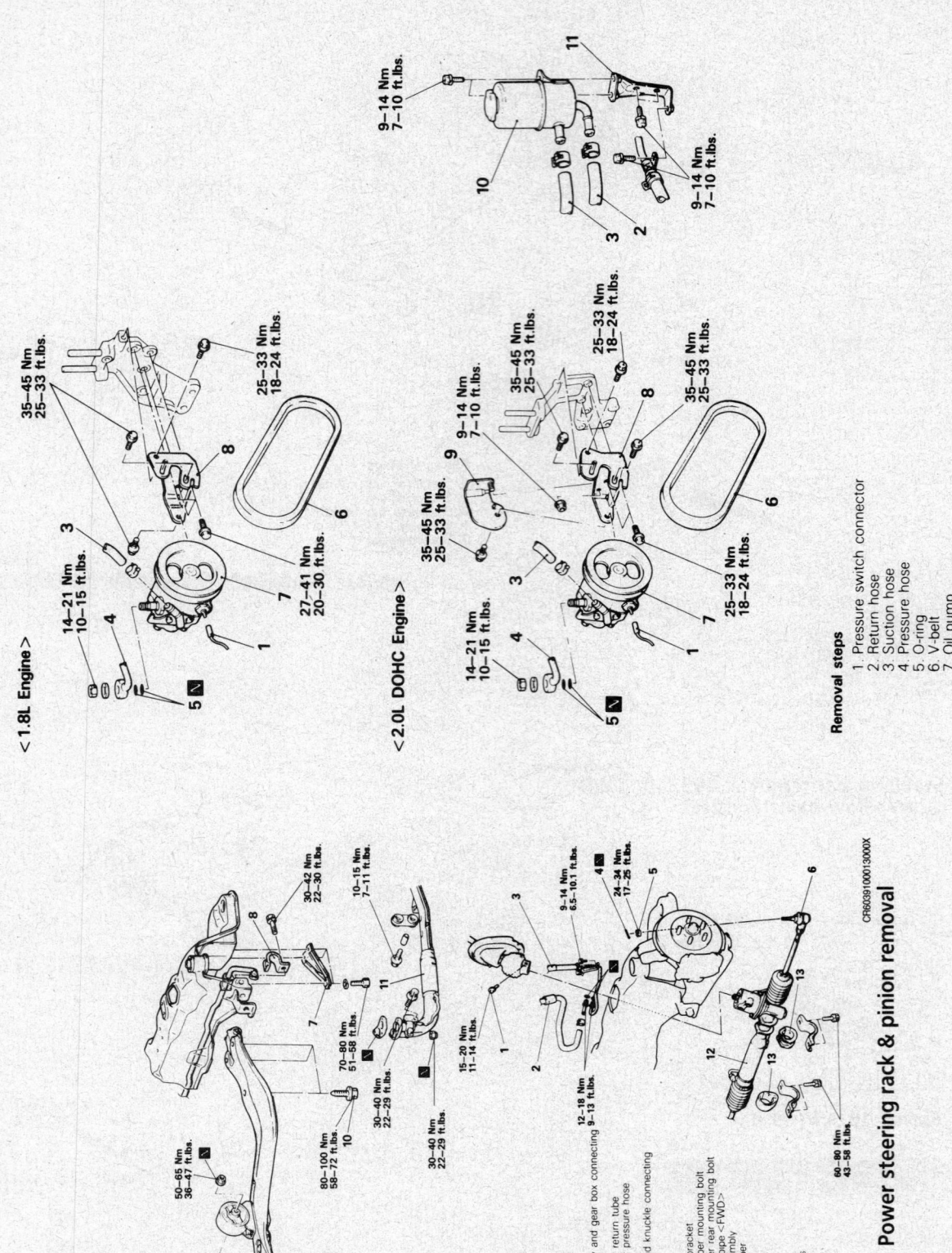

CR602910008l000X

9–14 Nm
7–10 ft.lbs.

11

10

9–14 Nm
7–10 ft.lbs.

3

2

☒ Non-reusable parts

< 1.8L Engine >

35–45 Nm
25–33 ft.lbs.

25–33 Nm
18–24 ft.lbs.

8

14–21 Nm
10–15 ft.lbs.

3

4

5 ☒

1

7

6

27–41 Nm
20–30 ft.lbs.

< 2.0L DOHC Engine >

9–14 Nm
7–10 ft.lbs.

9

35–45 Nm
25–33 ft.lbs.

25–33 Nm
18–24 ft.lbs.

8

35–45 Nm
25–33 ft.lbs.

6

14–21 Nm
10–15 ft.lbs.

4

5 ☒

1

3

7

25–33 Nm
18–24 ft.lbs.

Removal steps

1. Pressure switch connector
2. Return hose
3. Suction hose
4. Pressure hose
5. O-ring
6. V-belt
7. Oil pump
8. Oil pump bracket
9. Heat protector < 2.0L DOHC Engine >
10. Oil reservoir
11. Reservoir bracket

Fig. 25 Power steering pump removal. 1992–94

CR603910013000X

30–42 Nm
22–30 ft.lbs.

8

10–15 ft.lbs.
7–11 ft.lbs.

11

7

70–80 Nm
51–58 ft.lbs. ☒

80–100 Nm
58–72 ft.lbs. ☒

10

30–40 Nm
22–29 ft.lbs. ☒

30–40 Nm
22–29 ft.lbs.

50–65 Nm
36–47 ft.lbs. ☒

9

15–20 Nm
11–14 ft.lbs.

1

12–18 Nm
9–13 ft.lbs.

3

9–14 Nm
6.5–10.1 ft.lbs.

4 ☒

2

24–34 Nm
17–25 ft.lbs.

5

6

12

13

13

60–80 Nm
43–58 ft.lbs.

☒ Non-reusable parts

Removal steps

1. Joint assembly and gear box connecting bolt
2. Connection for return tube
3. Connection for pressure hose
4. Cotter pin
5. Tie-rod end and knuckle connecting nuts
6. Tie-rod end
7. Stay
8. Stabilizer bar bracket
9. Front roll stopper mounting bolt
10. Center member rear mounting bolt
11. Front exhaust pipe < FWD >
12. Gear box assembly
13. Mounting rubber

Fig. 24 Power steering rack & pinion removal

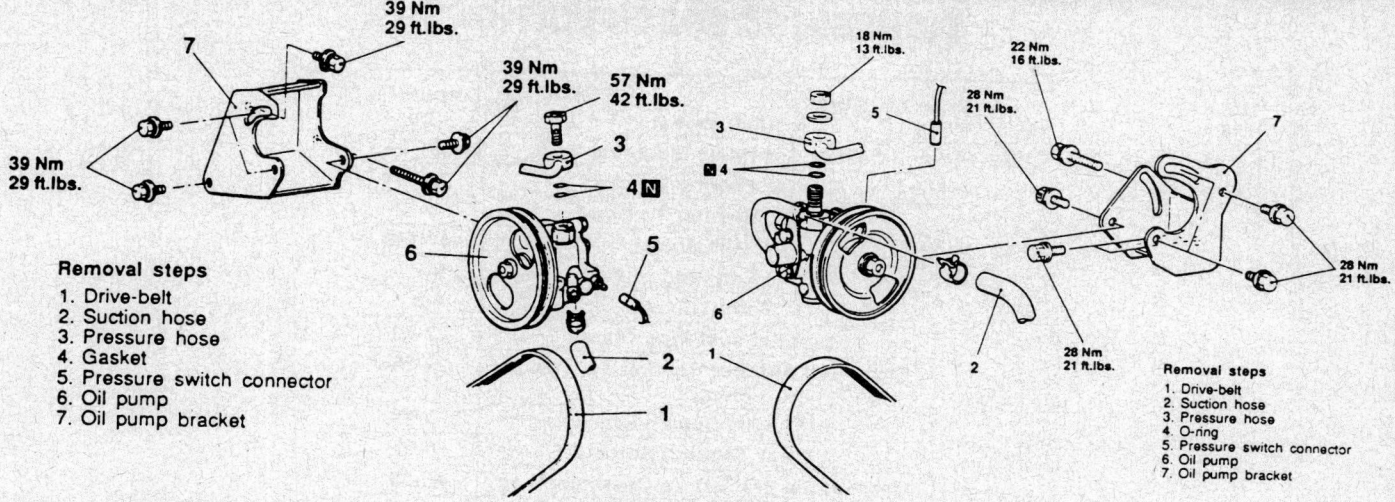

Removal steps
1. Drive-belt
2. Suction hose
3. Pressure hose
4. Gasket
5. Pressure switch connector
6. Oil pump
7. Oil pump bracket

39 Nm 29 ft.lbs.
39 Nm 29 ft.lbs.
57 Nm 42 ft.lbs.
39 Nm 29 ft.lbs.

CR6029500082000X

Fig. 26   Power steering pump removal. 1995 less turbo

Removal steps
1. Drive-belt
2. Suction hose
3. Pressure hose
4. O-ring
5. Pressure switch connector
6. Oil pump
7. Oil pump bracket

18 Nm 13 ft.lbs.
22 Nm 16 ft.lbs.
28 Nm 21 ft.lbs.
28 Nm 21 ft.lbs.
28 Nm 21 ft.lbs.

CR6029500083000X

Fig. 27   Power steering pump removal. 1995 w/turbo

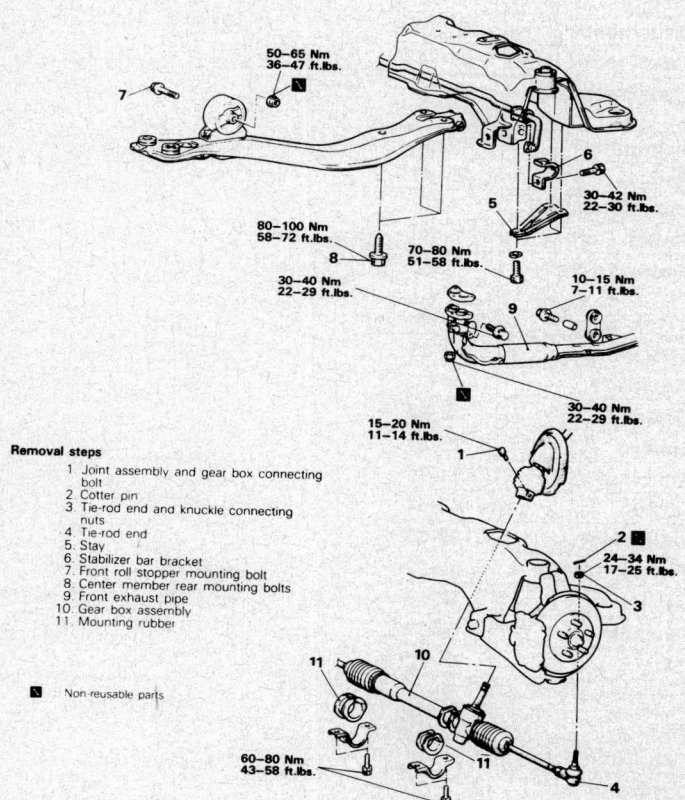

Removal steps
1. Joint assembly and gear box connecting bolt
2. Cotter pin
3. Tie-rod end and knuckle connecting nuts
4. Tie-rod end
5. Stay
6. Stabilizer bar bracket
7. Front roll stopper mounting bolt
8. Center member rear mounting bolts
9. Front exhaust pipe
10. Gear box assembly
11. Mounting rubber

◨ Non-reusable parts

50–65 Nm 36–47 ft.lbs.
30–42 Nm 22–30 ft.lbs.
80–100 Nm 58–72 ft.lbs.
70–80 Nm 51–58 ft.lbs.
10–15 Nm 7–11 ft.lbs.
30–40 Nm 22–29 ft.lbs.
30–40 Nm 22–29 ft.lbs.
15–20 Nm 11–14 ft.lbs.
24–34 Nm 17–25 ft.lbs.
60–80 Nm 43–58 ft.lbs.

CR6039100012000X

Fig. 28   Manual steering rack & pinion removal

1995

Remove steering pump in numbered sequence, **Figs. 26 and 27** noting the following:
1. Remove reservoir cap and disconnect return hose to drain fluid.
2. Raise and support vehicle.
3. Cover alternator (located under oil pump) if any hoses are removed
4. Reverse procedure to install, ensuring to install oil pump in a position towards the front of the bracket, and adjust the belt tension using the air conditioning tension pulley.

MANUAL STEERING GEAR
REPLACE

Remove rack & pinion in numbered sequence, **Fig. 28**, noting the following:
1. Turn rack completely to right, the disconnect gearbox from crossmember.
2. While tilting gearbox downward, remove from left side.
3. Reverse procedure to install.

TIGHTENING SPECIFICATIONS

Year	Component	Torque/Ft. Lbs.
1992–94	Caliper Assembly Mounting Bolt	58-72
	Center Bearing Bracket	26-33
	Center Member To Body	58-72
	Driveshaft Nut	144-188
	End Plug	36-51
	Feed Tubes	9-13
	Front Exhaust Pipe Clamp	22-29
	Front Roll Stopper Bracket To Center Member	29-36
	Front Speed Sensor Bracket	7-10
	Front Toothed Rotor	7-10
	Gearbox To Bracket To Crossmember	43-58
	Heat Protector Installation Nut	7-10
	Hub Assembly To Knuckle	144-188
	Joint Assembly	11-14
	Knuckle To Ball Joint	43-52
	Knuckle To Strut Assembly	80-101
	Lower Arm Clamp To Crossmember (Nut)	25-34
	Lower Arm Clamp To Crossmember (Bolt)	58-72
	Lower Arm To Crossmember	72-87
	Oil Pump To Bracket	25-33
	Oil Reservoir Bracket Installation Bolt	7-10
	Oil Reservoir Installation Bolt	7-10
	Pinion And Valve Assembly To Self-Locking Nut	14-22
	Pressure Hose To Gearbox	9-13
	Pressure Hose To Oil Pump	10-15
	Return Tube To Gearbox	9-13
	Stabilizer Bar Bracket	22-30
	Stabilizer Link	25-33
	Stay To Crossmember	51-58
	Strut Top End Nut	43-51
	Strut Upper Mounting Nut	29-39
	Terminal Assembly To Pump Body	18-22
	Tie Rod End Ball Joint	17-25
	Tie Rod End To Rack	58-72
	Wheel Lug Nuts	87-101
1995	Caliper Assembly Mounting Bolt	36-43
	Compression Lower Arm	51-60
	Dampener To Strut Collar	75
	Dampener Pivot	64
	Driveshaft Nut	145-188
	Dust Shield	6.5
	Hub Assembly To Knuckle	65
	Knuckle To Ball Joint	21
	Knuckle To Compression Lower Arm	43-52
	Knuckle Upper Mounting	21
	Lateral Lower Arm To Crossmember	71-85
	Lateral Lower Arm Ball Joint	60
	P. S. Oil Pump To Bracket	21-29
	Stabilizer Bar Bracket	28
	Stabilizer Link To Dampener	28

TIGHTENING SPECIFICATIONS—Continued

Year	Component	Torque/Ft. Lbs.
	Stay To Crossmember	51-58
	Strut Top End Nut	16
	Strut Lower Mounting	64
	Strut Upper Mounting Nut	32
	Tie Rod End Ball Joint	21
	Upper Arm Shaft Assembly	62
	Upper Arm Pivot	41
	Upper Arm To Knuckle	20
	Wheel Lug Nuts	88-108

Wheel Alignment

INDEX

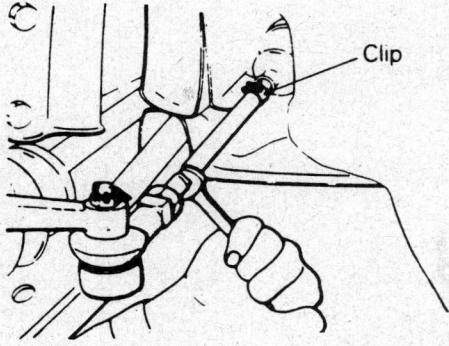

Fig. 1 Toe-in adjustment

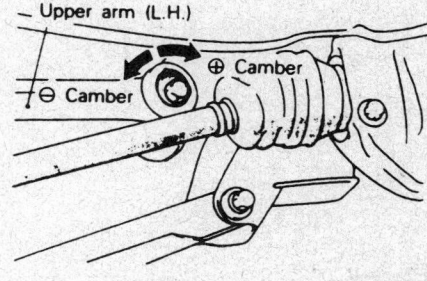

Fig. 2 Rear wheel camber adjustment. AWD

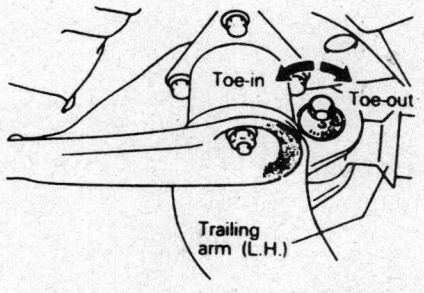

Fig. 3 Rear wheel toe-in adjustment. AWD

FRONT WHEEL ALIGNMENT

Prior to wheel alignment, ensure tires are at recommended pressure, are of equal size and have approximately the same wear pattern. Check front wheel and tire assembly for radial runout and inspect lower ball joints and steering linkage for looseness. Check front and rear springs for sagging or damage. Front suspension inspections should be performed on a level floor or alignment rack with fuel tank at capacity and vehicle free of luggage and passenger compartment load. The vehicle should be bounced an equal number of times from the center of the bumper alternately, first from the rear, then the front, releasing at the bottom of down cycle.

EAGLE TALON & PLYMOUTH LASER

CASTER & CAMBER

Caster and camber are preset at the factory and cannot be adjusted. If caster or camber are not within specifications, replace bent or damaged components.

TOE-IN

Adjust toe-in by undoing clips and turning each tie rod turnbuckle an equal amount in opposite directions, **Fig. 1.** Toe will move out as the left turnbuckle is turned toward front of vehicle and the right turnbuckle is turned toward rear of vehicle. For each half turn, toe-in will increase or decrease .24 inch.

REAR WHEEL ALIGNMENT

FWD MODELS

Camber and toe-in are preset at the factory and cannot be adjusted. If camber or toe-in are not within specifications, replace bent or damaged components.

AWD MODELS

Camber

Always adjust toe-in following a camber adjustment, toe in will vary .035 inch for every camber scale adjustment.

1. Measure camber using a camber/caster/kingpin gauge.
2. If camber is not within specifications, adjust by moving the mounting bolt located on the crossmember side of the arm, **Fig. 2.**

Toe-In

1. Measure toe-in using a toe-in gauge.
2. If toe-in is not within specifications, adjust by moving the mounting bolts located on the crossmember side of the trailing arm, **Fig. 3.**

COLT, COLT VISTA, SUMMIT & SUMMIT WAGON

NOTE: Refer To The Rear Of This Manual For Vehicle Manufacturer's Special Tool Suppliers.

INDEX OF SERVICE OPERATIONS

NOTE: For Service Operations Not Listed Below, Refer To The Table Of Contents In The Front Of This Manual.

Specifications
GENERAL ENGINE SPECIFICATIONS

Year	Engine Liter/CID [1]	Engine VIN Code [2]	Fuel System	Bore & Stroke	Comp. Ratio	Net Horsepower @ RPM [3]	Maximum Torque, Ft. Lbs. @ RPM	Normal Oil Pressure, psi [4]
1992	1.5L/4-90	A	MPI	2.97 x 3.23	9.2	92 @ 6000	93 @ 3000	11.4
	1.8L/4-110	D	MPI	3.19 x 3.50	8.5	113 @ 6000	116 @ 4500	11.4
	2.4L/4-146	W	MPI	3.41 x 3.94	8.5	116 @ 5000	136 @ 3500	11.4
1993	1.5L/4-90	A	MPI	2.97 x 3.23	9.2	92 @ 6000	93 @ 3000	11.4
	1.8L/4-110	D	MPI	3.19 x 3.50	9.5	113 @ 6000	116 @ 4500	11.4
	2.4L/4-146	W	MPI	3.41 x 3.94	9.5	136 @ 5500	145 @ 4250	11.4
1994-95	1.5L/4-90	A	MPI	2.97 x 3.23	9.2	92 @ 6000	93 @ 3000	11.4
	1.8L/4-110	C	MPI	3.19 x 3.50	9.5	113 @ 6000	116 @ 4500	11.4
	2.4L/4-146	W	MPI	3.41 x 3.94	9.5	136 @ 5500	145 @ 4250	11.4

MPI—Multi-Point Fuel Injection System.
[1]—Cubic inch displacement.
[2]—The eighth digit of the VIN denotes engine code.
[3]—Ratings are net, as installed in vehicle.
[4]—Minimum oil pressure at idle RPM, with oil temperature at 167 to 194°F.

TUNE UP SPECIFICATIONS

Engine/VIN	Spark Plug Gap	Ignition Timing, °BTDC Firing Order Fig.	Ignition Timing, °BTDC Man. Trans.	Ignition Timing, °BTDC Auto. Trans.	Mark Fig.	Curb Idle Speed Man. Trans.	Curb Idle Speed Auto. Trans.	Fast Idle Speed Man. Trans.	Fast Idle Speed Auto. Trans.	Fuel Pressure psi
1992										
1.5L/4-90/A	.041	C	5N[4]	5P[4]	A	750N[3]	750P[3]	[3]	[3]	[2] [5]
1.8L/4-110/D	.041	D	5[1]	5[1]	A	750N[3]	750N[3]	—	[3]	[2] [5]
2.4L/4-146/W	.041	B	5[1]	5[1]	A	750N[3]	750N[3]	—	[3]	[2] [5]
1993										
1.5L/4-90/A	.041	C	5N[4]	5P[4]	A	750N[3]	750P[3]	[3]	[3]	[2] [5]
1.8L/4-110/D	.041	D	5[1]	5[1]	A	750N[3]	750N[3]	[3]	[3]	[2] [5]
2.4L/4-146/W	.041	B	5[1]	5[1]	A	750N[3]	750N[3]	[3]	[3]	[2] [5]
1994-95										
1.5L/4-90/A	.041	C	5N[4]	5P[4]	A	750N[3]	750P[3]	[3]	[3]	[2] [5]
1.8L/4-110/C	.041	D	5[1]	5[1]	A	750N[3]	750N[3]	—	[3]	[2] [5]
2.4L/4-146/W	.041	B	5[1]	5[1]	A	750N[3]	750N[3]	—	[3]	[2] [5]

BTDC—Before top dead center.
N—Neutral.
P—Park.
[1]—With jumper wire connected between ignition timing adjustment connector and ground.
[2]—Vacuum hose connected to pressure regulator, 38 psi; vacuum hose disconnected from pressure regulator, 47–50 psi.
[3]—Controlled by Idle Speed Control (ISC).
[4]—With jumper wire connected between ignition timing adjustment connector & ground. Refer to Fig. E.
[5]—Disconnect fuel pump electrical connector, located at fuel tank. Start engine & operate until it stalls. Disconnect battery ground cable, then reconnect fuel pump electrical connector. Place shop towels around fuel high pressure hose at fuel delivery pipe side, then disconnect hose. Install suitable fuel pressure gauge between fuel delivery pipe & high pressure hose. Connect battery ground cable and check fuel pressure with engine idling.

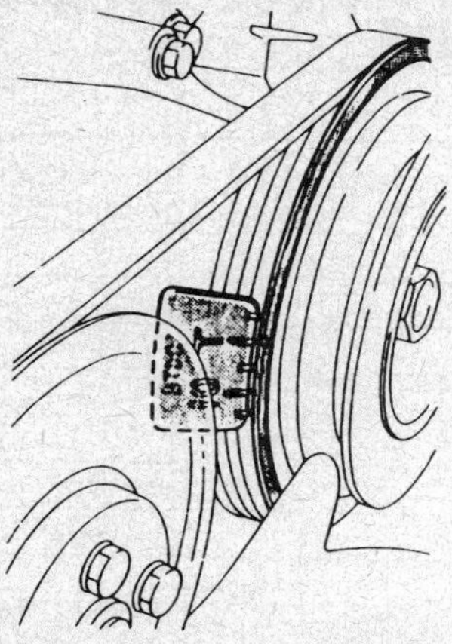

CR1139100183000X

Fig. A

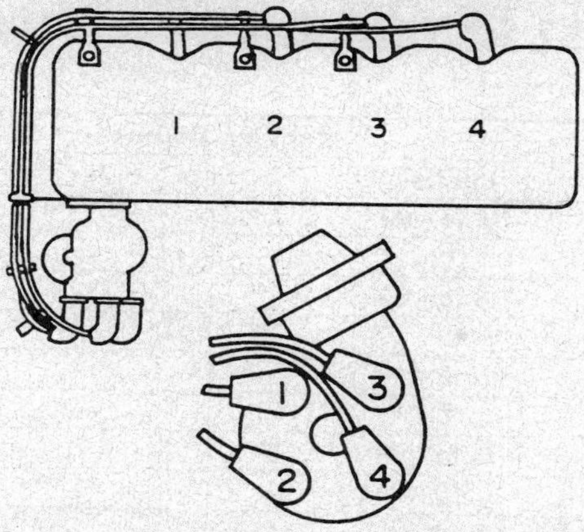

CR1139100184000X

Fig. B

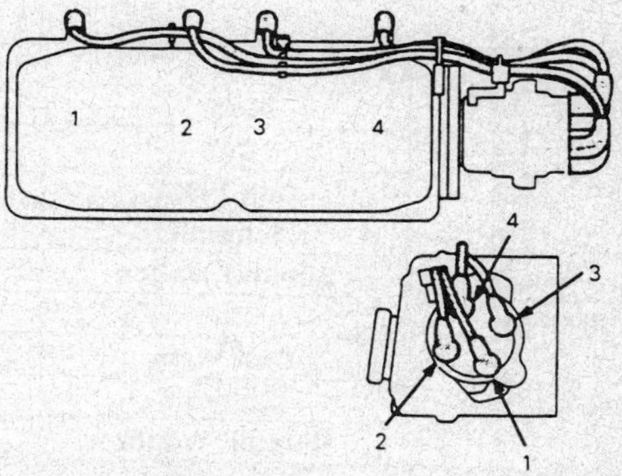

CR1139100185000X

Fig. C

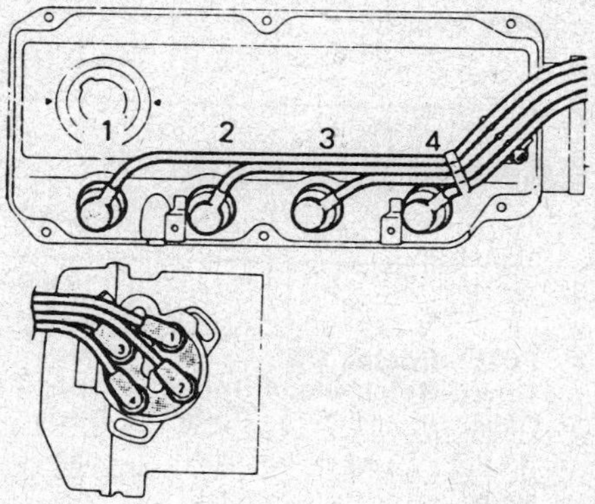

CR1139100186000X

Fig. D

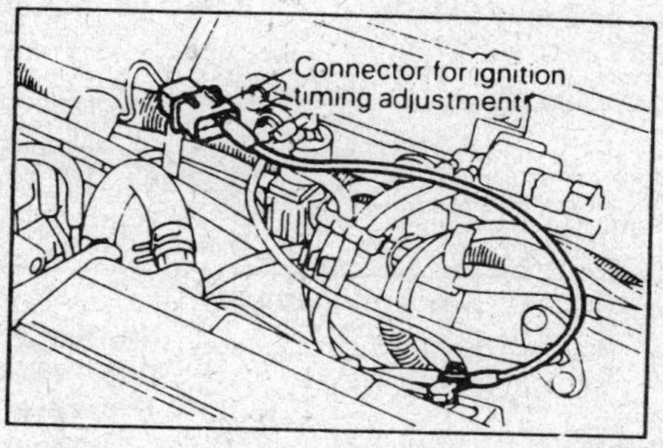

CR1139100187000X

Fig. E Ignition timing adjustment connector. Colt & Summit w/1.5L/4-90 engine

FRONT WHEEL ALIGNMENT SPECIFICATIONS

Year	Model	Caster Angle, Degrees		Camber Angle, Degrees		
		Limits	Desired	Limits	Desired	Toe-In
1992	Colt	+1 5/6 to +2 5/6	+2 1/3	-1/2 to +1/2	0	③
	Colt Vista ②	+1 1/2 to +2 5/6	+2 1/6	-1/6 to +5/6	+1/3	③
	Colt Vista ①	+1 5/12 to +2 3/4	+2 1/12	+1/6 to +1 1/6	+2/3	③
	Summit	+1 5/6 to +2 5/6	+2 1/3	-1/2 to +1/2	0	③
	Summit Wagon ②	+1 1/2 to +2 5/6	+2 1/6	-1/6 to +5/6	+1/3	③
	Summit Wagon ①	+1 5/12 to +2 3/4	+2 1/12	+1/6 to +1 1/6	+2/3	③
1993–94	Colt	+1 5/6 to +2 5/6	+2 1/3	-1/2 to +1/2	0	③
	Summit	+1 5/6 to +2 5/6	+2 1/3	-1/2 to +1/2	0	③
	Colt Vista ②	+1 1/2 to +2 5/6	+2 1/6	-1/6 to +5/6	+1/3	③
	Colt Vista ①	+1 5/12 to +2 3/4	+2 1/12	+1/6 to +1 1/6	+2/3	③
	Summit Wagon ②	+1 1/2 to +2 5/6	+2 1/6	-1/6 to +5/6	+1/3	③
	Summit Wagon ①	+1 5/12 to +2 3/4	+2 1/12	+1/6 to +1 1/6	+2/3	③
1995	Summit	+1 5/6 to +2 5/6	+2 1/3	-1/2 to +1/2	0	③
	Summit Wagon ②	+1 1/2 to +2 5/6	+2 1/6	-1/6 to +5/6	+1/3	③
	Summit Wagon ①	+1 5/12 to +2 3/4	+2 1/12	+1/6 to +1 1/6	+2/3	③

①—AWD.

②—FWD.

③—.12 inch toe in to .12 inch toe-out.

REAR WHEEL ALIGNMENT SPECIFICATIONS

Year	Model	Camber, Degrees		Toe In, Inch
		Limits	Desired	
1992	Colt	-1¼ to -1/12	-2/3	②
	Colt Vista	①	①	③
	Summit	-1¼ to -1/12	-2/3	②
	Summit Wagon	①	①	③
1993–94	Colt	-1¼ to -1/12	-2/3	②
	Colt Vista	①	①	③
	Summit	-1¼ to -1/12	-2/3	②
	Summit Wagon	①	①	③
1995	Summit	-1¼ to -1/12	-2/3	②
	Summit Wagon	①	①	③

①—Distance between stabilizer bar mounting nut and end of bolt, .98–1.60 inches.
②—.18 inch toe in to .18 inch toe out.
③—.08 inch toe in to .12 inch toe out.

COOLING SYSTEM & CAPACITY DATA

Year	Engine	Coolant Capacity, Qts. Less A/C	With A/C	Radiator Cap Relief Pressure, Lbs.	Thermo. Opening Temp.°F.	Fuel Tank Gals.	Engine Oil Refill, Qts.①	4 Speed, Pints	5 Speed, Pints	Auto. Trans., Qts.②	Rear Axle Oil, Pints
1992–95	1.5L/4-90	5.3	5.3	13	190	13.2	3.6	3.6	3.8	6.5	—
	1.8L/4-110	6.3	6.3	13	170	14.5	4	③	③	④	1.48
	2.4L/4-146	6.8	6.8	13	190	15.9	4.1	③	③	④	1.48

①—Includes filter.
②—Approximate, make final check with dipstick.
③—FWD, 3.8 pts.; AWD, 4.8 pts.; transfer, 1.2 pts.
④—FWD, 6.4 qts.; AWD, 6.9 qts.; transfer, 1.2 pts.

LUBRICANT DATA

Year	Model	Transmission Manual	Automatic	Transfer Case	Rear Axle	Power Steering	Brake System
1992–95	All	API GL4	①	API GL4	API GL4	①	DOT 3

①—Mopar ATF plus automatic transmission fluid type 7176/Dexron or Dexron II.

NOTE: On Air Bag Equipped Models, Refer To "Air Bag System Precautions" Located In The Front Of This Manual For System Disarming & Arming Procedures.

INDEX

PRECAUTIONS

AIR BAG SYSTEMS

Refer to "Air Bag System Precautions" in the front of this manual for system disarming and arming procedures.

FUSE PANEL & FLASHER LOCATION

The fuse panel is located behind the instrument panel access cover to the left of the steering column.

On Colt and Summit, the flasher unit is located on the fuse panel, behind instrument panel access cover to left of steering column.

On Colt Vista and Summit Wagon, the flasher unit is located on the lefthand kick panel, behind the instrument panel.

RELAY CENTER LOCATION

ENGINE COMPARTMENT

The engine compartment relay centers are located atop the right front fender apron and at the front lefthand corner of the engine compartment.

PASSENGER COMPARTMENT

The main passenger compartment relay center is located behind the lower lefthand side of the instrument panel, left of the steering column.

STARTER

REPLACE

1. Disconnect battery ground cable.

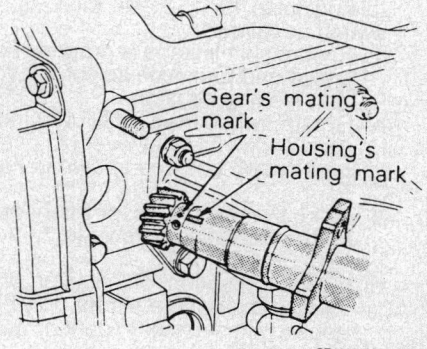

Fig. 1 Distributor shaft alignment. 1.5L/4-90 & 1.8L/4-110 engines

2. Remove air cleaner and intake manifold stay as needed to gain access to starter.
3. Disconnect starter wiring.
4. Remove starter mounting bolts, then remove starter motor.
5. Reverse procedure to install.

DISTRIBUTOR

REPLACE

REMOVAL

1. Disconnect battery ground cable.
2. Disconnect distributor wiring harness, then remove distributor cap with ignition cables attached and position aside.
3. Remove mounting bolt, then the distributor.

INSTALLATION

1. Rotate crankshaft until piston of No.1 cylinder is at top dead center on compression stroke.
2. Align mating mark line on distributor housing with corresponding mating mark on distributor gear, **Fig. 1.**
3. Install distributor onto cylinder head while aligning mating mark on distributor attaching flange with center of cylinder head distributor flange stud.
4. Install mounting nut, then vacuum hose(s), wiring harness and distributor cap.
5. Check and reset ignition timing if necessary.

IGNITION LOCK

REPLACE

The heads of the bolts securing the steering lock assembly shear off when the bolts are tightened. Replacement of the steering lock assembly may require that the steering column be removed, as these bolts must be cut or slotted to permit removal with a screwdriver. When the lock assembly is installed, new shear bolts must be used and the bolts should be tightened until the bolt heads twist off.

1. Disconnect battery ground cable, then remove steering wheel as described under "Steering Wheel, Replace."
2. **On Colt Vista and Summit Wagon,** remove lap heater duct.
3. **On Colt and Summit,** remove instrument undercover, then the foot and lap ducts.
4. **On all models,** remove upper and lower column covers, then the screws attaching combination switch to steering lock.
5. Disconnect steering lock electrical connector, then use a suitable tool to cut grooves in heads of attaching bolts and remove screws using a screwdriver.
6. Remove steering lock.
7. Reverse procedure to install.

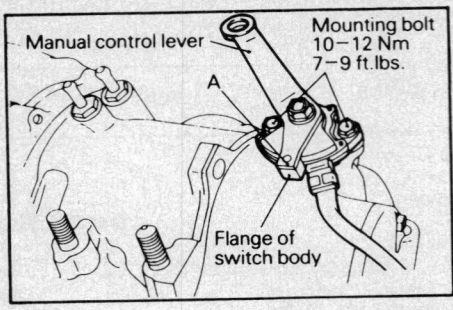

Fig. 2 Neutral safety switch adjustment

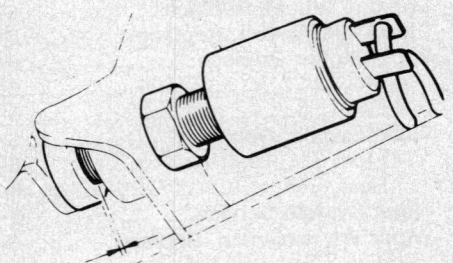

Fig. 3 Stop light switch clearance adjustment

1. Center panel
2. Knee protector or lower panel assembly
3. Meter bezel
4. Combination meter
5. Adapter

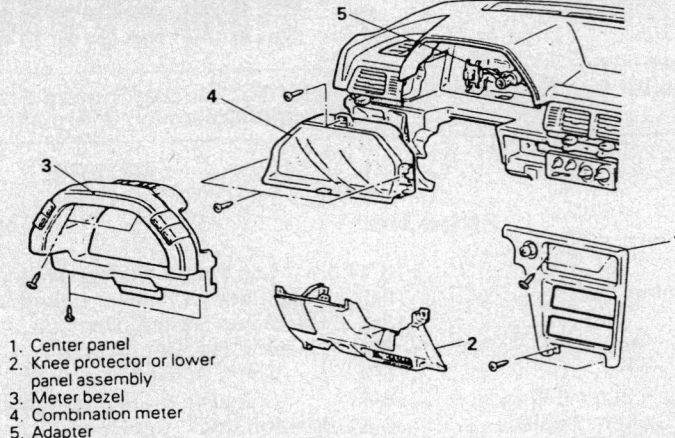

Fig. 4 Instrument cluster. Colt & Summit

IGNITION SWITCH
REPLACE

Ignition switch may be replaced without removing steering lock.
1. Disconnect battery ground cable.
2. **On Colt and Summit,** remove knee protector, then the upper and lower column covers.
3. **On Colt Vista and Summit Wagon,** remove hood lock release handle, instrument panel undercover, meter hood then the upper and lower column covers.
4. **On all models,** remove band securing electrical connector, then disconnect electrical connector.
5. **On Colt and Summit with automatic transaxle,** remove interlock cable cover, then disconnect interlock cable, spring and slide lever.
6. **On all models,** remove screws attaching ignition switch to ignition lock, then the switch from lock assembly.
7. Reverse procedure to install.

CLUTCH START SWITCH
REPLACE

1. Disconnect clutch switch electrical connector.
2. Remove locknut, then the clutch switch.
3. Reverse procedure to install.

NEUTRAL SAFETY SWITCH
REPLACE

1. Place selector lever in Neutral position.
2. Hold transaxle shift lever and remove retaining nut, then remove manual lever.
3. Disconnect switch electrical connector and remove retaining screws, then remove switch from transaxle.
4. Install replacement switch over selector shaft, loosely install retaining screws and connect electrical connector.
5. Install manual lever and **torque** retaining nut to 13-15 ft. lbs., then adjust switch as follows:
   a. Ensure shift linkage is properly adjusted and transaxle selector lever is in Neutral position.
   b. Rotate switch body until .472 inch wide end of manual lever (A) overlaps switch body as shown in **Fig. 2.**
   c. Hold switch in this position and **torque** retaining screws to 7–9 ft. lbs.
   d. Check operation of selector and switch, and ensure starter only engages with selector in park or neutral.

HEADLAMP SWITCH
REPLACE

Refer to "Combination Switch, Replace" for procedure.

STOP LIGHT SWITCH
REPLACE

1. Disconnect battery ground cable.
2. Disconnect electrical connector from stop light switch.
3. Remove retaining nut from bracket, then remove switch.
4. Reverse procedure to install. Ensure brake pedal height is correct, then adjust switch to obtain a clearance of .02 to .04 inch between switch housing and pedal stopper with pedal released, **Fig. 3.**

COMBINATION SWITCH
REPLACE

The combination switch includes the headlight, headlight dimmer, turn signal and wiper/washer switches.

1. Disconnect battery ground cable.
2. Remove steering wheel as described under "Steering Wheel, Replace."
3. **On Colt and Summit models,** remove knee protector.
4. **On 1992 Colt Vista and Summit Wagon models,** remove hood lock release handle, instrument panel undercover and meter hood.
5. **On all models,** remove upper and lower column covers.
6. Remove wiring harness retaining straps, then disconnect electrical connectors.
7. Remove attaching screws, then the combination switch assembly.
8. Reverse procedure to install.

STEERING WHEEL
REPLACE

1. Disconnect battery ground cable.
2. **On models less air bag,** remove steering wheel horn pad, then remove steering wheel to column shaft nut.
3. **On models with air bag,** remove air bag module from steering wheel, then remove steering wheel to column shaft nut. **Refer to "Precautions" for safety measures during this procedure.**
4. **On all models,** Use a suitable puller to remove steering wheel.
5. Reverse procedure to install. **Torque** steering wheel to column shaft attaching nut to 25 to 33 ft. lbs.

INSTRUMENT CLUSTER
REPLACE

COLT & SUMMIT

1. Disconnect battery ground cable.
2. Remove instrument panel lower center trim panel, **Fig. 4.**
3. Remove instrument panel lower left hand trim panel.
4. Remove instrument cluster bezel.
5. Remove instrument cluster attaching screws, pull cluster slightly outward and disconnect speedometer cable and electrical connectors.
6. Remove instrument cluster assembly.
7. Reverse procedure to install.

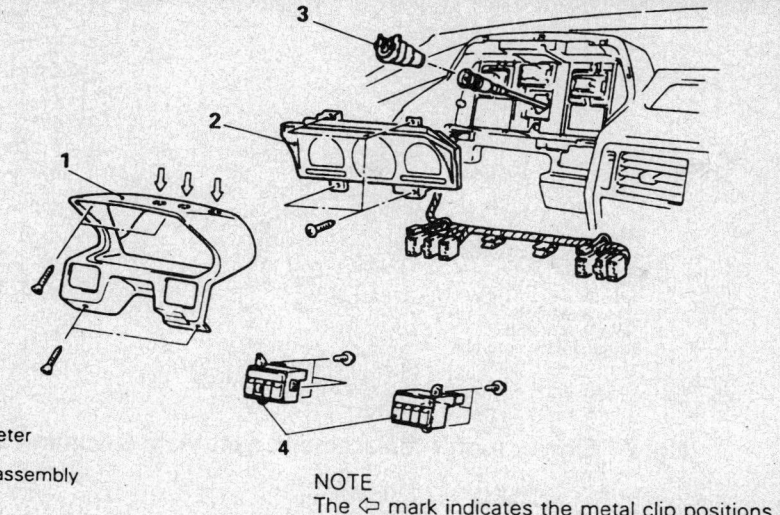

Removal steps
1. Meter hood
2. Combination meter
3. Adapter
4. Cluster switch assembly

NOTE
The ⇦ mark indicates the metal clip positions

CR9099100060000X

Fig. 5 Instrument cluster. Colt Vista & Summit Wagon

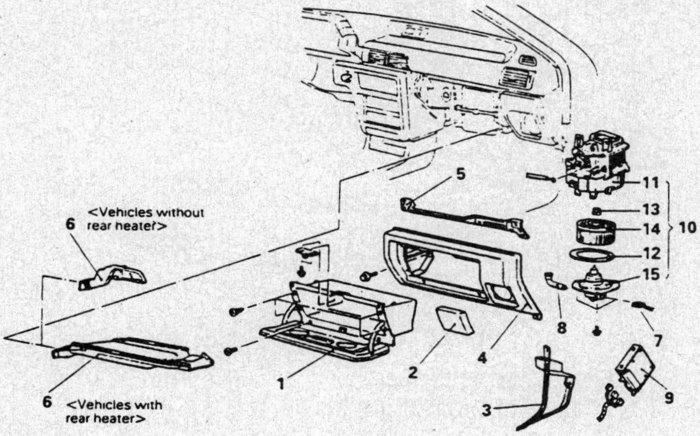

1. Glove box
2. Speaker cover
3. Cowl side trim, R.H.
4. Knee protector, R.H.
5. Glove box frame
6. Lap heater duct <vehicles without rear heater> or shower duct <vehicles with rear heater>
7. Blower motor connector
8. Hose
9. MPI control unit
10. Blower motor assembly
11. Blower case
12. Packing
13. Fan installation nut
14. Fan
15. Blower motor

CR7029100053000X

Fig. 6 Blower motor replacement. Colt & Summit

COLT VISTA & SUMMIT WAGON

1. Disconnect battery ground cable.
2. Remove meter hood, **Fig. 5.**
3. Disconnect combination meter then remove from instrument panel.
4. Remove adapter lock, pull speedometer cable slightly into the passenger compartment then the rear side of the adapter from the cable.
5. Turn adapter so notched section in aligned with tab on cable side, remove the adapter by sliding it backwards.
6. Remove cluster switch bolts, then the switch.
7. Reverse procedure to install.

WIPER MOTOR
REPLACE

FRONT

1. Disconnect battery ground cable.
2. Remove wiper motor attaching bolts or nuts, pull motor out slightly and disconnect linkage. **If it is necessary to remove crank arm, mark relationship of crank arm to motor prior to removal to ensure proper stop angle after installation.**
3. Remove wiper motor.
4. Reverse procedure to install. When installing crank arm on wiper motor, en-

sure reference marks made during removal are aligned.

REAR

1. Disconnect battery ground cable.
2. Remove wiper arm from shaft, then the washers and grommets, noting position for installation.
3. Remove liftgate trim panel, then disconnect wiper motor electrical connector.
4. Remove wiper motor attaching screws, then the motor from liftgate.
5. Reverse procedure to install. **On 1992 Colt Vista and Summit Wagon,** mount wiper arm so that when motor is in park position distance between tip of blade and lower window molding is .78–1.18 inch.

WIPER SWITCH
REPLACE

FRONT

Refer to "Combination Switch, Replace" for procedure.

REAR

Colt & Summit

1. Insert suitable tool behind switch, compress lock tab and pry switch from instrument panel. Taking care not to mar garnish or instrument panel.
2. Disconnect electrical connector and remove switch.
3. Reverse procedure to install.

Colt Vista & Summit Wagon

Refer to "Instrument Cluster, Replace" for switch removal procedure.

WIPER TRANSMISSION
REPLACE

1. Disconnect battery ground cable, then remove wiper arm and blade assemblies from pivots.
2. Remove front deck garnishes, then the pivot lock and attaching nuts.
3. **On all models,** remove wiper motor as described under "Wiper Motor, Replace."
4. Remove wiper transmission assembly.
5. Reverse procedure to install. **On Colt Vista and Summit Wagon,** mount wiper arms so that when motor is in park position, distance between wiper blade and bottom of windshield is 1.18 inch on left side and 1.37 inch on right side.

BLOWER MOTOR
REPLACE

COLT & SUMMIT

Refer to **Fig. 6** during replacement procedure.
1. Disconnect battery ground cable, then remove glove box assembly.
2. Remove righthand speaker cover, cowl side trim and knee protector.
3. Remove glove box frame, then the lap

heater duct on models without rear heater or shower duct on models with rear heater.
4. Disconnect blower motor electrical connector, then the drain hose.
5. Remove MPI control unit, then the blower motor from blower assembly.
6. Reverse procedure to install.

COLT VISTA & SUMMIT WAGON

Replace blower motor in numbered sequence shown in **Fig. 7**.

HEATER CORE
REPLACE

COLT & SUMMIT

Refer to **Fig. 8** during replacement procedure.
1. Disconnect battery ground cable.
2. Set temperature lever at the extreme hot position, then drain engine coolant and disconnect heater hoses.
3. Remove front seats and floor console, then the instrument panel as described in "Dash Panel Service" section.
4. Disconnect air selection, temperature control and mode selection control wires.
5. Remove heater control assembly, then disconnect MPI relay connector.
6. Remove instrument panel center stay assembly.
7. **On models with rear heater,** remove rear heater and shower ducts.
8. **On models less rear heater,** remove lap heater duct.
9. **On all models,** remove foot, lap and center ventilation ducts, then the heater unit mounting nuts.
10. **On models with ELC-4 automatic transmission,** remove ELC-4 A/T control unit.
11. **On models with A/C,** remove evaporator mounting nuts and clips, then pull evaporator outward to allow access to heater unit. **Be careful not to damage liquid pipe or suction hose.**
12. **On all models,** remove heater unit.
13. Remove side plate and heater core fastening clips from heater unit, then pull out heater core from heater unit.
14. Reverse procedure to install, noting the following:
    a. Place mode selector lever in Vent position; then, with mode selection damper lever pulled outward in direction indicated by arrow in **Fig. 9**, connect mode selection control wire to lever and secure outer cable using clip.
    b. Place temperature control lever in Cool position, then with blend air damper lever pressed completely downward in direction indicated by arrow in **Fig. 10**, connect temperature control wire to lever and secure outer cable using clip.
    c. Place air selection lever in Recirc position, then set air selection damper lever as it contacts stopper as shown in **Fig. 11**, connect air

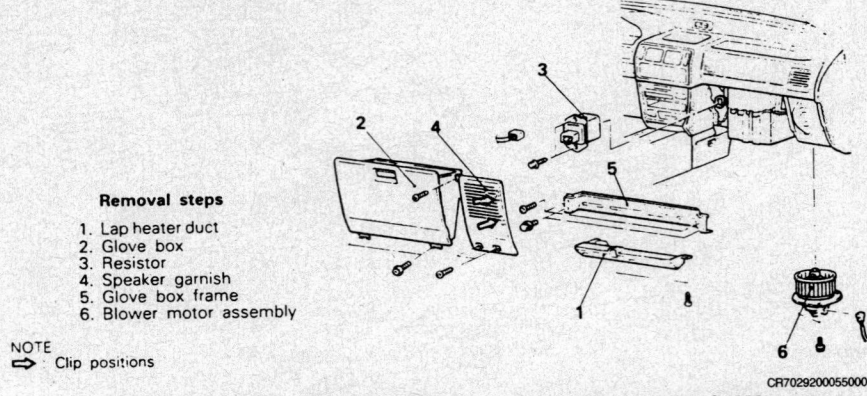

Removal steps
1. Lap heater duct
2. Glove box
3. Resistor
4. Speaker garnish
5. Glove box frame
6. Blower motor assembly

NOTE
⇨ : Clip positions

CR7029200055000X

Fig. 7   Blower motor replacement. Colt Vista & Summit Wagon

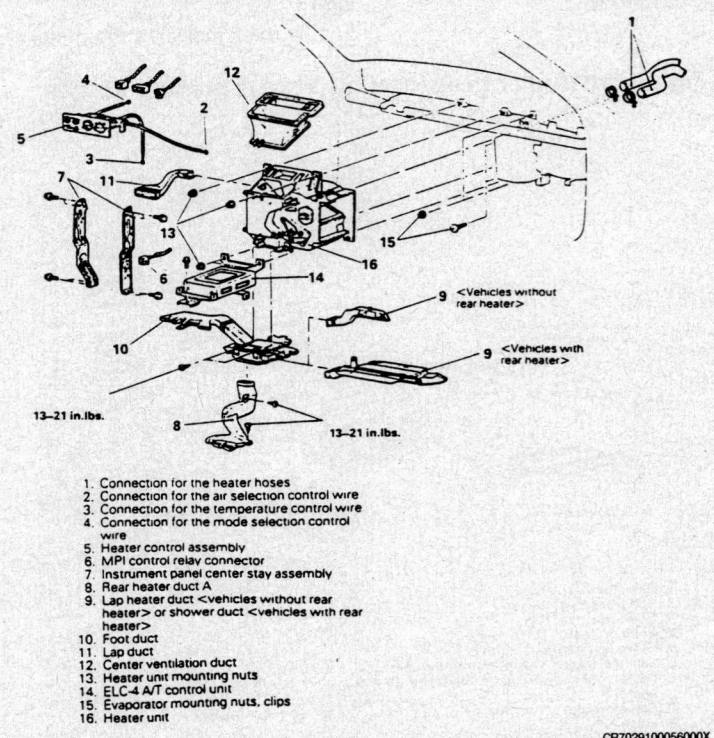

13–21 in.lbs.

13–21 in.lbs.

1. Connection for the heater hoses
2. Connection for the air selection control wire
3. Connection for the temperature control wire
4. Connection for the mode selection control wire
5. Heater control assembly
6. MPI control relay connector
7. Instrument panel center stay assembly
8. Rear heater duct A
9. Lap heater duct <vehicles without rear heater> or shower duct <vehicles with rear heater>
10. Foot duct
11. Lap duct
12. Center ventilation duct
13. Heater unit mounting nuts
14. ELC-4 A/T control unit
15. Evaporator mounting nuts, clips
16. Heater unit

CR7029100056000X

Fig. 8   Heater core replacement. Colt & Summit

selection control wire to lever and secure outer cable using clip.

COLT VISTA & SUMMIT WAGON

1. Raise and support vehicle then drain cooling system into a suitable container.
2. Remove floor console and instrument panel as outlined in "Dash Panel Service" section.
3. Replace heater core in numbered sequence shown in **Fig. 12**.
4. Reverse procedure to install.

EVAPORATOR CORE
REPLACE
COLT & SUMMIT

Refer to **Fig. 13** during replacement procedure.
1. Disconnect battery ground cable, then discharge refrigerant from A/C system as described in "Air Conditioning" section.
2. Remove canister from canister bracket in engine compartment and set aside, then disconnect liquid pipe and suction hose and cap fittings.
3. Remove evaporator drain hose, then the glove box assembly.
4. Remove lap heater duct on models less rear heater or shower duct on models with rear heater.

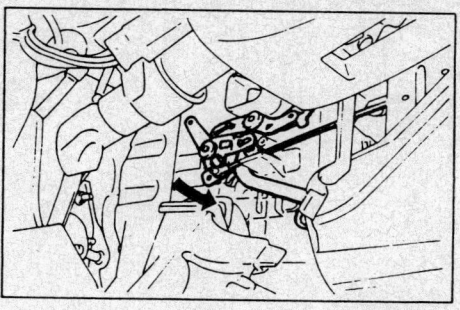

CR7029100057000X

Fig. 9 Mode selection damper lever position. Colt & Summit

CR7029100058000X

Fig. 10 Blend air damper lever position. Colt & Summit

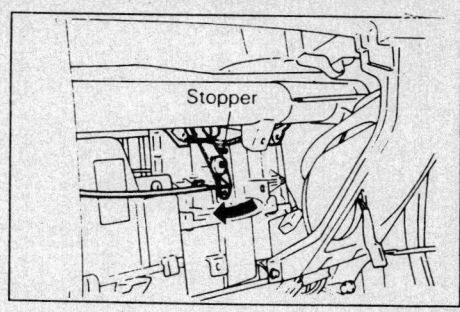

CR7029100059000X

Fig. 11 Air selection damper lever setting. Colt & Summit

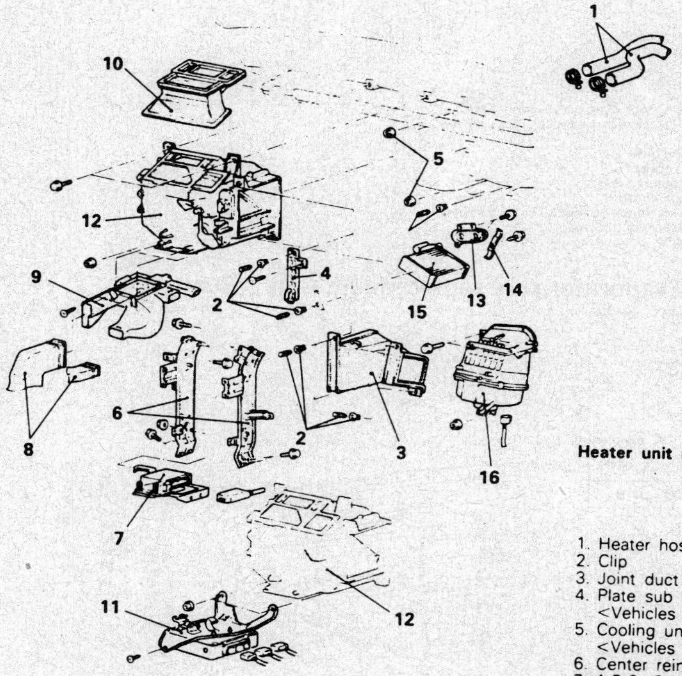

Heater unit removal steps

1. Heater hose connection
2. Clip
3. Joint duct
4. Plate sub assembly
   <Vehicles with air conditioner>
5. Cooling unit installation nut
   <Vehicles with air conditioner>
6. Center reinforcement
7. A.B.S. Control unit assembly
8. Rear heater duct connection
9. Foot distribution duct
10. Center ventilation duct assembly
11. Automatic transmission control unit
12. Heater unit
13. Plate
14. Clamp
15. Heater core

Blower assembly removal steps

2. Clip
3. Joint duct
16. Blower assembly

CR7029200060000X

Fig. 12 Heater core replacement. Colt Vista & Summit Wagon

5. Remove righthand cowl side trim, speaker cover and knee protector.
6. Remove glove box frame, then disconnect electrical connector from evaporator.
7. Remove evaporator assembly.
8. Remove clips attaching case halves, then disconnect expansion valve flare nut and remove evaporator core from case.

9. Reverse procedure to install. Apply compressor oil to O-rings and expansion valve of evaporator assembly.

COLT VISTA & SUMMIT WAGON

1. Discharge air conditioning system using suitable recovery system.
2. Remove and disassemble evaporator

housing in numbered sequence shown in **Fig. 14**, noting the following:
a. Remove retaining clips by pushing the center inward.
b. Remove evaporator housing clips using a suitable flat blade screwdriver.
c. Loosen flare nut on expansion valve using two wrenches.
3. Reverse procedure to install.

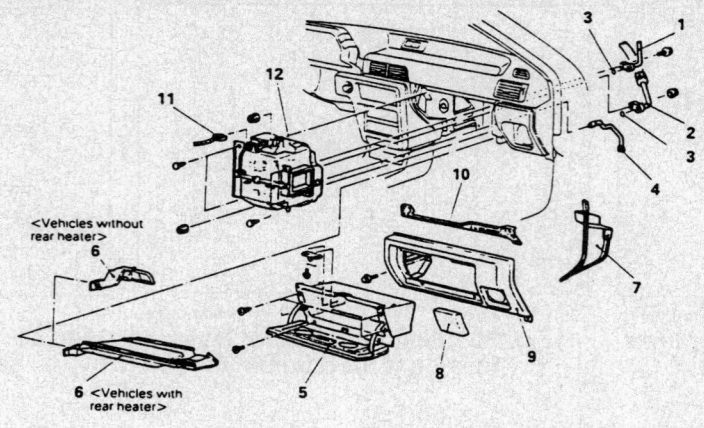

1. Liquid pipe connection
2. Suction hose connection
3. O-rings
4. Drain hose
5. Glove box
6. Lap heater duct <vehicles without rear heater> or shower duct <vehicles with rear heater>
7. Cowl side trim
8. Speaker cover
9. Knee protector, R.H.
10. Glove box frame
11. Connection of the connector (12P) for auto compressor control unit
12. Evaporator

CR7029100061000X

Fig. 13 Evaporator core replacement. Colt & Summit

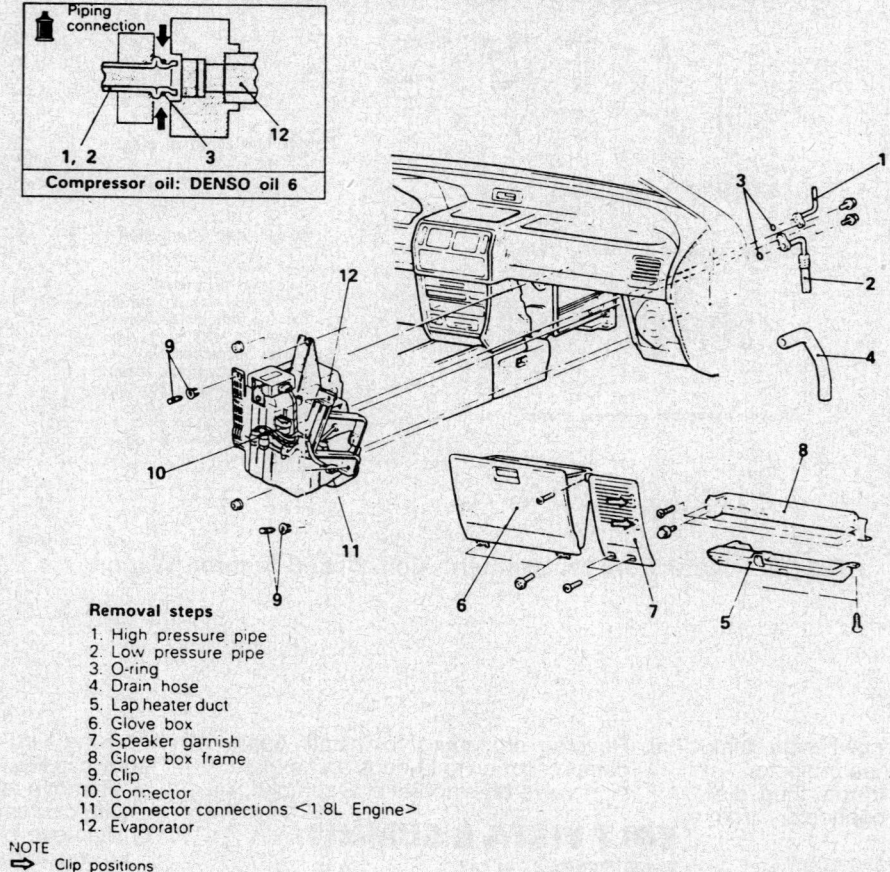

Removal steps
1. High pressure pipe
2. Low pressure pipe
3. O-ring
4. Drain hose
5. Lap heater duct
6. Glove box
7. Speaker garnish
8. Glove box frame
9. Clip
10. Connector
11. Connector connections <1.8L Engine>
12. Evaporator

NOTE
⇨ Clip positions

CR7029200062010X

Fig. 14 Evaporator core replacement (Part 1 of 2). Colt Vista & Summit Wagon

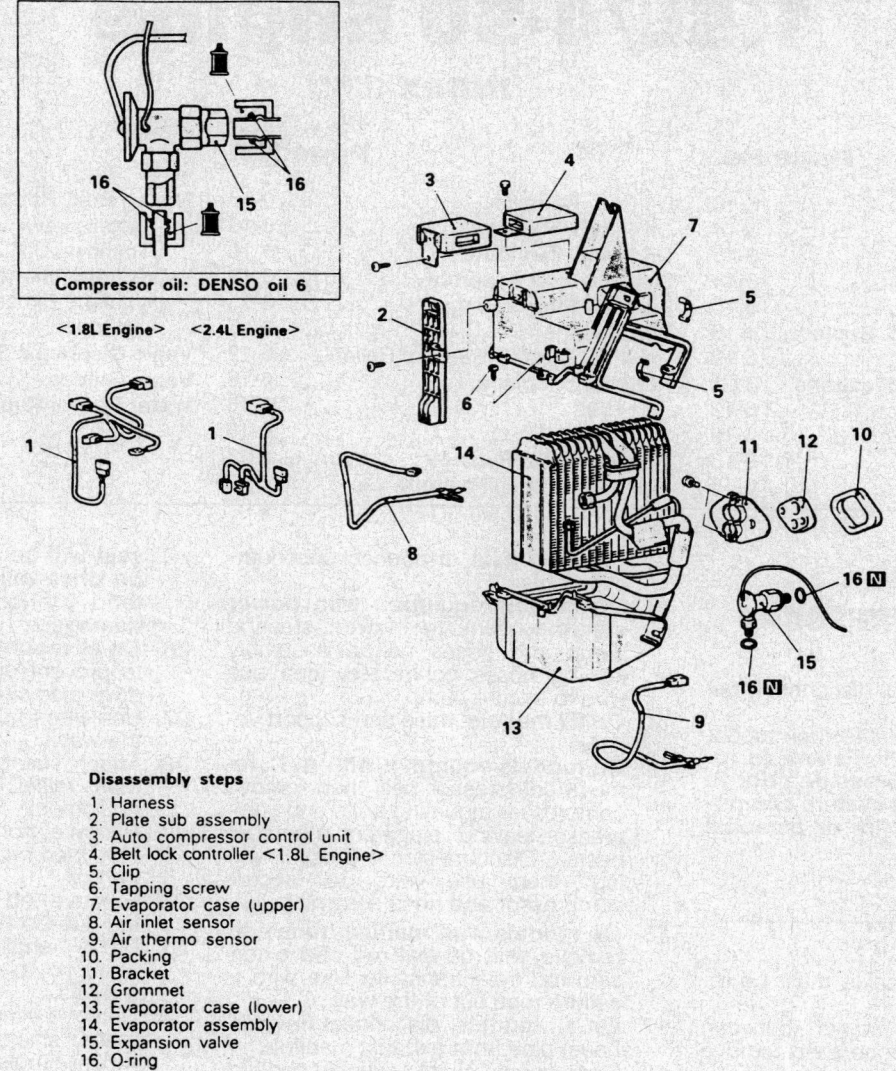

Compressor oil: DENSO oil 6

<1.8L Engine>   <2.4L Engine>

Disassembly steps

1. Harness
2. Plate sub assembly
3. Auto compressor control unit
4. Belt lock controller <1.8L Engine>
5. Clip
6. Tapping screw
7. Evaporator case (upper)
8. Air inlet sensor
9. Air thermo sensor
10. Packing
11. Bracket
12. Grommet
13. Evaporator case (lower)
14. Evaporator assembly
15. Expansion valve
16. O-ring

CR7029200062020X

Fig. 14 Evaporator core replacement (Part 2 of 2). Colt Vista & Summit Wagon

1.5L/4-90 Engine

INDEX

PRECAUTIONS

FUEL SYSTEM PRESSURE RELIEF

1. With engine running, disconnect fuel pump connector.
2. Allow engine to deplete fuel supply, then turn ignition Off. **Failure to relieve fuel system pressure prior to disconnecting fuel system components may cause fire or personal injury.**

ENGINE
REPLACE

The engine and transaxle must be removed as an assembly.

1. Scribe reference marks between hood and hood hinges, then remove hood.
2. Release fuel system pressure as outlined under "Precautions."
3. Disconnect battery cables, then remove battery and battery tray.
4. Remove air cleaner and engine undercover, if equipped.
5. Drain cooling system into suitable container.
6. **On models with automatic transaxle,** disconnect transaxle cooling hoses from transaxle.
7. **On all models,** disconnect heater and the upper and lower radiator hoses from engine, then disconnect cooling fan motor and remove radiator.
8. Mark and disconnect necessary vacuum hoses and engine/transaxle wiring that would interfere with engine removal.
9. Disconnect accelerator cable and brake booster vacuum hose.
10. **On models with manual transaxle,** disconnect control cable or clutch tube.
11. **On models with automatic transaxle,** disconnect automatic transaxle control cable. **Handle control cable very carefully so as not to bend inner cable.**

12. **On all models,** disconnect speedometer cable.
13. **On models equipped with power steering,** remove power steering pump and hoses as an assembly leaving hoses connected, then use wire to secure pump.
14. **On all models,** raise and support vehicle.
15. **On models equipped with A/C,** remove compressor belt, then remove compressor mounting bolts and compressor leaving refrigerant lines connected. Disconnect compressor wiring, then use wire to secure compressor and hose assembly.
16. **On models with manual transaxle,** remove shift control rod and extension rod from transaxle. Use wire to secure rods out of the way.
17. **On all models,** disconnect front exhaust pipe from exhaust manifold.
18. Drain engine oil into suitable container.
19. **On models with turbocharged engines,** remove oil cooler lines from engine.
20. **On all models,** disconnect stabilizer bar from lower control arm.
21. Loosen, but do not remove ball joint stud attaching nut, then disconnect ball joint from steering knuckle using puller tool No. MB991113 or equivalent.
22. Loosen, but do not remove tie rod end attaching nut, then disconnect tie rod end from steering knuckle using puller tool No. MB991113 or equivalent.
23. Drain transaxle oil.
24. **On models equipped with driveshaft center bearing,** remove snap ring securing center bearing, then using plastic hammer, lightly tap Double Offset Joint (DOJ) outer race to remove driveshaft from transaxle. Remove center bearing.
25. **On models not equipped with driveshaft center bearing,** insert suitable pry bar between transaxle case and driveshaft, then pry driveshaft from transaxle case. **Do not insert pry bar too deep or oil**

seal will be damaged. **Do not pull on drive axle and do not overextend CV joints, as joints will be damaged.**
26. **On all models,** cover transaxle holes to prevent entry of dirt and replace drive axle circlips.
27. Use wire to secure driveshafts out of the way.
28. Attach suitable engine lifting device, then raise lift enough to tension equipment.
29. Remove front roll stopper insulator bolt, then the rear roll stopper insulator bolt.
30. Remove left mount insulator attaching nut. **Do not remove bolt.**
31. Raise engine/transaxle assembly enough to remove weight from mounts.
32. Remove blind cover from inside right fender shield, then remove transaxle mount bracket bolt.
33. Remove left mount insulator bolt, then while directing transaxle side down, remove engine/transaxle assembly from vehicle.
34. Separate engine from transaxle as follows:
    a. Remove starter motor.
    b. **On models with automatic transaxle,** remove bolts securing torque converter to driveplate.
    c. **On all models,** remove engine-to-transaxle attaching bolts, then remove transaxle assembly.
35. Reverse procedure to install.

CYLINDER HEAD
REPLACE

1. Disconnect battery ground cable and drain cooling system.
2. Disconnect breather and secondary air hose, then remove air cleaner assembly, air intake duct and hot air duct.
3. Disconnect accelerator cable from throttle lever and brackets.
4. Disconnect upper radiator, heater and water hoses, fuel hoses and the brake booster hose.

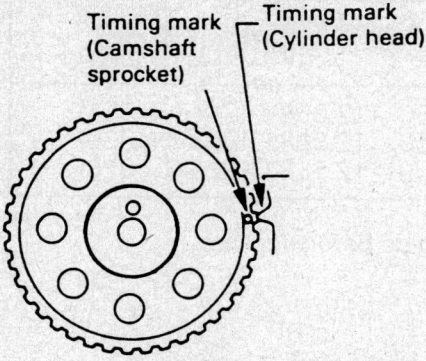

Fig. 1 Camshaft timing marks

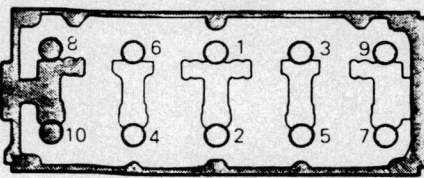

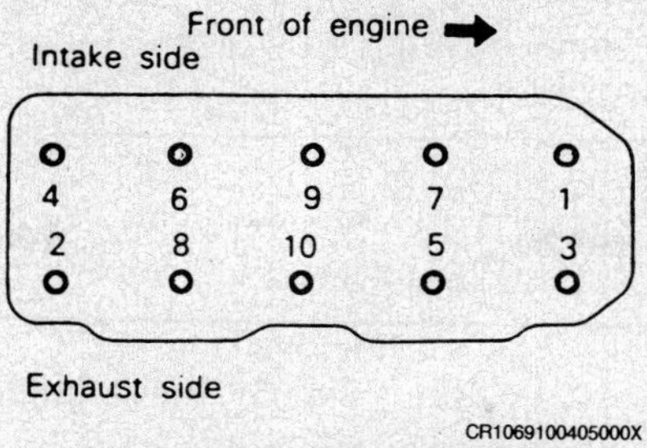

Fig. 2 Cylinder head bolt loosening sequence

Fig. 3 Cylinder head bolt tightening sequence

5. **On models with automatic transaxle,** disconnect throttle cable from engine.
6. **On models with manual transaxle,** disconnect clutch cable and secure aside.
7. **On all models,** mark and disconnect necessary electrical connectors and vacuum hoses, release harness clips and secure harnesses aside to prevent damage.
8. Disconnect ignition coil high tension lead, then remove distributor cap and plug wires.
9. Support engine as needed, then remove left engine mount bracket from cylinder head.
10. Remove exhaust manifold covers and disconnect exhaust pipe from manifold.
11. Remove engine oil dipstick and plug opening.
12. Remove upper timing belt cover, rocker arm cover and the gasket.
13. Rotate crankshaft in normal direction of rotation (clockwise) to bring No. 1 cylinder to top dead center compression stroke. The No. 1 cylinder is at top dead center compression stroke when the mark on the upper timing undercover is aligned with the mark on the camshaft sprocket, **Fig. 1.**
14. Place an alignment mark on timing belt, inline with mark on camshaft sprocket timing mark, **Fig. 1.**
15. Remove camshaft sprocket attaching bolt, then detach sprocket from camshaft with timing belt attached. Position camshaft sprocket on lower belt cover or suspend sprocket and belt from hood to maintain proper timing alignment. **Do not rotate crankshaft after removing sprocket from camshaft.**
16. Remove cylinder head attaching bolts in sequence shown in **Fig. 2.** Loosen bolts evenly, in three steps, to prevent cylinder head warpage, then remove cylinder head and gasket. Take care not to dislodge camshaft sprocket during cylinder head removal.
17. Reverse procedure to install, noting the following:
    a. Do not apply sealer to cylinder head gasket. Install gasket with I.D. mark toward timing belt.
    b. Prior to installing cylinder head on engine, ensure crankshaft and camshaft timing marks are aligned.
    c. Tighten cylinder head bolts in two or three steps in the sequence shown in **Fig. 3** until a final **torque of 53 ft. lbs. is reached. Cylinder head bolt tightening must be done in two or three steps to ensure correct cylinder head to cylinder block seating.**
    d. After cylinder head has been installed, adjust timing belt tension as outlined under "Timing Belt, Replace" and valve clearance as outlined under "Valve Adjustment."

VALVE CLEARANCE SPECIFICATIONS

| Year | Clearance, Inch | | | | |
	Hot		Cold		Jet Valve
1992	.0059	.0098	.0028	.0067	.0100
1993-95	.0080	.0100	.0040	.0070	—

VALVE ADJUSTMENT

On models equipped with jet valve, the jet valve must be adjusted before adjusting the intake valve.

JET VALVE

1. Following procedure for intake and exhaust valve adjustment, position No. 1 cylinder at top dead center compression stroke.
2. Loosen intake valve adjusting screw at least two turns, then loosen jet valve adjusting screw locknut.
3. Rotate jet valve adjusting screw counterclockwise and insert a .010 inch (.25mm) feeler gauge between jet valve stem and adjusting screw, **Fig. 4.**
4. Tighten jet valve adjusting screw until it contacts the feeler gauge blade, then while holding adjusting screw in position, tighten locknut.
5. After jet valve adjustment has been completed, adjust intake valve clearance. Continue to follow intake and exhaust valve adjustment procedure and adjust jet valves as necessary.

INTAKE & EXHAUST VALVES

1. With engine at operating temperature, remove rocker arm cover.
2. Disconnect high tension lead from ignition coil.
3. While observing rocker arms on No. 4 cylinder, rotate crankshaft clockwise until the exhaust valve is closing and the intake valve has just to open.
4. Ensure timing mark on crankshaft pulley is aligned with "T" mark on lower timing cover case. **At this position the No. 1 cylinder is at top dead center compression stroke.**
5. Check and adjust valve clearance for both intake and exhaust valves of No. 1 cylinder, intake valve of No. 2 cylinder and exhaust valve of No. 3 cylinder. If valve clearance is not as specified, adjust valves as follows:
    a. Loosen rocker arm locknut.
    b. Turn adjusting screw while measuring clearance with a feeler gauge, **Fig. 5,** until screw contacts feeler gauge.
    c. Intake and exhaust valve clearances should be as specified under "Valve Clearance Specifications."
    d. Hold adjusting screw in place and tighten locknut.
6. Rotate crankshaft clockwise 360 degrees, then check and adjust valve clearance for exhaust valve of No. 2 cylinder, intake valve of No. 3 cylinder and intake and exhaust valves of No. 4 cylinder.
7. After completing adjustment, install rocker arm cover and connect ignition coil high tension lead.

ROCKER ARMS
REPLACE

Refer to "Camshaft, Replace" for procedure.

VALVE GUIDES

1. Press old valve guide from cylinder head toward lower surface using the special valve guide tool and press.
2. Ream each valve guide bore in cylinder head to the O.D. of replacement valve guide, **Fig. 6. Never use a valve guide of the same size as the removed guide.**
3. Install new valve guides using special valve guide and stopper tools and

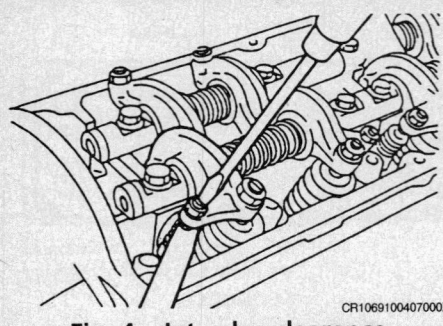

Fig. 4 Jet valve clearance adjustment

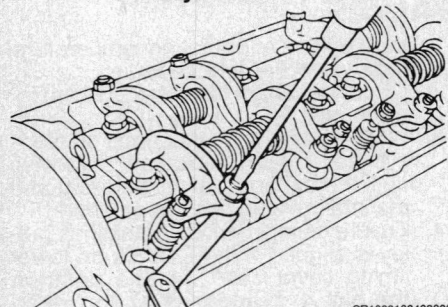

Fig. 5 Valve clearance adjustment

Size mm (in.)	Size mark	Cylinder head hole size mm (in.)
0.05 (.002) O.S.	5	12.050 – 12.068 (.4744 – .4751)
0.25 (.010) O.S.	25	12.250 – 12.268 (.4823 – .4830)
0.50 (.020) O.S.	50	12.500 – 12.518 (.4921 – .4928)

Fig. 6 Valve guide & guide bore oversizes

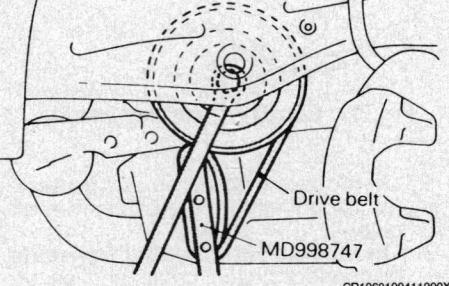

Fig. 7 Timing belt removal

press. **Intake valve guide length is 1.732 inches and exhaust valve guide length is 1.949 inches; as a result, they are not interchangeable.**

4. After installation of new valve guides, insert valve and ensure it slides freely, then check for proper clearance. If clearance is not correct, ream valve guide until proper clearance is obtained. Refer to "Valve Clearance Specifications" for stem to guide clearance.

TIMING BELT
REPLACE
REMOVAL

1. Remove battery ground cable.
2. Disconnect breather and secondary air hoses, then remove air cleaner assembly, air intake duct and heated air duct as needed.
3. Disconnect accelerator cable and oxygen sensor lead, and remove spark plug wires as needed.
4. Remove accessory drive belts.
5. Support engine as needed, then remove left engine mount bracket.
6. Remove power steering pump, if equipped and water pump pulleys.
7. Remove rocker arm cover, gasket and packing, and the upper timing belt cover.
8. Using Crankshaft Pulley Holder tool No. MD998747 or equivalent and a discarded drive belt, stop rotation of crankshaft pulley, remove A/C and crankshaft pulley, **Fig. 7.**
9. Rotate crankshaft in normal direction of rotation (clockwise) until timing marks are aligned, **Fig. 8,** loosen belt tensioner bolts and move timing belt tensioner fully toward the water pump, then tighten bolts to hold tensioner.

10. Remove timing belt. If the timing belt is to be reused, place an arrow mark indicating direction of normal engine rotation for belt installation reference.
11. Remove camshaft sprocket, crankshaft sprocket and flange, and timing belt tensioner as needed.
12. Inspect belt and replace if any of the following conditions are noted:
    a. Hardened back surface rubber, characterized by glossy back surface and non-elasticity.
    b. Cracked back surface rubber.
    c. Cracked or separated canvas.
    d. Cracks at tooth bottom or side of belt.

INSTALLATION

1. Install flange and crankshaft sprocket as shown in **Fig. 9.**
2. Tighten crankshaft sprocket bolt.
3. Install camshaft sprocket.
4. Install timing belt tensioner as follows:
    a. Mount tensioner, spring and spacer, then temporarily tighten pivot bolt.
    b. Temporarily tighten the adjusting bolt, then install bottom end of the spring into front case.
    c. Secure tensioner to the position nearest the water pump.
5. Ensure timing marks are aligned, **Fig. 8.**
6. Install timing belt over crankshaft sprocket, then the camshaft sprocket, keeping tension side of belt tight as belt is installed. If used belt is installed, ensure belt is installed in original direction.
7. Apply counterclockwise force to camshaft sprocket to tighten tension side of belt, ensuring that timing marks remain aligned.
8. Install crankshaft pulley to prevent belt from slipping off sprocket, then adjust belt tension as follows:
    a. Loosen tensioner bolts to allow tensioner to bear against belt, then tighten adjusting bolt and pivot bolt. **Tighten adjusting bolt first to prevent tensioner from rotating away from belt.**
    b. Rotate crankshaft clockwise one full revolution, then realign crankshaft sprocket timing mark with pointer. **Crankshaft must be rotated smoothly, in clockwise direction. Do not apply any force other than spring force of tensioner to timing belt.**
    c. Loosen tensioner pivot and adjusting bolts, then tighten adjuster bolt and pivot bolt. **Tighten adjusting**

bolt first to prevent tensioner from rotating away from belt.
    d. Check belt tension by holding belt as shown in **Fig. 10,** and applying thumb pressure to tension side of belt. Tension is correct when tooth of belt covers approximately 1/4 the width of the tensioner adjuster bolt.
    e. Rotate crankshaft clockwise one full revolution and ensure timing marks line up.
9. Reverse remaining procedure to complete installation, then adjust valve clearances as outlined under "Valve Adjustment."

CAMSHAFT
REPLACE
REMOVAL

1. Disconnect battery ground cable.
2. Remove the distributor as described under "Distributor, Replace" in "Electrical" section.
3. Disconnect breather hose and secondary air hose.
4. Remove air cleaner and timing belt cover.
5. Rotate crankshaft in normal direction of rotation (clockwise) to bring No. 1 cylinder to top dead center on compression stroke. The No. 1 cylinder is at top dead center on compression stroke when the mark on the upper timing undercover is aligned with the mark on the camshaft sprocket, **Fig. 1.**
6. Move timing belt tensioner fully toward the water pump assembly and temporarily secure it.
7. Remove camshaft sprocket attaching bolt, then detach sprocket from camshaft with timing belt attached. Position camshaft sprocket on lower belt cover or suspend sprocket and belt from hood to maintain proper timing alignment. **Do not rotate crankshaft after removing sprocket from camshaft.**

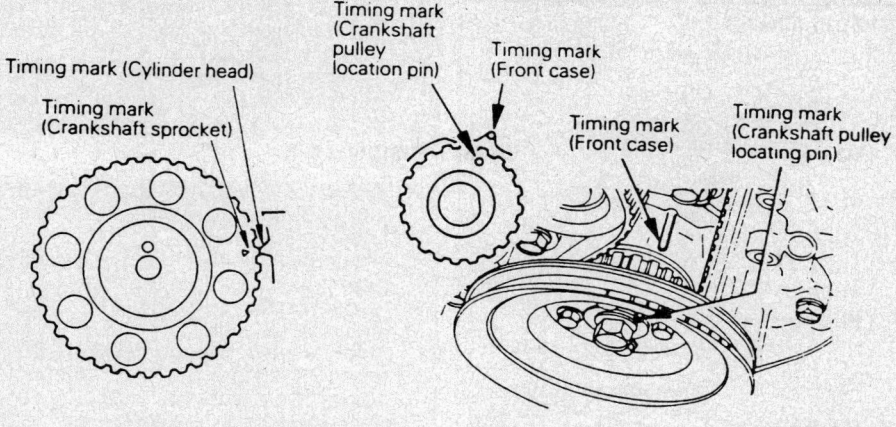

Fig. 8   Camshaft & crankshaft sprocket timing marks

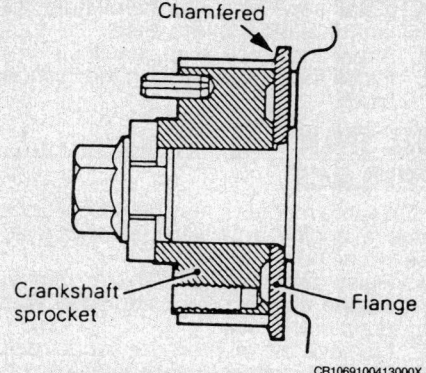

Fig. 9   Flange & crankshaft sprocket installation

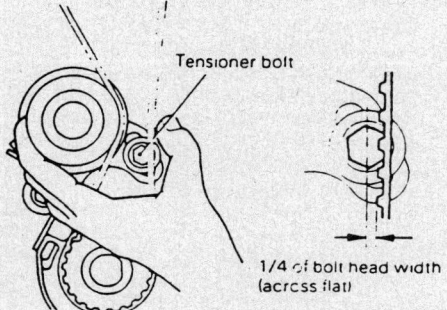

Fig. 10   Timing belt tension inspection

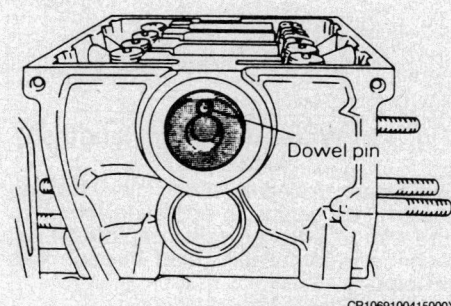

Fig. 11   Camshaft installation

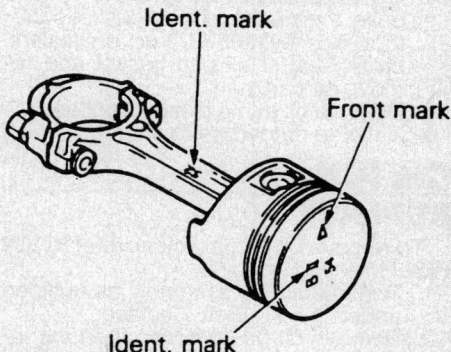

Fig. 12   Piston & rod assembly

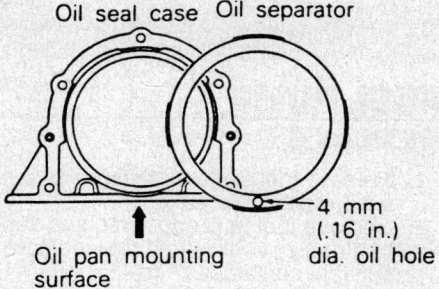

Fig. 13   Exploded view of oil seal case

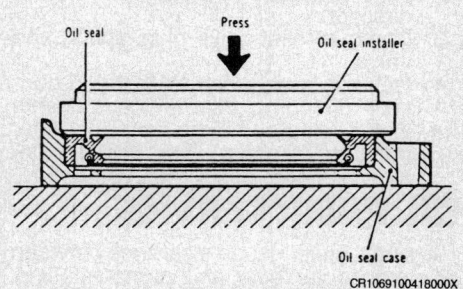

Fig. 14   Rear seal installation

8. Remove rocker cover and gasket, and note position of camshaft.
9. Remove rocker shaft assembly and cylinder head rear cover.
10. Remove camshaft thrust case tightening bolt, thrust case, camshaft and oil seal. Remove assembly toward transaxle side of cylinder head.
11. Remove oil seal, exhaust side, then intake side rocker arm assembly and camshaft.

INSTALLATION

1. Check camshaft journals for wear. If journals are badly worn, replace camshaft.
2. Lubricate, then install camshaft so dowel on camshaft is straight up in cylinder head, **Fig. 11**.

3. Install the intake, then exhaust side rocker arm assemblies. Tighten rocker arm shaft bolts in an even pattern to specifications.
4. Lubricate the surface of oil seal and end of camshaft. Using guide tool No. MD998307 and seal installer tool No. MD998306 or equivalents, install camshaft oil seal. Ensure seal is completely seated.
5. Install camshaft sprocket and timing belt, and ensure timing marks are aligned, **Fig. 1**. Tighten camshaft sprocket bolt to specifications.
6. Temporarily set valve clearances to specifications with engine cold.
7. Install gasket in rocker cover groove, then temporarily install rocker cover.
8. Start and operate engine at idle speed until normal operating temperature is reached and adjust valve clearances as described under "Valve Adjustment."
9. Install rocker cover and tighten bolts to specifications.
10. Install remaining hoses.

PISTON & ROD ASSEMBLY

The piston and rod is assembled with the indented arrow on the piston and the embossed numeral on the rod facing front of engine, **Fig. 12**.

PISTONS, PINS & RINGS

Pistons and rings are available in standard size and oversizes of .010, .020, .030

and .039 inch. Oversize pins are not available.

MAIN & ROD BEARINGS

Main and rod bearings are available in undersizes of .010, .020 and .030 inch.

The main bearing caps are installed with arrows facing front of engine.

CRANKSHAFT REAR OIL SEAL

REPLACE

1. Remove transmission, clutch assembly and flywheel or flex plate, as equipped.
2. Remove rear oil seal case and separate oil seal, case and separator, **Fig. 13**.
3. Drive in oil seal from inside of case using suitable tool, **Fig. 14**. Ensure oil seal plate fits properly in the inner contact surface of the seal case.

4. Install separator with the oil hole facing the bottom of the case.
5. Apply engine oil to oil seal lips.
6. Install the oil seal case in the cylinder block.

OIL PAN
REPLACE

On some models it may be necessary to remove engine from vehicle to gain access to oil pan.

1. Raise and support vehicle, remove engine splash pan, if equipped, then drain crankcase.
2. Remove the oil pressure sender unit.
3. **On turbocharged models,** disconnect oil drain hose and remove oil drain pipe.
4. **On all models,** remove the oil pan bolts; then, using oil pan gasket cutter tool No. MD998727 or equivalent, break seal of oil pan gasket and remove oil pan.
5. Remove oil pump pickup if necessary.
6. Reverse procedure to install.

OIL PUMP
REPLACE

To remove oil pump pickup, refer to "Oil Pan, Replace."

1. Remove timing assembly as outlined under "Timing Belt, Replace."
2. Remove oil pump cover, then the inner and outer gears from front case. Mark outer gear surface facing timing case so it can be installed in the same direction.
3. Remove relief valve plug, spring and valve.
4. Reverse procedure to install. Lubricate oil pump internal components with engine oil before installing. After installing oil pump cover, check to ensure oil pump gears rotate smoothly.

OIL PUMP SERVICE

Using a feeler gauge clearance between oil pump outer gear and pump housing. Check clearance between outer gear and pump crescent. Check clearance between inner gear and crescent. Using a straightedge and feeler gauge, measure gear side clearance. Verify clearance measured with value provided under "Engine Rebuilding Specifications" section.

BELT TENSION DATA

Component	Belt Deflection, Inch	
	New	Used ①
1992		
Alternator	.217-.276	.315
A/C	.197-.236	.236-.276
P.S.	.236-.254	.236-.254
1993-95		
Alternator	.220-.280	.310
A/C	.200-.240	.240-.280
P.S.	.160-.220	.220-.300

① —A new belt run 30 minutes is considered used.

COOLING SYSTEM BLEED

These engines do not require a speci-

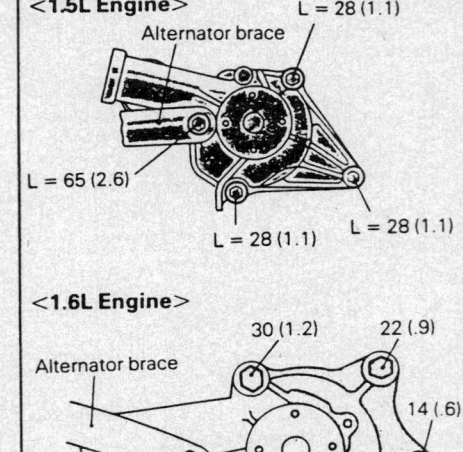

<1.5L Engine>
Alternator brace
L = 28 (1.1)
L = 65 (2.6)
L = 28 (1.1)
L = 28 (1.1)

<1.6L Engine>
Alternator brace
30 (1.2)   22 (.9)
14 (.6)
65 (2.6)
28 (1.1)
L = Length of bolt   mm (in.)

Fig. 15 Water pump bolt lengths & locations

fied bleed procedure. After filling cooling system, run engine to operating temperature with radiator/pressure cap off. Air will then be automatically bled through cap opening.

WATER PUMP
REPLACE

1. Disconnect battery ground cable and drain cooling system.
2. **On models with power steering,** remove power steering pump and bracket leaving hoses connected, and secure pump aside.
3. **On all models.** remove timing belt as outlined under "Timing Belt, Replace."
4. Remove alternator brace and disconnect hoses from water pump.
5. Remove water pump bolts, noting length and position for installation, then remove water pump, gasket and O-ring.
6. Reverse procedure to install. Refer to **Fig. 15,** for bolt length and position.

RADIATOR
REPLACE
1992

1. Disconnect battery ground cable, then remove radiator cap.
2. Place a suitable container below radiator drain plug, then remove plug and allow coolant to drain from radiator.
3. Remove radiator overflow tube and tank, then the upper and lower radiator hoses.
4. **On models with automatic transaxle,** disconnect transaxle oil cooler hoses at radiator and plug ends to prevent entry of foreign matter.
5. **On all models,** disconnect thermo sensor and radiator fan motor connectors.
6. **On models with A/C,** disconnect condenser fan motor connector.

7. **On all models,** remove radiator upper insulators, then lift radiator assembly from vehicle.
8. Reverse procedure to install. Refill engine coolant when installation is complete.

1993-95

1. Disconnect battery ground cable, then remove radiator overflow hose and reserve tank.
2. Place a suitable container below radiator drain plug, then remove plug and allow coolant to drain from radiator.
3. Remove coolant drain hose and upper and lower radiator hoses, then disconnect radiator fan motor connector.
4. **On models with automatic transaxle,** disconnect transaxle oil cooler lines at radiator and plug ends to prevent entry of foreign matter.
5. **On all models,** remove upper insulators and lift radiator and fan motor from vehicle as an assembly.
6. If necessary, disconnect engine coolant temperature switch connector and remove fan motor assembly from radiator.
7. Reverse procedure to install, noting the following:
   a. **On models with automatic transaxle,** connect transaxle oil cooler lines so that flexible hoses overlap 1 inch onto radiator fittings. Ensure hose clamps do not pinch fitting end bulges.
   b. **On all models,** slide radiator upper and lower hoses over water outlet and inlet fittings as far as small protrusions on each fitting will allow.
   c. Refill engine coolant when installation is complete.

FUEL PUMP
REPLACE

1. Release fuel system pressure as outlined under "Precautions."
2. Remove fuel tank cap, raise and support rear of vehicle and drain fuel into suitable container.
3. Disconnect filler hose from tank, support tank with suitable jack and remove nuts securing tank straps.
4. Lower fuel tank, then mark and disconnect fuel hoses, vapor hoses and electrical connectors.
5. Remove nuts securing fuel pump assembly, then the fuel pump and gasket.
6. Reverse procedure to install.

FUEL FILTER
REPLACE

1. Release fuel system pressure as outlined under "Precautions."
2. Remove air cleaner assembly.
3. Loosen eye bolt and fuel main pipe flare nut while holding fuel filter nut securely.
4. Remove fuel filter mounting bolts, then the fuel filter.
5. Reverse procedure to install.

TIGHTENING SPECIFICATIONS

Year	Component	Torque/Ft. Lbs.
1992–95	Camshaft Sprocket Bolt	47-54
	Connecting Rod Cap Nuts	①
	Crankshaft Pulley Bolts	9-11
	Crankshaft Sprocket	51-72
	Cylinder Head Bolts	②
	Exhaust Manifold Nuts & Bolts	11-14
	Flex Plate Bolts	94-101
	Flywheel Bolts	94-101
	Front Case Bolt	9-11
	Intake Manifold Nuts & Bolts	③
	Jet Valve Assembly	13-15
	Main Bearing Cap Bolts	36-40
	Oil Pan Bolts	4-6
	Oil Pan Drain Plug	26-32
	Oil Pressure Switch	11-16
	Oil Pump Cover	6-7

Year	Component	Torque/Ft. Lbs.
1992–95 —Cont'd	Oil Pump Relief Valve Plug	29-36
	Oil Screen	11-16
	Rocker Arm Cover Bolts	1.1-1.4
	Rocker Arm Shaft	④
	Spark Plug	15-21
	Timing Belt Cover Upper & Lower	7-9
	Timing Belt Tensioner	14-20

① —14.5 ft. lbs., then tighten an additional ¼ turn.
② —Refer to text.
③ —11–14 ft. lbs.
④ —21–25 ft. lbs.

1.8L/4-110 & 2.4L/4-146 Engines

INDEX

PRECAUTIONS

FUEL SYSTEM PRESSURE RELIEF

1. Remove floorpan grommet, then remove and disconnect the fuel pump connector.
2. After starting the engine and letting it stall, turn ignition switch to Off position.
3. Connect fuel pump connector and install grommet.

ENGINE MOUNT

REPLACE

Replace engine mounts in numbered sequence shown in **Figs. 1 and 2**, noting

the following:
1. Use a block of wood to distribute the load when raising the engine at the oil pan.
2. Check insulators and brackets for damage.
3. Engine mount stopper is properly installed when its arrow mark points at the center of the engine, **Fig. 3**.

ENGINE ROLL STOPPER

Replace engine roll stoppers in numbered sequence shown in **Figs. 4 and 5**, noting the following:
1. Check insulators and brackets for damage.
2. Install the front roll stopper assembly so that the end fitted with the round hole faces the front of the vehicle.

ENGINE

REPLACE

1. Relieve fuel system pressure as outlined under "Precautions."
2. Mark hood hinge location on hood, then remove hood.
3. **On models with 2.4L/4-146 engine**, remove engine undercover.
4. **On all models**, drain engine coolant.
5. Remove the radiator in numbered sequence shown in **Fig. 6**.
6. Remove the engine in numbered sequence shown in **Figs. 7 through 9**, noting the following:
   a. Without disconnecting its hydraulic lines, remove the power steering pump from its mounting bracket and support pump aside.

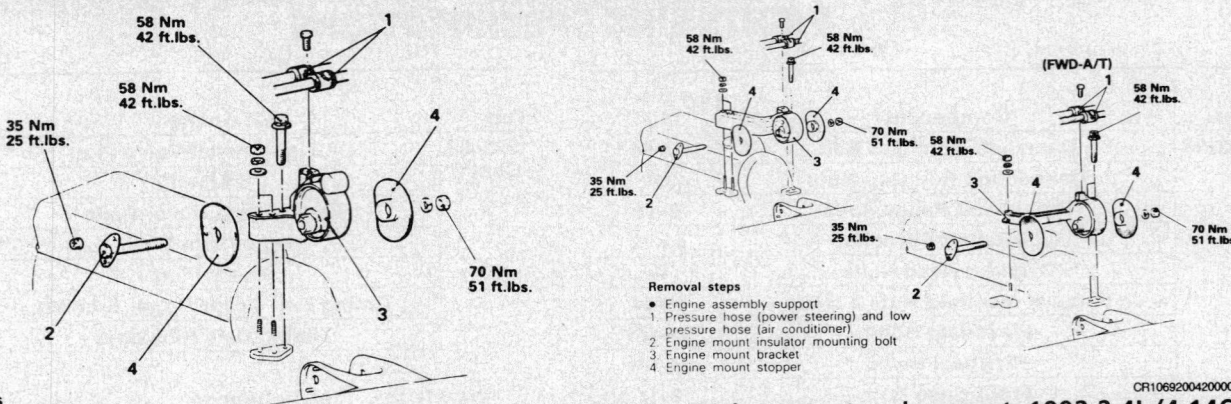

Removal steps
- Engine assembly support
1. Pressure hose (power steering) and low pressure hose (air conditioning)
2. Engine mount insulator mounting bolt
3. Engine mount bracket
4. Engine mount stopper

Fig. 1   Engine mount replacement. 1.8L/4-110 & 1993–95 2.4L/4-146 engines

Removal steps
- Engine assembly support
1. Pressure hose (power steering) and low pressure hose (air conditioner)
2. Engine mount insulator mounting bolt
3. Engine mount bracket
4. Engine mount stopper

Fig. 2   Engine mount replacement. 1992 2.4L/4-146 engine

b. **On models equipped with A/C,** let the refrigerant lines remain connected, then remove the compressor from its mounting bracket and carefully suspend it where it will not be a hindrance.

c. **On models with 1.8L/4-110 engine,** remove engine mount bracket as described under "Engine Mount, Replace."

d. **On models with 2.4L/4-146 engine,** remove center member mounting bolt as described under "Engine Mount, Replace."

e. **On all models,** ensure all hoses, cables, harness connections are disconnected.

7. Reverse procedure to install, ensuring not to pinch any cables, hoses, pipes or harnesses.

INTAKE MANIFOLD
REPLACE

1. Release fuel system pressure as outlined under "Precautions."
2. Drain engine coolant into a suitable container.
3. Remove intake manifold in numbered sequence shown in **Figs. 10 through 12.** Remove fuel rail assembly with injectors and regulator attached.
4. Reverse procedure to install. **On 2.4L/4-146 engine,** apply 3M No. 4171 adhesive or its equivalent to thermo valve thread, prior to valve installation on intake manifold.

EXHAUST MANIFOLD
REPLACE

1. Remove the power steering pump as outlined in the "Front Suspension & Steering" section.
2. Remove the exhaust manifold in numbered sequence shown in **Figs. 13 through 15.**
3. Reverse procedure to install.

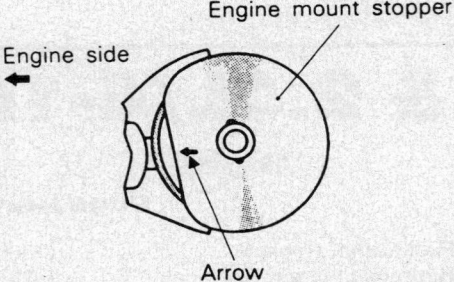

Fig. 3   Engine mount stopper orientation. 1.8L/4-110 & 1993–95 2.4L/4-146 engines

CYLINDER HEAD
REPLACE

1.8L/4-110 & 1993–95 2.4L/4-146 ENGINES

1. Release fuel system pressure as outlined under "Precautions."
2. Raise and support vehicle then drain cooling system and engine oil.
3. Remove cylinder head in numbered sequence shown in **Figs. 16 and 17,** noting the following:
   a. Rotate crankshaft clockwise direction and align the timing marks, **Figs. 18 and 19.**
   b. Tie camshaft sprocket and timing belt with a cord so that position of camshaft sprocket will not move with respect to the timing belt.
   c. Remove camshaft sprocket using spanner wrench tool Nos. MB990767 and MD998719 or equivalents.
   d. Remove cylinder head bolts in two or three steps in numbered sequence shown in **Fig. 20.**
4. Install cylinder head in reverse numbered sequence shown in **Figs. 16 and 17,** noting the following:

a. Place cylinder head gasket on block so that ID mark is facing upward.
b. Ensure length of cylinder head bolts do not exceed 3.795 inches on 1.8L/4-110 engine or 3.91 inches on 1993–95 2.4L/4-146 engine.
c. Apply engine oil to threads of cylinder head bolt before tightening.
d. Tighten cylinder head bolts in sequence shown in **Fig. 21,** using procedures and specifications shown in **Figs. 22 and 23.**
e. Loosen water inlet pipe bolt and apply sealant to thermostat case assembly as shown, **Figs. 24 and 25.**
f. Apply a small amount of water to O-ring of water inlet pipe and press thermostat case assembly onto water inlet pipe.

1992 2.4L/4-146 ENGINE

1. Release fuel system pressure as outlined under "Precautions."
2. Raise and support vehicle then drain cooling system and engine oil.
3. Remove cylinder head in numbered sequence shown in **Fig. 26,** noting the following:
   a. Remove engine mount as outlined under "Engine Mount, Replace."
   b. Rotate crankshaft in a clockwise direction and align the timing marks, **Fig. 27.**
   c. Tie camshaft sprocket and timing belt with a cord so that position of camshaft sprocket will not move with respect to the timing belt.
   d. Remove camshaft sprocket using spanner wrench tool Nos. MB990767 and MD998719 or equivalents.
   e. Remove cylinder head bolts in two or three steps in numbered sequence shown in **Fig. 28.**
4. Install cylinder head in reverse numbered sequence shown in **Fig. 26,** noting the following:
   a. Place cylinder head gasket on cylinder block so that ID mark is facing upward.
   b. Tighten cylinder head bolts in sequence shown in **Fig. 29** using procedure and specifications shown in **Fig. 22.**

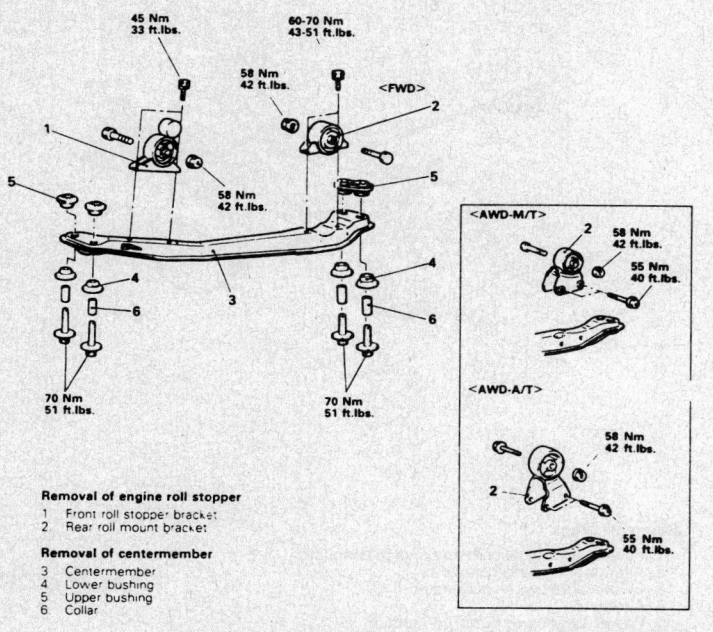

Removal of engine roll stopper
1. Front roll stopper bracket
2. Rear roll mount bracket

Removal of centermember
3. Centermember
4. Lower bushing
5. Upper bushing
6. Collar

CR1069300422000X

Fig. 4 Engine roll stopper & center member. 1.8L/4-110 & 1993–95 2.4L/4-146 engines

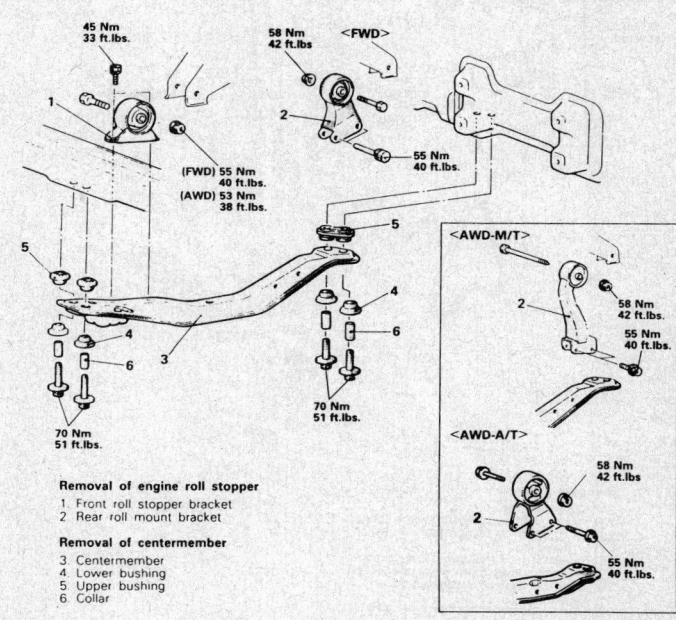

Removal of engine roll stopper
1. Front roll stopper bracket
2. Rear roll mount bracket

Removal of centermember
3. Centermember
4. Lower bushing
5. Upper bushing
6. Collar

CR1069200423000X

Fig. 5 Engine roll stopper & center member. 1992 2.4L/4-146 engine

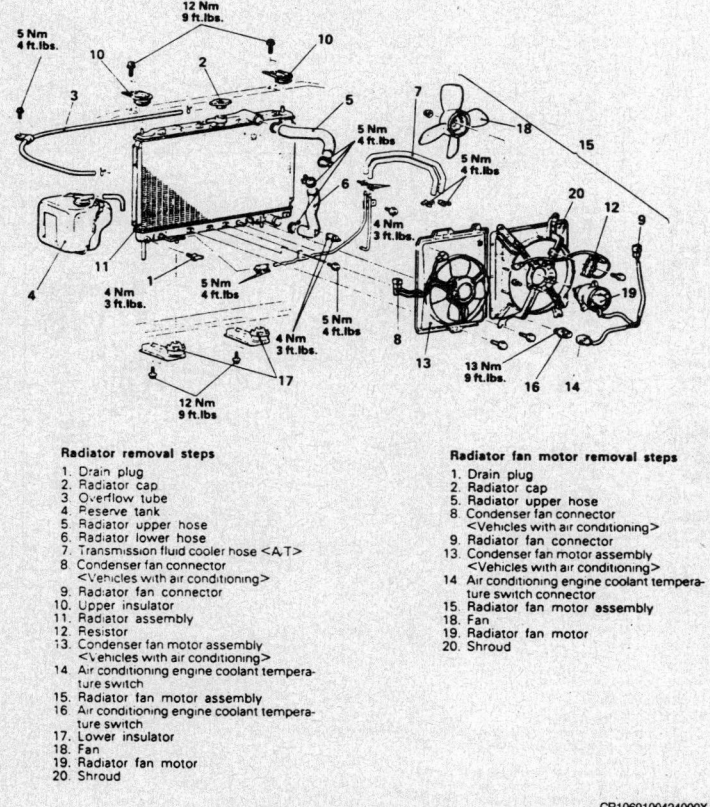

Radiator removal steps
1. Drain plug
2. Radiator cap
3. Overflow tube
4. Reserve tank
5. Radiator upper hose
6. Radiator lower hose
7. Transmission fluid cooler hose <A/T>
8. Condenser fan connector
   <Vehicles with air conditioning>
9. Radiator fan connector
10. Upper insulator
11. Radiator assembly
12. Resistor
13. Condenser fan motor assembly
    <Vehicles with air conditioning>
14. Air conditioning engine coolant tempera-
    ture switch
15. Radiator fan motor assembly
16. Air conditioning engine coolant tempera-
    ture switch
17. Lower insulator
18. Fan
19. Radiator fan motor
20. Shroud

Radiator fan motor removal steps
1. Drain plug
2. Radiator cap
5. Radiator upper hose
8. Condenser fan connector
   <Vehicles with air conditioning>
9. Radiator fan connector
13. Condenser fan motor assembly
    <Vehicles with air conditioning>
14. Air conditioning engine coolant tempera-
    ture switch connector
15. Radiator fan motor assembly
18. Fan
19. Radiator fan motor
20. Shroud

CR1069100424000X

Fig. 6 Radiator & attendant parts

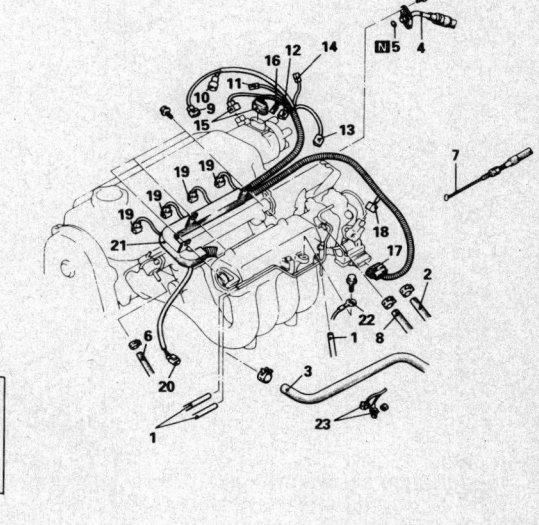

Removal steps
1. Vacuum hose connection
2. Heater hose connection
   (Thermostat housing → heater unit)
3. Heater hose connection
   (Heater unit → Water inlet pipe)
4. Fuel high pressure hose connection
5. O-ring
6. Fuel return hose connection
7. Accelerator cable connection
8. Brake booster vacuum hose connection
9. Air conditioning engine coolant
   temperature switch connector
10. Oxygen sensor connector <Except California>
11. Oil pressure switch connector
12. Water temperature gauge unit connector
13. Engine coolant temperature sensor connector
14. Air conditioning engine coolant
    temperature switch connector
    <for condenser fan>
15. Distributor connector
16. Condenser connector
17. Idle air control connector
18. TPS connector
19. Injector connector
20. EGR temperature sensor connector
    <California>
21. Control harness assembly
22. Ground wire
23. Generator harness connection

CR1069100425010X

Fig. 7 Engine removal (Part 1 of 2). 1.8L/4-110 engine

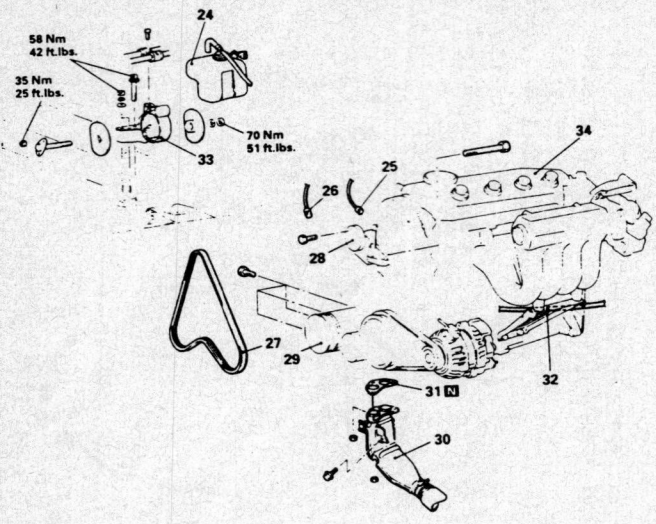

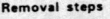

Removal steps
24. Condense tank
25. Power steering pressure switch connector
26. Air conditioning compressor connector
27. V-ribbed belt
28. Power steering oil pump connection
29. Air conditioning compressor connection
30. Front exhaust pipe connection
31. Gasket
32. Starter and generator harness clamp
33. Engine mount bracket
34. Engine assembly

CR1069100425020X

Fig. 7   Engine removal (Part 2 of 2). 1.8L/4-110 engine

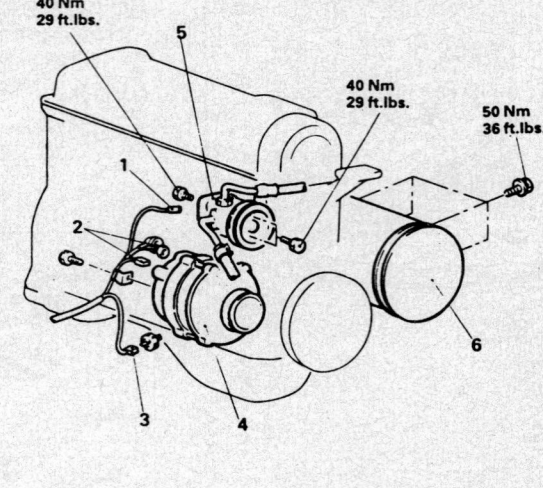

Removal steps
1. Power steering oil pressure switch connector
2. Alternator harness connector
3. Oil pressure switch connector
4. Alternator
5. Power steering oil pump connection
6. Air conditioner compressor connection (Vehicles with air conditioner)
   Removal of transaxle assembly

CR1069200426010X

Fig. 8   Engine removal (Part 1 of 3). 1992 2.4L/4-146 engine

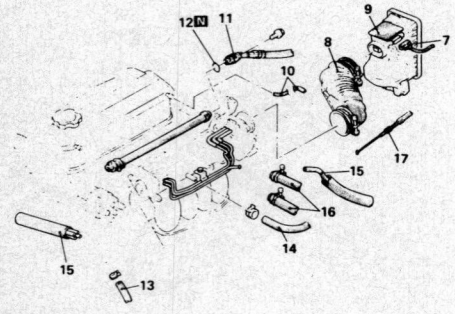

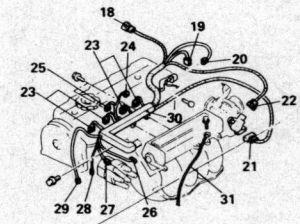

Removal steps
7. Air flow sensor connector
8. Air intake hose
9. Air cleaner case cover
10. Breather hose connection
11. Fuel hight pressure hose connection
12. O-ring
13. Fuel return hose connection
14. Brake booster vacuum hose connection
15. Vacuum hose connection
16. Heater hose connection
17. Accelerator cable connection
18. Oxygen sensor connector
19. Water temperature gauge unit connector
20. Engine coolant temperature sensor connector
21. Idle speed control connector
22. TPS connector
23. Injector connector
24. EGR temperature sensor connector
    <California>
25. Power transistor connector
26. Ignition coil connector
27. Distributor connector
28. Condenser connector
29. Air conditioner compressor connector
30. Control harness assembly
31. Ground wire

CR1069200426020X

Fig. 8   Engine removal (Part 2 of 3). 1992 2.4L/4-146 engine

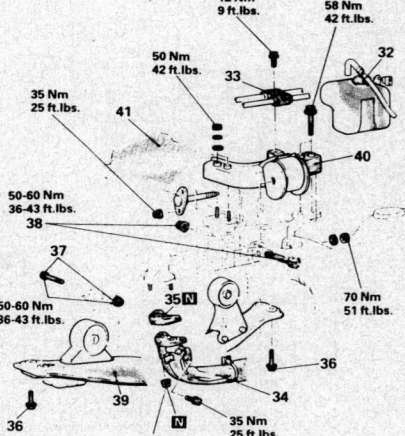

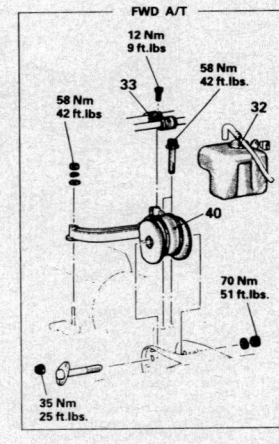

Removal steps
32. Condense tank
33. Power steering hose and air conditioner hose clamp part
34. Front exhaust pipe connection
35. Gasket
36. Center member mounting bolt <FWD>
37. Front roll stopper connection <FWD>
38. Rear roll stopper connection <FWD>
39. Center member assembly
40. Engine mount bracket
41. Engine assembly

CR1069200426030X

Fig. 8   Engine removal (Part 3 of 3). 1992 2.4L/4-146 engine

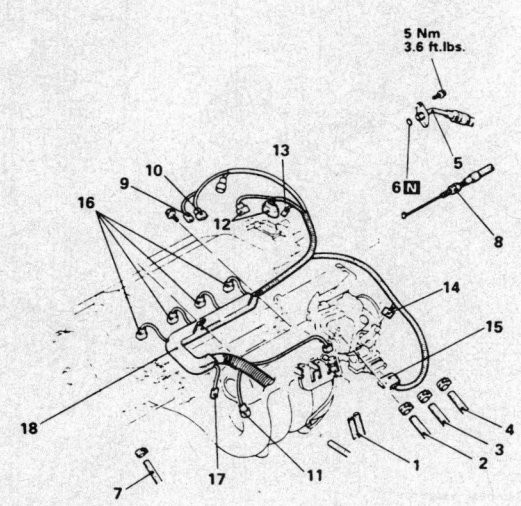

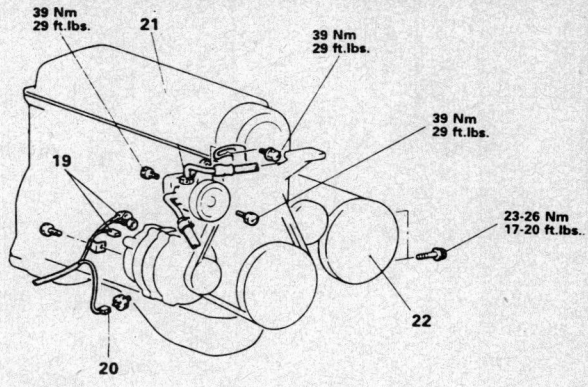

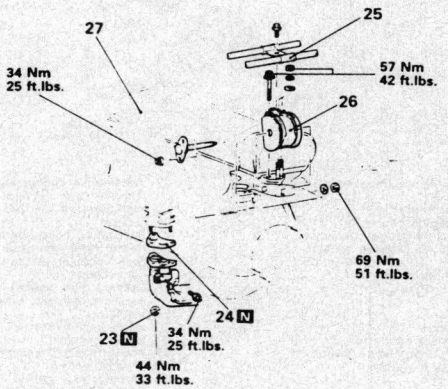

Removal steps

1. Vacuum hose connection
2. Brake booster vacuum hose connection
3. Heater hose connection (cylinder head → heater unit)
4. Heater hose connection (heater unit → water inlet pipe)
5. Fuel high pressure hose connection
6. O-ring
7. Fuel return hose connection
8. Accelerator cable connection
9. Engine coolant temperature gauge unit connector
10. Engine coolant temperature sensor connector
11. Oxygen sensor connector <Except California>
12. Distributor connector
13. Condenser connector
14. TPS connector
15. IAC connector
16. Injector connector
17. Air conditioning compressor connector
18. Control harness

CR1069300427010X

Fig. 9   Engine removal (Part 1 of 2). 1993–95 2.4L/4-146 engine

Removal steps

19. Connection for generator
20. Connection for oil pressure switch
• Drive belt tension adjustment

21. Power steering oil pump
22. Air conditioning compressor
23. Self-locking nuts
24. Gasket
25. Clamp of pressure hose (Power steering) and high pressure hose (Air conditioning)
26. Engine mount bracket
27. Engine assembly

CR1069300427020X

Fig. 9   Engine removal (Part 2 of 2). 1993–95 2.4L/4-146 engine

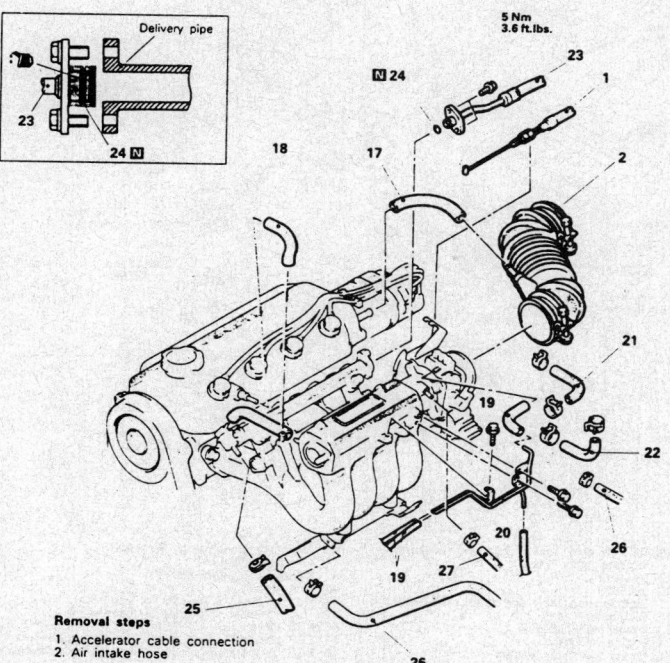

Removal steps

1. Accelerator cable connection
2. Air intake hose

CR1059100064010X

Fig. 10   Intake manifold removal (Part 1 of 2). 1.8L/4-110 engine

CAMSHAFT LOBE LIFT SPECIFICATIONS

Year	Intake Lobe	Exhaust Lobe
1.8L/4-110		
1992–95	1.4876	1.4996
2.4L/4-146		
1992	1.7531	1.7531
1993–95	1.4720	1.4752

VALVE CLEARANCE SPECIFICATIONS

On cold engines, correct valve clearance is .0035 inch for intake valves and .0079 inch for exhaust valves.

VALVE ADJUSTMENT

The 2.4L/4-146 engine employs hydraulic lifters and thus no adjustments are necessary or can be performed. Inspection

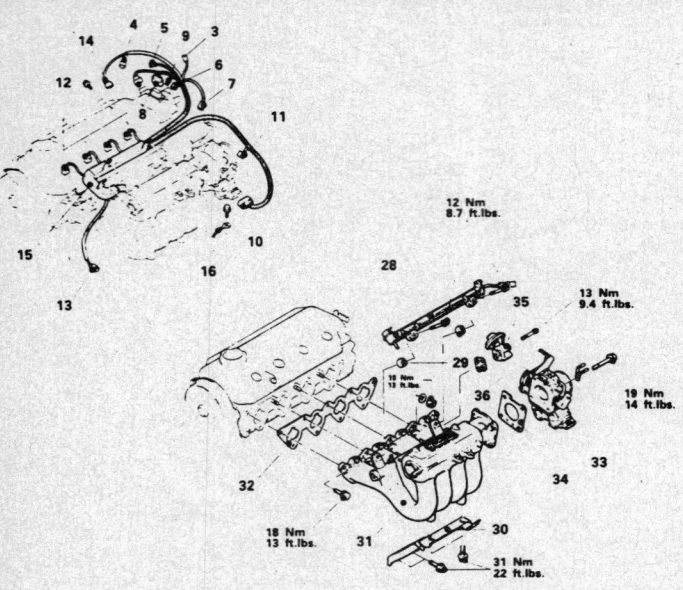

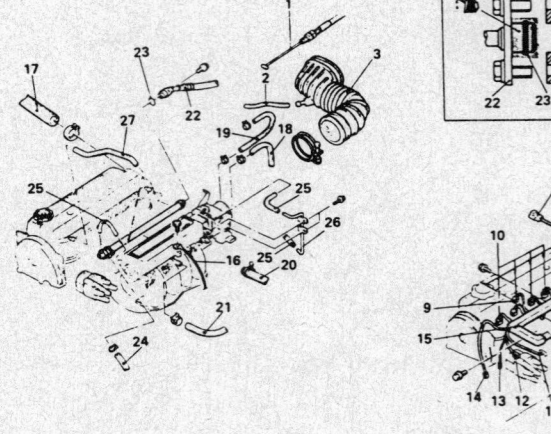

Fig. 11 Intake manifold removal (Part 1 of 2). 1992 2.4L/4-146 engine

Fig. 10 Intake manifold removal (Part 2 of 2). 1.8L/4-110 engine

Removal steps

1. Accelerator cable connection
2. Breather hose connection
3. Air intake hose
4. Oxygen sensor connector
5. Engine coolant temperature gauge unit connector
6. Engine coolant temperature sensor connector
7. ISC connector
8. Throttle position sensor
9. Power transistor connector
10. Injector connector
11. Ignition coil connector
12. Distributor connector
13. Condenser connector
14. Air Conditioner comperssor connector
15. Control harness

16. Ground wire
17. Radiator upper hose connection
18. Water by-pass hose connection
19. Water hose connection
20. Heater hose connection
21. Brake booster vacuum hose connection
22. Fuel high pressure hose connection
23. O-ring
24. Fuel return hose connection
25. Vacuum hoses connection
26. Vacuum pipe
27. PCV hose connection

---

3. Engine coolant temperature switch (A/C) connector
4. Oxygen sensor connector
5. Oil pressure switch connector
6. Water temperature gauge connector
7. Engine coolant temperature sensor connector
8. Distributor connector
9. Condenser connector
10. ISC connector
11. TPS connector
12. Injector connector
13. Detonation sensor connector
14. Engine coolant temperature switch
15. Control harness assembly
16. Ground wire
17. Breather hose connection
18. PCV hose connection
19. Vacuum hose connection
20. Vacuum pipe
21. Water hose connection (Thermostat case — Throttle body)

22. Water hose connection (Throttle body — Water inlet fitting)
23. High-pressure fuel hose connection
24. O-ring
25. Fuel return hose connection
26. Heater hose connection
27. Brake booster vacuum hose connection
28. Delivery pipe, injector and pressure regulator assembly
29. Insulator
30. Intake manifold stay
31. Intake manifold
32. Intake manifold gasket
33. Throttle body
34. Throttle body gasket
35. EGR valve (Vehicles for California)
36. EGR valve gasket (Vehicles for California)

of the 2.4L/4-146 engine auto lash adjuster is outlined under "Hydraulic Lifter, Replace." Adjustments to the 1.8L/4-110 engine may be made, however, by proceeding as follows:

1. Position the No. 1 cylinder at TDC on the compression stroke.
2. Adjust valve clearance at the points shown with the outlined arrow in **Fig. 30.**
3. Loosen adjusting screw locknut.
4. Using a feeler gauge, adjust the valve clearance by turning the adjusting screw. On cold engines, correct valve clearance for intake valves is .0035 inches, and .0079 inches for exhaust valves.
5. While holding the adjusting screw with a screwdriver, tighten the locknut.
6. Rotate the crankshaft one complete turn clockwise, then adjust valve clearance at the points shown with the solid arrow in **Fig. 30.**

ROCKER ARMS

1.8L/4-110 & 1993–95 2.4L/4-146 ENGINES

Replace rocker arms, rocker arm shafts and camshaft in numbered sequence shown in **Fig. 31**, noting the following:

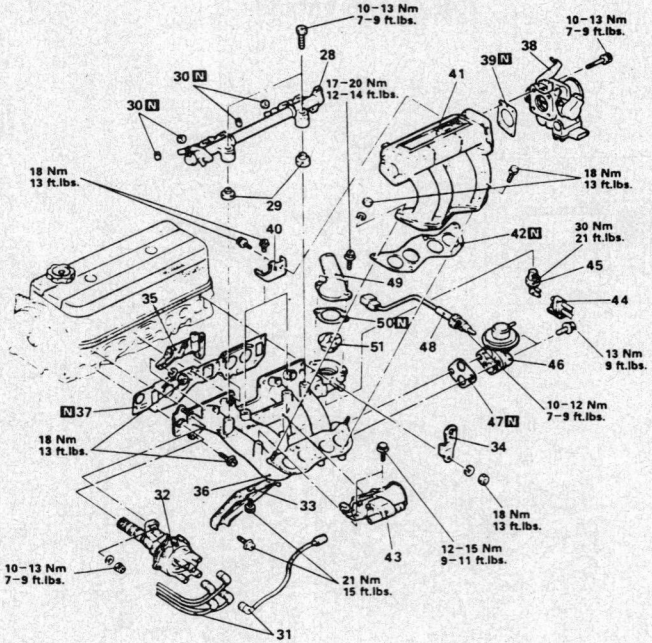

28. Delivery pipe, fuel injector and pressure regulator
29. Insulator
30. Insulator
31. High tension cable and spark plug cable
32. Distributor
33. Intake manifold stay
34. Engine hanger
35. Power transistor bracket
36. Intake manifold
37. Intake manifold gasket
38. Throttle body assembly
39. Gasket

40. Air intake plenum stay
41. Air intake plenum
42. Air intake plenum gasket
43. Ignition coil
44. Vacuum hose <Vehicles for Federal>
45. Thermo valve <Vehicles for Federal>
46. EGR valve
47. EGR gasket
48. EGR temperature sensor <Vehicles for California>
49. Water outlet fitting
50. Gasket
51. Thermostat

Fig. 11 Intake manifold removal (Part 2 of 2). 1992 2.4L/4-146 engine

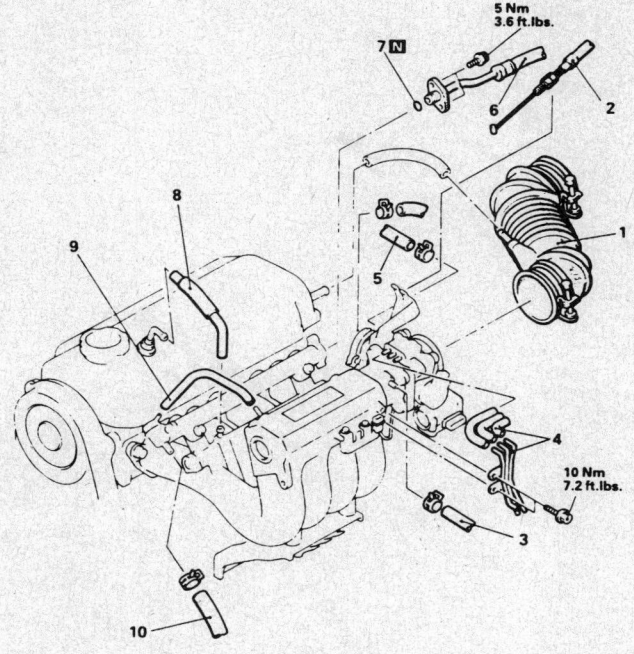

Removal steps

1. Air intake hose
2. Connection for accelerator cable
3. Connection for brake booster vacuum hose
4. Connection for vacuum pipe and hose assembly
5. Connection for water hose
6. Connection for fuel high pressure hose
7. O-ring
8. PCV hose
9. Connection for vacuum hose
10. Connection for fuel return hose

CR1059300066010X

Fig. 12   Intake manifold removal (Part 1 of 2). 1993–95 2.4L/4-146 engine

1. **On 2.4L/4-146 engines,** prior to removing rocker arms and shaft assemblies, install auto lash adjuster holder tool No. MD998443 or equivalent to prevent adjuster from dropping out.
2. Inspect auto lash adjuster as outlined under "Hydraulic Lifter, Replace."
3. Prior to installing the auto lash adjuster, prime the lash adjuster as follows:
   a. Immerse the auto lash adjuster in clean diesel fuel.
   b. Using a small wire, move plunger up and down four or five times while pushing down lightly on check ball to bleed out air, **Fig. 32.**
   c. Insert lash adjuster from below ensuring not to spill out the diesel fuel inside.
   d. Install auto lash adjuster holder tool No. MD998443 or equivalent.
4. **On all models,** temporarily tighten rocker arm shaft so all rocker arms on inlet side do not push the valves.
5. Fit rocker shaft spring from the above position so that it is at right angles to the plug guide, **Fig. 33.**
6. **On 2.4L/4-146 engines,** remove lash adjuster holder tool.
7. Ensure the notches of the rocker shafts are in the direction as shown in **Fig. 34.**

8. **On all models,** use seal installation tool No. MD998713 or equivalent to install camshaft oil seal.

1992 2.4L/4-146 ENGINE

Replace rocker arms, rocker arm shafts and camshaft in numbered sequence shown in **Fig. 35,** noting the following:
1. Prior to removing rocker arms and shaft assemblies, install auto lash adjuster holder tool No. MD998443 or equivalent to prevent adjuster from dropping out.
2. Inspect auto lash adjuster as outlined under "Auto Lash Adjuster Inspection."
3. Insert rocker arm shaft into front bearing so that notch on shaft faces upward, and insert the bolt without tightening it.
4. Install wave washer as shown **Fig. 36.**
5. Install bearing caps with their front marks pointing to camshaft sprocket side. **Bearing cap Nos. 2, 3 and 4 look very similar, identify using marks shown in Fig. 37.**
6. Prior to installing the auto lash adjuster, prime the lash adjuster as follows:
   a. Immerse the auto lash adjuster in clean diesel fuel.
   b. Using a small wire, move plunger up and down four or five times

while pushing down lightly on check ball to bleed out air, **Fig. 32.**
   c. Insert lash adjuster from below ensuring not to spill out the diesel fuel inside.
   d. Install auto lash adjuster holder tool No. MD998443 or equivalent.
7. Use seal installer tools No. MD998306 and MD998307 or equivalents to install the camshaft oil seal.
8. Apply sealant to the lower rounded edge of the semi-circular packing prior to installation.

HYDRAULIC LIFTERS
REPLACE
INSPECTION

1. Remove rocker arms as outlined under "Rocker Arms, Replace."
2. Remove auto lash adjuster from each rocker arm. **Keep lash adjusters and rocker arms in order to ensure proper installation.**
3. Immerse lash adjuster in clean diesel fuel.
4. While lightly pushing down inner steel ball using the small wire and retainer tool Nos. MD998442 and MD998441 or equivalents, move plunger up and down four or five times to bleed air, **Fig. 32.**
5. Remove small wire and test as follows:
   a. Press plunger and note resistance.
   b. If plunger is hard to press, the auto lash adjuster is normal.
   c. If plunger can be pressed easily, repeat steps 3 through 5.
   d. If plunger can still be pressed easily after re-bleeding, replace the auto lash adjuster.
6. After air bleeding, set lash adjuster on leak down test tool No. MD998440 or equivalent.
7. After plunger has dropped .008-.020 inch, measure time taken for plunger to drop an additional .04 inch.
8. If measured time is not within 4-20 seconds, replace auto lash adjuster.

FRONT COVER
REPLACE

Refer to **Timing Belt, Replace** for procedure.

TIMING BELT
REPLACE

1.8L/4-110 ENGINE
Removal

1. Release fuel system pressure as outlined under "Precautions."
2. Remove engine undercover.
3. Remove timing belt and covers in numbered sequence shown in **Fig. 38,** noting the following:

a. With tool No. MB990767 or equivalent in place to keep the crankshaft from turning, remove the crankshaft bolt.

b. Turn the crankshaft clockwise to align each timing mark and to set the No. 1 cylinder at compression TDC, **Fig. 18.**

c. Loosen the timing belt tensioner bolt.

d. Set a screwdriver to the timing belt tensioner and press it fully back in the direction of the arrow, **Fig. 39.**

e. Temporarily tighten the timing belt tensioner bolt in the slackened position.

f. Remove the timing belt. **If the timing belt is to be reinstalled, use chalk to mark the flat side of the belt with an arrow indicating the direction of rotation (right turn).**

Installation

Reverse the removal procedure to install, noting the following:

1. With the timing belt tensioner bolt loosened, use a screwdriver to fully turn the timing belt tensioner as close to the engine mount as possible, and then, for the time being, tighten the tensioner bolt.

2. Align each of the camshaft sprocket and the crankshaft timing marks, **Fig. 18.**

3. Without slackening its tension side, install the timing belt at first the crankshaft sprocket, then the water pump sprocket, then the camshaft sprocket, and lastly the tensioner pulley.

4. After installing the timing belt, apply force to turn the camshaft sprocket in the reverse direction, then recheck to be sure that the belt is fully tensioner and that each timing mark is in the proper position.

5. Set timing belt tension as follows:
   a. Loosen the fixing bolt of the tensioner pulley fixed to the engine mount side by 1/4–1/2 turn and use the force of the tensioner spring to apply tension to the belt.
   b. Turn the crankshaft in the proper rotation direction (right turn) for two rotations and recheck to be sure that the timing marks on each sprocket are aligned.

6. Install timing belt cover bolts in correct location as shown in **Fig. 40.** Bolts marked A are .72 inch long and bolts marked B are 1.18 inches long.

1992 2.4L/4-146 ENGINE

This engine is fitted with two timing belts, the camshaft timing belt and the silent shaft "B" belt.

Removal

1. Release fuel system pressure as outlined under "Precautions."
2. Remove engine undercover.
3. Remove camshaft timing belt in numbered sequence shown in **Fig. 41,** noting the following:
   a. Jack up engine at oil pan, then remove engine mount bracket. When lifting engine, use a piece of wood

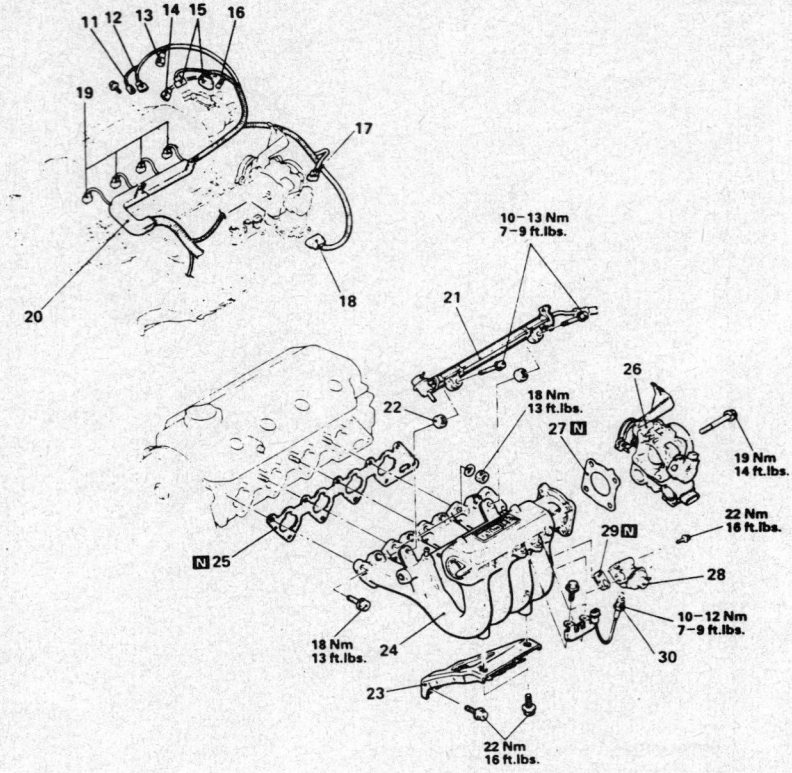

10–13 Nm	7–9 ft.lbs.
18 Nm	13 ft.lbs.
19 Nm	14 ft.lbs.
22 Nm	16 ft.lbs.
10–12 Nm	7–9 ft.lbs.
18 Nm	13 ft.lbs.
22 Nm	16 ft.lbs.

11. Engine coolant temperature gauge unit connector
12. Engine coolant temperature sensor connector
13. Air conditioning engine coolant temperature switch connector
14. Oxygen sensor connector <Vehicles for Federal and Canada>
15. Distributor connector
16. Condenser connector
17. TPS connector
18. IAC connector
19. Injector connector
20. Control harness
21. Fuel rail, fuel injector and pressure regulator
22. Insulator
23. Intake manifold stay
24. Intake manifold
25. Intake manifold gasket
26. Throttle body
27. Throttle body gasket
28. EGR valve
29. EGR gasket
30. EGR temperature sensor <Vehicles for California>

CR1059300066020X

Fig. 12   Intake manifold removal (Part 2 of 2). 1993–95 2.4L/4-146 engine

to help distribute load.

b. Turn crankshaft clockwise and align timing marks, **Fig. 27.**

c. Loosen timing belt tensioner bolts, **Fig. 42.**

d. Move the timing belt tensioner to the water pump side and temporarily tighten the bolt so that the tensioner doesn't return.

e. Remove the timing belt. **If the timing belt is to be reused, use chalk to mark its flat side with an arrow indicating the clockwise direction.**

Installation

Reverse the removal procedure to install, noting the following:

1. Install the timing belt tensioner, tensioner spring and tensioner spacer as follows:
   a. With the tensioner spring free and the tensioner placed most closely to the water pump side, temporarily tighten the tensioner mounting bolts.
   b. With pliers, set the tensioner spring into position.

2. Make sure that the timing marks of the of the camshaft sprocket, crankshaft sprocket and oil pump sprocket are all aligned.

3. After aligning the timing mark on the oil pump sprocket, remove the cylinder block plug and insert a Phillips screwdriver with a diameter of 8 mm and check that the screwdriver goes in 2.36 inches or more.

4. If the screwdriver will only go .79–.98 inch before it strikes against the counterbalance shaft, turn the sprocket once, realign the timing mark and check that the screwdriver goes in 2.36 inches or more. The screwdriver should not be taken out until the timing belt is installed.

5. Install the timing belt onto the crankshaft sprocket, the oil pump sprocket and the camshaft sprocket in that order, while making sure that the tension side of the belt is not slackened. **If the timing belt is reused, install so that the arrow marked on it during removal points in the clockwise direction.**

6. Adjust timing belt tension as follows:

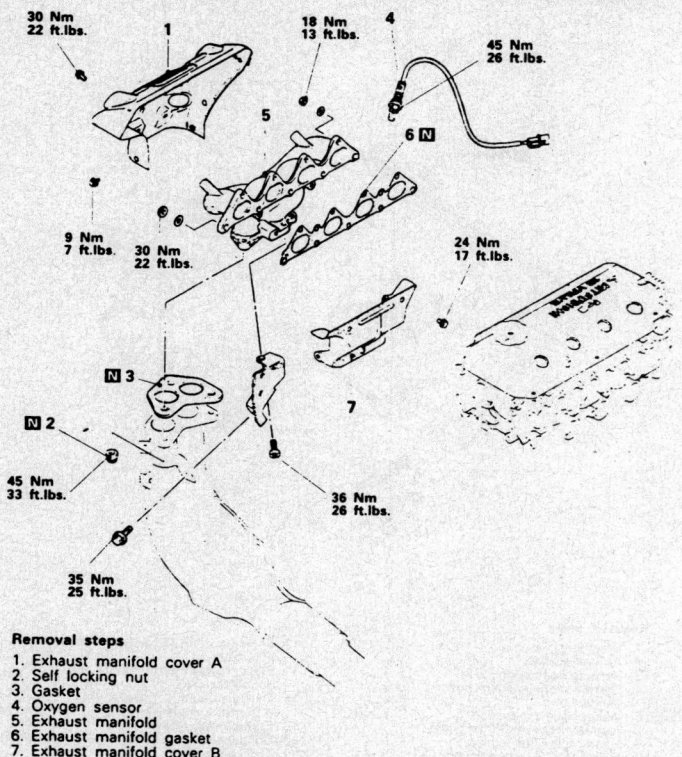

Removal steps
1. Exhaust manifold cover A
2. Self locking nut
3. Gasket
4. Oxygen sensor
5. Exhaust manifold
6. Exhaust manifold gasket
7. Exhaust manifold cover B

CR1079100009000X

Fig. 13   Exhaust manifold removal. 1.8L/4-110 engine

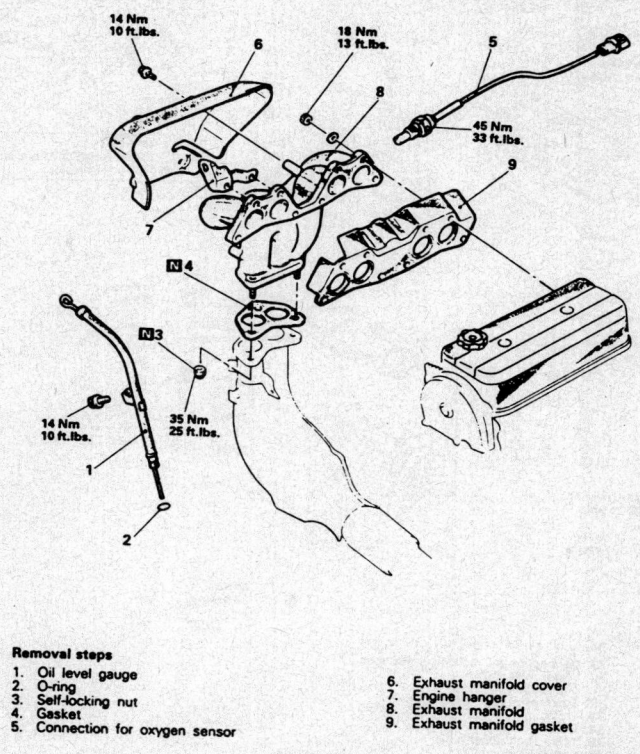

Removal steps
1. Oil level gauge
2. O-ring
3. Self-locking nut
4. Gasket
5. Connection for oxygen sensor

6. Exhaust manifold cover
7. Engine hanger
8. Exhaust manifold
9. Exhaust manifold gasket

CR1079200010000X

Fig. 14   Exhaust manifold removal. 1992 2.4L/4-146 engine

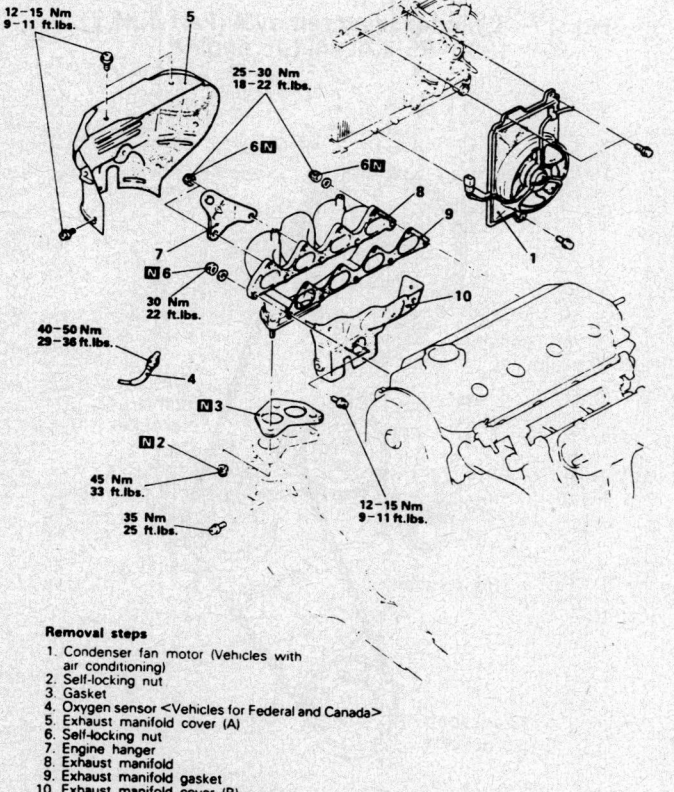

Removal steps
1. Condenser fan motor (Vehicles with air conditioning)
2. Self-locking nut
3. Gasket
4. Oxygen sensor <Vehicles for Federal and Canada>
5. Exhaust manifold cover (A)
6. Self-locking nut
7. Engine hanger
8. Exhaust manifold
9. Exhaust manifold gasket
10. Exhaust manifold cover (B) <Vehicles for Federal and Canada>

CR1079300011000X

Fig. 15   Exhaust manifold removal. 1993–95 2.4L/4-146 engine

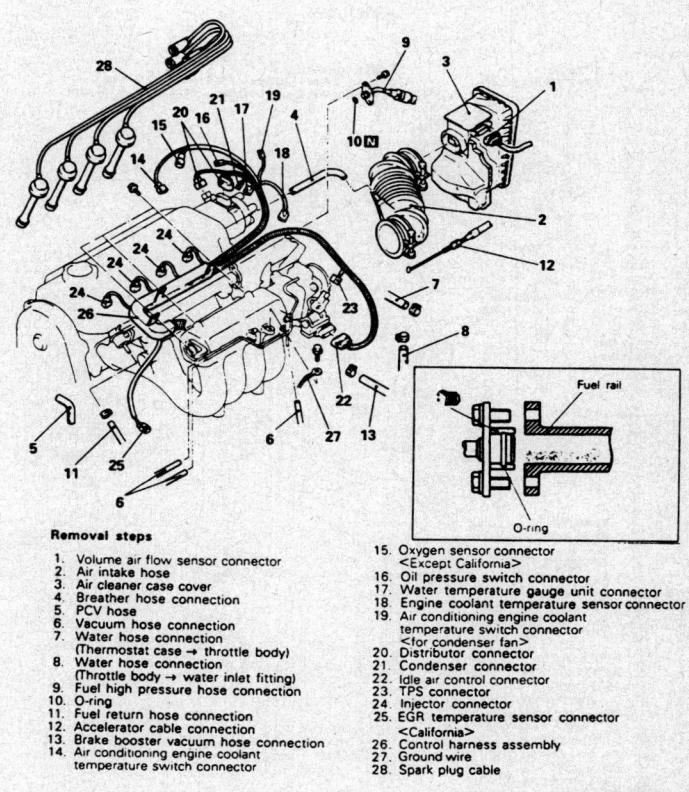

Removal steps
1. Volume air flow sensor connector
2. Air intake hose
3. Air cleaner case cover
4. Breather hose connection
5. PCV hose
6. Vacuum hose connection
7. Water hose connection (Thermostat case → throttle body)
8. Water hose connection (Throttle body → water inlet fitting)
9. Fuel high pressure hose connection
10. O-ring
11. Fuel return hose connection
12. Accelerator cable connection
13. Brake booster vacuum hose connection
14. Air conditioning engine coolant temperature switch connector

15. Oxygen sensor connector <Except California>
16. Oil pressure switch connector
17. Water temperature gauge unit connector
18. Engine coolant temperature sensor connector
19. Air conditioning engine coolant temperature switch connector <for condenser fan>
20. Distributor connector
21. Condenser connector
22. Idle air control connector
23. TPS connector
24. Injector connector
25. EGR temperature sensor connector <California>
26. Control harness assembly
27. Ground wire
28. Spark plug cable

CR1069100428010X

Fig. 16   Cylinder head removal (Part 1 of 2). 1.8L/4-110 engine

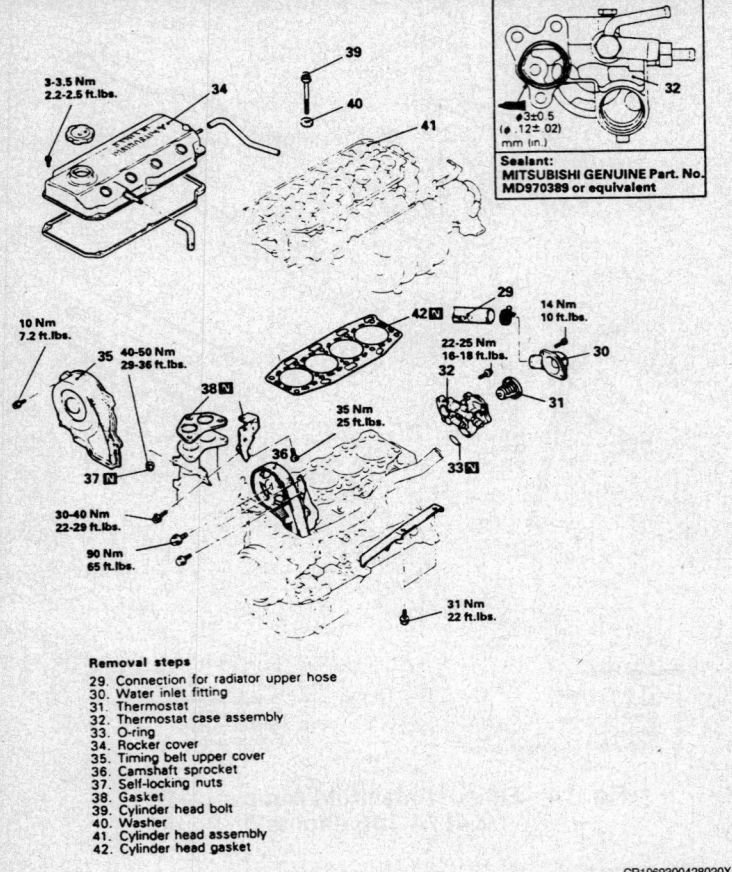

Removal steps

29. Connection for radiator upper hose
30. Water inlet fitting
31. Thermostat
32. Thermostat case assembly
33. O-ring
34. Rocker cover
35. Timing belt upper cover
36. Camshaft sprocket
37. Self-locking nuts
38. Gasket
39. Cylinder head bolt
40. Washer
41. Cylinder head assembly
42. Cylinder head gasket

CR1069300428020X

Fig. 16   Cylinder head removal (Part 2 of 2). 1.8L/4-110 engine

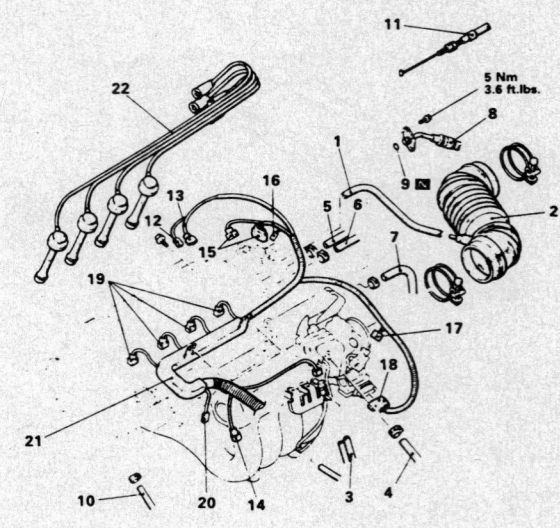

Removal steps

1. Breather hose
2. Air intake hose
3. Vacuum hose connection
4. Brake booster vacuum hose connection
5. Water hose connection (cylinder head → throttle body)
6. Heater hose connection (cylinder head → heater unit)
7. Water hose connection (throttle body → water inlet pipe)
8. Fuel high pressure hose connection
9. O-ring
10. Fuel return hose connection
11. Accelerator cable connection
12. Engine coolant temperature gauge unit connector
13. Engine coolant temperature sensor connector
14. Oxygen sensor connector <Except California>
15. Distributor connector
16. Condenser connector
17. TPS connector
18. IAC connector
19. Injector connector
20. Air conditioning compressor connector
21. Control harness
22. Spark plug cable

CR1069300429010X

Fig. 17   Cylinder head removal (Part 1 of 2). 1993–95 2.4L/4-146 engine

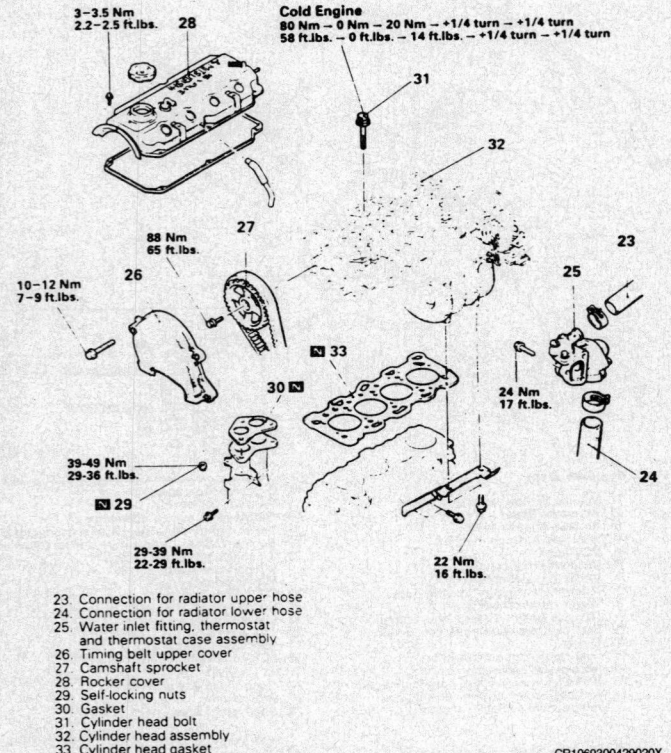

Cold Engine
80 Nm → 0 Nm → 20 Nm → +1/4 turn → +1/4 turn
58 ft.lbs. → 0 ft.lbs. → 14 ft.lbs. → +1/4 turn → +1/4 turn

23. Connection for radiator upper hose
24. Connection for radiator lower hose
25. Water inlet fitting, thermostat and thermostat case assembly
26. Timing belt upper cover
27. Camshaft sprocket
28. Rocker cover
29. Self-locking nuts
30. Gasket
31. Cylinder head bolt
32. Cylinder head assembly
33. Cylinder head gasket

CR1069300429020X

Fig. 17   Cylinder head removal (Part 2 of 2). 1993–95 2.4L/4-146 engine

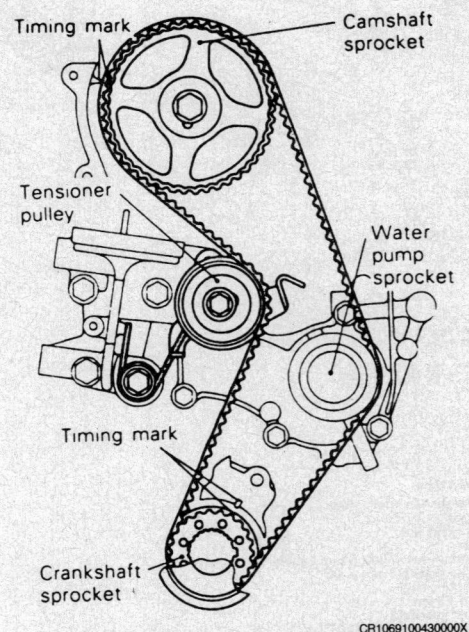

CR1069100430000X

Fig. 18   Timing mark alignment. 1.8L/4-110 engine

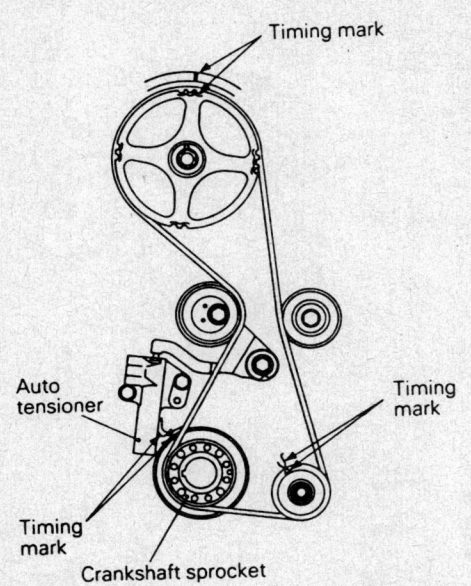

Fig. 19 Timing mark alignment. 1993–95 2.4L/4-146 engine

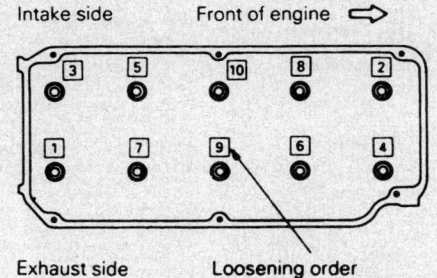

Fig. 20 Cylinder head bolt loosening sequence. 1.8L/4-110 & 1993–95 2.4L/4-146 engines

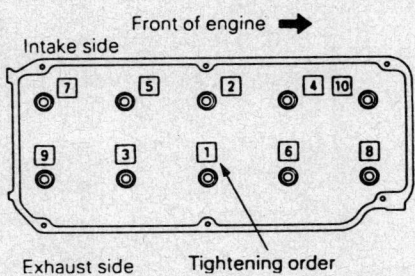

Fig. 21 Cylinder head bolt tightening sequence. 1.8L/4-110 & 1993–95 2.4L/4-146 engines

Procedure	Operation contents	Remarks
①	Tighten to 75 Nm (54 ft.lbs.)	Carry out in the order shown in the illustration.
②	Fully loosen.	Carry out in the reverse order to that shown in the illustration.
③	Tighten to 20 Nm (14 ft.lbs.)	Carry out in the order shown in the illustration.
④	Tighten by 1/4 turn (90°).	Carry out in the order shown in the illustration.
⑤	Tighten by 1/4 turn (90°).	Carry out in the order shown in the illustration.

CR1069100434000X

Fig. 22 Cylinder head bolt tightening procedure & specifications. 1.8L/4-110 & 1992 2.4L/4–146 engines

Procedure	Operation contents	Remarks
①	Tighten to 78 Nm (58 ft.lbs.)	Carry out in the order shown in the illustration.
②	Fully loosen.	Carry out in the reverse order to that shown in the illustration.
③	Tighten to 20 Nm (14 ft.lbs.)	Carry out in the order shown in the illustration.
④	Tighten by 1/4 turn (90°).	Carry out in the order shown in the illustration.
⑤	Tighten by 1/4 turn (90°).	Carry out in the order shown in the illustration.

CR1069100435000X

Fig. 23 Cylinder head bolt tightening procedure & specifications. 1993–95 2.4L/4-146 engine

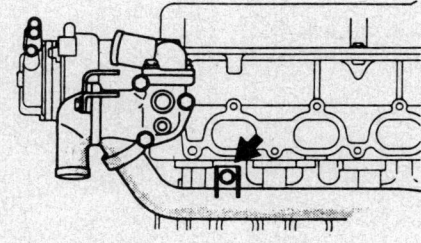

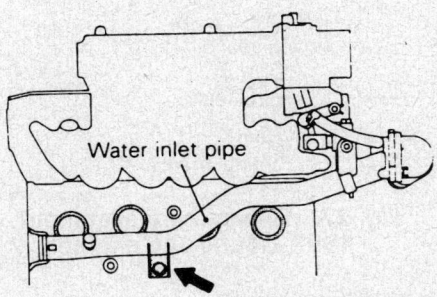

Fig. 24 Water inlet pipe bolt. 1.8L/4-110 engine

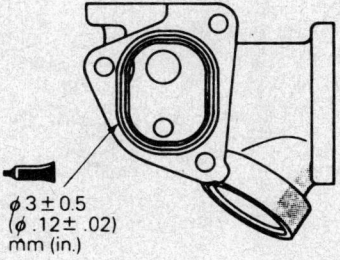

Fig. 25 Water inlet fitting installation. 1993–95 2.4L/4-146 engine

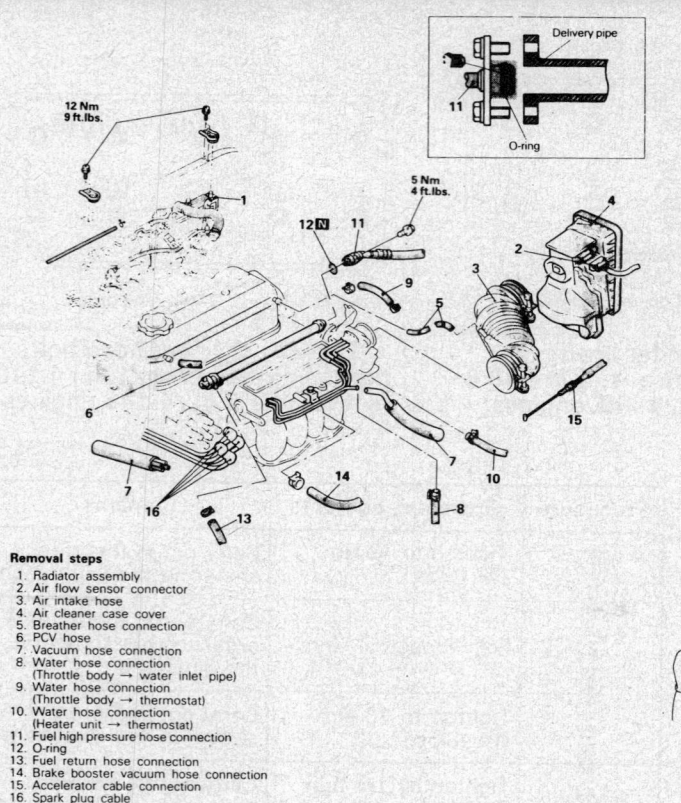

Removal steps
1. Radiator assembly
2. Air flow sensor connector
3. Air intake hose
4. Air cleaner case cover
5. Breather hose connection
6. PCV hose
7. Vacuum hose connection
8. Water hose connection
   (Throttle body → water inlet pipe)
9. Water hose connection
   (Throttle body → thermostat)
10. Water hose connection
    (Heater unit → thermostat)
11. Fuel high pressure hose connection
12. O-ring
13. Fuel return hose connection
14. Brake booster vacuum hose connection
15. Accelerator cable connection
16. Spark plug cable

Fig. 26 Cylinder head removal (Part 2 of 3). 1992 2.4L/4-146 engine

CR1069200438020X

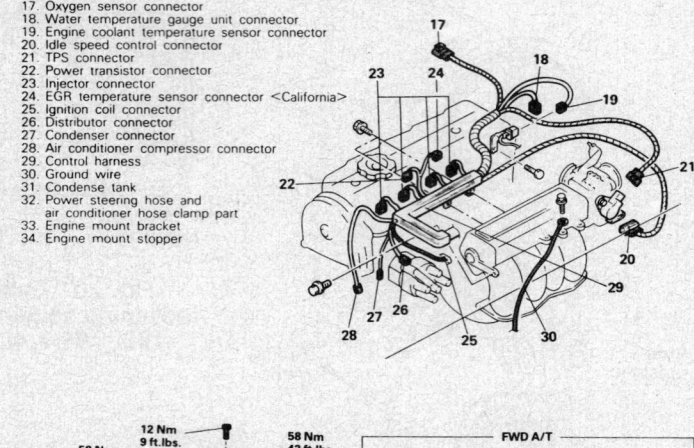

Removal steps
17. Oxygen sensor connector
18. Water temperature gauge unit connector
19. Engine coolant temperature sensor connector
20. Idle speed control connector
21. TPS connector
22. Power transistor connector
23. Injector connector
24. EGR temperature sensor connector <California>
25. Ignition coil connector
26. Distributor connector
27. Condenser connector
28. Air conditioner compressor connector
29. Control harness
30. Ground wire
31. Condense tank
32. Power steering hose and
    air conditioner hose clamp part
33. Engine mount bracket
34. Engine mount stopper

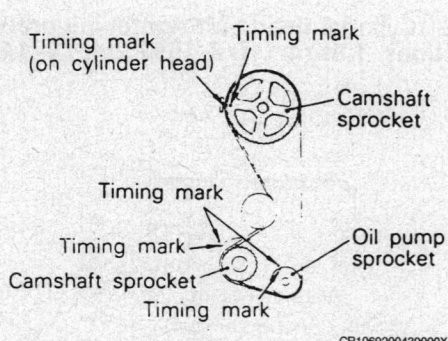

Fig. 26 Cylinder head removal (Part 3 of 3). 1992 2.4L/4-146 engine

CR1069200438030X

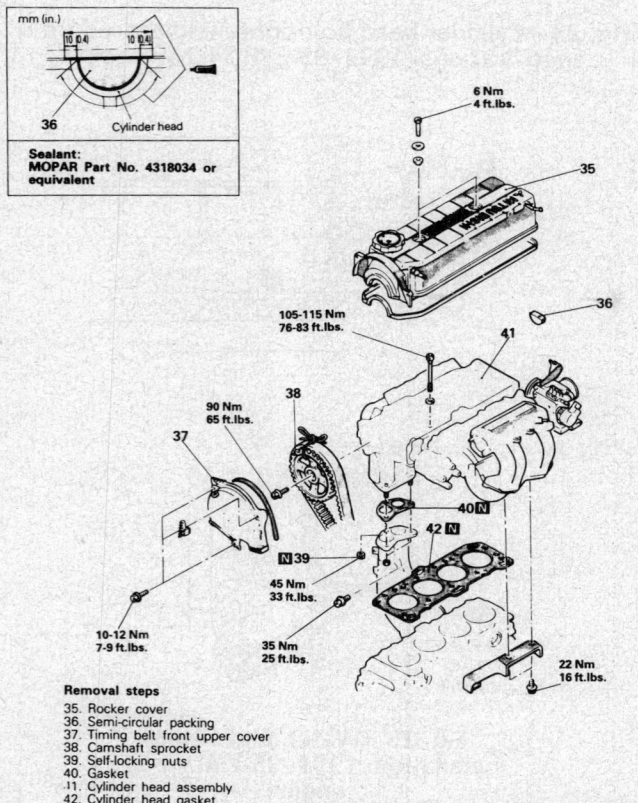

Removal steps
35. Rocker cover
36. Semi-circular packing
37. Timing belt front upper cover
38. Camshaft sprocket
39. Self-locking nuts
40. Gasket
41. Cylinder head assembly
42. Cylinder head gasket

Fig. 26 Cylinder head removal (Part 1 of 3). 1992 2.4L/4-146 engine

CR1069200438010X

Fig. 27 Timing mark alignment. 1992 2.4L/4-146 engine

CR1069200439000X

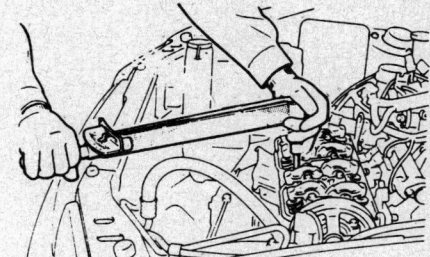

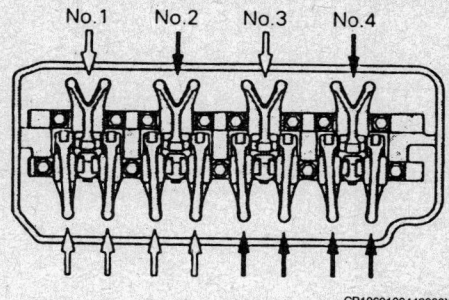

No.1   No.2   No.3   No.4

Fig. 30   Valve clearance adjustment. 1.8L/4-110 engine

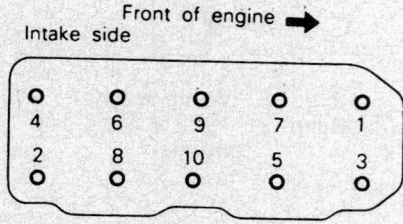

Front of engine →

Intake side

| 4 | 6 | 9 | 7 | 1 |
| 2 | 8 | 10 | 5 | 3 |

Exhaust side

Fig. 28   Cylinder head bolt loosening sequence. 1992 2.4L/4-146 engine

Front of engine →

Intake side

| 4 | 6 | 9 | 7 | 1 |
| 2 | 8 | 10 | 5 | 3 |

Exhaust side

Fig. 29   Cylinder head bolt tightening sequence. 1992 2.4L/4-146 engine

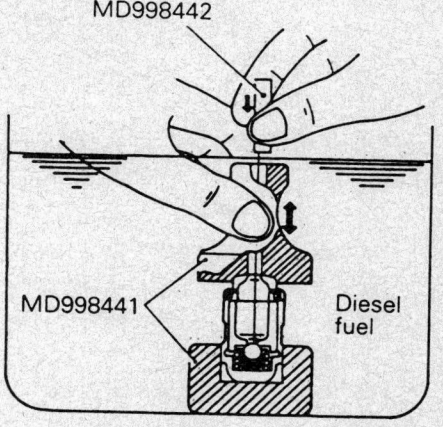

MD998442

MD998441   Diesel fuel

Fig. 32   Hydraulic lifter bleeding. 2.4L/4-146 engine

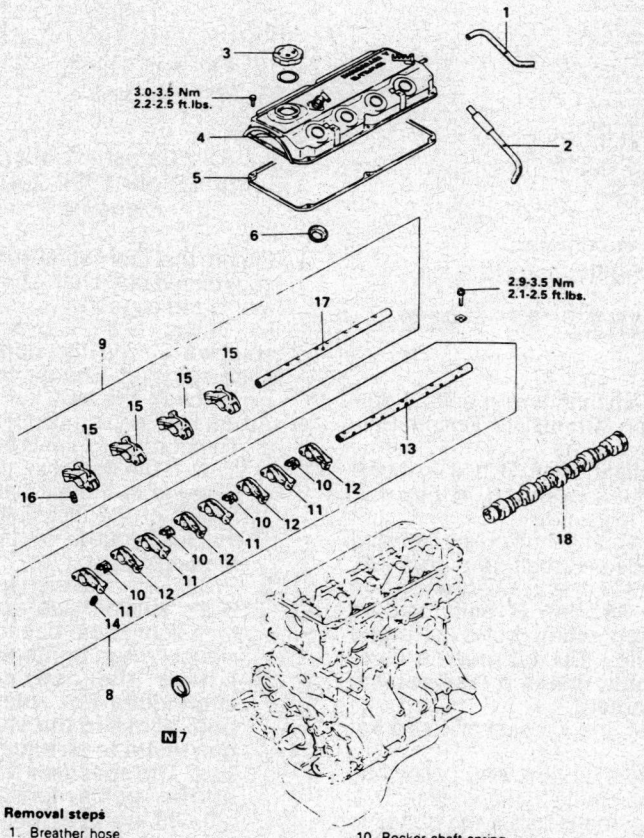

3
3.0-3.5 Nm
2.2-2.5 ft.lbs.
4
5
6

17
2.9-3.5 Nm
2.1-2.5 ft.lbs.
13
18

Removal steps

1. Breather hose
2. P.C.V. hose
3. Oil filler cap
4. Rocker cover
5. Rocker cover gasket
6. Oil seal
7. Oil seal
8. Rocker arms and rocker arm shaft
9. Rocker arms and rocker arm shaft
10. Rocker shaft spring
11. Rocker arm A
12. Rocker arm B
13. Rocker arm shaft (Intake side)
14. Lash adjuster
15. Rocker arm C
16. Rocker arm shaft (Exhaust side)
17. Lash adjuster
18. Camshaft

Fig. 31   Rocker arm, rocker arm shafts & camshaft replacement. 1.8L/4-110 & 1993–95 2.4L/4-146 engines

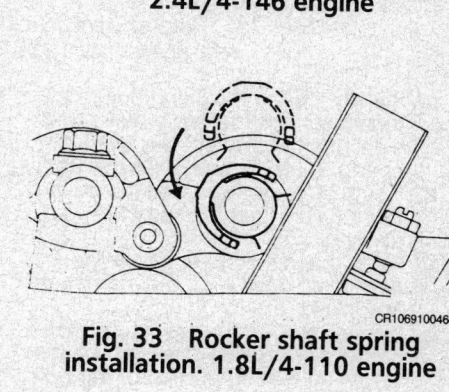

Fig. 33   Rocker shaft spring installation. 1.8L/4-110 engine

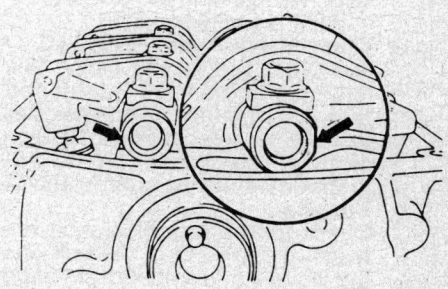

Fig. 34   Rocker arm shaft notches alignment. 1993–95 2.4L/4-146 engine

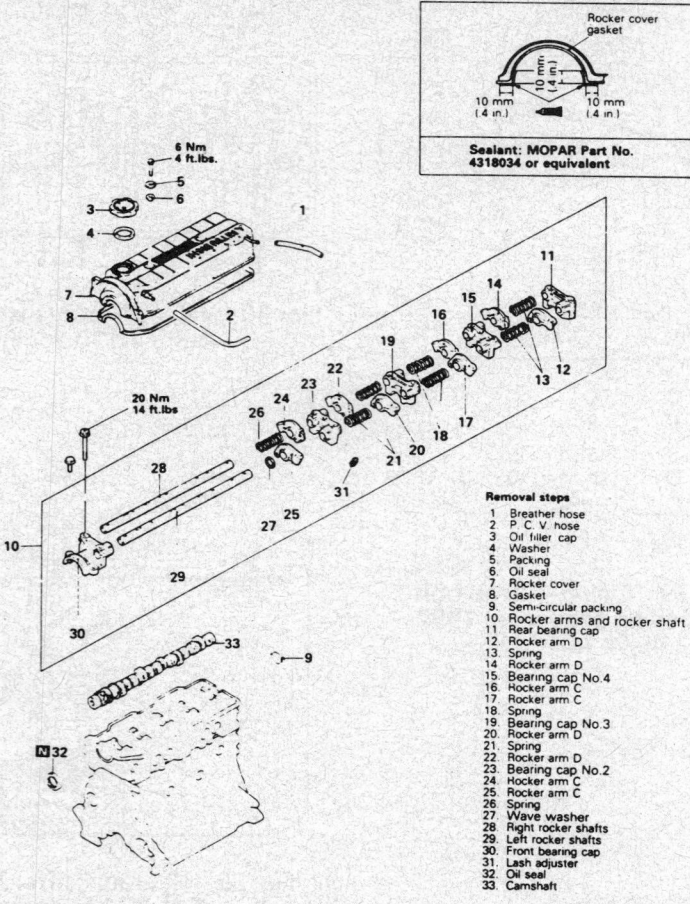

Fig. 35 Rocker arm, rocker arm shafts & camshaft replacement. 1992 2.4L/4-146 engine

Removal steps
1. Breather hose
2. P.C.V. hose
3. Oil filler cap
4. Washer
5. Packing
6. Oil seal
7. Rocker cover
8. Gasket
9. Semi-circular packing
10. Rocker arms and rocker shaft
11. Rear bearing cap
12. Rocker arm D
13. Spring
14. Rocker arm D
15. Bearing cap No.4
16. Rocker arm C
17. Rocker arm C
18. Spring
19. Bearing cap No.3
20. Rocker arm D
21. Spring
22. Rocker arm D
23. Bearing cap No.2
24. Rocker arm C
25. Rocker arm C
26. Spring
27. Wave washer
28. Right rocker shafts
29. Left rocker shafts
30. Front bearing cap
31. Lash adjuster
32. Oil seal
33. Camshaft

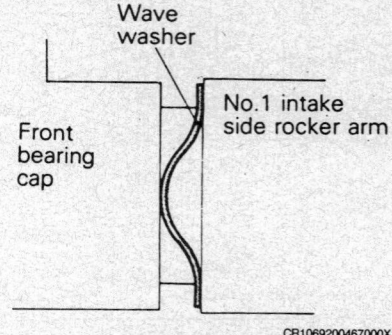

Fig. 36 Wave washer installation. 1992 2.4L/4-146 engine

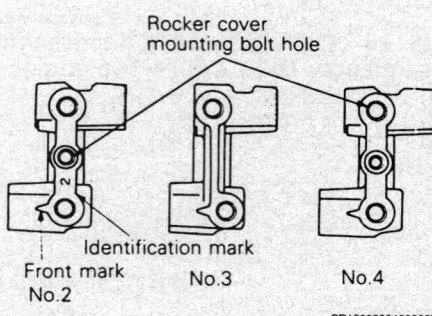

Fig. 37 Camshaft bearing cap identification. 1992 2.4L/4-146 engine

a. Initially loosen the fixing bolt of the tensioner fixed to the water pump side, use the force of the tensioner spring to apply tension to the belt.

b. Recheck to be sure that the timing marks on each sprocket are aligned.

c. Turn the crankshaft clockwise by two teeth (15°) of the camshaft sprocket.

d. Apply force on the timing belt tensioner toward the direction of the arrow so that no portion of the belt raises out in portion A, **Fig. 43**, then place the belt on the camshaft sprocket such that the belt sprocket teeth are fully engaged.

e. Tighten bolts A and B, **Fig. 43**, in that order and fix the timing belt tensioner. **If bolt B is tightened first, the timing belt tensioner will rotate with it and belt tension will be thrown out of adjustment. Always tighten the A bolt first.**

f. Check to see that clearance between the outside of the belt and the cover is within the standard value of approximately .55 inches by grasping the belt at the midpoint of its tension length.

7. Install the timing belt upper and lower covers.

SILENT SHAFT "B" BELT
Removal

1. Remove camshaft timing belt as outlined under "Camshaft Timing Belt, Replace."

2. Remove silent shaft B belt in numbered sequence shown in **Fig. 44**, noting the following:

a. Hold the crankshaft pulley by using the ribbed B belt and tool No. MD998747 or equivalent as shown in **Fig. 45. The B belt may be damaged when used to move the pulley. Do not reuse a damaged belt, install a new service replacement.**

b. Remove the crankshaft sprocket bolt.

c. Remove the crankshaft pulley and then the crankshaft sprocket.

d. Remove the B belt. If the belt is to be used again, use chalk to mark its flat side with an arrow to indicate clockwise travel.

Installation

Reverse the removal procedure to install, noting the following:

1. Ensure that crankshaft sprocket B and counterbalance shaft sprocket timing marks are aligned.

2. Fit timing belt B over crankshaft sprocket B and the counterbalance shaft sprocket. **Ensure that there is no slack in the belt.**

3. Adjust belt tension as follows:

a. Temporarily fix the B belt tensioner so that the center of the tensioner pulley is to the left and above the center of the installation bolt and that the flange is toward the front of the engine.

b. Position the tensioner so that the belt's tension side becomes taut, then tighten the bolt to fix the tensioner. **When tightening the bolt, ensure the tensioner pulley shaft does not rotate with the bolt, allowing the shaft to do so can result in an excessively taut belt. The specified tension value at the belt's tension side is .20-.28 inch.**

4. Install the flange.

5. Install the crankshaft sprocket as follows:

a. Install the sprocket, then the crankshaft pulley.

b. Using tool No. MD998747 or equivalent, hold pulley in place.

c. Tighten the crankshaft sprocket bolt to specification, then remove the crankshaft pulley.

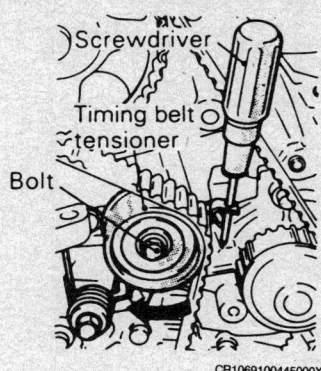

Fig. 39 Timing belt tension relief. 1.8L/4-110 engine

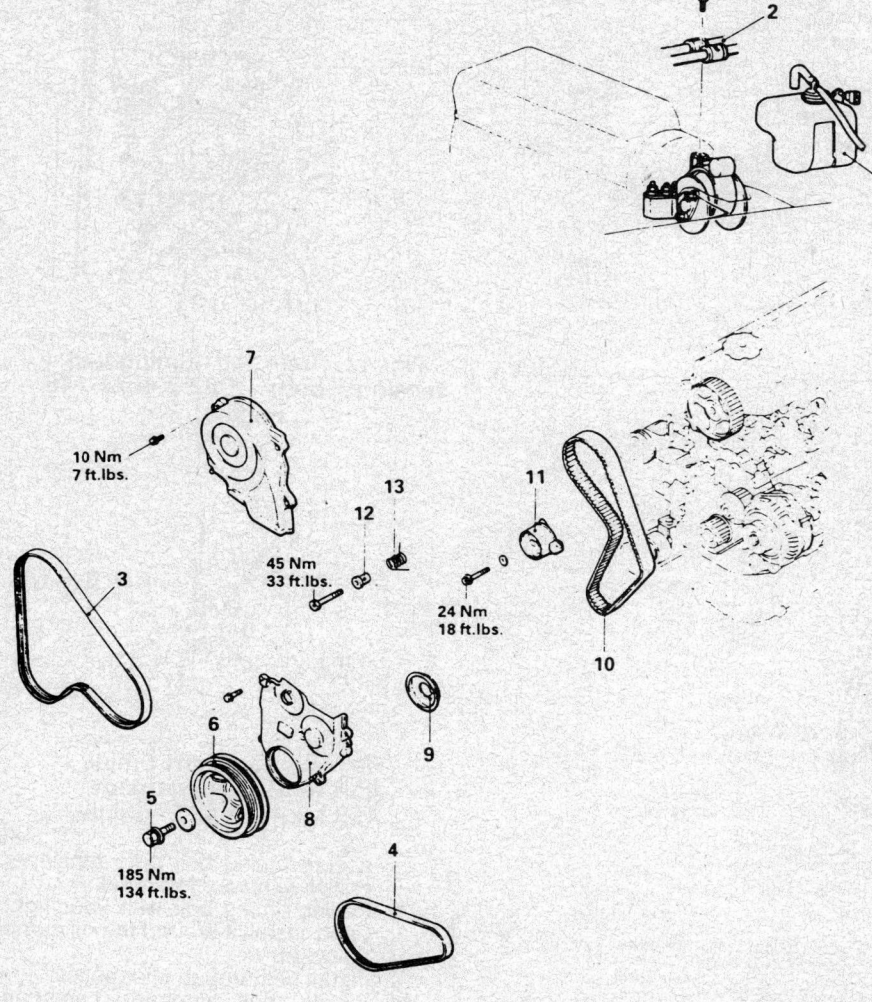

Removal steps
1. Condense tank
2. Clamp section of Air conditioner and Power steering hose
3. Drive belt (Power steering. Air conditioner)
4. Drive belt (Alternator)
5. Crankshaft bolt
6. Crankshaft pulley
7. Timing belt upper cover
8. Timing belt lower cover
9. Flange
● Adjustment of timing belt tension
10. Timing belt
11. Timing belt tensioner
12. Tensioner spacer
13. Tensioner spring

Fig. 38 Timing belt. 1.8L/4-110 engine

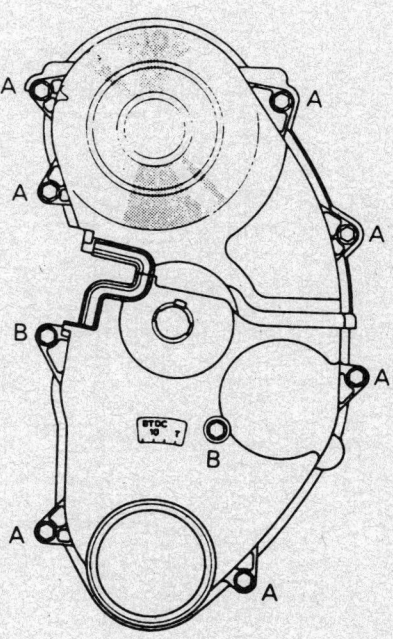

Fig. 40 Timing belt cover bolt installation. 1.8L/4-110 engine

1993—95 2.4L/4-146 ENGINE

Removal

Remove timing belt in numbered sequence shown in **Fig. 46**, noting the following:

1. Remove engine mount bracket as outlined under "Engine Mount, Replace."
2. Turn crankshaft clockwise and align timing marks to position No. 1 cylinder on its compression stroke at TDC, **Fig. 19**.
3. Remove the auto tensioner.
4. Mark belt rotating direction on belt.
5. Tie camshaft sprocket and timing belt with a cord so that the position of the camshaft sprocket will not move with respect to the timing belt.
6. Using spanner wrench tool Nos. MB990767 and MD998719 or equivalents, remove camshaft sprocket nut and sprocket.
7. Remove oil pump sprocket as follows:
   a. Remove plug on side of engine block, **Fig. 47**.
   b. Insert a Phillips screwdriver into hole to block the left silent shaft. If the screwdriver will only go in .79-.98 inch as it strikes against the counterbalance shaft, turn the sprocket once, realign the timing mark and check that the screwdriver goes in 2.36 inches or more. The screwdriver should not be taken out until the timing belt is installed.
   c. Remove oil pump sprocket nut then the sprocket.
8. Mark rotational direction on timing belt B prior to removal.

Installation

Install timing belt in numbered sequence shown in **Fig. 46**, noting the following:
1. Apply sealant to engine support bracket bolt shown in **Fig. 48**.
2. Install crankshaft sprocket B as shown in **Fig. 49**.
3. Install right silent shaft sprocket spacer with chamfered edge pointed toward the oil seal.
4. Ensure crankshaft sprocket B and the silent shaft sprocket timing marks are aligned then install timing belt B.
5. Adjust timing belt B tension as follows:

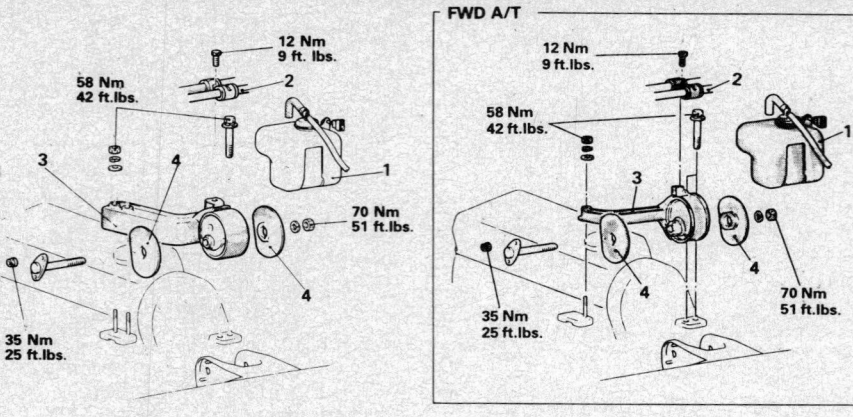

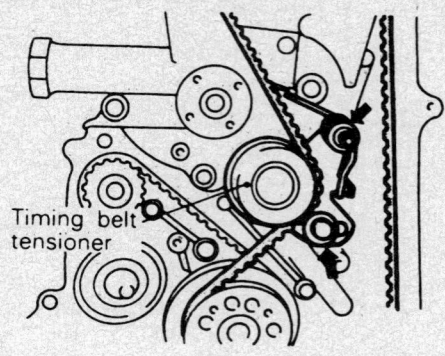

CR1069300448000X

Fig. 42 Camshaft timing belt tensioner bolts. 1992 2.4L/4-146 engine

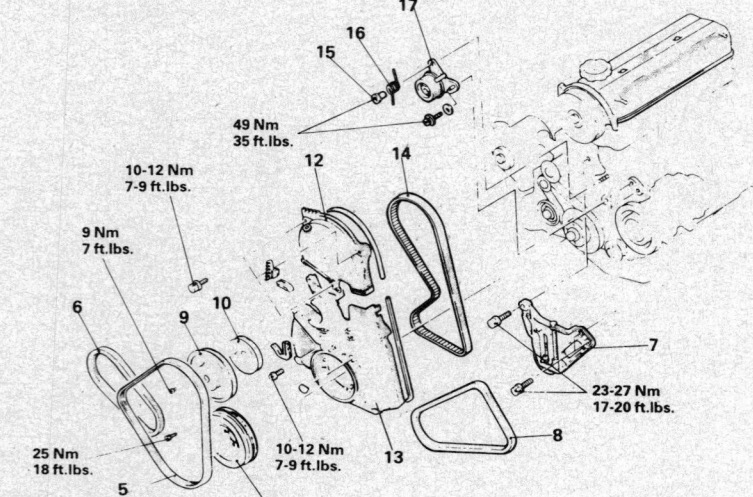

CR1069300447000X

Fig. 41 Camshaft timing belt. 1992 2.4L/4-146 engine

Removal steps

1. Condense tank
2. Power steering hose and air conditioner hose clamp part
3. Engine mount bracket
4. Engine mount stopper
5. Drive belt (Alternator)
6. Drive belt (Power steering oil pump)
7. Tension pulley bracket
8. Drive belt (Air conditioner compressor)
9. Water pump pulley
10. Water pump pulley for power steering
11. Crankshaft pulley
12. Timing belt front upper cover
13. Timing belt front lower cover
 • Adjustment of timing belt tension
14. Timing belt
15. Tension spacer
16. Tension spring
17. Timing belt tensioner

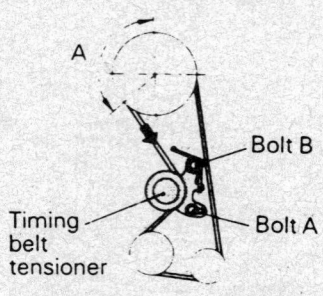

CR1069300449000X

Fig. 43 Camshaft timing belt tension adjustment. 1992 2.4L/4-146 engine

a. Temporarily install timing belt B tensioner to that center of tensioner is to the left and above the installation bolt.
b. Place tension on timing belt B so tension side of belt is tight then tighten tensioner bolt.
c. At the point marked "A" and ensure belt is within .20-.28 inch when depressed for correct tension, **Fig. 50.**
6. Install crankshaft flange and pulley as shown in **Fig. 51.**
7. Install auto tensioner as follows:
 a. Keeping auto tensioner level clamp it in a soft jawed vise. **If plug at bottom of tensioner protrudes, surround it with a washer to prevent the plug from being in direct contact with the vise.**
 b. Push in the rod slowly with vise until set holes are aligned, **Fig. 52.**
 c. Insert a wire .055 inch in diameter into set holes and release tensioner from vise.
 d. Install tensioner, keeping wire installed in set holes.
8. Install tensioner pulley onto tensioner arm. Position the pinhole in tensioner pulley shaft to the left of the center bolt, then tighten center bolt finger tight.
9. Ensure timing marks are aligned and remove plug on side of engine block, **Fig. 47.** Insert a Phillips screwdriver into hole to block the left silent shaft.
10. If screwdriver cannot be inserted 2.4 inch or more turn the oil pump sprocket one turn and realign timing marks. Ensure screwdriver can be inserted 2.4 inches or more. **Screwdriver should not be removed until installation of the timing belt is complete.**
11. Install timing belt as follows:
 a. Install timing belt around tensioner pulley and crankshaft sprocket and

secure timing belt onto tensioner pulley with your left hand.
 b. Pulling timing belt with your right hand, install it around the oil pump sprocket.
 c. Install belt around idler pulley.
 d. Install belt around camshaft sprocket.
 e. Gently raise tensioner pulley so that belt does not sag then temporarily tighten center bolt, **Fig. 53.**
12. Adjust timing belt tension as follows:
 a. Remove screwdriver and install plug in side of cylinder block.
 b. Turn crankshaft 90° (¼ turn) counterclockwise.
 c. Turn crankshaft back to position No. 1 cylinder at TDC.
 d. Loosen tensioner pulley center bolt, then attach socket wrench tool No. MD998752 or equivalent and a torque wrench and apply a **torque** of 1.88-2.03 ft. lbs., **Fig. 54.**
 e. Holding tensioner pulley with special tool, tighten center bolt to specification.
 f. Install setscrew tool No. MD998738 or equivalent into engine left support bracket until its end makes contact with tensioner arm, **Fig. 55.**
 g. Turn setscrew tool to increase the pressure on the tensioner arm then remove wire from tensioner set holes.
 h. Rotate crankshaft two complete turns clockwise and allow to sit for 15 minutes.

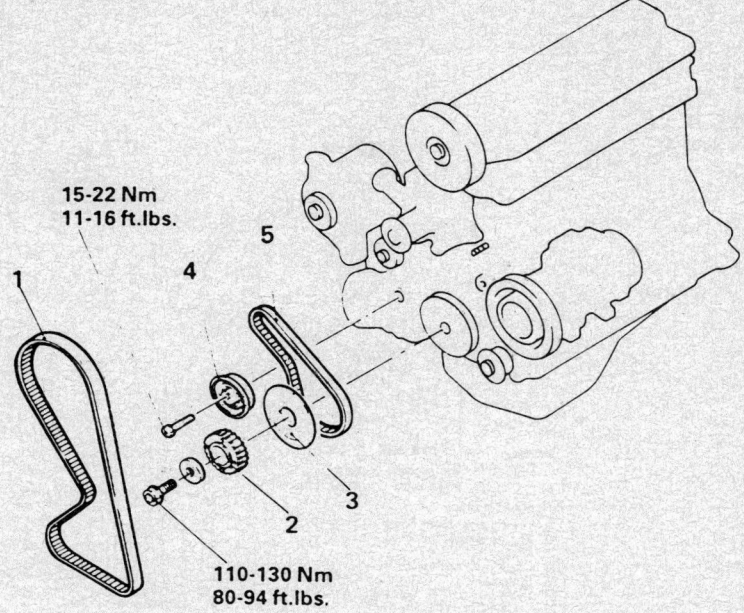

15-22 Nm
11-16 ft.lbs.

110-130 Nm
80-94 ft.lbs.

Removal steps

1. Timing belt
2. Crankshaft sprocket
3. Flange
4. Timing belt B tensioner
5. Timing belt B

Fig. 44 Silent shaft timing belt. 1992 2.4L/4-146 engine

i. After 15 minutes, measure auto tensioner rod protrusion, and verify that it is within the .15-.18 inch specification. If not as specified, repeat steps a through h.
j. Install rubber plug to the timing belt rear cover.

13. Install timing belt cover screws into proper location as shown in **Fig. 56.**

SILENT SHAFT
REPLACE

Refer to "Oil Pan , Replace" for procedure.

CRANKSHAFT REAR OIL SEAL
REPLACE

1. Remove transaxle as outlined under "Clutch & Manual Transaxle" section or in the "Automatic Transaxle" unit repair section.
2. Remove the flywheel or driveplate.
3. Remove rear plate and bellhousing cover.
4. Remove crankshaft rear main oil seal and retainer.
5. Remove oil seal from retainer.
6. Reverse procedure to install, apply sealant to shaded area shown in **Fig. 57,** prior to installation.

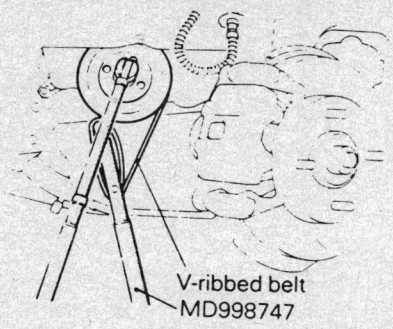

V-ribbed belt
MD998747

Fig. 45 Crankshaft pulley holder

OIL PAN
REPLACE
1.8L/4-110 ENGINE

Replace the oil pan & oil pump in numbered sequence shown in **Fig. 58,** noting the following:

1. To remove the oil pan, knock tool No. MD998727 or equivalent between oil pan and engine block. Dislodge the pan from the block by moving the tool along the pan lip.
2. Make alignment marks on the inner and outer rotors for assembling.

2.4L/4-146 ENGINE

Replace the oil pan, oil pump and silent shafts in numbered sequence shown in **Fig. 59,** noting the following:

1. **On AWD models,** oil pan removal requires that the transfer assembly first be removed as outlined under "Clutch & Manual Transaxle."
2. **On all models,** use a brass bar and tool No. MD998727 or equivalent to knock the oil pan loose from the block after removing the retaining bolts and nuts. Perform this operation with care so that the pan flange is not damaged.
3. Use special tool No. MD998162 or equivalent to remove the front case plug cap.

4. Remove the pump driven gear bolt by first removing the plug on the side of the cylinder block, and then inserting a Phillips screwdriver into the plug hold to block the silent shaft, **Fig. 47.**
5. Use tool No. MD998371 or equivalent to remove the silent shaft front bearing from the cylinder block, tool No. MD998372 or equivalent to remove the right silent shaft rear bearing and tool Nos. MD998372 and MD998374 or equivalents to remove the left shaft rear bearing.
6. Reverse procedure to install, noting the following:
   a. Use bearing installation tool Nos. MD998374 and MD998373 or equivalents when installing silent shaft bearings.
   b. Coat oil pump drive and driven gears with oil then install, aligning timing marks, **Fig. 60.**
   c. Install oil seals using seal installation tool No. C-3095-A or equivalent.
   d. Install front oil seal installer tool No. MD998285 or equivalent on crankshaft and apply oil to tool.
   e. Install front case assembly through new front case gasket and temporarily tighten flange bolts, **Fig. 61. Do not tighten filter bracket bolts.**
   f. Mount oil filter bracket and gasket on front case and install bolts.
   g. Tighten front case and oil filter bracket bolts to specifications, **Fig. 61.**
   h. Secure oil pump driven gear onto the left silent shaft.
   i. Install new O-ring and cap plug using socket tool No. MD998162 or equivalent.
   j. Apply a .16 inch bead of sealant to the oil pan flange as shown in **Fig. 62.**
   k. Note difference in length of oil pan bolt when installing oil pan, **Fig. 63.**

OIL PUMP
REPLACE

Refer to "Oil Pan, Replace" for procedure.

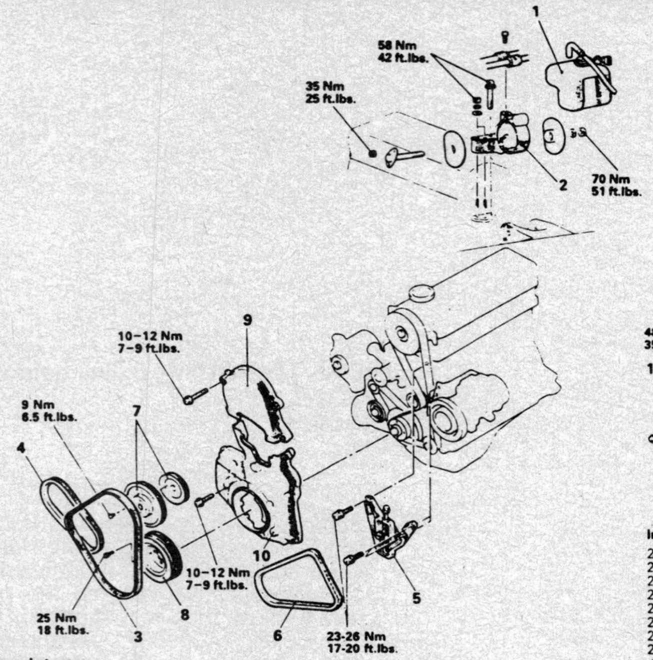

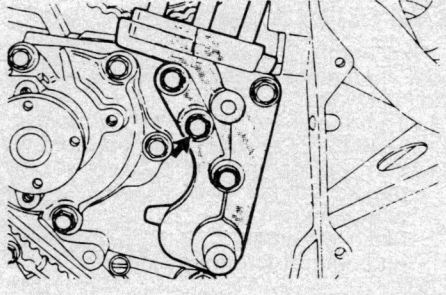

Removal steps

1. Condense tank
2. Engine mount bracket
3. Drive belt (generator)
4. Drive belt (power steering)
5. Tensioner pulley bracket
6. Drive belt (air conditioning)
7. Water pump pulley
8. Crankshaft pulley
9. Timing belt front upper cover
10. Timing belt front lower cover
11. Auto tensioner
12. Timing belt
13. Tensioner pulley
14. Tensioner arm
15. Idle pulley
16. Camshaft sprocket
17. Oil pump sprocket
18. Crankshaft sprocket bolt
19. Special washer
20. Crankshaft sprocket
21. Flange
22. Timing belt tensioner "B"
23. Timgin belt "B"
24. Right silent shaft sprocket
25. Spacer
26. Crankshaft sprocket "B"
27. Key
28. Engine support bracket
29. Timing belt under cover

CR1069300452010X

Fig. 46 Timing belt replacement (Part 1 of 2). 1993–95 2.4L/4-146 engine

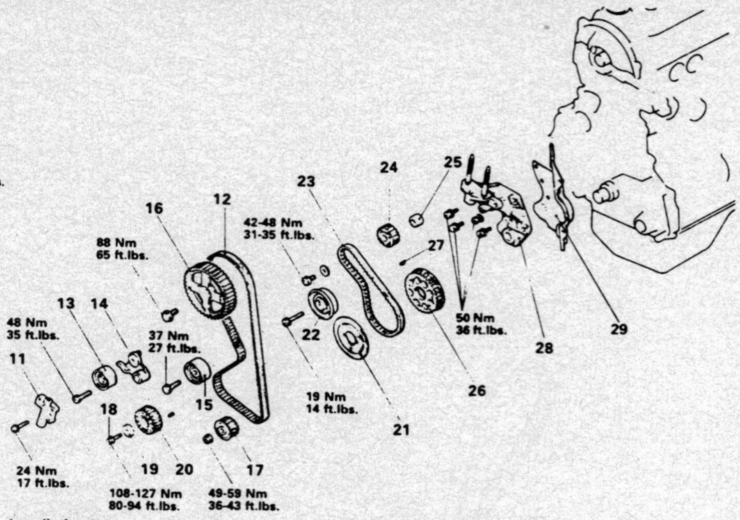

Installation steps

29. Timing belt under cover
28. Engine support bracket
27. Key
26. Crankshaft sprocket "B"
25. Spacer
24. Right silent shaft sprocket
22. Timing belt tensioner "B"
23. Timing belt "B"
- Adjustment of timing belt "B" tension
21. Flange
20. Crankshaft sprocket
19. Special washer
18. Crankshaft sprocket bolt
17. Oil pump sprocket
16. Camshaft sprocket
15. Idle pulley
11. Auto tensioner
14. Tensioner arm
13. Tensioner pulley
12. Timing belt
- Adjustment of timing belt tension
10. Timing belt front lower cover
9. Timing belt front upper cover
8. Crankshaft pulley
7. Water pump pulley
6. Drive belt (air conditioning)
5. Tensioner pulley bracket
4. Drive belt (power steering)
3. Drive belt (generator)
- Adjustment of drive belt tension

2. Engine mount bracket
1. Condense tank

CR1069300452020X

Fig. 46 Timing belt replacement (Part 2 of 2). 1993–95 2.4L/4-146 engine

CR1069300453000X

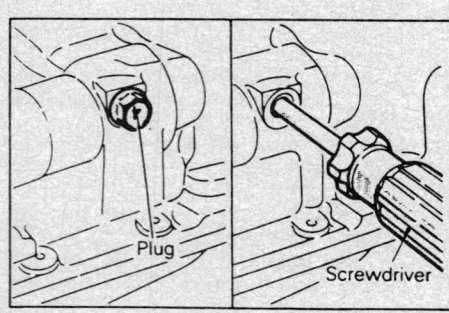

Fig. 47 Silent shaft lock. 1993–95 2.4L/4-146 engine

CR1069300454000X

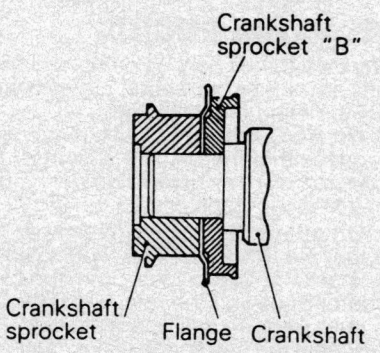

Fig. 48 Support bracket bolt. 1993–95 2.4L/4-146 engine

CR1069300455000X

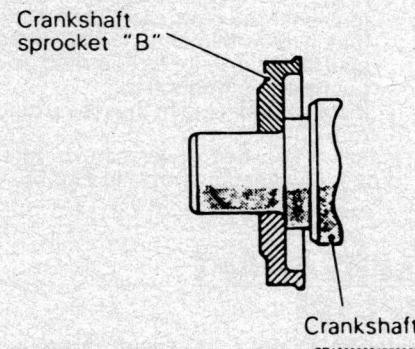

Fig. 49 Crankshaft sprocket B installation. 1993–95 2.4L/4-146 engine

CR1069300456000X

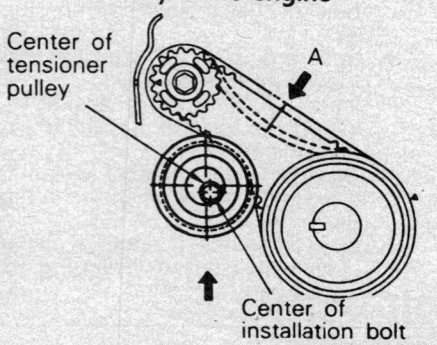

Fig. 50 Timing belt B tension inspection. 1993–95 2.4L/4-146 engine

CR1069300457000X

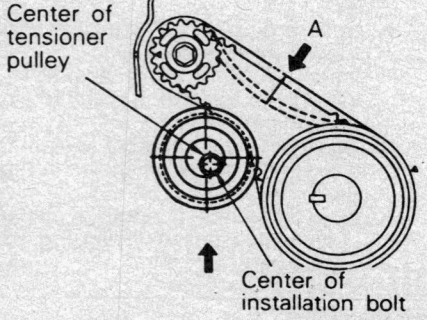

Fig. 51 Crankshaft flange & sprocket installation. 1993–95 2.4L/4-146 engine

CR1069300458000X

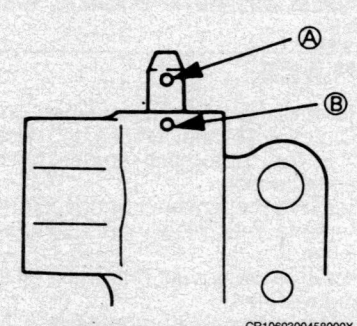

Fig. 52 Tensioner set hole alignment. 1993–95 2.4L/4-146 engine

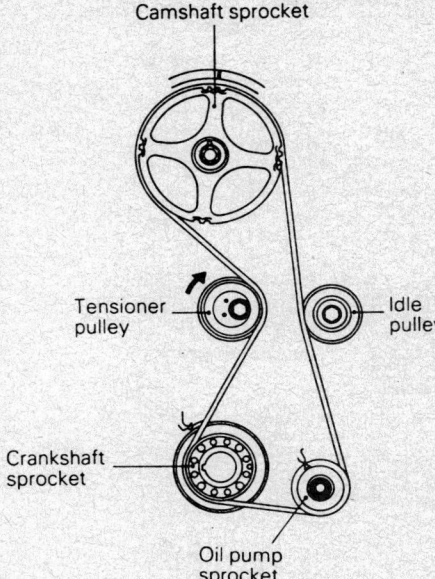

Fig. 53 Timing belt tension pulley position. 1993–95 2.4L/4-146 engine

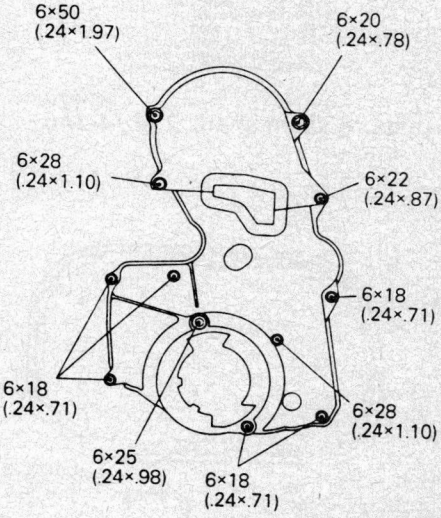

Fig. 56 Timing belt cover installation. 1993–95 2.4L/4-146 engine

BELT TENSION DATA

Component	Deflection, Inch①	Tension, lbs.
1.8L/4-110 Engine		
Alternator	.280–.340	—
Power Steering ②	.295–.354	143–187
Power Steering ③	.217–.236	165–176
A/C Compressor	.217–.236	165–176

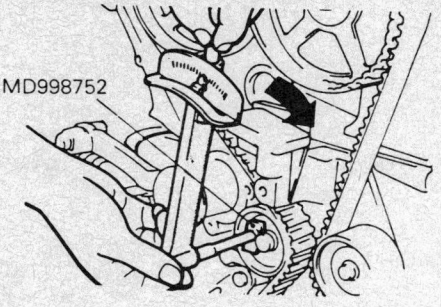

Fig. 54 Timing belt tension adjustment. 1993–95 2.4L/4-146 engine

Component	Deflection, Inch①	Tension, lbs.
2.4L/4-146 Engine		
Alternator	.300–.350	—
Power Steering	.180–.260	—
A/C Compressor	.170–.190	121–143

①—Applying a force of 22 lbs. at a center point between the longest distance between pulleys.
②—Models with A/C.
③—Models less A/C.

COOLING SYSTEM BLEED

1.8L/4-110 ENGINE

1. Drain coolant from engine.
2. Remove air bleed screw from top of thermostat housing, **Fig. 64.**
3. With all drain plugs installed, pour coolant into air bleed screw hole until coolant flows out.
4. Install air bleed screw.
5. Slowly pour coolant into radiator until full. Also fill reservoir tank to the FULL mark.
6. Install radiator cap and start engine.
7. Run engine until it reaches operating temperature.
8. After thermostat opens, race engine three times then stop engine.
9. After engine has cooled, check coolant level.
10. If coolant level has dropped, fill to full level and repeat steps 6 through 9.
11. When coolant level stops dropping, add coolant to condense tank.

2.4L/4-146 ENGINE

1. Drain coolant from engine.
2. Slowly pour coolant into radiator until full. Also fill reservoir tank to the FULL mark.
3. Install radiator cap and start engine.
4. Run engine until it reaches operating temperature.
5. After thermostat opens, race engine three times then stop engine.
6. After engine has cooled, check coolant level.
7. If coolant level has dropped, fill to full level and repeat steps 4 through 6.
8. When coolant level stops dropping, add coolant to condense tank.

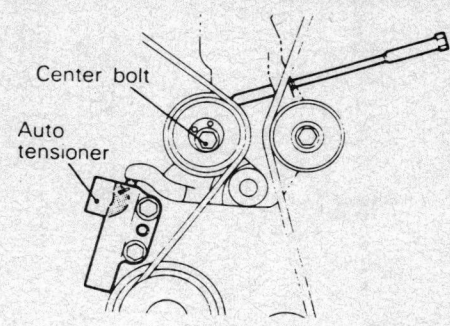

Fig. 55 Setscrew tool installation

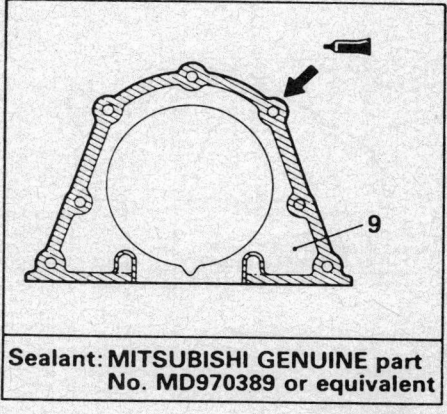

Sealant: MITSUBISHI GENUINE part No. MD970389 or equivalent

Fig. 57 Rear main oil seal retainer sealant location

THERMOSTAT
REPLACE

1. Drain engine coolant into a suitable container.
2. Disconnect upper radiator hose.
3. Remove water outlet fitting and the thermostat, **Fig. 65.**
4. Reverse procedure to install, ensuring jiggle valve on thermostat is aligned with mark on thermostat housing, **Fig. 66.**

WATER PUMP
REPLACE

1. Drain cooling system into a suitable container.
2. Remove timing belt as outlined under "Timing Belt, Replace."
3. **On 1.8L/4-110 engine,** remove timing belt rear cover then the water pump, **Fig. 67.**
4. **On 2.4L/4-146 engine,** remove alternator brace, water pump, gasket and O-ring, **Fig. 68.**
5. **On all engines,** reverse procedure to install, installing water pump bolts in locations shown in **Figs. 69 and 70.**

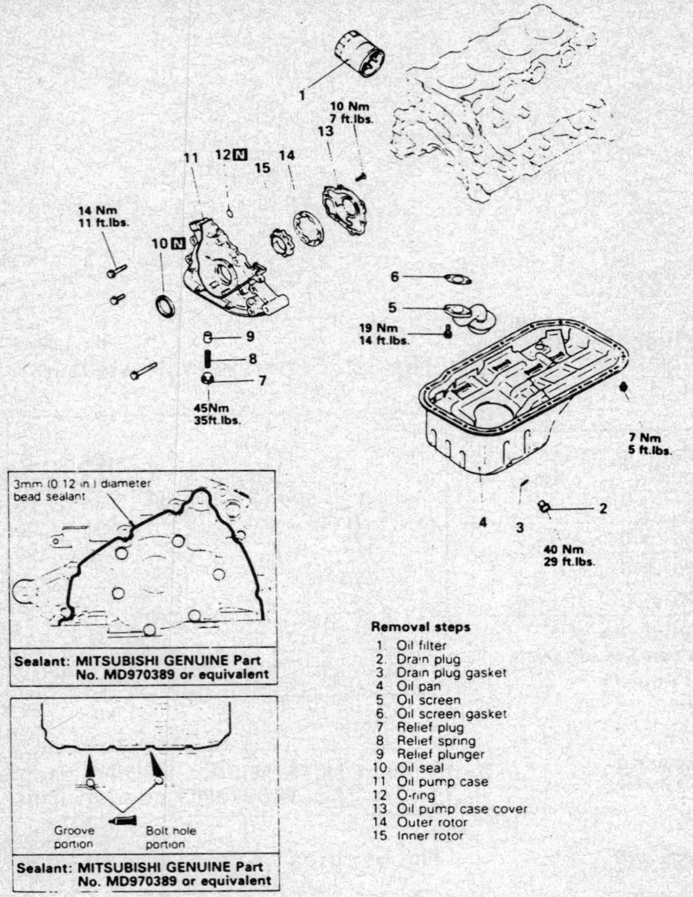

14 Nm
11 ft.lbs.

10 Nm
7 ft.lbs.

45 Nm
35 ft.lbs.

19 Nm
14 ft.lbs.

7 Nm
5 ft.lbs.

40 Nm
29 ft.lbs.

3mm (0.12 in.) diameter
bead sealant

Sealant: MITSUBISHI GENUINE Part
No. MD970389 or equivalent

Groove   Bolt hole
portion   portion

Sealant: MITSUBISHI GENUINE Part
No. MD970389 or equivalent

CR1099100062000X

Removal steps
1. Oil filter
2. Drain plug
3. Drain plug gasket
4. Oil pan
5. Oil screen
6. Oil screen gasket
7. Relief plug
8. Relief spring
9. Relief plunger
10. Oil seal
11. Oil pump case
12. O-ring
13. Oil pump case cover
14. Outer rotor
15. Inner rotor

Fig. 58 Oil pan and screen. 1.8L/4-110 engine

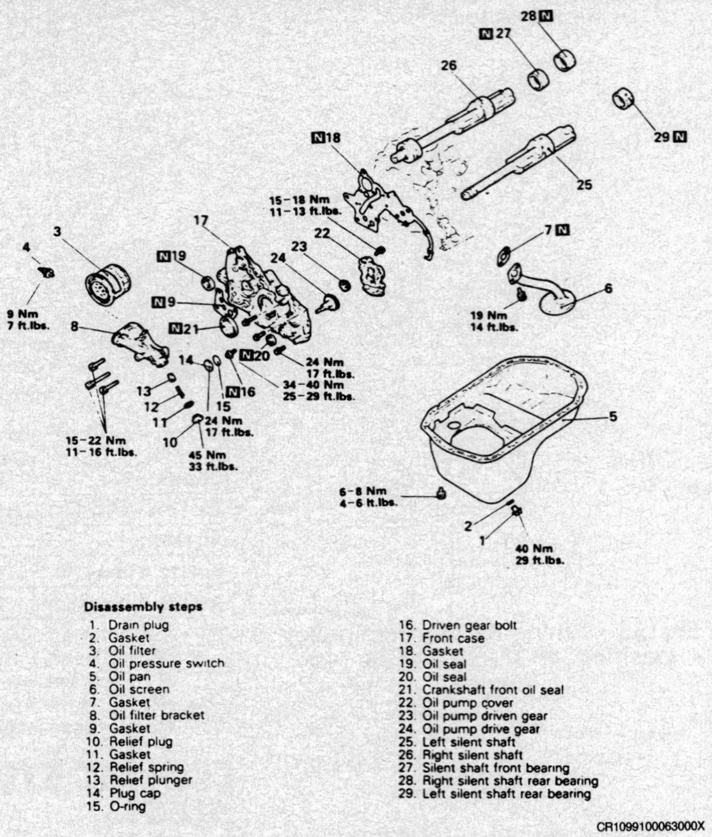

15-18 Nm
11-13 ft.lbs.

9 Nm
7 ft.lbs.

15-22 Nm
11-16 ft.lbs.

24 Nm
17 ft.lbs.

24 Nm
17 ft.lbs.

34-40 Nm
25-29 ft.lbs.

45 Nm
33 ft.lbs.

19 Nm
14 ft.lbs.

6-8 Nm
4-6 ft.lbs.

40 Nm
29 ft.lbs.

Disassembly steps
1. Drain plug
2. Gasket
3. Oil filter
4. Oil pressure switch
5. Oil pan
6. Oil screen
7. Gasket
8. Oil filter bracket
9. Gasket
10. Relief plug
11. Gasket
12. Relief spring
13. Relief plunger
14. Plug cap
15. O-ring
16. Driven gear bolt
17. Front case
18. Gasket
19. Oil seal
20. Oil seal
21. Crankshaft front oil seal
22. Oil pump cover
23. Oil pump driven gear
24. Oil pump drive gear
25. Left silent shaft
26. Right silent shaft
27. Silent shaft front bearing
28. Right silent shaft rear bearing
29. Left silent shaft rear bearing

CR1099100063000X

Fig. 59 Oil pan, oil pump & silent shaft. 2.4L/4-146 engine

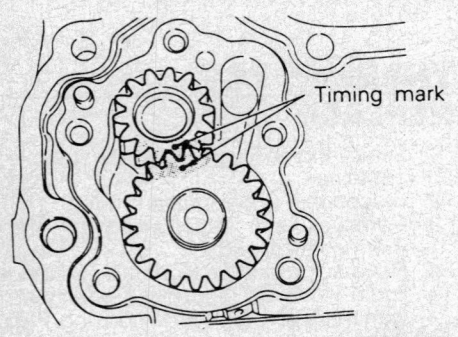

Timing mark

CR1099100064000X

Fig. 60 Oil pump drive gears alignment. 2.4L/4-146 engine

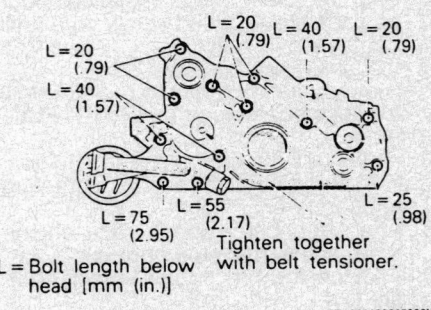

L = 20 (.79)
L = 40 (1.57)
L = 20 (.79)
L = 20 (.79)
L = 40 (1.57)
L = 75 (2.95)
L = 55 (2.17)
L = 25 (.98)

Tighten together with belt tensioner.

L = Bolt length below head [mm (in.)]

CR1099100065000X

Fig. 61 Front case assembly bolt locations. 2.4L/4-146 engine

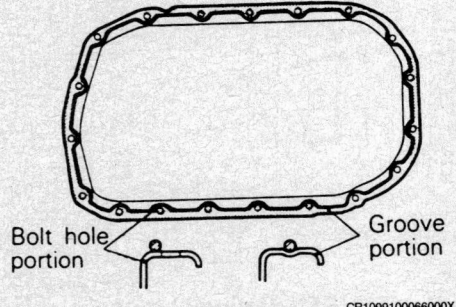

Bolt hole portion

Groove portion

CR1099100066000X

Fig. 62 Oil pan sealant locations. 2.4L/4-146 engine

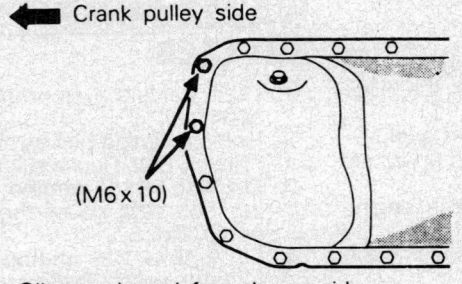

Crank pulley side

(M6 x 10)

Oil pan viewed from lower side

CR1099100067000X

Fig. 63 Oil pan bolt length. 2.4L/4-146 engine

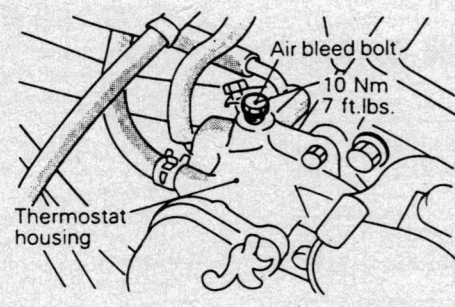

Air bleed bolt

10 Nm
7 ft.lbs.

Thermostat housing

CR1089100114000X

Fig. 64 Cooling system bleed screw location. 1.8L/4-110 engine

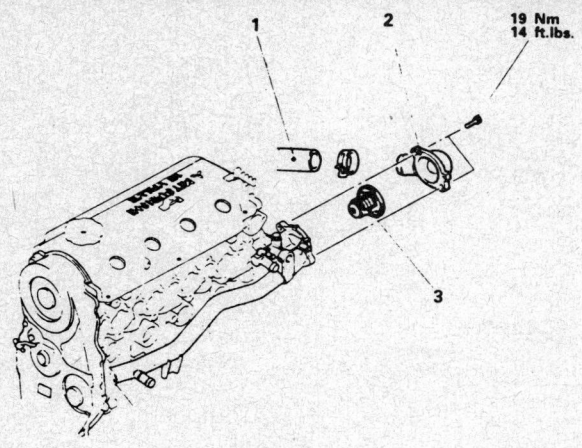

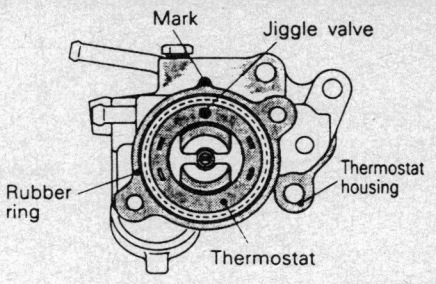

Fig. 66   Thermostat installation

Removal steps
1. Connection for radiator upper hose
2. Water outlet fitting
3. Thermostat

Fig. 65   Thermostat replacement

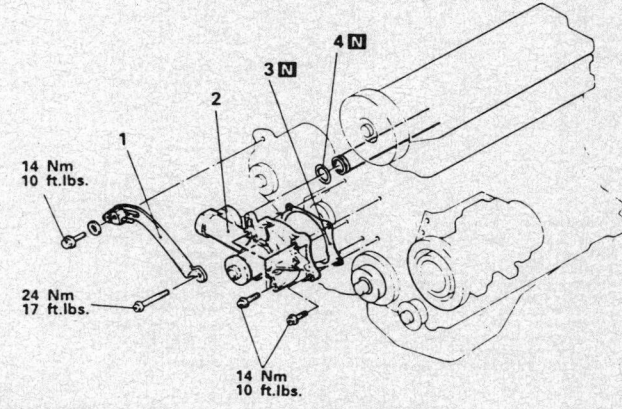

Removal steps
1. Alternator brace
2. Water pump
3. Water pump gasket
4. O-ring

Fig. 68   Water pump replacement. 2.4L/4-146 engine

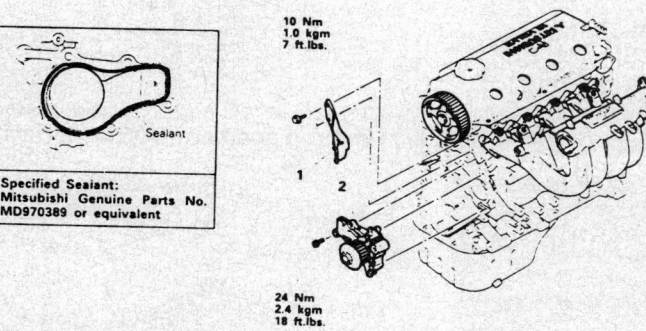

Specified Sealant:
Mitsubishi Genuine Parts No.
MD970389 or equivalent

Removal steps
1. Timing belt rear cover
2. Water pump

Fig. 67   Water pump replacement. 1.8L/4-110 engine

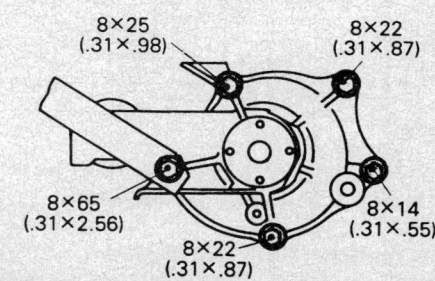

8×25 (.31×.98)
8×22 (.31×.87)
8×65 (.31×2.56)
8×22 (.31×.87)
8×14 (.31×.55)

Screw diameter × length: mm (in.)

Fig. 70   Water pump bolt locations. 2.4L/4-146 engine

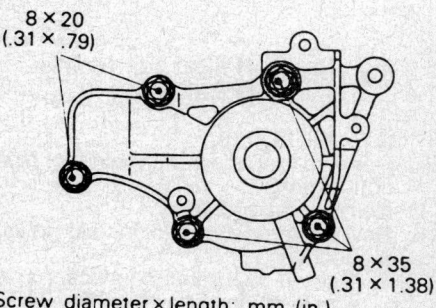

8×20 (.31×.79)

8×35 (.31×1.38)

Screw diameter × length: mm (in.)

Fig. 69   Water pump bolt locations. 1.8L/4-110 engine

RADIATOR
REPLACE

COLT VISTA & SUMMIT WAGON

1. Disconnect battery ground cable, then remove radiator cap.
2. Place a suitable container below radi-ator drain plug, then remove plug and allow coolant to drain from radiator.
3. Remove radiator overflow tube and tank, then the upper and lower radia-tor hoses.
4. **On models with automatic transax-le,** disconnect transaxle oil cooler hoses at radiator and plug ends to prevent entry of foreign matter.
5. **On all models,** disconnect thermo sensor and radiator fan motor con-nectors.
6. **On models with A/C,** disconnect condenser fan motor connector.
7. **On all models,** remove radiator up-per insulators, then lift radiator assem-bly from vehicle.
8. Reverse procedure to install. Refill en-gine coolant when installation is com-plete.

COLT & SUMMIT
1992

Refer to "Colt Vista & Summit Wagon" in this section for radiator replacement pro-cedure.

1993-95

1. Disconnect battery ground cable, then remove radiator overflow hose and reserve tank.
2. Place a suitable container below radi-ator drain plug, then remove plug and allow coolant to drain from radiator.
3. Remove coolant drain hose and up-per and lower radiator hoses, then dis-connect radiator fan motor connector.
4. **On models with automatic transax-le,** disconnect transaxle oil cooler lines at radiator and plug ends to pre-vent entry of foreign matter.
5. **On all models,** remove upper insula-tors and lift radiator and fan motor

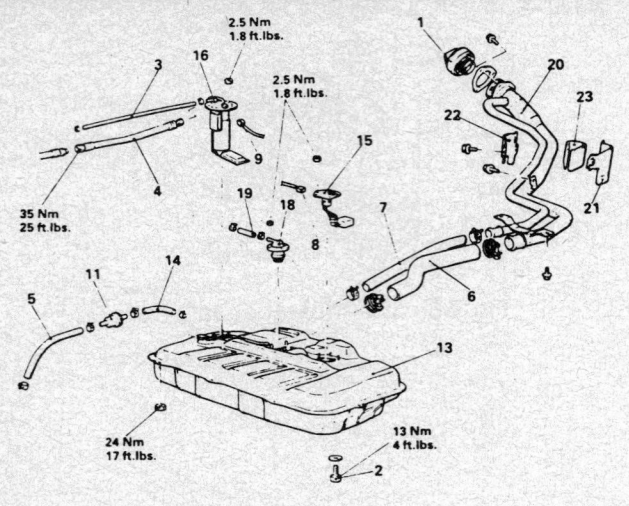

Removal steps

1. Fuel tank filler tube cap
2. Drain plug
3. Return hose
4. Fuel high-pressure hose
5. Vapor hose
6. Filler hose
7. Vapor hose
8. Fuel gauge unit connector
9. Fuel pump connector
11. Fuel tank pressure control valve

13. Fuel tank
14. Vapor hose
15. Fuel gauge unit
16. Fuel pump
18. Fuel cut off valve
19. Vapor hose
20. Fuel tank filler tube
21. Protector (A)
22. Protector (B)
23. Insulator

CR1029102525000X

Fig. 71   Fuel tank & pump replacement. FWD models

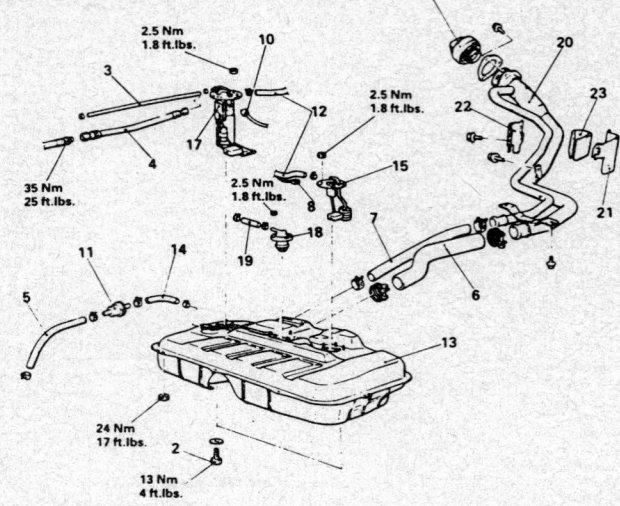

Removal steps

1. Fuel tank filler tube cap
2. Drain plug
3. Return hose
4. Fuel high-pressure hose
5. Vapor hose
6. Filler hose
7. Vapor hose
8. Fuel gauge unit connector
10. Fuel gauge and pump assembly connector
11. Fuel tank pressure control valve
12. Suction hose

13. Fuel tank
14. Vapor hose
15. Fuel gauge unit
17. Fuel gauge and pump assembly
18. Fuel cut off valve
19. Vapor hose
20. Fuel tank filler tube
21. Protector (A)
22. Protector (B)
23. Insulator

CR1029102526000X

Fig. 72   Fuel tank & pump replacement. AWD models

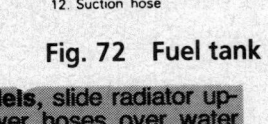

CR1029102527000X

Fig. 73   Fuel filter location

from vehicle as an assembly.
6. If necessary, disconnect engine coolant temperature switch connector and remove fan motor assembly from radiator.
7. Reverse procedure to install, noting the following:
   a. **On models with automatic transaxle**, connect transaxle oil cooler lines so that flexible hoses overlap 1 inch onto radiator fittings. Ensure hose clamps do not pinch fitting end bulges.

b. **On all models,** slide radiator upper and lower hoses over water outlet and inlet fittings as far as small protrusions on each fitting will allow.
c. Refill engine coolant when installation is complete.

FUEL PUMP
REPLACE

1. Release fuel system pressure as outlined under "Precautions."
2. Drain fuel tank into a suitable container.
3. **On AWD models,** disconnect propeller shaft and support out of the way.
4. Replace fuel tank and fuel pump in numbered sequence shown in **Figs. 71 and 72.**

FUEL FILTER
REPLACE

1. Release fuel system pressure as outlined under "Precautions."
2. Remove air cleaner and intake hose.
3. Hold fuel filter and loosen eye bolt and

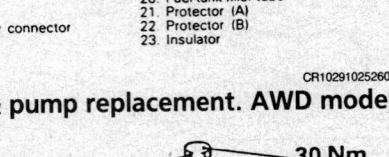

CR1029102528000X

Fig. 74   Fuel filter tightening specifications

flare nut, **Fig. 73.**
4. Remove fuel hose and main fuel pipe connections.
5. Remove the fuel filter.
6. Reverse procedure to install, noting the following:
   a. Tighten fuel filter connections to specifications shown in **Fig. 74.**
   b. Apply voltage to fuel pump and check system for leaks.

TIGHTENING SPECIFICATIONS
1.8L/4-110 ENGINE

Year	Component	Torque/Ft. Lbs.
1992-95	Bellhousing Cover To Engine Bolts	7
	Bellhousing Cover To Transaxle Bolts	③
	Camshaft Sprocket Bolt	65
	Connecting Rod Cap Nuts	15
	Crankshaft Pulley Center Bolt	134
	Cylinder Head Bolts	①
	Distributor Hold-Down Bolt	7-9
	EGR Valve Bolts	16
	Engine Hanger Bracket Bolts	9
	Engine Rear Plate Bolts	8
	Exhaust Manifold Nuts & Bolts	22
	Exhaust Pipe Support Bracket Bolts	26
	Exhaust Pipe To Manifold Bolts	33
	Flywheel Bolts	72
	High Pressure Fuel Hose Connection	42-48 ②
	Intake Manifold Nuts & Bolts	15
	Intake Manifold Stay Bolts	22
	Main Bearing Cap Bolts	14
	Oil Pan Bolts	5
	Oil Pan Drain Plug	29
	Oil Pressure Switch	7
	Oil Pump Case	11

Year	Component	Torque/Ft. Lbs.
	Oil Pump Case Cover	7
	Oil Pump Relief Valve Plug	35
	Oil Screen	14
	Rear Oil Seal Case Bolts	8
	Rocker Arm Adjustment Screw Locknut	7
	Rocker Arm Cover Bolts	24-36 ②
	Rocker Arm Shaft Bolts	23
	Thermostat Case To Block Bolts	16-18
	Throttle Body Bolts	14
	Timing Belt Cover, Upper & Lower	7
	Timing Belt Tensioner Center Bolt	18
	Timing Belt Tensioner Pivot Bolt	33
	Water Inlet Fitting Bolts	10
	Water Pump Pulley Bolts	7
	Water Pump To Engine	18

①—Refer to text.
②—Inch lbs.
③—Manual transaxle, 9-11 ft. lbs.;
automatic transaxle, 7-9 ft. lbs.

2.4L/4-146 ENGINE

Year	Component	Torque/Ft. Lbs.
1992-95	Bellhousing Cover To Engine Bolts	7
	Bellhousing Cover To Transaxle Bolts	③
	Camshaft Sprocket Bolt	65
	Connecting Rod Cap Nuts	15
	Crankshaft Pulley Bolts	18
	Crankshaft Timing Belt Sprocket Bolt	80-94
	Cylinder Head Bolts	①
	Distributor Hold-Down Bolt	7-9
	EGR Valve Bolts	16
	Engine Rear Plate Bolts	8
	Engine Support Bracket Bolts	36
	Exhaust Manifold Nuts & Bolts	22
	Exhaust Pipe Support Bracket Bolts	26
	Exhaust Pipe To Manifold Bolts	33
	Front Case Bolts	17
	Flywheel Bolts	72
	High Pressure Fuel Hose Connection	42-48 ②
	Intake Manifold Nuts & Bolts	15
	Intake Manifold Stay Bolts	16
	Main Bearing Cap Bolts	14
	Oil Pan Bolts	5
	Oil Pan Drain Plug	29
	Oil Pressure Switch	7
	Oil Pump Case	11
	Oil Pump Case Cover	7

Year	Component	Torque/Ft. Lbs.
	Oil Pump Relief Valve Plug	35
	Oil Pump Timing Belt Sprocket	36-43
	Oil Screen	14
	Rear Oil Seal Case Bolts	8
	Right Silent Shaft Timing Belt Sprocket	31-35
	Rocker Arm Adjustment Screw Locknut	7
	Rocker Arm Cover Bolts	24-36 ②
	Rocker Arm Shaft Bolts	23
	Thermostat Case To Block Bolts	16-18
	Throttle Body Bolts	14
	Timing Belt Auto Tensioner Bolt	17
	Timing Belt Cover, Upper & Lower	7-9
	Timing Belt Idler Pulley Bolt	27
	Timing Belt Tensioner "B" Bolt	14
	Timing Belt Tensioner Pulley Bracket	17-20
	Timing Belt Tensioner Pulley Pivot Bolt	35
	Water Inlet Fitting Bolts	17
	Water Pump Pulley Bolts	7
	Water Pump To Engine	18

①—Refer to text.
②—Inch lbs.
③—Manual transaxle, 9-11 ft. lbs.;
automatic transaxle, 7-9 ft. lbs.

INDEX

Year	Model	Pedal Height (A) Inch	Freeplay (B) Inch	Release Point (C) Inch ①
1992	Colt & Summit ②	6.61–6.73	.24–.51	2.8
	Colt & Summit ③	6.61–6.73	.80–1.18	3.2
	Colt Vista & Summit Wagon	7.68–7.87	.04–.12	1.77
1993–95	Colt & Summit ②	6.61–6.73	.24–.51	2.8
	Colt & Summit ③	6.61–6.73	.80–1.18	3.2
	Colt Vista & Summit Wagon	7.68–7.87	.04–.12	1.77

① —Minimum.
② —Hydraulic release.
③ —Cable release.

Fig. 1   Clutch pedal adjustment specifications

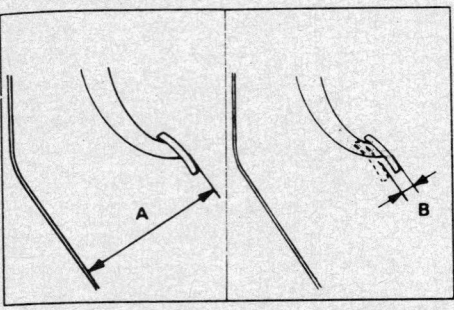

Fig. 2   Clutch pedal height (A), freeplay & clevis pin play (B) measurements

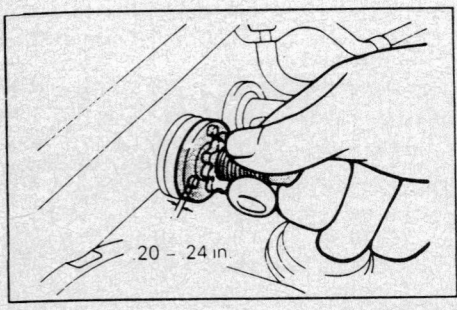

Fig. 3   Clutch cable adjustment

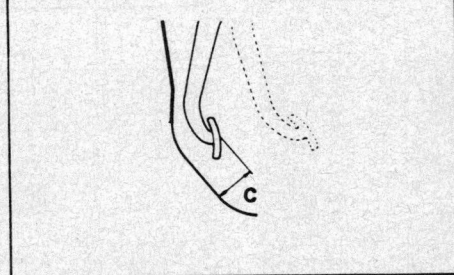

Fig. 4   Clutch release point measurement

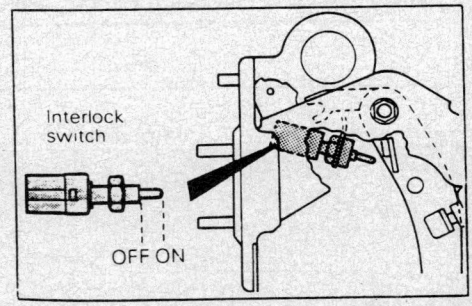

Fig. 5   Interlock switch adjustment inspection. Colt & Summit

ADJUSTMENTS

CLUTCH PEDAL

Refer to **Fig. 1** for clutch pedal height, freeplay and pedal height at clutch release point specifications.

Cable Release System

1. Measure clutch pedal height (A), **Fig. 2**. If height is not within specifications, check pedal bracket for damage and wear and repair as needed.
2. Measure clutch pedal freeplay (B), **Fig. 2**.
3. If freeplay is not within specifications, turn outer cable adjusting nut at toeboard until clutch cable freeplay is within .20-.24 inch, **Fig. 3**.

4. Depress clutch pedal several times, then check clutch pedal to floorboard clearance at clutch release point (C), **Fig. 4**.
5. If clutch pedal to floorboard clearance at release point is less than specified, check clutch assembly and release mechanism and repair as needed.
6. **On Colt and Summit,** ensure when clutch pedal is depressed all the way (5.9 inches of travel), interlock switch switches from on to off, **Fig. 5**.
7. If necessary, loosen locknut and adjust.

Hydraulic Release System

1. Measure clutch pedal height (A), **Fig. 2.**
2. If not within specifications, adjust as follows:

a. **On models less cruise control,** loosen locknut and turn adjusting bolt to bring height within specifications.
b. **On models with cruise control,** loosen locknut and turn clutch switch to bring height within specifications.
3. Measure clutch pedal clevis pin play (B), **Fig. 2,** should be .04-.12 inch.
4. If not within specifications, adjust clutch master cylinder pushrod as necessary to bring play within specifications. **Do not press pushrod into master cylinder when adjusting clevis pin clearance.**
5. **On Colt and Summit,** ensure when clutch pedal is depressed all the way (5.9 inches of travel), interlock switch switches from on to off, **Fig. 5**. If necessary, loosen locknut and adjust.
6. **On all models,** measure clutch pedal freeplay (B), **Fig. 2,** and clutch pedal

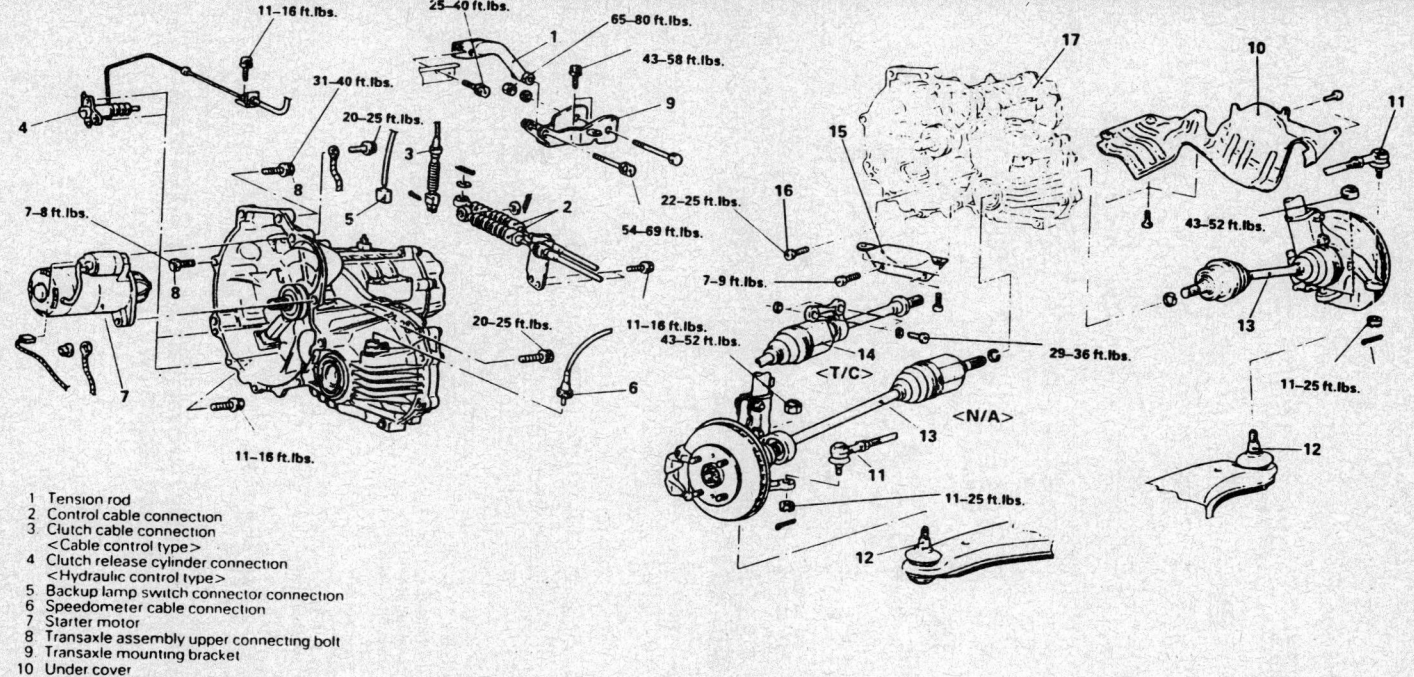

1. Tension rod
2. Control cable connection
3. Clutch cable connection
   <Cable control type>
4. Clutch release cylinder connection
   <Hydraulic control type>
5. Backup lamp switch connector connection
6. Speedometer cable connection
7. Starter motor
8. Transaxle assembly upper connecting bolt
9. Transaxle mounting bracket
10. Under cover
11. Tie rod end connection
12. Lower arm ball joint connection
13. Drive shaft connection
14. Drive shaft and inner shaft assembly
    connection
15. Bell housing cover
16. Transaxle assembly lower connecting bolt
17. Transaxle assembly

Fig. 6 Transaxle assembly removal. Colt & Summit

to floorboard clearance at clutch release point (C), **Fig. 4.**

7. If clearance and/or freeplay are not within specifications, hydraulic system requires bleeding or clutch is faulty.

HYDRAULIC SYSTEM SERVICE

CLUTCH SYSTEM BLEED

1. Connect a suitable hose to bleeder screw at slave cylinder, then loosen bleeder screw.
2. Push pedal down slowly until all air is expelled, hold clutch pedal down until bleeder screw is retightened.
3. Refill master cylinder as necessary.

SLAVE CYLINDER, REPLACE

1. Drain clutch fluid, then disconnect hydraulic line.
2. **On models with 1.5L/4-90 engine,** remove snap ring and clevis pin securing slave cylinder to clutch fork.
3. **On all models,** remove attaching bolts, then the slave cylinder.
4. Reverse procedure to install, noting the following:
   a. Apply multi-purpose grease to clevis pin or pushrod contact surfaces as equipped.
   b. Tighten attaching bolts to specifications.
   c. Bleed hydraulic system and adjust clutch pedal.

CLUTCH
REPLACE

1. Remove transmission or transaxle as described under "Transaxle, Replace."
2. With suitable clutch disc guide inserted in center hole to prevent clutch disc from dropping, evenly loosen bolts holding clutch cover assembly in a crossing pattern, then remove clutch cover assembly.
3. Remove clutch disc.
4. Reverse procedure to install, noting the following:
   a. Clean surface of flywheel thoroughly with fine sandpaper or crocus cloth and ensure all oil or grease has been removed.
   b. Apply a small amount of multipurpose grease to clutch disc and input shaft splines and groove of release bearing.
   c. Tighten clutch cover bolts to specifications.

TRANSAXLE
REPLACE

COLT & SUMMIT

Refer to **Fig. 6** during replacement procedures.
1. Disconnect battery ground cable, then remove the battery and battery tray.
2. Remove air cleaner assembly.
3. Drain transaxle oil.
4. Disconnect clutch cable or slave cyl-

inder as equipped and secure at body side, then the back-up lamp switch electrical connector and speedometer cable.
5. Remove starter motor, transaxle upper attaching bolts, transaxle mounting bracket and undercover.
6. Disconnect tie rod ends and lower ball joints using steering linkage puller tool No. MB990635 or equivalent.
7. Insert a pry bar between transaxle case and driveshaft and pry driveshaft from transaxle. Secure to body with wire.
8. Remove bellhousing cover and transaxle lower attaching bolts.
9. Support transaxle assembly on a suitable transaxle jack, then move assembly to right, lower and remove from vehicle.
10. Reverse procedure to install. Tighten attaching bolts to specifications.

COLT VISTA & SUMMIT WAGON

1. Remove air cleaner assembly.
2. Raise and support vehicle then drain transaxle fluid.
3. Remove transaxle in numbered sequence shown in **Figs. 7 and 8,** noting the following:
   a. Remove starter motor with starter motor harness attached, then suspend starter motor from frame.
   b. **On models with 1.8L/4-110 engine,** support engine using engine mount tool No. MB991191 or equivalent.

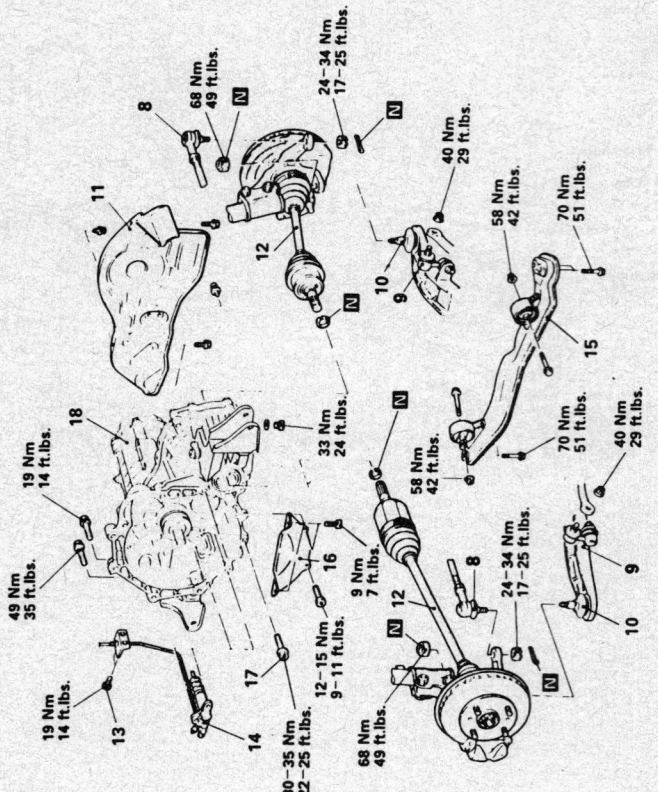

Fig. 7   Transaxle assembly removal (Part 2 of 2). Colt Vista & Summit Wagon FWD

- Lift up of the vehicle
8. Connection for tie rod end
9. Connection for stabilizer bar
10. Connection for lower arm ball joint
11. Under cover (RH)
- Draining of the transaxle oil
12. Drive shaft connection
13. Clutch oil line bracket bolt
14. Connection for release cylinder
15. Center member
16. Bell housing cover
17. Transaxle assembly lower part coupling bolts
18. Transaxle assembly

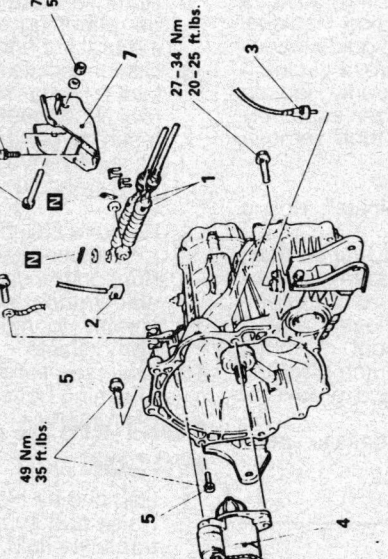

Removal steps
1 Control cable connection
2 Backup light switch connector
3 Speedometer cable connection
4 Starter motor
5 Transaxle assembly upper part coupling bolt
6 Transaxle mount bolt
7 Transaxle mount bracket

NOTE
For tightening locations indicated by the * symbol first tighten temporarily, and then make the final tightening with the entire weight of the engine applied to the vehicle body.

Fig. 7   Transaxle assembly removal (Part 1 of 2). Colt Vista & Summit Wagon FWD

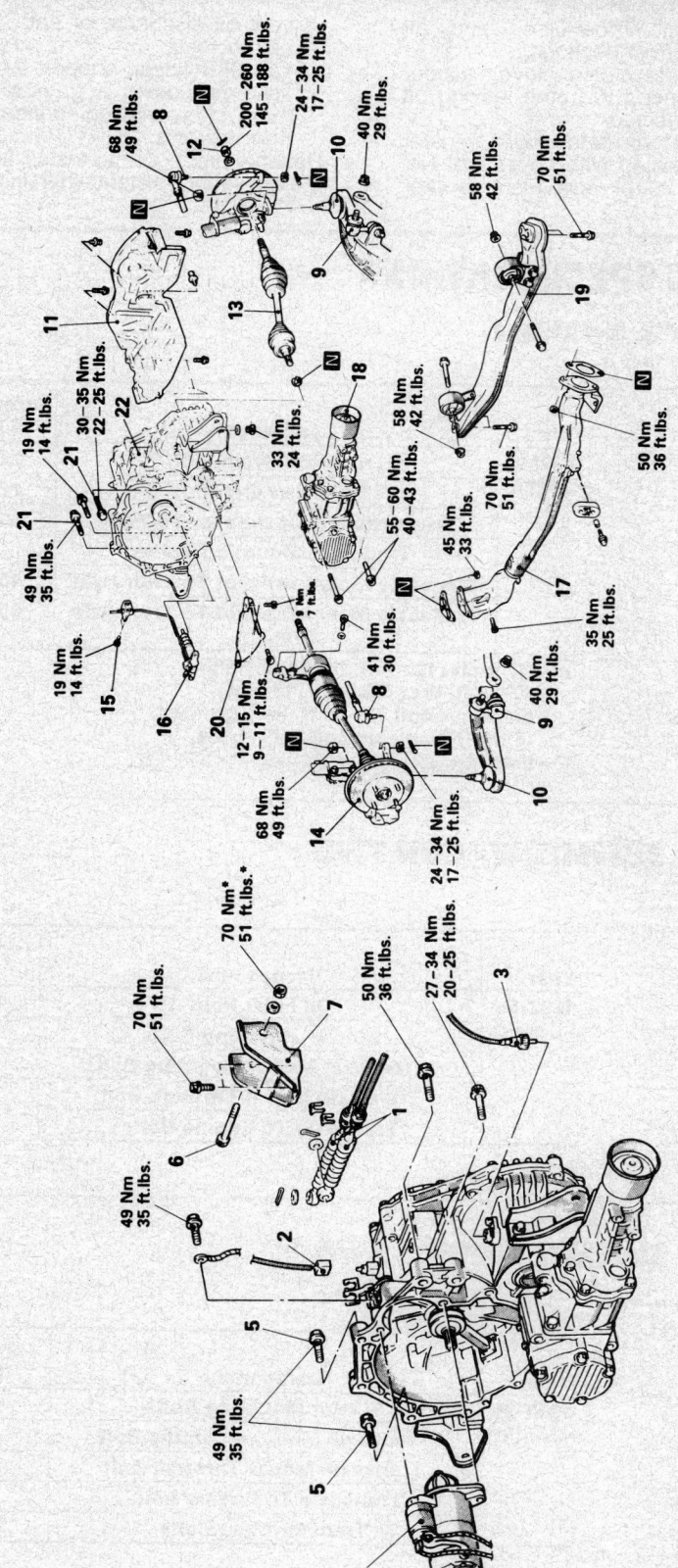

Fig. 8 Transaxle assembly removal (Part 2 of 2). Colt Vista & Summit Wagon AWD

Fig. 8 Transaxle assembly removal (Part 1 of 2). Colt Vista & Summit Wagon AWD

Removal steps

1. Control cable connection
2. Backup light switch connector
3. Speedometer cable connection
4. Starter motor
5. Transaxle assembly upper part coupling bolt
6. Transaxle mount bolt
7. Transaxle mount bracket

- Lifting up of the vehicle
8. Connection for tie rod end
9. Connection for stabilizer bar
10. Connection for lower arm ball joint
- Draining of the transaxle oil
11. Under cover (RH)
12. Drive shaft nut (RH)
13. Drive shaft (RH)
14. Connection for drive shaft and inner shaft
15. Clutch oil line bracket bolts
16. Connection for clutch release cylinder

17. Front exhaust pipe
18. Transfer assembly
19. Center member
20. Bell housing cover
21. Transaxle assembly lower part coupling bolts
22. Transaxle assembly

Transfer assembly removal steps

17. Front exhaust pipe
18. Transfer assembly

NOTE
For tightening locations indicated by the * symbol, first tighten temporarily, and then make the final tightening with the entire weight of the engine applied to the vehicle body.

c. **On models with 2.4L/4-146 engine,** support engine using a suitable floor jack.

d. **On all models,** disconnect tie rods and ball joints using steering linkage tool No. MB991113 or equivalent.

e. Remove driveshafts as outlined in the "Front Wheel Drive" and "All Wheel Drive" sections.

f. Disconnect clutch slave cylinder and suspend to frame leaving oil line connected.

g. **On AWD models,** cover transfer case opening with cover tool No. MB991193 or equivalent to prevent oil discharge or entry of foreign objects.

h. **On all models,** support transaxle assembly using a transaxle jack then after moving transaxle to right, lower it.

4. Reverse procedure to install, keeping the driveshaft straight when installing.

TIGHTENING SPECIFICATIONS

COLT & SUMMIT

Year	Component	Torque/Ft. Lbs.
1992–95	Bellhousing Cover To Transaxle	7-9
	Back-up Lamp Switch	22-25
	Clutch Cover	11-15
	Clutch Release Cylinder Mounting Bolts	11-15
	Clutch Tube To Transaxle	11-16
	Lever To Body	7-10
	Shift Lever To Bracket	14-20
	Speedometer Sleeve Bolt	36-48 ②
	Starter Mounting Bolts	20-25
	Transaxle Case Tightening Bolt	26-30

Year	Component	Torque/Ft. Lbs.
1992–95 —Cont'd	Transaxle Drain Plug	22-25
	Transaxle Filler Plug	22-25
	Transaxle Mount Bracket To Body	65-80
	Transaxle Mounting Bolts	①
	Transaxle Mount Bracket To Transaxle	43-58
	Transaxle Mount Bracket To Transaxle Bracket	65-80

① —.47 inch (12 mm) diameter bolt, 32–39 ft. lbs.; .39 inch (10 mm) diameter bolt, 22–25 ft. lbs.; .31 inch (8 mm) diameter bolt, 7–9 ft. lbs.

② —Inch lbs.

COLT VISTA & SUMMIT WAGON FWD

Year	Component	Torque/Ft. Lbs.
1992–95	Center Member To Body Bolts	51
	Clutch Cover Bolts	14
	Clutch Master Cylinder Nuts	9
	Clutch Slave Cylinder Bolt	14
	Hydraulic Clutch Hose Fittings	11
	Oil Drain Plug	22-25

Year	Component	Torque/Ft. Lbs.
1992–95 —Cont'd	Oil Filler Plug	22-25
	Starter Mounting Bolts	35
	Transaxle Mount Mounting Bolt	51
	Transaxle Mount Through Bolt	51
	Transaxle To Engine Bolts	35

COLT VISTA & SUMMIT WAGON AWD

Year	Component	Torque/Ft. Lbs.
1992–95	Clutch Cover Bolts	14
	Clutch Master Cylinder Nuts	9
	Clutch Slave Cylinder Bolt	14
	Hydraulic Clutch Hose Fittings	11
	Oil Drain Plug	22-25
	Oil Filler Plug	22-25

Year	Component	Torque/Ft. Lbs.
1992–95 —Cont'd	Starter Mounting Bolts	35
	Transaxle Mount Mounting Bolt	51
	Transaxle Mount Through Bolt	51
	Transaxle To Engine Bolts	35
	Transfer Case Bolts	40-43

INDEX

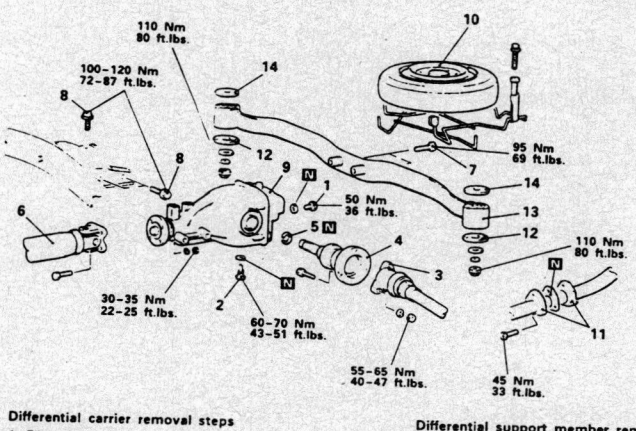

Differential carrier removal steps
1. Filler plug
2. Drain plug
3. Drive shaft connection
4. Companion shaft
5. Circlip
6. Propeller shaft connection
7. Bolts
8. Bolts
9. Differential Carrier

Differential support member removal steps
7. Bolts
10. Spare tire
11. Connection for main muffler and center exhaust pipe
12. Differential mount lower stopper
13. Differential support member
14. Differential mount upper stopper

Caution
If the thread section of the mounting bolts and nuts for the drive shaft and propeller shaft and the companion shaft have any oil or grease on them, there is a possibility that they may loosen, even if they are tightened to the specified torque, so the threads should always be cleaned before tightening.

CR3039100324000X

Fig. 1   Differential carrier removal. Colt Vista & Summit Wagon

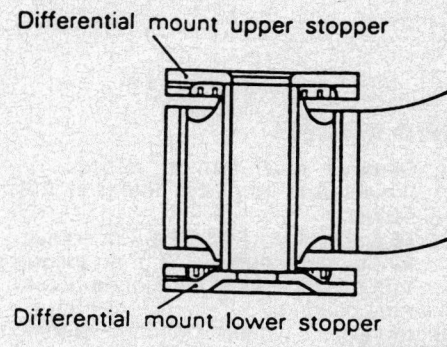

CR3039100325000X

Fig. 2   Differential mount stopper installation. Colt Vista & Summit Wagon

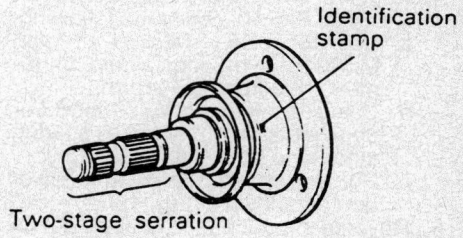

CR3039100326000X

Fig. 3   Companion flange identification. Colt Vista & Summit Wagon

DIFFERENTIAL CARRIER
REPLACE

COLT VISTA & SUMMIT WAGON

1. Remove differential carrier in sequence as shown in **Fig. 1**, noting the following:
   a. Make mating mark on differential companion flange and flange of yoke for reference during reassembly.
   b. Support lower section of differential carrier with a jack when removing carrier.
2. Reverse procedure to install, noting the following:
   a. Install mount stopper as shown in **Fig. 2**.
   b. Do not damage oil seal of differential carrier with spline section of companion shaft. The righthand

shaft on vehicles that have LSD with VCU has a two stage serration. The left and right end can be determined from stampings on companion shaft **Fig. 3**.
   c. Fill differential carrier with GL-5 gear oil or higher.

PROPELLER SHAFT
REPLACE

1. Remove propeller shaft in sequence as shown in **Fig. 4**, noting the following:
   a. Use tool No. MB990767 or equivalent to remove propeller shaft nut.
   b. Remove driveshaft from hub as shown in **Fig. 5**.
2. Reverse procedure to install.

HUB & BEARING
REPLACE

COLT VISTA & SUMMIT WAGON
FWD Models

1. Remove axle hub in sequence as shown in **Fig. 6**, noting the following:
   a. **On models with ABS**, ensure end pole piece does not contact teeth of rotor or other parts.
2. Reverse procedure to install noting the following:
   a. When installing flange nut, crimp nut to meet concave portion of the spindle.
   b. **On models with ABS**, adjust speed sensor by placing a feeler gauge speed sensors pole piece and rotors toothed surface. Gap should be between .008-.028 inches, then tighten speed sensor.

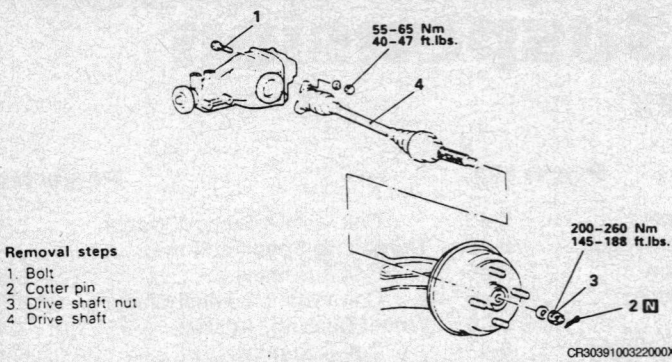

55-65 Nm
40-47 ft.lbs.

200-260 Nm
145-188 ft.lbs.

Removal steps
1. Bolt
2. Cotter pin
3. Drive shaft nut
4. Drive shaft

CR3039100322000X

Fig. 4 Propeller shaft removal. Colt Vista & Summit Wagon

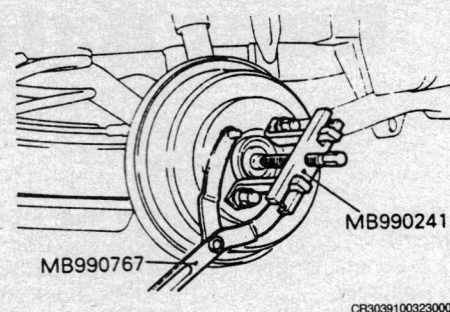

MB990241

MB990767

CR3039100323000X

Fig. 5 Propeller shaft nut removal. Colt Vista & Summit Wagon

AWD Models

1. Remove lower arm as describe in "Lower Arm Replace" found in this section.
2. Mount tool No. MB990998 or equivalent to lower arm **Fig. 7**, then **torque** tool to 145-188 ft. lbs. Rotate hub to seat bearing.
3. Measure wheel bearing starting torque as shown in **Fig. 8**; reading should be 9 inch lbs. or less.
4. Measure rear hub endplay as shown in **Fig. 9**. Limit is .0020 inches.
5. Remove axle hub in sequence as shown in **Fig. 10**, noting the following:
   a. Use tool Nos. MB990241 and MB990211 or equivalents to remove hub from lower arm.
   b. Using tool No. MB990560 or equivalent, remove wheel bearing inner race from hub, **Fig. 11**.
   c. Remove wheel bearing from lower arm as shown in **Fig. 12**.
6. Reverse procedure to install, noting the following:
   a. Press new wheel bearing on to lower arm as shown in **Fig. 13**.
   b. Press hub onto wheel bearing as shown **Fig. 14**.

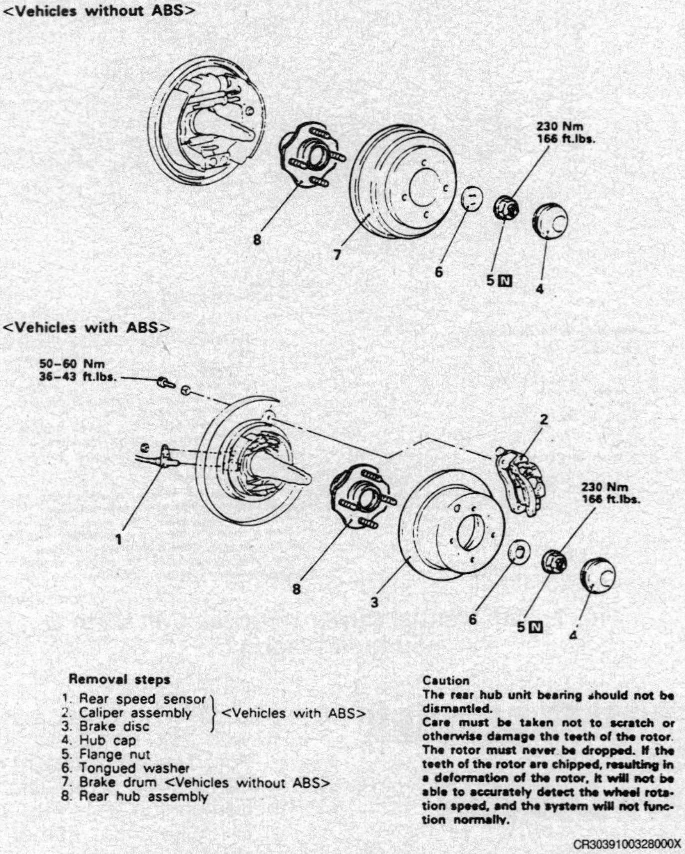

WHEEL BEARING
ADJUST

COLT & SUMMIT

1. Raise and support rear of vehicle and remove wheel.
2. Ensure parking brake is fully released.
3. Check wheel bearing endplay with suitable dial indicator. Maximum allowable endplay is as follows:
   a. **On 1992 models**, endplay should not exceed .008 inch.
   b. **On 1993-95 models**, endplay should not exceed .002 inch.
4. Check hub and drum starting torque by rotating hub with suitable spring scale. Maximum allowable starting torque is as follows:

<Vehicles without ABS>

230 Nm
166 ft.lbs.

<Vehicles with ABS>

50-60 Nm
36-43 ft.lbs.

230 Nm
166 ft.lbs.

Removal steps
1. Rear speed sensor
2. Caliper assembly <Vehicles with ABS>
3. Brake disc
4. Hub cap
5. Flange nut
6. Tongued washer
7. Brake drum <Vehicles without ABS>
8. Rear hub assembly

Caution
The rear hub unit bearing should not be dismantled.
Care must be taken not to scratch or otherwise damage the teeth of the rotor. The rotor must never be dropped. If the teeth of the rotor are chipped, resulting in a deformation of the rotor, it will not be able to accurately detect the wheel rotation speed, and the system will not function normally.

CR3039100328000X

Fig. 6 Axle hub removal. Colt Vista & Summit Wagon FWD

a. **On 1992 models**, starting **torque** should not exceed 4.9 lbs.
b. **On 1993-95 models**, starting **torque** should not exceed 4.0 lbs.
5. If endplay or starting torque exceed limits, loosen bearing retaining nut, then retighten nut to specifications.
6. If endplay or starting torque are still not within limits, replace wheel bearings as needed.

SHOCK ABSORBER
REPLACE

COLT & SUMMIT

1. Raise rear of vehicle and position jack stands under frame side rails.
2. Remove wheel and tire assembly.
3. Using a suitable jack, support lower

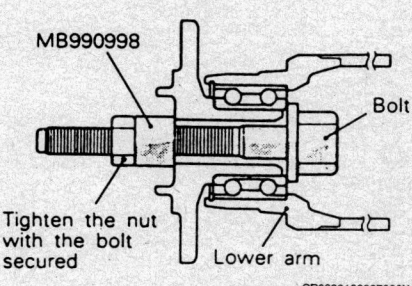

Fig. 7   Mount tool installation. Colt Vista & Summit Wagon AWD

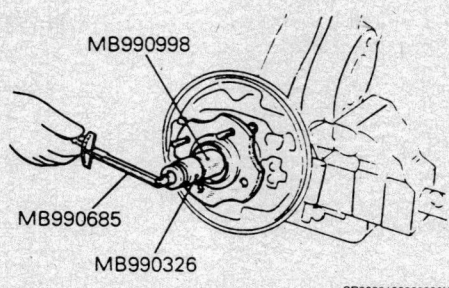

Fig. 8   Wheel bearing starting torque inspection. Colt Vista & Summit Wagon AWD

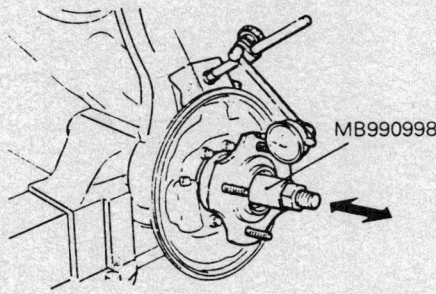

Fig. 9   Hub endplay inspection. Colt Vista & Summit Wagon AWD

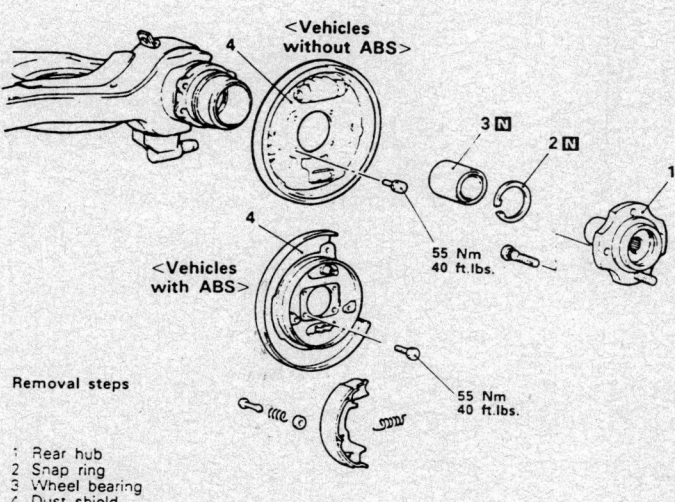

Fig. 10   Axle hub removal. Colt Vista & Summit Wagon AWD

Removal steps

1. Rear hub
2. Snap ring
3. Wheel bearing
4. Dust shield

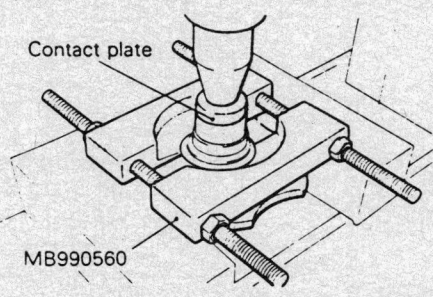

Fig. 11   Wheel bearing removal. Colt Vista & Summit Wagon AWD

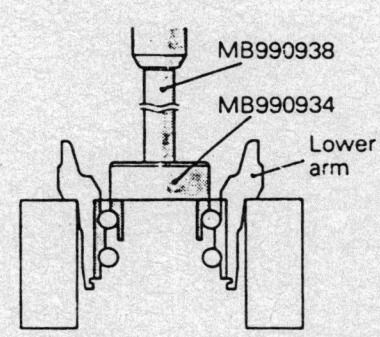

Fig. 12   Wheel bearing removal from lower arm. Colt Vista & Summit Wagon AWD

suspension arm, then disconnect shock absorber from upper and lower mounting and remove from vehicle.

4. Reverse procedure to install.

COLT VISTA & SUMMIT WAGON

When removing shock from vehicle, refer to **Fig. 15.**

1. Raise and support vehicle, then place jack under lower arm.
2. Remove lower shock absorber mounting nut, remove lid from inside vehicle, then cap.
3. Remove upper shock absorber mounting nut, then the shock assembly.
4. Reverse procedure to install.

COIL SPRING
REPLACE
COLT & SUMMIT

1. Raise rear of vehicle and position jack stands under frame side rails to support body.
2. Remove wheel and tire assembly, then remove rear drum brake assembly.
3. Disconnect muffler from exhaust pipe, then remove muffler assembly.
4. Position a suitable jack under suspension arm, then raise suspension arm slightly.
5. Disconnect shock absorber from upper and lower mounting.

6. Carefully lower jack to relieve spring tension, then remove coil spring. When removing spring, note location of upper and lower spring seats.
7. Reverse procedure to install. After completing installation, bleed brake system and adjust rear wheel bearings.

COLT VISTA & SUMMIT WAGON

1. Raise and support vehicle, then remove stabilizer bar, support lower arm

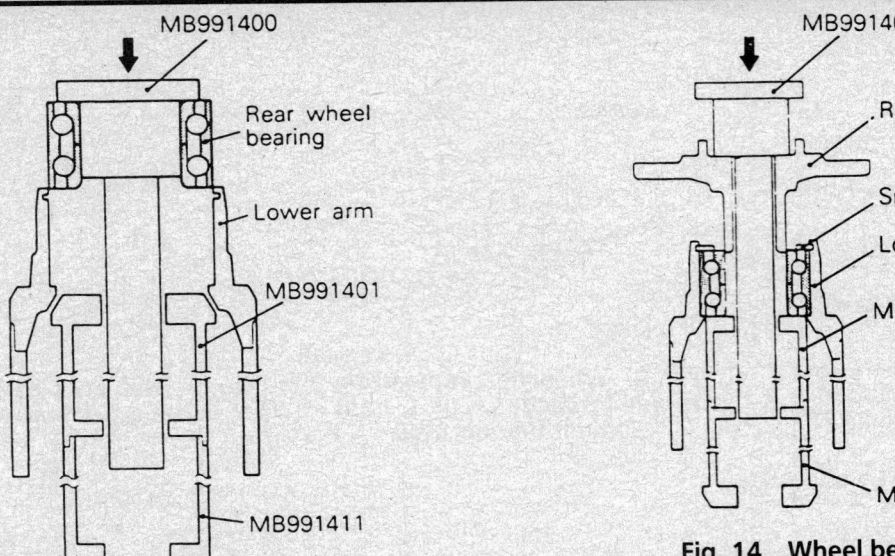

Fig. 13 Bearing installation in arm. Colt Vista & Summit Wagon AWD

Fig. 14 Wheel bearing installation. Colt Vista & Summit Wagon AWD

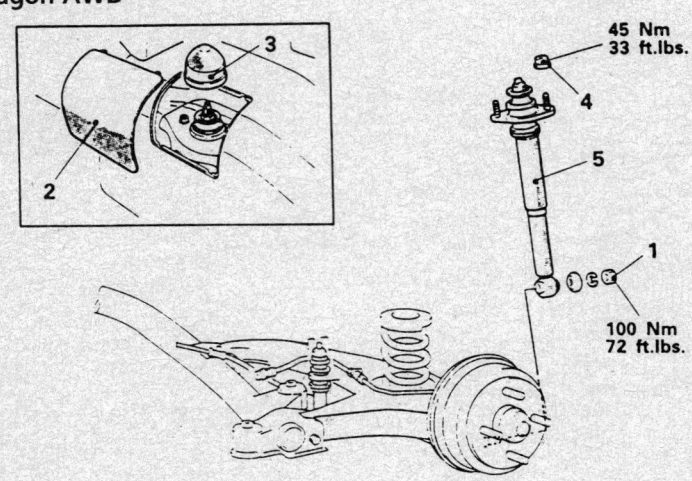

Removal steps
1. Nut
2. Lid (A)
3. Cap
4. Nut
5. Shock absorber assembly

Fig. 15 Shock absorber removal. Colt Vista & Summit Wagon

with suitable jack and remove lower shock mounting bolt and shock from lower arm.
2. **On AWD models,** remove bolt attaching driveshaft to rear carrier, then hang shaft from vehicle with wire.
3. **On models with ABS,** remove speed sensor clamp bolt.
4. **On all models,** make mating marks on lower arm shaft assembly and crossmember, then loosen shaft assembly nut.
5. Lower rear end of lower arm, then remove coil spring.
6. Reverse procedure to install, ensuring that both ends of coil spring are aligned with spring groove.

CONTROL ARM
REPLACE
LOWER
Colt Vista & Summit Wagon

1. When replacing lower arm, remove in sequence as shown in **Figs. 16 and 17,** noting the following:
   a. When removing shock absorbers from lower arm, support lower arm with suitable jack.
   b. Make mating marks on lower arm shaft assembly and crossmember, then loosen shaft assembly nut.
   c. Lower rear end of lower arm, then remove coil spring.

2. Reverse procedure to install, ensuring that both ends of coil spring are aligned with spring groove.

STABILIZER BAR
REPLACE

COLT VISTA & SUMMIT WAGON

1. When replacing stabilizer bar, refer to **Fig. 18.**
2. Reverse procedure to install noting

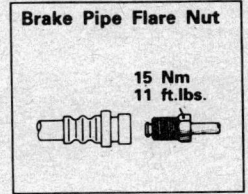

Brake Pipe Flare Nut

15 Nm
11 ft.lbs.

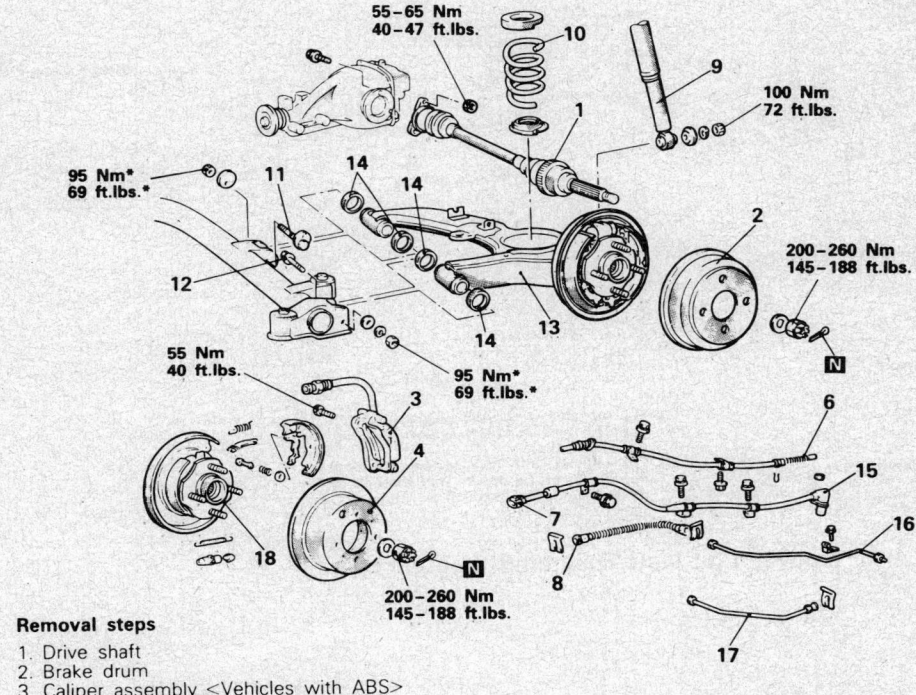

55–65 Nm
40–47 ft.lbs.

100 Nm
72 ft.lbs.

95 Nm*
69 ft.lbs.*

200–260 Nm
145–188 ft.lbs.

55 Nm
40 ft.lbs.

95 Nm*
69 ft.lbs.*

200–260 Nm
145–188 ft.lbs.

Removal steps

1. Drive shaft
2. Brake drum
3. Caliper assembly <Vehicles with ABS>
4. Brake disc <Vehicles with ABS>
6. Connection for parking brake cable and brake shoe

7. Rear sensor connector <Vehicles with ABS>
8. Brake hose
9. Shock absorber
10. Coil spring
11. Shaft assembly
12. Flange bolt
13. Lower arm assembly
14. Stopper
15. Rear speed sensor <Vehicles with ABS>
16. Brake pipe
17. Brake pipe <Vehicles with ABS>
18. Hub assembly

NOTE
*Indicates parts which should be temporarily tightened, and then fully tightened with the vehicles in the unladen condition.

Caution
(1) For vehicles with ABS, be careful not to damage the rotor teeth when removing the drive shaft.
(2) For vehicles with ABS, when removing the speed sensor, be careful that the end of the pole piece does not touch any other component.

CR2039100027000X

Fig. 16 Lower arm removal. Colt Vista & Summit Wagon AWD

the following:
a. Position stabilizer bar with painted

section aligned with fixture as shown in **Fig. 19.**

b. Install locknut to a value of A (A = .98–1.06 inches), **Fig. 20.**

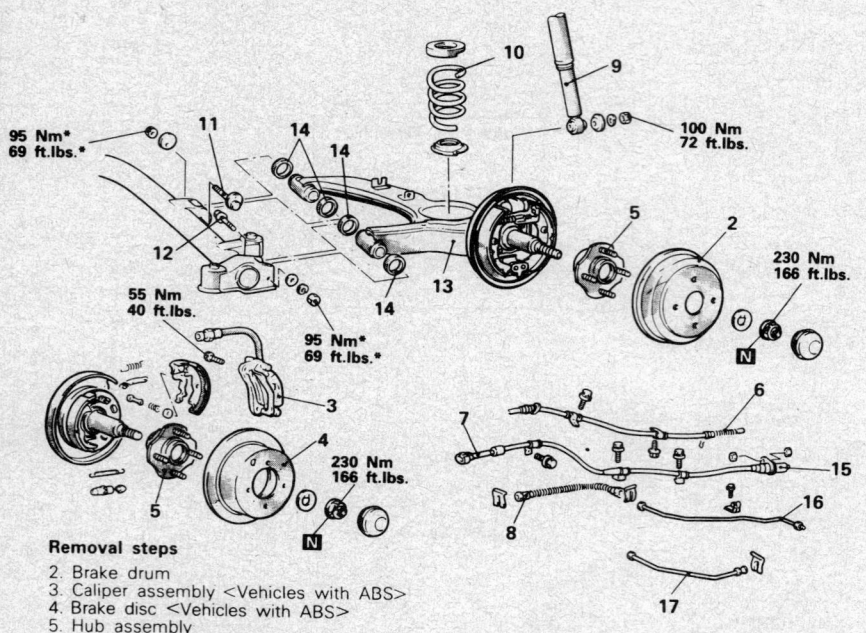

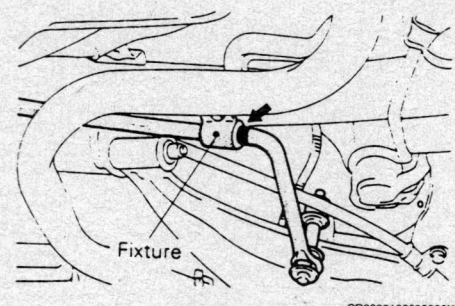

Fig. 19 Stabilizer fixture installation. Colt Vista & Summit Wagon

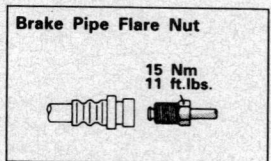

Brake Pipe Flare Nut

15 Nm
11 ft.lbs.

Removal steps
2. Brake drum
3. Caliper assembly <Vehicles with ABS>
4. Brake disc <Vehicles with ABS>
5. Hub assembly
6. Connection for parking brake cable and brake shoe

7. Rear sensor connector <Vehicles with ABS>
8. Brake hose
9. Shock absorber
10. Coil spring
11. Shaft assembly
12. Flange bolt
13. Lower arm assembly
14. Stopper
15. Rear speed sensor <Vehicles with ABS>
16. Brake pipe
17. Brake pipe <Vehicles with ABS>

NOTE
*Indicates parts which should be temporarily tightened, and then fully tightened with the vehicle in the unladen condition.

Caution
(1) For vehicles with ABS, be careful not to damage the rotor teeth when removing the hub assembly.
(2) For vehicles with ABS, when removing the speed sensor, be careful that the end of the pole piece does not touch any other component.

Fig. 17 Lower arm removal. Colt Vista & Summit Wagon FWD

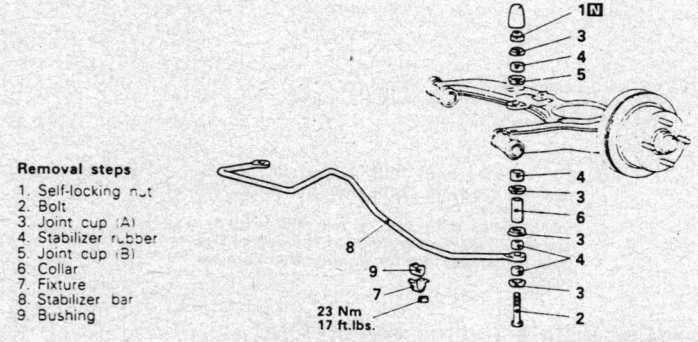

Removal steps
1. Self-locking nut
2. Bolt
3. Joint cup (A)
4. Stabilizer rubber
5. Joint cup (B)
6. Collar
7. Fixture
8. Stabilizer bar
9. Bushing

23 Nm
17 ft.lbs.

Fig. 18 Rear stabilizer bar removal. Colt Vista & Summit Wagon

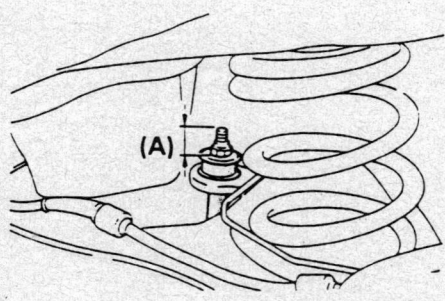

Fig. 20 Self locking nut installation. Colt Vista & Summit Wagon

TIGHTENING SPECIFICATIONS
COLT & SUMMIT

Year	Component	Torque/Ft. Lbs.
1992–95	Brake Adapter, Disc Brakes	36-43
	Dust Shield To Trailing Arm	36-43
	Lateral Rod To Axle	58-72
	Lateral Rod To Body	58-72
	Piston Rod Nut	14-22
	Shock Unit Lower Attachment	58-72

Year	Component	Torque/Ft. Lbs.
1992–95 —Cont'd	Shock Unit Upper Attachment	18-25
	Suspension Arm, Left To Right Hand	58-72
	Suspension Arm To Body	36-51
	Trailing Arm	98-108
	Wheel Bearing Nut	108-145
	Wheel Lug Nuts	65-80

COLT VISTA & SUMMIT WAGON

Year	Component	Torque/Ft. Lbs.
1992–95	Axle Hub Flange Nut ②	166
	Backing Plate Attaching Bolts	40
	Caliper Attaching Bolt ①	40
	Caliper Attaching Bolt ② ③	40
	Differential Carrier Drain Plug	43-51
	Differential Carrier Filler Plug	36
	Differential Support Member Attaching Nuts	80
	Differential Support Member To Carrier Attaching Nuts	69

Year	Component	Torque/Ft. Lbs.
1992–95 —Cont'd	Driveshaft Nut ①	145–188
	Driveshaft To Carrier Attaching Bolt & Nut ①	40–47
	Lower Arm To Crossmember ① ②	69
	Lower Shock Absorber Nut	72
	Propeller Shaft Attaching Nuts & Bolts	22–25
	Stabilizer Fixture Bar Attaching Nuts	17
	Upper Shock Absorber Nut	33

① —AWD Models.
② —FWD Models.
③ —With ABS.

Transfer Case

INDEX

TRANSFER CASE
REPLACE
COLT VISTA & SUMMIT WAGON

1. Remove transaxle as described under "Transaxle, Replace" in "Clutch & Manual Transaxle" section.
2. Remove bolts attaching transfer assembly to transaxle, then the transfer assembly.
3. Reverse procedure to install. Tighten attaching bolts to specifications.

TIGHTENING SPECIFICATIONS

Year	Component	Torque/Ft. Lbs.
1992–95	Transfer Assembly Adapter To Subassembly Bolts	28
	Transfer Assembly Extension Housing To Adapter Bolts	14
	Transfer Assembly To Transaxle Bolts	40–43

Front Suspension & Steering

INDEX

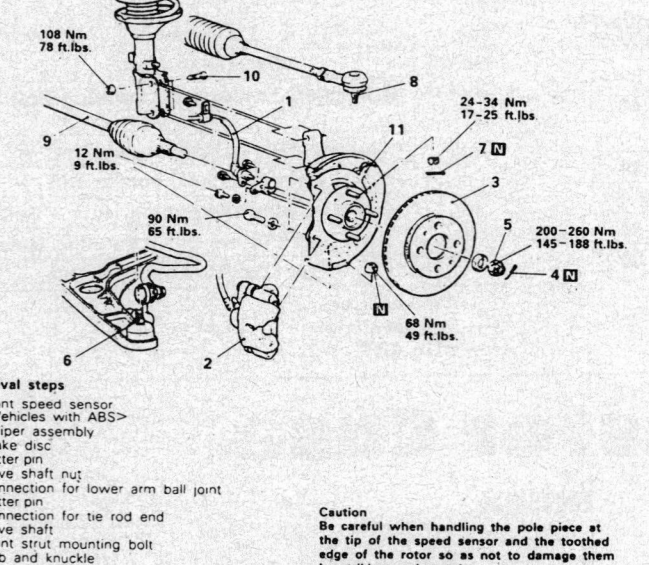

Removal steps
1. Front speed sensor <Vehicles with ABS>
2. Caliper assembly
3. Brake disc
4. Cotter pin
5. Drive shaft nut
6. Connection for lower arm ball joint
7. Cotter pin
8. Connection for tie rod end
9. Drive shaft
10. Front strut mounting bolt
11. Hub and knuckle

Caution
Be careful when handling the pole piece at the tip of the speed sensor and the toothed edge of the rotor so as not to damage them by striking against other parts.

CR3039100336000X

Fig. 1 Wheel hub removal. Colt Vista & Summit Wagon

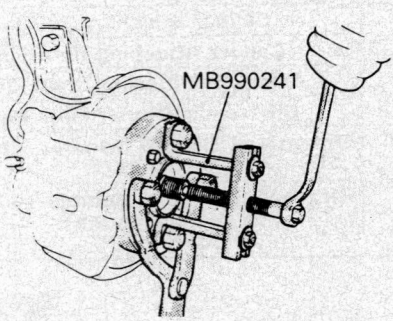

CR3039100337000X

Fig. 2 Driveshaft removal. Colt Vista & Summit Wagon

WHEEL HUB
REPLACE

COLT VISTA & SUMMIT WAGON

1. Remove axle hub in order as shown in **Fig. 1**, noting the following:
   a. Remove driveshaft nut from hub using tool No. MB990767 or equivalent.
   b. Using tool No. MB991113 or equivalent, disconnect lower arm ball joint from knuckle. **Tie cord of tool to nearby part, loosen nut but do not remove.**
   c. Using tool No. MB991113 or equivalent, disconnect tie rod from knuckle. **Tie cord of tool to nearby part, loosen nut but do not remove.**
   d. Using tool No. MB990241 or equivalent, push out driveshaft from front hub, **Fig. 2.**
2. Reverse procedure to install, noting the following:
   a. Install washer and driveshaft nut as shown in **Fig. 3.**
   b. Using tool No. MB990767 or equivalent, **Fig. 4**, tighten driveshaft nut to specifications.
   c. **On vehicles with anti-lock brakes,** install speed sensor to knuckle, insert feeler gauge into space between speed sensor pole piece and rotors toothed surface, **Fig. 5.**
   d. Obtain a reading between .012 and .035 inch, then tighten speed sensor.

BALL JOINT INSPECTION

1. Raise front of vehicle until both wheels are suspended.
2. Have an assistant shake bottom edge of tire in and out and inspect lower end of knuckle and lower control arm for movement.
3. If movement is observed, replace lower control arm assembly. Refer to "Lower Control Arm, Replace" for procedure.

BALL JOINT
REPLACE

COLT & SUMMIT

With load removed from lower ball joint, check starting torque with inch lb. wrench. If starting **torque** is not 21.7-86.8 inch lbs., replace lower control arm and ball joint as an assembly. Refer to "Control Arm, Replace" for procedure.

STRUT
REPLACE

COLT & SUMMIT

1. Raise and support front of vehicle.
2. Remove brake hose bracket to strut attaching screws, then the bracket.
3. Remove strut to knuckle attaching bolts.
4. Remove dust cover from top of strut.
5. Remove strut assembly flange nuts,

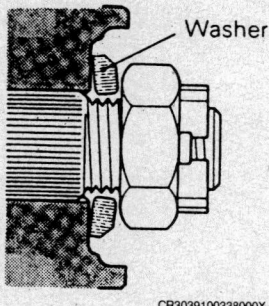

Fig. 3 Driveshaft washer & nut installation. Colt Vista & Summit Wagon

CR3039100338000X

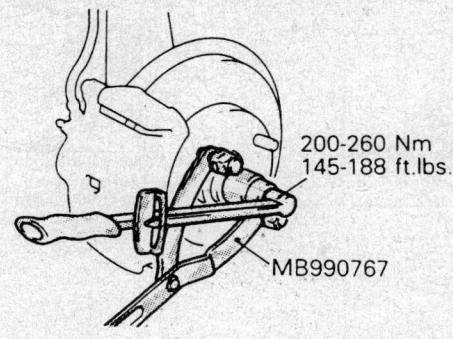

200-260 Nm
145-188 ft.lbs.

MB990767

Fig. 4 Driveshaft nut installation. Colt Vista & Summit Wagon

CR303910339000X

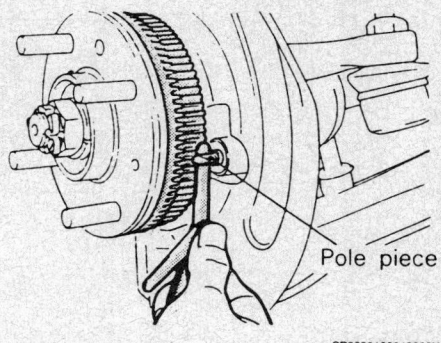

Pole piece

Fig. 5 Speed sensor adjustment. Colt Vista & Summit Wagon

CR3039100340000X

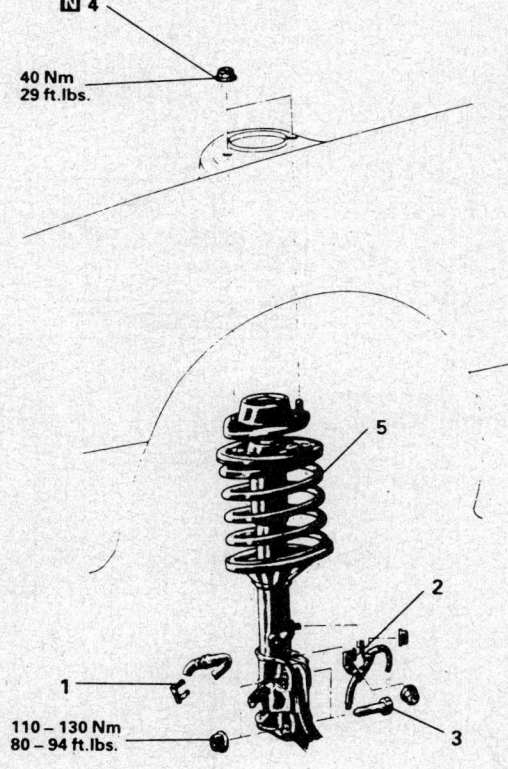

N 4

40 Nm
29 ft.lbs.

5

2

1

3

110 – 130 Nm
80 – 94 ft.lbs.

Removal steps
1. Brake hose clamp
2. Front speed sensor bracket <Vehicles with ABS>
3. Bolts
4. Flange nut
5. Strut assembly

CR2029200106000X

Fig. 6 Strut replacement. Colt & Summit

Fig. 6, then the strut.
6. Reverse procedure to install.

COLT VISTA & SUMMIT WAGON

1. **On models with speed control,** remove speed control actuator from righthand strut.
2. **On all models,** remove strut assembly as shown in **Fig. 7.** Suspend lower arm from vehicle with suitable wire.
3. Reverse procedure to install. When compressing spring, do not use air tools to tighten spring compressor tool.

STRUT SERVICE

Disassemble strut assembly as shown in **Fig. 8.** Compress coil spring with tool Nos. MB991238 and MB991237 or equivalents before removing locking nut, **Fig. 9.**
On Colt and Summit, the spring seat and pad, **Fig. 8,** are removed as a unit.

CONTROL ARM
REPLACE
LOWER
Colt & Summit
1. Raise and support vehicle.

2. Remove center member. On all models, remove chassis undercover, then disconnect stabilizer bar from lower control arm.
3. Disconnect ball joint from steering knuckle.
4. Loosen lower control arm to chassis attaching bolts, then remove lower control arm.
5. Replace ball joint dust cover.
6. Reverse procedure to install.

Colt Vista & Summit Wagon

1. Remove lower arm in sequence as shown in **Fig. 10,** noting the following:
   a. Using tool No. MB991113 or equivalent, disconnect knuckle from lower arm ball joint. **Tie cord of tool to nearby part, then loosen (but do not remove) nut.**
2. Check ball joint starting torque as shown in **Fig. 11.** Starting **torque** should be 17-78 inch lbs.
3. If not within specifications, replace ball joint.
4. Reverse procedure to install.

STEERING KNUCKLE
REPLACE

1. With vehicle on ground, remove cotter pin and loosen hub to driveshaft retaining nut.
2. Raise and support front of vehicle, then remove wheel and tire assembly and hub nut with washer.
3. **On models with ABS,** remove front wheel speed sensor.
4. **On all models,** remove front brake caliper and disc from hub; then, using suitable puller, disconnect tie rod end from steering knuckle. **It is not necessary to disconnect caliper hydraulic line; support caliper from frame to avoid damage.**
5. Using axle shaft puller tool No. MB990241 and holding tool No. MB990767 or equivalents, detach driveshaft from hub.
6. Disconnect steering knuckle from strut, then remove knuckle and hub as an assembly.
7. Reverse procedure to install. Install wheel speed sensor as described in "Anti-Lock Brakes" section.

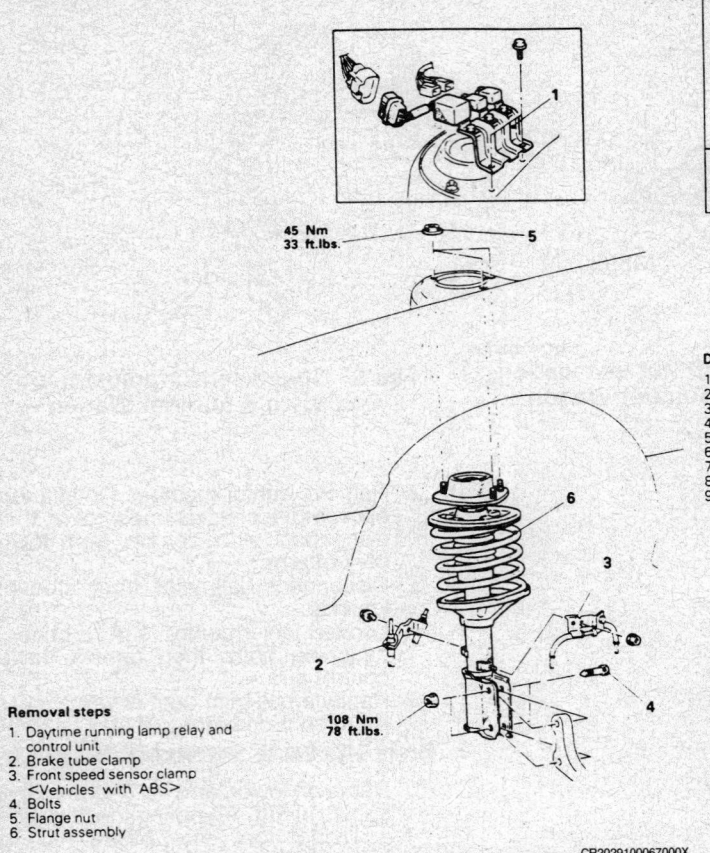

45 Nm
33 ft.lbs.

Grease: MOPAR Multi-mileage Lubricant Part No.2525035 or equivalent

108 Nm.
78 ft.lbs.

Removal steps
1. Daytime running lamp relay and control unit
2. Brake tube clamp
3. Front speed sensor clamp <Vehicles with ABS>
4. Bolts
5. Flange nut
6. Strut assembly

CR2029100067000X

Fig. 7 Strut replacement. Colt Vista & Summit Wagon

60–70 Nm
43–51 ft.lbs.

Disassembly steps
1. Dust cover
2. Self-locking nut
3. Strut insulator
4. Spring seat, upper
5. Spring pad, upper
6. Bump rubber
7. Dust cover
8. Coil spring
9. Strut assembly

CR2029100068000X

Fig. 8 Strut assembly service

Grease: MOPAR Multi-mileage lubricant Part No.2525035 or equivalent

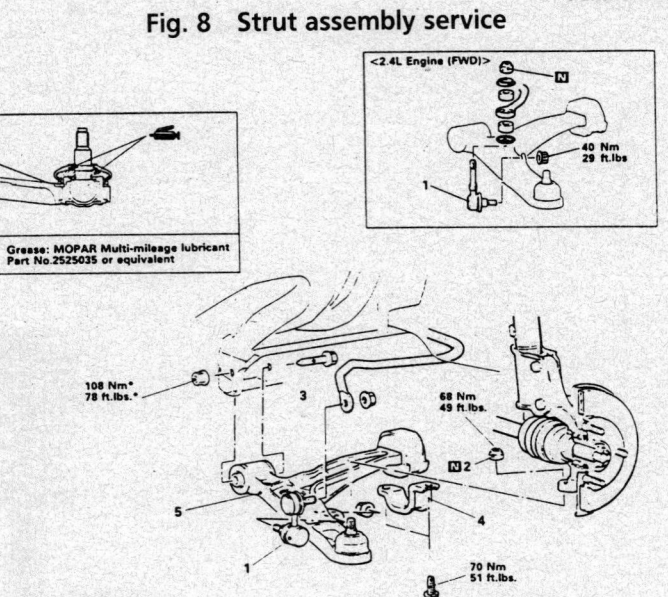

<2.4L Engine (FWD)>

40 Nm
29 ft.lbs.

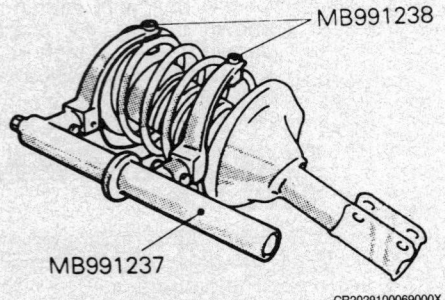

MB991238

MB991237

CR2029100069000X

Fig. 9 Self locking nut removal

108 Nm*
78 ft.lbs.*

68 Nm
49 ft.lbs.

70 Nm
51 ft.lbs.

Removal steps
1. Stabilizer link
2. Self-locking nut
3. Bolt
4. Clamp
5. Lower arm

NOTE
*: Indicates parts which should be temporarily tightened, and then fully tightened with the vehicle in the unladen condition.

CR2029100075000X

Fig. 10 Lower arm removal. Colt Vista & Summit Wagon

STABILIZER BAR
REPLACE

COLT & SUMMIT

1. Raise and support vehicle, then remove undercover attaching bolt, undercover and center member.
2. Remove stabilizer bar to lower control arm mounting bolt, nut and hardware.
3. Remove stabilizer bar bracket mounting bracket bolts, then the bracket and stabilizer bar.
4. Reverse procedure to install. Tighten stabilizer bar to lower control arm bushing attaching nuts until distance from top of threads to top of nuts is .83-.91 inch.

COLT VISTA & SUMMIT WAGON

2.4L/4-146 Engine w/AWD & 1.8L/4–110 Engine

1. Remove propeller shaft from vehicle.
2. Remove stabilizer bar in sequence as shown in **Fig. 12. When disconnecting front exhaust pipe assembly and exhaust manifold, take care not to bend flexible joint.**
3. Check ball joint starting torque, **Fig. 13.** Starting **torque** should be 15-28 inch lbs.
4. Reverse procedure to install.

2.4L/4-146 Engine w/FWD

1. Remove stabilizer bar in sequence shown in **Fig. 14.**
2. Check ball joint starting torque, **Fig. 13.** Starting **torque** should be 15-28 inch lbs.
3. Reverse procedure to install, noting the following:
   a. When installing stabilizer bolt, position bar so lengths of marking projecting from fixture are .27 inch (value A), then tighten mounting bolt to specifications, **Fig. 15.**
   b. Tighten nut on stabilizer bar to a value of A (A = .3-.4 inches), **Fig. 16.**

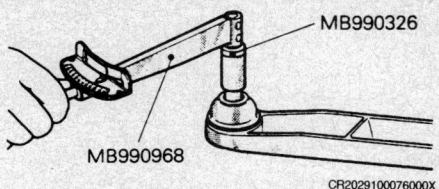

Fig. 11   Lower arm ball joint starting torque inspection. Colt Vista & Summit Wagon

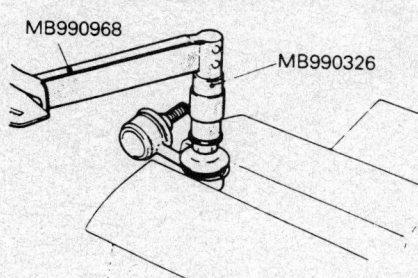

Fig. 13   Stabilizer ball joint starting torque inspection. Colt Vista & Summit Wagon

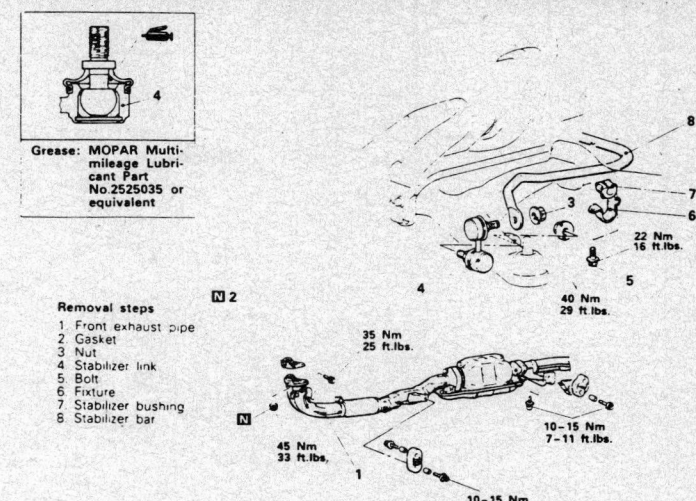

Grease: MOPAR Multi-mileage Lubricant Part No.2525035 or equivalent

Removal steps
1. Front exhaust pipe
2. Gasket
3. Nut
4. Stabilizer link
5. Bolt
6. Fixture
7. Stabilizer bushing
8. Stabilizer bar

Fig. 12   Stabilizer bar removal. Colt Vista & Summit Wagon w/2.4L/4-146 engine & AWD & 1.8L/4-110 engine

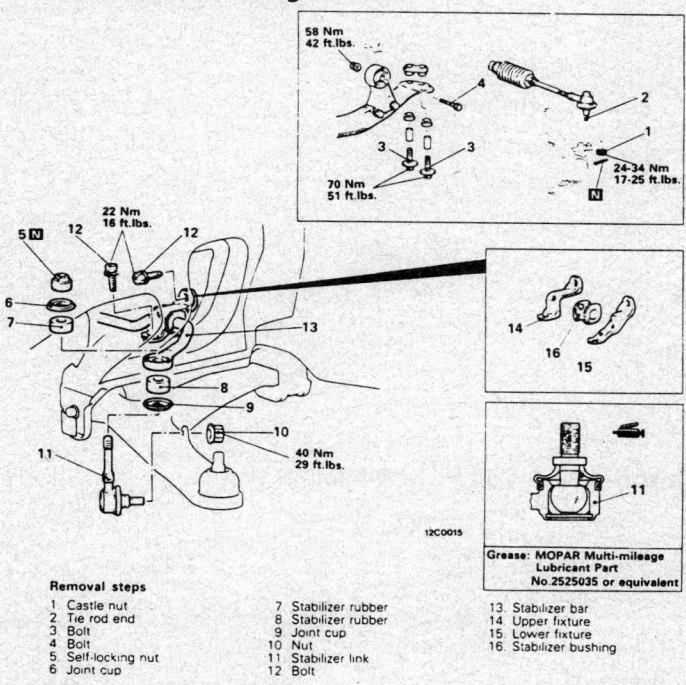

Removal steps

1. Castle nut	7. Stabilizer rubber
2. Tie rod end	8. Stabilizer rubber
3. Bolt	9. Joint cup
4. Bolt	10. Nut
5. Self-locking nut	11. Stabilizer link
6. Joint cup	12. Bolt

13. Stabilizer bar	
14. Upper fixture	
15. Lower fixture	
16. Stabilizer bushing	

Grease: MOPAR Multi-mileage Lubricant Part No.2525035 or equivalent

Fig. 14   Stabilizer bar removal. Colt Vista & Summit Wagon w/2.4L/4-146 engine & FWD

Fig. 15   Stabilizer bar installation. Colt Vista & Summit Wagon w/2.4L/4-146 engine & FWD

Fig. 16   Stabilizer bar self locking nut installation. Colt Vista & Summit Wagon w/2.4L/4-146 engine & FWD

POWER STEERING GEAR
REPLACE

COLT & SUMMIT

1. Raise and support front of vehicle.
2. Remove return hose from reservoir and allow fluid to drain into suitable container.
3. Remove steering shaft to gearbox pinion coupling bolt.
4. Remove tie rod ends from steering knuckles using steering linkage puller tool No. MB991113 or equivalent.
5. Remove pressure and return lines from steering gearbox.
6. Remove clamp from lower steering column dust cover.
7. Remove steering gear bracket bolts, then the brackets.
8. Remove mounting rubber, then the gearbox assembly.
9. Reverse procedure to install. When installing mounting rubber, apply adhesive to joints to prevent opening.

COLT VISTA & SUMMIT WAGON

1. Remove steering gearbox in sequence as shown in **Fig. 17**, noting the following:
   a. Remove tie rod ends using tool No. MB990635 or equivalent. **Tie cord of tool to nearby part and loosen (but do not remove)** nut.
2. Reverse procedure to install, adjusting tie rod ends as shown in **Fig. 18**.

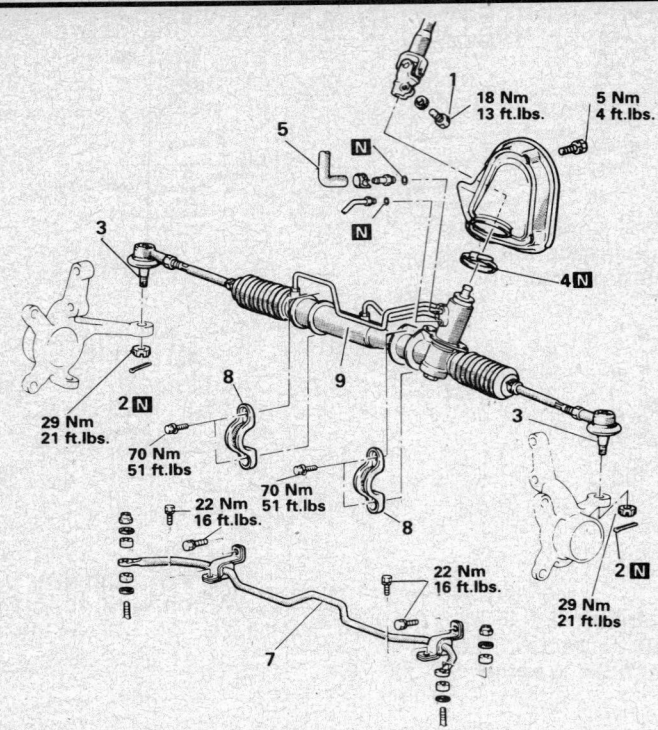

Removal steps
1. Joint assembly and gear box connecting bolt
2. Cotter pin
3. Connection for tie-rod end and knuckle
4. Band
5. Connection for return hose
6. Bracket <AWD>
7. Stabilizer bar <2.4L Engine (FWD)
8. Clamp
9. Gear box assembly

CR6039100015000X

Fig. 17 Power steering gearbox removal. Colt Vista & Summit Wagon

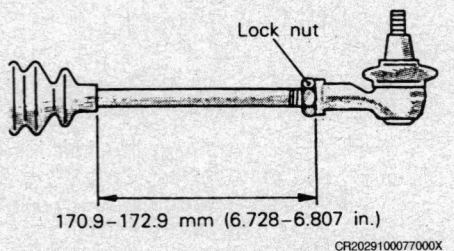

Lock nut

170.9–172.9 mm (6.728–6.807 in.)

CR2029100077000X

Fig. 18 Tie rod end adjustment. Colt Vista & Summit Wagon

POWER STEERING PUMP
REPLACE

COLT & SUMMIT

1. Disconnect power steering pressure switch electrical connector, if equipped.
2. Disconnect pressure and return hoses from power steering pump.
3. Loosen pump mounting bolts, then remove drive belt.

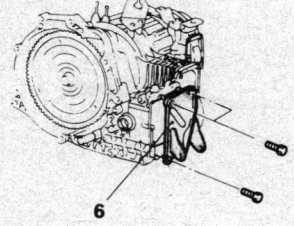

Removal steps
1. Pressure switch connector
2. Pressure hose
3. O-ring
4. Suction hose
5. Drive-belt
6. Oil pump
7. Oil pump bracket
8. Heat protector (2.4L Engine)

CR6039100016000X

Fig. 19 Power steering pump removal. Colt Vista & Summit Wagon

4. Remove power steering pump attaching bolts, then remove pump.
5. Reverse procedure to install.

COLT VISTA & SUMMIT WAGON

1. Remove drive belt, then drain power steering fluid.
2. Remove pump in sequence as shown in **Fig. 19. On models with 2.4L/4-146 engine,** alternator should be covered with a rag before removing power steering lines.
3. Reverse procedure to install.

MANUAL STEERING GEAR
REPLACE

1. Raise and support front of vehicle, then remove wheel and tire assembly.
2. Remove clamp bolt securing joint with pinion shaft.
3. Remove tie end stud nut, then using suitable puller disconnect tie rod from steering knuckle.
4. Remove steering gear clamp bolts from crossmember, then remove steering gear.
5. Reverse procedure to install.

TIGHTENING SPECIFICATIONS
COLT & SUMMIT

Year	Component	Torque/Ft. Lbs.
1992–95	Caliper To Knuckle	58-72
	Center Bearing Bracket To Engine	26-33
	Center Member Rear Mounting Bolt	43-58
	Connector To Power Steering Pump Body	36-51
	Driveshaft Nut	144-188
	Hub To Brake Rotor	36-43
	Knuckle To Strut Assembly	80-94
	Lower Arm Ball Joint	43-52
	Lower Arm Front Mounting Nut	69-87
	Lower Arm Rear Mounting Bolt	43-58
	Power Steering Cooler Tube Clamp Bolt	2-3
	Power Steering Cooler Tube To Body	7-10
	Power Steering Cooler Tube To Hood Stay	3-4
	Power Steering Gear End Plug	36-51
	Power Steering Gear Feed Tubes	9-13
	Power Steering Gear Pinion And Valve Assembly To Locknut	14-22
	Power Steering Gear Valve Housing Bolts	12-19
	Power Steering Pressure Hose To Pressure Tube	22-29
	Power Steering Pressure Hose To Pump	10-15
	Power Steering Pressure Tube To Steering Gear	9-13
	Power Steering Pump Bracket To Engine	18-24
	Power Steering Pump Cover To Pump Body	13-16

Year	Component	Torque/Ft. Lbs.
1992–95 —Cont'd	Power Steering Pump Heat Shield	7-10
	Power Steering Pump Reservoir Bolt	7-10
	Power Steering Pump Reservoir Bracket Bolt	7-10
	Power Steering Pump To Pump Bracket	33-40
	Power Steering Return Tube To Steering Gear	9-13
	Power Steering Suction Connector To Pump Body	4-7
	Rack Support Cover Locknut	36-51
	Rear Roll Stopper Mounting Nut	33-43
	Stabilizer Bar Mounting Bolt	12-19
	Stabilizer Link Mounting Nut	40-51
	Steering Column Lower Bracket	6-9
	Steering Column Upper Bracket	6-9
	Steering Gear To Body	43-58
	Steering Shaft Dust Cover	2.6-3.6
	Steering Shaft Joint To Steering Gear	11-14
	Steering Wheel Locknut	25-33
	Strut Top End Nut	43-57
	Strut Upper Mounting Nut	25-33
	Terminal Assembly To Power Steering Pump Body	18-22
	Tie Rod End Ball Joint	11-25
	Tie Rod End Locknut	25-36
	Tie Rod End To Rack	58-72
	Top Cover Locknut	36-51
	Wheel Lug Nuts	65-80

COLT VISTA & SUMMIT WAGON

Year	Component	Torque/Ft. Lbs.
1992–95	Caliper Mounting Bolts	65
	Exhaust Pipe Flange Mounting Nuts	33①
	Front Driveshaft Nut	145–188
	Front Strut Mounting Nut	78
	High Pressure Hose To Pump Attaching Nut	13
	Joint To Gearbox Connecting Bolt	13
	Lower Arm Attaching Nut	49
	Lower Arm Clamp Bolt	51
	Lower Arm To Frame	78
	Power Steering Gear Mounting Bracket Bolts	51
	Pump Mounting Bracket Mounting Bolts	29

Year	Component	Torque/Ft. Lbs.
1992–95 —Cont'd	Pump Pressure Switch Connector	29
	Stabilizer Bushing Bolt	16
	Stabilizer Link To Stabilizer Bar Mounting Nut	29①
	Stabilizer To Lower Arm Mounting Nut	29②
	Strut Self Locking Nut	43-51
	Tie Rod Mounting Nut	17-25
	Upper Strut Flange Nuts	33
	Wheel Lug Nuts	65-80

① —2.4L/4-146 engine w/AWD &
   1.8L/4-110 engine.
② —2.4L/4-146 engine w/FWD.

Wheel Alignment

INDEX

PRELIMINARY INSPECTION

1. Road test vehicle, noting any abnormal steering or handling characteristics.
2. Ensure tires are of proper type, are correctly inflated and that tires on each axle are the same size.
3. Ensure tires conform with size recommendations for vehicle.
4. Inspect ball joints, suspension arms, bushings and tie rods; repair or replace any component that is damaged or excessively worn.
5. Ensure wheel runout is not excessive, and that wheel bearings are properly adjusted.
6. Jounce vehicle several times to settle suspension.
7. Place vehicle on suitable alignment rack following manufacturer's instructions.
8. Check and correct alignment angles in the following sequence: rear toe and camber, caster, front camber and front toe.
9. Correct any angle that is not within specifications. If no adjustment is possible, check for damaged or worn suspension components and/or damaged or distorted chassis members and correct as needed.

FRONT WHEEL ALIGNMENT

On vehicles with aluminum wheels, attach camber/caster to driveshaft using tool No. MB991004 or equivalent.

CASTER

Caster is preset during production and is not adjustable. If caster is out of specifications, replace bent, worn or otherwise damaged parts.

CAMBER

The specified camber is built into the steering knuckle, which is part of the strut assembly. No adjustment is possible.

TOE-IN

Colt & Summit

Remove outer bellows clamp from tie rod before adjusting toe. After completing adjustment, reinstall clamp.

The amount of toe-in of the left front wheel is reduced by turning the tie rod turnbuckle toward the front of the car and the amount of toe-in on the right front wheel is reduced by turning it toward the rear of the car. After adjustment, the difference in length between the two tie rods should not exceed .2 inch (5 mm).

Colt Vista & Summit Wagon

Adjust toe-in by removing the left and right tie rod turnbuckle retaining clips, then turning the left and right turnbuckles the same amount in opposite directions. To reduce toe-in, turn the left turnbuckle toward the front of the vehicle and the right turnbuckle toward the rear of the vehicle. For each half turn of the turnbuckle, toe-in will be adjusted by approximately .24 inch.

REAR WHEEL ALIGNMENT

On vehicles with aluminum wheels, attach camber/caster to driveshaft using tool No. MB991004 or equivalent.

CAMBER

Rear camber is pre-set during vehicle assembly and cannot be adjusted. If camber is not within specifications, check for worn or damaged suspension component, and damaged or deformed floor pan or body and repair as needed.

TOE-IN

Colt & Summit

Rear toe is pre-set during vehicle assembly and cannot be adjusted. If toe is not within specifications, check for worn or damaged suspension components, and damaged or deformed floor pan or body and repair as needed.

Colt Vista & Summit Wagon

Toe is adjustable by rotating the outer and inner arm mounting bolts. If toe-in is not within specifications, rotate left and right outer arm and inner arm bolts, each by the same amount, to perform adjustment. An adjustment of approximately .08 inch (2 mm) will be made when the outer arm and inner arm bolts are turned the equivalent of 1 alignment mark.

VEHICLE RIDE HEIGHT

| Year | Model | Height ① | |
		Front Bumper To Ground	Rear Bumper To Ground
1992–94	Colt & Summit ②	23.5	25.0
	Colt & Summit ③	23.5	21.0
	Colt Vista & Summit Wagon	④	④
1995	Summit ②	23.5	25.0
	Summit ③	23.5	21.0
	Summit Wagon	④	④

①—Measured in degrees from bottom center of wheel to bottom of bumper. If not within specifications, check suspension components for wear and damage.
②—Hatchback.
③—Sedan.
④—Minimum running ground clearance, measured in front of front wheels, is 6.7 inches.

DODGE STEALTH

NOTE: Refer To Rear Of This Manual For Vehicle Manufacturer's Special Service Tool Suppliers.

INDEX OF SERVICE OPERATIONS

NOTE: For Service Operations Not Listed Below, Refer To The Table Of Contents In The Front Of This Manual.

Specifications

GENERAL ENGINE SPECIFICATIONS

Year	Engine Liter/CID	VIN Code	Fuel System	Bore & Stroke	Compression Ratio	Net H.P. @ RPM	Maximum Torque Ft. Lbs. @ RPM	Normal Oil Pressure, psi ③
1992–95	3.0L/V6-181 ①	S	MPI	3.58 x 2.99	8.9	164 @ 5500	185 @ 4000	11.4
	3.0L/V6-181 ④	B	MPI	3.58 x 2.99	10.0	222 @ 6000	201 @ 4500	11.4
	3.0L/V6-181 ②	C	MPI	3.58 x 2.99	8.0	300 @ 6000	307 @ 2500	11.4

MPI— Multi-Port Fuel Injection
① —Single over head cam.
② —Dual over head cam, turbocharged.
③ —Minimum at 700 RPM w/oil temperature at 167–174°F.
④ —Dual over head cam, except turbocharged.

TUNE UP SPECIFICATIONS

Year & Engine Liter/CID, VIN Code	Spark Plug Gap	Firing Order Fig. ②	Ignition Timing @ BTDC Man. Trans. ①	Ignition Timing @ BTDC Auto. Trans. ①	Mark Fig.	Curb Idle Speed, RPM Man. Trans.	Curb Idle Speed, RPM Auto. Trans.	Fast Idle Speed, RPM Man. Trans.	Fast Idle Speed, RPM Auto. Trans.	Fuel Pump Pressure, psi ③
1992–95										
3.0L/V6-181, S ④	.39–.43	A	5	5	C	600–800	600–800	⑧	⑧	47–50
3.0L/V6-181, B ⑤	.39–.43	B	5	5	⑦	600–800	600–800	⑧	⑧	47–50
3.0L/V6-181, C ⑥	.39–.43	B	5	5	⑦	600–800	600–800	⑧	⑧	43–45

BTDC-Before Top Dead Center.
① —With ignition timing adjusting terminal grounded.
② —Firing order, 1-2-3-4-5-6.
③ —With vacuum hose disconnected at curb idle speed.
④ —Single overhead cam.
⑤ —Dual overhead cam, except turbocharged.
⑥ —Dual overhead cam, turbocharged.
⑦ —Equipped w/crankshaft position sensor.
⑧ —Controlled by idle speed control system.

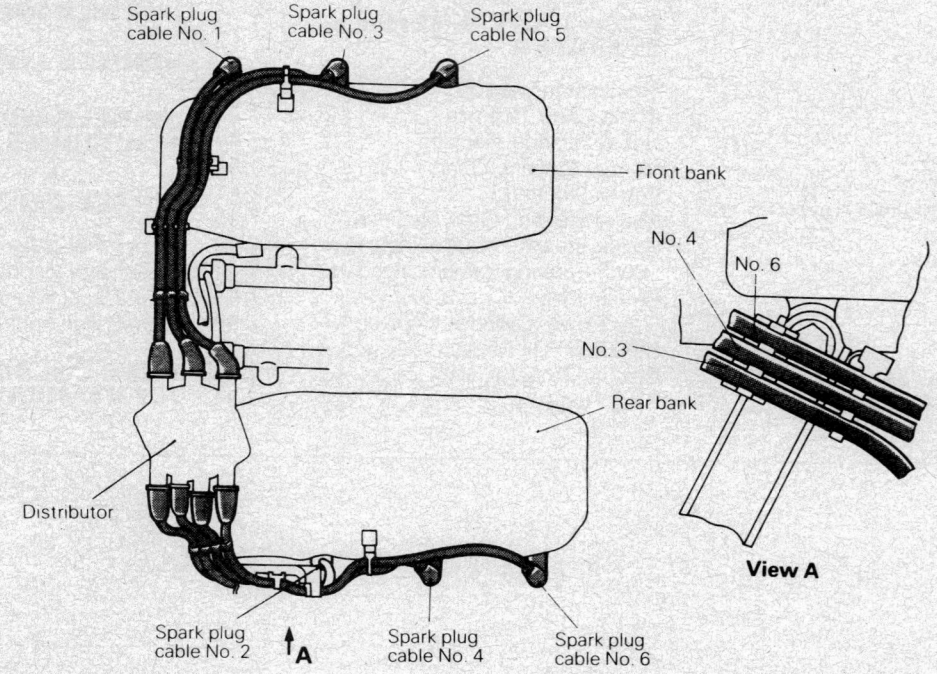

Fig. A

CR1139100189000X

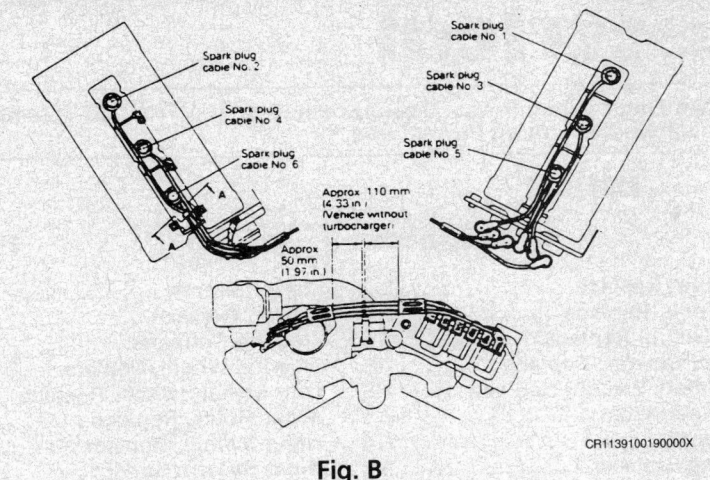

Fig. B

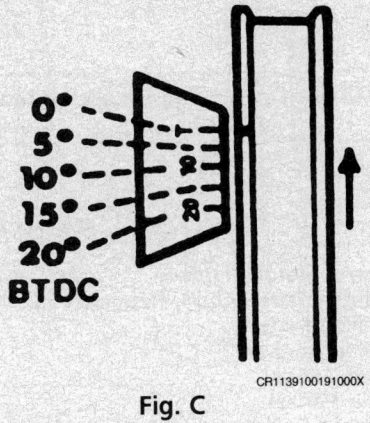

Fig. C

FRONT WHEEL ALIGNMENT SPECIFICATIONS

| Year | Model | Caster Angle, Degrees | | Camber Angle, Degrees | | Toe-In Inch |
		Limits	Desired	Limits	Desired	
1992–95	All	+ 3.42 to + 4.42	+ 3.92	-.5 to + .5	0	-.12 to + .12

REAR WHEEL ALIGNMENT SPECIFICATIONS

| Year | Model | Camber Angle, Degrees | | Toe-In Inch |
		Limits	Desired	
1992–95	FWD	-.5 to + .5	0	-.08 to + .12
	AWD	-1/3 to + 2/3	0	-.08 to + .12

COOLING SYSTEM & CAPACITY DATA

| Year | Engine, Liter/CID, VIN Code | Coolant Capacity, Qts. | | Radiator Cap Relief Pressure, Lbs. | Thermo. Opening Temp.°F | Fuel Tank, Gals. | Engine Oil Refill Qts.① | Transaxle Oil | |
		Less A/C	With A/C					Manual Transaxle, Pts.②	Auto. Transaxle, Qts.
1992–95	3.0L/V6-181, S	8.5	8.5	11–15	③	19.8	4.2	②	7.9

①—Add .5 quart for filter and/or oil cooler.
②—FWD, 2.4 quarts; AWD, 2.5 quarts.
③—SOHC, 180°F, DOHC, 170°F.

LUBRICANT DATA

| Year | Model | Lubricant Type | | | | | |
| | | Transaxle | | Transfer Case | Rear Axle | Power Steering | Brake System |
		Manual	Automatic				
1992–95	All	API GL-4	Dia ATF SP①	API GL-4	API GL-5	②	③

①—Automatic transmission fluid type 7176 or equivalent.
transmission fluid type 7176 or equivalent.
③—DOT 3 or DOT 4 brake fluid or equivalent.
②—Dexron or Dexron II automatic

Electrical

NOTE: On Air Bag Equipped Models, Refer To "Air Bag System Precautions" Located In The Front Of This Manual For System Disarming & Arming Procedures.

INDEX

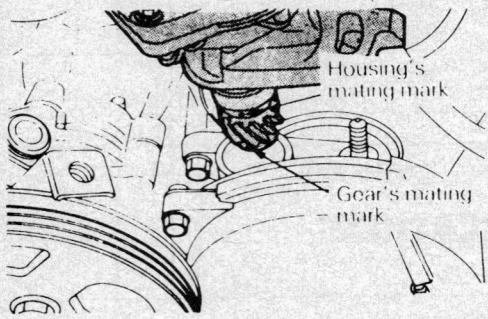

Fig. 1   Distributor alignment

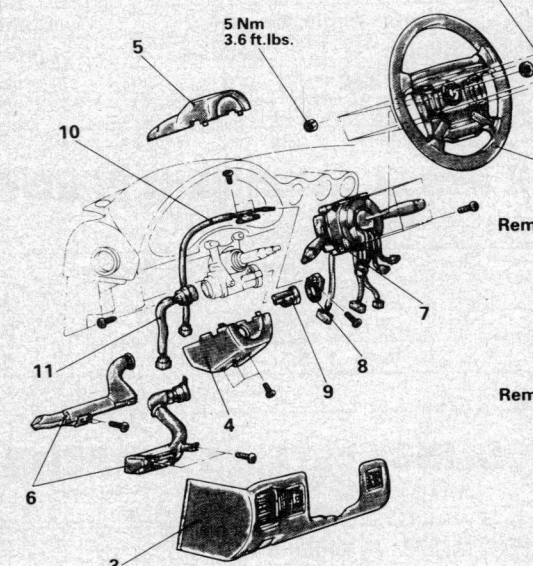

Removal steps of ignition switch segment

3. Knee protector

4. Column cover lower
5. Column cover upper
6. Lap cooler duct and foot shower duct
10. Key reminder switch segment
11. Ignition switch segment

Removal steps of steering lock cylinder

1. Air bag module

2. Steering wheel
3. Knee protector

4. Column cover lower
5. Column cover upper
6. Lap cooler duct and foot shower duct
7. Column switch and clock spring assembly
8. Ignition key illumination ring
9. Steering lock cylinder

Fig. 2   Ignition lock & ignition switch

PRECAUTIONS

AIR BAG SYSTEMS

Refer to "Air Bag System Precautions" in the front of this manual for system disarming and arming procedures.

FUSE PANEL & FLASHER LOCATION

The fuse panel is located under the instrument panel to the left of the steering column.

The turn signal and hazard flasher unit is located to the lower left of the steering column near the drivers door assembly.

RELAY CENTER LOCATION

The relay center is located at the right-hand front of the engine compartment.

STARTER
REPLACE

1. Disconnect battery ground cable.
2. Disconnect starter motor electrical connector.
3. Remove starter motor bracket attaching bolt.
4. Remove starter motor attaching nut, then remove starter motor assembly.

5. Reverse procedure to install. **Torque** starter motor bracket attaching bolt to 22 ft. lbs.

DISTRIBUTOR
REPLACE

1. Disconnect battery ground cable.
2. Disconnect spark plug wires.
3. Remove distributor assembly attaching nut, then remove distributor.
4. Reverse procedure to install, noting the following:
   a. Rotate crankshaft that No. 1 cylinder is at compression top dead center (TDC).
   b. Align distributor housing and gear mating marks, **Fig. 1.**
   c. **Torque** distributor assembly attaching nut to 11 ft. lbs.

IGNITION LOCK
REPLACE

1. Remove steering wheel as outlined under "Steering Wheel, Replace."
2. Remove instrument panel lower knee protector attaching screws.
3. Remove ignition lock cylinder as shown in **Fig. 2**, noting the following:
   a. Remove steering column cover upper to lower attaching screws, then carefully unsnap upper steering column cover from lower.
   b. To remove steering lock cylinder insert ignition key and place in "ACC" position.
   c. Using suitable Phillips head screwdriver, press lockpin inward to release lock cylinder.

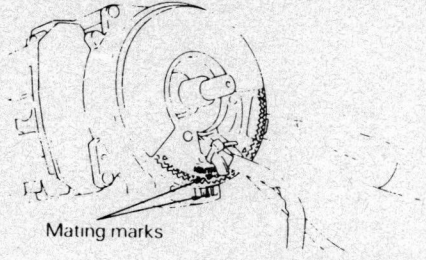

Fig. 3 Steering wheel clock spring alignment

4. Reverse procedure to install. Align Neutral mark of clock spring with mating marks, **Fig. 3.** If clock spring is not properly aligned, steering wheel may not be completely rotational, or flat cable within clock spring may be severed obstructing normal SRS operation which may cause personal injury.

IGNITION SWITCH
REPLACE

1. Remove instrument panel lower knee protector attaching screws.
2. Remove ignition switch as shown in **Fig. 2,** noting the following:
   a. Remove steering column cover upper to lower attaching screws, then carefully unsnap upper steering column cover from lower.
3. Reverse procedure to install.

NEUTRAL SAFETY SWITCH
REPLACE

1. Disconnect battery ground cable.
2. Disconnect neutral switch electrical connector.
3. Remove neutral switch assembly.
4. Reverse procedure to install. Adjust as follows:
   a. Place selector lever in "Neutral" position.
   b. Place manual control lever in "Neutral" position.
   c. Turn switch body, ensuring manual control lever end is aligned with opening in switch body flange.
   d. **Torque** switch attaching bolts to 7-9 ft. lbs.

HEADLAMP SWITCH
REPLACE

1. Disconnect battery ground cable.
2. Remove instrument panel lower knee protector attaching screws.
3. Remove headlamp switch as shown in **Fig. 4,** noting the following:
   a. Remove steering column cover upper to lower attaching screws, then carefully unsnap upper steering column cover from lower.
4. Reverse procedure to install.

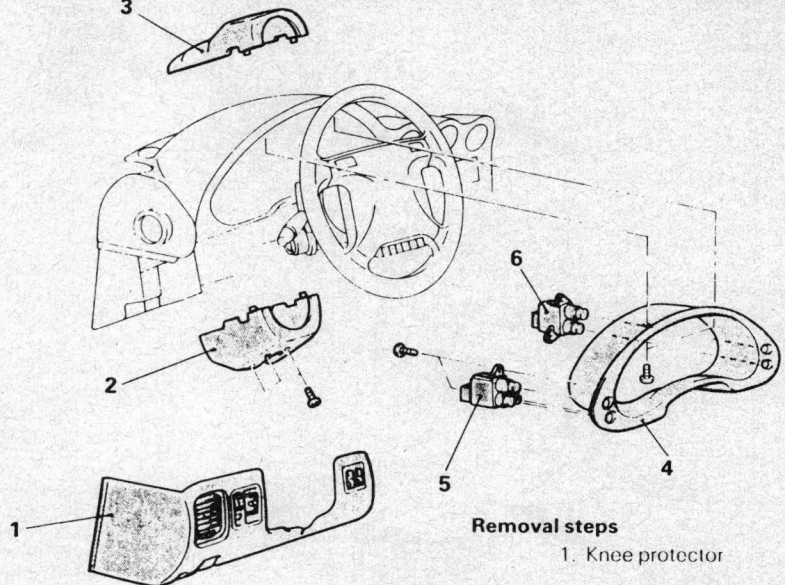

Removal steps

1. Knee protector
2. Column cover lower
3. Column cover upper
4. Meter bezel
5. Pop-up switch and fog light switch
6. Rear window defogger switch

Fig. 4 Headlight switch assembly

COMBINATION SWITCH
REPLACE

1. Disconnect battery ground cable.
2. Remove steering wheel as outlined under "Steering Wheel, Replace."
3. Remove turn signal switch as shown in **Fig. 5,** noting the following:
   a. Remove steering column cover upper to lower attaching screws, then carefully unsnap upper steering column cover from lower.
4. Reverse procedure to install.

TURN SIGNAL SWITCH
REPLACE

Refer to "Combination Switch, Replace" for turn signal switch replacement.

DIMMER SWITCH
REPLACE

Refer to "Combination Switch, Replace" for dimmer switch replacement.

STEERING WHEEL
REPLACE

1. Remove air bag module and air bag clock spring as outlined in the "Passive Restraints" section. **Do not use excessive force to disconnect clock spring. Store air bag assembly in dry place with pad cover face up.**
2. Remove steering wheel attaching nut.
3. Using suitable steering wheel removal tool, remove steering wheel. **Do not use hammer to remove steering wheel as damage may occur.**

4. Reverse procedure to install, noting the following:
   a. **Torque** steering wheel attaching nut to 29 ft. lbs.
   b. Install clock spring and air bag as outlined in the "Passive Restraints" section. **If clock spring is not properly aligned, steering wheel may not be completely rotational, or flat cable within clock spring may be severed obstructing normal SRS operation which may cause personal injury.**

INSTRUMENT CLUSTER
REPLACE

1. Remove instrument panel lower knee protector panel attaching screws.
2. Remove steering column cover upper to lower attaching screws, then carefully unsnap upper steering column cover from lower.
3. Remove instrument cluster as shown in **Fig. 6,** noting the following:
   a. **On models equipped with mechanical speedometer,** disconnect speedometer cable at transaxle, then pull toward interior, then disconnect instrument cluster speedometer adapter by turning right or left.
4. Reverse procedure to install.

RADIO
REPLACE

1. Disconnect battery ground cable.
2. Remove radio assembly as shown in **Fig. 7.**

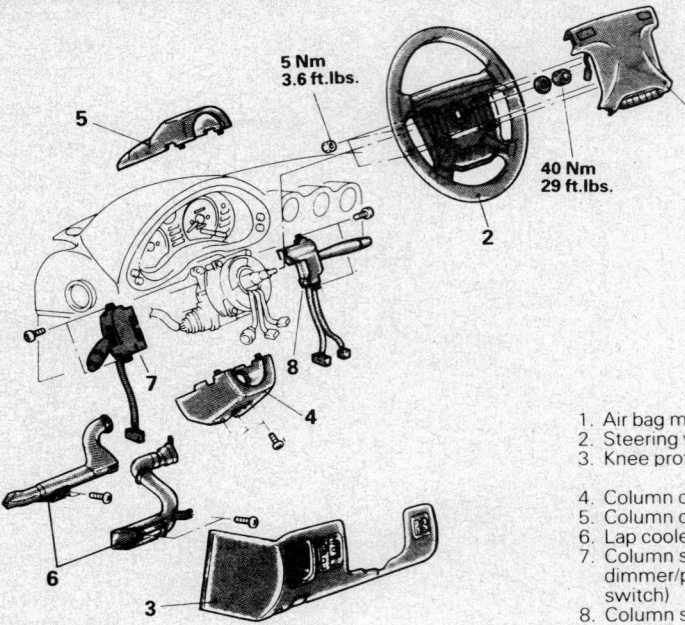

5 Nm
3.6 ft.lbs.

40 Nm
29 ft.lbs.

1. Air bag module
2. Steering wheel
3. Knee protector

4. Column cover lower
5. Column cover upper
6. Lap cooler duct and foot shower duct
7. Column switch left (For lighting switch, dimmer/passing switch and turn signal switch)
8. Column switch right (For wiper and washer switch)

CR6049100094000X

Fig. 5   Combination switch replacement

3. Remove front console assembly as shown in **Fig. 8**.
4. Reverse procedure to install.

WIPER MOTOR
REPLACE

1. Disconnect battery ground cable.
2. Remove wiper arm attaching bolt, then remove wiper arm.
3. Unsnap hole cover assembly, **Fig. 9**.
4. Disconnect wiper motor electrical connector.
5. Remove wiper motor attaching bolts, then remove wiper motor.
6. Reverse procedure to install. **Torque** wiper motor attaching bolts to 7 ft. lbs. **Torque** wiper arm attaching nuts to 9.4 ft. lbs.

WIPER SWITCH
REPLACE

Refer to "Combination Switch, Replace" for wiper switch replacement.

WIPER TRANSMISSION
REPLACE

1. Disconnect battery ground cable.
2. Remove wiper blade, then remove wiper arm attaching nut.
3. Remove front deck attaching screws, then remove front deck.
4. Remove RH air inlet assembly.
5. Unsnap hole cover assembly.
6. Remove wiper motor attaching bolts, then position wiper motor aside.
7. Remove wiper transmission attaching bolts, then remove wiper transmission assembly.
8. Reverse procedure to install. **Torque** linkage attaching bolts to 4 ft. lbs. **Torque** wiper motor attaching bolts to

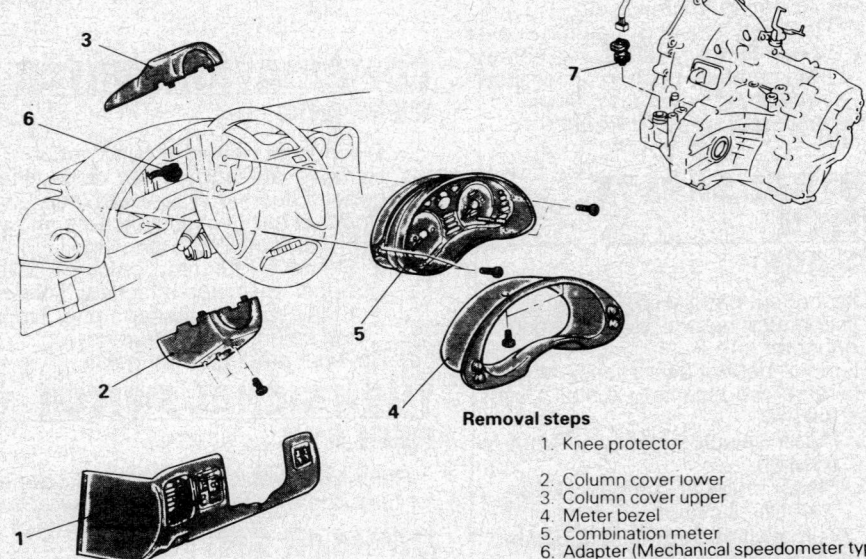

Removal steps
1. Knee protector
2. Column cover lower
3. Column cover upper
4. Meter bezel
5. Combination meter
6. Adapter (Mechanical speedometer type) / Washer tank
7. Vehicles speed sensor (Electrical speedometer type)

CR9099100061000X

Fig. 6   Instrument cluster

7 ft. lbs. **Torque** wiper arm attaching nuts to 9.4 ft. lbs.

BLOWER MOTOR
REPLACE

1. Disconnect battery ground cable.
2. Remove glove compartment attaching screws, then carefully push sides inward to remove.
3. Remove glove compartment latch attaching screws.
4. Remove four glove compartment outer case attaching screws.
5. Remove four right lower cover attaching screws.
6. Disconnect lower frame electrical connector, then remove lower frame attaching screws.
7. **On models equipped with A/C,** remove evaporator attaching bolt and nut.
8. **On all models,** disconnect air selection control wire at blower motor case.
9. Remove side frame attaching screws.
10. Disconnect blower motor electrical connectors.
11. Remove blower case attaching nuts, then remove blower motor case.

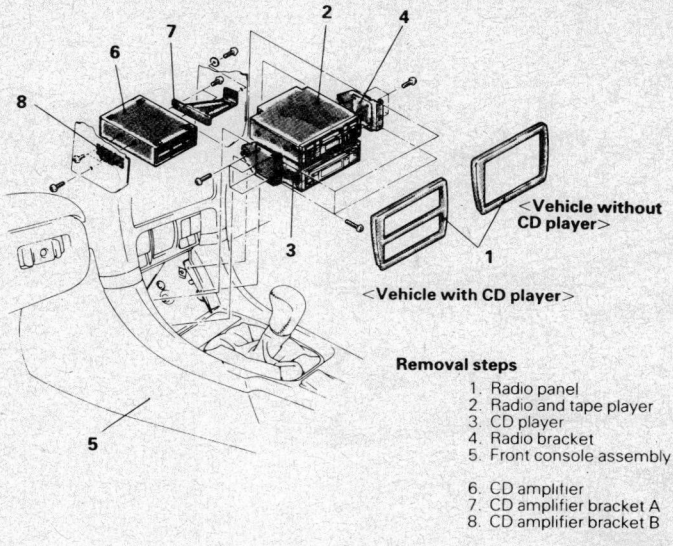

Removal steps

1. Radio panel
2. Radio and tape player
3. CD player
4. Radio bracket
5. Front console assembly

6. CD amplifier
7. CD amplifier bracket A
8. CD amplifier bracket B

<Vehicle without CD player>

<Vehicle with CD player>

CR9039100005000X

Fig. 7 Radio assembly

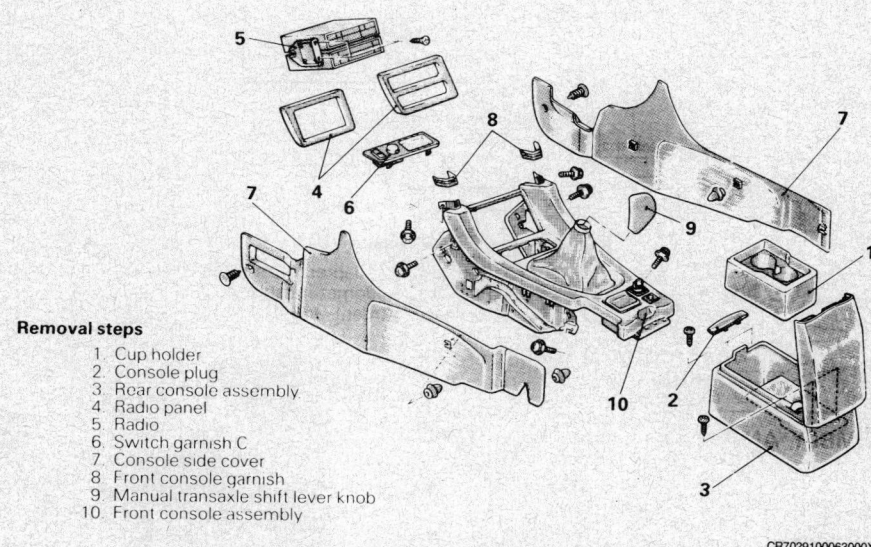

Removal steps

1. Cup holder
2. Console plug
3. Rear console assembly
4. Radio panel
5. Radio
6. Switch garnish C
7. Console side cover
8. Front console garnish
9. Manual transaxle shift lever knob
10. Front console assembly

CR7029100063000X

Fig. 8 Floor console assembly

---

12. Remove blower motor attaching bolt, then remove blower motor.
13. Reverse procedure to install, noting the following:
    a. Position air selection control lever as in **Fig. 10.**
    b. Press air selection damper inward, then connect inner cable of air selection wire to air selection lever, then secure outer cable with clip.

HEATER CORE
REPLACE

1. Disconnect battery ground cable.
2. Drain cooling system.

---

3. Remove floor console as shown in **Fig. 8.**
4. Remove instrument panel, as outlined under "Dash Panel Service."
5. Remove heater core as shown in **Fig. 11.** On models equipped with A/C, set inside/outside air selection damper to position that permits outside air introduction to prevent evaporator assembly attaching to enter the blower assembly.
6. Reverse procedure to install.

EVAPORATOR CORE
REPLACE

1. Discharge air conditioning system.

---

2. Remove battery cables, then remove battery assembly.
3. Remove evaporator case assembly as shown in **Fig. 12,** noting the following:
    a. Cap hoses and pipes to prevent entry of contaminates.
4. Disassemble evaporator case as shown in **Fig. 13,** noting the following:
    a. Disconnect evaporator cover attaching clips with suitable screwdriver covered with shop towel to prevent damage.
    b. Loosen expansion valve flare nut using two suitable wrenches.
5. Reverse procedure to install.

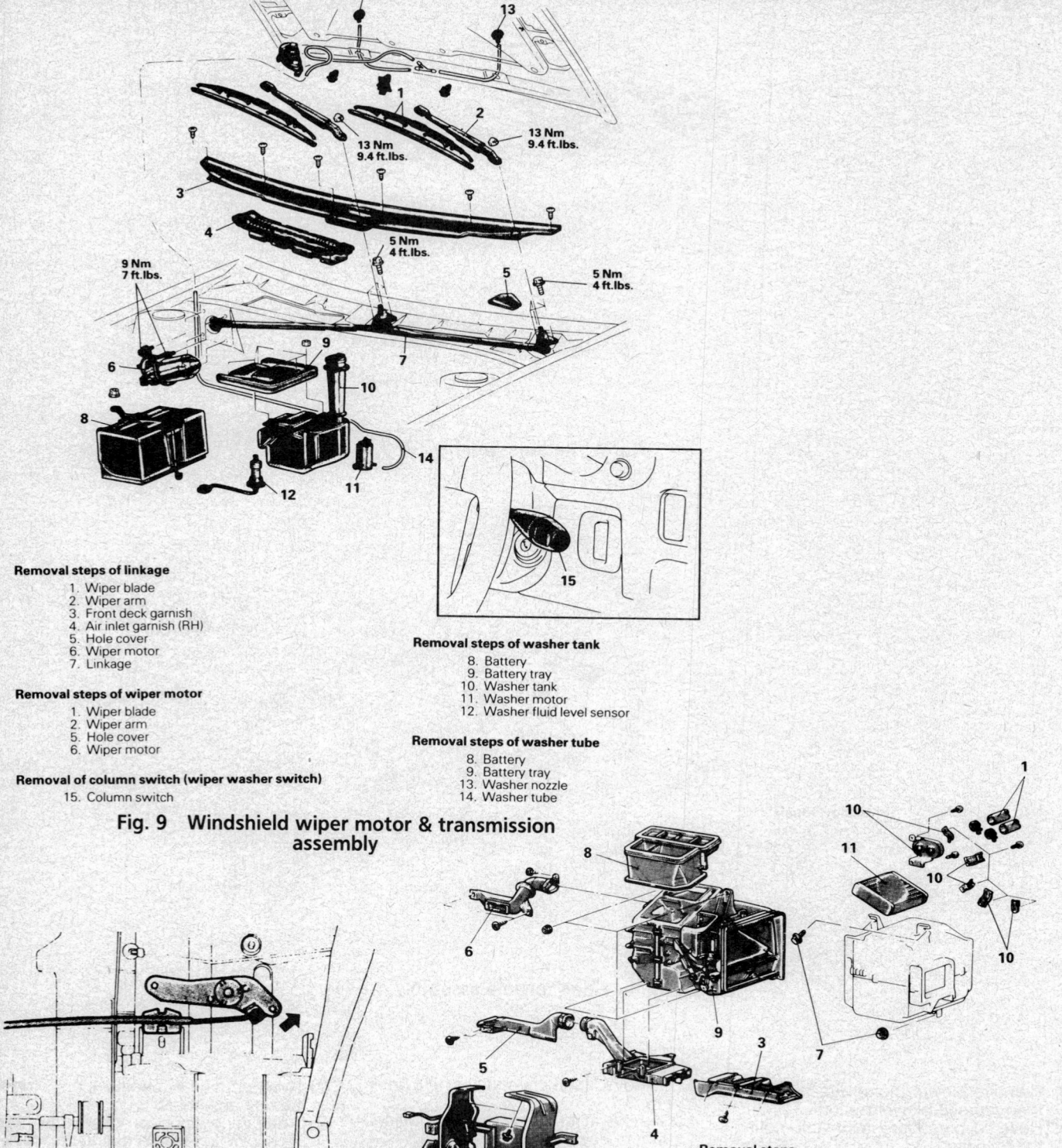

Removal steps of linkage

1. Wiper blade
2. Wiper arm
3. Front deck garnish
4. Air inlet garnish (RH)
5. Hole cover
6. Wiper motor
7. Linkage

Removal steps of wiper motor

1. Wiper blade
2. Wiper arm
5. Hole cover
6. Wiper motor

Removal of column switch (wiper washer switch)

15. Column switch

Removal steps of washer tank

8. Battery
9. Battery tray
10. Washer tank
11. Washer motor
12. Washer fluid level sensor

Removal steps of washer tube

8. Battery
9. Battery tray
13. Washer nozzle
14. Washer tube

Fig. 9 Windshield wiper motor & transmission assembly

Fig. 10 Air selection damper lever

CR7029100064000X

Removal steps

1. Connection of water hoses
2. Center reinforcement
3. Under cover
4. Distribution duct (foot)
5. Foot shower duct
6. Lap cooler duct
7. Evaporator mounting bolt and nut <Vehicles with air conditioner>
8. Center duct
9. Heater unit
10. Plate
11. Heater core

Fig. 11 Heater core assembly

CR7029100066000X

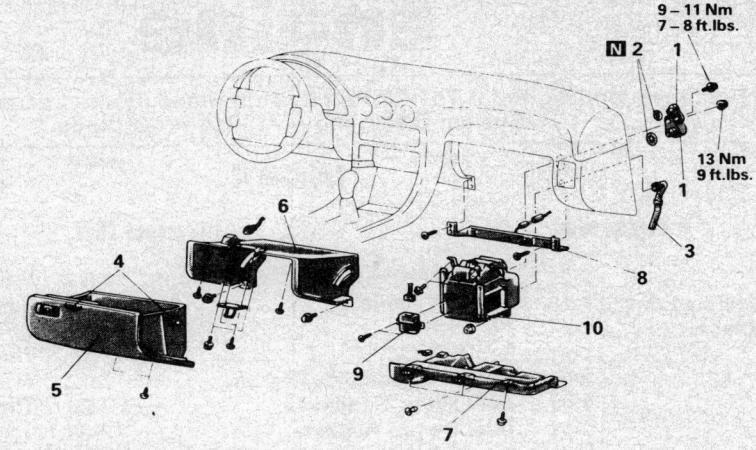

Removal steps

1. Connection of liquid pipe and suction hose
2. O-ring
3. Drain hose
4. Stopper
5. Glove box
6. Glove box outer case assembly
7. Under cover
8. Lower frame
9. A/C control unit
10. Evaporator

CR7029100067000X

Fig. 12 Evaporator case assembly

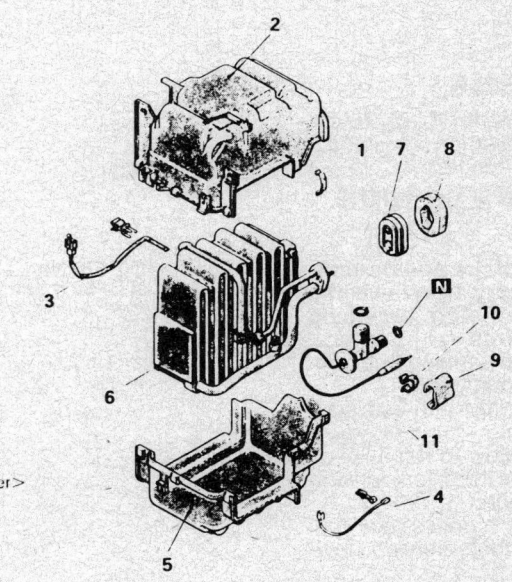

Disassembly steps

1. Clips
2. Evaporater case (upper)
3. Fin thermo sensor
4. Air inlet sensor
   Vehicles with manual air conditioner>
5. Evaporator case (lower)
6. Evaporator assembly
7. Grommet
8. Insulator
9. Rubber insulator
10. Clip
11. Expansion valve

CR7029100068000X

Fig. 13 Evaporator core assembly

Engine

NOTE: On Air Bag Equipped Models, Refer To "Air Bag System Precautions" Located In The Front Of This Manual For System Disarming & Arming Procedures.

INDEX

PRECAUTIONS

AIR BAG SYSTEMS

Refer to "Air Bag System Precautions" in the front of this manual for system disarming and arming procedures.

FUEL SYSTEM PRESSURE RELIEF

To reduce the risk of fire and personal injury, it is necessary to relieve the fuel system pressure before servicing fuel system components.

1. Remove fuel gauge sending unit cover in luggage compartment.
2. Disconnect fuel pump harness connector.
3. Start engine and allow to run.
4. After engine stop by itself, turn ignition switch to Off position.
5. Connect fuel pump harness after fuel system or components service have been completed.

ENGINE MOUNT
REPLACE
ENGINE ROLL STOPPER

Front

1. **On models with turbocharger, remove A/C condenser cooling fan assembly.**
2. **On models with turbocharger, remove left catalytic converter.**
3. Remove front engine roll stopper in order shown in **Fig. 1**.
4. Reverse procedure to install.

Rear

1. **On models with turbocharger, remove A/C condenser cooling fan assembly.**

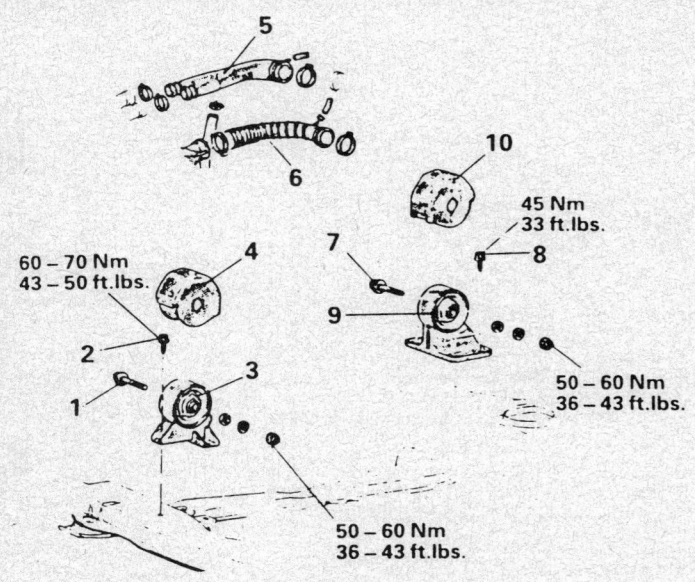

Front stopper bracket

1. Front roll stopper bracket and engine connection bolt
2. Front roll stopper bracket installation bolt
3. Front roll stopper bracket
4. Heat protector <Turbo>

Rear roll stopper bracket

5. Air hose A <Turbo>
6. Air intake hose C <Turbo>
7. Rear roll stopper bracket and engine connection bolt
8. Rear roll stopper bracket installation bolt
9. Rear roll stopper bracket
10. Heat protector <Turbo>

CR1069100492000X

Fig. 1 Engine roll stopper replacement

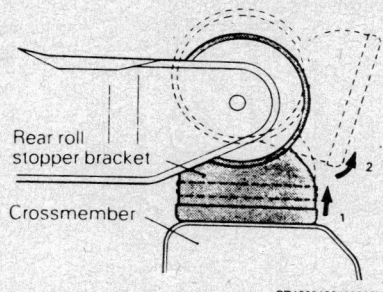

Fig. 2   Rear roll stopper mount installation

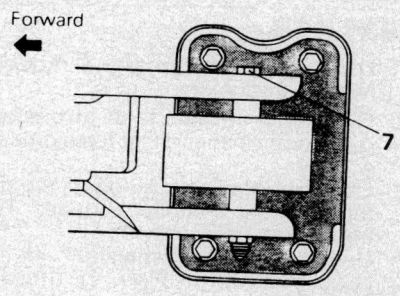

Fig. 3   Rear roll stopper mount bolt installation

2. **On models with turbocharger,** remove left catalytic converter.
3. **On all models,** remove rear roll stopper in order shown in **Fig. 1,** noting the following:
   a. Slightly raise rear roll stopper bracket while turning roll stopper as shown in **Fig. 2.**
4. Reverse procedure to install, noting the following:
   a. Install rear roll stopper bracket as shown in **Fig. 2.**
   b. Install through bolt as shown in **Fig. 3.**

ENGINE

1. Raise and support engine using suitable support tool.
2. Remove engine mount in order shown in **Fig. 4,** noting the following:
   a. Remove actuator and position aside.
3. Reverse procedure to install, noting the following:
   a. When installing engine mounting bracket, align arrow on mounting stopper as shown in **Fig. 5.**

TRANSAXLE

1. Raise and support transaxle using suitable support tool.
2. Remove air cleaner assembly.
3. Remove transaxle mount in order shown in **Fig. 6.**
4. Reverse procedure to install, noting the following:
   a. When installing transaxle mounting bracket, align arrow on mounting stopper as shown in **Fig. 7.**

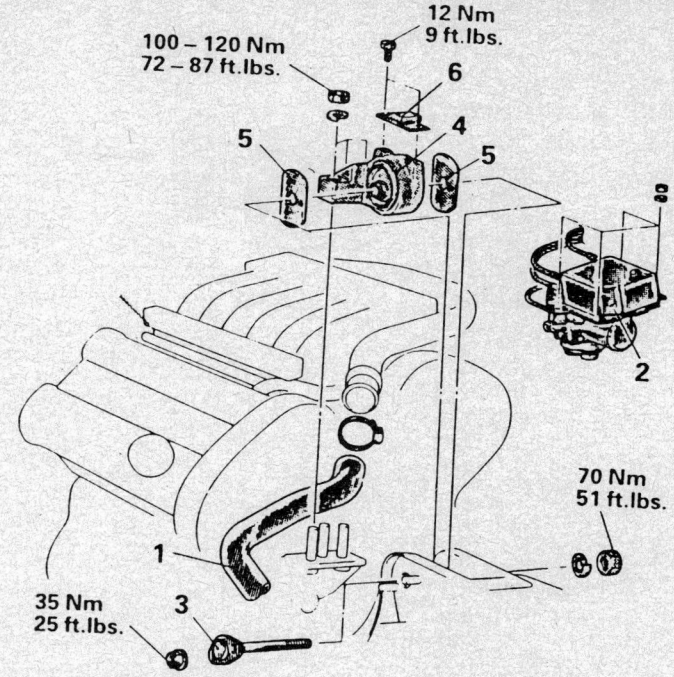

1 Connection for air hose G <Turbo>
2 Cruise control pump and link assembly <Vehicles with Cruise Control>
3 Engine mount bracket and body connection bolt
4 Engine mount bracket
5 Mounting stopper
6 Dynamic damper <DOHC>

Fig. 4   Engine mount replacement

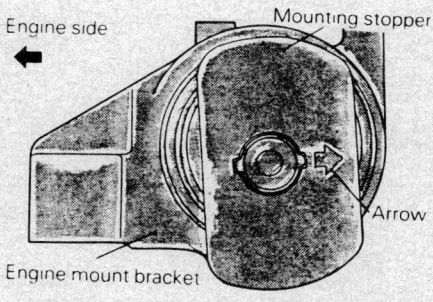

Fig. 5   Engine mount installation

ENGINE
REPLACE
SOHC

1. Relieve fuel system pressure as outlined under "Precautions."
2. Mark and remove hood assembly.
3. Disconnect and remove cruise control pump and link assembly.
4. Drain cooling system.
5. Remove front exhaust pipes.
6. Remove transaxle as outlined under "Clutch & Manual Transaxle."
7. Remove radiator assembly as outlined under "Radiator, Replace".
8. Remove engine assembly in order shown in **Fig. 8,** noting the following:

   a. Disconnect power steering pump and A/C compressor with hoses attached. Support aside with rope or other suitable material.
   b. Open relay box cover and disconnect alternator wiring harness.
   c. Disconnect oil pressure gauge connector from sending unit located near the oil filter.
   d. Remove engine mount as outlined under "Engine Mount, Replace."
   e. Ensure all necessary electrical connections and hoses are disconnected and positioned out of the way.
   f. Slowly raise engine assembly out of vehicle.
9. Reverse procedure to install.

DOHC

1. Relieve fuel system pressure as outlined under "Precautions."
2. Mark and remove hood assembly.
3. Disconnect and remove cruise control pump and link assembly.
4. **On turbocharged models,** remove air hose and air pipe.
5. **On all models,** remove front exhaust pipes.
6. Remove transaxle as outlined under "Clutch & Manual Transaxle."
7. Remove radiator assembly as outlined under "Radiator, Replace".

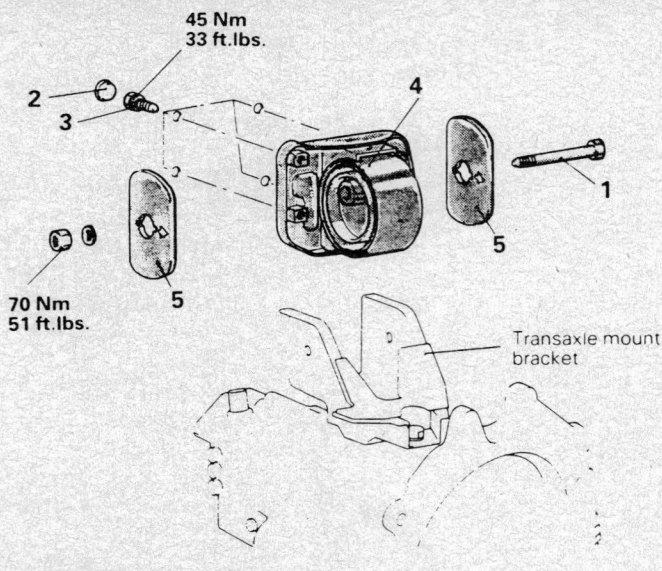

Removal steps

1. Transaxle mount bracket and transaxle connection bolt
2. Cap
3. Transaxle mount bracket installation bolt
4. Transaxle mount bracket
5. Mounting stopper

CR1069100490000X

Fig. 6 Transaxle mount replacement

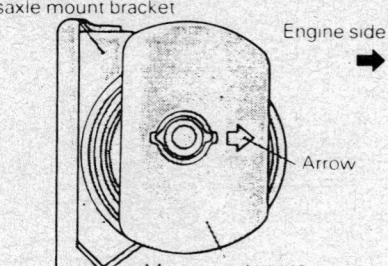

CR1069100491000X

Fig. 7 Transaxle mount installation

8. Remove engine assembly in order shown in **Fig. 9**, noting the following:
   a. Disconnect power steering pump and A/C compressor with hoses attached. Support aside with rope or other suitable material.
   b. Remove engine mount as outlined under "Engine Mount, Replace."
   c. Ensure all necessary electrical connections and hoses are disconnected and positioned out of the way.
   d. Slowly raise engine assembly out of vehicle.
9. Reverse procedure to install.

INTAKE AIR PLENUM
REPLACE

1. Remove intake air plenum in sequence shown in **Figs. 10 through 12**.
2. Install intake air plenum in reverse sequence shown in **Figs. 10 through 12**, noting the following:
   a. Install throttle body gasket with protrusion positioned as shown, **Fig. 13**.

INTAKE MANIFOLD
REPLACE

SOHC

1. Relieve fuel system pressure as outlined under "Precautions."
2. Drain engine coolant.
3. Remove intake air plenum as outlined under "Intake Air Plenum, Replace."
4. Remove intake manifold in sequence shown in **Fig. 14**, noting the following:

a. Disconnect delivery pipe with injectors attached.
5. Reverse procedure to install, noting the following:
   a. Install intake manifold gasket with adhesive coated side toward the intake manifold.
   b. Apply lubricant to the intake manifold nuts and tighten to specification.

DOHC

1. Relieve fuel system pressure as outlined under "Precautions."
2. Drain engine coolant.
3. Remove intake air plenum as outlined under "Intake Air Plenum, Replace."
4. Remove intake manifold in sequence shown in **Fig. 15**.
5. Reverse procedure to install, noting the following:
   a. Install intake manifold gaskets with protrusion position as shown, **Fig. 16**.
   b. On turbocharged models, **Torque** intake manifold front bank nuts to 2.2-3.6 ft. lbs.
   c. On turbocharged models, **Torque** intake manifold rear bank nuts to 9-11 ft. lbs.
   d. On turbocharged models, **Torque** intake manifold front bank nuts to 9-11 ft. lbs.
   e. **On turbocharged models**, repeat steps c and d one more time.
   f. **On except turbocharged models**, lubricate intake manifold nuts and tighten to specification.

EXHAUST MANIFOLD
REPLACE

1. **On except turbocharged models,** remove front exhaust pipe.
2. **On DOHC models less turbocharged,** remove condenser fan motor assembly.
3. **On turbocharged models,** remove turbocharger as outlined under "Turbocharger, Replace."
4. Remove exhaust manifold in sequence shown in **Figs. 17 through 19.**
5. **On except turbocharged models,** reverse procedure shown in **Fig. 17 and 18** to install.
6. **On turbocharged models,** install exhaust manifold in reverse sequence shown in **Fig. 19,** noting the following:
   a. **Torque** exhaust manifold nuts marked A to 22 ft. lbs., **Fig. 20.**
   b. **Torque** exhaust manifold nuts marked B to 34-38 ft. lbs., **Fig. 20.**
   c. Back off exhaust manifold nuts marked B to a **Torque** value of 7 ft. lbs.
   d. **Torque** exhaust manifold nuts marked B to 21-22 ft. lbs.
   e. Install exhaust manifold stay with it resting on exhaust manifold, fit it along with exhaust manifold over the studs.
   f. **Torque** exhaust manifold nuts marked C to 22 ft. lbs., **Fig. 21.**
   g. Temporarily tighten turbocharger to exhaust manifold.
   h. **Torque** nut marked D to 22 ft. lbs., **Fig. 21.**
   i. **Torque** exhaust manifold nuts marked E and F to 34-38 ft. lbs., **Fig. 21.**
   j. Back off exhaust manifold nuts marked E and F to a **Torque** value of 7 ft. lbs.
   k. **Torque** exhaust manifold nuts marked E and F to 21-22 ft. lbs., **Fig. 21.**

CYLINDER HEAD
REPLACE

SOHC

1. Remove exhaust manifold as outlined under "Exhaust Manifold, Replace."

Continued on page 7-18

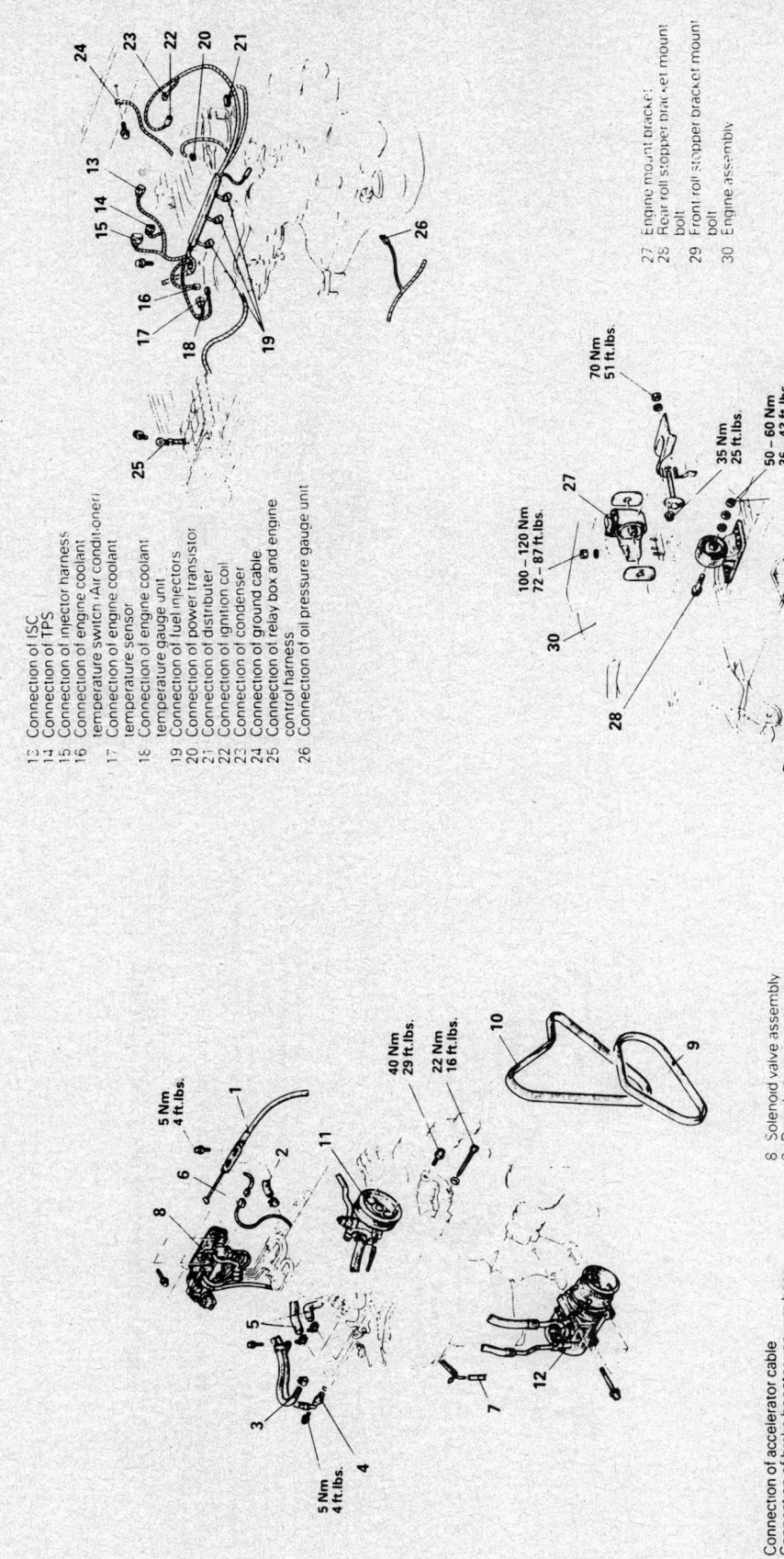

CR106910049502OX

13 Connection of ISC
14 Connection of TPS
15 Connection of injector harness
16 Connection of engine coolant
    temperature switch (Air conditioner)
17 Connection of engine coolant
    temperature sensor
18 Connection of engine coolant
    temperature gauge unit
19 Connection of fuel injectors
20 Connection of power transistor
21 Connection of distributor
22 Connection of ignition coil
23 Connection of condenser
24 Connection of ground cable
25 Connection of relay box and engine
    control harness
26 Connection of oil pressure gauge unit

27 Engine mount bracket
28 Rear roll stopper bracket mount
    bolt
29 Front roll stopper bracket mount
    bolt
30 Engine assembly

Fig. 8 Engine replacement (Part 2 of 2). SOHC

70 Nm
51 ft.lbs.

35 Nm
25 ft.lbs.

50 – 60 Nm
36 – 43 ft.lbs.

100 – 120 Nm
72 – 87 ft.lbs.

50 – 60 Nm
36 – 43 ft.lbs.

1   Connection of accelerator cable
2   Connection of brake booster vacuum hose
3   Connection of fuel return hose
4   Connection of fuel high pressure hose
5   Connection of heater hose
6   Connection of EGR temperature sensor
    <Vehicles for California>
7   Connection of vaper hose

8   Solenoid valve assembly
9   Drive belt (air conditioner)
10 Drive belt (alternator and power steering)
11 Power steering oil pump
12 Air conditioner compressor

5 Nm
4 ft.lbs.

40 Nm
29 ft.lbs.

22 Nm
16 ft.lbs.

5 Nm
4 ft.lbs.

CR106910049501OX

Fig. 8 Engine replacement (Part 1 of 2). SOHC

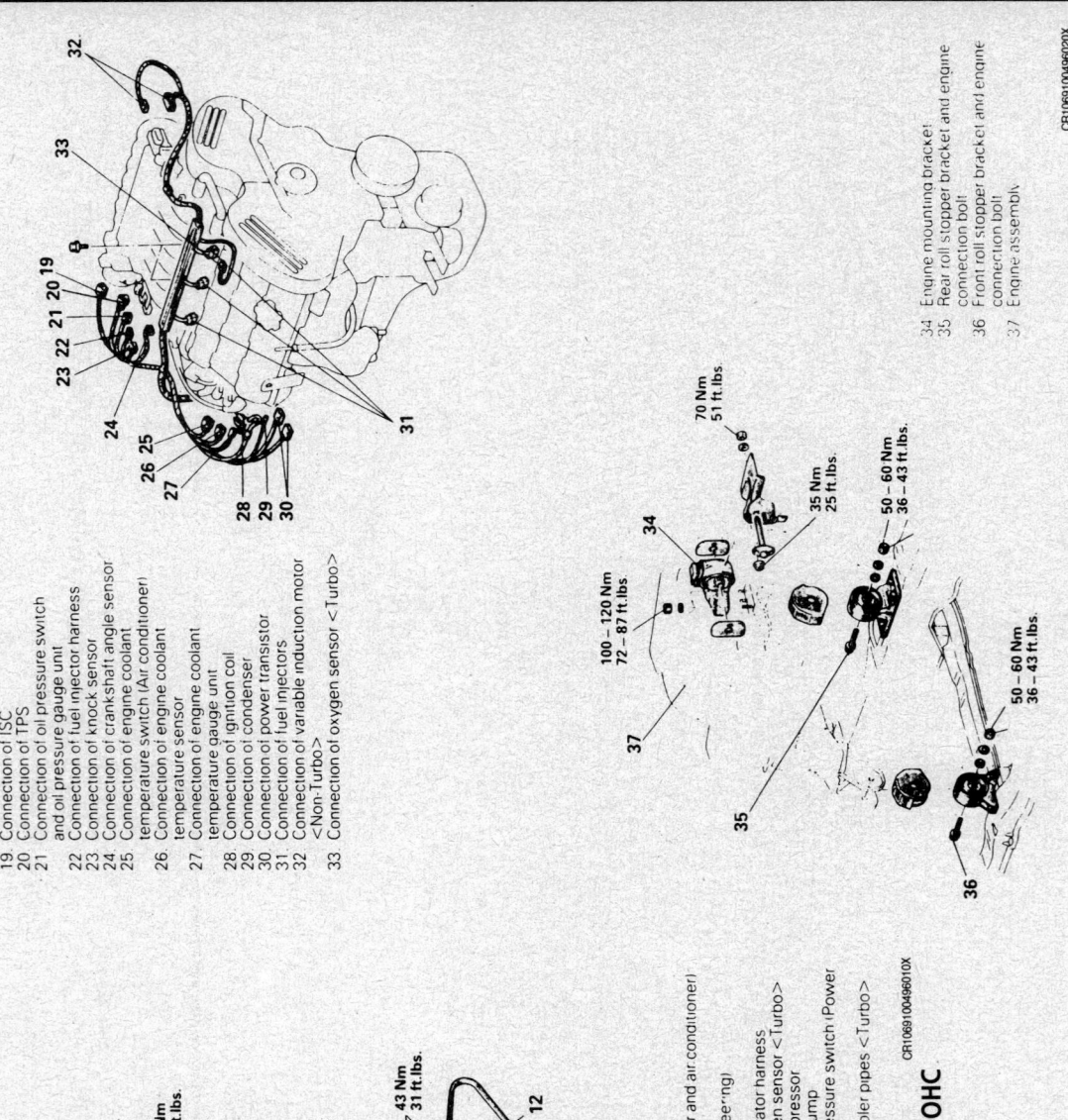

Fig. 9 Engine replacement (Part 2 of 2). DOHC

Fig. 9 Engine replacement (Part 1 of 2). DOHC

19 Connection of ISC
20 Connection of TPS
21 Connection of oil pressure switch and oil pressure gauge unit
22 Connection of fuel injector harness
23 Connection of knock sensor
24 Connection of crankshaft angle sensor
25 Connection of engine coolant temperature switch (Air conditioner)
26 Connection of engine coolant temperature sensor
27 Connection of engine coolant temperature gauge unit
28 Connection of ignition coil
29 Connection of condenser
30 Connection of power transistor
31 Connection of fuel injectors
32 Connection of variable induction motor <Non-Turbo>
33 Connection of oxygen sensor <Turbo>

34 Engine mounting bracket
35 Rear roll stopper bracket and engine connection bolt
36 Front roll stopper bracket and engine connection bolt
37 Engine assembly

1 Connection of accelerator cable
2 Connection of brake booster vacuum hose
3 Connection of booster vacuum hose <Turbo>
4 Connection of fuel return hose
5 Connection of fuel high pressure hose
6 Connection of ground cable
7 Solenoid valve assembly
8 Connection of vapor hose
9 Connection of heater hose
10 Connection of EGR temperature sensor <Vehicles for California>
11 Drive belt (Alternator and air conditioner)
12 Drive belt (Power steering)
13 Connection of alternator harness
14 Connection of oxygen sensor <Turbo>
15 Air conditioner compressor
16 Power steering oil pump
17 Connection of oil pressure switch (Power steering)
18 Connection of oil cooler pipes <Turbo>

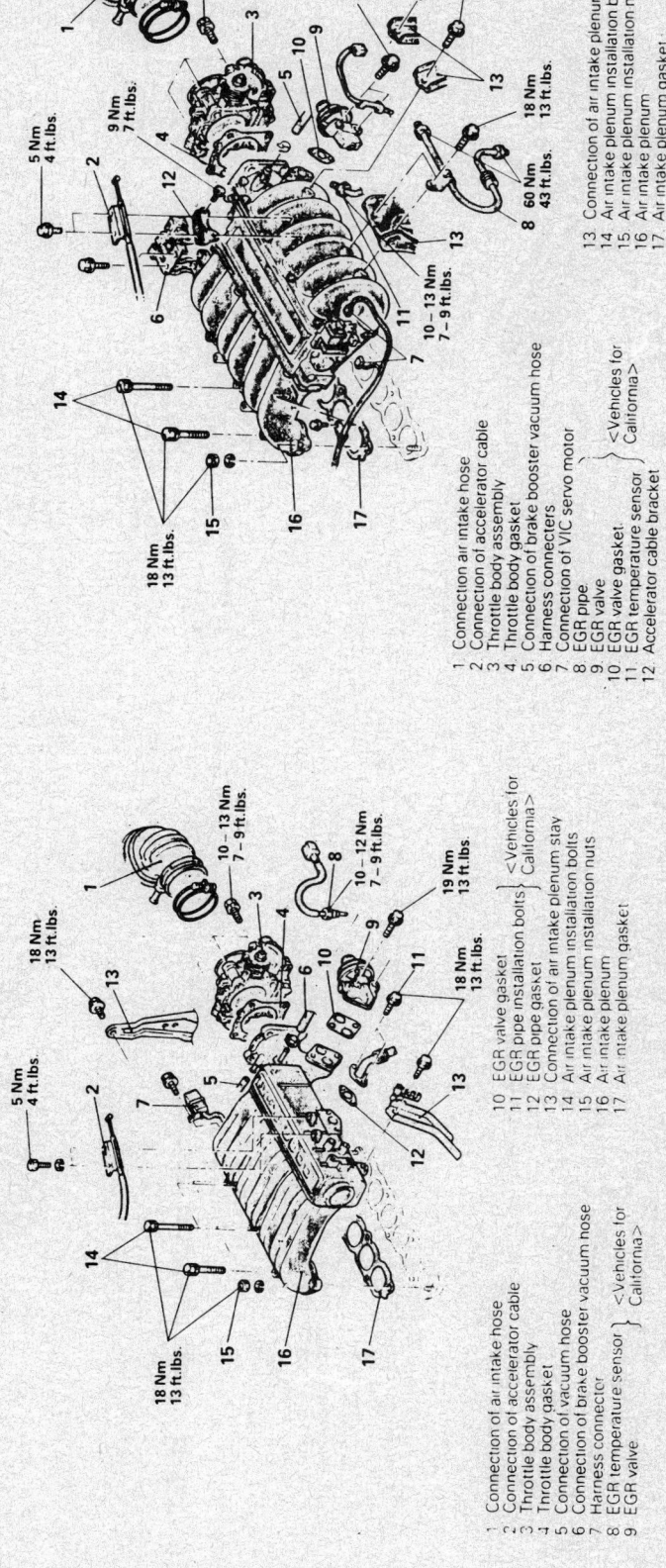

1 Connection air intake hose
2 Connection of accelerator cable
3 Throttle body assembly
4 Throttle body gasket
5 Connection of brake booster vacuum hose
6 Harness connecters
7 Connection of VIC servo motor
8 EGR pipe
9 EGR valve
10 EGR valve gasket.
11 EGR temperature sensor ⎫ <Vehicles for
                                ⎬ California>
12 Accelerator cable bracket

13 Connection of air intake plenum stay
14 Air intake plenum installation bolts
15 Air intake plenum installation nuts
16 Air intake plenum
17 Air intake plenum gasket

CR105910006700CX

Fig. 11 Intake air plenum replacement. DOHC except turbocharged

1 Connection of air intake hose
2 Connection of accelerator cable
3 Throttle body assembly
4 Throttle body gasket
5 Connection of vacuum hose
6 Connection of brake booster vacuum nose
7 Harness connector
8 EGR temperature sensor ⎫ <Vehicles for
                              ⎬ California>
9 EGR valve

10 EGR valve gasket
11 EGR pipe installation bolts ⎫ <Vehicles for
                                    ⎬ California>
12 EGR pipe gasket
13 Connection of air intake plenum stay
14 Air intake plenum installation bolts
15 Air intake plenum installation nuts
16 Air intake plenum
17 Air intake plenum gasket

CR1069100497000X

Fig. 10 Intake air plenum replacement. SOHC

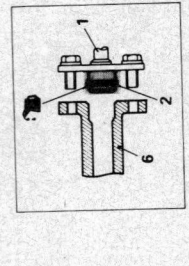

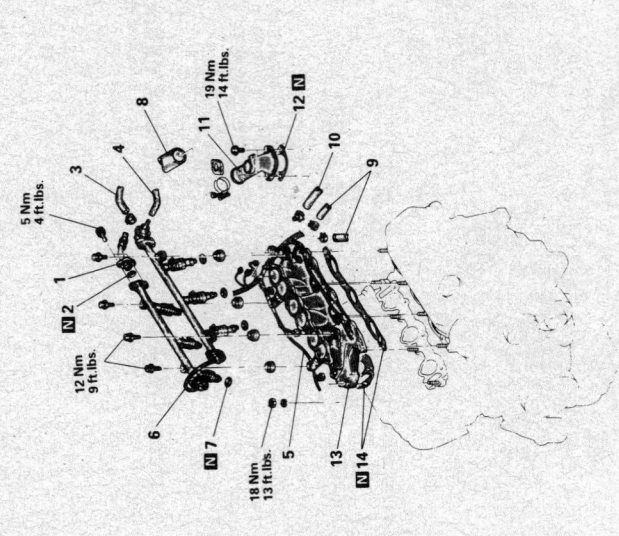

Removal steps

1. Connection for high-pressure fuel hose
2. O-ring
3. Connection for fuel return hose
4. Connection for vacuum hoses
5. Wiring harness connector
6. Delivery pipe (with injectors)
7. Insulators
8. Connection for radiator upper hose
9. Connection for heater hose
10. Connection for water hose
11. Water outlet fitting
12. Water outlet fitting gasket
13. Intake manifold
14. Intake manifold gasket

Fig. 14   Intake manifold replacement. SOHC

CR105910000700000X

5 Nm
4 ft.lbs.

12 Nm
9 ft.lbs.

18 Nm
13 ft.lbs.

19 Nm
14 ft.lbs.

---

5 Nm
4 ft.lbs.

10–13 Nm
7–9 ft.lbs.

19 Nm
13 ft.lbs.

18 Nm
13 ft.lbs.

18 Nm
13 ft.lbs.

10–13 Nm
7–9 ft.lbs.

10–13 Nm
7–9 ft.lbs.

Turbocharger

Grease: MOPAR Multi-mileage Lubricant Part No. 2525035 or equivalent

1. Connection air hose A
2. Connection of accelerator cable
3. Throttle body assembly
4. Throttle body gasket
5. Air pipe A
6. Connection of vacuum hose
7. Connection of brake booster vacuum hose
8. Harness connecter
9. Connection of clutch booster vacuum hose
10. EGR temperature sensor <vehicles for California>
11. EGR valve
12. EGR valve gasket
13. EGR pipe installation bolts
14. EGR pipe gasket
15. Connection of air intake plenum stay
16. Air intake plenum installation bolts
17. Air intake plenum installation nuts
18. Air intake plenum
19. Air intake plenum gasket

Fig. 12   Intake air plenum replacement. DOHC turbocharged

CR10591000680000X

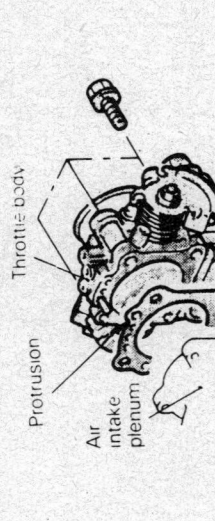

Throttle body

Protrusion

Air intake plenum

Fig. 13   Throttle body gasket installation

CR10591000690000X

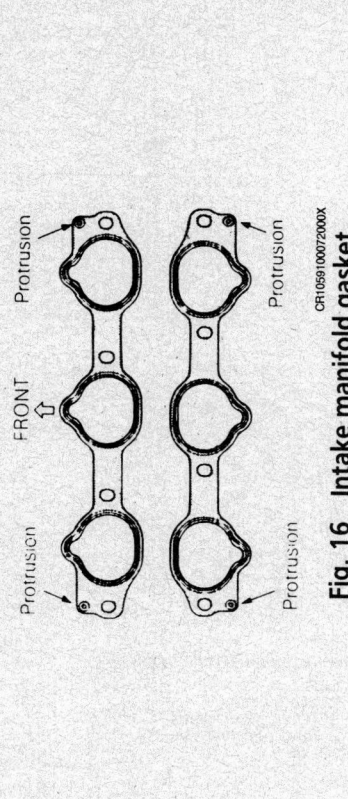

Fig. 16 Intake manifold gasket installation. DOHC

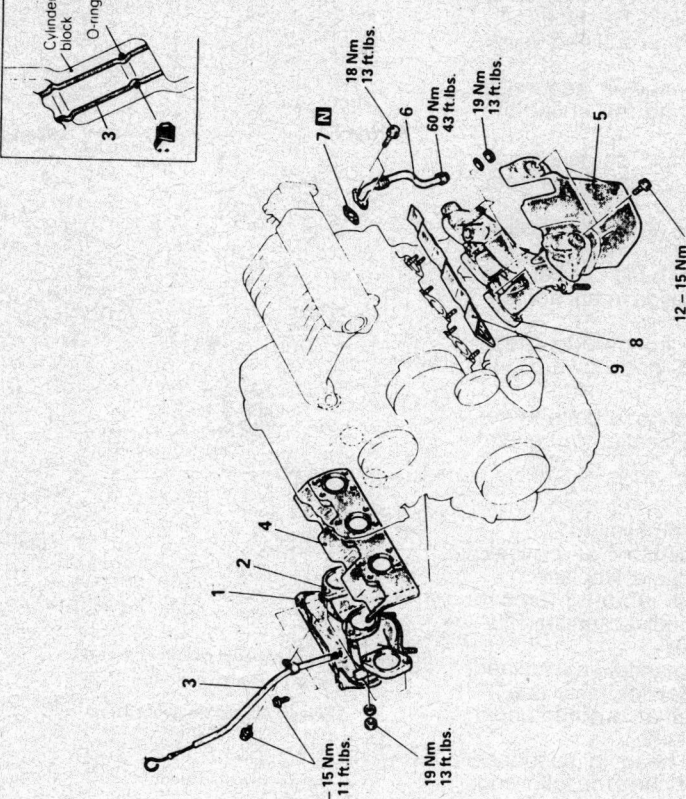

Removal steps of exhaust manifold (front)

1. Heat protector
2. Exhaust manifold (front)
3. Oil level gauge guide
4. Gasket

Removal steps of exhaust manifold (rear)

5. Heat protector
6. EGR pipe <Vehicles for California>
7. EGR gasket <Vehicles for California>
8. Exhaust manifold (rear)
9. Gasket

Fig. 17 Exhaust manifold replacement. SOHC

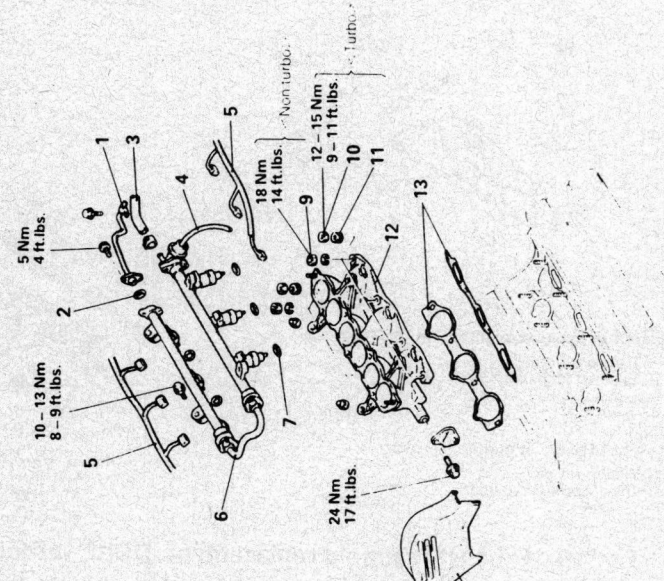

1. Connection for high-pressure fuel hose
2. O-ring
3. Connection for fuel return hose
4. Connection for vacuum hoses
5. Connection for injector connector
6. Delivery pipe (with injectors)
7. Insulators
8. Timing belt upper cover
9. Intake manifold mounting nut <Non turbo>
10. Intake manifold mounting nut <Turbo>
11. Cone disc spring <Turbo>
12. Intake manifold
13. Intake manifold gasket

Fig. 15 Intake manifold replacement. DOHC

2. Remove intake manifold as outlined under "Intake manifold, Replace."
3. Remove timing belt as outlined under "Timing Belt, Replace."
4. Remove cylinder head in sequence shown in **Fig. 22 and 23**, noting the following:
   a. Remove camshaft sprockets as outlined under "Camshaft Oil Seal, Replace."
5. Reverse procedure to install, noting the following:
   a. Ensure cylinder head gasket has proper identification mark for engine.
   b. Install marking on cylinder head gasket upward and toward the front.
   c. Tighten cylinder head bolts in sequence to specification in several steps, **Fig. 24**.

DOHC

1. Drain engine cooling system.
2. Remove intake manifold as outlined under "Intake manifold, Replace."
3. **On turbocharged models,** remove turbocharger as outlined under "Turbocharger, replace."
4. Remove exhaust manifold as outlined under "Exhaust Manifold, Replace."
5. Remove timing belt as outlined under "Timing Belt, Replace."
6. Remove cylinder head in sequence shown in **Fig. 25**, noting the following:
   a. Remove camshaft sprockets as outlined under "Camshaft Oil Seal, Replace."
7. Reverse procedure to install, noting the following:
   a. Ensure cylinder head gasket has proper identification mark for engine.
   b. Install marking on cylinder head gasket upward and toward the front.
   c. Tighten cylinder head bolts in sequence to specification in several steps, **Fig. 26**.

VALVE ARRANGEMENT

The exhaust valves are on the outboard side of the cylinder head and the intake valves are on the inboard side of the cylinder head.

CAMSHAFT LOBE LIFT SPECIFICATIONS

Engine	Camshaft	Standard, Inch	Limit, Inch
SOHC	Int.	1.6240	1.6430
	Exh.	1.6240	1.6430
DOHC	Int.	1.3972	1.3776
	Exh	1.3858	1.3661

VALVE ADJUSTMENT

These engines are equipped with hydraulic lifters, no adjustment required.

TIMING BELT

REPLACE

Replace timing belt every 60,000 miles or every five years to prevent cylinder head, valve train or piston damage.

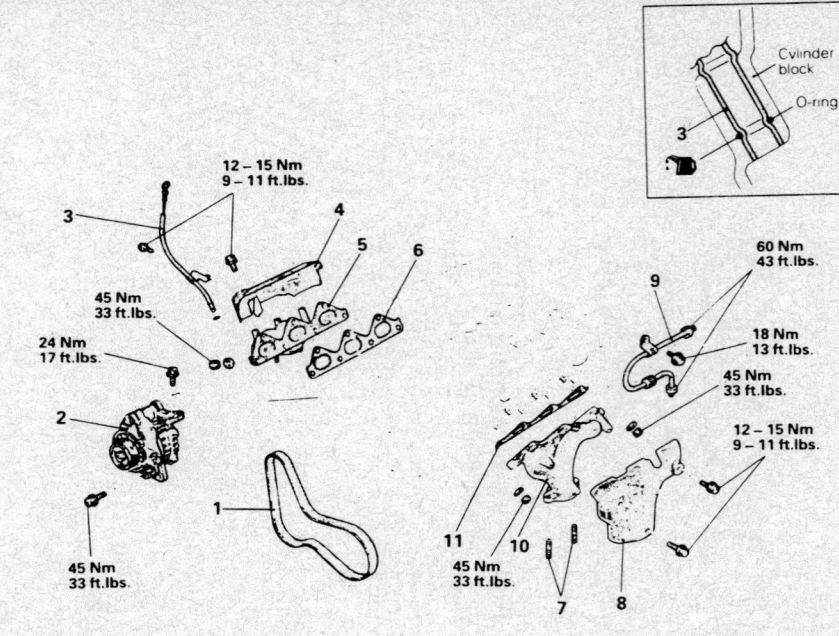

Removal steps of exhaust manifold (front)
1. Drive belt (Alternator)
   Service Adjustment procedures)
2. Alternator assembly
3. Oil level gauge guide
4. Heat protector
5. Exhaust manifold (front)
6. Gasket

Removal steps of exhaust manifold (rear)
7. Stud
8. Heat protector
9. EGR pipe <Vehicles for California>
10. Exhaust manifold (rear)
11. Gasket

CR1079100013000X

Fig. 18 Exhaust manifold replacement. DOHC except turbocharged

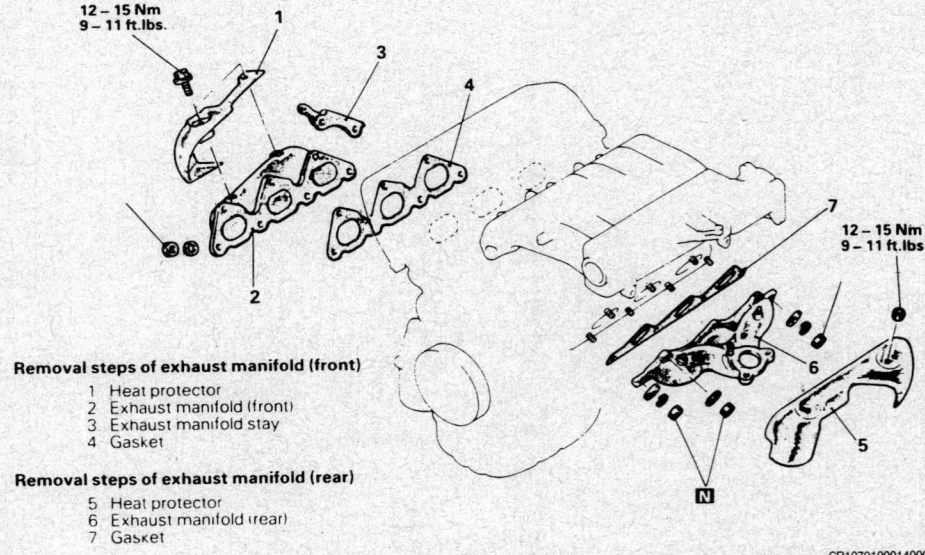

Removal steps of exhaust manifold (front)
1. Heat protector
2. Exhaust manifold (front)
3. Exhaust manifold stay
4. Gasket

Removal steps of exhaust manifold (rear)
5. Heat protector
6. Exhaust manifold (rear)
7. Gasket

CR1079100014000X

Fig. 19 Exhaust manifold replacement. DOHC turbocharged

SOHC

1. Remove lefthand front and side undercover.
2. Disconnect and remove cruise control pump and link assembly.
3. Raise and support engine assembly to take weight off engine mounts.
4. Remove timing belt in order shown in **Fig. 27**, noting the following:
   a. Disconnect power steering pump and A/C compressor with hoses attached. Support aside with rope or other suitable material.

Sealant: MOPAR Part No. 4318034 or equivalent

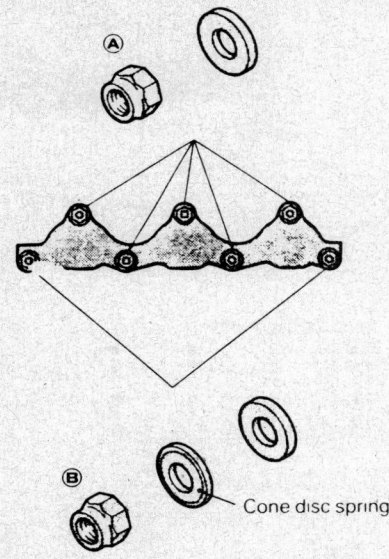

Fig. 20 Rear exhaust manifold installation. DOHC turbocharged

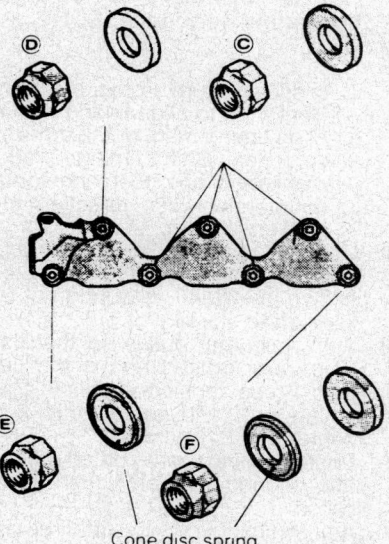

Fig. 21 Front exhaust manifold installation. DOHC turbocharged

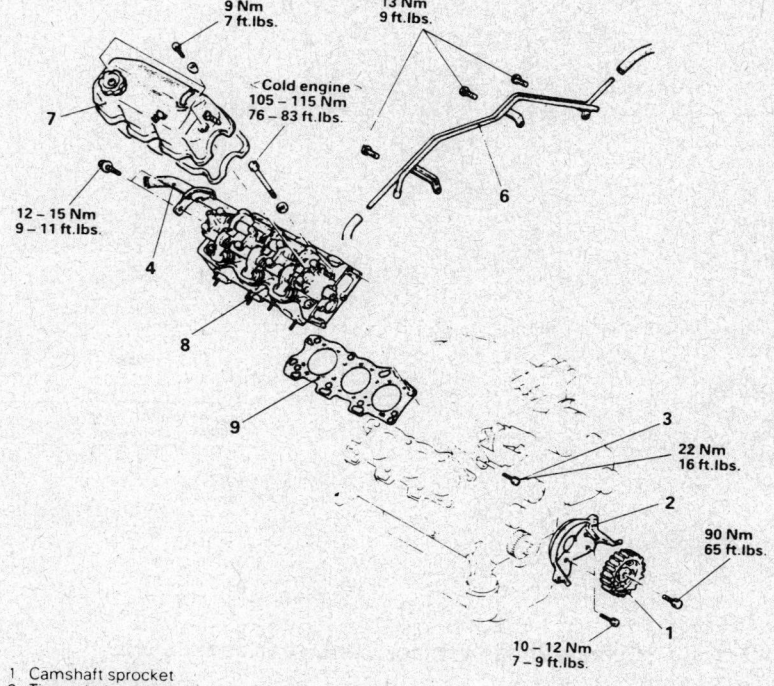

1. Camshaft sprocket
2. Timing belt rear cover
3. Connection of power steering pump bracket
4. Connection of water inlet pipe
6. Purge pipe assembly
7. Rocker cover
8. Cylinder head assembly
9. Cylinder head gasket

Fig. 22 Cylinder head replacement, front bank. SOHC

b. Remove engine mount as outlined under "Engine Mount, Replace."

c. Remove engine mount bracket in sequence shown in **Fig. 28**, lubricating reamer bolt indicated by arrow then remove bolt slowly. **Reamer bolt is sometimes heat seized on engine support bracket.**

d. Remove crankshaft pulley using end yoke holder tool No. MB990767 and crankshaft pulley holder tool No. MB998719, or equivalent, as shown in **Fig. 29**.

e. Align timing marks prior to timing belt removal.

f. Mark rotation direction on timing belt for installation if belt is to be re-used.

g. Loosen timing belt tensioner bolt and turn tensioner counterclockwise and tighten tensioner bolt.

h. Remove timing belt.

5. Reverse procedure to install, noting the following:

a. Align timing marks on camshaft and crankshaft sprockets, **Fig. 30**.

b. Install timing belt on crankshaft first, then working counterclockwise position belt over one camshaft sprocket, water pump pulley, other camshaft sprocket then over belt tensioner, **Fig. 31**.

c. Apply force counterclockwise to rear camshaft sprocket. Ensure timing marks are aligned.

d. Attach front flange then loosen timing belt tensioner bolt and allow tensioner to tighten belt using spring force.

e. Using crankshaft wrench tool No. MD998716, or equivalent, turn crankshaft two turns clockwise.

f. Re-align timing marks and tighten timing belt tensioner bolt to specifi-

cation.

g. Measure belt tension using a suitable belt tension gauge tool on timing belt opposite side of tensioner, **Fig. 32.**. Belt tension should be 46.3–68.3 ft. lbs.

h. Install timing cover bolts as shown in **Fig. 33**.

i. Install engine support bracket bolts in sequence shown in **Fig. 34**.

DOHC
Removal

1. Remove lefthand front and side undercover.

2. Disconnect and remove cruise control pump and link assembly.

3. Remove alternator assembly.

4. Raise and support engine assembly to take weight off engine mounts.

5. Remove timing belt in order shown in **Fig. 35**, noting the following:

a. Remove crankshaft pulley using end yoke holder tool No. MB990767 and crankshaft pulley

Rear bank

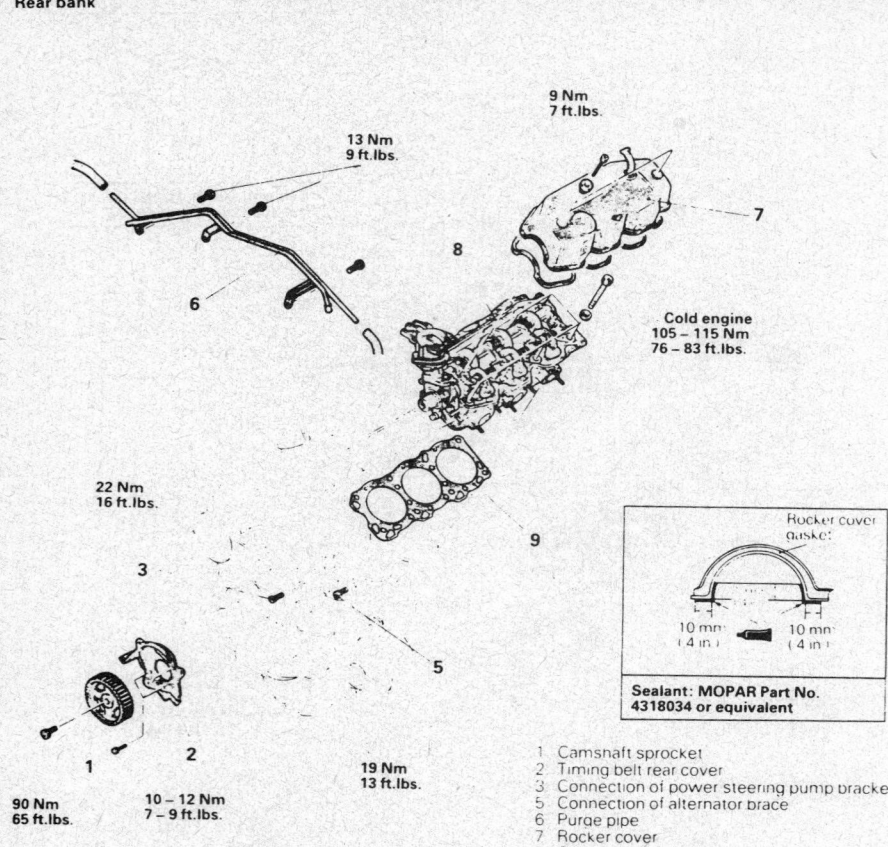

Sealant: MOPAR Part No. 4318034 or equivalent

1. Camshaft sprocket
2. Timing belt rear cover
3. Connection of power steering pump bracket
4. Connection of alternator brace
5. Connection of alternator brace
6. Purge pipe
7. Rocker cover
8. Cylinder head assembly
9. Cylinder head gasket

CR1069100499000X

Fig. 23 Cylinder head replacement, rear bank. SOHC

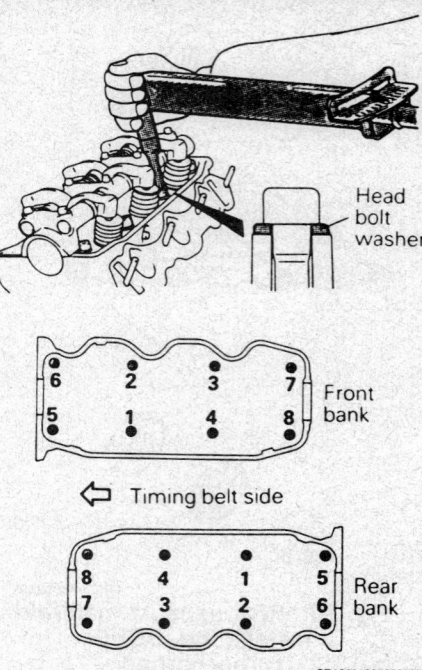

Head bolt washer

| 6 | 2 | 3 | 7 | Front bank |
| 5 | 1 | 4 | 8 | |

⇐ Timing belt side

| 8 | 4 | 1 | 5 | Rear bank |
| 7 | 3 | 2 | 6 | |

CR1069100500000X

Fig. 24 Cylinder head bolt tightening sequence. SOHC

holder tool No. MB998754, or equivalent.

b. Remove engine mount bracket in sequence shown in **Fig. 28**, lubricating reamer bolt indicated by arrow then remove bolt slowly. **Reamer bolt is sometimes heat seized on engine support bracket.**

c. Align timing marks prior to timing belt removal.

d. Mark rotation direction on timing belt for installation if belt is to be reused.

e. Loosen timing belt tensioner center bolt.

f. Remove timing belt.

Installation

1. Reset auto tensioner by placing auto tensioner level in a soft jawed vise.
2. Pushrod inward until set hole marked A is aligned with set hole marked B, **Fig. 36.**
3. Insert a .055 inch diameter wire into set holes.
4. Remove tensioner from vise then install tensioner onto engine.
5. Align timing marks for camshaft sprockets on the rear bank, **Fig. 37.**
6. Align timing marks for camshaft sprockets on the front bank, as follows:

a. Install the crankshaft pulley. Shift timing mark on crankshaft sprocket by three teeth to lower piston in No. 1 cylinder slightly from top dead center. **Turning camshaft sprocket with piston in No. 1 cylinder located at TDC may cause valves to interfere with piston.**

b. Make sure that timing marks on camshaft sprockets for intake and exhaust valves are not within range marked A, **Fig. 38.** If timing mark is within range marked A, turn camshaft sprocket to move timing mark to area closest to range marked A. **In range marked A, the cam lobe on the camshaft lifts the valve through the rocker arm and the camshaft sprocket is apt to rotate by reaction force of the valve spring.**

c. Turn camshaft sprocket to locate timing mark as shown in **Fig. 39.** If **the intake and exhaust valves of the same cylinder lift simultaneously, interference with each other may result. Therefore, turn the intake camshaft sprocket and the exhaust camshaft sprocket alternately.**

d. Turn camshaft sprocket clockwise to align the timing marks. If camshaft sprocket has been turned ex-

cessively, turn sprocket counterclockwise to align timing marks.

e. Align timing mark of the crankshaft sprocket. Shift timing mark of crankshaft sprocket one tooth in counterclockwise direction to install timing belt.

7. Using paper clips to hold timing belt in place, install timing belt in order shown in **Fig. 40**, ensuring not to allow belt to slack.

8. Turn tensioner pulley so that its pin holes are located above the center bolt. Press tensioner pulley against timing belt and temporarily tighten center bolt.

9. Ensure timing marks on all sprockets are aligned properly then remove clips.

10. Adjust timing belt by rotating crankshaft ¼ turn counterclockwise, then rotate it clockwise until timing marks are aligned.

11. Loosen tensioner pulley center bolt. Using tensioner pulley socket wrench tool No. MB998767, or equivalent, apply 7.2 ft.lbs of **Torque** to the timing belt and tighten tensioner pulley center bolt to specification, **Fig. 41.**

12. Remove set pin from auto tensioner and ensure the set pin can be easily removed.

13. Rotate crankshaft two times and leave it for five minutes or more. Ensure again that the set pin can be easily removed from and installed to the auto tensioner.

14. Ensure tensioner rod protrusion is within .149-.177 inch, **Fig. 42** If rod is out of specification repeat steps 5 through 9.

15. Ensure timing marks are aligned on all sprockets.

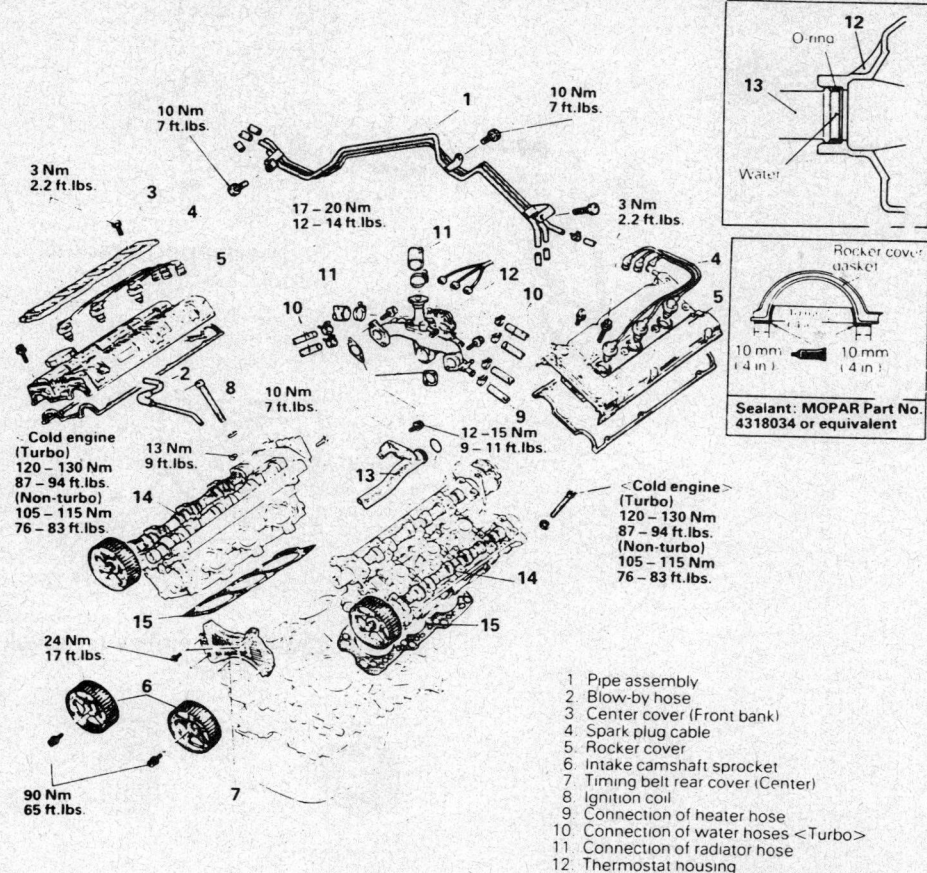

Fig. 25 Cylinder head replacement. DOHC

1. Pipe assembly
2. Blow-by hose
3. Center cover (Front bank)
4. Spark plug cable
5. Rocker cover
6. Intake camshaft sprocket
7. Timing belt rear cover (Center)
8. Ignition coil
9. Connection of heater hose
10. Connection of water hoses <Turbo>
11. Connection of radiator hose
12. Thermostat housing
13. Connection of water inlet pipe (Front bank)
14. Cylinder head assembly
15. Cylinder head gasket

CR1069100501000X

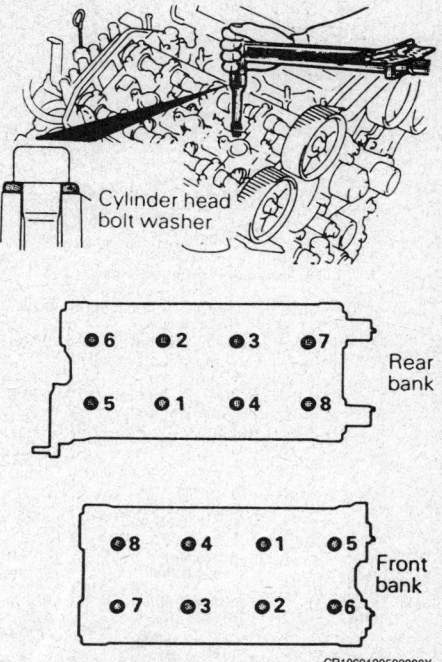

Fig. 26 Cylinder head bolt tightening sequence. DOHC

CR1069100502000X

16. Install lower timing belt cover bolts as shown in **Fig. 43.**
17. Install engine support bracket bolts in sequence shown in **Fig. 44.**
18. Reverse remaining removal procedure to install.

CAMSHAFT OIL SEAL
REPLACE

SOHC

1. Remove timing belt as outlined under "Timing Belt, Replace."
2. Remove camshaft sprockets by using yoke holder tool No. MB990767 and pulley holder tool No. MD998719.
3. Remove timing belt rear covers.
4. Remove oil seal by using a suitable pry tool.
5. Reverse procedure to install, noting the following:
   a. Install oil seal using seal installer tool No. MD998713, or equivalent.

DOHC

1. Remove timing belt as outlined under "Timing Belt, Removal."
2. Remove intake manifold as outlined under "Intake Manifold, Replace."
3. Remove camshaft oil seals in sequence shown in **Fig. 45,** noting the following:

a. Remove camshaft sprocket by holding camshaft on the hexagonal part and removing sprocket bolt, **Fig. 46.**
b. Cut out a portion of the camshaft seal then pry out seal using a suitable pry tool.
4. Reverse procedure to install, noting the following:
   a. Install camshaft oil seal using seal installer tool No. MD998671.
   b. Tighten rocker covers in sequence shown in **Fig. 47.** Rocker cover bolts are color code, front bank bolts are black and read bank bolts are green.

CAMSHAFT
REPLACE

SOHC

1. Remove camshaft in sequence shown in **Fig. 48,** noting the following:
   a. Install lash adjuster tool No. MD998443, or equivalent, to prevent lash adjuster from falling out.
2. Reverse procedure to install, noting the following:
   a. Install No. 1 bearing cap on shafts so that notch on end of shaft faces in direction shown in **Fig. 49.** Ensure oil grooves faces down-

ward as shown and oil port is located on rocker shaft side.
b. Install remaining bearing caps on shaft with arrow mark on each bearing cap points in same direction as No. 1 bearing cap.
c. Immerse lash adjuster in clean diesel fuel.
d. Using a small wire, move plunger up and down several times while pushing down lightly on check ball in order to bleed out air.
e. Install lash adjuster into rocker arms, using care not to spill out diesel fuel, then retain lash adjuster with lash adjuster retainer tool No. MD998443, or equivalent, **Fig. Fig. 50.**
f. Apply a small amount of sealant to areas shown, **Fig. 51.**
g. Install rocker arm shaft assembly bearing cap arrow marks in same direction as arrow mark on cylinder head.
h. Tighten bearing cap bolts to specification, then remove lash adjuster tool.
i. Install circular packing using seal installer tool No. MD998306, or equivalent.
j. Install camshaft oil seal and sprocket.

DOHC

1. Remove camshaft in sequence shown in **Fig. 52.**
2. Install camshaft in reverse sequence shown in **Fig. 52,** noting the following:
   a. Immerse lash adjuster in clean diesel fuel.
   b. Using a small wire, move plunger up and down several times while pushing down lightly on check ball

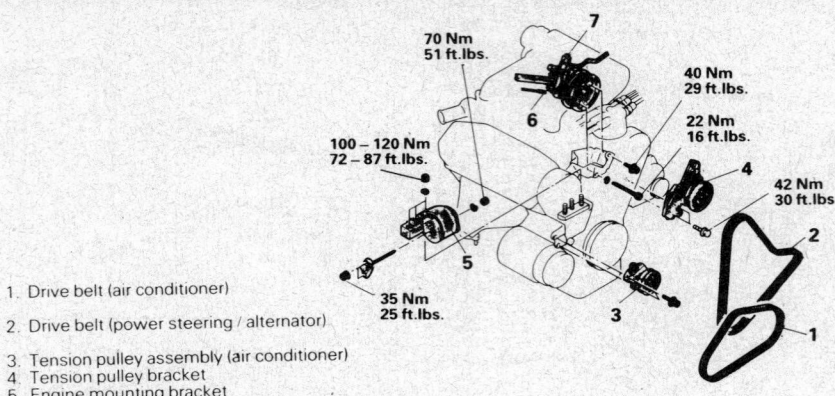

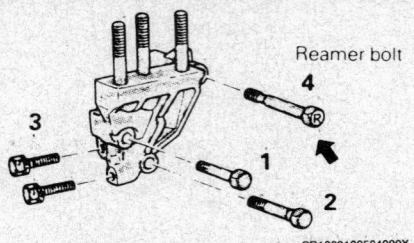

Fig. 28 Engine support bracket removal. SOHC

1. Drive belt (air conditioner)
2. Drive belt (power steering / alternator)
3. Tension pulley assembly (air conditioner)
4. Tension pulley bracket
5. Engine mounting bracket
6. Connection for power steering oil pump pressure switch connector
7. Power steering oil pump

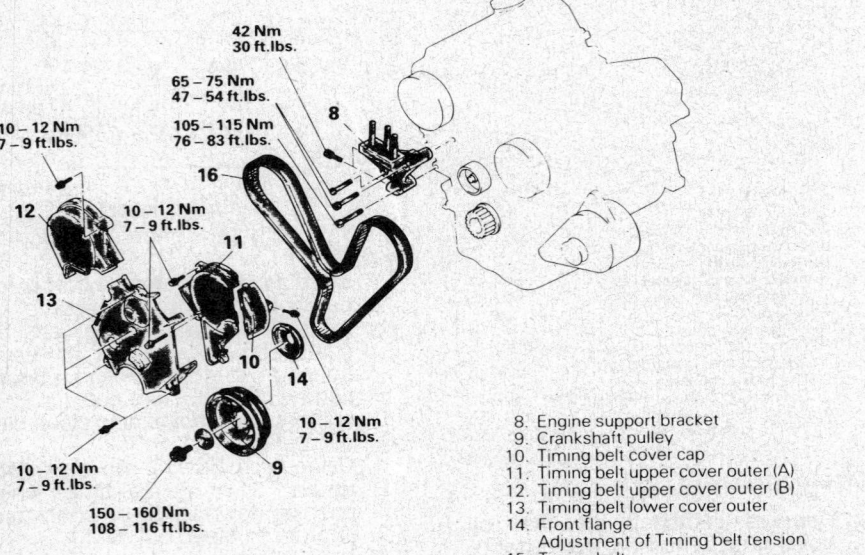

8. Engine support bracket
9. Crankshaft pulley
10. Timing belt cover cap
11. Timing belt upper cover outer (A)
12. Timing belt upper cover outer (B)
13. Timing belt lower cover outer
14. Front flange
    Adjustment of Timing belt tension
15. Timing belt

Fig. 27 Timing belt replacement. SOHC

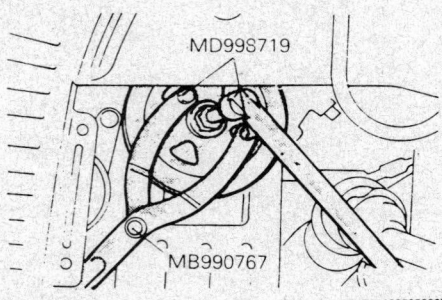

Fig. 29 Crankshaft pulley removal. SOHC

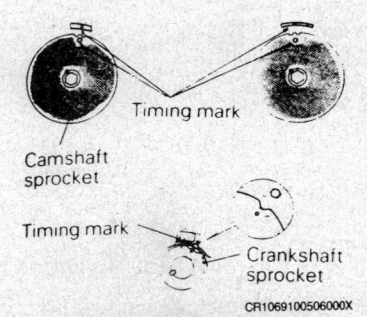

Fig. 30 Timing mark alignment. SOHC

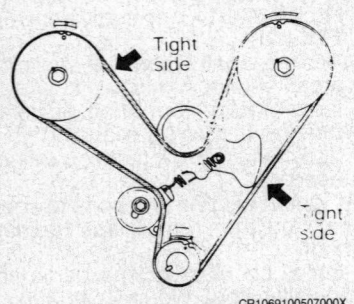

Fig. 31 Timing belt installation. SOHC

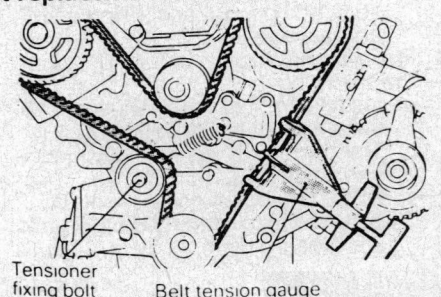

Fig. 32 Belt tension measurement. SOHC

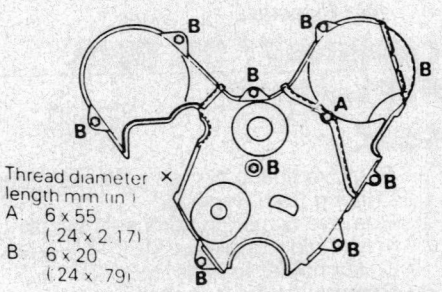

Fig. 33 Timing belt cover installation. SOHC

in order to bleed out air.

c. Install lash adjuster into rocker arms, using care not to spill out diesel fuel, then retain lash adjuster with lash adjuster retainer tool No. MD998443, or equivalent, **Fig. 50.**

d. Turn crankshaft to bring No. 1 cylinder to TDC.

e. Install intake camshaft, marked V, and exhaust camshaft, marked C, onto the cylinder head with dowel pins as shown in **Fig. 53.**

f. Install bearing caps, on proper camshaft, with arrow mark pointing in same direction as arrow mark on cylinder head.

g. Tighten bearing cap bolts to speci-

fication in several steps.

h. Install circular packing using seal installer tool No. MD998762, or equivalent.

i. Install camshaft oil seal and sprocket.

PISTON & ROD ASSEMBLY

1. Remove piston and rod assembly as

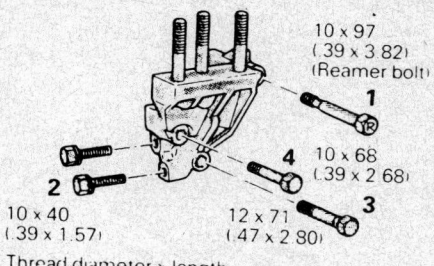

Fig. 34 Engine support bracket installation. SOHC

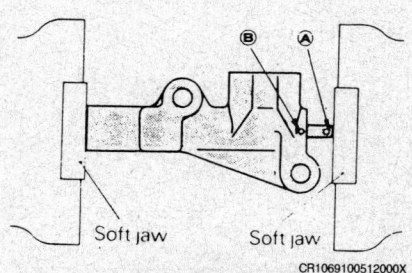

Fig. 36 Set hole alignment. DOHC

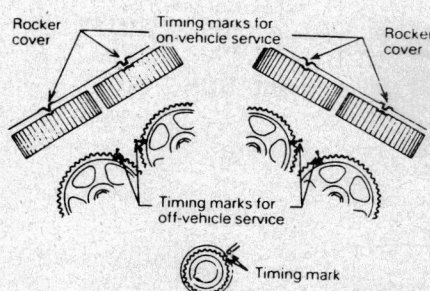

Fig. 37 Timing mark alignment. DOHC

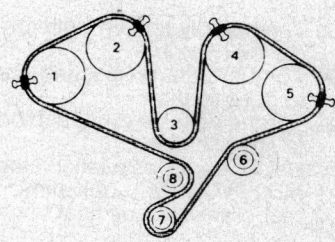

Fig. 40 Timing belt installation. DOHC

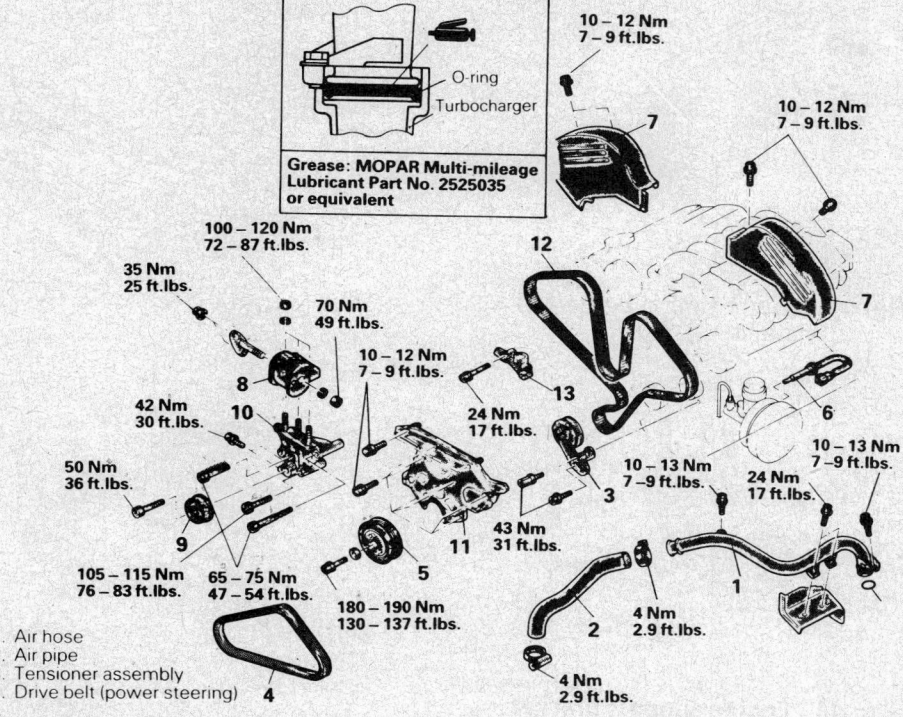

Grease: MOPAR Multi-mileage Lubricant Part No. 2525035 or equivalent

1. Air hose
2. Air pipe
3. Tensioner assembly
4. Drive belt (power steering)
5. Crankshaft pulley
6. Brake fluid level sensor
7. Timing belt upper cover
8. Engine mount bracket
9. Idler pulley (alternator / air conditioner)
10. Engine support bracket
11. Timing belt lower cover
    Adjustment of timing belt tension
12. Timing belt
13. Auto tensioner

Fig. 35 Timing belt removal. DOHC

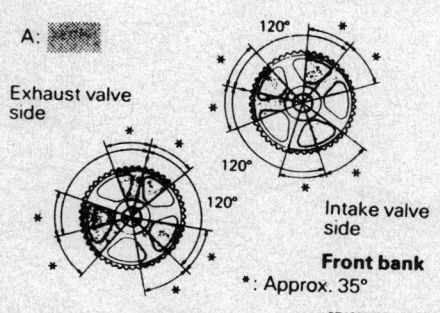

Fig. 38 Rear camshaft alignment position. DOHC

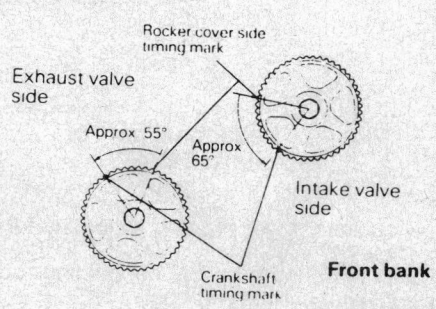

Fig. 39 Camshaft sprocket positioning. DOHC

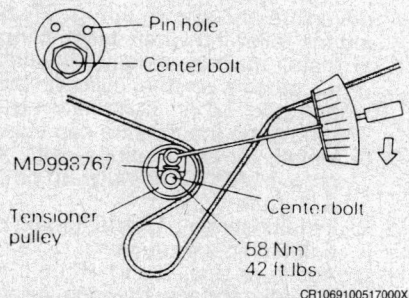

Fig. 41 Tightening tensioner pulley bolt. DOHC

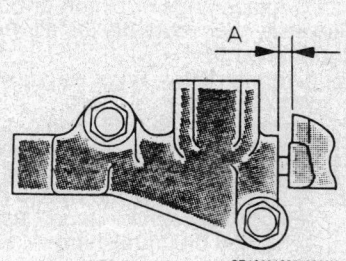

Fig. 42 Rod protrusion measurement

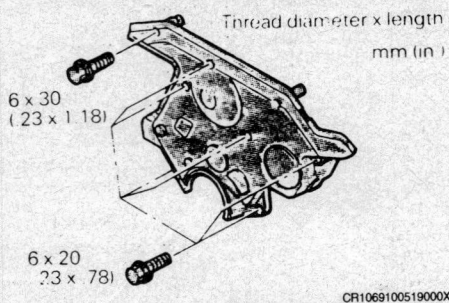

Fig. 43 Lower timing belt cover installation. DOHC

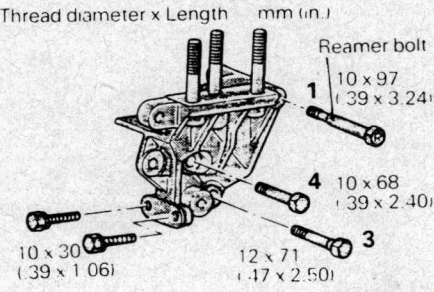

Fig. 44 Engine support bracket installation. DOHC

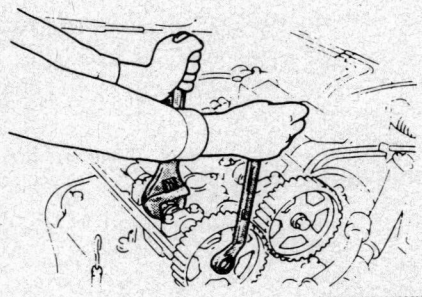

Fig. 46 Hexagonal part of camshaft. DOHC

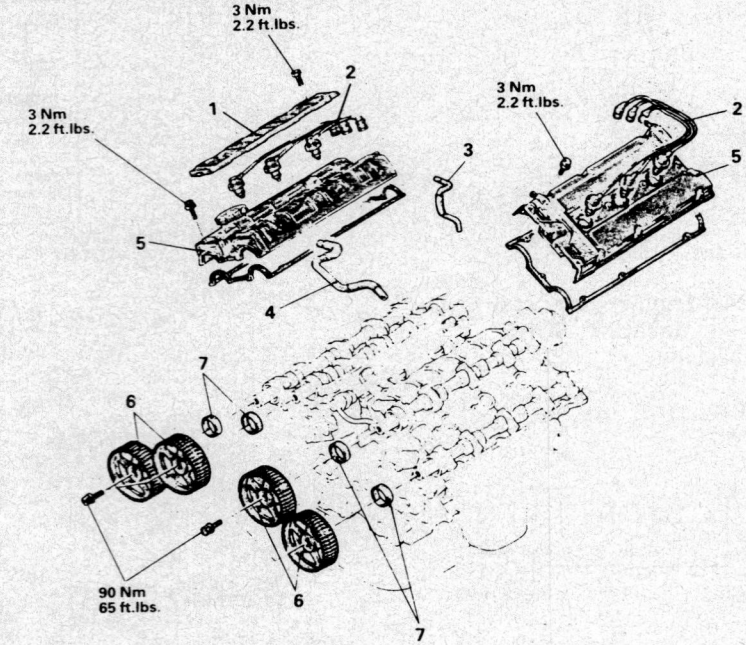

1. Center cover (front bank)
2. Connection for spark plug cables
3. Connection for breather hose
4. Connection for PCV hose
5. Rocker cover
6. Camshaft sprocket
7. Camshaft oil seals

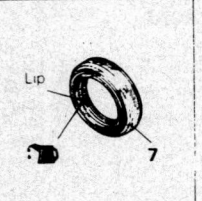

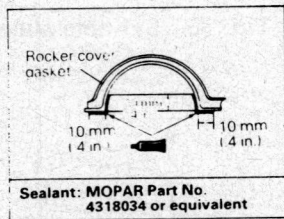

Fig. 45 Camshaft oil seal replacement. DOHC

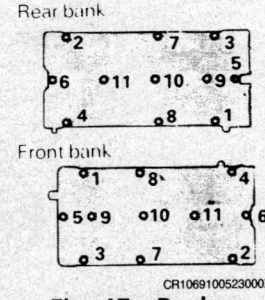

Fig. 47 Rocker cover installation. DOHC

outlined under **Fig. 54**, noting the following:
a. Mark large end of connecting rod with cylinder number.
b. Inspect side clearance between piston ring and ring groove. If side clearance is not as specified in "Engine Rebuilding Specifications," replace rings or piston or both.
2. Reverse procedure to install, noting the following:
a. Arrange piston rings as shown in **Fig. 55**.
b. Pistons for SOHC engines are identified for front and rear banks, **Fig. 56**.
c. Align connecting rod marks made during disassembly when assembling cod on crankshaft.

CRANKSHAFT
REPLACE

1. Replace crankshaft, flywheel and

driveplate and shown in **Fig. 57**, noting the following when assembling:
a. Install main bearings half with an oil groove on the cylinder block and the other half with no oil groove on the bearing cap side.
b. Install thrust bearings with the groove side facing outward on No. 3 journal.
c. Install bearing cap and tighten cap bolts to specification.
d. Apply engine oil to thread and bearing surface of each bearing cap stay bolts. Bearing cap stays A and B differ in shape, install in correct order, **Fig. 58**.

e. Temporarily tighten bolts on cylinder block side.
f. Torque bolts on bearing cap side to specification.
g. Torque bolts on cylinder block side to specification.
h. Using seal installation tool No. MD998718 or equivalent, install rear crankshaft oil seal.

OIL PAN
REPLACE

1. Remove timing belt as outlined under "Timing Belt, Replace."

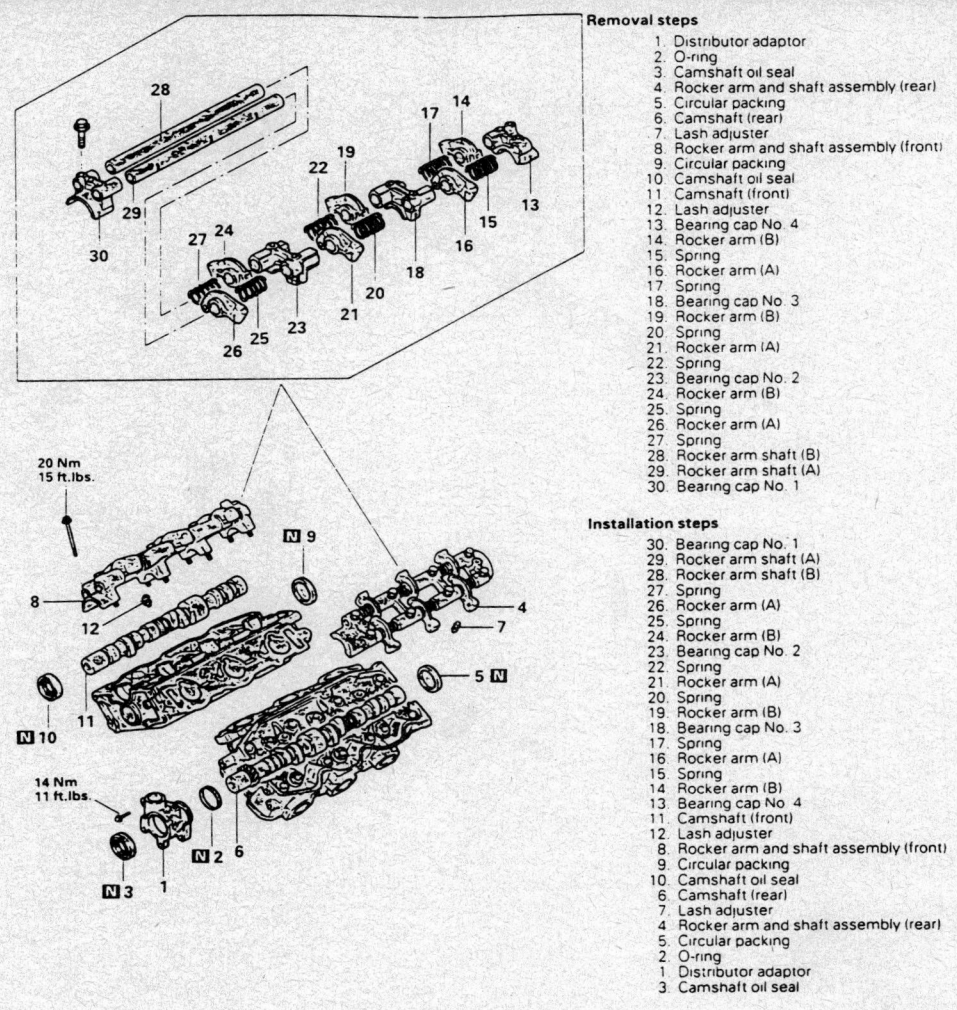

Removal steps

1. Distributor adaptor
2. O-ring
3. Camshaft oil seal
4. Rocker arm and shaft assembly (rear)
5. Circular packing
6. Camshaft (rear)
7. Lash adjuster
8. Rocker arm and shaft assembly (front)
9. Circular packing
10. Camshaft oil seal
11. Camshaft (front)
12. Lash adjuster
13. Bearing cap No. 4
14. Rocker arm (B)
15. Spring
16. Rocker arm (A)
17. Spring
18. Bearing cap No. 3
19. Rocker arm (B)
20. Spring
21. Rocker arm (A)
22. Spring
23. Bearing cap No. 2
24. Rocker arm (B)
25. Spring
26. Rocker arm (A)
27. Spring
28. Rocker arm shaft (B)
29. Rocker arm shaft (A)
30. Bearing cap No. 1

Installation steps

30. Bearing cap No. 1
29. Rocker arm shaft (A)
28. Rocker arm shaft (B)
27. Spring
26. Rocker arm (A)
25. Spring
24. Rocker arm (B)
23. Bearing cap No. 2
22. Spring
21. Rocker arm (A)
20. Spring
19. Rocker arm (B)
18. Bearing cap No. 3
17. Spring
16. Rocker arm (A)
15. Spring
14. Rocker arm (B)
13. Bearing cap No. 4
11. Camshaft (front)
12. Lash adjuster
8. Rocker arm and shaft assembly (front)
9. Circular packing
10. Camshaft oil seal
6. Camshaft (rear)
7. Lash adjuster
4. Rocker arm and shaft assembly (rear)
5. Circular packing
2. O-ring
1. Distributor adaptor
3. Camshaft oil seal

20 Nm
15 ft.lbs.

14 Nm
11 ft.lbs.

CR1069100524000X

Fig. 48   Camshaft replacement. SOHC

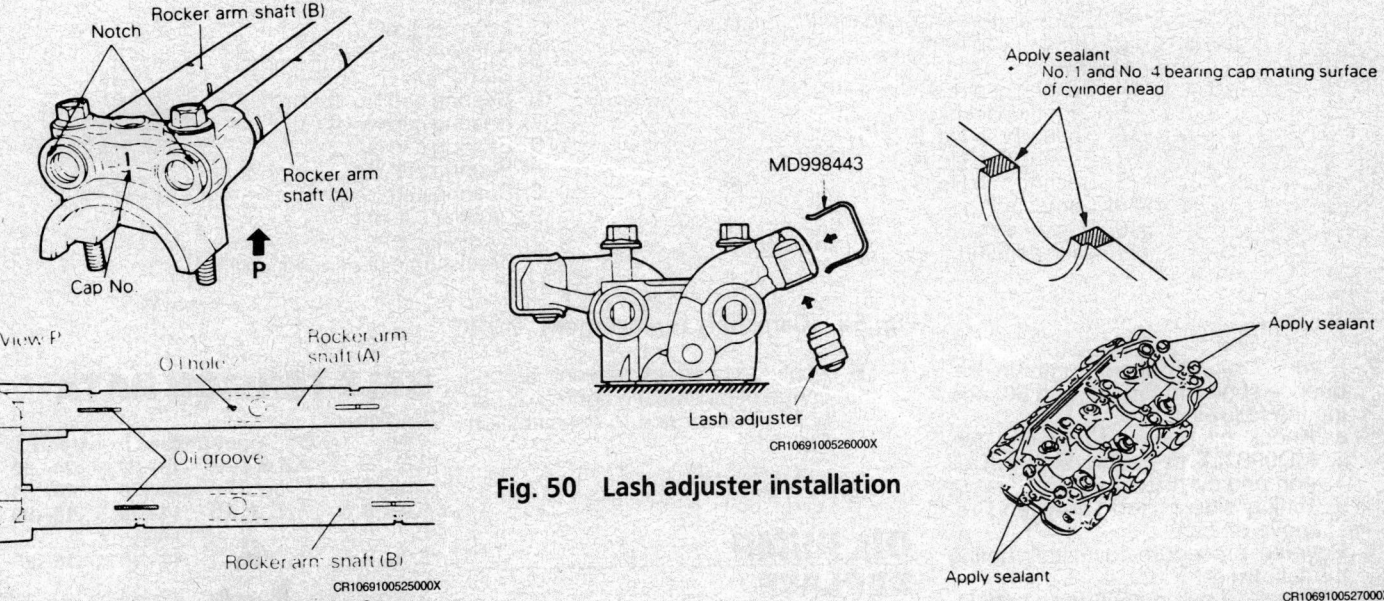

Fig. 49   Rocker arm shaft installation. SOHC

CR1069100525000X

MD998443

Lash adjuster

CR1069100526000X

Fig. 50   Lash adjuster installation

Apply sealant
• No. 1 and No. 4 bearing cap mating surface of cylinder head

Apply sealant

Apply sealant

CR1069100527000X

Fig. 51   Sealing camshaft. SOHC

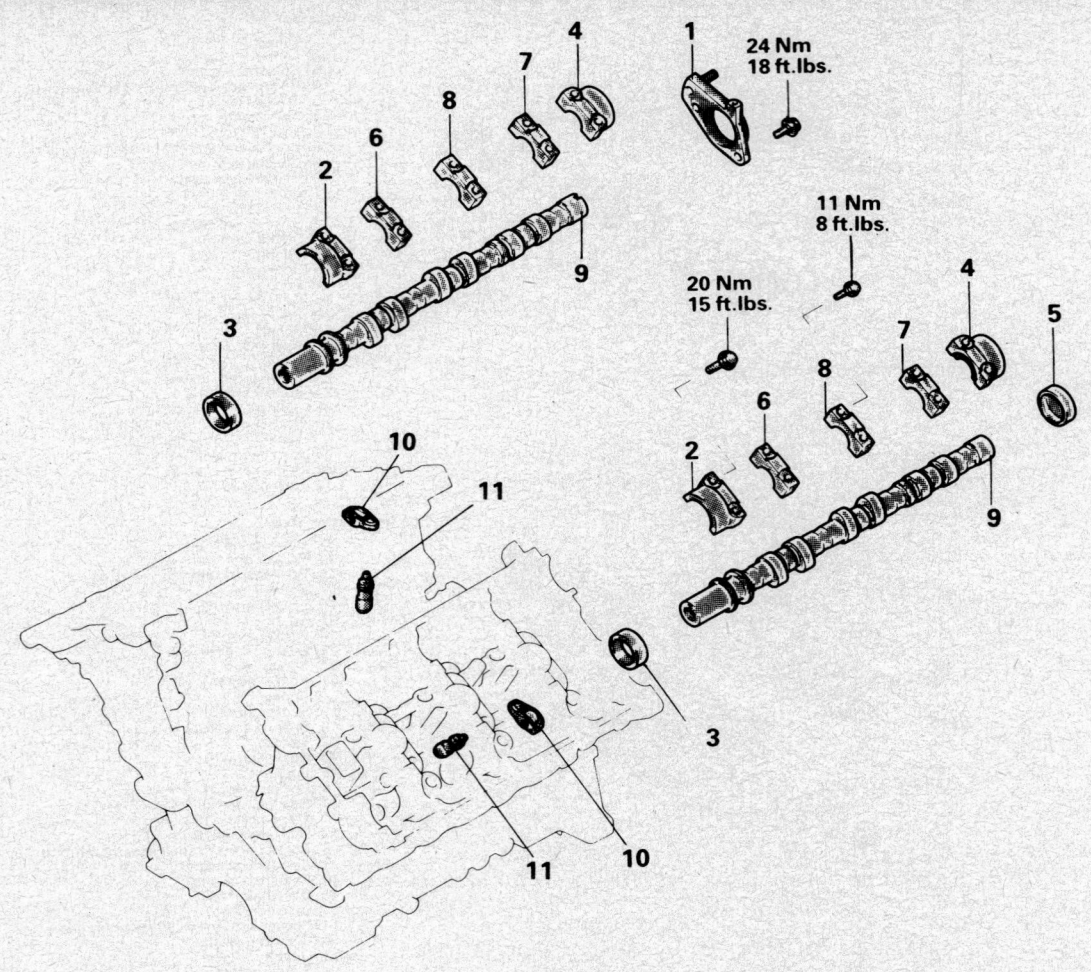

24 Nm
18 ft.lbs.

11 Nm
8 ft.lbs.

20 Nm
15 ft.lbs.

Removal steps

1. Crank angle sensor adaptor
2. Bearing cap front
3. Oil seal
4. Bearing cap rear
5. Circular packing
6. Bearing cap No. 2
7. Bearing cap No. 4
8. Bearing cap No. 3
9. Camshaft
10. Rocker arm
11. Lash adjuster

Installation steps

11. Lash adjuster
10. Rocker arm
9. Camshaft
8. Bearing cap No. 3
7. Bearing cap No. 4
6. Bearing cap No. 2
4. Bearing cap rear
2. Bearing cap front
5. Circular packing
3. Oil seal
1. Crank angle sensor adaptor

CR1069100528000X

Fig. 52   Camshaft replacement. DOHC

2. Remove oil pan and pump in sequence shown in **Fig. 59 and 60**, noting the following:
   a. Knock oil pan remover tool No. MD998727 in deeply between oil pan and cylinder block.
   b. Hitting side of tool, slide and remove oil pan.
3. Reverse procedure to install, noting the following:
   a. Install oil pump seal using seal installer tool No. MD998717, or equivalent.

b. Apply a bead of sealant around flange of oil pan and tighten oil pan bolts in sequence to specification, **Fig. 61.**

OIL PUMP
REPLACE

Refer to "Oil Pan, Replace," for oil pump replacement procedure.

BELT TENSION DATA

Engine, VIN	Component	New ①	Used ①
3.0L, S	Alt & P/S	.16–.20	.24–.32
3.0L, S	A/C	.26–.28	.28–.34
3.0L, B & C	A/C & Alt	.14–.16	.16–.20
3.0L, B & C	Alt	.14–.16	.16–.20
3.0L, B & C	P/S	.30–.35	.41–.49

① —Deflection Inch

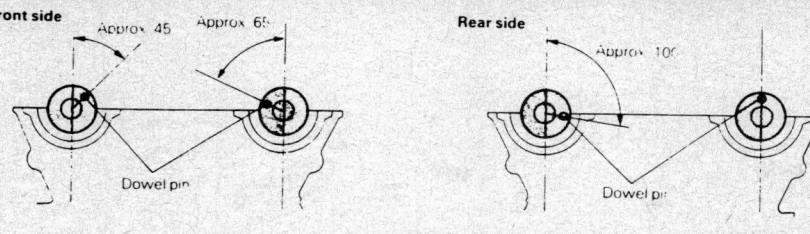

Fig. 53 Camshaft installation. DOHC

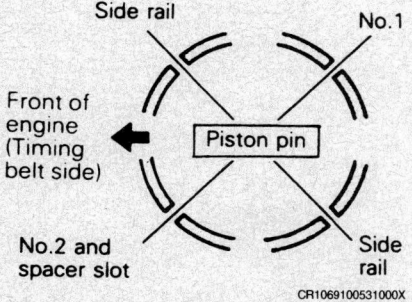

Fig. 55 Piston ring alignment

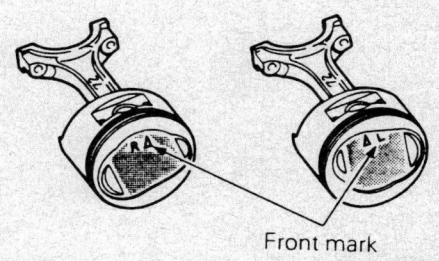

Front mark

Fig. 56 Piston installation direction. SOHC

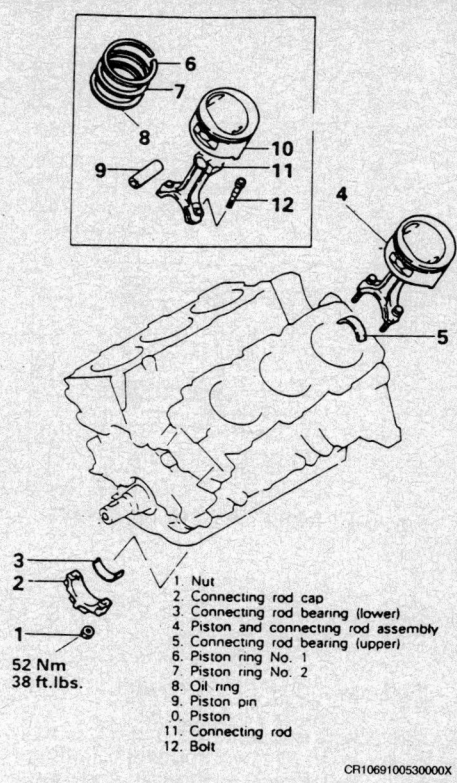

1. Nut 52 Nm / 38 ft.lbs.
2. Connecting rod cap
3. Connecting rod bearing (lower)
4. Piston and connecting rod assembly
5. Connecting rod bearing (upper)
6. Piston ring No. 1
7. Piston ring No. 2
8. Oil ring
9. Piston pin
0. Piston
11. Connecting rod
12. Bolt

Fig. 54 Piston, rings & rod assembly

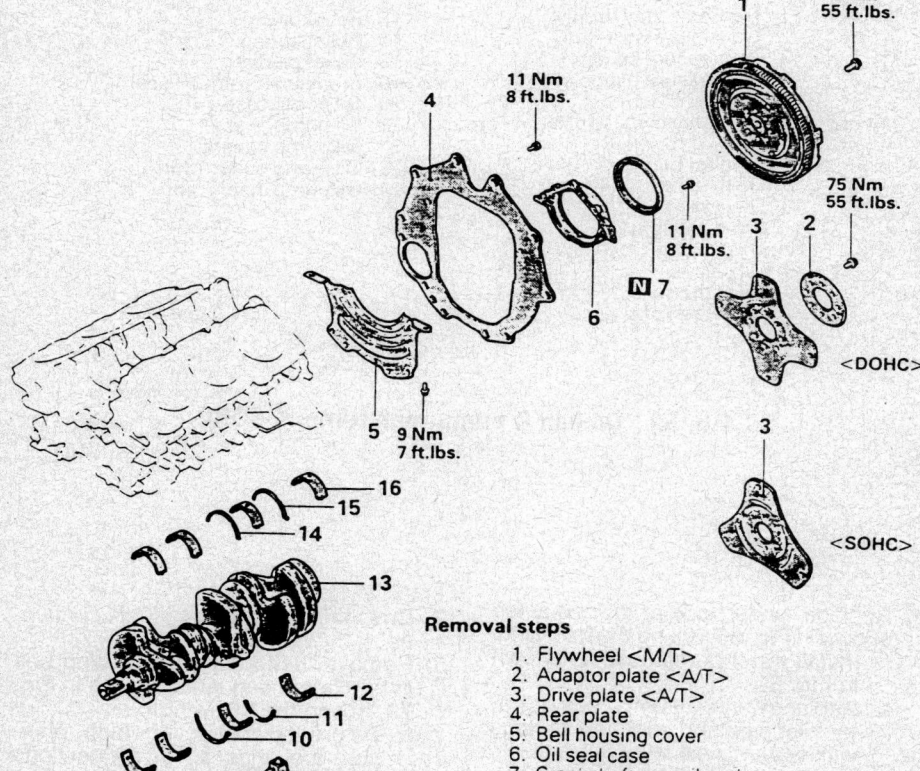

75 Nm
55 ft.lbs.

11 Nm
8 ft.lbs.

75 Nm
55 ft.lbs.

11 Nm
8 ft.lbs.

<N> 7

<DOHC>

9 Nm
7 ft.lbs.

<SOHC>

80 Nm
58 ft.lbs.

48 Nm
35 ft.lbs.

Removal steps
1. Flywheel <M/T>
2. Adaptor plate <A/T>
3. Drive plate <A/T>
4. Rear plate
5. Bell housing cover
6. Oil seal case
7. Crankshaft rear oil seal
8. Bearing cap stay <Turbo>
9. Bearing cap
10. Thrust bearing A
11. Thrust bearing B
12. Crankshaft bearing (lower)
13. Crankshaft
14. Thrust bearing B
15. Thrust bearing A
16. Crankshaft bearing (upper)

Fig. 57 Crankshaft replacement

SERPENTINE DRIVE BELT
ROUTING

Refer to **Fig. 62** for belt routing.

COOLING SYSTEM BLEED

These engines do not require a specified bleed procedure. After filling cooling system, run engine to operating temperature with radiator/pressure cap off. Air will then be automatically bled through cap opening.

THERMOSTAT
REPLACE

Do not remove pressure cap while engine is hot or under pressure.
1. Drain coolant to level below thermostat housing.
2. **On turbo models,** remove air intake hoses one (1) and two (2), **Fig. 63.**
3. **On non-turbo engines,** remove air intake hose (3).
4. **On DOHC models,** remove lower radiator hose (4), three housing retain-

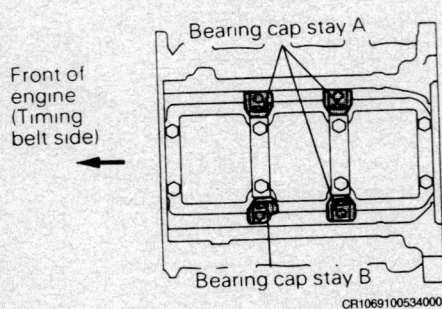

Fig. 58 Main bearing cap stays

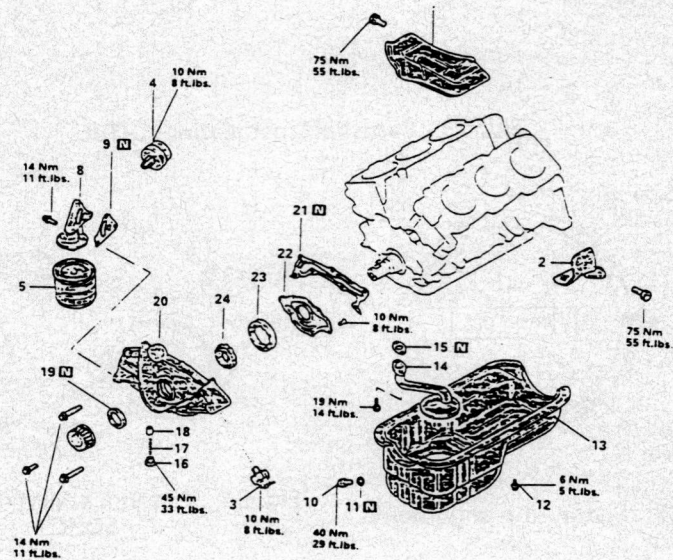

ing bolts. housing (5), gasket (8) and thermostat (9).

5. **On SOHC models,** remove upper radiator hose (6), two housing retaining bolts, housing (7), gasket (8) and thermostat (9).
6. Clean mating surfaces and close drain.
7. Reverse removal procedures to install.
8. Refer to **Fig. 64,** before installing thermostat.
9. Ensure that drain is closed, then refill coolant. Replace cap, start engine until warm. Check of leaks, then recheck coolant and fill if necessary.

1. Transaxle stay (front)
2. Transaxle stay (rear)
3. Oil pressure switch
4. Oil pressure gauge unit
5. Oil filter
6. Oil cooler by-pass valve <Turbo>
8. Oil filter bracket
9. Oil filter bracket gasket
10. Drain plug
11. Drain plug gasket
12. Oil pan bolt
13. Oil pan
14. Oil screen
15. Oil screen gasket
16. Relief plug
17. Relief spring
18. Relief plunger
19. Crankshaft front oil seal
20. Oil pump case
21. Oil pump gasket
22. Oil pump cover
23. Oil pump outer rotor
24. Oil pump inner rotor

Fig. 59 Oil pan & pump replacement. SOHC

WATER PUMP
REPLACE
SOHC

1. Drain engine cooling system.
2. Remove timing belt as outlined under "Timing Belt, Replace."
3. Replace water pump in sequence shown in **Fig. 65,** noting the following:
   a. **On models with automatic transaxle,** insert O-ring to water inlet pipe and coat outer circumference of O-ring with water.
   b. **On models with manual transaxles,** insert O-ring to water inlet pipe A and coat outer circumference of O-ring with water.
   c. **On models with manual transaxles,** insert O-ring to water inlet pipe B and coat outer circumference of O-ring with water.

DOHC

1. Drain engine cooling system.
2. Remove power transistor assembly.
3. Remove timing belt as outlined under "Timing Belt, Replace."

4. Replace water pump in sequence shown in **Fig. 66,** noting the following:
   a. Install water pump bolts as shown in **Fig. 67.**
   b. Replace O-ring at both ends of water inlet pipe and coat new O-rings with water to aid in installation.

RADIATOR
REPLACE

Refer to **Figs. 68 and 69 for radiator replacement procedure.**

FUEL PUMP
REPLACE

1. Release fuel system pressure as outlined under "Precautions."

2. Drain fuel tank into a suitable container.
3. Remove fuel pump and sending unit in numbered sequence shown in **Fig. 70,** noting the following:
   a. Before disconnecting high pressure fuel lines, cover connections with a rag to prevent residual fuel from splashing.
   b. Secure pump side nut of fuel line connections then loosen line side nut.
4. Reverse procedure to install, noting the following:
   a. Align three projections of packings with holes in fuel pump and fuel gauge unit assembly.
   b. Ensure not to twist fuel lines when tightening.

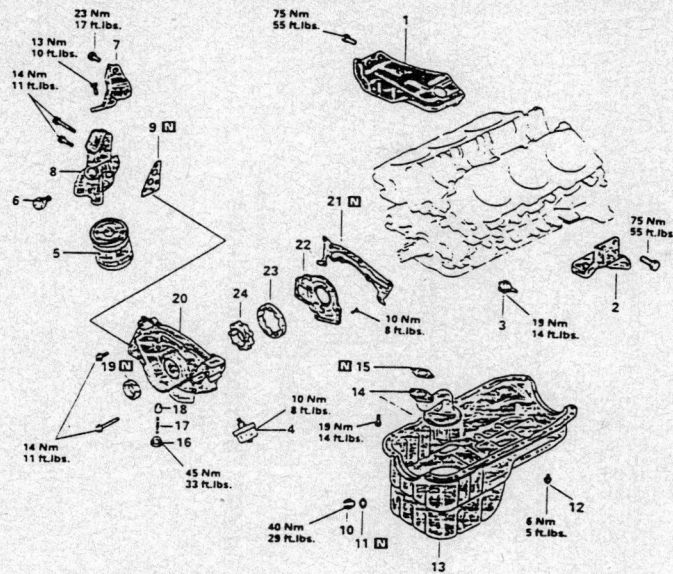

1. Transaxle stay (front)
2. Transaxle stay (rear)
3. Oil pressure switch
4. Oil pressure gauge unit
5. Oil filter
6. Oil cooler by-pass valve <Turbo>
7. Oil filter bracket stay <DOHC>
8. Oil filter bracket
9. Oil filter bracket gasket
10. Drain plug
11. Drain plug gasket
12. Oil pan bolt
13. Oil pan
14. Oil screen
15. Oil screen gasket
16. Relief plug
17. Relief spring
18. Relief plunger
19. Crankshaft front oil seal
20. Oil pump case
21. Oil pump gasket
22. Oil pump cover
23. Oil pump outer rotor
24. Oil pump inner rotor

CR1099100074000X

Fig. 60   Oil pan & pump replacement. DOHC

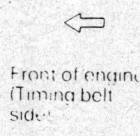

CR1099100075000X

Fig. 61   Oil pan installation

c. Install overfill limiter valve in correct direction, **Fig. 71.**
d. After installation, check for fuel leaks.

FUEL FILTER
REPLACE

1. Release fuel system pressure as outlined under "Precautions."
2. Disconnect battery cables, remove battery hold-down attaching nuts, then battery, **Fig. 72.**
3. Remove battery tray and washer reservoir assembly.
4. Remove fuel line eye bolt and washers, then high pressure fuel line.

5. Remove main fuel line, fuel filter mounting bolt, then fuel filter.
6. Remove high pressure fuel line eyebolt, gaskets, then high pressure fuel pipe connector.
7. Reverse procedure to install.

TURBOCHARGER
REPLACE
FRONT

1. Remove radiator assembly and transmission stay bracket.
2. Remove front exhaust pipe assembly.
3. Remove front turbocharger in sequence shown in **Fig. 73**, noting the

<SOHC>

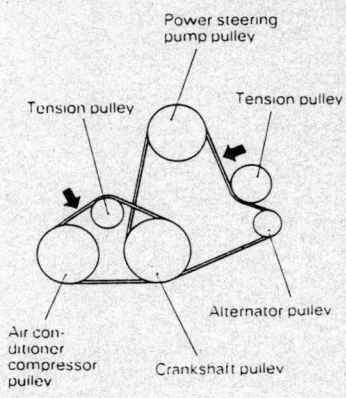

<DOHC <Vehicle without air conditioner>>

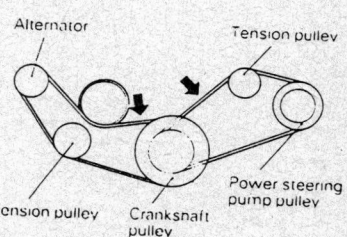

<Vehicle with air conditioner>

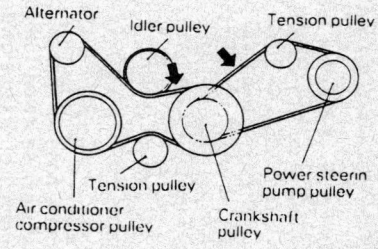

CR1069100535000X

Fig. 62   Drive belt routing

following:
a. Disconnect oxygen sensor connector and remove using oxygen wrench remover tool No. MD998770, or equivalent.
b. Disconnect A/C compressor with hoses attached. Position aside using suitable support wire.
4. Reverse procedure to install, noting the following:
a. Clean points marked in **Fig. 74.** and supply clean engine oil into oil pipe installation hole.
b. Install oxygen sensor using oxygen sensor wrench tool No. MD998770, or equivalent.
c. Align marks on air hose E and B indicated by arrows in **Fig. 75** and seat completely into stepper portion of pipe or until seated.
d. Align marks on air hose D/1 and C indicated by arrows in **Fig. 76** and seat completely into stepper portion of pipe or until seated.
e. Align and engage air intake hose notches mark with an arrow in **Fig. 77** until fully seated.

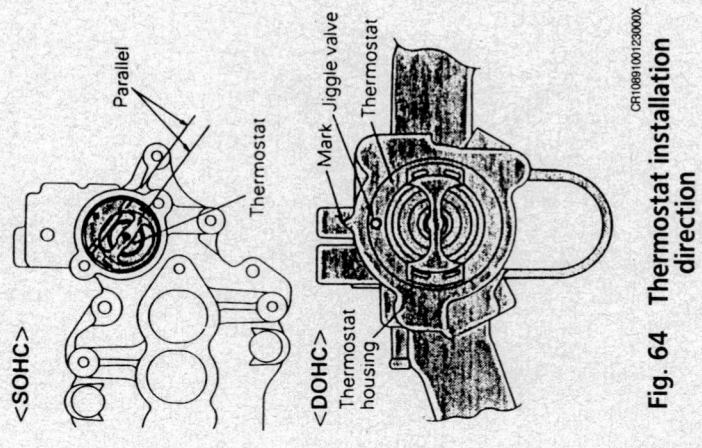

Parallel

Thermostat

<SOHC>

Mark Jiggle valve Thermostat

<DOHC>

Thermostat housing

CR108910012300X

Fig. 64 Thermostat installation direction

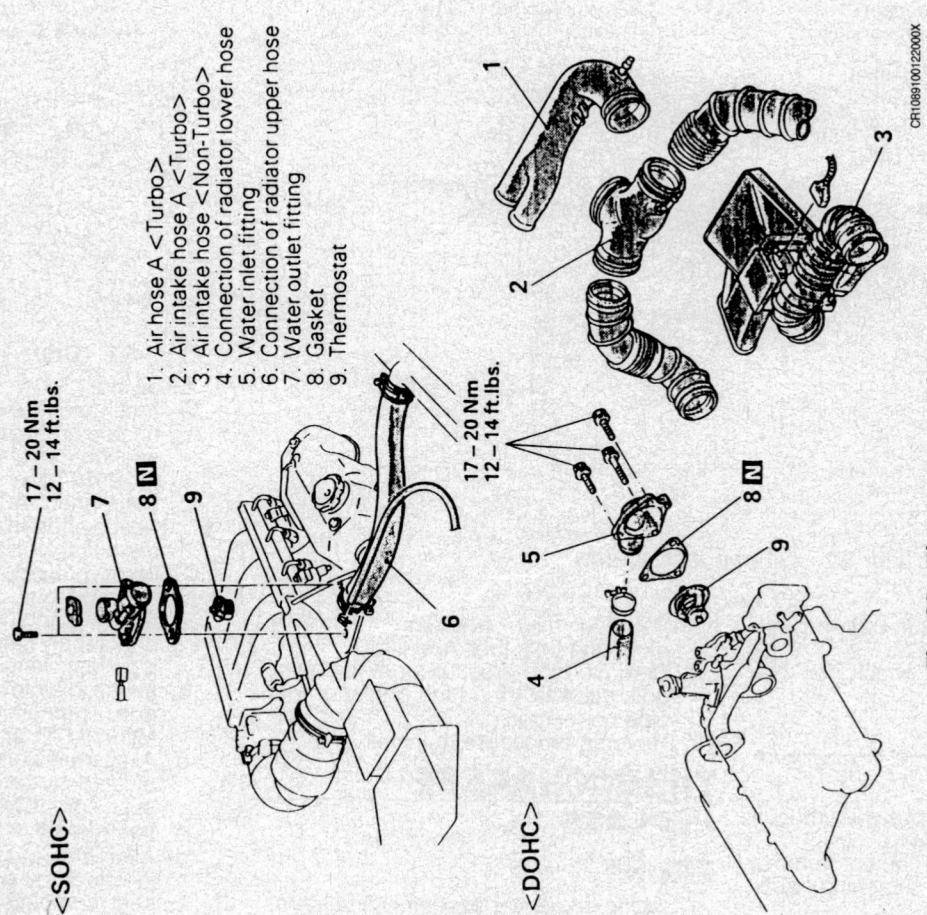

1. Air hose A <Turbo>
2. Air intake hose A <Turbo>
3. Air intake hose <Non-Turbo>
4. Connection of radiator lower hose
5. Water inlet fitting
6. Connection of radiator upper hose
7. Water outlet fitting
8. Gasket
9. Thermostat

17 – 20 Nm
12 – 14 ft.lbs.

17 – 20 Nm
12 – 14 ft.lbs.

<SOHC>

<DOHC>

CR108910012200X

Fig. 63 Thermostat replacement

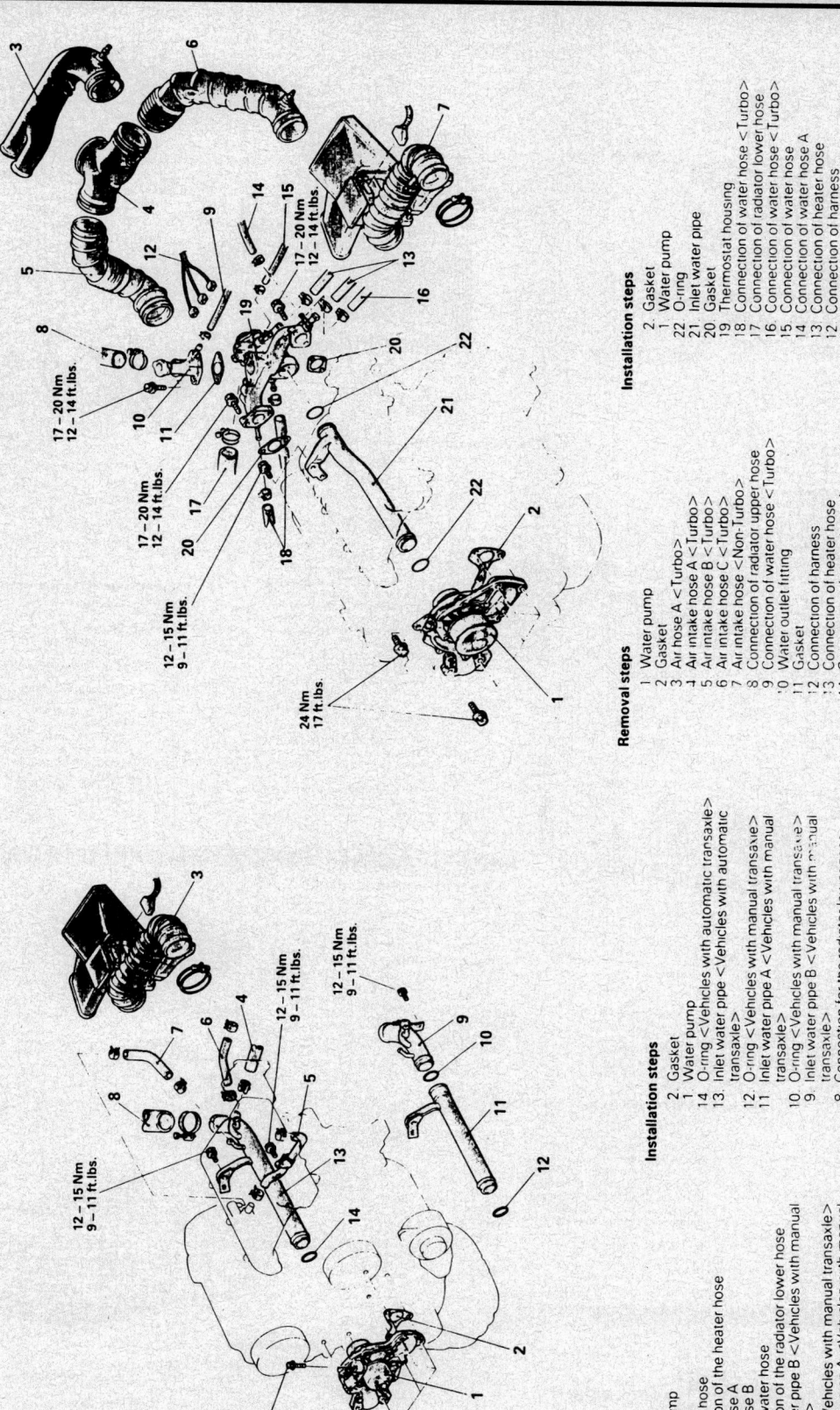

Removal steps

1 Water pump
2 Gasket
3 Air intake hose A <Turbo>
4 Air intake hose A <Turbo>
5 Air intake hose B <Turbo>
6 Air intake hose C <Turbo>
7 Air intake hose <Non-Turbo>
8 Connection of radiator upper hose
9 Connection of water hose <Turbo>
10 Water outlet fitting
11 Gasket
12 Connection of harness
13 Connection of heater hose
14 Connection of water hose A
15 Connection of water hose
16 Connection of radiator lower hose
17 Connection of water hose <Turbo>
18 Connection of water hose <Turbo>
19 Thermostat housing
20 Gasket
21 Inlet water pipe
22 O-ring

Installation steps

2 Gasket
1 Water pump
22 O-ring
21 Inlet water pipe
20 Gasket
19 Thermostat housing
18 Connection of water hose <Turbo>
17 Connection of water hose <Turbo>
16 Connection of radiator lower hose
15 Connection of water hose
14 Connection of water hose A
13 Connection of heater hose
12 Connection of harness
11 Gasket
10 Water outlet fitting
9 Connection of water hose <Turbo>
8 Connection of radiator upper hose
7 Air intake hose <Non-Turbo>
6 Air intake hose C <Turbo>
5 Air intake hose B <Turbo>
4 Air intake hose A <Turbo>
3 Air hose A <Turbo>

17 – 20 Nm
12 – 14 ft.lbs.

17 – 20 Nm
12 – 14 ft.lbs.

17 – 20 Nm
12 – 14 ft.lbs.

12 – 15 Nm
9 – 11 ft.lbs.

24 Nm
17 ft.lbs.

Fig. 66   Water pump replacement. DOHC

Removal steps

1 Water pump
2 Gasket
3 Air intake hose
4 Connection of the heater hose
5 Water hose A
6 Water hose B
7 By-pass water hose
8 Connection of the radiator lower hose
9 Inlet water pipe B <Vehicles with manual transaxle>
10 O-ring <Vehicles with manual transaxle>
11 Inlet water pipe A <Vehicles with manual transaxle>
12 O-ring <Vehicles with manual transaxle>
13 Inlet water pipe <Vehicles with automatic transaxle>
14 O-ring <Vehicles with automatic transaxle>

Installation steps

2 Gasket
1 Water pump
14 O-ring <Vehicles with automatic transaxle>
13 Inlet water pipe <Vehicles with automatic transaxle>
12 O-ring <Vehicles with manual transaxle>
11 Inlet water pipe A <Vehicles with manual transaxle>
10 O-ring <Vehicles with manual transaxle>
9 Inlet water pipe B <Vehicles with manual transaxle>
8 Connection for the radiator lower hose
7 By-pass water hose
6 Water hose B
5 Water hose A
4 Connection for the heater hose
3 Air intake hose

12 – 15 Nm
9 – 11 ft.lbs.

12 – 15 Nm
9 – 11 ft.lbs.

12 – 15 Nm
9 – 11 ft.lbs.

24 Nm
17 ft.lbs.

24 Nm
17 ft.lbs.

Fig. 65   Water pump replacement. SOHC

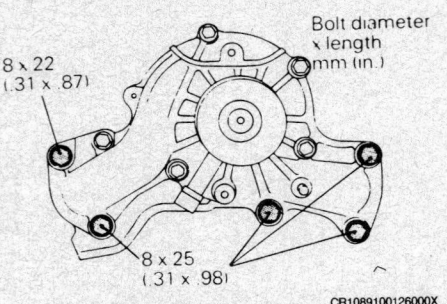

Fig. 67 Water pump bolts installation. DOHC

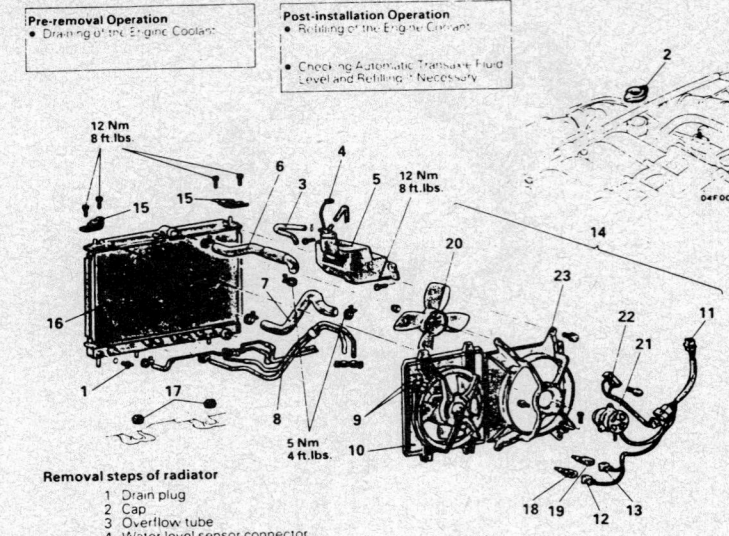

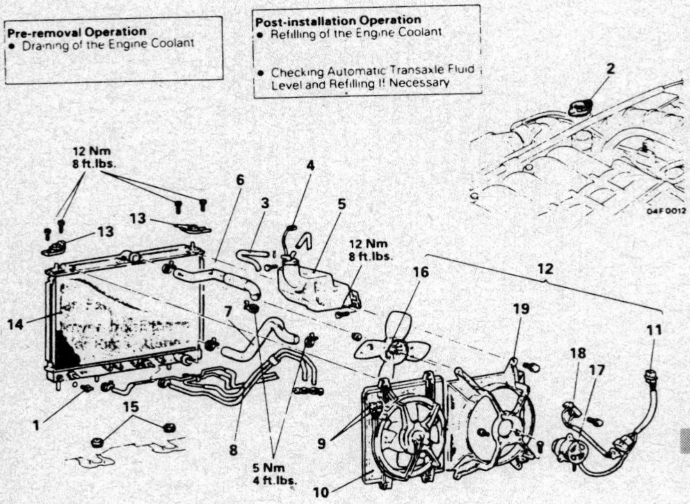

Pre-removal Operation
• Draining of the Engine Coolant

Post-installation Operation
• Refilling of the Engine Coolant

• Checking Automatic Transaxle Fluid Level and Refilling It Necessary

Removal steps of radiator

1. Drain plug
2. Cap
3. Overflow tube
4. Water level sensor connector
5. Reserve tank
6. Radiator upper hose
7. Radiator lower hose
8. Automatic transaxle oil cooler hoses <Vehicles with A.T>
9. Condenser fan motor connector <Vehicles with air conditioner>
10. Condenser fan motor assembly <Vehicles with air conditioner>
11. Radiator fan motor connector
12. Connection of thermo sensor (For radiator fan)
13. Connection of thermo sensor (For condenser fan) <Vehicles with air conditioner>
14. Radiator fan motor assembly
15. Upper insulator
16. Radiator assembly
17. Lower insulator
18. Thermo sensor (For radiator fan)
19. Thermo sensor (For condenser fan) <Vehicles with air conditioner>
20. Fan
21. Radiator fan motor
22. Resistor
23. Shroud

Removal steps of radiator fan motor assembly

1. Drain plug
2. Cap
6. Radiator upper hose
9. Condenser fan motor connector <Vehicles with air conditioner>
10. Condenser fan motor assembly <Vehicles with air conditioner>
11. Radiator fan motor connector
12. Connection of thermo sensor (For radiator fan)
13. Connection of thermo sensor (For condenser fan) <Vehicles with air conditioner>
14. Radiator fan motor assembly
20. Fan
21. Radiator fan motor
22. Resistor
23. Shroud

Fig. 68 Radiator replacement. 1992-93

Removal steps of radiator

1. Drain plug
2. Cap
3. Overflow tube
4. Water level sensor connector
5. Reserve tank
6. Radiator upper hose
7. Radiator lower hose
8. Automatic transaxle oil cooler hoses <Vehicles with A.T>
9. Condenser fan motor connector <Vehicles with air conditioning>
10. Condenser fan motor assembly <Vehicles with air conditioning>
11. Radiator fan motor connector
12. Radiator fan motor assembly
13. Upper insulator
14. Radiator assembly
15. Lower insulator
16. Fan
17. Radiator fan motor
18. Resistor
19. Shroud

Removal steps of radiator fan motor assembly

1. Drain plug
2. Cap
6. Radiator upper hose
9. Condenser fan motor connector <Vehicles with air conditioning>
10. Condenser fan motor assembly <Vehicles with air conditioning>
11. Radiator fan motor connector
12. Radiator fan motor assembly
16. Fan
17. Radiator fan motor
18. Resistor
19. Shroud

Fig. 69 Radiator replacement. 1994-95

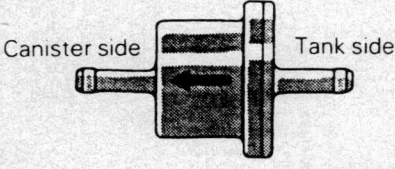

Canister side   Tank side

Fig. 71 Overflow limiter valve installation

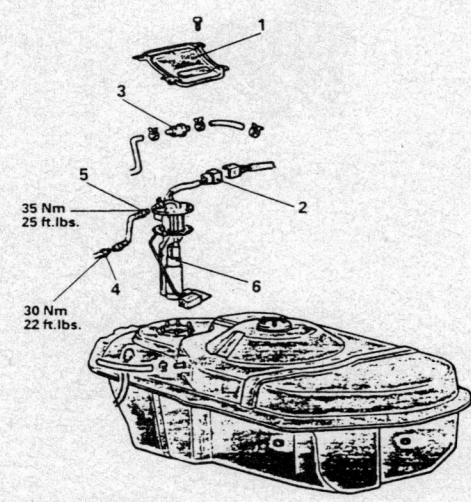

Removal steps

1. Fuel gauge cover
2. Fuel pump and fuel gauge unit assembly connector
3. Overfill limiter (Two-way valve)
4. High pressure fuel hose connection (body side)
5. High pressure fuel hose connection (fuel pump side)
6. Fuel pump and fuel gauge unit assembly

Fig. 70 Fuel pump replacement procedure

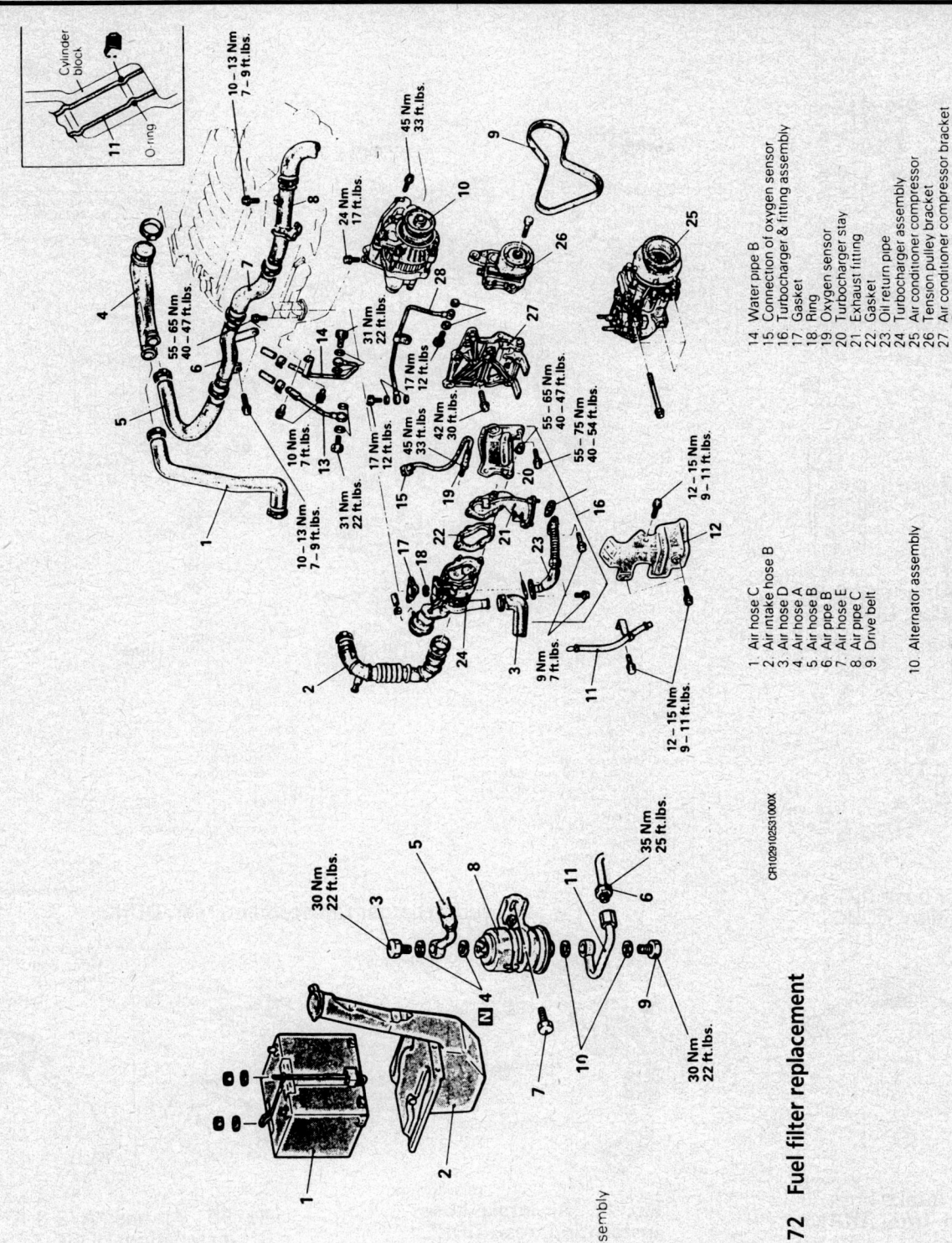

CR10591000730000X

Fig. 73 Turbocharger replacement, front. DOHC

1. Air hose C
2. Air intake hose B
3. Air hose A
4. Air hose B
5. Air hose B
6. Air pipe B
7. Air pipe E
8. Air pipe C
9. Drive belt

10. Alternator assembly

11. Engine oil level gauge guide
12. Heat protector B
13. Water pipe A

14. Water pipe B
15. Connection of oxygen sensor
16. Turbocharger & fitting assembly
17. Gasket
18. Ring
19. Oxygen sensor
20. Turbocharger stay
21. Exhaust fitting
22. Gasket
23. Oil return pipe
24. Turbocharger assembly
25. Air conditioner compressor
26. Tension pulley bracket
27. Air conditioner compressor bracket
28. Oil pipe

CR10291025310000X

Fig. 72 Fuel filter replacement

1. Battery
2. Battery tray with washer tank assembly
3. Eye bolt
4. Gasket
5. High pressure fuel hose
6. Connection of fuel main pipe
7. Mounting bolt
8. Fuel filter
9. Eye bolt
10. Gasket
11. High pressure fuel pipe

Cylinder block
O-ring

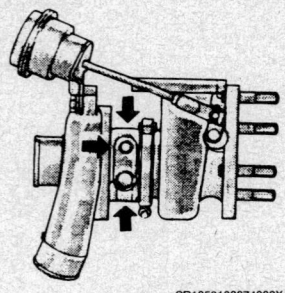

Fig. 74 Cleaning turbocharger. DOHC

CR1059100074000X

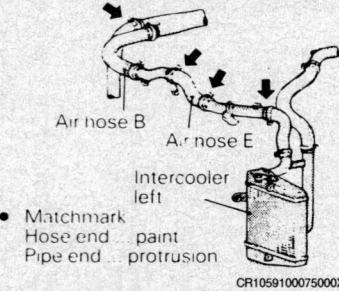

Air hose B
Air hose E
Intercooler left
- Matchmark
  Hose end ... paint
  Pipe end ... protrusion

CR1059100075000X

Fig. 75 Air hose E & B installation. DOHC

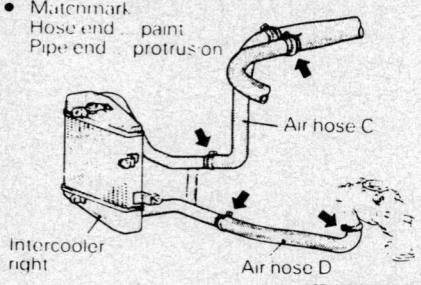

- Matchmark
  Hose end ... paint
  Pipe end ... protrusion

Air hose C
Intercooler right
Air hose D

CR1059100076000X

Fig. 76 Air hose D/1 & C installation. DOHC

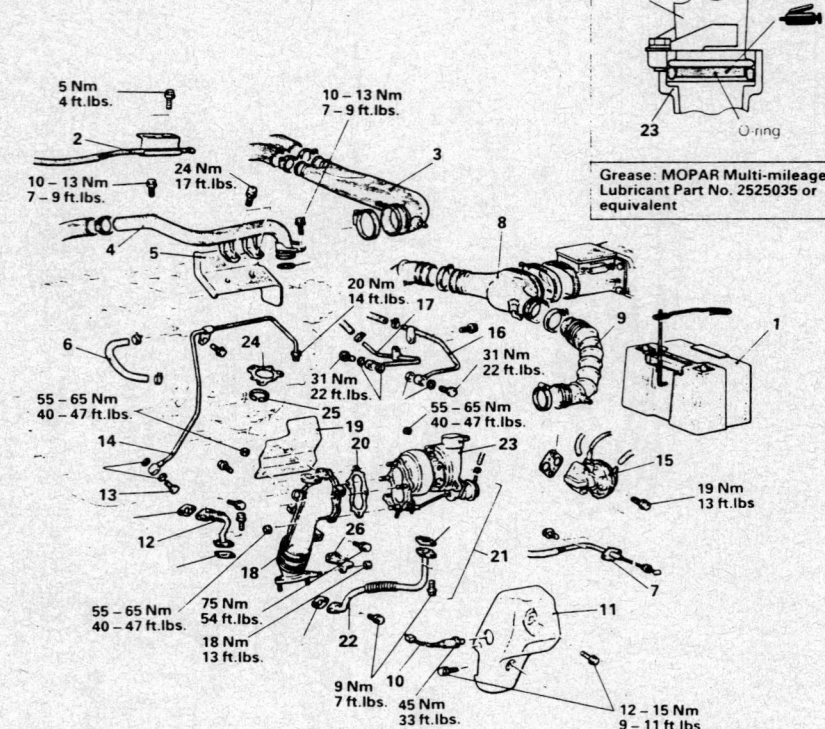

5 Nm
4 ft.lbs.

10 – 13 Nm
7 – 9 ft.lbs.

2

24 Nm
17 ft.lbs.

10 – 13 Nm
7 – 9 ft.lbs.

4

5

6

24

20 Nm
14 ft.lbs.

17

16

31 Nm
22 ft.lbs.

55 – 65 Nm
40 – 47 ft.lbs.

31 Nm
22 ft.lbs.

25

55 – 65 Nm
40 – 47 ft.lbs.

14

19

20

23

15

19 Nm
13 ft.lbs.

13

21

7

12

26

11

18

55 – 65 Nm
40 – 47 ft.lbs.

75 Nm
54 ft.lbs.

18 Nm
13 ft.lbs.

22

9 Nm
7 ft.lbs.

10

45 Nm
33 ft.lbs.

12 – 15 Nm
9 – 11 ft.lbs.

3

8

9

1

4

23   O-ring

Grease: MOPAR Multi-mileage Lubricant Part No. 2525035 or equivalent

1. Battery
2. Connection of accelerator cable (engine side)
3. Air hose A
4. Air pipe A
5. Heat protector F
6. Clutch booster vacuum hose
7. Connection of accelerator cable (pedal side)
8. Air intake hose A
9. Air intake hose C
10. Oxygen sensor
11. Heat protector D
12. EGR pipe
13. Eye bolt
14. Oil pipe
15. EGR valve
16. Water pipe A
17. Water pipe B
18. Exhaust fitting
19. Heat protector E
20. Gasket
21. Turbocharger & return pipe assembly
22. Oil return pipe
23. Turbocharger assembly
24. Gasket
25. Ring
26. Exhaust fitting stay

CR1059100078000X

Fig. 78 Turbocharger replacement, rear. DOHC

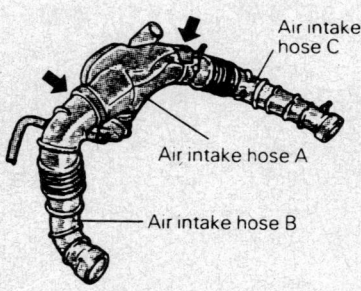
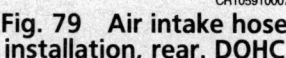

Air intake hose A
Air intake hose B

CR1059100077000X

Fig. 77 Intake hose installation, front. DOHC

Air intake hose C
Air intake hose A
Air intake hose B

CR1059100079000X

Fig. 79 Air intake hose installation, rear. DOHC

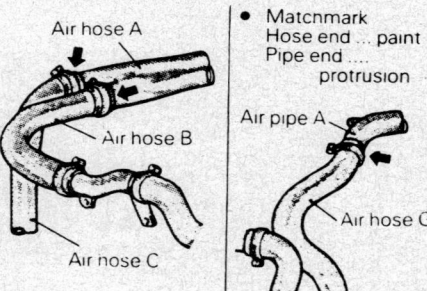

Air hose A
Air hose B
Air hose C

- Matchmark
  Hose end ... paint
  Pipe end .... protrusion

Air pipe A
Air hose G

CR1059100080000X

Fig. 80 Air hose A/3 & A installation. DOHC

REAR

1. Drain engine cooling system.
2. Remove front exhaust pipe.
3. Remove rear turbocharger in sequence shown in **Fig. 78**, noting the following:
   a. Disconnect oxygen sensor connector and remove using oxygen wrench remover tool No. MD998770, or equivalent.
4. Reverse procedure to install, noting

the following:
a. Clean points marked in **Fig. 74**. and supply clean engine oil into oil pipe installation hole.
b. Install oxygen sensor using oxygen sensor wrench tool No. MD998770, or equivalent.
c. Align and engage air intake hose notches mark with an arrow in **Fig. 79** until fully seated.
d. Align marks on air pipe A indicated

by arrows in **Fig. 80** and seat completely into stepper portion of pipe or until seated.

TIGHTENING SPECIFICATIONS

For engine tightening specifications, refer to individual repair procedure or illustrations.

Clutch & Manual Transaxle

INDEX

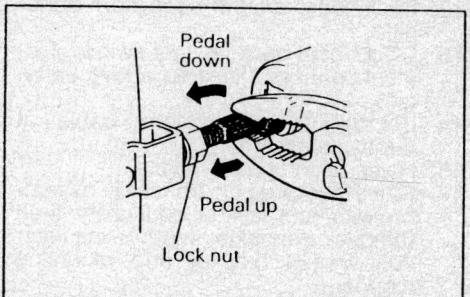

Fig. 1 Clutch pedal height pushrod adjustment

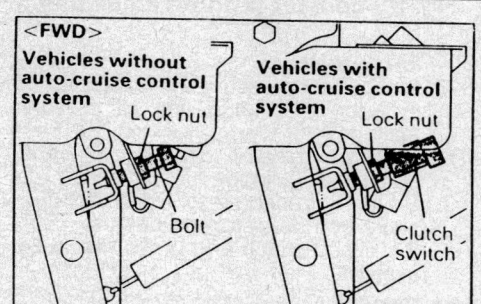

Fig. 2 Clutch pedal height adjusters

Fig. 3 Clutch interlock switch

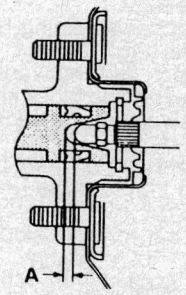

Fig. 4 Clutch booster piston to pushrod clearance

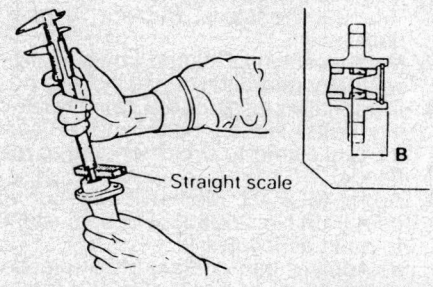

Fig. 5 Location of measurement "B"

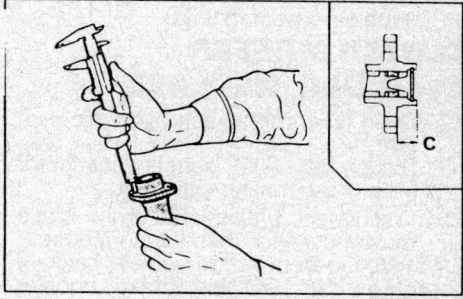

Fig. 6 Location of measurement "C"

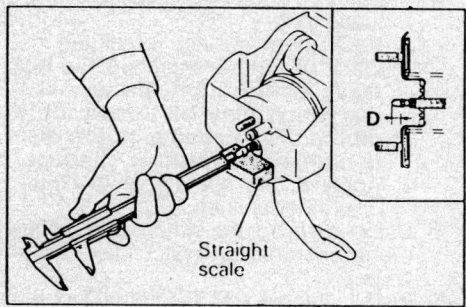

Fig. 7 Location of measurement "D"

ADJUSTMENTS

CLUTCH PEDAL HEIGHT

To determine if the pedal height requires adjustment, measure the distance from the floor pan to the upper center of pedal pad. The distance should be 6.97-7.17 inches.

If pedal height is lower than specified, loosen bolt or clutch switch, then turn the pushrod to adjust clutch pedal to specification **Fig. 1**. After making the adjustment, adjust the bolt or clutch switch to reach the pedal stopper and tighten locknut. If pedal height is higher than specified, use the following procedure:

1. **On vehicles less cruise control,** turn and adjust bolt located at top of pedal so that pedal height is within specification **Fig. 2**, then secure by tightening locknut.
2. **On vehicles equipped with cruise** control, disconnect clutch switch connector, then turn switch to adjust pedal height **Fig. 2**. Tighten switch locknut.
3. Ensure that clutch interlock switch is as shown in **Fig. 3**, when clutch pedal is fully depressed. If switch is not as shown, loosen locknut and adjust.

CLUTCH PEDAL FREEPLAY

On AWD vehicles, depress clutch pedal two to three times with the engine off to eliminate booster negative pressure before testing pedal freeplay.

To determine if the pedal freeplay is not within specification, depress clutch pedal by hand until clutch resistance is felt. Measure the distance between upper pedal height and where resistance is felt. Freeplay should be .24-.51 inch on FWD models or .49-.79 inch on AWD models. After pedal freeplay has been checked, measure the distance between the clutch pedal and the floorpan when the clutch disengages. On AWD vehicles, measure distance with engine running. Clearance should be 2.2 inches or greater.

If the pedal freeplay and/or clutch disengagement clearance is not within specification, bleed the clutch hydraulic system.

CLUTCH BOOSTER

Refer to **Fig. 4** when adjusting clearance between clutch booster pushrod and piston.

1. Measure and record dimensions B, C and D, **Figs. 5 through 7**.
2. Using measured values obtained in step one, add measurements C and D, then subtract that measurement from measurement B, this will give you di-

mension A in **Fig. 4**. Dimension A should be between .0082–.0181 inches.

3. If clearance is not within specification, adjust the pushrod length by turning the adjustable end of pushrod, **Fig. 8**. Improper clearance may cause excessive clutch drag.

HYDRAULIC SYSTEM SERVICE

HYDRAULIC SYSTEM BLEED

The clutch hydraulic system must be bled whenever the pressure line is disconnected or system component replacement is required.

The fluid in the reservoir must be maintained at the ¾ level or higher during air bleeding.
1. Remove bleeder cap from slave cylinder and attach vinyl hose to bleeder screw, then place other end of hose in container.
2. Slowly pump clutch pedal several times.
3. With clutch pedal depressed, loosen bleeder screw to release trapped air.
4. Tighten bleeder screw.
5. Repeat steps 2 through 4 until no air bubbles appear in fluid.

CLUTCH MASTER CYLINDER, REPLACE

1. Drain fluid from clutch hydraulic system.
2. Disconnect fluid sensor connector from brake master cylinder.
3. Disconnect brake lines from brake master cylinder, then vacuum hose.
4. Working from inside vehicle, remove clevis pin retaining brake booster pushrod to brake pedal.
5. Remove four brake booster retaining bolts from brake pedal support bracket.
6. Remove brake master cylinder and booster assembly from engine compartment.
7. Disconnect clutch pressure line from master cylinder.
8. **On AWD vehicles**, working form inside engine compartment, remove clutch master cylinder retaining bolts.
9. **On FWD models**, working from inside vehicle, remove master cylinder retaining nuts.
10. **On all models**, remove clutch master cylinder from engine compartment.
11. Reverse procedure to install, **Torque** clutch master cylinder retaining nuts to 9 ft. lbs. **Torque** brake master cylinder retaining nuts to 10 ft. lbs.

CLUTCH RELEASE CYLINDER, REPLACE

1. Remove air cleaner and intake hose assembly from vehicle.
2. **On AWD models**, remove vacuum pipe from above battery.
3. **On all models**, remove battery, then battery tray assembly from vehicle.
4. Remove windshield washer reservoir

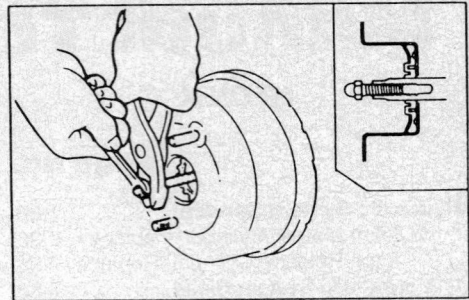

Fig. 8   Booster pushrod adjustment

from vehicle.
5. Disconnect pressure line from release cylinder, then plug line to prevent leakage.
6. Remove release cylinder retaining bolts, then cylinder.
7. Reverse procedure to install. **Torque** slave cylinder retaining bolts to 13 ft. lbs. Bleed clutch and brake hydraulic systems.

CLUTCH
REPLACE

1. Remove transaxle as described under "Manual Transaxle, Replace" procedure.
2. Mark position of clutch cover to flywheel for reference during installation.
3. Diagonally loosen clutch cover retaining bolts, loosen bolts one or two turns at a time, to avoid bending cover flange.
4. Apply MOPAR Multi-mileage Lubricant (Part No. 2525035) or equivalent to parts as follows:
   a. Apply a thin coating of to release arm fulcrum and point of contact with release bearing.
   b. To end of the release cylinders, pushrod and to pushrod hole in release fork.
   c. Pack inner surface of clutch release bearing and groove. **Do not leave excess lubricant on bearing which may be thrown onto clutch disc, causing clutch disc contamination and/or slippage.**
   d. Apply a thin coating of to clutch disc inner splines.
5. Using a universal clutch disc alignment tool, position clutch disc to flywheel.
6. Install clutch cover assembly. Tighten bolts a little at a time, working in a diagonal sequence. **Torque** bolts to 11–15 ft. lbs.

TRANSAXLE
REPLACE

1. Drain transaxle fluid.
2. **On vehicles equipped with SOHC engine**, drain engine coolant.
3. Remove front wheel and tire assemblies.
4. **On all models**, working from inside front inner fenderwells, remove engine splash shields.

5. **On AWD models**, remove vacuum pipe assembly from above battery.
6. **On all models**, remove battery and battery tray assembly.
7. Remove windshield washer reservoir from vehicle.
8. Disconnect air flow sensor.
9. Disconnect air duct hose and air cleaner cover from engine.
10. **On vehicles equipped with SOHC engine**, remove upper and lower radiator hoses.
11. **On all models**, disconnect pressure line from release cylinder, then plug pressure line.
12. Disconnect ground strap from transaxle.
13. Disconnect back-up light switch electrical connector located above transaxle.
14. Disconnect speedometer cable at transaxle assembly.
15. Raise and support vehicle.
16. Raise and support transaxle assembly with floor jack or equivalent, then remove transaxle mount insulator bolt, mount bracket and mounting stopper.
17. Disconnect front tie rod ends from steering knuckles.
18. Disconnect steering knuckle from lower control arm.
19. Remove right member, then starter assembly **Fig. 9**.
20. Remove lefthand bearing bracket retaining bolts, **Fig. 10**.
21. Insert a pry bar between bearing bracket and engine block, then pry lefthand driveshaft assembly from transaxle.
22. Remove lefthand driveshaft, hub and inner shaft from vehicle as a assembly.
23. Insert pry bar to protrusion shown in **Fig. 11** to remove righthand driveshaft assembly from transaxle.
24. **On AWD models**, remove driveshaft retaining bolts, then midship bearing retaining bolts and driveshaft from vehicle.
25. **On all models**, support transaxle with transmission jack or equivalent, then remove transaxle assembly lower coupling bolt.
26. Remove transaxle from vehicle.
27. Reverse procedure to install. **Torque** all bolts to specification.

TRANSFER CASE
REPLACE

1. Drain transaxle assembly.
2. Remove active front venturi skirt from vehicle.
3. Remove front exhaust pipe and main muffler assembly from vehicle.
4. Remove driveshaft retaining bolts, then midship bearing retaining bolts and driveshaft from vehicle.
5. Remove five transfer case retaining bolts, then transfer case.
6. Reverse procedure to install. **Torque** all bolts to specification.

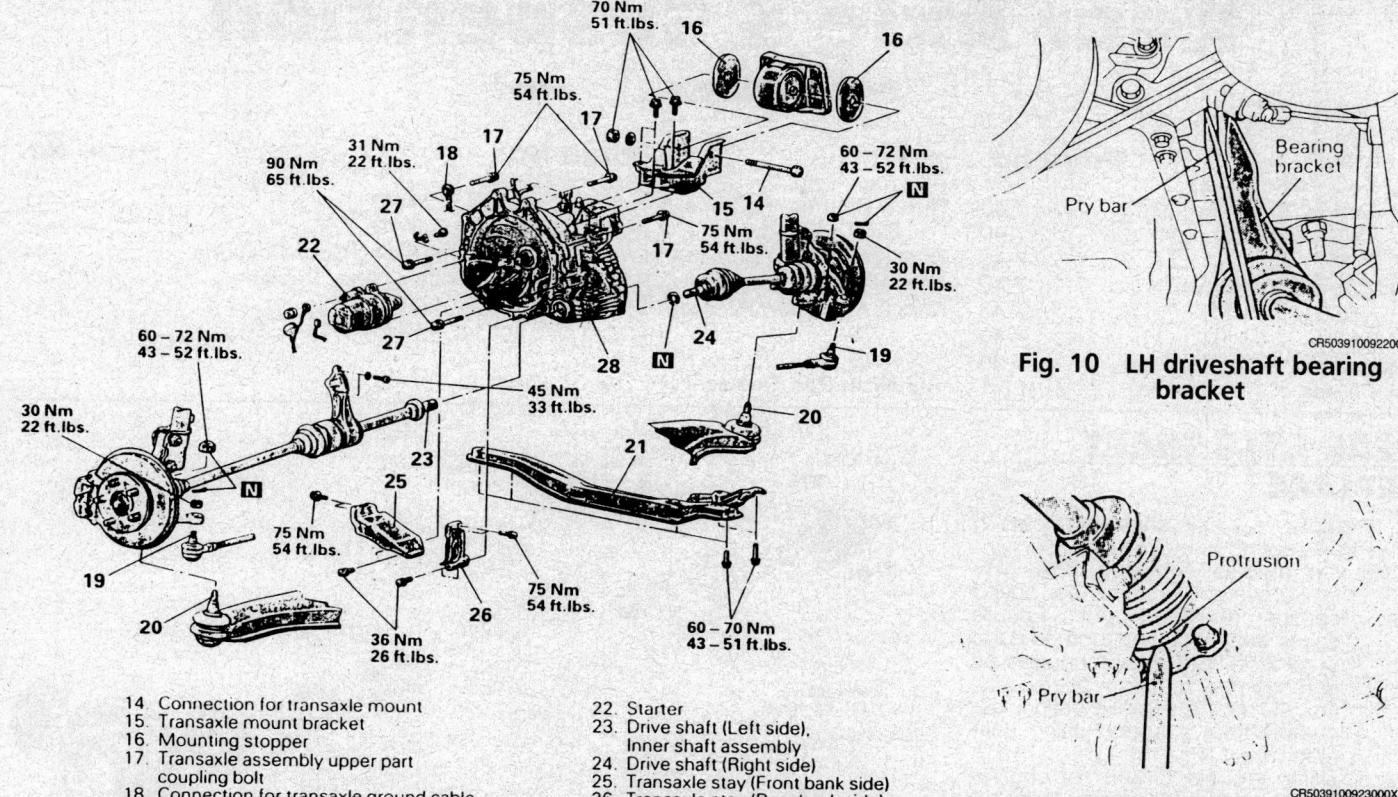

Fig. 10 LH driveshaft bearing bracket

Fig. 11 Location of righthand driveshaft protrusion

14. Connection for transaxle mount
15. Transaxle mount bracket
16. Mounting stopper
17. Transaxle assembly upper part coupling bolt
18. Connection for transaxle ground cable
19. Connection for tie rod end
20. Connection for lower arm ball joint
21. Right member

22. Starter
23. Drive shaft (Left side), Inner shaft assembly
24. Drive shaft (Right side)
25. Transaxle stay (Front bank side)
26. Transaxle stay (Rear bank side)
27. Transaxle assembly lower part coupling bolt
28. Transaxle assembly

Fig. 9 Transaxle replacement

TIGHTENING SPECIFICATIONS

Year	Component	Torque/Ft. Lbs.
1992–95	Back-Up Lamp Switch	14–22
	Brake Pedal Shaft	22
	Clutch Cover Bolt	11–15
	Clutch Master Cylinder Bolt	9
	Clutch Pedal Bolt	22
	Clutch Release Cylinder	13
	Clutch Tube Bolt	11
	Clutch Vacuum Line Bolt	11–13
	Flywheel Bolt	55

Year	Component	Torque/Ft. Lbs.
1992–95 -Cont'd	RH Member Bolt	43–51
	Starter Cover Bolt	7
	Stop Lamp Switch	10
	Tie Rod End	22
	Transaxle Coupling Bolt	65
	Transaxle Mount	33
	Transaxle Stay	54
	Transfer Case To Transaxle	64

Rear Axle & Suspension

INDEX

REAR AXLE SHAFT
REPLACE

1. Remove rear axle shaft as shown in **Fig. 1**, noting the following:
   a. On models equipped with ABS brake system, remove rear speed sensor attaching nut. Ensure speed sensor tip and toothed edge of rotor do not strike other parts, as damage may result.
   b. On all models, remove caliper assembly then suspend using suitable wire.
   c. Using tool No. C 3281 or equivalent, secure axle shaft, then remove companion flange self-locking nut.
   d. **On models equipped with ABS brake system,** using tool No. P 334 or equivalent, remove rear rotor from axle shaft assembly.
   e. **On all models,** using tool No. P334 or equivalent, remove outer bearing and dust shield assembly.
   f. Using tool No. C 4171 or equivalent, remove inner bearing and seal from axle housing.
2. Reverse procedure to install, noting the following:
   a. Using tool No. C 4171 or equivalent, press fit inner bearing onto axle housing.
   b. Using tool No. MB990641 or equivalent, press oil seal onto axle housing with oil seal depression facing upward, and until it contacts shoulder on inside of axle housing. Using suitable plastic hammer, lightly tap top and circumference of tool press fitting oil seal gradually and evenly.
   c. Using tool No. MB990799 or equivalent, press fit dust shield until it contacts with axle shaft shoulder. Using suitable plastic hammer, lightly tap top and circumference of tool press fitting oil seal gradually and evenly.
   d. Apply multipurpose grease around circumference of inner side of outer bearing seal lip.
   e. Using tool No. P 334 or equivalent, press fit outer bearing to axle shaft, ensuring bearing seal lip surface faces axle shaft flange.
   f. **On models equipped with ABS**

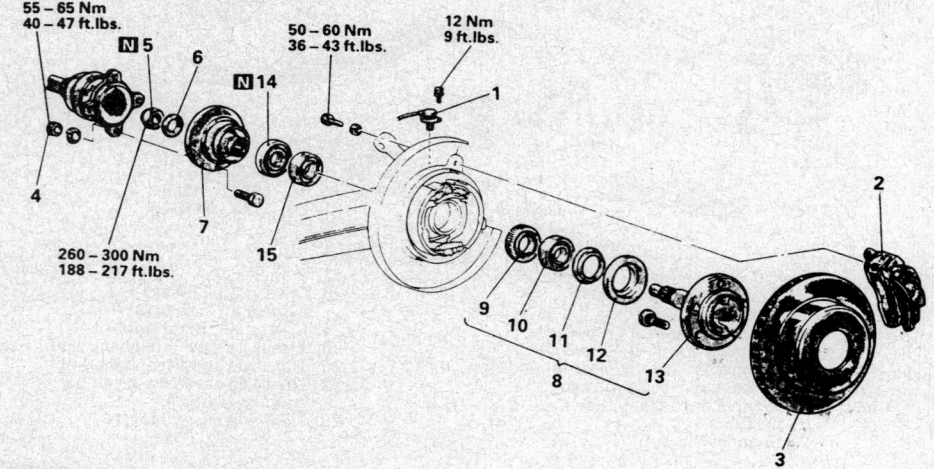

Removal steps

1. Rear speed sensor
   \<Vehicles with A.B.S.>
2. Brake caliper assembly
3. Brake disc
4. Drive shaft mounting nut
5. Self-locking nut
6. Washer
7. Companion flange
8. Axle shaft assembly
9. Rear rotor
   \<Vehicles with A.B.S.>
10. Outer bearing
11. Dust shield
12. Dust shield
13. Axle shaft
14. Oil seal
15. Inner bearing

CR3039100342000X

Fig. 1   Rear axle shaft assembly

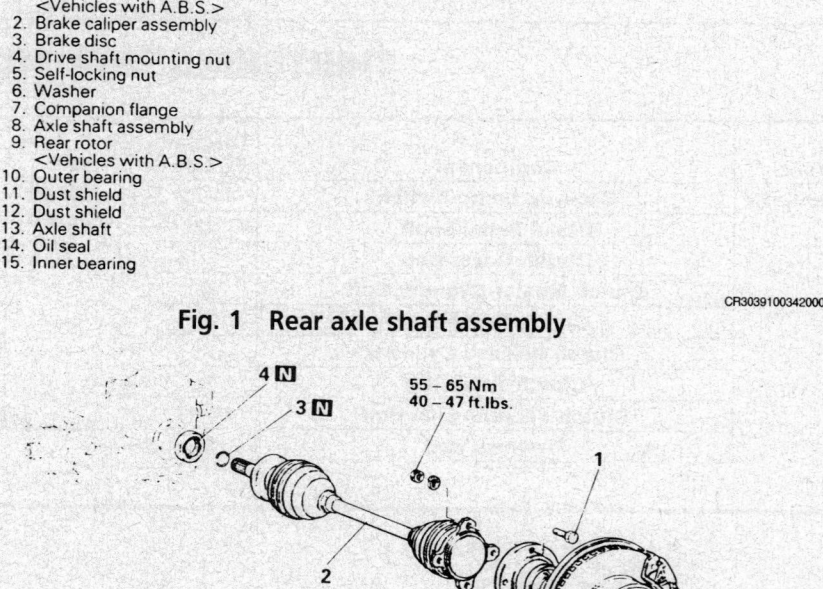

Removal steps

1. Bolt
2. Drive shaft
3. Circlip
4. Oil seal

CR3039100343000X

Fig. 2   Rear driveshaft assembly

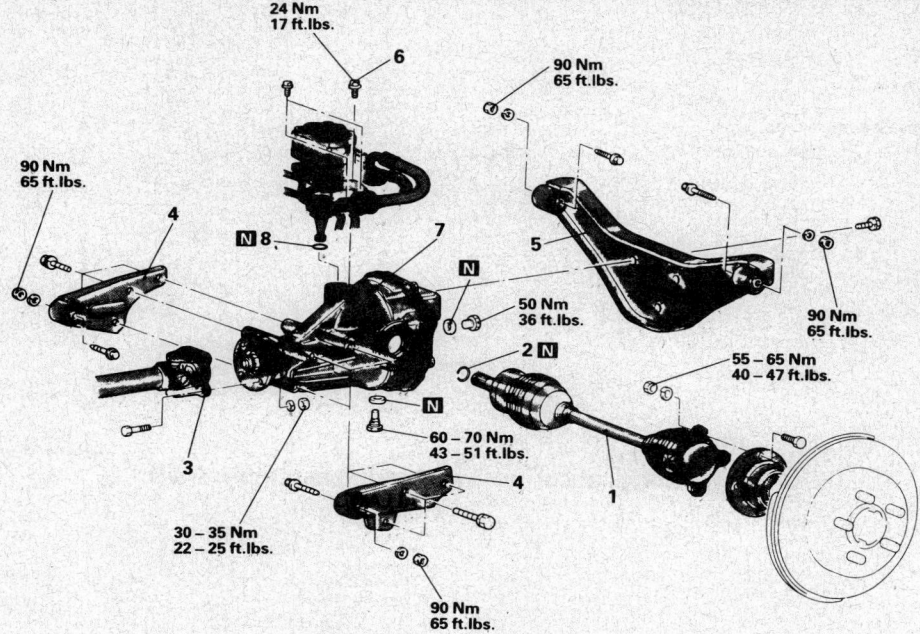

24 Nm
17 ft.lbs.

90 Nm
65 ft.lbs.

90 Nm
65 ft.lbs.

50 Nm
36 ft.lbs.

55 – 65 Nm
40 – 47 ft.lbs.

90 Nm
65 ft.lbs.

60 – 70 Nm
43 – 51 ft.lbs.

30 – 35 Nm
22 – 25 ft.lbs.

90 Nm
65 ft.lbs.

Removal steps
1. Drive shaft
2. Circlip
3. Propeller shaft connection
4. Differential support assembly
5. Differential support member assembly
6. Rear wheel oil pump installation bolt
7. Differential carrier
8. O-ring

Fig. 3   Rear differential carrier assembly

CR3039100344000X

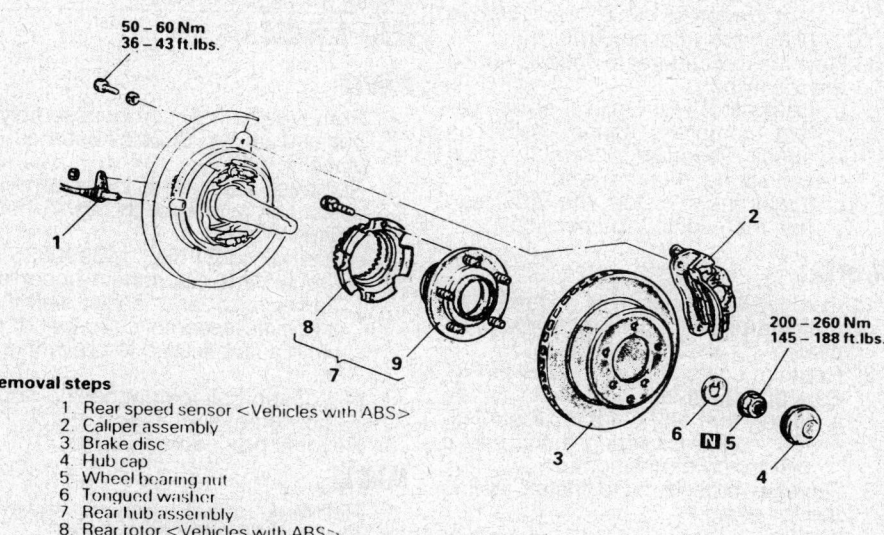

50 – 60 Nm
36 – 43 ft.lbs.

200 – 260 Nm
145 – 188 ft.lbs.

Removal steps
1. Rear speed sensor <Vehicles with ABS>
2. Caliper assembly
3. Brake disc
4. Hub cap
5. Wheel bearing nut
6. Tongued washer
7. Rear hub assembly
8. Rear rotor <Vehicles with ABS>
9. Rear hub unit bearing

Caution
Rear hub unit bearing cannot be disassembled.

CR3039100345000X

Fig. 4   Rear hub & bearing assembly. FWD

---

brake systems, using tool No. P 334 or equivalent, press fit rotor to axle shaft with rear rotor groove toward axle shaft flange.
g. **On all models,** using tool No. C3281 or equivalent, secure axle shaft, then tighten companion flange self-locking nut.

REAR HALFSHAFT
REPLACE

1. Remove driveshaft as shown in **Fig. 2,** noting the following:
   a. Using suitable tool, remove driveshaft from differential carrier. **Ensure differential carrier oil seal is not damaged by driveshaft spline.**
2. Reverse to install, noting the following:
   a. Using tool Nos. C4171 and MB991380 or equivalents, install oil seal.
   b. **Ensure differential carrier oil seal is not damaged by driveshaft spline.**
   c. **On models equipped with Limited Slip Differential (LSD) a Viscous coupling Unit (VCU) has a tow part serration, ensure installation on correct side.**
   d. Driveshaft LH boot band color on ball joint side is white, RH side is blue.

DIFFERENTIAL CARRIER
REPLACE

1. Drain differential gear oil.
2. Remove main muffler assembly as follows:
   a. Remove main muffler and center exhaust pipe attaching bolts and gasket.
   b. Remove rubber hanger attaching bolts.
   c. Remove main muffler assembly.
3. Remove differential carrier as shown in **Fig. 3,** noting the following:
   a. Using suitable tool, remove driveshaft from differential carrier. **Ensure differential carrier oil seal is not damaged by driveshaft spline.**
   b. Mark differential companion flange and propeller shaft flange yoke for installation alignment.
   c. Support propeller shaft with suitable wire.
   d. Hold bottom of differential carrier, then remove rear wheel oil pump through mounting hole, then remove differential carrier.
4. Reverse procedure to install, noting the following:
   a. Install rear wheel oil pump through mounting hole, then install differential carrier.
   b. Align flange yoke and companion flange mating mark, then install propeller shaft.

HUB & BEARING
REPLACE

FWD

1. Remove rear hub and bearing assembly as shown in **Fig. 4**, noting the following:
   a. **On models equipped with ABS brake system,** remove rear speed sensor attaching nut. Ensure speed sensor tip and toothed edge of rotor do not strike other parts, as damage may result.
   b. **On all models,** remove caliper assembly then suspend using suitable wire.
   c. **On models equipped with ABS brake system,** do not scratch or scar toothed surface of rotor, if rotor is deformed it may not be able to accurately sense wheel rotation speed and the system may perform normally.
2. Reverse procedure to install, noting the following:
   a. Align wheel bearing attaching nut with spindle indentation, then crimp.

SHOCK ABSORBER
REPLACE

FWD

1. Remove interior rear side trim panel to gain access to shock assembly.
2. Remove upper shock absorber attaching nut.
3. Remove ECS electrical connector.
4. Remove shock absorber upper cap.
5. Raise and support vehicle.
6. Remove brake line clamp attaching bolt.
7. Remove shock absorber lower attaching bolt, then remove shock assembly.
8. Reverse procedure to install. Tighten to specifications.

AWD

1. Remove interior rear side trim panel to gain access to shock assembly.
2. Remove upper shock absorber attaching nut.
3. Remove ECS electrical connector.
4. Remove shock absorber upper cap.
5. Raise and support vehicle.
6. Remove shock absorber lower attaching bolt, then remove shock assembly.
7. Reverse procedure to install. Tighten to specifications.

COIL SPRING
REPLACE

FWD

1. Remove shock absorber assembly as outlined under "Shock Absorber, Replace."
2. Remove coil spring as shown in **Fig. 5**, noting the following:

Disassembly steps

1. Piston rod tightening nut
2. Washer
3. Upper bushing (A)
4. Bracket assembly
5. Upper spring pad
6. Upper bushing (B)
7. Collar
8. Cup assembly
9. Dust cover
10. Bump rubber
11. Coil spring
12. Shock absorber

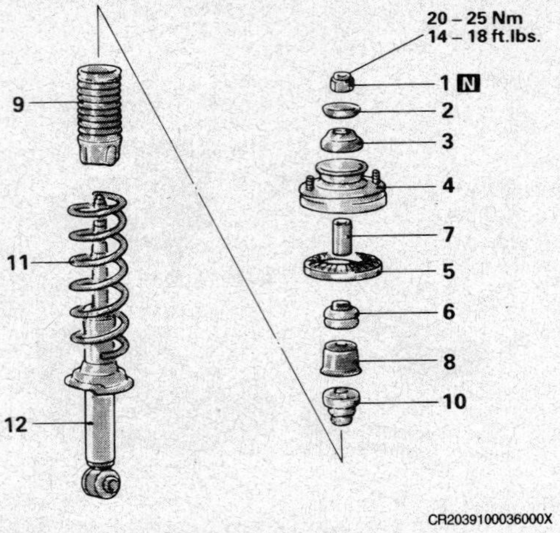

20 – 25 Nm
14 – 18 ft.lbs.

CR2039100036000X

Fig. 5   Shock absorber & coil spring assembly. FWD

Disassembly steps

1. Cap
2. Piston rod tightening nut
3. Washer
4. Upper bushing (A)
5. Bracket assembly
6. Spring pad
7. Upper bushing (B)
8. Collar
9. Cup assembly
10. Dust cover
11. Bump rubber
12. Coil spring
13. Shock absorber

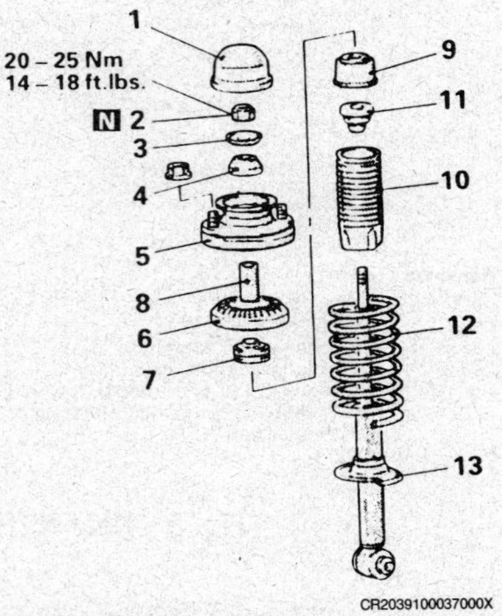

20 – 25 Nm
14 – 18 ft.lbs.

CR2039100037000X

Fig. 6   Shock absorber & coil spring assembly. AWD

   a. Using tool No. C-4838 or equivalent, compress spring, then remove piston rod attaching nut.
3. Reverse procedure to install, noting the following:
   a. Using tool No. L-4514 or equivalent, compress spring, install on shock absorber assembly, align coil spring in spring seat.
   b. Install new piston rod attaching nut, then tighten to specifications.

AWD

1. Remove shock absorber assembly as outlined under "Shock Absorber, Replace."
2. Remove coil spring as shown in **Fig. 6**, noting the following:
   a. Using tool No. C-4838 or equivalent, compress spring, then remove piston rod attaching nut.
3. Reverse procedure to install, noting the following:
   a. Using tool No. L-4514 or equivalent, compress spring, install on shock absorber assembly, align coil spring in spring seat.
   b. Install new piston rod attaching nut, then tighten to specifications.

CONTROL ARM
REPLACE

FWD

1. Remove shock absorber assembly as outlined under "Shock Absorber, Replace."
2. Remove upper arm, lower arm and assist link as shown in **Fig. 7**, noting the following:
   a. Using tool No. MB990635 or equivalent, disconnect upper arm, lower arm and assist link from knuckle assembly. Suspend tool with suitable rope to prevent dropping.
   b. Loosen ball joint attaching nut, do not remove.
3. Reverse procedure to install.

AWD

1. Remove control arms as shown in **Fig. 8**, noting the following:
   a. Using tool No. MB990635 or equivalent, disconnect upper arm ball joint from knuckle assembly. Suspend tool with suitable rope to prevent dropping.

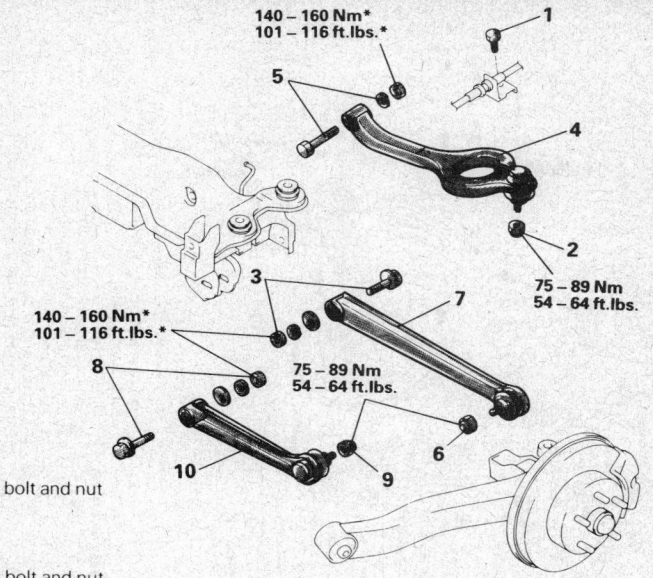

Upper arm removal steps
1. Brake line clamp bolt
2. Self-locking nut
3. Upper arm mounting bolt and nut
4. Upper arm

Lower arm removal steps
5. Lower arm mounting bolt and nut
6. Self-locking nut
7. Lower arm

Assist link removal steps
8. Assist link mounting bolt and nut
9. Self-locking nut
10. Assist link

NOTE
* : indicates parts which should be temporarily tightened, and then fully tightened with the vehicle in the unladen condition.

CR2039100032000X

Fig. 7   Upper & lower control arms & assist link. FWD

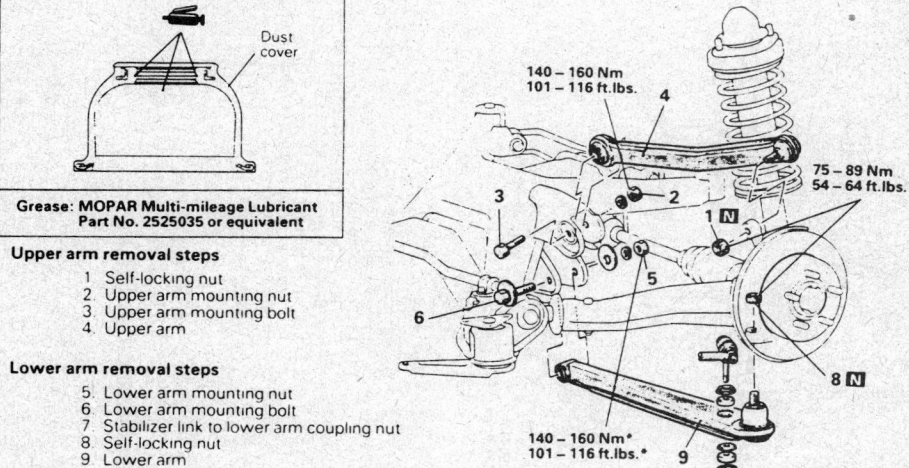

Upper arm removal steps
1. Self-locking nut
2. Upper arm mounting nut
3. Upper arm mounting bolt
4. Upper arm

Lower arm removal steps
5. Lower arm mounting nut
6. Lower arm mounting bolt
7. Stabilizer link to lower arm coupling nut
8. Self-locking nut
9. Lower arm

NOTE
For tightening points marked with *, first temporarily tighten and then ground the vehicle to torque to specification where the vehicle is empty

CR2039100033000X

Fig. 8   Upper & lower control arms assembly. AWD

b. Loosen ball joint attaching nut, do not remove.
c. Lower lower control arm at crossmember side. Using tool MB990635 or equivalent, disconnect lower arm ball joint from knuckle assembly.
d. Loosen ball joint attaching nut, do not remove.
2. Reverse procedure to install, noting the following:
  a. Hold stabilizer link ball studs with

suitable wrench, tighten self-locking nut so protrusion of stabilizer link is within .197-.276 inch.

TRAILING ARM
REPLACE
FWD

1. Remove trailing arm as shown in **Fig. 9**, noting the following:
  a. Using tool No. MB990635 or

equivalent, disconnect upper arm, lower arm and assist link from knuckle assembly. Suspend tool with suitable rope to prevent dropping.
  b. Loosen ball joint attaching nut, do not remove.
2. Reverse procedure to install, noting the following:
  a. Hold stabilizer link ball studs with suitable wrench, tighten self-locking nut so protrusion of stabilizer link is within .197-.276 inch.

AWD

1. Remove trailing arm as shown in **Fig. 10**, noting the following:
  a. Using tool No. C3281 or equivalent, secure rear axle, then remove self-locking nut.
  b. Using tool Nos. C637 and CT 1003 or equivalent, remove rear axle shaft.
  c. Using tool No. MB990635 or equivalent, disconnect ball joint from knuckle assembly. Suspend tool with suitable rope to prevent dropping.
  d. Loosen ball joint attaching nut, do not remove.
2. Reverse procedure to install.

STABILIZER BAR
REPLACE
FWD

1. Remove stabilizer bar as shown in **Fig. 11**.
2. Reverse procedure to install, noting the following:
  a. Hold stabilizer link ball studs with suitable wrench, tighten self-locking nut so protrusion of stabilizer link is within .197-.276 inch.
  b. Align LH stabilizer bar bushing with stabilizer bar marking end, then temporarily tighten attaching bolts.
  c. Install RH stabilizer bar bushing and bracket, then temporarily tighten attaching bolts.
  d. Install stabilizer bar to stabilizer link then tighten bracket attaching bolt to specifications.

AWD

1. Remove stabilizer bar as shown in **Fig. 12**, noting the following:
  a. Using suitable jack, support rear suspension assembly, then remove crossmember bracket and attaching nut.
  b. Lower suitable jack, to gain access between rear suspension and body, then using a suitable tool, remove stabilizer bar.
2. Reverse procedure to install, noting the following:
  a. Hold stabilizer link ball studs with suitable wrench, ensure protrusion of stabilizer link is within .197-.276 inch, install self-locking nut.

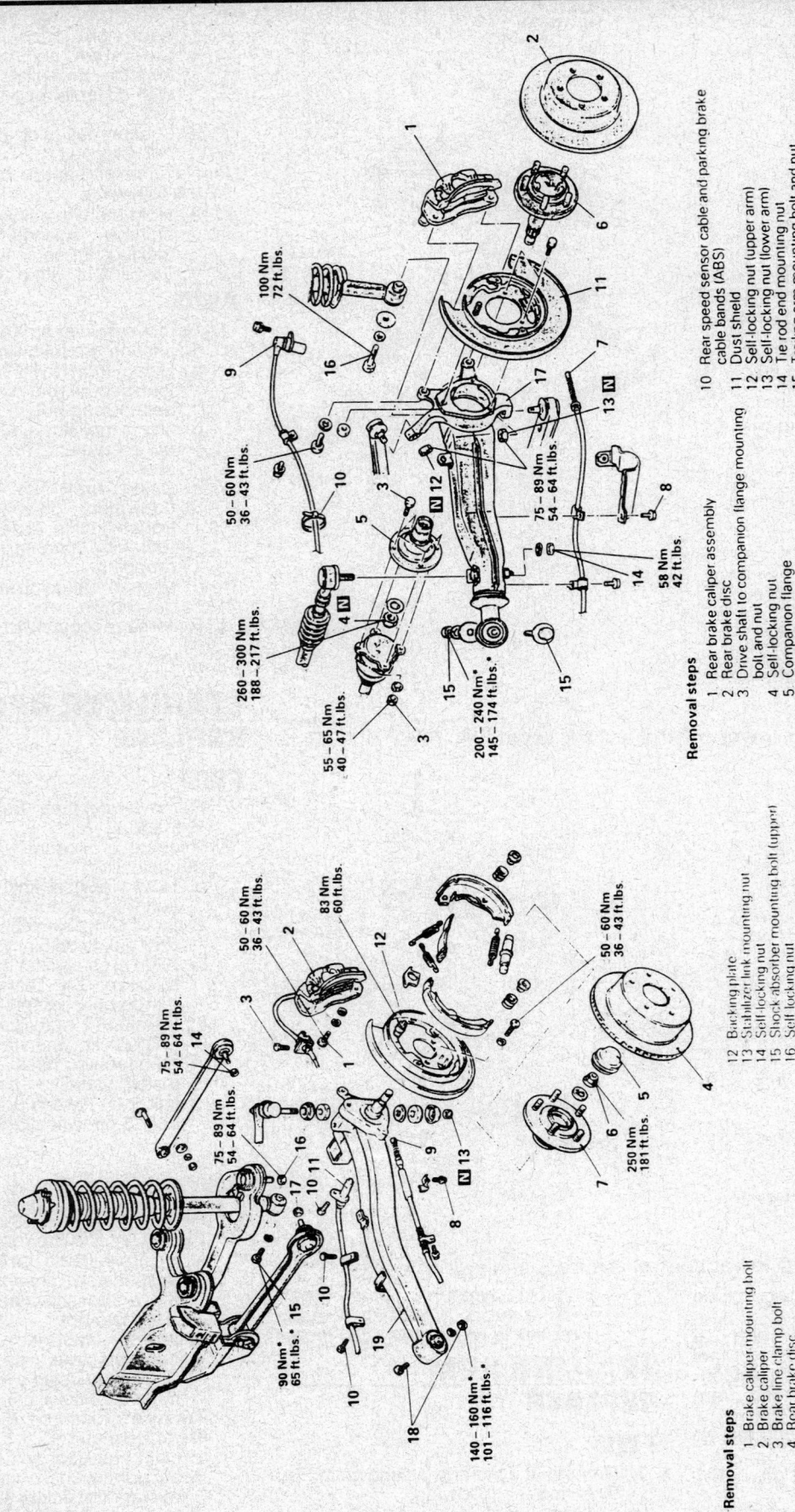

Fig. 10 Trailing arm assembly. AWD

CR2039100035000X

Removal steps

1. Rear brake caliper assembly
2. Rear brake disc
3. Drive shaft to companion flange mounting bolt and nut
4. Self-locking nut
5. Companion flange
6. Rear axle shaft
7. Parking brake cable end
8. Parking brake cable clamp bolt
9. Rear speed sensor (ABS)
10. Rear speed sensor cable and parking brake cable bands (ABS)
11. Dust shield
12. Self-locking nut (upper arm)
13. Self-locking nut (lower arm)
14. Tie rod end mounting nut
15. Trailing arm mounting bolt and nut
16. Rear shock absorber mounting bolt
17. Trailing arm

NOTE
For tightening points marked with *, first temporarily tighten and then ground the vehicle to torque to specification where the vehicle is empty.

100 Nm
72 ft.lbs.

50 – 60 Nm
36 – 43 ft.lbs.

75 – 89 Nm
54 – 64 ft.lbs.

58 Nm
42 ft.lbs.

260 – 300 Nm
188 – 217 ft.lbs.

55 – 65 Nm
40 – 47 ft.lbs.

200 – 240 Nm*
145 – 174 ft.lbs.

Fig. 9 Trailing arm assembly. FWD

CR2039100034000X

Removal steps

1. Brake caliper mounting bolt
2. Brake caliper
3. Brake line clamp bolt
4. Rear brake disc
5. Hub cap
6. Wheel bearing nut
7. Hub assembly
8. Parking brake cable clamp bolt
9. Parking brake cable end
10. Rear speed sensor clamp bolt (ABS)
11. ABS speed sensor (ABS)
12. Backing plate
13. Stabilizer link mounting nut
14. Self-locking nut
15. Shock absorber mounting bolt (upper)
16. Self locking nut
17. Self locking nut
18. Trailing arm mounting bolt and nut
19. Trailing arm assembly

83 Nm
60 ft.lbs.

50 – 60 Nm
36 – 43 ft.lbs.

50 – 60 Nm
36 – 43 ft.lbs.

75 – 89 Nm
54 – 64 ft.lbs.

75 – 89 Nm
54 – 64 ft.lbs.

250 Nm
181 ft.lbs.

90 Nm*
65 ft.lbs.

140 – 160 Nm*
101 – 116 ft.lbs.

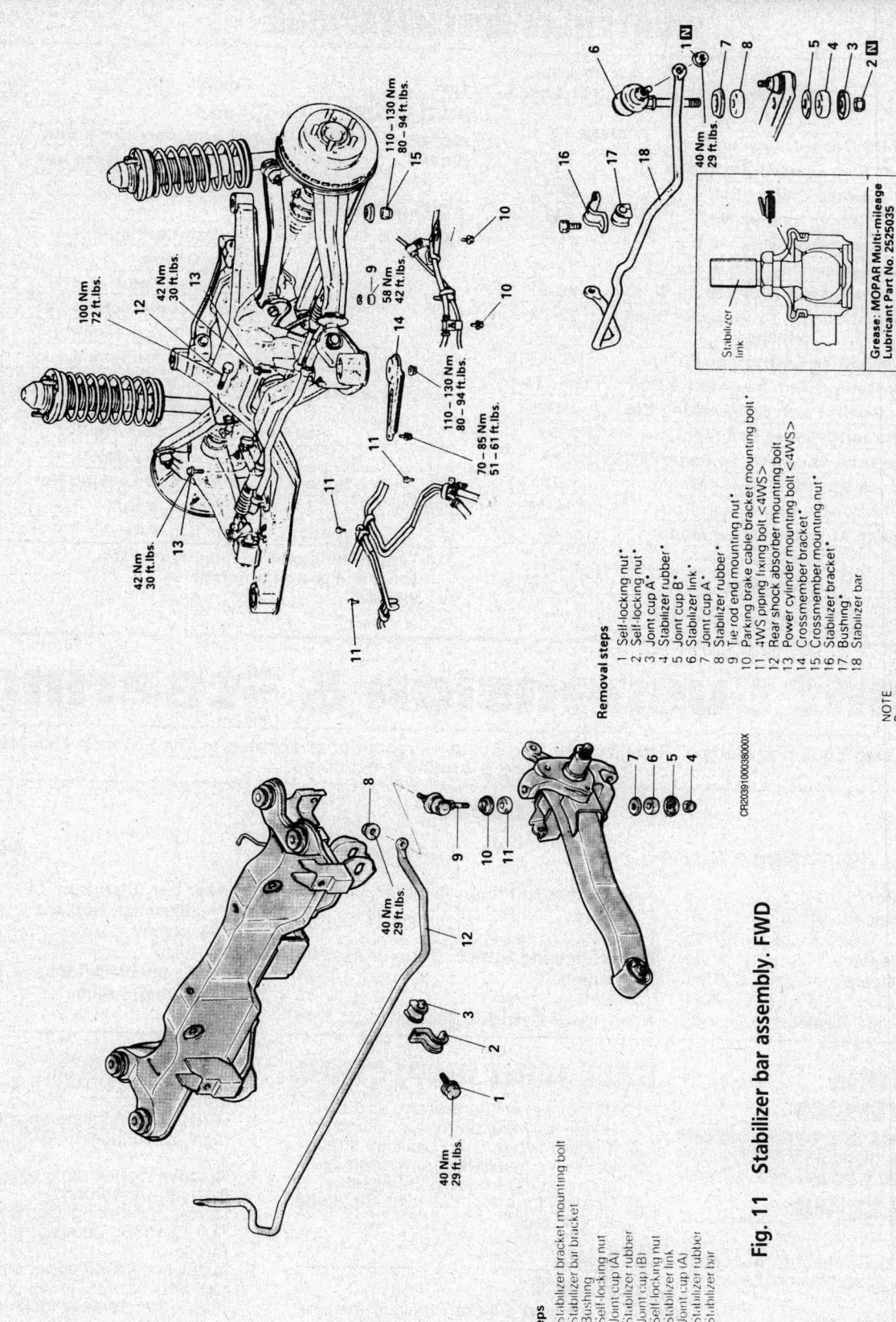

CR2039100039000X

100 Nm
72 ft. lbs.

42 Nm
30 ft. lbs.

110 – 130 Nm
80 – 94 ft. lbs.

42 Nm
30 ft. lbs.

58 Nm
42 ft. lbs.

110 – 130 Nm
80 – 94 ft. lbs.

70 – 85 Nm
51 – 61 ft. lbs.

42 Nm
30 ft. lbs.

40 Nm
29 ft. lbs.

Grease: MOPAR Multi-mileage
Lubricant Part No. 2525035
or equivalent

Stabilizer
link

Removal steps
1. Self-locking nut*
2. Self-locking nut*
3. Joint cup A*
4. Stabilizer rubber*
5. Joint cup B*
6. Stabilizer link*
7. Joint cup A*
8. Stabilizer rubber*
9. Tie rod end mounting nut*
10. Parking brake cable bracket mounting bolt*
11. 4WS piping fixing bolt <4WS>
12. Rear shock absorber mounting bolt
13. Power cylinder mounting bolt <4WS>
14. Crossmember bracket*
15. Crossmember mounting nut*
16. Stabilizer bracket*
17. Bushing*
18. Stabilizer bar

NOTE
Parts marked with * are symmetrical

Fig. 12   Stabilizer bar assembly, AWD

CR2039100038000X

40 Nm
29 ft. lbs.

40 Nm
29 ft. lbs.

Removal steps
1. Stabilizer bracket mounting bolt
2. Stabilizer bar bracket
3. Bushing
4. Self-locking nut (A)
5. Joint cup (A)
6. Stabilizer rubber
7. Joint cup (B)
8. Self-locking nut
9. Stabilizer link
10. Joint cup (A)
11. Stabilizer rubber
12. Stabilizer bar

Fig. 11   Stabilizer bar assembly, FWD

TIGHTENING SPECIFICATIONS

Year	Component	Torque/ Ft. Lbs.
AWD MODELS		
1992–95	**ABS Cable Attaching Bolt**	9
	ABS Rear Speed Sensor Bolt	9
	Brake Caliper Bolt	36–43
	Center Bearing Nut	22
	Crossmember Bracket Bolt	51–61
	Crossmember Bracket Nut	80–94
	Crossmember Nut (Differential Side)	80–94
	Differential Carrier To Propeller Shaft Coupling	22–25
	Driveshaft To Companion Flange	40–47
	Lower Control Arm Inner Nut & Bolt	101–116 ①
	Lower Control Arm Self-Locking Nut	54–64
	Power Cylinder Bolt (4WS)	30
	Pressure Tube Assembly To Pump (4WS)	25
	Shock Absorber Lower Mount	72
	Shock Absorber Piston Rod	14–18
	Shock Absorber Upper Mount	33
	Tie Rod End	42
	Trailing Arm	145–174 ①

Year	Component	Torque/ Ft. Lbs.
AWD MODELS–Continued		
1992–95 -Cont'd	**Upper Control Arm Inner Nut & Bolt**	101–116 ①
	Upper Control Arm Self-Locking Nut	54–64
	Wheel Lug Nuts	87–101
FWD MODELS		
1992–95	**Assist Arm Self-Locking Nut**	54–64
	Brake Caliper	36–43
	Crossmember Nut	65
	Lower Control Arm Self-Locking Nut	54–64
	Shock Absorber Lower Mount	65 ①
	Shock Absorber Piston Rod Nut	14–18
	Shock Absorber Upper Mount	33
	Stabilizer Bar Bolt	29
	Stabilizer Bar Self-Locking Nut	29
	Trailing Arm Nut & Bolt	101–116 ①
	Upper Control Arm Self-Locking Nut	54–64
	Wheel Bearing Nut	145–188
	Wheel Lug Nuts	87–101

①—Tighten temporarily, then tighten to specifications once vehicle is unladen.

Front Suspension & Steering

NOTE: On Air Bag Equipped Models, Refer To "Air Bag System Precautions" Located In The Front Of This Manual For System Disarming & Arming Procedures.

INDEX

PRECAUTIONS
AIR BAG SYSTEMS

Refer to "Air Bag System Precautions" in the front of this manual for system disarming and arming procedures.

WHEEL BEARING
ADJUST

Bearing preload is preset to the specified value by design and cannot be adjusted.

HUB & BEARING
REPLACE

Refer to the "Steering Knuckle, Replacement" procedure in this section to perform hub and bearing unit replacement.

BALL JOINT INSPECTION

1. Remove lower control arm as outlined under "Lower Control Arm, Replace."
2. Tighten two nuts on ball joint stud.
3. Using a suitable torque wrench, measure starting torque of ball joint.
4. Starting torque of ball joint should be 7-16 ft. lbs.

STRUT
REPLACE

1. Raise and support vehicle, then remove wheel and tire assembly.
2. Remove brake hose clamp retaining bolt, then brake hose from strut assembly.
3. Remove front speed sensor retaining nut from strut assembly, then position clamp aside.
4. Remove lower strut to steering knuckle retaining bolts.
5. Working from inside engine compartment, disconnect ECS connector, **Fig. 1.**
6. Remove upper strut retaining bolts, then strut assembly.
7. Using Coil Spring Compressor (tool No. C-4838) compress coil spring, **Fig. 2.**
8. Install coil spring upper seat retaining tool (tool No. CT-1112) or equivalent, **Fig. 3,** then remove locknut from strut assembly.
9. Reverse procedure to install noting the following:
   a. **Torque** all bolts to specification.
   b. Align front suspension to specification.

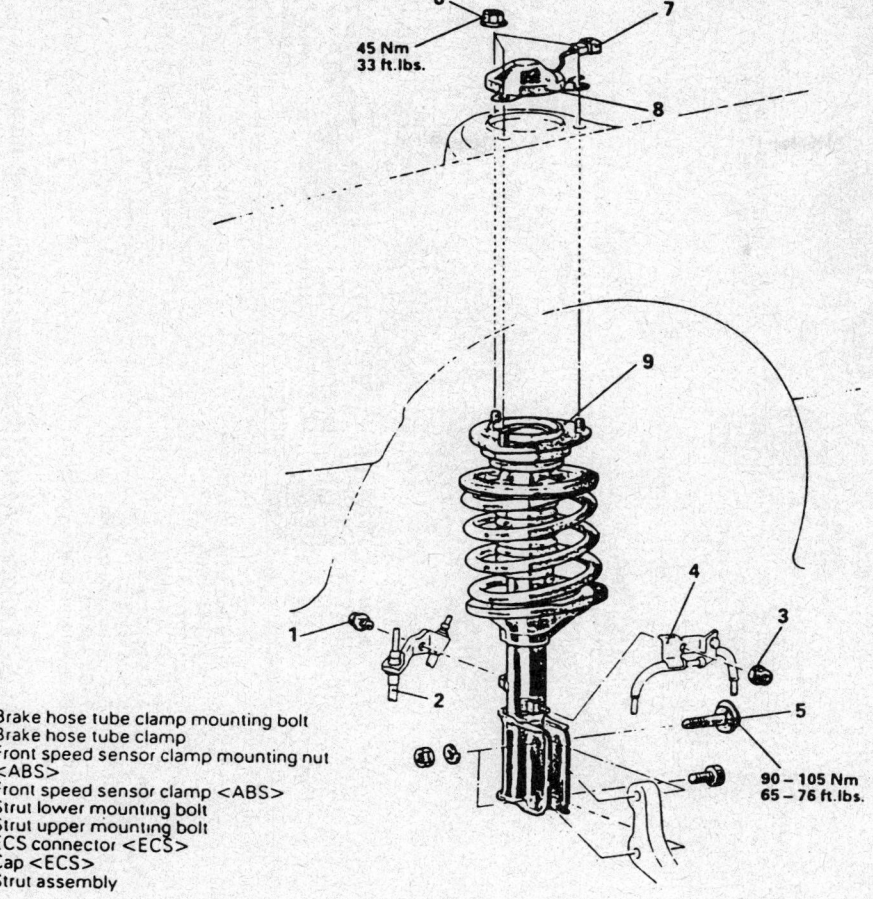

1. Brake hose tube clamp mounting bolt
2. Brake hose tube clamp
3. Front speed sensor clamp mounting nut <ABS>
4. Front speed sensor clamp <ABS>
5. Strut lower mounting bolt
6. Strut upper mounting bolt
7. ECS connector <ECS>
8. Cap <ECS>
9. Strut assembly

45 Nm 33 ft.lbs.

90 – 105 Nm 65 – 76 ft.lbs.

Fig. 1   Front strut component location

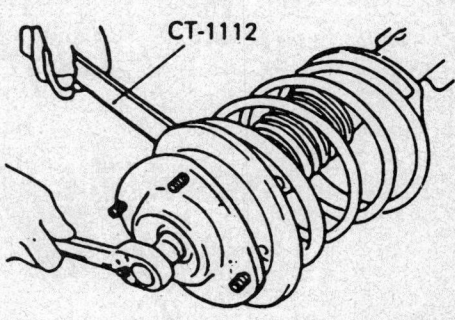

Fig. 2   Spring compressor tool installation

Fig. 3   Upper spring seat retaining tool installation

STRUT SERVICE

Refer to "Strut Replace" for strut service procedures.

CONTROL ARM
REPLACE

LOWER

1. Remove upper and lower stabilizer link mounting nuts, then stabilizer link, **Fig. 4.**
2. Remove lower ball joint to steering knuckle retaining nut, then press ball joint from steering knuckle assembly.
3. Remove lower control arm clamp mounting bolts.
4. Remove lower control arm mounting bolt, then lower control arm.
5. Reverse procedure to install. **Torque** all bolts to specification.

STEERING KNUCKLE
REPLACE

1. Raise and support vehicle.
2. Remove wheel and tire assembly.
3. Remove vehicle speed sensor retaining bolt from knuckle assembly, then suspend sensor.
4. Remove hub nut cotter pin, then hub nut.

5. Remove caliper retaining bolts, then suspend caliper out of way.
6. Remove front hub unit bearing retaining bolts from rear of steering knuckle assembly, then press driveshaft from hub unit and backing plate **Fig. 5.**
7. Remove tie rod end from steering knuckle assembly.
8. Press lower ball joint assembly from steering knuckle.
9. Suspend driveshaft assembly with wire, then swing steering knuckle clear of driveshaft assembly.
10. Remove steering knuckle to strut retaining bolts, then steering knuckle.
11. Reverse procedure to install. **Torque** all bolts to specification.

STABILIZER BAR
REPLACE

1. Raise and support vehicle.
2. **On AWD models equipped with automatic transaxle,** remove transaxle stay B, **Fig. 6.**
3. Remove transfer case assembly, refer to "Clutch & Manual Transaxle" section in this chapter for removal procedure.
4. **On all models,** remove stabilizer link.
5. Remove stabilizer bar bracket retaining bolts, then stabilizer bar from vehicle.

6. Reverse procedure to install. Torque all bolts to specification.

POWER STEERING GEAR
REPLACE

1. Center front wheels and remove ignition key. **Failure to do so mat damage SRS clock spring and render the SRS system inoperative, risking serious injury.**
2. Drain power steering fluid from system.
3. Raise and support vehicle.
4. Remove front exhaust pipe and main muffler assembly.
5. Remove transfer case assembly, refer to "Clutch & Manual Transaxle" section in this chapter.
6. Remove steering column to steering gear pinch bolt.
7. Separate tie rod ends from steering knuckle assemblies.
8. Support engine and transaxle assembly with transmission jack, then remove left member and right member, **Fig. 7.**
9. Disconnect pressure lines from steering gear assembly.
10. Remove steering gear retaining clamps, then steering gear.
11. Reverse procedure to install, noting the following:
    a. Check steering wheel position with wheels straight ahead for correct installation.
    b. Align front wheels to specification.
    c. Bleed power steering system.

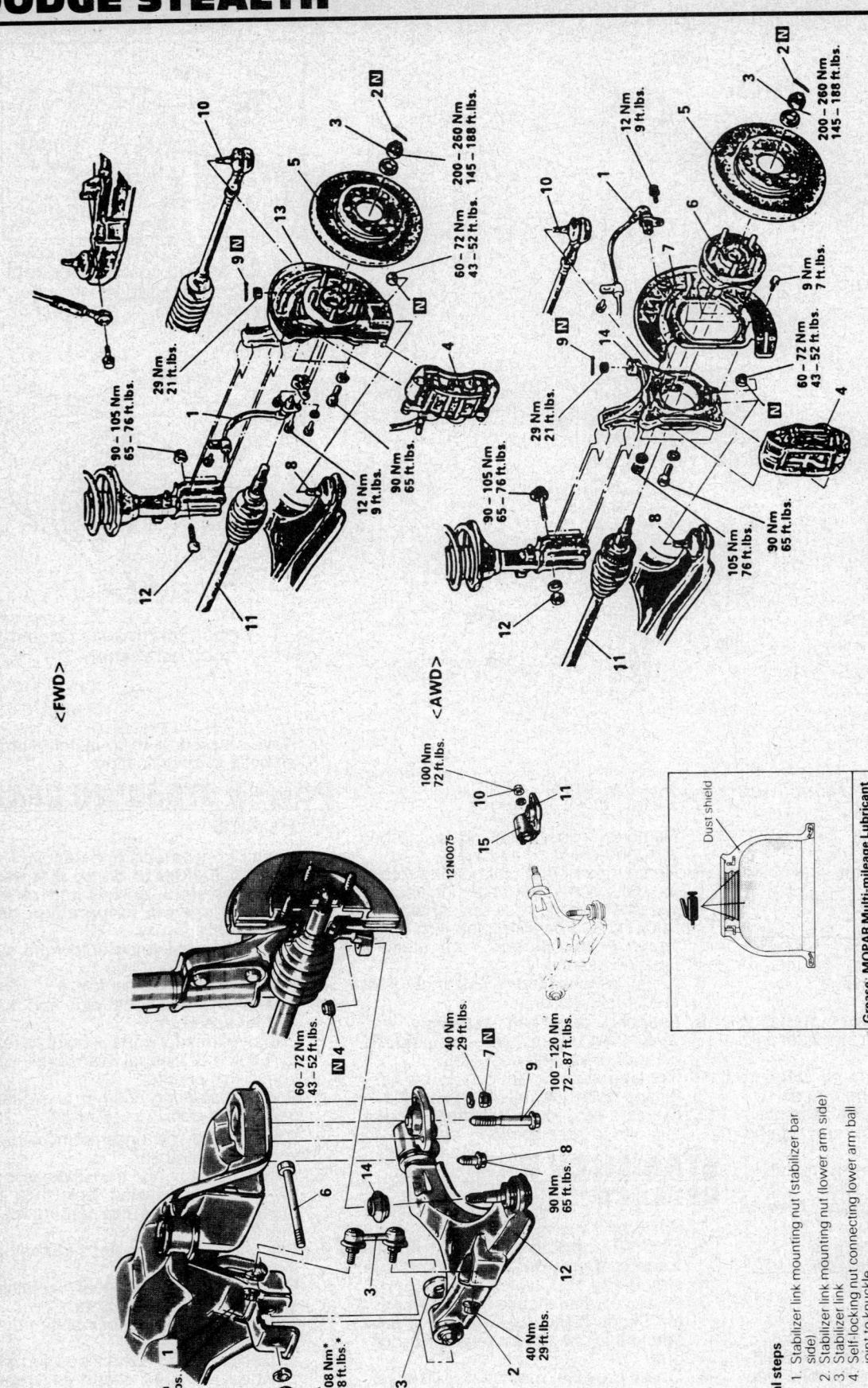

Fig. 5 Exploded view of front suspension components

1. Front speed sensor connection
   <Vehicles with A.B.S.>
2. Cotter pin
3. Drive shaft nut
4. Caliper assembly
5. Brake disc
6. Front hub unit bearing
7. Dust shield
8. Lower arm ball joint connection
9. Cotter pin
10. Tie rod end connection
11. Drive shaft
12. Front strut mounting bolt
13. Hub and knuckle
14. Hub

<FWD>

<AWD>

Fig. 4 Lower control arm replace

Removal steps

1. Stabilizer link mounting nut (stabilizer bar side)
2. Stabilizer link mounting nut (lower arm side)
3. Stabilizer link
4. Self-locking nut connecting lower arm ball joint to knuckle
5. Lower arm mounting nut
6. Lower arm mounting bolt
7. Clamp mounting self-locking nut
8. Clamp mounting bolt (small)
9. Clamp mounting bolt (large)
10. Lower arm clamp mounting self-locking nut
11. Lower arm mounting clamp
12. Lower arm
13. Stopper
14. Dust shield
15. Rod bushing

Grease: MOPAR Multi-mileage Lubricant Part No. 2525035 or equivalent

NOTE
For tightening points marked with *, first temporarily tighten them, then ground the vehicle and torque to specification where the vehicle is empty.

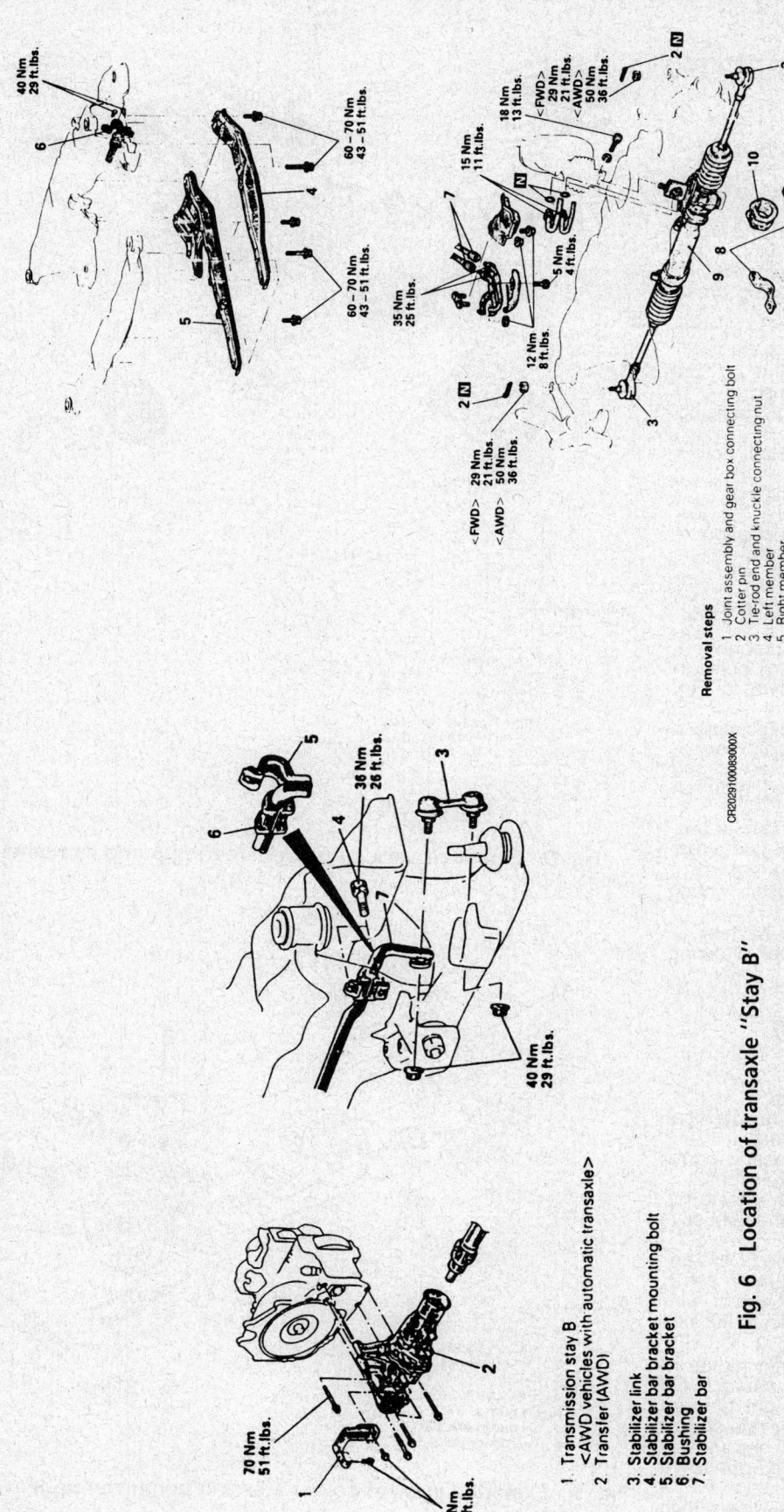

Removal steps

1 Joint assembly and gear box connecting bolt
2 Cotter pin
3 Tie-rod end and knuckle connecting nut
4 Left member
5 Right member
6 Stabilizer bar bracket
7 Connection of steering gear box with 4WS oil line
8 Clamp
9 Gear box assembly
10 Mounting rubber

Fig. 7 Power steering gear component location

40 Nm
29 ft.lbs.

60 – 70 Nm
43 – 51 ft.lbs.

60 – 70 Nm
43 – 51 ft.lbs.

15 Nm
11 ft.lbs.

35 Nm
25 ft.lbs.

12 Nm
8 ft.lbs.

5 Nm
4 ft.lbs.

18 Nm
13 ft.lbs.
<FWD>
29 Nm
21 ft.lbs.
<AWD>
50 Nm
36 ft.lbs.

70 Nm
51 ft.lbs.

<FWD>
29 Nm
21 ft.lbs.
<AWD>
50 Nm
36 ft.lbs.

CR6039100017000X

Fig. 6 Location of transaxle "Stay B"

1. Transmission stay B
   <AWD vehicles with automatic transaxle>
2. Transfer (AWD)
3. Stabilizer link
4. Stabilizer bar bracket mounting bolt
5. Stabilizer bar bracket
6. Bushing
7. Stabilizer bar

36 Nm
26 ft.lbs.

40 Nm
29 ft.lbs.

70 Nm
51 ft.lbs.

36 Nm
26 ft.lbs.

CR2029100083000X

POWER STEERING PUMP
REPLACE
FRONT

1. Drain power steering fluid from system.
2. Remove power steering pump drive belt.
3. Remove right front timing belt cover.
4. Remove timing belt cover cap.
5. Remove left front timing belt cover.
6. Remove power steering pump pressure hoses, **Fig. 8 and 9.**
7. Remove timing belt and camshaft sprocket, refer to "Camshaft Oil Seal, Replace" in engine section of this chapter for these procedures.
8. Remove power steering retaining bolts, then pump.
9. Reverse procedure to install, noting the following:
   a. Bleed power steering system.
   b. Adjust drive belt tension.
   c. Torque all bolts to specification.

REAR

1. Drain power steering fluid into a suitable container.
2. Remove main muffler assembly.
3. Remove rear power steering pump in numbered sequence shown in **Fig. 10,** noting the following:
   a. Support differential case using a suitable transmission jack, then remove crossmember bracket and crossmember mounting nuts on the differential side.
   b. Slightly lower crossmember assembly, then remove pump assembly.
4. Reverse procedure to install, noting the following:
   a. Bleed power steering system as outlined under "Power Steering System Bleed."

POWER STEERING SYSTEM BLEED

1. Raise and support vehicle.
2. Fill power steering pump to specification with recommended fluid.
3. Manually turn power steering pump by hand three or four revolutions.
4. Turn steering wheel with engine off, all the way to left and to the right several times.
5. Disable ignition system, on SOHC engines ground coil high tension cable. On DOHC engines disconnect wire harness connector at Distributor coil pack.
6. While operating the starter motor intermittently, turn steering wheel to full left position, then full right position several times. **Do not operate starter motor more than 15-20 seconds at a time without sufficient cool down time.**
7. Connect ignition system wiring, then start engine. Run at idle only.

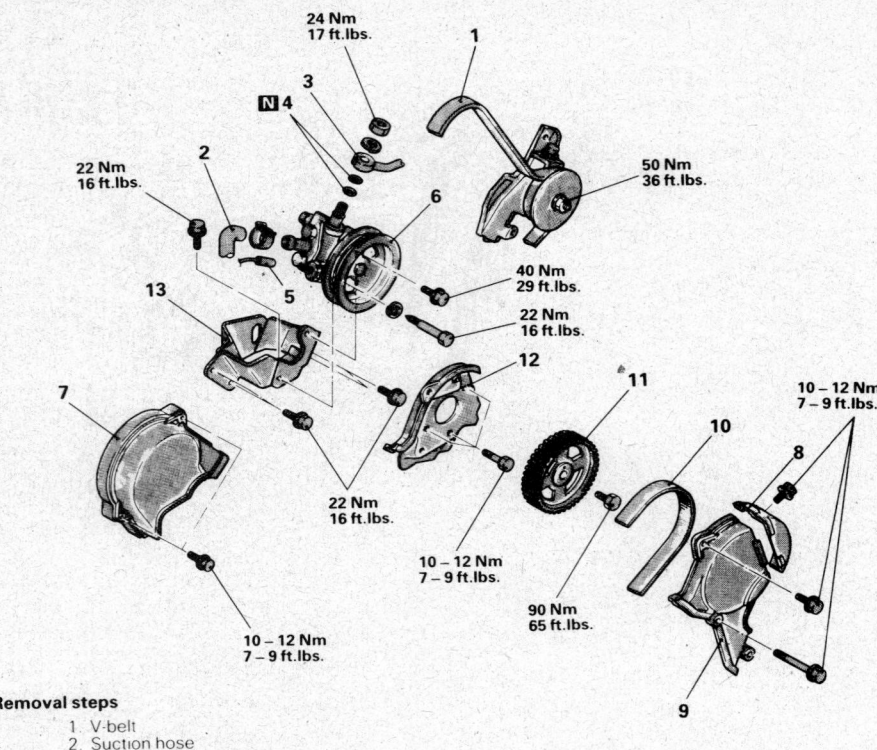

Removal steps

1. V-belt
2. Suction hose
3. Pressure hose
4. O-ring
5. Pressure switch connector
6. Oil pump
7. Front timing belt cover, right
8. Timing belt cover cap
9. Front timing belt cover, left
10. Timing belt
11. Camshaft sprocket
12. Rear timing belt cover, left
13. Oil pump bracket

CR6039100018000X

Fig. 8   Exploded view of power steering pump component locations. SOHC

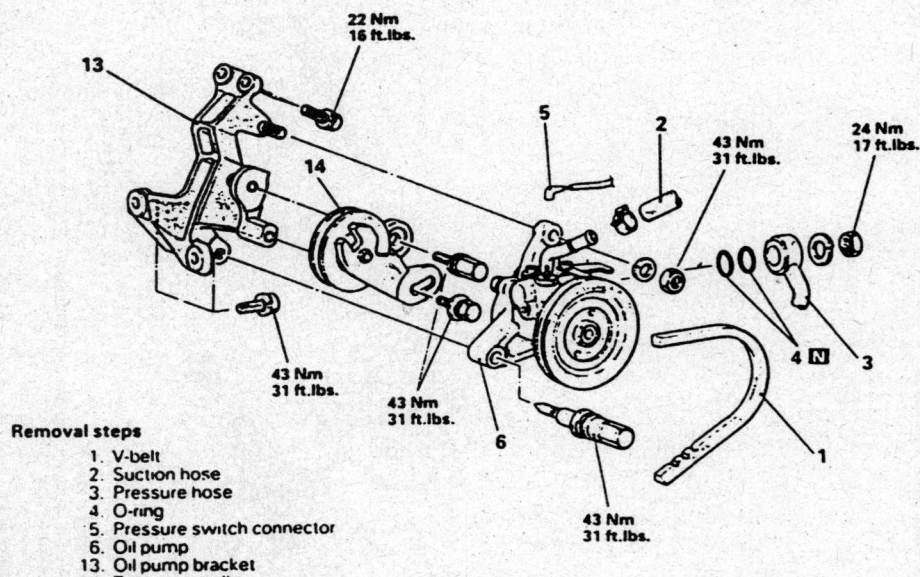

Removal steps

1. V-belt
2. Suction hose
3. Pressure hose
4. O-ring
5. Pressure switch connector
6. Oil pump
13. Oil pump bracket
14. Tensioner pulley

CR6039100019000X

Fig. 9   Exploded view of power steering pump component locations. DOHC

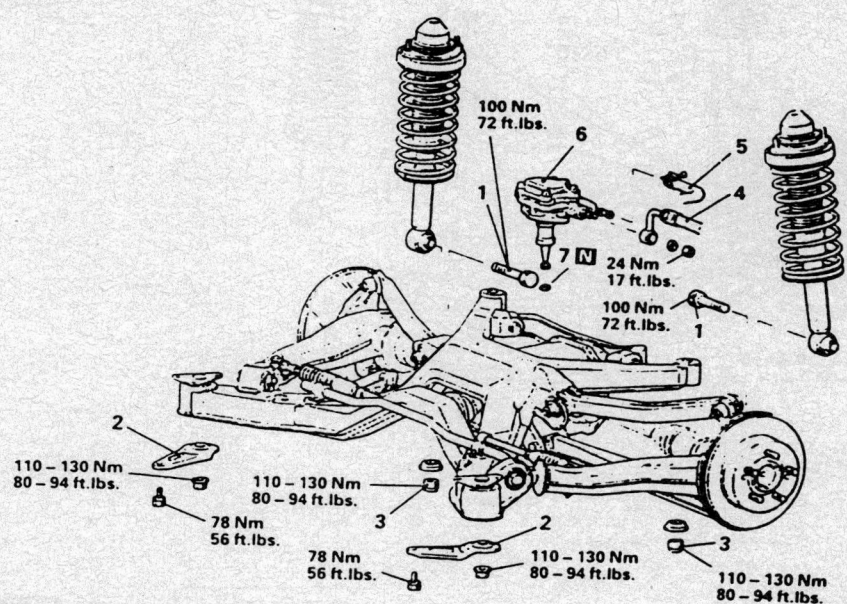

Removal steps

1. Rear shock absorber lower mounting bolt
2. Crossmember bracket
3. Crossmember mounting nut (on differential side)
4. Pressure hose
5. Suction hose
6. Rear-wheel oil pump
7. O-ring

NOTE
Do not disassemble the rear-wheel oil pump

CR6039100020000X

Fig. 10   Rear power steering oil pump removal

8. Recheck fluid level, then turn steering wheel to full left and to full right positions.
9. Ensure fluid level and composition of fluid in reservoir has not changed while engine is running or with engine stopped.

REAR POWER CYLINDER
REPLACE

1. Raise and support vehicle.
2. Clean steering system piping using suitable steam cleaner or equivalent.
3. Drain steering system fluid into a suitable container.
4. Remove main muffler assembly.
5. Remove rear power cylinder in numbered sequence shown in Fig. 11, noting the following:
   a. Before removing the crossmember self-locking nut, support differential case with a suitable transmission jack , then remove the self-locking nut.

b. Secure power cylinder on tie rod side with a suitable spanner wrench and remove power cylinder mounting nut.
6. Inspect the tie rod swing torque as follows:
   a. Swing tie rod ten times, hard.
   b. Point tie rod end down, then attach a suitable spring scale as shown and measure swing torque, Fig. 12.
   c. If swing torque is more than 26 inch lbs., replace the tie rod.
   d. If swing torque is less than 4 inch lbs., the ball joint may be reused as long as it operates smoothly and is not loose.
7. Inspect power cylinder slide resistance as follows:
   a. Place piston in neutral position.
   b. Wrap wire around tie rod end, then measure slide resistance using a suitable spring scale, Fig. 13.
   c. If slide resistance is more than 15 lbs., replace the power cylinder.
   d. If resistance is less than 15 lbs., the

power cylinder may be reused as long as it slides smoothly and is not loose.
8. Reverse procedure to install, noting the following:
   a. Secure power cylinder to crossmember.
   b. Move power cylinder piston rod over its full stroke to determine its neutral position.
   c. Align tie rod ends and installation holes at trailing arm.
   d. When tie rod ends and the installation holes on the trailing arm do not meet, loosen tie rod end securing nut, then adjust the length. **The dust cover fastener clip should be removed for this.**
   e. The difference between lengths of left and right tie rods should be less than .039 inch. **The threads of the tie rod ends may be used as a guide for this.**
   f. Bleed the Steering system as outlined under "Power Steering System Bleed."

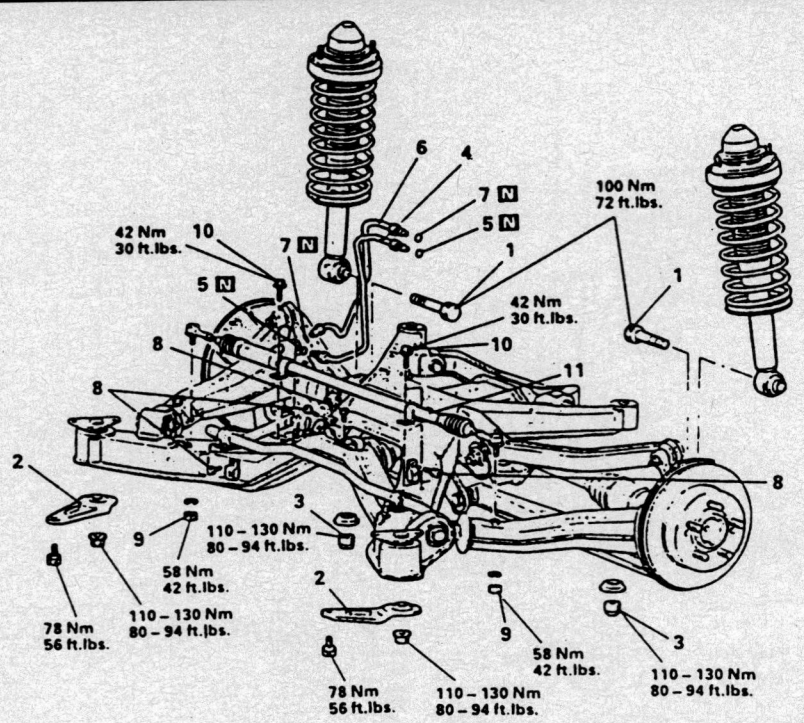

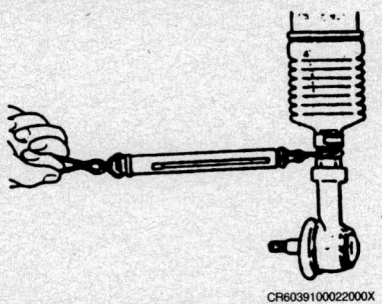

Fig. 12 Swing torque measurement

Removal steps

1. Rear shock absorber lower mounting bolt
2. Crossmember bracket
3. Crossmember mounting nut (on differential side)
4. Pressure tube (RL)
5. O-ring
6. Pressure tube (RR)
7. O-ring
8. Oil line clamp bolt
9. Tie rod end nut
10. Power cylinder installation bolt
11. Power cylinder

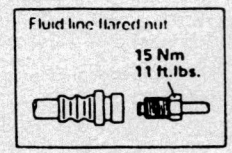

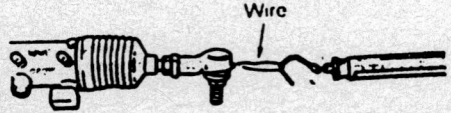

Fig. 13 Slide resistance of power cylinder measurement

Fig. 11 Rear power cylinder removal

TIGHTENING SPECIFICATIONS

Year	Component	Torque/ Ft. Lbs.
1992–95	Airbag Module	4
	Axle Shaft Nut	145–188
	Crossmember Attaching Bolt	43–51
	Crossmember Attaching Nut	58–72
	Crossmember Lower Plate Self-Locking Nut	65
	Dust Plate Bolt (AWD)	7
	Front Brake Caliper	65
	Front Roll Stopper Bolt	43–51
	Front Speed Sensor Attaching Bolt	9
	Front Strut Lower Mount Bolt	65–76
	Front Strut Piston Rod Nut	56
	Inner Shaft Bracket Bolt	33
	Lower Ball Joint Nut	43–52
	Lower Ball Joint To Steering Knuckle Nut	43–52
	Lower Control Arm Clamp Long Bolt	72–87
	Lower Control Arm Clamp Mounting Nut	72
	Lower Control Arm Clamp Nut	29

Continued

TIGHTENING SPECIFICATIONS-Continued

Year	Component	Torque/ Ft. Lbs.
1992-95 -Cont'd	Lower Control Arm Clamp Short Bolt	65 ①
	Lower Control Arm Nut	72–87 ①
	Power Steering Gearbox Line Fittings (4WS)	25
	Power Steering Line Fitting	11
	Power Steering Line Inner Bracket (4WS)	4
	Power Steering Line Outer Bracket (4WS)	8
	Power Steering Pump Bracket Lower Bolt	31
	Power Steering Pump Bracket Upper Bolt	16
	Power Steering Pump Plug	18–22
	Power Steering Pump Pressure Hose Nut	17
	Power Steering Pump Tensioner Pulley	31
	Power Steering Pump To Bracket	31
	Power Steering Rack Bracket Attaching Bolts	51
	Power Steering Rack To Steering Column Linkage	13
	Steering Column Shaft Joint	13
	Steering Column Support	8
	Steering Wheel	29
	Stabilizer Bar Bracket Bolt	26
	Stabilizer Link Nut	29
	Tie Rod End Attaching Nut	21-36
	Tie Rod End Locking Nut	36-40
	Wheel Lug Nuts	87-101

① —Tighten temporarily, tighten to specifications when vehicle is unladen.

Wheel Alignment

INDEX

PRELIMINARY INSPECTION

1. Road test vehicle noting any abnormal steering or handling characteristics.
2. Ensure tires are the proper type, correctly inflated and that tires on each axle are the same size.
3. Inspect ball joints, suspension arms, bushings and tie rods, and repair or replace any component that is damaged or excessively worn.
4. Ensure wheel runout is not excessive, and that wheel bearings are properly adjusted.
5. Jounce vehicle several times to settle suspension.
6. Place vehicle on suitable alignment rack following manufacturer's instructions.

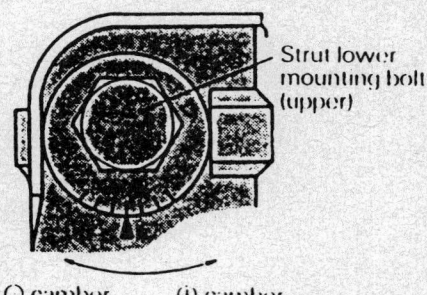

Strut lower mounting bolt (upper)

O camber ⊕ camber

CR2049100031000X

Fig. 1 Front camber adjustment

7. Check and correct alignment angles in the following sequence: Rear toe and camber, caster, front camber and front toe.
8. Correct any angle that is not within specifications. If no adjustment is possible, check for damaged or worn suspension components and/or damaged or distorted chassis and correct as needed.

FRONT WHEEL ALIGNMENT

Adjust front toe-in after front camber has been adjusted. One camber graduation change changes toe by about .02 inch.

CAMBER

To adjust camber, turn strut lower mounting bolt (upper), **Fig. 1.** One graduation is equivalent to about .33° in camber.

CASTER

Caster has been factory adjusted to the standard value and requires no adjustment.

TOE-IN

Adjust toe-in by releasing tie rod clips, then turning right and left tie rod jam nut, in opposite directions, and equal amount.

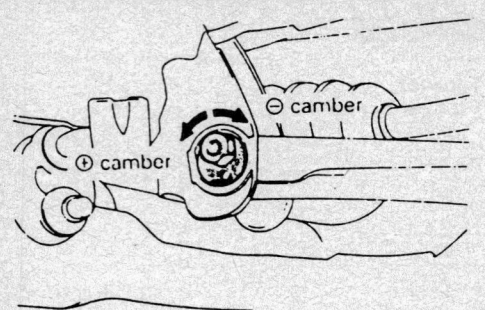

Fig. 2 Rear camber adjustment

REAR WHEEL ALIGNMENT

FWD

Adjust rear toe-in after rear camber has been adjusted. On models equipped with 4WS, disconnect 4WS tie rod end from trailing arm prior to making adjustments.

Camber

To adjust camber, turn lower control arm mounting bolt on the crossmember side, **Fig. 2.** At the left wheel turn the mounting bolt clockwise to indicate negative camber, at the right wheel turn the mounting bolt right to indicate positive camber. One graduation changes camber by about .2°. **Adjust eccentric cam bolt within 90° from central position.**

Toe-In

To adjust toe-in, turn right and left trailing arm mounting bolts on the crossmember side, the same amount. At the left wheel turn the mounting bolt clockwise to indicate toe-in, at the right wheel turn the mounting bolt clockwise to indicate toe-out, **Fig. 3.** One graduation changes toe by about .08 inch.

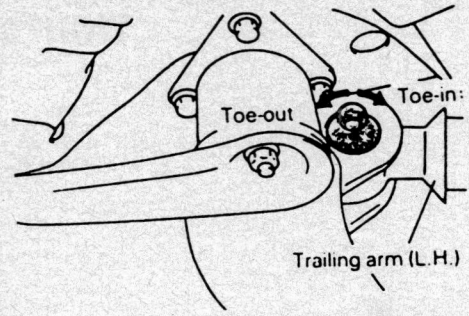

Fig. 3 Rear toe-in adjustment

AWD

Camber

1. Measure camber with a camber/caster/kingpin gauge.
2. Adjust camber by moving mounting bolt located on crossmember side of lower arm. One graduation changes camber by about 1/5°.

CHRYSLER CONCORDE, LHS & 1994-95 NEW YORKER, DODGE INTREPID & EAGLE VISION

NOTE: Refer To Rear Of This Manual For Vehicle Manufacturer's Special Service Tool Suppliers.

INDEX OF SERVICE OPERATIONS

NOTE: For Service Operations Not Listed Below, Refer To The Table Of Contents In The Front Of This Manual.

Specifications

GENERAL ENGINE SPECIFICATIONS

Year	Engine		Fuel System	Bore and Stroke Inch (Millimeters)	Compression Ratio	Brake HP @ RPM	Maximum Torque Ft. Lbs @ R.P.M.	Normal Oil Pressure psi. @ 2000 RPM
	Liter/CID ①	VIN Code ②						
1993	3.3L/V6-201	T	S.M.P.I. ③	3.661 x 3.188	8.9	153 @ 5300	177 @ 2800	30-80 ④
	3.5L/V6-215	F	S.M.P.I. ③	3.780 x 3.189	10.45	214 @ 5800	221 @ 2800	25-70 ④
1994	3.3L/V6-201	T	S.M.P.I. ③	3.661 x 3.188	8.9	161 @ 5300	181 @ 3200	30-80 ④
	3.5L/V6-215	F	S.M.P.I. ③	3.780 x 3.189	10.45	214 @ 5800	221 @ 2800	25-70 ④
1995	3.3L/V6-201	T	S.M.P.I. ③	3.661 x 3.188	8.9	161 @ 5300	181 @ 3200	30-80 ④
	3.3L/V6-201	U	S.M.P.I. ⑤	3.661 x 3.188	8.9	—	—	30-80 ④
	3.5L/V6-215	F	S.M.P.I. ③	3.780 x 3.189	10.45	214 @ 5800	221 @ 2800	25-70 ④

①—CID-cubic inch displacement.
②—The 8th digit of the VIN denotes engine code.
③—Sequential Multi-Port Fuel Injection.
④—At 300 RPM.
⑤—Flexible Fuel Sequential Multi-Port Fuel Injection.

TUNE UP SPECIFICATIONS

Liter/CID (VIN Code ①)	Spark Plug Gap	Ignition Timing @ BTDC				Curb Idle Speed ②	Fuel Pump Pressure psi.
		Firing Order Fig.	Man. Trans.	Auto. Trans.	Mark Fig.		
1993–94							
3.3L/V6-201 (T)	.048-.053	A	—	③	④	⑤	55 ⑥
3.5L/V6-215 (F)	.048-.053	A	—	③	④	⑤	48 ⑥
1995							
3.3L/V6-201 (T)	.048-.053	A	—	③	④	⑤	55 ⑥
3.3L/V6-201 (U) ⑦	.043-.048	A	—	③	④	⑤	55 ⑥
3.5L/V6-215 (F)	.048-.053	A	—	③	④	⑤	48 ⑥

①—The eighth digit of the Vehicle Identification Number (VIN) denotes engine code.
②—N: Neutral.
③—Direct Ignition System (DIS), not adjustable.
④—Equipped w/crankshaft position sensor.
⑤—Controlled by the Powertrain Control Module (PCM).
⑥—Without vacuum applied to pressure regulator.
⑦—Flexible Fuel Sequential Multi-Port Fuel Injection.

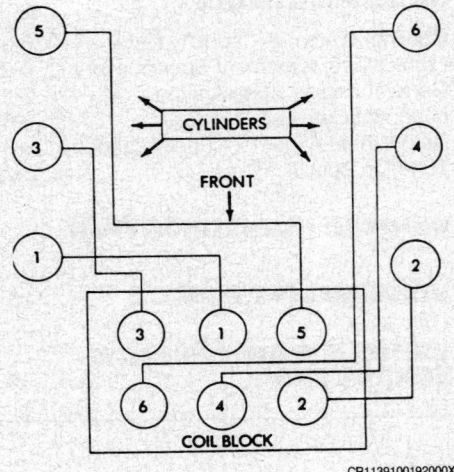

CR1139100192000X

Fig. A

FRONT WHEEL ALIGNMENT SPECIFICATIONS

Year	Model	Camber Angle, Degrees [1]		Caster Angle, Degrees [1]		Toe In, Degrees		Thrust Angle [1]
		Limits	Desired	Limits	Desired	Limits	Desired	
1993–95	All	-.6 to +.6 [2]	0	2 to 4 [3]	3	.4 In to 0	.2 In	—

[1]—Reference angle only, non adjustable.

[2]—Side to side differential not to exceed .7°.

[3]—Side to side differential not to exceed 1°.

REAR WHEEL ALIGNMENT SPECIFICATIONS

Year	Model	Camber Angle, Degrees [1]		Caster Angle, Degrees [1]		Toe In, Degrees		Thrust Angle [1]
		Limits	Desired	Limits	Desired	Limits	Desired	
1993–95	All	-.6 to +.4	-.1	—	—	.2 Out to .4 In	.1 In	-.15 to +.15

[1]—Reference angle only, non adjustable.

COOLING SYSTEM & CAPACITY DATA

Year	Engine Liter/ CID (VIN) [1]	Coolant Capacity		Radiator Cap Relief Pressure, Lbs.	Thermo. Opening Temp. Deg. F	Fuel Tank Gals.	Engine Oil Refill Qts. [3]	Transaxle Oil [2]
		Less A/C Qts.	With A/C Qts.					
1993–95	3.3L/V6-201 (T) (U)	10.17	10.17	16	195	18	5	9.9
	3.5L/V6-215 (F)	11.80	11.80	16	195	18	5.5	9.9

[1]—The eighth digit of Vehicle Identification Number (VIN) denotes engine code.

[2]—Approximate. Make final check with dipstick.

[3]—Includes oil filter.

LUBRICANT DATA

Year	Model	Lubricant Type		
		Transaxle	Power Steering	Brake System
1993–95	All	Mopar ATF Type 7176 [1]	4318055 [2]	DOT 3

[1]—Chrysler recommends only this type of transmission fluid be used.

[2]—Mopar Part No.

Electrical

NOTE: Refer To "Air Bag System Precautions" Located In The Front Of This Manual For System Disarming & Arming Procedures.

INDEX

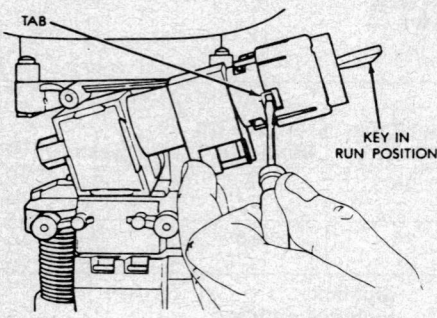

Fig. 1 Lock cylinder removal

PRECAUTIONS

AIR BAG SYSTEMS

Refer to "Air Bag System Precautions" in the front of this manual for system disarming and arming procedures.

FUSE PANEL & FLASHER LOCATION

The fuse panel/junction block is located under the LH side of the instrument panel. The hazard flasher unit is located under the LH side of the instrument panel between the junction block and the brake pedal.

STARTER
REPLACE

1. Disconnect battery ground cable.
2. Raise and support vehicle.
3. Remove three bolts from starter.
4. Remove starter assembly from engine.
5. Disconnect electrical connections from starter solenoid.
6. Reverse procedure to install.

DISTRIBUTOR
REPLACE

These models use a fixed ignition timing system known as Direct Ignition System (DIS). This system uses no distributor, only an electronic ignition coil pack.

The electronic ignition coil pack attaches to the LH cylinder head on 3.3L/V6-201 engines or to the RH cylinder head on 3.5L/V6-215 engines.

1. **On 3.5L/V6-215 engines,** remove air cleaner hose.
2. **On all engines,** disconnect electrical connector from coil pack.
3. Remove coil pack mounting screws.
4. Remove coil pack.
5. Transfer spark plug wires to new coil pack.
6. Reverse procedure to install.

IGNITION LOCK
REPLACE
CYLINDER

If the vehicle has a column shifter, install a new interlock cassette as outlined under "Ignition Interlock Service." If the vehicle has a floor shift, adjust the interlock cable as outlined under "Ignition Interlock Service."

1. Disconnect battery ground cable.
2. Remove tilt lever.
3. Remove upper and lower column covers.
4. Turn ignition key to Run position then depress the lock cylinder retaining tab and slide the cylinder out of the housing, **Fig. 1.**
5. Reverse procedure to instal.

HOUSING
Removal

1. Remove upper and lower column covers.
2. Remove tilt lever.
3. Remove ignition switch as outlined under "Ignition Switch, Replace."

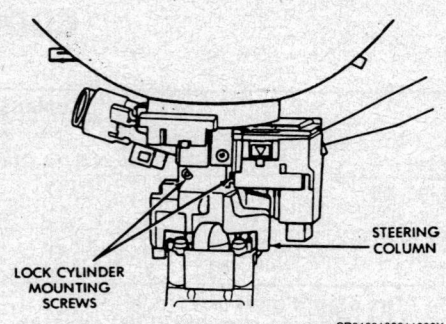

Fig. 2 Lock cylinder housing mounting screws

4. Center punch the tamper proof screws, **Fig. 2.**
5. Using a 1/4 inch drill bit, drill out the screw heads.
6. Remove lock cylinder housing from steering column.
7. Use suitable pliers to remove bolts from steering column.

Installation

1. Position lock cylinder housing on steering column.
2. Tighten new tamper proof screws until head twist off.
3. Install ignition switch, tilt lever and upper and lower column covers.

IGNITION SWITCH
REPLACE

1. Disconnect battery ground cable.
2. Remove tilt lever then upper and lower column covers.
3. Disconnect electrical connector from ignition switch.
4. Remove ignition switch mounting screws and ignition switch.
5. Reverse procedure to install, noting the following:
   a. Align tab on ignition switch with slot on lock housing.

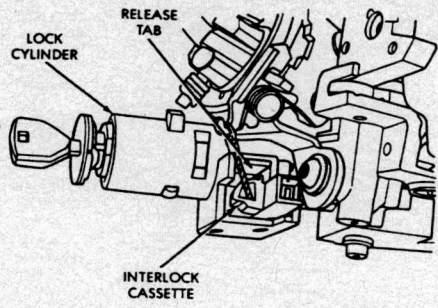

Fig. 3   Ignition interlock cassette

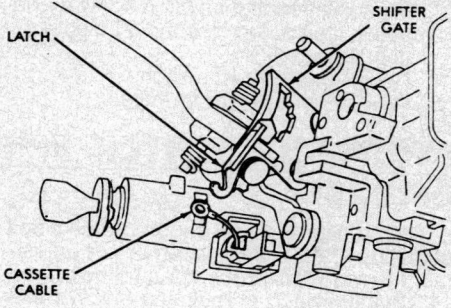

Fig. 4   Latch & shifter gate

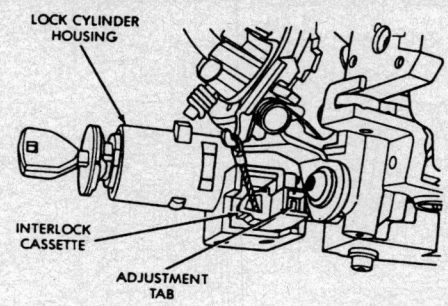

Fig. 5   Ignition interlock adjustment tab

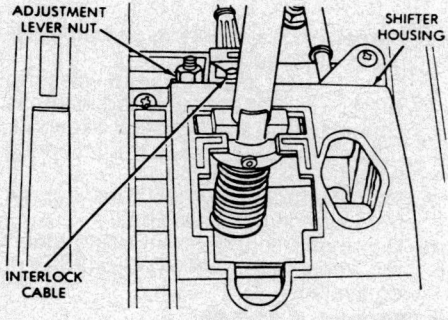

Fig. 6   Interlock adjustment lever nut

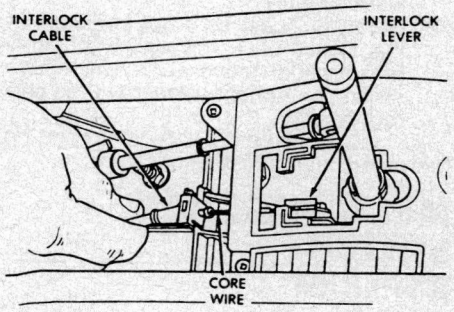

Fig. 7   Interlock cable at floor shifter

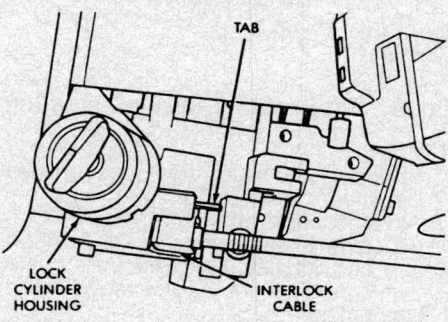

Fig. 8   Interlock cable at ignition switch

INTERLOCK CASSETTE, REPLACE

COLUMN SHIFT

The interlock cassette slides into the housing behind the lock cylinder. The cable at the rear of the cassette attaches to a locking arm on the shifter mechanism. **The column shift interlock system is only adjusted after installing a new cassette. The cassette cannot be adjusted more than once. If the system operates incorrectly, install and adjust a new interlock cassette.**

Removal

1. Disconnect battery ground cable.
2. Remove tilt lever then upper and lower column covers.
3. Depress tab on top of cassette, **Fig. 3**, then slide cassette out of housing.
4. Remove cable from locking arm on shifter mechanism.

Installation

1. Ensure latch rotates freely on shifter gate, **Fig. 4**.
2. With shifter in Park position and key removed, install cable over hook of locking arm of shifter mechanism.
3. Slide cassette into housing until it locks into place.
4. Push adjustment tab in until it stops, **Fig. 5**. The adjustment tab will click as it moves into position. Ensure the tab is fully depressed.

FLOOR SHIFT INTERLOCK SERVICE

The interlock cable slides into the lock housing behind the lock cylinder and at-taches to the floor mounted shifter. The floor shift interlock system is adjusted by a nut at the shifter.

Removal

1. Remove shifter handle.
2. Remove bezel from shifter console and drivers side kick panel center console.
3. Remove tilt lever then upper and lower column covers.
4. Loosen nut on interlock adjustment lever, **Fig. 6**.
5. Move ignition key to Run position.
6. Remove interlock cable from shifter housing by sliding cable out of groove in interlock lever, **Fig. 7**.
7. Depress lock tab on interlock cable and remove cable from lock cylinder housing, **Fig. 8**.

Installation

1. Place ignition switch in On position.
2. Route interlock cable as follows:
   a. Route cable down steering column, past air distribution duct.
   b. Route cable between support strut and air bag module mounting bracket then down to the shifter housing.
3. Slide interlock cable into lock cylinder housing until it snaps into place, **Fig. 8**.
4. Turn ignition lock to Off/Lock position.
5. Put shifter into Park position.
6. Slide interlock cable core wire into groove on adjustment lever. Ensure cable end seats into groove.
7. Slip cable into housing until it snaps into place.
8. Remove ignition key from ignition lock cylinder.
9. Loosen adjustment nut and allow ca-ble to adjust itself to correct position then tighten adjustment nut, **Fig. 6**.
10. Inspect interlock cable as follows:
    a. With lock cylinder in Off position and ignition key removed, cable core wire should not move when pulled.
    b. With lock cylinder in Run position, cable core wire should slide freely when pulled. Also, cable should return to the bottomed out position when released.
11. Inspect interlock cable adjustment as follows:
    a. With ignition lock in Off position, shifter should be locked in the Park position.
    b. Without starting engine, place ignition switch in the Run position. Move shifter to the reverse position. Ignition key should not be able to be removed from lock cylinder.
    c. Place shifter into Park position and turn ignition key to Off position. Ignition key should be able to be removed from the lock cylinder.
    d. If shifter and ignition key does not perform as described in previous steps, repeat adjustment procedure.
12. Install shifter console bezel, shifter handle, kick panel, tilt lever and upper and lower steering column covers.

FLOOR SHIFT INTERLOCK ADJUSTMENT

1. Remove shifter handle and console bezel.
2. Loosen adjustment nut on interlock lever, **Fig. 6**.
3. Place ignition in Run position.
4. Remove interlock cable from shifter

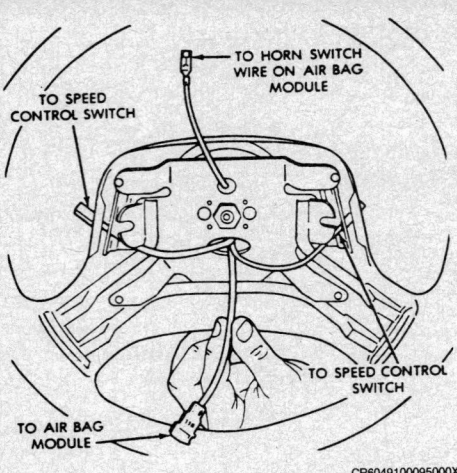

Fig. 9   Wire routing through steering wheel

housing and slide cable out of groove in interlock lever, **Fig. 7.**

5. Inspect cable as follows:
   a. With lock cylinder in Off position and ignition key removed, cable core wire should not move when pulled.
   b. With lock cylinder in Run position, cable core wire should slide freely when pulled. Also, cable should return to the bottomed out position when released.
6. Place shifter in Park position.
7. Slide interlock cable core wire into groove on adjustment lever. **Ensure cable end seats into groove.**
8. Slip cable into housing until it snaps into place.
9. Keeping shifter in Park position, place lock cylinder in Off position and remove ignition key.
10. Loosen adjustment nut and allow cable to adjust itself to correct position then tighten adjustment nut, **Fig. 6.**
11. Inspect interlock cable adjustment as follows:
   a. With ignition lock in Off position, shifter should be locked in the Park position.
   b. Without starting engine, place ignition switch in the Run position. Move shifter to the reverse position. Ignition key should not be able to be removed from lock cylinder.
   c. Place shifter into Park position and turn ignition key to Off position. Ignition key should be able to be removed from the lock cylinder.
   d. If shifter and ignition key does not perform as described in steps a through c, repeat adjustment procedure.
12. Install shifter console bezel and shifter handle.

HEADLAMP SWITCH
REPLACE

1. Open front door and remove left end cover.
2. Remove screw from left end of instrument panel and pull headlight bezel rearward to disengage clips.

3. Remove headlight switch screws and pull switch out to disconnect electrical connectors.
4. Remove headlight switch.
5. Reverse procedure to install.

STOP LIGHT SWITCH
REPLACE

The stop lamp switch incorporates a self adjusting feature. If replacement or adjustment is required, proceed as follows:
1. Install switch in retaining bracket and push switch forward as far as possible. The brake pedal will move forward slightly.
2. Gently pull back on brake pedal bringing striker back toward switch until brake pedal stops. This will cause switch to ratchet backward to the correct position.
Very little movement is required and no further adjustment is necessary.

MULTI-FUNCTION SWITCH
REPLACE

1. Disconnect battery ground cable.
2. Remove tilt lever and upper and lower steering column covers.
3. Remove multi-function switch to column retaining screws.
4. Disconnect multi-function switch electrical connections.
5. Reverse procedure to install, noting the following:
   a. **Torque** multi-function switch to column screws to 17 inch lbs.

TURN SIGNAL SWITCH
REPLACE

Refer to procedure found under "Multi-Function Switch, Replace" for turn signal switch replacement.

DIMMER SWITCH
REPLACE

Refer to procedure found under "Multi-Function Switch, Replace" for dimmer switch replacement.

STEERING WHEEL
REPLACE
REMOVAL

1. Disconnect battery ground cable.
2. Lock steering column by turning steering wheel 1/2 turn (180°) clockwise from the straight ahead position.
3. Place ignition in the Off/Lock position and remove ignition key. This will ensure no damage occurs to the clockspring.
4. Remove speed control switches from steering wheel to gain access to air bag module attaching screws. If vehicle is not equipped with speed control, pry out covers on sides of steering wheel for access.

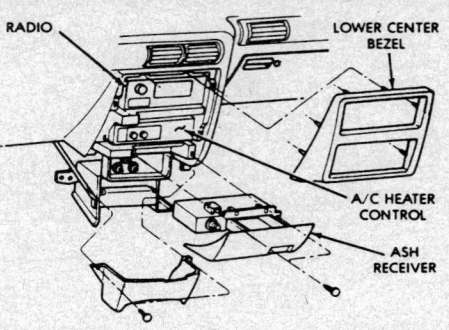

Fig. 10   Radio replacement

5. Remove bolts attaching air bag module to steering wheel.
6. Lift air bag module from steering wheel, disconnecting wiring harness connections from rear of air bag module and remove module from steering wheel.
7. Remove steering wheel retaining nut from steering column shaft.
8. Remove steering wheel using steering wheel puller tool No. C-3428-B, or equivalent.

INSTALLATION

1. Align splines on steering wheel and steering column then install steering on column routing wiring through steering wheel as shown in **Fig. 9.**
2. Install steering wheel retaining nut and tighten nut to draw steering wheel onto column. **Torque** steering column shaft nut to 45 ft. lbs.
3. Connect wiring harness on air bag module.
4. Install air bag module into steering wheel using care not to pinch any wires.
5. Install air bag retaining bolts, and center air bag module and **torque** air bag module to 8 ft. lbs.
6. Connect speed control switches then install switches on steering wheel. If vehicle is not equipped with speed control, install speed control switch covers.

INSTRUMENT CLUSTER
REPLACE

1. Disconnect battery ground cable.
2. Remove instrument panel left end cap.
3. Remove headlamp switch as outlined under "Headlight Switch, Replace."
4. Remove instrument panel upper center bezel. Refer to procedure found in "Dash Panel Service."
5. Remove hazard switch and steering column shroud then tilt steering wheel down.
6. Remove instrument panel cluster bezel.
7. Remove instrument cluster screws and disengage upper latch.
8. Remove instrument cluster from panel. **The instrument panel wiring harness connectors are mounted directly to the rear panel. A force of approximately 20 lbs. will be re-**

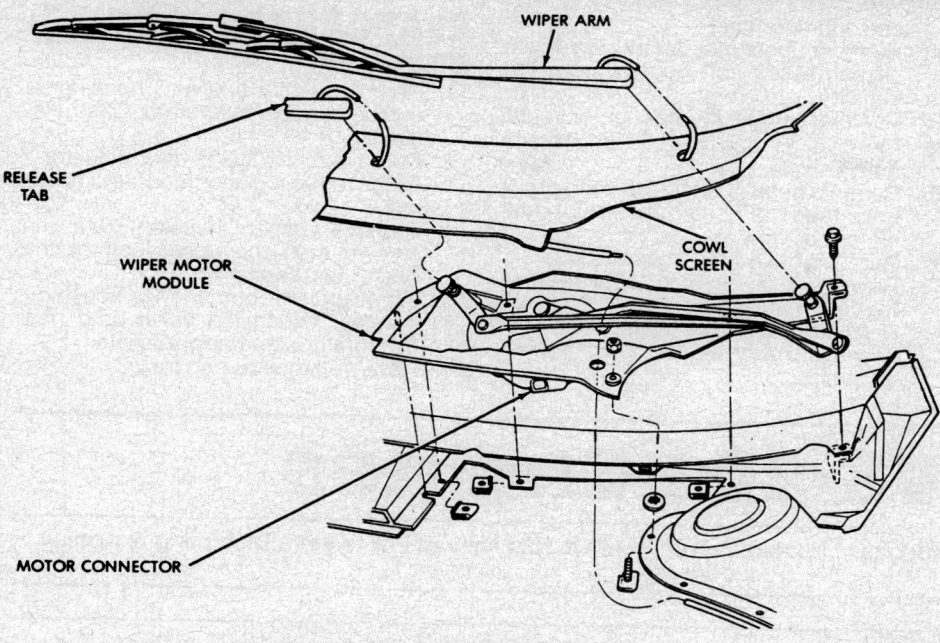

Fig. 11 Wiper motor & linkage module

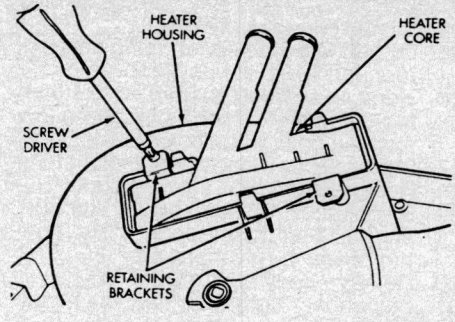

Fig. 12 Heater core replacement

quired to disengage the cluster from the connectors.
9. Reverse procedure to install.

RADIO
REPLACE

1. Remove lower center bezel and re-move radio retaining screws and re-move radio, **Fig. 10.**
2. Pull radio straight out and disconnect electrical and antenna connections.
3. Remove radio ground strap then the radio.
4. Reverse procedure to install.

WIPER MOTOR
REPLACE

1. Remove wiper arms and blades and disconnect hoses from in-line con-nector.
2. Remove rear hood seal with cowl top plastic screen and disconnect washer hose at in-line connector.
3. Disconnect motor connector at back side of housing, **Fig. 11.**
4. Remove wiper housing retaining screws then the wiper housing mod-ule.
5. Disconnect and remove wiper drive link from motor crank.
6. Remove motor mounting screws then lift motor and mounting plate out of housing.
7. Disconnect motor harness grommet from housing.
8. Reverse procedure to install, **torqu-ing** crank motor nut to 89-124 inch lbs. and motor mounting screws to 89-106 inch lbs.

WIPER SWITCH
REPLACE

Refer to procedure found under "Multi-Function Switch, Replace" for wiper switch replacement.

BLOWER MOTOR
REPLACE

1. Disconnect battery ground cable.
2. Remove lower right under panel si-lencer duct.
3. Remove blower motor housing cover.
4. Remove blower motor retaining screws, lower blower motor from housing.
5. Reverse procedure to install.

HEATER CORE
REPLACE

1. Remove heater and A/C housing as outlined under "Evaporator Case, Re-place."
2. Pull back heater core retaining clips, then pull the heater core out of the housing.
3. Install new heater core.
4. Place retaining brackets over heater core and fasten with screws provided with new heater core, **Fig. 12.**
5. Reinstall heater housing into vehicle as outlined under "Evaporator Case, Replace."

EVAPORATOR CASE
REPLACE

Refer to procedures found in the "Dash Panel Service" section when servicing the dash panel.
1. Disconnect battery ground cable.

2. Using a suitable A/C recovery unit, re-move all R-134a refrigerant from the A/C system. **R-134a service equip-ment or vehicle A/C system should not be pressure tested or leak tested with compressed air. Some mixtures of air and R-134a have been shown to be combusti-ble at elevated pressures. These mixtures are potentially dangerous and may result in fire or explosion causing injury or property damage.**
3. Remove air cleaner hose and air dis-tribution duct.
4. Drain engine cooling system.
5. Disconnect heater hoses at dash pan-el and plug heater core inlet tubes.
6. Remove both A/C lines from expan-sion valve, using line tool No. 7193 or equivalent.
7. Plug A/C lines and evaporator hous-ing inlets.
8. Remove heater & A/C housing stud nuts.
9. Remove right and left instrument pan-el end caps.
10. Remove right and left interior door post kick panel.
11. Remove right side bezel from instru-ment panel.
12. Remove radio center bezel then the radio and heater A/C control head.
13. Remove center instrument panel bez-el.
14. Remove center console from vehicle.
15. Remove right side air bag as outlined under the "Passive Restraints" sec-tion.
16. Remove lower bolster retaining screws.
17. Lower bolster and disconnect trunk release and glove box light wiring then remove bolster from the vehicle.
18. Remove instrument panel top cover.
19. Remove windshield A pillar trim cov-ers.
20. Remove instrument panel to cowl panel bolts.
21. Disconnect DRB II scan tool connec-tor brace.
22. Remove instrument panel ground strap from lower left side of center console.
23. Remove knee blocker support brack-et, under column duct and left floor duct.
24. Disconnect 60-way connector and all

25. Disconnect fuse panel wiring connectors and brake light switch.
26. Remove steering column covers then the column retaining bolts and allow steering column to lower to the floor.
27. Disconnect air bag connectors.
28. Remove right side floor air duct.
29. Disconnect 10-way, blower module and blower motor connectors from the heater & A/C housing.
30. Remove body controller.
31. Disconnect right side connector and antenna.
32. Remove right and left side upper instrument panel mounting screws located in door jamb.
33. Remove upper instrument panel with all harnesses and gauges from the vehicle.
34. Remove air duct for rear heater vents.
35. Remove air bag module and brace from vehicle.
36. Remove heater housing to dash panel bolts then roll heater and A/C housing out of vehicle.
37. Remove drain tube from housing.
38. Reverse procedure to install, noting the following:
   a. Install drain tube from underneath vehicle after heater housing is installed.

EVAPORATOR CORE
REPLACE

1. Remove heater and A/C housing as outlined under "Evaporator Case, Replace."
2. Remove recirculation door actuator.
3. Remove recirculation door and housing.
4. Remove upper housing retaining screws then the upper half of the heater housing.
5. Lift evaporator out of lower housing.
6. Transfer expansion valve onto new evaporator using new gaskets.
7. Reverse procedure to install.

3.3L/V6-201 Engines

NOTE: Refer To "Air Bag System Precautions" Located In The Front Of This Manual For System Disarming & Arming Procedures.

NOTE: For Procedures Not Found In This Section, Refer To The 3.3L & 3.8L Engines Section In The Acclaim/Spirit, Daytona, Dynasty/Imperial/New Yorker, LeBaron & Shadow/Sundance Section.

INDEX

PRECAUTIONS
AIR BAG SYSTEMS

Refer to "Air Bag System Precautions" in the front of this manual for system disarming and arming procedures.

FLEXIBLE FUEL MODELS

Flexible Fuel engine control systems allow engines to run on mixtures of methanol and unleaded gasoline. The system allows optimum engine operation with various mixtures of up to 85 percent methanol 15 percent unleaded gasoline.

A Methanol Concentration Sensor (MCS), containing a microprocessor, is used to sample fuel as it is pumped to the fuel injection system and determine the percentage of methanol and unleaded gasoline. This sensor sends a real-time correction signal to the Powertrain Control Module (PCM). The PCM then adjusts ignition and fuel injection functions to provide optimum engine performance. In the event of MCS failure, the PCM remembers the last correction signal and will use that information to enable a limp home mode.

Flexible Fuel Vehicles (FFV) use unique

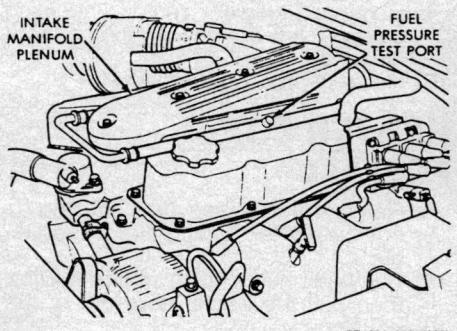

Fig. 1 Fuel pressure test port

methanol-compatible components. These items may be identified by either, a green tag or sticker or the component itself will be colored green.

Certain gasoline only (uncolored) components may appear identical to these FFV components. Under no circumstances may these components be interchanged.

FUEL SYSTEM PRESSURE RELEASE

When releasing fuel pressure on Flexi-

ble Fuel Vehicles (FFV) use methanol resistant gloves and eye protection. Avoid prolonged skin contact with liquid or breathing of vapors.

Persons taking medications containing DISULFIRAM such as ANTIBUSE should avoid contact with liquids or vapors from methanol based fuels.

1. Disconnect battery ground cable.
2. Remove fuel filler cap.
3. Remove protective cap from fuel pressure test port on fuel rail, **Fig. 1**.
4. Place open end of fuel pressure release hose tool No. C-4799-1 or equivalent into approved container.
5. Connect other end of hose to pressure test port.
6. Fuel pressure will bleed off through hose into container.

ENGINE MOUNT
REPLACE
FRONT

1. Remove insulator attaching nuts from top of mounting bracket.
2. Raise and support vehicle.
3. Support engine using a suitable jack stand and a block of wood across full width of oil pan.

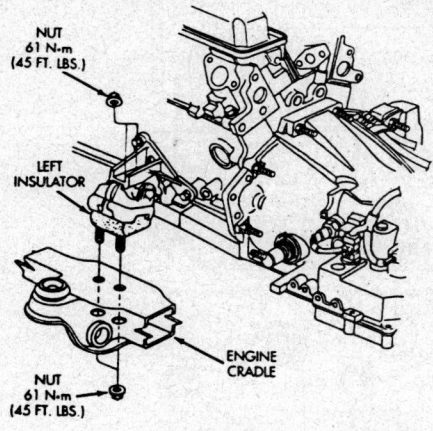

Fig. 2 Left engine mount

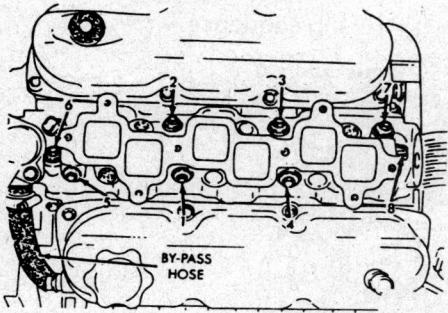

Fig. 5 Intake manifold bolts replacement sequence

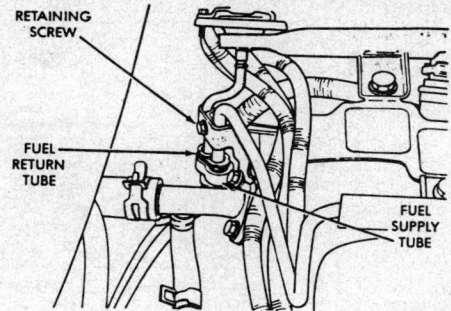

Fig. 3 Fuel supply & return tubes

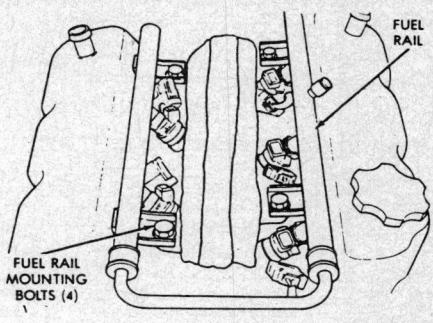

Fig. 4 Fuel rail

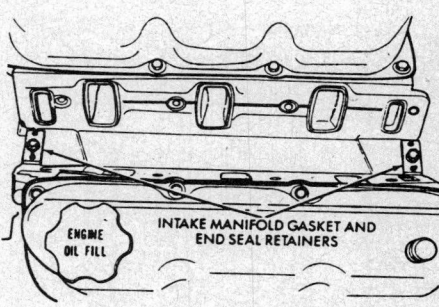

Fig. 6 Intake manifold seal retainer screws

4. Remove lower attaching nuts from bottom of insulator to frame, **Fig. 2.**
5. Raise engine enough to remove insulator.
6. Reverse procedure to install, tightening mount to specification.

REAR

1. Raise and support vehicle.
2. Support transaxle with suitable transmission jack.
3. Remove insulator through bolt from mount.
4. Remove rear mount retainers and remove mount.
5. Reverse procedure to install, tightening bolts to specifications.

ENGINE
REPLACE

1. Release fuel system pressure as outlined under "Precautions."
2. Disconnect battery ground cable.
3. Mark hood position at hinges then remove.
4. Drain cooling system.
5. Disconnect all electrical connections.
6. Remove coolant hoses from radiator and engine.
7. Remove radiator and fan assembly.
8. Disconnect fuel lines and accelerator cable.
9. Remove air cleaner assembly.
10. Raise and support vehicle then drain engine oil.
11. Remove air conditioning compressor mounting bolts and position compressor aside. **Do not allow compressor to hang by hoses, support using suitable wire to frame.**
12. Disconnect exhaust pipe at manifold.
13. Remove transaxle inspection cover and mark flex plate to torque converter position.
14. Remove bolts holding torque converter to flex plate and attach a C-clamp on bottom of converter housing to prevent torque converter from coming out.
15. Remove power steering pump mounting bolts and position pump aside. **Do not allow pump to hang by hoses, support using suitable wire to frame.**
16. Remove lower transmission to engine block bolts.
17. Remove starter assembly as outlined under "Starter, Replace" in the "Electrical" section.
18. Lower vehicle and disconnect vacuum lines and ground straps.
19. Support transaxle using a suitable floor jack.
20. Attach engine lifting device and support engine.
21. Remove upper transaxle to engine block bolts.
22. Remove front engine mounts as outlined under "Engine Mounts, Replace."
23. Remove engine from vehicle.
24. Reverse procedure to install, noting the following:
    a. Tighten all fasteners to specifications.
    b. Refer to "Cooling System Bleed" when filling cooling system with coolant.

INTAKE MANIFOLD
REPLACE

1. Release fuel system pressure as outlined under "Precautions."
2. Disconnect battery ground cable.
3. Drain cooling system.
4. Disconnect air tube from air cleaner and throttle body.
5. Hold throttle lever in wide open position then remove throttle and speed control cables from lever.
6. Compress locking tabs on throttle and speed control cables then remove cables from bracket.
7. Disconnect electrical connector from EGR solenoid valve transducer.
8. Disconnect PCV valve, brake booster, throttle body purge and fuel pressure regulator hoses.
9. Disconnect throttle position sensor and idle air control motor.
10. Remove EGR tube mounting screws at intake manifold.
11. Remove intake manifold plenum bolts then lift plenum up off engine.
12. Disconnect fuel supply and return tube quick disconnect fittings at rear of intake manifold, **Fig. 3.**
13. Remove screw from fuel tube clamp then separate fuel tubes from the bracket.
14. Rotate injectors toward center of engine, tag injector connectors with there cylinder number then disconnect each injector.
15. Remove fuel rail bolts then lift fuel rail and injectors straight up and off engine, **Fig. 4.**
16. Remove upper radiator and rear intake manifold hoses.
17. Remove intake manifold bolts then the intake manifold, **Fig. 5.**
18. Remove intake manifold seal retainer screws then the intake manifold gasket, **Fig. 6.**
19. Inspect for damage and cracks of each section.
20. Inspect for clogged water passages in end crossovers and for clogged gas passages.
21. Reverse procedure to install, noting the following:
    a. Clean all surfaces of cylinder block and heads.
    b. Place a 1/4 inch drop of Mopar Silicone Rubber Adhesive Sealant or equivalent onto each of the four manifold to cylinder head gasket corners, **Fig. 7.**
    c. Install intake manifold gasket then

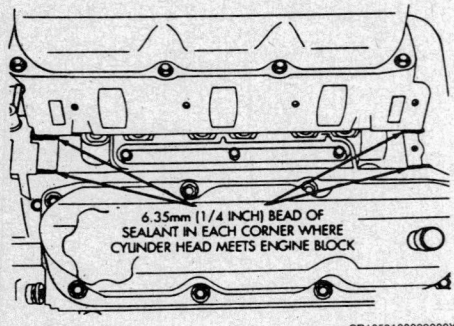

Fig. 7   Intake manifold sealant

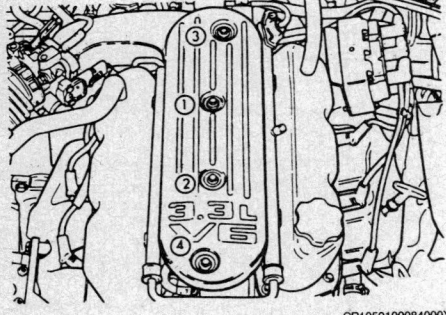

Fig. 8   Intake plenum bolt tightening sequence

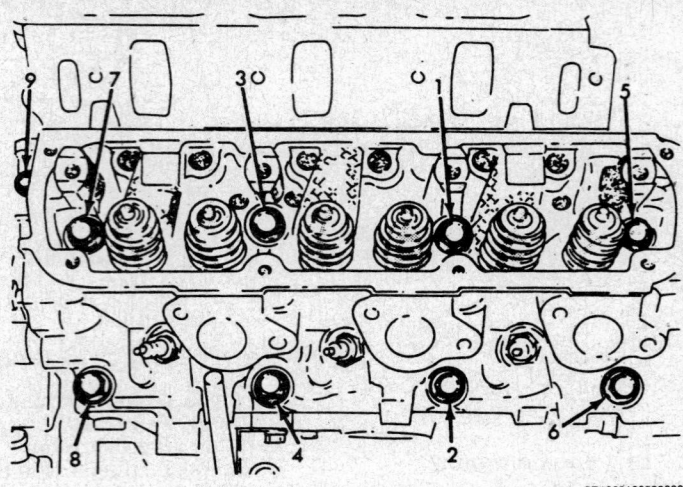

Fig. 9   Cylinder head bolt tightening sequence

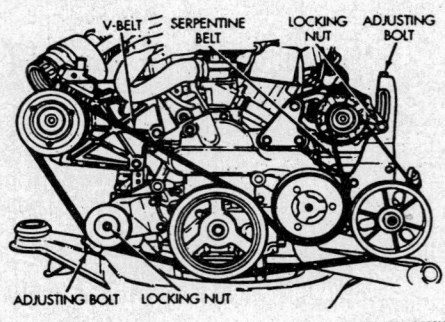

Fig. 10   Drive belt routing

tighten seal retainers to specifications.

d. Install intake manifold and tighten bolts in sequence shown in **Fig. 5**, as follows: **Torque** bolts in sequence to 10 inch lbs. **Torque** bolts in sequence to 200 inch lbs. Check bolts in sequence shown and ensure bolts are **torqued** to 200 inch lbs.

e. Ensure seal and gasket are in correct place.

f. Apply a light coat of clean engine oil to O-ring on each injector prior to installation.

g. Tighten plenum bolts in sequence shown in **Fig. 8**.

h. Bleed cooling system as outlined under "Cooling System Bleed."

CYLINDER HEAD
REPLACE

1. Disconnect battery ground cable from battery, then drain coolant from radiator.
2. Remove intake manifold and throttle body as outlined under "Intake Manifold, Replace".
3. Disconnect coil wires, sending unit wire, heater hoses and bypass hose from engine block.
4. Remove closed ventilation system, then evaporation control system.
5. Remove valve covers, then exhaust manifolds.
6. Remove rocker arm and shaft assemblies from each cylinder head. **Mark pushrods to ensure installation into original positions.**

7. Remove the nine cylinder head retaining bolts, then cylinder head from cylinder block.
8. Clean cylinder block and cylinder head mating surfaces, then inspect for cracks, damage and leakage.
9. Install new gaskets on cylinder block.
10. Tighten cylinder head bolts 1 through 8 in the sequence shown in **Fig. 9**, using the 4 step torque turn method. **Cylinder head bolts are torqued using the torque yield method and should be inspected before reuse. If the threads are stretched or the center of the threads is smaller than the rest of the bolt, they must replaced.** Tighten according to the following values:
    a. **Torque** cylinder head retaining bolts in sequence to 45 ft. lbs.
    b. **Torque** cylinder head retaining bolts again in sequence to 65 ft. lbs.
    c. **Torque** cylinder head retaining bolts again in sequence to 65 ft. lbs.
    d. **Do Not use a torque wrench for this step.** Tighten cylinder head bolts again 1/4 turn. Bolt torque should be over 90 ft. lbs. If not replace the bolt.
11. **Torque** head bolt No. 9 to 25 ft. lbs., after head bolts 1 through 8 have been torqued to specification.
12. Install pushrods in their original positions, then rocker arm and shaft as-

semblies. **Torque** rocker arm shaft retaining bolts to 12 ft. lbs.
13. Install valve covers, then intake manifold. Refer to "Intake Manifold, Replace," in this section.

VALVE ADJUSTMENT

This engine is equipped with hydraulic valve lash adjusters which are not adjustable.

SERPENTINE DRIVE BELT

DRIVE BELT ROUTING

Refer to **Fig. 10** for serpentine drive belt routing.

SERPENTINE BELT, REPLACE

The drive belt is provided with an adjusting screw on the generator mounting bracket, **Fig. 11**, to maintain proper belt tension. To remove or install belt, release tension by loosening generator mounting bolt (A) and adjusting bolt locknut (B) then loosen adjusting bolt. Reverse procedure to tighten belt to specified tension.

BELT TENSION DATA

Use belt tensioning special tool kit No. C-4162 or equivalent to tighten used belts to 120 lbs. and new belts to 140-160 lbs.

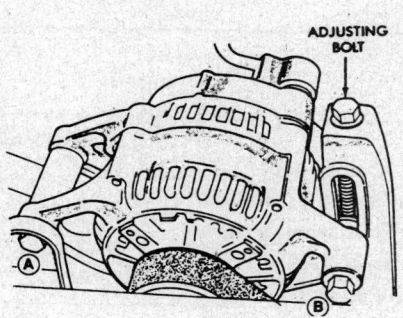

Fig. 11 Serpentine drive belt adjustment bolt

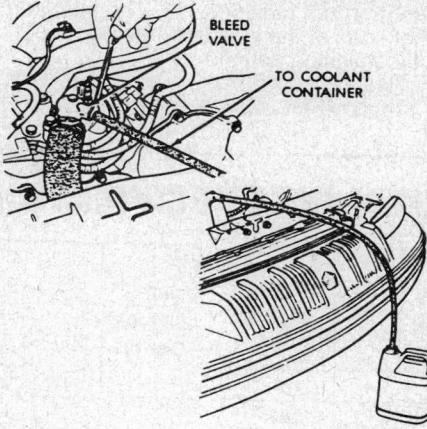

Fig. 12 Cooling system bleed screw location

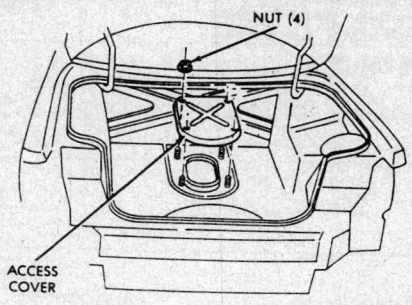

Fig. 13 Fuel pump access panel

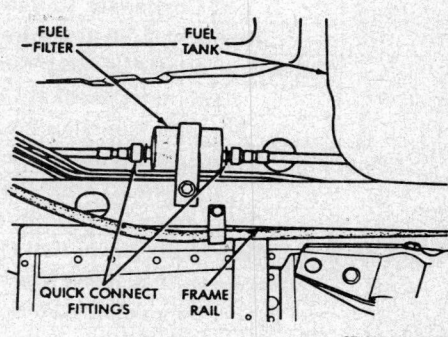

Fig. 16 Fuel filter location

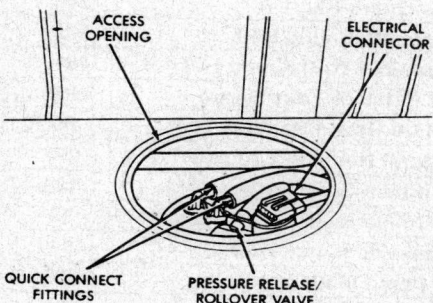

Fig. 14 Fuel pump module connections

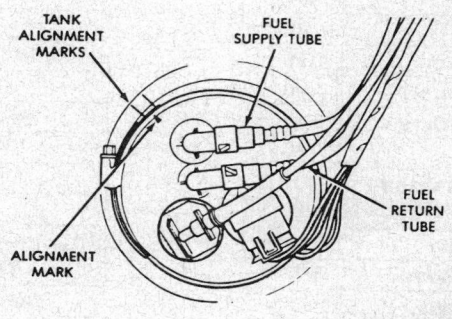

Fig. 15 Fuel pump alignment marks

d. Check automatic transaxle oil level and replenish as necessary.

FUEL PUMP
REPLACE

1. Release fuel system pressure as outlined under "Precautions."
2. Disconnect battery ground cable.
3. Remove trunk liner, access panel and gasket, **Fig. 13.**
4. Disconnect electrical connector from top of pump module.
5. Disconnect fuel supply and return hoses and pressure relief/rollover valve, **Fig. 14.**
6. Loosen band clamp until fuel pump module rises up from tank.
7. Place shop towels around access opening to absorb possible fuel spillage.
8. Without removing module, tip module backward to allow fuel to drain back into tank.
9. Tilt fuel pump module to prevent fuel level gauge float from catching on fuel tank when removing module.
10. Reverse procedure to install, noting the following:
    a. Align marks on module and tank when installing module, **Fig. 15.**
    b. Seat module into tank by pushing the top down. Ensure gasket does not slip over the outside or inside edge of fuel tank lip.
    c. Tighten fuel pump module band clamp to specification. **Do not over tighten band clamp.**
    d. Pressurize fuel system and test for leaks.

RADIATOR
REPLACE

1. Disconnect battery ground cable, then drain cooling system.
2. Remove the upper radiator crossmember, then remove coolant hose clamps and hoses from radiator.
3. Disconnect automatic transaxle cooler lines from radiator.
4. **On models with an auxiliary transaxle cooler,** disconnect rubber auxiliary cooler lines.
5. **On all models** disconnect radiator fan wiring from the RFI module.
6. Disconnect upper radiator mounting screws.
7. **On models with engine block heater** disconnect wiring.
8. Remove condenser to radiator mounting screws.
9. Using caution not to bend condenser inlet tube or damage cooling fins, lean condenser forward against bumper.
10. Lift radiator free of vehicle.
11. **On models with an auxiliary transaxle cooler,** remove plastic retaining straps and remove cooler.
12. Reverse procedure to install, noting the following:
    a. **Torque** A/C condenser mounting screws to 45 inch lbs.
    b. **Torque** radiator hose clamps to 22 inch lbs.
    c. Refill and bleed cooling system as

COOLING SYSTEM BLEED

1. Close radiator drain.
2. Install cylinder block drain plugs.
3. Attach one end of a .250 inch ID clear hose that is 48 inches long to bleed screw on thermostat housing, **Fig. 12.**
4. Route hose away from accessory drive belts and cooling fan and place into a clean suitable container.
5. Open bleed screw.
6. Slowly fill coolant pressure bottle until a steady stream of coolant flows from hose.
7. Gently squeeze upper radiator hose until all air is removed from system.
8. Close bleed valve and continue filling to top of coolant pressure bottle.
9. Install cap on coolant pressure bottle remove hose from bleed screw.

FUEL FILTER
REPLACE

The fuel filter is located on the frame rail in front of fuel tank, **Fig. 16.** The inlet and outlet ends of the filter are marked for correct installation as follows:

1. Release fuel system pressure as outlined under "Precautions."
2. Disconnect quick connect fitting from fuel filter.
3. Remove fuel filter mounting bracket and filter.
4. Reverse procedure to install.

TIGHTENING SPECIFICATIONS

Year	Component	Torque/Ft. Lbs.
1993–95	A/C Compressor Support Bolt	30①
	A/C Compressor To Bracket Bolt	50①
	A/C Condenser To Radiator	45
	Alternator Adjusting Strap Bolt	200
	Alternator Adjusting Strap Mounting Bolt	30①
	Alternator Bracket Bolt	30①
	Alternator Mounting Pivot Nut	30①
	Camshaft Sprocket Lockbolt	40①
	Camshaft Thrust Plate	105
	Chain Case Cover Bolt (8 mm)	20
	Chain Case Cover Bolt (11 mm)	40
	Condenser Inlet Tube Bracket Screw	45
	Connecting Rod Nut	②
	Crankshaft Pulley Screw To Crankshaft	40①
	Cylinder Head Bolt	③
	Cylinder Head Cover Bolt	105
	Engine Block To Transaxle Bolts	75①
	Engine Mount Attaching Nuts	45①
	Exhaust Crossover Pipe Flange Nut/Bolt	25①
	Exhaust Manifold Heat Shield Mounting Screw	200
	Exhaust Manifold Mounting Screw	200
	Exhaust Manifold Nuts To Front Down Pipes	20①
	Fan Blade Retaining Nut Left Side (Short Motor)	45
	Fan Module To Radiator	45
	Fan Motor To Shroud Screws (Left Side)	45
	Fan Motor To Shroud Screws (Right Side)	25
	Fuel Pump Band Clamp	31
	Fuel Rail Bolts	200
	Intake Manifold Bolt	③
	Intake Manifold Gasket Retainer Screws	105
	Intake Manifold Plenum Bolt	250

Year	Component	Torque/Ft. Lbs.
1993–95 —Cont'd	Main Bearing Cap Bolt	④
	Oil Filter Attaching Nipple	30①
	Oil Level Sensor Plug	20①
	Oil Pan Drain Plug	20①
	Oil Pan Screw	105
	Oil Pressure Sending Unit	60
	Oil Pump Cover Bolt	105
	Oil Pump Pick-Up Tube Screw	250
	PCV Valve	60
	Radiator (Cooling Module) To Body Screws	105
	Receiver/Drier Swivel Nut	45
	RFI Harness To Shroud Screw	25
	Rocker Shaft Bracket Bolt	250
	Spark Plug	20①
	Starter Mounting Bolt	50①
	Strut Intake Manifold To Cylinder Head Bolt	40①
	Tappet Retainer Yoke Screw	105
	Temperature Gauge Sending Unit	60
	Thermostat Housing Bolt Nut	250
	Timing Chain Snubber Screw	105
	Torque Converter To Flex Plate	55
	Transaxle Mount Bolt	45①
	Water Pump Mounting Bolts	105
	Water Pump Pulley Screw	250
	Water Pump To Chain Case Cover Bolt	105

①—Foot lbs.
②—Tighten in two steps, first to 40 ft. lbs. then tighten an additional ¼ turn.
③—Refer to text.
④—Tighten in two steps, first to 30 ft. lbs. then tighten an additional ¼ turn.

NOTE: Refer To "Air Bag System Precautions" Located In The Front Of This Manual For System Disarming & Arming Procedures.

NOTE: For Procedures Not Found In This Section, Refer To The 3.3L/V6-201 Engine Section In This Chapter.

INDEX

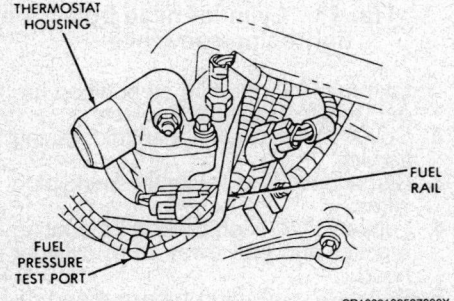

Fig. 1   Fuel pressure test port

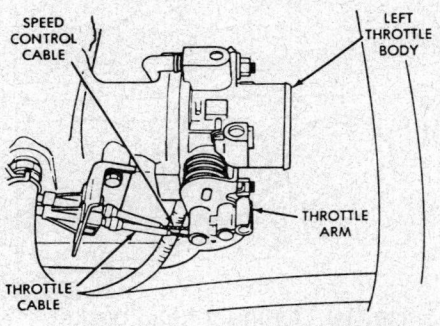

Fig. 2   Throttle lever

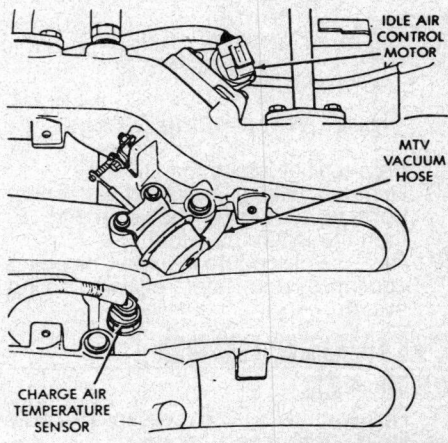

Fig. 3   Idle air control motor, charge air temperature sensor & MTV component location

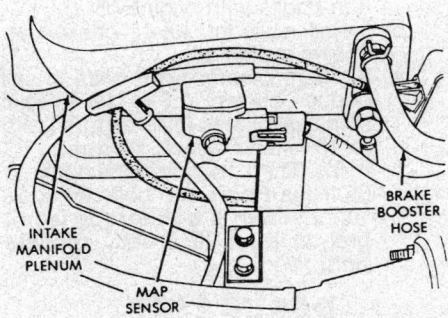

Fig. 4   MAP location

PRECAUTIONS

AIR BAG SYSTEMS

Refer to "Air Bag System Precautions" in the front of this manual for system disarming and arming procedures.

FUEL SYSTEM PRESSURE RELEASE

1. Disconnect battery ground cable.
2. Remove fuel filler cap.
3. Remove protective cap from fuel pressure test port on fuel rail, **Fig. 1.**
4. Place open end of fuel pressure release hose tool No. C-4799-1 or equivalent into approved container.
5. Connect other end of hose to pressure test port.
6. Fuel pressure will bleed off through hose into container.

INTAKE MANIFOLD

REPLACE

1. Release fuel system pressure as outlined under "Precautions."
2. Drain cooling system.
3. Remove engine cover from top of plenum.

4. Remove accelerator cable and speed control cable from throttle arm, **Fig. 2.**
5. Disconnect electrical connector from idle air control motor and charge air temperature sensor then remove vacuum hose from Manifold Tuning Valve (MTV), **Fig. 3.**
6. Remove ground screw from intake manifold.
7. Disconnect electrical connector from Manifold Absolute Pressure (MAP) sensor and Throttle Position Sensor (TPS), **Fig. 4.**
8. Disconnect purge hose from throttle bodies.
9. Disconnect PCV make up air hose and idle air control motor supply hose then remove the air inlet plenum from behind manifold.
10. Disconnect PCV, brake booster and remaining vacuum hoses from intake manifold.
11. Remove EGR tube mounting bolts at intake manifold plenum.
12. Remove air plenum support bracket on each side of manifold.
13. Remove intake manifold plenum mounting bolts. The plenum uses two different length bolts, **Fig. 5.**
14. Remove intake manifold plenum.
15. Remove upper radiator hose from thermostat housing and heater hose

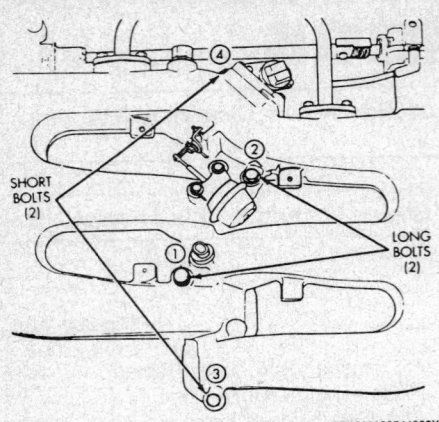

Fig. 5   Intake plenum bolt length identification

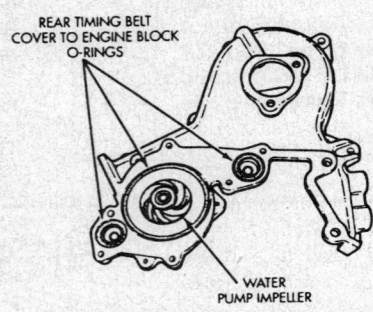

Fig. 8   Water pump O-rings

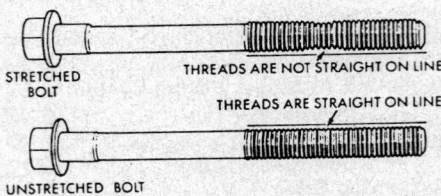

Fig. 6   Intake manifold replacement sequence

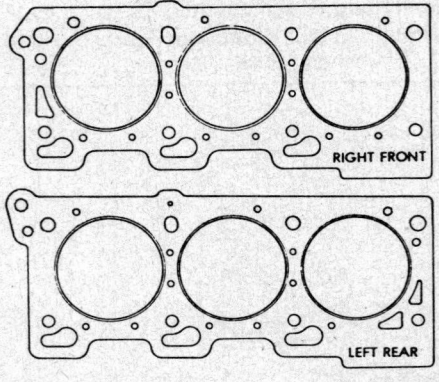

Fig. 9   Bolt check for stretching

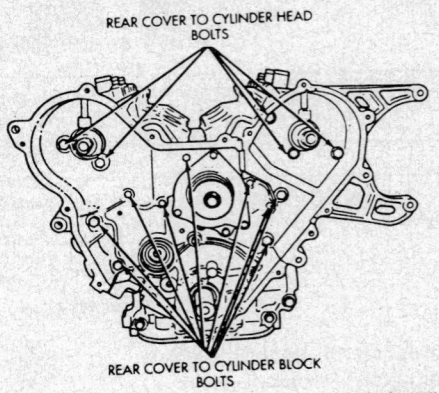

Fig. 7   Rear timing belt cover bolts

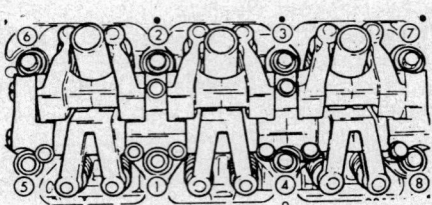

Fig. 11   Cylinder head bolt tightening sequence

Fig. 10   Cylinder head gasket identification

from rear of intake manifold.
16. Remove intake manifold attaching bolts in sequence shown in **Fig. 6,** then the intake manifold.
17. Reverse procedure to install, bleeding cooling system after refilling cooling system.

CYLINDER HEAD
REPLACE

1. Release fuel system pressure as outlined under "Precautions."
2. Remove camshaft sprockets as outlined under "Timing System & Seal Service."
3. Remove intake manifold as outlined under "Intake Manifold, Replace."
4. Remove timing belt cover to cylinder head fasteners, **Fig. 7.**
5. If right side timing belt cover is removed, there are O-rings located behind it for water pump passages, **Fig. 8.**
6. Remove cylinder head bolts then the cylinder head.
7. Check for cracks, leaks or damage.
8. Clean mating surfaces of cylinder head and engine block.
9. Clean cylinder head and oil passages.
10. Ensure cylinder head flatness is within .002 inch.
11. Check cylinder head bolts for necking by holding a scale or straightedge against threads. If all threads do not contact the scale, bolts should be replaced, **Fig. 9.**
12. Reverse procedure to install, noting the following:

a. Lightly coat threads of cylinder head bolts with engine oil.
b. Install cylinder head gasket as shown in **Fig. 10.**
c. Tighten cylinder head bolts in sequence shown in **Fig. 11,** in four steps as follows. First, **torque** bolts to 45 ft. lbs. Second, **torque** to 65 ft. lbs. Third, **torque** bolts again to 65 ft. lbs. Forth, turn bolts an additional 1/4 turn. **If bolt torque is not greater than 90 ft. lbs., replace bolt.**

VALVE LIFT SPECIFICATIONS

Engine	Year	Lift, Inch Intake	Exhaust
3.5L/V6-215	1993–94	.3209	.2571

VALVE COVER
REPLACE

1. Remove air cleaner assembly and in-

take manifold plenum as outlined under "Intake Manifold, Replace."
2. Cover lower intake manifold during service.
3. Disconnect and relocate spark plug wires.
4. Loosen A/C compressor mounting bracket and pull away from cylinder head.
5. Remove spark plug tube nut and O-ring.
6. Remove rocker cover screws and remove cover.
7. Reverse procedure to install.

VALVE ADJUSTMENT

This engine is equipped with hydraulic valve lash adjusters which are not adjustable.

TIMING SYSTEM & SEAL SERVICE

TIMING BELT COVER, REPLACE

1. Release fuel system pressure as outlined under "Precautions."
2. Drain cooling system and remove upper radiator hose for access to timing belt covers.
3. Remove accessory drive belts.
4. Remove stamped steel, cast and lower covers, **Fig. 12. Do not remove sealer on steel cover, it is reuseable.**
5. Reverse procedure to install.

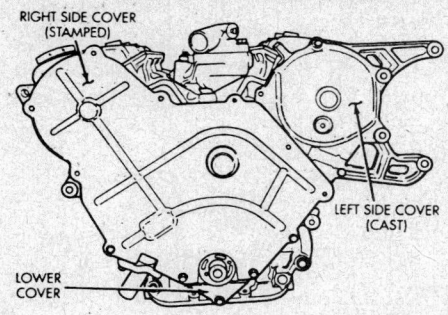

Fig. 12   Timing belt covers

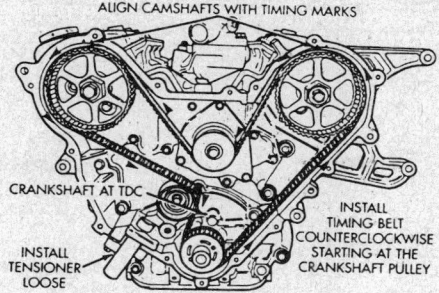

Fig. 13   Timing belt installation

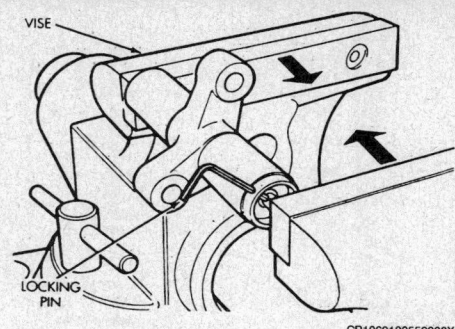

Fig. 14   Timing belt tensioner compression

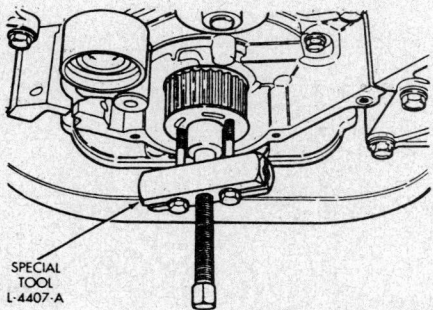

Fig. 15   Crankshaft sprocket removal

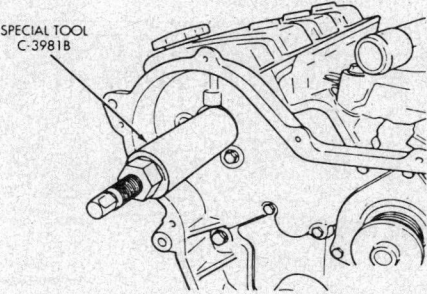

Fig. 16   Camshaft oil seal removal

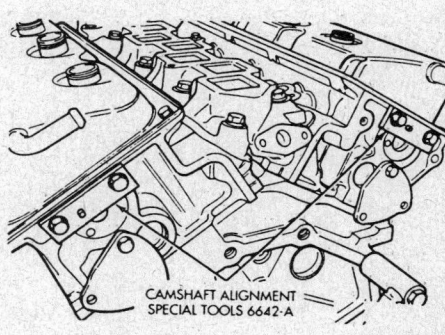

Fig. 17   Camshaft alignment tool

TIMING BELT, REPLACE
Removal

1. Remove timing belt covers as outlined under "Timing Belt Cover Replace."
2. Mark belt running direction for installation.
3. Align camshaft sprockets with marks on rear covers before timing belt is removed, **Fig. 13**.
4. Remove timing belt tensioner and the timing belt.

Installation

1. When tensioner is removed from engine, it is necessary to compress the plunger into the tensioner body.
2. Place tensioner into a vise and slowly compress the plunger, **Fig. 14**.
3. When plunger is compressed into tensioner body, install a pin through the body and plunger to retain plunger in place until tensioner is installed.
4. **If camshaft sprockets have been removed, refer to procedures found under "Camshaft Sprocket, Replace" to align camshafts prior to installing timing belt.**
5. Align crankshaft sprocket with the Top Dead Center TDC mark on oil pump cover, **Fig. 13**.
6. Align camshaft sprockets between marks on covers.
7. Install timing belt starting at the crankshaft sprocket in a counterclockwise direction. After belt is installed on the right sprocket keep tension on the belt until it is past the tensioner pulley.
8. Holding tensioner pulley against the belt, install tensioner into housing and **torque** to 250 inch lbs.

9. When tensioner is in place, pull retaining pin to allow tensioner to extend to the pulley bracket.
10. Rotate crankshaft sprocket two revolutions and check timing marks on camshafts and crankshaft. If marks do not line up repeat procedure.

CRANKSHAFT FRONT OIL SEAL, REPLACE

1. Remove timing belt as outlined under "Timing Belt, Replace."
2. Remove crankshaft sprocket using pulley puller tool No. L-4407-A or equivalent, **Fig. 15**.
3. Tap dowel pin out of crankshaft.
4. Remove crankshaft seal using seal remover tool No. 6341 or equivalent.
5. Shaft seal lip must be free of varnish, dirt or nicks. Polish with 400 grit paper if necessary.
6. Install crankshaft seal using seal installer tool No. 6342 or equivalent.
7. Install dowel pin into the crankshaft .047 inch.
8. Install crankshaft sprocket using sprocket tool No. C-4685-C1 or equivalent.
9. Install timing belt and covers.

CAMSHAFT SPROCKETS, REPLACE
Removal

1. Remove timing belt as outlined under "Timing Belt Replace."
2. Hold camshaft sprocket with 1 7/16 inch box wrench to loosen and remove sprocket bolt and washer. **To remove bolt with engine in vehicle, it may be necessary to lift that side of the engine to gain access for bolt removal.**

3. Remove camshaft sprocket from camshaft. Each sprocket had a "D" shaped hole that allows it to rotate several degrees in each direction on its shaft. This design must be timed with the engine to ensure proper engine performance. Refer to "Camshaft & Timing Belt Installation & Timing" for sprocket installation procedure.

Installation

Refer to "Camshaft & Timing Belt Installation & Timing" for sprocket installation procedure.

CAMSHAFT OIL SEAL, REPLACE

1. Remove camshaft sprockets as outlined under "Camshaft Sprockets, Replace."
2. Remove camshaft oil seals using oil seal remover tool No. C-3981B or equivalent, **Fig. 16**.
3. Reverse procedure to install, lubricating seal prior to installation using seal installer tool No. 6052.

CAMSHAFT & TIMING BELT INSTALLATION & TIMING

1. Place crankshaft sprocket to TDC mark on oil pump housing.
2. Install camshaft alignment tool No. 6642-A to rear of cylinder heads, **Fig. 17**.
3. Preload tensioner with a vise and install locking pin as outlined in the "Installation" procedure under "Timing Belt, Replace."
4. Install camshaft sprockets onto camshafts.

Fig. 18 No. 1 cylinder positioning at TDC

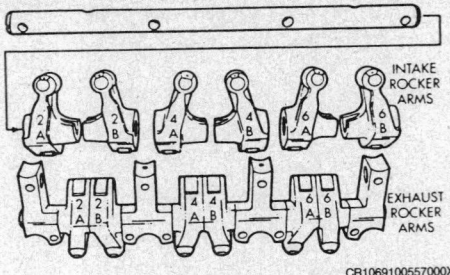

Fig. 19 Rocker arms & shaft identification

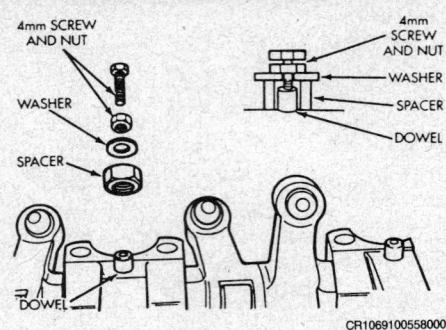

Fig. 20 Dowel pin removal

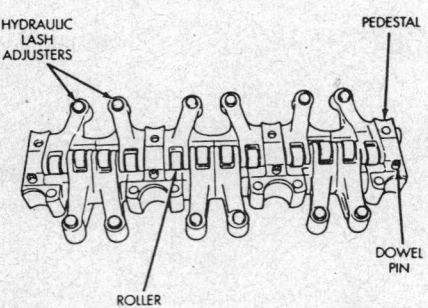

Fig. 21 Rocker arms & shaft assembly

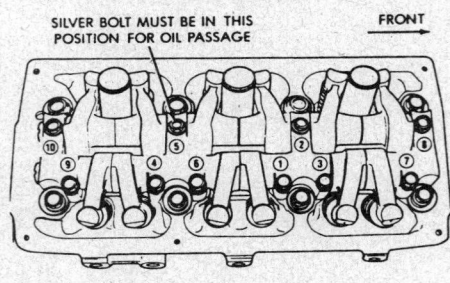

RIGHT SIDE SHOWN

Fig. 22 Rocker arm shaft bolt tightening sequence

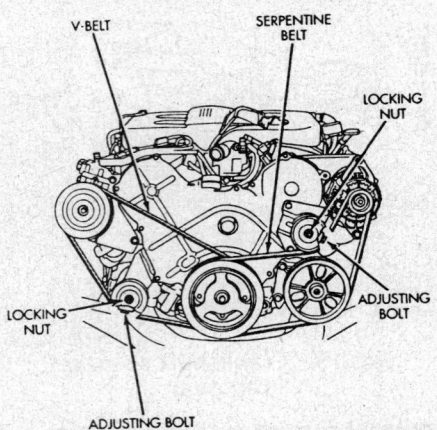

Fig. 23 Drive belt routing

5. Apply Loctite sealer No. 277 or equivalent to ends of bolts. The 10 inch bolt is installed into the left camshaft and the 8 3/8 inch bolt is installed into the right camshaft. **Do not tighten bolts.**
6. Position camshaft sprocket mark should be between marks on the cover, **Fig. 13.**
7. Install timing belt as outlined in the "Installation" procedure under "Timing Belt, Replace."
8. Install a dial indicator in number one cylinder to check TDC of piston, **Fig. 18.** Rotate crankshaft until piston is at exactly TDC.
9. With number one cylinder at TDC, hold camshaft sprocket with a 1 7/16 inch wrench and **torque** camshaft bolt to 95 ft. lbs. Repeat on other camshaft.
10. Remove dial indicator and install spark plugs.
11. Remove camshaft alignment tool and install camshaft covers and O-rings.
12. Install timing belt covers as outlined under "Timing Belt Cover Replace."

ROCKER ARMS
REPLACE
REMOVAL
1. Remove cylinder head covers as outlined under "Cylinder Head Cover, Replace."
2. Identify and mark rocker arm assembly and rocker arms before disassembly, **Fig. 19.**
3. Remove rocker arm assembly bolts then rocker arms.
4. Check rocker arms for the following wear or damage:

a. Roller scuffing or wear.
b. Bore scuffing or wear.
c. Swivel pad on lash adjuster missing or broken.
d. Rocker arm showing signs of fatigue or cracking.
e. Roller axle protruding from arm.
5. Remove dowel pin using a 4mm screw, nut, spacer and washer installed into pin, **Fig. 20.**
6. Remove rocker arms and pedestals in order, **Fig. 21.**
7. Check rocker arm mounting portion of shafts for wear or damage.
8. Check oil holes for clogging with small wire, clean as required.

INSTALLATION
1. Install rocker arms and pedestals onto shaft.
2. Install dowel pins in correct locations, **Fig. 21.** Dowel pins pass through pedestal into rocker shafts. Dowel pins should be pressed until they bottom out in pedestal.
3. Rotate camshaft placing lobes in a neutral position (no load on valves).
4. Install rocker arm assembly with identification marks toward front of engine.
5. Install oil feed bolt into correct location on rocker shaft retainer and tighten bolts in sequence to specification, **Fig. 22.**
6. Install cylinder head covers.

CAMSHAFT
REPLACE
1. Remove cylinder head as outlined under "Cylinder Head, Replace."
2. Mark then remove rocker arm assemblies as outlined under "Rocker Arms, Replace."

3. Remove rear camshaft cover and O-ring from head.
4. Carefully remove camshaft from rear of cylinder head. **Use care not to damage, nick or scratch camshaft journals when removing camshafts.**
5. Reverse procedure to install, lubricating camshaft journals and camshaft with clean engine oil prior to installation.

CAMSHAFT OIL SEAL
REPLACE
Refer to procedure found under "Timing System & Seal Service" when replacing the camshaft oil seals.

CRANKSHAFT SEAL
REPLACE
Refer to procedure found under "Timing System & Seal Service" when replacing the front crankshaft oil seal.

SERPENTINE DRIVE BELT
BELT ROUTING
Refer to **Fig. 23** for serpentine belt routing.

SERPENTINE BELT, REPLACE

The drive belt is provided with an adjustable tensioner pulley on the timing belt cover, **Fig. 23**, to maintain proper belt tension. To remove or install belt, release tension by loosening the tensioner pulley nut and adjustment bolt. Reverse procedure to tighten belt to specified tension.

SERPENTINE BELT TENSION DATA

Use tensioning special tool kit No. C-4162 or equivalent to tighten used belts to 120 lbs. and new belts to 140-160 lbs.

SEPARATED ACCESSORY DRIVE SYSTEM

A/C BELT ROUTING

Refer to **Fig. 23** for A/C drive belt routing.

A/C BELT, REPLACE

The drive belt is provided with an adjustable tensioner pulley , **Fig. 23**, to maintain proper belt tension.
1. Remove serpentine drive belt as outlined under "Serpentine Drive Belt."
2. Release tension by loosening the tensioner pulley locking nut, then the adjustment bolt
3. Remove belt.
4. Reverse procedure to install, noting the following:
   a. Tension belt as outlined under "A/C Belt Tension Data."
   b. **Torque** tensioner locking nut to 40 ft. lbs.

A/C BELT TENSION DATA

Use tensioning special tool kit No. C-4162 or equivalent to tighten used belts to 120 lbs. and new belts to 140-160 lbs.

WATER PUMP
REPLACE

1. Drain cooling system.
2. Remove timing belt as outlined under "Timing System & Seal Service."

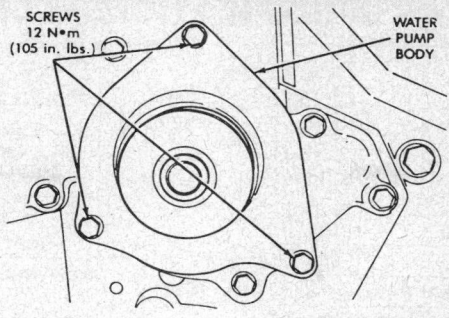

SCREWS 12 N•m (105 in. lbs.)

WATER PUMP BODY

CR108910012800X

Fig. 24   Water pump

3. Remove water pump mounting bolts then the water pump, **Fig. 24**.
4. Reverse procedure to install.

RADIATOR REPLACE
NEW YORKER & LHS

1. Disconnect battery ground cable, then drain cooling system.
2. Remove sight shields and right and left headlight modules.
3. Discharge air conditioning system as outlined under"Discharging System" in the "Air Conditioning" chapter of this manual.
4. Remove upper radiator crossmember, then the coolant hose clamps and hoses from radiator.
5. Disconnect automatic transaxle cooler lines from radiator.
6. **On models with an auxiliary transaxle cooler**, disconnect rubber auxiliary cooler lines.
7. **On all models**, disconnect radiator fan wiring from the RFI module.
8. Disconnect upper radiator mounting screws.
9. **On models with engine block heater**, disconnect wiring.
10. **On all models**, disconnect A/C lines from condenser.
11. Lift condenser and radiator unit from vehicle.
12. Remove A/C condenser mounting screws, then separate radiator from A/C condenser
13. **On models with an auxiliary transaxle cooler**, remove plastic retaining straps and remove cooler.

14. Reverse procedure to install, noting the following:
   a. **Torque** A/C condenser mounting screws to 45 inch lbs.
   b. **Torque** radiator hose clamps to 22 inch lbs.
   c. Refill and bleed cooling system as outlined under "Cooling System, Bleed".
   d. Check automatic transaxle oil level and replenish as necessary.
   e. Recharge air conditioning system as outlined under "Charging System" in the "Air Conditioning" chapter of this manual.

CONCORDE, INTREPID & VISION

1. Disconnect battery ground cable, then drain cooling system.
2. Remove upper radiator crossmember, then the coolant hose clamps and hoses from radiator.
3. Disconnect automatic transaxle cooler lines from radiator.
4. **On models with an auxiliary transaxle cooler**, disconnect rubber auxiliary cooler lines.
5. **On all models**, disconnect radiator fan wiring from the RFI module.
6. Disconnect upper radiator mounting screws.
7. **On models with engine block heater**, disconnect wiring.
8. Remove condenser to radiator mounting screws.
9. Using caution not to bend condenser inlet tube or damage cooling fins, lean condenser forward against bumper.
10. Lift radiator free of vehicle.
11. **On models with an auxiliary transaxle cooler**, remove plastic retaining straps and remove cooler.
12. Reverse procedure to install, noting the following:
   a. **Torque** A/C condenser mounting screws to 45 inch lbs.
   b. **Torque** radiator hose clamps to 22 inch lbs.
   c. Refill and bleed cooling system as outlined under "Cooling System, Bleed",
   d. Check automatic transaxle oil level and replenish as necessary.

TIGHTENING SPECIFICATIONS

Year	Component	Torque/Ft. Lbs.	Year	Component	Torque/Ft. Lbs.
1993–95	A/C Compressor Bracket To Engine Block	30	1993–95 —Cont'd	Connecting Rod Cap Nuts	40②
	A/C Compressor To Bracket	200①		Crankshaft Main Bearing Cap Bolts	30②
	A/C Condenser To Radiator	45①		Crankshaft Main Bearing Tie Bolts	40
	Alternator Bracket Bolts	30		Crankshaft Pulley Bolt	85
	Alternator Mounting Bolts	30		Cylinder Head Bolts	③
	Camshaft Bolt w/Loctite 277	95		Cylinder Head Cover Bolts	105①
	Camshaft Thrust Plate Bolt	250①		Engine Mount Bracket To Block Bolts	65
	Condenser Inlet Tube Bracket Screw	45①		Engine Mount Insulator Stud Nuts	45

Continued

TIGHTENING SPECIFICATIONS–Continued

Year	Component	Torque/ Ft. Lbs.
1993–95	Exhaust Front Down Pipe To Exhaust Support Bracket Screw	35
	Exhaust Manifold Heat Shield Mounting Screws	130①
	Exhaust Manifold Heat Shield	105①
	Exhaust Manifold Mounting	200①
	Exhaust Manifold Nuts To Front Down Pipe	20
	Exhaust Manifold To Cylinder Head	200①
	Exhaust Module Body Bracket Support	18
	Exhaust Pipe Flange Nuts	25
	Exhaust Support Bracket To Transaxle Screw	35
	Exhaust U-Bolt In Front Of Underfloor Converter Nut	24
	Fan Blade Retaining Nut	45①
	Fan Module To Radiator	45①
	Fan Motor To Shroud Screws (Left Side)	45①
	Fan Motor To Shroud Screws (Right Side)	25①
	Insulator Mounting Bolts	200①
	Intake Manifold Bolts	250①
	Intake Manifold Screws	250①
	Intake Plenum Attaching	250①
	Muffler Heat Shield Mounting Nuts	45①
	Oil Filter	15
	Oil Pan Bolts	105①
	Oil Pan Drain Plug	25

Year	Component	Torque/ Ft. Lbs.
1993–95	Oil Pump Cover Bolts	105①
	Oil Pump Pick Up Tube Screw	250①
	PCV Valve	60①
	Radiator To Body Screws	105①
	Rear Crankshaft Seal Retainer Bolts	105①
	Rear Insulator To Crossmember Flange Nut	30
	Receiver/Drier Swivel Nut	45①
	RFI Harness To Shroud Screw	25①
	Spark Plug Tubes	30
	Spark Plug	20
	Starter Mounting Bolt	30
	Thermostat Housing Bolt Nut	250①
	Throttle Body Bolts	105①
	Timing Belt Cover Bolts (6mm)	105①
	Timing Belt Cover Bolts (8mm)	250①
	Timing Belt Cover Bolts (10mm)	40
	Timing Belt Tensioner Pulley Assembly	30
	Timing Belt Tensioner	250①
	Upper Radiator Crossmember Bolts	250①
	Water Inlet Connector Bolt	250①
	Water Outlet Elbow Bolt	250①
	Water Pump Mounting Bolts	105①
	Water Pump To Timing Belt Cover Bolts	105①

① —Inch lbs.
② —Plus an additional ¼ turn.
③ —Refer to text.

Rear Axle & Suspension

INDEX

REAR WHEEL SPINDLE
REPLACE

1. Raise and support vehicle then remove rear tire and wheel assemblies.
2. **On models with rear disc brakes,** proceed as follows:
   a. Remove rear caliper assembly and support to frame using suitable wire.
   b. Remove rear disc brake rotor.
3. **On models with rear drum brakes,** proceed as follows:
   a. Remove brake flex hose bracket from support plate and wheel cylinder.
   b. Remove brake drum.
4. **On all models,** remove rear hub and bearing assembly.
5. **On models with drum brakes,** remove rear brake support plate with parking brake cable attached.
6. **On models with Anti-Lock Brake**

System (ABS), proceed as follows:
   a. Remove speed sensor head from rear disc brake adapter.
   b. Remove speed sensor cable routing tube from trailing arm.
7. **On models with rear disc brakes,** remove disc brake adapter, disc shield, park brake shoes and park brake cable as an assembly.
8. **On all models,** disconnect trailing arm from trailing arm bracket.
9. Disconnect lateral rod from spindle.
10. Loosen and remove rear spindle to strut assembly pinch bolt.
11. Tap a center punch into hole on spindle until punch is jammed into hole, **Fig. 1. Do not punch a hole in the strut with center punch.**
12. Using a hammer, tap on top surface of spindle, driving it down and off the strut assembly, **Fig. 2.**
13. Remove spindle from vehicle.
14. Reverse procedure to install, noting

the following:
   a. Install spindle assembly onto bottom of strut assembly. Push or tap spindle assembly onto strut until notch in spindle is tightly seated against locating tab on strut assembly.
   b. Check rear toe as outlined under "Rear Wheel Alignment" in the "Wheel Alignment" unit repair section.

STRUT
REPLACE

1. Raise and support vehicle then remove rear wheel and tire assembly.
2. **On models with rear disc brakes,** proceed as follows:
   a. Remove rear caliper assembly and support to frame using suitable wire.

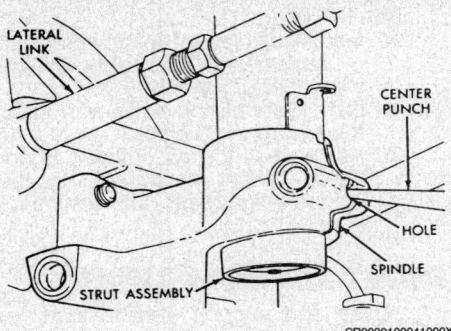

Fig. 1 Center punch installed in spindle

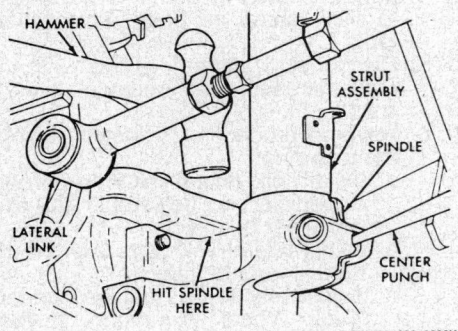

Fig. 2 Spindle removal

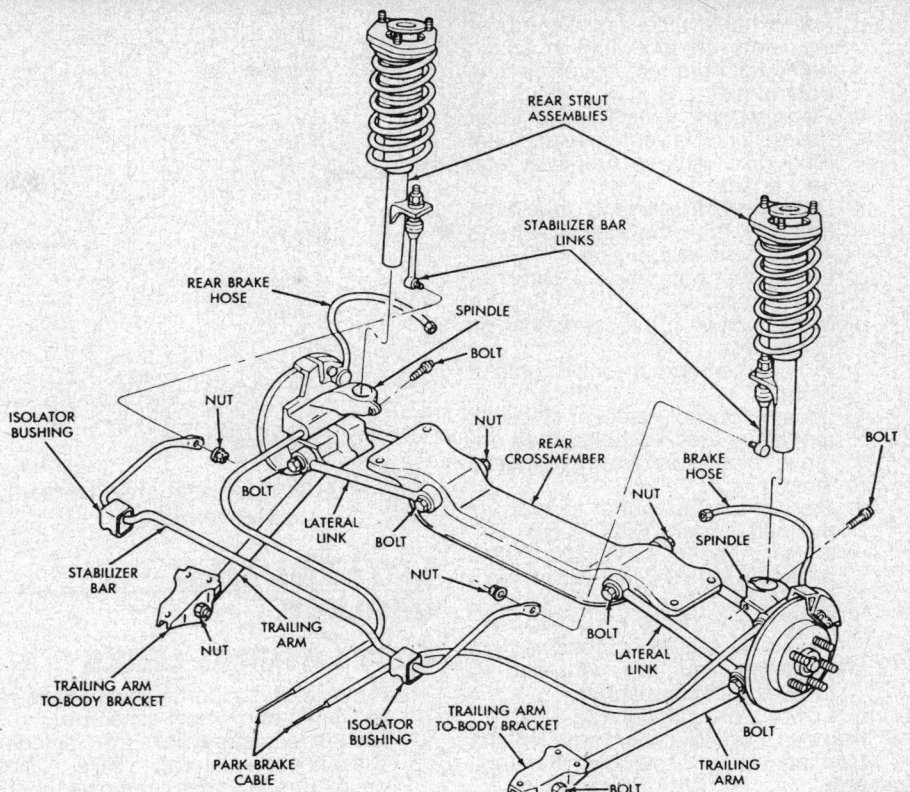

Fig. 3 Exploded view of rear suspension

b. Remove rear disc brake rotor.
3. **On models with rear drum brakes,** proceed as follows:
   a. Remove brake flex hose bracket from support plate and wheel cylinder.
   b. Remove speed sensor cable routing tube on trailing arm bracket to spindle.
4. **On all models,** remove bolt attaching lateral link to rear spindle assembly, **Fig. 3.**
5. Remove rear strut assembly to stabilizer bar attaching link at the stabilizer bar.
6. Loosen and remove rear spindle to strut assembly pinch bolt.
7. Tap a center punch into hole on spindle until punch is jammed into hole, **Fig. 1. Do not punch a hole in the strut with center punch.**
8. Using a hammer, tap on top surface of spindle, driving it down and off the strut assembly, **Fig. 2.**
9. Let rear spindle and assembled components hang from trailing arm while strut is out of vehicle.
10. Lower vehicle.
11. Remove rear upper strut mount from vehicle by accessing the upper strut mount tower and removing the three attaching nuts from trunk of vehicle.
12. Remove strut from vehicle.
13. Reverse procedure to install, noting the following:
    a. Install spindle assembly onto bottom of strut assembly. Push or tap spindle assembly onto strut until

notch in spindle is tightly seated against locating tab on strut assembly.
    b. Check rear toe as outlined under "Rear Wheel Alignment" in the "Wheel Alignment" unit repair section.

STRUT SERVICE

1. Remove strut assembly from vehicle as outlined under "Strut, Replace."
2. Position strut assembly in a vise.
3. Mark strut assembly lower spring isolator, spring and upper strut mount for indexing.
4. Position spring compressor tool No. C-4838 or equivalent on strut assembly spring and compress coil spring until all load is removed from upper strut mount assembly.
5. Install strut rod ratchet socket tool No. L-4558 or equivalent on strut nut.
6. Using an 8mm Allen wrench inserted into end of strut shaft and remove shaft nut from shaft.
7. Remove upper strut mount assembly from strut shaft.
8. Remove coil spring, spring compressor, plate, dust shield, jounce bumper and lower spring isolator.
9. Inspect all components for signs of abnormal wear or failure, replace any component as required.
10. Reverse procedure to install, aligning marks made during disassembly.

REAR CROSSMEMBER
REPLACE

1. Raise and support vehicle then remove rear tire and wheel assemblies.
2. Position a suitable jack under fuel tank just forward of crossmember to help support fuel tank when crossmember is removed.
3. Disconnect lateral link from spindle, **Fig. 3.**
4. Remove bolts attaching crossmember to frame rails.
5. Lower crossmember and lateral links out of vehicle as an assembly.
6. Reverse procedure to install, transferring lateral links to replacement crossmember.

STABILIZER BAR
REPLACE

1. Raise and support vehicle then remove rear tire and wheel assemblies.
2. Position a suitable jack under fuel tank just forward of crossmember to help support fuel tank when crossmember is removed.
3. Remove crossmember to frame rail bolts.
4. Remove fuel tank as follows:
   a. Release fuel system pressure as outlined under "Fuel System Pressure Release" in the "3.3L/V6-201 Engine" or the "3.5L/V6-215 Engine" section.
   b. Drain fuel tank into a suitable container.
   c. Disconnect battery ground cable.

d. Pull exhaust pipe hangers rubber insulators off mounting studs on frame rail from rear of vehicle and front of fuel tank.

e. Place alignment marks on fuel filler hose, filler tube vent hose and vent tube then remove fuel filler and vent hoses.

f. Disconnect fuel supply tube from fuel filter then the fuel return and vent tube near fuel filter.

g. Disconnect both ends of stabilizer bar from links.

h. Mark position of crossmember on frame rails.

i. Pull crossmember down until it stops.

j. Loosen, do not remove, stabilizer mounting bracket bolts, then remove heat shield and fuel tank strap, **Fig. 4.**

k. Disconnect fuel pump module as outlined under "Fuel Pump, Replace" in the "3.3L/V6-201 Engine" or the "3.5L/V6-215 Engine" section.

l. Slightly lower front of fuel tank then slide tank away from crossmember while pushing filler vent and fill tube over crossmember.

m. Lower tank from vehicle.

5. Remove stabilizer bar and isolator bushings as an assembly from vehicle.

6. Reverse procedure to install, aligning marks made during removal.

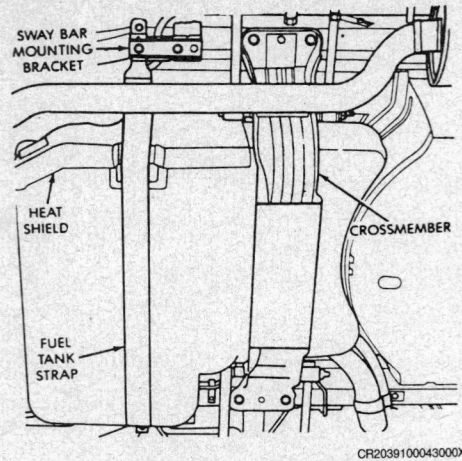

Fig. 4 Fuel tank heat shield & tank strap removal

LATERAL LINK
REPLACE

LEFT LATERAL LINKS

1. Raise and support vehicle then remove tire and wheel assembly.
2. Disconnect lateral links from spindle.
3. Disconnect lateral links from crossmember then remove lateral links.
4. Reverse procedure to install, noting the following:

a. Install solid lateral link toward front of vehicle and adjustable link toward rear of vehicle.

b. Install lateral link bolts with head toward front of vehicle.

c. Adjust rear toe as outlined under "Rear Wheel Alignment" in the "Wheel Alignment" unit repair section.

RIGHT LATERAL LINKS

1. Raise and support vehicle then remove tire and wheel assembly.
2. Disconnect lateral links from spindle.
3. Position a transmission jack under fuel tank.
4. Remove crossmember to frame rail bolts and lower crossmember enough to allow lateral link bolts to clear fuel tank.
5. Disconnect lateral links from crossmember then remove lateral links.
6. Reverse procedure to install, noting the following:

a. Install solid lateral link toward front of vehicle and adjustable link toward rear of vehicle.

b. Install lateral link bolts with head toward front of vehicle.

c. Adjust rear toe as outlined under "Rear Wheel Alignment" in the "Wheel Alignment" unit repair section.

TIGHTENING SPECIFICATIONS

Year	Component	Torque/ Ft. Lbs.
1993–95	Adjustable Link Jam Nut	65
	Bolt Hanger To Spindle	85
	Brake Hose Bolt	35
	Brake Hose Bracket Mounting Bolt	17
	Brake Support Plate To Spindle Bolts	80
	Caliper To Drum/Hat Assembly Bolt	16
	Drum/Hat To Spindle Bolt	85
	Hub & Bearing Assembly To Spindle Nut	125
	Link Assembly Nut	105
	Link To Hanger Bolt	70
	Rear Crossmember To Frame Rail Bolts	70
	Stabilizer Bar Link To Strut Nut	8
	Strut Assembly Shaft Nut	50
	Strut Assembly To Body Nuts	21
	Strut Assembly To Spindle Pinch Bolt	40
	Sway Bar Isolator Bushing Retainer To Frame Bolt	40
	Sway Bar To Rear Strut Attaching Link Nut	70
	Trailing Arm Bracket To Body Bolts	50

NOTE: On Air Bag Equipped Models, Refer To "Air Bag System Precautions" Located In The Front Of This Manual For System Disarming & Arming Procedures.

INDEX

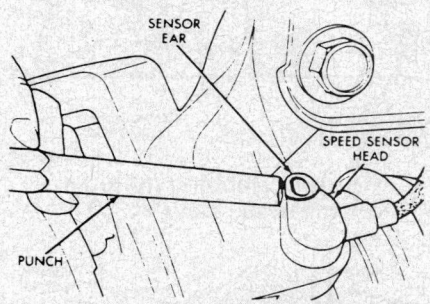

Fig. 1   Speed sensor, tapping loose when stuck

PRECAUTIONS

AIR BAG SYSTEMS

Refer to "Air Bag System Precautions" in the front of this manual for system disarming and arming procedures.

HUB & BEARING
REPLACE

1. Raise and support vehicle then remove tire and wheel assemblies.
2. Remove front caliper assembly and rotor from the steering knuckle as outlined under "Caliper, Replace" in the "Disc Brake" unit repair section.
3. **On models with ABS,** remove the speed sensor as follows:
   a. Remove bolt retaining sensor to steering knuckle.
   b. Slide sensor from steering knuckle. If sensor is stuck into knuckle **do not use pliers on sensor body.** Using a suitable punch, tap on sensor body ear to rock sensor loose from knuckle, **Fig. 1.**
4. **On all models,** remove hub and bearing to stub axle retaining nut.
5. Disconnect hub bolts, then remove hub and bearing assembly from steering knuckle by sliding it straight off end of stub axle. **If metal seal on hub and bearing assembly is seized to steering knuckle and becomes dislodged on hub and bearing assembly during removal, or when removing hub and bearing, the**

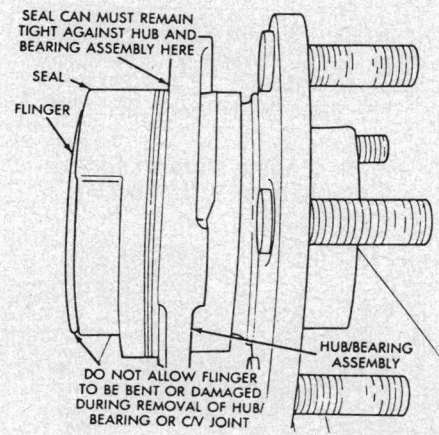

Fig. 2   Hub & bearing assembly

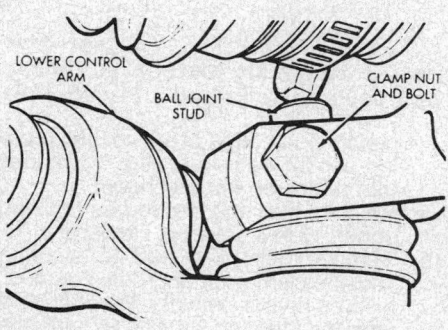

Fig. 4   Ball joint stud to steering knuckle clamp nut and bolt removal

flinger disc on hub becomes damaged, hub and bearing assembly must be replaced, Fig. 2.
6. If hub and bearing will not slide out of knuckle, insert a prybar between hub and steering knuckle and gently pry hub and bearing from knuckle, **Fig. 3.**
7. Reverse procedure to install, noting the following:
   a. Always use a new stub shaft nut when installing.
   b. Tighten stub shaft nut, lower vehicle and with brakes applied **torque** stub shaft nut to 70-90 ft. lbs.

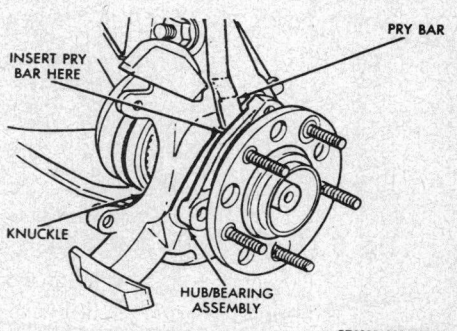

Fig. 3   Hub & bearing removal

BALL JOINT INSPECTION

The lower ball joint is serviced with the lower control arm.
1. Raise and support front of vehicle.
2. Grasp tire at top and bottom then apply an in and out force.
3. While applying force to tire, look for movement between lower ball joint and lower control arm.
4. If any movement is evident, the lower ball joint is worn and the lower control arm requires replacement.

CONTROL ARM
REPLACE
LOWER

1. Raise and support vehicle then remove tire and wheel assembly.
2. Remove ball joint stud to steering knuckle clamp nut and bolt, **Fig. 4.**
3. Insert a prybar between lower control arm and steering knuckle to separate ball joint stud from steering knuckle, **Fig. 5. Pulling steering knuckle out away from vehicle after releasing from ball joint can separate inner tripod joint.**
4. Remove and discard tension strut to cradle nut and washer from end of tension strut, **Fig. 6. Never reuse tension strut nut.**
5. Loosen and remove lower control arm pivot bushing bolt.
6. Separate lower control arm and tension strut from the cradle as an as-

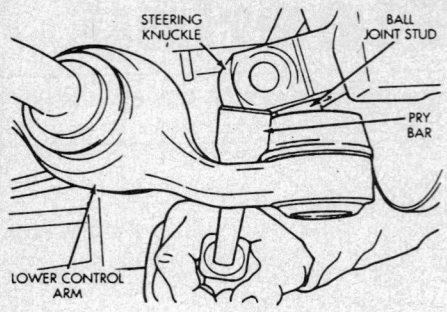

Fig. 5   Ball joint from steering knuckle, separation

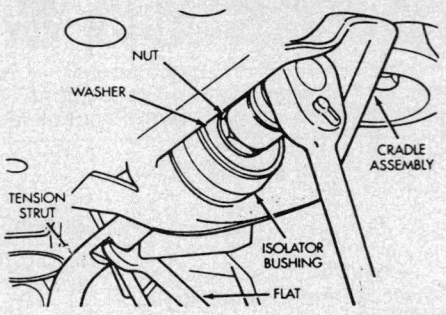

Fig. 6   Tension strut to cradle mounting

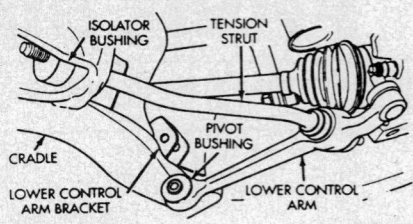

Fig. 7   Lower control arm removal

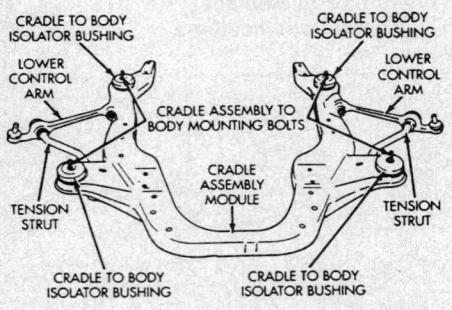

Fig. 8   Front cradle assembly

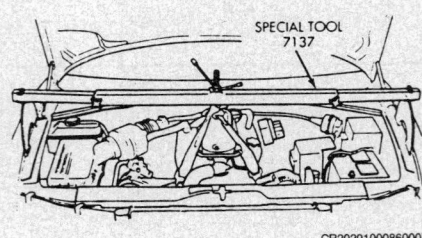

Fig. 9   Engine support fixture installation. 3.3L/V6-201

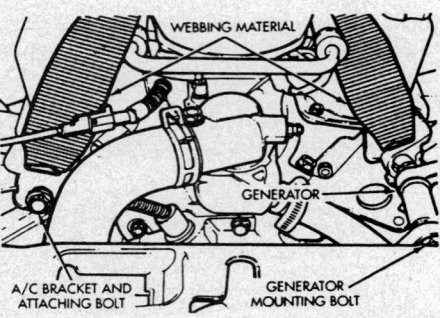

Fig. 10   Webbing material installation. 3.3L/V6-201

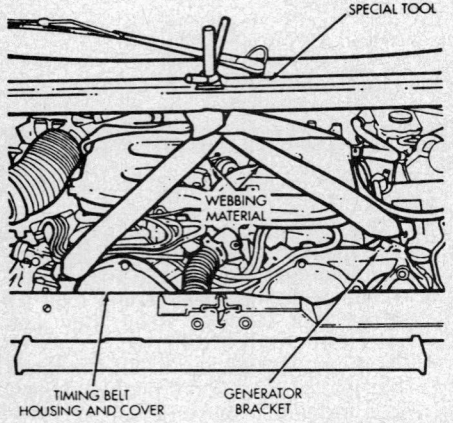

Fig. 11   Engine support fixture installation. 3.5L/V6-215

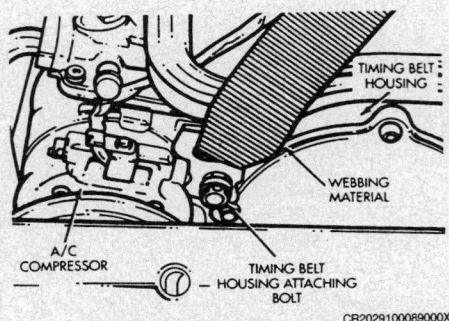

Fig. 12   Webbing material to timing belt cover installation. 3.5L/V6-215

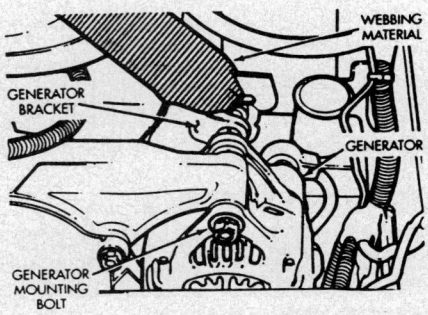

Fig. 13   Webbing material to generator bracket installation. 3.5L/V6-215

sembly by first removing pivot bushing from cradle and then sliding tension strut out of isolator bushing, **Fig. 7.**
7. Reverse procedure to install, tightening lower control arm pivot bushing to cradle bracket attaching bolt with full weight of vehicle on suspension.

STEERING KNUCKLE
REPLACE
1. Raise and support vehicle then remove tire and wheel assembly.
2. Remove brake caliper and rotor as outlined under "Caliper, Replace" in the "Disc Brake" unit repair section.
3. Remove ABS speed sensor screw.
4. Carefully remove speed sensor head from knuckle. If sensor has seized due to corrosion use a hammer and a

punch to tap edge of sensor ear, rocking sensor until free, **Fig. 1. Do not use pliers on sensor head.**
5. Remove hub and bearing as outlined under "Hub & Bearing, Replace."
6. Remove ball joint stud to steering knuckle clamp nut and bolt, **Fig. 4.**
7. Insert a prybar between lower control arm and steering knuckle to separate ball joint stud from steering knuckle, **Fig. 5. Do not pull steering knuckle out away from vehicle after releasing from ball joint as this can separate inner tripod joint.**
8. Remove strut assembly to steering knuckle attaching bolts. Strut bolts have a serrated shaft for a tight fit into steering knuckle. Turn nut on bolts only, do not turn bolts.
9. Remove steering knuckle from the vehicle.
10. Reverse procedure, noting the following:
    a. **Strut bolts have a serrated shaft so do not turn bolts in steering knuckle. Turn nut on bolts do not turn bolts.**

b. Coat speed sensor head with high temperature multi-purpose EP grease before installing.
c. Tighten new stub shaft retaining nut with vehicle brakes applied.

STABILIZER BAR
REPLACE
When removing the front stabilizer bar, it is necessary to support engine assembly and remove the entire front cradle module, **Fig. 8.**

SUPPORTING ENGINE
To allow removal of cradle module assembly from the vehicle, it will be necessary to support the engine and transaxle assembly using engine support fixture No. 7137 or equivalent. Refer to Figs. 9 through 13 for engine supporting locations.

3.3L/V6-201
1. Mount fixture across engine compartment.

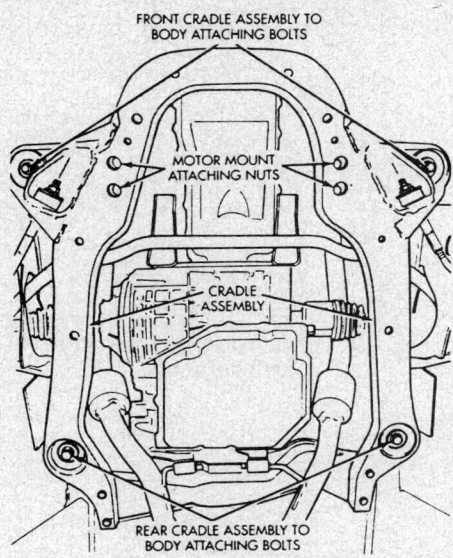

Fig. 14 Engine cradle assembly

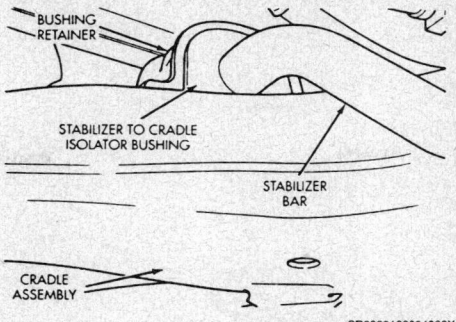

Fig. 15 Stabilizer bar isolator bushing & bracket

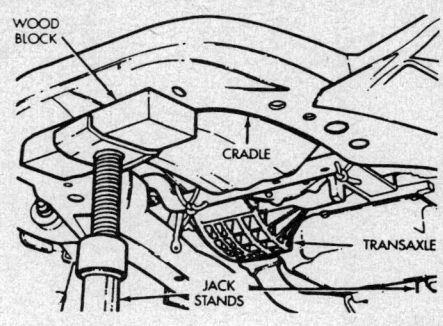

Fig. 16 Cradle & transaxle support

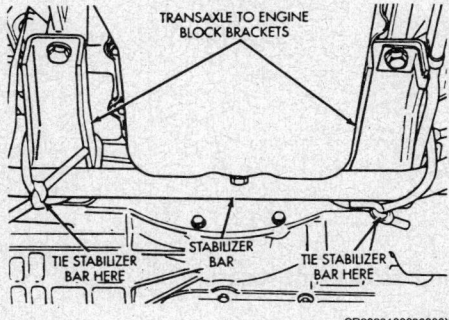

Fig. 17 Stabilizer bar location for cradle installation

2. Mount nylon webbing material, to the following locations.
   a. Remove bolt attaching A/C compressor bracket to front of engine. Install webbing material hook on A/C compressor bolt then install bolt and tighten, **Fig. 10.**
   b. Loosen, do not remove, generator to engine bolt, remove spacer between generator and engine. Install webbing material hook between generator and engine then install and tighten bolt, **Fig. 10.**
   c. Remove electronic ignition coil and mounting bracket bolt from rear of engine. Install webbing material hook on bracket bolt and reinstall and tighten bolt. **Route webbing material between fuel injector rail and valve cover.**
   d. Mount remaining piece of webbing material to threaded hole on back of left cylinder head using a suitable bolt.
3. Securely attach pieces of webbing material to hook on engine holding fixture. Tighten hook on fixture until all slack is removed from all webbing material.

3.5L/V6-215

1. Mount fixture across engine compartment.
2. Mount nylon webbing material, to the following locations.
   a. Remove bolt attaching timing belt housing to front of engine. Install webbing material hook on bolt then install bolt and tighten.
   b. Remove generator to generator mounting bracket nut and bolt. Install webbing material hook on generator mounting bolt then install and tighten nut and bolt.
   c. Mount remaining pieces of webbing material to threaded hole on back of each cylinder head using a suitable bolt.

3. Securely attach pieces of webbing material to hook on engine holding fixture. Tighten hook on fixture until all slack is removed from all webbing material.

CRADLE ASSEMBLY, REPLACE

Remove

1. Support engine and transaxle as outlined under "Supporting Engine."
2. Raise and support vehicle then remove tire and wheel assemblies.
3. Remove ball joint stud to steering knuckle clamp nut and bolt, **Fig. 4.**
4. Insert a prybar between lower control arm and steering knuckle to separate ball joint stud from steering knuckle, **Fig. 5. Pulling steering knuckle out away from vehicle after releasing from ball joint can separate inner tripod joint.**
5. Remove ground strap from cradle assembly.
6. Disconnect motor and transmission mounts from cradle assembly, **Fig. 14.**
7. Disconnect stabilizer bushing retainer from cradle, **Fig. 15.**
8. Position a jack stand under front of cradle and at center of transaxle cradle assembly mount. Raise jack stand at transaxle mount until transaxle just lifts off cradle assembly, **Fig. 16.**
9. Remove cradle assembly as follows:
   a. Loosen, do not remove, two rear cradle assembly to body bolts, **Fig. 14.**
   b. Loosen and remove two front cradle assembly to body attaching

bolts. **Ensure jack stand is properly placed under front of cradle to support cradle weight.**
   c. With a helper supporting rear of cradle and jack stand supporting transaxle, remove two rear cradle bolts and slowly lower front jack stand until weight of engine is supported by engine support fixture and motor bolts are clear of cradle assembly.
   d. Lift front of cradle off jack stand and remove cradle from vehicle.

Install

1. Install stabilizer bar, isolator and retainers into vehicle as an assembly. Ensure bar is installed through openings in splash shield.
2. Install stabilizer link attaching nuts.
3. Tie stabilizer bar up against transaxle to engine block brackets to keep bar clear when installing cradle, **Fig. 17.**
4. Install cradle assembly into vehicle resting front of cradle assembly on jack stand.
5. Install cradle into vehicle as follows:
   a. Raise rear of cradle far enough for rear two cradle bolts to support weight of cradle.
   b. Using jack stand, raise front of cradle up to bottom of motor mounts. **Ensure all four motor mount bolts come through holes in cradle assembly.**
   c. Continue to raise cradle assembly and engine using jack stand until front two cradle bolts can be installed.
   d. Lower transaxle and align mount with holes in cradle. Install mount nuts, do not tighten.
   e. Prior to tightening cradle bolts ensure all bolts are installed straight into mounting plates in frame rails and mounting plates are not cocked in frame rails.
   f. Tighten cradle bolts using a crisscross pattern until cradle seats against body. then tighten cradle bolts to specification.
6. Tighten transaxle mount bolts to specifications.
7. Untie stabilizer bar and align bushing retainers with holes in cradle. Install, do not tighten, retainer bolts.
8. Install motor mount nuts and tighten to specification.
9. Install ground strap.

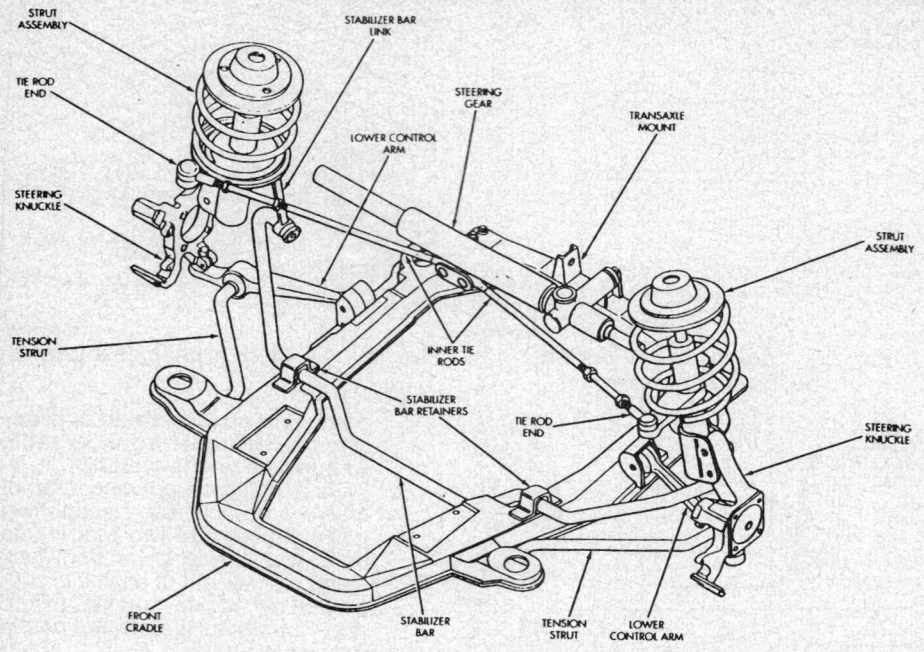

Fig. 18 Front suspension component location

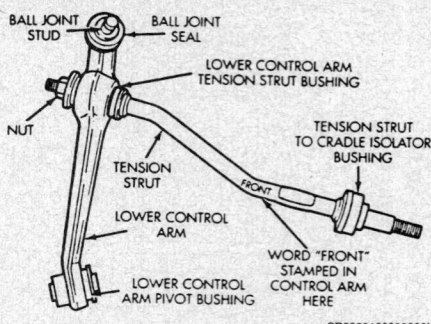

Fig. 19 Tension strut from control arm removal

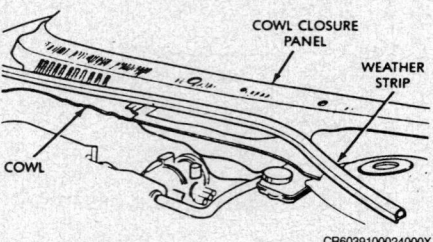

Fig. 20 Cowl closure panel replacement

10. Install lower ball joint studs into steering knuckle then the clamp bolts and nuts. Tighten to specification.
11. Install tire and wheel assembly.
12. Lower vehicle and with full weight on suspension, tighten stabilizer bar bushing bracket bolts to specification.
13. Remove engine support fixture and webbing material.
14. Check wheel alignment.

STABILIZER BAR, REPLACE

1. Support engine assembly as outlined under "Supporting Engine."
2. Remove engine cradle as outlined under "Cradle Assembly, Replace."
3. Remove stabilizer bar to links attaching nuts, Fig. 18.
4. Remove stabilizer bar assembly from vehicle.
5. Reverse procedure to install.

STRUT DAMPER
REPLACE

1. Raise and support vehicle then remove tire and wheel assembly.
2. Remove stabilizer bar link at strut assembly, Fig. 18.
3. Loosen, do not remove, outer tie rod end nut then remove outer tie rod end using suspension component puller tool No. MB-990635 or equivalent.
4. On models with anti-lock brakes, remove speed sensor cable routing bracket from strut assembly.
5. On all models, remove brake caliper and brake rotor as outlined under "Caliper Replace" in the "Disc Brake" unit repair section. Suspend caliper from frame using suitable wire.
6. Disconnect lower strut from steering knuckle. Strut bolts have a serrated

shaft for a tight fit into steering knuckle. Turn nut on bolts only, do not turn bolts.
7. Disconnect upper strut from shock tower and remove strut assembly from vehicle.
8. Reverse procedure to install. Strut bolts have a serrated shaft so do not turn bolts in steering knuckle. Turn nut on bolts do not turn bolts.

STRUT DAMPER SERVICE

1. Remove strut assembly as outlined under "Strut Damper, Replace."
2. Position strut assembly in a vise by clamping strut by steering arm.
3. Mark strut unit, lower spring isolator, spring and upper strut mount for indexing of parts during assembly.
4. Install spring compressor tool No. C-4838 or equivalent on coil spring and compress coil spring to release all load from upper strut mount assembly.
5. Install strut rod socket tool No. L-4558A or equivalent on strut shaft nut then using a 10 mm socket on strut shaft end, remove strut shaft nut.
6. Remove upper strut mount, jounce bumper, seat/bearing, dust shield, coil spring and lower spring mount from strut.
7. Reverse procedure to install, aligning marks made during disassembly.

TENSION STRUT
REPLACE

1. Remove lower control arm as outlined under "Control Arm, Replace."
2. Separate tension strut from lower control arm.

3. Install replacement tension strut into lower control arm. Position tension strut with word Front stamped in strut positioned away from control arm, Fig. 19.
4. Install lower control arm and tension strut into vehicle.
5. Install washer and new nut on tension strut.
6. Install tire and wheel assembly.
7. Tighten lower control arm pivot bushing to cradle bracket attaching bolt with full weight of vehicle on suspension.

POWER STEERING GEAR
REPLACE

REMOVAL

1. Disconnect battery ground cable.
2. Raise and support vehicle.
3. Disconnect gear shift cable from lever on transaxle then remove cable off transaxle.
4. Lower vehicle.
5. On models with 3.5L/V6-215 engine, disconnect throttle cable from throttle body and remove from cable bracket.
6. On all models, remove both wiper arm assemblies from pivots.
7. Remove cowl closure panel and weather-strip as an assembly from cowl, Fig. 20.
8. Disconnect air plenum from throttle bodies, PCV make up air tube and idle air control motor.
9. Remove plenum from right side of vehicle, Fig. 21.
10. Remove wiper module assembly as outlined under "Wiper Motor, Replace in the "Electrical" section.
11. Remove vacuum supply hose for

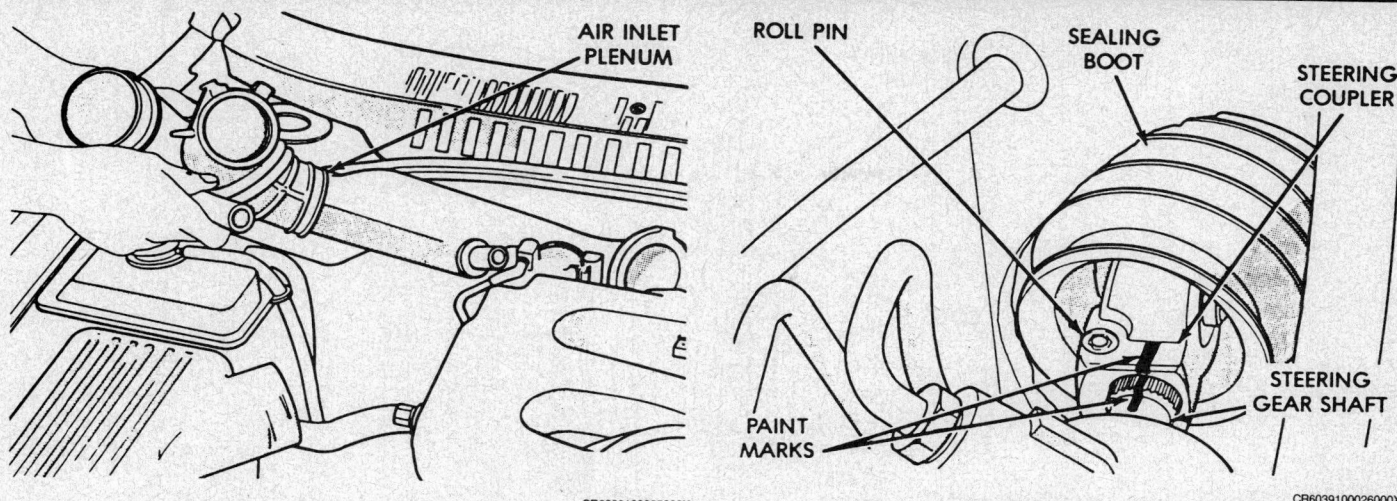

Fig. 21 Air intake plenum removal

Fig. 22 Steering gear coupler pin removal

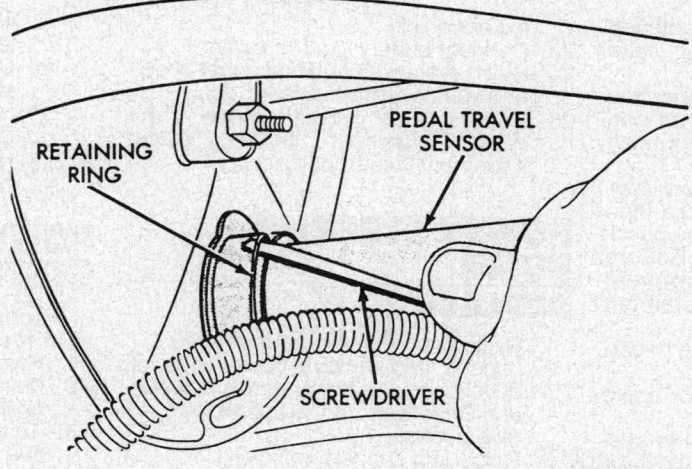

Fig. 23 Pedal sensor retaining ring removal

power brake booster at intake manifold and position hose out of the way.

12. Turn front wheels to full left turn position, then turn wheels back until roll pin is steering coupler is accessible, **Fig. 22.** Lock steering column in place using ignition key.

13. Mark steering coupler and gear shaft for assembly.

14. Remove steering coupler roll pin using correct pin punch.

15. Remove pedal travel sensor from brake booster as follows:
    a. Pump brake pedal 20 times to evacuate stored vacuum.
    b. Remove wiring harness connector from sensor.
    c. Using a small screwdriver, lift retaining ring from notch, then remove retaining ring from grommet, **Fig. 23.**
    d. Remove pedal travel sensor from brake booster by carefully pulling it out of its grommet. **Do Not Twist.**

16. Remove brake master cylinder with lines connected from brake booster.

17. Carefully position master cylinder against left shock tower.

18. Remove power steering pressure and return hoses from power steering gear.

19. Bend back retaining tabs on bolt attaching tie rods to steering gear then loosen and remove bolts attaching tie rods to steering gear. Lay tie rods, bolts and plate as an assembly on bellhousing of transaxle, **Fig. 24.**

20. Remove bolts attaching steering gear assembly to crossmember.

21. Slide steering gear forward in vehicle to disengage steering coupler. **After steering gear is disengaged from steering column, do not rotate steering gear shaft.**

22. Remove steering gear through area in cowl wiper module removal provided.

INSTALLATION

If a replacement steering gear assembly is being installed, the replacement gear will need to be positioned prior to installation.

1. Install steering gear assembly in vehicle through opening in cowl.

2. **When reusing original gear,** align paint marks on steering coupler and gear shaft then insert gear shaft into coupling.

3. **When using a replacement gear,** position gear by carefully grasping shaft of steering gear and rotating until steering gear is in a full left turn position.

4. **On all gears,** align steering gear with mounting holes in crossmember then install gear mounting bracket bolts. **Ensure brake line routing clip is installed under left steering gear mounting bracket.**

5. Install steering gear coupler retaining roll pin flush with top of steering coupler.

6. Attach power steering fluid pressure and return lines to proper ports of steering gear.

7. **On models with 3.5L/V6-215 engine,** correct orientation of power steering pressure hose at power steering pump must be maintained. Ensure power steering hose is installed in orientation clip at power steering pump prior to tightening tube fitting.

8. **On all models,** align center take off on power steering gear with tie rod assemblies then install tie rod bolts and washers, **Fig. 24.**

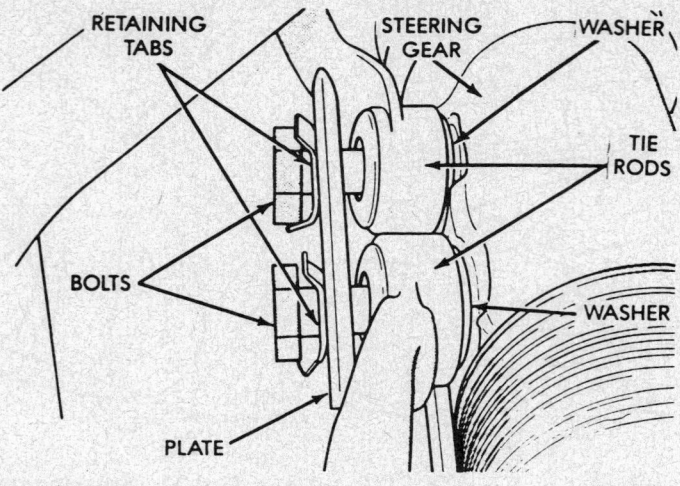

Fig. 24 Tie rod attachment to steering gear

9. After tie rod bolts have been tightened to specification, bend lock tabs against bolt heads.
10. Install pedal travel sensor retainer ring on sensor grommet with tab on ring located in top notch of mounting grommet.
11. Sparingly lubricate pedal travel sensor O-ring with fresh brake fluid then install sensor into grommet by pushing it straight into grommet. **Ensure sensor is installed into grommet until tab on sensor is past retaining ring on grommet.**
12. Install master cylinder on brake booster.
13. Install vacuum supply hose for brake booster on intake manifold.
14. Install windshield wiper module system.
15. Connect wiring harness from windshield wiper module into wiring harness.
16. **On models with 3.5L/V6-215 engines,** connect air intake plenum to throttle bodies, PCV make up air tube and idle air control motor.
17. **On all models,** install cowl closer panel and weather strip.
18. Install washer hoses on wiper arms then both wiper arms on pivots.
19. **On models with 3.5L/V6-215 engines,** install throttle cable in throttle cable bracket and on throttle body.
20. **On all models,** raise and support vehicle.
21. Install gear shift cable on shift lever and mounting bracket.
22. Install tire and wheel assemblies then

lower vehicle.
23. Connect battery ground cable.
24. Bleed system as outlined under "Power Steering System Bleed."
25. Adjust toe as outlined under "Front Wheel Alignment" in the "Wheel Alignment" unit repair section.

POWER STEERING PUMP
REPLACE

1. Disconnect battery ground cable.
2. Loosen and remove power steering drive belt as outlined under "Serpentine Drive Belt" in the appropriate engine section.
3. Raise and support vehicle.
4. Drain power steering fluid reservoir into a suitable container.
5. Loosen and remove power steering pressure hose from pump discharge fitting.
6. Loosen and remove bolts attaching pump to pump bracket through holes in pump drive pulley.
7. Remove pump and pulley as an assembly from the vehicle through bottom of engine compartment.
8. Reverse procedure to install, noting the following:
   a. **On models with 3.5L/V6-215 engine,** correct orientation of power steering pressure hose at power steering pump must be maintained. Ensure power steering hose is installed in orientation clip at power

steering pump prior to tightening tube fitting.
   b. **On all models,** install power steering drive belt as outlined under "Serpentine Drive Belt" in the appropriate engine section.
   c. Bleed system as outlined under "Power Steering System Bleed."

POWER STEERING SYSTEM BLEED

During bleeding procedure, keep fluid in reservoir at correct level.
1. Raise and support front of vehicle.
2. Manually turn oil pump pulley a few times.
3. Turn steering wheel from stop to stop five or six times.
4. Disconnect high tension cable then operate starter motor intermittently while turning the steering wheel from stop to stop five or six times.
5. Connect high tension cable and start engine.
6. Turn steering wheel from stop to stop until no bubbles appear in reservoir.
7. Ensure fluid is not milky and that at proper level.
8. Confirm there is little or no change in fluid level when steering wheel is turned from stop to stop.
9. Ensure fluid level is within .2 inch with the engine running and when it is stopped.
10. If fluid level is not as specified, the system is not completely bled. Repeat procedure.

TIGHTENING SPECIFICATIONS

Year	Component	Torque/ Ft. Lbs.
1993–95	Ball Joint Stud To Steering Knuckle Bolt	40
	Disc Brake Caliper Assembly To Steering Knuckle Bolts	16
	Front Cradle Assembly To Body Bolts	115
	Hub & Bearing Assembly To Steering Knuckle Bolts	80
	Inner Tie Rod To Adjustment Sleeve Jam Nut	55
	Lower Control Arm To Cradle Pivot Bolts	90
	Outer Tie Rod To Adjustment Sleeve Jam Nut	55
	Power Steering Fluid Pressure Hose To Discharge Fitting	25
	Power Steering Pressure Hose Tube Nut	23
	Power Steering Pump To Bracket Bolts	35
	Return Tube Nut	23
	Stabilizer Bar Attaching Link To Strut Nut	8
	Stabilizer Bar Bushing Retainer To Cradle Bolts	40
	Steering Gear To Crossmember Bolts	50
	Strut Assembly Shaft Nut	70
	Strut Assembly To Shock Tower Nuts	28
	Strut Assembly To Steering Knuckle Bolt Nut	125 ①
	Sway Bar To Strut Link Nut	70
	Tension Strut Nuts	130
	Tie Rod End To Strut Steering Arm Nut	27

①—Strut bolts have a serrated shaft so do not turn bolts in steering knuckle. Turn nuts on bolts. Do not turn bolts.

Wheel Alignment

INDEX

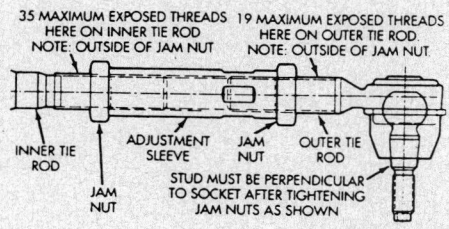

Fig. 1   Front tie rod adjustment dimensions

PRELIMINARY INSPECTION

Before any attempt is made to change or correct front wheel alignment, the fol-lowing inspections and necessary correc-tions must be made.

1. Ensure tire pressure is at recom-mended pressure, all tires should be the same size and in good condition and have the approximately the same wear.
2. Check front wheels and tire assembly for radial runout.
3. Inspect lower ball joint and steering linkage for looseness.
4. Check for broken or damaged front and rear springs.
5. Just prior to each alignment read-ing, then vehicle should be bounced (rear first then front) by grasping bumper at center and bouncing each end of vehicle an equal number of times. Always re-

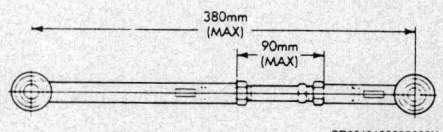

Fig. 2   Rear tie rod adjustment dimensions

lease bumpers at bottom of down cycle.

FRONT WHEEL ALIGNMENT

Front wheel alignment is the proper settings of all interrelated suspension angles affecting the running and steering of the front wheels of the vehicle. On these models, only the wheel toe is adjustable.

TOE ADJUST

1. Prepare vehicle as outlined under "Preliminary Inspection."
2. Center steering wheel and hold with steering wheel clamp.
3. Loosen tie rod adjustment sleeve jam nuts. Rotate adjustment sleeve to align tore to specifications.
4. **When setting toe, the maximum threads exposed on the inner and outer tie rod can not exceed the amounts shown in Fig. 1.**
5. When tightening the adjustment sleeve jam nuts, the following procedure must be followed to ensure adequate torquing and retention of adjustment sleeve jam nut is obtained.
   a. Install correct size open end wrench on flat of adjustment sleeve.
   b. While holding adjustment sleeve, **torque** outer tie rod to adjusting sleeve jam nut to 55 ft. lbs.
   c. While holding adjustment sleeve from turning, **torque** inner tie rod to adjustment sleeve jam nut to 55 ft. lbs.
6. **Torque** tie rod adjustment sleeve locknuts to 55 ft. lbs.
7. Remove steering wheel clamp.

REAR WHEEL ALIGNMENT

Rear wheel adjustments can only be made for the toe in setting on these models.

TOE ADJUST

1. Prepare vehicle as outlined under "Preliminary Inspection."
2. Loosen lateral link adjustment link jam nuts.
3. Rotate adjustment link as required to set rear wheel toe to specification. **Do not exceed maximum length dimension of lateral links, Fig. 2. Both dimensions must be checked.**
4. **Torque** lateral links locknuts to 55 ft. lbs.

AIR CONDITIONING

TABLE OF CONTENTS

System Testing

INDEX

PRECAUTIONS

R-12 SYSTEMS

The freon refrigerant used in these systems is known as R-12. It is odorless and colorless both as a gas and a liquid. Since it boils (vaporizes) at -21.7°F, it will usually be in a vapor state when being handled in a repair shop. But if a portion of the liquid coolant should come in contact with the hands or face, note that its temperature momentarily will be at least -22°F.

Protective goggles should be worn when opening any refrigerant lines. If liquid coolant does touch the eyes, bathe eyes quickly in cold water, then apply a bland disinfectant oil to eyes. See an eye doctor.

When checking a system for leaks with a torch type leak detector, do not breathe vapors coming from flame. Do not discharge refrigerant in an area of a live flame. A poisonous phosgene gas is produced when R-12 is burned. While the small amount of gas produced by a leak detector is not harmful unless inhaled directly at the flame, the quantity of refrigerant released into the air when a system is purged can be extremely dangerous if allowed to come in contact with an open flame. Thus, when purging a system, ensure that the discharge hose is routed to a well ventilated place where no flame is present. Under these conditions the refrigerant will be quickly dissipated into the surrounding air.

Never allow the temperature of refrigerant drums to exceed 125°F. The resultant increase in temperature will cause a corresponding increase in pressure which may cause the safety plug to release or the drum to burst.

If it is necessary to heat a drum of refrigerant when charging a system, the drum should be placed in water that is no hotter than 125°F. Never use a blow torch or other open flame. If possible, a pressure release mechanism should be attached before the drum is heated.

When connecting and disconnecting service gauges on A/C system, ensure that gauge hand valves are fully closed and that compressor service valves, if equipped, are in the back-seated (fully counterclockwise) position. Do not disconnect gauge hoses from service port adapters, if used, while gauges are connected to A/C system. To disconnect hoses, always remove adapter from service port. Do not disconnect hoses from gauge manifold while connected to A/C system, as refrigerant will be rapidly discharged.

After disconnecting gauge lines, check the valve areas to be sure service valves are correctly seated and Schraeder valves, if used, are not leaking.

R-134a SYSTEMS

R-134a refrigerant is a non-toxic, non-flammable, clear, colorless, odorless liquified gas.

R-134a refrigerant is not compatible with R-12 refrigerant. Even small amounts of R-12 in an R-134a system will cause lubricant contamination, compressor failure, or improper A/C performance. Never add R-12 to an R-134a system.

New service ports have been added to the compressor to prevent charging the system with R-12 refrigerant. R-134a systems require a special compressor lubricant. Use PAG compressor oil when servicing system.

Avoid breathing A/C R-134a refrigerant and lubricant vapor or mist. Exposure may irritate eyes, nose and throat. Use only approved service equipment to discharge R-134a systems.

EXERCISE SYSTEM

A/C units must be used periodically. Manufacturers caution that when the air conditioner is not used regularly, particularly during cold months, it should be turned on for a few minutes once every two or three weeks while the engine is running. This keeps the system in good operating condition.

Inspecting the system for effects of infrequent usage before the onset of summer is one of the most important aspects of A/C servicing.

First, clean out the condenser core, in all cases in front of the radiator. All obstructions, such as leaves, bugs and dirt, must be removed, as they will reduce heat transfer and impair the efficiency of the system. Make sure the space between the condenser and the radiator is also free of foreign matter.

Ensure evaporator water drain is open. The evaporator cools and dehumidifies the air before it enters the passenger compartment; there, the refrigerant is changed from a liquid to a vapor. As the core cools the air, moisture condenses on it but is prevented from collecting in the evaporator by the water drain.

Ambient Temperature	21°C (70°F)	26.5°C (80°F)	32°C (90°F)	37.5°C (100°F)	43°C (110°F)
Air Temperature at Center Panel Outlet	2-8°C (35-46°F)	4-10°C (39-50°F)	7-13°C (44-55°F)	10-17°C (50-62°F)	13-21°C (56-70°F)
Compressor Discharge Pressure	965-1448 kPa (140-210 PSI)	1240-1620 kPa (180-235 PSI)	1448-1860 kPa (210-270 PSI)	1655-2137 kPa (240-310 PSI)	1930-2413 kPa (280-350 PSI)
Evaporator Suction Pressure	69-241 kPa (10-35 PSI)	110-262 kPa (16-38 PSI)	138-290 kPa (20-42 PSI)	172-331 kPa (25-48 PSI)	207-379 kPa (30-55 PSI)

CR7029100027000X

Fig. 1   Performance temperature chart

PERFORMANCE TEST

EXCEPT COLT, COLT VISTA, CONCORDE, INTREPID, LASER, LHS, MONACO, NEON, PREMIER, STEALTH, SUMMIT, SUMMIT WAGON, TALON, VISION &1994 NEW YORKER

Air temperature in test room must be 70°F minimum for this test.
1. Connect tachometer and manifold gauge set to vehicle.
2. Set control to MAX A/C, temperature lever on full cool and blower on High.
3. Start engine and adjust to idle to 1000 RPM with A/C clutch engaged. Engine should be at normal operating temperature. Doors and windows should be closed.
4. Insert thermometer in left center A/C outlet and operate the engine for five minutes. The A/C clutch may cycle depending on ambient conditions.
5. With A/C clutch engaged, compare discharge air temperature to A/C performance temperature chart, **Fig. 1.**
6. Operate A/C for two minutes and take discharge air temperature readings. If temperature increased by more than 5°F, check blend air door for correct operation. If temperature does not increase more than 5°F, compare discharge air temperature, suction and discharge pressures with values in the performance chart corresponding with the ambient temperature.
7. If discharge air temperature fails to meet specifications further diagnosis of air conditioning system should be performed.

MONACO & PREMIER

Diagnosis of the refrigerant system is performed by analyzing the clutch cycle time rate. Refer to **Figs. 2 through 4** for testing of the A/C system.

COLT, COLT VISTA, SUMMIT & SUMMIT WAGON

1. Connect a suitable manifold gauge set and tachometer.
2. Position air temperature controls as follows:
   a. Select air conditioner.
   b. Position mode selection lever to "Face."
   c. Position temperature control lever to "Max" cooling.
   d. Position air selection lever to "Recirc."
   e. Position blower lever to high.
3. Start engine, then adjust RPM to 1000 with compressor clutch engaged.
4. Vehicle doors should be closed, windows up and engine should be at normal operating temperature.
5. Insert a thermometer in the left center vent and allow engine to run for 20 minutes.
6. Note the discharge temperature and compare with chart **Figs. 5 through 8.** Reading should be taken with compressor clutch engaged.

LASER, STEALTH & TALON

1. Connect a suitable manifold gauge set and tachometer.
2. Set controls of air conditioner as follows:
   a. Air conditioning switch to A/C On position.
   b. Place mode selection lever in Face position.
   c. Place temperature control lever in Max. cooling position.
   d. Place air selection lever in Recirculation position.
   e. Place blower switch to high position.
3. Start engine, then adjust idle to 1000 RPM with compressor clutch engaged.
4. Vehicle doors should be closed, windows up and engine should be at normal operating temperature.
5. Insert a thermometer in the left center vent and allow engine to run for 20 minutes.
6. Note discharge temperature and compare with chart, **Figs. 9 and 10. Reading should be taken with compressor clutch engaged.**

CONCORDE, INTREPID, LHS, VISION & 1994 NEW YORKER

1. Connect a suitable manifold gauge set and tachometer.
2. Start engine and hold at a steady 1000 rpm.
3. **On models with manual air conditioning,** set controls of air conditioner as follows:
   a. Air conditioning switch to A/C On position.
   b. Place air selection lever in Panel-Recirculation position.
   c. Place temperature control lever in Max. cooling position.
   d. Place blower switch to High position.
4. **On models with automatic temperature control,** set controls of air conditioner as follows:
   a. Air conditioning switch to A/C On position.
   b. Rotate blower knob to High , full clockwise position.
   c. Rotate temperature control knob to full cool, counterclockwise position.
   d. Push panel mode button.
   e. Push Recirculation button. A/C and REC buttons should now be lit.
5. **On all models,** insert a thermometer in the left center vent and allow engine to run for five minutes. The A/C clutch may cycle depending on ambient conditions.
6. Note discharge temperature and compare with chart, **Fig. 11. Reading should be taken with compressor clutch engaged.**

NEON

1. Connect a suitable manifold gauge set and tachometer.
2. Set controls to PANEL, FULL COOL, RECIRC, HIGH BLOWER with A/C on.

NORMAL CLUTCH CYCLE RATE PER MINUTE

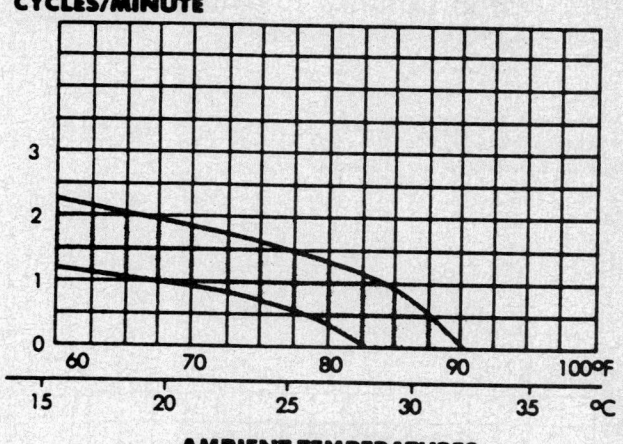

CYCLES/MINUTE

AMBIENT TEMPERATURES

NORMAL CENTER REGISTER DISCHARGE TEMPERATURES

CENTER REGISTER DISCHARGE AIR TEMPERATURE °F/°C

AMBIENT TEMPERATURES

THESE CONDITIONAL REQUIREMENTS FOR THE FIXED ORIFICE TUBE CYCLING CLUTCH SYSTEM TESTS MUST BE SATISFIED TO OBTAIN ACCURATE PRESSURE READINGS.

- STABILIZED IN CAR TEMPERATURE @ 70°F TO 80°F (21°C TO 27°C)
- MAXIMUM A/C (RECIRCULATING AIR)
- MAXIMUM BLOWING SPEED
- 1500 ENGINE RPM FOR 10 MINUTES

NORMAL FIXED ORIFICE TUBE CYCLING CLUTCH REFRIGERANT SYSTEM PRESSURES

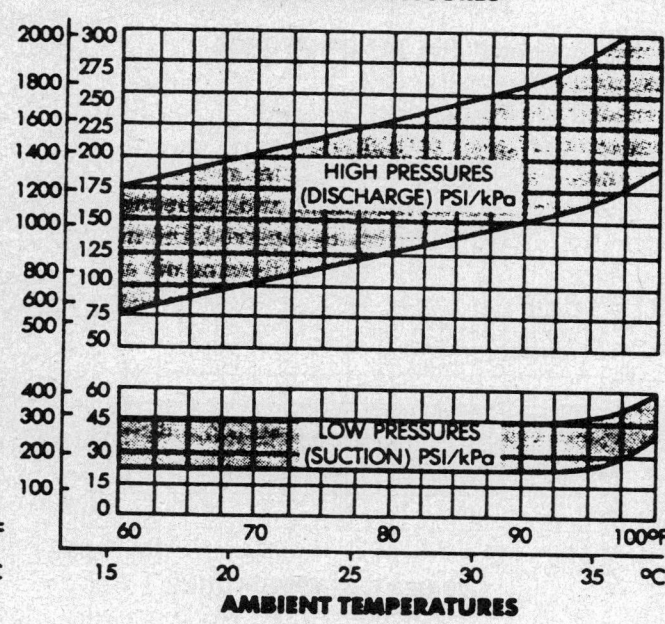

HIGH PRESSURES (DISCHARGE) PSI/kPa

LOW PRESSURES (SUCTION) PSI/kPa

AMBIENT TEMPERATURES

CR7029100028000X

Fig. 2   A/C preliminary diagnosis test. Monaco & Premier

3. Start engine, then adjust idle to 1000 RPM with compressor clutch engaged.
4. Vehicle doors should be closed, windows up and engine should be at normal operating temperature.
5. Insert a thermometer in the left center vent and allow engine to run for five minutes. The A/C clutch may cycle depending on ambient conditions.
6. Note discharge temperature and compare with chart, Fig. 12. **Reading should be taken with compressor clutch engaged.**

LEAK TEST

R-12 SYSTEMS

Testing the refrigerant system for leaks is one of the most important phases of troubleshooting. One or more of the methods outlined will prove useful in detecting leaks or checking connections if service work is performed. Before beginning any leak test, attach a manifold gauge set and note pressure. If little or no pressure is indicated, a partial charge must be installed. Check all connections, compressor head gasket, oil filler plug and compressor shaft seal for leaks.

Electronic Leak Detectors

There are a number of electronic leak detectors available to perform leak tests. Refer to operating instructions for the unit being used and observe these general procedures:

1. Move the detector probe one inch per second in areas of suspected leaks.
2. Position the probe below the test point, as refrigerant gas is heavier than air.
3. Be sure to check service access gauge port valve fittings, particularly when valve caps are missing, as dirt accumulations can destroy the sealing area of valve core when manifold gauge set is attached. Replace missing valve caps after cleaning valve core area. **Valve caps should only be finger tightened. Using pliers to tighten valve caps may distort sealing surface of valve.**
4. Check for leaks in manifold gauge set and hoses, as well as the rest of the system.

Flame-Type (Halide) Leak Detectors

When using flame-type detectors, avoid inhaling fumes produced by burning refrigerant. Do not use this type detector where concentrations of combustible or explosive gases, dusts or vapors may exist.

1. Adjust detector flame as low as possible to obtain maximum sensitivity. Be sure copper element is cherry red and not burned away. The flame will be almost colorless.
2. Slowly move detector along areas of suspected leaks. A slight leak will cause the flame to change to a bright yellow-green color. A significant leak will be indicated by a brilliant blue flame. Position detector under areas being tested as refrigerant gas is heavier than air. **The presence of dust in the pickup hose may cause a change in the color of the flame. If not recognized, a false diagnosis could be made. Store leak detector in a clean place and ensure hose is free of dust before leak testing.**

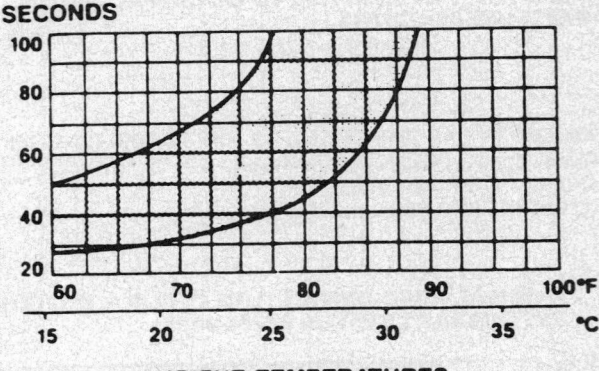

TOTAL CLUTCH
CYCLE TIME — SECONDS

SECONDS

AMBIENT TEMPERATURES

THESE CONDITIONAL REQUIREMENTS FOR THE
FIXED ORIFICE TUBE CYCLING CLUTCH SYSTEM
TESTS MUST BE SATISFIED TO OBTAIN
ACCURATE PRESSURE READINGS.

- Stabilized in Car Temperature @ 70°F to 80°F (21°C to 27°C)
- Maximum A/C (Recirculating Air)
- Maximum Blowing Speed
- 1500 Engine RPM For 10 Minutes

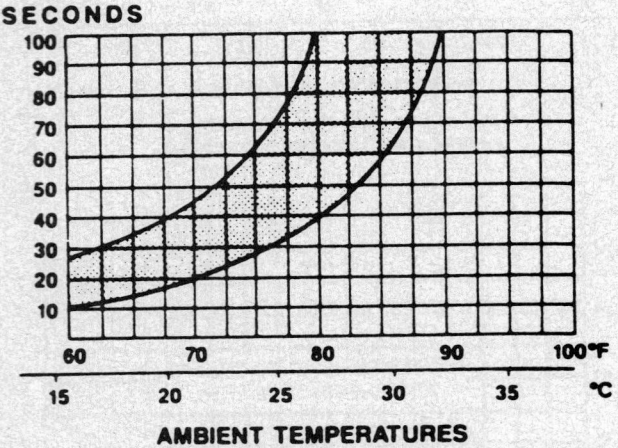

NORMAL CLUTCH
ON TIME — SECONDS

SECONDS

AMBIENT TEMPERATURES

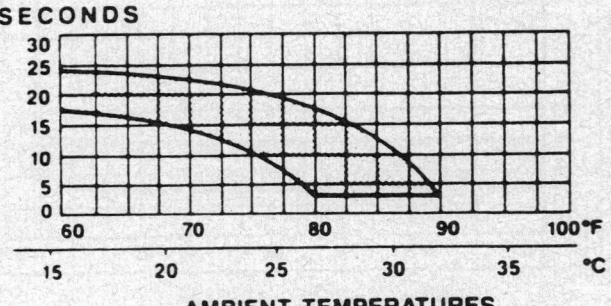

NORMAL CLUTCH
OFF TIME — SECONDS

SECONDS

AMBIENT TEMPERATURES

CR7029100029000X

Fig. 3   A/C clutch cycle time chart. Monaco & Premier

3. Check for leaks in the manifold gauge set and hoses, as well as the rest of the system.
4. Use a small fan to ventilate areas where the leak detector indicates refrigerant constantly. These areas are contaminated with refrigerant and must be ventilated before leak can be pinpointed.

Fluid Leak Detectors

Apply leak detector solution around joints to be tested. A cluster of bubbles will form immediately if there is a leak. A white foam that forms after a short while will indicate an extremely small leak. In some confined areas such as sections of the evaporator and condenser, electronic leak detectors will be more useful.

R-134a SYSTEMS

Do not pressure test R-134a systems with compressed air. Some mixtures of air/R-134a have been shown to be combustible at higher pressures.

A leak detector designed for R-12 will not detect leaks in a R-134a system.
1. Check charge level as described un-

der "Performance Test" in this section.
2. When performing this test with original discharge pressure less than 30 psi, reclaim remaining refrigerant, then connect suitable vacuum pump and evacuate system to lowest vacuum possible.
3. Ensure system holds vacuum reading for at least 15 minutes. If system holds vacuum for 15 minutes a leak is probably not present. If vacuum did not hold for 15 minutes proceed as follows:
   a. Ensure transaxle is in Park.
   b. Run engine for five minutes, then ensure engine is idling at 700 RPM.
   c. Charge system with 10 ounces of R-134a refrigerant.
   d. Set A/C control to 100 percent outside air.
   e. Set panel mode to full cool.
   f. Set blower to high speed.
   g. Place A/C button in ON position.
   h. Open vehicle windows open.
4. Shut engine Off, wait approximately 5 minutes, then use a suitable electrical leak detector designed for R-134a refrigerant systems and leak check system. If a leak is found repair as neces-

sary. If no leak was found fill system as outlined under "Performance Test" in this section.

DISCHARGING SYSTEM

The use of refrigerant recovery and recycling stations allows the recovery and reuse of refrigerant after contaminants and moisture have been removed.

When using a recovery or recycling station, follow the manufacturer's operating instructions, noting the following:
1. **Use extreme caution and observe all safety and service precautions related to use of refrigerants.**
2. Connect refrigerant recycling station hose(s) to vehicle A/C service port(s) and recovery station inlet fitting. Hoses used should have shutoff devices or check valve within 12 inches of hose ends to minimize introduction of air into recycling station and to minimize amount of refrigerant released when hose(s) is disconnected.
3. Turn recycling station On to start recovery process. Allow recycling station to pump refrigerant from A/C sys-

TEMP. °F	PRESS. PSI	TEMP. °F	PRESS. PSI	TEMP. °F	PRESS. PSI	TEMP. °F	PRESS. PSI	TEMP. °F	PRESS. PSI
0	9.1	35	32.5	60	57.7	85	91.7	110	136.0
2	10.1	36	33.4	61	58.9	86	93.2	111	138.0
4	11.2	37	34.3	62	60.0	87	94.8	112	140.1
6	12.3	38	35.1	63	61.3	88	96.4	113	142.1
8	13.4	39	36.0	64	62.5	89	98.0	114	144.2
10	14.6	40	36.9	65	63.7	90	99.6	115	146.3
12	15.8	41	37.9	66	64.9	91	101.3	116	148.4
14	17.1	42	38.8	67	66.2	92	103.0	117	151.2
16	18.3	43	39.7	68	67.5	93	104.6	118	152.7
18	19.7	44	40.7	69	68.8	94	106.3	119	154.9
20	21.0	45	41.7	70	70.1	95	108.1	120	157.1
21	21.7	46	42.0	71	71.4	96	109.8	121	159.3
22	22.4	47	43.6	72	72.8	97	111.5	122	161.5
23	23.1	48	44.6	73	74.2	98	113.3	123	163.8
24	23.8	49	45.6	74	75.5	99	115.1	124	166.1
25	24.6	50	46.6	75	76.9	100	116.9	125	168.4
26	25.3	51	47.6	76	78.3	101	118.8	126	170.7
27	26.1	52	48.7	77	79.2	102	120.6	127	173.1
28	26.8	53	49.8	78	81.1	103	122.4	128	175.4
29	27.6	54	50.9	79	82.5	104	124.3	129	177.8
30	28.4	55	52.0	80	84.0	105	126.2	130	182.2
31	29.2	56	53.1	81	85.5	106	128.1	131	182.6
32	30.0	57	55.4	82	87.0	107	130.0	132	185.1
33	30.9	58	56.6	83	88.5	108	132.1	133	187.6
34	31.7	59	57.1	84	90.1	109	135.1	134	190.1

CR7029100030000X

Fig. 4   Temperature-pressure relationship chart. Monaco & Premier

	21 (70)	26.7 (80)	32.2 (90)	37.8 (100)	43.3 (110)
Garage ambient temperature °C (°F)	21 (70)	26.7 (80)	32.2 (90)	37.8 (100)	43.3 (110)
Discharge air temperature °C (°F)	2.8 – 4.4 (37 – 40)	3.3 – 5.0 (38 – 41)	3.9 – 5.6 (39 – 42)	4.4 – 7.2 (40 – 45)	4.4 – 7.8 (40 – 46)
Compressor discharge pressure kPa (psi)	758 – 1,310 (110 – 190)	896 – 1,517 (130 – 220)	1,103 – 1,793 (160 – 260)	1,310 – 1,999 (190 – 290)	1,517 – 2,206 (220 – 320)
Compressor suction pressure kPa (psi)	131 – 165 (19 – 24)	138 – 179 (20 – 26)	145 – 186 (21 – 27)	152 – 193 (22 – 28)	159 – 200 (23 – 29)

CR7029100031000X

Fig. 5   Performance temperature chart. 1992–93 Colt & Summit

	21 (70)	26.7 (80)	32.2 (90)	37.8 (100)	43.3 (110)
Garage ambient temperature °C (°F)	21 (70)	26.7 (80)	32.2 (90)	37.8 (100)	43.3 (110)
Discharge air temperature °C (°F)	2.5 – 5.0 (36.5 – 41.0)	3.0 – 5.5 (37.4 – 41.9)	3.0 – 6.0 (37.4 – 42.8)	3.5 – 7.5 (38.3 – 45.5)	3.5 – 8.0 (38.3 – 46.4)
Compressor discharge pressure kPa (psi)	650 – 890 (92.5 – 126.6)	740 – 1,040 (105.3 – 147.9)	750 – 1,130 (106.7 – 160.7)	950 – 1,320 (135.1 – 187.7)	1,150 – 1,410 (163.6 – 200.5)
Compressor suction pressure kPa (psi)	140 – 210 (19.9 – 29.9)	140 – 210 (19.9 – 29.9)	140 – 210 (19.9 – 29.9)	150 – 220 (21.3 – 31.3)	150 – 220 (21.3 – 31.3)

CR7029400211000X

Fig. 6   Performance temperature chart. 1994 Colt & Summit

	21 (70)	26.7 (80)	32.2 (90)	37.8 (100)	43.3 (110)
Garage ambient temperature °C (°F)	21 (70)	26.7 (80)	32.2 (90)	37.8 (100)	43.3 (110)
Discharge air temperature °C (°F)	2.5–7.5 (36.5–45.5)	2.5–8.0 (36.5–46.5)	3.0–8.0 (37.4–46.5)	3.5–8.0 (38.3–46.5)	3.5–8.0 (38.3–46.5)
Compressor discharge pressure kPa (psi)	850–900 (121.0–128.1)	1,000–1,070 (142.3–152.3)	1,100–1,150 (156.5–163.6)	1,250–1,320 (177.9–187.8)	1,350–1,400 (192.1–199.2)
Compressor suction pressure kPa (psi)	130–190 (18.5–27.0)	140–190 (19.9–27.0)	140–200 (19.9–28.5)	160–200 (22.8–28.5)	165–210 (23.5–29.9)

CR7029200032000X

Fig. 7   Performance temperature chart. 1992–93 Colt Vista & Summit Wagon

tem until station pressure gauge indicates vacuum.
4. After vehicle A/C system has been evacuated, close station inlet valve, if equipped.
5. Turn station Off. On some stations the pump will automatically be turned Off by a low pressure switch.
6. Allow vehicle A/C system to remain closed for approximately two minutes. Observe vacuum level indicated on gauge. If pressure does not rise, disconnect recycling station hose(s).
7. If system pressure rises, repeat steps 3 through 6 until vacuum level remains stable for two minutes.
8. Service A/C system as necessary, then evacuate and recharge A/C system.

SYSTEM EVACUATION

USING VACUUM PUMP

Vacuum pumps suitable for removing air and moisture from A/C systems are commercially available. A specification for system pump-down used here is 26 to 29½ inches vacuum. This reading can be attained at or near sea level only. For each 1000 feet of altitude this operation is being performed, the reading will be 1 inch vacuum lower. As an example, at 5000 feet elevation, only 21–24½ inches of vacuum can be obtained.

The system must be completely discharged before it can be evacuated. Damage to vacuum pump may result if pressurized refrigerant is allowed to enter.

1. With gauges connected into system, remove cap from vacuum hose connector. Install center hose from gauge manifold to vacuum pump connector. Mid-position high and low side compressor service valves (if used). Open high and low side gauge manifold hand valves.
2. Operate vacuum pump a minimum of 30 minutes for air and moisture removal. Watch compound gauge that system pumps down into a vacuum. System will reach 26–29½ inches vacuum in not over 5 minutes. If system does not pump down, check all connections and leak-test if necessary.
3. Close gauge manifold hand valves and shutoff vacuum pump.
4. Check ability of system to hold vacuum. Watch compound gauge to see that gauge does not rise at a faster rate than 1 inch vacuum every 4 or 5 minutes. If compound gauge rises at too rapid a rate, install partial charge and leak-test. Then evacuate system as outlined above.
5. If system holds vacuum, charge system with refrigerant.

USING CHARGING STATION

On systems using R-134a refrigerant use a charging station designed for R-134a refrigerant systems.

A vacuum pump is built into the charging station and is constructed to withstand repeated and prolonged use without damage. Complete moisture removal from the system is possible only with a vacuum pump constructed for the purpose.

The system must be completely discharged before it can be evacuated. Damage to the vacuum pump may result if pressurized refrigerant is allowed to enter.

1. Connect hose to vacuum pump if system was discharged through charging station.
2. Open high and low side gauge valves of charging station.
3. Connect station into 110 volt current.
4. Engage "Off-On" switch to vacuum pump according to directions of specific station being used.
5. System should pump down into a 28-29½ inches vacuum in not more than 5 minutes. If system fails to meet this specification, repair as necessary.
6. Operate pump a minimum of 30 minutes to remove all air and moisture.
7. Close high and low side gauge valves. Open switch to turn off pump.
8. Check ability of system to hold vacuum by watching compound gauge to see that it does not rise at a rate higher than 1 inch of vacuum every 4 or 5 minutes. If rise rate is not within specifications, repair system as necessary. If rise rate is within specifications, charge system with refrigerant.

CHARGING SYSTEM

EXCEPT CONCORDE, INTREPID, LHS, MONACO, NEON, PREMIER, VISION & 1994 NEW YORKER

Never use cans to charge into high pressure side of system (compressor discharge port) or into system at high temperature, as high system pressure transferred into charging can may cause it to explode.

1. Attach center hose from manifold gauge set to refrigerant dispensing manifold. Turn refrigerant manifold valves completely counterclockwise to open fully, and remove protective caps from refrigerant manifold.
2. Screw refrigerant cans into manifold, ensuring gasket is in place and in good condition. **Torque** can and manifold nuts to 6-8 ft. lbs.
3. Turn refrigerant manifold valves clockwise to puncture cans, and close manifold valves.
4. Loosen charging hose at gauge set manifold and turn a refrigerant valve counterclockwise to release refrigerant and purge air from charging hose. When refrigerant gas escapes from loose connection, retighten hose.
5. Fully open all refrigerant manifold valves being used and place refrigerant cans into pan of hot water at 125°F to aid transfer of refrigerant gas. **Do not heat refrigerant cans over 125°F as they may explode.**

Garage ambient temperature	°C (°F)	20 (68)	25 (77)	35 (95)	45 (113)
Discharge air temperature	°C (°F)	10.8 (51.4)	16.8 (62.2)	23.5 (74.3)	24.3 (95.7)
Compressor discharge pressure	kPa (psi)	1,030 (149)	1,128 (164)	1,393 (202)	1,736 (252)
Compressor suction pressure	kPa (psi)	178 (26)	184 (27)	196 (28)	210 (30)

CR7029400212000X

Fig. 8   Performance temperature chart. 1994 Colt Vista & Summit Wagon

Garage ambient temperature °C (°F)	21 (70)	26.7 (80)	32.2 (90)	37.8 (100)	43.3 (110)
Discharge air temperature °C (°F)	2.0–8.0 (35.6–46.4)	2.0–8.0 (35.6–46.4)	2.0–8.0 (35.6–46.4)	4.0–11.0 (39.2–51.8)	6.0–14.0 (42.8–57.2)
Compressor discharge pressure kPa (psi)	900–1,300 (128–186)	1,000–1,400 (142–199)	1,100–1,500 (156–212)	1,300–1,700 (186–242)	1,500–1,900 (212–270)
Compressor suction pressure kPa (psi)	50–150 (7.1–21.3)	80–180 (11.4–25.6)	100–200 (14.2–28.4)	130–230 (18.5–32.7)	150–250 (21.3–35.6)

CR7029100033000X

Fig. 9   Performance temperature chart. Laser & Talon

Garage ambient temperature °C (°F)	21 (70)	26.7 (80)	32.2 (90)	37.8 (100)	43.3 (110)
Discharge air temperature °C (°F)	0.0 – 3.0 (32.0 – 37.4)	1.0 – 4.0 (33.8 – 39.2)	1.0 – 4.0 (33.8 – 39.2)	1.0 – 4.0 (33.8 – 39.2)	2.0 – 5.0 (35.6 – 41.0)
Compressor discharge pressure kPa (psi)	690 – 740 (98.1 – 105.3)	780 – 830 (110.9 – 118.1)	870 – 920 (123.7 – 130.9)	1,080 – 1,130 (153.6 – 160.7)	1,210 – 1,260 (172.1 – 179.2)
Compressor suction pressure kPa (psi)	130 – 190 (18.5 – 27.5)	130 – 190 (18.5 – 27.5)	130 – 190 (18.5 – 27.5)	130 – 190 (18.5 – 27.5)	130 – 190 (18.5 – 27.5)

CR7029100034000X

Fig. 10   Performance temperature chart. Stealth

Ambient Temperature	21°C (70°F)	26.5°C (80°F)	37.5°C (90°F)	37.5°C (100°F)	43°C (110°F)
Maximum Allowable Air Temperature at Center Left Panel Outlet	7°C (45°F)	9°C (49°F)	12°C (54°F)	13°C (56°F)	15°C (59°F)
Compressor Discharge Pressure	772-1448 kPa (112-210 PSI)	903-1475 kPa (131-214 PSI)	1241-1482 kPa (180-215 PSI)	1400-1986 kPa (203-288 PSI)	1600-2282 kPa (232-331 PSI)
Compressor Suction Pressure	69-255 kPa (10-37 PSI)	117-262 kPa (17-38 PSI)	145-324 kPa (21-47 PSI)	193-352 kPa (28-51 PSI)	207-365 kPa (30-53 PSI)

CR7029300227000X

Fig. 11   Performance temperature chart. Concorde, Intrepid, LHS, Vision & 1994 New Yorker

Place water pan and refrigerant cans on scale and note weight.
6. **On Colt, Colt Vista and Summit,** connect a jumper wire across cycling clutch switch terminals. This will engage clutch to compressor.
7. **On all models,** start engine and turn A/C On, then index blower switch to low position.
8. Low pressure cut-out switch will prevent clutch from engaging until refrigerant is added to system. If clutch does engage, replace switch before continuing.
9. Charge through suction side of system by slowly opening suction manifold valve. Adjust valve so charging pressure does not exceed 50 psi.
10. Adjust engine speed to fast idle of 1400-1550 RPM.
11. After specified refrigerant charge has entered system, close gauge set manifold valves and refrigerant manifold valves, then reconnect wiring.

Ambient Temperature	21°C (70°F)	26.5°C (80°F)	32°C (90°F)	37.5°C (100°F)	43°C (110°F)
Air Temperature at Left Center Panel Outlet	1-8°C (34-46°F)	3-9°C (37-49°F)	4-10°C (39-50°F)	6-11°C (43-52°F)	7-18°C (45-65°F)
Compressor Discharge Pressure	1034-1724 kPa (150-250 PSI)	1517-2275 kPa (220-330 PSI)	1999-2620 kPa (290-380 PSI)	2068-2965 kPa (300-430 PSI)	2275-3241 kPa (330-470 PSI)
Evaporator Suction Pressure	103-207 kPa (15-30 PSI)	117-221 kPa (17-32 PSI)	138-241 kPa (20-35 PSI)	172-269 kPa (25-39 PSI)	207-345 kPa (30-50 PSI)

CR7029500213000X

Fig. 12 Performance temperature chart. Neon

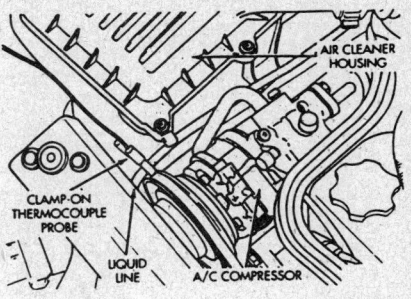

Fig. 1 Thermocouple clamp attachment to liquid line. Concorde, Intrepid, LHS, Vision & 1994 New Yorker

MONACO & PREMIER

Never use cans to charge into high pressure side of system (compressor discharge port) or into system at high temperature, as high system pressure transferred into charging can may cause it to explode.

1. Attach center hose from manifold gauge set to refrigerant dispensing manifold. Turn refrigerant manifold valves completely counterclockwise to open fully, and remove protective caps from refrigerant manifold.
2. Screw refrigerant cans into manifold, ensuring gasket is in place and in good condition.
3. Turn refrigerant manifold valves clockwise to puncture cans, and close manifold valves.
4. Loosen charging hose at gauge set manifold and turn a refrigerant valve counterclockwise to release refrigerant and purge air from charging hose. When refrigerant gas escapes from loose connection, retighten hose.
5. Fully open all refrigerant manifold valves being used and place refrigerant cans into pan of hot water at 125°F to aid transfer of refrigerant gas. Do not heat refrigerant cans over 125°F as they may explode.
6. Place water pan and refrigerant cans on scale and note weight.
7. Connect a jumper wire across cycling clutch switch terminals.
8. Open Manifold gauge low side valve and allow refrigerant to be drawn into system.
9. When no more refrigerant is being drawn into system, start engine and set controls to Max A/C, then select the high blower position.
10. Allow remaining refrigerant to be drawn into system, then close the manifold low side valve and refrigerant supply valve.
11. Remove jumper wire from clutch cycling pressure switch, then reconnect connector.
12. Operate system until pressures stabilize and normal operation is verified.

CONCORDE, INTREPID, LHS, VISION & 1994 NEW YORKER

1. Connect suitable pressure gauge to discharge side of compressor, then attach clamp on thermocouple part No. P.S.E. 66-324-0014 or 80PK-1A or equivalent to liquid line as shown in Fig. 1. It must be attached as close to condenser as possible to read liquid line temperature.
2. With transaxle in Park and engine idling at 700 RPM, set air conditioning controls as follows:
   a. A/C control set to outside air.
   b. Set panel mode to full cool.
   c. Blower to high speed.
   d. A/C button in On position.
   e. On models equipped with ATC, turn Off Recirc button.
3. On all models, operate system and allow to stabilize, then set system pressure to 260 psi by placing a piece of cardboard over part of condenser to obtain specified gauge reading.
4. Observe discharge pressure and liquid line temperature, then refer to charge determination graph, Fig. 2, to determine system charge.
5. If charge is not within specification, add or reclaim two ounces of refrigerant at a time, then read gauge pressure and liquid line temperature. Continue procedure until proper charge area on chart determination graph is obtained, Fig. 2.

NEON

1. Connect suitable pressure gauge to discharge side of compressor, then attach thermocouple part No. P.S.E. 66-324-0014, or equivalent, to liquid line, as close to filter-dryer as possible.
2. With transaxle in Park and engine idling, set air conditioning controls as follows:
   a. A/C control set to outside air.
   b. Set panel mode to full cool.
   c. Blower to high speed.
   d. A/C button in On position, with windows and doors closed.
3. Operate system for a few minutes to allow system to stabilize.
4. Observe filter-dryer pressure and liquid line temperature.
5. Using the Charge Determination graph, Fig. 15, determine where system is currently operating. If the system is not in the proper range, reclaim all the refrigerant and recharge per A/C label, using suitable refrigerant recovery and charging equipment.

TECHNICAL SERVICE BULLETINS

AIR CONDITIONING SYSTEM CHANGES TO DEFROST MODE WHEN ACCELERATING

1992 Acclaim, Daytona, Dynasty, Imperial, LeBaron, New Yorker, Shadow, Spirit & Sundance

On these models, the A/C system may change to defrost mode during a low vacuum condition such as trailer towing, hill climbing and acceleration.

To test components for this condition, proceed as follows:
1. Remove vacuum check valve from vacuum supply line near the brake booster and connect vacuum supply to hose going through dash panel.
2. Pull between 10-20 inches of vacuum with test vacuum source.
3. With test vacuum source shutoff, vacuum reading should remain constant for one minute.
4. If vacuum reading dropped within one minute, there is a leak in the system. Repair leak as needed.
5. If vacuum reading remains constant, install new vacuum check valve (Part No. 4677204) in vacuum line at same location as original check valve. Discard original check valve.

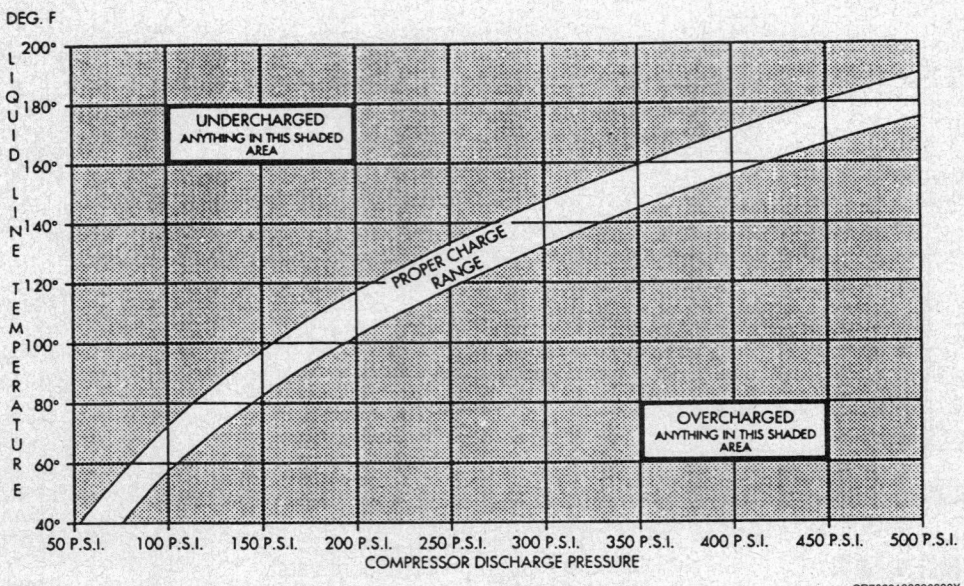

Fig. 2 Charge determination chart. Concorde, Intrepid, LHS, Vision & 1994 New Yorker

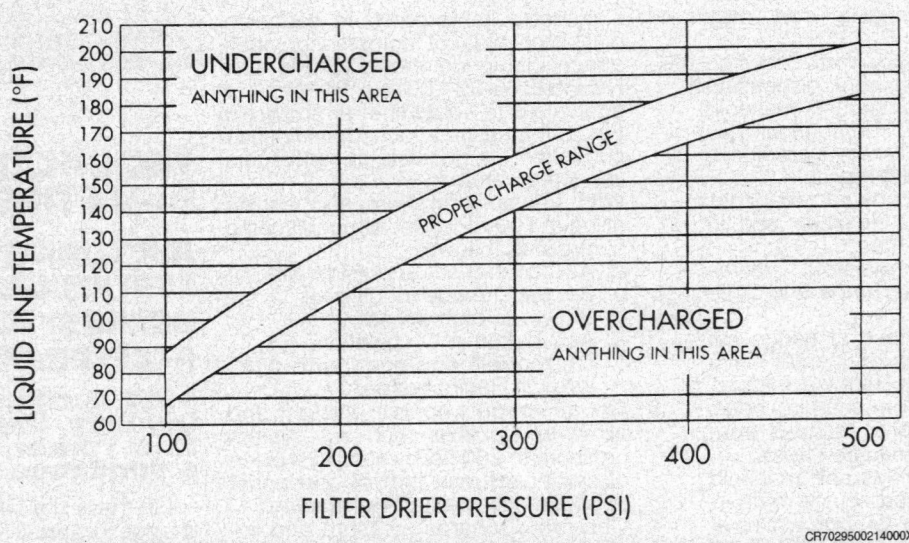

Fig. 3 Charge determination graph. Neon

INDEX

OIL CHARGE

Model	Year	Compressor	Component	Oil ① ⑤
Acclaim, Daytona, Dynasty, Fitfth Avenue, Imperial, LeBaron, New Yorker (1992-93), Shadow, Spirit & Sundance	1992-94	②	Evaporator	2
			Condenser	1
			Filter-Drier	1
Colt & Summit	1992-93	FX105V	Compressor	2.8
			Condenser	.5
			Evaporator	1.7
			Line	.35
	1994	FX105V	Evaporator	2.0
			Condenser	.5
			Low Pressure Hose	.3
			Receiver	.3
Colt Vista & Summit Wagon	1992-93	10PA15	Condenser	1
			Evaporator	1.3
			Lines	.3
			Receiver/Drier	.3
	1994	10A17C	Condenser	1.3
			Evaporator	1.3
			Suction Hose	.3
			Receiver	.3
Concorde, Intrepid, LHS, New Yorker (1994) & Vision ③	1993-94	10PA17-R-134a ④	Evaporator	2
			Condenser	1
			Receiver-Dryer	.2
			Lines	1.5
Laser & Talon	1992-94	10PA17	Condenser	.7
			Evaporator	1
			Receiver/Dryer	.3
			Lines	.1
Monaco & Premier	1992	SD-709	Compressor	1
			Accumulator/Drier	1
			Condenser	1
			Evaporator	3
Neon	1995	10PA17-R-134a ④	Condenser	1
			Evaporator	2
			Receiver/Dryer	1
			Lines	1.5
Stealth	1992-94	FX-105VS	Evaporator	2
			Condenser	.5
			Receiver-Drier	.3
			Lines	.3

①—Ounces.
②—A new service fixed displacement type compressor contains 7.25 ounces of refrigerant oil. A new service variable displacement type compressor contains 8.7 ounces of refrigerant oil. Before installing replacement compressor, drain oil from replacement and failed

OIL CHARGE-Continued

compressors (drain oil from suction port). Add same amount of oil to replacement compressor as drained from failed compressor.

③—When components of an A/C system utilizing R-134a refrigerant are replaced, use only ND8 PSG compressor oil No. 82300101, or equivalent.

④—The 10PA17–R12 compressor looks the same and has the same bolt pattern as the 10PA17–R134a through normal system servicing.

compressor. Ensure Proper compressor is used when replacement is necessary.

⑤—Refer Air Conditioning Specifications for refrigerant oil type.

MONACO & PREMIER

Mounting angle will affect reading on dipstick. This procedure is designed for compressor removed from vehicle and on flat surface.

1. Remove oil filler plug and, looking through plug hole, turn front clutch plate to position piston connecting rod in center of oil filler plug hole, **Fig. 1.**
2. Insert dipstick tool No. J-29642-12, or equivalent, through oil filler plug hole to the right of piston connecting rod until dipstick stop contacts compressor housing, **Fig. 2.**
3. Remove dipstick and note number of increments covered. When properly filled, the compressor should contain between six and eight increments of oil.
4. Adjust oil level as necessary and install oil fill plug.

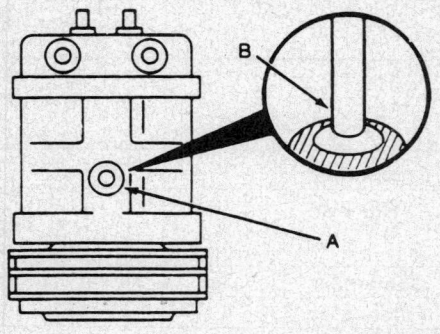

Fig. 1 Compressor connecting rod position. Monaco & Premier

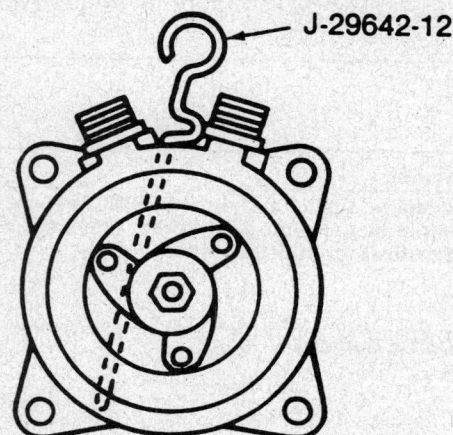

Fig. 2 Compressor oil level inspection with dipstick. Monaco, & Premier

OIL LEVEL CHECK

The oil level of these compressors should be checked whenever refrigerant has been lost due to leakage or

Air Conditioning Specifications

INDEX

A/C SPECIFICATIONS

Year	Model	Refrigerant Capacity, Lbs.	Type	Viscosity	Total System Capacity, Ounces	Compressor Oil Check	Compressor Clutch Air Gap, Inch
1992	Colt	2.25	R-12	500	5	①	.010-.020
	Colt Vista	1.86	R-12	500	4.9	①	.014-.026
	Except Colt, Colt Vista, Laser, Monaco, Premier, Stealth, Summit, Summit Wagon & Talon	2	R-12	500	④	①	⑥
	Laser & Talon	2.06	R-12	500	2.7	①	.014-.026
	Monaco & Premier	2.25	R-12	500	8.1	⑦	.016-.031
	Stealth	2.12	R-12	500	5.4	①	.010-.020
	Summit	2.25	R-12	500	5.0	①	.010-.020
	Summit Wagon	2.70	R-12	500	4.9	①	.014-.026

A/C SPECIFICATIONS-Continued

Year	Model	Refrigerant Capacity, Lbs.	Type	Viscosity	Total System Capacity, Ounces	Compressor Oil Check	Compressor Clutch Air Gap, Inch
1993	Colt	2.25	R-12	500	5.0	①	.010-.020
	Colt Vista	1.86	R-12	500	2.0-3.4	①	.014-.026
	Concorde	1.75	R-134a	②	4.75	①	.014-.026
	Except Colt, Colt Vista, Concorde, Intrepid, Laser, Stealth, Summit, Summit Wagon, Talon & Vision	⑤	R-12	500	④	①	.020-.035
	Intrepid	1.75	R-134a	②	4.75	①	.014-.026
	Laser	2.00	R-12	500	2.0-3.4	①	.014-.026
	Stealth	1.80	R-12	500	4.7-6.0	①	.010-.020
	Summit	1.62-1.87	R-12	500	4.4	①	.020-.030
	Summit Wagon	1.87	R-12	500	2.0-3.4	①	.014-.026
	Talon	2.00	R-12	500	2.7	①	.014-.026
	Vision	1.75	R-134a	②	4.75	①	.014-.026
1994	Acclaim	1.63	R-134a	②	7.25	①	.020-.035
	Colt	1.62-1.87	R-134a	②	4.4	①	.016-.026
	Colt Vista	1.68	R-134a	②	③	①	.014-.026
	Concorde	1.75	R-134a	②	4.75	①	.014-.026
	Intrepid	1.75	R-134a	②	4.75	①	.014-.026
	Laser	2.06	R-12	500	2.7	①	.014-.026
	LeBaron	1.63	R-134a	②	7.25	①	.020-.035
	LHS	1.75	R-134a	②	4.75	①	.014-.026
	New Yorker	1.75	R-134a	②	4.75	①	.014-.026
	Shadow	1.63	R-134a	②	7.25	①	.020-.035
	Spirit	1.63	R-134a	②	7.25	①	.020-.035
	Stealth	1.63	R-134a	②	5.33	①	.010-.020
	Summit	1.62-1.87	R-134a	②	4.4	①	.016-.026
	Summit Wagon	1.68	R-134a	②	③	①	.014-.026
	Sundance	1.63	R-134a	②	7.25	①	.020-.035
	Talon	2.06	R-12	500	2.7	①	.014-.026
	Vision	1.75	R-134a	②	4.75	①	.014-.026
1995	Neon	1.81	R-134a	⑧	4.75	①	.014-.026

PAG: Polyalkaline Glycol lubricant.

①—Oil Level cannot be checked. Refer to total capacity in ounces.

②—Use a polyalkalene glycol (PAG) lubricant ND8 or part No. 82300102, or equivalent, approved for use w/R-134a refrigerant systems.

③—Vehicles w/1.8L/4-107 engines, 4.1 oz.; vehicles w/2.4L/4-143 engines, 2.7 oz.

④—Fixed displacement compressor, 7.25 ounces; variable displacement compressor, 8.7 ounces.

⑤—Less rear A/C, 2 lbs.; with rear A/C, 2.68 lbs.

⑥— Fixed placement compressors, 10PA17, .016-.031; TR105, .013-.025. Variable displacement compressor 6C17, .020-.035

⑦—Can be measured with dipstick tool No. J-296420-12, or equivalent, when removed from vehicle.

⑧—PAG-Polyalkaline Glycol lubricant.

CHARGING VALVE LOCATION

EXCEPT COLT, COLT VISTA, CONCORDE, INTREPID, LHS, LASER, MONACO, NEON, PREMIER, STEALTH, SUMMIT, TALON, VISION & 1994 NEW YORKER

All low side valves are located on the compressor or on the suction line near the compressor. All high side valves are located on the discharge line between the compressor and condenser.

COLT, COLT VISTA, LASER, SUMMIT, SUMMIT WAGON & TALON

Low side valve is located on top of the compressor. High pressure valve is located on compressor discharge line.

MONACO & PREMIER

The low side valve is located on top of the accumulator/drier. The high pressure valve is located on the compressor discharge line.

STEALTH

The low side charging valves are located on the compressor and high side valves are located on the high pressure line.

CONCORDE, INTREPID, LHS, NEW YORKER & VISION

The high and low side pressure connectors are located on the A/C compressor.

NEON

The low side valve is located on the suction line. The high side valve is located on the filter-dryer.

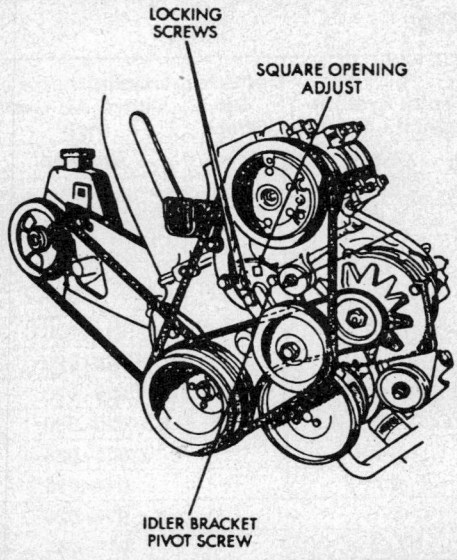

Fig. 1 Belt tension inspection. 2.2L/4–135 & 2.5L/4–153 engines

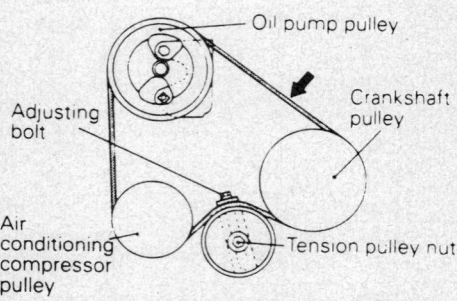

Fig. 4 Belt tension inspection. Colt & Summit w/1.8L/4-112 engine

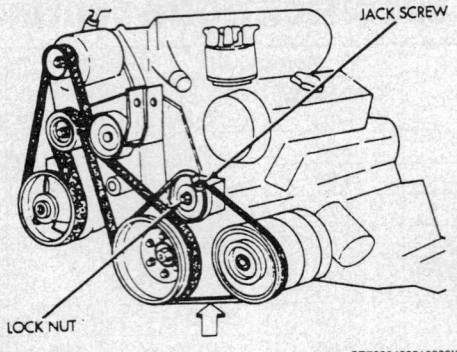

Fig. 2 Belt tension inspection. 3.0L/V6-181 engines

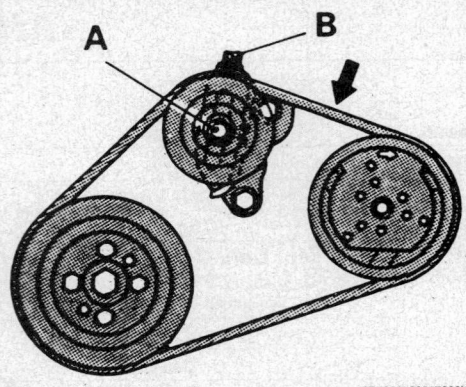

Fig. 3 Belt tension inspection. Colt & Summit w/1.5L/4-90 engine

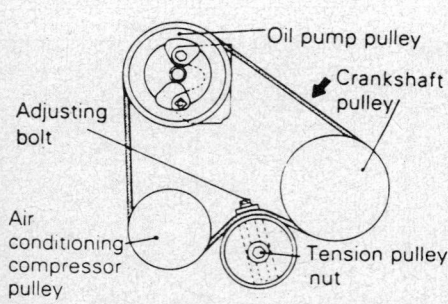

Fig. 5 Belt tension inspection. Colt Vista & Summit Wagon w/1.8L/4-110 engine

BELT TENSION

EXCEPT COLT, COLT VISTA, CONCORDE, INTREPID, LASER, LHS, MONACO, NEON, PREMIER, STEALTH, SUMMIT, SUMMIT WAGON, TALON, VISION & 1994 NEW YORKER

2.2L/4–135 & 2.5L/4–153 Engines

1. Install a suitable belt tension gauge in the middle of belt span.
2. Correct belt tension is 135 lbs. for new belts and 80 lbs. for used belts.
3. Adjust belt tension as follows:
   a. Loosen idler bracket pivot screw and locking screws, **Fig. 1**.
   b. Adjust tension by applying torque to square hole on idler bracket.
   c. Adjust new belt to 135 lbs. and used belt to 80 lbs.
   d. **Torque** locking screws, then pivot screw to 40 ft. lbs.
4. Check belt tension after driving vehicle.

3.0L/V6–181 Engine

1. Install a suitable belt tension gauge in the middle of belt span, **Fig. 2.**
2. Correct belt tension is 125 lbs for new belts and 80 lbs. for used belts.
3. Adjust belt tension as follows:
   a. Loosen idler pulley lock nut.
   b. Adjust tension by tightening jack screw.
   c. Adjust new belt to 125 lbs. and used belt to 80 lbs.
   d. **Torque** locking screws, then pivot screw to 40 ft. lbs.

COLT & SUMMIT

1.5L/4–90 Engine

1. Measure drive belt deflection by pulling or pushing at mid-point of the belt between pulleys as shown in **Fig. 3**, with a force of 22 lbs.
2. Deflection should be .24-.28 inch. If deflection is not within specifications, tighten belt as follows:
   a. Loosen tension pulley securing nut (A).
   b. Adjust tension to specification with adjusting bolt (B), .20-24 inch for a new belt and .24-.28 inch for used belt.
   c. Tighten securing nut.
3. Check belt tension after driving vehicle.

1.8L/4–112 Engine

1. Using a suitable belt tension gauge, measure drive belt deflection by pulling or pushing at mid-point of the belt between pulleys as shown in **Fig. 4**, **with a force of 22 lbs.**
2. Deflection should be .27-.30. If deflection is not within specifications, tighten belt as follows:
   a. Loosen tension pulley nut.
   b. Adjust tension to specification with adjusting bolt, .22-24 inch for a new belt and .27-.30 inch for used belt.
   c. Tighten securing nut.
3. Check belt tension after driving vehicle.

COLT VISTA & SUMMIT WAGON

1.8L/4–110 Engine

1. Using a suitable belt tension gauge, measure drive belt deflection by pulling or pushing at mid-point of the belt between pulleys as shown in **Fig. 5**, with a force of 22 lbs.
2. Deflection should be .27-.30 inch. If deflection is not within specifications, tighten belt as follows:
   a. Loosen tension pulley nut.
   b. Adjust tension to specification with adjusting bolt, .22-27 inch for a new belt and .27-.30 inch for used belt.
   c. Tighten securing nut.
3. Check belt tension after driving vehicle.

2.4L/4–146 Engine

1. Using a suitable belt tension gauge, measure drive belt deflection by pulling or pushing at mid-point of the belt between pulleys as shown in **Fig. 6**, with a force of 22 lbs.
2. Deflection should be .21-.24 inch. If deflection is not within specifications, tighten belt as follows:
   a. Loosen tension pulley nut (A).
   b. Adjust tension to specification with adjusting bolt (B), .17-.19 inch for a new belt and .21-.24 inch for used belt.

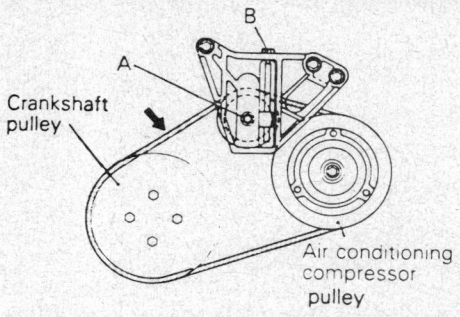

Fig. 6 Belt tension inspection. Colt Vista & Summit Wagon w/2.4L/4-146 engine

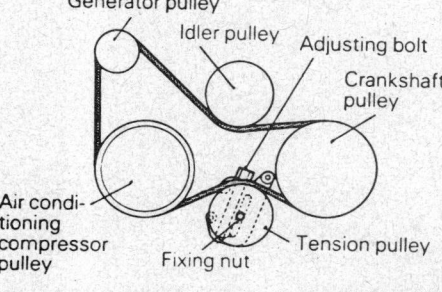

Fig. 9 Belt tension inspection. Stealth w/3.0L/V6-181 DOHC engine

c. Tighten securing nut.
3. Check belt tension after driving vehicle.

LASER & TALON

1.8L/4–107 SOHC Engine

1. Using a suitable belt tension gauge, measure drive belt deflection by pulling or pushing at mid-point of the belt between pulleys as shown in Fig. 7, with a force of 22 lbs.
2. Deflection should be .22-.24 inch. If deflection is not within specifications, tighten belt as follows:
   a. Loosen tension pulley securing nut.
   b. Adjust tension to specification with adjusting bolt, .16-.20 inch for a new belt and .22-.24 inch for used belt.
   c. **Torque** securing nut to 24-36 ft. lbs.
3. Check belt tension after driving vehicle.

2.0L/4–122 DOHC Engine

1. Using a suitable belt tension gauge, measure drive belt deflection by pulling or pushing at mid-point of the belt between pulleys as shown in Fig. 7, with a force of 22 lbs.
2. Deflection should be .22-.24 inch. If deflection is not within specifications, tighten belt as follows:
   a. Loosen tension pulley securing nut.

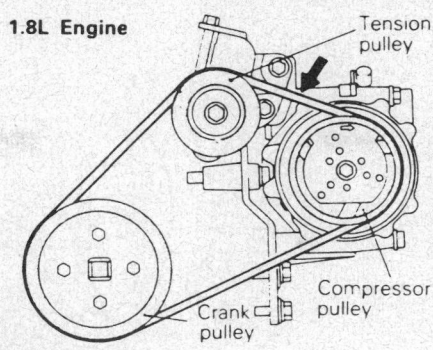

1.8L Engine

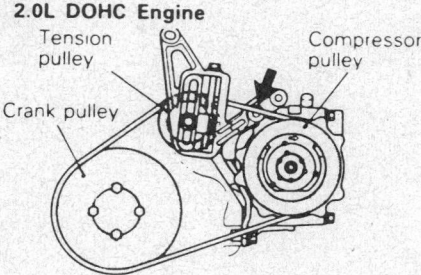

2.0L DOHC Engine

Fig. 7 Belt tension inspection. Laser & Talon

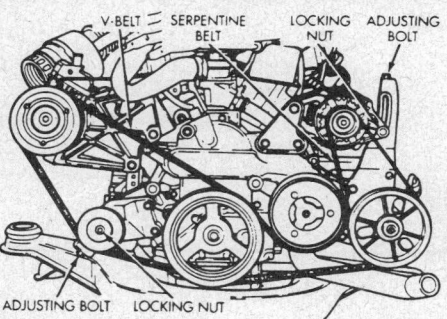

Fig. 10 Belt tension inspection. Concorde, Intrepid, LHS, Vision & 1994 New Yorker w/3.3L/V6-201 engine

   b. Adjust tension to specification with adjusting bolt, .18-.20 inch for a new belt and .22-.24 inch for used belt.
   c. **Torque** securing nut to 24-36 ft. lbs.
3. Check belt tension after driving vehicle.

MONACO & PREMIER

1. Install a suitable belt tension gauge in the middle of belt span.
2. Tighten adjusting bolt until correct tension is obtained; 180-220 lbs. for new belt, 140-160 lbs. for used belt.
3. **Torque** pivot bolt to 30 ft. lbs.
4. Check belt tension after driving vehicle.

STEALTH

3.0L/V6–181 SOHC Engine

1. Using a suitable belt tension gauge, measure drive belt deflection by pull-

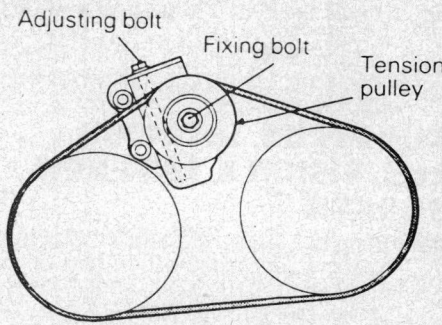

Fig. 8 Belt tension inspection. Stealth w/3.0L/V6-181 SOHC engine

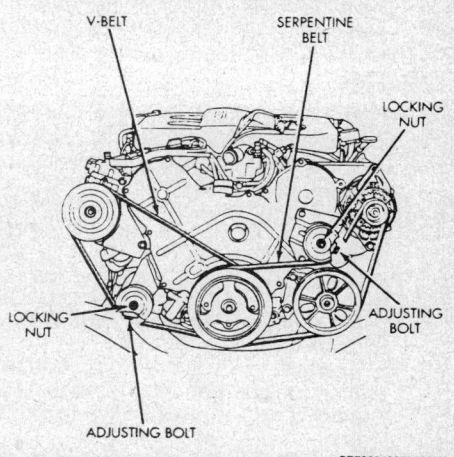

Fig. 11 Belt tension inspection. Concorde, Intrepid, LHS, Vision & 1994 New Yorker w/3.5L/V6-215 engine

ing or pushing at mid-point of the belt between pulleys as shown in Fig. 8, with a force of 22 lbs.
2. Deflection should be .28-.34 inch. If deflection is not within specifications, tighten belt as follows:
   a. Loosen tension pulley securing nut.
   b. Adjust tension to specification with adjusting bolt, .26-.28 inch for a new belt and .28-.34 inch for used belt.
   c. **Torque** securing nut to 30 ft. lbs.
3. Check belt tension after driving vehicle.

3.0L/V6–181 DOHC Engine

1. Using a suitable belt tension gauge, measure drive belt deflection by pulling or pushing at mid-point of the belt between pulleys as shown in Fig. 9, with a force of 22 lbs.
2. Deflection should be .16-.20 inch. If deflection is not within specifications, tighten belt as follows:
   a. Loosen tension pulley securing nut.
   b. Adjust tension to specification with adjusting bolt, .14-.16 inch for a

new belt and .16–.20 inch for used belt.

c. **Torque** securing nut to 30 ft. lbs.

3. Check belt tension after driving vehicle.

CONCORDE, INTREPID, LHS, VISION & 1994 NEW YORKER

1. Using belt tensioning tool No. C-4162, or equivalent, ensure belt tension is 120 lbs. If not within specification, tighten belt as follows:
   a. Loosen tensioner pulley locking nut, **Figs. 10 and 11.**
   b. Adjust tension to specification with adjusting bolt, 150 lbs. for a new belt and 120 lbs. for used belt.
   c. **Torque** locking nut to 40 ft. lbs.
2. Check belt tension after driving vehicle.

NEON

1. Using belt tensioning tool No. C-4162, or equivalent, ensure belt tension is 100 lbs. If not within specification, tighten belt as follows:
   a. Loosen power steering pump locking bolts A and B **Fig. 12**, then loosen pivot bolt C.
   b. Adjust tension by applying torque to square hole on idler bracket, 135 lbs. for a new belt and 100 lbs. for used belt.
   c. **Torque** in order, locking bolt A, then locking bolt B to 20 ft. lbs. Finally, **Torque** pivot bolt C to 40 ft. lbs.
2. Check belt tension after driving vehicle.

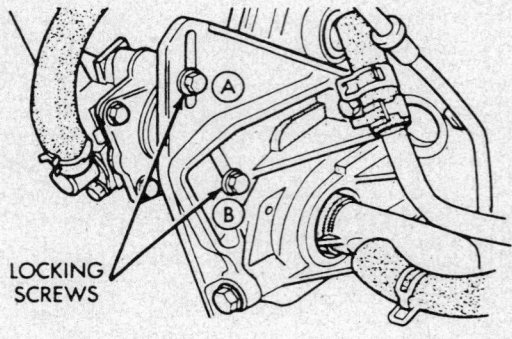

LOCKING SCREWS

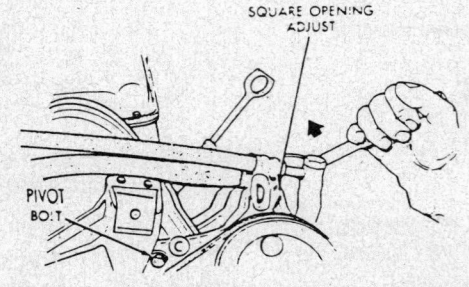

SQUARE OPENING ADJUST

PIVOT BOLT

CR7029500226000X

Fig. 12   Belt tension inspection. Neon

COOLING FANS

NOTE: Electrical Symbol And Wire Color Code Identification Located In Front Of This Manual Can Be Used As An Aid When Using Wiring Circuits Found In This Section.

INDEX

Switch conditions		Fan rotating condition	
Air conditioner switch	Thermo sensor	Cooling (radiator) fan	Condenser fan
LO (0V)	OFF	OFF	OFF
LO (0V)	ON	HIGH	OFF
HI (12V)	OFF	LOW	LOW
HI (12V)	ON	HIGH	HIGH

CR1089100044000X

Fig. 1 Fan operating mode conditions. Laser & Talon

Switch conditions				Fan revolving operation condition	
Air conditioner switch	Thermo sensor		Engine coolant temperature switch (for air conditioner cut-off) OFF at 115 ± 3°C (239 ± 5°F) or over. ON at 108°C (226°F) or less	Radiator fan motor	Condenser fan motor
	For radiator fan ON at 85 ± 4°C (185 ± 7°F) or more OFF at 77°C (171°F) or less	For condenser fan ON at 95 ± 4°C (203 ± 7°F) or more OFF at 87°C (189°F) or less			Condenser fan motor operates in HIGH only when it receives input from condenser fan motor relay (HI) and (LO)
OFF	OFF	OFF	–	OFF	OFF
	ON	OFF		LOW	OFF
		ON		HIGH	LOW
ON	OFF	OFF	ON	LOW	LOW
	ON	OFF		LOW	LOW
		ON		HIGH	HIGH
		OFF	OFF	HIGH	LOW

CR1089100045000X

Fig. 2 Fan operating mode conditions. Stealth

DESCRIPTION

EXCEPT COLT, COLT VISTA, CONCORDE, INTREPID, LHS, SUMMIT, SUMMIT WAGON, VISION & 1994 NEW YORKER

Except Dynasty, Fifth Avenue, Imperial & New Yorker Salon w/V6 Engine & Laser, Monaco, Premier, Stealth & Talon

Fan control is accomplished two ways.

The fan will always run when the A/C compressor clutch is engaged or when the engine coolant temperature set limit has been exceeded and the engine controller turns on the fan through the fan relay.

Switching through the engine controller provides fan control for the following conditions:

1. The fan will not run during engine cranking until the engine starts, regardless of engine temperature.
2. The fan will always run when the A/C compressor clutch is engaged.
3. The fan will run at vehicle speeds above 40 mph only if coolant temperature reaches 230°F and will turn off when temperatures drops to 220°F.

At speeds below 40 mph the fan switches on at 210°F and off at 200°F.
4. To help prevent steaming, the fan will run below 60°F ambient temperatures with coolant temperature between 100–195° and engine at idle and then only for three minutes.

New Yorker Salon, Dynasty, Fifth Avenue & Imperial w/V6 Engine

Fan control is accomplished based on coolant temperature and A/C head pressure.

The fan will go on when coolant temperature reaches 210°F and turn off at 200°F regardless of vehicle speed.

On models with A/C, when A/C head pressure reaches 220 psi cooling fan system will engaged, and when head pressure drops to 160 psi cooling fan will turn off.

Laser & Talon

Refer to **Fig. 1** for fan operation modes.

Monaco & Premier

The fan(s) will turn On when the contacts of the cooling fan relay close and supply battery voltage to the motor from a fuse link. There is only one fan relay that controls both fans. The cooling fan will turn On if engine coolant temperature is above 220°F or if the A/C compressor clutch is engaged, which will cause both fans operate.

Stealth

Refer to **Fig. 2** for fan operating mode conditions.

COLT & SUMMIT

The electric cooling fan is controlled by a thermo sensor and a relay, the thermo sensor, is located in the radiator lower tank. When coolant temperature reaches approximately 185°F, the thermo sensor contacts close, providing a ground circuit to the fan relay, which provides voltage to the fan motor.

When coolant temperature drops to approximately 178°F, the thermo sensor contacts open, opening the fan relay and shutting off the fan.

COLT VISTA & SUMMIT WAGON

The electric cooling fan is controlled by a thermo sensor, radiator fan relay and an engine coolant temperature switch, **Fig. 3.** When coolant temperature reaches approximately 185°F, the thermo sensor contacts close, providing a ground circuit to the fan relay, which provides voltage to the fan motor.

When coolant temperature drops to approximately 171°F, the thermo sensor contacts open, opening the fan relay and shutting off the cooling fan.

CONCORDE, INTREPID, LHS, VISION & 1994 NEW YORKER

Radiator fan control is accomplished in two ways. A pressure transducer on the compressor discharge line sends a signal to the powertrain control module (PCM) which will activate the fans. The fans are also turned on by a coolant temperature sensor, which sends a message to the engine controller. The engine controller then sends a signal to the fan relay which in turn switches the coolant fans on.

Switching through the engine controller provides fan control for the following conditions:

1. Fans will not run during cranking until engine starts, no matter what coolant temperature is.
2. Fan runs according to chart shown in **Fig. 4.**

SYSTEM DIAGNOSIS & TESTING

EXCEPT COLT, COLT VISTA, CONCORDE, INTREPID, LHS, SUMMIT, SUMMIT WAGON, VISION & 1994 NEW YORKER

Refer to **Figs. 5 through 25** for cooling fan wiring diagrams.

COLT & SUMMIT

Refer to **Figs. 26 through 29** for cooling fan relay wiring diagrams.

COLT VISTA & SUMMIT WAGON

Refer to **Fig. 30** for cooling fan wiring diagram when testing system.

CONCORDE, INTREPID, LHS, VISION & 1994 NEW YORKER

Refer to **Fig. 31** for wiring diagrams.

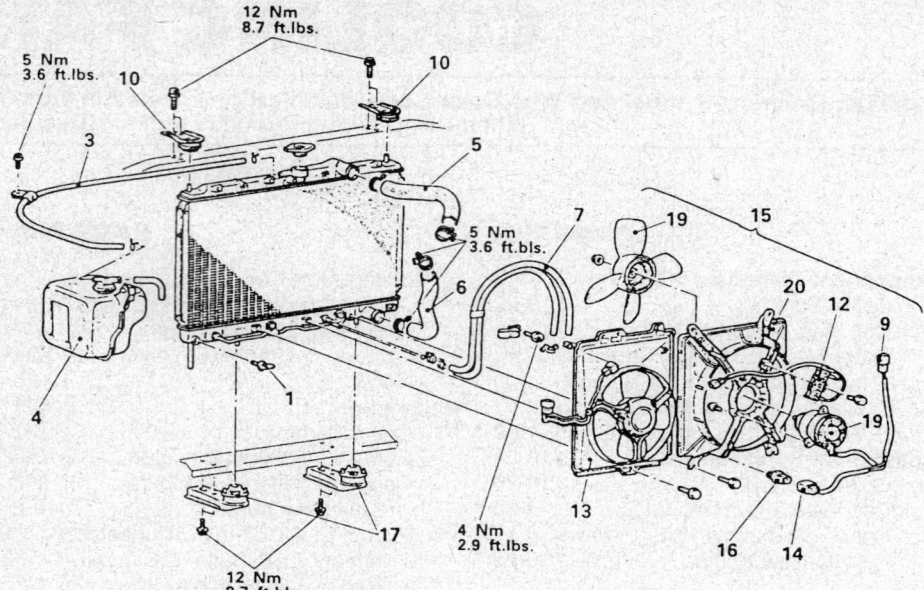

Radiator fan motor removal steps

1. Drain plug
2. Radiator cap
5. Radiator upper hose
8. Condenser fan connector <Vehicles with air conditioner>
9. Radiator fan connector
13. Condenser fan motor assembly <Vehicles with air conditioner>
14. Engine coolant temperature switch connector
15. Radiator fan motor assembly
18. Fan
19. Radiator fan motor
20. Shroud

CR1089200084000X

Fig. 3   Electric cooling fan. Colt Vista & Summit Wagon

RADIATOR COOLING FAN OPERATION	ENGINE COOLANT TEMPERATURE	
	3.3L ENGINE	3.5L ENGINE
Low Speed Fan ON	99°C (211°F)	104°C (219°F)
Low Speed Fan OFF	93°C (199°F)	99°C (210°F)
High Speed Fan ON	110°C (230°F)	110°C (230°F)
High Speed Fan OFF	104°C (219°F)	105°C (221°F)

Air Conditioning NOT activated

CR1089100094000X

Fig. 4   Fan operating mode conditions. Concorde, Intrepid, LHS, Vision & 1994 New Yorker

COMPONENT DIAGNOSIS & TESTING

EXCEPT COLT, COLT VISTA, CONCORDE, INTREPID, LHS, SUMMIT, SUMMIT WAGON, VISION & 1994 NEW YORKER

COOLANT TEMPERATURE SENSOR

1992 Except Laser, Stealth & Talon

1. With key Off, disconnect coolant temperature sensor connector.
2. Measure resistance between sensor terminals.
3. If resistance is not 700-1000 ohms at temperature of 200°F, replace sensor.

Stealth

1. Remove engine coolant temperature sensor from intake manifold.
2. With sensing end immersed in hot water resistance should be 5800 ohms at 32°F; 2400 ohms at 68°F; 1100 ohms at 104°F; and 300 ohms at 176°F.
3. If resistance is not as indicated, replace sensor.

Laser & Talon

1. Remove engine coolant temperature sensor and immerse in hot water.
2. Connect a suitable ohmmeter across terminals of sensor. At 68°F resistance should be 2210-2690 ohms; at 176°F, resistance should be 264-328 ohms.
3. If not within specifications, replace sensor.

COOLANT TEMPERATURE SWITCH

Laser, Stealth & Talon

1. Place sensor in oil up to mounting thread.
2. Connect a suitable ohmmeter across terminals of coolant temperature switch, then increase oil temperature.
3. Ensure switch is switched OFF when oil temperature at 234-244°F, replace sensor if necessary.

Continued on page 10-22
COOLING FANS

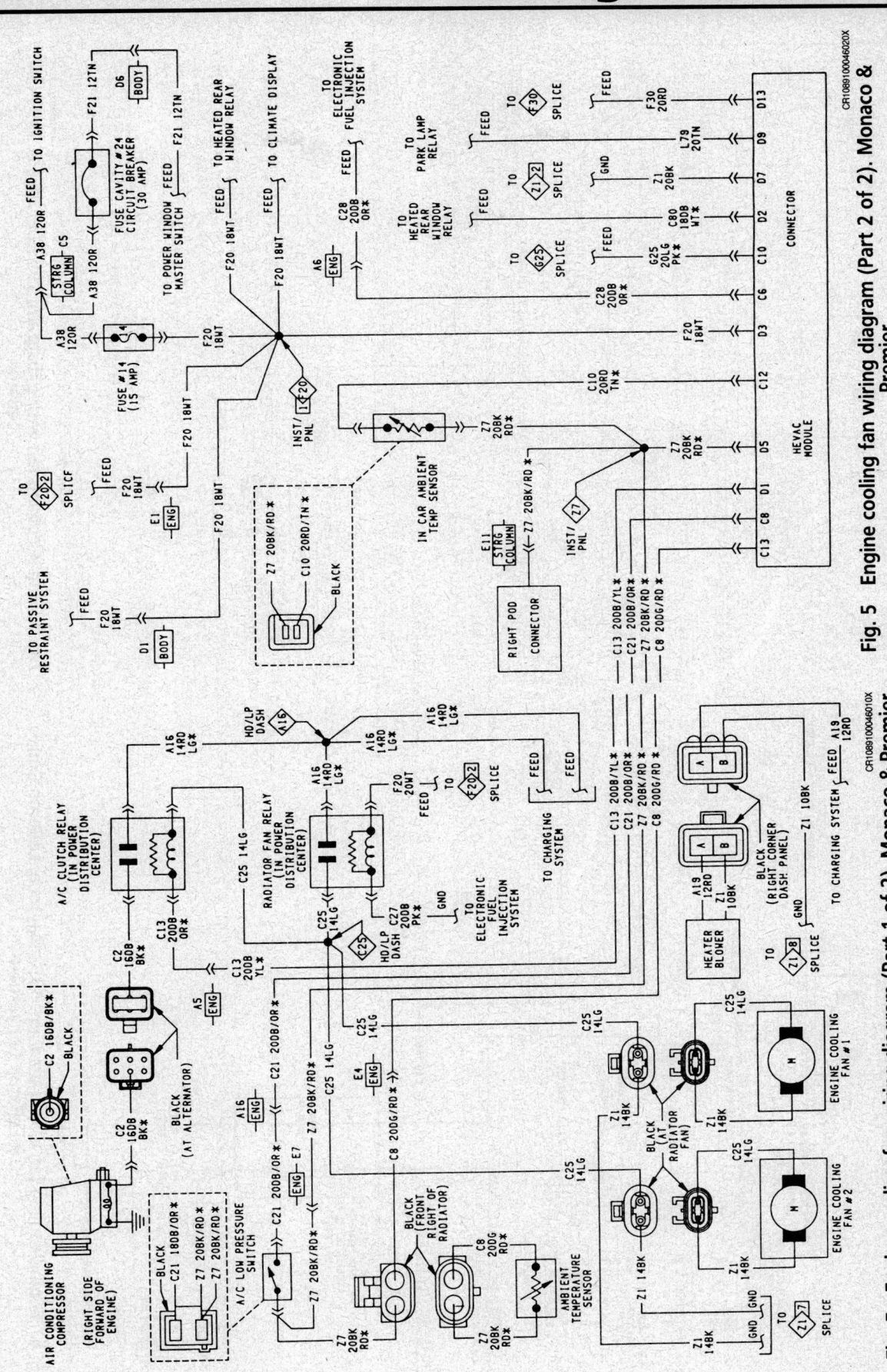

Fig. 5 Engine cooling fan wiring diagram (Part 2 of 2). Monaco & Premier

Fig. 5 Engine cooling fan wiring diagram (Part 1 of 2). Monaco & Premier

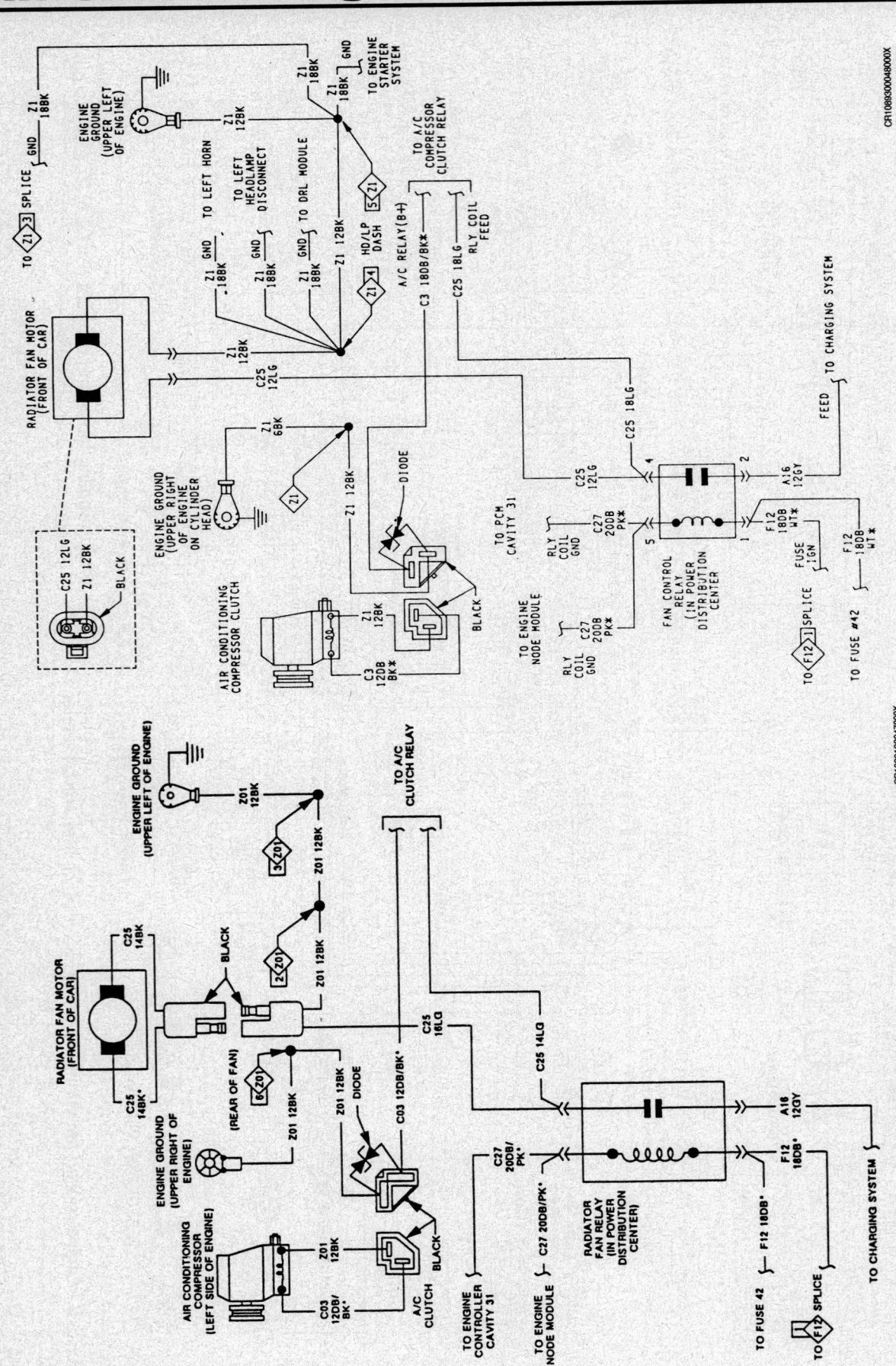

Fig. 7 Engine cooling fan wiring diagram. 1993 Daytona & 1993–94 LeBaron

Fig. 6 Engine cooling fan wiring diagram. 1992 Daytona, LeBaron Coupe & LeBaron Convertible

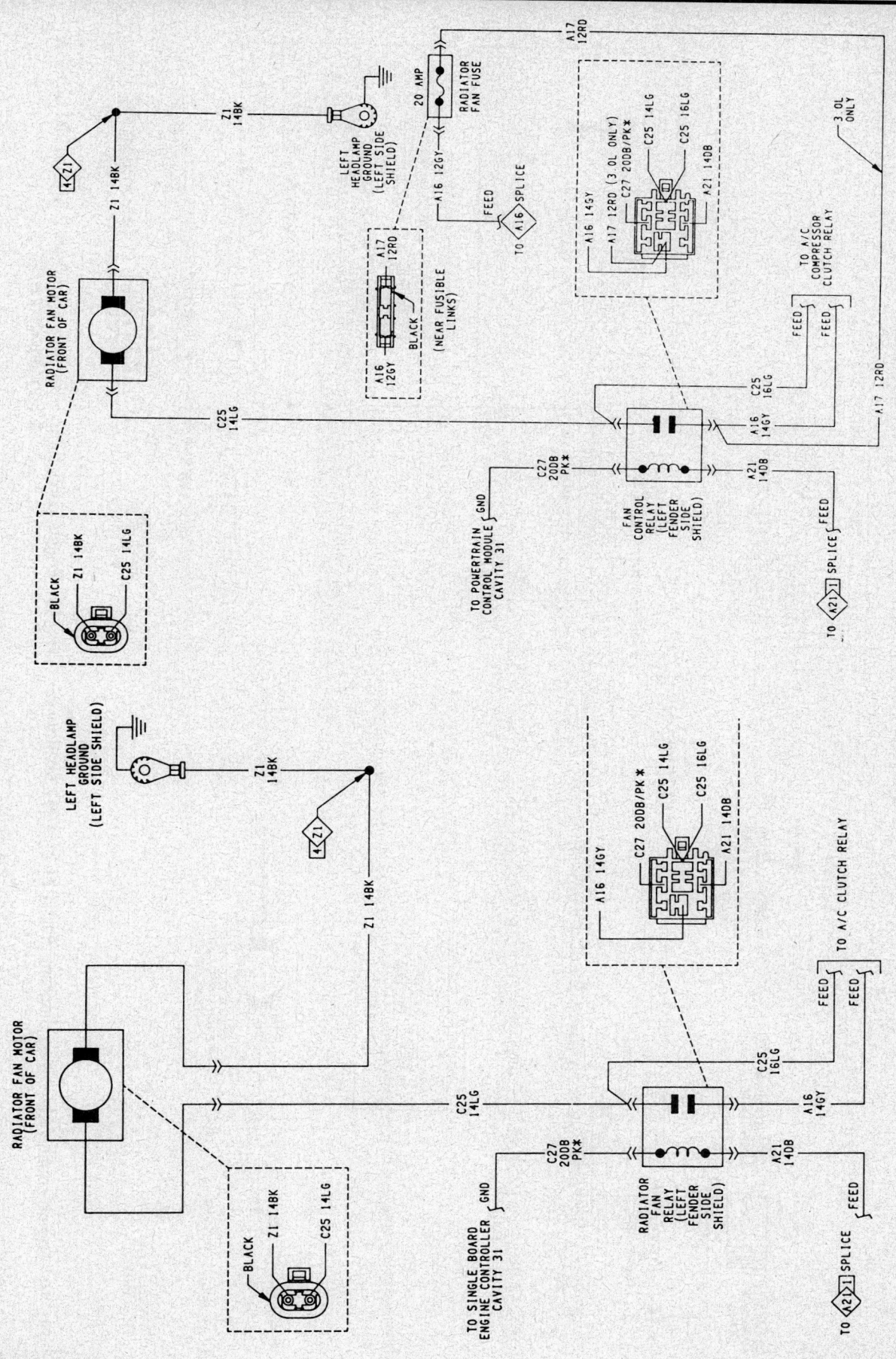

Fig. 9 Engine cooling fan wiring diagram. 1993–94 Shadow & Sundance less A/C

Fig. 8 Engine cooling fan wiring diagram. 1992 Shadow & Sundance less A/C

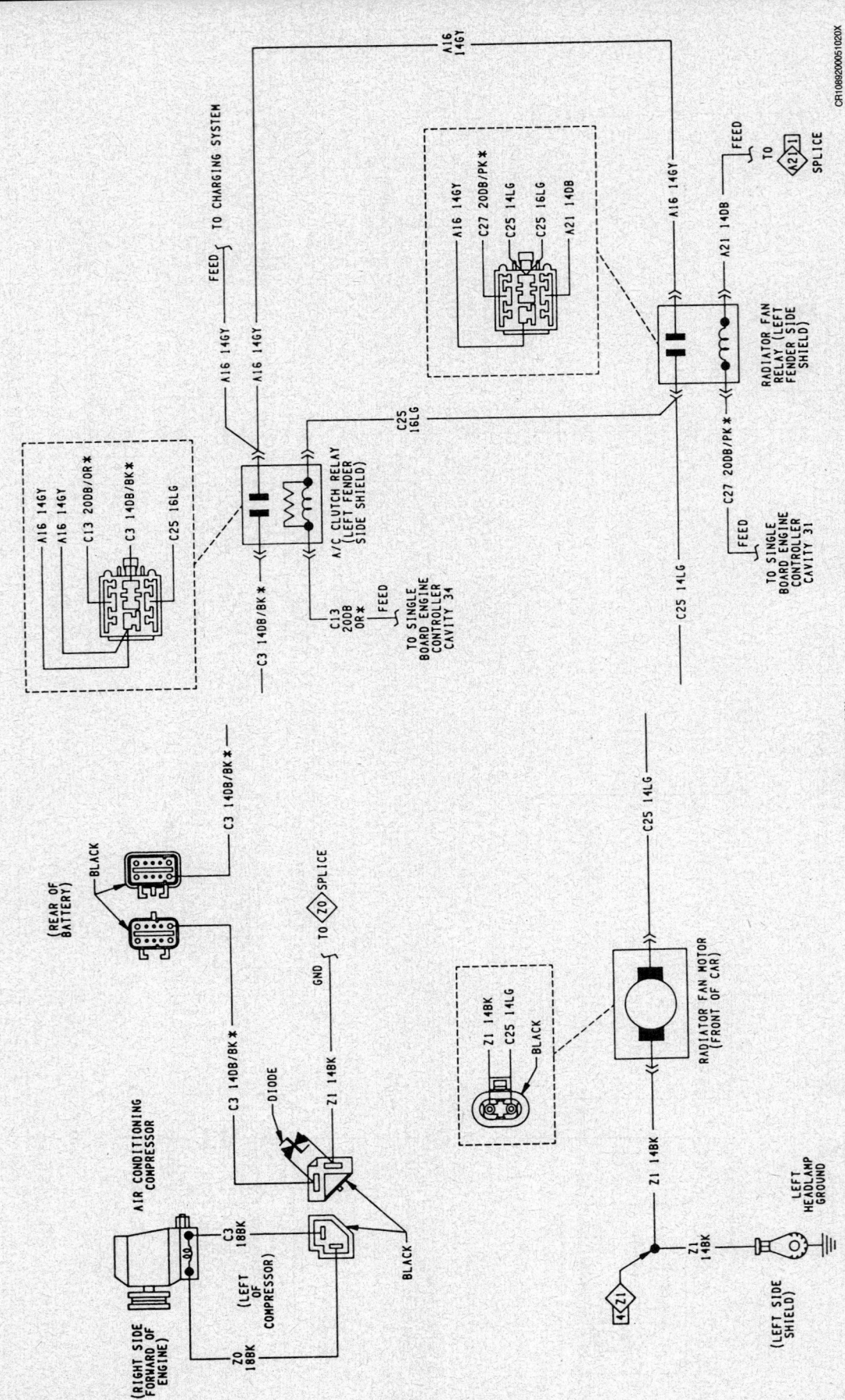

Fig. 10 Engine cooling fan wiring diagram (Part 2 of 2). 1992 Shadow & Sundance w/A/C

Fig. 10 Engine cooling fan wiring diagram (Part 1 of 2). 1992 Shadow & Sundance w/A/C

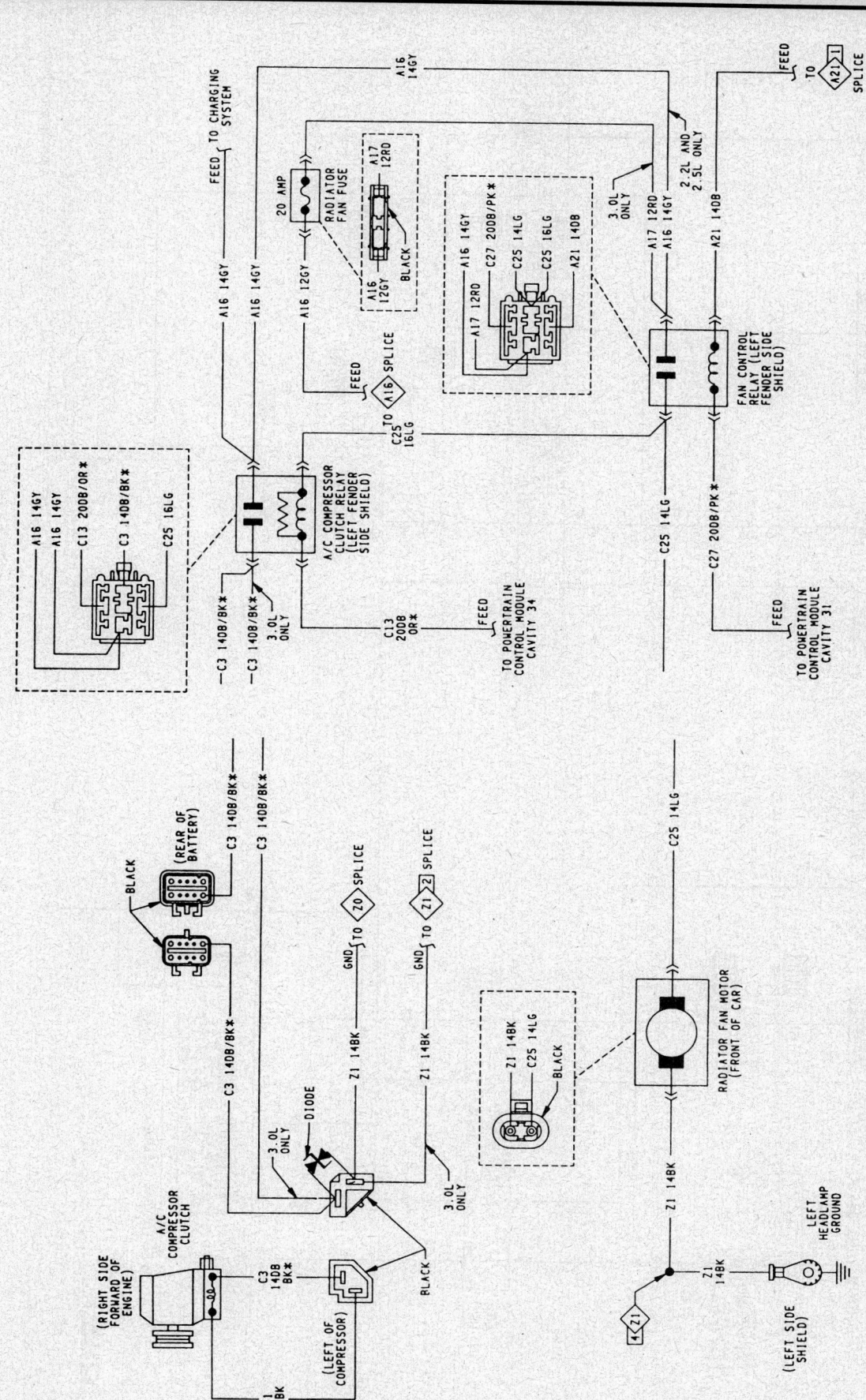

Fig. 11 Engine cooling fan wiring diagram (Part 2 of 2). 1993–94 Shadow & Sundance w/A/C

Fig. 11 Engine cooling fan wiring diagram (Part 1 of 2). 1993–94 Shadow & Sundance w/A/C

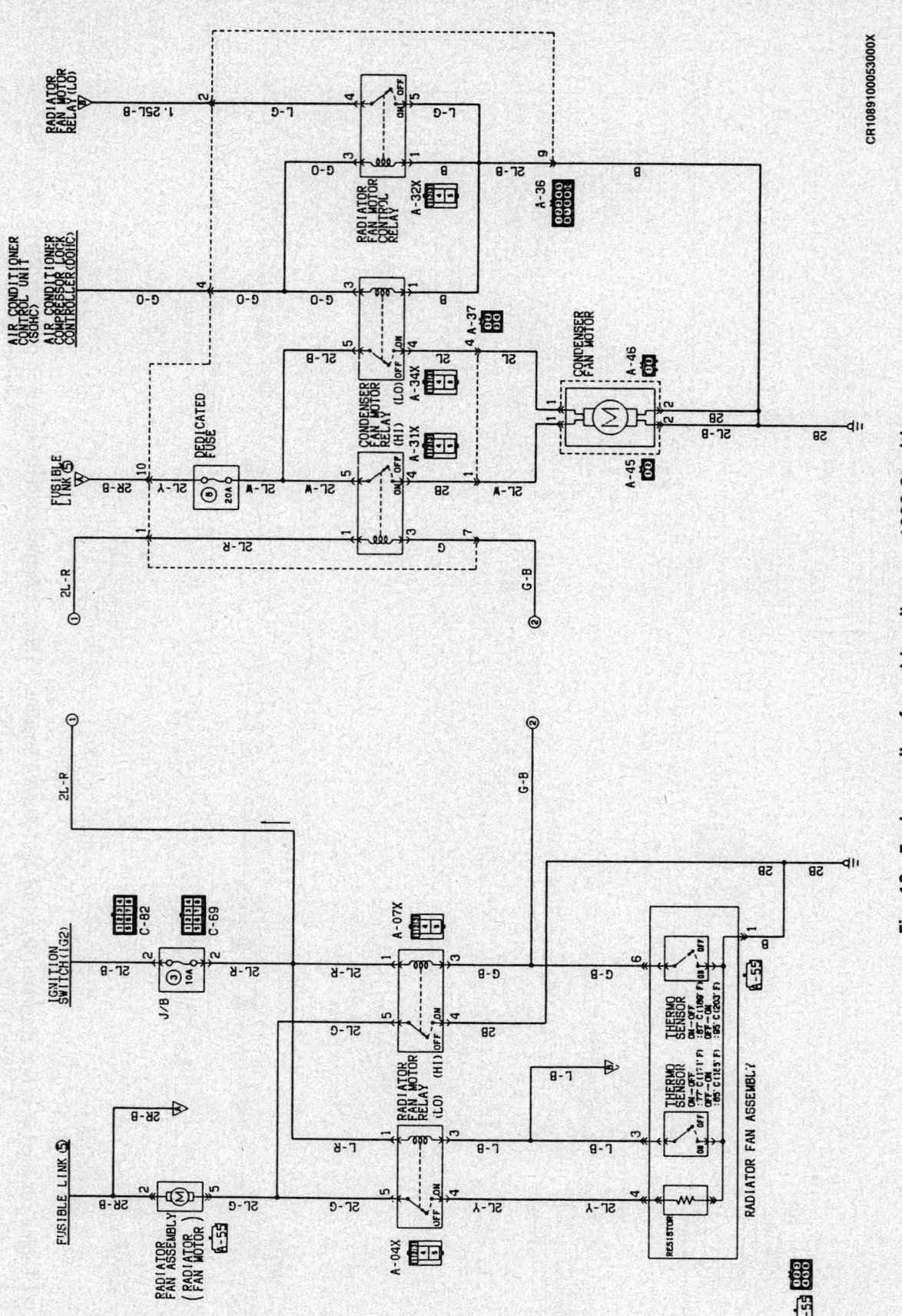

Fig. 12 Engine cooling fan wiring diagram. 1992 Stealth

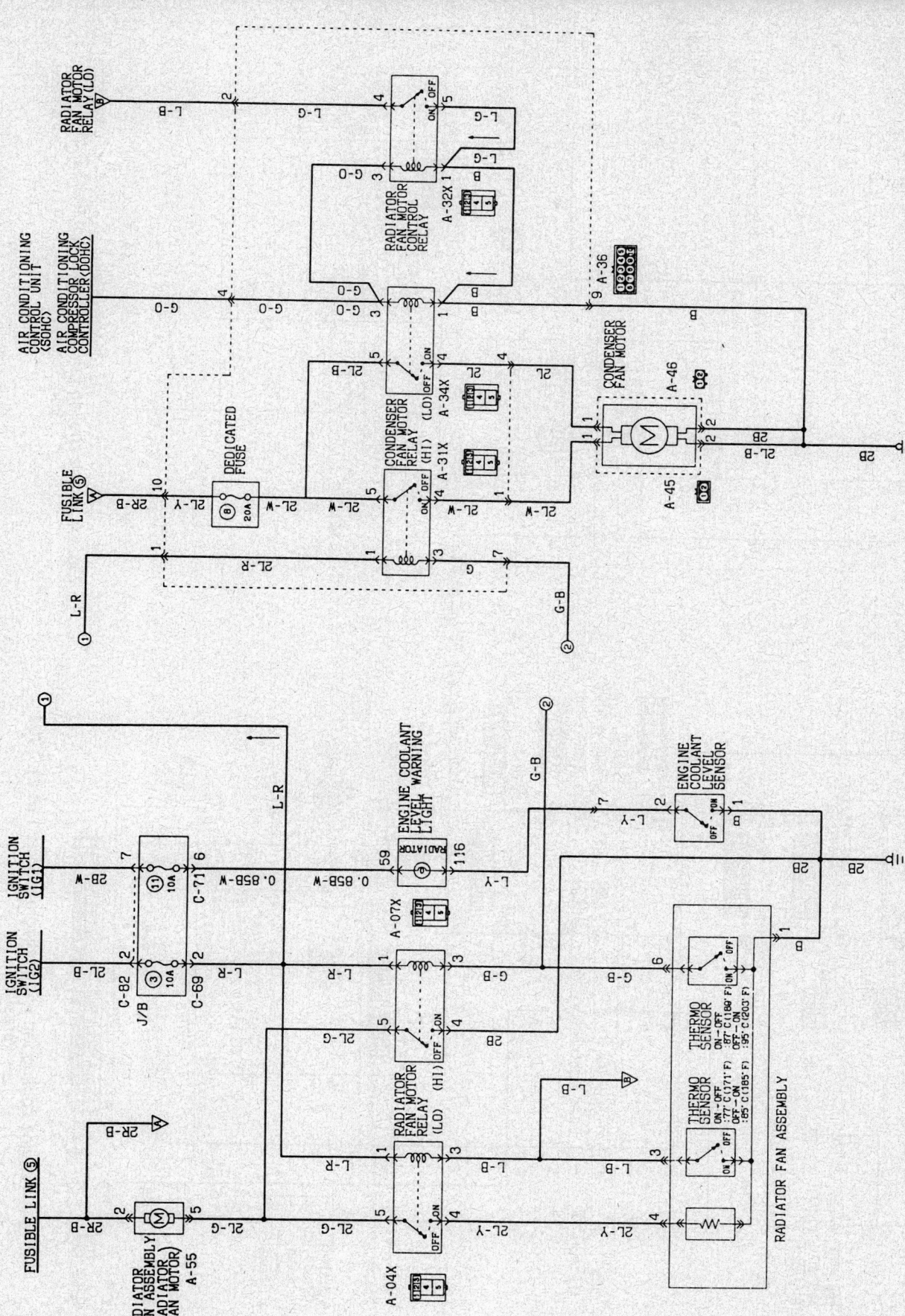

Fig. 13 Engine cooling fan wiring diagram (Part 2 of 2). 1993 Stealth

Fig. 13 Engine cooling fan wiring diagram (Part 1 of 2). 1993 Stealth

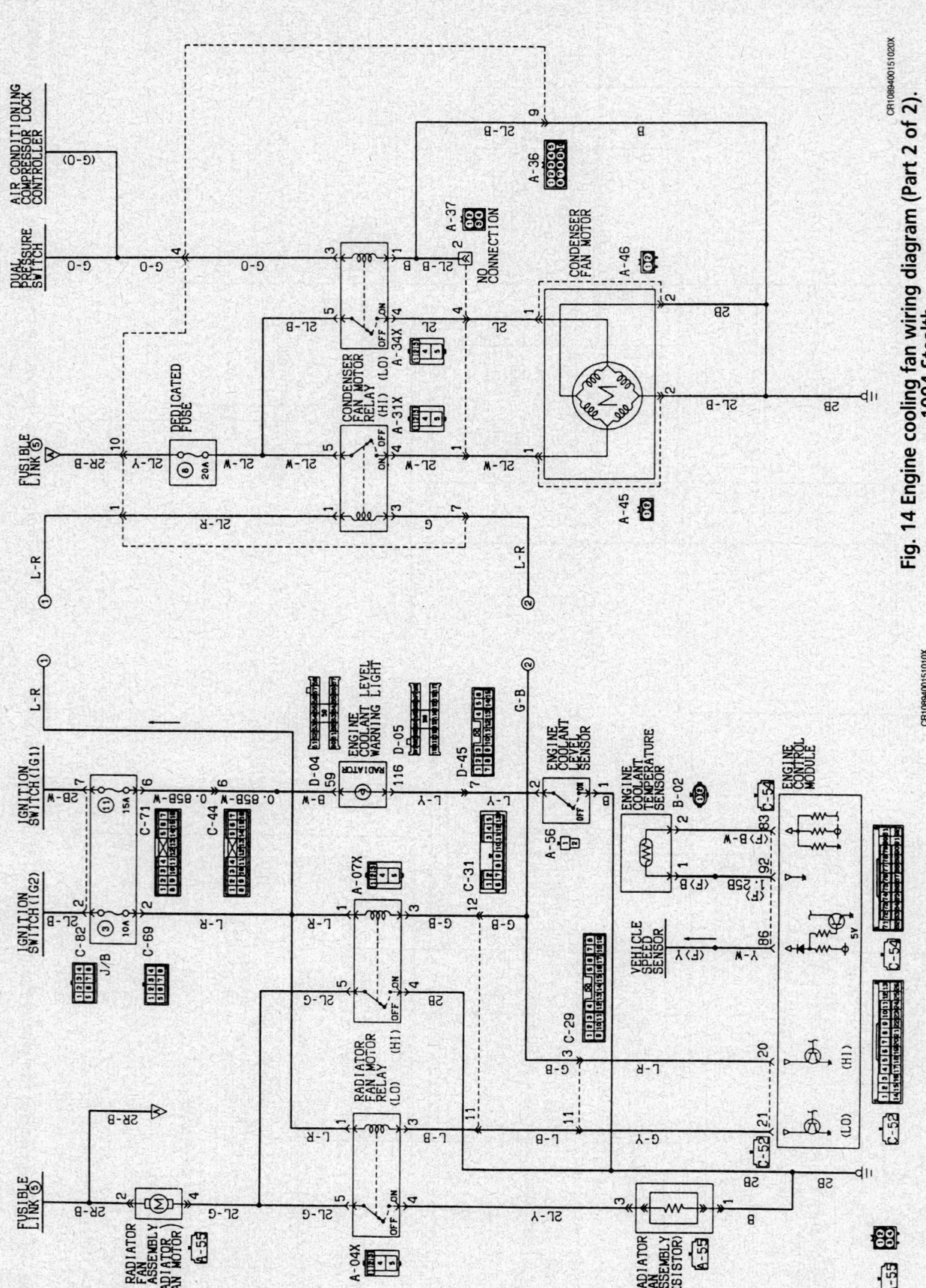

Fig. 14 Engine cooling fan wiring diagram (Part 2 of 2). 1994 Stealth

Fig. 14 Engine cooling fan wiring diagram (Part 1 of 2). 1994 Stealth

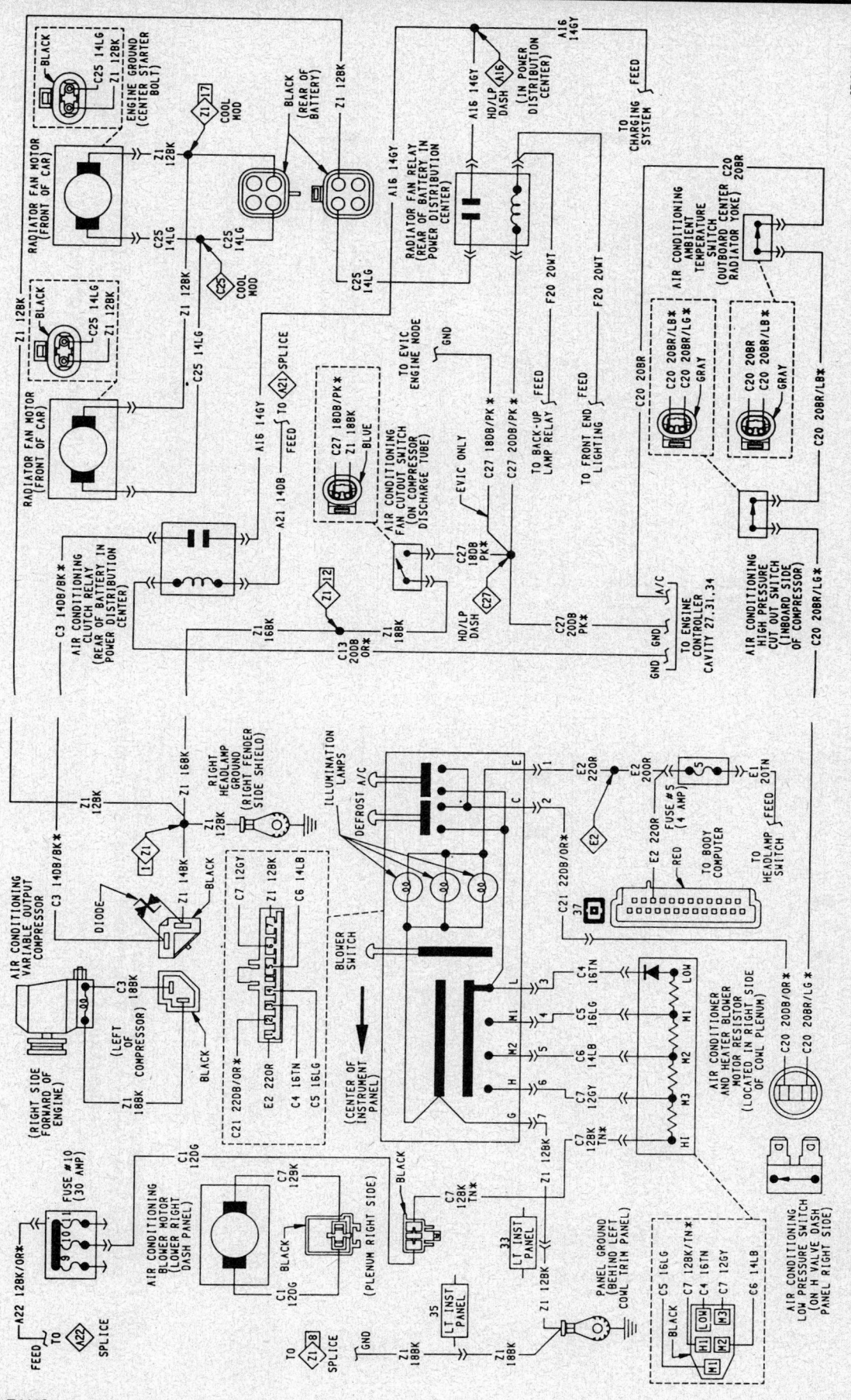

Fig. 15 Engine cooling fan wiring diagram (Part 2 of 2). 1992-93 Dynasty, Imperial, New Yorker & New Yorker 5th Avenue w/6 cylinder engines less Automatic Temperature Control

Fig. 15 Engine cooling fan wiring diagram (Part 1 of 2). 1992-93 Dynasty, Imperial, New Yorker & New Yorker 5th Avenue w/6 cylinder engines less Automatic Temperature Control

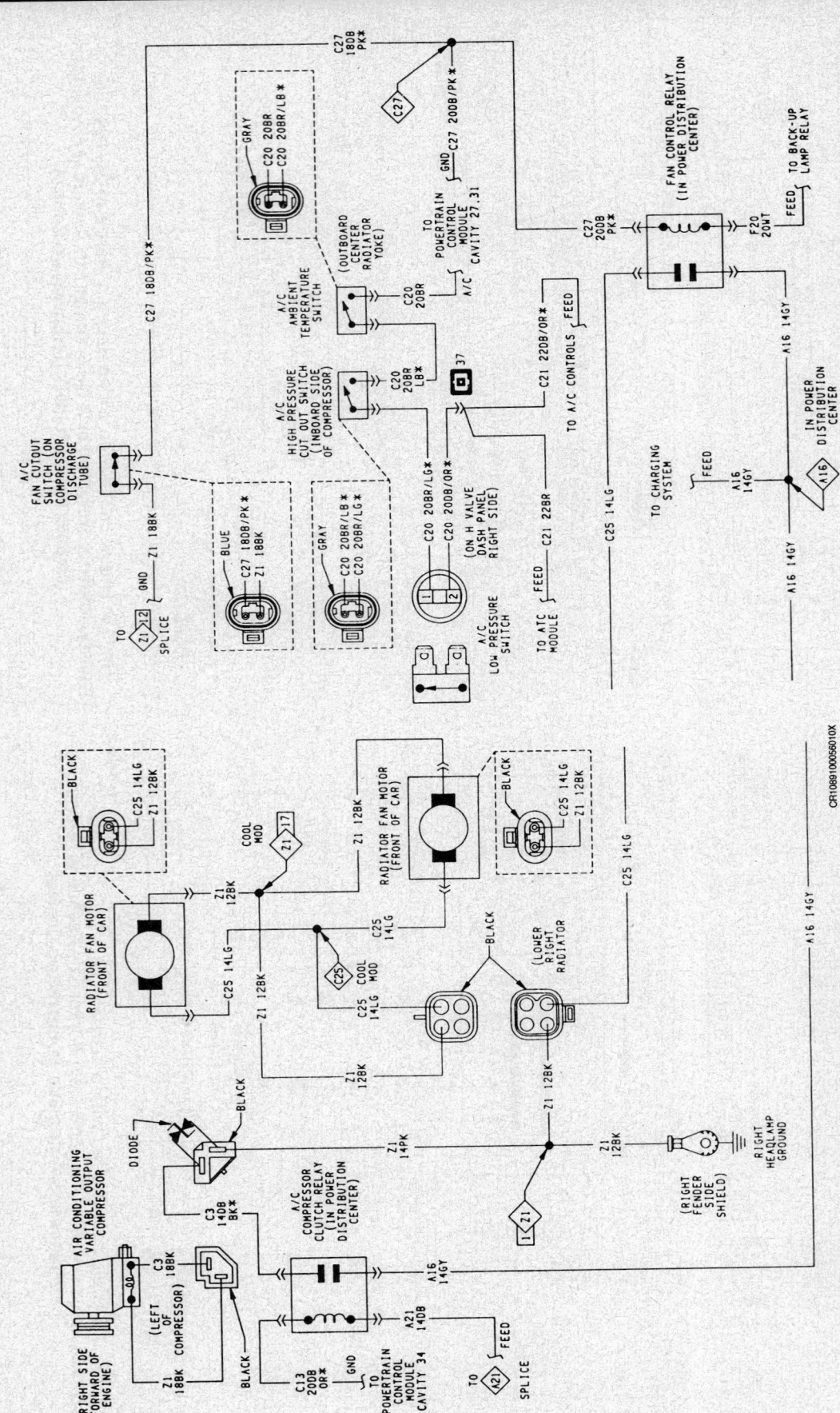

CR108910005602OX

Fig. 16 Engine cooling fan wiring diagram (Part 2 of 2). 1992-93 Dynasty, Imperial, New Yorker & New Yorker 5th Avenue w/Automatic Temperature Control

CR108910005601OX

Fig. 16 Engine cooling fan wiring diagram (Part 1 of 2). 1992-93 Dynasty, Imperial, New Yorker & New Yorker 5th Avenue w/Automatic Temperature Control

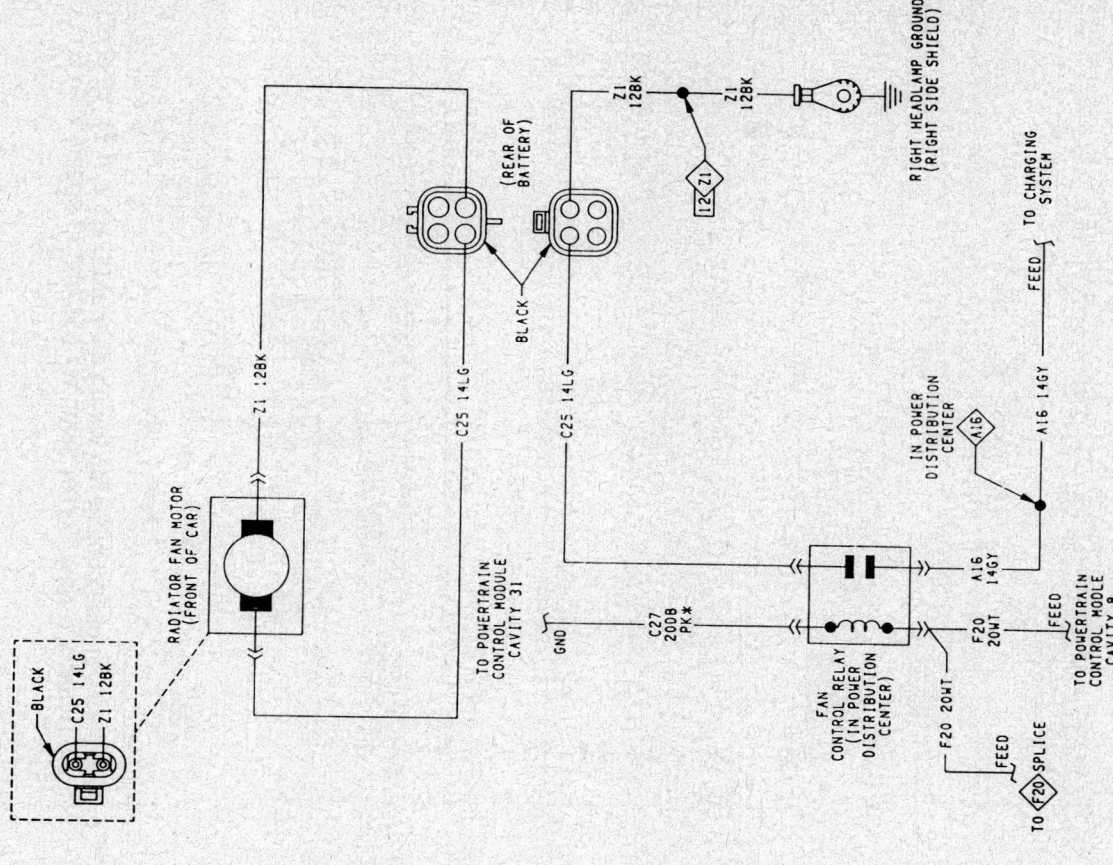

Fig. 18 Engine cooling fan wiring diagram. 1993 Dynasty & New Yorker Salon w/2.5L/4-153 engine less A/C

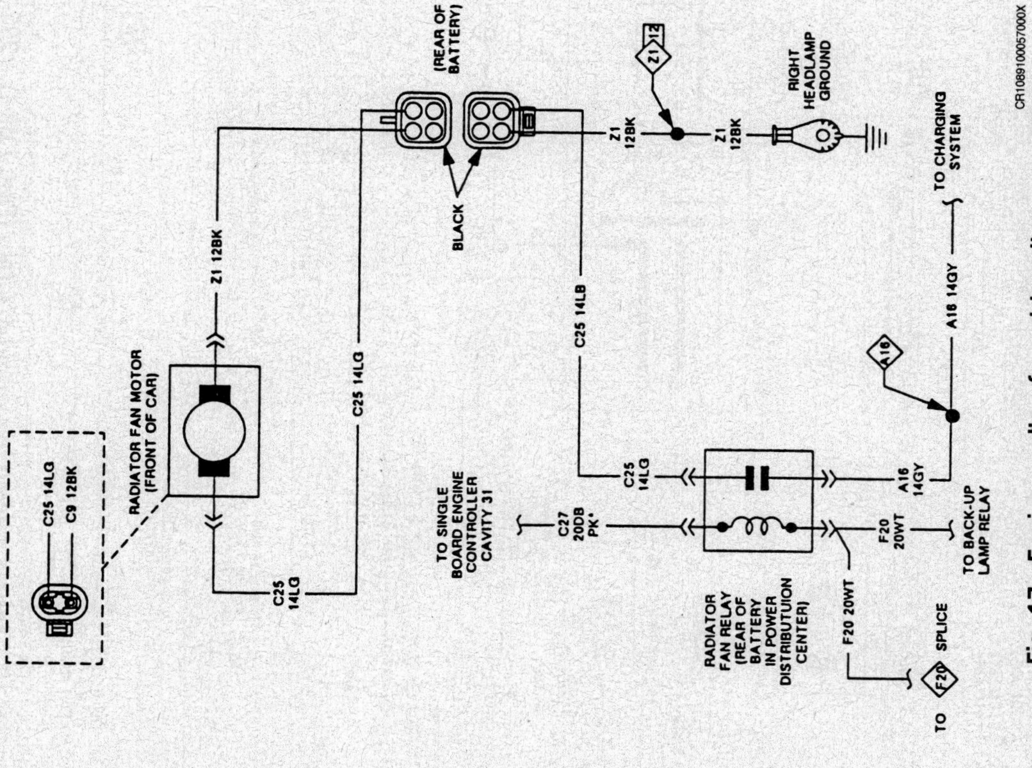

Fig. 17 Engine cooling fan wiring diagram. 1992 Dynasty & New Yorker Salon w/2.5L/4-153 engine less A/C

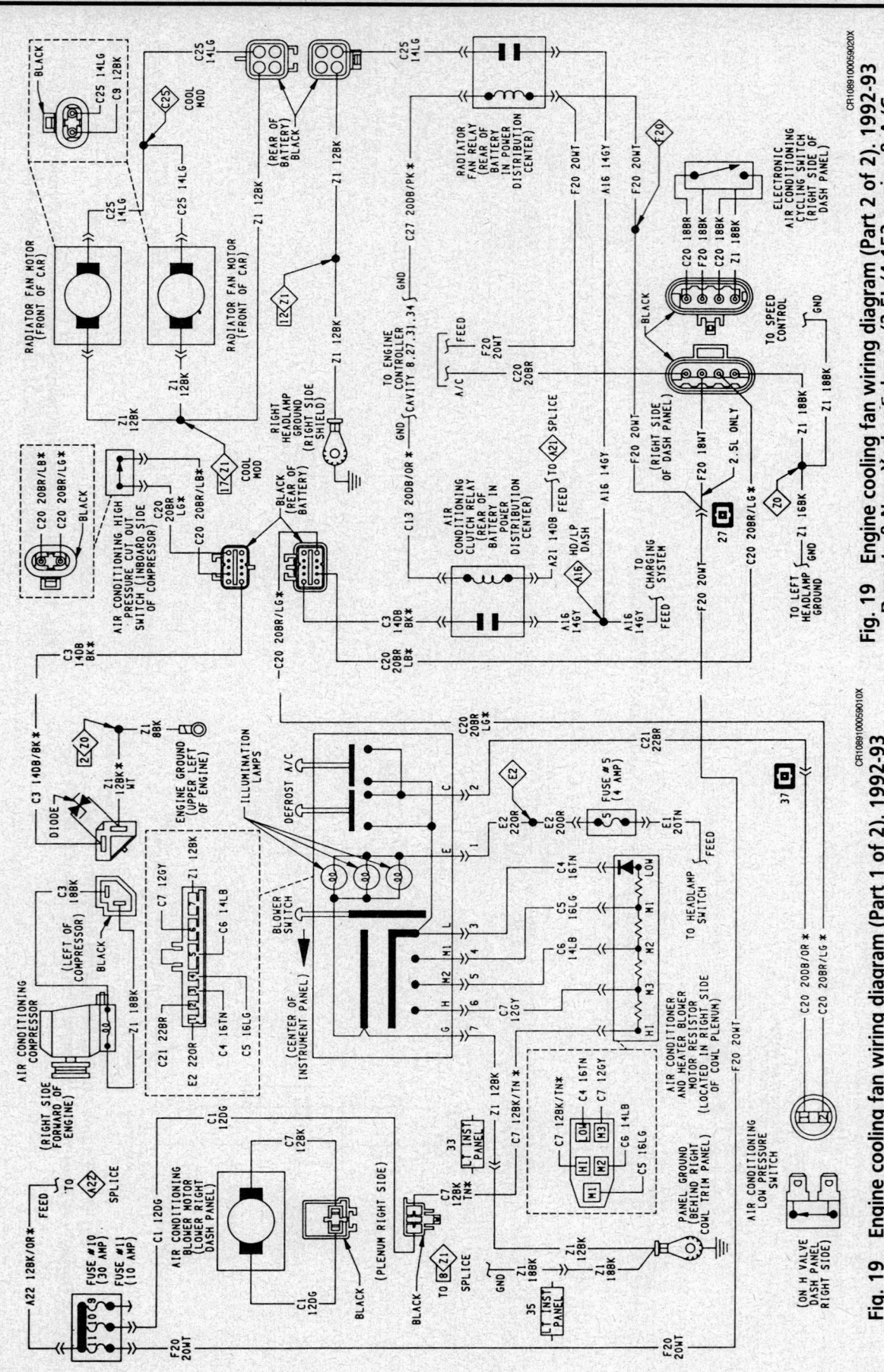

Fig. 19 Engine cooling fan wiring diagram (Part 2 of 2). 1992-93 Dynasty & New Yorker Salon w/2.5L/4-153 engine & A/C

Fig. 19 Engine cooling fan wiring diagram (Part 1 of 2). 1992-93 Dynasty & New Yorker Salon w/2.5L/4-153 engine & A/C

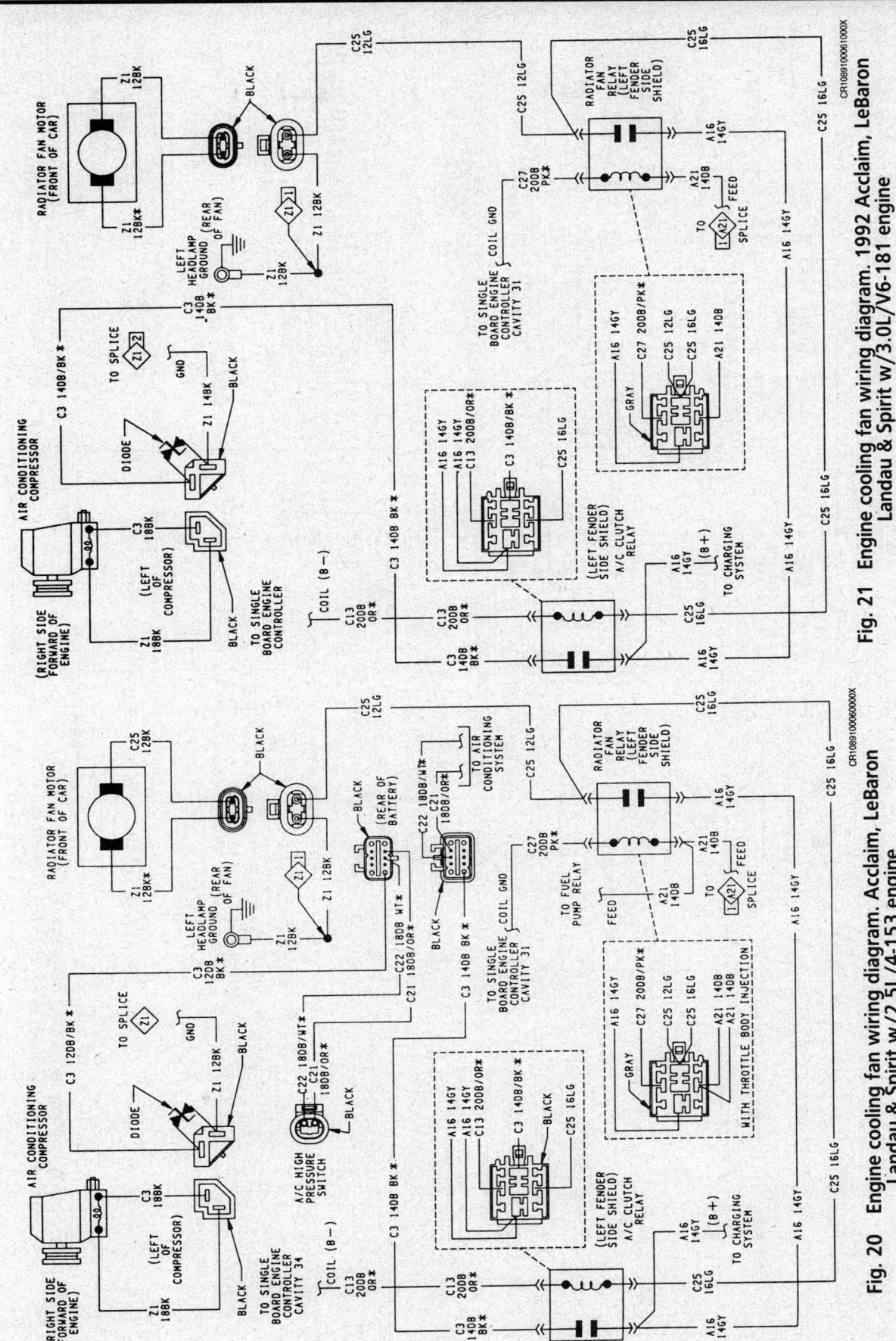

Fig. 21 Engine cooling fan wiring diagram. 1992 Acclaim, LeBaron Landau & Spirit w/3.0L/V6-181 engine

Fig. 20 Engine cooling fan wiring diagram. Acclaim, LeBaron Landau & Spirit w/2.5L/4-153 engine

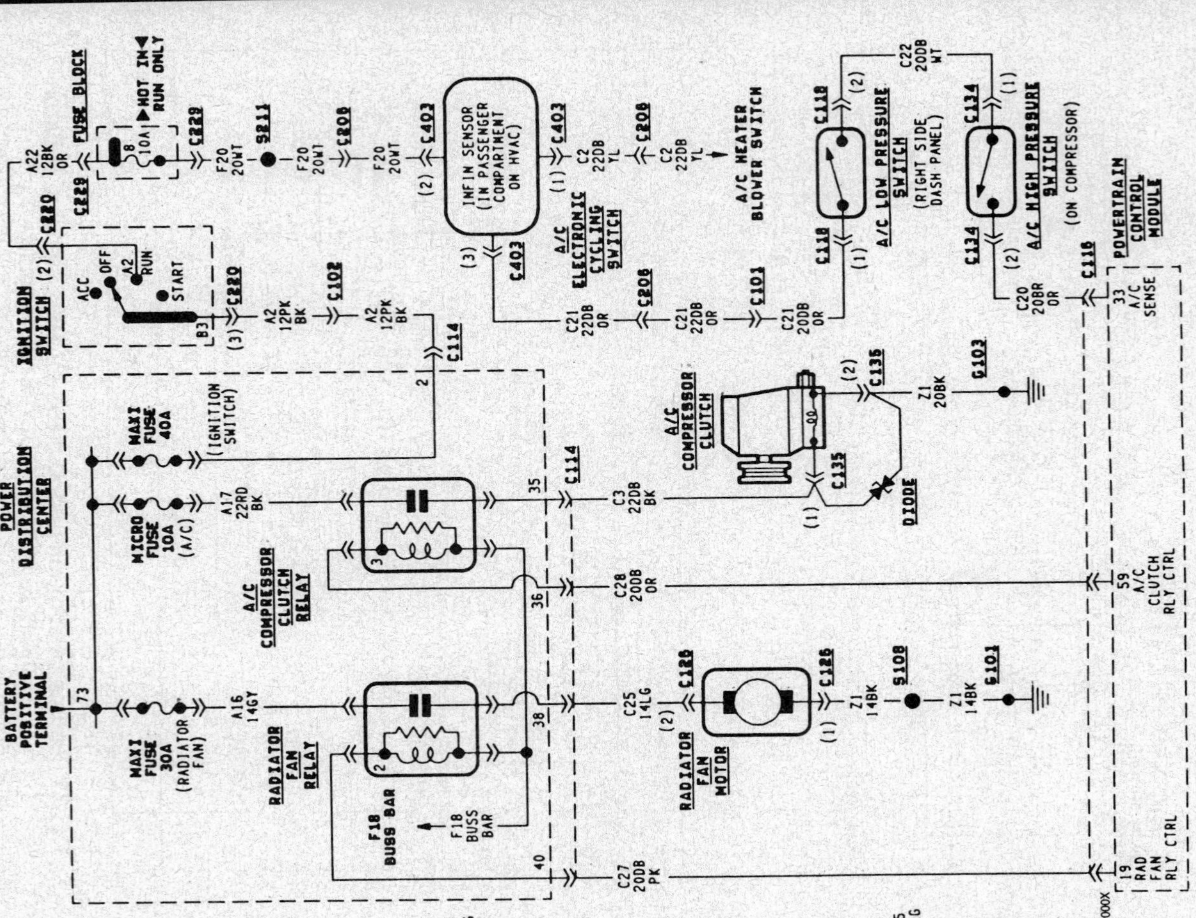

Fig. 10   Fig. 23 Engine cooling fan wiring diagram. Neon

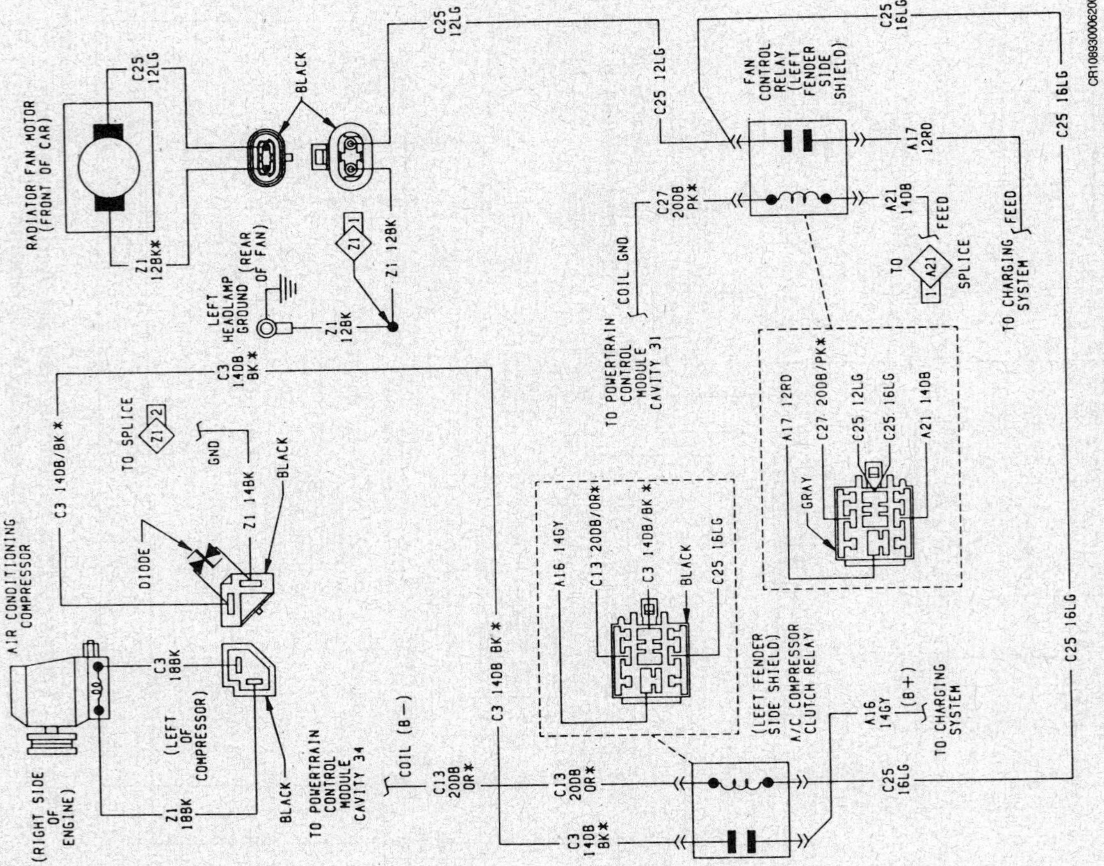

Fig. 22   Engine cooling fan wiring diagram. 1993-94 Acclaim, LeBaron Landau & Spirit w/3.0L/V6-181 engine

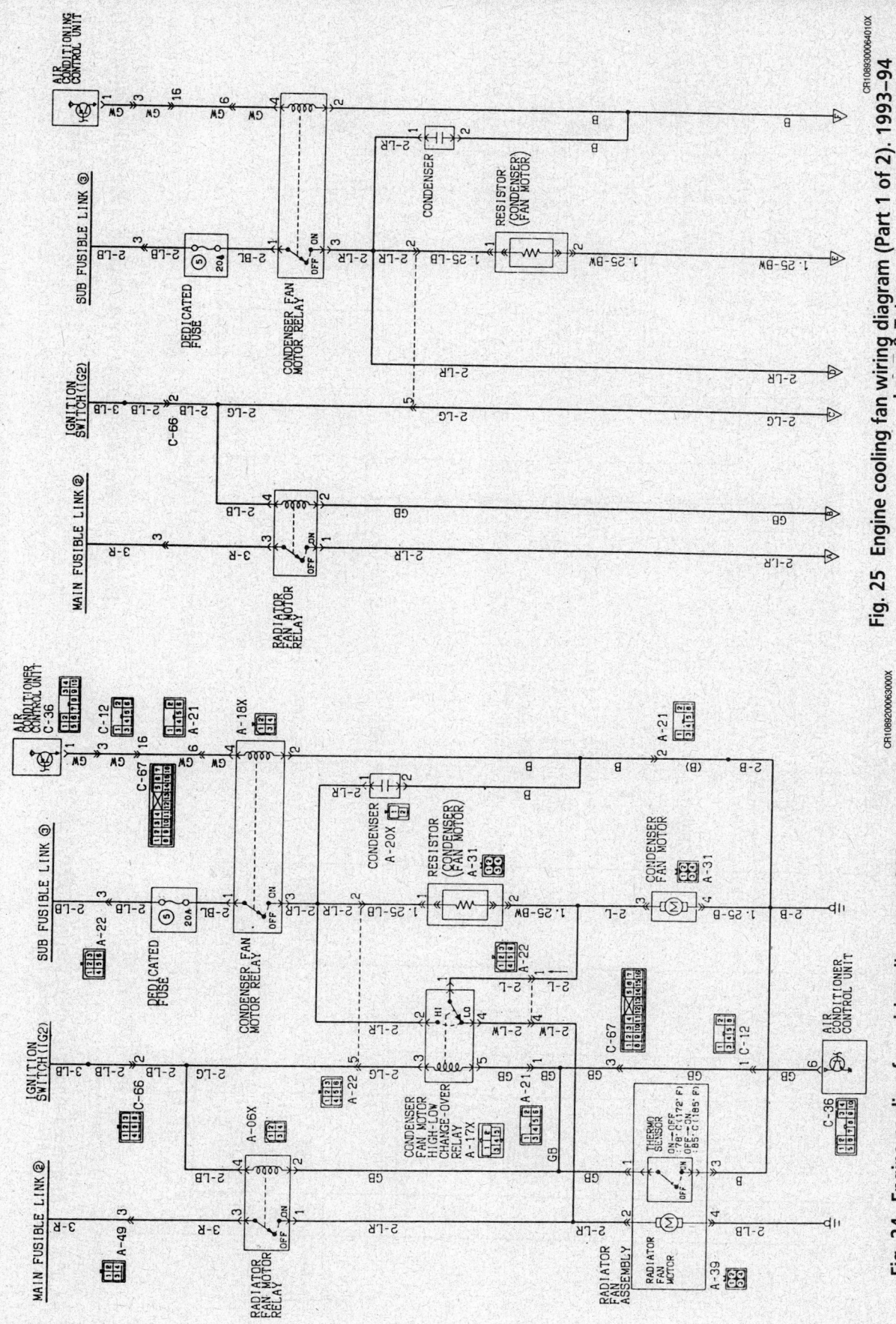

Fig. 25 Engine cooling fan wiring diagram (Part 1 of 2). 1993–94 Laser & Talon

Fig. 24 Engine cooling fan wiring diagram. 1992 Laser & Talon

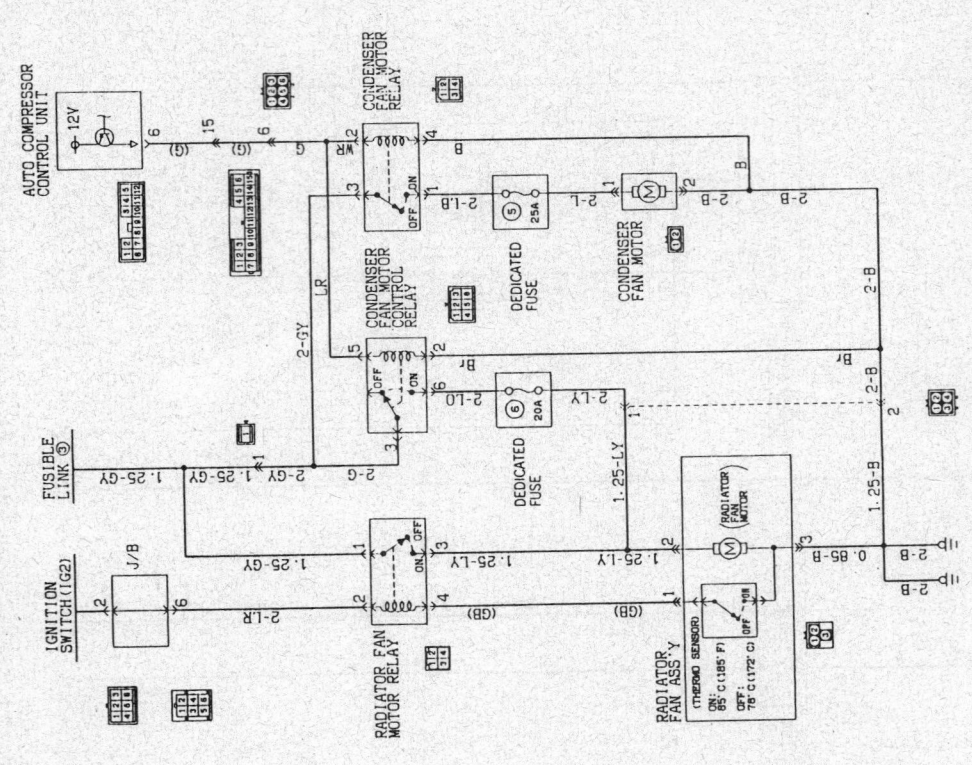

Fig. 26 Engine cooling fan wiring diagram. 1992 Colt & Summit

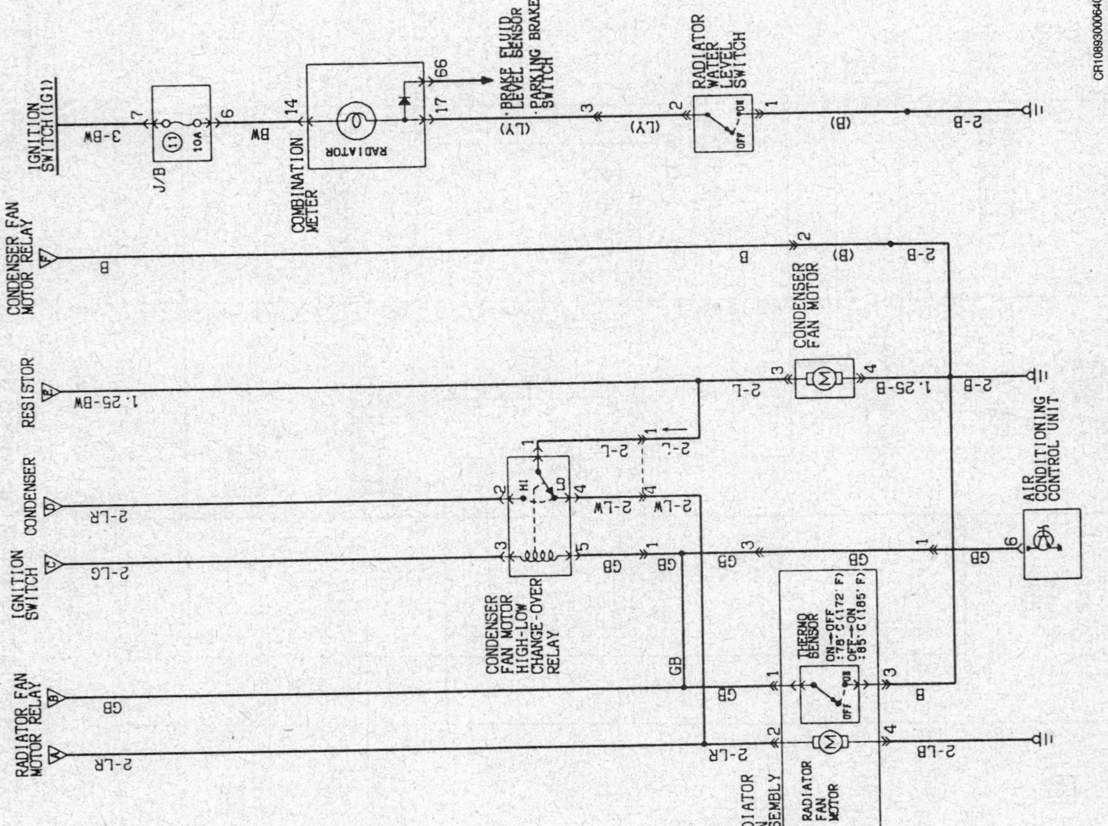

Fig. 25 Engine cooling fan wiring diagram (Part 2 of 2). 1993–94
Laser & Talon

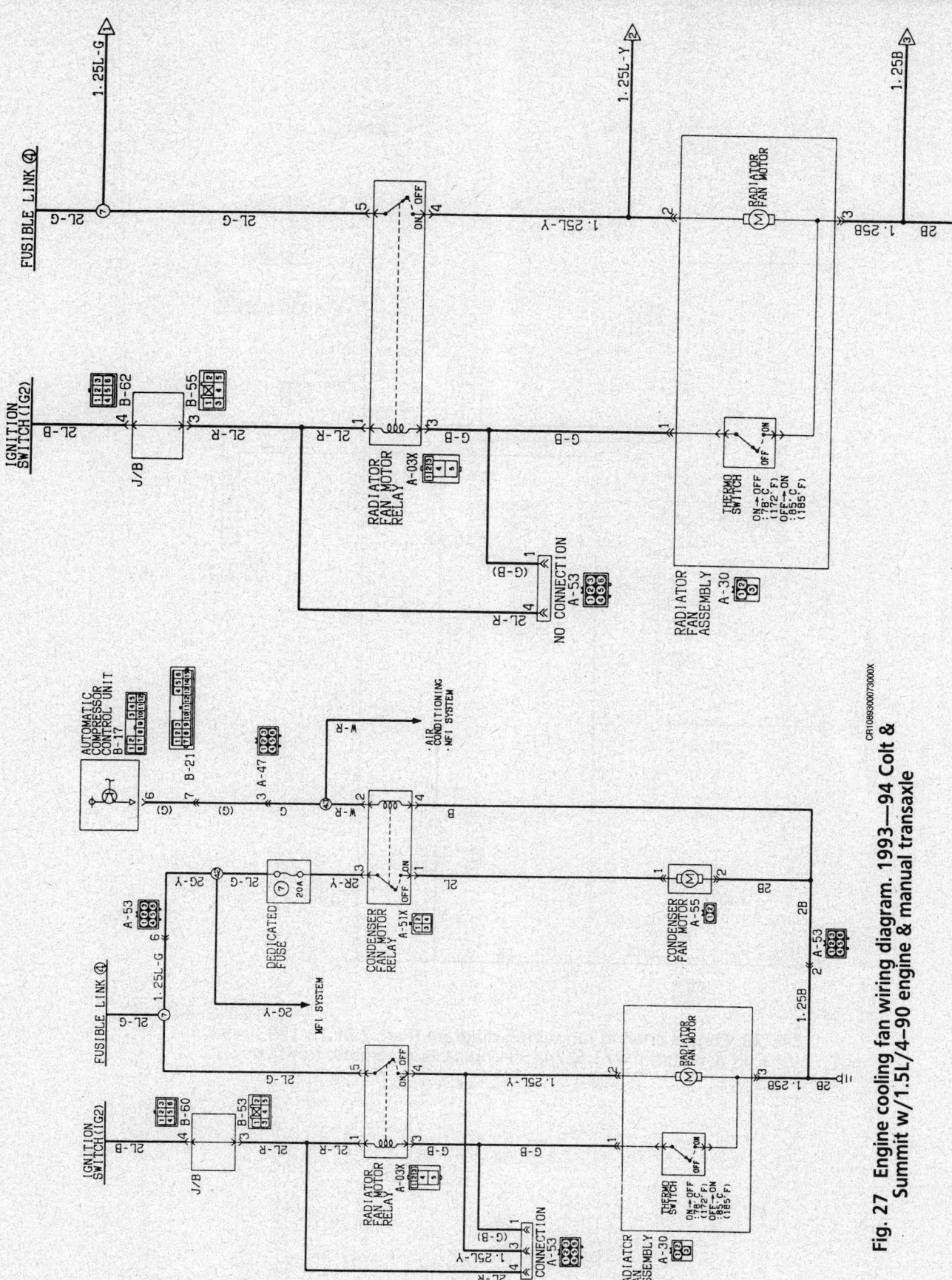

Fig. 28 Engine cooling fan wiring diagram (Part 1 of 2). 1993—94 Colt & Summit w/1.5L/4-90 engine & automatic transaxle

Fig. 27 Engine cooling fan wiring diagram. 1993—94 Colt & Summit w/1.5L/4-90 engine & manual transaxle

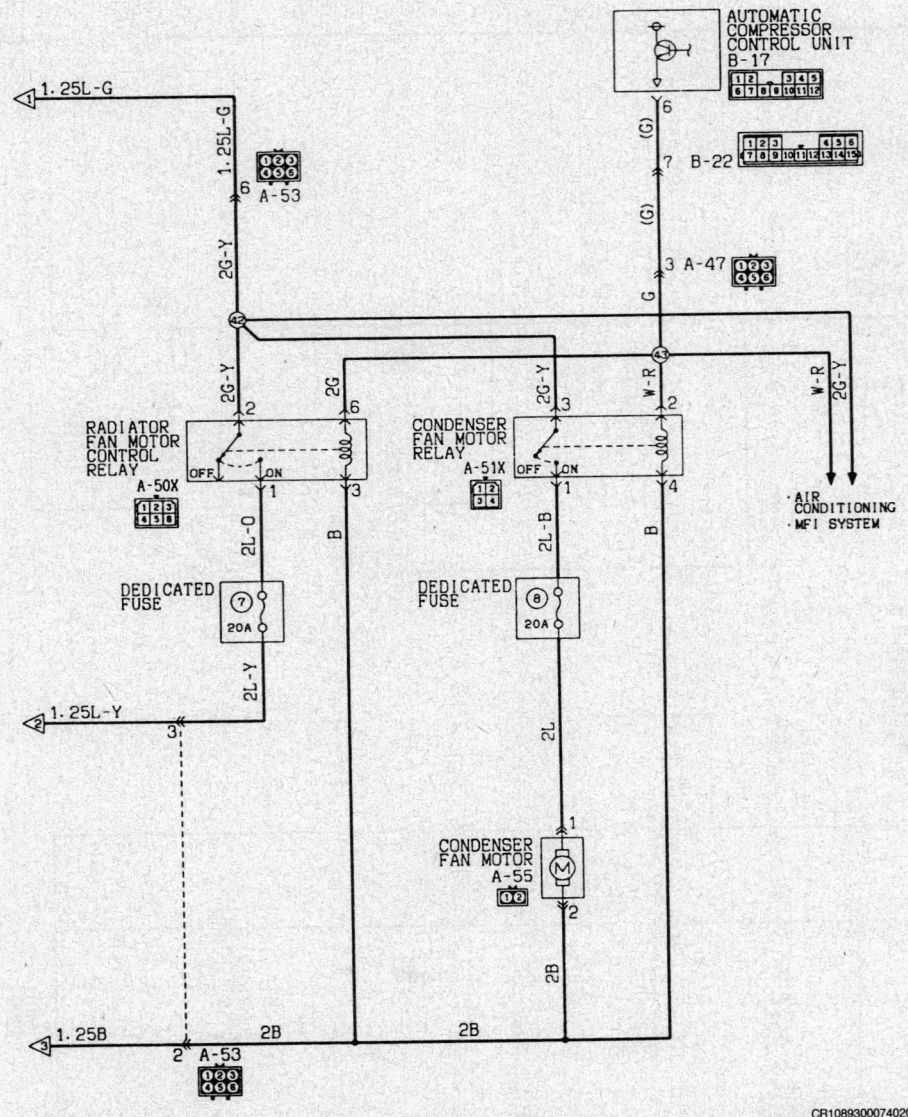

Fig. 28 Engine cooling fan wiring diagram (Part 2 of 2). 1993—94 Colt & Summit w/1.5L/4—90 engine & automatic transaxle

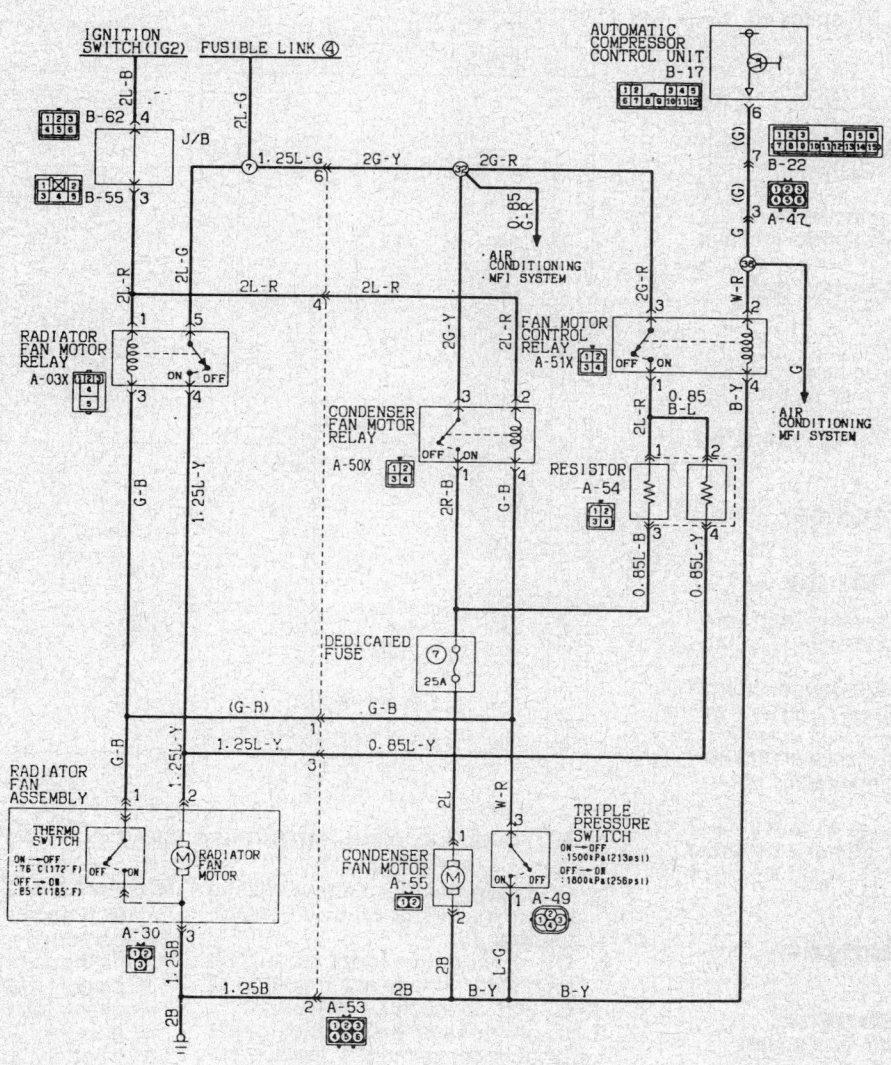

Fig. 29 Engine cooling fan wiring diagram. 1993—94 Colt & Summit w/1.8L/4–110 engine

CR1089300075000X

THERMO SENSOR

Laser & Talon

1. Place sensor in hot water up to mounting thread.
2. Check for continuity between terminals on sensor.
3. Continuity should exist with water temperature at 180-190°F. Continuity should not exist with water temperature at 172°F or less.
4. If continuity is not as specified, replace sensor.

Stealth

1. Place sensor in hot water up to mounting thread.
2. Change water temperature, then check for continuity between terminals of sensor.
3. Refer to **Fig. 32** for specifications.
4. If not within specifications, replace thermo sensor.

RADIATOR FAN RESISTOR

Stealth

1. Measure resistance between connector terminals 1 and 4 of radiator fan connector, **Fig. 33**.
2. If resistance is not .29-.35 ohms, replace resistor.

RADIATOR FAN MOTOR RELAY

Laser, Stealth & Talon

1. Remove radiator fan relay from relay box located at RH side of engine compartment.
2. Check for continuity between terminals 1 and 3, **Fig. 34**. If continuity exists, replace relay.
3. Check for continuity between terminals 2 and 4. If continuity does not exist, replace relay.
4. Supply battery voltage to terminals 2 and 4. Check for continuity between terminals 1 and 3. If continuity does not exist, replace relay.

RADIATOR FAN MOTOR CIRCUIT TEST

Except Laser, Monaco, Premier, Stealth & Talon

1. Run engine to normal operating temperature.
2. Check wiring connector in C25, C9 and C26 for proper engagement.
3. Connect diagnostic read out tool DRB II to diagnostic connector. Check for fault codes.
4. If fault code 88, 12, 35 or 55 is detected, proceed with next step.
5. With ignition switch in Run position, test for battery voltage at fan relay single pin connector. If battery voltage is detected or if voltage reads at zero to one volt, proceed with next step.
6. With ignition switch in Off position, disconnect the 60-way connector from engine controller and return ignition switch to Run position, then proceed as follows:

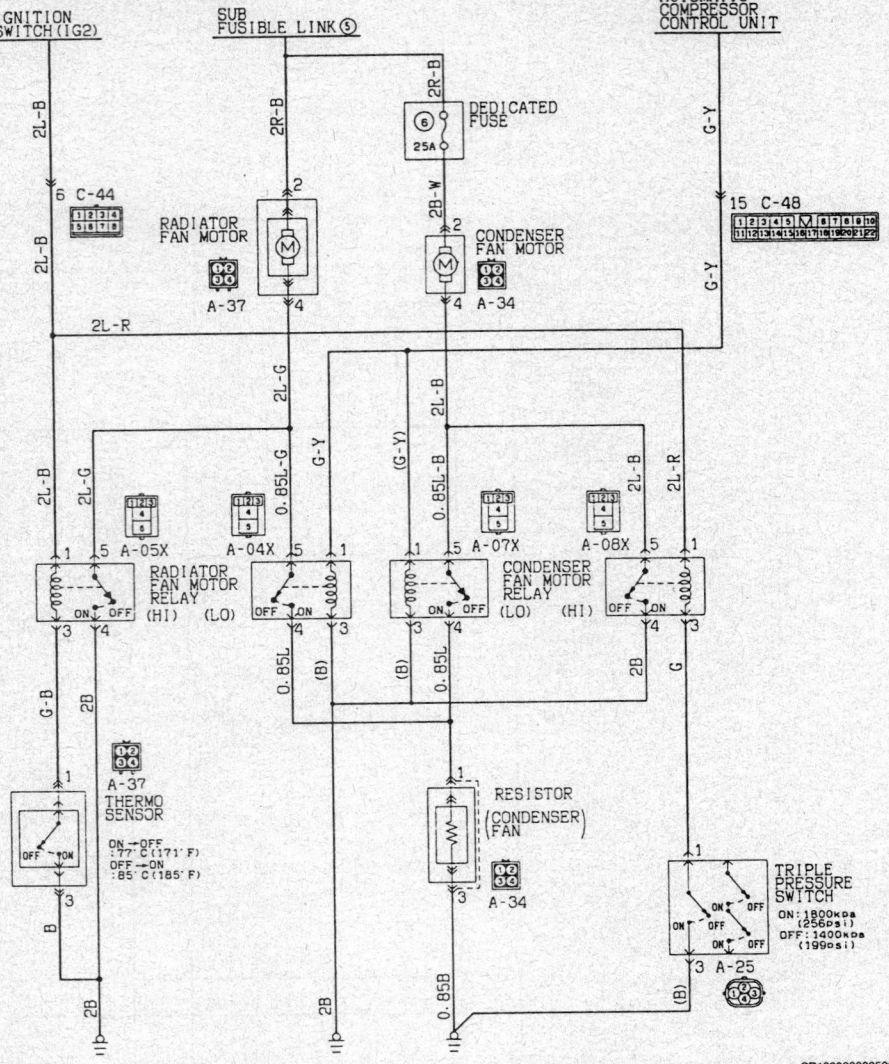

   a. **On Neon**, test for battery voltage at terminal 19 of 60-way connector, **Fig. 35**.
   b. **On all models except Neon**, test for battery voltage at terminal 31 of 60-way connector, **Fig. 35**.
7. If battery voltage exists and female terminal is not damaged, replace engine controller. If no battery voltage exists, repair open or short in circuit C27.
8. With ignition switch in Off position, disconnect 60-way connector from engine controller and return ignition switch to Run position. Test for battery voltage at single pin connector on fan relay. If battery voltage exists, replace engine controller. If voltage is zero to one volt proceed to last step.
9. With ignition switch in Run position, test for battery voltage at wire C27 in 3-way connector of fan relay. If battery voltage exists, replace fan relay. If voltage is zero to one, repair open or short in circuit C27.
10. Turn ignition switch Off, connect 60-way connector and test system.

Fig. 30 Engine cooling fan wiring diagram. Colt Vista & Summit Wagon

Monaco & Premier

1. Run engine to normal operating temperature.
2. If fans do not come on, shut off engine, place ignition in Run position, then check for battery voltage at fan connectors.
3. If battery voltage is present and one or both fans do not operate, replace defective fan motor(s).
4. If battery voltage is not present, repair open or short in electrical wiring.

Laser & Talon

1. Disconnect fan motor connector and connect to battery positive to terminal 2, and battery negative to terminal 4, **Fig. 36**.
2. If fan does not run normally or make abnormal noises, replace fan motor assembly.

Stealth

1. Disconnect fan motor connector and connect to battery positive to terminal 2 and battery negative to terminal 5, **Fig. 33**.

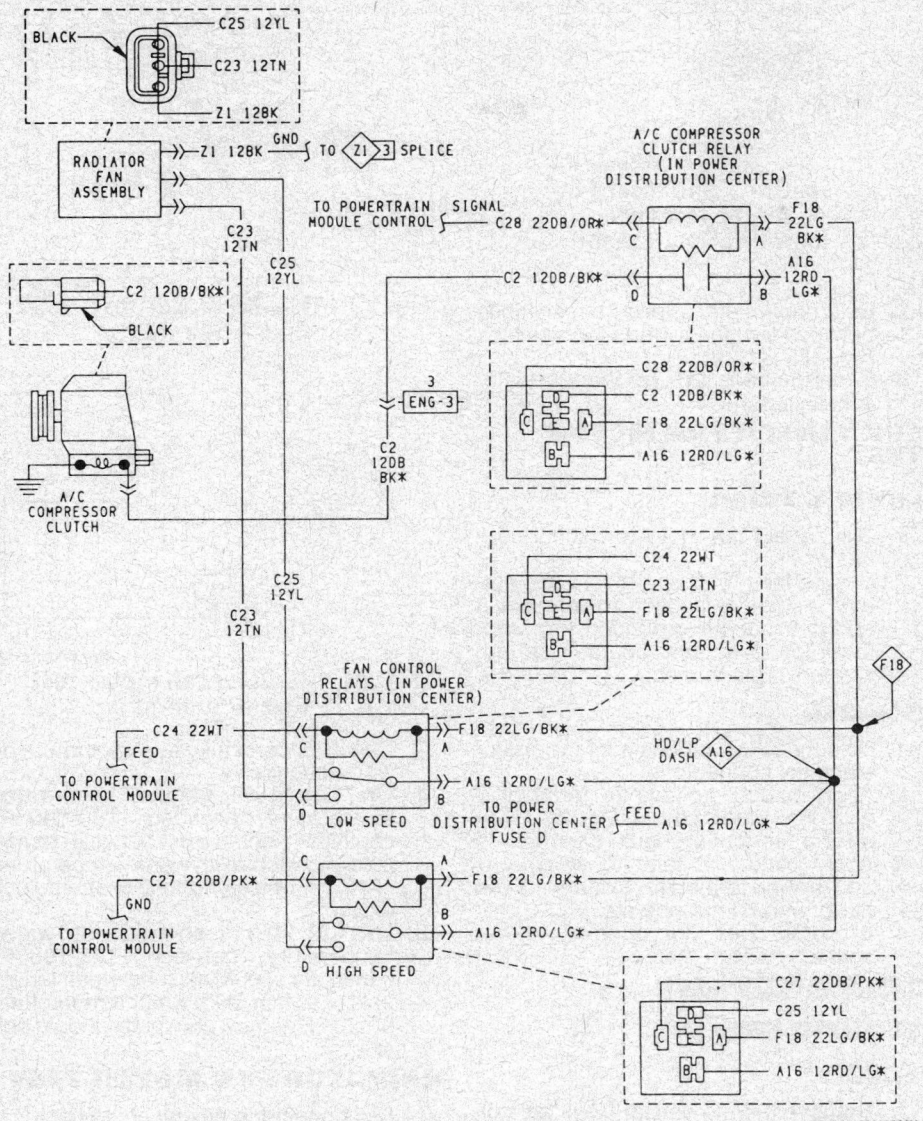

Fig. 31 Engine cooling fan wiring diagram. Concorde, Intrepid, LHS, Vision & 1994 New Yorker

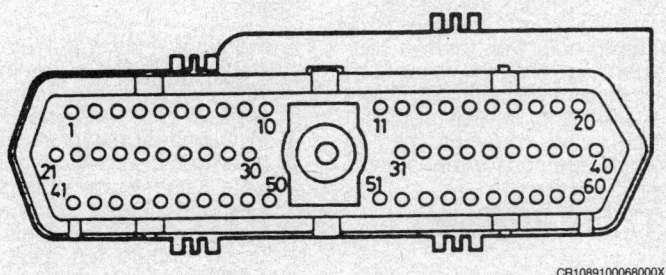

Fig. 35 Engine controller 60-way connector. Except Laser, Monaco, Premier, Stealth & Talon

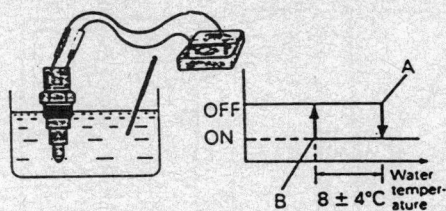

Fig. 32 Thermo sensor inspection. Stealth

Item	For condenser fan	For radiator fan
With continuity (temperature of point A)	91 – 99°C (196 – 210°F)	81 – 89°C (178 – 192°F)
Without continuity (temperature of point B)	87°C (189°F) or less	77°C (171°F) or less

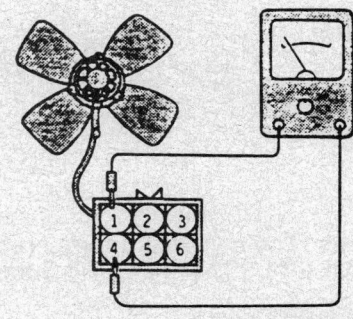

Fig. 33 Radiator fan connector terminals. Stealth

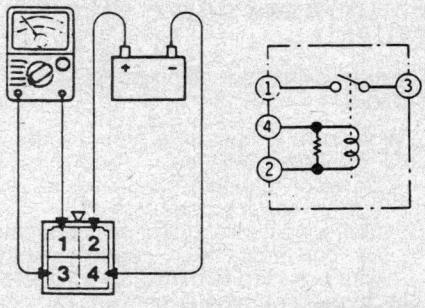

Fig. 34 Radiator fan motor relay. Laser, Stealth & Talon

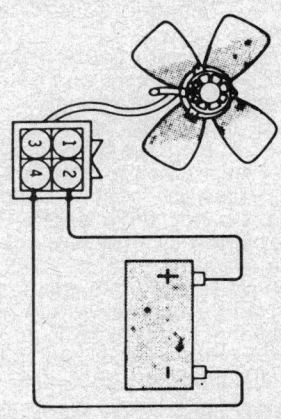

Fig. 36 Fan motor terminal identification. Laser & Talon

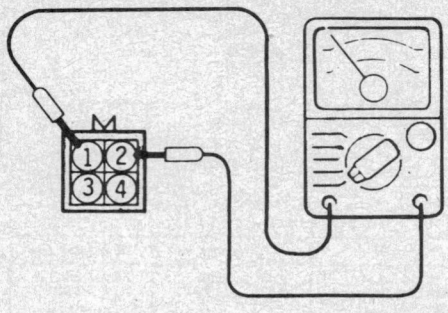

Fig. 37 Condenser fan resistor terminal identification. Laser & Talon

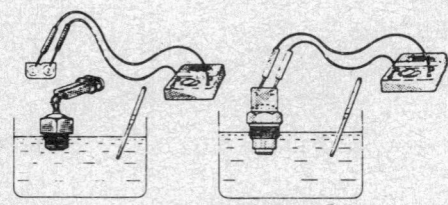

Fig. 40 Engine coolant temperature switch test. 1993–94 Colt & Summit

2. If fan does not run normally or makes abnormal noises, replace fan motor assembly.

CONDENSER FAN CONTROL SWITCH

Except Laser, Stealth & Talon

Work area temperature must be above 70°F to perform this test.
1. Connect manifold gauge set to A/C system service ports.
2. Disconnect fan control switch electrical connector, then connect jumper wire between terminals in connector.
3. Connect ohmmeter between fan control switch terminals.
4. Start engine and set idle at 1300 RPM. Radiator fan should run constantly.
5. Set A/C controls to A/C and high blower.
6. If high pressure gauge reads below 160 psi, continuity should not exist between switch terminals.
7. Block radiator air flow with suitable cover to increase high side pressure to at least 230 psi. Continuity should exist between control switch terminals. **Do not allow engine to overheat when air flow is blocked.**
8. Remove cover from radiator. Allow high side pressure to decrease. When pressure drops below 160 psi, continuity should not exist.
9. If fan control switch does not operate as specified, replace switch.

CONDENSER FAN RESISTOR

Laser & Talon

1. Disconnect resistor electrical connector.

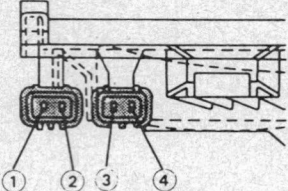

Fig. 38 Condenser fan motor terminal identification. Stealth

2. Using ohmmeter, measure resistance between terminals 1 and 2 of resistor, **Fig. 37.**
3. If resistance is .26-.32 ohms, resistor is satisfactory.

CONDENSER FAN MOTOR TEST

Laser & Talon

1. Disconnect fan motor electrical connector.
2. Ensure fan motor operates when battery voltage is applied to terminal 3 and terminal 4 is grounded, **Fig. 36.**
3. If motor does not operate as described, replace motor.

Stealth

1. Disconnect condenser fan motor electrical connectors.
2. Apply battery voltage to terminal 3 and ground terminal 4, **Fig. 38.** Condenser fan motor should operate.
3. Apply battery voltage to terminal 1 and ground terminal 2. Condenser fan motor should not operate.
4. If motor does not operate as described, replace motor.

COLT & SUMMIT

THERMO SENSOR

1992

1. Remove thermo sensor from radiator.
2. Submerge sensor end of thermo sensor in water as shown in **Fig. 39.**
3. Connect ohmmeter across thermo sensor terminal and casing, then heat water.
4. When water temperature reaches approximately 185°F, the thermo sensor contacts should close and continuity should exist between sensor terminals.
5. Allow water to cool with thermo sensor still submerged. When water temperature drops to approximately 172°F, the thermo sensor contacts should open and continuity should not exist between sensor terminals.

ENGINE COOLANT TEMPERATURE SWITCH

1993–94

1. Remove temperature switch from radiator.
2. Immerse switch in warm water and connect ohmmeter as shown in **Fig. 40.**

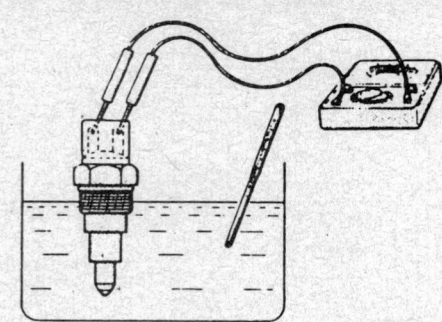

Fig. 39 Thermo sensor test. 1992 Colt & Summit

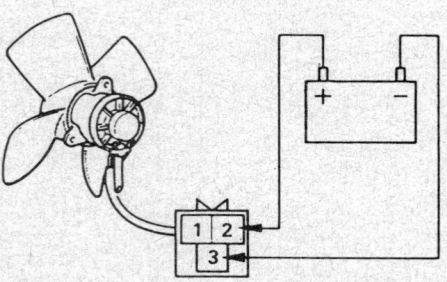

Fig. 41 Radiator fan motor test. Colt & Summit

3. Check for continuity as temperature of water changes.
4. **On 1.5L/4-90 engine,** with water temperature between 180-190°F, continuity should exist between terminals of switch. With water temperature of 172°F or less, continuity should not exist.
5. **On 1.8L/4-110 engine,** with water temperature between 178-190°F, continuity should exist between terminals of switch. With water temperature of 171°F or less, continuity should not exist.

RADIATOR FAN MOTOR TEST

1. Disconnect fan electrical connector.
2. Connect 12 power supply as shown in **Fig. 41.** Fan motor should operate smoothly.
3. If motor does not operate as specified, replace fan motor.

RADIATOR FAN MOTOR RELAY TEST

1992

1. Remove relay from relay box, apply battery positive to terminal No. 2 and battery negative to terminal No. 1 to relay side of connector, **Fig. 42.**
2. With battery power supplied connect a suitable ohmmeter between terminals 3 and 4, continuity should exist.
3. Remove battery voltage from relay, check between terminals 3 and 4 continuity should not exist, then check between terminals 1 and 2, continuity should exist.

1993–94

Refer to **Fig. 43** when performing this test.

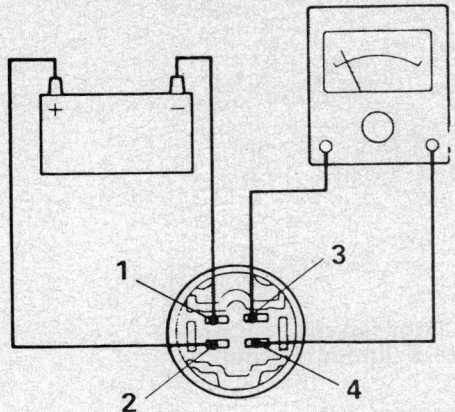

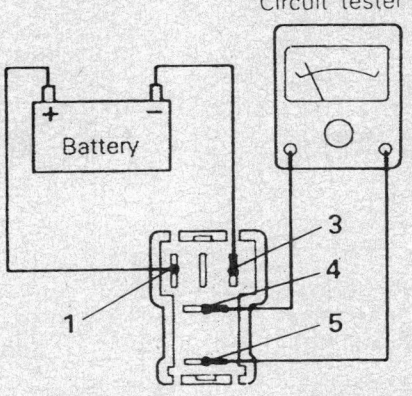

Circuit tester

Fig. 43 Radiator fan motor relay test. 1993–94 Colt & Summit

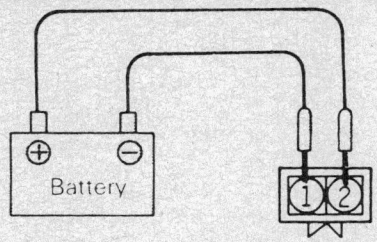

Fig. 44 Condenser fan motor test. Colt & Summit

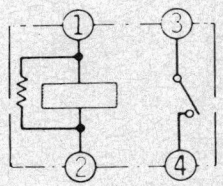

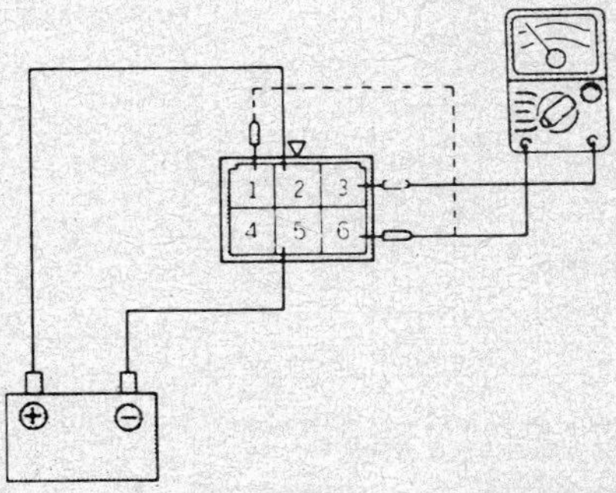

Fig. 42 Radiator fan motor relay test. 1992 Colt & Summit

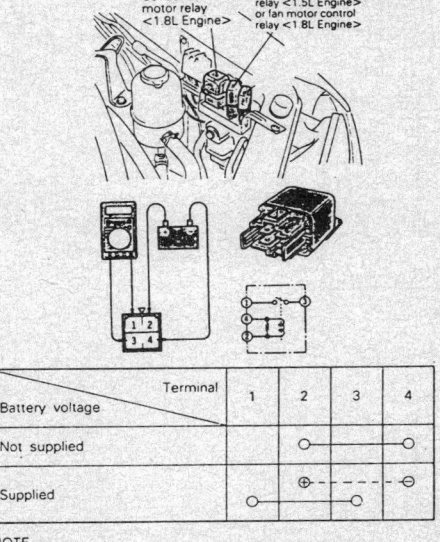

Terminal	1	2	3	4
Battery voltage				
Not supplied		○────	────○	
Supplied	○────	⊕─ ─ ─	────○	

NOTE
○──○ indicates that there is continuity between the terminals.
⊕──○ indicates terminals to which battery voltage is applied.

Fig. 46 Condenser fan motor relay & fan motor control relay test. 1993–94 Colt & Summit

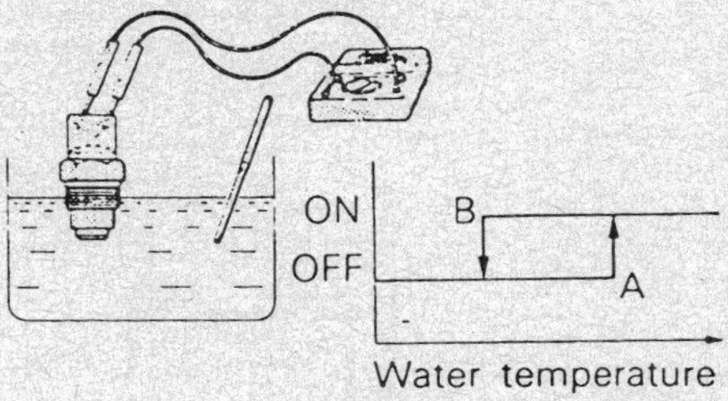

Items	For radiator fan
Temperature at point A (OFF→ON)	81°C–88°C (178°F–190°F)
Temperature at point B (ON→OFF)	77°C (171°F)

Fig. 47 Engine coolant temperature switch inspection. Colt Vista & Summit Wagon

7. Check for continuity between terminals 3 and 6, of relay. Continuity should exist.
8. If relay does not operate as specified, replace relay.

CONDENSER FAN MOTOR RELAY & FAN MOTOR CONTROL RELAY TEST

1993–94

Refer to **Fig. 46** for this test.

COLT VISTA & SUMMIT WAGON

Engine Coolant Temperature Switch

1. Remove engine coolant temperature switch from radiator, then immerse switch in warm water or oil.
2. Connect a suitable ohmmeter across switch, then refer to **Fig. 47** for specifications.
3. If not within specifications, replace coolant temperature switch.

Radiator Fan Motor

1. Disconnect fan motor connector, apply battery positive to terminal 2 of fan motor connector and battery negative to terminal 4, **Fig. 48**.
2. Ensure fan motor operates properly and no abnormal noise is produced. Replace if necessary.

Radiator Fan Motor Relay

1. Remove radiator fan motor HI and LO

Fig. 45 Condenser fan motor relay test. 1992 Colt & Summit

1. Remove radiator fan motor relay from relay box inside engine compartment.
2. Check for continuity between terminals 1 and 3. Continuity should exist.
3. Check for continuity between terminals 4 and 5. Continuity should not exist.
4. Connect 12 power supply between terminals 1 and 3.
5. Check for continuity between terminals 4 and 5. Continuity should exist.
6. If continuity is not as specified, replace relay.

CONDENSER FAN MOTOR TEST

1. Disconnect fan electrical connector.
2. Connect 12 power supply as shown in **Fig. 44**. Fan motor should operate smoothly.
3. If motor does not operate as specified, replace fan motor.

CONDENSER FAN MOTOR RELAY TEST

1992

Refer to **Fig. 45** when performing this test.
1. Remove condenser fan motor relay from relay box located in engine compartment.
2. Check for continuity between terminals 1 and 3, of relay. Continuity should exist.
3. Check for continuity between terminals 3 and 6, of relay. Continuity not should exist.
4. Check for continuity between terminals 2 and 5, of relay. Continuity should exist.
5. Connect 12 volt power supply to terminal 2, then ground terminal 5.
6. Check for continuity between terminals 1 and 3, of relay. Continuity not should exist.

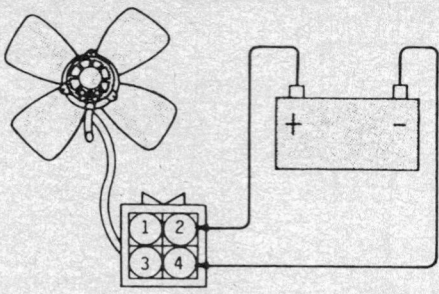

Fig. 48   Radiator fan motor terminal identification. Colt Vista & Summit Wagon

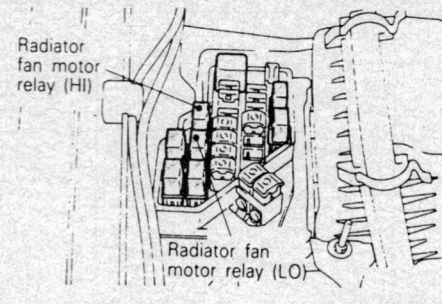

Fig. 49   Radiator fan relay location. Colt Vista & Summit Wagon

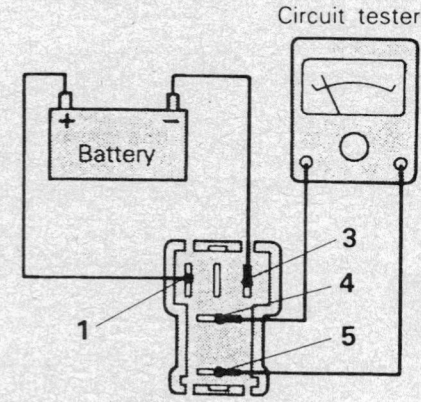

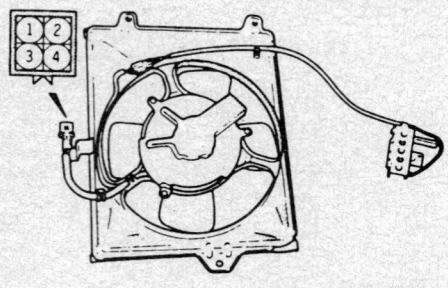

Fig. 51   Condenser fan motor terminal identification. Colt Vista & Summit Wagon

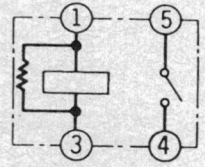

Fig. 50   Radiator fan relay terminal identification. Colt Vista & Summit Wagon

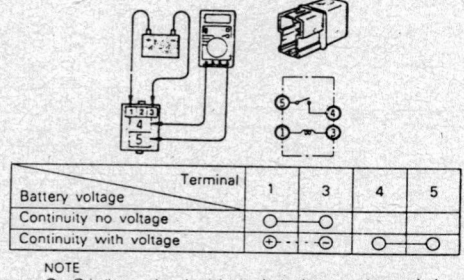

Terminal	1	3	4	5
Battery voltage				
Continuity no voltage	O——O			
Continuity with voltage	⊕-- ⊖		

NOTE
O——O indicates that there is continuity between the terminals.
⊕-- ⊖ indicates terminals to which battery voltage is applied.

Fig. 52   Condenser fan motor relay test. Colt Vista & Summit Wagon

relays from relay box located in engine compartment, **Fig. 49.**
2. Check continuity between terminals 1 and 3, continuity should exist, then check between terminals 4 and 5, continuity should not exist, **Fig. 50.**
3. Connect battery positive to terminal 1 and battery negative to terminal 3, then check continuity between terminals 4 and 5 continuity should exist. **Fig. 50.**
4. If not within specifications, replace HI or LO relay.

Engine Coolant Temperature Sensor

1. Remove engine coolant temperature sensor from intake manifold.
2. With sensing end immersed in hot water resistance should be 5.8 k at 32°F, 2.4 k at 68°F; 1.1 k at 104°F and 0.3 k at 176°F.
3. If resistance is not approximate to specifications above, replace sensor.

Thermo Sensor

Remove thermo sensor place in warm water, when water temperature reaches approximately 185°F, continuity should exist. At 171°F or lower continuity should not exist.

Condenser Fan Motor

1. Disconnect condenser fan motor electrical connector.
2. Connect 12 power supply to terminal 3 and ground terminal 1, **Fig. 51.**
3. Condenser fan motor should run smoothly.
4. If motor does not operate as specified, replace fan motor.

Condenser Fan Motor Relay

Refer to **Fig. 52** for condenser fan motor relay test.

COMPONENT REPLACEMENT

EXCEPT COLT, COLT VISTA, CONCORDE, INTREPID, LHS, NEON, SUMMIT, SUMMIT WAGON, VISION & 1994 NEW YORKER

Condenser And/Or Radiator Fan Motor

1. Disconnect battery negative cable, then disconnect fan motor electrical connector.
2. Remove fan motor, fan and fan shroud or support as an assembly from radiator support.
3. Remove fan blade from motor, then motor from shroud.
4. Reverse procedure to install.

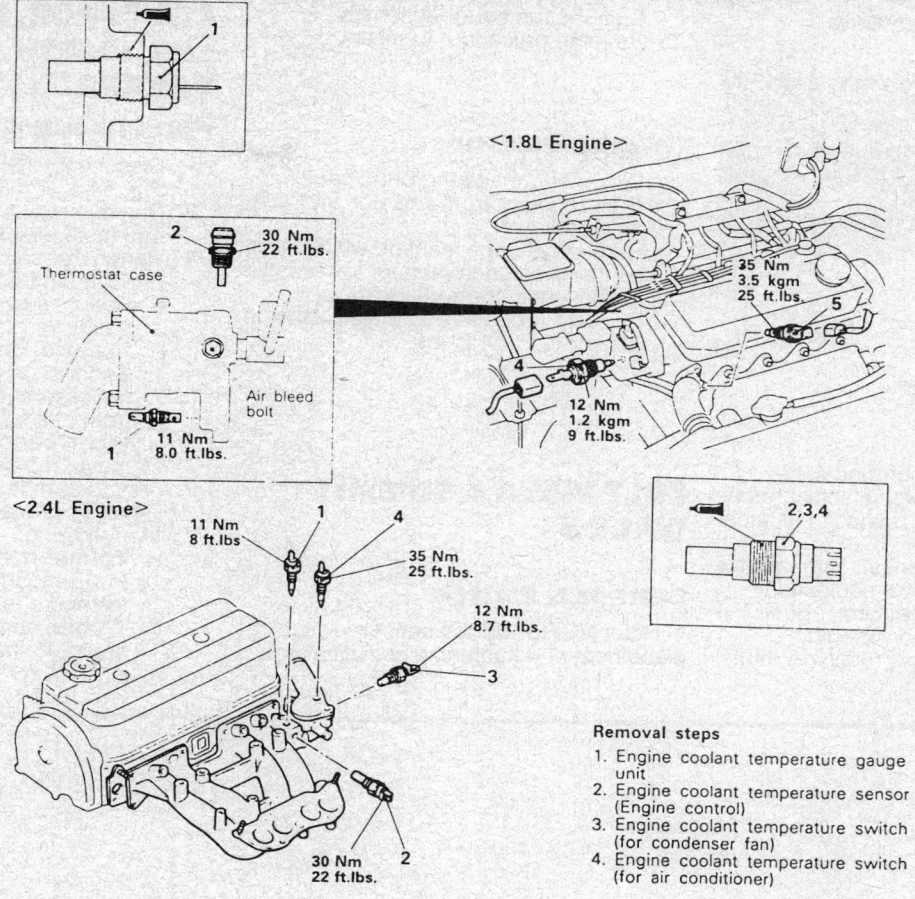

Fig. 53 Sensor & switch replacement. Colt Vista & Summit Wagon

Removal steps
1. Engine coolant temperature gauge unit
2. Engine coolant temperature sensor (Engine control)
3. Engine coolant temperature switch (for condenser fan)
4. Engine coolant temperature switch (for air conditioner)

CR1089200092000X

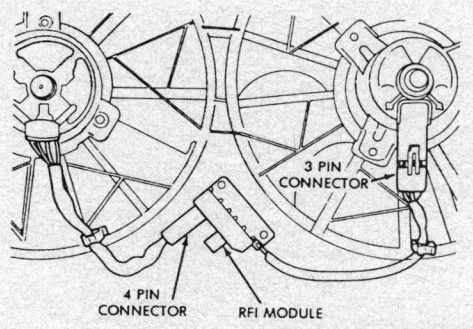

Fig. 54 RFI module location.
Concorde, Intrepid, LHS, Vision & 1994
New Yorker

CR1089100095000X

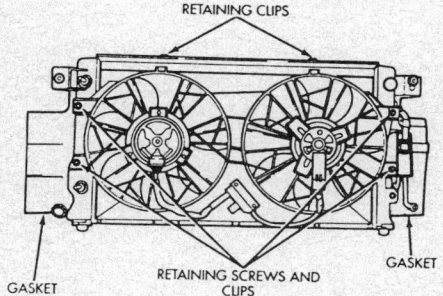

Fig. 55 Fan module removal.
Concorde, Intrepid, LHS, Vision &
1994 New Yorker

CR1089100096000X

Coolant Temperature Sensor

The coolant temperature sensor is located in the thermostat housing. Ensure coolant does not contact accessory drive belt or pulleys. Flush any spilled coolant with water.

1. Drain coolant from cylinder block by removing drain plug, located behind and below exhaust manifold.
2. Disconnect coolant temperature sensor electrical connector, then remove sensor.

3. Reverse procedure to install. Refill cooling system.

NEON

Fan Motor

1. Remove fan motor fasteners from motor support, then remove motor.
2. Reverse procedure to install. **Torque** fasteners to 25 inch lbs.

Fan Blade

The fan blade cannot be repaired in any way. Warpage, cracking or other damage can only be remedied by blade replacement. To remove from motor shaft, proceed as follows:

1. Support motor and shaft. Failure to do so may result in damage from excessive force.
2. Remove retaining clip from front of shaft, then draw fan blade off shaft. It may be necessary to eliminate burrs from shaft prior to blade removal.
3. Reverse procedure to install. Ensure motor and shaft are supported during fan blade retaining clip installation.

Coolant Temperature Sensor

1. Drain coolant from cylinder block by removing drain plug, located behind and below exhaust manifold.
2. Disconnect coolant temperature sensor electrical connector, then remove sensor.
3. Reverse procedure to install. Refill cooling system.

COLT & SUMMIT

Fan Motor

1. Disconnect battery ground cable.
2. Disconnect fan motor electrical connector and thermo sensor electrical connectors.
3. Disconnect condenser fan motor electrical connector, if equipped.
4. Remove upper radiator hose, if equipped with air conditioning.
5. Remove fan motor retaining bolts, then the fan motor assembly.
6. Reverse procedure to install.

Thermo Sensor

1. Disconnect battery ground cable.
2. Drain coolant from radiator into suitable container.
3. Remove thermo sensor wiring from sensor located in radiator lower tank.
4. Remove sensor from radiator.
5. Reverse procedure to install. **Torque** sensor to 7–14 ft. lbs.

COLT VISTA & SUMMIT WAGON

Sensor & Switch

Refer to **Fig. 53** for sensor, switch replacement and tightening specifications.

CONCORDE, INTREPID, LHS, VISION & 1994 NEW YORKER

Fan Shroud & Fan Motors

1. Disconnect RFI electrical connector, **Fig. 54**.
2. Remove fan module to radiator clips and fasteners, **Fig. 55**.
3. Remove assembly from radiator, then remove fan blades as follows:
   a. Bench support motor and motor shaft.
   b. Remove fan retaining clip or nut. Surface or burr removal may be necessary before removing fans from shaft. **Do not let fan blades touch bench when removing.**
4. Remove motor fasteners from support, then motor from support.
5. Reverse procedure to install, noting the following:
   a. **Torque** right fan motor fasteners to 25 inch lbs. and left fan motor fasteners to 45 inch lbs.
   b. **Torque** shroud to radiator fasteners to 45 inch lbs.

DASH GAUGES

NOTE: On Air Bag Equipped Models, Refer To "Air Bag System Precautions" Located In The Front Of This Manual For System Disarming & Arming Procedures.

INDEX

PRECAUTIONS

AIR BAG SYSTEMS

Refer to "Air Bag System Precautions" in the front of this manual for system disarming and arming procedures.

GAUGES

VOLTAGE LIMITER (CONSTANT VOLTAGE) TYPE

The voltage limiter type indicator gauge is a bi-metal resistance type system consisting of a voltage limiter, an indicator gauge and a variable resistance sending unit. Current to the system is applied to the gauge terminals by the voltage limiter, which maintains an average pulsating value of 5 volts.

The indicator gauge consists of a pointer which is attached to a wire-wound bi-metal strip. Current passing through the coil heats the bi-metal strip, causing the pointer to move. As more current passes through the coil, heat increases, moving the pointer farther.

The circuit is completed through a sending unit which contains a variable resistor. When resistance is high, less current is allowed to pass through the gauge, and the pointer moves very little. As resistance decreases due to changing conditions in the system being monitored, current increases through the gauge coil, causing the pointer to move farther.

DIAGNOSIS & TESTING

Gauge failures are often caused by defective wiring or grounds. The first step in locating trouble should be a thorough inspection of all wiring, terminals and printed circuits. If wiring is secured by clamps, check to see whether the insulation has been severed, thereby grounding the wire. In the case of a fuel gauge, rust may cause failure by corrosion at the ground connection of the tank unit.

Voltage Limiter Test

1. Using a suitable voltmeter, connect one lead to the temperature sending unit and other lead to ground. Do not disconnect sending unit lead from sending unit.
2. Turn ignition switch to On position and observe voltmeter.
3. A fluctuating voltmeter indicates that voltage limiter is operating properly.

Fuel Tank Sending Unit Test

1. Disconnect wiring from fuel tank sending unit.
2. Connect wiring to a known good sending unit.
3. Connect a jumper wire between sending unit pick up tube and ground.
4. Check fuel gauge as follows:
   a. **Allow at least two minutes for gauge to settle at each test point.**
   b. Move float arm to its empty stop and turn ignition to On position; gauge should read Empty or below.
   c. Move float arm to Full position; gauge should read Full or above.
5. If gauge does not meet specifications, check the following items for possible malfunction:
   a. Wiring and connections between gauge sending unit and multiple connector behind left kick panel.
   b. Wiring and connections between multiple connector and printed circuit board terminals.
   c. Circuit continuity between printed circuit board terminals and gauge terminals.
   d. If above items are satisfactory, gauge is defective and must be replaced.
6. If fuel gauge meets specifications, check fuel tank sending unit. Remove fuel tank sending unit from fuel tank and connect a jumper wire between sending unit pick up tube and ground, then repeat fuel gauge inspection procedure.
7. If fuel gauge is now within specifications, check the following:
   a. Ground wire from sending unit to left side cowl. Ensure continuity exists.
   b. Sending unit mechanical condition. Ensure float arm moves freely and pick up tube is not bent.
   c. Sending unit float. Ensure there are no leaks or deformations.
   d. Sending unit installation. Ensure unit is installed correctly.
   e. Sending unit mounting flange on fuel tank. Ensure flange is not deformed.
   f. Fuel tank bottom. If deformed, pick up tube may be improperly positioned.

Oil & Temperature Sending Unit Test

1. Test dash gauge and voltage limiter as outlined under "Voltage Limiter Test."
2. If system is satisfactory, start engine and allow it to reach operating temperature.
3. If no reading is indicated on gauge, remove wire from sending unit and momentarily ground this wire to a clean, unpainted portion of engine.
4. If gauge remains motionless, wire is defective. Repair or replace wire.
5. If grounding new or repaired wire activates dash gauge, sending unit is faulty. Replace as necessary.

VARIABLE VOLTAGE TYPE

The variable voltage type dash gauge consists of two magnetic coils to which battery voltage is applied. The coils act on the gauge pointer and pull in opposite directions. One coil is grounded directly to the chassis, while the other coil is grounded through a variable resistor within the sending unit. Resistance through the sending unit determines current flow through its coil, and therefore determines pointer position.

When resistance is high in the sending unit, less current is allowed to flow through its coil, causing the gauge pointer to move toward the directly grounded coil. When resistance in the sending unit decreases, more current is allowed to pass through its coil, increasing the magnetic field. The gauge pointer is then attracted toward the coil which is grounded through the sending unit.

ELECTRICAL TYPE

TEMPERATURE GAUGE

This system consists of a sending unit, located on the cylinder head, electrical temperature gauge and an instrument voltage regulator. As engine temperature increases or decreases, resistance of the sending unit changes, in turn controlling current flow to the gauge. When engine temperature is low, the resistance of the sending unit is high, restricting current flow to the gauge, in turn indicating low engine temperature. As engine temperature increases, resistance of the sending unit decreases, permitting an increased current flow to the gauge, resulting in an increased temperature reading.

Troubleshooting

Disconnect terminal from temperature sending unit on engine, then connect test lead of tester tool No. C-3826A or equivalent to terminal and second test lead to ground. Place pointer of gauge tester on E position and turn ignition switch to the On position. The temperature gauge should show C plus or minus 1/8 inch.

Place pointer of tester on the 1/2 position, the gauge should advance to the operating range left of 1/2 position of the dial. Place pointer of the tester in the F position, gauge should advance to H position of the dial. If gauge responds to test correctly, but does not operate when terminal is attached to sending unit, replace gauge.

OIL PRESSURE GAUGE

The oil pressure indicating system consists a instrument voltage regulator, electrical oil pressure gauge and a sending unit which are connected in series. The sending unit consists of a diaphragm, contact and a variable resistor. As oil pressure increases or decreases, the diaphragm actuates the contact on the variable resistor, in turn controlling current flow to the gauge. When oil pressure is low, the resistance of the variable resistor is high, restricting current flow to the gauge, in turn indicating low oil pressure. As oil pressure increases, the resistance of the variable resistor is lowered, increasing current flow to the gauge, resulting in an increased gauge reading.

Troubleshooting

Disconnect oil pressure gauge electrical connector from the sending unit, then connect a 12 volt test lamp between the gauge connector and ground, then turn ignition to the On position. If test lamp flashes, the instrument voltage regulator is functioning properly and the gauge circuit is not broken. If the test lamp remains lit, the instrument voltage regulator is defective and must be replaced. If the test lamp does not light, check the instrument voltage regulator for proper ground or an open circuit. Also, check for an open in the instrument voltage regulator to oil pressure gauge wire or in the gauge. **If test lamp flashes and gauge is not accurate,**

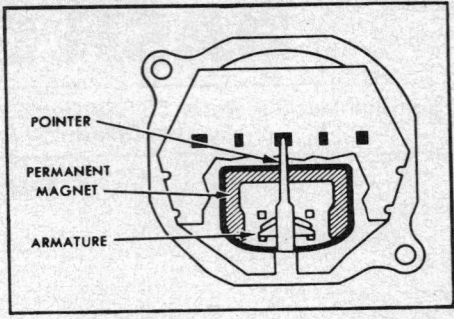

Fig. 1 Conventional type ammeter (typical)

CR9099100055000X

gauge may be out of calibration. Replace gauge.

METERS

AMMETER

The ammeter is used to indicate current flow into and out of the battery. When electrical accessories in the vehicle draw more current than the alternator can supply, current flows from the battery and the ammeter indicates a discharge (-) condition. When electrical loads of the vehicle are less than alternator output, current is available to charge the battery, and the ammeter indicates a charge (+) condition. If battery is fully charged, the voltage regulator reduces alternator output to meet only immediate vehicle electrical loads. When this happens, the ammeter will read zero.

VARIABLE VOLTAGE TYPE

A conventional ammeter is connected between the battery and alternator in order to indicate current flow. This type of ammeter, **Fig. 1**, consists of a frame to which a permanent magnet is attached. The frame also supports an armature and pointer assembly. Current in this system flows from the alternator through the ammeter, then to the battery or from the battery through the ammeter into the vehicle electrical system, depending on vehicle operating conditions.

When current flow is not present through the ammeter, the magnet holds the pointer armature so the pointer stands centered in the dial. When current passes in either direction through the ammeter, the resulting magnetic field attracts the armature away from the effect of the permanent magnet, giving a reading proportional to the strength of the current flowing.

Troubleshooting

When the ammeter fails to register correctly, the trouble may be in the alternator, battery, or the wiring from the ammeter to the alternator and battery.

Check connections at the ammeter, ignition switch, battery and alternator. Repair as necessary.

All wires with chafed, burned or broken insulation should be repaired or replaced. After repairs have been made, and all con-

nections are tightened, connect the battery cable and turn ignition switch to the On position. The needle should point slightly to the discharge (-) side.

Start engine and raise engine speed. The ammeter needle should then move to the charge side.

If the ammeter fails to operate correctly, replace the ammeter.

SHUNT TYPE

The shunt type ammeter is a specially calibrated voltmeter. It's purpose is to read voltage drop across a resistance wire (shunt) between the battery and condition is indicated for an extended period, the battery and charging system should be checked. The shunt is located in the vehicle wiring or within the ammeter.

When voltage is higher at the alternator end of the shunt, the meter indicates a charge (+) condition. When voltage is higher at the battery end of the shunt, the meter indicates a discharge (-) condition. When voltage is equal at both ends of the shunt, the meter reads zero.

Troubleshooting

Ammeter accuracy can be determined by comparing reading with an ammeter of known accuracy.

1. With engine stopped and ignition switch in On position, turn on headlamps and heater fan. Meter should indicate a discharge (-) condition.
2. If ammeter pointer does not move, check ammeter terminals for proper connection and open circuit in wiring harness. If connections and wiring harness are satisfactory, ammeter is defective.
3. If ammeter indicates a charge (+) condition, wiring harness connections are reversed at ammeter.

VOLTMETER

The voltmeter gauge measures electrical flow from the battery to indicate battery output tolerances. The voltmeter reading may range from 13.5–14.0 volts under normal operating conditions.

Troubleshooting

To check voltmeter turn headlights on, then turn key to the On position. Pointer

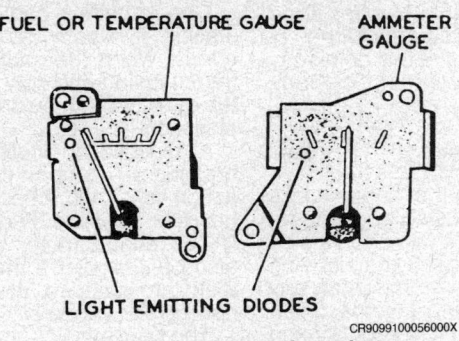

FUEL OR TEMPERATURE GAUGE   AMMETER GAUGE

LIGHT EMITTING DIODES

CR9099100056000X

Fig. 2   Gauge LED locations

should move to 12.5 volts. If needle movement is not present, check connections from battery to circuit breaker. If connections are tight and meter shows no movement, check wire continuity. If continuity is satisfactory, meter is inoperative and must be replaced.

WARNING LAMPS

LOW FUEL WARNING LAMP

When the ignition is turned to the On position current flows to the low-fuel warning sensor. If the fuel level falls below the preset level, the fuel level sensor, which is normally submerged in fuel, is exposed to air and resistance to the sensor decreases to a low level, in turn causing the warning light to go on.

OIL PRESSURE INDICATOR LAMP

A warning lamp on the instrument panel is used in place of the conventional dash indicating gauge to warn the driver when oil pressure is low. The warning lamp is wired in series with the ignition switch and the oil sending unit.

The oil pressure switch contains a diaphragm and contacts. When the ignition switch is turned to the On position, the warning lamp circuit is energized and the circuit is completed through the closed contacts in the pressure switch. When the engine is started, build-up of oil pressure compresses the diaphragm, opening the contacts, thereby breaking the circuit.

Troubleshooting

When the ignition is turned on, the oil pressure warning lamp should light. If the lamp does not light, disconnect the sending unit electrical connector from the engine unit and ground wire to the frame or cylinder block. If the warning lamp still does not light with the ignition switch on, replace the bulb.

If the warning lamp lights when the wire is grounded, check the unit for looseness or improper grounding. If the unit is found to be tight and properly grounded, replace unit.

If the warning lamp remains lit under normal conditions, replace the unit before proceeding further to determine the cause for a low pressure indication.

Under normal conditions, the warning lamp will sometimes light or flicker when the engine is idling. However, the lamp should go out when engine idle is raised.

TEMPERATURE INDICATOR LAMP

If the engine cooling system is not functioning properly, causing coolant temperature to exceed a predetermined value, the coolant temperature warning lamp will illuminate.

Troubleshooting

If the lamp is not lit when engine is being cranked, check for a defective bulb, open in the light circuit, or a defective ignition switch.

If the lamp is lit when the engine is running, check for overheated cooling system, defective temperature switch, or wiring between lamp and switch for short to ground.

WARNING SYSTEM

DESCRIPTION

The fuel, temperature and ammeter gauges are equipped with a Light Emitting Diode (LED) mounted in each of the gauge dials, **Fig. 2**. This diode will illuminate and alert the driver that the system is malfunctioning. The electronic sensor circuit is mounted on the gauge housing. The printed circuit board is permanently attached and is not serviceable. If the LED is malfunctioning, the gauge and the printed circuit board must be replaced as an assembly.

The oil pressure warning switch, mounted on the engine, is controlled by engine oil pressure.

When engine oil pressure is high (normal operating condition) the switch is held in the Off position allowing no current to flow to the oil pressure warning lamp on the instrument panel.

When engine oil pressure is low the switch is in the On position allowing current to flow to the oil pressure warning lamp on the instrument panel causing the instrument panel to be illuminated. When the switch is in the Off position it completes the circuit for the electric choke heater.

OPERATION

Fuel Gauge

When the gauge indicator shows approximately 1/8 tank of fuel remaining, the LED will light, alerting the driver to a low fuel condition.

Temperature Gauge

When the gauge indicator shows engine temperature to be 240° to 260°, the LED will light, alerting the driver to an overheating condition.

Ammeter Gauge

This LED operates independently of the gauge indicator and monitors system voltage. The LED will alert the driver of the following three charging system potential malfunctions:

1. A discharging condition, caused by excessive electrical demand on charging system (engine at idle RPM).
2. A weak or defective battery with ignition switch in On position (before ignition switch is moved to Start position).
3. A weak or defective battery with minimum demand on charging system, while vehicle is being used in stop and go driving (intermittent LED illumination occurring).

TESTING

Fuel & Temperature LED

Use tester tool No. C-3826 or equivalent when diagnosing systems.

Ammeter LED

Proceed with the following test only if the battery and charging system are functioning properly.

Turn ignition switch to the On position and turn on headlights, windshield wipers and stoplights. This will cause excessive demand on charging system activating the LED immediately or within approximately one minute. If the LED does not light, there is a malfunction in the system. If LED lights, run engine at approximately 2000 RPM, LED should stop emitting light. If the LED continues to emit light there is a malfunction in the system. **In all cases of system malfunctions, the complete gauge must be replaced.**

SPEEDOMETERS

The speedometer has two main parts: the indicator head and the speedometer drive cable. When the speedometer fails to indicate speed or mileage, the cable or housing is probably broken.

SPEEDOMETER CABLE

Most cables are broken due to lack of lubrication or a sharp bend or kink in the housing.

A cable might break because the speedometer head mechanism binds. If such is the case, the speedometer head should be repaired or replaced before a new cable or housing is installed.

A jumpy or noisy pointer condition is due to a dry or kinked speedometer cable. The kinked cable rubs on the housing and winds up, slowing down the pointer. The cable then unwinds and the pointer jumps.

To check for kinks, remove the cable, lay it on a flat surface and twist one end with the fingers. If it turns over smoothly the cable is not kinked. But if part of the cable flops over as it is twisted, the cable is kinked and should be replaced.

LUBRICATION

The speedometer cable should be lubricated with special cable lubricant every 10,000 miles.

Fill the ferrule on the upper end of the housing with the cable lubricant. Insert the cable in the housing, starting at the upper end. Turn the cable around carefully while feeding it into the housing. Repeat filling the ferrule except for the last six inches of cable. Too much lubricant at this point may cause the lubricant to work into the indicating hand.

INSTALLING CABLE

During installation, if the cable sticks when inserted in the housing and will not go through, the housing is damaged inside or kinked. Be sure to check the housing from one end to the other. Straighten any sharp bends by relocating clamps or elbows. Replace housing if it is badly kinked or broken. Position the cable and housing so that they lead into the head as straight as possible.

Check the new cable for kinks before installing it. Use wide, sweeping, gradual curves when the cable comes out of the transmission and connects to the head so the cable will not be damaged during its installation.

If inspection indicates that the cable and housing are in good condition, yet pointer action is erratic, check the speedometer head for possible binding.

The speedometer drive pinion should also be checked. If the pinion is dry or its teeth are stripped, the speedometer may not register properly.

The transmission mainshaft nut must be tight or the speedometer drive gear may slip on the mainshaft and cause slow speed readings.

STARTER MOTORS

TABLE OF CONTENTS

Bosch Starter Motors

INDEX

APPLICATION CHART

Model	Engine Liter/CID	Starter Type
1992		
Acclaim	2.2L/4-135	Gear Reduction
	2.5L/4-153	Gear Reduction
	3.0L/V6-181	Gear Reduction
Daytona	2.2L/4-135	Gear Reduction
	2.5L/4-153	Gear Reduction
	3.0L/V6-181	Gear Reduction
Dynasty	2.5L/4-153	Gear Reduction
	3.0L/V6-181	Gear Reduction
LeBaron Coupe/Convertible	2.5L/4-153	Gear Reduction
	3.0L/V6-181	Gear Reduction
LeBaron Landau	2.5L/4-153	Gear Reduction
	3.0L/V6-181	Gear Reduction
Shadow	2.5L/4-153	Gear Reduction
Spirit	2.2L/4-135	Gear Reduction
	2.5L/4-153	Gear Reduction
	3.0L/V6-181	Gear Reduction
Sundance	2.5L/4-153	Gear Reduction
1993		
Acclaim	2.2L/4-135	Gear Reduction
	2.5L/4-153	Gear Reduction
	3.0L/V6-181	Gear Reduction
Daytona	2.2L/4-135	Gear Reduction
	2.5L/4-153	Gear Reduction
	3.0L/V6-181	Gear Reduction

Model	Engine Liter/CID	Starter Type
1993 -Continued		
Dynasty	2.5L/4-153	Gear Reduction
	3.0L/V6-181	Gear Reduction
LeBaron Coupe/Convertible	2.5L/4-153	Gear Reduction
	3.0L/V6-181	Gear Reduction
LeBaron Landau	2.5L/4-153	Gear Reduction
	3.0L/V6-181	Gear Reduction
Shadow	2.5L/4-153	Gear Reduction
Spirit	2.2L/4-135	Gear Reduction
	2.5L/4-153	Gear Reduction
	3.0L/V6-181	Gear Reduction
Sundance	2.5L/4-153	Gear Reduction
1994		
Acclaim	2.2L/4-135	Gear Reduction
	2.5L/4-153	Gear Reduction
	3.0L/V6-181	Gear Reduction
LeBaron	2.5L/4-153	Gear Reduction
	3.0L/V6-181	Gear Reduction
Shadow	2.5L/4-153	Gear Reduction
Spirit	2.2L/4-135	Gear Reduction
	2.5L/4-153	Gear Reduction
	3.0L/V6-181	Gear Reduction
Sundance	2.5L/4-153	Gear Reduction
1995		
Neon	2.0L/4-122	Gear Reduction

DESCRIPTION

Bosch starter motors incorporate an overrunning clutch type starter drive. A solenoid switch is mounted on the starter motor, **Fig. 1**.

The Bosch starter is a gear reduction starter. This starter uses six permanent magnets in place of conventional wound field magnets to save weight, eliminate field winding to case shorts and improve cold start performance. The gear reduction system uses a planetary gear train to transmit armature rotation to the pinion shaft. A solenoid switch is mounted on the starter motor drive end shield.

TROUBLESHOOTING

Refer to **Fig. 2** when troubleshooting the starting system.

DIAGNOSIS & TESTING
IN-VEHICLE TESTING

Before starting any tests, ensure that the battery is fully charged and that all connections are good, then disable ignition system as follows:
1. **On models with distributor ignition system,** disconnect ignition coil cable from distributor cap. Connect a suitable jumper wire between coil cable end terminal and a good body ground.
2. **On models with direct ignition system,** disconnect ignition coils electrical connector.

STARTER FEED CIRCUIT TEST

The following test will require a suitable volt-ohmmeter tester.
1. Connect tester to battery terminals following manufactures instructions.
2. Disable ignition system.
3. Ensure all electrical accessories are Off, transmission in Park or Neutral and the parking brake is set.
4. Turn ignition switch to Start position and observe tester.
5. If voltage reads above 9.6 volts and amperage draw reads above 250 amps, perform test shown under "Starter Feed Circuit Resistance Test.
6. If voltage reads 12.4 volts or more and amperage reads 0-10 amps, perform "Starter Control Circuit Test" in this section.
7. After starting system problems have been corrected, verify battery is fully charged. Disconnect all testing equipment and connect ignition system. Start vehicle several times to ensure system is operating correctly.

STARTER FEED CIRCUIT RESISTANCE TEST

The following test will require a voltmeter accurate to 1/10 volt.
1. Disable ignition system.
2. With wiring harnesses and components connected properly, proceed as follows:
   a. Connect positive lead of voltmeter to negative battery post and negative lead to negative battery cable clamp. Turn ignition switch to Start position and observe voltmeter. If voltage is detected, correct poor contact between cable clamp and post.
   b. Connect positive lead of voltmeter to negative battery terminal and negative lead to engine block near battery cable attaching point. Turn ignition switch to Start position and observe voltmeter. If voltage reads above .2 volts, correct poor connection at ground cable attaching point. If voltmeter still reads above .2 volts after correcting poor contacts, replace ground cable.
3. Remove starter heat shield, then proceed as follows:
   a. Connect positive voltmeter lead to starter motor housing and negative lead to negative battery terminal. Turn ignition switch to Start position. If voltage reads above .2 volts, correct poor starter to engine ground.
   b. Connect positive voltmeter lead to positive battery terminal and negative lead to battery cable terminal on starter solenoid. Turn ignition switch to Start position. If voltage reads above .2 volts, correct poor contact at battery cable solenoid connection. If reading is still above .2 volts after correcting contact points, replace positive battery cable.
4. If resistance tests detect no feed circuit failures, remove starter motor and perform test under "Bench Testing."

STARTER CONTROL CIRCUIT TEST

The starter control circuit consists of the starter solenoid, starter relay, ignition switch, neutral safety switch and all related wiring and connections.

Starter Solenoid Test

1. Verify battery is fully charged and in good condition.
2. Raise and support vehicle.
3. Inspect starter and starter solenoid for corrosion or loose wiring.
4. Lower vehicle.
5. Locate starter relay as follows:
   a. **On all models except Acclaim, LeBaron Landau, Sundance, Shadow and Spirit,** the starter relay is located in the power distribution center mounted near the LH strut tower.
   b. **On Acclaim, LeBaron Landau, Sundance, Shadow and Spirit,** the starter relay is located on the front of the LH strut tower.
6. Remove starter relay from connector.
7. Connect a remote starter switch or a jumper wire between the battery positive post and terminal 87 on starter relay connector, **Fig. 3.**
8. If engine cranks, starter and starter solenoid is operating correctly, perform starter relay test.
9. If engine does not crank or solenoid chatters, check wiring and connectors from relay to starter for loose or corroded connections.
10. Repeat test and, if engine still does not crank properly, repair or replace starter or starter solenoid as necessary.

Starter Relay Test

1. Verify battery is fully charged and in good condition.
2. Perform starter solenoid test.
3. Remove starter relay.
4. Perform starter relay test shown in **Fig. 4.**

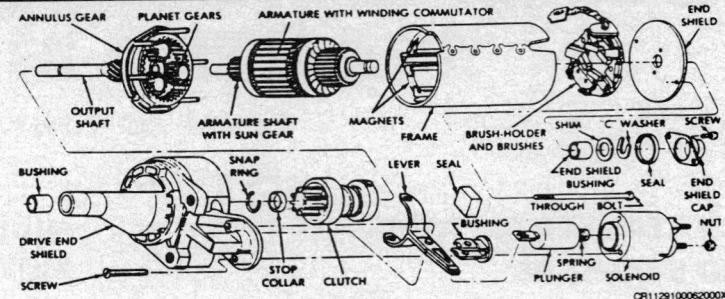

Fig. 1 Bosch starter motor

SYMPTOM STARTER FAILS TO ENGAGE. NO SOUNDS	SYMPTOM STARTER FAILS TO ENGAGE. SOLENOID OR RELAY CLICKS	SYMPTOM STARTER ENGAGES, FAILS TO TURN ENGINE. DOME LIGHT DIMS	SYMPTOM STARTER ENGAGES, DRIVE CLUTCH SPINS OUT	SYMPTOM STARTER DOES NOT DISENGAGE AFTER ENGINE STARTS
POSSIBLE CAUSE ↓ STARTER CONTROL CIRCUIT FAULTY ↓ IGNITION SWITCH FAULTY ↓ NEUTRAL SAFETY SWITCH (AUTO TRANS.) FAULTY OR MISADJUSTED ↓ CLUTCH PEDAL SWITCH (MANUAL TRANS.) FAULTY OR MISADJUSTED ↓ STARTER RELAY FAULTY ↓ STARTER ASSEMBLY FAULTY	POSSIBLE CAUSE ↓ RESISTANCE TOO HIGH IN STARTER FEED CIRCUIT ↓ STARTER CONTROL CIRCUIT FAULTY ↓ STARTER SOLENOID FAULTY ↓ STARTER ASSEMBLY FAULTY	POSSIBLE CAUSE ↓ RESISTANCE TOO HIGH IN STARTER FEED CIRCUIT ↓ ENGINE SEIZED ↓ STARTER ASSEMBLY FAULTY	POSSIBLE CAUSE ↓ DRIVE CLUTCH FAULTY ↓ BROKEN TEETH ON RING GEAR ↓ STARTER ASSEMBLY FAULTY	POSSIBLE CAUSE ↓ IGNITION SWITCH FAULTY ↓ STARTER RELAY FAULTY ↓ STARTER ASSEMBLY FAULTY

REFER TO PROPER SERVICE AND TEST PROCEDURES FOR THE COMPONENTS INVOLVED

Fig. 2 Starting system troubleshooting chart

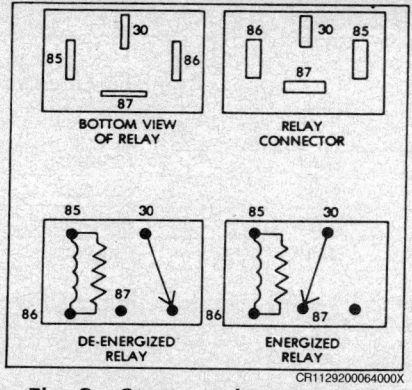

Fig. 3 Starter relay terminal identification

Ignition Switch Test

After testing starter solenoid and relay, test ignition switch and wiring. Check all wiring for opens and shorts and all connectors for looseness or corrosion.

BENCH TESTING

Starter Solenoid

1. Disconnect field coil wire from field coil terminal.
2. Check for continuity between solenoid terminal and field coil terminal. There should be continuity.
3. Check for continuity between sole-

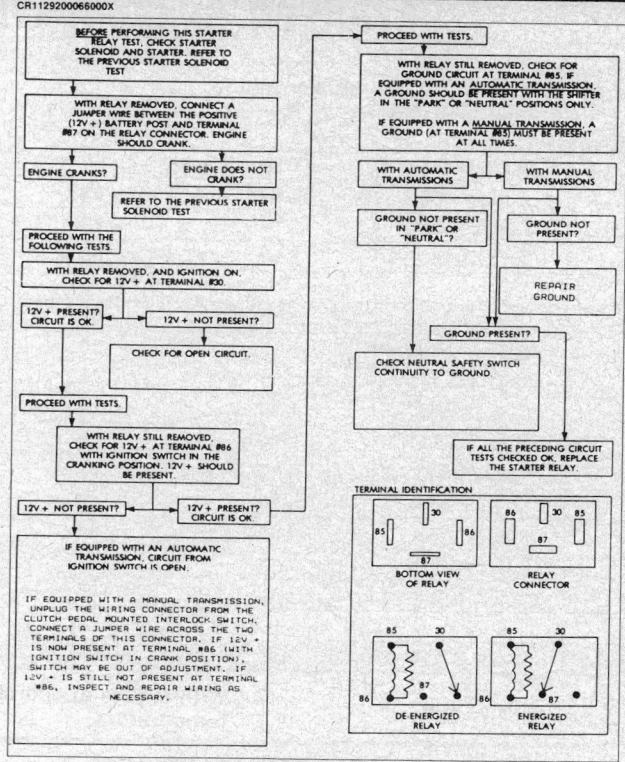

Fig. 4 Starter relay test

noid terminal and solenoid housing. There should be continuity.

4. If there is no continuity in either test, replace solenoid assembly.

STARTER SPECIFICATIONS

Model	Engine Liter/CID	Power Rating, Kw	Free Speed Test		RPM②	Cranking Amp Draw Test③
			Amps①	Volts		
1992						
Acclaim	2.2L/4-135	1.10	69	11	3447	150-220
	2.5L/4-153	1.10	69	11	3447	150-220
	3.0L/V6-181	1.10	73	11	3473	150-220
Daytona	2.2L/4-135	1.10	69	11	3447	150-220
	2.5L/4-153	1.10	69	11	3447	150-220
	3.0L/V6-181	1.10	73	11	3473	150-220
Dynasty	2.5L/4-153	1.10	69	11	3447	150-220
	3.0L/V6-181	1.10	73	11	3473	150-220
LeBaron Coupe/ Convertible	2.5L/4-153	1.10	69	11	3447	150-220
	3.0L/V6-181	1.10	73	11	3473	150-220
LeBaron Landau	2.5L/4-153	1.10	69	11	3447	150-220
	3.0L/V6-181	1.10	73	11	3473	150-220
Shadow	2.5L/4-153	1.10	69	11	3447	150-220
Spirit	2.2L/4-135	1.10	69	11	3447	150-220
	2.5L/4-153	1.10	69	11	3447	150-220
	3.0L/V6-181	1.10	73	11	3473	150-220
Sundance	2.5L/4-153	1.10	69	11	3447	150-220
1993						
Acclaim	2.2L/4-135	1.10	69	11	3447	150-220
	2.5L/4-153	1.10	69	11	3447	150-220
	3.0L/V6-181	1.10	73	11	3473	150-220
Daytona	2.2L/4-135	1.10	69	11	3447	150-220
	2.5L/4-153	1.10	69	11	3447	150-220
	3.0L/V6-181	1.10	73	11	3473	150-220
Dynasty	2.5L/4-153	1.10	69	11	3447	150-220
	3.0L/V6-181	1.10	73	11	3473	150-220
LeBaron Coupe/ Convertible	2.5L/4-153	1.10	69	11	3447	150-220
	3.0L/V6-181	1.10	73	11	3473	150-220
LeBaron Landau	2.5L/4-153	1.10	69	11	3447	150-220
	3.0L/V6-181	1.10	73	11	3473	150-220
Shadow	2.5L/4-153	1.10	69	11	3447	150-220

| Model | Engine Liter/CID | Free Speed Test | | | | Cranking Amp Draw Test[3] |
		Power Rating, Kw	Amps[1]	Volts	RPM[2]	
1993 -Continued						
Spirit	2.2L/4-135	1.10	69	11	3447	150-220
	2.5L/4-153	1.10	69	11	3447	150-220
	3.0L/V6-181	1.10	73	11	3473	150-220
Sundance	2.5L/4-153	1.10	69	11	3447	150-220
1994						
Acclaim	2.2L/4-135	1.10	69	11	3447	150-220
	2.5L/4-153	1.10	69	11	3447	150-220
	3.0L/V6-181	1.10	73	11	3473	150-220
LeBaron	2.5L/4-153	1.10	69	11	3447	150-220
	3.0L/V6-181	1.10	73	11	3473	150-220
Shadow	2.5L/4-153	1.10	69	11	3447	150-220
Spirit	2.2L/4-135	1.10	69	11	3447	150-220
	2.5L/4-153	1.10	69	11	3447	150-220
	3.0L/V6-181	1.10	73	11	3473	150-220
Sundance	2.5L/4-153	1.10	69	11	3447	150-220
1995						
Neon	2.0L/4-122	.95	—	—	—	150-280

①—Maximum.
②—Minimum.
③—With engine at operating temperature.

Mitsubishi Starter Motors

INDEX

APPLICATION CHART

Model	Engine Liter/CID	Starter Type
1992		
Colt	1.5L/4-90	Direct Drive
Colt Vista	1.8L/4-110①	Direct Drive
	1.8L/4-110②	Gear Reduction
	2.4L/4-146①	Direct Drive
	2.4L/4-146②	Gear Reduction
Laser	1.8L/4-107	Direct Drive
	2.0L/4-122	Gear Reduction
Monaco	3.0L/V6-181	—
Premier	3.0L/V6-181	—
Stealth	3.0L/V6-181	Gear Reduction
Summit	1.5L/4-90	Direct Drive
Summit Wagon	1.8L/4-110①	Direct Drive
	1.8L/4-110②	Gear Reduction
	2.4L/4-146①	Direct Drive
	2.4L/4-146②	Gear Reduction
Talon	1.8L/4-107	Direct Drive
	2.0L/4-122	Gear Reduction

Model	Engine Liter/CID	Starter Type
1993		
Colt	1.5L/4-90	Direct Drive
	1.8L/4-110①	Direct Drive
	1.8L/4-110②	Gear Reduction
Colt Vista	1.8L/4-110①	Direct Drive
	1.8L/4-110②	Gear Reduction
	2.4L/4-146	Gear Reduction
Laser	1.8L/4-107	Direct Drive
	2.0L/4-122	Gear Reduction
Stealth	3.0L/V6-181	Gear Reduction
Summit	1.5L/4-90	Direct Drive
	1.8L/4-110①	Direct Drive
	1.8L/4-110②	Gear Reduction
Summit Wagon	1.8L/4-110①	Direct Drive
	1.8L/4-110②	Gear Reduction
	2.4L/4-146	Gear Reduction
Talon	1.8L/4-107	Direct Drive
	2.0L/4-122	Gear Reduction

Continued

APPLICATION CHART –Continued

Model	Engine Liter/CID	Starter Type	Model	Engine Liter/CID	Starter Type
1994			**1994 –Continued**		
Colt	1.5L/4-90	Direct Drive	**Summit**	1.5L/4-90	Direct Drive
	1.8L/4-110①	Direct Drive		1.8L/4-110①	Direct Drive
	1.8L/4-110②	Gear Reduction		1.8L/4-110②	Gear Reduction
Colt Vista	1.8L/4-110①	Direct Drive	**Summit Wagon**	1.8L/4-110①	Direct Drive
	1.8L/4-110②	Gear Reduction		1.8L/4-110②	Gear Reduction
	2.4L/4-146	Direct Drive		2.4L/4-146	Direct Drive
Laser	1.8L/4-107	Direct Drive	**Talon**	1.8L/4-107	Direct Drive
	2.0L/4-122	Gear Reduction		2.0L/4-122	Gear Reduction
Stealth	3.0L/V6-181	Gear Reduction			

①—Manual transaxle.
②—Automatic transaxle.

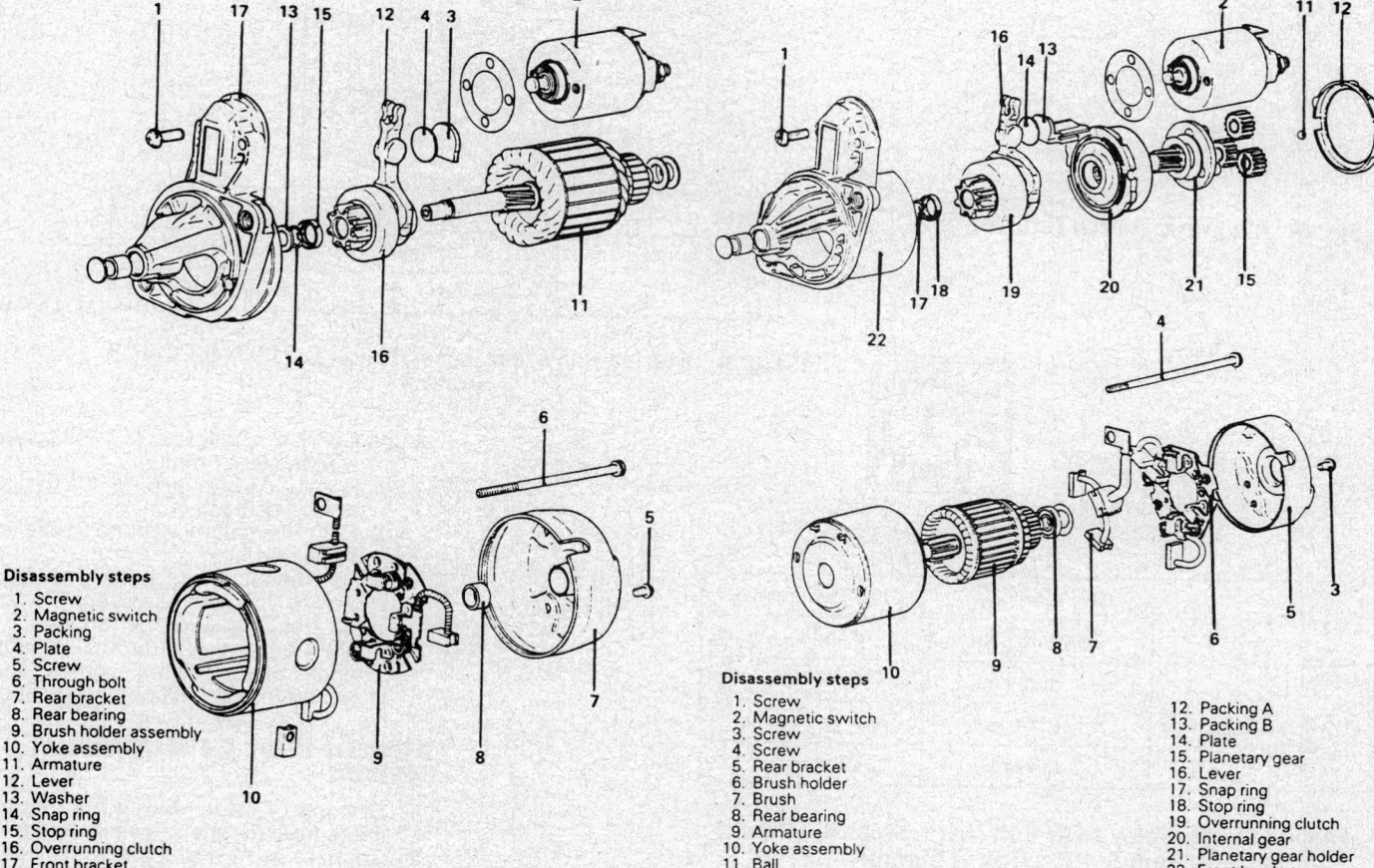

Disassembly steps
1. Screw
2. Magnetic switch
3. Packing
4. Plate
5. Screw
6. Through bolt
7. Rear bracket
8. Rear bearing
9. Brush holder assembly
10. Yoke assembly
11. Armature
12. Lever
13. Washer
14. Snap ring
15. Stop ring
16. Overrunning clutch
17. Front bracket

CR1129100067000X

Fig. 1 Exploded view of Mitsubishi direct drive starter

Disassembly steps
1. Screw
2. Magnetic switch
3. Screw
4. Screw
5. Rear bracket
6. Brush holder
7. Brush
8. Rear bearing
9. Armature
10. Yoke assembly
11. Ball

12. Packing A
13. Packing B
14. Plate
15. Planetary gear
16. Lever
17. Snap ring
18. Stop ring
19. Overrunning clutch
20. Internal gear
21. Planetary gear holder
22. Front bracket

CR1129100068000X

Fig. 2 Exploded view of Mitsubishi gear reduction starter

DESCRIPTION

Mitsubishi starters are either direct drive or gear reduction type. The unit shown in **Fig. 1** is a direct drive starter motor with an overrunning clutch type starter drive. A solenoid switch is mounted on the starter motor. The unit shown in **Fig. 2** is a gear reduction type utilizing a planetary gear assembly to obtain higher rotational speeds with the same torque output.

TROUBLESHOOTING
STARTER MOTOR DOES NOT OPERATE AT ALL

1. Check starter coil.
2. Check for poor contact at battery terminals and starter.
3. Check park/neutral position switch.
4. Check clutch pedal position switch.
5. Check starter relay.
6. Check theft-alarm starter relay.
7. Check key reminder switch.

DIAGNOSIS & TESTING
EXCEPT MONACO & PREMIER
Pull-In Test Of Magnetic Switch

1. Disconnect field coil wire from M-terminal, **Fig. 3**.

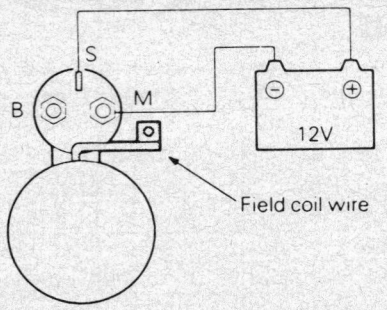

Fig. 3 Magnetic switch pull-in test

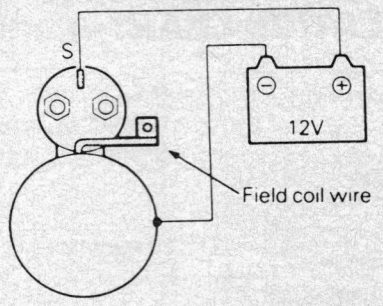

Fig. 4 Magnetic switch hold-in test

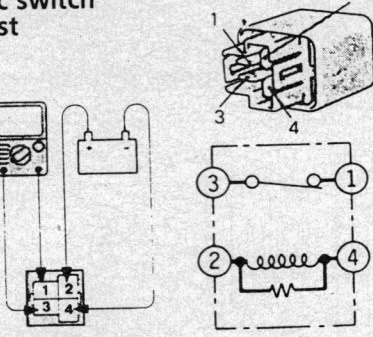

Fig. 5 Free running test

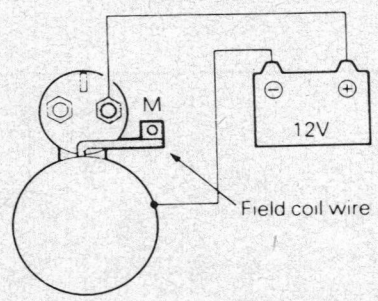

Fig. 6 Magnetic switch return test

Power is supplied	1–3 terminals	No continuity
Power is not supplied	1–3 terminals	Continuity
	2–4 terminals	Continuity

Fig. 8 Starter relay test. Laser, Talon & 1992–93 Colt & Summit

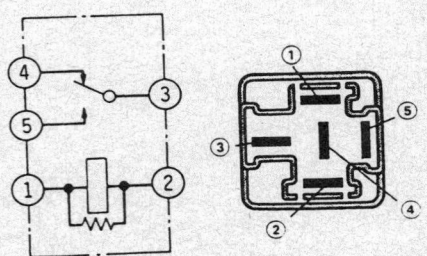

	3-4 terminals	No continuity
Power is supplied	3-5 terminals	Continuity
	3-4 terminals	Continuity
Power is not supplied	3-5 terminals	No continuity
	1-2 terminals	Continuity

Fig. 7 Starter relay test. Colt Vista, Stealth, Summit Wagon & 1994 Colt & Summit

2. Connect a 12 volt battery between terminals S and M.
3. If pinion moves out, then pull-in coil is good.
4. If pinion does not move out, replace magnetic switch.

Hold-In Test Of Magnetic Switch

1. Disconnect field coil wire from terminal M of switch, **Fig. 4**.
2. Connect a 12 volt battery between terminal S and starter body. **This test must be performed quickly to prevent coil from burning.**

3. If pinion remains out, switch is operating correctly.
4. If pinion moves in, hold-in circuit is open. Replace magnetic switch.

Free Running Test

1. Place starter motor assembly in a soft jawed vise.
2. Connect a fully charged battery to starter motor as follows:
   a. Connect a test voltmeter (100 ampere scale) and carbon pile rheostat in series with battery positive post and starter motor terminal, **Fig. 5**.

b. Connect a voltmeter (15 volt scale) across starter motor.
c. Rotate carbon pile to full resistance position.
d. Connect battery ground cable to starter body.
3. Adjust rheostat until battery voltage shown by voltmeter is voltage shown in "Starter Specifications" chart.
4. Confirm amperage is as indicated in "Starter Specifications" chart and starter motor turns smoothly and freely.

Return Test Of Magnetic Switch

1. Disconnect field coil wire from terminal M from magnetic switch, **Fig. 6**.
2. Connect a 12 volt battery between terminals M and starter body. **This test must be performed quickly to prevent coil from burning.**
3. Pull pinion out and release.
4. If pinion quickly returns to original position, switch is operating correctly.
5. If pinion does not quickly return to original position, replace magnetic switch.

Starter Relay Test

Refer to **Figs. 7 and 8** for starter relay continuity tests.

MONACO & PREMIER

Refer to "Bosch Starter Motors" for starter diagnosis & testing procedures.

STARTER SPECIFICATIONS

Model	Engine Liter/ CID	Free Speed Test			
		Power Rating	Amps①	Volts	RPM②
1992					
Colt	1.5L/4-90③	.9	60	11.5	6600
	1.5L/4-90③	.7	60	11.5	6500
Colt Vista	1.8L/4-107④	.8	53	11.5	6000
	1.8L/4-107③	1.0	90	11	3000
	2.4L/4-146④	.9	60	11.5	6600
	2.4L/4-146③	1.2	90	11	3000
Laser	1.8L/4-107	.9	60	11.5	6600
	2.0L/4-122	1.2	90	11	3000
Monaco	3.0L/V6-181	—	80	11.2	2500
Premier	3.0L/V6-181	—	80	11.2	2500
Stealth	3.0L/V6-181	1.2	90	11	3000
Summit	1.5L/4-90④	.9	60	11.5	6600
	1.5L/4-90④	.7	60	11.5	6500
Summit Wagon	1.8L/4-107④	.8	53	11.5	6000
	1.8L/4-107③	1.0	90	11	3000
	2.4L/4-146④	.9	60	11.5	6600
	2.4L/4-146③	1.2	90	11	3000
Talon	1.8L/4-107	.9	60	11.5	6600
	2.0L/4-122	1.2	90	11	3000
1993					
Colt	1.5L/4-90④	.7	60	11.5	6600
	1.5L/4-90③	.9	60	11.5	6600
	1.8L/4-110④	.8	53	11.5	6000
	1.8L/4-110③	1.0	90	11	3000
Colt Vista	1.8L/4-110④	.8	53	11.5	6000
	1.8L/4-110③	1.0	90	11	3000
	2.4L/4-146	1.2	90	11	3000
Laser	1.8L/4-107	.9	60	11.5	6600
	2.0L/4-122	1.2	90	11	3000
Stealth	3.0L/V6-181	1.2	90	11	3000
Summit	1.5L/4-90④	.7	60	11.5	6600
	1.5L/4-90③	.9	60	11.5	6600
	1.8L/4-110④	.8	53	11.5	6000
	1.8L/4-110③	1.0	90	11	3000
Summit Wagon	1.8L/4-110④	.8	53	11.5	6000
	1.8L/4-110③	1.0	90	11	3000
	2.4L/4-146	1.2	90	11	3000
Talon	1.8L/4-107	.9	60	11.5	6600
	2.0L/4-122	1.2	90	11	3000
1994					
Colt	1.5L/4-90④	.7	60	11.5	6600
	1.5L/4-90③	.9	60	11.5	6600
	1.8L/4-110④	.9	60	11.5	6600
	1.8L/4-110③	1.0	90	11	3000
Colt Vista	1.8L/4-110④	.9	60	11.5	6000
	1.8L/4-110③	1.0	90	11	3000
	2.4L/4-146	.9	60	11.5	6600
Laser	1.8L/4-107	.9	60	11.5	6600
	2.0L/4-122	1.2	90	11	3000

Continued

STARTER SPECIFICATIONS—Continued

Model	Engine Liter/ CID	Free Speed Test			RPM②
		Power Rating	Amps①	Volts	
1994 -Continued					
Stealth	3.0L/V6-181	1.2	90	11	3000
Summit	1.5L/4-90④	.7	60	11.5	6600
	1.5L/4-90③	.9	60	11.5	6600
	1.8L/4-110④	.9	60	11.5	6600
	1.8L/4-110③	1.0	90	11	3000
Summit Wagon	1.8L/4-110④	.9	60	11.5	6000
	1.8L/4-110③	1.0	90	11	3000
	2.4L/4-146	.9	60	11.5	6600
Talon	1.8L/4-107	.9	60	11.5	6600
	2.0L/4-122	1.2	90	11	3000

①—Maximum.
②—Minimum.
③—Automatic transmission.
④—Manual transmission.

Nippondenso Starter Motors

INDEX

APPLICATION CHART

Model	Engine Liter/CID	Starter Type
1992		
Acclaim	3.0L/V6-181	Direct Drive
Daytona	3.0L/V6-181	Direct Drive
Dynasty	3.0L/V6-181	Direct Drive
	3.3L/V6-201	Direct Drive
Imperial	3.8L/V6-231	Direct Drive
LeBaron	3.0L/V6-181	Direct Drive
New Yorker	3.3L/V6-201	Direct Drive
	3.8L/V6-231	Direct Drive
Spirit	3.0L/V6-181	Direct Drive
1993		
Acclaim	3.0L/V6-181	Direct Drive
Concorde	3.3L/V6-201	Gear Reduction
Daytona	3.0L/V6-181	Direct Drive
Dynasty	3.0L/V6-181	Direct Drive
Imperial	3.8L/V6-231	Direct Drive

Model	Engine Liter/CID	Starter Type
1993 -Continued		
Intrepid	3.3L/V6-201	Gear Reduction
LeBaron	3.0L/V6-181	Direct Drive
New Yorker	3.3L/V6-201	Direct Drive
	3.8L/V6-231	Direct Drive
Spirit	3.0L/V6-181	Direct Drive
Vision	3.3L/V6-201	Gear Reduction
1994		
Acclaim	3.0L/V6-181	Gear Reduction
Concorde	3.3L/V6-201	Gear Reduction
Intrepid	3.3L/V6-201	Gear Reduction
LeBaron	3.0L/V6-181	Gear Reduction
LHS	3.3L/V6-201	Gear Reduction
New Yorker	3.3L/V6-201	Gear Reduction
Spirit	3.0L/V6-181	Gear Reduction
Vision	3.3L/V6-201	Gear Reduction

DESCRIPTION

Nippondenso starters, **Figs. 1 and 2,** are either direct drive or gear reduction types. The direct drive starter has an overrunning clutch type starter drive and a solenoid switch is mounted on the starter motor. The structure of the reduction gear type starter differs from that of the direct drive type, but the electrical wiring is the same for both types.

DIAGNOSIS & TESTING

IN-VEHICLE TESTING

Before starting any tests, ensure that the battery is fully charged and that all connections are good, then disable ignition system as follows:
1. **On models with distributor ignition system,** disconnect ignition coil cable from distributor cap. Connect a suitable jumper wire between coil cable end terminal and a good body ground.
2. **On models with direct ignition system,** disconnect ignition coils electrical connector.

STARTER FEED CIRCUIT TEST

The following test will require a suitable volt-ohmmeter tester.
1. Connect tester to battery terminals following manufactures instructions.

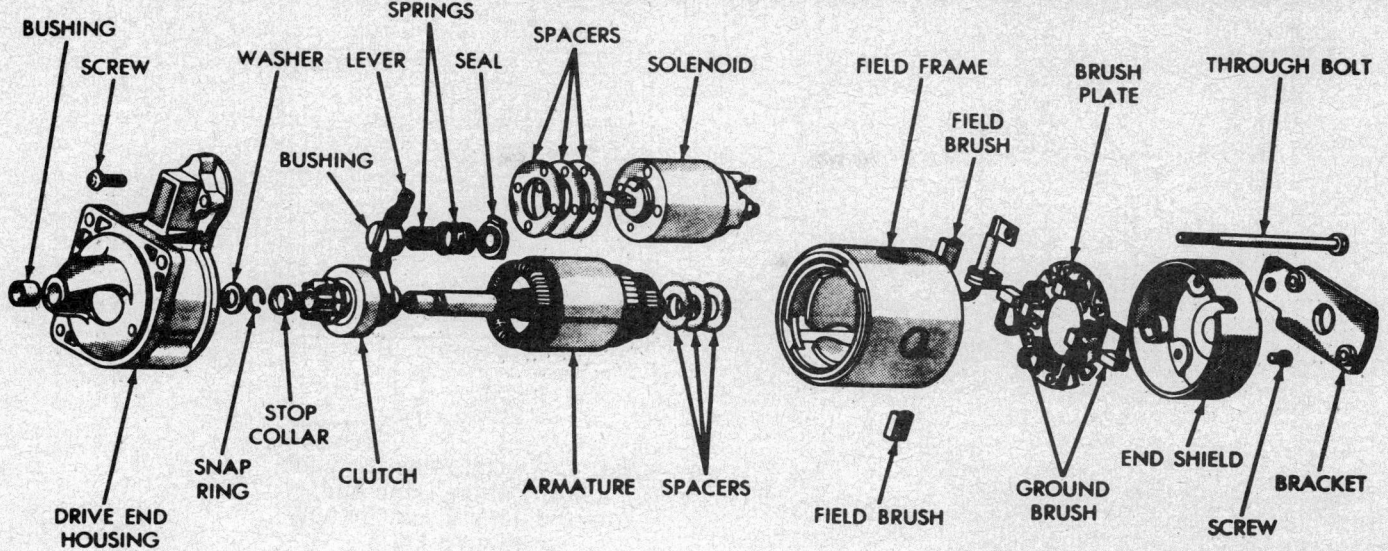

Fig. 1   Exploded view of Nippondenso direct drive starter

CR1129100075000X

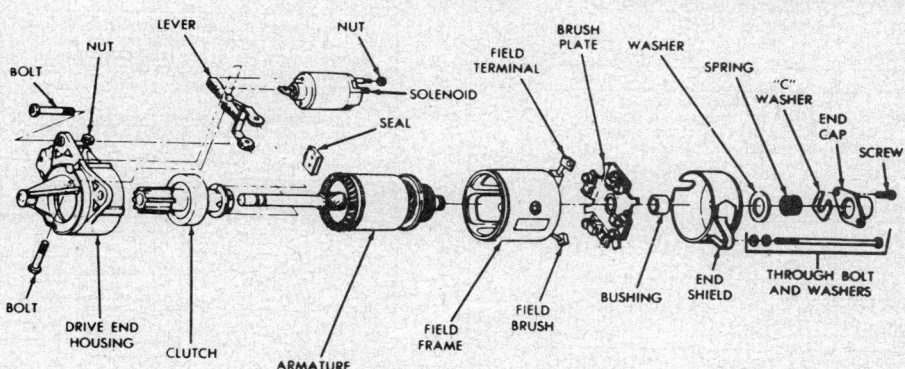

Fig. 2   Exploded view of Nippondenso gear reduction starter

CR1129100076000X

2. Disable ignition system.
3. Ensure all electrical accessories are Off, transmission in Park or Neutral and the parking brake is set.
4. Turn ignition switch to Start position and observe tester.
5. If voltage reads above 9.6 volts and amperage draw reads above 250 amps, perform test shown under "Starter Feed Circuit Resistance Test."
6. If voltage reads 12.4 volts or more and amperage reads 0-10 amps, perform test shown under "Starter Control Circuit Test."
7. After starting system problems have been corrected, verify battery is fully charged. Disconnect all testing equipment and connect ignition system. Start vehicle several times to ensure system is operating correctly.

STARTER FEED CIRCUIT RESISTANCE TEST

The following test will require a voltmeter accurate to $1/10$ volt.
1. Disable ignition system.
2. With wiring harnesses and components connected properly, proceed as follows:

a. Connect positive lead of voltmeter to negative battery post and negative lead to negative battery cable clamp. Turn ignition switch to Start position and observe voltmeter. If voltage is detected, correct poor contact between cable clamp and post.
b. Connect positive lead of voltmeter to negative battery terminal and negative lead to engine block near battery cable attaching point. Turn ignition switch to Start position and observe voltmeter. If voltage reads above .2 volts, correct poor connection at ground cable attaching point. If voltmeter still reads above .2 volts after correcting poor contacts, replace ground cable.
3. Remove starter heat shield, then proceed as follows:
a. Connect positive voltmeter lead to starter motor housing and negative lead to negative battery terminal. Turn ignition switch to Start position. If voltage reads above .2 volts, correct poor starter to engine ground.

b. Connect positive voltmeter lead to positive battery terminal and negative lead to battery cable terminal on starter solenoid. Turn ignition switch to Start position. If voltage reads above .2 volts, correct poor contact at battery cable solenoid connection. If reading is still above .2 volts after correcting contact points, replace positive battery cable.
4. If resistance tests detect no feed circuit failures, remove starter motor and perform tests under "Bench Testing."

STARTER CONTROL CIRCUIT TEST

The starter control circuit consists of the starter solenoid, starter relay, ignition switch, neutral safety switch and all related wiring and connections.

Starter Solenoid Test

1. Verify battery is fully charged and in good condition.
2. Raise and support vehicle.
3. Inspect starter and starter solenoid for corrosion or loose wiring.
4. Lower vehicle.
5. Remove starter relay from connector.
6. Connect a remote starter switch or a jumper wire between the battery positive post and terminal 87 on starter relay connector on all models except Concorde, Intrepid, LHS, Vision and 1994 New Yorker, or between the battery positive post and terminal D on starter relay connector on Concorde, Intrepid, LHS, Vision and 1994 New Yorker, **Figs. 3 and 4.**
7. If engine cranks, starter and starter solenoid is operating correctly, perform starter relay test.
8. If engine does not crank or solenoid chatters, check wiring and connectors from relay to starter for loose or corroded connections.
9. Repeat test and, if engine still does not crank properly, repair or replace

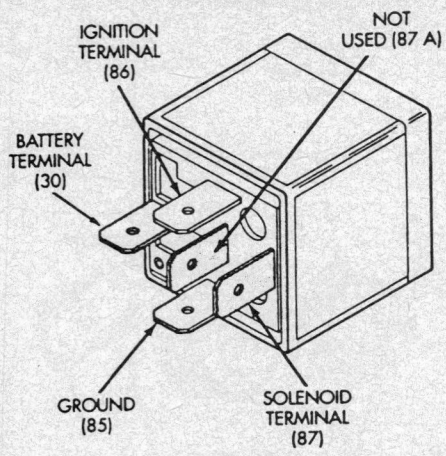

Fig. 3 Starter relay terminal identification. Except Concorde, Intrepid, LHS, Vision & 1994 New Yorker

Fig. 4 Starter relay terminal identification. Concorde, Intrepid, LHS, Vision & 1994 New Yorker

starter or starter solenoid as necessary.

Starter Relay Test

1. Verify battery is fully charged and in good condition.
2. Perform starter solenoid test.
3. Remove starter relay.
4. Perform starter relay test shown in **Fig. 5.**

Ignition Switch Test

After testing starter solenoid and relay, test ignition switch and wiring. Check all wiring for opens or shorts and all connectors for being loose or corroded.

BENCH TESTING

Starter Solenoid

1. Disconnect field coil wire from field coil terminal.
2. Check for continuity between solenoid terminal and field coil terminal. There should be continuity.
3. Check for continuity between solenoid terminal and solenoid housing. There should be continuity.
4. If there is no continuity in either test, replace solenoid assembly.

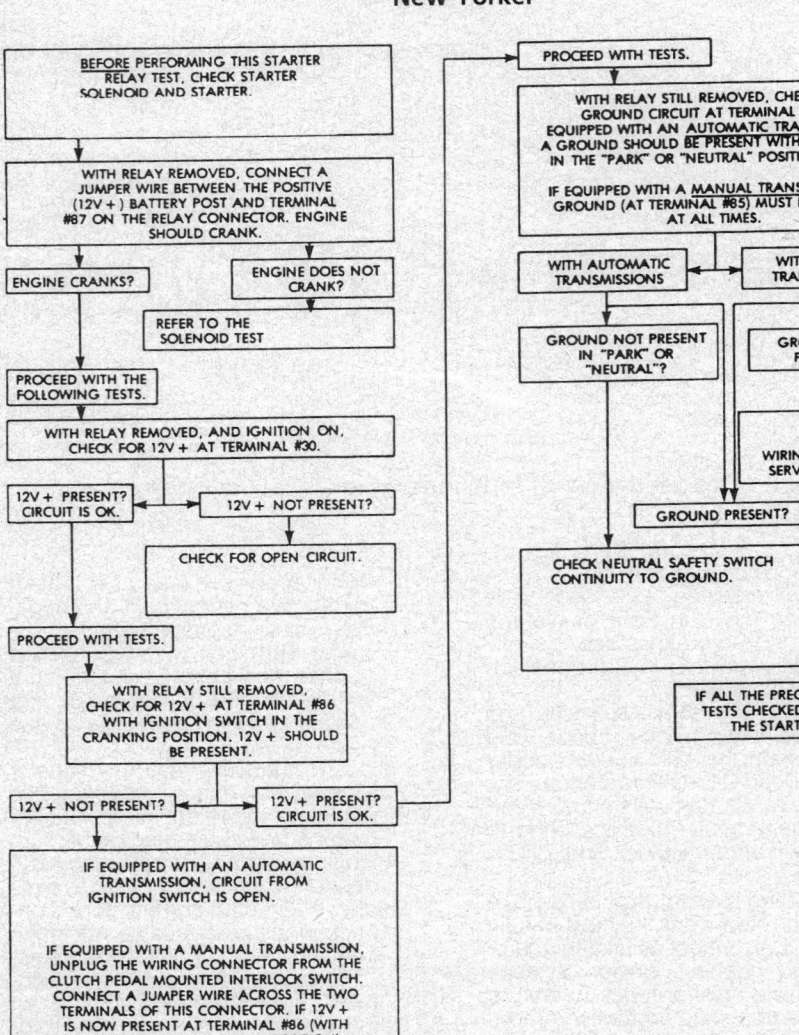

Fig. 5 Starter relay test

STARTER SPECIFICATIONS

Model	Engine Liter/CID	Free Speed Test			RPM②	Cranking Amp Draw Test③
		Power Rating	Amps①	Volts		
1992						
Acclaim	3.0L/V6-181	1.4	73	11	3601	150-220
Daytona	3.0L/V6-181	1.4	73	11	3601	150-220
Dynasty	3.0L/V6-181	1.4	73	11	3601	150-220
	3.3L/V6-201	1.4	73	11	3401	150-200
Imperial	3.8L/V6-231	1.4	73	11	3601	150-220
LeBaron	3.0L/V6-181	1.4	73	11	3601	150-220
New Yorker Fifth Avenue	3.3L/V6-201	1.4	73	11	3401	150-200
	3.8L/V6-231	1.4	73	11	3601	150-220
New Yorker Salon	3.3L/V6-201	1.4	73	11	3601	150-220
Spirit	3.0L/V6-181	1.4	73	11	3601	150-220
1993						
Acclaim	3.0L/V6-181	1.4	73	11	3601	150-220
Concorde	3.3L/V6-201	1.2	—	12	—	150-280
Daytona	3.0L/V6-181	1.4	73	11	3601	150-220
Dynasty	3.0L/V6-181	1.4	73	11	3601	150-220
	3.3L/V6-201	1.4	73	11	3401	150-200
Imperial	3.8L/V6-231	1.4	73	11	3601	150-220
Intrepid	3.3L/V6-201	1.2	—	12	—	150-280
LeBaron	3.0L/V6-181	1.4	73	11	3601	150-220
New Yorker Fifth Avenue	3.3L/V6-201	1.4	73	11	3401	150-200
	3.8L/V6-231	1.4	73	11	3601	150-220
New Yorker Salon	3.3L/V6-201	1.4	73	11	3401	150-200
Spirit	3.0L/V6-181	1.4	73	11	3601	150-220
Vision	3.3L/V6-201	1.2	—	12	—	150-280
1994						
Acclaim	3.0L/V6-181	1.4	73	11	3601	150-220
Concorde	3.3L/V6-201	1.2	—	12	—	150-280
Intrepid	3.3L/V6-201	1.2	—	12	—	150-280
LeBaron	3.0L/V6-181	1.4	73	11	3601	150-220
LHS	3.3L/V6-201	1.2	—	12	—	150-280
New Yorker	3.3L/V6-201	1.2	—	12	—	150-280
Spirit	3.0L/V6-181	1.4	73	11	3601	150-220
Vision	3.3L/V6-201	1.2	—	12	—	150-280

①—Maximum.
②—Minimum.
③—With engine at operating temperature.

Melco Starters

INDEX

APPLICATION CHART

Model	Engine Liter/CID	Starter Type
1993		
Concorde	3.5L/V6-215	Gear Reduction
Intrepid	3.5L/V6-215	Gear Reduction
Vision	3.5L/V6-215	Gear Reduction
1994		
Concorde	3.5L/V6-215	Gear Reduction
Intrepid	3.5L/V6-215	Gear Reduction
LHS	3.5L/V6-215	Gear Reduction
New Yorker	3.5L/V6-215	Gear Reduction
Vision	3.5L/V6-215	Gear Reduction

DESCRIPTION

Melco starters are reduction gear type starters. The reduction gear type starter has an overrunning clutch type starter drive and a solenoid switch mounted on the starter motor.

DIAGNOSIS & TESTING

Refer to "Nippondenso Starter Motors" for Melco starter diagnosis and testing procedures.

STARTER SPECIFICATIONS

Model	Engine Liter/CID	Free Speed Test Power Rating	Amps①	Volts	RPM②	Cranking Amp Draw Test③
1993						
Concorde	3.5L/V6-215	1.2	—	12	—	150-280
Intrepid	3.5L/V6-215	1.2	—	12	—	150-280
Vision	3.5L/V6-215	1.2	—	12	—	150-280
1994						
Concorde	3.5L/V6-215	1.2	—	12	—	150-280
Intrepid	3.5L/V6-215	1.2	—	12	—	150-280
LHS	3.5L/V6-215	1.2	—	12	—	150-280
New Yorker	3.5L/V6-215	1.2	—	12	—	150-280
Vision	3.5L/V6-215	1.2	—	12	—	150-280

① —Maximum.
② —Minimum.
③ —With engine at operating temperature.

ALTERNATORS
TABLE OF CONTENTS

Bosch & Nippondenso Alternators

INDEX

APPLICATION CHART

Model	Engine	Type	Id. No.
1992			
Acclaim, LeBaron Landau & Spirit	2.2L/4-135	Bosch 90HS	4557431
		Nippondenso 75HS	4557301
		Nippondenso 90HS	5234031
	2.5L/4-153	Bosch 90HS	4557431
		Nippondenso 90HS	5234031
	3.0L/V6-181	Bosch 90HS	4557432
		Nippondenso 90HS	5234032
		Nippondenso 120HS	5234033
Daytona	2.2L/4-135	Bosch 90HS	4557431
		Nippondenso 75HS	4557301
		Nippondenso 90HS	5234031
	2.5L/4-153	Bosch 90HS	4557431
		Nippondenso 90HS	5234031
	3.0L/V6-181	Bosch 90HS	4557432
		Nippondenso 90HS	5234032
		Nippondenso 120HS	5234033
Dynasty & New Yorker Salon	2.5L/4-153	Bosch 90HS	4557431
		Nippondenso 90HS	5234031
	3.0L/V6-181	Bosch 90HS	4557432
		Nippondenso 90HS	5234032
		Nippondenso 120HS	5234033
	3.3L/V6-201	Nippondenso 90HS	5234032
		Nippondenso 120HS	5234033
Imperial & New Yorker Fifth Avenue	3.3L/V6-201	Nippondenso 90HS	5234032
		Nippondenso 120HS	5234033
	3.8L/V6-231	Nippondenso 90HS	5234032
		Nippondenso 120HS	5234033

Continued

Model	Engine	Type	Id. No.
1992			
LeBaron Coupe/Convertible	2.5L/4-153	Bosch 90HS	4557431
		Nippondenso 90HS	5234031
	3.0L/V6-181	Bosch 90HS	4557432
		Nippondenso 90HS	5234032
		Nippondenso 120HS	5234033
Shadow & Sundance	2.5L/4-153	Bosch 90HS	4557431
		Nippondenso 90HS	5234031
1993			
Acclaim, LeBaron Landau & Spirit	2.2L/4-135	Bosch 90HS	4557431
		Nippondenso 75HS	4557301
		Nippondenso 90HS	5234031
	2.5L/4-153	Bosch 90HS	4557431
		Nippondenso 90HS	5234031
	3.0L/V6-181	Bosch 90HS	4557432
		Nippondenso 90HS	5234032
		Nippondenso 120HS	5234033
Concorde, Intrepid &Vision	All	Nippondenso	—
Daytona	2.2L/4-135	Bosch 90HS	4557431
		Nippondenso 75HS	4557301
		Nippondenso 90HS	5234031
	2.5L/4-153	Bosch 90HS	4557431
		Nippondenso 90HS	5234031
	3.0L/V6-181	Bosch 90HS	4557432
		Nippondenso 90HS	5234032
		Nippondenso 120HS	5234033
Dynasty & New Yorker Salon	2.5L/4-153	Bosch 90HS	4557431
		Nippondenso 90HS	5234031
	3.0L/V6-181	Bosch 90HS	4557432
		Nippondenso 90HS	5234032
		Nippondenso 120HS	5234033
	3.3L/V6-201	Nippondenso 90HS	5234032
		Nippondenso 120HS	5234033
Imperial & New Yorker Fifth Avenue	3.3L/V6-201	Nippondenso 90HS	5234032
		Nippondenso 120HS	5234033
	3.8L/V6-231	Nippondenso 90HS	5234032
		Nippondenso 120HS	5234033
LeBaron Coupe/Convertible	2.5L/4-153	Bosch 90HS	4557431
		Nippondenso 90HS	5234031
	3.0L/V6-181	Bosch 90HS	4557432
		Nippondenso 90HS	5234032
		Nippondenso 120HS	5234033
Shadow & Sundance	2.5L/4-153	Bosch 90HS	4557431
		Nippondenso 90HS	5234031
1994			
Acclaim, LeBaron & Spirit	2.2L/4-135	Bosch 90HS	4557431
		Nippondenso 75HS	4557301
		Nippondenso 90HS	5234031
	2.5L/4-153	Bosch 90HS	4557431
		Nippondenso 90HS	5234031

Continued

APPLICATION CHART-Continued

Model	Engine	Type	Id. No.
1994-Continued			
	3.0L/V6-181	Bosch 90HS	4557432
		Nippondenso 90HS	5234032
		Nippondenso 120HS	5234033
Concorde, Intrepid, LHS, New Yorker & Vision	All	Nippondenso	—
Shadow & Sundance	2.5L/4-153	Bosch 90HS	4557431
		Nippondenso 90HS	5234031
1995			
Neon	All	Nippondenso	—

PRECAUTIONS

The power source of the charging system is the alternator. Current is transmitted from the field terminal of the regulator through a slip ring to the field coil and back to ground through another slip ring. The strength of the field regulates the output of the alternating current. The alternating current is then transmitted from the alternator to the rectifier where it is converted to direct current.

The main components of the alternator are the rotor, stator, rectifier, end shields and drive pulley. Direct current is available at the output "B+" terminal.

These alternators employ a three-phase stator winding in which the phase windings are electrically 120° apart. The rotor consists of a field coil encased between interleaved sections producing a magnetic field with alternate north and south poles. By rotating the rotor inside the stator, the alternating current is induced in the stator windings. This alternating current is rectified (changed to DC) by silicon diodes and brought back to the output terminal of the alternator.

1. Ensure battery polarity is correct when servicing units. Reversed battery polarity will damage rectifiers and regulators.
2. If booster battery is used for starting, be sure to use correct polarity in hook up.
3. When a fast charger is used to charge a vehicle battery, vehicle battery cables should be disconnected unless fast charger is equipped with a special alternator protector, in which case vehicle battery cables need not be disconnected. Also, fast chargers should never be used to start a vehicle, as damage to rectifiers will result.
4. Lead connections to grounded rectifiers (negative) should never be soldered, as excessive heat may damage rectifiers.
5. Unless system includes a load relay or field relay, grounding alternator output terminal will damage alternator and/or circuits. This is true even when system is not in operation, since no circuit breaker is used and battery voltage is applied to alternator output terminal at all times. Field or load relay acts as a circuit breaker in that it is controlled by ignition switch.
6. Before making any in-vehicle tests of alternator or regulator, battery should be checked and circuit inspected for faulty wiring or insulation, loose or corroded connections and poor ground circuits.
7. Check alternator belt tension to ensure belt is tight enough to prevent slipping under load.
8. To prevent system damage, place ignition switch in Off position and disconnect battery ground cable before making any test connections.
9. The vehicle battery must be fully charged or a fully charged battery may be installed for test purposes.

DESCRIPTION

The main components of the alternator are the rotor, stator, rectifier, end shields and drive pulley. Direct current is available at the output "B + " terminal.

Alternator output is controlled by voltage regulator circuitry contained within the power and logic modules of the Engine Controller.

DIODE RECTIFIERS

Six or more silicon diode rectifiers are used and act as electrical one-way valves. One half of the diodes have ground polarity and are pressed or screwed into a heat sink which is grounded. The other diodes (ungrounded) are pressed or screwed into and insulated from the end head. These diodes are connected to the alternator output terminal.

Since the diodes have a high resistance to the flow of current in one direction and a low resistance in the opposite direction, they may be connected in a manner which allows current to flow from the alternator to the battery in the low resistance direction. The high resistance in the opposite direction prevents the flow of current from the battery to the alternator. Because of this feature no circuit breaker is required between the alternator and battery.

DIAGNOSIS & TESTING
OUTPUT WIRE VOLTAGE DROP TEST
Concorde, Intrepid, LHS, Neon, Vision & 1994 New Yorker

1. Ensure battery is fully charged.
2. Check generator ground path using an ohmmeter. Resistance should not exceed .3 Mohms.
3. Connect positive lead of an 18 volt voltmeter to positive lead for generator (B +) output terminal.
4. Connect negative lead to positive battery post.
5. Connect an engine tachometer.
6. Place transaxle in park position and apply parking brake.
7. Start engine and allow to idle for ten minutes.
8. Operate blower motor on high speed and turn headlamps on high beam.
9. Increase engine speed to 2400 RPM and observe voltmeter. Voltmeter should not exceed .8 volts.
10. If a higher voltage drop is indicated, clean and tighten all connections between generator and battery.
11. If voltage drop is as specified, system is operating correctly.

CHARGING CIRCUIT RESISTANCE TEST

1. Disconnect battery ground cable and "Bat" lead from alternator output terminal.
2. Complete test connections as shown in **Fig. 1**.
3. Remove air hose between engine controller and air cleaner.
4. **On non-turbocharged models,** connect a suitable jumper wire from green (R3) terminal to ground. **Do not connect blue J2 circuit to ground.**
5. **On turbocharged models,** connect a suitable jumper wire from green R3 lead wire on dash side of black 8 way connector to ground. **Do not connect blue J2 lead of 8 way wiring connector to ground.**
6. **On all models,** connect battery ground cable, then start engine and operate at idle.
7. Adjust engine speed and carbon pile rheostat to obtain 20 amps in circuit, then check voltmeter reading. Reading should not exceed .5 volts. If a higher voltage drop is indicated, inspect, clean and tighten all connections in circuit. A voltage drop test at

each connection can be performed to isolate problem.

CURRENT OUTPUT TEST

Except Concorde, Intrepid, LHS, Neon, Vision & 1994 New Yorker

1. Disconnect battery ground cable and "Bat" lead from alternator output terminal.
2. Complete test connections as shown in **Fig. 2.**
3. Remove air hose between engine controller and air cleaner.
4. **On non-turbocharged models, connect a suitable jumper wire from green (R3) terminal to ground. Do not connect blue J2 circuit to ground.**
5. **On turbocharged models,** connect a suitable jumper wire from green R3 lead wire on dash side of black 8 way connector to ground. **Do not connect blue J2 lead of 8 way wiring connector to ground.**
6. **On all models,** connect battery ground cable, then start engine and operate at idle.
7. Adjust carbon pile rheostat and engine speed to obtain 15 volts at 1250 RPM. **While increasing engine speed, do not allow voltage to exceed 16 volts.**
8. If ammeter reading is not within limits shown in "Alternator Specifications," replace alternator.

OUTPUT VOLTAGE TEST

Concorde, Intrepid, LHS, Neon, Vision & 1994 New Yorker

1. Ensure battery is fully charged.
2. Connect voltmeter leads across battery terminals as shown in **Fig. 3.**
3. Record base voltage with all electrical components and ignition switch in Off position.
4. Place transaxle in park position and apply parking brake.
5. Start engine.
6. With engine at 1800 RPM and no other electrical loads, battery voltage should not be more than 2.7 volts above base voltage. If voltage is not as specified, perform on-board diagnostics procedures for overcharging.
7. Record battery voltage with engine at 2400 RPM, blower motor on high speed and headlamps on high beam. Battery voltage should be a minimum of .4 volts above base voltage. If voltage is not as specified, perform on-board diagnostic procedures for inadequate or low charging.

ON-BOARD DIAGNOSTIC SYSTEM

The on-board diagnostic system can be used to help determine charging system malfunctions. This system monitors, then stores information that can be retrieved by using a DRBII diagnostic tool. For proper code diagnostic procedures, install DRBII

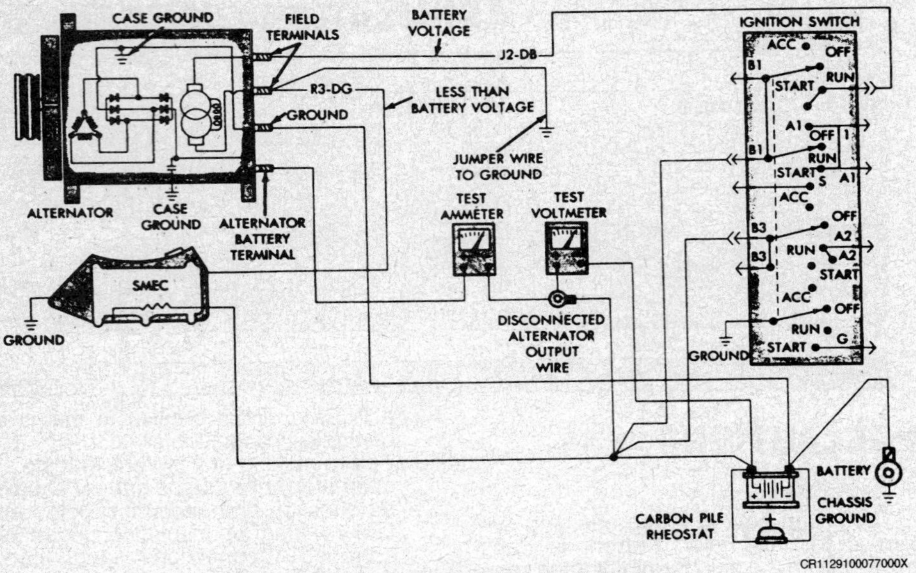

Fig. 1 Charging circuit resistance test

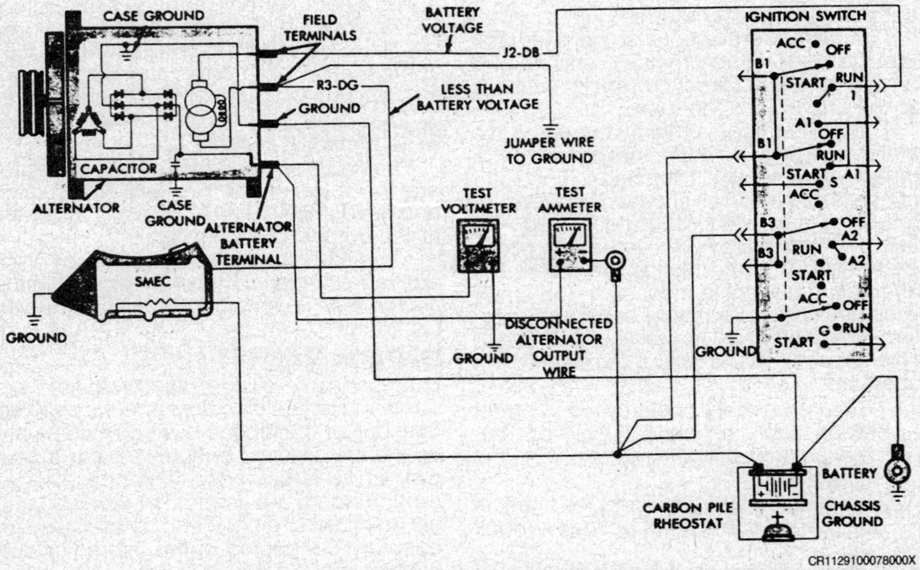

Fig. 2 Current output test. Except Concorde, Intrepid, LHS, Neon, Vision & 1994 New Yorker

on vehicle and refer to **Figs. 4 through 12** for 1992 models, **Figs. 13 through 22** for 1993 models except Concorde, Intrepid and Vision, **Figs. 13 and 23 through 34** for 1994 models except Concorde, Intrepid, LHS, Vision and New Yorker, or **Figs. 35 through 44** for Concorde, Intrepid, LHS, Vision and 1994 New Yorker. Perform all available VER verification tests after each procedure.

If a diagnostic tool is not available, the diagnostic trouble codes can be retrieved by using the "Check Engine" lamp on the instrument cluster. Cycle the ignition switch On-Off-On-Off-On without starting the engine. The light will go on for two seconds as a bulb check; the diagnostic trouble code will follow immediately. Count the number of flashes; for example, "flash, pause, flash, flash" indicates Diagnostic Trouble Code 12. Refer to **Figs. 45 through 47** for diagnostic trouble codes and diagnostic trouble code diagnosis. All diagnostic trouble codes are two digit numbers; there will be a four second pause between different diagnostic trouble codes.

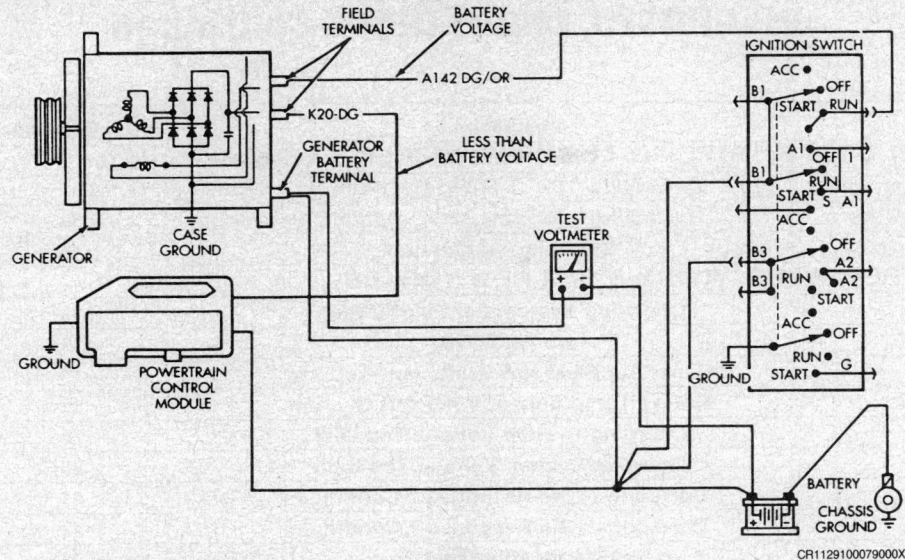

Fig. 3 Output voltage test. Concorde, Intrepid, LHS, Neon, Vision & 1994 New Yorker

DIAGNOSTIC CHART INDEX

Test	Description	Page No. 13-	Fig. No.
1992			
Test CH-1A	Testing Battery	6	4
Test CH-1B	Load Testing Battery & Reading Faults	6	5
Test CH-2A	Alternator Field Not Switching Properly	7	6
Test CH-2C	Checking Field Control For Shorts	7	7
Test CH-3A	Charging System Voltage Too Low	8	8
Test CH-4A	Charging System Voltage Too High	8	9
Test CH-4B	Checking Engine Controller Regulating Circuit	9	10
Test CH-5A	Checking For Intermittent Problems	9	11
Test CH-VER	Charging Verification	9	12
1993 EXCEPT CONCORDE, INTREPID & VISION			
Test CH-1A	Testing Battery	10	13
Test CH-1B	Load Testing Battery & Reading Faults	10	14
Test CH-2A	Alternator Field Not Switching Properly	11	15
Test CH-2B	Alternator Field Not Switching Properly	11	16
Test CH-2C	Checking Field Driver Circuit For Shorts	11	17
Test CH-3A	Charging System Voltage Too Low	12	18
Test CH-4A	Charging System Voltage Too High	12	19
Test CH-4B	Checking Powertrain Control Module Regulating Circuit	12	20
Test CH-5A	Checking Charging System No Faults	13	21
Test CH-VER	Charging Verification	13	22
1994 EXCEPT CONCORDE, INTREPID, LHS, NEW YORKER & VISION			
Test TC-1A	Checking The System For Trouble Codes	13	23
Test TC-34A	Generator Field Not Switching Properly	13	24
Test TC-34B	Checking Field Driver Circuit For Shorts	14	25
Test TC-35A	Charging System Voltage Too Low	14	26
Test TC-36A	Charging System Voltage Too High	14	27
Test TC-36B	Checking Powertrain Control Module Regulating Circuit	15	28
Test TC-38A	Battery Temp Sensor Volts Out Of Limit	15	29
Test CH-1A	Checking Charging System No Trouble Codes	15	30
Test NS-6A	Correcting " No Response" Condition	16	31
Test NS-6B	Correcting " No Response" Condition	17	32

Continued

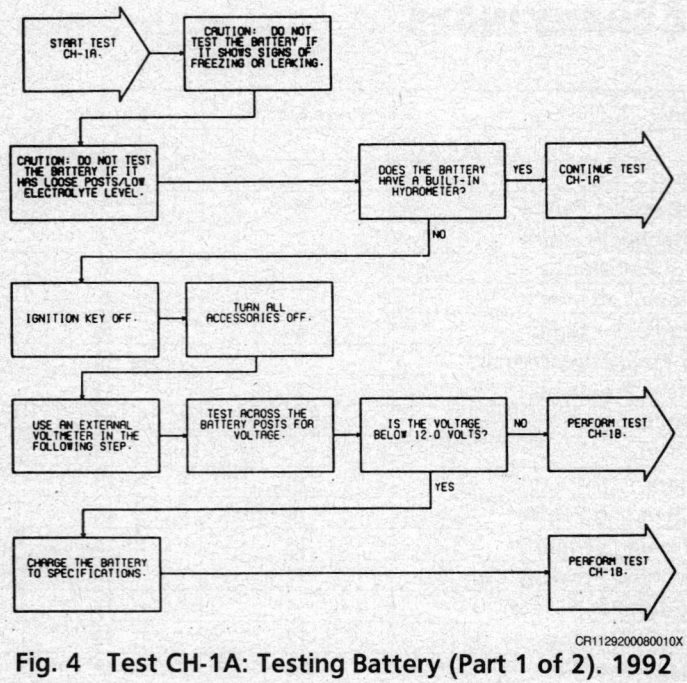

Fig. 4   Test CH-1A: Testing Battery (Part 1 of 2). 1992

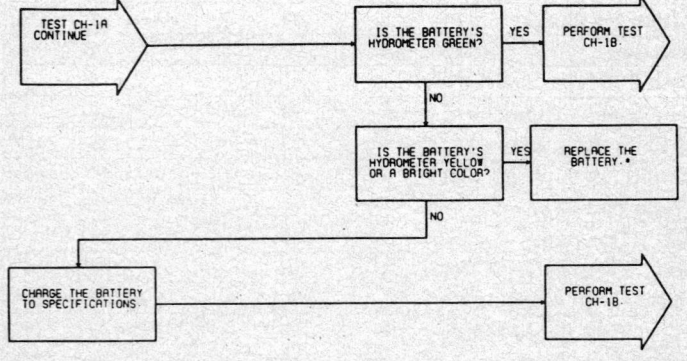

Fig. 4   Test CH-1A: Testing Battery (Part 2 of 2). 1992

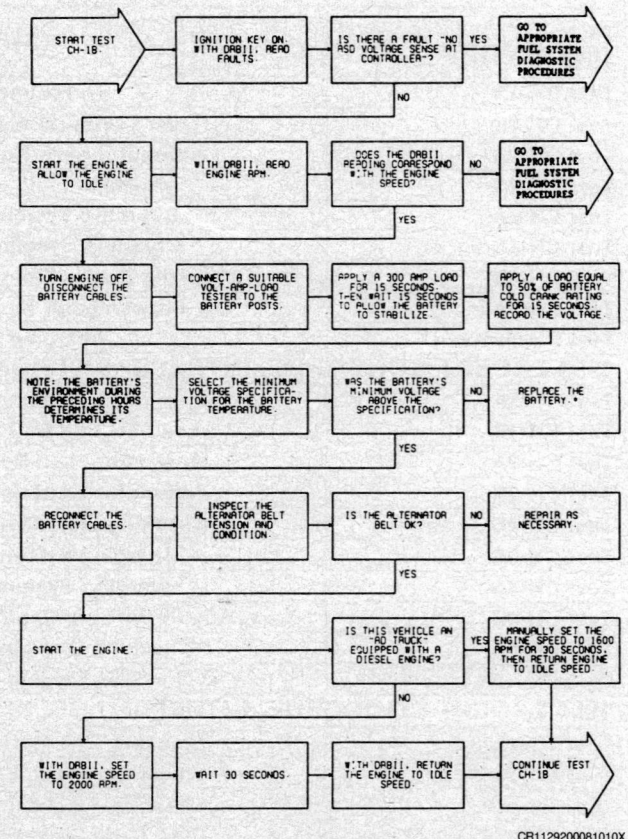

Fig. 5   Test CH-1B: Load Testing Battery & Reading Faults (Part 1 of 2). 1992

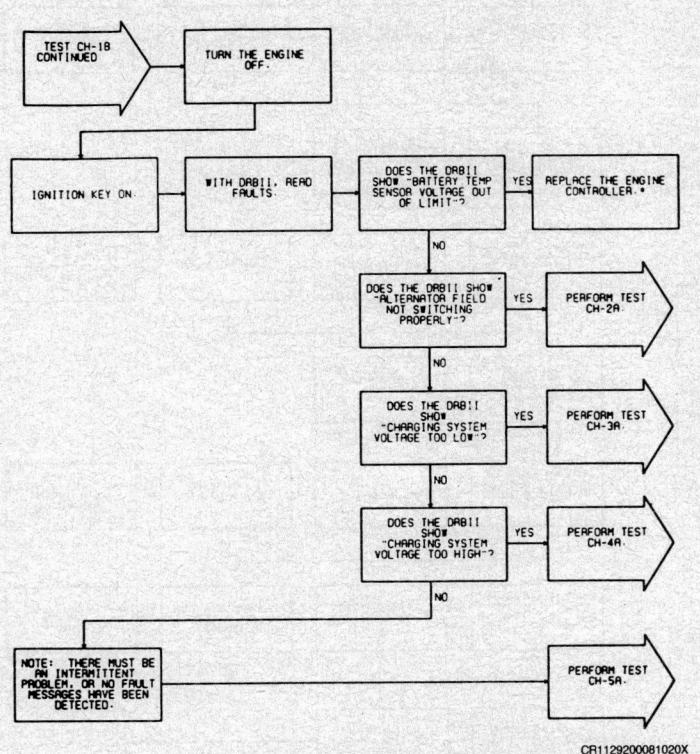

Fig. 5 Test CH-1B: Load Testing Battery & Reading Faults (Part 2 of 2). 1992

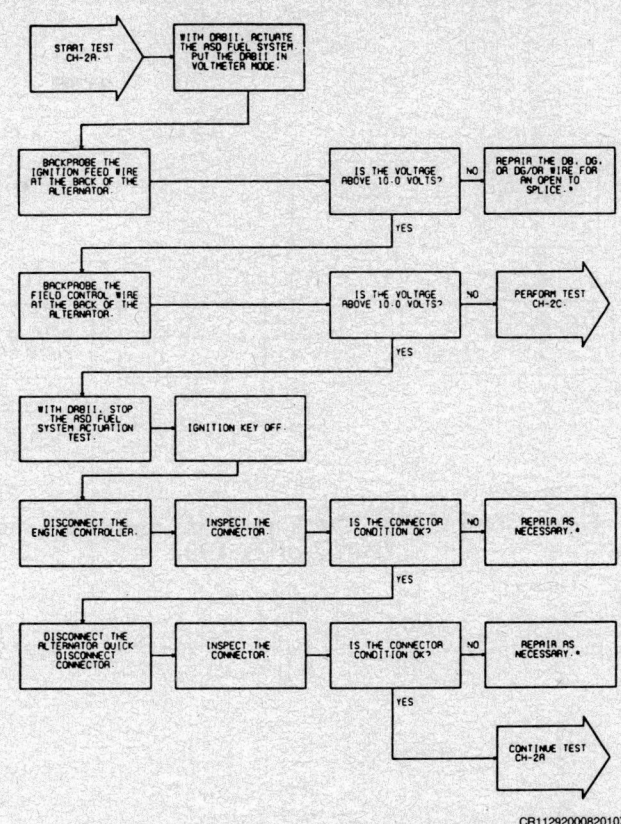

Fig. 6 Test CH-2A: Alternator Field Not Switching Properly (Part 1 of 2). 1992

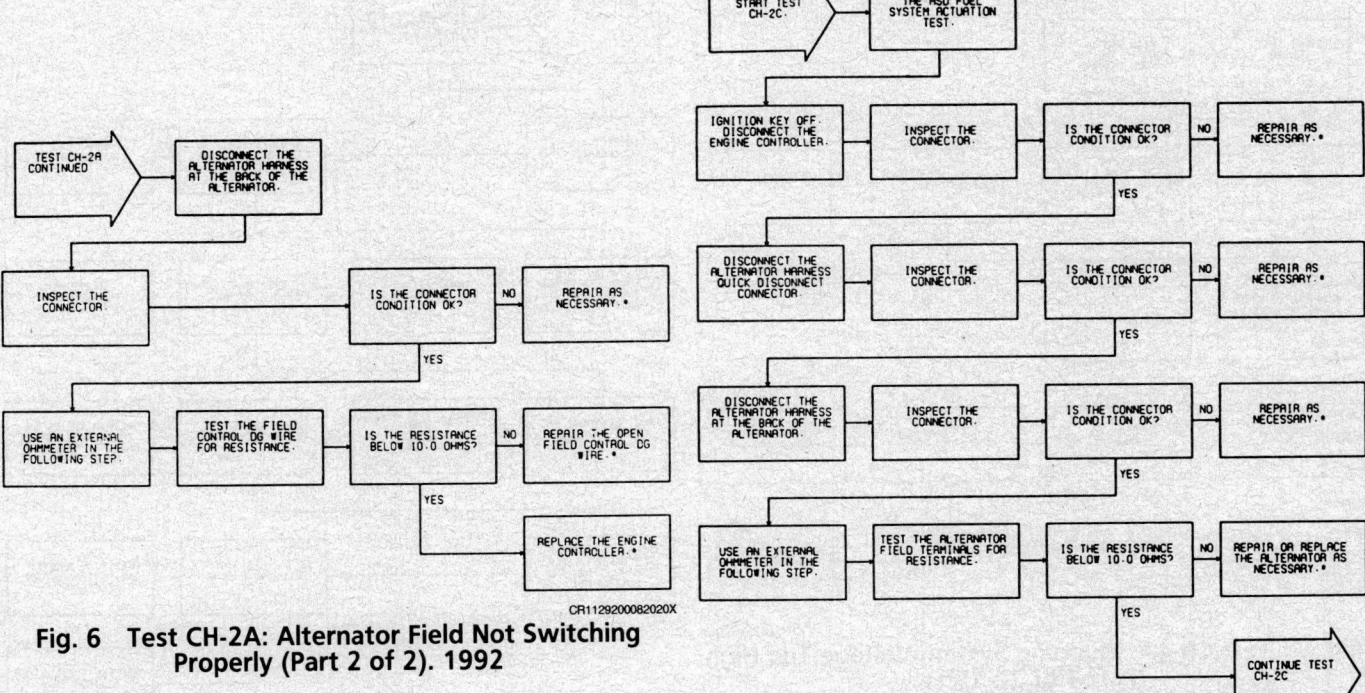

Fig. 6 Test CH-2A: Alternator Field Not Switching Properly (Part 2 of 2). 1992

Fig. 7 Test CH-2C: Checking Field Control For Shorts (Part 1 of 2). 1992

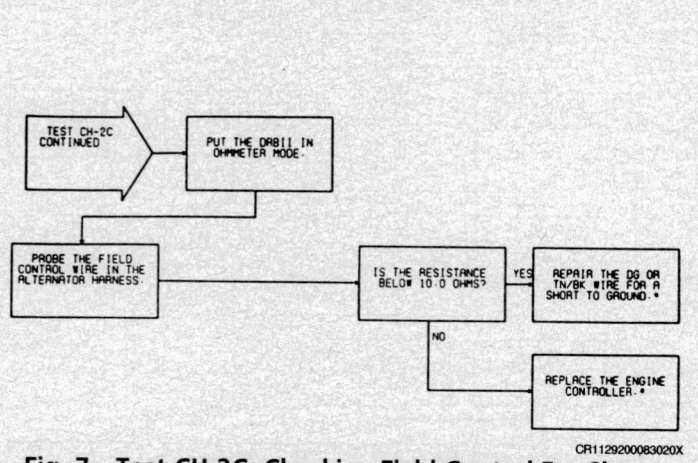

Fig. 7   Test CH-2C: Checking Field Control For Shorts (Part 2 of 2). 1992

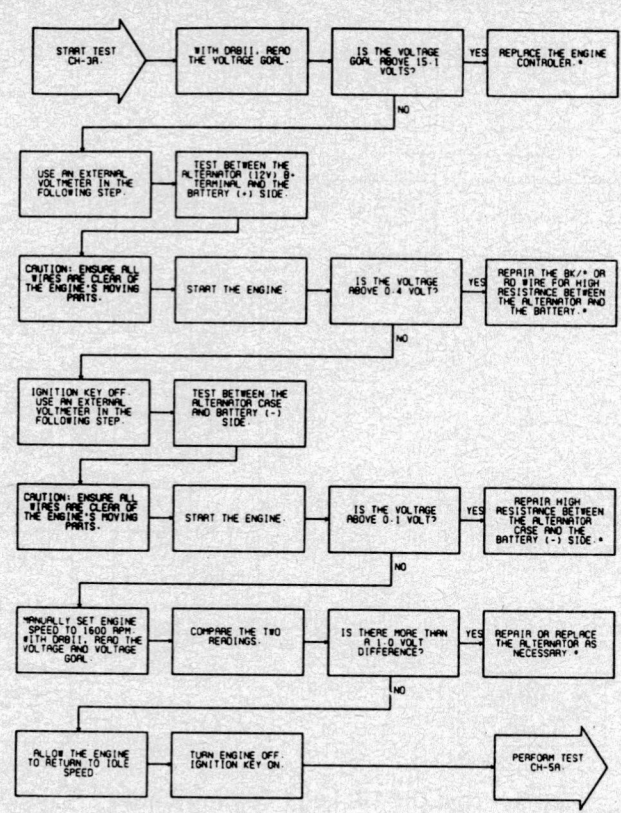

Fig. 8   Test CH-3A: Charging System Voltage Too Low. 1992

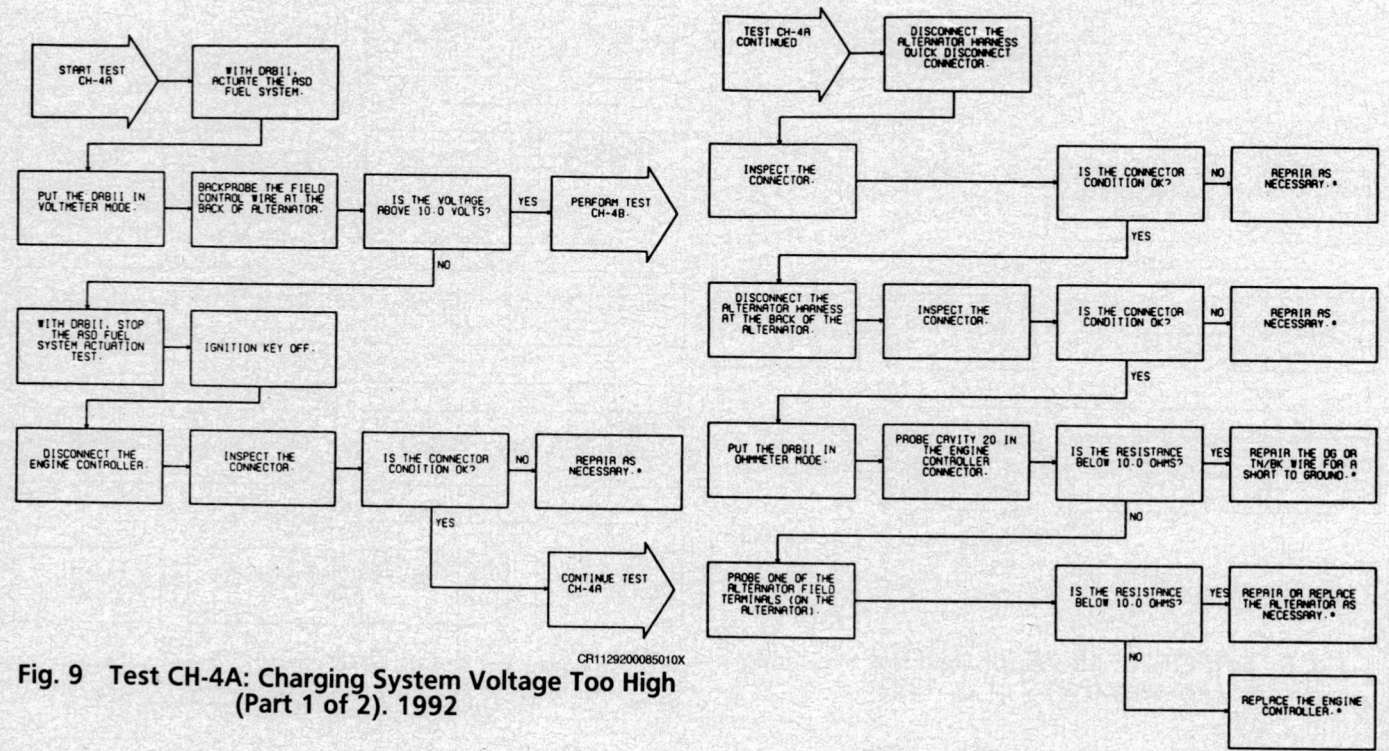

Fig. 9   Test CH-4A: Charging System Voltage Too High (Part 1 of 2). 1992

Fig. 9   Test CH-4A: Charging System Voltage Too High (Part 2 of 2). 1992

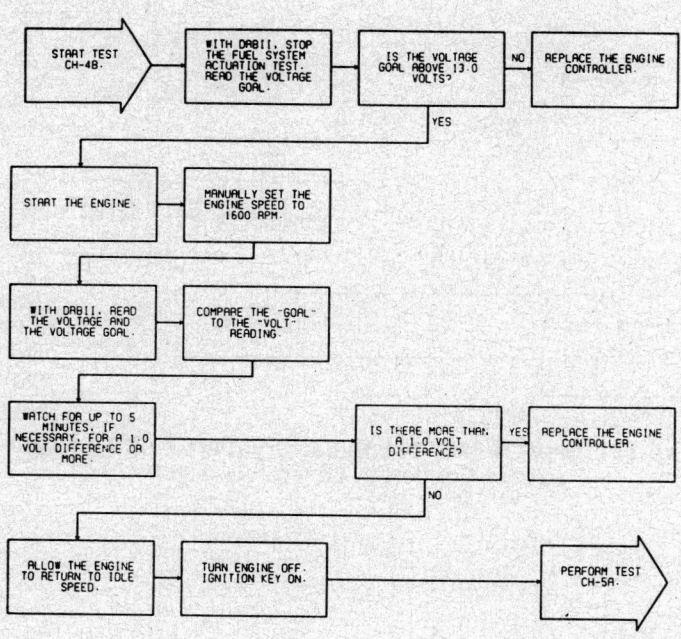

CR1129100086000X

Fig. 10 Test CH-4B: Checking Engine Controller Regulating Circuit. 1992

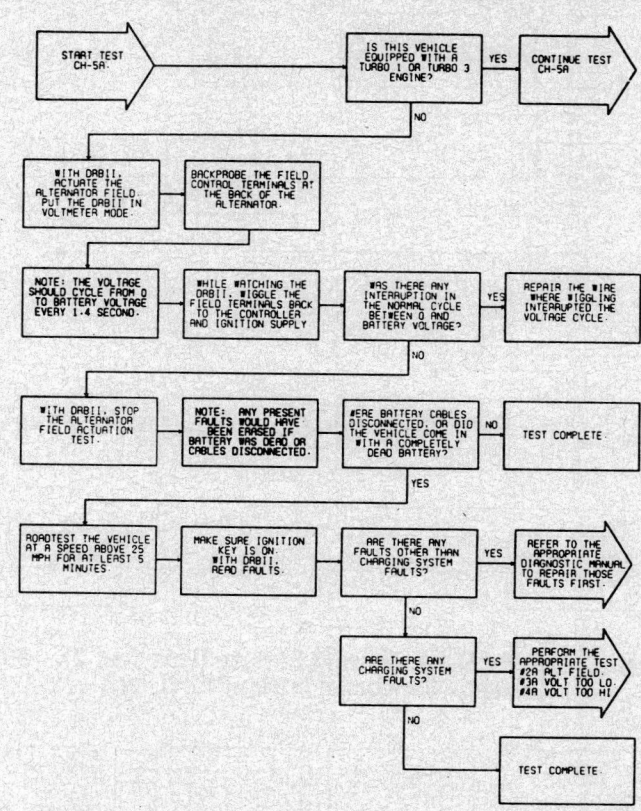

CR1129200087010X

Fig. 11 Test CH-5A: Checking For Intermittent Problems (Part 1 of 2). 1992

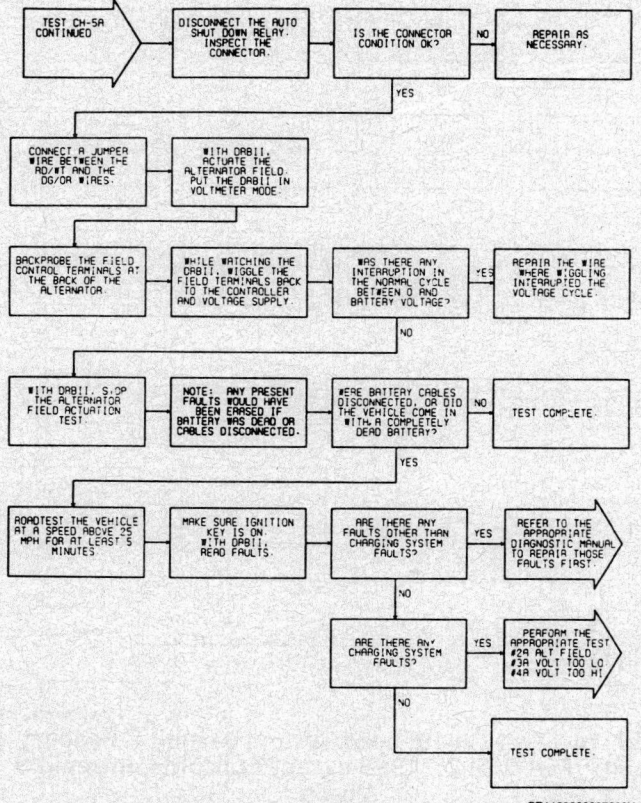

CR1129200087020X

Fig. 11 Test CH-5A: Checking For Intermittent Problems (Part 2 of 2). 1992

Inspect the vehicle to ensure that all engine components are connected. Reassemble and reconnect components as necessary.

If the engine controller has been changed, do the following:

1. If the vehicle is equipped with a factory theft alarm, start the vehicle at least 20 times so that the alarm system may be activated when desired.

2. If the vehicle is a minivan or a truck, the vehicle's mileage must be copied from its odometer to a memory location within the replacement controller. This will enable the new controller to operate the EMR lamp properly.

Connect the DRBII to the engine diagnostic connector and erase the faults.

Ensure no other charging system problems remain by doing the following:

1. Start the engine.

2. Raise the engine speed to 2000 rpm (1600 rpm for diesel) for at least 30 seconds.

3. Allow the engine to idle.

4. Turn the engine off.

5. Turn ignition key on.

6. With the DRBII, read fault messages.

If the repaired fault has reset, or another one has set, check all pertinent TECHNICAL SERVICE BULLETINS and return to TEST CH-1A if necessary.

If there are no other faults, the repair is now complete.

CR1129200088000X

Fig. 12 Test CH-VER: Charging Verification. 1992

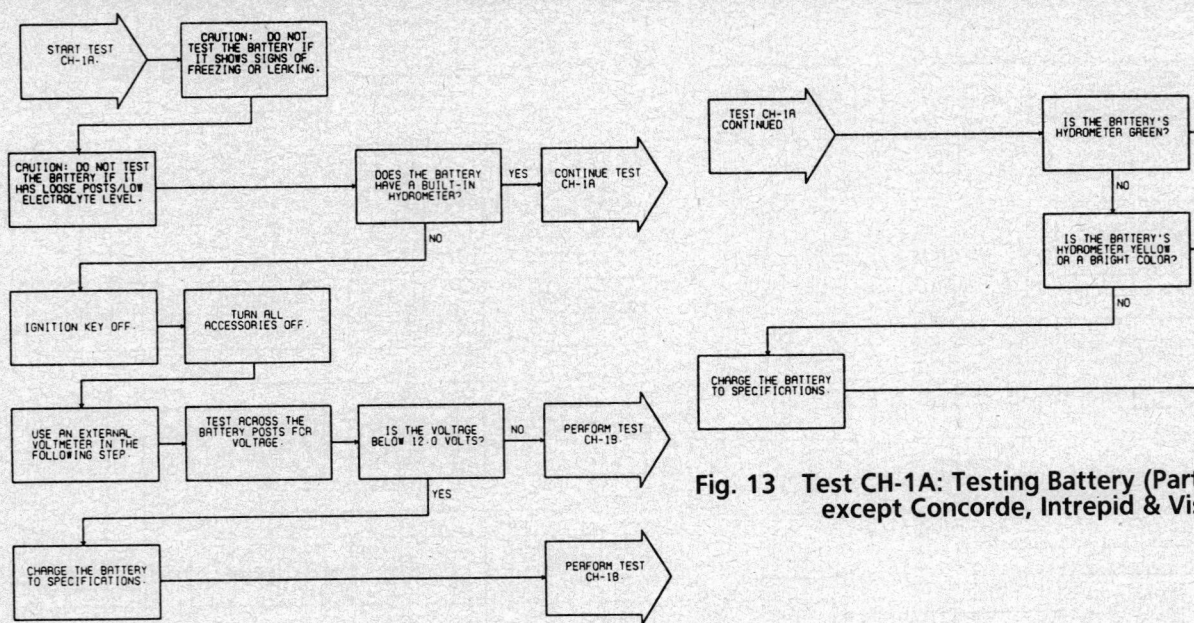

Fig. 13   Test CH-1A: Testing Battery (Part 1 of 2). 1993 except Concorde, Intrepid & Vision

CR1129300089010X

Fig. 13   Test CH-1A: Testing Battery (Part 2 of 2). 1993 except Concorde, Intrepid & Vision

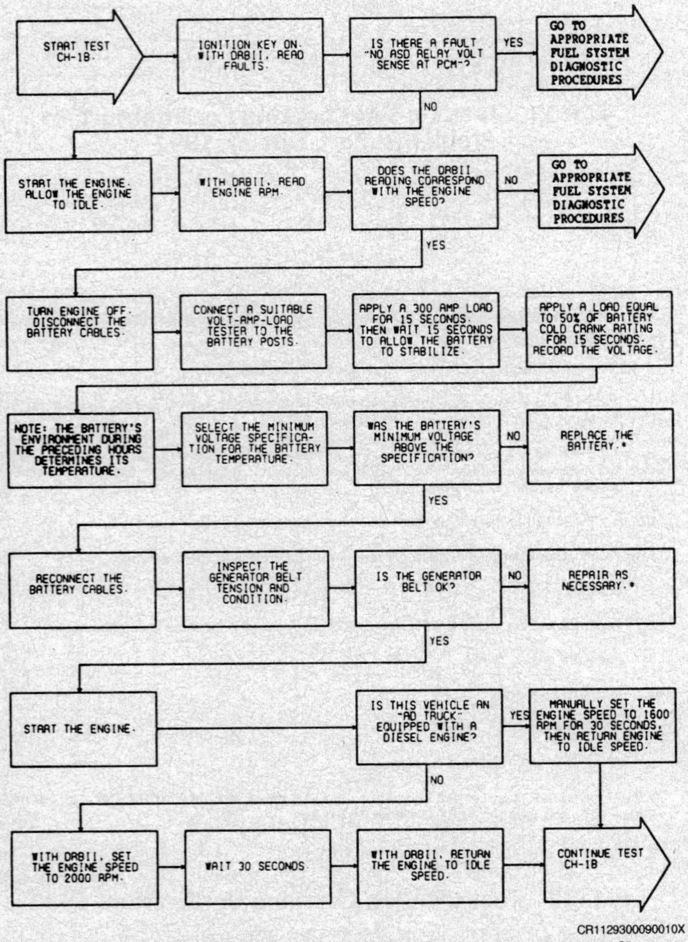

CR1129300089020X

Fig. 14   Test CH-1B: Load Testing Battery & Reading Faults (Part 1 of 2). 1993 except Concorde, Intrepid & Vision

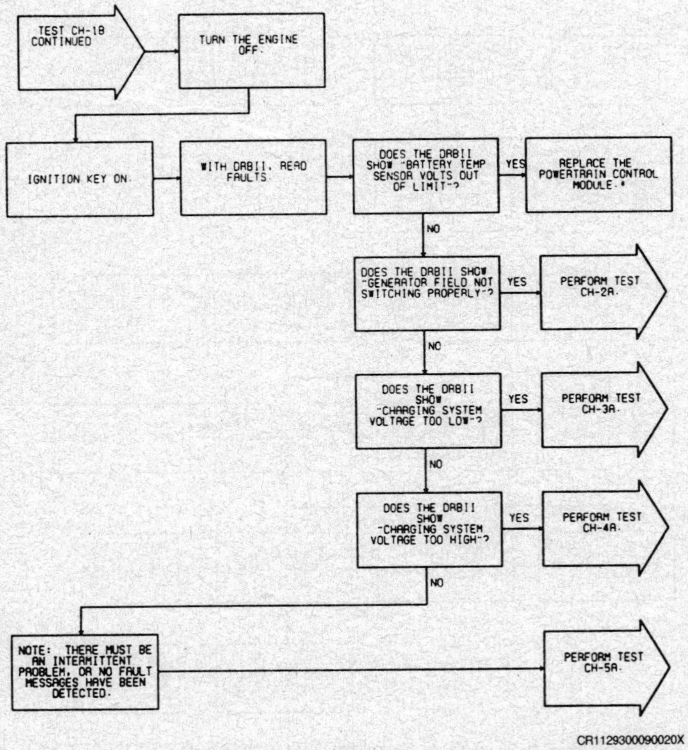

CR1129300090010X

Fig. 14   Test CH-1B: Load Testing Battery & Reading Faults (Part 2 of 2). 1993 except Concorde, Intrepid & Vision

CR1129300090020X

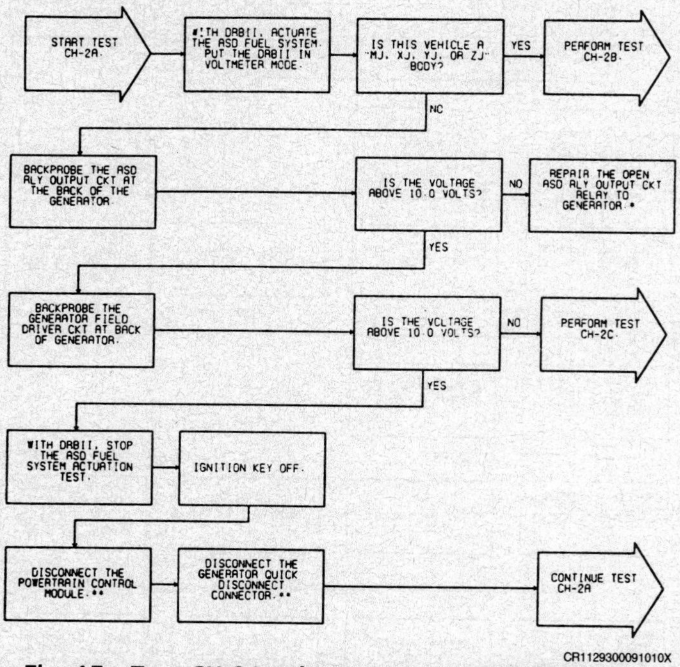

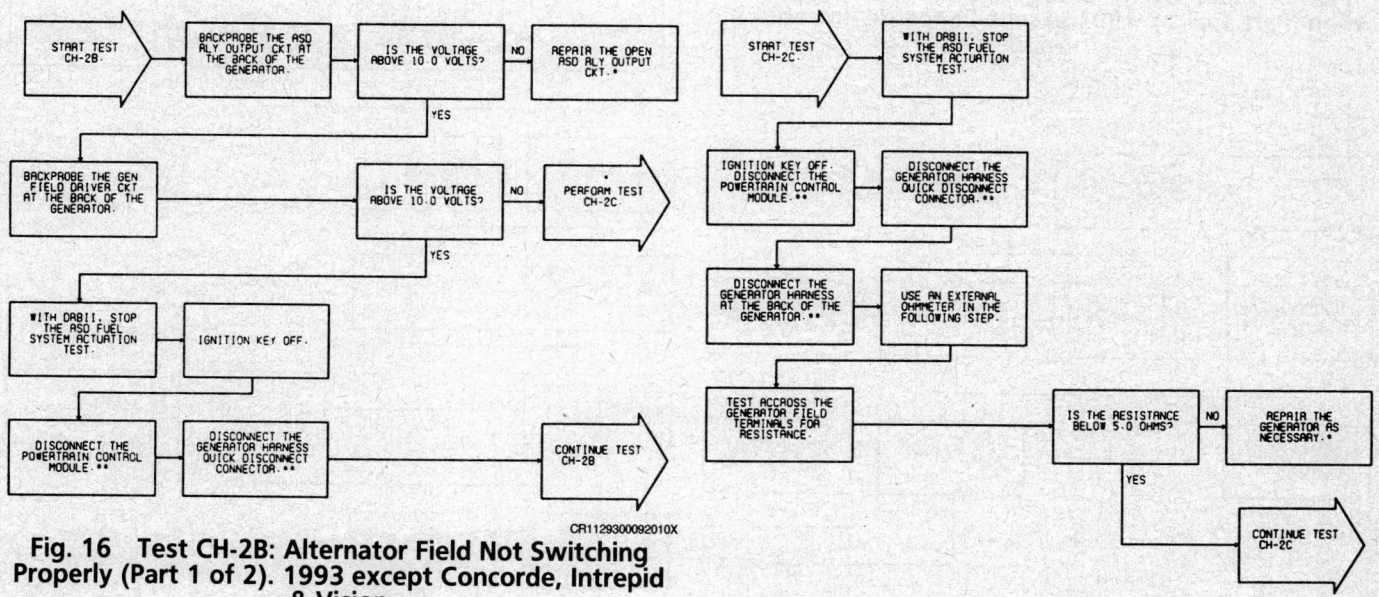

Fig. 15 Test CH-2A: Alternator Field Not Switching Properly (Part 2 of 2). 1993 except Concorde, Intrepid & Vision

Fig. 15 Test CH-2A: Alternator Field Not Switching Properly (Part 1 of 2). 1993 except Concorde, Intrepid & Vision

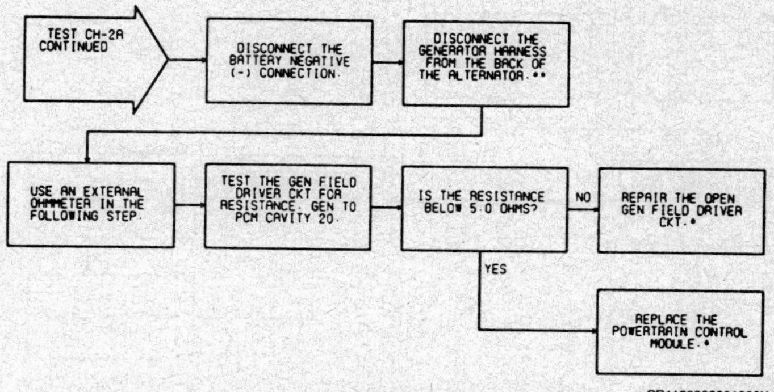

Fig. 16 Test CH-2B: Alternator Field Not Switching Properly (Part 2 of 2). 1993 except Concorde, Intrepid & Vision

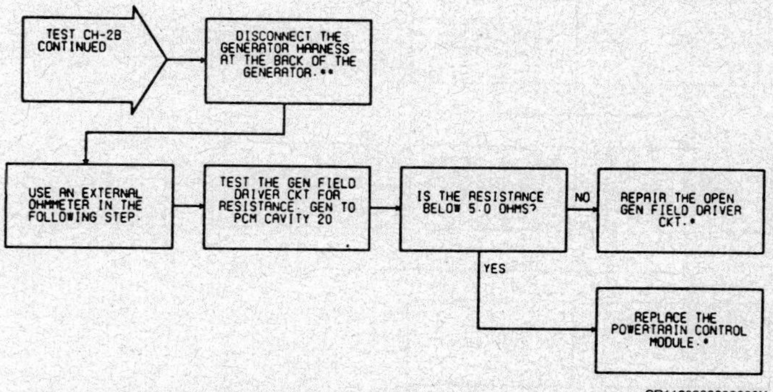

Fig. 16 Test CH-2B: Alternator Field Not Switching Properly (Part 1 of 2). 1993 except Concorde, Intrepid & Vision

Fig. 17 Test CH-2C: Checking Field Driver Circuit For Shorts (Part 1 of 2). 1993 except Concorde, Intrepid & Vision

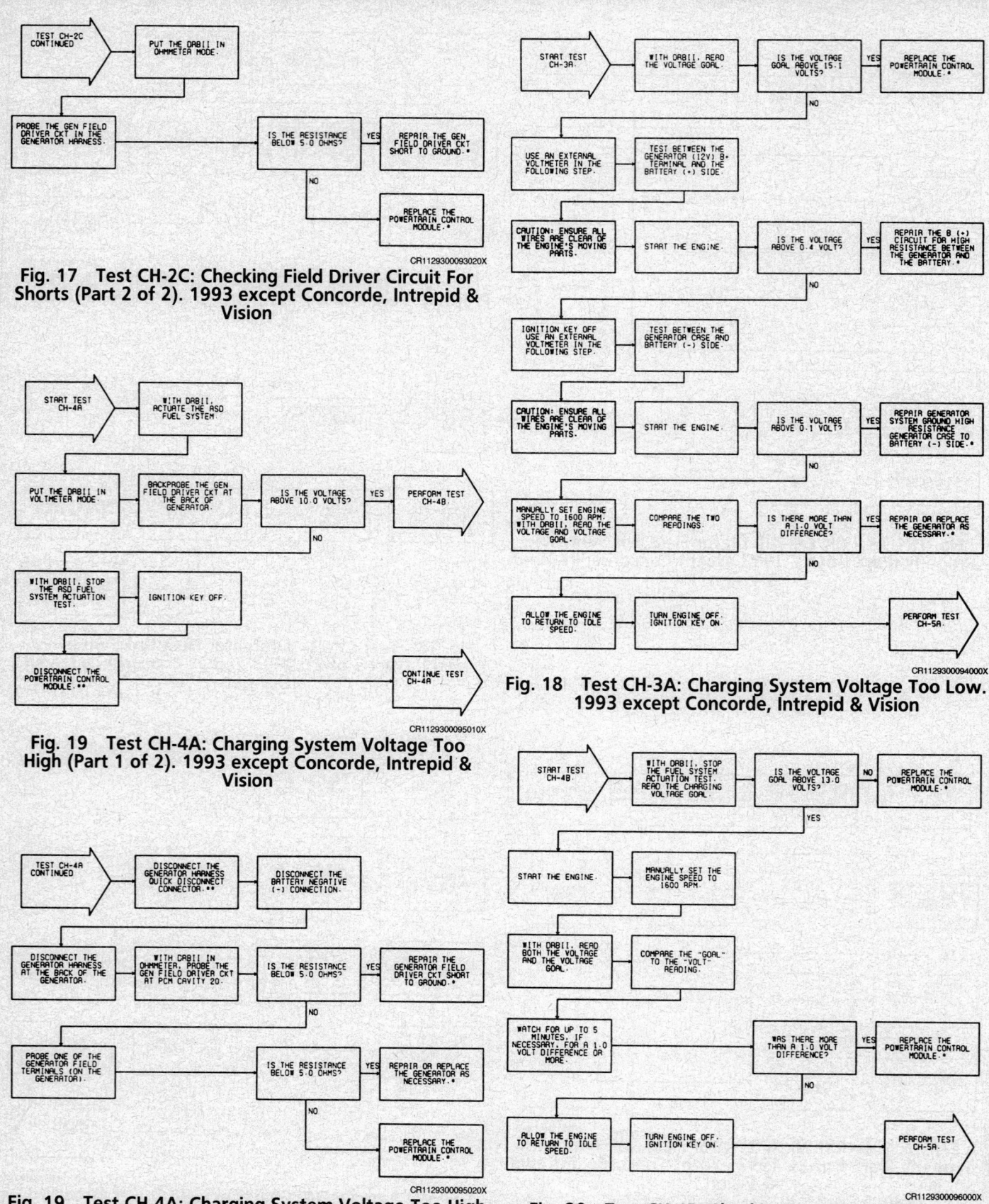

Fig. 17   Test CH-2C: Checking Field Driver Circuit For Shorts (Part 2 of 2). 1993 except Concorde, Intrepid & Vision

Fig. 19   Test CH-4A: Charging System Voltage Too High (Part 1 of 2). 1993 except Concorde, Intrepid & Vision

Fig. 19   Test CH-4A: Charging System Voltage Too High (Part 2 of 2). 1993 except Concorde, Intrepid & Vision

Fig. 18   Test CH-3A: Charging System Voltage Too Low. 1993 except Concorde, Intrepid & Vision

Fig. 20   Test CH-4B: Checking Powertrain Control Module Regulating Circuit. 1993 except Concorde, Intrepid & Vision

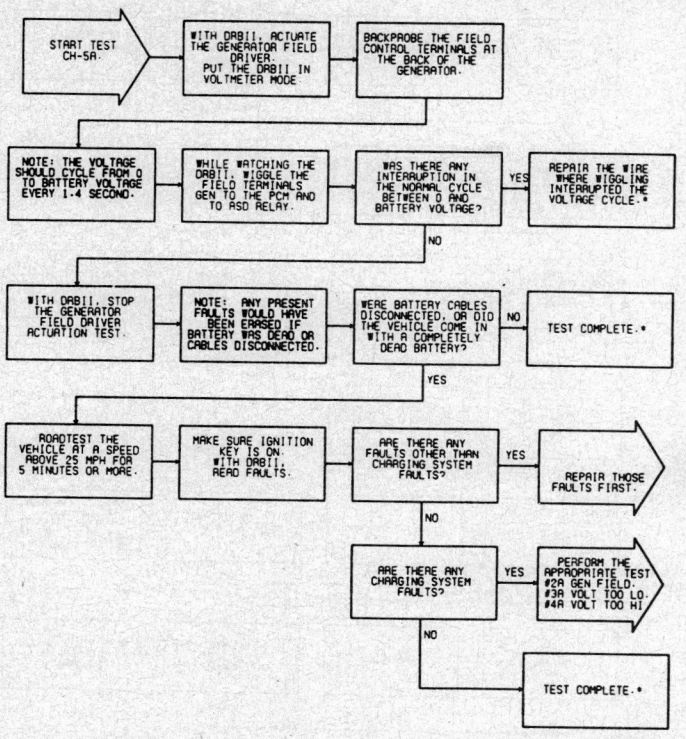

Fig. 21 Test CH-5A: Checking Charging System No Faults. 1993 except Concorde, Intrepid & Vision

Inspect the vehicle to ensure that all engine components are connected. Reassemble and reconnect components as necessary.

If the powertrain control module has been changed, do the following:

1. If the vehicle is equipped with a factory theft alarm, start the vehicle at least 20 times so that the alarm system may be activated when desired.

Connect the DRB to the PCM data link connector and erase the codes.

Ensure no other charging system problems remain by doing the following:

1. Start the engine.

2. Raise the engine speed to 2000 rpm for at least 30 seconds.

3. Allow the engine to idle.

4. Turn the engine off.

5. Turn the ignition key on.

6. With the DRB, read trouble code messages.

If the repaired code has reset, or another one has set, check all pertinent Technical Service Bulletins.

If there are no codes, the repair is now complete.

CR1129300098000A

Fig. 22 Test CH-VER: Charging Verification. 1993–94 except Concorde, Intrepid, LHS, Vision & 1994 New Yorker

DRB MESSAGE	DIAGNOSTIC TEST
GENERATOR FIELD NOT SWITCHING PROPERLY	TC-34A
CHARGING SYSTEM VOLTAGE TOO LOW	TC-35A
CHARGING SYSTEM VOLTAGE TOO HIGH	TC-36A
BATTERY TEMP SENSOR VOLTS OUT OF LIMIT	TC-38A

Engine is Cold Too Long - engine does not warm to 176°F while driving 20 minutes after start. This may set in error during very cold slow speed driving.

CR1129400131020X

Fig. 23 Test TC-1A: Checking The System For Trouble Codes (Part 2 of 2). 1994 except Concorde, Intrepid, LHS, New Yorker & Vision

NOTE: The battery must be fully charged for any test.

Attempt to start the engine. Crank for up to 10 seconds if necessary.

Connect the DRB to the engine diagnostic connector. Write down trouble code messages that are displayed.

If the DRB screen displays "No Response," go to **TEST NS-6A.**

If trouble code messages are displayed, refer to the trouble code list for the appropriate test.

CR1129400131010X

Fig. 23 Test TC-1A: Checking The System For Trouble Codes (Part 1 of 2). 1994 except Concorde, Intrepid, LHS, New Yorker & Vision

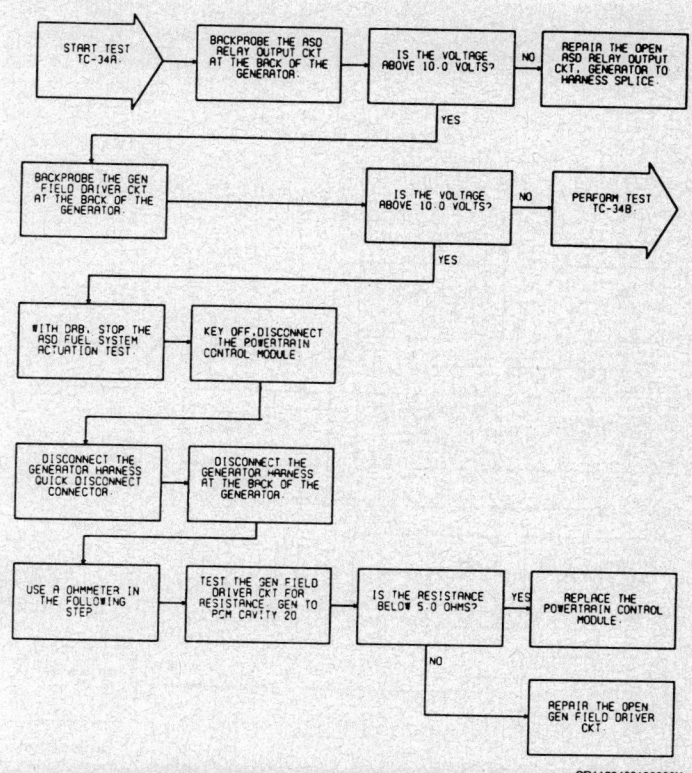

CR1129400132000X

Fig. 24 Test TC-34A: Generator Field Not Switching Properly. 1994 Except Concorde, Intrepid, LHS, New Yorker & Vision

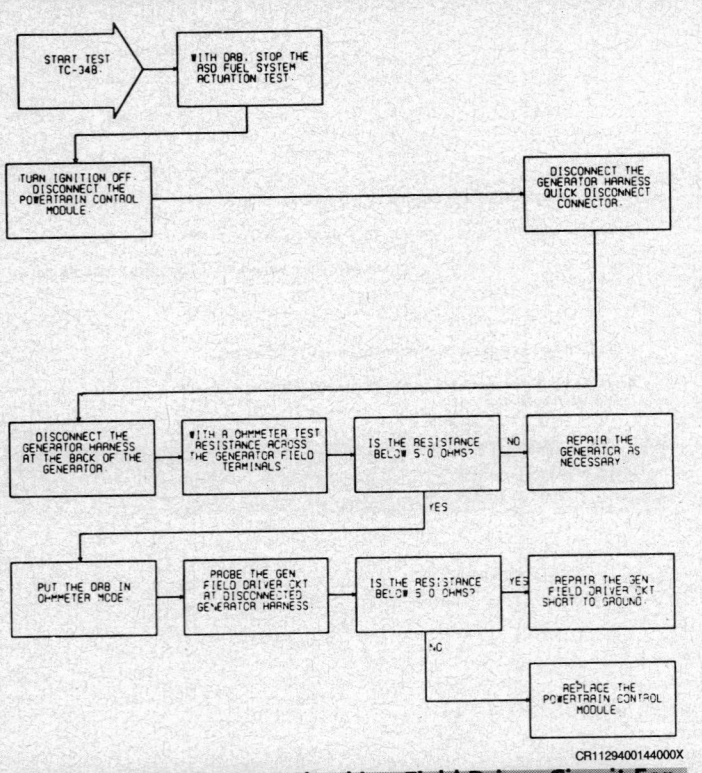

Fig. 25   Test TC-34B: Checking Field Driver Circuit For Shorts. 1994 except Concorde, Intrepid, LHS, New Yorker & Vision

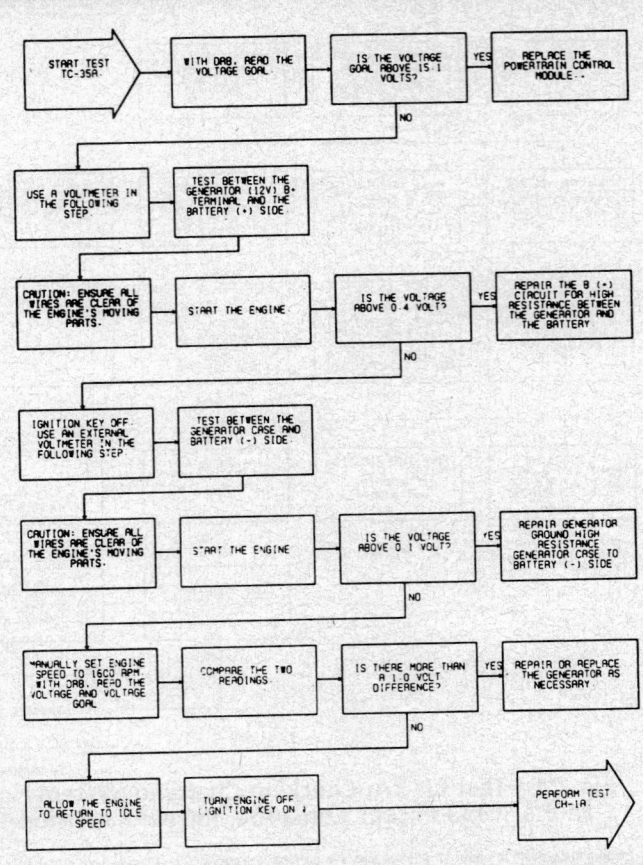

Fig. 26   Test TC-35A: Charging System Voltage Too Low. 1994 except Concorde, Intrepid, LHS, New Yorker & Vision

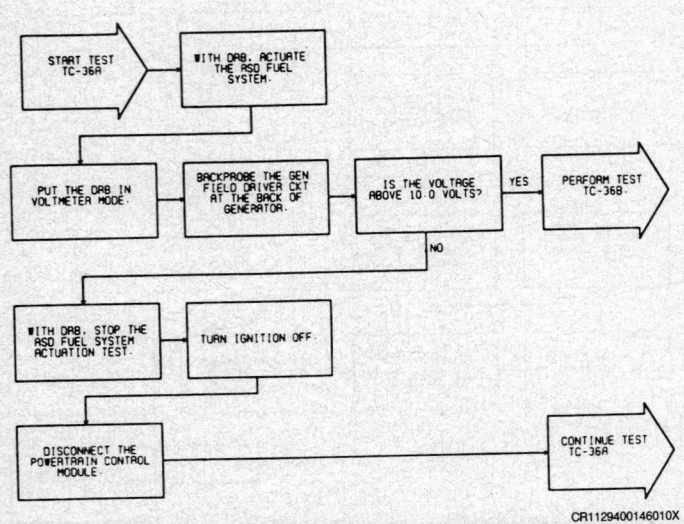

Fig. 27   Test TC-36A: Charging System Voltage Too High (Part 1 of 2). 1994 except Concorde, Intrepid, LHS, New Yorker & Vision

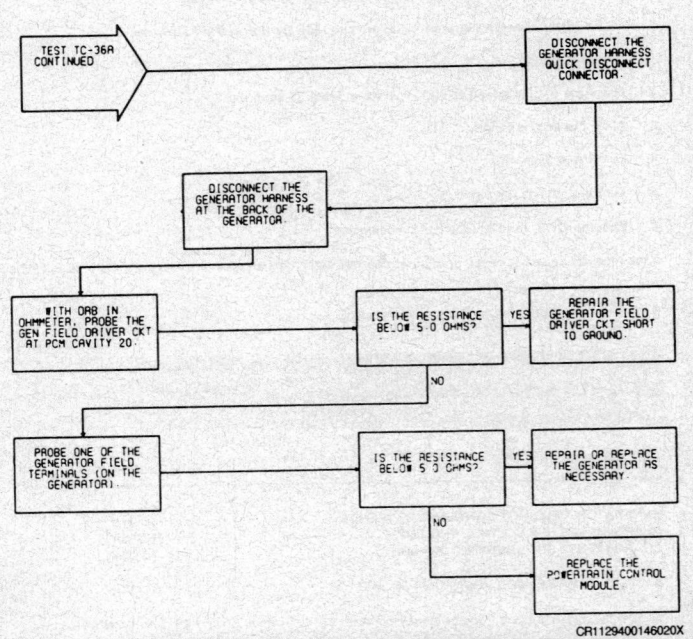

Fig. 27   Test TC-36A: Charging System Voltage Too High (Part 2 of 2). 1994 except Concorde, Intrepid, LHS, New Yorker & Vision

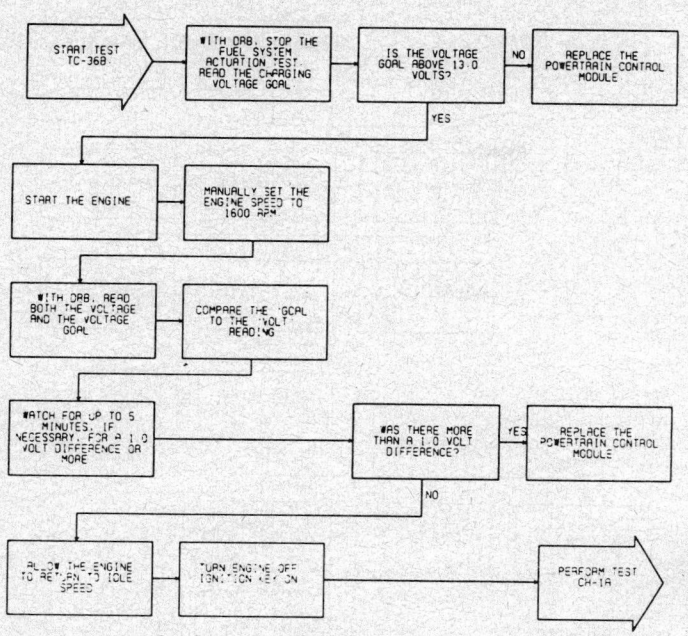

Fig. 28   Test TC-36B: Checking Powertrain Control Module Regulating Circuit. 1994 except Concorde, Intrepid, LHS, New Yorker & Vision

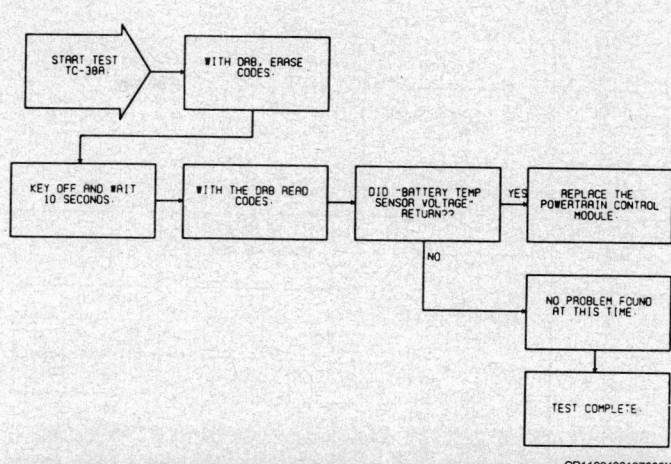

Fig. 29   Test TC-38A: Battery Temp Sensor Volts Out Of Limit. 1994 except Concorde, Intrepid, LHS, New Yorker & Vision

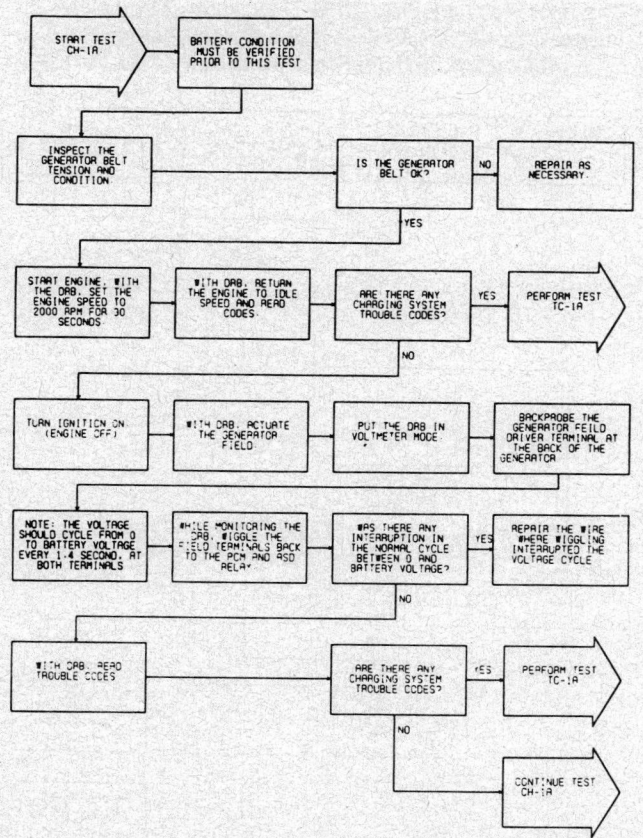

Fig. 30   Test CH-1A: Checking Charging System No Trouble Codes (Part 1 of 3). 1994 except Concorde, Intrepid, LHS, New Yorker & Vision

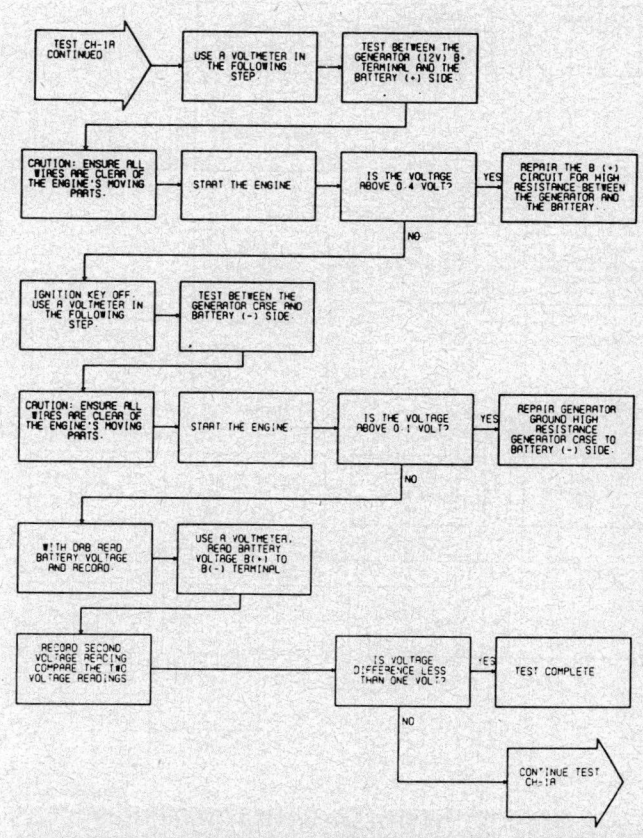

Fig. 30   Test CH-1A: Checking Charging System No Trouble Codes (Part 2 of 3). 1994 except Concorde, Intrepid, LHS, New Yorker & Vision

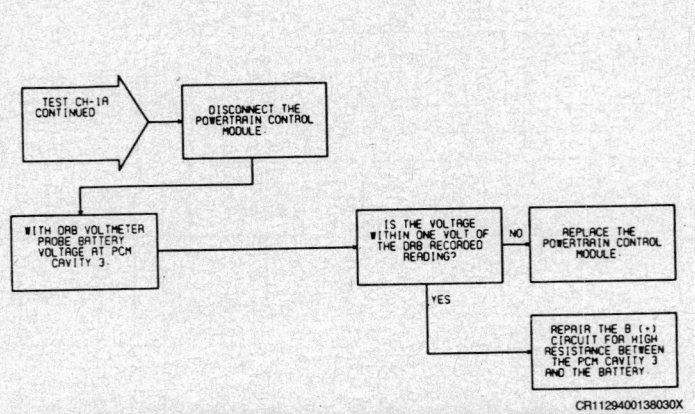

Fig. 30   Test CH-1A: Checking Charging System No Trouble Codes (Part 3 of 3). 1994 except Concorde, Intrepid, LHS, New Yorker & Vision

CR1129400138030X

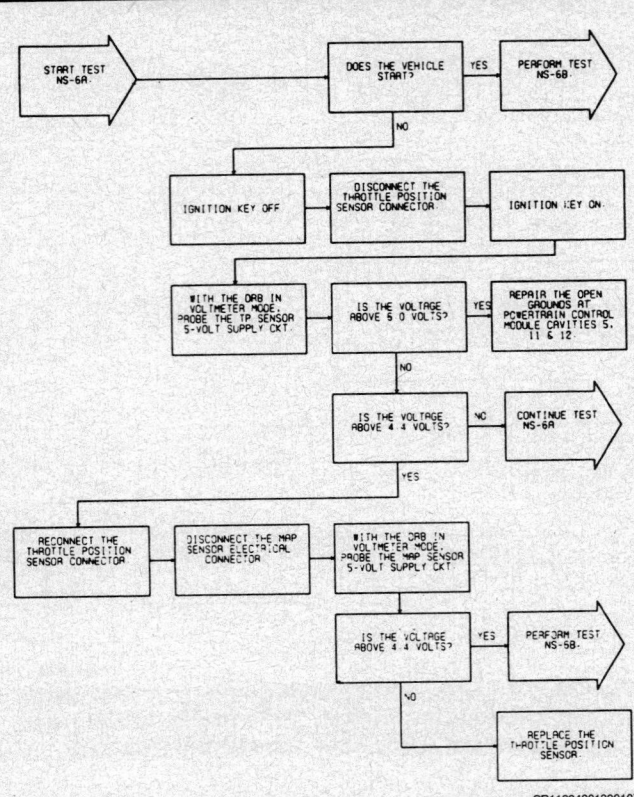

CR1129400139010X

Fig. 31   Test NS-6A: Correcting "No Response" Condition (Part 1 of 5). 1994 except Concorde, Intrepid, LHS, New Yorker & Vision

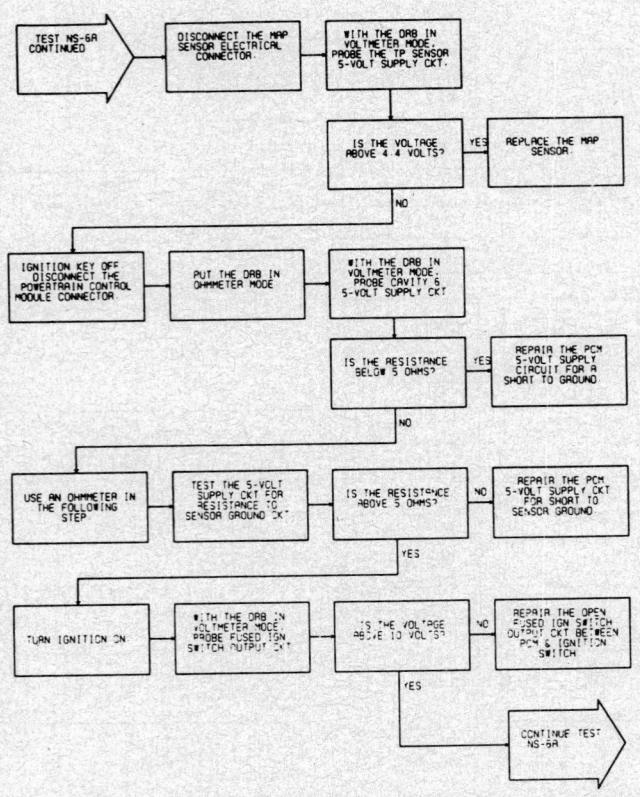

CR1129400139020X

Fig. 31   Test NS-6A: Correcting "No Response" Condition (Part 2 of 5). 1994 except Concorde, Intrepid, LHS, New Yorker & Vision

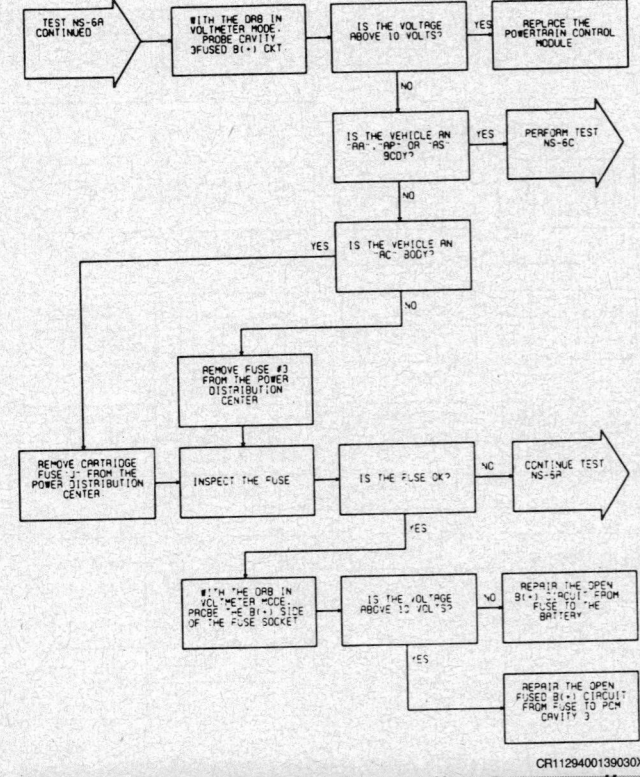

CR1129400139030X

Fig. 31   Test NS-6A: Correcting "No Response" Condition (Part 3 of 5). 1994 except Concorde, Intrepid, LHS, New Yorker & Vision

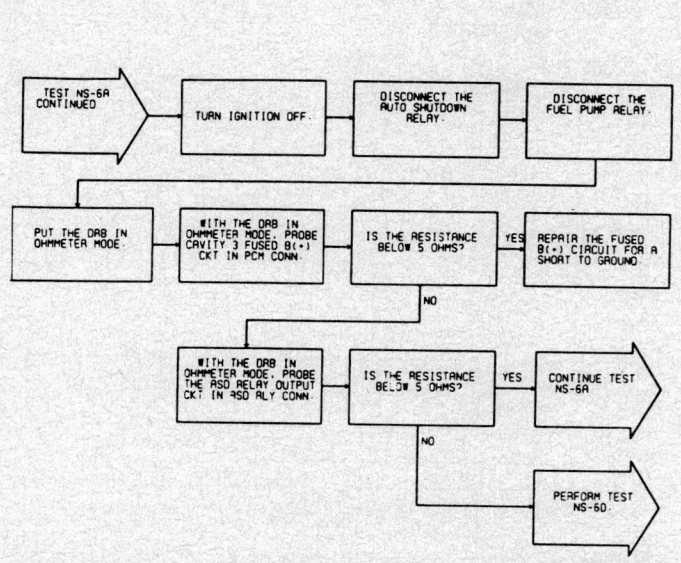

Fig. 31   Test NS-6A: Correcting "No Response" Condition (Part 4 of 5). 1994 except Concorde, Intrepid, LHS, New Yorker & Vision

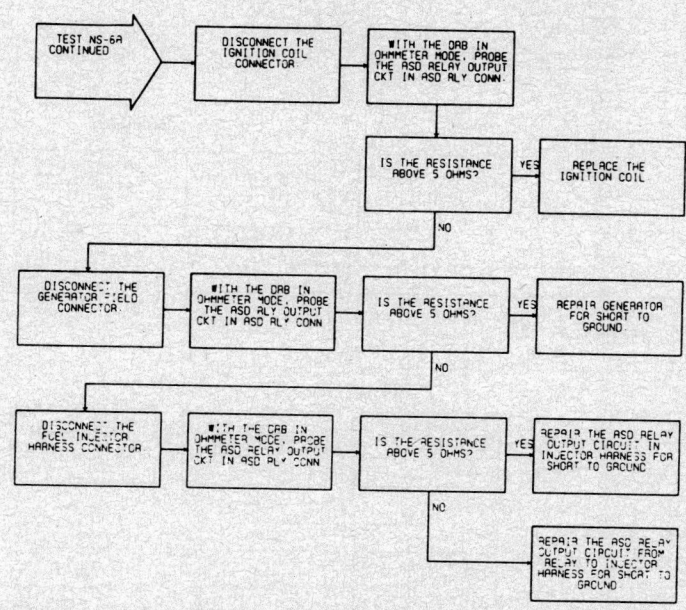

Fig. 31   Test NS-6A: Correcting "No Response" Condition (Part 5 of 5). 1994 except Concorde, Intrepid, LHS, New Yorker & Vision

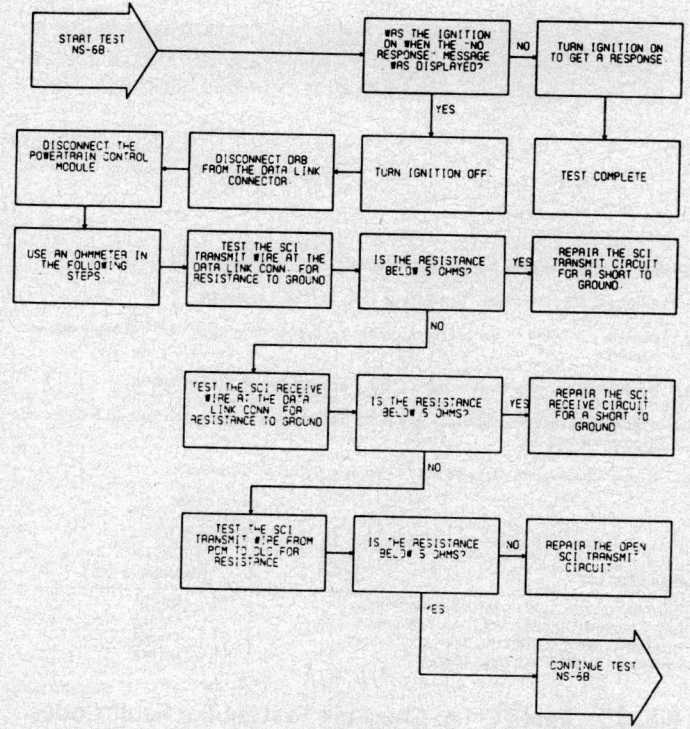

Fig. 32   Test NS-6B: Correcting "No Response" Condition (Part 1 of 2). 1994 except Concorde, Intrepid, LHS, New Yorker & Vision

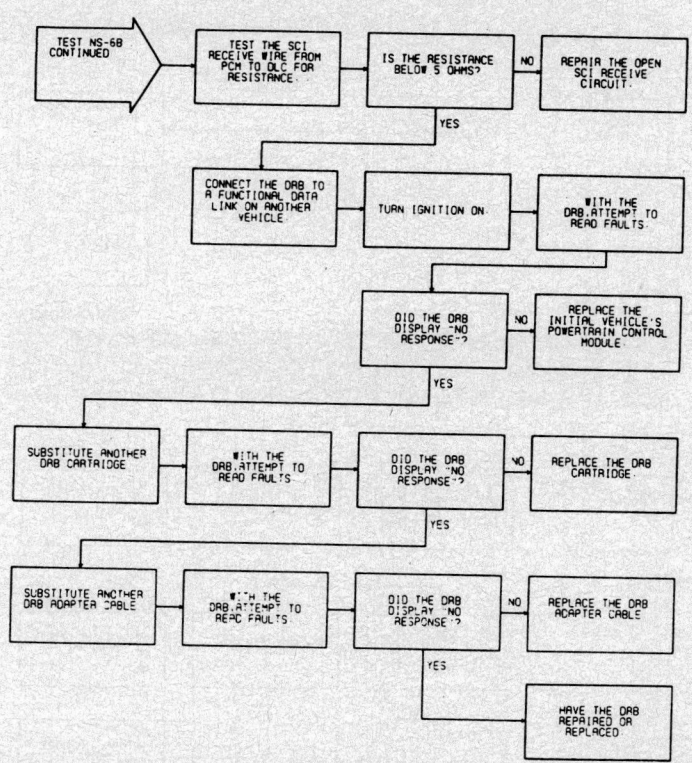

Fig. 32   Test NS-6B: Correcting "No Response" Condition (Part 2 of 2). 1994 except Concorde, Intrepid, LHS, New Yorker & Vision

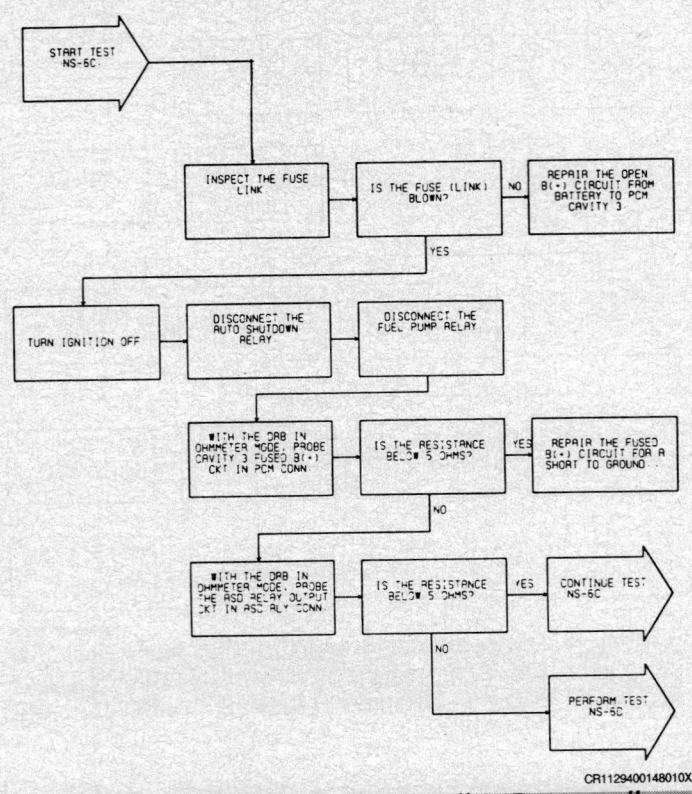

Fig. 33 Test NS-6C: Correcting "No Response" Condition (Part 1 of 2). 1994 except Concorde, Intrepid, LHS, New Yorker & Vision

CR1129400148010X

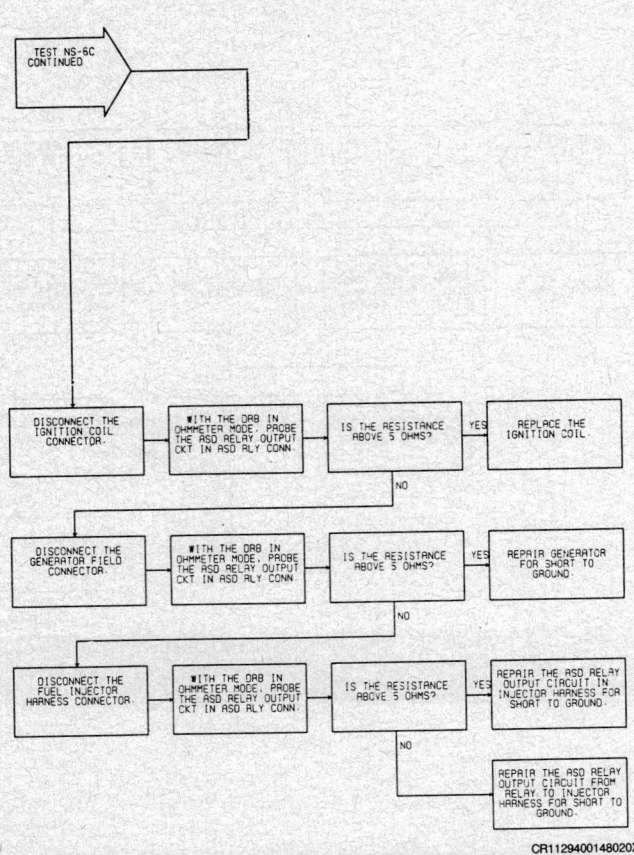

Fig. 33 Test NS-6C: Correcting "No Response" Condition (Part 2 of 2). 1994 except Concorde, Intrepid, LHS, New Yorker & Vision

CR1129400148020X

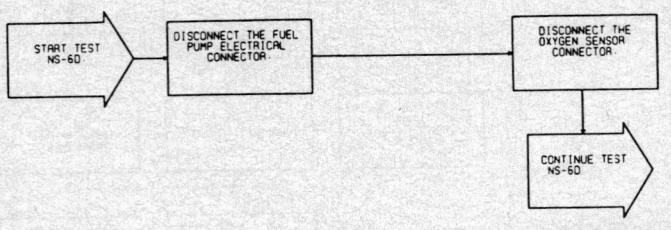

Fig. 34 Test NS-6D: Correcting "No Response" Condition (Part 1 of 2). 1994 except Concorde, Intrepid, LHS, New Yorker & Vision

CR1129400142010X

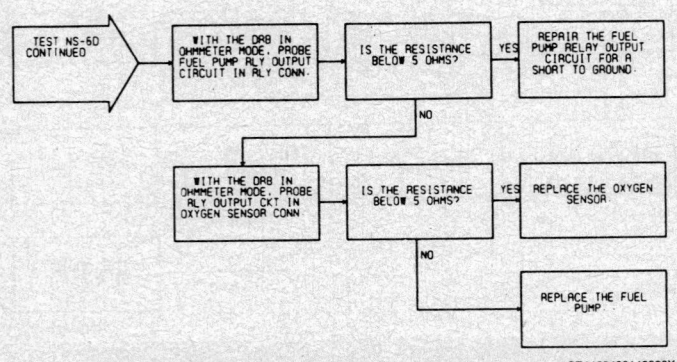

Fig. 34 Test NS-6D: Correcting "No Response" Condition (Part 2 of 2). 1994 except Concorde, Intrepid, LHS, New Yorker & Vision

CR1129400142020X

NOTE: The battery must be fully charged for any test in this manual.

1. Attempt to start the engine. Crank for up to 10 seconds if necessary.

2. Connect the DRBII to the engine diagnostic connector. Write down fault messages that are displayed.

3. If the DRBII screen is blank or has a DRBII error message, go to TEST NS-6A.

4. If fault messages are displayed, refer to the fault code list below and on the next page for the appropriate test.

5. If there are no faults displayed refer to Charging problems CH-NF-1

DRBII MESSAGE	DIAGNOSTIC TEST
GENERATOR FIELD NOT SWITCHING PROPERLY	CH-48A
BATTERY TEMP SENSOR VOLTS OUT OF LIMIT	CH-49A
CHARGING SYSTEM VOLTAGE TOO LOW	CH-50A
CHARGING SYSTEM VOLTAGE TOO HIGH	CH-51A

CR1129100099000X

Fig. 35 Test FC-1A: Checking System For Fault Codes. Concorde, Intrepid, LHS, Vision & 1994 New Yorker

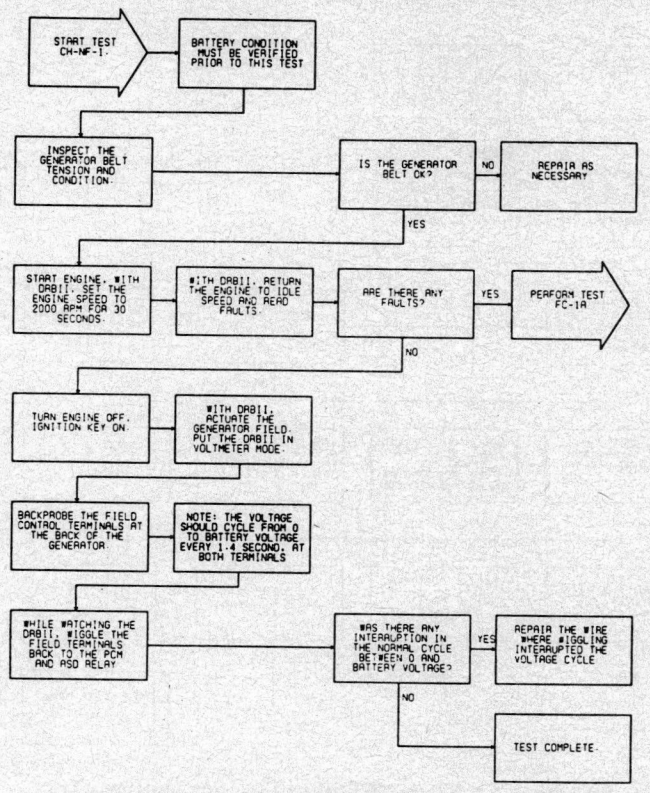

Fig. 36   Test CH-NF-1: No Fault Test. Concorde, Intrepid, LHS, Vision & 1994 New Yorker

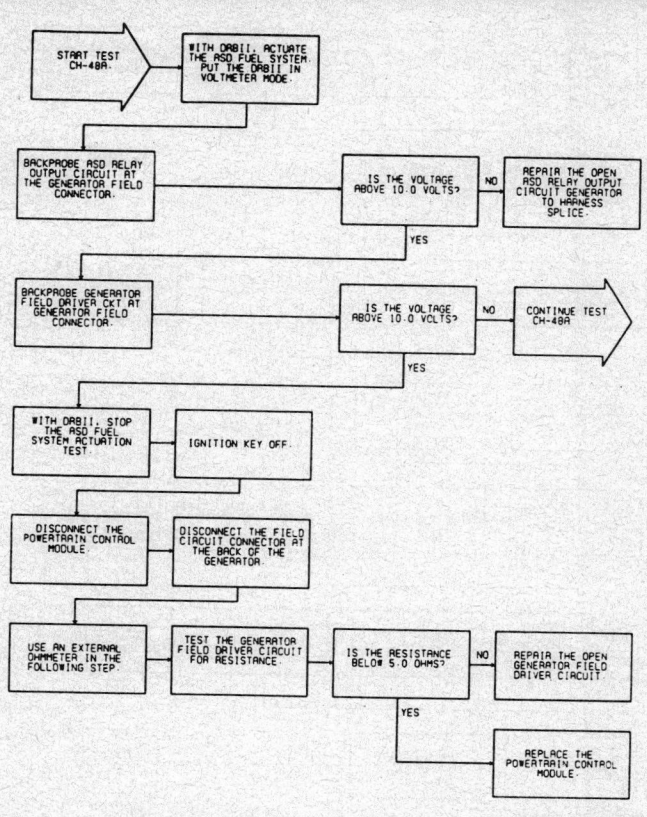

Fig. 37   Test CH-48A: Generator Field Not Switching Properly (Part 1 of 2). Concorde, Intrepid, LHS, Vision & 1994 New Yorker

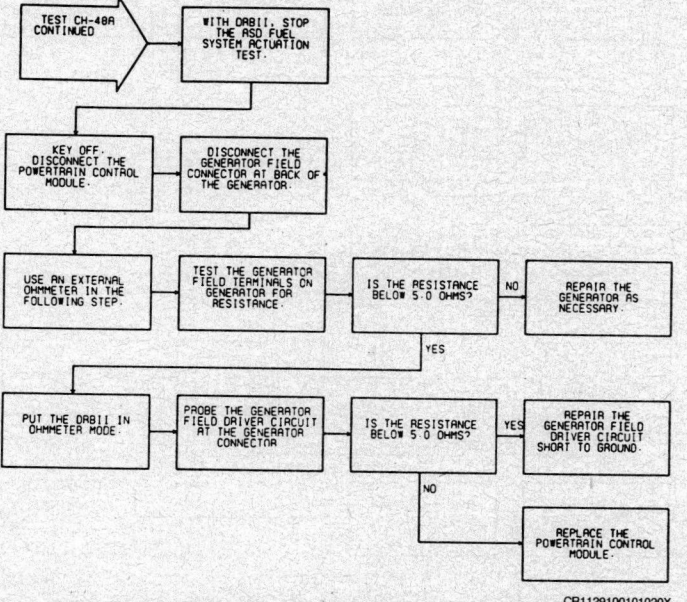

Fig. 37   Test CH-48A: Generator Field Not Switching Properly (Part 2 of 2). Concorde, Intrepid, LHS, Vision & 1994 New Yorker

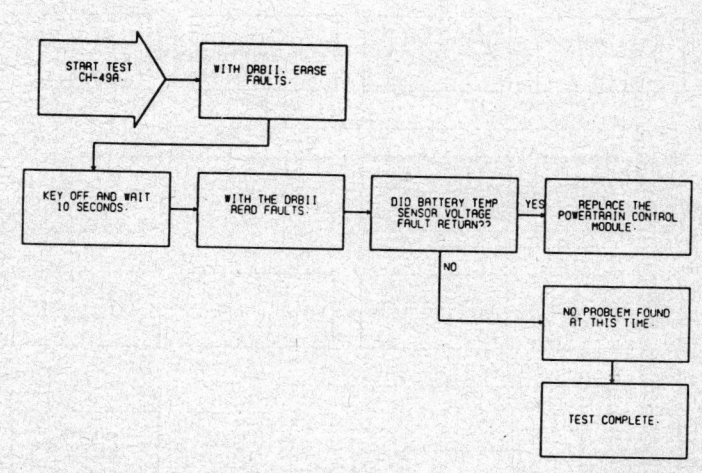

Fig. 38   Test CH-49A: Battery Temp Sensor Volts Out Of Limit. Concorde, Intrepid, LHS, Vision & 1994 New Yorker

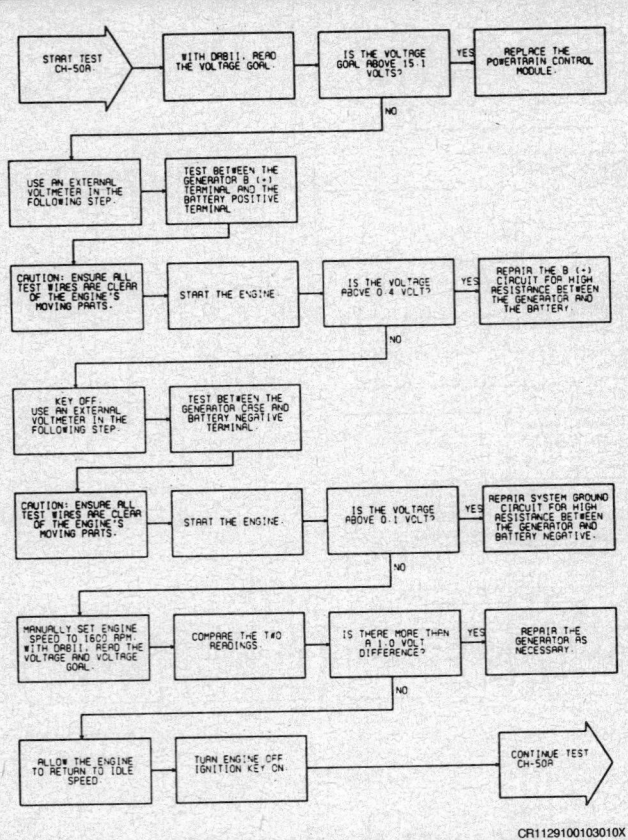

Fig. 39   Test CH-50A: Charging System Voltage Too Low (Part 1 of 2). Concorde, Intrepid, LHS, Vision & 1994 New Yorker

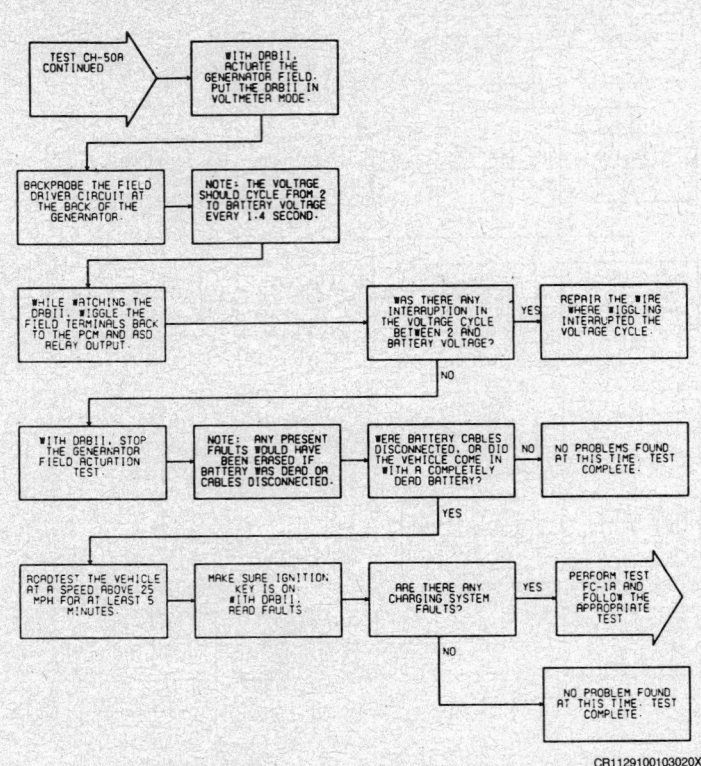

Fig. 39   Test CH-50A: Charging System Voltage Too Low (Part 2 of 2). Concorde, Intrepid, LHS, Vision & 1994 New Yorker

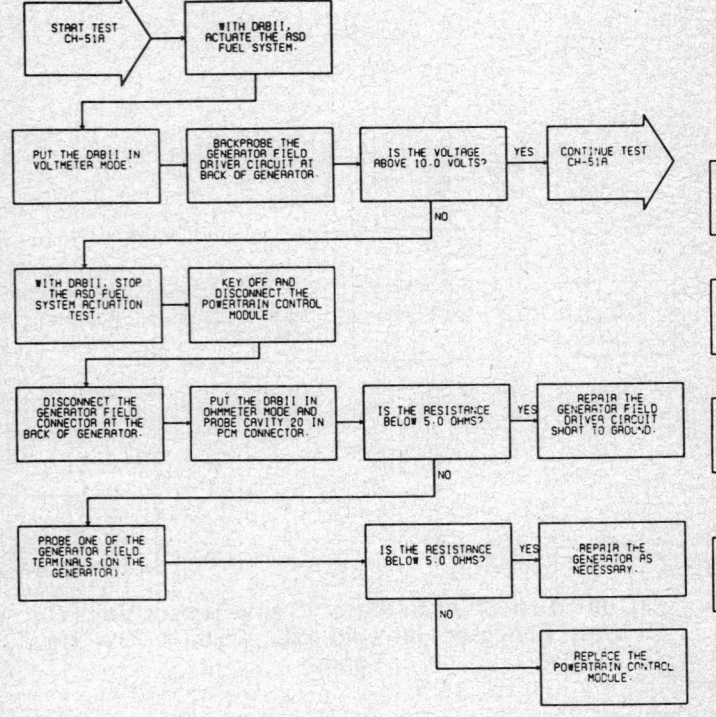

Fig. 40   Test CH-51A: Charging System Voltage Too High (Part 1 of 2). Concorde, Intrepid, LHS, Vision & 1994 New Yorker

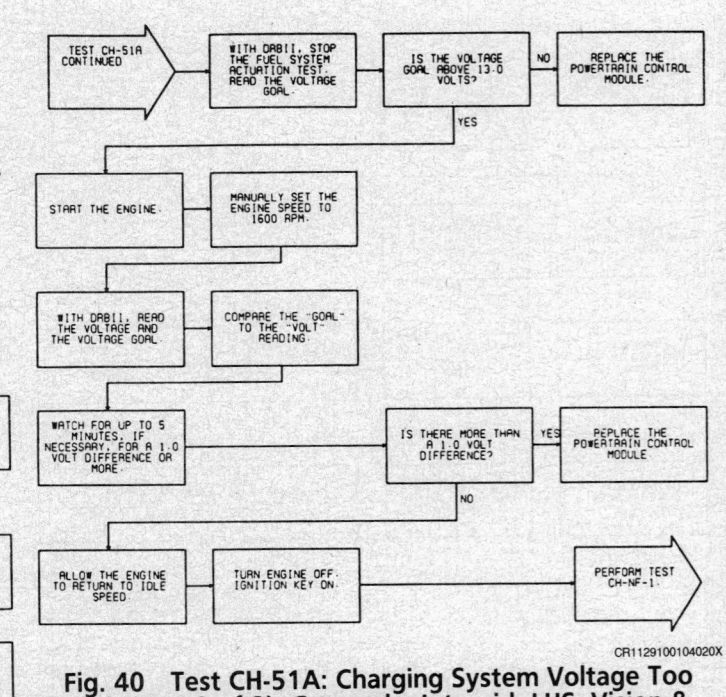

Fig. 40   Test CH-51A: Charging System Voltage Too High (Part 2 of 2). Concorde, Intrepid, LHS, Vision & 1994 New Yorker

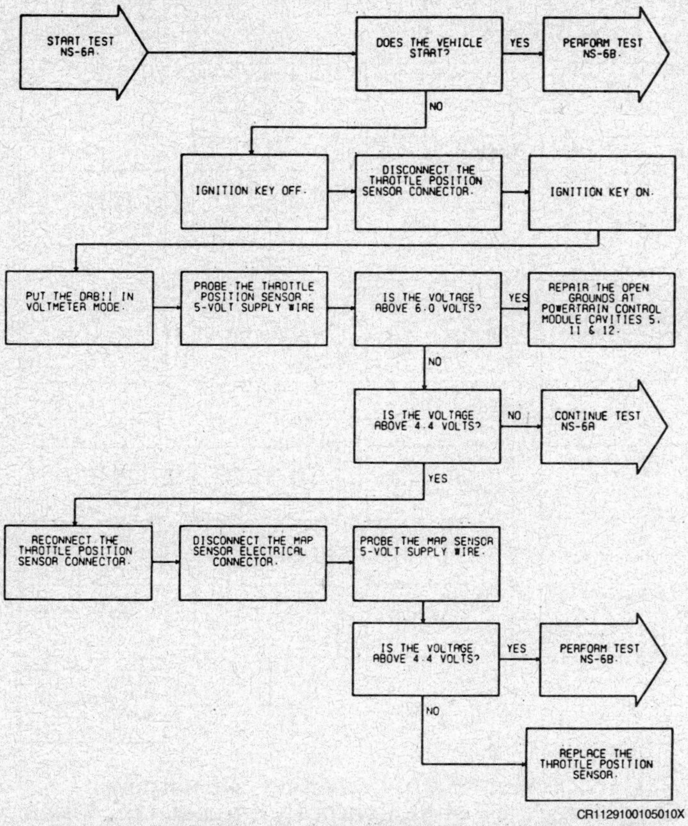

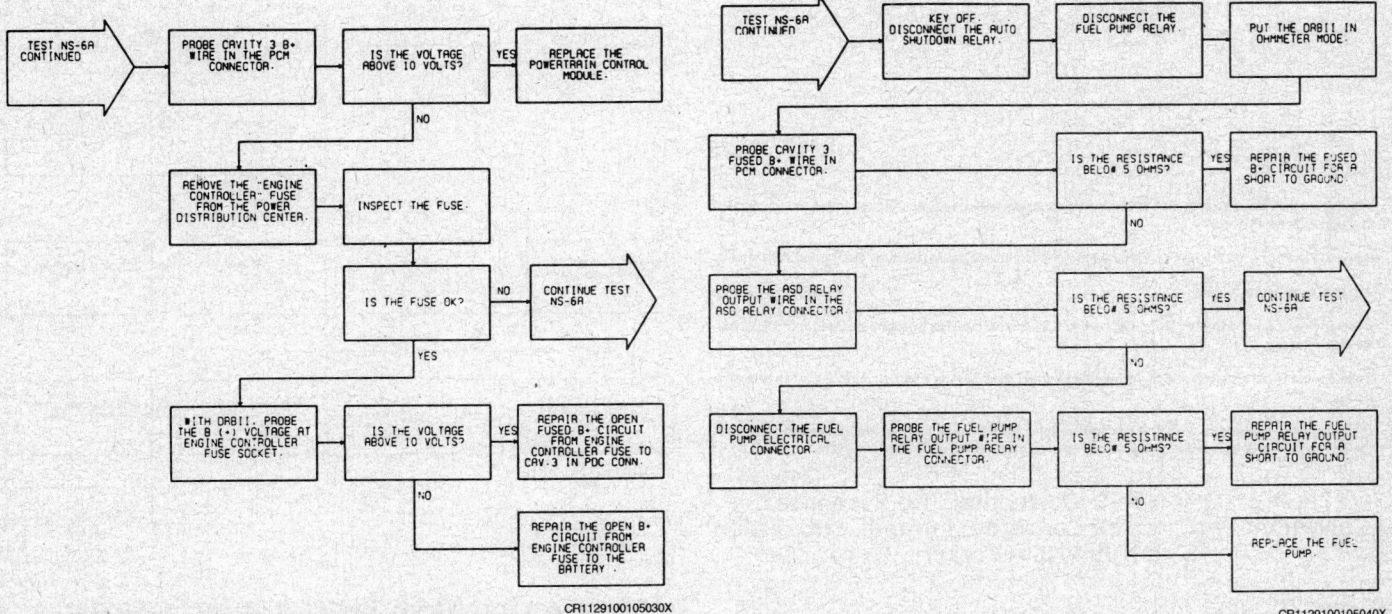

Fig. 41   Test NS-6A: Correcting "No Response"
Condition (Part 1 of 6). Concorde, Intrepid, LHS, Vision &
1994 New Yorker

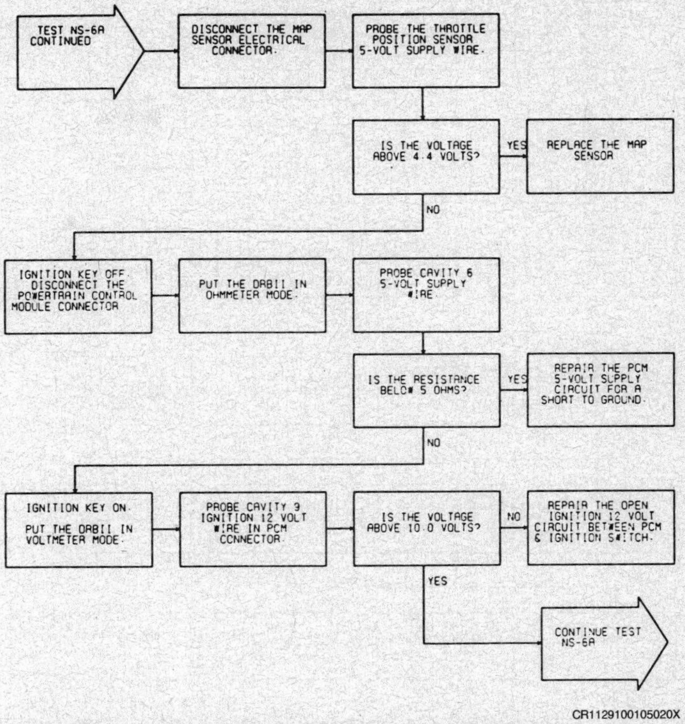

Fig. 41   Test NS-6A: Correcting "No Response"
Condition (Part 2 of 6). Concorde, Intrepid, LHS, Vision &
1994 New Yorker

Fig. 41   Test NS-6A: Correcting "No Response"
Condition (Part 3 of 6). Concorde, Intrepid, LHS, Vision
& 1994 New Yorker

Fig. 41   Test NS-6A: Correcting "No Response"
Condition (Part 4 of 6). Concorde, Intrepid, LHS, Vision
& 1994 New Yorker

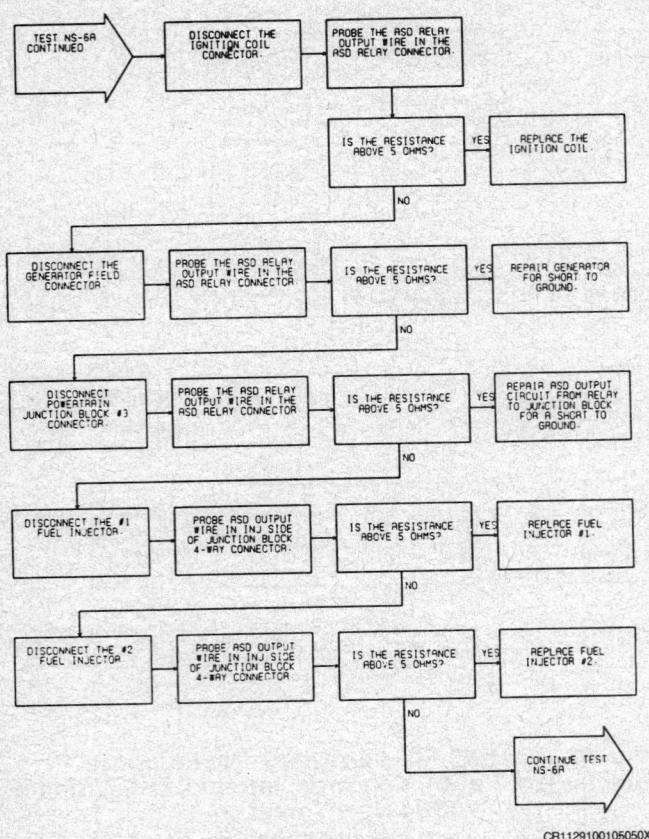

Fig. 41 Test NS-6A: Correcting "No Response" Condition (Part 5 of 6). Concorde, Intrepid, LHS, Vision & 1994 New Yorker

Fig. 41 Test NS-6A: Correcting "No Response" Condition (Part 6 of 6). Concorde, Intrepid, LHS, Vision & 1994 New Yorker

Inspect the vehicle to ensure that all engine components are connected. Reassemble and reconnect components as necessary.

Inspect the engine oil for fuel contamination. If it is contaminated, change the oil and filter.

Attempt to start the engine.

If the engine is unable to start, check all pertinent Technical Service Bulletins and return to **TEST FC-1A** if necessary.

If the engine is able to start and the powertrain control module has been changed, the repair is now complete.

If the engine is not able to start and the powertrain control module has not been changed, connect the DRBII to the data link connector and erase faults. The repair is now complete.

Fig. 42 Test NS-6B: Correcting "No Response" Condition (Part 1 of 2). Concorde, Intrepid, LHS, Vision & 1994 New Yorker

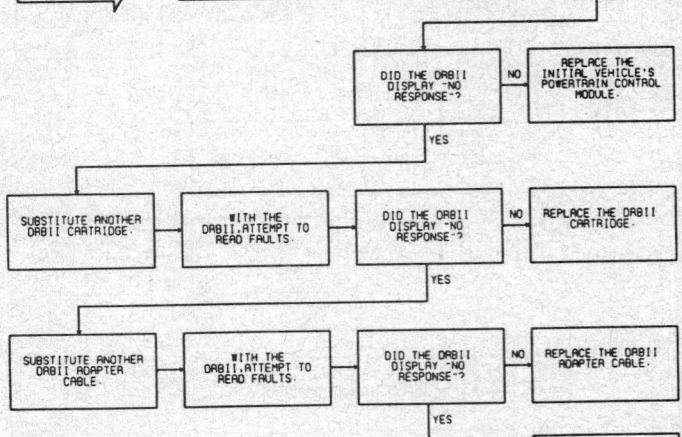

Fig. 42 Test NS-6B: Correcting "No Response" Condition (Part 2 of 2). Concorde, Intrepid, LHS, Vision & 1994 New Yorker

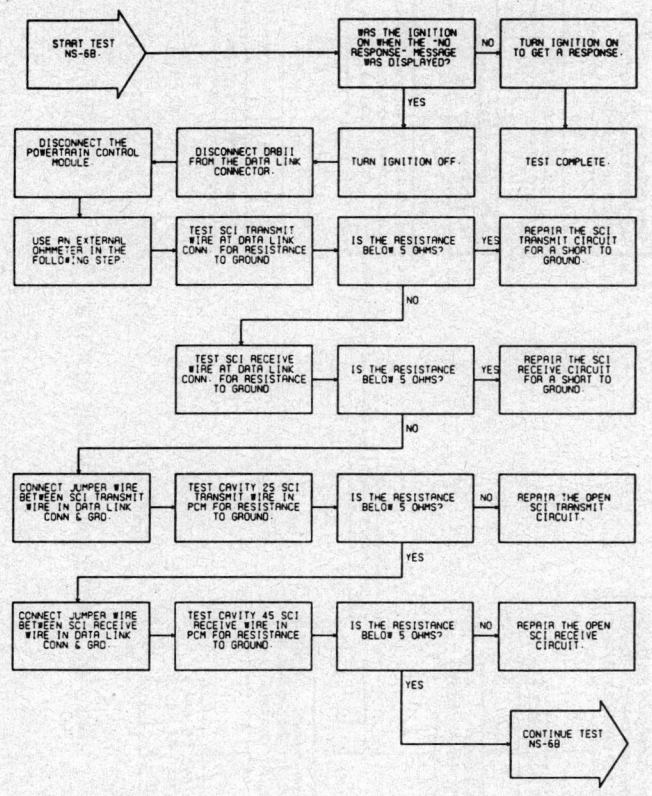

Fig. 43 Test VER-1: Verification Test 1. Concorde, Intrepid, LHS, Vision & 1994 New Yorker

CR1129100107000X

Inspect the vehicle to ensure that all engine components are connected. Reassemble and reconnect components as necessary.

If another fault was read previously that has not been dealt with, return to **TEST FC-1A** and follow the path specified by the other fault.

If the powertrain control module has not been changed, do the following:

a. Connect the DRBII to the data link connector and erase faults.

b. With DRBII, reset all values in adaptive memory.

c. Disconnect the DRBII.

Ensure no other fault remains by doing the following:

a. If the vehicle is equipped with air conditioning, turn on the air conditioning and blower.

b. Drive the vehicle for at least five minutes and at some point attain a speed of 40 mph. Ensure the transmission shifts through all gears. Upon the completion of the road test, turn the engine off.

c. Start the engine. Allow the engine to idle for at least two minutes.

d. Turn the engine off.

e. Connect the DRBII to the data link connector.

f. With the DRBII, read all fault messages.

If the repaired fault has reset, the repair is not complete. Check all pertinent Technical Service Bulletins and return to **TEST FC-1A** if necessary.

If there is another fault, return to **TEST FC-1A** and follow the path specified by the other fault.

If there are no faults, the repair is now complete.

CR1129100108000X

Fig. 44 Test VER-2: Verification Test 2. Concorde, Intrepid, LHS, Vision & 1994 New Yorker

Fault Code	Type	Check Engine Lamp	Circuit	When Monitored By The Logic Module	When Put Into Memory
12	Indication	No	Battery Feed to the Logic Module Controller	All the time when the ignition switch is on.	If the battery feed to the logic module has been disconnected within the last 50-100 engine starts.
41	Fault	Yes	Alternator Field Control (Charging System)	All the time when the ignition switch is on.	If the field control fails to switch properly.
46	Fault	Yes	Battery Voltage Sensing (Charging System)	All the time when the engine is running.	If the battery sense voltage is more than 1 volt above the desired control voltage for more than 20 seconds.
47	Fault	Yes	Battery Voltage Sensing (Charging System)	Engine rpm above 1,500 rpm.	If the battery sense voltage is less than 1 volt below the desired control voltage for more than 20 seconds and active test indicates a starter problem.
55	Indication	No			Indicates end of diagnostic mode.

CR1129100109000X

Fig. 45 Alternator diagnostic trouble codes

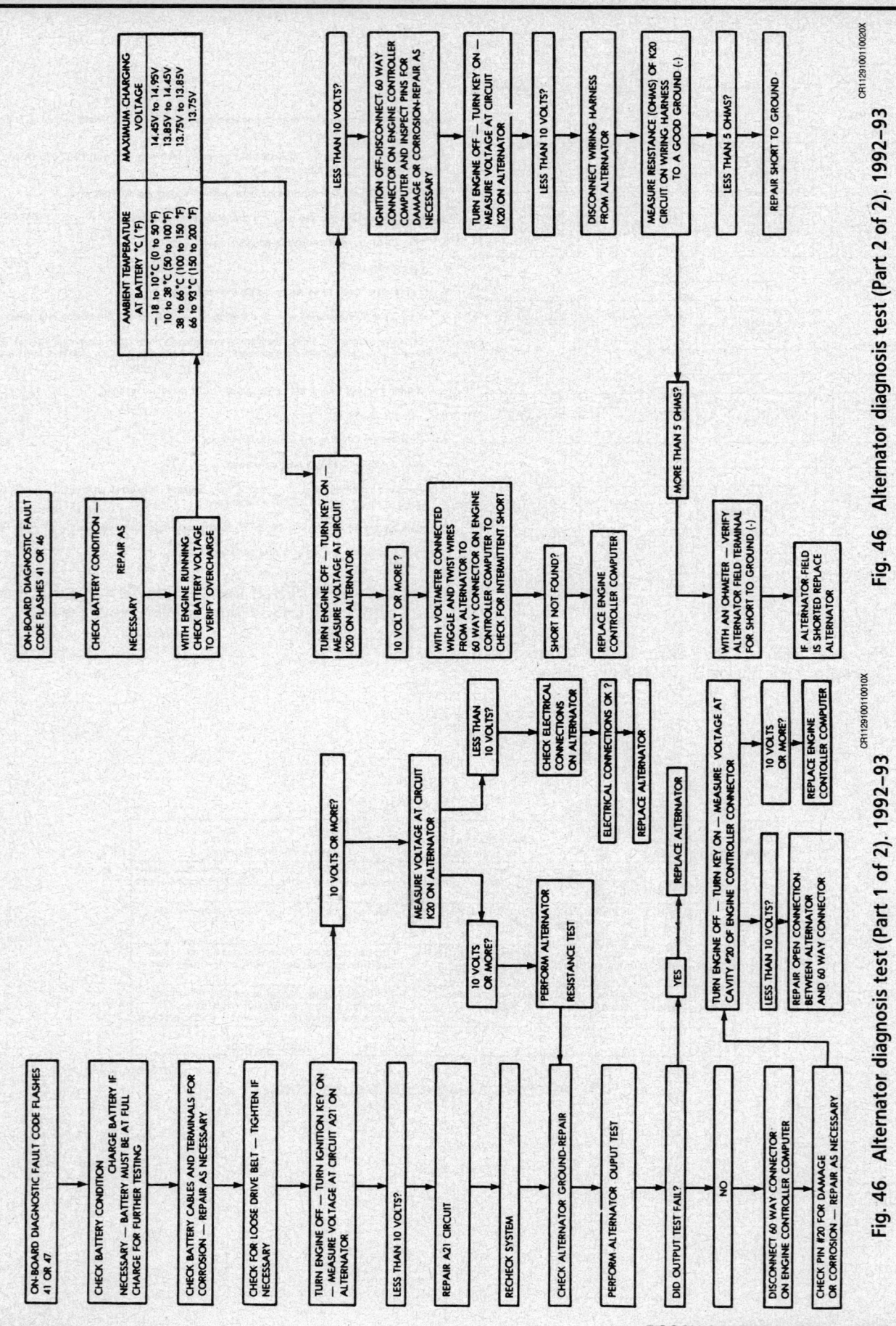

Fig. 46 Alternator diagnosis test (Part 2 of 2). 1992-93

Fig. 46 Alternator diagnosis test (Part 1 of 2). 1992-93

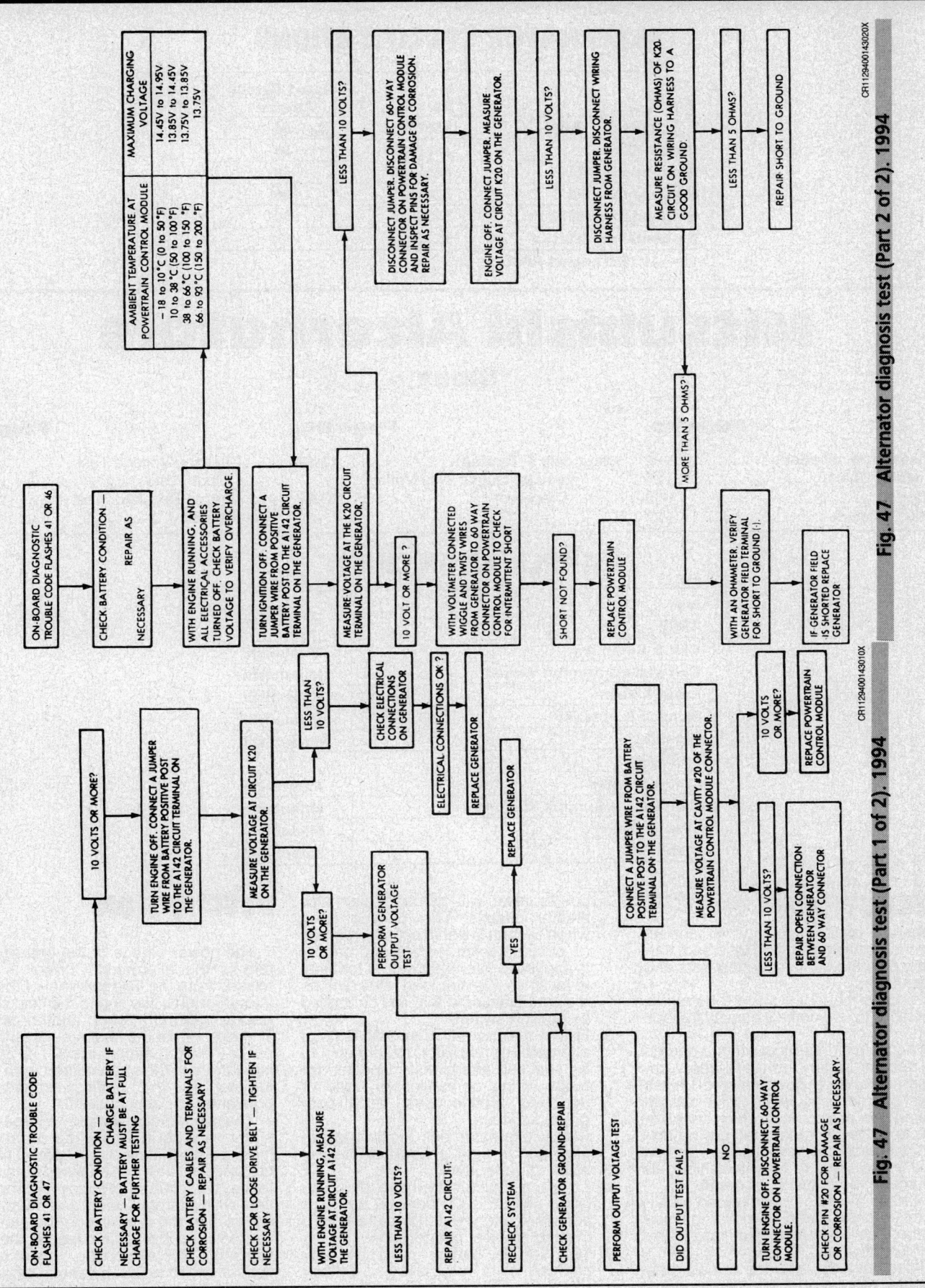

Fig. 47 Alternator diagnosis test (Part 2 of 2). 1994

Fig. 47 Alternator diagnosis test (Part 1 of 2). 1994

ALTERNATOR SPECIFICATIONS

Type	Part No.	Rated Output Amps ①
Bosch 90HS	4557431	84
Bosch 90HS	4557432	86
Nippondenso 75HS	4557301	68
Nippondenso 90HS	5234031	86
Nippondenso 90HS	5234032	90
Nippondenso 120HS	5234033	102

① —At 1250 engine RPM.

Mitsubishi Alternators

INDEX

APPLICATION CHART

Model	Type
1992	
Colt & Summit	Mitsubishi
Colt Vista & Summit Wagon	Mitsubishi
Laser & Talon	Mitsubishi
Monaco & Premier	Mitsubishi
Stealth	Mitsubishi
1993-94	
Colt & Summit	Mitsubishi
Colt Vista & Summit Wagon	Mitsubishi
Laser & Talon	Mitsubishi
Stealth	Mitsubishi

PRECAUTIONS

1. Ensure battery polarity is correct when servicing units. Reversed battery polarity will damage rectifiers and regulators.
2. If booster battery is used for starting, be sure to use correct polarity in hook up.
3. When a fast charger is used to charge a vehicle battery, vehicle battery cables should be disconnected unless fast charger is equipped with a special alternator protector, in which case vehicle battery cables need not be disconnected. Also, fast chargers should never be used to start a vehicle, as damage to rectifiers will result.
4. Lead connections to grounded rectifiers (negative) should never be soldered, as excessive heat may damage rectifiers.
5. Unless system includes a load relay or field relay, grounding alternator output terminal will damage alternator and/or circuits. This is true even when system is not in operation, since no circuit breaker is used and battery is applied to alternator output terminal at all times. Field or load relay acts as a circuit breaker in that it is controlled by ignition switch.
6. Before making any in-vehicle tests of alternator or regulator, battery should be checked and circuit inspected for faulty wiring or insulation, loose or corroded connections and poor ground circuits.
7. Check alternator belt tension to ensure belt is tight enough to prevent slipping under load.
8. To prevent system damage, place ignition switch in Off position and disconnect battery ground cable before making any test connections.
9. The vehicle battery must be fully charged or a fully charged battery may be installed for test purposes.

DESCRIPTION

The power source of the charging system is the alternator. Current is transmissed from the field terminal of the regulator through a slip ring to the field coil and back to ground through another slip ring. The strength of the fiedl regulates the output of the alternating current. The alternating current is then transmitted from the alternator to the rectifier where it is converted to direct current.

These alternators employ a three-phase stator winding in which the phase windings are electrically 120° apart. The rotor consists of a field coil encased between interleaved sections producing a magnetic field with alternate north and south poles. By rotating the rotor inside the stator, the alternating current is induced in the stator windings. This alternating current is rectified (changed to DC) by silicon diodes and brought back to the output terminal of the

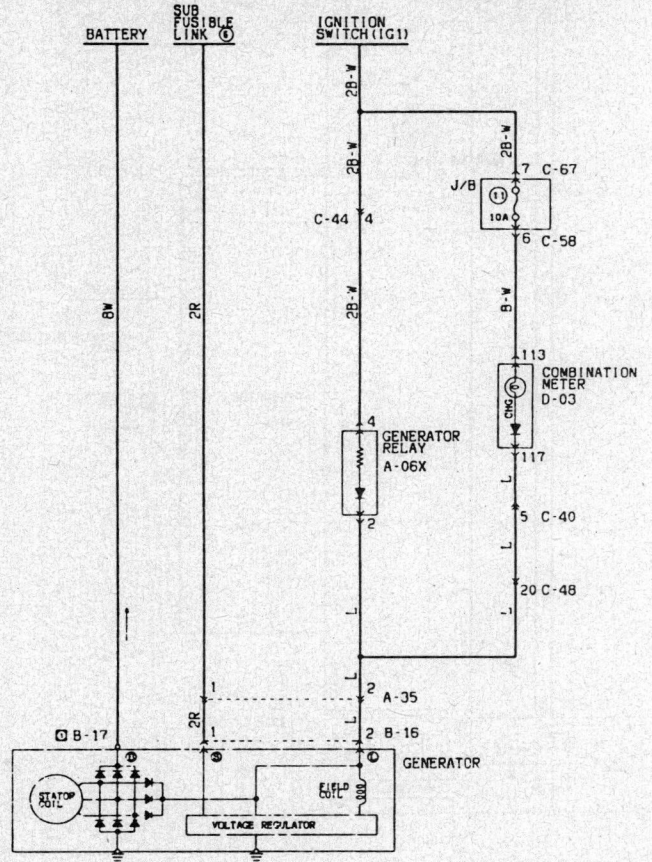

Fig. 1 Charging system wiring diagram. Colt Vista & Summit Wagon w/1.8L/4-110 engine

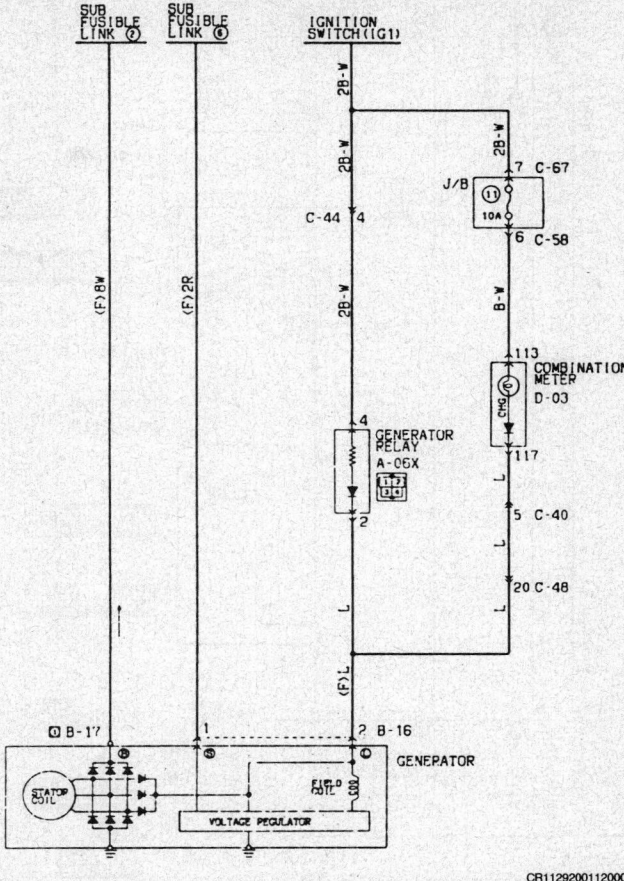

Fig. 2 Charging system wiring diagram. Colt Vista & Summit Wagon w/2.4L/4-146 engine

alternator.

On these units, the regulator is incorporated into the alternator rear housing, **Figs. 1 through 10**. The electronic voltage regulator has the ability to vary regulated system voltage upward or downward as temperature changes. No voltage regulated adjustments are required on these units.

DIODE RECTIFIERS

Six or more silicon diode rectifiers are used and act as electrical one-way valves. One half of the diodes have ground polarity and are pressed or screwed into a heat sink which is grounded. The other diodes (ungrounded) are pressed or screwed into and insulated from the end head. These diodes are connected to the alternator output terminal.

Since the diodes have a high resistance to the flow of current in one direction and a low resistance in the opposite direction, they may be connected in a manner which allows current to flow from the alternator to the battery in the low resistance direction. The high resistance in the opposite direction prevents the flow of current from the battery to the alternator. Because of this

feature no circuit breaker is required between the alternator and battery.

DIAGNOSIS & TESTING
CHARGING VOLTAGE TEST

1. With ignition switch in Off position, disconnect battery ground cable and connect a digital voltmeter between alternator S terminal, **Fig. 11**, and ground.
2. Disconnect alternator output wire from alternator B terminal, then connect a DC ammeter in series between B terminal and disconnected output wire. Connect positive lead of ammeter to B terminal. Connect negative lead to disconnected output wire.
3. Install engine tachometer and reconnect battery ground cable.
4. Place ignition switch in On position and observe voltmeter. Reading should equal battery voltage. If reading is 0, check for an open circuit in wire between alternator S terminal and battery positive terminal or a blown fusible link.
5. Start engine, keeping all accessories and lights off. Run engine at a cons-

tant 2500 RPM and read voltmeter when alternator output current drops to 10 amps or less.

ALTERNATOR OUTPUT WIRE VOLTAGE DROP TEST

1. Disconnect battery ground cable.
2. Disconnect alternator output lead from alternator "B +" terminal, **Fig. 12**, then connect a DC ammeter between "B +" and disconnected output lead. Connect positive lead of ammeter to "B +" terminal and negative lead to disconnected output wire.
3. Connect a digital voltmeter between alternator "B +" terminal and battery positive terminal. Connect positive lead of voltmeter to "B +" terminal and negative lead wire to positive battery terminal.
4. Connect battery ground cable, then start engine.
5. Obtain an ammeter reading of 20 A by adjusting engine speed and current draw by turning lights on and off. Voltmeter should read 0.2 V maximum.

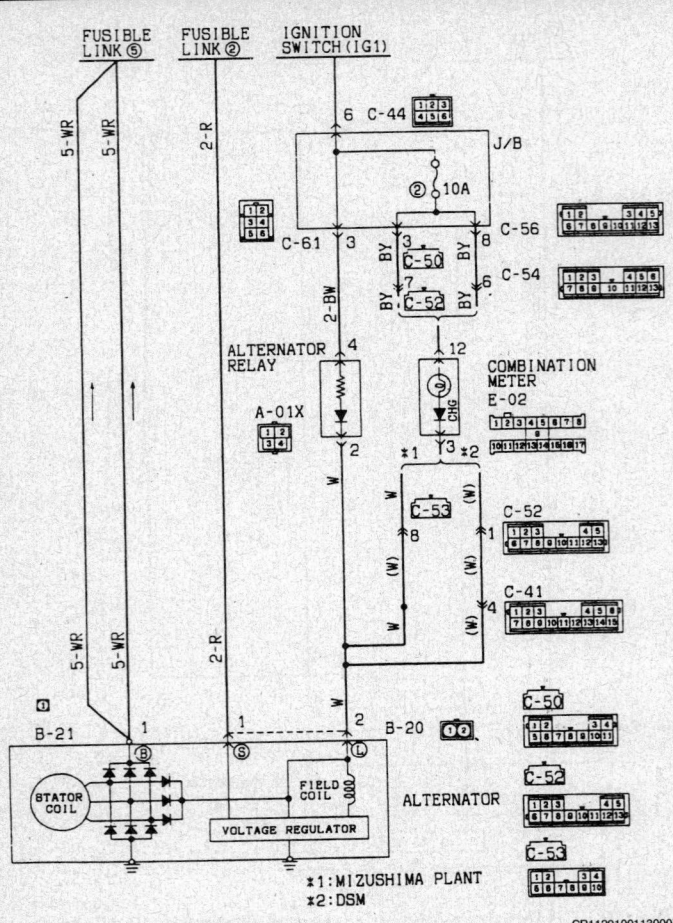

Fig. 3 Charging system wiring diagram. 1992 Colt & Summit

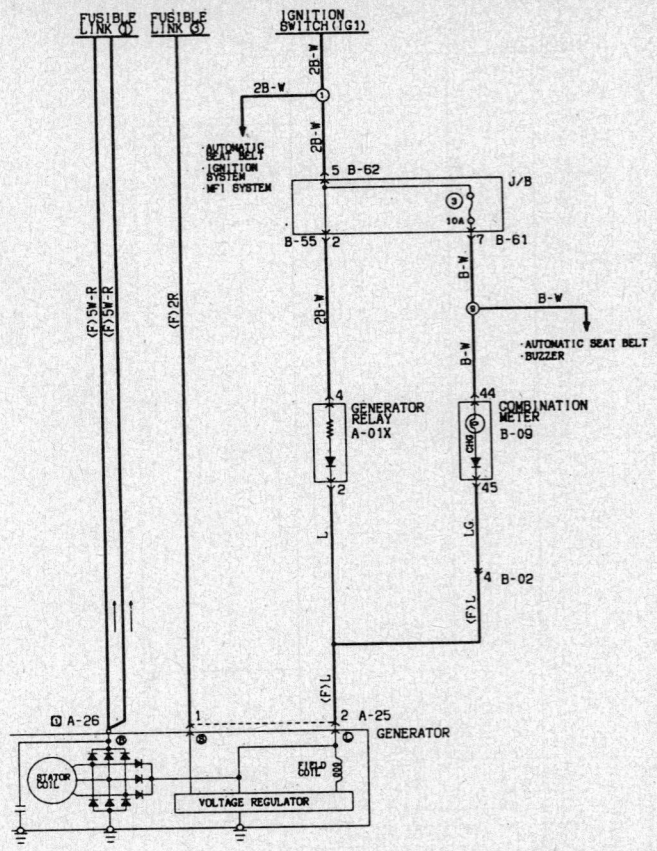

Fig. 4 Charging system wiring diagram. 1993–94 Colt & Summit w/1.5L/4-90 engine

6. If voltmeter reading is higher than specified, wiring may be at fault. Check wiring from alternator "B +" terminal to battery for proper connections or signs of overheating.

OUTPUT TEST

1. With ignition switch in Off position, disconnect battery cables.
2. Disconnect wire from terminal "B +" of alternator, then connect an ammeter between battery positive cable and alternator "B +" terminal, **Fig. 13.**
3. Connect a voltmeter between B + terminal and ground, **Fig. 13.**
4. Connect battery ground cable to battery ground post, then note voltmeter reading. Voltmeter should indicate battery voltage.
5. Connect a tachometer to engine, then start engine and turn on lights and heater blower to high.
6. Operate engine at approximately 2500 RPM and note ammeter reading. Reading must be higher than limit value given in "Alternator Specifications." **After engine has been started, ammeter reading will gradually decrease as battery approaches a fully charged condition. Note ammeter indication at its maximum value while increasing engine RPM.**

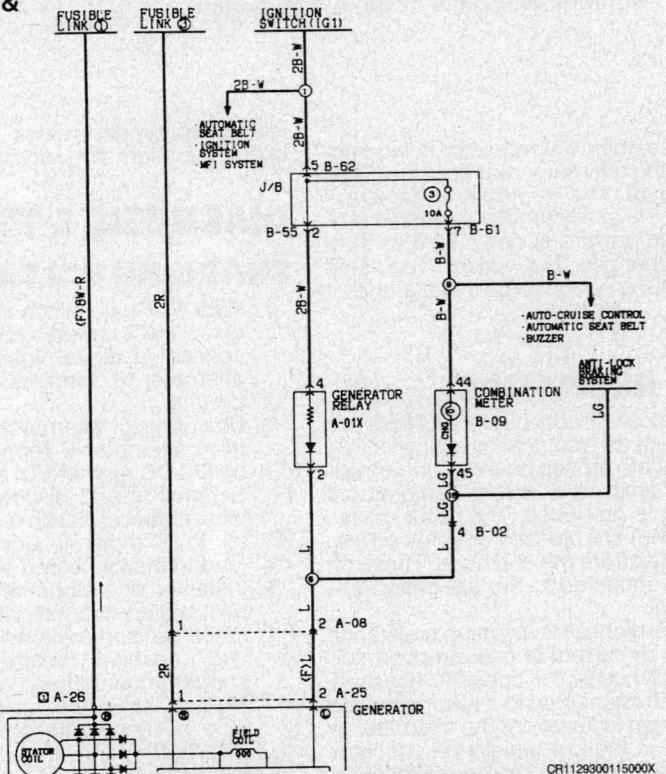

Fig. 5 Charging system wiring diagram. 1993–94 Colt & Summit w/1.8L/4-110 engine

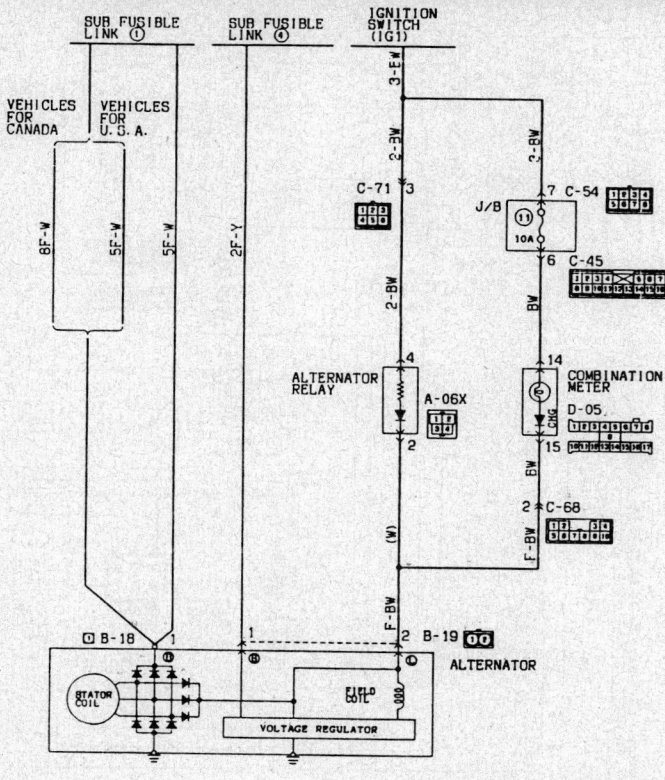

Fig. 6 Charging system wiring diagram. 1992 Laser & Talon

CR1129100116000X

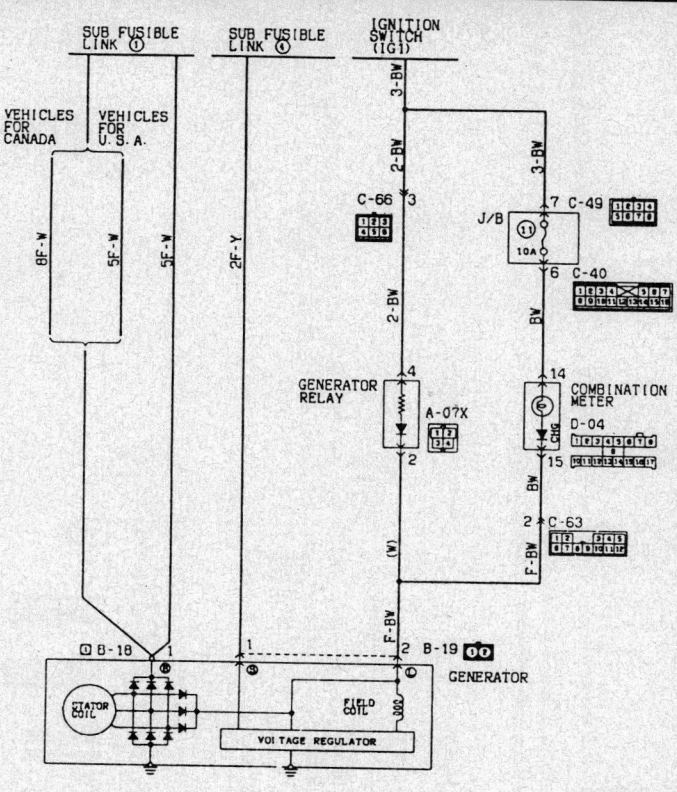

Fig. 7 Charging system wiring diagram. 1993–94 Laser & Talon

CR1129300117000X

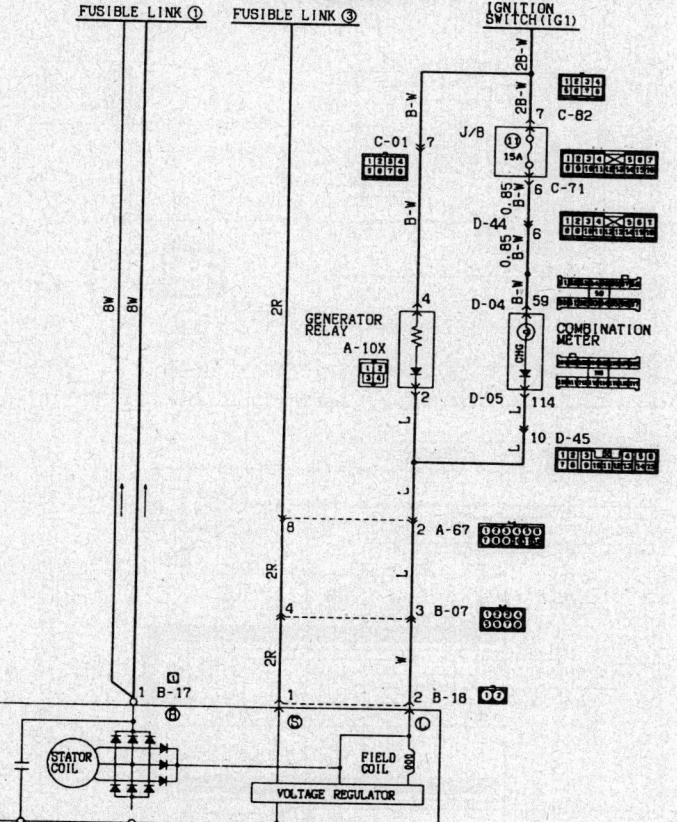

Fig. 8 Charging system wiring diagram. Stealth w/SOHC engine

CR1129200118000X

VOLTAGE REGULATOR TEST

1. With ignition switch in Off position, disconnect battery ground cable and connect a digital voltmeter between alternator S terminal **Fig. 14**, and ground.
2. Disconnect alternator output wire from alternator B terminal, then connect a DC ammeter in series between B terminal and output wire. Connect positive lead of ammeter to B terminal. Connect negative lead to output wire.
3. Install a tachometer per manufacturers instructions, then connect battery ground cable.
4. Place ignition switch in On position and observe voltmeter. Reading should equal battery voltage. If reading is 0, check for an open circuit in wire between alternator S terminal and battery positive terminal or a blown fusible link.
5. Start engine, keeping all accessories and lights off. Run engine at a constant 2500 RPM and read voltmeter, when alternator output current drops to 10 amps or less, voltage reading should read 13.9-14.9 at 68°F or 13.4-14.6 at 140°F.

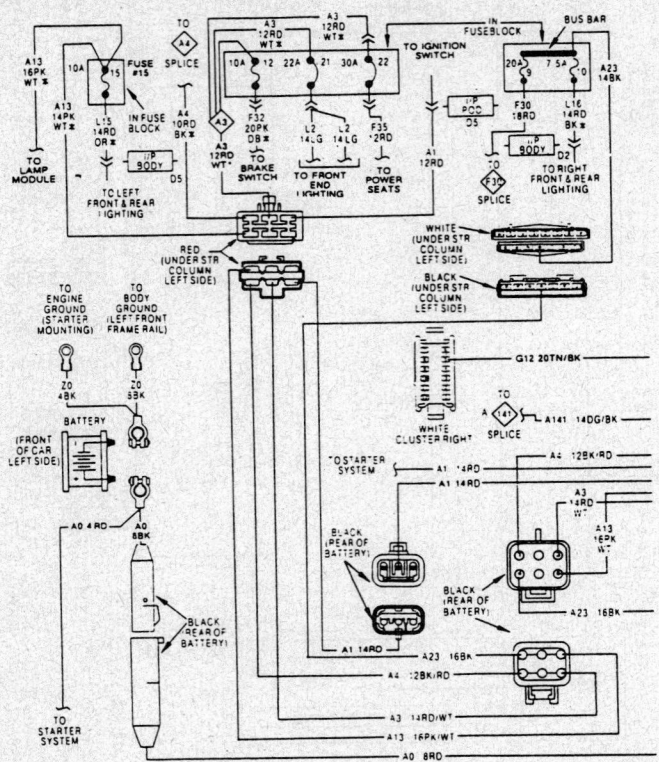

Fig. 10 Charging system wiring diagram (Part 1 of 2). Monaco & Premier

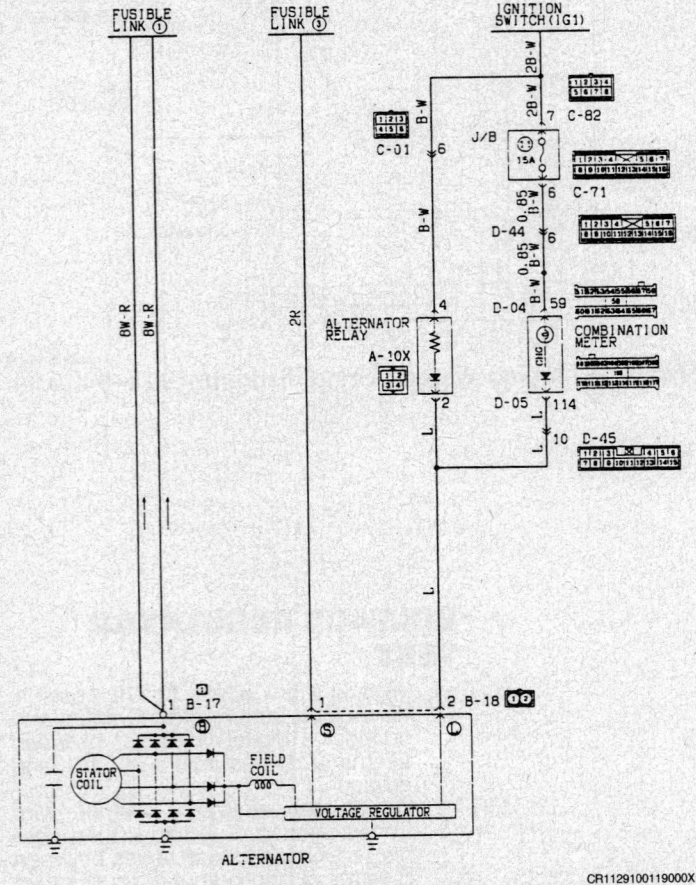

Fig. 9 Charging system wiring diagram. Stealth w/DOHC engine

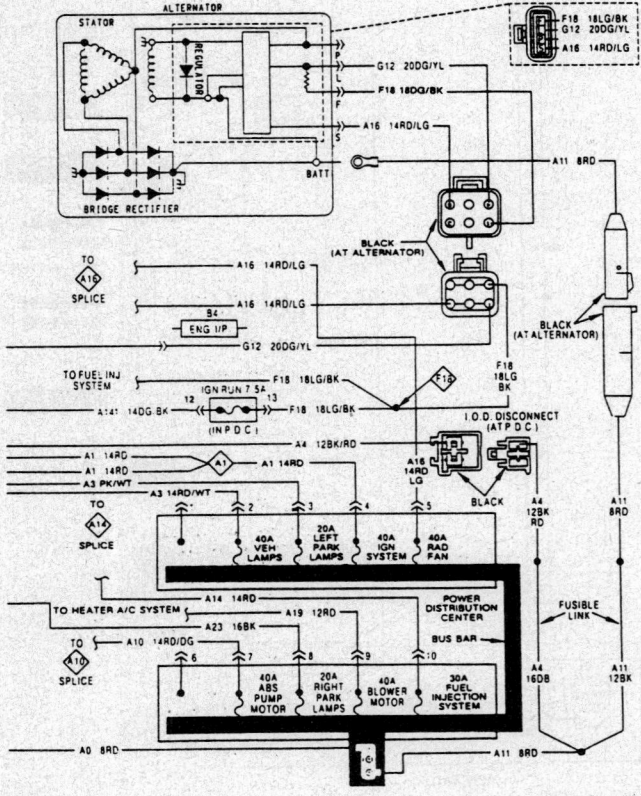

Fig. 10 Charging system wiring diagram (Part 2 of 2). Monaco & Premier

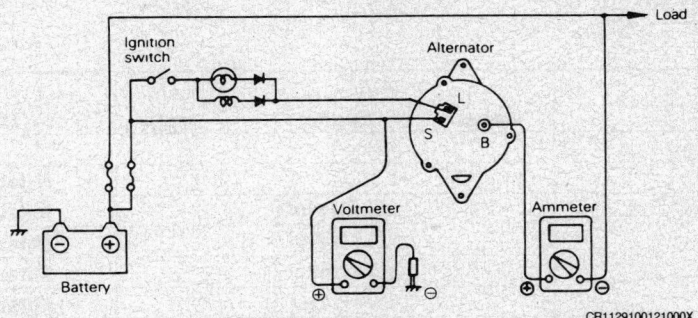

Fig. 11 Alternator charging voltage test connection.
Battery voltage sensing type alternator

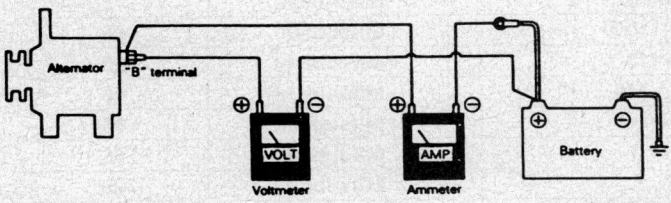

Fig. 12 Alternator output wire voltage drop test connection

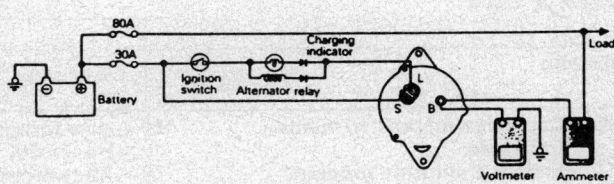

Fig. 13 Alternator output test connection.
Battery voltage type sensor

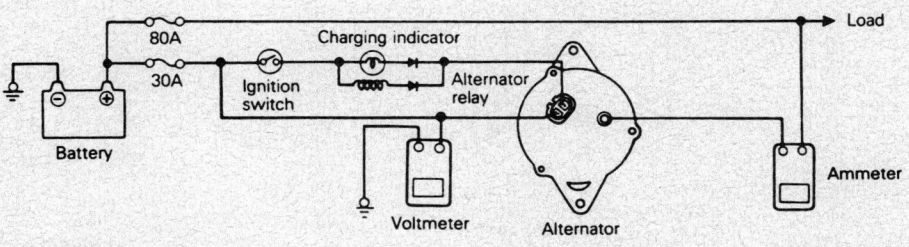

Fig. 14 Voltage regulator test connections

ALTERNATOR SPECIFICATIONS

Model	Engine	Type	Rated Output Amps
1992			
Colt & Summit	③	Mitsubishi	75
Colt Vista & Summit Wagon	1.8L/4-110 ⑥	Mitsubishi	60
	1.8L/4-110 ⑦	Mitsubishi	65
	2.4L/4-146 ② ⑥	Mitsubishi	65
	2.4L/4-146 ① ⑦	Mitsubishi	75
Laser & Talon	④	Mitsubishi	65
	⑤	Mitsubishi	75
Monaco & Premier	3.0L/V6-181	Mitsubishi	65 ⑩
Stealth	3.0L/V6-181 ⑧	Mitsubishi	90
	3.0L/V6-181 ⑨	Mitsubishi	110
1993-94			
Colt & Summit	1.5L/4-90	Mitsubishi	75
	1.8L/4-110 ⑥	Mitsubishi	65
	1.8L/4-110 ⑦	Mitsubishi	70
Colt Vista & Summit Wagon	1.8L/4-110	Mitsubishi	60
	2.4L/4-146	Mitsubishi	75
Laser & Talon	④	Mitsubishi	65
	⑤	Mitsubishi	75
Stealth	3.0L/V6-181 ⑧	Mitsubishi	90
	3.0L/V6-181 ⑨	Mitsubishi	110

① —California models w/manual transaxle.
② —Except California models.
③ —All available engines.
④ —Non-turbocharged engine & manual transaxle.
⑤ —All turbocharged engines & non-turbocharged models w/automatic transaxle.
⑥ —Manual transaxle.
⑦ —Automatic transaxle.
⑧ —SOHC.
⑨ —DOHC.
⑩ —At 1250 engine RPM.

SPEED CONTROL SYSTEMS

TABLE OF CONTENTS

Application Chart

Year	Model	Type	Page No.
1992	Monaco	1	14-1
	Premier	1	14-1
1992-93	Daytona	1	14-1
	Dynasty	1	14-1
	Fifth Avenue	1	14-1
	Imperial	1	14-1
	LeBaron Coupe	1	14-1
	New Yorker Salon	1	14-1
1992-94	Acclaim	1	14-1
	Colt	2	14-26
	Colt Vista	2	14-26
	Laser	2	14-26
	LeBaron Convertible	1	14-1
	LaBaron Sedan	1	14-1

Year	Model	Type	Page No.
1992-94 —Cont'd	Shadow	1	14-1
	Spirit	1	14-1
	Stealth	2	14-26
	Summit	2	14-26
	Summit Wagon	2	14-26
	Sundance	1	14-1
	Talon	2	14-26
1993-94	Concorde	3	14-60
	Intrepid	3	14-60
	Vision	3	14-60
1994	New Yorker	3	14-60
	LHS	3	14-60
1995	Neon	4	14-73

Type 1

NOTE: Electrical Symbol & Wire Color Code Identification Located In The Front Of This Manual May Be Used As An Aid When Using Wiring Circuits Found In This Section.

NOTE: On Air Bag Equipped Models, Refer To Air Bag System Precautions Located In The Front Of This Manual For System Disarming & Arming Procedures.

INDEX

DESCRIPTION

This Speed Control System is electrically actuated and vacuum operated. The controls are located on the steering wheel and these controls consist of a SET/DECEL, RESUME/ACCEL and ON/OFF buttons. This system is designed to operate at speed exceeding 35 mph.

To activate the system push ON/OFF button to ON. When desired speed is obtained push the SET/DECEL button to engage system. To deactivate system push ON/OFF button or lightly tap on brake pedal. On models with manual transaxles depressing the clutch pedal will also deactivate system.

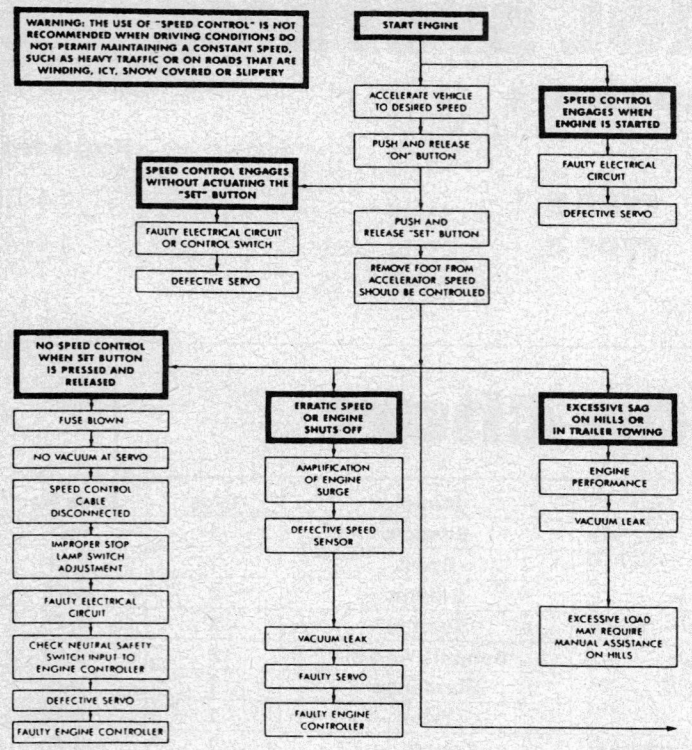

Fig. 1   Cruise control system troubleshooting (Part 1 of 2)

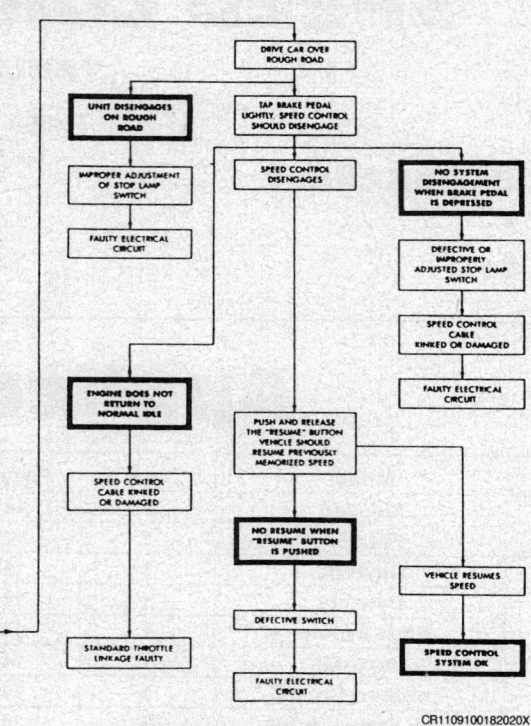

Fig. 1   Cruise control system troubleshooting (Part 2 of 2)

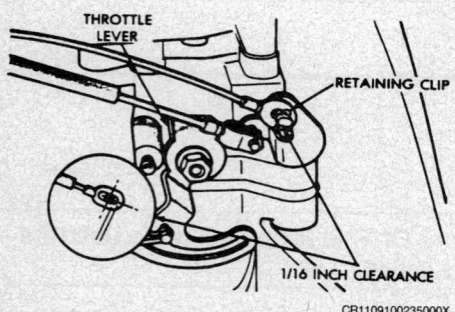

Fig. 2   Speed control cable adjustment

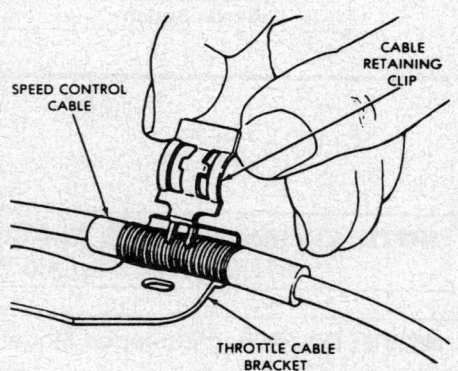

Fig. 3   Cable retaining clip

ADJUSTMENTS

SPEED CONTROL CABLE

2.2L/4-135 & 2.5L/4-153

1. Clearance between throttle stud and cable clevis should be 1/16 inch, **Fig. 2.**
2. Adjust cable by removing cable retaining clip at throttle bracket, **Fig. 3. Do not pull throttle away from curb idle.**
3. Reinstall cable retaining clip.

SYSTEM DIAGNOSIS & TESTING

ROAD TEST

Road test vehicle to verify reports of speed control system malfunction. The road test should include attention to the speedometer. Speedometer operation should be smooth and without flutter at all speeds or surging may be caused in the speed control system.

INOPERATIVE SYSTEM

If road test verifies an inoperative system check and verify the following:
1. Inspect system electrical connections for loose, corrosion or bent terminals.
2. Verify correct installation and condition of vacuum hoses.
3. Check for correct installation of vacuum check valve. End marked VAC must point toward vacuum source.

CHECKING FOR DIAGNOSTIC TROUBLE CODES

When trying to verify a speed control system electronic malfunction, one of two methods may be used and are described as follows:

PRECAUTIONS

AIR BAG SYSTEM

Refer to Air Bag Systems Precautions in the front of this manual for system disarming and arming procedures.

TROUBLESHOOTING

Refer to **Fig. 1** when troubleshooting the speed control system.

DIAGNOSTIC CHART INDEX

Test No.	Description	Page No.	Fig. No.
SP-1A	Reading Fault Codes	14-4	4
SP-2A	Repairing Power & Ground Supply For Open To Servo Solenoids	14-4	5
SP-2B	Repairing Speed Control Vacuum Solenoid Control Circuit	14-4	6
SP-2C	Repairing Speed Control Vent Solenoid Control Circuit	14-5	7
SP-3A	Repairing Fault "No Vehicle Speed Signal"	14-5	8
SP-3B	Repairing Fault "No Vehicle Speed Signal"	14-6	9
SP-3C	Repairing Fault "No Vehicle Speed Signal"	14-6	10
SP-4A	Checking Speed Control Switches	14-7	11
SP-5A	Checking Speed Control Switches	14-7	12
SP-5B	Repairing Speed Control Switch Circuits For A Short To Ground	14-8	13
SP-5C	Checking Switch Wiring For A Short To Ground	14-8	14
SP-5D	Checking Switch Wiring For Open Circuit	14-9	15
SP-6A	Checking Speed Control Resume Switch Circuit	14-9	16
SP-6B	Checking Speed Control Resume Switch Circuit	14-9	17
SP-7A	Checking Speed Control Set Switch Circuit	14-10	18
SP-7B	Checking Speed Control Set Switch Circuit	14-10	19
SP-9A	Testing Speed Control Switch Circuits	14-10	20
SP-9B	Testing Clockspring Circuit For Shorts	14-11	21
SP-9C	Testing Clockspring Circuit For Open	14-11	22
SP-10A	Repairing Speed Control Switch Circuits For A Short To Ground	14-11	23
SP-11A	Checking Brake Switch Circuits For Open	14-12	24
SP-11B	Checking Brake Switch Circuits For Shorts	14-12	25
SP-12A	Checking Speed Control Servo Operation	14-13	26
SP-12B	Checking Vacuum To Speed Control Servo	14-13	27
SP-13A	Checking Park/Neutral Safety Switch	14-13	28
SP-14A	Checking For Intermittent Faults	14-14	29
SP-15A	Reading Faults	14-14	30
SP-16A	Repairing Fault "Speed Control Power Relay Circuit"	14-15	31
SP-17A	Repairing Fault "Speed Control Solenoid Circuit"	14-15	32
SP-17B	Repairing Speed Control Vacuum Solenoid Control Circuit	14-16	33
SP-17C	Repairing Speed Control Vent Solenoid Control Circuit	14-16	34
SP-18A	Repairing Fault "No Vehicle Speed Signal"	14-16	35
SP-19A	Checking Speed Control Switches	14-17	36
SP-20A	Testing Speed Control Switches Output	14-17	37
SP-21A	Checking Brake Switch Circuits For Open	14-18	38
SP-21B	Checking Brake Switch Circuits For Shorts	14-19	39
SP-22A	Checking Park/Neutral Safety Switch	14-19	40
SP-VER	Speed Control Verification	14-20	41

USING DIAGNOSTIC TOOL

If a DRB II Diagnostic Tool is available, plug tool into diagnostic connector and verify that either a Diagnostic Trouble Code 15 or 34 on all except Monaco & Premier is indicated or Diagnostic Trouble Codes 15, 34 or 77 on Monaco & Premier is indicated, then refer to the appropriate diagnostic chart shown in **Figs. 4 through 41.** After all tests have been completed perform verification TEST SP-VER. Follow tool manufacturers instructions for proper installation of the tool prior to testing speed control system.

If no problems were found, replace engine controller.

USING VOLTMETER

If a DRB II Diagnostic tool is not available, check for Diagnostic Trouble Codes as follows:

1. Cycle ignition switch to On position three times. On third cycle, leave switch in On position.
2. Observe Check Engine indicator on instrument cluster. If a Diagnostic Trouble Code is present, indicator lamp will flash (blink) in a series which will show which Diagnostic Trouble Code is the problem.
3. If Diagnostic Trouble Code 34 is observed, determine source of problem by performing tests described under "Component Diagnosis & Testing." Refer to **Figs. 42 through 46** for speed control system wiring diagrams.
4. If Diagnostic Trouble Code 15 is present, testing of the distance sensor is required. **Testing of the distance sensor requires the use of the DRB II diagnostic tool.**
5. **On Monaco & Premier,** if Diagnostic Trouble Code 77 is present, perform "Speed Control Relay Test" under "Component Diagnosis & Testing."
6. **On all models,** if no problems were found, replace engine controller.

Continued on page 14-24

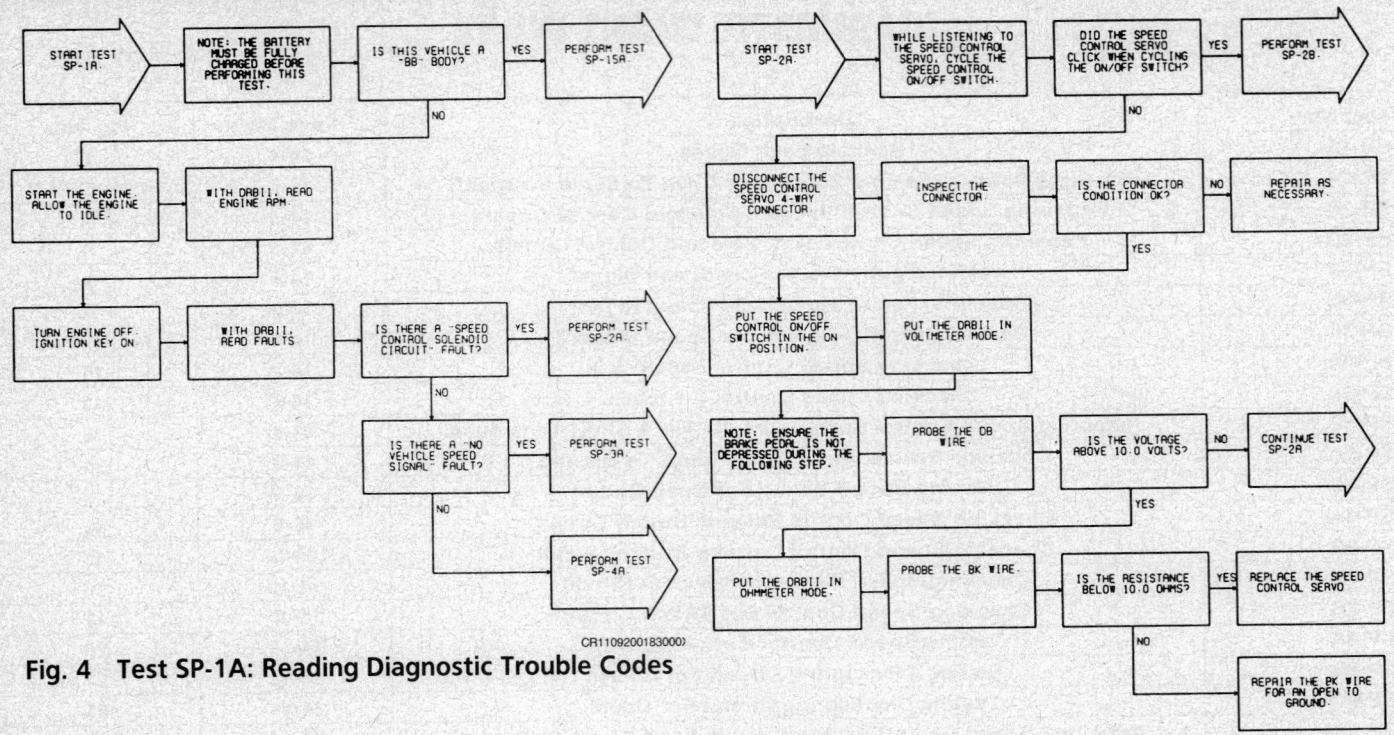

Fig. 4   Test SP-1A: Reading Diagnostic Trouble Codes

Fig. 5   Test SP-2A: Repairing Power & Ground Supply For Open To Servo Solenoids (Part 1 of 2)

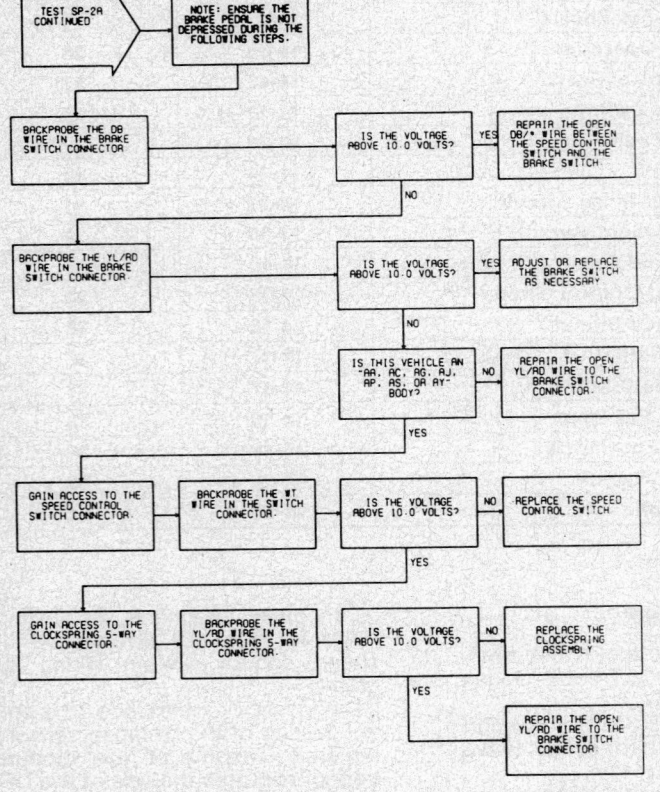

Fig. 5   Test SP-2A: Repairing Power & Ground Supply For Open To Servo Solenoids (Part 2 of 2).

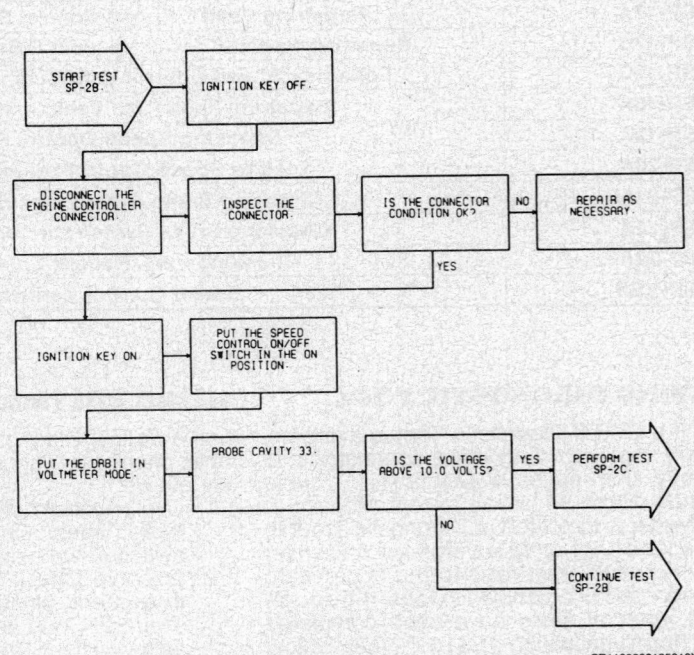

Fig. 6   Test SP-2B: Repairing Speed Control Vacuum Solenoid Control Circuit (Part 1 of 2)

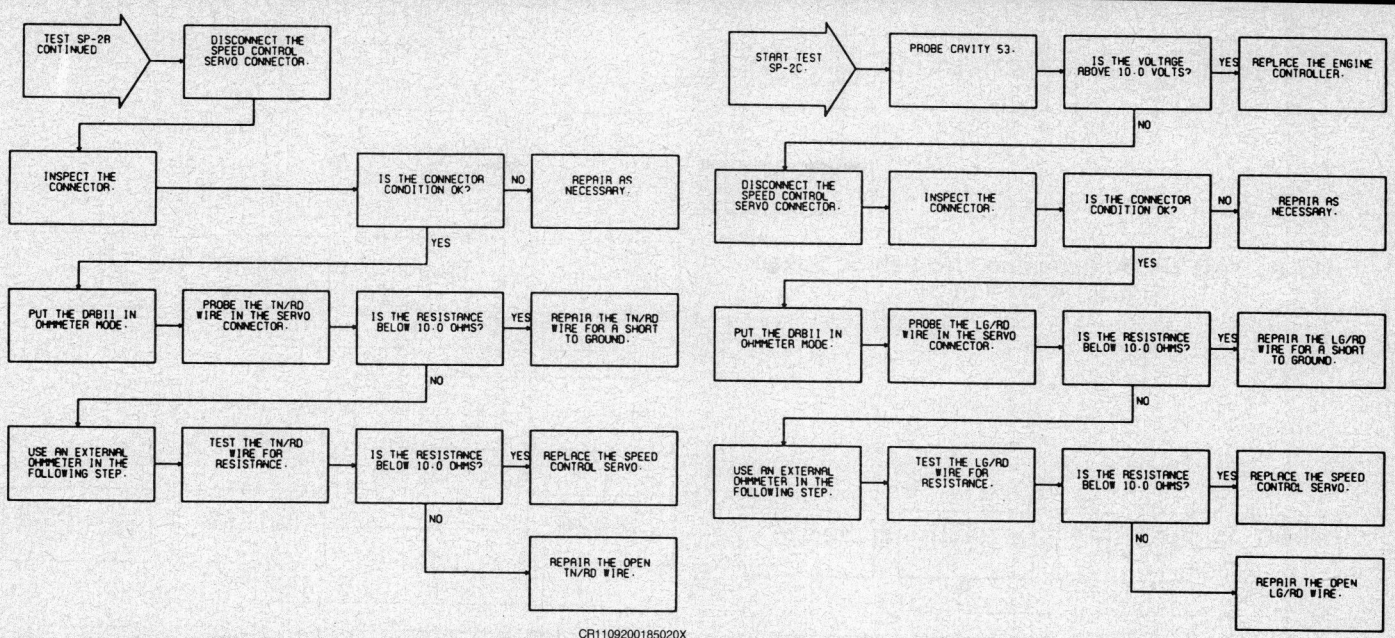

CR1109200185020X

Fig. 6 Test SP-2B: Repairing Speed Control Vacuum Solenoid Control Circuit (Part 2 of 2)

CR1109200186000X

Fig. 7 Test SP-2C: Repairing Speed Control Vent Solenoid Control Circuit

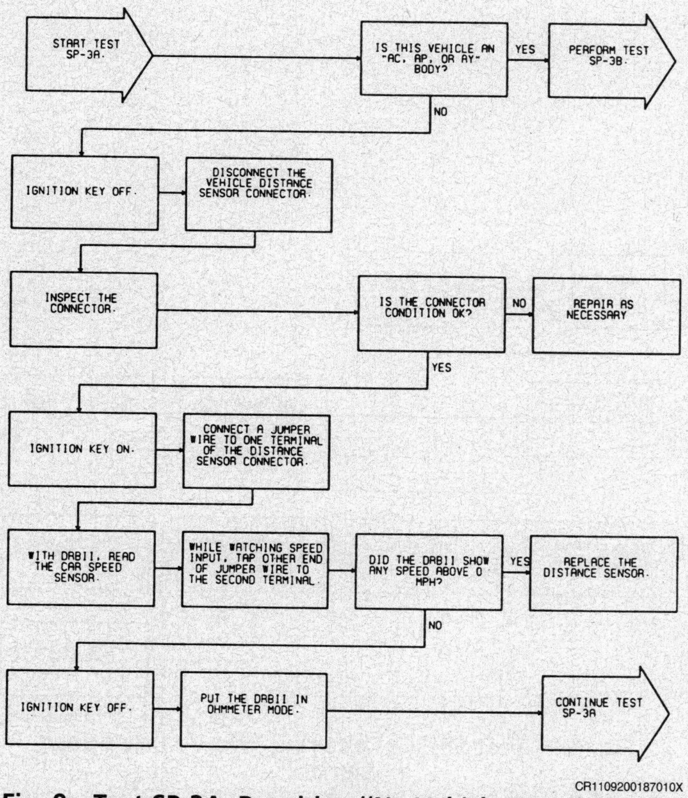

CR1109200187010X

Fig. 8 Test SP-3A: Repairing "No Vehicle Speed Signal" (Part 1 of 3)

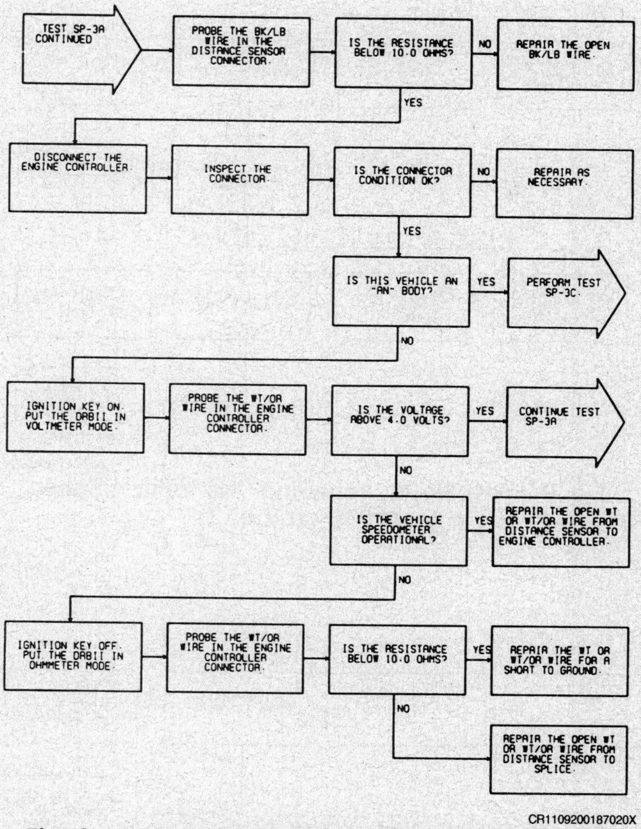

CR1109200187020X

Fig. 8 Test SP-3A: Repairing "No Vehicle Speed Signal" (Part 2 of 3)

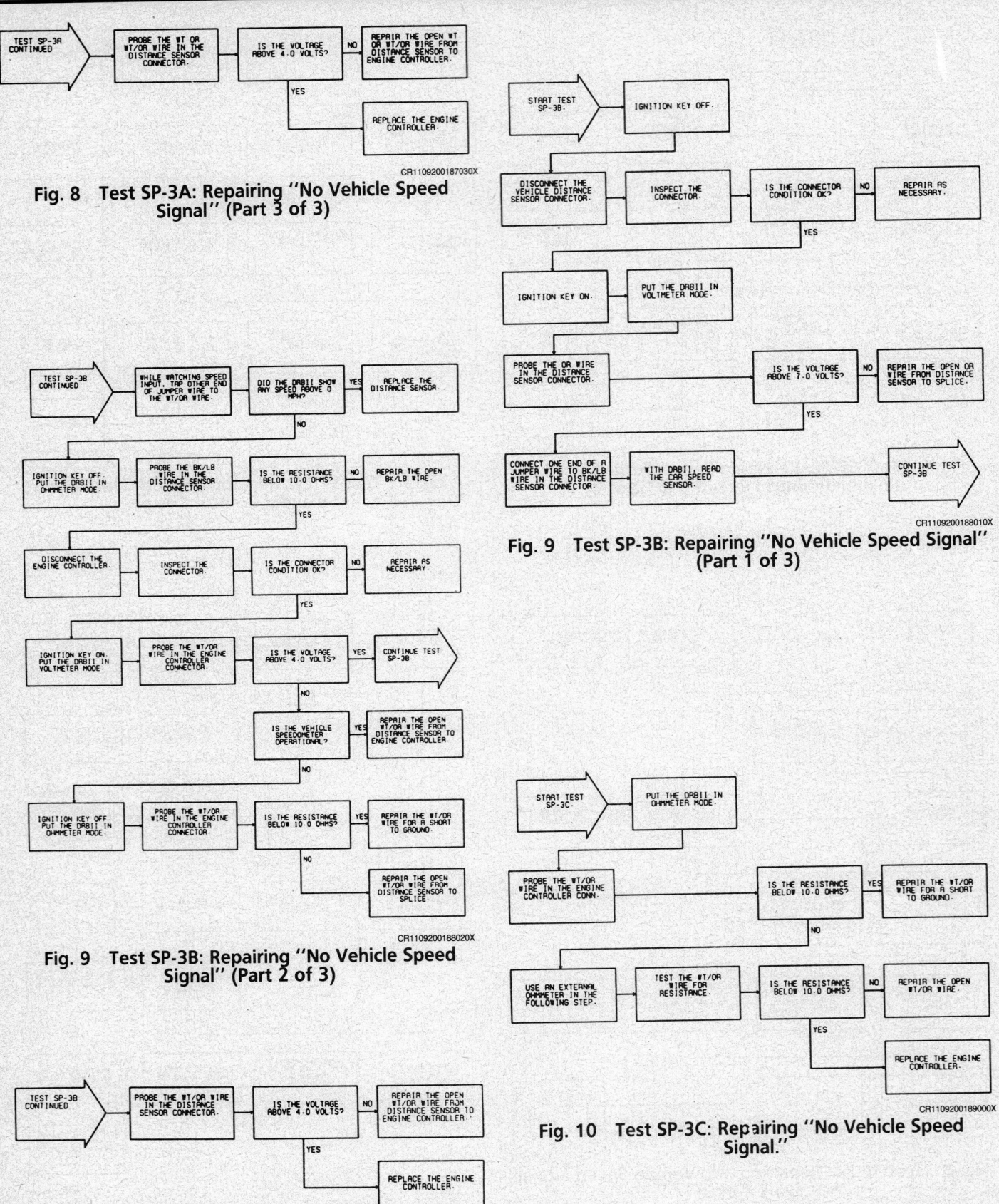

Fig. 8 Test SP-3A: Repairing "No Vehicle Speed Signal" (Part 3 of 3)

CR1109200187030X

Fig. 9 Test SP-3B: Repairing "No Vehicle Speed Signal" (Part 1 of 3)

CR1109200188010X

Fig. 9 Test SP-3B: Repairing "No Vehicle Speed Signal" (Part 2 of 3)

CR1109200188020X

Fig. 10 Test SP-3C: Repairing "No Vehicle Speed Signal."

CR1109200189000X

Fig. 9 Test SP-3B: Repairing "No Vehicle Speed Signal" (Part 3 of 3)

CR1109200188030X

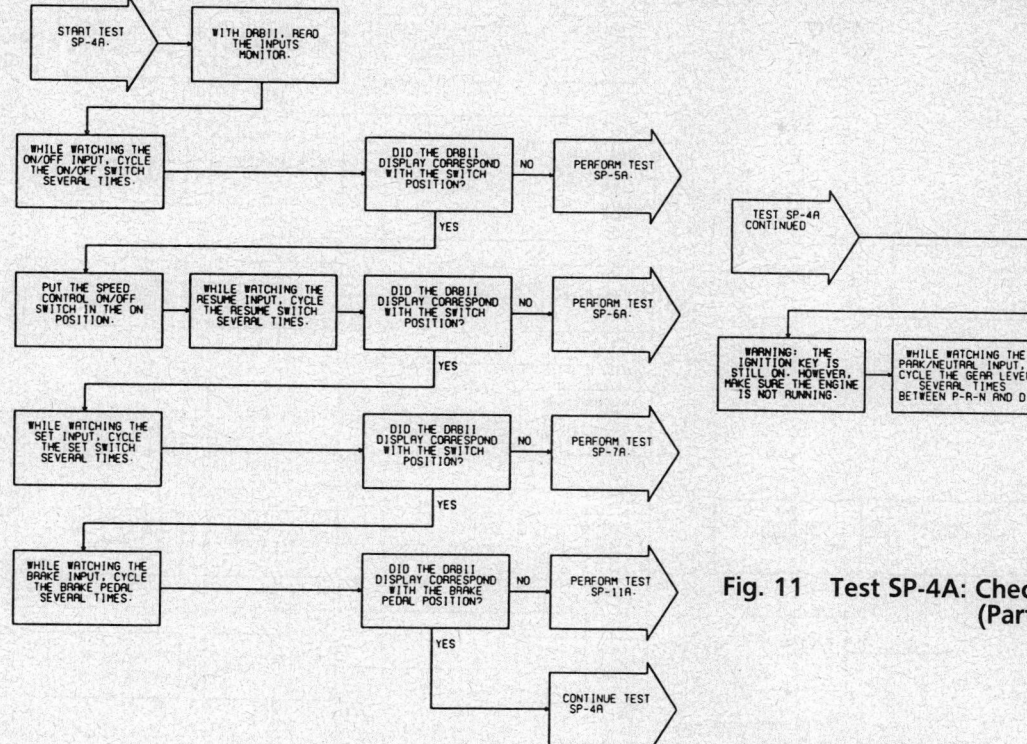

Fig. 11   Test SP-4A: Checking Speed Control Switches
(Part 1 of 2)

Fig. 11   Test SP-4A: Checking Speed Control Switches
(Part 2 of 2)

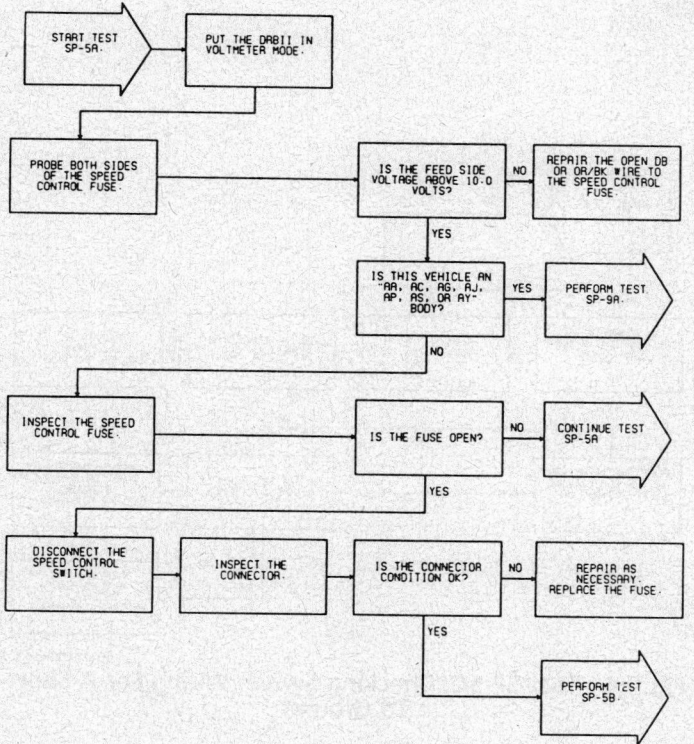

Fig. 12   Test SP-5A: Checking Speed Control Switches
(Part 1 of 2)

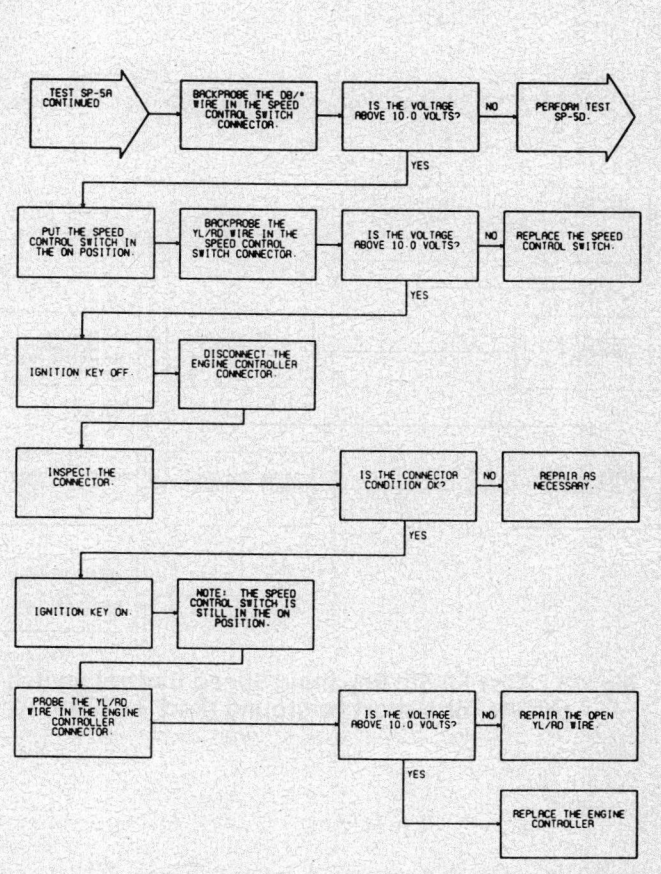

Fig. 12   Test SP-5A: Checking Speed Control
Switches (Part 2 of 2)

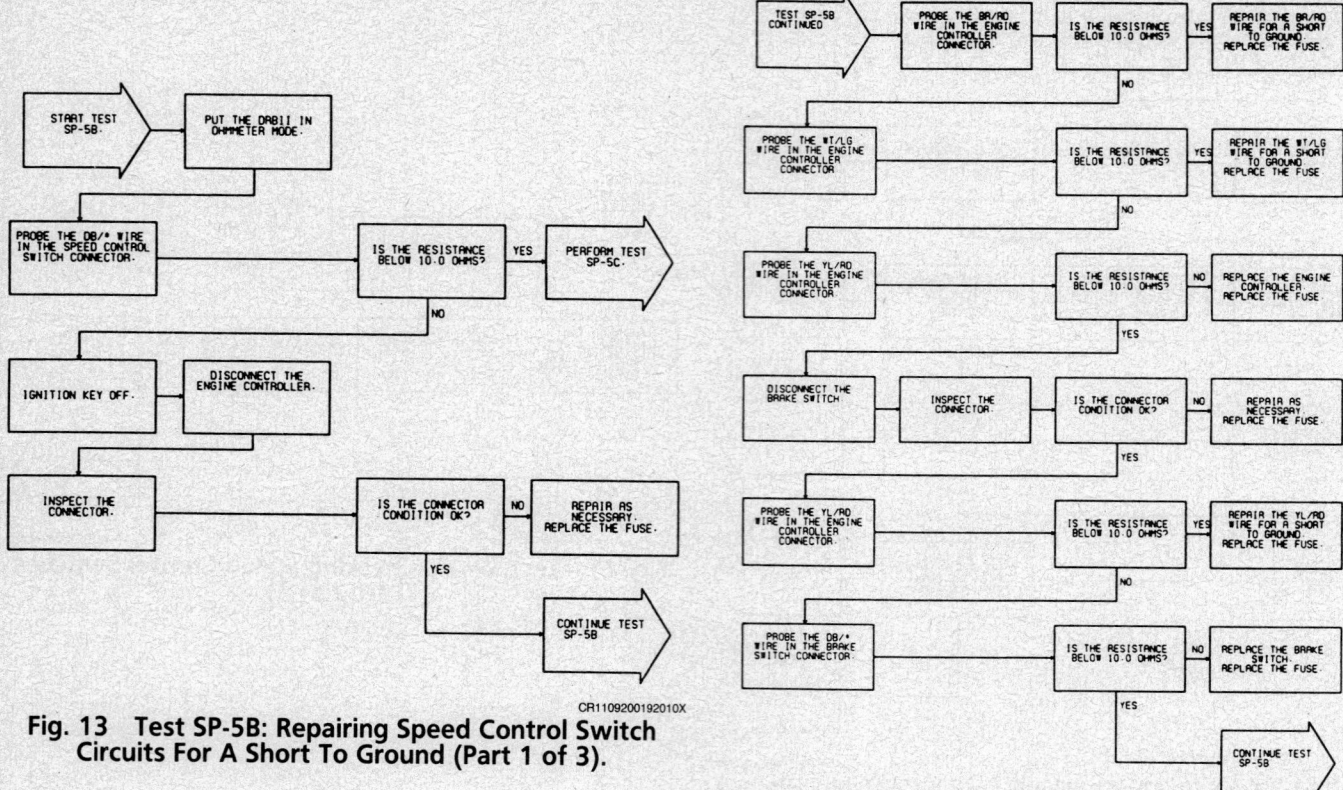

Fig. 13 Test SP-5B: Repairing Speed Control Switch Circuits For A Short To Ground (Part 1 of 3).

Fig. 13 Test SP-5B: Repairing Speed Control Switch Circuits For A Short To Ground (Part 2 of 3)

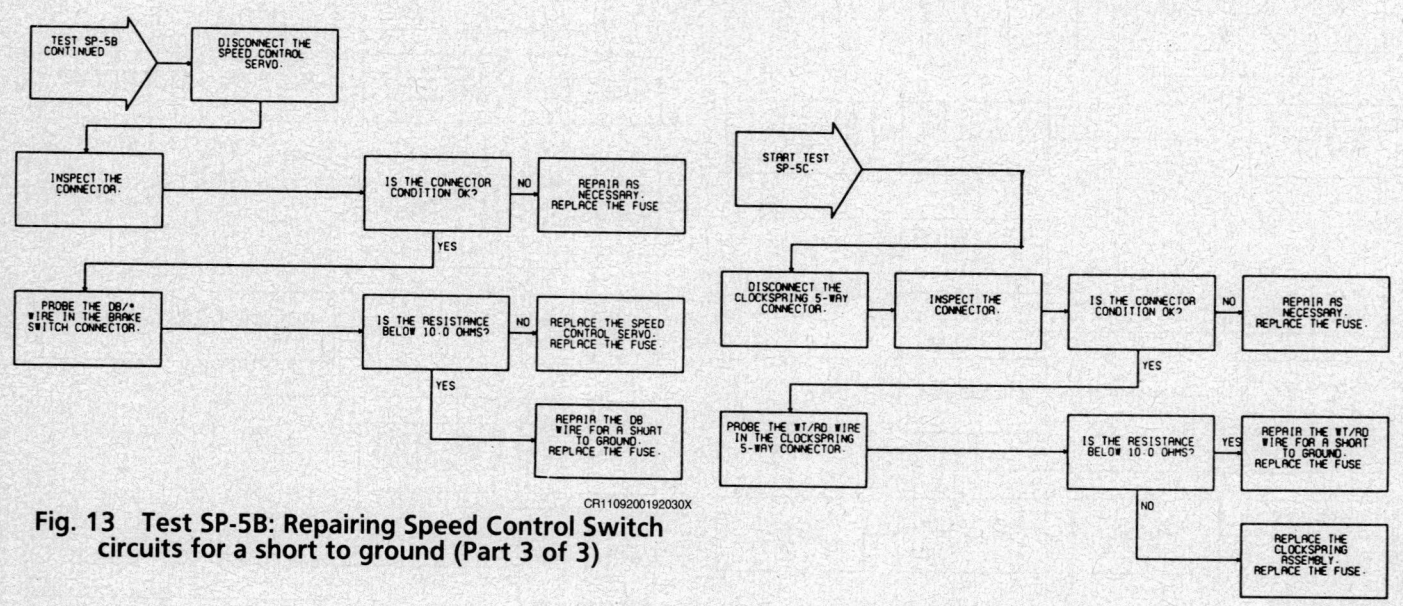

Fig. 13 Test SP-5B: Repairing Speed Control Switch circuits for a short to ground (Part 3 of 3)

Fig. 14 Test SP-5C: Checking Switch Wiring For A Short To Ground

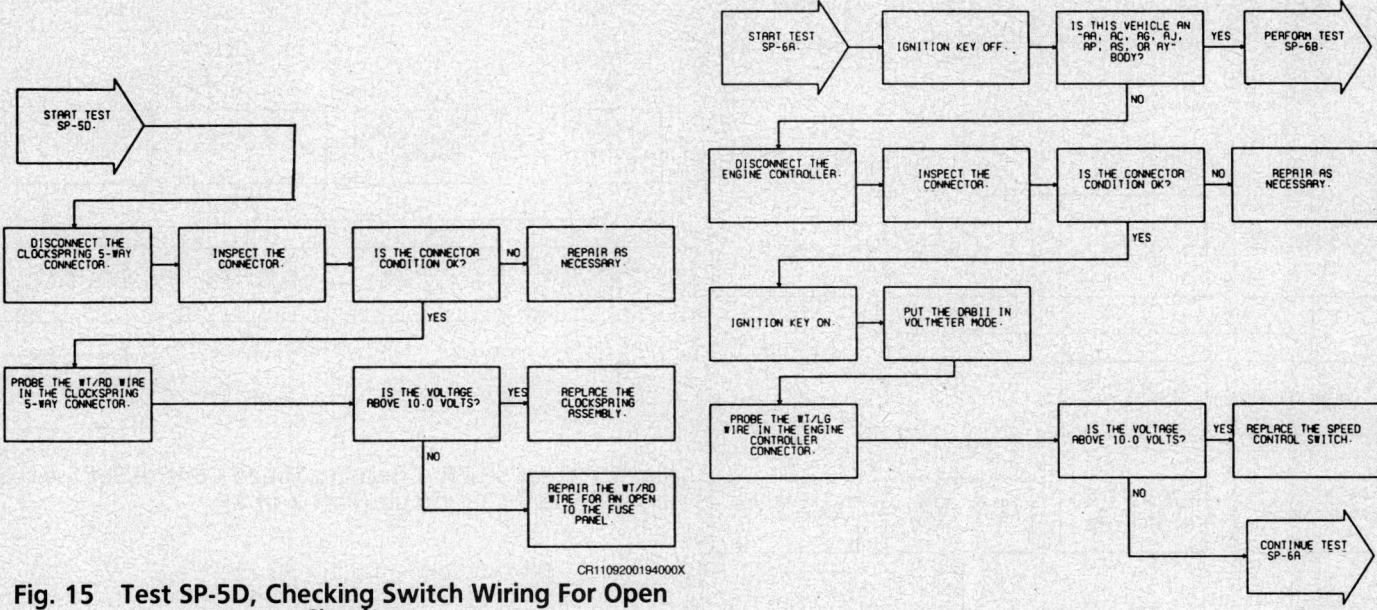

Fig. 15   Test SP-5D, Checking Switch Wiring For Open Circuit

Fig. 16   Test SP-6A: Checking Speed Control Resume Switch circuit (Part 1 of 2)

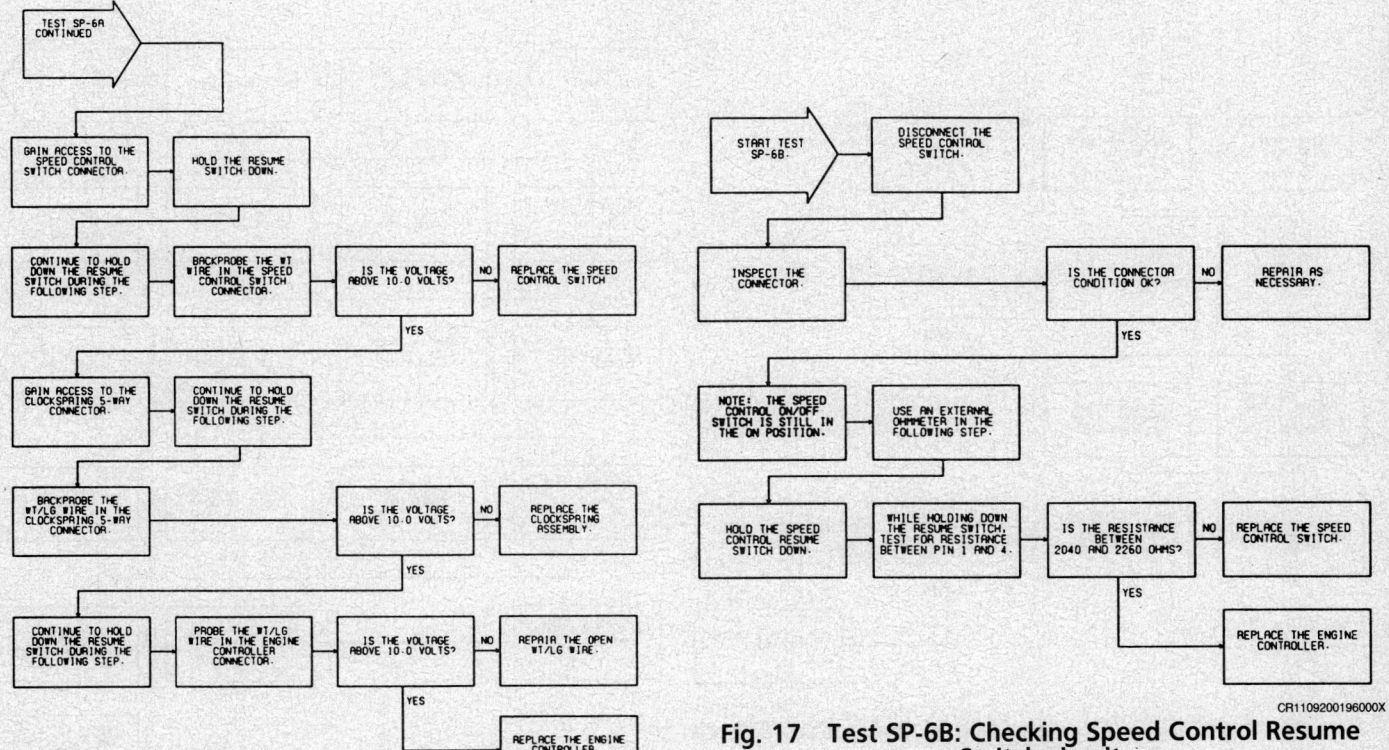

Fig. 16   Test SP-6A: Checking Speed Control Resume Switch circuit (Part 2 of 2)

Fig. 17   Test SP-6B: Checking Speed Control Resume Switch circuit

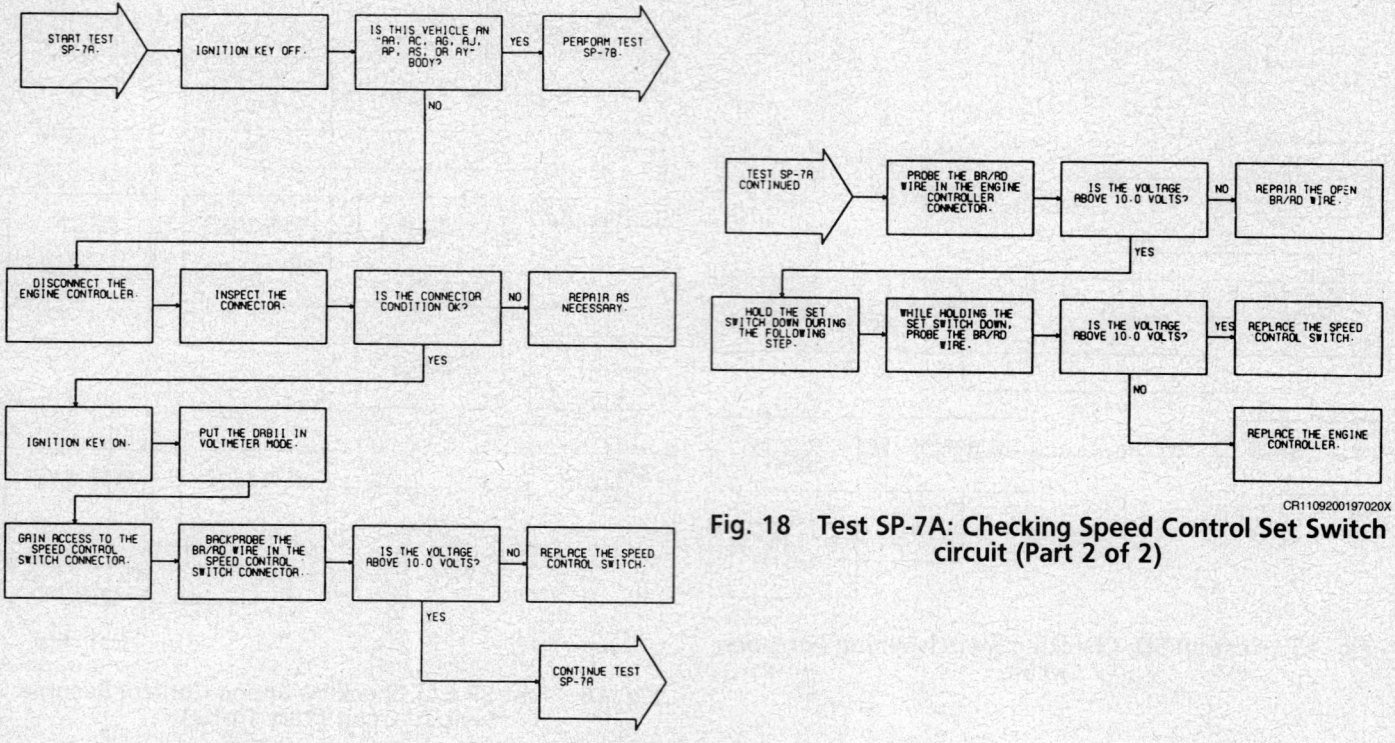

Fig. 18   Test SP-7A: Checking Speed Control Set Switch circuit (Part 1 of 2)

Fig. 18   Test SP-7A: Checking Speed Control Set Switch circuit (Part 2 of 2)

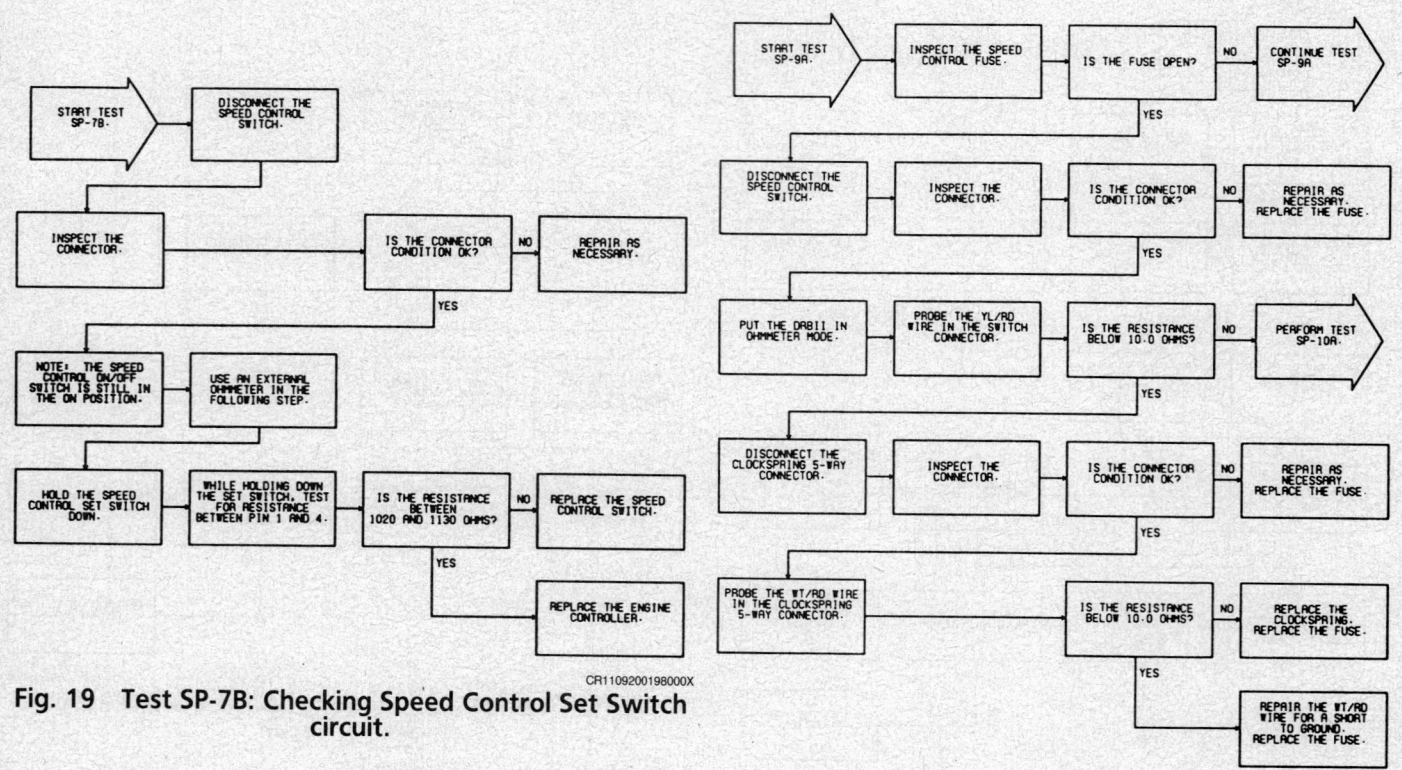

Fig. 19   Test SP-7B: Checking Speed Control Set Switch circuit.

Fig. 20   Test SP-9A: testing Speed Control Switch circuits (Part 1 of 3)

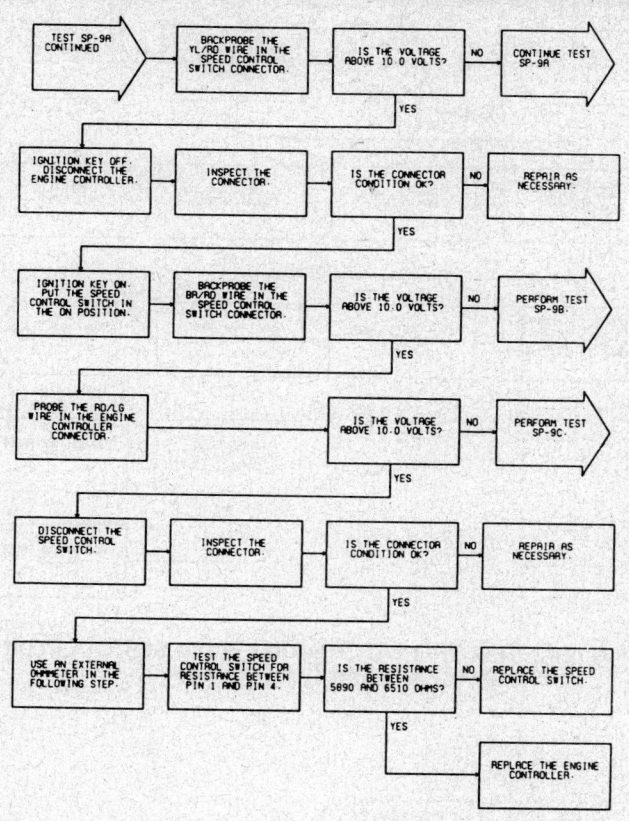

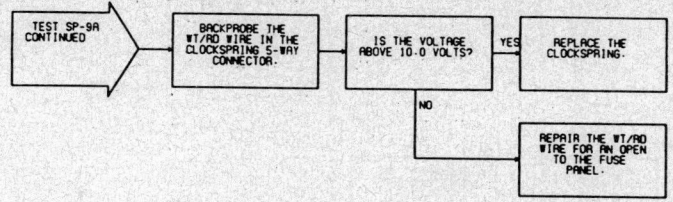

Fig. 20 Test SP-9A: testing Speed Control Switch circuits (Part 3 of 3)

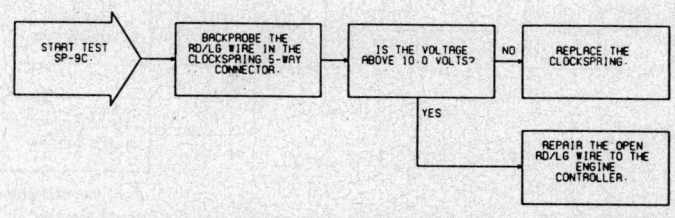

Fig. 22 Test SP-9C: Testing Clockspring Circuit For Open

Fig. 20 Test SP-9A: testing Speed Control Switch circuits (Part 2 of 3)

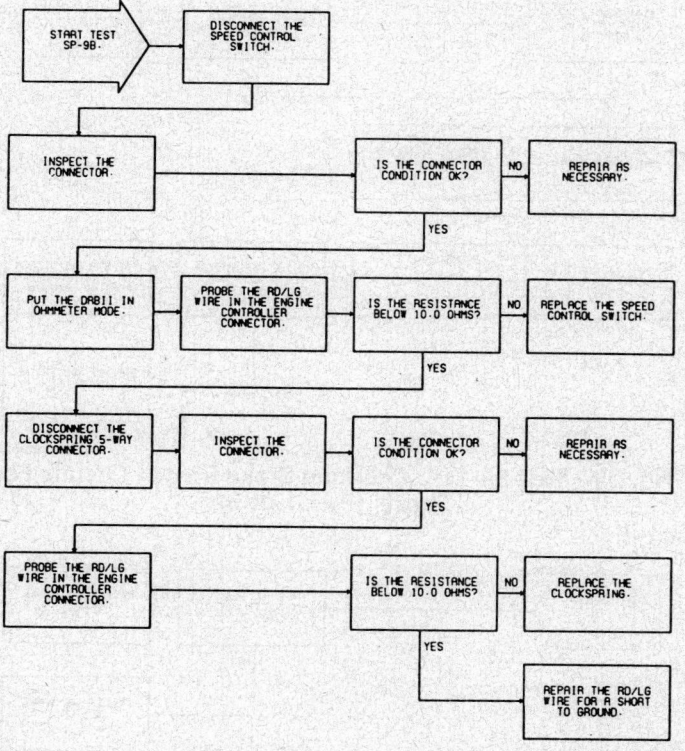

Fig. 21 Test SP-9B: Testing Clockspring Circuit For Shorts

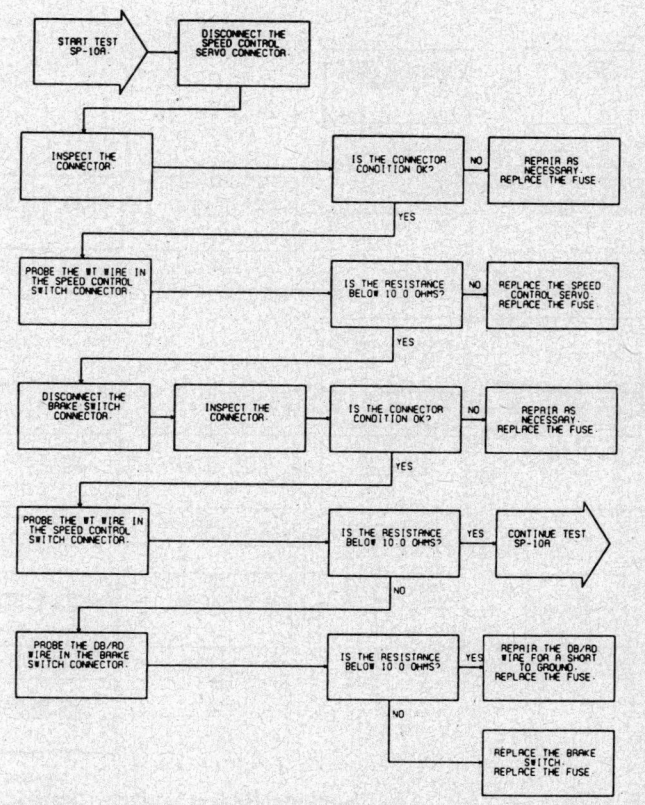

Fig. 23 Test SP-10A: Repairing Speed Control Switch circuits for a short to ground (Part 1 of 2)

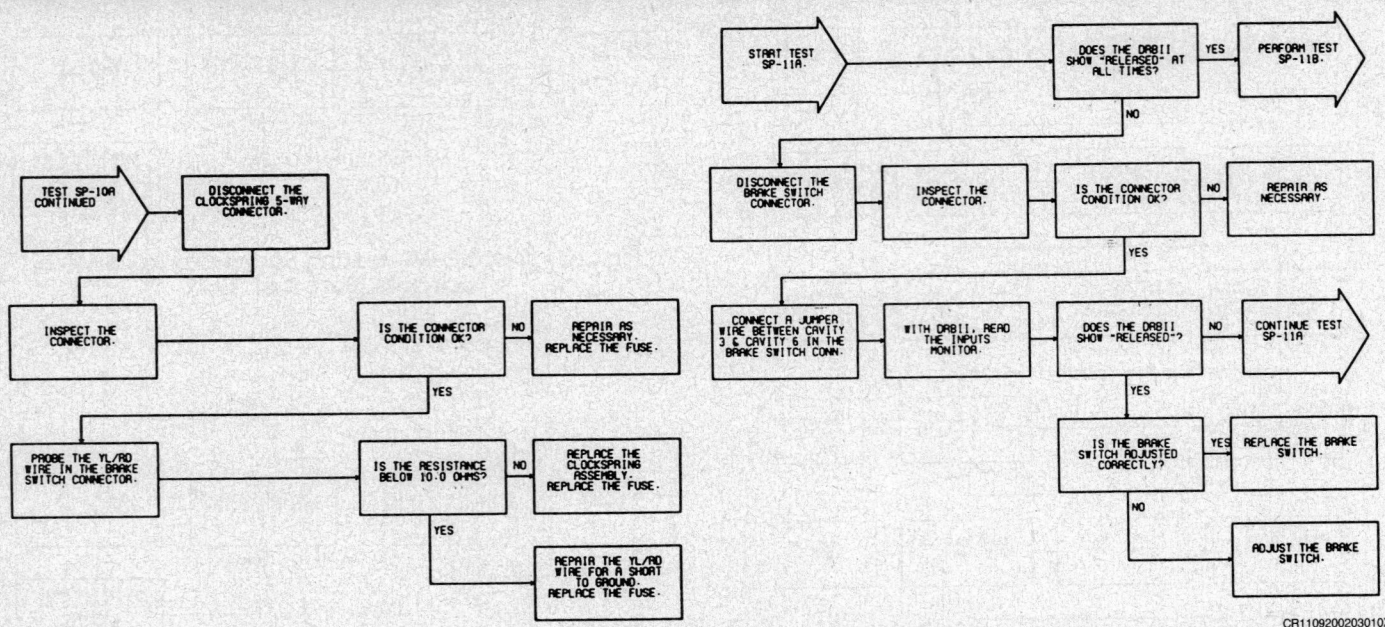

Fig. 23   Test SP-10A: Repairing Speed Control Switch Circuits For A Short To Ground (Part 2 of 2)

CR1109200202020X

Fig. 24   Test SP-11A: Checking Brake Switch Circuits For Open (Part 1 of 2)

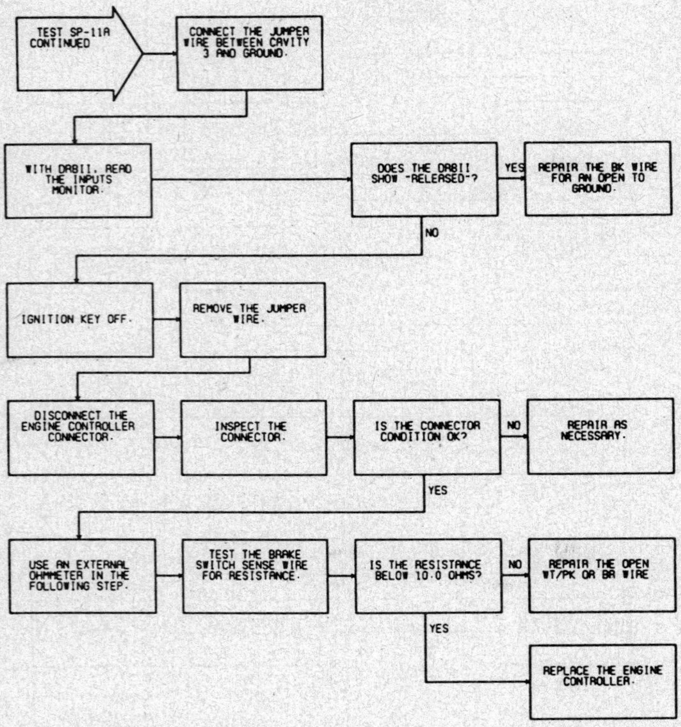

CR1109200203010X

Fig. 24   Test SP-11A: Checking Brake Switch Circuits For Open (Part 2 of 2)

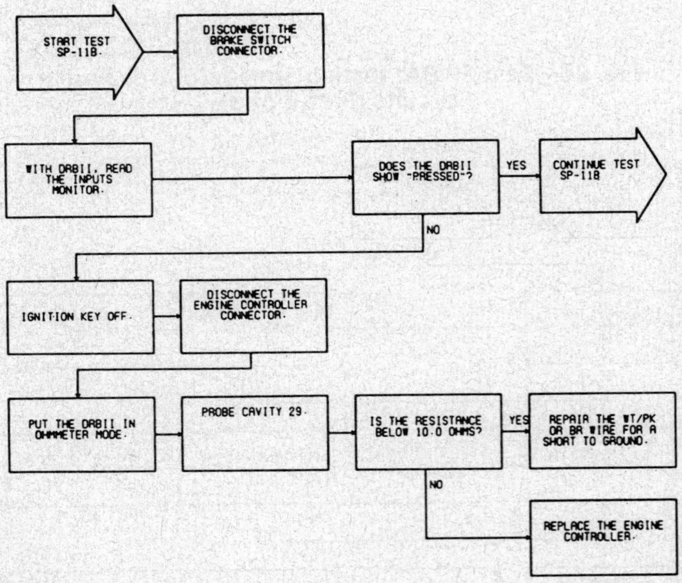

CR1109200203020X

Fig. 25   Test SP-11B: Checking Brake Switch Circuits For Shorts (Part 1 of 2)

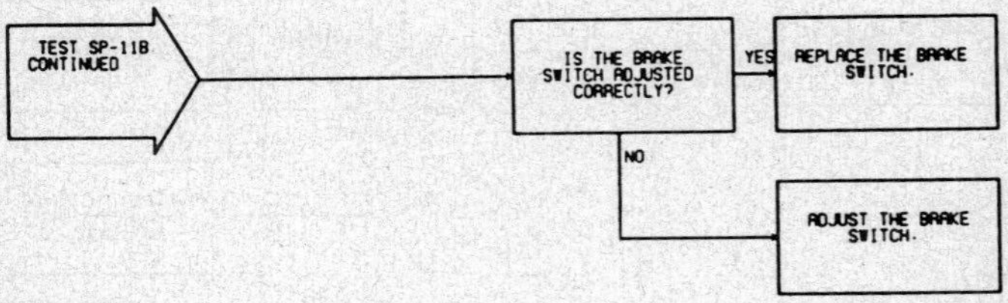

CR1109200204010X

Fig. 25   Test SP-11B: Checking Brake Switch Circuits For Shorts (Part 2 of 2)

CR1109200204020X

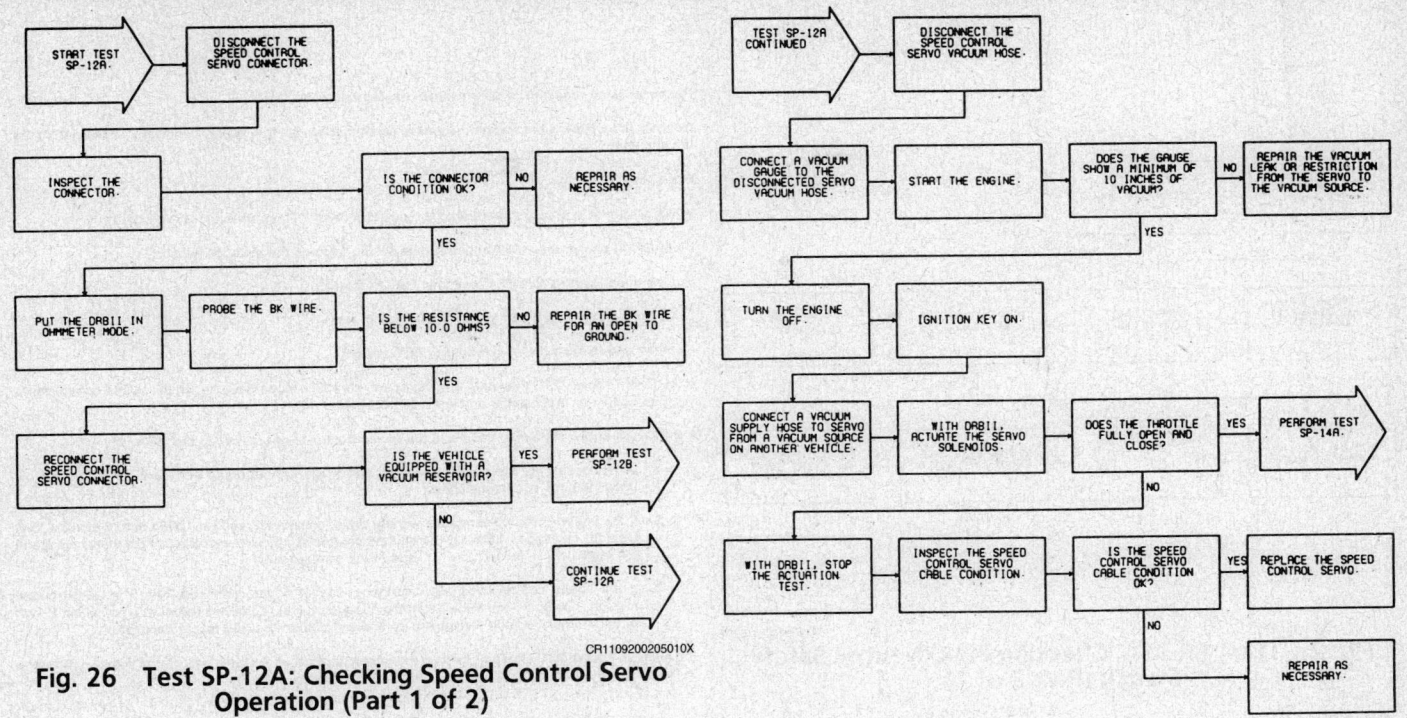

Fig. 26   Test SP-12A: Checking Speed Control Servo Operation (Part 1 of 2)

CR1109200205010X

Fig. 26   Test SP-12A: Checking Speed Control Servo Operation (Part 2 of 2)

CR1109200205020X

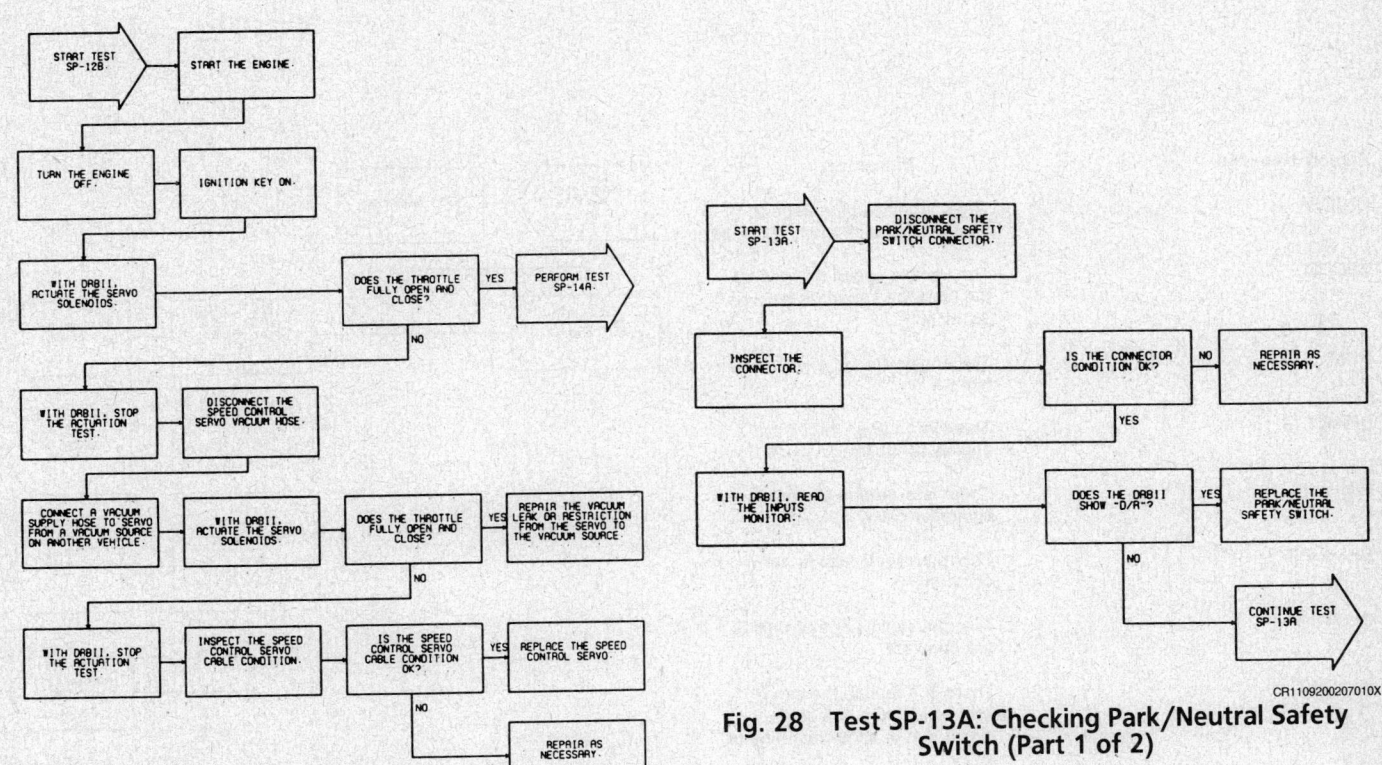

Fig. 27   Test SP-12B: Checking Vacuum To Speed Control Servo

CR1109200206000X

Fig. 28   Test SP-13A: Checking Park/Neutral Safety Switch (Part 1 of 2)

CR1109200207010X

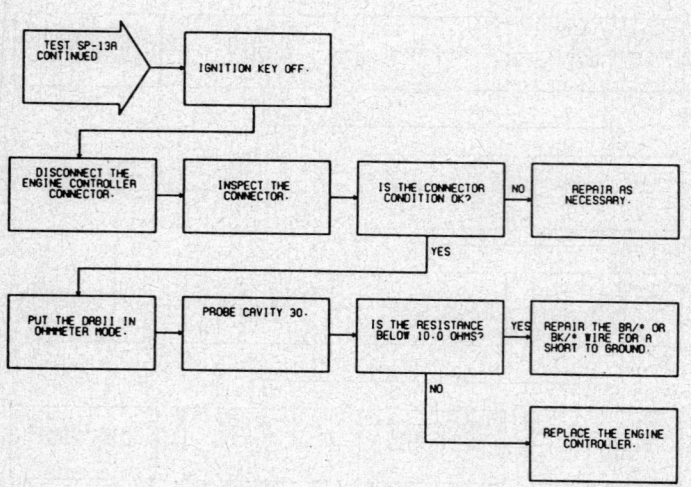

Fig. 28   Test SP-13A: Checking Park/Neutral Safety Switch (Part 2 of 2)

CR1109200207020X

Reconnect and reassemble all previously tested components.

Connect the DRBII to the engine diagnostic connector so that the display can safely be seen from the driver's seat.

Road test the vehicle.

While driving at a steady speed, read the cutout monitor. Have passenger read DRBII.

If the DRBII shows the vehicle speed to be erratic, replace the distance sensor.

Put the speed control ON/OFF switch in the ON position.

Drive the vehicle above 35 mph for the following steps.

Depress and release the speed control SET switch.

If the DRBII shows "S/C Allowed," and the speed control is inoperative, repair the speed control servo vacuum supply or mechanical problems as necessary.

If the DRBII shows "S/C Allowed," and the speed control is operative, do the following:

1. While looking for the speed control to disengage without driver command, drive the vehicle under various road conditions.

2. If the speed control disengages without driver command, read the DRBII cutout monitor "S/C Denied" message. Look up the intermittent circuit problem associated with this message in the chart following and repair as necessary.*

3. If the speed control does not disengage without driver command, read the DRBII cutout monitor. Compare the "Goal" with the "Speed" value. If the two values are not within 2 mph of each other, replace the engine controller.* Otherwise, the test is complete.*

If the DRBII shows "S/C Denied," look up the intermittent circuit problem associated with this message in the chart on the following page, and repair as necessary.

CR1109200208010X

Fig. 29   Test SP-14A: Checking For Intermittent Diagnostic Trouble Codes (Part 1 of 2)

Denied Message	Indication
ON/OFF	There is a lack of voltage at engine controller cavity 23 or 49.
SPEED	The vehicle speed as read by the distance sensor is below 35 mph.
RPM	The engine rpm is excessively high.
BRAKE	There is an open circuit at engine controller cavity 29.
P/N	There is a ground at engine controller cavity 30.
RPM/SPD	The rpm/speed ratio is not constant.
CLUTCH	The rpm/vehicle speed ratio is not constant.
SOL FLT	There is a fault in the servo vent or vacuum solenoid circuit that is either maturing or set.

CR1109200208020X

Fig. 29   Test SP-14A: Checking For Intermittent Diagnostic Trouble Codes (Part 2 of 2)

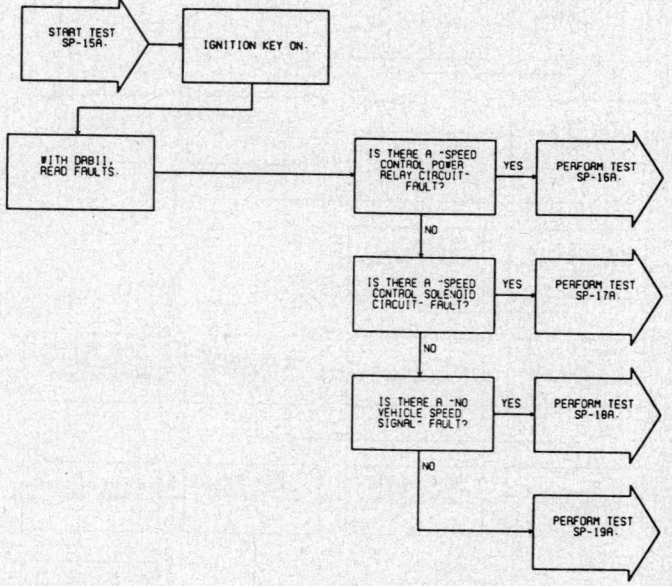

CR1109200209000X

Fig. 30   Test SP-15A: Reading Diagnostic Trouble Codes

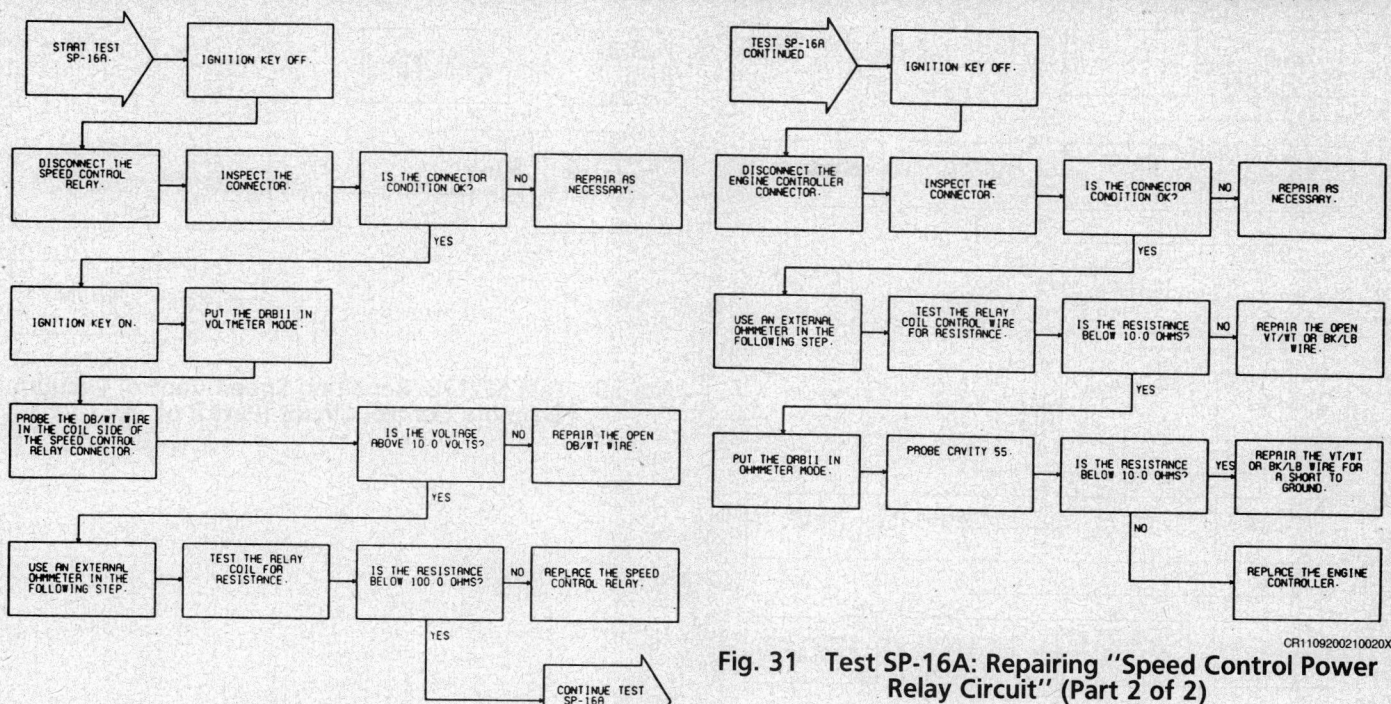

Fig. 31   Test SP-16A: Repairing "Speed Control Power Relay Circuit" (Part 1 of 2)

Fig. 31   Test SP-16A: Repairing "Speed Control Power Relay Circuit" (Part 2 of 2)

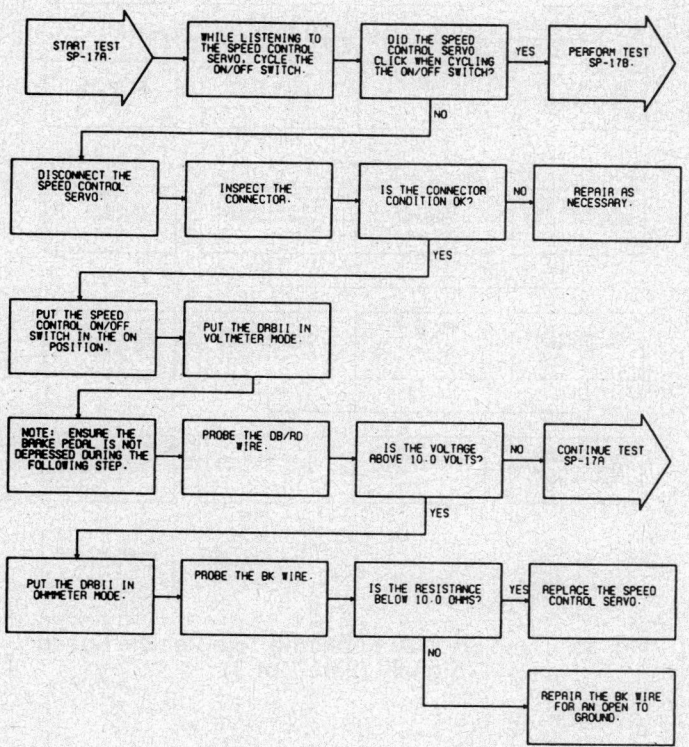

Fig. 32   Test SP-17A: Repairing "Speed Control Solenoid Circuit" (Part 1 of 2)

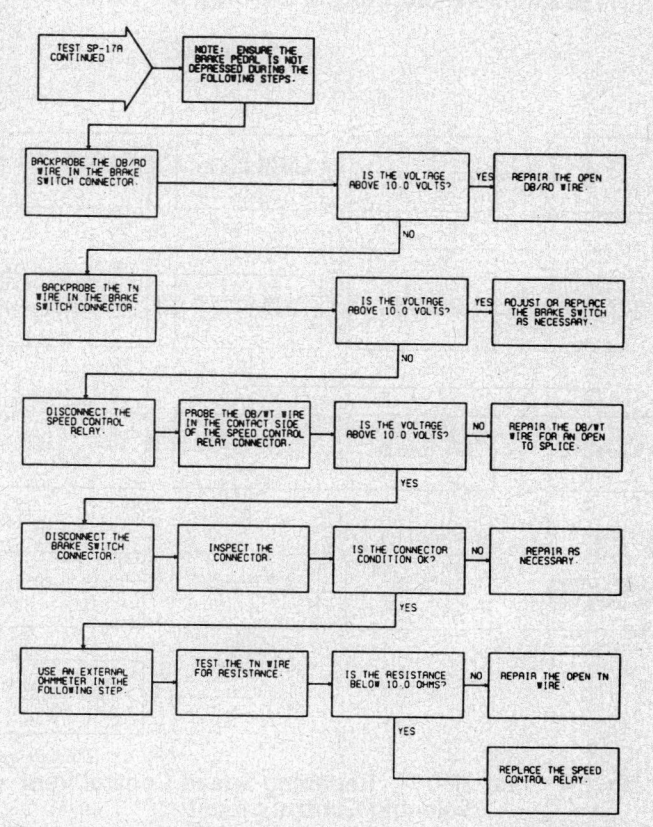

Fig. 32   Test SP-17A: Repairing "Speed Control Solenoid Circuit" (Part 2 of 2)

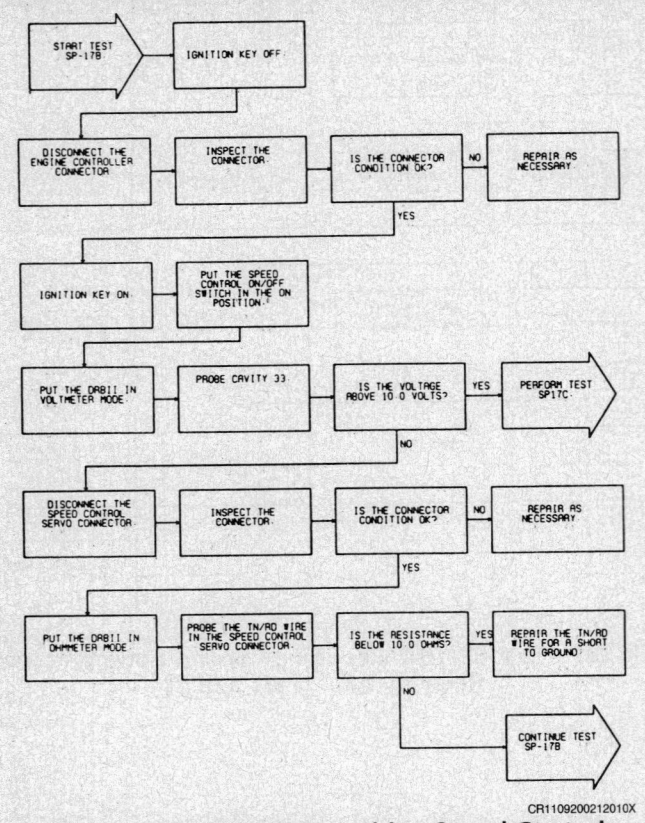

Fig. 33   Test SP-17B: Repairing Speed Control Vacuum Solenoid Control Circuit (Part 1 of 2)

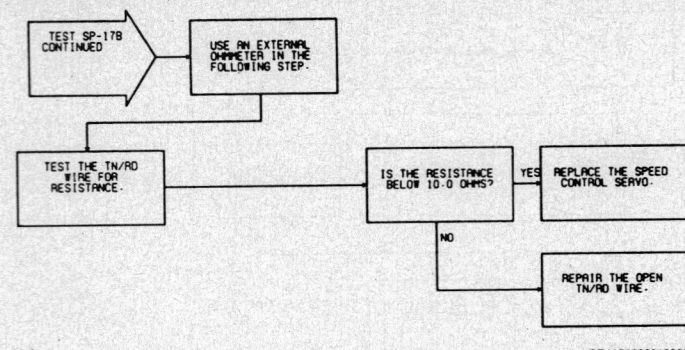

Fig. 33   Test SP-17B: Repairing Speed Control Vacuum Solenoid Control Circuit (Part 2 of 2)

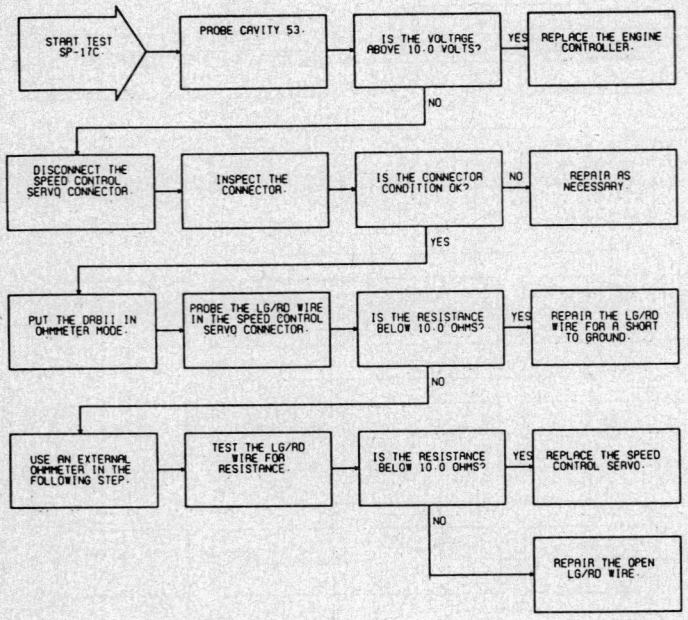

Fig. 34   Test SP-17C: Repairing Speed Control Vent Solenoid Control Circuit

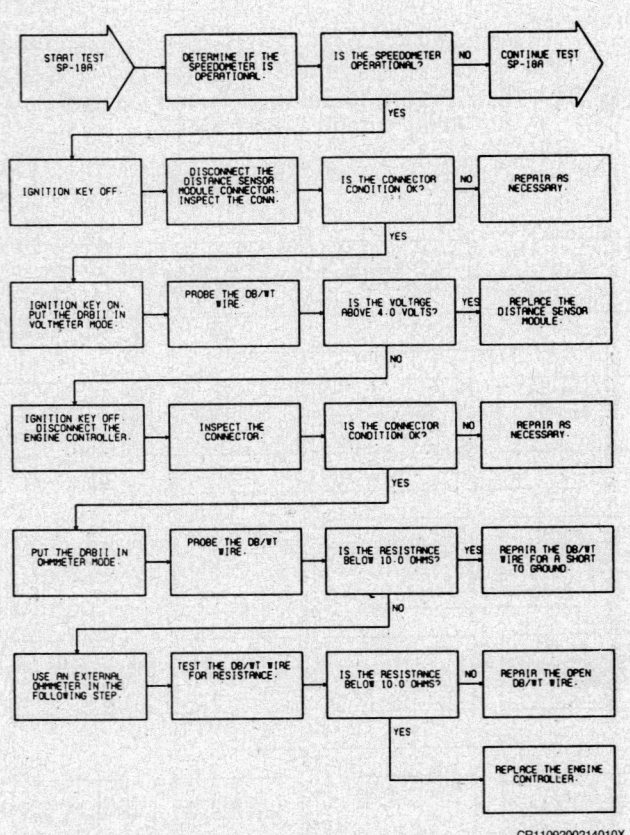

Fig. 35   Test SP-18A: Repairing "No Vehicle Speed Signal" (Part 1 of 3)

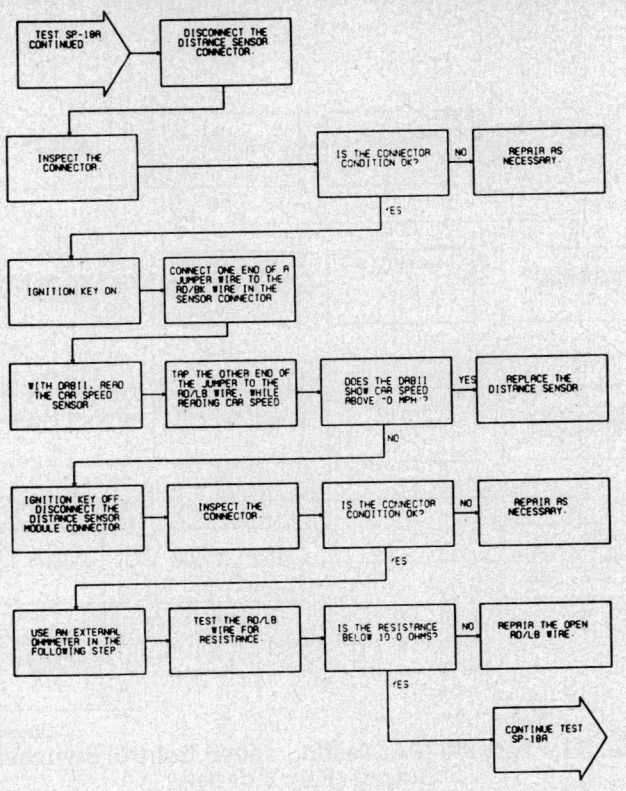

Fig. 35 Test SP-18A: Repairing "No Vehicle Speed Signal" (Part 2 of 3)

CR1109200214020X

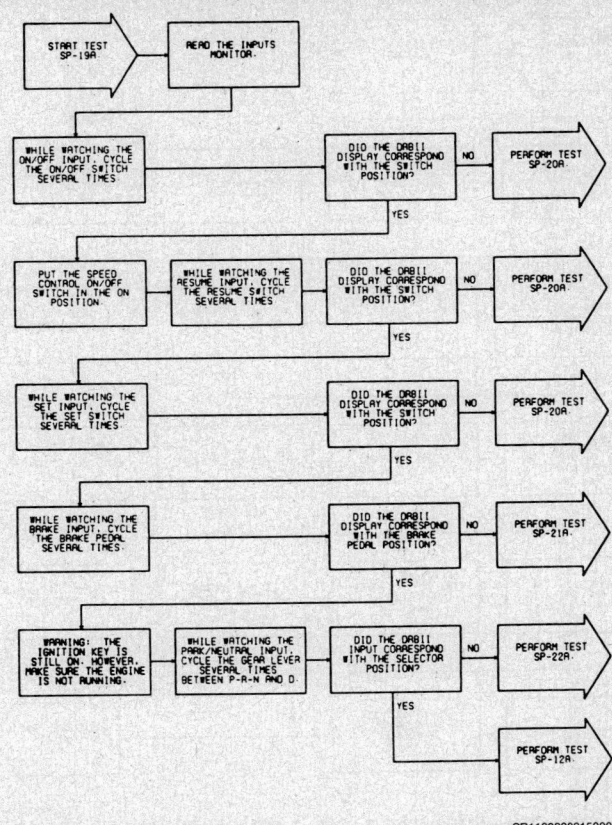

Fig. 36 Test SP-19A: Checking Speed Control Switches

CR1109200215000X

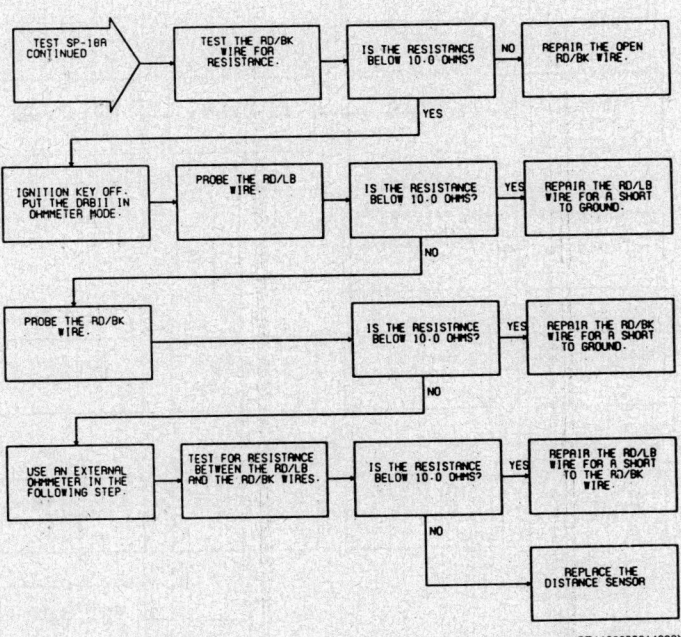

Fig. 35 Test SP-18A: Repairing "No Vehicle Speed Signal" (Part 3 of 3)

CR1109200214030X

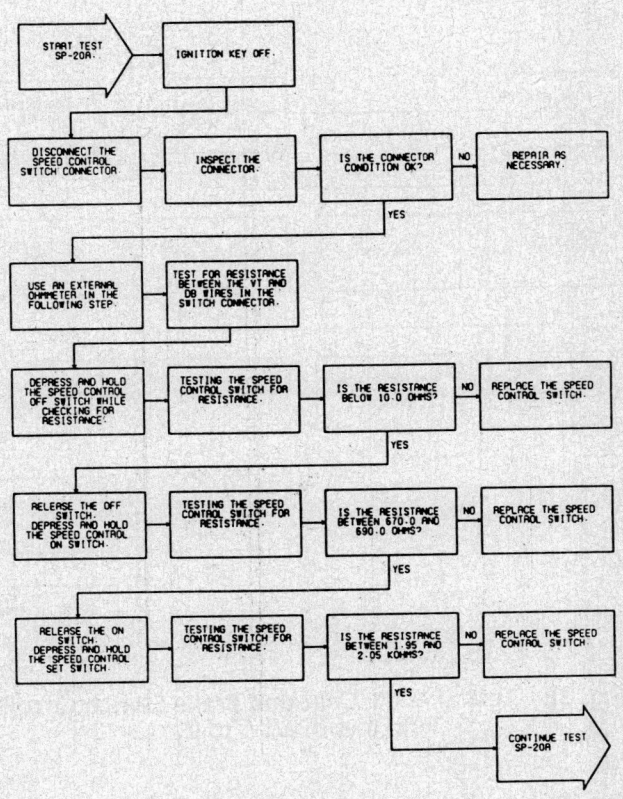

Fig. 37 Test SP-20A: Testing Speed Control Switches Output (Part 1 of 3)

CR1109200216010X

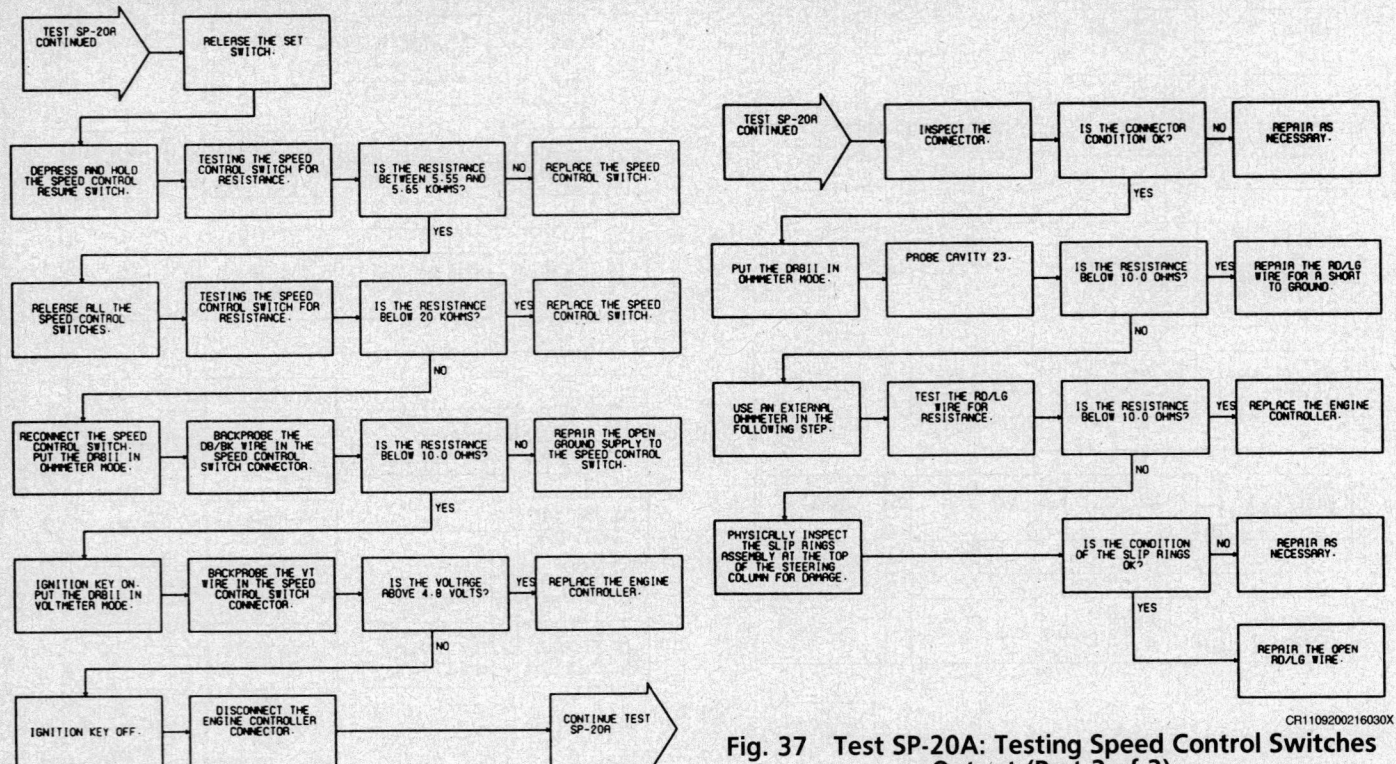

Fig. 37   Test SP-20A: Testing Speed Control Switches Output (Part 2 of 3)

Fig. 37   Test SP-20A: Testing Speed Control Switches Output (Part 3 of 3)

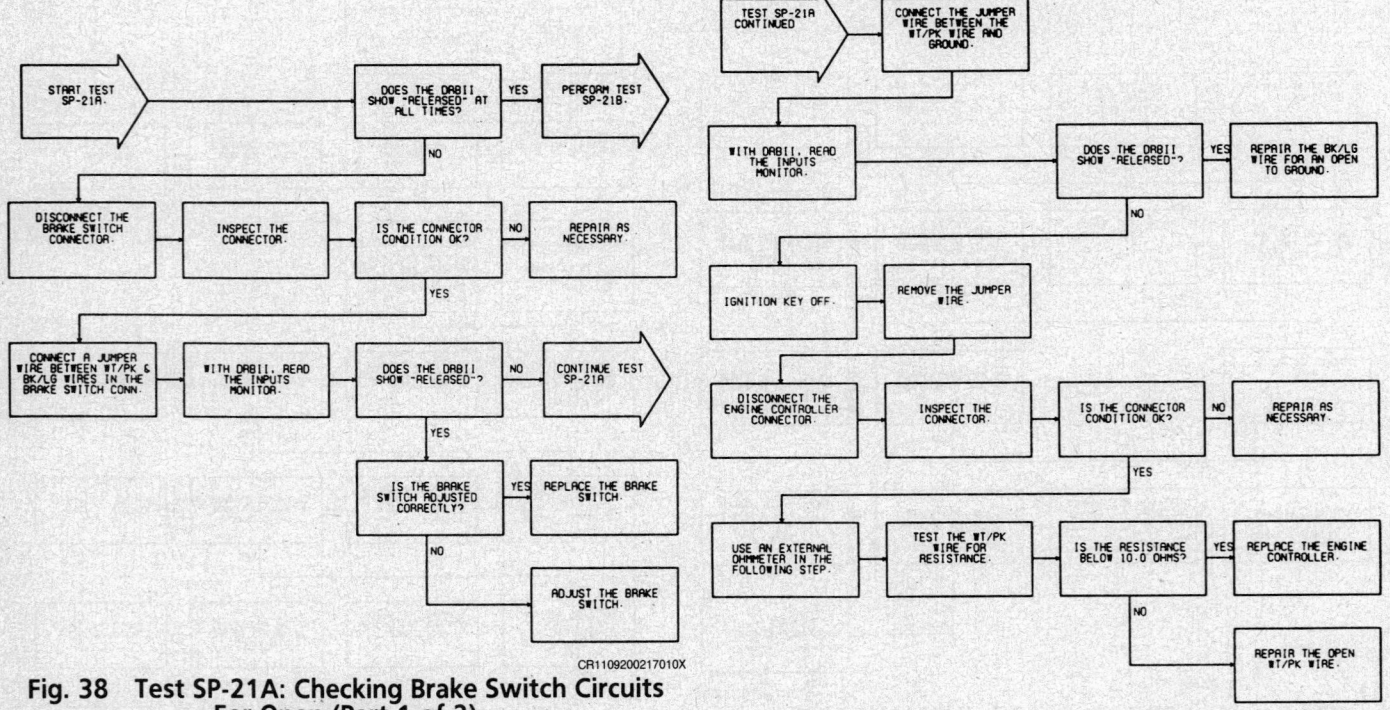

Fig. 38   Test SP-21A: Checking Brake Switch Circuits For Open (Part 1 of 2)

Fig. 38   Test SP-21A: Checking Brake Switch Circuits For Open (Part 2 of 2)

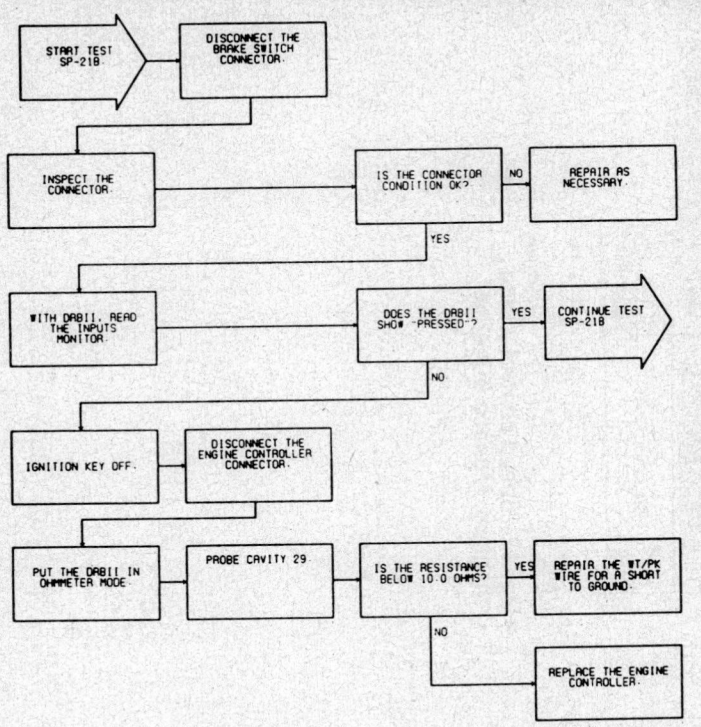

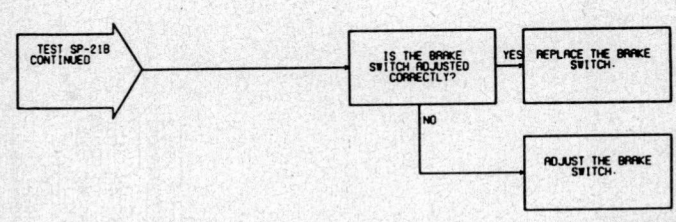

Fig. 39 Test SP-21B: Checking Brake Switch Circuits For Shorts (Part 2 of 2)

Fig. 39 Test SP-21B: Checking Brake Switch Circuits For Shorts (Part 1 of 2)

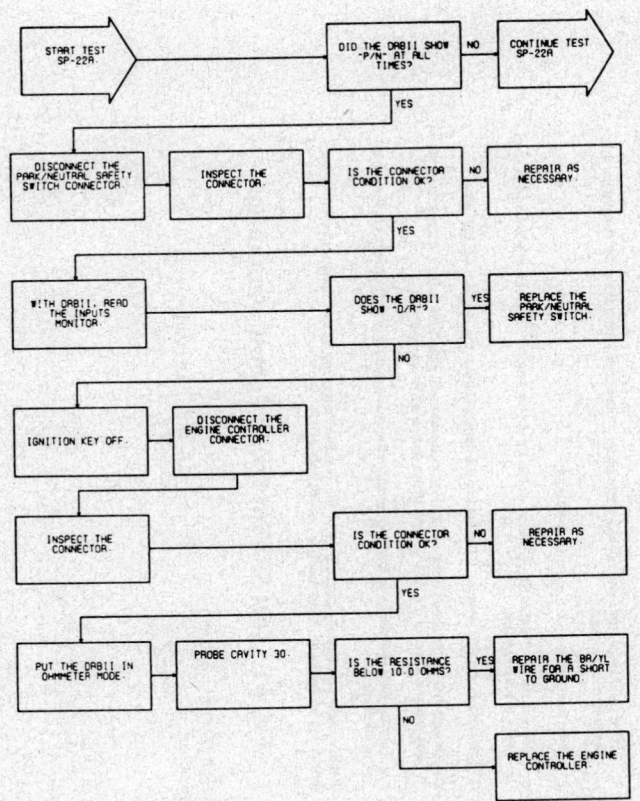

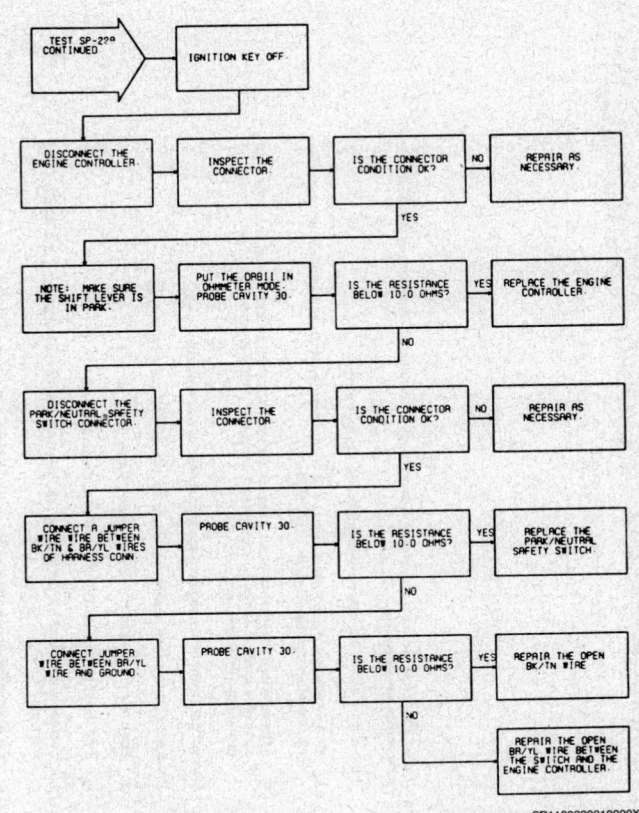

Fig. 40 Test SP-22A: Checking park/Neutral Safety Switch (Part 1 of 2)

Fig. 40 Test SP-22A: Checking Park/Neutral Safety Switch (Part 2 of 2)

Inspect the vehicle to ensure that all engine components are connected. Reassemble and reconnect components as necessary.

If the engine controller has been changed, do the following:

a. If the vehicle is equipped with a factory theft alarm, start the vehicle at least 20 times so that the alarm system may be activated when desired.

b. If the vehicle is a minivan or a truck, the vehicle's mileage must be copied from its odometer to a memory location within the replacement controller. This will enable the new controller to operate the EMR lamp properly.

Connect the DRBII to the engine diagnostic connector and erase the faults.

Ensure no other speed control problems remain by doing the following:

a. Road test the vehicle at a speed above 35 mph.

b. Turn the speed control ON/OFF switch to the on position.

c. Depress and release the SET switch. If the speed control did not engage, the repair is not complete.*

d. For stalk switch equipped vehicles, quickly depress and release the SET switch.

For steering wheel switch equipped vehicles, quickly depress and release the RESUME/ACCEL switch. If the vehicle speed did not increase by 2 mph, the repair is not complete.

e. Using caution, depress and release brake pedal. If the speed control did not disengage, the repair is not complete.*

f. Bring the vehicle speed back up to 35 mph.

g. Depress the RESUME/ACCEL switch. If the s/c did not resume the previously set speed, the repair is not complete.

h. Hold down the SET switch. If the vehicle did not decelerate, the repair is not complete.

i. Ensure the vehicle speed is greater than 35 mph and release the SET switch. If the vehicle did not adjust and set at the new vehicle speed, the repair is not complete.

j. Turn the ON/OFF switch to the off position. If the speed control did not disengage, the repair is not complete.

If the vehicle successfully passed all of the previous tests, the speed control system is now functioning as designed. The repair is now complete.

CR110920022000X

Fig. 41   Test SP-VER: Speed Control Verification

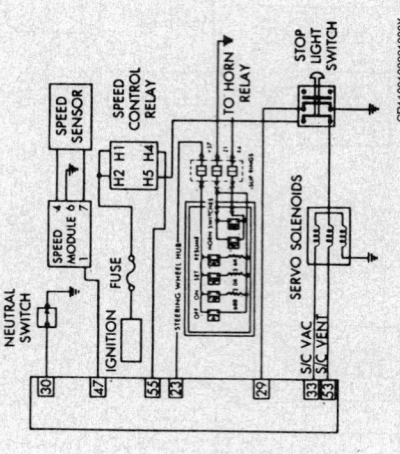

Fig. 42   Speed control wiring diagram. Monaco & Premier

CR11091002221000X

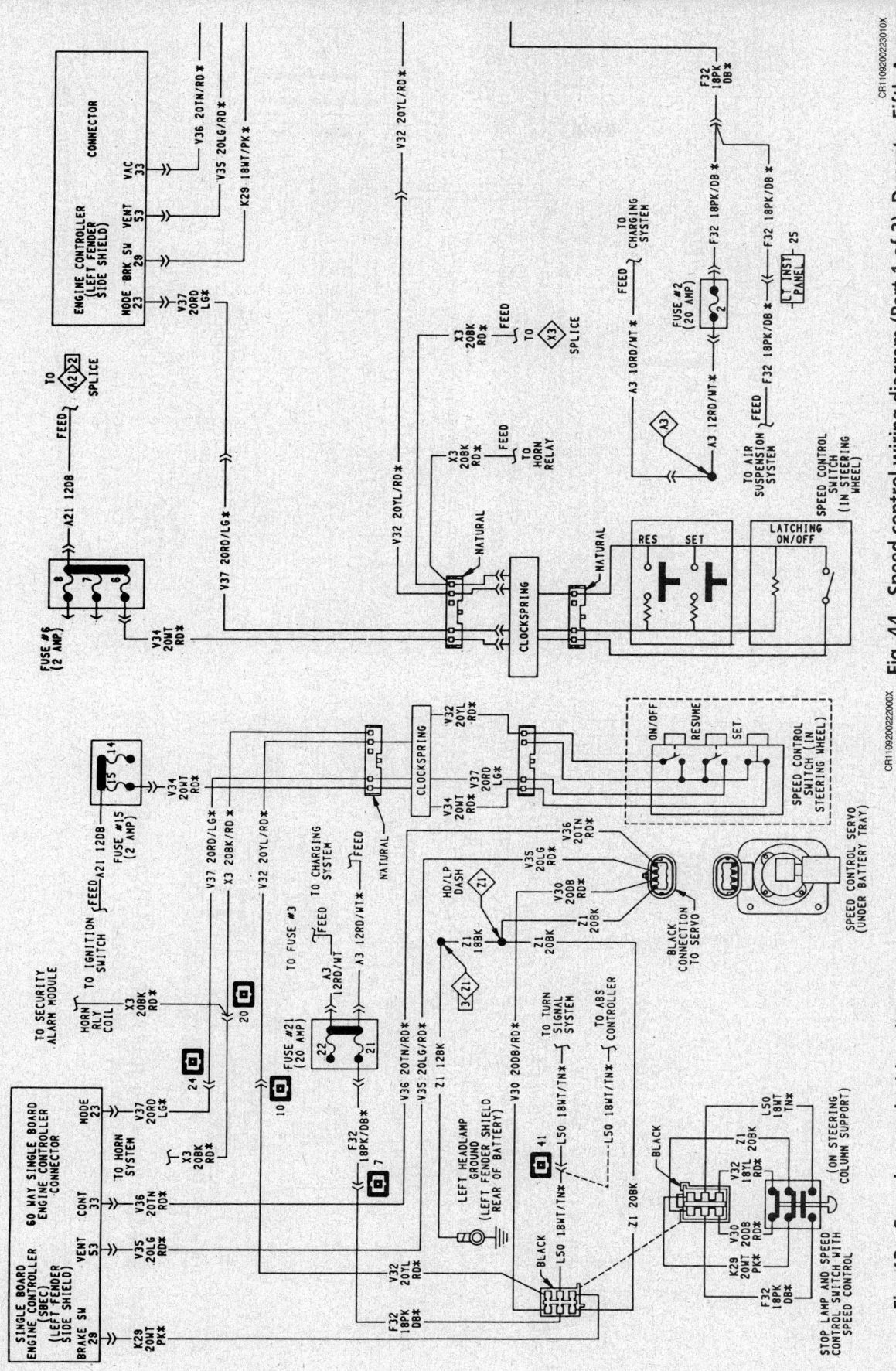

Fig. 44   Speed control wiring diagram (Part 1 of 2). Dynasty, Fifth Ave., Imperial & New Yorker

Fig. 43   Speed control wiring diagram. Daytona & LeBaron 2 door/convertible

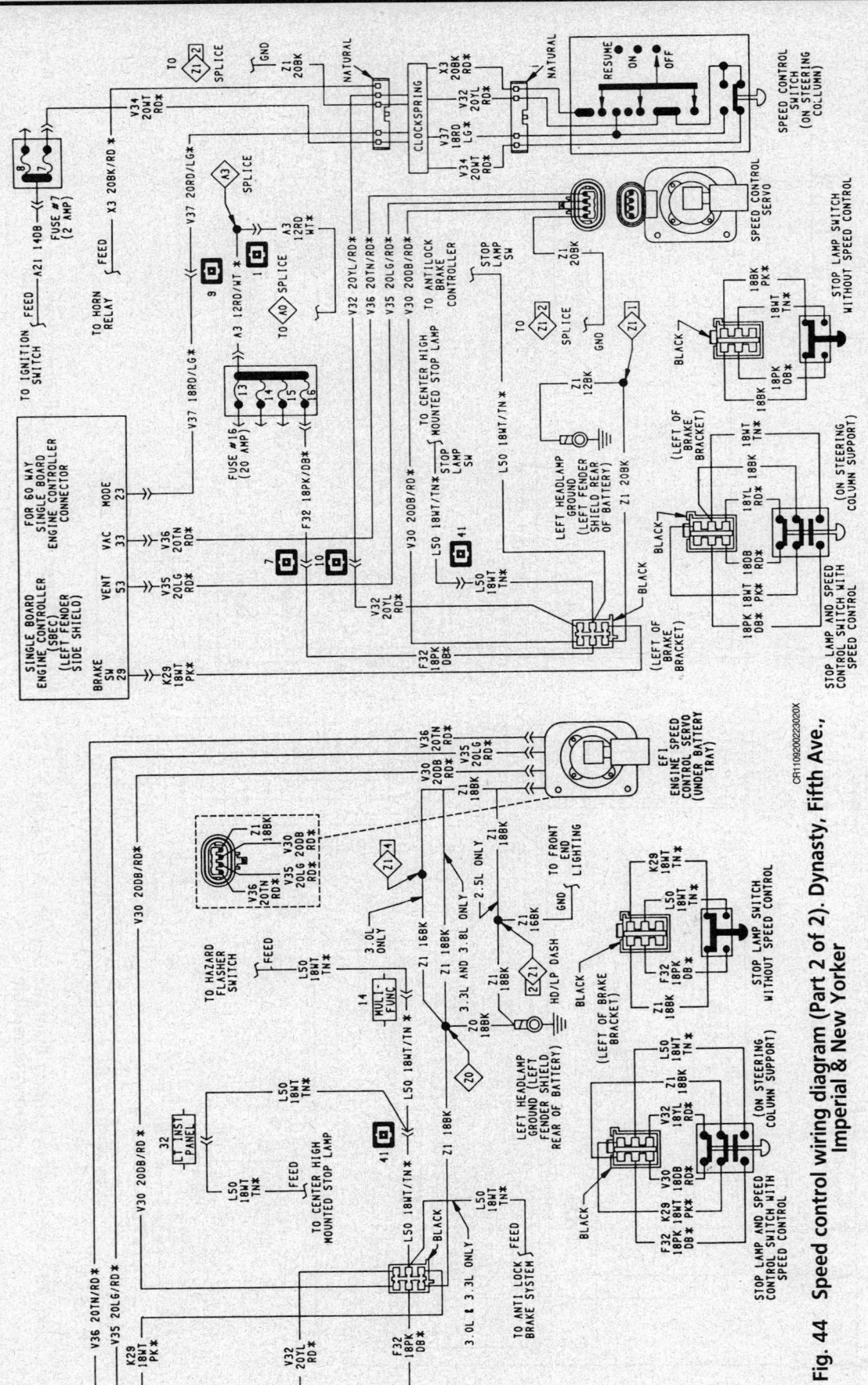

Fig. 45 Speed control wiring diagram. Acclaim, LeBaron & Spirit

Fig. 44 Speed control wiring diagram (Part 2 of 2). Dynasty, Fifth Ave., Imperial & New Yorker

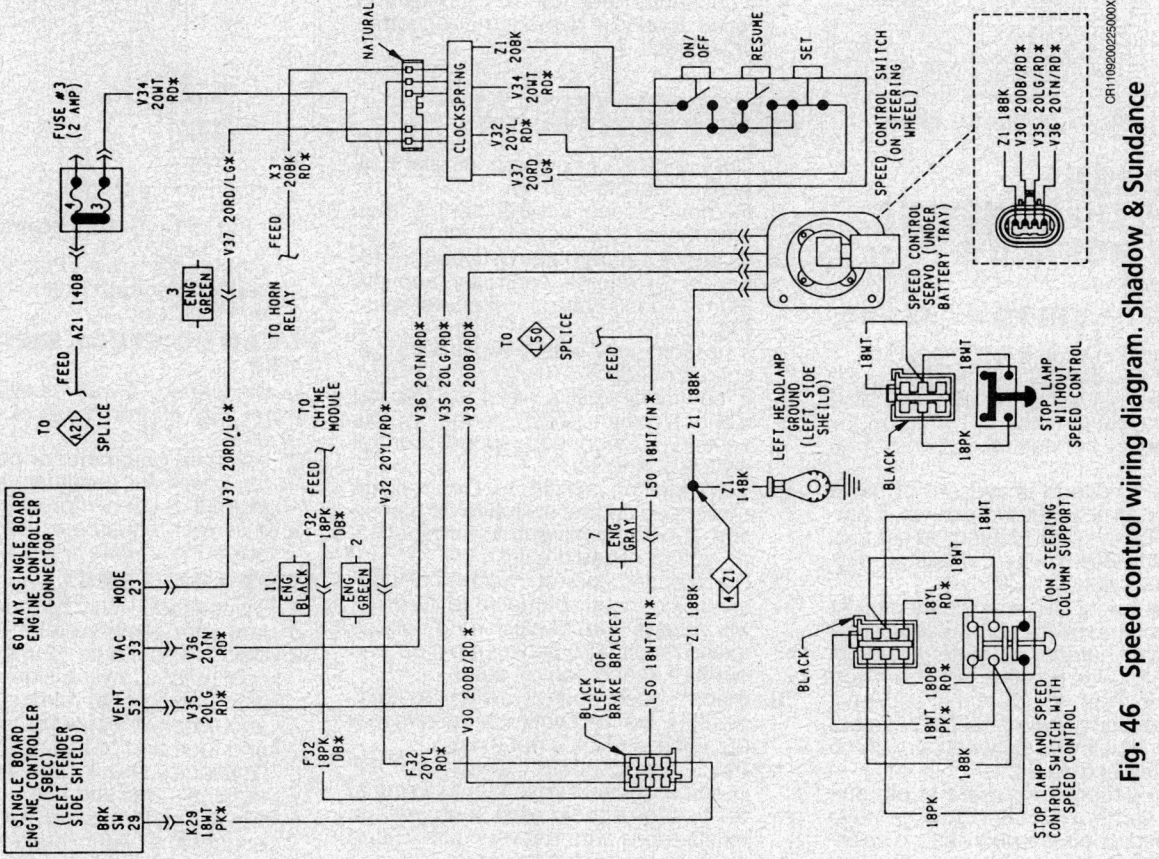

Fig. 46 Speed control wiring diagram. Shadow & Sundance

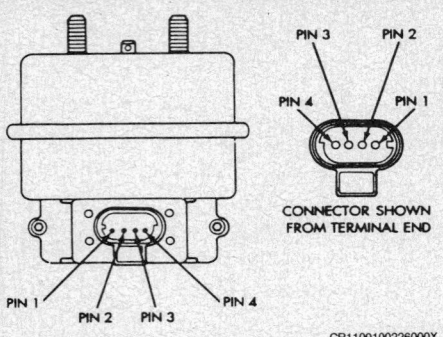

CR1109100226000X

Fig. 47 Servo harness connector

TERMINAL VIEW

CR1109100227000X

Fig. 48 Engine controller connector

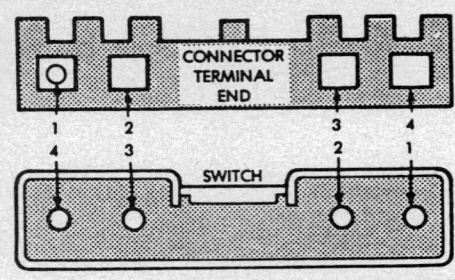

CR1109100228000X

Fig. 49 4-way electrical connector

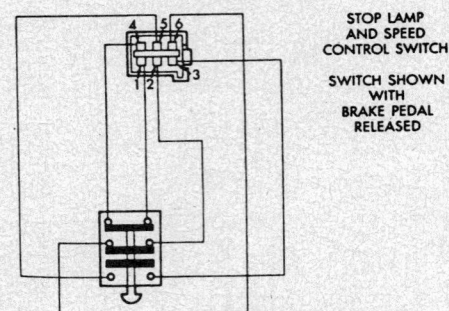

CR1109100230000X

Fig. 51 6-way connector

SWITCH POSITION	CONTINUITY BETWEEN	RANGE
OFF	PIN 3 AND PIN 4	5890-6510
	PIN 1 AND PIN 3	NO CONTINUITY
ON	PIN 1 AND PIN 4	5890-6510
	PIN 1 AND PIN 3	CONTINUITY
ON/SET	PIN 1 AND PIN 4	1020-1130 Ω
ON/RESUME	PIN 3 AND PIN 4	2040-2260 Ω

Fig. 50 Continuity chart

COMPONENT DIAGNOSIS & TESTING
EXCEPT MONACO & PREMIER
ELECTRICAL TESTS AT SERVO

1. Turn ignition switch to On position.
2. With speed control switch in On position, connect voltmeter negative lead to a chassis ground.
3. Disconnect connector at servo, **Fig. 47.**
4. If battery voltage is present at pin 2 proceed to next numbered step, if battery voltage is not present at pin 2 of main harness 4-way connector, proceed as follows:
   a. Disconnect six way connector at stop lamp switch and test pin one of main harness for battery voltage, if voltage is present perform "Stop Lamp Test" found in this section.
   b. If stop lamp switch test is satisfactory, repair wire between stop lamp switch and servo.
   c. If no voltage is present at pin one of six way connector, remove speed control switch and disconnect four way connector. Test pin one for battery voltage.
   d. If voltage is present, perform "Speed Control Switch Test" found in this section.
   e. If speed control switch is satisfactory, check continuity across clockspring. If continuity exists, repair wire between stop lamp switch and clockspring.
   f. If no voltage is present at pin one of four way speed control switch connector, test for battery voltage between ignition and the fuse, if satisfactory, check fuse. If fuse is satisfactory, repair wire between fuse and clockspring.
5. Connect a suitable jumper wire between pin No. 2 of 4-way connector and pin No. 2 of speed control servo.
6. In battery voltage is not present at remaining pin at servo, replace speed control servo.
7. Using suitable ohmmeter, connect negative lead to chassis ground and positive lead to pin 1 of 4-way connector.
8. If continuity does not exist, check and repair loose or damaged connectors or harness.

ELECTRICAL TESTS AT ENGINE CONTROLLER

1. Unplug 60-way engine controller harness connector **Fig. 48.**
2. Remove speed control switch, then disconnect four way connector.
3. Connect a ohmmeter between terminal 23 of engine controller and pin four of speed control switch harness **Fig. 49, .**
4. If no continuity exists, repair wire circuit as needed.
5. If continuity exists, refer to "Speed Control Switch Test" found in this section. Reconnect speed control switch connector.
6. Turn ignition switch to On position and speed control switch to OFF position, connect voltmeter to terminal 53, no voltage should exist.
7. Place speed control switch to ON position, connect voltmeter to terminal 53, voltage should exist. If no voltage exists repair wire between pin 53 and pin 3 of speed control servo.
8. Place speed control switch to OFF position, connect voltmeter to terminal 33, voltage should not exist.
9. Place speed control switch to OFF position, connect voltmeter to terminal 33, voltage should exist. If no voltage exists repair wire between pin 33 and pin 4 of speed control servo.
10. Connect one lead of a ohmmeter to ground and other lead to terminal 29, with brake pedal released continuity should exist. With brake pedal depressed continuity should not exist.
11. If continuity exists when pedal is depressed, check for continuity between terminal 29 of engine controller and pin 3 of stop lamp connector. If no continuity exists, repair wiring. If continuity does exist test stop lamp switch. Refer to "Stop Lamp Switch Test" found in this section.
12. If stop lamp switch test is satisfactory, test continuity between pin six of stop lamp switch and ground.
13. Connect one lead of an ohmmeter to ground and one lead to pin 30, place transaxle in Drive, no continuity should not exist. Place selector in Park or Neutral, continuity should exist.

SPEED CONTROL SWITCH TEST

1. Disconnect 4-way electrical connector, **Fig. 49** from base of steering column
2. Using an ohmmeter or continuity tester, check for continuity according to **Fig. 50** at connector wires.
3. If correct results are not attained, replace the switch.

STOP LAMP TEST

1. Disconnect 6-way connector, **Fig. 51,** from stop lamp switch.
2. Using a suitable ohmmeter, check continuity at switch side of connector with brake pedal released. Continuity should exist between terminals one and four, and terminals three and six. Continuity should not exist between terminals two and five.
3. Check continuity at switch side of connector with brake pedal depressed. Continuity should not exist between terminals one and four, and terminals three and six. Continuity should exist between terminals two and five.
4. If proper results are not obtained, the stop lamp switch should be adjusted or replaced.

VACUUM SUPPLY TEST

1. Disconnect vacuum hose from servo and install a vacuum gauge in hose.
2. Start engine and run at idle. Vacuum gauge should read 10 inches Hg.
3. If vacuum is below 10 inches Hg, check for vacuum leaks or poor engine performance.

SERVO VACUUM TEST

1. Remove speed control cable at throttle body end, then disconnect four

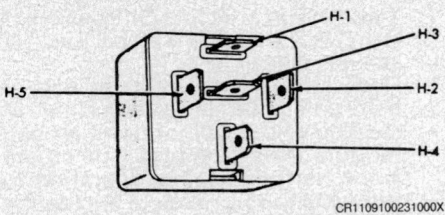

Fig. 52 Speed control relay. Monaco & Premier

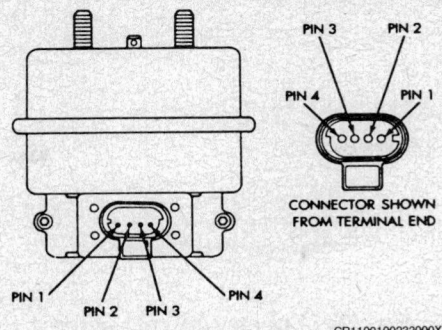

Fig. 53 Speed control servo. Monaco & Premier

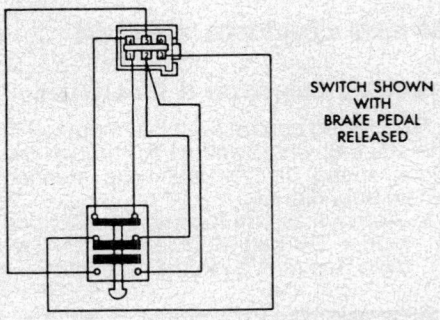

Fig. 55 Stop lamp switch circuit. Monaco & Premier

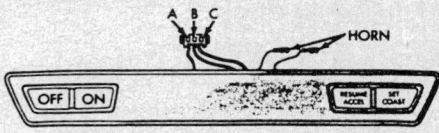

Fig. 54 Speed control switch pod. Monaco & Premier

way electrical connector and vacuum harness at the servo, **Fig. 47.**

2. Connect battery voltage to pin two of servo, then ground remaining three pins.
3. Connect a hand held vacuum pump to servo, then apply 15 inches of vacuum. Cable should pull in and stay as long as vacuum is applied.

MONACO & PREMIER

Speed Control Relay Test

1. With ignition switch in Off position, remove speed control power relay located in the instrument panel relay bank, **Fig. 52.**
2. With ignition switch in On position, measure voltage at pin 4 of the relay connector.
3. If voltage is less than 10 volts, check fuse or repair open wire between relay and fuse panel or between ignition and fuse panel.
4. Remove speed control relay from relay bank and measure resistance between terminals H2 and H5. If resistance is greater than 100 ohms, replace the relay.
5. With ignition switch in Off position, disconnect engine controller. Measure resistance between engine controller connector terminal 55 and relay connector terminal H4, **Fig. 52.**
6. If resistance is greater than 10 ohms, repair open circuit.
7. With ignition in Off position, measure resistance between engine controller connector terminal 55 and ground. If resistance is less than 10 ohms, repair wire for a short to ground.
8. If resistance is above 10 ohms, replace the engine controller.

Electrical Test At Servo

1. Turn ignition switch to On position
2. Press speed control switch On, immediately after the speed control relay becomes energized. Test for battery voltage.
3. Disconnect 4-way connector from speed control servo, **Fig. 53.** Using a voltmeter, test pin 2 on connector. If voltage is 12 volts, proceed to step 5.
4. If voltage is less than 12 volts, disconnect 6-way connector on stop lamp switch. Measure voltage at dash harness circuit No. 42 at brake lamp switch. If voltage is 12 volts, perform tests under "Stop Lamp Switch Test."
5. Measure voltage at speed control relay connector H4, **Fig. 52.** If battery voltage is present, repair circuit between relay and brake switch.

6. If no voltage is present, re-check for Diagnostic Trouble Code 77. If Diagnostic Trouble Code 77 is found, perform tests under "Speed Control Relay Test."
7. If code 77 is not present, perform tests under "Speed Control Switch Test."

Speed Control Switch Test

1. Remove speed control switch as outlined under "Speed Control Switch" under "Component Replacement."
2. Measure resistance at terminals B and C of speed control switch with switches pressed, **Fig. 54** resistance should be as follows:
   a. With switch in Off position, 0–5 ohms.
   b. With switch in On position, 645–715 ohms.
   c. With switch Resume/Accel switch pressed, 1900–2100 ohms.
   d. With switch Set/Coast switch pressed, 5370–5925 ohms.
3. If resistance is not as specified, replace the speed control switch bar.
4. Disconnect turn signal cancel switch 8-way connector located in the lower steering column.
5. Install a suitable jumper wire between speed control switch terminal C to terminal E (white wire) and between speed control switch terminal B to terminal F (blue wire). With jumpers in place, press speed control On switch. Speed control relay should now be energized and battery voltage should be at servo terminal 2, **Fig. 53.**
6. If battery voltage is present at servo,

repair open or replace turn signal cancel cam and switch.

7. If voltage is not present at servo, disconnect engine controller and test for continuity from connector terminal 23 to turn signal cancel cam switch connector terminal E (white wire). Repair any open or short to ground.
8. Check for continuity to ground or an open from turn signal cancel switch harness connector terminal F (blue wire) and ground. Repair any open circuit.
9. Connect negative lead of ohmmeter to ground near engine controller. Place ignition switch in Off position, press speed control switch Off.
10. Measure resistance between ground and engine controller connector terminal 53 then between ground and servo connector terminal 3. Repair any short to ground.
11. Measure resistance between engine controller connector terminal 53 and servo connector terminal 3. If resistance is less than 10 ohms there is a short to ground.
12. Measure resistance between engine controller connector terminal 33 and the servo connector terminal 2. Resistance should be less than 10 ohms. Repair circuit if resistance is not as specified.

Stop Lamp Switch Test

1. Disconnect 6-way connector at stop lamp switch.
2. Using an ohmmeter, and with brake pedal released, continuity should be present between switch terminals, **Fig. 55,** as follows:
   a. Between terminals 1 and 4.
   b. Between terminals 3 and 6.
3. No continuity should exists between switch terminals 2 and 5 with brake pedal released.
4. With brake pedal depressed, continuity should not be present between switch terminals as follows:
   a. Between terminals 1 and 4.
   b. Between terminals 3 and 6.
5. Continuity should exists with brake pedal depressed between switch terminals 2 and 5.
6. If continuity tests are not as specified, replace stop lamp switch.

Vacuum Supply Test

1. Disconnect vacuum hose from servo and install a vacuum gauge in hose.
2. Start engine and run at idle. Vacuum gauge should read 10 inches Hg.
3. If vacuum is below 10 inches Hg check for vacuum leaks or poor engine performance.

COMPONENT REPLACEMENT

SPEED CONTROL SERVO

1. Remove speed control cable and mounting bracket to servo attaching nuts.
2. Remove screws attaching servo mounting bracket, then servo mounting bracket.
3. Disconnect vacuum and electrical connector.
4. Pull cable away from servo to expose retaining clip, then remove clip attaching cable and servo.
5. To install, place throttle in wide open position, align hole in speed control cable sleeve with hole in servo pin, then install retaining clip.
6. Reconnect vacuum hose and electrical connector.
7. Install mounting bracket and attaching screws, **torque** attaching screws to 105 inch lbs.
8. Install servo and servo attaching nuts, **torque** nuts to 60 inch lbs.

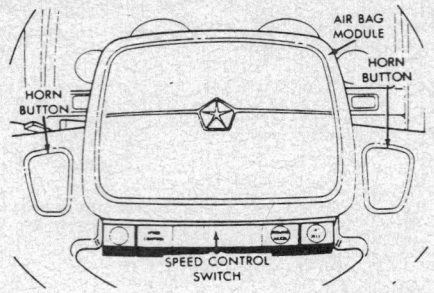

Fig. 56   Speed control switch location. 1992 models, except Monaco & Premier

SPEED CONTROL SWITCH

Except Monaco & Premier

The speed control switch is mounted in the steering wheel and wired through the clock spring device under the steering wheel hub, **Fig. 56.**
1. Remove air bag module as described under "Air bag Module" in the "Passive Restraint Systems" section.

2. Turn ignition switch to Off position.
3. Remove two screws from back side of steering wheel.
4. Rock switch away from air bag or horn pad while lifting switch out of steering wheel. **Do not point air bag module toward yourself or others when performing this operation to prevent injury in case of accidental deployment of air bag module.**
5. Disconnect 4-way electrical connector.
6. Reverse procedure to install, sliding the forward edge of switch under air bag or horn pad. Line up locating pins on switch with holes in steering wheel frame. **Do not point air bag module toward yourself or others when performing this operation to prevent injury in case of accidental deployment of air bag module.**

Monaco & Premier

1. Pull rearward on horn cover.
2. Disconnect horn wires.
3. Disconnect speed control electrical connector.
4. Pry up on switch panel and remove panel from steering wheel.
5. Reverse procedure to install.

Type 2

NOTE: Electrical Symbol & Wire Color Code Identification Located In The Front Of This Manual May Be Used As An Aid When Using Wiring Circuits Found In This Section.

NOTE: On Air Bag Equipped Models, Refer To Air Bag System Precautions Located In The Front Of This Manual For System Disarming & Arming Procedures.

INDEX

DESCRIPTION

The speed control system, performs control functions for setting or cancellation of fixed-speed driving speed based upon data provided by input signals. When the speed control system is cancelled, the cause is memorized in a separate circuit by the ECU whether the condition is normal or abnormal. This provides the ECU with a self-diagnosis function by monitoring certain fixed patterns and is able to check whether the ECU input switch or sensor is normal. When using these functions time required for checking and repair can be shortened.

PRECAUTIONS

AIR BAG SYSTEM

Refer to Air Bag Systems Precautions in the front of this manual for system disarming and arming procedures.

ADJUSTMENTS

LASER & TALON

Accelerator Cables

1. Confirm there are no sharp bends in accelerator cables.
2. Check inner cables for correct slack.
3. If slack is incorrect, adjust as follows:
   a. Remove actuator protector.
   b. **On single overhead cam engines,** turn ignition switch to the On position and leave in this position for approximately 15 seconds.
   c. **On all models,** loosen adjusting bolts, then adjust accelerator cable B, **Fig. 1,** to achieve freeplay of .04-.08 inch. If there is too much slack in the cable, the vehicle speed drop will be great when climbing a slope. If there is no slack in the cable, idle speed will increase.
4. After adjusting accelerator cable B, ensure the throttle lever touches the idle switch.
5. Adjust accelerator cable A: by loosening the locknut, **Fig. 2.** Correct freeplay should measure 0.0-0.4 inch for manual transaxles and .08-.12 inch for automatic transaxles.

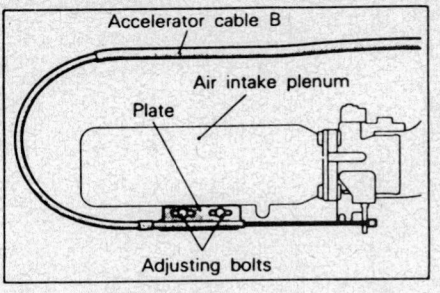

Fig. 1 Accelerator cable B adjustment. Laser & Talon

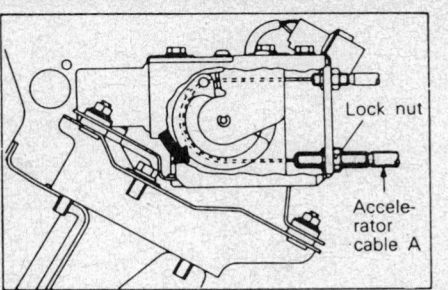

Fig. 2 Accelerator cable A adjustment. Laser & Talon

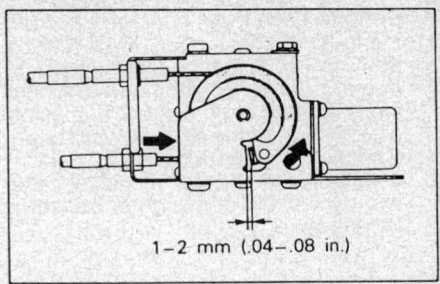

Fig. 3 Accelerator cable adjustment check. Laser & Talon

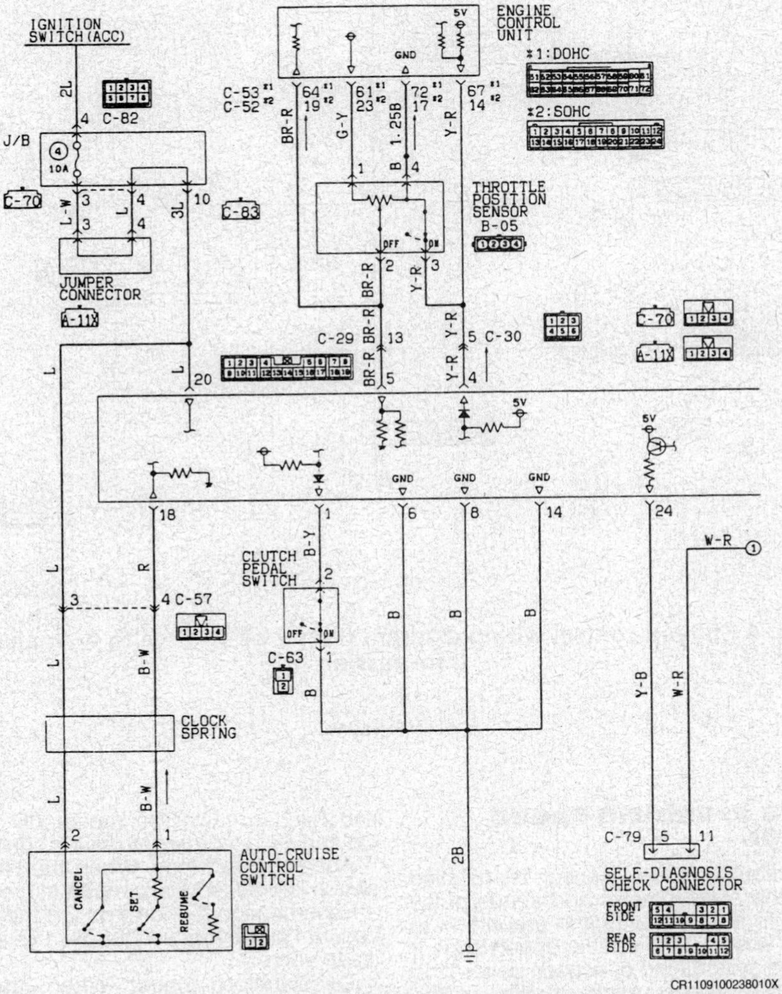

Fig. 4 Speed control wiring diagram (Part 1 of 3). Stealth w/manual transmission

6. After making cable adjustments, ensure the throttle lever at the engine side is caused to move .04-.08 inch when the actuator link is turned, as shown in **Fig. 3**.
7. Install actuator protector, then ensure throttle valve opens and closes fully by use of the accelerator pedal.

SYSTEM DIAGNOSIS & TESTING

Refer to **Figs. 4 through 11** for wiring circuits when diagnosing and testing the speed control system.

SELF DIAGNOSIS

Ensure (ECU) power supply is left on until checking is completed.

1. Connect a voltmeter between ground and auto-cruise control terminal of diagnosis harness connector, located on lower left side of instrument panel, **Fig. 12**.
2. There are up to six diagnosis codes, including one for normal condition. Check voltmeter readings with display patterns shown in **Figs. 13 and 14**, then refer to the appropriate circuit check chart indicated. On except Laser and Talon, refer to **Figs. 15 through 37** on Laser Talon, refer to text shown under "Circuit Tests." Diagnostic Trouble Code indicated by an asterisk can be caused by an intermittent condition. Check related connectors and wiring circuits.

SYMPTOM DIAGNOSIS

Refer to **Figs. 38 through 40** for symptom diagnosing the speed control system, then refer to the appropriate circuit check chart indicated. On except Laser and Talon, refer to **Figs. 15 through 37** on Laser and Talon, refer to text shown under "Circuit Tests."

INPUT TEST

Input test should be performed when the speed control system cannot be set, but necessary to check if the signals are normal when system malfunctions.

Laser, Stealth, Talon, Colt & Summit

1. Connect a voltmeter between ground and auto-cruise control terminal of diagnosis harness connector, located on lower left side of instrument panel, **Fig. 12**.
2. Turn ignition switch to On position and cruise control switch to Off position.
3. Turn Set switch On, turn Cruise switch On then within one second, turn Resume switch to On position.

4. Perform each input operation according to input check chart, **Figs. 41 and 42.** Each code will be displayed in order of priority, beginning with check No. 1. If there is no display, a possible malfunction of the ECU power supply. Check using circuit tests.

5. If output code is not displayed after two cycles, either switch or sensor is defective.

CIRCUIT TESTS

EXCEPT LASER & TALON

Refer to **Figs. 15 through 37,** for individual circuit tests.

LASER & TALON

Check 1, Control Unit Power Supply

When the ignition and main switches are in the On position current flows to the ignition switch, fuse 11 of the junction block, cruise control switch, control unit and to ground.

Check 2, Set Switch

When the ignition, cruise control and Set switches are in the On position, with the vehicle at the desired speed, vehicle speed should remain constant.

Constant speed can gradually be reduced when the Set switch is pressed and held while the vehicle is traveling at the previously set speed. The vehicle will coast to reduced speeds. When the desired speed is achieved, release the Set switch and the vehicle will remain at the new set speed.

Current flows to the control unit, cruise control Set switch and to ground.

Check 3, Resume Switch

The set speed prior to cancellation should resume when the resume switch is placed in the On position even if the constant speed control has been cancelled.

When the Resume switch is placed in the On position and held while the vehicle is traveling at the previously set constant speed, the vehicle speed will increase. When the switch is released, that speed will be the new set speed.

The set speed should not resume, even if the Resume switch remains in the On position, if the Main switch is turned off and vehicle speed falls below 25 mph.

Current flows to the control unit, Resume switch and to ground.

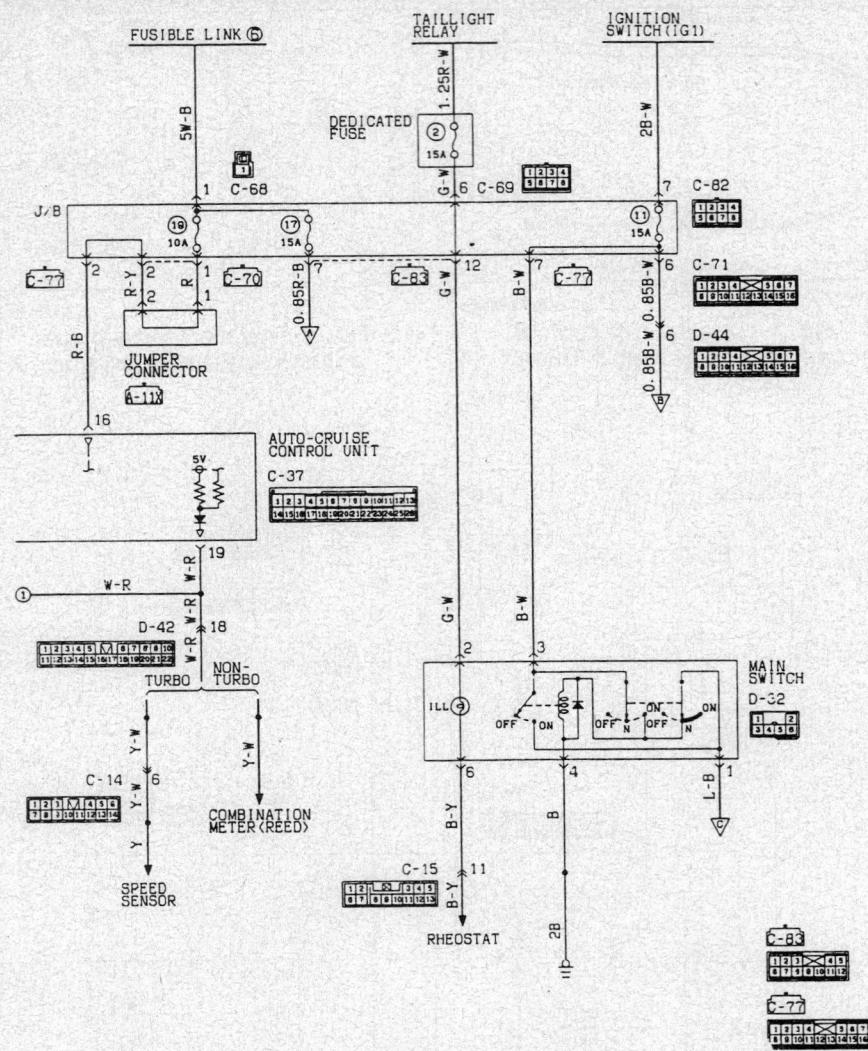

Fig. 4   Speed control wiring diagram (Part 2 of 3). Stealth w/manual transmission

Check 4, Vehicle Speed Sensor

The vehicle speed sensor is installed within the speedometer and sends pulse signals to the control unit in proportion to vehicle speed. The vehicle speed sensor is a reed switch type of sensor, generating four pulse signals each rotation of the speedometer driven gear.

Check 5, Cruise Control Vacuum Pump

Hold Mode. When the Set switch is On and the Cruise switch is On, when a determined speed is reached the control unit receives a set signal and turns the cruise vacuum pump motor On. After constant speed is reached the motor, control valve and release valve are repeatedly turned On and Off according to driving conditions.

Acceleration Mode. When the Resume switch is pressed, the control unit receives a Resume signal and turns On the cruise vacuum pump motor, control valve and release valve.

Deceleration Mode. When the Set switch in held depressed, the control unit receives a set signal and turns the cruise vacuum pump and control valve Off and turns the release valve On.

Release Mode. When the Set switch is turned Off, the control unit receives a cancel signal and turns Off the cruise vacuum pump motor, control valve and release valve.

Measure voltage at terminal No. 26 then at terminal No. 13, vacuum pump drive and control valve open/close. Voltage should measure 12 volts or 0 volts during the Hold mode, 0 volts during the Acceleration

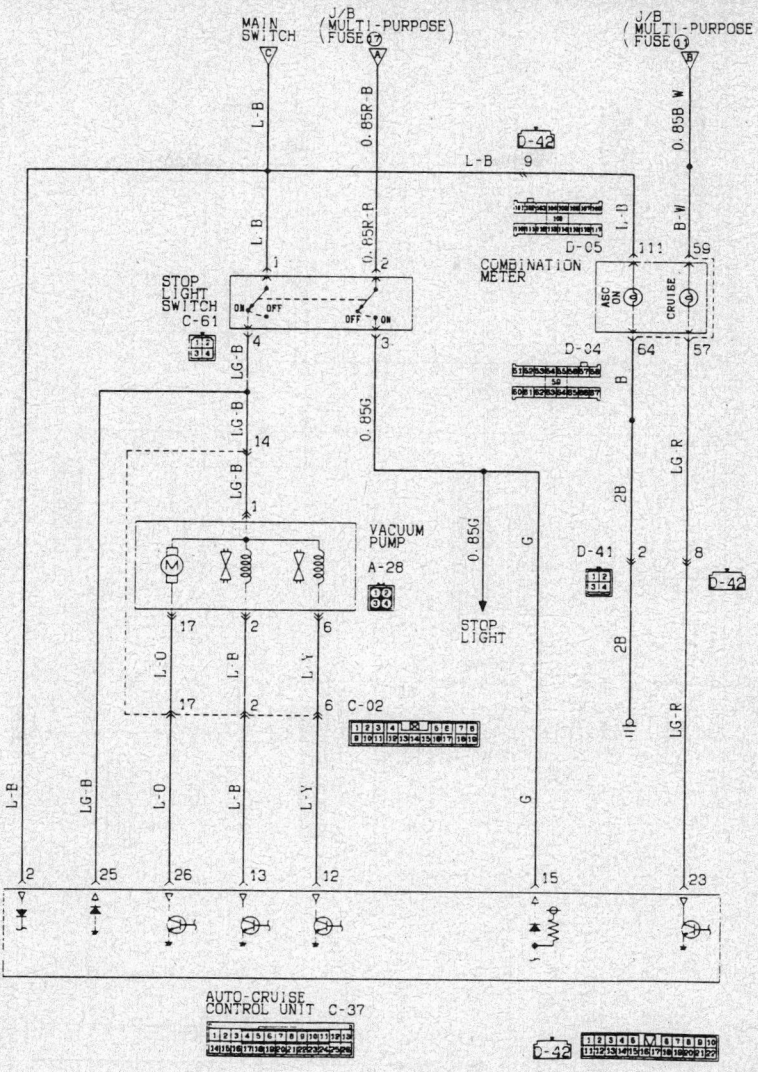

Fig. 4   Speed control wiring diagram (Part 3 of 3). Stealth w/manual transmission

CR1109100238030X

mode and 12 volts during both the Deceleration and Release modes.

Measure voltage at terminal No. 12 release valve open/close. Voltage should measure 12 volts or 0 volts during the Hold mode, 0 volts during both the Acceleration and Deceleration modes and 12 volts during the Release mode.

Check 6-1, Stop Light Switch

When the brake pedal is depressed during constant speed travel, the stop light switch contacts for the cruise control system open, creating an interruption in the signal to the actuator electromagnetic clutch, cancelling the constant speed travel.

The flow of current is from the battery to fuse No. 17 of the junction block, stop light switch, to the control unit.

Check 6-2, Inhibitor Switch

The inhibitor switch also functions as the switch for the starter. If the selector handle is moved to the N position during constant speed, a cancel signal is sent to the control unit, cancelling the constant speed travel.

Check 6-3, Clutch Circuit Switch

If the clutch pedal is depressed during constant speed travel, the contacts of the clutch switch close, sending a cancel signal to the control unit, cancelling the constant speed travel.

The flow of current is to the ignition switch, fuse No. 11 of the junction block, clutch switch, then the control unit.

Measure voltage at terminal No. 1, clutch switch. With the clutch pedal depressed, voltage should measure 12 volts. With the clutch pedal at rest, voltage should measure 0 volts.

Check 7, Accelerator Switch Off Function

The accelerator switch detects the operational status of the accelerator pedal.

During constant speed driving, the accelerator pedal is not operational. The ground circuit of the accelerator switch if off during constant speed driving, as to not interfere with the function of the automatic transaxle.

Check 8, Overdrive Cancellation Function

Overdrive is cancelled if the Resume switch is used, or if the vehicle speed drops 1 mph below the vehicle set speed. At this time, the signals to the control unit are cancelled. Drive will then be controlled in third gear.

Continued on page 14-54

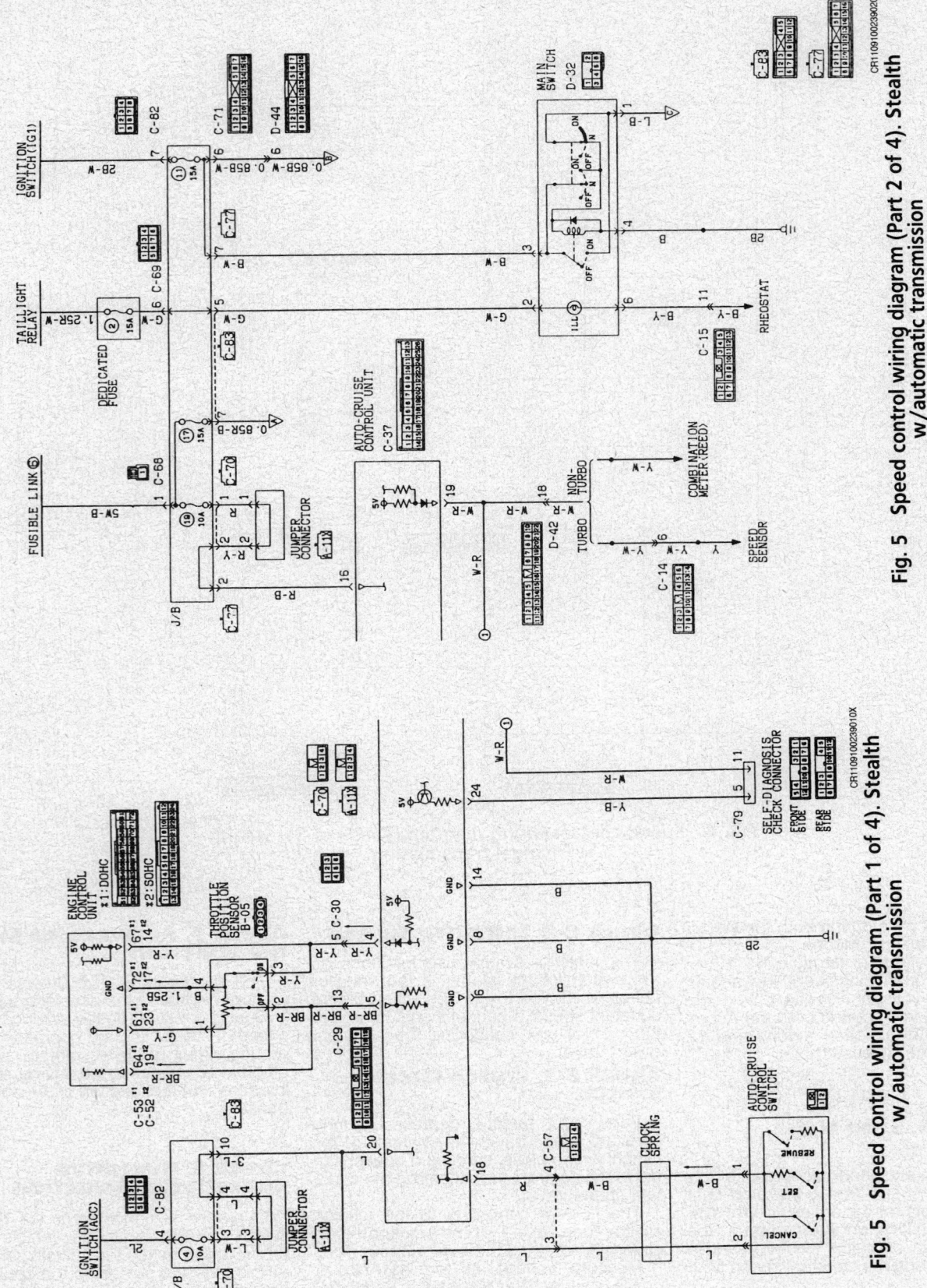

Fig. 5 Speed control wiring diagram (Part 2 of 4). Stealth w/automatic transmission

Fig. 5 Speed control wiring diagram (Part 1 of 4). Stealth w/automatic transmission

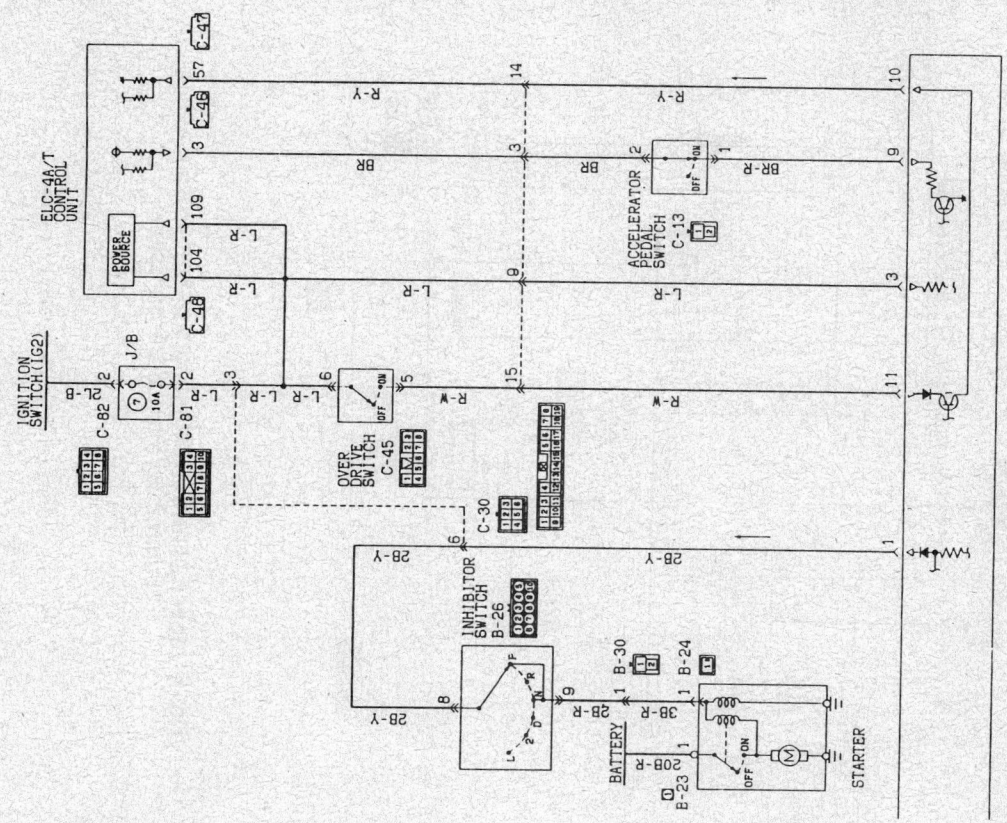

Fig. 5 Speed control wiring diagram (Part 4 of 4). Stealth w/automatic transmission

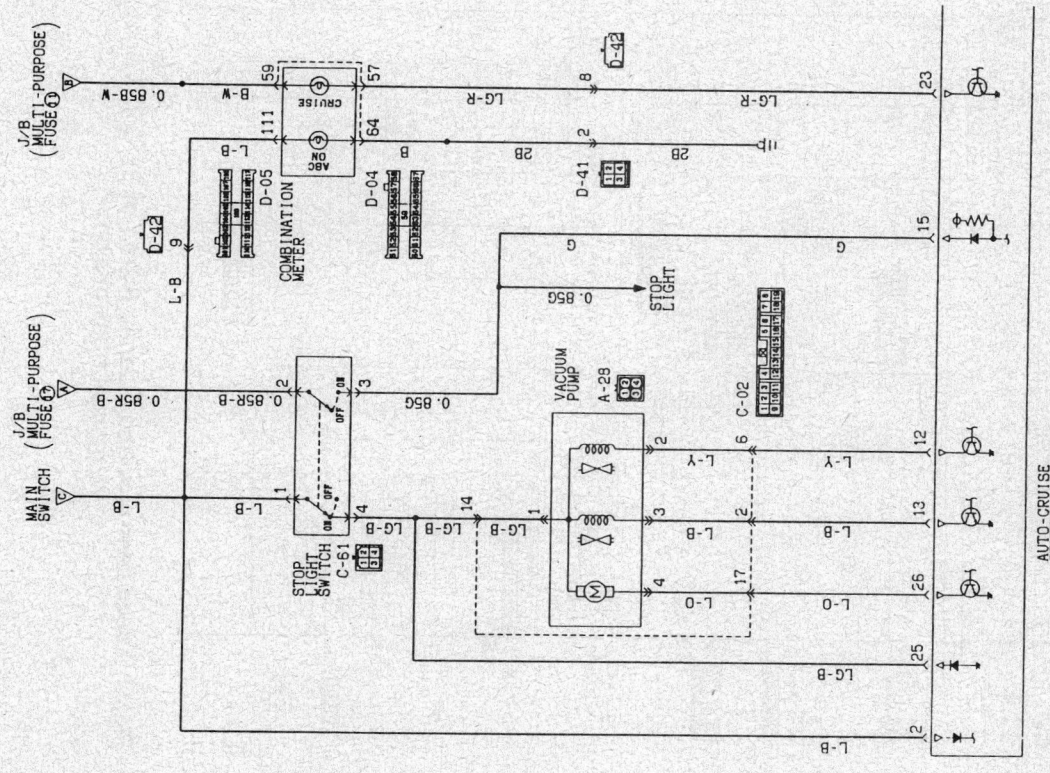

Fig. 5 Speed control wiring diagram (Part 3 of 4). Stealth w/automatic transmission

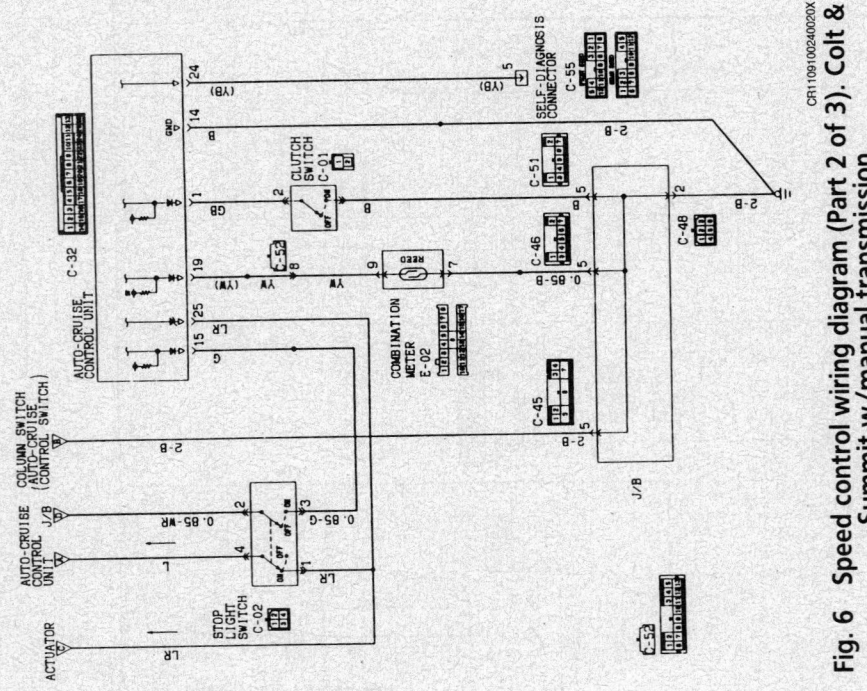

Fig. 6 Speed control wiring diagram (Part 2 of 3). Colt & Summit w/manual transmission

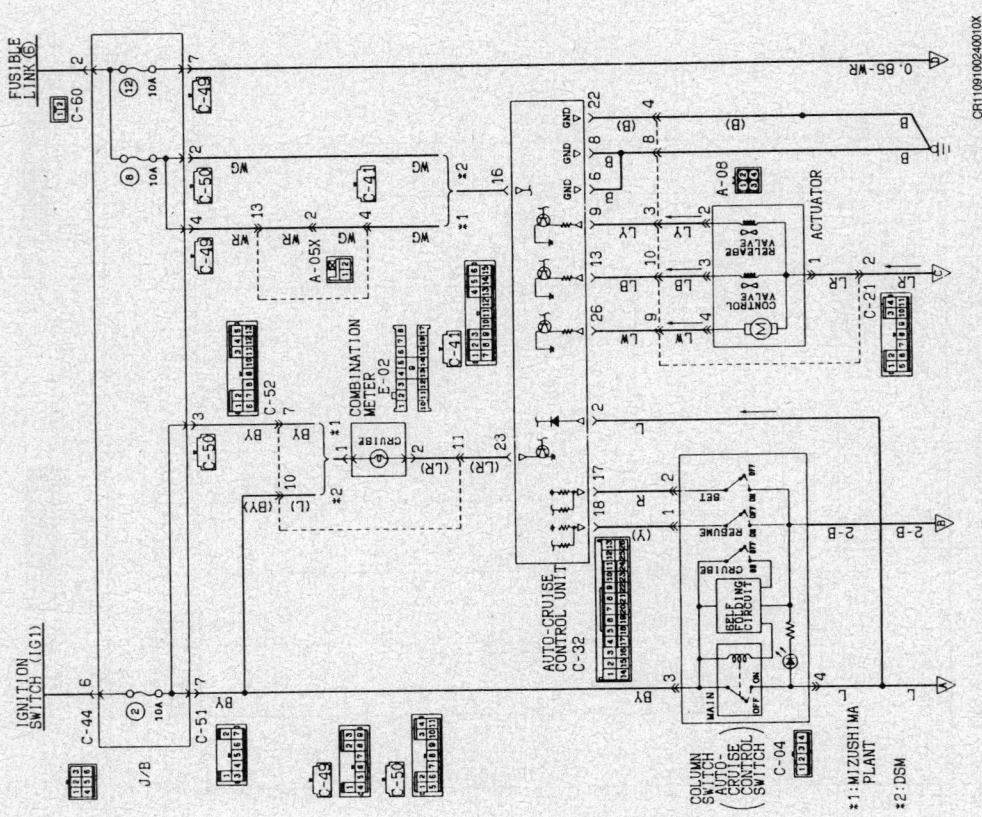

Fig. 6 Speed control wiring diagram (Part 1 of 3). Colt & Summit w/manual transmission

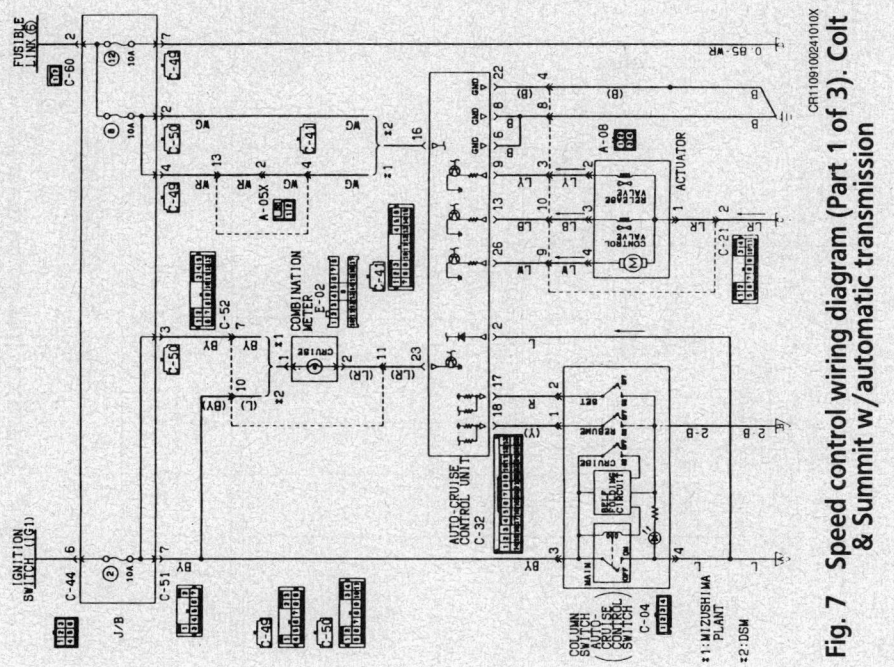

Fig. 7 Speed control wiring diagram (Part 1 of 3). Colt & Summit w/automatic transmission

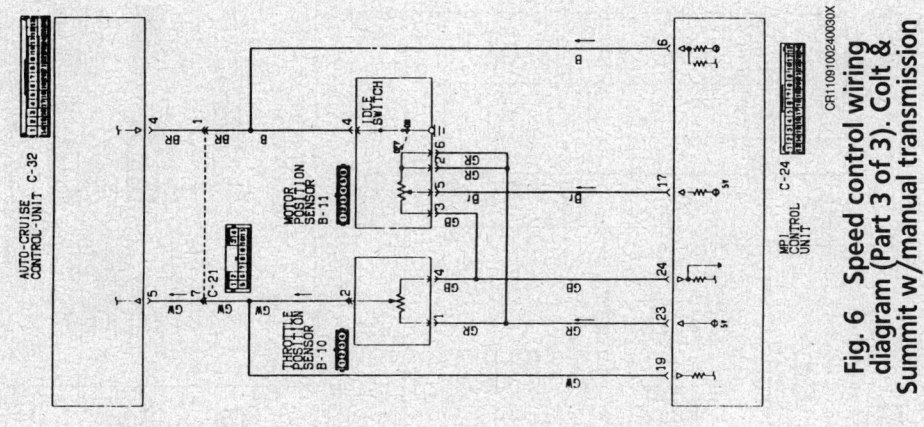

Fig. 6 Speed control wiring diagram (Part 3 of 3). Colt & Summit w/manual transmission

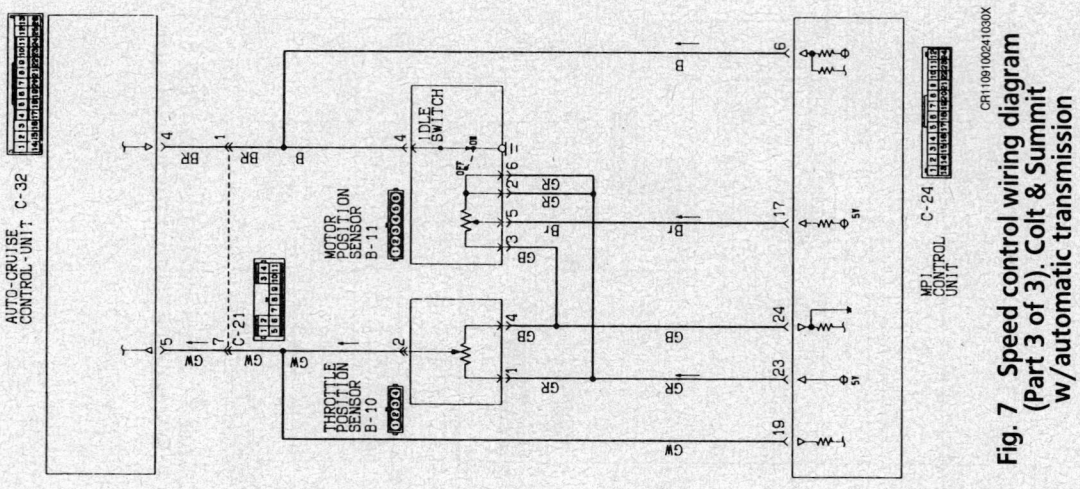

Fig. 7 Speed control wiring diagram (Part 3 of 3). Colt & Summit w/automatic transmission

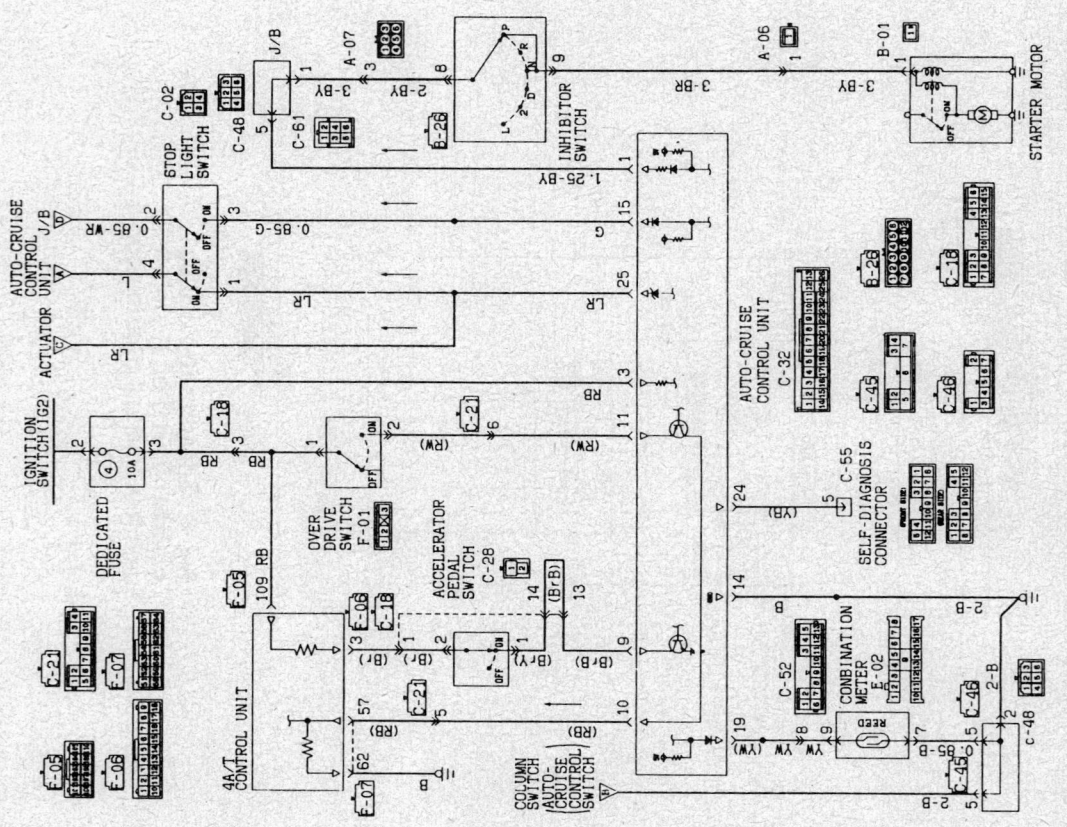

Fig. 7 Speed control wiring diagram (Part 2 of 3). Colt & Summit w/automatic transmission

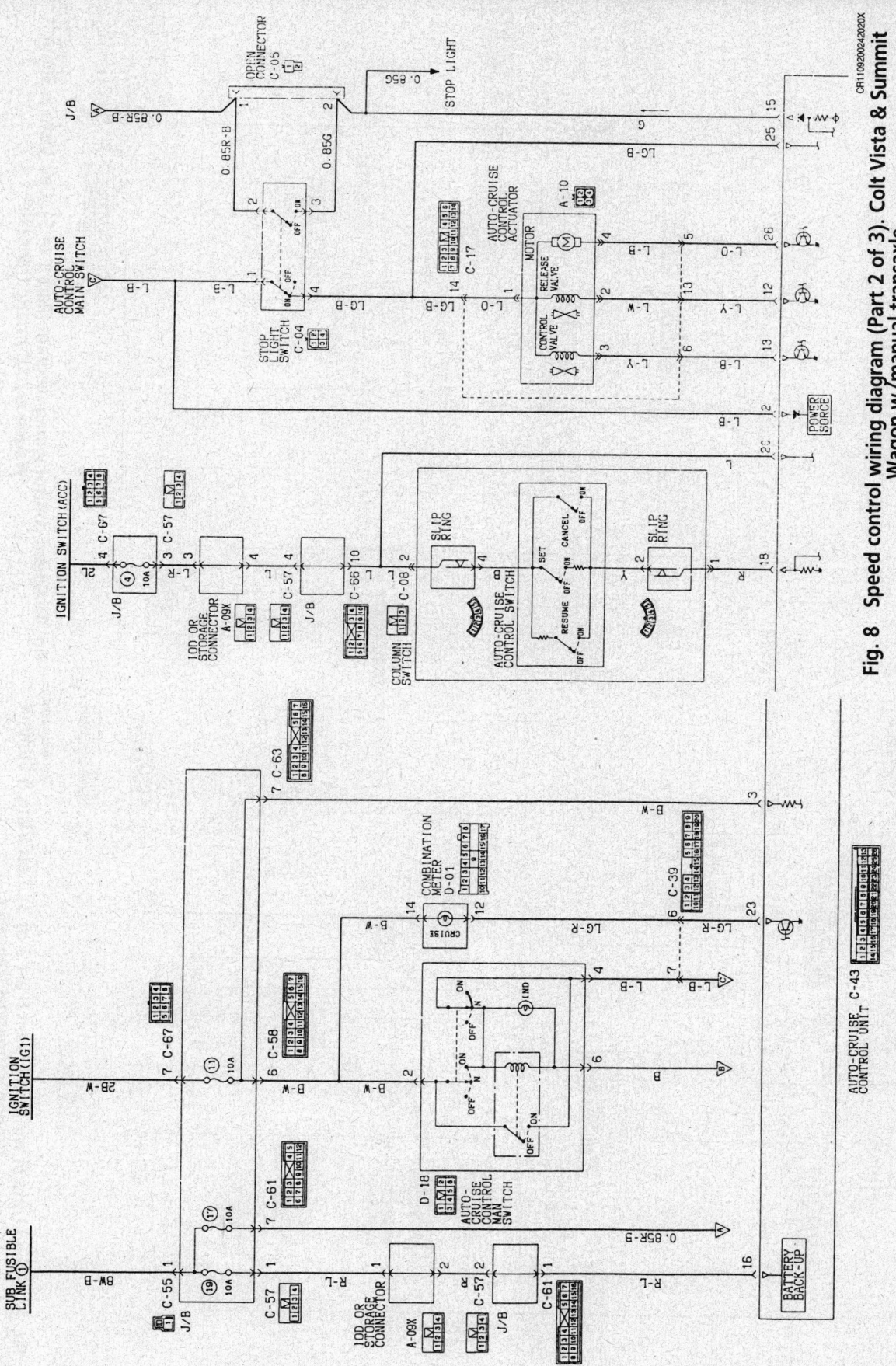

Fig. 8 Speed control wiring diagram (Part 2 of 3). Colt Vista & Summit Wagon w/manual transaxle

Fig. 8 Speed control wiring diagram (Part 1 of 3). Colt Vista & Summit Wagon w/manual transaxle

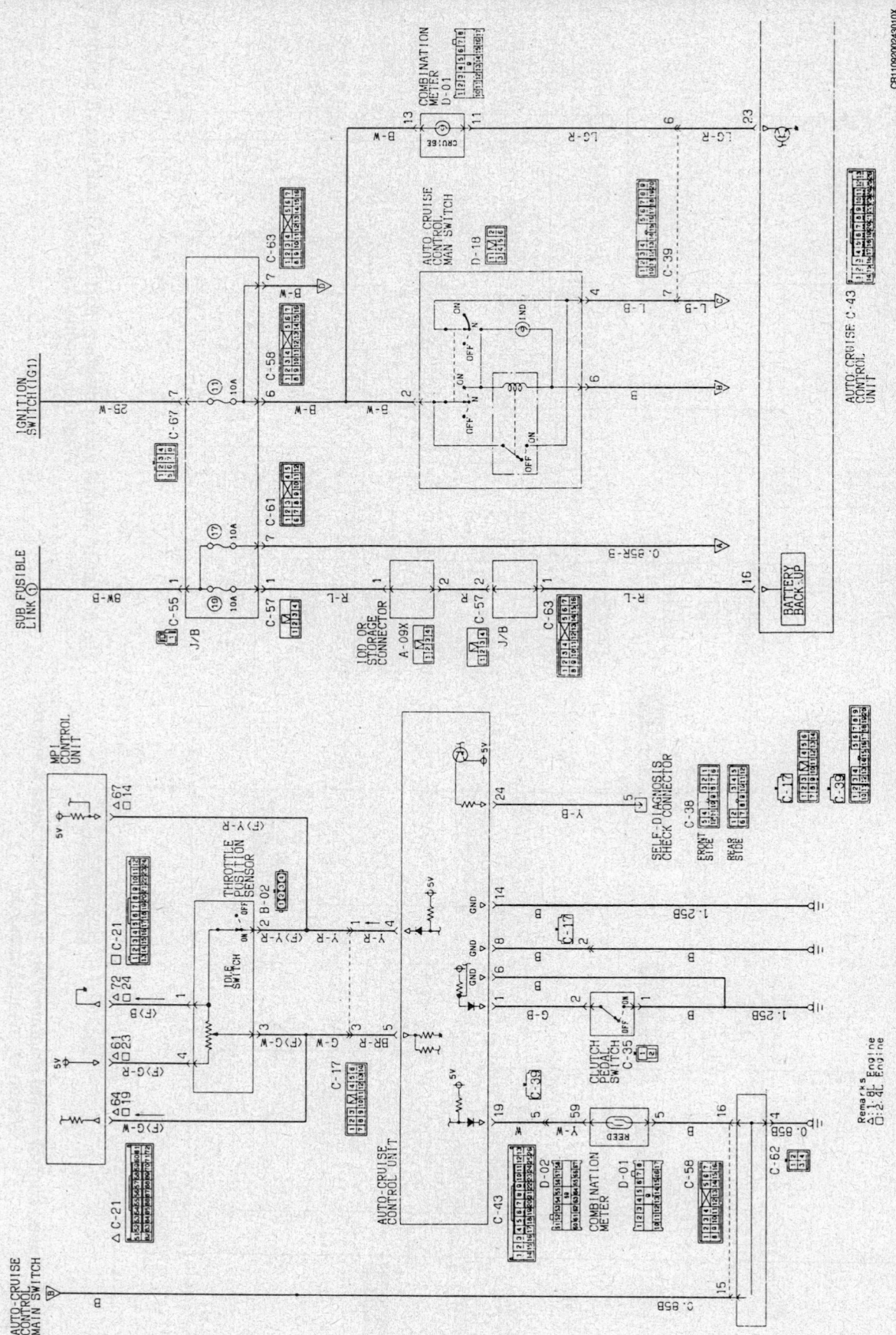

Fig. 9 Speed control wiring diagram (Part 1 of 5). Colt Vista & Summit Wagon w/automatic transaxle

Fig. 8 Speed control wiring diagram (Part 3 of 3). Colt Vista & Summit Wagon w/manual transaxle

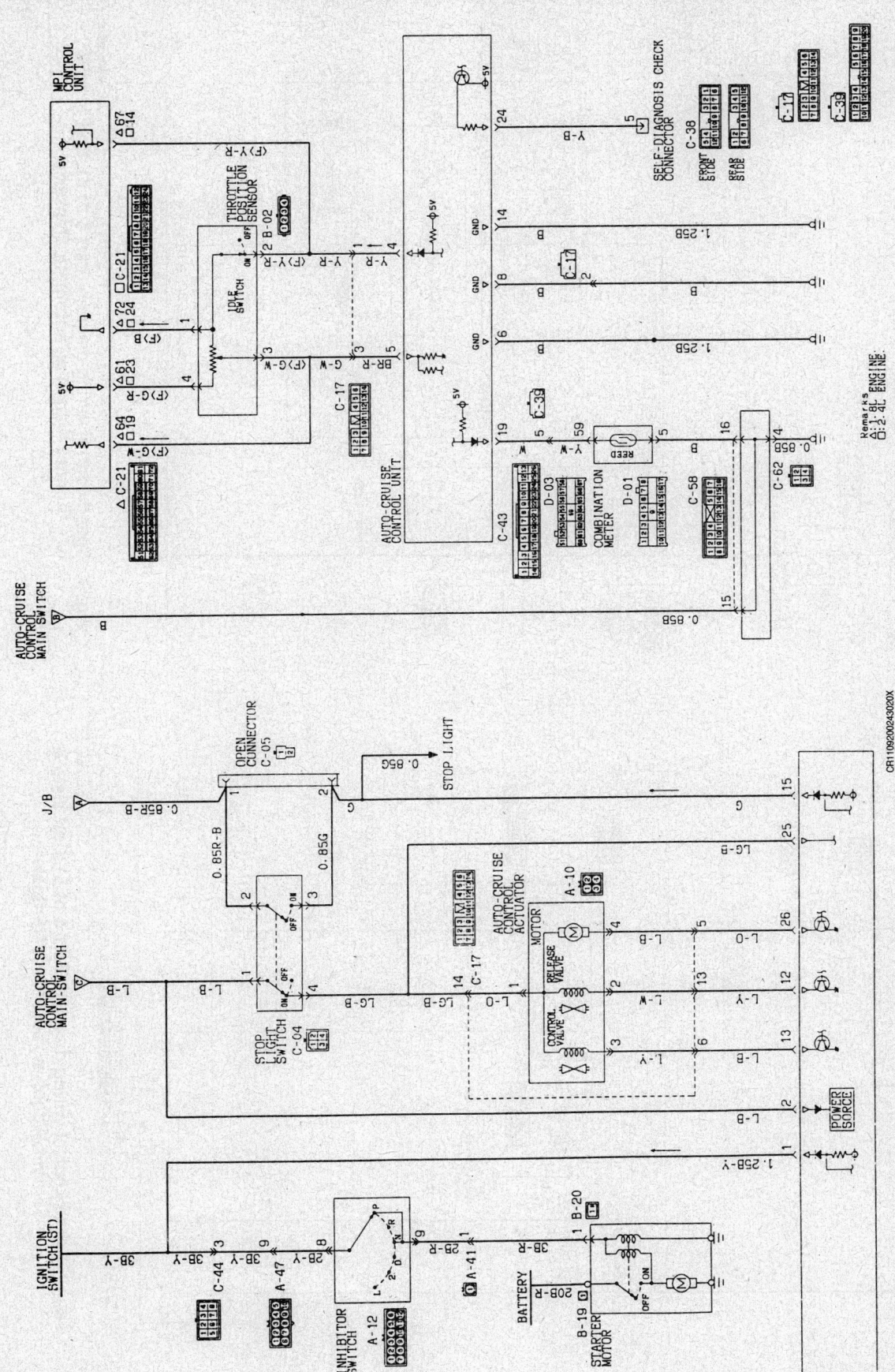

Fig. 9   Speed control wiring diagram (Part 3 of 5). Colt Vista &
Summit Wagon w/automatic transaxle

Fig. 9   Speed control wiring diagram (Part 2 of 5). Colt Vista & Summit
Wagon w/automatic transaxle

TYPE 2

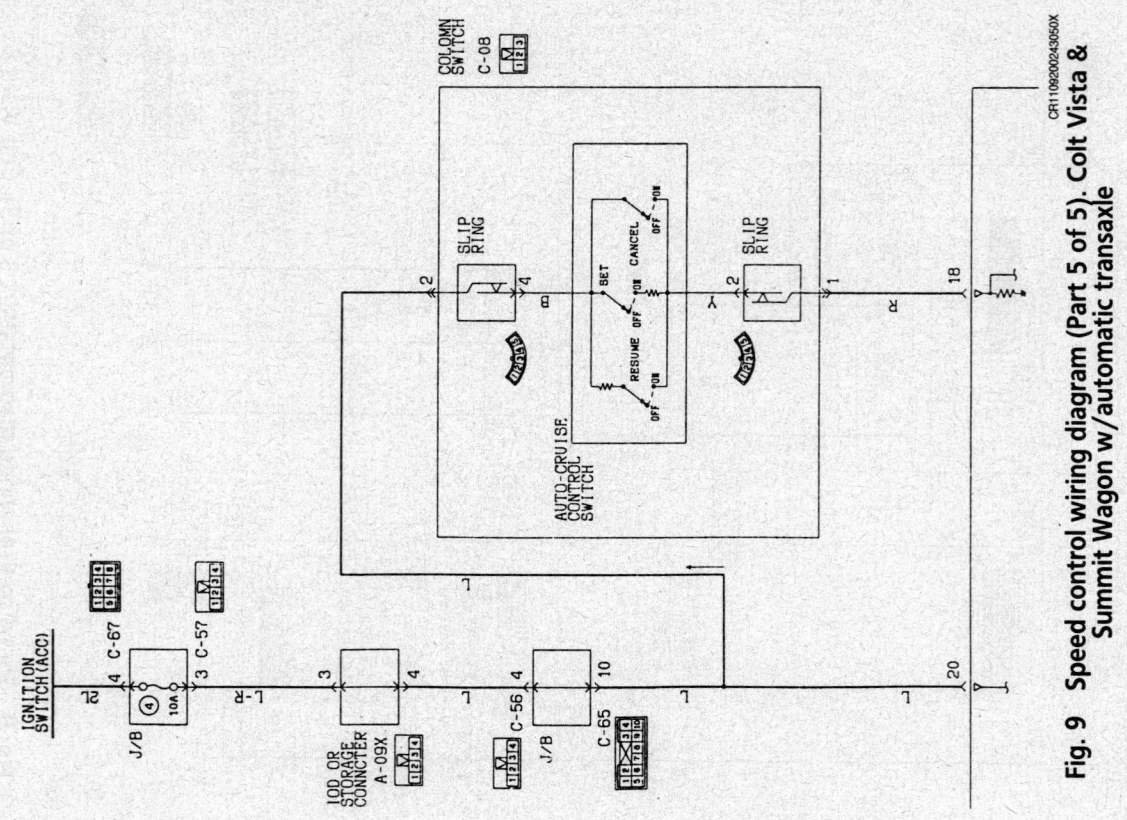

Fig. 9 Speed control wiring diagram (Part 5 of 5). Colt Vista & Summit Wagon w/automatic transaxle

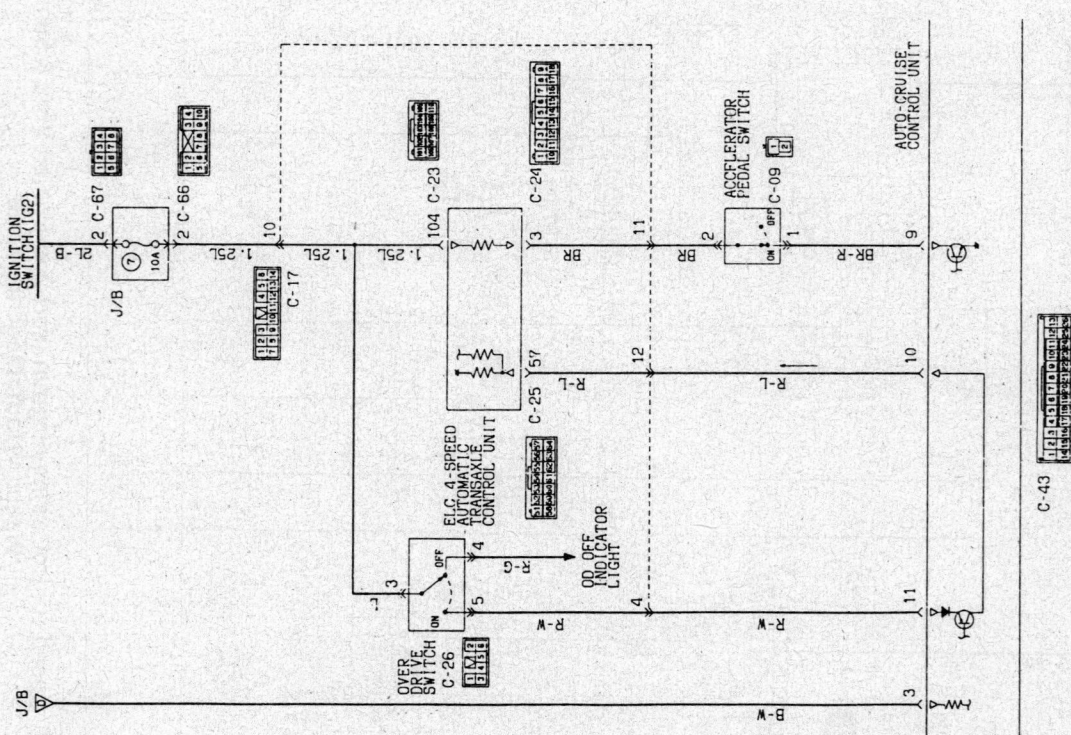

Fig. 9 Speed control wiring diagram (Part 4 of 5). Colt Vista & Summit Wagon w/automatic transaxle

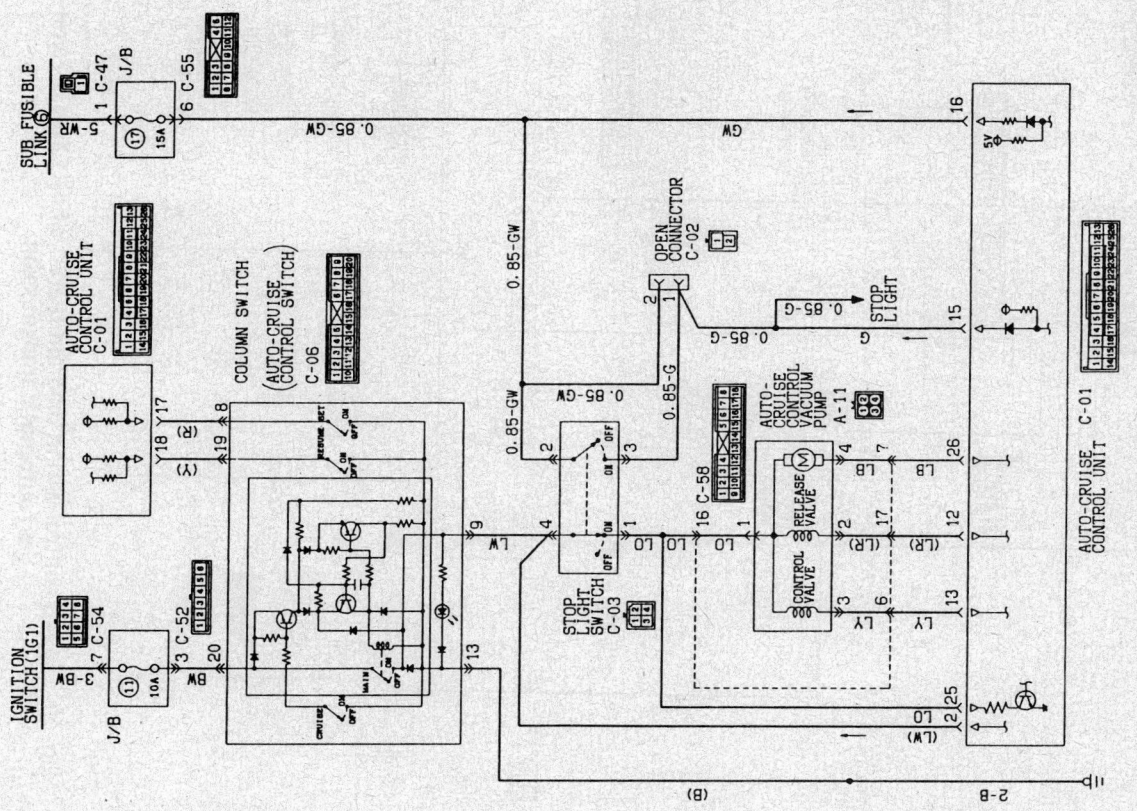

Fig. 10 Speed control wiring diagram (Part 2 of 3). Laser & Talon w/manual transmission

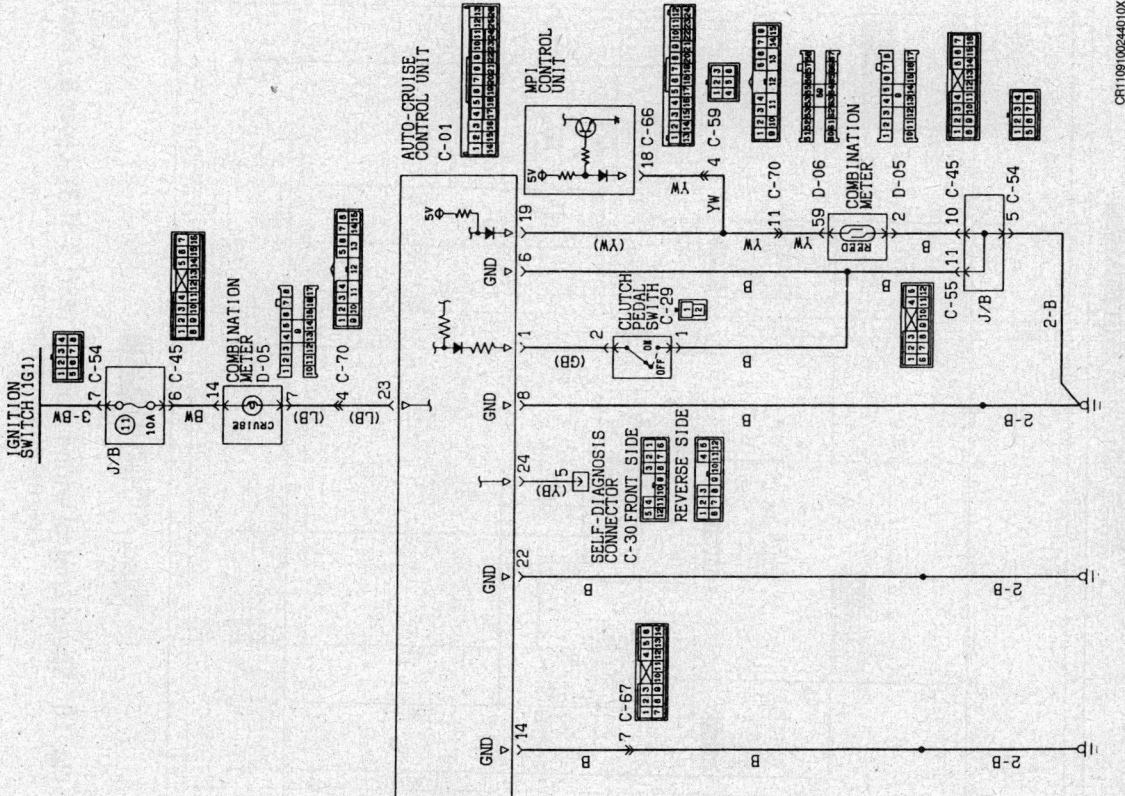

Fig. 10 Speed control wiring diagram (Part 1 of 3). Laser & Talon w/manual transmission

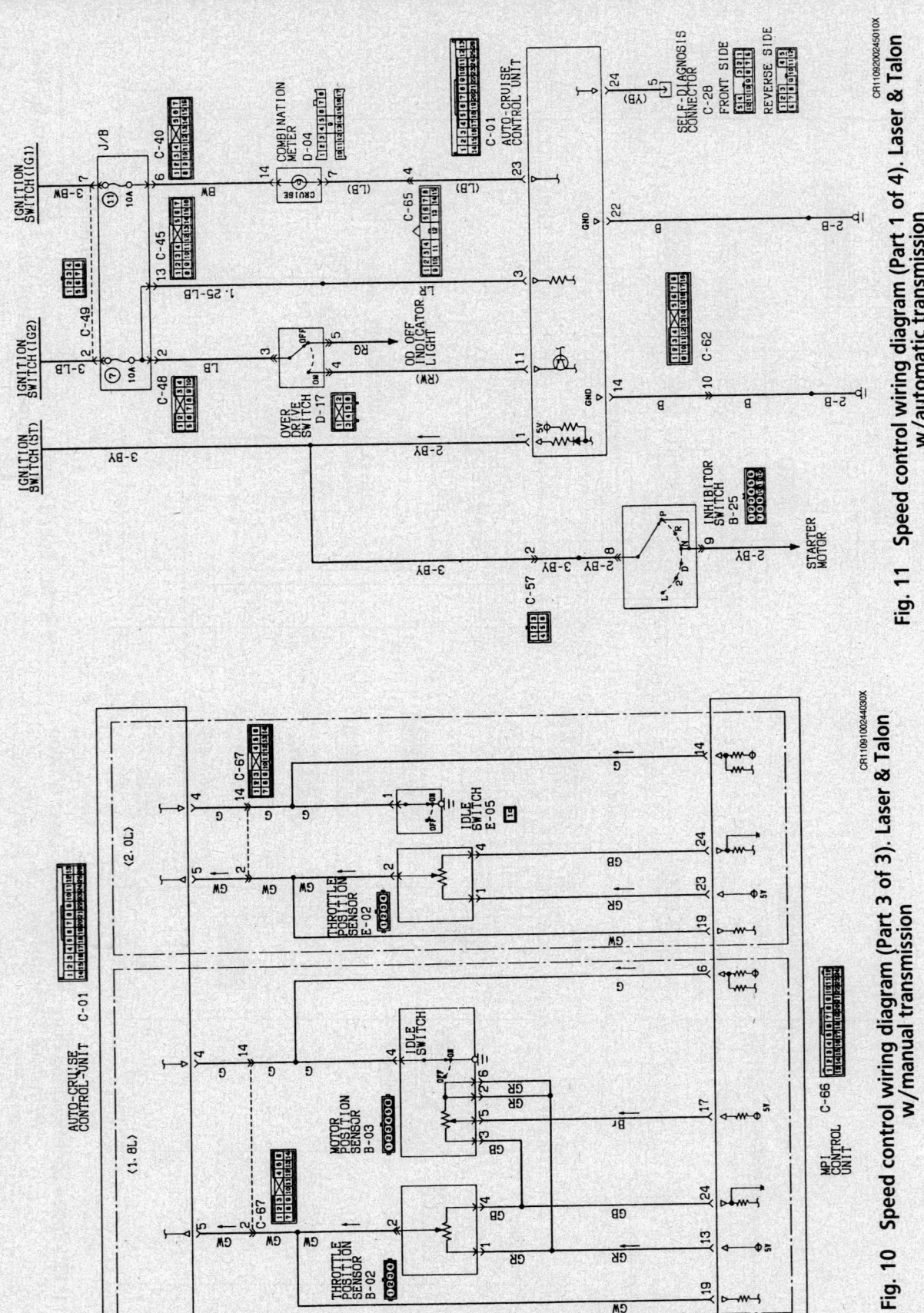

Fig. 11 Speed control wiring diagram (Part 1 of 4). Laser & Talon w/automatic transmission

Fig. 10 Speed control wiring diagram (Part 3 of 3). Laser & Talon w/manual transmission

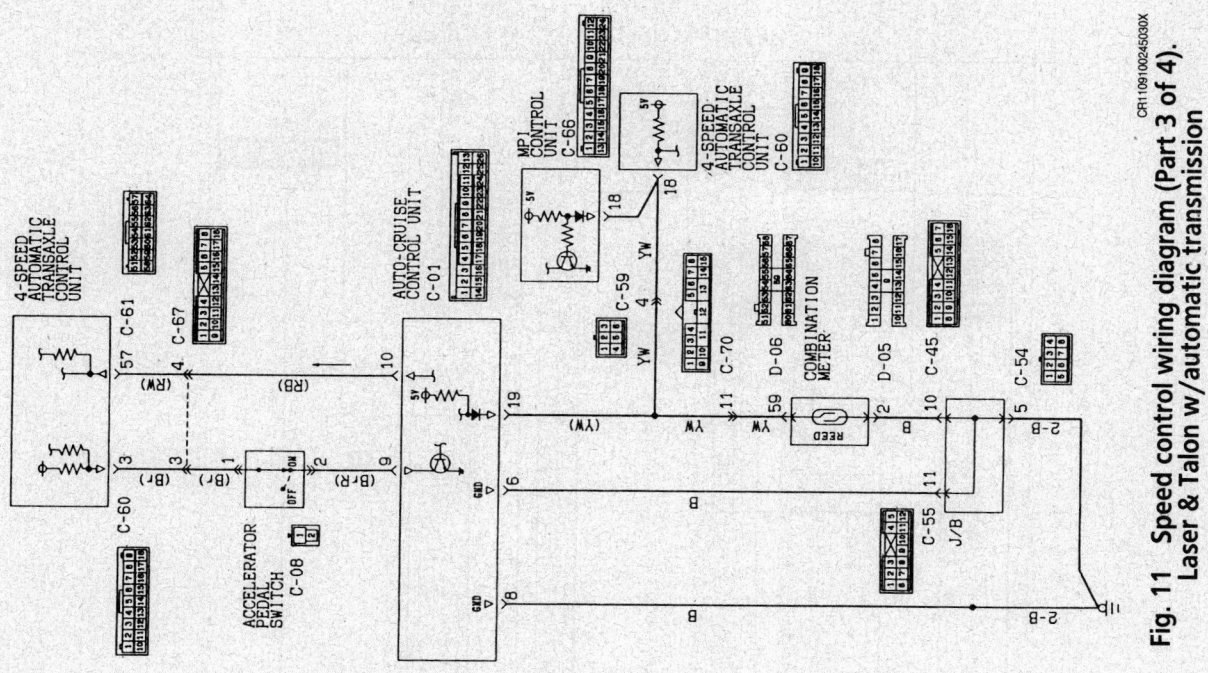

Fig. 11   Speed control wiring diagram (Part 3 of 4). Laser & Talon w/automatic transmission

Fig. 11   Speed control wiring diagram (Part 2 of 4). Laser & Talon w/automatic transmission

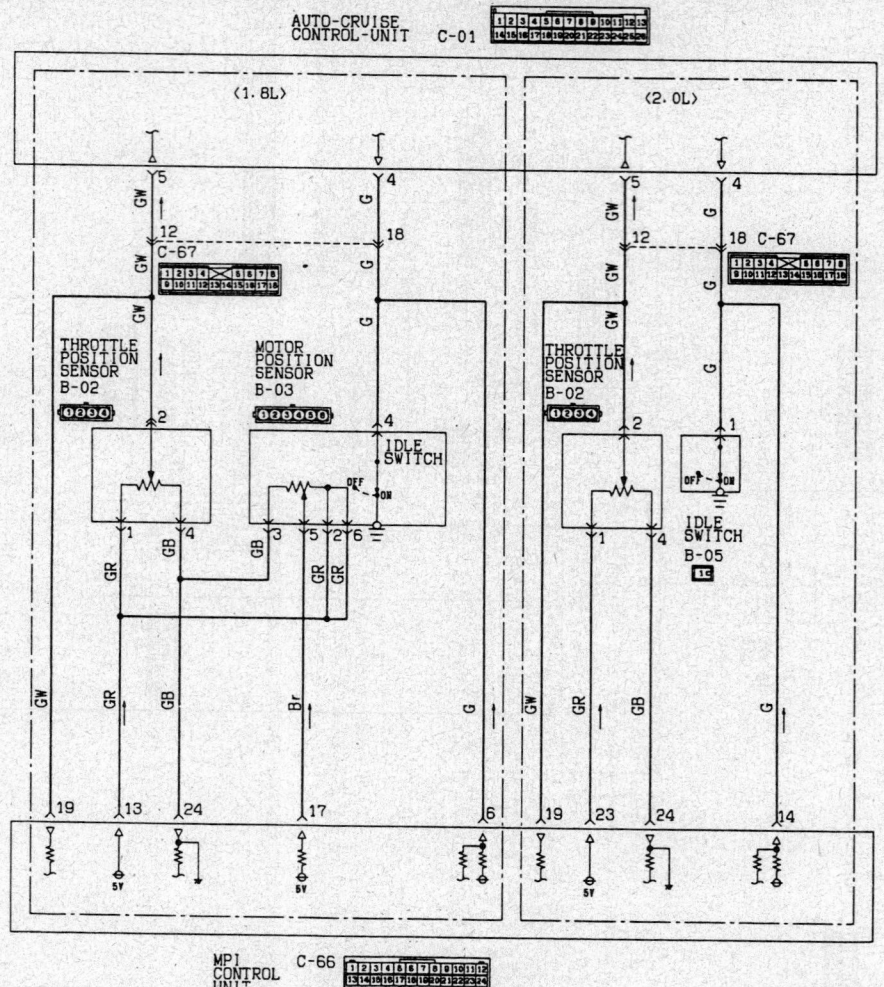

Fig. 11 Speed control wiring diagram (Part 4 of 4). Laser & Talon w/automatic transmission

CR1109100245040X

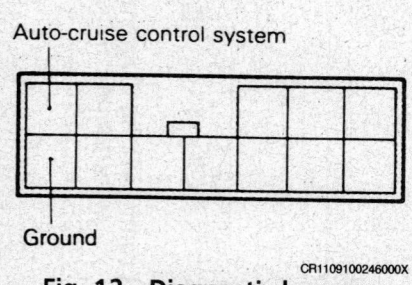

Auto-cruise control system

Ground

CR1109100246000X

Fig. 12 Diagnostic harness connector

Code No.	Display patterns (output codes)	Probable cause	Check chart No.
11		Abnormal condition of actuator clutch coil drive system	4
12		Abnormal condition of vehicle-speed signal system	3
13*		Low-speed limiter activation (The system is normal if it can be reset.)	—
14*		Automatic cancelation activated by vehicle speed reduction. (The system is normal if it can be reset.)	—
15*		Control switch malfunction (when SET and RESUME switches switched ON simultaneously)	1 2
16*		Cancel switch ON signal input (including stop light switch input wiring damage or disconnection)	5-1 5-2 5-3

CR1109100247000X

Fig. 13 Diagnosis display patterns. Colt, Summit & Laser & Talon

Code No.	Display patterns (output codes) (Use with voltmeter)	Probable cause	Check chart No.
11	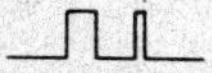 _(waveform)_ The same pattern repeatedly displayed	Vacuum pump assembly drive output system out of order	5
12	 _(waveform)_	Vehicle speed signal system out of order	4
15	 _(waveform)_	Control switch out of order (When SET or RESUME switch is kept in ON state continuously for more than 60 seconds)	2
16	 _(waveform)_	Control unit out of order	—
17*	 _(waveform)_	Throttle position sensor or idle switch out of order	9

CR1109100248000X

Fig. 14 Diagnosis display patterns. Colt Vista, Stealth & Summit Wagon

DIAGNOSTIC CHART INDEX

Test	Description	Page No.	Fig. No.
Colt & Summit			
—	Symptom Diagnosis Chart	14-48	38
1	Control Unit Power Supply Circuit	14-44	15
2	Set Switch Wiring Circuit	14-44	16
3	Resume Switch Wiring Circuit	14-44	17
4	Indicator Light Wiring Circuit	14-44	18
5	Vehicle Speed Sensor Wiring Circuit	14-44	19
6	Vacuum Pump Drive Wiring Circuit	14-45	20
7	Stop Light Switch Wiring Circuit	14-45	21
8	Clutch Switch Wiring Circuit M/T	14-45	22
9	Inhibitor Switch Wiring Circuit A/T	14-45	23
10	Throttle Position Sensor & Idle Switch Wiring Circuit	14-45	24
11	Accelerator Switch Off Function Related Circuits	14-46	25
12	Overdrive Cancellation Function Related Circuits	14-46	26
Laser & Talon			
—	Symptom Diagnosis Chart	14-51	40
1	Control Unit Power Supply	14-28	—
2	Set Switch	14-28	—
3	Resume Switch	14-28	—
4	Vehicle Speed Sensor	14-28	—
5	Cruise Control Vacuum Pump	14-28	—
6-1	Stop Light Switch	14-29	—
6-2	Inhibitor Switch	14-29	—
6-3	Clutch Circuit Switch	14-29	—
7	Accelerator Switch Off Function	14-29	—
8	Overdrive Cancellation Function	14-29	—
Stealth			
—	Symptom Diagnosis Chart	14-49	39
1	Control Unit Power Supply Circuit	14-46	27
2	Control Switch Wiring Circuit	14-46	28
3	Indicator Light Wiring Circuit	14-46	29
4	Vehicle Speed Sensor Wiring Circuit	14-46	30
5	Vacuum Pump Drive Wiring Circuit	14-47	31
6	Stop Light Switch Wiring Circuit	14-47	32
7	Clutch Switch Wiring Circuit M/T	14-47	33
8	Inhibitor Switch Wiring Circuit A/T	14-47	34
9	Throttle Position Sensor & Idle Switch Wiring Circuit	14-47	35
10	Accelerator Switch Off Function Related Circuits	14-48	36
11	Overdrive Cancellation Function Related Circuits	14-48	37

Continued

DIAGNOSTIC CHART INDEX–Continued

Test	Description	Page No.	Fig. No.
Colt Vista & Summit Wagon			
—	Symptom Diagnosis Chart	14-49	39
1	Control Unit Power Supply Circuit	14-46	27
2	Control Switch Wiring Circuit	14-46	28
3	Indicator Light Wiring Circuit	14-46	29
4	Vehicle Speed Sensor Wiring Circuit	14-46	30
5	Vacuum Pump Drive Wiring Circuit	14-47	31
6	Stop Light Switch Wiring Circuit	14-47	32
7	Clutch Switch Wiring Circuit M/T	14-47	33
8	Inhibitor Switch Wiring Circuit A/T	14-47	34
9	Throttle Position Sensor & Idle Switch Wiring Circuit	14-47	35
10	Accelerator Switch Off Function Related Circuits	14-48	36
11	Overdrive Cancellation Function Related Circuits	14-48	37

Terminal No.	Signal	Conditions	Terminal voltage
2	Control unit power supply	When the auto-cruise control switch (CRUISE) is switched ON	System voltage
8, 14	Control unit ground	At all times	0V
16	Control unit backup power supply	At all times	System voltage

CR1109100249000X

Fig. 15 Test No. 1: Control Unit Power Supply Circuit. Colt & Summit

Terminal No.	Signal	Conditions	Terminal voltage
17	SET switch	When the SET switch is switched ON	0V
		When the SET switch is switched OFF	System voltage

CR1109100250000X

Fig. 16 Test No. 2: Set Switch Wiring Circuit. Colt & Summit

Terminal No.	Signal	Conditions	Terminal voltage
18	RESUME switch	When the RESUME switch is switched ON	0V
		When the RESUME switch is switched OFF	System voltage

CR1109100251000X

Fig. 17 Test No. 3: Resume Switch Wiring Circuit. Colt & Summit

Terminal No.	Signal	Conditions	Terminal voltage
23	Auto-cruise control (CRUISE) indicator light	When auto-cruise control is active	System voltage
		When auto-cruise control is inactive	0V

CR1109100252000X

Fig. 18 Test No. 4: Indicator Light Wiring Circuit. Colt & Summit

Terminal No.	Signal	Conditions	Terminal voltage
19	Vehicle speed sensor	Move the vehicle forward slowly.	0V – 0.6V ↕ Flashing 2V or higher

CR1109100253000X

Fig. 19 Test No. 5: Vehicle Speed Sensor Wiring Circuit. Colt & Summit

Terminal No.	Signal	Conditions	Terminal voltage
9	Release valve drive signal	When release valve is ON	0V
		When release valve is OFF	System voltage
13	Control valve drive signal	When control valve is ON	0V
		When control valve is OFF	System voltage
26	DC motor drive signal	When DC motor is driven	0V
		When DC motor is stopped	System voltage
25	Surge absorption circuit terminal	When control switch is ON	System voltage

CR1109100254000X

Fig. 20   Test No. 6: Vacuum Pump Drive Wiring Circuit. Colt & Summit

Terminal No.	Signal	Conditions	Terminal voltage
15	Stop light switch	When brake pedal is depressed	System voltage
		When brake pedal is not depressed	0V

NOTE
(1)   NC: Indicates ON at all times.
(2)   NO: Indicates OFF at all times.

CR1109100255000X

Fig. 21   Test No. 7: Stop Light Switch Wiring Circuit. Colt & Summit

Terminal No.	Signal	Conditions	Terminal voltage
1	Clutch switch	When clutch pedal is depressed	0V
		When clutch pedal is not depressed	System voltage

CR1109100256000X

Fig. 22   Test No. 8: Clutch Switch Wiring Circuit M/T. Colt & Summit

Terminal No.	Signal	Conditions	Terminal voltage
1	Inhibitor switch	Inhibitor switch is at "N" or "P" position	0V
		Inhibitor switch is at "D", "2", "L" or "R" position	System voltage

CR1109100257000X

Fig. 23   Test No. 9: Inhibitor Switch Wiring Circuit A/T. Colt & Summit

Terminal No.	Signal	Conditions	Terminal voltage
4	Idle switch	When accelerator pedal is depressed	System voltage
		When accelerator pedal is not depressed	0V
5	Throttle position sensor	When accelerator is in idling position	0.45 to 0.55V
		When accelerator is in fully opened position	4.5 to 5.5V

CR1109100258000X

Fig. 24   Test No. 10: Throttle Position Sensor & Idle Switch Wiring Circuit. Colt & Summit

Terminal No.	Signal	Conditions	Terminal voltage
3	Accelerator pedal switch control power supply	When ignition switch is switched ON	System voltage
9	Accelerator pedal switch	When accelerator pedal is depressed	0V
		When accelerator pedal is not depressed	System voltage

CR1109100259000X

Fig. 25   Test No. 11: Accelerator Switch Off Function Related Circuits. Colt & Summit

Terminal No.	Signal	Conditions	Terminal voltage
3	Overdrive signal control power supply	When ignition switch is switched ON	System voltage
10	4 A/T control unit	When overdrive is ON	System voltage
		When overdrive is OFF	0V
11	Overdrive switch	When overdrive switch is ON	System voltage
		When overdrive switch is OFF	0V

CR1109100260000X

Fig. 26   Test No. 12: Overdrive Cancellation Function Related Circuits. Colt & Summit

Terminal No.	Signal name	Condition	Terminal voltage
2	Control unit power supply	Main switch ON and neutral position thereafter	System voltage
		Main switch OFF and neutral position thereafter	0V
8, 14	Control unit ground	At all times	0V
16	Control unit back up power supply	At all times	System voltage

CR1109100261000X

Fig. 27   Test No. 1: Control Unit Power Supply Circuit. Stealth & Colt Vista/Summit Wagon

Terminal No.	Signal name	Condition	Terminal voltage
18	Control switch	When all switches are OFF	0V
		When SET switch is ON	3V
		When RESUME switch is ON	6V
		When CANCEL switch is ON	System voltage

CR1109100262000X

Fig. 28   Test No. 2: Control Switch Wiring Circuit. Stealth & Colt Vista/Summit Wagon

Terminal No.	Signal name	Condition	Terminal voltage
23	Cruise control (CRUISE) indicator light	When cruise control is active	System voltage
		When cruise control is inactive	0V

CR1109100263000X

Fig. 29   Test No. 3: Indicator Light Wiring Circuit. Stealth & Colt Vista/Summit Wagon

Terminal No.	Signal name	Condition	Terminal voltage
19	Vehicle speed sensor	Slowly drive forward with SELECT lever at "D" or "1st Speed"	0 to 0.6V ↕ Flashing 2V or more

CR1109100264000X

Fig. 30   Test No. 4: Vehicle Speed Sensor Wiring Circuit. Stealth & Colt Vista/Summit Wagon

Terminal No.	Signal name	Condition	Terminal voltage
12	Relief valve drive signal	When relief valve is ON	0V
		When relief valve is OFF	System voltage
13	Control valve drive signal	When control valve is ON	0V
		When control valve is OFF	System voltage
26	DC motor drive signal	When DC motor is running	0V
		When DC motor is stationary	System voltage
25	Surge absorption circuit terminal	When main switch is ON	System voltage

CR1109100265000X

Fig. 31   Test No. 5: Vacuum Pump Drive Wiring Circuit. Stealth & Colt Vista/Summit Wagon

Terminal No.	Signal name	Condition	Terminal voltage
15	Stop light switch	When brake pedal is depressed	System voltage
		When brake pedal is not depressed	0V

CR1109100266000X

Fig. 32   Test No. 6: Stop Light Switch Wiring Circuit. Stealth & Colt Vista/Summit Wagon

Terminal No.	Signal name	Condition	Terminal voltage
1	Clutch switch	When clutch pedal is depressed	0V
		When clutch pedal is not depressed	System voltage

CR1109100267000X

Fig. 33   Test No. 7: Clutch Switch Wiring Circuit M/T. Stealth & Colt Vista/Summit Wagon

Terminal No.	Signal name	Condition	Terminal voltage
1	Inhibitor switch	Inhibitor switch in "N" or "P" position	0V
		Inhibitor switch in "D", "2", "L" or "R" position	System voltage

CR1109100268000X

Fig. 34   Test No. 8: Inhibitor Switch Wiring Circuit A/T. Stealth & Colt Vista/Summit Wagon

Terminal No.	Signal name	Condition	Terminal voltage
4	Idle switch	When accelerator pedal is depressed	0V
		When accelerator pedal is not depressed	4.5 – 5.5V
5	Throttle position sensor	During idle	0.48 – 0.72V
		When fully opened	4.0 – 5.5V

CR1109100269000X

Fig. 35   Test No. 9: Throttle Position Sensor & Idle Switch Wiring Circuit. Stealth & Colt Vista/Summit Wagon

Terminal No.	Signal name	Condition	Terminal voltage
3	Accelerator pedal switch control power supply	When ignition switch is placed at ON	System voltage
9	Accelerator pedal switch	When accelerator pedal is depressed	0V
		When accelerator pedal is not depressed	System voltage

CR1109100270000X

Fig. 36   Test No. 10: Accelerator Switch Off Function Related Circuits. Stealth & Colt Vista/Summit Wagon

Terminal No.	Signal name	Condition	Terminal voltage
3	OD signal control power supply	When ignition switch is ON	System voltage
10	ELC-4A/T control unit	When overdrive mode is active	System voltage
		When overdrive mode is inactive	0V
11	OD switch	When OD switch is ON	System voltage
		When OD switch is OFF	0V

CR1109100271000X

Fig. 37   Test No. 11: Overdrive Cancellation Function Related Circuits. Stealth & Colt Vista/Summit Wagon

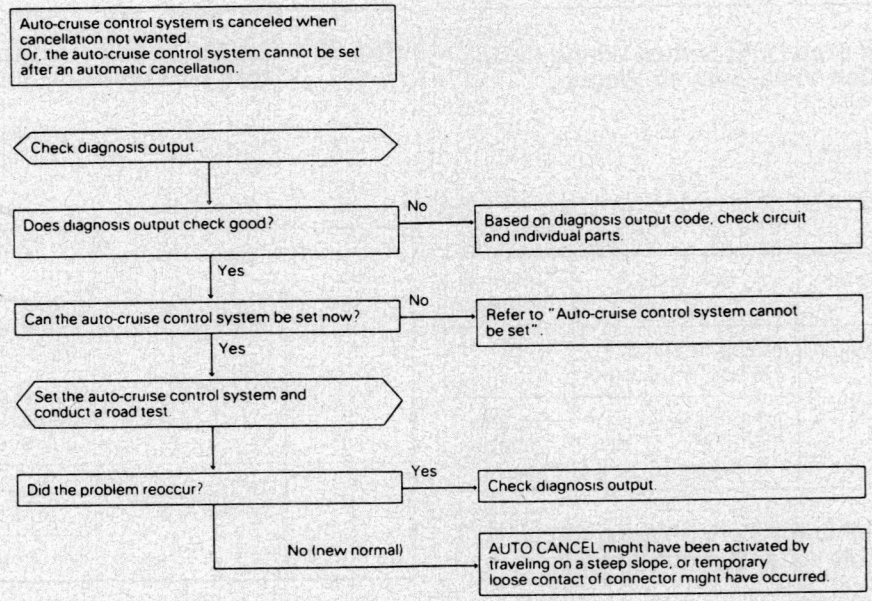

CR1109100333010X

Fig. 38   Symptom diagnosis chart (Part 1 of 4). Colt & Summit

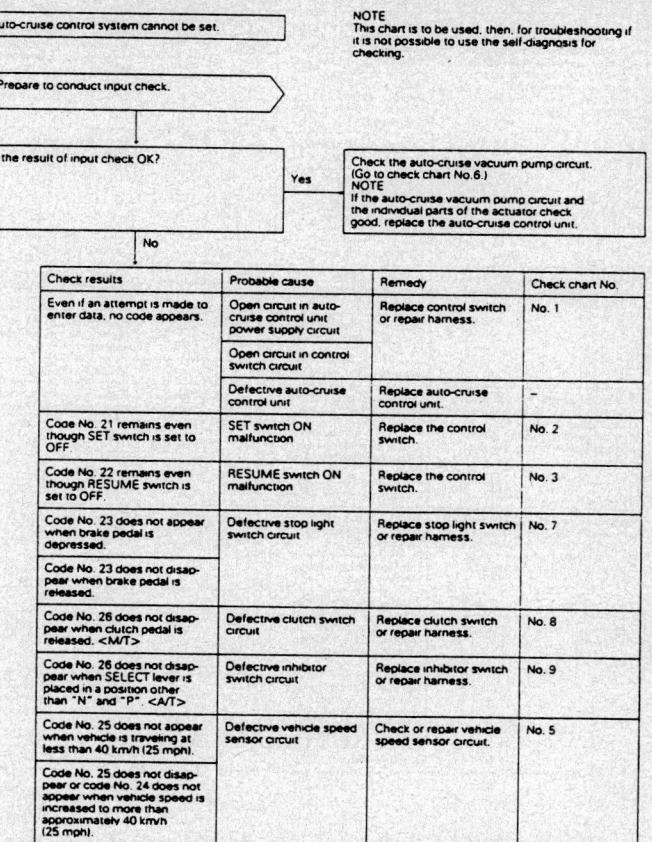

Auto-cruise control system cannot be set.

NOTE
This chart is to be used, then, for troubleshooting if it is not possible to use the self-diagnosis for checking.

Prepare to conduct input check.

Is the result of input check OK? — Yes → Check the auto-cruise vacuum pump circuit. (Go to check chart No. 6.)
NOTE
If the auto-cruise vacuum pump circuit and the individual parts of the actuator check good, replace the auto-cruise control unit.

No

Check results	Probable cause	Remedy	Check chart No.
Even if an attempt is made to enter data, no code appears.	Open circuit in auto-cruise control unit power supply circuit	Replace control switch or repair harness.	No. 1
	Open circuit in control switch circuit		
	Defective auto-cruise control unit	Replace auto-cruise control unit.	—
Code No. 21 remains even though SET switch is set to OFF.	SET switch ON malfunction	Replace the control switch.	No. 2
Code No. 22 remains even though RESUME switch is set to OFF.	RESUME switch ON malfunction	Replace the control switch.	No. 3
Code No. 23 does not appear when brake pedal is depressed.	Defective stop light switch circuit	Replace stop light switch or repair harness.	No. 7
Code No. 23 does not disappear when brake pedal is released.			
Code No. 26 does not disappear when clutch pedal is released. <M/T>	Defective clutch switch circuit	Replace clutch switch or repair harness.	No. 8
Code No. 26 does not disappear when SELECT lever is placed in a position other than "N" and "P". <A/T>	Defective inhibitor switch circuit	Replace inhibitor switch or repair harness.	No. 9
Code No. 25 does not appear when vehicle is traveling at less than 40 km/h (25 mph).	Defective vehicle speed sensor circuit	Check or repair vehicle speed sensor circuit.	No. 5
Code No. 25 does not disappear or code No. 24 does not appear when vehicle speed is increased to more than approximately 40 km/h (25 mph).			

CR1109100272020X

Fig. 38   Symptom diagnosis chart (Part 2 of 4). Colt & Summit

Trouble symptom	Probable cause	Check chart No.	Remedy
• The set vehicle speed varies greatly upward or downward. • "Hunching" (repeated alternating acceleration and deceleration) occurs after setting is made.	Malfunction of the vehicle speed sensor circuit	No. 5	Repair the vehicle speed sensor system, or replace the part.
	Malfunction of the speedometer cable or speedometer drive gear		
	Auto-cruise vacuum pump circuit poor contact	No. 6	Repair the auto-cruise vacuum pump system, or replace the part.
	Malfunction of the auto-cruise vacuum pump		
	Malfunction of the auto-cruise control unit	—	Replace the auto-cruise control unit.
The auto-cruise control system is not canceled when the brake pedal is depressed.	Brake switch (for auto-cruise control) malfunction (short-circuit)	No. 7	Repair the harness or replace the stop light switch.
	Auto-cruise vacuum pump drive circuit short-circuit	No. 6	Repair the harness or replace the auto-cruise vacuum pump.
	Malfunction of the auto-cruise control unit	—	Replace the auto-cruise control unit.
The auto-cruise control system is not canceled when the clutch pedal is depressed. <M/T> (It is canceled, however, when the brake pedal is depressed.)	Damaged or disconnected wiring of clutch switch input circuit	If the input check code No. 26 indicates a malfunction. No. 8	Repair the harness, or repair or replace the clutch switch.
	Clutch switch improper installation (won't switch ON)		
	Malfunction of the auto-cruise control unit	—	Replace the auto-cruise control unit.
The auto-cruise control system is not canceled when the shift lever is moved to the "N" position. <A/T> (It is canceled, however, when the brake pedal is depressed.)	Damaged or disconnected wiring of inhibitor switch input circuit	If the input check code No. 26 indicates a malfunction. No. 9	Repair the harness, or repair or replace the inhibitor switch.
	Improper adjustment of inhibitor switch		
	Malfunction of the auto-cruise control unit	—	Replace the auto-cruise control unit.

CR1109100272030X

Fig. 38   Symptom diagnosis chart (Part 3 of 4). Colt & Summit

Trouble symptom	Probable cause	Check chart No	Remedy
Cannot decelerate by using the SET switch.	Temporary damaged or disconnected wiring of SET switch input circuit	No. 2	Repair the harness or replace the SET switch.
	Auto-cruise vacuum pump circuit poor contact	No. 6	Repair the harness or replace the auto-cruise vacuum pump and actuator
	Malfunction of the auto-cruise vacuum pump and actuator (including blocking of negative pressure passage)		
	Malfunction of the auto-cruise control unit	—	Replace the auto-cruise control unit.
Cannot accelerate or resume speed by using the RESUME switch.	Open or short circuit in RESUME switch circuit in control switch	No. 3	Replace the control switch.
	Auto-cruise vacuum pump circuit poor contact	No. 6	Repair the harness or replace the auto-cruise vacuum pump and actuator
	Malfunction of the auto-cruise vacuum pump and actuator (including air leaks from negative pressure passage)		
	Malfunction of the auto-cruise control unit	—	Replace the auto-cruise control unit.
Auto-cruise control system can be set while traveling at a vehicle speed of less than 40 km/h (25 mph), or there is no automatic cancellation at that speed.	Malfunction of the vehicle speed sensor circuit	No. 5	Repair the vehicle speed sensor system, or replace the part.
	Malfunction of the speedometer cable or the speedometer drive gear		
	Malfunction of the auto-cruise control unit	—	Replace the auto-cruise control unit.
The auto-cruise control switch indicator light does not illuminate. (But auto-cruise control system is normal.)	Damaged or disconnected bulb of auto-cruise control switch indicator	No. 4	Repair the harness or replace the control switch.
	Harness damaged or disconnected		
Malfunction of control function by ON/OFF switching of 4 A/T accelerator switch (Non-operation of damper clutch, 2nd gear hold, etc.)	Malfunction of circuit related to accelerator switch OFF function	No. 11	Repair the harness or replace the part.
	Malfunction of the auto-cruise control unit		
Overdrive is not canceled during fixed speed driving <A/T>	Malfunction of circuit related to overdrive cancellation, or malfunction of auto-cruise control unit	No. 12	Repair the harness or replace the part.
No shift to overdrive during manual driving <A/T>			
The auto-cruise control indicator light does not illuminate. (But auto-cruise control system is normal.)	Damaged or disconnected bulb of indicator light	No. 4	Repair the harness or replace the bulb.
	Harness damaged or disconnected		

CR1109100272040X

Fig. 38   Symptom diagnosis chart (Part 4 of 4). Colt & Summit

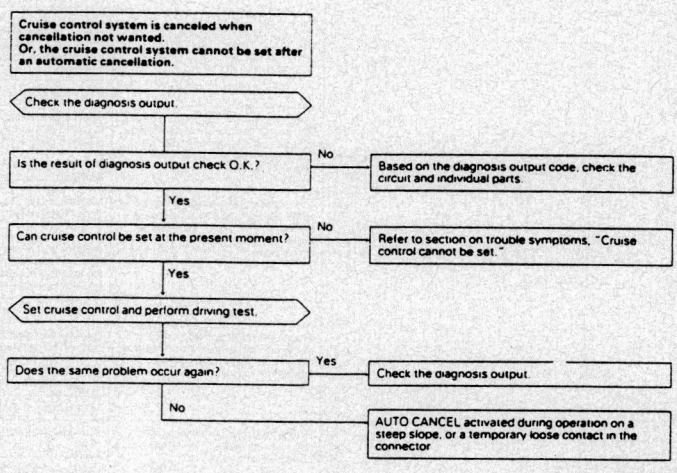

Cruise control system is canceled when cancellation not wanted.
Or, the cruise control system cannot be set after an automatic cancellation.

Check the diagnosis output.

Is the result of diagnosis output check O.K.? — No → Based on the diagnosis output code, check the circuit and individual parts.

Yes

Can cruise control be set at the present moment? — No → Refer to section on trouble symptoms, "Cruise control cannot be set."

Yes

Set cruise control and perform driving test.

Does the same problem occur again? — Yes → Check the diagnosis output.

No

AUTO CANCEL activated during operation on a steep slope, or a temporary loose contact in the connector

CR1109100273010X

Fig. 39   Symptom diagnosis chart (Part 1 of 4). Stealth & Colt Vista/Summit Wagon

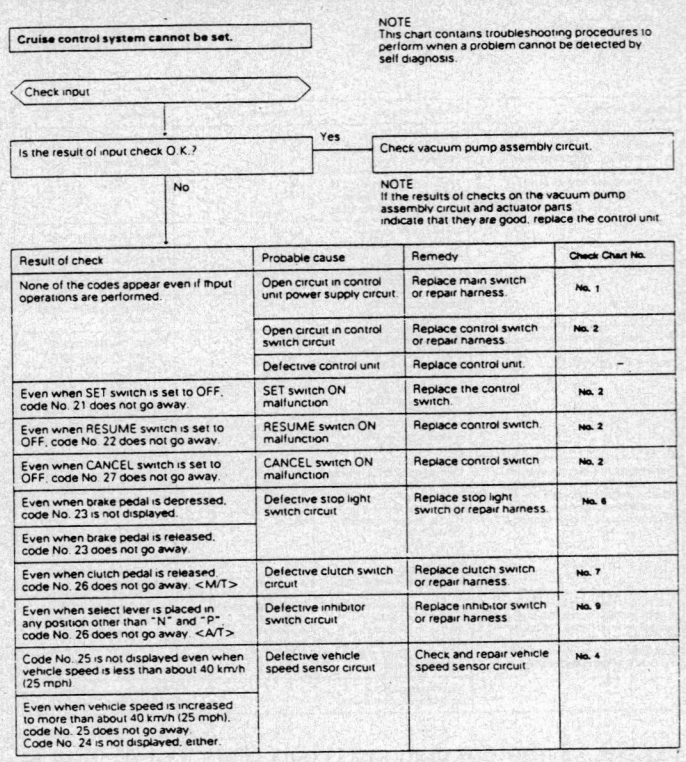

Cruise control system cannot be set.

↓

Check input

↓

Is the result of input check O.K.? → Yes → Check vacuum pump assembly circuit.

↓ No

NOTE
This chart contains troubleshooting procedures to perform when a problem cannot be detected by self diagnosis.

NOTE
If the results of checks on the vacuum pump assembly circuit and actuator parts indicate that they are good, replace the control unit.

Result of check	Probable cause	Remedy	Check Chart No.
None of the codes appear even if input operations are performed.	Open circuit in control unit power supply circuit.	Replace main switch or repair harness.	No. 1
	Open circuit in control switch circuit	Replace control switch or repair harness.	No. 2
	Defective control unit	Replace control unit.	—
Even when SET switch is set to OFF, code No. 21 does not go away.	SET switch ON malfunction	Replace the control switch.	No. 2
Even when RESUME switch is set to OFF, code No. 22 does not go away.	RESUME switch ON malfunction	Replace control switch.	No. 2
Even when CANCEL switch is set to OFF, code No. 27 does not go away.	CANCEL switch ON malfunction	Replace control switch.	No. 2
Even when brake pedal is depressed, code No. 23 is not displayed.	Defective stop light switch circuit	Replace stop light switch or repair harness.	No. 6
Even when brake pedal is released, code No. 23 does not go away.			
Even when clutch pedal is released, code No. 26 does not go away. <M/T>	Defective clutch switch circuit	Replace clutch switch or repair harness.	No. 7
Even when select lever is placed in any position other than "N" and "P", code No. 26 does not go away. <A/T>	Defective inhibitor switch circuit	Replace inhibitor switch or repair harness.	No. 9
Code No. 25 is not displayed even when vehicle speed is less than about 40 km/h (25 mph).	Defective vehicle speed sensor circuit	Check and repair vehicle speed sensor circuit.	No. 4
Even when vehicle speed is increased to more than about 40 km/h (25 mph), code No. 25 does not go away. Code No. 24 is not displayed, either.			

CR1109100273020X

Fig. 39 Symptom diagnosis chart (Part 2 of 4). Stealth & Colt Vista/Summit Wagon

Trouble symptom	Probable cause	Check chart No.	Remedy
• The set vehicle speed varies greatly upward or downward. • "Hunching" (repeated alternating acceleration and deceleration) occurs after setting is made.	Malfunction of the vehicle speed sensor circuit	No. 4	Repair the vehicle speed sensor system, or replace the part.
	Malfunction of the speedometer cable or speedometer drive gear <Non turbo>		
	Vacuum pump assembly circuit poor contact	No. 5	Repair the actuator system, or replace the part.
	Malfunction of the vacuum pump assembly (including air leaks from negative pressure passage)		
	Malfunction of the ECU	—	Replace the ECU.
The cruise control system is not canceled when the brake pedal is depressed.	Brake switch (for cruise control) malfunction (short-circuit)	No. 6	Repair the harness or replace the stop light switch.
	Vacuum pump assembly drive circuit short-circuit	No. 5	Repair the harness or replace the vacuum pump assembly.
	Malfunction of the ECU	—	Replace the ECU.
The cruise control system is not canceled when the clutch pedal is depressed <M/T> (It is canceled, however, when the brake pedal is depressed.)	Damaged or disconnected wiring of clutch switch input circuit	If the input check code No. 26 indicates a malfunction. No. 7	Repair the harness, or repair or replace the clutch switch.
	Clutch switch improper installation (won't switch ON)		
	Malfunction of the ECU	—	Replace the ECU.
The cruise control system is not canceled when the shift lever is moved to the "N" position. <A/T> (It is canceled, however, when the brake pedal is depressed.)	Damaged or disconnected wiring of inhibitor switch input circuit	If the input check code No. 26 indicates a malfunction. No. 8	Repair the harness, or repair or replace the inhibitor switch.
	Improper adjustment of inhibitor switch		
	Malfunction of the ECU	—	Replace the ECU.
Cannot decelerate by using the SET switch.	Temporary damaged or disconnected wiring of control switch input circuit	No. 2	Repair the harness or replace the control switch
	Vacuum pump assembly circuit poor contact	No. 5	Repair the harness or replace the vacuum pump assembly.
	Malfunction of the vacuum pump assembly		
	Malfunction of the ECU	—	Replace the ECU.

NOTE
ECU: Electronic control unit

CR1109100273030X

Fig. 39 Symptom diagnosis chart (Part 3 of 4). Stealth & Colt Vista/Summit Wagon

Trouble symptom	Probable cause	Check chart No.	Remedy
Cannot accelerate or resume speed by using the RESUME switch.	Open or short circuit in RESUME switch circuit in control switch	No. 2	Replace the control switch.
	Vacuum pump assembly circuit poor contact	No. 5	Repair the harness or replace the vacuum pump assembly.
	Malfunction of the vacuum pump assembly (including air leaks from negative pressure passage)		
	Malfunction of the ECU	—	Replace the ECU.
Even when CANCEL switch is set to ON, cruise control is not canceled (Cruise control, however, is canceled when brake pedal is depressed.)	Open or short circuit in CANCEL switch circuit in control switch	If the input check code No. 27 indicates a malfunction. No. 2	Replace the control switch
	Malfunction of the ECU	—	Replace the ECU
The cruise control system can be set while traveling at a vehicle speed of less than 40 km/h (25 mph), or there is no automatic cancellation at that speed.	Malfunction of the vehicle-speed sensor circuit	No. 4	Repair the vehicle speed sensor system, or replace the part.
	Malfunction of the speedometer cable or the speedometer drive gear <Non turbo>		
	Malfunction of the ECU	—	Replace the ECU.
The cruise control indicator light of the combination meter does not illuminate. (But cruise control system is normal)	Damaged or disconnected bulb of indicator light	No. 3	Repair the harness or replace the light bulb.
	Harness damaged or disconnected		
	Malfunction of the ECU	—	Replace the ECU.
Cruise control ON indicator light does not come on. (However, cruise control is functional.)	Burned-out indicator light bulb	No. 3	Repair the harness or replace the main switch.
	Open or short circuit in harness		
Malfunction of control function by ON/OFF switching of ELC 4 A/T accelerator switch. (Non-operation of damper clutch, 2nd gear hold, etc.)	Malfunction of circuit related to accelerator switch OFF function	No. 10	Repair the harness or replace the part.
	Malfunction of the ECU		
Overdrive is not canceled during fixed speed driving <A/T>	Malfunction of circuit related to overdrive cancellation, or malfunction of ECU	No. 11	Repair the harness or replace the part.
No shift to overdrive during manual driving. <A/T>			

CR1109100273040X

Fig. 39 Symptom diagnosis chart (Part 4 of 4). Stealth & Colt Vista/Summit Wagon

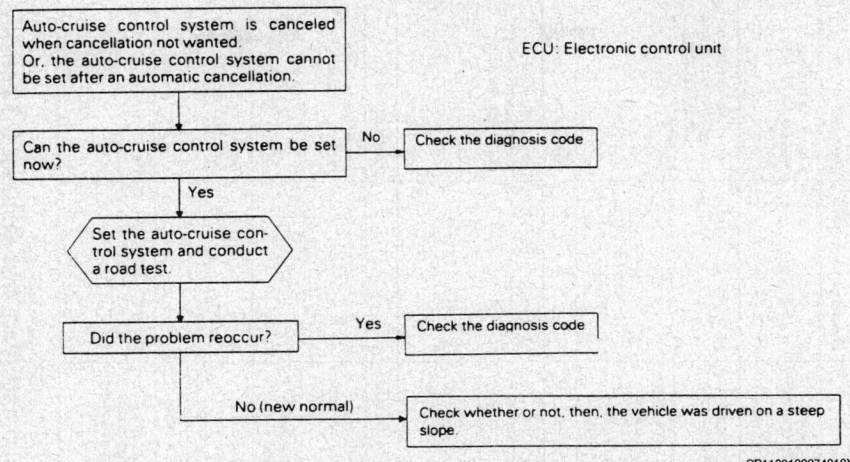

Fig. 40   Symptom diagnosis chart (Part 1 of 4). Laser & Talon

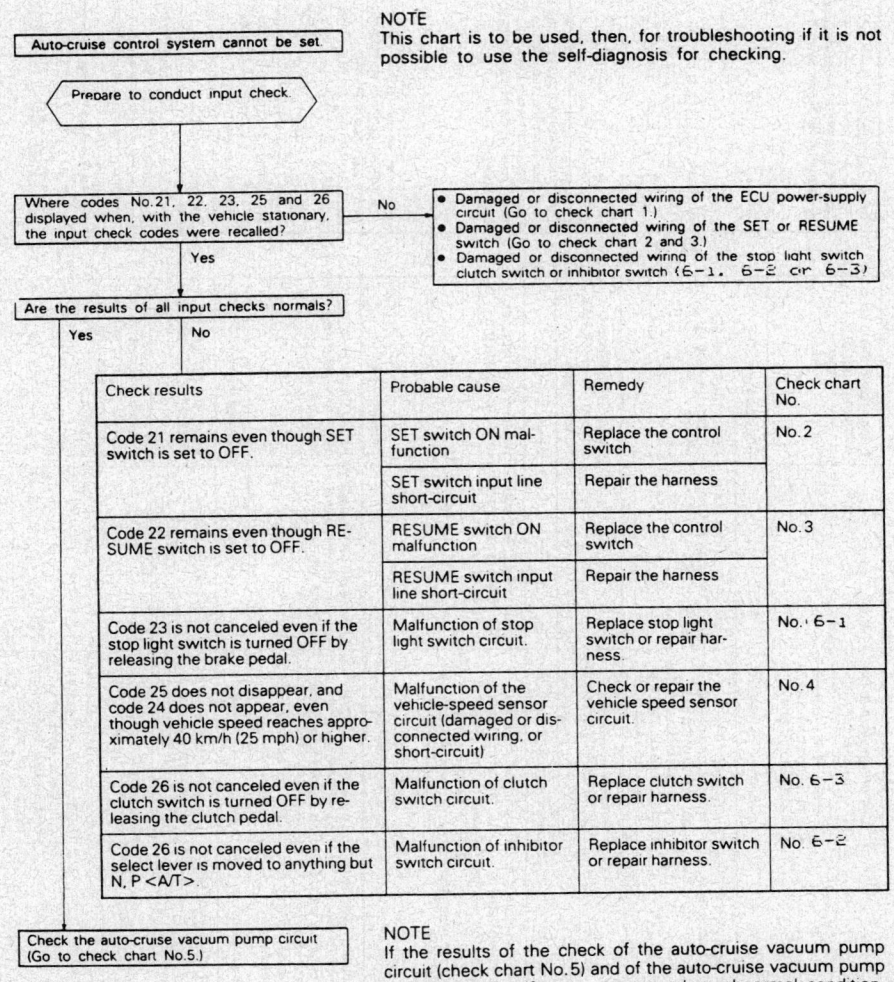

NOTE
This chart is to be used, then, for troubleshooting if it is not possible to use the self-diagnosis for checking.

Check results	Probable cause	Remedy	Check chart No.
Code 21 remains even though SET switch is set to OFF.	SET switch ON malfunction	Replace the control switch	No. 2
	SET switch input line short-circuit	Repair the harness	
Code 22 remains even though RESUME switch is set to OFF.	RESUME switch ON malfunction	Replace the control switch	No. 3
	RESUME switch input line short-circuit	Repair the harness	
Code 23 is not canceled even if the stop light switch is turned OFF by releasing the brake pedal.	Malfunction of stop light switch circuit.	Replace stop light switch or repair harness.	No. 6-1
Code 25 does not disappear, and code 24 does not appear, even though vehicle speed reaches approximately 40 km/h (25 mph) or higher.	Malfunction of the vehicle-speed sensor circuit (damaged or disconnected wiring, or short-circuit)	Check or repair the vehicle speed sensor circuit.	No. 4
Code 26 is not canceled even if the clutch switch is turned OFF by releasing the clutch pedal.	Malfunction of clutch switch circuit.	Replace clutch switch or repair harness.	No. 6-3
Code 26 is not canceled even if the select lever is moved to anything but N, P <A/T>.	Malfunction of inhibitor switch circuit.	Replace inhibitor switch or repair harness.	No. 6-2

NOTE
If the results of the check of the auto-cruise vacuum pump circuit (check chart No.5) and of the auto-cruise vacuum pump and actuator itself   reveal no abnormal condition, replace the electronic control unit (ECU).

Fig. 40   Symptom diagnosis chart (Part 2 of 4). Laser & Talon

Trouble symptom	Probable cause	Check chart No.	Remedy
Cannot accelerate or resume speed by using the RESUME switch.	Damaged or disconnected wiring, or short-circuit, of RESUME switch input circuit	No. 3	Repair the harness or replace the RESUME switch.
	Auto-cruise vacuum pump circuit poor contact	No. 5	Repair the harness or replace the auto-cruise vacuum pump and actuator.
	Malfunction of the auto-cruise vacuum pump and actuator (including air leak from negative pressure passage)		
	Malfunction of the ECU	–	Replace the ECU.
Auto-cruise control system can be set while traveling at a vehicle speed of less than 40 km/h (25 mph), or there is no automatic cancellation at that speed.	Malfunction of the vehicle-speed sensor circuit	No. 4	Repair the vehicle-speed sensor system, or replace the part.
	Malfunction of the speedometer cable or the speedometer drive gear		
	Malfunction of the ECU	–	Replace the ECU.
The indicator light of combination meter does not illuminate. (But auto-cruise control system is normal.)	Damaged or disconnected bulb of indicator light	–	Repair the harness or replace the bulb.
	Harness damaged or disconnected		
Malfunction of control function by ON/OFF switching of ELC 4 A/T accelerator switch (Non-operation of damper clutch, 2nd gear hold, etc.)	Malfunction of circuit related to accelerator switch OFF function	No. 7	Repair the harness or replace the part.
	Malfunction of the ECU		
Overdrive is not canceled during fixed speed driving. <A/T>	Malfunction of circuit related to overdrive cancellation, or malfunction of ECU	No. 8	Repair the harness or replace the part.
No shift to overdrive during manual driving. <A/T>			

CR1091002740040X

Fig. 40 Symptom diagnosis chart (Part 4 of 4). Laser & Talon

Trouble symptom	Probable cause	Check chart No.	Remedy
• The set vehicle speed varies greatly upward or downward. • "Hunching" (repeated alternating acceleration and deceleration) occurs after setting is made.	Malfunction of the vehicle speed sensor circuit	No. 4	Repair the vehicle speed sensor system, or replace the part.
	Malfunction of the speedometer cable or speedometer drive gear		
	Auto-cruise vacuum pump circuit poor contact	No. 5	Repair the auto-cruise vacuum pump, or replace the part.
	Malfunction of the auto-cruise vacuum pump		
	Malfunction of the ECU	–	Replace the ECU
The auto-cruise control system is not canceled when the brake pedals is depressed.	Damaged or disconnected wiring of the stop light switch input circuit; brake switch (for auto-cruise control) malfunction (short-circuit)	If the input check code No. 23 indicates a malfunction. No. 6-1	Repair the harness or replace the stop light switch.
	Auto-cruise vacuum pump drive circuit short-circuit	No. 5	Repair the harness or replace the auto-cruise vacuum pump.
	Malfunction of the ECU	–	Replace the ECU.
The auto-cruise control system is not canceled when the clutch pedal is depressed. (vehicles with a manual transaxle) (It is canceled, however, when the brake pedal is depressed.)	Damaged or disconnected wiring of clutch switch input circuit	If the input check code No. 26 indicates a malfunction. No. 6-3	Repair the harness, or repair or replace the clutch switch.
	Clutch switch improper installation (won't switch ON)		
	Malfunction of the ECU	–	Replace the ECU.
The auto-cruise control system is not canceled when the shift lever is moved to the "N" position. (vehicles with an automatic transaxle) (It is canceled, however, when the brake pedal is depressed.)	Damaged or disconnected wiring of inhibitor switch input circuit	If the input check code No. 26 indicates a malfunction. No. 6-2	Repair the harness, or repair or replace the inhibitor switch.
	Improper adjustment of inhibitor switch		
	Malfunction of the ECU	–	Replace the ECU.
Cannot decelerate by using the SET switch	Temporary damaged or disconnected wiring of SET switch input circuit	No. 2	Repair the harness or replace the SET switch.
	Auto-cruise vacuum pump circuit poor contact	No. 5	Repair the harness or replace the auto-cruise vacuum pump and actuator.
	Malfunction of the auto-cruise vacuum pump and actuator (including clogging of negative pressure passage)		
	Malfunction of the ECU	–	Replace the ECU

CR1091002740030X

Fig. 40 Symptom diagnosis chart (Part 3 of 4). Laser & Talon

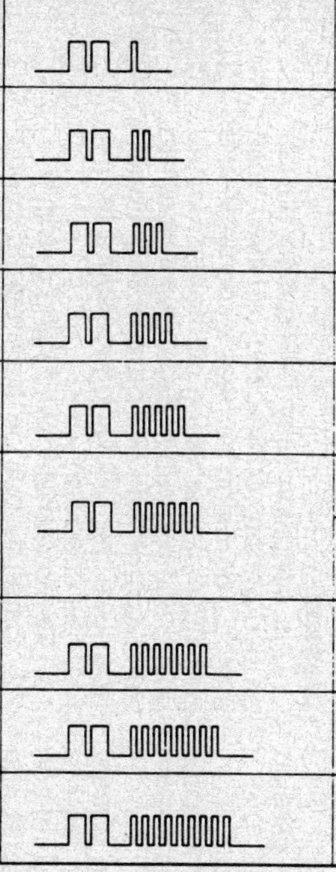

Fig. 42 Input check table. Colt & Summit

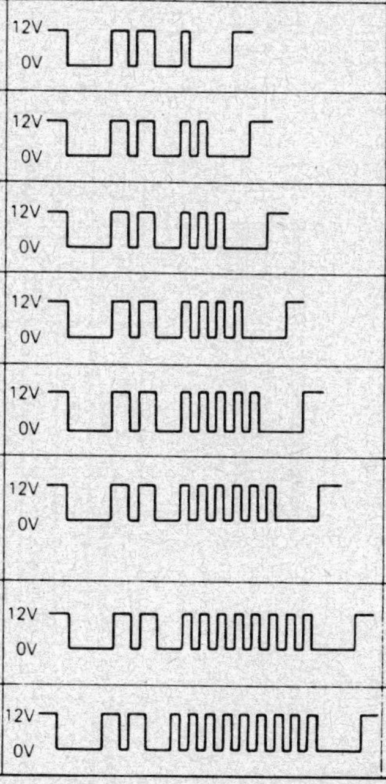

Check No.	Input operation	Code No.	Display patterns (output codes) (use with voltmeter)	Check results
1	SET switch ON	21		SET switch circuit normal
2	RESUME switch ON	22		RESUME switch circuit normal
3	Stop light switch ON (brake pedal depressed)	23		Stop light switch normal
4	Driving at approximately to 40 km/h (25 mph) or higher	24		When both No 4 and No. 5 can be confirmed, vehicle speed sensor circuit normal
5	Driving at less than approximately 40 km/h (25 mph) or stopped	25		
6	1. Clutch switch ON (clutch pedal depressed) <M T> 2. Inhibitor switch ON (shift lever to "N" or "P" range) <A T>	26		Clutch switch, inhibitor switch normal
7	Throttle position sensor output voltage 1.5V or more (when accelerator pedal is depressed more than half the way)	28		Throttle position sensor normal
8	Idle switch OFF (accelerator pedal depressed)	29		Idle switch normal

CR1109200276000X

Fig. 41 Input check table. Stealth, Talon & Colt Vista/Summit Wagon

Code No.	Display patterns (output codes) (use with voltmeter)	Input operation		Check results
21		SET switch ON		SET switch circuit normal
22		RESUME switch ON		RESUME switch circuit normal
23		Stop light switch ON (brake pedal depressed)		Stop light switch circuit normal
24		Vehicle speed more than approx. 40 km/h (25 mph)		Vehicle speed sensor circuit normal if code Nos. 24 and 25 are displayed
25		Vehicle speed less than approx. 40 km/h (25 mph)		
26		M/T	Clutch switch ON (clutch pedal depressed)	Clutch switch circuit normal
		A/T	Inhibitor switch ON (SELECT lever placed in "N" position)	Inhibitor switch circuit normal
27		CANCEL switch ON		CANCEL switch circuit normal
28		TPS output voltage 1 5 V or more (Accelerator pedal depressed more than half the way)		Throttle position sensor circuit normal
29		Idle switch OFF (Accelerator pedal depressed)		Idle switch circuit normal

CR1109100275000X

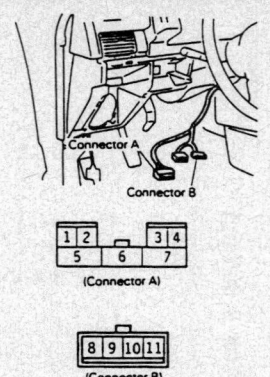

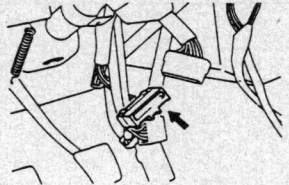

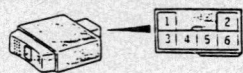

(Connector A)

(Connector B)

Switch position \ Terminal	7	9	8
OFF			
SET switch ON	O—O		
RESUME switch ON		O—O	

NOTE
If the continuity is other than shown, replace the column switch.

CR1109100277000X

Fig. 43 Speed control main switch test. Colt & Summit

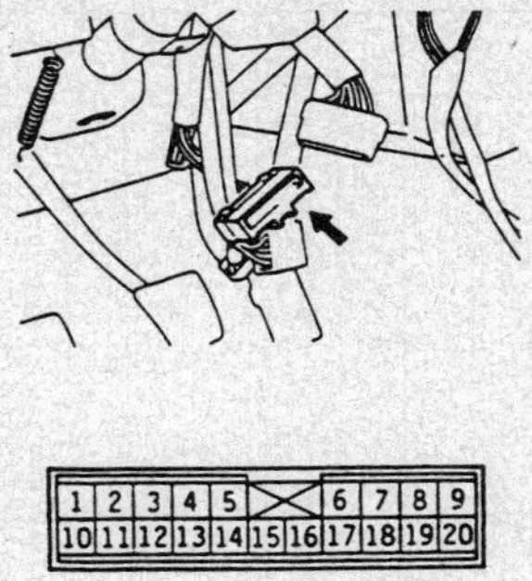

O—O: continuity

Switch position \ Terminal	13	8	9	19	20
OFF					
SET switch ON	O—O				
Neutral					
RESUME switch ON			O—O		

NOTE
If there is an abnormal condition (any condition not described in the table above), replace the column switch.

CR1109100278000X

Fig. 44 Speed control main switch test. Laser & Talon

Terminal No. \ Switch state	1	ILL	2	3	4	5
Press OFF	O—	(ⓘ)	—O			
Neutral position		(ⓘ)			O—	—O
Press ON.	O—	(ⓘ)	—O	O—		—O

NOTE
(1) O—O denotes continuity across the terminals.
(2) ILL: Illumination light

CR1109100279000X

Fig. 45 Speed control main switch test. Stealth

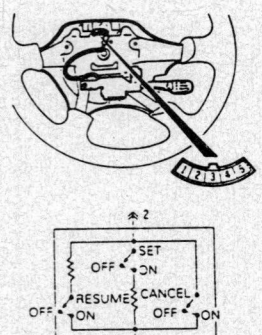

Switch operation	Resistance between terminals
When switch is not operated	No continuity
When CANCEL switch is set to ON	Approx. 0 Ω
When RESUME switch is set to ON	Approx. 820 Ω
When STE switch is set to ON	Approx. 2,700 Ω

CR1109200282000X

Fig. 48 Cruise control switch test. Colt Vista/Summit Wagon

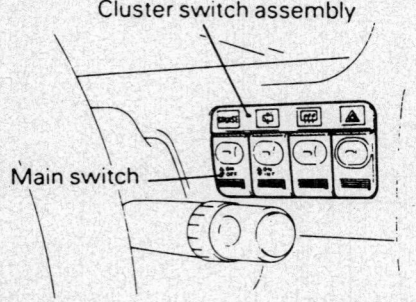

Fig. 46 Cluster switch assembly removal. Colt Vista/Summit Wagon

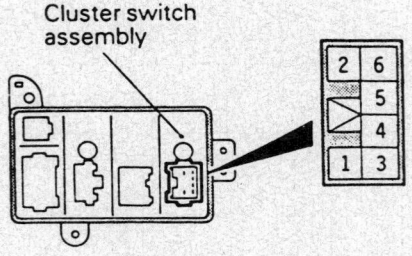

Terminal No. \ Switch state	2	4	6
Press OFF			
Neutral position		O—O	
Press ON	O—		—O

NOTE
O—O denotes continuity across the terminals.

CR1109200281000X

Fig. 47 Speed control main switch test. Colt Vista/Summit Wagon

COMPONENT TESTING

SPEED CONTROL SWITCH

Except Stealth & Colt Vista/Summit Wagon

Gain access and disconnect connector to speed control main switch and check for continuity between terminals as shown in **Figs. 43 and 44.**

Stealth

1. Remove main switch and garnish from console.
2. Remove switch from garnish.
3. Operate main switch and check for continuity across terminals as shown in **Fig. 45.**
4. Connect a positive lead from battery to terminal 3 and a negative lead to terminal 5. Check that battery voltage is available between terminals 4 and 5 when the switch is turned On and when the switch is turned Off.
5. Check that when turned to Off position thereafter, the battery voltage

across terminal 4 and 5 is reduced to 0 volts.

Speed control will not remain On when the main On/Off switch is depressed.

This condition may be caused be improper wiring connection at the main switch. The wiring harness is too short and partially pulls the wiring off the back of the speed control switch. **Replacement of the main switch will not correct this condition.** Use the following procedure to correct this condition.

1. Remove main switch and garnish.
2. Carefully pull on main speed control switch wiring harness to gain an additional 1/16–1/8 inch of wiring.
3. Install main speed control switch and garnish.

MAIN SWITCH TEST

Colt Vista/Summit Wagon

1. Remove main cluster switch, **Fig. 46,** then operate switch and check continuity across terminal as shown in **Fig. 47.**
2. Ensure battery voltage is present between terminal four and ground, and that indicator lamp comes On when main switch is turned On with terminal two connected to battery positive and terminal six is connected to terminal six.
3. Ensure no battery voltage between terminal four and ground is present when main switch is turned Off.

CRUISE CONTROL SWITCH TEST

Colt Vista/Summit Wagon

1. Remove steering wheel horn pad.
2. Measure resistance between terminals as shown in **Fig. 48.** If resistance is not as specified, replace switch.

STOP LIGHT/BRAKE SWITCH

1. Disconnect electrical connector from switch.

	Switch	Brake switch		Stop light switch	
	Terminal	3	4	1	2
Measurement conditions					
When brake pedal depressed.				○──────○	
When brake pedal not depressed		○──────○			

○─○: continuity

CR1109100283000X

Fig. 49   Stoplight/brake switch test

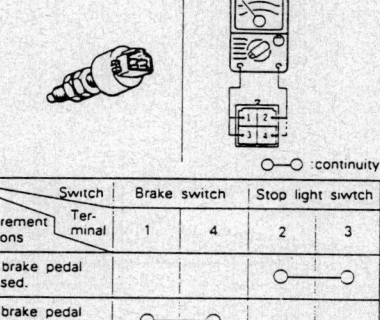

○─○: continuity

	Switch	Brake switch		Stop light siwtch	
Measurement conditions	Terminal	1	4	2	3
When brake pedal depressed.				○──────○	
When brake pedal not depressed.		○──────○			

CR1109100284000X

Fig. 50   Stoplight/brake switch test. Laser & Talon

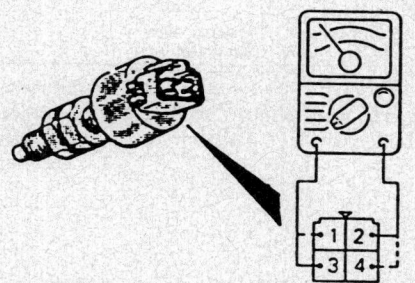

	Switch	Used for stop light circuit		Used for cruise control circuit	
Measurement conditions	Terminal	2	3	1	4
When brake pedal depressed.		○──────○			
When brake pedal not depressd.				○──────○	

NOTE
○──○ denotes continuity across the terminals.

CR1109200285000X

Fig. 51   Stoplight/brake switch test. Colt Vista/Summit Wagon

2. Check for continuity between terminal of switch, **Figs. 49 through 51.**

CLUTCH SWITCH
1. Disconnect electrical connector from switch.
2. Check for continuity between terminals when clutch pedal is depressed.

INHIBITOR SWITCH
1. Disconnect electrical connector from switch.
2. Ensure there is continuity between connector terminals 8 and 9 when shift lever is moved to N range, **Fig. 52.**

ACTUATOR
Laser & Talon
Measure resistance value of each clutch coil and ensure value is 50-60 ohms.

Stealth, Colt & Summit & Laser/Talon & Colt Vista/Summit Wagon
1. Remove actuator.
2. Apply vacuum to actuator and ensure that holder moves more than 1.4 inches.
3. Ensure that no change in holder position as vacuum is maintained.

VACUUM PUMP TEST
Colt Vista/Summit Wagon
1. Disconnect electrical connector from vacuum pump assembly, then measure resistance between terminal one

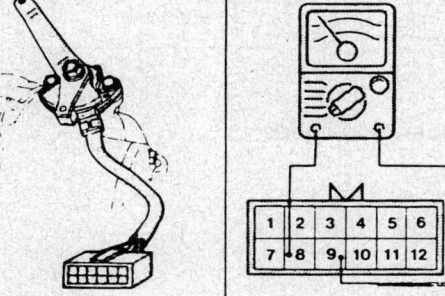

CR1109100286000X

Fig. 52   Inhibitor switch N & P position check. Stealth, Colt & Summit

and two and terminals one and three, **Fig. 53,** resistance should be between 50-60 ohms.
2. Apply battery voltage between terminal one and two and terminals one and three, ensure operating sounds of solenoid valves are heard.
3. If solenoid valves are defective, replace vacuum pump assembly.
4. Check motor by applying battery voltage across terminals one and four, ensure motor operates, if not replace motor.

ACTUATOR OPERATION CHECK
Colt, Summit
1. Connect terminal 3 of actuator through ammeter, to battery positive terminal, **Fig. 54.**
2. Connect terminal 1 to battery negative terminal.
3. Solenoid should emit an audible click and ammeter should measure .5-.7 amps. If not, proceed as follows:
   a. If no solenoid sound is heard and ammeter reads 0 amps, check for damaged or disconnected clutch coil wiring.
   b. If no solenoid sound is heard, but ammeter reads infinite, check for clutch coil short circuit.

Laser & Talon
1. Remove actuator.
2. Apply vacuum to actuator and ensure that holder moves more than 1.4 inches.

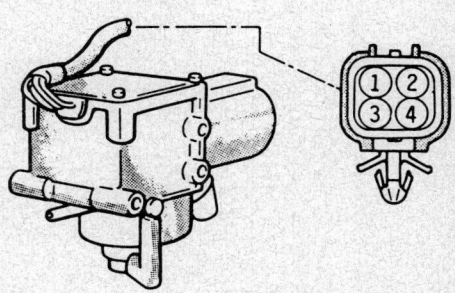

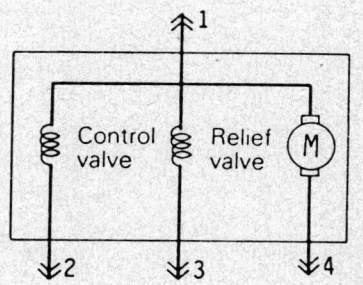

CR1109200287000X

Fig. 53   Testing speed control vacuum pump. Colt Vista/Summit Wagon

3. Ensure that no change in holder position as vacuum is maintained.
4. Refer to **Fig. 55** for actuator testing.

COMPONENT REPLACEMENT
COLT, COLT VISTA, LASER, STEALTH, SUMMIT, SUMMIT WAGON & TALON
Remove components in order as shown in **Figs. 56 through 59,** when replacing actuator and speed control components. Reverse procedure to install.

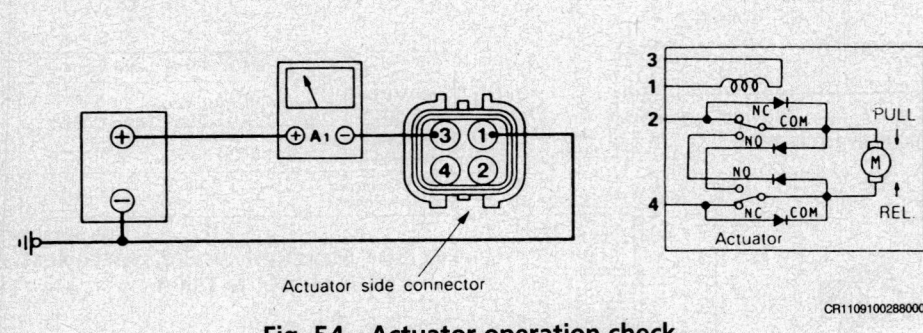

Fig. 54 **Actuator operation check**

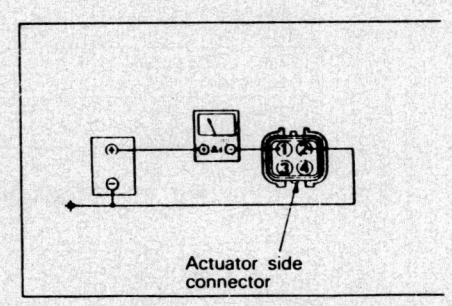

CR1109100289000X

Fig. 55 **Actuator connector. Laser & Talon**

CR1109100288000X

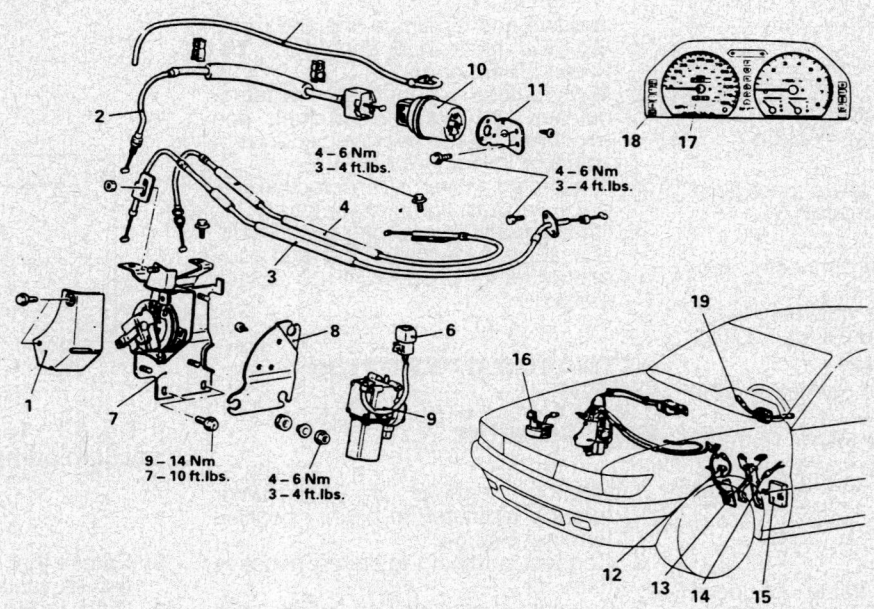

4 – 6 Nm
3 – 4 ft.lbs.

4 – 6 Nm
3 – 4 ft.lbs.

9 – 14 Nm
7 – 10 ft.lbs.

4 – 6 Nm
3 – 4 ft.lbs.

Removal steps of actuator

Air cleaner

1. Link protector
2. Auto-cruise control cable
3. Accelerator cable
4. Throttle cable
5. Vacuum hose
6. Auto-cruise control vacuum pump connector
7. Link assembly
8. Pump bracket
9. Auto-cruise control vacuum pump
10. Auto-cruise control actuator
11. Actuator bracket

Removal steps of sensor and switches

12. Accelerator switch <A/T>
13. Clutch switch <M/T>
14. Stop light switch
15. Auto-cruise control unit
16. Inhibitor switch <A/T>
17. Vehicle speed sensor
18. Auto-cruise control indicator light
19. Auto-cruise control switch

CR1109100297000X

Fig. 56 **Component location. Colt & Summit**

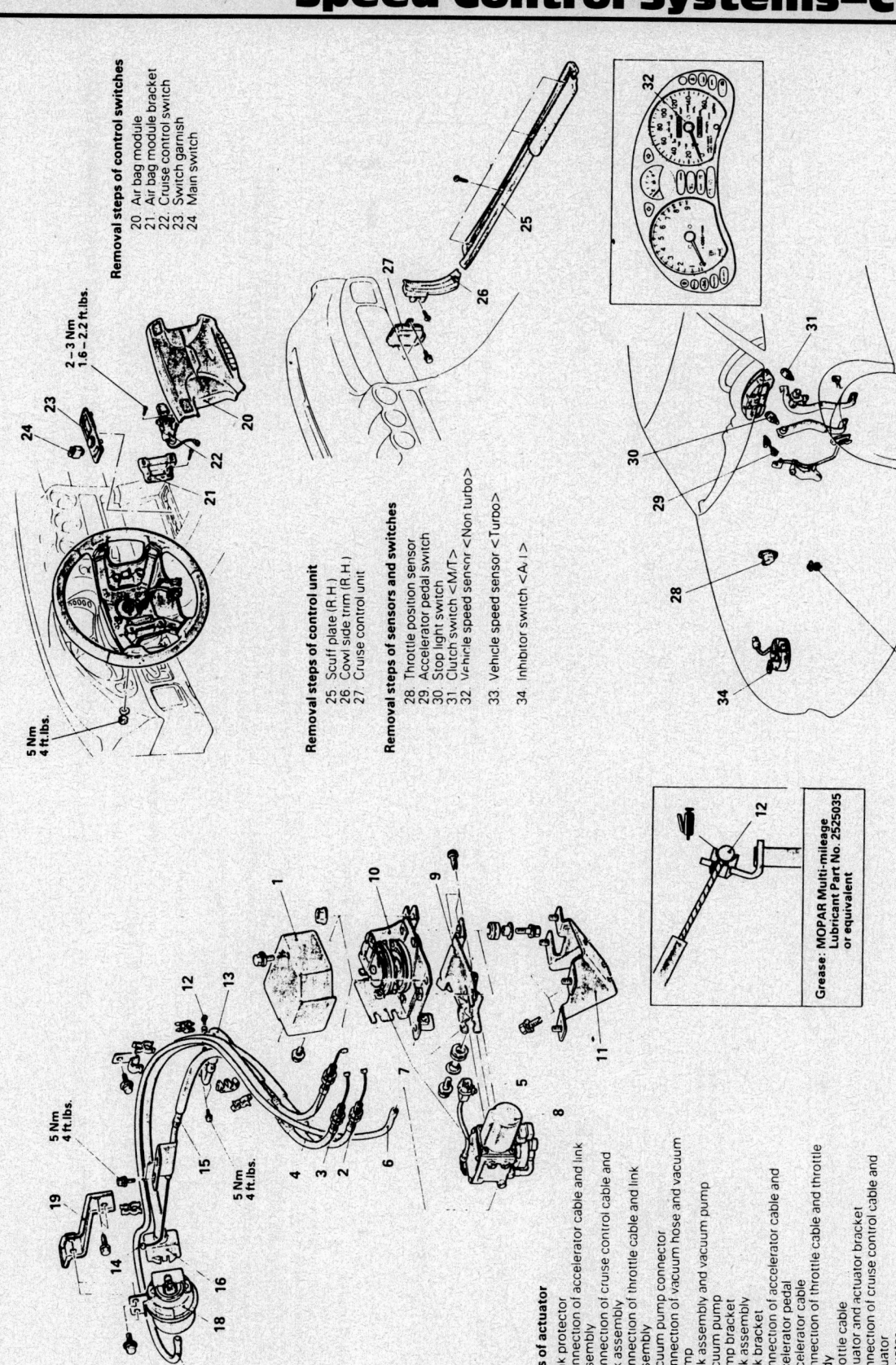

Removal steps of control switches

20. Air bag module
21. Air bag module bracket
22. Cruise control switch
23. Switch garnish
24. Main switch

2–3 Nm
1.6–2.2 ft.lbs.

5 Nm
4 ft.lbs.

Removal steps of control unit

25. Scuff plate (R.H.)
26. Cowl side trim (R.H.)
27. Cruise control unit

Removal steps of sensors and switches

28. Throttle position sensor
29. Accelerator pedal switch
30. Stop light switch
31. Clutch switch <M/T>
32. Vehicle speed sensor <Non turbo>
33. Vehicle speed sensor <Turbo>
34. Inhibitor switch <A/J>

Fig. 57 Component location (Part 2 of 2). Stealth

Removal steps of actuator

1. Link protector
2. Connection of accelerator cable and link assembly
3. Connection of cruise control cable and link assembly
4. Connection of throttle cable and link assembly
5. Vacuum pump connector
6. Connection of vacuum hose and vacuum pump
7. Link assembly and vacuum pump
8. Vacuum pump
9. Pump bracket
10. Link assembly
11. Link bracket
12. Connection of accelerator cable and accelerator pedal
13. Accelerator cable
14. Connection of throttle cable and throttle body
15. Throttle cable
16. Actuator and actuator bracket
17. Connection of cruise control cable and actuator
18. Actuator
19. Actuator bracket

5 Nm
4 ft.lbs.

5 Nm
4 ft.lbs.

Grease: MOPAR Multi-mileage
Lubricant Part No. 2525035
or equivalent

Fig. 57 Component location (Part 1 of 2). Stealth

CR11091002980020X

CR11091002980010X

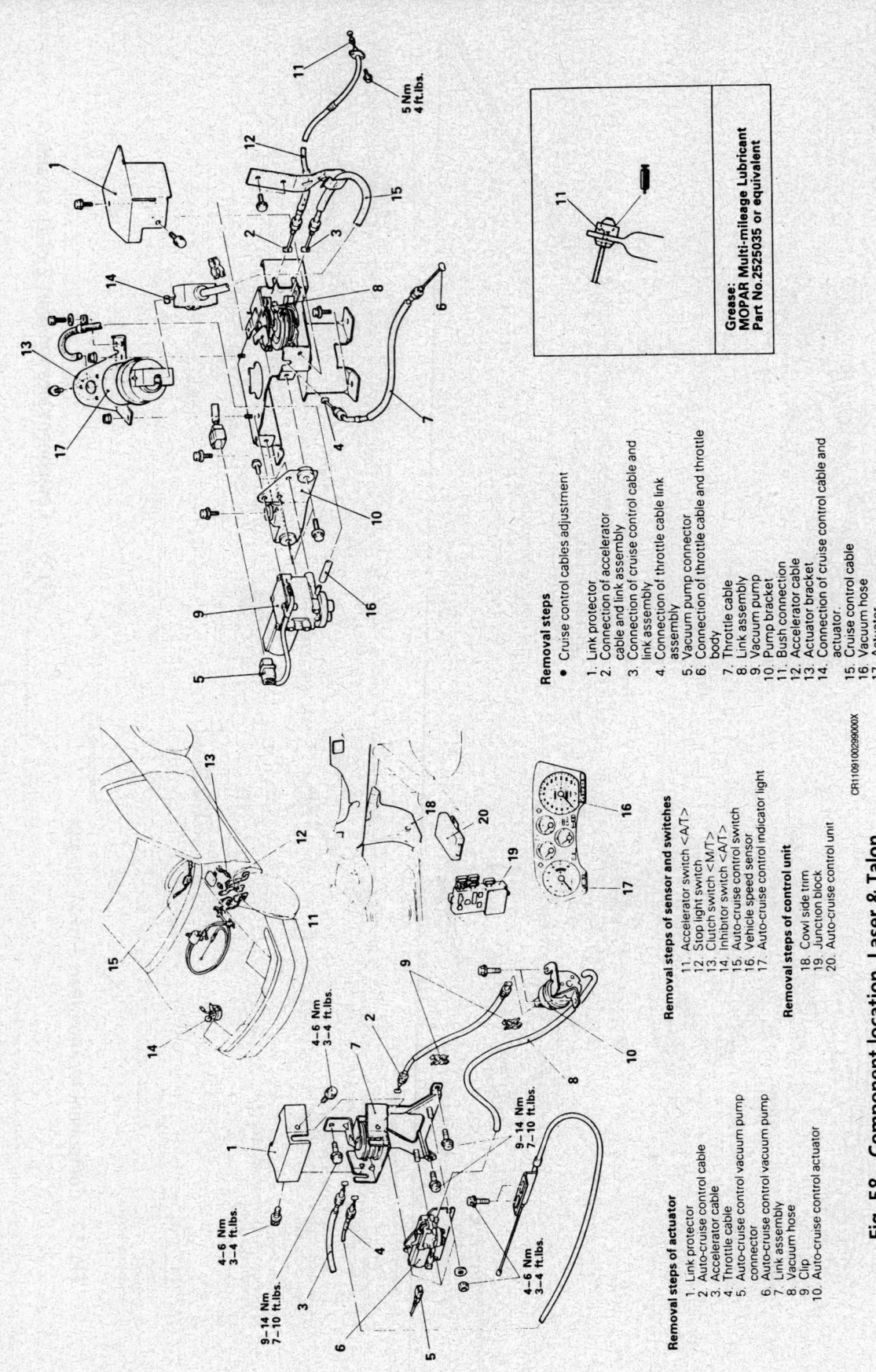

Grease:
MOPAR Multi-mileage Lubricant
Part No.252503S or equivalent

CR11092003000010X

Removal steps

● Cruise control cables adjustment

1. Link protector
2. Connection of accelerator cable and link assembly
3. Connection of cruise control cable and link assembly
4. Connection of throttle cable link assembly
5. Vacuum pump connector
6. Connection of throttle cable and throttle body
7. Throttle cable
8. Link assembly
9. Vacuum pump
10. Pump bracket
11. Bush connection
12. Accelerator cable
13. Actuator bracket
14. Connection of cruise control cable and actuator.
15. Cruise control cable
16. Vacuum hose
17. Actuator

Fig. 59 Component location (Part 1 of 2). Colt Vista/Summit Wagon

CR1091002990000X

Removal steps of actuator

1. Link protector
2. Auto-cruise control cable
3. Accelerator cable
4. Throttle cable
5. Auto-cruise control vacuum pump connector
6. Auto-cruise control vacuum pump
7. Link assembly
8. Vacuum hose
9. Clip
10. Auto-cruise control actuator

Removal steps of sensor and switches

11. Accelerator switch <A/T>
12. Stop light switch
13. Clutch switch <M/T>
14. Inhibitor switch <A/T>
15. Auto-cruise control switch
16. Vehicle speed sensor
17. Auto-cruise control indicator light

Removal steps of control unit

18. Cowl side trim
19. Junction block
20. Auto-cruise control unit

Fig. 58 Component location. Laser & Talon

Control switch and control unit removal steps

18. Horn pad
19. Control switch
20. Meter hood
21. Main switch (Cluster switch assembly)
  • Instrument under cover

22. Control unit

Sensor and switches removal steps

23. Inhibitor switch
24. Accelerator pedal switch <A/T>
25. Stop light switch
26. Clutch switch <M/T>
27. Throttle position sensor (with built-in idle switch)
28. Vehicle speed sensor

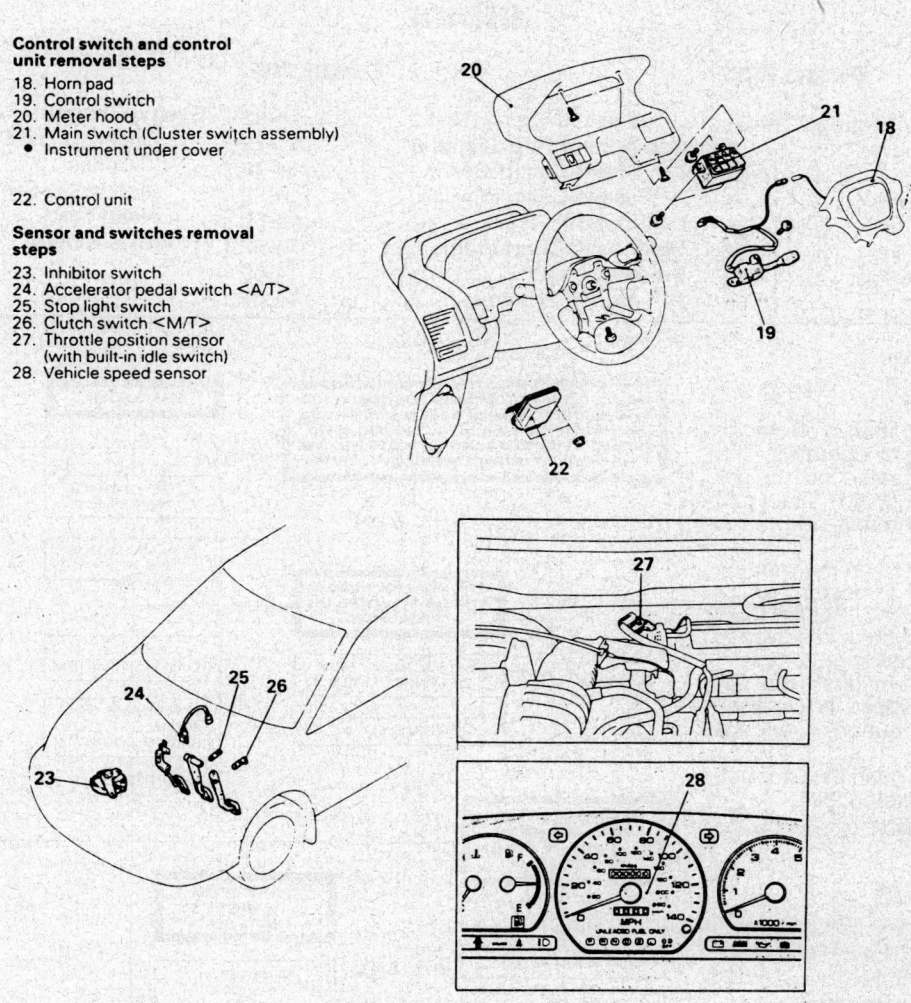

CR1109200300020X

Fig. 59 Component location (Part 2 of 2). Colt Vista/Summit Wagon

Type 3

NOTE: Electrical Symbol & Wire Color Code Identification Located In The Front Of This Manual May Be Used As An Aid When Using Wiring Circuits Found In This Section.

NOTE: On Air Bag Equipped Models, Refer To Air Bag System Precautions Located In The Front Of This Manual For System Disarming & Arming Procedures.

INDEX

DESCRIPTION

This Speed Control System is electrically controlled and vacuum operated. The electronic control is integrated into the powertrain control module (PCM). The PCM is located under the righthand side of the air cleaner.

The controls are located on the steering wheel. The controls consist of a SET/COAST, RESUME/ACCEL and ON and OFF buttons. This system is designed to operate at speed exceeding 35 mph.

To activate the system push the ON button. When desired speed is obtained push the SET/COAST button to engage system.

To deactivate system push the OFF button or lightly tap on brake pedal.

PRECAUTIONS

AIR BAG SYSTEM

Refer to Air Bag Systems Precautions in the front of this manual for system disarming and arming procedures.

TROUBLESHOOTING

When troubleshooting speed control system, refer to **Fig. 1** for troubleshooting chart.

SYSTEM DIAGNOSIS & TESTING

ROAD TEST

Road test vehicle to verify speed control system malfunction. The road test should include attention to the speedometer. Speedometer operation should be smooth and without flutter at all speeds or surging may be caused in the speed control system.

INOPERATIVE SYSTEM

If road test verifies an inoperative system, check and verify the following:

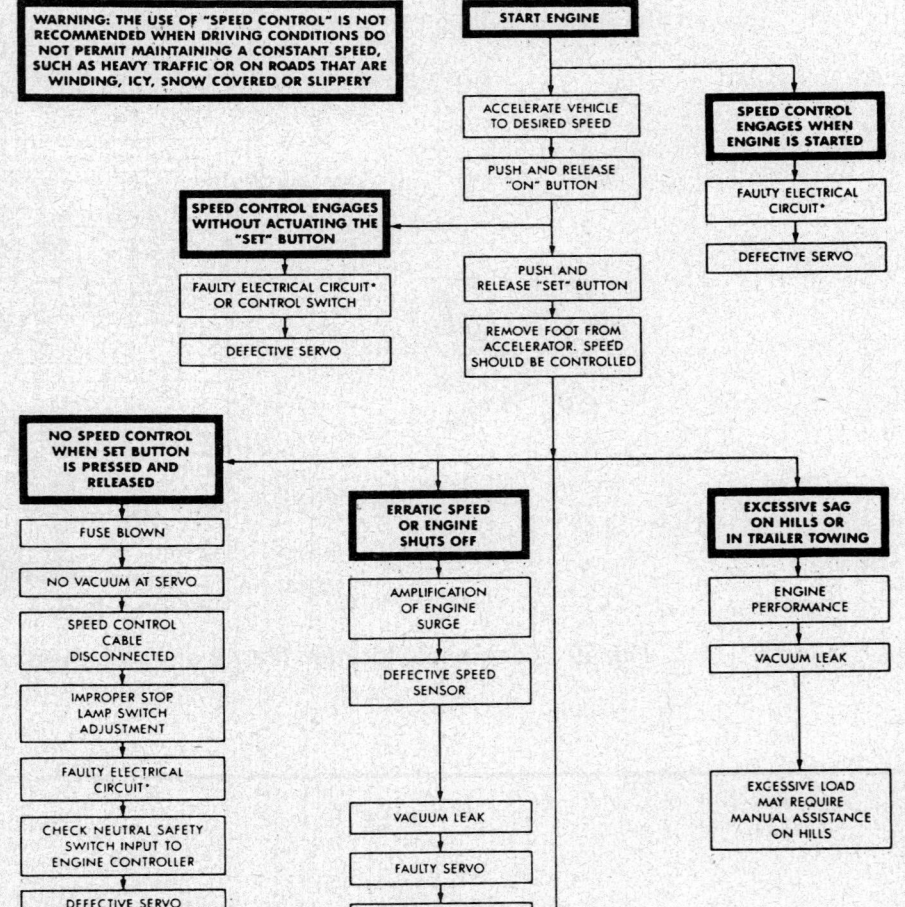

Fig. 1   Speed control troubleshooting chart (Part 1 of 2)

1. Inspect vacuum hose and electrical connections for loose, corrosion or bent terminals at servo.
2. Ensure both ends of speedometer are securely attached.
3. Check Fuse No. 14.

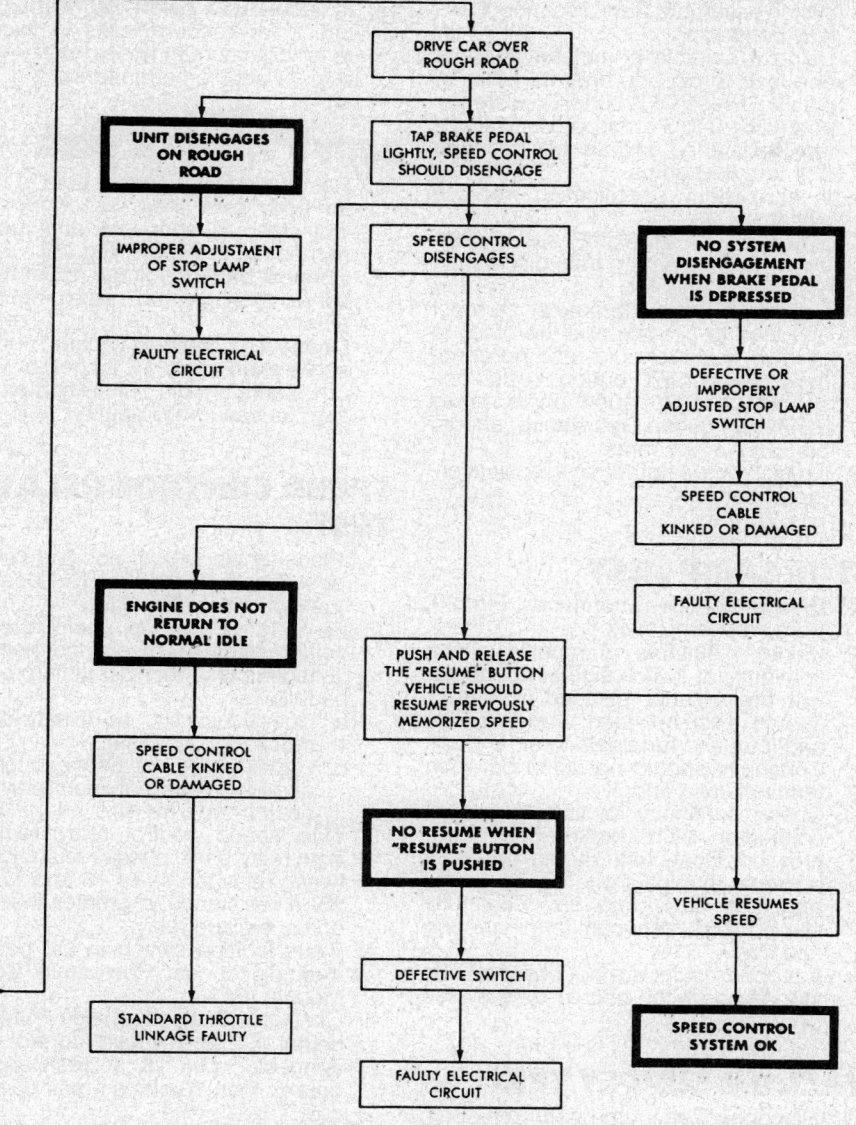

Fig. 1 Speed control troubleshooting chart (Part 2 of 2)

CR1109100304020X

quires the use of the DRB II diagnostic tool.
5. If Diagnostic Trouble Code 77 is present, refer to "Speed Control Relay Test" found in this section.
6. Repair any problems found, then recheck for Diagnostic Trouble Codes after repairs have been completed.
7. If no problems were found, replace powertrain control module.

COMPONENT DIAGNOSIS & TESTING

ELECTRICAL TESTS AT SERVO
1. Turn ignition switch to On position.
2. With speed control switch in On position, connect voltmeter negative lead to a chassis ground.
3. Disconnect 4-way connector at servo, **Fig. 25.**
4. If battery voltage is present at pin 2 proceed to step six, if battery voltage is not present at pin 2 of main harness 4-way connector, proceed as follows:
   a. Disconnect six way connector at stop lamp switch and test pin one of main harness for battery voltage, if voltage is present perform "Stop Lamp Test" found in this section.
   b. If stop lamp switch test is satisfactory, repair wire between stop lamp switch and servo.
   c. If no voltage at pin one of six way connector, remove ON/OFF speed control switch on steering wheel and disconnect two way connector. Test pin one for battery voltage.
   d. If voltage is present, perform "Speed Control Switch Test" found in this section.
   e. If speed control switch is satisfactory, check continuity across clockspring. If continuity exists, repair wire between stop lamp switch and clockspring.
   f. If no voltage exists at pin one of both switches, test for battery voltage between ignition and the fuse, if satisfactory check fuse. If fuse is satisfactory, repair wire between fuse and clockspring.
5. Connect a suitable jumper wire between pin No. 2 of 4-way connector and pin No. 2 of speed control servo.
6. In battery voltage is not present at remaining pin at servo, replace speed control servo.
7. Using suitable ohmmeter, connect negative lead to chassis ground and positive lead to pin 1 of 4-way connector.
8. If continuity does not exist, check and repair loose or damaged connectors or harness.

ELECTRICAL TESTS AT ENGINE CONTROLLER
1. Unplug 60-way engine controller harness connector from powertrain control module which is located under air cleaner.

CHECKING FOR DIAGNOSTIC TROUBLE CODES

When trying to verify a speed control system electronic malfunction, one of two methods may be used, the DRB II Diagnostic Tool or a Voltmeter.

Using Diagnostic Tool

If a DRB II Diagnostic Tool is available, plug tool into six way diagnostic connector located at right hand side of steering column, and verify that either a diagnostic trouble code 15, 34 or 77 is indicated. Refer to the appropriate diagnostic chart shown in **Figs. 2 through 21.** After performing test NS-6A and NS-6B, **Fig. 3 and 4,** perform verification test VER-1, **Fig. 22.** After performing all other diagnostic tests, perform verification test VER-2, **Fig. 23.** Refer to **Fig. 24** for speed control system wiring diagram. Follow tool manufacturers instructions for proper installation of the

tool prior to testing speed control system. If no problems were found, replace engine controller.

Using Voltmeter

If a DRB II Diagnostic tool is not available, check for Diagnostic Trouble Codes as follows:
1. Cycle ignition switch to On position three times. On third cycle, leave switch in On position.
2. Observe Check Engine indicator on instrument cluster. If a Diagnostic Trouble Code is present, CHECK ENGINE indicator lamp will flash (blink) in a series which will show which Diagnostic Trouble Code is the problem.
3. If no Diagnostic Trouble Code, or if code 34 is observed, perform "Electrical Test At Servo," "Speed Control Switch Test" and "Powertrain Control Module Test" found in this section.
4. If Diagnostic Trouble Code 15 is present, test Vehicle Speed Sensor. **Testing of Vehicle Speed Sensor re-**

2. Remove steering wheel speed control switches, then disconnect two way connector.
3. Connect a ohmmeter between terminal 23 of powertrain control module and pin one of speed control switch harnesses.
4. If no continuity exists, repair wire circuit as needed.
5. If continuity exists, refer to "Speed Control Switch Test" found in this section. Reconnect speed control switch connector.
6. Turn ignition switch to On position, connect voltmeter to terminal 53. Press OFF switch, no voltage should exist.
7. Depress ON switch, voltage should exist. If no voltage exists repair wire between pin 53 and pin 2 of speed control servo.
8. Connect voltmeter to terminal 33, depress OFF switch, voltage should not exist.
9. Depress ON switch, voltage should exist. If no voltage exists repair wire between pin 33 and pin 1 of speed control servo.
10. Connect one lead of a ohmmeter to ground and other lead to terminal 29, with brake pedal released continuity should exist. With brake pedal depressed continuity should not exist.
11. If continuity exists when pedal is depressed, check for continuity between terminal 29 of engine controller and pin 3 of stop lamp connector. If no continuity exists, repair wiring. If continuity does exist test stop lamp switch. Refer to "Stop Lamp Switch Test" found in this section.
12. If stop lamp switch test is satisfactory, test continuity between pin six of stop lamp switch and ground.
13. Connect one lead of an ohmmeter to ground and one lead to pin 30, place transaxle in Drive, no continuity should not exist. Place selector in Park or Neutral, continuity should exist.

SPEED CONTROL SWITCH TEST

1. Remove ON/OFF speed control switch assembly, then disconnect two way connector.
2. Using a suitable ohmmeter connect one lead to pin one and the other to pin two. Press OFF button, resistance should be 0 to 5 ohms, press ON button, resistance should be between 674 and 688 ohms.
3. If not within specification, replace switch.
4. Remove SET/RESUME speed control switch assembly, then disconnect two way connector.
5. Using a suitable ohmmeter connect one lead to pin one and the other to pin two, meter should read no continuity. Press SET button, resistance should be 1978-2002 ohms, press RESUME button, resistance should be 5558-5682 ohms.
6. If resistance is not within specification, replace switch.

STOP LAMP TEST

1. Disconnect 6-way connector, **Fig. 26**, from stop lamp switch.
2. Using a suitable ohmmeter, check continuity at switch side of connector with brake pedal released. Continuity should exist between terminals one and four, and terminals three and six. Continuity should not exits between terminals two and five.
3. Check continuity at switch side of connector with brake pedal depressed. Continuity should not exist between terminals one and four, and terminals three and six. Continuity should exits between terminals two and five.
4. If proper results are not obtained, the stop lamp switch should be adjusted or replaced.

VACUUM SUPPLY TEST

1. Disconnect vacuum hose from servo and install a vacuum gauge in hose.
2. Start engine and run at idle. Vacuum gauge should read 10 inches Hg.
3. Shut engine Off, vacuum should still read 10 inches Hg.

4. If vacuum is below 10 inches Hg, check for vacuum leaks in vacuum reservoir, vacuum hoses, check valve or poor engine performance.

SERVO VACUUM TEST

1. Remove speed control cable at throttle body end, then disconnect four way electrical connector and vacuum harness at the servo, **Fig. 25**.
2. Connect battery voltage to pin two of servo, then ground remaining three pins.
3. Connect a hand held vacuum pump to servo, then apply 15 inches of vacuum. Cable should pull in and stay as long as vacuum is applied.

SPEED CONTROL RELAY TEST

1. Place ignition in Off position, remove speed control relay which is located in junction block, **Fig. 27**.
2. Place ignition in On position, check voltage at pin 16 of relay connector. If voltage is less than 10 volts proceed as follows:
   a. Check fuse No. 14, if satisfactory proceed to next step.
   b. Repair open wire between ignition and fuse 14 or between relay connector and fuse 14.
3. With speed control relay removed from relay bank, check resistance between relay terminals 16 and 17, **Fig. 28**. If resistance is greater than 100 ohms, replace relay.
4. Place ignition switch in Off position, then disconnect Powertrain Control Module (PCM).
5. Check resistance between PCM connector 55 and speed control relay connector pin 18, if resistance is greater than 10 ohms repair open circuit.
6. Check resistance between pin 55 of PCM and ground, if resistance is below 10 ohms repair short to ground. If resistance is greater than 10 ohms, replace PCM.

DIAGNOSTIC CHART INDEX

Test	Description	Page No.	Fig. No.
FC-1A	Checking System For Fault Codes	14-63	2
NS-6A	Correcting "No Response" Condition	14-63	3
NS-6B	Correcting "No Response" Condition	14-65	4
SC-52A	Repairing Fault Speed Control Solenoid Circuits	14-65	5
SC-52B	Repairing Fault Speed Control Solenoid Circuits	14-66	6
SC-52C	Repairing Fault Speed Control Solenoid Circuits	14-66	7
SC-53A	Repairing Fault Speed Control Switch Always High	14-66	8
SC-53B	Repairing Fault Speed Control Switch Always High	14-67	9
SC-54A	Repairing Fault Speed Control Switch Always Low	14-67	10
SC-55A	Repairing Fault Speed Control Power Relay Circuit	14-67	11
SC-NF-1	Checking Speed Control Switches	14-68	12
SC-NF-2	Checking Park/Neutral Circuit	14-68	13

Continued

DIAGNOSTIC CHART INDEX—Continued

Test	Description	Page No.	Fig. No.
SC-NF-3	Checking Speed Control Servo Vacuum & Actuation	14-68	14
SC-NF-4	Checking Speed Control Cable	14-69	15
SC-NF-5	Repairing Speed Control Set/Resume Switch Open	14-69	16
SC-NF-6	Repairing Brake Switch Sense Circuit For A Short To Ground	14-69	17
SC-NF-7	Repairing Brake Switch Open Or Adjustment	14-69	18
SC-NF-8	Repairing Brake Switch Sense Circuit Open	14-69	19
SC-NF-9	Checking Brake Adjustment	14-69	20
SC-NF-10	Speed Control Road Test & Indicators	14-70	21
VER-1	Verification Test 1	14-70	22
VER-2	Verification Test 2	14-70	23

NOTE: The battery must be fully charged for any test in this manual.

1. Attempt to start the engine. Crank for up to 10 seconds if necessary.

2. Connect the DRBII to the engine diagnostic connector. Write down fault messages that are displayed.

3. If the DRBII screen is blank or has a DRBII error message, go to TEST NS-6A.

4. If fault messages are displayed, refer to the fault code list below for appropriate test.

5. If there are no faults displayed refer to Speed Control problems SC-NF-1

DRBII MESSAGE	DIAGNOSTIC TEST
SPEED CONTROL SOLENOID CIRCUITS	SC-52A
SPEED CONTROL SWITCH ALWAYS HIGH	SC-53A
SPEED CONTROL SWITCH ALWAYS LOW	SC-54A
SPEED CONTROL POWER RELAY CIRCUIT	SC-55A

CR1109100305000X

Fig. 2 Test FC-1A: Checking system for Diagnostic Trouble Codes

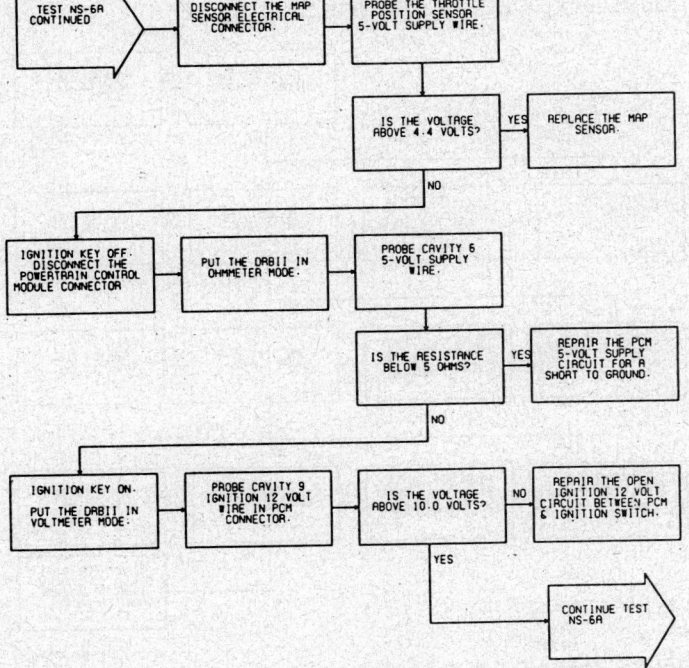

CR1109100306020X

Fig. 3 Test NS-6A: Correcting "No Response" Condition (Part 2 of 6)

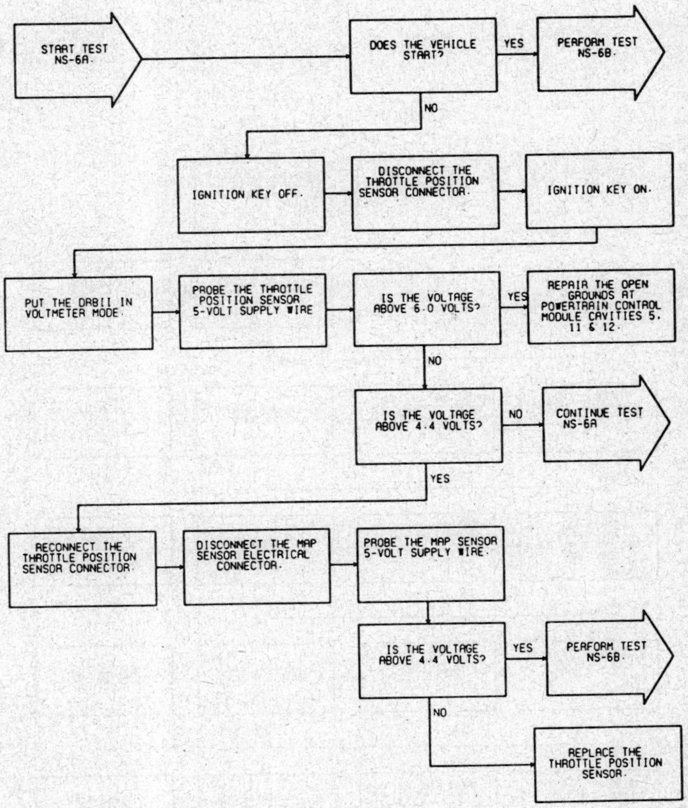

CR1109100306010X

Fig. 3 Test NS-6A: Correcting "No Response" Condition (Part 1 of 6)

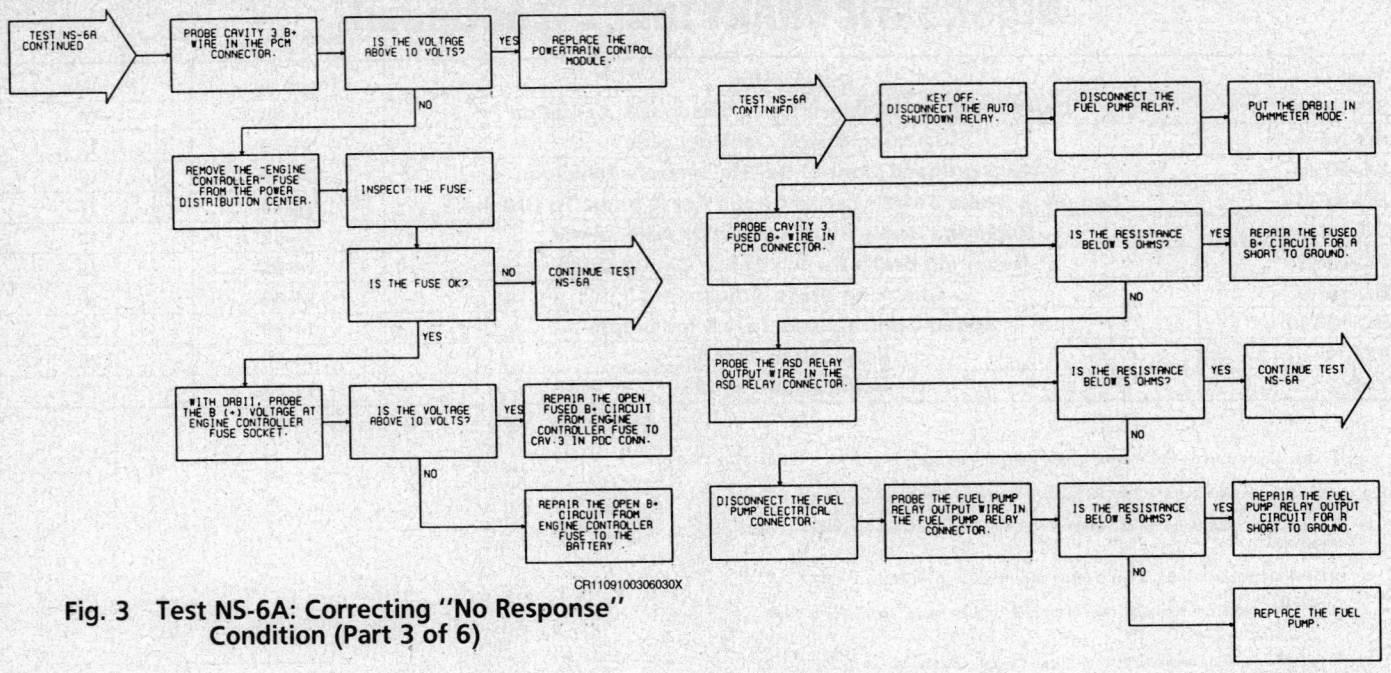

Fig. 3 Test NS-6A: Correcting "No Response" Condition (Part 3 of 6)

CR1109100306030X

Fig. 3 Test NS-6A: Correcting "No Response" Condition (Part 4 of 6)

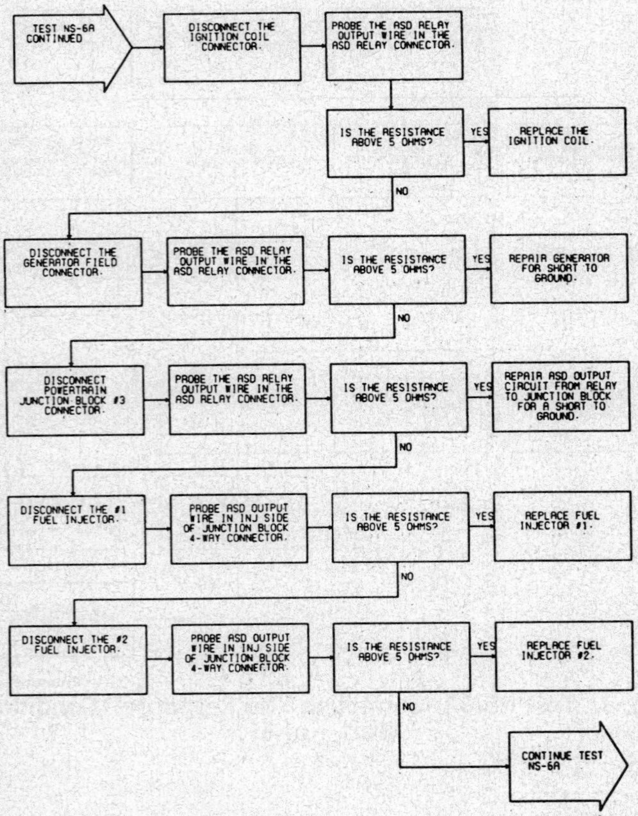

CR1109100306040X

Fig. 3 Test NS-6A: Correcting "No Response" Condition (Part 5 of 6)

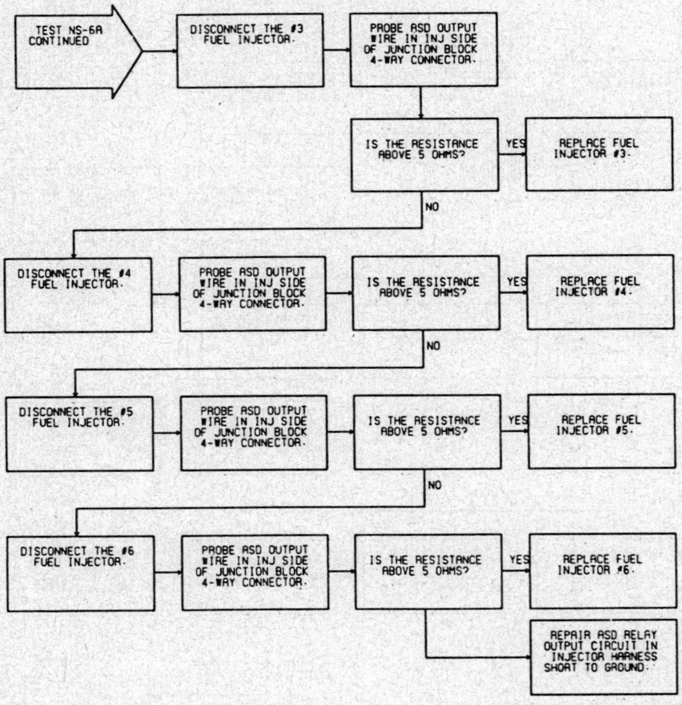

CR1109100306050X

Fig. 3 Test NS-6A: Correcting "No Response" Condition (Part 6 of 6)

CR1109100306060X

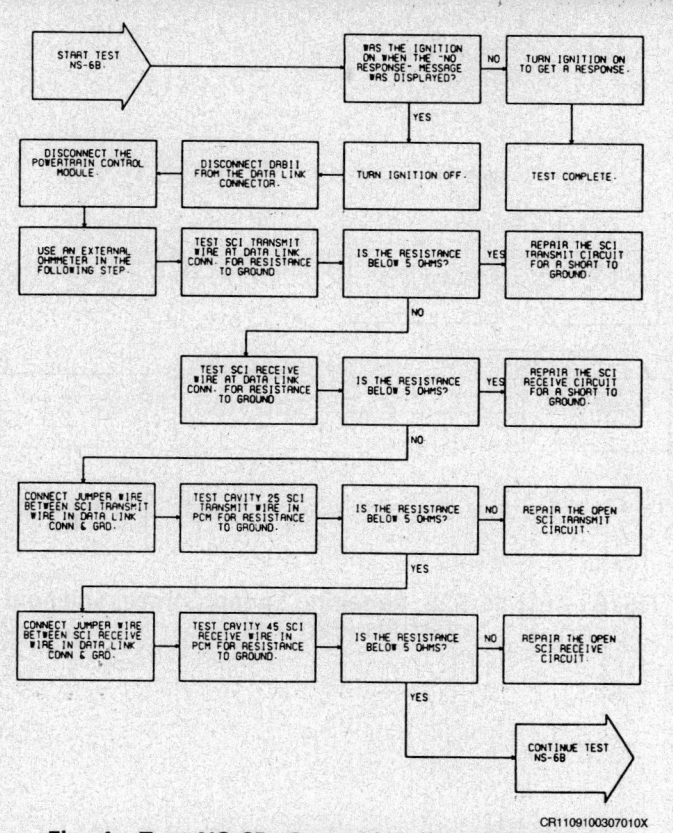

Fig. 4 Test NS-6B: Correcting "No Response"
Condition (Part 1 of 2)

Fig. 4 Test NS-6B: Correcting "No Response" Condition
(Part 2 of 2)

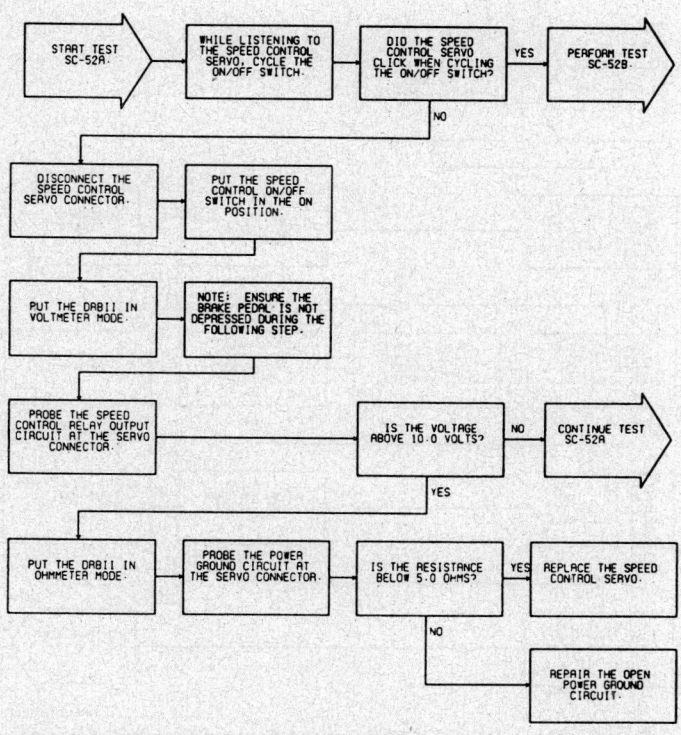

Fig. 5 Test SC-52A: Repairing Speed Control Solenoid
Circuits (Part 1 of 2)

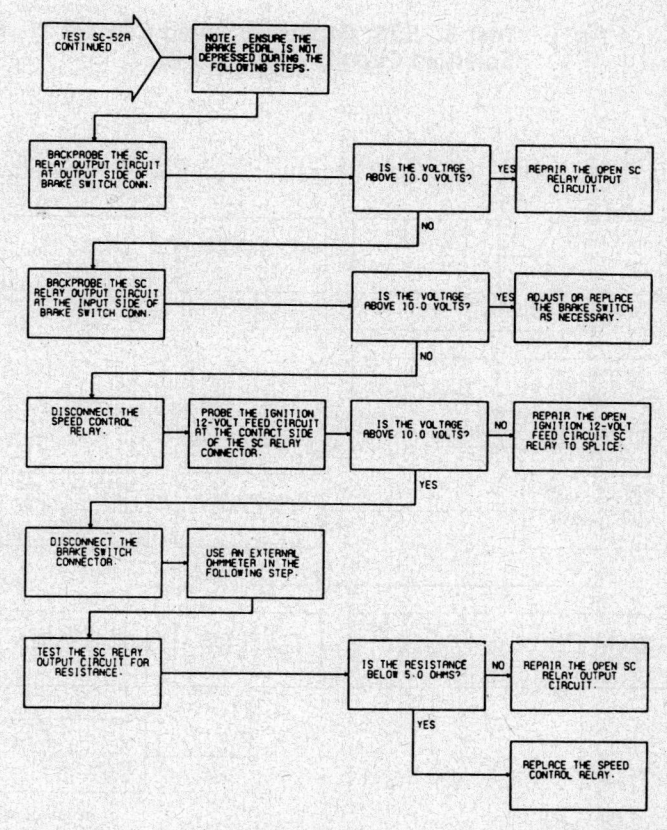

Fig. 5 Test SC-52A: Repairing Speed Control
Solenoid Circuits (Part 2 of 2)

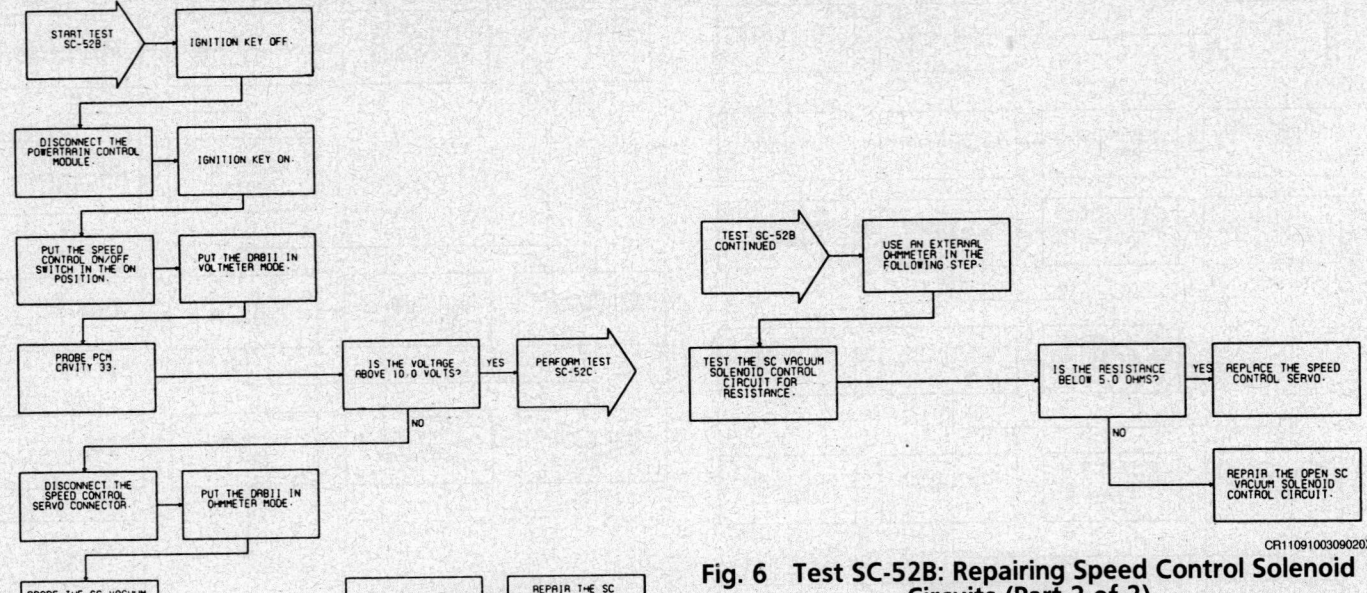

Fig. 6   Test SC-52B: Repairing Speed Control Solenoid Circuits (Part 1 of 2)

Fig. 6   Test SC-52B: Repairing Speed Control Solenoid Circuits (Part 2 of 2)

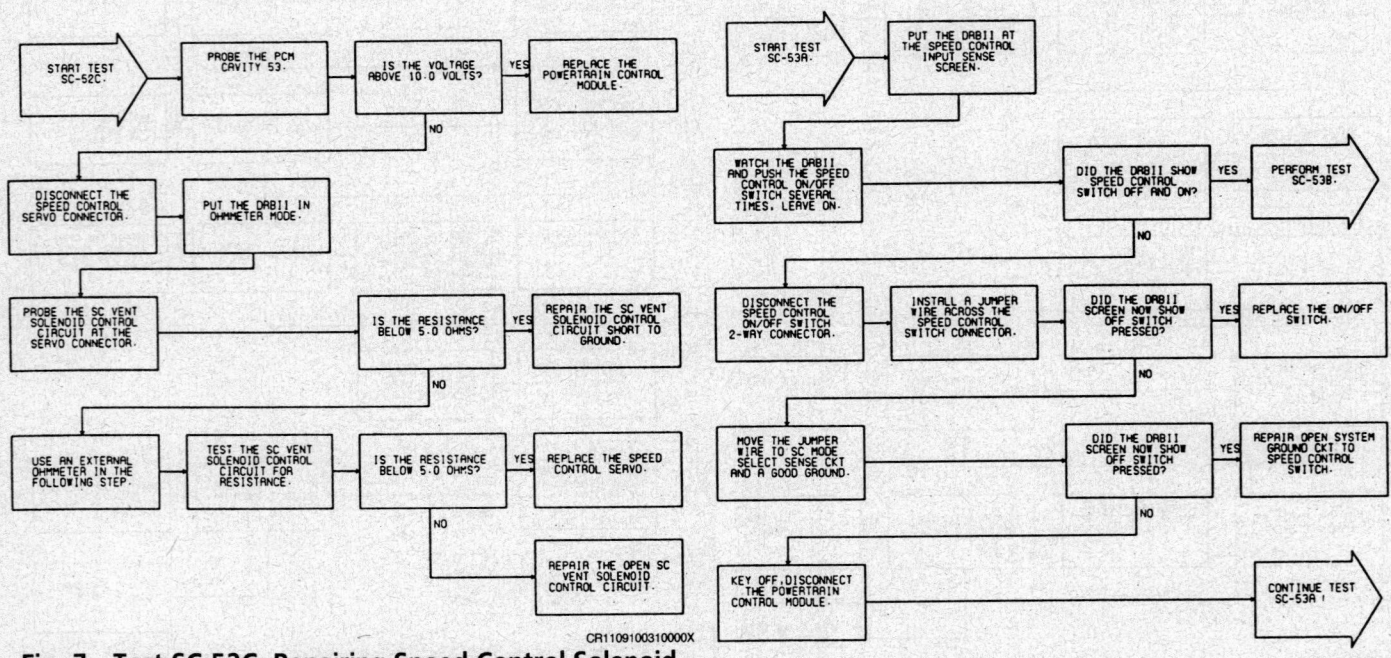

Fig. 7   Test SC-52C: Repairing Speed Control Solenoid Circuits

Fig. 8   Test SC-53A: Repairing Speed Control Switch Always High (Part 1 of 2)

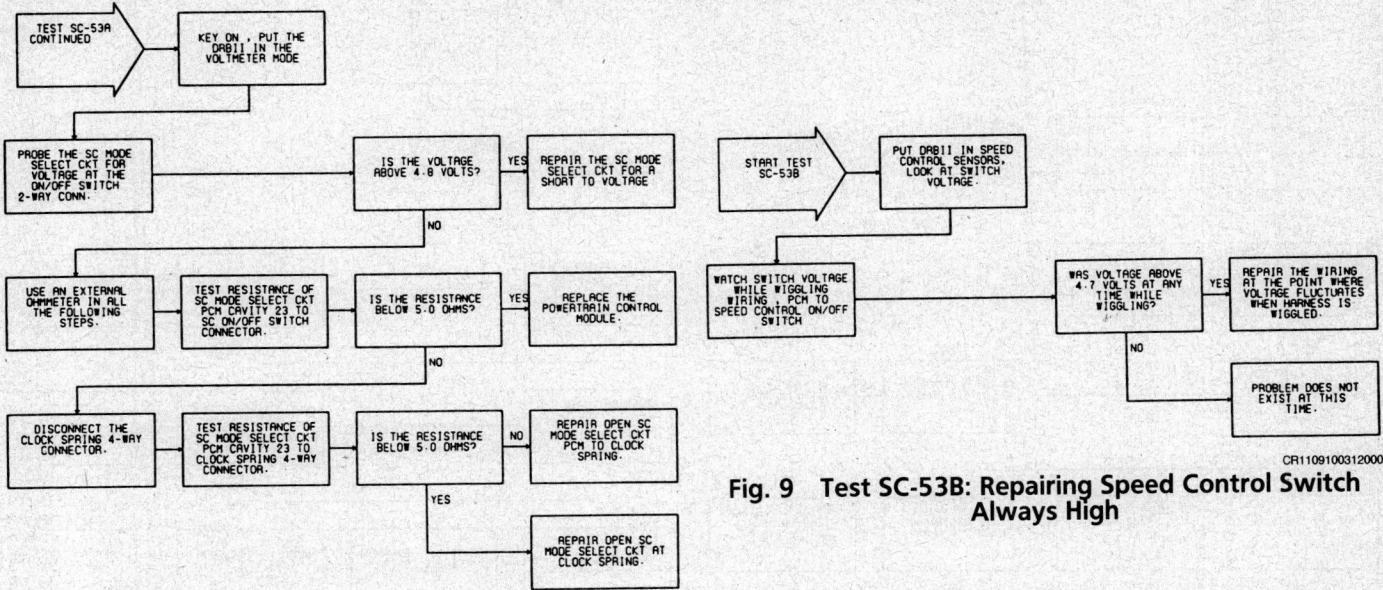

**Fig. 8   Test SC-53A: Repairing Speed Control Switch
Always High (Part 2 of 2)**

CR1109100311020X

**Fig. 9   Test SC-53B: Repairing Speed Control Switch
Always High**

CR1109100312000X

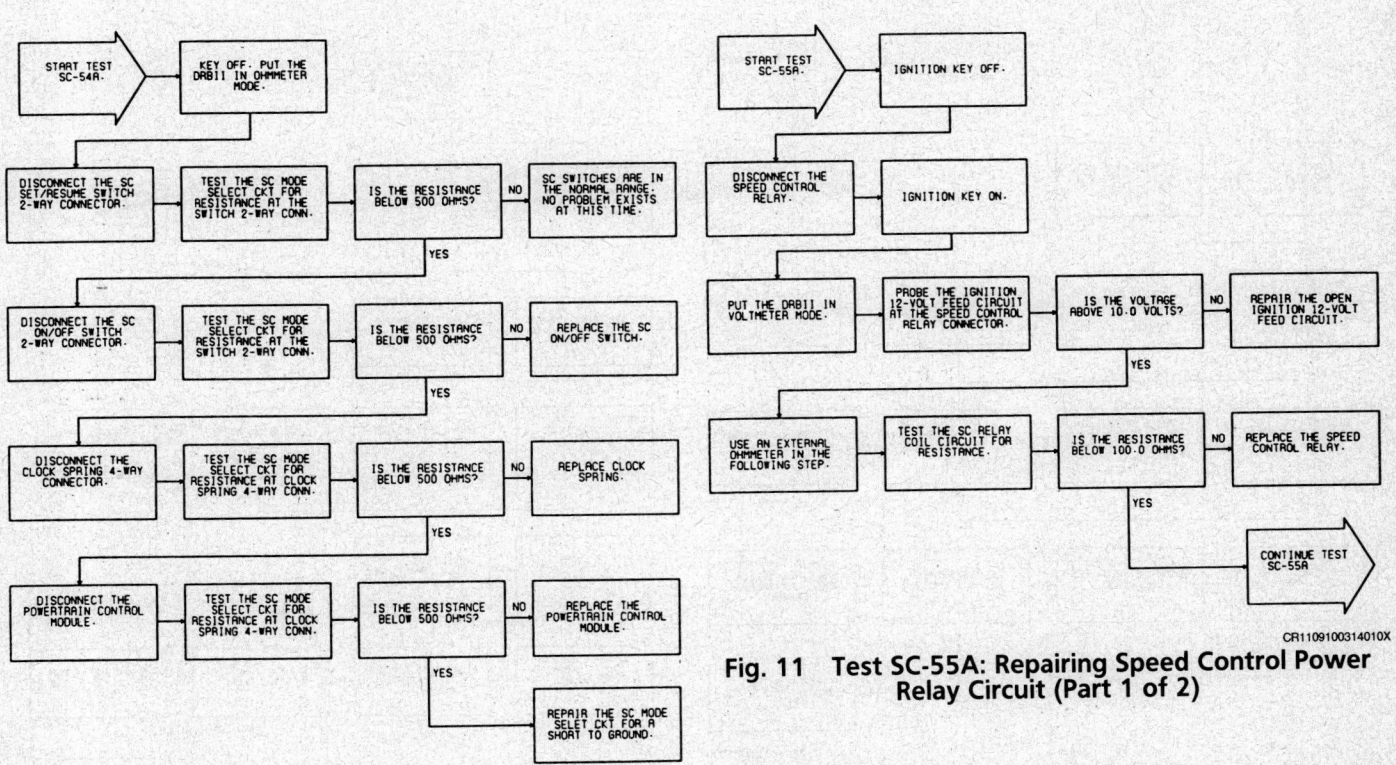

**Fig. 10   Test SC-54A: Repairing Speed Control Switch
Always Low**

CR1109100313000X

**Fig. 11   Test SC-55A: Repairing Speed Control Power
Relay Circuit (Part 1 of 2)**

CR1109100314010X

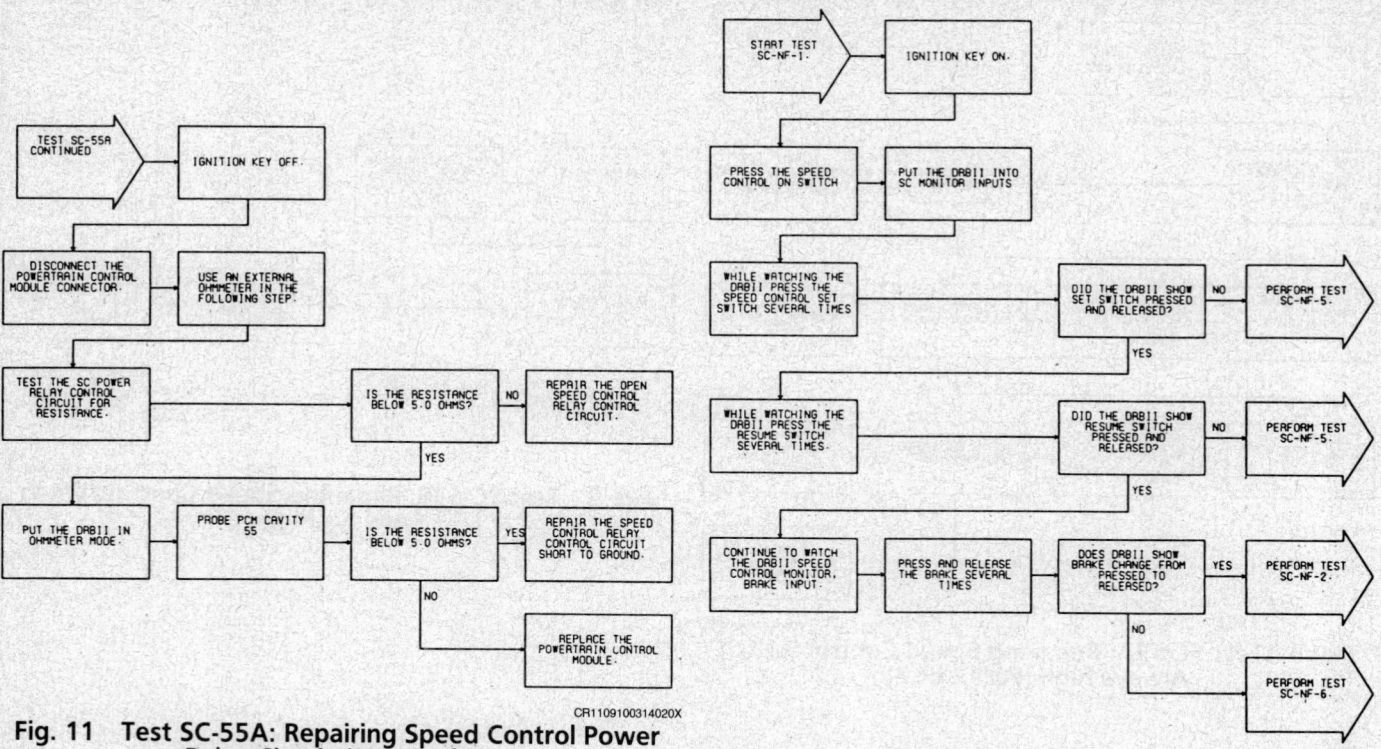

Fig. 11 Test SC-55A: Repairing Speed Control Power Relay Circuit (Part 2 of 2)

CR1109100314020X

Fig. 12 Test SC-NF-1, Checking Speed Control Switches

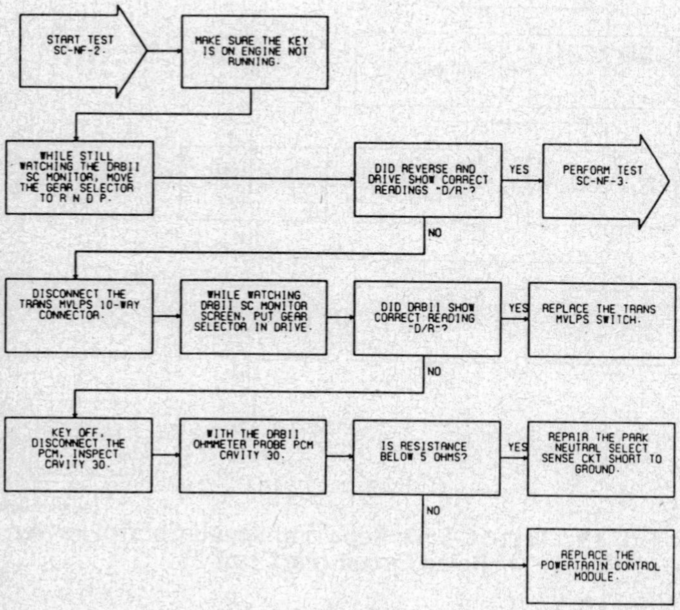

CR1109100315000X

Fig. 13 Test SC-NF-2, Checking Park/Neutral Circuit

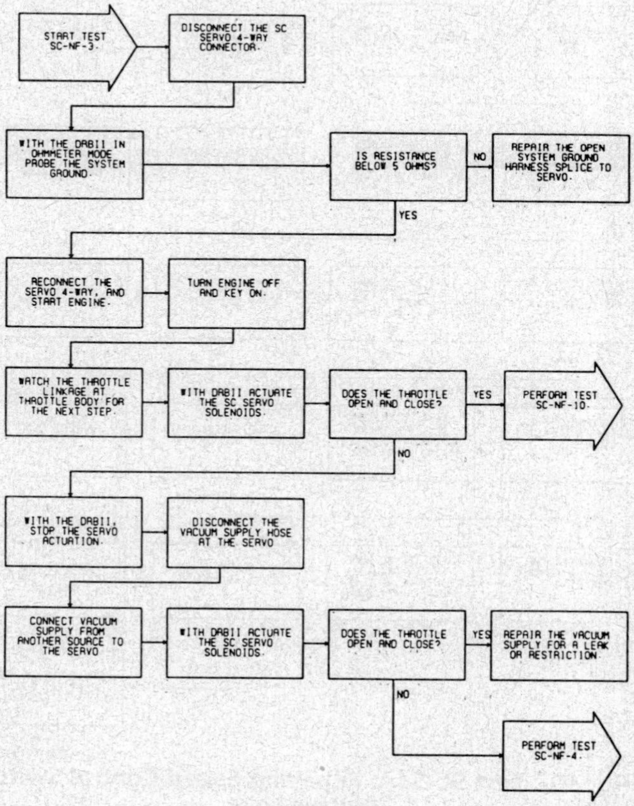

CR1109100316000X

Fig. 14 Test SC-NF-3, Checking Speed Control Servo Vacuum & Actuation

CR1109100317000X

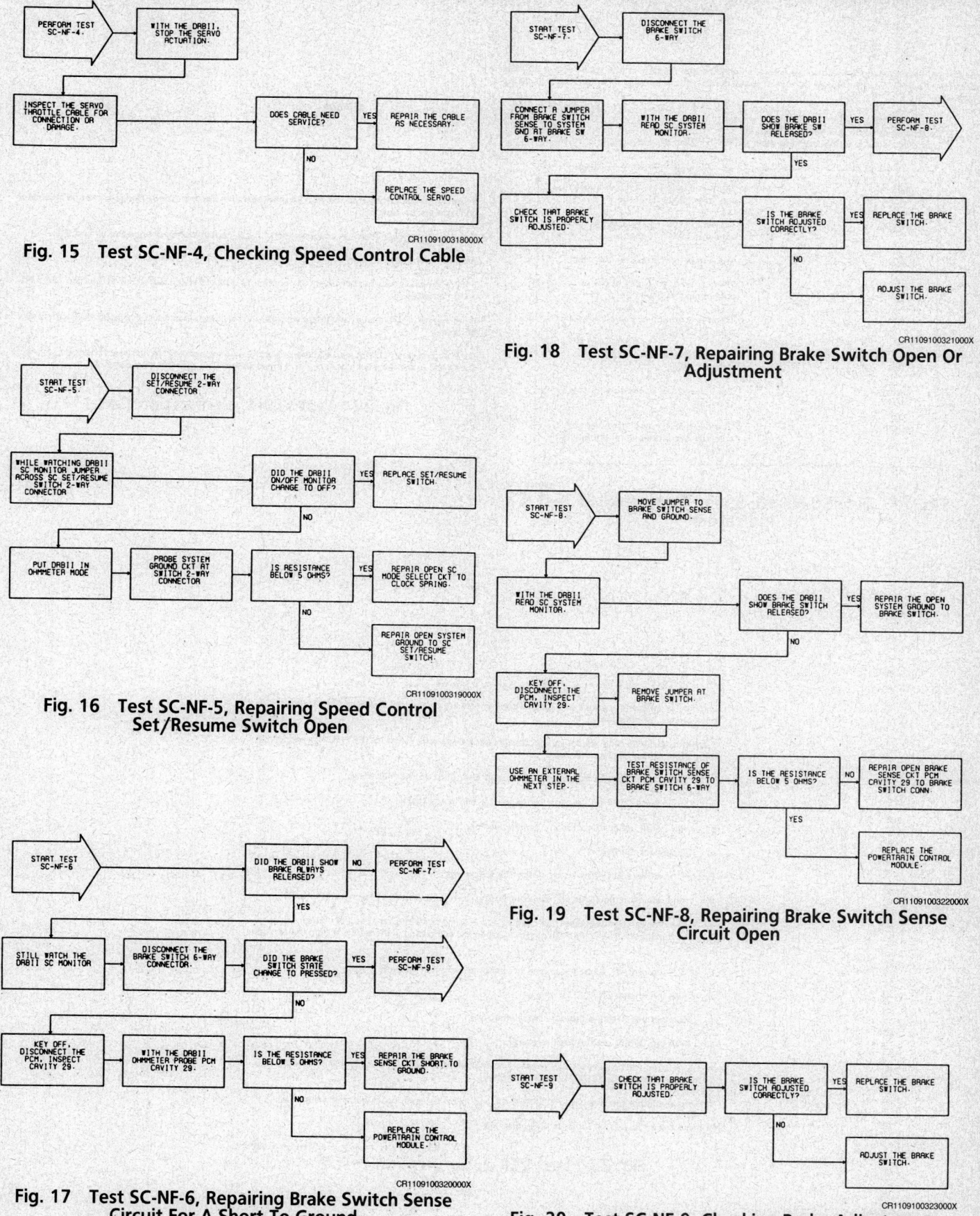

Fig. 15   Test SC-NF-4, Checking Speed Control Cable

Fig. 16   Test SC-NF-5, Repairing Speed Control Set/Resume Switch Open

Fig. 17   Test SC-NF-6, Repairing Brake Switch Sense Circuit For A Short To Ground

Fig. 18   Test SC-NF-7, Repairing Brake Switch Open Or Adjustment

Fig. 19   Test SC-NF-8, Repairing Brake Switch Sense Circuit Open

Fig. 20   Test SC-NF-9, Checking Brake Adjustment

All components checked indicate speed control should operate. Test drive at a speed above 30 miles per hour. Attempt to set the Speed Control. If speed control will not set after repeated attempts, do the following:

1. Read the DRBII Speed Control Status screen.
2. Look at what is the last denied message.
3. Use that message in the following table for the indicated area of trouble.

Denied Message	Indication
ON/OFF	There is a lack of voltage at engine controller cavity 23 or 49.
SPEED	The vehicle speed as read by the distance sensor is below 35 mph.
RPM	The engine rpm is excessively high.
BRAKE	There is an open circuit at power control module cavity 29.
P/N	There is a ground at powertrain control module cavity 30.
RPM/SPD	The rpm/vehicle speed ratio is not constant.
CLUTCH	The rpm/vehicle speed ratio is not constant.
SOL FLT	There is a fault in the servo vent or solenoid circuit that is either maturing or set.

CR1109100324000X

Fig. 21   Test SC-NF-10, Speed Control Road Test & Indicators

Inspect the vehicle to ensure that all engine components are connected. Reassemble and reconnect components as necessary.

Inspect the engine oil for fuel contamination. If it is contaminated, change the oil and filter.

Attempt to start the engine.

If the engine is unable to start, check all pertinent Technical Service Bulletins and return to **TEST FC-1A** if necessary.

If the engine is able to start and the powertrain control module has been changed, the repair is now complete.

If the engine is not able to start and the powertrain control module has not been changed, connect the DRBII to the data link connector and erase faults. The repair is now complete.

CR1109100325000X

Fig. 22   Test VER-1, Verification Test 1

Inspect the vehicle to ensure that all engine components are connected. Reassemble and reconnect components as necessary.

If another fault was read previously that has not been dealt with, return to **TEST FC-1A** and follow the path specified by the other fault.

If the powertrain control module has not been changed, do the following:

a.   Connect the DRBII to the data link connector and erase faults.

b.   With DRBII, reset all values in adaptive memory.

c.   Disconnect the DRBII.

Ensure no other fault remains by doing the following:

a.   If the vehicle is equipped with air conditioning, turn on the air conditioning and blower.

b.   Drive the vehicle for at least five minutes and at some point attain a speed of 40 mph. Ensure the transmission shifts through all gears. Upon the completion of the road test, turn the engine off.

c.   Start the engine. Allow the engine to idle for at least two minutes.

d.   Turn the engine off.

e.   Connect the DRBII to the data link connector.

f.   With the DRBII, read all fault messages.

If the repaired fault has reset, the repair is not complete. Check all pertinent Technical Service Bulletins and return to **TEST FC-1A** if necessary.

If there is another fault, return to **TEST FC-1A** and follow the path specified by the other fault.

If there are no faults, the repair is now complete.

CR1109100326000X

Fig. 23   Test VER-2, Verification Test 2

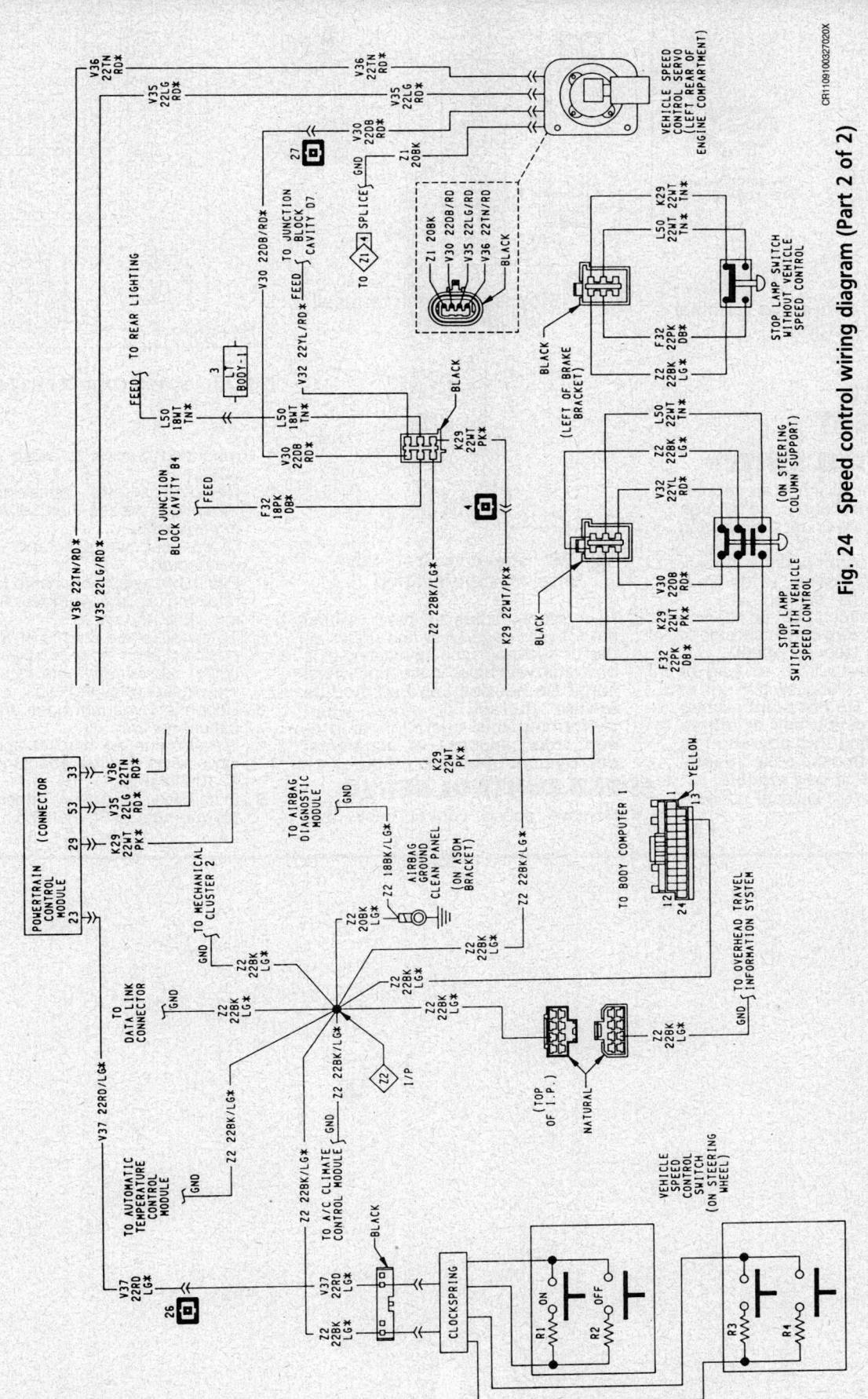

Fig. 24 Speed control wiring diagram (Part 2 of 2)

Fig. 24 Speed control wiring diagram (Part 1 of 2)

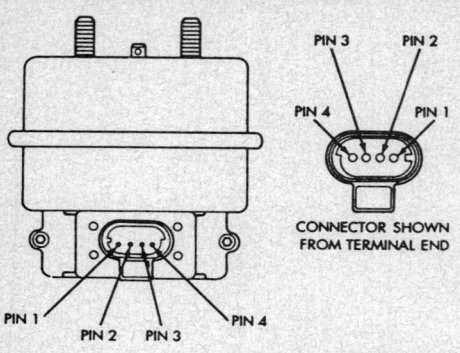

Fig. 25 Speed control servo terminal identification

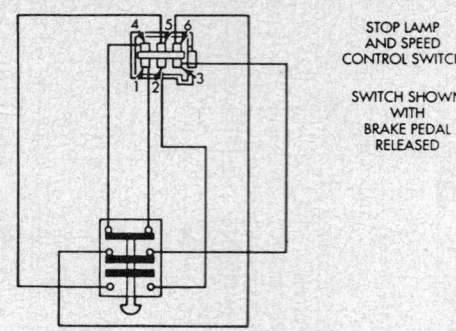

Fig. 26 Stop lamp switch terminal identification

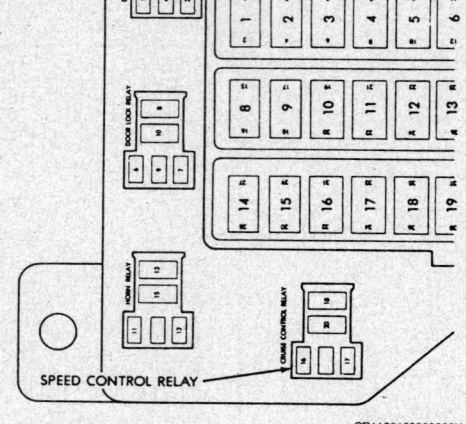

Fig. 27 Speed control relay location

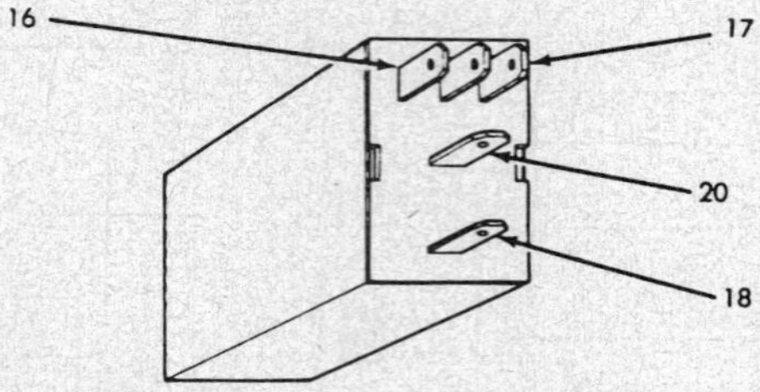

COMPONENT REPLACEMENT

SPEED CONTROL SWITCH

The speed control switches are mounted in the steering wheel and wired through the clock spring device under the steering wheel hub.

If removal of air bag module is necessary, refer to "Air bag Module" in the "Passive Restraint Systems" section.

1. Turn ignition switch to Off position.
2. Remove two screws from back side of each switch on steering wheel.
3. Rock switch away from air bag or horn pad while lifting switch out of steering wheel. **Do not point air bag module toward yourself or others when performing this operation to prevent injury in case of accidental deployment of air bag module.**
4. Disconnect 2-way electrical connector.

Fig. 28 Speed control relay terminal identification

5. Reverse procedure to install, sliding the forward edge of switch under air bag or horn pad. Line up locating pins on switch with holes in steering wheel frame. **Do not point air bag module toward yourself or others when performing this operation to prevent injury in case of accidental deployment of air bag module.**

SPEED CONTROL SERVO

1. Remove speed control cable and mounting bracket to servo attaching nuts.
2. Remove screws attaching servo mounting bracket, then servo mounting bracket.
3. Disconnect vacuum and electrical connector.
4. Pull cable away from servo to expose retaining clip, then remove clip attaching cable and servo.
5. To install, place throttle in wide open position, align hole in speed control cable sleeve with hole in servo pin, then install retaining clip.
6. Reconnect vacuum hose and electrical connector.
7. Install mounting bracket and attaching screws, **torque** attaching screws to 105 inch lbs.
8. Install servo and servo attaching nuts, **torque** nuts to 60 inch lbs.

NOTE: Electrical Symbol & Wire Color Code Identification Located In The Front Of This Manual May Be Used As An Aid When Using Wiring Circuits Found In This Section.

NOTE: On Air Bag Equipped Models, Refer To Air Bag System Precautions Located In The Front Of This Manual For System Disarming & Arming Procedures.

INDEX

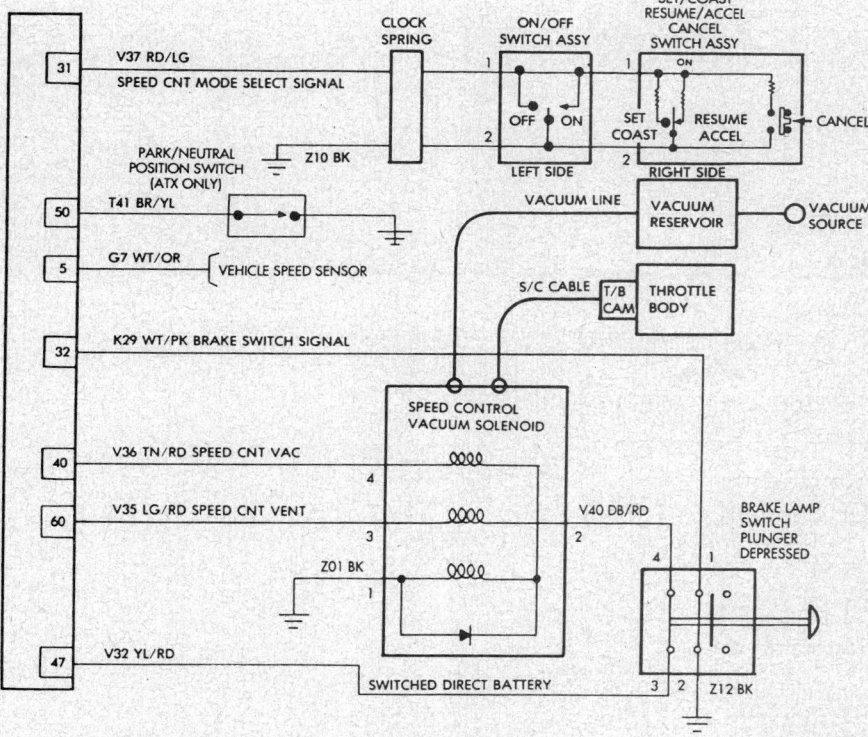

Fig. 1   Speed control circuit

CR1109500335000X

TROUBLESHOOTING

When troubleshooting speed control system, refer to **Fig. 1** for wiring diagram.

SYSTEM DIAGNOSIS & TESTING

ROAD TEST

Road test vehicle to verify speed control system malfunction. The road test should include attention to the speedometer. Speedometer operation should be smooth and at all speeds or surging may be caused in the speed control system.

INOPERATIVE SYSTEM

If road test verifies an inoperative system, check and verify the following:
1. Check Fuse No. 25 in the power distribution center.
2. Inspect vacuum hose and electrical connections for loose, corrosion or bent terminals at servo.
3. Check for correct position of the vacuum check valve in the hose from servo to vacuum source. The word **VAC** on the valve must point toward the vacuum source.
4. Ensure both ends of speedometer are securely attached.

CHECKING FOR DIAGNOSTIC TROUBLE CODES

When trying to verify a speed control system electronic malfunction, one of two methods may be used; the DRB II Diagnostic Tool or by reading the Malfunction Indicator Lamp (MIL) on the instrument cluster.

Using Diagnostic Tool

If a DRB II Diagnostic Tool is available, plug tool into six way diagnostic connector located at righthand side of steering column, at lower edge of knee bolster, and verify that either a diagnostic trouble code 15, 34 is indicated. Refer to the appropriate diagnostic chart, **Figs. 2 through 11**.

DESCRIPTION

This Speed Control System is electrically controlled and vacuum operated. The electronic control is integrated into the powertrain control module (PCM). The PCM is located on the left fender shield.

The controls are located on the steering wheel. The controls consist of two switch pods. The ON and OFF buttons are located on the upper left side of the air bag module. The RESUME/ACCEL, SET/COAST and CANCEL buttons are located on the upper right side of the air bag module. This system is designed to operate at speeds exceeding 30 mph.

To activate the system, push the ON button. When the desired speed is obtained, push the SET/COAST button to engage the system.

To deactivate the system, push the OFF button, lightly tap on brake pedal, or push the CANCEL button, which will disengage the speed control without erasing the speed set in memory.

PRECAUTIONS

AIR BAG SYSTEM

Refer to "Air Bag Systems Precautions" in the front of this manual for system disarming and arming procedures.

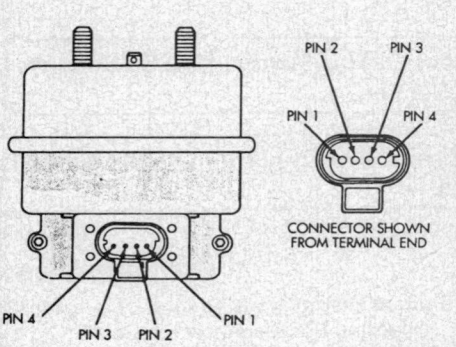

Fig. 2   Servo harness connector

CONNECTOR SHOWN
FROM TERMINAL END

PIN 2   PIN 3
PIN 1   PIN 4

PIN 4   PIN 3   PIN 2   PIN 1

CR1109500336000X

Reading Malfunction Indicator Lamp (MIL)

1. With key inserted in ignition switch, cycle switch to ON position three times. On third cycle, leave switch in ON position.
2. Observe the Malfunction Indicator Lamp (MIL) on the instrument cluster. If a Diagnostic Trouble Code is present, the lamp will flash in a series which will indicate the problem. For example; a series of three flashes in rapid succession, a slight pause, then four flashes in rapid succession would indicate Diagnostic Trouble Code 34.
3. If no Diagnostic Trouble Code appears or Diagnostic Trouble Code 15 or 34 is observed, refer to **Figs. 2** through 11.

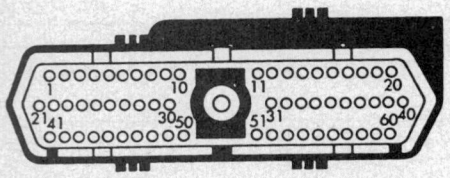

Fig. 3   60–way connector

CR1109500337000X

DIAGNOSTIC CHART INDEX

Description	Page No.	Fig. No.
Will Not Set or Disengage	14-74	4
Accelerates By Itself	14-75	5
Slows Down By Itself	14-75	6
Resumes By Itself	14-76	7
Sets By Itself	14-76	8
Will Not Resume But Sets Properly	14-76	9
Will Not Resume But Sets Properly	14-77	10
Will Not Slow Down When COAST Button Is Pressed	14-77	11

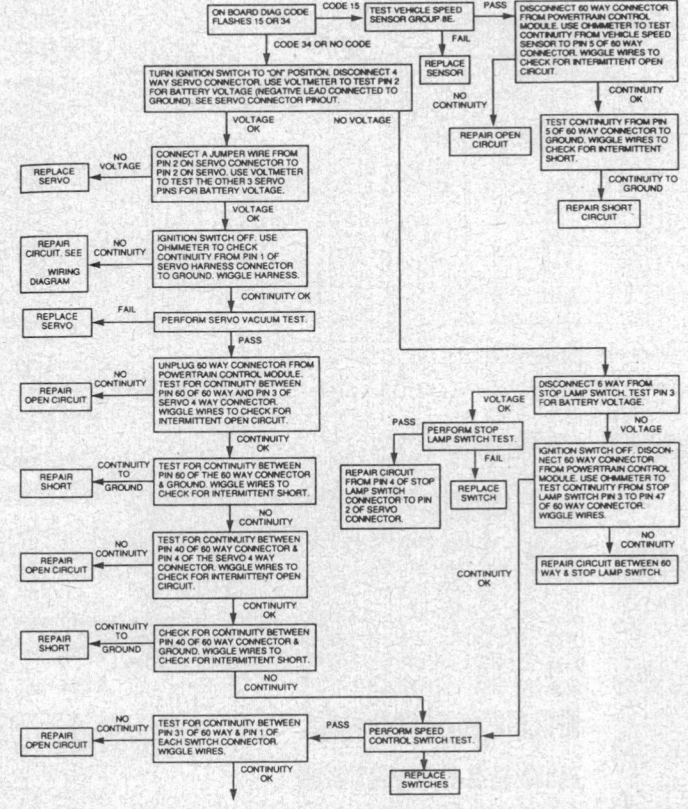

CR1109500338010X

Fig. 4   Will Not Set or Disengage (Part 1 of 2)

CR1109500338020X

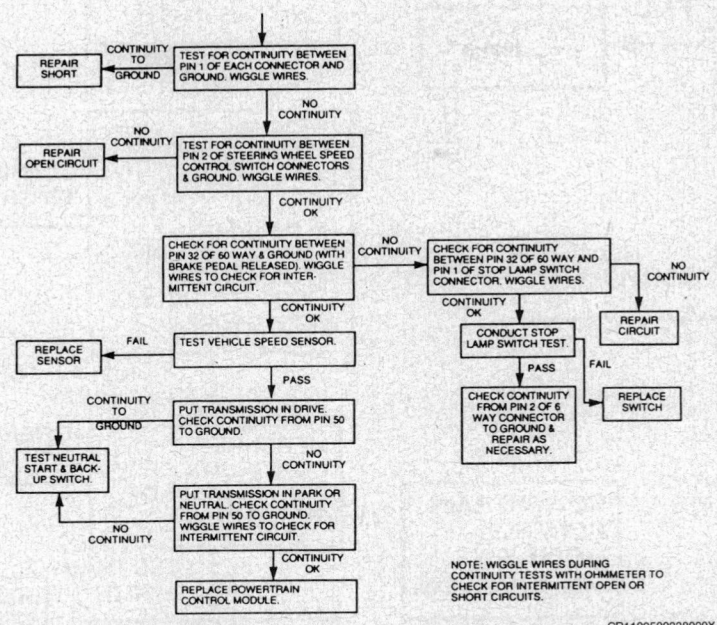

Fig. 4 Will Not Set or Disengage (Part 2 of 2)

CR1109500339000X

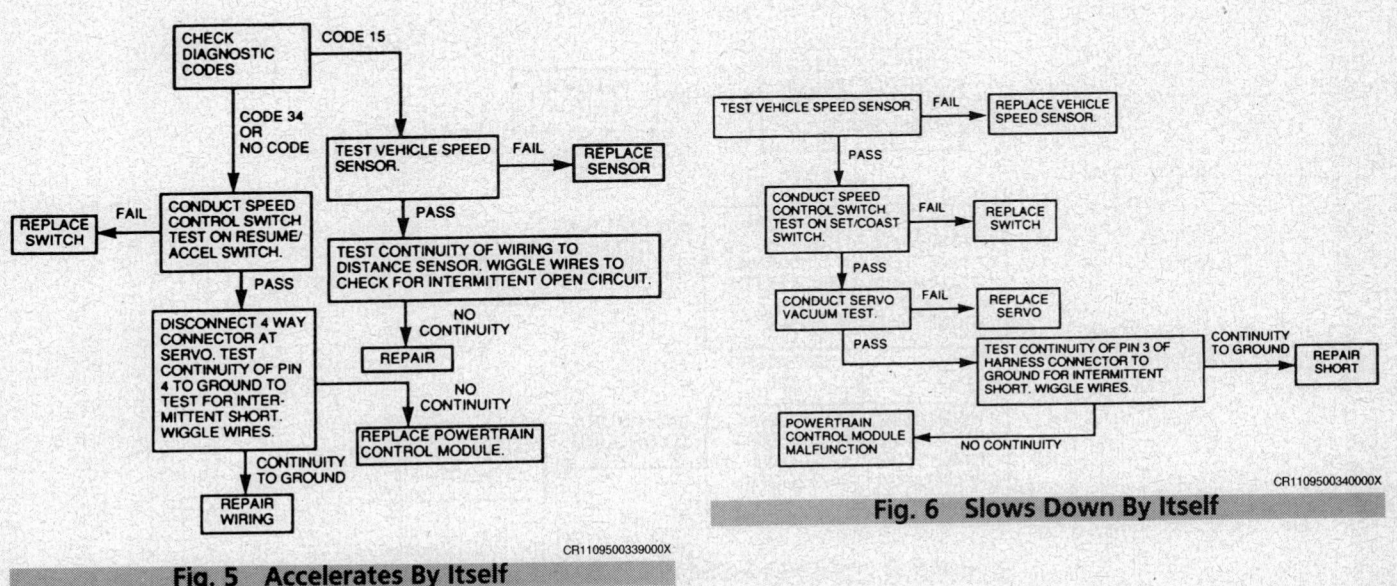

Fig. 5 Accelerates By Itself

CR1109500340000X

Fig. 6 Slows Down By Itself

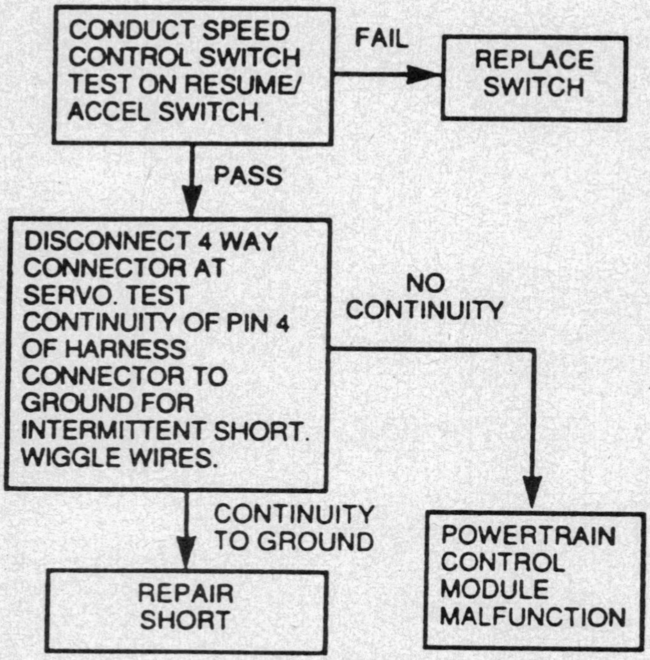

CONDUCT SPEED CONTROL SWITCH TEST ON RESUME/ACCEL SWITCH. → **FAIL** → REPLACE SWITCH

↓ **PASS**

DISCONNECT 4 WAY CONNECTOR AT SERVO. TEST CONTINUITY OF PIN 4 OF HARNESS CONNECTOR TO GROUND FOR INTERMITTENT SHORT. WIGGLE WIRES. → **NO CONTINUITY** → POWERTRAIN CONTROL MODULE MALFUNCTION

↓ **CONTINUITY TO GROUND**

REPAIR SHORT

Fig. 7 Resumes By Itself

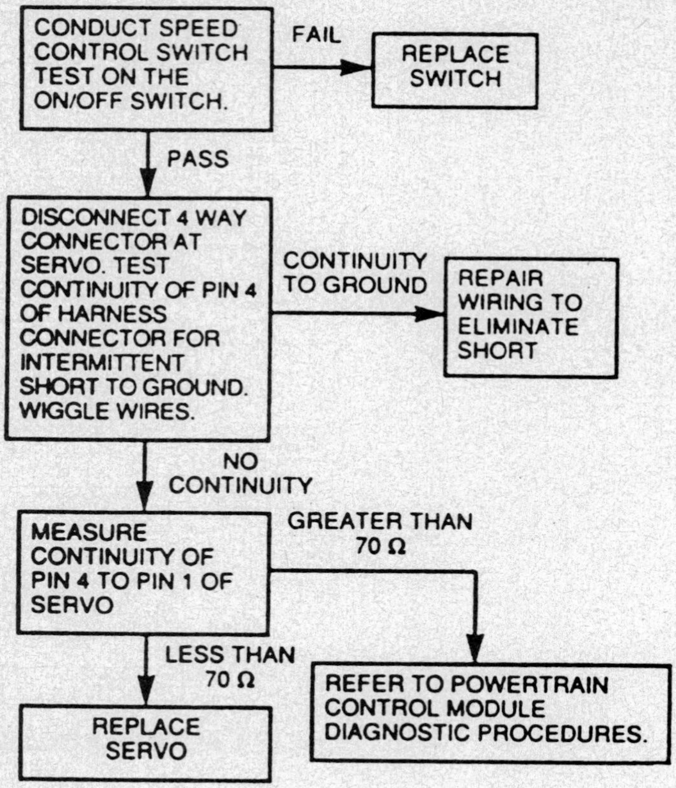

CR1109500341000X

CONDUCT SPEED CONTROL SWITCH TEST ON THE ON/OFF SWITCH. → **FAIL** → REPLACE SWITCH

↓ **PASS**

DISCONNECT 4 WAY CONNECTOR AT SERVO. TEST CONTINUITY OF PIN 4 OF HARNESS CONNECTOR FOR INTERMITTENT SHORT TO GROUND. WIGGLE WIRES. → **CONTINUITY TO GROUND** → REPAIR WIRING TO ELIMINATE SHORT

↓ **NO CONTINUITY**

MEASURE CONTINUITY OF PIN 4 TO PIN 1 OF SERVO → **GREATER THAN 70 Ω** → REFER TO POWERTRAIN CONTROL MODULE DIAGNOSTIC PROCEDURES.

↓ **LESS THAN 70 Ω**

REPLACE SERVO

Fig. 8 Sets By Itself

CR1109500342000X

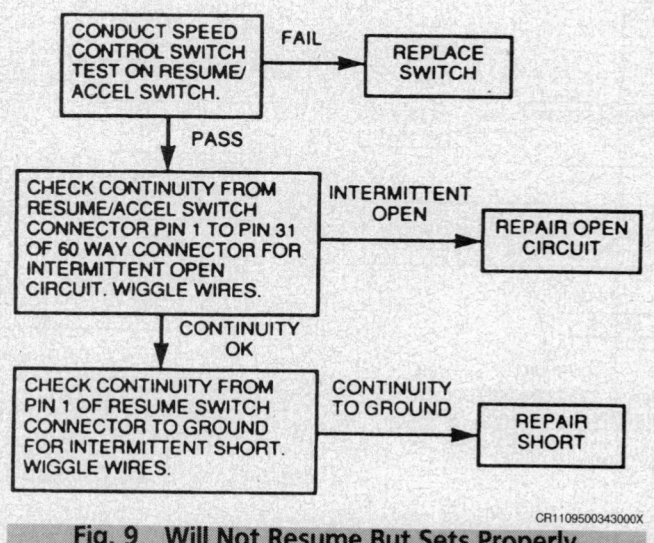

CONDUCT SPEED CONTROL SWITCH TEST ON RESUME/ACCEL SWITCH. → **FAIL** → REPLACE SWITCH

↓ **PASS**

CHECK CONTINUITY FROM RESUME/ACCEL SWITCH CONNECTOR PIN 1 TO PIN 31 OF 60 WAY CONNECTOR FOR INTERMITTENT OPEN CIRCUIT. WIGGLE WIRES. → **INTERMITTENT OPEN** → REPAIR OPEN CIRCUIT

↓ **CONTINUITY OK**

CHECK CONTINUITY FROM PIN 1 OF RESUME SWITCH CONNECTOR TO GROUND FOR INTERMITTENT SHORT. WIGGLE WIRES. → **CONTINUITY TO GROUND** → REPAIR SHORT

CR1109500343000X

Fig. 9 Will Not Resume But Sets Properly

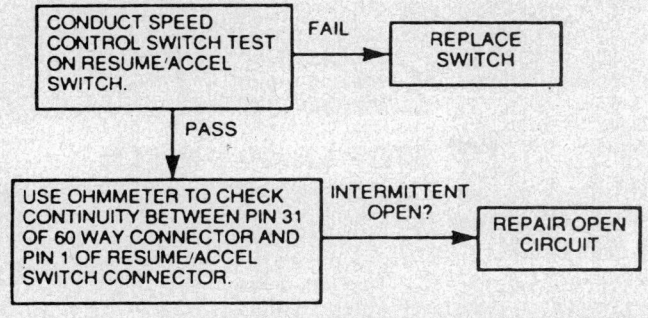

```
CONDUCT SPEED          FAIL      REPLACE
CONTROL SWITCH TEST  ────────►   SWITCH
ON RESUME/ACCEL
SWITCH.

     │ PASS
     ▼
USE OHMMETER TO CHECK   INTERMITTENT     REPLACE OPEN
CONTINUITY BETWEEN PIN 31   OPEN?    ──► CIRCUIT
OF 60 WAY CONNECTOR AND
PIN 1 OF RESUME/ACCEL
SWITCH CONNECTOR.
```

CR1109500344000X

Fig. 10   Will Not Resume But Sets Properly

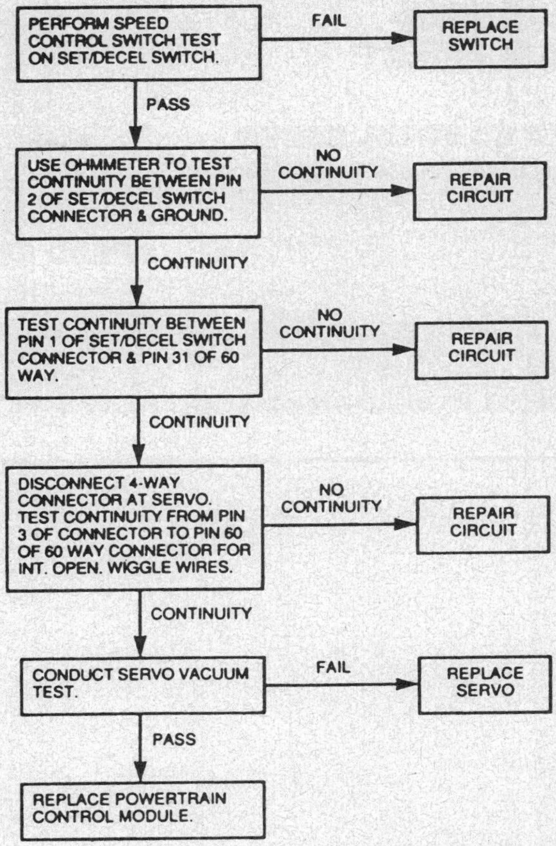

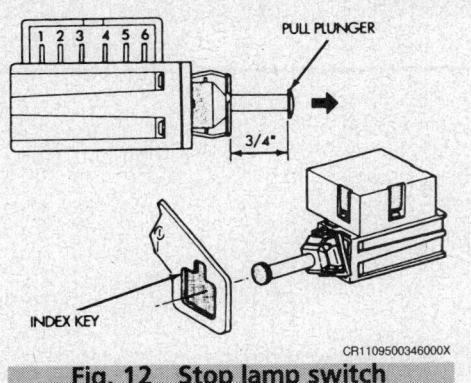

PULL PLUNGER

3/4"

INDEX KEY

CR1109500346000X

Fig. 12   Stop lamp switch

```
PERFORM SPEED           FAIL      REPLACE
CONTROL SWITCH TEST  ────────►   SWITCH
ON SET/DECEL SWITCH.

     │ PASS
     ▼
USE OHMMETER TO TEST      NO          REPAIR
CONTINUITY BETWEEN PIN  CONTINUITY ──► CIRCUIT
2 OF SET/DECEL SWITCH
CONNECTOR & GROUND.

     │ CONTINUITY
     ▼
TEST CONTINUITY BETWEEN    NO          REPAIR
PIN 1 OF SET/DECEL SWITCH  CONTINUITY ──► CIRCUIT
CONNECTOR & PIN 31 OF 60
WAY.

     │ CONTINUITY
     ▼
DISCONNECT 4-WAY           NO          REPAIR
CONNECTOR AT SERVO.      CONTINUITY ──► CIRCUIT
TEST CONTINUITY FROM PIN
3 OF CONNECTOR TO PIN 60
OF 60 WAY CONNECTOR FOR
INT. OPEN. WIGGLE WIRES.

     │ CONTINUITY
     ▼
CONDUCT SERVO VACUUM    FAIL      REPLACE
TEST.                ────────►   SERVO

     │ PASS
     ▼
REPLACE POWERTRAIN
CONTROL MODULE.
```

CR1109500345000X

Fig. 11   Will Not Slow Down When COAST Button Is Pressed

COMPONENT DIAGNOSIS & TESTING

SPEED CONTROL SWITCH TEST

1. Remove ON/OFF speed control switch assembly and disconnect connector.
2. Using a suitable ohmmeter, ensure there is no continuity between switch terminals. Press the OFF button and ohmmeter should read 0—0.5 ohms. Press the ON button and ohmmeter should read 15,245—15,555 ohms. If resistance does not fall within these values, replace switch.
3. Remove RESUME/SET/CANCEL speed control switch assembly and disconnect connector.
4. Using a suitable ohmmeter, ensure there is no continuity between switch terminals. Press the SET button and ohmmeter should read 2,910—2,970 ohms. Press the RESUME button and ohmmeter should read 6,580—6,750 ohms. Press the CANCEL button and ohmmeter should read 900—920 ohms. If resistance does not fall within these values, replace switch.

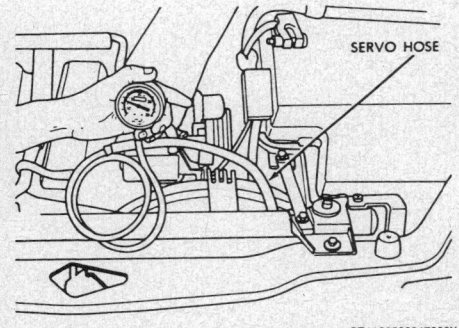

SERVO HOSE

CR1109500347000X

Fig. 13   Vacuum supply test

STOP LAMP SWITCH TEST

1. Remove stop lamp switch assembly and disconnect connector, **Fig. 12.**
2. Using a suitable ohmmeter, ensure there is continuity between switch terminals 5 and 6. When plunger is de-

pressed, there should be continuity between terminals 1 and 2 and between terminals 3 and 4.
3. If above results are not obtained, switch is defective or out of adjustment. Switch is adjusted by pulling out plunger to end of travel which is   inch.

VACUUM SUPPLY TEST

1. Disconnect vacuum hose at servo and install a suitable vacuum gauge in the hose, **Fig. 13.**
2. Start engine and observe gauge at idle. Vacuum should read at least 10

inches of mercury. Shut off engine and ensure vacuum holds.
3. If vacuum does not meet the above requirements, check for leaks in vacuum lines, check valve, vacuum reservoir or poor engine performance

SERVO VACUUM TEST

1. Turn ignition switch to ON position without starting engine.
2. Activate speed control ON switch.
3. Disconnect 4-way electrical connector and vacuum harness at servo, **Fig. 2.**
4. Connect a jumper wire from pin 2 of the servo to pin 2 of the wire connector.
5. Ground pins 1, 3 and 4 in the servo connector
6. Connect a suitable hand held vacuum pump to the vacuum nipple of the servo and apply 10-15 inches of vacuum.
7. Ensure throttle cable pulls in and holds as long as long as vacuum pump is connected. After one minute, ensure cable is still holding . If cable does not hold, replace servo.
8. Disconnect pin 3 from ground. Cable should return to rest position. If cable does not return, replace servo.

COMPONENT REPLACEMENT

SPEED CONTROL SERVO

1. Disconnect battery cables, then remove battery thermoguard, battery hold down and battery.
2. Remove power distribution center from back of battery tray.
3. Disconnect speed control cable from throttle body.
4. Remove screw holding support strut to front of battery tray.
5. Remove top battery tray fasteners.
6. Slide tray up and disconnect speed control servo wiring and vacuum harness from servo.
7. Remove attaching nuts and then speed control assembly from bottom of battery tray
8. Reverse procedure to install ensuring servo wiring connector points toward the left front corner of vehicle when battery tray is installed. **Torque** nuts to 60 inch lbs.

SPEED CONTROL SWITCH

The speed control switches are mounted in the steering wheel and wired through the clock spring device under the air bag module .

1. Ensure ignition switch is in OFF position.
2. Remove screws from each side of switch, then gently pull switch away from steering wheel assembly using a rocking motion.
3. Reverse procedure to install.

STOP LAMP SWITCH

1. Depress brake pedal while rotating switch in a counterclockwise direction approximately 30 degrees. Pull switch out of bracket and disconnect wiring harness connector.
2. Reverse procedure to install ensuring to pull switch plunger out to full length of travel and align switch with index key on bracket during installation **Fig. 12.**

WIPER SYSTEMS

NOTE: On Air Bag Equipped Models, Refer To "Air Bag System Precautions" Located In The Front Of This Manual For System Disarming & Arming Procedures.

INDEX

PRECAUTIONS

AIR BAG SYSTEMS

Refer to "Air Bag System Precautions" in the front of this manual for system disarming and arming procedures.

DESCRIPTION

ACCLAIM, DAYTONA, DYNASTY, FIFTH AVENUE, IMPERIAL, LEBARON, SHADOW, SPIRIT, SUNDANCE & 1992–93 NEW YORKER

Windshield wiper operation is controlled by a dash or column mounted switch. Wiper motors have permanent magnet fields, and high and low speeds are determined by current flow to the appropriate set of brushes. Delay operation on intermittent systems is controlled by a variable resistor in the wiper switch, a dwell switch in the wiper motor and a control unit/relay assembly.

Wiper arms on both systems return to a park position when the system is switched off with ignition in on position. Standard two-speed systems complete the wipe cycle and stop in park position, while intermittent systems complete a full wipe cycle before parking.

CONCORDE, INTREPID, LHS, VISION & 1994 NEW YORKER

The wiper system operates only when the ignition switch is On or in the Accesso-ry position. The wiper motor has permanent magnet fields, and high and low speeds are determined by current flow to the appropriate set of brushes.

The intermittent wiper system in addition to HI and Low speeds, has a delay mode. The delay mode is done by a variable resistor in the wiper switch and two relays. One relay turns the wipers On/Off and the other changes the speed.

The wiper system completes wipe cycle when the switch is turned Off and the blades park in lowest portion of wipe pattern.

MONACO & PREMIER

A two-speed intermittent windshield wiper motor is employed within this system. The intermittent operation is controlled by an adjustable pause between wipe cycles. The controls are located in a pod, attached to LH side of steering column.

LASER & TALON

A two-speed intermittent windshield wiper motor is employed within this system. The intermittent operation is controlled by an adjustable pause between wipe cycles.

NEON

The wiper system operates only when the ignition switch is On or in the Accesso-ry position. The wiper motor has permanent magnet fields, and high and low speeds are determined by current flow to the appropriate set of brushes.

The optional Intermittent Wiper System, in addition to HI and Low speeds, has a Delay Mode and a Pulse Mode. The Delay Mode, with a delay range of one to fifteen seconds, is controlled by a variable resistor in the wiper switch and two relays. One relay turns the wipers On/Off and the other changes the speed. The Pulse mode allows one or two sweeps of the wiper system at the drivers command. With the switch in either Off or Delay position, a momentary movement of the switch into Wash position will activate Pulse Mode.

The wiper system completes wipe cycle when the switch is turned Off and the blades park in lowest portion of wipe pattern.

TROUBLESHOOTING

ACCLAIM, DAYTONA, DYNASTY, FIFTH AVENUE, IMPERIAL, LEBARON, SHADOW, SPIRIT, SUNDANCE & 1992–93 NEW YORKER

STANDARD FRONT WIPERS

Whenever a wiper motor malfunction occurs, first ensure wiper motor wire harness is properly connected before starting with normal diagnosis and repair procedures.

Motor Will Not Run In Any Switch Position

1. Check for blown fuse.
2. If fuse is defective, replace and recheck motor operation in all switch positions.
3. If motor is still inoperative and fuse does not blow, place switch in Low speed position and proceed to next step.
4. If replacement fuse blows, disconnect motor wiring and replace fuse.
5. Place switch in Low speed position.

6. Listen for motor operation sound. If motor sound is not heard, proceed to step 9.
7. If motor sound is heard, check motor output shaft.
8. If shaft is not turning, replace motor assembly. If motor shaft is turning, check for proper connection of drive link or linkage.
9. Connect a voltmeter between motor terminal 3 and ground.
10. If no or little voltage is present, move negative test lead to battery ground terminal.
11. If an increase in voltage is noticed, problem is a bad ground circuit. Ensure motor mounting is free of paint and all attaching bolts are tight.
12. If there is still no indication of voltage, problem is an open circuit in wiring harness or wiper switch.
13. If no more than 3 volt increase in voltage is observed, problem is a faulty motor assembly.
14. Disconnect motor wiring connector and replace fuse.
15. If fuse does not blow, motor is defective.
16. If fuse blows, switch or wiring is at fault.

Motor Runs Slowly At all Speeds

1. Disconnect wiring harness connector at motor.
2. Remove wiper arms and blades.
3. Connect an ohmmeter between battery positive terminal and terminal 3 on motor.
4. If motor runs and average ammeter reading is more than 6 amps, proceed to motor linkage test step.
5. If motor runs and average ammeter reading is less than 6 amps, proceed to wire harness test step.
6. Check wiper linkage or pivots for binding. Disconnect drive link from motor.
7. If motor now runs and draws less than 3 amps, repair linkage system.
8. If motor continues to draw more than 3 amps, replace motor assembly.
9. Check motor wiring harness for shorting between high and low speed wires as follows:
   a. Connect a voltmeter or test lamp to motor ground strap.
   b. Set wiper switch on Low position.
   c. Connect other lead to terminal 4 of wiring harness.
   d. If voltage is present, there is a short in the wiring or the wiper switch. If no voltage is present, proceed to next step.
   e. Set switch to High position.
   f. Move voltmeter lead from terminal 4 to terminal 3.
   g. If voltage is present, there is a short in the wiring or wiper switch.

Motor Will Not Run At High Speed, But Not At Low Speed; Motor Will Run At Low Speed, But Not At High Speed

1. If motor will not run at high speed,

place switch in High position and connect a test lamp between motor terminal 4 and ground.
2. If motor will not run on low speed, place switch in Low position and connect a test lamp to motor terminal 3 and ground.
3. If test lamp does not light at motor terminal, there is an open in wiring or switch.
4. If test lamp lights, replace motor assembly.

Motor Keeps Running w/Switch In Off Position

Remove wiring harness. Connect a jumper wire between terminals 1 and 3 on motor. Connect a second jumper wire from terminal 2 to battery positive terminal. If motor runs to park position and stops, wiper switch is faulty. If motor continues to operate, replace motor assembly.

Motor Will Stop Wherever It Is When Switch Is Placed In Off Position; Wipers Do Not Continue Running To Park Position

1. Disconnect motor wiring harness connector and clean terminals. Reconnect connector and test motor.
2. If condition persists, set wiper switch to Off position. Disconnect motor wiring connector. Connect a voltmeter to motor ground strap and other lead to terminal 2 on harness connector.
3. If voltage is not present, check for an open circuit in wiring harness or wiper control switch.
4. If voltage is present, connect an ohmmeter between terminals 3 and 1.
5. If continuity exists, problem is a defective motor.
6. If no continuity exists, problem is an open circuit in wiper control switch or wiring harness.

INTERMITTENT FRONT WIPERS

On models with intermittent wipers, the intermittent wipe function is controlled by the body controller, located in the passenger compartment behind the right side kick panel.

To diagnose system malfunctions that do not involve the delay function, refer to "Two-Speed Motor Function Test."

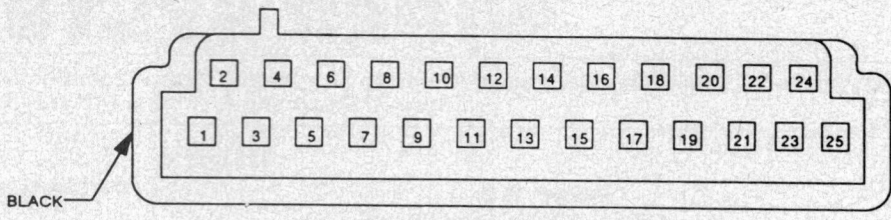

CR9029100039000X

Fig. 1 Body controller 25-way connector

Wipers Do Not Come On When Switch Is In Delay Position

1. Disconnect the 25-way (black) connector from the body controller.
2. Place wiper control switch in maximum delay position.
3. Connect positive lead of voltmeter to pin 9 of black connector and negative lead to metal case of body controller, **Fig. 1.**
4. If no voltage is present, check switch and wiring for an open circuit.
5. If voltage is present, connect positive lead of voltmeter to pin 22 black connector and negative to a good ground.
6. If no voltage is present, check fuses and wiring for an open circuit.
7. If voltage is present, reconnect body controller.
8. Connect positive lead of voltmeter to pin 24 and negative lead to metal case of body controller.
9. Disconnect wiring harness from wiper motor. Set control switch to minimum delay mode.
10. If no voltage is present, check wiring from intermittent wipe switch to body controller for an open circuit.
11. If voltage is present, connect voltmeter to pin L of intermittent wiper switch. Place intermittent wiper switch in maximum delay position.
12. If no voltage is present, replace intermittent wiper switch.
13. If voltage is present, check wiring between intermittent wiper switch and wiper motor for an open circuit.
14. If all tests have been perform and problem was not found, replace body controller.

Wipers Start To Wipe But Stop Before one Complete Cycle & Do Not Return To Park Position

1. Verify that motor will park when switch is in Off position.
2. Set wiper control switch to maximum delay and allow motor to run until it stops during a wipe cycle then disconnect 25-way (black) connector from body controller.
3. Connect positive lead of a voltmeter to pin 20 of black connector and negative lead to metal case of body controller, **Fig. 1.**
4. If no voltage is present, check wiring for an open circuit.
5. If voltage is present, check for continuity between the following terminals

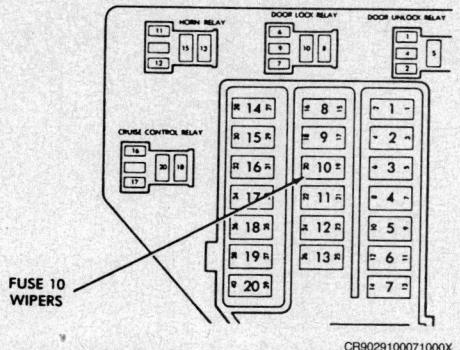

Fig. 2   Junction Block. Concorde, Intrepid & Vision

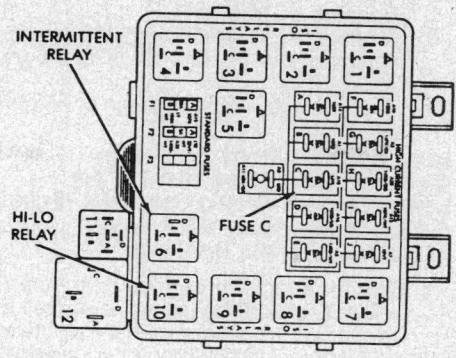

Fig. 3   Power distribution center. Concorde, Intrepid & Vision

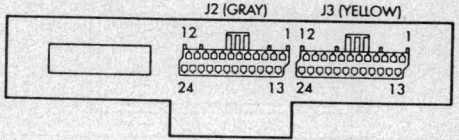

Fig. 4   Body Controller J3, 24 way connector. Concorde, Intrepid & Vision

CONCORDE, INTREPID, LHS, VISION & 1994 NEW YORKER

Motor Will Not Run In Any Switch Position

1. Check for blown fuse No. 10 in junction block and No. C in power distribution center, **Figs. 2 and 3.**
2. If fuses are defective replace, then check motor operation in all switch positions. If motor is still inoperative and fuse does not blow proceed to next step. If replacement fuse blows proceed to step 12.
3. Disconnect motor wire connector, check motor Low speed operation by disconnecting wiper motor connector, using two jumper wires connect one wire between battery positive terminal and terminal 3 of motor connector, then connect other wire to battery negative and terminal four of motor connector, **Fig. 4.**
4. Check High speed operation by connecting battery positive jumper to terminal two of motor connector and battery negative to terminal four of motor connector.
5. If motor has no High or Low speed, using a suitable ohmmeter check for a good ground at terminal four of motor wiring harness connector. If satisfactory, replace motor. If ground is not satisfactory repair ground circuit as needed.
6. If motor runs, using a suitable ohmmeter check for battery voltage at terminal D of intermittent relay in distribution center, **Fig. 3.** If no voltage check fuse C, if satisfactory proceed to next step. If not repair as necessary.
7. Using a suitable ohmmeter check terminal D of HI-LO wiper relay to terminal two of wiring harness connector at motor for continuity. Check from terminal E of HI-LO wiper relay to terminal three of wiring harness connector at motor for continuity. If satisfactory proceed to next step. If not repair as necessary.
8. Using a suitable ohmmeter check continuity between HI-LO wiper relay and intermittent wiper relay. Check from terminal B of HI-LO wiper relay to terminal B of intermittent wiper relay. If satisfactory check for defective relays. If not repair as necessary.
9. Disconnect J3 24-way connector from body controller, **Fig. 4.**
10. Using a suitable ohmmeter, check for continuity between terminal one of 24

---

of the body controller connector:
  a. Between terminals 20 and 24.
  b. Reverse ohmmeter leads then check between terminals 20 and 24.
6. If continuity does not exist between terminals 20 and 24 in both directions, replace body controller.

Excessive Delay Of More Than 30 Seconds Or Inadequate Variation In Delay

1. Verify delay as follows:
  a. Minimum delay is ½ to 2 seconds.
  b. Maximum delay is 15 to 25 seconds.
2. If there is excessive delay or no variations in delay, remove wiper motor wiring harness while motor is parked in Off position.
3. Remove 25-way (Black) body controller connector, **Fig. 1.**
4. Set wiper control to maximum delay position.
5. With ignition switch in On position, measure voltage between terminal 9 and body ground.
6. If voltage is present, remove wiper motor circuit fuse.
7. If no voltage is present, set wiper control switch to minimum delay position and measure voltage between terminal 9 and body ground. If no voltage is present, check for an open circuit in the intermittent wipe wiring harness.
8. Remove wiper motor circuit fuse.
9. Using an ohmmeter, measure resistance between pins 9 and 22 of the black connector with wiper control first set to minimum delay and then maximum delay.
10. If resistance at minimum delay is between 0–15 ohms and resistance at maximum delay is between 240,000–330,000 ohms, replace body controller.
11. If resistance is not as specified, replace wiper control switch.

Wipers Do Not Run Continually When Wash Control Is Operated During Delay

1. Disconnect 25-way (black) body controller connector, **Fig. 1.**

---

2. Using a voltmeter, connect positive lead to pin 10 and negative lead to body controller metal case.
3. Set wiper control switch to Delay position.
4. Depress wash switch.
5. If no voltage is present, check switch relay and wiring.
6. If voltage is present, replace body controller.

In Delay Mode, Wipers Run Continually When Wash Is Operated But Do Not Provide Four Extra Wipes When Wash Control Is Released

1. Replace body controller.

Wipers Start Erratically During Delay Mode

1. Verify that ground connections at instrument panel and motor mounting bolts are tight.
2. Verify motor ground strap is making good contact.
3. Verify that wiring connections to body controller, wiper motor and wiper motor switch are tight and free of corrosion.
4. If condition is not corrected, replace body controller.

REAR WIPERS

1. Remove lower cover on liftgate.
2. Disconnect feed connector from wiper motor.
3. With ignition switch in On position, check for voltage at blue wire.
4. With both ignition and wiper switches in On position, check for voltage at blue and brown wires.
5. If battery voltage is not present, check fuse, liftgate wiper switch and wiring.
6. With ignition switch in On position and wiper switch in Off position, check for battery voltage between blue and brown wires.
7. If no voltage is present, check ground wire to liftgate switch.
8. If battery voltage is present in steps 3 and 4, replace motor.

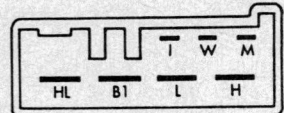

SWITCH POSITION		TERMINALS	RESISTANCE VALUE
OFF		PIN I to M	OPEN ≥ 300 K OHMS
DELAY LEVEL	1	PIN I to M	9.72 K OHMS
	2	PIN I to M	8.22 K OHMS
	3	PIN I to M	6.61 K OHMS
	4	PIN I to M	5.12 K OHMS
	5	PIN I to M	3.67 K OHMS
	6	PIN I to M	2.22 K OHMS
LOW		PIN I to M	1.02 K OHMS
HIGH		PIN I to M	0.51 K OHMS
WASH		PIN I to W	OPEN
RESISTANCE AT MAXIMUM DELAY POSITION SHOULD BE			9,720 K OHMS
RESISTANCE AT MINIMUM DELAY POSITION SHOULD BE			2,220 K OHMS

CR9029100075000X

Fig. 5 Ammeter to wiper motor connection. Concorde, Intrepid & Vision

way connector to terminal C of intermittent wiper relay. If satisfactory proceed to next step. If not repair as necessary.

11. With wiper switch connected, using a suitable voltmeter connect positive lead to terminal one of wiper switch, then turn ignition switch to ON position. Move wiper switch from OFF position to High position, then proceed as follows:
   a. If no voltage is present, replace wiper switch. If voltage is present, check continuity from terminal one of wiper switch to terminal 16 of body controller J3.
   b. Turn ignition Off, using a suitable ohmmeter check for continuity between fuse No. 10 and terminal 1 and 18 of body controller J3. If no continuity is present, check HI-LO and intermittent relays. If relays are satisfactory, repair wire circuit as necessary.
   c. If voltage increases from zero to approximately 10 volts in HIGH position replace body controller.
12. Disconnect motor connector and replace fuse No. 10 from junction block, if fuse does not blow, return to step 3. If fuse blows, wiper control circuitry is at fault, repair as necessary.

Motor Runs Slowly At all Speeds

1. Remove wiper arms and blades, disconnect wiper motor connector, then drive link from motor.
2. Connect a suitable ammeter between positive terminal and terminal three of motor connector, **Fig. 5.** Connect a ground wire to terminal four of motor connector. **When replacing drive link nut, torque nut to 98-106 inch lbs.**
3. If motor runs and average ammeter reading is higher than six amps, proceed to next step. If motor runs and average ammeter reading is less than

six amps go to step 5.
4. Connect a suitable ohmmeter, check high and low circuits for a short to ground.
5. Check to see if wiper linkage or pivots are binding.

Motor Will Run At High Speed, But Not Move At Low Speed & Motor Will Run At Low Speed, But Not Move at High Speed

1. Disconnect motor connector. If motor will not run on low speed, connect a jumper wire between battery positive and terminal three of motor connector. Connect a second jumper between battery ground and terminal four of motor connector, **Fig. 6.**
2. If motor does not run, replace motor. If motor runs proceed to step 4.
3. If motor will not run at high speed, connect a jumper wire between battery positive terminal and terminal two. Connect a second jumper wire between ground and terminal four of motor connector.
4. If wipers will not run at low speed use a suitable ohmmeter, check for open circuit. Check between terminal E of HI-LO wiper relay to terminal three of wiper motor wire harness connector for continuity. If satisfactory proceed to step 6, if not repair as necessary.
5. If wiper will not run at high speed, using a suitable ohmmeter, check for an open circuit. Check between terminal D of HI-LO wiper relay and terminal two of wiper motor wire harness connector for continuity. If satisfactory proceed to next step. If not satisfactory repair as necessary.
6. Check for faulty HI-LO wiper relay.

Wipers Run At High Speed With Switch In Low Speed & Wipers Operate In Intermittent Mode, But Each Wipe Is At High Speed

1. Disconnect motor connector, using two jumper wires connect one between battery positive and terminal three of motor wiring harness connector. Connect second lead between battery negative and terminal four of motor wiring harness connector, **Fig. 6.**
2. If motor runs at low speed, check for faulty HI-LO wiper relay, then check for crossed wires in harness from HI-LO relay motor.
3. If motor runs at high speed, check for crossed wires in motor pigtail wire connector.
4. Using a suitable ohmmeter, check for short to ground. Disconnect J3 24 way connector from body controller and remove intermittent wiper relay.
5. If none of the above conditions are present, replace body controller.

Wipers Run At Low Speed With Switch In High Speed Position

1. Check for faulty HI-LO wiper relay.
2. Using a suitable ohmmeter check for

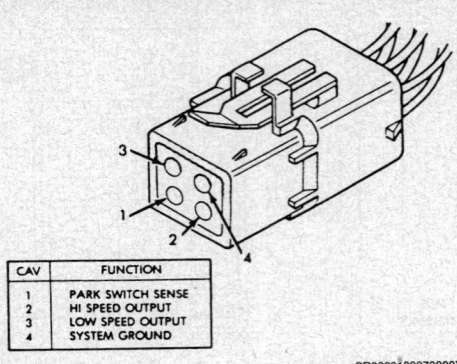

CAV	FUNCTION
1	PARK SWITCH SENSE
2	HI SPEED OUTPUT
3	LOW SPEED OUTPUT
4	SYSTEM GROUND

CR9029100073000X

Fig. 6 Wiper motor connector identification. Concorde, Intrepid & Vision

open circuit between terminal C of HI-LO wiper relay and terminal 18 of body controller J3. If satisfactory check wiper switch. In not satisfactory repair as necessary.

Motor Will Keep Running With Switch In Off Positions

1. Check wiper motor wiring harness for shorts between low speed motor feed terminal three or high speed motor feed terminal two and battery or ignition.
2. Check for faulty wiper intermittent or HI-LO relays, then check circuit from intermittent relay cavity B to HI-LO relay cavity B for short to battery or ignition.
3. Disconnect body controller 3 connector. Check circuit from terminal 1 of J3 24 way connector **Fig. 4** to terminal C of intermittent wiper relay for short to ground.
4. Using a suitable voltmeter connect positive lead to terminal 16 of body controller. Connect negative lead to ground.
5. If voltmeter reads greater than zero volts, check wiper switch and wiring.
6. Connect voltmeter positive lead to terminal 10 of body controller connector, of voltmeter read 10 to 15 volts, check circuit for short to battery or ignition. If voltmeter read zero volts, replace body controller.

Wiper Will Run Continuously With Switch In Intermittent Position. When Column Switch Is Turned Off Wipers Stop Wherever They Are Without Returning To Park Position

1. Check for ground at wiper motor wire connector terminal four.
2. Using a suitable ohmmeter and with wiper motor in PARK position, check for continuity between terminal one and terminal four of motor connector. If satisfactory proceed to next step. If not satisfactory replace motor.
3. Check for continuity between terminal one of motor wire harness connector and terminal 2 of J3 24 way connector

Phenomenon		Inspection method
Wipers do not operate continuously	Washer does not operate.	• Check the multi-purpose fuse No. ⑨.
	Washer operates.	• Check the wiper motor. • Check the column switch.
Low-speed (or high-speed) wiper operation only is inoperative.		• Check the column switch.
Wipers do not operate intermittently. (They operate continuously.)		• Check the wiper switch "INT" input signal. • • Check the column switch.
Wipers do not stop.		• Check the wiper switch "INT" input signal. • Check the column switch. • Check the wiper motor.
The intermittent time will not vary even if the variable intermittent wiper control switch is operated.		• Check the variable intermittent wiper control switch input signal. • Check the column switch.
Even if the washer switch is on for 0.6 second or more, the washer will not operate.	The wipers linked with the washer operate.	• Check the washer motor. • Check the washer nozzle and washer tube.
	The wipers linked with the washer do not operate.	• Check the washer switch input signal. • Check the washer switch.

CR9029200052000X

Fig. 7 Wiper system troubleshooting. Stealth

of body controller. Using a suitable voltmeter check for short circuit to battery or ignition feed in this circuit.

Wipers Do Not Run When Washer Motor Is Engaged

1. Disconnect J3 24 way connector from body controller.
2. Using a suitable voltmeter, connect positive lead to terminal 10 of 24 way connector.
3. Engage washer switch so that washer motor runs continuously.
4. If voltage is zero, check wiring between washer motor and body controller, repair if necessary.
5. If voltage is 10 to 15 volts, replace body controller.

COLT & SUMMIT

Wipers Do Not Operate

1. Check multi-purpose fuse 1.
2. Defective wiper switch.
3. Defective wiper motor.
4. Check ground connection.
5. Check wiper linkage.

Wipers Do Not Operate At Low Speed Or High Speed

1. Defective wiper switch.
2. Defective wiper motor.
3. Check wiring harness connection.

Wipers Do Not Operate In Intermittent Mode

1. Check intermittent wiper relay terminal voltage with relay energized.
2. Connect a voltmeter between terminal No. 3 and ground.
3. If voltmeter indicates zero voltage, check wiper switch.
4. If voltmeter indicates 12 volts, check intermittent wiper relay.
5. If voltmeter changes between zero volts and 12 volts repeatedly, system is operating satisfactory.

Wipers Fail To Stop

1. Check wiper motor.

Interval Period Will Not Adjust

1. Check interval adjustment switch.
2. Check intermittent wiper relay.

Washer Is Inoperative

1. Check washer motor.
2. Check washer switch.

Wiper Operation Not Coordinated w/Washer

1. Check intermittent wiper relay.

COLT VISTA & SUMMIT WAGON

Wipers Do Not Operate

1. Check for blown multi-purpose fuse 9.
2. Defective wiper switch.
3. Defective wiper motor.
4. Defective intermittent wiper relay.
5. Check ground connection.
6. Defective variable intermittent wiper switch.
7. Check wiper linkage.

STEALTH

Refer to **Fig. 7** when troubleshooting wiper system.

MONACO & PREMIER

Refer to **Figs. 8 and 9** when troubleshooting wiper system.

LASER & TALON

Wipers Or Washers Do Not Operate

1. Check multi-purpose fuse No. 9.
2. Check ground.

Wipers Operate Only At Low Or High Speed

1. Check Wiper Switch.

Wipers Do Not Stop

1. Check wiper motor.
2. Check intermittent wiper relay.
3. Check wiper switch.

Wipers Do Not Operate On Intermittent Wipe

1. Check terminal voltage at steering column switch connector terminal 3.
2. If voltage is 0 volts, check intermittent wiper relay or wiper switch.
3. If voltage is 12 volts, Check intermittent wiper relay.
4. If voltage alternates from 0 to 12 volts, system is operating normally.

Length Of Pause For Intermittent Operation Cannot Be Varied

1. Check variable intermittent wiper control switch.
2. Check intermittent wiper relay.

Washer Only Is Inoperative

1. Check washer motor.

Washer-Wiper Operation Is Inoperative

1. Check intermittent relay.

NEON

STANDARD WIPERS

Motor Will Not Operate In Some Or All Switch Positions

1. Check fuse fifteen in fuse block:
   a. If fuse is OK proceed to next step.
   b. If fuse is bad, replace, then check wiper functions in all switch positions. If fuse blows again proceed to voltmeter test step below.
   c. If replaced fuse does not blow and motor does not run, proceed to next step.
2. Disconnect motor connector, refer to **Fig. 10** for following tests:
   a. Connect jumper wire from battery negative terminal to motor ground strap.
   b. Connect jumper wire from battery positive terminal to pin two of connector, then move jumper wire from battery positive terminal to pin one of connector.
   c. If motor runs OK check wiring circuits **Fig. 12**. Check wiper switch as outlined under "Component Diagnosis & Testing."
   d. If motor does not run proceed to next step.
3. Using a suitable ohmmeter check ground strap at motor:
   a. If ground strap is OK, replace motor.
   b. If not OK, repair ground as necessary.
4. Using a suitable voltmeter, with wiper switch connected:
   a. Connect voltmeter positive lead to terminal P1 **Fig. 11** and negative lead to motor ground.
   b. If no voltage repair wiring circuits as necessary **Fig. 12**.
   c. If voltage is OK, connect voltmeter positive lead to wiper switch terminal L, then move switch to low speed position. If no voltage replace switch.

d. Repeat above test for wiper switch terminal H.
e. If all tests OK, proceed to next step.
5. Disconnect motor connector, then replace fuse fifteen in fuse block:
   a. If fuse does not blow, replace motor.
   b. If fuse blows, disconnect wiper switch and replace fuse fifteen in fuse block.
   c. If fuse does not blow replace switch.
   d. If fuse blows check and repair wiring circuits **Fig. 12** as necessary.

Wipers Operate Slowly At All Speeds

Refer to "Component Diagnosis & Testing"

Wipers Run Fast In Low Switch Position Or Slow In Fast Switch Position

1. Check for crossed wires in wiper motor connectors **Fig. 12**.
2. Check for crossed wires in wiper switch connectors.
3. If OK replace wiper switch.

Wipers Do Not Operate In Washer Or Pulse Mode

Using a suitable ohmmeter check motor ground, if OK replace wiper switch. If not OK repair ground.

INTERMITTENT WIPERS

For operation not covered in this section refer to "Standard Wipers."

Motor Will Not Operate In Some Or All Switch Positions

1. Check fuse fifteen in fuse block:
   a. If fuse is OK proceed to next step.
   b. If fuse is bad, replace, then check wiper functions in all switch positions. If fuse blows again proceed to voltmeter test step below.
   c. If replaced fuse does not blow and motor does not run, proceed to next step.
2. Disconnect motor connector, refer to **Fig. 10** for following tests:
   a. Connect jumper wire from battery negative terminal to motor ground strap.
   b. Connect jumper wire from battery positive terminal to pin two of connector, then move jumper wire from battery positive terminal to pin one of connector.
   c. If motor runs OK check wiring circuits **Fig. 12** and wiper switch as outlined under "Component Diagnosis & Testing"
   d. If motor does not run proceed to next step.
3. Using a suitable ohmmeter check ground strap at motor:
   a. If ground strap is OK, replace motor.
   b. If not OK, repair ground as necessary.
4. Using a suitable ohmmeter, check continuity from terminal E of wiper switch **Fig. 11** to ground:

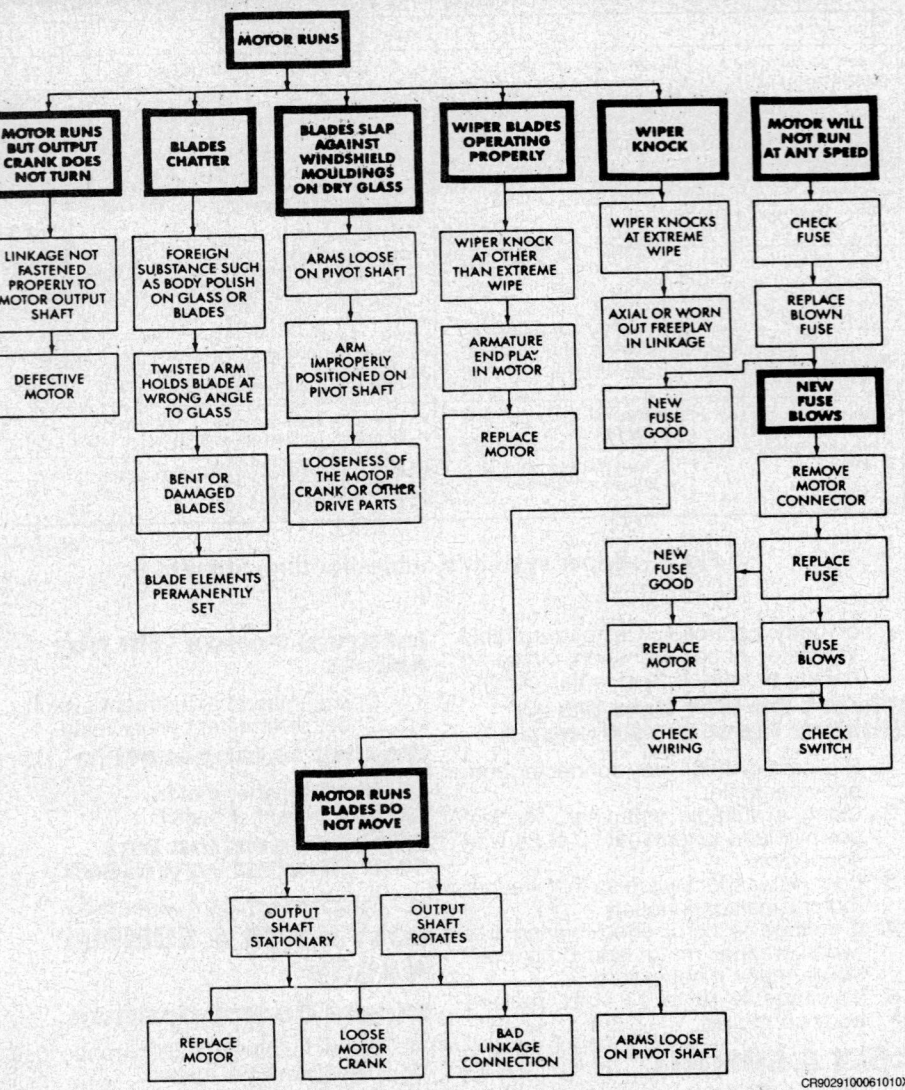

Fig. 8   Wiper system troubleshooting charts (Part 1 of 2). Monaco & Premier

Windshield Wipers Inoperative—Ignition Switch in RUN, Wiper Switch in LO or HI Position

TEST	OK	NOT OK
Inspect fuse	Not blown	Replace 20 A fuse
Battery side of fuse	Battery voltage	Repair open from ignition S
Ground on wiper motor frame	Ground	Repair open ground
Connector 4 on motor switch on LO	Battery voltage	Repair lead from switch or check switch
Connector 1 on motor switch on HI	Battery voltage	Repair lead from switch or check switch

Windshield Wipers Inoperative in Intermittent Mode, OK in HI and LO—Ignition Switch in RUN, Wiper Switch in Intermittent Mode—See Intermittent Wiper Module

Windshield Wipers do Not Park

TEST	OK	NOT OK
Turn motor to OFF	Blades at bottom of wipe pattern	Loose linkage at motor crank or next test
Connector 3 on motor	Battery voltage	Repair lead from 20 A fuse
Connector 2 on motor	0 voltage when connected to wiring. If OK replace motor	Repair lead to I wipe modul or check I wipe module or wiper switch

Windshield Wipers Inoperative During Washer Operation—Ignition in RUN, Wiper Switch in Wash-Replace Switch

Windshield Washer Inoperative—Ignition in RUN, Wiper Switch in Wash

TEST	OK	NOT OK
Washer pump motor Terminal A	Battery voltage	Repair open from wiper switch
Washer pump motor Terminal B	Zero ohms. If zero ohms replace pump motor	Repair open to ground

CR9029100061020X

Fig. 8   Wiper system troubleshooting charts (Part 2 of 2). Monaco & Premier

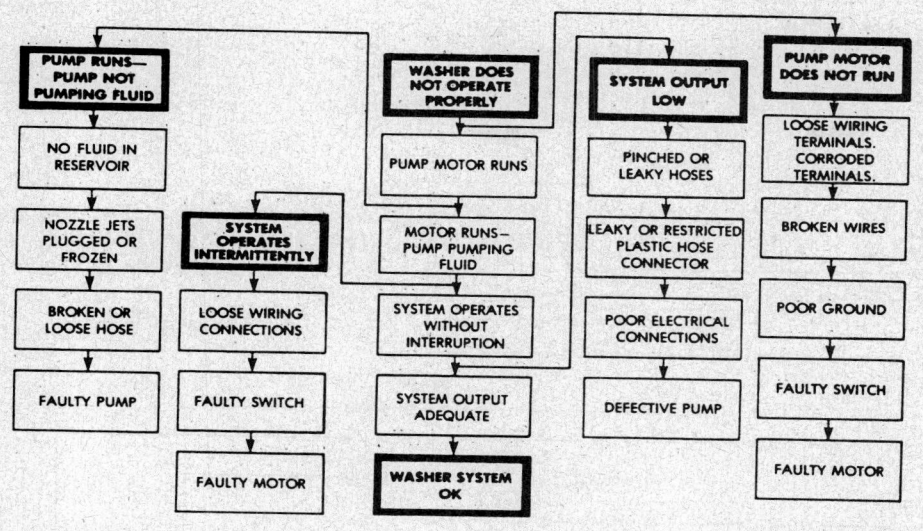

Fig. 9   Washer system troubleshooting chart. Monaco & Premier

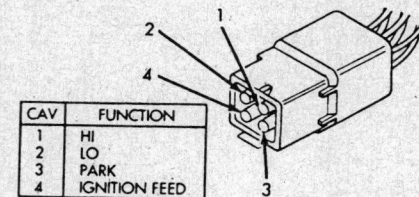

Fig. 10   Wiper motor connector. Neon

CAV	FUNCTION
1	HI
2	LO
3	PARK
4	IGNITION FEED

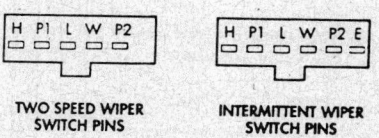

SWITCH POSITION	CONTINUITY BETWEEN
OFF	PIN P2 and PIN L
LOW	PIN P1 and PIN L
HIGH	PIN P1 and PIN H
WASH	PIN P1 and PIN W
INTERMITTENT	CANNOT BE CHECKED

Fig. 11   Wiper switch tests. Neon

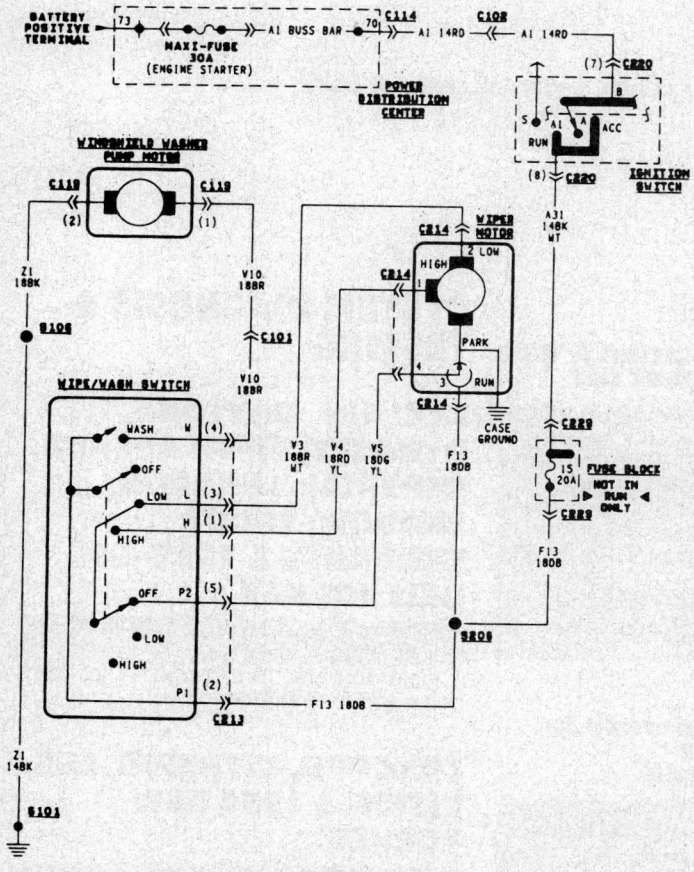

Fig. 12   Wiper system wiring diagram. (Part 1 of 2) Neon

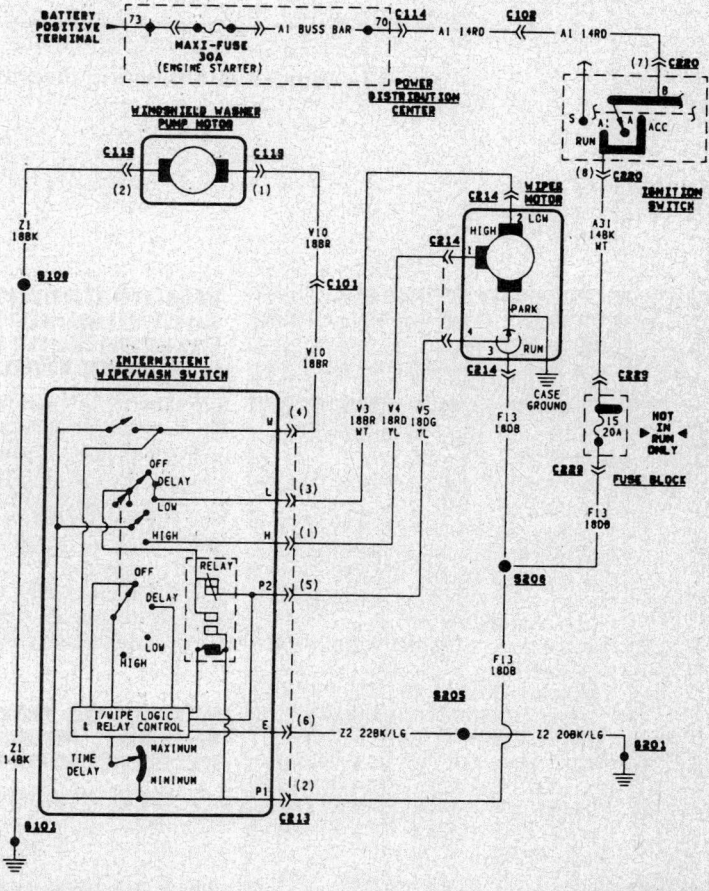

Fig. 12   Wiper system wiring diagram. (Part 2 of 2) Neon

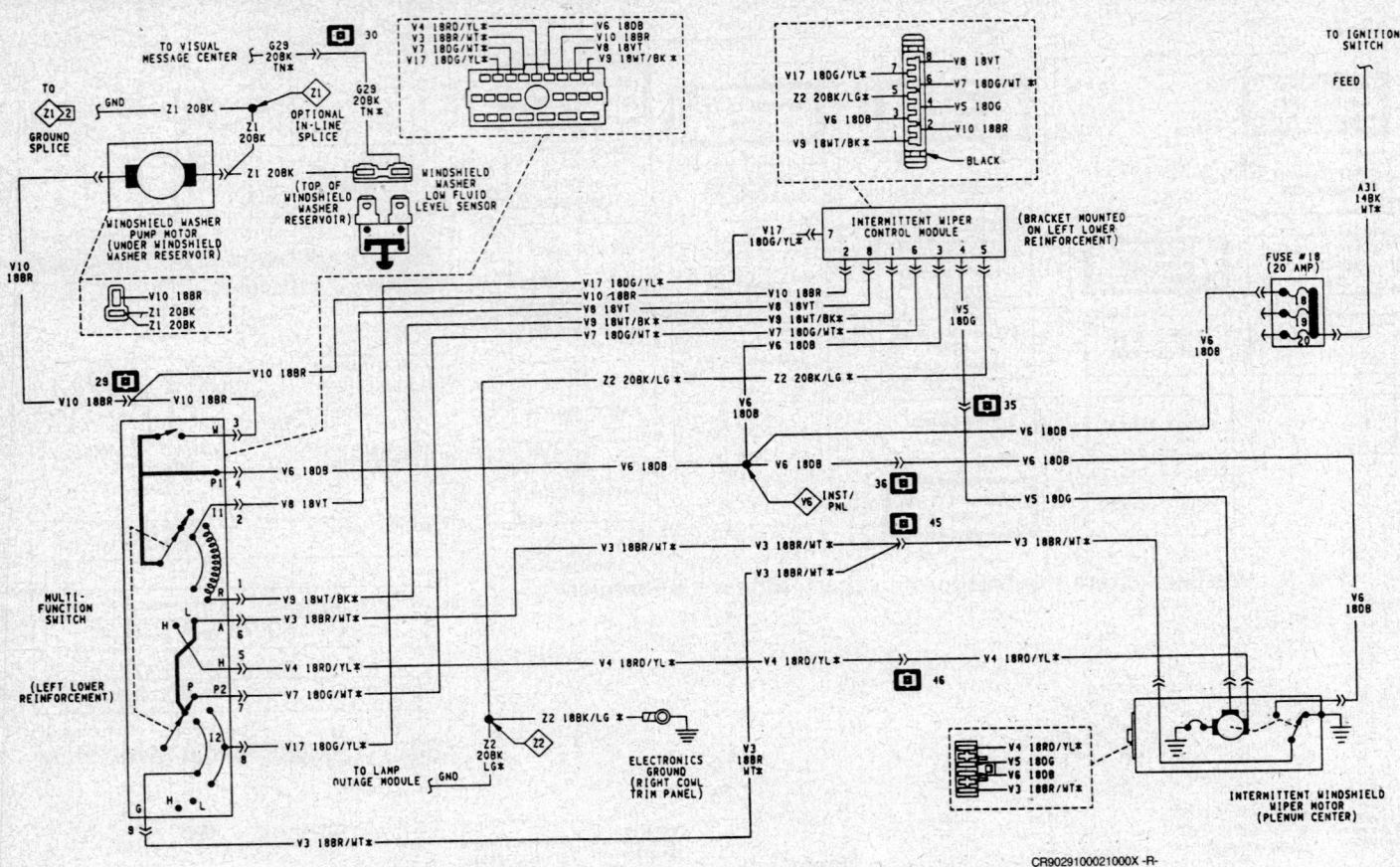

Fig. 13 Wiper system wiring diagram. Acclaim, LeBaron Landau & Spirit

a. If OK, proceed to next step.
b. If not OK, repair wiring circuit to ground **Fig. 12.**
5. Using a suitable voltmeter, with wiper switch connected:
   a. Connect voltmeter positive lead to terminal P1 **Fig. 11** and negative lead to motor ground.
   b. If no voltage repair wiring circuits as necessary **Fig. 12.**
   c. If voltage is OK, connect voltmeter positive lead to wiper switch terminal L, then move switch to low speed position. If no voltage replace switch.
   d. Repeat above test for wiper switch terminal H.
   e. If all tests OK, proceed to next step.
6. Disconnect motor connector, then replace fuse fifteen in fuse block:
   a. If fuse does not blow, replace motor.
   b. If fuse blows, disconnect wiper switch and replace fuse fifteen in fuse block.
   c. If fuse does not blow replace switch.
   d. If fuse blows check and repair wiring circuits **Fig. 12** as necessary.

Wipers Operate Continuously In Intermittent Position & Will Not Park When Shut Off

1. Using a suitable ohmmeter, check motor ground and repair if necessary.
2. With ignition switch in OFF position and wiper motor in park position:
   a. Using a suitable ohmmeter, check for continuity between pin three of wiper motor connector **Fig. 10** and ground.
   b. If OK, replace wiper switch.
   c. If not OK, repair wiring circuits as necessary **Fig. 12.**

Wipers Do Not Operate In Washer, Pulse Or Intermittent Mode

1. Using a suitable ohmmeter, check motor ground and continuity from terminal E of wiper switch **Fig. 11** to ground.
2. If OK, replace wiper switch.
3. If not OK, Repair wiring circuit as necessary **Fig. 12.**

SYSTEM DIAGNOSIS & TESTING

ACCLAIM, DAYTONA, DYNASTY, FIFTH AVENUE, IMPERIAL, LEBARON, SHADOW, SPIRIT, SUNDANCE & 1992–93 NEW YORKER

Refer to **Figs. 13 through 15** when performing system diagnosis.
Refer to **Figs. 16 through 41** for diagnosis and testing procedures.

CONCORD, INTREPID, LHS, VISION & 1994 NEW YORKER

Refer to **Fig. 42** when performing system diagnosis.
Refer to **Figs. 43 through 62** for diagnosis and testing procedures.

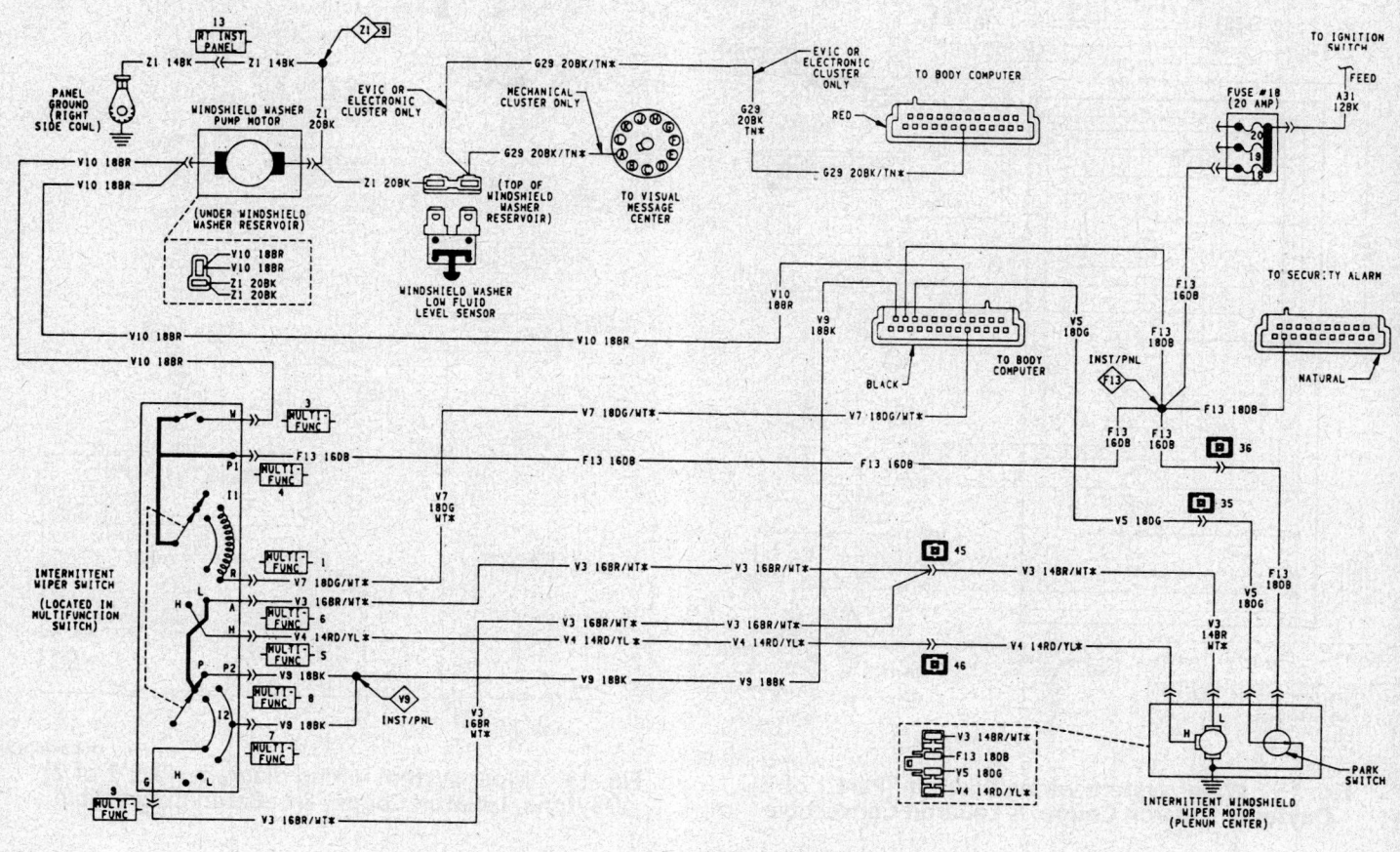

Fig. 14 Wiper system wiring diagram. Dynasty, Fifth Avenue, Imperial & 1992–93 New Yorker

COLT & SUMMIT

Refer to **Figs. 63** and **64** when performing system diagnosis.

COLT VISTA & SUMMIT WAGON

Refer to **Figs. 65** and **66** when performing system diagnosis.

STEALTH

Refer to **Figs. 67 through 70** when performing system diagnosis.

INPUT SIGNAL TO ECU TEST

1. Ensure ignition switch is in Off position, then connect test equipment, **Figs. 71** and **72**.
2. If scan tool is not used, operate (turn On/Off) each switch function, a voltage pulse indicates that a correct signal has been sent to the ECU.
3. If scan tool is used, operate (turn On/Off) each switch function, a BUZZ or PEEP tone from the Scan Tool indi-

cates that a correct signal has been sent to the ECU.

MONACO & PREMIER

Refer to **Fig. 73** when performing system diagnosis.

NEON

Refer to **Fig. 12** when performing system diagnosis.

Continued on page 15-32

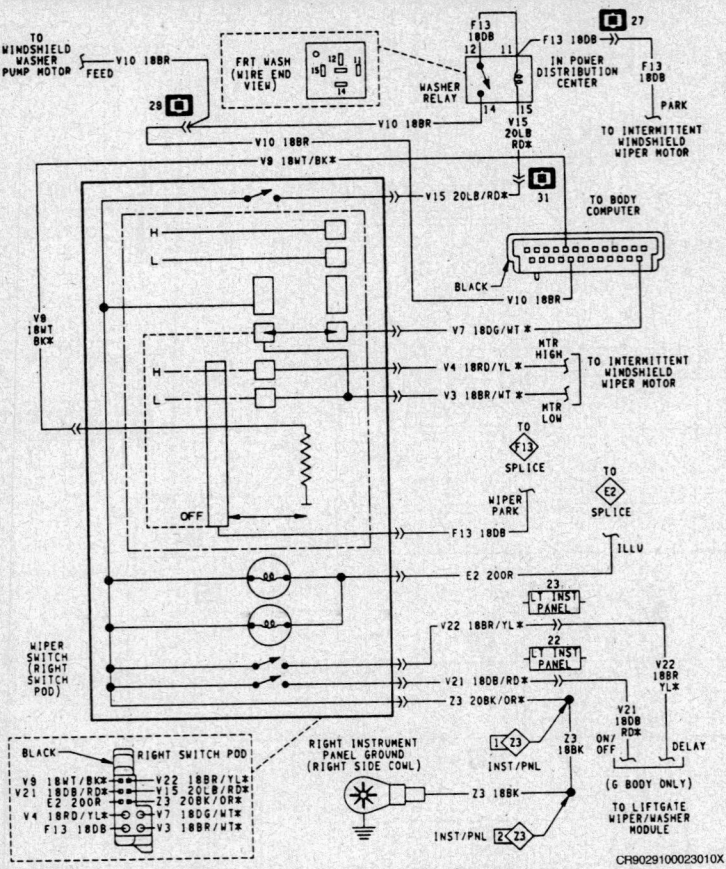

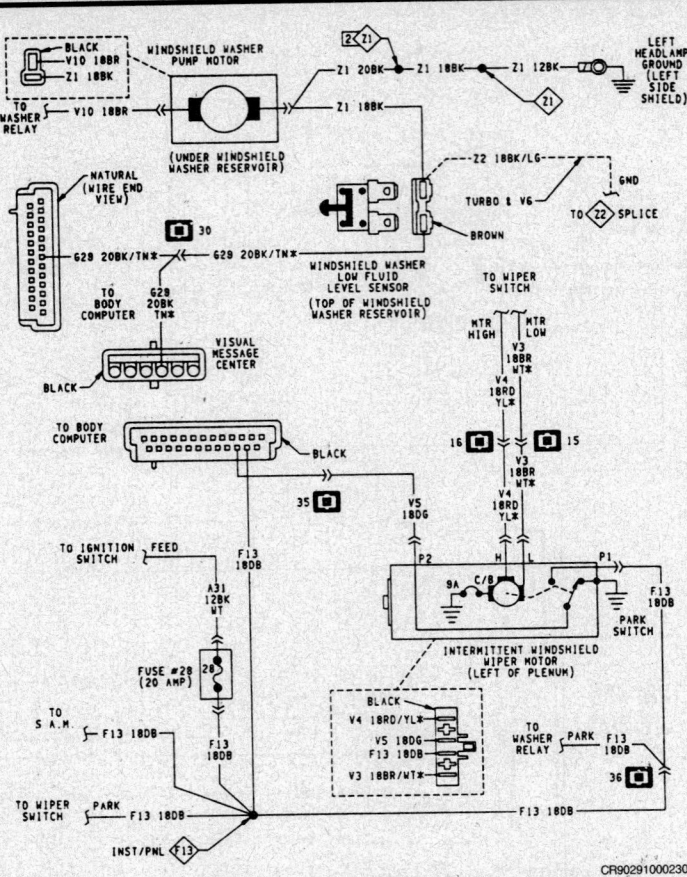

Fig. 15 Wiper system wiring diagram (Part 1 of 2). Daytona, LeBaron Coupe, & LeBaron Convertible

Fig. 15 Wiper system wiring diagram (Part 2 of 2). Daytona, LeBaron Coupe, & LeBaron Convertible

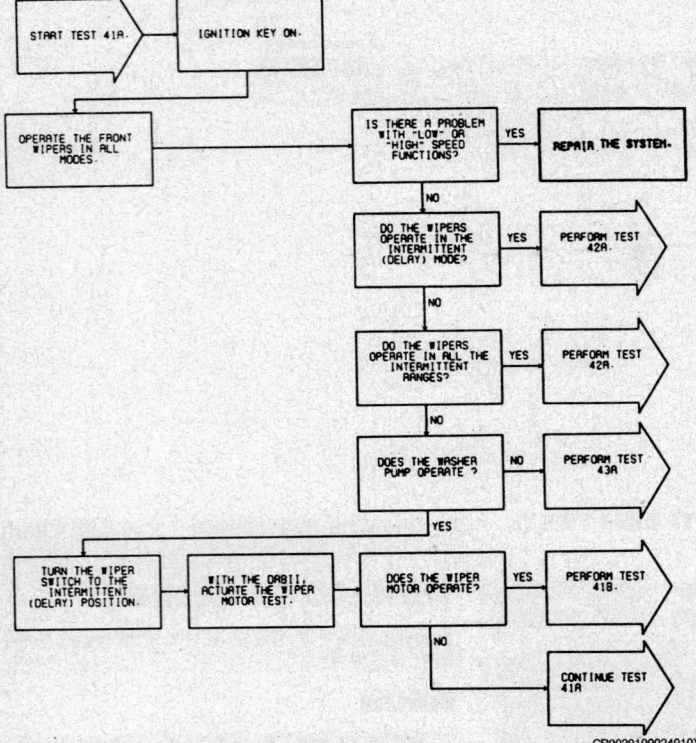

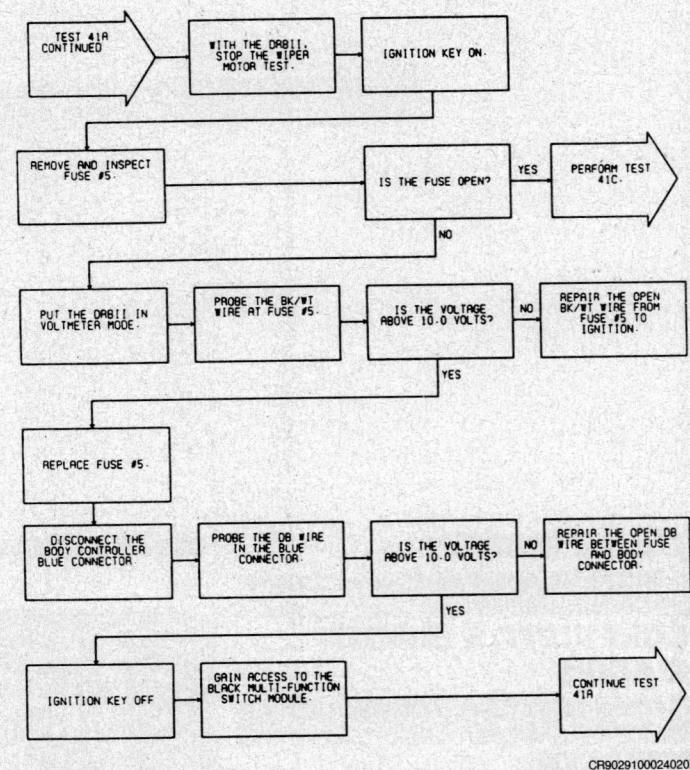

Fig. 16 Test 41A: Wiper System Testing (Part 1 of 3). 1992 Acclaim, LeBaron Landau & Spirit

Fig. 16 Test 41A: Wiper System Testing (Part 2 of 3). 1992 Acclaim, LeBaron Landau & Spirit

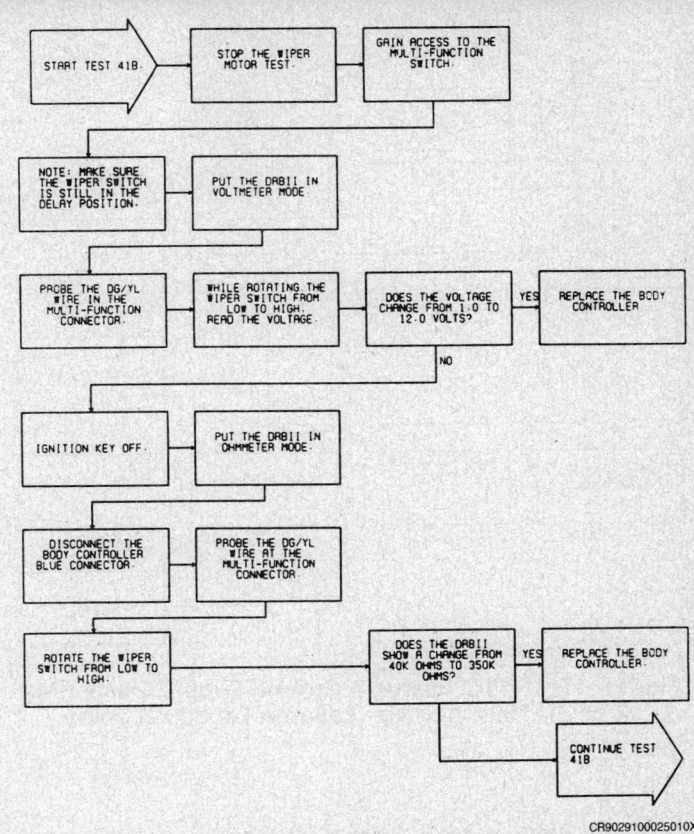

Fig. 17 Test 41B: Controller & Wiper Switch Check (Part 1 of 2). 1992 Acclaim, LeBaron Landau & Spirit

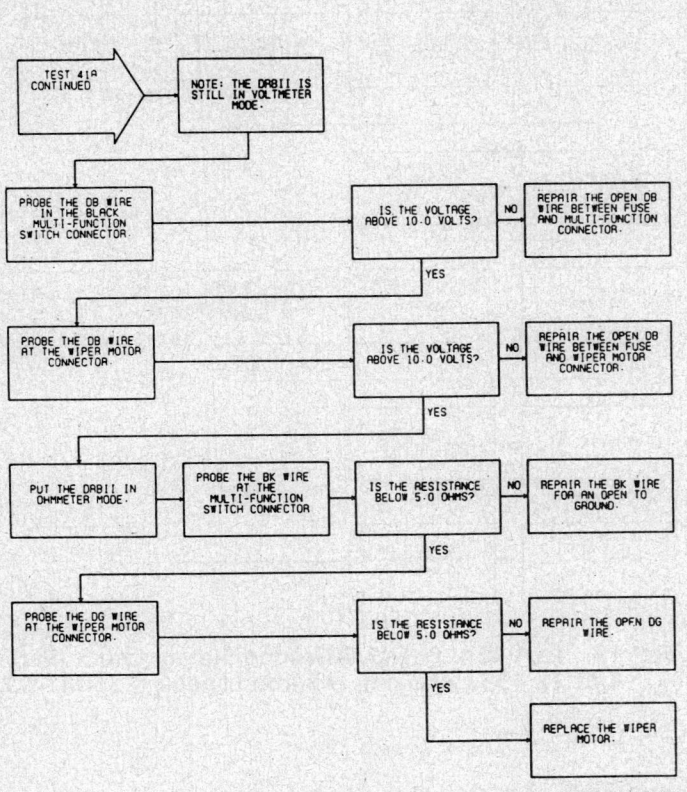

Fig. 16 Test 41A: Wiper System Testing (Part 3 of 3). 1992 Acclaim, LeBaron Landau & Spirit

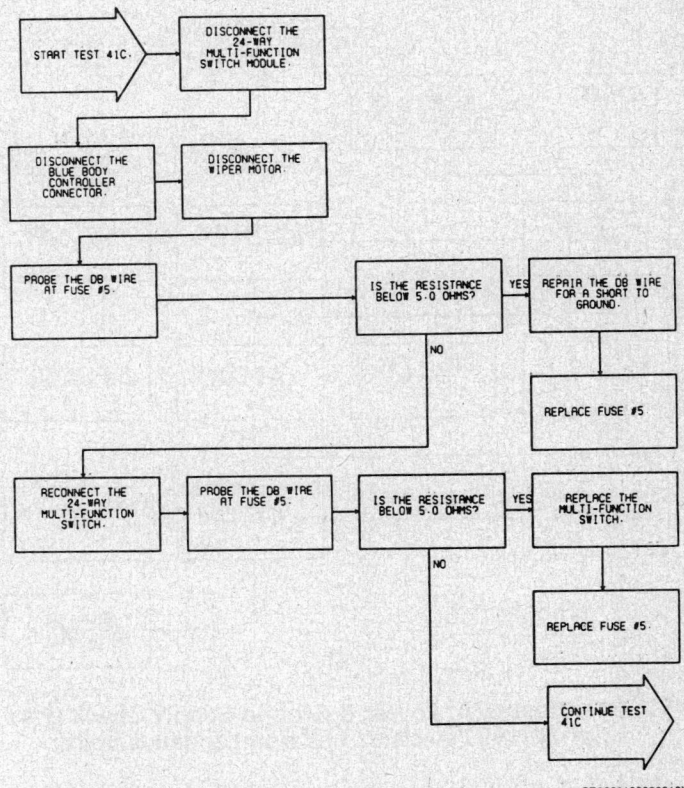

Fig. 18 Test 41C: Power & Ground Supply Check (Part 1 of 2). 1992 Acclaim, LeBaron Landau & Spirit

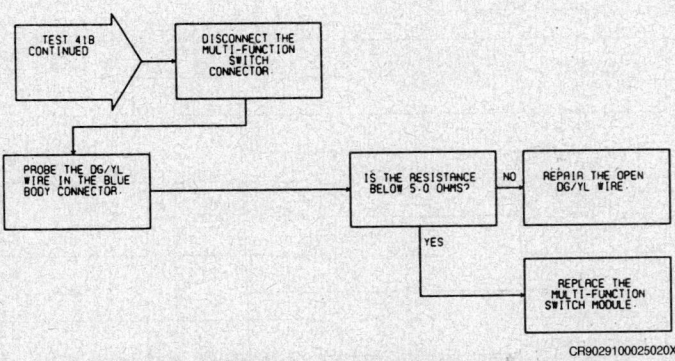

Fig. 17 Test 41B: Controller & Wiper Switch Check (Part 2 of 2). 1992 Acclaim, LeBaron Landau & Spirit

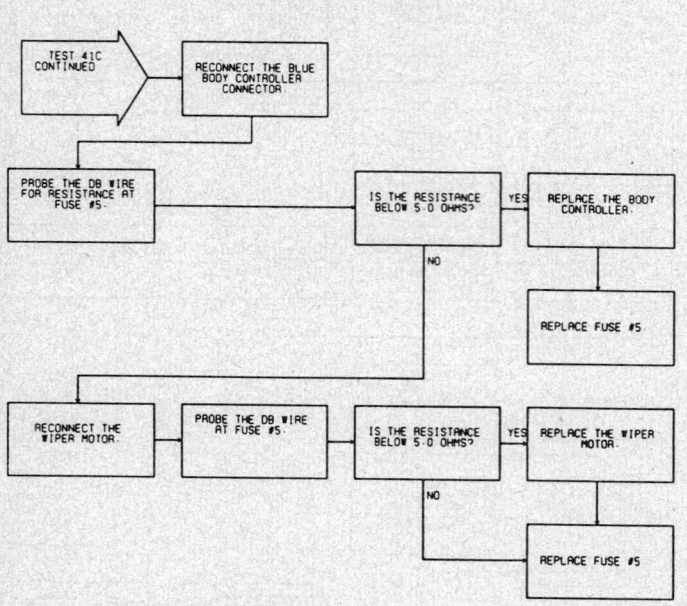

Fig. 18   Test 41C: Power & Ground Supply Check (Part 2 of 2). 1992 Acclaim, LeBaron Landau & Spirit

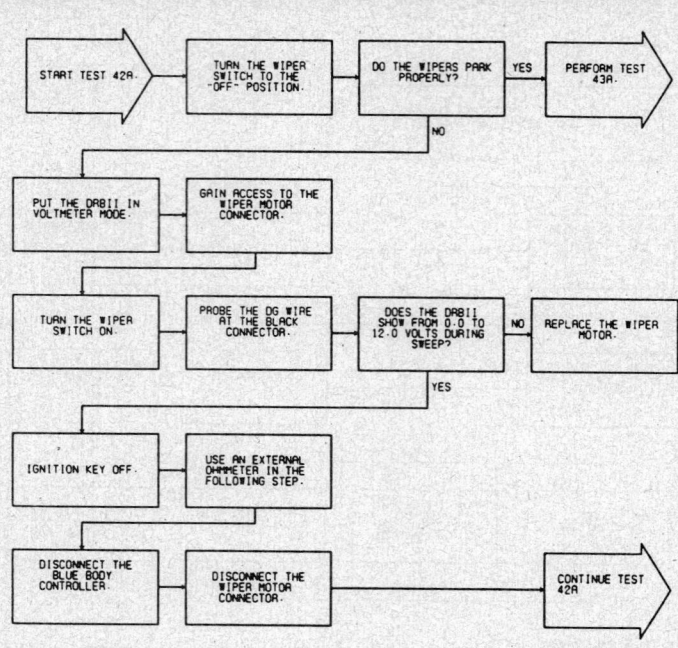

Fig. 19   Test 42A: Power & Ground Supply Check (Part 1 of 2). 1992 Acclaim, LeBaron Landau & Spirit

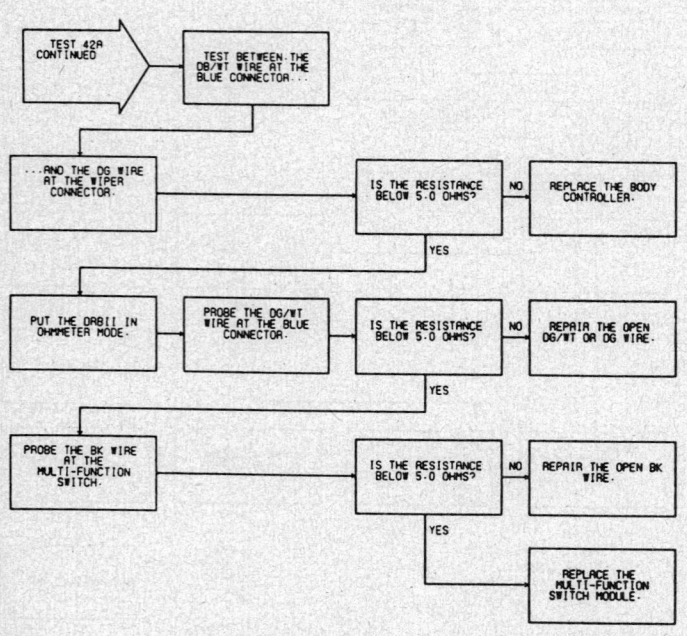

Fig. 19   Test 42A: Power & Ground Supply Check (Part 2 of 2). 1992 Acclaim, LeBaron Landau & Spirit

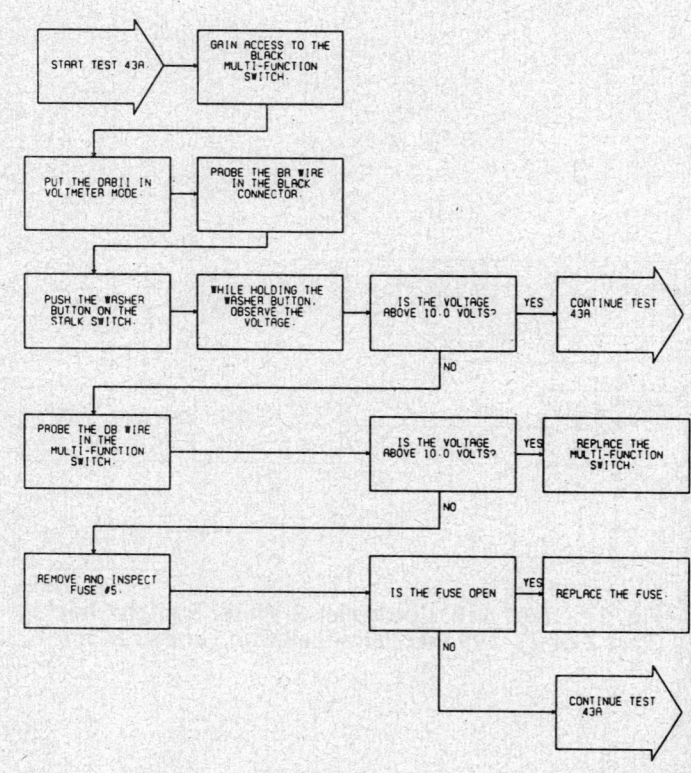

Fig. 20   Test 43A: Washer Pump Operation Check (Part 1 of 2). 1992 Acclaim, LeBaron Landau & Spirit

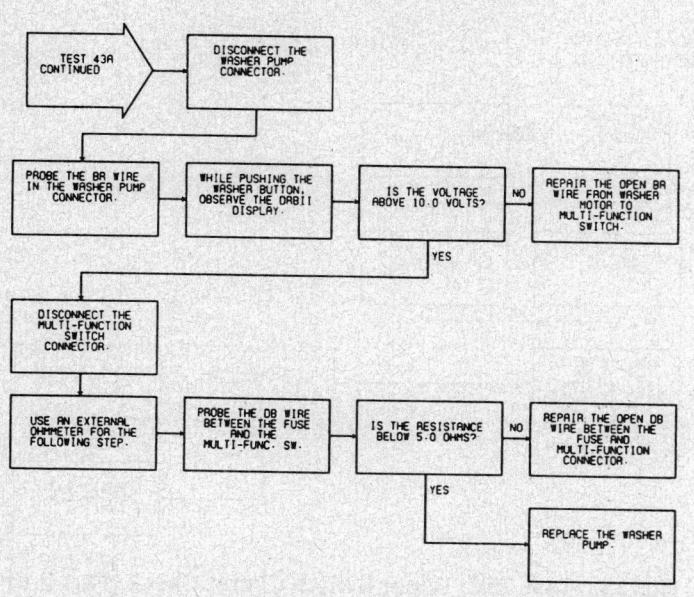

Fig. 20   Test 43A: Washer Pump Operation Check (Part 2 of 2). 1992 Acclaim, LeBaron Landau & Spirit

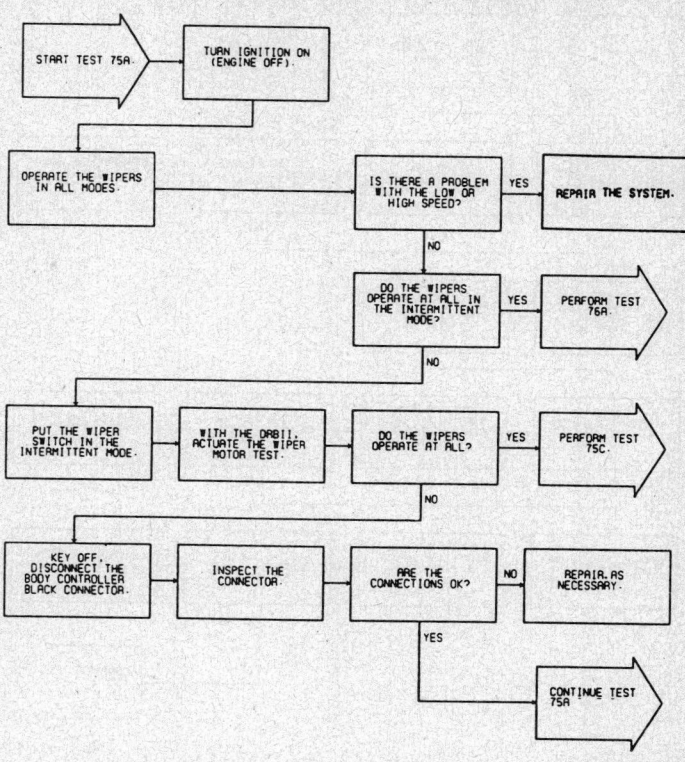

Fig. 21   Test 75A: Wiper System Testing (Part 1 of 2). 1992 Dynasty, Fifth Avenue, Imperial & 1992–93 New Yorker

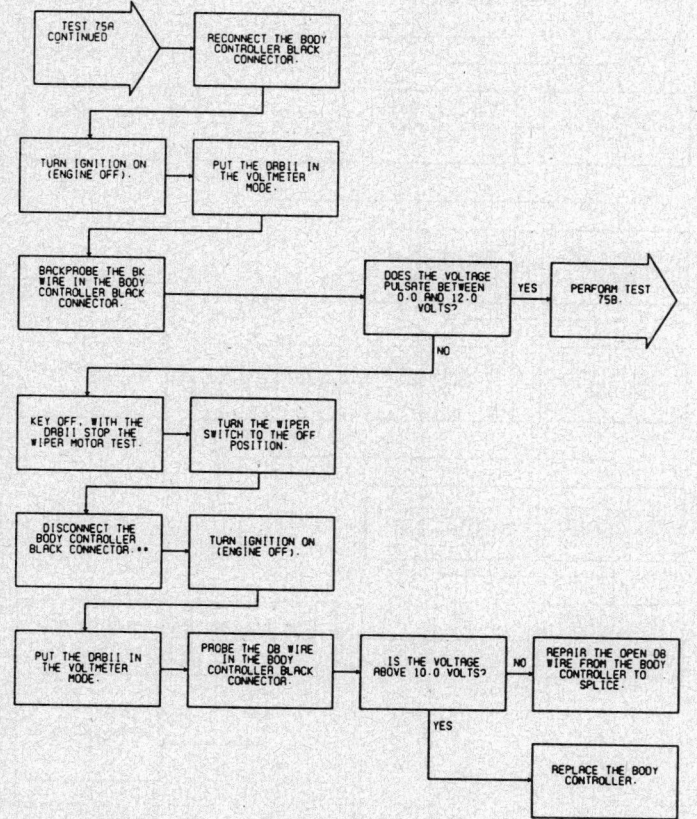

Fig. 21   Test 75A: Wiper System Testing (Part 2 of 2). Dynasty, Fifth Avenue, Imperial & 1992–93 New Yorker

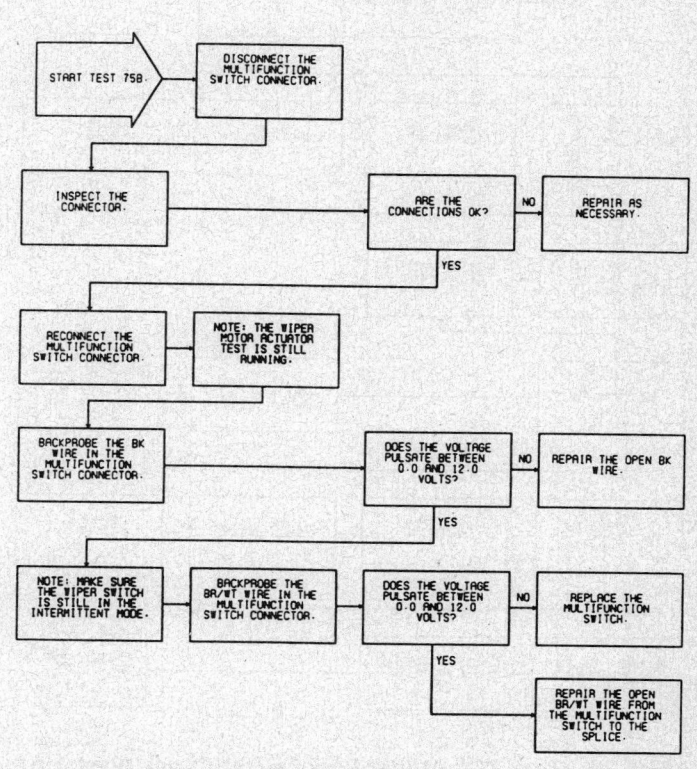

Fig. 22   Test 75B: Wiper System Testing. Dynasty, Fifth Avenue, Imperial & 1992–93 New Yorker

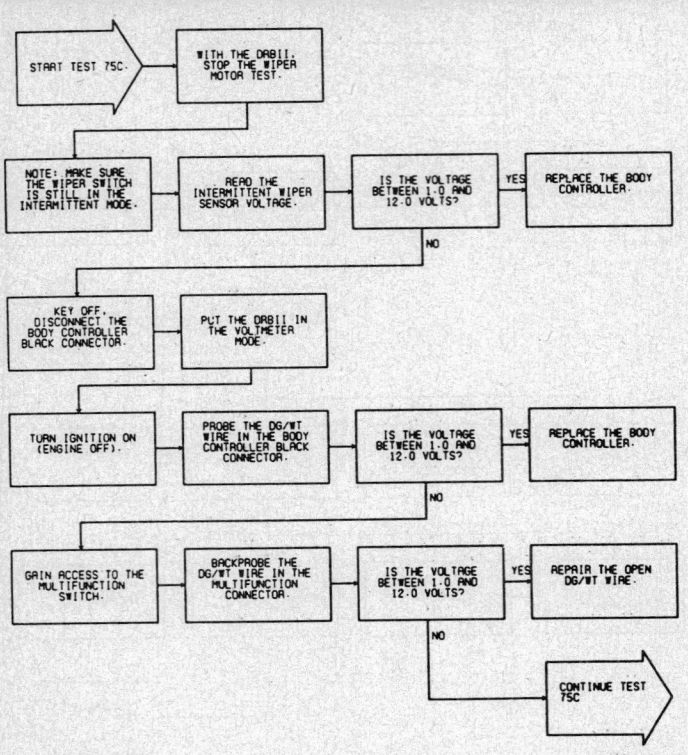

Fig. 23   Test 75C: Wiper Switch Circuit Check (Part 1 of 2). Dynasty, Fifth Avenue, Imperial & 1992–93 New Yorker

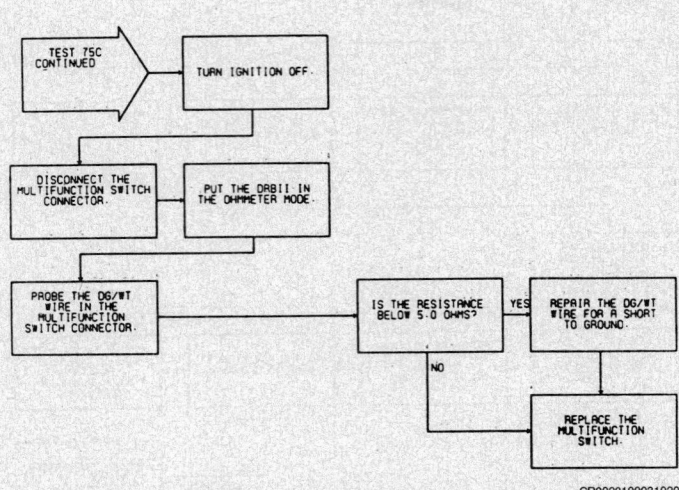

Fig. 23   Test 75C: Wiper Switch Circuit Check (Part 2 of 2). Dynasty, Fifth Avenue, Imperial & 1992–93 New Yorker

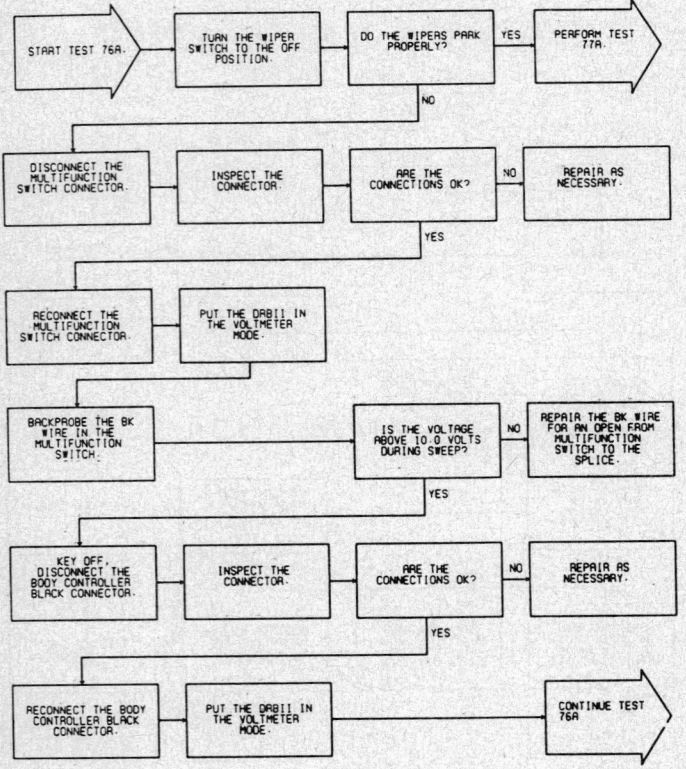

Fig. 24   Test 76A: Wiper Park Circuit Check (Part 1 of 2). Dynasty, Fifth Avenue, Imperial & 1992–93 New Yorker

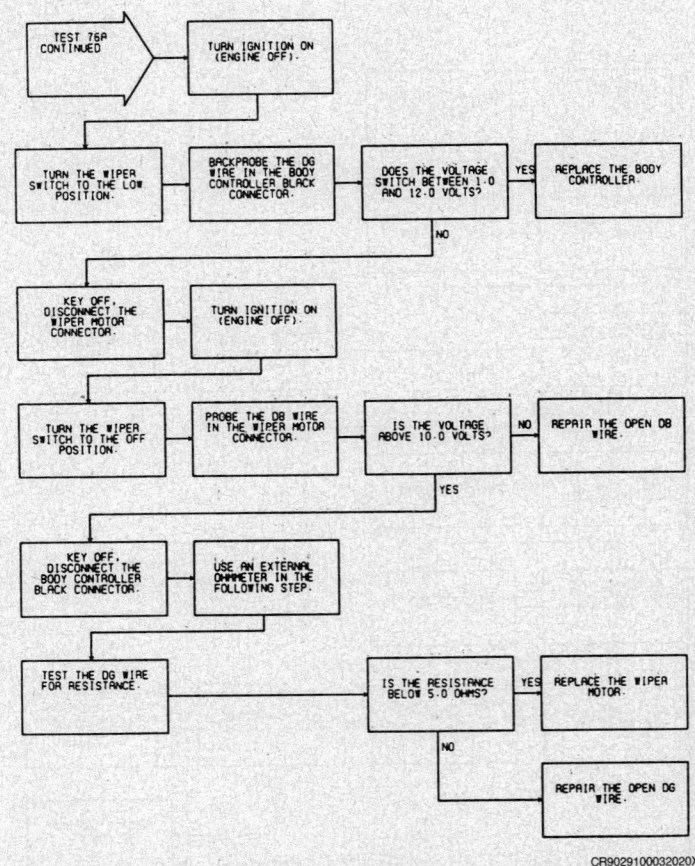

Fig. 24   Test 76A: Wiper Park Circuit Check (Part 2 of 2). Dynasty, Fifth Avenue, Imperial & 1992–93 New Yorker

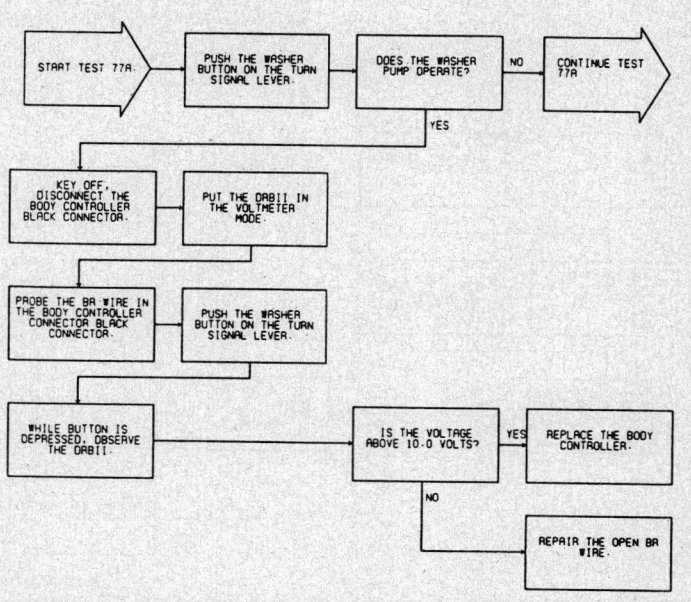

Fig. 25   Test 77A: Washer Pump Circuit Check (Part 1 of 2). Dynasty, Fifth Avenue, Imperial & 1992–93 New Yorker

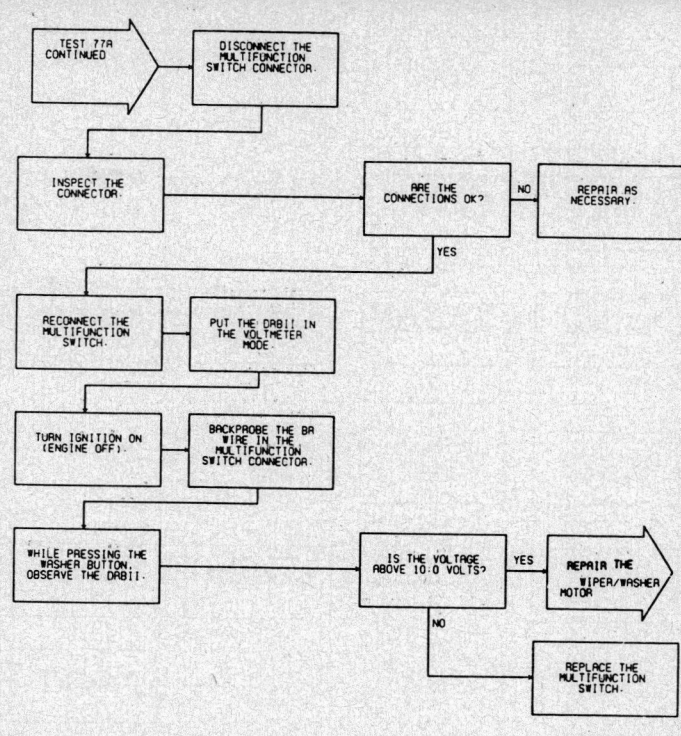

Fig. 25   Test 77A: Washer Pump Circuit Check (Part 2 of 2). Dynasty, Fifth Avenue, Imperial & 1992–93 New Yorker

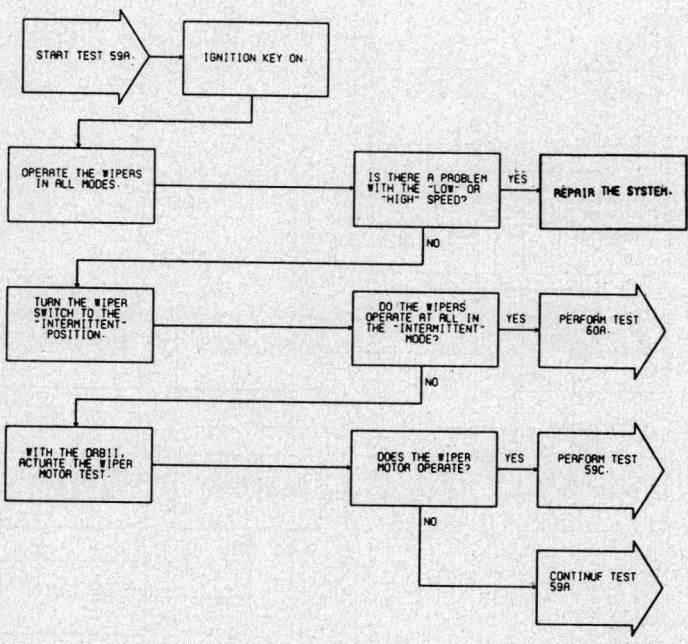

Fig. 26   Test 59A: Wiper Switch, Controller & Related Wiring Diagnosis (Part 1 of 3). 1992 Daytona, LeBaron Coupe, & LeBaron Convertible

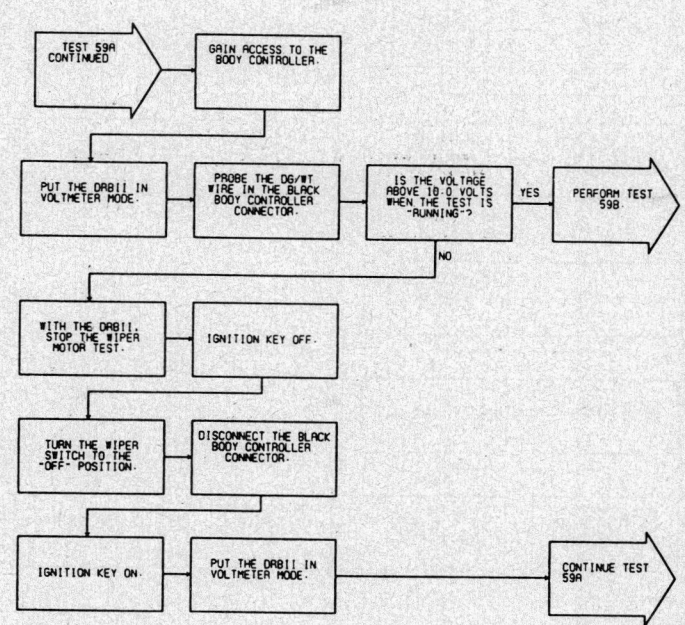

Fig. 26   Test 59A: Wiper Switch, Controller & Related Wiring Diagnosis (Part 2 of 3). 1992 Daytona, LeBaron Coupe, & LeBaron Convertible

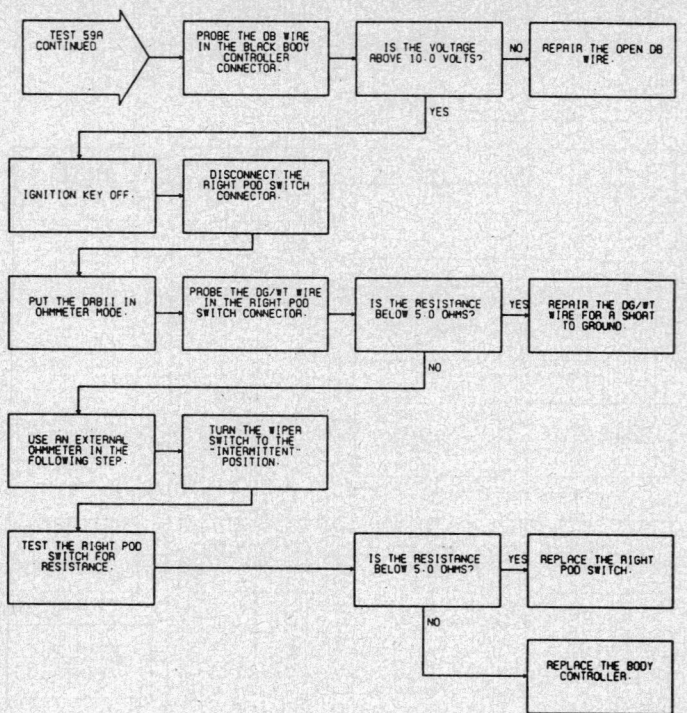

Fig. 26   Test 59A: Wiper Switch, Controller & Related Wiring Diagnosis (Part 3 of 3). 1992 Daytona, LeBaron Coupe, & LeBaron Convertible

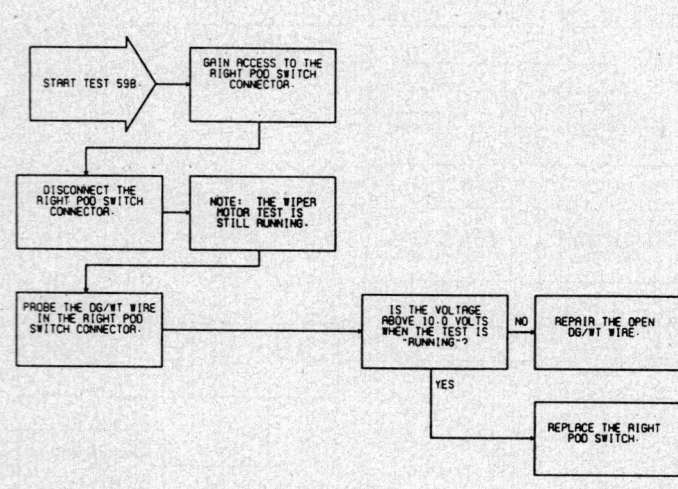

Fig. 27   Test 59B: Controller Signal & Switch Continuity Check. 1992 Daytona, LeBaron Coupe, & LeBaron Convertible

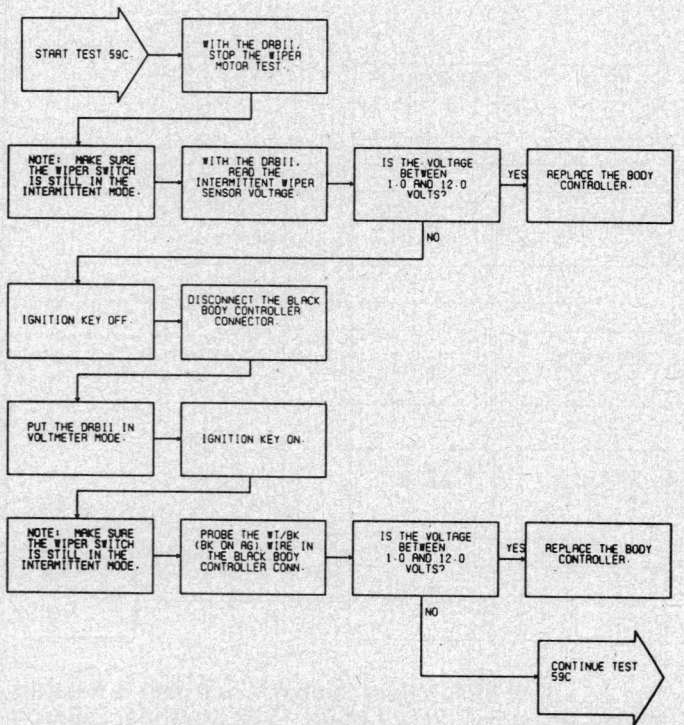

Fig. 28   Test 59C: Body Controller Input Check (Part 1 of 2). 1992 Daytona, LeBaron Coupe, & LeBaron Convertible

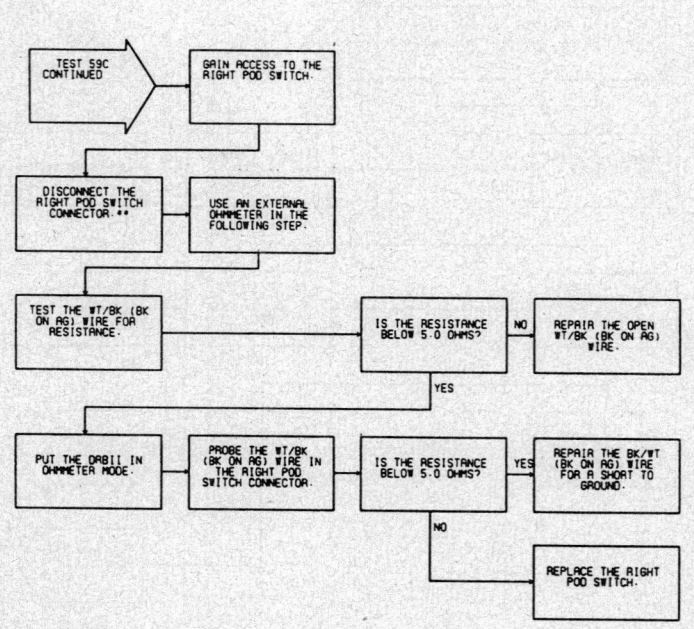

Fig. 28   Test 59C: Body Controller Input Check (Part 2 of 2). 1992 Daytona, LeBaron Coupe, & LeBaron Convertible

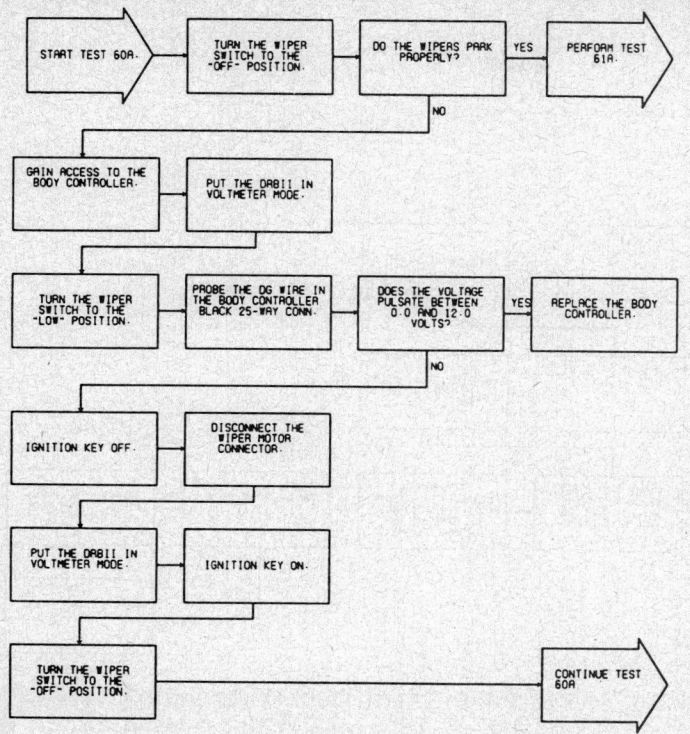

Fig. 29   Test 60A: Wiper Motor & Motor Control Check (Part 1 of 2). 1992 Daytona, LeBaron Coupe, & LeBaron Convertible

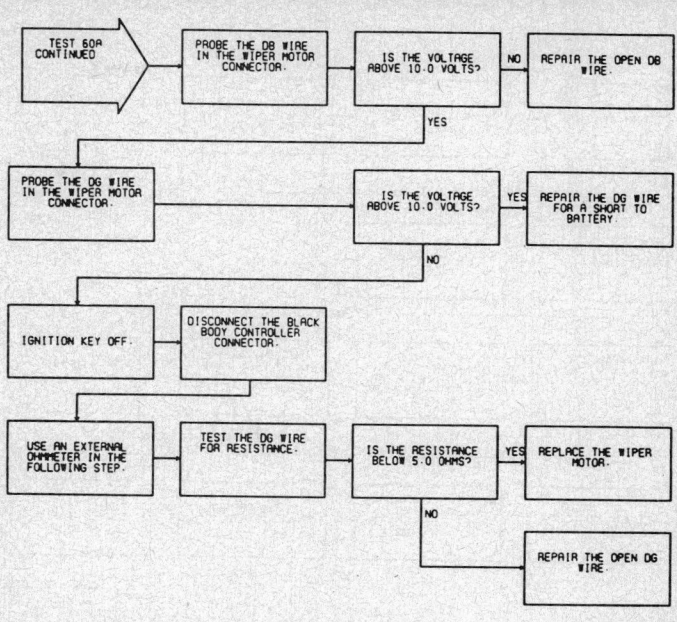

Fig. 29   Test 60A, Wiper Motor & Motor Control Check (Part 2 of 2). 1992 Daytona, LeBaron Coupe, & LeBaron Convertible

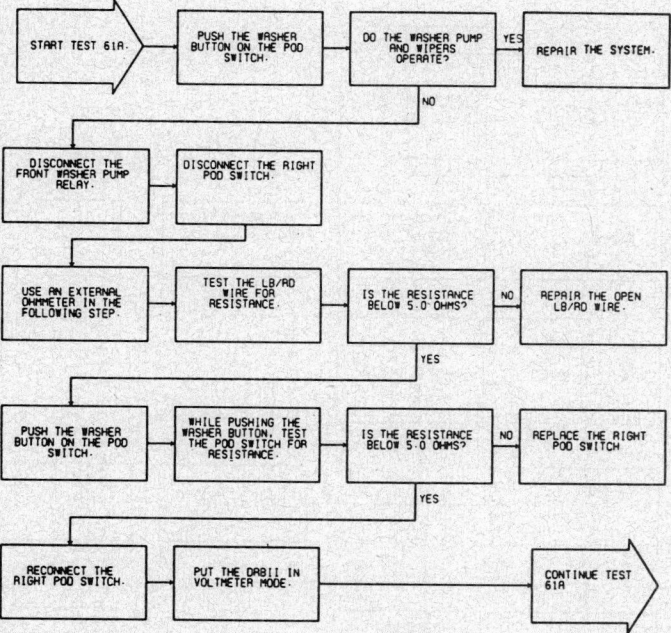

Fig. 30   Test 61A: Pod Switch & Windshield Washer Function Test (Part 1 of 2). 1992 Daytona, LeBaron Coupe, & LeBaron Convertible

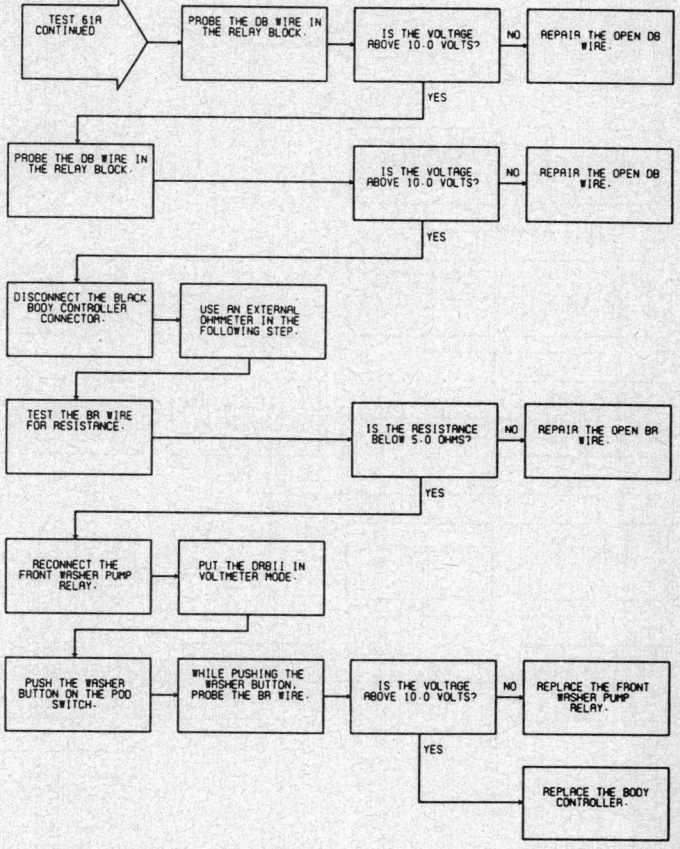

Fig. 30   Test 61A: Pod Switch & Windshield Washer Function Test (Part 2 of 2). 1992 Daytona, LeBaron Coupe, & LeBaron Convertible

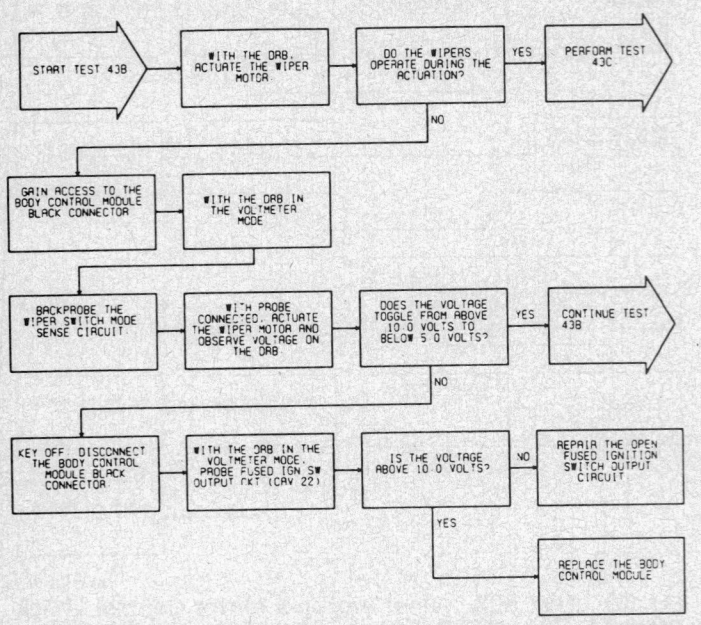

Fig. 31 Test 43B: Intermittent Wiper System Testing (Part 1 Of 2). 1993-94 Daytona & LeBaron

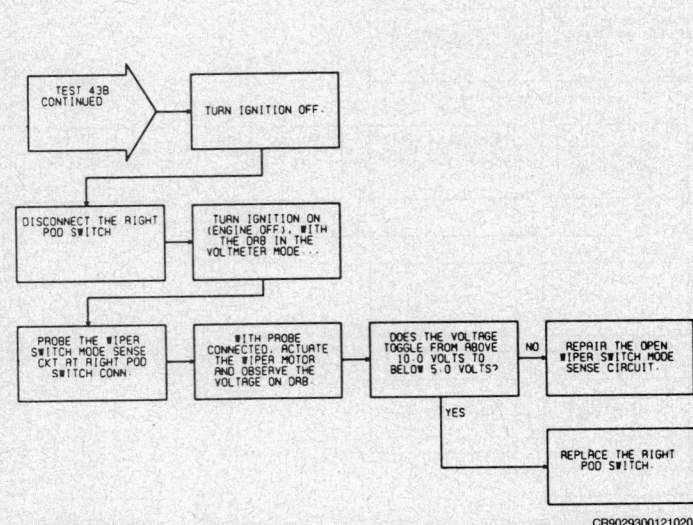

Fig. 31 Test 43B: Intermittent Wiper System Testing (Part 2 Of 2). 1993-94 Daytona & LeBaron

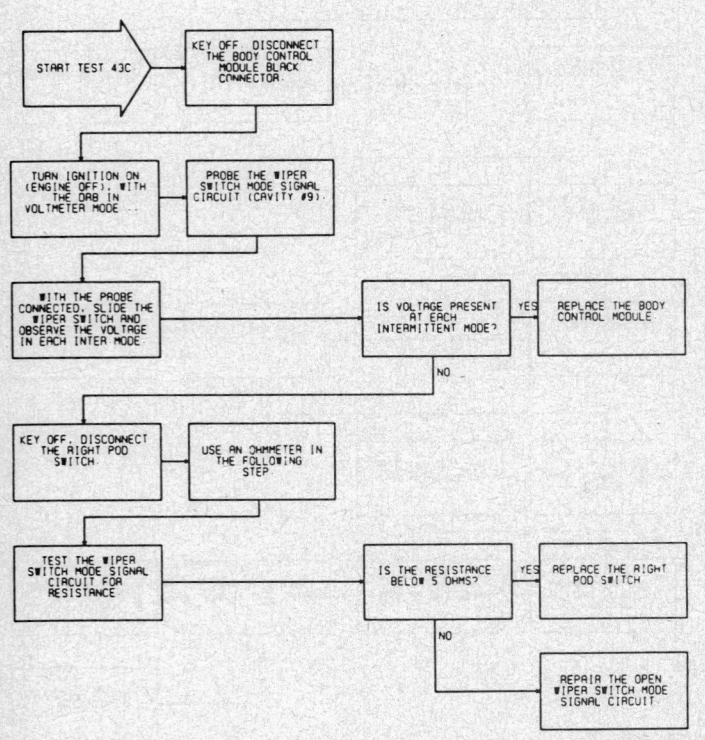

Fig. 32 Test 43C: Intermittent Wiper Systems Testing. 1993-94 Daytona & LeBaron

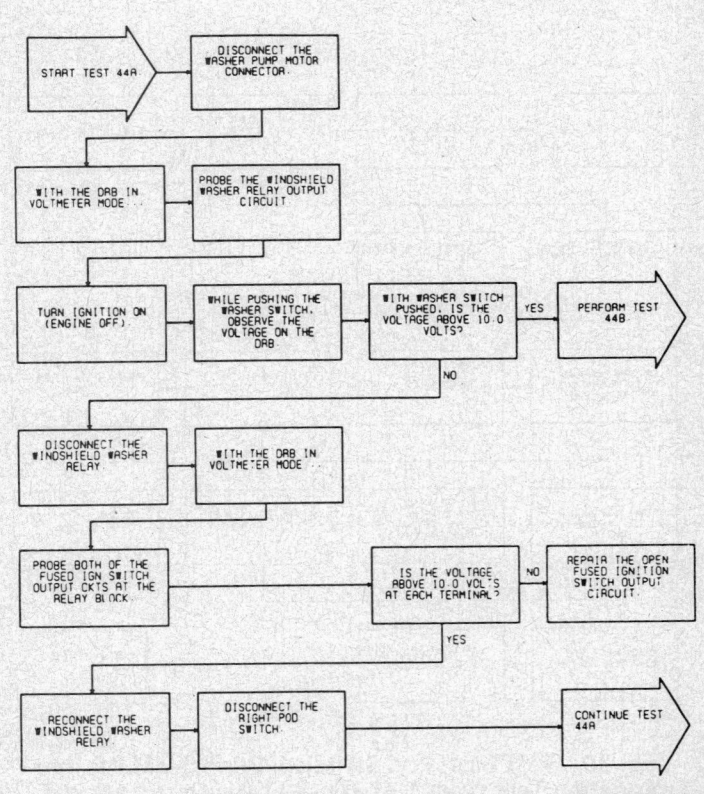

Fig. 33 Test 44A: Washer Pump System Testing (Part 1 Of 2). 1993-94 Daytona & LeBaron

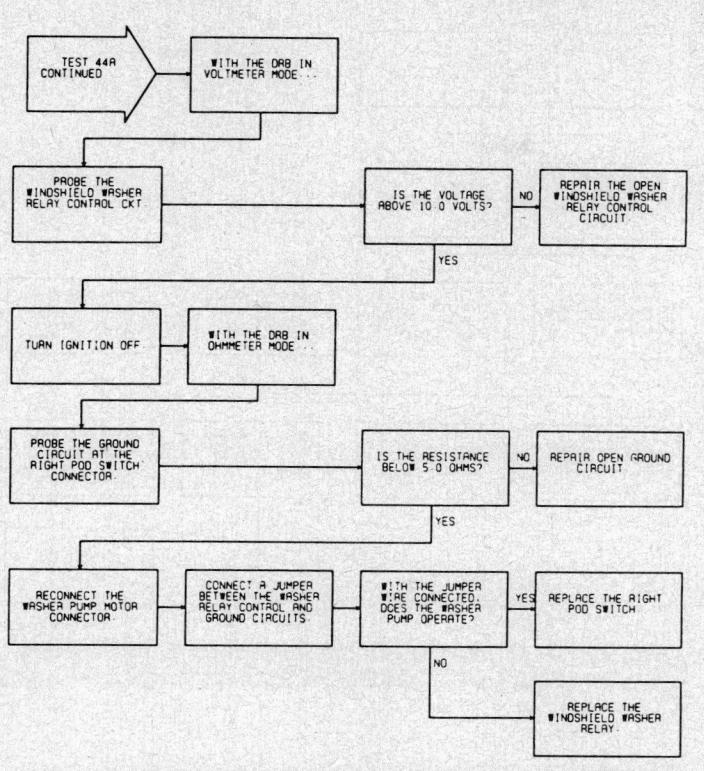

Fig. 33   Test 44A: Washer Pump System Testing (Part 2 Of 2). 1993-94 Daytona & LeBaron

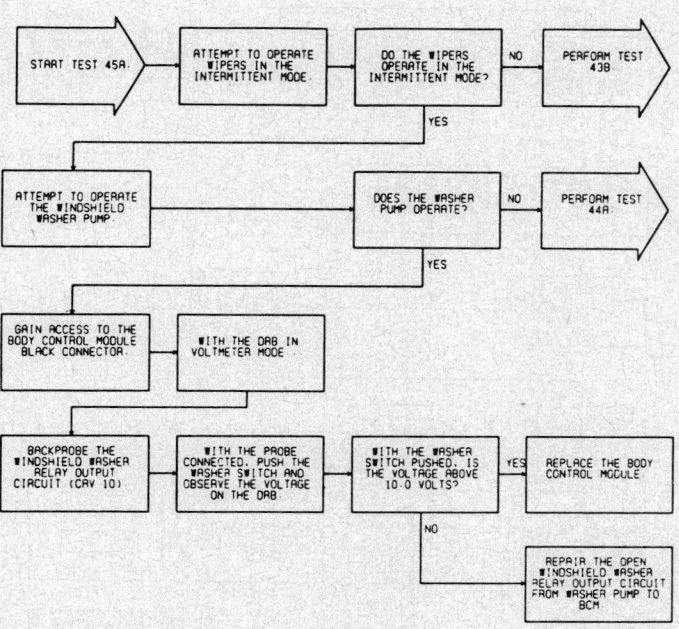

Fig. 35   Test 45A: Washer Cycle Testing. 1993-94 Daytona & LeBaron

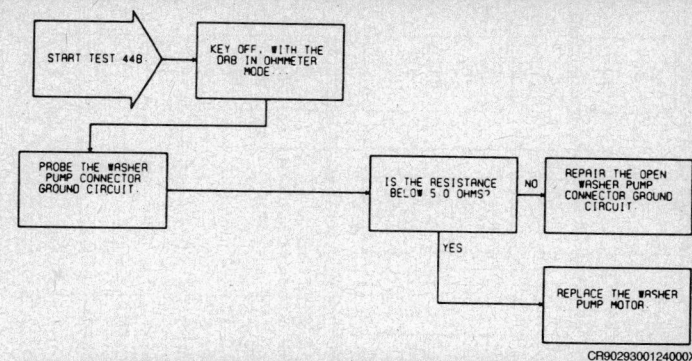

Fig. 34   Test 44B: Washer Pump Testing. 1993-94 Daytona & LeBaron

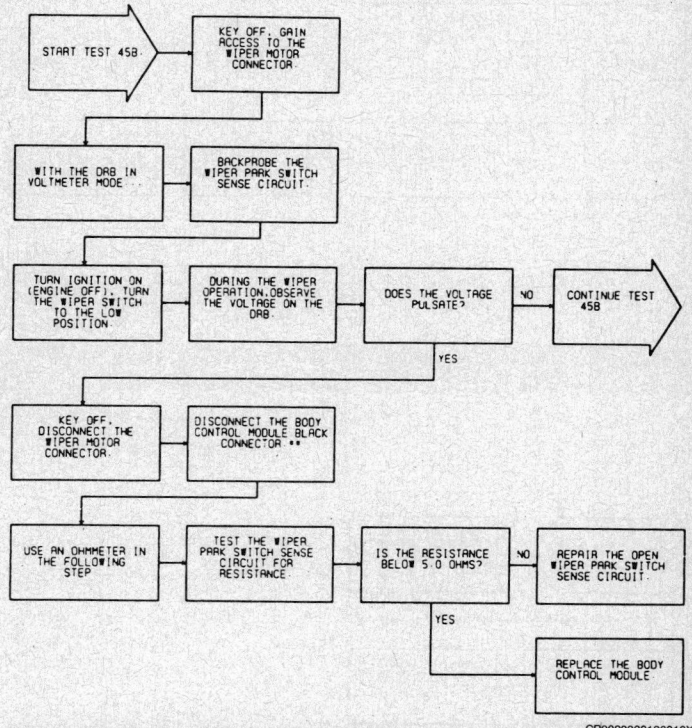

Fig. 36   Test 45B: Wipers Will Not Park Testing (Part 1 Of 2). 1993-94 Daytona & LeBaron

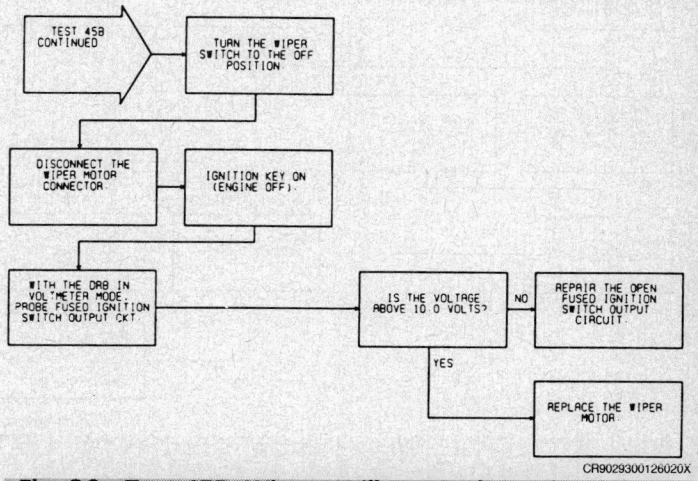

Fig. 36   Test 45B: Wipers Will Not Park Testing (Part 2 Of 2). 1993-94 Daytona & LeBaron

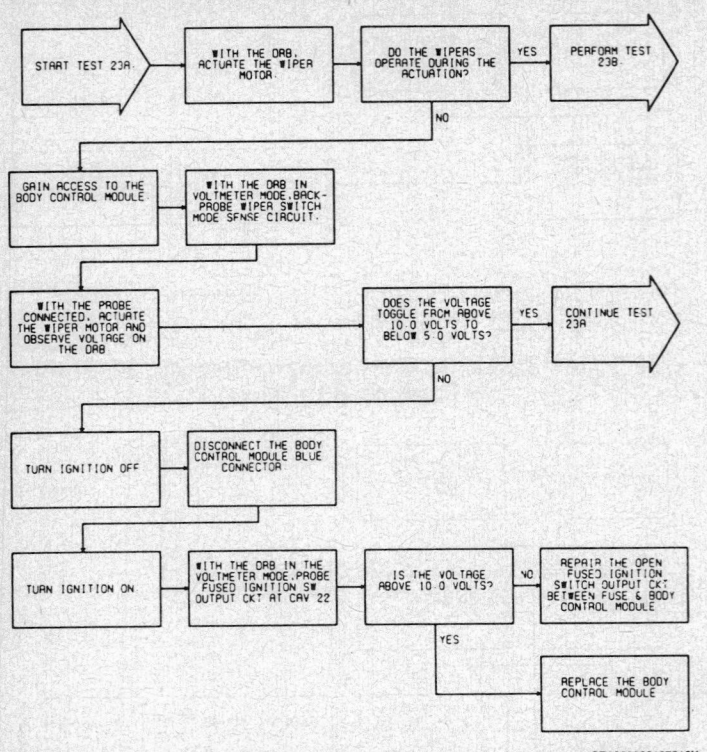

Fig. 37   Test 23A: Intermittent Wiper System Testing (Part 1 Of 2). 1993–94 Acclaim & Spirit

CR9029300127010X

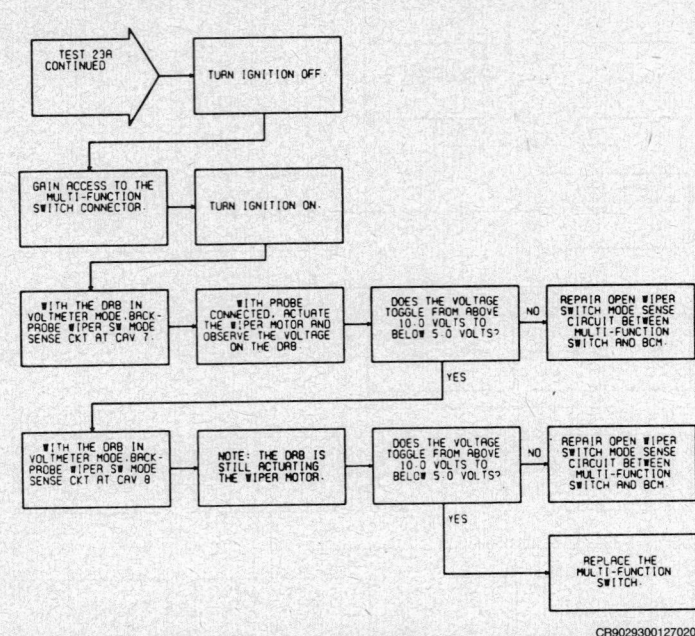

Fig. 37   Test 23A: Intermittent Wiper System Testing (Part 2 Of 2). 1993–94 Acclaim & Spirit

CR9029300127020X

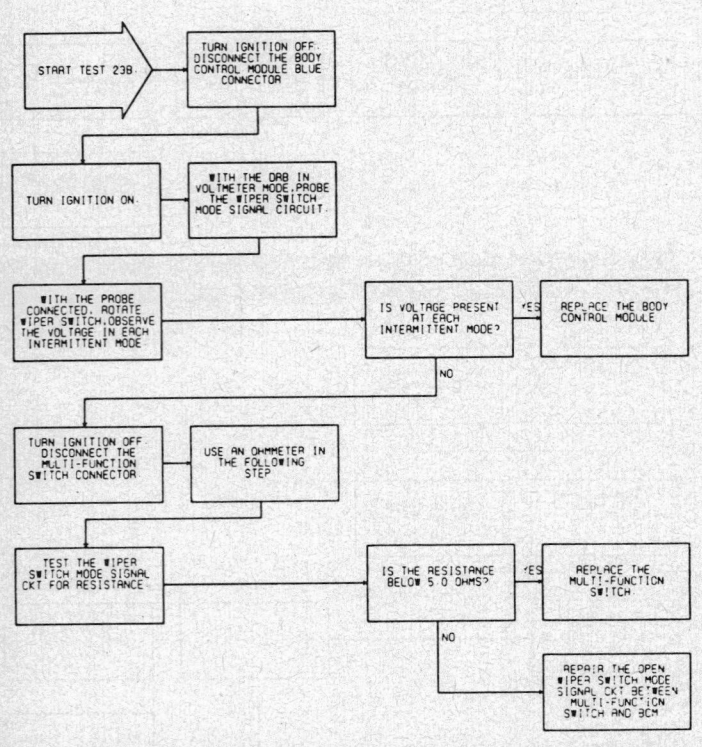

Fig. 38   Test 23B: Wiper Switch Testing For Open In Signal Circuit. 1993–94 Acclaim & Spirit

CR9029300128000X

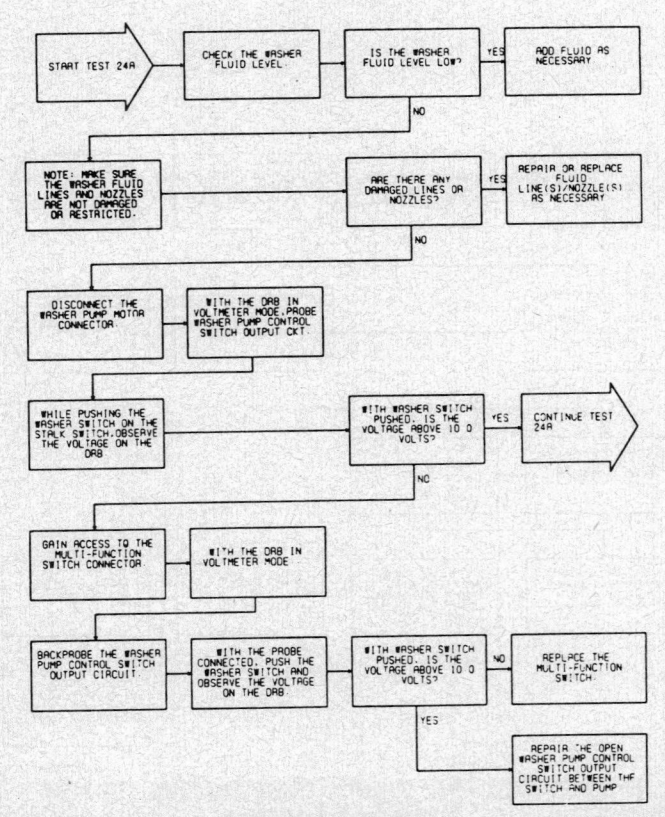

Fig. 39   Test 24A: Washer Pump System Testing (Part 1 Of 2). 1993–94 Acclaim & Spirit

CR9029300129010X

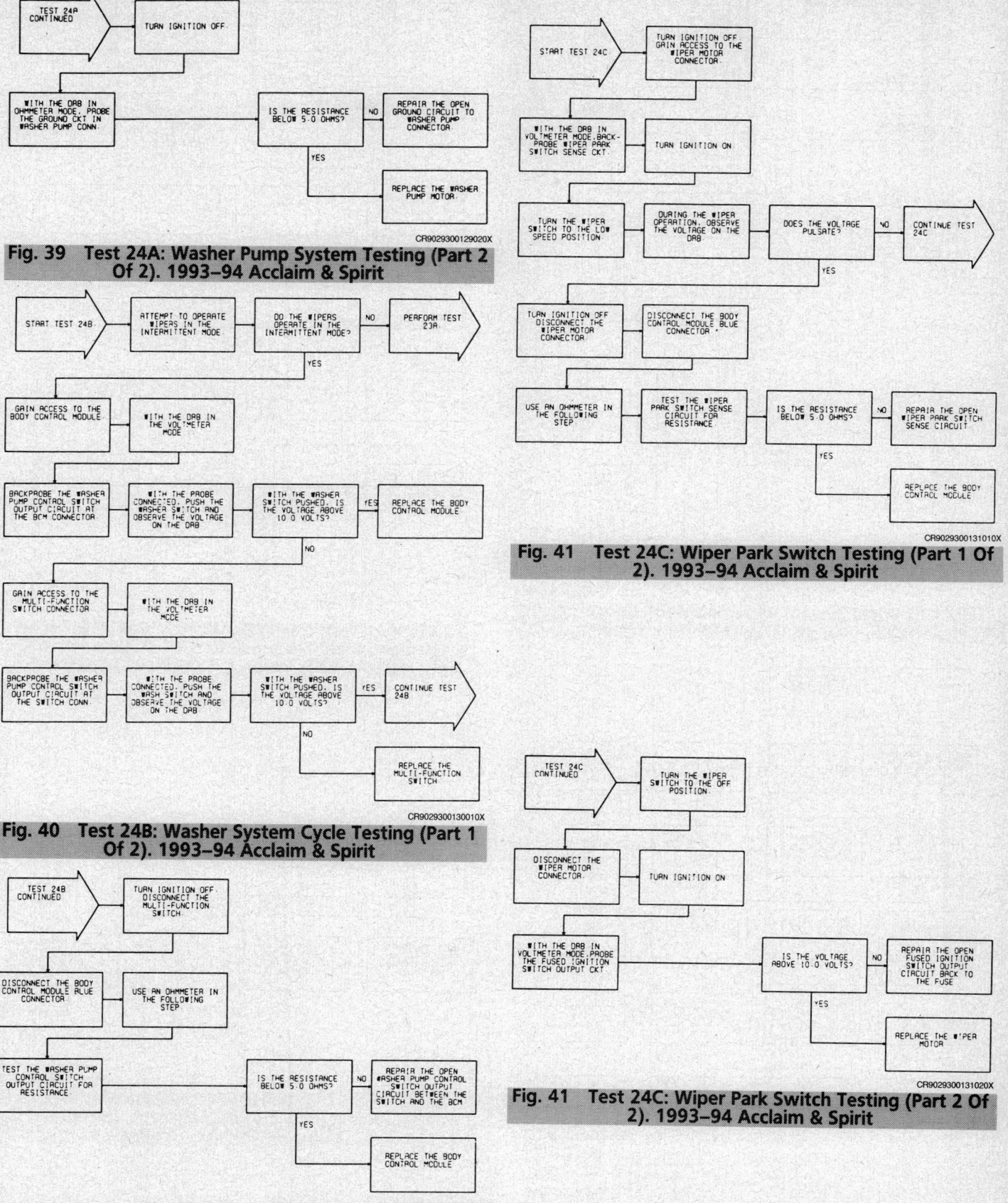

Fig. 39 Test 24A: Washer Pump System Testing (Part 2 Of 2). 1993–94 Acclaim & Spirit

Fig. 40 Test 24B: Washer System Cycle Testing (Part 1 Of 2). 1993–94 Acclaim & Spirit

Fig. 40 Test 24B: Washer System Cycle Testing (Part 2 Of 2). 1993–94 Acclaim & Spirit

Fig. 41 Test 24C: Wiper Park Switch Testing (Part 1 Of 2). 1993–94 Acclaim & Spirit

Fig. 41 Test 24C: Wiper Park Switch Testing (Part 2 Of 2). 1993–94 Acclaim & Spirit

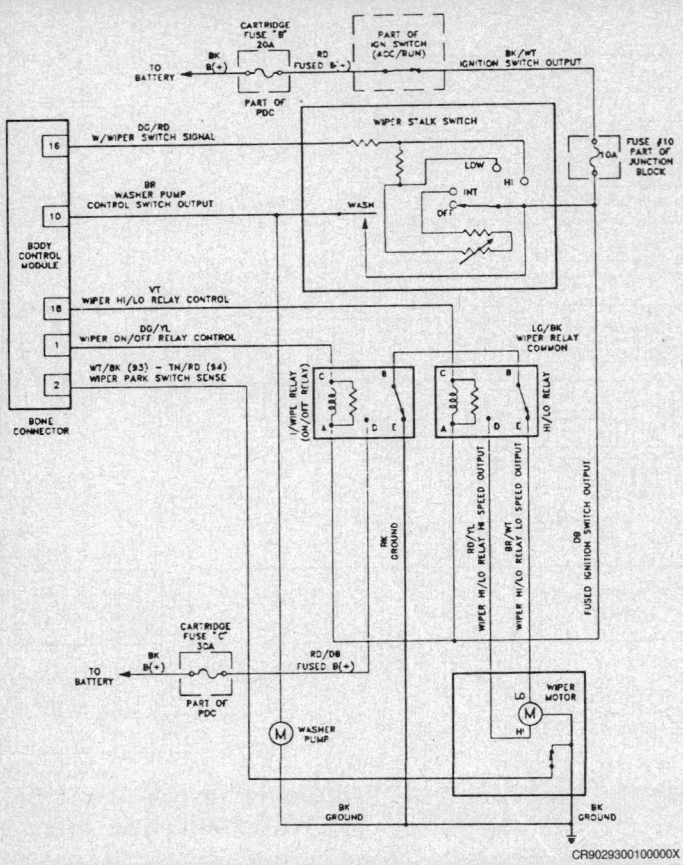

Fig. 42   Wiper system wiring diagram. Concorde, Intrepid, LHS, Vision & 1994 New Yorker

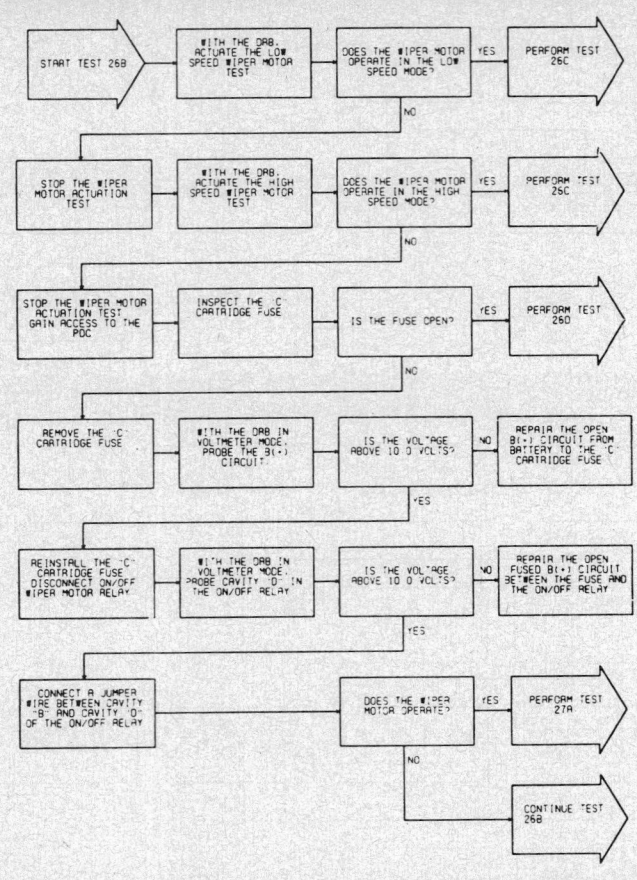

Fig. 43   Test 26B: Wiper Switch, Controller & Power Supply Testing (Part 1 of 3). Concorde, Intrepid, LHS, Vision & 1994 New Yorker

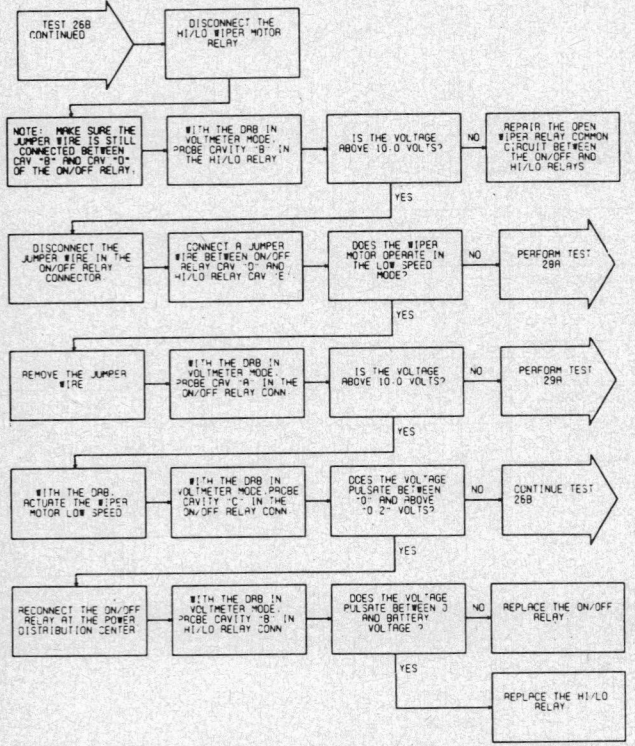

Fig. 43   Test 26B: Wiper Switch, Controller & Power Supply Testing (Part 2 of 3). Concorde, Intrepid, LHS, Vision & 1994 New Yorker

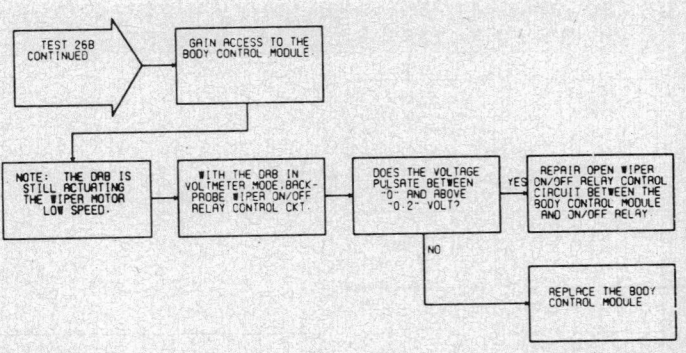

Fig. 43   Test 26B: Wiper Switch, Controller & Power Supply Testing (Part 3 of 3). Concorde, Intrepid, LHS, Vision & 1994 New Yorker

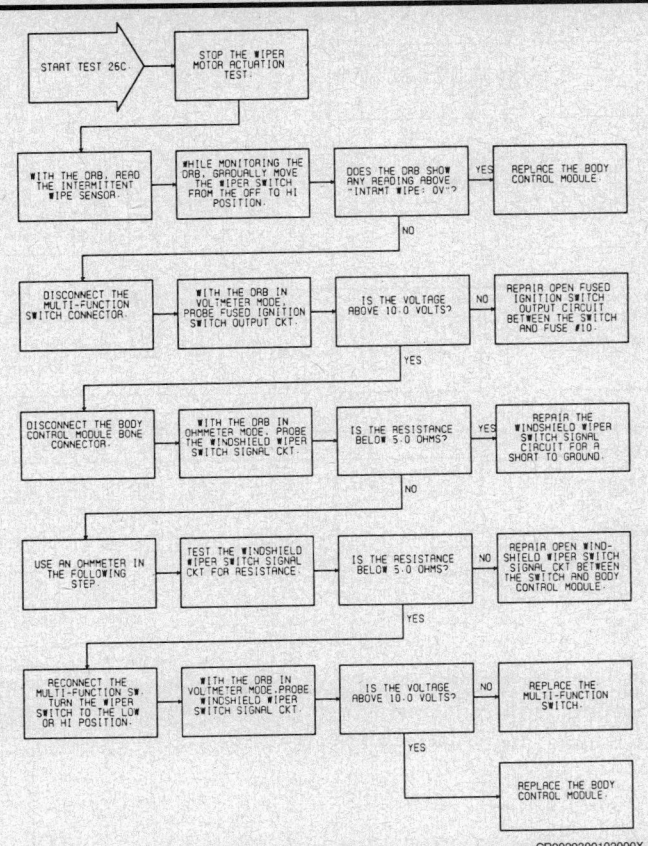

Fig. 44   Test 26C: Wiper Switch Mode Sense Circuit Testing. Concorde, Intrepid, LHS, Vision & 1994 New Yorker

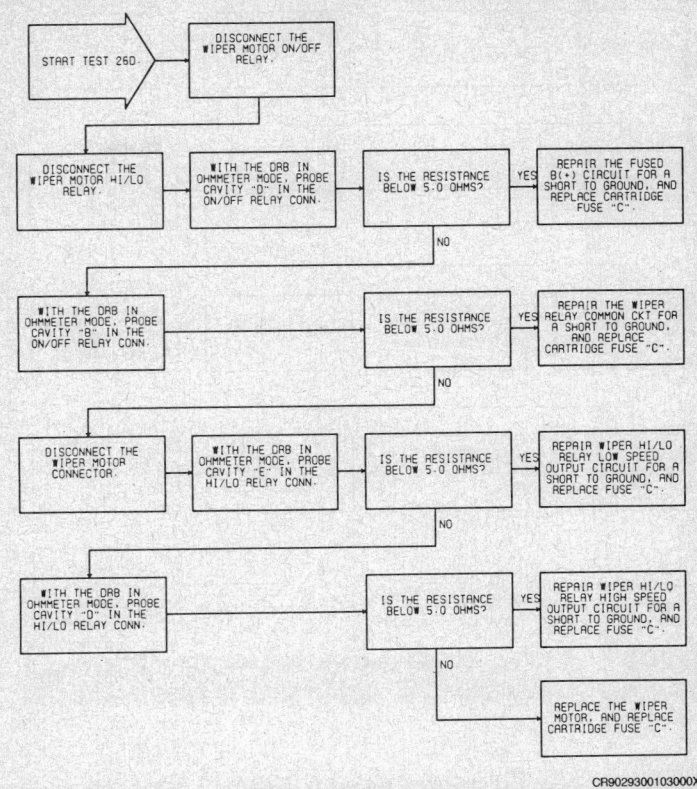

Fig. 45   Test 26D: Wiper Motor Output Circuit, Testing For Shorts. Concorde, Intrepid, LHS, Vision & 1994 New Yorker

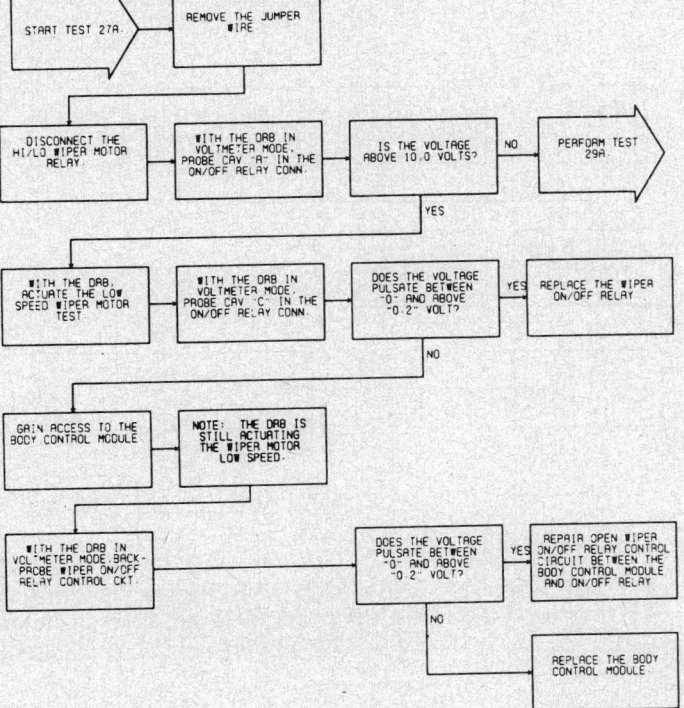

Fig. 46   Test 27A: Low Speed Wiper Motor Relay & Control Testing. Concorde, Intrepid, LHS, Vision & 1994 New Yorker

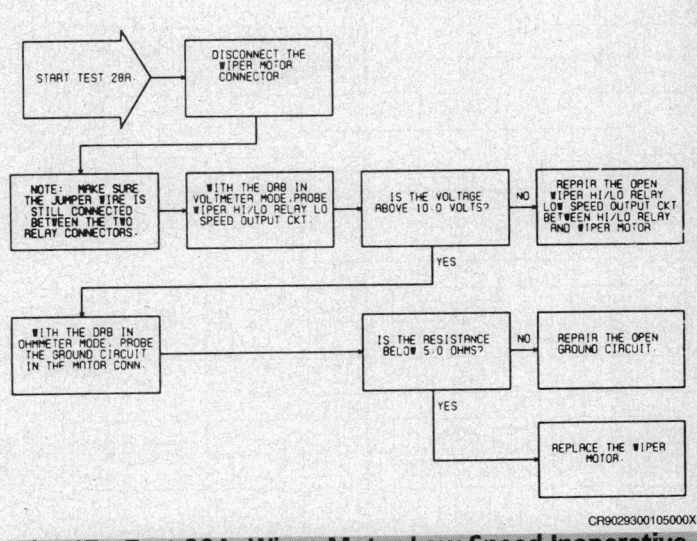

Fig. 47   Test 28A: Wiper Motor Low Speed Inoperative Testing. Concorde, Intrepid, LHS, Vision & 1994 New Yorker

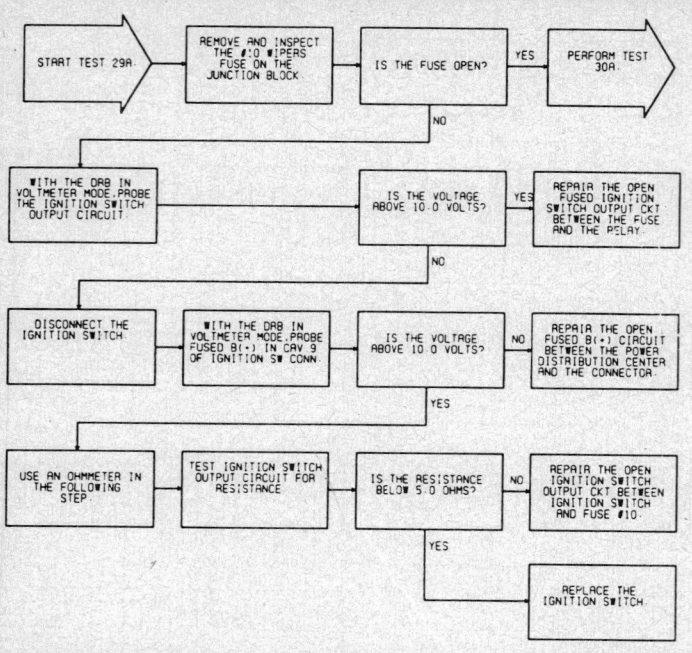

Fig. 48   Test 29A: Wiper Switch Power Supply Testing. Concorde, Intrepid, LHS, Vision & 1994 New Yorker

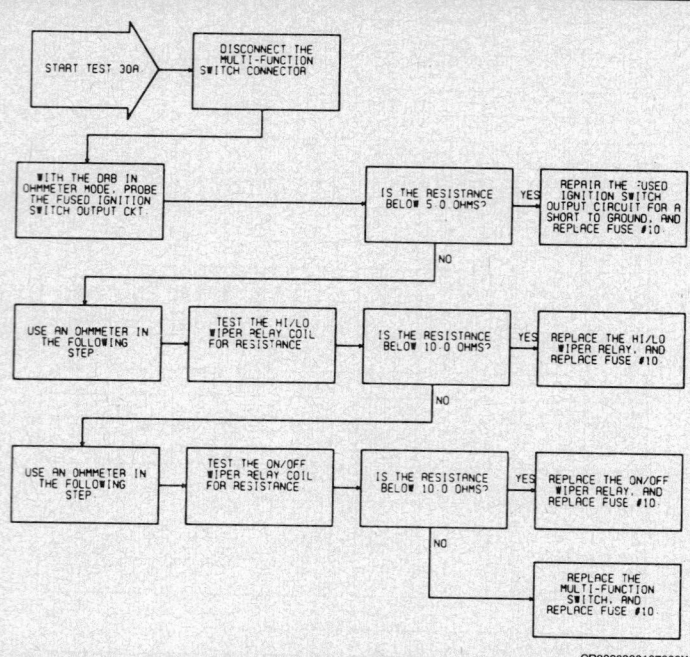

Fig. 49   Test 30A: Wiper Switch Power Supply Short To Ground Testing. Concorde, Intrepid, LHS, Vision & 1994 New Yorker

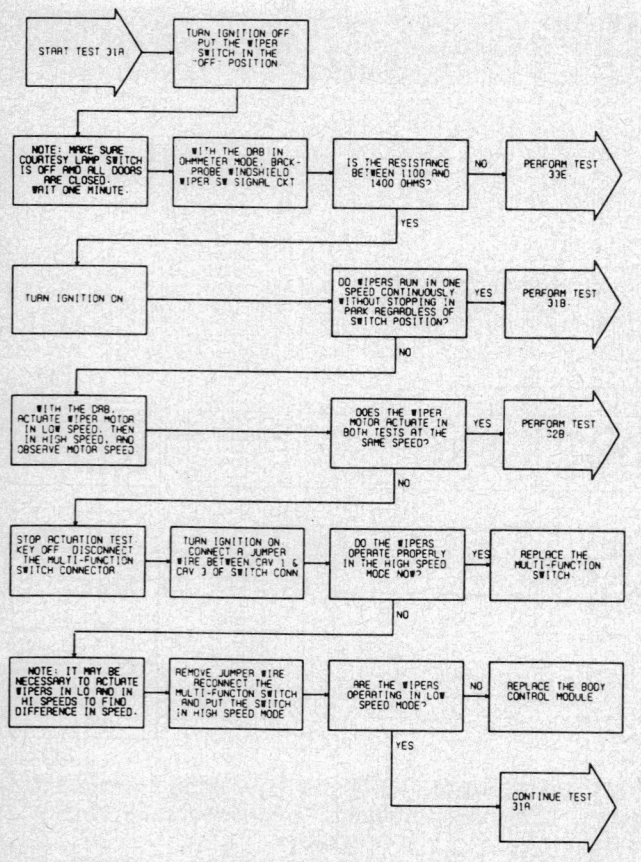

Fig. 50   Test 31A: Wiper Motor High Speed Operation Testing (Part 1 Of 3). Concorde, Intrepid, LHS, Vision & 1994 New Yorker

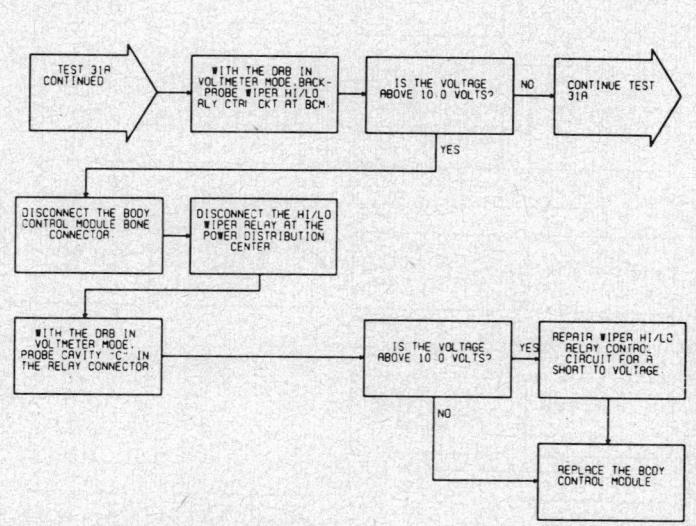

Fig. 50   Test 31A: Wiper Motor High Speed Operation Testing (Part 2 Of 3). Concorde, Intrepid, LHS, Vision & 1994 New Yorker

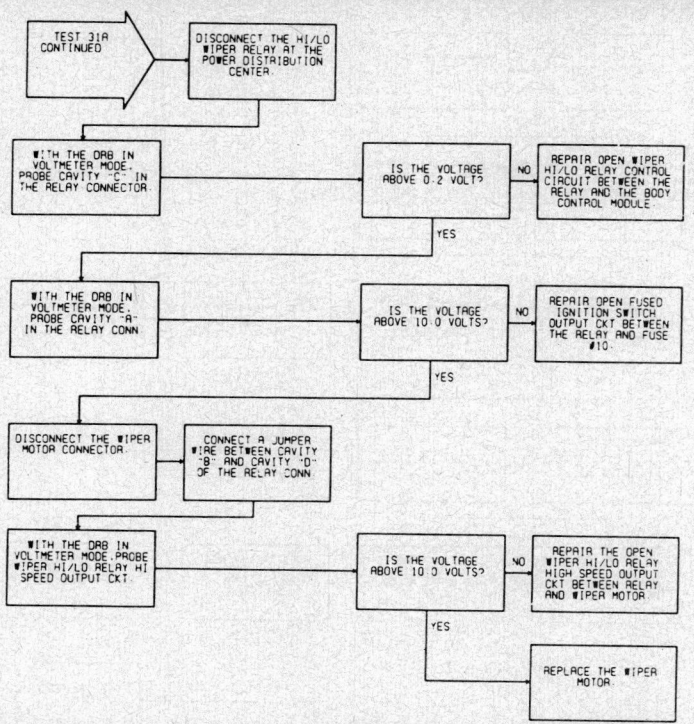

Fig. 50 Test 31A: Wiper Motor High Speed Operation Testing (Part 3 Of 3). Concorde, Intrepid, LHS, Vision & 1994 New Yorker

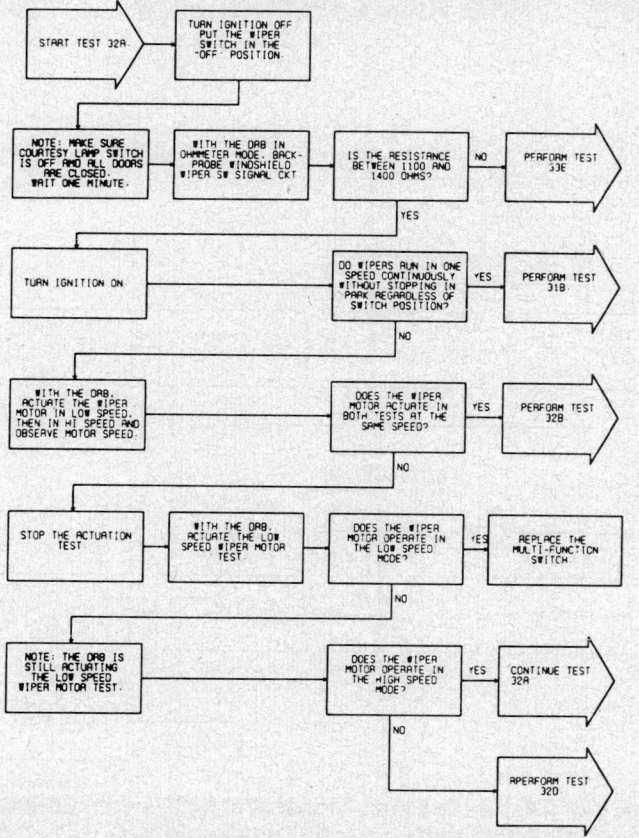

Fig. 52 Test 32A: Wiper Motor Low Speed Operation Testing (Part 1 Of 2). Concorde, Intrepid, LHS, Vision & 1994 New Yorker

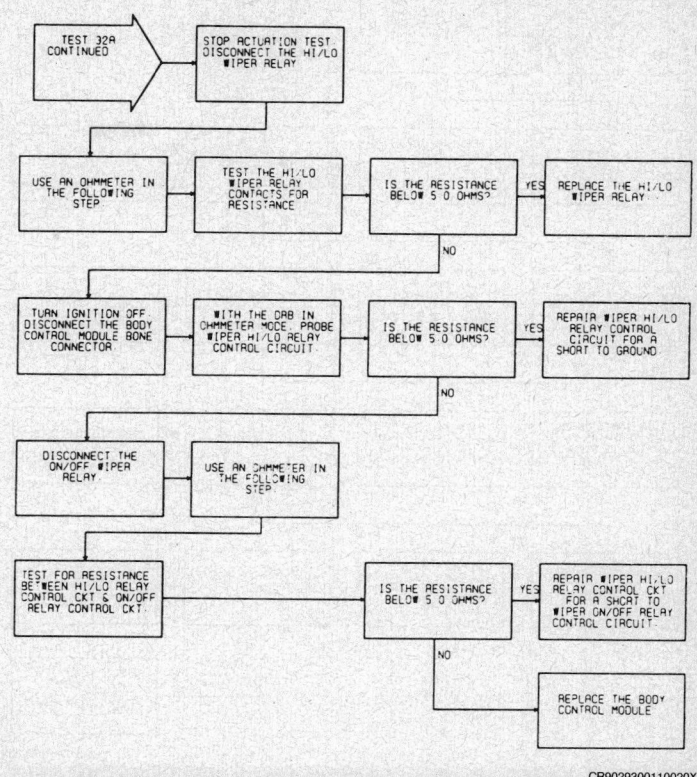

Fig. 52 Test 32A: Wiper Motor Low Speed Operation Testing (Part 2 Of 2). Concorde, Intrepid, LHS, Vision & 1994 New Yorker

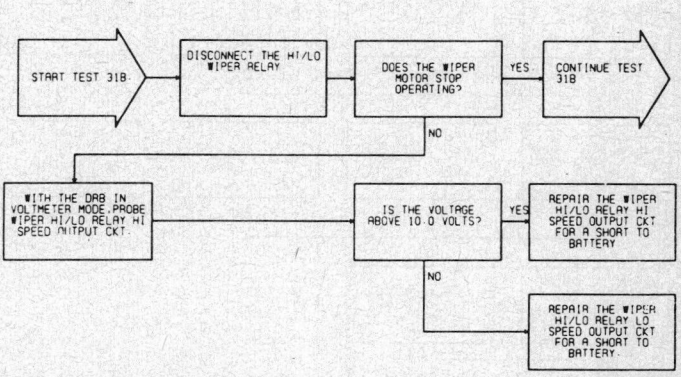

Fig. 51 Test 31B: Wiper Motor Does Not Shut Off (Part 1 Of 2). Concorde, Intrepid, LHS, Vision & 1994 New Yorker

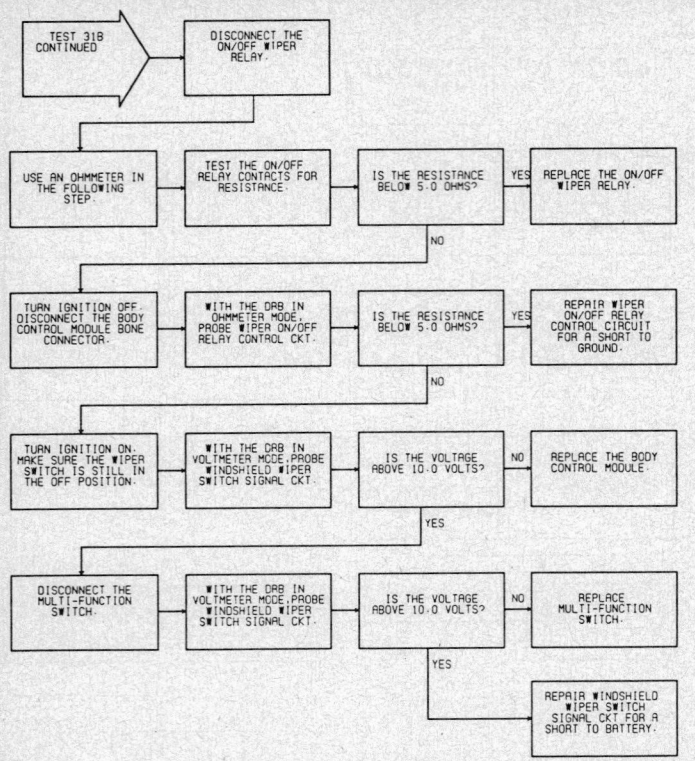

Fig. 51   Test 31B: Wiper Motor Does Not Shut Off (Part 2 Of 2). Concorde, Intrepid, LHS, Vision & 1994 New Yorker

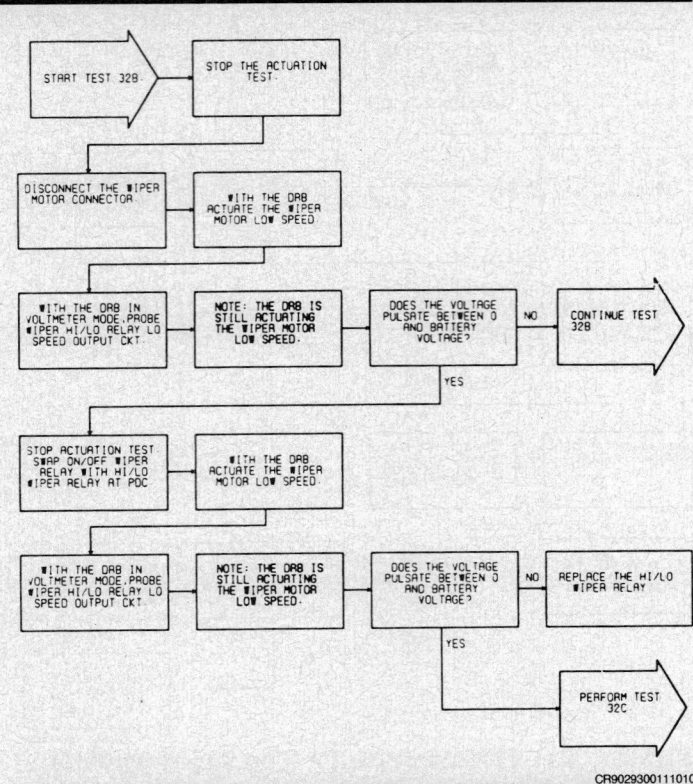

Fig. 53   Test 32B: Wiper Motor Will Not Switch Between High & Low Speeds (Part 1 Of 2). Concorde, Intrepid, LHS, Vision & 1994 New Yorker

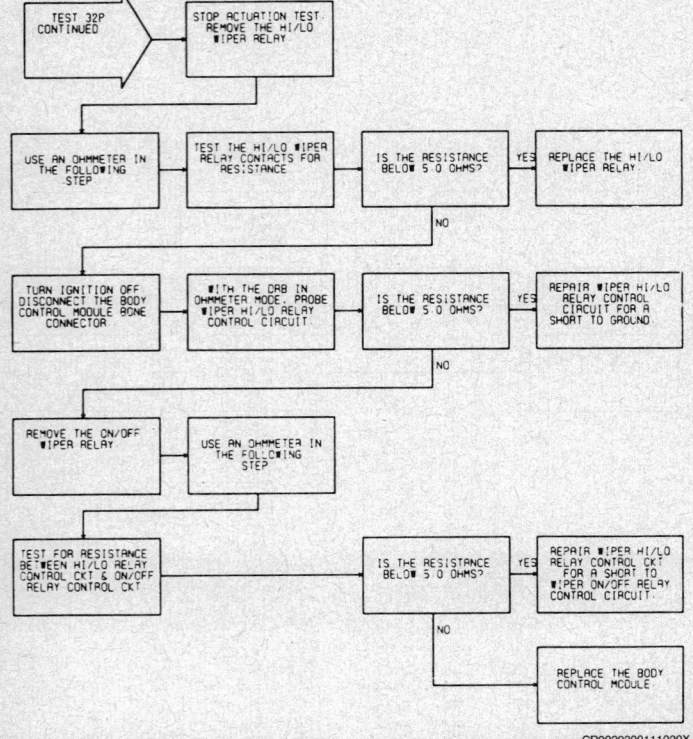

Fig. 53   Test 32B: Wiper Motor Will Not Switch Between High & Low Speeds (Part 2 Of 2). Concorde, Intrepid, LHS, Vision & 1994 New Yorker

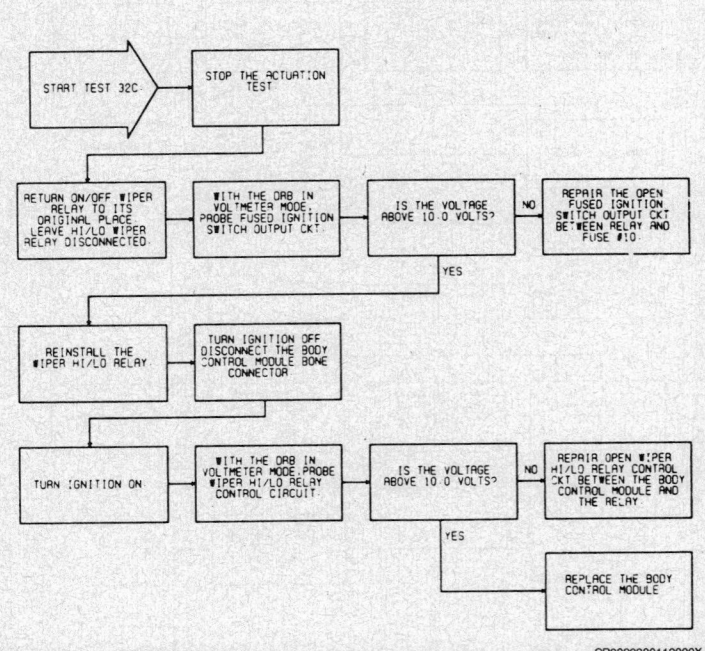

Fig. 54   Test 32C: Wiper Motor Will Not Switch Between High & Low Speeds. Concorde, Intrepid, LHS, Vision & 1994 New Yorker

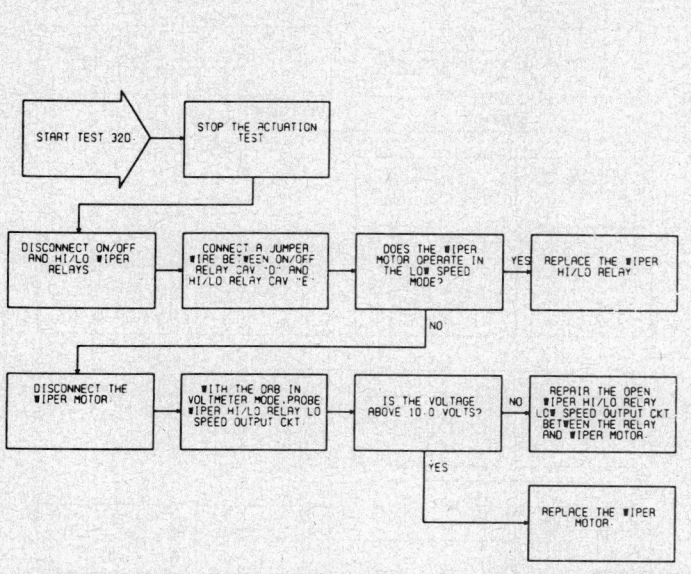

Fig. 55   Test 32D: Wiper Motor Low Speed Operation. Concorde, Intrepid, LHS, Vision & 1994 New Yorker

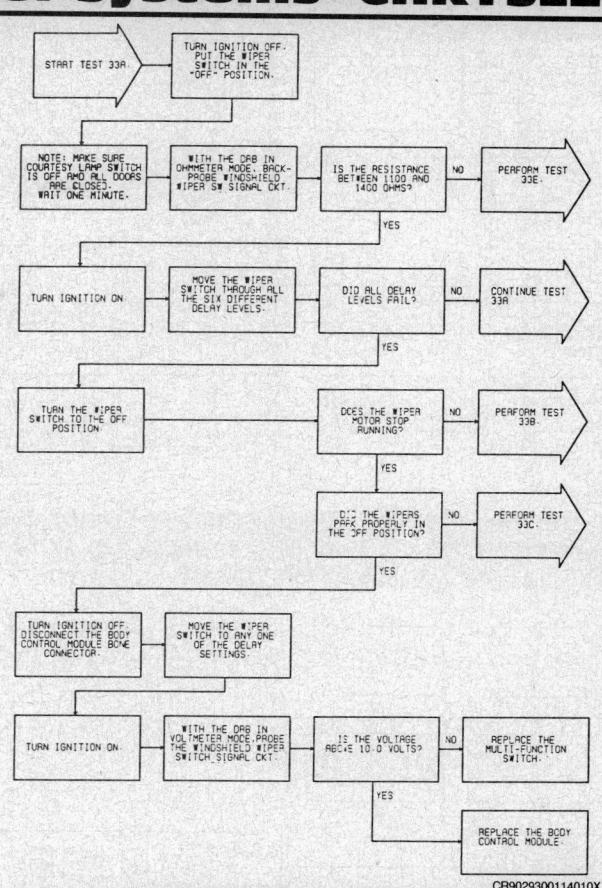

Fig. 56   Test 33A: Wiper Motor Intermittent Speed Operation Testing (Part 1 Of 2). Concorde, Intrepid, LHS, Vision & 1994 New Yorker

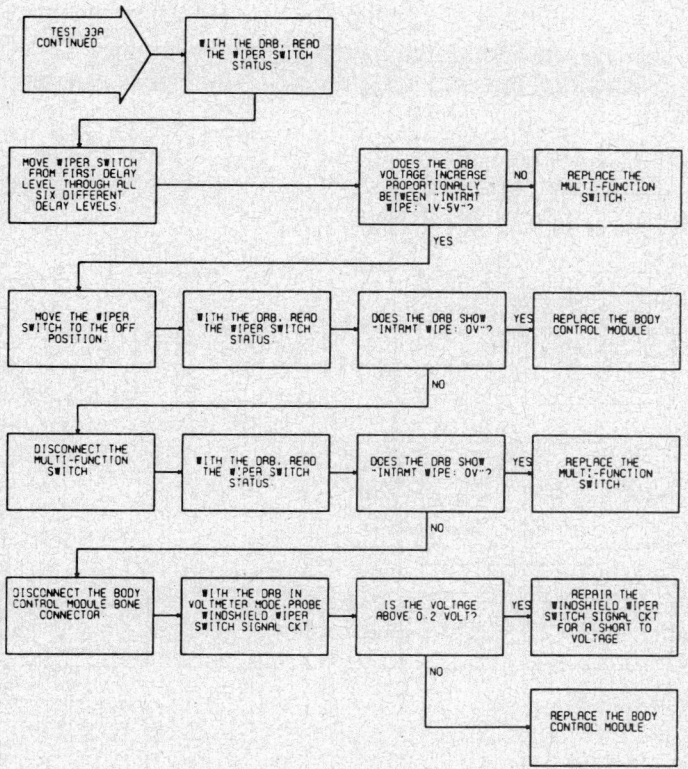

Fig. 56   Test 33A: Wiper Motor Intermittent Speed Operation Testing (Part 2 Of 2). Concorde, Intrepid, LHS, Vision & 1994 New Yorker

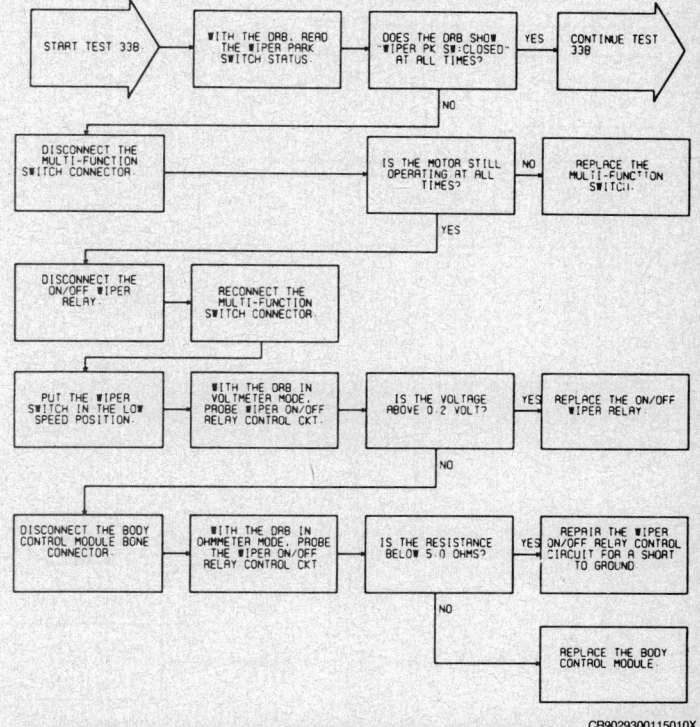

Fig. 57   Test 33B: Wiper Motor ON/OFF Control Circuit Testing (Part 1 Of 2). Concorde, Intrepid, LHS, Vision & 1994 New Yorker

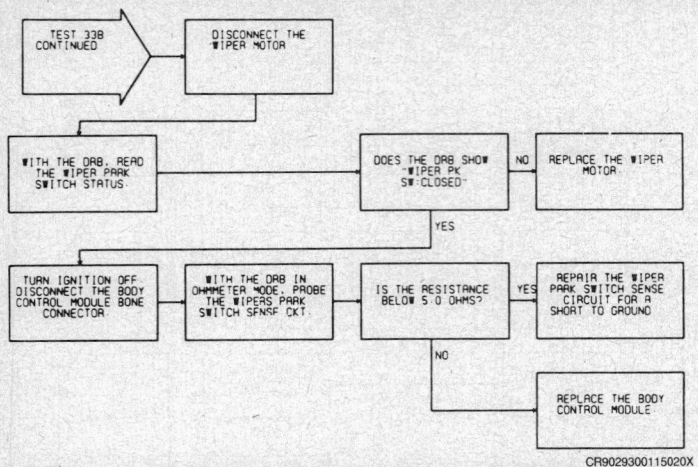

Fig. 57 Test 33B: Wiper Motor ON/OFF Control Circuit Testing (Part 2 Of 2). Concorde, Intrepid, LHS, Vision & 1994 New Yorker

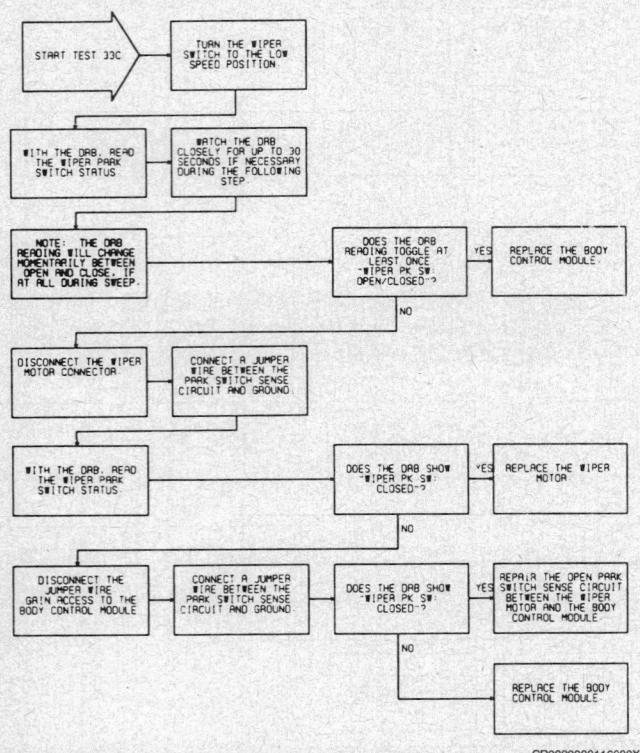

Fig. 58 Test 33C: Park Switch Sense Circuit, Test For Open. Concorde, Intrepid, LHS, Vision & 1994 New Yorker

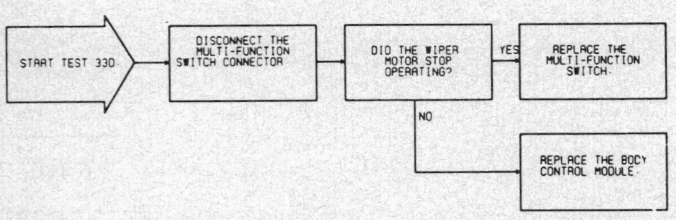

Fig. 59 Test 33D: Wipers Do Not Park In The OFF Position. Concorde, Intrepid, LHS, Vision & 1994 New Yorker

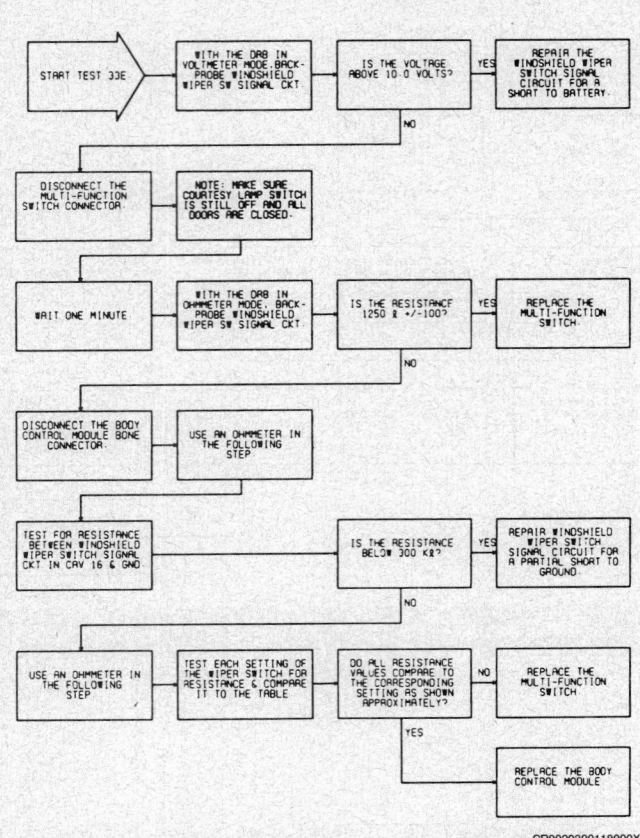

Fig. 60 Wiper Switch Signal Circuit Testing. Concorde, Intrepid, LHS, Vision & 1994 New Yorker

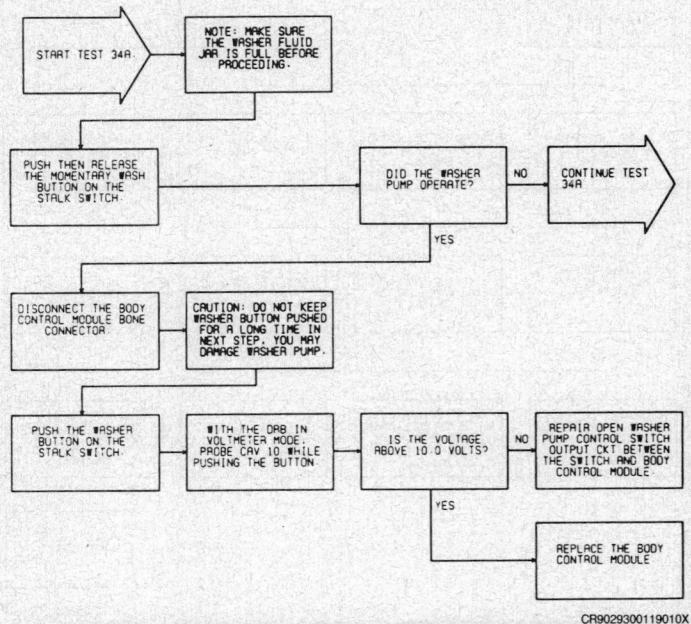

Fig. 61 Test 34A: Washer Pump Operation Testing (Part 1 Of 2). Concorde, Intrepid, LHS, Vision & 1994 New Yorker

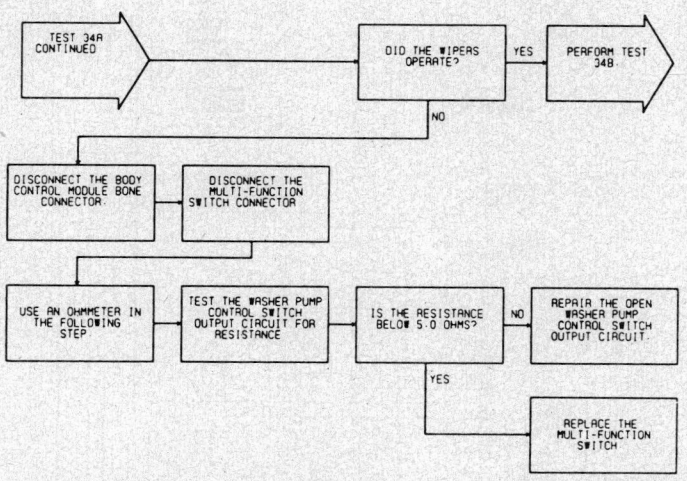

Fig. 61   Test 34A: Washer Pump Operation Testing (Part 2 Of 2). Concorde, Intrepid, LHS, Vision & 1994 New Yorker

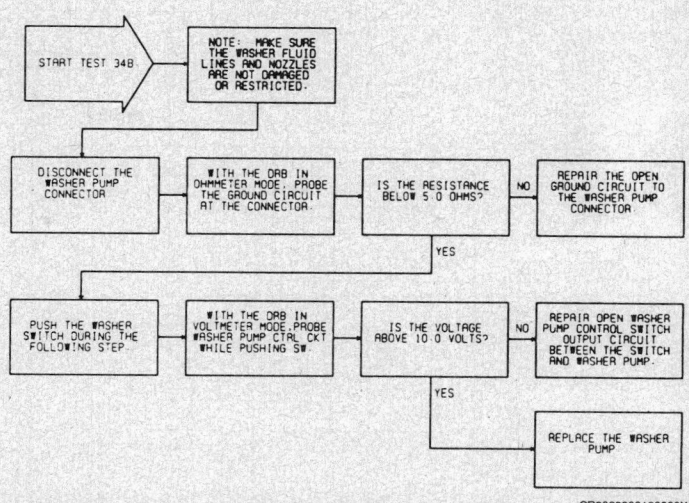

Fig. 62   Test 34B: Washer Pump Control Testing. Concorde, Intrepid, LHS, Vision & 1994 New Yorker

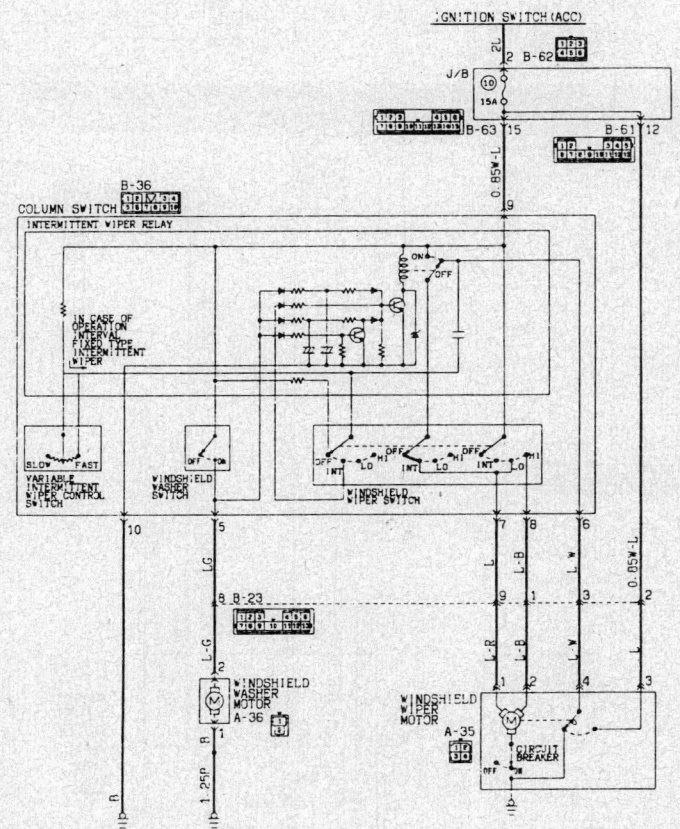

Fig. 63   Wiring diagram intermittent wiper system. Colt & Summit

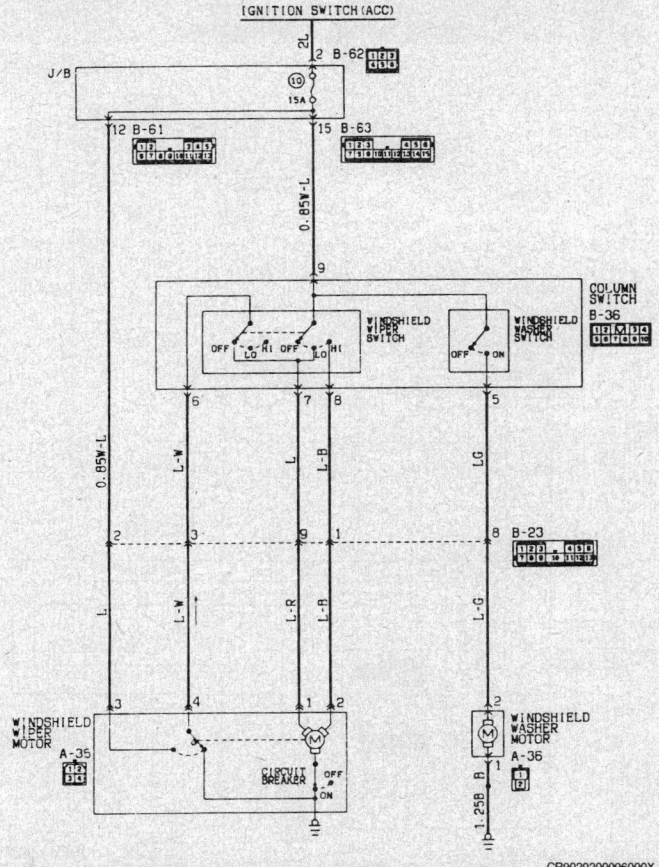

Fig. 64   Wiring diagram standard wiper system. Colt & Summit

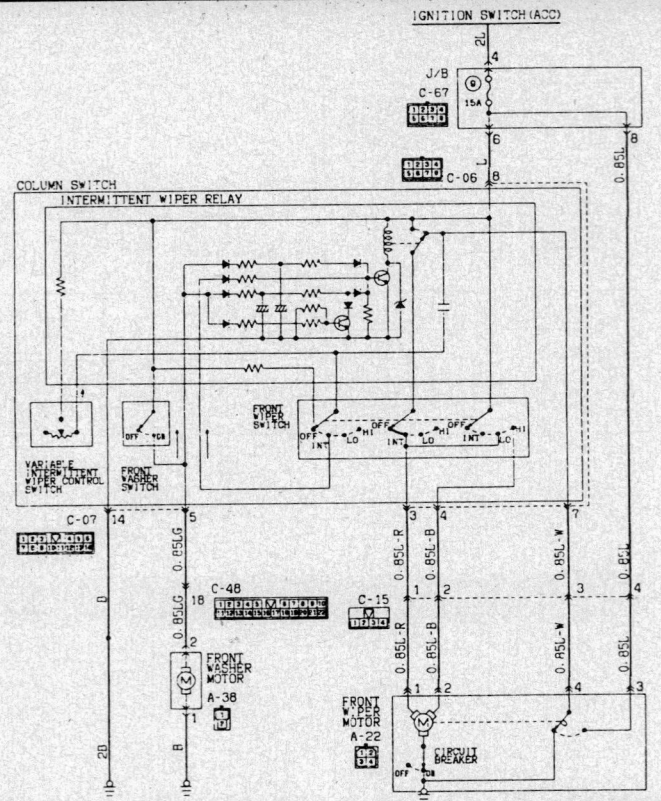

Fig. 65 Wiring diagram, front wiper system. Colt Vista & Summit Wagon

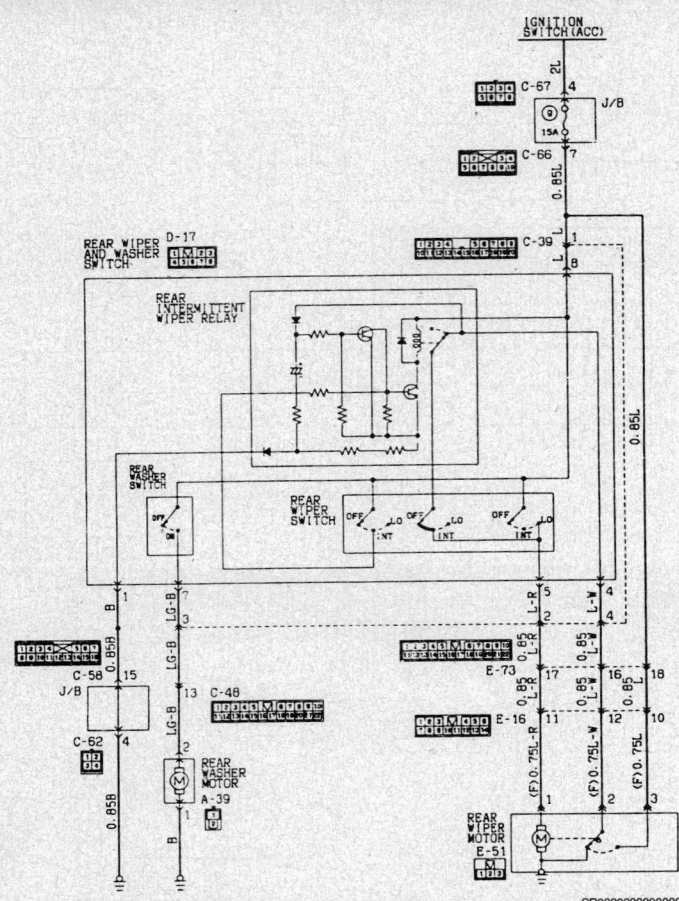

Fig. 66 Wiring diagram, rear wiper system, Colt Vista & Summit Wagon

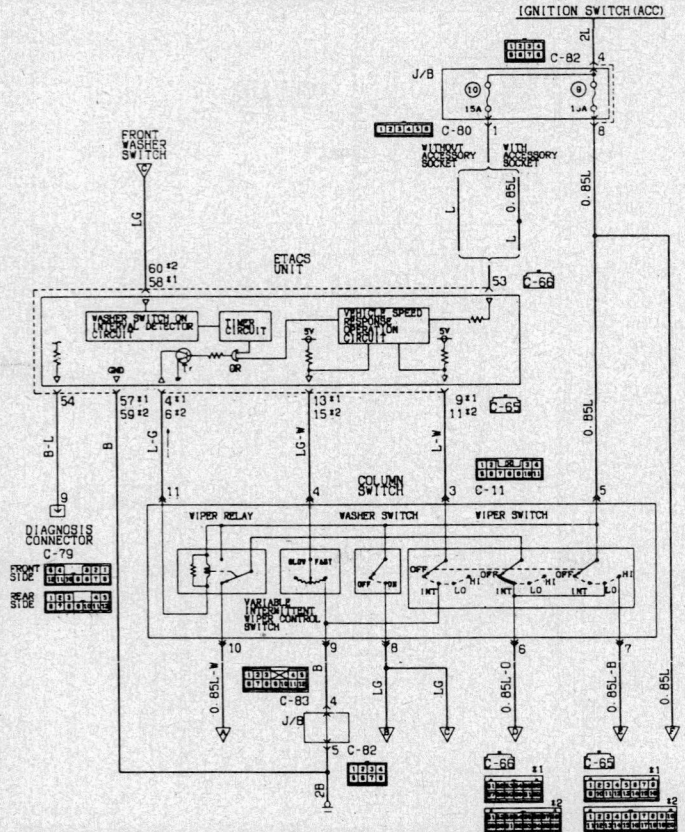

Fig. 67 Front wiper wiring circuit (Part 1 of 2). 1992 Stealth

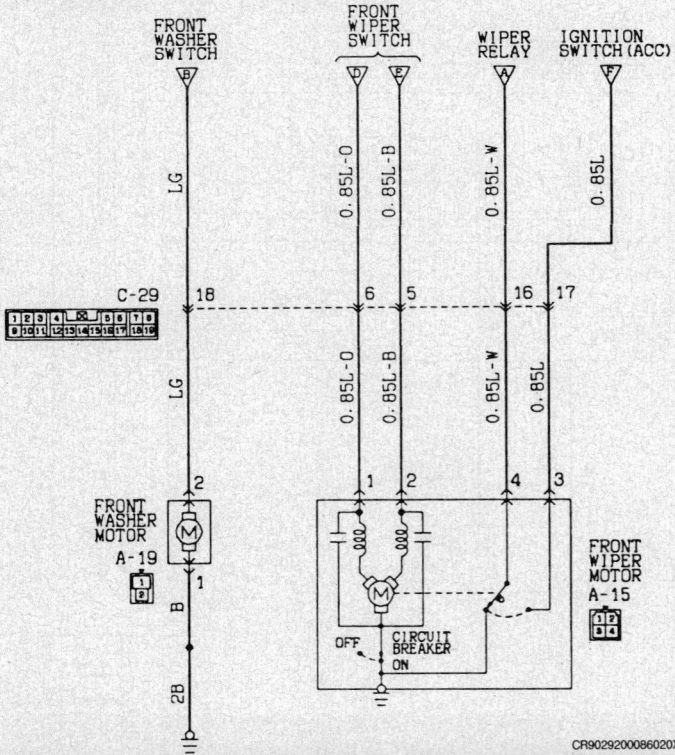

Fig. 67 Front wiper wiring circuit (Part 2 of 2). 1992 Stealth

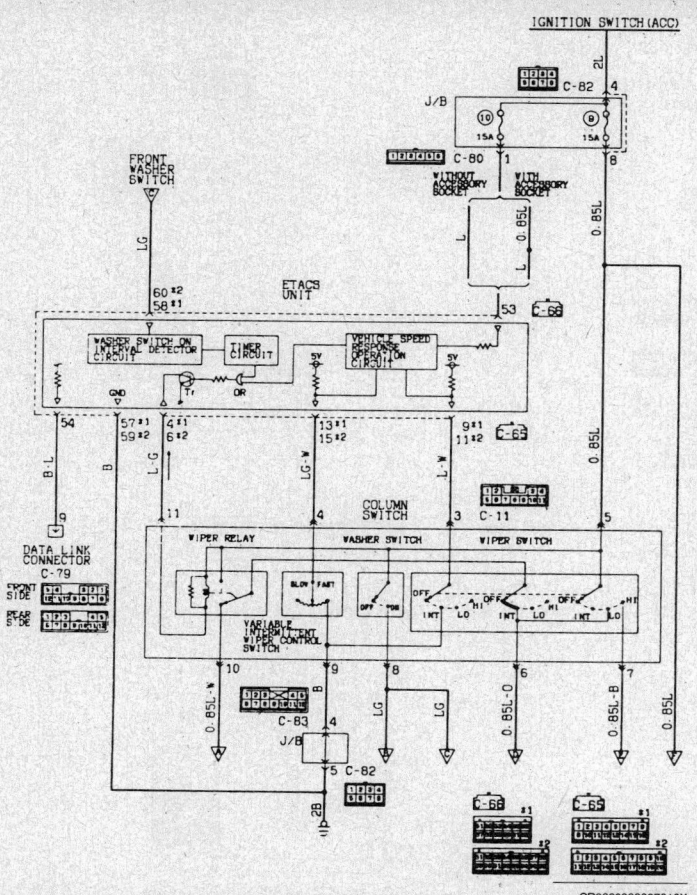

Fig. 68   Front wiper wiring circuit (Part 1 of 2). 1993 Stealth

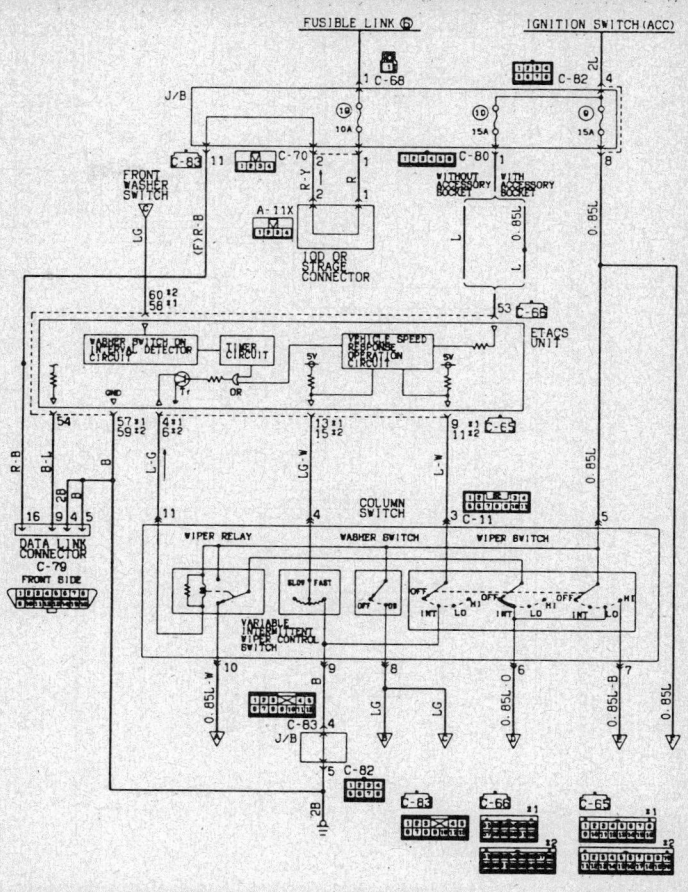

Fig. 69   Front wiper wiring circuit (Part 1 of 2). 1994 Stealth

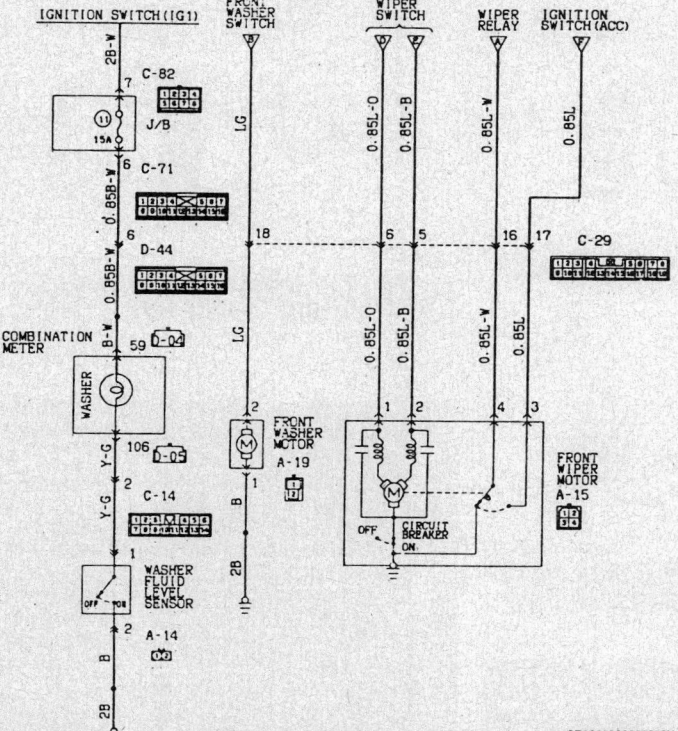

Fig. 68   Front wiper wiring circuit (Part 2 of 2). 1993 Stealth

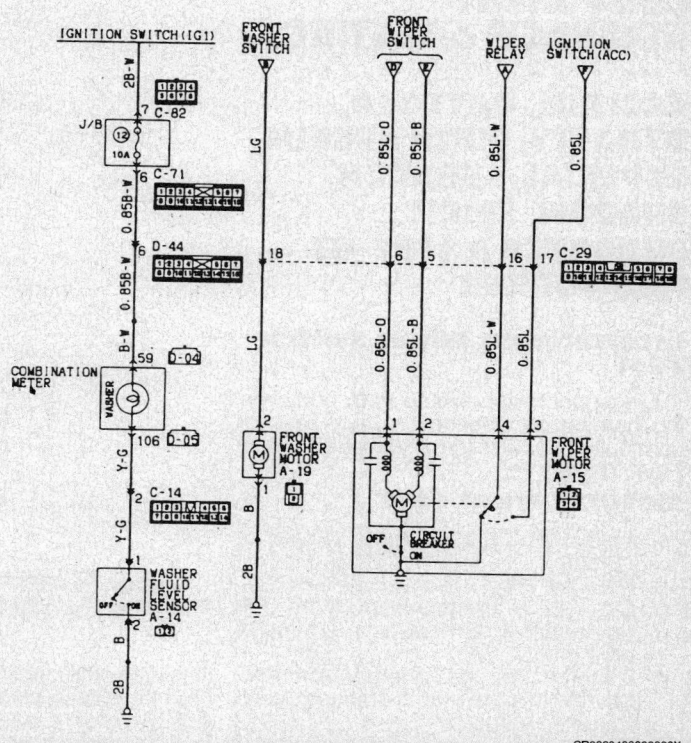

Fig. 69   Front wiper wiring circuit (Part 2 of 2). 1994 Stealth

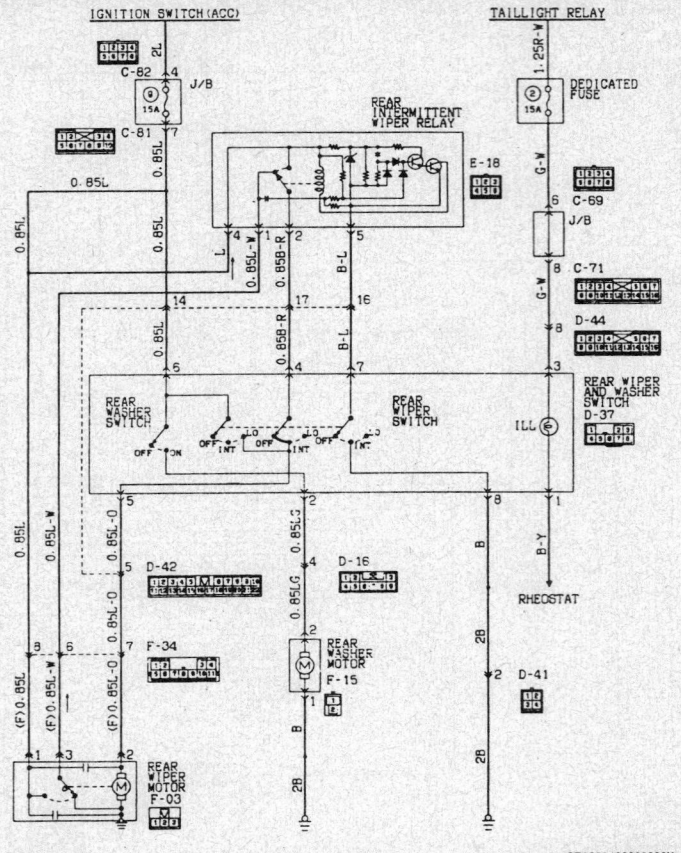

Fig. 70   Rear wiper wiring circuit. Stealth

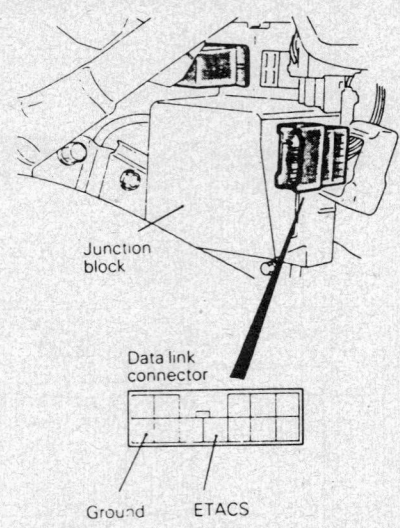

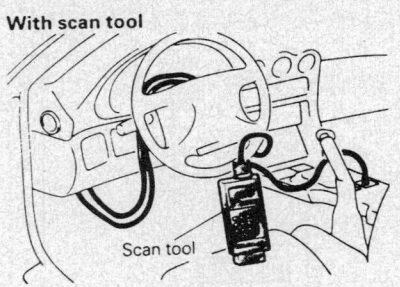

COMPONENT DIAGNOSIS & TESTING

ACCLAIM, DAYTONA, DYNASTY, FIFTH AVENUE, IMPERIAL, LEBARON, SHADOW, SPIRIT, SUNDANCE & 1992–93 NEW YORKER

Intermittent Wiper Switch Test

Disconnect wipe switch from body wiring harness in steering column. Test for continuity between terminals as shown in Figs. 74 and 75.

Motor Current Test

1. Disconnect wiring harness connector at motor.
2. Remove wiper arms and blades.
3. Connect an ohmmeter between battery positive terminal and terminal 3 on motor.
4. If motor runs and average ammeter reading is more than 6 amps, proceed to motor linkage test step.
5. If motor runs and average ammeter reading is less than 6 amps, proceed to wire harness test step.

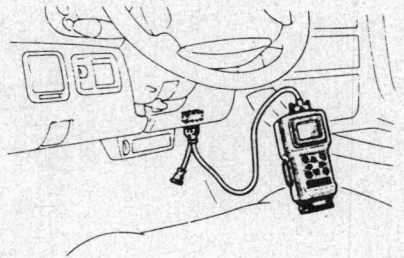

Fig. 72   Input signal testing. 1994 Stealth

6. Check wiper linkage or pivots for binding. Disconnect drive link from motor.
7. If motor now runs and draws less than 3 amps, repair linkage system.
8. If motor continues to draw more than 3 amps, replace motor assembly.

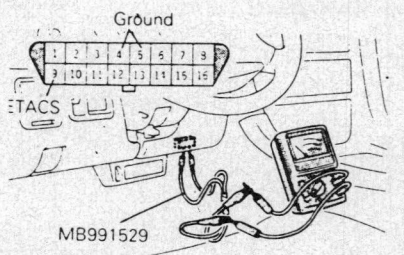

Fig. 71   Input signal testing. 1992–93 Stealth

9. Check motor wiring harness for shorting between high and low speed wires as follows:
   a. Connect a voltmeter or test lamp to motor ground strap.
   b. Set wiper switch on Low position.
   c. Connect other lead to terminal 4 of wiring harness.
   d. If voltage is present, there is a short in the wiring or wiper switch. If no voltage is present, proceed to next step.
   e. Set switch to high position.
   f. Move voltmeter lead from terminal 4 to terminal 3.
   g. If voltage is present, there is a short in the wiring or wiper switch.

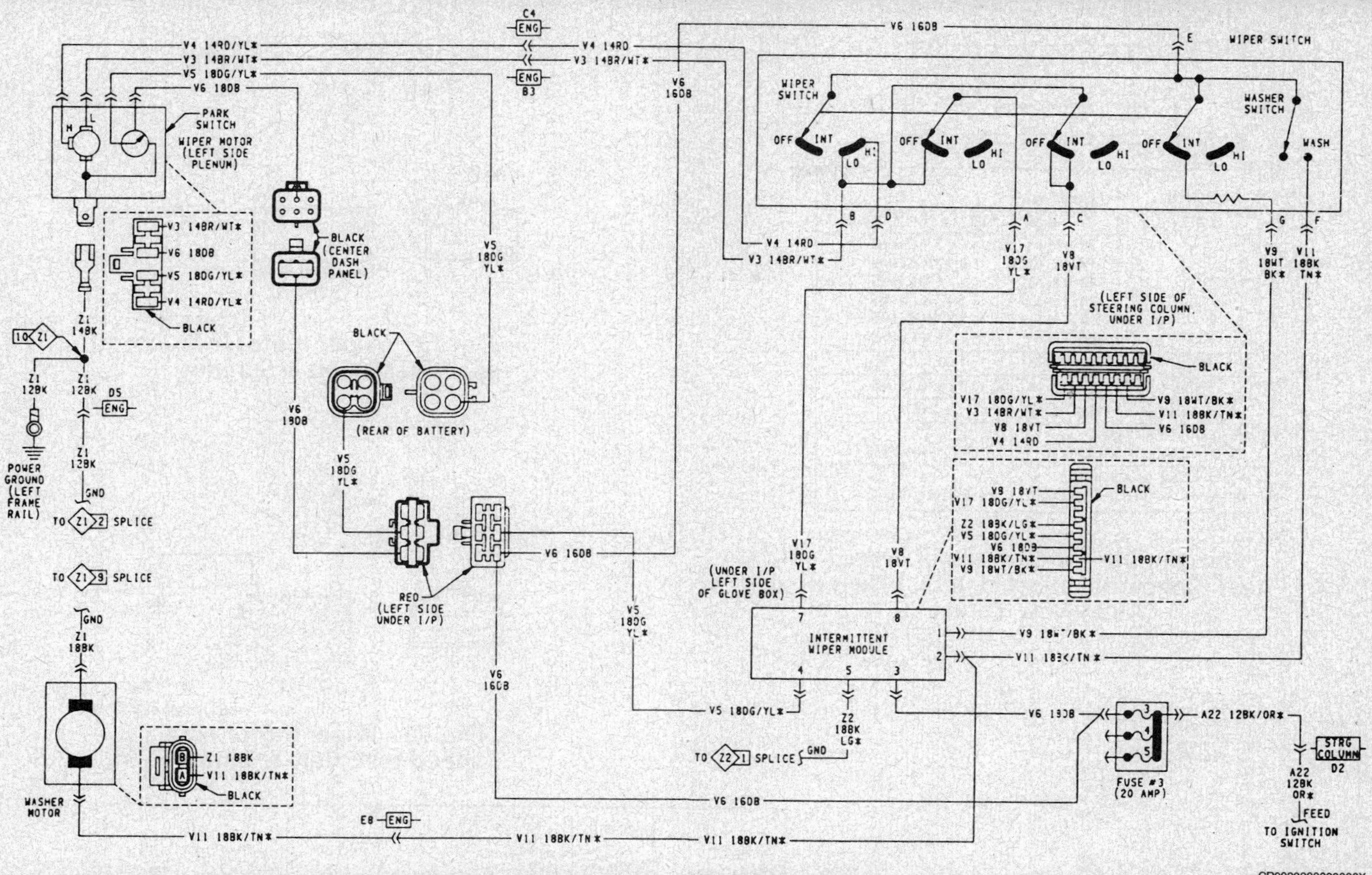

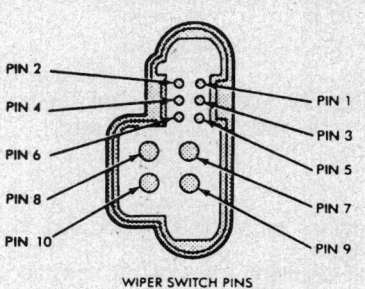

Fig. 73 Wiper system wiring diagram. Monaco & Premier

CR9029200099000X

MULTIFUNCTION SWITCH PINS

SWITCH POSITION	CONTINUITY BETWEEN
OFF	PIN 6 AND PIN 7
DELAY	PIN 8 AND PIN 9
	PIN 2 AND PIN 4
	PIN 1 AND PIN 2
	PIN 1 AND PIN 4
LOW	PIN 4 AND PIN 6
HIGH	PIN 4 AND PIN 5
WASH	PIN 3 AND PIN 4

*RESISTANCE AT MAXIMUM DELAY POSITION SHOULD BE BETWEEN 270,000 OHMS AND 330,000 OHMS.

*RESISTANCE AT MINIMUM DELAY POSITION SHOULD BE ZERO WITH OHMMETER SET ON HIGH OHM SCALE.

CR9029100040000X

Fig. 74 Wiper switch connector continuity check. Except Daytona & LeBaron

CONCORD, INTREPID, LHS, VISION & 1994 NEW YORKER

Motor Test

1. Remove wiper arms and blades, disconnect wiper motor connector, then drive link from motor.
2. Connect a suitable ammeter between positive terminal and terminal three of

motor connector, **Fig. 5.** Connect a ground wire to terminal four of motor connector. **When replacing drive link nut, torque nut to 98-106 inch lbs.**
3. If motor runs and average ammeter reading is higher than six amps, proceed to next step. If motor runs and average ammeter reading is less than six amps go to step 5.
4. Connect a suitable ohmmeter, check high and low circuits for a short to ground.
5. Check to see if wiper linkage or pivots are binding.

Intermittent Wiper Switch Test

1. Disconnect switch wires from body wiring in steering column. Using a suitable ohmmeter, test for continuity between terminals of switch as shown in **Fig. 76.**
2. When testing switch the first position is OFF, the next six are delay wipe. Low is the next detent, and high is full counterclockwise detent position.

COLT & SUMMIT

FRONT

Wiper Motor

1. Connect battery to wiper motor, **Fig. 77,** and ensure motor operation at low speed.

WIPER SWITCH PINS

SWITCH POSITION	CONTINUITY BETWEEN
OFF	PIN 8 AND PIN 10
DELAY	PIN 1 AND PIN 9
LOW	PIN 9 AND PIN 10
HIGH	PIN 9 AND PIN 7

CR9029100041000X

Fig. 75 Wiper switch connector continuity check. Daytona & LeBaron

2. Connect battery to wiper motor, **Fig. 78,** and ensure motor operates at high speed.

Wiper & Washer Switch

1. Remove lower panel assembly and the column cover, **Fig. 79.**
2. Disconnect column switch electrical connector, then check continuity be-

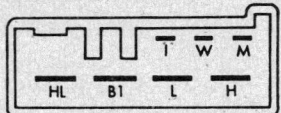

SWITCH POSITION		TERMINALS	RESISTANCE VALUE
OFF		PIN I to M	OPEN ≥ 300 K OHMS
DELAY LEVEL	1	PIN I to M	9.72 K OHMS
	2	PIN I to M	8.22 K OHMS
	3	PIN I to M	6.61 K OHMS
	4	PIN I to M	5.12 K OHMS
	5	PIN I to M	3.67 K OHMS
	6	PIN I to M	2.22 K OHMS
LOW		PIN I to M	1.02 K OHMS
HIGH		PIN I to M	0.51 K OHMS
WASH		PIN I to W	OPEN
RESISTANCE AT MAXIMUM DELAY POSITION SHOULD BE			9,720 K OHMS
RESISTANCE AT MINIMUM DELAY POSITION SHOULD BE			2,220 K OHMS

CR9029100076000X

Fig. 76   Intermittent wiper switch test. Concorde, Intrepid, LHS, Vision & 1994 New Yorker

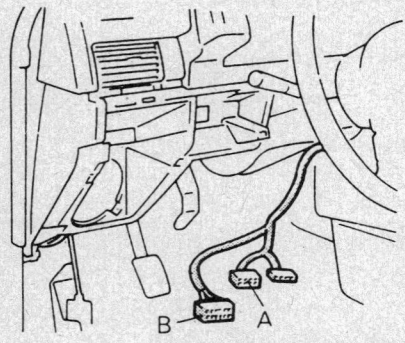

CR9029100044000X

Fig. 79   Wiper/washer switch removal. Colt & Summit

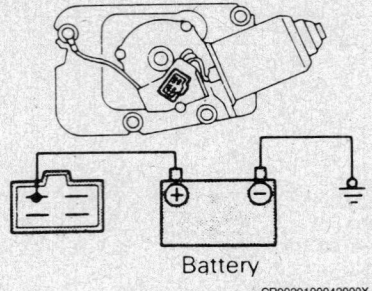

CR9029100042000X

Fig. 77   Wiper motor low speed test. Colt & Summit

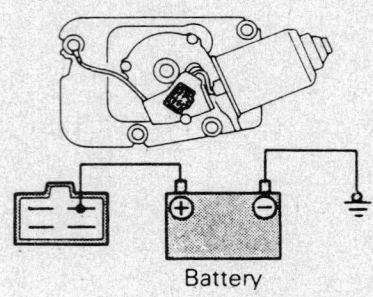

CR9029100043000X

Fig. 78   Wiper motor high speed test. Colt & Summit

Switch position \ Terminal	10	17	18	4	14
OFF		○——○		○-----○	
*INT	○——○	○——○		○-----○	
1		○——○		○-----○	
2	○——○		○——○	○-----○	

Connector A   Connector B

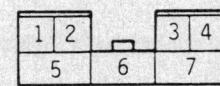   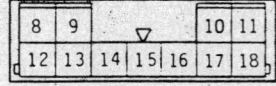

CR9029100045000X

Fig. 80   Wiper/washer continuity chart. Colt & Summit

tween terminals for each switch, **Fig. 80.**
3. If continuity is not as specified, replace switch, **Fig. 79.**

REAR

Wiper & Washer Switch

1. Disconnect wiper/washer switch electrical connector.
2. Check continuity between terminals, **Fig. 81.**
3. If continuity is not as specified, replace switch.

COLT VISTA & SUMMIT WAGON

FRONT

Operation At Low Speed Or High Speed

1. Connect battery to wiper motor as shown in **Fig. 82.**
2. Ensure motor works at both HI and Low speeds.
3. Replace motor if necessary.

Operation Of Wiper Motor At Stop Position

1. Run motor at Low speed, disconnect battery and stop motor, **Fig. 82.**
2. Reconnect battery and ensure after motor starts turning at Low speed it stops at the automatic position.

Wiper & Washer Switch

1. Disconnect column switch connector, then check continuity between terminal for each switch as shown in **Fig. 83.**

2. If not as specified, replace wiper washer switch.

Intermittent Wiper Relay

With column switch connected, ignition switch in ACC position, wiper switch in INT position, check voltage between terminal three and ground. Voltage should alternate from zero to system volts.

Washer Motor

Ensure washer tank is full, then connect battery as shown in **Fig. 84,** ensure water squirts out strongly. Replace motor if necessary.

1	2	3	☒	4	5	6
7	8	9	10	11	12	13

Terminal Switch position		8	9	7	10
Wiper switch	OFF	O——O			
	ON	O——|————O			O
Washer switch	OFF				
	ON			O——O	

NOTE
O—O indicates that there is continuity between the terminals.

Fig. 81   Rear wiper/washer continuity chart. Colt & Summit

CR9029100046000X

Operation check

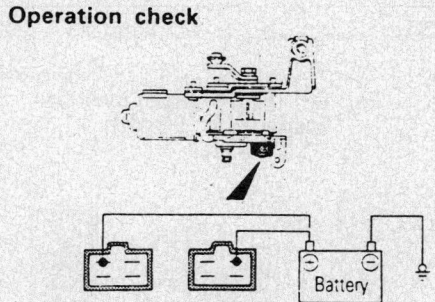

Low speed   High speed   Battery

Stop position check

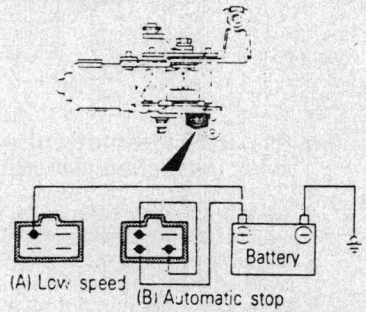

(A) Low speed   (B) Automatic stop   Battery

CR9029200047000X

Fig. 82   Wiper motor operation. Colt Vista & Summit Wagon

REAR

Operation Of Wiper Motor

1. Disconnect wiper motor connector, the connect a battery to wiper motor as shown in **Fig. 85.**
2. Ensure motor operates properly, replace motor if necessary.

Operation Of Wiper Motor At Stop Position

1. Run rear wiper motor, disconnect battery and stop motor.
2. Reconnect battery as shown in **Fig. 85,** ensure after motor starts turning, it stops at the automatic stop position.

1	2	3	4
5	6	7	8

9	10	11	▽	12	13	14
15	16	17	18	19	20	21	22

Terminal Switch position		3	4	7	8	13	22
Wiper switch	OFF	O——	——O				
	LO	O——	——	——O			
	HI				O		
	INT	O——	——O——O	O——	——O		
Washer switch	ON				O——O		

NOTE
O—O indicates that there is continuity between the terminals.

CR9029200048000X

Fig. 83   Wiper/washer switch test. Colt Vista & Summit Wagon

Rear Wiper & Washer Switch

Remove cluster switch, then check continuity between terminal for each switch as shown in **Fig. 86.** If not as specified, replace switch.

Rear Intermittent Wiper Relay

With rear wiper switch connected, ignition switch in ACC position, wiper switch in INT position, check voltage between terminal five and ground. Voltage should alternate from zero to system volts.

STEALTH

FRONT

Front Wiper Motor

Connect battery voltage to wiper motor as shown in **Fig. 87,** and ensure it operates at slow and high speeds.

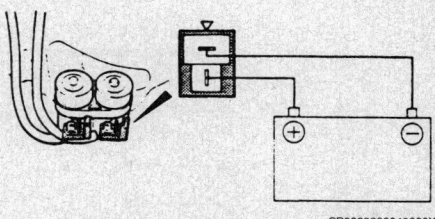

CR9029200049000X

Fig. 84   Washer motor test. Colt Vista & Summit Wagon

Operation check

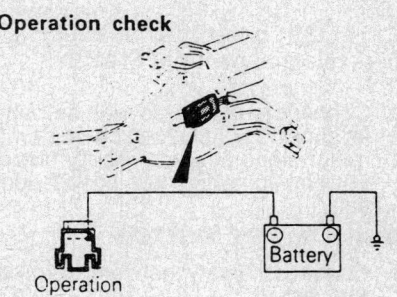

Operation   Battery

Stop position check

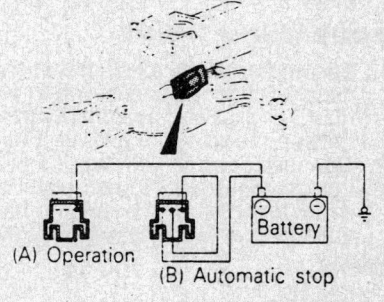

(A) Operation   (B) Automatic stop   Battery

CR9029200050000X

Fig. 85   Rear wiper motor test. Colt Vista & Summit Wagon

Front Wiper Motor Stop Position

1. Operate wiper motor at low speed and intermediately disconnect battery to allow wiper motor to stop.

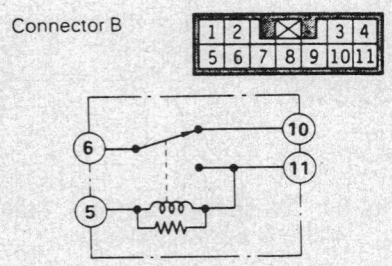

Fig. 86 Rear wiper/washer switch test. Colt Vista & Summit Wagon

Switch position	Terminal	1	4	5	7	8
Wiper switch	OFF		○——○			
	ON			○——○		○
	INT	○		○——○		○
Washer switch					○——○	○

NOTE
○——○ indicates that there is continuity between the terminals.

CR9029200051000X

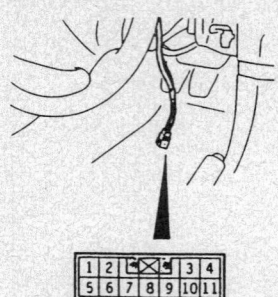

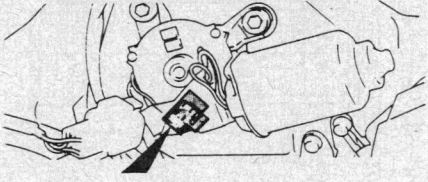

Inspection of Operation

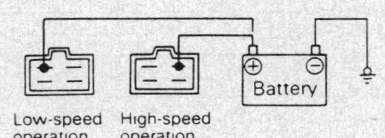

Low-speed operation   High-speed operation

Inspection of Stop Position

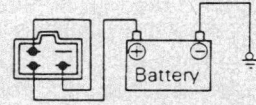

Fig. 87 Front wiper motor inspection. Stealth

CR9029100056000X

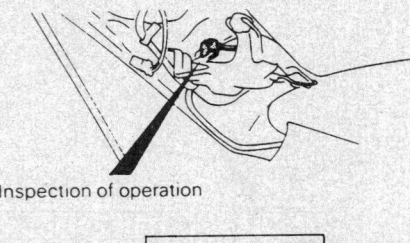

Inspection of operation

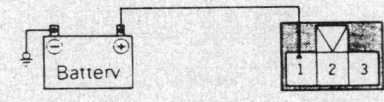

Inspection of stop position

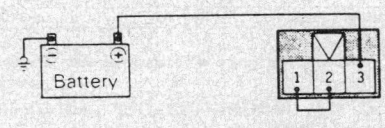

Fig. 90 Rear wiper motor inspection. Stealth

CR9029100059000X

Switch position	Terminal No.	3	4	5	6	7	8	9	10
Wiper switch	OFF				○				○
	INT	○			○			○——○	
	LO				○——○				
	HI				○	○——○			
Variable intermittent wiper control switch			○	○					
Washer switch			○——○				○——○		

NOTE
○—○ denotes that there is continuity between the terminals.

CR9029100057000X

Fig. 88 Front wiper switch inspection. Stealth

Connector B

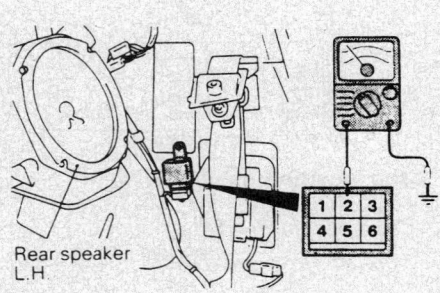

Rear speaker L.H.

CR9029100060000X

Fig. 91 Rear intermittent wiper relay inspection. Stealth

Fig. 89 Intermittent wiper relay inspection. Stealth

CR9029100058000X

2. Connect terminals as well as battery as shown in **Fig. 87**, and ensure wiper motor stops at automatically stopped position following low speed operation.

Front Wiper Switch

1. Check continuity between terminals, **Fig. 88**.
2. If continuity is not as specified, replace switch.

Front Wiper Relay

1. Ensure continuity exists between terminals 5 and 11 and between terminals 6 and 10 and no continuity exists between terminals 6 and 11, **Fig. 89**.
2. Connect positive terminal of battery voltage to terminal 5 and negative terminal to terminal 11 to ensure battery voltage is available at terminal 6.

REAR

Rear Wiper Motor

Connect battery voltage as shown in **Fig. 90**, and ensure motor operates.

Rear Wiper Motor Stop Position

1. Operate wiper motor and intermediately disconnect battery to allow wiper motor to stop.
2. Connect terminals as well as battery

as shown in **Fig. 90**, and ensure wiper motor stops at automatically stopped position following low speed operation.

Rear Intermittent Wiper Relay

1. Remove quarter trim panel.
2. With relay connected and wipers operating at intermittent mode, ensure battery voltage exists at terminal 2, **Fig. 91**.

MONACO & PREMIER

INTERMITTENT WIPER FUNCTION TEST

Excessive Delay Of More Than 30 Seconds or Inadequate Variation In Delay

1. Verify wiper delay as follows:

a. Minimum delay should be at intervals of 1.5 to 2 seconds.
b. Maximum delay should be at intervals of 10 to 30 seconds.

2. If wiper verification is not as specified, perform "Intermittent Wiper Switch Test."

In Delay Mode Wipers Run Continually When Wash Is Operated But Do Not Provide An Extra Wipe When The Wash Control Is Released

Replace the control unit.

Wipers Start Erratically During Delay Mode

1. Verify that motor ground strap is making good contact and that motor mounting bolts are tight.
2. Verify that wiring ground connections for intermittent wipe control unit and that wiper switch are tight.
3. If condition in not corrected, replace control unit.

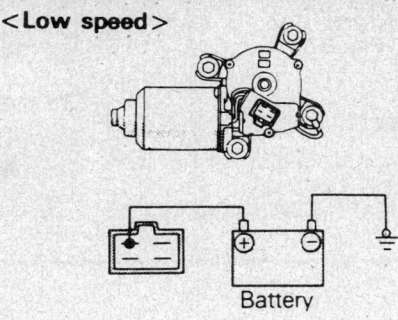

<Low speed>

Battery

<High speed>

Fig. 92 Intermittent wiper switch test. Monaco & Premier

SWITCH POSITION	CONTINUITY BETWEEN
Off	Pin A and Pin B
Delay	Pin E and Pin C
	Pin E and Pin G
	Pin A and Pin B
Low	Pin E and Pin B
High	Pin E and Pin D
Wash (Button pushed in)	Pin E and Pin F

Battery

Fig. 93 Front wiper motor inspection. Laser & Talon

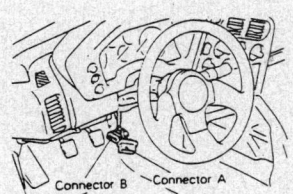

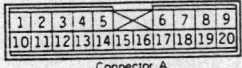

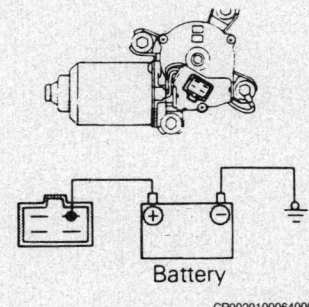

	Terminal	23	24	27	28
Switch position					
Wiper switch	OFF				
	INT				
	LO				
	HI				

	Terminal	7	28
Switch position			
OFF			
ON			

NOTE
○—○ indicates that there is continuity between the terminals.

Fig. 94 Front wiper/washer switch inspection. Laser & Talon

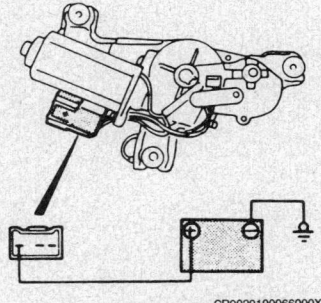

Fig. 95 Rear wiper motor inspection. Laser & Talon

	Terminal	2	4	5	6	7	8	3	1
Switch position									
Wiper switch	OFF								
	ON								
	INT								
Washer switch									

NOTE
○—○ indicates that there is continuity between the terminals.

Fig. 96 Rear wiper/washer switch inspection. Laser & Talon

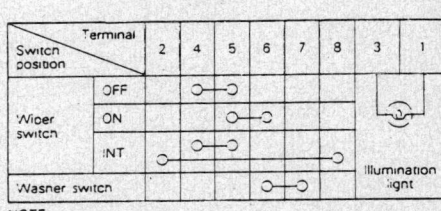

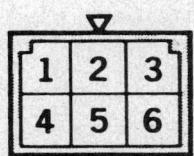

Fig. 97 Rear intermittent wiper relay inspection. Laser & Talon

LASER & TALON

FRONT

Wiper Motor

Connect a battery as shown in **Fig. 93** to check wiper motor low and high speed operation.

Wiper/Washer Switch & Intermittent Wiper Relay

Disconnect wiper switch connector and check for continuity as shown in **Fig. 94.**

REAR

Wiper Motor

Connect a battery as shown in **Fig. 95** to check wiper motor operation.

Wiper/Washer Switch

Disconnect wiper switch connector and check for continuity as shown in **Fig. 96.**

INTERMITTENT WIPER SWITCH TEST

1. Disconnect wiper switch wires from switch body in steering column.
2. Using an ohmmeter, test for continuity between terminals of switch as shown in **Fig. 92.**

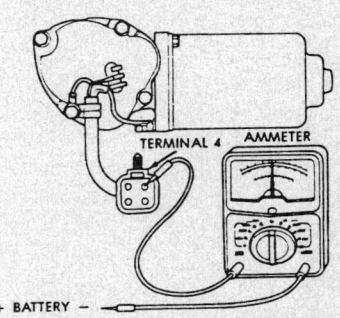

Fig. 98 Wiper motor current test. Neon

Intermittent Wiper Relay

With relay connector connected, ensure no voltage is present at terminal 2 when rear wiper stops and 12 volts when rear wiper operates, **Fig. 97.**

NEON

Wiper Switch

1. Disconnect wiper switch wiring from main wiring at steering column
2. Using a suitable ohmmeter test continuity between connector pins as shown in **Fig. 11**

Wiper Motor Runs Slow

1. Remove wiper arms and cowl panel.
2. Disconnect wiper linkage and wiring connector from motor.
3. Connect a suitable ammeter between motor and battery positive terminal **Fig. 98.**
4. With motor running, if current draw is greater than six amps, check for binding in shafts and linkage.
5. With motor running, if current draw is less than six amps, use a suitable ohmmeter and check wiper circuits for short to ground **Fig. 12.**

PASSIVE RESTRAINT SYSTEMS

TABLE OF CONTENTS

Air Bag System

INDEX

AIR BAG SYSTEM DISARMING & ARMING

Disarming

It may be necessary to access and record all diagnostic trouble codes prior to disarming the Supplemental Restraint System (SRS).

1. Place ignition switch in lock position.
2. Disconnect and tape battery ground cable connector.
3. **Wait at least 2 minutes after disconnecting battery ground cable before doing any further work on vehicle. The SRS system is designed to retain enough voltage to deploy air bag for a short time even after battery has been disconnected.**

Arming

1. Connect battery ground cable.
2. From passenger side of vehicle, turn ignition switch to On position.
3. SRS warning light should illuminate for 6 to 8 seconds, then remain off for at least 45 seconds to indicate if SRS system is functioning correctly.
4. If SRS indicator does not perform as described, refer to "Diagnosis & Testing" section.

PRECAUTIONS EXCEPT COLT VISTA, STEALTH & SUMMIT WAGON

General Safety Precautions

Always wear safety glasses when servicing an air bag equipped vehicle or when handling an air bag module.

Because this system is a sensitive, complex electro-mechanical unit, before attempting to diagnose, remove or install any air bag system component, you must first disarm the air bag system as outlined under "Air Bag System Disarming & Arming."

Replace air bag components with Chrysler Mopar specified replacement parts. Substitute parts may visually appear interchangeable but internal differences may result in inferior occupant protection.

The fasteners, screws and bolts used for air bag components have special coatings and are specifically designed for the air bag system. They must not be replaced with substitutes. If fastener replacement is required, use the correct fasteners provided in the service package.

Ensure no one is inside the vehicle when the air bag system is rearmed as outlined under "Air Bag System Disarming & Arming."

Handling & Storage Of Live Module

At no time should any source of electricity be permitted near the inflator on the back of the module. When carrying a live module, the trim cover of the air bag module should be pointed away from the body to minimize injury in the event of an accidental deployment.

When handling a steering column with an air bag module attached, never place column on floor or other surface with steering wheel or module facing down. When handling a passenger air bag module, never place it on a surface with the paper-like tyvek cover face down and the saddle brackets pointing up.

Handling Of Deployed Module

The vehicle interior may contain a very small amount of sodium hydroxide powder, a by-product of air bag deployment. Since this powder can irritate the skin, eyes, nose or throat, wear safety glasses, rubber gloves, particle dust mask and protective clothing with long sleeves during cleanup.

If you find that the cleanup is irritating your skin, run cool water over effective area. Also, if you experience nasal or throat irritation, exit vehicle for fresh air until irritation ceases. If irritation continues, see a physician.

Clean Up Procedure

Wear safety glasses, rubber gloves, particle dust mask and protective clothing with long sleeves, then place tape over exhaust vents in the air bag so that no additional powder will escape into the vehicle. Roll or fold passengers air bag toward the instrument panel surface and close the cover over the folded air bag. Tape the cover closed. Remove the drivers air bag module from the vehicle then the passengers air bag module.

Use a vacuum cleaner to remove any residual powder from the vehicle interior working from the outside to the center of the vehicle. Ensure to vacuum the heater and A/C ducts as well. Run the blower motor on low speed and vacuum any powder expelled from the plenum. It may be necessary to vacuum the interior of the vehicle a second time to ensure all powder is recovered.

Vehicle Scrapping

Prior to scrapping a vehicle equipped with an air bag, the air bag module must be deployed. Refer to Chrysler Corporation for proper deployment procedures.

Air Bag Disposal Procedure

Place deployed bag and module in a suitable automotive scrap bin.

COLT VISTA, STEALTH & SUMMIT WAGON

General Safety Precautions

Always wear safety glasses when servicing an air bag equipped vehicle and when handling an air bag module.

Because this system is a sensitive, complex electro-mechanical unit, before attempting to diagnose, remove or install any air bag system component, you must first disarm the air bag system as outlined under "Air Bag System Disarming & Arming."

Only use a digital multi-meter with a maximum test current of 2mA or less, at the minimum ranger of resistance measurement, when diagnosing the system.

Never attempt to repair the front impact sensors, the Air Bag Control Module

(ACM) (Air bag System Diagnostic Module (ASDM)), clockspring or the air bag module. If any of these components are diagnosed as faulty, they should be replaced.

Never attempt to repair the wiring harness connectors of the SRS. If any connectors are diagnosed as faulty, replace the wiring harness. If the wires are diagnosed as faulty, replace or repair the wiring harness.

SRS system components should not be exposed to temperatures higher than 200°F.

Replace air bag components with Chrysler Mopar specified replacement parts. Substitute parts may visually appear interchangeable but internal differences may result in inferior occupant protection.

The fasteners, screws and bolts used for air bag components have special coatings and are specifically designed for the air bag system. They must not be replaced with substitutes. If fastener replacement is required, use the correct fasteners provided in the service package.

Ensure no one is inside the vehicle when the air bag system is rearmed as outlined under "Air Bag System Disarming & Arming."

Handling & Storage Of Module

Never attempt to disassemble or repair the air bag module or clockspring. Do not drop the air bag module or clockspring or allow contact with water, grease or oil.

The air bag module should be stored on a flat surface and placed so that bag surface is facing upward. Do not place anything on top of module.

After an air bag has deployed, replace with a new air bag module and check SRS operability. Wear safety glasses, rubber gloves, particle dust mask and protective clothing with long sleeves during cleanup. Dispose air bag as outlined under "Air Bag Disposal Procedure."

Air Bag Disposal Procedure

Place deployed bag and module in a suitable automotive scrap bin.

Clean Up Procedure

Wear safety glasses, rubber gloves, particle dust mask and protective clothing with long sleeves, then place tape over exhaust vents in the air bag so that no additional powder will escape into the vehicle. Remove the driver air bag module from the vehicle.

Use a vacuum cleaner to remove any residual powder from the vehicle interior working from the outside to the center of the vehicle. Ensure to vacuum the heater and A/C ducts as well. Run the blower motor on low speed and vacuum any powder expelled from the plenum. It may be necessary to vacuum the interior of the vehicle a second time to ensure all powder is recovered.

Vehicle Scrapping

Prior to scrapping an air bag module or a vehicle equipped with an air bag, the air bag module must be deployed. Deploy the air bag module inside the

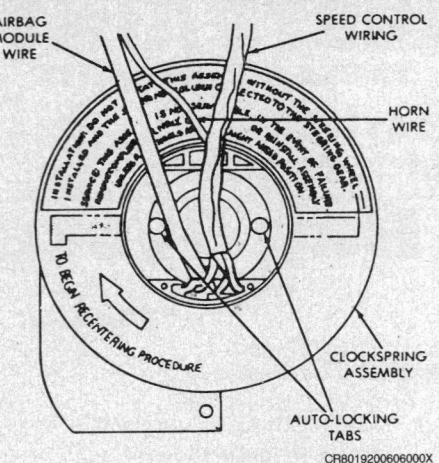

Fig. 1 Auto-locking type clockspring. Except Concorde, Intrepid, LHS, Vision & 1994 New Yorker

vehicle if the vehicle is to be scrapped. If the vehicle will continue to operate, remove the air bag module and deploy it outside of the vehicle. Since there is a loud noise when air bag is deployed, give warning to any one standing nearby.

COLLISION INSPECTION

EXCEPT COLT VISTA, STEALTH & SUMMIT WAGON

After all collisions, minor or major, proper system operation must be verified by performing the appropriate system diagnostic checks. Refer to MOTOR's Air Bag Manual for further information.

COLT VISTA, STEALTH & SUMMIT WAGON

Air Bag Deploys

1. Replace the following components:
   a. Front impact sensors.
   b. Air bag Control Module (ACM) (Air bag System Diagnostic Module (ASDM)).
   c. Air bag module.
   d. Clockspring.
   e. Steering wheel, steering column and intermediate joint.
2. Check all harnesses for binding, connectors for damage, poor connections and terminals for deformities.
3. Inspect all wiring harnesses.

Air Bag Does Not Deploy

Check and replace air bag system components if any visible signs of damage, dents, cracks or deformation. Inspect and replace each of the following components as required.

1. **Front Impact Sensors.**
   a. Check front upper frame lower for deformities or rust.
   b. Check front impact sensors for dents, cracks or deformities.
   c. Check sensor harness for binds,

connectors for damage and terminals for deformities.
2. **Air Bag Control Module (ACM) (Air bag System Diagnostic Module (ASDM)).**
   a. Check control unit case and brackets for dents, cracks or deformities.
   b. Check connectors and lock lever for damage and terminals for deformities.
3. **Air Bag Module.**
   a. Check pad cover for dents, cracks or deformities.
   b. Check hooks and connectors for damage, terminals deformities and harness for binds.
   c. Check air bag inflator case for dents, cracks or deformities.
   d. Install air bag module on steering wheel to check fit or alignment with wheel.
4. **Clockspring.**
   a. Check clockspring connectors and protective tube for damage and terminals for deformities.
   b. Visually check the case and gears for damage.
5. **Steering Wheel, Steering Column and Intermediate Joint.**
   a. Check wiring harness built into steering wheel and connectors for damage and terminals for deformities.
   b. Install air bag module on steering wheel to check fit or alignment with wheel.
   c. Check steering wheel for noise, binds or difficult operation and excessive freeplay.
6. **Body and Front Wiring Harness.**
   a. Check harness for binding, connectors for damage, poor connections and terminals for deformities.

DIAGNOSIS & TESTING

Refer to MOTOR's Air Bag Manual for air bag system diagnosis and testing procedures.

COMPONENT SERVICE

CLOCKSPRING, REPLACE

Before attempting to diagnose, remove or install any air bag system components, unless otherwise noted, you must first disconnect and isolate battery ground cable. Failure to do so could result in accidental deployment and possible personal injury. Refer to the "Precautions" section for proper air bag system disarming procedures.

EXCEPT CONCORDE, INTREPID, LHS, STEALTH, VISION & 1994 COLT VISTA, NEW YORKER & SUMMIT WAGON

The clockspring used is a automatic lock type, which engages when the steering wheel is removed. Automatic locking clocksprings can be identified by the lack of a setscrew and tether strap.

Removal

1. Ensure front wheels are in straight ahead position.

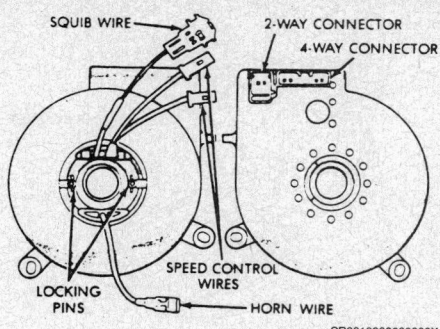

Fig. 2 Auto-locking type clockspring. Concorde, Intrepid, LHS, Vision & 1994 New Yorker

2. Disconnect and isolate battery ground cable, wait minimum of 2 minutes before working on vehicle.
3. Remove air bag module.
4. Remove speed control switch and connector, if equipped.
5. Remove steering wheel and vibration damper, if equipped.
6. Disconnect horn terminals.
7. Remove upper and lower steering column shrouds, then disconnect the connectors between clockspring and instrument panel wiring harness at base of steering column.
8. Remove clockspring by lifting locating tabs as necessary, **Fig. 1.**

Centering

1. Place front wheels in straight ahead position.
2. Depress two plastic lockpins or spread apart two metal locking tabs in center of clockspring, **Fig. 1.**
3. At the same time, rotate clockspring rotor **clockwise** to the end of its travel.
4. From this position, rotate clockspring rotor counterclockwise 2 1/2 turns. The horn wire should be at the top and the squib wire at the bottom. While turning the rotor, visually inspect flat cable for bends or kinks. If clockspring is bent or kinked, replace clockspring assembly.

Installation

1. Snap clockspring onto steering column. Ensure clockspring is centered; if not, follow clockspring centering procedure.
2. Connect clockspring assembly to instrument panel wiring harness, ensure wiring locator clips are properly seated on outside of wiring trough and locking tabs are engaged.
3. Install steering column shrouds, ensure wire is inside shroud.
4. Ensure front wheels are in straight ahead position. Install steering wheel and vibration damper, if equipped. **Torque** to 45 ft. lbs. Fit flats on hub of steering wheel with formations on inside of clockspring.
5. Ensure to pull horn lead through upper smaller hole and clockspring lead through bottom larger hole.
6. Connect horn lead wire, then air bag lead wire to air bag module. To assure

complete connections, latching arms must be visible on top of connector housing.
7. Install air bag module and **torque** nuts to 80 to 100 inch lbs.
8. Rearm air bag system as described under "Air Bag System Arming & Disarming."

CONCORDE, INTREPID, LHS, VISION & 1994 NEW YORKER

Removal

1. Ensure front wheels are in straight ahead position.
2. Rotate steering wheel clockwise 180° (1/2 turn) and lock in place using ignition lock cylinder.
3. Disconnect and isolate battery ground cable, wait minimum of 2 minutes before working on vehicle.
4. Remove air bag module.
5. Remove speed control switch and connector, if equipped.
6. Disconnect horn terminals.
7. Remove steering wheel and the tilt lever.
8. Remove upper and lower steering column shrouds, then disconnect the connectors between clockspring and instrument panel wiring harness at base of steering column.
9. Remove halo light wire from clip on side of clockspring.
10. Remove two mounting screws and pull clockspring assembly from steering shaft, **Fig. 2.**

Centering

1. With clockspring removed, depress two plastic locking pins to disengage locking mechanism, **Fig. 2.**
2. Keeping locking mechanism disengaged, rotate clockspring rotor clockwise to the end of its travel. **Do not apply excessive torque.**
3. From end of travel, rotate rotor 2 1/2 turns counterclockwise. **At this position the horn wire should end up at the bottom and the squib wire at the top. If not, rotate the rotor counterclockwise until the wires are properly positioned, but not more than 180° (1/2 turn).**
4. Release pins and allow clockspring locking device to engage.
5. Install clock spring.

Installation

1. Ensure steering wheel is 180° (1/2 turn) to the right (clockwise) and is locked in place.
2. Ensure turn signal stalk in the neutral position.
3. Install clockspring on steering shaft and push down on rotor until clockspring is fully seated on steering column.
4. Fasten clockspring to steering column using proper mounting bolts then **torque** bolts to 14-34 inch lbs. **Tighten screw near ignition switch halo light first.**
5. Properly route clockspring harness then connect to instrument panel harness.
6. Ensure harness connectors are prop-

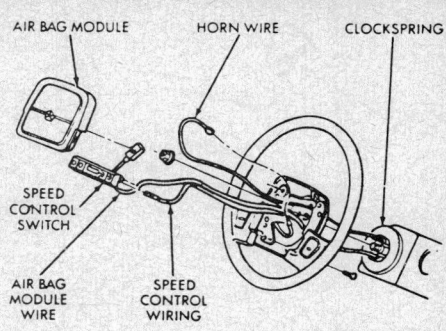

Fig. 3 Driver's side air bag module removal. Except Colt Vista, Concorde, Intrepid, LHS, Stealth, Summit Wagon, Vision & 1994 New Yorker

erly engaged.
7. Connect halo light and position wire on clockspring.
8. Install steering column shrouds and tilt lever.
9. Install steering wheel ensuring the flats on hub align with the clockspring. Pull yellow horn lead through smaller round hole and the air bag and speed control through larger slot. **Ensure wires do not get pinched under steering wheel.**
10. Connect horn and air bag connectors to the air bag module.
11. Install air bag module and **torque** bolts to 105-125 inch lbs.
12. Connect speed control and install switches, then **torque** screws to 12-18 inch lbs.
13. Rearm air bag system as described under "Air Bag System Arming & Disarming."

COLT VISTA, STEALTH & SUMMIT WAGON

Refer to the procedure found under "Air Bag Module, Replace."

AIR BAG MODULE, REPLACE

Before attempting to diagnose, remove or install any air bag system components, you must first disconnect and isolate the battery ground cable. Failure to do so could result in accidental deployment and possible personal injury. Refer to the "Precautions" section for proper air bag system disarming procedures.

Refer to "Precautions" prior to removing air bag module.

EXCEPT COLT VISTA, CONCORDE, INTREPID, LHS, STEALTH, SUMMIT WAGON, VISION & 1994 NEW YORKER

Driver's Side

1. Disconnect and isolate battery ground cable. **Wait minimum of 2 minutes before working on vehicle.**
2. Remove four holding air bag module in place on steering wheel, **Fig. 3.**
3. Lift module high enough to remove clockspring connecting wire and remove air bag module.

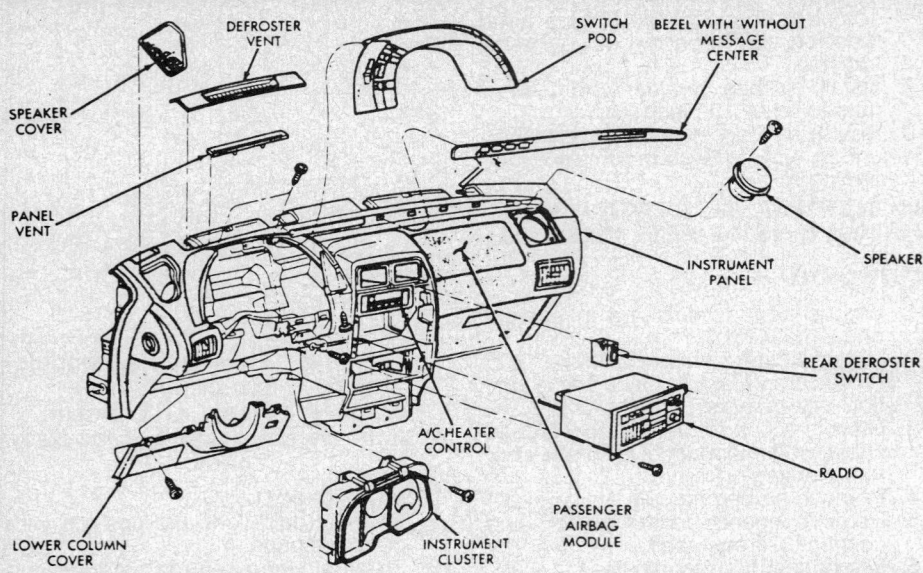

Fig. 4 Instrument panel. 1994 Acclaim, LeBaron, Shadow, Spirit & Sundance

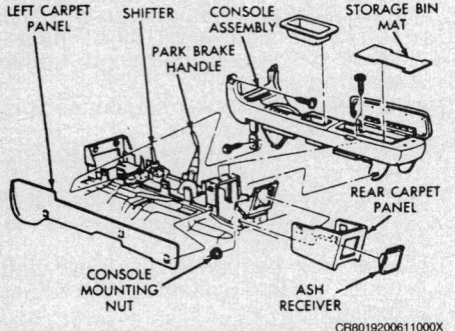

Fig. 6 Transmission range cable routing. 1994 Acclaim, LeBaron, Shadow, Spirit & Sundance

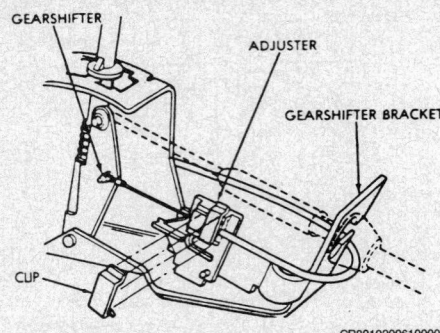

Fig. 5 Center console. 1994 Acclaim, LeBaron, Shadow, Spirit & Sundance

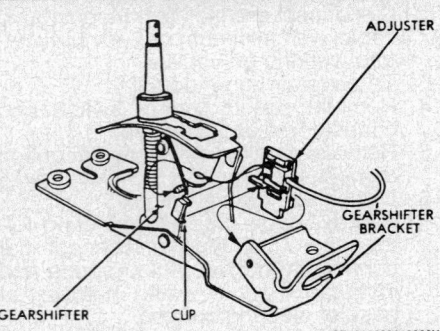

Fig. 7 Transmission range cable adjustment. 1994 Acclaim, LeBaron, Shadow, Spirit & Sundance

4. If replacing a deployed module, clock-spring must also be replaced. Refer to procedure outlined under "Clockspring, Replace."
5. Reverse procedure to install and **torque** nuts to 80-100 inch lbs.
6. Rearm air bag system as described under "Air Bag System Arming & Disarming."

Passenger's Side

1. Disconnect and isolate battery ground cable.
2. Remove instrument panel center bezel, **Fig. 4.**
3. Remove upper and lower steering column covers, then the left under panel silencer.
4. Set parking brake, then remove side carpet panels, **Fig. 5.**
5. Remove center console assembly.
6. Remove transmission range clip and cable loop end from post to gear shifter, **Fig. 6.**
7. Remove adjuster tab on gear shifter bracket, by pushing locking tab on adjuster and sliding adjuster off tab on gear shifter bracket.
8. Remove two Air Bag Diagnostic Module (ADM) attaching screws and slide module out of right side of instrument panel center stack area, then disconnect ADM wiring.
9. Remove screw from instrument panel dimmer module at left of steering column and lower module.
10. Remove fuse block attaching screws and lower fuse block.
11. Remove three hood release attaching screws, then lower hood release handle.
12. Remove flasher relay from bracket on center distribution duct.
13. Remove ATC sensor motor assembly attaching screw and unhook from bracket.
14. Remove radio ground screw, then the center distribution duct screw from left lower instrument panel brace.
15. Remove four left lower brace attaching screws, then the brace.
16. Remove five steering column support nuts and lower steering column.
17. Remove compact disc player or cubby box attaching screws, then disconnect coax cable from compact disc player.
18. Remove Electronic Vehicle Information Center (EVIC) or traveler from the vehicle.
19. Remove radio and heater-A/C controls.
20. Squeeze latches on side of rear window defogger switch and remove.
21. Snap off cluster lower trim bezel, switch pod vent grill, speaker grill and defroster grilles.
22. Remove switch pod assembly, cluster assembly and instrument panel speakers.
23. Snap out bezel with message center and disconnect wiring.
24. Open glove compartment door, squeeze sides and roll glove compartment completely open, then remove glove compartment light and disconnect glove compartment wires.

25. Loosen right cowl side pivot bolt through the glove compartment opening, then close glove compartment.
26. Loosen left cowl side pivot, then remove four top instrument panel attaching screws and roll panel out.
27. Pull wiring, antenna cable, A/C cable and vacuum lines out of instrument panel.
28. Disconnect demister hose and remove instrument panel with ducts attached.
29. Remove three nut/cone washers and three passenger air bag module attaching screws, then the air bag module from the vehicle.
30. Reverse procedure to install, noting the following:
    a. **Torque** air bag module nuts to 105 inch lbs.
    b. Insert transmission range cable into adjuster with gear shifter in low position, **Fig. 7.**
    c. Check gear selector indicator for proper alignment.
    d. Attach transmission range clip to adjuster to secure cable.
    e. Rearm air bag system as described under "Air Bag System Arming & Disarming."

COLT VISTA & SUMMIT WAGON

Removal

1. Ensure front wheels are in straight ahead position.
2. Disconnect and isolate battery ground cable. **Wait minimum of 2 minutes**

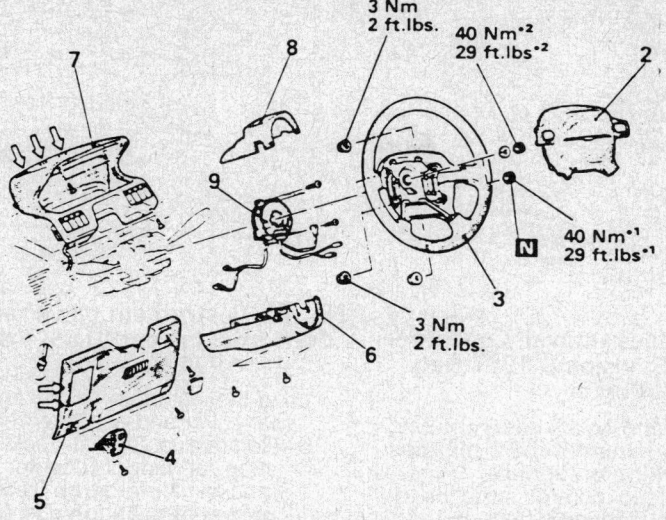

Fig. 8 Air bag module & clockspring removal. Colt
Vista & Summit Wagon

Fig. 9 Clockspring installation. Colt
Vista & Summit Wagon

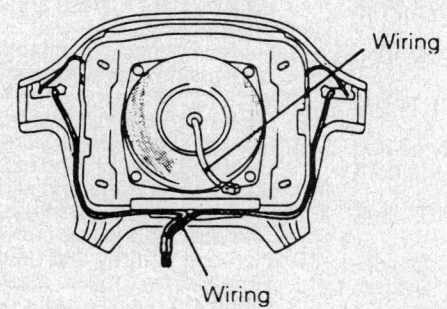

Fig. 10 Air bag wiring routing.
Colt Vista & Summit Wagon

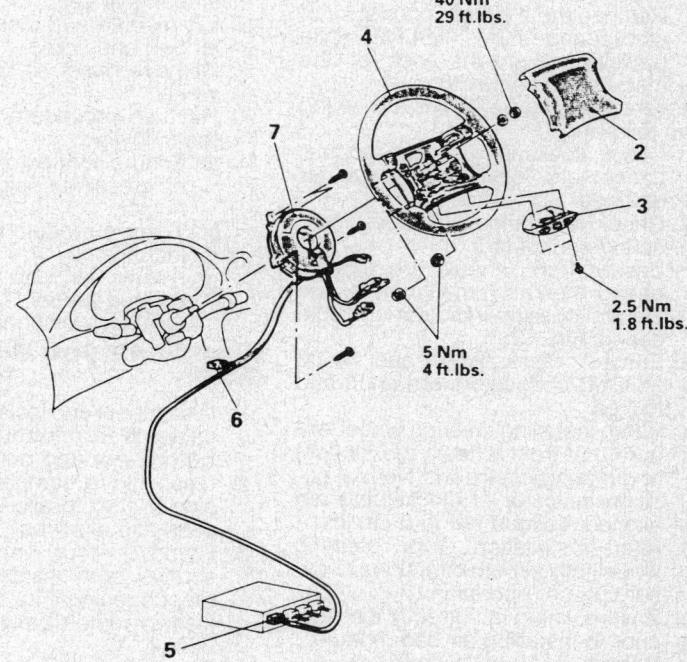

Fig. 11 Air bag module & clockspring removal. Stealth

before working on vehicle.
3. Remove air bag module and clockspring in numbered sequence shown in **Fig. 8,** noting the following:
   a. Remove air bag module mounting nut using a socket wrench from rear.
   b. Disconnect connector of clockspring from air bag module by pressing air bag lock toward outer side spreading it open, then gently pry connector out.
   c. Air bag module should be stored in a clean, dry place with pad cover facing up.
   d. Remove steering wheel using appropriate steering wheel puller.

Installation

1. Prior to installation, check clockspring, air bag module, connectors, case and gear for damage. If clockspring or any other components, including connectors are damaged, replace as necessary.
2. Prior to installing clockspring, check resistance between No. 2 and No. 5 connectors using SRS check harness tool No. MB991349 or equivalent and a suitable digital volt/ohmmeter. Resistance must be less than 0.4 ohms; if not, replace clockspring.
3. Ensure front wheels are straight

ahead, then align mating mark and Neutral position indicator of clockspring, **Fig. 9.**
4. Connect clockspring and ACM (ASDM) connectors; ensure connectors are snug and locked.
5. Install steering wheel, ensure that front wheels are straight and mating marks and Neutral position indicator of clockspring are aligned. **Torque** nut to 29 ft. lbs.
6. After installation of steering wheel, turn wheel fully in both directions to ensure proper operation.
7. Ensure wiring is correctly installed, **Fig. 10,** then install air bag module.
8. Rearm air bag system as described under "Air Bag System Arming & Disarming."

STEALTH
Driver's Side

1. Ensure front wheels are in straight ahead position.
2. Disconnect and isolate battery ground cable. **Wait minimum of 2 minutes before working on vehicle.**
3. Remove air bag module and clockspring in numbered sequence shown in **Fig. 11,** noting the following:
   a. Remove air bag module mounting nut using a socket wrench from rear.
   b. Disconnect connector of clockspring from air bag module by pressing air bag lock toward outer side spreading it open, then gently pry connector out.

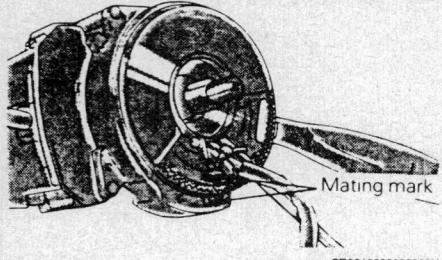

Fig. 12 Clockspring installation. Stealth

c. Air bag module should be stored in a clean, dry place with pad cover facing up.
d. Remove steering wheel using appropriate steering wheel puller.
e. Remove rear console assembly.
f. Disconnect SRS from Air bag Control Module (ACM) (Air Bag System Diagnostic Module (ASDM)), using screwdriver to push in lock spring of lock lever.
g. Remove the 2 pin red connector of clockspring ACM (ASDM) while pressing down the lock of the clockspring connector.

4. Reverse procedure to install, noting the following:
   a. Check clockspring, air bag module, connectors, case and gear for damage.
   b. Check resistance between clockspring connectors.
   c. Ensure front wheels are straight ahead, then align mating mark and Neutral position indicator of clockspring, **Fig. 12.**
   d. Ensure clockspring and ACM (ASDM) connectors are snug and locked.
   e. When installing steering wheel, ensure that front wheels are straight and mating marks and Neutral position indicator of clockspring are aligned. **Torque** nut to 29 ft. lbs.
   f. After installation, turn steering wheel fully in both directions to ensure proper operation.
   g. Ensure wiring is correctly installed prior to installing air bag module.
   h. Rearm air bag system as described under "Air Bag System Arming & Disarming."

Passenger's Side

1. Disconnect and isolate battery ground cable. **Wait minimum of 2 minutes before continuing work on vehicle.**
2. Remove glove compartment assembly.
3. Remove cross pipe cover from rear of glove compartment opening.
4. Remove air bag module.
5. Reverse procedure to install. Rearm air bag system as described under "Air Bag System Arming & Disarming.

CONCORDE, INTREPID, LHS, VISION & 1994 NEW YORKER

Driver's Side

1. Ensure front wheels are in straight ahead position.

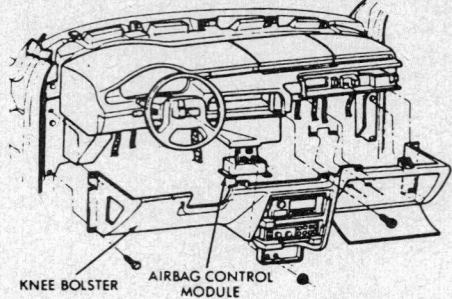

Fig. 13 Module removal. Concorde, Intrepid, LHS, Vision & 1994 New Yorker

2. Disconnect and isolate battery ground cable. **Wait minimum of 2 minutes before working on vehicle.**
3. Remove speed control switches or covers from steering wheel and disconnect wiring.
4. Remove bolts securing air bag to steering wheel.
5. Lift module and disconnect wiring to air bag and horn.
6. Remove driver air bag from steering wheel.
7. Reverse procedure to install, noting the following:
   a. Ensure connectors are fully seated by pressing straight in on the connector.
   b. **Torque** module bolts to 105-125 inch lbs.
   c. Rearm air bag system as described under "Air Bag System Arming & Disarming."

Non-Deployed Passenger's Side

1. Disconnect and isolate battery ground cable. **Wait minimum of 2 minutes before working on vehicle.**
2. Open glove compartment and push side inward to allow door bumper to pass and allow box to open fully.
3. Remove four module attaching screws from inside glove compartment opening, **Fig. 13.**
4. Remove knee bolster and right spot cooler.
5. Disconnect wire connector from module.
6. Lift module up and turn it so it can be lowered through the mounting brackets.
7. Reverse procedure to install. Rearm air bag system as described under "Air Bag System Arming & Disarming.

Deployed Passenger's Side

1. Disconnect and isolate battery ground cable. **Wait minimum of 2 minutes before working on vehicle.**
2. Roll/fold air bag toward instrument panel.
3. Close door over folded bag and tape door closed.
4. Open both vehicle doors and remove both instrument panel end covers.
5. **On 1994 models,** proceed as follows:
   a. Remove floor console if equipped

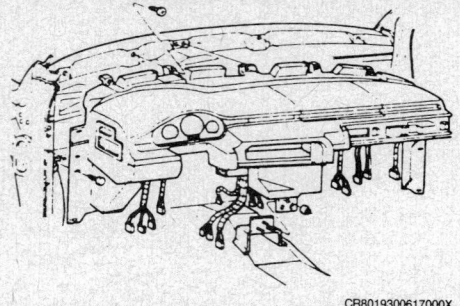

Fig. 14 Instrument panel removal. Concorde, Intrepid, LHS, Vision & 1994 New Yorker

or the instrument panel lower center cover and ash receiver.
b. Remove screw at radio ground strap at side of center support bracket. **Note strap routing for proper installation and radio operation.**

6. **On all models,** open glove compartment and push side inward to allow door bumper to pass and allow box to open fully.
7. Remove module attaching screws from inside glove compartment opening, **Fig. 13.**
8. Remove center distribution duct.
9. Remove instrument panel top cover by prying up each end of the top cover then lift rear edge and sliding top cover rearward to disengage front clips and remove the top cover.
10. Remove ashtray and center bezel.
11. Remove two lower steering column mounting bracket bolts.
12. Remove two upper mounting bracket nuts and lower column.
13. Remove instrument panel mounting screws, **Fig. 14.**
14. Disconnect wiring connectors as necessary.
15. Remove right spot cooler duct.
16. Remove upper instrument panel with passenger air bag module attached.
17. Reverse procedure to install, noting the following:
    a. **Torque** air bag module to collar bracket mounting screws to 35 inch lbs.
    b. **Torque** module to knee bolster attaching screws to 20 inch lbs.
    c. Rearm air bag system as described under "Air Bag System Arming & Disarming."

AIR BAG CONTROL MODULE (ACM/SDU) AIR BAG SYSTEM DIAGNOSTIC MODULE (ASDM), REPLACE

Before attempting to diagnose, remove or install any air bag system components, you must first disconnect and isolate the battery ground cable. Failure to do so could result in accidental deployment and possible personal injury.

The ACM (ASDM) contains one of the impact sensors which enables the system

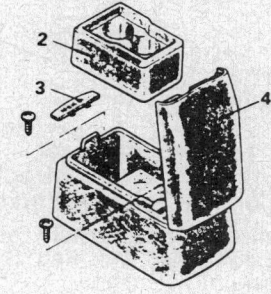

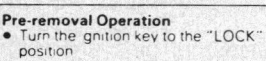

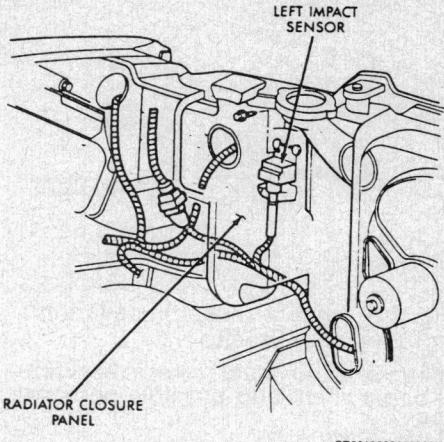

RADIATOR CLOSURE
PANEL

CR8019200623000X

Fig. 16 Left impact sensor. Except Colt Vista, Concorde, Intrepid, LHS, Stealth, Summit Wagon, Vision & 1994 New Yorker

4. Reverse procedure to install. Ensure connectors are properly connected. Rearm air bag system as described under "Air Bag System Arming & Disarming."

CONCORDE, INTREPID, LHS, VISION & 1994 NEW YORKER

Removal

1. **Disconnect battery ground cable, then wait at least 2 minutes before working on vehicle.**
2. **On five passenger models,** remove upper console seal and ash receiver, then the shifter knob and bezel.
3. **On six passenger models,** remove lower center retaining screws and the trim cover.
4. **On all models,** disconnect Air bag Control Module (ACM) (Air bag System Diagnostic Module (ASDM)) 4-way and 13-way connectors.
5. Remove module mounting screws and the module.

Installation

1. Install ACM (ASDM) (arrow pointing forward) in instrument panel support bracket ensuring insert tab on ACM (ASDM) is in slot on support bracket.
2. Attach ACM (ASDM) to support bracket and **torque** to 105-125 inch lbs.
3. Connect 4-way and 13-way connectors ensuring both connectors and all locking tabs are engaged.
4. **On five passenger models,** install shifter bezel and knob then the ash receiver and upper console.
5. **On six passenger models,** in stall lower trim cover and retaining screws.
6. Rearm air bag system as described under "Air Bag System Arming & Disarming."

FRONT IMPACT SENSORS, REPLACE

Before attempting to diagnose, remove or install any air bag system components, you must first disconnect and isolate the battery ground cable.

Removal steps

Post-installation inspection
1 Connection for the negative (−) battery cable
2 Cup holder
3 Console plug
4 Rear console assembly
5 SRS diagnosis unit and each harness connector connection
6 SRS diagnosis unit (SDU) Pre-installation inspection

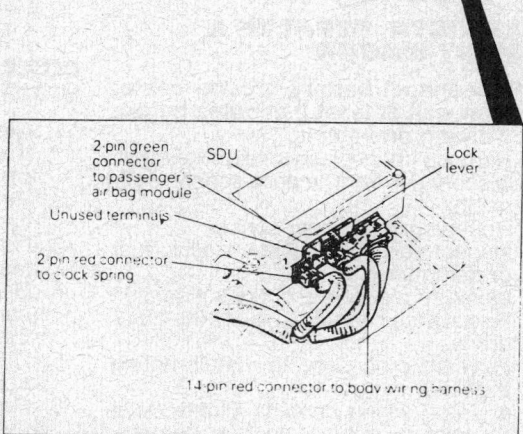

CR8019200621000X

Fig. 15 ACM/SDU replacement. Stealth

to activate the air bag. To avoid accidental deployment, never connect ACM (ASDM) electrically to system unless it is bolted to vehicle.

EXCEPT CONCORDE, INTREPID, LHS, STEALTH, VISION & 1994 NEW YORKER

Removal

1. Disconnect and isolate battery ground cable.
2. Remove floor console, vertical console trim bezel, vertical console carrier and radio as necessary.
3. Remove glove compartment, and the left side fasteners on instrument panel reinforcement, if necessary.
4. Disconnect electrical connectors and remove ACM (ASDM).

Installation

1. Install ACM (ASDM) (arrow pointing forward) in instrument panel support bracket, or on console reinforcement, as applicable, ensuring insert tab on ACM (ASDM) is in slot on support bracket.
2. Attach ACM (ASDM) to support bracket and **torque** to 15-20 inch lbs.
3. Remount instrument panel center support bracket to left and right instrument panel reinforcements.
4. Connect ACM (ASDM) electrical connectors.

5. Install vertical console carrier and floor console.
6. Rearm air bag system as described under "Air Bag System Arming & Disarming."

STEALTH

1. Note the following before servicing the ACM/SDU (ASDM):
   a. After air bag deployment, replace ACM/SDU (ASDM).
   b. The ACM/SDU (ASDM) is not serviceable, if faulty replace.
   c. Do not expose unit to vibration or drop.
   d. Do not use volt/ohmmeter on or near ACM/SDU (ASDM). Use only specified equipment.
2. **Disconnect battery ground cable, then wait 2 minutes before working on vehicle.**
3. Remove ACM/SDU (ASDM) from vehicle in numbered sequence shown in **Fig. 15**, noting the following:
   a. Disconnect SRS connector from ACM/SDU (ASDM), using screwdriver to push in lock spring of lock lever.
   b. Disconnect the red 14-pin connector from the ACM/SDU (ASDM) while pressing down the lock of connector.
   c. Check ACM/SDU (ASDM) case, brackets and connectors for deformities.

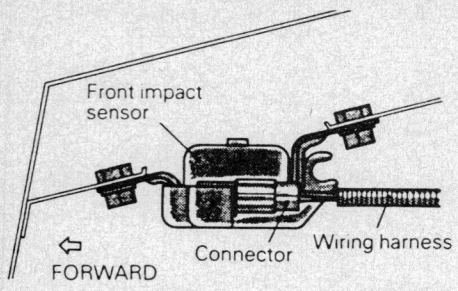

Fig. 17   Impact sensor installation. Stealth

Failure to do so could result in accidental deployment and possible personal injury.

EXCEPT COLT VISTA, CONCORDE, INTREPID, LHS, STEALTH, SUMMIT WAGON, VISION & 1994 NEW YORKER

Left Sensor

1. **Disconnect battery ground cable, then wait 2 minutes before working on vehicle.**
2. Disconnect speed control servo from battery tray.
3. Remove battery, battery tray and coolant bottle.
4. Disconnect sensor electrical connector.
5. Remove three screws holding sensor to radiator closure panel and remove sensor, **Fig. 16.**
6. Reverse procedure to install, noting the following:
   a. **Torque** mounting screws to 100 inch lbs.

b. Rearm air bag system as described under "Air Bag System Arming & Disarming."

Right Sensor

1. **Disconnect battery ground cable, then wait 2 minutes before working on vehicle.**
2. Disconnect sensor electrical connector.
3. Remove three screws holding sensor to engine side of closure panel and remove right sensor.
4. Reverse procedure to install, noting the following:
   a. **Torque** mounting screws to 100 inch lbs.
   b. Rearm air bag system as described under "Air Bag System Arming & Disarming."

COLT VISTA, STEALTH & SUMMIT WAGON

1. **Disconnect battery ground cable, then wait at least 2 minutes before working on vehicle.**
2. Remove front splash shield extension.
3. Disconnect front impact sensor connector.
4. Remove front impact sensor.
5. Inspect sensor for dents, cracks, rust or deformities.
6. Measure resistance of impact sensor. Resistance should be 1960-2040 ohms.
7. Reverse procedure to install, noting the following:
   a. Bend wiring harness slightly, to a point to reduce slack in harness, and clip securely to clip of front impact sensor.
   b. Install impact sensor so that there is close adherence to the upper surface of the front impact sensor and installation surface of the upper frame, **Fig. 17.**

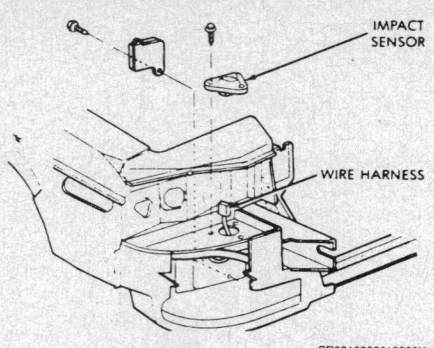

Fig. 18   Impact sensor replacement. Concorde, Intrepid, LHS, Vision & 1994 New Yorker

   c. Rearm air bag system as described under "Air Bag System Arming & Disarming."

CONCORDE, INTREPID, LHS, VISION & 1994 NEW YORKER

1. **Disconnect battery ground cable, then wait 2 minutes before working on vehicle.**
2. Remove headlamp pins then the headlamp.
3. Remove headlamp carrier securing fasteners then the carrier.
4. Remove screws holding impact sensor to headlamp carrier surface then the sensor, **Fig. 18.**
5. Disconnect impact sensor electrical connector.
6. Reverse procedure to install, noting the following:
   a. Install impact sensor with arrow on sensor pointing forward.
   b. **Torque** sensor screws to 25-45 inch lbs.
   c. Rearm air bag system as described under "Air Bag System Arming & Disarming."

TIGHTENING SPECIFICATIONS

Year	Component	Torque/Inch lbs.
EXCEPT COLT VISTA, CONCORDE, INTREPID, LHS, STEALTH, SUMMIT WAGON, VISION & 1994 NEW YORKER		
1992-94	Air Bag Module Nut (Drivers Side)	80-100
	Air Bag Module Nut (Passenger Side)	105
	Air Bag Control Module (ACM) (Air bag System Diagnostic Module (ASDM))	15-20 ①
	Impact Sensor Screws	90-120
	Steering Wheel Nut	45 ①
COLT VISTA, STEALTH & SUMMIT WAGON		
1992-94	Air Bag Module Nut	48
	Steering Wheel Nut	29 ①
	Steering Wheel Switches	21

Year	Component	Torque/Inch lbs.
CONCORDE, INTREPID, LHS, VISION & 1994 NEW YORKER		
1993-94	Air Bag Module Nut (Driver Side)	105-125
	Air Bag Module To Collar Bracket Screws (Passenger Side)	35
	Air Bag Module To Knee Bolster (Passenger Side)	20
	Air Bag Control Module (ACM) (Air bag System Diagnostic Module (ASDM))	105-125
	Clockspring screws	14-34
	Impact Sensor Screws	25-45
	Steering Wheel Nut	45 ①
	Steering Wheel Switches	12-18

①—Ft. lbs.

INDEX

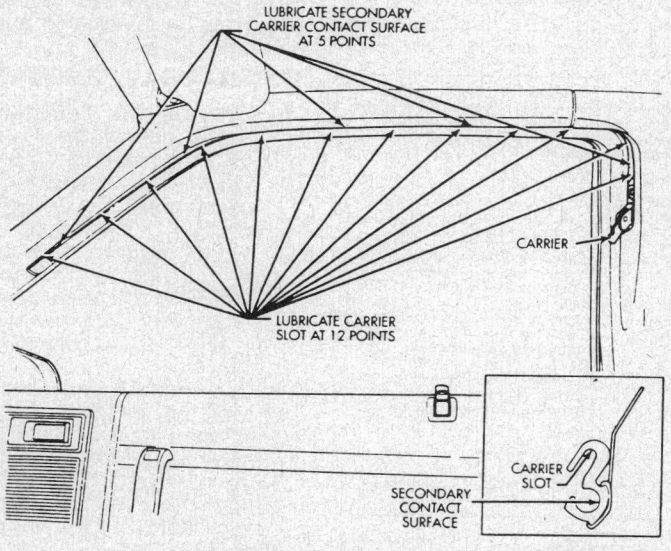

LUBRICATE SECONDARY CARRIER CONTACT SURFACE AT 5 POINTS

CARRIER

LUBRICATE CARRIER SLOT AT 12 POINTS

CARRIER SLOT

SECONDARY CONTACT SURFACE

CR8029400016000X

Fig. 1 Automatic seat belt track lubricant points. Acclaim, LeBaron Sedan, Shadow, Spirit & Sundance

DESCRIPTION

The automatic seat belt system incorporates the use of both mechanical and electronic components. The system operates mechanically by the use of track and drive assemblies, lap belt retractor assemblies and a console mounted retractor. Electronically, the system uses a passive belt control module which controls motors, tension eliminators and the system warning lamp. Inputs from the ignition switch, retractor and limit switches and distance sensor are used by the control module to operate the outputs to the motors and warning lamp.

TROUBLESHOOTING

ACCLAIM, LEBARON SEDAN, SHADOW, SPIRIT & SUNDANCE

Motorized Seat Belt Moves Slowly In Either Direction

This condition is most likely the result of insufficient lubricant in the track assembly. Proceed as follows:
1. Cover passenger's seat with a disposable cloth, then place ignition switch in On position and disconnect shoulder belt buckle from carrier.
2. After belt retracts to B-pillar, apply 1/4 inch diameter spots of Mopar Passive Restraint Track Lubricant or equivalent at 5 points along secondary carrier contact surface on rail, then apply at 12 points along carrier slot in rail, **Fig. 1.**
3. Connect shoulder belt carrier, then open and close door several times and allow belt retraction and extension to distribute lubricant along length of track.
4. Place ignition switch in Off position.

COLT, COLT VISTA, LASER, SUMMIT, SUMMIT WAGON & TALON

Refer to **Fig. 2** when troubleshooting these systems.

MONACO & PREMIER

SHOULDER BELT DOES NOT OPERATE

With control module connectors disconnected, ignition switch in Run position, both shoulder belts buckled and doors closed, proceed as follows:
1. Measure resistance from terminals 1, 21 and 27 with shoulder belt in forward position.
2. Resistance should be 0 ohms. If not as specified, check for open ground.
3. Measure resistance from terminals 4 and 28 with shoulder belt in rearward position.
4. Resistance should be 0 ohms. If not as specified, check for open ground.
5. Measure resistance from terminals 12, 35, 5 and 6.
6. Resistance should be zero. If not as specified, repair short.
7. Measure voltage at terminals 8 and 30.
8. Voltage should be approximately 12 volts. If not as specified, check fuses and/or repair short to fuse block.
9. Disconnect speed sensor module, then check for continuity.
10. If continuity exists, replace seat belt control module. If no continuity is present, check for open wire.

SEAT BELT INDICATOR OR CHIME MODULE DOES NOT OPERATE

With ignition switch in Run position and shoulder belts buckled, proceed as follows:
1. Check for approximately 12 volts at terminal 34, **Fig. 3.**
2. If not as specified, replace shoulder belt control module.

SHOULDER BELTS FAIL TO MOVE IN FORWARD DIRECTION

Motor Relay Connector Inspection

With ignition in run position, shoulder belts buckled, doors open, LH or RH front motor relay disconnected, shoulder belt control module disconnected and terminals 8 and 36 RH side or 8 and 25 LH side jumpered, proceed as follows:

1. Measure voltage between terminals 4 and 5; approximately 12 volts should be indicated. If not, check for a short in wiring.
2. Measure resistance to ground from terminals 2 and 3. Resistance should be 0 ohms. If not, check for a short to ground.
3. Measure voltage at terminal 1; approximately 12 volts should be indicated. If not, replace relay.

Motor Connector Inspection

With LH side or RH seat belt motor disconnected, shoulder belt control module disconnected, terminals 8 and 25 RH side or 8 and 36 LH side jumpered, proceed as follows:

1. Measure voltage at terminal C. Voltage should be approximately 12 volts; if not as specified, check wire(s) from front motor relay.
2. Measure resistance from ground to terminal D. If resistance is 0 ohms, replace seat belt motor. If not, check wiring for shorts; if wiring is good, replace control module.

SHOULDER BELTS FAIL TO MOVE IN REARWARD DIRECTION

Motor Relay Inspection

With ignition switch in Run position, shoulder belts buckled, doors closed, LH side or RH side back motor relay disconnected, shoulder belt control module disconnected, terminals 8 and 23 RH side or 8 and 24 LH side jumpered, proceed as follows:

1. Measure voltage between terminals 4 and 5; approximately 12 volts should be indicated. If not, check wire from front relay.
2. Measure resistance between ground and terminals 2 and 3. Resistance should read 0 ohms. If correct, replace seat belt motor; if not, check ground wire.
3. Measure voltage at terminal 1. Voltage should be approximately 12 volts; if not, replace relay.

Motor Connector Inspection

With LH side or RH side seat belt motor disconnected, seat belt control module disconnected and terminals 8 and 25 RH side or 8 and 36 LH side jumpered, proceed as follows:

1. Measure voltage at terminal D; approximately 12 volts should be indicated. If not, check front motor relay wire.
2. Measure resistance from ground to terminal C; resistance should read 0 ohms. If so, replace seat belt motor; if not, check for open wiring.
3. If open wiring is not at fault, replace control module.

SHOULDER BELT INDICATOR LAMP DOES NOT LIGHT

1. With belt not buckled and using suit-

Trouble symptom	Cause
Driver's and/or front passenger's system does not function	Fuse blown or disconnected
	Open harness wire or disconnected connector
	Defective switch
	Defective motor
	Defective relay
	Defective control unit
Warning light does not illuminate or flash	Fuse blown or disconnected
	Open harness wire or disconnected connector
	Defective switch
	Warning light bulb blown or in poor contact
	Defective control unit
Buzzer does not sound	Fuse blown or disconnected
	Defective buzzer
	Open harness wire or disconnected connector
	Defective control unit
The slide anchor does not move from the "fasten" range into "release" range, or from the "release" range into the "fasten" range	Defective driving device, or problem in electrical circuit
Slide anchor moves too slowly	Defective control unit
	Foreign matter in guide rail
Slide anchor stops halfway	Defective retractor (remains in locked state)
	Defective driving device or problem in electrical circuit

CR8019100278000X

Fig. 2 Troubleshooting chart. Colt, Colt Vista, Laser, Summit, Summit Wagon & Talon

able volt/ohmmeter, check control module terminal 30 for voltage. Voltage should read approximately 12 volts.
2. If not as specified, check for open circuit.
3. Check control module terminal 1 for resistance. Resistance should be 0 ohms.
4. If not as specified, check for open circuit.
5. Check control module terminal 33 for test voltage. Voltage should be approximately 12 volts.
6. If not as specified, replace lamp and/or check terminal 6 and 5 for closed circuit and if OK, replace module.

SHOULDER BELT INDICATOR DOES NOT GO OFF

1. With belt buckled and using suitable volt/ohmmeter check terminals 5 and 6 for resistance. Resistance should be 0 ohms.
2. If not as specified, check for short and if not fault, replace switch.

3. Check for resistance between terminals 27 and 28. Resistance should be 0 ohms.
4. If not as specified, check for short; if no short is present, replace switch.

DIAGNOSIS & TESTING

Acclaim, LeBaron Sedan, Shadow, Spirit & Sundance

SYSTEM TESTING

Refer to **Figs. 4 and 5** for wiring diagrams when diagnosing the automatic seat belt system.

To perform testing of the automatic seat belt system, the use of a DRBII or equivalent scan tool or suitable volt/ohmmeter is required. Follow tool manufacturer's instructions for installation and operation of scan tool, if used.

USING VOLT/OHMMETER

1. **On Acclaim, LeBaron Sedan and Spirit**, inspect circuit breaker in cavity 13 and fuse in cavity 8 of fuse block.
2. **On Shadow and Sundance**, inspect circuit breaker in cavity 11 and fuse in cavity 4 of fuse block.
3. **On all models**, replace circuit breaker and/or fuse as required, then use voltmeter to check for battery voltage at pin 6 of Passive Seat Belt Module (PSBM) 10-way electrical connector, **Fig. 6.**
4. If voltmeter indicates that less than 9 volts are present, inspect all harness connectors and repair as necessary, then recheck voltage.
5. If voltmeter indicates that 9 volts or more are present, check for ground at pin 1 of PSBM 10-way connector, **Fig. 6.**
6. If ground is not indicated, inspect all harness connectors and repair as necessary, then check again for ground.
7. If ground is indicated, place ignition switch in On position, then use a voltmeter to check for battery voltage at pin 16 of PSBM 21-way connector, **Fig. 6.**
8. If battery voltage is not present, proceed as follows:
   a. **On Acclaim, LeBaron Sedan and Spirit**, inspect fuse in cavity 8 of fuse block. Replace as necessary.
   b. **On Shadow and Sundance**, inspect fuse in cavity 4 of fuse block. Replace as necessary.
9. If battery voltage is present, check PSBM output voltage to seat belt motor as follows:
   a. Disconnect PSBM 10-way connector from module; allow 21-way connector to remain connected.
   b. Connect voltmeter leads between pins 5 and 10 of module 10-way connector. With ignition switch in On position, passenger door opening or closing and shoulder belt buckled to track and drive carrier,

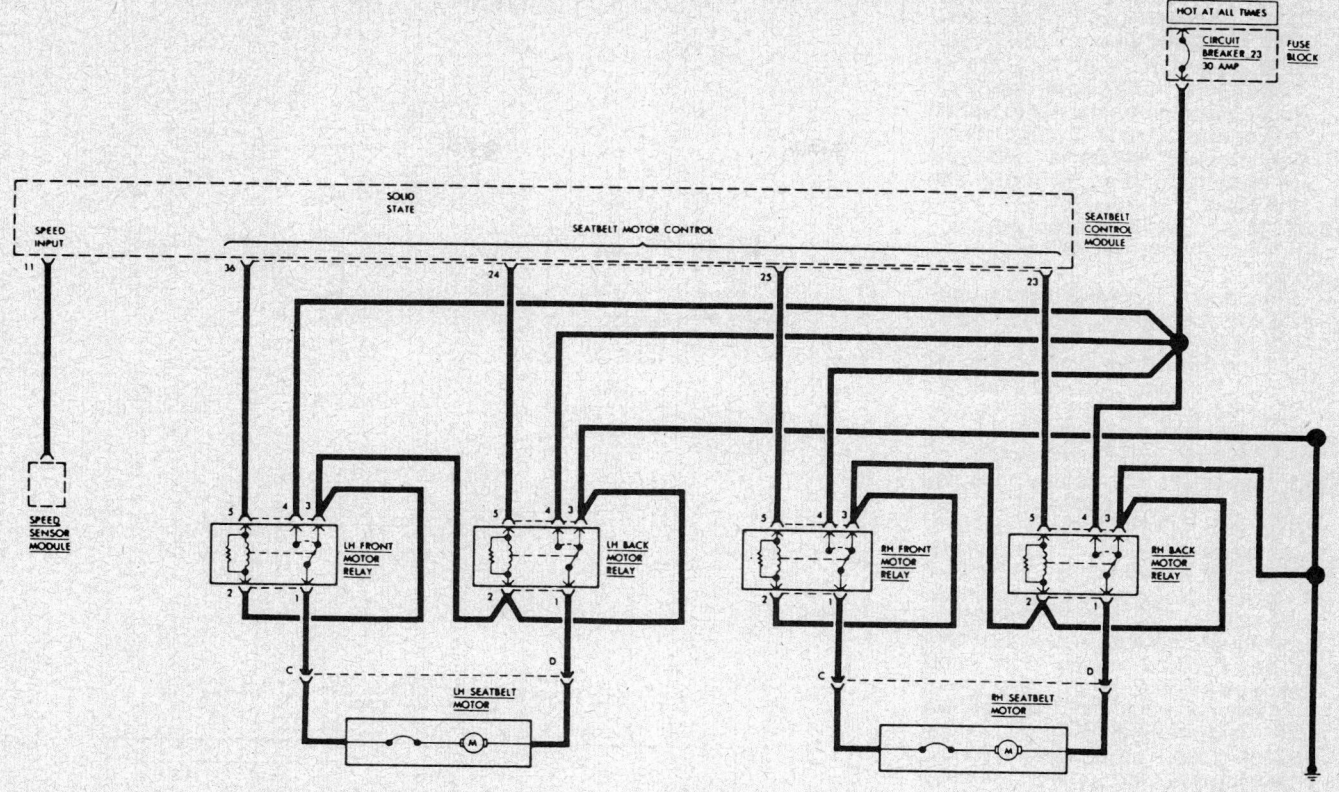

Fig. 3 Automatic seat belt system circuit diagram (Part 1 of 2). Monaco & Premier

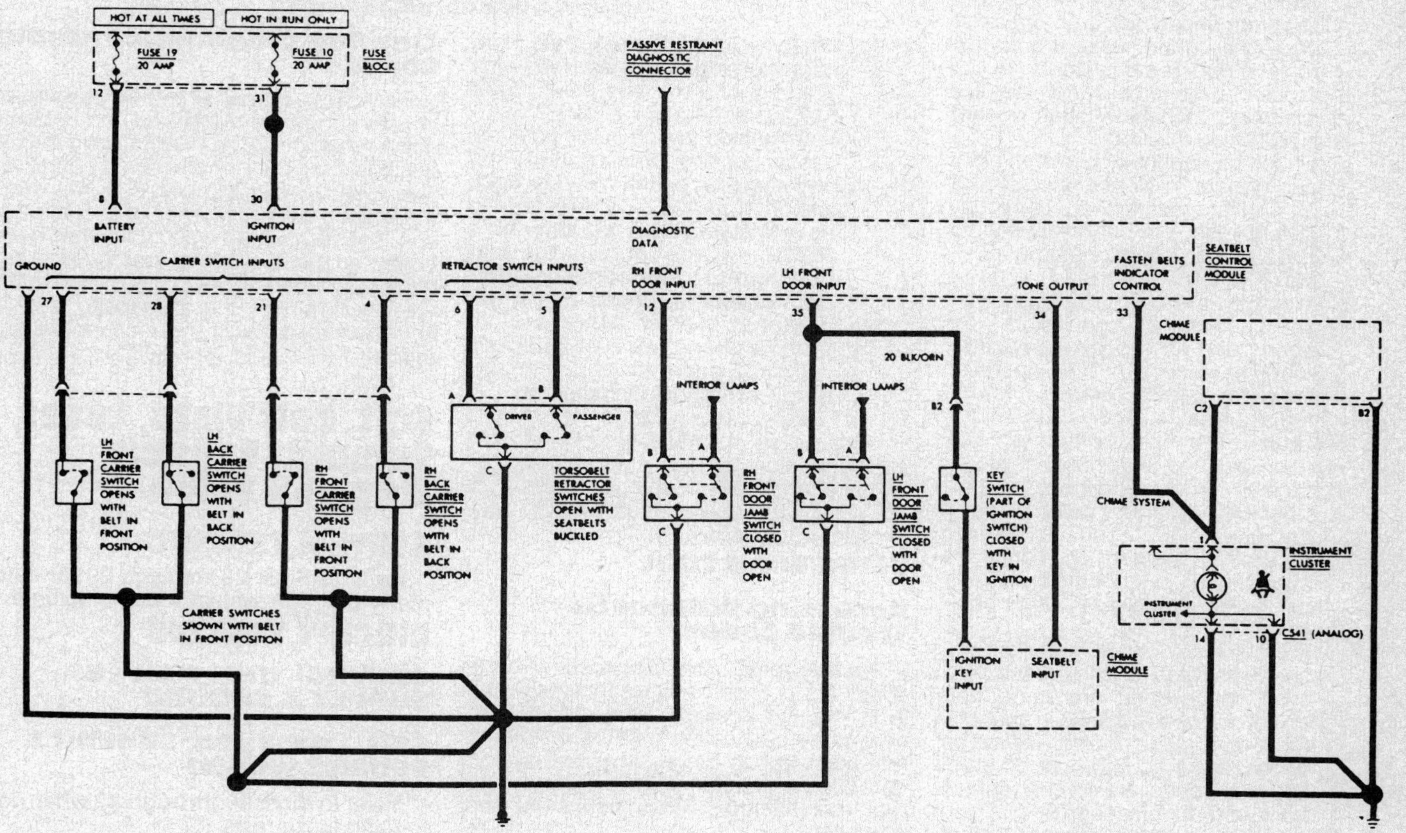

CR8019100272010X

Fig. 3 Automatic seat belt system circuit diagram (Part 2 of 2). Monaco & Premier

CR8019100272020X

7-12 volts should be indicated. **There will only be a PSBM voltage output to seat belt motor immediately after door opens or closes and when carrier is not at either end of track. Voltage must be checked within 30 seconds of placing ignition switch in On position.**

10. If PSBM output voltage is not as specified, inspect shoulder belt switch as follows:

    a. Disconnect PSBM 21-way connector; then, using an ohmmeter, check for continuity from pin 15 to ground. No continuity should be indicated when shoulder belt is buckled to track and drive carrier, but continuity should exist when belt is fully coiled on retractor.

    b. If results are not as specified, inspect harness connectors for opens and for proper connection; repair as necessary. If no opens or improper connections are found, replace shoulder belt retractor assembly.

11. If results of shoulder belt switch test are as specified, inspect door jamb switch as follows:

    a. Check for continuity between pin 14 and ground. With passenger door closed, no continuity should exist; with door open, continuity should exist.

    b. If results are not as specified, inspect harness connectors for opens and for proper connection; repair as necessary. If no opens or improper connections are found, replace door jamb switch.

12. If results of door jamb switch test are as specified, inspect A-pillar forward limit switch as follows:

    a. Check for continuity between pin 5 and ground. With belt latch carrier at A-pillar position, no continuity should exist, but continuity should exist with carrier in any other position.

    b. If results are not as specified, inspect harness connectors for opens and for proper connection; repair as necessary. If no opens or improper connections are found, replace track and drive assembly.

13. If results of forward limit switch test are as specified, inspect B-pillar reverse limit switch as follows:

    a. Check for continuity between pin 7 and ground. With belt latch carrier at B-pillar position, no continuity should exist, but continuity should exist with carrier in any other position.

    b. If results are not as specified, inspect harness connectors to ensure connections are good and check for opens between module, track and drive motor; repair as necessary. If no improper connections or opens are found, replace track and drive assembly.

14. Check PSBM output voltage at seat belt motor as follows:

    a. Connect both module connectors

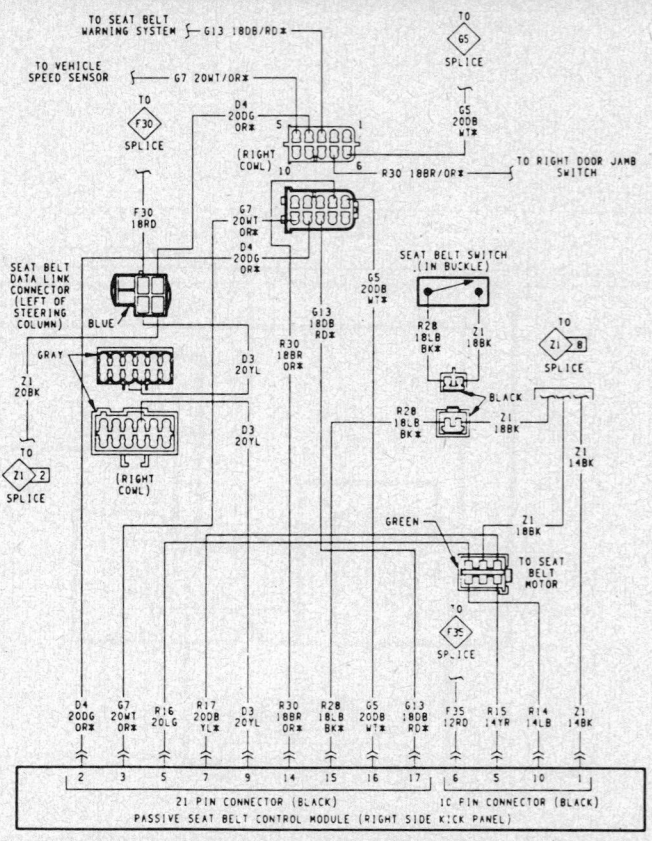

Fig. 4 Automatic seat belt system circuit diagram. Acclaim, LeBaron Sedan & Spirit

(10-way and 21-way), then connect voltmeter leads between pins 1 and 3 of track and drive motor 6-way connector.

   b. With ignition switch in On position, passenger door opening or closing and shoulder belt buckled to track and drive carrier, 7-12 volts should be indicated. **There will only be a PSBM voltage output to seat belt motor immediately after door opens or closes and when carrier is not at either end of track. Voltage must be checked within 30 seconds of placing ignition switch in On position.**

15. If PSBM output voltage test results are not as specified, inspect harness connectors for opens and for improper connections; repair as necessary. If results are as specified, replace track and drive assembly.

USING SCAN TOOL

Accessing Diagnostic Trouble Codes

Passive seat belt diagnostic trouble codes are only active while ignition switch is in the On position. They can be accessed by connecting a DRBII or equivalent scan tool to the passive belt system data link connector, **Fig. 7**. Follow scan tool manufacturer's instructions for tool operation.

Refer to **Figs. 8 through 22** for diagnostic flowcharts.

Clearing Diagnostic Trouble Codes

Because passive seat belt diagnostic trouble codes are not stored and are only active when the ignition switch is in the On position, they are not retained by the Passive Belt Control Module (PBCM) when the ignition switch is turned to the Off position. Therefore, if the malfunction has been corrected, the diagnostic trouble code will be erased when the switch is cycled to the Off position, but the diagnostic trouble code will reappear if the malfunction still exists.

Colt, Colt Vista, Laser, Summit, Summit Wagon & Talon

SYSTEM TESTING

Refer to **Figs. 23 through 29** for automatic seat belt system wiring diagrams.

CIRCUIT TESTING

CONTROL UNIT POWER SUPPLY & GROUND

Colt, Colt Vista, Summit & Summit Wagon

Refer to **Figs. 30 through 32** when performing these tests.

1. Disconnect control unit harness connector.

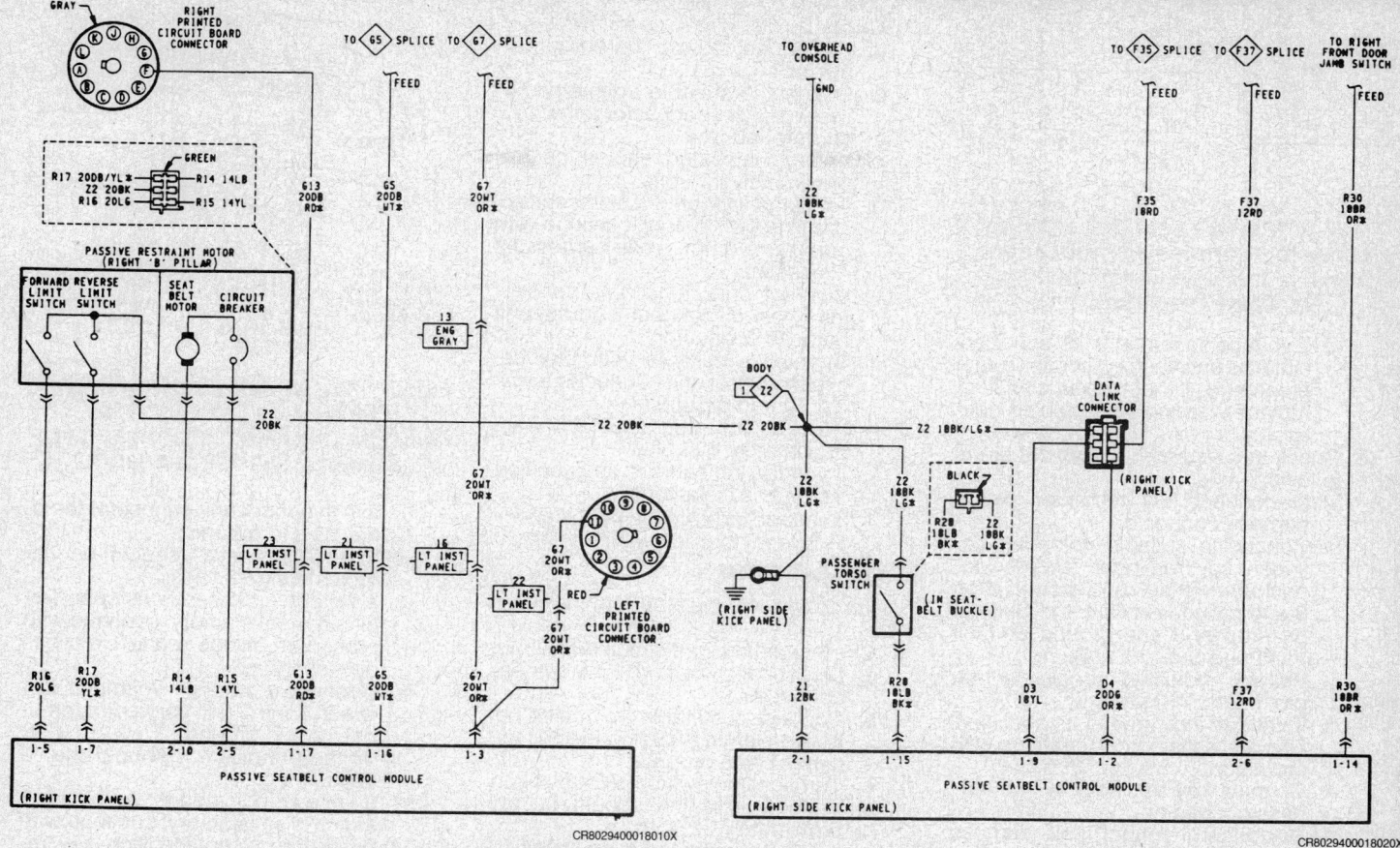

Fig. 5   Automatic seat belt system circuit diagram. Shadow & Sundance

2. Connect a suitable voltmeter between control unit connector terminal 11 and ground.
3. Voltage indicated should be approximately 12 volts.
4. If voltage indicated is as specified, circuit is satisfactory; continue with procedure. If not, repair circuit as necessary.
5. Connect a suitable voltmeter between control unit connector terminal 1 and ground.
6. Turn ignition switch to On position.
7. Voltage indicated should be approximately 12 volts.
8. If voltage indicated is as specified, circuit is satisfactory; continue with procedure. If not, repair circuit as necessary.
9. Connect a suitable ohmmeter between control unit connector terminal 7 and ground, then terminal 17 and ground.
10. Turn ignition switch to Off position.
11. Ohmmeter should indicate continuity.
12. If continuity is indicated, circuit is satisfactory.
13. If continuity is not indicated, repair circuit as necessary.

Laser & Talon

Refer to **Figs. 33 and 34** when perform-

ing these tests.
1. Disconnect control unit harness connector.
2. Connect a suitable voltmeter between control unit connector terminal 11 and ground.
3. Voltage indicated should be approximately 12 volts.
4. If voltage indicated is as specified, circuit is satisfactory; continue with procedure. If not, repair circuit as necessary.
5. Connect a suitable voltmeter between control unit connector terminal 1 and ground.
6. Turn ignition switch to On position.
7. Voltage indicated should be approximately 12 volts.
8. If voltage indicated is as specified, circuit is satisfactory; continue with procedure. If not, repair circuit as necessary.
9. Connect a suitable ohmmeter between control unit connector terminal 7 and ground, then terminal 17 and ground.
10. Turn ignition switch to Off position.
11. Ohmmeter should indicate continuity.
12. If continuity is indicated, circuit is satisfactory.
13. If continuity is not indicated, repair circuit as necessary.

WARNING LIGHT, KEY REMINDER SWITCH & BUZZER

Colt, Colt Vista, Summit & Summit Wagon

Refer to **Figs. 35 through 39** when performing these tests.
1. Check warning light circuit as follows:
   a. Disconnect warning light harness connector.
   b. Connect a suitable voltmeter between warning light connector terminal 10 and ground.
   c. Turn ignition switch to On position.
   d. Voltage indicated should be approximately 12 volts.
   e. If voltage indicated is as specified, circuit is satisfactory; continue with procedure. If not, repair circuit as necessary.
   f. Connect warning light harness connector.
   g. Disconnect control unit harness connector.
   h. Connect a suitable voltmeter between control unit connector terminal 10 and ground.
   i. Turn ignition switch to On position.
   j. Voltage indicated should be approximately 12 volts.

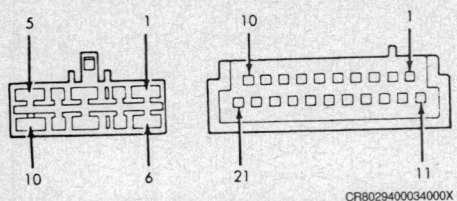

Fig. 6 Passive seat belt module connector terminal identification. Acclaim, LeBaron Sedan, Shadow, Spirit & Sundance

k. If voltage indicated is as specified, circuit is satisfactory; continue with procedure. If not, repair circuit or replace warning light bulb as necessary.
2. Check key reminder switch circuit as follows:
   a. Disconnect key reminder switch harness connector.
   b. Connect a suitable voltmeter between key reminder switch connector terminal 7 and ground, then 3 and ground on Colt and Summit or terminal 2 and ground on Colt Vista and Summit Wagon.
   c. Voltage indicated should be approximately 12 volts.
   d. If voltage indicated is as specified, circuit is satisfactory; continue with procedure.
   e. Connect key reminder switch harness connector.
   f. Disconnect control unit harness connector.
   g. Remove key from ignition switch.
   h. Connect a suitable voltmeter between control unit connector terminal 13 and ground.
   i. Voltage indicated should be approximately 12 volts.
   j. If voltage indicated is as specified, circuit is satisfactory; continue with procedure. If not, repair circuit as necessary.
   k. Connect a suitable voltmeter between control unit connector terminal 12 and ground.
   l. Voltage indicated should be 0 volts.
   m. If voltage indicated is as specified, circuit is satisfactory; continue with procedure. If not, replace key reminder switch.
   n. Insert ignition key.
   o. Connect a suitable voltmeter between control unit connector terminal 13 and ground.
   p. Voltage indicated should be 0 volts.
   q. If voltage indicated is as specified, circuit is satisfactory; continue with procedure. If not, replace key reminder switch.
   r. Connect a suitable voltmeter between control unit connector terminal 12 and ground.
   s. Voltage indicated should be approximately 12 volts.
   t. If voltage indicated is as specified, circuit is satisfactory; continue with procedure. If not, repair harness as necessary.

3. Check buzzer circuit as follows:
   a. Disconnect buzzer harness connector.
   b. Connect a suitable voltmeter between buzzer connector terminal 2 and ground.
   c. Voltage indicated should be approximately 12 volts.
   d. If voltage indicated is as specified, circuit is satisfactory; continue with procedure. If not, repair harness as necessary.
   e. Connect buzzer harness connector, then disconnect control unit harness connector.
   f. Connect a suitable voltmeter between control unit connector terminal 20 and ground.
   g. Voltage indicated should be approximately 12 volts.
   h. If voltage indicated is as specified, circuit is satisfactory.
   i. If voltage indicated is not as specified, repair harness as necessary.

Laser & Talon

Refer to **Fig. 40** when performing these tests.
1. Check warning light circuit as follows:
   a. Disconnect warning light harness connector.
   b. Connect a suitable voltmeter between warning light connector terminal 1 and ground.
   c. Turn ignition switch to On position.
   d. Voltage indicated should be approximately 12 volts.
   e. If voltage indicated is as specified, circuit is satisfactory; continue with procedure. If not, repair circuit as necessary.
   f. Connect warning light harness connector.
   g. Disconnect control unit harness connector.
   h. Connect a suitable voltmeter between control unit connector terminal 1 and ground.
   i. Turn ignition switch to On position.
   j. Voltage indicated should be approximately 12 volts.
   k. If voltage indicated is as specified, circuit is satisfactory; continue with procedure. If not, repair circuit or replace warning light bulb as necessary.
2. Check key reminder switch circuit as follows:
   a. Disconnect key reminder switch harness connector.
   b. Connect a suitable voltmeter between key reminder switch connector terminal 1 and ground, then terminal 3 and ground.
   c. Voltage indicated should be approximately 12 volts.
   d. If voltage indicated is as specified, circuit is satisfactory; continue with procedure. If not, repair circuit as necessary.
   e. Connect key reminder switch harness connector.
   f. Disconnect control unit harness connector.
   g. Remove key from ignition switch.
   h. Connect a suitable voltmeter be-

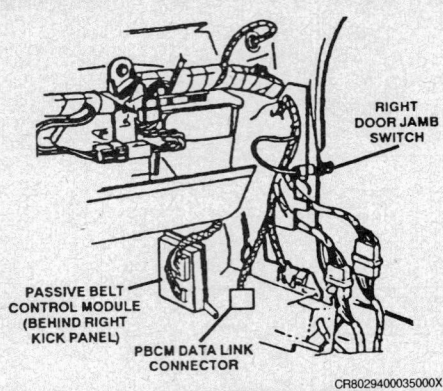

Fig. 7 Passive Belt Control Module (PBCM) data link connector location. Acclaim, LeBaron Sedan, Shadow, Spirit & Sundance

tween control unit connector terminal 13 and ground.
   i. Voltage indicated should be approximately 12 volts.
   j. If voltage indicated is as specified, circuit is satisfactory; continue with procedure. If not, repair circuit as necessary.
   k. Connect a suitable voltmeter between control unit connector terminal 12 and ground.
   l. Voltage indicated should be 0 volts.
   m. If voltage indicated is as specified, circuit is satisfactory; continue with procedure. If not, replace key reminder switch.
   n. Insert ignition key.
   o. Connect a suitable voltmeter between control unit connector terminal 13 and ground.
   p. Voltage indicated should be 0 volts.
   q. If voltage indicated is as specified, circuit is satisfactory; continue with procedure. If not, replace key reminder switch.
   r. Connect a suitable voltmeter between control unit connector terminal 12 and ground.
   s. Voltage indicated should be approximately 12 volts.
   t. If voltage indicated is as specified, circuit is satisfactory; continue with procedure. If not, repair harness as necessary.
3. Check buzzer circuit as follows:
   a. Disconnect buzzer harness connector.
   b. Connect a suitable voltmeter between buzzer connector terminal 1 and ground.
   c. Voltage indicated should be approximately 12 volts.
   d. If voltage indicated is as specified, circuit is satisfactory; continue with procedure. If not, repair harness as necessary.
   e. Connect buzzer harness connector, then disconnect control unit harness connector.
   f. Connect a suitable voltmeter between control unit connector terminal 20 and ground.

g. Voltage indicated should be approximately 12 volts.
h. If voltage indicated is as specified, circuit is satisfactory.
i. If voltage indicated is not as specified, repair harness as necessary.

MOTOR POWER SUPPLY & DRIVE

Colt, Colt Vista, Summit & Summit Wagon

Refer to **Figs. 41 through 44** when performing these tests.

1. Disconnect motor relay harness connector.
2. Connect a suitable ohmmeter between motor relay connector terminals 1 and 3 (motor relay side).
3. Ohmmeter should indicate continuity.
4. If continuity is indicated, circuit is satisfactory; continue with procedure. If continuity is not indicated, replace motor and track assembly.
5. Connect ohmmeter between motor relay connector terminal 5 (harness side) and ground.
6. Ohmmeter should indicate continuity.
7. If continuity is indicated, circuit is satisfactory; continue with procedure. If continuity is not indicated, repair harness as necessary.
8. Disconnect control unit harness connector.
9. Connect ohmmeter between motor relay connector terminal 1 (motor relay side) and ground, then between terminal 3 (motor relay side) and ground.
10. Ohmmeter should indicate continuity.
11. If continuity is indicated, circuit is satisfactory; continue with procedure. If continuity is not indicated, replace motor and track assembly.
12. Connect a suitable voltmeter between motor relay connector terminal 2 (harness side) and ground, then between terminal 6 (harness side) and ground. On Colt Vista & Summit Wagon, repeat test using terminals 2 and 7 to test left motor relay.
13. Voltage indicated should be approximately 12 volts.
14. If voltage indicated is as specified, circuit is satisfactory; continue with procedure. If voltage indicated is not as specified, repair harness as necessary.
15. Connect motor relay harness connector.
16. Connect voltmeter between control unit connector terminals 8, 9 and ground (left side), then between terminals 18, 19 and ground (right side).
17. Voltage indicated should be approximately 12 volts.
18. If voltage indicated is as specified, circuit is satisfactory; if voltage indicated is not as specified, repair harness or replace motor and track assembly as necessary.

Laser & Talon

Refer to **Fig. 45** when performing these tests.

1. Disconnect motor relay harness connector.
2. Connect a suitable ohmmeter between motor relay connector terminals 1 and 3 (motor relay side).
3. Ohmmeter should indicate continuity.
4. If continuity is indicated, circuit is satisfactory; continue with procedure. If not, replace motor and track assembly.
5. Connect ohmmeter between motor relay connector terminal 5 (harness side) and ground.
6. Ohmmeter should indicate continuity.
7. If continuity is indicated, circuit is satisfactory; continue with procedure. If not, repair harness as necessary.
8. Disconnect control unit harness connector.
9. Connect ohmmeter between motor relay connector terminal 2 (motor relay side) and ground, then between terminal 6 (motor relay side) and ground.
10. Ohmmeter should indicate continuity.
11. If continuity is indicated, circuit is satisfactory; continue with procedure. If not, replace motor and track assembly.
12. Connect a suitable voltmeter between motor relay connector terminal 2 (harness side) and ground, then between terminal 6 (harness side) and ground.
13. Voltage indicated should be approximately 12 volts.
14. If voltage indicated is as specified, circuit is satisfactory; continue with procedure. If not, repair harness as necessary.
15. If voltage indicated is not as specified, repair harness as necessary.
16. Connect motor relay harness connector.
17. Connect voltmeter between control unit connector terminals 8, 9 and ground (left side), then between terminals 18, 19 and ground (right side).
18. Voltage indicated should be approximately 12 volts.
19. If voltage indicated is as specified, circuit is satisfactory.
20. If voltage indicated is not as specified, repair harness or replace motor and track assembly as necessary.

RELEASE SWITCH (DRIVER'S SIDE), BUCKLE SWITCH & OUTER SWITCH

1992–93 Colt, Colt Vista, Summit & Summit Wagon

Refer to **Figs. 46 through 48** when performing these tests.

1. Check release switch (driver's side) circuit as follows:
   a. Disconnect release switch harness connector.
   b. Connect a suitable ohmmeter between release switch connector terminal 1 and ground.
   c. Ohmmeter should indicate continuity.
   d. If continuity is indicated, circuit is satisfactory; continue with procedure. If continuity is not indicated, repair harness as necessary.
   e. Connect release switch harness connector, then disconnect control unit harness connector.
   f. Connect ohmmeter between control unit connector terminal 5 and ground.
   g. Observe ohmmeter while moving slide anchor.
   h. Ohmmeter should indicate continuity when slide anchor is not in release (switch on) range.
   i. Ohmmeter should indicate infinite ohms when slide anchor is in release (switch off) range.
   j. If resistance indicated is as specified, circuit is satisfactory; continue with procedure. If resistance indicated is not as specified, repair harness or replace motor and track assembly as necessary.
   k. If resistance indicated is not as specified, repair harness or replace motor and track assembly as necessary.
2. Check buckle switch circuit as follows:
   a. Disconnect buckle switch harness connector.
   b. Connect a suitable ohmmeter between buckle switch connector terminal 2 and ground.
   c. Ohmmeter should indicate continuity.
   d. If continuity is indicated, circuit is satisfactory; continue with procedure. If not, repair harness as necessary.
   e. Connect buckle switch harness connector, then disconnect control unit harness connector. Ensure lap belt is unfastened (buckle switch on).
   f. Connect ohmmeter between control unit connector terminal 2 and ground.
   g. Ohmmeter should indicate continuity.
   h. If continuity is indicated, circuit is satisfactory; continue with procedure. If continuity is not indicated, repair harness or replace buckle as necessary.
3. Check outer switch circuit as follows:
   a. Disconnect outer switch harness connector.
   b. Connect ohmmeter between outer switch connector (harness side) terminal 1 and ground, then terminal 3 and ground.
   c. Ohmmeter should indicate continuity.
   d. If continuity is indicated, circuit is satisfactory; continue with procedure. If continuity is not indicated, repair harness as necessary.
   e. Connect ohmmeter between outer switch connector (switch side) terminals 1 and 2 (left side), then between terminals 3 and 4 (right side).
   f. Observe ohmmeter while pulling out and retracting shoulder belt.
   g. From shoulder belt full retracted position to halfway out (outer switch off), infinite ohms should be indicated.

h. With shoulder belt pulled halfway out (outer switch on), continuity should be indicated.

i. If resistance indicated is as specified, circuit is satisfactory; continue with procedure. If not, replace shoulder belt retractor assembly.

j. If resistance indicated is not as specified, replace shoulder belt retractor assembly.

k. Connect shoulder belt to slide anchor (outer switch on). Connect outer switch harness connector, then disconnect control unit harness connector.

l. Connect ohmmeter between control unit connector terminal 3 and ground, then terminal 14 and ground.

m. Ohmmeter should indicate continuity. If continuity is indicated, circuit is satisfactory; if not, repair harness as necessary.

Laser & Talon

Refer to **Fig. 49** when performing these tests.

1. Check release switch (driver side) circuit as follows:
   a. Disconnect release switch harness connector.
   b. Connect a suitable ohmmeter between release switch connector terminal 1 and ground.
   c. Ohmmeter should indicate continuity.
   d. If continuity is indicated, circuit is satisfactory; continue with procedure. If not, repair harness as necessary.
   e. Connect release switch harness connector, then disconnect control unit harness connector.
   f. Connect ohmmeter between control unit connector terminal 5 and ground.
   g. Observe ohmmeter while manually moving slide anchor.
   h. Ohmmeter should indicate continuity when slide anchor is not in release (switch on) range.
   i. Ohmmeter indicate infinite ohms when slide anchor is in release (switch off) range.
   j. If resistance indicated is as specified, circuit is satisfactory; continue with procedure. If not, repair harness or replace motor and track assembly as necessary.

2. Check buckle switch circuit as follows:
   a. Disconnect buckle switch harness connector.
   b. Connect a suitable ohmmeter between buckle switch connector terminal 2 and ground.
   c. Ohmmeter should indicate continuity.
   d. If continuity is indicated, circuit is satisfactory; continue with procedure. If not, repair harness as necessary.
   e. Connect buckle switch harness connector, then disconnect control unit harness connector.
   f. Connect ohmmeter between control unit connector terminal 2 and

ground. **Ensure lap belt is not fastened.**
   g. Ohmmeter should indicate continuity.
   h. If continuity is indicated, circuit is satisfactory; continue with procedure. If not, repair harness or replace buckle switch as necessary.

3. Check outer switch circuit as follows:
   a. Disconnect outer switch harness connector.
   b. Connect ohmmeter between outer switch connector (harness side) terminal 2 and ground, then terminal 4 and ground.
   c. Ohmmeter should indicate continuity.
   d. If continuity is indicated, circuit is satisfactory; continue with procedure. If not, repair harness as necessary.
   e. Connect ohmmeter between outer switch connector (switch side) terminals 1 and 2 (left side), then between terminals 3 and 4 (right side).
   f. Observe ohmmeter while pulling out and retracting shoulder belt.
   g. With shoulder belt fully retracted to pulled out approximately half way (outer switch off), infinite ohms should be indicated.
   h. With shoulder belt pulled half way out to fully pulled out position (outer switch on), continuity should be indicated.
   i. If resistance indicated is as specified, circuit is satisfactory; continue with procedure. If not, replace shoulder belt retractor assembly.
   j. Connect shoulder belt to slide anchor (outer switch on). Connect outer switch harness connector, then disconnect control unit harness connector.
   k. Connect ohmmeter between control unit connector terminal 3 and ground, then terminal 14 and ground.
   l. Ohmmeter should indicate continuity.
   m. If continuity is indicated, circuit is satisfactory.
   n. If continuity is not indicated, repair harness as necessary.

BUCKLE SWITCH, OUTER SWITCH & DOOR SWITCH 1994 Colt, Colt Vista, Summit & Summit Wagon

1. Unplug connector from buckle switch, **Figs. 50 and 51**, then measure continuity as follows:
   a. **On Colt and Summit,** measure between buckle switch harness side connector terminal 1 and ground.
   b. **On Colt Vista and Summit Wagon,** measure between buckle switch harness side connector terminal 2 and ground.

2. If resistance is 0, circuit is satisfactory; if resistance is infinite, check for an open harness wire between buckle switch and ground or an improper ground connection and repair as necessary.

3. Connect buckle switch connector, then disconnect control unit connector and leave lap belt unfastened so that buckle switch will be on.

4. Measure continuity between control unit harness side connector terminal 2 and ground. If resistance is 0, circuit is satisfactory; if resistance is infinite, check for an open harness wire between buckle switch and control unit. Repair open wire or replace buckle switch as necessary.

5. Disconnect outer switch connector, then measure continuity as follows:
   a. **On Colt and Summit,** measure between outer switch harness side connector terminal 1 and ground.
   b. **On Colt Vista and Summit Wagon,** measure between outer switch harness side connector terminal 3 and ground.

6. If resistance is 0, circuit is satisfactory; if resistance is infinite, check for an open harness wire between outer switch and ground or an improper ground connection and repair as necessary.

7. Pull out and retract shoulder belt, then measure continuity as follows:
   a. **On Colt and Summit,** measure terminal to ground continuity at outer switch side connectors 1 and 2.
   b. **On Colt Vista and Summit Wagon,** measure terminal to ground continuity at outer switch side connectors 3 and 4.

8. Ensure resistance is infinite as belt is pulled from its fully retracted position to its approximate midpoint, then is 0 from that point to its fully extended position.

9. If results are as specified, continue with procedure; if not, replace shoulder belt retractor.

10. Attach shoulder belt to slide anchor (outer switch on), then connect outer switch connector and disconnect control unit connector.

11. Measure continuity between control unit harness side connector terminal 14 and ground. If resistance is 0, circuit is satisfactory; if not, an open may exist between control unit and outer switch. Repair harness as necessary.

12. **On Colt and Summit,** inspect door switch as follows:
    a. Disconnect control unit connector, then measure continuity between control unit harness side connector terminal 6 and ground while opening and closing driver's door.
    b. Ensure resistance is 0 when door is open and is infinite when door is closed.
    c. If results are not as specified, replace door switch, repair harness and connector or improve ground connection as necessary.

DOOR LATCH SWITCH (DRIVER'S SIDE) & FASTEN SWITCH

Colt, Colt Vista, Summit & Summit Wagon

Refer to **Figs. 52 through 55** when performing these tests.

1. Disconnect door latch switch harness connector.
2. Connect a suitable ohmmeter between door latch switch terminals 1 and 3, then terminals 2 and 3.
3. Observe ohmmeter while opening and closing door.
4. Infinite ohms should be indicated between terminals 1 and 3 when door is open, continuity should be indicated between terminals 1 and 3 when door is closed.
5. Continuity should be indicated between terminals 2 and 3 when door is open, infinite ohms should be indicated between terminals 2 and 3 when door is closed.
6. If resistance indicated is as specified, circuit is satisfactory; continue with procedure. If not, replace door latch switch.
7. Connect ohmmeter between door latch switch connector terminal 3 and ground.
8. Ohmmeter should indicate continuity.
9. If continuity is indicated, circuit is satisfactory; continue with procedure. If not, repair harness as necessary.
10. Connect door latch switch harness connector, then disconnect control unit harness connector.
11. Connect ohmmeter between control unit connector terminal 6 and ground.
12. Observe ohmmeter while opening and closing door.
13. Continuity should be indicated when door is open, infinite ohms should be indicated when door is closed.
14. If resistance indicated is as specified, circuit is satisfactory; continue with procedure. If not, repair harness as necessary.
15. If resistance indicated is not as specified, repair harness as necessary.
16. Disconnect fasten switch harness connector.
17. Connect ohmmeter between fasten switch connector terminal 1 and ground.
18. Observe ohmmeter while opening and closing door.
19. Infinite ohms should be indicated when door is open, continuity should be indicated when door is closed.
20. If resistance indicated is as specified, circuit is satisfactory; continue with procedure. If not, repair harness as necessary.
21. Connect fasten switch harness connector.
22. Connect ohmmeter between control unit connector terminal 4 and ground.
23. Close door.
24. Infinite ohms should be indicated when slide anchor is in fasten range (fasten switch Off), continuity should be indicated when slide anchor is not in fasten range (fasten switch On).
25. If resistance indicated is as specified, circuit is satisfactory.
26. If resistance is not as specified, replace motor and track assembly.

Laser & Talon

Refer to **Fig. 56** when performing these tests.

1. Disconnect door latch switch harness connector.
2. Connect a suitable ohmmeter between door latch switch terminals 1 and 3, then terminals 2 and 3.
3. Observe ohmmeter while opening and closing door.
4. Infinite ohms should be indicated between terminals 1 and 3 when door is open, continuity should be indicated between terminals 1 and 3 when door is closed.
5. Continuity should be indicated between terminals 2 and 3 when door is open, infinite ohms should be indicated between terminals 2 and 3 when door is closed.
6. If resistance indicated is as specified, circuit is satisfactory; continue with procedure. If not, replace door latch switch.
7. Connect ohmmeter between door latch switch connector terminal 3 and ground.
8. Ohmmeter should indicate continuity.
9. If continuity is indicated, circuit is satisfactory; continue with procedure. If not, repair harness as necessary.
10. Connect door latch switch harness connector, then disconnect control unit harness connector.
11. Connect ohmmeter between control unit connector terminal 6 and ground.
12. Observe ohmmeter while opening and closing door.
13. Continuity should be indicated when door is open, infinite ohms should be indicated is closed.
14. If resistance indicated is as specified, circuit is satisfactory; continue with procedure. If not, repair harness as necessary.
15. Disconnect fasten switch harness connector.
16. Connect ohmmeter between fasten switch connector terminal 6 and ground.
17. Observe ohmmeter while opening and closing door.
18. Infinite ohms should be indicated when door is open, continuity should be indicated when door is closed.
19. If resistance indicated is as specified, circuit is satisfactory; continue with procedure. If not, repair harness as necessary.
20. Connect fasten switch harness connector.
21. Connect ohmmeter between control unit connector terminal 4 and ground.
22. Close door.
23. Infinite ohms should be indicated when slide anchor is in fasten range (fasten switch Off), continuity should be indicated when slide anchor is not in fasten range (fasten switch On).
24. If resistance indicated is as specified, circuit is satisfactory.
25. If resistance is not as specified, replace motor and track assembly.

RELEASE SWITCH, DOOR LATCH SWITCH & FASTEN SWITCH (PASSENGER'S SIDE) Colt, Colt Vista, Summit & Summit Wagon

Refer to **Figs. 52 through 55** when performing these tests.

1. Disconnect door latch switch harness connector.
2. Connect a suitable ohmmeter between door latch switch terminals 1 and 3, then terminals 2 and 3.
3. Observe ohmmeter while opening and closing door.
4. Infinite ohms should be indicated between terminals 1 and 3 when door is open; continuity should be indicated between terminals 1 and 3 when door is closed.
5. Continuity should be indicated between terminals 2 and 3 when door is open; infinite ohms should be indicated between terminals 2 and 3 when door is closed.
6. If resistance indicated is as specified, circuit is satisfactory; continue with procedure. If not, replace door latch switch.
7. Connect ohmmeter between door latch switch connector terminal 3 and ground.
8. Ohmmeter should indicate continuity.
9. If continuity is indicated, circuit is satisfactory; continue with procedure. If not, repair harness as necessary.
10. If continuity is not indicated, repair harness as necessary.
11. Connect door latch switch harness connector, then disconnect release switch harness connector.
12. Connect ohmmeter between release switch connector terminal 1 and ground on Colt and Summit or between terminal 2 and ground on Colt Vista and Summit Wagon.
13. Observe ohmmeter while opening and closing door.
14. Continuity should be indicated when door is open, infinite ohms should be indicated is closed.
15. If resistance indicated is as specified, circuit is satisfactory; continue with procedure. If not, repair harness as necessary.
16. Connect release switch harness connector, then disconnect control unit harness connector.
17. Connect ohmmeter between control unit connector terminal 16 and ground on Colt and Summit or between terminal 15 and ground on Colt Vista and Summit Wagon.
18. Observe ohmmeter while opening and closing door.
19. Continuity should be indicated when door is open; infinite ohms should be indicated when door is closed.
20. If resistance indicated is as specified, circuit is satisfactory; continue with procedure. If not, repair harness or replace motor and track assembly as necessary.
21. Disconnect fasten switch harness connector.
22. Connect ohmmeter between fasten switch connector terminal 1 and ground.
23. Observe ohmmeter while opening and closing door.
24. Infinite ohms should be indicated when door is open; continuity should be indicated when door is closed.

25. If resistance indicated is as specified, circuit is satisfactory; continue with procedure. If not, repair harness as necessary.
26. Connect fasten switch harness connector.
27. Connect ohmmeter between control unit connector terminal 15 and ground on Colt and Summit or between terminal 16 and ground on Colt Vista and Summit Wagon.
28. Observe ohmmeter while opening and closing door.
29. Continuity should be indicated when door is open and slide anchor is not in fasten range (fasten switch on), infinite ohms should be indicated when door is closed and slide anchor is in fasten range (fasten switch off).
30. If resistance indicated is as specified, circuit is satisfactory.
31. If resistance is not as specified, repair harness or replace motor and track assembly as necessary.

Laser & Talon

Refer to **Fig. 56** when performing these tests.
1. Disconnect door latch switch harness connector.
2. Connect a suitable ohmmeter between door latch switch terminals 1 and 3, then terminals 2 and 3.
3. Observe ohmmeter while opening and closing door.
4. Infinite ohms should be indicated between terminals 1 and 3 when door is open, continuity should be indicated between terminals 1 and 3 when door is closed.
5. Continuity should be indicated between terminals 2 and 3 when door is open, infinite ohms should be indicated between terminals 2 and 3 when door is closed.
6. If resistance indicated is as specified, circuit is satisfactory; continue with procedure. If not, replace door latch switch.
7. Connect ohmmeter between door latch switch connector terminal 3 and ground.
8. Ohmmeter should indicate continuity.
9. If continuity is indicated, circuit is satisfactory; continue with procedure. If not, repair harness as necessary.
10. Connect door latch switch harness connector, then disconnect release switch harness connector.
11. Connect ohmmeter between release switch connector terminal 1 and ground.
12. Observe ohmmeter while opening and closing door.
13. Continuity should be indicated when door is open, infinite ohms should be indicated is closed.
14. If resistance indicated is as specified, circuit is satisfactory; continue with procedure. If not, repair harness as necessary.
15. Connect release switch harness connector, then disconnect control unit harness connector.
16. Connect ohmmeter between control unit connector terminal 16 and ground.

17. Observe ohmmeter while opening and closing door.
18. Continuity should be indicated when door is open, infinite ohms should be indicated when door is closed.
19. If resistance indicated is as specified, circuit is satisfactory; continue with procedure. If not, repair harness or replace motor and track assembly as necessary.
20. Disconnect fasten switch harness connector.
21. Connect ohmmeter between fasten switch connector terminal 6 and ground.
22. Observe ohmmeter while opening and closing door.
23. Infinite ohms should be indicated when door is open, continuity should be indicated when door is closed.
24. If resistance indicated is as specified, circuit is satisfactory; continue with procedure. If not, repair harness as necessary.
25. Connect fasten switch harness connector.
26. Connect ohmmeter between control unit connector terminal 15 and ground.
27. Observe ohmmeter while opening and closing door.
28. Continuity should be indicated when door is open and slide anchor is not in fasten range (fasten switch on), infinite ohms should be indicated when door is closed and slide anchor is in fasten range (fasten switch off).
29. If resistance indicated is as specified, circuit is satisfactory.
30. If resistance is not as specified, repair harness or replace motor and track assembly as necessary.

COMPONENT TESTING
MOTOR

1. Disconnect the automatic seat belt motor relay connector.
2. Connect the terminals of the automatic seat belt wiring harness connector to the battery as shown in **Fig. 57.** Ensure motor operates smoothly.
3. Reverse the polarity and ensure motor operates smoothly in reverse position.

RELEASE SWITCH
Colt, Colt Vista, Summit & Summit Wagon

1. Remove the release switch.
2. Using a suitable ohmmeter, check for continuity between switch terminals, **Fig. 58.**
3. Continuity should be present with switch knob released and no continuity should be present with the knob pushed in.

RELEASE & FASTEN SWITCH
Laser & Talon

1. Remove release and fasten switch.
2. Check for continuity between terminals 1 and 2, then between terminals 4 and 6, **Fig. 59.**

3. If continuity does not exists for either switch, replace the release and fasten switch.

FASTEN SWITCH
Colt, Colt Vista, Summit & Summit Wagon

1. Remove the fasten switch.
2. Using a suitable ohmmeter, check for continuity between switch terminals 1 and 2 on 1992 Colt and Summit, between terminals 4 and 6 on Colt Vista and Summit Wagon or between terminals 1 and 5 on 1993-94 Colt and Summit, **Figs. 60 and 61.**
3. Continuity should be present with switch knob released and no continuity should be present with the knob pushed in.

SEAT BELT MOTOR RELAY

1. Remove the relay.
2. Using a suitable ohmmeter, check for continuity between switch terminals as shown, **Fig. 62.**

OUTER SWITCH

1. Disconnect the outer switch connector.
2. Pull the shoulder belt out farther than its midpoint.
3. Using a suitable ohmmeter, check continuity as shown, **Fig. 63.**
4. Continuity should be present with the belt pulled out past its midpoint.
5. No continuity should be present when belt is pulled out less then its midpoint.

BUCKLE SWITCH

1. Disconnect the buckle switch connector.
2. Using a suitable ohmmeter, check continuity between terminals of connector.
3. Continuity should be present with the buckle unlocked; no continuity should be present when the buckle is locked.

DOOR LATCH SWITCH
Colt Vista & Summit Wagon

Check for continuity as shown in **Fig. 64.** If not as specified, replace switch.

Monaco & Premier
SYSTEM TESTING

Refer to passive belt system wiring diagram, **Fig. 3,** when diagnosing the automatic seat belt system.

To perform testing of the automatic seat belt system, the use of a DRBII readout box or equivalent is required to obtain system diagnostic trouble codes. Follow tool manufacturer's instructions for installation and operation of readout box.

Refer to **Figs. 65 through 94** for component location, connector location, terminal identification and diagnostic flow charts.

COMPONENT TESTING
Carrier Switches

1. Using suitable volt/ohmmeter, check resistance at open switch position at cavity 27 (LH side, carrier front position switch circuit), and 28 (rear position), **Fig. 3.** Resistance should be greater than 3,000 ohms.
2. Check resistance at open switch position at cavity 21 (RH side, carrier front position switch circuit), and 4 (rear position). Resistance should be greater than 3,000 ohms.

3. Check resistance at closed switch position at cavity 27 (RH side, carrier front position switch circuit), and 28 (rear position). Resistance should be less than 100 ohms.
4. Check resistance at closed switch position at cavity 21 (RH side, carrier front position switch circuit), and 4 (rear position). Resistance should be less than 100 ohms.
5. Ensure voltage is concurrent with **Fig. 95.**

Shoulder Belt Retractor Switches

1. Using suitable volt/ohmmeter, check resistance in open switch of RH switch at cavity 6 and LH switch at cavity 5, **Fig. 3.** Resistance should be more than 3,000 ohms.
2. Check resistance in closed switch of RH switch at cavity 6 and LH switch at cavity 5, **Fig. 3.** Resistance should be less than 40 ohms.
3. Ensure voltage is concurrent with **Fig. 96.**

Continued on page 16-57

DIAGNOSTIC CHART INDEX

Test	Code	Description	Page No. 16-	Fig. No.
ACCLAIM, LEBARON SEDAN, SHADOW, SPIRIT & SUNDANCE				
Test 1A	—	Testing System Function	20	8
Test 2A	—	Repairing A Blank DRB Screen	20	9
Test 3A	—	Repairing A No Response From PBCM	20	10
Test 4A	—	Passive Belt Control Module Codes	21	11
Test 5A	—	Repairing Seat Belt Switch Sense Circuit For Short	21	12
Test 6A	—	Repairing Passenger Seat Belt Sense Circuit For Open	21	13
Test 7A	—	Repairing Seat Belt Lamp Driver Circuit	22	14
Test 8A	—	Repairing Lamp Test Failure	22	15
Test 9A	—	Repairing Vehicle Speed Sensor Signal Circuit Input	22	16
Test 10A	—	Repairing Passenger's Side Time Limit Exceeded	23	17
Test 11A	—	Repairing Passenger A & B-Pillar Switch Open	23	18
Test 12A	—	Repairing Carrier Not Seen At Passenger A-Pillar	24	19
Test 13A	—	Repairing Carrier Not Seen At Passenger B-Pillar	24	20
Test 14A	—	Repairing Right Front Door Jamb Switch Sense Circuit	24	21
Test VER-1	—	Passive Belt System Verification Test	25	22
MONACO & PREMIER				
Test 1A	—	Passive Restraint System Functional Test	47	71
Test 2A	403	Speed Sensor Not Seen	48	72
Test 3A	405	Driver Door Switch Closed	48	73
Test 4A	406	Driver Door Switch Open	48	74
Test 5A	407	Driver Forward Station Seen	49	75
Test 5B	407	Diagnosing Relays & Wiring	49	76
Test 5C	407	Diagnosing Relays & Wiring	50	77
Test 6A	408	Driver Forward Station Not Seen	50	78
Test 7A	409	Driver Rear Station Seen	50	79
Test 7B	409	Diagnosing Relays & Wiring	51	80
Test 7C	409	Diagnosing Relays & Wiring	52	81
Test 8A	410	Driver Rear Station Not Seen	52	82
Test 9A	411	Driver Belt On Carriage Seen	52	83
Test 10A	412	Driver Belt On Carriage Not Seen	52	84
Test 11A	413	Passenger Door Switch Closed	53	85
Test 12A	414	Passenger Door Switch Open	53	86
Test 13A	415	Passenger Forward Station Seen	53	87
Test 13B	415	Diagnosing Relays & Wiring	54	88
Test 13C	415	Diagnosing Relays & Wiring	54	89
Test 14A	416	Passenger Forward Station Not Seen	55	90
Test 15A	417	Passenger Rear Station Seen	55	91
Test 15B	417	Diagnosing Relays & Wiring	55	92
Test 15C	417	Diagnosing Relays & Wiring	56	93
Test 16A	418	Passenger Rear Station Not Seen	56	94

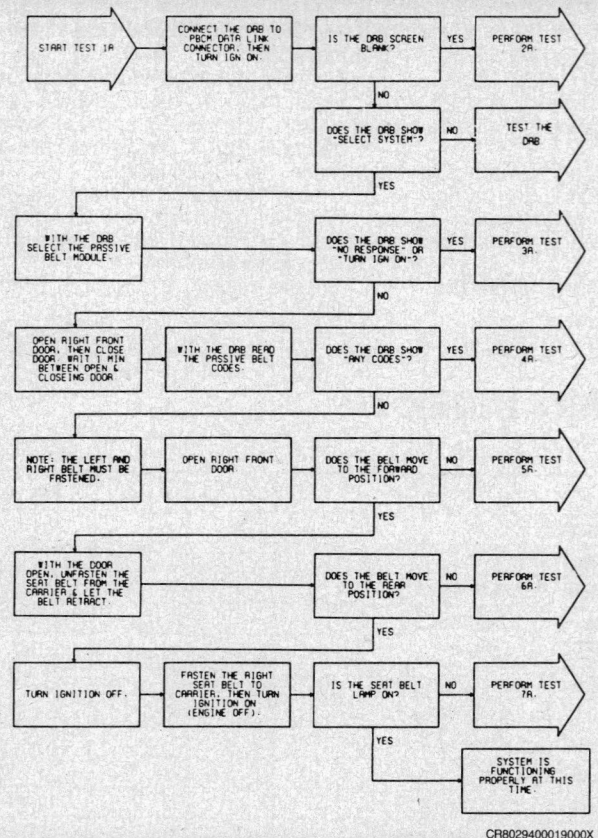

Fig. 8   Test 1A: Testing System Function. Acclaim, LeBaron Sedan, Shadow, Spirit & Sundance

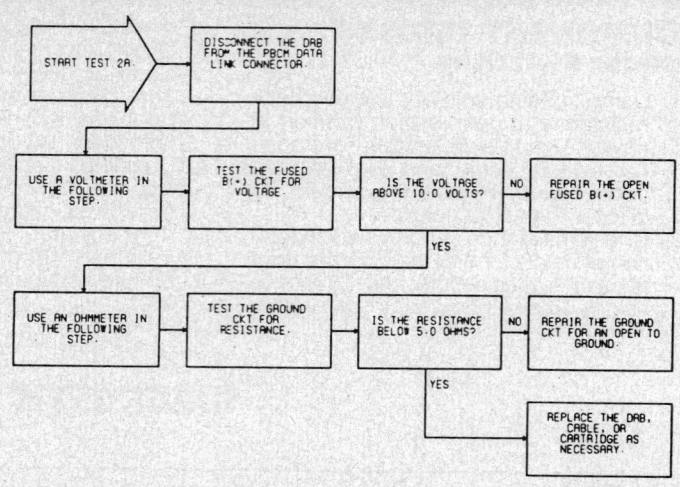

Fig. 9   Test 2A: Repairing A Blank DRB Screen. Acclaim, LeBaron Sedan, Shadow, Spirit & Sundance

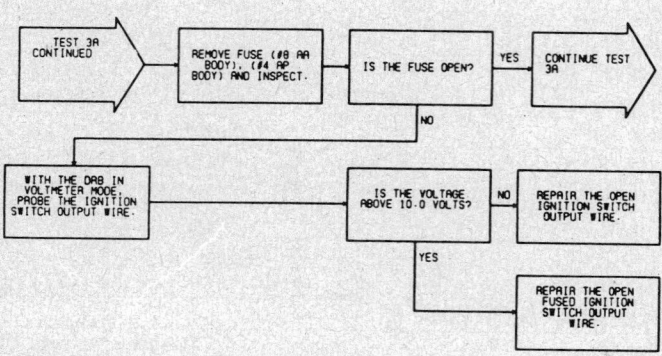

Fig. 10   Test 3A: Repairing A No Response From PBCM (Part 2 of 3). Acclaim, LeBaron Sedan, Shadow, Spirit & Sundance

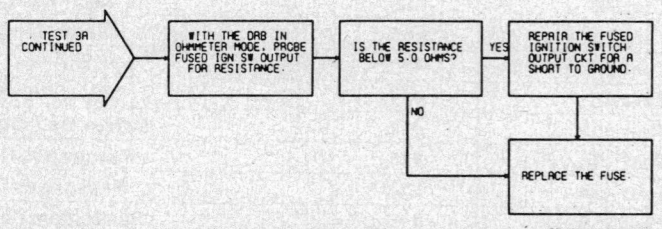

Fig. 10   Test 3A: Repairing A No Response From PBCM (Part 3 of 3). Acclaim, LeBaron Sedan, Shadow, Spirit & Sundance

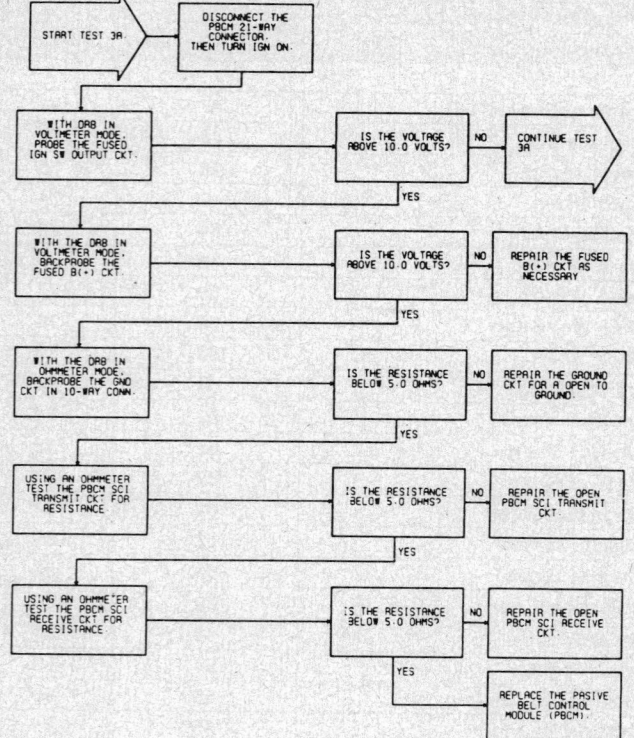

Fig. 10   Test 3A: Repairing A No Response From PBCM (Part 1 of 3). Acclaim, LeBaron Sedan, Shadow, Spirit & Sundance

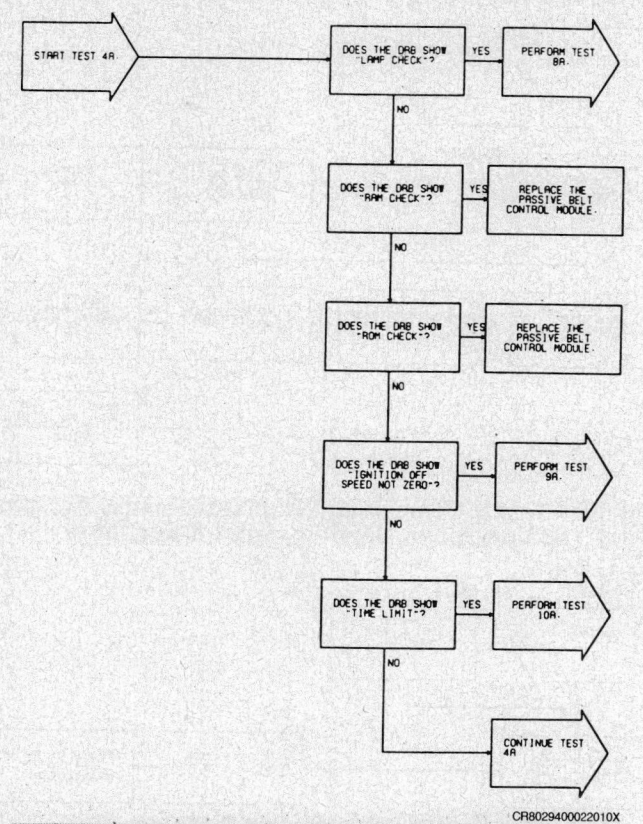

Fig. 11   Test 4A: Passive Belt Control Module Codes (Part 1 of 2). Acclaim, LeBaron Sedan, Shadow, Spirit & Sundance

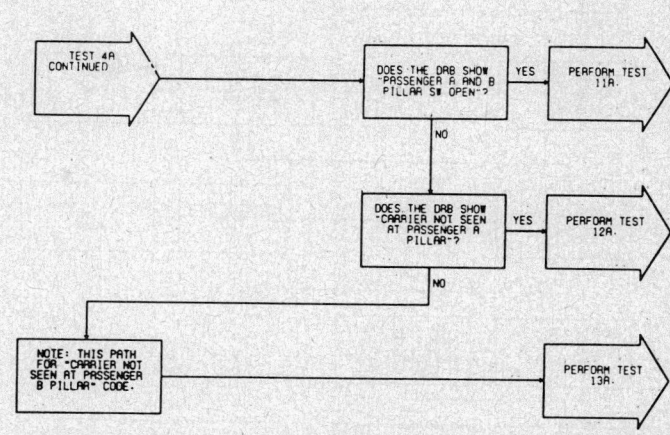

Fig. 11   Test 4A: Passive Belt Control Module Codes (Part 2 of 2). Acclaim, LeBaron Sedan, Shadow, Spirit & Sundance

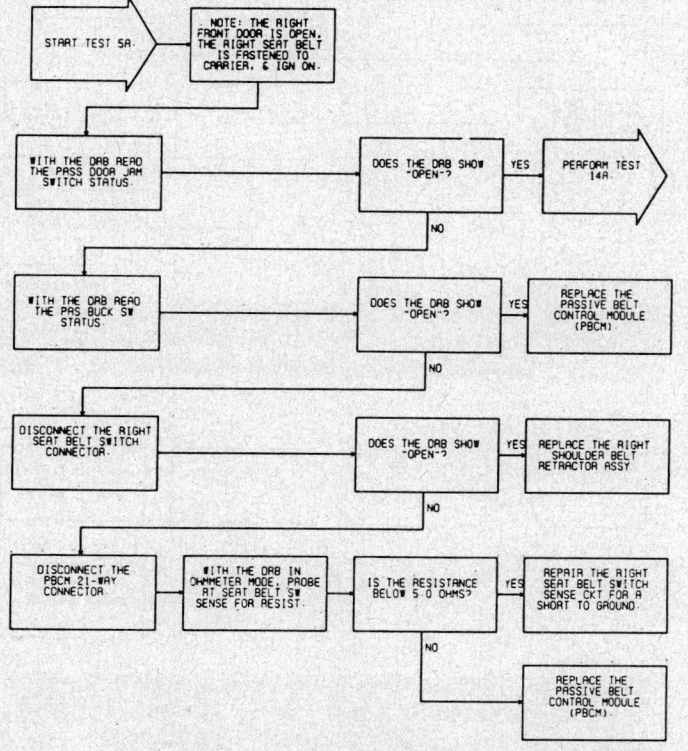

Fig. 12   Test 5A: Repairing Seat Belt Switch Sense Circuit For Short. Acclaim, LeBaron Sedan, Shadow, Spirit & Sundance

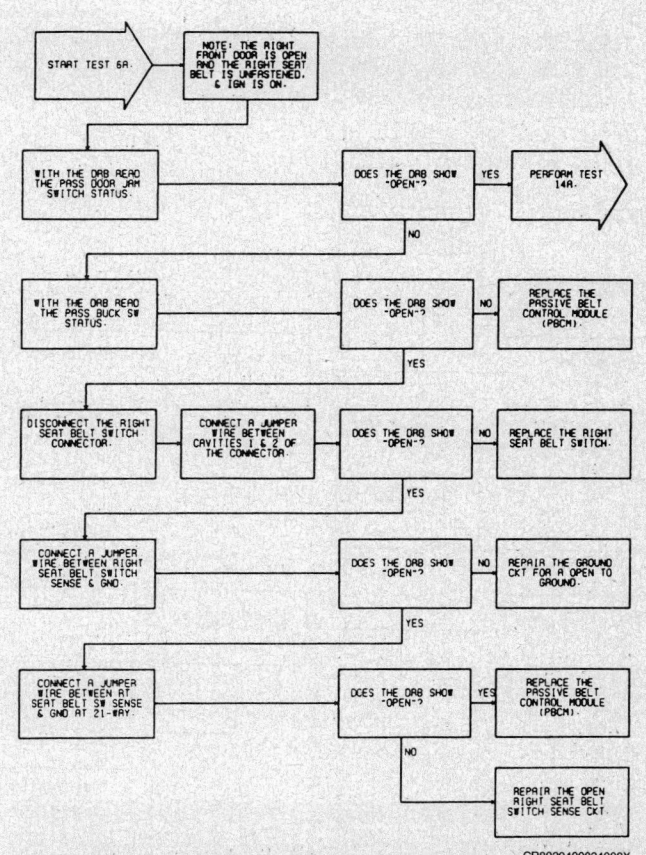

Fig. 13   Test 6A: Repairing Passenger Seat Belt Sense Circuit For Open. Acclaim, LeBaron Sedan, Shadow, Spirit & Sundance

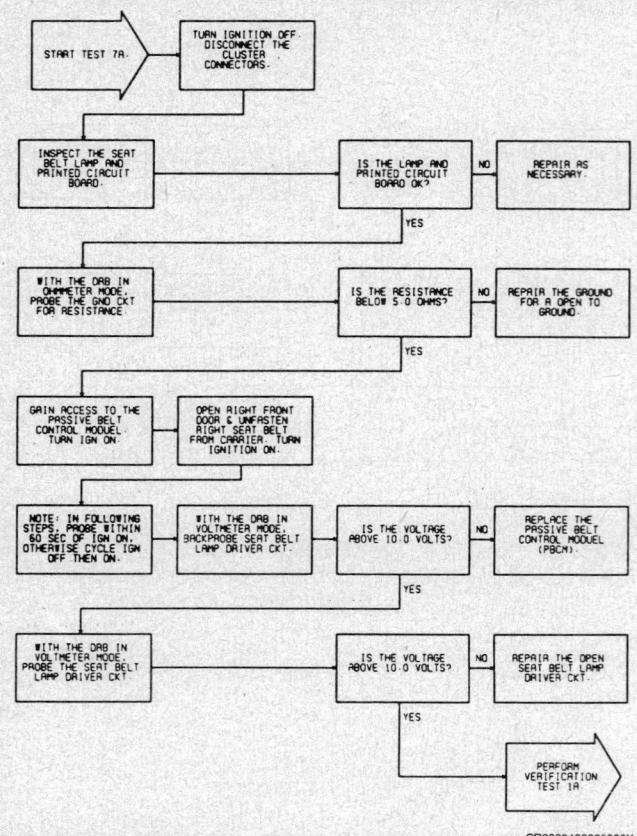

Fig. 14   Test 7A: Repairing Seat Belt Lamp Driver Circuit. Acclaim, LeBaron Sedan, Shadow, Spirit & Sundance

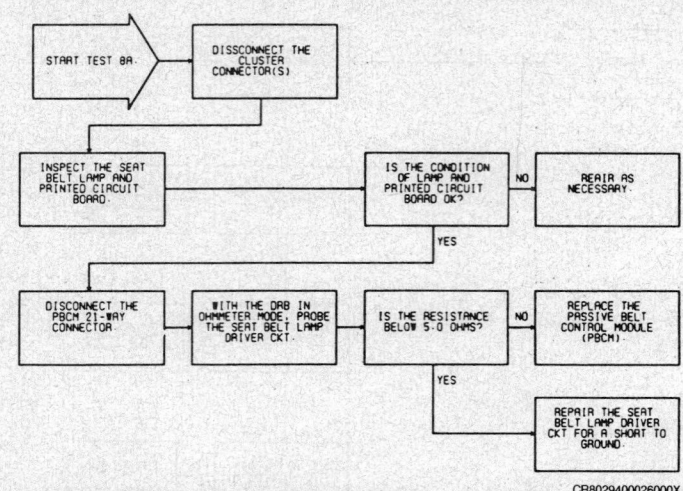

Fig. 15   Test 8A: Repairing Lamp Test Failure. Acclaim, LeBaron Sedan, Shadow, Spirit & Sundance

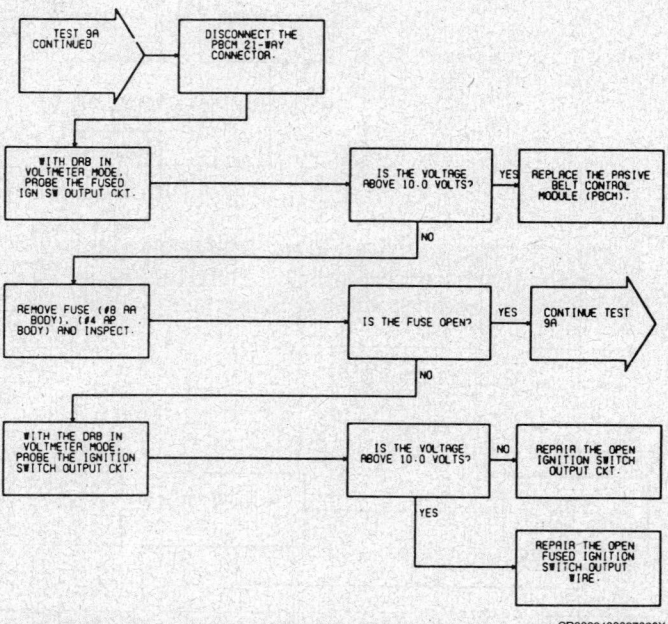

Fig. 16   Test 9A: Repairing Vehicle Speed Sensor Signal Circuit Input (Part 2 of 3). Acclaim, LeBaron Sedan, Shadow, Spirit & Sundance

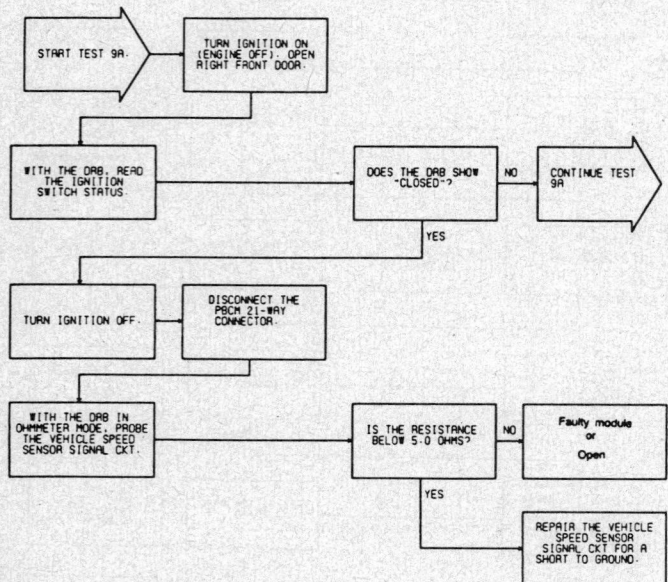

Fig. 16   Test 9A: Repairing Vehicle Speed Sensor Signal Circuit Input (Part 1 of 3). Acclaim, LeBaron Sedan, Shadow, Spirit & Sundance

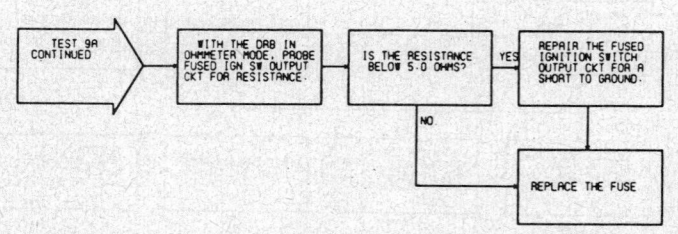

Fig. 16   Test 9A: Repairing Vehicle Speed Sensor Signal Circuit Input (Part 3 of 3). Acclaim, LeBaron Sedan, Shadow, Spirit & Sundance

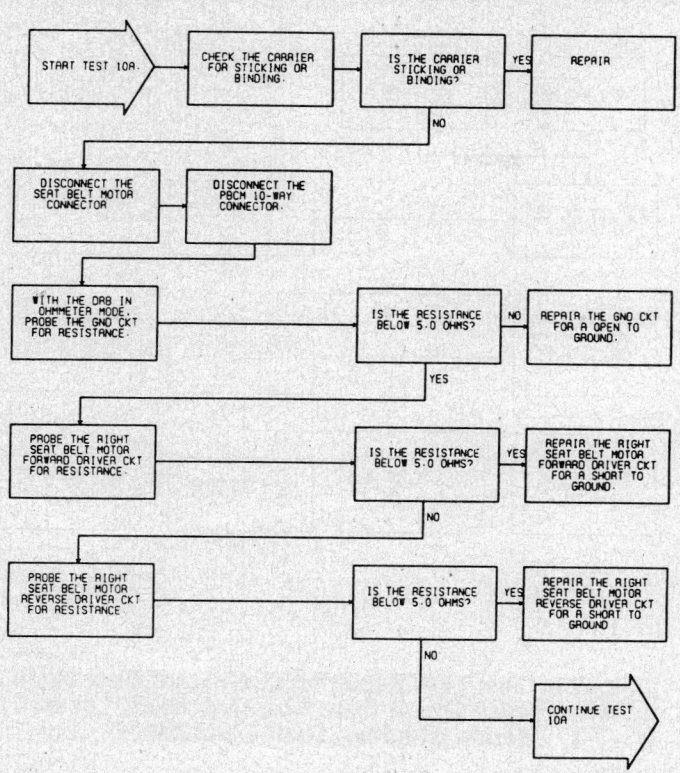

CR8029400028010X

Fig. 17 Test 10A: Repairing Passenger's Side Time Limit Exceeded (Part 1 of 3). Acclaim, LeBaron Sedan, Shadow, Spirit & Sundance

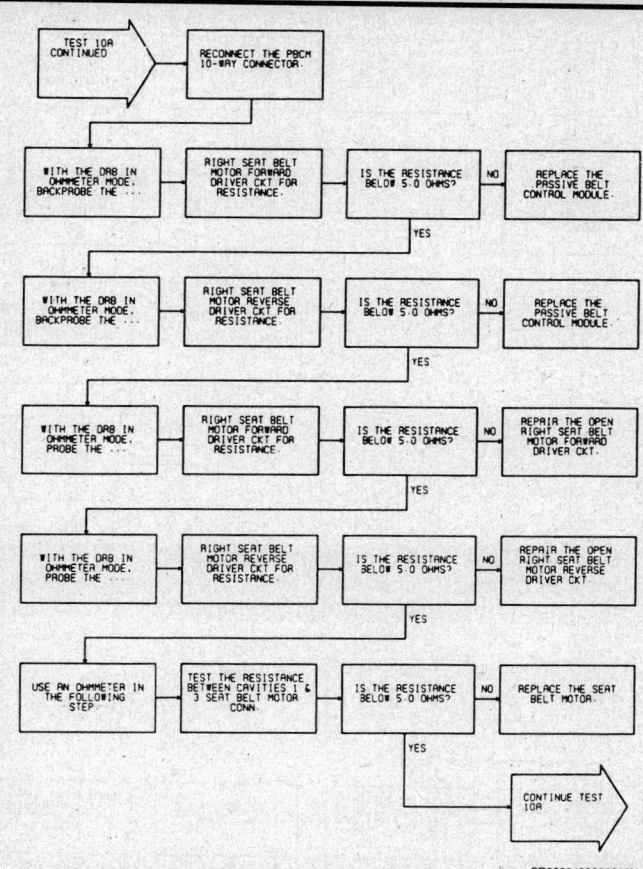

CR8029400028020X

Fig. 17 Test 10A: Repairing Passenger's Side Time Limit Exceeded (Part 2 of 3). Acclaim, LeBaron Sedan, Shadow, Spirit & Sundance

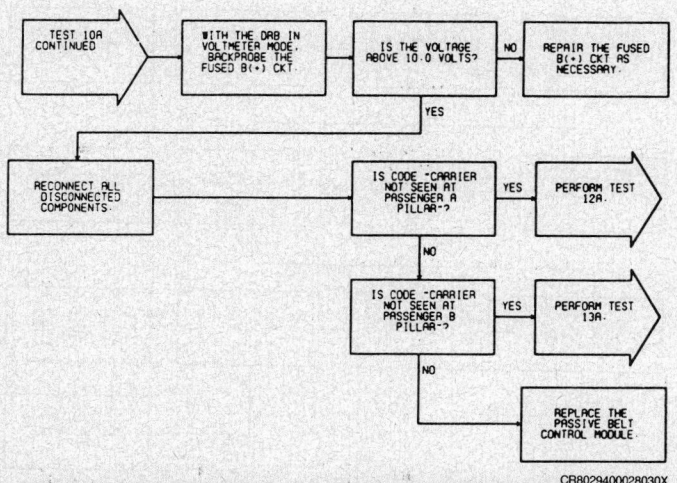

CR8029400028030X

Fig. 17 Test 10A: Repairing Passenger's Side Time Limit Exceeded (Part 3 of 3). Acclaim, LeBaron Sedan, Shadow, Spirit & Sundance

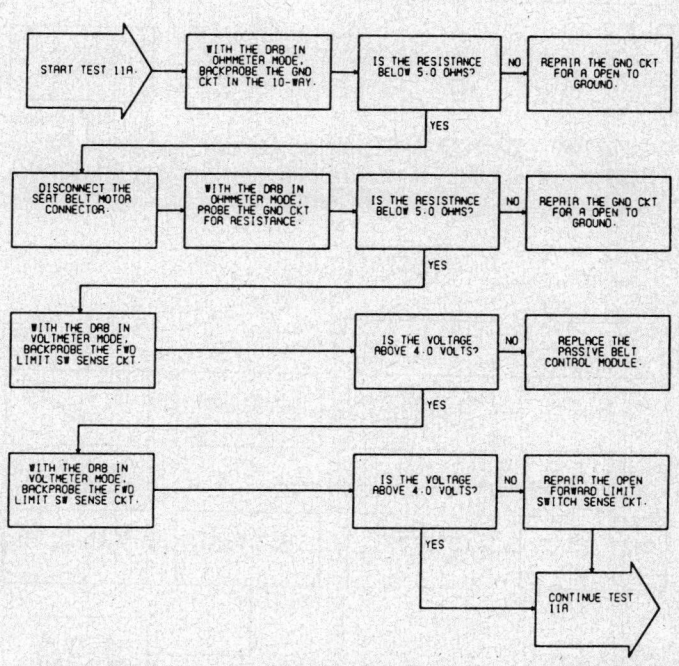

CR8029400029010X

Fig. 18 Test 11A: Repairing Passenger A & B-Pillar Switch Open (Part 1 of 2). Acclaim, LeBaron Sedan, Shadow, Spirit & Sundance

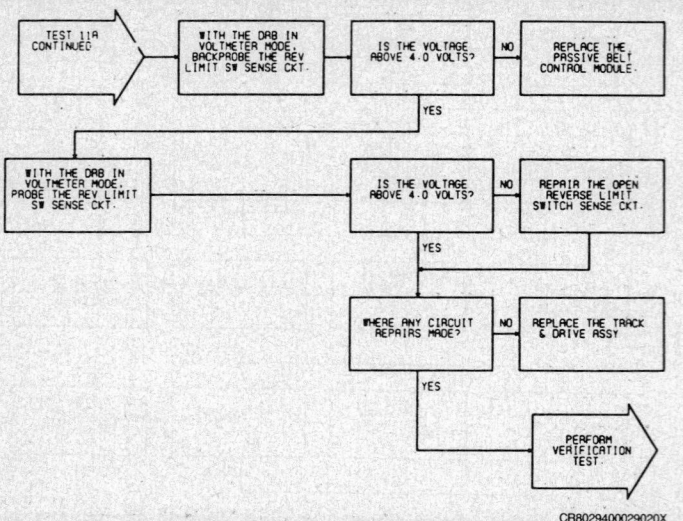

Fig. 18 Test 11A: Repairing Passenger A & B-Pillar Switch Open (Part 2 of 2). Acclaim, LeBaron Sedan, Shadow, Spirit & Sundance

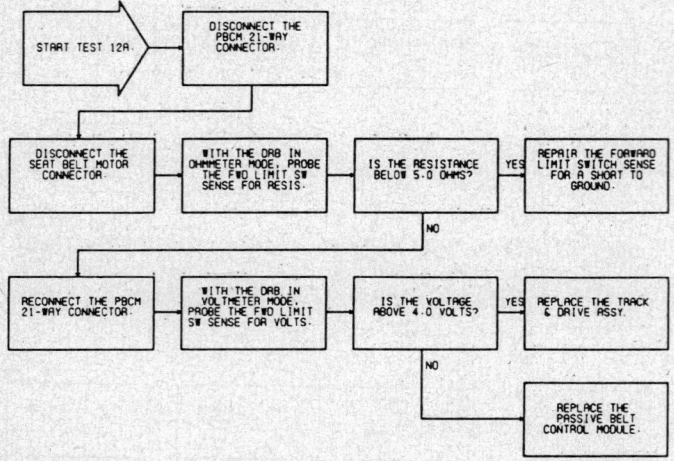

Fig. 19 Test 12A: Repairing Carrier Not Seen At Passenger A-Pillar. Acclaim, LeBaron Sedan, Shadow, Spirit & Sundance

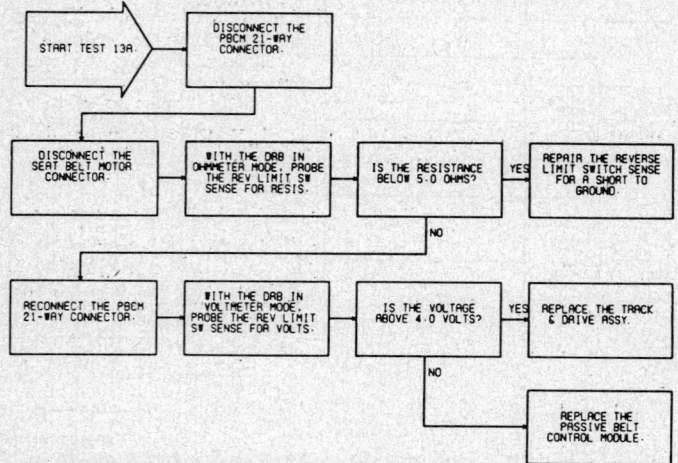

Fig. 20 Test 13A: Repairing Carrier Not Seen At Passenger B-Pillar. Acclaim, LeBaron Sedan, Shadow, Spirit & Sundance

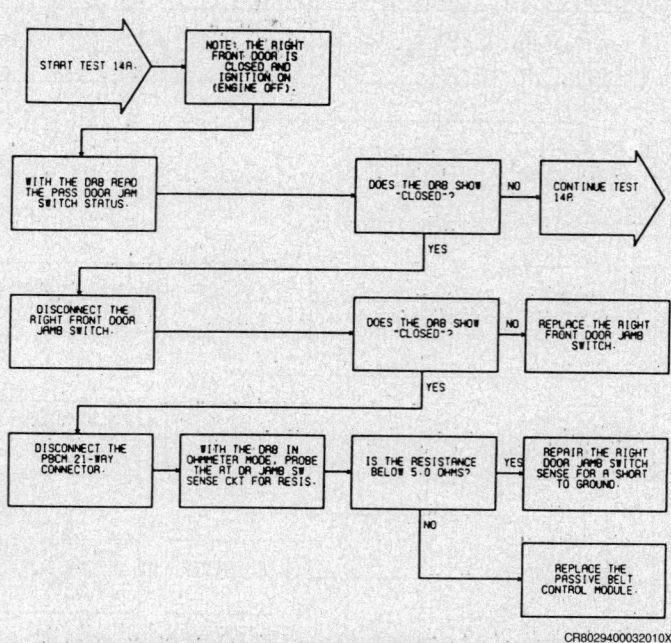

Fig. 21 Test 14A: Repairing Right Front Door Jamb Switch Sense Circuit (Part 1 of 2). Acclaim, LeBaron Sedan, Shadow, Spirit & Sundance

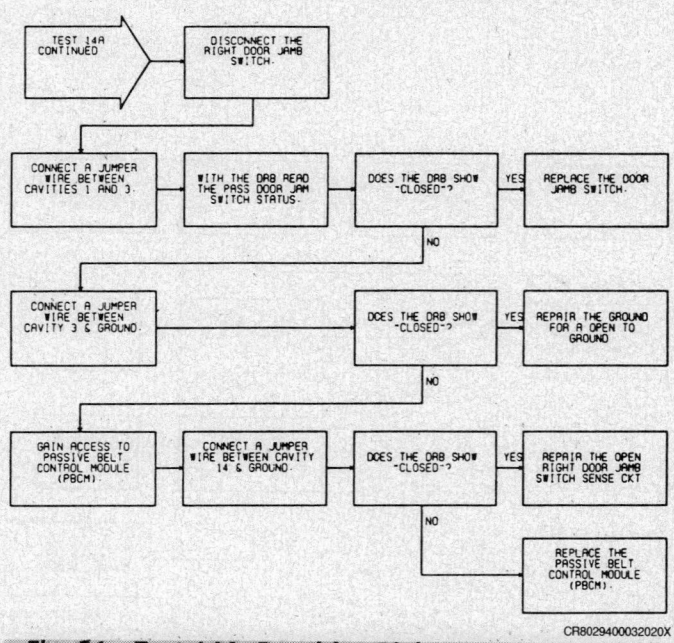

Fig. 21 Test 14A: Repairing Right Front Door Jamb Switch Sense Circuit (Part 2 of 2). Acclaim, LeBaron Sedan, Shadow, Spirit & Sundance

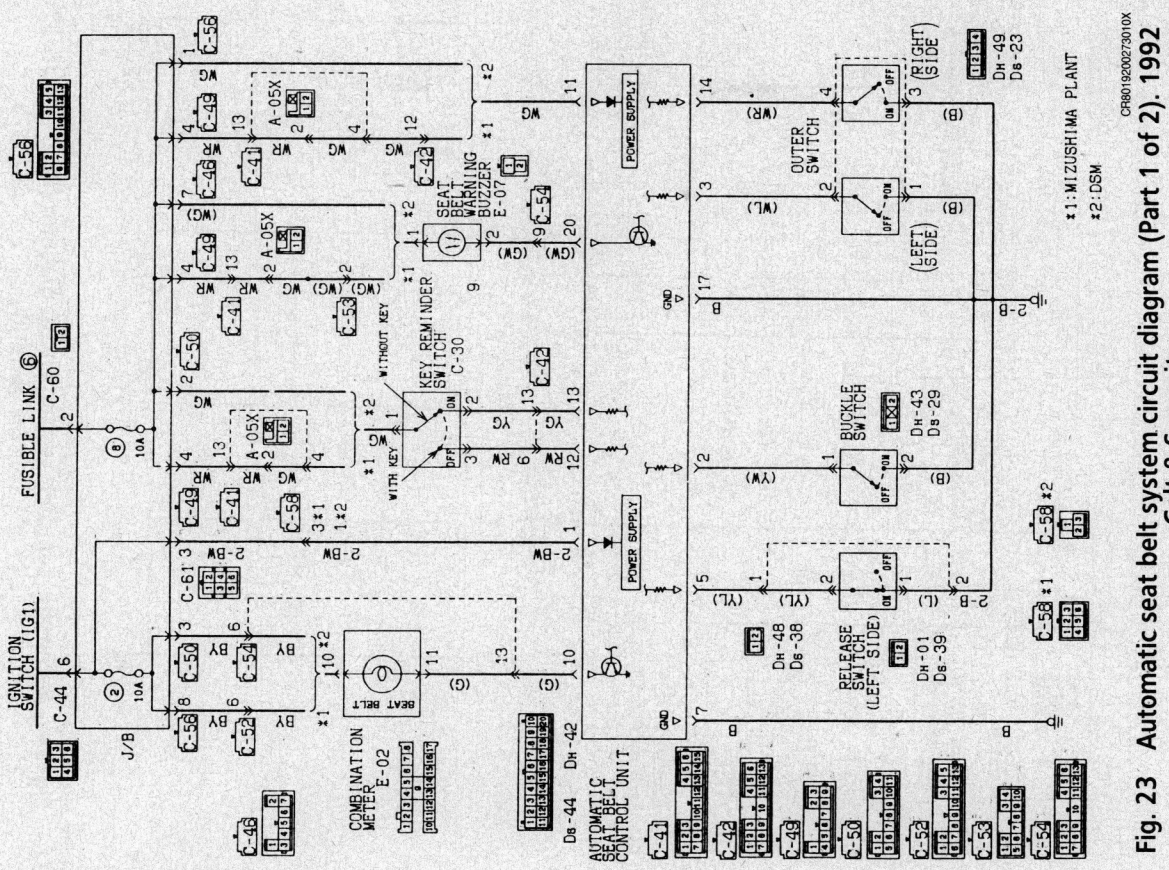

Fig. 23 Automatic seat belt system circuit diagram (Part 1 of 2). 1992 Colt & Summit

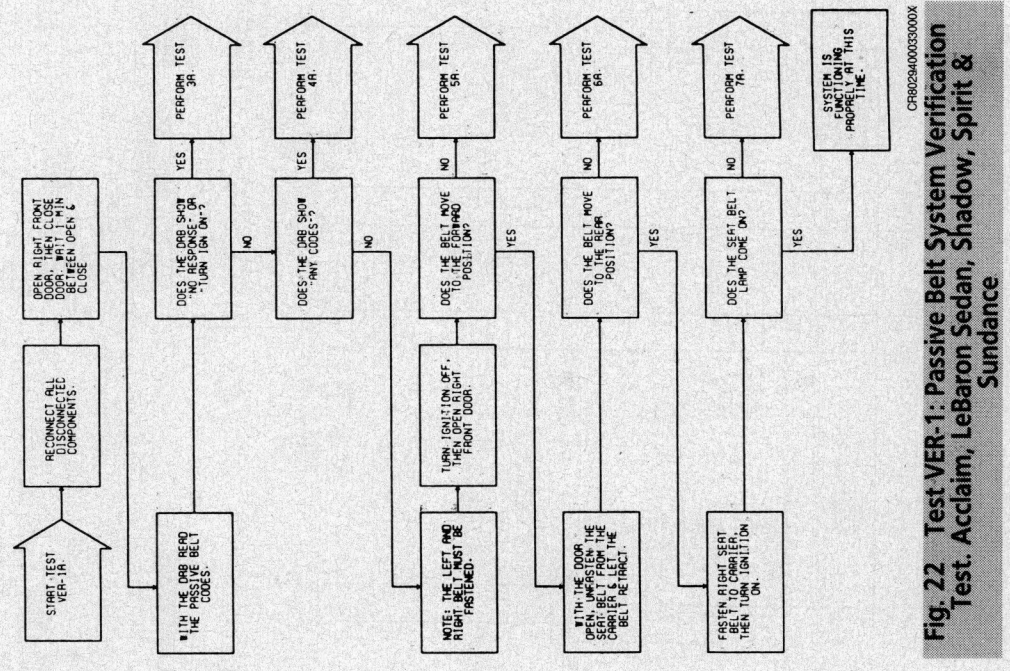

Fig. 22 Test VER-1: Passive Belt System Verification Test. Acclaim, LeBaron Sedan, Shadow, Spirit & Sundance

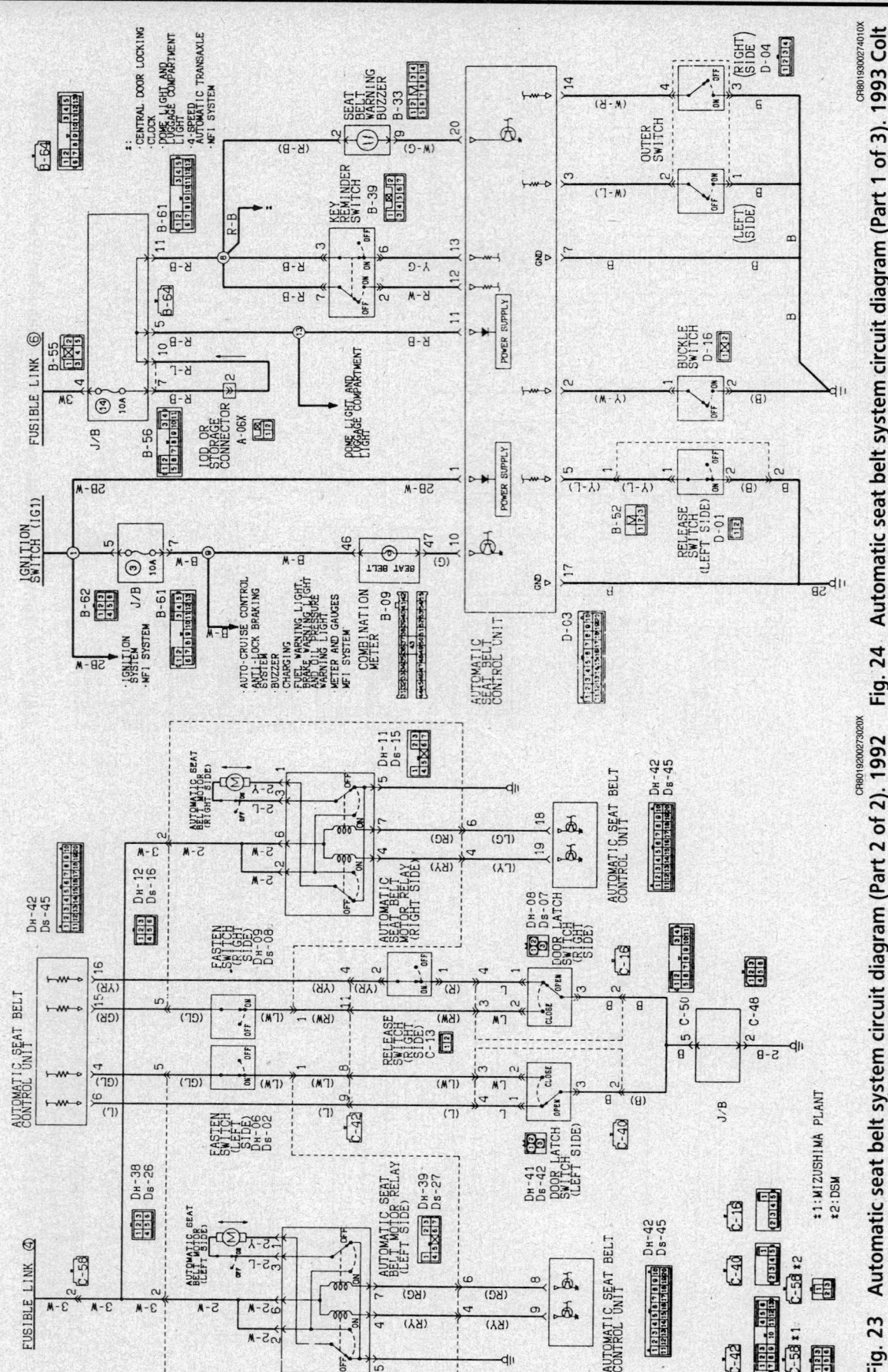

Fig. 24 Automatic seat belt system circuit diagram (Part 1 of 3). 1993 Colt & Summit

Fig. 23 Automatic seat belt system circuit diagram (Part 2 of 2). 1992 Colt & Summit

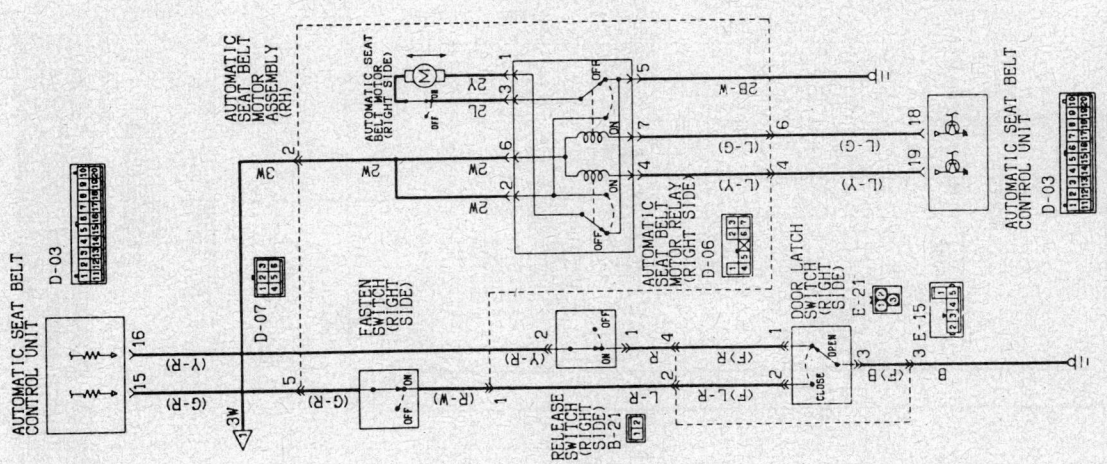

Fig. 24 Automatic seat belt system circuit diagram (Part 3 of 3). 1993 Colt & Summit

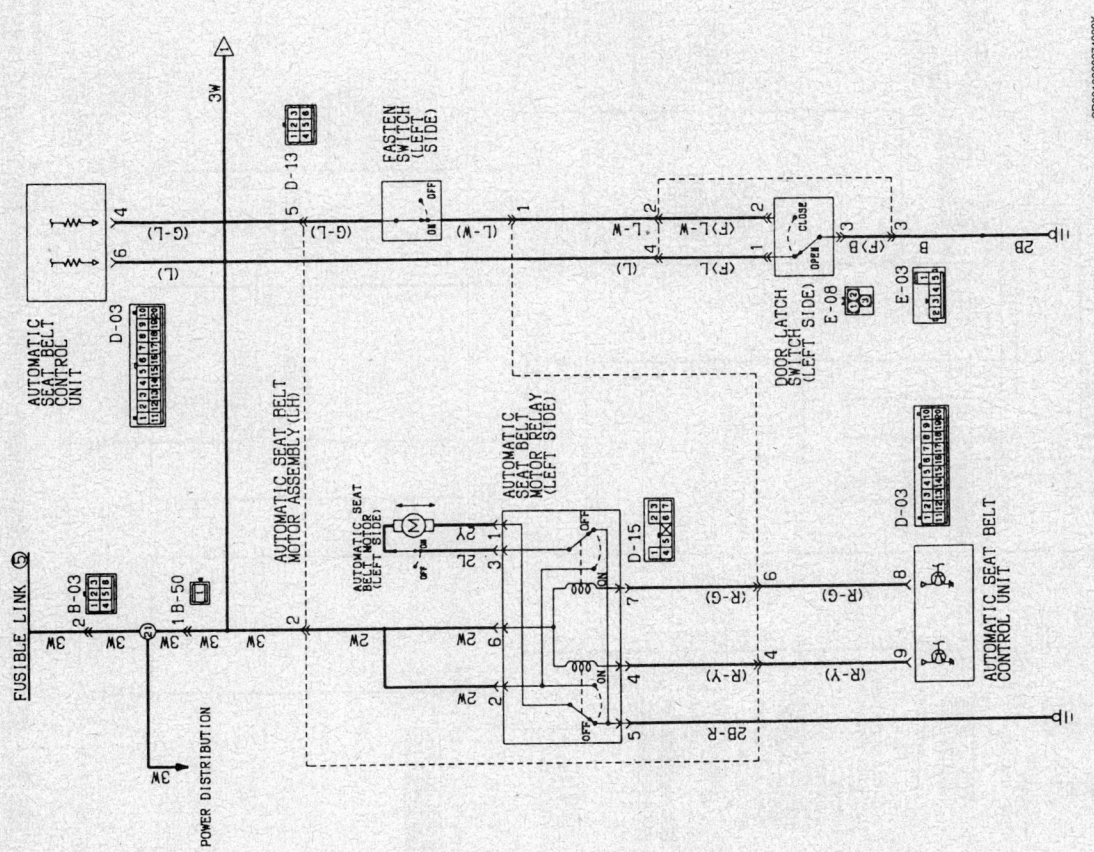

Fig. 24 Automatic seat belt system circuit diagram (Part 2 of 3). 1993 Colt & Summit

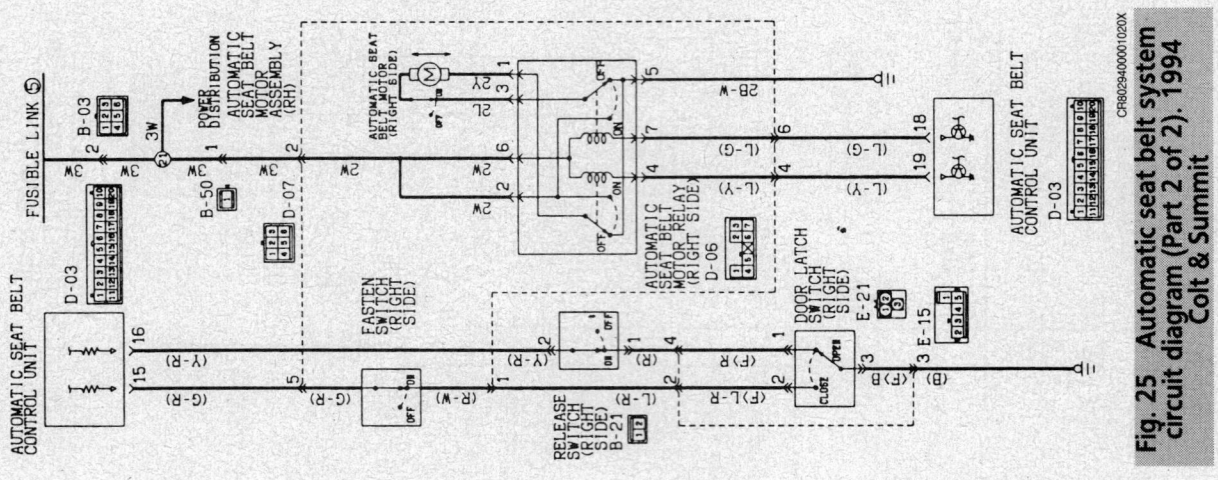

Fig. 25 Automatic seat belt system circuit diagram (Part 2 of 2). 1994 Colt & Summit

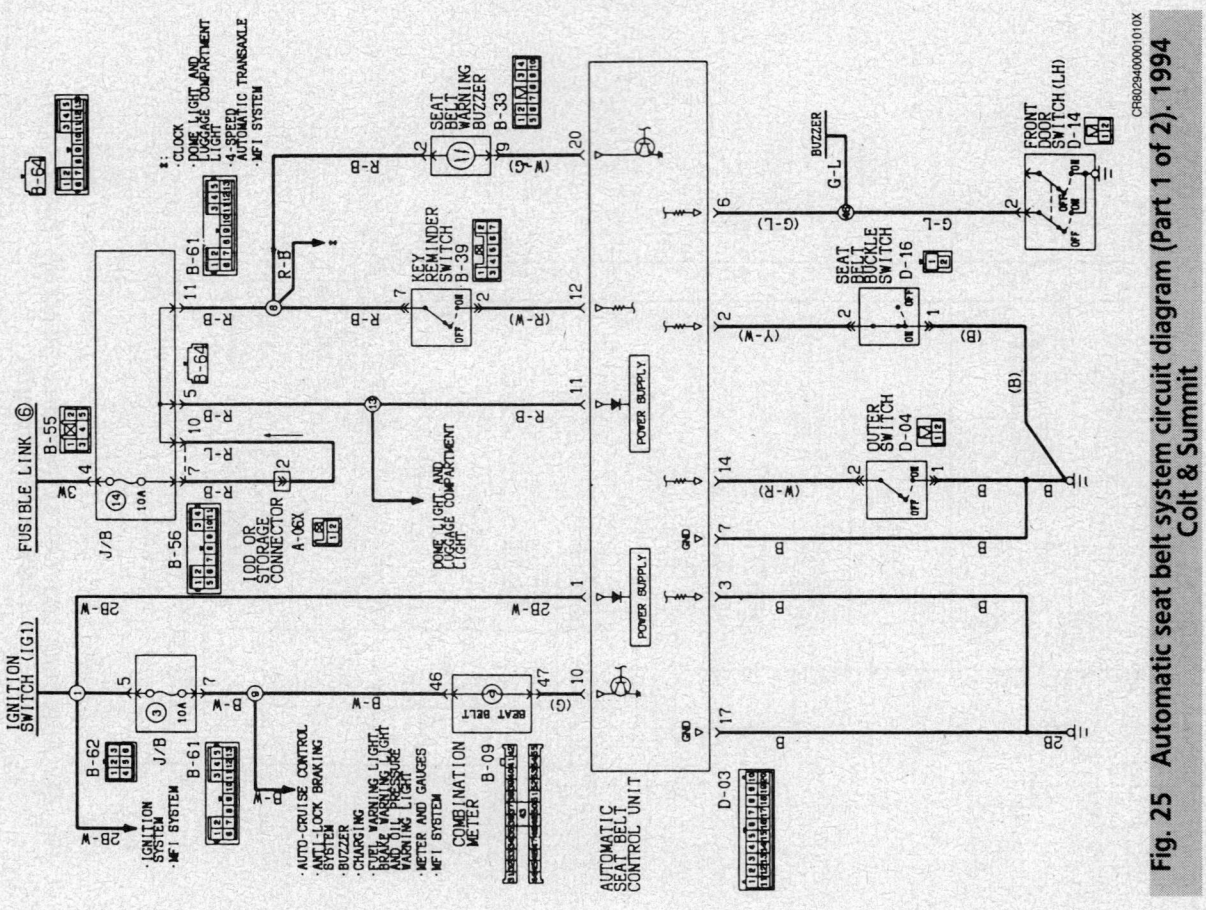

Fig. 25 Automatic seat belt system circuit diagram (Part 1 of 2). 1994 Colt & Summit

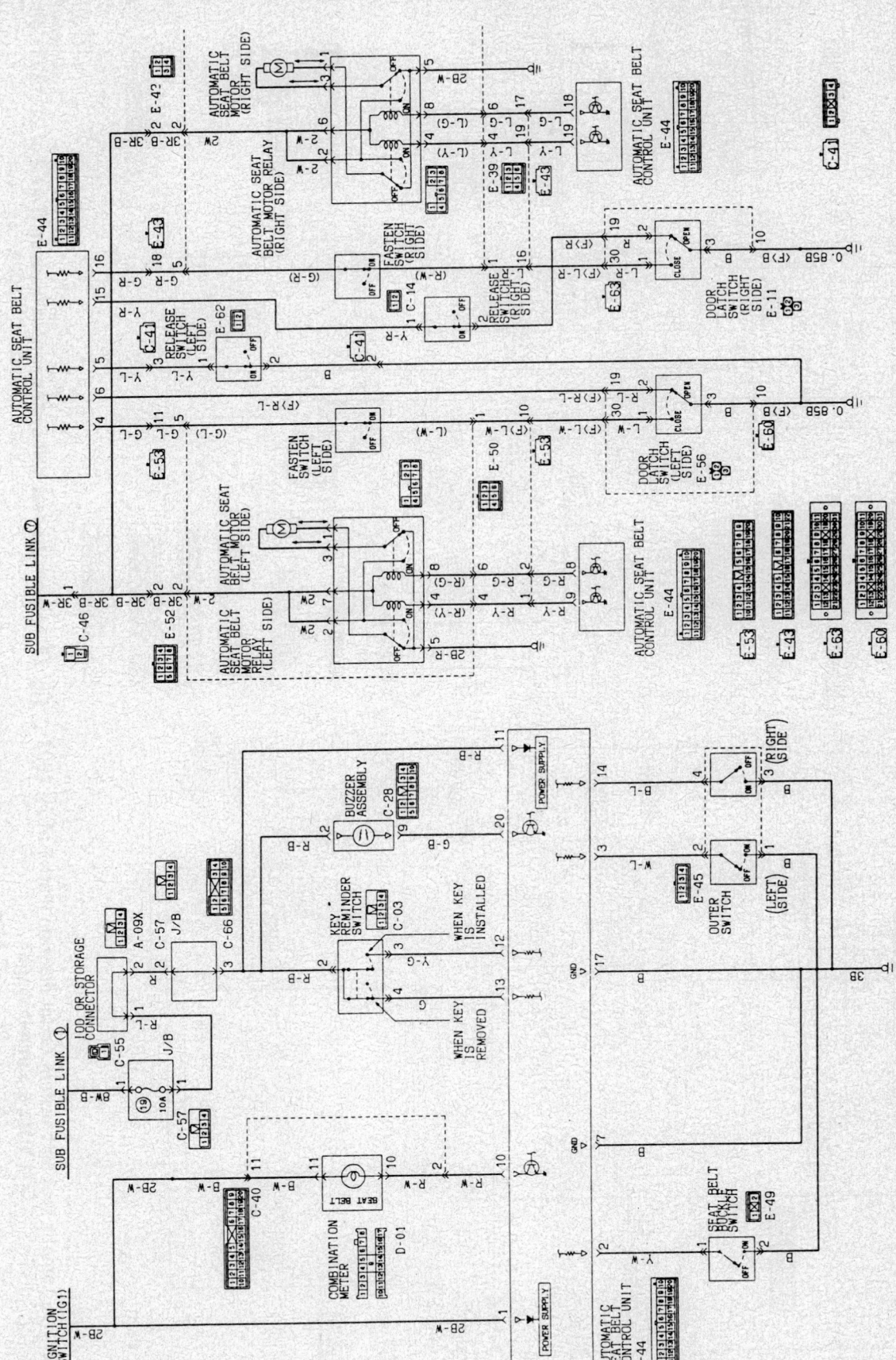

Fig. 26 Automatic seat belt system circuit diagram (Part 2 of 2). 1992 Colt Vista & Summit Wagon

Fig. 26 Automatic seat belt system circuit diagram (Part 1 of 2). 1992 Colt Vista & Summit Wagon

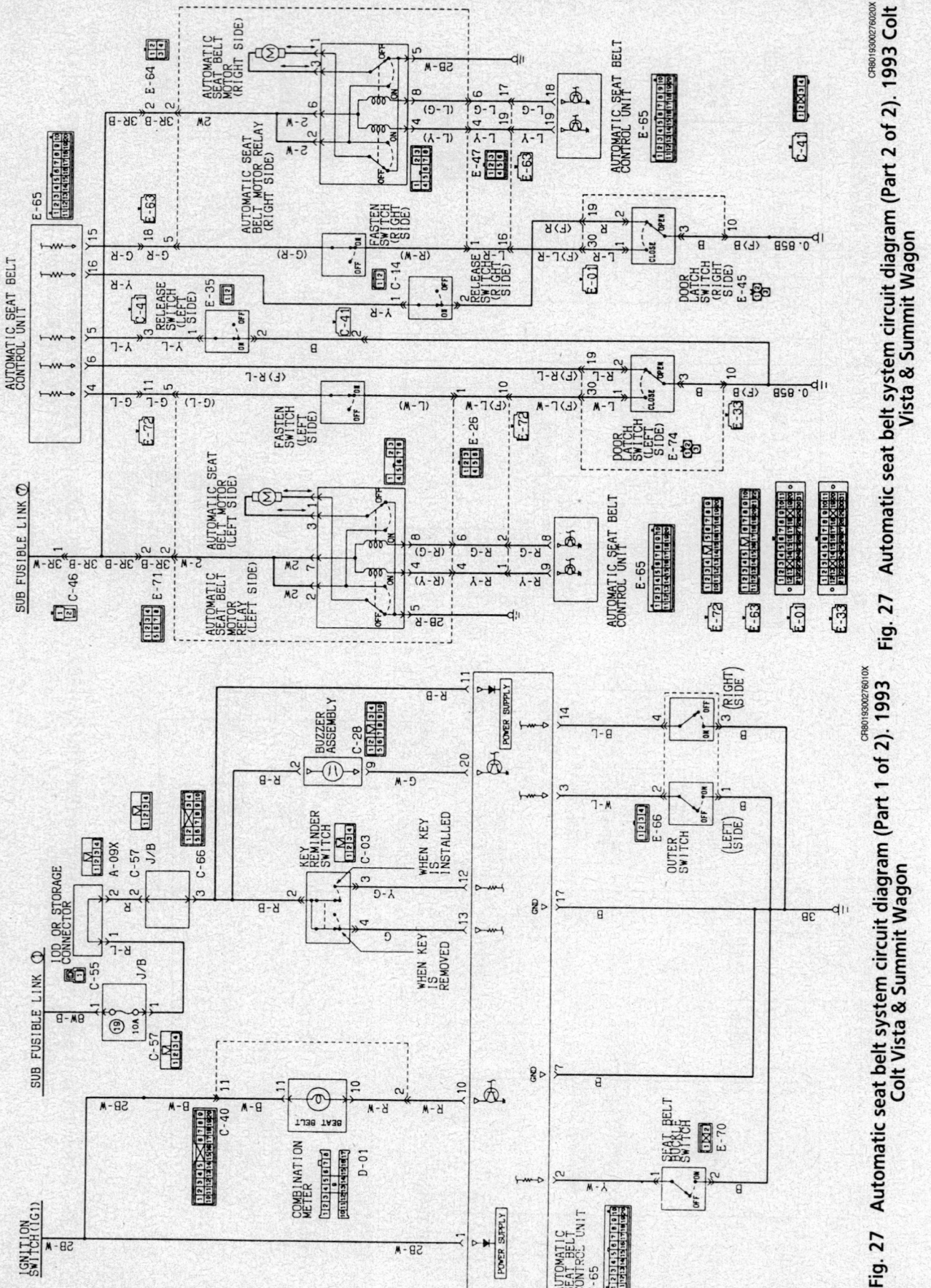

Fig. 27 Automatic seat belt system circuit diagram (Part 2 of 2). 1993 Colt Vista & Summit Wagon

Fig. 27 Automatic seat belt system circuit diagram (Part 1 of 2). 1993 Colt Vista & Summit Wagon

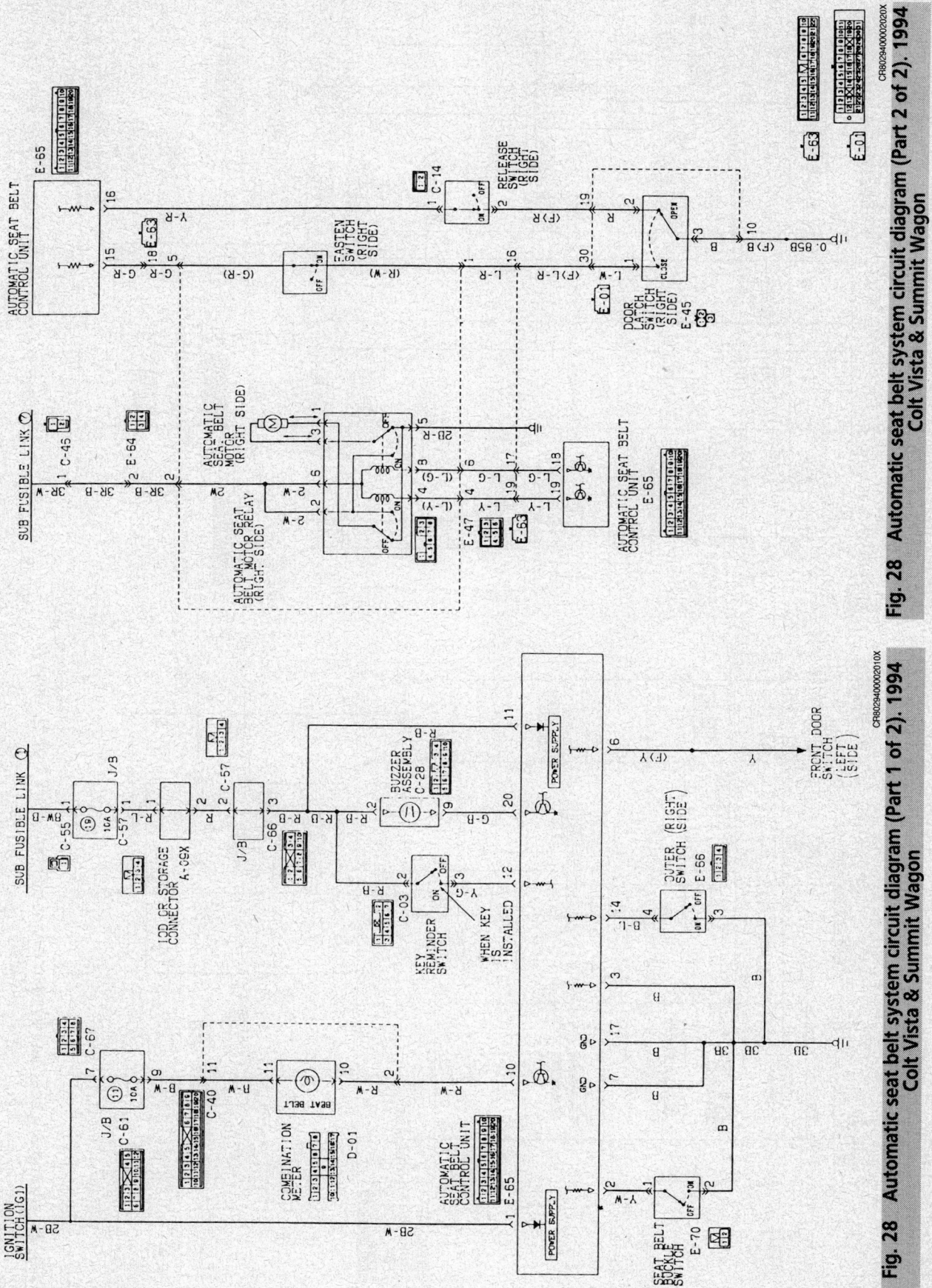

Fig. 28   Automatic seat belt system circuit diagram (Part 2 of 2). 1994 Colt Vista & Summit Wagon

Fig. 28   Automatic seat belt system circuit diagram (Part 1 of 2). 1994 Colt Vista & Summit Wagon

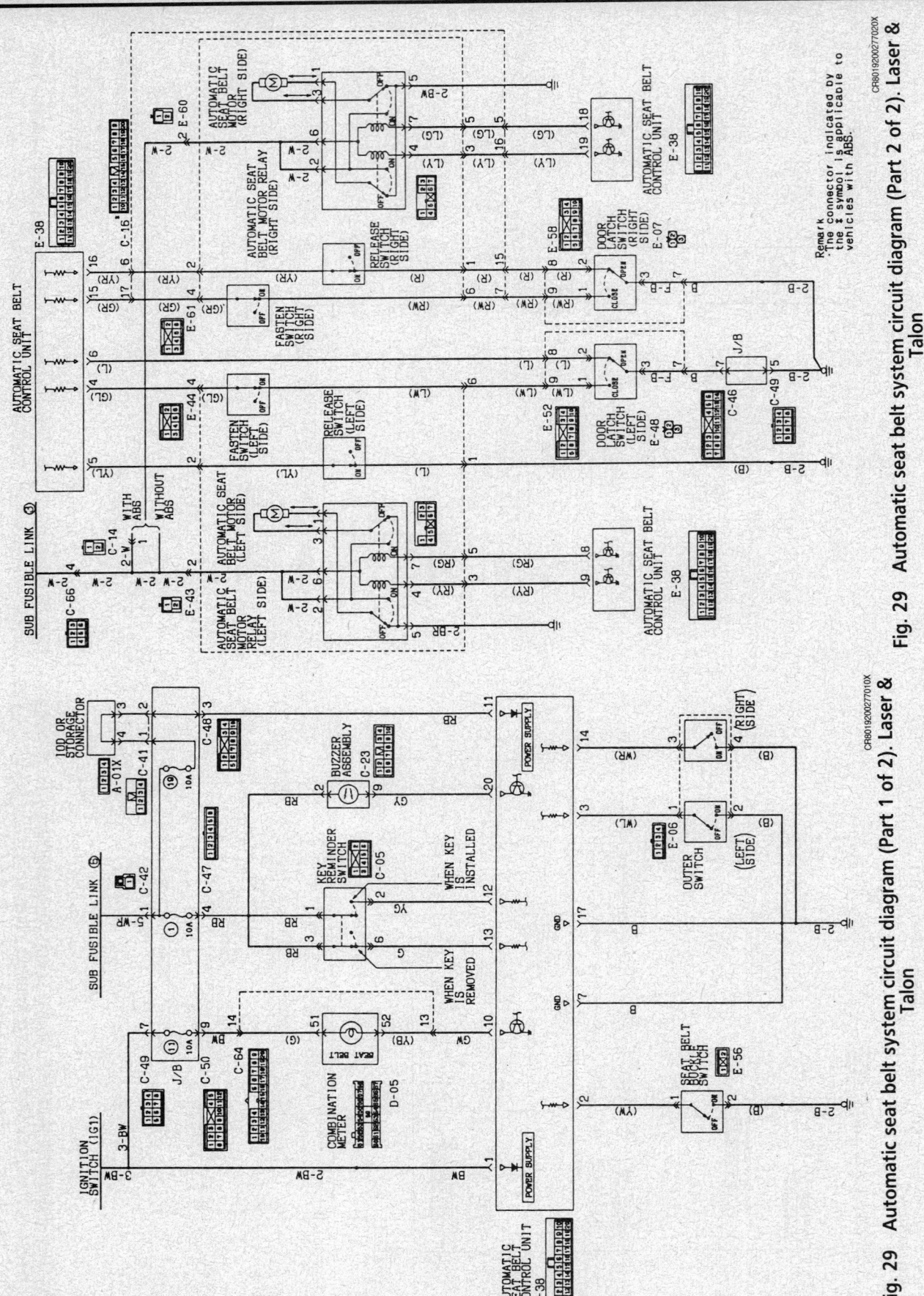

Fig. 29 Automatic seat belt system circuit diagram (Part 2 of 2). Laser & Talon

Fig. 29 Automatic seat belt system circuit diagram (Part 1 of 2). Laser & Talon

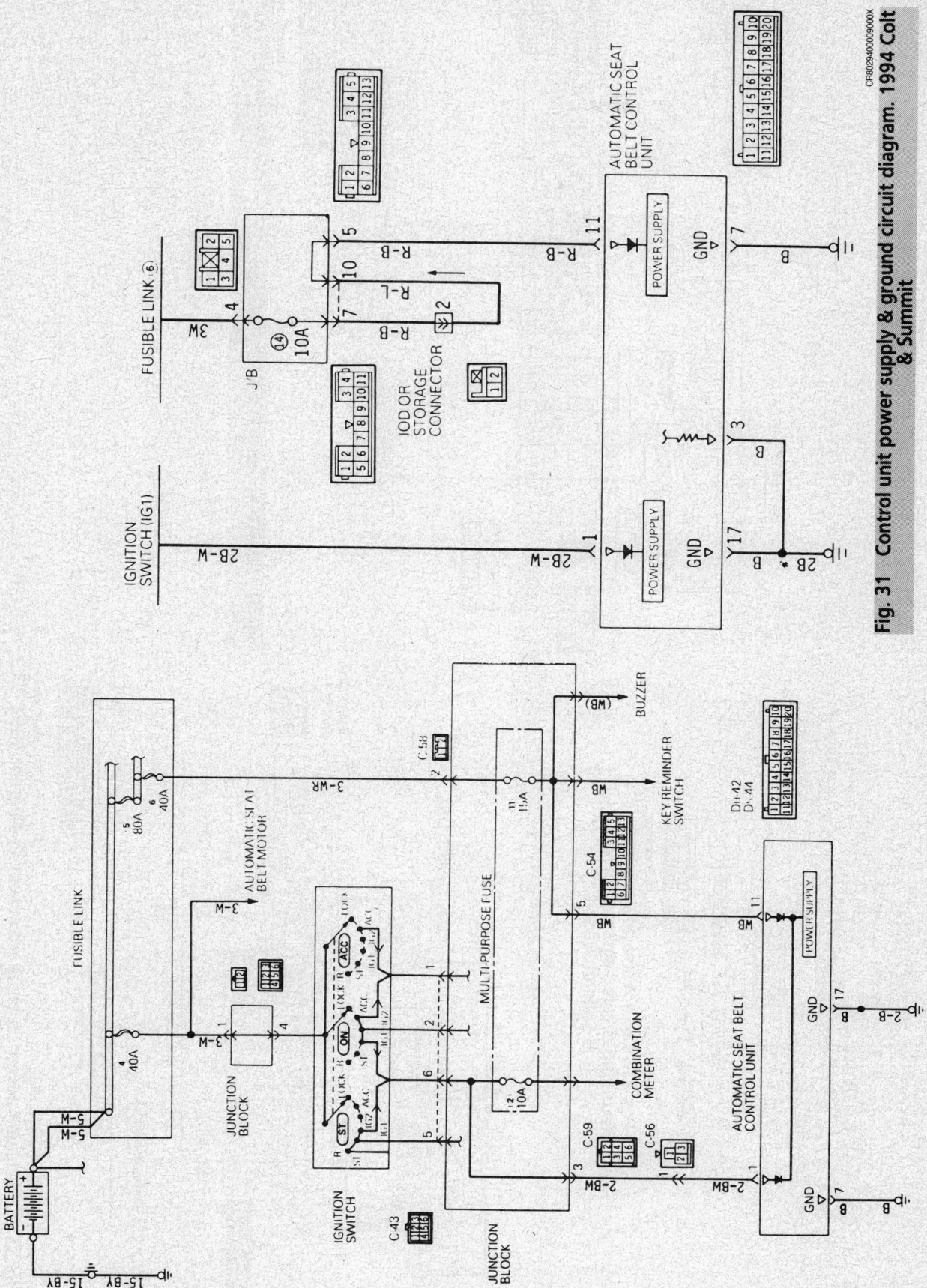

Fig. 31 Control unit power supply & ground circuit diagram. 1994 Colt & Summit

Fig. 30 Control unit power supply & ground circuit diagram. 1992–93 Colt & Summit

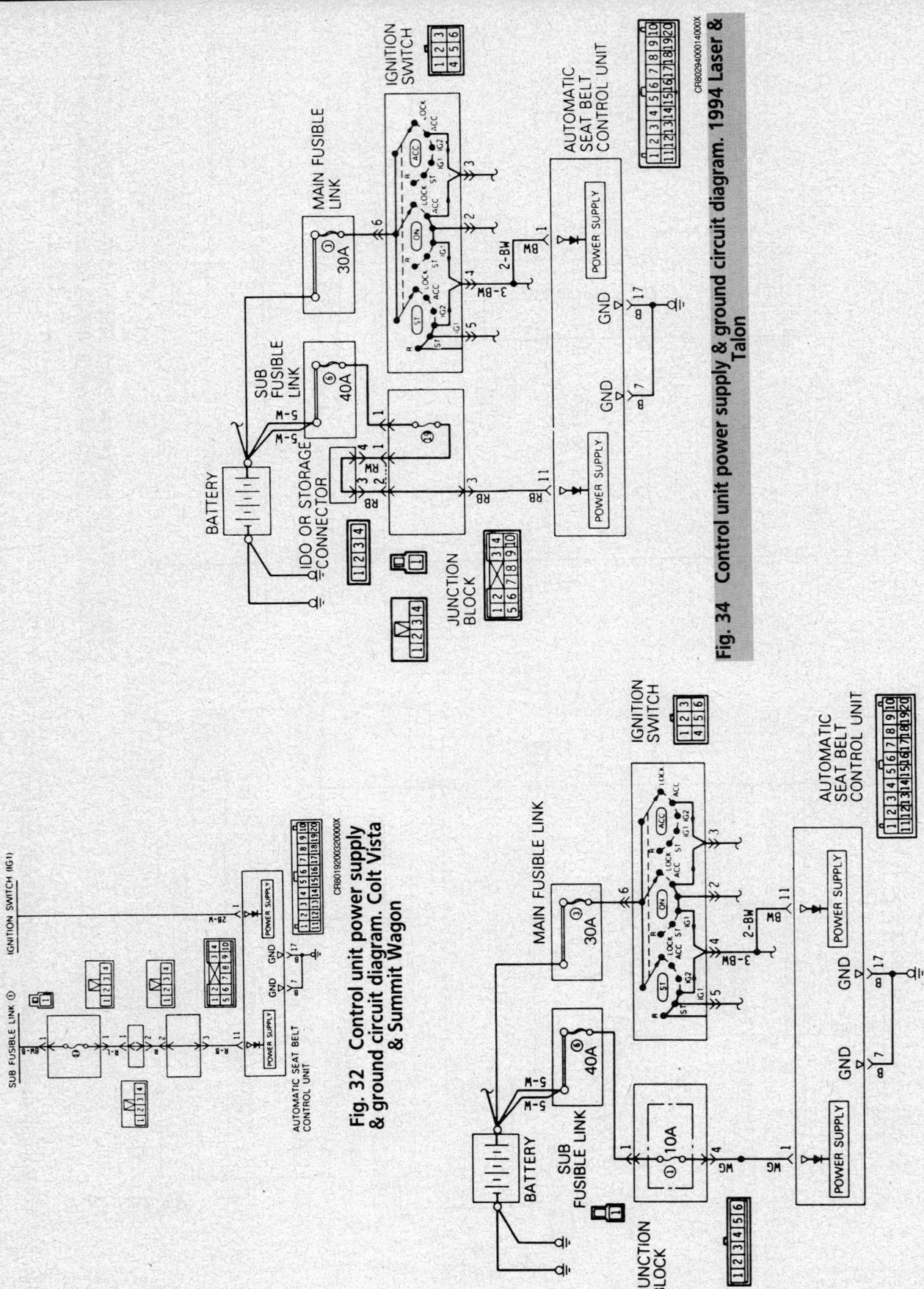

Fig. 34 Control unit power supply & ground circuit diagram. 1994 Laser & Talon

Fig. 32 Control unit power supply & ground circuit diagram. Colt Vista & Summit Wagon

Fig. 33 Control unit power supply & ground circuit diagram. 1992–93 Laser & Talon

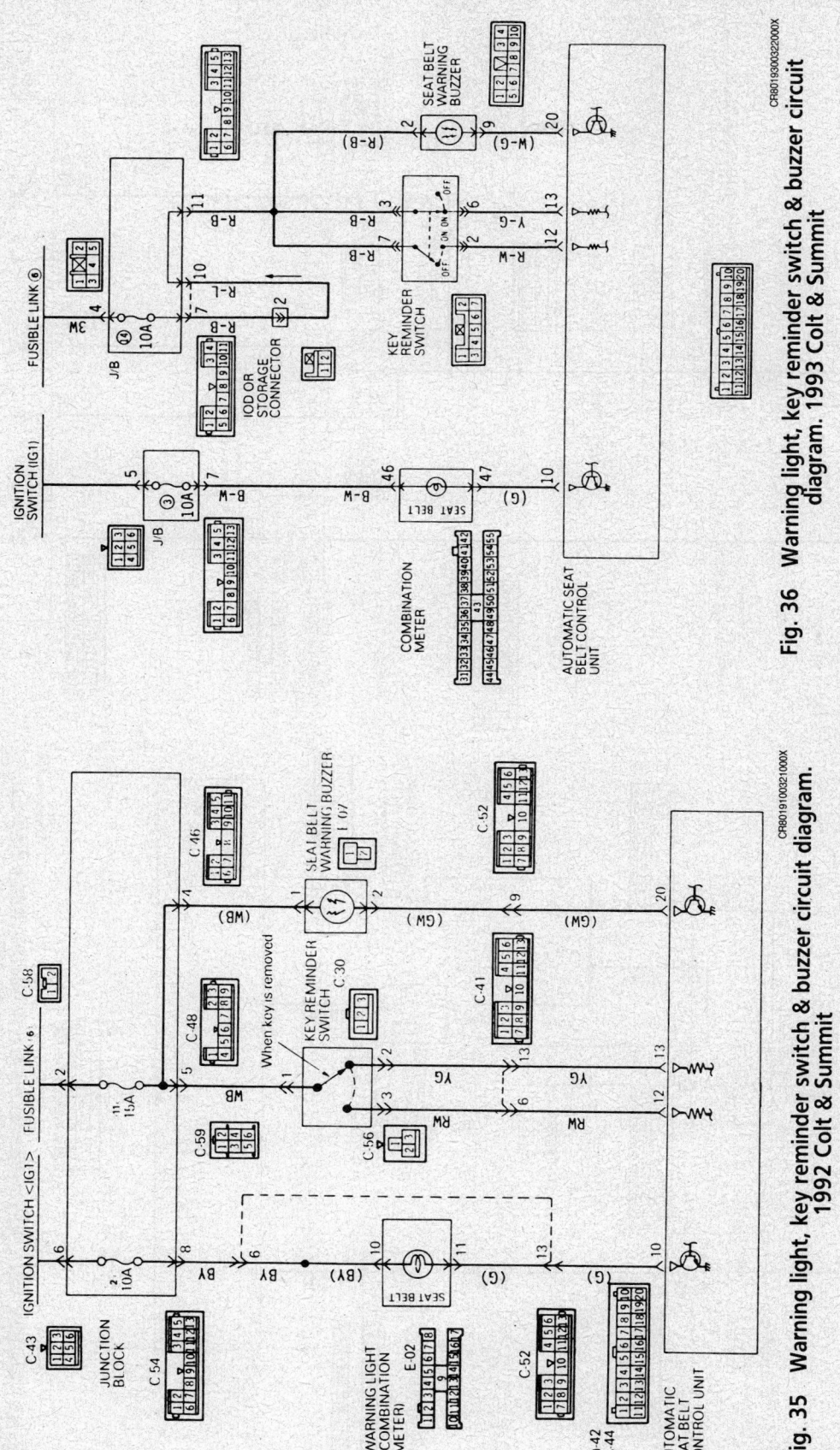

Fig. 36 Warning light, key reminder switch & buzzer circuit diagram. 1993 Colt & Summit

Fig. 35 Warning light, key reminder switch & buzzer circuit diagram. 1992 Colt & Summit

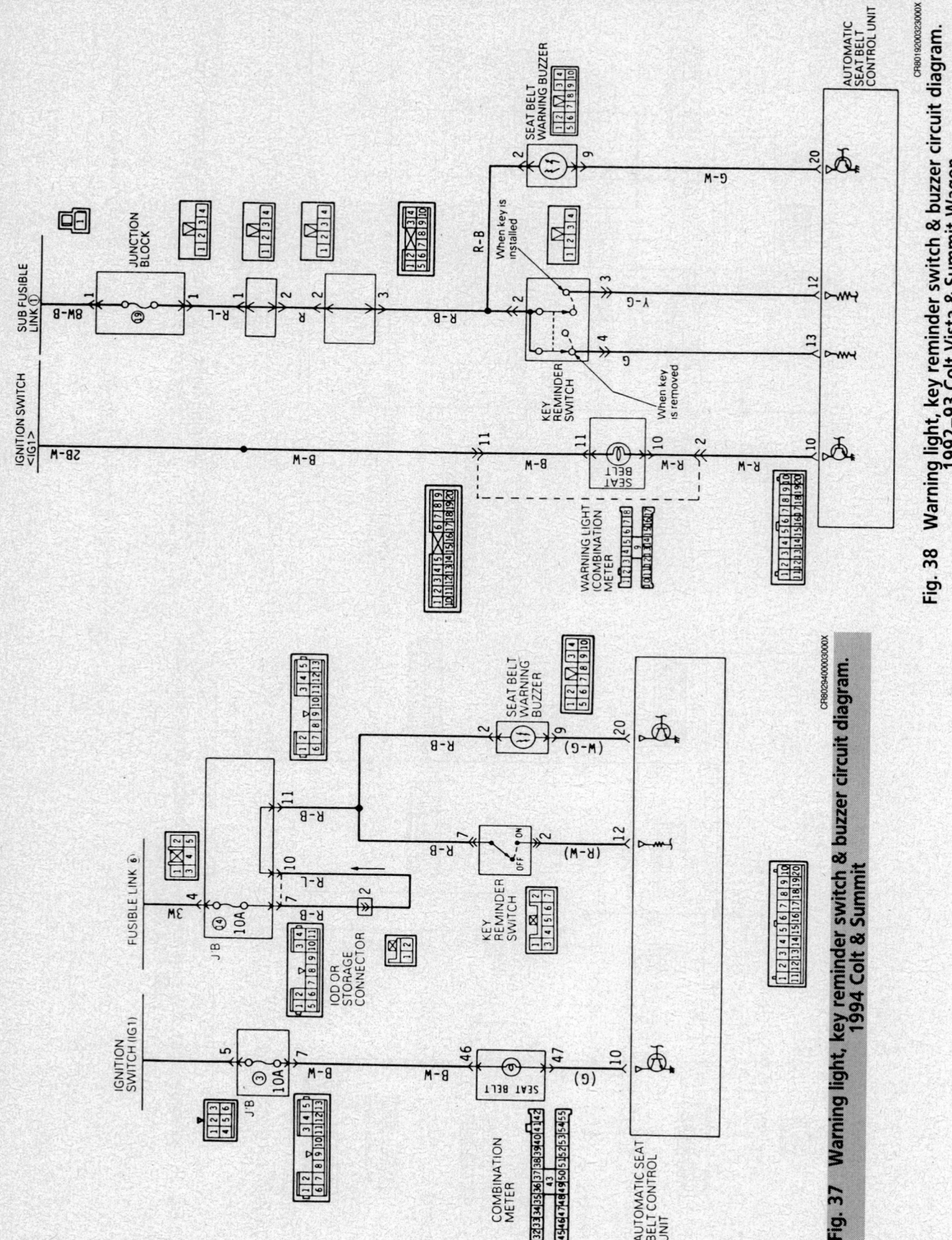

Fig. 38 Warning light, key reminder switch & buzzer circuit diagram.
1992–93 Colt Vista & Summit Wagon

Fig. 37 Warning light, key reminder switch & buzzer circuit diagram.
1994 Colt & Summit

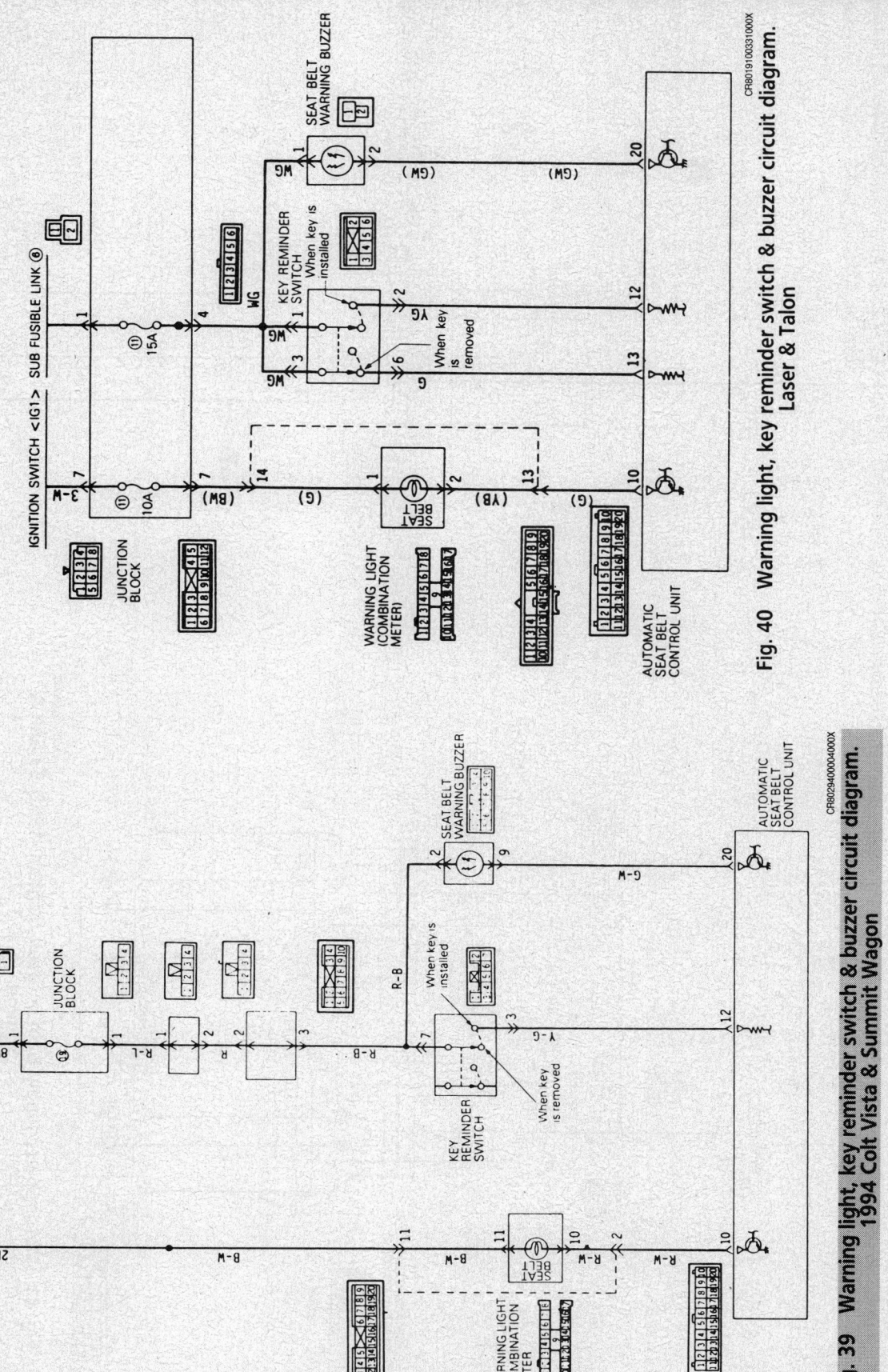

Fig. 40 Warning light, key reminder switch & buzzer circuit diagram. Laser & Talon

Fig. 39 Warning light, key reminder switch & buzzer circuit diagram. 1994 Colt Vista & Summit Wagon

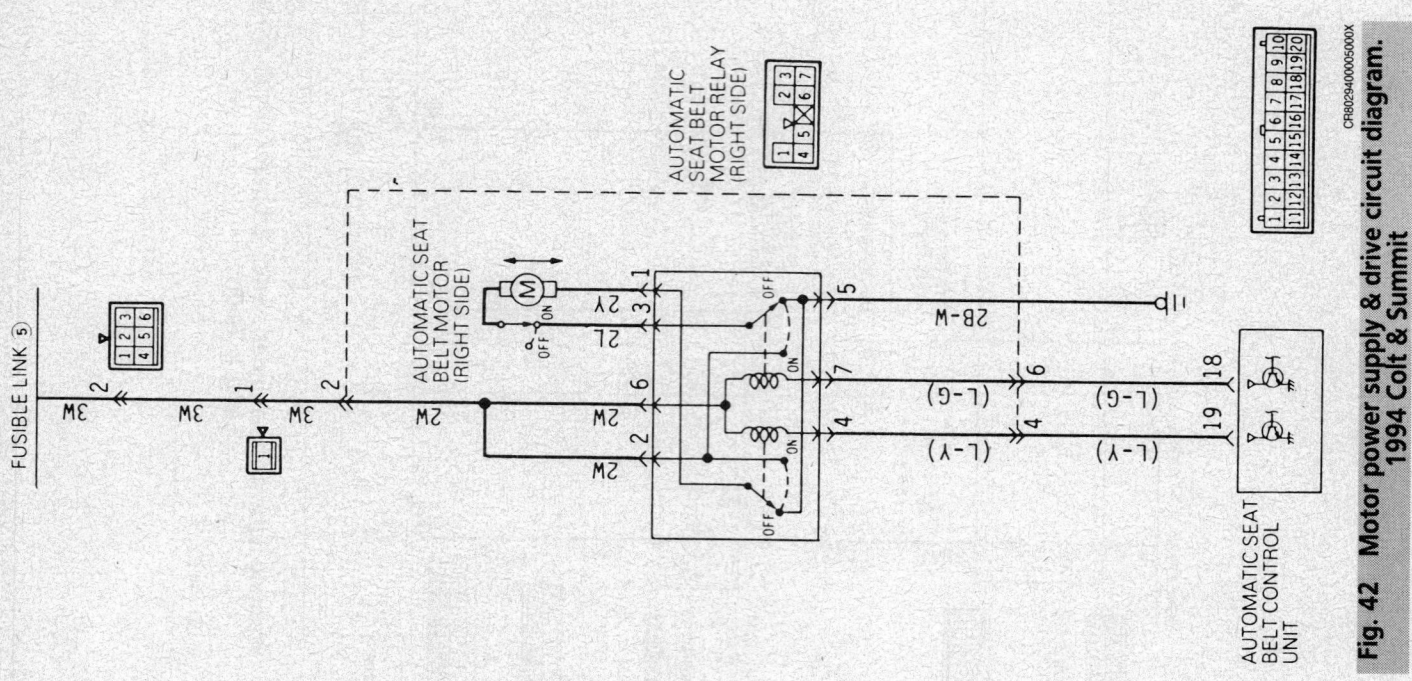

Fig. 42 Motor power supply & drive circuit diagram. 1994 Colt & Summit

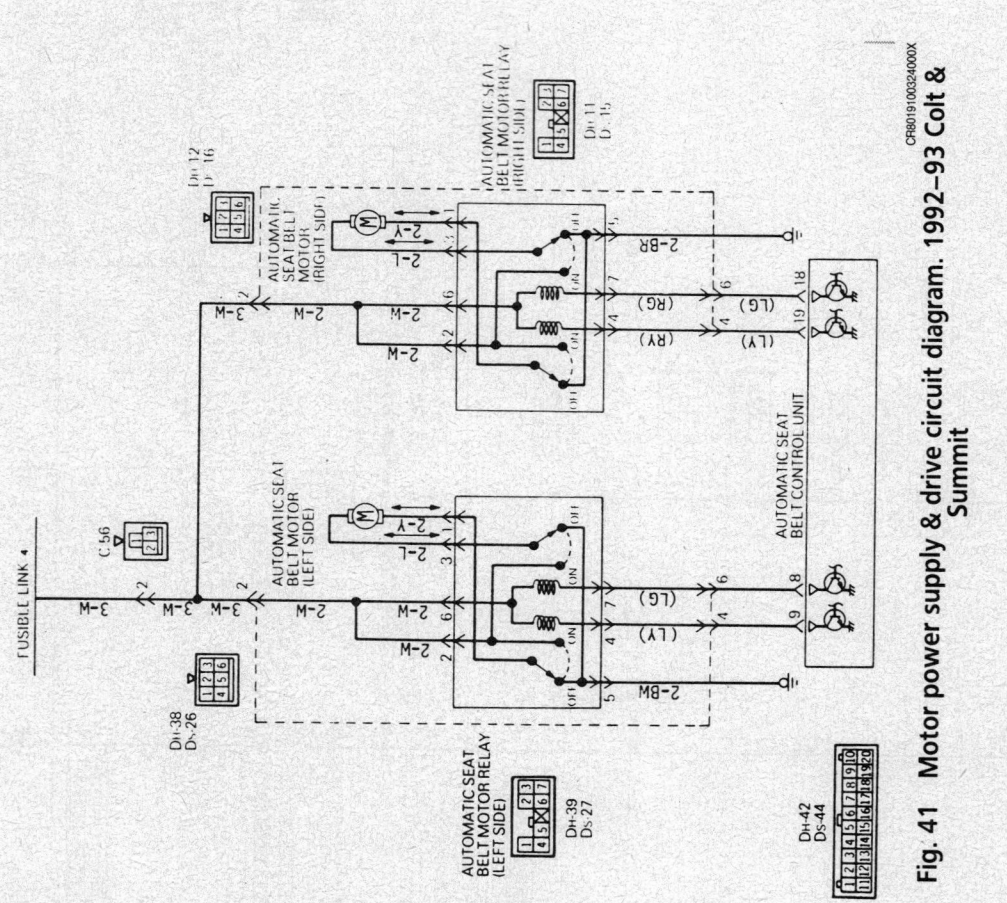

Fig. 41 Motor power supply & drive circuit diagram. 1992–93 Colt & Summit

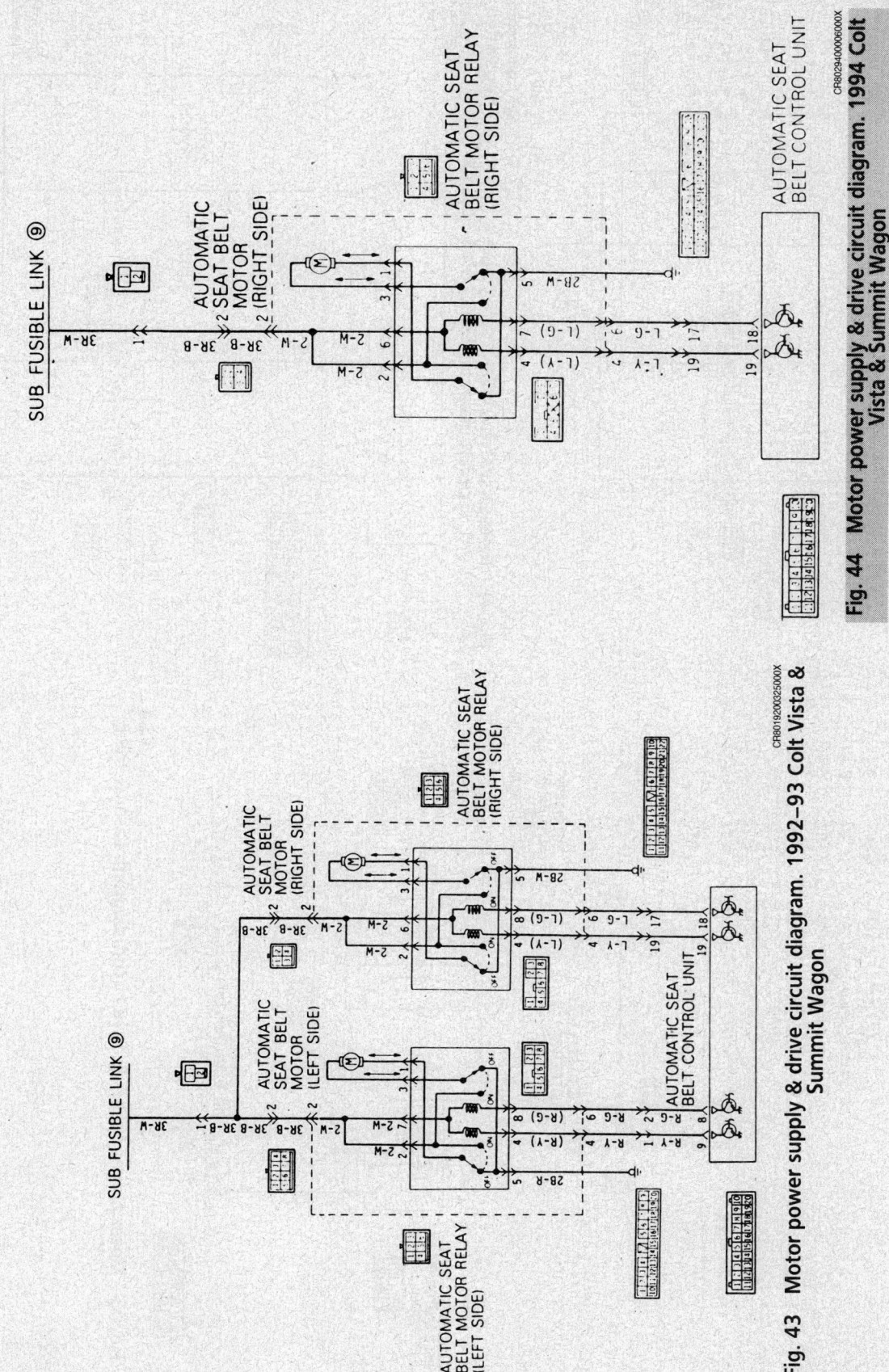

Fig. 44 Motor power supply & drive circuit diagram. 1994 Colt Vista & Summit Wagon

Fig. 43 Motor power supply & drive circuit diagram. 1992–93 Colt Vista & Summit Wagon

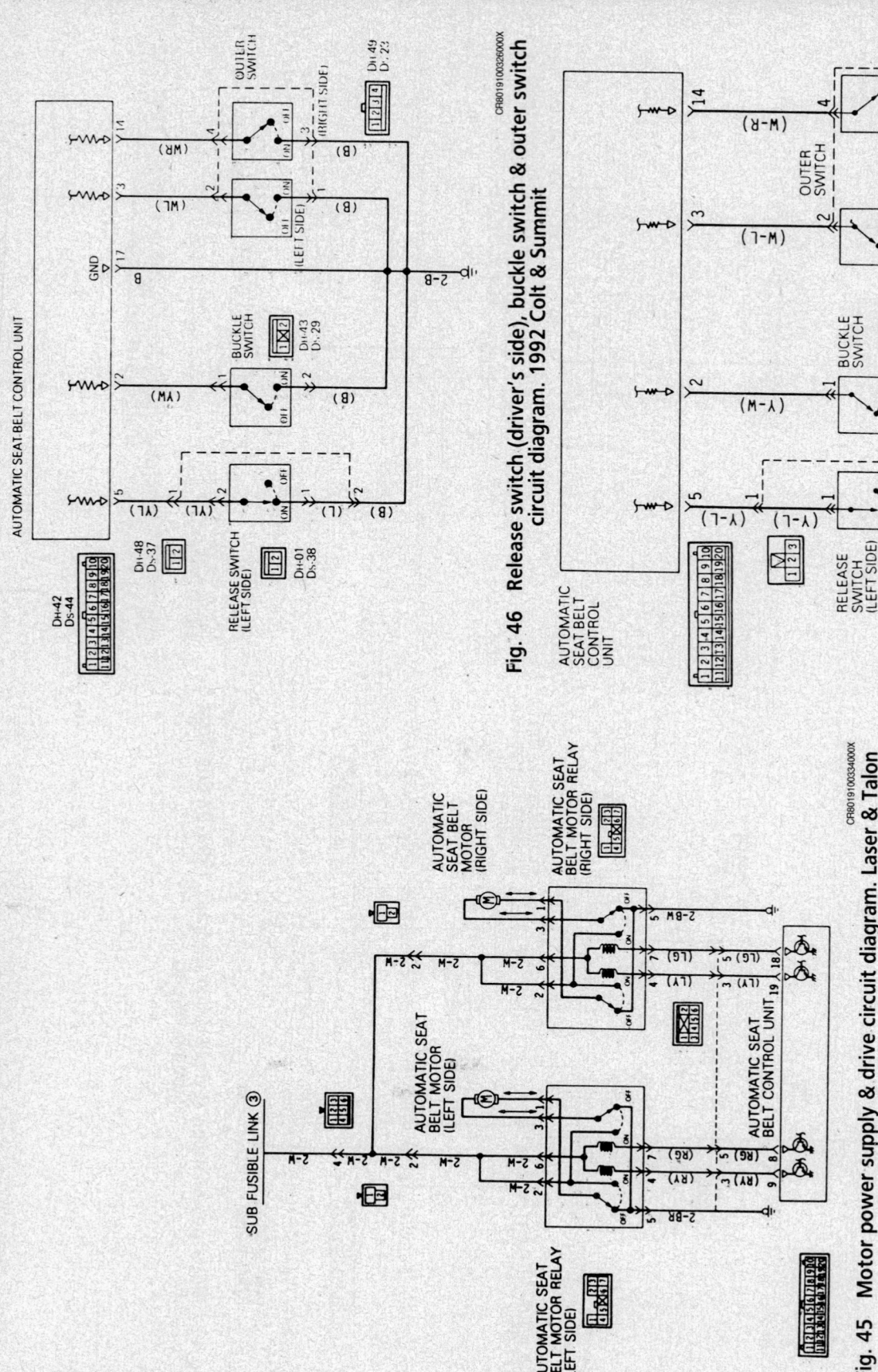

Fig. 46 Release switch (driver's side), buckle switch & outer switch circuit diagram. 1992 Colt & Summit

Fig. 47 Release switch (driver's side), buckle switch & outer switch circuit diagram. 1993 Colt & Summit

Fig. 45 Motor power supply & drive circuit diagram. Laser & Talon

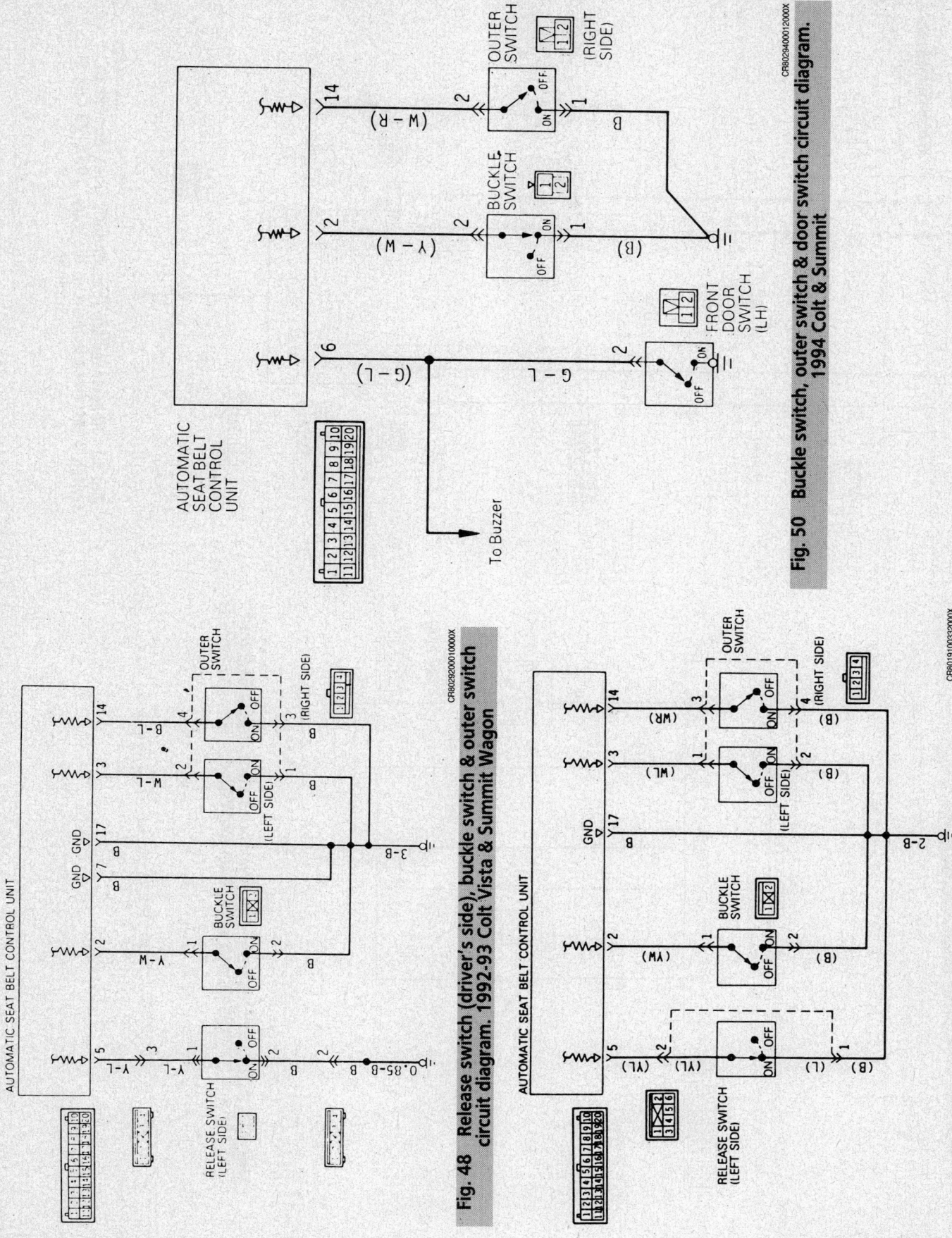

Fig. 50 Buckle switch, outer switch & door switch circuit diagram. 1994 Colt & Summit

Fig. 48 Release switch (driver's side), buckle switch & outer switch circuit diagram. 1992-93 Colt Vista & Summit Wagon

Fig. 49 Release switch (driver's side), buckle switch & outer switch circuit diagram. Laser & Talon

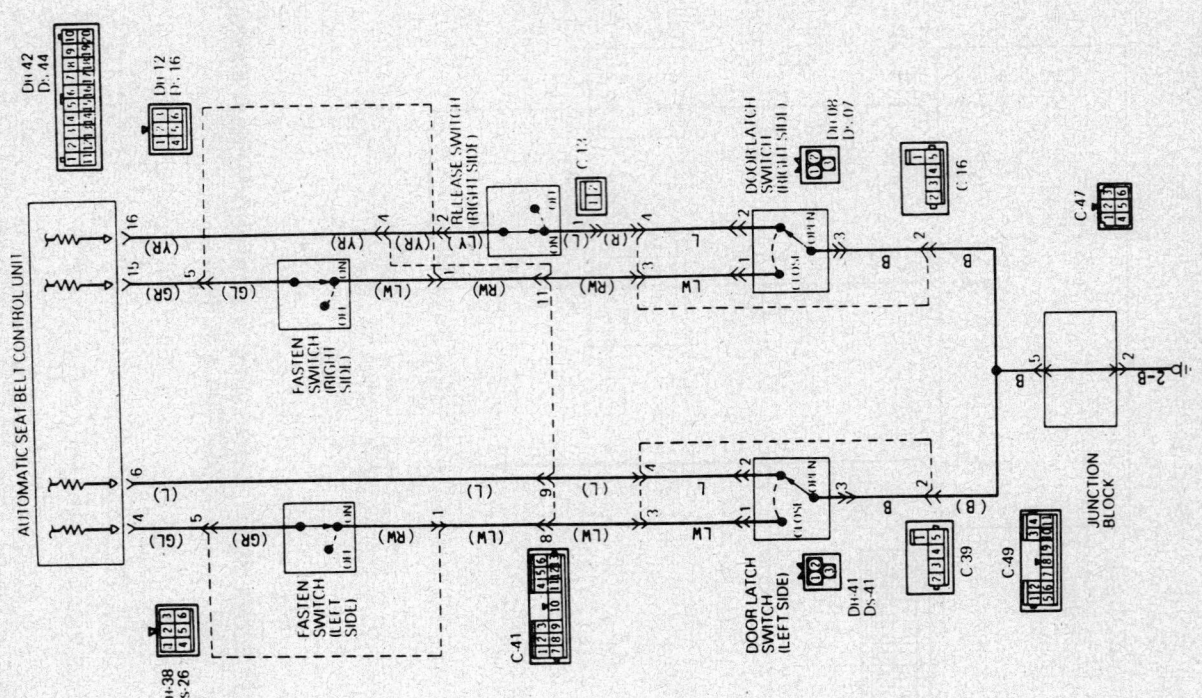

Fig. 52 Release switch (passenger's side), door latch switch & fasten switch circuit diagram. 1992-93 Colt & Summit

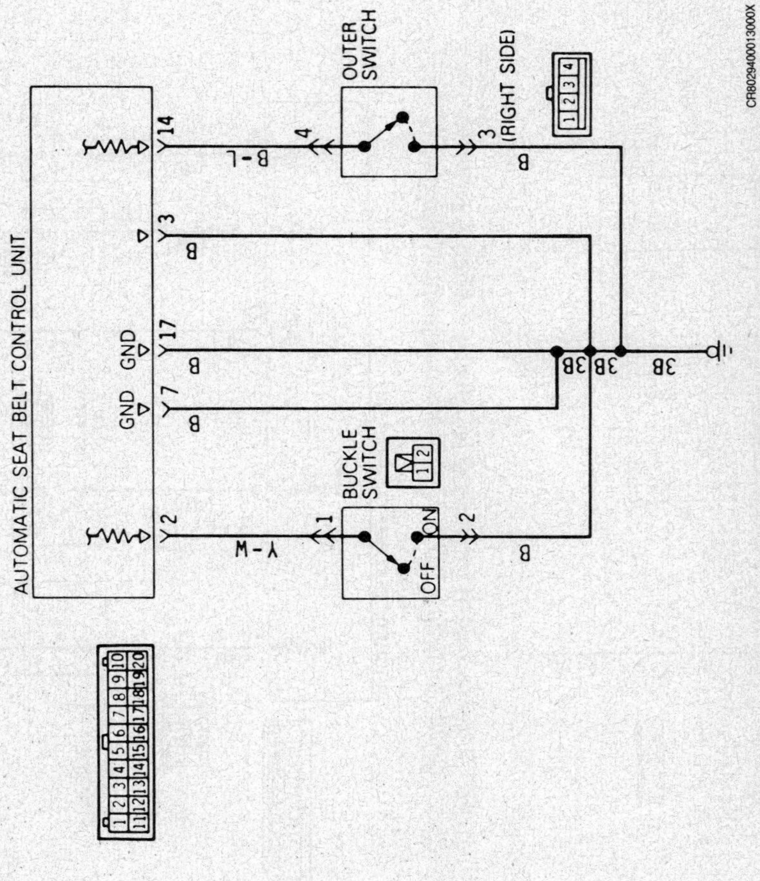

Fig. 51 Buckle switch, outer switch & door switch circuit diagram. 1994 Colt Vista & Summit Wagon

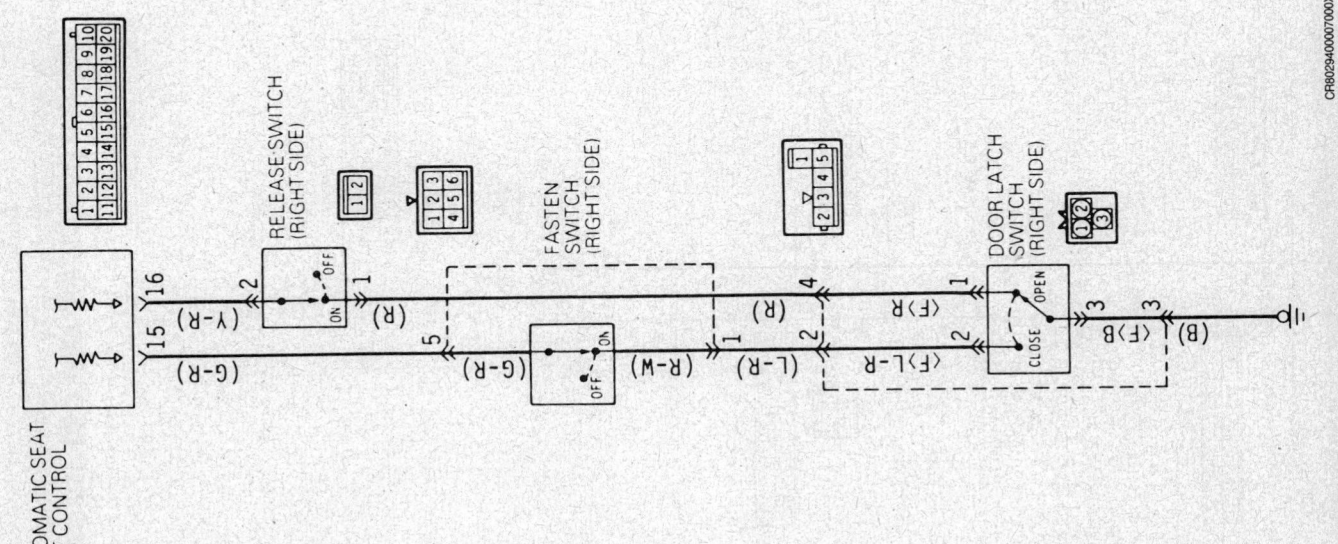

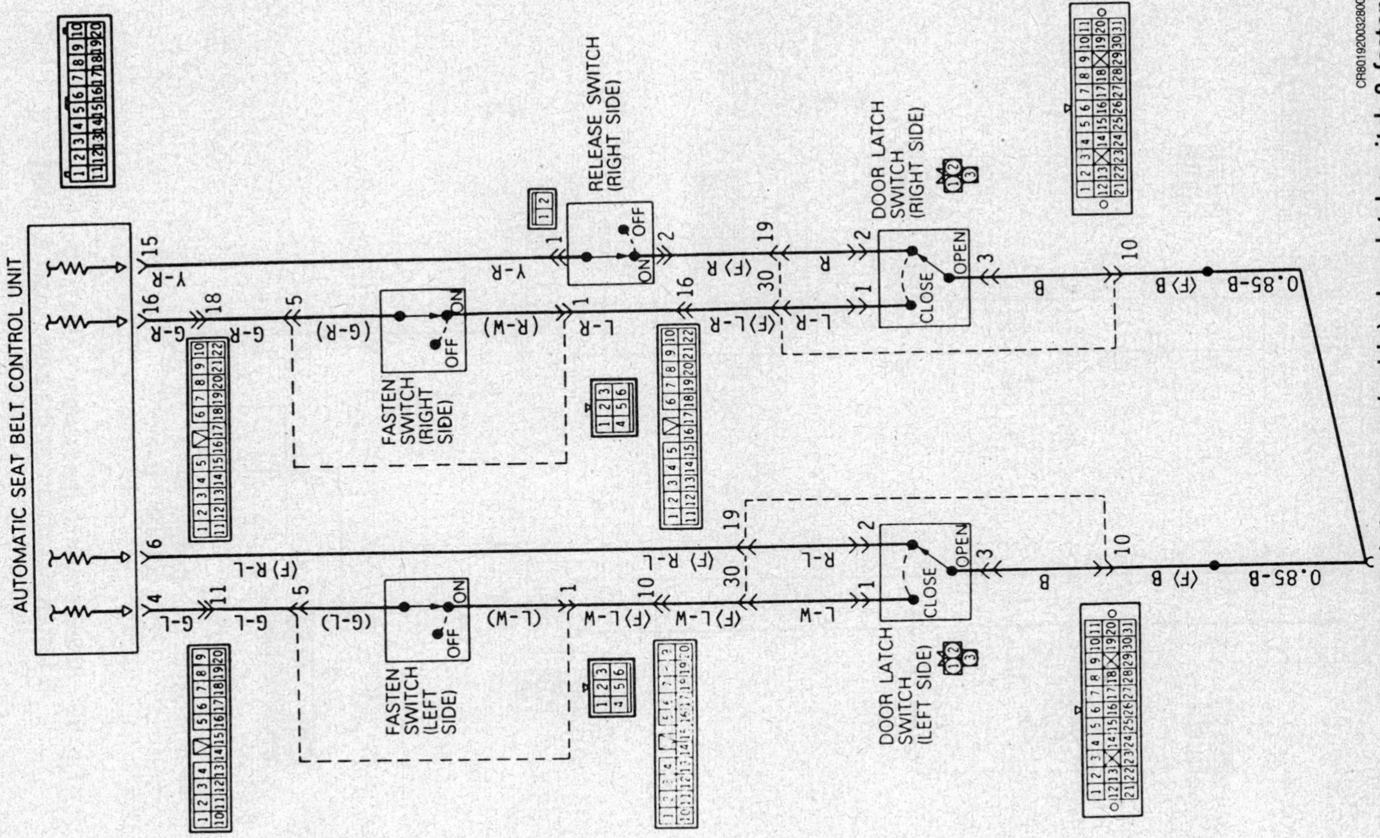

Fig. 54 Release switch (passenger's side), door latch switch & fasten switch. 1992-93 Colt Vista & Summit Wagon

Fig. 53 Door latch switch, fasten switch & release switch circuit. 1994 Colt & Summit

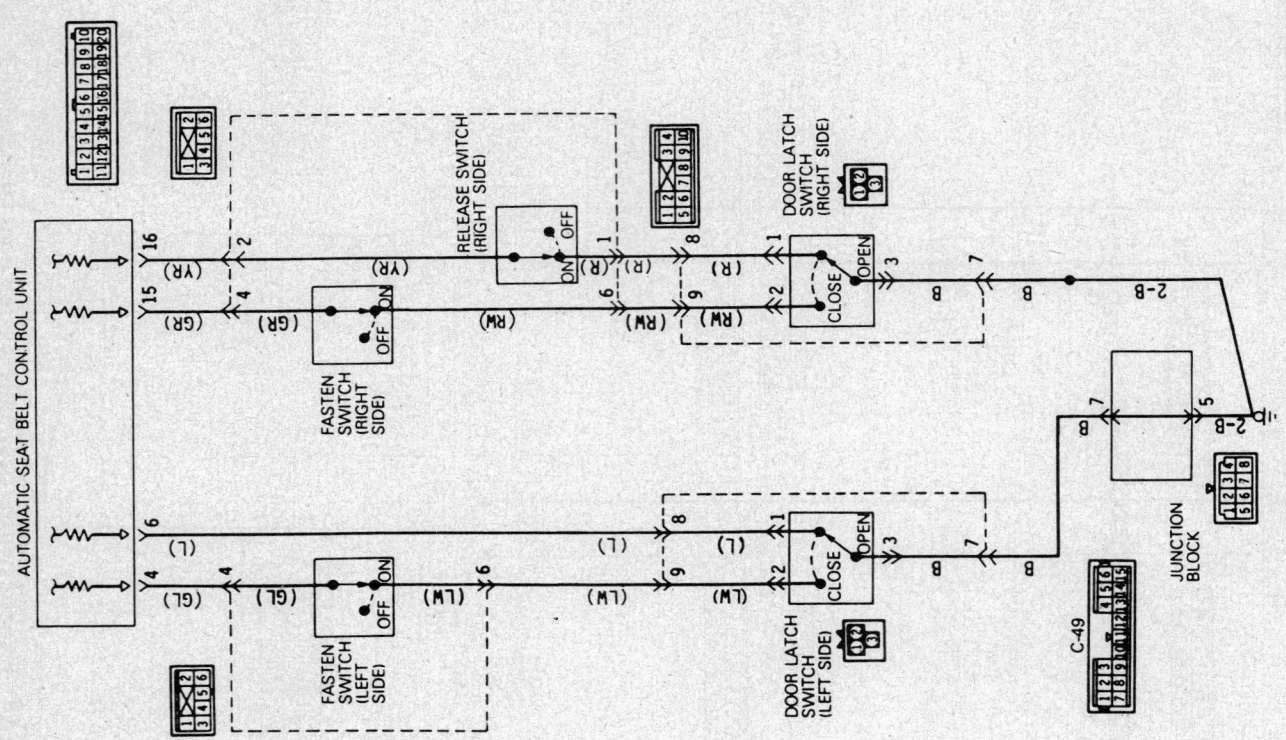

Fig. 56 Release switch (passenger's side), door latch switch & fasten switch circuit diagram. Laser & Talon

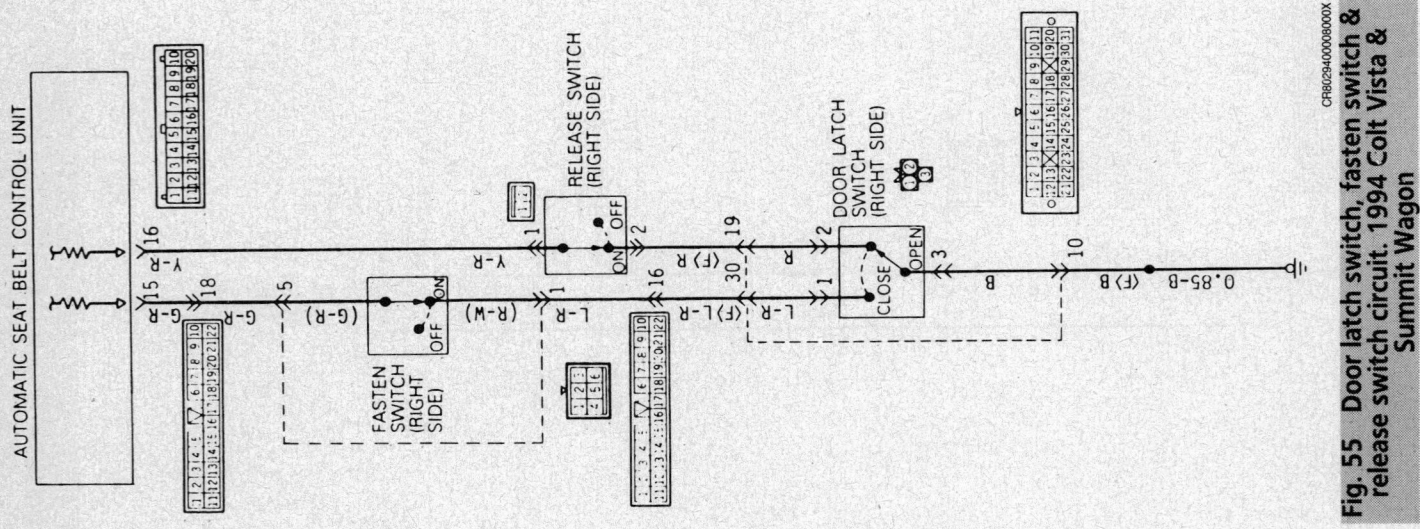

Fig. 55 Door latch switch, fasten switch & release switch circuit. 1994 Colt Vista & Summit Wagon

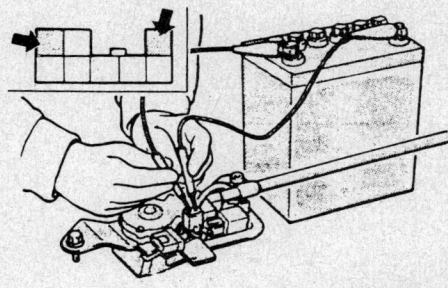

Fig. 57 Seat belt motor inspection. Colt, Colt Vista, Laser, Summit, Summit Wagon & Talon

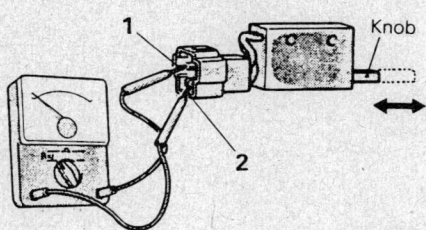

Fig. 58 Release switch inspection. Colt, Colt Vista, Summit & Summit Wagon

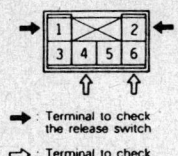

→ : Terminal to check the release switch

⇒ : Terminal to check the fasten switch

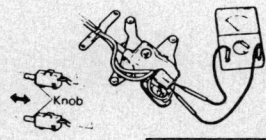

		Release switch		Fasten switch	
Condition	Terminal	1	2	4	6
Release the switch knob		○—○		○—○	
Push the switch knob					

NOTE
○—○ indicates that there is continuity between the terminals.

Fig. 59 Release & fasten switch inspection. Laser & Talon

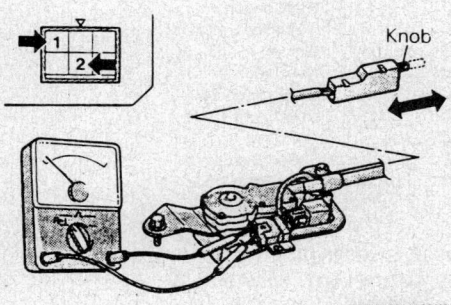

Fig. 60 Fasten switch inspection. 1992 Colt & Summit

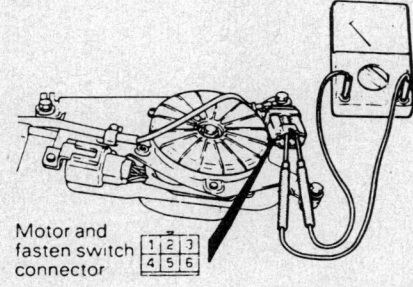

Motor and fasten switch connector

Fig. 61 Fasten switch inspection. Colt Vista, Summit Wagon & 1993–94 Colt & Summit

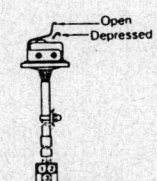

		Terminal	1	2	3
Switch position					
Switch	Open (door open)			○—○	
	Depressed (door close)		○—○		

NOTE
○—○ indicates that there is continuity between the terminals.

Fig. 64 Door latch switch inspection. Colt Vista & Summit Wagon

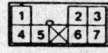

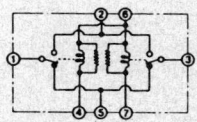

	Terminal	1	2	3	4	5	6	7
Battery voltage								
Continuity no voltage		○—○			○—○			
			○—○			○—○		
Continuity with voltage						⊕---⊕		
		○—○					⊕—⊕	

Fig. 62 Motor relay inspection. Colt, Colt Vista, Laser, Summit, Summit Wagon & Talon

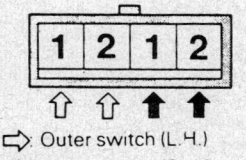

⇨ Outer switch (L.H.)
➡ Outer switch (R.H.)

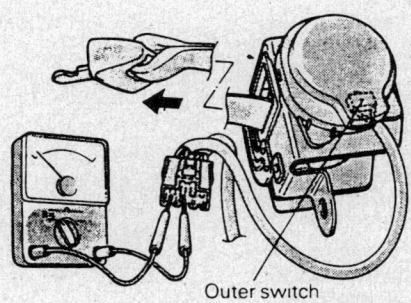

Outer switch

Fig. 63 Outer switch inspection. Colt, Colt Vista, Laser, Summit, Summit Wagon & Talon

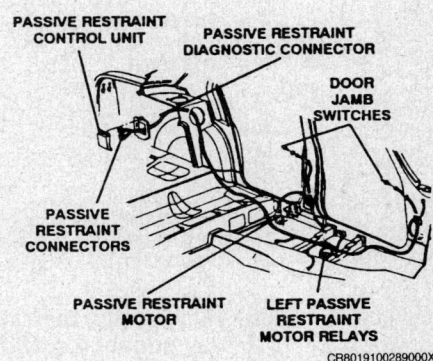

Fig. 65 Component & connector location (LH side). Monaco & Premier

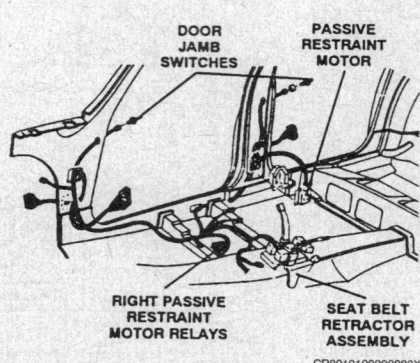

Fig. 66   Component & connector location (RH side). Monaco & Premier

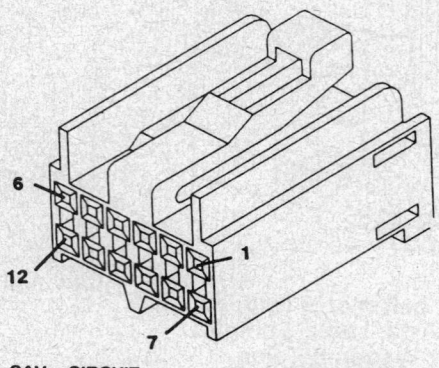

CAV	CIRCUIT	FUNCTION
1	Z1 BK	Ground
2		Not Used
3		Not Used
4	R17 DB/YL	Carrier Switch Right Rear Position (Right)
5	R28 LB/BK	Retractor Switch (Passenger)
6	R27 YL/BK	Retractor Switch (Driver)
7		Not Used
8	F30 RD	B+ For Module
9		Not Used
10		Not Used
11	G7 WT/OR	Speed Signal
12	R30 BR/OR	Right Front Door Jamb Switch

Fig. 67   Passive restraint module black 12 way connector. Monaco & Premier

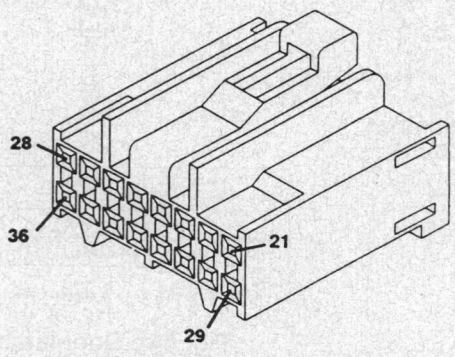

CAV	CIRCUIT	FUNCTION
21	R16 LG	Carrier Switch Front Position (Right)
22		Not Used
23	R24 VT	Right Rear Motor Relay
24	R26 VT/WT	Left Rear Motor Relay
25	R23 GY	Right Front Motor Relay
26		Not Used
27	R18 DG	Carrier Switch Front Position (Left)
28	R19 LB/WT	Carrier Switch Right Rear Position (Left)
29		Not Used
30	F20 WT	Fused Ignition "C"
31		Not Used
32	D10 PK/WT	Diagnostic
33	G11 WT/YL	Seat Belt Warning Lamp
34	G80 VT/BK	Warning Tone
35	G16 BK/LB	Left Front Door Jamb
36	R25 GY/WT	Left Passenger Relay

Fig. 68   Passive restraint module black 16 way connector. Monaco & Premier

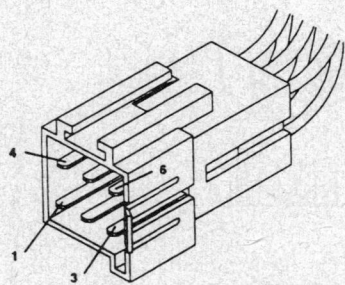

CAV	CIRCUIT	FUNCTION
1		Not Used
2	F30 19RD	Battery 12V
3		Not Used
4		Not Used
5	D10 PK/WT	Data Out From Passive Module
6	Z1 BK	Ground

Fig. 69   Passive restraint module diagnostic connector. Monaco & Premier

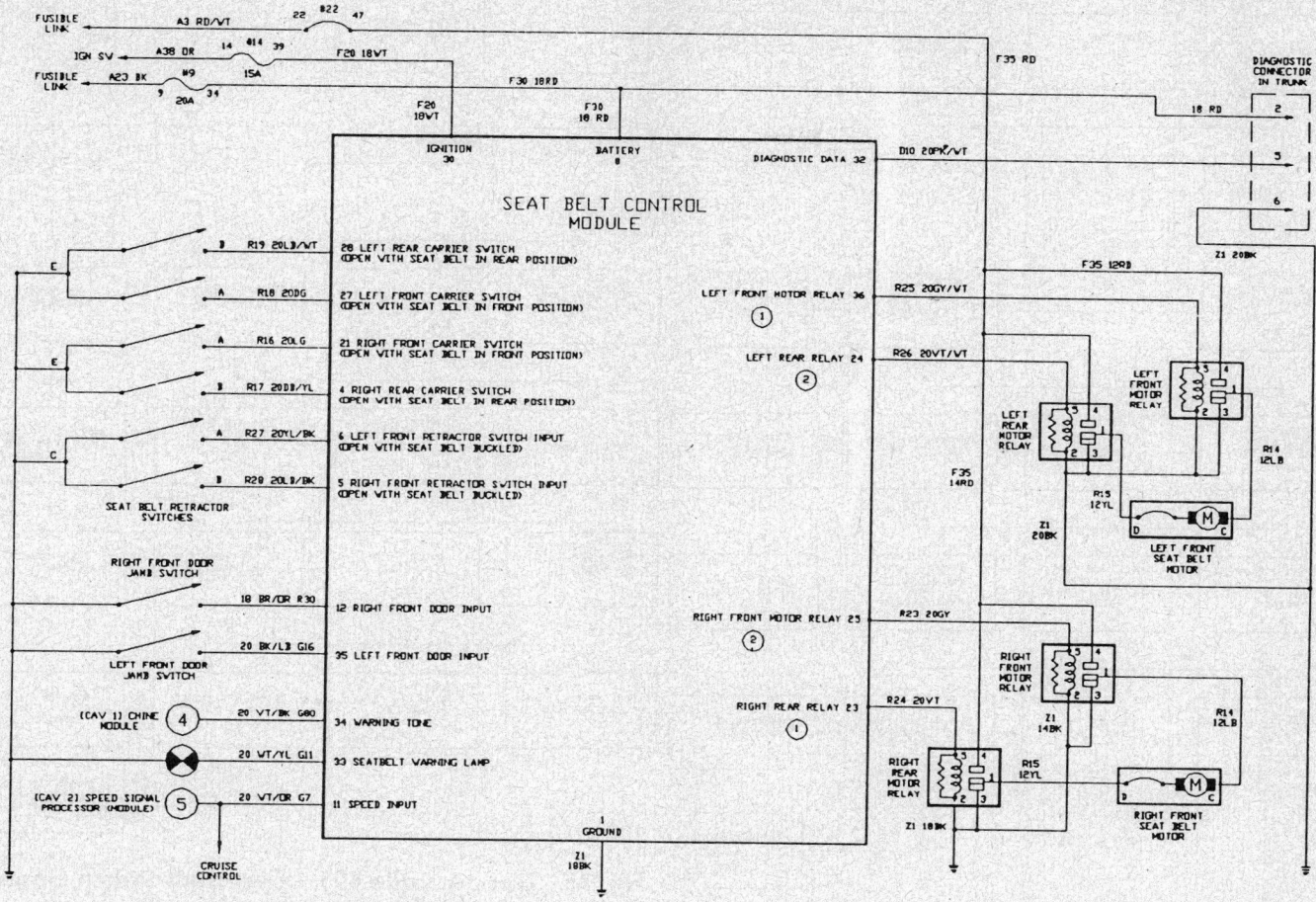

CR801910029400X

Fig. 70   Passive restraint system schematic. Monaco & Premier

1. Turn the ignition key to the on position.

2. Plug the DRBII in the diagnostic connector (left right side of trunk).

3. Select the system test and follow the DRBII Instructions.

   If you are prompted by the DRBII to perform an instruction, do it. If the DRBII does not respond within 5 seconds or if the component is in the specified position, press and hold the ENTER key until the command is confirmed.

NOTE: Skip this note if any fault is detected on the DRBII. If no faults are detected and the belt does not travel to the far front when opening the door, replace the seat belt motor assembly.

Refer to the following table for fault identification:

DRBII FAULT CODES	DIAGNOSTIC TEST
No Response	Refer to the vehicle communication manual.
Fault 403	2A
Fault 404	Replace the passive restraint module.
Fault 405	3A
Fault 406	4A
Fault 407	5A
Fault 408	6A
Fault 409	7A
Fault 410	8A
Fault 411	9A
Fault 412	10A
Fault 413	11A
Fault 414	12A
Fault 415	13A
Fault 416	14A
Fault 417	15A
Fault 418	16A
Fault 419	17A
Fault 420	18A

CR8019100295000X

Fig. 71   Test 1A: Passive Restraint System Functional Test. Monaco & Premier

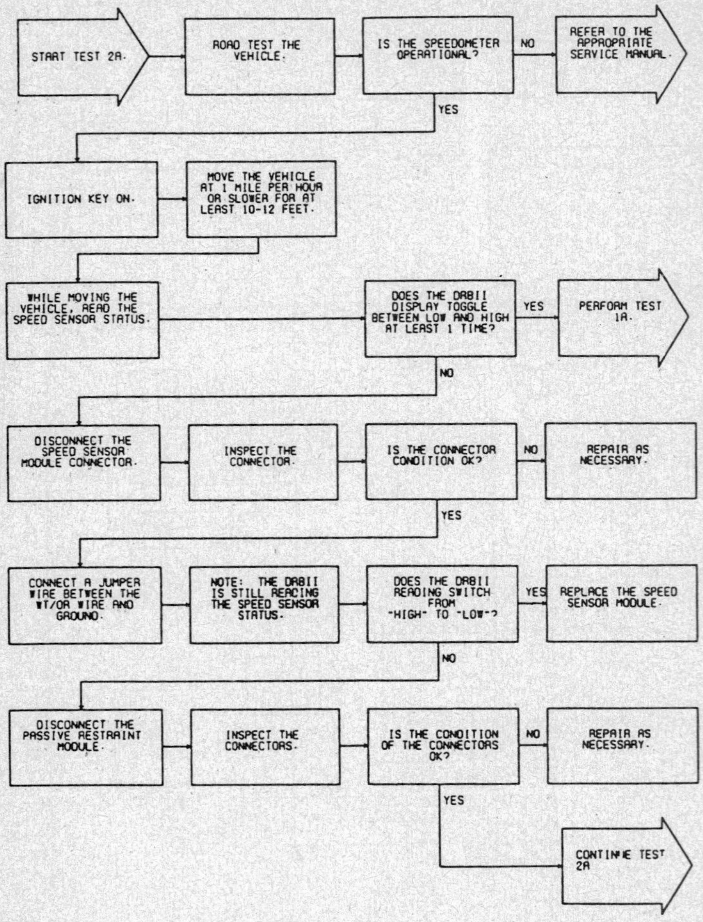

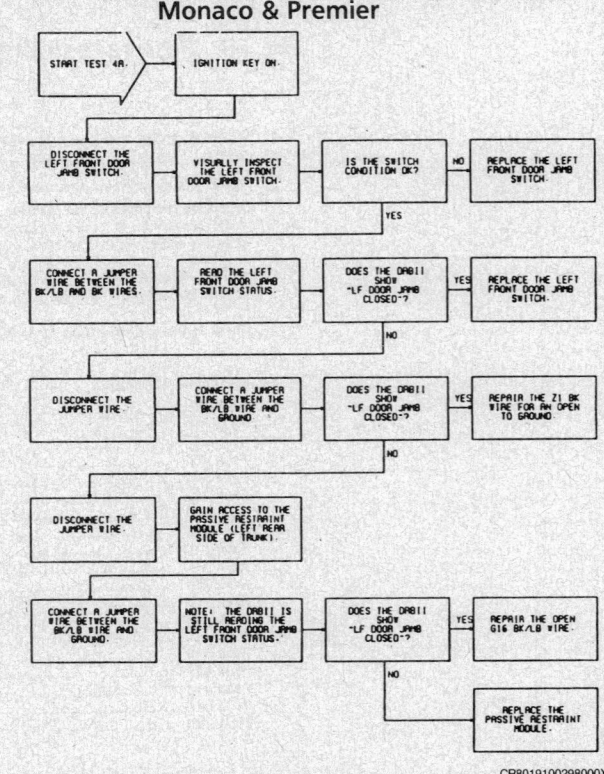

Fig. 72 Test 2A: Code 403, Speed Sensor Not Seen (Part 1 of 2). Monaco & Premier

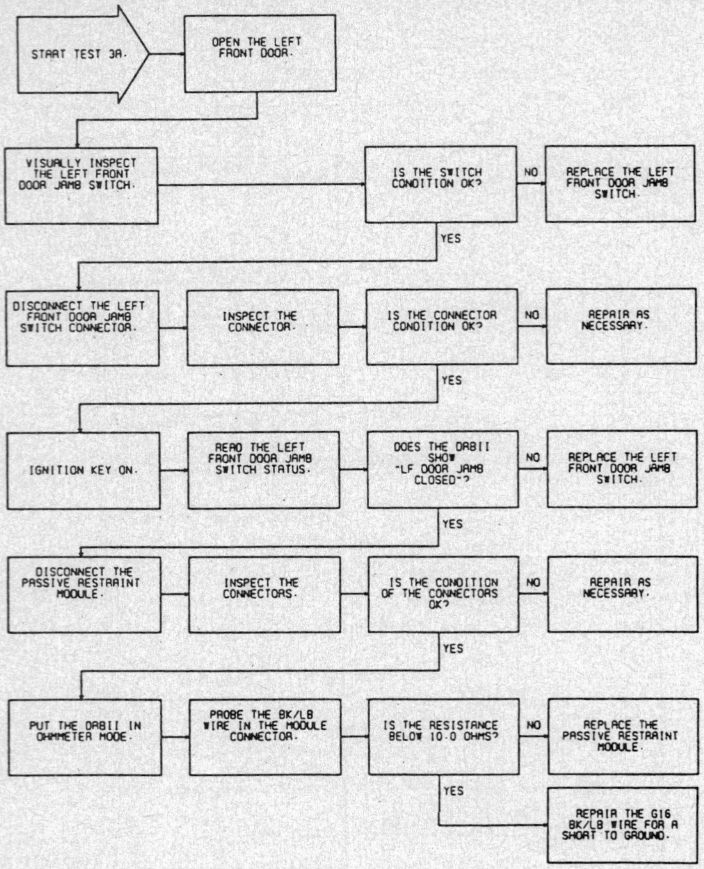

CR8019100296010X

Fig. 73 Test 3A: Code 405, Driver Door Switch Closed. Monaco & Premier

CR8019100297000X

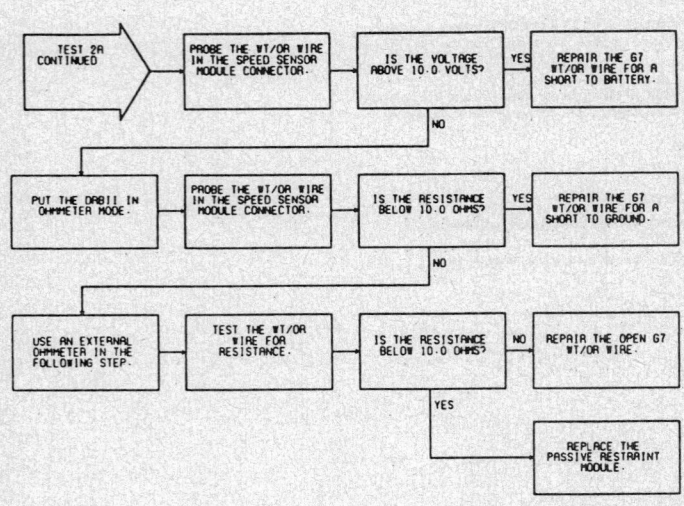

CR8019100296020X

Fig. 72 Test 2A: Code 403, Speed Sensor Not Seen (Part 2 of 2). Monaco & Premier

CR8019100298000X

Fig. 74 Test 4A: Code 406, Driver Door Switch Open. Monaco & Premier

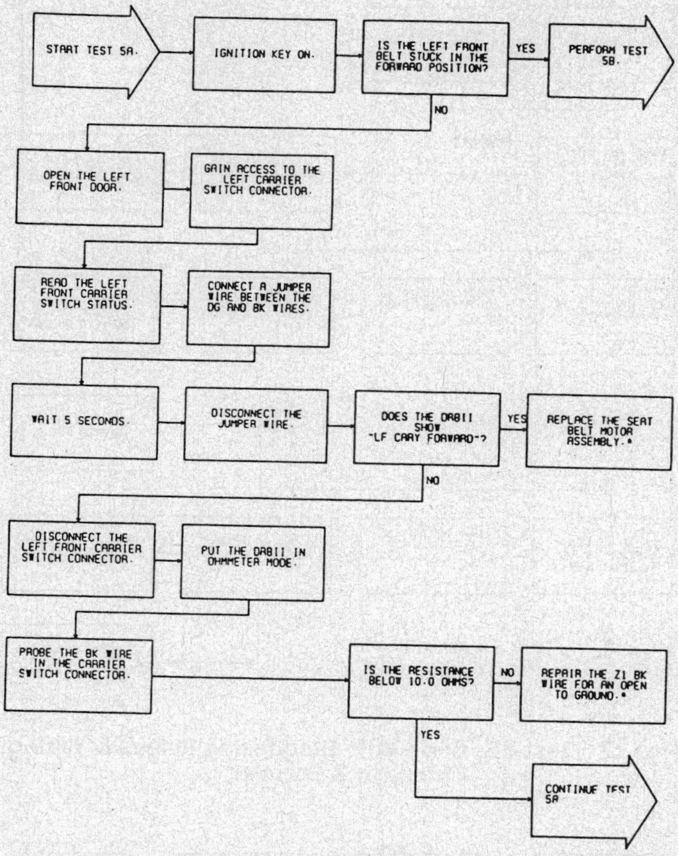

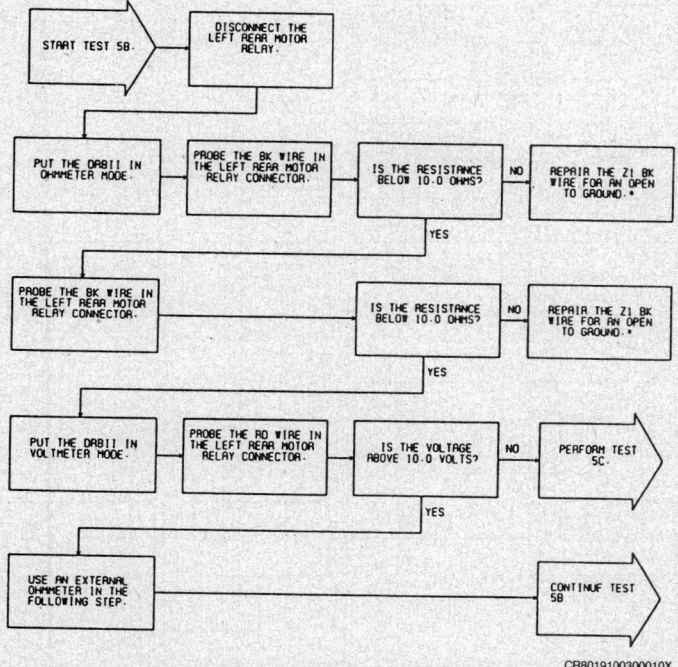

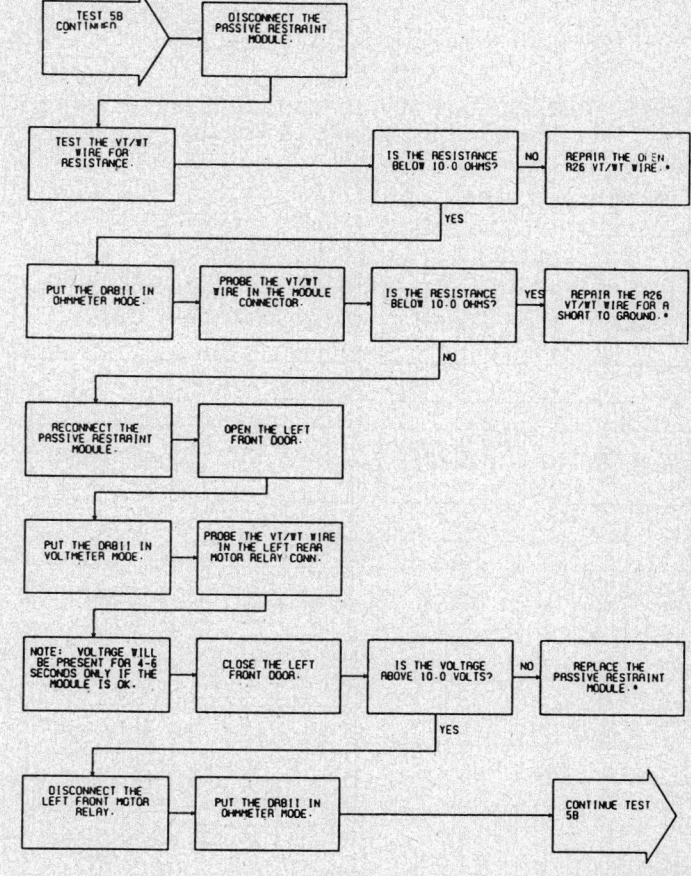

CR8019100299010X

Fig. 75 Test 5A: Code 407, Driver Forward Station Seen (Part 1 of 2). Monaco & Premier

CR8019100299020X

Fig. 75 Test 5A: Code 407, Driver Forward Station Seen (Part 2 of 2). Monaco & Premier

CR8019100300010X

Fig. 76 Test 5B: Code 407, Diagnosing Relays & Wiring (Part 1 of 3). Monaco & Premier

CR8019100300020X

Fig. 76 Test 5B: Code 407, Diagnosing Relays & Wiring (Part 2 of 3). Monaco & Premier

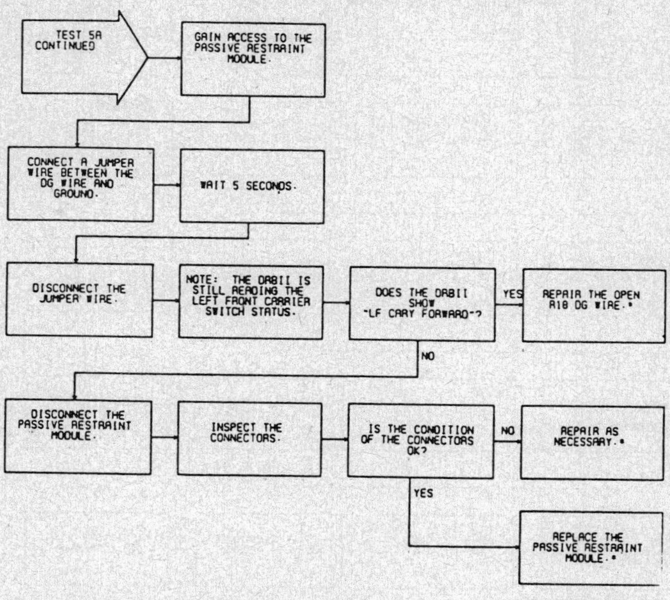

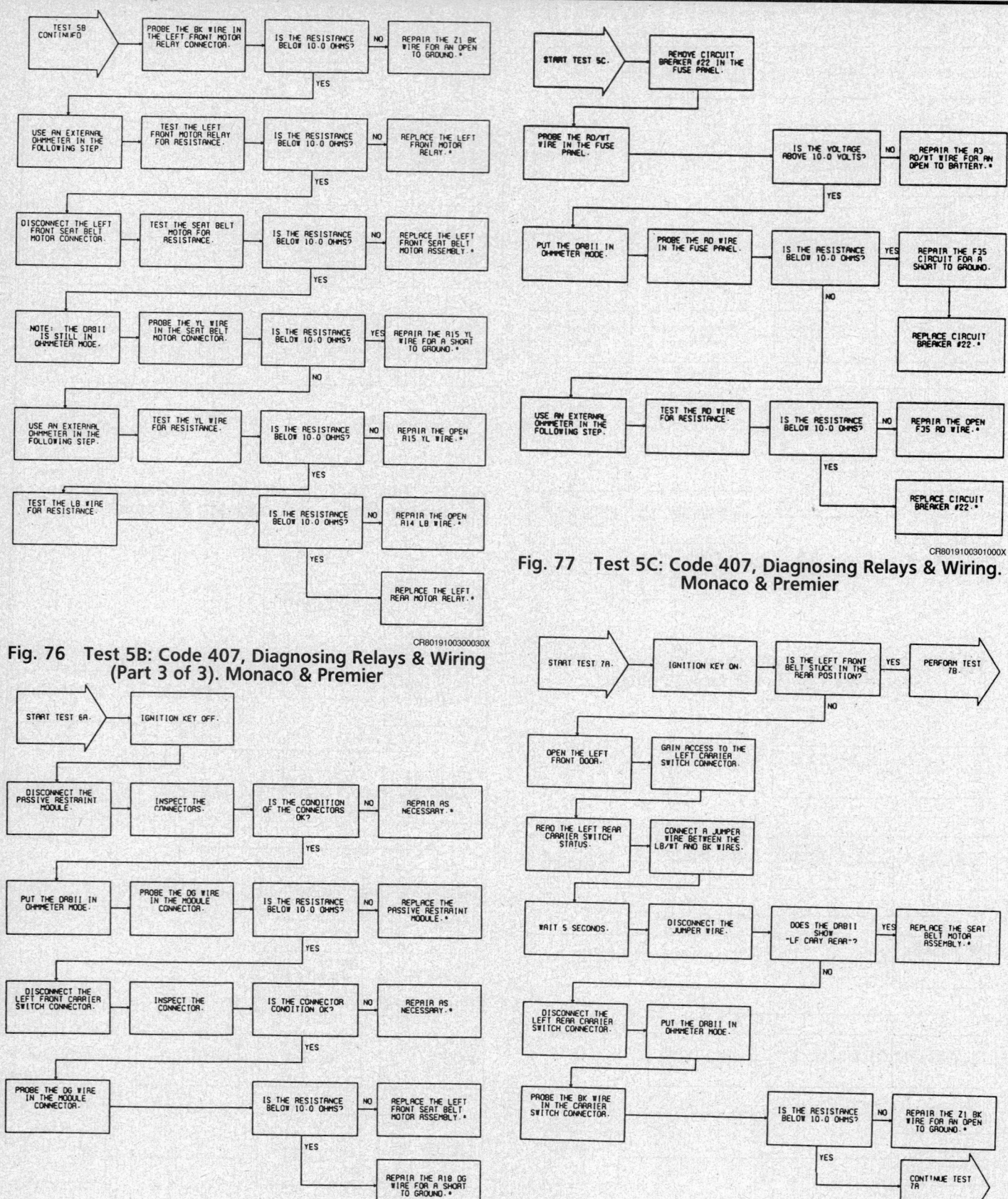

Fig. 76 Test 5B: Code 407, Diagnosing Relays & Wiring (Part 3 of 3). Monaco & Premier

Fig. 77 Test 5C: Code 407, Diagnosing Relays & Wiring. Monaco & Premier

Fig. 78 Test 6A: Code 408, Driver Forward Station Not Seen. Monaco & Premier

Fig. 79 Test 7A: Code 409, Driver Rear Station Seen (Part 1 of 2). Monaco & Premier

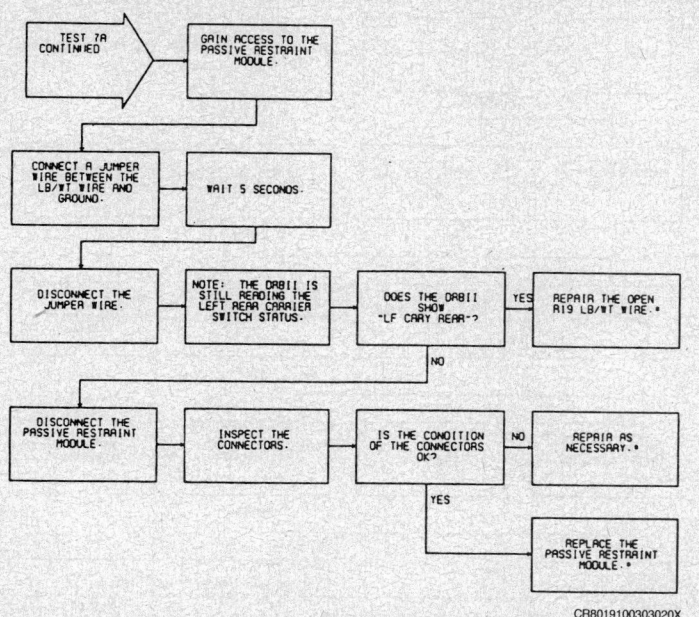

Fig. 79   Test 7A: Code 409, Driver Rear Station Seen (Part 2 of 2). Monaco & Premier

CR8019100303020X

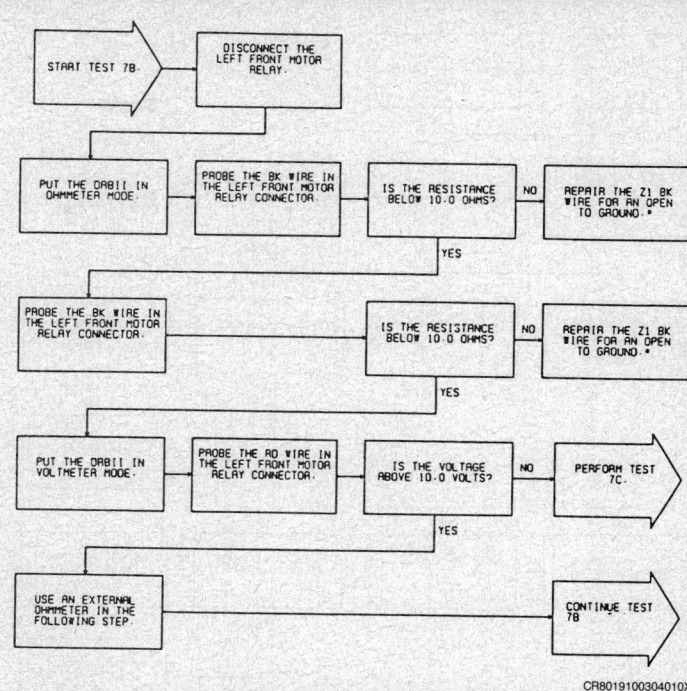

CR8019100304010X

Fig. 80   Test 7B: Code 409, Diagnosing Relays & Wiring (Part 1 of 3). Monaco & Premier

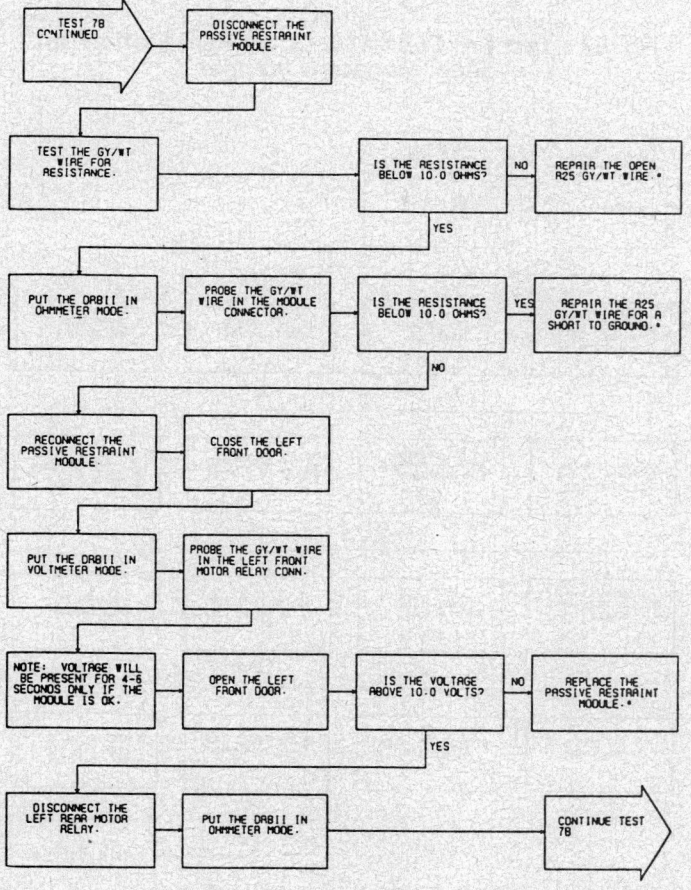

CR8019100304020X

Fig. 80   Test 7B: Code 409, Diagnosing Relays & Wiring (Part 2 of 3). Monaco & Premier

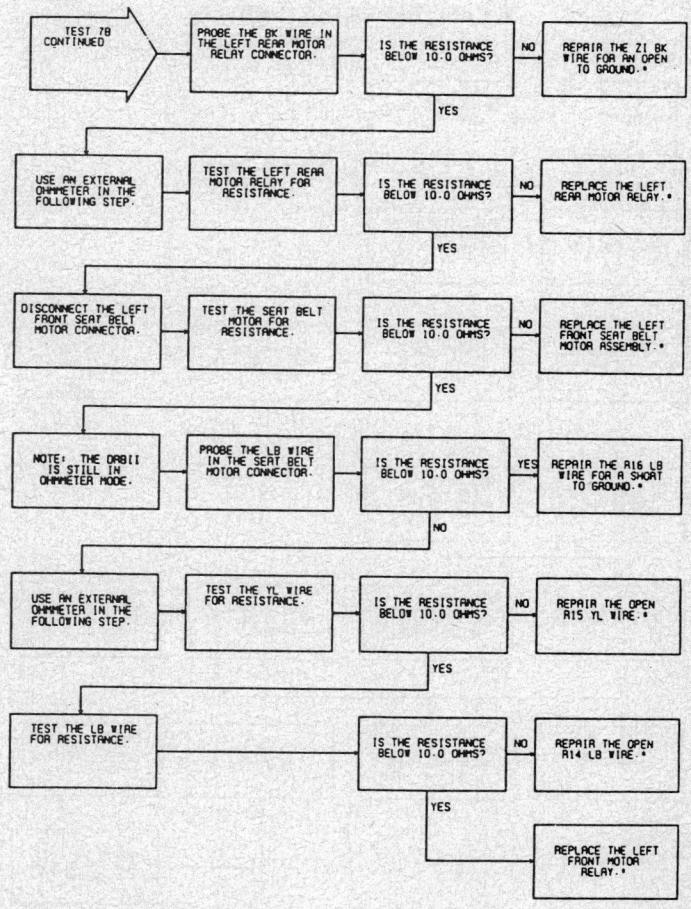

CR8019100304030X

Fig. 80   Test 7B: Code 409, Diagnosing Relays & Wiring (Part 3 of 3). Monaco & Premier

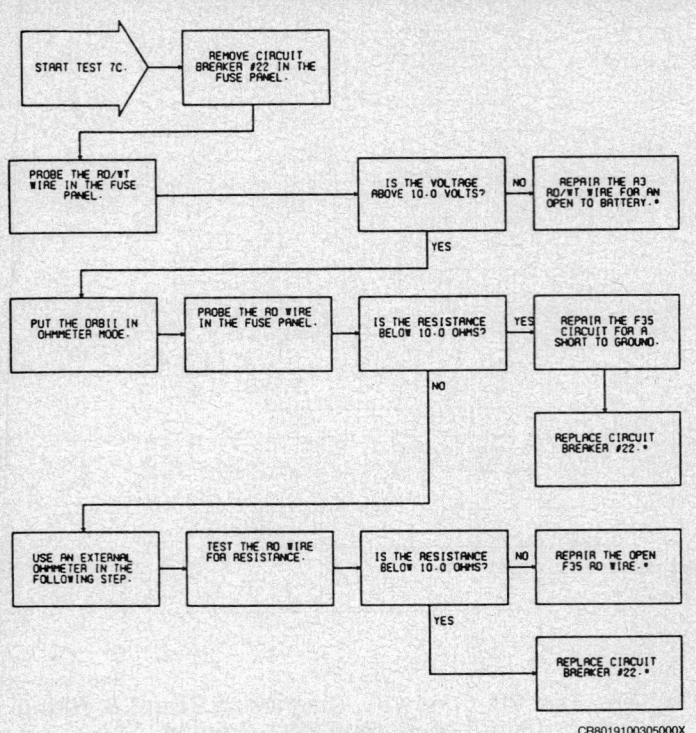

Fig. 81 Test 7C: Code 409, Diagnosing Relays & Wiring. Monaco & Premier

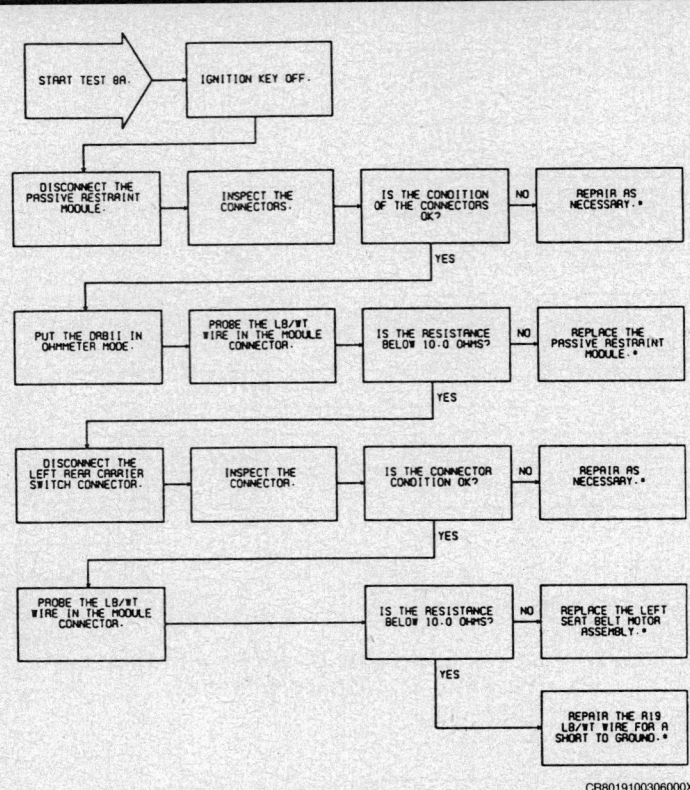

Fig. 82 Test 8A: Code 410, Driver Rear Station Not Seen. Monaco & Premier

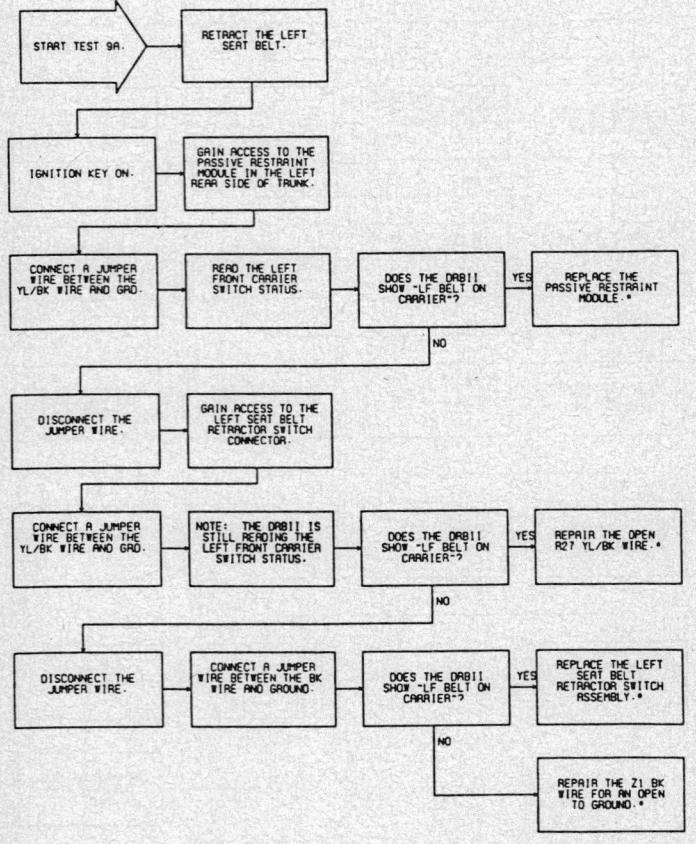

Fig. 83 Test 9A: Code 411, Driver Belt On Carriage Seen. Monaco & Premier

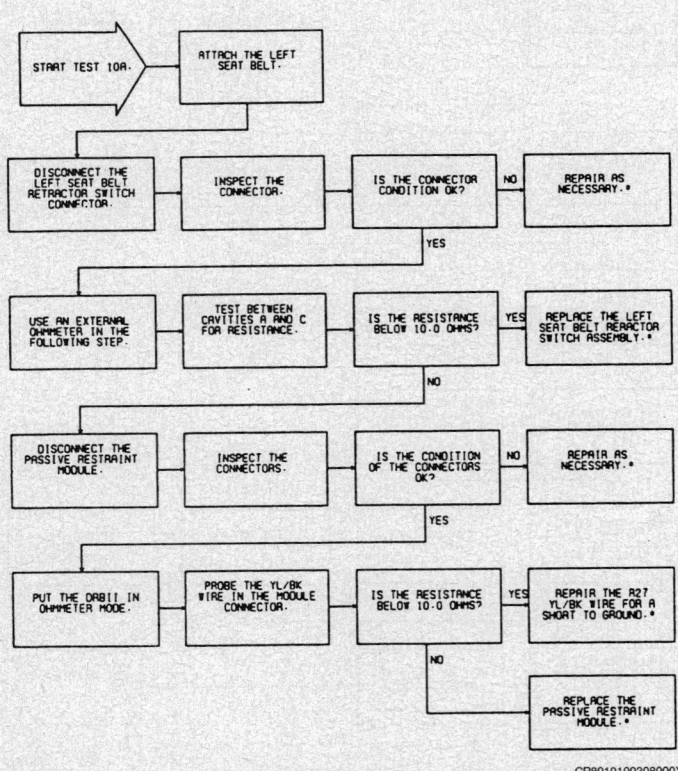

Fig. 84 Test 10A: Code 412, Driver Belt On Carriage Not Seen. Monaco & Premier

CR8019100309000X

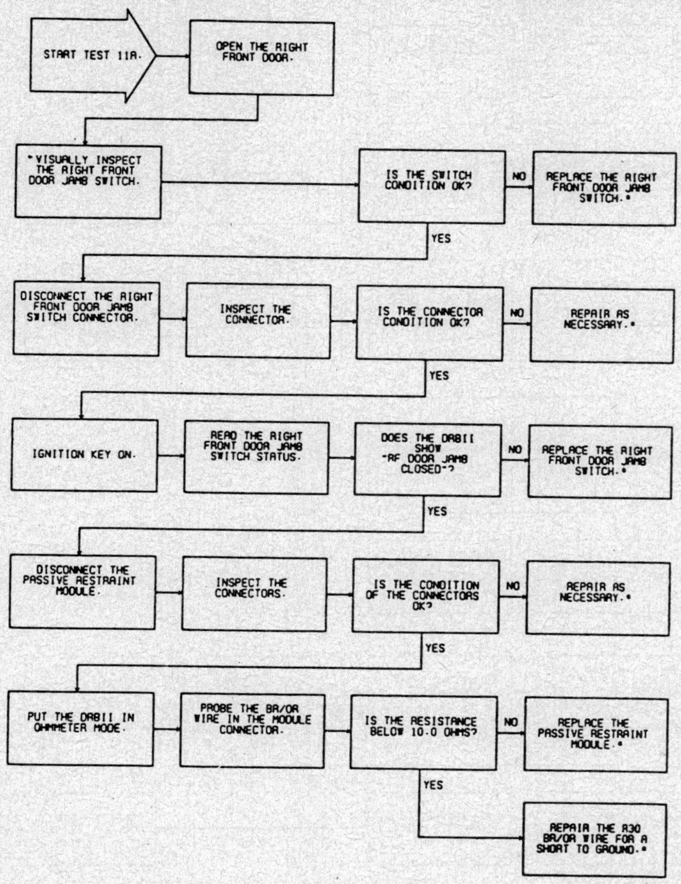

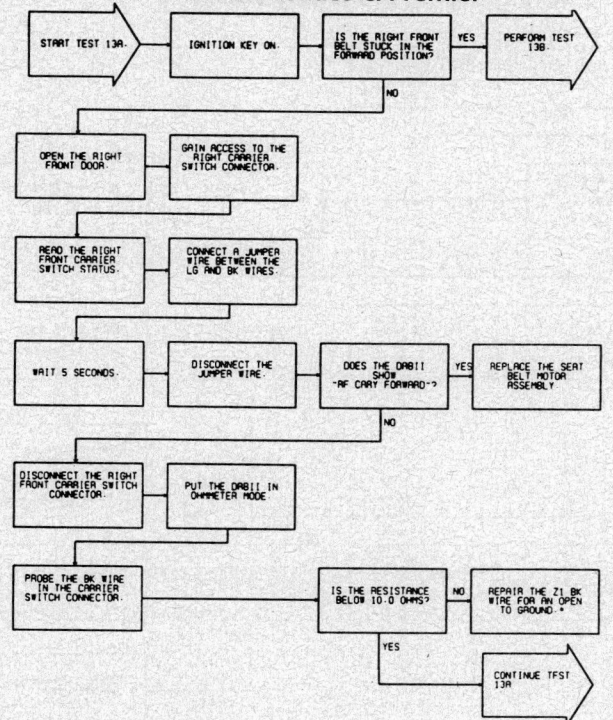

Fig. 85 Test 11A: Code 413, Passenger Door Switch Closed. Monaco & Premier

CR8019100310000X

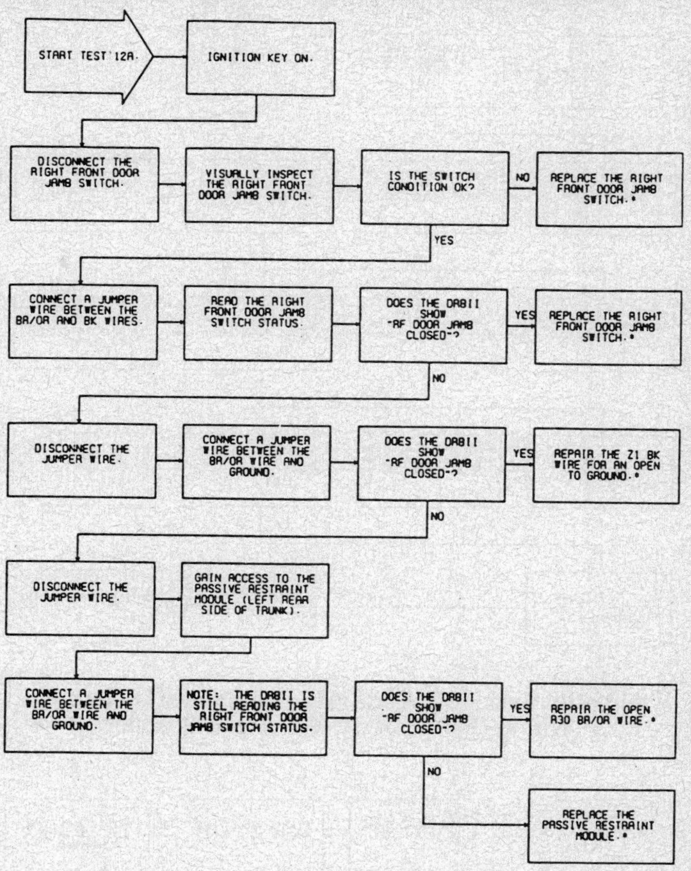

Fig. 86 Test 12A: Code 414, Passenger Door Switch Open. Monaco & Premier

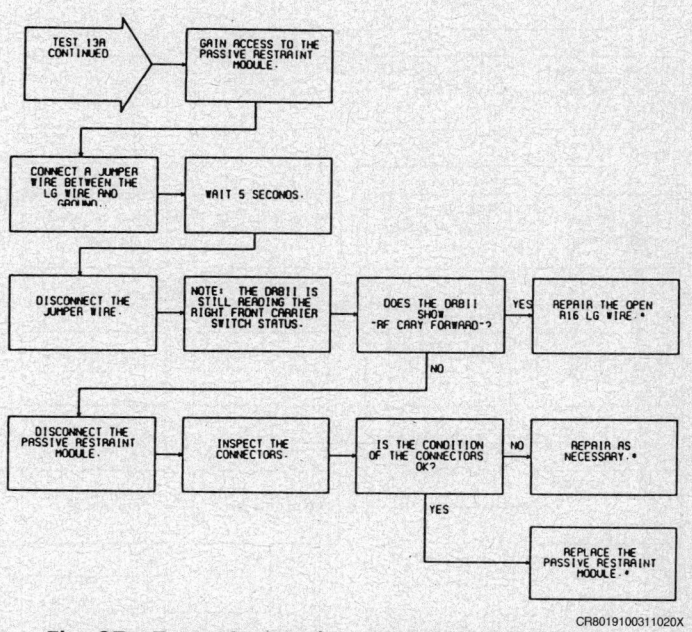

CR8019100311010X

Fig. 87 Test 13A: Code 415, Passenger Forward Station Seen (Part 1 of 2). Monaco & Premier

CR8019100311020X

Fig. 87 Test 13A: Code 415, Passenger Forward Station Seen (Part 2 of 2). Monaco & Premier

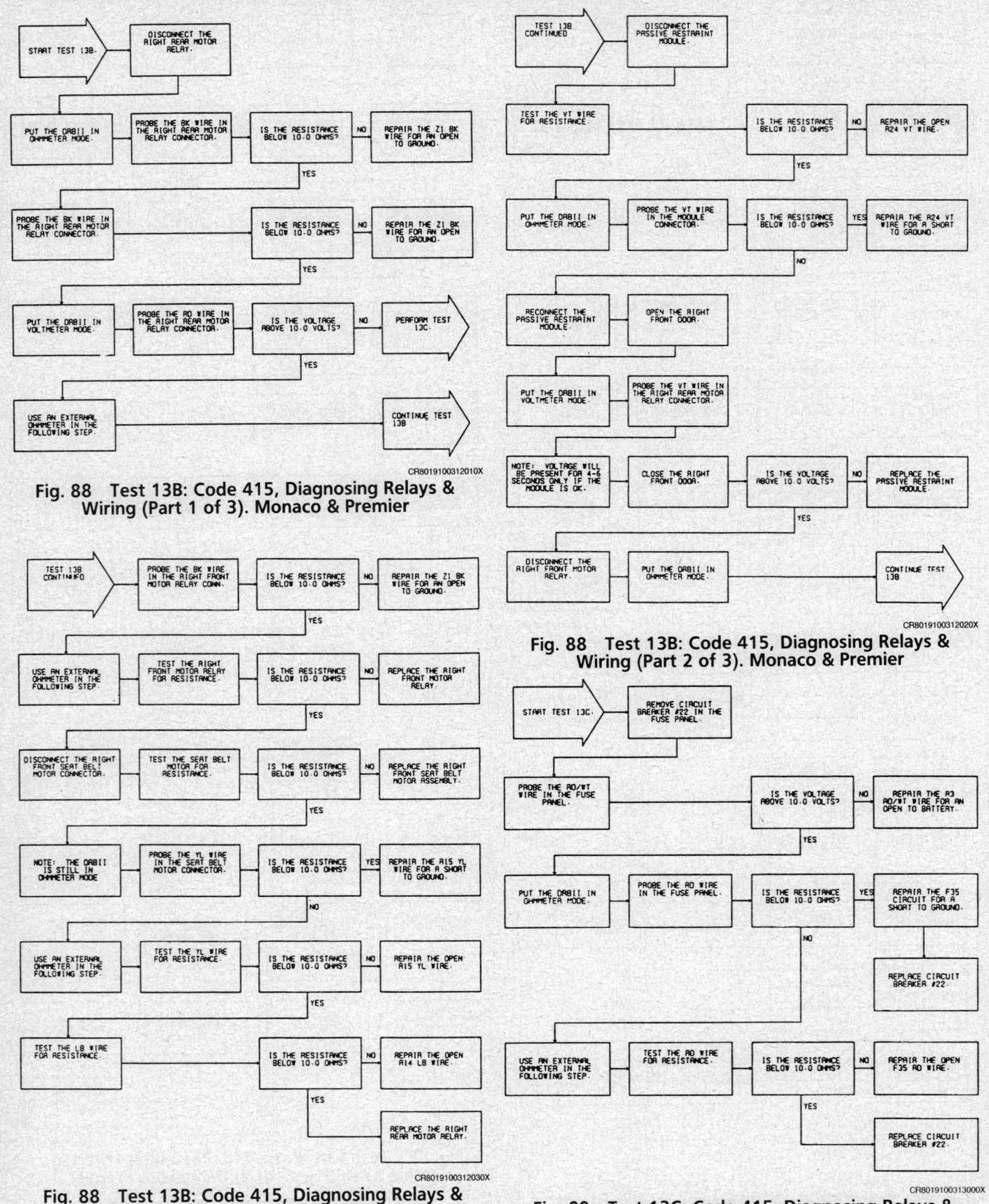

Fig. 88   Test 13B: Code 415, Diagnosing Relays & Wiring (Part 1 of 3). Monaco & Premier

Fig. 88   Test 13B: Code 415, Diagnosing Relays & Wiring (Part 2 of 3). Monaco & Premier

Fig. 88   Test 13B: Code 415, Diagnosing Relays & Wiring (Part 3 of 3). Monaco & Premier

Fig. 89   Test 13C: Code 415, Diagnosing Relays & Wiring. Monaco & Premier

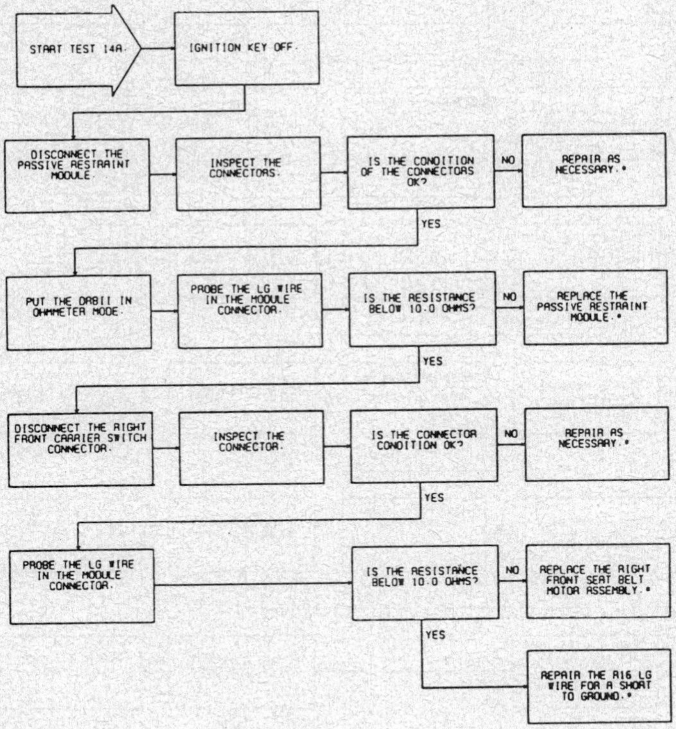

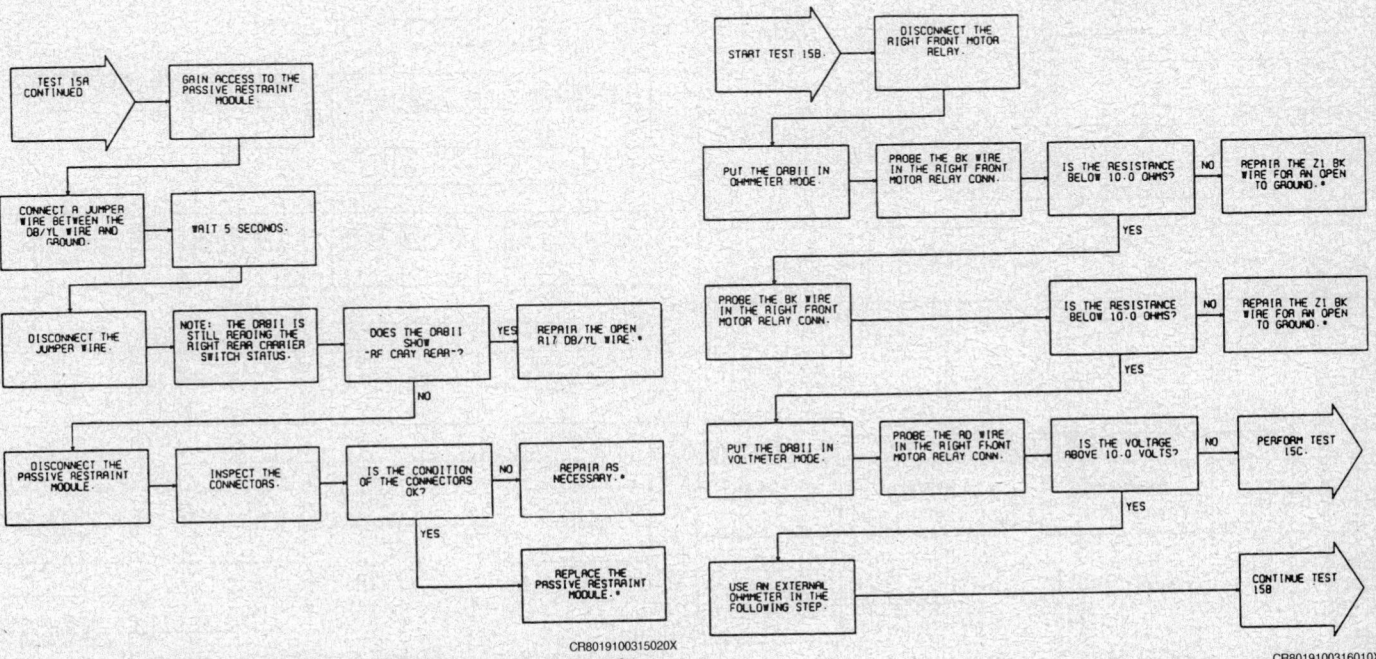

Fig. 90   Test 14A: Code 416, Passenger Forward Station Not Seen. Monaco & Premier

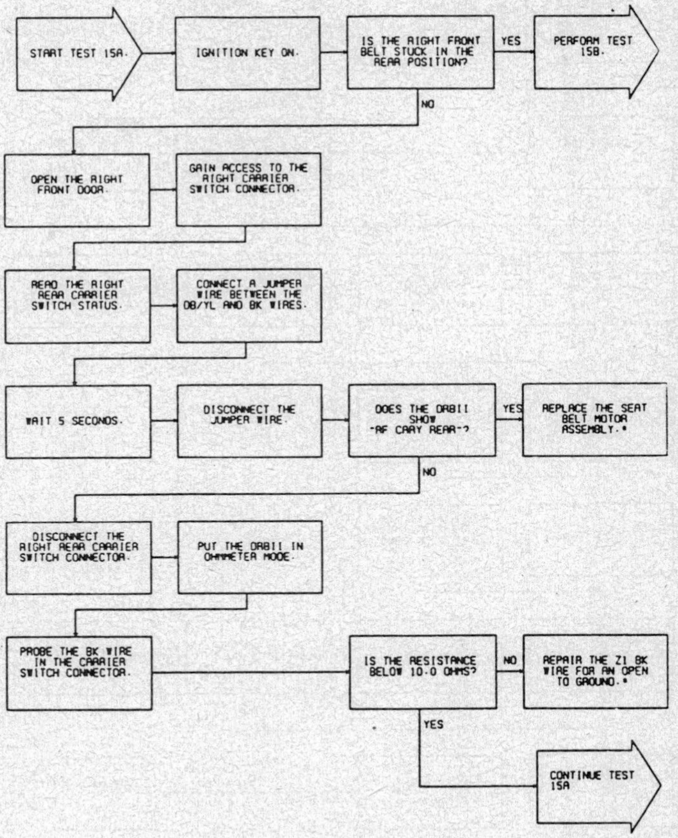

CR8019100314000X

Fig. 91   Test 15A: Code 417, Passenger Rear Station Seen (Part 1 of 2). Monaco & Premier

CR8019100315010X

Fig. 91   Test 15A: Code 417, Passenger Rear Station Seen (Part 2 of 2). Monaco & Premier

CR8019100315020X

Fig. 92   Test 15B: Code 417, Diagnosing Relays & Wiring (Part 1 of 3). Monaco & Premier

CR8019100316010X

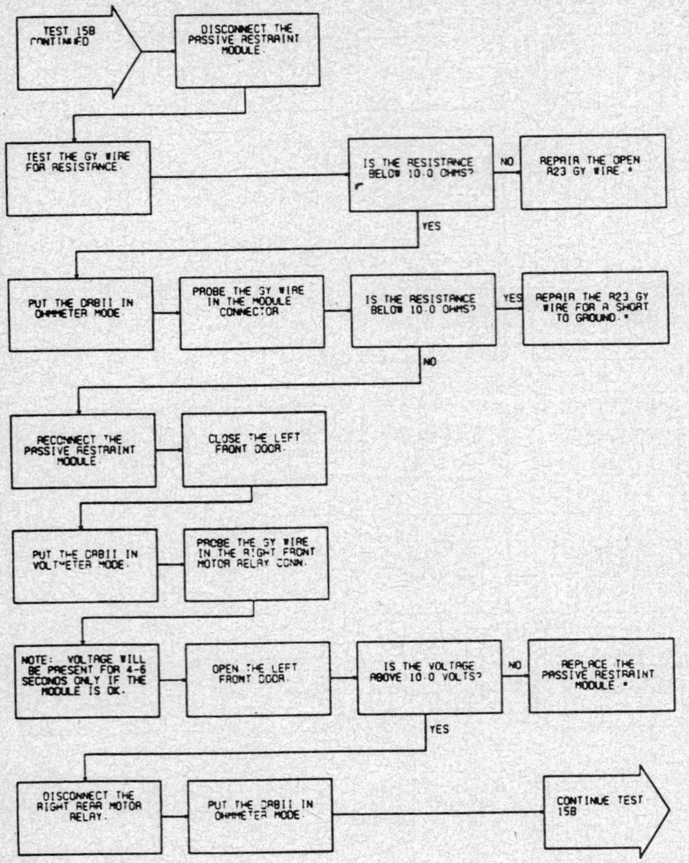

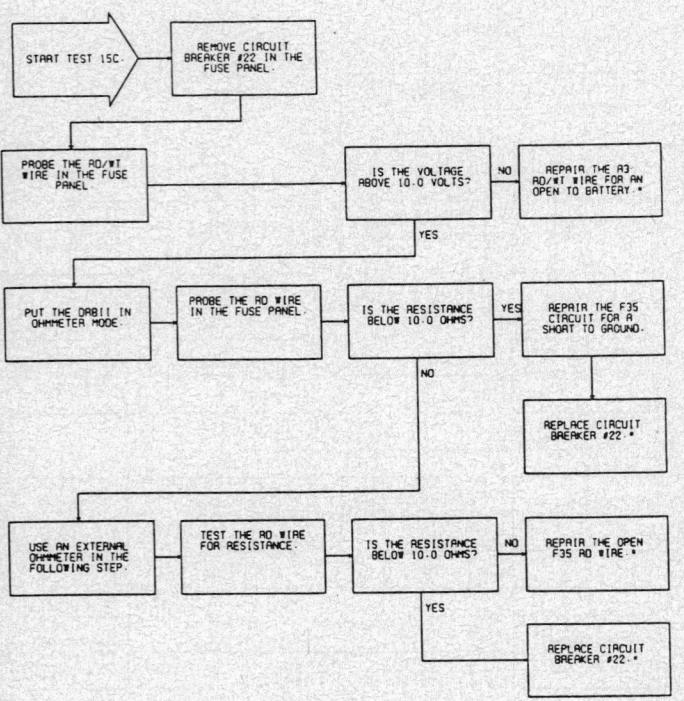

Fig. 92   Test 15B: Code 417, Diagnosing Relays &
Wiring (Part 2 of 3). Monaco & Premier

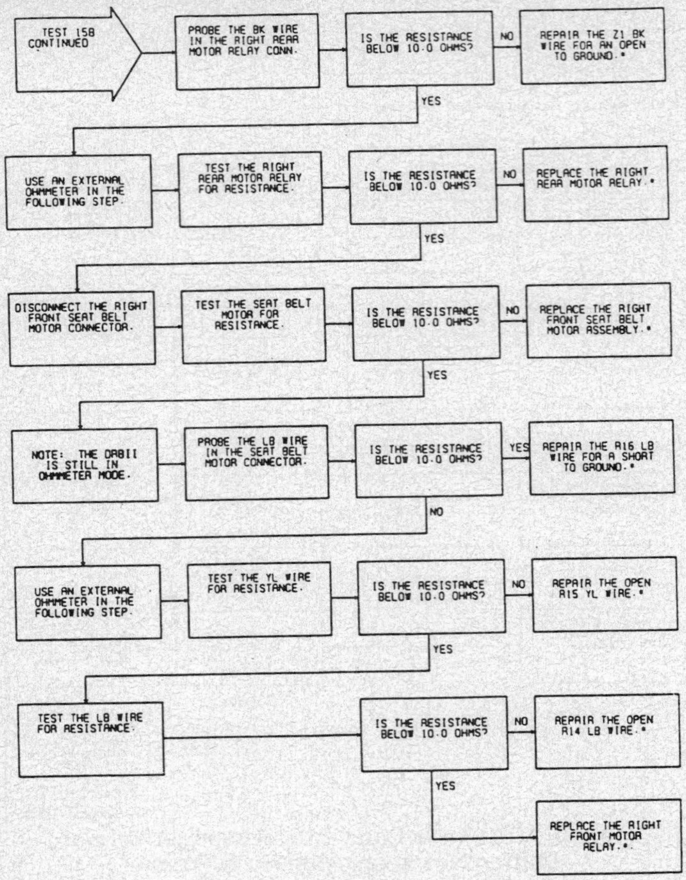

CR8019100316020X

Fig. 92   Test 15B: Code 417, Diagnosing Relays &
Wiring (Part 3 of 3). Monaco & Premier

CR8019100316030X

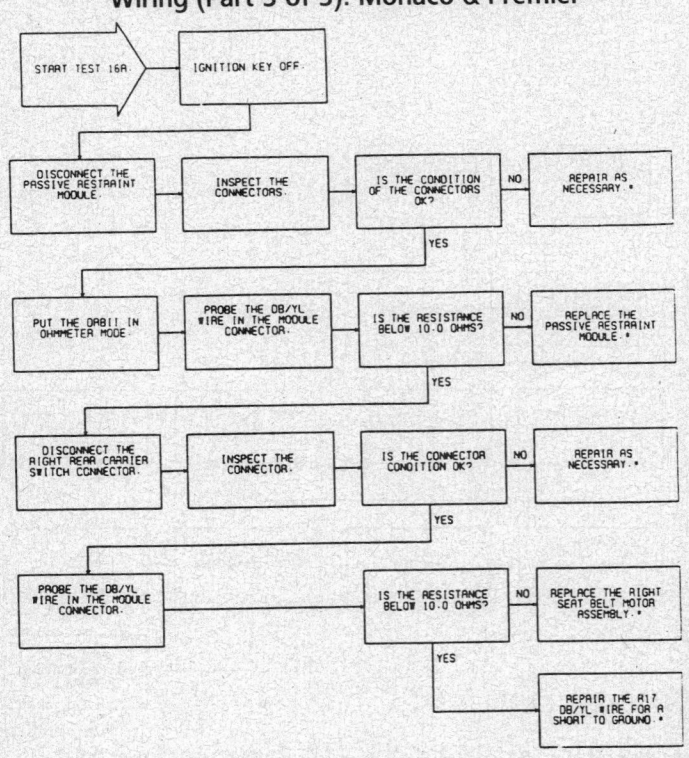

Fig. 93   Test 15C: Code 417, Diagnosing Relays &
Wiring. Monaco & Premier

CR8019100317000X

Fig. 94   Test 16A: Code 418, Passenger Rear Station
Not Seen. Monaco & Premier

CR8019100318000X

Front Position Switch "A"	Rear Position Switch "B"	Tab Or Carrier Position
Closed 0v	Open 12v	Tab or carrier in rear position
Open 12v	Closed 0v	Tab or carrier in front position
Closed 0v	Closed 0v	Tab or carrier leaving rear and moving to front
Closed 0v	Closed 0v	Tab or carrier leaving front and moving to rear

CR8019100287000X

Fig. 95 Carrier switch voltage. Monaco & Premier

Switch Position	Shoulder Belt Position
Open 12v	Shoulder belt should be extended and connected to the carrier or tab
Closed 0v	Shoulder belt retracted and/or disconnected from the carrier

CR8019100288000X

Fig. 96 Shoulder belt retractor switch voltage. Monaco & Premier

COMPONENT REPLACEMENT

MOTOR & TRACK ASSEMBLY

ACCLAIM, LEBARON SEDAN, SHADOW, SPIRIT & SUNDANCE

1. Remove interior trim panels as necessary to gain access to motor and track components, then disconnect electrical connector from motor.
2. Remove motor attaching nut, **Fig. 97**, then the two cable guide tube screws.
3. Remove track screws and lock box bolt, then remove track and drive assembly from vehicle.
4. Reverse procedure to install, noting the following:
   a. **Torque** drive motor mounting nut to 15 ft. lbs.
   b. **On Acclaim, LeBaron Sedan and Spirit, torque** forward track screw to 36 inch lbs. and remaining track screws to 35 inch lbs.
   c. **On Shadow & Sundance, torque** forward track screw to 36 inch lbs. and track bolts to 12 ft. lbs.
   d. **On all models, torque** lock box bolt to 29 ft. lbs. and cable guide tube screws to 17 inch lbs.

COLT & SUMMIT

1992

Refer to **Fig. 98** when performing the following procedure.
1. **On Colt and Summit hatchback,** proceed as follows:
   a. Remove scuff plate, then upper and lower quarter trim.
   b. Remove front pillar trim, then the front belt rail trim.
   c. Remove headliner.
2. **On Colt and Summit sedan,** proceed as follows:
   a. Remove front and rear scuff plates.
   b. Remove center pillar upper and lower trim panels.
   c. Remove front pillar trim panel, then the front belt rail trim.
   d. Remove headliner.
3. **On all models,** remove shoulder belt tongue plate.
4. Disconnect release switch connector.

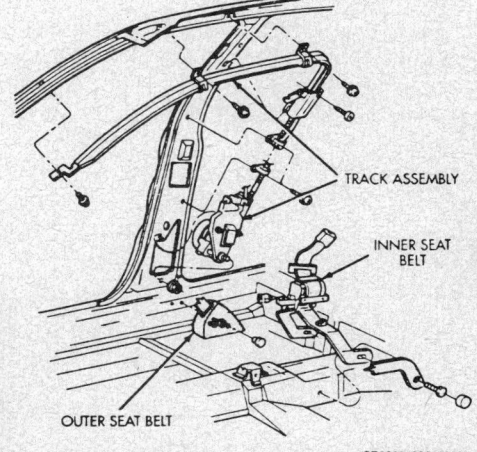

Fig. 97 Seat belt motor & track replacement. Acclaim, LeBaron Sedan, Shadow, Spirit & Sundance

CR8029400036000X

5. Disconnect seat belt wiring harness connector.
6. Remove outer casing mounting bolts.
7. Remove motor mounting bolts.
8. Remove guide rail mounting bolts, then the track and motor assembly.
9. Reverse procedure to install.

1993–94

Replace automatic seat belt components in numbered sequence shown in **Fig. 99**.

COLT VISTA & SUMMIT WAGON

1992

Refer to **Fig. 100** when performing the following procedure.
1. Remove front and rear scuff plates.
2. Remove center pillar corner garnish.
3. Remove center pillar upper and lower trim panels.
4. Remove front pillar trim panel, then the flange trim.
5. Remove shoulder belt tongue plate.
6. Disconnect release switch connector.
7. Disconnect seat belt wiring harness connector.
8. Remove outer casing mounting bolts.
9. Remove motor mounting bolts.
10. Remove guide rail mounting bolts, then the track and motor assembly.
11. Reverse procedure to install.

1993

Replace automatic seat belt components in numbered sequence shown in **Fig. 101**.

1994

Replace automatic seat belt components in numbered sequence shown in **Fig. 102**.

LASER & TALON

Refer to **Fig. 103** when performing the following procedure.
1. Remove scuff plates, quarter trim, center and front pillar trim.
2. Disconnect seat belt wiring harness connector.
3. Remove outer casing mounting bolts.
4. Remove motor mounting bolts.
5. Remove guide rail mounting bolts, then the track and motor assembly.
6. Reverse procedure to install.

MONACO & PREMIER

1. Remove front door garnish molding, then the B-pillar trim, **Fig. 104**.
2. Remove lower door opening trim, then move trim back to gain access to motor mounting bolts.
3. Disconnect electrical connector at motor.
4. Remove track and motor assembly.
5. Reverse procedure to install. **Torque** motor mounting bolts to 3.7 ft. lbs., lock box mounting bolt to 24 ft. lbs. and track mounting bolts to 12 inch lbs.

SHOULDER BELT

Colt, Colt Vista, Laser, Summit, Summit Wagon & Talon

1. Remove shoulder belt tongue plate, then the guide ring.
2. Remove rear console box.
3. Disconnect outer switch connector, then remove retractor assembly.
4. Reverse procedure to install.

SHOULDER BELT RETRACTOR

Acclaim, LeBaron Sedan & Spirit w/Floor Console

1. Disconnect shoulder belt buckle from carrier, then remove bolt covers, lock

Continued on page 16-63

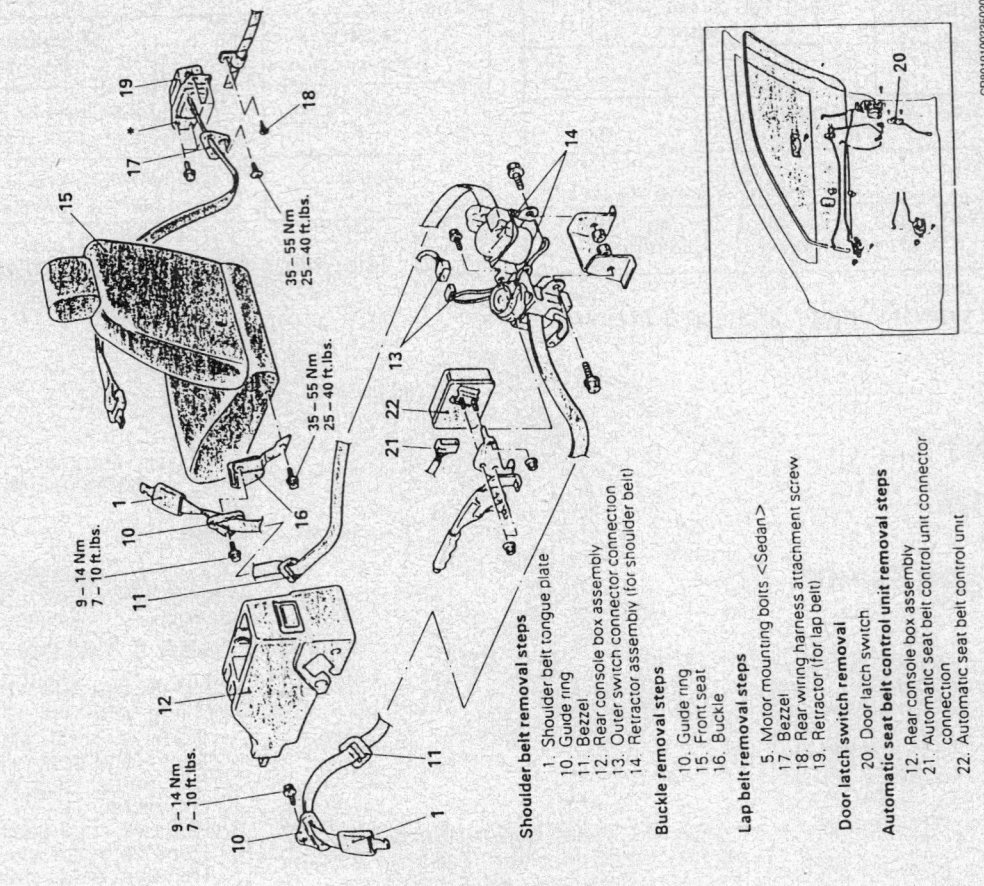

Fig. 98 Automatic seat belt system (Part 2 of 2). 1992 Colt & Summit

Shoulder belt removal steps
1. Shoulder belt tongue plate
10. Guide ring
11. Bezzel
12. Rear console box assembly
13. Outer switch connector connection
14. Retractor assembly (for shoulder belt)

Buckle removal steps
10. Guide ring
15. Front seat
16. Buckle

Lap belt removal steps
5. Motor mounting bolts <Sedan>
17. Bezzel
18. Rear wiring harness attachment screw
19. Retractor (for lap belt)

Door latch switch removal
20. Door latch switch

Automatic seat belt control unit removal steps
12. Rear console box assembly
21. Automatic seat belt control unit connector connection
22. Automatic seat belt control unit

35 – 55 Nm
25 – 40 ft.lbs.

9 – 14 Nm
7 – 10 ft.lbs.

Fig. 98 Automatic seat belt system (Part 1 of 2). 1992 Colt & Summit

<Automatic Seat Belt – Hatchback>

<Automatic Seat Belt – Sedan>

Driving device assembly removal steps
1. Shoulder belt tongue plate
2. Release switch connector connection
3. Automatic seat belt wiring harness connector connection
4. Outer casing mounting bolts
5. Motor mounting bolts
6. Guide rail mounting bolts (A)
7. Guide rail mounting bolts (B)
8. Guide rail mounting bolts (C)
9. Driving device assembly

16 – 23 Nm
12 – 17 ft.lbs.

4 – 6 Nm
3 – 4 ft.lbs.

35 – 55 Nm
25 – 40 ft.lbs.

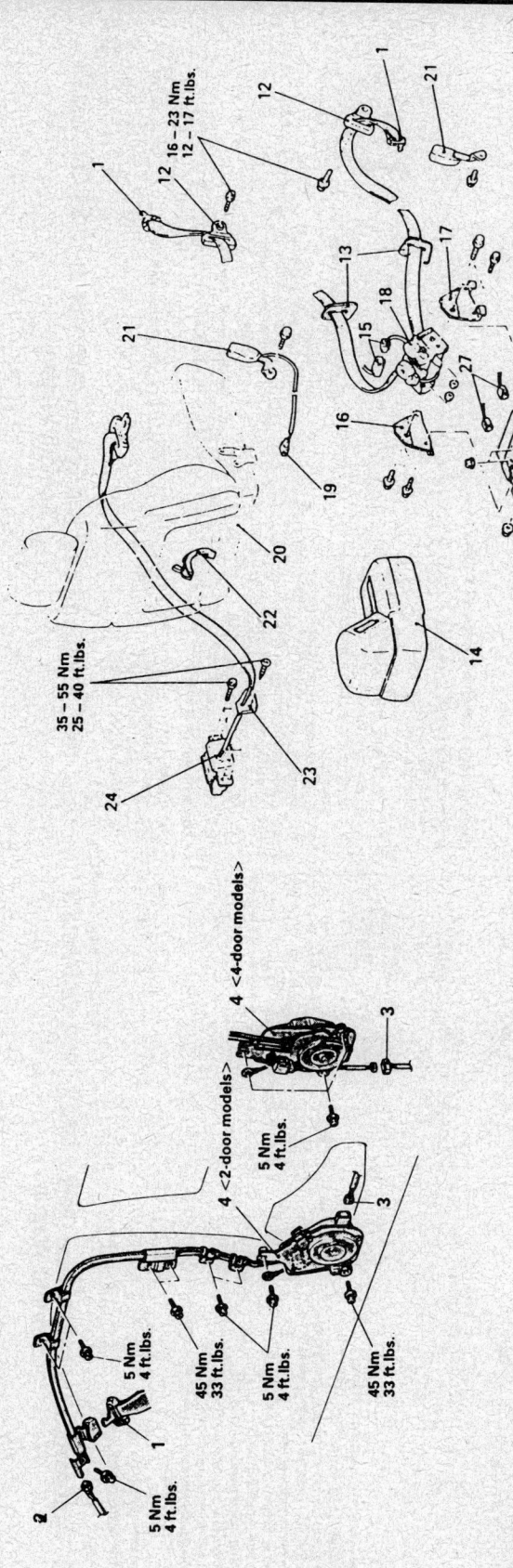

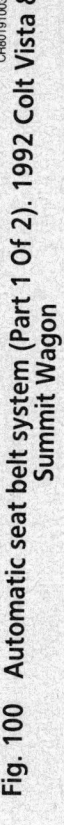

2
5 Nm
4 ft.lbs.
1
5 Nm
4 ft.lbs.
45 Nm
33 ft.lbs.
5 Nm
4 ft.lbs.
4 <2-door models>
4 <4-door models>
5 Nm
4 ft.lbs.
45 Nm
33 ft.lbs.
3
3

Driving device assembly removal steps

- Front pillar trim
1. Shoulder belt tongue plate
2. Release switch connector
3. Harness connector
4. Driving device assembly

Shoulder belt removal steps

- Rear console box assembly

5. Outer switch connector
6. Automatic seat belt control unit connector
7. Automatic seat belt control unit
8. Retractor assembly (for shoulder belt)

Buckle removal steps

- Rear console box assembly

9. Harness connector <driver's side>
10. Front seat
- Front seat hinge cover
11. Buckle

Lap belt removal steps

- Scuff plate or center pillar lower trim

12. Retractor assembly (for lap belt)

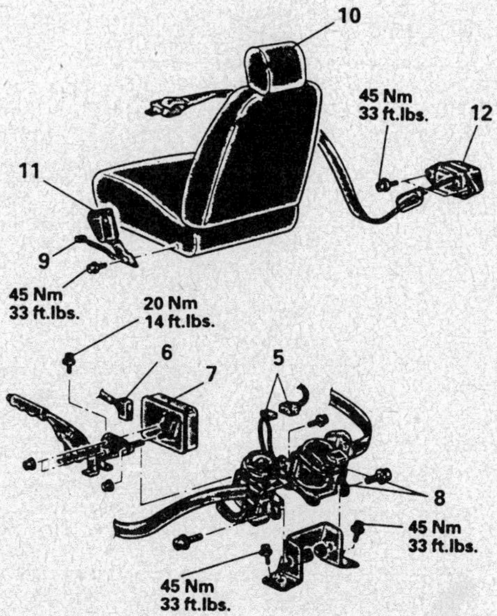

10
45 Nm
33 ft.lbs.
12
11
9
45 Nm
33 ft.lbs.
20 Nm
14 ft.lbs.
6
7
5
8
45 Nm
33 ft.lbs.
45 Nm
33 ft.lbs.

CR8019100336000X

Fig. 99 Automatic seat belt system. 1993–94 Colt & Summit

35 – 55 Nm
25 – 40 ft.lbs.
24
1
21
12
16 – 23 Nm
12 – 17 ft.lbs.
12
22
20
23
19
16
13
15
18
1
21
17
27
14
25
28
26

Shoulder belt removal steps

1. Shoulder belt tongue plate
12. Guide ring
13. Bezzel
14. Rear console box assembly
15. Outer switch connector connection
16. Retractor bracket (L.H)
17. Retractor bracket (R.H.)
18. Retractor assembly (for shoulder belt)

Buckle removal steps

12. Guide ring
19. Buckle switch connector connection
20. Front seat
21. Buckle

Lap belt removal steps

22. Removal of lap belt from belt holder
23. Bezzel
24. Retractor (for lap belt)

Automatic seat belt control unit removal steps

14. Rear console box assembly
25. Automatic seat belt control unit connector connection
26. Automatic seat belt control unit

Automatic seat belt motor relay removal steps

14. Rear console box assembly
27. Automatic seat belt motor relay connector connection
28. Automatic seat belt motor relay

CR8019100337010X

Fig. 100 Automatic seat belt system (Part 1 Of 2). 1992 Colt Vista & Summit Wagon

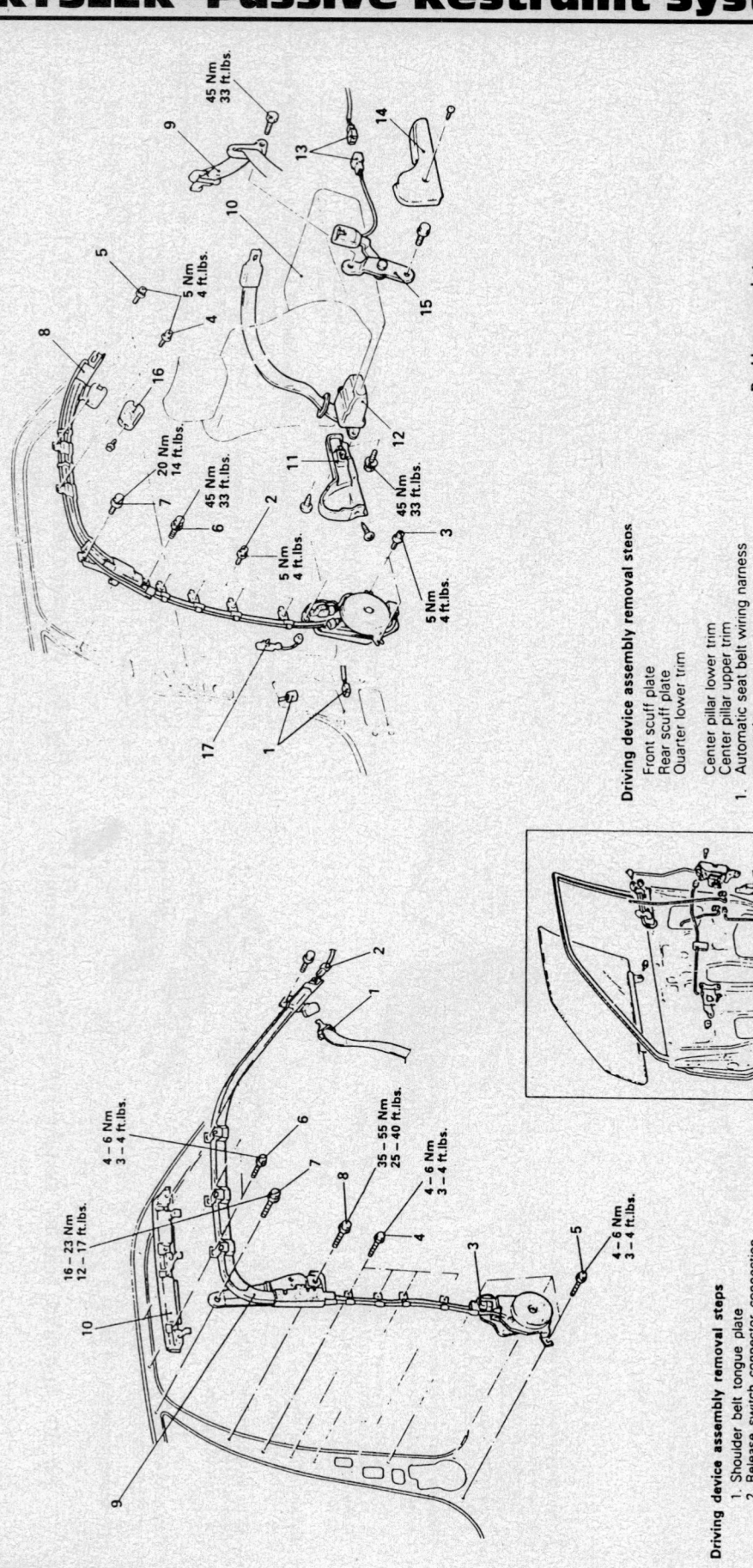

CRB0193003380I0X

Driving device assembly removal steps

Front scuff plate
Rear scuff plate
Quarter lower trim

Center pillar lower trim
Center pillar upper trim
1. Automatic seat belt wiring harness connector
2. Outer casing mounting bolt
3. Motor mounting bolt
4. Guide rail mounting bolt (A)
5. Guide rail mounting bolt (B)
6. Guide rail mounting bolt (C)
7. Guide rail mounting bolt (D)
8. Driving device assembly

Lap belt removal steps
9. Guide ring
10. Front seat assembly
11. Front seat side shield
12. Retractor (for lap belt)

Buckle removal steps
9. Guide ring
10. Front seat assembly
13. Seat belt switch connector (L.H. only)
14. Free hinge cover
15. Buckle

Buckle cover removal
16. Buckle cover

Door latch switch removal
17. Door latch switch

Fig. 101 Automatic seat belt system (Part 1 of 2). 1993 Colt Vista & Summit Wagon

CRB0191003370Z0X

Driving device assembly removal steps
1. Shoulder belt tongue plate
2. Release switch connector connection
3. Automatic seat belt wiring harness connector connection
4. Outer casing connection
5. Motor mounting bolts
6. Guide rail mounting bolts (A)
7. Guide rail mounting bolts (B)
8. Guide rail mounting bolts (C)
9. Driving device assembly
10. Roof side bracket

Door latch switch removal
11. Door latch switch

Fig. 100 Automatic seat belt system (Part 2 of 2). 1992 Colt Vista & Summit Wagon

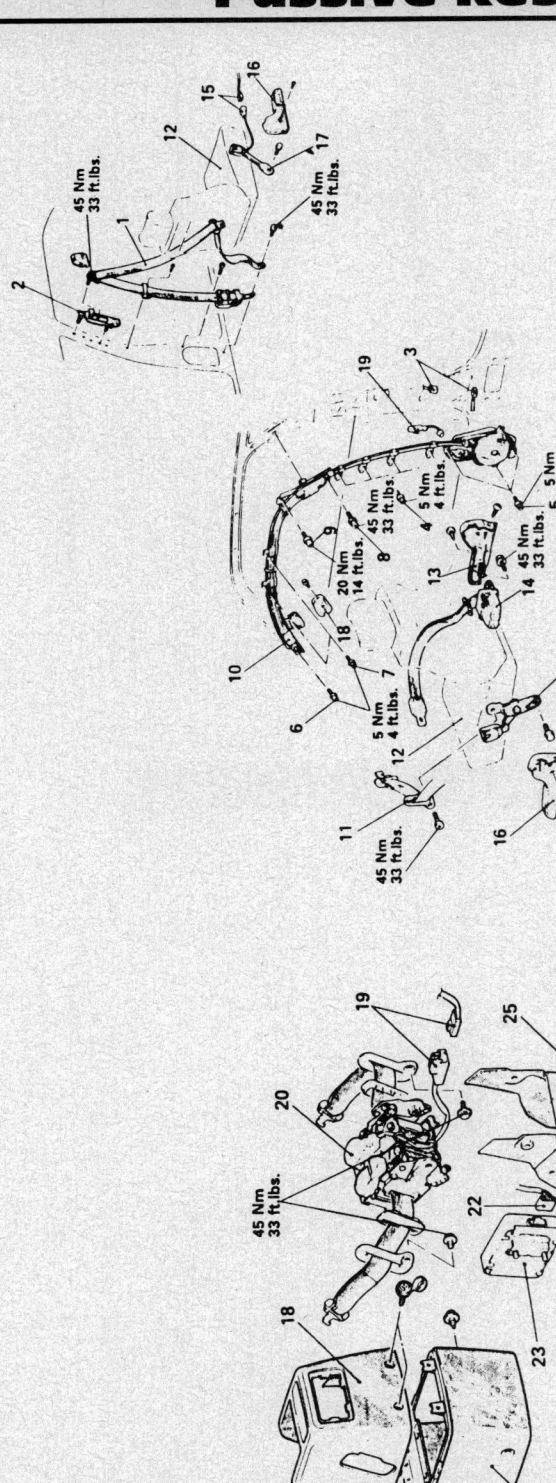

Retractor assembly removal steps

18. Rear console upper
19. Harness connector
20. Retractor assembly (for shoulder belt)

Control unit removal steps

18. Rear console upper
21. Rear console lower
22. Harness connector
23. Control unit

Retractor mounting bracket removal steps

18. Rear console upper
20. Retractor assembly (for shoulder belt)
21. Rear console lower
23. Control unit
24. Floor console
25. Retractor mounting braket

Buzzer removal steps

Instrument under cover
26. Buzzer

Fig. 101 Automatic seat belt system (Part 2 of 2). 1993 Colt Vista & Summit Wagon

CR801930003B020X

Front seat belt assembly removal steps

- Center pillar lower trim
- Center pillar upper trim

1. Front seat belt assembly
2. Slider

Driving device assembly removal steps

- Front scuff plate
- Rear scuff plate
- Quarter lower trim

- Center pillar lower trim
- Center pillar upper trim

3. Automatic seat belt wiring harness connector
4. Outer casing mounting bolt
5. Motor mounting bolt
6. Guide rail mounting bolt (A)
7. Guide rail mounting bolt (B)
8. Guide rail mounting bolt (C)
9. Guide rail mounting bolt (D)
10. Driving device assembly

Lap belt removal steps

11. Guide ring
12. Front seat assembly
13. Front seat side shield
14. Retractor (for lap belt)

Buckle removal steps

11. Guide ring
12. Front seat assembly
15. Buckle switch connector (L.H. only)
16. Free hinge cover
17. Buckle

Buckle cover removal

18. Buckle cover

Door latch switch removal

19. Door latch switch

Fig. 102 Automatic seat belt components (Part 1 of 2). 1994 Colt Vista & Summit Wagon

CR802940001S010X

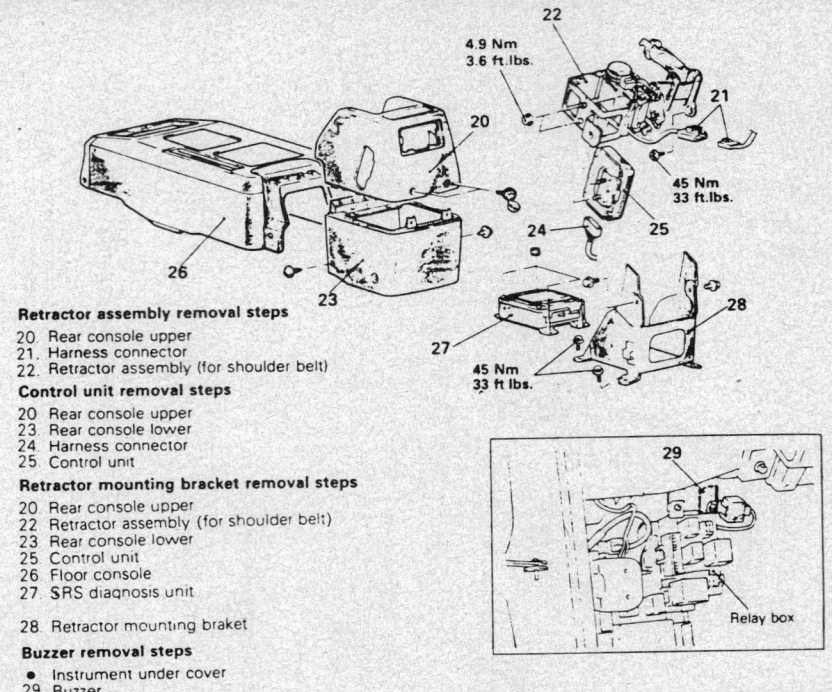

Retractor assembly removal steps

20. Rear console upper
21. Harness connector
22. Retractor assembly (for shoulder belt)

Control unit removal steps

20. Rear console upper
23. Rear console lower
24. Harness connector
25. Control unit

Retractor mounting bracket removal steps

20. Rear console upper
22. Retractor assembly (for shoulder belt)
23. Rear console lower
25. Control unit
26. Floor console
27. SRS diagnosis unit

28. Retractor mounting braket

Buzzer removal steps

- Instrument under cover
29. Buzzer

Fig. 102 Automatic seat belt components (Part 2 of 2). 1994 Colt Vista & Summit Wagon

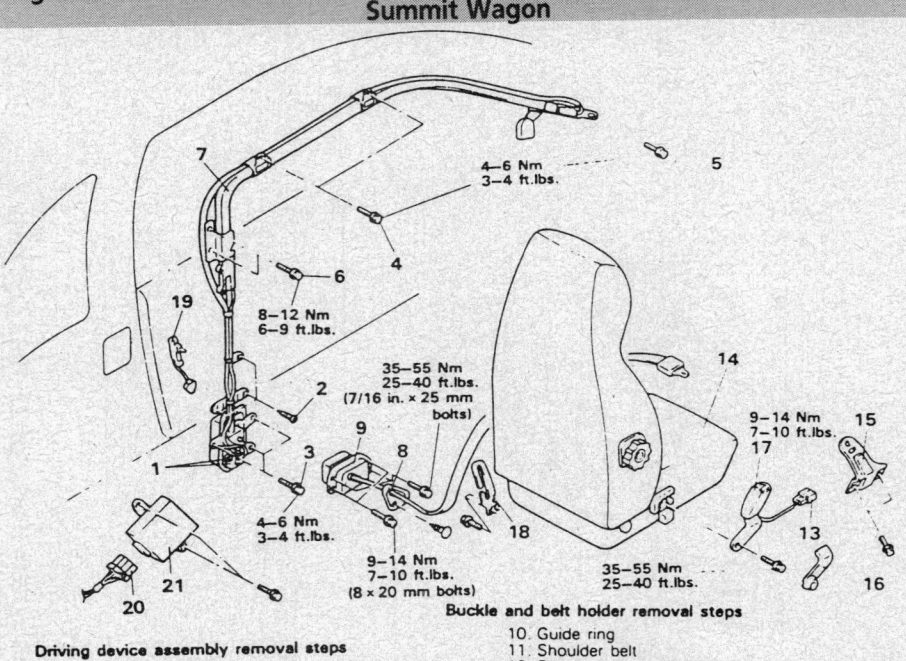

Driving device assembly removal steps

Scuff plate
Quarter trim
Center pillar trim
Front pillar trim
1. Automatic seat belt wiring harness connector connection
2. Outer casing mounting screws
3. Motor mounting bolts
4. Guide rail mounting bolts (A)
5. Guide rail mounting bolt (B)
6. Guide rail mounting bolts (C)
7. Driving device assembly

Lap belt removal steps

Scuff plate
Quarter trim
8. Bezzel
9. Retractor (for lap belt)

Buckle and belt holder removal steps

10. Guide ring
11. Shoulder belt
12. Floor console assembly
13. Seat belt switch connector connection (L.H. only)
14. Front seat assembly
15. Guide ring bracket
16. Buckle cover
17. Buckle
18. Belt holder

Door latch switch removal

19. Door latch switch

Automatic seat belt control unit removal steps

Scuff plate
Quarter trim
20. Automatic seat belt control unit connector connection
21. Automatic seat belt control unit

Fig. 103 Automatic seat belt system (Part 1 Of 2). Laser & Talon

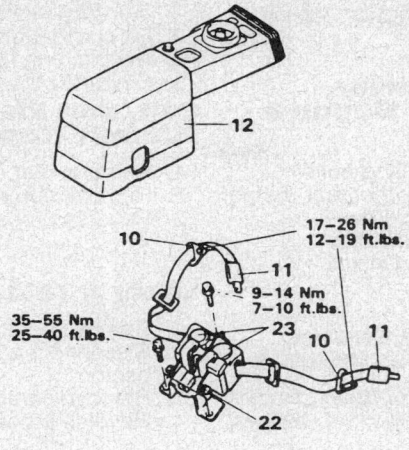

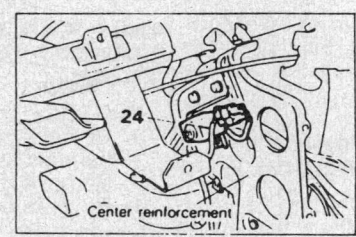

17—26 Nm
12—19 ft.lbs.

9—14 Nm
7—10 ft.lbs.

35—55 Nm
25—40 ft.lbs.

Center reinforcement

Shoulder belt removal steps

10. Guide ring
11. Shoulder belt
12. Floor console assembly
22. Outer switch connector connection
23. Retractor assembly (for shoulder belt)

Buzzer removal steps

Instrument panel assembly

24. Buzzer

CR8019100339020X

Fig. 103   Automatic seat belt system (Part 2 Of 2). Laser & Talon

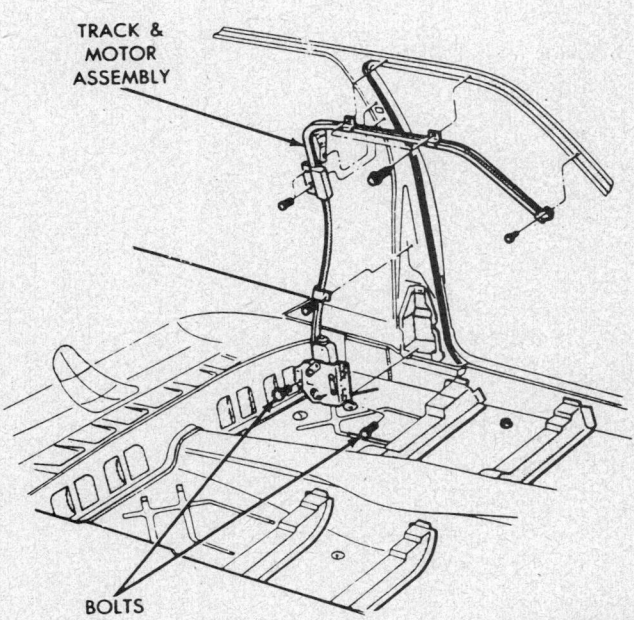

TRACK & MOTOR ASSEMBLY

BOLTS

CR8019100340000X

Fig. 104   Track & motor assembly. Monaco & Premier

bar bolts and seat belt bolts.
2. Remove console and cupholder side plugs to gain access to screws, then remove screws and lift console out of position.
3. Disconnect electrical connector, then remove console and retractor assembly from vehicle.
4. If necessary, separate retractor from console by releasing bezel from console opening. **Do not attempt to separate bezel from retractor assembly.**
5. Reverse procedure to install, noting the following:
   a. **Torque** rear console to front console screws to 17 inch lbs. and console to body screws to 16 ft. lbs.
   b. **Torque** lock bar and seat belt bolts to 29 ft. lbs.

Shadow & Sundance

1. Disconnect shoulder belt buckle from carrier, then remove armrest and disconnect electrical connector at front of console.
2. Remove stub nuts and driver's side buckle, then remove bolt and washer from floor on passenger's side and lift retractor assembly out of position.
3. Reverse procedure to install. **Torque** driver's side buckle bolt and passenger's side bolt and washer to 29 ft. lbs., stub nuts to 9 ft. lbs. and armrest screws to 17 inch lbs.

Monaco & Premier

1. Remove center console as follows:
   a. Remove ash tray and ash tray receiver, the disconnect connector from cigar lighter.

CHRYSLER—Passive Restraint Systems

b. Remove armrest, then console.
2. From inside of vehicle, remove retractor assembly.
3. Reverse procedure to install. **Torque** retractor bolts to 27 ft. lbs. and seat belt anchor brace to 26 ft. lbs.

BUCKLE

Colt, Colt Vista, Laser, Summit, Summit Wagon & Talon

1. Remove guide ring, then the front seat.
2. Remove buckle.
3. Reverse procedure to install.

Shadow & Sundance

Refer to "Shoulder Belt Retractor" in this section when replacing buckle.

LAP BELT

Colt, Colt Vista, Laser, Summit, Summit Wagon & Talon

1. Remove motor mounting bolts.
2. Remove bezel, then the rear wiring harness attachment screw.
3. Remove retractor assembly.
4. Reverse procedure to install.

CONTROL UNIT

Acclaim, LeBaron Sedan, Shadow, Spirit & Sundance

1. With passenger's door open, remove kick panel and scuff plate screws, then lift panel and plate out of position.
2. Disconnect electrical connectors and remove unit.
3. Reverse procedure to install.

Colt, Colt Vista, Summit & Summit Wagon

1. Remove rear console assembly.
2. Remove control unit.
3. Reverse procedure to install.

Laser & Talon

1. Remove scuff plate and quarter trim
2. Disconnect control unit harness connector.
3. Remove control unit.
4. Reverse procedure to install.

DASH PANEL SERVICE

NOTE: On Air Bag Equipped Models, Refer To Air Bag System Precautions Located In Front Of This Manual For System Disarming & Arming Procedures.

INDEX

PRECAUTIONS

AIR BAG SYSTEMS

Refer to "Air Bag System Precautions" in the front of this manual for system disarming and arming procedures.

DASH PANEL
REPLACE

ACCLAIM, LEBARON LANDAU & SPIRIT

1. Remove left and right side A pillar trim by disengaging retaining clips.
2. Remove left and right cowl side trim panels as follows:
   a. Remove four scuff plate/cowl panel assembly attaching screws, then the cowl side trim panels.
3. Remove glove compartment assembly as follows:
   a. Open glove compartment door, then disconnect check strap.
   b. Remove glove compartment switch and light by pulling rearward, then disconnecting wiring connectors.
   c. Remove attaching screws, then the glove compartment assembly.
4. Remove four relays located above glove compartment assembly.
5. Reach through glove compartment opening, then disconnect A/C heater control vacuum lines, radio noise suppressor wires and blower motor/cycling switch wires.
6. Remove hood release handle.
7. Remove lower steering column cover as follows:
   a. Disconnect parking brake release rod from parking brake.
   b. Remove fuse panel access door, then remove one screw from lower column cover, **Fig. 1.**
   c. Remove six screws from lower cover, four across top of panel and two on bottom, then remove lower steering column cover.
8. Remove lower left instrument panel silencer and reinforcement as follows:
   a. Remove two screws from front of silencer, **Fig. 2.**

b. Remove one push nut, then disconnect courtesy lamp and remove silencer.
9. Remove instrument panel center bezel by pulling straight back, disengaging five clips.
10. Remove floor console as follows:
   a. Place transaxle shifter in N position.
   b. Remove both side carpet panels from front console.
   c. Remove two screw cover plates from rear console, **Fig. 3.**
   d. Remove coin holder, then the two rear console to front console attaching screws.
   e. Remove two rear console to mounting bracket screws, then the rear console assembly.
   f. **On models equipped with automatic transaxle,** remove shift lever bezel as follows: (1) Remove two screws, then pull up to remove automatic transaxle shift knob; (2) Lift shift lever bezel from front to unsnap from console, then disconnect wiring harness and remove shift lever bezel.
   g. **On models equipped with manual transaxle,** remove shift lever bezel as follows: (1) Unscrew shifter knob from shifter; (2) Remove nut, then lift ring from shaft; (3) Lift shift lever bezel from front to unsnap from console, then remove shift lever bezel.
   h. **On all models,** remove two console to mounting bracket screws.
   i. Remove six console to instrument panel screws.
   j. Slide console assembly rearward to unlatch console from instrument panel, then remove console assembly.
11. Remove radio assembly as follows:
   a. Remove radio mounting screws.
   b. Pull radio from panel, disconnect wiring, ground strap and antenna lead from radio, then remove radio.
12. Remove A/C heater control as follows:
   a. Remove two A/C heater control mounting screws, **Fig. 4.**
   b. Slide A/C heater control rearward, disconnect temperature control cable and wiring, then remove A/C heater control.

13. Remove cigar lighter assembly as follows:
   a. Remove two screws from lighter assembly.
   b. Pull lighter assembly rearward, disconnect wiring, then remove lighter assembly.
14. Remove message center/traveler as follows:
   a. Remove four attaching screws.
   b. Pull unit rearward, disconnect wiring, then remove message center/traveler.
15. Disconnect demister hoses.
16. Remove instrument panel top cover as follows:
   a. Lift up rear edge of instrument panel top panel up, **Fig. 5.**
   b. Remove panel by pulling rearward.
17. Remove instrument cluster, then the radio and rear window defogger bezels.
18. Remove nuts attaching steering column bracket to instrument panel support and lower bracket support, then lower steering column.
19. Loosen instrument panel pivot bolts, **Fig. 5.**
20. Remove screws attaching instrument panel to cowl panel.
21. Allow instrument panel to roll down slightly, then disconnect remaining electrical connections.
22. With the aid of a helper, remove panel pivot bolts, then the instrument panel from vehicle.
23. Reverse procedure to install.

DAYTONA & LEBARON COUPE/CONVERTIBLE

1. Remove instrument panel center bezel, **Fig. 6.**
2. Remove lower steering column cover as follows:
   a. Remove screws along top edge of lower cover, then screws at lower corners of cover.
   b. Remove lower cover.
3. Remove left under panel silencer, then set parking brake.
4. Remove console side carpet panels, **Fig. 7.**
5. Position front seats fully forward, then remove rear ashtray.

6. Remove rear lower carpeted end cover, then the nuts holding console to floor bracket.
7. Position front seats fully rearward.
8. Raise console storage bin cover and remove bottom mat, then remove screws holding bottom of storage bin to floor bracket.
9. Remove screws holding console side panels to instrument panel. Disengage hook and loop fasteners and separate side panels from console.
10. **On models with automatic transaxle,** disconnect shift indicator cable and clips from shift mechanism through right side panel opening.
11. **On all models,** disengage clips holding parking brake lever cover to console, then separate cover from vehicle.
12. Remove center instrument panel bezel as follows:
    a. Using a straightedge tool, pry out one end of bezel and continue to disengage six clips along length of bezel. If equipped with message center, disconnect electrical connectors.
13. Remove screws holding console to lower instrument panel, then bolts holding console to forward floor mounting bracket.
14. Remove gear selector knob, then separate console from floor and remove from vehicle.
15. Remove PRNDL clip and cable loop end from post on gear shifter.
16. Remove adjuster from tab on gear shifter bracket by pushing in locking knob on adjuster and sliding adjuster off tab on gear shifter bracket.
17. Remove Air bag diagnostic module mounting screws, then slide module out right side of instrument panel center stack area and disconnect module wiring.
18. Remove dimmer module mounting screw at left of steering column, then lower dimmer module.
19. Remove fuse block mounting screws, then lower fuse block.
20. Remove hood release mounting screws, then lower hood release.
21. Remove flasher relay from bracket on center distribution duct.
22. Remove screw from ATC sensor motor assembly, then the sensor from bracket, if equipped.
23. Remove radio ground screw above flasher relay mount.
24. Remove center distribution duct screw from left instrument panel lower brace, then four screws to from left lower brace.
25. Remove five steering column retaining nut, then lower column. Remove two upper column attaching studs.
26. Remove two screw and pull out compact disc player or cubby box, then disconnect co-axial cable from disc player.
27. Remove Electronic Vehicle Information Center (EVIC) or Traveler from vehicle.
28. Remove radio, ATC, A/C or heater controls.

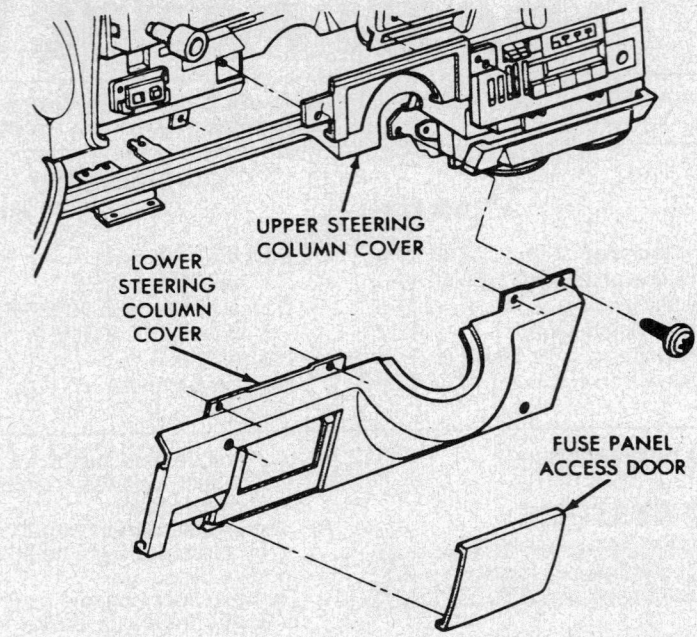

Fig. 1 Lower steering column cover. Acclaim & Spirit

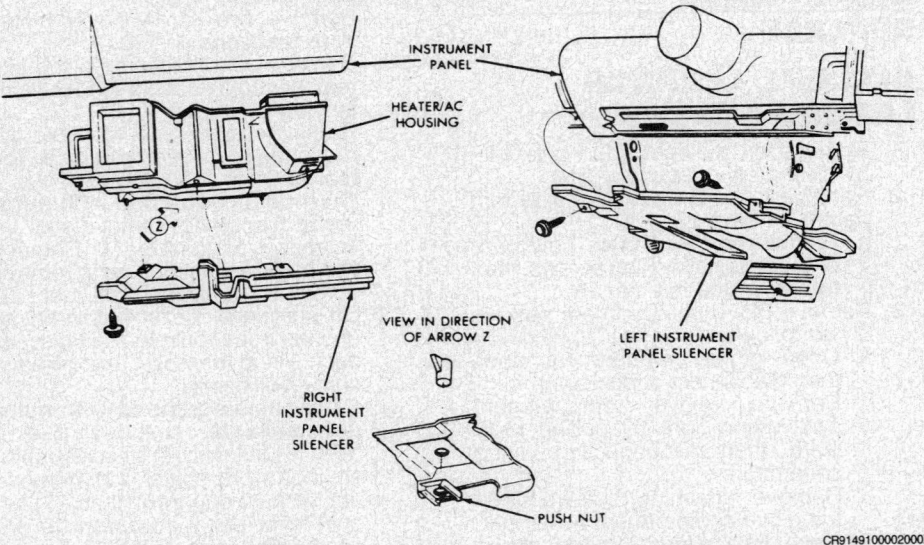

Fig. 2 Instrument panel silencers. Acclaim & Spirit

29. Remove rear window defogger switch by squeezing latches on side of switch.
30. Remove cluster lower trim bezel, switch pod vent grille, speaker grilles and defroster grilles.
31. Remove switch pod assembly as follows:
    a. Remove two screws located under panel vent grille, then two screws under pod assembly.
    b. Position tilt steering wheel to lowest setting.
    c. Slightly pull switch module rearward, the disconnect electrical connectors.
    d. Remove switch pod from vehicle.
32. Remove cluster assembly, then dash speakers.
33. Open glove compartment door, squeeze side and roll glove compartment completely open, then remove glove compartment light switch and disconnect wires.
34. Loosen right cowl side pivot bolt through glove compartment opening, the close glove compartment.
35. Loosen left cowl side pivot.
36. Remove four screw attachments at top of instrument panel, then roll panel out.
37. Pull wiring, antenna cable, A/C cable and vacuum lines out of instrument panel.
38. Disconnect demister hose and remove instrument panel with ducts attached.
39. Reverse procedure to install. If new in-

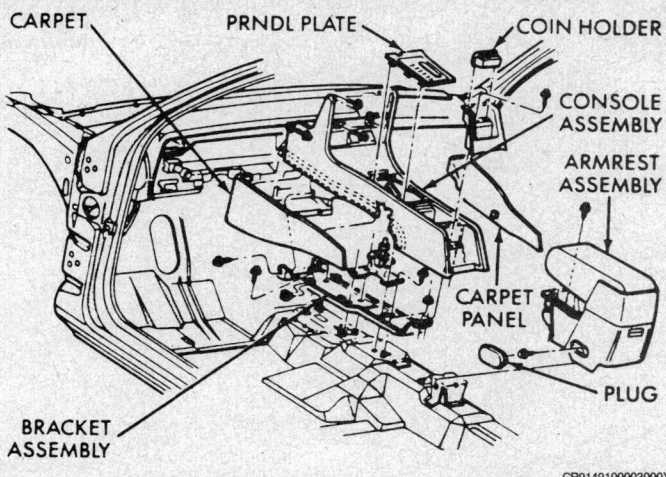

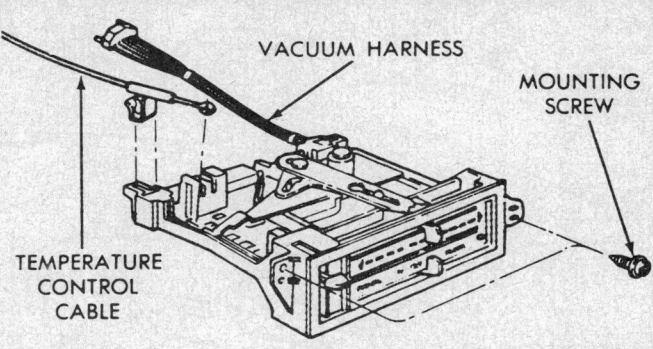

Fig. 4 A/C heater control. Acclaim & Spirit

Fig. 3 Exploded view of console assembly . Acclaim & Spirit

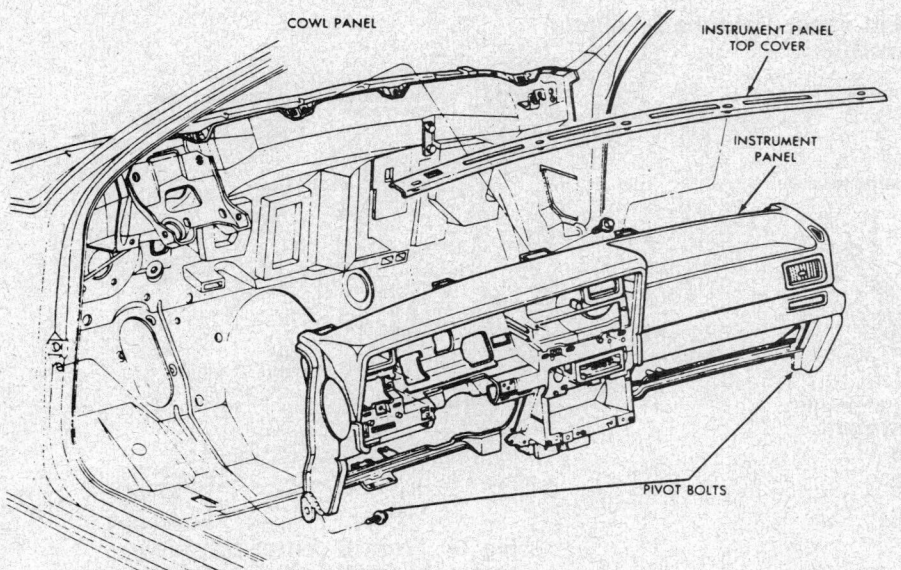

Fig. 5 Instrument panel, top cover & mounting bolts. Acclaim & Spirit

strument panel is to be installed, transfer ducts and brackets onto new panel.

40. Install PRNDL cable as follows:
   a. Place gear shifter in low position.
   b. Insert cable into adjuster, then line up cable up with end of adjuster, **Fig. 8**.
   c. Check gear selector indicator for proper alignment.
   d. Attach PRNDL clip to adjuster to secure cable.

SHADOW & SUNDANCE

1. Remove windshield wiper arms. Open hood and remove cowl top plastic cover.
2. Remove windshield washer reservoir.
3. Pull connector loose from A/C resistor block, then push wiring and grommet through bulkhead into passenger compartment.

4. Remove console assemblies as follows:
   a. Position front seats fully forward.
   b. **On models with automatic transaxle**, remove gear selector knob and shift plate, **Fig. 9**. Remove illumination lamp socket. Position socket aside.
   c. **On models with manual transaxle**, lift gear shift boot adapter from console, then push adapter through opening in console, **Fig. 9**.
   d. **On all models**, unsnap power mirror/window switch bezel, if equipped, then disconnect switch wiring.
   e. Remove bolts holding arm rest riser to floor bracket, then separate rear console from floor and remove from vehicle.
   f. Open armrest lid and remove three screws attaching armrest to console retractor bracket.

   g. Remove armrest and center console section as a unit by lifting and unsnapping from front console section.
   h. Position front seats fully rearward.
   i. Remove center module bezel.
   j. Remove front console and side walls as a unit by removing six screws attaching side wall to instrument panel and console bracket.
   k. Slide front console assembly rearward, then lift to remove.
5. Disconnect passive restraint seat belt logic control module wiring connector.
6. Remove six attaching nuts securing instrument panel to console support brace.
7. Remove instrument to console support brace with passive restraint seat belt logic control module attached.
8. Remove right and left cowl side and scuff plate trim mouldings as follows:
   a. Remove three scuff plate trim moulding attaching screws.
   b. Remove cowl side trim attaching screw and lower most push pin from A pillar trim mouldings.
   c. Remove side cowl and scuff plate trim mouldings.
9. Remove right and left A pillar trim mouldings by removing remaining push pins.
10. Remove instrument panel top cover as follows:
   a. Insert suitable trim stick tool in groove between instrument panel top cover and instrument panel pad surface, **Fig. 10**.
   b. Pry cover up and forward until cover is released from instrument panel pad.
   c. Lift top cover up and rearward to remove.
11. Remove lower steering column cover as follows:
   a. Remove two screws attaching hood release handle, then the handle.
   b. Remove fuse access door, then remove lower steering column cover attaching screw located directly above fuse block, **Fig. 11**.
   c. Remove six attaching screws around outside of steering column cover, then the cover.
12. Disconnect steering column wiring from 25-way connector.

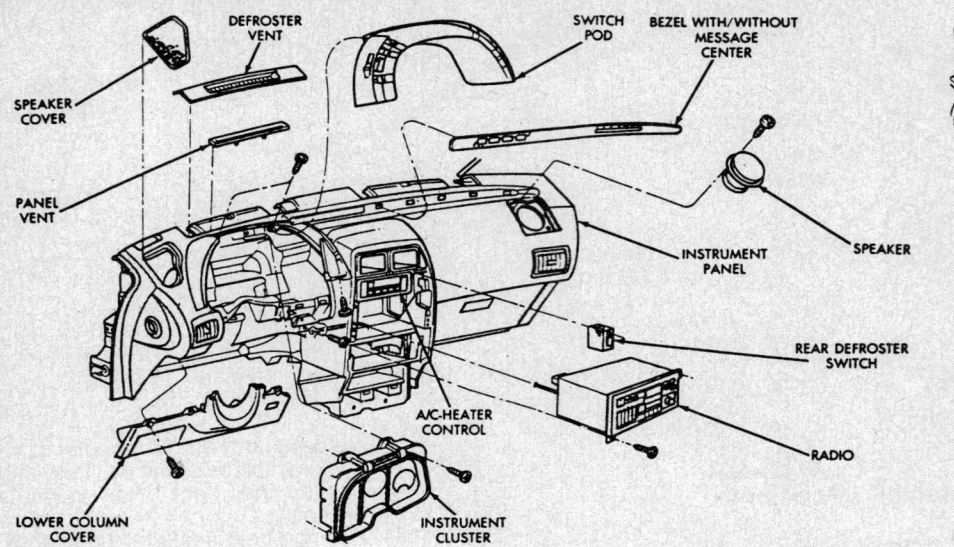

Fig. 6 Exploded view of instrument panel. Daytona & LeBaron Coupe/Convertible

Fig. 7 Exploded view of center console. Daytona & LeBaron Coupe/Convertible

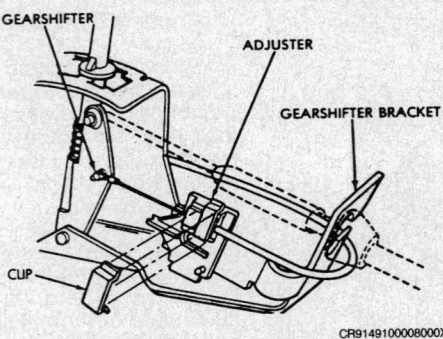

Fig. 8 PRNDL cable adjustment. Daytona & LeBaron Coupe/Convertible

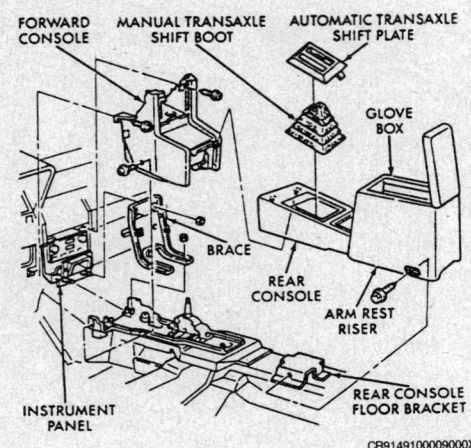

Fig. 9 Front & center console assembly. Shadow & Sundance

13. Disconnect parking brake, stop lamp and cruise control wiring, if equipped.
14. Remove five steering column support nuts, lower steering column, then remove two column attaching studs.
15. Disconnect engine wiring harness from 18-way and 16-way connectors located on left side panel support bracket.
16. Remove glove compartment, then loosen instrument panel pivot bolts, **Fig. 10.**
17. Remove defroster duct adapter from defroster duct, then the screws attaching instrument panel to cowl panel.
18. Roll instrument panel down, attach heavy wire to hold in position, then remove defroster duct retaining screws.
19. Disconnect body wiring from right side 18-way connector and left side 25-way connector.
20. Disconnect temperature mode cable at inline connector, then the resistor block and blower motor wiring connections.
21. Disconnect antenna cable.
22. Disconnect left and right demister hoses from demister outlets on panel.

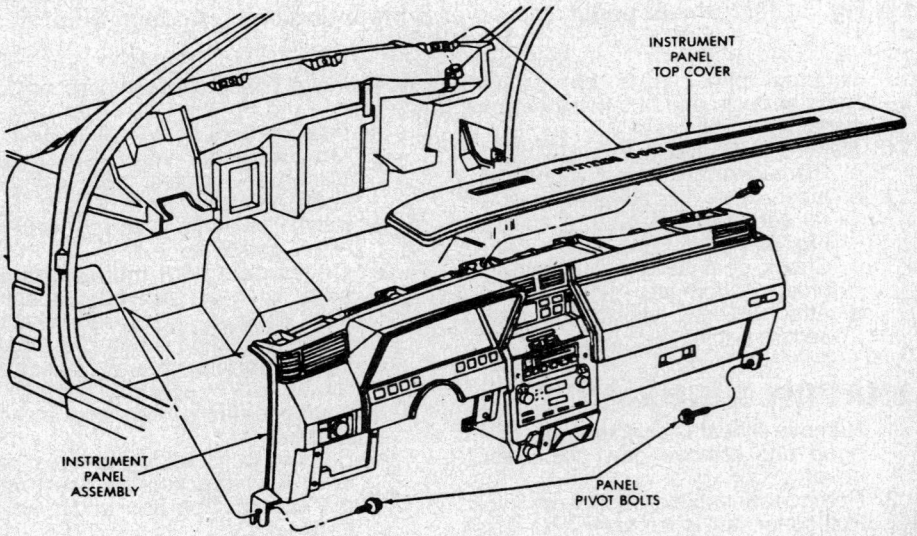

Fig. 10 Instrument panel & top cover. Shadow & Sundance

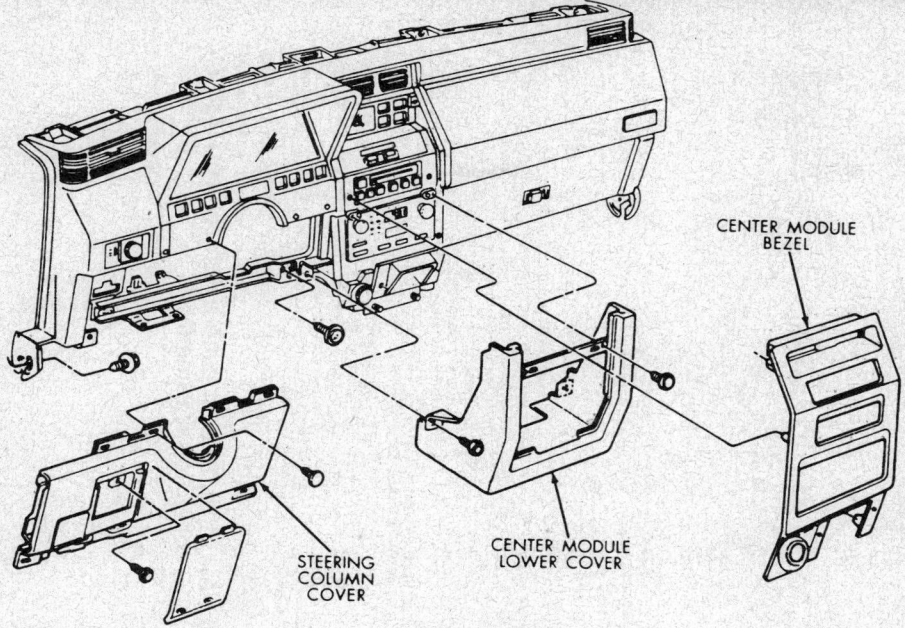

Fig. 11 Lower instrument panel components. Shadow & Sundance

CR9149100011000X

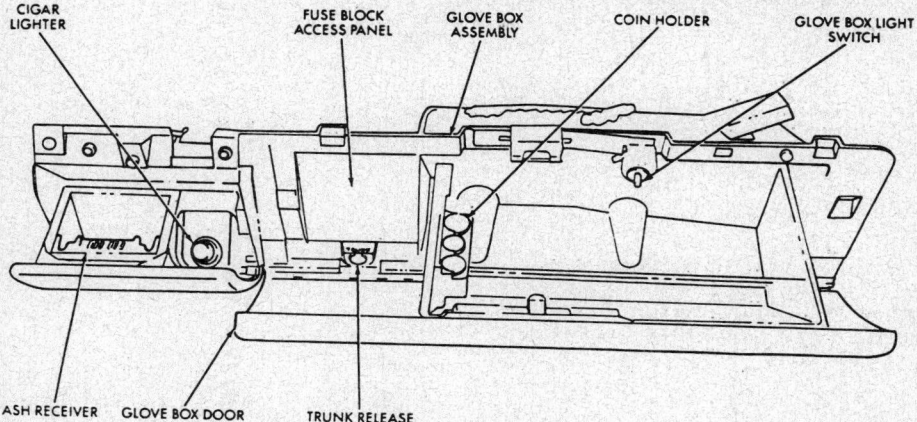

Fig. 12 Glove compartment & ash tray assembly. Dynasty, Imperial & 1992–93 New Yorker

CR9149100012000X

23. Remove instrument panel pivot bolts, then the instrument panel.
24. Reverse procedure to install.

DYNASTY, IMPERIAL & 1992–93 NEW YORKER

1. Remove left instrument panel silencer.
2. Remove right and left cowl side and scuff plate attaching screws, then the scuff plates.
3. Remove right and left A pillar trim mouldings by removing two push pin fasteners per side and disengaging from clip on B pillar trim.
4. Remove instrument panel top cover by pushing forward and prying up, using a straightedge to aid in removal.
5. Disconnect bulkhead connector from brace under left side of instrument panel.
6. Remove glove compartment/ash receiver module, **Fig. 12**, as follows:
   a. Open upper storage bin door, then remove two screws attaching front wall of storage bin to mounting bracket.
   b. Remove console and drawer.
   c. Remove two screws attaching mounting bracket to lower instrument panel, then the mounting bracket.
   d. Disconnect glove compartment/ash receiver wiring connectors.
   e. Remove ten screws around edge of glove compartment/ash receiver assembly, then the assembly.
7. Remove right instrument panel silencer, then the center panel support brace and Air bag diagnostic module.
8. Disconnect Air bag module electrical connectors, then remove upper and lower cluster bezels.

9. Remove steering column cover.
10. Remove steering column mounting nuts, then lower steering column.
11. Unhook shift indicator cable eyelet from steering column actuator.
12. Unlatch lock tab in shift indicator column insert and squeeze legs together to remove from steering column.
13. Remove cluster assembly while guiding PRNDL indicator guide tube through access hole in base panel.
14. Remove instrument panel steering column opening support/hood release handle assembly.
15. Remove two steering column upper studs, then loosen side cowl tie down bolts.
16. Remove steering column tilt lever, then the upper and lower lock housing shroud.
17. Remove lower fixed shroud, then the upper fixed shroud.
18. Disconnect Air bag pigtail, ignition switch and halo light/key buzzer switch wiring.
19. Disconnect multi function switch by loosening connector jack screw and pulling connector from switch.
20. Disconnect Air bag pigtail from wiring trough housing by pulling two push fasteners.
21. Remove wiring trough from steering column, then the defroster ducts.
22. Remove five screws attaching instrument panel to cowl panel.
23. Loosen instrument panel pivot bolts, roll instrument panel down, attach a hook to hold panel in position.
24. Open hood and remove plenum grill.
25. Disconnect washer bottle, resistor block and under hood lamp wiring. Washer bottle must be removed to gain access.
26. Remove grommet and pull plenum wiring into vehicle through plenum panel.
27. Disconnect right demister hose from instrument panel, then the antenna cable.
28. Disconnect right and left 25-way body wiring connectors.
29. Disconnect A/C heater unit control cables, wiring connectors and vacuum harness.
30. Remove right side instrument panel ground wire, then disconnect body controller wiring.
31. Remove instrument panel pivot bolts, then the instrument panel.
32. Reverse procedure to install.

COLT & SUMMIT
1992

Remove both side cowl trim panels. Remove components in order as they appear in **Fig. 13**, noting the following:
1. Remove glass pocket (3) using a plastic trim stick.
2. Remove instrument panel lower covers (13) by pulling forward.
3. Remove speedometer cable adapter (17) as follows:
   a. Disconnect speedometer cable from transaxle end of cable.

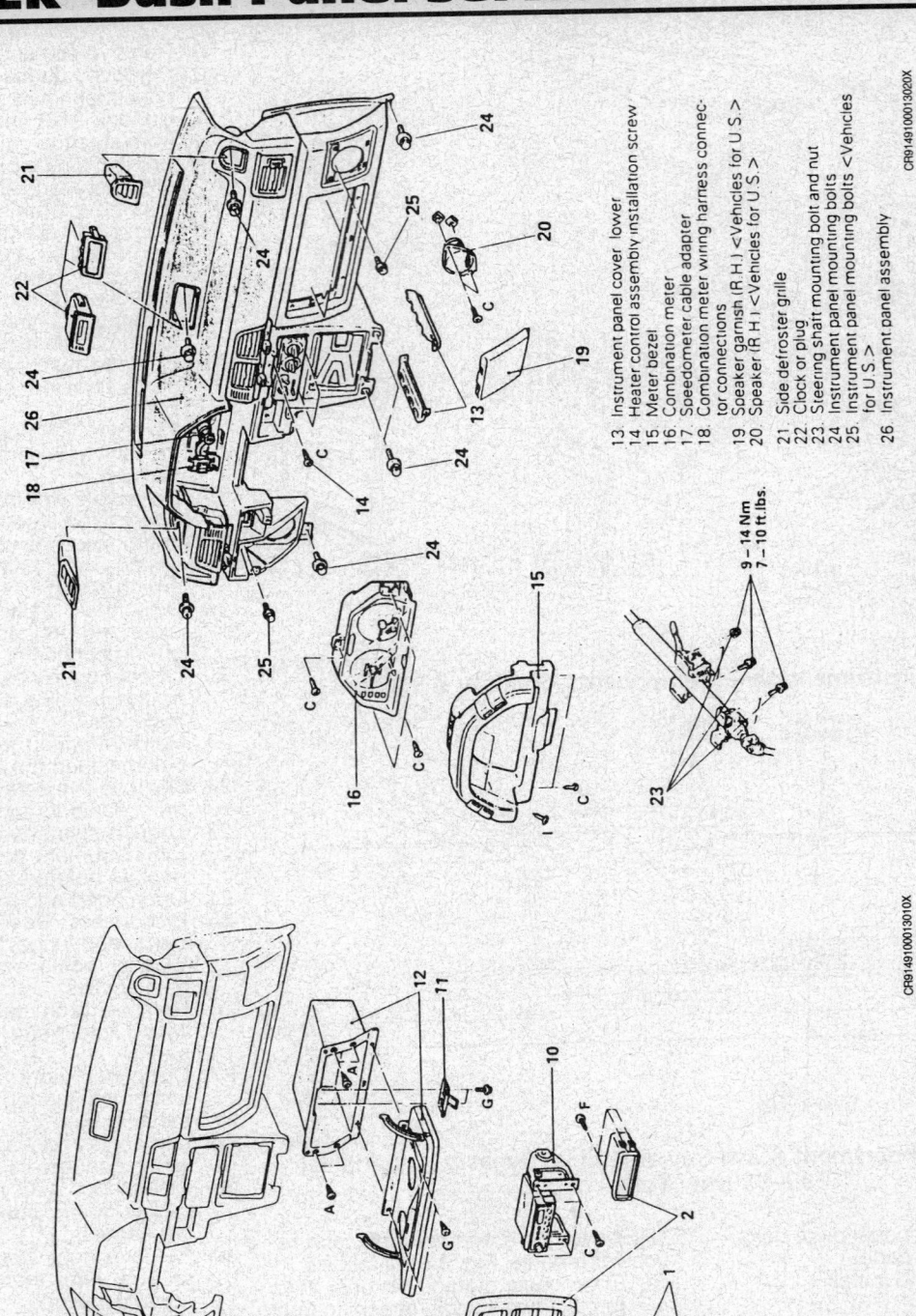

1. Ashtray
2. Center panel
3. Sunglass pocket
4. Side panel assembly <Vehicles for U.S.>
5. Knee protector assembly (L.H.) <Vehicles for U.S.>
6. Lower panel assembly <Vehicles for Canada>
7. Hood lock release handle
8. Column cover, lower
9. Column cover, upper
10. Radio
11. Striker <Vehicles for U.S.>
12. Glove box assembly <Vehicles for U.S.>

Fig. 13   Exploded view of instrument panel assembly (Part 1 of 2). 1992 Colt & Summit

CR91491000013010X

13. Instrument panel cover, lower
14. Heater control assembly installation screw
15. Meter bezel
16. Combination meter
17. Speedometer cable adapter
18. Combination meter wiring harness connector connections
19. Speaker garnish (R.H.) <Vehicles for U.S.>
20. Speaker (R.H.) <Vehicles for U.S.>
21. Side defroster grille
22. Clock or plug
23. Steering shaft mounting bolt and nut
24. Instrument panel mounting bolts
25. Instrument panel mounting bolts <Vehicles for U.S.>
26. Instrument panel assembly

9 – 14 Nm
7 – 10 ft.lbs.

Fig. 13   Exploded view of instrument panel assembly (Part 2 of 2). 1992 Colt & Summit

CR91491000013020X

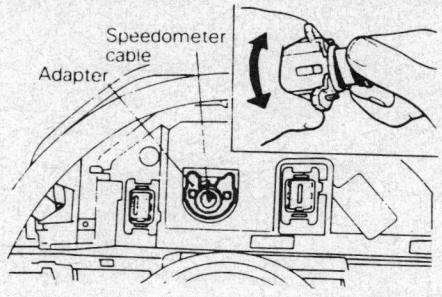

Fig. 14 Speedometer cable adapter removal. 1992 Colt & Summit

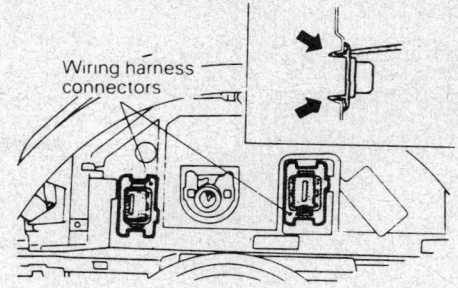

Fig. 15 Combination meter wiring connectors. 1992 Colt & Summit

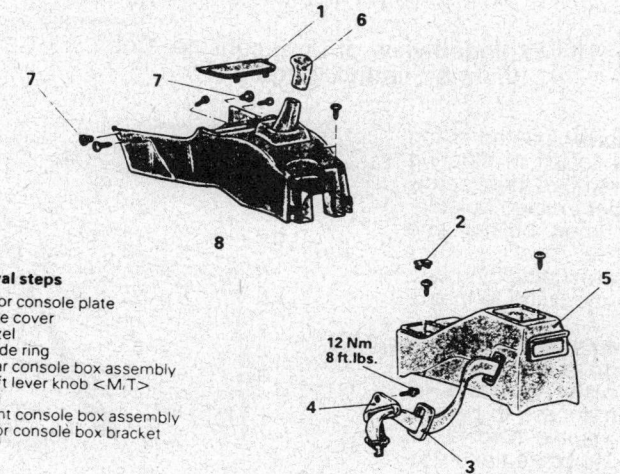

Removal steps
1. Floor console plate
2. Hole cover
3. Bezel
4. Guide ring
5. Rear console box assembly
6. Shift lever knob <M.T>
7. Clip
8. Front console box assembly
9. Floor console box bracket

12 Nm
8 ft.lbs.

Fig. 16 Exploded view of floor console. 1993–94 Colt & Summit

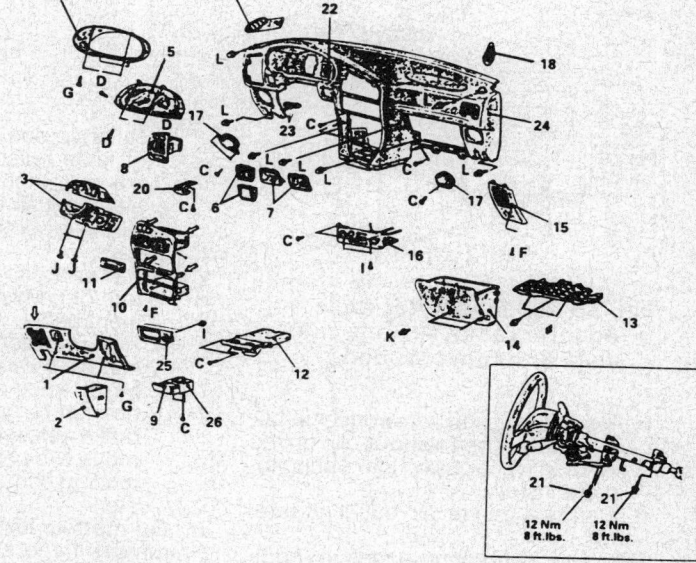

12 Nm
8 ft.lbs.

12 Nm   12 Nm
8 ft.lbs.   8 ft.lbs.

Removal steps
1. Knee protector or instrument lower panel assembly
2. Sunglass pocket
3. Column cover
4. Meter bezel
5. Combination meter
6. Remote control mirror switch rheostat or plug
7. Coin box or rear wiper washer switch
8. Air outlet panel assembly
9. Ashtray
10. Air outlet center panel assembly
11. Radio plug
12. Cup holder
13. Under cover

14. Glove box
15. Corner panel
16. Heater control assembly
17. Speaker
18. Side defroster grille (RH)
19. Side defroster grille (LH)
20. Hood lock release handle
21. Steering column assembly installation bolts
22. Adapter
23. Harness connector
24. Instrument panel assembly
25. Ashtray panel
26. Ashtray bracket

Fig. 17 Exploded view of instrument panel. 1993–94 Colt & Summit

b. Pull speedometer cable slightly toward vehicle interior, release lock by turning speedometer cable adapter to left or right, **Fig. 14,** then remove adapter.
4. Disconnect combination meter wiring harness connectors (18) as follows:
   a. Using a flat tip screwdriver, open tabs of connectors, **Fig. 15,** then remove harness connectors.
5. Remove righthand speaker garnish (19) and side defroster grilles (21) using a plastic trim stick.
6. Remove clock or plug (22) using a plastic trim stick, disconnect clock harness connector, if equipped, then remove clock.
7. Reverse procedure to install, **torquing** steering shaft mounting nuts and bolts (23) to 7–10 ft. lbs.

1993–94

1. Remove floor console components in numbered sequence, **Fig. 16.**
2. Remove instrument panel components in numbered sequence, **Fig. 17,** noting the following:
   a. Remove cool air bypass lever cable from heater unit.

b. Remove air outlet center panel assembly mounting screws, then the assembly.
c. Remove heater control cables from heater unit and blower assembly.
d. Remove heater control assembly in order shown in **Fig. 18.**
e. Remove adapter lock from instrument panel. Pull speedometer cable slightly into passenger compartment, then remove adapter.
3. Reverse procedure to install, noting the following:
   a. Turn cool air bypass lever of air outlet center panel assembly fully upward.
   b. Turn cool air bypass damper lever at heater unit fully downward, then install cool air bypass lever cable.

COLT VISTA & SUMMIT WAGON

1. Remove floor console in numbered sequence, **Fig. 19.**
2. Remove speedometer cable adapter, **Fig. 20,** (13) as follows:
   a. Remove adapter lock.
   b. Pull speedometer cable slightly toward vehicle interior, then remove rear of adapter from cable.
   c. Turn adapter so notched section is aligned with tab on cable section, then remove adapter by sliding it in the reverse direction.
3. Remove center air outlet assembly, **Fig. 21,** as follows:
   a. Remove clip on lower section of assembly.

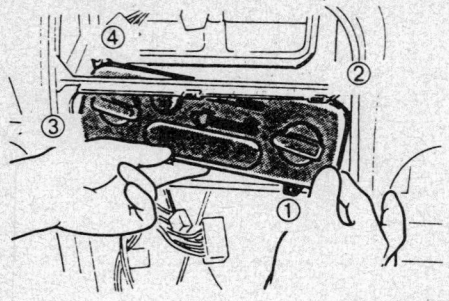

Fig. 18   Heater control assembly removal. 1993–94 Colt & Summit

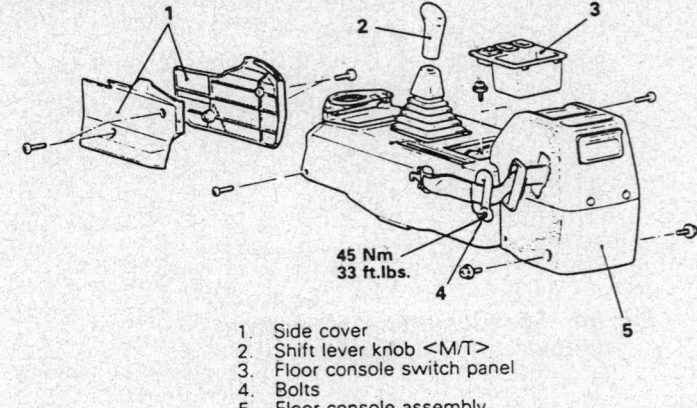

1. Side cover
2. Shift lever knob <M/T>
3. Floor console switch panel
4. Bolts
5. Floor console assembly

45 Nm
33 ft.lbs.

Fig. 19   Exploded view of floor console. Colt Vista & Summit Wagon

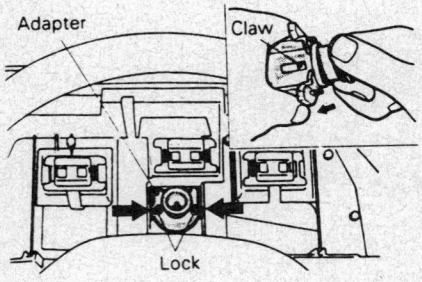

Fig. 20   Speedometer cable adapter removal. Colt Vista & Summit Wagon

b. Insert flat tipped screwdriver in between fins, then remove clip on top section while pulling lock spring toward inside.

c. Remove center air outlet assembly.

4. Remove instrument panel in numbered sequence, **Fig. 22.**

5. Reverse numbered sequence, **Figs. 19 and 22,** to install.

MONACO & PREMIER

1. **On models equipped with passive restraints,** proceed as follows:
    a. Remove ashtray by pulling up and out of ashtray receiver, **Fig. 23.**
    b. Remove one screw attaching ashtray receiver, disconnect wire from cigar lighter, then remove receiver.
    c. Remove two screws attaching front of console to bracket.
    d. Remove three screws attaching armrest assembly to console, then remove armrest by pulling up and out of console.
    e. Remove two screws attaching rear of console to bracket.
    f. Reach inside console and push out seat belt guides, then remove console.
    g. Remove two bolts attaching pivot bracket to knee bolster, **Fig. 24.**
    h. Loosen, but do not remove, two pivot bracket bolts.
    i. Remove one screw and two Torx bolts attaching front console bracket to floor, then slide console bracket back.
    j. Remove two screws attaching center of knee bolster to instrument panel.

k. Remove one screw located at top of knee bolster to left of steering column, then remove one screw attaching air duct to knee bolster.

l. Remove both knee bolster end caps.

m. Remove one screw attaching bottom of garnish moulding to instrument panel.

n. Remove four nuts attaching ends of knee bolster to instrument panel.

o. Move knee bolster rearward far enough to gain access to parking brake release handle screws, remove two parking brake handle attaching screws, then the knee bolster.

2. **On models less passive restraints,** remove three attaching screws, then the instrument panel lower cover, **Fig. 25.**

3. **On all models,** remove steering column as outlined under applicable section of "Steering Columns" chapter.

4. Remove defroster grille, **Fig. 26,** then the four upper instrument panel attaching bolts, **Fig. 27.**

5. **Loosen, but do not remove,** one nut located near parking brake release handle, **Fig. 28,** and one nut located on passenger side kick panel, **Fig. 29.**

6. **On models less passive restraints,** proceed as follows:
    a. Remove two parking brake release handle attaching screws, the lower the parking brake release handle assembly.
    b. Remove ashtray by releasing tab, then ashtray pulling forward and out of instrument panel.
    c. Disconnect cigar lighter connectors, then remove one screw from ashtray cavity, **Fig. 30.**

7. **On all models,** remove one bolt from brake sled, **Fig. 31.**

8. Disconnect all electrical connectors shown in **Fig. 32.**

9. **On models less passive restraints,** remove two bolts attaching instrument panel to center floor bracket, **Fig. 33.**

10. **On all models,** open glove compartment door, remove six glove compart-

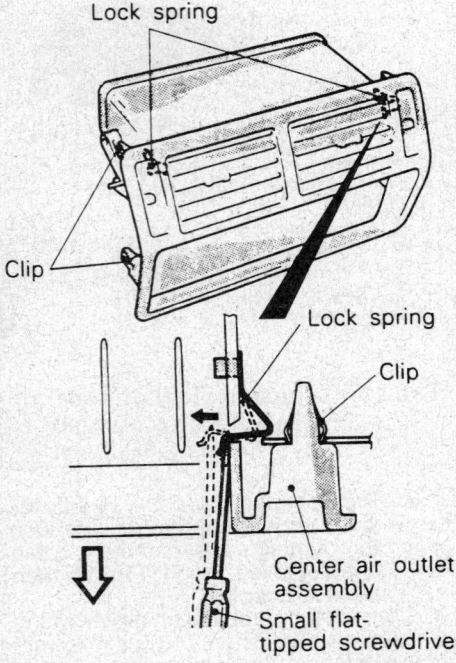

Lock spring

Clip

Lock spring

Clip

Center air outlet assembly

Small flat-tipped screwdriver

Fig. 21   Center air outlet assembly removal

ment liner attaching screws, then the glove compartment liner, **Fig. 34.**

11. Reach through glove compartment opening and remove plastic fastener attaching interior temperature sensor, **Fig. 35.**

12. Disconnect interior temperature sensor by pressing tabs together, **Fig. 36**, and pressing air temperature sensor hose rearward.

13. Carefully lift instrument panel up and rearward to disengage, then remove the instrument panel.

14. Reverse procedure to install, noting the following:
    a. When installing instrument panel, position instrument panel ensuring instrument panel mounting brackets engage studs on kick panels.

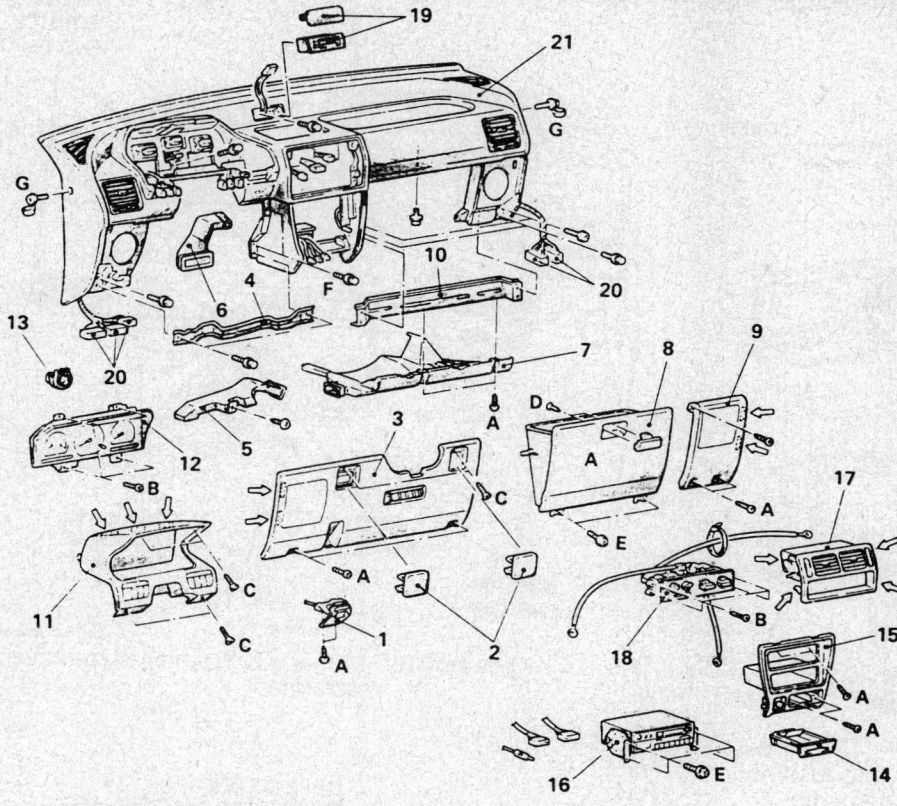

1. Hood lock release handle
2. Knee pro plug
3. Instrument under cover
4. Lower frame
5. Foot duct
6. Lap duct
7. Lap heater duct
8. Glove box
9. Speaker garnish
10. Glove box frame
11. Meter hood

12. Combination meter
13. Adapter
14. Ashtray
15. Center panel
16. Radio or radio and tape player
17. Center air outlet assembly
18. Heater control assembly
19. Clock or plug
20. Harness connector
21. Instrument panel assembly

CR9149200022000X

Fig. 22 Exploded view of instrument panel. Colt Vista & Summit Wagon

b. Ensure wire harness is routed behind center mounting bracket.
c. Connect all electrical connections and interior temperature sensor.
d. **Torque** nuts and bolts attaching steering column to instrument panel to 35 ft. lbs.

LASER & TALON

1. Remove floor console in numbered sequence, **Fig. 37.**
2. Remove instrument panel in numbered sequence, **Fig. 38,** noting the following:
3. Use a suitable screwdriver to pry back retaining pawls of center air outlet assembly, **Fig. 39,** then remove using a plastic trim tool.
4. When removing speedometer cable adapter, disconnect cable from the transaxle and pull the cable slightly toward the vehicle interior. Release the lock by turning the adapter to the left or right, then remove adapter, **Fig. 40.**
5. Remove bolts, then lower steering column to allow clearance for removal

of instrument panel.
6. Reverse numbered sequence **Figs. 37 and 38,** to install, ensuring all connectors are securely connected and wiring harnesses are not pinched.

STEALTH

1. Remove console assembly as follows:
   a. Remove cup holder and console plug, **Fig. 41.**
   b. Remove rear console assembly.
   c. Remove radio panel and radio.
   d. Remove switch trim panel C and console side cover.
   e. Remove front console trim panel.
   f. **On models with manual transaxle,** remove shift lever knob.
   g. **On all models,** remove front console assembly.
2. Remove hood release handle and rheostat, **Fig. 42.**
3. Remove switch trim panel B and knee protector assembly.
4. Remove steering column cover.

5. Remove glove compartment striker, glove compartment and cross pipe cover.
6. Using a flat tip screwdriver, remove center air outlet assembly.
7. Remove heater control assembly retaining screws.
8. Remove meter bezel.
9. Remove combination meter.
10. **On models with mechanical speedometer,** disconnect speedometer at transaxle, then remove adapter locks from instrument panel.
11. Pull lightly on speedometer cable toward passenger compartment and remove adapter.
12. **On all models,** remove speaker or instrument panel top covers.
13. Remove steering column retaining bolts.
14. Remove instrument panel assembly.
15. Reverse procedure to install.

CONCORDE, INTREPID, LHS, VISION & 1994 NEW YORKER

Refer to **Fig. 43** when performing the following procedure.
1. Remove two air bag fuses, then open doors and remove right and left end covers.
2. **On models with floor console,** remove floor console as follows:
   a. Place gear selector in Neutral position, the loosen setscrew holding gear shift knob to gear shift.
   b. Pull gear shift knob from gear shift, then rubber molding from gap at top of console, if equipped.
   c. Remove ashtray, then console bezel retaining screw.
   d. Disengage clips holding rear of bezel to center console, then remove console bezel.
   e. Remove retaining screws from forward crossmember to floor mounting bracket.
   f. Remove retaining screws from bottom of glove compartment to rear mounting bracket.
   g. Remove console from vehicle.
3. **On models less floor console,** remove instrument panel lower center cover and ashtray.
4. **On all models,** remove radio ground strap screw at side of center support bracket. **Proper routing of radio ground strap is necessary for radio operation.**
5. Open glove compartment door, flex sides of glove compartment inward to swing glove compartment door down to floor. Remove mounting bolts from top of glove compartment.
6. Remove two nuts from center support bracket at ashtray support.
7. Remove mounting screws from center outlet bezel opening and right bezel opening.
8. Remove mounting screw from end cover area of instrument panel, if equipped.
9. With steering column in upward tilt position, remove two screws at ends

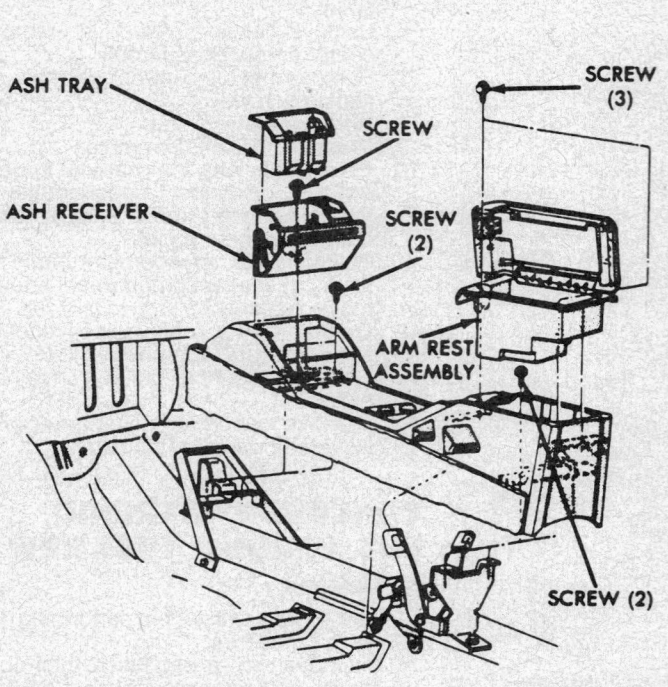

Fig. 23 Exploded view of center console assembly. Monaco & Premier w/passive restraints

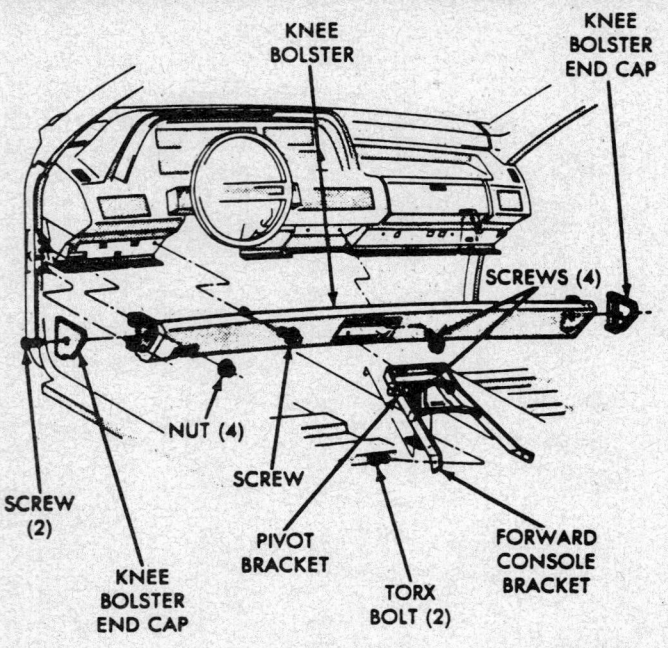

Fig. 24 Knee bolster. Monaco & Premier w/passive restraints

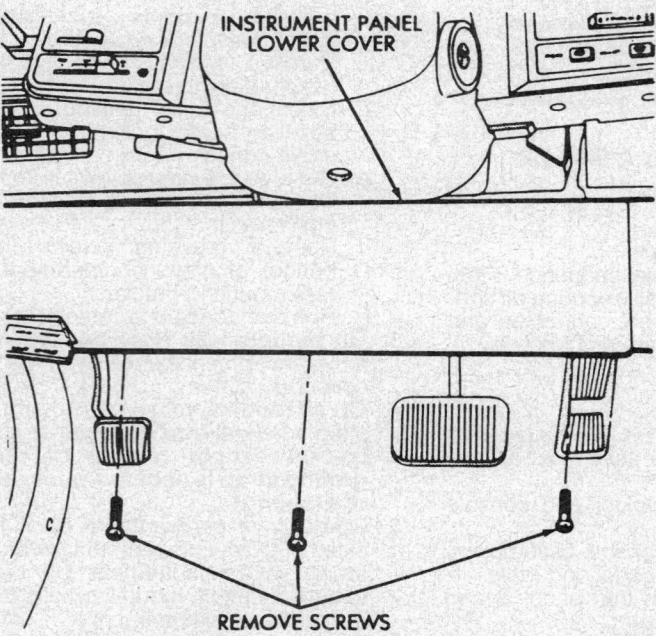

Fig. 25 Lower instrument panel. Monaco & Premier less air bag

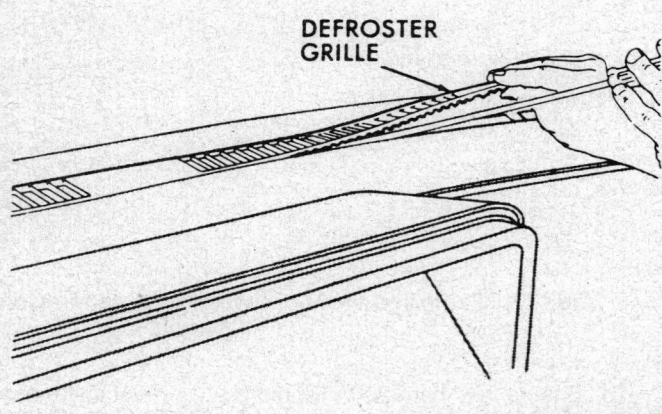

Fig. 26 Defroster grille removal. Monaco & Premier

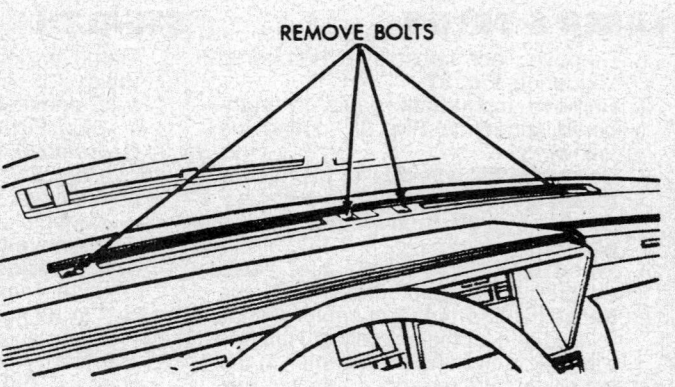

Fig. 27 Upper instrument panel attaching bolts. Monaco & Premier

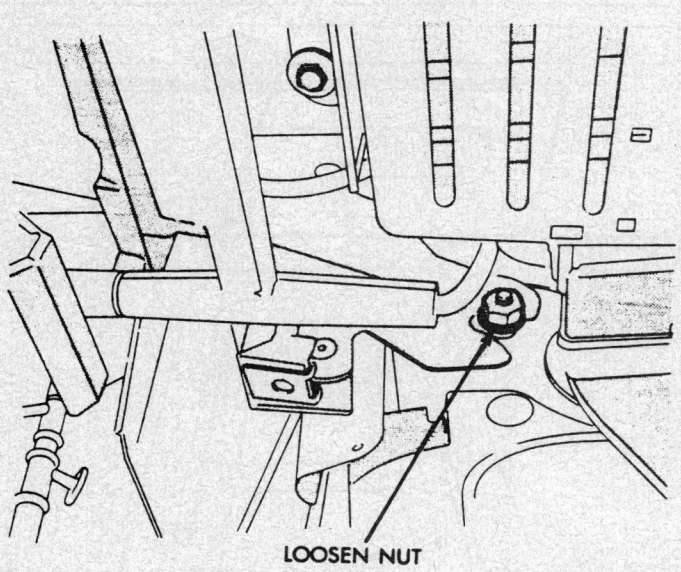

LOOSEN NUT

CR9149100028000X

Fig. 28 Left side lower instrument panel bracket nut. Monaco & Premier

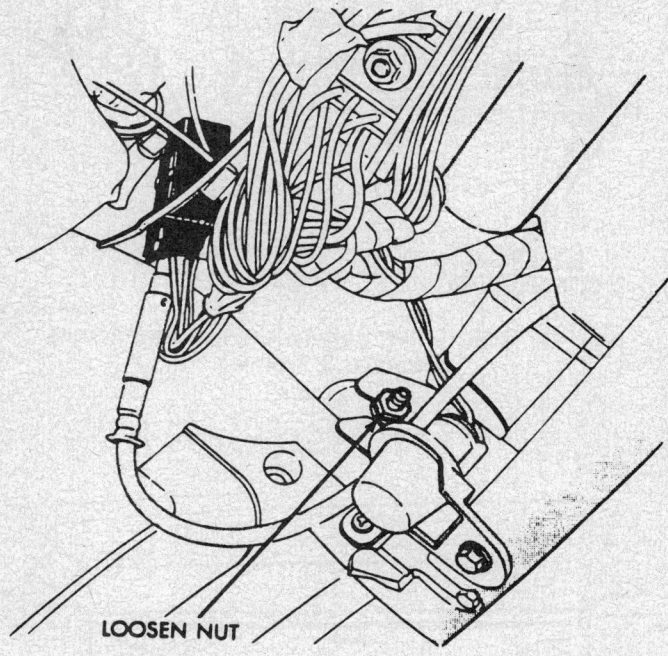

LOOSEN NUT

CR9149100029000X

Fig. 29 Right side lower instrument panel bracket nut. Monaco & Premier

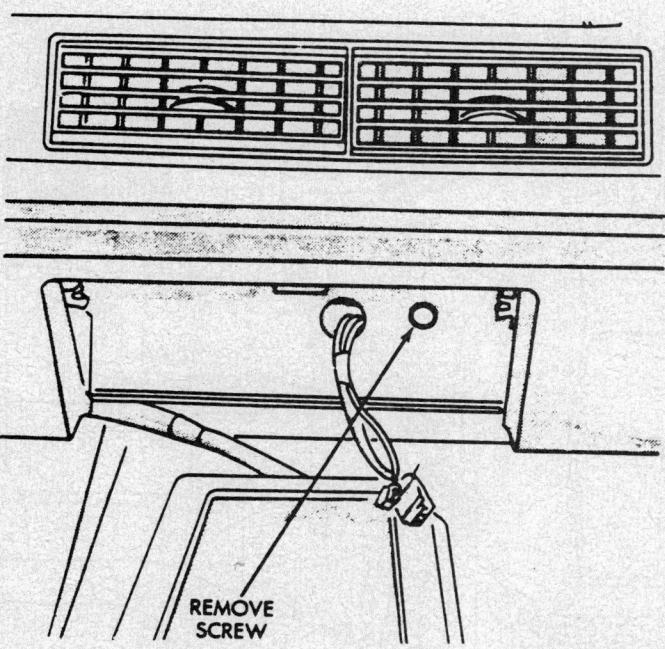

REMOVE SCREW

CR9149100030000X

Fig. 30 Instrument panel attaching screw. Monaco & Premier

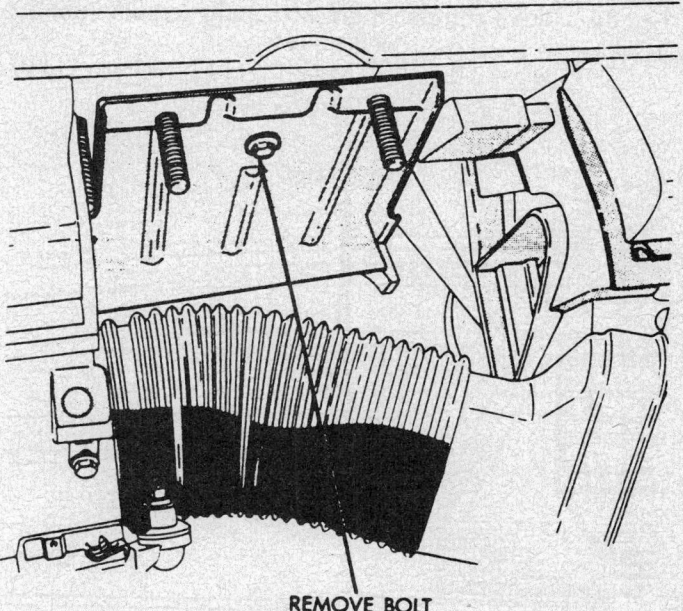

REMOVE BOLT

CR9149100031000X

Fig. 31 Brake sled bolt. Monaco & Premier

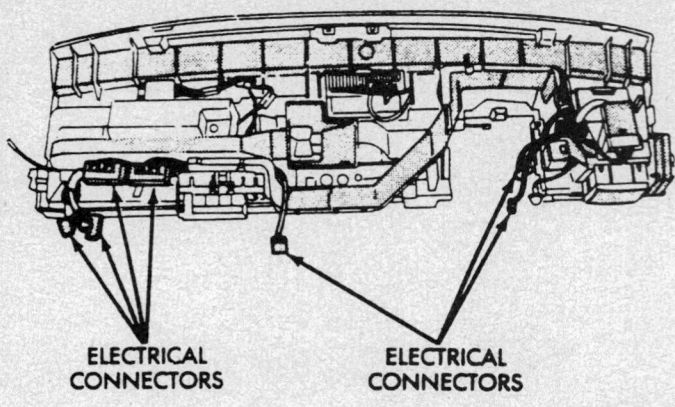

ELECTRICAL CONNECTORS

ELECTRICAL CONNECTORS

CR9149100032000X

Fig. 32   Instrument panel electrical connectors. Monaco & Premier

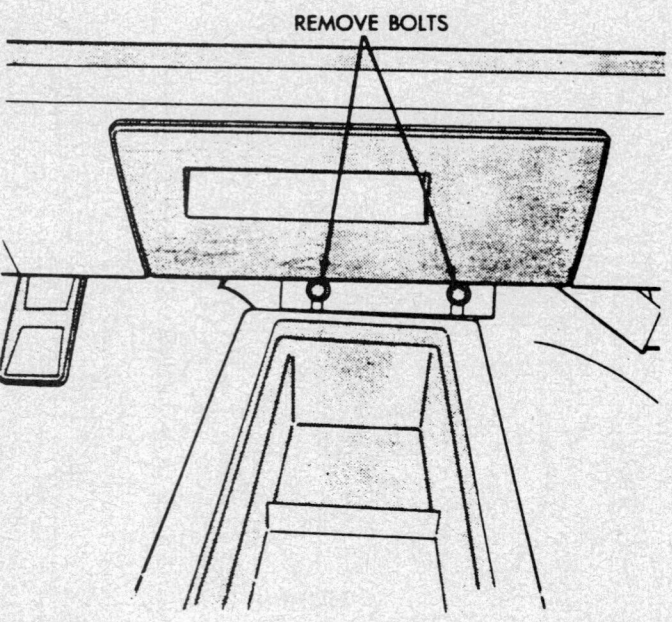

REMOVE BOLTS

CR9149100033000X

Fig. 33   Instrument panel to center floor bracket attaching bolts. Monaco & Premier less passive restraints

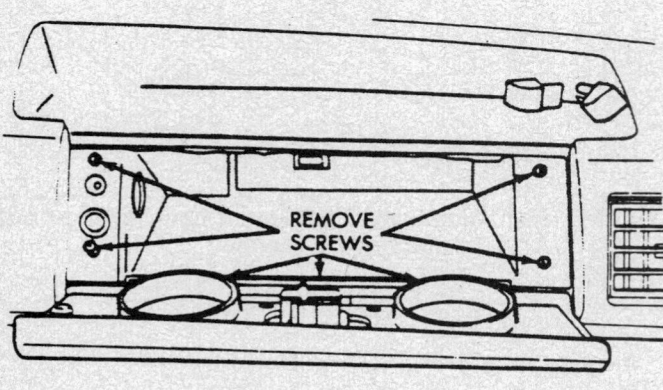

REMOVE SCREWS

CR9149100034000X

Fig. 34   Glove compartment attaching screws. Monaco & Premier

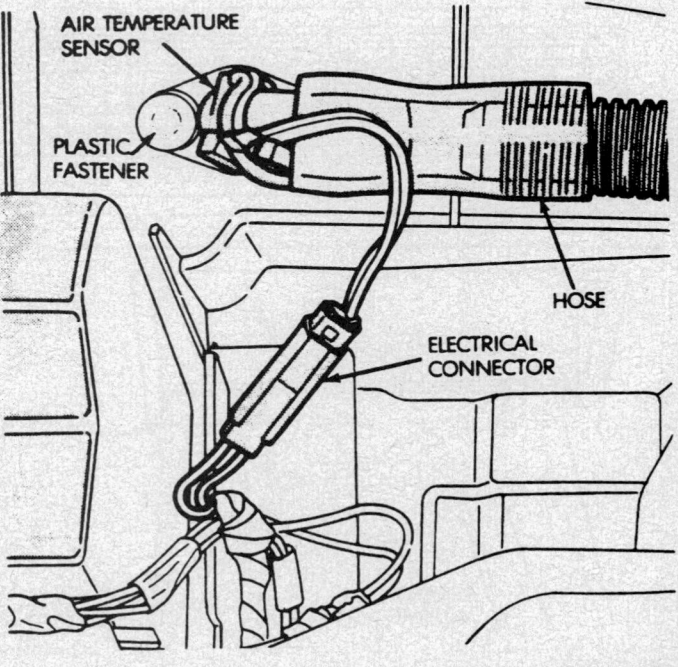

AIR TEMPERATURE SENSOR

PLASTIC FASTENER

HOSE

ELECTRICAL CONNECTOR

CR9149100035000X

Fig. 35   Air temperature sensor fastener. Monaco & Premier

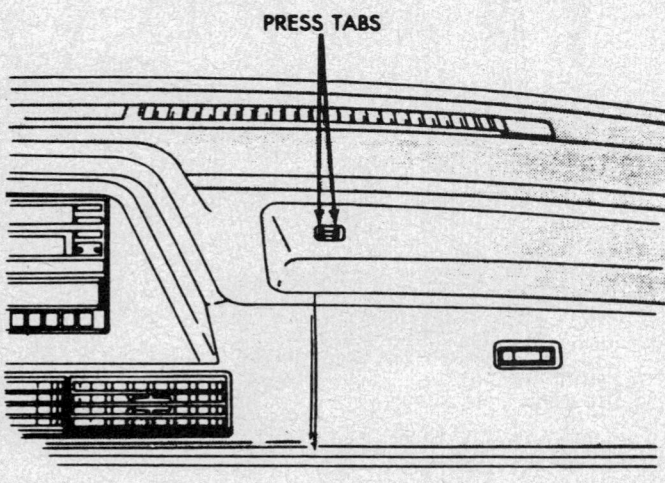

PRESS TABS

CR9149100036000X

Fig. 36   Air temperature sensor retaining tabs. Monaco & Premier

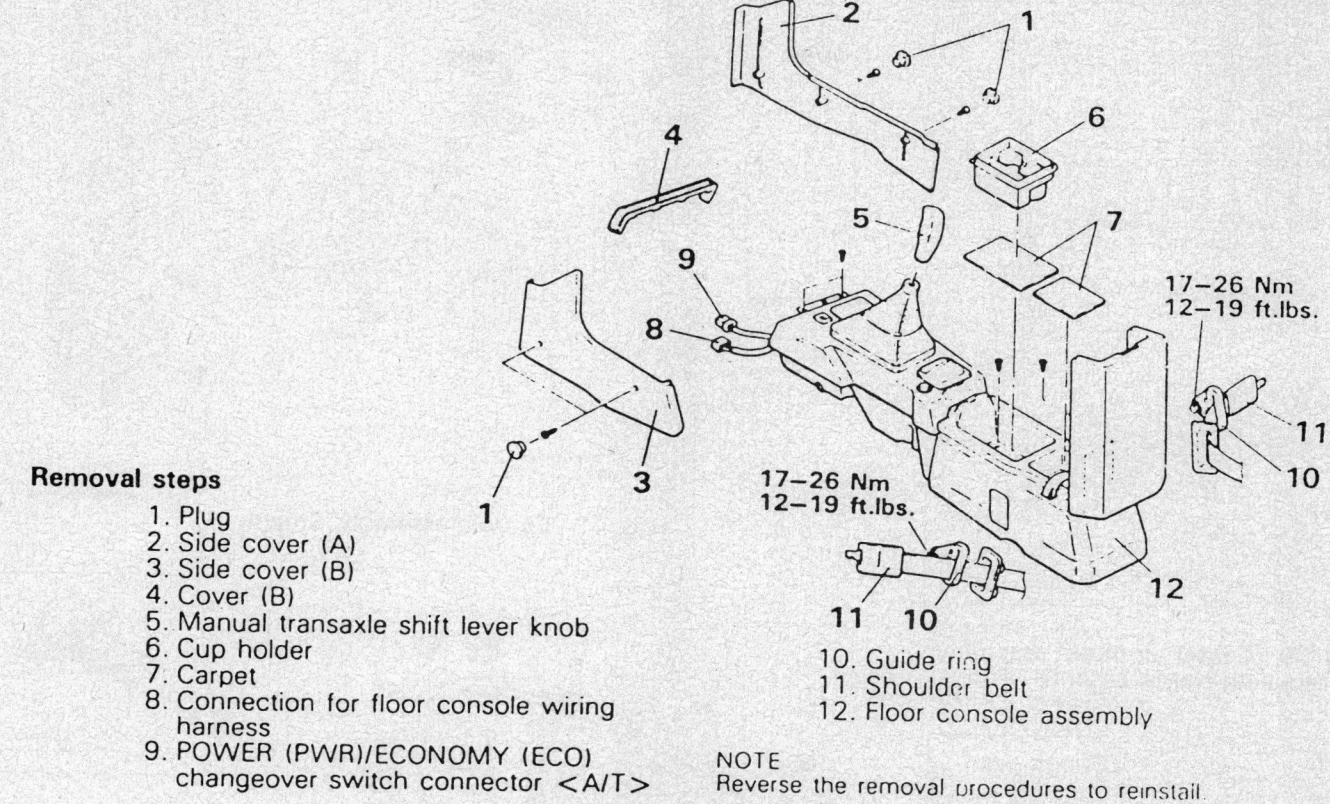

Removal steps

1. Plug
2. Side cover (A)
3. Side cover (B)
4. Cover (B)
5. Manual transaxle shift lever knob
6. Cup holder
7. Carpet
8. Connection for floor console wiring harness
9. POWER (PWR)/ECONOMY (ECO) changeover switch connector <A/T>

10. Guide ring
11. Shoulder belt
12. Floor console assembly

NOTE
Reverse the removal procedures to reinstall.

17–26 Nm
12–19 ft.lbs.

17–26 Nm
12–19 ft.lbs.

CR9149100037000X

Fig. 37 Exploded view of floor console. Laser & Talon

8–12 Nm
6–9 ft.lbs.

Removal steps

1. Plug
2. Knee protecter assembly
3. Hood lock release handle
4. Column cover lower
5. Column cover upper
6. Cover (A)
7. Cluster panel assembly (A)
8. Radio panel
9. Radio or radio and tape player
10. Center air outlet assembly
11. Dial knob (A)
12. Cluster panel assembly (B)
13. Stopper
14. Glove box assembly

15. Combination meter
16. Speedometer cable adapter
17. Speaker garnishes
18. Bracket
19. Heater control assembly installation screws
20. Lap cooler duct
21. Shower duct (L.H.)
22. Steering shaft installing bolt(s)
23. Instrument panel mounting screws
24. Instrument panel mounting bolts
25. Instrument panel assembly

NOTE
Reverse the removal procedures to reinstall.

Fig. 38 Exploded view of instrument panel. Laser & Talon

CR9149100038000X

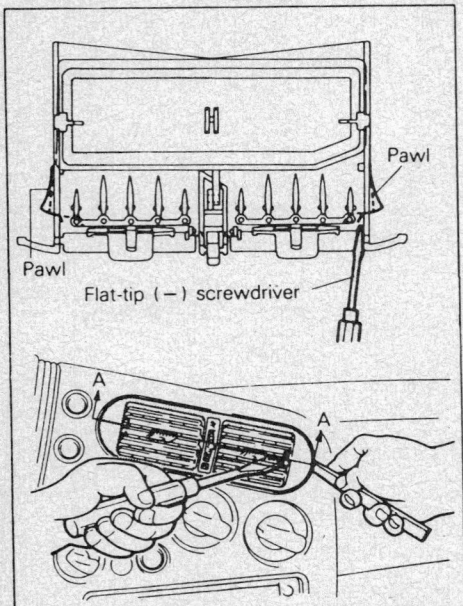

Fig. 39 Center air outlet assembly retaining pawls. Laser & Talon

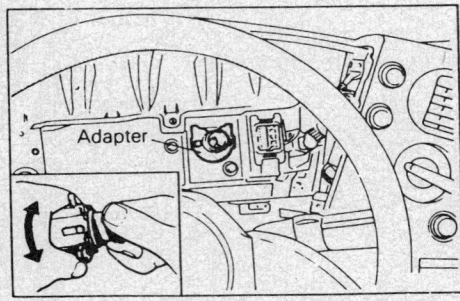

Fig. 40 Speedometer cable adapter removal. Laser & Talon

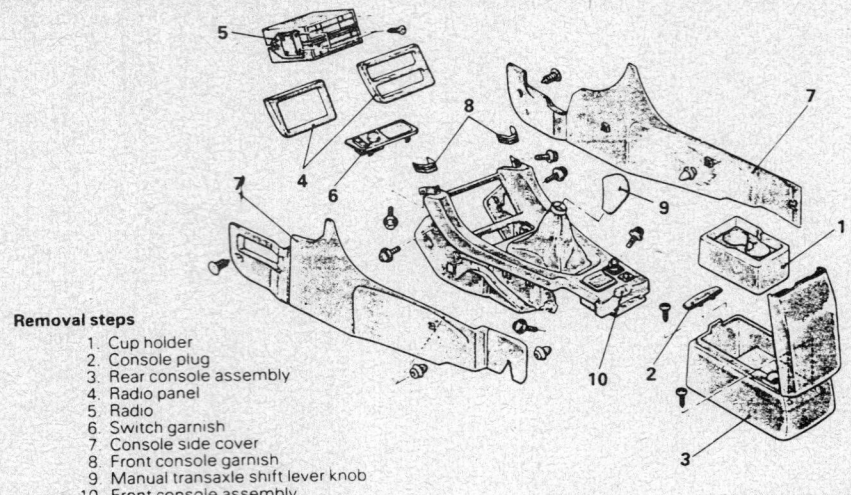

Removal steps
1. Cup holder
2. Console plug
3. Rear console assembly
4. Radio panel
5. Radio
6. Switch garnish
7. Console side cover
8. Front console garnish
9. Manual transaxle shift lever knob
10. Front console assembly

Fig. 41 Console assembly. Stealth

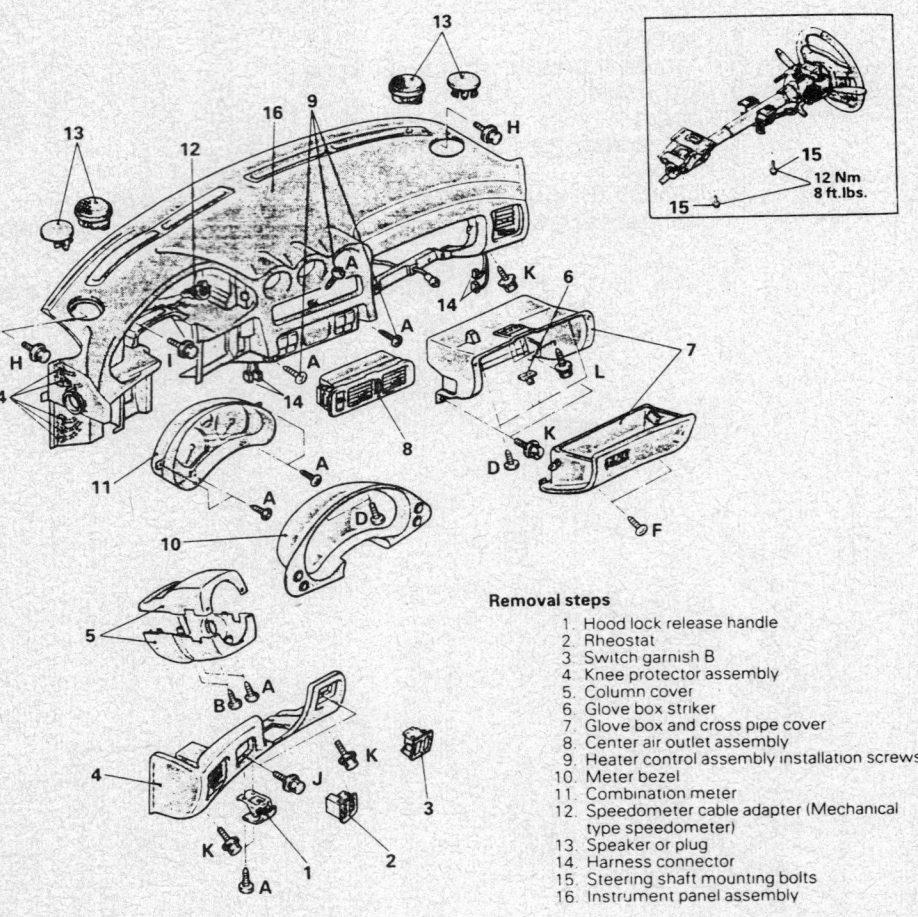

Removal steps
1. Hood lock release handle
2. Rheostat
3. Switch garnish B
4. Knee protector assembly
5. Column cover
6. Glove box striker
7. Glove box and cross pipe cover
8. Center air outlet assembly
9. Heater control assembly installation screws
10. Meter bezel
11. Combination meter
12. Speedometer cable adapter (Mechanical type speedometer)
13. Speaker or plug
14. Harness connector
15. Steering shaft mounting bolts
16. Instrument panel assembly

Fig. 42 Dash panel assembly. Stealth

of instrument panel (cowl sides), then detach lower instrument panel from upper instrument panel.
10. Disconnect the following electrical connectors:
   a. Trunk release and glove compartment light switches.
   b. Radio/antenna connectors.
   c. Heater-A/C and cigar lighter connectors.
   d. Ashtray light.
11. Remove left under instrument panel silencer/duct as follows:
   a. Remove push in fastener under left end of instrument panel.
   b. Pull silencer/duct off brake bracket stud and center floor distribution duct.
12. Remove instrument panel top cover as follows:
   a. Pry up each end of top cover, disengaging clip.
   b. Using straightedge tool along rear edge, lift rear edge of top cover and slide top cover rearward disengaging clips.

13. Remove A pillar trim panels, then the body controller module at right end of instrument panel.
14. Remove two impact brackets from steering column, then the left outlet duct.
15. Remove steering column shrouds, then disconnect six electrical connec-

tors. Slide wiring trough retainer off trough. Position wiring aside.
16. Loosen two lower screws and remove two upper nuts on steering column assembly. Position column on floor.
17. Disconnect the following electrical connectors:
   a. Power antenna and cable at right

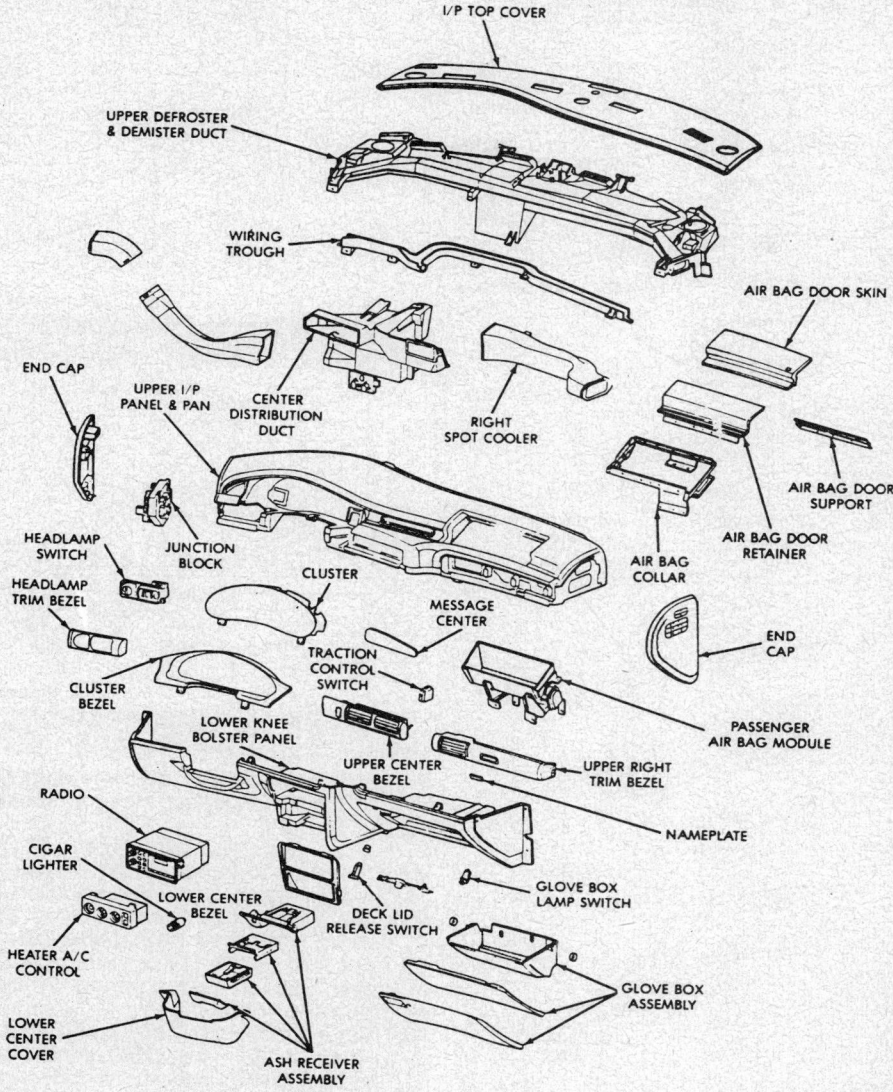

I/P TOP COVER

UPPER DEFROSTER & DEMISTER DUCT

WIRING TROUGH

AIR BAG DOOR SKIN

END CAP

UPPER I/P PANEL & PAN

CENTER DISTRIBUTION DUCT

RIGHT SPOT COOLER

AIR BAG DOOR SUPPORT

AIR BAG DOOR RETAINER

HEADLAMP SWITCH

JUNCTION BLOCK

CLUSTER

MESSAGE CENTER

AIR BAG COLLAR

HEADLAMP TRIM BEZEL

TRACTION CONTROL SWITCH

END CAP

CLUSTER BEZEL

LOWER KNEE BOLSTER PANEL

UPPER CENTER BEZEL

UPPER RIGHT TRIM BEZEL

PASSENGER AIR BAG MODULE

RADIO

NAMEPLATE

CIGAR LIGHTER

LOWER CENTER BEZEL

DECK LID RELEASE SWITCH

GLOVE BOX LAMP SWITCH

HEATER A/C CONTROL

LOWER CENTER COVER

ASH RECEIVER ASSEMBLY

GLOVE BOX ASSEMBLY

CR9149100043000X

Fig. 43 Exploded view of instrument panel. Concorde, Intrepid, LHS, Vision & 1994 New Yorker

cowl side.
b. Body wiring at right end of A/C unit.
c. Three ATC unit connectors at center of unit.
d. Ground wire at left of center support.
e. DRB II connector at left brace.
f. Two Air bag diagnostic module connectors.
g. Three inline bracket connectors including 40-way jack screw, then remove hazard relay.
h. Four outboard connector to junction block.
i. Headliner connector at top of panel.
18. Remove upper instrument panel attaching bolts, two at each cowl side and five bolts along top of panel.
19. Lift upper instrument panel rearward off lower attaching studs. Remove instrument panel from vehicle.
20. Reverse procedure to install.

NEON

Refer to **Fig. 44** when performing the following operations.
1. Disconnect battery ground cable.
2. Remove center console unit as follows:
   a. **On models with automatic transaxle,** loosen set screw under left side of shift knob button, then pull up to remove shift knob.
   b. **On models with manual transaxle,** pull shifter boot down to expose knob locking tabs.
   c. Release lock tabs, then pull up knob to slide it off shaft.
   d. **On all models** remove screw found under plug in each forward cup holder, **Fig. 45.**
   e. **On models with center armrest,** remove four screws inside console bin.
   f. **On models less center armrest,**

remove two screws at rear end of console.
   g. **On all models,** fully engage parking brake.
   h. Lift console from rear until indicator lamp socket is accessible, then remove indicator lamp.
3. Remove right and left lower kick panel trim.
4. Remove screws along bottom edge of steering column cover, then pull cover out to disengage clips.
5. Remove two screws in upper area and one screw in lower left area of steering column cover liner, then remove liner.
6. Remove top dash cover and instrument bezel unit by carefully prying out lower edge of bezel and lower edge of top dash cover, then pull unit rearward to disengage clips.
7. Remove instrument cluster as follows:
   a. Remove four screws holding instrument cluster to base panel.
   b. Pull cluster rearward to expose electrical connectors, then disconnect connectors.
   c. Remove cluster assembly from dash.
8. Remove right instrument panel trim as follows:
   a. Reach inside dash area and disconnect rear window defogger and/or fog light switch.
   b. Disengage left bezel latch, then pull switch and bezel from dash.
   c. Remove six attaching screws along edge of right dash trim.
   d. Lift edge of panel to disengage three locator pins.
   e. Pull trim panel rearward until lower clips disengage.
9. Remove left instrument panel trim by removing one upper and two lower screws, then pull panel rearward.
10. Lift and remove upper defroster duct.
11. Remove A/C heater control as follows:
   a. Open ash tray door, then pull center bezel rearward to disengage clips.
   b. Remove three screws retaining A/C heater control, **Fig. 46.**
   c. Pull control unit until wiring connector are accessible, then disconnect wiring.
   d. Using a suitable tool, disengage control cable clips, then disconnect cables.
12. Remove screws along bottom edge of glove compartment.
13. Open clove box door.
14. Using suitable tool, depress glove compartment sides, while pulling compartment rearward, to clear door stop bumpers and remove.
15. Remove steering column shroud, if required, as follows:
   a. Insert a suitable tool through access hole in lower steering column cover to depress the ignition lock cylinder button while rotating ignition key between On and Start position.
   b. Remove ignition lock cylinder.

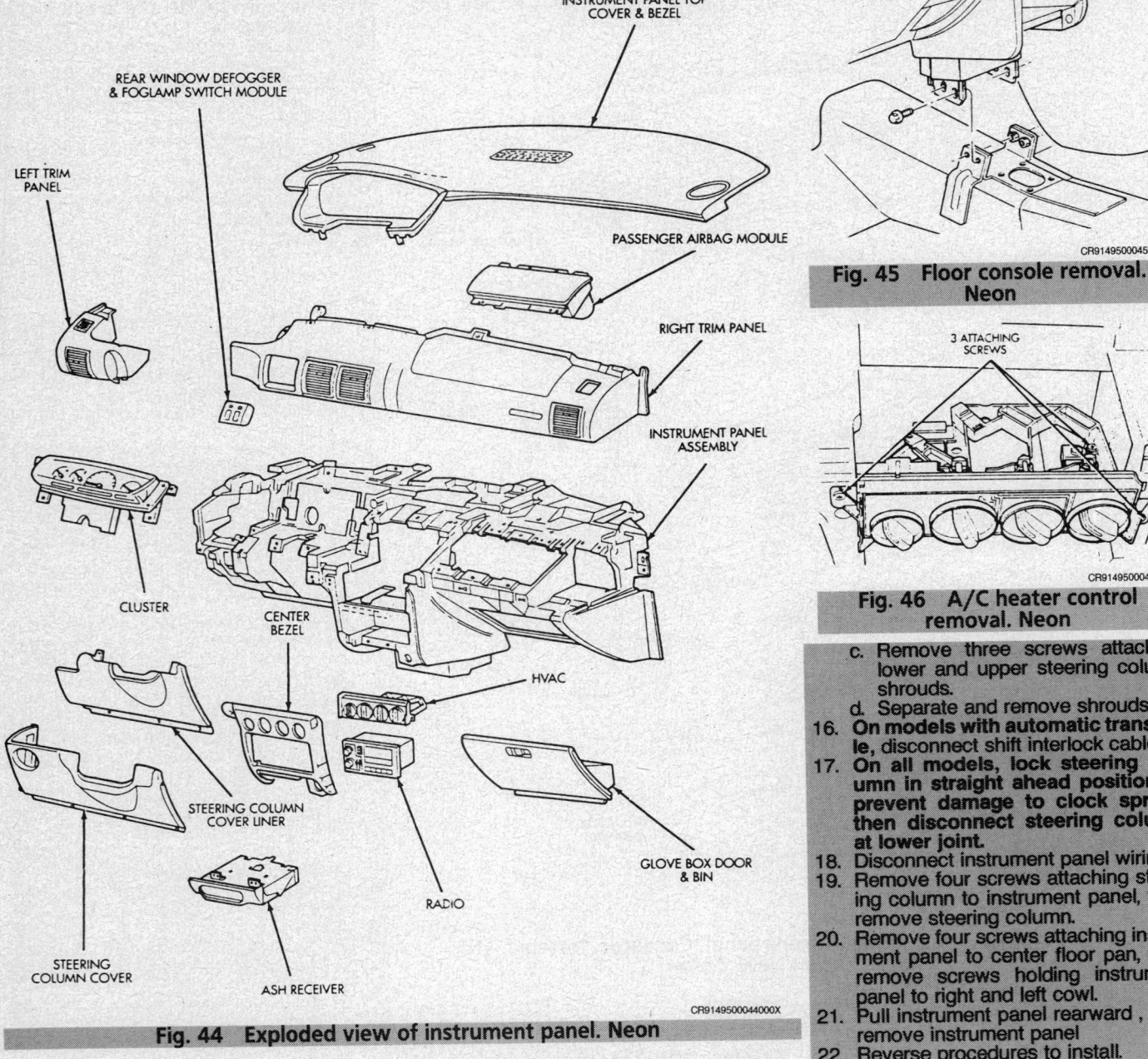

INSTRUMENT PANEL TOP
COVER & BEZEL

REAR WINDOW DEFOGGER
& FOGLAMP SWITCH MODULE

LEFT TRIM
PANEL

PASSENGER AIRBAG MODULE

RIGHT TRIM PANEL

INSTRUMENT PANEL
ASSEMBLY

CLUSTER

CENTER
BEZEL

HVAC

STEERING COLUMN
COVER LINER

STEERING
COLUMN COVER

RADIO

ASH RECEIVER

GLOVE BOX DOOR
& BIN

CR9149500044000X

Fig. 44   Exploded view of instrument panel. Neon

CR9149500045000X

**Fig. 45   Floor console removal.
Neon**

3 ATTACHING
SCREWS

CR9149500046000X

**Fig. 46   A/C heater control
removal. Neon**

   c. Remove three screws attaching
lower and upper steering column
shrouds.
   d. Separate and remove shrouds.
16. **On models with automatic transaxle,** disconnect shift interlock cable.
17. **On all models, lock steering column in straight ahead position to
prevent damage to clock spring,
then disconnect steering column
at lower joint.**
18. Disconnect instrument panel wiring.
19. Remove four screws attaching steering column to instrument panel, then
remove steering column.
20. Remove four screws attaching instrument panel to center floor pan, then
remove screws holding instrument
panel to right and left cowl.
21. Pull instrument panel rearward , then
remove instrument panel
22. Reverse procedures to install.

STEERING COLUMNS

NOTE: On Air Bag Equipped Models, Refer To "Air Bag System Precautions" Located In The Front Of This Manual For System Disarming & Arming Procedures.

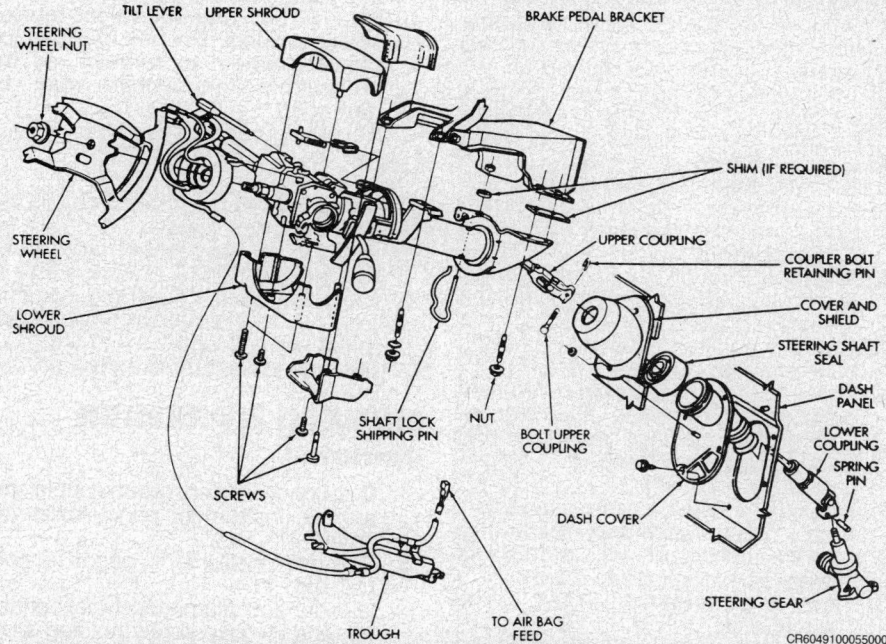

Fig. 1 Exploded view of steering column assembly. Acclaim, Daytona, Dynasty, Imperial, LeBaron, Shadow, Spirit, Sundance & 1992-93 New Yorker

PRECAUTIONS

AIR BAG SYSTEMS

Refer to "Air Bag System Precautions" in the front of this manual for system disarming and arming procedures.

SERVICE PRECAUTIONS

When servicing collapsible steering columns, care should be exercised since they are extremely susceptible to damage. Dropping of or leaning on column or striking sharp blows on end of steering shaft or shift levers could loosen or shear plastic fasteners which maintain column rigidity.

It is important that only the specified screws, bolts and nuts be used during the mandatory reassembly sequence and tightened to specifications to insure proper breakaway action of column under impact. Avoid using excessively long bolts, as they may prevent a portion of the steering column from collapsing under impact.

If there is evidence of a sheared plastic shift tube injection, a new shift tube must be installed. If plastic injections are sheared but steering shaft is not bent, repairs may be possible using Service Steering Shaft Repair Kit part number 3514996. The kit contains instructions and dimensions for all steering columns. On some models, the retaining brackets will shear under impact and must also be replaced.

STEERING COLUMN

REPLACE

ACCLAIM, DAYTONA, DYNASTY, IMPERIAL, LEBARON, SHADOW, SPIRIT, SUNDANCE & 1992-93 NEW YORKER

The steering column used on these models, **Fig. 1**, has been designed to be serviced as an assembly except for wiring, switches, shrouds and the steering wheel. Also, most steering column components can be serviced without removing the column from the vehicle.

1. Ensure wheels are in a straight ahead position.
2. Disconnect battery ground cable.
3. **On models with column shift,** disconnect link rod by prying it out of grommet in shift lever.
4. **On models less air bag,** remove steering wheel center pad.
5. **On models with air bag,** remove air bag as outlined under "Passive Restraint Systems."
6. **On all models,** disconnect electrical components.
7. Remove steering wheel nut, then steering wheel using puller tool No. C-3228-B or equivalent. **Do not bump or hammer on steering column shaft to remove wheel.**
8. Remove lower steering column, then the upper coupling retaining pin.
9. Remove nut and bolt from upper coupling then separate the upper coupling from the lower coupling.
10. **On models with column shift,** proceed as follows:
    a. Place gear shift lever in Neutral or Park position.
    b. Remove PRNDL indicator cable from actuating arm, then release lock bar on column insert, **Fig. 2.**

c. Squeeze legs of column insert together and remove insert from steering column, **Fig. 2.**

d. Position insert and actuation cable aside.

11. **On models with tilt steering,** remove tilt lever.

12. **On all models,** remove upper and lower lock housing shrouds.

13. Remove lower fixed shroud Torx head screws and shroud.

14. Remove turn signal multi-function switch.

15. Remove electrical connections from key-in light, main ignition switch, horn and/or air bag clock spring. Remove clock spring electrical connections as outlined under "Passive Restraint Systems."

16. Loosen upper support bracket nuts then remove upper fixed shroud.

17. Remove wiring harness by prying out plastic retainer buttons.

18. Remove lower dash panel and support bracket standoff fasteners.

19. Remove column through passenger compartment.

20. Reverse procedure to install, noting the following:

    a. **On models with column shift,** replace shift rod grommet.

    b. **On all models,** ensure ground clip on left capsule slot in place.

    c. Ensure to install upper coupling bolt retainer pin.

    d. Ensure breakaway capsules are fully seated in slots in column bracket, then **torque** bracket nuts to 105 inch lbs.

    e. **Torque** steering wheel nut to 45 ft. lbs. **Do not force steering wheel on column shaft by driving wheel with a heavy object. Use retaining nut.**

NEON

Refer to **Figs. 3 and 4** throughout the following procedure.

1. Disconnect and isolate battery ground cable, then ensure front wheels are directed straight ahead.

2. Remove steering column cover trim panel and cover liner from lower instrument panel, then remove steering wheel trim covers and, if necessary, speed control switches from steering wheel.

3. Remove two bolts securing air bag module to steering wheel, **Fig. 5,** then lift module carefully from center of steering wheel and disconnect clockspring electrical connector from rear of module.

4. Disconnect clockspring electrical connectors from horn switches, then remove steering wheel retaining nut and dampener weight.

5. Install steering wheel puller tool No. C-3428-B or equivalent upon steering wheel, then tighten tool center bolt until wheel can be slid from steering shaft. **Do not hammer on tool or steering wheel during removal.**

6. Place key lock cylinder in On position, then use a small screwdriver or other

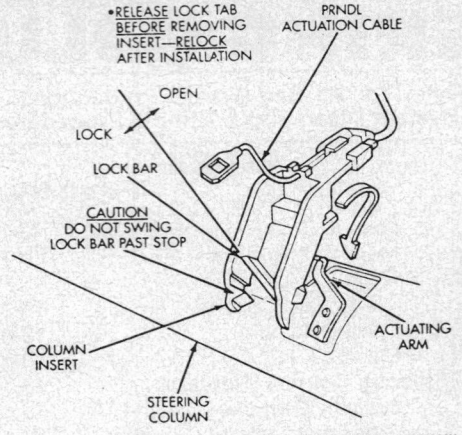

Fig. 2   PRNDL cable replacement. Acclaim, Daytona, Dynasty, Imperial, LeBaron, Shadow, Spirit, Sundance & 1992–93 New Yorker

suitable tool to depress lock cylinder retaining tab through tab access hole, **Fig. 6.**

7. Remove key lock cylinder assembly from steering column, then remove steering column lower shroud.

8. Tilt steering column to lowest position and remove upper shroud, then slip retaining pin out of upper to lower column pinch bolt.

9. Remove pinch bolt nut, separate upper and lower coupler shafts. **Pinch bolt cannot be removed from coupler assembly.**

10. Remove through bolt from lower steering column bearing housing and mounting bracket, then remove upper steering column assembly batwing bracket bolts.

11. Lower steering column in instrument panel access opening, then disconnect wiring harness at wiper and multi-function switches and disengage from clips.

12. Remove wiring harness connectors from ignition switch and clockspring, then lift steering column assembly out of vehicle through driver's door.

13. Reverse procedure to install, noting the following:

    a. **Torque** upper steering column bracket to support bolts to 9 ft. lbs.

    b. **Torque** pinch bolt nut to 21 ft. lbs. and ensure its retaining pin is installed.

    c. **Torque** steering wheel retaining nut to 45 ft. lbs.

    d. Use only original or correct replacement bolts when installing air bag module. **Torque** bolts to 90 inch lbs.

COLT & SUMMIT

1992–93

Refer to **Fig. 7** for steering column removal, noting the following:

1. Disconnect battery ground cable.

2. Remove trim clip (2), **Fig. 7,** by lightly pushing pin at center of clip with a Phillips screwdriver, then pull out clip.

Do not push pin in any further than necessary.

3. Remove steering wheel using a suitable puller. **Do not hammer on steering wheel to remove, as the collapsible mechanism may be damaged.**

4. Reverse procedure to install.

1994

Refer to **Fig. 8** for steering column removal, noting the following:

1. Use puller tool No. MB990803 or equivalent to remove steering wheel.

2. Refer to "Passive Restraint Systems" for air bag component removal procedures & precautions.

3. Reverse procedure to install.

COLT VISTA & SUMMIT WAGON

1992–93

Refer to **Fig 9** for steering column removal, noting the following:

1. Disconnect battery ground cable.

2. Remove steering wheel retaining nut; then, using steering wheel puller tool No. DT-1001-A or equivalent, remove steering wheel. **Do not hammer on steering wheel to remove, as the collapsible mechanism may be damaged.**

3. Reverse procedure to install.

1994

Refer to **Fig. 10** for steering column removal, noting the following:

1. Remove steering wheel using puller tool No. MB990803 or equivalent.

2. Refer to "Passive Restraint Systems" for air bag component removal procedures and precautions.

3. Reverse procedure to install.

MONACO & PREMIER

Removal

1. Disconnect battery ground cable, then remove instrument panel lower trim cover.

2. Remove instrument panel support rod, **Fig. 11.**

3. Disconnect column electrical connector, and remove screw holding steering column wiring harness bulkhead connector, **Fig. 12.**

4. Disconnect automatic transaxle shift cable with a screwdriver, **Fig. 13.**

5. Disconnect shift cable from steering column. Compress cable retainer tangs with pliers, then slide out of column bracket, **Fig. 14.**

6. Remove shift indicator bracket mounting screw, and lift indicator wire off the pin.

7. Unsnap the steering column boot and slide down the steering column.

8. Scribe reference marks on steering column shaft and intermediate shaft U-joint for assembly reference.

9. Remove hold-down bolt from intermediate steering shaft, **Fig. 15** then remove bolts and nuts holding steering column to instrument panel.

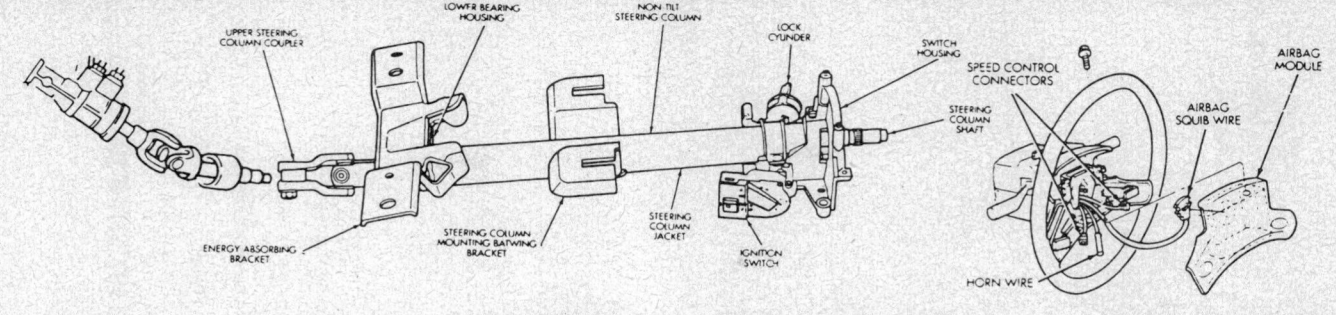

Fig. 3 Exploded view of steering column. Neon w/standard column

CR6049500097000X

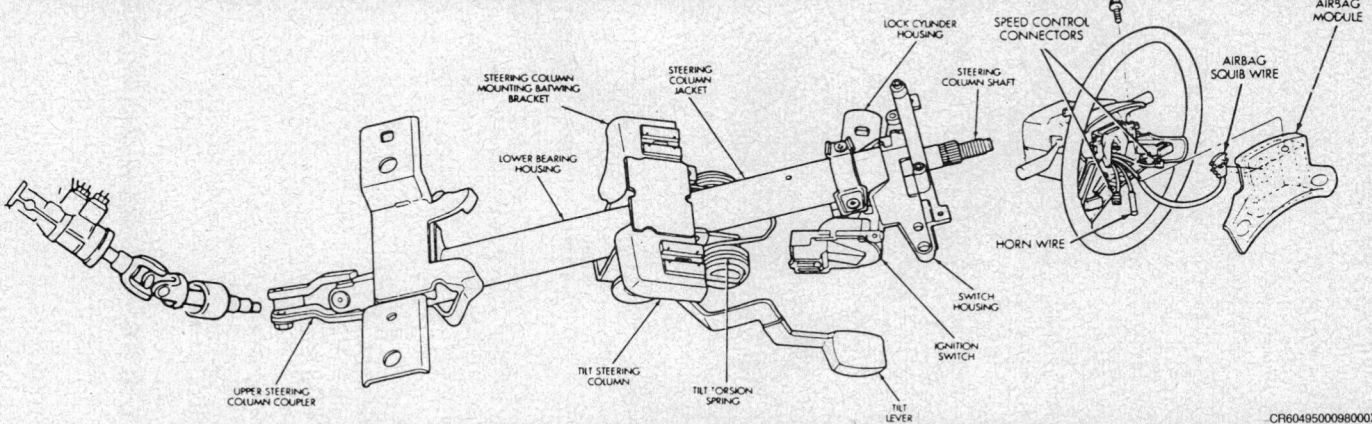

Fig. 4 Exploded view of steering column. Neon w/tilt column

CR6049500098000X

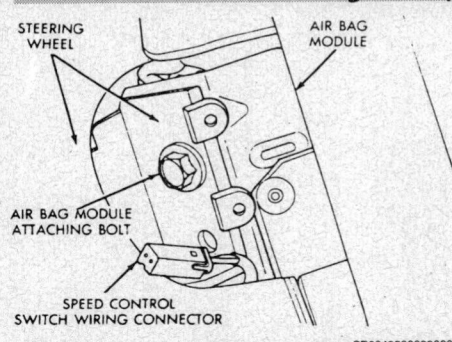

Fig. 5 Air bag module mounting bolt locations. Neon

CR6049500099000X

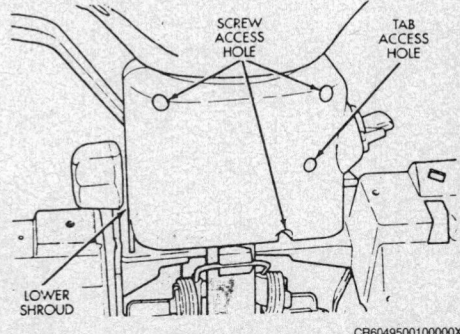

Fig. 6 Ignition key lock cylinder retaining tab access hole location. Neon

CR6049500100000X

10. Carefully lower steering assembly and separate steering column shaft from intermediate shaft, then remove from vehicle.

Installation

1. Align and insert steering column shaft in intermediate steering shaft U-joint using the marks made during disassembly, then install but do not torque U-joint bolt.
2. Position column and install nuts and bolts retaining column to instrument panel and **torque** to 35 ft. lbs.
3. Tighten intermediate shaft U-joint bolt.
4. Loop shift indicator wire on mounting pin, then install bracket retaining screw.
5. Snap shift cable into steering column bracket, then snap shift cable head onto mounting ball in shift arm.
6. Move gearshift lever into N position and check that shift pointer is aligned

correctly. Adjust by loosening indicator bracket screw, and moving into position as needed.
7. Install bulkhead connector and retaining screw, then connect column connector.
8. Install instrument panel support rod and tighten screws securely.
9. Align the two halves of steering shaft boot with the "X" mark of lower half is centered in the oval mark on the upper half. Alignment mark on metal boot flange should be at the 6 o'clock position, **Fig. 16.**
10. Install instrument panel lower trim cover, then connect battery ground cable.

LASER & TALON

Refer to **Fig. 17** for steering column assembly replacement.

STEALTH

1. Remove air bag module as outlined under "Passive Restraint Systems."
2. Replace the steering column in numbered sequence shown in **Fig. 18.**

CONCORDE, INTREPID, LHS, VISION & 1994 NEW YORKER

Refer to **Fig. 19** when performing this procedure.

1. Turn steering wheel ½ turn from straight ahead position, then remove key from lock cylinder.
2. Disconnect battery ground cable.
3. **On models with speed control,** remove speed control switches from

steering wheel.
4. **On models less speed control,** remove steering wheel side covers.
5. **On all models,** remove air bag module mounting bolts, then slightly lift module. Disconnect module electrical connectors and remove module from steering wheel.
6. Remove steering wheel retaining nut, then the steering wheel using puller tool No. C-3428-B or equivalent. Do not bump or hammer on steering column shaft to remove wheel.
7. Remove instrument panel end covers, then air bag fuses 7 and 19 from fuse panel.
8. Remove cowl trim panels, then the console or instrument panel lower center cover and ashtray.
9. Remove left under instrument panel

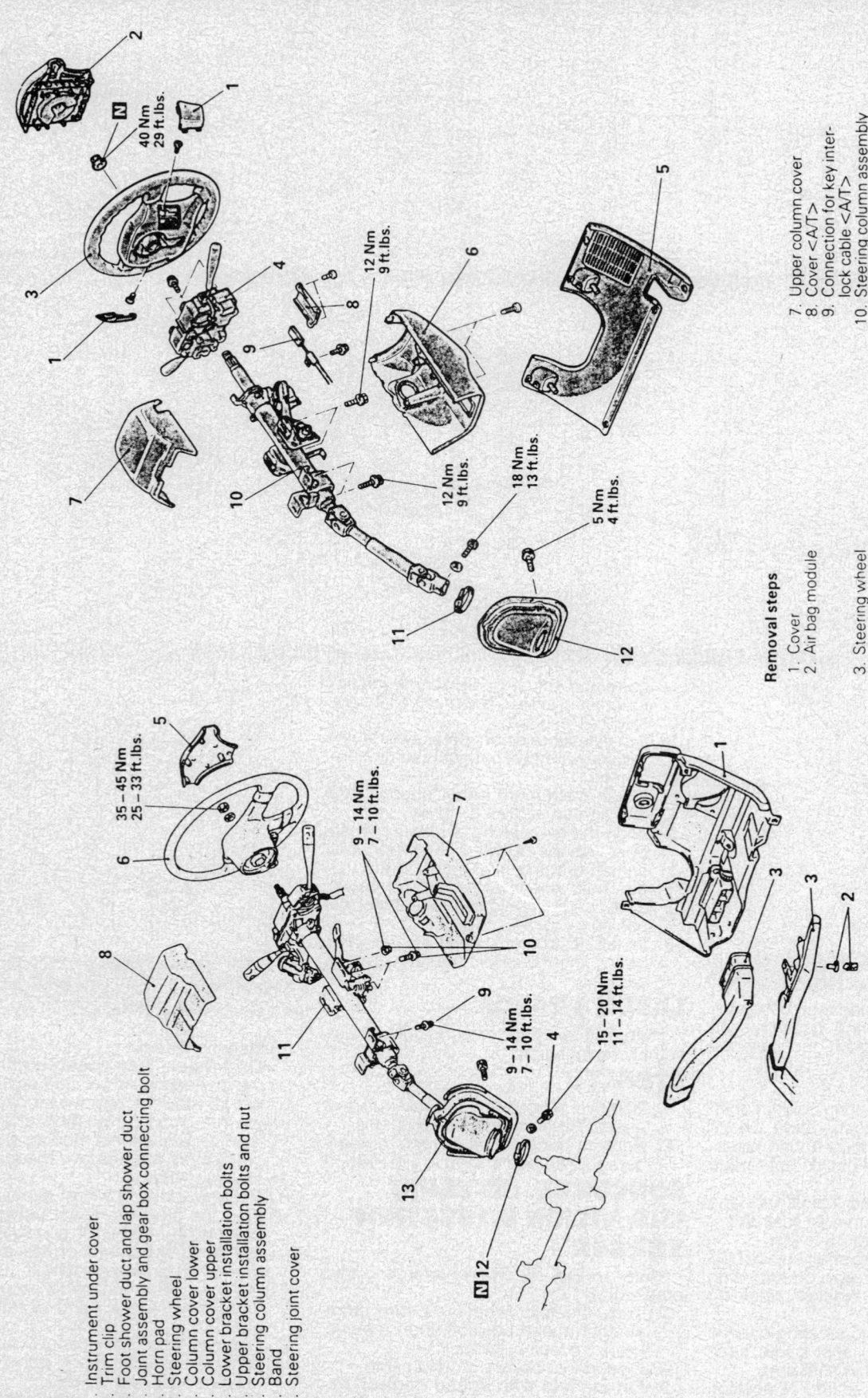

Removal steps

1. Cover
2. Air bag module

3. Steering wheel
4. Column switch assembly
5. Knee protector or instrument under cover
6. Lower column cover

7. Upper column cover
8. Cover <A/T>
9. Connection for key inter-lock cable <A/T>
10. Steering column assembly
11. Band
12. Steering cover

Fig. 8   Exploded view of steering column. 1994 Colt & Summit

1. Instrument under cover
2. Trim clip
3. Foot shower duct and lap shower duct
4. Joint assembly and gear box connecting bolt
5. Horn pad
6. Steering wheel
7. Column cover lower
8. Column cover upper
9. Upper bracket installation bolts
10. Lower bracket installation bolts and nut
11. Steering column assembly
12. Band
13. Steering joint cover

Fig. 7   Exploded view of steering column assembly. 1992–93 Colt & Summit

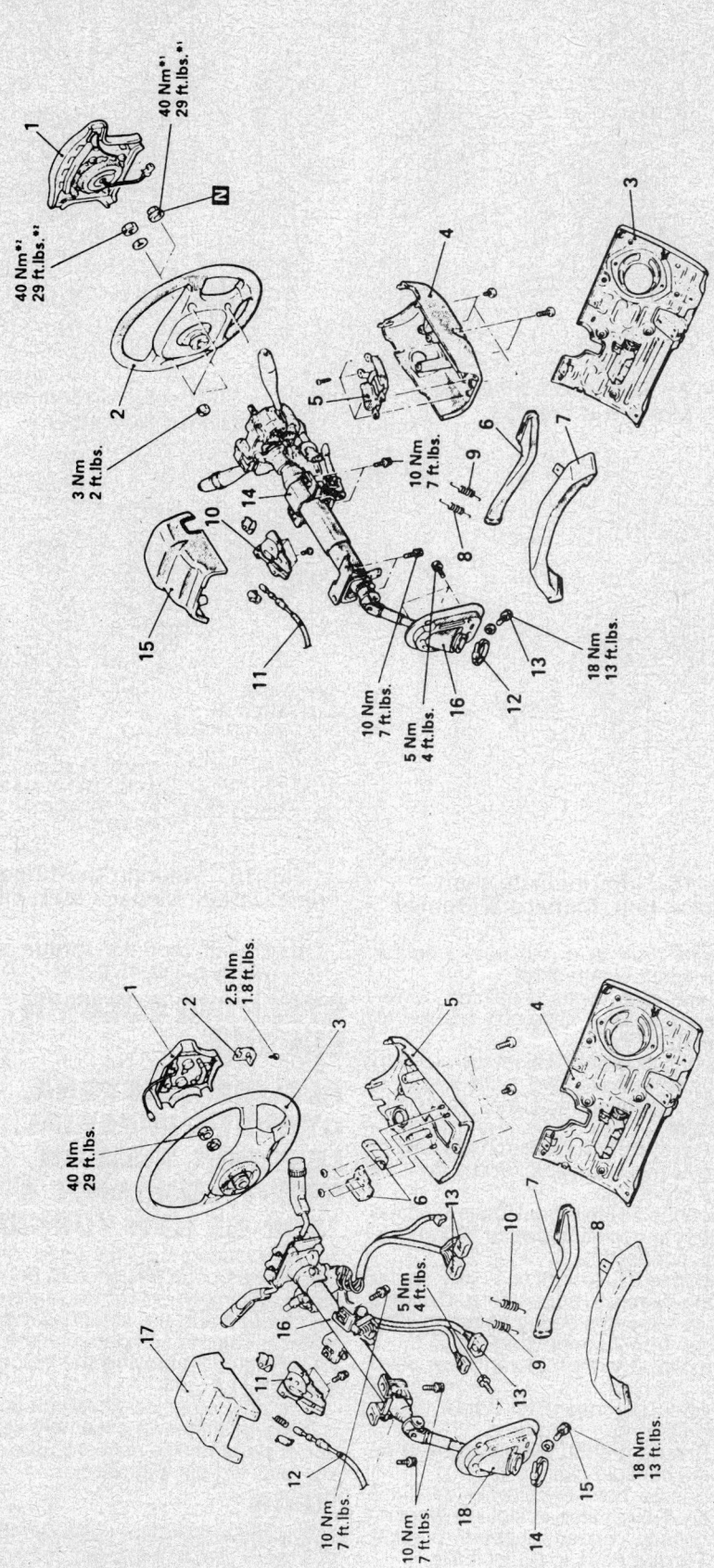

Removal steps

1. Air bag module
2. Steering wheel
3. Instrument under cover
4. Lower column cover
5. Protector
6. Lap duct
7. Foot duct
8. Brake pedal return spring
9. Clutch pedal return spring <M/T>

10. Cover <A/T>
11. Key-interlock cable <A/T>
12. Band
13. Joint assembly and gear box connecting bolt
14. Steering column assembly
15. Upper column cover
16. Steering joint cover assembly

NOTE
*1 : Case of self locking nut
*2 : Case of nut and spring washer

CR60494001020000X

Fig. 10 Exploded view of steering column. 1994 Colt Vista & Summit Wagon

Removal steps

1. Horn pad
2. Spring holder
3. Steering wheel
4. Instrument under cover
5. Lower column cover
6. Column cover protector
7. Lap duct
8. Foot duct
9. Brake pedal return spring
10. Clutch pedal return spring <M/T>

11. Cover <A/T>
12. Key-interlock cable <A/T>
13. Harness connector
14. Band
15. Joint assembly and gear box connecting bolt
16. Steering column assembly
17. Upper column cover
18. Steering joint cover assembly

CR60492000580000X

Fig. 9 Exploded view of steering column assembly. 1992–93 Colt Vista & Summit Wagon

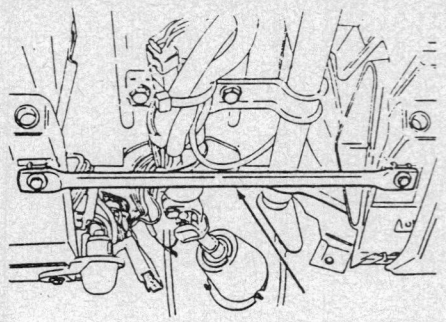

Fig. 11   Instrument panel support rod. Monaco & Premier

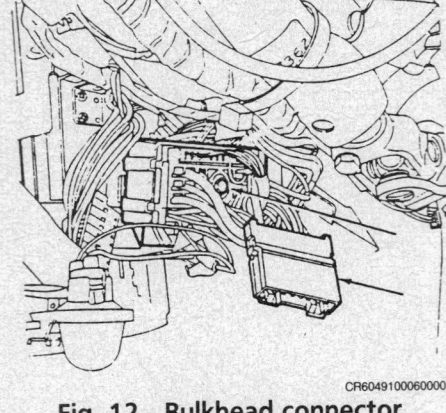

Fig. 12   Bulkhead connector. Monaco & Premier

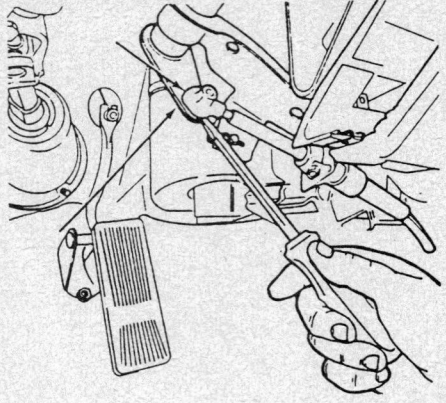

Fig. 13   Shift cable disconnected. Monaco & Premier

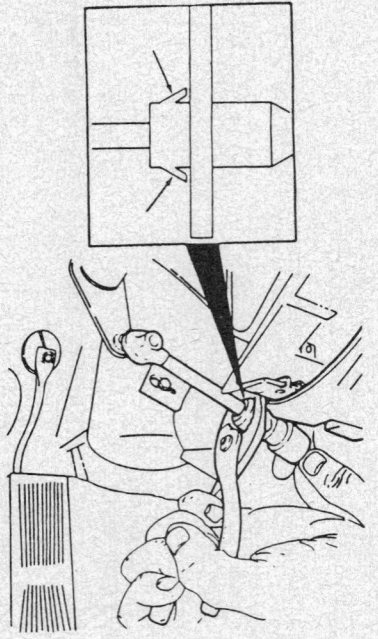

Fig. 14   Cable retainer disconnected. Monaco & Premier

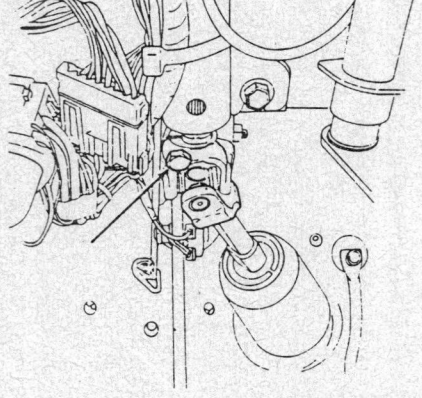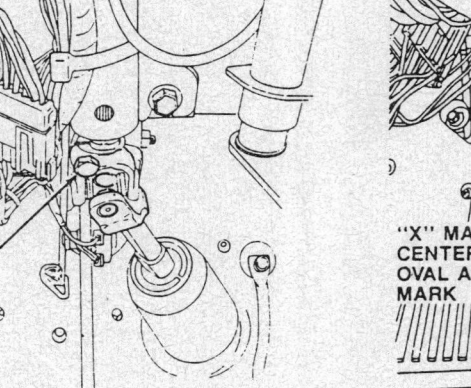

Fig. 15   Intermediate shaft hold-down bolt. Monaco & Premier

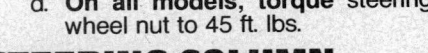

"X" MARK CENTERED IN OVAL ALIGNMENT MARK

BOOT FLANGE ALIGNMENT MARK AT 6 O'CLOCK POSITION

Fig. 16   Steering shaft boot installation. Monaco & Premier

silencer/duct, then the lower dash panel assembly.

10. Remove under steering column air outlet duct, then tilt steering column to full down position.

11. Remove tilt lever and steering column shrouds.

12. **On models equipped with column shift lever,** remove shift cable as follows:
   a. Install tilt lever, then tilt steering column to full up position.
   b. Pry shift cable off shifter pin, then remove shift cable retaining clip at shift cable support bracket. Do not bend cable bracket.
   c. Remove tilt lever.

13. **On all models,** turn ignition key to run position, unlocking steering column. Depress tab and remove floor shift interlock cable from steering column socket.

14. Remove retaining pin, from lower steering column coupler bolt. Remove coupler bolt and separate coupler from intermediate shaft.

15. Loosen two bolts retaining lower steering column assembly bracket to mount bracket.

16. While supporting weight of steering column, remove two nuts retaining upper steering column mounting bracket.

17. Remove steering column assembly from its mounting bracket and lay it on floor of vehicle.

18. Disconnect turn signal/multi-function switch and ignition switch wiring harness connectors.

19. Disconnect halo light and clock spring wiring harness connectors. Depress tab to remove steering column wiring trough from its mounting bracket.

20. Remove steering column from vehicle.

21. Reverse procedure to install, noting the following:
   a. Ensure ground clip is installed on left capsule slot.
   b. Ensure both breakaway capsules are fully seated in slots of steering column upper support bracket. **Torque** bolts to 95 inch lbs.
   c. **On models with column shifter,** a new interlock cassette must be installed.

   d. **On all models, torque** steering wheel nut to 45 ft. lbs.

STEERING COLUMN SERVICE

ACCLAIM, DAYTONA, DYNASTY, IMPERIAL, LEBARON, SHADOW, SPIRIT, SUNDANCE & 1992–93 NEW YORKER

The steering column used on these models has been designed to be serviced as an assembly except for wiring, switches, shrouds and the steering wheel. Most steering column components can be serviced without removing the column from the vehicle, **Fig. 1.**

The only other serviceable component is the gear shift lever assembly. Use a drift and a suitable size socket to drive out lever retaining pin, **Fig. 20.**

NEON

The steering column used on this model, **Figs. 3 and 4,** has been designed to be serviced as an assembly except for wiring, switches, shrouds and the steering wheel. Most steering column components can be

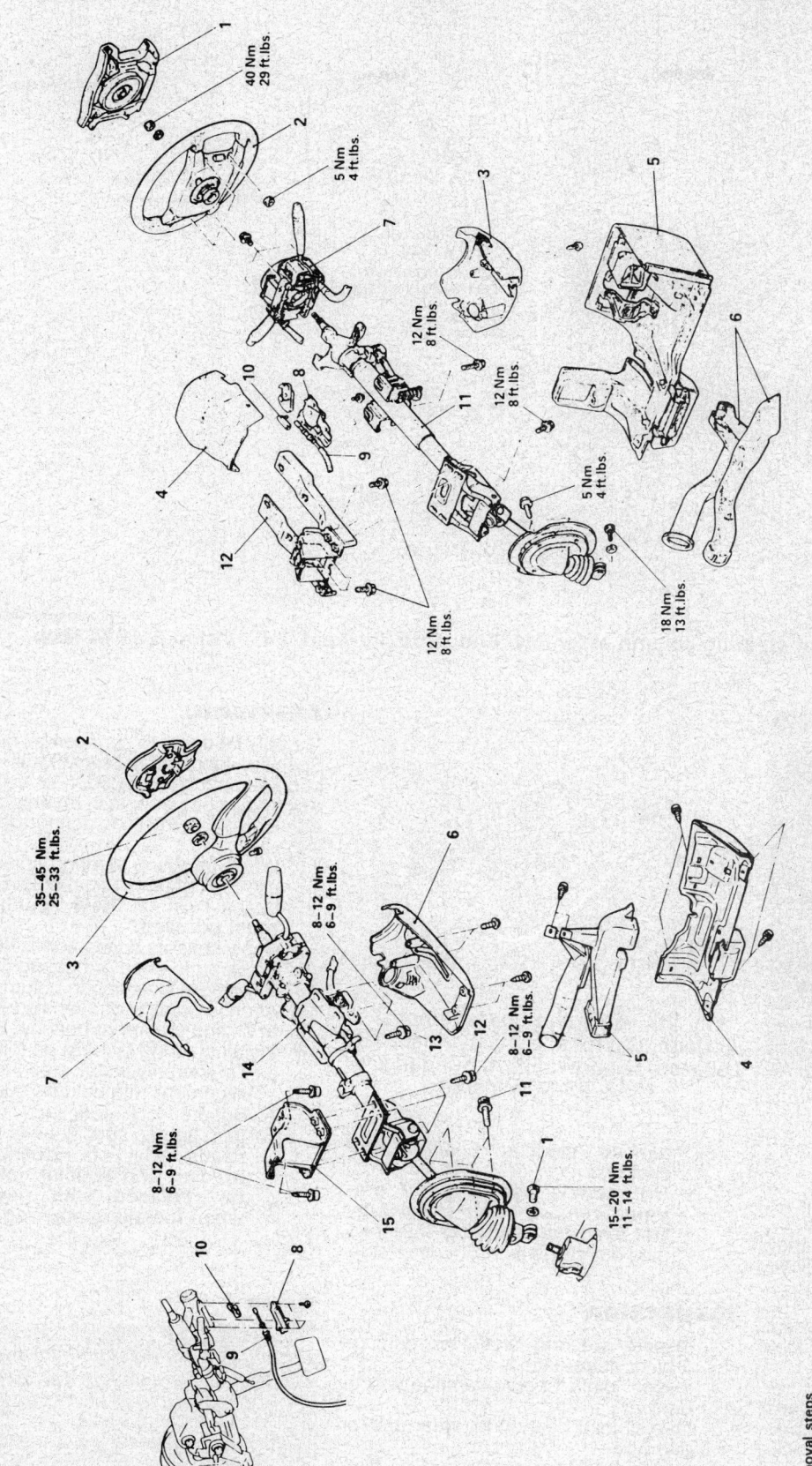

Removal steps

1. Air bag module
2. Steering wheel
3. Lower column cover
4. Upper column cover
5. Knee protector
6. Lap cooler duct and foot shower duct
7. Column switch assembly
8. Cover
9. Key interlock cable   <Automatic transaxle vehicles>
10. Slide lever
11. Steering column assembly
12. Column support assembly

Fig. 18 Exploded view of steering column assembly. Stealth

Removal steps

1. Joint assembly and gear box connecting bolt
2. Horn pad
3. Steering wheel
4. Instrument under cover
5. Foot shower duct and lap shower duct
6. Column cover lower
7. Column cover upper
8. Cover <A/T>
9. Key interlock cable (steering lock assembly side) <A/T>
10. Slide lever <A/T>
11. Cover attaching bolts
12. Lower bracket installation bolts
13. Tilt bracket installation bolts
14. Steering column assembly
15. Column support

Fig. 17 Exploded view of steering column assembly. Laser & Talon

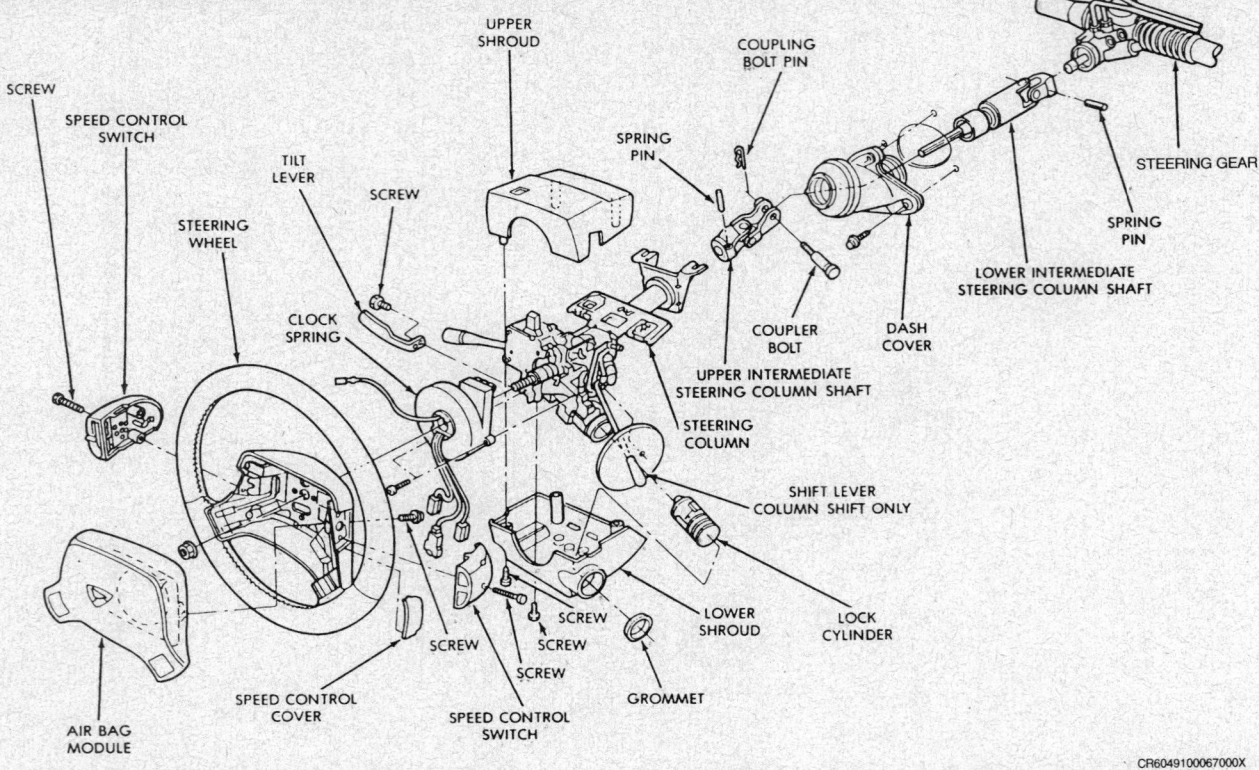

Fig. 19   Exploded view of steering column assembly. Concorde, Intrepid, LHS, Vision & 1994 New Yorker

serviced without removing the column from the vehicle.

The only other serviceable component is the steering column shaft coupler. If the coupler requires replacement due to a seized bearing, insufficient bearing staking or improper bearing seating, proceed as follows:

1. Remove steering column assembly as described under "Steering Column, Replace."
2. Remove spring pin from coupler and slide coupler from end of steering shaft. **Ensure lower shaft coupler is supported during spring pin removal and installation to prevent bearing damage.**
3. Reverse procedure to install.

COLT & SUMMIT

1992–93

Disassemble

1. Remove steering column as outlined under "Steering Column, Replace."
2. Remove components in order as they appear in **Fig. 21**, noting the following:
   a. If removal of steering lock (4) is necessary, use a hacksaw to cut special bolts at steering lock bracket side.
   b. Remove snap ring (5), then remove steering shaft (6) downward.
   c. If removal of steering column bracket(s) is necessary, use a hacksaw to cut a groove in head of special bolts, then use a screwdriver to

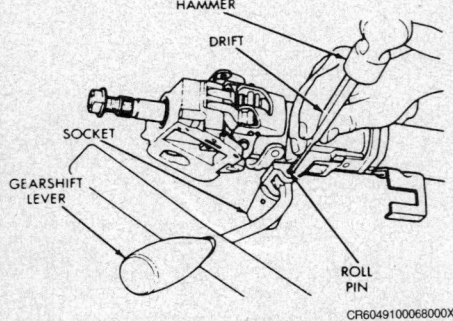

Fig. 20   Gear shift lever removal. Acclaim, Daytona, Dynasty, Imperial, LeBaron, Shadow, Spirit, Sundance & 1992–93 New Yorker

remove steering column bracket(s).
   d. **On models with Type 2 columns,** remove clevis pin (15) by first removing snap ring, then tapping out clevis pin from inner side.

Inspection

1. Inspect steering shaft for damage and/or deformation.
2. Inspect joints for play, damage and/or binding.
3. Inspect joint bearing for wear and/or damage.
4. Inspect bushing for wear and/or damage.

Assemble

Apply lubricant to surfaces as indicated. Specified lubricant is Mopar Multi-mileage Lubricant part No. 2525035 or equivalent. Assemble components in reverse order as they appear in **Fig. 21**, noting the following:

1. When installing steering column bracket(s), tighten special bolts until bolt heads twist off. **New special bolts must be used.**
2. Apply suitable drying adhesive to outer circumference of bearing (11), **Fig. 22,** before installing in column tube.
3. Apply a coating of specified lubricant to sliding portion of bearing, **Fig. 22.**
4. Install steering lock (8) as follows:
   a. Temporarily install steering lock in alignment with column boss.
   b. Ensure lock functions correctly, then tighten special bolts until bolt heads twist off. **Steering lock bracket and special bolts must be replaced with new ones when installing steering lock.**

1994

Disassemble column in sequence shown, **Fig. 23,** noting the following:

1. If steering lock cylinder is to be removed, cut special bolts at bracket side with a hacksaw.
2. Inspect universal joint for endplay and steering column for signs of bending.
3. Reverse procedure to assemble.

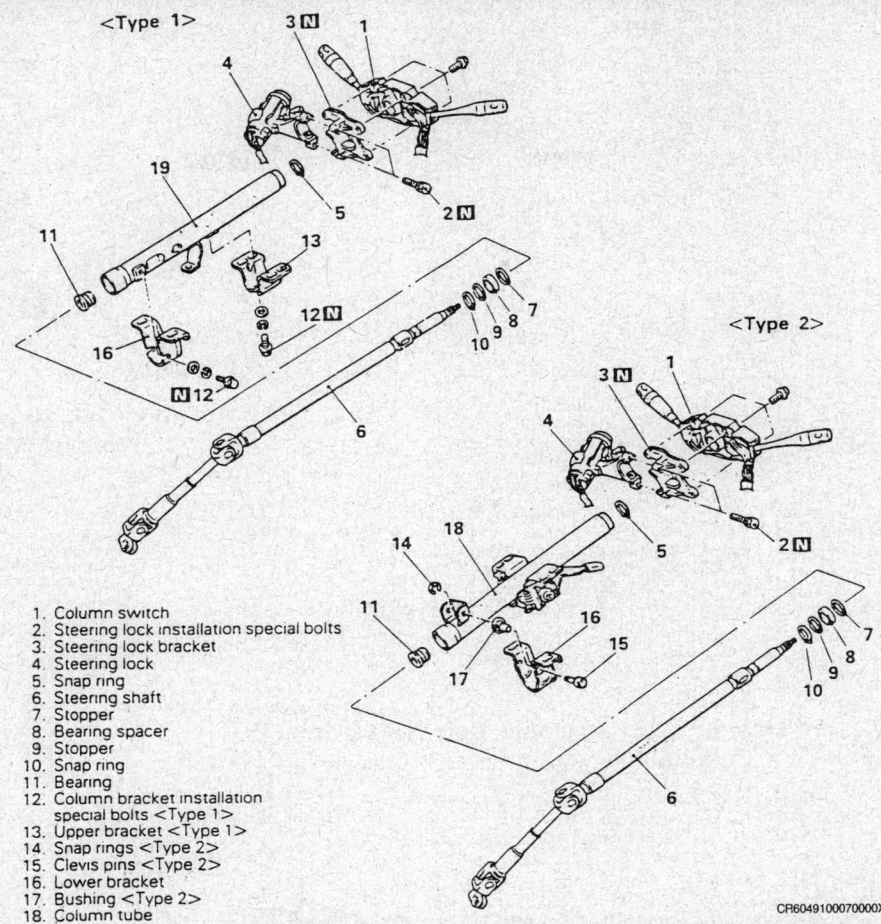

Fig. 21 Exploded view of steering column assembly. 1992-93 Colt & Summit

1. Column switch
2. Steering lock installation special bolts
3. Steering lock bracket
4. Steering lock
5. Snap ring
6. Steering shaft
7. Stopper
8. Bearing spacer
9. Stopper
10. Snap ring
11. Bearing
12. Column bracket installation special bolts <Type 1>
13. Upper bracket <Type 1>
14. Snap rings <Type 2>
15. Clevis pins <Type 2>
16. Lower bracket
17. Bushing <Type 2>
18. Column tube

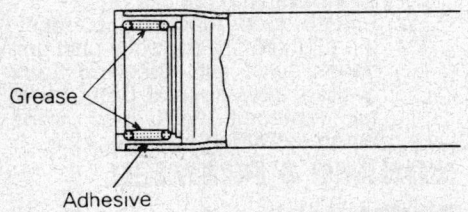

Fig. 22 Bearing installation. 1992-93 Colt & Summit

COLT VISTA & SUMMIT WAGON

Disassemble

1. Remove steering column as outlined under "Steering Column, Replace."
2. Remove components in order as they appear in **Fig. 24**, noting the following:
   a. If removal of steering wheel lock assembly is necessary, use a hacksaw to cut a groove in head of special bolts, then use a screwdriver to remove steering lock.
   b. If removal of steering column bracket(s) is necessary, use a hacksaw to cut a groove in head of special bolts, then use a screwdriver to

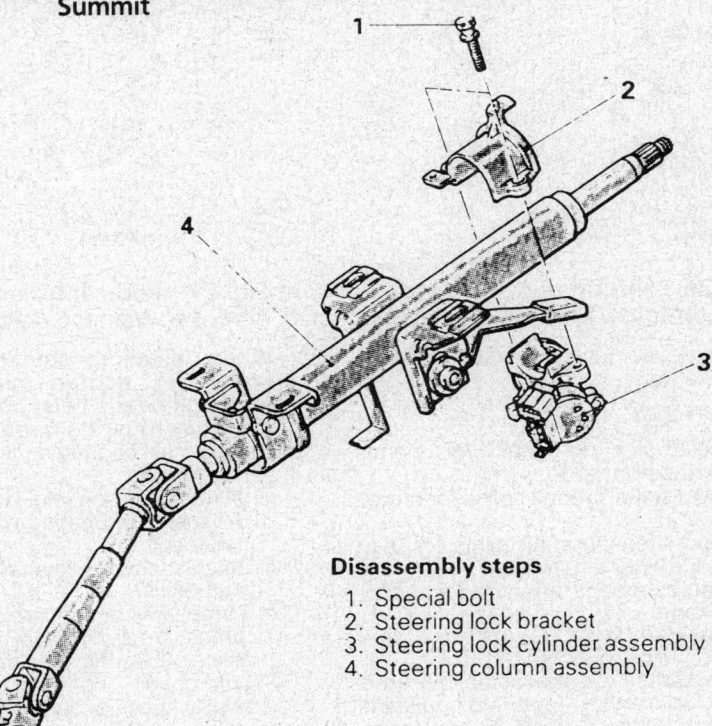

Disassembly steps

1. Special bolt
2. Steering lock bracket
3. Steering lock cylinder assembly
4. Steering column assembly

Fig. 23 Steering column service. 1994 Colt & Summit

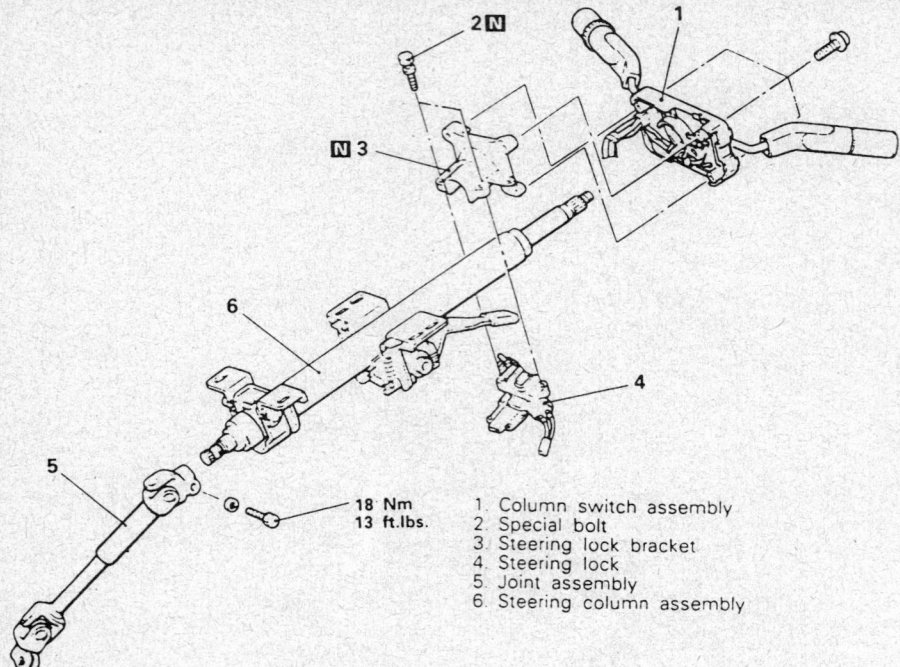

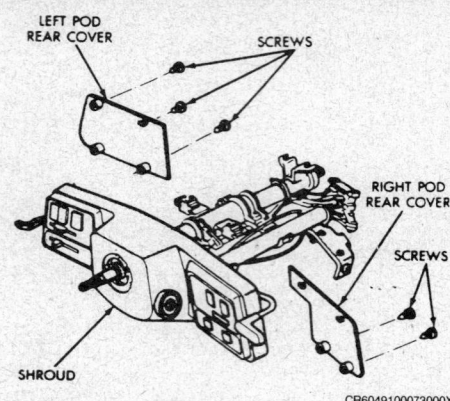

Fig. 25   Shroud pod rear cover removal. Monaco & Premier

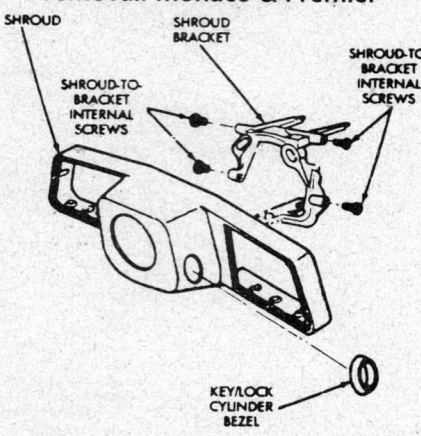

18 Nm
13 ft.lbs.

1. Column switch assembly
2. Special bolt
3. Steering lock bracket
4. Steering lock
5. Joint assembly
6. Steering column assembly

Fig. 24   Exploded view of steering shaft assembly. Colt Vista & Summit Wagon

Fig. 28   Shroud removal. Monaco & Premier

a. Temporarily install steering lock in alignment with column boss.
b. Ensure lock functions correctly, then tighten special bolts until bolt heads twist off. **Steering lock bracket and special bolts must be replaced with new ones when installing steering lock.**

MONACO & PREMIER

Disassemble

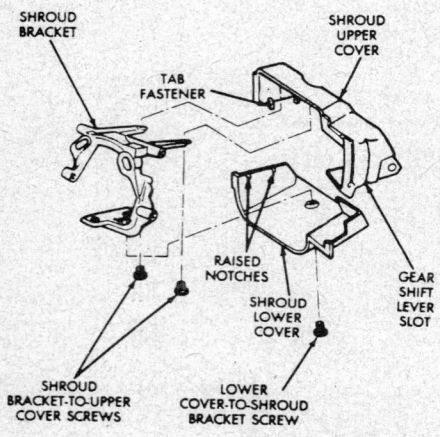

Fig. 26   Shroud upper & lower cover removal. Monaco & Premier

remove steering column bracket(s).

Inspection

1. Inspect steering shaft for bends and/or deformation.
2. Inspect steering shaft spline for breakage.
3. Inspect steering shaft joints for play, damage and/or binding.
4. Inspect rubber parts for cracks and/or breakage.

Assemble

Apply lubricant to surfaces as indicated. Specified lubricant is Mopar Multi-mileage Lubricant part No. 2525035 or equivalent. Assemble components in reverse order as they appear in **Fig. 24**, noting the following:

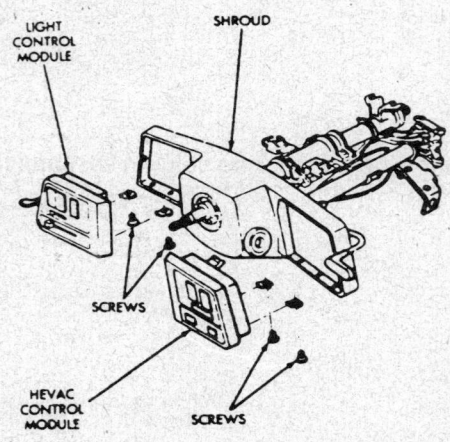

Fig. 27   Pod control module removal. Monaco & Premier

1. **When installing steering column bracket(s), tighten special bolts until bolt heads twist off. New special bolts must be used.**
2. Install cover, bearing and joint assembly as follows:
   a. Install cover on joint assembly.
   b. Fill inside of bearing with specified lubricant.
   c. Install bearings to shaft of joint assembly.
   d. Wrap vinyl tape approximately 1½ times around concave circumference of bearing, then press bearing into cover.
   e. Apply specified lubricant to mating surfaces of joint and cover assemblies.
3. Install steering wheel lock assembly as follows:

1. Disconnect battery ground cable.
2. Remove steering wheel and column as outlined under "Steering Column, Replace."
3. Remove steering column shroud as follows:
   a. Remove three screws retaining rear cover to left shroud pod, **Fig. 25.**
   b. Remove two screws retaining rear cover to right shroud pod, **Fig. 25.**
   c. Remove rear covers from both shroud pods.
   d. Remove lower cover to shroud bracket screw, then carefully separate lower cover from upper cover by detaching upper cover tab fasteners from lower cover notches, **Fig. 26.**
   e. Remove two shroud bracket to upper cover screws, then the upper shroud cover. Slide shroud upper cover off gearshift lever.

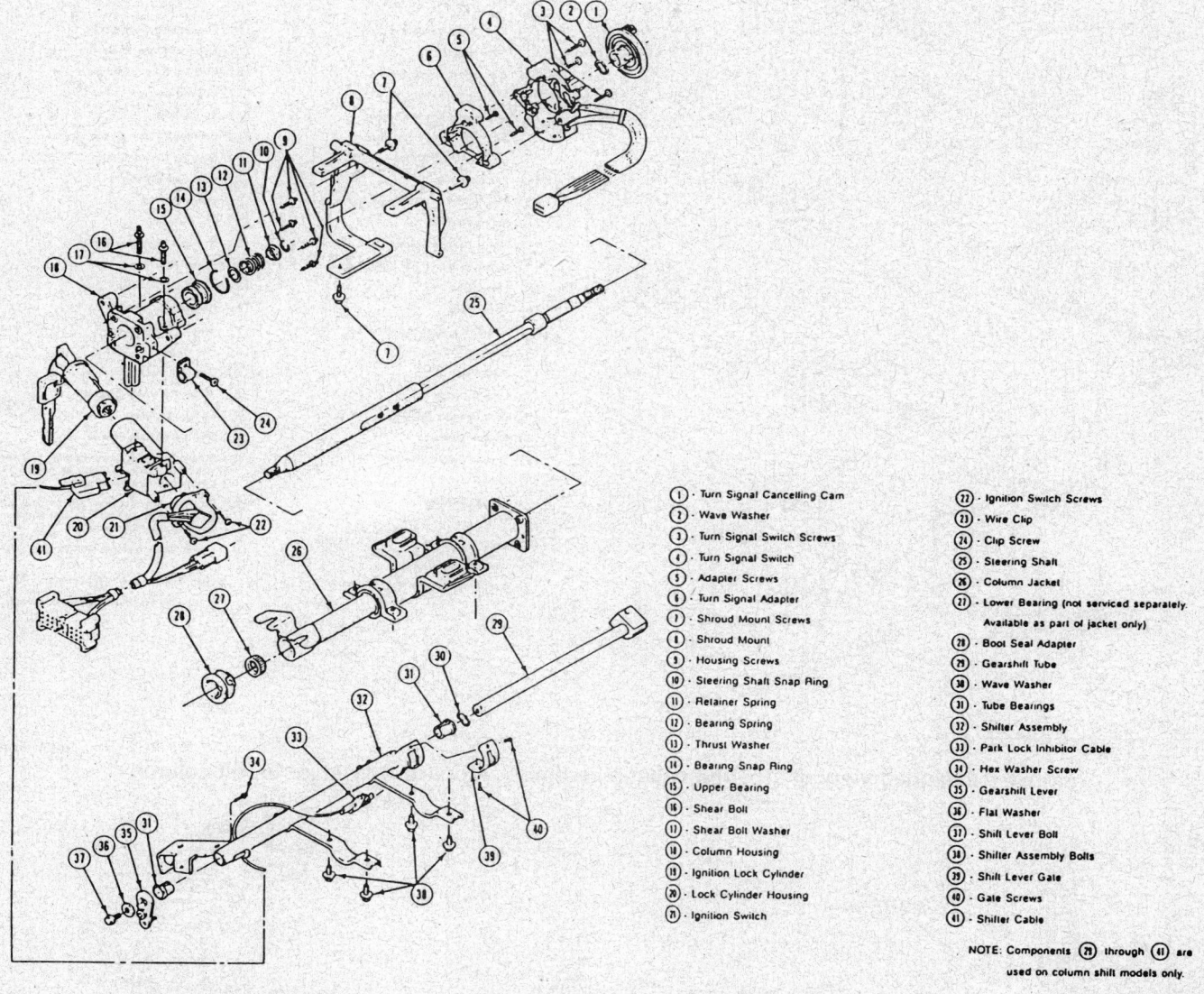

Fig. 29 Exploded view of steering column assembly. Monaco & Premier w/standard column

1. Turn Signal Cancelling Cam
2. Wave Washer
3. Turn Signal Switch Screws
4. Turn Signal Switch
5. Adapter Screws
6. Turn Signal Adapter
7. Shroud Mount Screws
8. Shroud Mount
9. Housing Screws
10. Steering Shaft Snap Ring
11. Retainer Spring
12. Bearing Spring
13. Thrust Washer
14. Bearing Snap Ring
15. Upper Bearing
16. Shear Bolt
17. Shear Bolt Washer
18. Column Housing
19. Ignition Lock Cylinder
20. Lock Cylinder Housing
21. Ignition Switch

22. Ignition Switch Screws
23. Wire Clip
24. Clip Screw
25. Steering Shaft
26. Column Jacket
27. Lower Bearing (not serviced separately. Available as part of jacket only)
28. Boot Seal Adapter
29. Gearshift Tube
30. Wave Washer
31. Tube Bearings
32. Shifter Assembly
33. Park Lock Inhibitor Cable
34. Hex Washer Screw
35. Gearshift Lever
36. Flat Washer
37. Shift Lever Bolt
38. Shifter Assembly Bolts
39. Shift Lever Gate
40. Gate Screws
41. Shifter Cable

NOTE: Components 27 through 41 are used on column shift models only.

CR6049100077000X

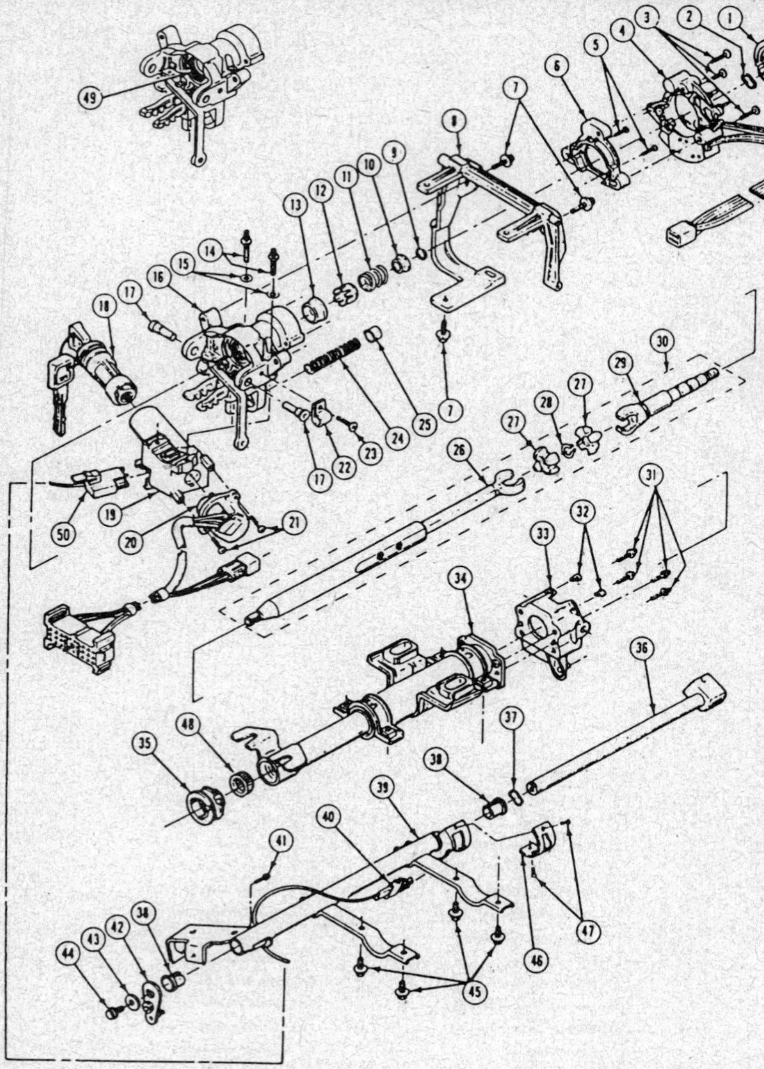

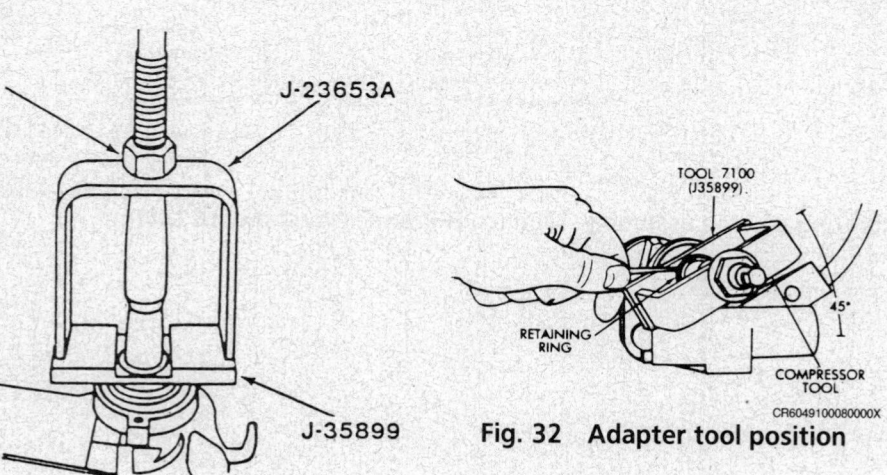

Fig. 30   Exploded view of steering column assembly. Monaco & Premier w/tilt column

CR6049100078000X

1 - Turn Signal Cancelling Cam
2 - Wave Washer
3 - Turn Signal Switch Screws
4 - Turn Signal Switch
5 - Turn Signal Adapter Screws
6 - Turn Signal Switch Adapter
7 - Shroud Mount Screws
8 - Shroud Mount
9 - Steering Shaft Retaining Snap Ring
10 - Spring Retainer
11 - Upper Bearing Spring
12 - Upper Bearing Inner Race Seat
13 - Inner Race
14 - Shear Bolts
15 - Shear Bolt Washer (Hardened)
16 - Steering Column Housing
17 - Pivot Pins
18 - Lock Cylinder
19 - Lock Cylinder Housing
20 - Ignition Switch
21 - Ignition Switch Screws
22 - Wire Clip
23 - Wire Clip Screw
24 - Tilt Spring
25 - Spring Retainer
26 - Lower Steering Shaft
27 - Centering Spheres (Flex Joint)

28 - Flex Joint Preload Spring
29 - Upper Steering Shaft
30 - Steering Shaft Assembly
31 - Support Screw
32 - Tilt Bumpers
33 - Steering Column Support
34 - Steering Column Jacket
35 - Boot Seal Adapter
36 - Gearshift Tube
37 - Wave Washer
38 - Gearshift Tube Bearing
39 - Shifter Assembly
40 - Park Lock Inhibitor Cable
41 - Hex Washer Screw
42 - Gearshift Lever
43 - Flat Washer
44 - Gearshift Lever Bolt
45 - Shifter Assembly Bolts
46 - Shift Lever Gate
47 - Shift Lever Gate Screws
48 - Steering Column Lower Bearing (not serviced separately. Available as part of column jacket assembly only.)
49 - Steering Column Upper Bearing (not serviced separately. Available as part of column housing assembly only.)
50 - Shifter Cable (column shift models only)

NOTE: Components ③⑥ through ④⑦ are used on column shift models only.

Fig. 31   Steering shaft spring compressor. Monaco & Premier

J-23653A

J-35899

CR6049100079000X

Fig. 32   Adapter tool position

TOOL 7100 (J35899)

RETAINING RING

COMPRESSOR TOOL

45°

CR6049100080000X

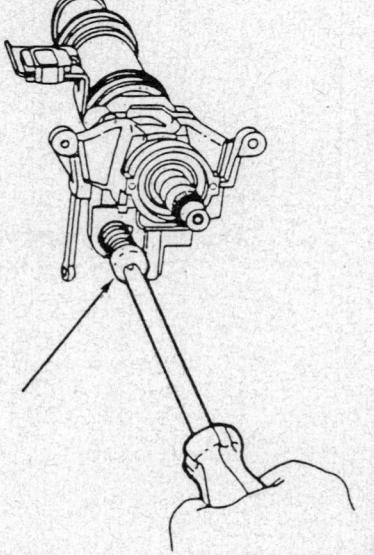

Fig. 33   Tilt spring retainer removal. Monaco & Premier

CR6049100081000X

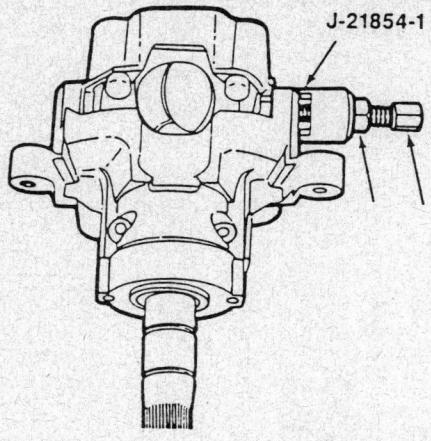

Fig. 34 Pivot pin removal.
Monaco & Premier

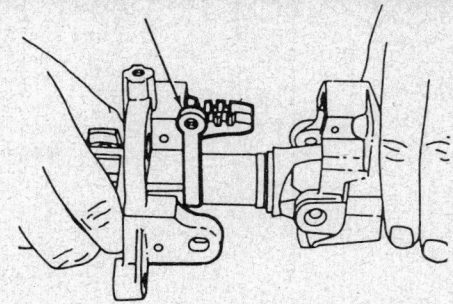

Fig. 35 Lock shoe retracting lever.
Monaco & Premier

f. Remove shroud to control module screws, then remove both control modules from pods, **Fig. 27**. This will provide access to four shroud to bracket internal screws.
g. Remove key/lock cylinder bezel from shroud.
h. Cover tilt lever stalk with a shop towel and remove from tilt lever using locking pliers. **Use caution not to damage stalk with plier teeth.**
i. Remove four shroud to bracket internal screws, then the shroud from bracket, **Fig. 28**.

4. Remove cancelling cam, wave washer and turn signal switch, **Figs. 29 and 30**.

5. Remove shroud bracket, then the two ignition switch retaining screws and switch from key/lock cylinder housing. Turn ignition key to unmarked position, push the cylinder lock tab inward and remove.

6. Remove turn signal adapter screws and the adapter.

7. Remove steering shaft snap ring, bearing retainer, retainer spring and thrust washer as follows:
   a. Install adapter tool No. J-35899 or equivalent on spring retainer, **Fig. 31. Use caution as snap ring and retainer are under spring pressure. Do not attempt to remove steering shaft without proper tools. Adapter tool must be positioned at a 45° angle from key/lock cylinder housing as shown in Fig. 32, to avoid damaging steering column housing.**
   b. Thread compressor tool No. J-23653-A or equivalent on steering column shaft.
   c. Tighten compressor tool nut, **Fig. 31**, to compress retainer spring, then unseat and remove snap ring. Discard the snap ring.
   d. Loosen compressor tool nut, then remove compressor and adapter.
   e. Remove spring, washer and retainer.

8. Remove shift cable from housing by pressing the retaining tab.

9. **On models with tilt steering column**, temporarily remove the tilt lever, then remove lock cylinder housing on all models as follows:
   a. Center punch the tamper proof bolts, then drill them out with a 1/4 inch drill bit. Drill down until bit contacts hardened washer.

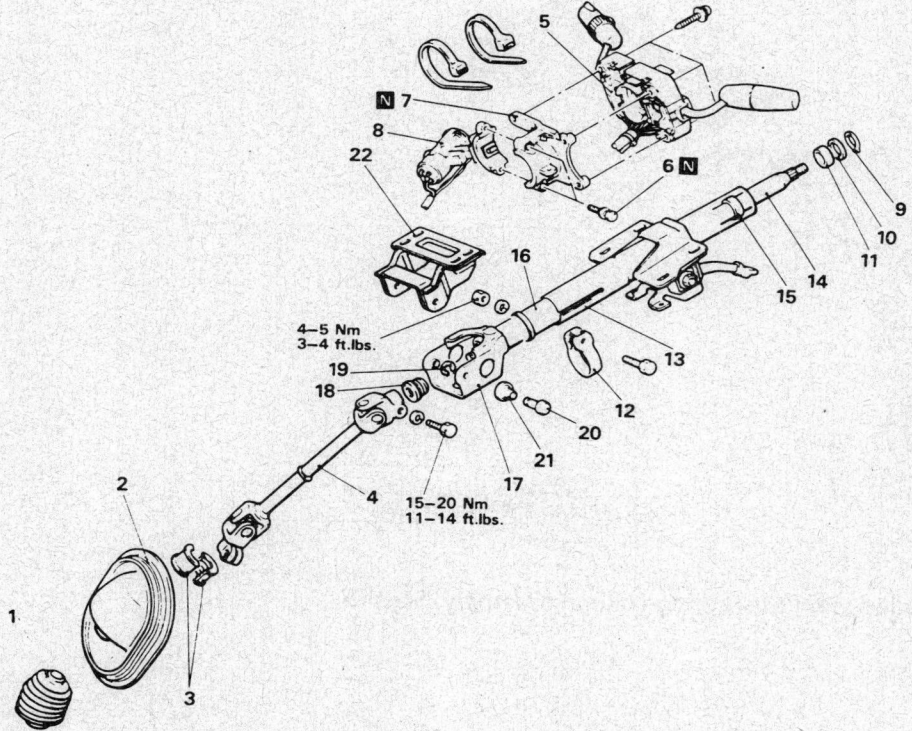

Disassembly steps

1. Boot	15. Bearing spacer
2. Cover assembly	16. Column bushing
3. Bearing	17. Column tube lower
4. Joint assembly	18. Bearing
5. Column switch	19. Snap ring
6. Steering lock installation special bolt	20. Clevis pin
7. Steering lock bracket	21. Bushing
8. Steering lock	22. Lower bracket
9. Snap ring	
10. Stopper	
11. Bearing spacer	
12. Column tube clamp	
13. Column tube upper	
14. Steering shaft	

Ⓝ Non-reusable parts

Fig. 36 Exploded view of steering column assembly. Laser & Talon

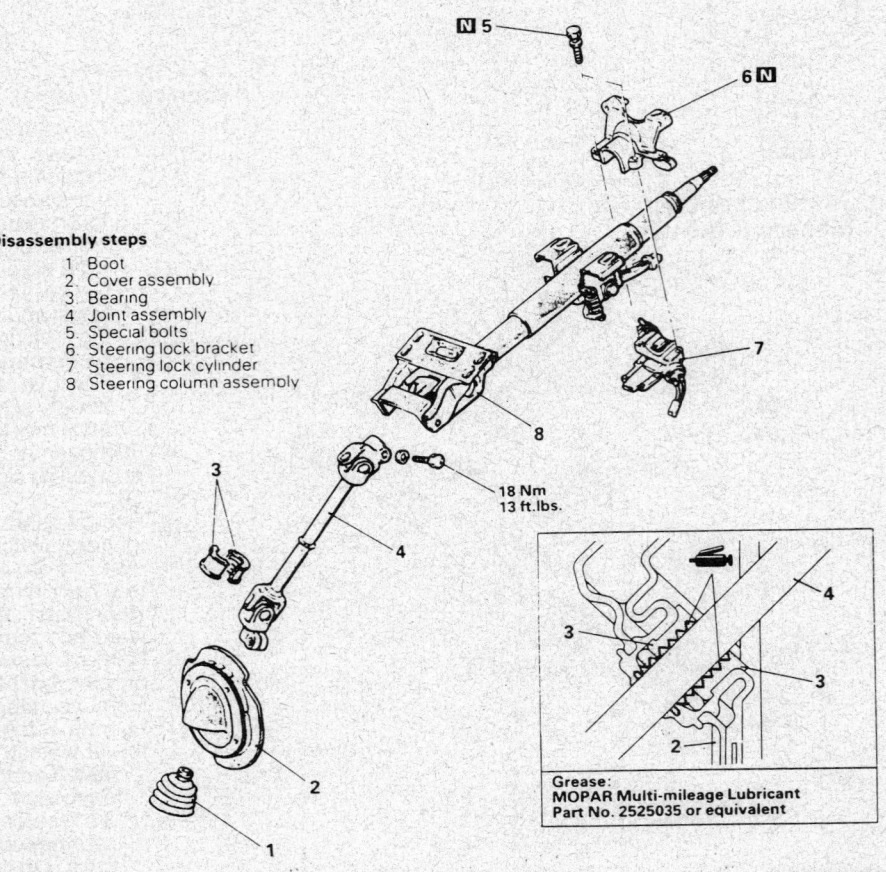

Disassembly steps

1. Boot
2. Cover assembly
3. Bearing
4. Joint assembly
5. Special bolts
6. Steering lock bracket
7. Steering lock cylinder
8. Steering column assembly

18 Nm
13 ft.lbs.

Grease:
MOPAR Multi-mileage Lubricant
Part No. 2525035 or equivalent

CR6049100085000X

Fig. 37 Exploded view of steering column assembly. Stealth

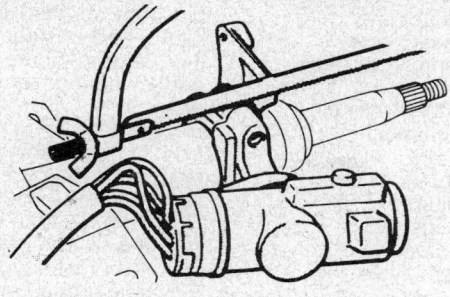

Fig. 38   Steering lock removal. Laser, Stealth & Talon

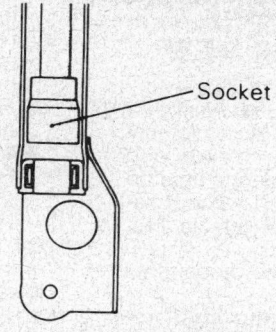

Fig. 39   Lower bearing removal. Laser & Talon

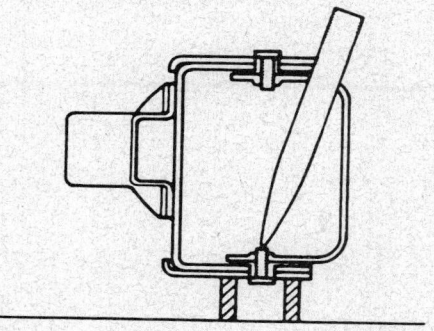

Fig. 40   Clevis pin removal. Laser & Talon

b. Remove lock cylinder housing, then the drilled out bolts with pliers.
10. Proceed as follows to remove tilt spring and retainer:
   a. Reinstall tilt lever and adjust to full upward tilt position.
   b. Remove tilt spring retainer using a large Phillips screwdriver. Press retainer in and turn clockwise to unlock, **Fig. 33,** then remove retainer and spring.
   c. Place column in center position and remove pivot pins using pin removal tool No. J-21854-1 or equivalent.
   d. Thread tool into each pin, then tighten tool nut to pull pin from housing, **Fig. 34.**
   e. Move tilt lever to disengage lock shoes and slide housing off column jacket.
11. **On all models,** pull steering shaft straight out of column to remove. **Do not strike the shaft as shear pins could be damaged.**
12. **On models with tilt steering column,** remove support screws and support from column jacket, then disassemble steering shaft by separating at flex joint.
13. **On models with standard column,** remove upper bearing from housing. Remove snap ring, and press bearing out of housing using two suitable size sockets or lengths of steel tube as driver and receiver.

Inspection

1. Inspect all column components, **Figs. 29 and 30,** for wear or damage and replace as necessary.

2. If standard column lower bearing, or either upper or lower tilt column bearing needs replacement, the entire column jacket assembly must be replaced.

Assemble

1. Press upper bearing into housing using two suitable size sockets as press tool and support.
2. **On models with tilt column,** proceed as follows:
   a. Install support and assemble steering shafts.
   b. Insert steering shaft into support and column jacket, then install housing over steering shaft onto support.
   c. Align pivot pin and support holes. Housing lock shoes must be retracted with lever, **Fig. 35,** in order to align holes.
   d. Insert and seat pivot pins with a punch and hammer, then stake each pin in two places.
   e. Install tilt spring in column and position retainer on spring.
   f. Using a large Phillips screwdriver, push retainer in and turn counterclockwise to lock.
3. **On models with standard column,** lubricate column bearings with chassis grease, then insert steering shaft into column jacket and secure with four Torx bolts.
4. **On all models,** position lock cylinder housing on column housing and secure with replacement tamper proof bolts and torque until bolt head shears off.
5. Press tab and install shift cable on housing.
6. Position washer, spring and retainer for standard columns, or race, seat and spring for tilt columns, on steering shaft.
7. Position a new snap ring, then using adapter tool No. J-35899 and compressor tool No. J-23653-A or equivalents, compress retainer spring as outlined under "Disassemble" in this section.
8. Seat snap ring in the bottom groove of steering shaft and remove tools and adapter.
9. Install ignition switch, then the shroud mount on column.
10. Install turn signal switch adapter and

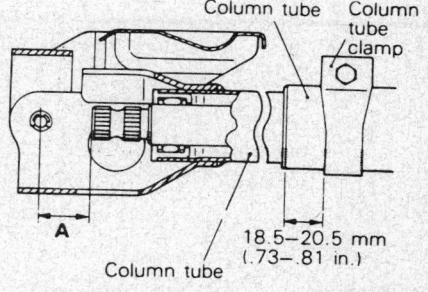

Fig. 41   Column tube clamp installation. Laser & Talon

turn signal switch.
11. Install wave washer, cancelling cam and ignition lock cylinder in housing.
12. Reverse disassembly procedure to install remaining components.

LASER, STEALTH & TALON

1. Remove steering column as outlined under "Steering Column, Replace."
2. Disassemble steering column in numbered sequence shown in **Figs. 36 and 37,** noting the following:
   a. If it is necessary to remove the steering lock, use a hacksaw to cut the special bolts at steering lock bracket side, **Fig. 38.**
   b. **On Laser and Talon,** use a socket wrench or a 1.2 inch outer diameter tool to remove lower bearing, **Fig. 39.**
   c. Remove the snap ring, then tap out clevis pin from inner side of column lower tube, **Fig. 40.**
3. **On all models,** reverse procedure to install, noting the following:
   a. **On Laser and Talon,** apply a thin coat of multipurpose grease to sliding part of lower bearing.
   b. Press oil seal into lower column tube.
   c. Apply multipurpose bearing grease which contacts steering shaft.
   d. Slide column tube and adjust so dimension marked A is .98-.99 inch, **Fig. 41.**
   e. Install column tube clamp at position as shown in **Fig. 41.**
   f. **On all models,** after ensuring steering lock operates correctly, tighten special bolts until heads twist off.

CHRYSLER—Steering Columns

CONCORDE, INTREPID, LHS, VISION & 1994 NEW YORKER

The Saginaw steering column has been designed to be serviced as an assembly except for wiring, switches, shrouds and steering wheel. Also most steering column components can be serviced without removing the column from the vehicle, **Fig. 19.**

The only other serviceable components are as follows:

1. **On models with column shift,** replace gear shift lever assembly as follows:
   a. Remove gear shift cable from retaining pin on gear shift assembly, then unlock shift cable adjuster.
   b. Remove three Torx head screws retaining shifter assembly to tilt housing.
   c. Remove shifter assembly from tilt housing and unhook interlock cable from shifter assembly.
   d. Remove and discard interlock cassette from steering column.
   e. Reverse procedure to install.
2. **On all models,** replace steering column jacket bushing assembly as follows:
   a. Remove steering column as outlined under "Steering Column, Replace."
   b. Remove steering coupler from steering shaft by removing spring pin from coupler and sliding coupler of end or steering shaft. Steering column shaft must be supported during removal of spring pin.
   c. Separate steering column bracket from jacket bushing, by depressing retaining tabs on bushing and lifting bracket off bushing.
   d. Using a pin punch lightly tap jacket bushing off end of steering column jacket and steering shaft.
   e. Reverse procedure to install, use arbor press and installer tool No. MB-990800 or equivalent to install bushing. Ensure 3 retaining tabs are expanded out past edge of lower bracket.

MANUAL STEERING GEARS

NOTE: On Air Bag Equipped Models, Refer To "Air Bag System Precautions" Located In The Front Of This Manual For System Disarming & Arming Procedures.

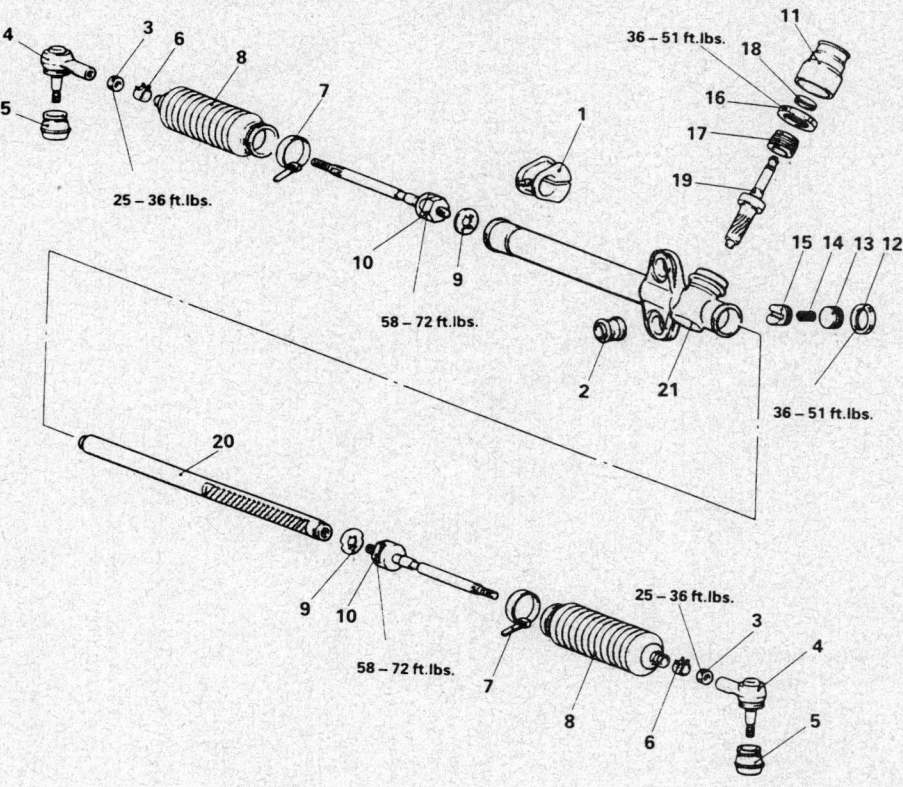

1. Mounting rubber
2. Mounting bush
3. Tie rod end locking nuts
4. Tie rod end
5. Dust covers
6. Bellows clips
7. Bellows bands
8. Bellows
9. Tab washers
10. Tie rod
11. Joint cover
    Adjustment of total pinion torque
12. Locking nut
13. Rack support cover
14. Rack support spring
15. Rack support
16. Locking nut
17. Top cover
18. Oil seal
19. Pinion
20. Rack
21. Rack housing

CR6039100010000X

Fig. 1   Manual steering gear assembly. 1992–93 Colt & Summit

PRECAUTIONS

AIR BAG SYSTEMS

Refer to "Air Bag System Precautions" in the front of this manual for system disarming and arming procedures.

STEERING GEAR SERVICE

COLT & SUMMIT

1992–93

Refer to **Fig. 1** when performing the following procedure.

Disassemble

1. Place steering gear assembly in a suitable soft-jawed vise.
2. Remove mounting rubber and bushings, outer tie rod ends, locking nuts, dust covers, bands, clips and bellows.
3. Separate tab washers from inner tie rods using a chisel, then remove inner tie rods and tab washers.
4. Remove joint cover, locking nut, then the rack support cover using torque wrench socket tool No. MB990607-A or equivalent.
5. Remove rack support spring and rack support.
6. Remove pinion locking nut, top cover, oil seal, then the pinion.
7. Remove rack from gear housing by pulling in direction shown in **Fig. 2.** **If rack is pulled from housing in wrong direction, rack bushing in gear housing may be damaged by rack threads.**
8. Inspect rack support for uneven wear or damage, rack support spring for deterioration, rack pinion tooth surfaces for wear or damage, pinion bearing for noise, uneven rotation or damage and rack bushing for damage. Replace as necessary.

Assemble

1. Apply Mopar multi-mileage lubricant 2525035 or equivalent to rack tooth surfaces and rack bushing. **Ensure grease does not obstruct air passage of rack bushing.**
2. Install rack into gear housing opposite of removal.
3. Apply multi-mileage lubricant to toothed surface of pinion, then install into rack housing.
4. Press oil seal into top cover, then apply semi-drying sealant to threaded portion of top cover.
5. Install top cover and locking nut, then tighten locking nut to specifications.
6. Apply a coating of multi-mileage lubricant to surface of rack support that contacts rack, then install rack support.
7. Fill inner side of rack support spring with multi-mileage lubricant, then install rack support spring.
8. Apply a coating of semi-drying sealant to threaded part of rack support cover, then install rack support cover.
9. With rack placed in center position, tighten cover to specifications using torque wrench socket.

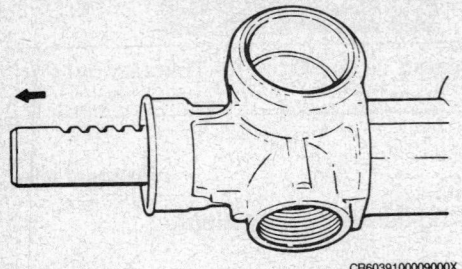

Fig. 2 Rack removal direction

10. In neutral position, rotate pinion shaft at a rate of one revolution every 4 to 6 seconds using preload socket tool No. CT-1108 or equivalent and a suitable torque wrench. Back off cover approximately 30-60° and adjust torque to 3-12 inch lbs. **When adjusting, set torque at its highest end, ensure there is no ratcheting or catching when operating rack towards shaft direction. Measure total rotating torque through whole stroke of rack.**
11. Install and tighten locking nut to specifications.
12. Install joint cover, tab washers and inner tie rods, then tighten inner tie rods to specifications.
13. Secure inner tie rods by bending tab washers onto tie rod stepped portions.
14. Apply multi-mileage lubricant to mounting surfaces of bellows, install bellows into position and ensure they are not twisted, then the clips and bands.
15. Fill inside and lip of dust cover with multi-mileage lubricant, install onto outer tie rod end.
16. Install outer tie rod end locknuts, then the tie rod ends.
17. Adjust so that length between outer lip of bellows and inner side of locknut is 7.2 inches, then tighten locknuts to specifications and recheck length.
18. Install mounting rubber and bushings.

1994

1. Disassemble manual steering gear in numbered sequence shown, **Fig. 3,** noting the following:
   a. Use torque wrench socket tool No. MB990607, or equivalent, to remove rack support cover.
   b. Remove rack from steering gear housing in direction shown, **Fig. 2. If rack is pulled out in opposite direction, rack threads may damage gear box bushing.**
2. Reverse procedure to assemble, noting the following:
   a. Press oil seal into top cover using seal installation tools as shown, **Fig. 4.**
   b. Lubricate and seal steering gear components as shown, **Fig. 5.**
   c. When installing outer tie rod ends, thread in until distance between end of tie rod boot and inside of outer locknut is 7.38 inches. Do not tighten locknut fully until gear box is installed and toe-in is adjusted.
3. Adjust total pinion preload as follows:

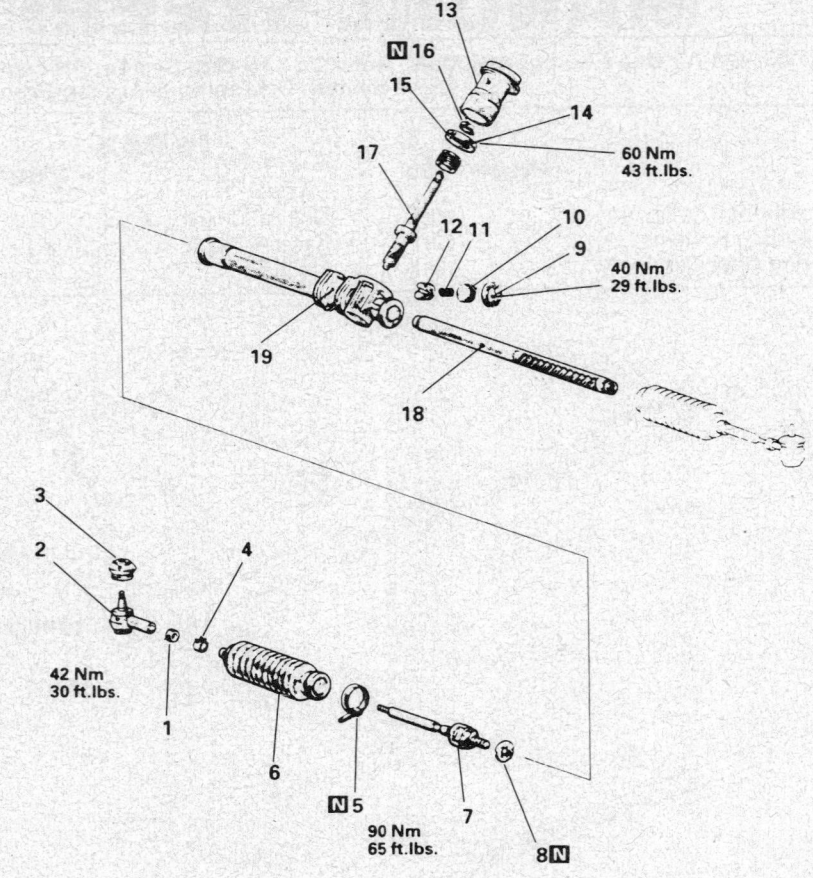

Disassembly steps

1. Tie-rod end locking nut
2. Tie-rod end
3. Dust cover
4. Bellows clip
5. Bellows band
6. Bellows
7. Tie-rod
8. Tab washer
   • Adjustment of total pinion preload
9. Locking nut
10. Rack support cover
11. Rack support spring
12. Rack support
13. Joint cover
14. Locking nut
15. Top cover
16. Oil seal
17. Pinion
18. Rack
19. Gear housing

Fig. 3 Manual steering gear assembly. 1994 Colt & Summit

a. Position rack at centered position and tighten rack support cover to specifications.
b. Using torque wrench tool No. MB991006 or equivalent, rotate pinion shaft clockwise at one rotation per 4-6 seconds.
c. Return support cover 30°-60° and adjust preload **torque** to 3-12 inch lbs., then lock rack support cover with locknut.

LASER & TALON

Refer to **Fig. 6** when performing the following procedure.

Disassemble

1. Place steering gear assembly in a suitable soft-jawed vise.
2. Remove outer tie rod ends and locking nuts, then place tie rod ends in a suitable soft-jawed vise and remove dust covers using a hammer and screwdriver.
3. Remove bellows clips, bands, and bellows.
4. Separate tab washers from inner tie rods using a chisel, then remove inner tie rods and tab washers.
5. Remove rack support cover locknut, rack support cover, rack support spring, cushion rubber and rack support.
6. Remove top plug locknut, top plug, pinion oil seal, pinion collar, then the pinion and bearing assembly.
7. Remove pinion bearing from pinion using a suitable press and steering/pinion gear replacement tool No. MB990783 or equivalent.
8. Remove rack from gear housing by pulling in direction shown in Fig. 2. If **rack is pulled from housing in**

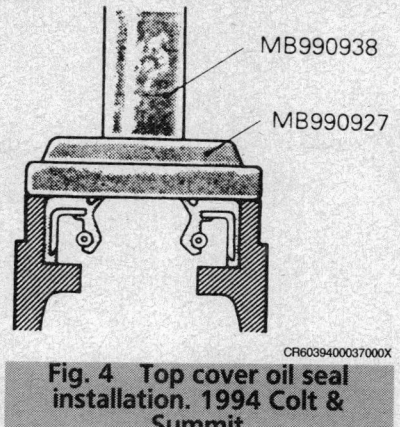

MB990938

MB990927

CR6039400037000X

Fig. 4   Top cover oil seal installation. 1994 Colt & Summit

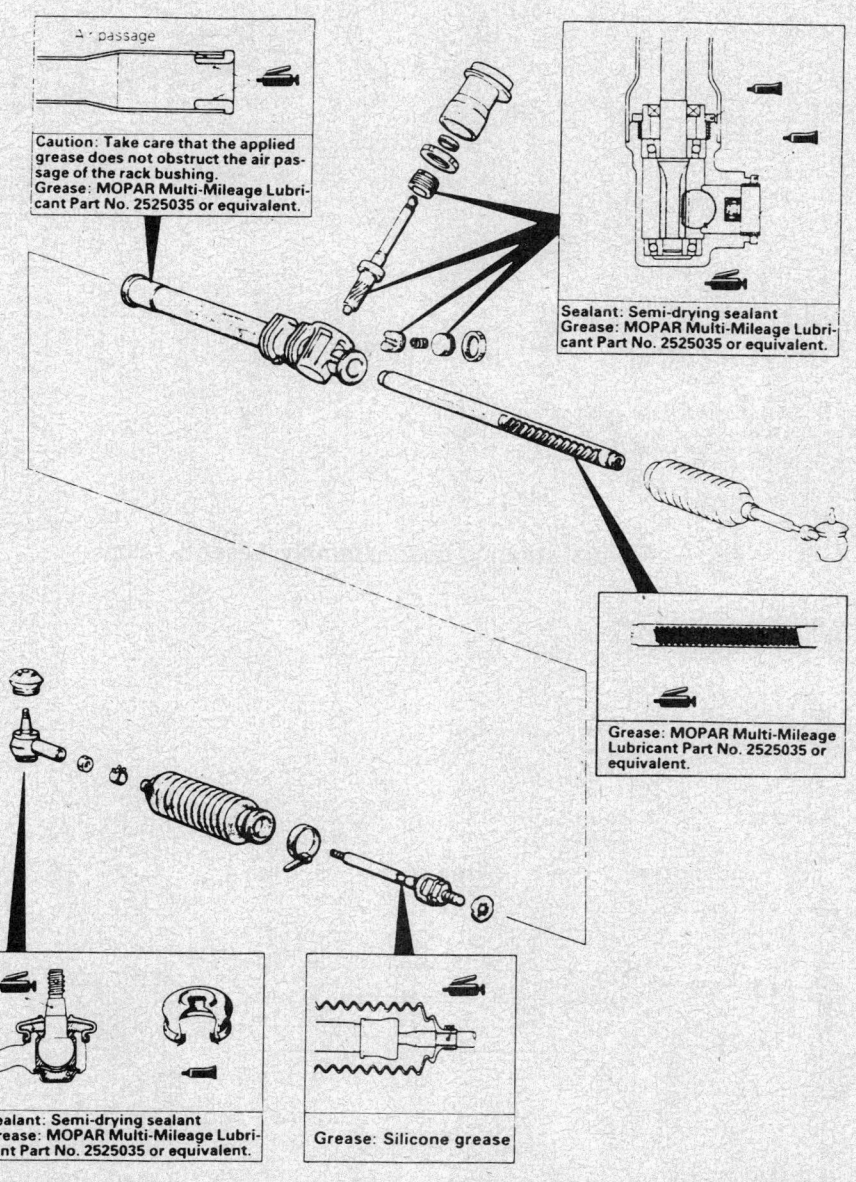

Air passage

Caution: Take care that the applied grease does not obstruct the air passage of the rack bushing.
Grease: MOPAR Multi-Mileage Lubricant Part No. 2525035 or equivalent.

Sealant: Semi-drying sealant
Grease: MOPAR Multi-Mileage Lubricant Part No. 2525035 or equivalent.

Grease: MOPAR Multi-Mileage Lubricant Part No. 2525035 or equivalent.

Sealant: Semi-drying sealant
Grease: MOPAR Multi-Mileage Lubricant Part No. 2525035 or equivalent.

Grease: Silicone grease

CR6039400038000X

Fig. 5   Steering gear lubrication & sealant application specifications. 1994 Colt & Summit

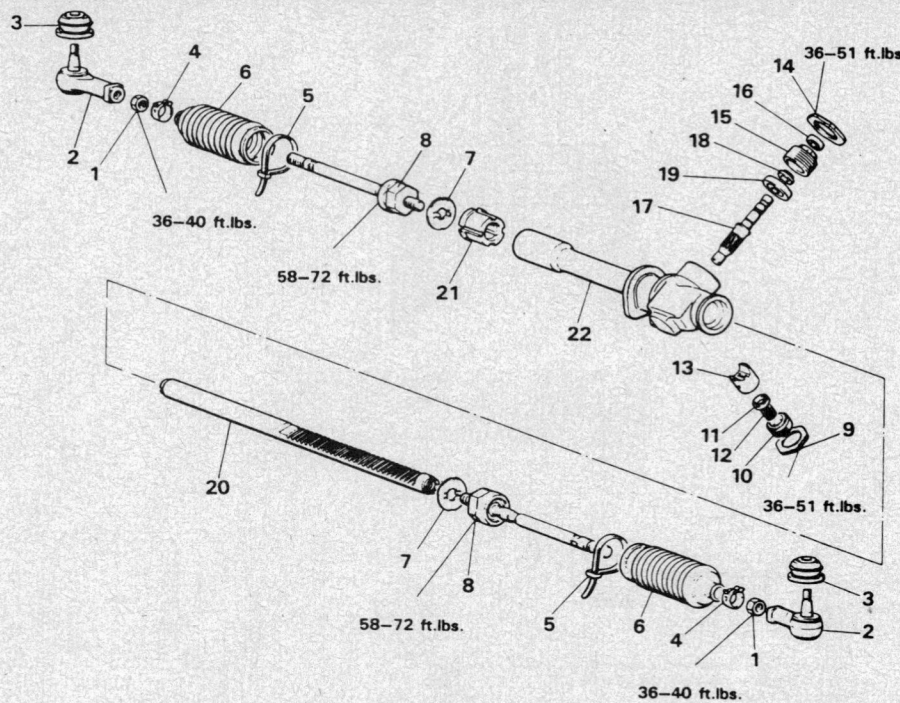

1. Tie-rod end locking nuts
2. Tie-rod end
3. Dust covers
4. Bellows clips
5. Bellows bands
6. Bellows
7. Tab washers
8. Tie-rod
    Adjustment of total pinion torque
9. Locking nut
10. Rack support cover
11. Cushion rubber
12. Rack support spring
13. Rack support

14. Locking nut
15. Top plug
16. Oil seal
17. Pinion
18. Pinion collar
19. Ball bearing
20. Rack
21. Rack bushing
22. Rack housing

CR6039100011000X

Fig. 6   Manual steering gear assembly. Laser & Talon

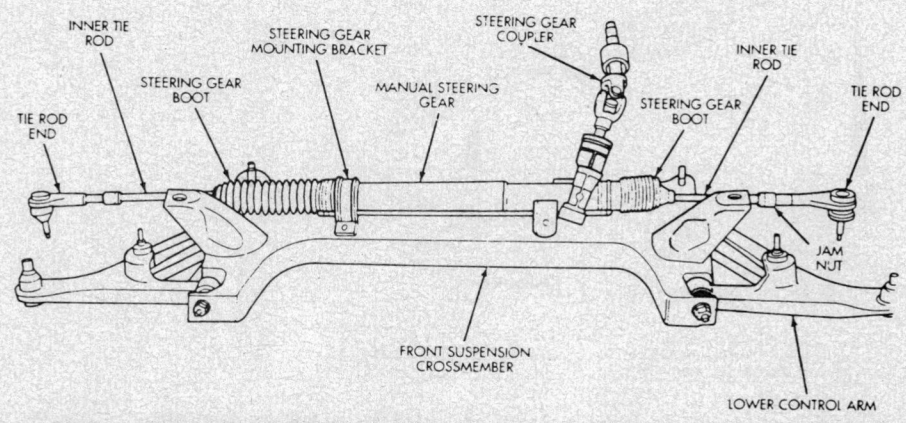

CR6039500039000X

Fig. 7   Manual steering gear assembly. Neon

wrong direction, rack bushing in gear housing may be damaged by rack threads.

9. Remove rack bushing from rack housing.
10. Inspect rack support for uneven wear or damage, rack support spring for deterioration, rack pinion tooth surfaces for wear or damage, pinion bearing for noise, uneven rotation or damage and rack bushing for damage. Replace as necessary.

Assemble

1. Apply Mopar multi-mileage lubricant 2525035 or equivalent to rack tooth surfaces, rack bushing and pinion needle bearing in rack housing.
2. Install rack bushing, then the rack into gear housing opposite of removal.
3. Press pinion bearing onto pinion using steering/pinion gear remover/installer MB990783 or equivalent.
4. Apply multi-mileage lubricant to toothed surface of pinion, install pinion and bearing assembly into housing, then the pinion collar.
5. Press oil seal into top plug, apply semi-drying sealant to threaded portion of top plug, install top plug, then the top plug locking nut and tighten to specifications.
6. Apply multi-mileage lubricant to surface of rack support that contacts rack, then install rack support to rack housing.
7. Apply multi-mileage lubricant to inner side of rack support spring, then install rack support spring to rack housing.
8. Install rubber cushion to rack support cover, apply a coating of semi-drying sealant to threaded part of rack support cover, install rack support cover to rack housing, then the locknut.
9. With rack placed in center position, tighten cover to specifications.

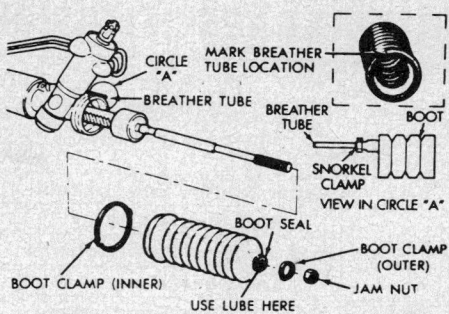

Fig. 8 Inner tie rod boot replacement. Neon

CR6039500040000X

10. In a neutral position, rotate pinion shaft at a rate of one revolution every 4 to 6 seconds using preload socket tool No. CT-1108 or equivalent and a suitable torque wrench. Return rack support cover 30-60° and adjust torque as follows:
    a. From 0-90°, **torque** should be 5-11 inch lbs.; from 90-650°, **torque** should be 2-9 inch lbs.
11. When adjusting, set at highest value, ensure there is no ratcheting or catching when operating rack towards shaft direction.
12. If specified values cannot be obtained, check rack support cover components and replace as necessary.
13. Install and tighten locking nut to specifications.
14. Install tab washers and inner tie rods, then tighten inner tie rods to specifications.
15. Secure inner tie rods by bending tab washers onto tie rod stepped portions.
16. Pack tie rod bellows lock groove with suitable silicone grease, install bellows into position and ensure they are not twisted, then the clips and bands.
17. Fill inside and lip of dust covers with multi-mileage lubricant, apply semi-drying sealant to dust covers, then press dust covers onto tie rod ends using front axle base tool No. MB990776-A or equivalent.
18. Install outer tie rod end locknuts, then the tie rod ends.
19. Adjust so that length between outer lip of bellows and inner side of tie rod end is 7.24-7.32 inches, then tighten locknuts to specifications and recheck length.

NEON

The manual steering gear assembly, Fig. 7, should not be serviced or adjusted. In the event of damage or a malfunction such as an oil leak, the entire assembly should be replaced. However, the inner tie rod boots and outer tie rod ends can be replaced as follows:

1. Loosen inner to outer tie rod jam nut; then, if assembly is still in vehicle, remove nut securing outer tie rod end to steering knuckle.
2. Separate outer tie rod from steering knuckle using remover tool No. MB990635 or equivalent, then expand tie rod boot to inner tie rod clamp using suitable pliers.
3. Remove clamp from steering gear boot, then expand boot snorkel clamp using suitable pliers.
4. Slip clamp from boot, then remove inner tie rod boot to steering gear clamp, **Fig. 8**.
5. Using a small screwdriver, gently lift lip of inner tie rod boot out of retaining groove in steering gear, then remove boot from gear.
6. Reverse procedure to install, noting the following:
    a. Lubricate inner tie rod boot groove and boot end seal, **Fig. 8**, with suitable silicone lubricant.
    b. Tighten inner to outer tie rod jam nut and outer tie rod end to steering knuckle nut to specifications.

TIGHTENING SPECIFICATIONS

Model	Year	Component	Torque/Ft. Lbs.
Colt & Summit	1992-93	Inner Tie Rod End	58–72
		Outer Tie Rod End Locknut	25–36
		Rack Support Cover	11
		Rack Support Cover Locknut	36–51
		Top Cover Locknut	36–51
	1994	Outer Tie Rod End Locknut	30
		Rack Support Cover Locknut	29
		Tie Rod	65
		Top Cover Locknut	43
Laser & Talon	1992-94	Inner Tie Rod End	58–72
		Outer Tie Rod End Locknut	36–40
		Rack Support Cover	11
		Rack Support Cover Locknut	36–51
		Top Cover Locknut	36–51
Neon	1995	Inner To Outer Tie Rod Jam Nut	45
		Tie Rod End To Steering Knuckle Nut	45

POWER STEERING

TABLE OF CONTENTS

Power Steering Pressure Secifications

Model	Year	Power Steering Pump Pressure, psi			Output Flow ④
		Test Valve Open	Test Valve Closed	Max Relief Pressure	
Acclaim, Concorde, Daytona, Dynasty, Ffith Avenue, Imperial, Intrepid, LeBaron, LHS, New Yorker, Shadow, Spirit, Sundance & Vision	1992-94	50-80①	1200-1300②	1200-1300	1.7
Colt & Summit	1992	114-142	782-882③	782-881	—
	1993-94	114-142	1351-1451③	1351-1451	—
Colt Vista & Summit Wagon	1992-94	114-142	1067-1166③	1067-1166	—
Laser & Talon	1992-94	114-142	1067-1166③	1067-1166	—
Monaco & Premier	1992	150⑤	1100-1200②	1100-1200	—
Neon	1995	50-80①	1195-1293②	1195-1293	—
Stealth	1992-94	114-142	1067-1166③	1067-1166	—

①—Initial pressure.
②—Do not leave valve closed for more than five seconds.
③—Do not leave valve closed for more than ten seconds.
④—At 1500 RPM & minimum pressure.
⑤—Maximum.

Acclaim, Daytona, Dynasty, Imperial, LeBaron, Monaco, Neon, Premier, Shadow, Spirit, Sundance & 1992–93 New Yorker

NOTE: On Air Bag Equipped Models, Refer To "Air Bag System Precautions" Located In The Front Of This Manual For System Disarming & Arming Procedures.

INDEX

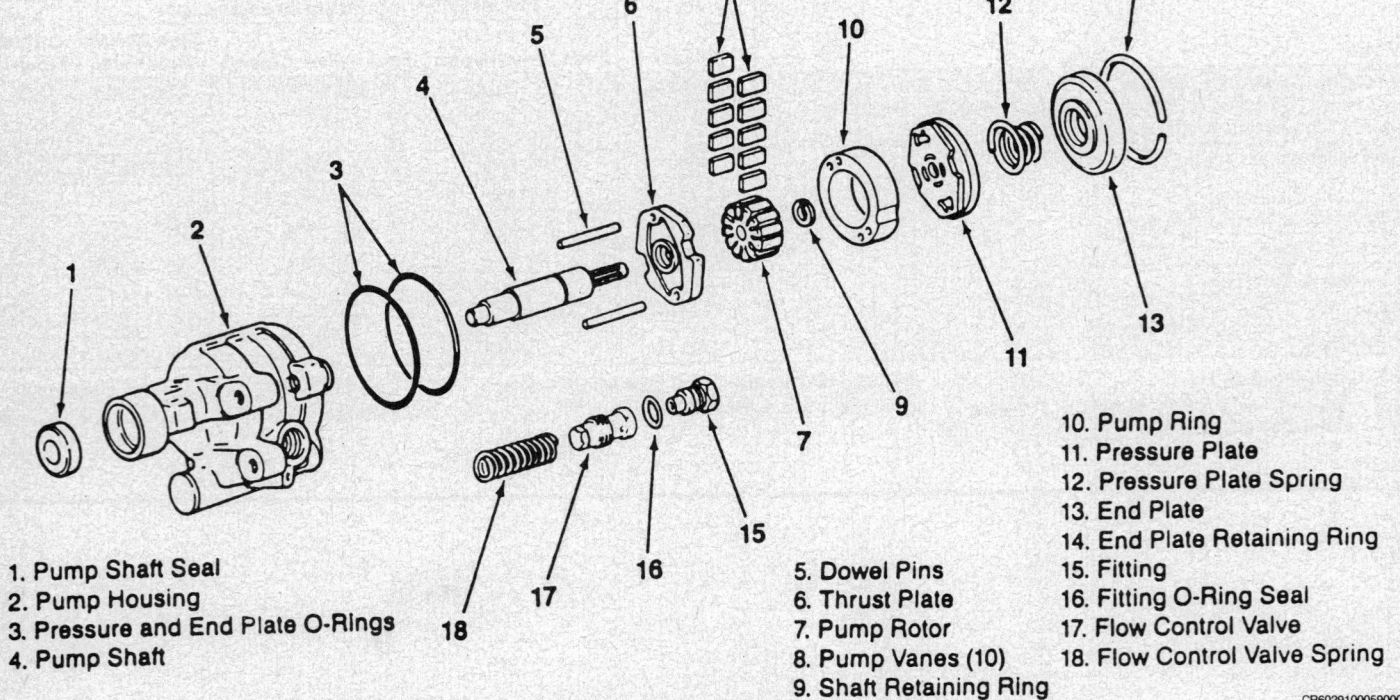

1. Pump Shaft Seal
2. Pump Housing
3. Pressure and End Plate O-Rings
4. Pump Shaft
5. Dowel Pins
6. Thrust Plate
7. Pump Rotor
8. Pump Vanes (10)
9. Shaft Retaining Ring
10. Pump Ring
11. Pressure Plate
12. Pressure Plate Spring
13. End Plate
14. End Plate Retaining Ring
15. Fitting
16. Fitting O-Ring Seal
17. Flow Control Valve
18. Flow Control Valve Spring

CR6029100059000X

Fig. 1 Exploded view of power steering pump. Monaco & Premier

PRECAUTIONS

AIR BAG SYSTEMS

Refer to "Air Bag System Precautions" in the front of this manual for system disarming and arming procedures.

POWER STEERING PUMP APPLICATIONS

Due to the unique shaft bearings, flow control levels and pump displacements, the power steering pumps used on these models may not be interchanged with pumps from other vehicles.

DESCRIPTION
POWER STEERING PUMP
Monaco & Premier

These models are equipped with an N-series pump, **Fig. 1**, which is a vane type pump utilizing a remote fluid reservoir located near the front of the left cylinder head.

Neon

This model is equipped with a TTA constant displacement, vane type pump, **Fig. 2**. The pump utilizes a remote fluid reservoir, mounted at the rear of the cylinder head on the passenger side of the vehicle.

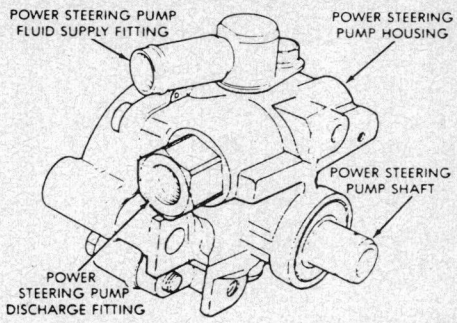

Fig. 2 TTA power steering pump. Neon

2.2L/4–135, 2.5L/4–153 & 3.0L/V6–181 Engines Except Monaco & Premier

These models are equipped with a Saginaw "Ham Can" style power steering pump, **Fig. 3.** The pump housing and internal components are combined with the reservoir.

Models w/3.3L/V6–201, 3.5L/V6–215 & 3.8L/V6–231 Engines

These models are equipped with a Saginaw TC-series power steering pump, **Fig. 4,** which consists of the power steering pump internal components and pump housing. It utilizes a remote fluid reservoir located at the left inner fender panel.

STEERING GEAR

The rack and pinion power steering gear used on these models should not be serviced or adjusted. If a malfunction or oil leak should occur, the complete steering gear should be replaced.

TROUBLESHOOTING

Refer to **Figs. 5 and 6** when troubleshooting the power steering system.

DIAGNOSIS & TESTING

PUMP PRESSURE TEST
Neon

1. Check and adjust power steering pump drive belt tension as required, then disconnect fluid pressure hose at power steering pump.
2. Connect pressure gauge tool No. 6815 or equivalent to both hoses using suitable adapter fittings, **Fig. 7.**
3. Connect spare pressure hose to power steering pump pressure hose banjo fitting, then fully open pressure gauge tool valve.
4. Start engine and allow to idle until power steering fluid has circulated through flow/pressure test and air has been evacuated from fluid, then stop engine.
5. Check and add fluid as required, then start engine and observe pressure gauge. Reading should be below 125 psi; if not, inspect hoses for crimping

or other restrictions and repair as necessary.
6. Observe pressure gauge and flow meter. Initial pressure reading should be as specified under "Power Steering Pressure Specifications" and flow meter should indicate 1.3–1.9 gpm.
7. Fully close pressure gauge valve 3 times for no longer than 5 seconds per closure, recording highest pressure indicated each time. Readings must be within specifications and within 50 psi of one another. **If valve remains closed for more than 5 seconds, pump damage is likely to occur.**
8. If readings are not as indicated, replace power steering pump.
9. Open test valve and rotate steering wheel from stop to stop, recording highest pressure indicated at each position. **Do not hold wheel against either stop for more than 5 seconds, as pump may be damaged.**
10. If highest output pressures recorded for left and right stop differ significantly, steering gear is leaking internally and should be replaced.

2.2L/4–135, 2.5L/4–153 & 3.0L/V6–181 Engines Except Monaco & Premier

1. Ensure fluid level and drive belt tension are correct, disconnect pressure hose and cap, then connect a spare pressure hose to pump fitting.
2. Connect spare pressure hose to gauge side of tool No. C-3309-E or equivalent, then the pressure hose from gear valve to valve side of tool Nos. L-4601 and C-3309-E or their equivalents. **New fittings will be required on tool No. C-3309-E or equivalent to adapt to new O-ring type hose tube ends.**
3. Open hand valve on special tool, insert a thermometer into fluid reservoir, start engine and allow fluid to reach a temperature of 150-170°F. Turn wheels from stop to stop to aid in warming fluid. **Do not hold wheels against stop for an extended period. Internal pump overheating may result.**
4. With engine at idle speed and gauge valve open, check initial pressure. Results should be as specified under "Power Steering Pressure Specifications."
5. If pressure is in excess of 100 psi, check hoses for restrictions and/or crimped oil lines.
6. Close gauge valve completely three times and record highest pressure attained each time. **Do not leave valve closed for more than 5 seconds; pump could be damaged.**
7. If recorded pressures are within specifications and range of readings are within 50 psi, pump is operating properly.
8. If recorded pressures are high, but do not repeat within 50 psi, flow control valve in pump is sticking. Remove valve, clean and remove any burrs with crocus cloth. If system contains

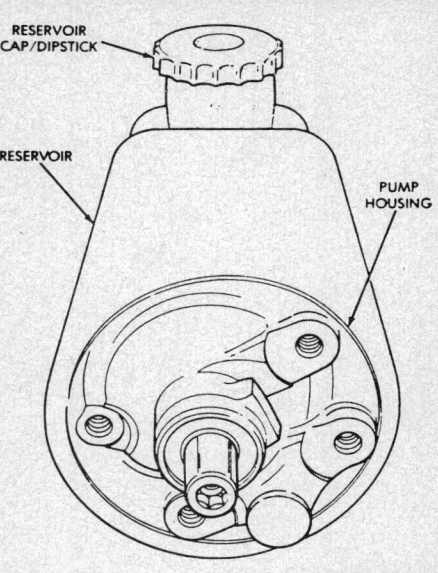

Fig. 3 Saginaw "Ham Can" power steering pump. Models w/2.2L/4-135, 2.5L/4-153 & 3.0L/V6-181 engines except Monaco & Premier

some dirt, it must be thoroughly flushed. If it is exceptionally dirty, both pump and gear must be removed, completely disassembled, cleaned and reassembled before further usage.
9. If recorded pressures are constant, but less than minimum specification, clean or replace pressure relief valve assembly. If pressures are still low, repair or replace pump.
10. If pump is within specifications, leave gauge valve open and turn steering wheel from stop to stop with engine idling. Record highest pressures attained at each wheel stop and compare with maximum pump pressure recorded previously. If this pressure cannot be obtained in either side of gear, gear is leaking internally and must be disassembled and repaired.
11. Shut engine off, remove tool No. C-3309-E or equivalent, reconnect pressure hose, then perform repairs as necessary.

Models w/3.3L/V6–201, 3.5L/V6–215 & 3.8L/V6–231 Engines, Monaco & Premier

1. Ensure drive belt tension is correct, then place a drip pan under engine and disconnect pump high pressure hose at steering gear. Hold hose end raised above reservoir to prevent fluid loss.
2. Connect one side of a suitable pressure test gauge to pump high pressure hose with an adapter, then the other side of gauge to power steering pump with an adapter hose as shown in **Fig. 8. Ensure that test gauge is connected in fluid high pressure circuit between pump and steering gear.**
3. Open test valve completely, fill fluid

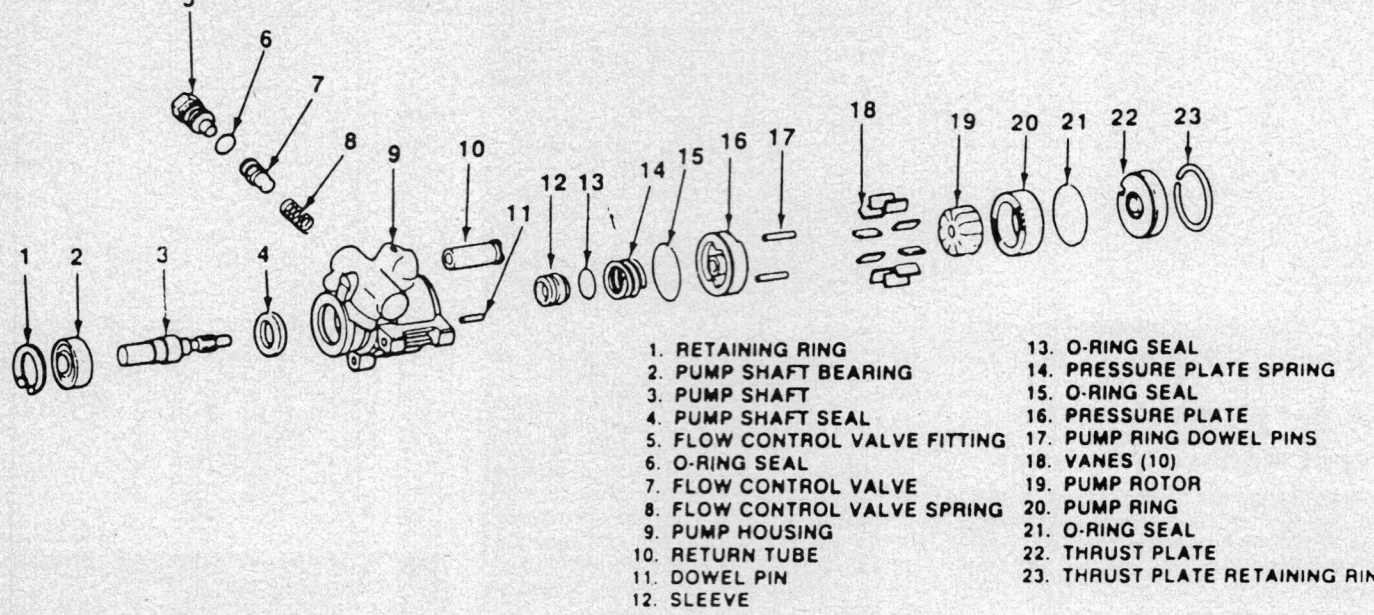

1. RETAINING RING
2. PUMP SHAFT BEARING
3. PUMP SHAFT
4. PUMP SHAFT SEAL
5. FLOW CONTROL VALVE FITTING
6. O-RING SEAL
7. FLOW CONTROL VALVE
8. FLOW CONTROL VALVE SPRING
9. PUMP HOUSING
10. RETURN TUBE
11. DOWEL PIN
12. SLEEVE

13. O-RING SEAL
14. PRESSURE PLATE SPRING
15. O-RING SEAL
16. PRESSURE PLATE
17. PUMP RING DOWEL PINS
18. VANES (10)
19. PUMP ROTOR
20. PUMP RING
21. O-RING SEAL
22. THRUST PLATE
23. THRUST PLATE RETAINING RING

CR6029100048000X

Fig. 4 Exploded view of power steering pump. Models w/3.3L/V6–201, 3.5L/V6–215 & 3.8L/V6–231 engines

reservoir with power steering fluid as necessary, then start engine and allow fluid to reach normal operating temperature of approximately 170°F.

4. Observe pressure test gauge, pressure should be within specifications. Refer to "Power Steering Pressure Specifications."

5. If pressure is greater than specified, check hoses for restrictions and repair as necessary.

6. Close test valve completely for 2-4 seconds, then immediately open. Repeat this procedure three times and record maximum pressure indicated on pressure test gauge each time test valve is closed. **Do not leave valve closed for more than 5 seconds, pump could be damaged.**

7. Compare maximum indicated pressures. If pressures are within specifications and variance of three indicated pressures are within 50 psi of each other, pump is operating properly.

8. If maximum indicated pressures are greater than specified and are not within 50 psi of each other, flow control valve is not functioning properly. Remove and clean valve.

9. If maximum indicated pressures are within specifications and within 50 psi of each other, open test valve completely, then turn wheels to extreme left and right positions to force pump to operate against steering stops.

10. Record pressure at each extreme position, then compare extreme left and right pressures with previously recorded maximum pressures. If pump maximum output pressure are not repeated when pump is forced to operate against either stop, steering gear is leaking internally and must be disassembled and repaired.

PUMP NOISE

There is some noise in all power steering systems. One of the most common is a hissing sound evident at standstill parking. Hiss is a high frequency noise similar to that experienced while slowly closing a water tap. The noise is present in every valve and results from high velocity fluid passing valve orifice edges. There is no relationship between this noise and performance of the steering. Hiss may be expected when steering wheel is at end of travel or when slowly turning at standstill.

CONDITION	POSSIBLE CAUSE	CORRECTION
OBJECTIONAL HISS OR WHISTLE	1. Noisy valve in gear	1. Check for proper seal between steering column coupling and dash seal. Ensure steering column lower coupling has no metal-to-metal contact within the coupling by performing an electrical continuity check. (Remove coupling for check.) If hiss is still extremely objectionable, replace steering gear.
RATTLE OR CLUNK	1. Gear loose on front crossmember	1. Check gear-to-crossmember mounting bolts. Tighten to specification.
	2. Crossmember-to-frame bolts or studs loose	2. Torque bolts and studs to specifications.
	3. Tie rod looseness (outer or inner)	3. Check tie rod pivot points for wear. Replace if necessary.
	4. Pressure hose touching other parts of vehicle	4. Adjust hose to proper position by loosening, repositioning, and retightening fitting. Do not bend tubing.
	5. Noise internal to gear	5. Replace gear.
CHIRP OR SQUEAL (IN THE AREA OF PUMP) PARTICULARLY NOTICEABLE AT FULL WHEEL TRAVEL AND DURING STANDSTILL PARKING	1. Loose belt	1. Adjust belt tension to specification.

CR6029100036010X

Fig. 5 Power steering system troubleshooting (Part 1 Of 6). Acclaim, Daytona, Dynasty, Imperial, LeBaron, Neon, Shadow, Spirit, Sundance & 1992–93 New Yorker

BINDS STICKS SEIZED

CONDITION	POSSIBLE CAUSE	CORRECTION
CATCHES, STICKS IN CERTAIN POSITIONS OR DIFFICULT TO TURN	1. Low fluid level	1. Fill to proper level and perform leakage diagnosis.
	2. Tires not properly inflated	2. Inflate tires to proper pressure.
	3. Lack of lube in ball joints	3. Lubricate where possible.
	4. Lack of lube in outer tie rod ends	4. Lubricate where possible.
	5. Loose pump belt	5. Tighten or replace belt.
	6. Faulty pump flow control (Verify cause using Pump Test Procedure)	6. Replace pump.
	7. Excessive friction in steering column or intermediate shaft	7. Correct condition.
	8. Steering column coupling binding	8. Realign as necessary.
	9. Excessive friction in gear	9. Replace gear.

SHAKE SHUDDER VIBRATION

CONDITION	POSSIBLE CAUSE	CORRECTION
VIBRATION OF THE STEERING WHEEL AND/OR DASH DURING DRY PARK OR LOW SPEED STEERING MANEUVERS	1. Air in the power steering system	1. Steering shudder can be expected in new vehicles and vehicles with recent steering system repairs. Shudder should improve after the vehicle has been driven several weeks.
	2. Tires not properly inflated	2. Inflate tires to proper pressure.
	3. Excessive engine vibration	3. Make sure that engine is running properly.
	4. Faulty accessory drive belt vibration (Poly-V belt systems only)	4. Check dynamic belt tensioner for abnormal vibration.
	5. Overcharged air conditioner	5. Check air conditioning pump head pressure.

CR60291000360030X

Fig. 5 Power steering system troubleshooting (Part 3 Of 6). Acclaim, Daytona, Dynasty, Imperial, LeBaron, Neon, Shadow, Spirit, Sundance & 1992-93 New Yorker

PUMP GROWL

Pump growl results from the development of high pressure fluid flow. Normally this noise should not be high enough to be objectionable. Abnormal situations, such as a low oil level causing aeration or hoses touching the vehicle body, can create a noise level that could bring complaints.

CONDITION	POSSIBLE CAUSE	CORRECTION
WHINE OR GROWL (PUMP NOISE)	1. Low fluid level	1. Fill to proper level and perform leakage diagnosis. (Recheck after system is free of aeration.)
	2. Hose touching vehicle body or frame	2. Reposition hose. Replace hose if tube ends are bent.
	3. Extreme wear of pump internal parts	3. Replace pump and flush system.
SUCKING AIR SOUND	1. Loose return line clamp	1. Tighten or replace clamp.
	2. Missing O-ring on hose connection	2. Inspect connection and replace o-ring as required.
	3. Low fluid level	3. Fill to proper level and perform leakage diagnosis.
	4. Air leak between reservoir and pump	4. Inspect and replace reservoir or pump.
SQUEAK OR RUB SOUND	1. Sound from steering column	1. Check for squeak in steering column. Inspect for contact between shroud, intermediate shaft, column, and wheel. (Realign if necessary.)
	2. Sound internal to steering gear	2. Replace gear.
SCRUBBING/KNOCKING	1. Incorrect tire size	1. Verify tire size is the same as originally supplied.
	2. Check clearance between tires and other vehicle components, through full travel	2. Correct as necessary.
	3. Check for interference between steering gear and other components	3. Correct as necessary.
	4. Incorrect gear supplied	4. Replace gear.

CR60291000360020X

Fig. 5 Power steering system troubleshooting (Part 2 Of 6). Acclaim, Daytona, Dynasty, Imperial, LeBaron, Neon, Shadow, Spirit, Sundance & 1992-93 New Yorker

LOW ASSIST, NO ASSIST, OR HARD STEERING

CONDITION	POSSIBLE CAUSE	CORRECTION
STIFF, HARD TO TURN, SURGES, MOMENTARY INCREASE IN EFFORT WHEN TURNING	1. Tires not properly inflated 2. Low fluid level 3. Loose belt 4. Lack of ball joint lubrication 5. Low pressure pump (Verify using Pump Test Procedure) 6. High internal leak gear	1. Inflate tires to proper pressure. 2. Add power steering fluid as required and perform leakage diagnosis. 3. Tighten or replace belt. 4. Lubricate or replace as required. 5. Verify cause using Pump Test Procedure. Replace pump if necessary. 6. Check steering system using test procedure. If steering gear is at fault, replace steering gear.

LOOSE STEERING

CONDITION	POSSIBLE CAUSE	CORRECTION
EXCESSIVE WHEEL KICKBACK OR TOO MUCH STEERING WHEEL PLAY	1. Air in system 2. Gear loose on crossmember 3. Worn/broken intermediate shaft 4. Free play in steering column 5. Loose ball joints 6. Front wheel bearings loose or worn 7. Loose outer tie rod ends 8. Loose inner tie rod ends 9. Defective steering gear rotary valve	1. Add fluid. 2. Check gear to crossmember mounting bolts. Tighten to specification. 3. Check for worn universal joint and broken isolator. Replace intermediate shaft if worn. 4. Check and replace as required. 5. Check and replace as required. 6. Tighten hub nut or replace with new parts as necessary. 7. Check and replace as required. 8. Replace gear. 9. Replace gear.

POOR RETURN TO CENTER

CONDITION	POSSIBLE CAUSE	CORRECTION
STEERING WHEEL DOES NOT WANT TO RETURN TO CENTER POSITION	1. Tires not properly inflated 2. Improper front wheel alignment 3. Lack of lubrication in ball joint 4. Steering column U-joints misaligned 5. Mispositioned dash cover 6. Steering wheel rubbing 7. Tight steering shaft bearings 8. Excessive friction coupling universal joint 9. High friction in the steering gear	1. Inflate tires to proper pressure. 2. Check and adjust as necessary. 3. Replace as required or lubricate. 4. Realign steering column U-joints. 5. Reposition dash cover. To evaluate items 6 and 7, disconnect the intermediate steering shaft. Turn the steering wheel and listen for internal rubbing in column. 6. Adjust covers. 7. Replace bearings. 8. Replace U-joints. 9. Replace steering gear.

VEHICLE LEADS TO THE SIDE

CONDITION	POSSIBLE CAUSE	CORRECTION
WHEEL DOES NOT WANT TO RETURN TO CENTER POSITION	1. Radial tire lead 2. Front end misaligned 3. Wheel braking 4. Unbalanced steering gear valve. (If this is the cause, the steering efforts will be very light in direction of lead and heavier in the opposite direction)	1. Rotate tires as recommended in Tire Service. 2. Align front end as recommended in Wheel Alignment Service Procedure. 3. Check for dragging brakes as directed in Brake Service Procedure. 4. Checking for pull with outer tie rod end disconnected. If verified, replace gear.

CR6029100036040X

Fig. 5 Power steering system troubleshooting (Part 4 Of 6). Acclaim, Daytona, Dynasty, Imperial, LeBaron, Neon, Shadow, Spirit, Sundance & 1992-93 New Yorker

CR6029100036050X

Fig. 5 Power steering system troubleshooting (Part 5 Of 6). Acclaim, Daytona, Dynasty, Imperial, LeBaron, Neon, Shadow, Spirit, Sundance & 1992-93 New Yorker

CR60291000370I0X

CONDITION	POSSIBLE CAUSE	CORRECTION
CHIRP NOISE IN STEERING PUMP	(1) Loose belt.	(1) Adjust belt tension to specification.
BELT SQUEAL (PARTICULARLY NOTICEABLE AT FULL WHEEL TRAVEL AND STAND STILL PARKING)	(1) Loose belt.	(1) Adjust belt tension to specification.
GROWL NOISE IN STEERING PUMP	(1) Excessive back pressure in hoses or steering gear caused by restriction.	(1) Locate restriction and correct. Replace part if necessary.
GROWL NOISE IN STEERING PUMP (PARTICULARLY NOTICEABLE AT STAND STILL PARKING)	(1) Scored pressure plates, thrust plate or rotor. (2) Extreme wear of cam ring.	(1) Replace parts and flush system. (2) Replace parts.
GROAN NOISE IN STEERING PUMP	(1) Low oil level. (2) Air in the oil. Poor pressure hose connection.	(1) Fill reservoir to proper level. (2) Tighten connector to specified torque. Bleed system by operating steering from right to left - full turn.
RATTLE NOISE IN STEERING PUMP	(1) Vanes not installed properly. (2) Vanes sticking in rotor slots.	(1) Install properly. (2) Free up by removing burrs, varnish, or dirt.
SWISH NOISE IN STEERING PUMP	(1) Defective flow control valve.	(1) Replace part.
WHINE NOISE IN STEERING PUMP	(1) Pump shaft bearing scored.	(1) Replace housing and shaft. Flush system.
HARD STEERING OR LACK OF ASSIST	(1) Loose pump belt. (2) Low oil in reservoir. NOTE: Low oil level will also result in excessive pump noise. (3) Steering gear to column misalignment. (4) Lower coupling flange rubbing against steering gear adjuster. (5) Tires not properly inflated.	(1) Adjust belt tension to specification. (2) Fill to proper level. If excessively low, check all lines and joints for evidence of external leakage. Tighten loose connectors. (3) Align steering column. (4) Loosen pinch bolt and assemble properly. (5) Inflate to recommended pressure.

Fig. 6   Power steering pump troubleshooting (Part 1 Of 3). Monaco & Premier

FLUID LEAK

CONDITION	POSSIBLE CAUSE	CORRECTION
LOW FLUID LEVEL WITH: • NO VISIBLE SIGNS OF LEAKS ON THE STEERING GEAR, PUMP, ON FLOOR, OR ANYWHERE ELSE — LOW FLUID LEVEL WITH: • VISIBLE LEAK ON STEERING GEAR, PUMP, FLOOR, OR ANYWHERE ELSE	1. Overfilled reservoir. 2. Hose connections at pump or gear. 3. Pump or gear leak.	1. Adjust fill level. 2. Check for loose fittings and tighten to specifications. If fittings are tight, examine for damaged or missing O-ring and replace as required. 3. Identify location of leak and repair or replace as indicated.

CR60291000360600X

Fig. 5   Power steering system troubleshooting (Part 6 Of 6). Acclaim, Daytona, Dynasty, Imperial, LeBaron, Neon, Shadow, Spirit, Sundance & 1992–93 New Yorker

FOAMY OR MILKY FLUID

CONDITION	POSSIBLE CAUSE	CORRECTION
AERATION AND OVERFLOW OF FLUID	1. Air leaks 2. Low fluid level 3. Cracked pump housing 4. Water contamination	1. Check for air leak as described under sucking air and correct. 2. Extremely cold temperatures may cause system aeration if the oil level is low. Add fluid as required. 3. Remove pump from vehicle and separate reservoir from housing. Check expansion plug and housing for cracks. Replace pump as required. 4. Drain and refill fluid if there is evidence of contamination.

11. Shut engine off, remove test equipment, reconnect pressure hose, then perform repairs as necessary.

POWER STEERING SYSTEM SERVICE

Power Steering System Bleed

1. Ensure power steering fluid reservoir is full, then start and run engine. If fluid level drops after engine has been run, fill and run again until level remains constant.
2. Raise and support front of vehicle, then start engine and turn steering wheel slowly from stop to stop.
3. Stop engine and add fluid as necessary, then lower vehicle and restart engine.
4. Turn steering wheel slowly from stop to stop, then stop engine again and add fluid as necessary.
5. Inspect fluid condition. If it appears extremely foamy, do not disturb vehicle for several minutes, then repeat bleed procedure. Check for leaks.

Component Service

POWER STEERING PUMP

MODELS w/2.2L/4—135, 2.5L/4—153 & 3.0L/V6—181 ENGINES EXCEPT MONACO & PREMIER

On these models, the power steering pump is not serviceable except for the following items:
1. Power steering pump oil seals except for the pump shaft seal.
2. Power steering pump reservoirs and related components.
3. Power steering pump reservoir filler cap/dipstick.

Refer to **Fig. 9** when replacing these parts.

NEON & MODELS w/3.3L/V6—201, 3.5L/V6—215 & 3.8L/V6—231 ENGINES

The power steering pump is not serviceable except for the reservoirs and related components, filler cap/dipstick and any oil seals other than the pump shaft seal.

MONACO & PREMIER

Disassembly

1. Remove pump, pump mounting brackets and pump pulley.
2. Remove pump end plate retaining ring as follows:
   a. Position a socket (1) on the pump shaft and end plate, **Fig. 10**.
   b. Mount pump and sockets in a vise as shown in **Fig. 10**.
   c. Tighten fixture slightly to compress spring under end plate. **End plate is under spring pressure. Use caution when removing retaining ring to avoid personal injury.**
   d. Insert a punch (2), **Fig. 10**, into access hole in pump and push ring outward.
   e. Remove retaining ring (3), **Fig. 10**, with a screwdriver, release vise jaws and remove pump and sockets from vise.
3. Place pump into vise with wood blocks between shaft end of pump housing and vise jaws, **Fig. 11**.
4. Remove end plate by gently rocking back and forth, or tapping with a soft mallet.
5. Remove high pressure fitting and O-ring from housing, then remove flow control valve and spring noting position for assembly, **Fig. 12**.
6. Remove pressure plate spring and pressure plate.
7. Tap pump shaft from housing, then remove shaft retaining ring, pump ring,

CONDITION	POSSIBLE CAUSE	CORRECTION
	Further possible causes could be:	
	(6) Sticking flow control valve.	In order to diagnose conditions such as listed in (6), (7), (8), (9) a pressure test of the entire power steering system is required.
	(7) Insufficient pump pressure output.	
	(8) Excessive internal pump leakage.	
	(9) Excessive internal gear leakage.	
FOAMING MILKY POWER STEERING FLUID, LOW FLUID LEVEL AND POSSIBLE LOW PRESSURE	(1) Air in the fluid, and loss of fluid due to internal pump leakage causing overflow.	(1) Check for leaks and correct. Bleed system. Extremely cold temperatures will cause system aeration should the oil level be low. If oil level is correct and pump still foams, remove pump from vehicle and separate reservoir from body. Check welsh plug and body for cracks. If plug is loose or body is cracked, replace body.
LOW PUMP PRESSURE	(1) Flow control valve stuck or inoperative.	(1) Remove burrs or dirt or replace. Flush system.
	(2) Pressure plate not flat against cam ring.	(2) Correct.
MOMENTARY INCREASE IN EFFORT WHEN TURNING WHEEL FAST TO RIGHT OR LEFT	(1) Low oil level in pump.	(1) Add power steering fluid as required.
	(2) Pump belt slipping.	(2) Tighten or replace belt.
	(3) High internal leakage.	(3) Check pump pressure. (See pressure test.)
STEERING WHEEL SURGES OR JERKS WHEN TURNING WITH ENGINE RUNNING ESPECIALLY DURING PARKING	(1) Low oil level.	(1) Fill as required.
	(2) Loose pump belt.	(2) Adjust tension to specification.
	(3) Steering linkage hitting engine oil pan at full turn.	(3) Correct clearance.
	(4) Insufficient pump pressure.	(4) Check pump pressure. (See pressure test.) Replace flow control valve if defective.
	(5) Sticking flow control valve.	(5) Inspect for varnish or damage, replace if necessary.
EXCESSIVE WHEEL KICKBACK OR LOOSE STEERING	(1) Air in system.	(1) Add oil to pump reservoir and bleed by operating steering. Check hose connectors for proper torque and adjust as required.

CR6029100037020X

Fig. 6   Power steering pump troubleshooting (Part 2 Of 3). Monaco & Premier

CONDITION	POSSIBLE CAUSE	CORRECTION
LOW PUMP PRESSURE	(1) Flow control valve stuck or inoperative.	(1) Remove burrs or dirt. Replace valve if damaged.
	(2) Pump pressure plate not seating (flat) against cam ring.	(2) Disassemble pump and correct.
	(3) Extreme wear of cam ring.	(3) Replace parts. Flush system.
	(4) Scored pressure plate, thrust plate, or rotor.	(4) Replace parts. Flush system.
	(5) Vanes not installed properly.	(5) Install properly.
	(6) Vanes sticking in rotor slots.	(6) Freeup by removing burrs, varnish, or dirt.
	(7) Cracked or broken thrust or pressure plate.	(7) Replace part.

CR6029100037030X

Fig. 6   Power steering pump troubleshooting (Part 3 Of 3). Monaco & Premier

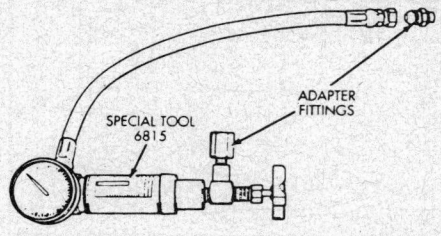

Fig. 7   Pressure gauge tool connections. Neon

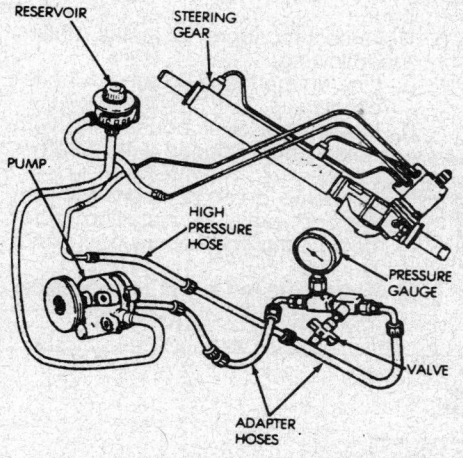

Fig. 8   Pump pressure test equipment

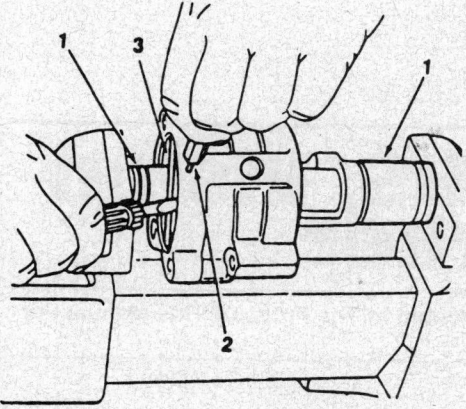

Fig. 10   End plate retaining ring removal. Monaco & Premier

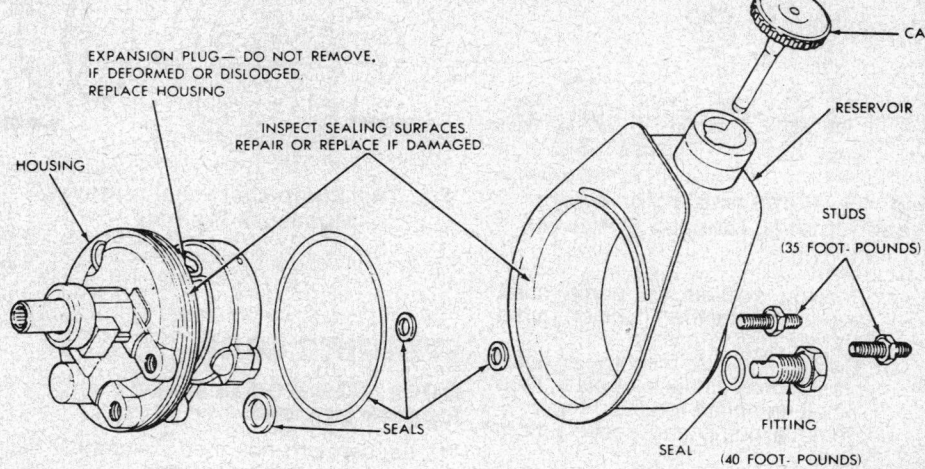

Fig. 9   Power steering pump & reservoir assembly. Models w/2.2L/4–135, 2.5L/4–153 & 3.0L/V6–181 engines except Monaco & Premier

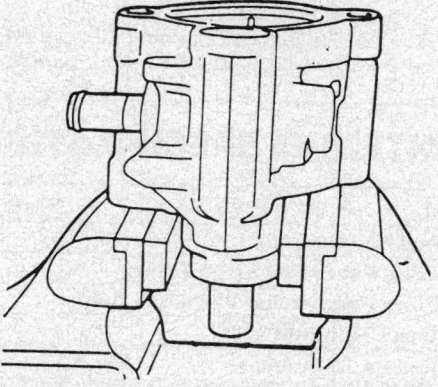

Fig. 11   End plate removal. Monaco & Premier

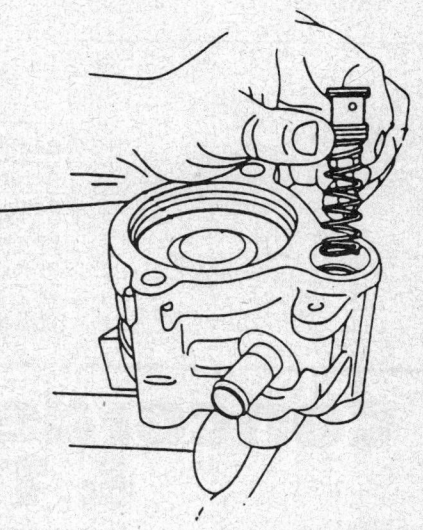

Fig. 12   Flow control valve removal. Monaco & Premier

rotor and vanes and thrust plate from the shaft, **Fig. 13.**
8. Remove thrust plate and dowel pins, **Fig. 13.**
9. Remove pressure plate and end plate O-rings, and shaft seal from pump housing, **Fig. 14.**

Inspection

1. Clean all parts with solvent and blow dry with compressed air.
2. Inspect flow control valve for nicks, scratches and burrs. Clean up minor surface marks with crocus cloth. Re-

place valve as an assembly if damaged.
3. Check pressure and thrust plates for flatness and replace if worn or scored.
4. Inspect pump ring and replace if damaged in any way.
5. Inspect thrust plate dowels, pressure plate spring, rotor, splines and surfaces for distortion or any other damage. Replace as needed.
6. Inspect pump shaft and splines and replace if scored or damaged. Replace shaft retaining ring.
7. Inspect pump housing and bores, and pump fittings for wear and porosity. Replace as necessary.
8. Inspect end plate and end plate retaining ring. Replace if damaged or distorted in any way.

Assembly

Ensure all parts are clean and lubricated with clean power steering fluid. Dirt will cause noise, leaks, and accelerated wear.
1. Install pump shaft seal with installer tool No. J-7728 or equivalent.
2. Install pressure plate and end plate O-

rings in housing, then install thrust plate dowels in housing.
3. Install thrust plate and rotor on pump shaft. Be sure rotor is installed with counterbore facing thrust plate, then secure rotor to shaft with retaining ring.
4. Align thrust plate to dowels and install shaft, rotor, and plate in pump.
5. Align pump ring to dowels and install over rotor. Ensure directional arrows are facing up, **Fig. 15.**
6. Install rotor vanes with rounded edges facing outward.
7. Install pressure plate with spring groove facing upward, then install spring in groove.
8. Install end plate then end plate retaining ring as follows:

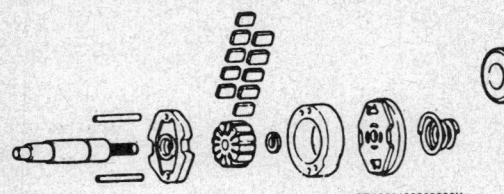

Fig. 13   Pump ring, rotor & rotor vane removal. Monaco & Premier

Fig. 14   Pump shaft seal removal. Monaco & Premier

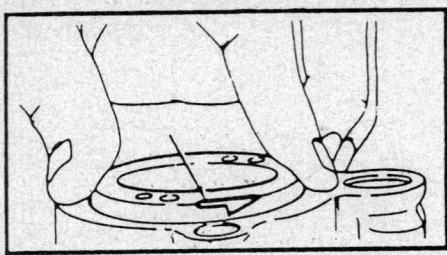

Fig. 15   Pump ring installation. Monaco & Premier

a. Position sockets on pump shaft and end plate, then position pump and sockets in a vise.

b. Tighten the vise slightly to compress spring under end plate, then install end plate retaining ring.

c. Remove pump and sockets from vise.

9. Install flow control valve and spring with hex nut side of valve toward bore.

10. Install O-ring and fitting in the flow control valve bore and tighten to specifications, then position pulley on pump.

11. Install pump and fill reservoir to specified level.

STEERING GEAR

Outer Tie Rod & Boot Replacement

1. Loosen jam nut, then disconnect tie rod from steering knuckle.
2. Remove outer tie rod and jam nut, then the outer boot clamp.
3. Use pliers to expand boot snorkel clamp, then slide clamp onto breather tube.
4. Remove inner boot clamp, then mark breather tube location and remove boot.
5. Reverse procedure to install, noting the following:
   a. Line up mark and breather tube location.
   b. Install boot over housing lip with hole in boot aligned with breather tube.
   c. Lubricate outer boot groove with silicone prior to installing outer boot clamp and ensure boot is not twisted.
   d. Tighten tie rod jam nut to specifications.

TIGHTENING SPECIFICATIONS

Component	Torque/Ft. Lbs.
Outer Tie Rod End Locknut	②
Power Steering Pump Discharge Fitting	①
Power Steering Pump Relief Valve Ball Seat	4
Pressure Hose Banjo Bolt	25

① —1992 models, 55 ft. lbs.

② —Neon, 45 ft. lbs.; all other models, 55 ft. lbs.

Concorde, Intrepid, LHS, Vision & 1994 New Yorker

NOTE: On Air Bag Equipped Models, Refer To "Air Bag System Precautions" Located In The Front Of This Manual For System Disarming & Arming Procedures.

INDEX

PRECAUTIONS

AIR BAG SYSTEMS

Refer to "Air Bag System Precautions" in the front of this manual for system disarming and arming procedures.

DESCRIPTION

POWER STEERING PUMP

These models are equipped with a Saginaw TC-Series power steering pump, **Fig. 1**, which consists of the power steering pump internal components and pump housing. It utilizes a remote fluid reservoir located at the left inner fender panel.

STEERING GEAR

The rack and pinion power steering gear used on these models, **Fig. 2**, should not

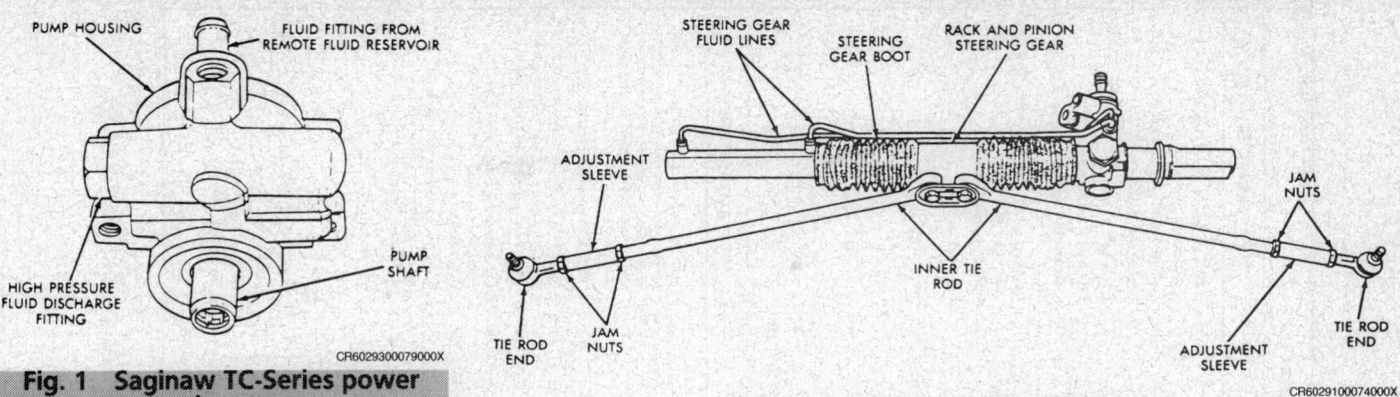

Fig. 1 Saginaw TC-Series power steering pump

Fig. 2 Rack & pinion steering gear

STEERING NOISES

There is some noise in all power steering systems. One of the most common is a hissing sound evident at standstill parking. Hiss is a high frequency noise similar to that experienced while slowly closing a water tap. The noise is present in every valve and results from high velocity fluid passing valve orifice edges. There is no relationship between this noise and performance of the steering. Hiss may be expected when steering wheel is at end of travel or when slowly turning at standstill.

CONDITION	POSSIBLE CAUSE	CORRECTION
OBJECTIONAL HISS OR WHISTLE	1. Noisy valve in gear	1. Check for proper seal between steering column coupling and dash seal. 2. Ensure steering column lower coupling has no metal-to-metal contact within the coupling by performing an electrical continuity check. (Remove coupling for check.) 3. If hiss is still extremely objectionable, replace steering gear.
RATTLE OR CLUNK	1. Gear loose on front crossmember 2. Crossmember-to-frame bolts or studs loose 3. Tie rod looseness (outer or inner) 4. Pressure hose touching other parts of vehicle 5. Noise internal to gear	1. Check gear-to-crossmember mounting bolts. Tighten to specification. 2. Torque bolts and studs to specifications. 3. Check tie rod pivot points for wear. Replace if necessary. 4. Adjust hose to proper position by loosening, repositioning, and retightening fitting. Do not bend tubing. 5. Replace gear.
CHIRP OR SQUEAL (IN THE AREA OF PUMP) PARTICULARLY NOTICEABLE AT FULL WHEEL TRAVEL AND DURING STANDSTILL PARKING	1. Loose belt	1. Adjust belt tension to specification.

Fig. 3 Power steering system troubleshooting (Part 1 of 6)

be serviced or adjusted. If a malfunction or oil leak should occur, the complete steering gear should be replaced.

TROUBLESHOOTING

Refer to **Fig. 3** when troubleshooting the power steering system.

DIAGNOSIS & TESTING
POWER STEERING PUMP

Refer to "Acclaim, Daytona, Dynasty, Imperial, LeBaron, Monaco, Neon, Premier, Shadow, Spirit, Sundance & 1992-93 New Yorker" section for power steering pump diagnosis and testing procedures.

POWER STEERING SYSTEM SERVICE
Power Steering System Bleed

1. Ensure power steering fluid remote reservoir is full, then start engine and turn steering wheel from stop to stop several times.
2. Stop engine and check fluid level again. If necessary, add fluid until correct fluid level is reached.
3. Repeat procedure until fluid level is consistent. Inspect system for leaks.

Component Service
OUTER TIE ROD & BOOT REPLACEMENT

1. Raise and support vehicle then remove tire and wheel assembly.
2. Loosen tie rod adjustment sleeve locknut.
3. Loosen, do not remove, outer tie rod to steering arm nut.
4. Using tie rod remover tool No. MB990635, or equivalent, remove tie rod end from steering arm.
5. Remove tie rod from adjustment sleeve.
6. Reverse procedure to install, noting the following:
   a. Check toe setting prior to tightening adjustment sleeve locknut.
   b. Ensure maximum exposed threads requirements are not exceeded, **Fig. 4.**

BINDS STICKS SEIZED

CONDITION	POSSIBLE CAUSE	CORRECTION
CATCHES, STICKS IN CERTAIN POSITIONS OR DIFFICULT TO TURN	1. Low fluid level	1. Fill to proper level and perform leakage diagnosis.
	2. Tires not properly inflated	2. Inflate tires to proper pressure.
	3. Lack of lube in ball joints	3. Lubricate where possible.
	4. Lack of lube in outer tie rod ends	4. Lubricate where possible.
	5. Loose pump belt	5. Tighten or replace belt.
	6. Faulty pump flow control (Verify cause using Pump Test Procedure)	6. Replace pump.
	7. Excessive friction in steering column or intermediate shaft	7. Correct condition. (See Steering Column Service Procedure.)
	8. Steering column coupling binding	8. Realign as necessary.
	9. Excessive friction in gear	9. Replace gear.

SHAKE SHUDDER VIBRATION

CONDITION	POSSIBLE CAUSE	CORRECTION
VIBRATION OF THE STEERING WHEEL AND/OR DASH DURING DRY PARK OR LOW SPEED STEERING MANEUVERS	1. Air in the power steering system	1. Steering shudder can be expected in new vehicles and vehicles with recent system repairs. Shudder should improve after the vehicle has been driven several weeks.
	2. Tires not properly inflated	2. Inflate tires to proper pressure.
	3. Excessive engine vibration	3. Make sure that engine is running properly.
	4. Loose tie rod end	4. Check inner and outer tie rod and jam nut for excessive free play.
	5. Faulty accessory drive belt tensioner. (Poly-V belt systems only)	5. Check dynamic belt tensioner for abnormal vibration. (See Drive Belt Adjustments.)
	6. Overcharged air conditioner	6. Check air conditioning pump head pressure. (See Air Conditioning Refrigerant System Diagnosis.)

Fig. 3   Power steering system troubleshooting (Part 3 of 6)

STEERING NOISES (Continued)

There is some noise in all power steering systems. One of the most common is a hissing sound evident at standstill parking. Hiss is a high frequency noise similar to that experienced while slowly closing a water tap. The noise is present in every valve and results from high velocity fluid passing valve orifice edges. There is no relationship be-tween this noise and performance of the steering. Hiss may be expected when steering wheel is at end of travel or when slowly turning at standstill.

CONDITION	POSSIBLE CAUSE	CORRECTION
WHINE OR GROWL (PUMP NOISE) — Pump growl results from the development of high pressure fluid flow. Normally this noise should not be high enough to be objectionable. Abnormal situations, such as a low oil level causing aeration or hoses touching the vehicle body, can create a noise level that could bring complaints.	1. Low fluid level	1. Fill to proper level and perform leakage diagnosis. (Recheck after system is free of aeration.)
	2. Hose touching vehicle body or frame	2. Reposition hose. Replace hose if tube ends are bent.
	3. Extreme wear of pump internal parts	3. Replace pump and flush system.
SUCKING AIR SOUND	1. Loose return line clamp	1. Tighten or replace clamp.
	2. Missing O-ring on hose connection	2. Inspect connection and replace o-ring as required.
	3. Low fluid level	3. Fill to proper level and perform leakage diagnosis.
	4. Air leak between reservoir and pump	4. Inspect and replace reservoir as required.
SQUEAK OR RUB SOUND	1. Sound from steering column	1. Check for squeak in steering column. Inspect for contact between shroud intermediate shaft, column, and wheel. (Realign if necessary.)
		2. Check for lack of grease on steering column, dash to lower coupling seal.
	2. Sound internal to steering gear	1. Replace gear.
SCRUBBING/KNOCKING	1. Incorrect tire size	1. Verify tire size is the same as originally supplied.
	2. Check clearance between tires and other vehicle components, through full travel	2. Correct as necessary.
	3. Check for interference between steering gear and other components	3. Correct as necessary.
	4. Incorrect gear supplied	4. Replace gear.

Fig. 3   Power steering system troubleshooting (Part 2 of 6)

CR60291000400050X

LOW ASSIST, NO ASSIST, OR HARD STEERING

CONDITION	POSSIBLE CAUSE	CORRECTION
STIFF, HARD TO TURN, SURGES, MOMENTARY INCREASE IN EFFORT WHEN TURNING	1. Tires not properly inflated 2. Low fluid level 3. Loose belt 4. Lack of ball joint lubrication 5. Low pressure pump (Verify using Pump Test Procedure) 6. High internal leak gear	1. Inflate tires to proper pressure. 2. Add power steering fluid as required and perform leakage diagnosis. 3. Tighten or replace belt. 4. Lubricate or replace as required. 5. Verify cause using Pump Test Procedure. Replace pump if necessary. 6. Check steering system using test procedure. If steering gear is at fault, replace steering gear.

LOOSE STEERING

CONDITION	POSSIBLE CAUSE	CORRECTION
EXCESSIVE WHEEL KICKBACK OR TOO MUCH STEERING WHEEL PLAY	1. Air in system 2. Gear loose on crossmember 3. Worn/broken intermediate shaft 4. Free play in steering column 5. Loose ball joints 6. Pinch bolt loose on ball joint 7. Front wheel bearings loose or worn 8. Loose outer tie rod ends 9. Loose inner tie rod ends 10. Defective steering gear rotary valve	1. Add fluid. 2. Check gear to crossmember mounting bolts. Tighten to specification. 3. Check for worn intermediate shaft universal joint and broken isolator. Replace intermediate shaft if worn. 4. Check and replace as required. 5. Check and replace as required. 6. Check pinch bolts and tighten as required to specified torque. 7. Tighten hub nut or replace with new parts as necessary. 8. Check and replace as required. 9. Replace gear. 10. Replace gear.

Fig. 3   Power steering system troubleshooting (Part 5 of 6)

POOR RETURN TO CENTER

CONDITION	POSSIBLE CAUSE	CORRECTION
STEERING WHEEL DOES NOT WANT TO RETURN TO CENTER POSITION	1. Tires not properly inflated 2. Improper front wheel alignment 3. Lack of lubrication in ball joint 4. Steering column U-joints misaligned 5. Mispositioned dash cover 6. Steering wheel rubbing 7. Tight steering shaft bearings 8. Excessive friction coupling universal joint 9. High friction in the steering gear	1. Inflate tires to proper pressure. 2. Check and adjust as necessary. 3. Replace as required or lubricate. 4. Realign steering column U-joints. 5. Reposition dash cover. To evaluate items 6 and 7, disconnect the intermediate steering shaft. Turn the steering wheel and listen for internal rubbing in column. 6. Adjust covers. 7. Replace bearings. 8. Replace U-joints. 9. Replace steering gear.

VEHICLE LEADS TO THE SIDE

CONDITION	POSSIBLE CAUSE	CORRECTION
WHEEL DOES NOT WANT TO RETURN TO CENTER POSITION	1. Radial tire lead 2. Front end misaligned 3. Wheel braking 4. Unbalanced steering gear valve. (If this is the cause, the steering efforts will be very light in direction of lead and heavier in the opposite direction)	1. Rotate tires as recommended in Tire Service. 2. Align front end as recommended in Wheel Alignment Service Procedure. 3. Check for dragging brakes as directed in Brake Service Procedure. 4. Checking for pull with outer tie rod end disconnected. If verified, replace gear.

CR602910004040X

Fig. 3   Power steering system troubleshooting (Part 4 of 6)

FLUID LEAK

CONDITION	POSSIBLE CAUSE	CORRECTION
LOW FLUID LEVEL WITH: • NO VISIBLE SIGNS OF LEAKS ON THE STEERING GEAR, PUMP, ON FLOOR, OR ANYWHERE ELSE LOW FLUID LEVEL WITH: • VISIBLE LEAK ON STEERING GEAR, PUMP, FLOOR, OR ANYWHERE ELSE	1. Overfilled reservoir 2. Hose connections at pump or gear 3. Pump or gear leak	1. Adjust fill level. 2. Check for loose fittings and tighten to specifications. If fittings are tight, examine for damaged or missing O-ring and replace as required. 3. Identify location of leak and repair or replace as indicated

FOAMY OR MILKY FLUID

CONDITION	POSSIBLE CAUSE	CORRECTION
AERATION AND OVERFLOW OF FLUID	1. Air leaks 2. Low fluid level 3. Cracked pump housing 4. Water contamination	1. Check for air leak as described under sucking air and correct. 2. Extremely cold temperatures may cause system aeration if the oil level is low. Add fluid as required. 3. Remove pump from vehicle and separate reservoir from housing. Check expansion plug and housing for cracks. Replace pump as required. 4. Drain and refill fluid if there is evidence of contamination.

Fig. 3   Power steering system troubleshooting (Part 6 of 6)

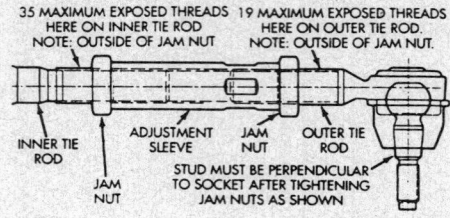

Fig. 4   Tie rod end thread requirements

SOLENOID CONTROL VALVE CONTROL MODULE REPLACEMENT

Models w/Speed Proportional Steering

1. Remove electrical connector from control module.
2. Depress 2 locking tabs on bottom of control module, then detach control module from steering gear end cap.
3. Rotate control module upward, until retaining tabs can be removed from steering gear end cap. Remove control module from steering gear.
4. Reverse procedure to install.

SOLENOID CONTROL VALVE REPLACEMENT

Models w/Speed Proportional Steering

1. Remove solenoid control valve electrical connector from control module.
2. Remove power steering pressure and return hoses from steering gear.
3. Using a $1^5/_{16}$ inch crow foot wrench, loosen solenoid control valve from steering gear.
4. Remove control valve from steering gear.
5. Reverse procedure to install. **Torque** valve to 10 ft. lbs.

TIGHTENING SPECIFICATIONS

Component	Torque/Ft. Lbs.
Outer Tie Rod End Nut	27
Power Steering Pressure Hose Banjo Bolt	25
Tie Rod Adjusting Sleeve Jamb Nut	55

Colt, Colt Vista, Laser, Stealth, Summit, Summit Wagon & Talon

NOTE: On Air Bag Equipped Models, Refer To "Air Bag System Precautions" Located In The Front Of This Manual For System Disarming & Arming Procedures.

INDEX

PRECAUTIONS

AIR BAG SYSTEMS

Refer to "Air Bag System Precautions" in the front of this manual for system disarming and arming procedures.

TROUBLESHOOTING

Refer to **Figs. 1 and 2** when troubleshooting power steering system.

DIAGNOSIS & TESTING

POWER STEERING PUMP PRESSURE TEST

1. Disconnect pressure hose from pump and install gauge and shut-off valve tool No. C-3309-E and hose tools No. C-4535 or their equivalents as shown in **Fig. 3**. Install adapter as shown.
2. Bleed power steering system as described under "Power Steering System Service," then start engine and allow fluid to reach a temperature of approximately 131°F.
3. Set engine speed to 1000 RPM, then completely close shut-off valve. **Do not close shut-off valve for more than 3 seconds, as damage to pump may occur.**
4. If pressure is not within specifications, repair or replace pump. Refer to "Power Steering Pressure Specifications."
5. Completely open shut-off valve. If pressure is not within minimum specifications, check for clogged or collapsed oil line, or clogged oil line inside gearbox and repair as necessary.
6. With shut-off valve completely open, turn wheels completely right or left. If pressure is not within minimum specifications, valve of gearbox is faulty, replace gearbox.

REAR SYSTEM POWER STEERING PUMP DISCHARGE FLOW VOLUME TEST

Stealth

1. Disconnect pressure hose from pump and install adapter tool No. MB991217-A or equivalent with a suitable hose, then place hose in a container which permits measurement of flow rate (graduated cylinder).
2. Start engine, increase idle speed slowly, then hold an indicated speed of 31 mph, measuring discharge flow volume for 30 seconds. **While performing this test, continuously add fluid to reservoir.**
3. If discharge flow volume is extremely higher or lower than 1.06 quarts, replace pump.

POWER STEERING SYSTEM SERVICE

Power Steering System Bleed

EXCEPT STEALTH REAR POWER STEERING SYSTEM

During bleeding procedure, keep fluid in reservoir at correct level.
1. Raise and support front of vehicle.
2. Manually rotate oil pump pulley several times.
3. Turn steering wheel from stop to stop five or six times.
4. Disconnect high tension cable then operate starter motor intermittently while turning the steering wheel from stop to stop five or six times.
5. Connect high tension cable and start engine.
6. Turn steering wheel from stop to stop until no bubbles appear in reservoir.
7. Ensure fluid is not milky and that at proper level.
8. Confirm there is little or no change in fluid level when steering wheel is turned from stop to stop.
9. Ensure fluid level with engine stopped is within .2 inch of level measured with engine running.
10. If fluid level is not as specified, the system is not completely bled; repeat procedure as necessary.

STEALTH REAR POWER STEERING SYSTEM

1. Bleed front power steering system as outlined under "Except Stealth Rear Power Steering System" in this section.
2. Raise and support vehicle. **Because wheels will be moving during this procedure, ensure vehicle is secured properly and do not allow anyone near drive wheels or other moving components.**
3. Start engine and allow to idle.
4. Loosen bleeder screw on LH side of control valve.
5. Connect one end of a vinyl hose on the bleeder screw and the other into a suitable container.
6. Turn steering wheel to left stop and back to center.
7. Repeat step 6 until no air remains in system.
8. Repeat steps 4 through 7 for the RH side, turning steering wheel to the right stop.
9. Loosen power cylinder bleeder screws and place a vinyl hose between the bleeder screws.

Fig. 1 — Power steering system troubleshooting. Colt, Laser, Stealth, Summit & Talon

Symptom	Probable cause	Remedy
Excessive play of steering wheel	Loose rack support cover	Retighten
	Loose steering gear mounting bolts	Retighten
	Loose or worn stud of tie-rod end	Retighten or replace as necessary
Steering wheel operation is hard (Improper power assist)	V-belt slippage	Check
	Damaged V-belt	Replace
	Low fluid level	Refill
	Air in the fluid	Bleed
	Twisted or damaged hoses	Correct the routing or replace
	Improper oil pump pressure	Repair or replace oil pump
	Sticky flow control valve	Replace
	Excessive internal oil pump leakage	Replace damaged parts
	Excessive oil leaks from rack & pinion in gear box	Replace damaged parts
	Bent or damaged gear box or valve body seal ring	Replace
Steering wheel does not return properly	Excessive turning resistance of tie-rod ball joint	Replacee
	Excessively tightened rack support cover	Adjust
	Rough turning of inner tie-rod and/or ball joint	Replace
	Worn steering shaft joint and/or body grommet	Correct or replace
	Bent rack	Replace
	Damaged pinion bearing	Replace
	Twisted or damaged hoses	Reroute or replace
	Damaged oil pressure control valve	Replace
	Damaged oil pump input shaft bearing	Replace
Noise	**Hissing Noise in Steering Gear** There is some noise in all power steering systems. One of the most common is a hissing sound when the steering wheel is turned and the car is not moving. This noise will be most evident when turning the wheel while the brakes are applied. There is no relationship between this noise and steering performance. Do not replace the valve unless the "hissing" noise is extremely objectionable. A replacement valve will also have a slight noise, and is not always a cure for the condition.	
Rattling or chucking noise in rack & pinion	Pressure hose touching other parts of vehicle	Reroute
	Loose gear box bracket	Retighten
	Loose tie-rod end ball joint	Retighten
	Worn tie-rod end ball joint	Replace
Groaning noise in oil pump	Low fluid level	Refill
	Air in the fluid	Bleed
	Loose pump mounting bolts	Retighten

Fig. 1   Power steering system troubleshooting. Colt, Laser, Stealth, Summit & Talon

Fig. 2 — Power steering system troubleshooting (Part 1 of 2). Colt Vista & Summit Wagon

Symptom	Probable cause	Remedy
Steering operation is "hard" (at low speed and in all gears), or there is notable torque unevenness when the steering wheel is turned	Loose drive belt	Adjust
	Insufficient fluid*1	Replenish
	Fluid leakage*2	Retighten or replace
	Twisted or damaged hoses	Correct the routing or replace
	No increase in oil pump pressure	Repair or replace (oil pump, gear box);
	Incorrect mounting of the steering gear box on the crossmember	Retighten
	Twisted firewall cover with steering shaft	
	Improper front wheel alignment	Adjust
	Damaged drive belt	Replace
	Excessive friction around steering linkage	
	Pinion and valve malfunction (seal damage, etc)	
The steering wheel does not return properly	Rack piston seal damage	
	Malfunction of ball joint (s) (excessive swinging torque or starting torque)	
	Incorrect front wheel alignment	Adjust
	Friction of steering shaft joint and/or body grommet	Correct or replace
	Rough turning of tie rod end and/or ball joint	Apply grease or replace
	Excessive turning resistance of tie rod ball joint	
	Gear sliding or rotating part if damaged	Replace
Lack of driving stability	Bent rack	
	Incorrect installation of gear box cross-member	Replace
		Retighten
	Loosened steering linkage ball joint	Retighten or replace
	Malfunction of ball joint (s) (insufficient swinging torque or starting torque)	Replace
Drifts to one side	Loose installation of gear box and cross-member	Retighten
	Tires (Assuming that the tire inflation pressure, tire wear, front alignment, and front wheels are all normal)	Rotate

Fig. 2   Power steering system troubleshooting (Part 1 of 2). Colt Vista & Summit Wagon

Symptom	Probable cause	Remedy
Abnormal noise (hissing sound, whistling sound)	Air in system due to insufficient fluid	Replenish or bleed air
	Air trapped in pipes	Retighten or replace or bleed air
	Crushed suction hose	Replace
Abnormal noise (creaking sound, squeaking sound)	Slipping drive belt	Adjust or replace
	Damaged drive belt	Replace
	Burned out oil pump	
Abnormal noise (rattling sound, clunking sound)	Loose gear box bracket mounting	Retighten
	Loose oil pump bracket and/or oil pump mounting bolts	
	Loose steering linkage or ball joint	
	Play in steering linkage or ball joint	Replace
	Interference between chassis and piping	Repair

NOTE
(1) *¹ Because fluid leakage is a possible, check carefully. Especially check the inside of the gear bellows for leakage.
(2) *² Because the gear-box-to-piping coupling is sealed by an O-ring, carefully check whether it is damaged before retightening.
(3) A soft humming sound can be heard from the oil pump when the steering wheel is turned while the vehicle is standing still. This sound is caused by the pulsing of the fluid inside the pump, and does not indicate a malfunction.
(4) If the steering wheel is turned while the brake pedal is being depressed, some sound may be heard from the brakes. This sound is caused by the sticking of the brake pads as the tires turn, and does not indicate a malfunction.
(5) When the steering wheel is turned while the vehicle is standing still, hissing sounds can be heard. These sounds are caused by the fluid flowing through the pressure control valve, and do not indicate a malfunction.

Fig. 2   Power steering system troubleshooting (Part 2 of 2). Colt Vista & Summit Wagon

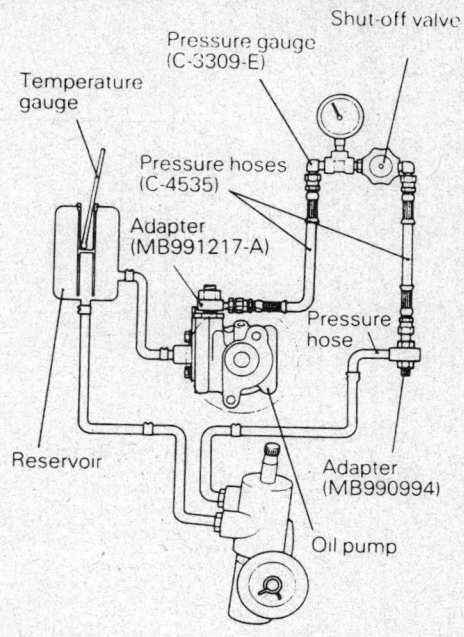

CR6029100069000X

Fig. 3   Pump pressure test equipment

10. Start engine and raise indicated vehicle speed to 43-50 mph.
11. Maintain an indicated speed of 19-25 mph while turning steering wheel from stop to stop. When wheel is turned to either stop position, pressure will rise and air will circulate inside vinyl hose. Ensure air is discharged into reservoir.
12. Repeat step 11 several times until no air appears in vinyl hose.
13. Ensure there is no more than .2 inch difference in fluid level when engine is running and when it is stopped. If difference is more than .2 inch, air is still trapped in system.

Power Steering Fluid Replacement

1. Raise and support front of vehicle.
2. Disconnect return hose, connect one end of a clear vinyl hose to the return hose and the other into a suitable container.
3. Disconnect high tension cable then operate starter motor intermittently while turning steering wheel from stop to stop until fluid is drained from system.
4. Fill reservoir with specified fluid and bleed air from system as outlined under "Power Steering System Bleed" in this section.

Component Service

POWER STEERING PUMP
EXCEPT STEALTH REAR POWER STEERING PUMP
Disassembly

Disassemble pump in numbered sequence shown in **Figs. 4 through 6**, noting the following:
1. Tap rotor side of pulley assembly slightly with a plastic hammer, then remove from pump housing.
2. **Do not disassemble flow control valve.**

Inspection

1. Clean all parts in a suitable cleaning fluid.
2. Check fit of vanes in slots of rotor for tightness or excessive looseness. Vanes must fit snugly but slide freely in slots in rotor. Replace rotor if excessive looseness exists between rotor and vanes. Replace vanes if worn or scored.
3. Inspect pump housing for cracks or damage. Check housing for evidence of wear or scoring.
4. Check all springs for free length, distortion or collapsed coils.
5. Inspect locating dowel pins for distortion.
6. Examine outer diameter of flow control valve for scoring or roughness. Slight damage may be cleaned up with crocus cloth. Check valve assembly for freedom of movement in bore of pump housing.
7. Check all oil passages in pump parts for obstruction.
8. Check bushing in pump housing for wear or damage.

Assembly

Reassemble pump in reverse order of numbered sequence shown in **Figs. 4 through 6**, noting the following:
1. Apply power steering fluid to all O-rings prior to installation.
2. Install rotor with countersunk part facing pump cover.
3. Ensure that rotor snap ring is secured in countersunk part of rotor.
4. Install cam ring with punched mark facing pump body and dowel pin holes aligned with dowel pins on pump body.

STEALTH REAR POWER STEERING PUMP

The rear system power steering pump is not serviceable. If a malfunction or leak should occur, the pump assembly should be replaced.

STEERING GEAR
Disassembly

Disassemble rack and pinion in numbered sequence shown in **Figs. 7 through 9**, noting the following:
1. Separate tab washers from inner tie rods using a chisel, then remove inner tie rods and tab washers.
2. Remove rack support cover locknut, then the rack support cover using torque wrench socket tool No. MB990607-A or equivalent.
3. Using a plastic hammer, gently tap pinion to remove.
4. Remove oil seal and ball bearing simultaneously from valve housing using a suitable socket to drive out.
5. Remove rack stopper circlip by turning rack stopper clockwise until end of circlip comes out of slot in gear housing, then when end of circlip comes out of notched hole of housing, turn rack stopper counterclockwise and remove circlip.
6. Pull rack out slowly while simultaneously removing rack stopper and bushing.
7. Use a suitable brass drift to remove pinion lower bearing, oil seal and needle bearing.

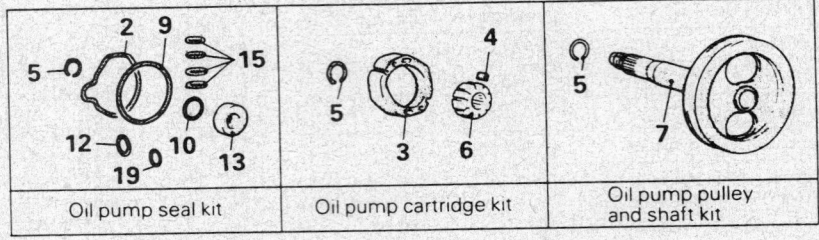

| Oil pump seal kit | Oil pump cartridge kit | Oil pump pulley and shaft kit |

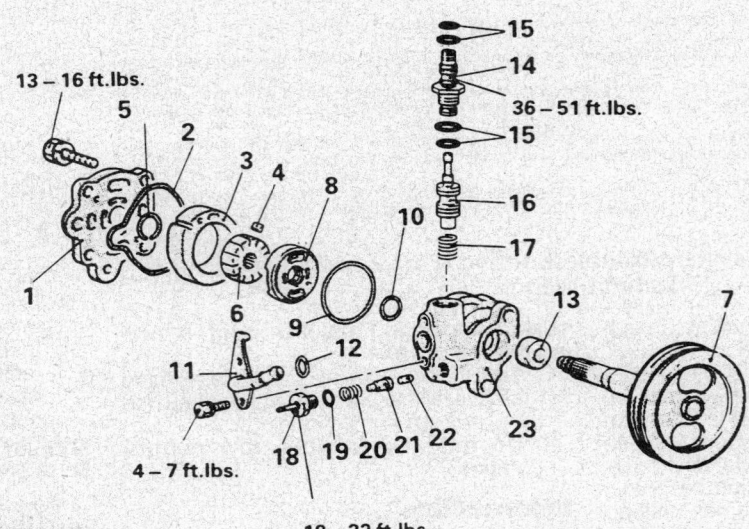

Disassembly steps
1. Pump cover
2. O-ring
3. Cam ring
4. Vanes
5. Snap ring
6. Rotor
7. Pulley assembly
8. Side plate
9. O-ring
10. O-ring
11. Suction connector
12. O-ring
13. Oil seal
14. Connector
15. O-ring
16. Flow control valve
17. Flow control spring
18. Terminal assembly
19. O-ring
20. Spring
21. Plunger
22. Piston rod
23. Oil pump body

Fig. 4   Vane type power steering pump assembly. 1992 Colt & Summit

CR6029100067000X

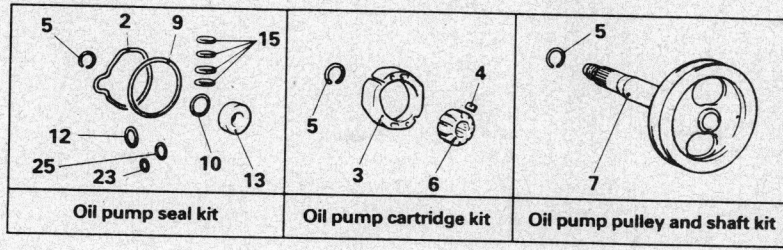

Oil pump seal kit | Oil pump cartridge kit | Oil pump pulley and shaft kit

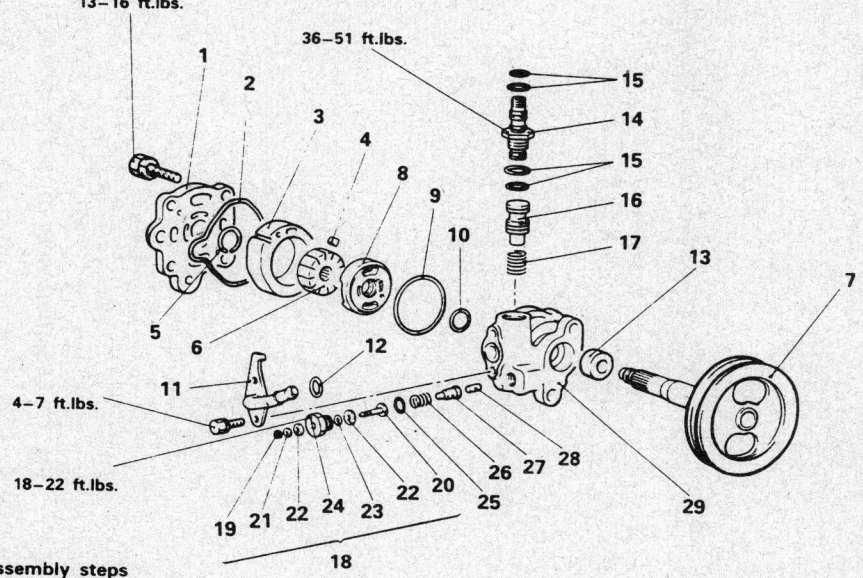

Disassembly steps

1. Pump cover
2. O-ring
3. Cam ring
4. Vanes
5. Snap ring
6. Rotor
7. Pulley assembly
8. Side plate
9. O-ring
10. O-ring
11. Suction connector
12. O-ring
13. Oil seal
14. Connector
15. O-ring
16. Flow control valve
17. Flow control spring
18. Terminal assembly

19. Snap ring
20. Terminal
21. Washer
22. Insulator
23. O-ring
24. Plug
25. O-ring
26. Spring
27. Plunger
28. Piston rod
29. Oil pump body

CR6029100068000X

Fig. 5 Vane type power steering pump assembly. Colt Vista, Laser, Summit Wagon, Talon & 1993–94 Colt & Summit

8. Use a suitable pipe to remove to remove back-up washer and oil seal from housing.

Inspection

1. Check rack teeth and pinion teeth for wear.
2. Check rack for distortion.
3. Check ball and needle bearings for seizure, uneven rotation and excessive play.
4. Check bellows for cracks and deformation.
5. Check gear housing for rust.

Assembly

Assemble rack and pinion in reverse order of the numbered sequence shown in **Figs.**

7 through 9, noting the following:

1. Apply Dexron or Dexron II automatic transmission fluid to O-rings, seal rings, entire surface of oil seals and rack.
2. Apply Mopar multi-mileage lubricant or equivalent to ball bearings, entire surface of needle bearings, rack teeth and pinion teeth.
3. Using suitable tools, press back-up washer and oil seal, pinion needle roller bearing and ball bearing and housing oil seals into housing.
4. Cover rack teeth with rack installer tool No. MB991212 or equivalent, apply Dexron or Dexron II to installer, then match oil seal center with rack to prevent retainer spring from slipping

and slowly insert rack from power cylinder side.

5. Wrap vinyl tape around end of rack, then install rack bushing and stopper. Push stopper in until circlip groove of stopper is aligned with notched hole of housing, then install circlip while turning stopper. **Circlip end should be visible through notched hole of housing.**
6. Using suitable tools, press oil seal and ball bearing into valve housing.
7. Use seal ring installer tool No. MB991317 or equivalent to compress pinion seal rings during installation.
8. Wrap vinyl tape around pinion teeth, then install seal using a suitable pipe.
9. Secure inner tie rods by bending tab washers onto tie rod stepped portions.
10. Apply semi-drying sealant to threaded section of rack support cover, then secure temporarily with locknut.
11. Apply semi-drying sealant to threaded section of end plug, install end plug, then stake at two points with a punch.
12. Fill outer tie rod end dust cover inner side and lip with multi-mileage lubricant.
13. Adjust tie rod length between end of bellows and inner side of tie rod locknut to 7.1 inches.
14. Inspect and adjust pinion total preload as described under "Adjustments" in this section.

RACK & PINION POWER CYLINDER
Stealth

The outer tie rod ends are the only serviceable components on the power cylinder. When reinstalling tie rod ends, adjust length between end of boot and center of tie rod end ball joint to 2.82 inches.

Adjustments
STEERING GEAR PINION TOTAL PRELOAD

1. With rack placed in center position, attach rack support cover to gear housing, then tighten cover to specifications using torque wrench socket tool No. MB990607-A or equivalent. Back off cover approximately 30–60°, then install and tighten locking nut to specifications.
2. In neutral position, rotate pinion shaft clockwise at a rate of one revolution every 4 to 6 seconds using preload socket tool No. CT-1108 or equivalent and a suitable torque wrench. Return rack support cover 30–60° and tighten to specifications. Pinion preload **torque should be 5–11 inch lbs. Measure starting torque through entire stroke of rack.**
3. If measured values are not within specifications, readjust rack support cover, then recheck.
4. If still not within specifications, check rack support cover, rack support spring and rack support and replace parts as necessary.

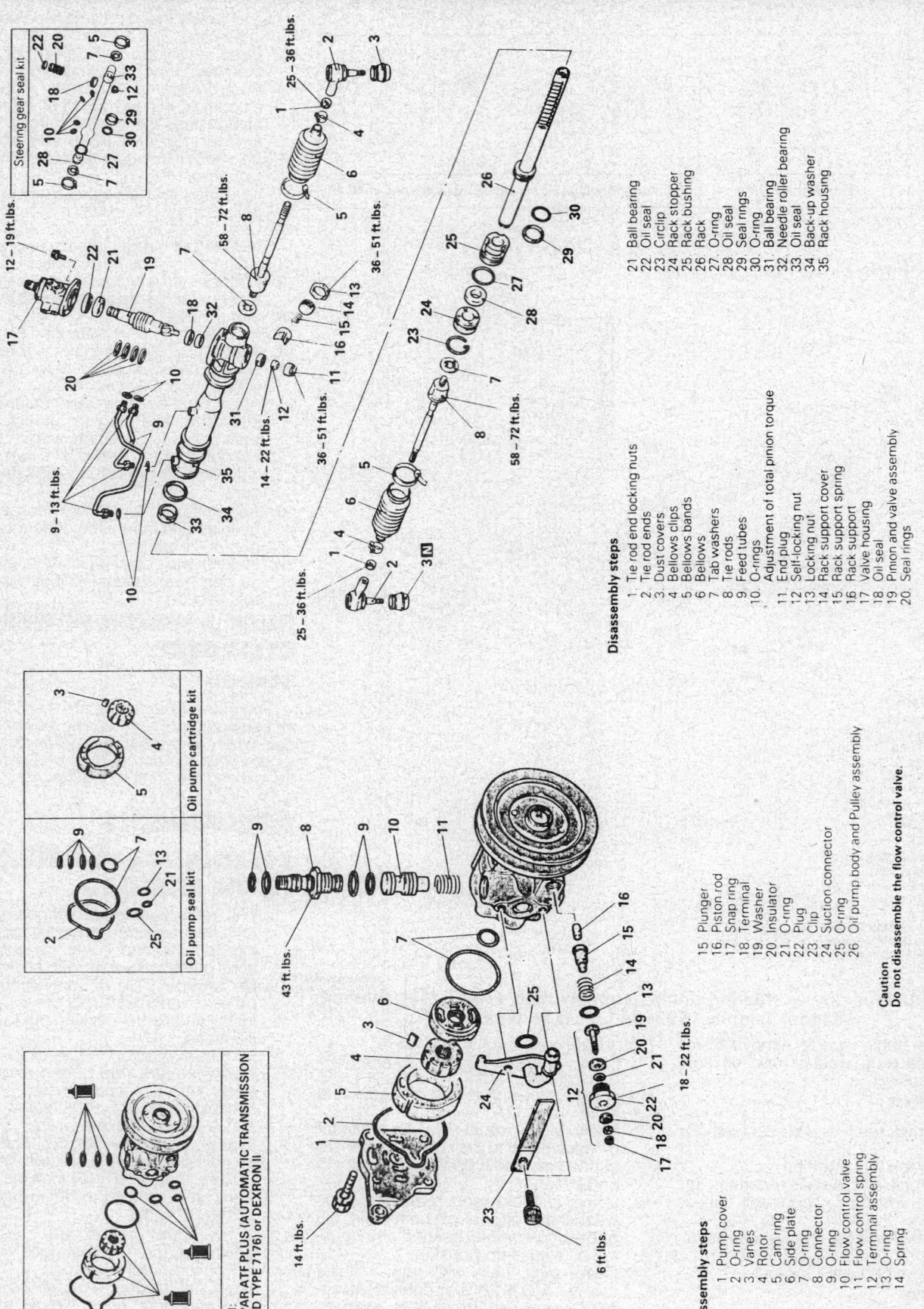

Steering gear seal kit

CR60291000071000X

Disassembly steps

1. Tie rod end locking nuts
2. Tie rod ends
3. Dust covers
4. Bellows clips
5. Bellows bands
6. Bellows
7. Tab washers
8. Tie rods
9. Feed tubes
10. O-rings
11. End plug
12. Self-locking nut
13. Locking nut
14. Rack support cover
15. Rack support spring
16. Rack support
17. Valve housing
18. Oil seal
19. Pinion and valve assembly
20. Seal rings

21. Ball bearing
22. Oil seal
23. Circlip
24. Rack stopper
25. Rack bushing
26. Rack
27. O-ring
28. Oil seal
29. Seal rings
30. O-ring
31. Ball bearing
32. Needle roller bearing
33. Oil seal
34. Back-up washer
35. Rack housing

Adjustment of total pinion torque

Fig. 7 Exploded view of rack & pinion steering gear. Colt & Summit

CR60291000070000X

Oil pump cartridge kit

Oil pump seal kit

Fluid:
MOPAR ATF PLUS (AUTOMATIC TRANSMISSION
FLUID TYPE 7176) or DEXRON II

Disassembly steps

1. Pump cover
2. O-ring
3. Vanes
4. Rotor
5. Cam ring
6. Side plate
7. O-ring
8. Connector
9. O-ring
10. Flow control valve
11. Flow control spring
12. Terminal assembly
13. O-ring
14. Spring

15. Plunger
16. Piston rod
17. Snap ring
18. Terminal
19. Washer
20. Insulator
21. O-ring
22. Plug
23. Clip
24. Suction connector
25. O-ring
26. Oil pump body and Pulley assembly

Caution
Do not disassemble the flow control valve.

Fig. 6 Vane type front power steering pump assembly. Stealth

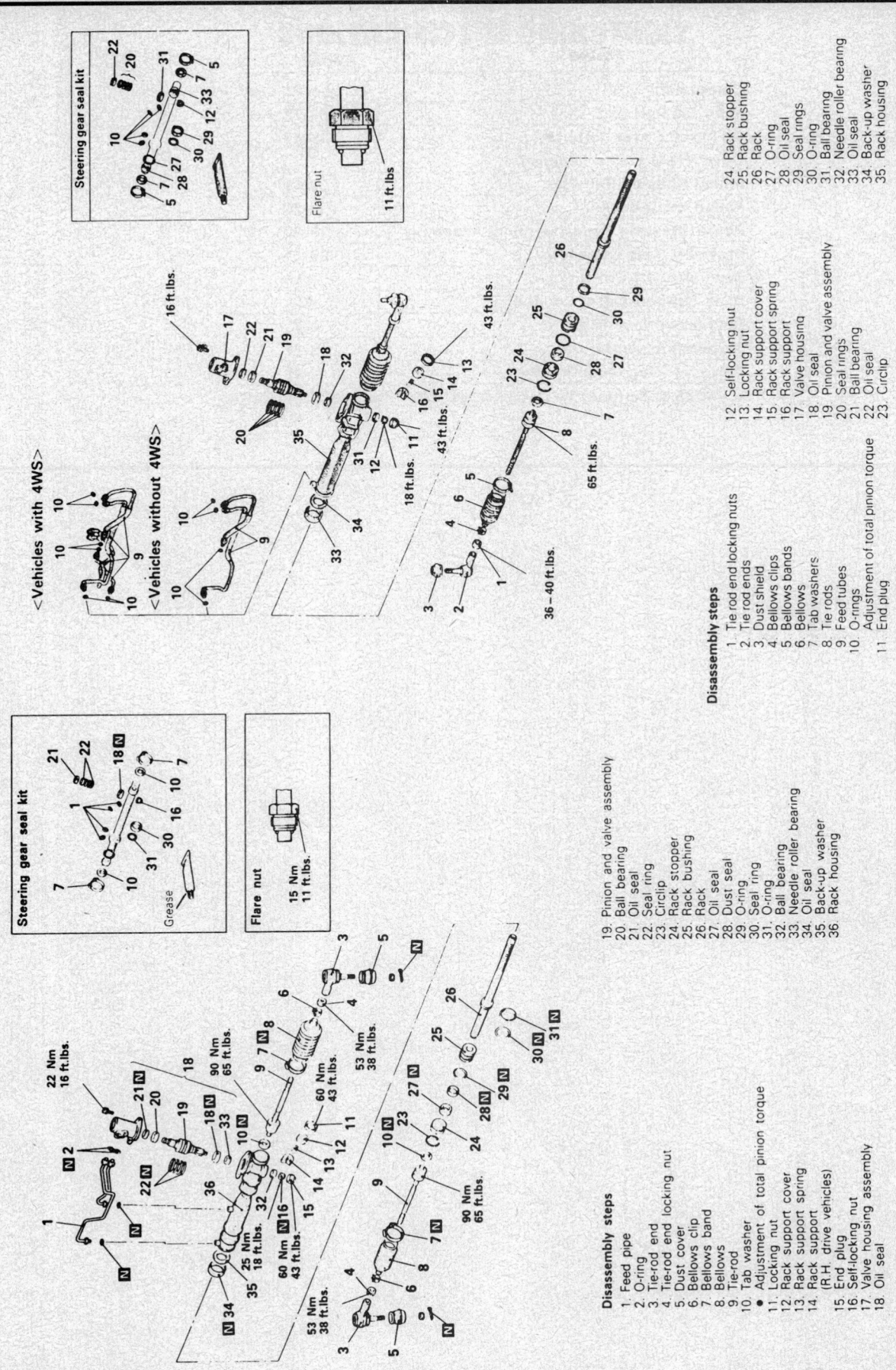

Disassembly steps

1. Feed pipe
2. O-ring
3. Tie-rod end
4. Tie-rod end locking nut
5. Dust cover
6. Bellows clip
7. Bellows band
8. Bellows
9. Tie-rod
10. Tab washer
11. Adjustment of total pinion torque
12. Locking nut
13. Rack support cover
14. Rack support
15. End plug (R.H. drive vehicles)
16. Self-locking nut
17. Valve housing assembly
18. Oil seal
19. Pinion and valve assembly
20. Ball bearing
21. Oil seal
22. Seal ring
23. Circlip
24. Rack stopper
25. Rack bushing
26. Rack
27. Oil seal
28. Dust seal
29. O-ring
30. Seal ring
31. O-ring
32. Ball bearing
33. Needle roller bearing
34. Oil seal
35. Back-up washer
36. Rack housing

Fig. 8 Exploded view of rack & pinion steering gear. Colt Vista & Summit Wagon

Disassembly steps

1. Tie rod end locking nuts
2. Tie rod ends
3. Dust shield
4. Bellows clips
5. Bellows bands
6. Bellows
7. Tab washers
8. Tie rods
9. Feed tubes
10. O-rings
11. End plug
12. Self-locking nut
13. Locking nut
14. Rack support cover
15. Rack support spring
16. Rack support
17. Valve housing
18. Oil seal
19. Pinion and valve assembly
20. Seal rings
21. Ball bearing
22. Oil seal
23. Circlip
24. Rack stopper
25. Rack bushing
26. Rack
27. O-ring
28. Oil seal
29. Seal rings
30. O-ring
31. Ball bearing
32. Needle roller bearing
33. Oil seal
34. Back-up washer
35. Rack housing

Fig. 9 Exploded view of rack & pinion steering gear. Laser, Stealth & Talon

TIGHTENING SPECIFICATIONS

Component	Torque/Ft. Lbs.
Inner Tie Rod End	58–72
Oil Pump Cover Bolts	13–16
Outer Tie Rod End Locknut	①
Pinion Housing End Plug	36–51
Pinion Shaft Locknut	14–22
Power Steering Pump Terminal Assembly	18–22
Pressure Hose Connector	36–51
Rack Support Cover	11
Rack Support Cover Locknut	43
Suction Connector Bolts	4–7
Terminal Assembly Plug	18–22
Valve Housing Mounting Bolt	12–19

①—Colt & Summit, 25–36 ft. lbs.; all other models, 36–40 ft. lbs.

DISC BRAKES

TABLE OF CONTENTS

Application Chart

Model	Year	Disc Brake Type
FRONT		
Acclaim	1992–94	6
Colt	1992–94	9
Colt Vista	1992–94	9
Concorde	1993–94	6
Daytona	1992–93	6
Dynasty	1992–93	5
Imperial	1992–93	5
Intrepid	1993–94	6
Laser	1992	9
Laser AWD	1993–94	1
Laser FWD	1993–94	9
LeBaron	1992–94	6
LeBaron Landau	1992–93	6
LHS	1994	6
Monaco	1992	5
Neon	1995	6
New Yorker	1992–93	5
	1994	6
New Yorker Fifth Avenue	1992–93	5
Premier	1992	5
Shadow	1992–94	6
Spirit	1992–94	6
Stealth AWD	1992–94	8
Stealth FWD	1992–94	1

Model	Year	Disc Brake Type
FRONT-CONTINUED		
Summit	1992–94	9
Summit Wagon	1992–94	9
Sundance	1992–94	6
Talon	1992	9
Talon AWD	1993–94	1
Talon FWD	1993–94	9
Vision	1993–94	6
REAR		
Acclaim	1992–94	7
Colt	1993–94	3
Colt Vista	1992–94	2
Concorde	1993–94	7
Daytona	1992–93	7
Dynasty	1992–93	7
Imperial	1992–93	7
Intrepid	1993–94	7
Laser	1992–94	3
LeBaron	1992–94	7
LeBaron Landau	1992–93	7
LHS	1994	7
Monaco	1992	4
Neon	1995	7
New Yorker	1992–94	7
New Yorker Fifth Avenue	1992–93	7

Continued

APPLICATION CHART-Continued

Model	Year	Disc Brake Type
REAR-Continued		
Premier	1992	4
Spirit	1992–94	7
Stealth AWD	1992-93	2
	1994	10
Stealth FWD	1992-94	2

Model	Year	Disc Brake Type
REAR-Continued		
Summit	1993	3
Summit Wagon	1992-93	2
Talon	1992-94	3
Vision	1993-94	7

Type 1–MR56W & MR57W Dual Piston Floating Caliper Disc Brake, Front

INDEX

TROUBLESHOOTING

Refer to **Fig. 1** for brake system troubleshooting.

LATERAL RUNOUT CHECK

Refer to "Disc Brake Specifications" for runout specifications.

1. Raise and support vehicle, then remove wheels.
2. If applicable, ensure wheel bearings are properly adjusted.
3. Using suitable spacers install lug nuts or bolts, then torque to specifications.
4. Mount a dial indicator to a convenient part of the vehicle (steering knuckle, tie rod, disc brake caliper housing).
5. Position dial indicator plunger so it contacts the disc at a point one inch from the outer edge.
6. Rotate the rotor and note the dial indicator readings. Perform this check on both inboard and outboard rotor faces.
7.
8. If runout exceeds specifications proceed as follows:
   a. Reposition rotor on the hub, then recheck runout.
   b. If runout still exceeds specifications, replace or machine the rotor.

PARALLELISM CHECK

Refer to "Disc Brake Specifications" for parallelism specifications.

1. Using a suitable micrometer, measure the rotor at 12 equally spaced points at a radius approximately one inch from edge of disc.
2. If measurements exceed specifica-

tions and the rotor cannot be machined, replace it.
3. If measurements exceed specifications and the rotor can be machined, resurface it.
4. Recheck parallelism. If measurements still exceed specifications, replace the rotor.

BRAKE SYSTEM BLEED

Bleeding the hydraulic brake system is necessary if air has entered the system. Symptoms can be noted by loss of brake operation, and/or a low or spongy brake pedal.

The brake system is bled or flushed from the system through bleeder valves located on the calipers, wheel cylinders, and some master cylinders. When bleeding the hydraulic brake system, use only specified brake fluid. **Never use old brake fluid removed from the system.**

PRESSURE BLEEDING

Pressure bleeding is recommended for all hydraulic brake systems. It is the fastest method because the master cylinder is automatically fed brake fluid from the pressure bleeder reservoir, and no pedal pumping is needed so only one person is required to perform the procedure. However, if pressure bleeding equipment is not available, the hydraulic system may be bled as described under "Manual Bleeding."

While pressure bleeding, to prevent air from getting into the hydraulic system, do not shake the pressure tank. Set the tank in the required location, bring the air hose

to the tank, and do not move it during the bleeding operation. The tank should be kept at least 1/3 full.

The bleeder valves should be opened at least one full turn, and intermittently closed at about four-second intervals. This gives a whirling action to fluid in the hydraulic system, and helps expel the air.

MANUAL BLEEDING

On models with power brakes, bleed the hydraulic system without the engine running. Reduce vacuum in the power unit to zero by pumping the brake pedal several times with the engine off.

1. Ensure master cylinder reservoir is full.
2. Raise and support vehicle.
3. Position a drain pan under the wheel being bled.
4. Have an assistant depress the brake pedal with a slow even strokes until pressure is felt, then hold it. **Do not depress brake pedal fully to the end of the master cylinder stroke. This may cause damage to the master cylinder.**
5. Starting at the bleeder screw farthest from the master cylinder, using a suitable wrench, open the bleeder valve one full turn allowing trapped air in the system to exit.
6. With the brake pedal still depressed, close the bleeder valve.
7. Have assistant pump the brake pedal several times, then repeat procedure until air no longer is noticed when bleeder is opened.
8. Repeat previous steps for all bleeders. Ensure all air is removed from the hy-

Symptom	Probable cause	Remedy
Vehicle pulls to one side when brakes are applied	Grease or oil on pad or lining surface	Replace
	Inadequate contact of pad or lining	Correct
	Auto adjuster malfunction	Adjust
	Drum eccentricity or uneven wear	Repair or replace as necessary
Insufficient braking power	Low or deteriorated brake fluid	Refill or change
	Air in brake system	Bleed air
	Overheated brake rotor due to dragging of pad or lining	Correct
	Grease or oil on pad, or lining surface	Replace
	Inadequate contact of pad or lining	Correct
	Brake booster malfunction	Correct
	Auto adjuster malfunction	Adjust
	Clogged brake line	Correct
	Proportioning valve malfunction	Replace
Increased pedal stroke (Reduced pedal to floorboard clearance)	Air in brake system	Bleed air
	Worn lining or pad	Replace
	Broken vacuum hose	Replace
	Brake fluid leaks	Correct
	Auto adjuster malfunction	Adjust
	Excessive push rod to master cylinder clearance	Adjust
	Faulty master cylinder	Replace
Brake drag	Incomplete release of parking brake	Correct
	Incorrect parking brake adjustment	Adjust
	Worn brake pedal return spring	Replace
	Broken rear drum brake shoe return spring	Replace
	Lack of lubrication in sliding parts	Lubricate
	Improper push rod to master cylinder clearance	Adjust
	Faulty master cylinder piston return spring	Replace
	Clogged master cylinder return port	Correct

CR4079100038010X

Fig. 1   Brake system troubleshooting (Part 1 of 3)

draulic system. **While bleeding the brake system, check brake fluid supply in the master cylinder ensuring master cylinder does not run out of fluid.**

9. Upon completion of hydraulic system bleeding proceed as follows:
   a. Lower vehicle. Ensure master cylinder reservoir is full.
   b. Ensure brake pedal is firm and braking operation is normal.

BRAKE PAD SERVICE

1. Remove approximately 1/3 of brake fluid from master cylinder.
2. Raise and support vehicle, then remove tire and wheel assembly.
3. Remove guide pin, **Fig. 2**, then lift caliper body upward and secure with wire.
4. Remove outer shims, brake pad assemblies and pad clips from support mounting.
5. Press caliper piston into caliper bore with suitable tool.
6. Install upper and lower pad clips, pad assemblies and outer shims into support mounting.
7. Lower caliper body, then install guide pin.
8. Depress brake pedal several times to seat pads, then check and replenish brake fluid as necessary.
9. Install wheel and tire assembly and lower vehicle.

CALIPER SERVICE
CALIPER, REPLACE

1. Raise and support vehicle, then remove wheel and tire assembly.
2. Disconnect brake hose at caliper strut and brake caliper, then cap brake line.
3. Remove brake pads as outlined under "Brake Pad Service".
4. Remove caliper support to steering knuckle attaching bolts, then caliper support.
5. Reverse procedure to install, noting the following:
   a. Tighten bolts to specifications.
   b. Bleed brakes as outlined under "Brake System Bleed".

CALIPER OVERHAUL

1. Remove caliper assembly as described under "Caliper, Replace."
2. Remove lockpin, bushing, caliper support, pin boot and boot ring, **Fig. 2**.
3. Using compressed air, remove two piston boots and pistons. **To prevent damage to pistons, place a suitable block of wood in caliper when removing pistons.**

4. Using finger tip, remove piston seal.
5. Reverse procedure to assemble, noting the following:
   a. Inspect cylinders and pistons for wear, damage and/or corrosion.
   b. Inspect caliper body and sleeve for wear.
   c. Apply suitable brake fluid to cylinders, then install piston seals into cylinder groove. **Do not wipe grease from piston seal.**
   d. Apply brake fluid to pistons and insert into cylinders by pushing downward into caliper. **Ensure not to twist pistons into caliper.**
   e. Fill piston edges with grease supplied with seal and boot repair kit, then install piston boots.
   f. Lubricate sliding surface of guide, lockpins and boots with grease supplied with seal and boot repair kit.
   g. Install guide and lockpins. Ensure head marks match with identification marks on caliper body.

ROTOR
REPLACE

Remove caliper as outlined under "Caliper Service," then remove rotor. If necessary use a suitable soft face hammer to tap rotor free of hub.

TYPE 1-MR56W & MR57W DUAL PISTON FLOATING CALIPER DISC BRAKE, FRONT

Symptom	Probable cause	Remedy
Insufficient parking brake function	Worn brake lining or pads	Replace
	Excessive parking brake lever stroke	Adjust the parking brake lever stroke or check the parking brake cable routing
	Grease or oil on lining or pad surface	Replace
	Auto adjuster malfunction	Adjust
	Parking brake cable sticking	Replace
	Stuck wheel cylinder or caliper piston	Replace
Scraping or grinding noise when brakes are applied	Worn brake linings or pads	Replace
	Caliper to wheel interference	Correct or replace
	Dust cover to disc interference	Correct or replace
	Bent brake backing plate	Correct or replace
	Cracked drums or brake disc	Correct or replace
Squealing, groaning or chattering noise when brakes are applied	Disc brakes – missing or damaged brake pad shim	Replace
	Brake drums and linings, discs and pads worn or scored	Correct or replace
	Improper lining parts	Correct or replace
	Disc brakes – burred or rusted calipers	Clean or deburr
	Dirty, greased, contaminated or glazed linings	Clean or replace
	Drum brakes – weak, damaged or incorrect shoe hold-down springs, loose or damaged shoe hold-down pins and springs	Correct or replace
	Incorrect brake pedal or booster push rod	Adjust
Squealing noise when brakes are not applied	Bent or warped backing plate causing interference with drum	Replace
	Improper machining of drum causing interference with backing plate or shoe	Replace drum
	Disc brakes – rusted, stuck	Lubricate or replace
	Worn, damaged or insufficiently lubricated wheel bearings	Lubricate or replace
	Drum brakes – weak, damaged or incorrect shoe-to-shoe spring	Replace
	Loose or extra parts in brakes	Retighten

CR4079100038020X

Fig. 1   Brake system troubleshooting (Part 2 of 3)

Symptom	Probable cause	Remedy
Squealing noise when brakes are not applied	Improper positioning of pads in caliper	Correct
	Improper installation of support mounting to caliper body	Correct
	Poor return of brake booster or master cylinder or wheel cylinder	Replace
	Incorrect brake pedal or booster push-rod	Adjust
Groaning, clicking or rattling noise when brakes are not applied	Stones or foreign material trapped inside wheel covers	Remove stones, etc.
	Loose wheel nuts	Retighten
	Disc brakes – failure of shim	Replace
	Disc brakes – loose installation bolt	Retighten
	Worn, damaged or dry wheel bearings	Lubricate or replace
	Disc brakes – wear on sleeve	Replace
	Incorrect brake pedal or booster push-rod	Adjust

CR4079100038030X

Fig. 1   Brake system troubleshooting (Part 3 of 3)

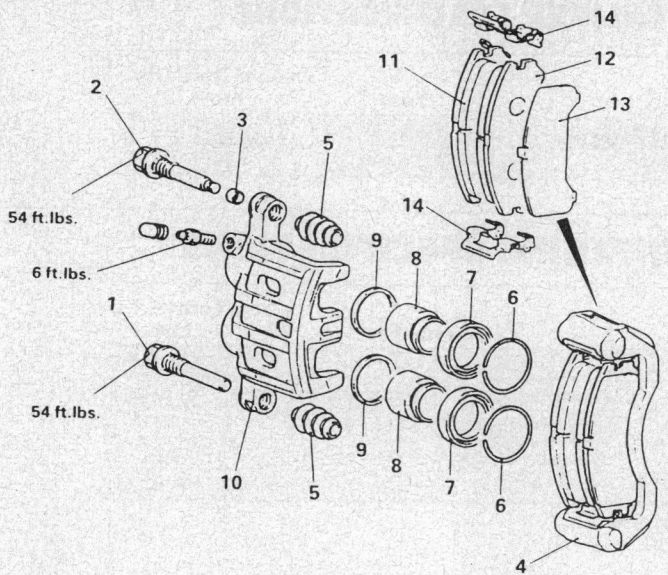

1. Guide pin
2. Lock pin
3. Bushing
4. Caliper support (pad, clip, shim)
5. Pin boot
6. Boot ring
7. Piston boot
8. Piston
9. Piston seal
10. Caliper body
11. Pad & wear indicator
12. Pad assembly
13. Outer shim
14. Clip

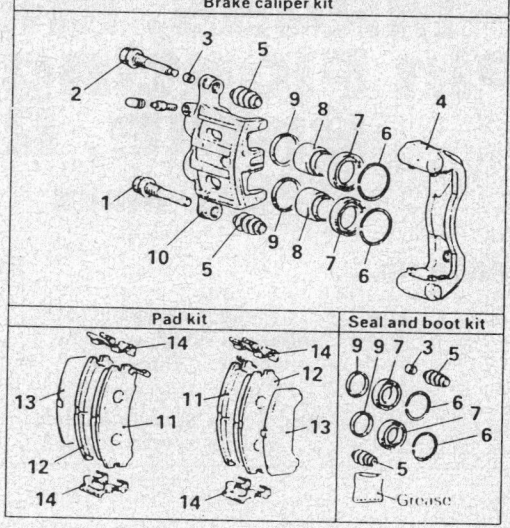

CR4079100043000X

**Fig. 2   MR56w & MR57W dual piston floating caliper disc brake assembly.
1992-93 Stealth FWD & 1993-94 Laser/Talon AWD**

DISC BRAKE SPECIFICATIONS
ROTOR SPECIFICATIONS

Year	Model	Nominal Thickness, Inch	Minimum Allowable Thickness, Inch	Thickness Variation Parallelism, Inch	Lateral Runout (T.I.R.)	Finish (Micro-Inch)
1992-94	**Stealth FWD**	.9400	.8800	.0006	.0040	—
1993-94	**Laser/Talon AWD**	.9400	.8800	.0006	.0028	—

TYPE 1-MR56W & MR57W DUAL PISTON FLOATING CALIPER DISC BRAKE, FRONT

CALIPER SPECIFICATIONS

Model	Year	Caliper Bore Dia. Inch
Laser/Talon AWD	1993–94	1.6250
Stealth FWD	1992–94	1.6875

TIGHTENING SPECIFICATIONS

Year	Component	Torque/Ft. Lbs.
1992-94	Bleed Screws	5–7
	Caliper Support To Front Axle①	58–72
	Caliper Support To Front Axle②	65
	Caliper Guide And Lockpins	54
	Wheel Lug Nuts	87–101

①—Except Stealth.
②—Stealth.

Type 2–MR45S, MR45V & MR58V Dual Pin Floating Caliper Disc Brake, Rear

INDEX

TROUBLESHOOTING

Refer to "Type 1-MR56W & MR57W Dual Piston Floating Caliper Disc Brake, Front" for system troubleshooting.

LATERAL RUNOUT CHECK

Refer to "Disc Brake Specifications" for runout specifications.

1. Raise and support vehicle, then remove wheels.
2. If applicable, ensure wheel bearings are properly adjusted.
3. Install lug nuts to ensure rotor does not move.
4. Mount a dial indicator to a convenient part of the vehicle (steering knuckle, tie rod, disc brake caliper housing).
5. Position dial indicator plunger so it contacts the disc at a point one inch from the outer edge.
6. Rotate the rotor and note the dial indicator readings. Perform this check on both inboard and outboard rotor faces.

BRAKE SYSTEM BLEED

Bleeding the hydraulic brake system is necessary if air has entered the system. Symptoms can be noted by loss of brake operation, and/or a low or spongy brake pedal.

The brake system is bled or flushed from the system through bleeder valves located on the calipers, wheel cylinders, and some master cylinders. When bleeding the hydraulic brake system, use only specified brake fluid. **Never reuse brake fluid that was removed from the system.**

PRESSURE BLEEDING

Pressure bleeding is recommended for all hydraulic brake systems. It is the fastest method because the master cylinder is automatically fed brake fluid from the pressure bleeder reservoir, and no pedal pumping is needed so only one person is required to perform the procedure. However, if pressure bleeding equipment is not available, the hydraulic system may be bled as described under "Manual Bleeding."

While pressure bleeding, to prevent air from getting into the hydraulic system, do not shake the pressure tank. Set the tank in the required location, bring the air hose to the tank, and do not move it during the bleeding operation. The tank should be kept at least one-third full.

The bleeder valves should be opened at least one full turn, and intermittently closed at about four-second intervals. This gives a whirling action to fluid in the hydraulic system, and helps expel the air.

MANUAL BLEEDING

On models with power brakes, bleed the hydraulic system without the engine running. Reduce vacuum in the power unit to zero by pumping the brake pedal several times with the engine off.

1. Ensure master cylinder reservoir is full.
2. Raise and support vehicle.

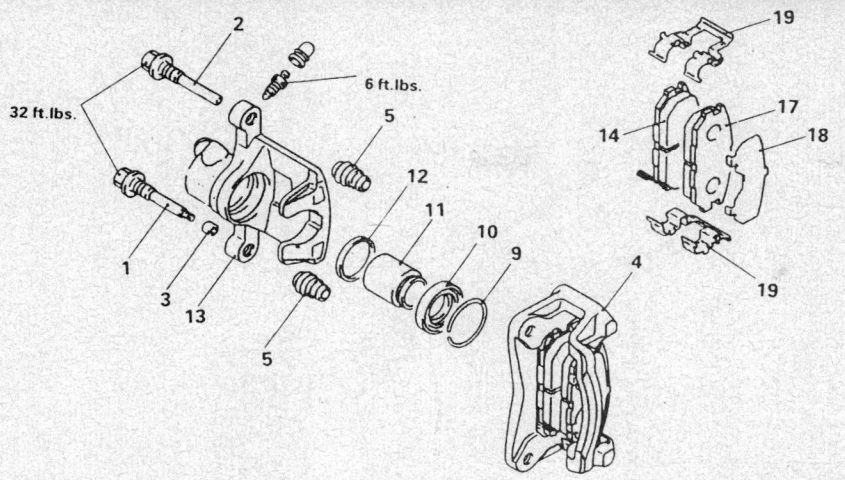

1. Lock pin
2. Guide pin
3. Bushing
4. Caliper support (pad, clip, shim)
5. Pin boot
9. Boot ring
10. Piston boot
11. Piston
12. Piston seal
13. Caliper body
14. Pad and wear indicator assembly
17. Pad assembly
18. Outer shim
19. Clip

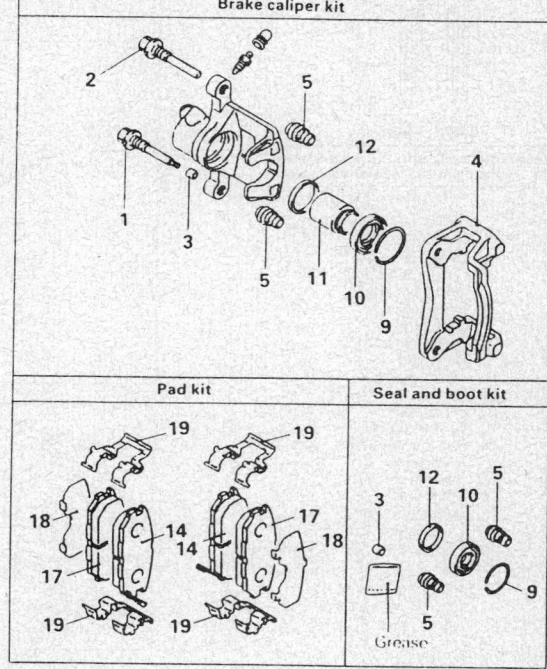

Brake caliper kit

Pad kit

Seal and boot kit

Grease

CR4079100045000X

**Fig. 1   MR45S & MR45V dual pin floating caliper disc brake assembly.
Stealth FWD & Colt Vista/Summit Wagon w/ABS**

4. Remove inner and outer shims, brake pad assemblies and pad clips from support mounting.
5. Press caliper piston into caliper bore with suitable tool.
6. Install upper and lower pad clips, pad assemblies and inner and outer shims into support mounting.
7. Lower caliper body, then install lockpin.
8. Depress brake pedal several times to seat pads, then check and replenish brake fluid as necessary.
9. Install wheel and tire assembly and lower vehicle.
10. Adjust parking brake as outlined under "Adjustments."

CALIPER SERVICE

CALIPER, REPLACE

1. Raise and support vehicle, then remove wheel assembly.
2. Disconnect brake hose.
3. Remove brake assembly attaching bolts, then brake assembly.
4. Remove brake pads and shims, then separate caliper body from caliper support, **Figs. 1 and 2.**
5. Reverse procedure to install.

CALIPER OVERHAUL

1. Remove caliper assembly as described under "Caliper Replace."
2. **On Stealth FWD, Colt Vista & Summit Wagon models,** remove guide pin and bushing, **Fig. 1.**
3. **On all models,** remove caliper support, **Fig. 1 and 2.**
4. **On 1992-93 Stealth AWD models,** remove sleeve, **Fig. 2.**
5. **On all models,** remove pin boots and boot ring.
6. Position a suitable wood block in caliper body, then apply compressed air through the brake hose fitting hole to remove piston and dust boot.
7. Using finger tip, remove piston seal.
8. Reverse procedure to assemble, noting the following:
   a. Inspect cylinder and piston for wear, damage and/or corrosion. Inspect caliper body and sleeve for wear.
   b. Apply brake fluid to inner cylinder, then install piston seal into cylinder groove. **Do not wipe grease from piston seal.**
   c. Apply brake fluid to pistons and insert into cylinders by pushing downward into caliper. **Ensure not to twist pistons into caliper.**
   d. Fill piston edge with grease from seal and boot repair kit, then install piston boot.
   e. Lubricate bushing, pin boot and slide pins with grease from seal and boot repair kit.
   f. Install guide and lockpins. Ensure head marks match with identification marks on caliper body.

3. Position a drain pan under the wheel being bled.
4. Have an assistant depress the brake pedal with a slow even strokes until pressure is felt, then hold it. **Do not depress brake pedal fully to the end of the master cylinder stroke. This may cause damage to the master cylinder.**
5. Starting at the bleeder screw farthest from the master cylinder, using a suitable wrench, open the bleeder valve one full turn allowing trapped air in the system to exit.
6. With the brake pedal still depressed, close the bleeder valve.
7. Have assistant pump brake pedal several times, then repeat procedure until air no longer is noticed when bleeder is opened.
8. Repeat previous steps for all bleeders.

Ensure all air is removed from the hydraulic system. **While bleeding the brake system, check brake fluid supply in the master cylinder ensuring master cylinder does not run out of fluid.**
9. Upon completion of hydraulic system bleeding proceed as follows:
   a. Lower the vehicle. Ensure master cylinder reservoir is full.
   b. Ensure brake pedal is firm and braking operation is normal.

BRAKE PAD SERVICE

1. Remove approximately 1/3 of brake fluid from master cylinder.
2. Raise and support vehicle, then remove tire and wheel assembly.
3. Remove lockpin, **Figs. 1 and 2,** then lift caliper body upward and secure with wire.

ADJUSTMENTS

PARKING BRAKE LEVER

1. Pull parking brake lever while counting number of clicks.
2. Lever should click 3-5 times on Stealth FWD, or 4-6 on Colt Vista and Summit Wagon.
3. If not within specifications, remove cup holder and plug, then turn adjusting nut located behind parking brake lever as necessary to bring parking brake within specifications.

PARKING BRAKE SHOE

1. Raise and support vehicle, then remove rear wheels.
2. **On All Wheel Drive Models** disconnect drive axles from companion flange.
3. **On all models** firmly apply, then fully release parking brake lever several times to seat and center parking brake shoes.
4. Remove adjusting hole plug from hub of brake disc.
5. Using a suitable tool, turn adjusting nut until brake disc cannot be turned by hand.
6. Back off adjusting nut five notches.
7. Repeat above steps on opposite side.
8. **On All Wheel Drive Models** connect drive axles to companion flange.
9. **On all models** firmly apply, then fully release parking brake lever several times to seat and center parking brake shoes.
10. Adjust parking brake lever as outlined under "Parking Brake Lever, Adjust"
11. Install rear wheels, then lower vehicle.

ROTOR
REPLACE

1. Remove caliper as outlined under "Caliper Service,".
2. Remove parking brake adjustment hole plug from hub of brake disc.
3. Using a suitable tool, turn parking brake adjusting nut until brake disc can be removed.
4. Reverse procedure to install, adjust parking brake as outlined under "Adjustments"

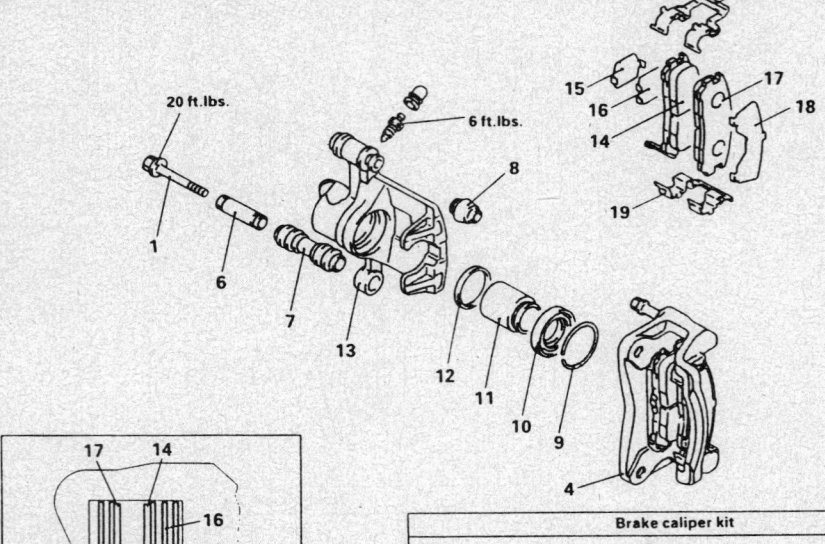

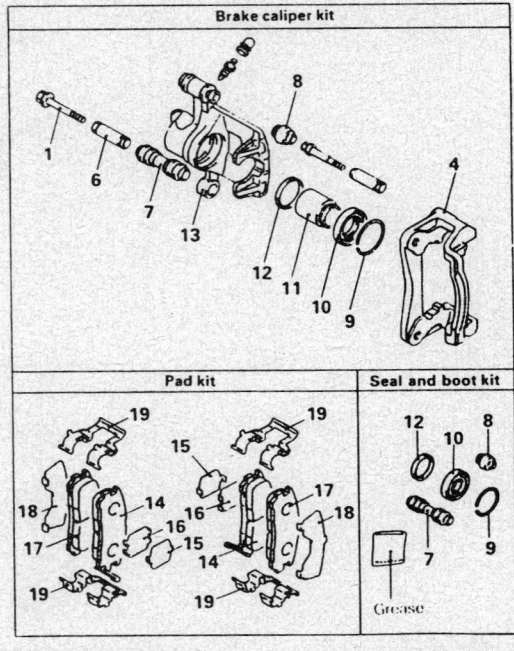

Grease: MOPAR Multi-Purpose Grease Part No. 2932524 or equivalent

1. Lock pin
4. Caliper support (pad, clip, shim)
6. Sleeve
7. Lock pin boot
8. Guide pin boot
9. Boot ring
10. Piston boot
11. Piston
12. Piston seal
13. Caliper body
14. Pad and wear indicator assembly
15. Inner shim
16. Inner shim
17. Pad assembly
18. Outer shim
19. Clip

Brake caliper kit

Pad kit

Seal and boot kit

CR4079100046000X

Fig. 2   MR58V dual pin floating caliper disc brake assembly. 1992–93 Stealth AWD

DISC BRAKE SPECIFICATIONS
ROTOR SPECIFICATIONS

Year	Model	Nominal Thickness (Inches)	Minimum Allowable Thickness (Inches)	Thickness Variation Parallelism (Inches)	Lateral Runout (T.I.R.)	Finish (Micro-Inch)
1992-94	Colt Vista/Summit Wagon	.390	.330	—	.0031	—
1992-93	Stealth AWD	.790	.720	—	.0031	—
1992-94	Stealth FWD	.710	.650	—	.0031	—

CALIPER SPECIFICATIONS

Model	Year	Caliper Bore Dia. Inch
Colt Vista/Summit Wagon	1992–94	1.375
Stealth AWD	1992–93	1.500
Stealth FWD	1992–94	1.375

TIGHTENING SPECIFICATIONS

Year	Component	Torque/Ft. Lbs.
1992–94	Backing Plate Bolts	36–43
	Brake Hose To Rear Caliper Banjo Bolt	18–25
	Bleed Screws	5–7
	Caliper Support To Rear Axle	36–43
	Caliper Guide And Lockpins, Rear	①
	Wheel Lug Nuts	87–101

①—MR45V & MR45S, 20 ft. lbs.; MR58V, 32 ft. lbs.

Type 3–AD30P & AD35P Dual Pin Floating Caliper Disc Brake, Rear

INDEX

TROUBLESHOOTING

Refer to "Type 1–MR56W & MR57W Dual Piston Floating Caliper Disc Brake, Front" for system troubleshooting.

LATERAL RUNOUT CHECK

Refer to "Disc Brake Specifications" for runout specifications.

1. Raise and support vehicle, then remove wheels.
2. If applicable, ensure wheel bearings are properly adjusted.
3. Using suitable spacers install lug nuts or bolts, then torque to specifications.
4. Mount a dial indicator to a convenient part of the vehicle (steering knuckle, tie rod, disc brake caliper housing).
5. Position dial indicator plunger so it contacts the disc at a point one inch from the outer edge.
6. Rotate the rotor and note the dial indicator readings. Perform this check on both inboard and outboard rotor faces.

7. If runout exceeds specifications proceed as follows:
   a. Reposition rotor on the hub, then recheck runout.
   b. If runout still exceeds specifications, replace or machine the rotor.

BRAKE SYSTEM BLEED

Bleeding the hydraulic brake system is necessary if air has entered the system. Symptoms can be noted by loss of brake operation, and/or a low or spongy brake pedal.

The hydraulic fluid is bled or flushed from the system through bleeder valves located on the calipers, wheel cylinders, and some master cylinders. When bleeding the hydraulic brake system, use only specified brake fluid. **Never reuse old brake fluid removed from the system.**

PRESSURE BLEEDING

Pressure bleeding is recommended for all hydraulic brake systems. It is the fastest method because the master cylinder is automatically fed brake fluid from the pressure bleeder reservoir, and no pedal pumping is needed so only one person is required to perform the procedure. However, if pressure bleeding equipment is not available, the hydraulic system may be bled as described under "Manual Bleeding."

While pressure bleeding, to prevent air from getting into the hydraulic system, do not shake the pressure tank. Set the tank in the required location, bring the air hose to the tank, and do not move it during the bleeding operation. The tank should be kept at least one-third full.

The bleeder valves should be opened at least one full turn, and intermittently closed at about four-second intervals. This gives a whirling action to fluid in the hydraulic system, and helps expel the air.

MANUAL BLEEDING

On models with power brakes, bleed the hydraulic system without the engine run-

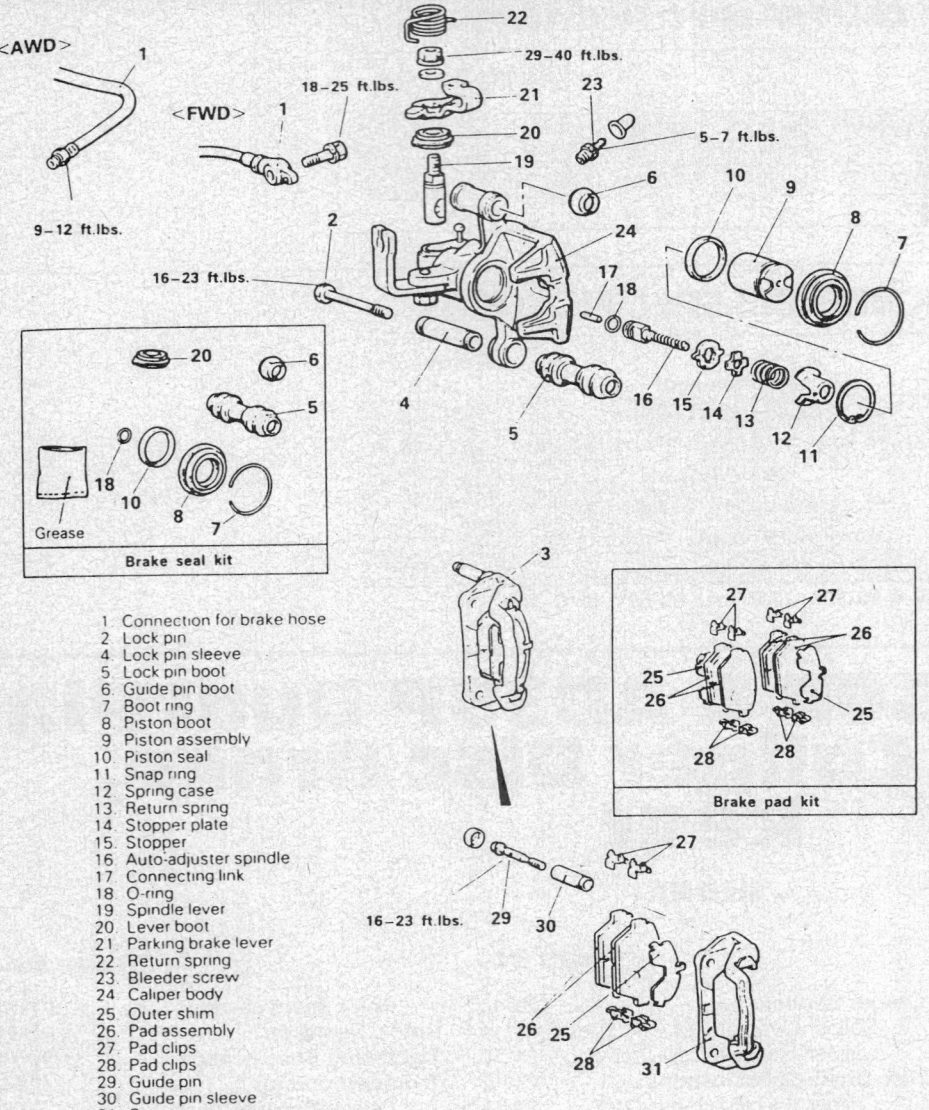

1. Connection for brake hose
2. Lock pin
4. Lock pin sleeve
5. Lock pin boot
6. Guide pin boot
7. Boot ring
8. Piston boot
9. Piston assembly
10. Piston seal
11. Snap ring
12. Spring case
13. Return spring
14. Stopper plate
15. Stopper
16. Auto-adjuster spindle
17. Connecting link
18. O-ring
19. Spindle lever
20. Lever boot
21. Parking brake lever
22. Return spring
23. Bleeder screw
24. Caliper body
25. Outer shim
26. Pad assembly
27. Pad clips
28. Pad clips
29. Guide pin
30. Guide pin sleeve
31. Support mounting

Fig. 1 AD30P & AD35P dual pin floating caliper disc brake assembly. Laser/Talon & Colt/Summit w/ABS

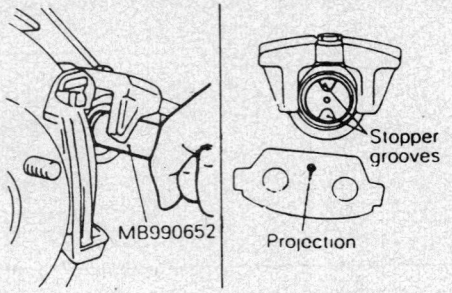

Fig. 2 Aligning caliper piston stopper grooves

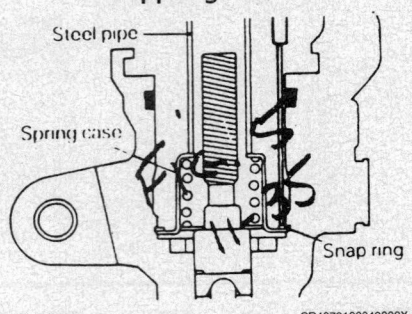

Fig. 3 Compressing spring case

is proper.

BRAKE PAD SERVICE

1. Remove approximately 1/3 of brake fluid from master cylinder.
2. Raise and support vehicle, then remove wheel assembly.
3. Loosen parking brake cable at lever underneath console, then disconnect cable from caliper.
4. Remove lower caliper lockpin, then pivot caliper up and support with wire to prevent damage to brake hose.
5. Remove brake pads, shims and pad clips, **Fig. 1.**
6. Using piston driver, tool No. MB990652 or equivalent, thread caliper piston into bore and ensure that piston stopper grooves are aligned as shown in **Fig. 2**, so that they will interlock with projections on pad assembly.
7. Install brake pads, shims and pad clips, then lower caliper and install lockpin.
8. Depress brake pedal several times to seat pads, then check and replenish brake fluid as necessary.
9. Connect parking brake cable, then install wheel and tire assembly and lower vehicle.
10. Adjust parking brake cable as described under "Adjustments."

CALIPER SERVICE

CALIPER, REPLACE

1. Raise and support vehicle, then remove wheel assembly.
2. Disconnect brake hose, then parking brake cable from brake assembly.
3. Remove brake assembly attaching bolts, then brake assembly.

ning, first reduce vacuum in the power unit to zero by pumping the brake pedal several times with the engine off.

1. Ensure master cylinder reservoir is full.
2. Raise and support vehicle.
3. Position a drain pan under the wheel being bled.
4. Have an assistant depress the brake pedal with a slow even strokes until pressure is felt, then hold it. **Do not depress brake pedal fully to the end of the master cylinder stroke. This may cause damage to the master cylinder.**
5. Starting at the bleeder screw farthest from the master cylinder, using a suitable wrench, open the bleeder valve one full turn. Watch for air bubbles in the fluid, and listen for air escaping from the system.
6. With the brake pedal still depressed, close the bleeder valve.

7. Have the assistant pump the brake pedal several times, then repeat procedure until air no longer is noticed when bleeder is opened. **Do not depress brake pedal fully to the end of the master cylinder stroke, this may cause damage to the master cylinder.**
8. Repeat previous steps for all bleeders. Ensure all air is removed from the hydraulic system. **While bleeding the system, recheck brake fluid supply in the master cylinder often so as not to allow the master cylinder to run dry.**
9. Upon completion of hydraulic system bleeding proceed as follows:
   a. Ensure the master cylinder reservoir is full. Add suitable brake fluid as needed, and securely reinstall the master cylinder cap.
   b. Lower the vehicle. Ensure brake pedal is firm and braking operation

4. Remove brake pads and shims, then separate caliper body from caliper support, **Fig. 1**.
5. Reverse procedure to install.

CALIPER OVERHAUL

1. Remove caliper assembly as described under "Caliper Replace."
2. Remove lockpin sleeve, lockpin boot, guide pin boot, boot ring and piston boot, **Fig. 1**.
3. Remove piston assembly using piston driver tool No. MB990652 or equivalent to twist piston out of caliper body.
4. Remove piston seal using finger tips. **Do not use flat blade screwdriver or other tool to prevent damage to inner cylinder.**
5. Compress spring case into caliper body using a ³⁄₄ inch steel pipe as shown in **Fig. 3**, then remove snap ring using suitable snap ring pliers.
6. Remove spring case, return spring, stopper plate and stopper.
7. Remove auto-adjuster spindle, connecting link, O-ring, spindle lever and lever boot.
8. Remove parking brake lever, return spring and bleeder screw.
9. Inspect the following:
   a. Connecting link and spindle for wear or damage.
   b. Caliper body for rust or cracks.
   c. Spindle lever shaft and piston for rust.
   d. Bearing for wear, piston seal and boot for wear, cracks or deterioration.
10. Reverse procedure to assemble, noting the following:
   a. Apply grease supplied in brake seal kit to lever boot, spindle lever, O-ring, connecting link and auto-adjuster spindle.
   b. Compress spring case into caliper body using a ³⁄₄ inch steel pipe as shown in **Fig. 3**, then install snap ring using suitable snap ring pliers. **Install snap ring to caliper body with opening facing bleeder.**
   c. Apply grease supplied in brake seal kit to cylinder walls, piston seal and piston, then install piston seal into cylinder.
   d. Using piston driver MB990652 or equivalent, press piston into caliper body with stopper grooves aligned, **Fig. 2**.
   e. Apply grease supplied in brake seal kit to piston boot mounting grooves in caliper body and piston, then install piston boot.
   f. Apply grease supplied in brake seal kit to guide pin boot inner surface, lockpin boot inner surface and lockpin sleeve.
   g. Adjust parking brake cable.

ADJUSTMENTS
PARKING BRAKE

1. Pull parking brake lever with a force of approximately 45 lbs. while counting number of clicks.
2. Lever should click 5-7 times.
3. If not within specifications, remove console and release parking brake lever, then turn adjusting nut located behind parking brake lever as necessary to bring parking brake within specifications.

ROTOR
REPLACE

1. Remove caliper as outlined under "Caliper Service,".
2. If necessary use a suitable soft face hammer to tap rotor free of hub.
3. Reverse procedure to install.

DISC BRAKE SPECIFICATIONS
ROTOR SPECIFICATIONS

Year	Model	Nominal Thickness (Inches)	Minimum Allowable Thickness (Inches)	Thickness Variation Parallelism (Inches)	Lateral Runout (T.I.R.)	Finish (Micro-Inch)
1993-94	Colt/Summit	.390	.330	—	.0031	—
1992-94	Laser/Talon	.390	.331	—	.0031	—

CALIPER SPECIFICATIONS

Model	Year	Caliper Bore Dia. Inch
Colt/Summit	1993-94	1.1875
Laser/Talon AWD	1992-94	1.3750
Laser/Talon FWD	1992-94	1.1875

TIGHTENING SPECIFICATIONS

Year	Component	Torque/Ft. Lbs.
1992-94	Backing Plate Bolts	36-43
	Brake Hose To Rear Caliper Banjo Bolt	18-25
	Bleed Screws	5-7
	Caliper Support To Rear Axle	36-43
	Caliper Guide And Lockpins, Rear	16-23
	Wheel Lug Nuts	①

①—Colt/Summit: 65-80 ft. lbs.; Laser/Talon: 87-101 ft. lbs.

TYPE 3-AD30P & AD35P DUAL PIN FLOATING CALIPER DISC BRAKE, REAR

Type 4—Dual Pin Sliding Caliper Disc Brake, Rear

INDEX

TROUBLESHOOTING

Refer to **Fig. 1** for system troubleshooting procedures.

LATERAL RUNOUT CHECK

Refer to "Disc Brake Specifications" for runout specifications.

1. Raise and support vehicle, then remove wheels.
2. If applicable, ensure wheel bearings are properly adjusted.
3. Using suitable spacers install lug nuts or bolts, then torque to specifications.
4. Mount a dial indicator to a convenient part of the vehicle (steering knuckle, tie rod, disc brake caliper housing).
5. Position dial indicator plunger so it contacts the disc at a point one inch from the outer edge.
6. Rotate the rotor and note the dial indicator readings. Perform this check on both inboard and outboard rotor faces.
7. If runout exceeds specifications, proceed as follows:
   a. Reposition rotor on the hub, then recheck runout.
   b. If runout still exceeds specifications, replace or machine the rotor.

PARALLELISM CHECK

Refer to "Disc Brake Specifications" for parallelism specifications.

1. Using a suitable micrometer, measure the rotor at 12 equally spaced points at a radius approximately one inch from edge of disc.
2. If measurements exceed specifications and the rotor cannot be machined, replace it.
3. If measurements exceed specifications and the rotor can be machined, resurface it.
4. Recheck parallelism. If measurements still exceed specifications, replace the rotor.

BRAKE SYSTEM BLEED

Bleeding the hydraulic brake system is necessary if air has entered the system. Symptoms can be noted by loss of brake operation, and/or a low or spongy brake pedal.

The hydraulic fluid is bled or flushed from the system through bleeder valves

INCIDENTS	POSSIBLE CAUSES
Brakes binding or grabbing	· Linings not chamfered
	· Oil or grease on linings
	· Caliper seized
	· Weak return springs
Brakes pulsating	· Oval drums
	· Excessive disc run-out
	· Discs not of even thickness
	· Abnormal deposit on discs (corrosion between lining and disc).
	· Linings cracked or broken
Front brakes pulling to one side	· Check front end alignment
	· Check front axle, suspension and steering
	· Piston seized*
	· Tires (worn - incorrect inflation pressure)
	· Pinched brake-line.
	*ATTENTION: Pulling to one side indicates a seized piston on the opposite side.
Rear brakes pulling to one side	· Incorrect compensator or limiter setting
	· Piston seized
	· Incorrect shoe adjustment manual adjustment: shoe too far from drum
	automatic adjustment: handbrake cable too tight.
	NOTE: Automatic wear take-up is performed by the brake pedal provided the handbrake cable is not abnormally tight when in off position
	· Return spring
Overheating brakes	· Master cylinder operating clearance insufficient to allow master cylinder to return to neutral position.
	· Master cylinder operating clearance insufficient to allow master cylinder to return to neutral position.
	· Piston seized or not returning properly.
	· Pinched brake line
	· Handbrake mechanism seized
	· Incorrect handbrake adjustment

CR4079100039010X

Fig. 1   Brake system troubleshooting (Part 1 of 2). Premier & Monaco

INCIDENT	POSSIBLE CAUSES

"Hard pedal":
 	
Great effort Needed and only a slight deceleration noticed in vehicle.
	- Power servo defective
	
	- Linings/pads
	
	  - oily
	  - glazed, not to specification
	  - overheating (due to excessive braking) or not to specification
	  - seized piston
	  - pinched brake line
	  - pads/linings worn:

"Soft pedal"
 	
Note: since the power servo system on current vehicles is very effective, the impression may be given that the pedal is "soft". To find out whether an incident has occurred or the braking system is operating normally, two tests must be performed.
 	
1. Vehicle moving
  - Assessment test: relation between pedal travel and vehicle deceleration.
 	
2. Vehicle stationary with ignition off
  - Additional test on pedal travel: depress the brake pedal 5 times to empty the brake servo, before assessing the result of the test.
	- Air in system: poor bleeding
	
	- Internal leakage in braking system
	
	- Lack of fluid in reservoir (external leak in braking system).

"Long" pedal travel Test to be performed with vehicle stationary and ignition off. Note: The brake pedal must be depressed 5 times in order to empty the brake servo before taking account of the test results.	- Incorrect shoe adjustment Drum brakes - Manual adjustments: shoes too far from drum surface. Disc and drum brakes - Automatic adjustment: handbrake cable too tight. Note: Automatic wear take-up is performed by by the brake pedal, provided the handbrake is not abnormally tight in the off position. - Excessively worn pads/linings of pads/linings not symmetrical (or crossed) - Excessive master cylinder operating clearance. - Brake fluid boiling or has heated up.
Pedal "travels to floor" Test to be performed on stationary vehicle with ignition off. Note: The brake pedal must be depressed 5 times in order to empty the brake servo before taking account of the test results.	- Fluid loss (check for leaks) - Faulty sealing cup between the two master cylinder circuits. - Brake fluid boiling.

CR4079100039020X

Fig. 1   Brake system troubleshooting (Part 2 of 2). Premier & Monaco

located on the calipers, wheel cylinders, and some master cylinders. When bleeding the hydraulic brake system, use only specified brake fluid. **Never reuse old brake fluid removed from the system.**

PRESSURE BLEEDING

Pressure bleeding is recommended for all hydraulic brake systems. It is the fastest method because the master cylinder is automatically fed brake fluid from the pressure bleeder reservoir, and no pedal pumping is needed so only one person is required to perform the procedure. However, if pressure bleeding equipment is not available, the hydraulic system may be bled as described under "Manual Bleeding."

While pressure bleeding, to prevent air from getting into the hydraulic system, do not shake the pressure tank. Set the tank in the required location, bring the air hose to the tank, and do not move it during the bleeding operation. The tank should be kept at least one-third full.

The bleeder valves should be opened at least one full turn, and intermittently closed at about four-second intervals. This gives a whirling action to fluid in the hydraulic system, and helps expel the air.

MANUAL BLEEDING

On models with power brakes, bleed the hydraulic system without the engine running, first reduce vacuum in the power unit to zero by pumping the brake pedal several times with the engine off.

1. Ensure master cylinder reservoir is full.
2. Raise and support vehicle.
3. Position a drain pan under the wheel being bled.
4. Have an assistant depress the brake pedal with a slow even strokes until pressure is felt, then hold it. **Do not depress brake pedal fully to the end of the master cylinder stroke. This may cause damage to the master cylinder.**
5. Starting at the bleeder screw farthest from the master cylinder, using a suitable wrench, open the bleeder valve one full turn. Watch for air bubbles in the fluid, and listen for air escaping from the system.
6. With the brake pedal still depressed, close the bleeder valve.
7. Have the assistant pump the brake pedal several times, then repeat procedure until air no longer is noticed when bleeder is opened. **Do not depress brake pedal fully to the end of the master cylinder stroke, this may cause damage to the master cylinder.**
8. Repeat previous steps for all bleeders. Ensure all air is removed from the hydraulic system. **While bleeding the system, check brake fluid supply in the master cylinder often so as not to allow the master cylinder to run dry.**
9. Upon completion of hydraulic system bleeding proceed as follows:
   a. Ensure the master cylinder reservoir is full. Add suitable brake fluid as needed, and securely reinstall the master cylinder cap.
   b. Lower the vehicle. Ensure brake pedal is firm and braking operation is proper.

BRAKE PAD SERVICE

1. Remove approximately 1/3 of brake fluid from master cylinder.
2. Raise and support vehicle, then remove tire and wheel assembly.
3. Disconnect parking brake cable operating lever return spring, **Fig. 2.**
4. Remove bolt attaching operating lever to caliper, then use a scribe to mark position of operating lever and remove operating lever using a suitable flat blade screwdriver.
5. Disconnect parking brake cable from mounting flange, then remove upper slide pin.
6. Loosen lower slide pin and tilt caliper downward.
7. Remove brake pad retaining pin using a suitable pin punch, then the lower slide pin and lift caliper off rotor and secure with wire.
8. Remove anti-rattle spring, then the brake pads.
9. Remove rotor retaining nuts, then the rotor.

TYPE 4-DUAL PIN SLIDING CALIPER DISC BRAKE, REAR

10. Inspect parking brake operating lever return spring, brake pad retaining pin, slide pins and bushings, and replace as necessary.
11. Bottom caliper piston in its bore, then temporarily mount caliper on axle shaft. Install and tighten slide pins just enough to hold caliper in place.
12. Using a 3/8 inch drive extension, ratchet and 7/16 inch deep well socket, insert spanner 6366 or equivalent into deep well socket.
13. Insert spanner tool lugs into matching holes in caliper piston face, and rotate piston in a clockwise direction until fully seated in bore.
14. Remove caliper slide pins and caliper, then install rotor and retaining nuts.
15. Install new pads in caliper, then the caliper on rotor and axle shaft.
16. Install caliper slide pins and tighten to specifications.
17. Install anti-rattle spring and ensure that spring is positioned so brake pad retaining pin will go through loops at each end of spring.
18. Insert parking brake cable in mounting flange, then position return spring on caliper and install operating lever on parking brake cable.
19. Pull parking brake lever rearward and install operating lever on caliper.
20. Connect return spring to operating lever first, then hook spring onto caliper with a long screwdriver. **Rounded end of return spring attaches to operating lever and square end goes to caliper.**
21. Install wheel and tire, lower vehicle, then apply brakes several times to seat pads and equalize parking brake adjustment.

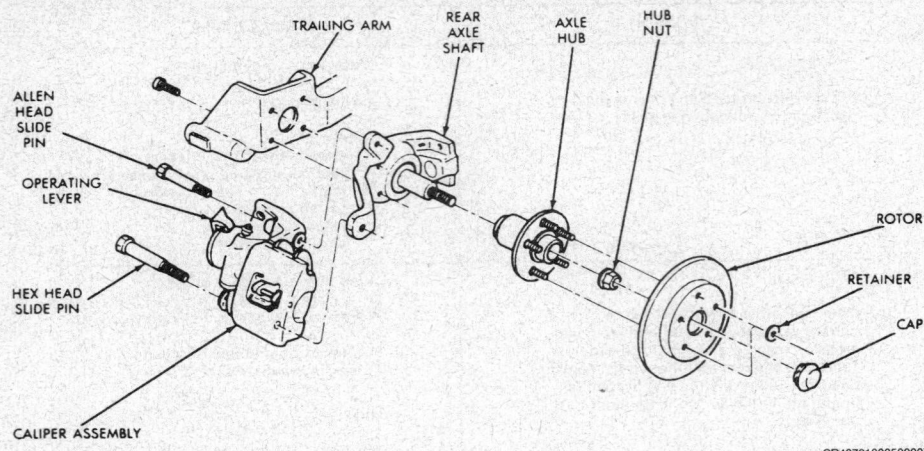

Fig. 2   Dual pin sliding caliper disc brake assembly. Monaco & Premier

CALIPER SERVICE
CALIPER, REPLACE

Refer to "Brake Pads, Replace" for procedure.

CALIPER OVERHAUL

These calipers are not serviceable, and must be replaced if worn or damaged.

ADJUSTMENTS
PARKING BRAKE

1. Apply and release parking brake 5 times to center pads, then press pedal down to first detent (one click).
2. Raise and support vehicle, then tighten adjusting nut until a slight drag is felt at one or both rear wheels when tires are rotated.
3. Loosen adjusting nut one turn, apply parking brake pedal once and release, then check for drag at rear wheels.

ROTOR
REPLACE

1. Remove caliper as outlined under "Caliper Service,".
2. Remove parking brake adjustment hole plug from hub of brake disc.
3. Using a suitable tool, turn parking brake adjusting nut until brake disc can be removed.
4. Reverse procedure to install, adjust parking brake as outlined under "Adjustments"

DISC BRAKE SPECIFICATIONS

ROTOR SPECIFICATIONS

Year	Model	Nominal Thickness (Inches)	Minimum Allowable Thickness (Inches)	Thickness Variation Parallelism (Inches)	Lateral Runout (T.I.R.)	Finish (Micro-Inch)
1992	Monaco/Premier	.394	.374	.001	.003	—

CALIPER SPECIFICATIONS

Model	Year	Caliper Bore Dia., Inch
Monaco/Premier	1992	1.41

TIGHTENING SPECIFICATIONS

Year	Component	Torque/Ft. Lbs.
1992	Brake Line Fittings	11-15①
	Bleed Screws	5-7
	Caliper Mounting Bolts	70
	Caliper Slide Pins	15-22
	Wheel Lug Nuts	63

①—Inch lbs.

Type 5–Kelsey-Hayes Dual Pin Floating Caliper Disc Brake, Front

INDEX

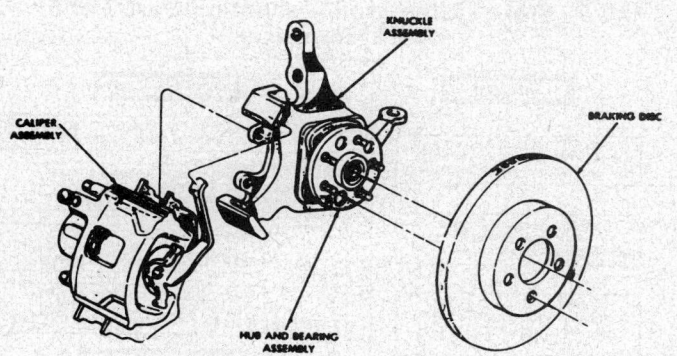

Fig. 1   Kelsey-Hayes dual pin floating caliper disc brake assembly

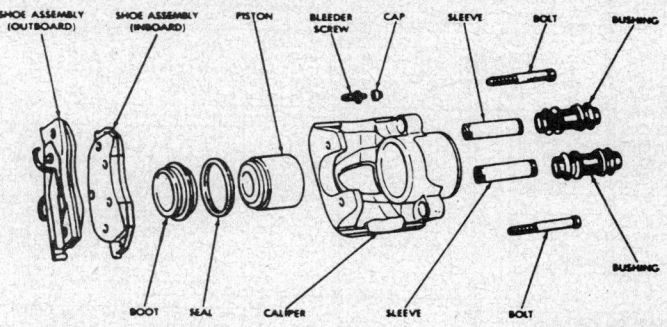

Fig. 2   Exploded view of Kelsey-Hayes disc brake caliper

DESCRIPTION

The single piston, floating caliper disc brake assembly, **Fig. 1**, consists of the rotor, caliper, pads and the driving hub. The caliper, **Fig. 2**, is mounted through bushings and sleeves by two through bolts threaded into the steering knuckle. Two machined abutments on the steering knuckle position and align the caliper fore and aft. The mounting bolts and bushings control the movement of the caliper and the piston seal to assist in maintaining proper pad clearance.

This assembly has an anti-rattle clip attached to the outer pad and an inner pad-piston retainer clip.

All of the braking force is taken directly by the steering knuckle. The caliper is a one piece casting with the inboard side containing a single piston cylinder bore.

A square cut rubber piston seal is located in a machined groove in the caliper bore and provides a seal between piston and caliper bore.

A molded rubber dust boot installed in a groove in the cylinder bore and piston keeps contamination from the caliper bore and piston. The boot mounts in the caliper bore and in a groove in the piston.

TROUBLESHOOTING

Refer to **Fig. 3** for troubleshooting procedures.

LATERAL RUNOUT CHECK

Refer to "Disc Brake Specifications" for runout specifications.

1. Raise and support vehicle, then remove wheels.
2. If applicable, ensure wheel bearings are properly adjusted.
3. Using suitable spacers install lug nuts or bolts, then torque to specifications.
4. Mount a dial indicator to a convenient part of the vehicle (steering knuckle, tie rod, disc brake caliper housing).
5. Position dial indicator plunger so it contacts the disc at a point one inch from the outer edge.
6. Rotate the rotor and note the dial indicator readings. Perform this check on both inboard and outboard rotor faces.
7. If runout exceeds specifications proceed as follows:
   a. Reposition rotor on the hub, then recheck runout.
   b. If runout still exceeds specifications, replace or machine the rotor.

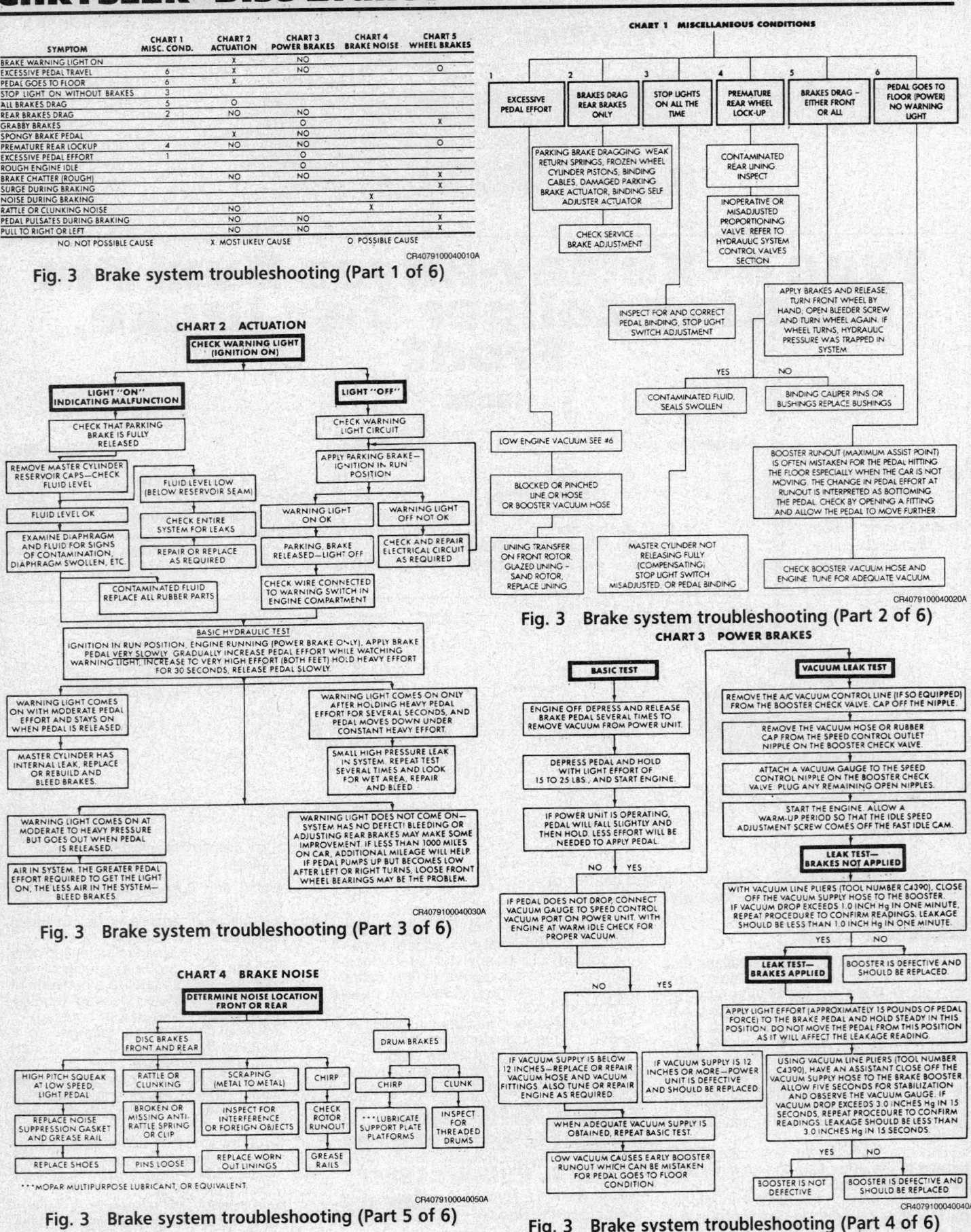

CHART 1 MISCELLANEOUS CONDITIONS

SYMPTOM	CHART 1 MISC. COND.	CHART 2 ACTUATION	CHART 3 POWER BRAKES	CHART 4 BRAKE NOISE	CHART 5 WHEEL BRAKES
BRAKE WARNING LIGHT ON		X	NO		
EXCESSIVE PEDAL TRAVEL	6	X	NO		O
PEDAL GOES TO FLOOR	6	X			
STOP LIGHT ON WITHOUT BRAKES	3				
ALL BRAKES DRAG	5	O			
REAR BRAKES DRAG	2	NO	NO		
GRABBY BRAKES			O		X
SPONGY BRAKE PEDAL		X	NO		
PREMATURE REAR LOCKUP	4	NO	NO		
EXCESSIVE PEDAL EFFORT	1		O		
ROUGH ENGINE IDLE			O		
BRAKE CHATTER (ROUGH)		NO	NO		X
SURGE DURING BRAKING					X
NOISE DURING BRAKING				X	
RATTLE OR CLUNKING NOISE		NO		X	
PEDAL PULSATES DURING BRAKING		NO	NO		X
PULL TO RIGHT OR LEFT		NO	NO		X

NO: NOT POSSIBLE CAUSE   X: MOST LIKELY CAUSE   O: POSSIBLE CAUSE

CR4079100040010A

Fig. 3   Brake system troubleshooting (Part 1 of 6)

CR4079100040020A

Fig. 3   Brake system troubleshooting (Part 2 of 6)

CHART 2   ACTUATION

CR4079100040030A

Fig. 3   Brake system troubleshooting (Part 3 of 6)

CHART 3   POWER BRAKES

CHART 4   BRAKE NOISE

***MOPAR MULTIPURPOSE LUBRICANT, OR EQUIVALENT.

CR4079100040050A

Fig. 3   Brake system troubleshooting (Part 5 of 6)

CR4079100040040A

Fig. 3   Brake system troubleshooting (Part 4 of 6)

TYPE 5-KELSEY-HAYES DUAL PIN FLOATING CALIPER DISC BRAKE, FRONT

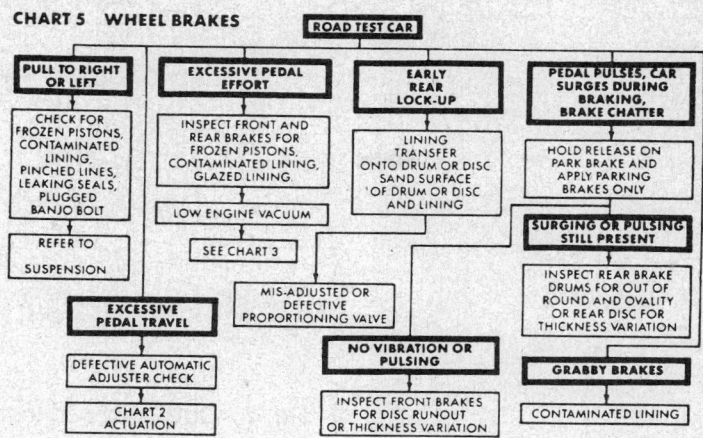

CHART 5 WHEEL BRAKES

Fig. 3 Brake system troubleshooting (Part 6 of 6)

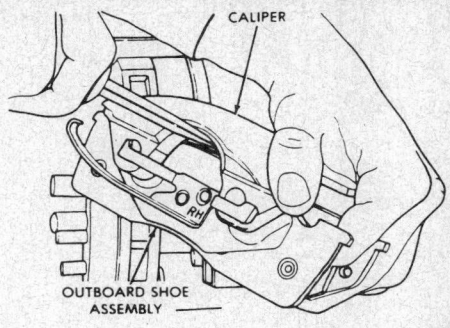

Fig. 4 Outboard pad removal

PARALLELISM CHECK

Refer to "Disc Brake Specifications" for parallelism specifications.
1. Using a suitable micrometer, measure the rotor at 12 equally spaced points at a radius approximately one inch from edge of disc.
2. If measurements exceed specifications and the rotor cannot be machined, replace it.
3. If measurements exceed specifications and the rotor can be machined, resurface it.
4. Recheck parallelism. If measurements still exceed specifications, replace the rotor.

BRAKE SYSTEM BLEED

Bleeding the hydraulic brake system is necessary if air has entered the system. Symptoms can be noted by loss of brake operation, and/or a low or spongy brake pedal.

The hydraulic fluid is bled or flushed from the system through bleeder valves located on the calipers, wheel cylinders, and some master cylinders. When bleeding the hydraulic brake system, use only specified brake fluid. **Never reuse old brake fluid removed from the system.**

PRESSURE BLEEDING

Pressure bleeding is recommended for all hydraulic brake systems. It is the fastest method because the master cylinder is automatically fed brake fluid from the pressure bleeder reservoir, and no pedal pumping is needed so only one person is required to perform the procedure. However, if pressure bleeding equipment is not available, the hydraulic system may be bled as described under "Manual Bleeding."

While pressure bleeding, to prevent air from getting into the hydraulic system, do not shake the pressure tank. Set the tank in the required location, bring the air hose to the tank, and do not move it during the bleeding operation. The tank should be kept at least one-third full.

The bleeder valves should be opened at least one full turn, and intermittently closed

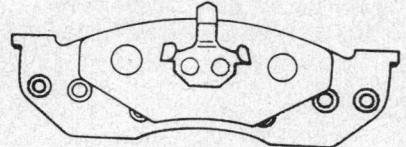

INBOARD SHOE ASSEMBLY
(RIGHT AND LEFT COMMON)

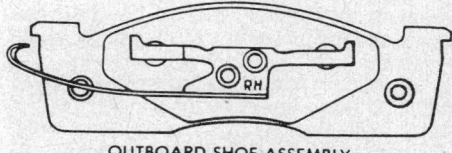

OUTBOARD SHOE ASSEMBLY
(RIGHT SIDE SHOWN)

Fig. 5 Brake pad identification

at about four-second intervals. This gives a whirling action to fluid in the hydraulic system, and helps expel the air.

MANUAL BLEEDING

On models with power brakes, bleed the hydraulic system without the engine running, first reduce vacuum in the power unit to zero by pumping the brake pedal several times with the engine off.
1. Ensure master cylinder reservoir is full.
2. Raise and support vehicle.
3. Position a drain pan under the wheel being bled.
4. Have an assistant depress the brake pedal with a slow even strokes until pressure is felt, then hold it. **Do not depress brake pedal fully to the end of the master cylinder stroke. This may cause damage to the master cylinder.**
5. Starting at the bleeder screw farthest from the master cylinder, using a suitable wrench, open the bleeder valve one full turn. Watch for air bubbles in the fluid, and listen for air escaping from the system.
6. With the brake pedal still depressed, close the bleeder valve.
7. Have the assistant pump the brake pedal several times, then repeat pro-

cedure until air no longer is noticed when bleeder is opened. **Do not depress brake pedal fully to the end of the master cylinder stroke, this may cause damage to the master cylinder.**
8. Repeat previous steps for all bleeders. Ensure all air is removed from the hydraulic system. **While bleeding the system, recheck brake fluid supply in the master cylinder often so as not to allow the master cylinder to run dry.**
9. Upon completion of hydraulic system bleeding proceed as follows:
   a. Ensure the master cylinder reservoir is full. Add suitable brake fluid as needed, and securely reinstall the master cylinder cap.
   b. Lower the vehicle. Ensure brake pedal is firm and braking operation is proper.

BRAKE PAD SERVICE

REMOVAL

1. Remove 1/2 of brake fluid from reservoir.
2. Raise and support front of vehicle.
3. Remove wheel and tire assembly.
4. Remove caliper-to-steering knuckle attaching bolts.
5. Remove caliper and brake pads as an assembly by pulling lower end of caliper outward from steering knuckle, then sliding assembly away from braking disc. **Suspend caliper with wire to avoid damaging brake hose.**
6. Remove outboard pad by prying between pad and caliper, **Fig. 4. Support caliper to avoid damage to brake hose.**
7. Remove inboard pad by pulling away from caliper piston.

INSTALLATION

The inboard pads are interchangeable and may be used on either side of vehicle. The outboard pads are not interchangeable and are marked "L" for left side or "R" for right side of vehicle, **Fig. 5.**
1. Lubricate adapter ways with suitable grease.
2. Install inboard pad in caliper, entering retainer into bore of piston, **Fig. 6.**
3. Position properly marked outboard

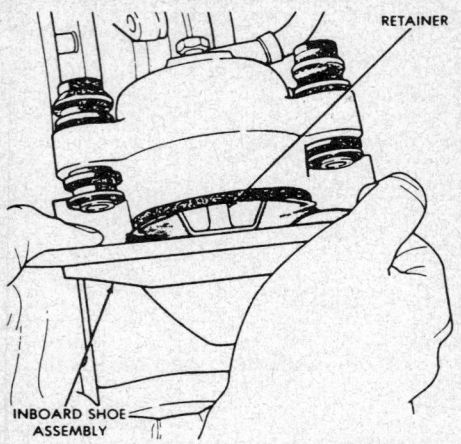

Fig. 6   Inboard pad installation

pad hold-down spring into caliper as shown in **Fig. 7.**

4. Lower caliper over braking disc, then install attaching bolts. Tighten bolts to specifications.
5. Install tire and wheel assembly and lower vehicle.

CALIPER SERVICE
CALIPER REPLACE

1. Remove caliper as outlined under "Brake Pad Service."
2. Disconnect Brake Line.
3. Reverse Procedure to install, bleed brakes as outlined under "Brake System Bleed."

CALIPER OVERHAUL

Disassemble

1. Remove caliper assembly as described under "Caliper Replace."

2. Place a wood block between caliper piston and caliper fingers. With brake hose attached to caliper, carefully depress brake pedal to push piston out of caliper bore. Prop brake pedal to any position below first inch of brake pedal travel to prevent brake fluid loss.
3. If piston are to be removed from both calipers, disconnect brake hose at frame bracket after removing piston, then cap brake line and repeat procedure to remove piston from other caliper.
4. Disconnect brake hose from caliper.
5. Mount caliper in a soft jawed vise.
6. Support caliper, then remove and discard dust boot.
7. Using a small wooden or plastic stick, remove seal from groove in piston bore and discard. **Do not use a screwdriver or other metal tool, as this may scratch caliper bore.**
8. Remove caliper bushings.

Assemble

1. Mount caliper in a soft jawed vise.
2. Lubricate piston seal with clean brake fluid and install seal in caliper bore groove. Ensure seal is properly seated.
3. Lubricate piston boot with clean brake fluid and position over piston.
4. Install piston and boot assembly, pushing it past piston seal until it bottoms into caliper bore.
5. Using a hammer and dust boot installer, tool No. C-4689 with tool No. C-4171 handle, drive dust boot into counterbore until properly seated.

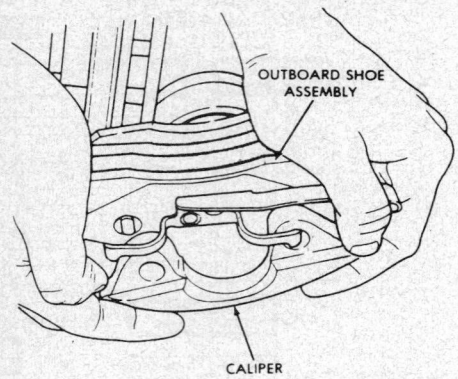

Fig. 7   Outboard pad installation

6. On models where bushings require replacement, compress flanges of bushings and install on caliper housing. Ensure bushing flanges extend evenly over caliper housing on both sides. Remove Teflon sleeves from guide pin bushings prior to installing bushings into caliper. After bushings are installed into caliper, reinstall Teflon sleeves into bushings.
7. Connect brake hose to brake line at frame bracket.
8. Install caliper on vehicle as described under "Brake Pad, Service."
9. Bleed brakes as outlined under "Brake System Bleed."

ROTOR
REPLACE

Remove caliper as outlined under "Caliper Service," then remove rotor. If necessary use a suitable soft face hammer to tap rotor free of hub.

DISC BRAKE SPECIFICATIONS
ROTOR SPECIFICATIONS

Year	Model	Nominal Thickness (Inches)	Minimum Allowable Thickness (Inches)	Thickness Variation Parallelism (Inches)	Lateral Runout (T.I.R.)	Finish (Micro-Inch)
1992	Monaco/Premier	.9500	.8900	.0010	.0030	—
1992-93	Dynasty, Fifth Avenue, Imperial & New Yorker	.9300-.9400	.8820	.0005	.0050	15-80

CALIPER SPECIFICATIONS

Model	Year	Caliper Bore Dia. Inch
Dynasty, Fifth Avenue, Imperial, Monaco/Premier & New Yorker	1992	2.362
Dynasty, Fifth Avenue, Imperial & New Yorker	1993	2.362

TIGHTENING SPECIFICATIONS

Year	Component	Torque/Ft. Lbs.
1992-93	Bearing Retainer Bolts	21
	Brake Hose To Caliper Banjo Bolt	35
	Front Brake Hose Intermediate Bracket	105①
	Bleed Screws	125①
	Caliper Mounting Bolts	160
	Caliper Guide Pins	30
	Wheel Lug Nuts	85-110

① —Inch lbs.

Type 6—Kelsey-Hayes Dual Pin Floating Caliper Disc Brake, Front

INDEX

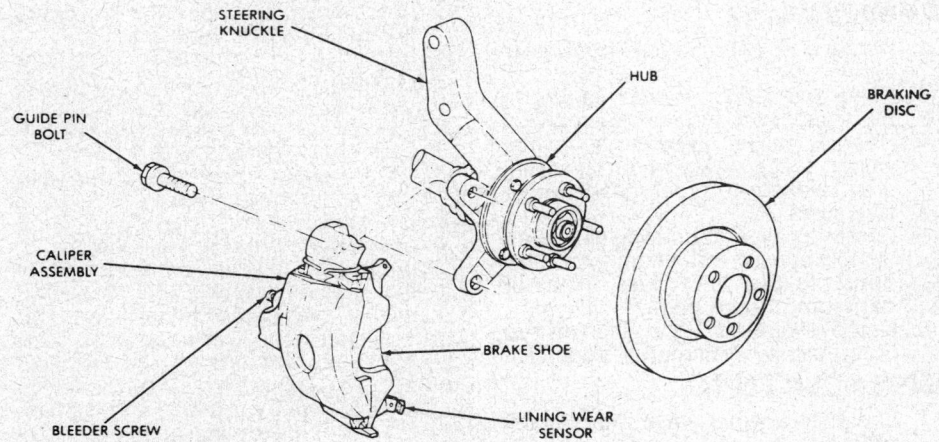

Fig. 1   Kelsey-Hayes dual pin floating caliper disc brake assembly

DESCRIPTION

The single piston, floating caliper disc brake assembly, **Fig. 1**, consists of the rotor, caliper, pads and the driving hub. The caliper is mounted through bushings and sleeves by two through bolts threaded into an adapter. Two machined abutments on the adapter position and align the caliper fore and aft. The mounting bolts and bushings control the movement of the caliper and the piston seal to assist in maintaining proper pad clearance.

This assembly has an anti-rattle clip attached to the outer pad and an inner pad-piston retainer clip.

All of the braking force is taken directly by the adapter. The caliper is a one piece casting with the inboard side containing a single piston cylinder bore.

A square cut rubber piston seal is located in a machined groove in the caliper bore and provides a seal between piston and caliper bore.

A molded rubber dust boot installed in a groove in the cylinder bore and piston keeps contamination from the caliper bore and piston. The boot mounts in the caliper bore and in a groove in the piston.

TROUBLESHOOTING

Refer to "Type 5–Kelsey Hayes Dual Pin Floating Disc Brake, Front" troubleshooting section for system troubleshooting.

LATERAL RUNOUT CHECK

Refer to "Disc Brake Specifications" for runout specifications.

1. Raise and support vehicle, then remove wheels.
2. If applicable, ensure wheel bearings are properly adjusted.
3. Using suitable spacers install lug nuts or bolts, then torque to specifications.
4. Mount a dial indicator to a convenient part of the vehicle (steering knuckle, tie rod, disc brake caliper housing).
5. Position dial indicator plunger so it contacts the disc at a point one inch from the outer edge.
6. Rotate the rotor and note the dial indicator readings. Perform this check on both inboard and outboard rotor faces.

7. If runout exceeds specifications proceed as follows:
   a. Reposition rotor on the hub, then recheck runout.
   b. If runout still exceeds specifications, replace or machine the rotor.

PARALLELISM CHECK

Refer to "Disc Brake Specifications" for parallelism specifications.

1. Using a suitable micrometer, measure the rotor at 12 equally spaced points at a radius approximately one inch from edge of disc.
2. If measurements exceed specifications and the rotor cannot be machined, replace it.
3. If measurements exceed specifications and the rotor can be machined, resurface it.
4. Recheck parallelism. If measurements still exceed specifications, replace the rotor.

BRAKE SYSTEM BLEED

Bleeding the hydraulic brake system is necessary if air has entered the system. Symptoms can be noted by loss of brake operation, and/or a low or spongy brake pedal.

The hydraulic fluid is bled or flushed from the system through bleeder valves located on the calipers, wheel cylinders, and some master cylinders. When bleeding the hydraulic brake system, use only specified brake fluid. **Never reuse old brake fluid removed from the system.**

PRESSURE BLEEDING

Pressure bleeding is recommended for all hydraulic brake systems. It is the fastest method because the master cylinder is automatically fed brake fluid from the pressure bleeder reservoir, and no pedal pumping is needed so only one person is required to perform the procedure. However, if pressure bleeding equipment is not available, the hydraulic system may be bled as described under "Manual Bleeding."

While pressure bleeding, to prevent air from getting into the hydraulic system, do not shake the pressure tank. Set the tank in the required location, bring the air hose to the tank, and do not move it during the bleeding operation. The tank should be kept at least one-third full.

The bleeder valves should be opened at least one full turn, and intermittently closed at about four-second intervals. This gives a whirling action to fluid in the hydraulic system, and helps expel the air.

MANUAL BLEEDING

On models with power brakes, bleed the hydraulic system without the engine running, first reduce vacuum in the power unit to zero by pumping the brake pedal several times with the engine off.

1. Ensure master cylinder reservoir is full.
2. Raise and support vehicle.
3. Position a drain pan under the wheel being bled.

4. Have an assistant depress the brake pedal with a slow even strokes until pressure is felt, then hold it. **Do not depress brake pedal fully to the end of the master cylinder stroke. This may cause damage to the master cylinder.**
5. Starting at the bleeder screw farthest from the master cylinder, using a suitable wrench, open the bleeder valve one full turn. Watch for air bubbles in the fluid, and listen for air escaping from the system.
6. With the brake pedal still depressed, close the bleeder valve.
7. Have the assistant pump the brake pedal several times, then repeat procedure until air no longer is noticed when bleeder is opened. **Do not depress brake pedal fully to the end of the master cylinder stroke, this may cause damage to the master cylinder.**
8. Repeat previous steps for all bleeders. Ensure all air is removed from the hydraulic system. **While bleeding the system, recheck brake fluid supply in the master cylinder often so as not to allow the master cylinder to run dry.**
9. Upon completion of hydraulic system bleeding proceed as follows:
   a. Ensure the master cylinder reservoir is full. Add suitable brake fluid as needed, and securely reinstall the master cylinder cap.
   b. Lower the vehicle. Ensure brake pedal is firm and braking operation is proper.

BRAKE PAD SERVICE
REMOVAL

1. Remove 1/2 of brake fluid from reservoir.
2. Raise and support front of vehicle.
3. Remove wheel and tire assembly.
4. Remove caliper guide pin bolts, then wedge caliper away from rotor using a screwdriver to break gasket adhesive seals.
5. Remove caliper by slowly sliding assembly out and away from rotor. **Suspend caliper with wire to avoid damaging brake hose.**
6. Remove outboard pad, then the inboard pad by sliding off of adapter.

INSTALLATION

1. Lubricate adapter ways with suitable grease.
2. Install inboard pad, then the outboard pad onto adapter.
3. Lower caliper over rotor and pad assemblies, then install guide pins. Tighten pins to specifications.
4. Install tire and wheel assembly and lower vehicle.

CALIPER SERVICE
CALIPER REPLACE

1. Remove caliper as outlined under "Brake Pad Service."

2. Disconnect Brake Line.
3. Reverse Procedure to install, bleed brakes as outlined under "Brake System Bleed."

CALIPER OVERHAUL
Disassemble

1. Remove caliper assembly as described under "Brake Pad, Service."
2. Place a wood block between caliper piston and caliper fingers. With brake hose attached to caliper, carefully depress brake pedal to push piston out of caliper bore. Prop brake pedal to any position below first inch of brake pedal travel to prevent brake fluid loss.
3. If piston are to be removed from both calipers, disconnect brake hose at frame bracket after removing piston, then cap brake line and repeat procedure to remove piston from other caliper.
4. Disconnect brake hose from caliper.
5. Mount caliper in a soft jawed vise.
6. Support caliper, then remove and discard dust boot.
7. Using a small wooden or plastic stick, remove seal from groove in piston bore and discard. **Do not use a screwdriver or other metal tool, as this may scratch caliper bore.**
8. Remove caliper bushings.

Assemble

1. Mount caliper in a soft jawed vise.
2. Lubricate piston seal with clean brake fluid and install seal in caliper bore groove. Ensure seal is properly seated.
3. Lubricate piston boot with clean brake fluid and position over piston.
4. Install piston and boot assembly, pushing it past piston seal until it bottoms into caliper bore.
5. Using a hammer and dust boot installer, tool No. C-4689 with tool No. C-4171 handle, drive dust boot into counterbore until properly seated.
6. On models where bushings require replacement, compress flanges of bushings and install on caliper housing. Ensure bushing flanges extend evenly over caliper housing on both sides. Remove Teflon sleeves from guide pin bushings prior to installing bushings into caliper. After bushings are installed into caliper, reinstall Teflon sleeves into bushings.
7. Connect brake hose to brake line at frame bracket.
8. Install caliper on vehicle as described under "Brake Pad, Service."
9. Bleed brakes as outlined under "Brake System Bleed."

ROTOR
REPLACE

Remove caliper as outlined under "Caliper Service," then remove rotor. If necessary use a suitable soft face hammer to tap rotor free of hub.

SPECIFICATIONS DISC BRAKE
ROTOR SPECIFICATIONS

Year	Model	Nominal Thickness (Inches)	Minimum Refinish Thickness (Inches)	Thickness Variation Parallelism (Inches)	Lateral Runout (T.I.R.)	Finish (Micro-Inch)
1992	Acclaim, Daytona, LeBaron, LeBaron Landau, Shadow, Spirit & Sundance	.870-.861	.803	.0005	.005	15-80
1993	Acclaim, Daytona, LeBaron, LeBaron Landau, Shadow, Spirit & Sundance	.930-.940	.882	.0005	.005	15-80
1994	Concorde, Intrepid & Vision	.940-.950	.882	.0005	.003	15-80
1994	Acclaim, Daytona, LeBaron & Spirit	.930-.940	.882	.0005	.005	15-80
1994	Concorde, Intrepid, LHS, New Yorker & Vision	.940-.950	.882	.0005	.003	15-80
1995	Neon	.782-.792	.724	.0005	.005	15-80

CALIPER SPECIFICATIONS

Model	Year	Caliper Bore Dia. Inch
Acclaim, Daytona, LeBaron, LeBaron Landau, Shadow, Spirit & Sundance	1992-94	2.126
Concorde, Intrepid & Vision	1993-94	2.362
LHS & New Yorker	1994	2.362
Neon	1995	—

TIGHTENING SPECIFICATIONS

Year	Component	Torque/Ft. Lbs.
1992-95	Bearing Retainer Bolts	21
	Brake Hose To Caliper Banjo Bolt	35
	Brake Line Fitting	12
	Front Brake Hose Intermediate Bracket	105①
	Bleed Screws	125①
	Caliper Mounting Bolts	16
	Caliper Guide Pins	30
	Wheel Lug Nuts	85-110

①—Inch lbs.

TYPE 6-KELSEY-HAYES DUAL PIN FLOATING CALIPER DISC BRAKE, FRONT

Type 7—Kelsey-Hayes Dual Pin Floating Caliper Disc Brake, Rear

INDEX

DESCRIPTION

This single piston, floating caliper rear disc brake assembly, **Fig. 1**, includes a hub assembly, adapter, rotor, caliper, shoes and pads. The parking brake system consists of a small duo-servo brake mounted to an adapter which expands out against the hat section on the inside of the rotor. The caliper has either a 1.338 (34 mm) or 1.42 inch (36 mm) piston located on the inboard side.

The caliper floats on rubber bushings with metal sleeves on two bolts that are threaded into the adapter. Two machined abutments on the adapter position and align the caliper and brake pads for movement fore and aft.

TROUBLESHOOTING

Refer to "Type 5–Kelsey Hayes Dual Pin Floating Disc Brake, Front" troubleshooting section for system troubleshooting.

LATERAL RUNOUT CHECK

Refer to "Disc Brake Specifications" for runout specifications.

1. Raise and support vehicle, then remove wheels.
2. If applicable, ensure wheel bearings are properly adjusted.
3. Using suitable spacers install lug nuts or bolts, then torque to specifications.
4. Mount a dial indicator to a convenient part of the vehicle (steering knuckle, tie rod, disc brake caliper housing).
5. Position dial indicator plunger so it contacts the disc at a point one inch from the outer edge.
6. Rotate the rotor and note the dial indicator readings. Perform this check on both inboard and outboard rotor faces.
7. If runout exceeds specifications, proceed as follows:
   a. Reposition rotor on the hub, then recheck runout.
   b. If runout still exceeds specifications, replace or machine the rotor.

PARALLELISM CHECK

Refer to "Disc Brake Specifications" for parallelism specifications.

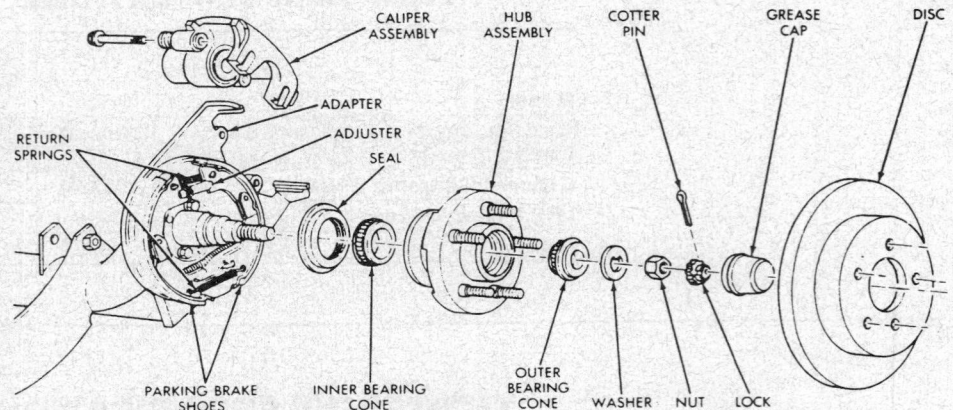

Fig. 1   Kelsey-Hayes dual pin floating caliper disc brake assembly

1. Using a suitable micrometer, measure the rotor at 12 equally spaced points at a radius approximately one inch from edge of disc.
2. If measurements exceed specifications and the rotor cannot be machined, replace it.
3. If measurements exceed specifications and the rotor can be machined, resurface it.
4. Recheck parallelism. If measurements still exceed specifications, replace the rotor.

BRAKE SYSTEM BLEED

Bleeding the hydraulic brake system is necessary if air has entered the system. Symptoms can be noted by loss of brake operation, and/or a low or spongy brake pedal.

The hydraulic fluid is bled or flushed from the system through bleeder valves located on the calipers, wheel cylinders, and some master cylinders. When bleeding the hydraulic brake system, use only specified brake fluid. **Never reuse old brake fluid removed from the system.**

PRESSURE BLEEDING

Pressure bleeding is recommended for all hydraulic brake systems. It is the fastest method because the master cylinder is automatically fed brake fluid from the pressure bleeder reservoir, and no pedal pumping is needed so only one person is required to perform the procedure. However, if pressure bleeding equipment is not available, the hydraulic system may be bled as described under "Manual Bleeding."

While pressure bleeding, to prevent air from getting into the hydraulic system, do not shake the pressure tank. Set the tank in the required location, bring the air hose to the tank, and do not move it during the bleeding operation. The tank should be kept at least one-third full.

The bleeder valves should be opened at least one full turn, and intermittently closed at about four-second intervals. This gives a whirling action to fluid in the hydraulic system, and helps expel the air.

MANUAL BLEEDING

On models with power brakes, bleed the hydraulic system without the engine running, first reduce vacuum in the power unit to zero by pumping the brake pedal several times with the engine off.

1. Ensure master cylinder reservoir is full.
2. Raise and support vehicle.

3. Position a drain pan under the wheel being bled.
4. Have an assistant depress the brake pedal with a slow even strokes until pressure is felt, then hold it. **Do not depress brake pedal fully to the end of the master cylinder stroke. This may cause damage to the master cylinder.**
5. Starting at the bleeder screw farthest from the master cylinder, using a suitable wrench, open the bleeder valve one full turn. Watch for air bubbles in the fluid, and listen for air escaping from the system.
6. With the brake pedal still depressed, close the bleeder valve.
7. Have the assistant pump the brake pedal several times, then repeat procedure until air no longer is noticed when bleeder is opened. **Do not depress brake pedal fully to the end of the master cylinder stroke, this may cause damage to the master cylinder.**
8. Repeat previous steps for all bleeders. Ensure all air is removed from the hydraulic system. **While bleeding the system, recheck brake fluid supply in the master cylinder often so as not to allow the master cylinder to run dry.**
9. Upon completion of hydraulic system bleeding proceed as follows:
   a. Ensure the master cylinder reservoir is full. Add suitable brake fluid as needed, and securely reinstall the master cylinder cap.
   b. Lower the vehicle. Ensure brake pedal is firm and braking operation is proper.

BRAKE PAD SERVICE

1. Raise and support vehicle.
2. Remove rear wheel and tire assembly.
3. Remove caliper retaining bolts, then lift caliper away from adapter rails. **Hang caliper from wire away from rotor.**
4. Remove outer brake pad by prying pad retaining clip over raised area on caliper, then sliding it down and off caliper.
5. Remove inner brake pad by pulling it away from the piston.
6. Retract piston, then reverse procedure to install. Tighten caliper retaining bolts to specifications.

CALIPER SERVICE

CALIPER OVERHAUL

1. Remove caliper from rotor as described under "Brake Pads, Service."
2. Place a small piece of wood between piston and caliper fingers, then carefully depress brake pedal to hydraulically push piston out of bore. Prop

brake pedal to any position below first inch of brake pedal travel to prevent brake fluid loss.
3. If pistons are to be removed from both calipers, disconnect brake hose at frame bracket after removing piston, then cap brake line and repeat procedure to remove piston from other caliper.
4. Disconnect brake hose from caliper.
5. Mount caliper in a soft jawed vise.
6. Support caliper, then remove and discard dust boot.
7. Using a small wooden or plastic stick, remove seal from groove in piston bore and discard. **Do not use a screwdriver or other metal tool, as this may scratch caliper bore.**
8. If necessary, remove bushing and sleeve assembly, as follows:
   a. Using fingers, push inner sleeve until it pops out of bushing, then pull inner sleeve completely out of bushing.
   b. Using fingers collapse one side of bushing. Pull opposite side of bushing to remove from caliper.
9. Using denatured alcohol or equivalent, thoroughly clean piston and caliper grooves, caliper housing and bushing mounting surfaces.
10. Dip new piston seal in clean brake fluid and install in groove in bore.
11. Coat new piston boot with clean brake fluid leaving a generous amount inside boot.
12. Coat piston with clean brake fluid, then position dust boot over piston.
13. Install piston into bore pushing it past piston seal until it bottoms in bore.
14. Position dust boot in counterbore, then using a hammer and installer, tool No. C-4383-7 or equivalent, drive boot into counterbore of caliper.
15. If removed, install guide pin sleeve bushings as follows:
   a. Fold bushing in half lengthwise at solid middle section.
   b. Using fingers, insert folded bushing into caliper. Do not use sharp object to perform this step.
   c. Using wooden dowel, unfold bushing until it is fully seated in caliper. Flanges should be seated evenly on both sides of bushing hole.
16. If removed, install guide pin sleeve as follows:
   a. Hold end of bushing, then push sleeve through bushing until end of bushing is fully seated into seal groove of sleeve.
   b. Holding sleeve in place, install other end of bushing into seal groove.
   c. Ensure bushing is in seal groove on both sides.
17. Install brake fluid line, then install caliper as outlined under "Brake Pad Service."
18. Bleed brakes as outlined under "Brake System Bleed."

PARKING BRAKE SERVICE

PARKING BRAKE SHOES, REPLACE

1. Raise and support vehicle.
2. Remove rear wheel and tire assembly.
3. Remove caliper from rotor as described under "Brake Pads, Service."
4. Remove rotor from hub.
5. Remove grease cap, cotter pin, locknut, retaining nut, washer, hub and bearings.
6. Using a suitable tool, remove forward hold-down clip.
7. Turn adjuster wheel until adjuster is at its shortest length, then remove adjuster assembly.
8. Remove upper shoe to shoe spring.
9. Pull front shoe away from anchor, then remove front shoe and lower spring.
10. Using a suitable tool, remove rear hold-down clip and shoe.
11. Reverse procedure to install noting the following:
   a. Adjust shoe diameter to 6.75 inches.
   b. Tighten wheel bearing adjusting nut to specifications while rotating hub to seat bearings, back off adjusting nut 1/4 turn, then tighten finger tight.
   c. Align nut-to-spindle holes for cotter pin insertion.

ADJUSTMENTS

PARKING BRAKE

1. Release parking brake.
2. Raise and support vehicle.
3. Adjust parking brake cable until there is slack in the cable.
4. Tighten adjusting nut until a slight drag is felt when rotating the rear wheels.
5. Back off adjusting nut two full turns past the point when both rear wheels rotate freely.
6. Check parking brake operation.

ROTOR

REPLACE

1. Remove caliper as outlined under "Caliper Service,".
2. Remove parking brake adjustment hole plug from hub of brake disc.
3. Using a suitable tool, turn parking brake adjusting nut until brake disc can be removed.
4. Reverse procedure to install, adjust parking brake as outlined under "Adjustments"

DISC BRAKE SPECIFICATIONS

ROTOR SPECIFICATIONS

Year	Model	Nominal Thickness (Inches)	Minimum Allowable Thickness (Inches)	Thickness Variation Parallelism (Inches)	Lateral Runout (T.I.R.)	Finish (Micro-Inch)
1992	Acclaim, Daytona, LeBaron, LeBaron Landau, Shadow, Spirit & Sundance ①	.467-478	.409	.0005	.005	15-80
	Daytona & LeBaron ②	.856-.876	.797	.0005	.005	15-80
1993	Acclaim, Concorde, Daytona, Intrepid, LeBaron, LeBaron Landau, Shadow, Spirit, Sundance & Vision ①	.467-478	.409	.0005	.005	15-80
	Daytona & LeBaron ②	.856-.876	.797	.0005	.005	15-80
1994	Acclaim, Concorde, Daytona, Intrepid, LeBaron, LHS New Yorker, Spirit & Vision	.467-.478	.409	.0005	.005	15-80
1995	Neon	—	③	—	—	—

①—Solid rotor.
②—Vented Rotor.

CALIPER SPECIFICATIONS

Model	Year	Caliper Bore Dia. Inch
Vehicles Equipped With 14 Inch Wheels	1992-94	1.338
Vehicles Equipped With 15 Inch Wheels	1992-93	1.417
Neon	1995	—

TIGHTENING SPECIFICATIONS

Year	Component	Torque/Ft. Lbs.
1992-95	Bearing Retainer Bolts	21
	Brake Hose To Caliper Banjo Bolt	35
	Brake Line Fitting	12
	Support Plate To Rear Axle	80
	Bleed Screws	125 ①
	Caliper Mounting Bolts	16
	Caliper Guide Pins	30
	Wheel Lug Nuts	85-110

①—Inch lbs.

TYPE 7-KELSEY-HAYES DUAL PIN FLOATING CALIPER DISC BRAKE, REAR

Type 8–MR66Z & MR76Z 4 Piston Rigid Caliper Disc Brake, Front

INDEX

TROUBLESHOOTING

Refer to "Type 1–MR56W & MR57W Dual Piston Floating Caliper Disc Brake, Front" for system troubleshooting.

LATERAL RUNOUT CHECK

Refer to "Disc Brake Specifications" for runout specifications.

1. Raise and support vehicle, then remove wheels.
2. If applicable, ensure wheel bearings are properly adjusted.
3. Using suitable spacers install lug nuts or bolts, then torque to specifications.
4. Mount a dial indicator to a convenient part of the vehicle (steering knuckle, tie rod, disc brake caliper housing).
5. Position dial indicator plunger so it contacts the disc at a point one inch from the outer edge.
6. Rotate the rotor and note the dial indicator readings. Perform this check on both inboard and outboard rotor faces.
7. If runout exceeds specifications, proceed as follows:
   a. Reposition rotor on the hub, then recheck runout.
   b. If runout still exceeds specifications, replace or machine the rotor.

PARALLELISM CHECK

Refer to "Disc Brake Specifications" for parallelism specifications.

1. Using a suitable micrometer, measure the rotor at 12 equally spaced points at a radius approximately one inch from edge of disc.
2. If measurements exceed specifications and the rotor cannot be machined, replace it.
3. If measurements exceed specifications and the rotor can be machined, resurface it.
4. Recheck parallelism. If measurements still exceed specifications, replace the rotor.

BRAKE SYSTEM BLEED

Bleeding the hydraulic brake system is necessary if air has entered the system. Symptoms can be noted by loss of brake operation, and/or a low or spongy brake pedal.

The hydraulic fluid is bled or flushed from the system through bleeder valves located on the calipers, wheel cylinders, and some master cylinders. When bleeding the hydraulic brake system, use only specified brake fluid. **Never reuse old brake fluid removed from the system.**

PRESSURE BLEEDING

Pressure bleeding is recommended for all hydraulic brake systems. It is the fastest method because the master cylinder is automatically fed brake fluid from the pressure bleeder reservoir, and no pedal pumping is needed so only one person is required to perform the procedure. However, if pressure bleeding equipment is not available, the hydraulic system may be bled as described under "Manual Bleeding."

While pressure bleeding, to prevent air from getting into the hydraulic system, do not shake the pressure tank. Set the tank in the required location, bring the air hose to the tank, and do not move it during the bleeding operation. The tank should be kept at least one-third full.

The bleeder valves should be opened at least one full turn, and intermittently closed at about four-second intervals. This gives a whirling action to fluid in the hydraulic system, and helps expel the air.

MANUAL BLEEDING

On models with power brakes, bleed the hydraulic system without the engine running, first reduce vacuum in the power unit to zero by pumping the brake pedal several times with the engine off.

1. Ensure master cylinder reservoir is full.
2. Raise and support vehicle.
3. Position a drain pan under the wheel being bled.
4. Have an assistant depress the brake pedal with a slow even strokes until pressure is felt, then hold it. **Do not depress brake pedal fully to the end of the master cylinder stroke. This may cause damage to the master cylinder.**
5. Starting at the bleeder screw farthest from the master cylinder, using a suitable wrench, open the bleeder valve one full turn. Watch for air bubbles in the fluid, and listen for air escaping from the system.

6. With the brake pedal still depressed, close the bleeder valve.
7. Have the assistant pump the brake pedal several times, then repeat procedure until air no longer is noticed when bleeder is opened. **Do not depress brake pedal fully to the end of the master cylinder stroke, this may cause damage to the master cylinder.**
8. Repeat previous steps for all bleeders. Ensure all air is removed from the hydraulic system. **While bleeding the system, recheck brake fluid supply in the master cylinder often so as not to allow the master cylinder to run dry.**
9. Upon completion of hydraulic system bleeding proceed as follows:
   a. Ensure the master cylinder reservoir is full. Add suitable brake fluid as needed, and securely reinstall the master cylinder cap.
   b. Lower the vehicle. Ensure brake pedal is firm and braking operation is proper.

BRAKE PAD SERVICE

1. Remove approximately 1/3 of brake fluid from master cylinder.
2. Raise and support front of vehicle, then remove tire and wheel assembly.
3. Remove the clip, then while holding cross spring, remove pad pins, **Fig. 1.**
4. Remove brake pad assemblies and shims.
5. Press caliper piston into caliper bore with suitable tool.
6. Apply a suitable multi-purpose grease to both sides of inner shims, then install pad assemblies and shims, pad pins and clip.
7. Depress brake pedal several times to seat pads, then check and replenish brake fluid as necessary.
8. Install wheel and tire assembly and lower vehicle.

CALIPER SERVICE

CALIPER, REPLACE

1. Raise and support vehicle, then remove wheel and tire assembly.
2. Disconnect brake hose at caliper strut, then at the brake caliper.
3. Remove brake pads.

4. Remove caliper to steering knuckle attaching bolts, then remove caliper assembly.
5. Reverse procedure to install, then bleed brakes as outlined under"Brake System, Bleeding"

CALIPER OVERHAUL

1. Remove pads as described under "Brake Pad, Service."
2. Disconnect brake hose at brake tube connection and caliper, then remove caliper mounting bolts and caliper.
3. Place caliper on a suitable work bench, remove retaining rings and piston boots, **Fig. 1**, then install a wooden block in center of caliper body and apply compressed air to evenly remove the four pistons. **Keep fingers away from piston area to avoid being pinched. Wear safety glasses to avoid brake fluid from getting into eyes.**
4. Remove piston seals using a suitable screwdriver, then the washers. **Do not damage cylinder inner surface.**
5. Reverse procedure to assemble, noting the following:
   a. Inspect cylinders and pistons for wear or damage and/or corrosion. Inspect caliper body for wear.
   b. Apply suitable brake fluid to inner cylinders, then install piston seals into cylinder groove. **Do not use grease from seal and boot repair kit on piston seals.**
   c. Apply suitable brake fluid to pistons and insert into cylinder without twisting.
   d. Fill piston edges with grease from seal and boot repair kit, then install piston boots.
   e. Bleed brakes as outlined under "Brake System, Bleeding."

ROTOR
REPLACE

Remove caliper as outlined under "Caliper Service," then remove rotor. If necessary use a suitable soft face hammer to tap rotor free of hub.

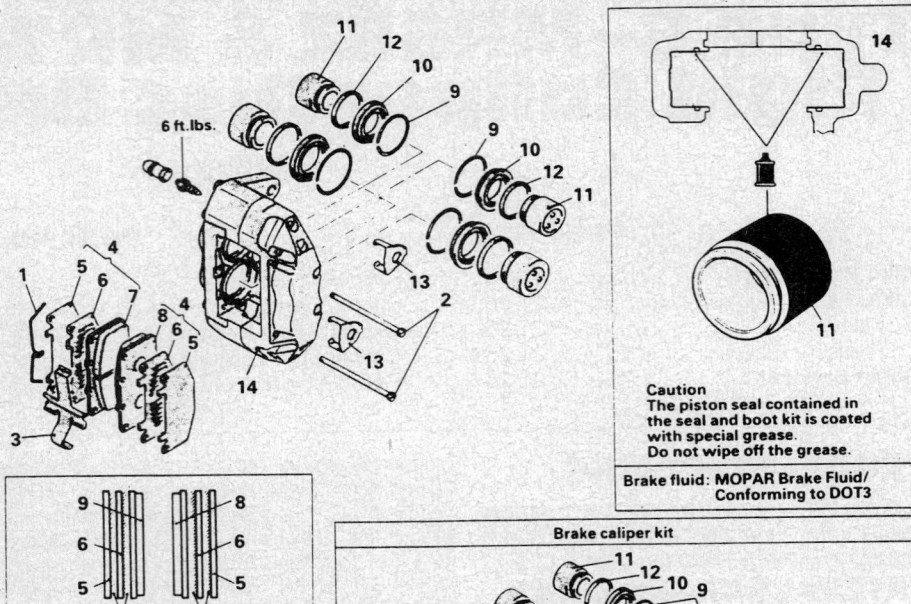

Caution
The piston seal contained in the seal and boot kit is coated with special grease.
Do not wipe off the grease.

Brake fluid: MOPAR Brake Fluid/ Conforming to DOT3

Grease: MOPAR Multi-Purpose Grease Part No. 2932524 or equivalent

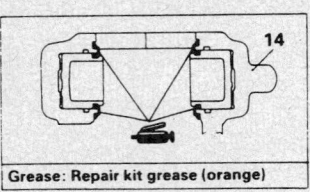

Grease: Repair kit grease (orange)

1. Clip
2. Pad pin
3. Cross spring
4. Pad assembly
5. Shim
6. Shim
7. Inner pad (with wear indicator)
8. Outer pad
9. Retaining ring
10. Piston boot
11. Piston
12. Piston seal
13. Washer
14. Caliper body

Brake caliper kit

Pad kit   Seal-and-boot kit

Grease

CR4079100044000X

Fig. 1   MR66Z & MR76Z 4-piston rigid caliper disc brake assembly. Stealth AWD

DISC BRAKE SPECIFICATIONS

ROTOR SPECIFICATIONS

Yea	Model	Nominal Thickness (Inches)	Minimum Allowable Thickness (Inches)	Thickness Variation Parallelism (Inches)	Lateral Runout (T.I.R.)	Finish (Micro-Inch)
1992-93	Stealth AWD ①	1.1800	1.1200	.0006	.0040	—
1994	Stealth AWD ②	1.1800	1.1200	.0006	.0040	—

① —9.8 inch rotor.
② —10.7 inch rotor.

CALIPER SPECIFICATIONS

Model	Year	Caliper Bore Dia. Inch
Stealth AWD	1992-94	①

① —Two pistons at 1.5938 inch & two at 1.6875 inch.

TIGHTENING SPECIFICATIONS

Year	Component	Torque/Ft. Lbs.
1992-94	Bleed Screws	5–7
	Caliper Support To Front Axle	65
	Caliper Guide And Lockpins,	54
	Wheel Lug Nuts	87-101

Type 9–MR31S, MR34V, MR44V & MR46V Dual Pin Floating Caliper Disc Brake, Front

INDEX

TROUBLESHOOTING

Refer to "Type 1–MR56W & MR57W Dual Piston Floating Caliper Disc Brake, Front" for system troubleshooting.

LATERAL RUNOUT CHECK

Refer to "Disc Brake Specifications" for runout specifications.

1. Raise and support vehicle, then remove wheels.
2. If applicable, ensure wheel bearings are properly adjusted.
3. Using suitable spacers install lug nuts or bolts, then torque to specifications.
4. Mount a dial indicator to a convenient part of the vehicle (steering knuckle, tie rod, disc brake caliper housing).
5. Position dial indicator plunger so it contacts the disc at a point one inch from the outer edge.
6. Rotate the rotor and note the dial indicator readings. Perform this check on both inboard and outboard rotor faces.
7. If runout exceeds specifications proceed as follows:

a. Reposition rotor on the hub, then recheck runout.
b. If runout still exceeds specifications, replace or machine the rotor.

PARALLELISM CHECK

Refer to "Disc Brake Specifications" for parallelism specifications.

1. Using a suitable micrometer, measure the rotor at 12 equally spaced points at a radius approximately one inch from edge of disc.
2. If measurements exceed specifications and the rotor cannot be machined, replace it.
3. If measurements exceed specifications and the rotor can be machined, resurface it.
4. Recheck parallelism. If measurements still exceed specifications, replace the rotor.

BRAKE SYSTEM BLEED

Bleeding the hydraulic brake system is necessary if air has entered the system. Symptoms can be noted by loss of brake operation, and/or a low or spongy brake pedal.

The hydraulic fluid is bled or flushed from the system through bleeder valves located on the calipers, wheel cylinders, and some master cylinders. When bleeding the hydraulic brake system, use only specified brake fluid. **Never reuse old brake fluid removed from the system.**

PRESSURE BLEEDING

Pressure bleeding is recommended for all hydraulic brake systems. It is the fastest method because the master cylinder is automatically fed brake fluid from the pressure bleeder reservoir, and no pedal pumping is needed so only one person is required to perform the procedure. However, if pressure bleeding equipment is not available, the hydraulic system may be bled as described under "Manual Bleeding."

While pressure bleeding, to prevent air from getting into the hydraulic system, do not shake the pressure tank. Set the tank in the required location, bring the air hose to the tank, and do not move it during the bleeding operation. The tank should be kept at least one-third full.

The bleeder valves should be opened at least one full turn, and intermittently closed at about four-second intervals. This gives a whirling action to fluid in the hydraulic system, and helps expel the air.

MANUAL BLEEDING

On models with power brakes, bleed the hydraulic system without the engine running, first reduce vacuum in the power unit to zero by pumping the brake pedal several times with the engine off.

1. Ensure master cylinder reservoir is full.
2. Raise and support vehicle.
3. Position a drain pan under the wheel being bled.
4. Have an assistant depress the brake pedal with a slow even strokes until pressure is felt, then hold it. **Do not depress brake pedal fully to the end of the master cylinder stroke. This may cause damage to the master cylinder.**
5. Starting at the bleeder screw farthest from the master cylinder, using a suitable wrench, open the bleeder valve one full turn. Watch for air bubbles in the fluid, and listen for air escaping from the system.
6. With the brake pedal still depressed, close the bleeder valve.
7. Have the assistant pump the brake pedal several times, then repeat procedure until air no longer is noticed when bleeder is opened. **Do not depress brake pedal fully to the end of the master cylinder stroke, this may cause damage to the master cylinder.**
8. Repeat previous steps for all bleeders. Ensure all air is removed from the hydraulic system. **While bleeding the system, recheck brake fluid supply in the master cylinder often so as not to allow the master cylinder to run dry.**
9. Upon completion of hydraulic system bleeding proceed as follows:
   a. Ensure the master cylinder reservoir is full. Add suitable brake fluid as needed, and securely reinstall the master cylinder cap.
   b. Lower the vehicle. Ensure brake pedal is firm and braking operation is proper.

BRAKE PAD SERVICE

1. Remove approximately 1/3 of brake fluid from master cylinder.
2. Raise and support vehicle, then remove tire and wheel assembly.
3. Remove guide pin or lower slide pin, **Fig. 1 and 2,** then lift caliper body upward and secure with wire.
4. Remove inner shims, anti-squeak shims, brake pad assemblies and pad clips from support mounting.
5. Press caliper piston into caliper bore with suitable tool.
6. Install upper and lower pad clips, pad assemblies, inner shims and anti-squeak shims into support mounting.
7. Lower caliper body, then install lockpin.

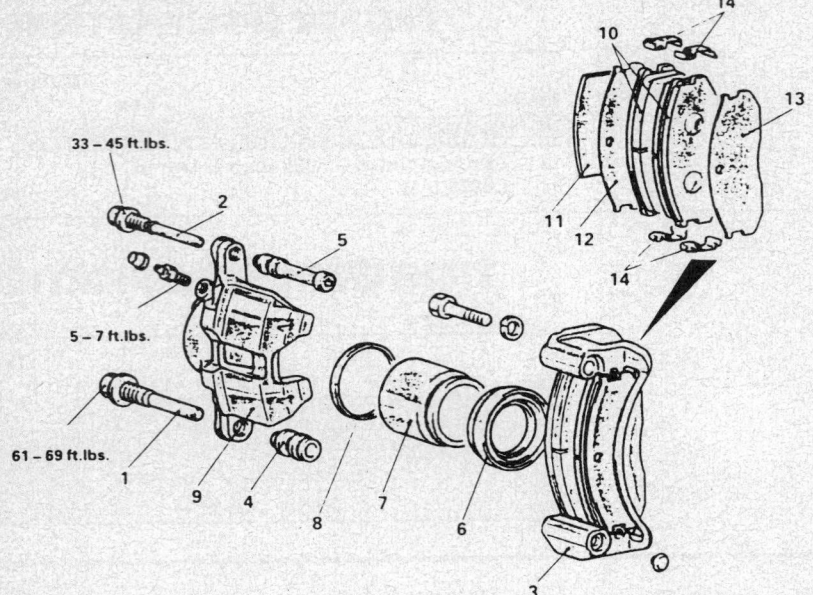

33 – 45 ft.lbs.

5 – 7 ft.lbs.

61 – 69 ft.lbs.

1. Slide pin (M14)
2. Slide pin (M10)
3. Torque member (pad, pad liner, shim)
4. Pin boot
5. Bushing
6. Piston boot
7. Piston
8. Piston seal
9. Caliper body
10. Pad assembly
11. Inner shim
12. Inner shim
13. Outer shim
14. Pad liner

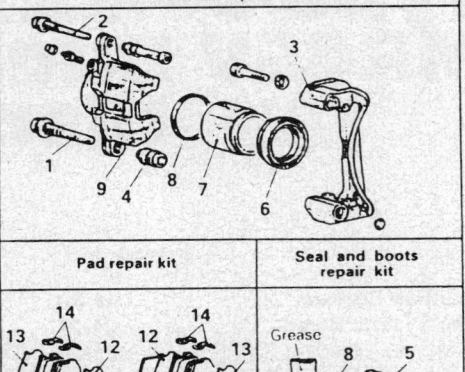

Brake caliper kit

Pad repair kit

Seal and boots repair kit

Grease

CR4079100059000X

Fig. 1   MR31S dual pin floating caliper disc brake assembly. Colt

8. Depress brake pedal several times to seat pads, then check and replenish brake fluid as necessary.
9. Install wheel and tire assembly and lower vehicle.

CALIPER SERVICE
CALIPER, REPLACE

1. Raise and support vehicle, then remove wheel and tire assembly.
2. Disconnect brake hose at caliper strut, then at the brake caliper. Cap vehicle brake line.
3. Remove brake pads as outlined under "Brake Pad Service".
4. Remove caliper support to steering knuckle attaching bolts, then caliper support.
5. Reverse procedure to install, noting the following:
   a. Tighten bolts to specifications.
   b. Bleed brakes as outlined under "Brake System Bleed".

CALIPER OVERHAUL
Colt

1. Remove caliper assembly as described under "Caliper, Replace."
2. Remove upper slide pin, torque member, pin boot and bushing, **Fig. 1.**
3. Position a shop towel in caliper body, then apply compressed air through the brake hose fitting hole to remove piston and dust boot. **Apply air gently.**
4. Remove piston seal using finger tips. **Do not use screwdriver or other tool to prevent damage to inner cylinder.**
5. Reverse procedure to assemble, noting the following:
   a. Inspect cylinder and piston for wear or damage and/or corrosion. Inspect caliper body and sleeve for wear.
   b. Apply suitable brake fluid to inner

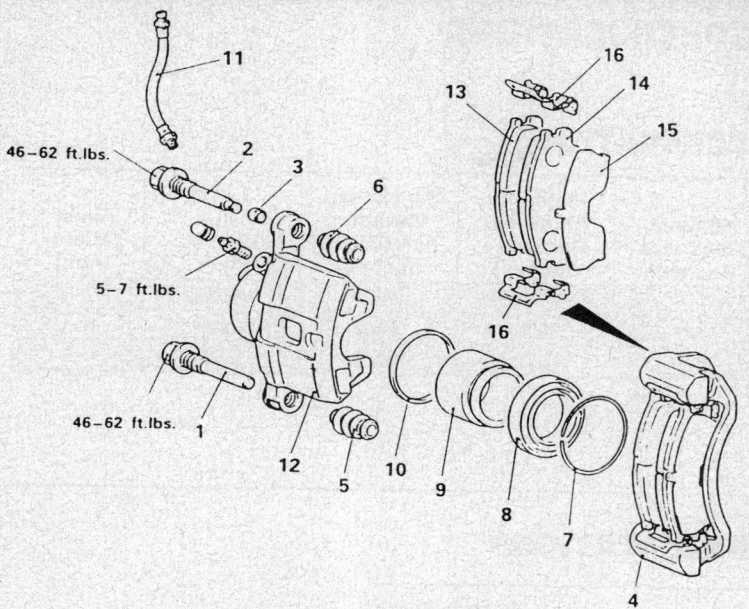

1. Guide pin
2. Lock pin
3. Bushing
4. Caliper support (Pad. clip. shim)
5. Guide pin boot
6. Lock pin boot
7. Boot ring
8. Piston boot
9. Piston
10. Piston seal
11. Brake hose
12. Caliper body
13. Pad and wear indicator assembly
14. Pad assembly
15. Outer shim
16. Clip

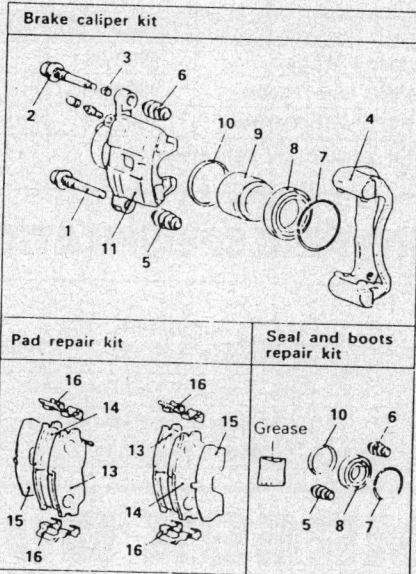

Brake caliper kit

Pad repair kit

Seal and boots
repair kit

Grease

CR4079100060000X

Fig. 2   MR34V, MR44V & MR46V dual pin floating caliper disc brake assembly. Except Colt

cylinder, then install piston seal into cylinder groove. **Do not wipe special grease from piston seal.**

c. Apply suitable brake fluid to piston and insert into cylinder without twisting.

d. Fill piston edge with grease from seal and boot repair kit or equivalent, then install piston boot.

e. Lubricate bushing, pin boot and slide pins with grease from seal and boot repair kit.

Except Colt

1. Remove caliper assembly as described under "Caliper, Replace."
2. Remove lockpin, bushing, caliper support, guide pin and lockpin boots, **Fig. 2.**
3. Remove boot ring using a suitable flat blade screwdriver.
4. Position a shop towel in caliper body, then apply compressed air through the brake hose fitting hole to remove piston and dust boot. **Apply air gently.**
5. Remove piston seal using finger tips. **Do not use screwdriver or other tool to prevent damage to inner cylinder.**
6. Reverse procedure to assemble, noting the following:
   a. Inspect cylinder and piston for wear or damage and/or corrosion. Inspect caliper body and sleeve for wear.
   b. Apply suitable brake fluid to inner cylinder, then install piston seal into cylinder groove. **Do not wipe special grease from piston seal.**
   c. Apply suitable brake fluid to piston and insert into cylinder without twisting.
   d. Fill piston edge with grease from seal and boot repair kit or equivalent, then install piston boot.
   e. Lubricate sliding surface of lockpin and guide pin boots, caliper support and bushing with grease from seal and boot repair kit.
   f. Install guide and lockpins with their head marks matched with identification marks on caliper body.

ROTOR REPLACE

Remove caliper as outlined under "Caliper Service," then remove rotor. If necessary use a suitable soft face hammer to tap rotor free of hub.

DISC BRAKE SPECIFICATIONS

ROTOR SPECIFICATIONS

Year	Model	Nominal Thickness (Inches)	Minimum Allowable Thickness (Inches)	Thickness Variation Parallelism (Inches)	Lateral Runout (T.I.R.)	Finish (Micro-Inch)
1992-94	Colt/Summit	①	②	.0006	.0028	—
1992-94	Colt Vista & Summit Wagon	.945	.882	.0006	.0028	—
1992-94	Laser & Talon	.940	.882	.0006	.0028	—

①—Solid rotor .511 inch; vented rotor .710 inch.

②—Solid rotor .450 inch; vented rotor .650 inch.

CALIPER SPECIFICATIONS

Model	Year	Caliper Bore Dia. Inch
Colt/Summit	1992-94	①
Colt Vista/Summit Wagon	1992-94	2.375
Laser/Talon FWD less Turbo	1992-94	2.125
Laser/Talon FWD with Turbo	1992-94	2.375

①—Solid rotor 2.010 inch; vented rotor 2.125 inch.

TIGHTENING SPECIFICATIONS

Year	Component	Torque/Ft. Lbs.
1992-94	Bleed Screws	5–7
	Caliper Support To Front Axle	65
	Caliper Guide And Lockpins,	54
	Wheel Lug Nuts	87–101

Type 10—MR68X Dual Piston, Rigid Caliper Disc Brake, Rear

INDEX

TROUBLESHOOTING

Refer to "Type 1-MR56W & MR57W Dual Piston Floating Caliper Disc Brake, Front" for system troubleshooting.

LATERAL RUNOUT CHECK

Refer to "Disc Brake Specifications" for runout specifications.

1. Raise and support vehicle, then remove wheels.
2. If applicable, ensure wheel bearings are properly adjusted.
3. Using suitable spacers install lug nuts or bolts, then torque to specifications.
4. Mount a dial indicator to a convenient part of the vehicle (steering knuckle, tie rod, disc brake caliper housing).
5. Position dial indicator plunger so it contacts the disc at a point one inch from the outer edge.
6. Rotate the rotor and note the dial indicator readings. Perform this check on both inboard and outboard rotor faces.

TYPE 10-MR68X, DUAL PISTON, RIGID CALIPER DISC BRAKE, FRONT

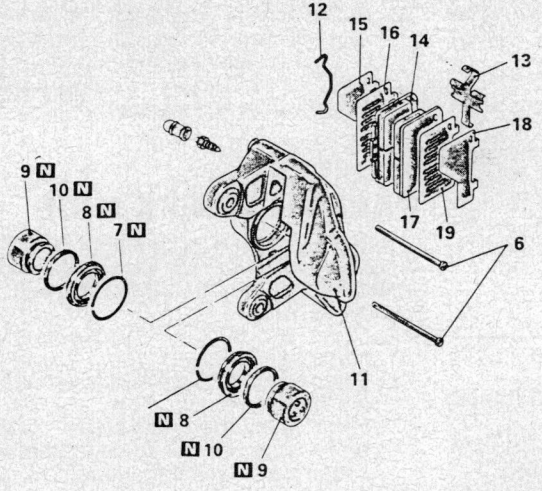

Caliper assembly disassembly steps

- 6 Pad pin
- 7 Retaining ring
- ◆◆ 8 Piston boot
- ◆◆ 9 Piston
- ◆◆ 10 Piston seal
- 11 Caliper body

Pad assembly disassembly steps

- 6 Pad pin
- 12 Clip
- 13 Cross spring
- 14 Pad and wear indicator assembly
- 15 Inner shim B
- 16 Inner shim A
- 17 Pad assembly
- 18 Outer shim B
- 19 Outer shim A

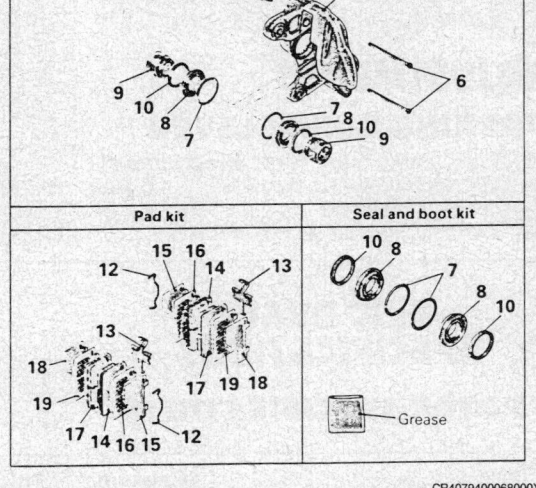

Brake caliper kit

Pad kit

Seal and boot kit

Grease

CR4079400068000X

Fig. 1 MR68X dual piston rigid caliper rear disk brake assembly. Stealth AWD

7. If runout exceeds specifications proceed as follows:
   a. Reposition rotor on the hub, then recheck runout.
   b. If runout still exceeds specifications, replace or machine the rotor.

BRAKE SYSTEM BLEED

Bleeding the hydraulic brake system is necessary if air has entered the system. Symptoms can be noted by loss of brake operation, and/or a low or spongy brake pedal.

The hydraulic fluid is bled or flushed from the system through bleeder valves located on the calipers, wheel cylinders, and some master cylinders. When bleeding the hydraulic brake system, use only specified brake fluid. **Never reuse old brake fluid removed from the system.**

PRESSURE BLEEDING

Pressure bleeding is recommended for all hydraulic brake systems. It is the fastest method because the master cylinder is automatically fed brake fluid from the pressure bleeder reservoir, and no pedal pumping is needed so only one person is required to perform the procedure. However, if pressure bleeding equipment is not available, the hydraulic system may be bled as described under "Manual Bleeding."

While pressure bleeding, to prevent air from getting into the hydraulic system, do not shake the pressure tank. Set the tank in the required location, bring the air hose to the tank, and do not move it during the bleeding operation. The tank should be kept at least one-third full.

The bleeder valves should be opened at least one full turn, and intermittently closed at about four-second intervals. This gives a whirling action to fluid in the hydraulic system, and helps expel the air.

MANUAL BLEEDING

On models with power brakes, bleed the hydraulic system without the engine running, first reduce vacuum in the power unit to zero by pumping the brake pedal several times with the engine off.

1. Ensure master cylinder reservoir is full.
2. Raise and support vehicle.
3. Position a drain pan under the wheel being bled.
4. Have an assistant depress the brake pedal with a slow even strokes until pressure is felt, then hold it. **Do not depress brake pedal fully to the end of the master cylinder stroke. This may cause damage to the master cylinder.**
5. Starting at the bleeder screw farthest from the master cylinder, using a suitable wrench, open the bleeder valve one full turn. Watch for air bubbles in the fluid, and listen for air escaping from the system.
6. With the brake pedal still depressed, close the bleeder valve.
7. Have the assistant pump the brake pedal several times, then repeat procedure until air no longer is noticed when bleeder is opened. **Do not depress brake pedal fully to the end of the master cylinder stroke, this may cause damage to the master cylinder.**
8. Repeat previous steps for all bleeders. Ensure all air is removed from the hydraulic system. **While bleeding the system, recheck brake fluid supply in the master cylinder often so as not to allow the master cylinder to run dry.**
9. Upon completion of hydraulic system bleeding proceed as follows:
   a. Ensure the master cylinder reservoir is full. Add suitable brake fluid as needed, and securely reinstall the master cylinder cap.
   b. Lower the vehicle. Ensure brake pedal is firm and braking operation is proper.

BRAKE PAD SERVICE

1. Remove approximately ⅓ of brake fluid from master cylinder.
2. Raise and support vehicle, then remove tire and wheel assembly.
3. Remove the clip, then while holding cross spring, remove pad pins, **Fig. 1.**
4. Remove brake pad assemblies and shims.
5. Press caliper piston into caliper bore with suitable tool.
6. Apply a suitable multi-purpose grease to both sides of inner shims, then install pad assemblies and shims, pad pins and clip.
7. Depress brake pedal several times to seat pads, then check and replenish brake fluid as necessary.
8. Install wheel and tire assembly and lower vehicle.

CALIPER SERVICE

CALIPER, REPLACE

1. Raise and support vehicle, then remove wheel and tire assembly.
2. Disconnect brake hose at caliper strut, then at the brake caliper. Cap vehicle brake line.
3. Remove brake pads as outlined under

"Brake Pad Service".

4. Remove caliper support to steering knuckle attaching bolts, then caliper support.

5. Reverse procedure to install, noting the following:
   a. Tighten bolts to specifications.
   b. Bleed brakes as outlined under "Brake System Bleed".

CALIPER OVERHAUL

1. Remove pads as described under "Brake Pad, Service."

2. Disconnect brake hose at brake tube connection and caliper, then remove caliper mounting bolts and caliper.

3. Place caliper on a suitable work bench, remove retaining rings and piston boots, **Fig. 1** then install a wooden block in center of caliper body and apply compressed air to evenly remove the four pistons. **Keep fingers away from piston area to avoid being pinched. Wear safety glasses to avoid brake fluid from getting into eyes.**

4. Remove piston seals using a suitable screwdriver, then the washers. **Do not damage cylinder inner surface.**

5. Reverse procedure to assemble, noting the following:
   a. Inspect cylinders and pistons for wear or damage and/or corrosion. Inspect caliper body for wear.
   b. Apply suitable brake fluid to inner cylinders, then install piston seals into cylinder groove. **Do not wipe special grease from piston seals.**
   c. Apply suitable brake fluid to pistons and insert into cylinder without twisting.
   d. Fill piston edges with grease from seal and boot repair kit or equivalent, then install piston boots.
   e. Bleed brakes as outlined under "Brake System, Bleeding"

ROTOR
REPLACE

1. Remove caliper as outlined under "Caliper Service."

2. Remove parking brake adjustment hole plug from hub of brake disc.

3. Using a suitable tool, turn parking brake adjusting nut until brake disc can be removed.

4. Reverse procedure to install, adjust parking brake as outlined under "Adjustments"

ADJUSTMENTS
PARKING BRAKE LEVER

1. Pull parking brake lever with a force of approximately 45 lbs. while counting number of clicks.

2. Lever should click 3-5 times .

3. If not within specifications, remove cup holder and plug, then turn adjusting nut located behind parking brake lever as necessary to bring parking brake within specifications.

PARKING BRAKE SHOE

If parking brake application is unbalanced or if repairs are made to parking brake system, shoe adjustment will be necessary

1. Raise and support vehicle, then remove rear wheels.

2. Disconnect drive axles from companion flange.

3. Firmly apply, then fully release parking brake lever several times to seat and center parking brake shoes.

4. Remove adjusting hole plug from hub of brake disc.

5. Using a suitable tool, turn adjusting nut until brake disc cannot be turned by hand.

6. Back off adjusting nut five notches.

7. Repeat above steps on opposite side.

8. Connect drive axles to companion flange.

9. Firmly apply, then fully release parking brake lever several times to seat and center parking brake shoes.

10. Adjust parking brake lever as outlined under "Parking Brake Lever Adjust"

11. Install rear wheels, then lower vehicle

DISC BRAKE SPECIFICATIONS

ROTOR SPECIFICATIONS

Year	Model	Nominal Thickness (Inches)	Minimum Refinish Thickness (Inches)	Thickness Variation Parallelism (Inches)	Lateral Runout (T.I.R.)	Finish (Micro-Inch)
1994	Stealth AWD	.790	.720	—	.0031	—

CALIPER SPECIFICATIONS

Model	Year	Caliper Bore Dia. Inch
Stealth AWD	1994	1.500

TIGHTENING SPECIFICATIONS

Year	Component	Torque/Ft. Lbs.
1994	Bleed Screws	5–7
	Caliper Support To Front Axle	65
	Caliper Guide And Lockpins,	54
	Wheel Lug Nuts	87–101

TYPE 10-MR68X, DUAL PISTON, RIGID CALIPER DISC BRAKE, FRONT

DRUM BRAKES

TABLE OF CONTENTS

Application Chart

Model	Year	Drum Brake Type
Colt/Summit	1992–94	4
Colt Vista/Summit Wagon	1992–94	5
Except Colt/Summit, Colt Vista/Summit Wagon, Neon & Monaco	1992–94	2/3
Monaco	1992	1
Neon	1995	2

Type 1—Leading Trailing Drum Brake

INDEX

PRECAUTIONS

When working on or around brake assemblies, care must be taken to prevent breathing asbestos dust, as many manufacturers incorporate asbestos fibers in the production of brake linings. During routine service operations, the amount of asbestos dust from brake lining wear is at a low level due to a chemical breakdown during use. A few precautions will minimize exposure.

Do not sand or grind brake linings unless suitable local exhaust ventilation equipment is used to prevent excessive asbestos exposure.
1. Wear a suitable respirator approved for asbestos dust use during all repair procedures.
2. When cleaning brake dust from brake parts, use a vacuum cleaner with a highly efficient filter system. If a suitable vacuum cleaner is not available, use a water soaked rag. **Do not use compressed air or dry brush to clean brake parts.**
3. Keep work area clean using same equipment as for cleaning brake parts.
4. Properly dispose of rags and vacuum cleaner bags by placing them in plastic bags.
5. Do not smoke or eat while working on brake systems.
6. Never use any fluid containing mineral oil to clean brake system components. This will damage the rubber caps and seals. If system contamination is suspected, check brake fluid in the reservoir for dirt, discoloration, or separation (breakdown) of the brake fluid into distinct layers. Drain and flush the hydraulic system with clean brake fluid if contamination is suspected.

pected.

INSPECTION

1. Inspect components for damage and unusual wear. Replace as necessary.
2. Inspect wheel cylinders. Boots which are torn, cut, or heat damaged indicate need for wheel cylinder replacement. Fluid spilling from boot center hole, or wetness around wheel cylinder ends indicates cup leakage and need for wheel cylinder replacement. **A small amount of fluid is always present and is considered normal, acting as a lubricant for the cylinder pistons.**
3. Inspect backing plate for evidence of seal leakage. If leakage exists, refer to individual car chapters for axle seal replacement procedure.
4. Inspect backing plate attaching bolts

5. Check adjuster screw operation. If satisfactory, lightly lubricate adjusting screw and washer with suitable brake lube. If operation is unsatisfactory, replace.

6. Using fine emery cloth or other suitable abrasive, clean rust and dirt from shoe contact surfaces on backing plate. Apply brake lube to contact surfaces and to park brake lever pivot pin.

BRAKE DRUMS

Any time the brake drums are removed for brake service, the braking surface diameter should be checked with a suitable brake drum micrometer at several points to determine if they are within the safe oversize limit stamped on the brake drum outer surface. If the braking surface diameter exceeds specifications, the drum must be replaced. If the braking surface diameter is within specifications, drums should be cleaned and inspected for cracks, scores, deep grooves, taper, out of round and heat spotting. If drums are cracked or heat spotted, they must be replaced. Scoring and grooves in the braking surface can only be removed by machining with special equipment, as long as the braking surface is within specifications. Any brake drum showing taper or sufficiently out of round to cause vehicle vibration or noise while braking should also be machined, removing only enough stock to true up the drum.

After a brake drum is machined, wipe the braking surface diameter with a denatured alcohol soaked cloth. If one brake drum is machined, the other should also be machined to the same diameter to maintain equal braking forces.

BRAKE LININGS & SPRINGS

Inspect brake linings for excessive wear, damage, oil, grease or brake fluid contamination. If any of the above conditions exist, brake linings should be replaced as an axle set to maintain equal braking forces. Examine brake shoe webbing, hold-down and return springs for signs of overheating indicated by a slight blue color. Any component which exhibits overheating signs should be replaced. Overheated springs lose their pull and could cause brake linings to wear out prematurely. Inspect all springs for sags, bends and external damage and replace as necessary.

Inspect hold-down retainers and pins for bends, rust and corrosion. If any of the above is found, replace as required.

BACKING PLATE

Inspect backing plate shoe contact surface for grooves that may restrict shoe movement and cannot be removed by lightly sanding with emery cloth or other suitable abrasive. If backing plate exhibits above condition, it should be replaced. Also inspect for signs of cracks, warpage and excessive rust, indicating need for replacement.

ADJUSTER MECHANISM

Inspect all components for rust, corrosion, bends and fatigue. Replace as necessary. On adjuster mechanism equipped with adjuster cable, inspect cable for kinks, fraying or elongation of eyelet and replace as necessary.

PARKING BRAKE CABLE

Inspect parking brake cable end for kinks, fraying and elongation and replace as necessary. Use a small hose clamp to compress clamp where it enters backing plate to remove.

TROUBLESHOOTING

Refer to **Fig. 1.** for brake systems and troubleshooting.

INCIDENTS	POSSIBLE CAUSES
Brakes binding or grabbing	- Linings not chamfered
	- Oil or grease on linings
	- Caliper seized
	- Weak return springs
Brakes pulsating	- Oval drums
	- Excessive disc run-out
	- Discs not of even thickness
	- Abnormal deposit on discs (corrosion between lining and disc).
	- Linings cracked or broken
Front brakes pulling to one side	- Check front end alignment
	- Check front axle, suspension and steering
	- Piston seized*
	- Tires (worn - incorrect inflation pressure)
	- Pinched brake-line.
	*ATTENTION: Pulling to one side indicates a seized piston on the opposite side.
Rear brakes pulling to one side	- Incorrect compensator or limiter setting
	- Piston seized
	- Incorrect shoe adjustment manual adjustment: shoe too far from drum
	automatic adjustment: handbrake cable too tight.
	NOTE: Automatic wear take-up is performed by the brake pedal provided the handbrake cable is not abnormally tight when in off position
	- Return spring
Overheating brakes	- Master cylinder operating clearance insufficient to allow master cylinder to return to neutral position.
	- Master cylinder operating clearance insufficient to allow master cylinder to return to neutral position.
	- Piston seized or not returning properly.
	- Pinched brake line
	- Handbrake mechanism seized
	- Incorrect handbrake adjustment

CR4089200017010X

Fig. 1   Brake system troubleshooting (Part 1 of 2)

BRAKE SERVICE
REMOVAL

1. Raise and support vehicle.
2. Remove rear wheel and tire assembly.
3. Remove brake drum. If brake lining is dragging on brake drum, remove access plug from backing plate and back off brake adjustment by rotating adjustment screw.
4. Install suitable wheel cylinder clamp over ends of wheel cylinder to retain pistons in bore.
5. Remove upper and lower return springs, **Fig. 2,** using suitable brake spring pliers.

INCIDENT	POSSIBLE CAUSES

"Hard pedal":
 	
Great effort Needed and only a slight deceleration noticed in vehicle.
	· Power servo defective
	
	· Linings/pads
	
	  · oily
	  · glazed, not to specification
	  · overheating (due to excessive braking) or not to specification
	  · seized piston
	  · pinched brake line
	  · pads/linings worn:

"Soft pedal"
 	
Note: since the power servo system on current vehicles is very effective, the impression may be given that the pedal is "soft". To find out whether an incident has occurred or the braking system is operating normally, two tests must be performed.
 	
1. Vehicle moving
  · Assessment test: relation between pedal travel and vehicle deceleration.
 	
2. Vehicle stationary with ignition off
  · Additional test on pedal travel: depress the brake pedal 5 times to empty the brake servo, before assessing the result of the test.
	· Air in system: poor bleeding
	
	· Internal leakage in braking system
	
	· Lack of fluid in reservoir (external leak in braking system).

"Long" pedal travel Test to be performed with vehicle stationary and ignition off. Note: The brake pedal must be depressed 5 times in order to empty the brake servo before taking account of the test results.	· Incorrect shoe adjustment Drum brakes · Manual adjustments: shoes too far from drum surface. Disc and drum brakes · Automatic adjustment: handbrake cable too tight. Note: Automatic wear take-up is performed by by the brake pedal, provided the handbrake is not abnormally tight in the off position. · Excessively worn pads/linings of pads/linings not symmetrical (or crossed) · Excessive master cylinder operating clearance. · Brake fluid boiling or has heated up.
Pedal "travels to floor" Test to be performed on stationary vehicle with ignition off. Note: The brake pedal must be depressed 5 times in order to empty the brake servo before taking account of the test results.	· Fluid loss (check for leaks) · Faulty sealing cup between the two master cylinder circuits. · Brake fluid boiling.

Fig. 1   Brake system troubleshooting (Part 2 of 2)   CR4089200017020X

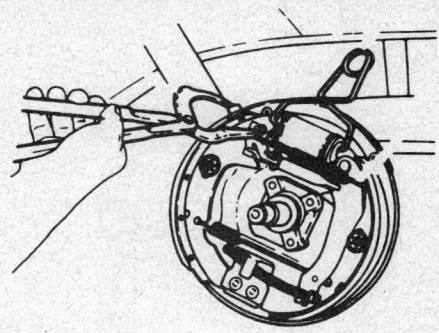

Fig. 2   Upper & lower return spring removal   CR4089100007000X

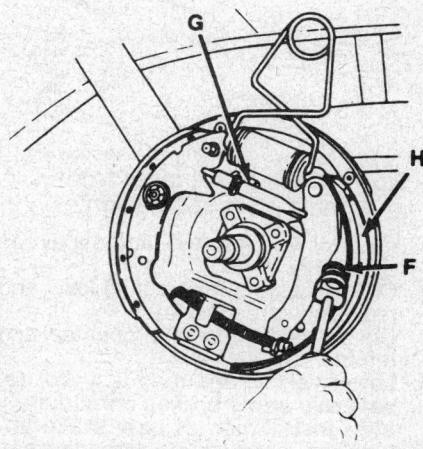

Fig. 3   Primary shoe, hold-down spring & self-adjusting lever removal   CR4089100008000X

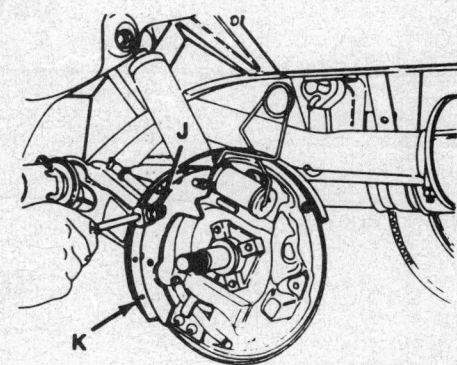

Fig. 4   Secondary shoe & hold-down spring removal   CR4089100009000X

6. Remove adjuster lever, then the parking brake cable from parking brake lever.
7. Using suitable tool, compress and remove rear hold-down spring (F), then remove self-adjusting screw (G) and primary brake shoe (H), **Fig. 3.**
8. Remove front hold-down spring (J), then the secondary brake shoe (K), **Fig. 4.**
9. Using snap ring pliers, remove clip from pivot pin on primary shoe, **Fig. 5,** then separate park brake lever from shoe.
10. Clean dirt from backing plate, brake drum and hardware.

INSTALLATION

1. Install park brake lever on primary brake shoe, compressing clip around pivot pin.
2. Using brake spring pliers, install park brake cable to park brake lever.
3. Install primary brake shoe, hold-down spring and self-adjusting screw.
4. Install secondary brake shoe and hold-down spring. **Ensure shoe is installed into larger (A) of two notches in adjuster lever, Fig. 6.**
5. Remove wheel cylinder clamp, then install adjuster lever (U) to pin (W), **Fig. 7,** and into self-adjusting screw.

Ensure lever is installed into smaller (B) of two notches in adjuster lever, Fig. 6.
6. Install upper and lower return springs.
7. Ensure brake shoes are centered on backing plate.
8. Install brake drum, wheel and tire assembly.
9. If any hydraulic brake connections have been opened, bleed brake system.
10. Adjust parking brake.
11. Inspect all hydraulic lines and con-

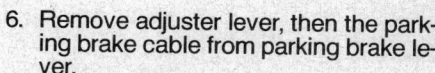

TYPE 1-LEADING TRAILING DRUM BRAKE

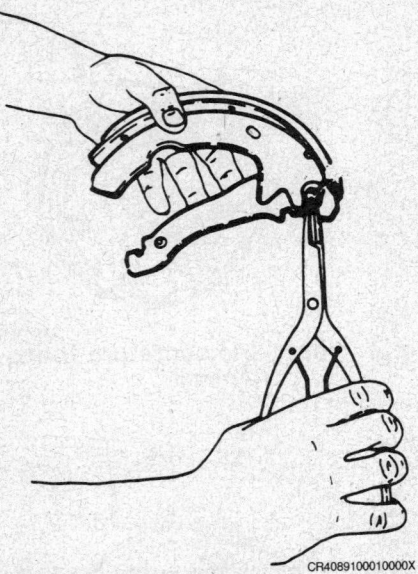

Fig. 5 Park brake lever from primary shoe separation

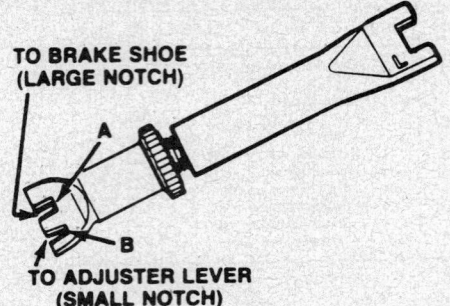

TO BRAKE SHOE (LARGE NOTCH)

A

B

TO ADJUSTER LEVER (SMALL NOTCH)

CR4089100011000X

Fig. 6 Self-adjusting screw notch locations

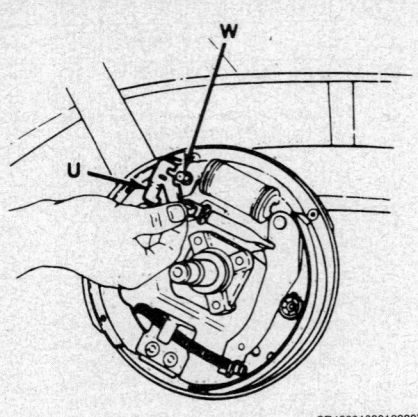

CR4089100012000X

Fig. 7 Adjuster lever installation

nections for leakage and repair as necessary.

12. Check master cylinder fluid level and replenish as necessary.
13. Check brake pedal for proper feel and return.
14. Lower vehicle and road test. **Do not severely apply brakes immediately after installation of new brake linings or permanent damage may occur to linings, and/or brake drums may become scored.**

Brakes must be used moderately during first several hundred miles of operation to ensure proper burnishing of linings.

ADJUSTMENTS

SERVICE BRAKE

1. Each backing plate has two adjusting hole covers; remove the rear cover and turn the adjusting screw upward with a screwdriver or other suitable tool to expand the shoes until a slight drag is felt when the drum is rotated.
2. While holding the adjustment lever out of engagement with the adjusting screw, back off the adjusting screw one complete turn.
3. Install wheel and adjusting hole cover.
4. Lower vehicle and ensure proper brake operation.

PARKING BRAKE

1. Push down on parking brake pedal until one click is heard. **Pedal must be in this position for proper cable adjustment.**
2. Attach a suitable torque wrench to adjusting tool No. J-34651-A, or equivalent.
3. Align notches in tool head with center of parking brake cable.
4. Tighten adjusting nut to remove slack from cable.
5. **Torque** cable to 100-110 inch lbs. using adjusting tool No. J-34651-A, or equivalent, while tightening adjustment nut. To achieve proper adjustment, pointer on tool must be located in one of four dark bands on tool face.

DRUM BRAKE SPECIFICATIONS

Year	Model	Brake Drum Inside Dia. Inch	Rear Wheel Cylinder Bore Dia. Inch
1992	Monaco	8.858	.807

TIGHTENING SPECIFICATIONS

Year	Component	Torque/Ft. Lbs.
1992	Brake Line Fittings	11-15
	Master Cylinder To Booster Nuts	9-13

Type 2 & 3—Kelsey-Hayes & Varga Leading Trailing Drum Brakes

INDEX

PRECAUTIONS

When working on or around brake assemblies, care must be taken to prevent breathing asbestos dust, as many manufacturers incorporate asbestos fibers in the production of brake linings. During routine service operations, the amount of asbestos dust from brake lining wear is at a low level due to a chemical breakdown during use. A few precautions will minimize exposure.

Do not sand or grind brake linings unless suitable local exhaust ventilation equipment is used to prevent excessive asbestos exposure.

1. Wear a suitable respirator approved for asbestos dust use during all repair procedures.
2. When cleaning brake dust from brake parts, use a vacuum cleaner with a highly efficient filter system. If a suitable vacuum cleaner is not available, use a water soaked rag. **Do not use compressed air or dry brush to clean brake parts.**
3. Keep work area clean using same equipment as for cleaning brake parts.
4. Properly dispose of rags and vacuum cleaner bags by placing them in plastic bags.
5. Do not smoke or eat while working on brake systems.
6. Never use any fluid containing mineral oil to clean brake system components. This will damage the rubber caps and seals. If system contamination is suspected, check brake fluid in the reservoir for dirt, discoloration, or separation (breakdown) of the brake fluid into distinct layers. Drain and flush the hydraulic system with clean brake fluid if contamination is suspected.

INSPECTION

BRAKE DRUMS

Any time the brake drums are removed for brake service, the braking surface diameter should be checked with a suitable brake drum micrometer at several points to determine if they are within the safe oversize limit stamped on the brake drum outer surface. If the braking surface diameter exceeds specifications, the drum must be replaced. If the braking surface diameter is within specifications, drums should be cleaned and inspected for cracks, scores, deep grooves, taper, out of round and heat spotting. If drums are cracked or heat spotted, they must be replaced. Scoring and grooves in the braking surface can only be removed by machining with special equipment, as long as the braking surface is within specifications. Any brake drum showing taper or sufficiently out of round to cause vehicle vibration or noise while braking should also be machined, removing only enough stock to true up the drum.

After a brake drum is machined, wipe the braking surface diameter with a denatured alcohol soaked cloth. If one brake drum is machined, the other should also be machined to the same diameter to maintain equal braking forces.

BRAKE LININGS & SPRINGS

Inspect brake linings for excessive wear, damage, oil, grease or brake fluid contamination. If any of the above conditions exist, brake linings should be replaced as an axle set to maintain equal braking forces. Examine brake shoe webbing, hold-down and return springs for signs of overheating indicated by a slight blue color. Any component which exhibits overheating signs should be replaced. Overheated springs lose their pull and could cause brake linings to wear out prematurely. Inspect all springs for sags, bends and external damage and replace as necessary.

Inspect hold-down retainers and pins for bends, rust and corrosion. If any of the above is found, replace as required.

BACKING PLATE

Inspect backing plate shoe contact surface for grooves that may restrict shoe movement and cannot be removed by lightly sanding with emery cloth or other suitable abrasive. If backing plate exhibits above condition, it should be replaced. Also inspect for signs of cracks, warpage and excessive rust, indicating need for replacement.

ADJUSTER MECHANISM

Inspect all components for rust, corrosion, bends and fatigue. Replace as necessary. On adjuster mechanism equipped with adjuster cable, inspect cable for kinks, fraying or elongation of eyelet and replace as necessary.

PARKING BRAKE CABLE

Inspect parking brake cable end for kinks, fraying and elongation and replace as necessary. Use a small hose clamp to compress clamp where it enters backing plate to remove.

TROUBLESHOOTING

Refer to **Fig. 1.** for brake systems and troubleshooting.

BRAKE SERVICE

REMOVAL

1. Raise and support rear of vehicle.
2. Remove tire and wheel assembly, then remove brake drum. If brake lining is dragging on brake drum, back off brake adjustment by rotating adjustment screw.
3. Using suitable pliers, remove adjuster lever spring, **Fig. 2.**
4. Remove adjuster lever.
5. Turn automatic adjuster screw out to expand shoes past wheel cylinder boot.
6. Disconnect parking brake cable from parking brake lever.
7. **On Type 2—Kelsey Hayes,** using suitable tool, remove hold-down springs.
8. Pull brake shoe assembly down and away from anchor plate, then remove brake shoe springs and adjusting screw assembly.
9. **On Type 3—Varga,** remove upper shoe to shoe return spring on leading shoe, **Fig. 3,** leading shoe hold-down spring, shoe to shoe spring at anchor plate, then the shoe and adjuster assembly.

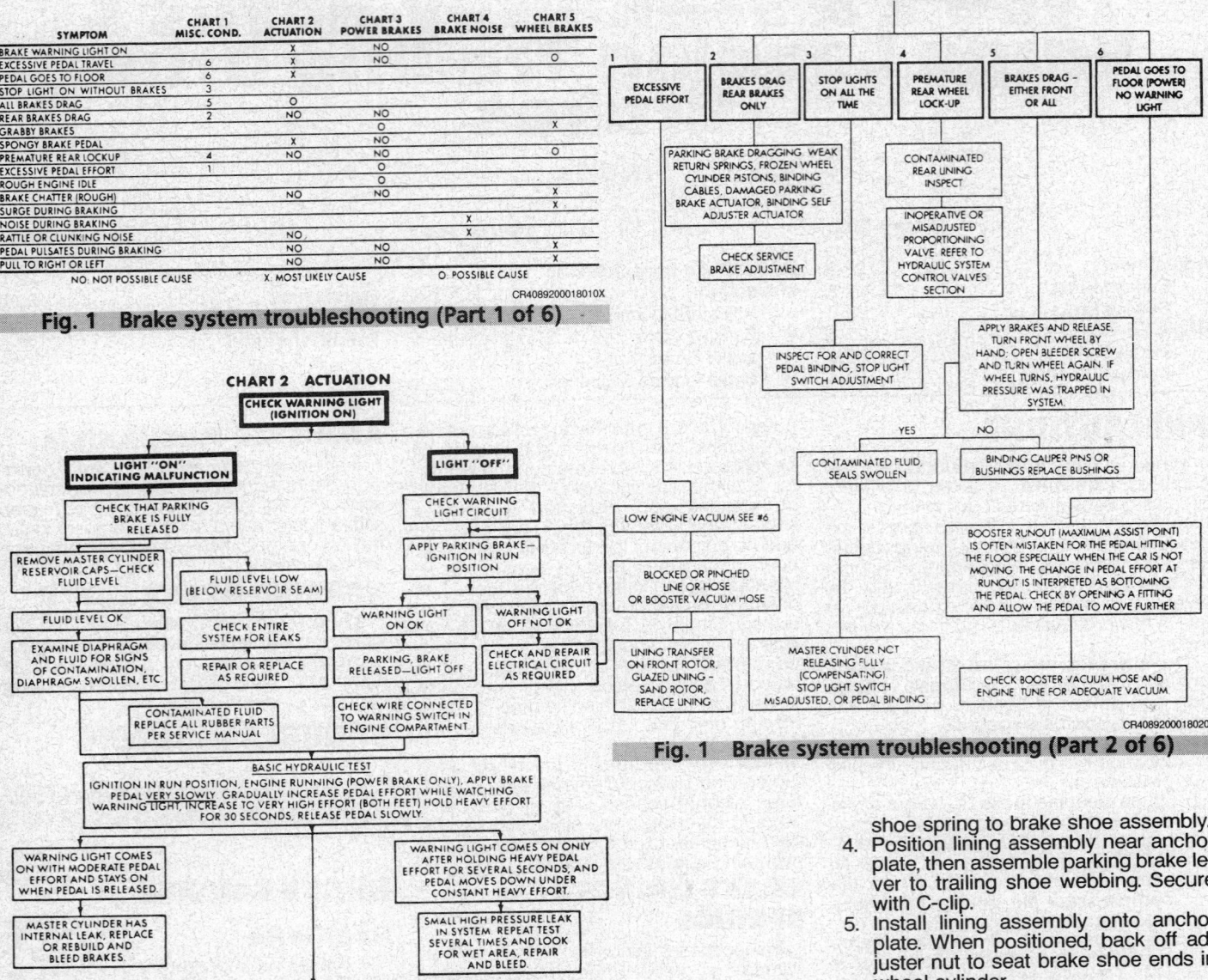

SYMPTOM	CHART 1 MISC. COND.	CHART 2 ACTUATION	CHART 3 POWER BRAKES	CHART 4 BRAKE NOISE	CHART 5 WHEEL BRAKES
BRAKE WARNING LIGHT ON		X	NO		
EXCESSIVE PEDAL TRAVEL	6	X	NO		O
PEDAL GOES TO FLOOR	6	X			
STOP LIGHT ON WITHOUT BRAKES	3				
ALL BRAKES DRAG	5	O			
REAR BRAKES DRAG	2	NO	NO		
GRABBY BRAKES		O	NO		X
SPONGY BRAKE PEDAL		X	NO		
PREMATURE REAR LOCKUP	4	NO	O		O
EXCESSIVE PEDAL EFFORT	1		O		
ROUGH ENGINE IDLE			O		
BRAKE CHATTER (ROUGH)		NO	NO		X
SURGE DURING BRAKING					X
NOISE DURING BRAKING				X	
RATTLE OR CLUNKING NOISE		NO		X	
PEDAL PULSATES DURING BRAKING		NO	NO		X
PULL TO RIGHT OR LEFT		NO	NO		X

NO: NOT POSSIBLE CAUSE   X: MOST LIKELY CAUSE   O: POSSIBLE CAUSE

CR4089200018010X

Fig. 1   Brake system troubleshooting (Part 1 of 6)

CR4089200018020X

Fig. 1   Brake system troubleshooting (Part 2 of 6)

CR4089200018030X

Fig. 1   Brake system troubleshooting (Part 3 of 6)

10. Remove hold-down spring and lower shoe to anchor plate spring for trailing shoe.
11. **On Type 2—Kelsey Hayes,** remove C-clip retaining parking brake lever to trailing brake shoe webbing.
12. **On Type 3—Varga,** remove parking brake lever from trailing shoe by prying retainer tangs apart.
13. Clean dirt from brake drum, anchor plate and all other components. **Do not use compressed air or dry brush to clean brake parts. Many brake parts contain asbestos fibers, which, if inhaled, can cause serious injury. To clean brake parts, use a water soaked rag or a suitable vacuum cleaner to minimize airborne dust.**

INSTALLATION

Type 2—Kelsey-Hayes

1. Lightly lubricate anchor plate shoe contact surfaces with suitable brake lube.
2. Remove brake drum hub grease seal and bearings, then clean and repack bearings and reinstall. Install new grease seal.
3. Assemble automatic adjuster screw assembly, return spring and shoe-to-shoe spring to brake shoe assembly.
4. Position lining assembly near anchor plate, then assemble parking brake lever to trailing shoe webbing. Secure with C-clip.
5. Install lining assembly onto anchor plate. When positioned, back off adjuster nut to seat brake shoe ends in wheel cylinder.
6. Install hold-down springs.
7. Position adjuster lever, then using suitable pliers, install adjuster lever spring.
8. Install brake drum and bearings. Refer to individual car chapter for wheel bearing adjustment procedure.
9. Adjust brakes.
10. Install tire and wheel assembly.
11. If any hydraulic connections have been opened, bleed brake system.
12. Check master cylinder level, and replenish as necessary.
13. Check brake pedal for proper feel and return.
14. Lower vehicle and road test. **Do not severely apply brakes immediately after installation of new brake linings or permanent damage may occur to linings and/or brake drums may become scored. Brakes must be used moderately during first several hundred miles of operation to ensure proper burnishing.**

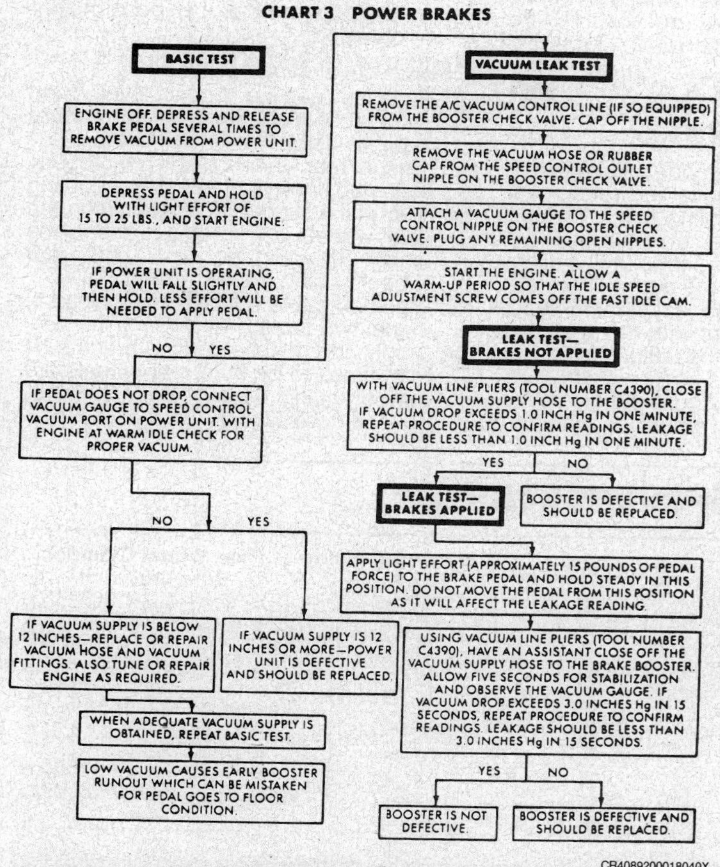

CHART 3 POWER BRAKES

BASIC TEST

ENGINE OFF. DEPRESS AND RELEASE BRAKE PEDAL SEVERAL TIMES TO REMOVE VACUUM FROM POWER UNIT.

DEPRESS PEDAL AND HOLD WITH LIGHT EFFORT OF 15 TO 25 LBS., AND START ENGINE.

IF POWER UNIT IS OPERATING, PEDAL WILL FALL SLIGHTLY AND THEN HOLD. LESS EFFORT WILL BE NEEDED TO APPLY PEDAL.

— NO / YES —

IF PEDAL DOES NOT DROP, CONNECT VACUUM GAUGE TO SPEED CONTROL VACUUM PORT ON POWER UNIT. WITH ENGINE AT WARM IDLE CHECK FOR PROPER VACUUM.

— NO / YES —

IF VACUUM SUPPLY IS BELOW 12 INCHES—REPLACE OR REPAIR VACUUM HOSE AND VACUUM FITTINGS. ALSO TUNE OR REPAIR ENGINE AS REQUIRED.

IF VACUUM SUPPLY IS 12 INCHES OR MORE—POWER UNIT IS DEFECTIVE AND SHOULD BE REPLACED.

WHEN ADEQUATE VACUUM SUPPLY IS OBTAINED, REPEAT BASIC TEST.

LOW VACUUM CAUSES EARLY BOOSTER RUNOUT WHICH CAN BE MISTAKEN FOR PEDAL GOES TO FLOOR CONDITION.

VACUUM LEAK TEST

REMOVE THE A/C VACUUM CONTROL LINE (IF SO EQUIPPED) FROM THE BOOSTER CHECK VALVE. CAP OFF THE NIPPLE.

REMOVE THE VACUUM HOSE OR RUBBER CAP FROM THE SPEED CONTROL OUTLET NIPPLE ON THE BOOSTER CHECK VALVE.

ATTACH A VACUUM GAUGE TO THE SPEED CONTROL NIPPLE ON THE BOOSTER CHECK VALVE. PLUG ANY REMAINING OPEN NIPPLES.

START THE ENGINE. ALLOW A WARM-UP PERIOD SO THAT THE IDLE SPEED ADJUSTMENT SCREW COMES OFF THE FAST IDLE CAM.

LEAK TEST— BRAKES NOT APPLIED

WITH VACUUM LINE PLIERS (TOOL NUMBER C4390), CLOSE OFF THE VACUUM SUPPLY HOSE TO THE BOOSTER. IF VACUUM DROP EXCEEDS 1.0 INCH Hg IN ONE MINUTE, REPEAT PROCEDURE TO CONFIRM READINGS. LEAKAGE SHOULD BE LESS THAN 1.0 INCH Hg IN ONE MINUTE.

— YES / NO —

LEAK TEST— BRAKES APPLIED

BOOSTER IS DEFECTIVE AND SHOULD BE REPLACED.

APPLY LIGHT EFFORT (APPROXIMATELY 15 POUNDS OF PEDAL FORCE) TO THE BRAKE PEDAL AND HOLD STEADY IN THIS POSITION. DO NOT MOVE THE PEDAL FROM THIS POSITION AS IT WILL AFFECT THE LEAKAGE READING.

USING VACUUM LINE PLIERS (TOOL NUMBER C4390), HAVE AN ASSISTANT CLOSE OFF THE VACUUM SUPPLY HOSE TO THE BRAKE BOOSTER. ALLOW FIVE SECONDS FOR STABILIZATION AND OBSERVE THE VACUUM GAUGE. IF VACUUM DROP EXCEEDS 3.0 INCHES Hg IN 15 SECONDS, REPEAT PROCEDURE TO CONFIRM READINGS. LEAKAGE SHOULD BE LESS THAN 3.0 INCHES Hg IN 15 SECONDS.

— YES / NO —

BOOSTER IS NOT DEFECTIVE.

BOOSTER IS DEFECTIVE AND SHOULD BE REPLACED.

CR4089200018040X

Fig. 1 Brake system troubleshooting (Part 4 of 6)

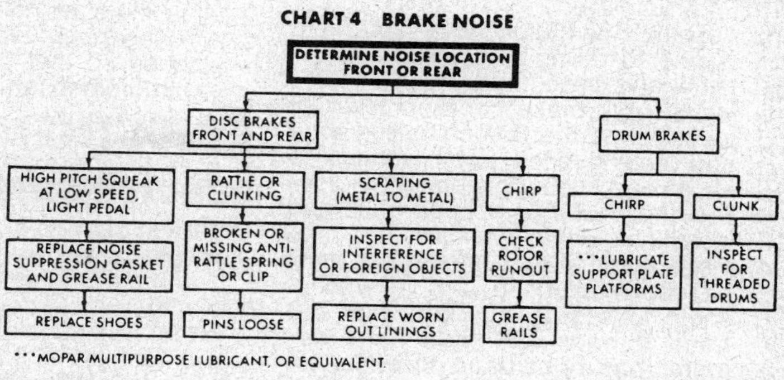

CHART 4 BRAKE NOISE

DETERMINE NOISE LOCATION FRONT OR REAR

DISC BRAKES FRONT AND REAR

HIGH PITCH SQUEAK AT LOW SPEED, LIGHT PEDAL — REPLACE NOISE SUPPRESSION GASKET AND GREASE RAIL — REPLACE SHOES

RATTLE OR CLUNKING — BROKEN OR MISSING ANTI-RATTLE SPRING OR CLIP — PINS LOOSE

SCRAPING (METAL TO METAL) — INSPECT FOR INTERFERENCE OR FOREIGN OBJECTS — REPLACE WORN OUT LININGS

CHIRP — CHECK ROTOR RUNOUT — GREASE RAILS

DRUM BRAKES

CHIRP — ***LUBRICATE SUPPORT PLATE PLATFORMS

CLUNK — INSPECT FOR THREADED DRUMS

***MOPAR MULTIPURPOSE LUBRICANT, OR EQUIVALENT.

CR4089200018050X

Fig. 1 Brake system troubleshooting (Part 5 of 6)

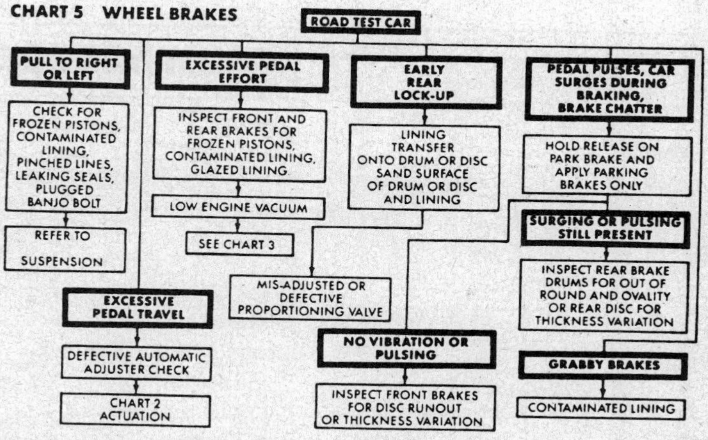

CHART 5 WHEEL BRAKES

ROAD TEST CAR

PULL TO RIGHT OR LEFT

CHECK FOR FROZEN PISTONS, CONTAMINATED LINING, PINCHED LINES, LEAKING SEALS, PLUGGED BANJO BOLT

REFER TO SUSPENSION

EXCESSIVE PEDAL TRAVEL

DEFECTIVE AUTOMATIC ADJUSTER CHECK

CHART 2 ACTUATION

EXCESSIVE PEDAL EFFORT

INSPECT FRONT AND REAR BRAKES FOR FROZEN PISTONS, CONTAMINATED LINING, GLAZED LINING.

LOW ENGINE VACUUM

SEE CHART 3

MIS-ADJUSTED OR DEFECTIVE PROPORTIONING VALVE

EARLY REAR LOCK-UP

LINING TRANSFER ONTO DRUM OR DISC SAND SURFACE OF DRUM OR DISC AND LINING

NO VIBRATION OR PULSING

INSPECT FRONT BRAKES FOR DISC RUNOUT OR THICKNESS VARIATION

PEDAL PULSES, CAR SURGES DURING BRAKING, BRAKE CHATTER

HOLD RELEASE ON PARK BRAKE AND APPLY PARKING BRAKES ONLY

SURGING OR PULSING STILL PRESENT

INSPECT REAR BRAKE DRUMS FOR OUT OF ROUND AND OVALITY OR REAR DISC FOR THICKNESS VARIATION

GRABBY BRAKES

CONTAMINATED LINING

CR4089200018060X

Fig. 1 Brake system troubleshooting (Part 6 of 6)

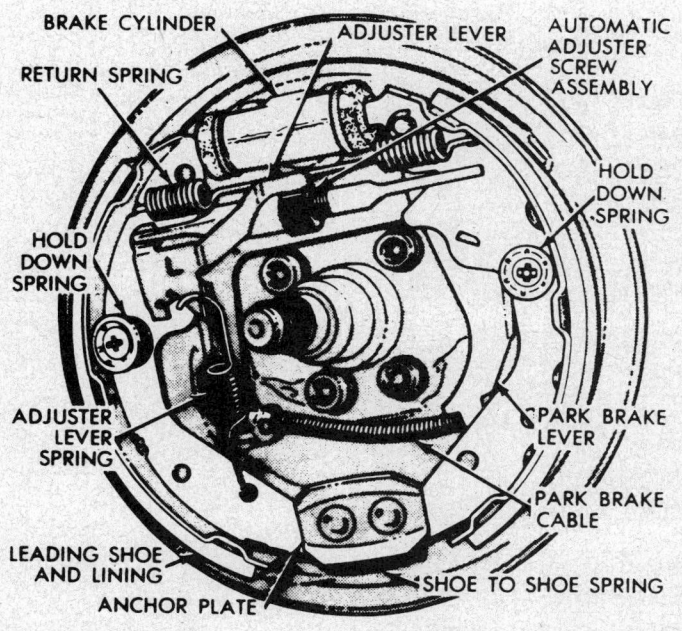

Fig. 2 Kelsey-Hayes leading trailing drum brake assembly. Type 2

Labels: BRAKE CYLINDER, ADJUSTER LEVER, AUTOMATIC ADJUSTER SCREW ASSEMBLY, RETURN SPRING, HOLD DOWN SPRING, HOLD DOWN SPRING, ADJUSTER LEVER SPRING, PARK BRAKE LEVER, PARK BRAKE CABLE, LEADING SHOE AND LINING, ANCHOR PLATE, SHOE TO SHOE SPRING

CR4089100013000X

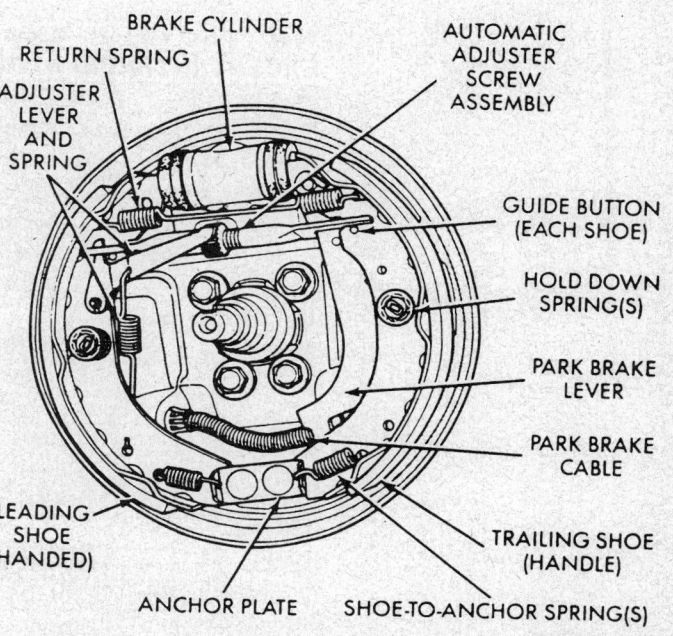

Fig. 3 Varga leading trailing drum brake assembly. Type 3

Labels: BRAKE CYLINDER, RETURN SPRING, ADJUSTER LEVER AND SPRING, AUTOMATIC ADJUSTER SCREW ASSEMBLY, GUIDE BUTTON (EACH SHOE), HOLD DOWN SPRING(S), PARK BRAKE LEVER, PARK BRAKE CABLE, LEADING SHOE (HANDED), ANCHOR PLATE, SHOE-TO-ANCHOR SPRING(S), TRAILING SHOE (HANDLE)

CR4089100014000X

Type 3—Varga

1. Assemble park brake lever and wave washer to trailing shoe, then install retainer and close ends.
2. Install park brake cable in lever of trailing shoe, then attach trailing shoe and leading shoe lower springs to shoes and anchor plate.
3. Position shoes on support plate and install hold-down springs.
4. Install automatic adjusters, ends must be above extruded pins in web of shoe. **Left side adjuster has left hand threads and right hand adjuster has right hand threads, do not interchange.**
5. Install upper shoe to shoe spring, then rotate adjuster to remove freeplay from adjuster assembly.
6. Install adjuster lever on leading pivot pin and attach short end of adjuster spring in hole of lever and long end in leading shoe hole.
7. Connect park brake cable and adjust shoes so that they do not interfere with drum installation.

ADJUSTMENTS
SERVICE BRAKE

1. Each backing plate has two adjusting hole covers; remove the rear cover and turn the adjusting screw upward with a screwdriver or other suitable tool to expand the shoes until a slight drag is felt when the drum is rotated.
2. While holding the adjustment lever out of engagement with the adjusting screw, back off the adjusting screw until wheel rotates freely with no drag.
3. Install wheel and adjusting hole cover. Adjust brakes on remaining wheel in the same manner.
4. If pedal height is not satisfactory, drive the vehicle and perform sufficient reverse stops until proper pedal height is obtained.

PARKING BRAKE

1. Release parking brake lever, then loosen cable adjusting nut and ensure cable is slack.
2. Ensure rear wheel brakes are properly adjusted, then tighten cable adjusting nut until a slight drag is felt when the rear wheels are rotated. Loosen the cable adjusting nut until both rear wheels rotate freely.
3. Back off cable adjusting nut an additional two turns.
4. Apply and release parking brake several times to be sure rear wheels are not dragging when cable is in released position.

DRUM BRAKE SPECIFICATIONS

Year	Model	Brake Drum Inside Dia. Inch	Rear Wheel Cylinder Bore Dia. Inch
1992	Acclaim, Dynasty, Fifth Avenue, Imperial, New Yorker & Spirit	8.661	.625
	Daytona, LeBaron, Shadow & Sundance	7.874	.625
1993	Acclaim, Daytona, Dynasty, Fifth Avenue, Imperial, LeBaron, New Yorker & Spirit	8.661	.625
	Intrepid & Vision	8.661	.724
	Shadow & Sundance	7.874	.625
1994	Acclaim, LeBaron & Spirit	7.874	.625
	Intrepid & Vision	8.661	.724
	Shadow & Sundance	7.874	.625
1995	Neon	7.880	—

TIGHTENING SPECIFICATIONS

Year	Component	Torque/Ft. Lbs.
EXCEPT INTREPID & VISON		
1992–94	Bearing Retainer Bolts	250①
	Brake Booster To Dash	250①
	Brake Line Fittings	143①
	Support Plate To Rear Axle	80
	Wheel Cylinder Bleed Screws	80①
	Wheel Cylinder To Support Plate	75①
	Wheel Lug Nuts	85–110
INTREPID & VISION		
1993–94	Bearing Retainer Bolts	124
	Brake Line Fittings	143①
	Support Plate To Rear Axle	80
	Wheel Cylinder Bleed Screws	80①
	Wheel Cylinder To Support Plate	75①
	Wheel Lug Nuts	85–115
NEON		
1995	Brake Line Fittings	145①
	Wheel Cylinder To Backing Plate	75①
	Wheel Lug Nut	80–110①

①—Inch lbs.

Types 4 & 5—Leading Trailing Drum Brakes

INDEX

PRECAUTIONS

When working on or around brake assemblies, care must be taken to prevent breathing asbestos dust, as many manufacturers incorporate asbestos fibers in the production of brake linings. During routine service operations, the amount of asbestos dust from brake lining wear is at a low level due to a chemical breakdown during use. A few precautions will minimize exposure.

Do not sand or grind brake linings unless suitable local exhaust ventilation equipment is used to prevent excessive asbestos exposure.

1. Wear a suitable respirator approved for asbestos dust use during all repair procedures.
2. When cleaning brake dust from brake parts, use a vacuum cleaner with a highly efficient filter system. If a suitable vacuum cleaner is not available, use a water soaked rag. **Do not use compressed air or dry brush to clean brake parts.**
3. Keep work area clean using same equipment as for cleaning brake parts.
4. Properly dispose of rags and vacuum cleaner bags by placing them in plastic bags.
5. Do not smoke or eat while working on brake systems.
6. Never use any fluid containing mineral oil to clean brake system components. This will damage the rubber caps and seals. If system contamination is suspected, check brake fluid in the reservoir for dirt, discoloration, or separation (breakdown) of the brake fluid into distinct layers. Drain and flush the hydraulic system with clean brake fluid if contamination is suspected.

INSPECTION

BRAKE DRUMS

Any time the brake drums are removed for brake service, the braking surface diameter should be checked with a suitable brake drum micrometer at several points to determine if they are within the safe oversize limit stamped on the brake drum outer surface. If the braking surface diameter exceeds specifications, the drum must be replaced. If the braking surface diame-

ter is within specifications, drums should be cleaned and inspected for cracks, scores, deep grooves, taper, out of round and heat spotting. If drums are cracked or heat spotted, they must be replaced. Scoring and grooves in the braking surface can only be removed by machining with special equipment, as long as the braking surface is within specifications. Any brake drum showing taper or sufficiently out of round to cause vehicle vibration or noise while braking should also be machined, removing only enough stock to true up the drum.

After a brake drum is machined, wipe the braking surface diameter with a denatured alcohol soaked cloth. If one brake drum is machined, the other should also be machined to the same diameter to maintain equal braking forces.

BRAKE LININGS & SPRINGS

Inspect brake linings for excessive wear, damage, oil, grease or brake fluid contamination. If any of the above conditions exist, brake linings should be replaced as an axle set to maintain equal braking forces. Examine brake shoe webbing, hold-down and return springs for signs of overheating indicated by a slight blue color. Any component which exhibits overheating signs should be replaced. Overheated springs lose their pull and could cause brake linings to wear out prematurely. Inspect all springs for sags, bends and external damage and replace as necessary.

Inspect hold-down retainers and pins for bends, rust and corrosion. If any of the above is found, replace as required.

BACKING PLATE

Inspect backing plate shoe contact surface for grooves that may restrict shoe movement and cannot be removed by lightly sanding with emery cloth or other suitable abrasive. If backing plate exhibits above condition, it should be replaced. Also inspect for signs of cracks, warpage and excessive rust, indicating need for replacement.

ADJUSTER MECHANISM

Inspect all components for rust, corrosion, bends and fatigue. Replace as necessary. On adjuster mechanism equipped with adjuster cable, inspect cable for kinks,

fraying or elongation of eyelet and replace as necessary.

PARKING BRAKE CABLE

Inspect parking brake cable end for kinks, fraying and elongation and replace as necessary. Use a small hose clamp to compress clamp where it enters backing plate to remove.

TROUBLESHOOTING

Refer to **Fig. 1.** for brake systems and troubleshooting.

BRAKE SERVICE

For drum brake service procedures, refer to **Figs. 2 and 3.**

ADJUSTMENTS

SERVICE BRAKES

These brakes are equipped with self adjusting mechanisms, therefore periodic adjustments are not necessary. If stopping power is insufficient, or if brake pedal travel is excessive, brakes should be cleaned and inspected, and the self-adjusting mechanisms should be checked.

After performing brake service, adjust brake shoes as follows:

1. Ensure shoes are centered on backing plate and measure width of brake shoes using suitable caliper. On Colt Vista models, also measure inside diameter of brake drum.
2. Adjust width of brake shoes to approximately 7.06 inches for Colt and Summit. On Colt Vista, adjust brake shoes to a width approximately .060 inch less than inside diameter of brake drum.
3. Install brake drums and adjust parking brake as described.
4. After adjusting parking brake, release parking brake lever and ensure shoe actuating lever is not being pulled by parking brake cable. **If shoe actuating lever is pulled by parking brake cable, self-adjusters will not operate.**

PARKING BRAKE

1. Apply parking brake lever with a force of approximately 45 lbs. while count-

Symptom	Probable cause	Remedy
Vehicle pulls to one side when brakes are applied	Grease or oil on pad or lining suface	Replace
	Inadequate contact of pad or lining	Correct
	Auto adjuster malfunction	Adjust
	Drum out of round or uneven wear	Repair or replace as necessary
Insufficient braking power	Low or deteriorated brake fluid	Refill or change
	Air in brake system	Bleed air from system
	Overheated brake rotor due to dragging of pad or lining	Correct
	Inadequate contact of pad or lining	
	Brake booster malfunction	
	Clogged brake line	
	Grease or oil on pad or lining surface	Replace
	Proportioning valve malfunction	
	Auto adjuster malfunction	Adjust
Increased pedal stroke (Reduced pedal to floor-board clearance)	Air in brake system	Bleed air from system
	Worn lining or pad	Replace
	Broken vacuum hose	
	Faulty master cylinder	
	Brake fluid leaks	Correct
	Auto adjuster malfunction	Adjust
	Excessive push rod to master cylinder clearance	
Brake drag	Incomplete release of parking brake	Correct
	Clogged master cylinder return port	
	Incorrect parking brake adjustment	Adjust
	Incorrect push rod to master cylinder clearance	
	Faulty master cylinder piston return spring	Replace
	Worn brake pedal return spring	
	Broken rear drum brake shoe return spring	
	Lack of lubrication in sliding parts	Lubricate

CR4089200019010X

Fig. 1   Brake system troubleshooting (Part 1 of 3)

Symptom	Probable cause	Remedy
Insufficient parking brake function	Worn brake lining or pad	Replace
	Grease or oil on lining or pad surface	
	Parking brake cable sticking	
	Stuck wheel cylinder or caliper piston	
	Excessive parking brake lever stroke	Adjust the parking brake lever stroke or check the parking brake cable routing
	Auto adjuster malfunction	Adjust
Scraping or grinding noise when brakes are applied	Worn brake lining or pad	Replace
	Caliper to wheel interference	Correct or replace
	Dust cover to disc interference	
	Bent brake backing plate	
	Cracked drums or brake disc	
Squealing, groaning or chattering noise when brakes are applied	Missing or damaged brake pad anti-squeak shim	Replace
	Brake drums and linings, discs and pads worn or scored	Correct or replace
	Incorrect parts	
	Burred or rusted calipers	Clean or deburr
	Dirty, greased, contaminated or glazed linings	Clean or replace
	Drum brakes-weak, damaged or incorrect shoe hold-down springs, loose or damaged shoe hold-down pins and springs	Correct or replace
	Incorrect brake pedal or booster push rod	Adjust
Squealing, noise when brakes are not applied	Bent or warped backing plate causing interference with drum	Replace
	Drum brakes-weak, damaged or incorrect shoe-to-shoe spring	
	Poor return of brake booster or master cylinder or wheel cylinder	
	Loose or extra parts in brakes	Retighten
	Improper positioning of pads in caliper	Correct
	Improper installation of support mounting to caliper body	
	Improper machining of drum causing interference with backing plate or shoe	Replace drum
	Disc brakes-rusted, stuck	Lubricate or replace
	Worn, damaged or insufficiently lubricated wheel bearings	
	Incorrect brake pedal or booster push-rod	Adjust

CR4089200019020X

Fig. 1   Brake system troubleshooting (Part 2 of 3)

Symptom	Probable cause	Remedy
Groaning, clicking or rattling noise when brakes are not applied	Stones or foreign material trapped inside wheel covers	Remove stones, etc
	Loose wheel nuts	Retighten
	Disc brakes-loose installation bolt	
	Worn, damaged or dry wheel bearings	Lubricate or replace
	Disc brakes-failure of anti-rattle shim	Replace
	Disc brakes-wear on sleeve	
	Incorrect brake pedal or booster push-rod setting	Adjust
Brake drag	Incomplete release of parking brake	Correct
	Incorrect parking brake adjustment	Adjust
Insufficient parking brake function	Worn brake pad	Replace
	Excessive parking brake lever stroke	Adjust the parking brake lever stroke or check the parking brake cable routing
	Grease or oil on pad surface	Replace
	Parking brake cable sticking	Replace

CR4089200019030X

Fig. 1   Brake system troubleshooting (Part 3 of 3)

ing number of clicks. Lever should click 5-7 times.
2. If not within specifications, release parking brake lever and remove center console, if equipped.
3. Loosen adjusting nut on parking brake lever to free parking brake cables, then depress brake pedal several times to ensure shoe to drum clearance is properly maintained by self-adjusters.
4. Tighten adjusting nut until brake lever can be raised 5-7 notches with a force of approximately 45 lbs. **If adjusting nut is tightened excessively, self-adjuster mechanism will be inoperative.**
5. After adjustment, raise rear of vehicle, ensuring brakes do not drag with parking brake lever released.

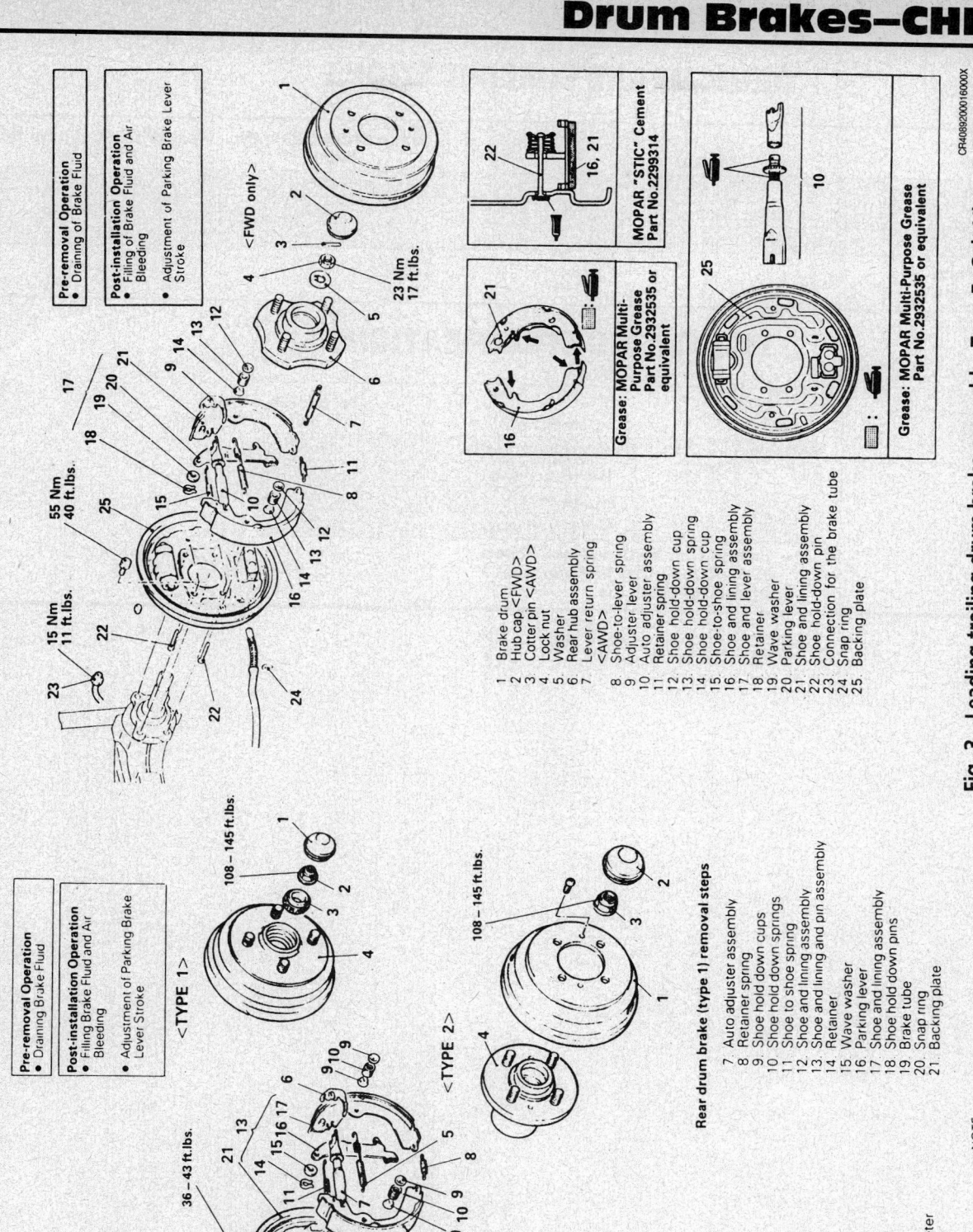

Pre-removal Operation
• Draining of Brake Fluid

Post-installation Operation
• Filling of Brake Fluid and Air Bleeding
• Adjustment of Parking Brake Lever Stroke

<FWD only>

23 Nm
17 ft.lbs.

55 Nm
40 ft.lbs.

15 Nm
11 ft.lbs.

MOPAR "STIC" Cement
Part No.2299314

Grease: MOPAR Multi-Purpose Grease
Part No.2932535 or equivalent

Grease: MOPAR Multi-Purpose Grease
Part No.2932535 or equivalent

CR408920000016000X

1. Brake drum
2. Hub cap <FWD>
3. Cotter pin <AWD>
4. Lock nut
5. Washer
6. Rear hub assembly
7. Lever return spring <AWD>
8. Shoe-to-lever spring
9. Adjuster lever
10. Auto adjuster assembly
11. Retainer spring
12. Shoe hold-down cup
13. Shoe hold-down spring
14. Shoe hold-down cup
15. Shoe-to-shoe spring
16. Shoe and lining assembly
17. Shoe and lever assembly
18. Retainer
19. Wave washer
20. Parking lever
21. Shoe and lining assembly
22. Shoe hold-down pin
23. Connection for the brake tube
24. Snap ring
25. Backing plate

Fig. 3 Leading trailing drum brake assembly. Type 5, Colt Vista & Summit Wagon

CR408910015000X

Pre-removal Operation
• Draining Brake Fluid

Post-installation Operation
• Filling Brake Fluid and Air Bleeding
• Adjustment of Parking Brake Lever Stroke

<TYPE 1>

108 – 145 ft.lbs.

<TYPE 2>

108 – 145 ft.lbs.

36 – 43 ft.lbs.

9 – 12 ft.lbs.

1. Hub cap
2. Wheel bearing nut
3. Outer bearing inner race
4. Brake drum
5. Adjustment of shoe outside diameter
6. Shoe to lever spring
7. Adjuster lever
8. Auto adjuster assembly
9. Retainer spring
10. Shoe hold down cups
11. Shoe hold down springs
12. Shoe to shoe spring
13. Shoe and lining assembly
14. Shoe and lining and pin assembly
15. Retainer
16. Wave washer
17. Parking lever
18. Shoe hold down pins
19. Brake tube
20. Snap ring
21. Backing plate

Rear drum brake (type 1) removal steps

7. Auto adjuster assembly
8. Retainer spring
9. Shoe hold down cups
10. Shoe hold down springs
11. Shoe to shoe spring
12. Shoe and lining assembly
13. Shoe and lining and pin assembly
14. Retainer
15. Wave washer
16. Parking lever
17. Shoe and lining assembly
18. Shoe hold down pins
19. Snap ring
20. Backing plate

Rear drum brake (type 2) removal steps

1. Brake drum
2. Adjustment of shoe outside diameter
3. Hub cap
4. Wheel bearing nut
5. Rear hub assembly
6. Shoe to lever spring
7. Adjuster lever

NOTE
(1) Reverse the disassembly procedures to reassemble.

Fig. 2 Leading trailing drum brake assembly. Type 4, Colt & Summit

DRUM BRAKE SPECIFICATIONS

Year	Model	Brake Drum Inside Dia. Inch	Rear Wheel Cylinder Bore Dia. Inch
1992–94	Colt/Summit	7.086	.751
	Colt Vista/Summit Wagon ①	7.992	1.374
	Colt Vista/Summit Wagon ②	8.999	1.374

①—With 8 inch drum.
②—With 9 inch drum.

TIGHTENING SPECIFICATIONS

Year	Component	Torque/Ft. Lbs.
1992–94	Backing Plate Bolts	36–43
	Bleed Screws	5–7
	Wheel Cylinder	6–9
	Wheel Lug Nuts	①

①—Except Colt Vista w/steel wheels, 65-80 ft. lbs.; Colt Vista w/steel wheels, 50-57 ft. lbs.

HYDRAULIC BRAKE SYSTEMS

NOTE: Refer To "Anti-Lock Brakes" Chapter When Servicing ABS Systems.

INDEX

MASTER CYLINDER APPLICATIONS

Model	Year	Type No.
Acclaim	1992–94	1
Colt	1992–94	5
Colt Vista	1992–94	3
Concorde	1993-94	4
Daytona	1992–93	1
Dynasty	1992–93	1
Imperial	1992–93	1
Intrepid	1993-94	4
Laser	1992–94	6
LeBaron	1992–94	1
LHS	1994	4
Neon	1995	8
Monaco	1992	2

Model	Year	Type No.
New Yorker	1994	4
New Yorker Landau/Salon	1992–93	1
New Yorker Fifth Avenue	1992–93	1
Premier	1992	2
Shadow	1992–94	1
Spirit	1992–94	1
Stealth	1992–94	7
Summit	1992–94	5
Summit Wagon	1992–94	3
Sundance	1992–94	1
Talon	1992–94	6
Vision	1993–94	4

HYDRAULIC CONTROLS APPLICATIONS

Model	Year	Type No.
Acclaim	1992–94	1
Colt	1992–94	3
Colt Vista	1992–94	3
Concorde	1993-94	5
Daytona	1992–93	1
Dynasty	1992–93	1
Imperial	1992–93	1
Intrepid	1993-94	5
Laser	1992–94	3
LeBaron	1992–94	1
LHS	1994	5
Neon	1995	6
Monaco	1992	2

Model	Year	Type No.
New Yorker	1994	5
New Yorker Landau/Salon	1992–93	1
New Yorker Fifth Ave.	1992–93	1
Premier	1992	2
Shadow	1992–94	1
Spirit	1992–94	1
Stealth	1992–94	3
Summit	1992–94	3
Summit Wagon	1992–94	3
Sundance	1992–94	1
Talon	1992–94	3
Vision	1993–94	5

DESCRIPTION

FRONT & REAR SPLIT HYDRAULIC BRAKE SYSTEMS

When the brake pedal is depressed, both the primary (front brake) and the secondary (rear brake) master cylinder pistons are moved simultaneously to exert hydraulic fluid pressure on their respective independent hydraulic systems. The fluid displacement of the two master cylinders is proportioned to fulfill the requirements of each of the two independent hydraulic brake systems, **Fig. 1.**

If a failure of a rear (secondary) brake system should occur, initial brake pedal movement causes the unrestricted secondary piston to bottom in the master cylinder bore. Primary piston movement displaces hydraulic fluid in the primary section of the dual master cylinder to actuate the front brake system.

Should the front (primary) brake system fail, initial brake pedal movement causes the unrestricted primary piston to bottom out against the secondary piston. Continued downward movement of the brake pedal moves the secondary piston to displace hydraulic fluid in the rear brake system to actuate the rear brakes.

The increased pedal travel and the increased pedal effort required to compensate for the loss of the failed portion of the brake system provides a warning that a partial brake system failure has occurred. When the ignition switch is turned on, a brake warning light on the instrument panel provides a visual indication that one of the dual brake systems has become inoperative.

Should a failure of either the front or rear brake hydraulic system occur, the hydraulic fluid pressure differential resulting from pressure loss of the failed brake system forces the valve toward the low pressure area to light the brake warning lamp.

DIAGONALLY SPLIT HYDRAULIC BRAKE SYSTEMS

This system operates on the same principles as conventional front and rear split systems using primary and secondary master cylinders moving simultaneously to exert hydraulic pressure on their respective systems.

The hydraulic brake lines on this system, however, have been diagonally split front to rear (left front to right rear and right front to left rear) in place of separate lines to the front and rear wheels, **Fig. 2.**

In the event of a system failure this would cause the remaining good system to do all the braking on one front wheel and the opposite rear wheel, thus maintaining 50% of the total braking force. The hydraulic pressure loss would result in a pressure differential in the system and cause a warning light on the dashboard to glow as in front and rear split systems.

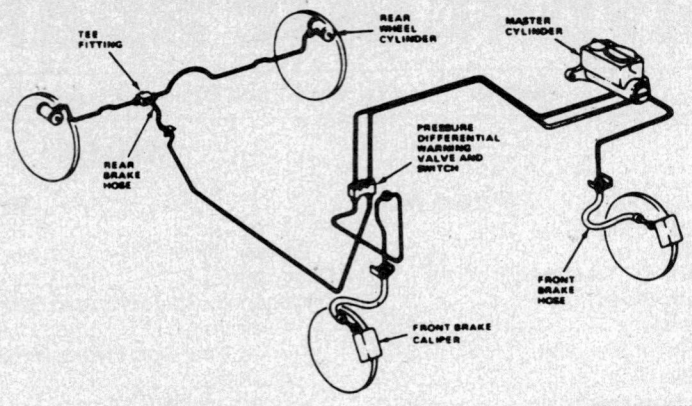

Fig. 1 Hydraulic front & rear split brake system schematic

CR4099100011000X

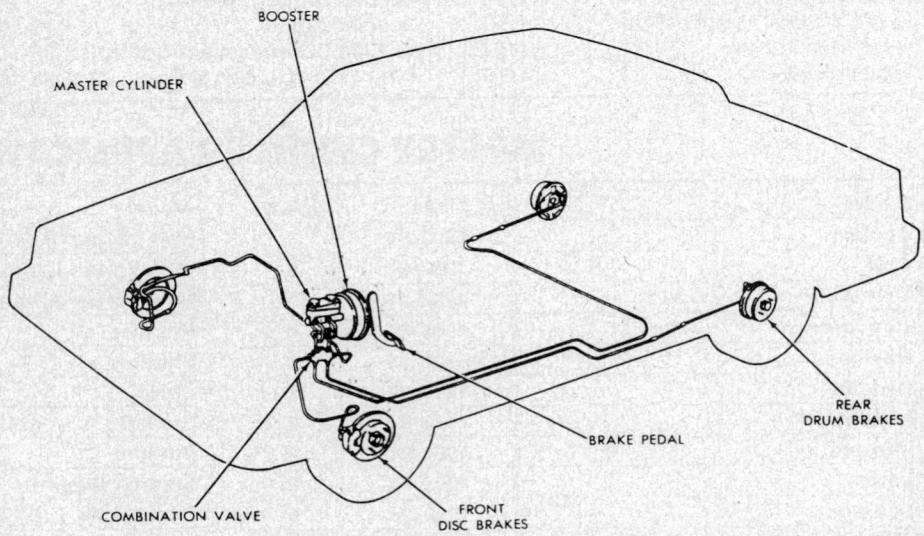

Fig. 2 Hydraulic diagonally split brake system schematic

CR4099100012000X

MASTER CYLINDERS

Type 1

This master cylinder, **Fig. 3**, is comprised of an aluminum body, pistons, springs, O-rings, cup seals, and a reinforced nylon reservoir. The bore of the aluminum body is anodized for durability, and to prevent corrosion and pitting. The reservoir caps contain diaphragms with precision slits for controlled equalization of pressure.

Type 2

This type of master cylinder design is of the primary piston style. The aluminum bodied unit is mounted on the front of the booster unit. This master cylinder is not serviceable and the unit must be replaced if diagnosis indicates a malfunction.

Types 3, 5, 6 & 7

These master cylinders are of the serviceable types. They consist of plastic reservoirs mounted on cast bodies and use replaceable springs, grommets and O-rings.

Type 4

The master cylinders used on standard or ABS brake systems are unique to themselves. The only serviceable component on both master cylinders are the reservoir and the sealing grommets. Neither of the master cylinder assemblies can be serviced, and must be replaced as an assembly.

Type 8

This type of master cylinder, designed for the Neon, utilizes screw-in proportioning valves at the master cylinder instead of a combination valve. With this new design, the chassis brake tubes connect directly from the master cylinder to the brake flex hose.

Vehicles not equipped with ABS use a standard compensating port design, while vehicles equipped with ABS use a center valve design. In addition, the non-ABS master cylinders are a four outlet design with two screw-in proportioning valves attached directly to the inboard side of the master cylinder housing, **Fig. 4.**

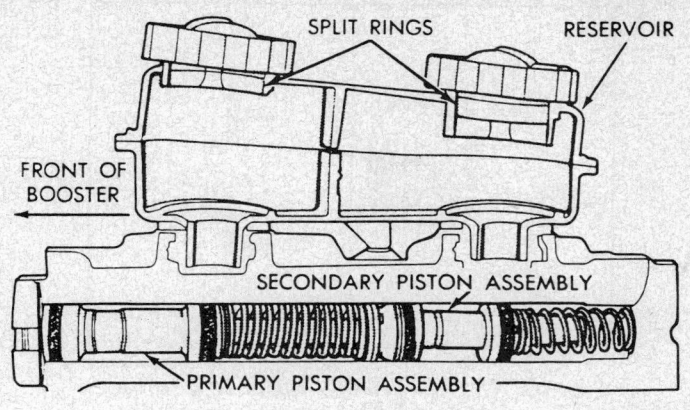

Fig. 3   Master cylinder. Type 1

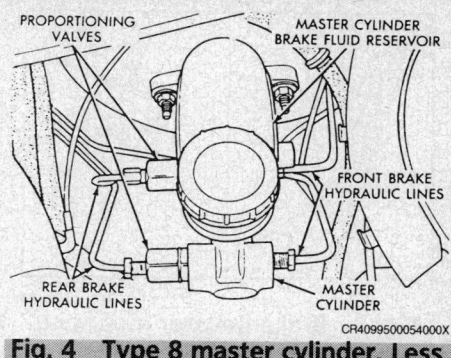

Fig. 4   Type 8 master cylinder. Less ABS

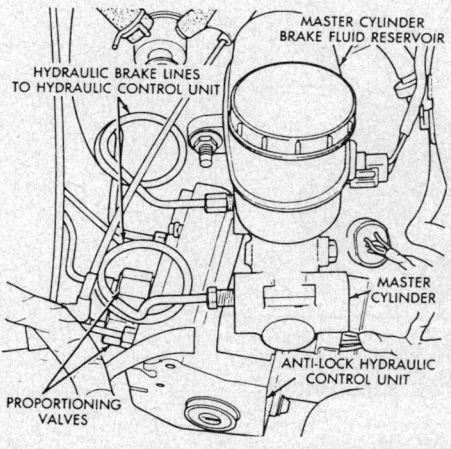

Fig. 5   Type 8 master cylinder. With ABS

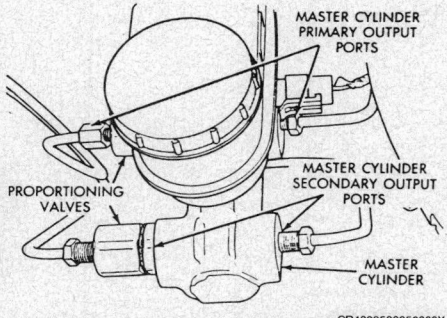

Fig. 6   Type 8 primary & secondary output ports. Less ABS

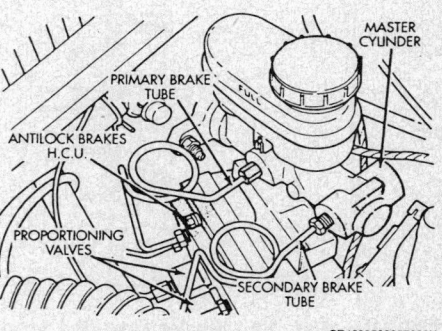

Fig. 7   Type 8 primary & secondary output ports. With ABS

The ABS master cylinders are a two outlet design with the screw-in proportioning valves attached to the ABS Hydraulic Control Unit (HCU), **Fig. 5.** Vehicles equipped with rear drum brakes use a master cylinder with a 21 mm bore, while vehicles equipped with rear disc brakes use a $7/8$ inch bore master cylinder.

The body of the master cylinder is an anodized aluminum casting. It has a machined bore to accept the master cylinder piston and threaded ports with seats for hydraulic brake line connections. The brake fluid reservoir assembly is made of polypropelene plastic.

The only serviceable component on both master cylinders are the reservoir and the sealing grommets. Neither of the master cylinder assemblies can be serviced, and must be replaced as an assembly.

On non-ABS master cylinders, the primary outlet ports supply hydraulic pressure to the left front and right rear brakes. The secondary outlet ports supply hydraulic pressure to the right front and left rear brakes, **Fig. 6.**

On ABS master cylinders, the primary outlet ports supply hydraulic pressure to the right front and left rear brakes. the secondary outlet ports supply hydraulic pressure to the left front and right rear brakes, **Fig. 7.**

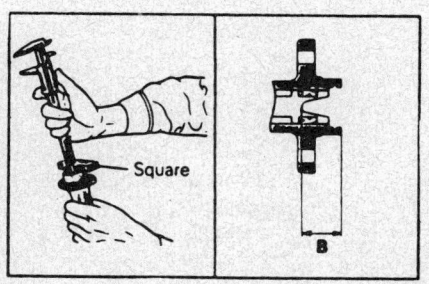

Fig. 8   Master cylinder end face to piston measurement

TROUBLESHOOTING

Refer to "Troubleshooting," in "Disc Brakes" for troubleshooting of the hydraulic brake system.

DIAGNOSIS & TESTING

TYPE 1 MASTER CYLINDER

Ensure the master cylinder compensates in both ports by applying the brake pedal lightly (engine running with power brakes) and observing brake fluid squirting up in the reservoir chambers. Due to a baffle incorporated in the master cylinder, only a minor fluid disturbance may be noticed in the rear chamber of the reservoir.

TYPE 4 MASTER CYLINDER

1. Ensure master cylinder vents at both ports.

2. With engine running apply slight pressure to brake pedal, check for fluid squirting or swirling into reservoir. A special baffle reduces amount of fluid entering secondary reservoir, so only a small disturbance may be noticed.

ADJUSTMENTS
TYPES 3, 5, 6 & 7 MASTER CYLINDERS
Brake Booster Pushrod-To-Primary Piston Clearance

1. With master cylinder removed from vehicle, as described under "Component Replacement," proceed as follows:
   a. Measure distance between master cylinder end face and the piston, **Fig. 8.** Position a square (straight scale) against edge of master cylinder, then measure and subtract thickness of the square to determine dimension B.
   b. Find dimension C by measuring distance between brake booster mounting surface and the end face, **Fig. 9.**
   c. Measure distance between master cylinder mounting surface and the pushrod end, **Fig. 10.** Find dimension D by subtracting the square's thickness from the measurement taken.
   d. Find brake booster-to-primary piston clearance dimension A, **Fig.**

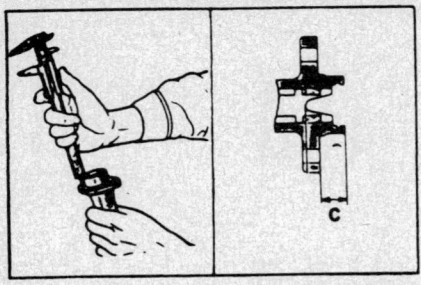

Fig. 9 Brake booster mounting surface to end face distance measurement

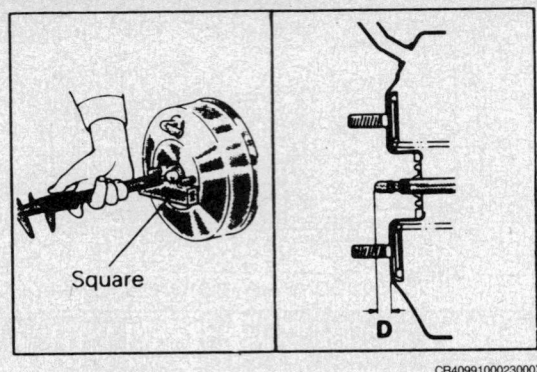

Fig. 10 Master cylinder mounting surface to pushrod end distance measurement

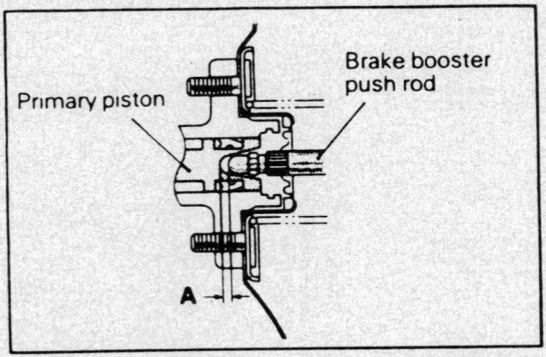

Fig. 11 Brake booster to primary piston clearance dimension A

Fig. 12 Brake booster pushrod adjustment

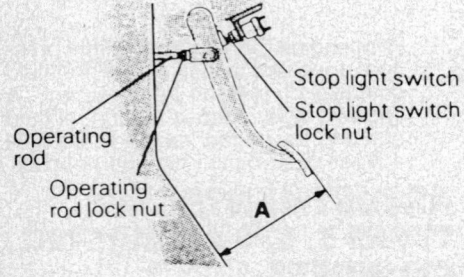

Fig. 13 Brake pedal height dimension "A"

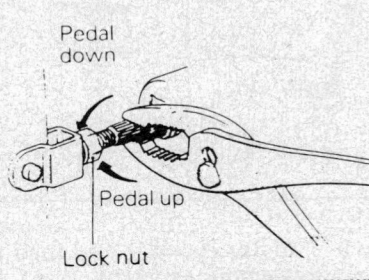

Fig. 14 Brake pedal height adjustment

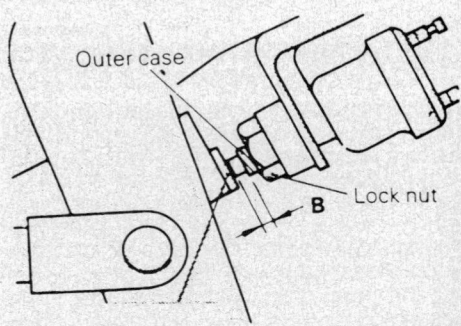

Fig. 15 Stop light switch reference dimension "B"

11, using the formula A = B-C-D. Refer to the "Hydraulic Brake System Specifications" chart for proper clearance specifications.

  e. If dimension A is not as specified, adjust brake booster pushrod as shown, **Fig. 12.**

Brake Pedal Height

1. Measure brake pedal height dimension "A," as shown in **Fig. 13.**
2. Standard height is 6.2-6.4 inches on Colt Wagon, 6.6-6.7 inches on Colt and Summit, 6.9-7.1 inches on Laser and Talon, 7.0-7.2 inches on Stealth, and 7.6-7.8 inches on 1992-93 Colt Vista and Summit Wagon.
3. If pedal height is not within standard, adjust as follows:
  a. Disconnect stop light switch electrical connector, then loosen locknut and move stop light switch to a position were it does not contact brake pedal arm.

b. Adjust brake pedal height by turning operating rod with pliers, **Fig. 14,** until correct brake pedal height is obtained.
c. **On Colt and Summit models,** remove clevis pin that connects master cylinder pushrod and clutch pedal, then the nuts that secure clutch master cylinder, and pull master cylinder slightly toward engine compartment.
d. **On all models,** screw in stop light switch until it contacts brake pedal stopper, ensure that brake pedal does not move, then return stop light switch 1/2-1 turn and secure by tightening locknut.
e. Connect stop light switch electrical connector and ensure that stop

light is not illuminated with brake pedal unpressed, then check reference dimension "B" as shown in, **Fig. 15,** distance should be 0.02-0.04 inch.
f. **On models with shift lock mechanism,** check adjustment of shift lock after brake pedal height has been adjusted, refer to "Automatic Transaxles" section and adjust if necessary.
g. **On all models,** with engine stopped, depress brake pedal two or three times to eliminate vacuum in power brake booster, then press pedal down by hand and confirm that amount of freeplay, dimension "C," **Fig. 16,** before resistance is felt is within 0.1-0.3 inch on all

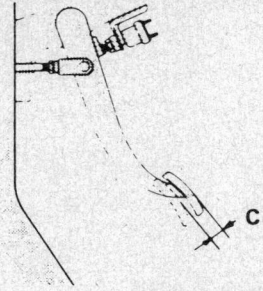

Fig. 16 Brake pedal freeplay dimension "C"

CR4099100029000X

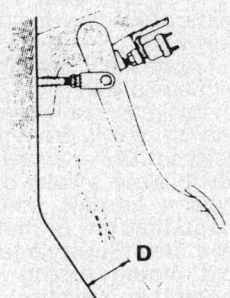

CR4099100030000X

Fig. 17 Clearance between brake pedal & floor board dimension "D"

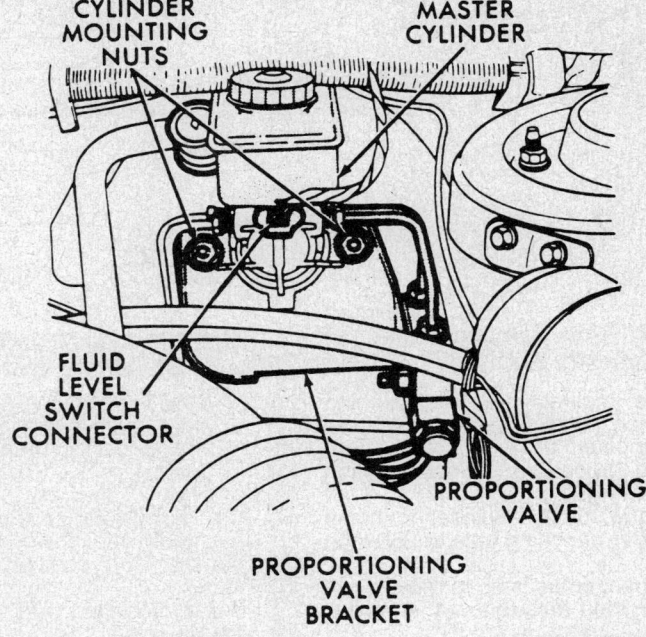

CR4099100015000X

Fig. 18 Type 2 master cylinder replacement

models except Colt Wagon or 0.4-0.6 inch on Colt Wagon.

h. If freeplay is less than 0.1 inch, ensure that clearance between stop light switch and brake pedal is within specifications.

i. If freeplay is greater than 0.4 inch, it is probably due to excessive play between clevis pin and brake pedal arm. Check for excessive clearance and replace defective components as necessary.

j. Start engine, then depress brake pedal with approximately 110 lbs. of force and measure clearance dimension "D" between brake pedal and floorboard, **Fig. 17.** Clearance should be 3.1 inch or more.

k. If clearance is less than 3.1 inch, check for air trapped in brake lines, fluid leaks, excessive brake shoe clearance due to faulty self-adjusters and repair or replace defective components as necessary.

COMPONENT REPLACEMENT

MASTER CYLINDER

TYPE 1

1. Place drain pan under the master cylinder.
2. Using a suitable wrench, disconnect brake lines from the master cylinder. Plug all lines and fittings.
3. Remove master cylinder-to-brake booster attaching nuts.

4. Pull master cylinder outward and away from brake booster.
5. Reverse procedure to install noting the following:
   a. Prior to installing a new or rebuilt master cylinder, it should be bench bled as described under "Brake System Bleed."
   b. **Torque** master cylinder-to-brake booster attaching nuts to 170-230 inch lbs.
   c. **Torque** brake line fittings to 170 inch lbs.

TYPE 2

Refer to **Fig. 18** when replacing master cylinder.
1. Position a drain pan under the master cylinder.
2. Disconnect electrical connector from reservoir, if equipped.
3. Loosen brake lines at top of the proportioning valve, then disconnect brake lines from the master cylinder. Plug all lines and fittings.
4. Remove master cylinder-to-brake booster attaching nuts.
5. Remove proportioning valve mounting bracket.
6. Pull master cylinder outward and away from brake booster.
7. Reverse procedure to install noting the following:
   a. Use caution during master cylinder to brake booster installation. The primary piston protrudes beyond the end cap, and may be damaged if not centered to the booster cavity.
   b. **Torque** brake lines to 11—15 ft. lbs., master cylinder to booster nuts to 9-13 ft. lbs. and proportioning valve bracket to 4-6 ft. lbs.

c. Bleed hydraulic system as described under "Brake System Bleed."

TYPES 3, 5, 6 & 7

1. **On Stealth models,** disconnect low-pressure hose.
2. **On all models,** disconnect brake fluid sensor electrical connector from master cylinder reservoir.
3. Position a drain pan under the master cylinder, then drain master cylinder.
4. **On models with separately mounted reservoir,** disconnect reservoir hoses from the master cylinder.
5. **On all models,** use a suitable wrench to disconnect brake lines from the master cylinder. Plug all lines and fittings.
6. Remove master cylinder-to-brake booster attaching nuts.
7. **On Colt, Colt Vista and Summit models,** remove proportioning valve.
8. **On all models,** pull master cylinder outward and away from brake booster.
9. Reverse procedure to install noting the following:
   a. Prior to master cylinder installation, check brake booster pushrod-to-primary piston clearance as described under "Adjustments," and adjust if necessary.
   b. Fill master cylinder reservoir, then bleed hydraulic system as described under "Brake System Bleed."
   c. Check adjustment of brake pedal as described under "Adjustments," and adjust if necessary.

TYPE 4

1. Disconnect primary and secondary brake lines from master cylinder, then install plugs at brake line outlets.

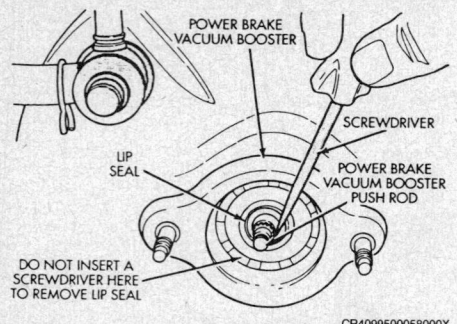

Fig. 19   Type 8 vacuum seal removal. With ABS

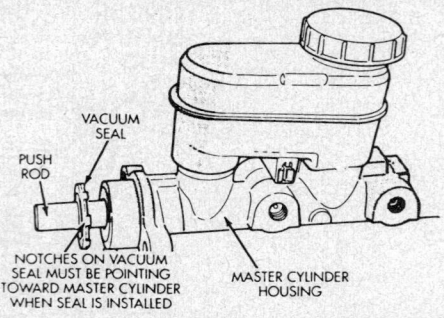

Fig. 20   Type 8 vacuum seal installation. With ABS

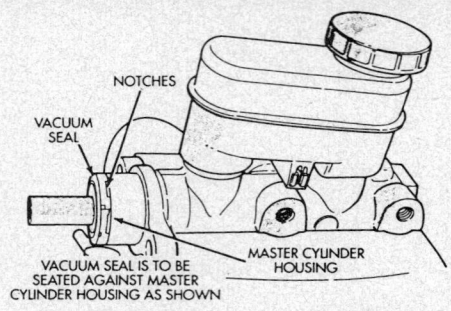

Fig. 21   Type 8 vacuum seal seating. With ABS

2. Remove master cylinder attaching nuts, then slide cylinder away from brake booster.
3. Reverse procedure to install noting the following:
   a. **Torque** master cylinder to brake booster attaching nuts to 250 inch lbs.
   b. Connect brake lines to master cylinder, then **torque** to 145 inch lbs.

TYPE 8

Removal

When replacing master cylinder on vehicles equipped with ABS, vacuum in power booster must be pumped down before removing master cylinder to prevent booster from sucking in any contamination. This can be done by pumping the brake pedal until it is firm, with the ignition off.

1. **On models with ABS**, ensure engine is not running and brake pedal has been pumped until firm.
2. **On all models**, remove wiring harness connector from brake fluid level sensor mounted on fluid reservoir.
3. Disconnect the primary and secondary brake tubes from master cylinder housing. Install suitable plugs at all open brake tube outlets on master cylinder assembly.
4. **On models with ABS**, clean area where master cylinder attaches to power brake vacuum booster using a suitable brake cleaner.
5. **On all models**, remove nuts attaching master cylinder to power brake vacuum booster.
6. Slide master cylinder forward out of power brake vacuum booster.
7. **On vehicles equipped with ABS, the vacuum seal in the front of the power brake vacuum booster must be replaced.** Remove vacuum seal in front of power brake vacuum booster by carefully inserting a suitable, small, screwdriver between master cylinder push rod and vacuum seal and prying seal out of booster, **Fig. 19. Do not attempt to pry seal out by inserting screwdriver between seal and booster.**

Installation

1. **On models with ABS**, install new vacuum seal as follows:
   a. Lubricate master cylinder push rod using suitable silicone lubricant.

   b. Slide vacuum seal onto master cylinder push rod with notches on seal pointing toward and seated against master cylinder housing, **Figs. 20 and 21.**
2. **On all models**, slide master cylinder assembly into power brake vacuum booster and position on mounting studs.
3. Install mounting nuts and **torque** to 250 inch lbs.
4. Connect brake tubes to master cylinder primary and secondary ports and **torque** tube nuts to 145 inch lbs.

FLUID RESERVOIR

TYPE 1

Refer to **Fig. 22** when performing this procedure.

Removal

1. Remove master cylinder from vehicle as described previously.
2. Thoroughly clean reservoir and housing.
3. Remove reservoir caps, then drain the brake fluid.
4. Clamp housing in a vise.
5. Grasp reservoir by hand, then separate it from the housing by rocking it from side to side. **Do not pry reservoir from the housing.**
6. Remove grommets from housing.

Installation

1. Install grommets in housing.
2. Apply clean brake fluid to reservoir mounting surface.
3. Position reservoir to housing so wording on reservoir reads from left to right from the front of the housing, **Fig. 22.**
4. Press reservoir into housing while rocking it from side to side. Reservoir is properly seated when bottom of reservoir touches the grommet.
5. Refer to "Brake System Bleed" to bleed the hydraulic system.

TYPE 5

1. Clean master cylinder housing, then remove reservoir caps.
2. Using a suitable tool remove brake fluid from reservoir, then secure master cylinder in a suitable vise.
3. Remove two reservoir to master cylinder retaining pins, **Fig. 23.**
4. Rock reservoir from side to side and remove from master cylinder. **Do not use any tools when removing reservoir from master cylinder, damage to reservoir may result.**

5. Remove sealing grommets.
6. Reverse procedure to install noting the following:
   a. Lubricate new sealing grommets with brake fluid.
   b. Ensure reservoir is seated properly against sealing grommets.
   c. Refer to "Brake System Bleed" to bench bleed master cylinder. **The Type 4 models use ISO style flares that are of metric dimension. Use ISO style tubing flares and metric tubing when performing any repairs.**

TYPE 8

Removal

1. Clean master cylinder housing and brake fluid reservoir.
2. Remove reservoir cap and remove as much brake fluid as possible using suitable syringe or similar tool.
3. Rock reservoir from side to side while pulling upward to remove from master cylinder housing, **Fig. 24.** Do not pry off using a tool as damage to reservoir may result.
4. Remove reservoir grommets from master cylinder housing.

Installation

1. Install new reservoir grommets in master cylinder housing.
2. Lubricate reservoir mounting area with fresh, clean brake fluid.
3. Install reservoir by pushing downward and rocking from side to side. Ensure reservoir is fully seated.

WHEEL CYLINDER

Removal

1. Remove wheel, drum and brake shoes.
2. Loosen brake line fitting at wheel cylinder. Do not pull metal line away from cylinder.
3. Remove screws holding cylinder to backing plate.
4. Separate wheel cylinder from brake line and backing plate by pulling the cylinder outward and away from backing plate.

Installation

1. Wipe end of hydraulic line to remove any foreign matter.
2. Position wheel cylinder to backing plate. Install brake line to cylinder and start connecting fitting.

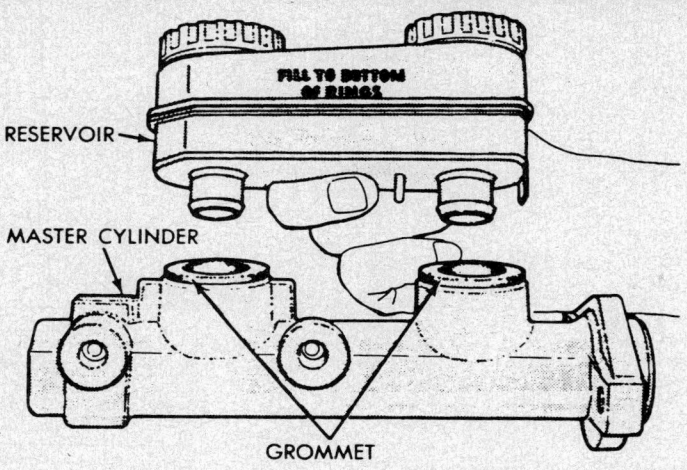

Fig. 22 Type 1 master cylinder reservoir replacement

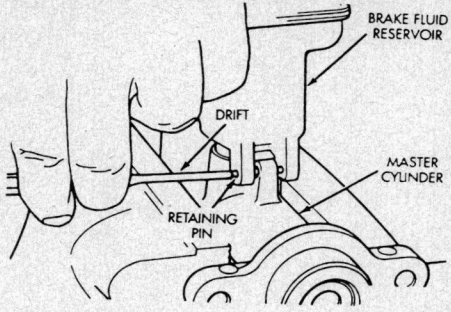

Fig. 23 Type 4 reservoir retaining pin removal. Concorde, Intrepid & Vision

3. Secure wheel cylinder to backing plate, then complete tightening of brake line fitting.
4. Install brake shoes, drum and wheel.
5. Bleed system as outlined previously, and adjust brakes.

COMPONENT SERVICE

MASTER CYLINDER

When disassembling the master cylinder, note the position of all parts as they are removed for proper installation.

When disassembled, wash all parts in denatured alcohol or clean brake fluid only. Use an air hose to blow out all passages, orifices and valve holes. Air dry and place parts on clean paper or lint-free cloth.

Inspect master cylinder bore for scoring, rust, pitting or etching. Any of these conditions will require replacement of the housing. Never hone the bore of the master cylinder as this will remove the anodized surface. Inspect master cylinder pistons for scoring, pitting or distortion. Replace piston if any of these conditions exist. If either the master cylinder housing or piston is replaced, clean the new parts with denatured alcohol or clean brake fluid, and blow out all passages with air hose.

Examine reservoirs for foreign matter and check all passages for restrictions. If there is any indication of contamination or evidence of corrosion, service the hydraulic system as needed, and flush the entire system as described under "Brake System Bleed."

When reassembling the master cylinder, use all parts contained in the repair kit. Dip all component parts in clean brake fluid, and place them on a clean surface. To prevent faulty operation, when installing seals inspect through side outlet of the dual master cylinder housing to make certain cup lips do not hang up on edge of hole or turn back. A piece of 3/16 inch rod with an end rounded off will be helpful in guiding cups past the hole.

When performing overhaul procedures, refer to **Figs. 25 through 28.**

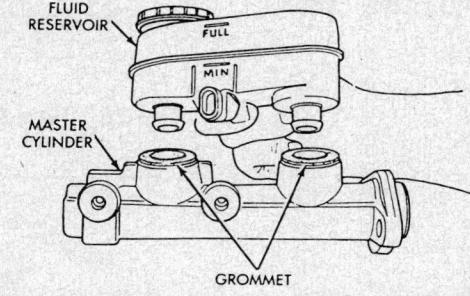

Fig. 24 Type 8 brake fluid reservoir removal

Disassemble

When disassembling the master cylinder, note the position of all parts as they are removed for proper installation.

1. Use a wooden stick or dowel to depress primary piston into cylinder bore.
2. With pushrod depressed, remove piston stopper bolt, then piston stopper ring.
3. Release pushrod, then remove piston assemblies. If secondary piston assembly is stuck in the bore, apply a light amount of compressed air to the secondary outlet port until piston assembly works free.

Cleaning & Inspection

Examine reservoirs for foreign matter and check all passages for restrictions. If there is any indication of contamination or evidence of corrosion, service the hydraulic system as needed, then flush the entire system as described under "Brake System Bleed."

When disassembled, wash all parts in denatured alcohol or clean brake fluid. Use an air hose to blow out all passages, orifices and valve holes. Air dry and place parts on clean paper or lint-free cloth.

1. Check components for wear, damage, or corrosion. Replace as needed.
2. Check master cylinder bore for scoring, rust, pitting or etching. Replace as necessary.

Assemble

When assembling the master cylinder, **Figs. 25 through 28,** use all parts contained in the repair kit. Coat all components in clean brake fluid, and place on a clean surface.

WHEEL CYLINDER

Note position of all parts as they are removed for proper installation.

Disassemble

1. Refer to **Fig. 29,** then remove boots, pistons, cups and spring from wheel cylinder.
2. Wipe cylinder walls with denatured alcohol or clean brake fluid.
3. Examine cylinder bore. A scored bore may be honed providing the bore diameter is not increased more than .005 inch. Replace as necessary.
4. Check pistons for wear or damage. Replace as necessary.

Assemble

1. Before assembling, wash hands with soap and water so as not to contaminate rubber parts.
2. Use all parts contained in repair kit. Lubricate cylinder wall and rubber cups with brake fluid.
3. Properly install spring, cups, pistons and boots in housing.

HYDRAULIC TUBING

Never use copper tubing as a replacement for steel tubing. Copper tubing is subject to fatigue cracking and corrosion which could result in brake system failure.

Steel tubing is used to transfer hydraulic pressure to the brakes. All fittings, tubing and hose should be inspected for rust, damage or defective flared seats. The tubing is equipped with a double flare/inverted seat or ISO flare to ensure more positive seating in the fitting.

DOUBLE FLARE/INVERTED SEAT

1. Using the tool shown in **Fig. 30,** or equivalent, cut off the damaged seat or damaged tubing.
2. Ream out any burrs or rough edges showing on inside edges of tubing. This will make the ends of the tubing

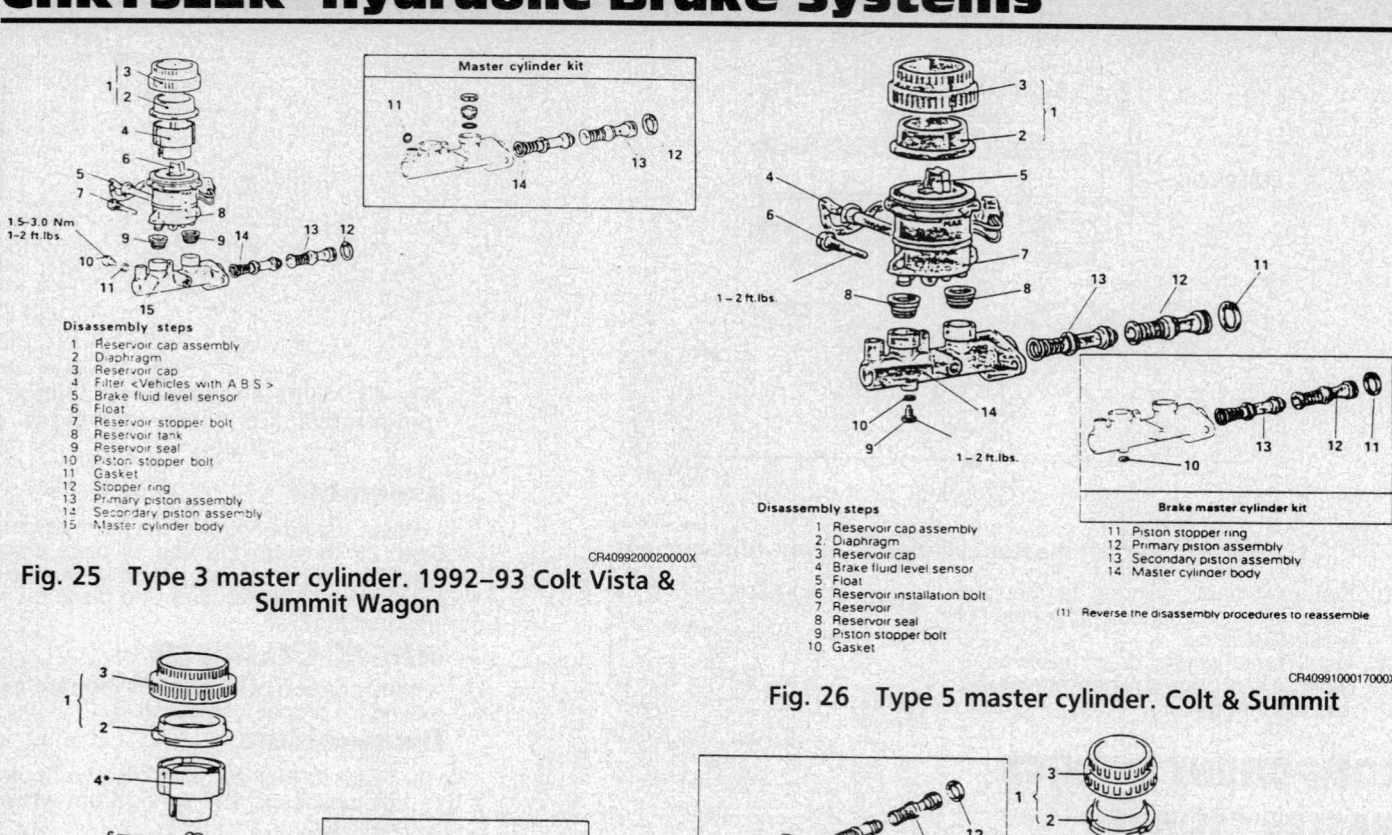

Fig. 25   Type 3 master cylinder. 1992–93 Colt Vista & Summit Wagon

Disassembly steps
1. Reservoir cap assembly
2. Diaphragm
3. Reservoir cap
4. Filter <Vehicles with A.B.S.>
5. Brake fluid level sensor
6. Float
7. Reservoir stopper bolt
8. Reservoir tank
9. Reservoir seal
10. Piston stopper bolt
11. Gasket
12. Stopper ring
13. Primary piston assembly
14. Secondary piston assembly
15. Master cylinder body

1.5–3.0 Nm
1–2 ft.lbs.

CR4099200020000X

Fig. 26   Type 5 master cylinder. Colt & Summit

Disassembly steps
1. Reservoir cap assembly
2. Diaphragm
3. Reservoir cap
4. Brake fluid level sensor
5. Float
6. Reservoir installation bolt
7. Reservoir
8. Reservoir seal
9. Piston stopper bolt
10. Gasket

11. Piston stopper ring
12. Primary piston assembly
13. Secondary piston assembly
14. Master cylinder body

1–2 ft.lbs.
1–2 ft.lbs.

(1) Reverse the disassembly procedures to reassemble

CR4099100017000X

Fig. 27   Type 6 master cylinder. Laser & Talon

Disassembly steps
1. Reservoir cap assembly
2. Diaphragm
3. Reservoir cap
4. Filter
5. Brake fluid level sensor
6. Float
7. Reservoir
8. Nipple
9. Reservoir seal
10. Piston stopper bolt

11. Gasket
12. Piston stopper ring
13. Primary piston assembly
14. Secondary piston assembly
15. Master cylinder body

(1) Reverse the disassembly procedures to reassemble.

Vehicles with ABS

1–2 ft.lbs.
1–2 ft.lbs.
1–2 ft.lbs.

CR4099100018000X

Fig. 28   Type 7 master cylinder. Stealth

Disassembly steps
1. Reservoir cap assembly
2. Diaphragm
3. Reservoir cap
4. Filter <Vehicles with ABS>
5. Brake fluid level sensor
6. Float
7. Reservoir stopper bolt
8. Reservoir
9. Reservoir seal
10. Piston stopper bolt
11. Gasket
12. Piston stopper ring
13. Primary piston assembly
14. Secondary piston assembly
15. Master cylinder body

1.4 ft.lbs.

CR4099100019000X

square and insure better seating on the flared end. Before flaring tubing, place a compression nut on tubing.
3. Open handles of flaring tool and rotate jaws of tool until mating jaws of tubing size are centered in the area between vertical posts.
4. Slowly close handles with tubing inserted in jaws but do not apply heavy pressure to handle as this will lock tubing in place.
5. Referring to **Fig. 30**, place gauge on edge over end of tubing and push tubing through jaws until end of tubing

contacts recessed notch of gauge matching size of tubing.
6. Squeeze handles of flaring tool and lock tubing in place.
7. Place proper size plug of gauge down in end of tubing. Swing compression disc over gauge and center tapered flaring screw in recess in disc.
8. Lubricate taper of flaring or screw and screw in until plug gauge has seated in jaws of flaring tool. This action has started to invert the extended end of tubing.
9. Remove gauge and apply lubricant to

tapered end of flaring screw and continue to screw down until tool is firmly seated in tubing.
10. Remove tubing from flaring tool and inspect the seat. If seat is cracked, cut off cracked end and repeat flaring operation.

BRAKE SYSTEM BLEED

Bleeding the hydraulic brake system is necessary if air has entered the system. A few causes for this condition are low fluid level, a hydraulic fluid leak, a hydraulic line is opened, or replacement of a hydraulic system component. Symptoms can be noted by an improper or loss of brake operation, and/or a low or spongy brake pedal.

Flushing the hydraulic brake system is necessary if contaminants are found in the

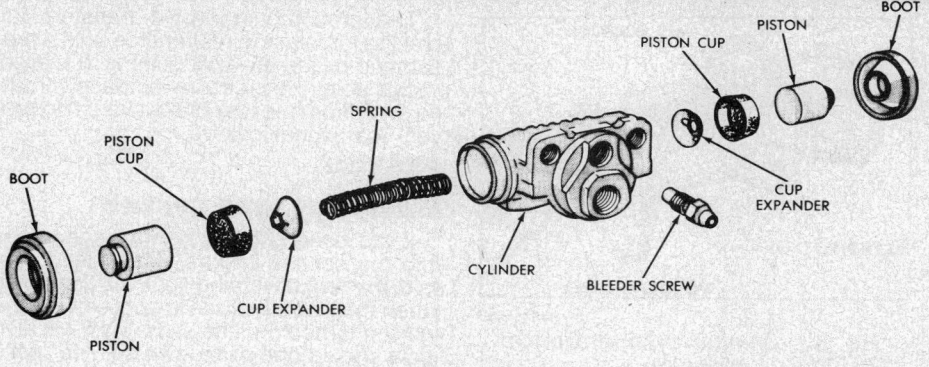

Fig. 29   Disassembled view of typical wheel cylinder

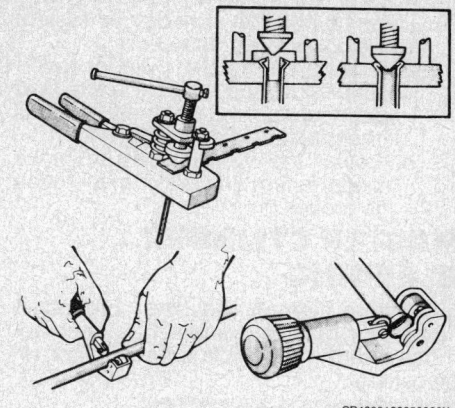

Fig. 30   Flaring hydraulic brake tubing

Premier

Use brake bleeding apparatus M.S.815 as shown, **Fig. 31.** When bleeding the hydraulic brake system, always support rear wheels at their normal curb height, and never start the engine. Open fluid feed valve until reservoir is full, then turn on compressed air to a minimum pressure of 73 psi. Upon completion, fill reservoir as needed.

MANUAL BLEEDING

On models with power brakes, if bleeding the hydraulic system without the engine running, first reduce vacuum in the power unit to zero by pumping the brake pedal several times with the engine off.

1. Ensure master cylinder reservoir is full. Add suitable brake fluid as needed, and securely reinstall the master cylinder cap.
2. Raise and support vehicle.
3. Position a drain pan under the wheel being bled. Refer to "Hydraulic Brake System Specifications" chart for proper wheel bleeding sequence.
4. Have an assistant depress the brake pedal with a slow even pressure and hold it. **Do not depress brake pedal fully to the end of the master cylinder stroke. This may cause damage to the master cylinder.**
5. Using a suitable wrench, open the bleeder valve one full turn. Watch for air bubbles in the fluid, and listen for air escaping from the system.
6. With the brake pedal still depressed, close the bleeder valve.
7. Have the assistant pump the brake pedal several times. **Do not depress brake pedal fully to the end of the master cylinder stroke, as this may cause damage to the master cylinder.**
8. Repeat steps 4 through 7 following the wheel bleeding sequence specified in "Hydraulic Brake System Specifications" chart. Ensure all air is removed from the hydraulic system. **While bleeding the system, recheck brake fluid supply in the master cylinder often so as not to allow the master cylinder to run dry.**

Fig. 31   Power bleeding brakes. Premier

hydraulic system. A few causes for hydraulic system contamination are moisture, age of hydraulic system parts and fluid, or improper fluid used in the system. Symptoms can be noted by an improper or loss of brake operation, swollen and deteriorated cups and other rubber parts, and/or a discoloration of the brake fluid.

The hydraulic fluid is bled or flushed from the system through bleeder valves located on the calipers, wheel cylinders, and some master cylinders. When bleeding the hydraulic brake system, use only specified brake fluid, and never reuse old brake fluid removed from the system.

PRESSURE BLEEDING

Pressure bleeding is recommended for all hydraulic brake systems. It is the fastest method because the master cylinder is automatically fed brake fluid from the pressure bleeder reservoir, and no pedal pumping is needed so only one person is required to perform the procedure. However, if pressure bleeding equipment is not available, the hydraulic system may be bled as described under "Manual Bleeding."

When pressure bleeding, to prevent air from getting into the hydraulic system, do not shake the pressure tank. Set the tank in the required location, bring the air hose to the tank, and do not move it during the bleeding operation. The tank should be kept at least one-third full.

The bleeder valve should be opened at least one full turn, and intermittently closed at about four-second intervals. This gives a whirling action to fluid in the hydraulic system, and helps expel the air. Refer to "Hydraulic Brake System Specifications" chart for proper wheel bleeding sequence.

Precautions
Except Premier

Normal pressure from the pressure bleeder should not be greater than about 35 psi. On vehicles equipped with plastic reservoirs, do not exceed 25 psi bleeding pressure.

On models with hold-off valves contained in the combination valve, the valve stem on the outside of the combination valve must be held in position during bleeding using valve holding tool No. C-4121, or equivalent.

9. Upon completion of hydraulic system bleeding proceed as follows:
   a. Ensure the master cylinder reservoir is full. Add suitable brake fluid as needed, and securely reinstall the master cylinder cap.
   b. Lower the vehicle. Ensure brake pedal is firm and braking operation is proper.

MASTER CYLINDER BLEEDING

Refer to "Bench Bleeding" procedure first if the master cylinder has been removed from the vehicle for service or replacement.

ON-VEHICLE SERVICE

Master cylinders may be bled manually or by pressure bleeding. It is recommended that the master cylinder be bled before bleeding the wheel cylinders and calipers.

Pressure Bleeding

1. Ensure master cylinder reservoir is full. Add suitable brake fluid as needed.
2. Install pressure bleeder according to manufacturer specifications.
3. Position a drain pan under the master cylinder.
4. Loosen brake lines, or bleeder valves if equipped, at the master cylinder. Watch for air bubbles in the fluid and listen for air escaping from the system.
5. Retighten brake lines or bleeder valves.
6. Bleed the master cylinder until all air is removed. Upon completion of bleeding, proceed as follows:
   a. Ensure the master cylinder reservoir is full. Add suitable brake fluid as needed, and securely reinstall the master cylinder cap.
   b. Ensure brake pedal is firm, and braking operation is proper.

Manual Bleeding

1. Ensure master cylinder reservoir is full. Add suitable brake fluid as needed, and securely reinstall the master cylinder cap.
2. Position a drain pan under the master cylinder.
3. Have an assistant depress the brake pedal with a slow even pressure and hold it. **Do not depress brake pedal fully to the end of the master cylinder stroke. This may cause damage to the master cylinder.**
4. Loosen the brake lines, or bleeder valves if equipped, at the master cylinder. Watch for air bubbles in the fluid and listen for air escaping from the system. **While bleeding the system, recheck brake fluid supply in the master cylinder often so as not to allow the master cylinder to run dry.**
5. With brake pedal still depressed, tighten the brake lines or bleeder valves.
6. Bleed the master cylinder until all air is removed. Upon completion of bleeding, proceed as follows:
   a. Ensure the master cylinder reser-

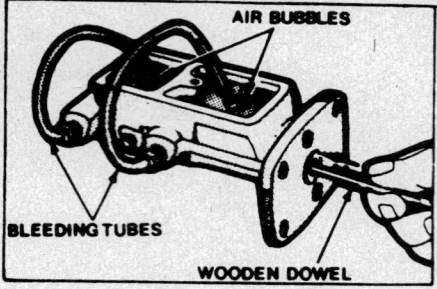

Fig. 32 Master cylinder bench bleeding

voir is full. Add suitable brake fluid as needed, and securely reinstall the master cylinder cap.
   b. Ensure brake pedal is firm, and braking operation is proper.

BENCH BLEEDING

When replacing or overhauling a master cylinder it is advisable to bleed it before installing it on the car.
1. Properly support master cylinder assembly and attach special bleeding tubes as shown in, **Fig. 32.**
2. Fill reservoir with approved brake fluid.
3. Using a wooden stick or dowel (cars with power brakes) depress pushrod slowly and allow the pistons to return under pressure of the springs. Do this several times until all air bubbles are expelled.
4. Remove bleeding tubes from cylinder and install reservoir cover.
5. Install master cylinder onto vehicle as described under "Component Replacement."
6. Bleed the entire hydraulic system as described previously.

Precautions

Combination valves containing brake warning or pressure differential type valves are self-centering. They will reset after hydraulic system pressure is equalized, and by doing the following: Upon completion of bleeding the hydraulic system, depress the brake pedal with moderate force. The brake warning lamp will turn off when the switch is re-centered.

HYDRAULIC BRAKE SYSTEM CONTROLS

TYPE 1 COMBINATION VALVE

This valve assembly, **Fig. 33,** is comprised of a warning switch, and a dual proportioning valve.

The warning switch detects system failure when a pressure difference occurs between the diagonally split systems. In such a case, the valve piston shuttles toward the side with the low pressure forcing the switch plunger upward over the piston's tapered shoulder. This movement closes the switch contacts causing the brake warning lamp to illuminate. Upon restoration of equalized system pressure the brake warning switch will reset.

The proportioning valve transfers full braking force to the rear brakes until a preset ratio called the split point is achieved. At this point the pressure increase is routed away from the rear brake system to prevent rear wheel lock-up.

TESTING

Warning Light System

If the parking brake light is connected into the service brake warning light system, the brake warning light will flash only when the parking brake is applied with the ignition turned on. The same light will also glow should one of the two service brake systems fail when the brake pedal is applied.

To test the system, turn the ignition on and apply the parking brake. If the lamp fails to light, inspect for a burned out bulb, disconnected socket, a broken or disconnected wire at the switch.

To test the brake warning system, raise the car and open a wheel bleeder valve while a helper depresses the brake pedal and observes the warning light on the instrument panel. If the bulb fails to light, inspect for a burned out bulb, disconnected socket, or a broken or disconnected wire at the switch. If the bulb is not burned out, and the wire continuity is proven, replace the brake warning switch.

Proportioning Valve

On vehicles with Bosch ABS-3, Bendix Anti-Lock 6 or Bendix Anti-Lock 10, refer to "Anti-Lock Brakes" section for testing procedures.

If premature rear wheel skid occurs on hard brake application, it could be an indication of a malfunctioning proportioning valve unit.

The proportioning valve is designed with two separate systems. One half controls the right rear brake, and the other half controls the left rear brake. A road test to determine which rear brake slides first must be performed.
1. To test proportioning valve when right rear wheel slides first, leave front brakes connected to valve, then proceed as follows:
   a. Install gauge set tool No. C-4007A , or equivalent, as shown in **Fig. 34.** A special adapter may be fabricated from a short piece of brake tube and two 3/8 X 24 tube nuts.
   b. Bleed the hose and gauge set.
   c. While watching pressure gauges, have an assistant depress the brake pedal. Note gauge readings, then refer to "Hydraulic Brake Controls Specifications" chart.
2. To test proportioning valve when left rear wheel slides first, leave front brakes connected to valve, then proceed as follows:
   a. Install gauge set tool No. C-4007A , or equivalent, as shown in **Fig. 35.** A special adapter may be fabricated from a 7/16 X 24 tube nut, a short piece of brake tube and a 3/8 X 24 tube nut.
   b. Bleed hose and gauge set.
   c. While watching pressure gauges, have an assistant depress the

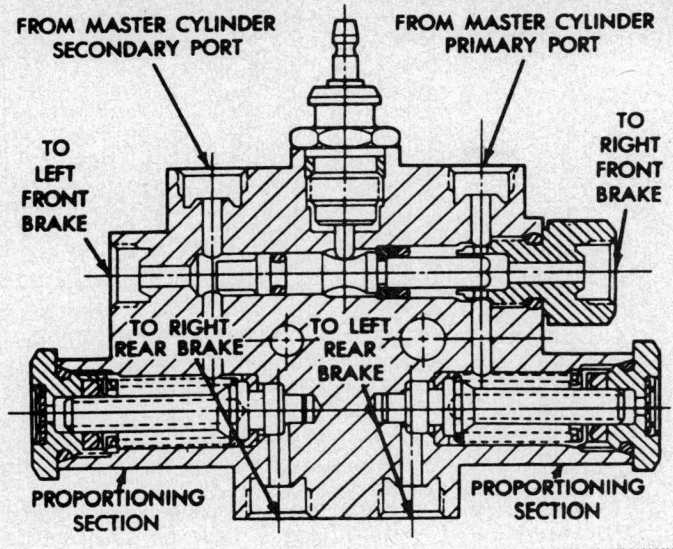

Fig. 33   Type 1 combination valve

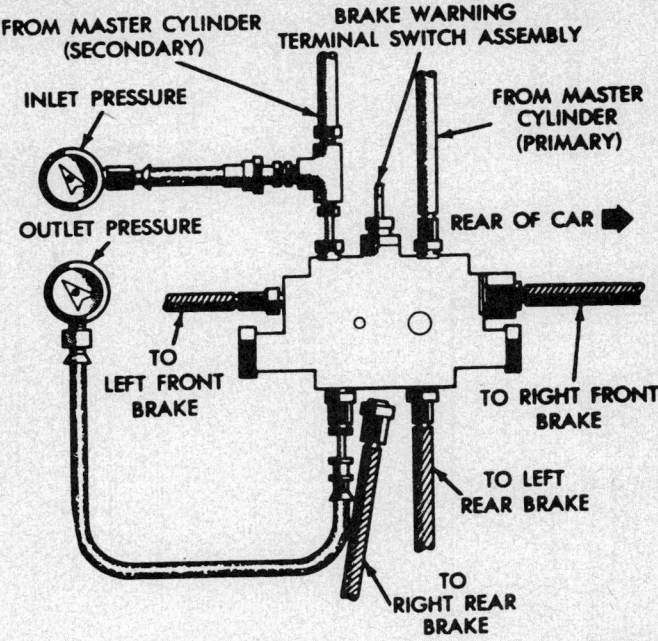

Fig. 34   Type 1 combination valve pressure gauge test connections. Right wheel malfunction

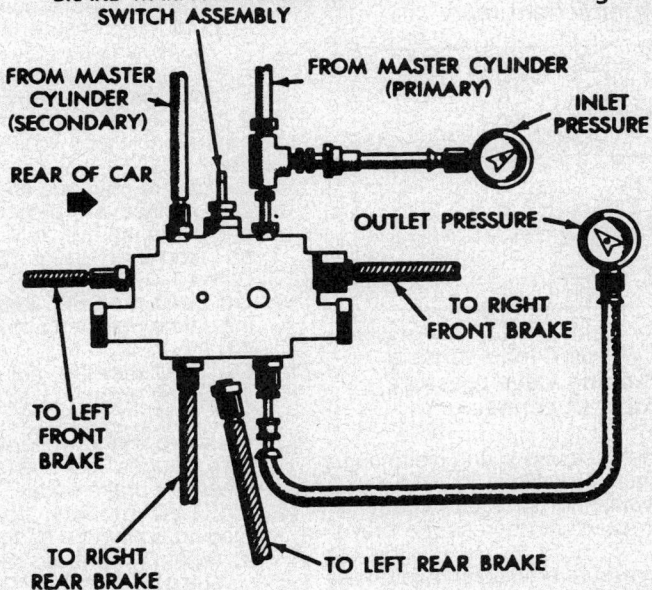

Fig. 35   Type 1 combination valve pressure gauge test connections. Left wheel malfunction

brake pedal. Note gauge readings, then refer to "Hydraulic Brake Controls Specifications" chart.

3. If pressure readings are not as specified for left or right rear wheel, replace the combination valve noting the following:
   a. After installing a new combination valve, bleed hydraulic brake system as described under "Brake System Bleed."
   b. After bleeding brake system, reset brake warning switch by depressing brake pedal with moderate force. Brake warning lamp will turn off when switch is reset.

TYPE 2 PROPORTIONING VALVE

Description

This system utilizes a proportioning valve with a diagonally split hydraulic system. The proportioning valve is incorporated into the hydraulic system to control braking force to the rear brakes.

Testing

On models with Bendix Anti-Lock 10, refer to "Anti-Lock Brakes" section for testing procedures.

1. Ensure that vehicle is unloaded, weight is on tires, one person is on board and fuel tank is full, also rear brake adjustment should be within specifications.
2. Remove bleed screws from right front caliper and left rear wheel cylinder or caliper.
3. Install pressure gauge No. 7212 or equivalent in each caliper or wheel cylinder in place of bleed screws as shown in **Fig. 36.**
4. Bleed air out through gauge bleed valves, then start engine and observe gauge readings while a helper applies brake pedal, refer to "Hydraulic Brake Controls Specifications" chart.
5. Stop engine, then remove pressure gauges and install bleed screws. Bleed right front caliper and left rear wheel cylinder or caliper prior to continuing, refer to "Brake System Bleed."
6. Remove bleed screws from left front caliper and right rear wheel cylinder or caliper.
7. Install pressure gauge No. 7212 or equivalent in each caliper or wheel cylinder in place of bleed screws as shown in **Fig. 37.**
8. Repeat steps 4 and 5, then if gauge readings are within specifications valve is operating properly, if not, replace valve.

TYPE 3 PROPORTIONING VALVE

Testing

1. Install suitable pressure gauges, one each on input side and output side of proportioning valve as shown in **Fig. 38.**
2. Bleed brake line and pressure gauge, then gradually depress brake pedal

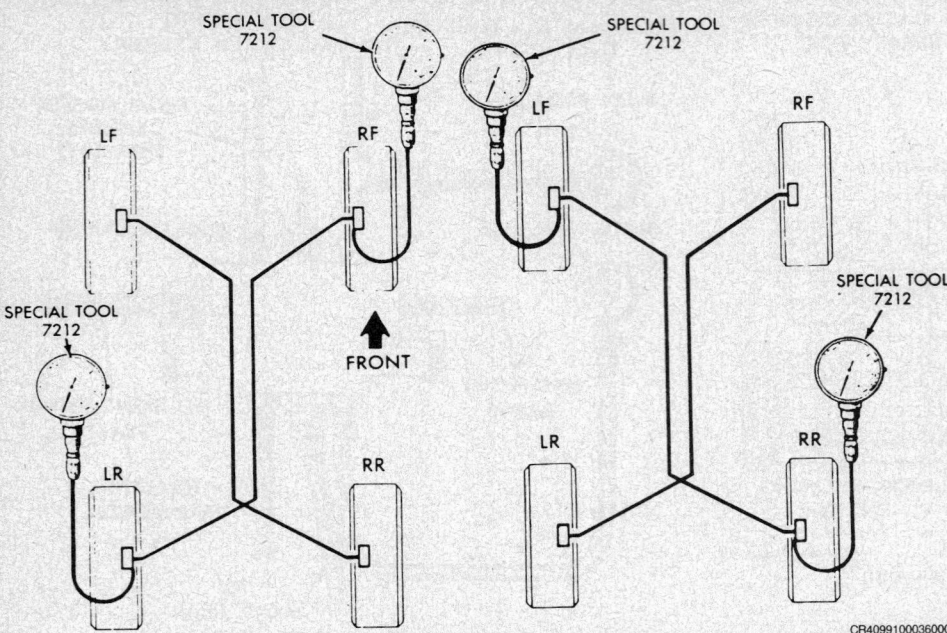

Fig. 36 Type 2 proportioning valve pressure gauge test connections. Right front & left rear

Fig. 37 Type 2 proportioning valve pressure gauge test connections. Left front & right rear

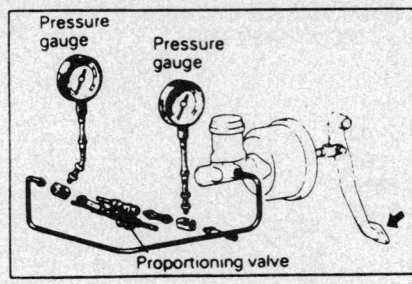

Fig. 38 Type 3 proportioning valve pressure gauge test connection

and observe gauge readings. Refer to "Hydraulic Brake Controls Specifications" chart.

3. Observe left and right output pressures, pressure difference between left and right should not be greater than 57 psi.
4. If gauge readings are not within specifications, replace proportioning valve.

TYPE 4 LOAD SENSING PROPORTIONING VALVE

Prior to performing the following test procedures, park vehicle on a level surface, ensure vehicle is unloaded and at normal curb height.

TESTING

Colt Vista

1. Install suitable gauge set as shown in **Fig. 39.**
2. Bleed hose and gauge set.
3. Loosen load sensing unit adjusting nuts, **Fig. 40.**
4. While watching pressure gauges, have an assistant depress the brake pedal.
5. Gauge pressure reading should be as follows:
   a. When input pressure is 740 psi, output pressure should read 307-377 psi.
   b. When input pressure is 1991 psi, output pressure should read 660-774 psi.
   c. Output pressure side to side difference should not exceed 57 psi.
6. If pressure readings are as specified proceed to step 7. If pressure readings are not as specified, replace the proportioning valve and bleed the hydraulic brake system as described under "Brake System Bleed."

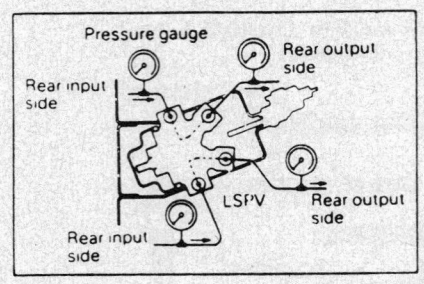

Fig. 39 Type 4 load sensing proportioning valve pressure gauge test connection

7. Adjust load sensing spring distance L to 4.07 inch, **Fig. 40.**
8. While watching pressure gauges, have an assistant depress the brake pedal.
9. Gauge pressure reading should be as follows:
   a. When input pressure is 1991 psi, output pressure should read 1228-1580.
   b. Output pressure side to side difference should not exceed 121 psi.
10. If pressure readings are as specified, proceed to step 11. If pressure readings are not as specified, replace the proportioning valve and bleed the hydraulic brake system as described under "Brake System Bleed."
11. Adjust load sensing spring distance L to 3.42-3.50 inch, **Fig. 40.**

Colt Wagon

1. Install suitable gauge set as shown in **Fig. 39.**
2. Bleed the hose and gauge set.
3. **On 2WD models,** loosen load sensing unit adjusting nuts, **Fig. 41.**

4. **On 4WD models,** loosen mounting brackets to free operating lever, **Fig. 42.**
5. **On all models,** while watching pressure gauges, have an assistant depress the brake pedal.
6. Gauge pressure reading should be as follows:
   a. When input pressure is 889 psi, output pressure should read 455-526 psi.
   b. When input pressure is 1991 psi, output pressure should read 765-879 psi.
   c. Output pressure side to side difference should not exceed 57 psi.
7. If pressure readings are as specified proceed to steps 9 or 10 as applicable.
8. If pressure readings are not as specified, replace the proportioning valve and bleed the hydraulic brake system as described under "Brake System Bleed."
9. **On 2WD models,** adjust load sensing spring distance L to 4.10 inch, **Fig. 41.**
10. **On 4WD models,** adjust load sensing spring distance L to 3.97 inch, **Fig. 42.**
11. **On all models,** while watching pressure gauges, have an assistant depress the brake pedal.
12. **On 2WD models,** gauge pressure reading should be as follows:
   a. When input pressure is 1991 psi, output pressure should read 1254-1496 psi.
   b. Output pressure side to side difference should not exceed 121 psi.
13. **On 4WD models,** gauge pressure reading should be as follows:
   a. When input pressure is 1991 psi, output pressure should read 1249-1491 psi.
   b. Output pressure side to side difference should not exceed 121 psi.
14. **On all models,** if pressure readings are as specified, proceed to steps 16 or 17 as applicable.
15. If pressure readings are not as specified, replace the proportioning valve and bleed the hydraulic brake system as described under "Brake System Bleed."
16. **On 2WD models,** adjust load sensing spring distance L to 3.51-3.59 inch, **Fig. 41.**

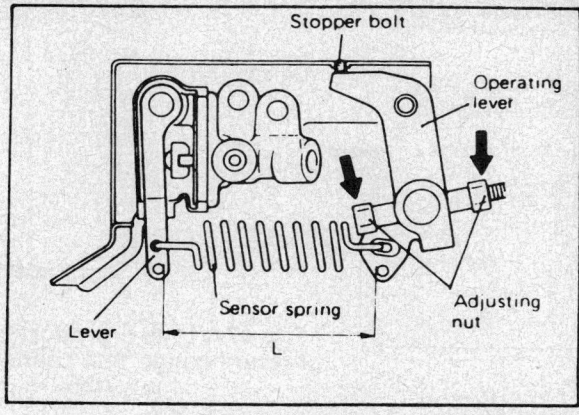

Fig. 40   Type 3 load sensing proportioning valve sensor spring. Colt Vista

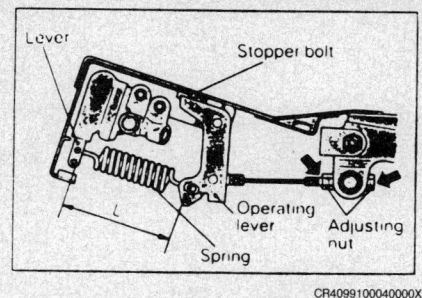

Fig. 41   Type 3 load sensing proportioning valve sensor spring. Colt Wagon 2WD

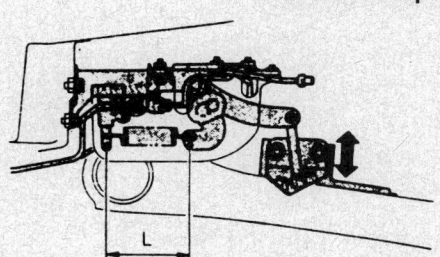

Fig. 42   Type 3 load sensing proportioning valve sensor spring. Colt Wagon 4WD

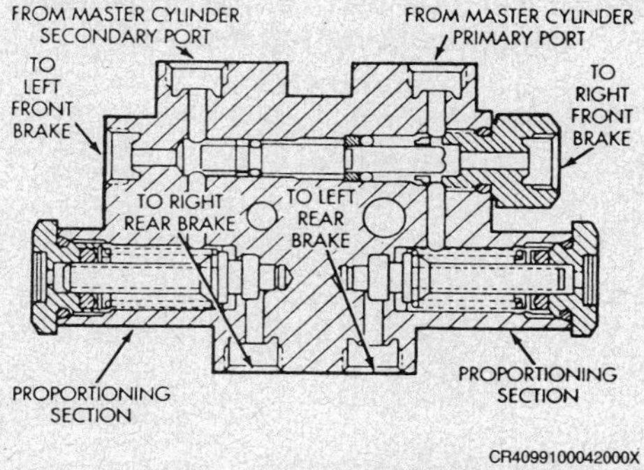

17. **On 4WD models,** Adjust load sensing spring distance L to 3.47–3.55 inch, **Fig. 42.**

TYPE 5 PROPORTIONING VALVES

DESCRIPTION

This valve assembly on non-ABS models, **Fig. 43,** is of a dual proportioning valve design.

The proportioning valve on non-ABS models transfers full braking force to the rear brakes until a preset ratio called the split point is achieved. At this point the pressure increase is routed away from the rear brake system to prevent rear wheel lock-up.

On models with ABS, two screw in proportioning valves are used, **Fig. 44.** These proportioning valves are attached to the rear brake outlets of the hydraulic control unit (HCU).

The brake warning light will come on when the parking brake is applied with the ignition turned On. The same light will also come on when one of the two service brake systems fail.

TESTING

Less Anti-Lock Brake System

If premature rear wheel skid occurs on hard brake application, it could be an indication of a malfunctioning proportioning valve unit.

The proportioning valve is designed

Fig. 43   Type 5, proportioning valve. Concorde, Intrepid & Vision less ABS

with two separate systems. One half controls the right rear brake, and the other half controls the left rear brake. A road test to determine which rear brake slides first must be performed.

1. If right rear wheel slides first, leave front brakes connected to valve, then proceed as follows:
   a. Install one gauge of set tool No. C-4007A, or equivalent, between brake line from master cylinder secondary port and brake valve assembly, **Fig. 45.**
   b. Install second gauge of set tool No. C-4007A, or equivalent, as shown in **Fig. 45.** A special adapter may be fabricated from a short piece of brake tube and one 3/8 X 24 tube nuts and one M10 X 1 tube nut.
   c. Bleed the hose and gauge set.
   d. While watching pressure gauges, have an assistant depress the brake pedal. Note gauge readings, then refer to "Hydraulic Brake Controls Specifications" chart.
2. If left rear wheel slides first, leave front brakes connected to valve, then proceed as follows:
   a. Install one gauge of set tool No. C-4007A, or equivalent, between brake line from master cylinder secondary port and brake valve assembly, **Fig. 46.**
   b. Install gauge set tool No. C-4007A, or equivalent, as shown in **Fig. 46.** A special adapter may be fabricated from a M12x1 tube nut, a short

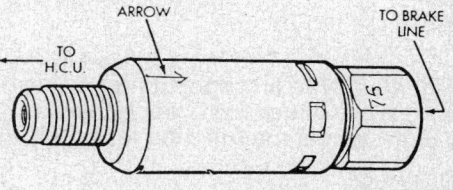

Fig. 44   Type 5 proportioning valve. Concorde, Intrepid & Vision w/ABS

piece of brake tube and a 3/8 X 24 tube nut.
   c. Bleed hose and gauge set.
   d. While watching pressure gauges, have an assistant depress the brake pedal. Note gauge readings, then refer to "Hydraulic Brake Controls Specifications" chart.
3. If pressure readings are not as specified for left or right rear wheel, replace the combination valve. After installing a new combination valve, bleed hydraulic brake system as described under "Brake System Bleed."

w/Anti-Lock Brake System

On vehicles with Teves Mark IV ABS system refer to "Anti-Lock Brakes" section for testing procedures.

All ABS components use an ISO type tubing flare. Ensure proper adapters with ISO type flare are used when installing test gauges.

1. Install one gauge of set tool No. C-700A, or equivalent, between hydraulic assembly and male end (inlet) of valve.
2. Install second gauge of set tool No. C-700A, or equivalent, at female end (outlet) of valve, **Fig. 47.**
3. While watching inlet and outlet pressure gauges, have an assistant depress the brake pedal. Note gauge readings, then refer to "Hydraulic Brake Controls Specifications" chart.
4. If pressures are not within specifications replace proportioning valve.

TYPE 6 PROPORTIONING VALVES

Description

This system uses proportioning valves to balance front to rear braking by controlling, at a given ratio, the increase in rear brake system hydraulic pressure above a preset level. Under light pedal application,

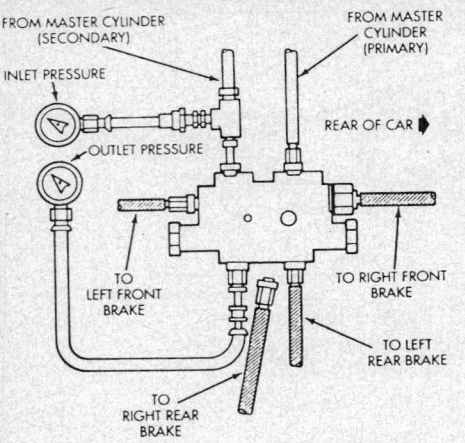

Fig. 45 Type 5 proportioning valve pressure gauge test connections. Right wheel malfunction less ABS

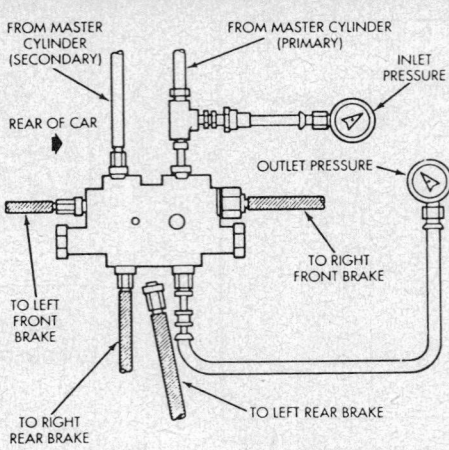

Fig. 46 Type 5 proportioning valve pressure gauge test connections. Left wheel malfunction less ABS

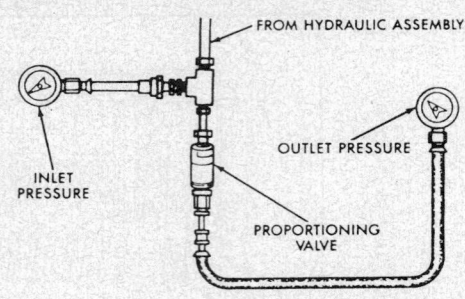

Fig. 47 Type 5 proportioning valve pressure gauge test connections. With ABS

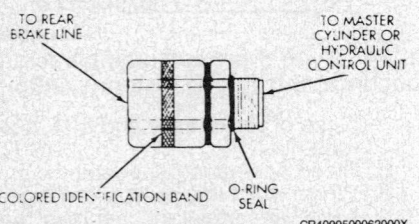

Fig. 48 Type 6, proportioning valve identification

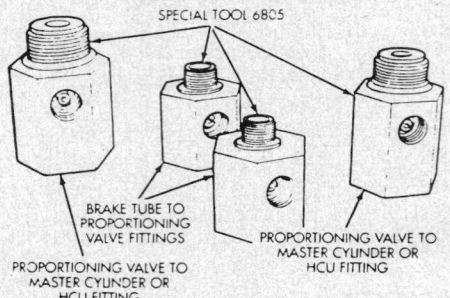

Fig. 49 Type 6, proportioning valve pressure test fittings

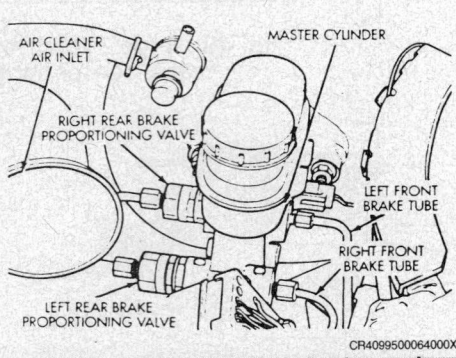

Fig. 50 Type 6, proportioning valve location. Less ABS

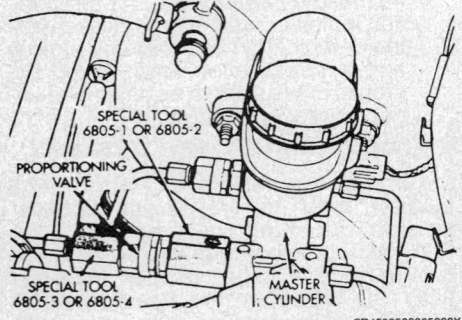

Fig. 51 Type 6, pressure test fitting installation. Less ABS

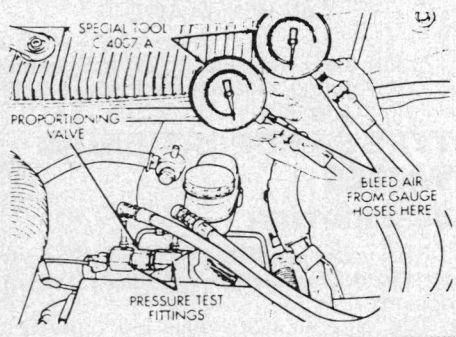

Fig. 52 Type 6, pressure testing. Less ABS

the proportioning valves allow full hydraulic pressure to be applied to the rear brakes.

There are two proportioning valve assemblies used in each vehicle. Due to differences in thread size, each valve has a different part number. During any service procedures, identify valve assemblies by part number or color code, **Fig. 48.**

TESTING

The in-line proportioning valves used in this system require special pressure fittings set No. 6805, or equivalent, to test for proper valve function, **Fig. 49.** The fittings are installed before and after the proportioning valve being tested to verify valve is maintaining the required hydraulic pressure to the rear wheel brake which it controls. The pressure gauges used for testing the in-line proportioning valves on both

non-ABS and ABS systems is Pressure Gauge Set No. C-4007-A, or equivalent

If a condition of premature wheel skid occurs on a vehicle, the proportioning valve should always be tested prior to being replaced as there are conditions other than a faulty proportioning valve that can cause premature wheel skid, such as worn, contaminated or improper brake linings.

Less Anti-Lock Brake System

1. Road test vehicle to determine which rear wheel exhibits premature wheel skid. Refer to **Fig. 50** to determine which proportioning valve needs to be tested.
2. Remove hydraulic brake line from proportioning valve to be tested, then remove valve from master cylinder outlet port.
3. Install Pressure Test Fitting No. 6805-1 or 6805-2, or equivalent, depending on the thread size, into outlet port of master cylinder.
4. Install proportioning valve into pressure test fitting in master cylinder outlet port.
5. Install Pressure Test Fitting No. 6805-3 or 6805-4, or equivalent, depending on the thread size, into outlet port of proportioning valve, **Fig. 51.**
6. Connect brake hydraulic line onto

pressure test fitting on proportioning valve.
7. Install Pressure Gauge Set No. C-4007-A, or equivalent, into test fitting and bleed air from pressure gauge hose, **Fig. 52.**
8. Apply pressure to brake pedal until reading on proportioning valve inlet test fitting is appropriate, then check the pressure reading on the outlet test fitting. If the pressure on the outlet test fitting is not within specifications, **Fig. 53,** replace proportioning valve.
9. Install proportioning valve into master cylinder body until O-ring is seated, then **torque** proportioning valve to 30 ft. lbs.
10. Install brake tube onto proportioning valve and **torque** tube nut to 145 inch lbs.
11. Bleed brake line as outlined under "Brake System Bleed".

System Type	Split Point	ID	Inlet Pressure	Outlet Pressure
14" Disc/Drum	400 psi	Black Band	1000 psi	600-700 psi
13" Disc/Drum	400 psi	Gold Band	1000 psi	550-650 psi
14" Disc/Disc	400 psi	Gold Band	1000 psi	550-650 psi
14" Disc/Disc w/ABS	400 psi	Gold Band	1000 psi	550-650 psi
13" Disc/Drum w/ABS	400 psi	Gold Band	1000 psi	550-650 psi
14" Disc/Drum w/ABS	400 psi	Gold Band	1000 psi	550-650 psi

CR4099500067000X

Fig. 53   Type 6, proportioning valve specifications

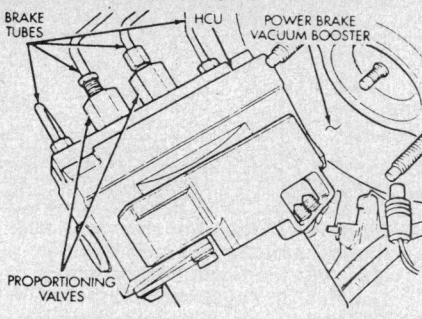

CR4099500068000X

Fig. 54   Type 6, proportioning valve location. With ABS

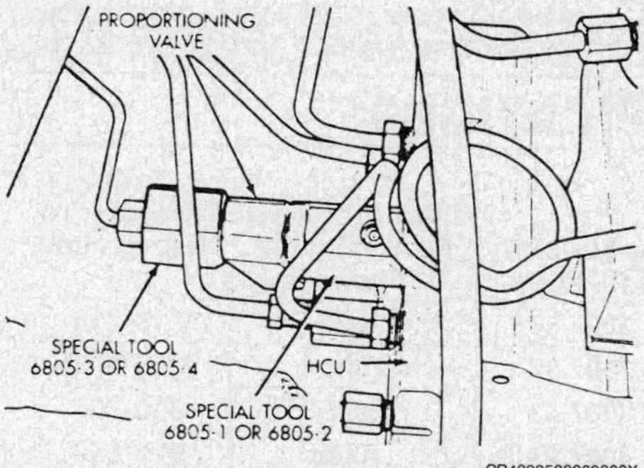

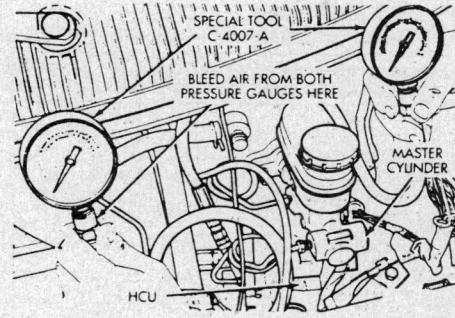

CR4099500069000X

Fig. 55   Type 6, pressure test fitting installation. With ABS

CR4099500070000X

Fig. 56   Type 6, pressure testing. With ABS

With Anti-Lock Brake System

1. Road test vehicle to determine which rear wheel exhibits premature wheel skid. Refer to **Fig. 54** to determine which proportioning valve needs to be tested.
2. Remove hydraulic brake line from proportioning valve to be tested, then remove valve from master cylinder outlet port.
3. Install Pressure Test Fitting No. 6805-1 or 6805-2, or equivalent, depending on the thread size, into outlet port of master cylinder.
4. Install proportioning valve into pressure test fitting in master cylinder outlet port.
5. Install Pressure Test Fitting No. 6805-3 or 6805-4, or equivalent, depending on the thread size, into outlet port of proportioning valve, **Fig. 55**.
6. Connect brake hydraulic line onto pressure test fitting on proportioning valve.
7. Install Pressure Gauge Set No. C-4007-A, or equivalent, into test fitting and bleed air from pressure gauge hose, **Fig. 56**.
8. Apply pressure to brake pedal until reading on proportioning valve inlet test fitting is appropriate, then check the pressure reading on the outlet test fitting. If the pressure on the outlet test fitting is not within specifications, **Fig. 53**, replace proportioning valve.
9. Install proportioning valve into master cylinder body until O-ring is seated, then **torque** proportioning valve to 30 ft. lbs.
10. Install brake tube onto proportioning valve and **torque** tube nut to 145 inch lbs.
11. Bleed brake line as outlined under "Brake System Bleed."

HYDRAULIC BRAKE SYSTEM SPECIFICATIONS

Year	Model	Master Cylinder Bore Dia. Inch	Booster to Primary Piston Clearance Inch	Wheel Bleeding Sequence
1992	Monaco & Premier	.944	—	RR,LR,RF,LF
1992-93	Daytona	④	—	RR,LR,RF,LF
	Dynasty & New Yorker Landau/Salon	④	—	RR,LR,RF,LF
	Fifth Avenue & Imperial	④	—	RR,LR,RF,LF
1992-94	Acclaim & Spirit	④	—	RR,LR,RF,LF
	Colt & Summit Hatchback	.8125	.020-.028	LR,RF,RR,LF
	Colt Vista	.937 ③	①	LR,RF,RR,LF
	Colt Vista	1.00 ②	①	LR,RF,RR,LF
	LeBaron	④	—	RR,LR,RF,LF
	Laser & Talon AWD ⑤	1.00	.020-.028	RR,LF,LR,RF
	Laser & Talon FWD ⑤	.9375	.020-.028	RR,LF,LR,RF
	Laser & Talon FWD ⑥	.874 ③	.020-.028	RR,LF,LR,RF
	Laser & Talon FWD ⑥	.937 ②	.031-.039	RR,LF,LR,RF
	Shadow & Sundance	④	—	RR,LR,RF,LF
	Summit Sedan	.8750	.024-.031	LR,RF,RR,LF
	Summit Wagon	.937 ③	①	LR,RF,RR,LF
	Summit Wagon	1.00 ②	①	LR,RF,RR,LF
	Stealth AWD	1.0625	.026-.033	RR,LF,LR,RF
	Stealth FWD	1.00	.022-.030	RR,LF,LR,RF

Continued

HYDRAULIC BRAKE SYSTEM SPECIFICATIONS -Continued

Year	Model	Master Cylinder Bore Dia. Inch	Booster to Primary Piston Clearance Inch	Wheel Bleeding Sequence
1993-94	Concorde, Intrepid & Vision	.937	—	RR,LF,LR,RF
1994	New Yorker & LHS	.937	—	RR,LF,LR,RF
1995	Neon	⑦	—	LR,RF,RR,LF

①—Models w/7 inch booster, .020–.028 inches; models w/8 inch booster, .024–.031 inches; model w/9 inch booster, .031–.039 inches.
②—With Anti-Lock Brakes.
③—Less Anti-Lock Brakes.
④—.875 & .944 inch.
⑤—Turbo models.
⑥—Non turbo models.
⑦—Models w/front disc brakes and rear drum brakes, 21 mm; models w/four wheel disc brakes, .875 in.

HYDRAULIC BRAKE CONTROLS SPECIFICATIONS

Year	Model	Valve Identification	Valve Tag Color ①	Split Point psi/Slope	Inlet Pressure From Master Cylinder psi	Outlet Pressure To Rear Brakes psi
1992	Monaco Except LE & Premier ⑩	⑨	—	300/.37	2000	710-810
	Monaco LE ⑪	⑨	—	430/.37	2000	950-1070
1992-93	Daytona ⑭ ④	⑨	Yellow	400/.43	1000	600-700
	Daytona ⑤ ④	⑨	White	400/.27	1000	525-600
	Daytona ⑤ ③	⑨	—	435/.45	1000	640-720
	Dynasty & New Yorker/Salon ③	⑥	—	290/.3	1000	460-540
	Fifth Avenue & Imperial ⑬ ④	⑨	Black	500/.59	1000	725-850
	Fifth Avenue & Imperial ⑫ ③	⑨	—	290/.3	1000	460-540
	Stealth AWD	⑨	—	533-604	1138	744-815
1992-94	Acclaim, LeBaron Landau & Spirit ⑫ ④	⑨	White	400/.27	—	525–600
	Acclaim, LeBaron Landau & Spirit ⑬ ④	⑨	Yellow	400/.43	1000	600-700
	Acclaim, LeBaron Landau & Spirit ⑫ ③	⑨	—	290/.45	1000	—
	Acclaim, LeBaron Landau & Spirit ⑤ ③	⑨	—	430/.45	1000	640-720
	Colt	⑨	—	348-420	953	519-590
	Colt Vista ⑭	⑨	—	391–462	966	604
	Colt Vista ⑮	⑨	—	462–533	1067	676
	Laser & Talon AWD	⑨	—	491-561	1095	661-732
	Laser & Talon FWD	⑨	—	562-633	1163	732-804
	LeBaron Except Landau ⑬ ④	⑨	Yellow	400/.43	1000	600-700
	LeBaron Except Landau ⑤ ④	⑨	Yellow	400/.43	1000	600-700
	LeBaron Except Landau ⑫ ④	⑨	Gray	500/.27	1000	725-850
	LeBaron Except Landau ⑤ ③	⑨	—	435/.45	1000	640-720
	Shadow & Sundance ⑬	⑨	Yellow	400/.43	1000	600-700
	Shadow & Sundance ⑫	⑨	Yellow	400/.43	1000	600-700
	Stealth FWD	⑨	—	533-604	1138	744-815
	Summit Hatchback	⑨	—	348-420	953	519-590
	Summit Sedan	⑨	—	420-491	1024	590-661
	Summit Wagon ⑭	⑨	—	391–462	966	604
	Summit Wagon ⑮	⑨	—	462–533	1067	676
1993-94	Concorde, Intrepid & Vision ②	⑨	Black	430/.43	1000	525-600
	Concorde, Intrepid & Vision ⑧	⑨	White	500/.43	1000	725-850
	Concorde, Intrepid & Vision ⑦	⑨	—	435/.45	1000	640-720
1994	New Yorker & LHS ②	⑨	Black	430/.43	1000	525–600
	New Yorker & LHS ⑦	⑨	—	435/.45	1000	640-720
1995	Neon	⑨	Black	400/.43	1000	600-700
	Neon	⑨	Gold	400/.34	1000	550-650

①—Color tag located under boot of valve stem.
②—Four wheel disc brakes less ABS.
③—With ABS.
④—Less ABS.
⑤—With 15 inch disc.
⑥—Differential-Proportioning Valve.
⑦—Four wheel disc brakes w/ABS.
⑧—Front disc brakes, rear drum brakes less ABS.
⑨—Proportioning Valve.
⑩—10.43 inch disc-disc.
⑪—10.43 inch disc-drum.
⑫—14 inch disc-disc.
⑬—14 inch disc-drum.
⑭—FWD w/anti-lock brakes.
⑮—Except FWD w/anti-lock brakes.

POWER BRAKE UNITS

INDEX

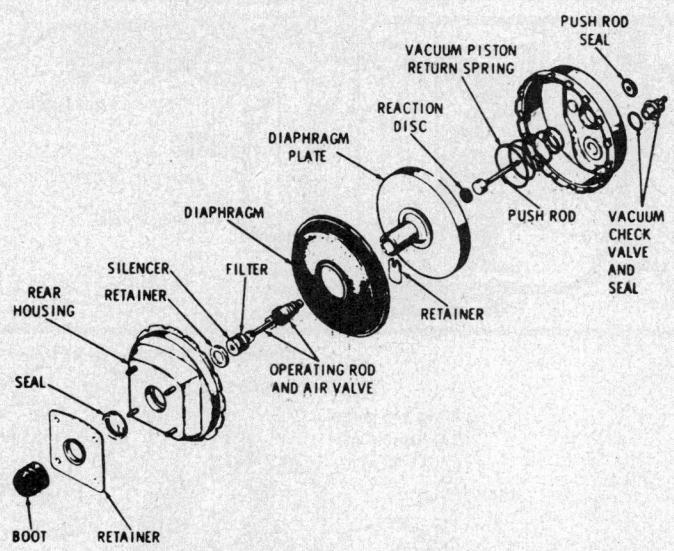

CR4099100052000X

Fig. 1 Bendix single diaphragm power brake unit

DESCRIPTION

SYSTEM

These units are of the vacuum suspended type. Some units are of the single diaphragm type, **Fig. 1,** while others are of the tandem diaphragm type, **Fig. 2.** Both single piston and double piston or split system type master cylinders are used.

The vacuum suspended diaphragm type units utilize engine manifold vacuum and atmospheric pressure for its power. It consists of three basic elements combined into a single power unit. The three basic elements of the single diaphragm type are:

1. A vacuum power section which includes a front and rear shell, a power diaphragm, a return spring and a pushrod.
2. A control valve, built integral with the power diaphragm and connected through a valve rod to the brake pedal, controls the degree of brake application or release in accordance with the pressure applied to the brake pedal.
3. A hydraulic master cylinder, attached to the vacuum power section which contains all the elements of the conventional brake master cylinder ex-

cept for the pushrod, supplies fluid under pressure to the wheel brakes in proportion to the pressure applied to the brake pedal.

OPERATION

Upon application of the brakes, the valve rod and plunger move to the left in the power diaphragm to close the vacuum port and open the atmospheric port to admit air through the air cleaner and valve at the rear diaphragm chamber. With vacuum present in the rear chamber, a force is developed to move the power diaphragm, hydraulic pushrod and hydraulic piston or pistons to close the compensating port or ports and force fluid under pressure through the residual check valve or valves and lines into the front and rear wheel cylinders to actuate the brakes.

As pressure is developed within the master cylinder a counter force acting through the hydraulic pushrod and reaction disc against the vacuum power diaphragm and valve plunger sets up a reaction force opposing the force applied to the valve rod and plunger. This reaction force tends to close the atmospheric port and reopen the vacuum port. Since this force is in opposition to the force applied to the brake pedal by the driver it gives the driver a "feel" of the amount of brake applied.

The proportion of reactive force applied to the valve plunger through the reaction disc is designed into the Master-Vac to assure maximum power consistent with maintaining pedal feel. The reaction force is in direct proportion to the hydraulic pressure developed within the brake system.

TROUBLESHOOTING

DECREASING BRAKE PEDAL TRAVEL

If a decreasing brake pedal is encountered, the power brake unit may be binding internally. To test the power brake unit for this condition proceed as follows:

1. Place transmission shift lever into Neutral and start engine.
2. Increase engine speed to approximately 1500 RPM, close throttle and completely depress brake pedal.
3. Slowly release brake pedal and stop engine.
4. Remove vacuum check valve and hose from power brake unit. Observe for backward movement of brake pedal.
5. If brake pedal moves backward, power brake unit has internal binding.
6. Replace power brake unit.

HARD BRAKE PEDAL

An internal bind or a failed vacuum check valve would cause this condition. Refer to Decreasing Brake Pedal Travel to test power brake unit for an internal bind. To check for a failed vacuum check valve proceed as follows:

1. Start engine and increase engine speed to approximately 1500 RPM, then close throttle and stop engine.
2. Wait 90 seconds, then try brake action.
3. If brakes are not vacuum assisted for two or more applications, replace check valve.

DRAGGING BRAKES

If slow or incomplete release of brakes (dragging brakes) is encountered the power brake unit has an internal bind condition. Test for an internal bind condition as described previously.

ADJUSTMENTS

PUSHROD ADJUSTMENT

In some cases adjustment of the brake booster pushrod is necessary to ensure proper operation of the power brake system. A pushrod that is too long will cause the master cylinder piston to close off the compensating port, preventing hydraulic pressure from being released and resulting in brake drag. A pushrod that is too short will cause excessive brake pedal travel and cause groaning noises to come from the booster when the brakes are applied. A properly adjusted pushrod that remains assembled to the booster with which is was matched during production should not require service adjustment. However, if the booster, master cylinder or pushrod are serviced, the pushrod may require adjustment.

Colt, Colt Vista, Laser, Summit, Summit Wagon & Talon

Refer to "Types 3, 5, 6, & 7 Master Cylinders" in the "Hydraulic Brake System" chapter under "Adjustments," or pushrod adjustment procedure.

GENERAL SERVICE

In order to properly service and repair available brake systems, a thorough understanding of the power assist systems is necessary. The vacuum assist diaphragm assembly multiplies the force exerted on the master cylinder piston in order to increase the hydraulic pressure delivered to the wheel cylinders or calipers while decreasing the effort necessary to obtain acceptable stopping performance.

Vacuum assist units get their energy by opposing engine vacuum to atmospheric pressure. A piston, cylinder and flexible diaphragm utilize this energy to provide brake assistance. The diaphragm is balanced with engine vacuum until the brake pedal is depressed, allowing atmospheric pressure to unbalance the unit and apply force to the brake system.

Brakes will operate even if the power unit fails. This means the conventional brake system and the power assist system are completely separate. Troubleshooting conventional and power assist systems are exactly the same until the power unit is reached. As with conventional hydraulic brakes, a spongy pedal still means air is trapped in the hydraulic system. Power brakes give higher line pressure, making leaks more critical.

CHECKING COMPLAINTS

Complaints about power brake operation should be handled as if two separate systems exist. Check for faults in the hydraulic system first. If it is satisfactory, start inspecting the power brake circuit. For a quick check of proper power unit operation, press the brake pedal firmly and then start the engine. The pedal should fall away slightly and less pressure should be needed to maintain the pedal in any position.

Another check begins with installation of a suitable pressure gauge in the brake hydraulic system. Take a reading with the engine off and the power unit not operating. Maintaining the same pedal height, start the engine and take another reading. There should be a substantial pressure in-

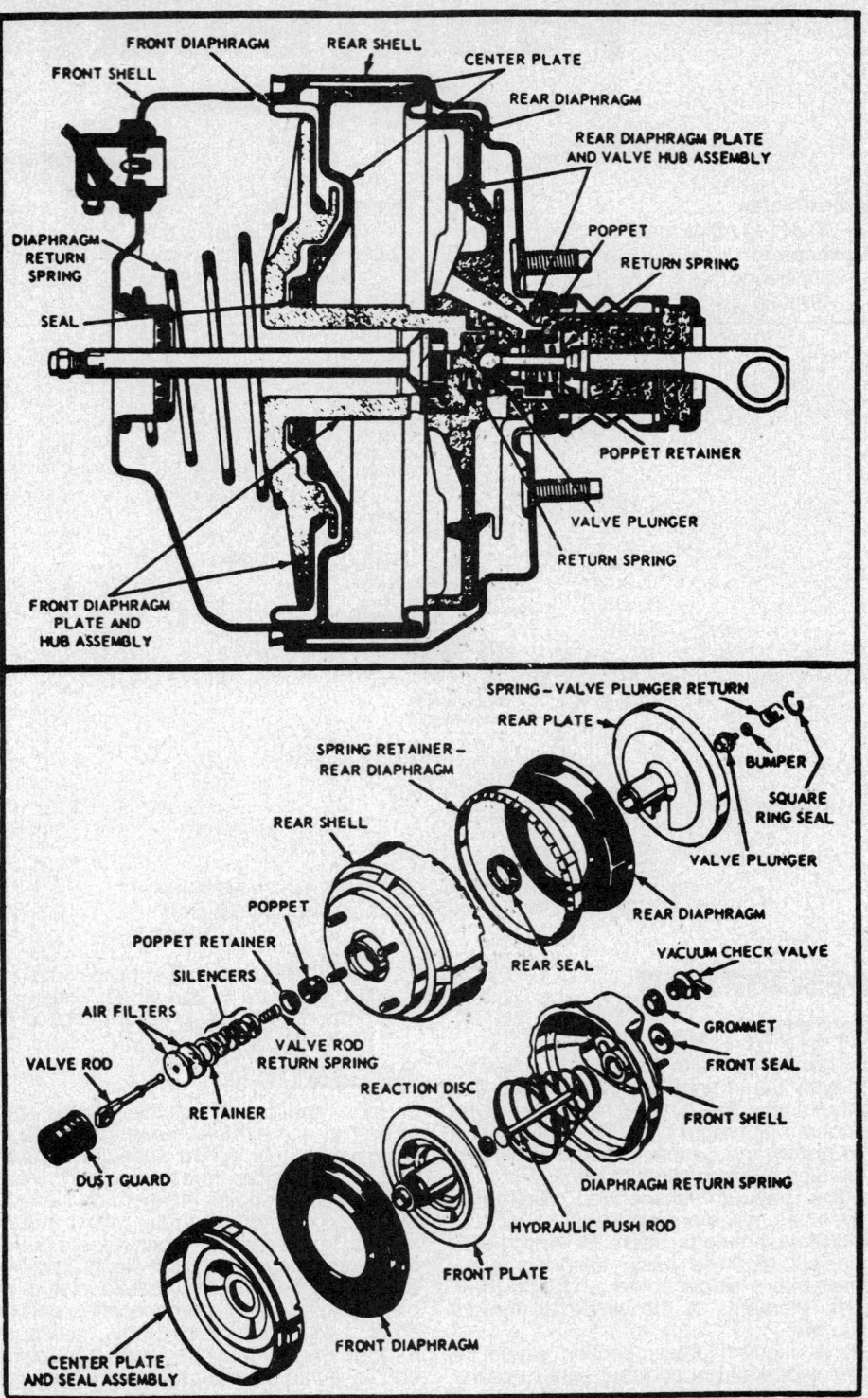

crease in the second reading.

Pedal free travel and total travel are critical on cars equipped with power brakes. Pedal travel should be kept strictly to specifications.

Take a manifold vacuum reading if the power unit isn't giving enough assistance. Remember, though, currently produced emission controlled engines, manifold vac-

uum readings may be less than 15 inches Hg at idle. If manifold vacuum is abnormally low, tune the engine and then try the power brakes again. Naturally, loose vacuum lines and clogged air intake filters will cut down brake efficiency. Most units have a check valve that retains some vacuum in the system when the engine is off. A vacuum gauge check of this valve will tell you

CR4099100053000X

Fig. 2   Bendix tandem diaphragm power brake

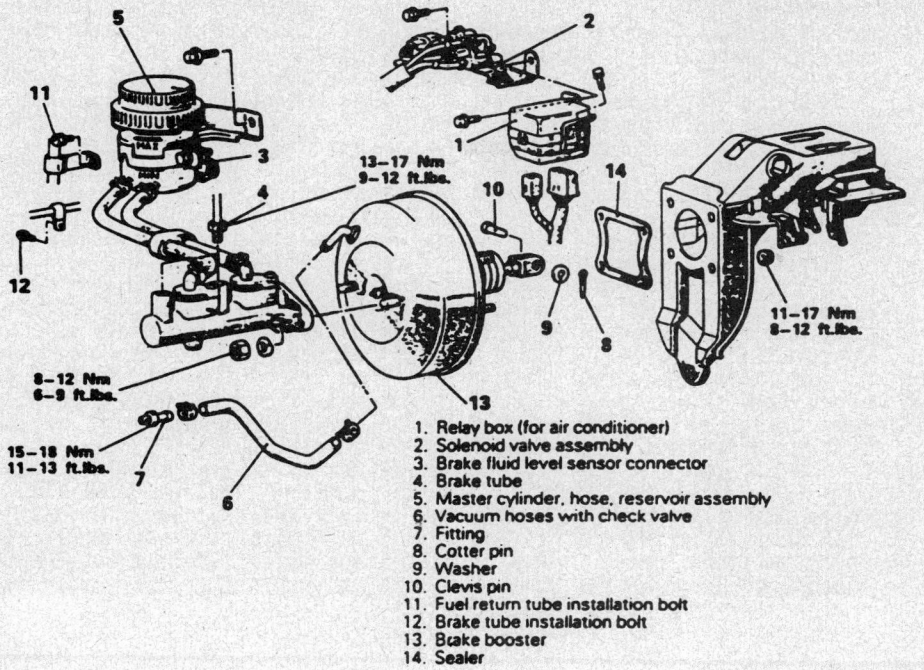

1. Relay box (for air conditioner)
2. Solenoid valve assembly
3. Brake fluid level sensor connector
4. Brake tube
5. Master cylinder, hose, reservoir assembly
6. Vacuum hoses with check valve
7. Fitting
8. Cotter pin
9. Washer
10. Clevis pin
11. Fuel return tube installation bolt
12. Brake tube installation bolt
13. Brake booster
14. Sealer

CR4099100051000X

Fig. 3 Power brake unit replacement. Laser & Eagle Talon

when it is restricted or stuck open or closed.

Failure of the brakes to release in most instances is caused by a tight or mis-aligned connection between the power unit and the brake linkage. If this connection is free, look for a broken piston, diaphragm or bellows and return spring.

A simple check of the hydraulic system should be made before proceeding. Loosen the connection between the master cylinder and the brake booster. If the brakes release, the trouble is in the power unit; if the brakes still will not release, look for a restricted brake line or similar difficulties in the hydraulic circuit.

A residual pressure check valve is usually included immediately under the brake line connection on hydraulic assist power brakes. This valve maintains a slight hydraulic pressure within the brake lines and wheel cylinders or caliper to give better pedal response. If it is sticking, the brakes may not release.

Power brakes that have a hard pedal are usually suffering from a milder form of the same ills that cause complete power unit failure. Collapsed or leaking vacuum lines or insufficient manifold vacuum, as well as punctured diaphragms or bellows and leaky piston seals, all lead to weak power unit operation. A steady hiss when the brake is held down means a vacuum leak that will cause poor power unit operation.

Do not immediately condemn the power unit if the brakes grab. First look for all the usual causes, such as greasy linings, scored rotors or drums. Then investigate the power unit. When the trouble has been traced to the power unit, check for a damaged reaction control. The reaction control is usually made up of a diaphragm, spring and valves that tends to resist pedal ac-

tion. It is put in the system to give the pedal "feel."

POWER BRAKE UNIT SERVICE

POWER BOOSTER, REPLACE

Acclaim, Daytona, Dynasty, Fifth Avenue, Imperial, LeBaron, Shadow, Spirit, Sundance & 1992-93 New Yorker

1. Remove master cylinder attaching nuts, disconnect brake tubes between master cylinder and valve assembly, then remove master cylinder.
2. Remove clutch cable mounting bracket, if equipped.
3. Disconnect vacuum hose from check valve on power brake unit. **Do not remove check valve from booster.**
4. Pull wiring harness away from and up shock tower. If more slack is required, disconnect wiring harness from bulkhead connector.
5. From under instrument panel, install a suitable screwdriver between center tang on retainer clip and brake pedal pin. Rotate screwdriver so retainer center tang will pass over brake pedal pin. Pull retainer clip from pin.
6. Remove power brake unit attaching nuts and power brake unit from vehicle.
7. Reverse procedure to install. Bleed brake system.

Monaco & Eagle Premier

1. Disconnect battery ground cable.

2. Remove vacuum supply hose from check valve.
3. Remove throttle cable attaching clip and position cable aside.
4. Remove intake hose at air cleaner and throttle body, then position hose aside.
5. Remove master cylinder as outlined in "Type 2 Master Cylinder." under "Component Replacement" in "Hydraulic Brake System" section.
6. Remove retaining clip attaching booster pushrod to brake pedal and discard.
7. Remove power brake unit attaching nuts and the unit.
8. Reverse procedure to install.

Laser & Eagle Talon

Remove power brake unit in numbered sequence, **Fig. 3**, noting the following:
1. Check valve is integral with vacuum line. If valve is defective, replace as an assembly.
2. When installing vacuum hose fitting, apply semi-drying sealant to threaded portion.
3. Reverse procedure to install.

Colt, Colt Vista, Colt Wagon, Stealth, Summit & Summit Wagon

1. Remove master cylinder as described in "Type 3, 5, 6, & 7 Master Cylinders." under "Component Replacement" in "Hydraulic Brake System" section.
2. Disconnect vacuum hose from power brake unit.
3. Remove pin connecting power brake rod with brake pedal.
4. Remove power brake unit attaching nuts and the power brake unit.
5. Reverse procedure to install.

Concorde, Intrepid, Vision, LHS & 1994 New Yorker

Do not attempt to disassemble or service power brake unit. Brake unit is serviced only as a complete unit.
1. Remove both wiper arm assemblies, then cowl panel cover from cowl.
2. Remove five screws that attach windshield wiper module from dash panel.
3. Remove two master cylinder to brake booster attaching nuts, then slide master cylinder off mounting studs.
4. Disconnect vacuum hose from booster check valve. **Do not remove check valve from booster.**
5. From under instrument panel position small screwdriver between center tang of booster input rod to brake pedal pin retaining clip, then rotate screwdriver so retainer clip center tang passes over end of brake pedal pin and pull retainer clip off. Discard old retainer clip.
6. From under instrument panel remove four booster attaching nuts, slide booster up and to right on dash panel, then tilt outward and up to remove.
7. Reverse procedure to install noting the following:
   a. **Torque** booster to dash panel and master cylinder to booster attaching nuts to 250 inch lbs.

b. When connecting booster input rod to brake pedal pin use new retainer clip.

c. Ensure brake lights work properly.

Neon

When repairing vehicles equipped with ABS systems, the vacuum in the power booster must be pumped down before removing the master cylinder to avoid drawing in any contamination. This can be done simply by pumping the brake until a firm pedal is achieved, with ignition off.

1. **On models with ABS systems,** ensure ignition switch is Off and brake pedal has been pumped until firm.

2. **On all models,** disconnect wiring harness from brake fluid level sensor mounted on fluid reservoir.

3. Disconnect primary and secondary brake tubes from master cylinder housing and plug outlets on master cylinder.

4. **On models with ABS systems,** clean area where master cylinder attaches to power booster using a suitable cleaner.

5. **On all models,** remove mounting nuts and slide master cylinder forward out of booster.

6. **On vehicles equipped with ABS, the vacuum seal in the front of the power brake vacuum booster must be replaced.** Remove vacuum seal in front of power brake vacuum booster by carefully inserting a small screwdriver between the master cylinder push rod and vacuum seal and prying the seal out of the booster. **Do not attempt to pry seal out by inserting screwdriver between seal and booster.**

7. **On all models,** disconnect vacuum hoses from power booster check valve. **Do not remove check valve from power booster.**

8. **On models with ABS systems,** remove Hydraulic Control Unit (HCU).

9. **On all models,** locate power booster input rod to brake pedal attachment under instrument panel. Position a suitable small screwdriver between center tang on input rod to brake pedal pin retaining clip. Rotate screwdriver to allow retaining clip center tang to pass over end of brake pedal pin. Discard retaining clip.

10. Remove power booster mounting nuts holding unit to dash panel.

11. Slide power booster forward until mounting studs clear dash, then tilt unit upward to remove.

12. Reverse procedure to install noting the following:

a. **On models with ABS,** install new vacuum seal by lubricating master cylinder push rod using suitable silicone lubricant and slide vacuum seal onto master cylinder push rod with notches on seal pointing toward and seated against master cylinder housing.

b. **On all models,** install mounting nuts and **torque** to 250 inch lbs.

c. Connect brake tubes to master cylinder primary and secondary ports and **torque** tube nuts to 145 inch lbs.

ANTI-LOCK BRAKES

TABLE OF CONTENTS

Application Chart

Year	Model	Body Code	System Type	Page No.
1992	Acclaim	AA	2	25-23
	Colt Vista	—	4	25-120
	Daytona Shelby	AG	2	25-23
	Daytona	AG	2	25-23
	Dynasty	AC	3	25-57
	Imperial	AY	3	25-57
	Laser	—	4	25-120
	LeBaron Landau	AA	2	25-23
	LeBaron	AJ	2	25-23
	Monaco	BB	3	25-57
	New Yorker Fifth Avenue	AY	3	25-57
	New Yorker Salon	AC	3	25-57
	New Yorker	AC	3	25-57
	Premier	BB	3	25-57
	Spirit	AA	2	25-23
	Stealth	—	4	25-120
	Summit Wagon	—	4	25-120
	Talon	—	4	25-120
1993	Acclaim	AA	①	—
	Colt	—	5	25-151
	Colt Vista	—	4	25-120
	Concorde	LH	6	25-166
	Daytona Shelby	AG	2	25-23
	Daytona	AG	2	25-23
	Dynasty	AC	3	25-57
	Imperial	AY	3	25-57
	Intrepid	LH	6	25-166
	Laser	—	4	25-120
	LeBaron Landau	AA	①	—
	LeBaron	AJ	①	—
	Monaco	BB	3	25-57

Year	Model	Body Code	System Type	Page No.
1993	New Yorker Fifth Avenue	AY	3	25-57
	New Yorker Salon	AC	3	25-57
	New Yorker	AC	3	25-57
	Premier	BB	3	25-57
	Shadow	AP	3	25-57
	Spirit	AA	①	—
	Stealth	—	4	25-120
	Summit	—	5	25-151
	Summit Wagon	—	4	25-120
	Sundance	AP	3	25-57
	Talon	—	4	25-120
	Vision	LH	6	25-166
1994	Acclaim	AA	1	25-2
	Colt	—	5	25-151
	Colt Vista	—	4	25-120
	Concorde	LH	6	25-166
	Intrepid	LH	6	25-166
	Laser	—	4	25-120
	LeBaron	AJ	1	25-2
	LHS	LH	6	25-166
	New Yorker	LH	6	25-166
	Shadow	AP	1	25-2
	Spirit	AA	1	25-2
	Stealth	—	4	25-120
	Summit	—	5	25-151
	Summit Wagon	—	4	25-120
	Sundance	AP	1	25-2
	Talon	—	4	25-120
	Vision	LH	6	25-166
1995	Neon	PL	1	25-2

①—Vehicles built after 4/19/93 at Newark Assembly Plant (VIN code F), Type 1; all other vehicles, Type 2.

Type 1—Bendix Anti-Lock 4 Braking System

NOTE: On Air Bag Equipped Models, Refer To "Air Bag System Precautions" Located In The Front Of This Manual For System Disarming & Arming Procedures.

INDEX

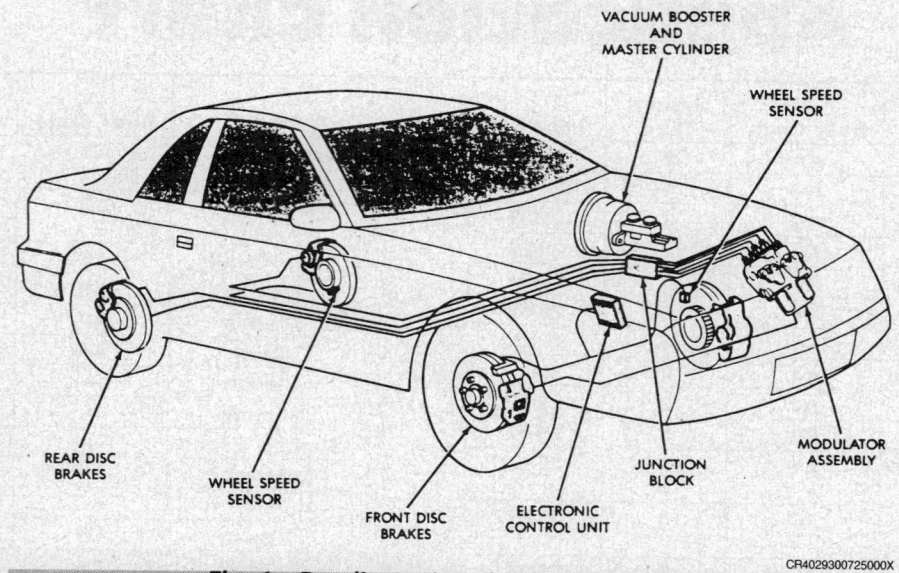

Fig. 1   Bendix Anti-Lock 4 brake system

PRECAUTIONS

AIR BAG SYSTEMS

Refer to "Air Bag System Precautions" in the front of this manual for system disarming and arming procedures.

DESCRIPTION

The Anti-Lock Braking System (ABS) prevents the wheels from locking up when braking, regardless of the surface conditions. This allows the car to stop in a shorter distance, and allows the driver to maintain directional control of the vehicle during heavy braking conditions.

Refer to **Fig. 1** for system components and locations.

TROUBLESHOOTING

Refer to **Figs. 2 through 7** when troubleshooting this system.

DIAGNOSIS & TESTING

Accessing Diagnostic Trouble Codes

This ABS system has a self-diagnosis connector located under the fuse panel access cover. The access cover is located on the lower section of the instrument panel to the left of the steering column. The ABS diagnostic connector is a blue 6-way connector which can be connected to a DRB II diagnostic readout box.

After connecting the DRB II to the diagnostic connector, follow the tool manufacturer's instructions to further diagnose the ABS system, noting the following:

1. **All diagnostic test procedures assume a Chrysler Diagnostic Readout Box (DRB II) is being used.** Tests have been designed specifically for the DRB II.

2. After completing diagnosis and repair of the system, perform any verification test provided.

Diagnostic Trouble Code Interpretation

Refer to **Fig. 8** for diagnostic trouble code interpretation and for direction to the proper diagnostic flow charts, **Figs. 9 through 45.**

Clearing Diagnostic Trouble Codes

Diagnostic trouble codes (DTCs) can be cleared using the DRB II diagnostics tester, or they will be automatically cleared after 50 ignition switch ON/OFF cycles.

Continued on page 25-20

SYMPTOM	CHART 1 MISC. COND.	CHART 2 ACTUATION	CHART 3 POWER BRAKES	CHART 4 BRAKE NOISE	CHART 5 WHEEL BRAKES
BRAKE WARNING LIGHT ON		X	NO		
EXCESSIVE PEDAL TRAVEL	6	X	NO		O
PEDAL GOES TO FLOOR	6	X			
STOP LIGHT ON WITHOUT BRAKES	3				
ALL BRAKES DRAG	5	O			
REAR BRAKES DRAG	2	NO	NO		
GRABBY BRAKES			O		X
SPONGY BRAKE PEDAL		X	NO		
PREMATURE REAR LOCKUP	4	NO	NO		O
EXCESSIVE PEDAL EFFORT	1		O		
ROUGH ENGINE IDLE			O		
BRAKE CHATTER (ROUGH)		NO	NO		X
SURGE DURING BRAKING					X
NOISE DURING BRAKING				X	
RATTLE OR CLUNKING NOISE		NO		X	
PEDAL PULSATES DURING BRAKING		NO	NO		X
PULL TO RIGHT OR LEFT		NO	NO		X

NO: NOT POSSIBLE CAUSE   X: MOST LIKELY CAUSE   O: POSSIBLE CAUSE

CR4029300714000X

Fig. 2   Troubleshooting symptom chart

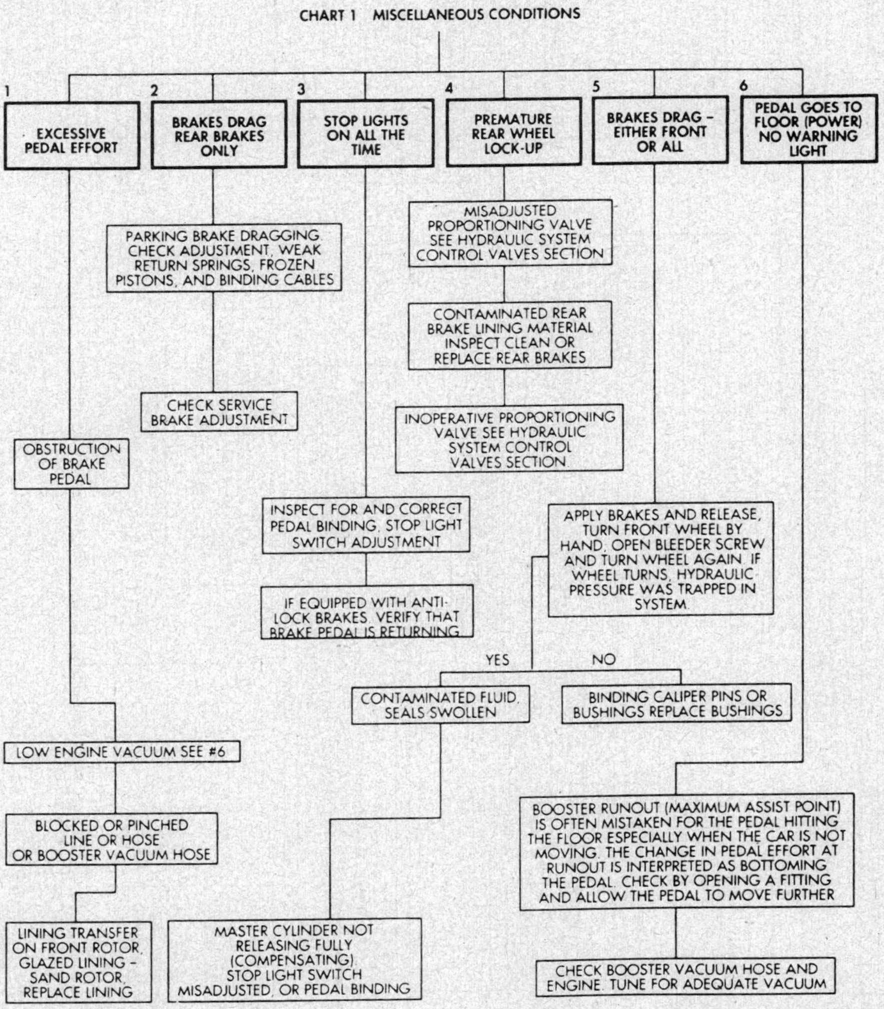

Fig. 3   Troubleshooting chart 1, miscellaneous conditions

CR4029300715000X

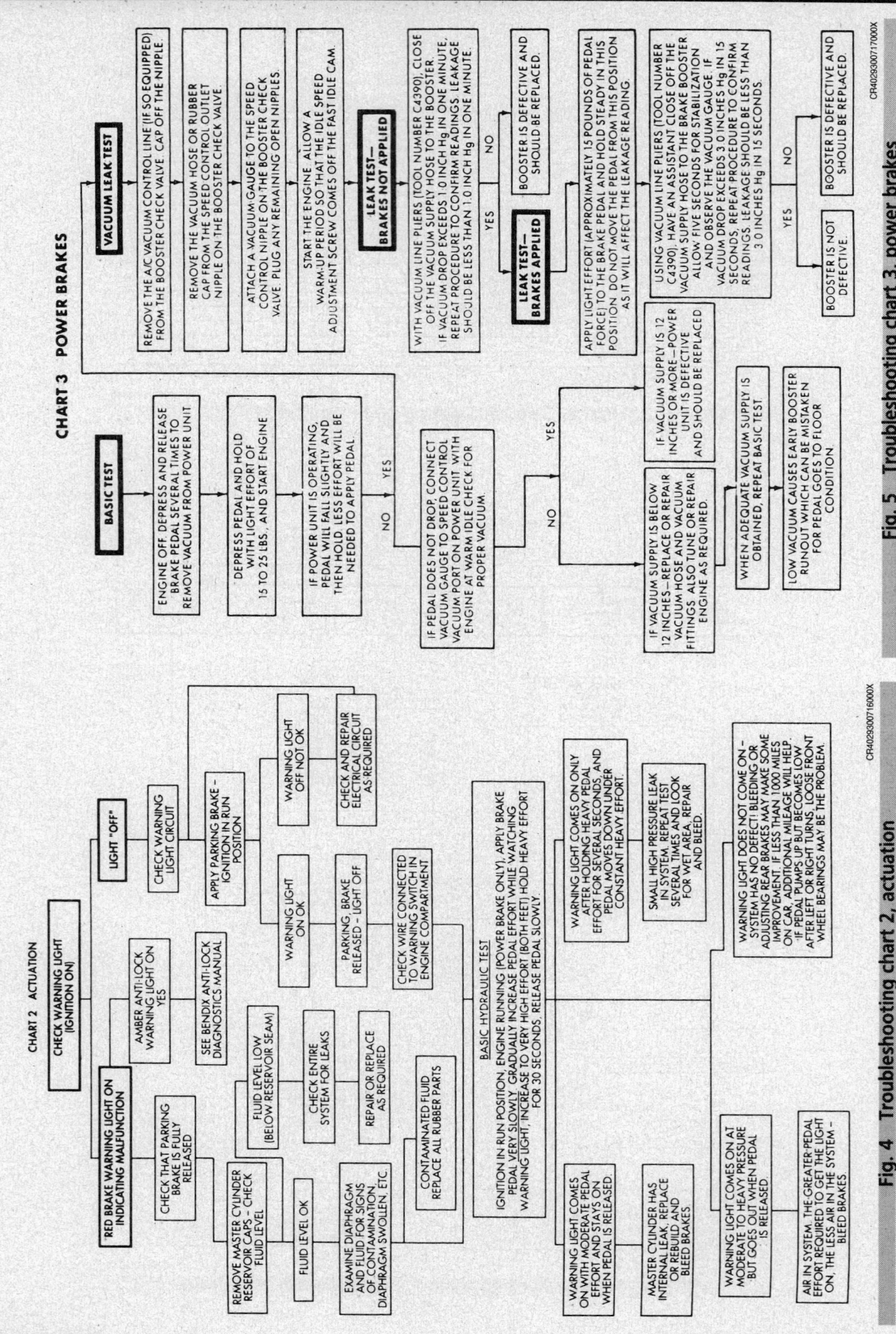

Fig. 5 Troubleshooting chart 3, power brakes

Fig. 4 Troubleshooting chart 2, actuation

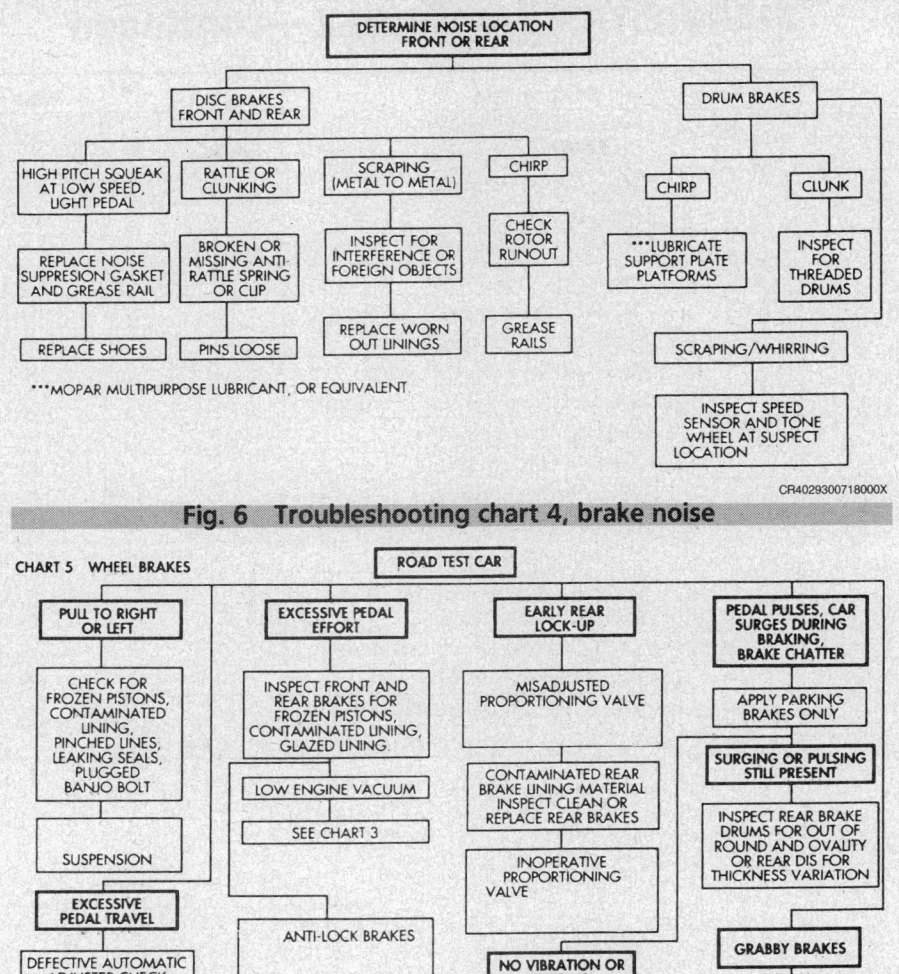

Fig. 6 Troubleshooting chart 4, brake noise

Fig. 7 Troubleshooting chart 5, wheel brakes

DIAGNOSTIC CHART INDEX

Test	Description	Page No.	Fig. No.
1A	Checking System For Trouble Codes (DTCs)	25-6	8
2A	Anti-Lock Lamp Diode Circuit	25-6	9
3A	Anti-Lock Lamp Circuit	25-7	10
3B	Anti-Lock Lamp Circuit	25-8	11
3C	Anti-Lock Lamp Circuit	25-8	12
4A	Excess Decay	25-8	13
4B	Excess Decay	25-8	14
5A	Left Front Wheel Speed Sensor	25-9	15
6A	Left Rear Wheel Speed Sensor	25-9	16
7A	Left Front Speed Sensor Continuity	25-9	17
8A	Left Rear Wheel Speed Sensor Continuity	25-10	18
9A	Modulator Circuit	25-10	19
9B	Modulator Circuit	25-11	20
9C	Modulator Circuit	25-11	21
9D	Modulator Circuit	25-11	22
9E	Modulator Circuit	25-12	23
9F	Modulator Circuit	25-12	24

Continued

DIAGNOSTIC CHART INDEX—Continued

Test	Description	Page No.	Fig. No.
10A	Pump/Motor Circuit	25-12	25
10B	Pump/Motor Circuit	25-13	26
10C	Pump/Motor Circuit	25-13	27
10D	Pump/Motor Circuit	25-13	28
10E	Pump/Motor Circuit	25-14	29
10F	Pump/Motor Circuit	25-14	30
11A	Right Front Wheel Speed Sensor Continuity	25-14	31
12A	Right Front Wheel Speed Sensor	25-15	32
13A	Right Rear Wheel Speed Sensor	25-15	33
14A	Right Rear Wheel Speed Sensor Continuity	25-15	34
15A	Solenoid Undervoltage	25-16	35
15B	Solenoid Undervoltage	25-16	36
15C	Solenoid Undervoltage	25-17	37
15D	Solenoid Undervoltage	25-17	38
16A	System Relay Circuit	25-18	39
16B	System Relay Circuit	25-18	40
16C	System Relay Circuit	25-18	41
17A	Repairing DRB "No Response" Message	25-18	42
18A	Repairing Blank DRB Screen	25-29	43
VER-1A	Anti-Lock System Repair Verification	25-19	44
VER-1B	Anti-Lock System Operation Verification	25-19	45

In some instances the cause of one fault message may trigger the setting of an additional diagnostic trouble code. If multiple trouble codes appear on the DRB when reading trouble codes, code repairs must be performed in the order in which they are displayed in the top portion of the chart below. If only one code has occurred, perform the indicated test for that trouble code.

NOTE: When inspecting connectors, look at both sides of the connector for any corrosion, pin push-outs, or spread cavities. Ensure that the connector is properly wired by verifying the wire color in each against the appropriate pinout illustration.

DRB MESSAGE	DIAGNOSTIC TEST
CONTROLLER ANTI-LOCK BRAKE (CAB)	REPLACE THE CAB
MODULATOR CIRCUIT	TEST 9A
SYSTEM RELAY CIRCUIT	TEST 16A
PUMP/MOTOR CIRCUIT	TEST 10A
SOLENOID UNDERVOLTAGE	TEST 15A
ANTILOCK LAMP DIODE CIRCUIT	TEST 2A
ANTILOCK LAMP CIRCUIT	TEST 3A
EXCESS DECAY	TEST 4A
LEFT FRONT WHEEL SPEED SENSOR	TEST 5A
LEFT REAR WHEEL SPEED SENSOR	TEST 6A
LF WHEEL SPEED SENSOR CONTINUITY	TEST 7A
LR WHEEL SPEED SENSOR CONTINUITY	TEST 8A
RF WHEEL SPEED SENSOR CONTINUITY	TEST 11A
RIGHT FRONT WHEEL SPEED SENSOR	TEST 12A
RIGHT REAR WHEEL SPEED SENSOR	TEST 13A
RR WHEEL SPEED SENSOR CONTINUITY	TEST 14A
DRB "NO RESPONSE" MESSAGE	TEST 17A
DRB BLANK SCREEN	TEST 18A
VERIFICATION PROCEDURE	VER-1A

CR4029300726000X

Fig. 8 Test 1A: Checking System For Diagnostic Trouble Codes

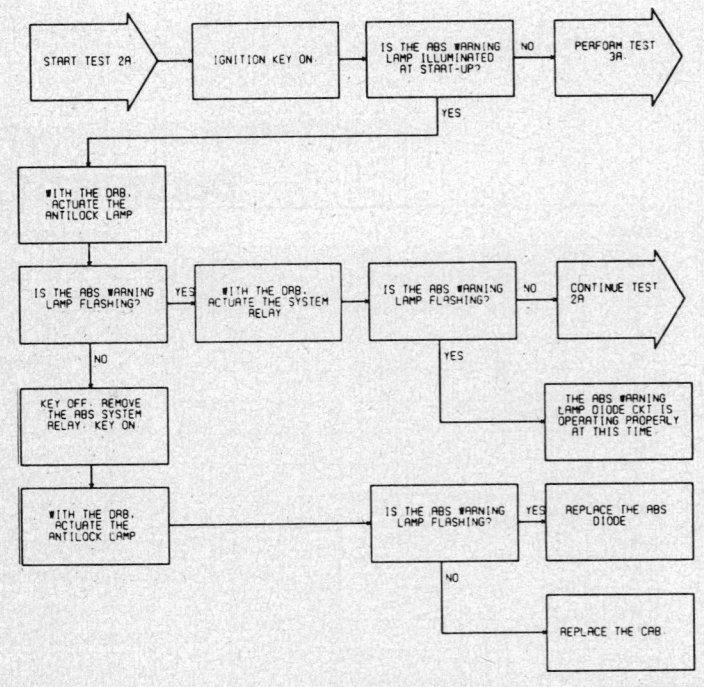

CR4029300727010X

Fig. 9 Test 2A: Anti-Lock Lamp Diode Circuit (Part 1 of 3)

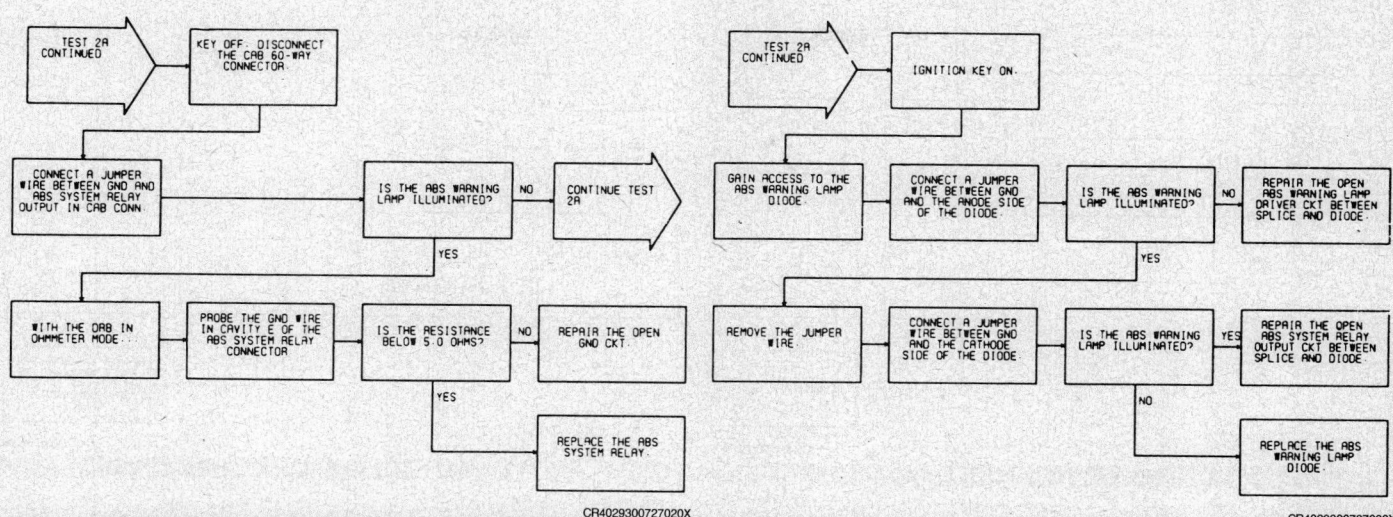

Fig. 9   Test 2A: Anti-Lock Lamp Diode Circuit (Part 2 of 3)

Fig. 9   Test 2A: Anti-Lock Lamp Diode Circuit (Part 3 of 3)

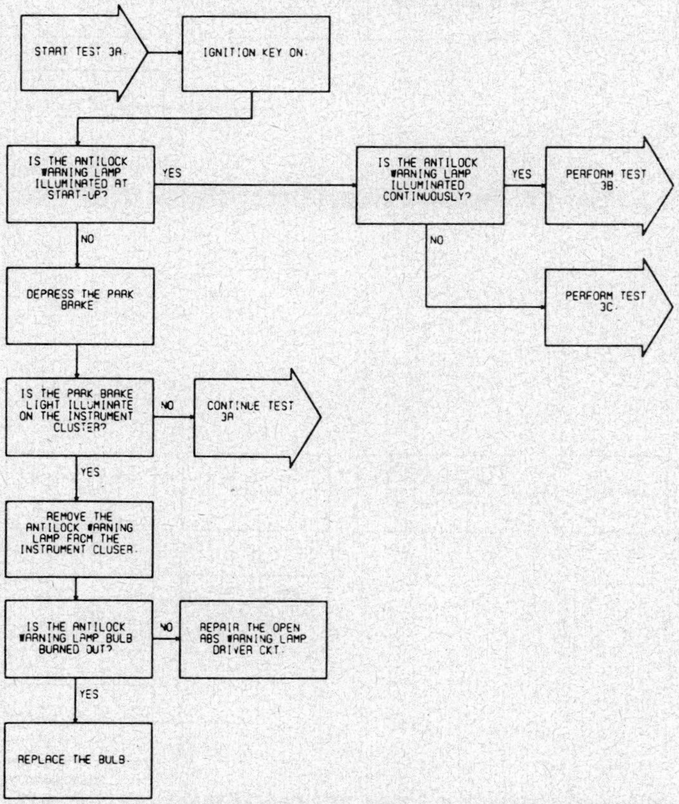

CR4029300727020X

CR4029300727030X

Fig. 10   Test 3A: Anti-Lock Lamp Circuit (Part 1 of 2)

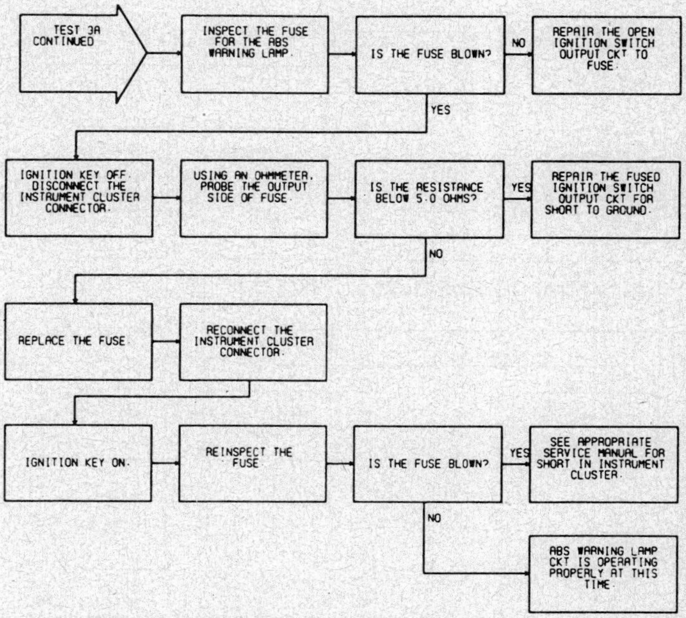

Fig. 10   Test 3A: Anti-Lock Lamp Circuit (Part 2 of 2)

CR4029300728010X

CR4029300728020X

TYPE 1-BENDIX ANTI-LOCK 4 BRAKING SYSTEM

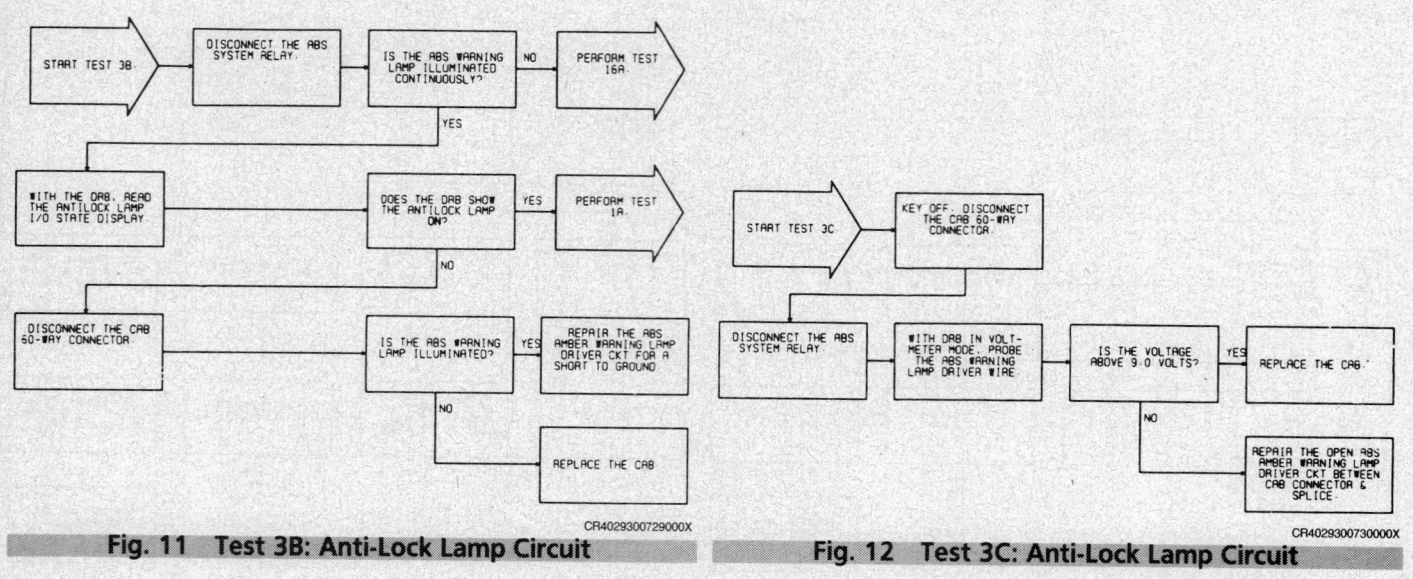

Fig. 11   Test 3B: Anti-Lock Lamp Circuit

CR4029300729000X

Fig. 12   Test 3C: Anti-Lock Lamp Circuit

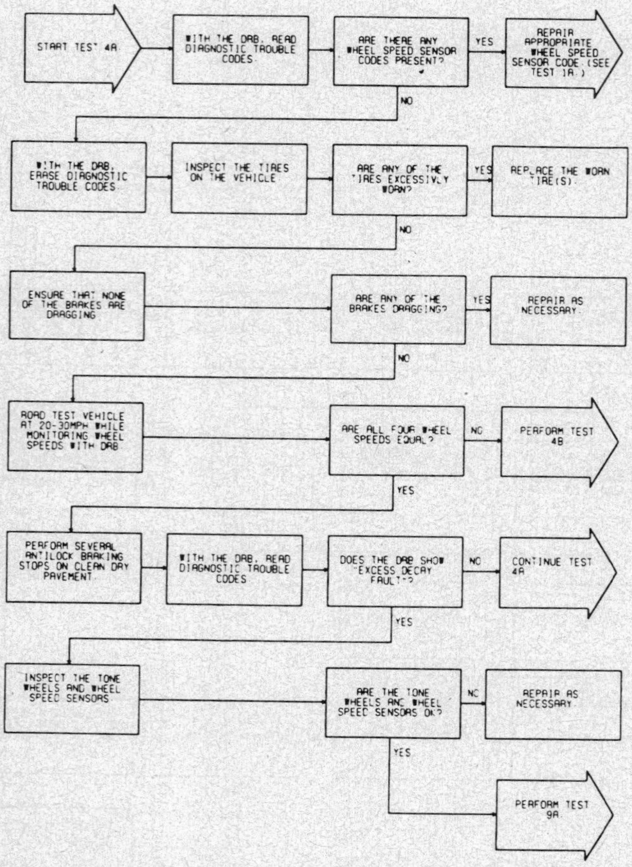

CR4029300730000X

Fig. 13   Test 4A: Excess Decay (Part 2 of 2)

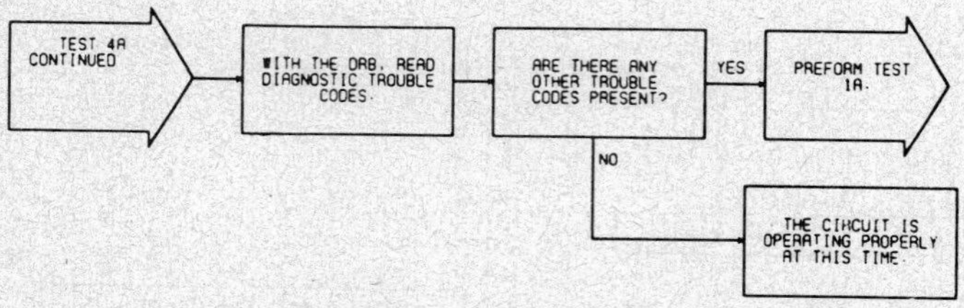

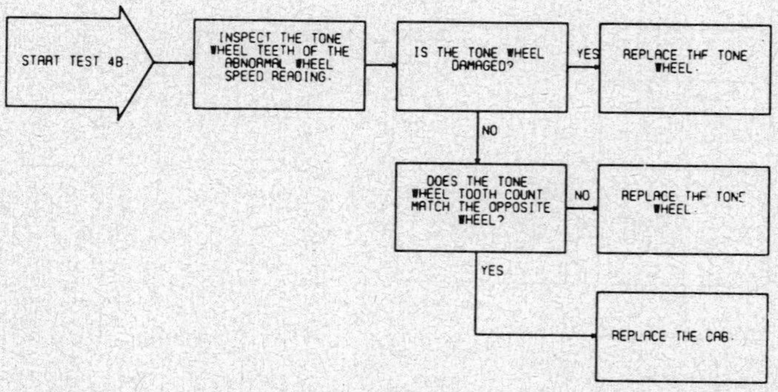

CR4029300731020X

Fig. 13   Test 4A: Excess Decay (Part 1 of 2)

CR4029300731010X

Fig. 14   Test 4B: Excess Decay

CR4029300732000X

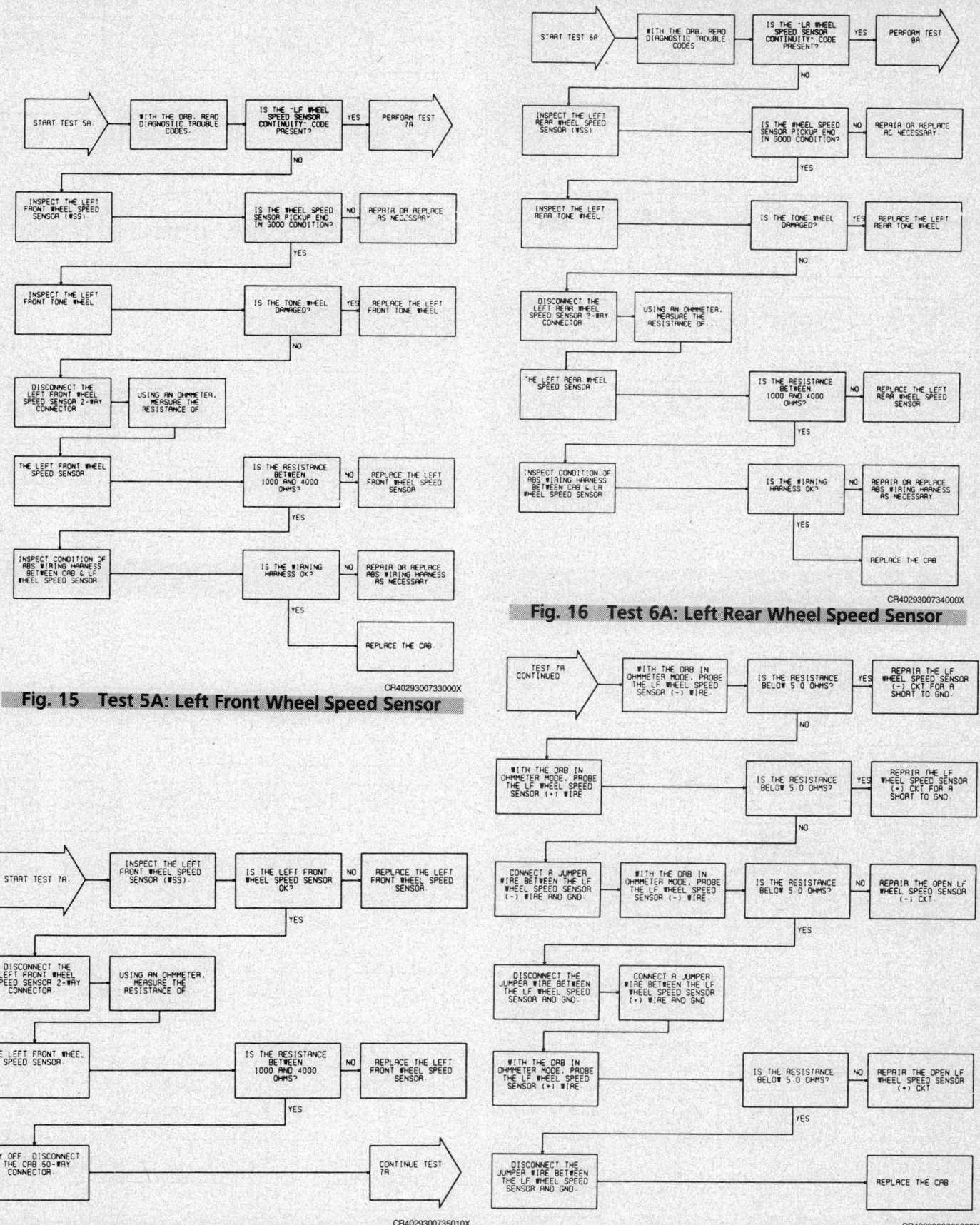

Fig. 15   Test 5A: Left Front Wheel Speed Sensor

CR4029300733000X

Fig. 16   Test 6A: Left Rear Wheel Speed Sensor

CR4029300734000X

Fig. 17   Test 7A: Left Front Wheel Speed Sensor Continuity (Part 1 of 2)

CR4029300735010X

Fig. 17   Test 7A: Left Front Wheel Speed Sensor Continuity (Part 2 of 2)

CR4029300735020X

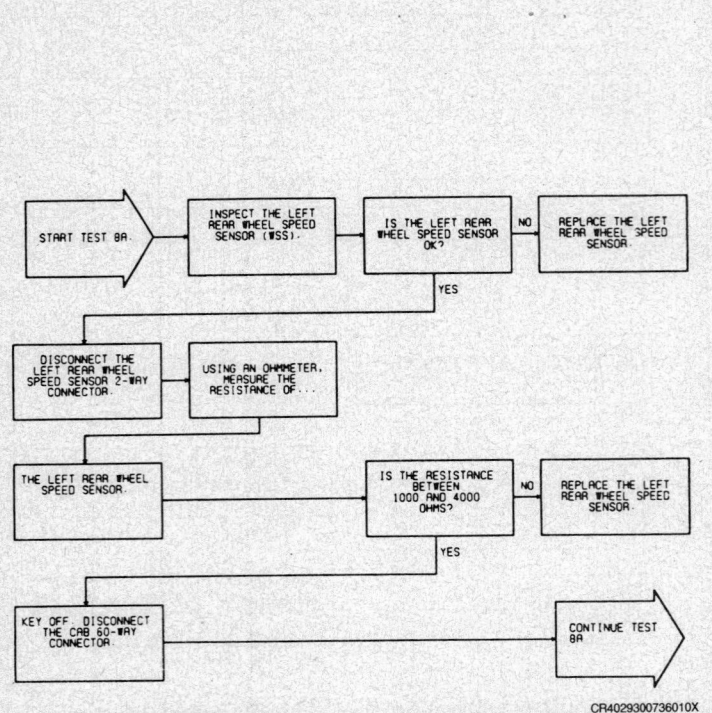

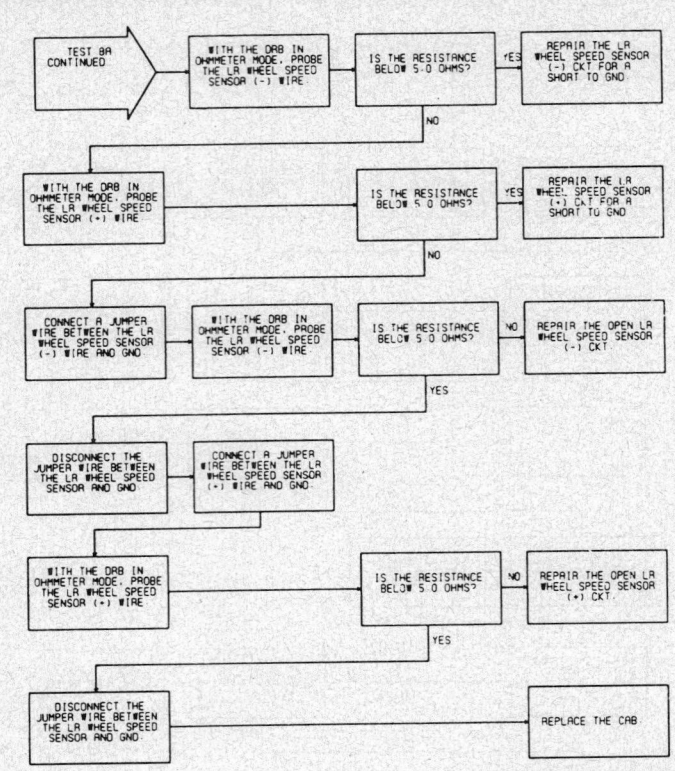

Fig. 18   Test 8A: Left Rear Wheel Speed Sensor Continuity (Part 1 of 2)

Fig. 18   Test 8A: Left Rear Wheel Speed Sensor Continuity (Part 2 of 2)

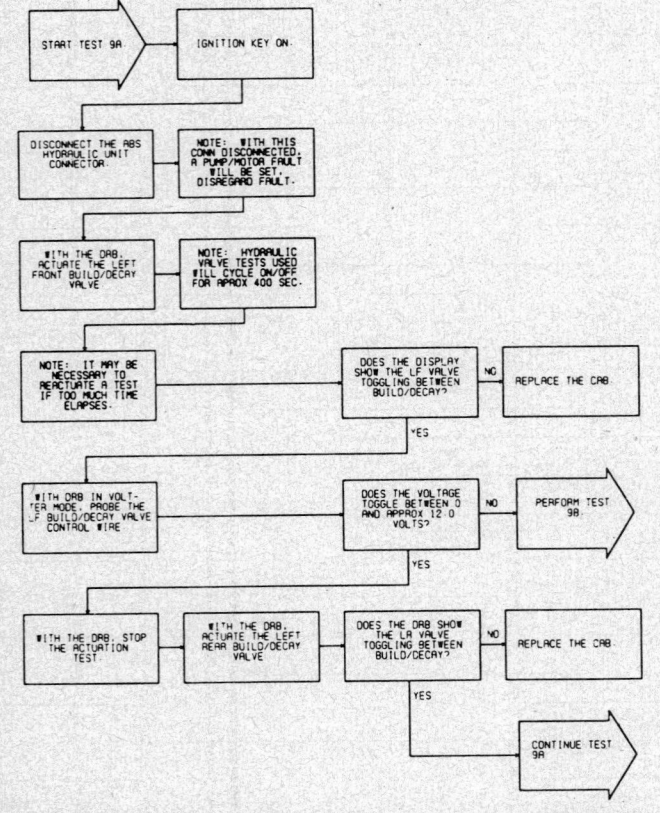

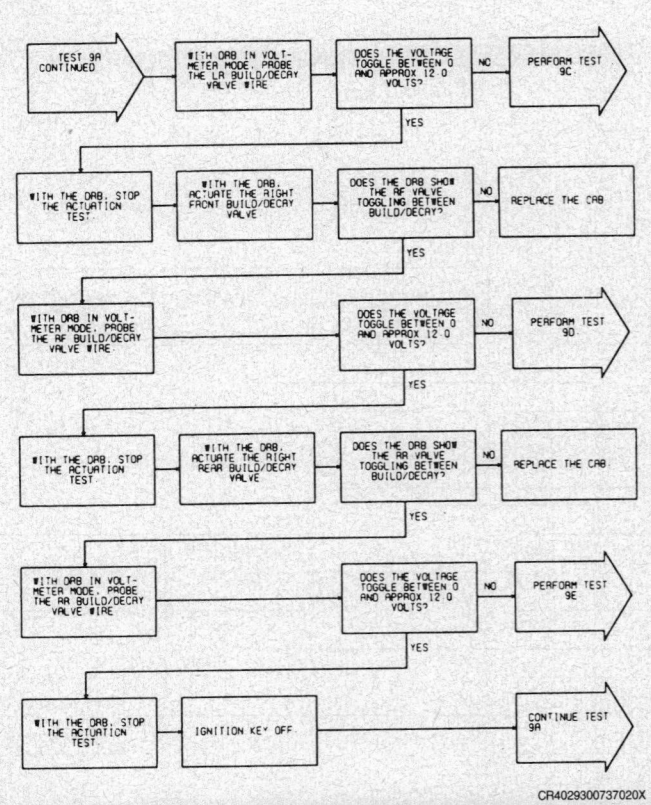

Fig. 19   Test 9A: Modulator Circuit (Part 1 of 3)

Fig. 19   Test 9A: Modulator Circuit (Part 2 of 3)

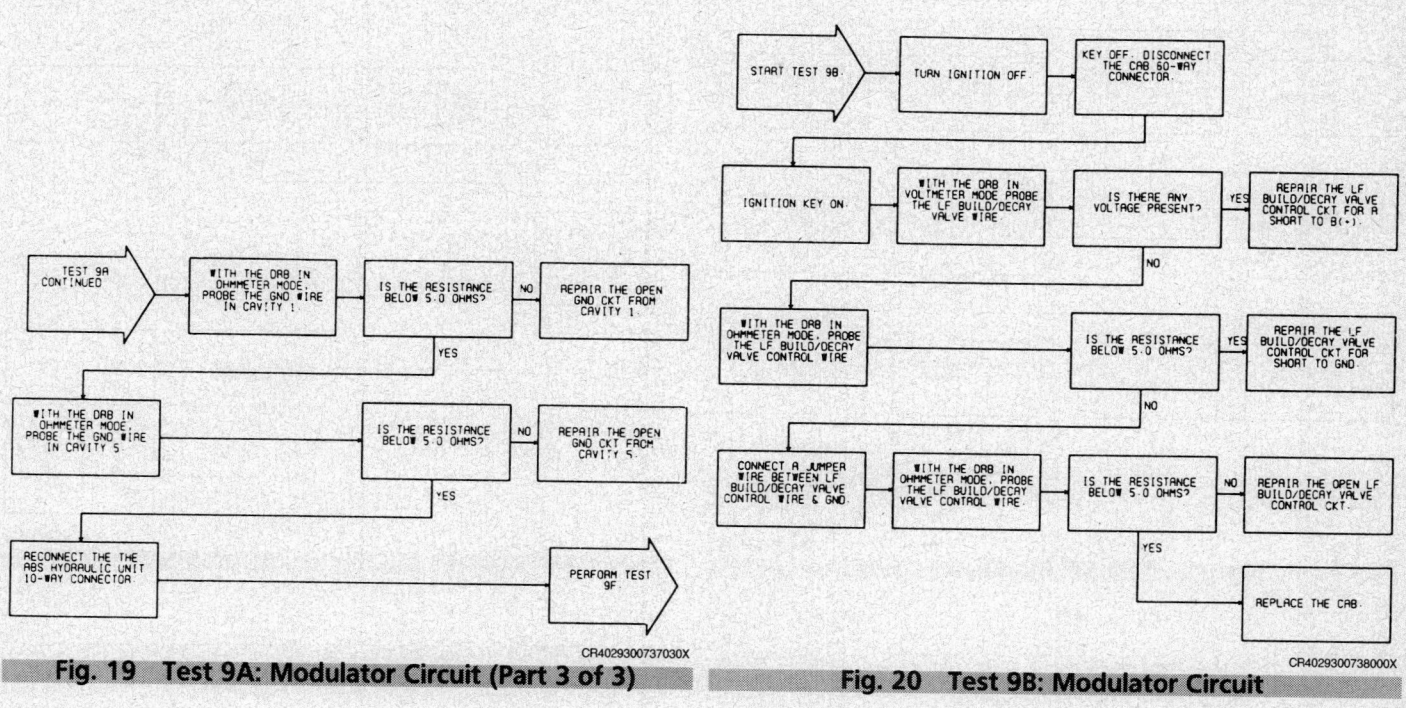

Fig. 19   Test 9A: Modulator Circuit (Part 3 of 3)

Fig. 20   Test 9B: Modulator Circuit

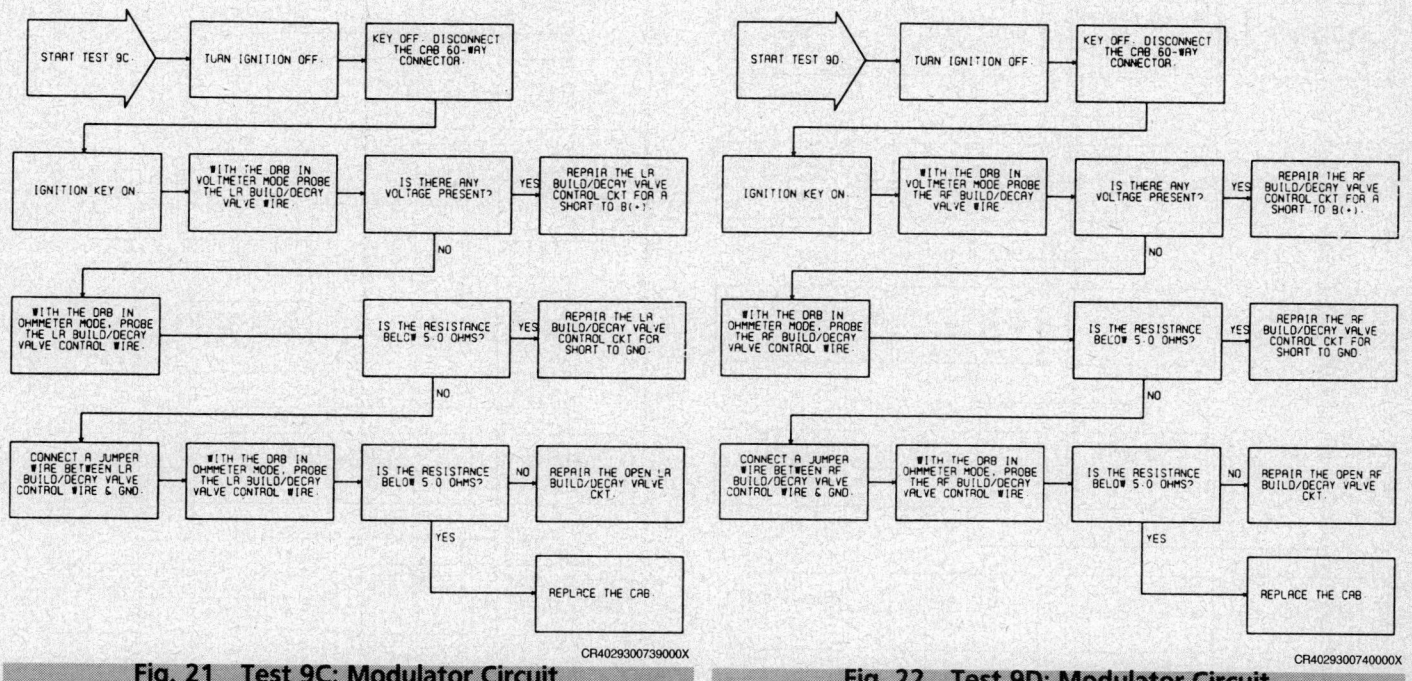

Fig. 21   Test 9C: Modulator Circuit

Fig. 22   Test 9D: Modulator Circuit

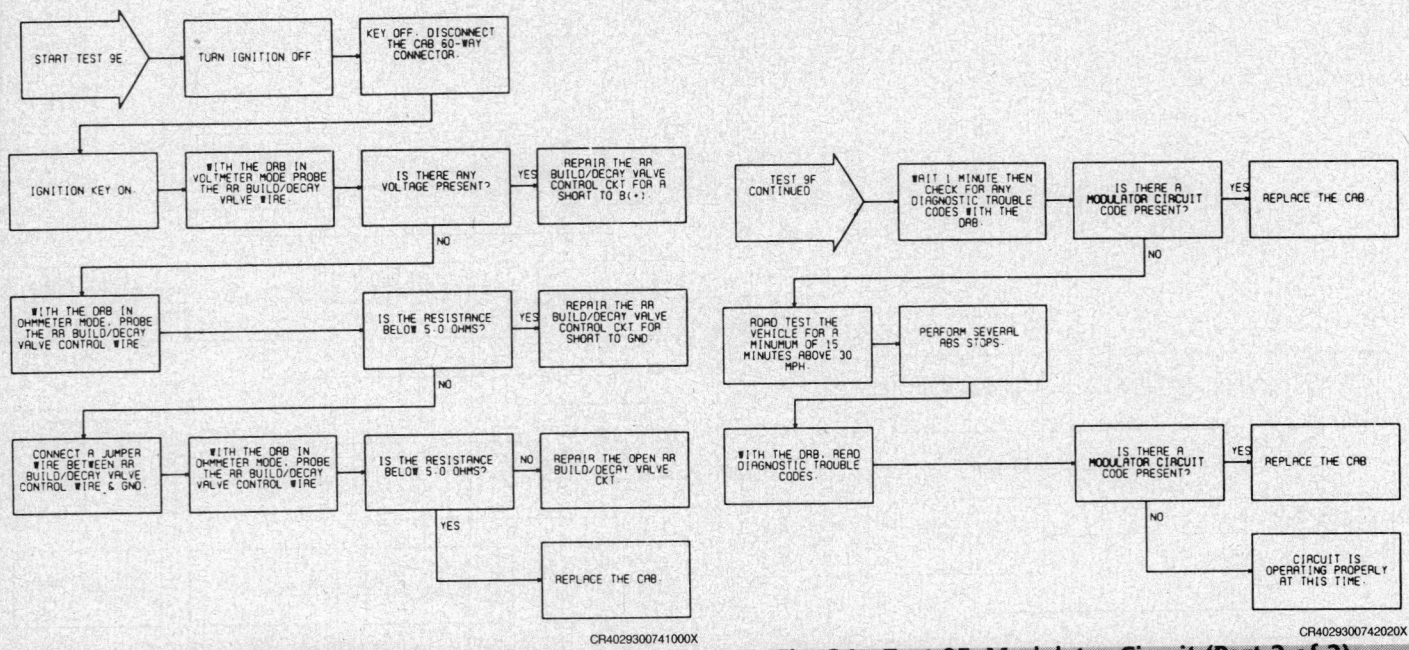

Fig. 23 Test 9E: Modulator Circuit

Fig. 24 Test 9F: Modulator Circuit (Part 2 of 2)

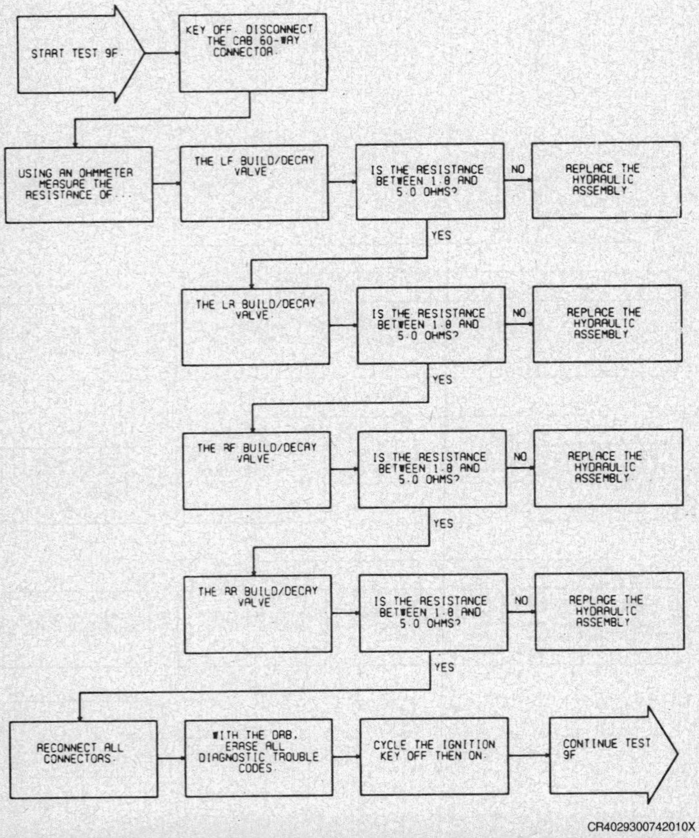

Fig. 24 Test 9F: Modulator Circuit (Part 1 of 2)

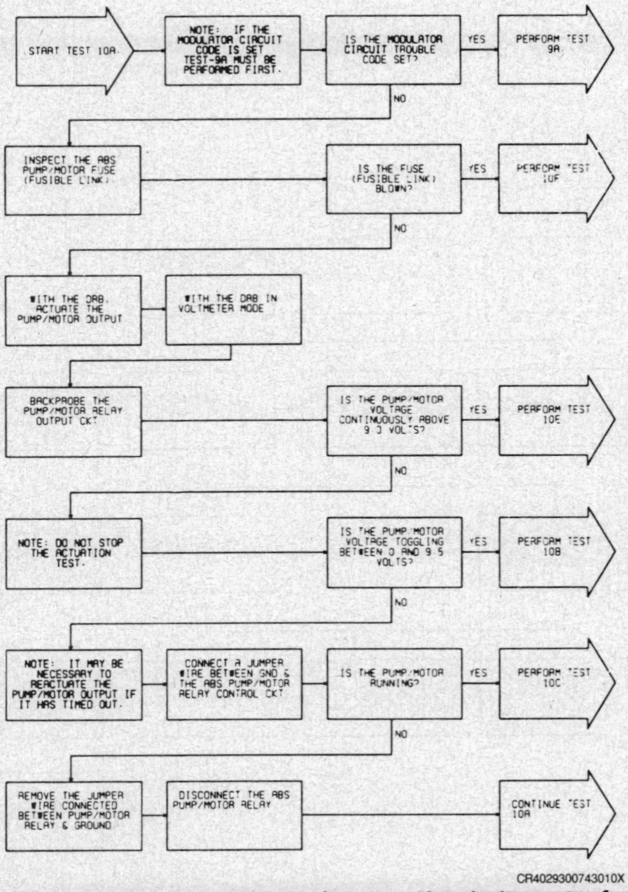

Fig. 25 Test 10A: Pump/Motor Circuit (Part 1 of 2)

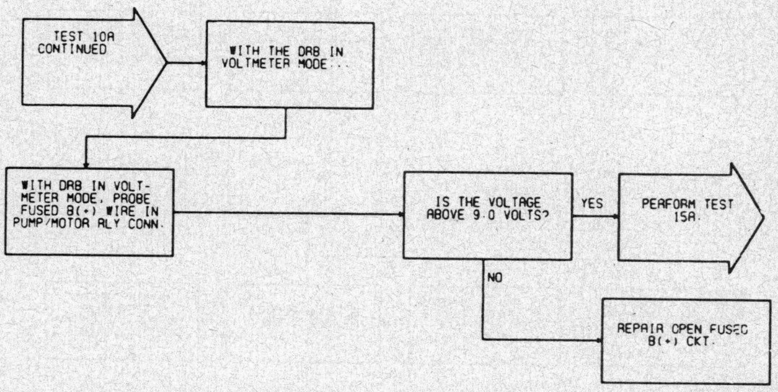

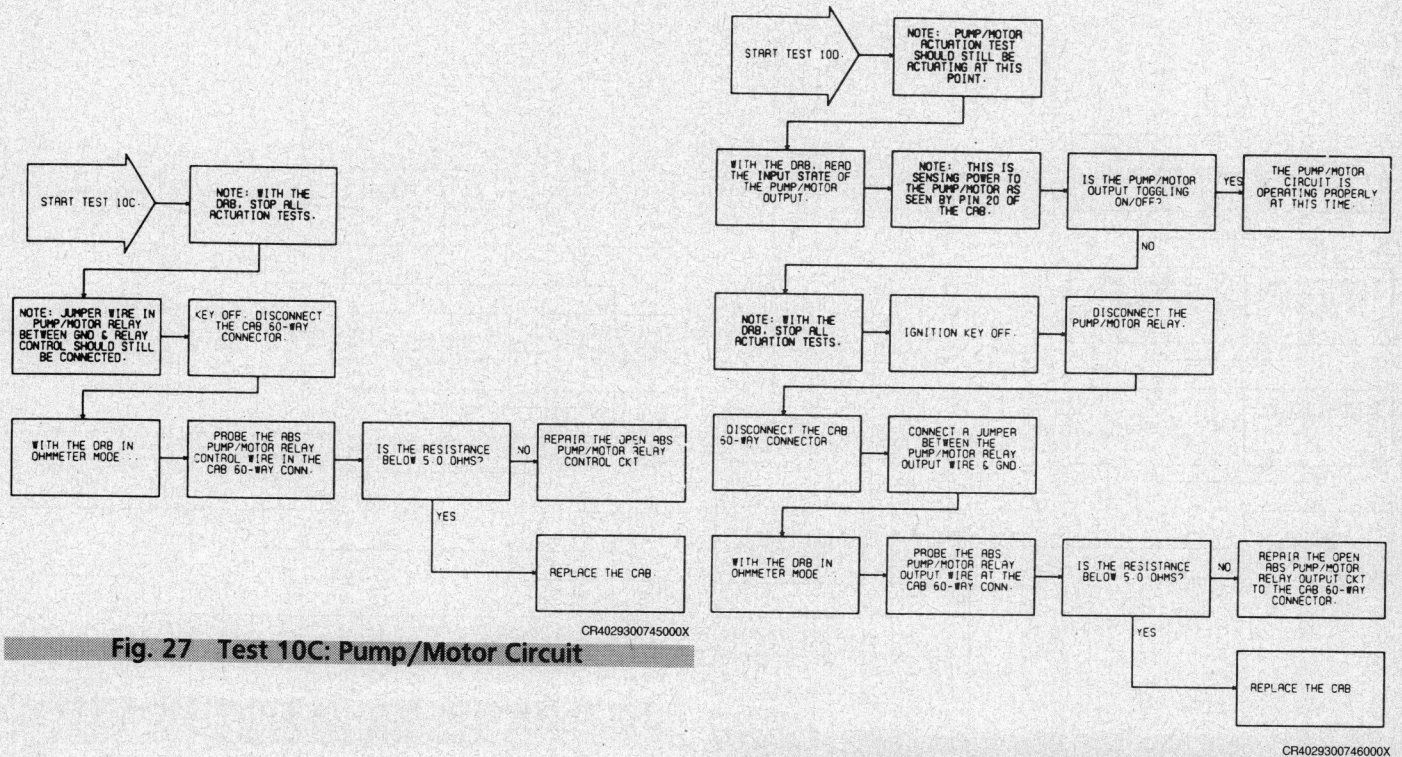

Fig. 25   Test 10A: Pump/Motor Circuit (Part 2 of 2)

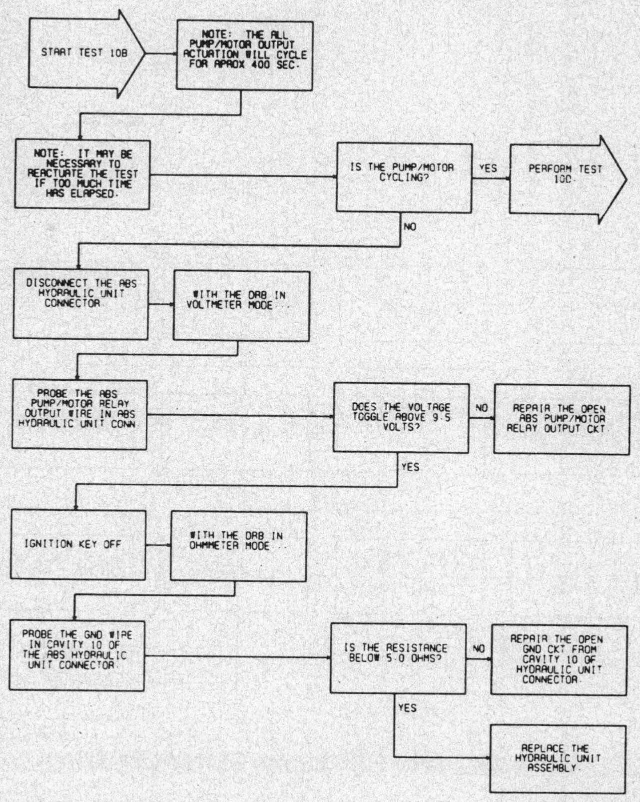

CR4029300743020X

Fig. 26   Test 10B: Pump/Motor Circuit

CR4029300744000X

Fig. 27   Test 10C: Pump/Motor Circuit

CR4029300745000X

Fig. 28   Test 10D: Pump/Motor Circuit

CR4029300746000X

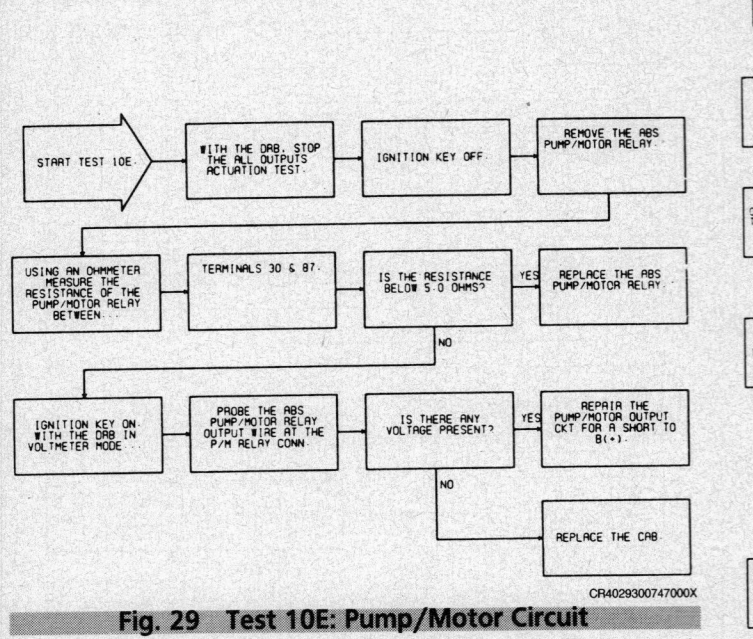

Fig. 29   Test 10E: Pump/Motor Circuit

CR4029300747000X

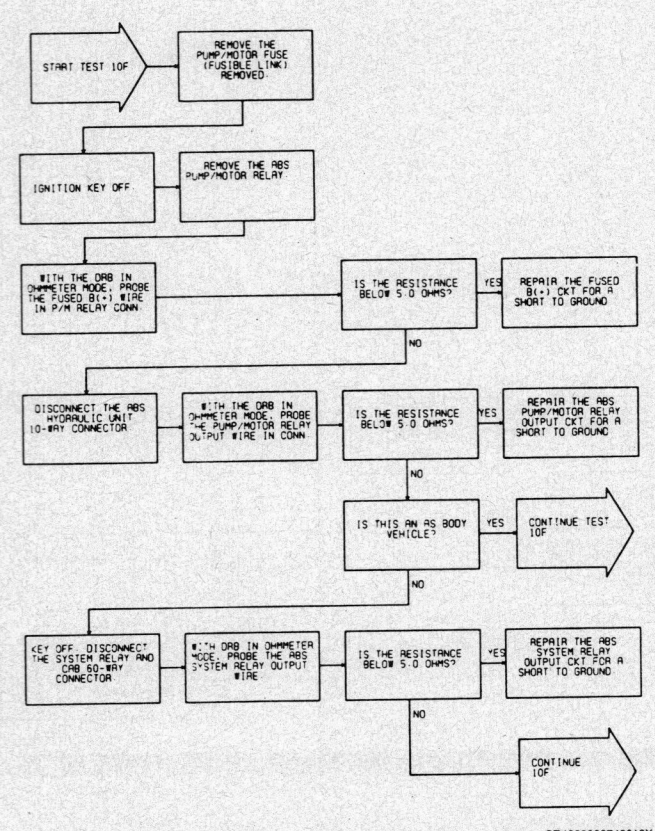

CR4029300748010X

Fig. 30   Test 10F: Pump/Motor Circuit (Part 1 of 2)

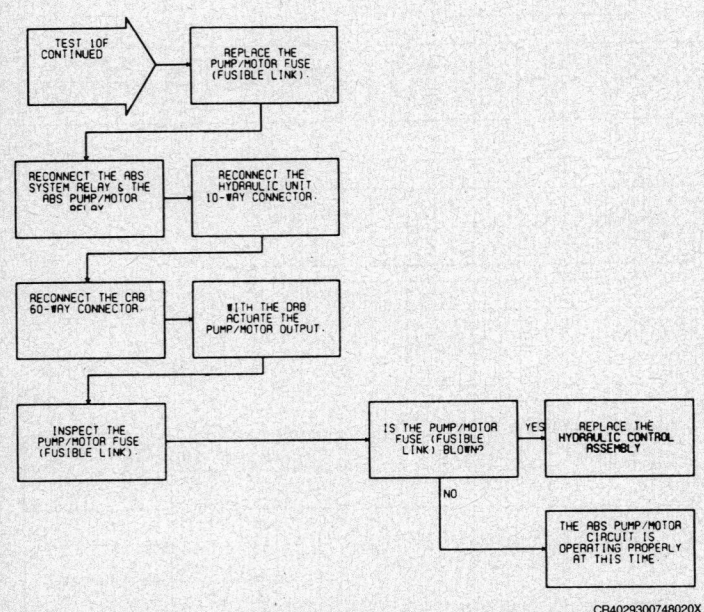

CR4029300748020X

Fig. 30   Test 10F: Pump/Motor Circuit (Part 2 of 2)

CR4029300749010X

Fig. 31   Test 11A: Right Front Wheel Speed Sensor Continuity (Part 1 of 2)

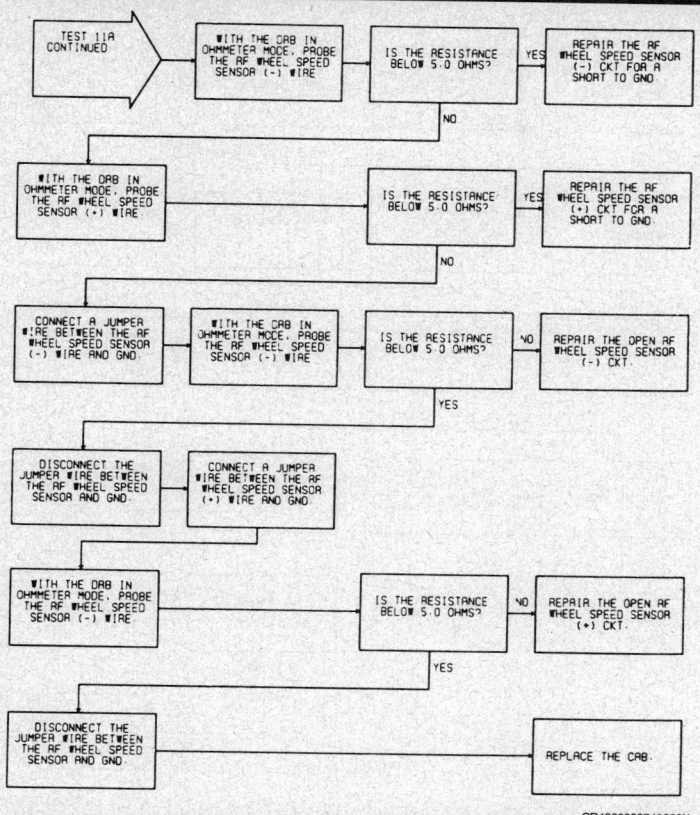

Fig. 31   Test 11A: Right Front Wheel Speed Sensor Continuity (Part 2 of 2)

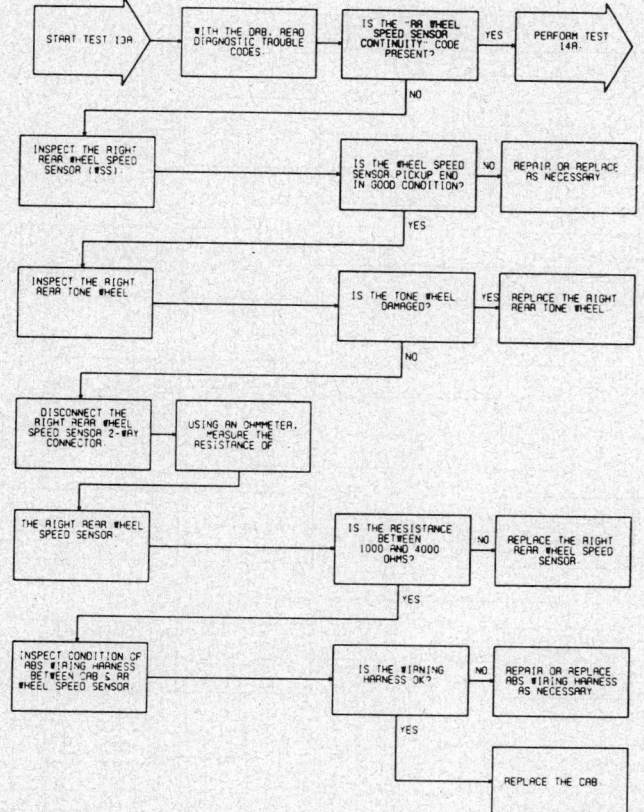

Fig. 33   Test 13A: Right Rear Wheel Speed Sensor

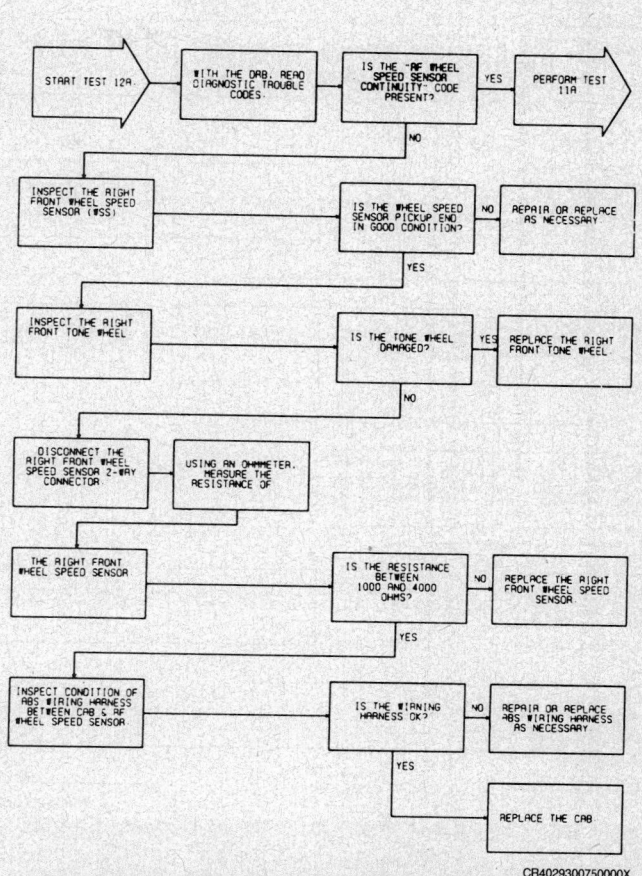

Fig. 32   Test 12A: Right Front Wheel Speed Sensor

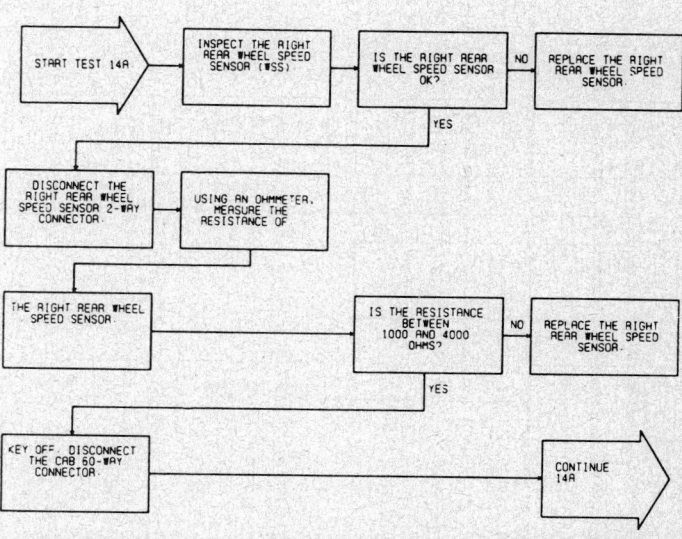

Fig. 34   Test 14A: Right Rear Wheel Speed Sensor Continuity (Part 1 of 2)

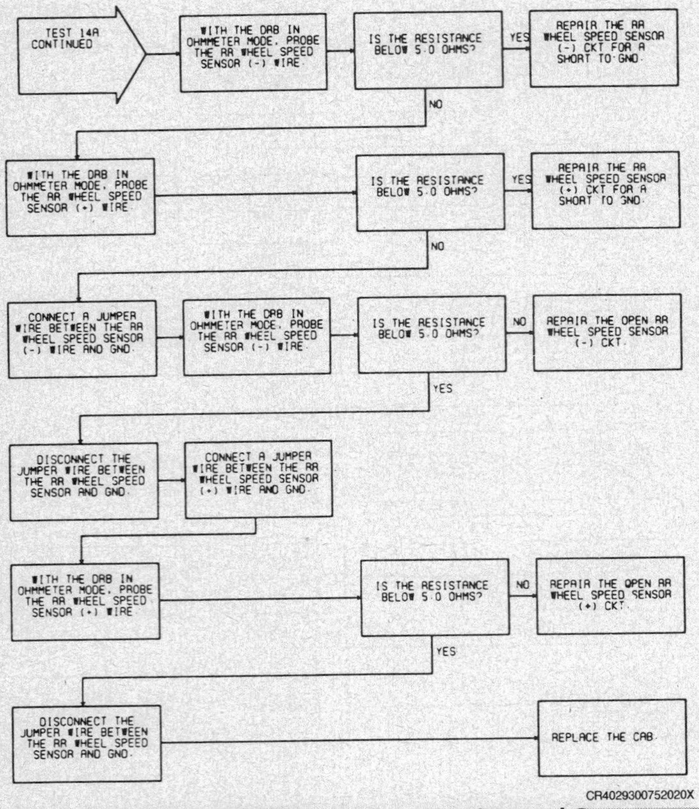

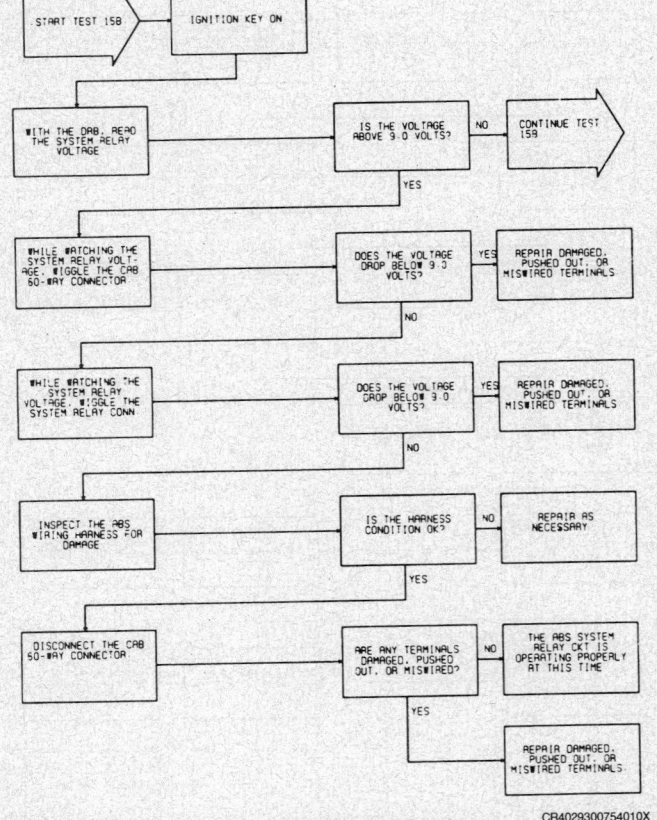

Fig. 34 Test 14A: Right Rear Wheel Speed Sensor Continuity (Part 2 of 2)

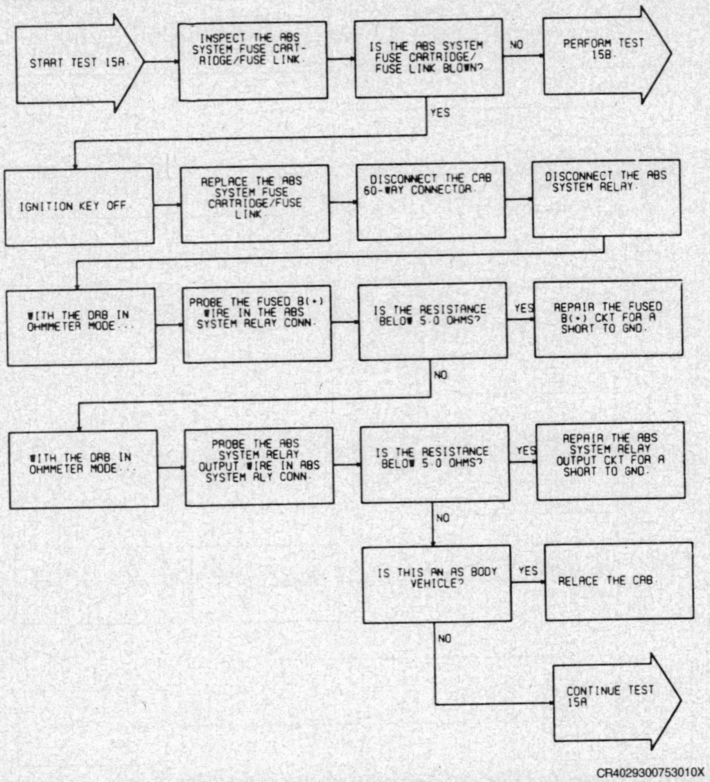

CR4029300752020X

Fig. 35 Test 15A: Solenoid Undervoltage (Part 1 of 2)

CR4029300753010X

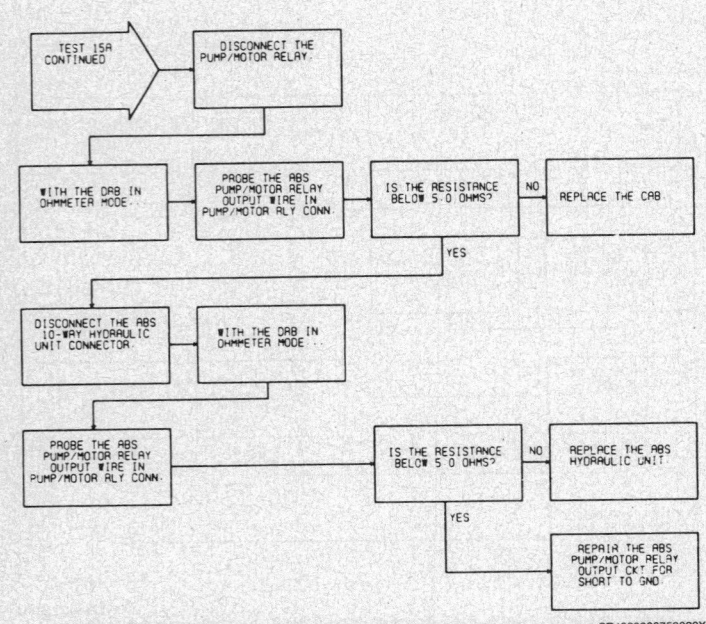

Fig. 35 Test 15A: Solenoid Undervoltage (Part 2 of 2)

CR4029300753020X

Fig. 36 Test 15B: Solenoid Undervoltage (Part 1 of 4)

CR4029300754010X

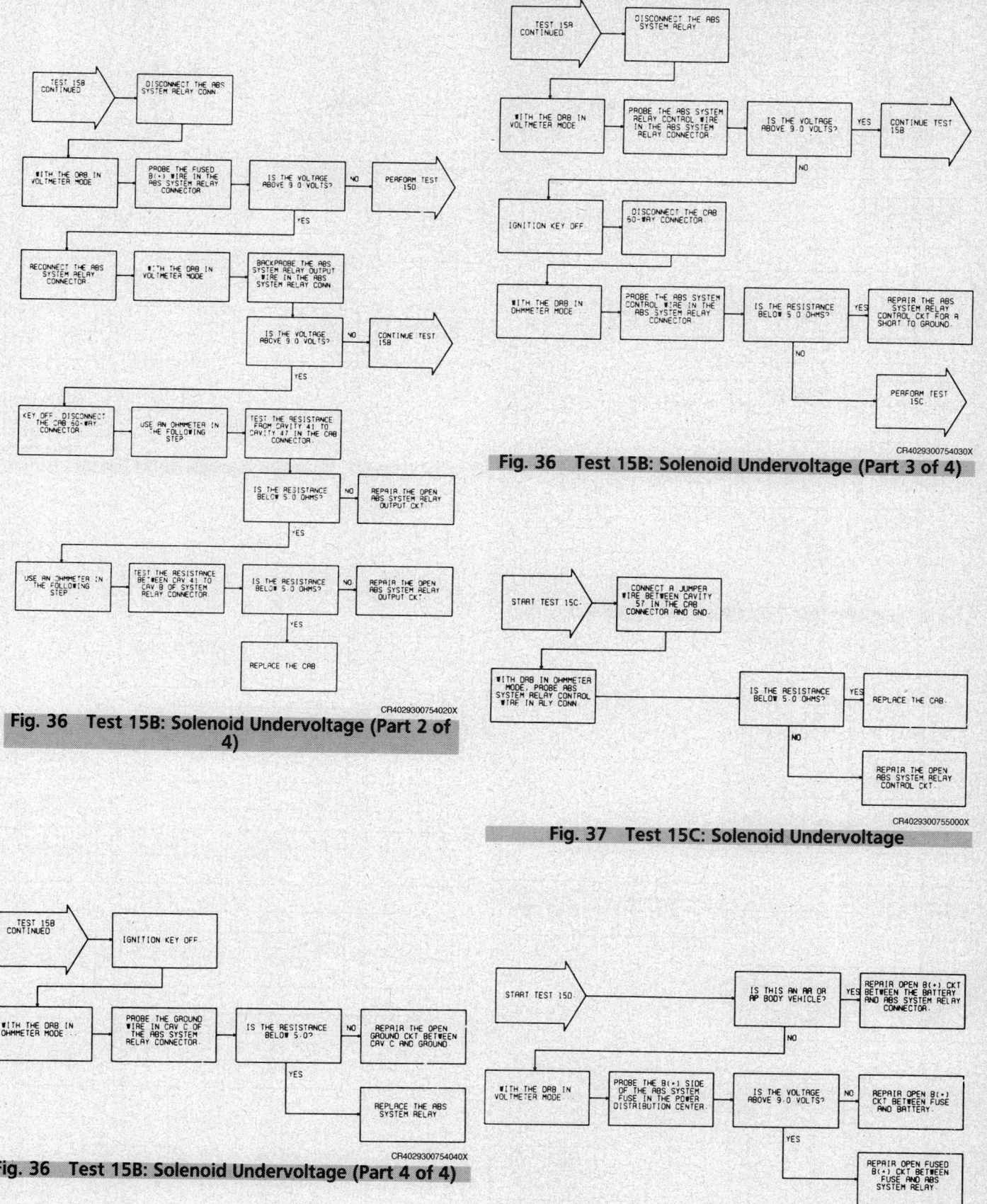

Fig. 36   Test 15B: Solenoid Undervoltage (Part 2 of 4)

CR4029300754020X

Fig. 36   Test 15B: Solenoid Undervoltage (Part 3 of 4)

CR4029300754030X

Fig. 37   Test 15C: Solenoid Undervoltage

CR4029300755000X

Fig. 36   Test 15B: Solenoid Undervoltage (Part 4 of 4)

CR4029300754040X

Fig. 38   Test 15D: Solenoid Undervoltage

CR4029300756000X

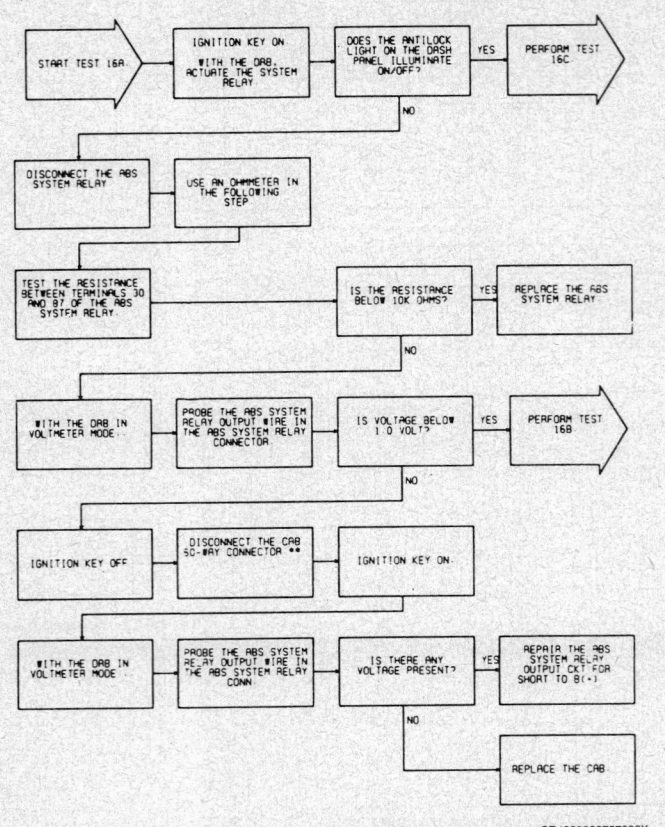

Fig. 39   Test 16A: System Relay Circuit

CR4029300757000X

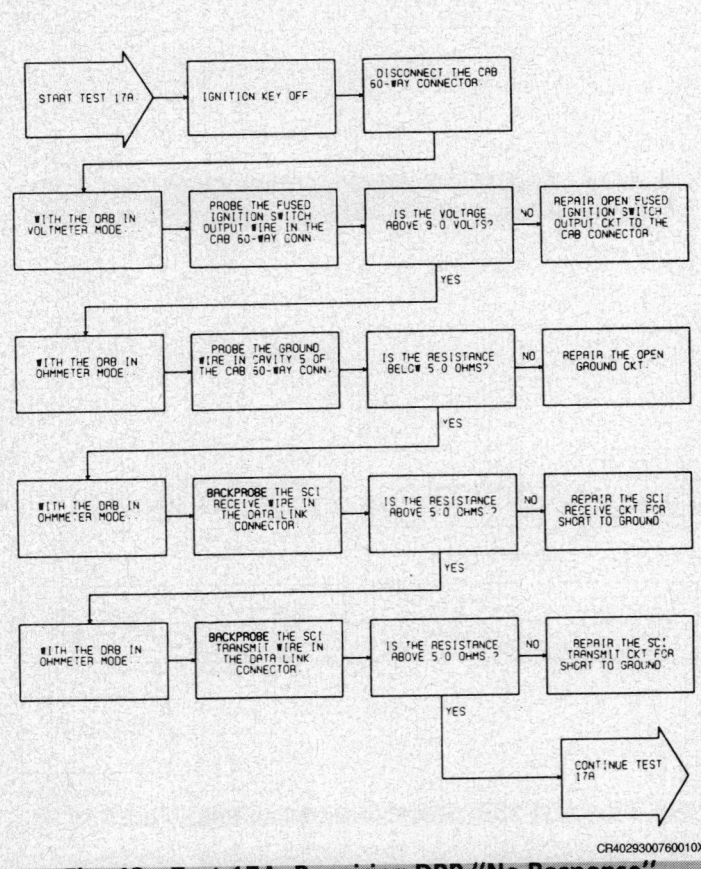

Fig. 40   Test 16B: System Relay Circuit

CR4029300758000X

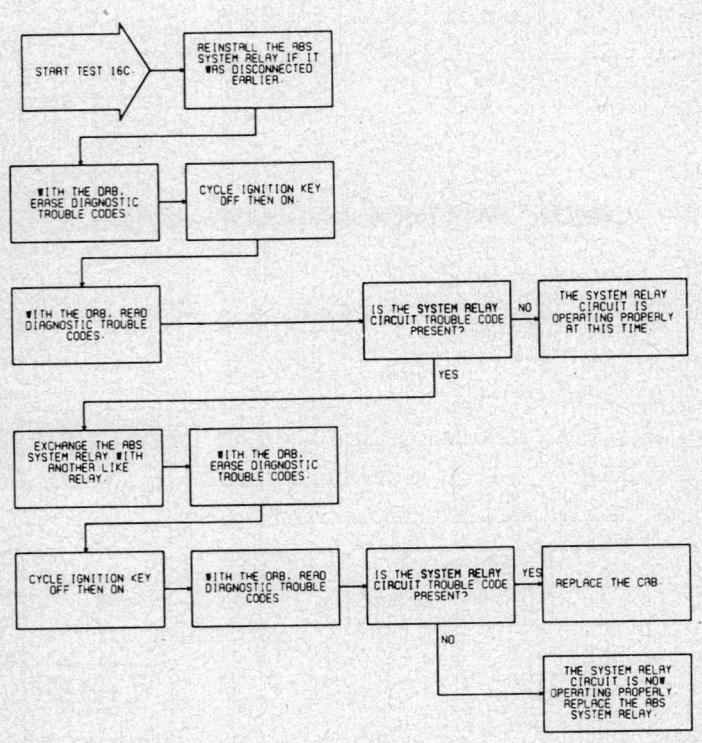

Fig. 41   Test 16C: System Relay Circuit

CR4029300759000X

Fig. 42   Test 17A: Repairing DRB "No Response" Message (Part 1 of 2)

CR4029300760010X

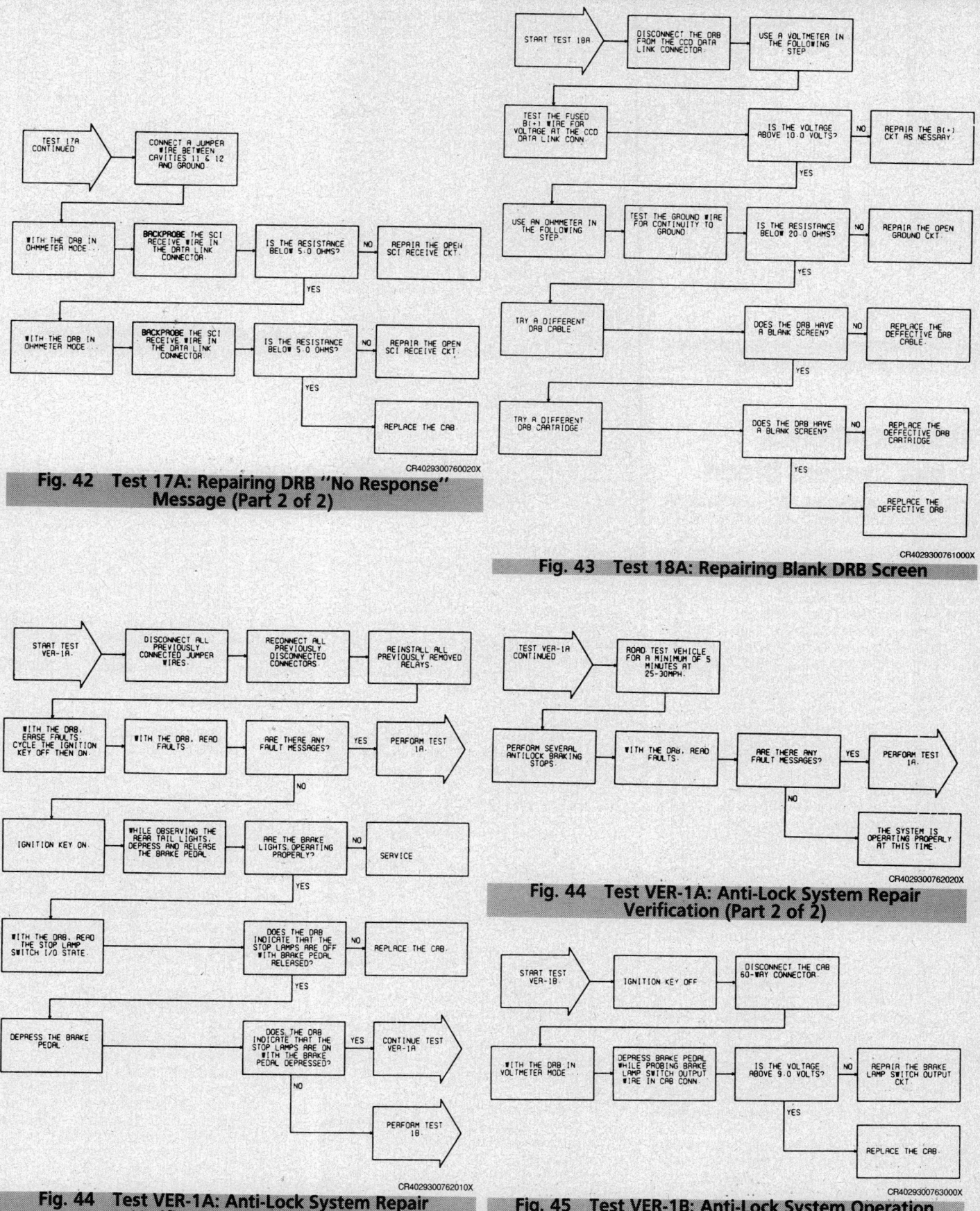

Fig. 42   Test 17A: Repairing DRB "No Response" Message (Part 2 of 2)

CR4029300760020X

Fig. 43   Test 18A: Repairing Blank DRB Screen

CR4029300761000X

Fig. 44   Test VER-1A: Anti-Lock System Repair Verification (Part 2 of 2)

CR4029300762020X

Fig. 44   Test VER-1A: Anti-Lock System Repair Verification (Part 1 of 2)

CR4029300762010X

Fig. 45   Test VER-1B: Anti-Lock System Operation Verification

CR4029300763000X

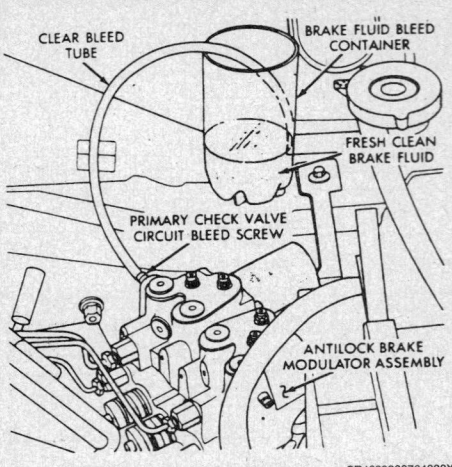

Fig. 46 Modulator assembly primary check valve circuit bleed

SYSTEM SERVICE
Brake System Bleed

The ABS and non-ABS portions of this system must be bled independently of one another. However, the ABS portion of the brake system cannot be bled using a hydraulic pressure bleeder because such equipment does not produce sufficient pressure to purge all air from the system.

1. Ensure master cylinder cover and surrounding components are free of debris, grime and any other substances that may contaminate brake fluid.
2. Using bleeder tank tool No. C-3496-B and adapter tool No. C-4578 or equivalents, pressurize non-ABS portion of system for bleeding. Follow equipment manufacturer's instructions during pressure bleeding.
3. Bleed line to right rear wheel first, then to left front, left rear and finally to right front wheel as follows:
   a. Attach a clear plastic hose to bleeder screw at wheel, then place other end of hose in a clear jar containing clean brake fluid.
   b. Open bleeder screw at least one full turn. This should allow brake fluid to flow steadily through clear hose and into jar.
   c. After 4 to 8 ounces of fluid (per wheel) has been dispensed, observe fluid condition. If it appears to be free of air bubbles and is flowing freely, bleeding is complete and next wheel in sequence may be bled. Tighten bleeder screw after bleeding each wheel.
   d. **Do not allow pressure bleeder tank to run dry during bleed procedure.**
   e. If, after all 4 wheels have been bled, brake pedal travel is not satisfactory, repeat procedure to purge remaining air from system.
4. If pressure bleeding equipment is not available, brakes may be bled manually (using same wheel sequence as described for pressure bleeding) as follows:
   a. With an assistant inside vehicle to operate brake pedal, connect one end of a clear plastic hose to bleeder screw and submerge other end in a clear container of clean brake fluid. **Ensure master cylinder reservoir is full.**
   b. Pump brake pedal several times, then hold it down and loosen bleeder screw at least one full turn; pedal should sink to floor and fluid should flow through clear tube.
   c. Without releasing brake pedal, tighten bleeder screw.
   d. After screw is tight, release pedal and repeat previous steps until fluid flowing through tube is free of air bubbles.
   e. Repeat procedure for remaining wheels.
   f. If, after all 4 wheels have been bled, brake pedal travel is not satisfactory, repeat procedure to purge remaining air from system.
5. Disconnect battery cables and remove battery, tray and acid shield from vehicle, then reconnect battery to cables using suitable jumper cables.
6. Connect DRB scan tool to vehicle diagnostic connector, located behind fuse panel access cover on lower left-hand side of instrument panel.
7. Ensure there are no diagnostic trouble codes stored by the Controller Anti-Lock Brake (CAB). If any diagnostic trouble codes are logged, erase them with scan tool.
8. Bleed modulator primary check valve circuit, then secondary check valve circuit as follows:
   a. Connect a clear bleed tube to check valve circuit bleeder screw, **Figs. 46 and 47**, then submerge other end of tube in a clear container of clean brake fluid.
   b. Have an assistant pump brake pedal several times, then maintain a constant, relatively heavy pressure on pedal.
   c. Open check valve circuit bleeder screw at least one full turn; when brake pedal bottoms, tighten screw, then release pedal.
   d. Repeat steps until fluid flowing through clear tube is free of air bubbles, then **torque** bleeder screw to 80 inch lbs.
9. Bleed modulator assembly primary sump circuit as follows:
   a. Connect clear bleed tube to primary sump bleeder screw, **Fig. 48**, then submerge other end of tube in a clear container of clean brake fluid.
   b. Have an assistant pump brake pedal several times, then maintain a constant, relatively heavy pressure on pedal.
   c. Open modulator assembly primary sump circuit bleeder screw at least one full turn; then, using DRB scan tool, select "Bleed ABS Hydraulic

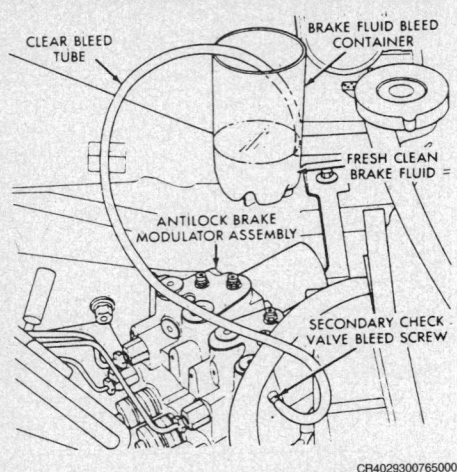

Fig. 47 Modulator assembly secondary check valve circuit bleed

Unit" mode.
   d. While in this mode, select "Primary Circuit" continuously until fluid flows freely through bleed tube without air bubbles.
   e. If brake pedal bottoms out before an air free flow of fluid can be maintained, repeat sump circuit bleed procedure.
   f. When sump circuit has been fully bled, **torque** bleeder screw to 80 inch lbs.
10. Bleed modulator assembly primary accumulator circuit as follows:
   a. Connect clear bleed tube to primary accumulator bleeder screw, **Fig. 49**, then submerge other end of tube in a clear container of clean brake fluid.
   b. Have an assistant pump brake pedal several times, then maintain a constant, relatively heavy pressure on pedal.
   c. Using DRB scan tool, select "Bleed ABS Hydraulic Unit" mode.
   d. While in this mode, select "Primary Circuit Valves," then open modulator assembly primary sump circuit bleeder screw at least one full turn.
   e. Allow fluid to flow continuously until it appears to be free of air bubbles. If brake pedal bottoms out before bubbles cease, repeat accumulator circuit bleed procedure.
   f. Close bleeder screw only snugly (without final tightening), then release brake pedal.
   g. Disconnect scan tool, then pump brake pedal several times and maintain a constant, relatively heavy pressure on pedal.
   h. Open primary accumulator circuit bleed screw, **Fig. 49**, then continue to bleed circuit until a clear, bubble-free flow of fluid can be maintained.

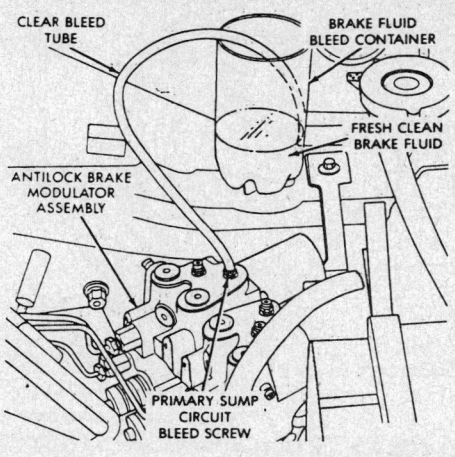

Fig. 48 Modulator assembly primary sump circuit bleed

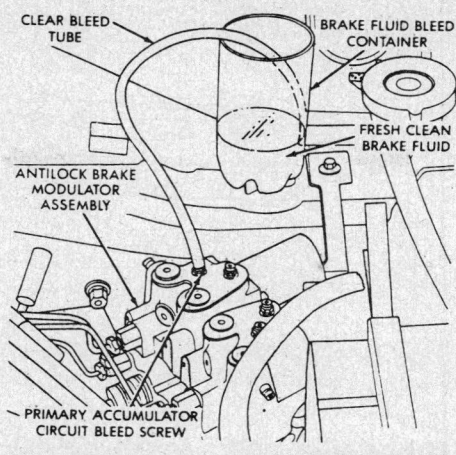

Fig. 49 Modulator assembly primary accumulator circuit bleed

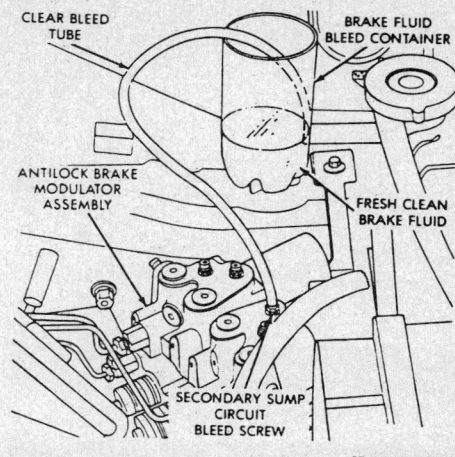

Fig. 50 Modulator assembly secondary sump circuit bleed

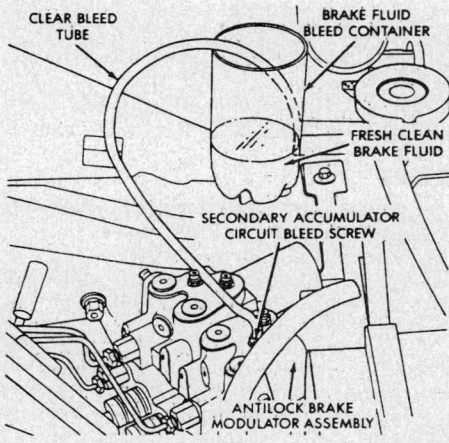

Fig. 51 Modulator assembly secondary accumulator circuit bleed

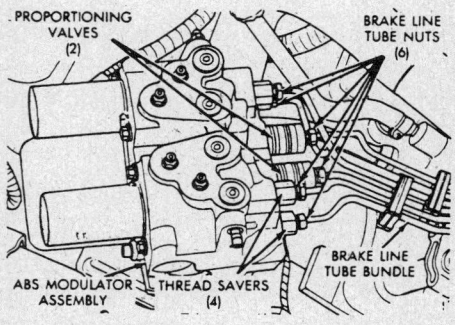

Fig. 52 Hydraulic tube bundle & ABS modulator assembly

i. Close bleeder screw, then release brake pedal and **torque** bleeder screw to 80 inch lbs.

11. Bleed modulator assembly secondary sump circuit as follows:
   a. Connect clear bleed tube to secondary sump bleeder screw, **Fig. 50**, then submerge other end of tube in a clear container of clean brake fluid.
   b. Have an assistant pump brake pedal several times, then maintain a constant, relatively heavy pressure on pedal.
   c. Open modulator assembly secondary sump circuit bleeder screw at least one full turn; then, using DRB scan tool, select "Bleed ABS Hydraulic Unit" mode.
   d. While in this mode, select "Secondary Circuit" continuously until fluid flows freely through bleed tube without air bubbles.
   e. If brake pedal bottoms out before an air free flow of fluid can be maintained, repeat sump circuit bleed procedure.

f. When sump circuit has been fully bled, **torque** bleeder screw to 80 inch lbs.

12. Bleed modulator assembly secondary accumulator circuit as follows:
   a. Connect clear bleed tube to secondary accumulator bleeder screw, **Fig. 51**, then submerge other end of tube in a clear container of clean brake fluid.
   b. Have an assistant pump brake pedal several times, then maintain a constant, relatively heavy pressure on pedal.
   c. Using DRB scan tool, select "Bleed ABS Hydraulic Unit" mode.
   d. While in this mode, select "Secondary Circuit Valves," then open modulator assembly secondary sump circuit bleeder screw at least one full turn.
   e. Allow fluid to flow continuously until it appears to be free of air bubbles. If brake pedal bottoms out before bubbles cease, repeat accumulator circuit bleed procedure.
   f. Close bleeder screw only snugly (without final tightening), then release brake pedal.
   g. Disconnect scan tool, then pump brake pedal several times and maintain a constant, relatively heavy pressure on pedal.
   h. Open secondary accumulator circuit bleed screw, **Fig. 51**, then continue to bleed circuit until a clear, bubble-free flow of fluid can be maintained.
   i. Close bleeder screw, then release brake pedal and **torque** bleeder screw to 80 inch lbs.

Component Replace

MODULATOR ASSEMBLY

1. Raise and support vehicle, then disconnect and remove battery cables.
2. Remove battery heat shield, hold-down clamp and battery from tray, then lift access cover off tray.

3. Remove speed control vacuum reservoir from battery tray without disconnecting vacuum lines, then remove battery tray from vehicle.
4. Remove battery acid shield from modulator assembly, then remove 6 nuts securing tube bundle to modulator, **Fig. 52**.
5. Separate tube bundle from modulator assembly, then disconnect 10-way connector at modulator.
6. Remove bolts securing front and lower portions of modulator assembly to mounting bracket, then remove assembly from vehicle.
7. Reverse procedure to install, noting the following:
   a. **Torque** modulator assembly mounting bolts to 21 ft. lbs.
   b. **Torque** tube bundle fittings to 13 ft. lbs.
   c. Bleed ABS components and basic brake system as described under "System Service."

PROPORTIONING VALVES

Proportioning valves should never be disassembled.
1. Raise and support vehicle, then disconnect and remove battery cables.
2. Remove battery heat shield, hold-

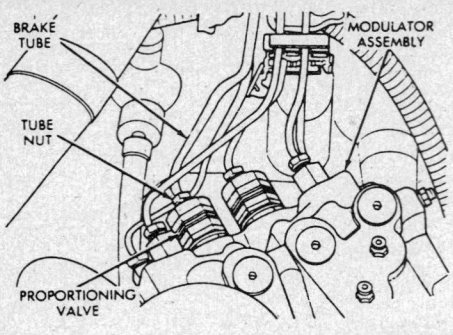

Fig. 53 Proportioning valve replacement

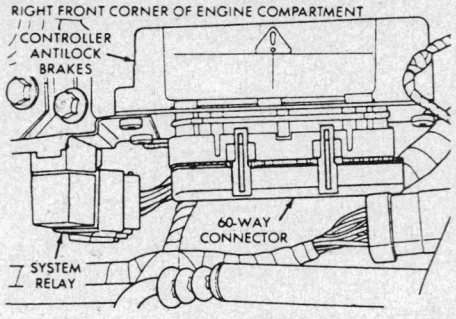

Fig. 54 Controller Anti-Lock Brake (CAB) & ABS relay

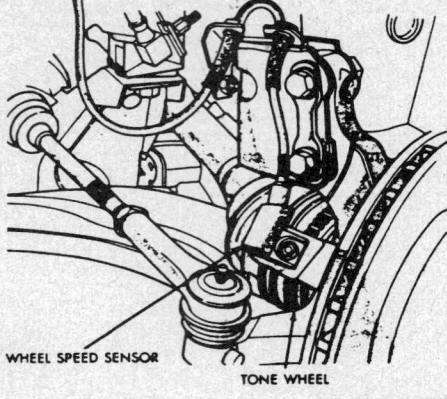

Fig. 55 Front wheel speed sensor

down clamp and battery from tray, then lift access cover off tray.

3. Remove speed control vacuum reservoir from battery tray without disconnecting vacuum lines, then remove battery tray from vehicle.

4. Remove battery acid shield from modulator assembly, then remove brake tube from proportioning valve, **Fig. 53.**

5. Remove proportioning valve from modulator assembly.

6. Reverse procedure to install, noting the following:
   a. Prior to installing proportioning valve, moisten sealing O-ring with clean brake fluid.
   b. **Torque** proportioning valve to 26 ft. lbs. and brake tube nut to 13 ft. lbs.

CONTROLLER ANTI-LOCK BRAKE (CAB)

1. Ensure ignition switch is in Off position, then disconnect wiring harness connector from ABS relay, **Fig. 54.**

2. Loosen 60-way connector bolt at CAB, then disconnect connector from CAB by pulling straight out. **Do not twist connector during removal.**

3. Remove CAB module mounting bracket to frame rail bolts, then remove CAB and mounting bracket from vehicle.

4. Remove ABS relay and bracket assembly from CAB module and mounting bracket.

5. Reverse procedure to install, noting the following:
   a. **Torque** ABS relay mounting bracket screw to 9 ft. lbs. and CAB mounting bracket to frame rail bolts to 21 ft. lbs.

b. **Ensure ignition switch is still in Off position before connecting 60-way connector to CAB module.**

ABS RELAY

Refer to "Controller Anti-Lock Brake (CAB)" replacement procedure for ABS relay replacement.

ABS PUMP MOTOR RELAY

1. While holding pump motor relay, pull wiring harness connector straight off relay terminals, then remove relay from vehicle.

2. Reverse procedure to install.

WHEEL SPEED SENSORS

Front

1. Raise and support vehicle, then remove wheel and tire assembly.

2. Remove screw securing grommet to fender shield, then the two screws securing sensor routing tube to frame rail, **Fig. 55.**

3. Pull sensor grommet carefully away from fender shield, then disconnect speed sensor connector from vehicle wiring harness.

4. Remove sensor grommets from retainer brackets, then remove sensor head screw and lift sensor from steering knuckle. **If corrosion impedes removal, do not use pliers to free sensor. Use a hammer and suitable punch to tap gently upon sensor mount until sensor is free.**

5. Reverse procedure to install, noting the following:
   a. Coat speed sensor with high tem-

perature grease prior to installation.
   b. **Torque** sensor screw to 60 inch lbs.
   c. Ensure cables are installed as shown, **Fig. 55.**

Rear

1. Raise and support vehicle, then remove wheel and tire assembly.

2. Remove sensor grommet from vehicle underbody, then pull harness through hole and disconnect sensor connector from harness.

3. Remove sensor grommets from batwing bracket, located just ahead of trailing arm bushing, then remove sensor and brake tube assembly clip from inside portion of trailing arm.

4. Remove sensor wire fastener from rear brake hose bracket, then remove retainer nut from outboard sensor assembly.

5. Remove sensor head screw, then carefully separate sensor head from adapter assembly. **If corrosion impedes removal, do not use pliers to free sensor. Use a hammer and suitable punch to tap gently upon sensor mount until sensor is free.**

6. Reverse procedure to install, noting the following:
   a. Coat speed sensor with high temperature grease prior to installation.
   b. **Torque** sensor screw to 60 inch lbs.

Type 2—Bendix Anti-Lock 6 Braking System

NOTE: On Air Bag Equipped Models, Refer To "Air Bag System Precautions" Located In The Front Of This Manual For System Disarming & Arming Procedures.

INDEX

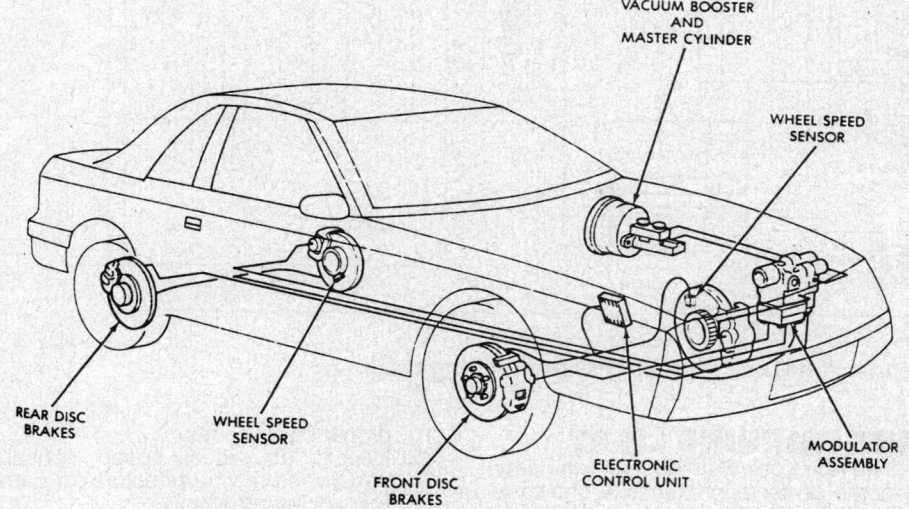

Fig. 1 Bendix Anti-Lock 6 braking system components

PRECAUTIONS

AIR BAG SYSTEMS

Refer to "Air Bag System Precautions" in the front of this manual for system disarming and arming procedures.

DESCRIPTION

The Anti-Lock Braking System (ABS) prevents the wheels from locking up when braking, regardless of the surface conditions. This allows the car to stop in a shorter distance, and allows the driver to maintain directional control of the vehicle during heavy braking.

During normal braking conditions, the ABS operates like a conventional diagonally split, hydraulic power assist system. During heavy braking, however, each wheel's braking pressure is modulated according to its speed. To maintain vehicle stability, both rear wheels receive the same signal.

There are four major components, **Fig. 1**, in the ABS which act in unison to control brake operation.

SYSTEM COMPONENTS

Master Cylinder & Brake Booster

This system uses the vehicles standard master cylinder and power brake booster. The master cylinder primary and secondary outputs are connected directly to the modulator assembly.

Modulator & Pump Motor Assembly

This assembly contains the wheel circuit valves used for brake pressure modulation and the pump motor.

The pump motor pumps brake fluid at a low pressure into the ABS accumulator during a stop that requires the ABS system to become operational.

Wheel Speed Sensors (WSS)

These sensors located at each wheel transmit information to the Controller Anti-Lock Brake (CAB).

Controller-Anti-Lock Brake (CAB)

This control computer uses signals from the wheel speed sensors to control and monitor Anti-Lock system operation.

TROUBLESHOOTING

Visually inspect system components and their connectors as described below prior to troubleshooting system or performing diagnostic tests.
1. Inspect brake fluid level and ensure fluid is not contaminated.
2. Inspect brake lines and master cylinder for leaks and/or damage.
3. Inspect ABS hydraulic unit for leaks, and ensure that hydraulic unit 10-way and differential pressure switch (Delta P) electrical connectors are not damaged or disconnected.
4. Inspect CAB for a secure mounting, and ensure that its electrical connector is not damaged or loose.
5. Inspect pump/motor, warning lamp and system relay connectors for any terminal corrosion, damage or improper connections.
6. Inspect all wheel speed sensors (WSS) and their connectors for damage or disconnection.

Refer to wiring diagram and connector identification, **Figs. 2 and 3**, when performing testing procedures.

DIAGNOSIS & TESTING

Accessing Diagnostic Trouble Codes

This ABS system has a self-diagnosis connector located under the fuse panel access cover. The access cover is located on the lower section of the instrument panel to the left of the steering column. The ABS diagnostic connector is a blue 6-way connector which can be connected to a DRB II diagnostic readout box.

After connecting the DRB II to the diagnostic connector, follow the tool manufacturer's instructions to further diagnose the

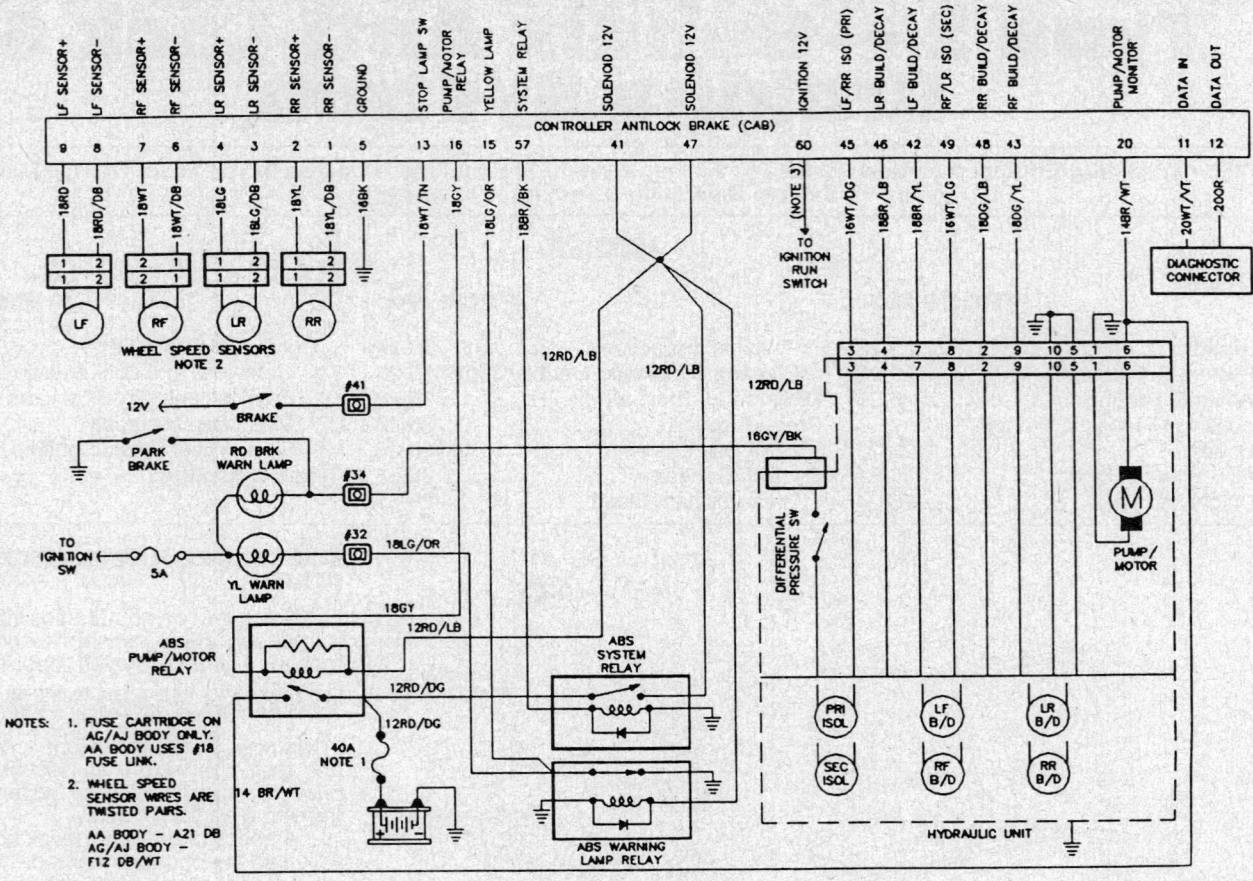

Fig. 2 Bendix Anti-Lock 6 braking system wiring diagram

ABS system. Note the following:
1. **All diagnostic test procedures assume a Chrysler Diagnostic Read-out Box (DRB II) is being used. Tests have been designed specifically for the DRB II.**
2. After completing diagnosis and repair of the system, perform any verification test provided.

Refer to wiring diagram and connector identification, **Figs. 2 and 3**, when performing testing procedures.

The Bendix Anti-Lock 6 Braking System has self diagnosis capability. The self diagnosis cycle begins when the ignition switch is in the ON position. An electrical check is completed on the ABS components such as wheel speed sensors continuity, system continuity and other relay continuity. During this check the Anti-Lock Light will be on for approximately one to two seconds.

Once the vehicle is set into motion the solenoid valves and pump motor are activated briefly to verify proper operation. The voltage output of the speed sensors is verified to be within the correct operating range.

If the vehicle is not set into motion within three minutes from the time the ignition switch is turned to the On position, the solenoid test is bypassed but the pump motor will be activated briefly to verify proper operation.

ABS WARNING LIGHT

The Anti-Lock warning light will normally come on for approximately one to two seconds when the ignition switch is first turned to the ON position.

Anytime the Controller Anti-Lock Brake (CAB) detects a condition which results in a shutdown of the ABS function other than when the ignition switch is first turned on it will activate the ABS warning lamp. When the light is on only the Anti-Lock function of the brake system is affected. The standard brake system and ability to stop the vehicle will not be affected.

VISUAL INSPECTION

Visually inspect system components and their connectors as described below prior to performing diagnostic tests.
1. Inspect brake fluid level, and ensure that fluid is not contaminated.
2. Inspect brake lines and master cylinder for leaks and/or damage.
3. Inspect ABS hydraulic unit for leaks, and ensure that hydraulic unit 10-way and differential pressure switch (Delta P) electrical connectors are not damaged or disconnected.
4. Inspect CAB for a secure mounting, and ensure that its electrical connector is not damaged or loose.
5. Inspect pump/motor, warning lamp and system relay connectors for any terminal corrosion, damage or im-

proper connections.
6. Inspect all wheel speed sensors (WSS) and their connectors for damage or disconnection.

DIAGNOSTIC TESTS

1992

Start with diagnostic test 1A, **Fig. 4**, then proceed as instructed to diagnostic charts 2A through 19A, **Figs. 5 through 37.** Starting at any other test other than test 1A may give incorrect results resulting in a misdiagnosed system. After each test is performed, perform verification test 20A, **Fig. 38**, before proceeding.

1993

Perform visual inspection shown in test 1A, **Fig. 39**, prior to performing test 1A, then proceed as instructed to diagnostic charts 2A through 21B, **Figs. 40 through 76.** Starting at any other test other than test 1A may give incorrect results resulting in a misdiagnosed system. After each test is performed, perform verification test VER-1A, **Fig. 77**, before proceeding.

Clearing Diagnostic Trouble Codes

Diagnostic trouble codes can be cleared using the DRB II diagnostics tester, or they will be automatically cleared after 50 ignition switch ON/OFF cycles.

Continued on page 25-55

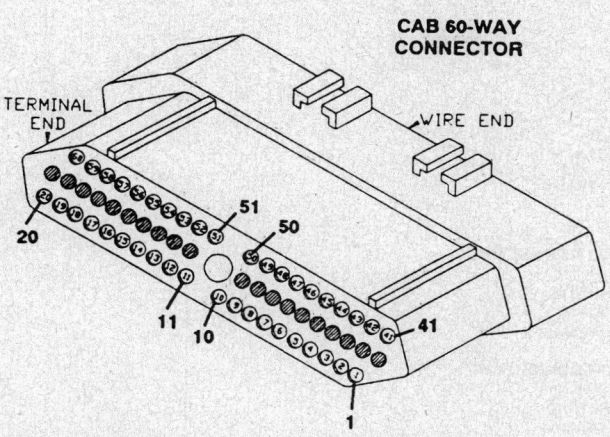

CAB 60-WAY CONNECTOR

TERMINAL END

WIRE END

20 · 51 · 50 · 11 · 10 · 41 · 1

CAV ..	CIRCUIT	FUNCTION
1	B01 18YL/DB	Right Rear Sensor -
2	B02 18YL	Right Rear Sensor +
3	B03 18LG/DB	Left Rear Sensor -
4	B04 18LG	Left Rear Sensor +
5	Z01 16BK	Ground
6	B06 18WT/DB	Right Front Sensor -
7	B07 18WT	Right Front Sensor +
8	B08 18RD/DB	Left Front Sensor -
9	B09 18RD	Left Front Sensor +
10		Not Used
11	D11 20WT/VT	Serial Data Input
12	D12 20OR	Serial Data Output
13	L50 18WT/TN	Stop Lamp Switch
14		Not Used
15	G19 18LG/OR	Yellow Light
16	B116 18 GY	Pump/Motor Relay
17-19		Not Used
20	B120 14BR/WT	Pump/Motor Monitor
21-40		Not Used
41	B47 112RD/LB	Solenoid +12V
42	B142 18BR/YL	LF Build/Decay Valve
43	B143 18DG/YL	RF Build/Decay Valve
44		Not Used
45	B145 16WT/DG	LF RR Isolation Valve
46	B146 18BR/LB	LR Build/Decay Valve
47	B47 12RD/LB	Solenoid +12V
48	B148 18DG/LB	RR Build/Decay Valve
49	B149 16WT/LG	RF/LR Isolation Valve
50-56		Not Used
57	B57 18BR/BK	System Relay
58-59		Not Used
60	A21 14DB	Ignition +12V (AA Body)
	F12 18DB/WT	Ignition +12V (AG/AJ Body)

ABS HYDRAULIC UNIT CONNECTOR

CAV ..	CIRCUIT	FUNCTION
1	Z01 12BK	Ground, Pump/Motor
2	B148 18DG/LB	Right Rear Build/Decay Valve
3	B145 16WT/LG	Left Front/Right Rear Isolation Valve
4	B146 18BR/LB	Left Rear Build/Decay Valve
5	Z01 12BK	Ground
6	B120 14BR/WT	Pump/Motor
7	B142 18BR/YL	Left Front Build/Decay Valve
8	B149 16WT/LG	Right Front/Left Rear Isolation Valve
9	B143 18DG/YL	Right Front Build/Decay Valve
10	Z01 12BK	Ground

BUS DIAGNOSTIC CONNECTOR

CAV ..	CIRCUIT	FUNCTION
1	D11 20WT/VT	Data In
2	F30 18RD	Battery 12V
3	D02 20WT/BK	Serial Data Bus (-)
4	D01 20VT/BR	Serial Data Bus (+)
5	D12 20OR	Data Out
6	Z02 20BK/LG	Ground

ABS PUMP/MOTOR RELAY CONNECTOR

CAV ..	CIRCUIT	FUNCTION
A	B47 12RD/LB	System Relay Voltage
B	A20 12RD/DG	Battery 12V
C	B116 18GY	Pump/Motor Grd., CAB Controlled
D	B120 14BR/WT	Pump/Motor and CAB Motor Monitor

ABS SYSTEM RELAY CONNECTOR

CAV ..	CIRCUIT	FUNCTION
A	B57 18BR/BK	System Relay Actuation
B	A20 12RD/DG	Battery 12V
C	Z02 18BK	Ground
D	B47 12RD/LB	System Relay Voltage
E		Not Used

ABS WARN LAMP RELAY CONNECTOR

CAV ..	CIRCUIT	FUNCTION
A	B47 12RD/LB	System Relay Voltage
B	G19 18LG/OR	CAB-Antilock Warning Light and Antilock Warning Light Bulb (Double Crimped at Relay Terminal)
C	Z01 18BK	Ground
D		Not Used
E	Z01 18BK	Ground

ABS HYDRAULIC UNIT CONNECTOR

BUS DIAGNOSTIC CONNECTOR

ABS PUMP/MOTOR RELAY CONNECTOR

SYSTEM RELAY AND WARNING LAMP RELAY CONNECTOR

SYSTEM RELAY AND WARNING LAMP RELAY CONNECTOR

CR4029100298010X

Fig. 3   Bendix Anti-Lock 6 braking system connector identification (Part 1 of 2)

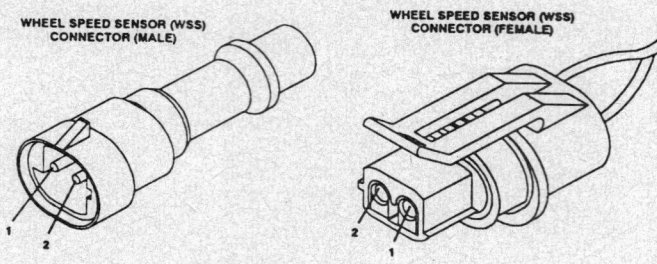

RR WHEEL SPEED SENSOR CONNECTOR

CAV.. CIRCUIT .... FUNCTION
1 ...... B02 18YL .... RR Sensor +
2 ...... B01 18YL/DB ...... RR Sensor -

LR WHEEL SPEED SENSOR CONNECTOR

CAV.. CIRCUIT .... FUNCTION
1 ...... B04 18LG............ LR Sensor +
2 ...... B03 18LG/DB ...... LR Sensor -

RF WHEEL SPEED SENSOR CONNECTOR

CAV.. CIRCUIT .... FUNCTION
1 ...... B06 18WT/DB .... RF Sensor -
2 ...... B07 18WT .... RF Sensor +

LF WHEEL SPEED SENSOR CONNECTOR

CAV.. CIRCUIT .... FUNCTION
1 ...... B09 18RD .... LF Sensor +
2 ...... B08 18RD/DB...... LF Sensor -

CR402910029802OX

Fig. 3   Bendix Anti-Lock 6 braking system connector
identification (Part 2 of 2)

DIAGNOSTIC CHART INDEX

Test No.	Symptom	Page No.	Fig. No.
1992			
1A	Reading Fault Messages	25-28	4
2A	Cab Fault	25-28	5
3A	Modulator Fault	25-28	6
3B	Modulator Fault, Left Front Build/Decay Valve	25-29	7
3C	Modulator Fault, Left Rear Build/Decay Valve	25-29	8
3D	Modulator Fault, Right Front Build/Decay Valve	25-29	9
3E	Modulator Fault, Right Rear Build/Decay Valve	25-30	10
3F	Modulator Fault, Left Front/Right Rear Isolation Valve	25-30	11
3G	Modulator Fault, Right Front/Left Rear Isolation Valve	25-30	12
4A	Solenoid Under Voltage Fault	25-30	13
4B	Solenoid Under Voltage Fault	25-31	14
5A	System Relay Fault	25-32	15
5B	System Relay Fault	25-32	16
6A	Pump/Motor Fault	25-33	17
6B	Pump/Motor Fault	25-33	18
6C	Pump/Motor Fault	25-33	19
6D	Pump/Motor Fault	25-33	20
7A	Anti-Lock Lamp Fault	25-34	21
7B	Anti-Lock Lamp Fault	25-34	22
8A	Anti-Lock Lamp Relay Fault	25-34	23
8B	Anti-Lock Lamp Relay Fault	25-35	24
8C	Anti-Lock Lamp Relay Fault	25-35	25

Continued

Test No.	Symptom	Page No.	Fig. No.
1992			
9A	Right Rear Wheel Speed Sensor Continuity Fault	25-36	26
10A	Left Rear Wheel Speed Sensor Continuity Fault	25-36	27
11A	Right Front Wheel Speed Sensor Continuity Fault	25-37	28
12A	Left Front Wheel Speed Sensor Continuity Fault	25-37	29
13A	Right Rear Wheel Speed Sensor Fault	25-38	30
14A	Left Rear Wheel Speed Sensor Fault	25-38	31
15A	Right Front Wheel Speed Sensor Fault	25-38	32
16A	Left Front Wheel Speed Sensor Fault	25-38	33
17A	Excess Decay Valve Fault	25-39	34
18A	Red Brake Warning Lamp Input Test	25-39	35
18B	Red Brake Warning Lamp Input Test	25-39	36
19A	Stop Lamp Switch Input Test	25-39	37
20A	System Verification Test	25-40	38
1993			
1A	Reading Fault Messages	25-40	39
2A	Testing Blank DRB II Message Screen	25-40	40
3A	Testing DRB II " No Response" Message	25-41	41
4A	Antilock Lamp Fault	25-41	42
4B	Antilock Lamp Fault	25-42	43
5A	Antilock Lamp Relay Fault	25-42	44
5B	Antilock Lamp Relay Fault	25-42	45
6A	CAB Fault	25-43	46
7A	Excess Decay Valve Fault	25-43	47
8A	LF Wheel Speed Sensor Continuity Fault	25-43	48
9A	Left Front Wheel Speed Sensor Fault	25-44	49
10A	LR Wheel Speed Sensor Continuity Fault	25-44	50
11A	Left Rear Wheel Speed Sensor Fault	25-45	51
12A	Modulator Fault	25-45	52
12B	Modulator Fault (Left Front Build/Decay Valve)	25-46	53
12C	Modulator Fault (Left Rear Build/Decay Valve)	25-47	54
12D	Modulator Fault (Right Front Build/Decay Valve)	25-47	55
12E	Modulator Fault (Right Rear Build/Decay Valve)	25-47	56
12F	Modulator Fault (Left Front/Right Rear Isolation Valve)	25-47	57
12G	Modulator Fault (Right Front/Left Rear Isolation Valve)	25-48	58
12H	Modulator Fault Solenoid Valve Resistance Check	25-48	59
13A	Stop Lamp Switch Input Test	25-48	60
14A	Pump/Motor Fault	25-49	61
14B	Pump/Motor Fault	25-49	62
14C	Pump/Motor Fault	25-49	63
14D	Pump/Motor Fault	25-50	64
15A	Red Brake Warning Lamp Input Test	25-50	65
15B	Red Brake Warning Lamp Input Test	25-50	66
16A	RF Wheel Speed Sensor Continuity Fault	25-50	67
17A	Right Front Wheel Speed Sensor Fault	25-51	68
18A	RR Wheel Speed Sensor Continuity Fault	25-51	69
19A	Right Rear Wheel Speed Sensor Fault	25-52	70
20A	Solenoid Undervoltage Fault	25-52	71
20B	Solenoid Undervoltage Fault	25-53	72
20C	Solenoid Undervoltage Fault	25-54	73
20D	Solenoid Undervoltage Fault	25-54	74
21A	System Relay Fault	25-54	75
21B	System Relay Fault	25-55	76
VER-1A	System Verification	25-55	77

TYPE 2-BENDIX ANTI-LOCK 6 BRAKING SYSTEM

Read faults.   If there are no fault messages present, perform TEST 19A.

In some instances the cause of one fault message may trigger the setting of an additional fault message. If multiple fault messages appear on the DRBII when reading faults, <u>fault repairs must be performed</u> in the order in which they are displayed in the chart below. If only one fault has occurred, perform the indicated test for that fault message.

NOTE: If a fault has occurred more than 2 key cycles ago, perform the Verification Test procedure (TEST 20A) before any attempt is made to diagnose that particular fault message.

CAB FAULT	PERFORM TEST 2A
MODULATOR FAULT	PERFORM TEST 3A
SOLENOID UNDERVOLTAGE FAULT	PERFORM TEST 4A
SYSTEM RELAY FAULT	PERFORM TEST 5A
PUMP/MOTOR FAULT	PERFORM TEST 6A
ANTILOCK LAMP FAULT	PERFORM TEST 7A
ANTILOCK LAMP RELAY FAULT	PERFORM TEST 8A
RR WHEEL SPEED SENS CONTINUITY FAULT	PERFORM TEST 9A
LR WHEEL SPEED SENS CONTINUITY FAULT	PERFORM TEST 10A
RF WHEEL SPEED SENS CONTINUITY FAULT	PERFORM TEST 11A
LF WHEEL SPEED SENS CONTINUITY FAULT	PERFORM TEST 12A
RIGHT REAR WHEEL SPEED SENSOR FAULT	PERFORM TEST 13A
LEFT REAR WHEEL SPEED SENSOR FAULT	PERFORM TEST 14A
RIGHT FRONT WHEEL SPEED SENSOR FAULT	PERFORM TEST 15A
LEFT FRONT WHEEL SPEED SENSOR FAULT	PERFORM TEST 16A
EXCESS DECAY FAULT	PERFORM TEST 17A

CR4029100299000X

Fig. 4   Test 1A: Fault message interpretation. 1992

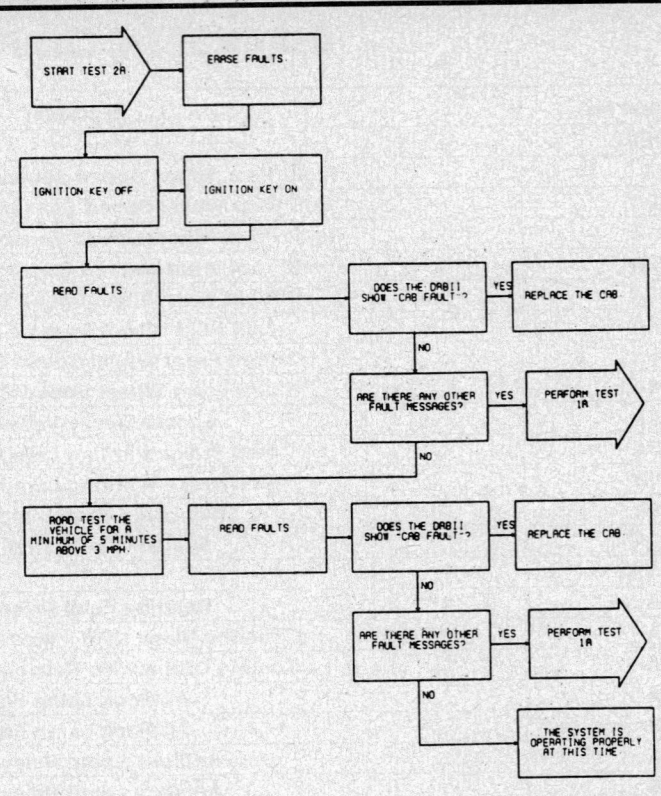

CR4029100300000X

Fig. 5   Test 2A: CAB Fault. 1992

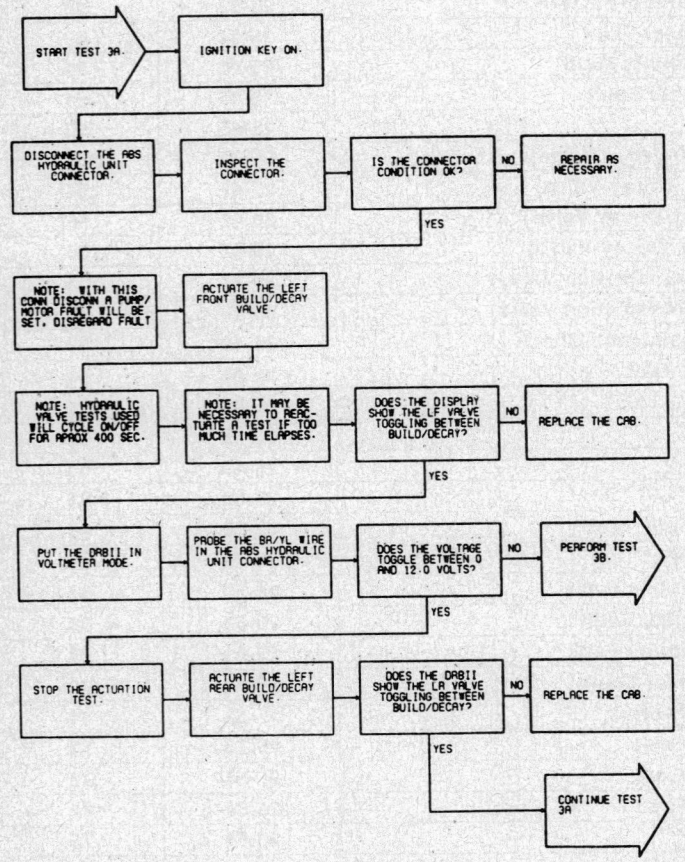

CR4029100301010X

Fig. 6   Test 3A: Modulator Fault (Part 1 of 3). 1992

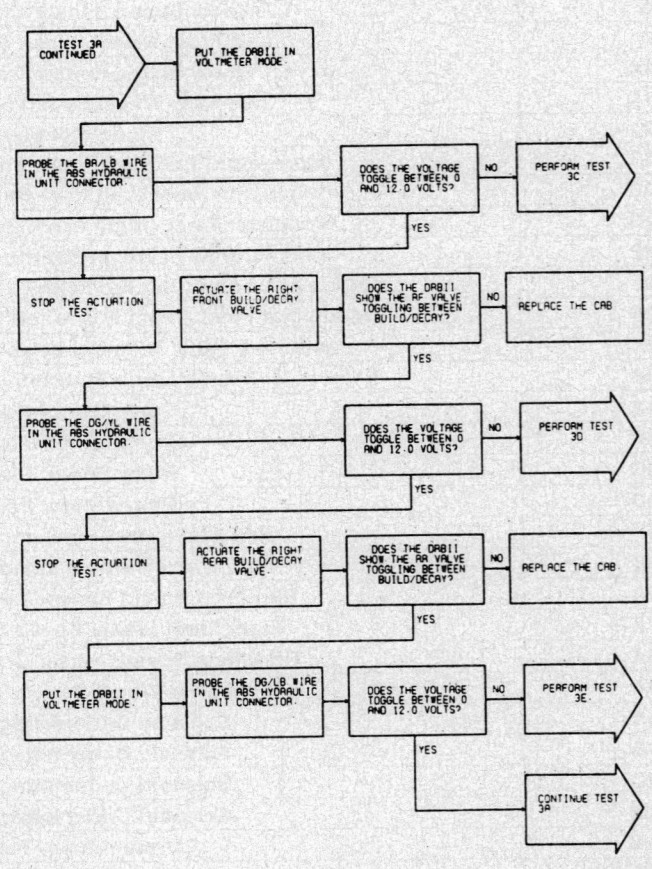

CR4029100301020X

Fig. 6   Test 3A: Modulator Fault (Part 2 of 3). 1992

CR4029100301030X

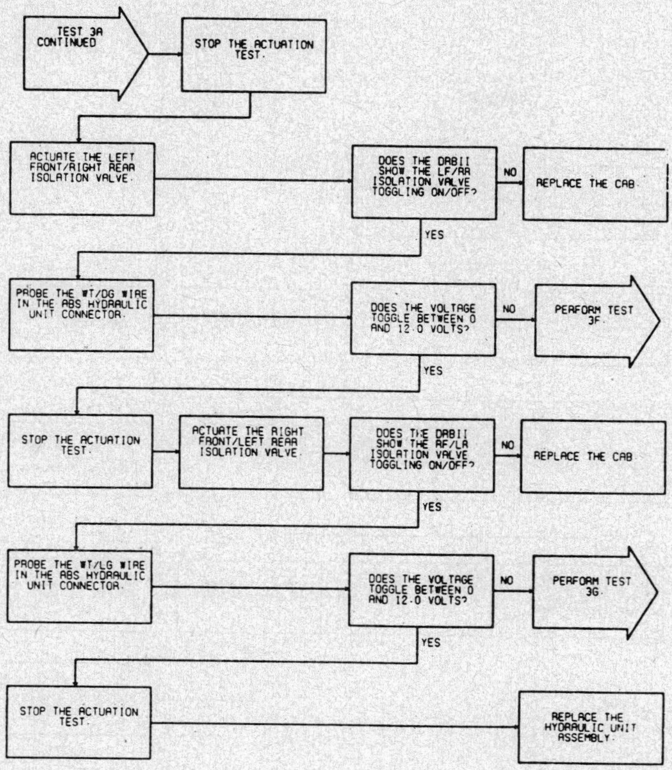

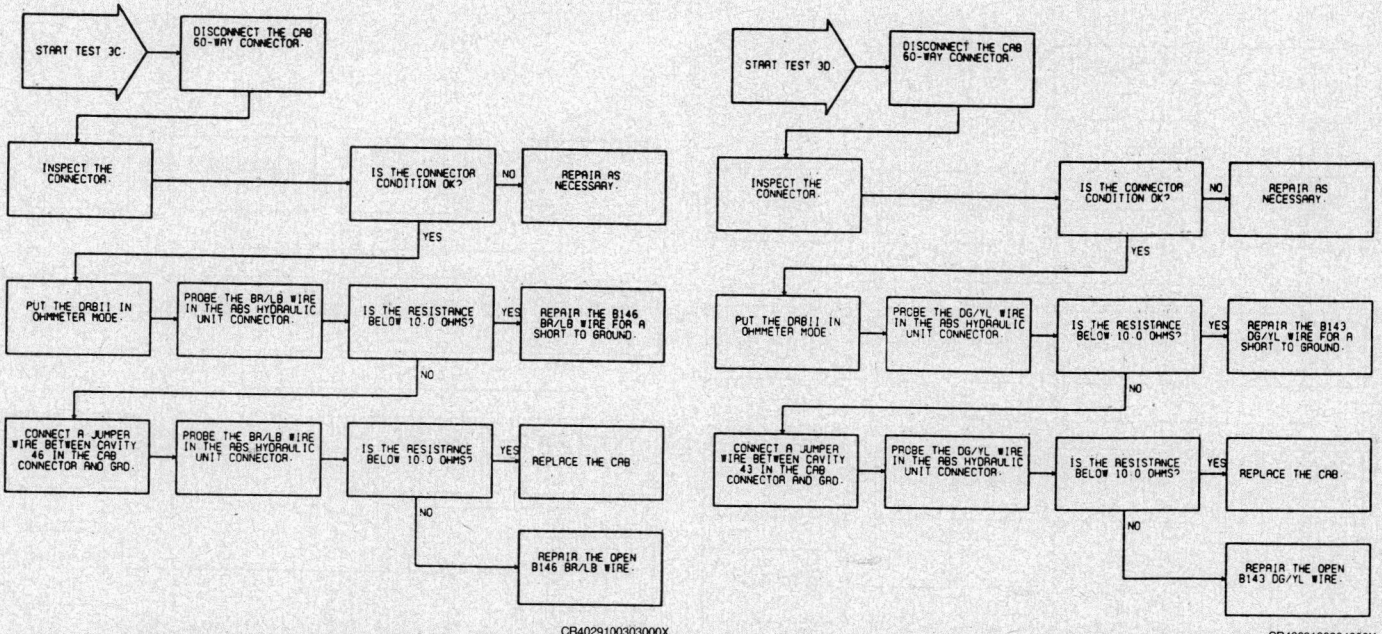

Fig. 6 Test 3A: Modulator Fault (Part 3 of 3). 1992

CR4029100302000X

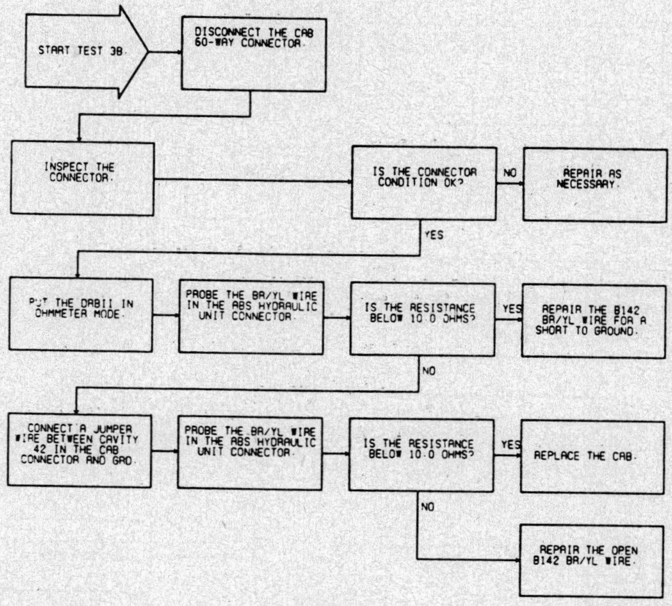

Fig. 7 Test 3B: Modulator Fault, Left Front Build/Decay Valve. 1992

CR4029100303000X

Fig. 8 Test 3C: Modulator Fault, Left Rear Build/Decay Valve. 1992

CR4029100304000X

Fig. 9 Test 3D: Modulator Fault, Right Front Build/Decay Valve. 1992

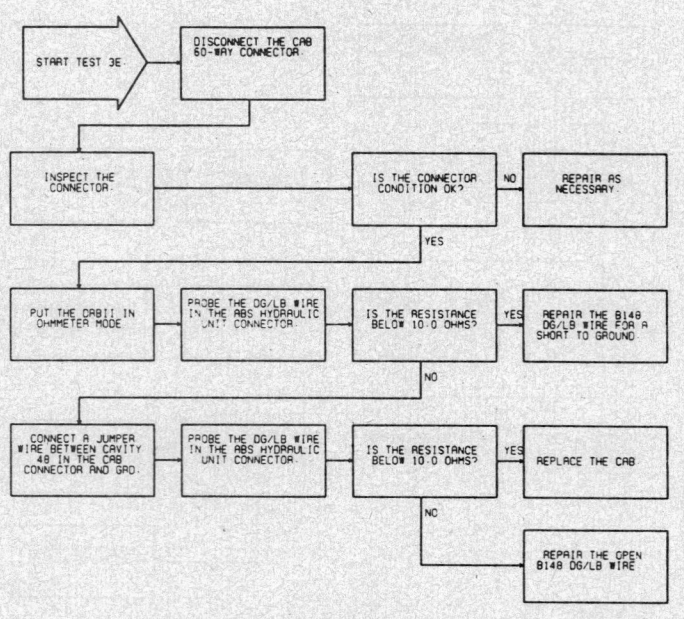

Fig. 10   Test 3E: Modulator Fault, Right Rear Build/Decay Valve. 1992

CR4029100305000X

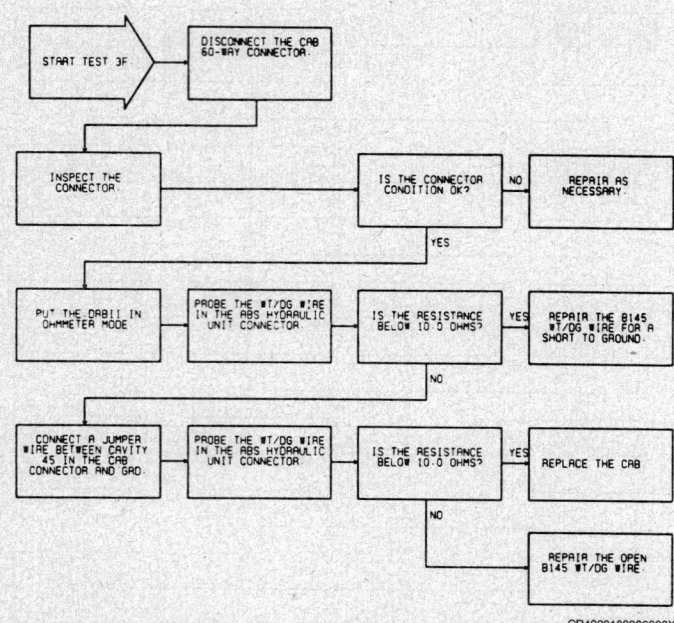

Fig. 11   Test 3F: Modulator Fault, Left Front/Right Rear Isolation Valve. 1992

CR4029100306000X

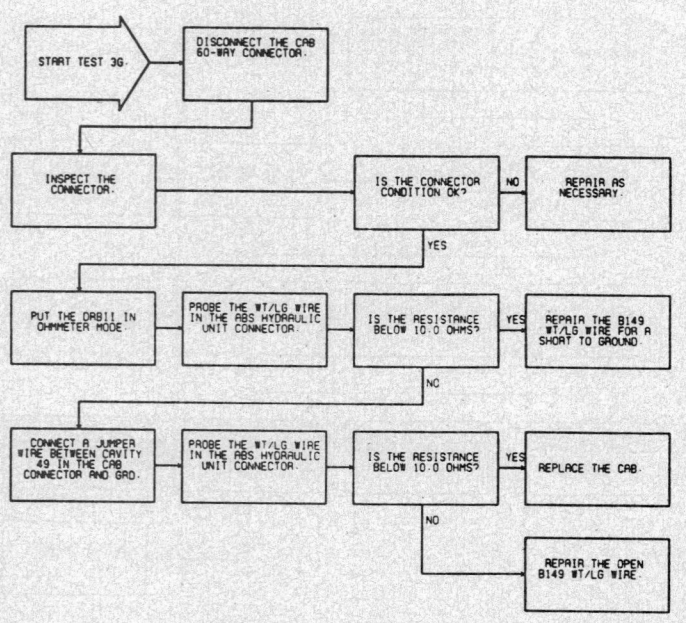

Fig. 12   Test 3G: Modulator Fault, Right Front/Left Rear Isolation Valve. 1992

CR4029100307000X

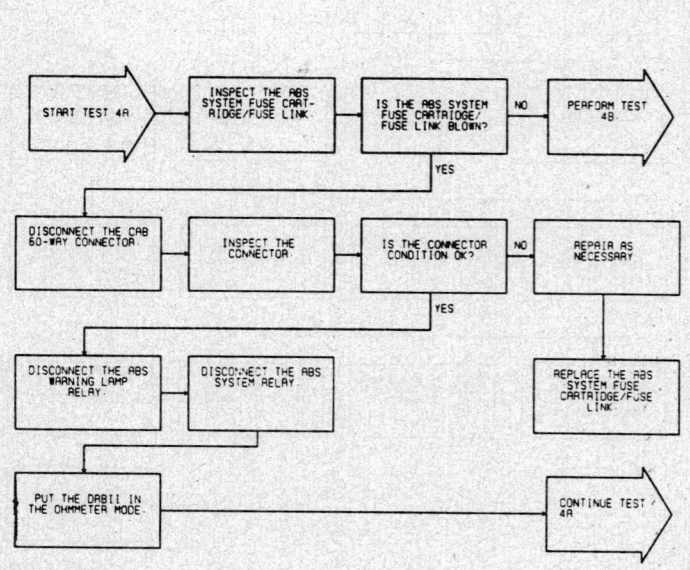

Fig. 13   Test 4A: Solenoid Under Voltage Fault (Part 1 of 2). 1992

CR4029100308010X

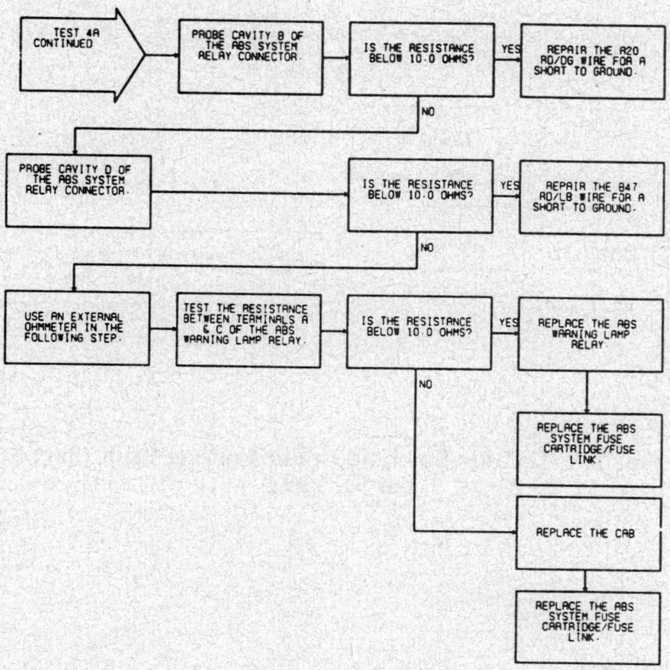

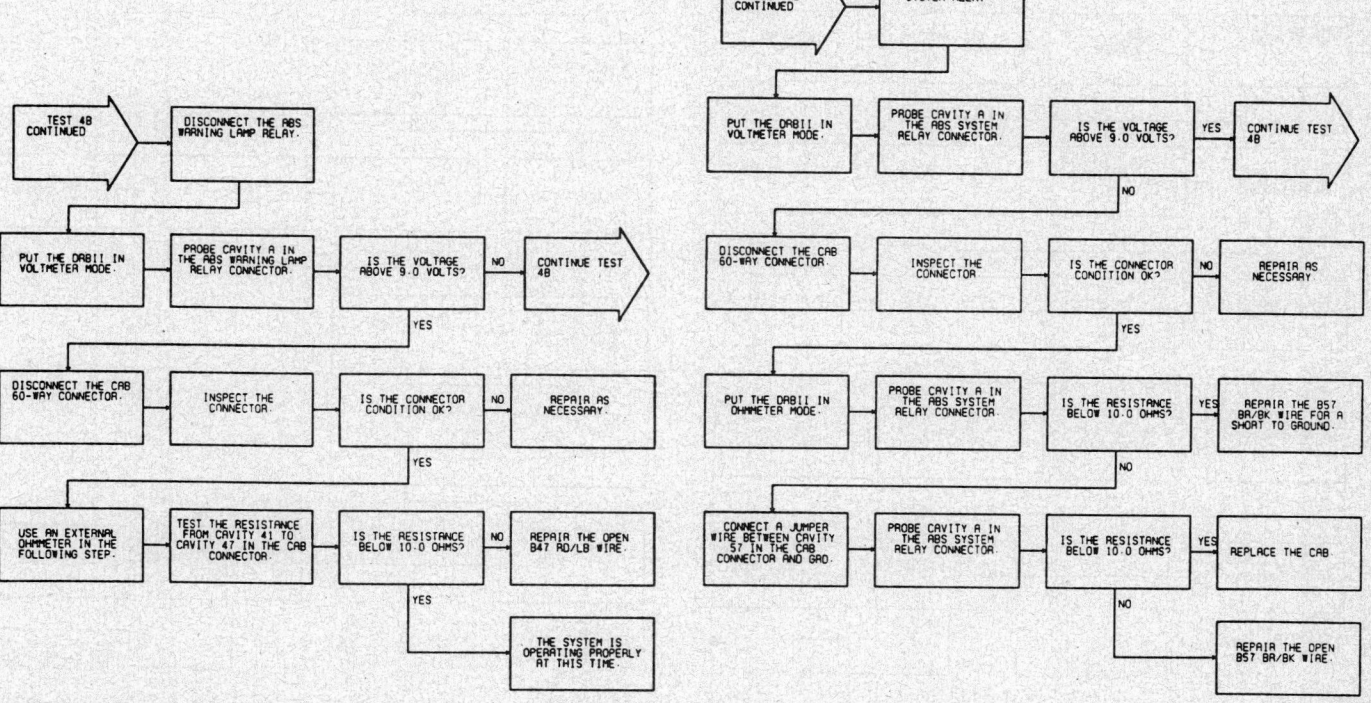

Fig. 13 Test 4A: Solenoid Under Voltage Fault (Part 2 of 2). 1992

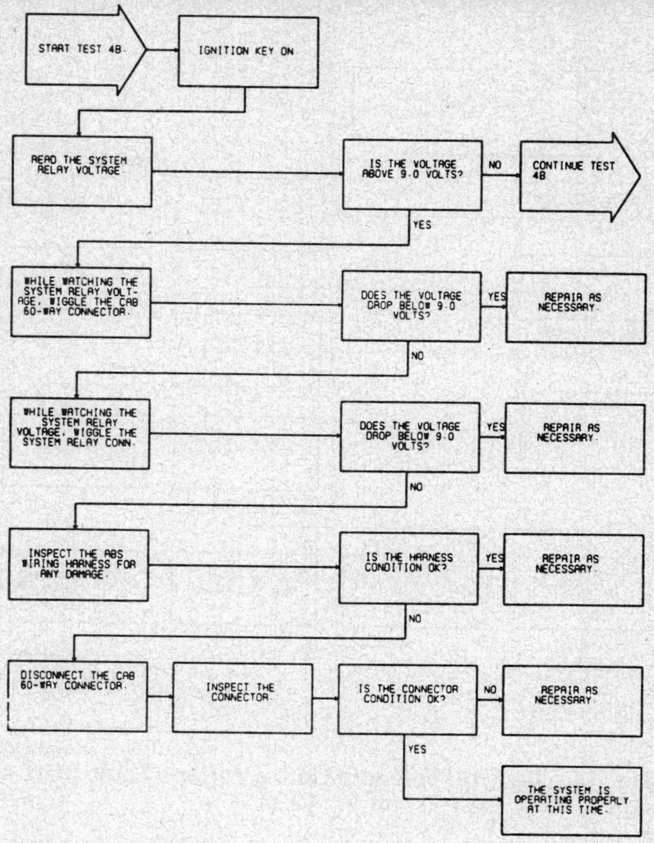

CR4029100308020X

Fig. 14 Test 4B: Solenoid Under Voltage Fault (Part 1 of 5). 1992

CR4029100309010X

Fig. 14 Test 4B: Solenoid Under Voltage Fault (Part 2 of 5). 1992

CR4029100309020X

Fig. 14 Test 4B: Solenoid Under Voltage Fault (Part 3 of 5). 1992

CR4029100309030X

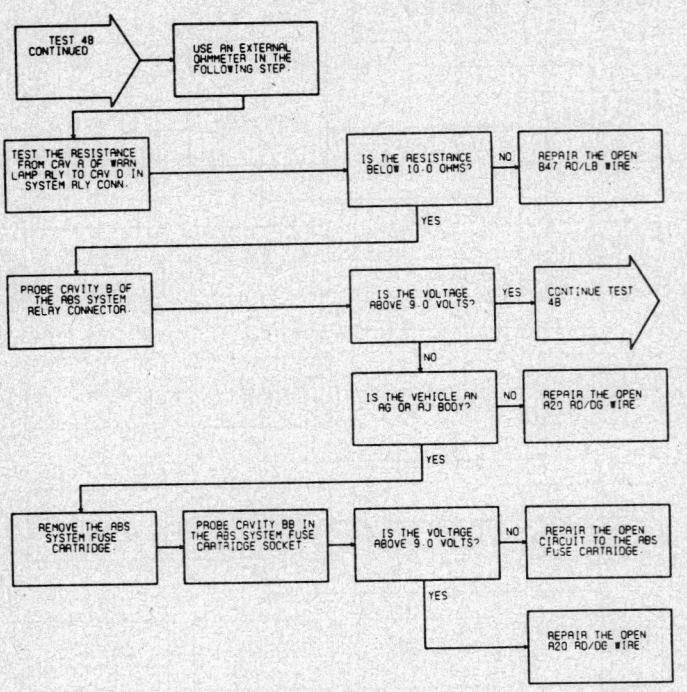

Fig. 14   Test 4B: Solenoid Under Voltage Fault (Part 4 of 5). 1992

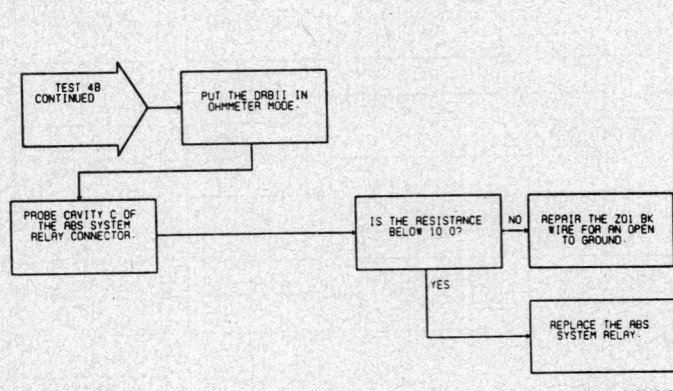

Fig. 14   Test 4B: Solenoid Under Voltage Fault (Part 5 of 5). 1992

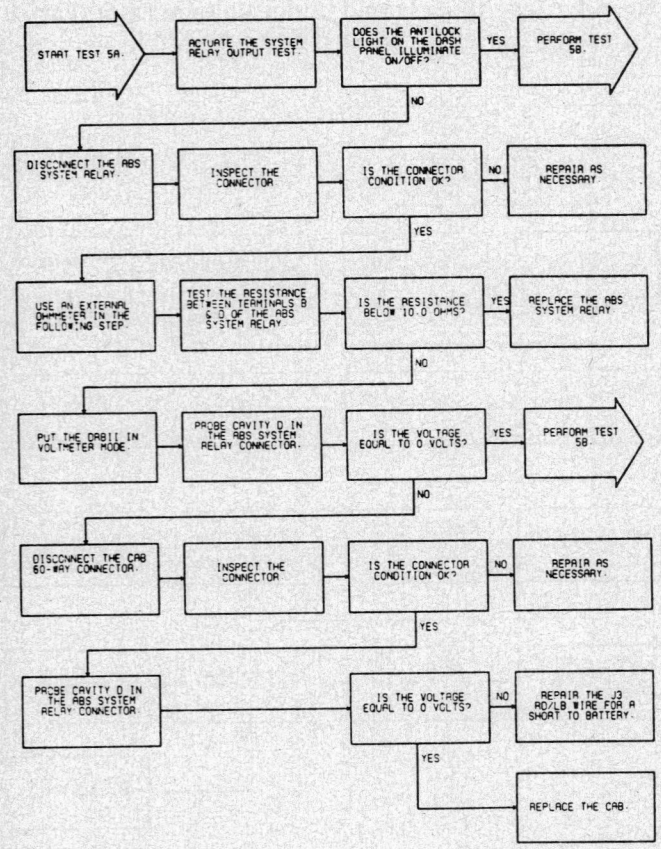

Fig. 15   Test 5A: System Relay Fault. 1992

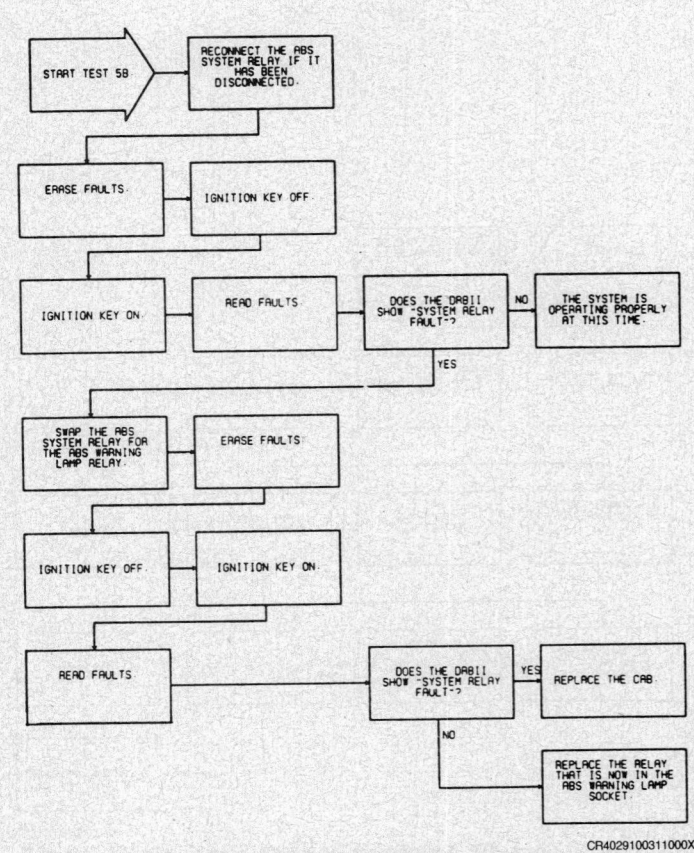

Fig. 16   Test 5B: System Relay Fault. 1992

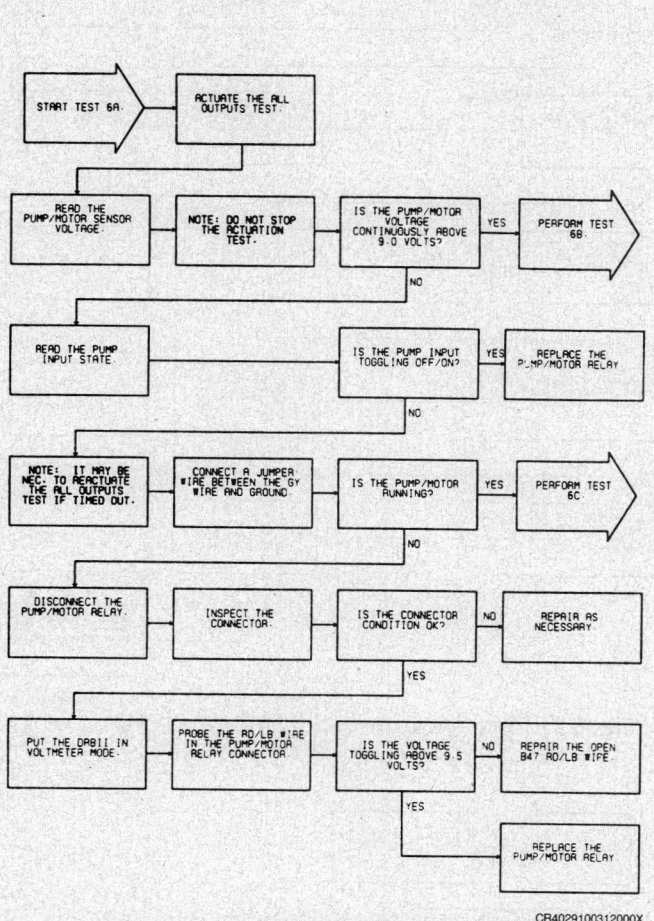

Fig. 17   Test 6A: Pump/Motor Fault. 1992

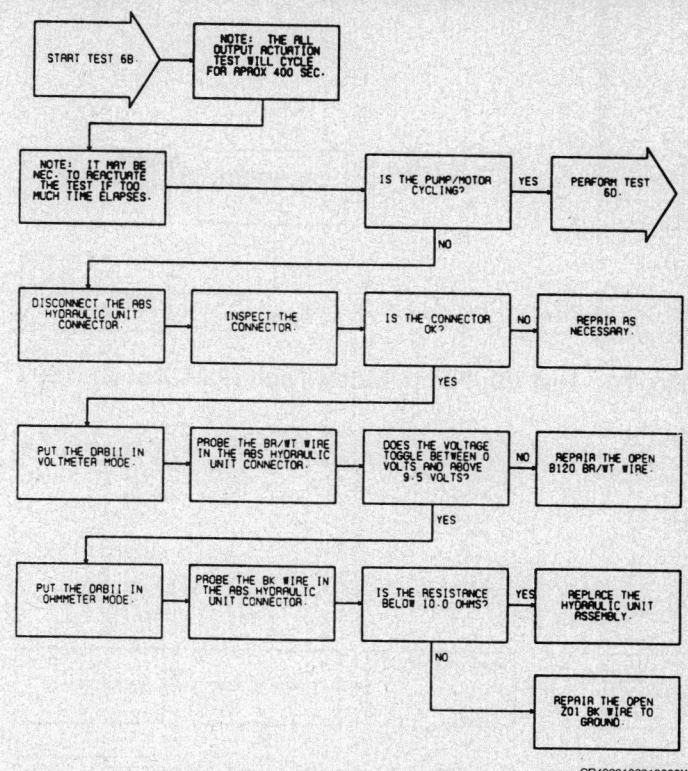

Fig. 18   Test 6B: Pump/Motor Fault. 1992

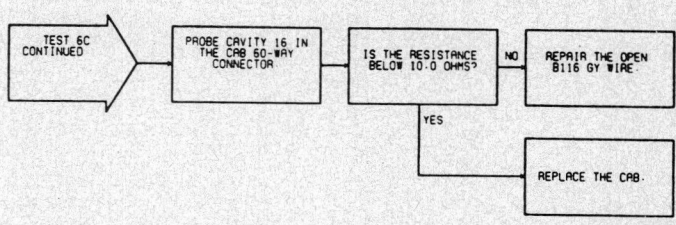

Fig. 19   Test 6C: Pump/Motor Fault (Part 2 of 2). 1992

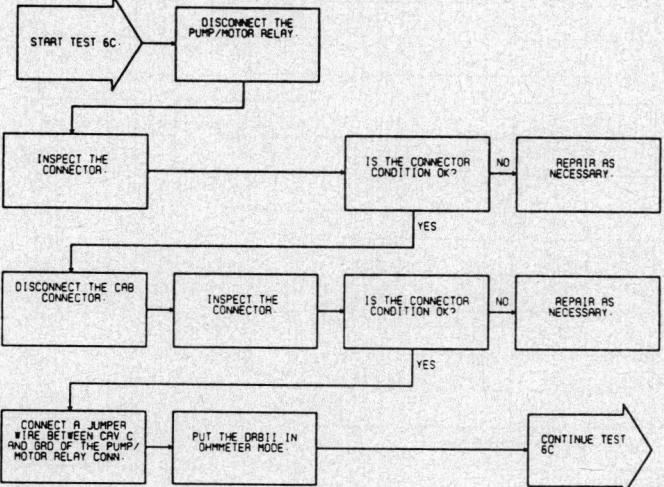

Fig. 19   Test 6C: Pump/Motor Fault (Part 1 of 2). 1992

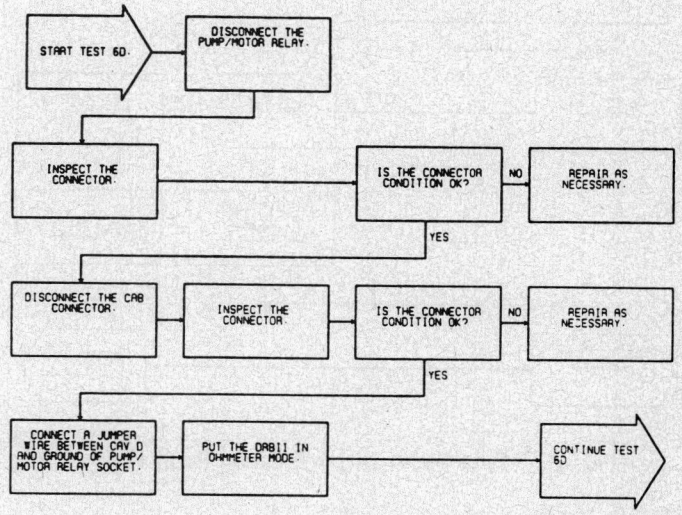

Fig. 20   Test 6D: Pump/Motor Fault (Part 1 of 2). 1992

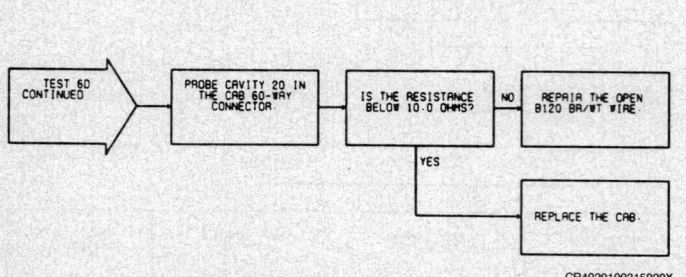

Fig. 20   Test 6D: Pump/Motor Fault (Part 2 of 2). 1992

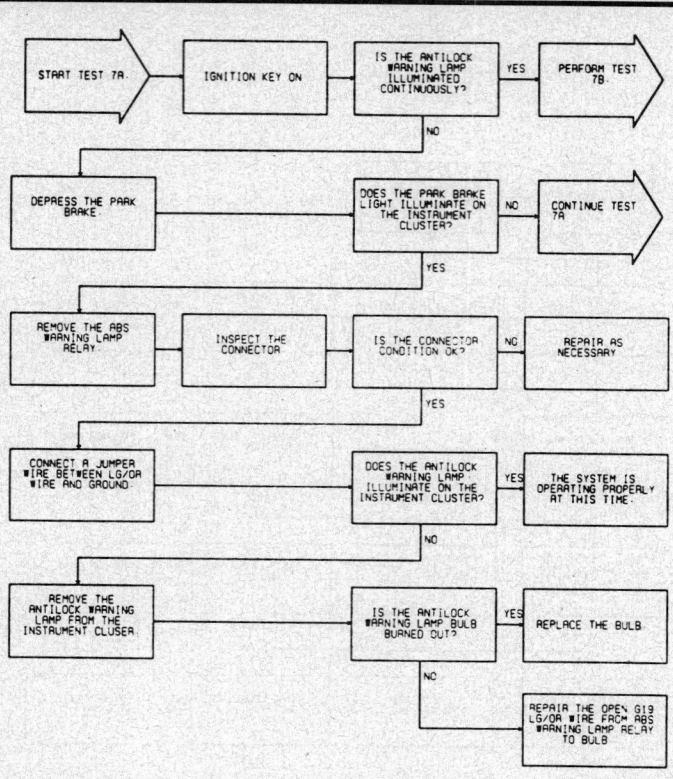

Fig. 21   Test 7A: Anti-Lock Lamp Fault (Part 1 of 2). 1992

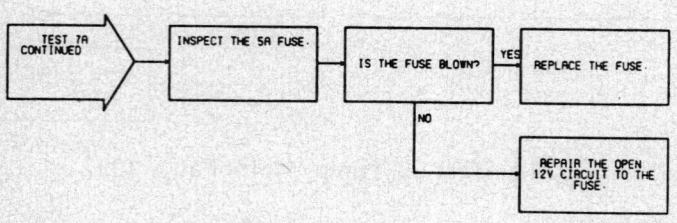

Fig. 21   Test 7A: Anti-Lock Lamp Fault (Part 2 of 2). 1992

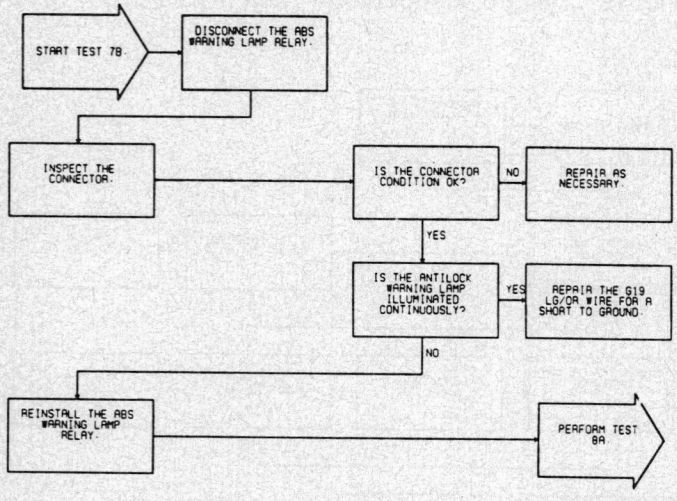

Fig. 22   Test 7B: Anti-Lock Lamp Fault. 1992

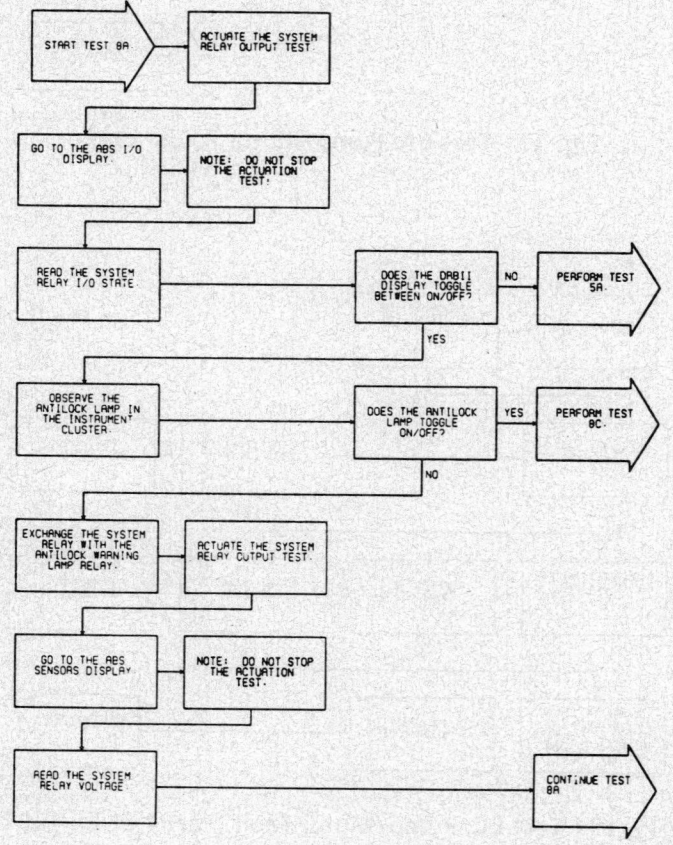

Fig. 23   Test 8A: Anti-Lock Lamp Relay Fault (Part 1 of 2). 1992

TYPE 2-BENDIX ANTI-LOCK 6 BRAKING SYSTEM

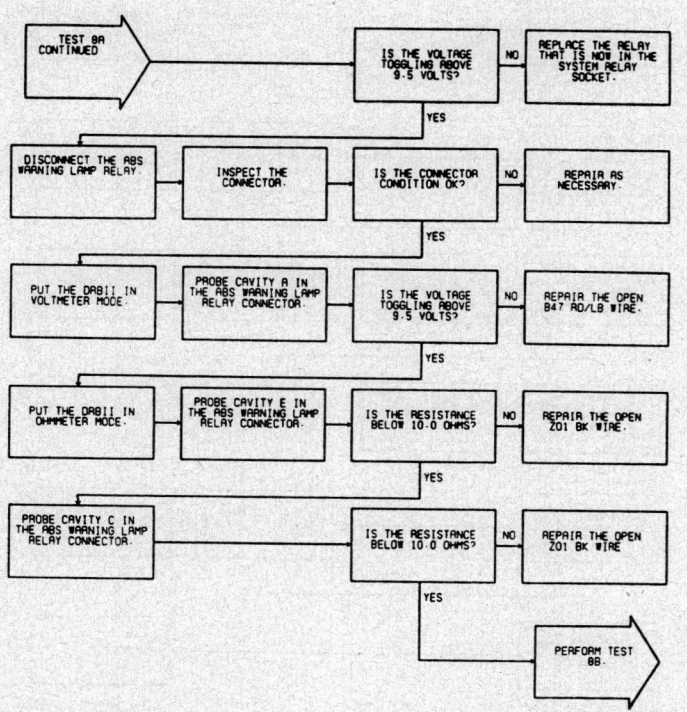

Fig. 23   Test 8A: Anti-Lock Lamp Relay Fault (Part 2 of 2). 1992

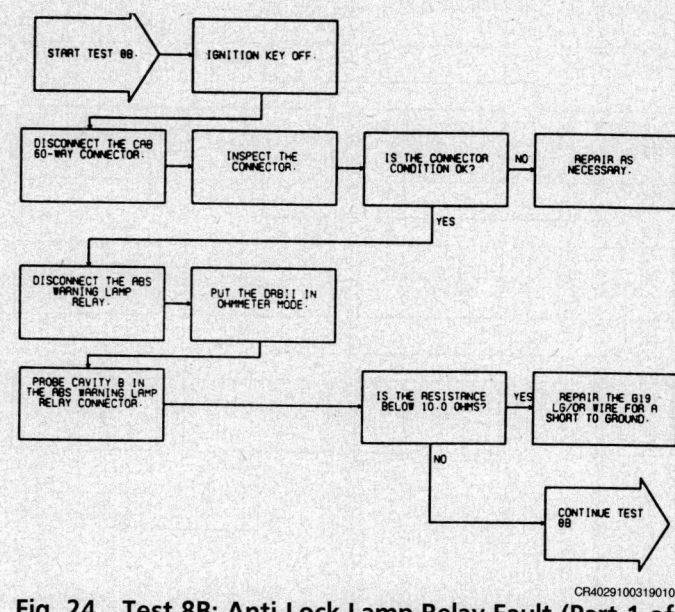

Fig. 24   Test 8B: Anti-Lock Lamp Relay Fault (Part 1 of 2). 1992

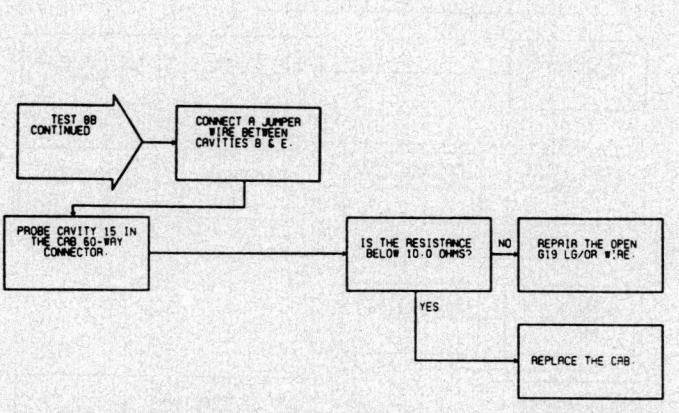

Fig. 24   Test 8B: Anti-Lock Lamp Relay Fault (Part 2 of 2). 1992

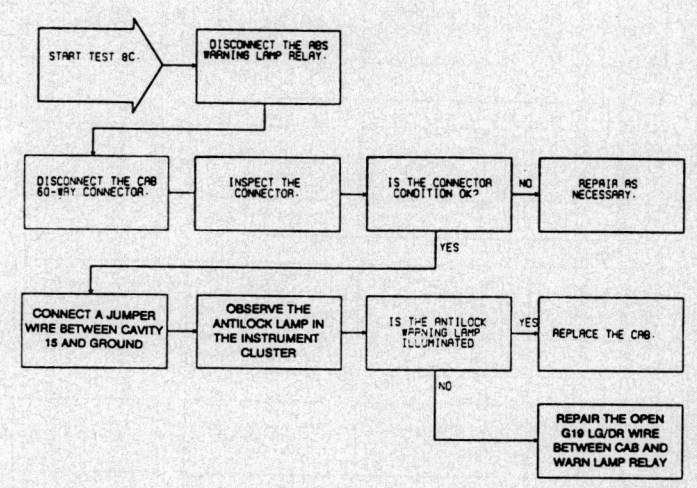

Fig. 25   Test 8C: Anti-Lock Lamp Relay Fault. 1992

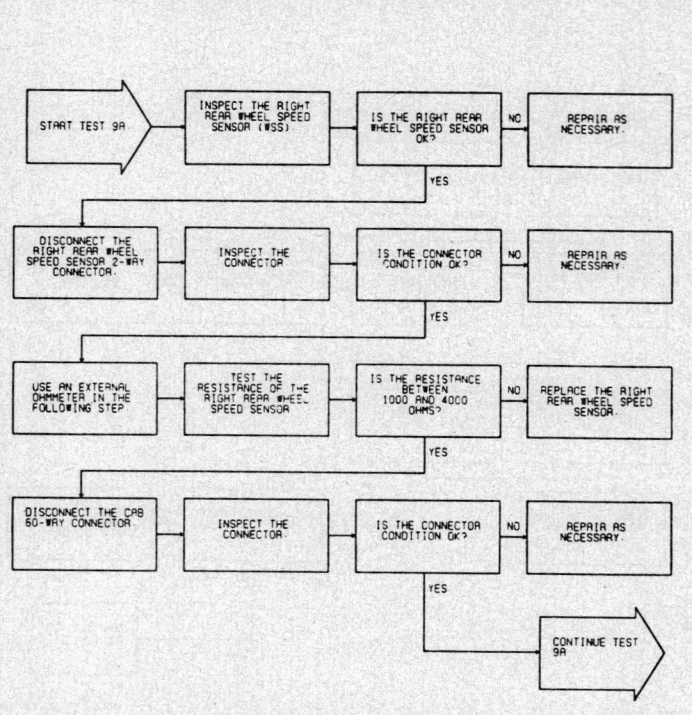

Fig. 26 Test 9A: Right Rear Wheel Speed Sensor Continuity Fault (Part 1 of 2). 1992

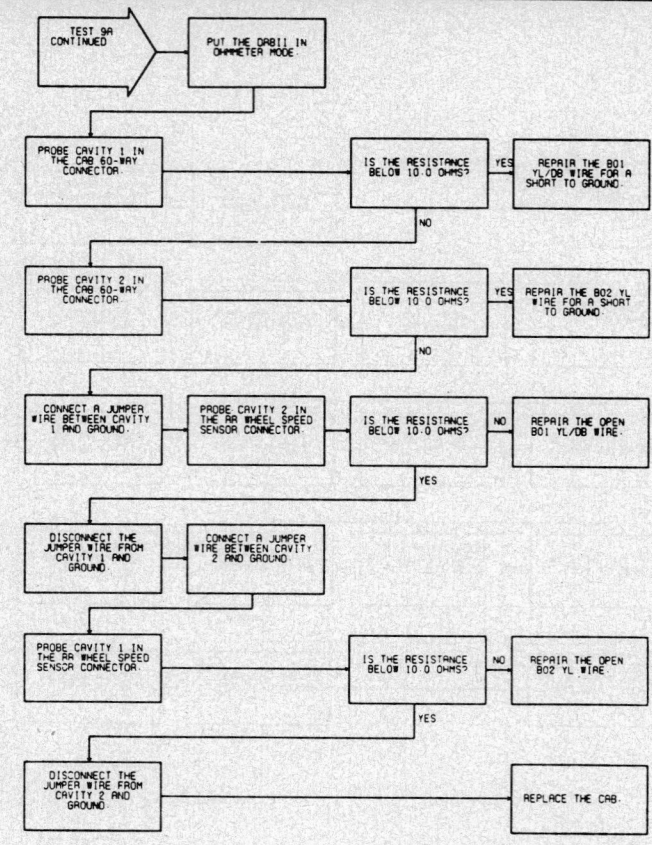

Fig. 26 Test 9A: Right Rear Wheel Speed Sensor Continuity Fault (Part 2 of 2). 1992

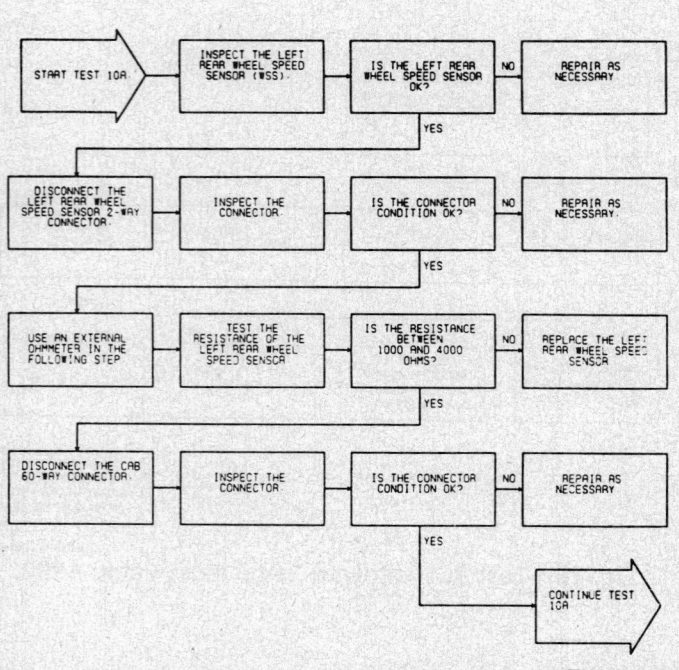

Fig. 27 Test 10A: Left Rear Wheel Speed Sensor Continuity Fault (Part 1 of 2). 1992

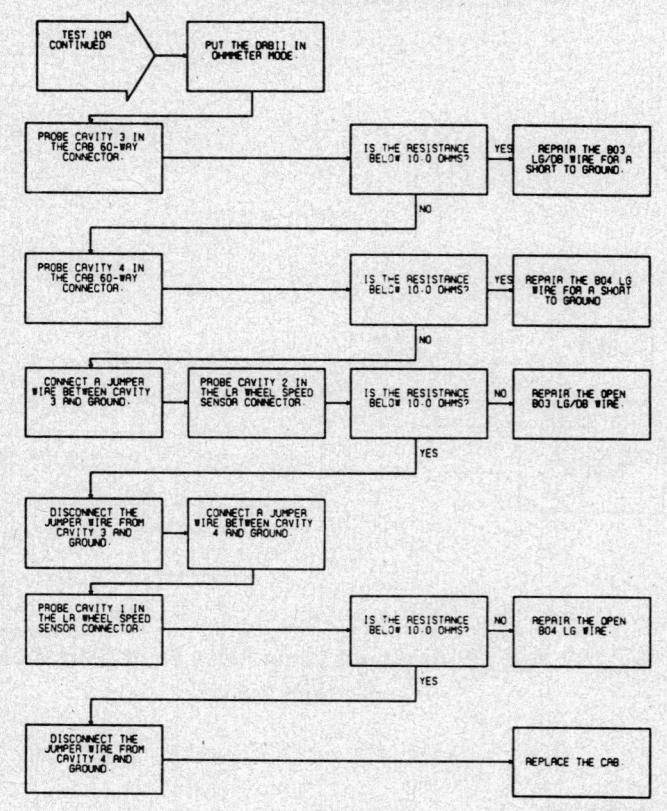

Fig. 27 Test 10A: Left Rear Wheel Speed Sensor Continuity Fault (Part 2 of 2). 1992

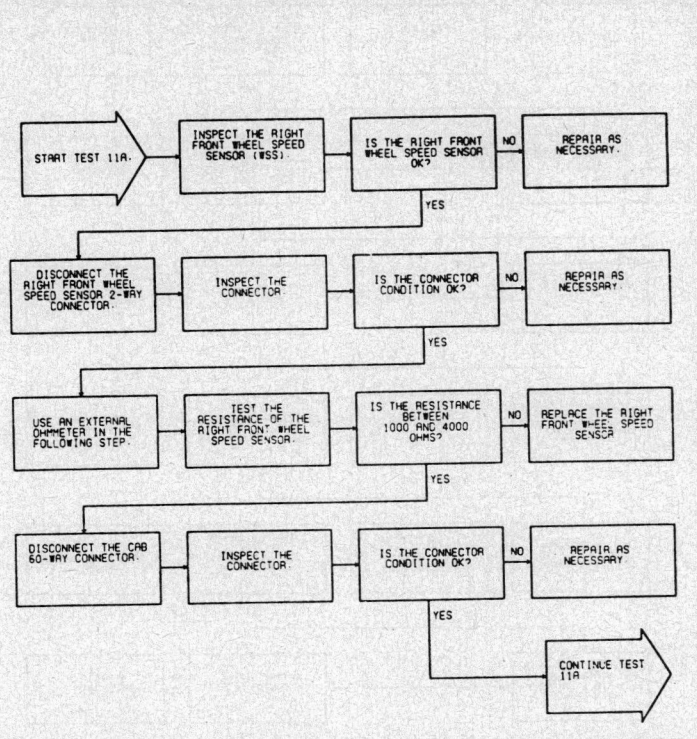

CR4029100323010X

Fig. 28 Test 11A: Right Front Wheel Speed Sensor Continuity Fault (Part 1 of 2). 1992

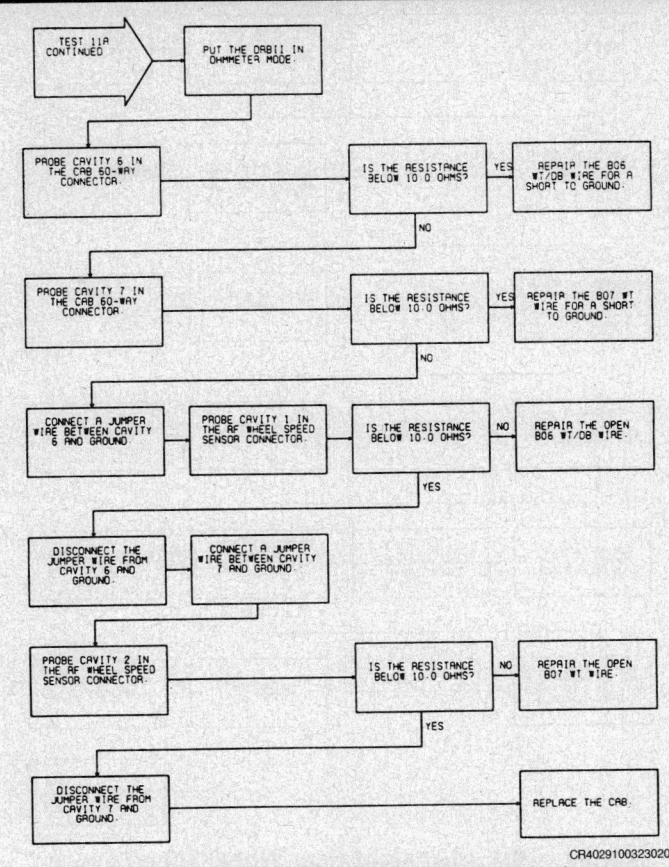

CR4029100323020X

Fig. 28 Test 11A: Right Front Wheel Speed Sensor Continuity Fault (Part 2 of 2). 1992

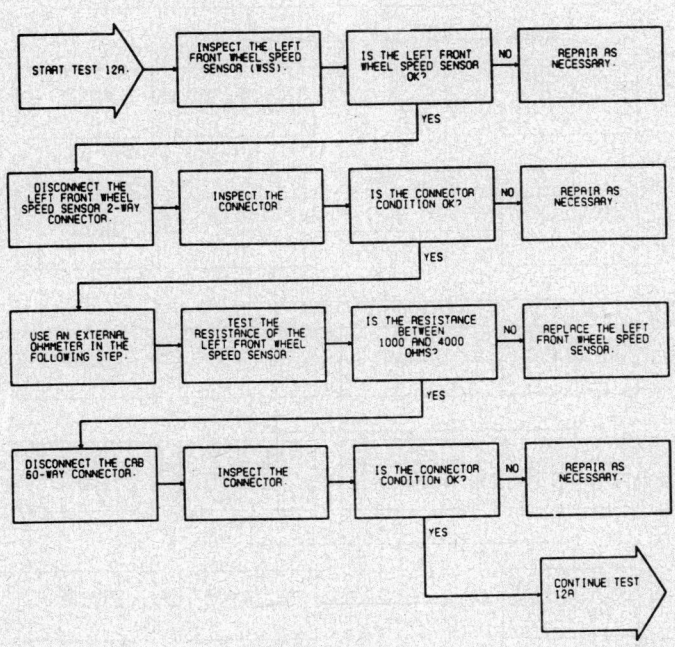

CR4029100324010X

Fig. 29 Test 12A: Left Front Wheel Speed Sensor Continuity Fault (Part 1 of 2). 1992

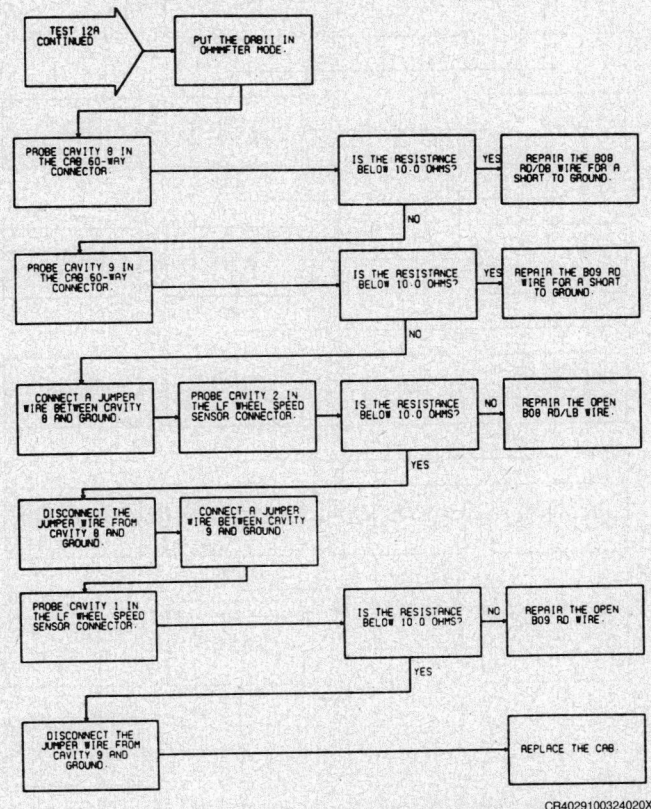

CR4029100324020X

Fig. 29 Test 12A: Left Front Wheel Speed Sensor Continuity Fault (Part 2 of 2). 1992

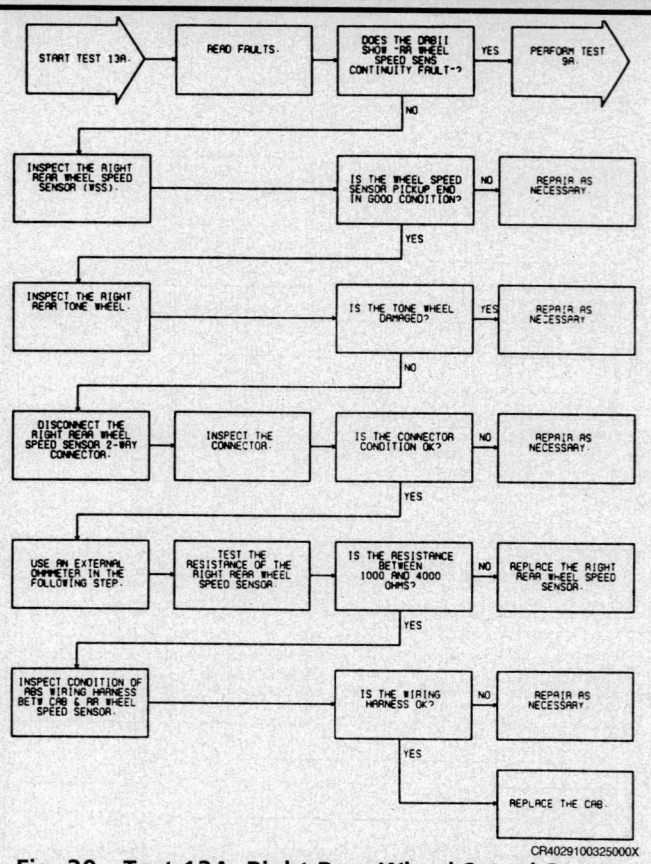

Fig. 30 Test 13A: Right Rear Wheel Speed Sensor Fault. 1992

CR4029100325000X

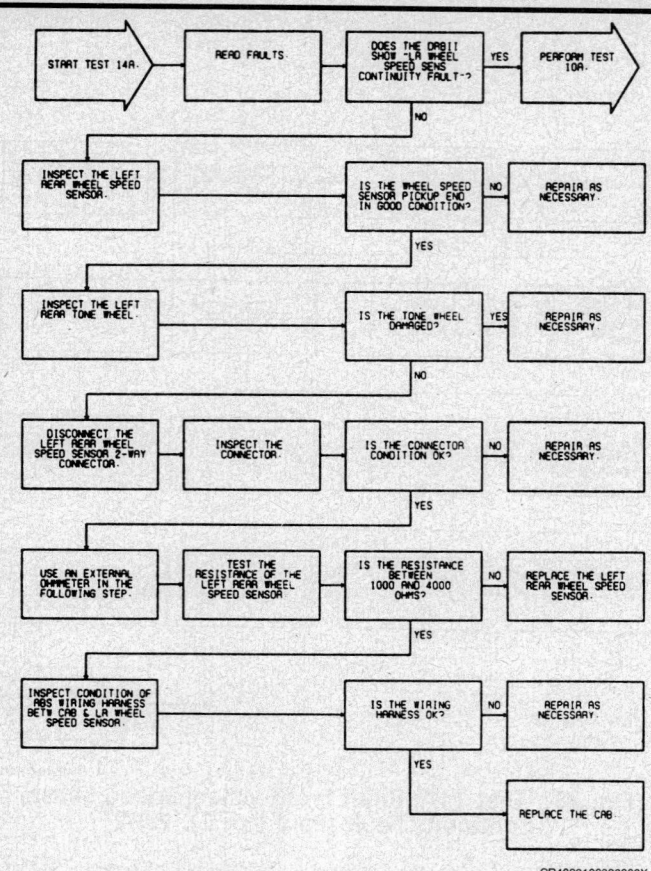

Fig. 31 Test 14A: Left Rear Wheel Speed Sensor Fault. 1992

CR4029100326000X

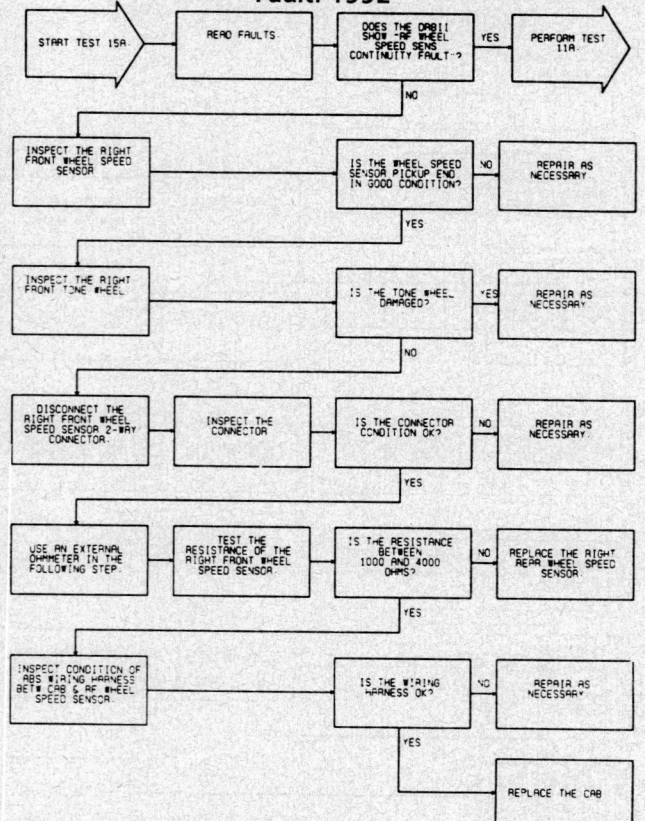

Fig. 32 Test 15A: Right Front Wheel Speed Sensor Fault. 1992

CR4029100327000X

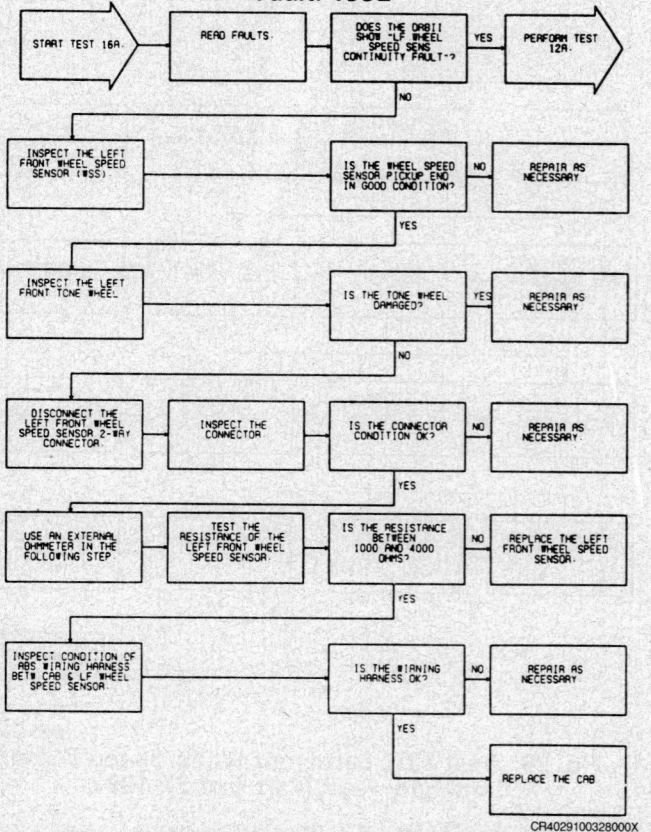

Fig. 33 Test 16A: Left Front Wheel Speed Sensor Fault. 1992

CR4029100328000X

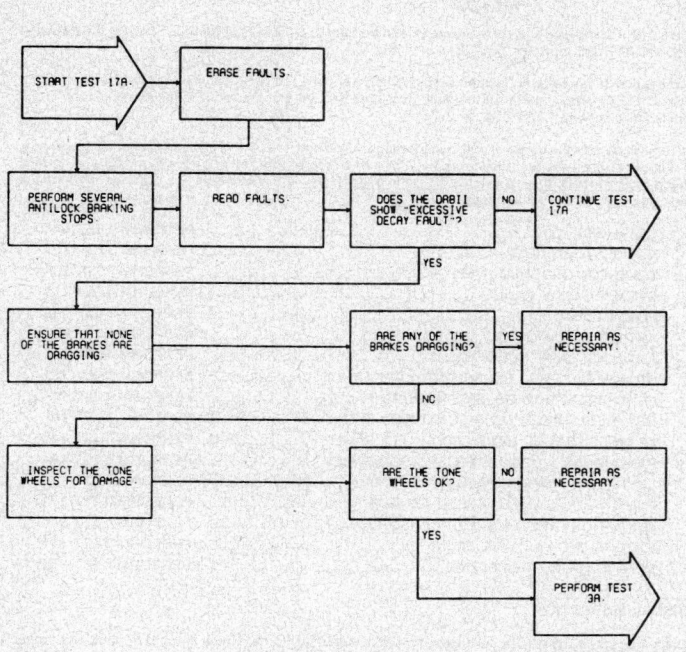

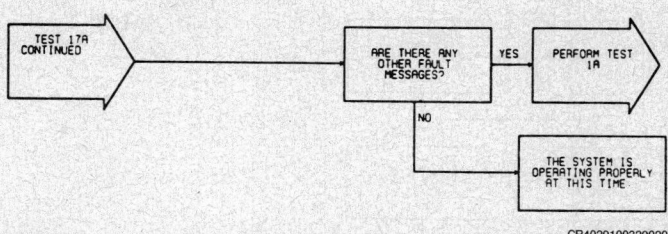

Fig. 34   Test 17A: Excess Decay Valve Fault (Part 2 of 2). 1992

Fig. 34   Test 17A: Excess Decay Valve Fault (Part 1 of 2). 1992

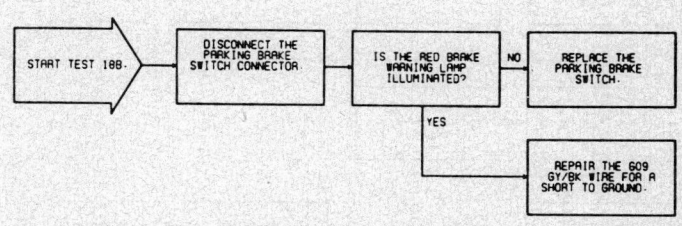

Fig. 36   Test 18B: Red Brake Warning Lamp Input Test. 1992

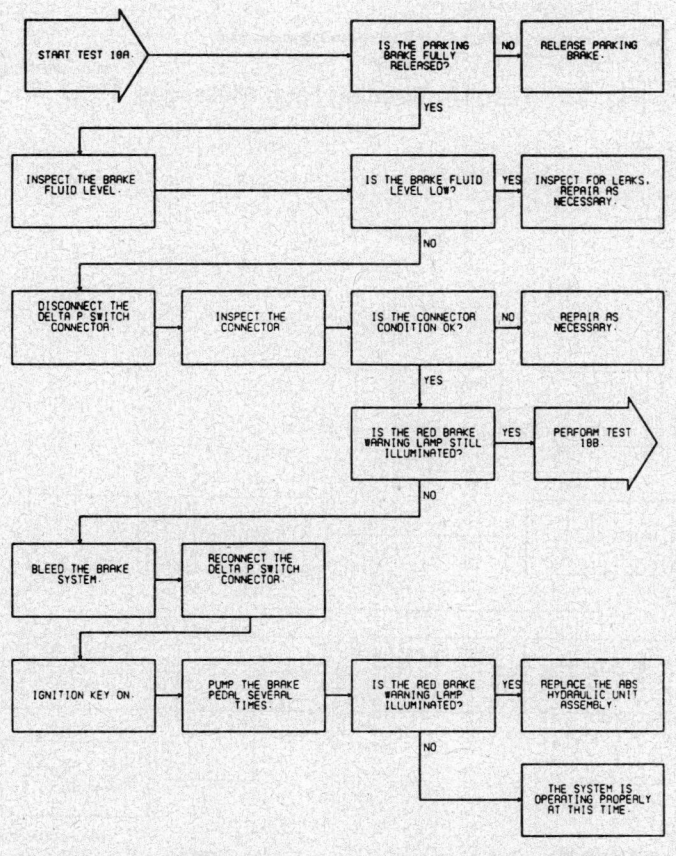

Fig. 35   Test 18A: Red Brake Warning Lamp Input Test. 1992

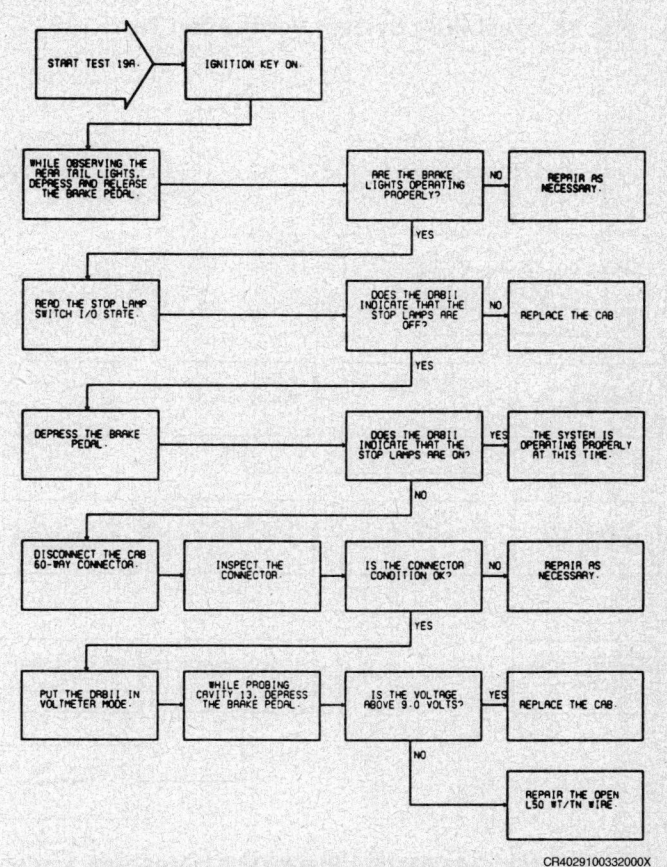

Fig. 37   Test 19A: Stop Lamp Switch Input Test. 1992

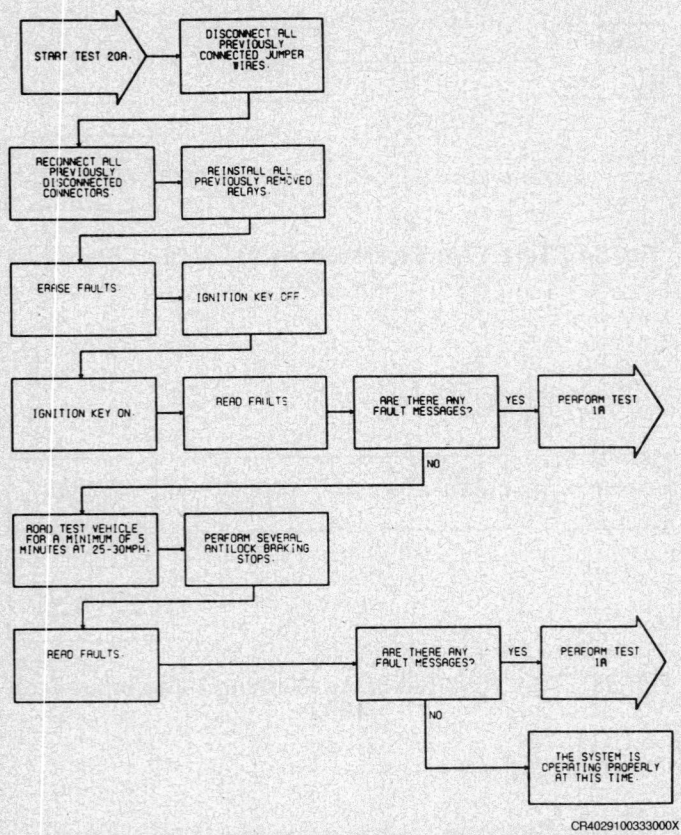

Fig. 38   Test 20A: System Verification Test. 1992

CR4029100333000X

If the DRBII is showing a blank message screen perform TEST 2A. If the DRBII is showing the message "NO RESPONSE" perform TEST 3A.

Read faults. If there are no fault messages present and the red "BRAKE" warning lamp is illuminated, perform TEST 15A. If there are no fault messages present and the red "PARK" warning lamp is not illuminated, perform TEST 13A.

In some instances the cause of one fault message may trigger the setting of an additional fault message. If multiple fault messages appear on the DRBII when reading faults, fault repairs must be performed in the order in which they are displayed in the chart below. If only one fault has occurred, perform the indicated test for that fault message.

CAB FAULT	PERFORM TEST 6A
MODULATOR FAULT	PERFORM TEST 12A
SOLENOID UNDERVOLTAGE FAULT	PERFORM TEST 20A
SYSTEM RELAY FAULT	PERFORM TEST 21A
PUMP/MOTOR FAULT	PERFORM TEST 14A
ANTILOCK LAMP FAULT	PERFORM TEST 4A
ANTILOCK LAMP RELAY FAULT	PERFORM TEST 5A
RR WHEEL SPEED SENS CONTINUITY FAULT	PERFORM TEST 18A
LR WHEEL SPEED SENS CONTINUITY FAULT	PERFORM TEST 10A
RF WHEEL SPEED SENS CONTINUITY FAULT	PERFORM TEST 16A
LF WHEEL SPEED SENS CONTINUITY FAULT	PERFORM TEST 8A
RIGHT REAR WHEEL SPEED SENSOR FAULT	PERFORM TEST 19A
LEFT REAR WHEEL SPEED SENSOR FAULT	PERFORM TEST 11A
RIGHT FRONT WHEEL SPEED SENSOR FAULT	PERFORM TEST 17A
LEFT FRONT WHEEL SPEED SENSOR FAULT	PERFORM TEST 9A
EXCESS DECAY VALVE FAULT	PERFORM TEST 7A
VERIFICATION PROCEDURE	PERFORM TEST VER-1A

VISUAL INSPECTION

Each time you disconnect a connector, inspect it thoroughly to determine that it is in good and proper condition. Focus on the circuit being checked. Each fault is created by an error in the respective circuit. Connectors and terminals can create these error messages.

>> Visually inspect the CAB, relay, wheel speed sensor and hyrdaulic unit connections for damage or disconnection.

>> Inspect both sides of the connector noting any corrosion, pin push-outs or spread cavities.

>> Ensure that the connector is properly wired by verifying the wire color in each cavity against the appropriate pinout illustration.

>> Clean, repair or replace the connector or harness as necessary.

CR4029300334000X

Fig. 39   Test 1A: Reading Fault Messages. 1993

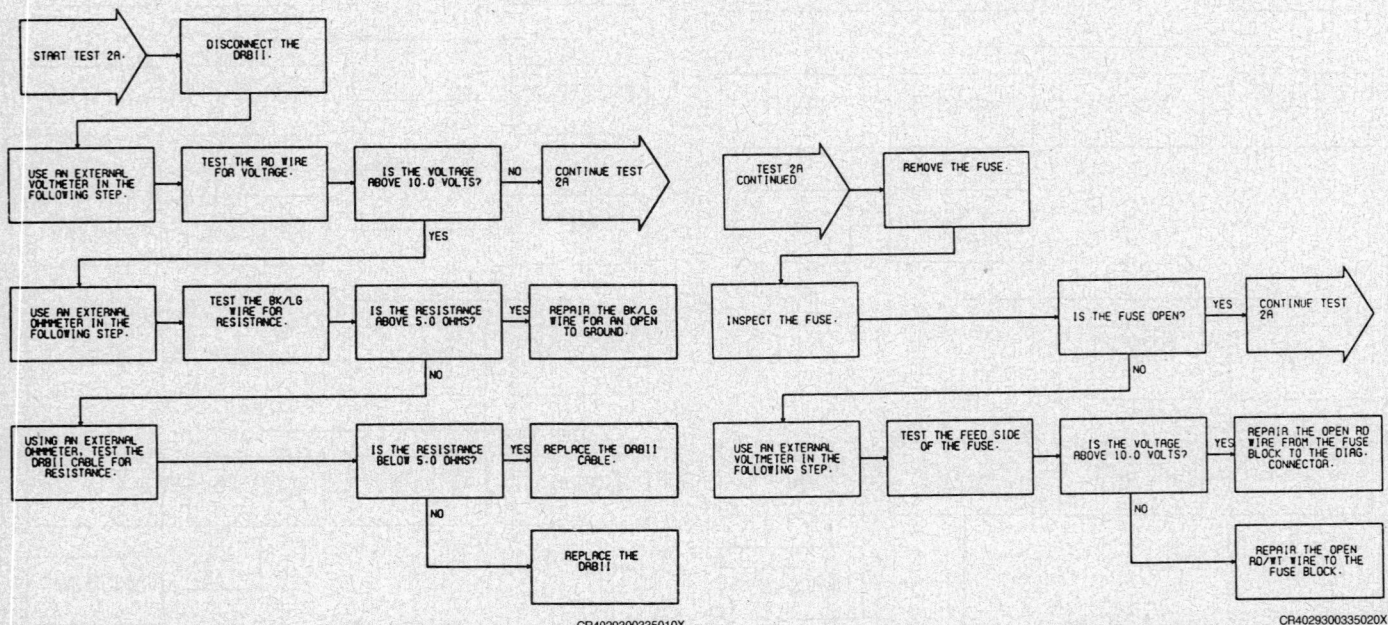

CR4029300335010X

Fig. 40   Test 2A: Testing Blank DRB II Message Screen (Part 1 of 3). 1993

CR4029300335020X

Fig. 40   Test 2A: Testing Blank DRB II Message Screen (Part 2 of 3). 1993

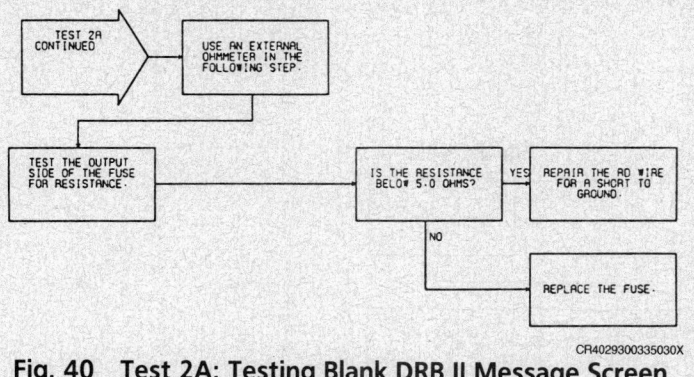

Fig. 40   Test 2A: Testing Blank DRB II Message Screen (Part 3 of 3). 1993

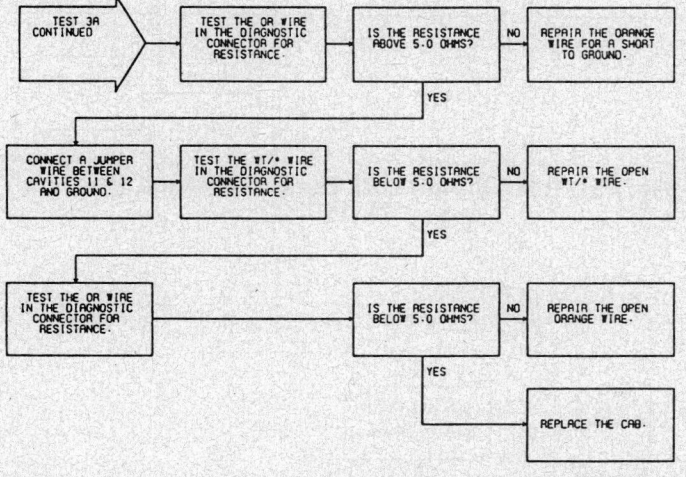

Fig. 41   Test 3A: Testing DRB II "No Response" Message (Part 2 of 2). 1993

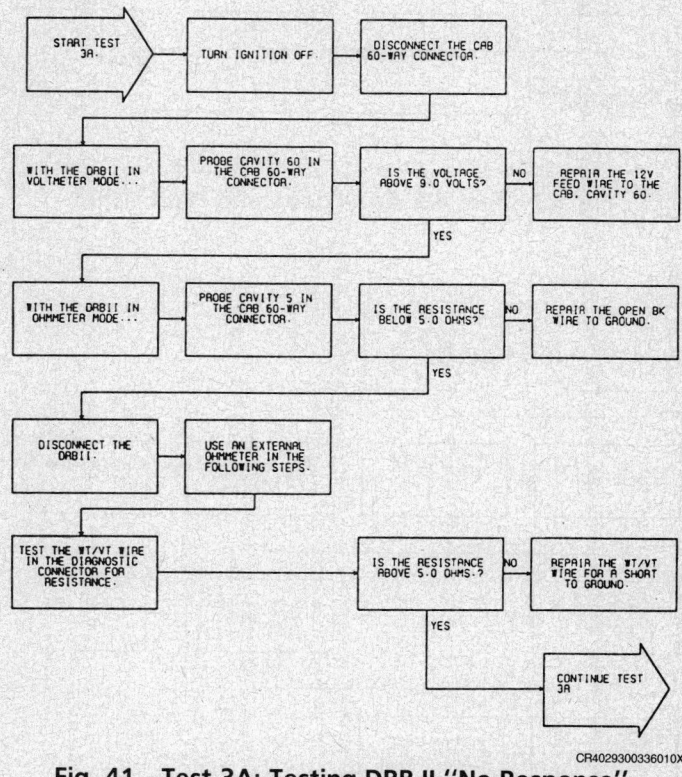

Fig. 41   Test 3A: Testing DRB II "No Response" Message (Part 1 of 2). 1993

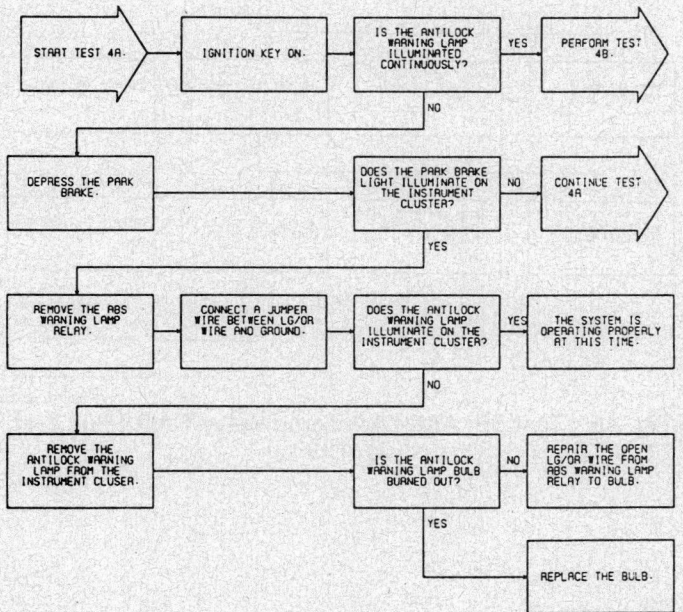

Fig. 42   Test 4A: Anti-Lock Lamp Fault (Part 1 of 2). 1993

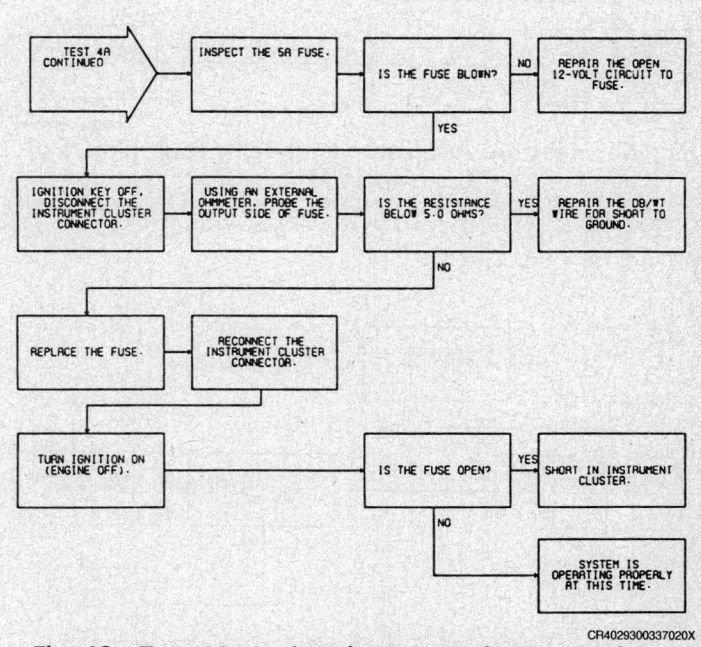

Fig. 42   Test 4A: Anti-Lock Lamp Fault (Part 2 of 2). 1993

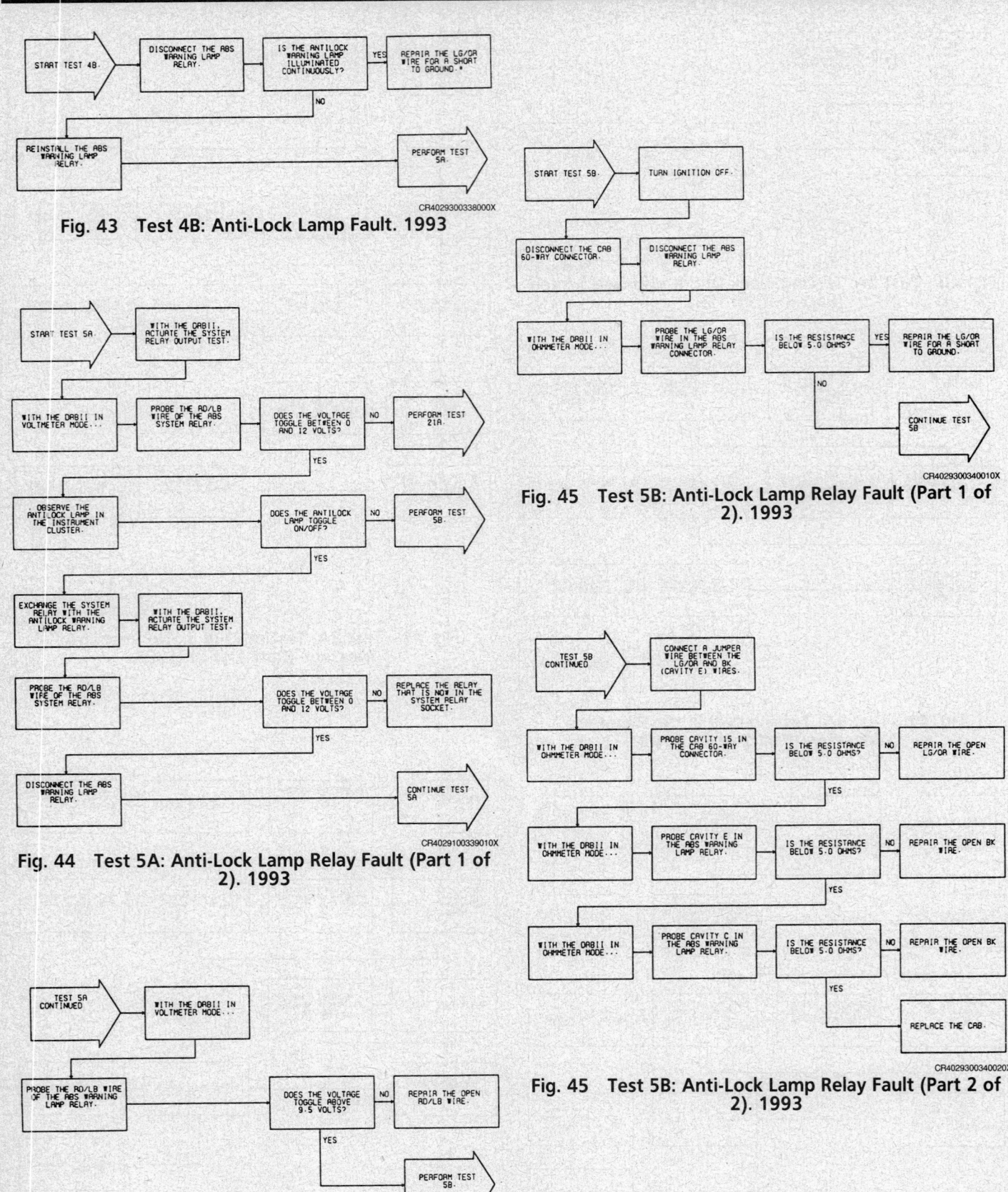

Fig. 43   Test 4B: Anti-Lock Lamp Fault. 1993

CR4029300338000X

Fig. 45   Test 5B: Anti-Lock Lamp Relay Fault (Part 1 of 2). 1993

CR4029300340010X

Fig. 44   Test 5A: Anti-Lock Lamp Relay Fault (Part 1 of 2). 1993

CR4029100339010X

Fig. 45   Test 5B: Anti-Lock Lamp Relay Fault (Part 2 of 2). 1993

CR4029300340020X

Fig. 44   Test 5A: Anti-Lock Lamp Relay Fault (Part 2 of 2). 1993

CR4029100339020X

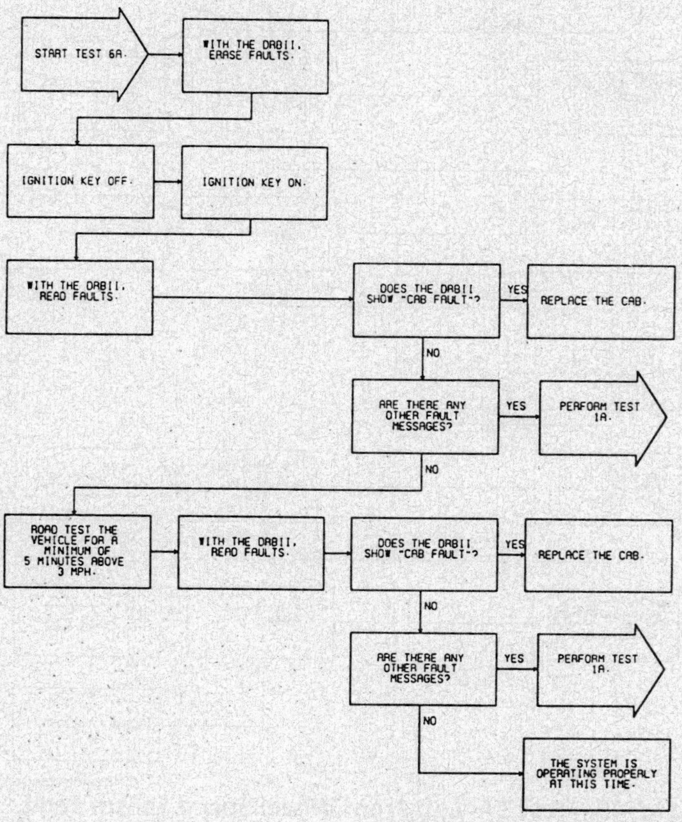

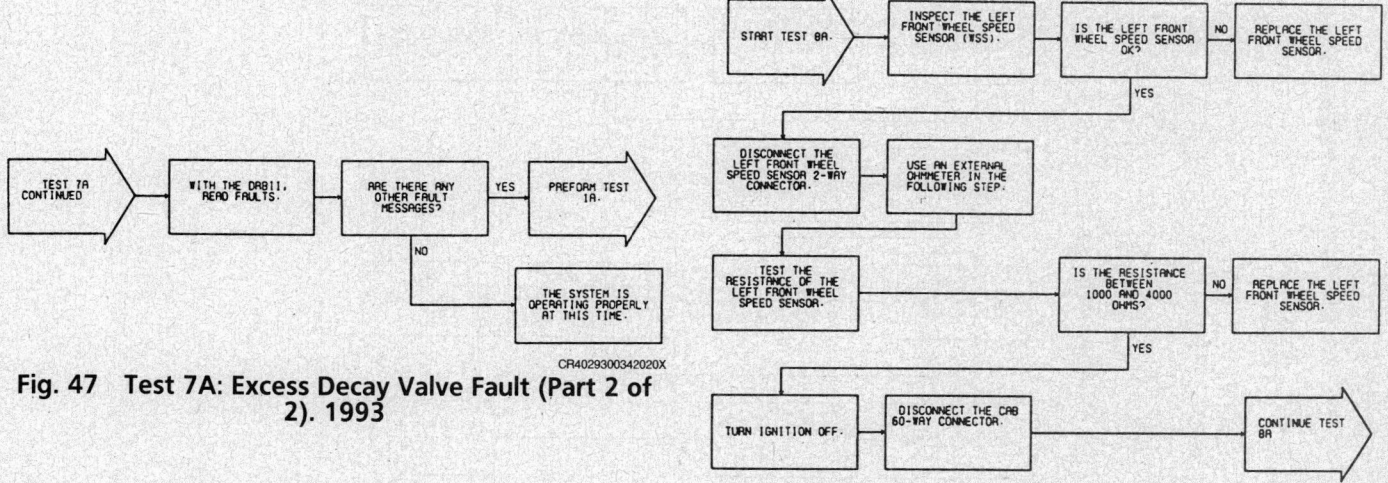

Fig. 46   Test 6A: CAB Fault. 1993

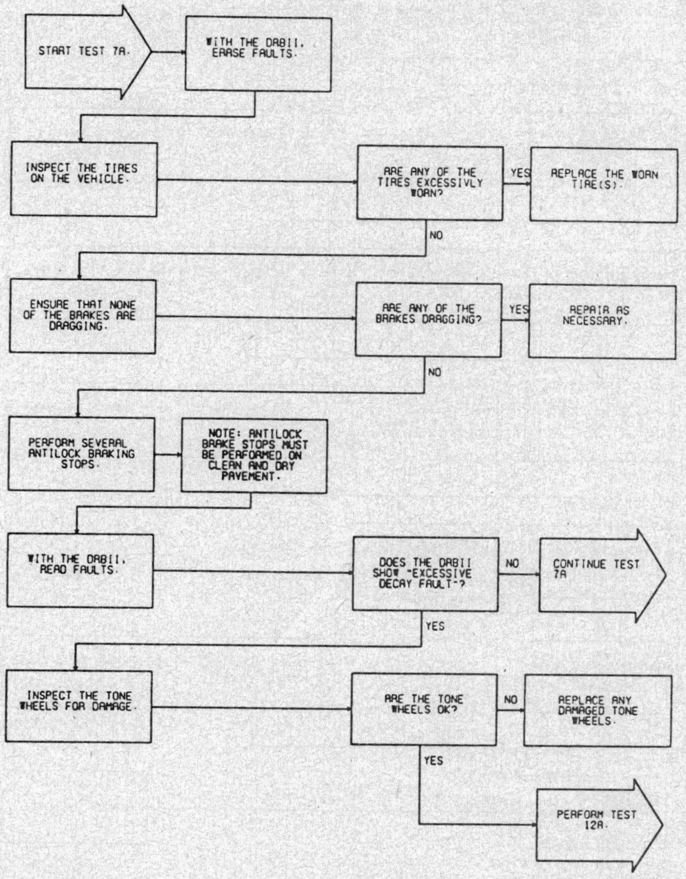

Fig. 47   Test 7A: Excess Decay Valve Fault (Part 1 of 2). 1993

Fig. 47   Test 7A: Excess Decay Valve Fault (Part 2 of 2). 1993

Fig. 48   Test 8A: LF Wheel Speed Sensor Continuity Fault (Part 1 of 2). 1993

TYPE 2-BENDIX ANTI-LOCK 6 BRAKING SYSTEM

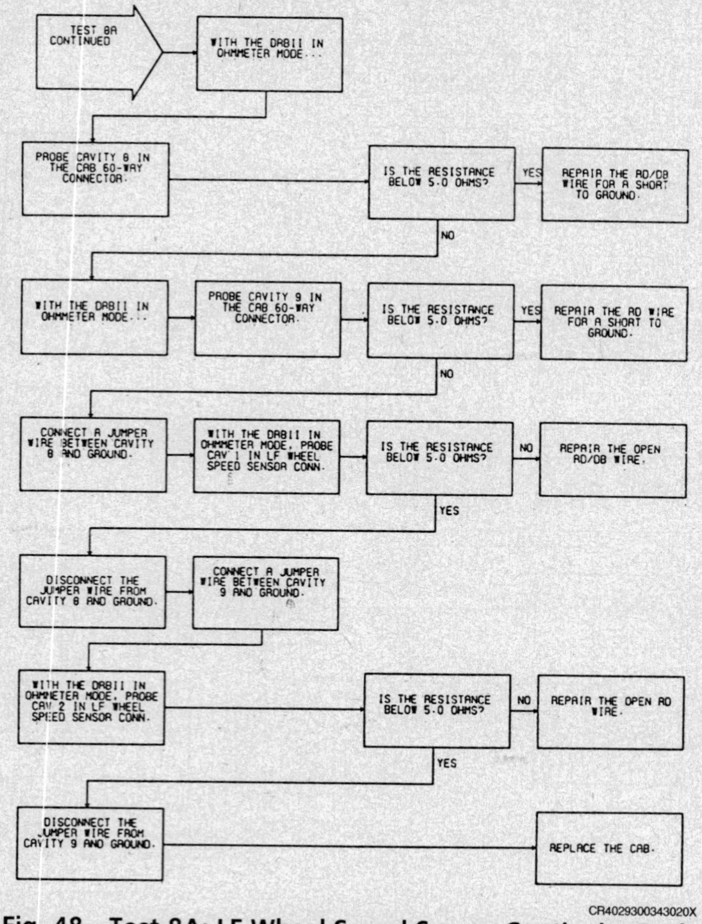

Fig. 48 (Test 8A flowchart)

TEST 8A CONTINUED → WITH THE DRBII IN OHMMETER MODE...

PROBE CAVITY 8 IN THE CAB 60-WAY CONNECTOR. → IS THE RESISTANCE BELOW 5.0 OHMS? — YES → REPAIR THE RD/DB WIRE FOR A SHORT TO GROUND.

NO ↓

WITH THE DRBII IN OHMMETER MODE... → PROBE CAVITY 9 IN THE CAB 60-WAY CONNECTOR. → IS THE RESISTANCE BELOW 5.0 OHMS? — YES → REPAIR THE RD WIRE FOR A SHORT TO GROUND.

NO ↓

CONNECT A JUMPER WIRE BETWEEN CAVITY 8 AND GROUND. → WITH THE DRBII IN OHMMETER MODE, PROBE CAV 1 IN LF WHEEL SPEED SENSOR CONN. → IS THE RESISTANCE BELOW 5.0 OHMS? — NO → REPAIR THE OPEN RD/DB WIRE.

YES ↓

DISCONNECT THE JUMPER WIRE FROM CAVITY 8 AND GROUND. → CONNECT A JUMPER WIRE BETWEEN CAVITY 9 AND GROUND.

WITH THE DRBII IN OHMMETER MODE, PROBE CAV 2 IN LF WHEEL SPEED SENSOR CONN. → IS THE RESISTANCE BELOW 5.0 OHMS? — NO → REPAIR THE OPEN RD WIRE.

YES ↓

DISCONNECT THE JUMPER WIRE FROM CAVITY 9 AND GROUND. → REPLACE THE CAB.

CR4029300343020X

Fig. 48   Test 8A: LF Wheel Speed Sensor Continuity Fault (Part 2 of 2). 1993

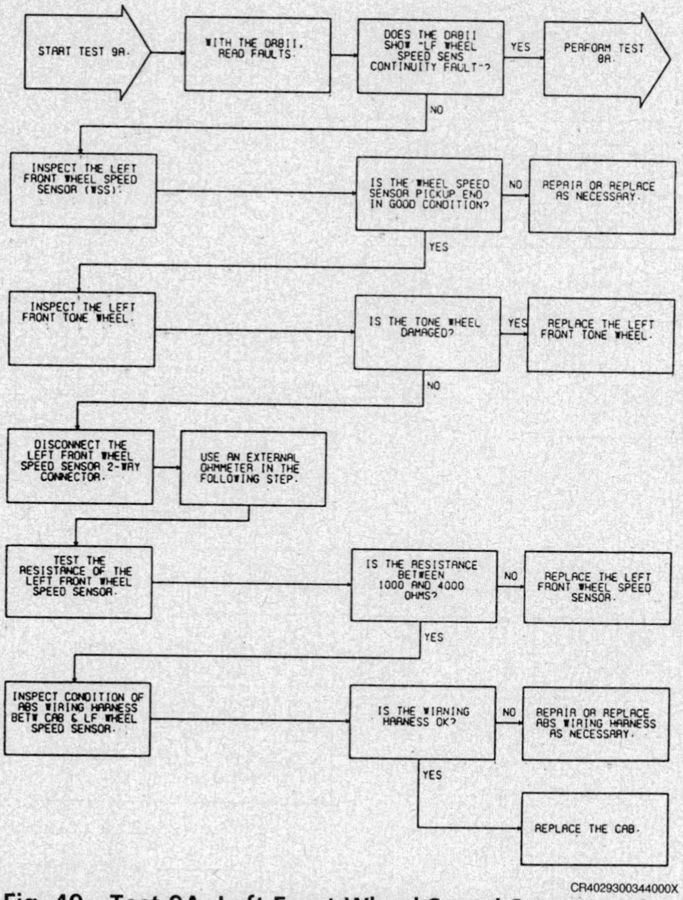

Fig. 49 (Test 9A flowchart)

START TEST 9A → WITH THE DRBII, READ FAULTS. → DOES THE DRBII SHOW "LF WHEEL SPEED SENS CONTINUITY FAULT"? — YES → PERFORM TEST 8A.

NO ↓

INSPECT THE LEFT FRONT WHEEL SPEED SENSOR (WSS). → IS THE WHEEL SPEED SENSOR PICKUP END IN GOOD CONDITION? — NO → REPAIR OR REPLACE AS NECESSARY.

YES ↓

INSPECT THE LEFT FRONT TONE WHEEL. → IS THE TONE WHEEL DAMAGED? — YES → REPLACE THE LEFT FRONT TONE WHEEL.

NO ↓

DISCONNECT THE LEFT FRONT WHEEL SPEED SENSOR 2-WAY CONNECTOR. → USE AN EXTERNAL OHMMETER IN THE FOLLOWING STEP.

TEST THE RESISTANCE OF THE LEFT FRONT WHEEL SPEED SENSOR. → IS THE RESISTANCE BETWEEN 1000 AND 4000 OHMS? — NO → REPLACE THE LEFT FRONT WHEEL SPEED SENSOR.

YES ↓

INSPECT CONDITION OF ABS WIRING HARNESS BETW CAB & LF WHEEL SPEED SENSOR. → IS THE WIRING HARNESS OK? — NO → REPAIR OR REPLACE ABS WIRING HARNESS AS NECESSARY.

YES ↓

REPLACE THE CAB.

CR4029300344000X

Fig. 49   Test 9A: Left Front Wheel Speed Sensor Fault. 1993

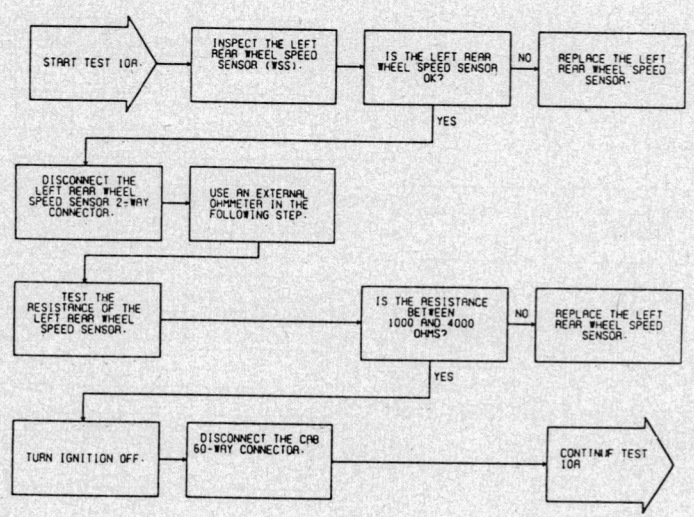

START TEST 10A → INSPECT THE LEFT REAR WHEEL SPEED SENSOR (WSS). → IS THE LEFT REAR WHEEL SPEED SENSOR OK? — NO → REPLACE THE LEFT REAR WHEEL SPEED SENSOR.

YES ↓

DISCONNECT THE LEFT REAR WHEEL SPEED SENSOR 2-WAY CONNECTOR. → USE AN EXTERNAL OHMMETER IN THE FOLLOWING STEP.

TEST THE RESISTANCE OF THE LEFT REAR WHEEL SPEED SENSOR. → IS THE RESISTANCE BETWEEN 1000 AND 4000 OHMS? — NO → REPLACE THE LEFT REAR WHEEL SPEED SENSOR.

YES ↓

TURN IGNITION OFF. → DISCONNECT THE CAB 60-WAY CONNECTOR. → CONTINUE TEST 10A

CR4029300345010X

Fig. 50   Test 10A: LR Wheel Speed Sensor Continuity Fault (Part 1 of 2). 1993

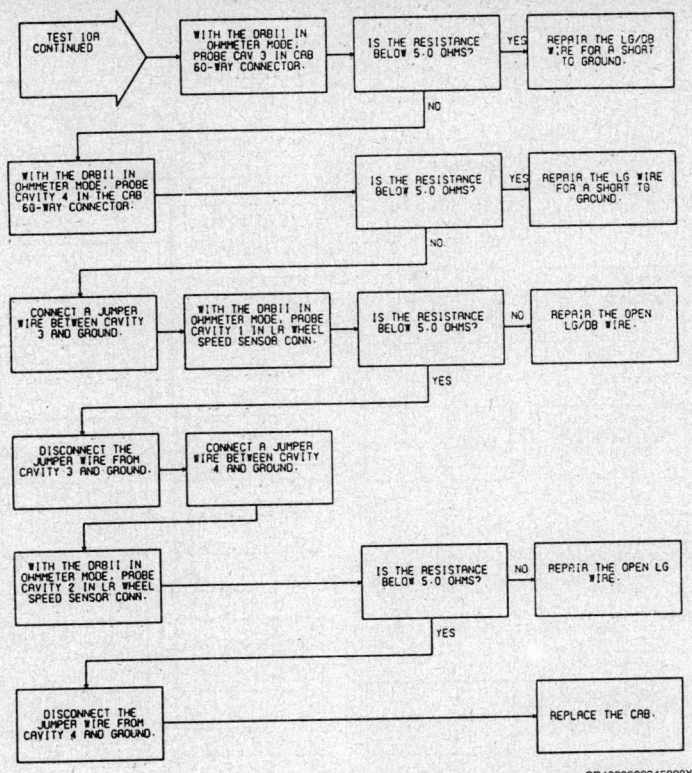

Fig. 50   Test 10A: LR Wheel Speed Sensor Continuity Fault (Part 2 of 2). 1993

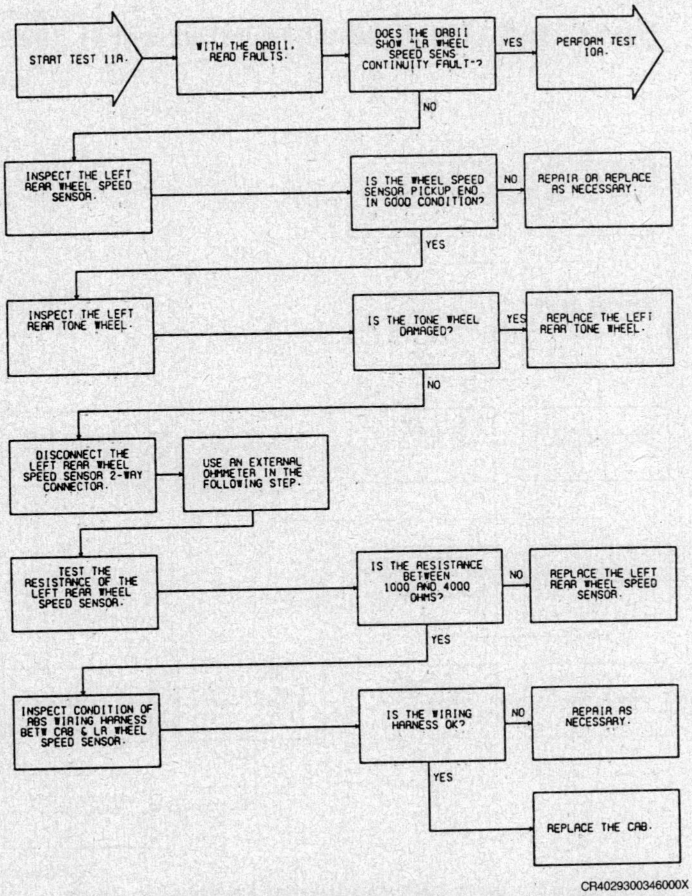

CR4029300345020X

CR4029300346000X

CR4029300347010X

Fig. 51   Test 11A: Left Rear Wheel Speed Sensor Fault. 1993

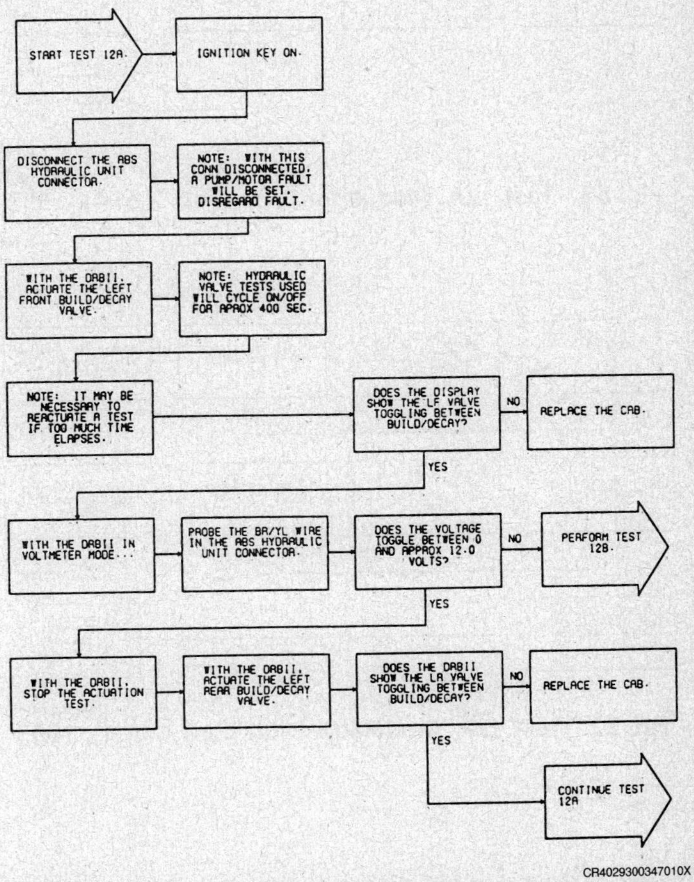

Fig. 52   Test 12A: Modulator Fault (Part 1 of 4). 1993

TYPE 2-BENDIX ANTI-LOCK 6 BRAKING SYSTEM

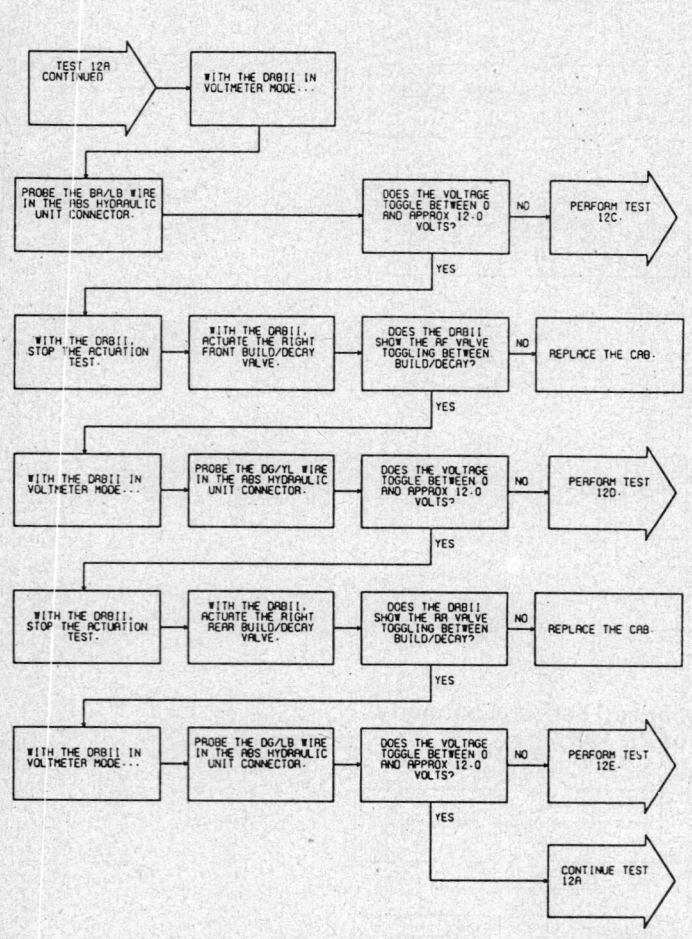

Fig. 52   Test 12A: Modulator Fault (Part 2 of 4). 1993

CR4029300347020X

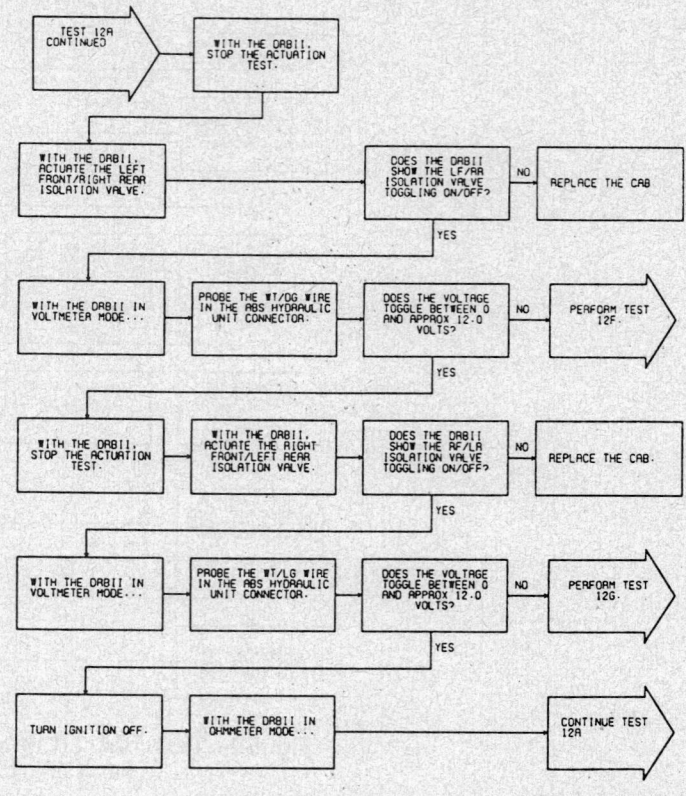

Fig. 52   Test 12A: Modulator Fault (Part 3 of 4). 1993

CR4029300347030X

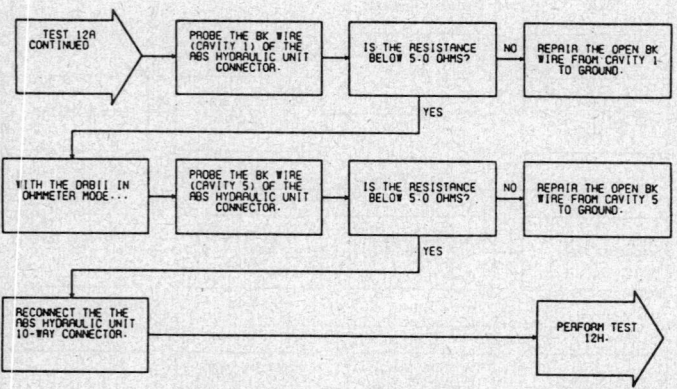

Fig. 52   Test 12A: Modulator Fault (Part 4 of 4). 1993

CR4029300347040X

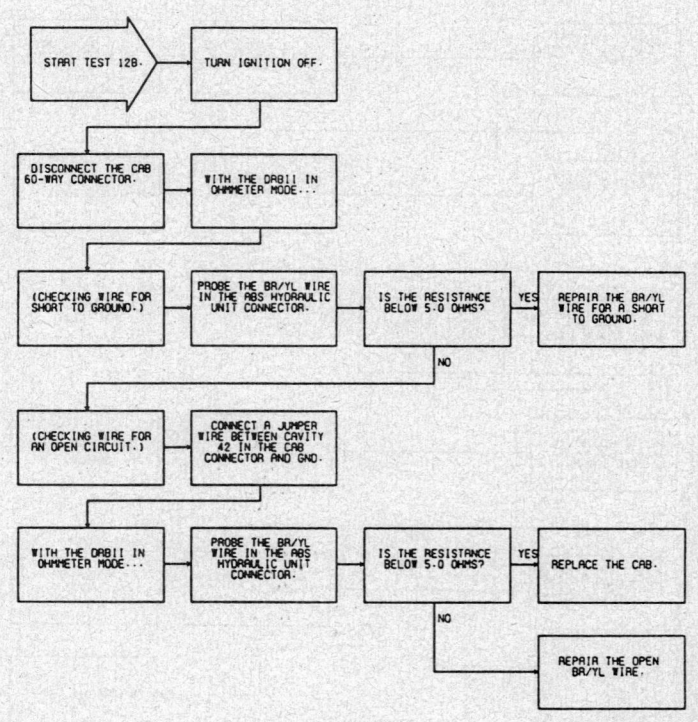

Fig. 53   Test 12B: Modulator Fault, Left Front Build/Decay Valve. 1993

CR4029300348000X

TYPE 2-BENDIX ANTI-LOCK 6 BRAKING SYSTEM

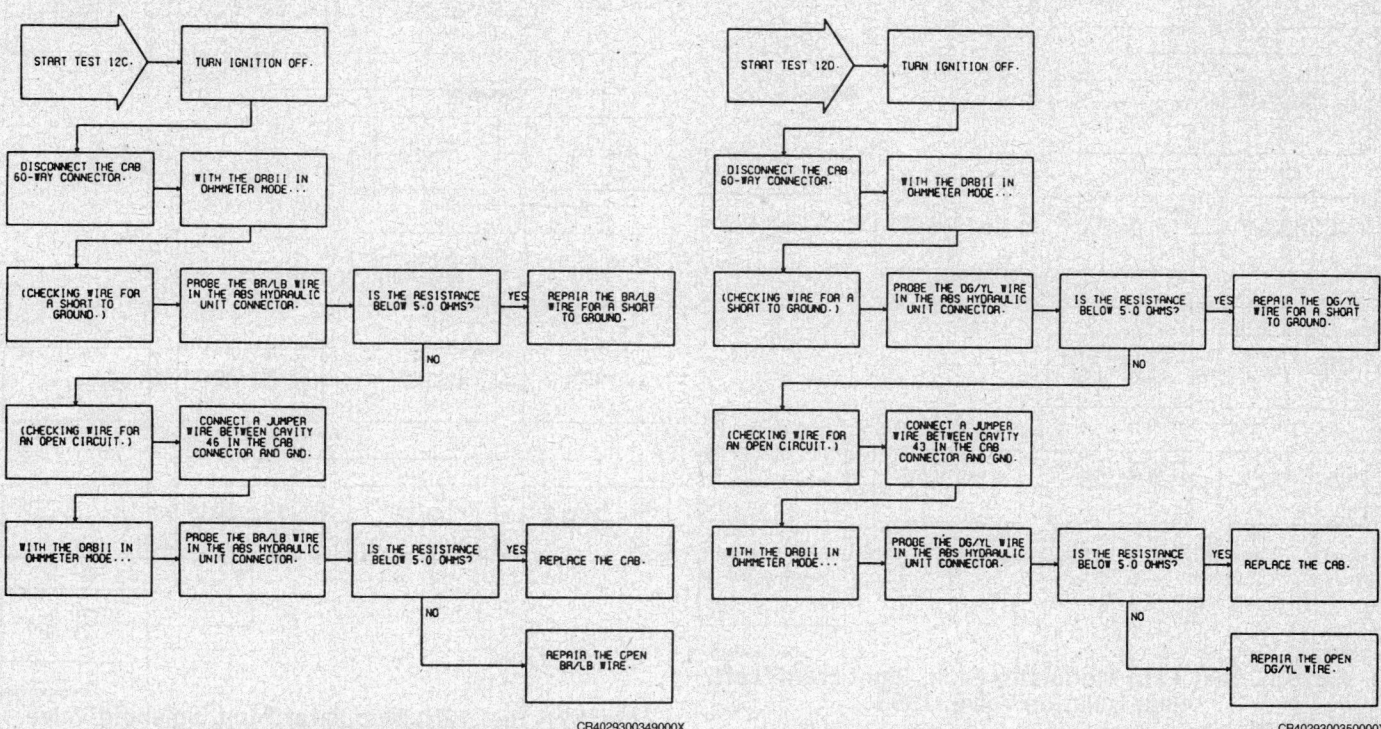

Fig. 54   Test 12C: Modulator Fault, Left Rear Build/Decay Valve. 1993

Fig. 55   Test 12D: Modulator Fault, Right Front Build/Decay Valve. 1993

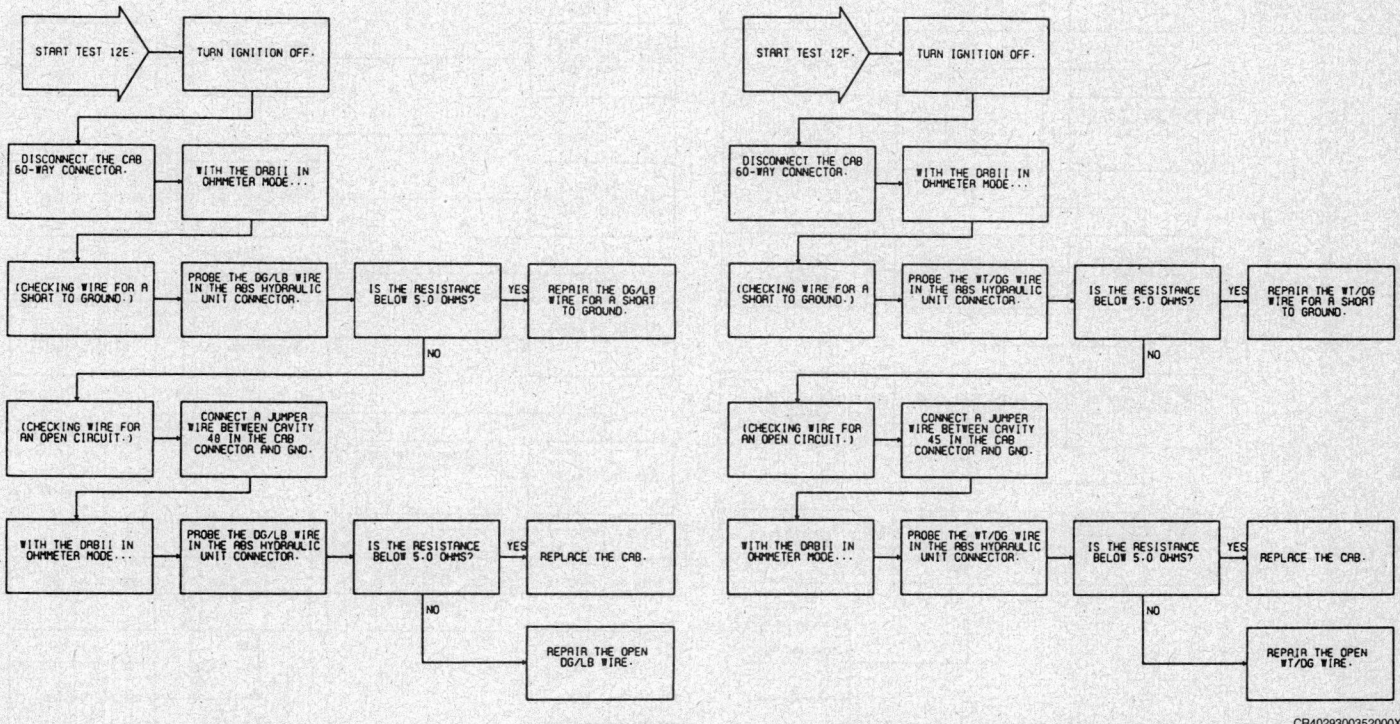

Fig. 56   Test 12E: Modulator Fault, Right Rear Build/Decay Valve. 1993

Fig. 57   Test 12F: Modulator Fault, Left Front/Right Rear Isolation Valve. 1993

TYPE 2-BENDIX ANTI-LOCK 6 BRAKING SYSTEM

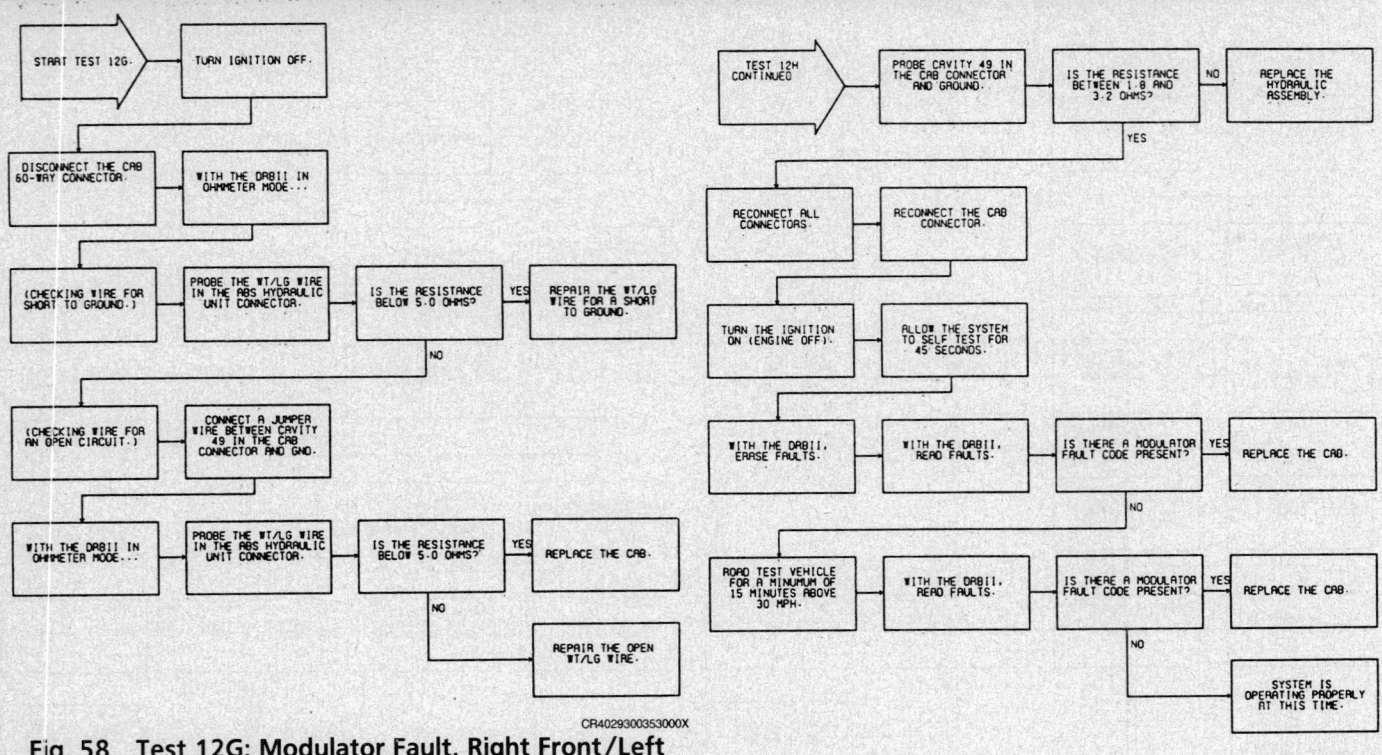

Fig. 58   Test 12G: Modulator Fault, Right Front/Left Rear Isolation Valve. 1993

CR4029300353000X

Fig. 59   Test 12H: Modulator Fault, Solenoid Valve Resistance Check (Part 2 of 2). 1993

CR4029300354020X

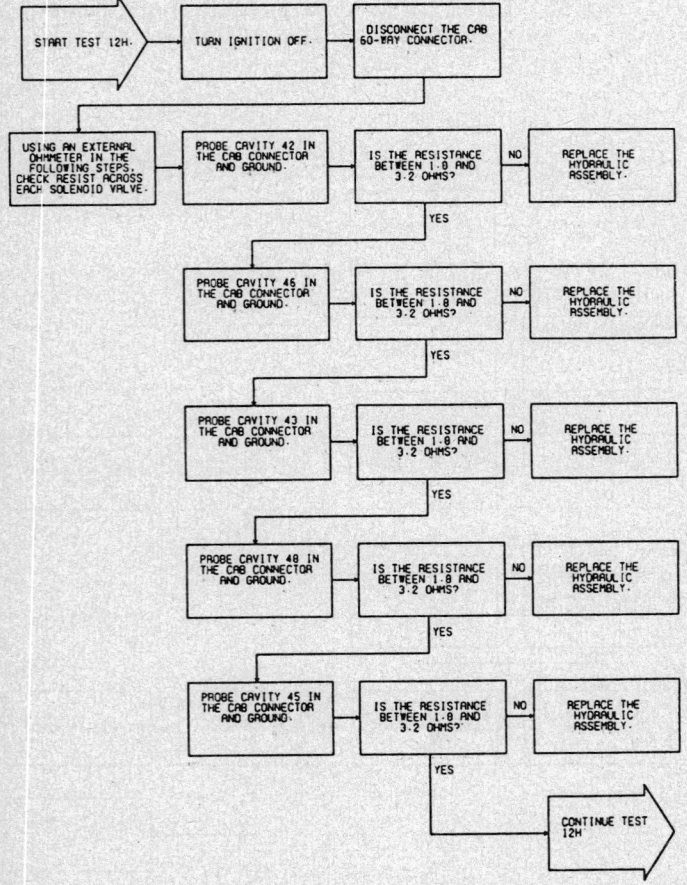

CR4029300354010X

Fig. 59   Test 12H: Modulator Fault, Solenoid Valve Resistance Check (Part 1 of 2). 1993

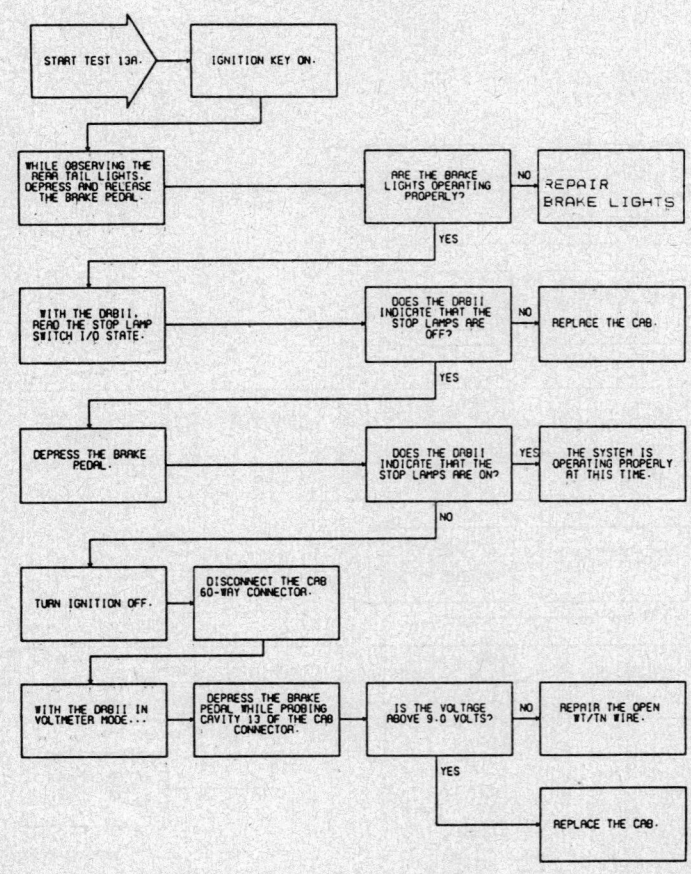

CR4029300355000X

Fig. 60   Test 13A: Stop Lamp Switch Input Test. 1993

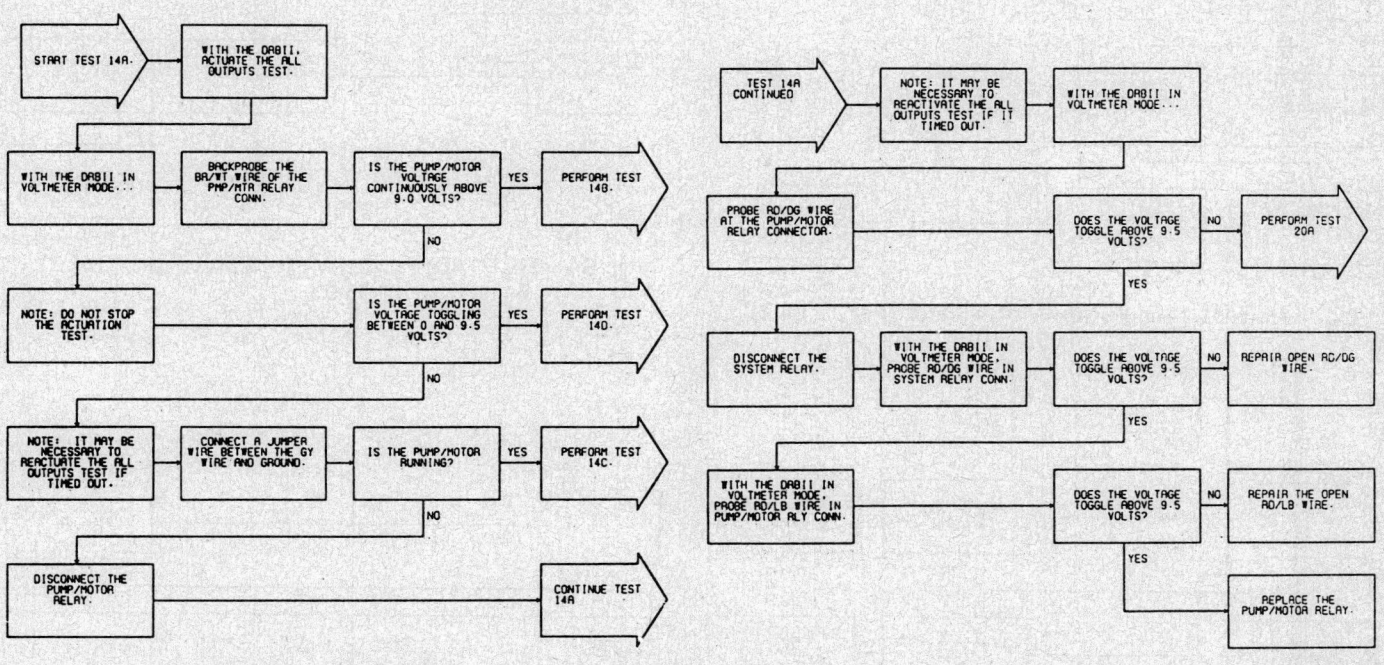

Fig. 61   Test 14A: Pump/Motor Fault (Part 1 of 2). 1993

Fig. 61   Test 14A: Pump/Motor Fault (Part 2 of 2). 1993

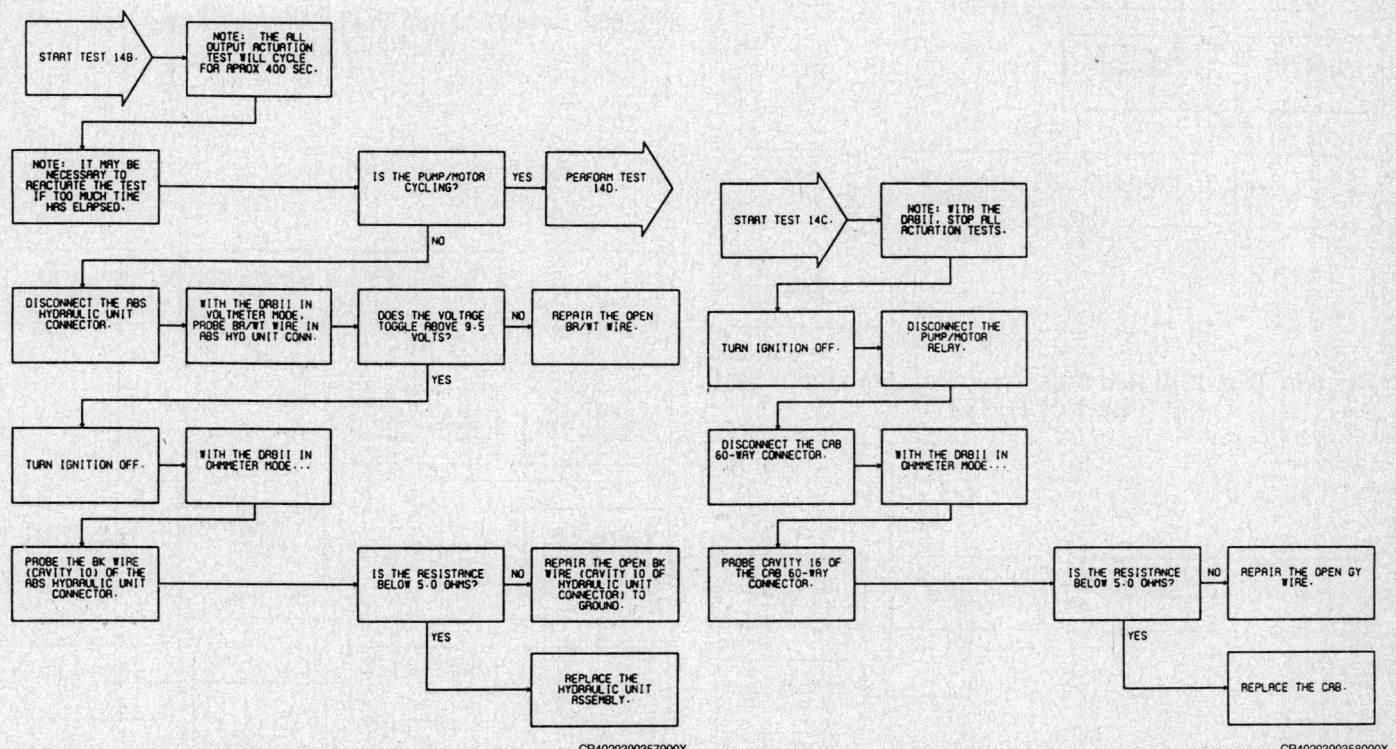

Fig. 62   Test 14B: Pump/Motor Fault. 1993

Fig. 63   Test 14C: Pump/Motor Fault. 1993

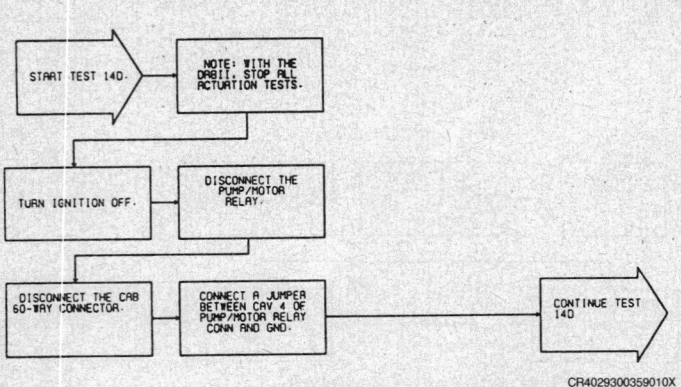

CR4029300359010X

Fig. 64   Test 14D: Pump/Motor Fault (Part 1 of 2). 1993

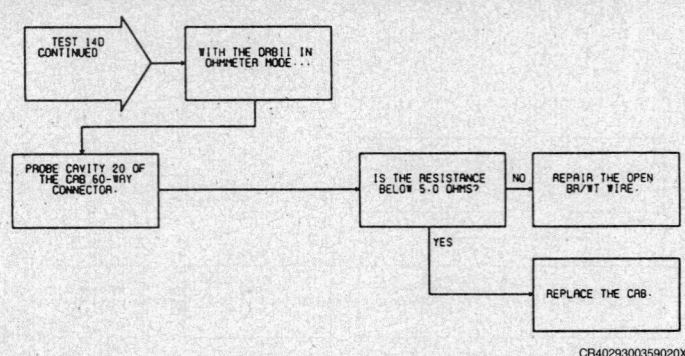

CR4029300359020X

Fig. 64   Test 14D: Pump/Motor Fault (Part 2 of 2). 1993

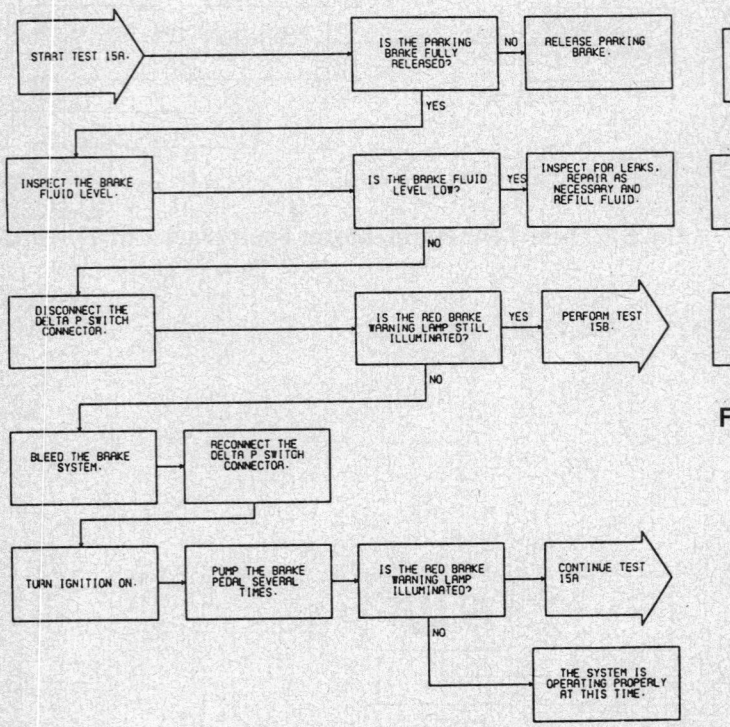

CR4029300360010X

Fig. 65   Test 15A: Red Brake Warning Lamp Input Test (Part 1 of 2). 1993

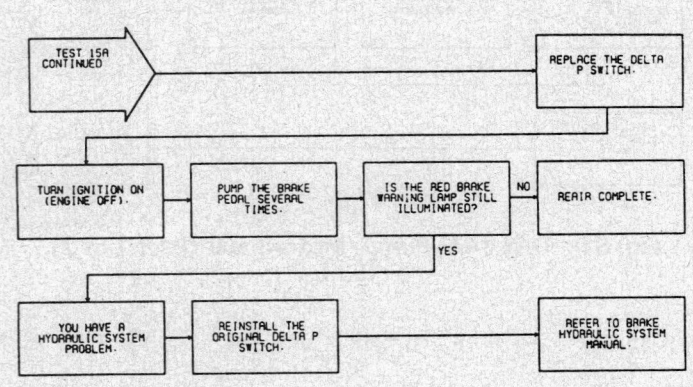

CR4029300360020X

Fig. 65   Test 15A: Red Brake Warning Lamp Input Test (Part 2 of 2). 1993

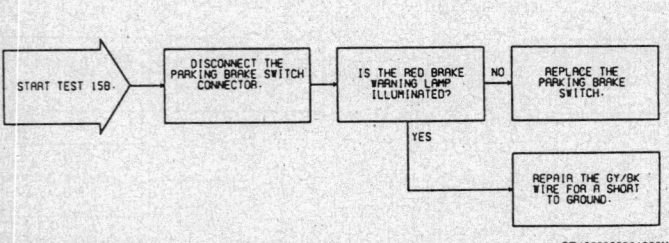

CR4029300361000X

Fig. 66   Test 15B: Red Brake Warning Lamp Input Test. 1993

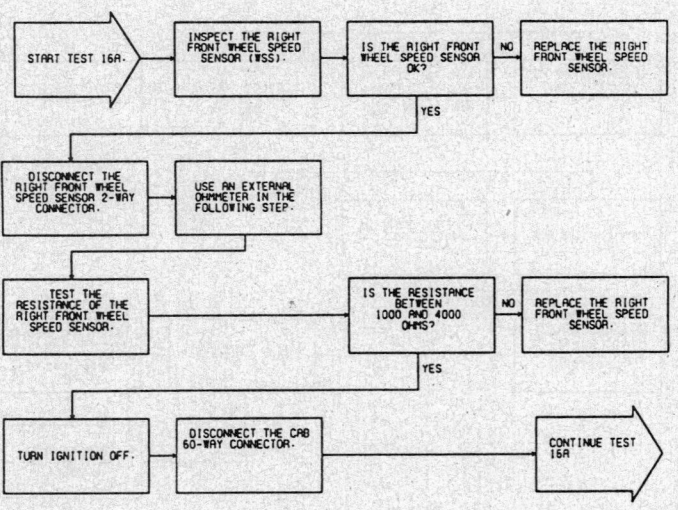

CR4029300362010X

Fig. 67   Test 16A: RF Wheel Speed Sensor Continuity Fault (Part 1 of 2). 1993

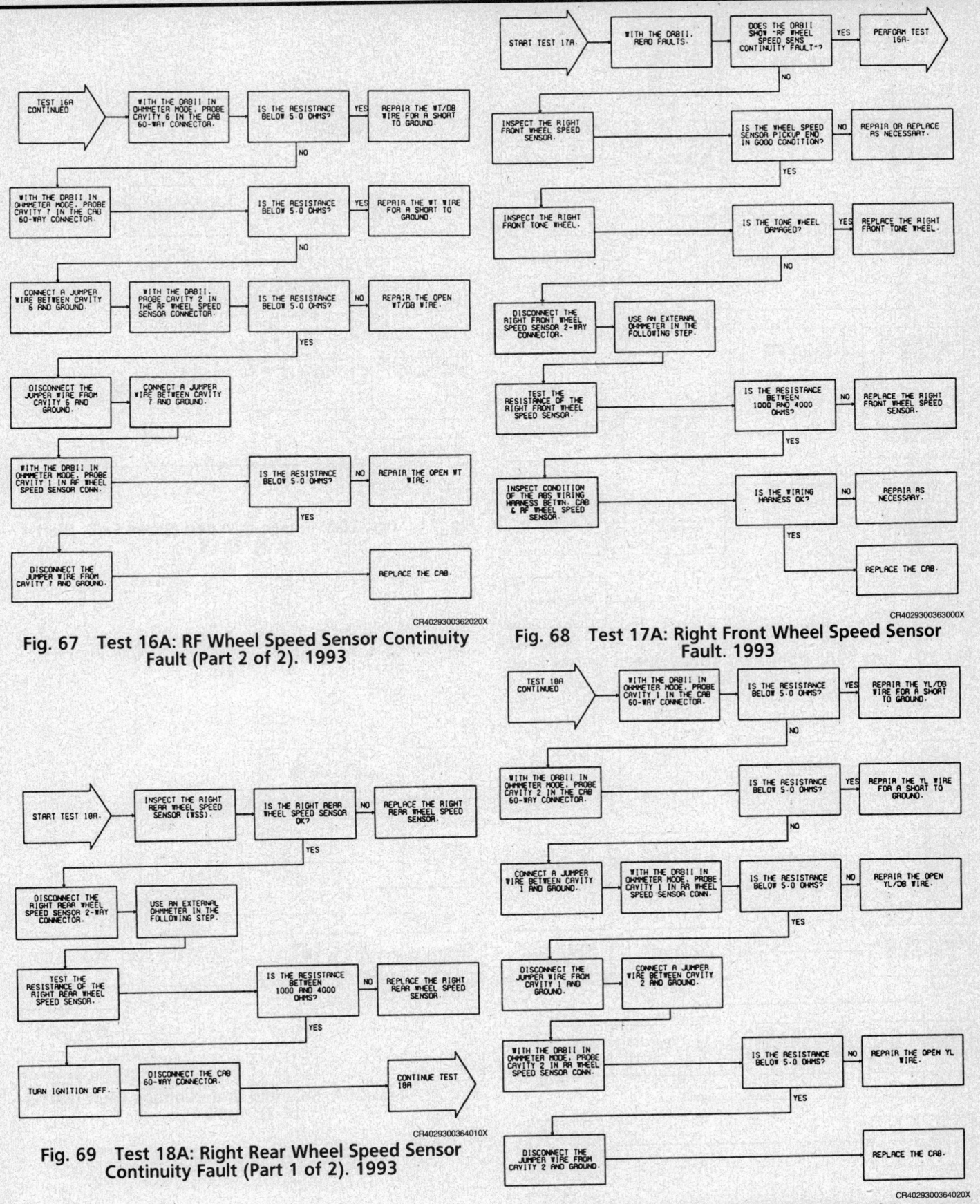

Fig. 67   Test 16A: RF Wheel Speed Sensor Continuity Fault (Part 2 of 2). 1993

Fig. 68   Test 17A: Right Front Wheel Speed Sensor Fault. 1993

Fig. 69   Test 18A: Right Rear Wheel Speed Sensor Continuity Fault (Part 1 of 2). 1993

Fig. 69   Test 18A: Right Rear Wheel Speed Sensor Continuity Fault (Part 2 of 2). 1993

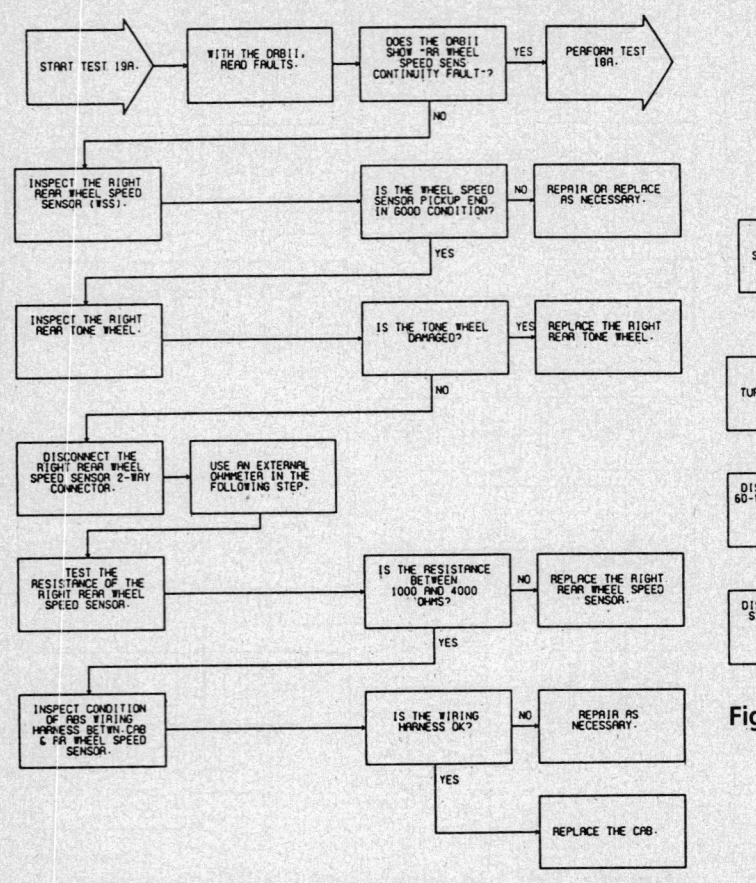

Fig. 70   Test 19A: Right Rear Wheel Speed Sensor Fault. 1993

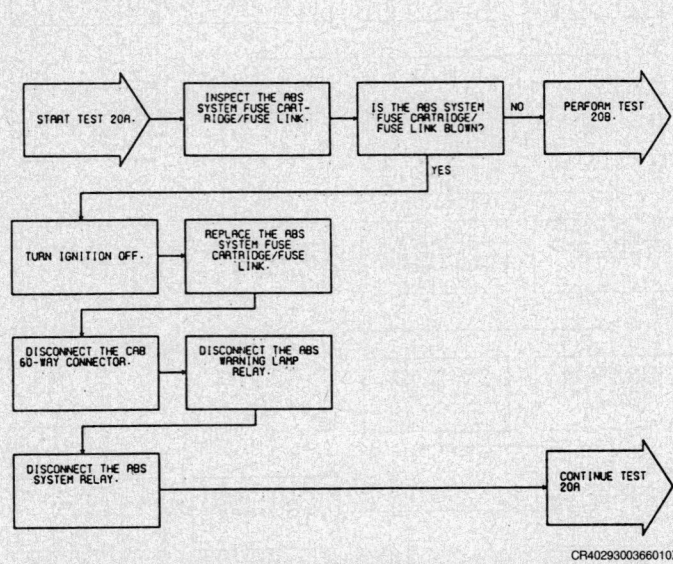

Fig. 71   Test 20A: Solenoid Undervoltage Fault (Part 1 of 3). 1993

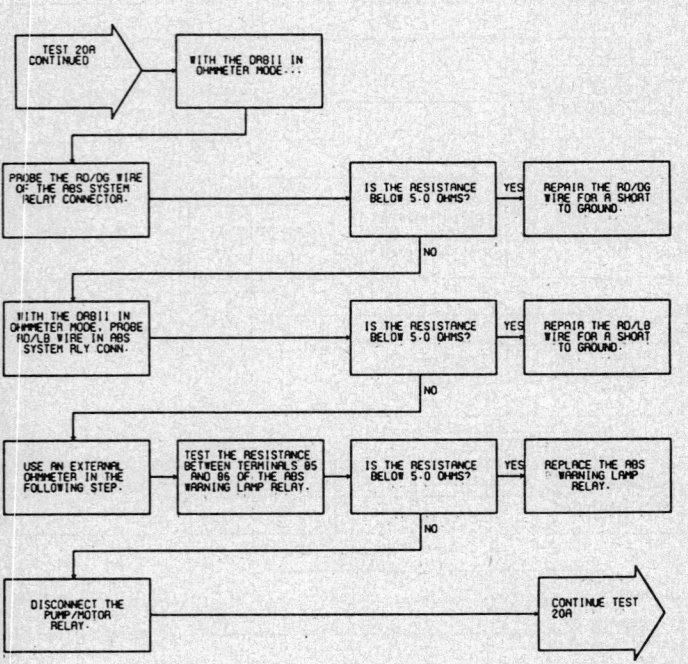

Fig. 71   Test 20A: Solenoid Undervoltage Fault (Part 2 of 3). 1993

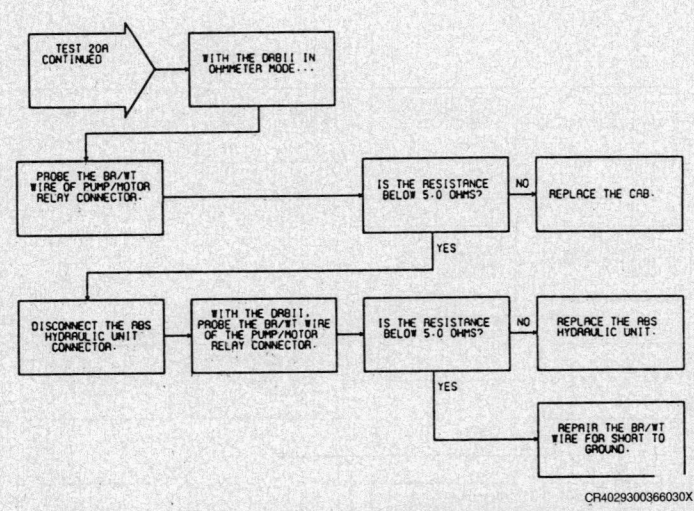

Fig. 71   Test 20A: Solenoid Undervoltage Fault (Part 3 of 3). 1993

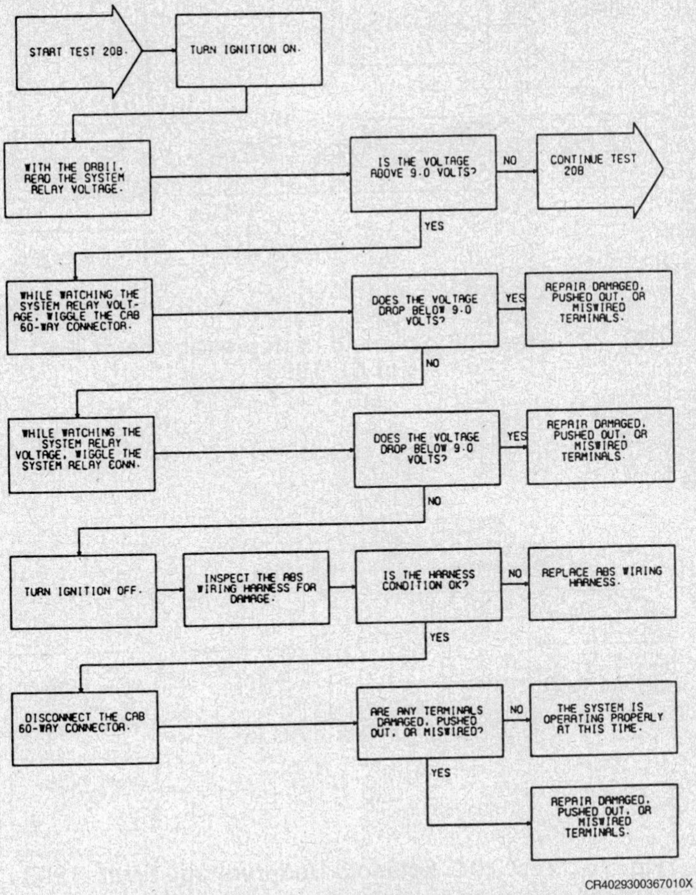

Part 1 flowchart:

START TEST 20B → TURN IGNITION ON.

WITH THE DRBII, READ THE SYSTEM RELAY VOLTAGE. → IS THE VOLTAGE ABOVE 9.0 VOLTS? → NO → CONTINUE TEST 20B

YES ↓

WHILE WATCHING THE SYSTEM RELAY VOLTAGE, WIGGLE THE CAB 60-WAY CONNECTOR. → DOES THE VOLTAGE DROP BELOW 9.0 VOLTS? → YES → REPAIR DAMAGED, PUSHED OUT, OR MISWIRED TERMINALS.

NO ↓

WHILE WATCHING THE SYSTEM RELAY VOLTAGE, WIGGLE THE SYSTEM RELAY CONN. → DOES THE VOLTAGE DROP BELOW 9.0 VOLTS? → YES → REPAIR DAMAGED, PUSHED OUT, OR MISWIRED TERMINALS

NO ↓

TURN IGNITION OFF. → INSPECT THE ABS WIRING HARNESS FOR DAMAGE. → IS THE HARNESS CONDITION OK? → NO → REPLACE ABS WIRING HARNESS.

YES ↓

DISCONNECT THE CAB 60-WAY CONNECTOR. → ARE ANY TERMINALS DAMAGED, PUSHED OUT, OR MISWIRED? → NO → THE SYSTEM IS OPERATING PROPERLY AT THIS TIME.

YES → REPAIR DAMAGED, PUSHED OUT, OR MISWIRED TERMINALS.

CR4029300367010X

Fig. 72   Test 20B: Solenoid Undervoltage Fault (Part 1 of 5). 1993

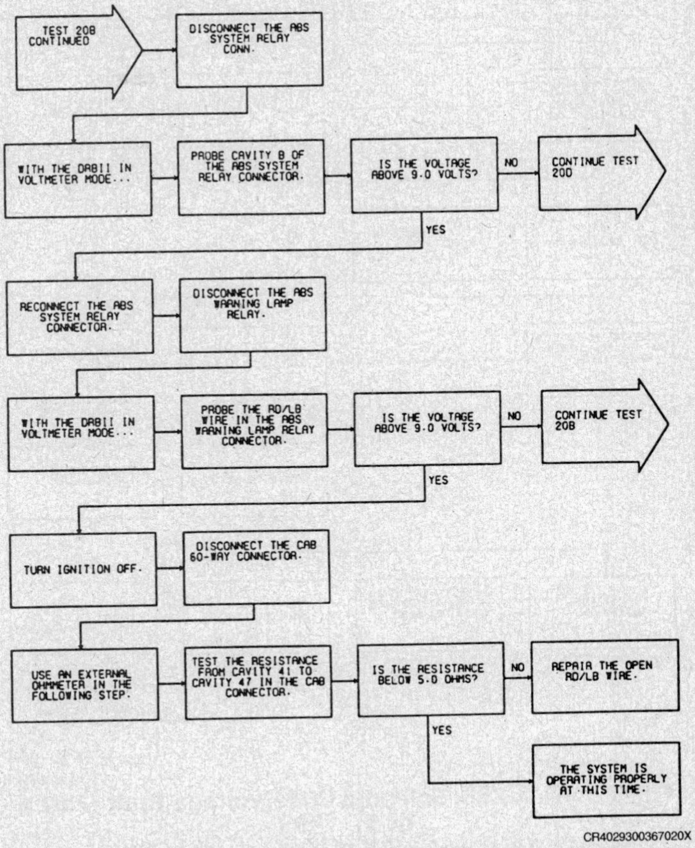

Part 2 flowchart:

TEST 20B CONTINUED → DISCONNECT THE ABS SYSTEM RELAY CONN.

WITH THE DRBII IN VOLTMETER MODE... → PROBE CAVITY B OF THE ABS SYSTEM RELAY CONNECTOR. → IS THE VOLTAGE ABOVE 9.0 VOLTS? → NO → CONTINUE TEST 20D

YES ↓

RECONNECT THE ABS SYSTEM RELAY CONNECTOR. → DISCONNECT THE ABS WARNING LAMP RELAY.

WITH THE DRBII IN VOLTMETER MODE... → PROBE THE RD/LB WIRE IN THE ABS WARNING LAMP RELAY CONNECTOR. → IS THE VOLTAGE ABOVE 9.0 VOLTS? → NO → CONTINUE TEST 20B

YES ↓

TURN IGNITION OFF. → DISCONNECT THE CAB 60-WAY CONNECTOR.

USE AN EXTERNAL OHMMETER IN THE FOLLOWING STEP. → TEST THE RESISTANCE FROM CAVITY 41 TO CAVITY 47 IN THE CAB CONNECTOR. → IS THE RESISTANCE BELOW 5.0 OHMS? → NO → REPAIR THE OPEN RD/LB WIRE.

YES → THE SYSTEM IS OPERATING PROPERLY AT THIS TIME.

CR4029300367020X

Fig. 72   Test 20B: Solenoid Undervoltage Fault (Part 2 of 5). 1993

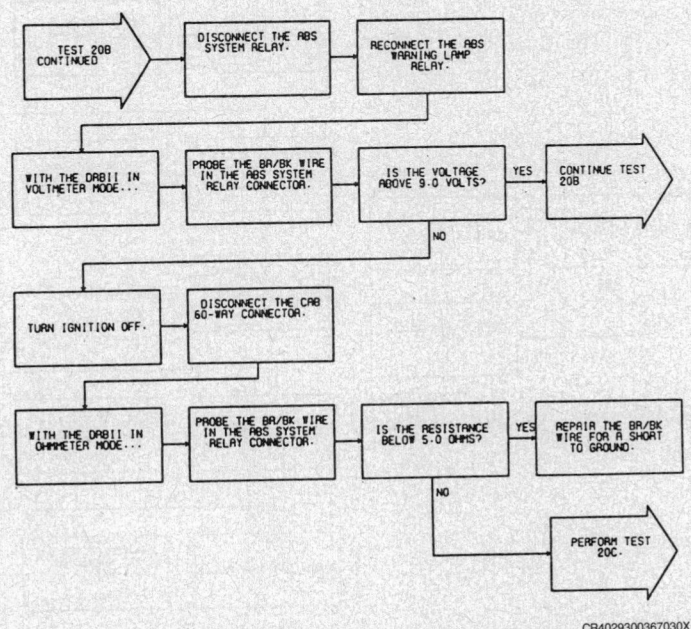

Part 3 flowchart:

TEST 20B CONTINUED → DISCONNECT THE ABS SYSTEM RELAY. → RECONNECT THE ABS WARNING LAMP RELAY.

WITH THE DRBII IN VOLTMETER MODE... → PROBE THE BR/BK WIRE IN THE ABS SYSTEM RELAY CONNECTOR. → IS THE VOLTAGE ABOVE 9.0 VOLTS? → YES → CONTINUE TEST 20B

NO ↓

TURN IGNITION OFF. → DISCONNECT THE CAB 60-WAY CONNECTOR.

WITH THE DRBII IN OHMMETER MODE... → PROBE THE BR/BK WIRE IN THE ABS SYSTEM RELAY CONNECTOR. → IS THE RESISTANCE BELOW 5.0 OHMS? → YES → REPAIR THE BR/BK WIRE FOR A SHORT TO GROUND.

NO → PERFORM TEST 20C.

CR4029300367030X

Fig. 72   Test 20B: Solenoid Undervoltage Fault (Part 3 of 5). 1993

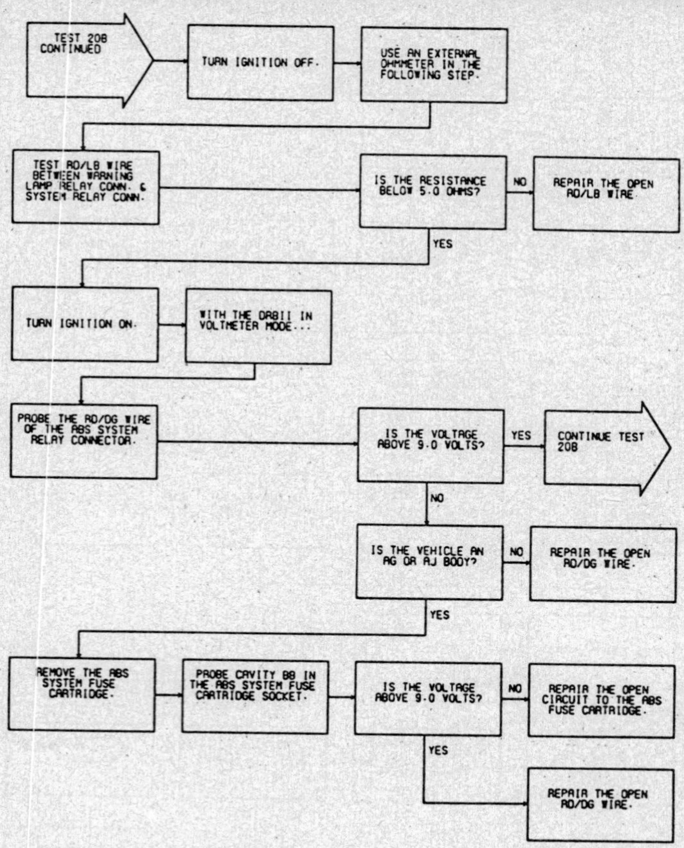

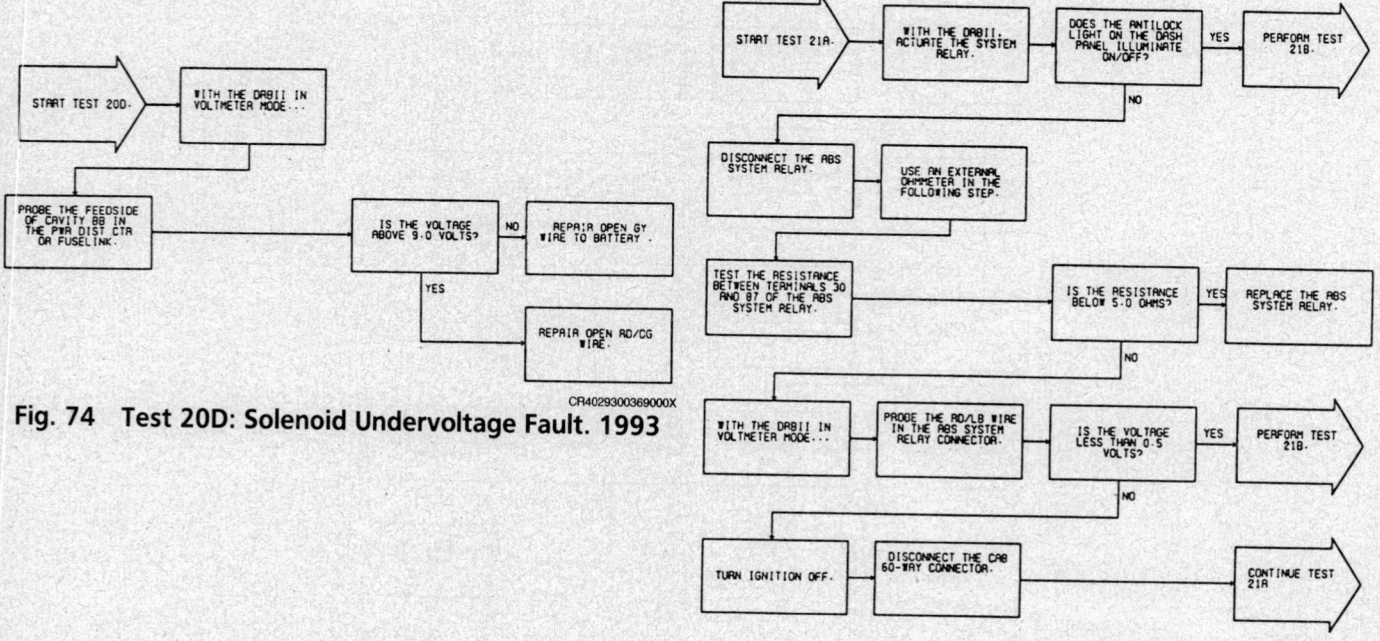

TEST 20B CONTINUED → TURN IGNITION OFF. → USE AN EXTERNAL OHMMETER IN THE FOLLOWING STEP.

TEST RO/LB WIRE BETWEEN WARNING LAMP RELAY CONN. & SYSTEM RELAY CONN. → IS THE RESISTANCE BELOW 5.0 OHMS? → NO → REPAIR THE OPEN RO/LB WIRE.

YES

TURN IGNITION ON. → WITH THE DRBII IN VOLTMETER MODE...

PROBE THE RO/DG WIRE OF THE ABS SYSTEM RELAY CONNECTOR. → IS THE VOLTAGE ABOVE 9.0 VOLTS? → YES → CONTINUE TEST 20B

NO

IS THE VEHICLE AN AG OR AJ BODY? → NO → REPAIR THE OPEN RO/DG WIRE.

YES

REMOVE THE ABS SYSTEM FUSE CARTRIDGE. → PROBE CAVITY 88 IN THE ABS SYSTEM FUSE CARTRIDGE SOCKET. → IS THE VOLTAGE ABOVE 9.0 VOLTS? → NO → REPAIR THE OPEN CIRCUIT TO THE ABS FUSE CARTRIDGE.

YES

REPAIR THE OPEN RO/DG WIRE.

Fig. 72   Test 20B: Solenoid Undervoltage Fault (Part 4 of 5). 1993

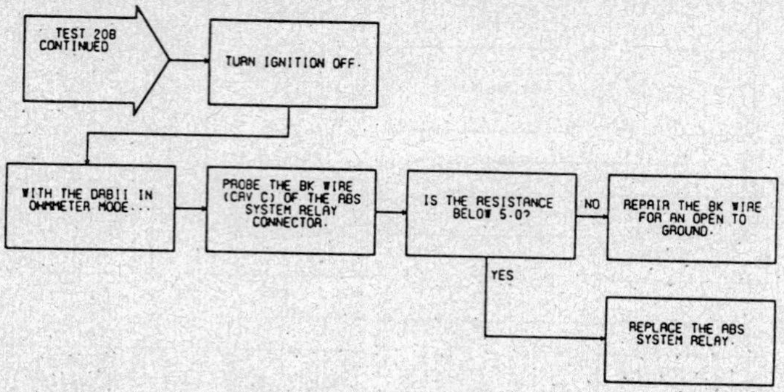

CR4029300367040X

TEST 20B CONTINUED → TURN IGNITION OFF.

WITH THE DRBII IN OHMMETER MODE... → PROBE THE BK WIRE (CAV C) OF THE ABS SYSTEM RELAY CONNECTOR. → IS THE RESISTANCE BELOW 5.0? → NO → REPAIR THE BK WIRE FOR AN OPEN TO GROUND.

YES

REPLACE THE ABS SYSTEM RELAY.

CR4029300367050X

Fig. 72   Test 20B: Solenoid Undervoltage Fault (Part 5 of 5). 1993

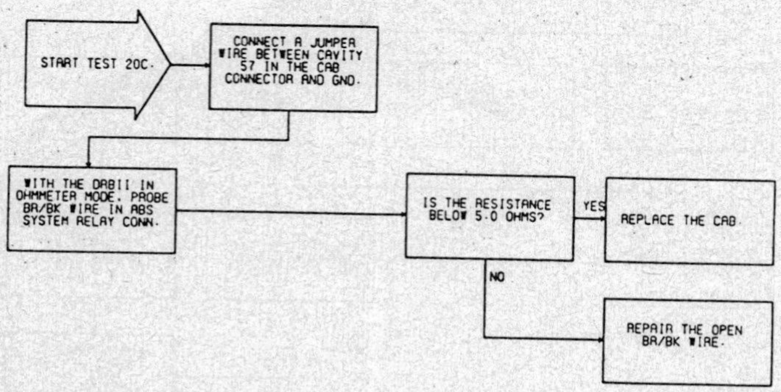

START TEST 20C. → CONNECT A JUMPER WIRE BETWEEN CAVITY 57 IN THE CAB CONNECTOR AND GND.

WITH THE DRBII IN OHMMETER MODE. PROBE BR/BK WIRE IN ABS SYSTEM RELAY CONN. → IS THE RESISTANCE BELOW 5.0 OHMS? → YES → REPLACE THE CAB.

NO

REPAIR THE OPEN BR/BK WIRE.

CR4029300368000X

Fig. 73   Test 20C: Solenoid Undervoltage Fault. 1993

START TEST 20D. → WITH THE DRBII IN VOLTMETER MODE...

PROBE THE FEEDSIDE OF CAVITY 88 IN THE PWR DIST CTR OR FUSELINK. → IS THE VOLTAGE ABOVE 9.0 VOLTS? → NO → REPAIR OPEN GY WIRE TO BATTERY.

YES

REPAIR OPEN RO/DG WIRE.

CR4029300369000X

Fig. 74   Test 20D: Solenoid Undervoltage Fault. 1993

START TEST 21A. → WITH THE DRBII, ACTUATE THE SYSTEM RELAY. → DOES THE ANTILOCK LIGHT ON THE DASH PANEL ILLUMINATE ON/OFF? → YES → PERFORM TEST 21B.

NO

DISCONNECT THE ABS SYSTEM RELAY. → USE AN EXTERNAL OHMMETER IN THE FOLLOWING STEP.

TEST THE RESISTANCE BETWEEN TERMINALS 30 AND 87 OF THE ABS SYSTEM RELAY. → IS THE RESISTANCE BELOW 5.0 OHMS? → YES → REPLACE THE ABS SYSTEM RELAY.

NO

WITH THE DRBII IN VOLTMETER MODE... → PROBE THE RO/LB WIRE IN THE ABS SYSTEM RELAY CONNECTOR. → IS THE VOLTAGE LESS THAN 0.5 VOLTS? → YES → PERFORM TEST 21B.

NO

TURN IGNITION OFF. → DISCONNECT THE CAB 60-WAY CONNECTOR. → CONTINUE TEST 21A.

CR4029300370010X

Fig. 75   Test 21A: System Relay Fault (Part 1 of 2). 1993

TYPE 2-BENDIX ANTI-LOCK 6 BRAKING SYSTEM

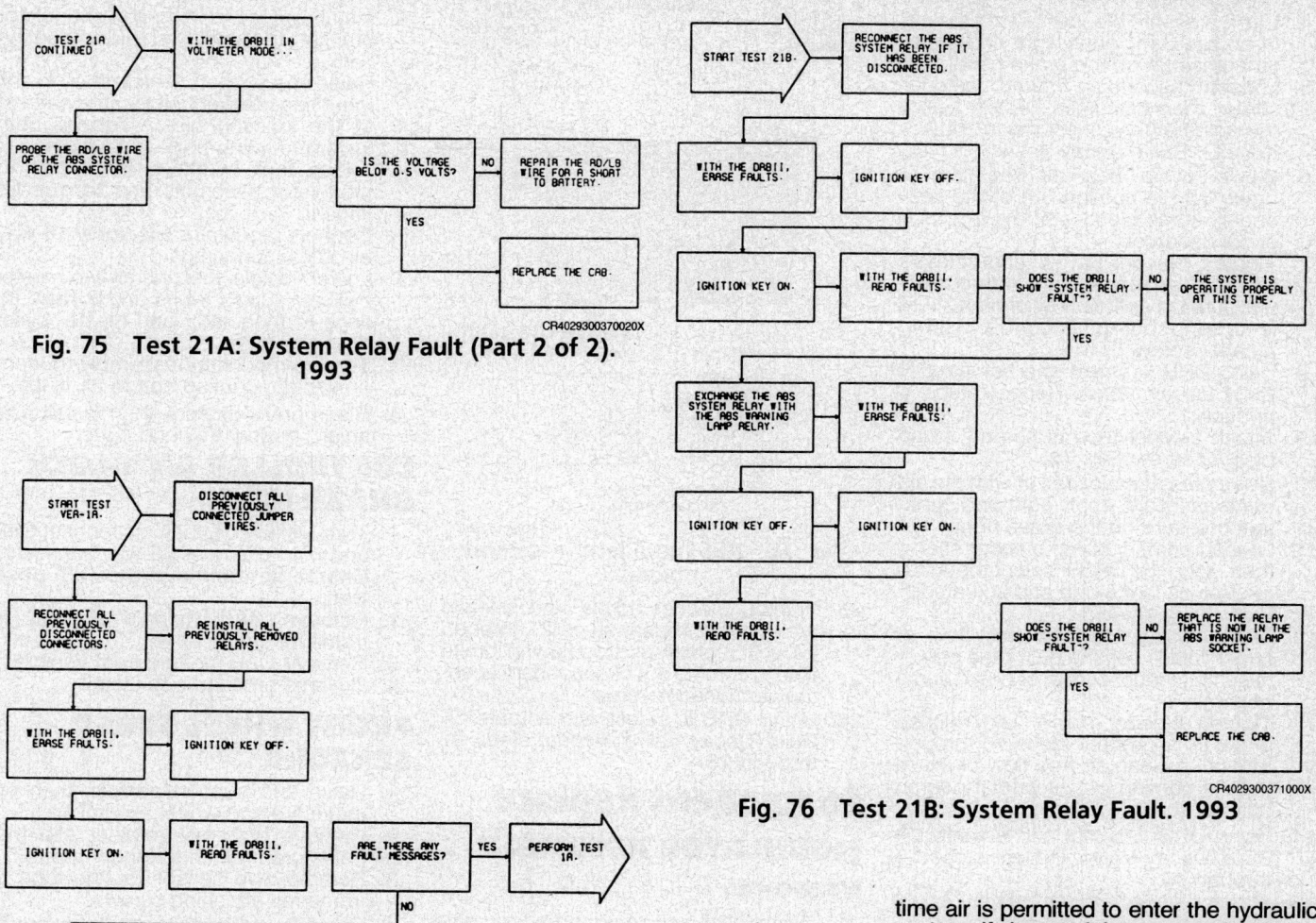

Fig. 75   Test 21A: System Relay Fault (Part 2 of 2). 1993

Fig. 76   Test 21B: System Relay Fault. 1993

Fig. 77   Test VER-1A: System Verification. 1993

SYSTEM SERVICE

Certain components of the ABS system are not intended to be serviced individually. Attempting to remove or disconnect certain system components, may result in personal injury and/or improper system operation. Only the components with removal and installation procedures should be serviced.

Use the following general precautions whenever servicing the ABS system:

1. If any welding work is to be performed using an arc welder, CAB should be disconnected.
2. When the ignition switch is in the ON position, the CAB and modulator assembly 10-way connector should not be disconnected or connected.
3. Some components of the ABS system are not serviced separately and must be serviced as complete assemblies. Do not disassemble any component which is designated as non-serviceable.

Brake System Bleed

The anti-lock system must be bled any-time air is permitted to enter the hydraulic system. If the modulator assembly is removed from the vehicle. Both the hydraulic and anti-lock systems will have to be bled. The ABS must be bled separately from the hydraulic portion of the braking system using a DRB II tester.

During bleeding procedures, ensure that the brake fluid level remains close to the full level in the reservoir. Check the fluid periodically during the bleeding procedure.

When bleeding the modulator assembly, wear safety glasses. A bleed tube should be attached to the bleeder screws, to direct flow of brake fluid away from the painted surfaces of the vehicle. Brake fluid at high pressure may come out of the bleeder screws when they are opened.

The modulator assembly must be bled in the following sequence; No. 1 secondary sump, No. 2 primary sump, No. 3 primary accumulator and No. 4 secondary accumulator. To ensure proper operation of the ABS system.

1. Remove battery to gain access to modulator assembly No. 4 bleeder screws, then connect a battery to the vehicle using jumper cables.
2. Connect DRB II to diagnostic connector and ensure that CAB has no diagnostic trouble codes stored in its memory.
3. Attach bleeder tube to secondary sump bleeder screw, **Fig. 78.**

4. Use a pressure bleeder, or with the aid of an assistant, apply light and constant pressure on the brake pedal.
5. Loosen secondary sump bleeder screw, then using the DRB II select the Actuate Valves test mode and actuate LF Build/Decay Valve.
6. Bleed until a clear air free flow of brake fluid is coming out of the secondary sump bleeder screw, or brake pedal bottoms.
7. Tighten bleeder screw and release brake pedal, repeat steps 4 through 6 until a clean air free flow of brake fluid is coming out of secondary sump bleeder screw.
8. Using DRB II, select and actuate RR Build/Decay Valve. Repeat steps 4 through 7.
9. Attach bleeder tube to primary sump bleeder screw, **Fig. 78.**
10. Use a pressure bleeder, or with the aid of an assistant, apply light and constant pressure on the brake pedal.
11. Loosen primary sump bleeder screw, then using the DRB II select the Actuate Valves test mode and actuate RF Build/Decay Valve.
12. Bleed until a clear air free flow of brake fluid is coming out of the primary sump bleeder screw, or brake pedal bottoms.
13. Tighten bleeder screw and release brake pedal, repeat steps 10 through 12 until a clean air free flow of brake fluid is coming out of primary sump bleeder screw.
14. Using DRB II, select and actuate LR Build/Decay Valve. Repeat steps 10 through 13.
15. Attach bleeder tube to primary accumulator bleeder screw, **Fig. 78.**
16. Use a pressure bleeder, or with the aid of an assistant, apply light and constant pressure on the brake pedal.
17. Loosen primary accumulator bleeder screw, then using the DRB II select the Actuate Valves test mode and actuate RF/LR Isolation Valve.
18. Bleed until a clear air free flow of brake fluid is coming out of the primary accumulator bleeder screw, or brake pedal bottoms.
19. Tighten bleeder screw and release brake pedal, repeat steps 16 through 18 until a clean air free flow of brake fluid is coming out of primary accumulator bleeder screw.
20. Using DRB II, select and actuate RF Build/Decay Valve. Repeat steps 16 through 19.
21. Attach bleeder tube to secondary accumulator bleeder screw, **Fig. 78.**
22. Use a pressure bleeder, or with the aid of an assistant, apply light and constant pressure on the brake pedal.
23. Loosen secondary accumulator bleeder screw, then using the DRB II select the Actuate Valves test mode and actuate LF/RR Isolation Valve.
24. Bleed until a clear air free flow of brake fluid is coming out of the secondary accumulator bleeder screw, or brake pedal bottoms.

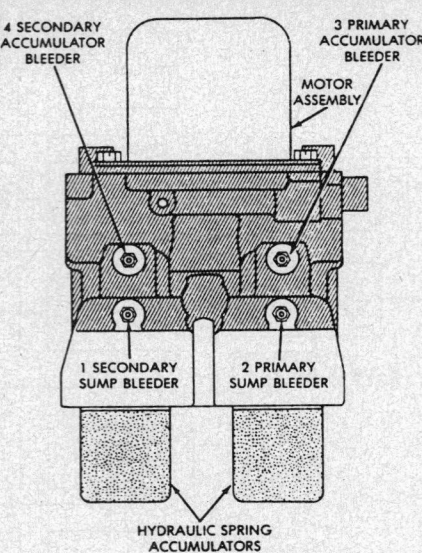

Fig. 78   ABS modulator assembly bleed

25. Tighten bleeder screw and release brake pedal, repeat steps 21 through 24 until a clean air free flow of brake fluid is coming out of secondary accumulator bleeder screw.
26. Using DRB II, select and actuate LF Build/Decay Valve. Repeat steps 21 through 25.

Component Replace
MODULATOR ASSEMBLY
Removal

1. Disconnect and remove battery, battery tray and acid shield that covers the modulator assembly.
2. Disconnect delta switch electrical connector from modulator assembly.
3. Remove top modulator assembly bracket to fender shield mounting bolt.
4. Disconnect two master cylinder supply tubes at modulator assembly, then loosen the tubes at the master cylinder so tubes can be swung out of the way without kinking them.
5. Raise and support vehicle.
6. Disconnect modulator assembly 10-way connector, then remove remaining hydraulic brake lines from modulator.
7. Remove modulator assembly bracket mounting bolt that is nearest the junction block.
8. Loosen but do not remove mounting bracket bolt that is nearest the radiator.
9. Lower vehicle, then remove modulator and bracket assembly.

Installation

1. Install modulator assembly into vehicle, using protruding tab on modulator to locate and hold assembly in place. Ensure bracket is held by front mounting bolt.

2. Install but do not tighten modulator bracket to fender shield mounting bolt.
3. Raise and support vehicle, then install mounting bracket bolt located nearest to the junction block. **Torque** both lower mounting bolts to 21 ft. lbs.
4. Attach four hydraulic fluid lines to modulator assembly and **torque** fittings to 12 ft. lbs.
5. Connect modulator assembly 10-way electrical connector.
6. Lower vehicle, then install two master cylinder supply tubes and **torque** fittings at modulator and master cylinder to 12 ft. lbs.
7. **Torque** modulator assembly to fender shield mounting bolt to 21 ft. lbs.
8. Bleed brake system, then install acid shield, battery tray and battery.

CONTROLLER ANTI-LOCK BRAKE (CAB)

1. Turn ignition off, then disconnect CAB and wiring harness 60-way connector. **Ensure ignition is in the OFF position.**
2. Remove CAB module bracket to frame mounting bolts.
3. Remove CAB module from vehicle.
4. Reverse procedure to install.

FRONT WHEEL SPEED SENSORS

1. Raise and support vehicle, then remove tire and wheel assembly.
2. Remove grommet retainer clip that holds grommet in to fender shield.
3. Remove two sensor routing tube to frame rail attaching screws.
4. Carefully pull sensor assembly grommet from fender shield.
5. Unplug connector from harness, then remove triangular retainer clip from bracket on strut damper.
6. Remove sensor head screw, then the sensor head from steering knuckle.
7. Reverse procedure to install.

REAR WHEEL SPEED SENSORS

1. Raise and support vehicle, then remove tire and wheel assemblies.
2. Remove sensor assembly grommet from underbody and pull harness through hole in underbody.
3. Unplug connector from harness, then remove sensor assembly grommets from bracket which is screwed into the body hose bracket, just forward of trailing arm bushing.
4. Remove sensor and brake tube assembly clip, located on inboard side of trailing arm.
5. Remove sensor wire fastener from rear brake hose bracket.
6. Remove outboard sensor assembly retainer nut, then the sensor head screw.
7. Remove sensor head from adapter assembly.
8. Reverse procedure to install.

Type 3—Bendix Anti-Lock 10 Braking System

NOTE: On Air Bag Equipped Models, Refer To "Air Bag System Precautions" Located In The Front Of This Manual For System Disarming & Arming Procedures.

INDEX

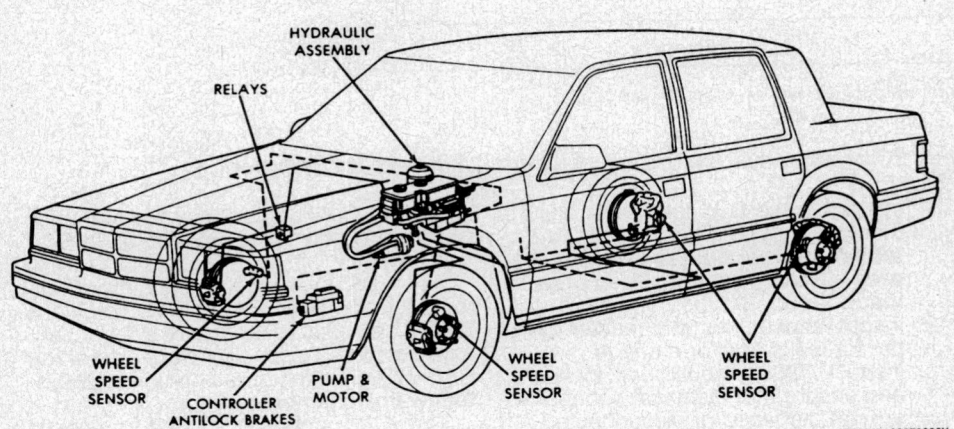

Fig. 1   Bendix Anti-Lock 10 brake system components

PRECAUTIONS

AIR BAG SYSTEMS

Refer to "Air Bag System Precautions" in the front of this manual for system disarming and arming procedures.

GENERAL

Use the following general precautions whenever servicing the ABS system:
1. If any welding work is to be performed using an arc welder, CAB should be disconnected.
2. When the ignition switch is in the ON position, the CAB electrical connector should not be disconnected or connected.
3. Some components of the ABS system are not serviced separately and must be serviced as complete assemblies.

Do not disassemble any component which is designated as non-serviceable.

DE-PRESSURIZING HYDRAULIC ACCUMULATOR

The ABS pump/motor assembly will keep the hydraulic accumulator charged to a pressure between 1600-2000 psi anytime the ignition is in the ON position. The pump/motor cannot run if the ignition is off or either battery cable is disconnected.

The hydraulic accumulator should be depressurized before disassembling any portion of the hydraulic system.
1. Turn ignition switch to the OFF position, or disconnect battery ground cable.
2. Pump brake pedal a minimum of 40 times using approximately 50 pounds

of pedal force. Pedal feel should change noticeably when accumulator is discharged.
3. After a definite increase in pedal effort is felt, pump pedal a few additional times. This will remove all hydraulic pressure from the system.

DESCRIPTION

SYSTEM

The Anti-Lock Braking System (ABS) prevents the wheels from locking up when braking, regardless of the surface conditions. This allows the car to stop in a shorter distance, and allows the driver to maintain directional control of the vehicle during heavy braking.

During normal braking conditions, the ABS operates like a conventional diagonally split, hydraulic power assist system. During heavy braking, however, each wheel's braking pressure is modulated according to its speed. To maintain vehicle stability, both rear wheels receive the same signal.

There are four major components, **Fig. 1**, in this ABS system that act in unison to control brake operation.

COMPONENTS

ABS Warning Lamp

The Anti-Lock warning light will normally come on for approximately one to two seconds when the ignition switch is first turned to the ON position.

Anytime the Controller Anti-Lock Brake (CAB) detects a condition which results in a shutdown of the ABS function other than when the ignition switch is first turned on it will activate the ABS warning lamp. When the light is on only the Anti-Lock function of the brake system is affected. The standard brake system and ability to stop the vehicle will not be affected.

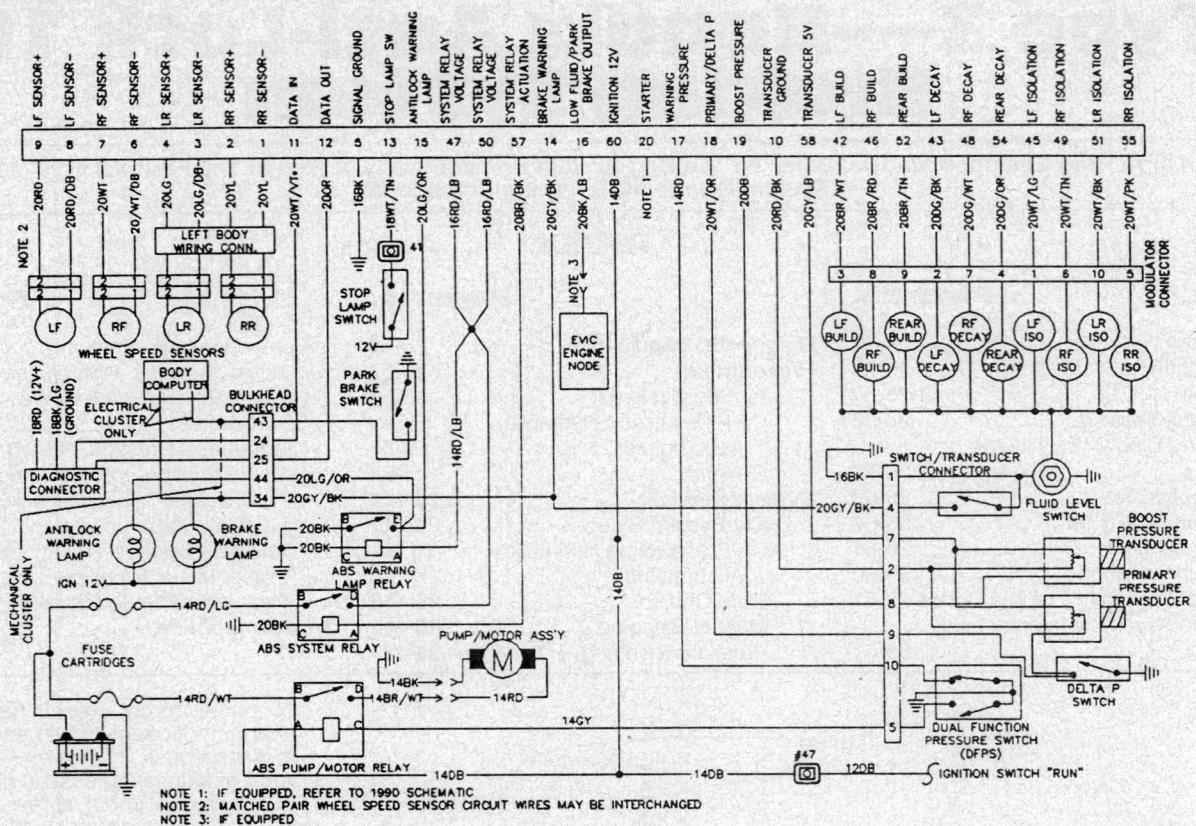

Fig. 2 Bendix Anti-Lock 10 braking system wiring diagram. 1992 except Premier

Hydraulic Assembly

This ABS system uses an integral hydraulic assembly which contains the wheel circuit valves used for brake pressure modulation.

Wheel Speed Sensors

The wheel speed sensors are located at each wheel and transmit wheel speed information to the Controller Anti-Lock Brake.

Controller Anti-Lock Brake (CAB)

The Controller Anti-Lock Brake (CAB) is located on the front lefthand side of the engine compartment. The CAB uses the wheel speed information from the wheel speed sensors to control the ABS system function. The CAB also monitors ABS operation and detects system faults.

Pump/Motor Assembly

The Pump/Motor assembly is located under the hydraulic assembly at the rear lefthand side of the engine compartment. This pump is electrically driven and takes low pressure brake fluid from the hydraulic assembly reservoir and pressurizes it for storage in two accumulators for power assist and anti-lock braking.

TROUBLESHOOTING

Visually inspect system components and their connectors as described below prior to troubleshooting the system or performing diagnostic tests.

1. Inspect brake fluid level, and ensure that fluid is not contaminated. **To establish proper fluid level, fully depress brake pedal 40 times prior to inspection.**
2. Inspect brake lines and master cylinder for leaks and/or damage.
3. Inspect ABS hydraulic unit for leaks, and ensure that electrical connectors are not damaged or disconnected.
4. Inspect Power Distribution Center (PDC) and ensure that all ABS relays are properly installed.
5. Inspect CAB for a secure mounting, and ensure that its electrical connector is not damaged or loose.
6. Inspect all wheel speed sensors (WSS) and their connectors for damage or improper connections.

Refer to wiring diagrams and connector identifications, **Figs. 2 through 6,** when performing testing procedures.

DIAGNOSIS & TESTING

Accessing Diagnostic Trouble Codes

The Bendix Anti-Lock 10 Brake System has self diagnosis capability. The self diagnosis cycle begins when the ignition switch is in the On position. An electrical check is completed on the ABS components such as wheel speed sensor continuity, system continuity and other relay continuity. During this check the Anti-Lock Light will be on for approximately one to two seconds.

The ABS system is constantly monitored by the CAB. If the CAB detects a fault, it can disable the brake system anti-lock function. Depending on the fault the CAB will light either one or both brake system warning lamps.

The CAB contains a Self-Diagnostic Program which activates the indicator lights when a system fault is detected. Faults are stored in a diagnostic program memory. There are 19 diagnostic trouble codes which may be stored in the CAB and displayed through the DRB II. These diagnostic trouble codes will remain in the memory even after the ignition switch is turned off.

The ABS system has a self diagnostic connector located under the lefthand side of the instrument panel, left of the steering column. The diagnostic connector is a blue 6-way connector which can be connected to a DRB II readout box.

After connecting the DRB II the the diagnostic connector follow the DRB I manufacture instructions to further diagnose the ABS system.

1. **All diagnostic test procedures assume a Chrysler Diagnostic Readout Box (DRB II) is being used. Tests have been designed specifically for the DRB II.**
2. After completion of diagnosis and repair of the system, perform any verification test provided.

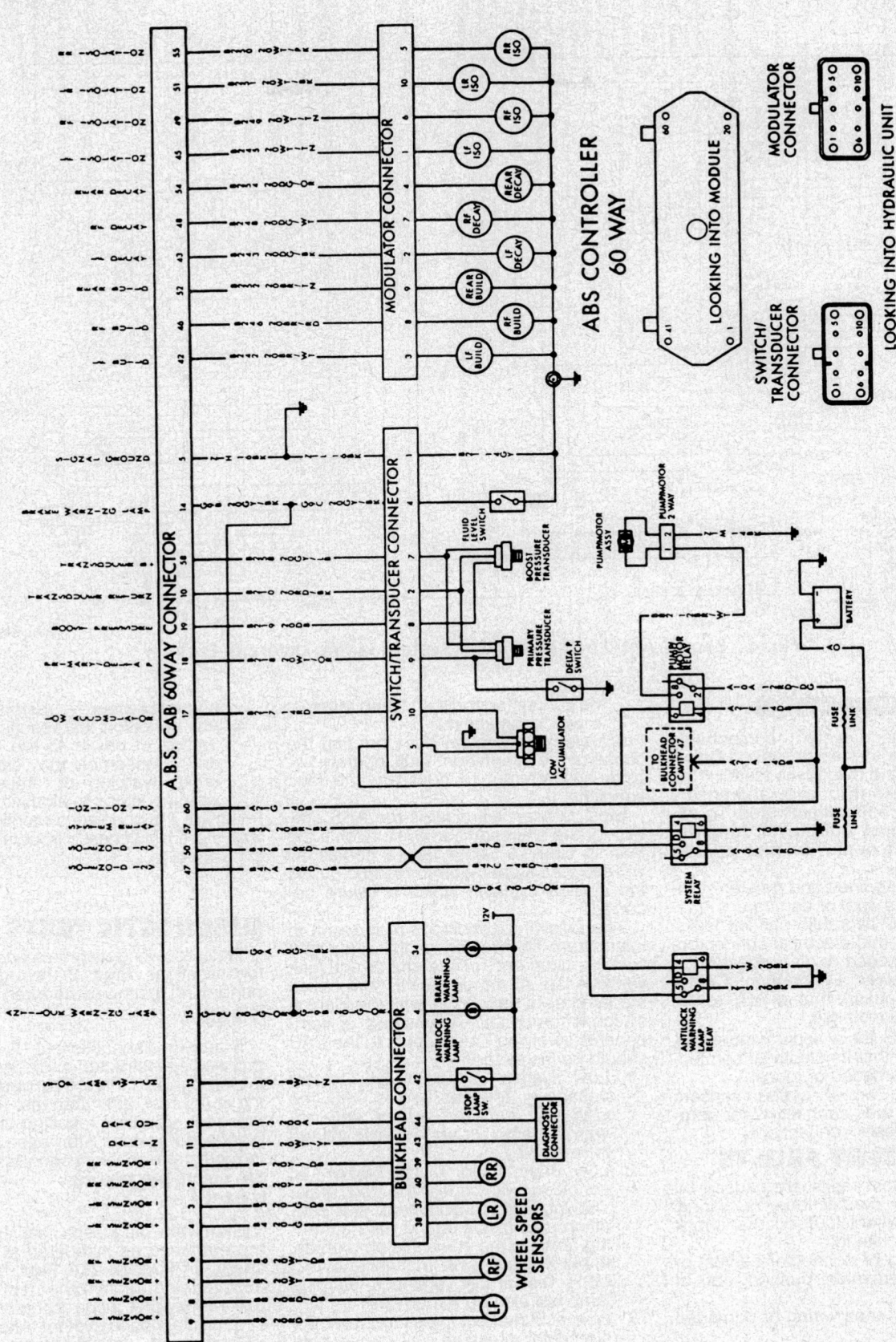

Fig. 3 Bendix Anti-Lock 10 braking system wiring diagram. 1993

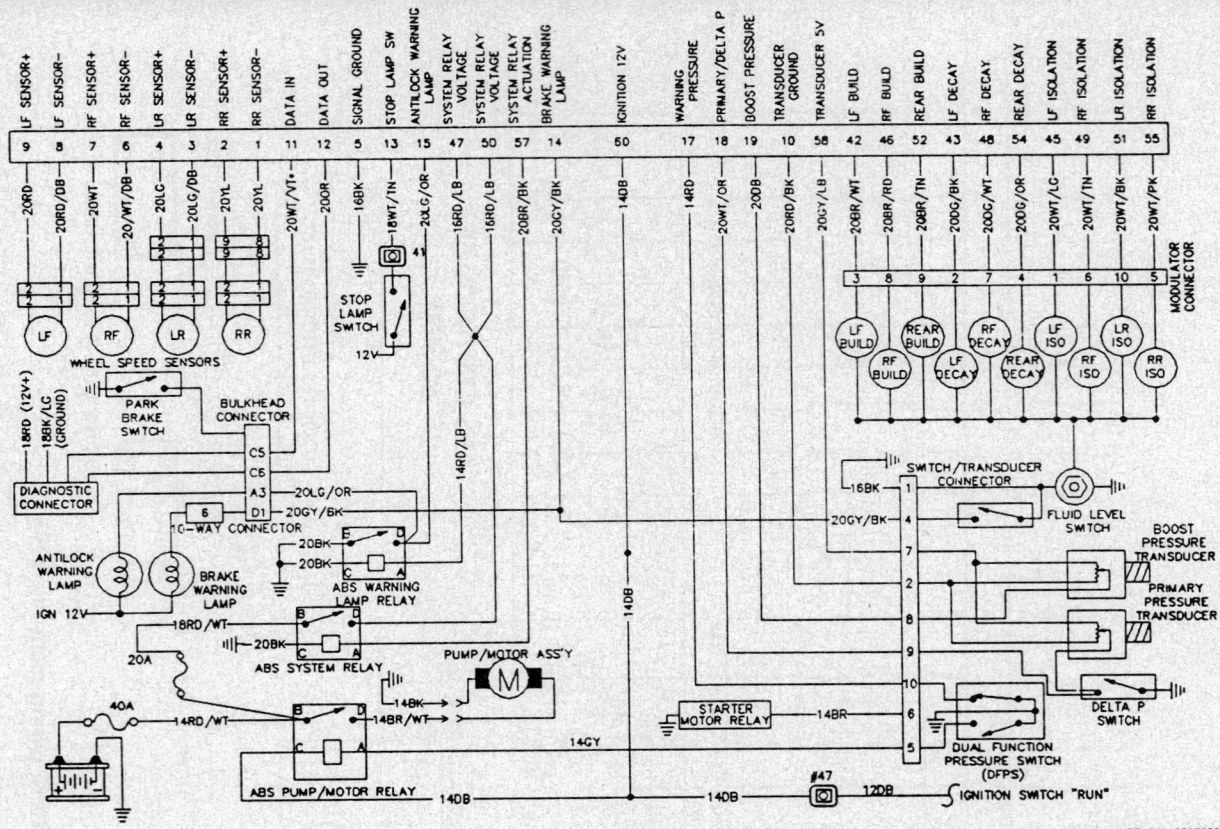

Fig. 4 Bendix Anti-Lock 10 braking system wiring diagram. Premier

VISUAL INSPECTION

Visually inspect system components and their connectors as described below prior to performing diagnostic tests.

1. Inspect brake fluid level, and ensure that fluid is not contaminated. **To establish proper fluid level, fully depress brake pedal 40 times prior to inspection.**
2. Inspect brake lines and master cylinder for leaks and/or damage.
3. Inspect ABS hydraulic unit for leaks, and ensure that electrical connectors are not damaged or disconnected.
4. Inspect Power Distribution Center (PDC) and ensure that all ABS relays are properly installed.
5. Inspect CAB for a secure mounting, and ensure that its electrical connector is not damaged or loose.
6. Inspect all wheel speed sensors (WSS) and their connectors for damage or improper connections.

INTERMITTENT FAULTS

Most intermittent faults are caused by faulty electrical connections or wiring. When an intermittent fault occurs, check the following circuits for:

1. Poor mating of connector halves, or electrical terminals pushed out of connectors.
2. Improperly routed wiring or damaged connectors.
3. Poor terminal to wire contact. This requires removal of the terminal from

the connector and inspection terminal to wire connection.

If a visual inspection does not find the cause of the intermittent fault, operate vehicle and attempt to duplicate the fault condition.

Most failures will disable the ABS system for the entire ignition cycle even if the fault is cleared. Some failure conditions will allow ABS operation to resume during the ignition cycle in which a failure occurred.

The following conditions may result in intermittent illumination of the red brake warning lamp and/or the amber anti-lock warning lap. All other failures will cause the lamp(s) to reman On until the ignition switch is turned Off. Circuits and/or components involving these inputs to the CAB should be inspected.

1. Low system voltage. If low system voltage is detected by the CAB, the CAB will turn the amber anti-lock warning lamp On until normal voltage is restored.
2. Low Brake Fluid. A low brake fluid condition will cause the red brake warning lamp to illuminate. This condition may exists during hard cornering or while the vehicle is on a grade. If the vehicle is in motion above 3 MPH the amber anti-lock warning lamp will also be turned On.
3. Low accumulator pressure. Low accumulator pressure will cause both the red brake warning and amber anti-lock warning lamps to illuminate until

normal pressure is restored.

4. Any condition that results in an interruption of power to the CAB or hydraulic assembly may cause the red brake warning or amber anti-lock warning lamps to illuminate.

Any of the conditions mentioned above can store a diagnostic trouble code in the CAB module.

DIAGNOSTIC TESTS

Refer to wiring diagrams and connector identifications, **Figs. 2 through 6,** when performing testing procedures.

1992

Start with diagnostic test 1A, **Fig. 7,** then proceed as instructed to diagnostic charts 2A through 25C, **Figs. 8 through 88.** Starting at any test other than test 1A may give incorrect results resulting in a misdiagnosed system. After each test is performed, perform verification test 24A, **Fig. 85,** before proceeding.

1993

Start with diagnostic test 1A, **Fig. 89,** then proceed as instructed to diagnostic charts 2A through 26A, **Figs. 90 through 155.** Starting at any other test other than test 1A may give incorrect results resulting in a misdiagnosed system. After each test is performed, perform verification tests VER-1A through VER-1E, **Figs. 156 through 160,** before proceeding.

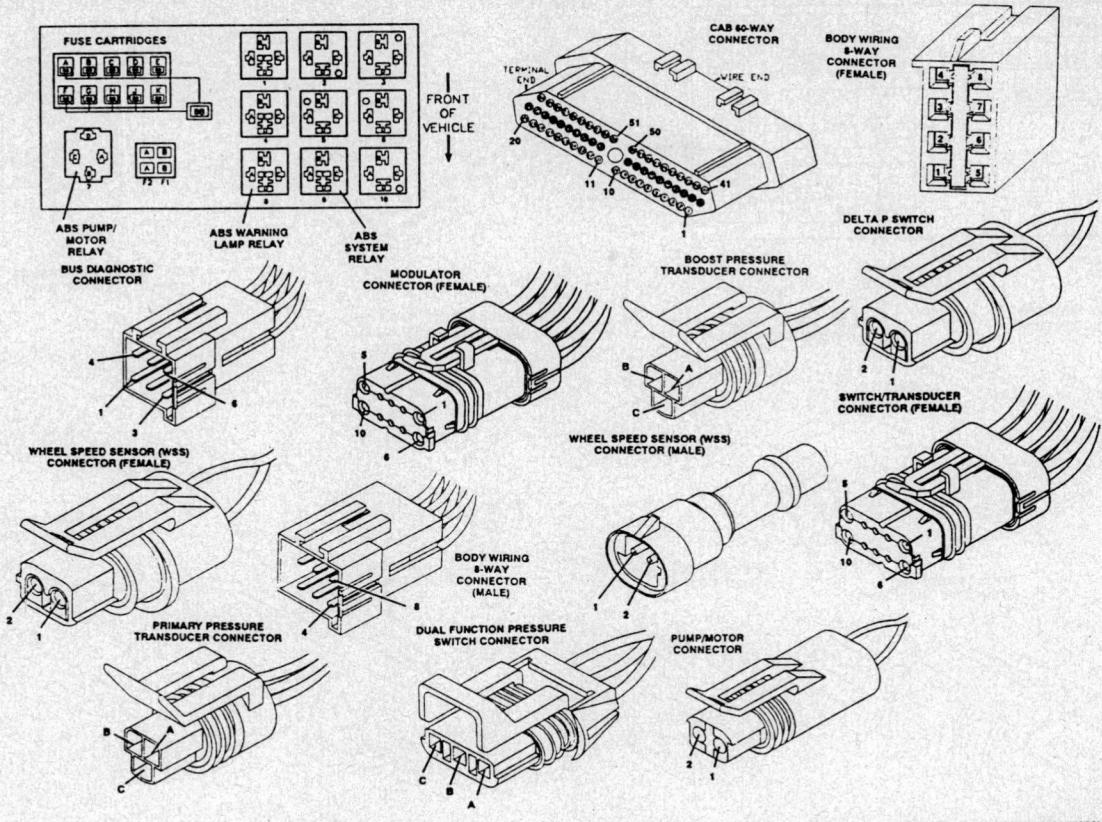

Fig. 5   Bendix Anti-Lock 10 braking system connector identification. Except Premier

PRESSURE TESTER

Some diagnostic procedures require the use of pressure tester gauge tool No. MST-6163 or equivalent and an adapter. The pressure gauge is required to measure accumulator pressure during certain phases of ABS operation. The pressure gauge should be installed as follows:

1. De-pressurize the system as outlined under "Precautions."
2. Remove hydraulic assembly accumulator port plug located on the right side of the assembly, **Fig. 161.**
3. Connect pressure gauge to hydraulic assembly adapter tool No. MST-6491A or equivalent, then install into accumulator port of hydraulic assembly and **torque** adapter to 7.5 ft. lbs.
4. Install pressure gauge and hose assembly tool No. MST-6163 or equivalent onto adapter tool No. MST-6505 or equivalent and **torque** hose fitting to 11 ft. lbs.
5. Install pressure gauge and hose assembly onto adapter installed on hydraulic assembly. Install the retaining clip into groove on adapter. **Ensure retaining clip is installed on the adapter correctly before proceeding.**
6. After test is performed, de-pressure hydraulic accumulator, remove special tools and install accumulator port plug and **torque** to 9 ft. lbs.

It is not necessary to bleed the brake system after installation and removal of the pressure gauge unless additional tubes or fittings were removed or loosened.

Clearing Diagnostic Trouble Codes

Diagnostic trouble codes can be cleared by using the DRB II diagnostics tester, or they will be automatically cleared after 50 ignition switch ON/OFF cycles.

Hydraulic Assembly Internal Leak Test

Some diagnostic procedures require testing the hydraulic assembly for internal leaks. This is made possible by using the ABS hydraulic circuit test gauge tool No. 6685 or equivalent. The test gauge installation and operation procedure is as follows:

1. De-pressurize the system as outlined under "Precautions."
2. Remove wiring harness connector from dual function pressure switch on bottom of hydraulic assembly.
3. Connect wiring harness from test gauge tool into wiring harness removed from dual function pressure switch.

4. Locate high pressure brake fluid hose going rom hydraulic assembly to pump/motor.
5. Remove high pressure hose tube nut from fitting on hydraulic assembly, **Fig. 162.**
6. Verify shutoff valve on test gauge in in the open position then install test gauge tool inline with high pressure hose. **Torque** test gauge tool to hydraulic assembly fitting and high pressure brake fluid hose to test gauge tool fitting to 145 inch lbs.
7. Install MST-6163 pressure tester tool or equivalent as outlined under "Pressure Tester" in this section.
8. Perform the required diagnostic test to diagnose the failure and make required repairs.
9. De-pressurize the system as outlined under "Precautions."
10. Remove all special tools.
11. Install accumulator port plug and **torque** to 9 ft. lbs.
12. Install high pressure brake fluid hose and **torque fitting to 145 inch lbs.**
13. Turn ignition switch to the Run position to energize the pump/motor assembly and pressurize hydraulic assembly system then check for leaks.
14. Again de-pressurize the system as outlined under "Precautions."
15. Check brake fluid level in the hydraulic assembly reservoir. If low, fill with DOT 3 brake fluid.

Continued on page 25-117

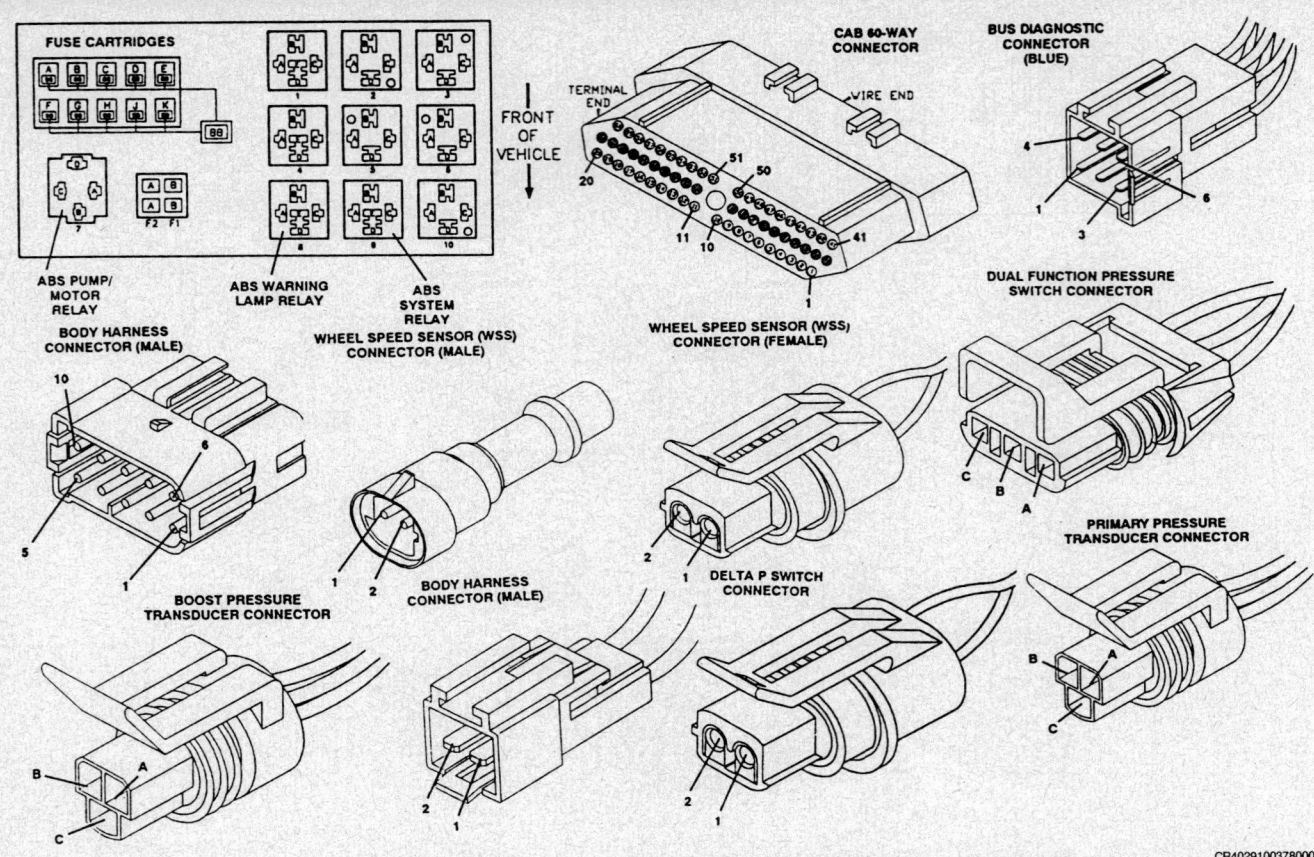

Fig. 6   Bendix Anti-Lock 10 braking system connector identification. Premier

CR4029100378000X

DIAGNOSTIC CHART INDEX

Test No.	Symptom	Page No.	Fig. No
1992			
1A	**Read Fault Message**	25-65	7
1B	**Read Fault Message**	25-65	8
2A	**Modulator Fault**	25-66	9
3A	**Modulator Fault**	25-66	10
3B	**Modulator Fault**	25-67	11
3C	**Modulator Fault**	25-67	12
3D	**Modulator Fault**	25-67	13
3E	**Modulator Fault**	25-68	14
3F	**Modulator Fault**	25-68	15
3G	**Modulator Fault**	25-68	16
3H	**Modulator Fault**	25-68	17
3J	**Modulator Fault**	25-69	18
3K	**Modulator Fault**	25-69	19
3L	**Modulator Fault**	25-69	20
4A	**Solenoid Undervoltage Fault**	25-69	21
4B	**Solenoid Undervoltage Fault**	25-70	22
5A	**Low Fluid/Park Brake Fault**	25-71	23
5B	**Low Fluid/Park Brake Fault**	25-72	24
5C	**Low Fluid/Park Brake Fault**	25-72	25
5D	**Low Fluid/Park Brake Fault**	25-72	26
5E	**Low Fluid/Park Brake Fault**	25-73	27
5F	**Low Fluid/Park Brake Fault**	25-73	28
6A	**System Relay Fault**	25-73	29

Continued

DIAGNOSTIC CHART INDEX—Continued

Test No.	Symptom	Page No.	Fig. No.
1992 -Continued			
7A	Low Accumulator Fault	25-74	30
8A	Boost Pressure Fault	25-74	31
8B	Boost Pressure Fault	25-74	32
8C	Boost Pressure Fault	25-75	33
8D	Boost Pressure Fault	25-75	34
9A	Right Rear Wheel Speed Sensor Continuity Fault	25-76	35
9B	Right Rear Wheel Speed Sensor Continuity Fault	25-76	36
9C	Right Rear Wheel Speed Sensor Continuity Fault	25-76	37
9D	Right Rear Wheel Speed Sensor Continuity Fault	25-76	38
9E	Right Rear Wheel Speed Sensor Continuity Fault	25-77	39
9F	Right Rear Wheel Speed Sensor Continuity Fault	25-77	40
9G	Right Rear Wheel Speed Sensor Continuity Fault	25-77	41
9H	Right Rear Wheel Speed Sensor Continuity Fault	25-77	42
9J	Right Rear Wheel Speed Sensor Continuity Fault	25-77	43
9K	Right Rear Wheel Speed Sensor Continuity Fault	25-78	44
9L	Right Rear Wheel Speed Sensor Continuity Fault	25-78	45
9M	Right Rear Wheel Speed Sensor Continuity Fault	25-78	46
9N	Right Rear Wheel Speed Sensor Continuity Fault	25-78	47
10A	Left Rear Wheel Speed Sensor Continuity Fault	25-78	48
10B	Left Rear Wheel Speed Sensor Continuity Fault	25-79	49
10C	Left Rear Wheel Speed Sensor Continuity Fault	25-79	50
10D	Left Rear Wheel Speed Sensor Continuity Fault	25-79	51
10E	Left Rear Wheel Speed Sensor Continuity Fault	25-79	52
10F	Left Rear Wheel Speed Sensor Continuity Fault	25-79	53
10G	Left Rear Wheel Speed Sensor Continuity Fault	25-80	54
10H	Left Rear Wheel Speed Sensor Continuity Fault	25-80	55
10J	Left Rear Wheel Speed Sensor Continuity Fault	25-80	56
10K	Left Rear Wheel Speed Sensor Continuity Fault	25-80	57
10L	Left Rear Wheel Speed Sensor Continuity Fault	25-80	58
10M	Left Rear Wheel Speed Sensor Continuity Fault	25-80	59
10N	Left Rear Wheel Speed Sensor Continuity Fault	25-81	60
11A	Right Front Wheel Speed Sensor Continuity Fault	25-81	61
12A	Left Front Wheel Speed Sensor Continuity Fault	25-81	62
13A	Right Rear Wheel Speed Sensor Fault	25-82	63
14A	Left Rear Wheel Speed Sensor Fault	25-82	64
15A	Right Front Wheel Speed Sensor Fault	25-82	65
16A	Left Front Wheel Speed Sensor Fault	25-83	66
17A	Primary Pressure/Delta P Fault	25-83	67
17B	Primary Pressure/Delta P Fault	25-84	68
17C	Primary Pressure/Delta P Fault	25-84	69
17D	Primary Pressure/Delta P Fault	25-84	70
17E	Primary Pressure/Delta P Fault	25-85	71
18A	Anti-Lock Lamp Fault	25-85	72
18B	Anti-Lock Lamp Fault	25-85	73
19A	Anti-Lock Lamp Relay Fault	25-85	74
19B	Anti-Lock Lamp Relay Fault	25-86	75
20A	Excess Decay Fault	25-86	76
21A	Hydraulic Pump/Motor Circuit Test	25-87	77
21B	Hydraulic Pump/Motor Circuit Test	25-87	78
21C	Hydraulic Pump/Motor Circuit Test	25-88	79
21D	Hydraulic Pump/Motor Circuit Test	25-88	80
21E	Hydraulic Pump/Motor Circuit Test	25-89	81

Continued

DIAGNOSTIC CHART INDEX —Continued

Test No.	Symptom	Page No.	Fig. No.
1992 -Continued			
22A	Hydraulic Pressure Performance Test	25-89	82
22B	Hydraulic Pressure Performance Test	25-89	83
23A	Stop Lamp Switch Input Test	25-90	84
24A	System Verification Test	25-90	85
25A	DRB II Error Messages	25-90	86
25B	DRB II Error Messages	25-90	87
25C	DRB II Error Messages	25-91	88
1993			
1A	Checking System For Faults	25-91	89
2A	Repairing " Cab Fault"	25-92	90
3A	Repairing " Modulator Fault"	25-92	91
3B	Repairing " Modulator Fault," LF Build Valve	25-93	92
3C	Repairing " Modulator Fault," RF Build Valve	25-93	93
3D	Repairing " Modulator Fault," RR/LR Build Valve	25-93	94
3E	Repairing " Modulator Fault," LF Decay Valve	25-94	95
3F	Repairing " Modulator Fault," RF Decay Valve	25-94	96
3G	Repairing " Modulator Fault," RR/LR Decay Valve	25-94	97
3H	Repairing " Modulator Fault," LF Isolation Valve	25-94	98
3J	Repairing " Modulator Fault," RF Isolation Valve	25-95	99
3K	Repairing " Modulator Fault," LR Isolation Valve	25-95	100
3L	Repairing " Modulator Fault," RR Isolation Valve	25-95	101
4A	Repairing " Solenoid Undervoltage Fault"	25-95	102
4B	Repairing " Solenoid Undervoltage Fault"	25-96	103
4C	Repairing " Solenoid Undervoltage Fault"	25-97	104
5A	Repairing " Low Fluid/Parking Brake" Fault	25-97	105
5B	Repairing " Low Fluid/Parking Brake" Fault	25-97	106
5C	Repairing " Low Fluid/Parking Brake" Fault	25-97	107
5D	Repairing " Low Fluid/Parking Brake" Fault	25-98	108
6A	Repairing " System Relay Fault"	25-98	109
6B	Repairing " System Relay Fault"	25-98	110
7A	Repairing " Low Accumulator Fault"	25-99	111
7B	Repairing " Low Accumulator Fault"	25-99	112
8A	Repairing " Boost Pressure Fault"	25-100	113
8B	Repairing " Boost Pressure Fault"	25-100	114
8C	Repairing " Boost Pressure Fault"	25-100	115
8D	Repairing " Boost Pressure Fault"	25-101	116
9A	Repairing " RR Wheel Speed Sensor Continuity Faulty"	25-101	117
9B	Repairing " RR Wheel Speed Sensor Continuity Faulty"	25-101	118
9C	Repairing " RR Wheel Speed Sensor Continuity Faulty"	25-102	119
9D	Repairing " RR Wheel Speed Sensor Continuity Faulty"	25-102	120
9E	Repairing " RR Wheel Speed Sensor Continuity Faulty"	25-103	121
10A	Repairing " LR Wheel Speed Sensor Continuity Fault"	25-103	122
10B	Repairing " LR Wheel Speed Sensor Continuity Fault"	25-104	123
10C	Repairing " LR Wheel Speed Sensor Continuity Fault"	25-104	124
10D	Repairing " LR Wheel Speed Sensor Continuity Fault"	25-105	125
10E	Repairing " LR Wheel Speed Sensor Continuity Fault"	25-105	126
11A	Repairing " RF Wheel Speed Sensor Continuity Fault"	25-106	127
12A	Repairing " LF Wheel Speed Sensor Continuity Fault"	25-106	128
13A	Repairing " Right Rear Wheel Speed Sensor Fault"	25-107	129
14A	Repairing " Left Rear Wheel Speed Sensor Fault"	25-107	130
15A	Repairing " Right Front Wheel Speed Sensor Fault"	25-107	131
16A	Repairing " Left Front Speed Sensor Fault"	25-108	132

Continued

DIAGNOSTIC CHART INDEX—Continued

Test No.	Symptom	Page No.	Fig. No.
1993			
17A	Repairing " Primary Pressure/Delta Pressure Fault"	25-108	133
17B	Repairing " Primary Pressure/Delta Pressure Fault"	25-108	134
17C	Repairing " Primary Pressure/Delta Pressure Fault"	25-109	135
17D	Repairing " Primary Pressure/Delta Pressure Fault"	25-109	136
17E	Repairing " Primary Pressure/Delta Pressure Fault"	25-109	137
17F	Repairing " Primary Pressure/Delta Pressure Fault"	25-109	138
18A	Repairing " Anti-lock Lamp Fault"	25-110	139
18B	Repairing " Anti-lock Lamp Fault"	25-110	140
19A	Repairing " Anti-lock Lamp Relay Fault"	25-110	141
20A	Repairing " Excess Decay Fault"	25-111	142
21A	Hydraulic Pump/Motor Circuit Test	25-111	143
21B	Hydraulic Pump/Motor Circuit Test	25-111	144
21C	Hydraulic Pump/Motor Circuit Test	25-112	145
22A	Hydraulic Pressure Performance Test	25-113	146
22B	Hydraulic Pressure Performance Test	25-113	147
22C	Hydraulic Pressure Performance Test	25-113	148
22D	Hydraulic Pressure Performance Test	25-114	149
23A	Correcting " No Response" Condition	25-114	150
24A	Complaint " Hard" Pedal Or Clicking Noise	25-115	151
24B	Complaint " Hard" Pedal Or Clicking Noise	25-115	152
24C	Complaint " Hard" Pedal Or Clicking Noise	25-115	153
25A	Complaint Of Noisy Pump/Motor Or Excessive Run Time	25-115	154
26A	Complaint Of Scraping/Whirring Noise	25-115	155
VER-1A	Verification Test	25-116	156
VER-1B	Repairing Stop Lamp Switch Sense Input Circuit	25-116	157
VER-1C	Repairing Accumulator Switch Sense Circuit	25-116	158
VER-1D	Repairing Pressure Transducer Return Circuit	25-116	159
VER-1E	Repairing Pressure Transducer 5-Volt Feed Circuit	25-117	160

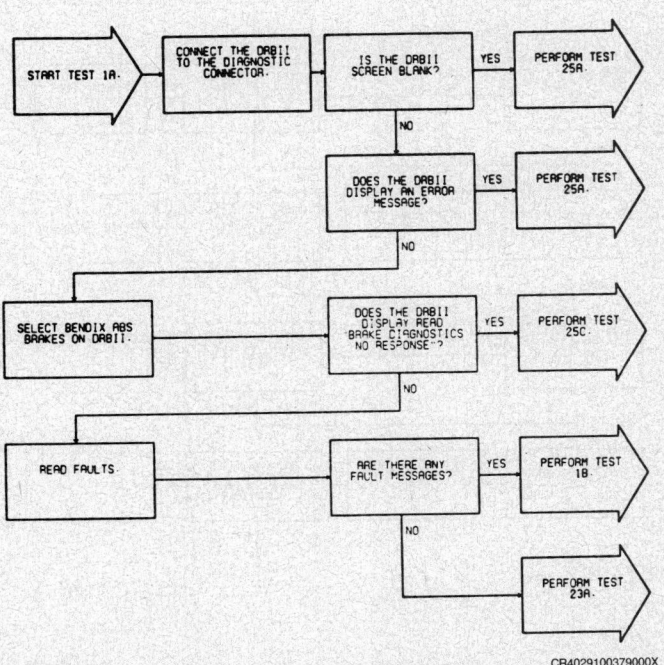

FAULT MESSAGES

CAB FAULT	Perform TEST 2A
MODULATOR FAULT	Perform TEST 3A
SOLENOID UNDERVOLT	Perform TEST 4A
LOW FLUID/PARK BRAKE	Perform TEST 5A
SYSTEM RELAY	Perform TEST 6A
LOW ACCUMULATOR	Perform TEST 7A
PRIMARY PRESS/DELTA P	Perform TEST 17A
BOOST PRESSURE	Perform TEST 8A
RIGHT REAR CONTIN	Perform TEST 9A
LEFT REAR CONTIN	Perform TEST 10A
RIGHT FRONT CONTIN	Perform TEST 11A
LEFT FRONT CONTIN	Perform TEST 12A
RIGHT REAR SENSOR	Perform TEST 13A
LEFT REAR SENSOR	Perform TEST 14A
RIGHT FRONT SENSOR	Perform TEST 15A
LEFT FRONT SENSOR	Perform TEST 16A
ANTILOCK LIGHT	Perform TEST 18A
ANTILOCK LIGHT RELAY	Perform TEST 19A
EXCESS DECAY FAULT	Perform TEST 20A

CR4029100379000X   CR4029100380000X

Fig. 7   Test 1A: Read Fault Message   **Fig. 8   Test 1B: Read Fault Message**

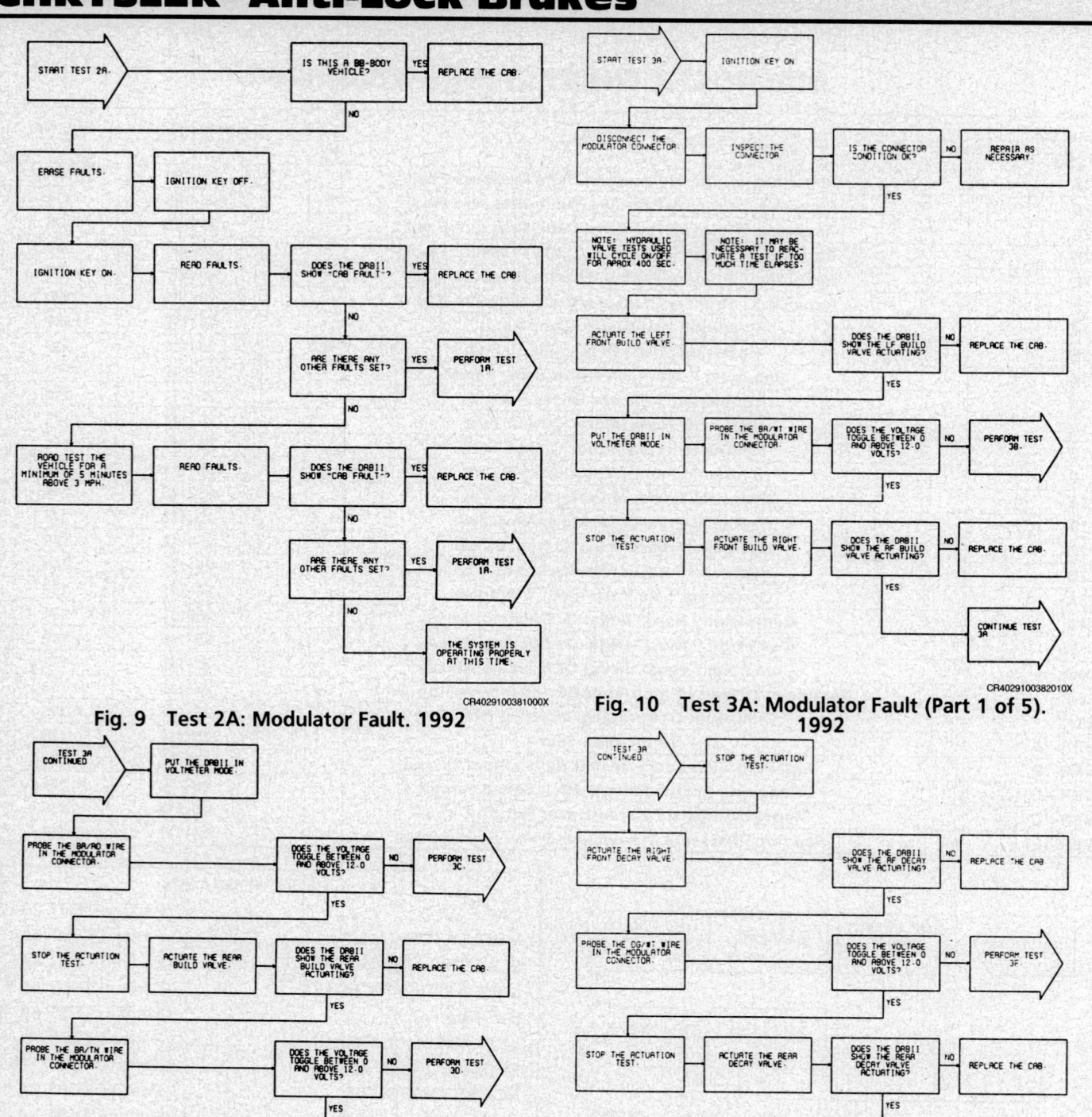

Fig. 9 Test 2A: Modulator Fault. 1992

Fig. 10 Test 3A: Modulator Fault (Part 1 of 5). 1992

Fig. 10 Test 3A: Modulator Fault (Part 2 of 5). 1992

Fig. 10 Test 3A: Modulator Fault (Part 3 of 5). 1992

TYPE 3-BENDIX ANTI-LOCK 10 BRAKING SYSTEM

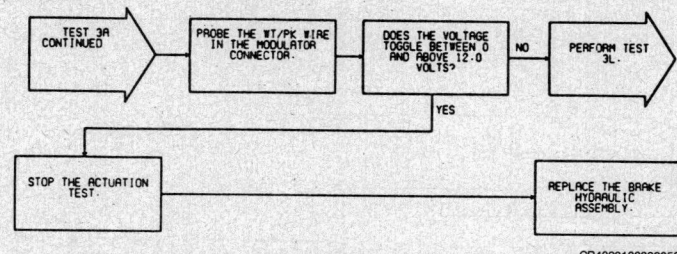

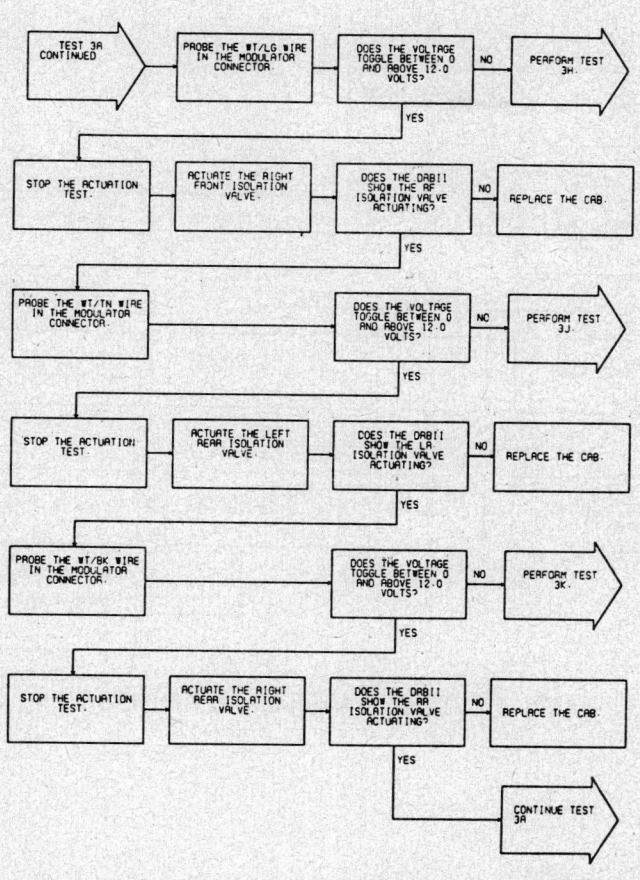

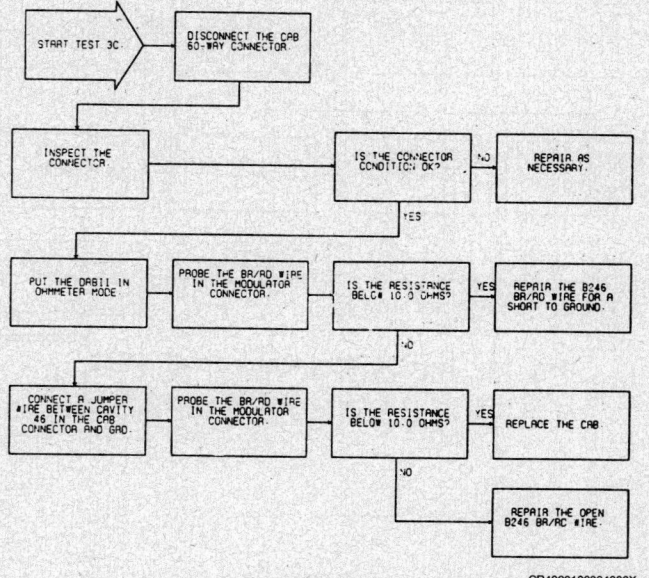

Fig. 10   Test 3A: Modulator Fault (Part 5 of 5). 1992

Fig. 10   Test 3A: Modulator Fault (Part 4 of 5). 1992

Fig. 12   Test 3C: Modulator Fault. 1992

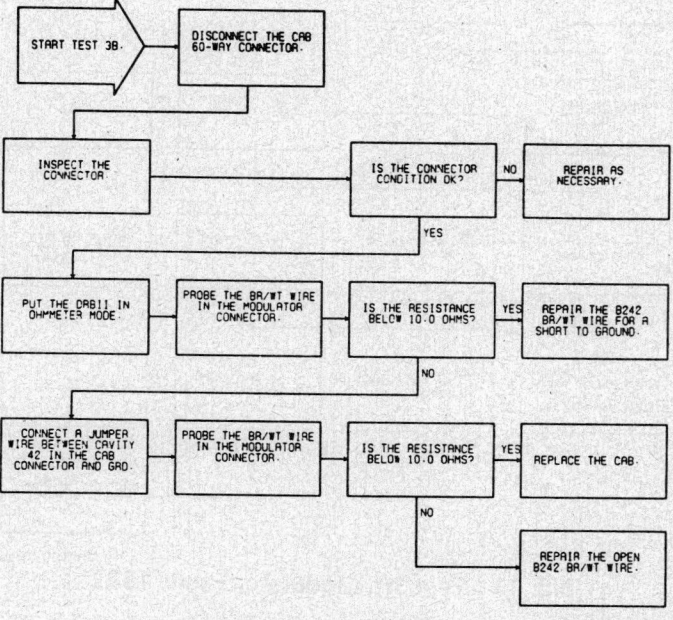

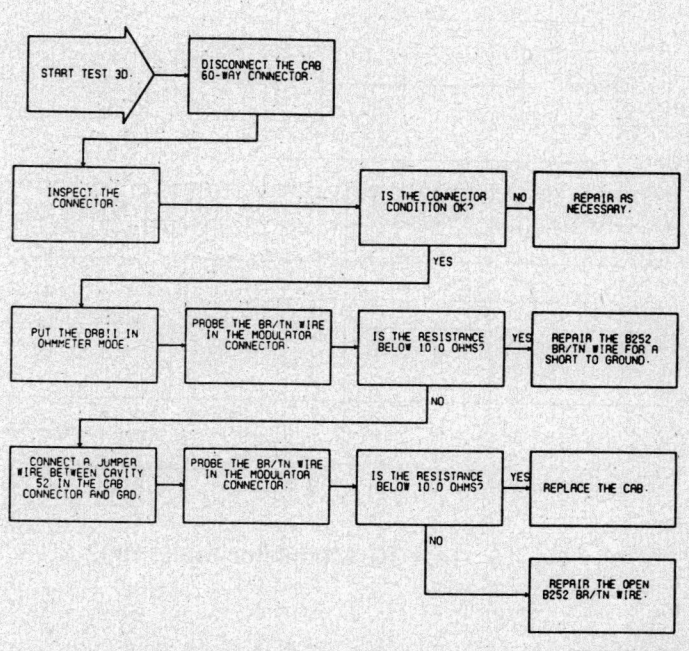

Fig. 11   Test 3B: Modulator Fault. 1992

Fig. 13   Test 3D: Modulator Fault. 1992

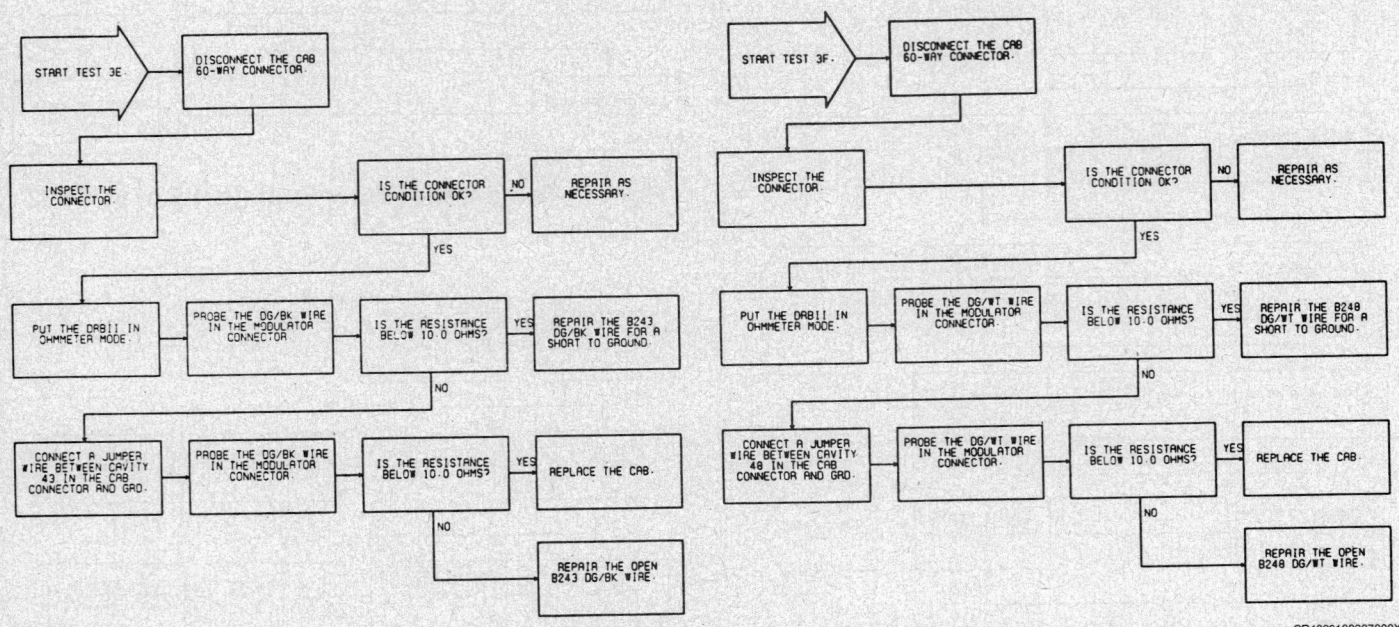

Fig. 14 Test 3E: Modulator Fault. 1992

Fig. 15 Test 3F: Modulator Fault. 1992

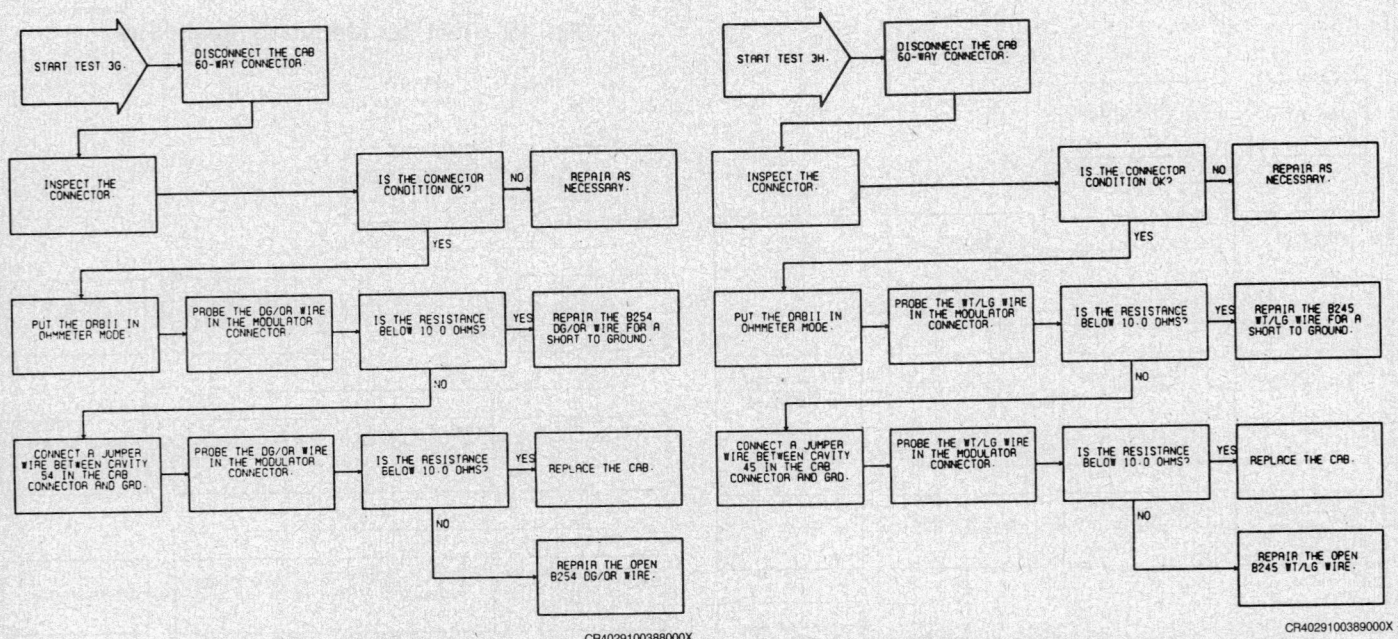

Fig. 16 Test 3G: Modulator Fault. 1992

Fig. 17 Test 3H: Modulator Fault. 1992

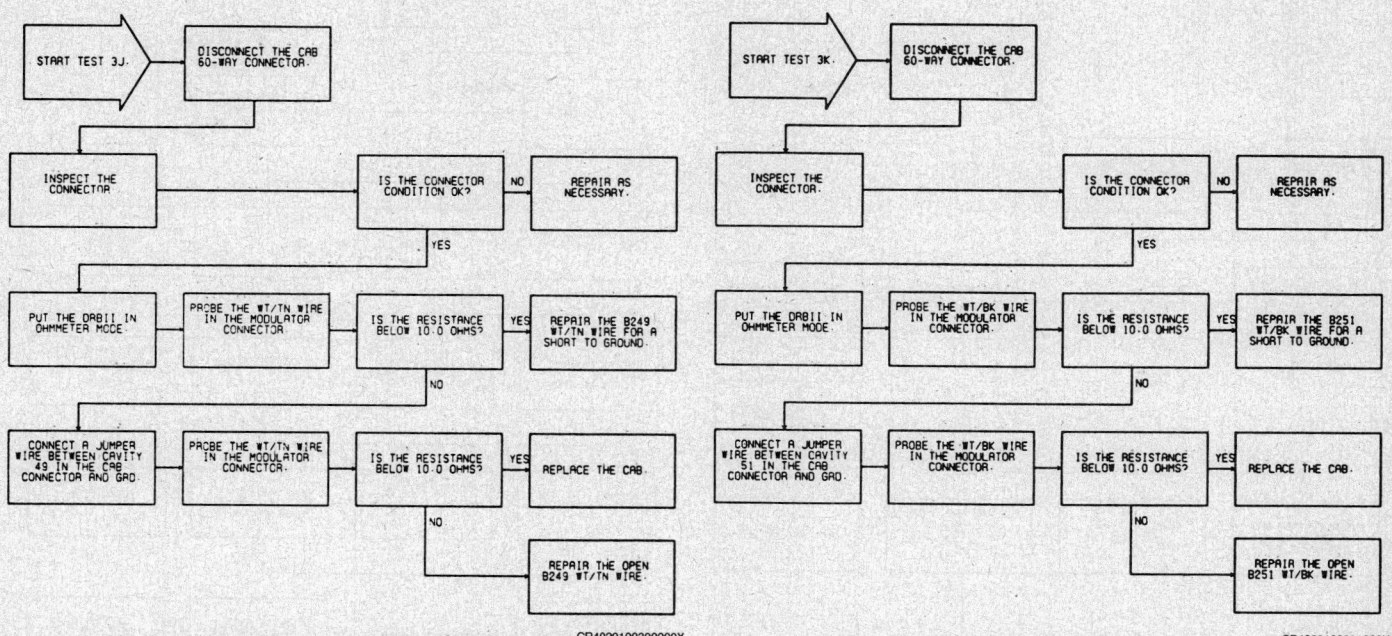

Fig. 18   Test 3J: Modulator Fault. 1992

Fig. 19   Test 3K: Modulator Fault. 1992

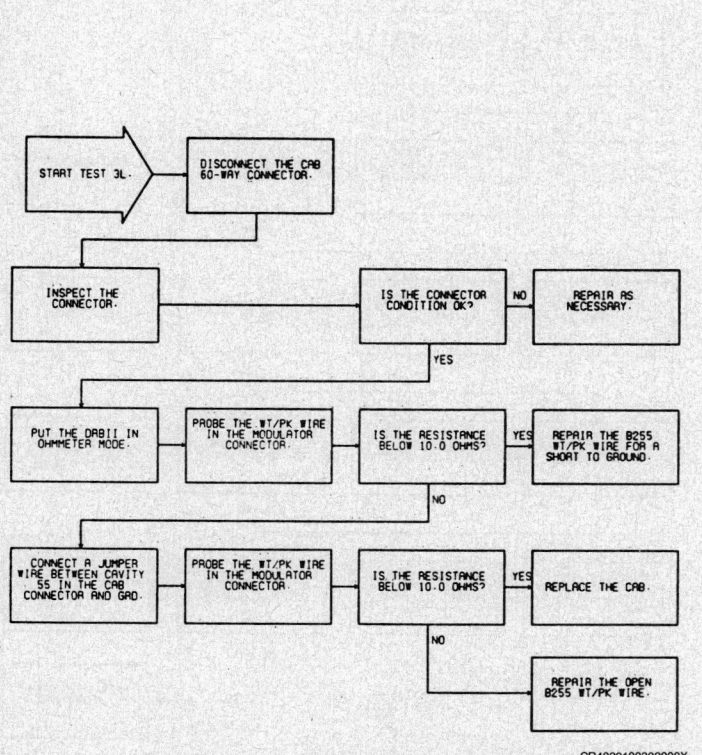

Fig. 20   Test 3L: Modulator Fault. 1992

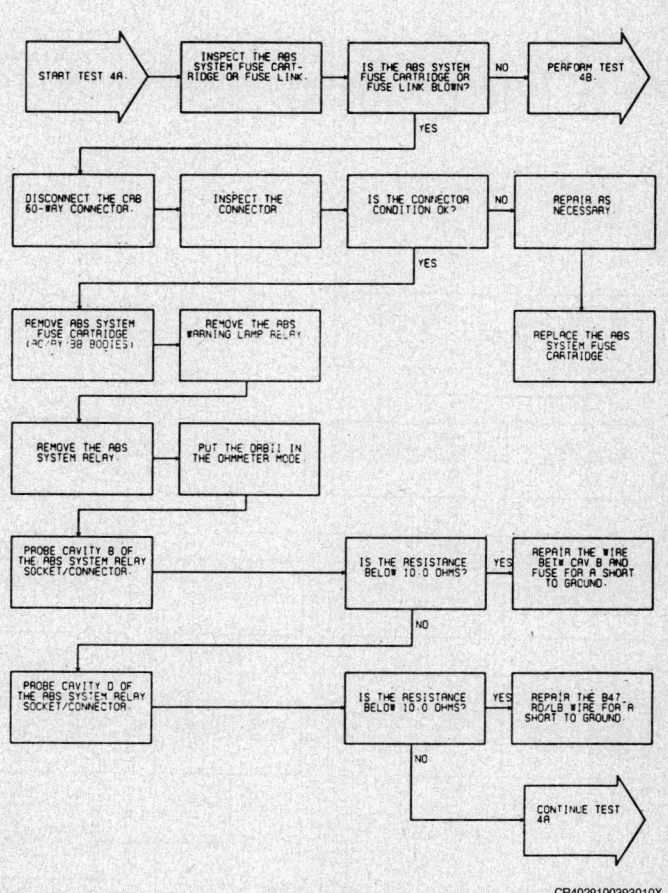

Fig. 21   Test 4A: Solenoid Undervoltage Fault (Part 1 of 2). 1992

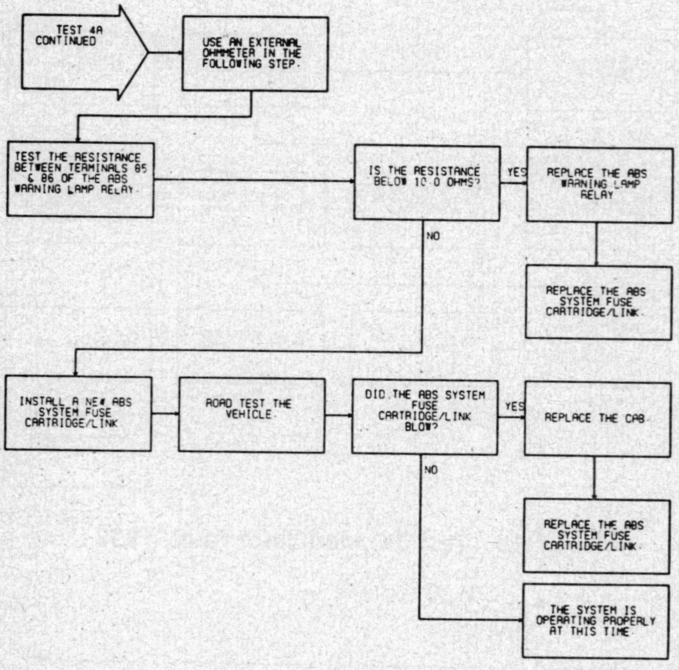

CHRYSLER—Anti-Lock Brakes

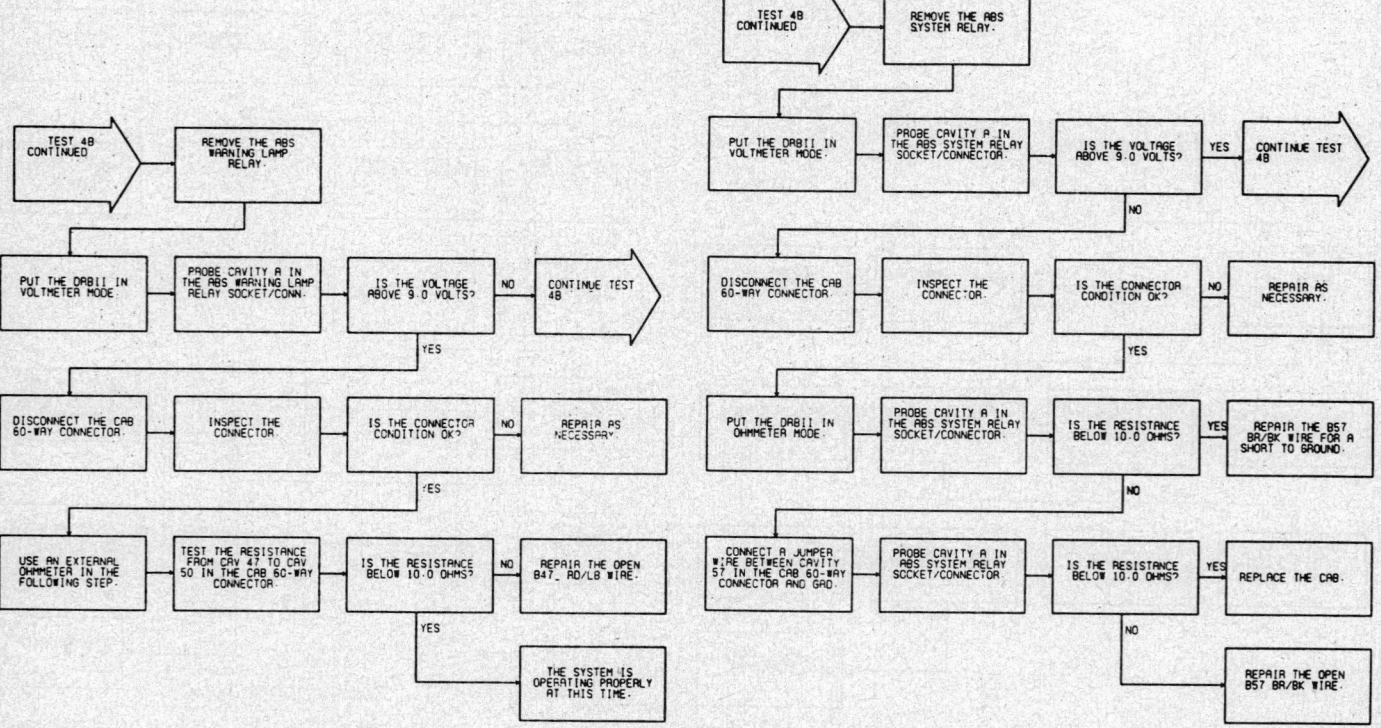

Fig. 21   Test 4A: Solenoid Undervoltage Fault (Part 2 of 2). 1992

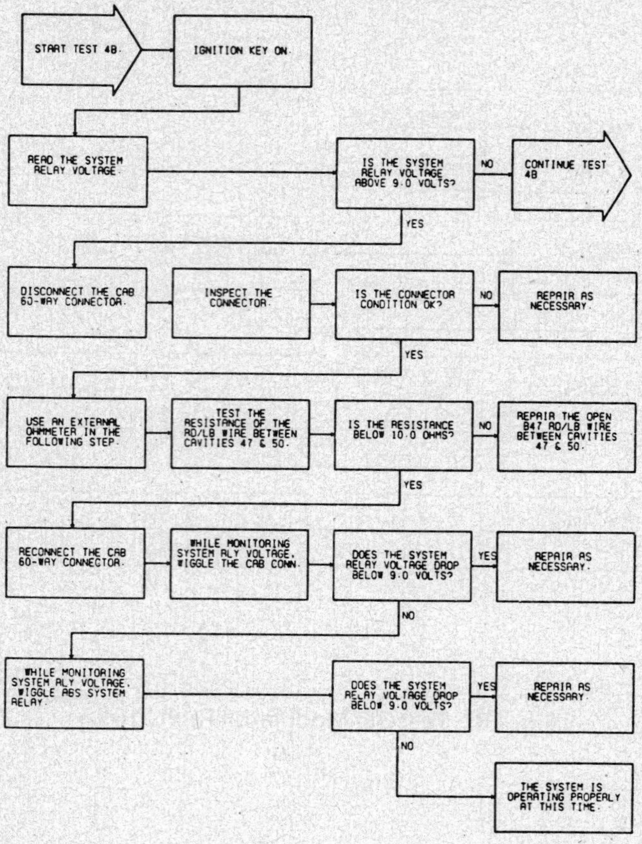

Fig. 22   Test 4B: Solenoid Undervoltage Fault (Part 1 of 6). 1992

Fig. 22   Test 4B: Solenoid Undervoltage Fault (Part 2 of 6). 1992

Fig. 22   Test 4B: Solenoid Undervoltage Fault (Part 3 of 6). 1992

25-70

TYPE 3-BENDIX ANTI-LOCK 10 BRAKING SYSTEM

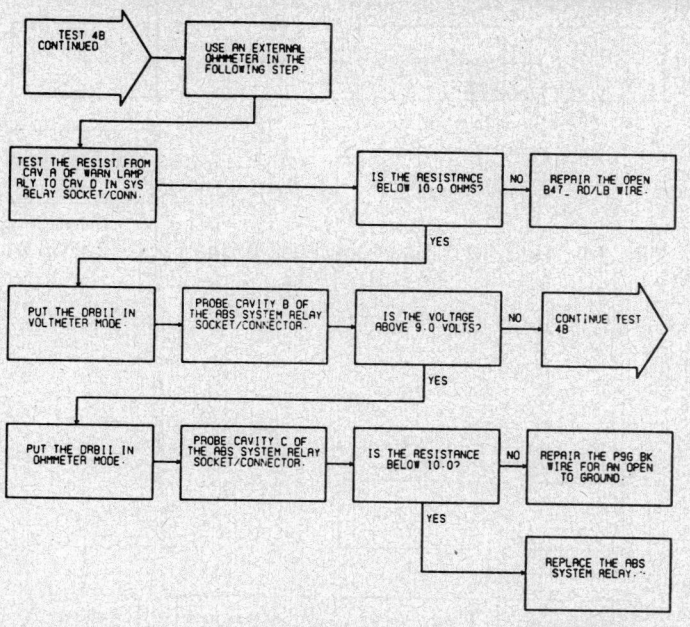

Fig. 22   Test 4B: Solenoid Undervoltage Fault (Part 4 of 6). 1992

CR4029100394040X

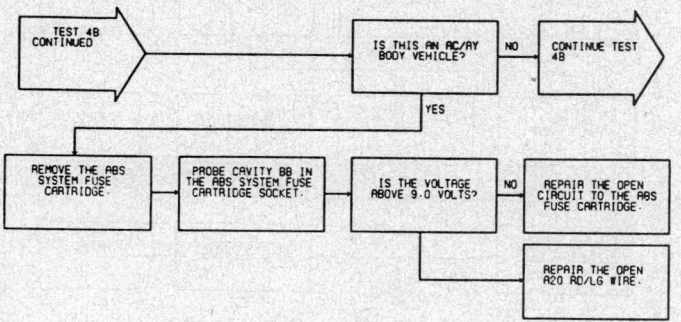

Fig. 22   Test 4B: Solenoid Undervoltage Fault (Part 5 of 6). 1992

CR4029100394050X

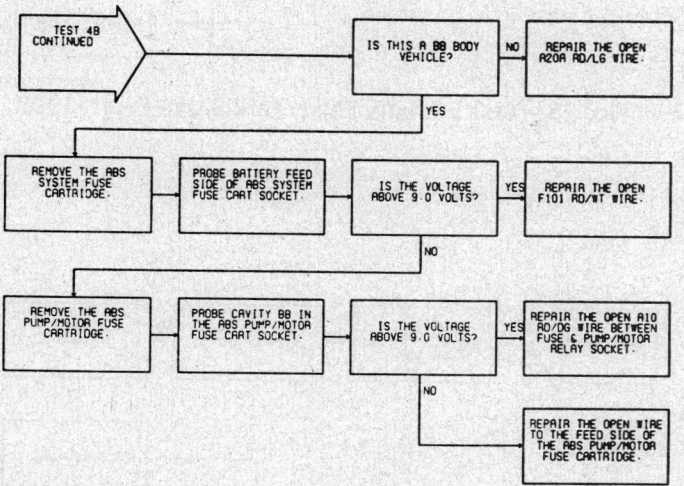

Fig. 22   Test 4B: Solenoid Undervoltage Fault (Part 6 of 6). 1992

CR4029100394060X

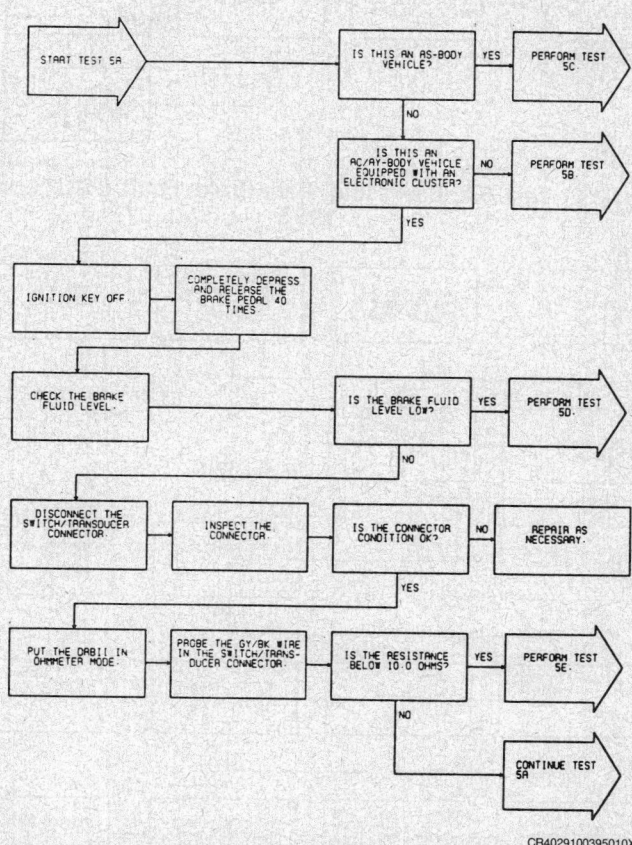

Fig. 23   Test 5A: Low Fluid/Park Brake Fault (Part 1 of 3). 1992

CR4029100395010X

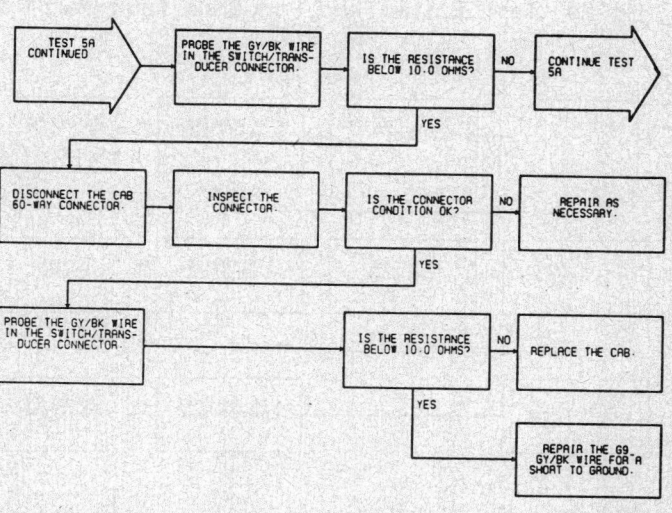

Fig. 23   Test 5A: Low Fluid/Park Brake Fault (Part 2 of 3). 1992

CR4029100395020X

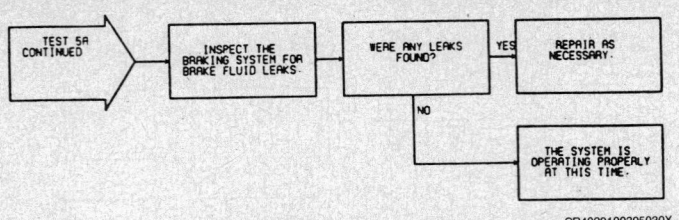

Fig. 23   Test 5A: Low Fluid/Park Brake Fault (Part 3 of 3). 1992

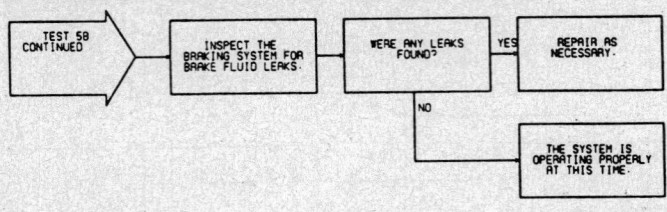

Fig. 24   Test 5B: Low Fluid/Park Brake Fault (Part 3 of 3). 1992

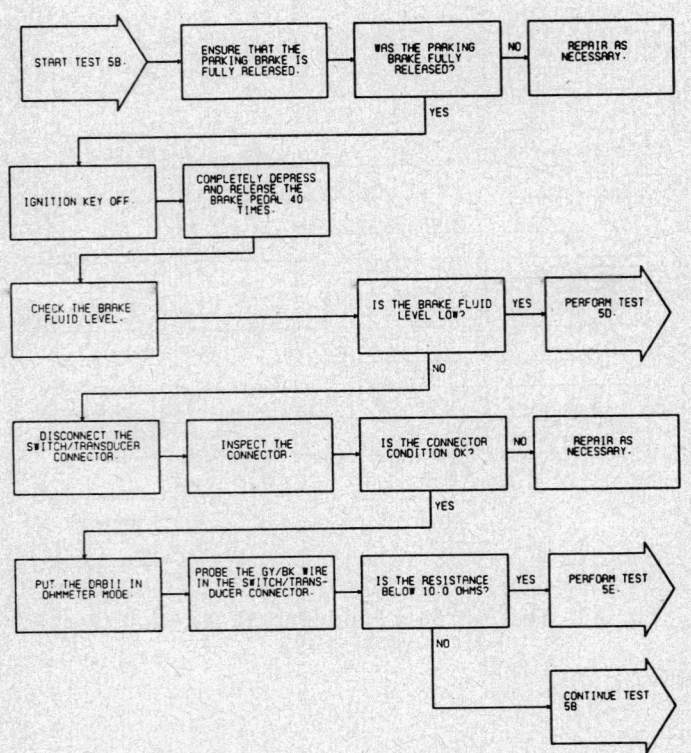

Fig. 24   Test 5B: Low Fluid/Park Brake Fault (Part 1 of 3). 1992

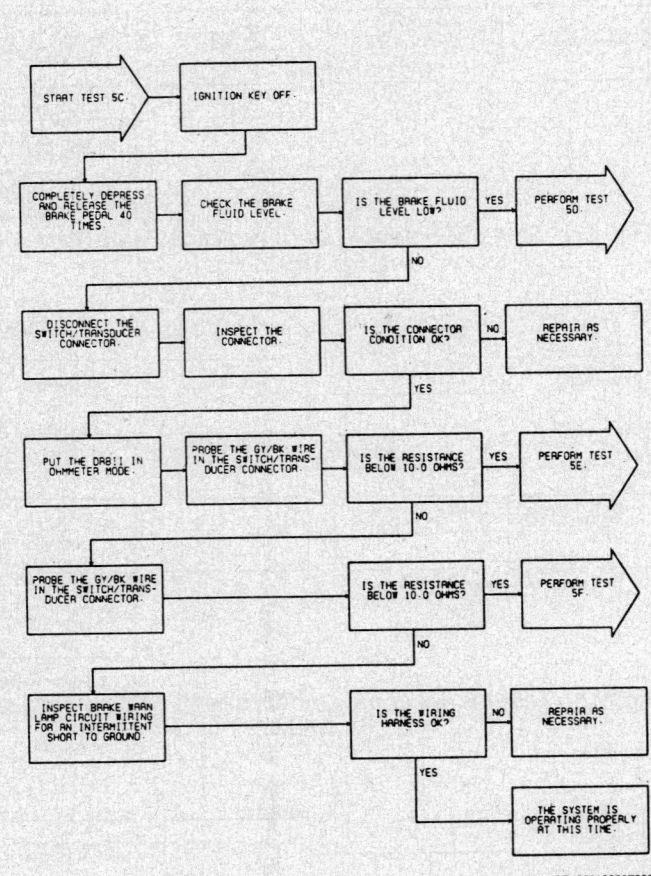

Fig. 25   Test 5C: Low Fluid/Park Brake Fault. 1992

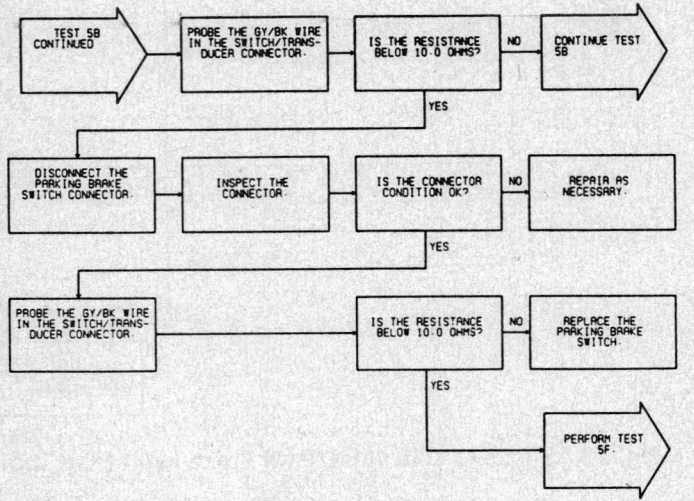

Fig. 24   Test 5B: Low Fluid/Park Brake Fault (Part 2 of 3). 1992

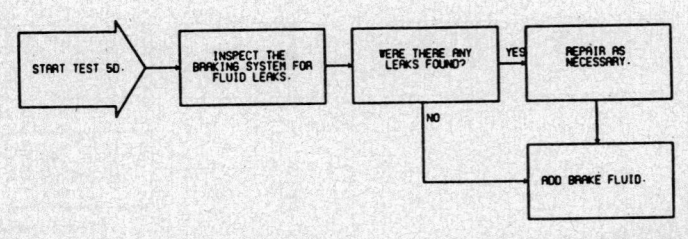

Fig. 26   Test 5D: Low Fluid/Park Brake Fault. 1992

CR4029100399000X

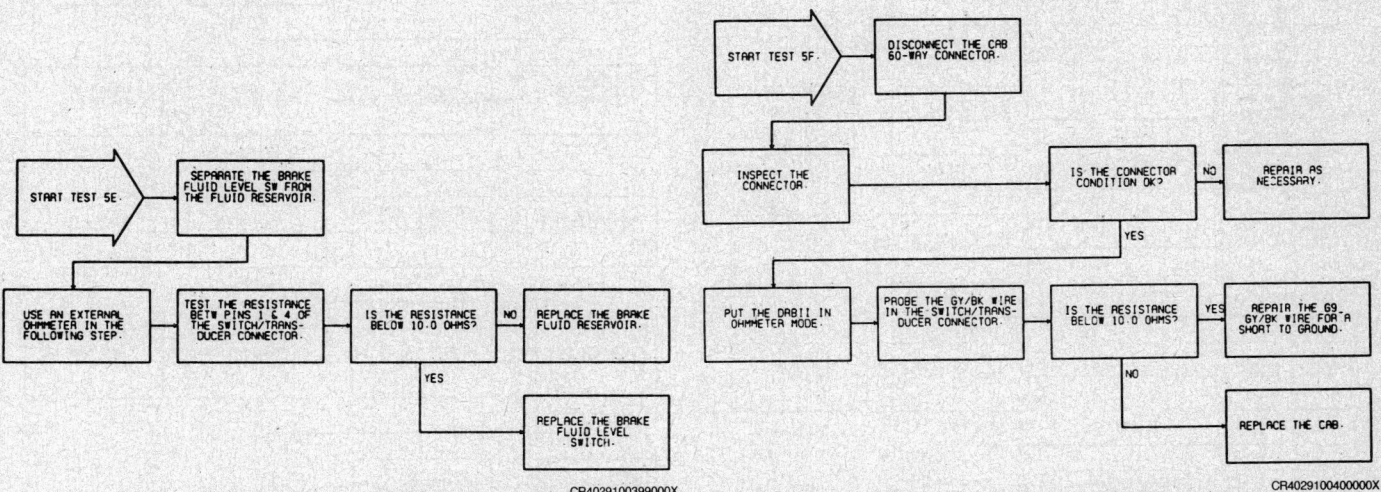

Fig. 27 Test 5E: Low Fluid/Park Brake Fault. 1992

CR4029100400000X

Fig. 28 Test 5F: Low Fluid/Park Brake Fault. 1992

CR4029100401010X

Fig. 29 Test 6A: System Relay Fault (Part 1 of 2). 1992

CR4029100401020X

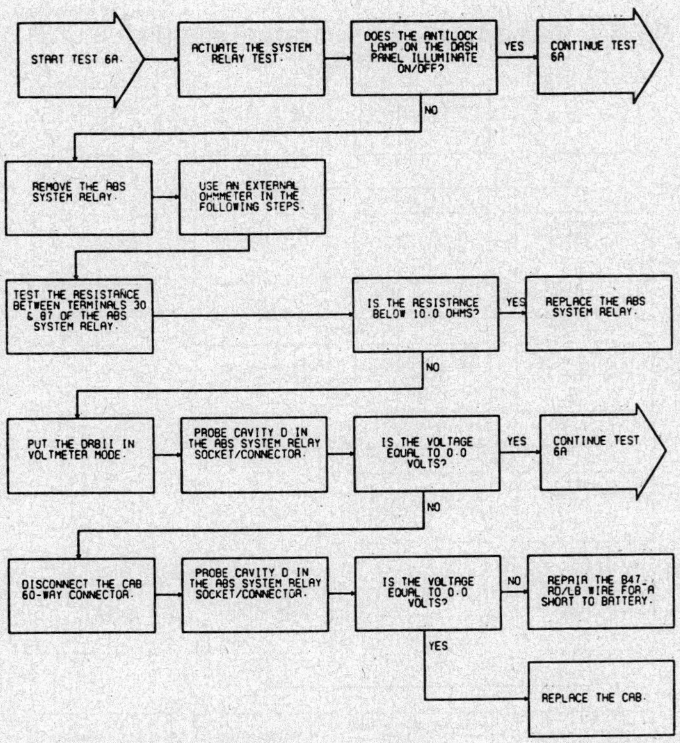

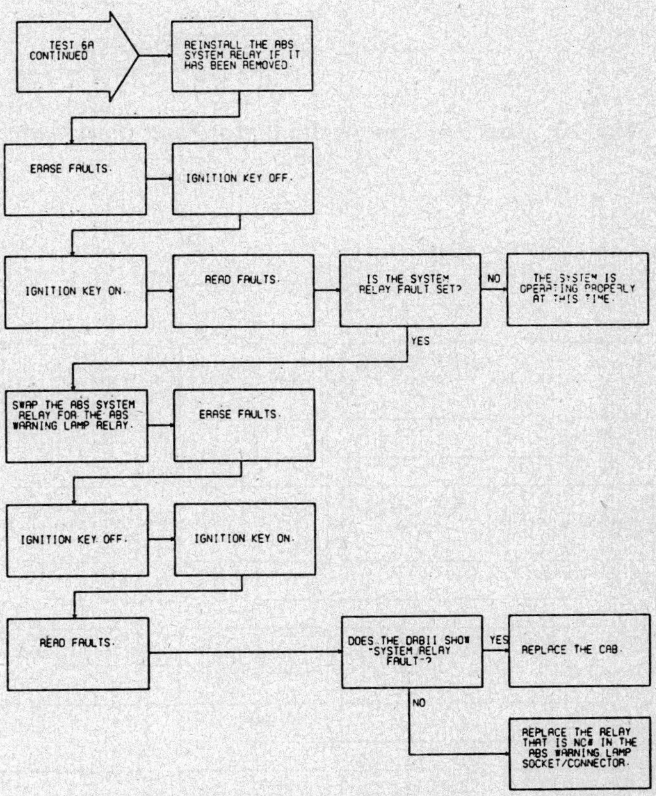

Fig. 29 Test 6A: System Relay Fault (Part 2 of 2). 1992

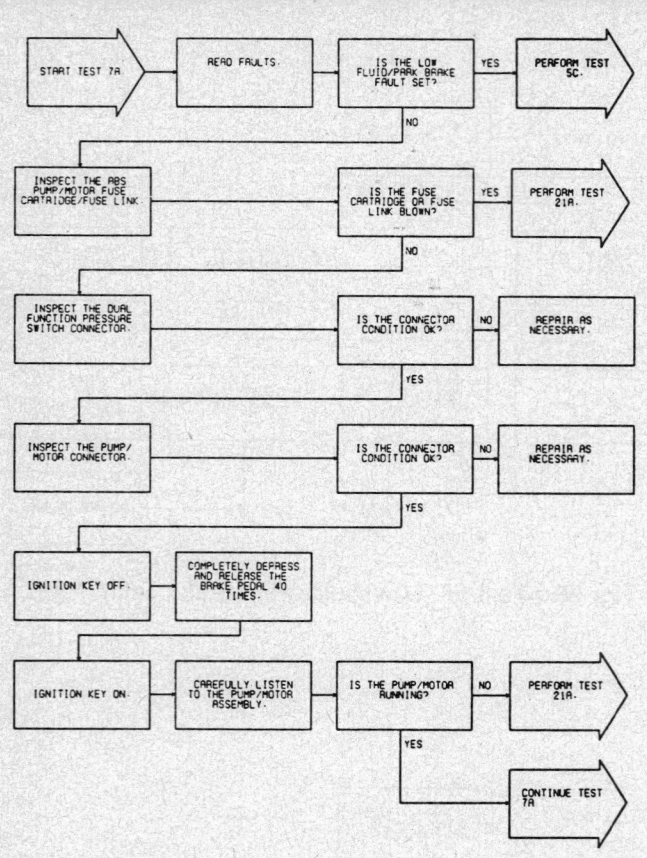

Fig. 30   Test 7A: Low Accumulator Fault (Part 1 of 2). 1992

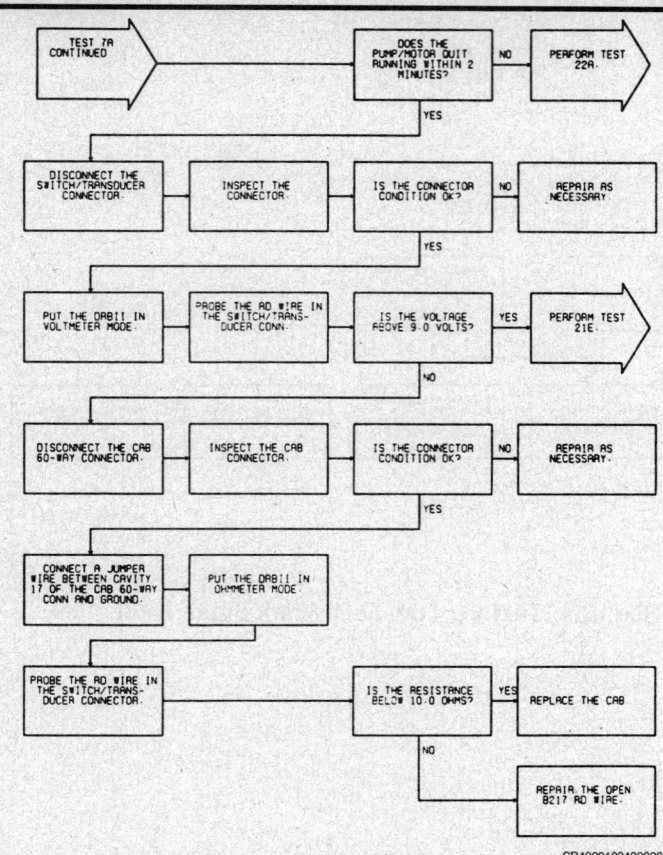

Fig. 30   Test 7A: Low Accumulator Fault (Part 2 of 2). 1992

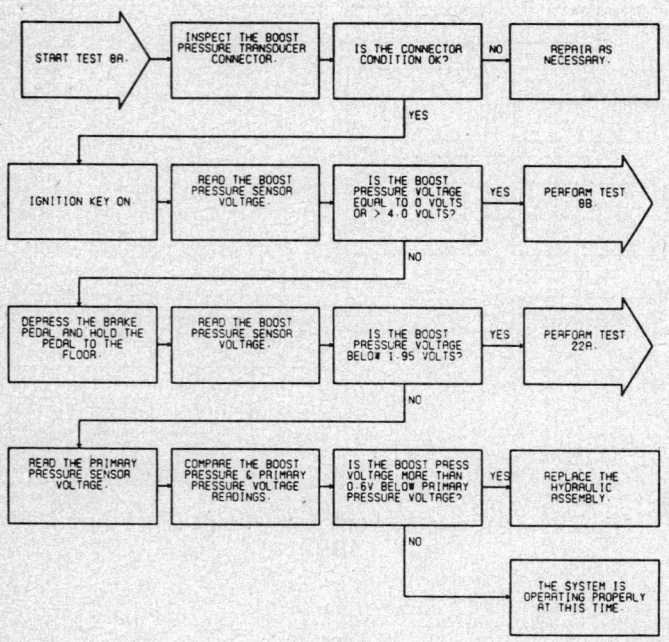

Fig. 31   Test 8A: Boost Pressure Fault

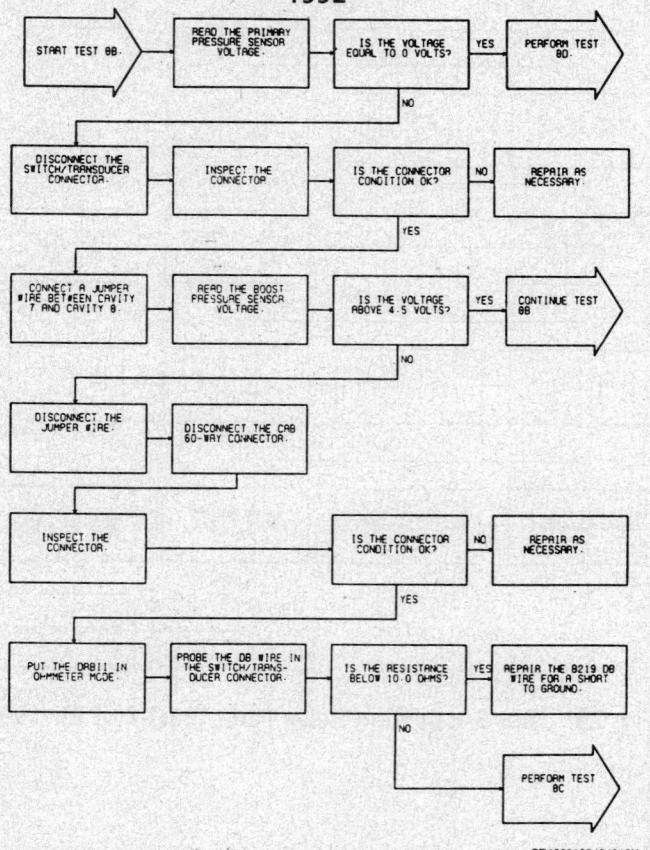

Fig. 32   Test 8B: Boost Pressure Fault (Part 1 of 3). 1992

TYPE 3-BENDIX ANTI-LOCK 10 BRAKING SYSTEM

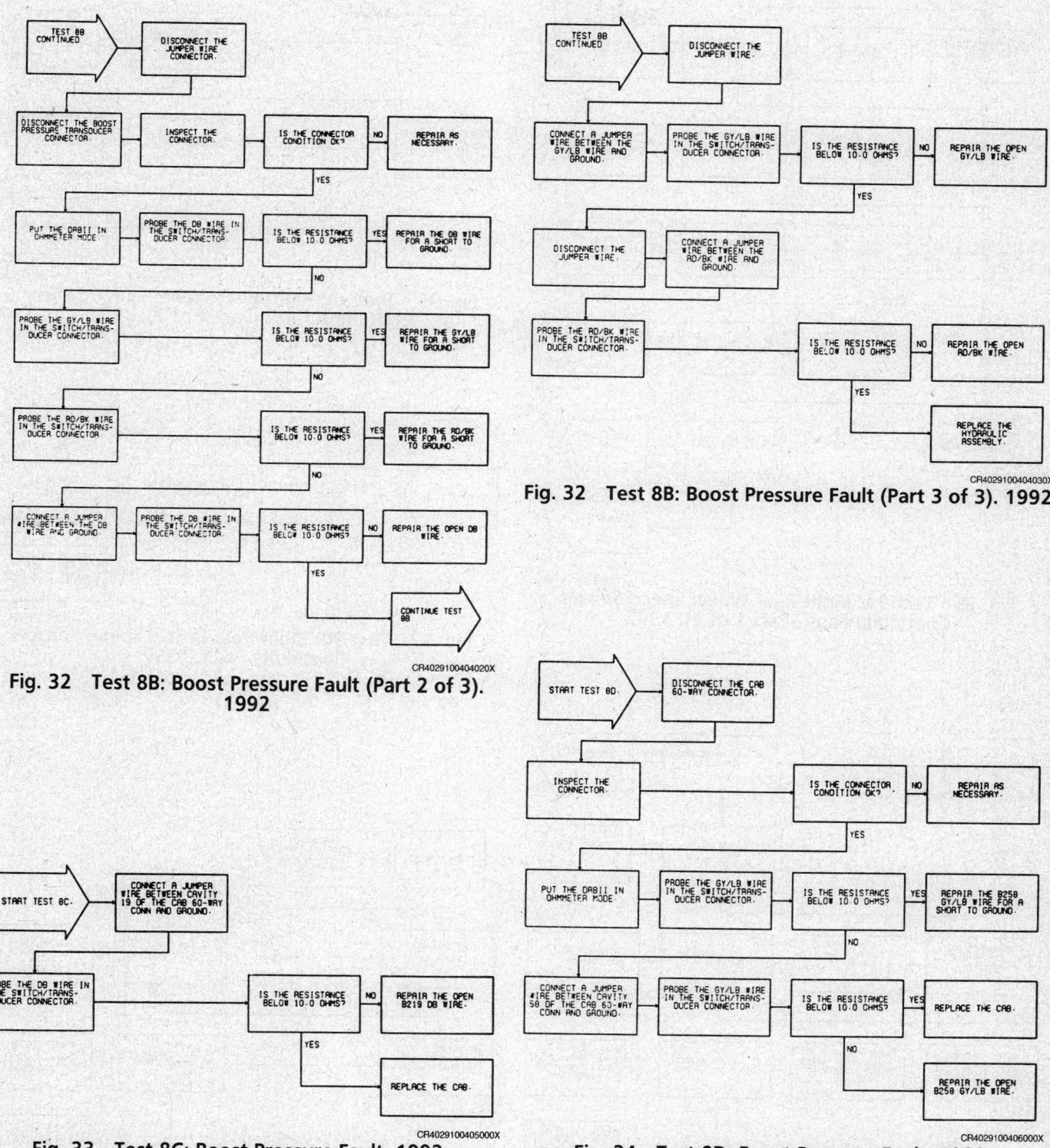

Fig. 32   Test 8B: Boost Pressure Fault (Part 2 of 3). 1992

CR4029100404020X

Fig. 32   Test 8B: Boost Pressure Fault (Part 3 of 3). 1992

CR4029100404030X

Fig. 33   Test 8C: Boost Pressure Fault. 1992

CR4029100405000X

Fig. 34   Test 8D: Boost Pressure Fault. 1992

CR4029100406000X

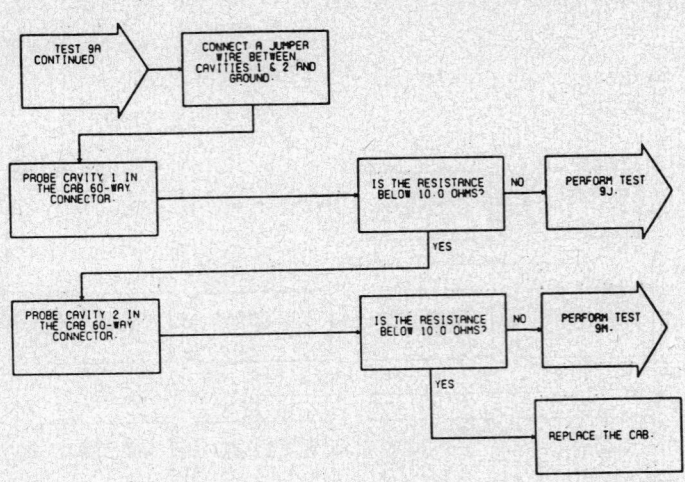

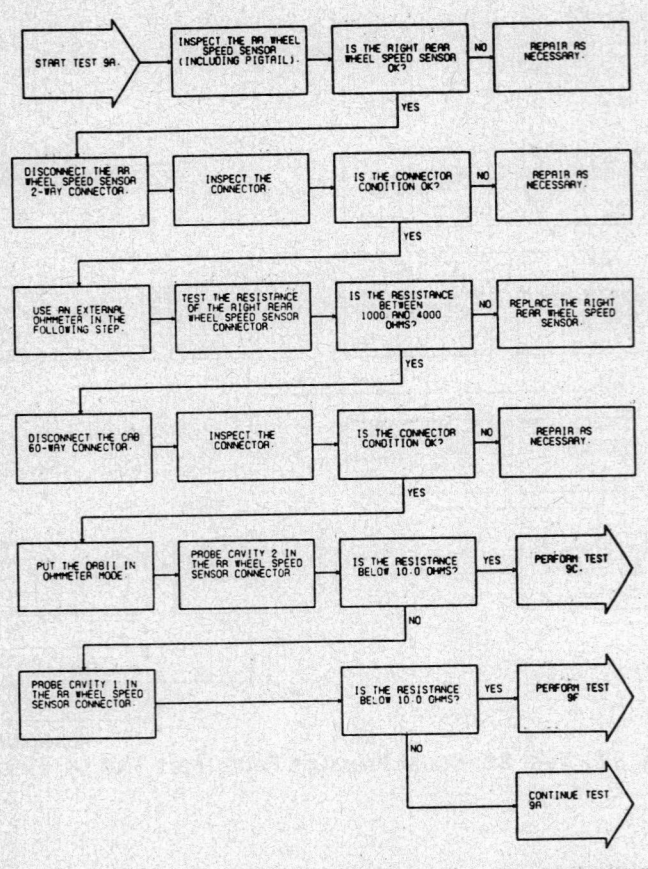

Fig. 35 Test 9A: Right Rear Wheel Speed Sensor Continuity Fault (Part 2 of 2). 1992

Fig. 35 Test 9A: Right Rear Wheel Speed Sensor Continuity Fault (Part 1 of 2). 1992

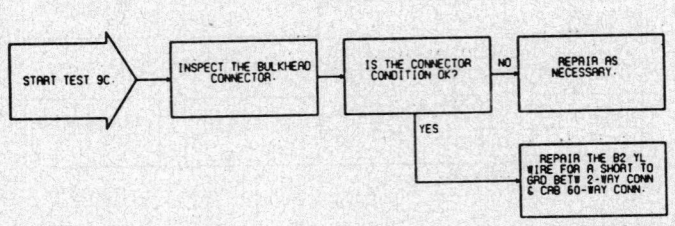

Fig. 37 Test 9C: Right Rear Wheel Speed Sensor Continuity Fault. 1992

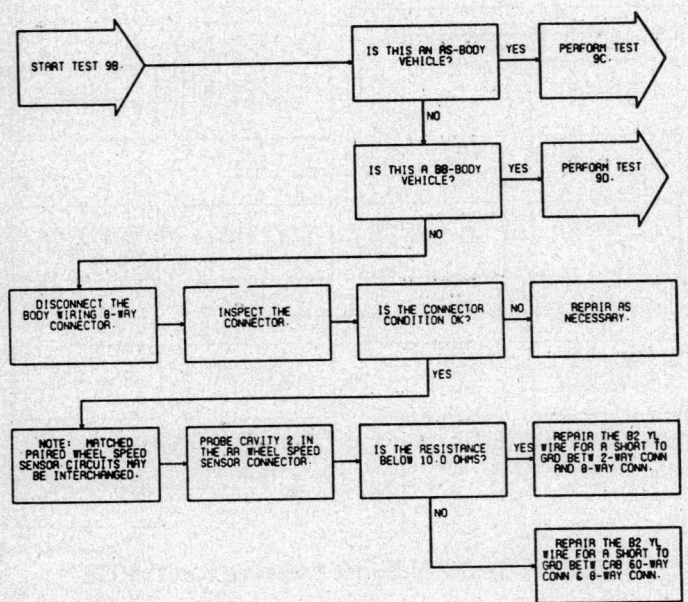

Fig. 36 Test 9B: Right Rear Wheel Speed Sensor Continuity Fault. 1992

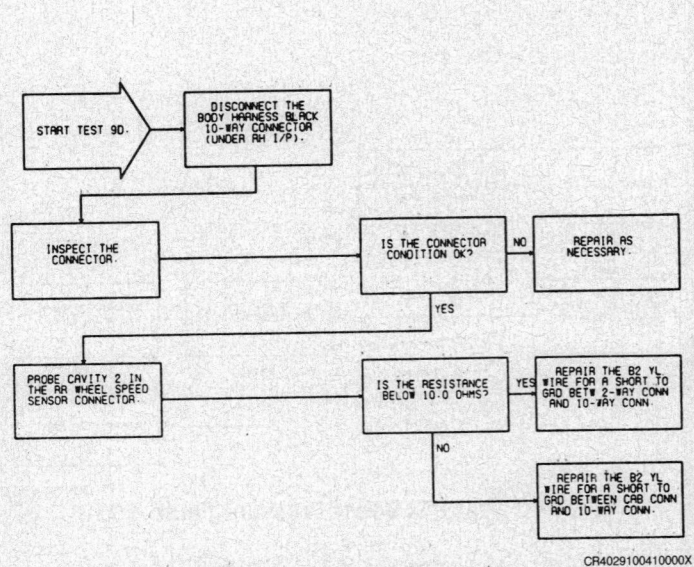

Fig. 38 Test 9D: Right Rear Wheel Speed Sensor Continuity Fault. 1992

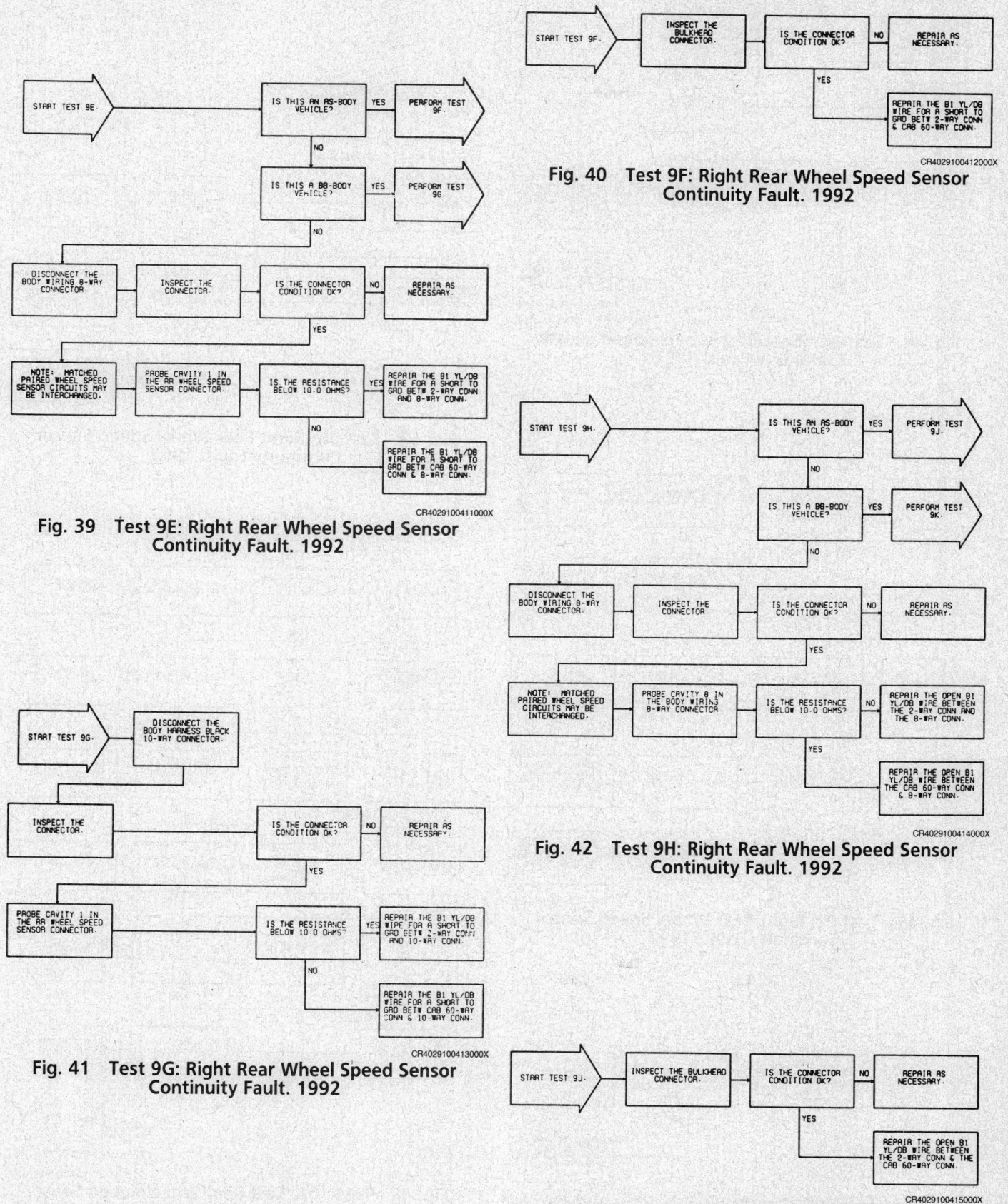

Fig. 39   Test 9E: Right Rear Wheel Speed Sensor Continuity Fault. 1992

CR4029100411000X

Fig. 40   Test 9F: Right Rear Wheel Speed Sensor Continuity Fault. 1992

CR4029100412000X

Fig. 41   Test 9G: Right Rear Wheel Speed Sensor Continuity Fault. 1992

CR4029100413000X

Fig. 42   Test 9H: Right Rear Wheel Speed Sensor Continuity Fault. 1992

CR4029100414000X

Fig. 43   Test 9J: Right Rear Wheel Speed Sensor Continuity Fault. 1992

CR4029100415000X

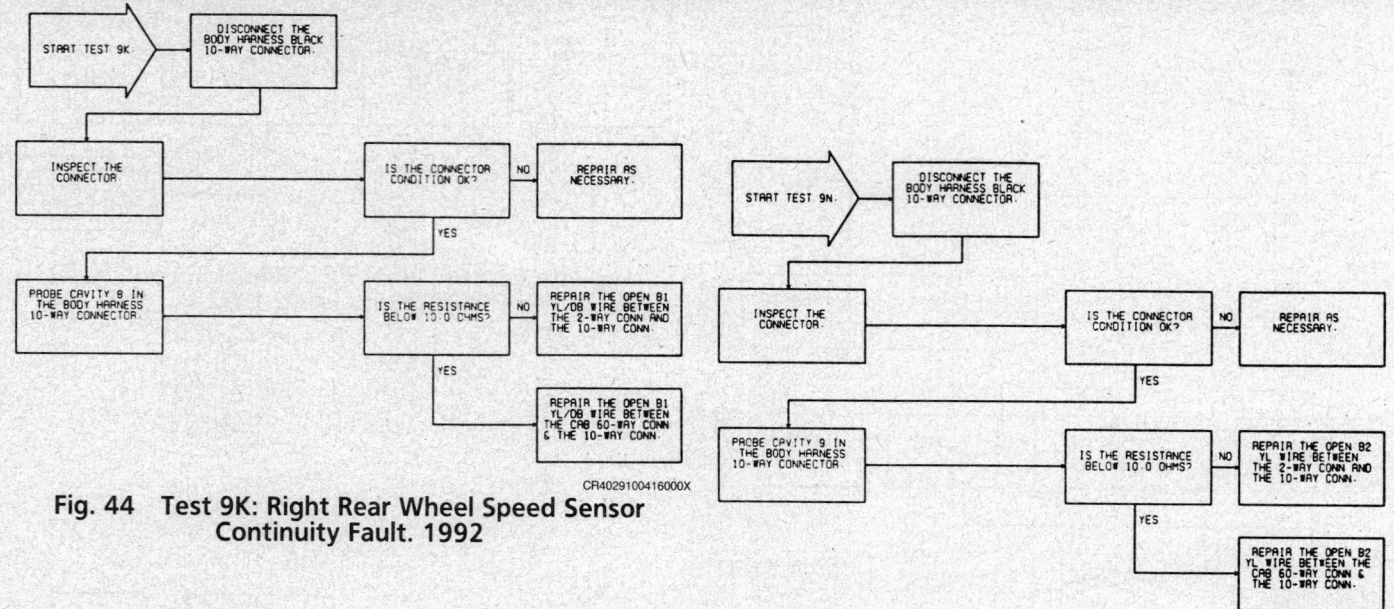

Fig. 44 Test 9K: Right Rear Wheel Speed Sensor Continuity Fault. 1992

Fig. 47 Test 9N: Right Rear Wheel Speed Sensor Continuity Fault. 1992

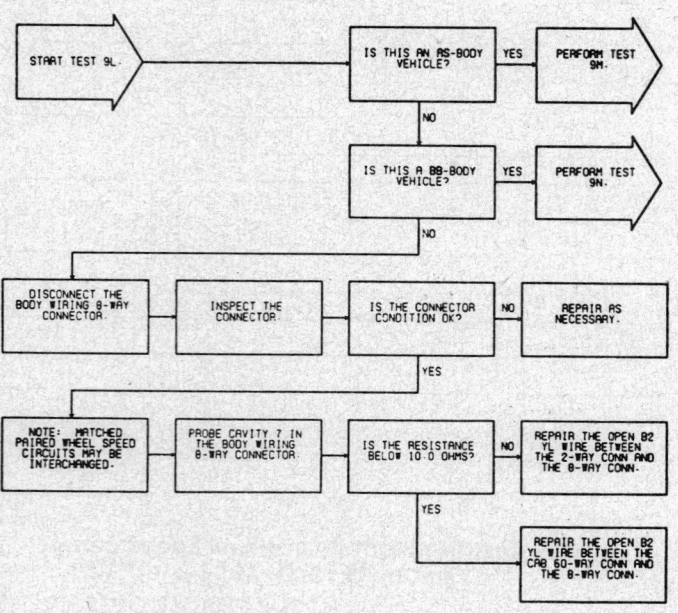

Fig. 45 Test 9L: Right Rear Wheel Speed Sensor Continuity Fault. 1992

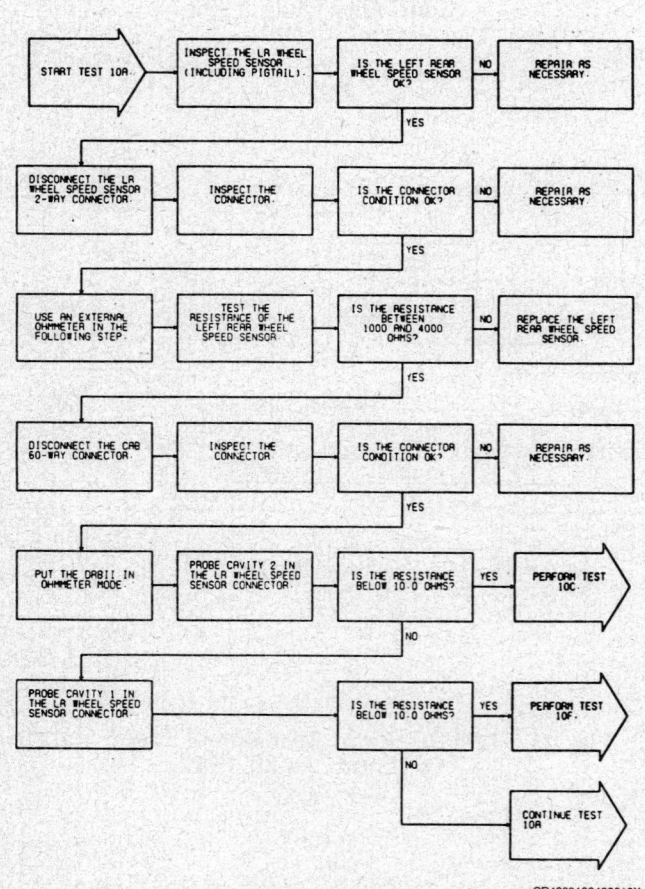

Fig. 48 Test 10A: Left Rear Wheel Speed Sensor Continuity Fault (Part 1 of 2). 1992

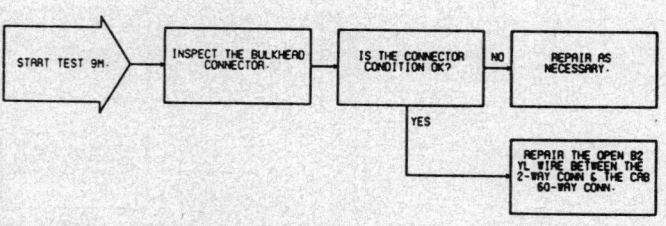

Fig. 46 Test 9M: Right Rear Wheel Speed Sensor Continuity Fault. 1992

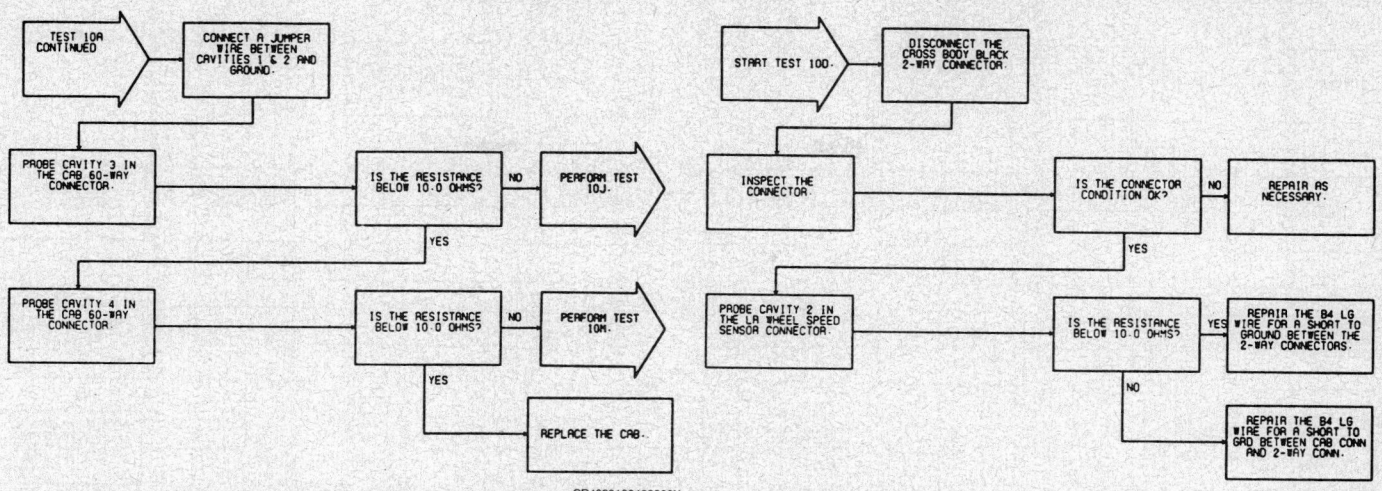

Fig. 48   Test 10A: Left Rear Wheel Speed Sensor Continuity Fault (Part 2 of 2). 1992

Fig. 51   Test 10D: Left Rear Wheel Speed Sensor Continuity Fault. 1992

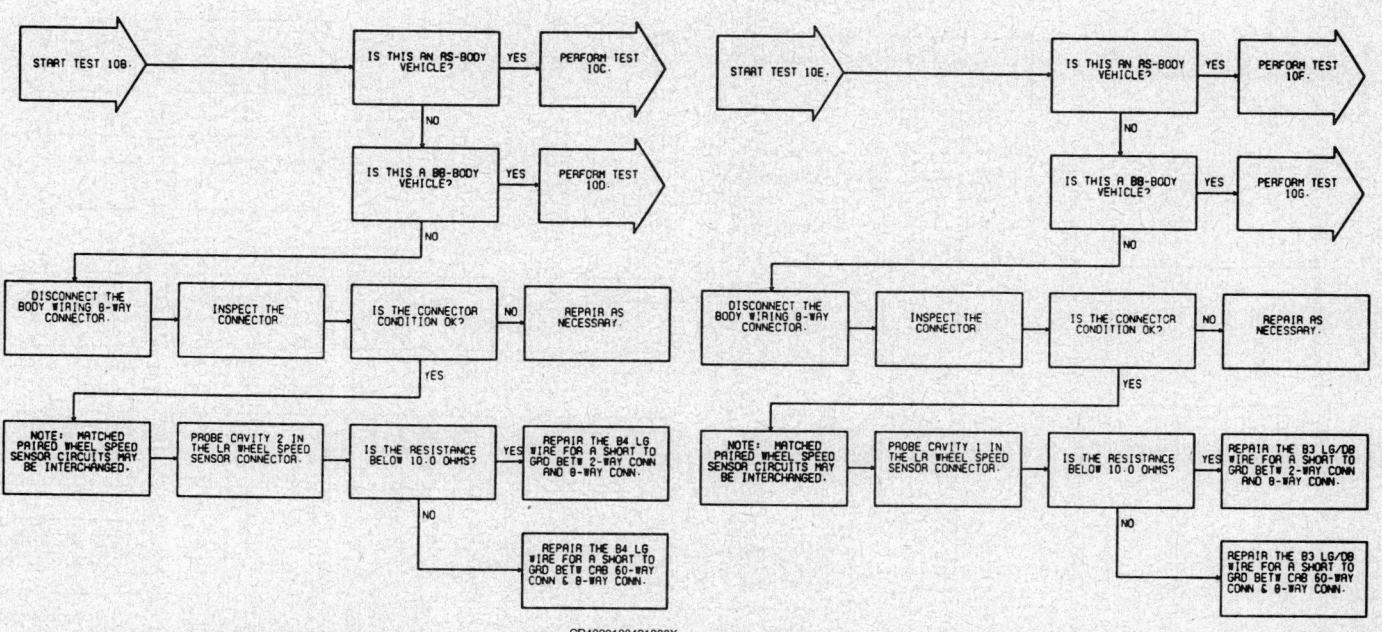

Fig. 49   Test 10B: Left Rear Wheel Speed Sensor Continuity Fault. 1992

Fig. 52   Test 10E: Left Rear Wheel Speed Sensor Continuity Fault. 1992

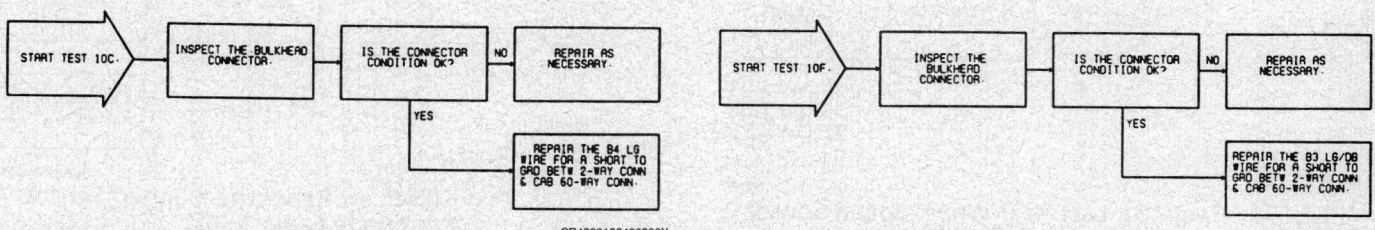

Fig. 50   Test 10C: Left Rear Wheel Speed Sensor Continuity Fault. 1992

Fig. 53   Test 10F: Left Rear Wheel Speed Sensor Continuity Fault. 1992

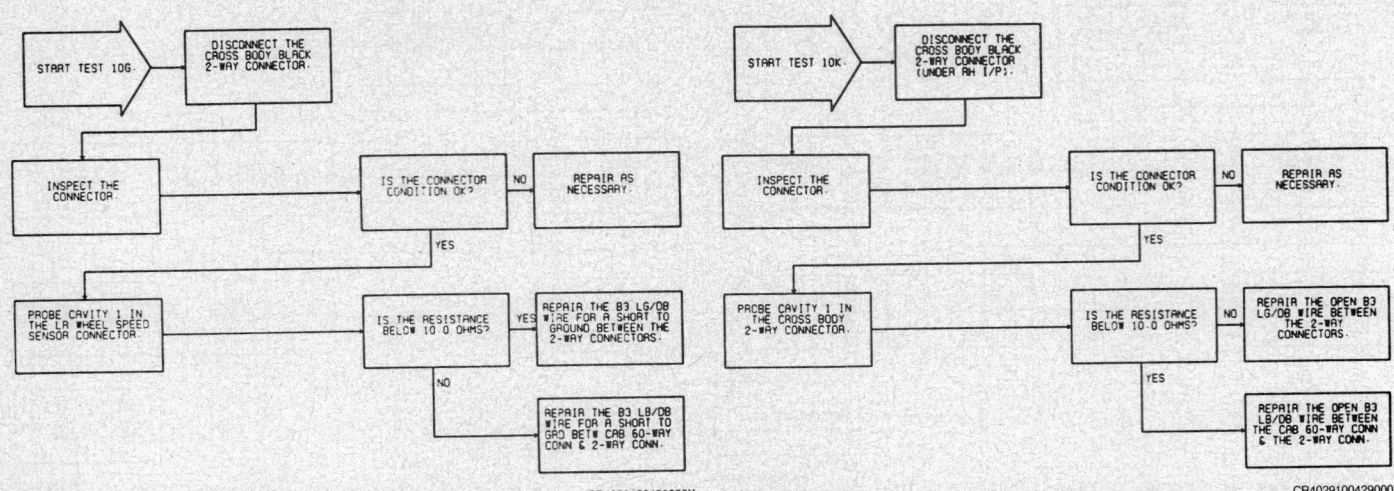

Fig. 54   Test 10G: Left Rear Wheel Speed Sensor Continuity Fault. 1992

Fig. 57   Test 10K: Left Rear Wheel Speed Sensor Continuity Fault. 1992

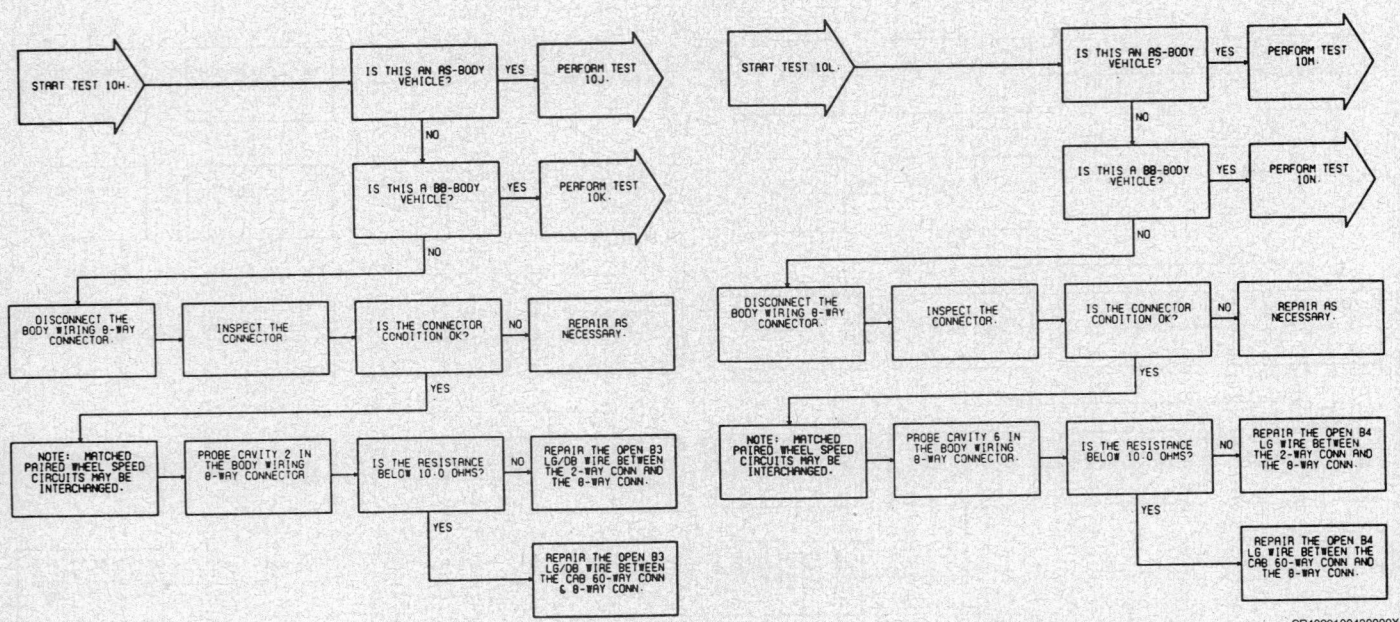

Fig. 55   Test 10H: Left Rear Wheel Speed Sensor Continuity Fault. 1992

Fig. 58   Test 10L: Left Rear Wheel Speed Sensor Continuity Fault. 1992

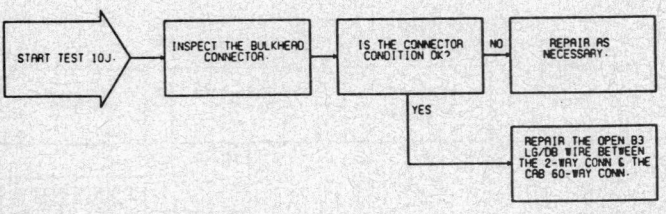

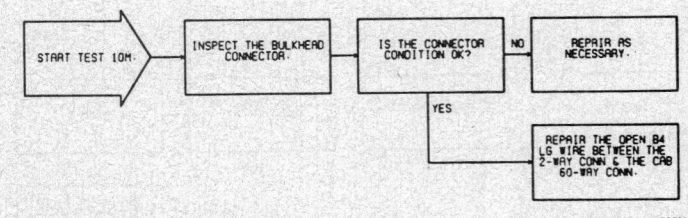

Fig. 56   Test 10J: Left Rear Wheel Speed Sensor Continuity Fault. 1992

Fig. 59   Test 10M: Left Rear Wheel Speed Sensor Continuity Fault. 1992

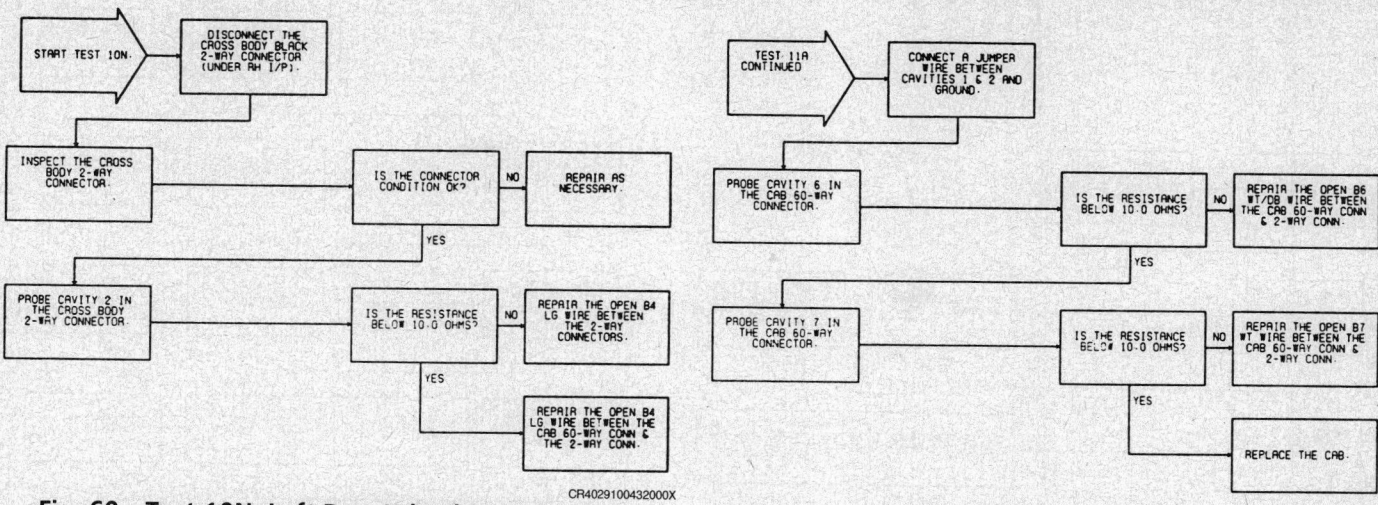

Fig. 60   Test 10N: Left Rear Wheel Speed Sensor Continuity Fault. 1992

Fig. 61   Test 11A: Right Front Wheel Speed Sensor Continuity Fault (Part 2 of 2). 1992

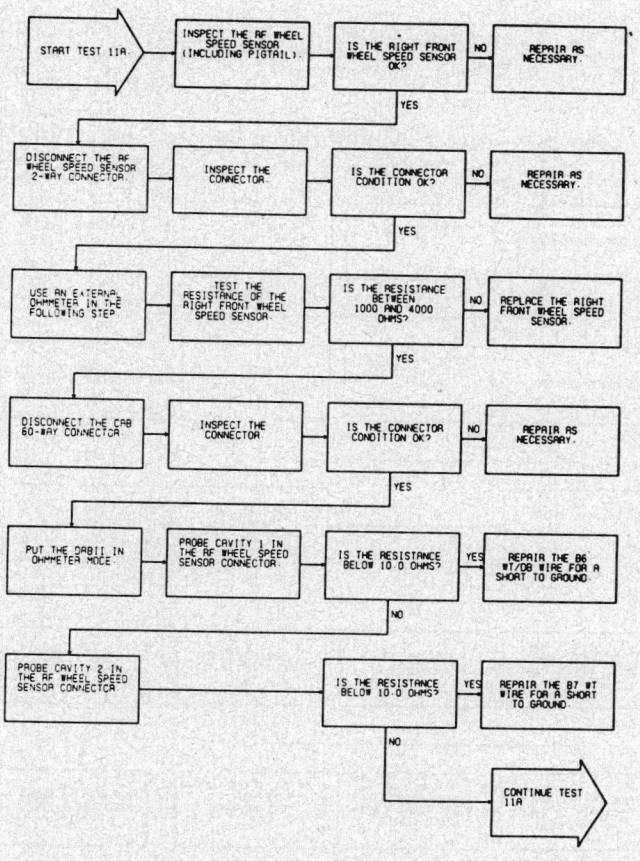

Fig. 61   Test 11A: Right Front Wheel Speed Sensor Continuity Fault (Part 1 of 2). 1992

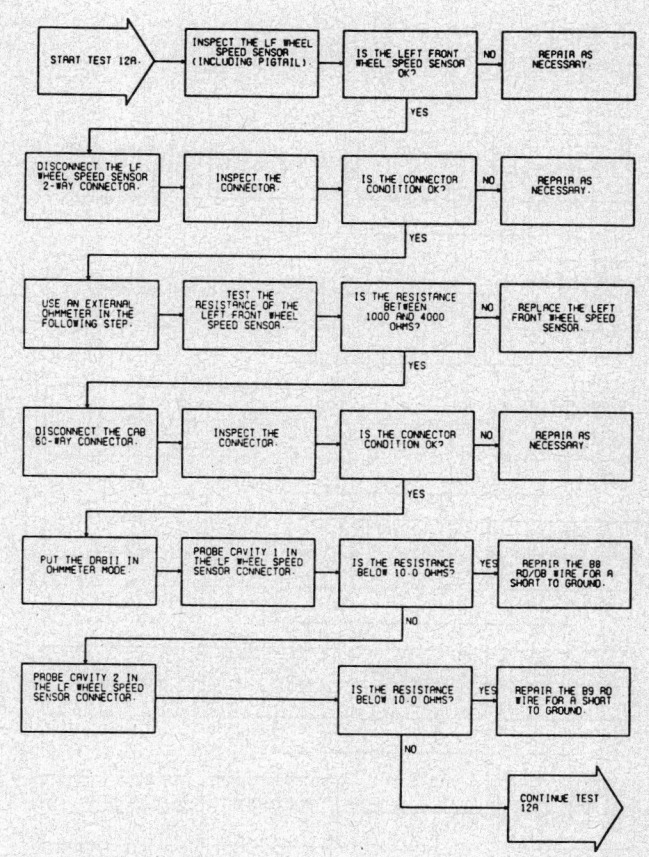

Fig. 62   Test 12A: Left Front Wheel Speed Sensor Continuity Fault (Part 1 of 2). 1992

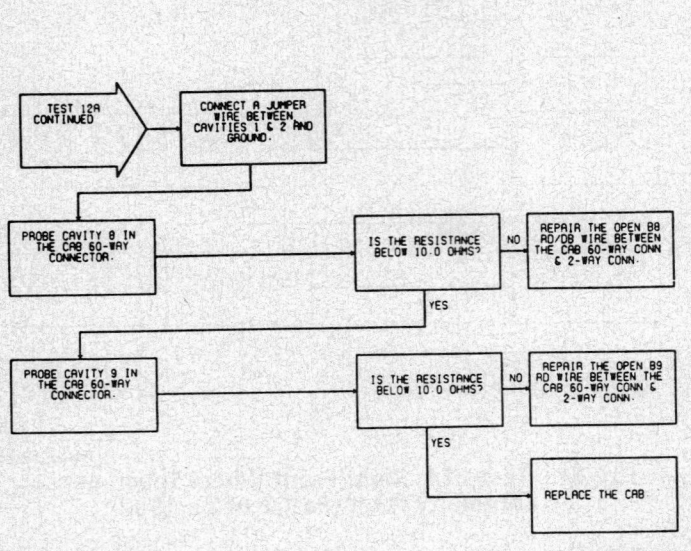

Fig. 62   Test 12A: Left Front Wheel Speed Sensor Continuity Fault (Part 2 of 2). 1992

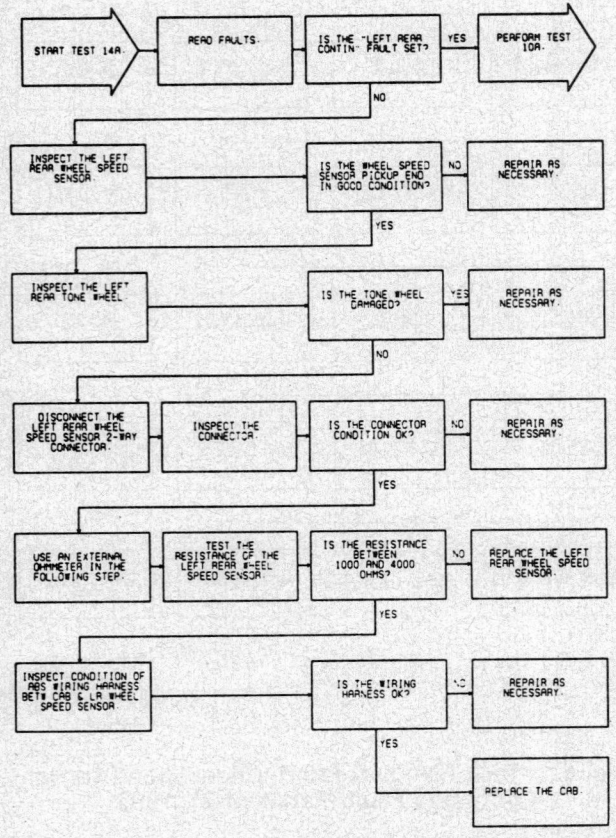

Fig. 64   Test 14A: Left Rear Sensor Fault. 1992

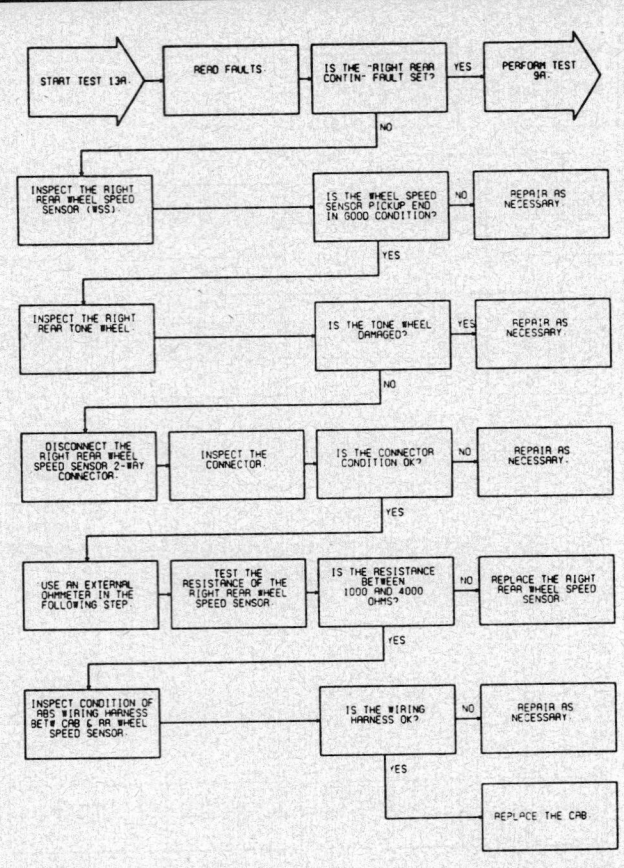

Fig. 63   Test 13A: Right Rear Sensor Fault. 1992

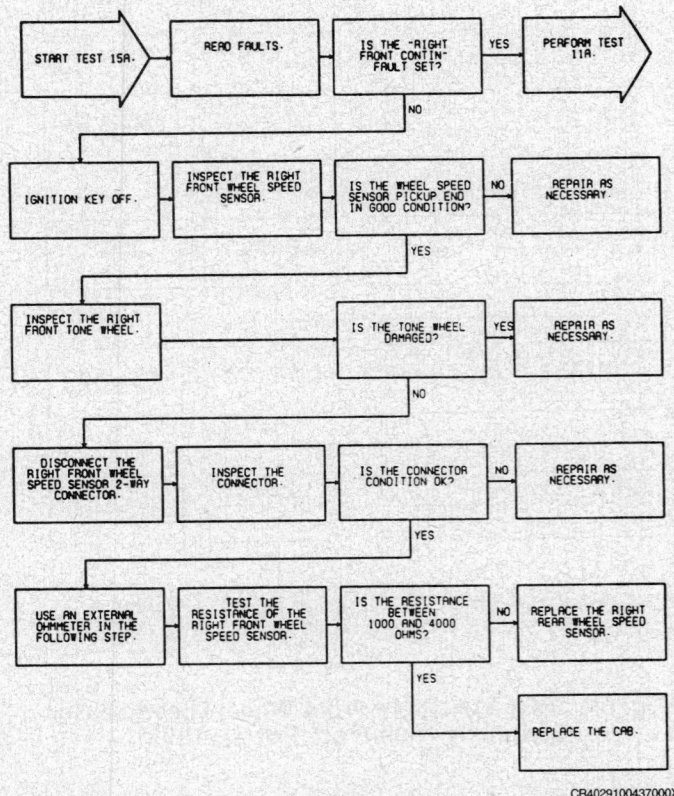

Fig. 65   Test 15A: Right Front Sensor Fault. 1992

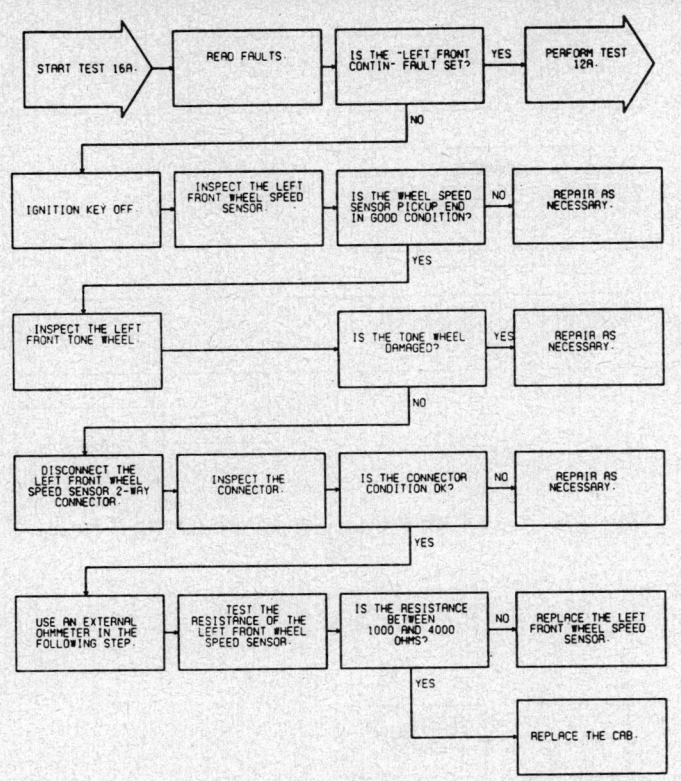

Fig. 66   Test 16A: Left Front Sensor Fault. 1992

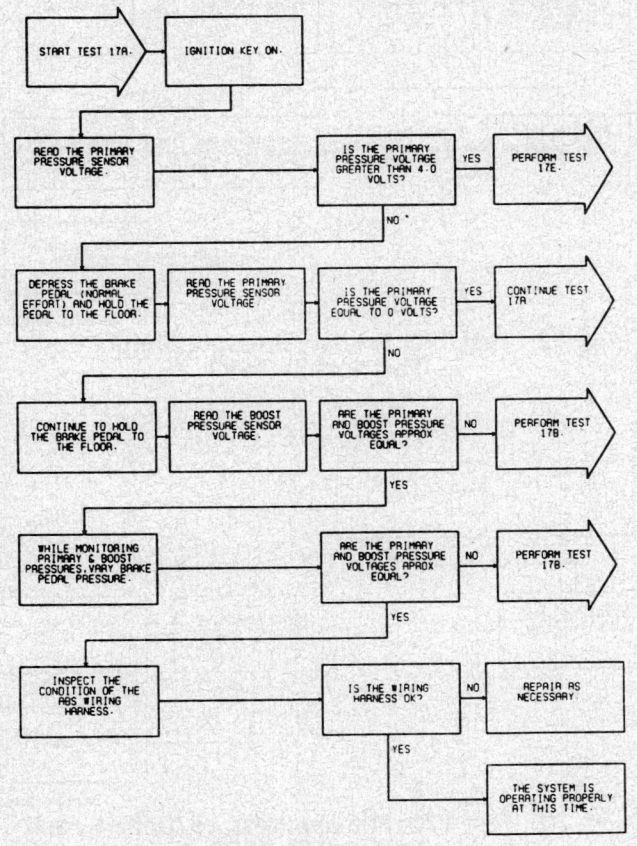

Fig. 67   Test 17A: Primary Pressure/Delta P Fault
(Part 1 of 4). 1992

Fig. 67   Test 17A: Primary Pressure/Delta P Fault (Part
2 of 4). 1992

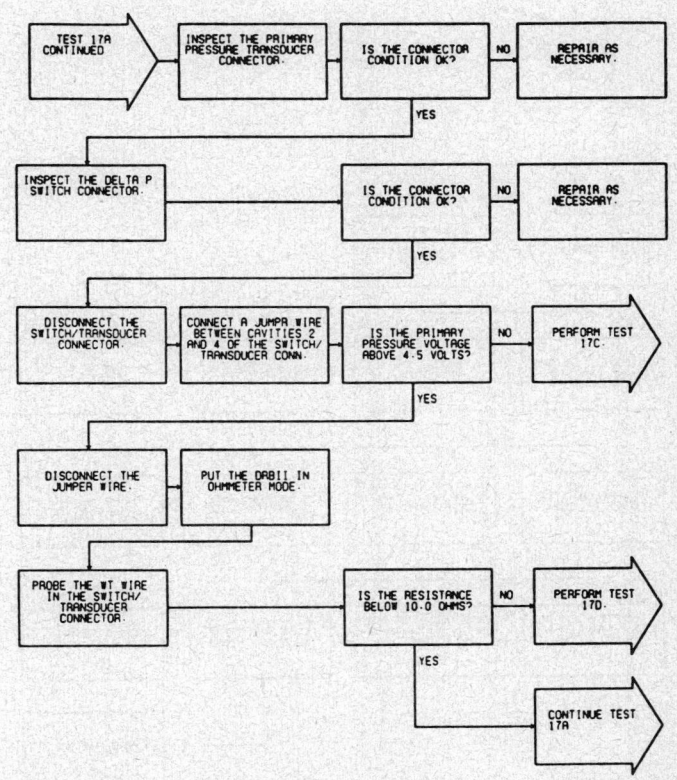

Fig. 67   Test 17A: Primary Pressure/Delta P Fault (Part
3 of 4). 1992

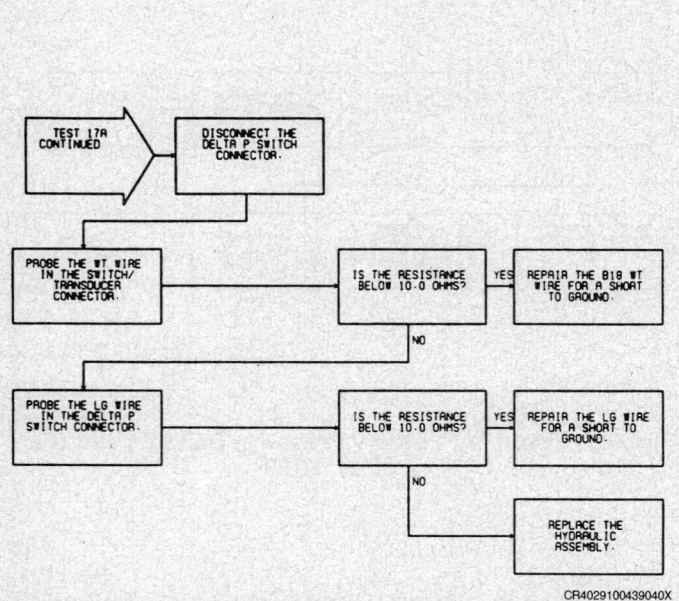

Fig. 67   Test 17A: Primary Pressure/Delta P Fault (Part 4 of 4). 1992

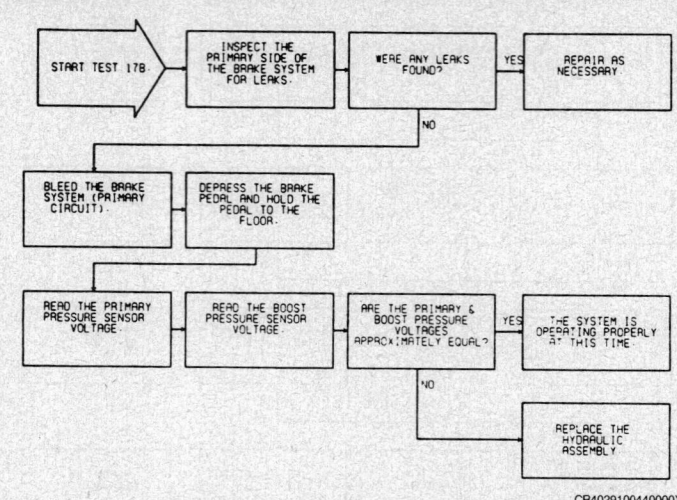

CR4029100440000X

Fig. 68   Test 17B: Primary Pressure/Delta P Fault. 1992

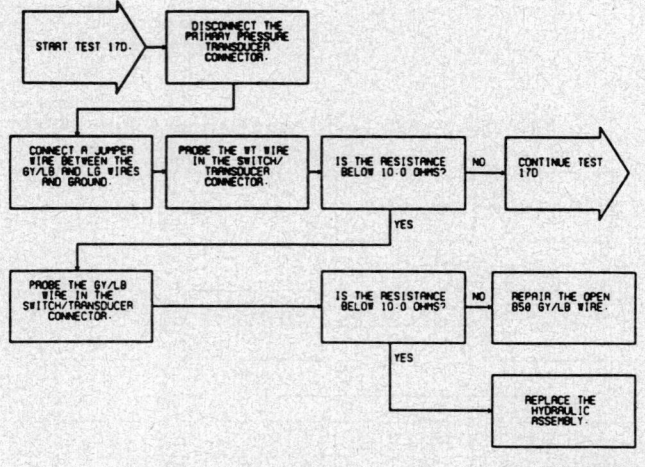

CR4029100442010X

Fig. 70   Test 17D: Primary Pressure/Delta P Fault (Part 1 of 2). 1992

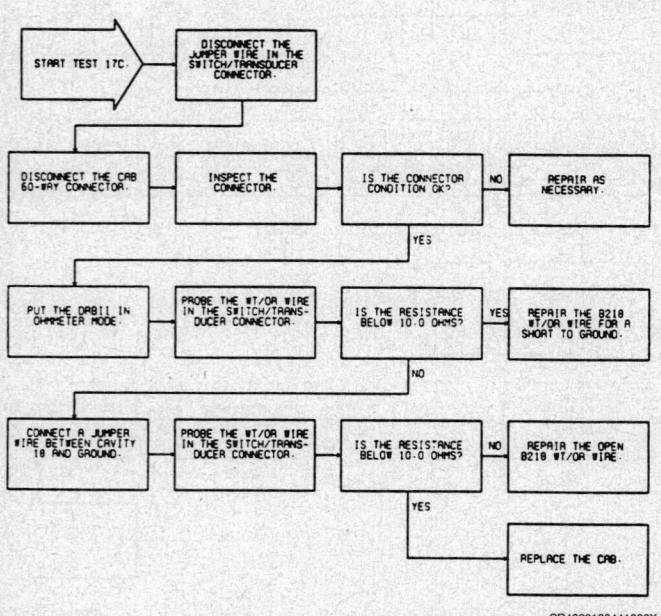

CR4029100441000X

Fig. 69   Test 17C: Primary Pressure/Delta P Fault. 1992

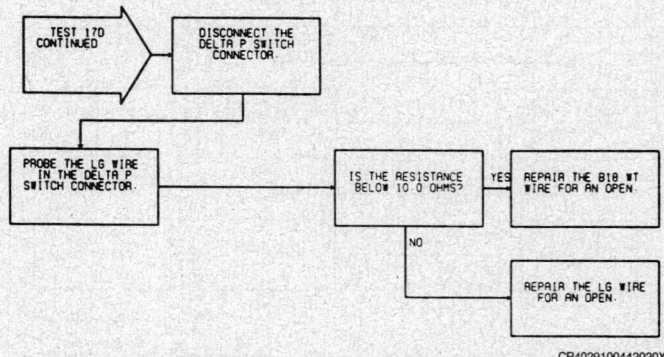

CR4029100442020X

Fig. 70   Test 17D: Primary Pressure/Delta P Fault (Part 2 of 2). 1992

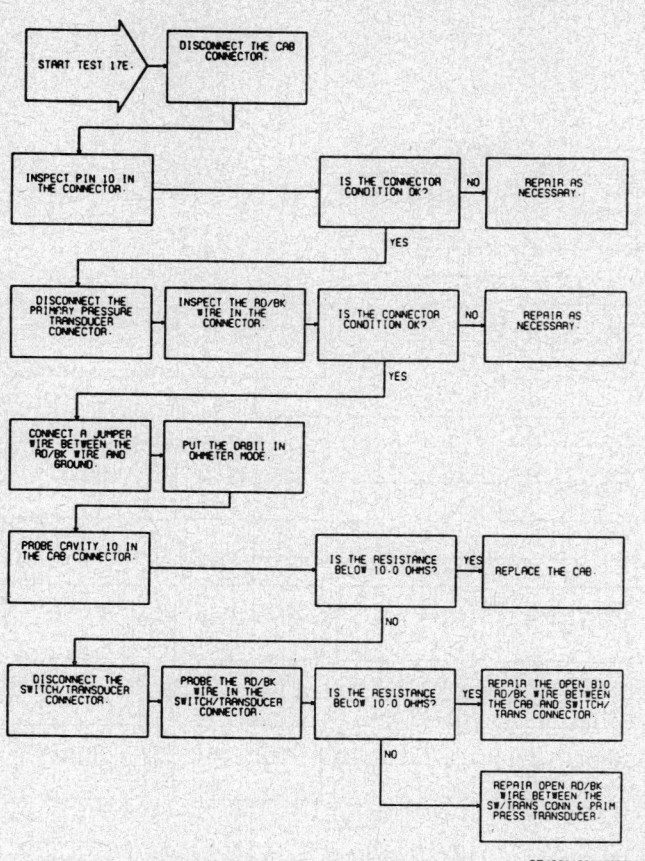

Fig. 71 Test 17E: Primary Pressure/Delta P Fault.
1992

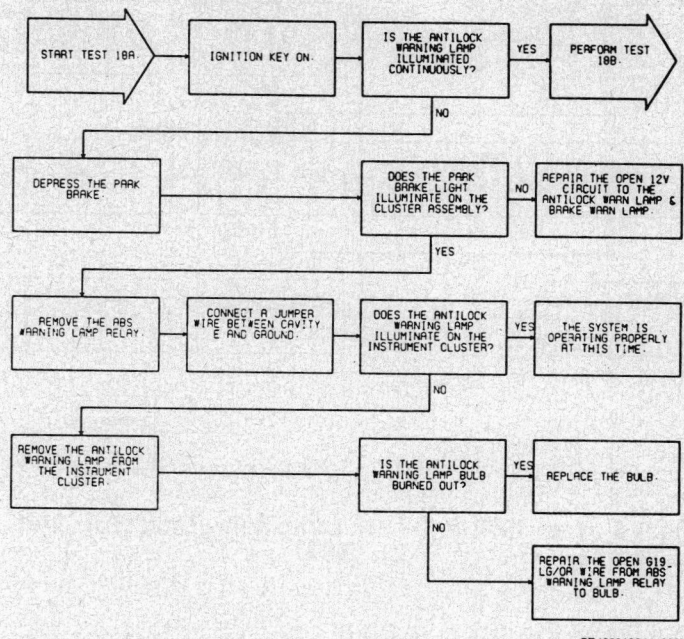

Fig. 72 Test 18A: Anti-Lock Lamp Fault. 1992

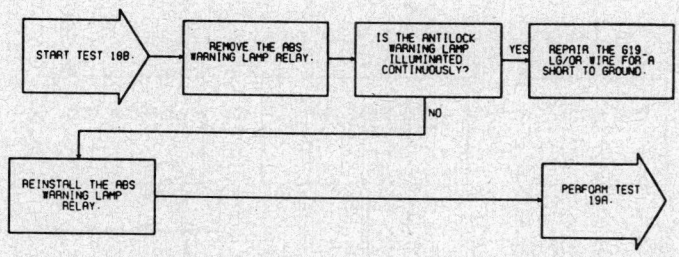

Fig. 73 Test 18B: Anti-Lock Lamp Fault. 1992

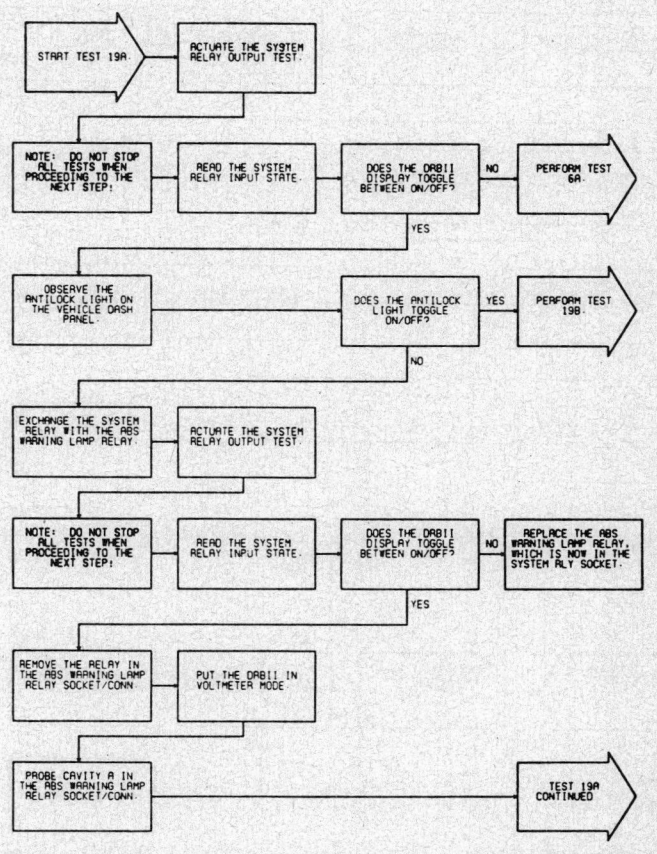

Fig. 74 Test 19A: Anti-Lock Lamp Relay Fault (Part
1 of 2). 1992

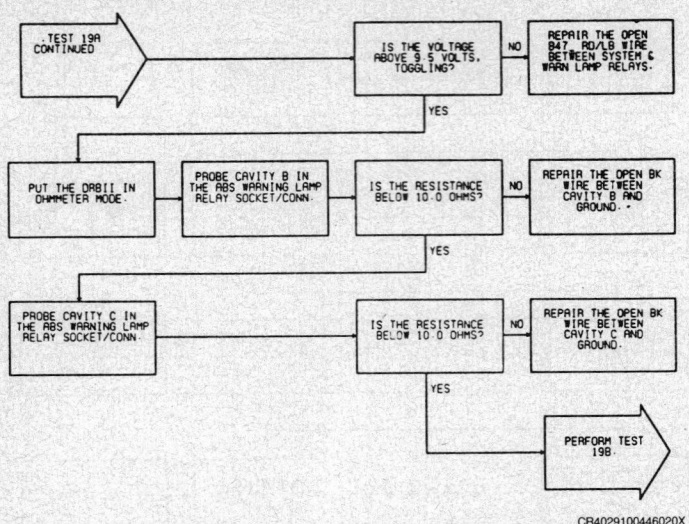

CR4029100446020X

Fig. 74 Test 19A: Anti-Lock Lamp Relay Fault (Part 2 of 2). 1992

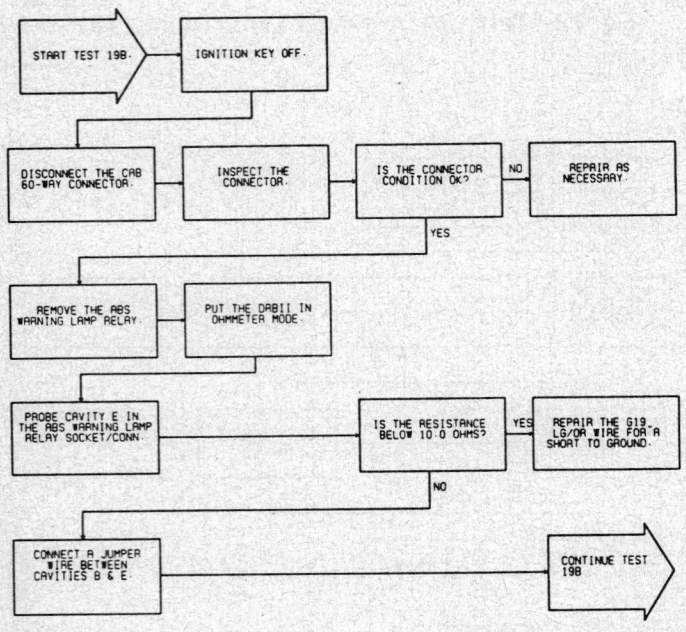

CR4029100447010X

Fig. 75 Test 19B: Anti-Lock Lamp Relay Fault (Part 1 of 2). 1992

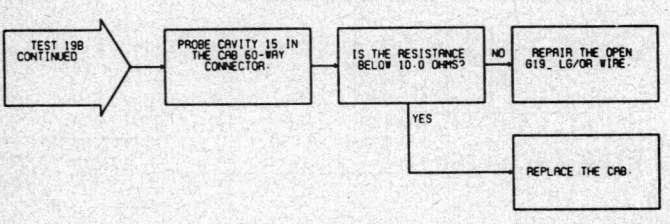

CR4029100447020X

Fig. 75 Test 19B: Anti-Lock Lamp Relay Fault (Part 2 of 2). 1992

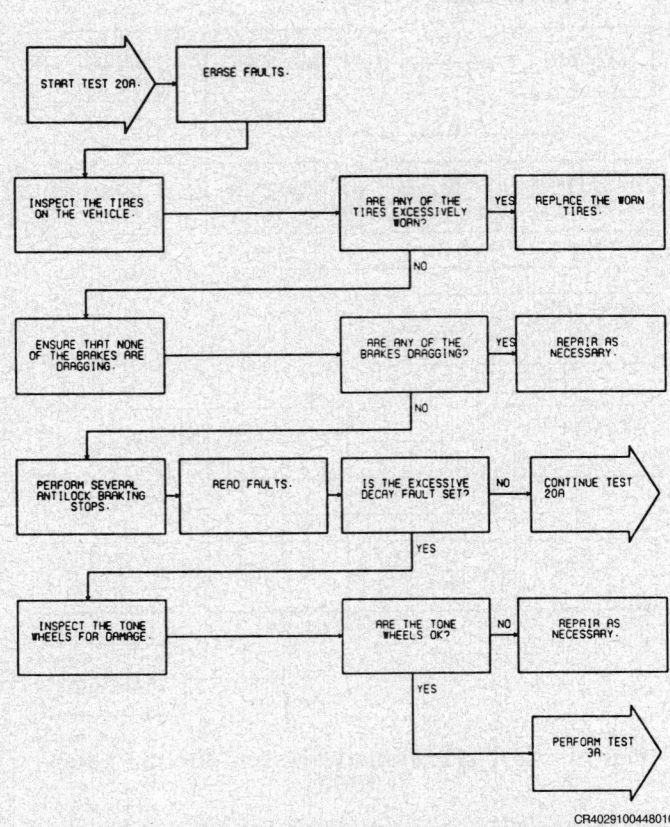

CR4029100448010X

Fig. 76 Test 20A: Excess Decay Fault (Part 1 of 2). 1992

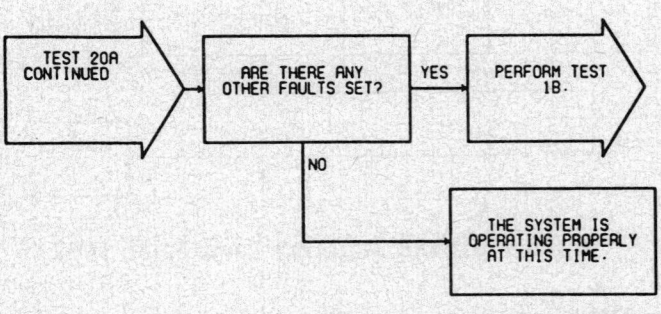

CR4029100448020X

Fig. 76 Test 20A: Excess Decay Fault (Part 2 of 2). 1992

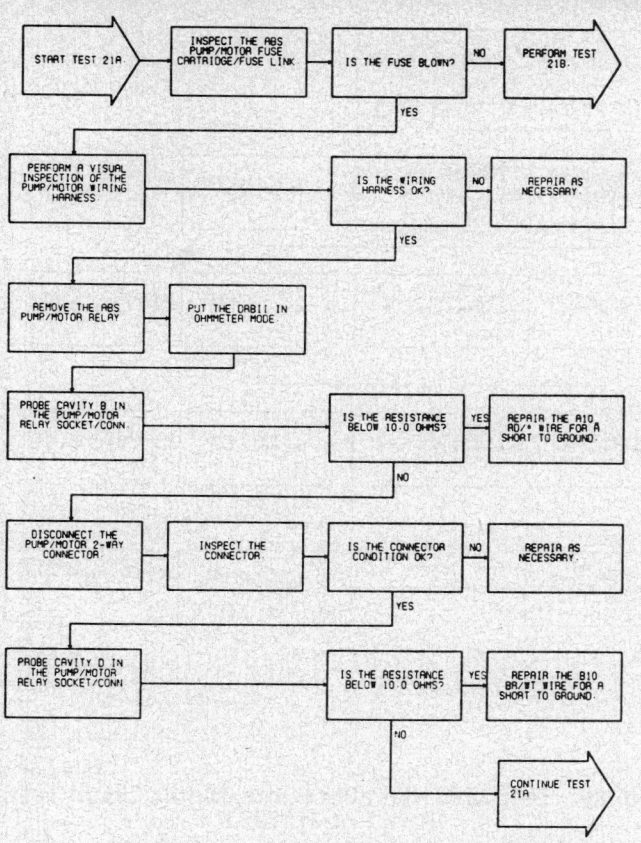

Fig. 77   Test 21A: Hydraulic Pump/Motor Circuit Test (Part 1 of 2). 1992

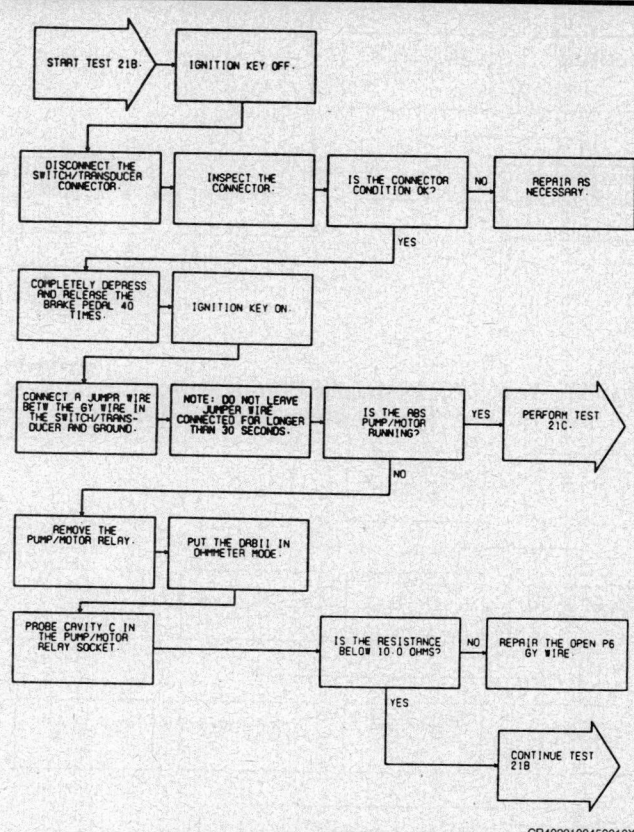

Fig. 78   Test 21B: Hydraulic Pump/Motor Circuit Test (Part 1 of 3). 1992

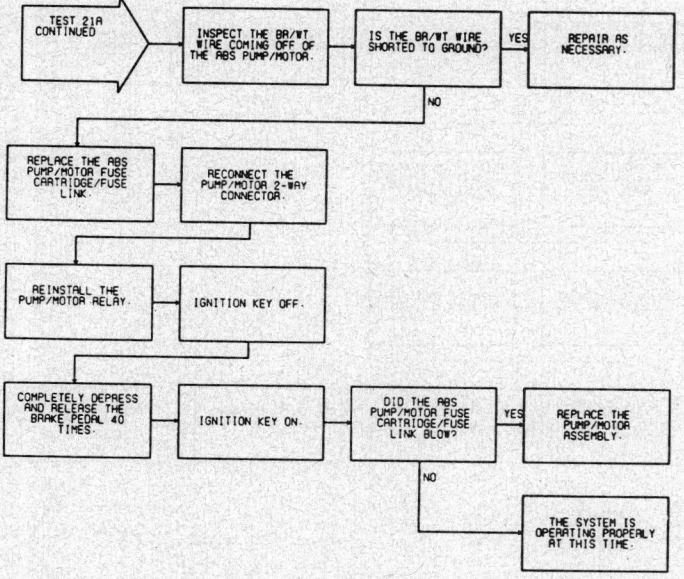

Fig. 77   Test 21A: Hydraulic Pump/Motor Circuit Test (Part 2 of 2). 1992

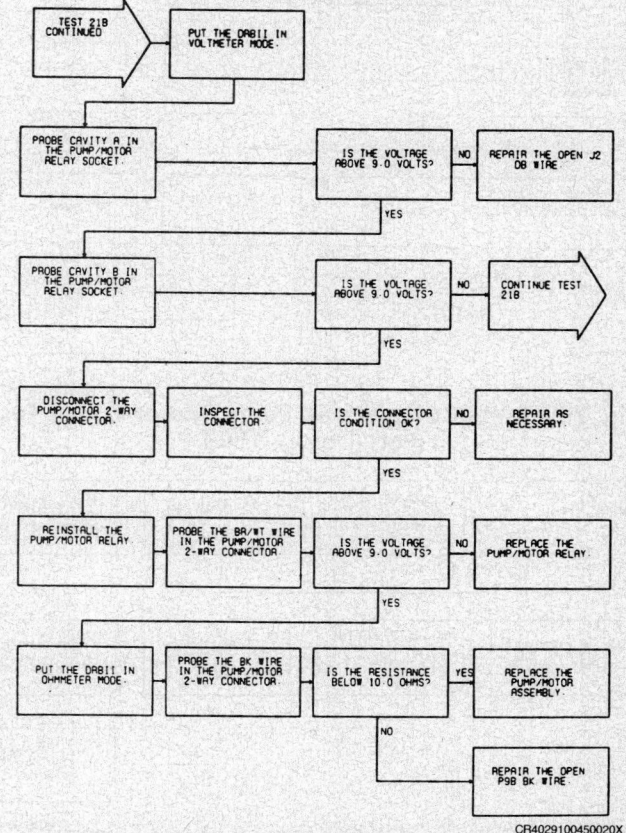

Fig. 78   Test 21B: Hydraulic Pump/Motor Circuit Test (Part 2 of 3). 1992

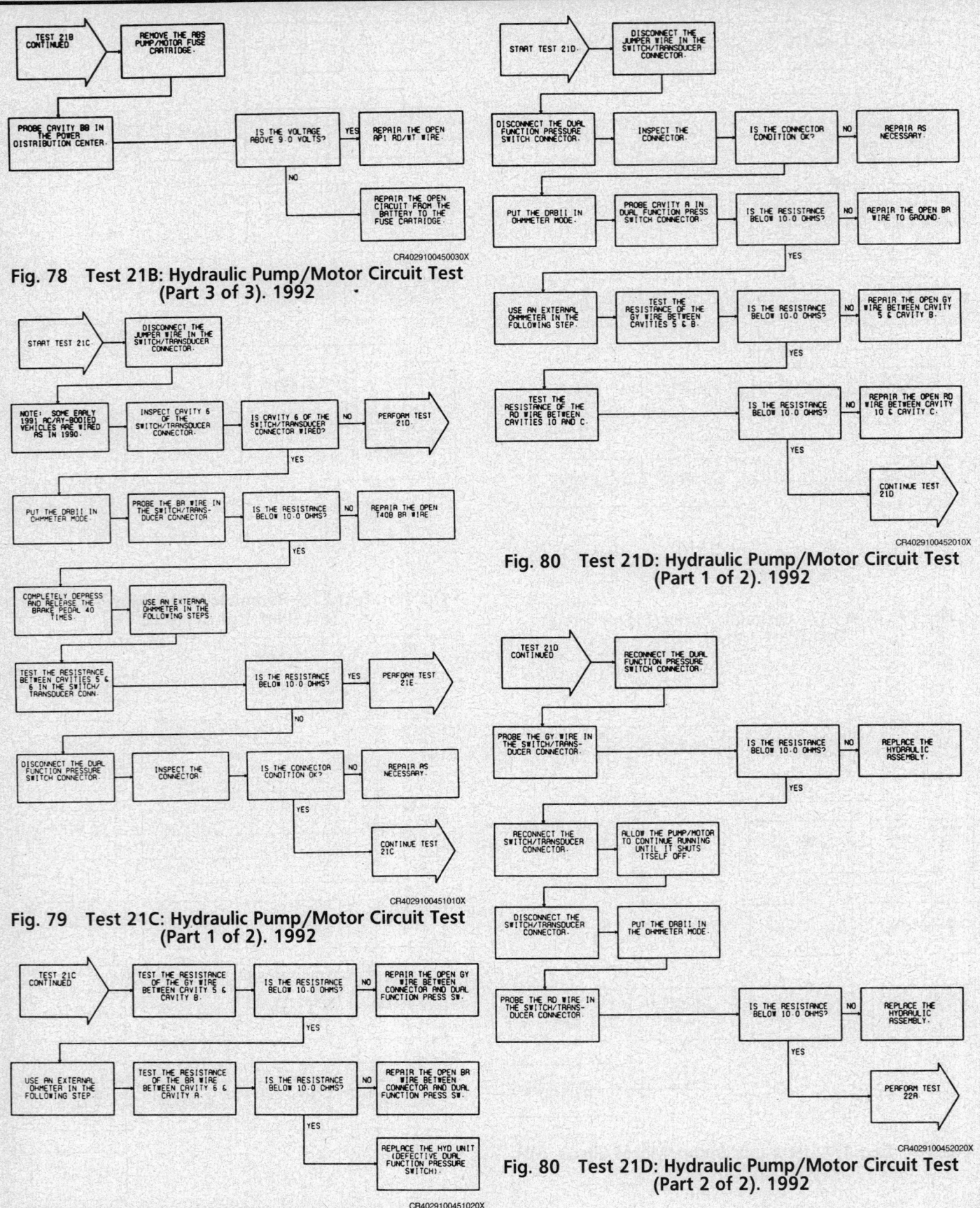

Fig. 78   Test 21B: Hydraulic Pump/Motor Circuit Test (Part 3 of 3). 1992

Fig. 79   Test 21C: Hydraulic Pump/Motor Circuit Test (Part 1 of 2). 1992

Fig. 79   Test 21C: Hydraulic Pump/Motor Circuit Test (Part 2 of 2). 1992

Fig. 80   Test 21D: Hydraulic Pump/Motor Circuit Test (Part 1 of 2). 1992

Fig. 80   Test 21D: Hydraulic Pump/Motor Circuit Test (Part 2 of 2). 1992

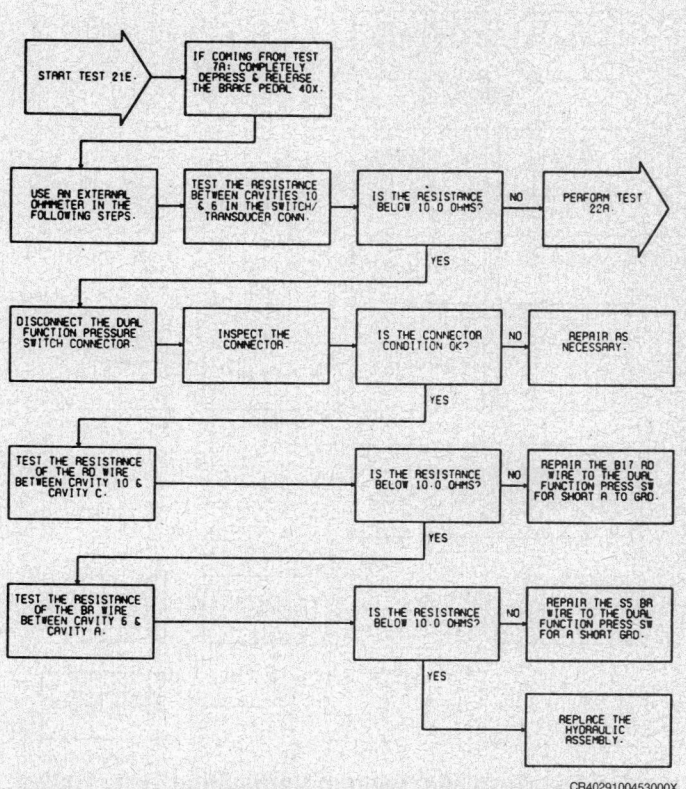

Fig. 81 Test 21E: Hydraulic Pump/Motor Circuit Test. 1992

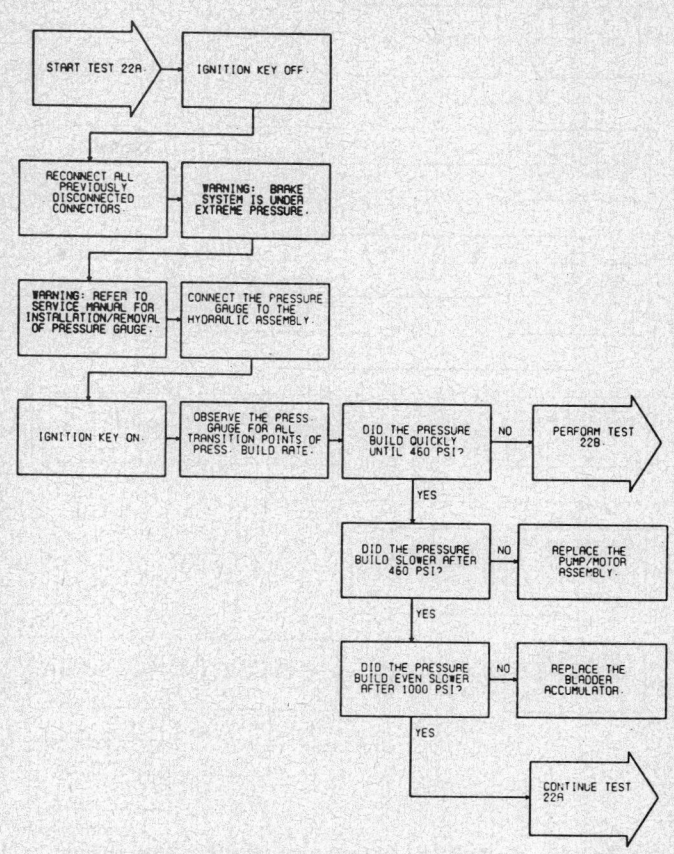

Fig. 82 Test 22A: Hydraulic Pressure Performance Test (Part 1 of 2). 1992

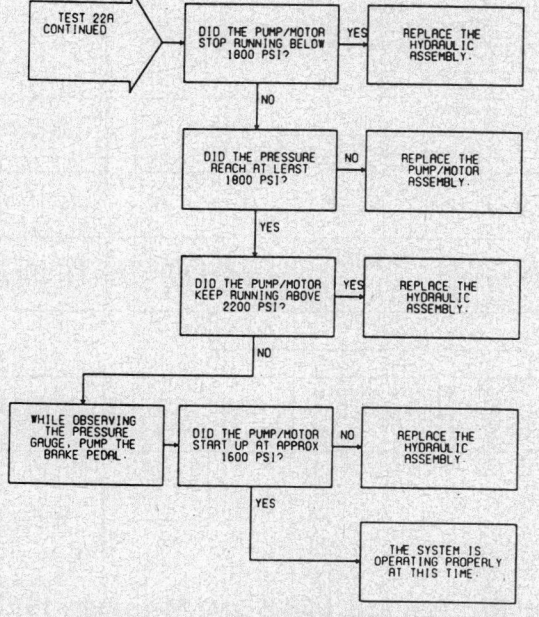

Fig. 82 Test 22A: Hydraulic Pressure Performance Test (Part 2 of 2). 1992

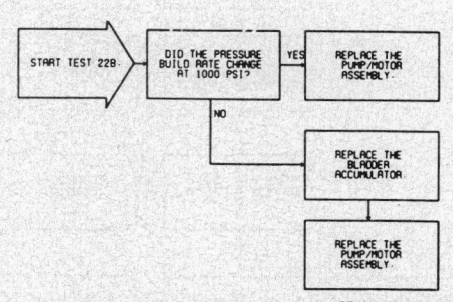

Fig. 83 Test 22B: Hydraulic Pressure Performance Test. 1992

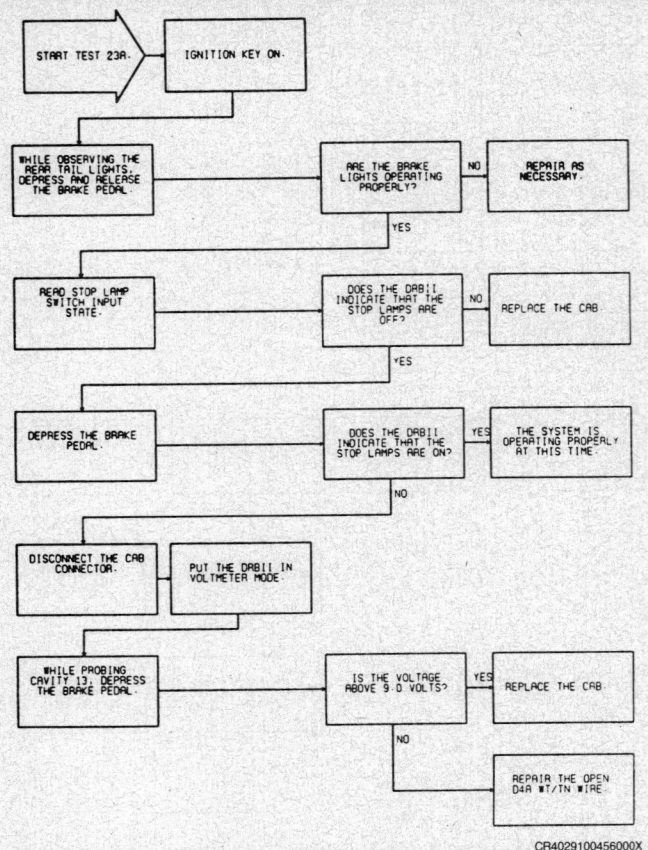

Fig. 84 Test 23A: Stop Lamp Switch Input Test. 1992

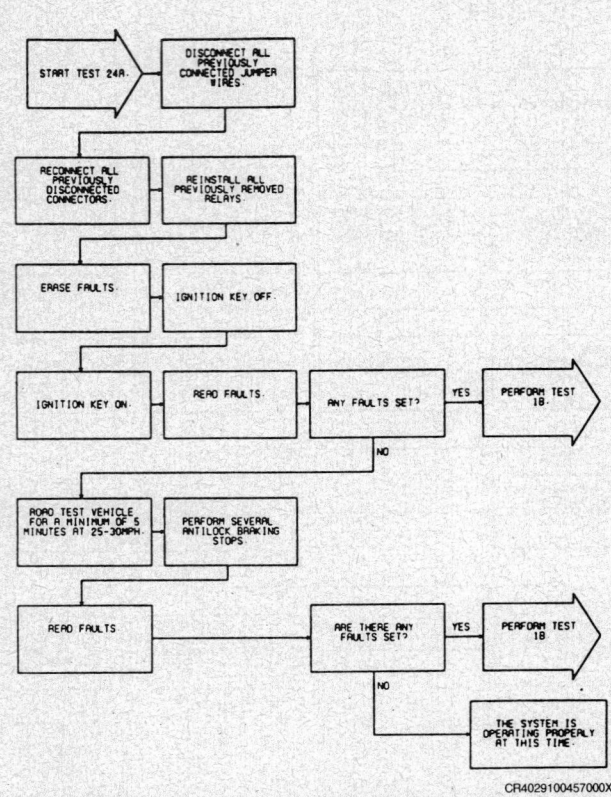

Fig. 85 Test 24A: System Verification Test. 1992

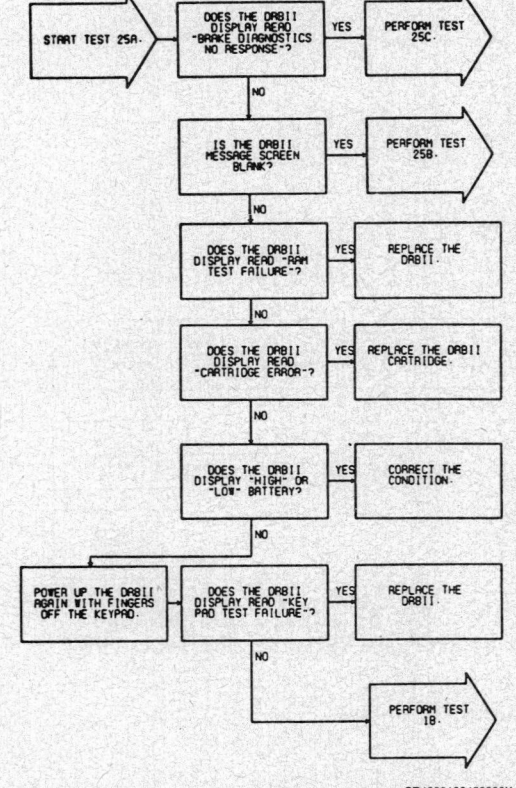

Fig. 86 Test 25A: DRB II Error Messages. 1992

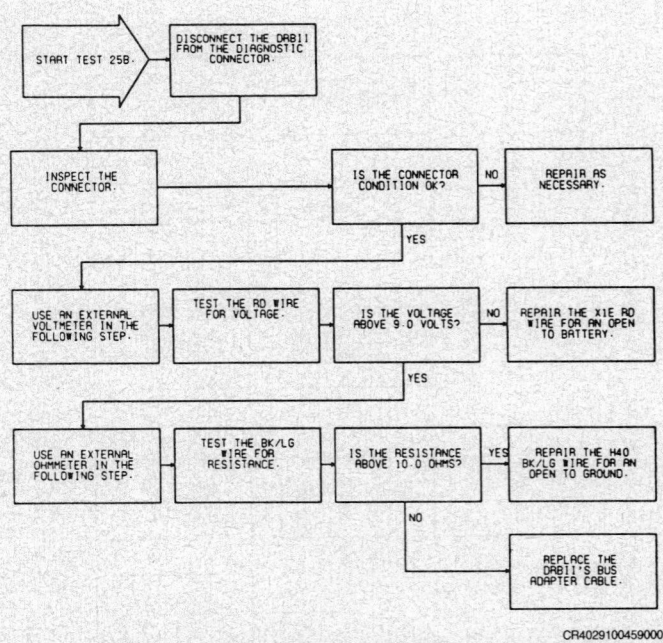

Fig. 87 Test 25B: DRB II Error Messages. 1992

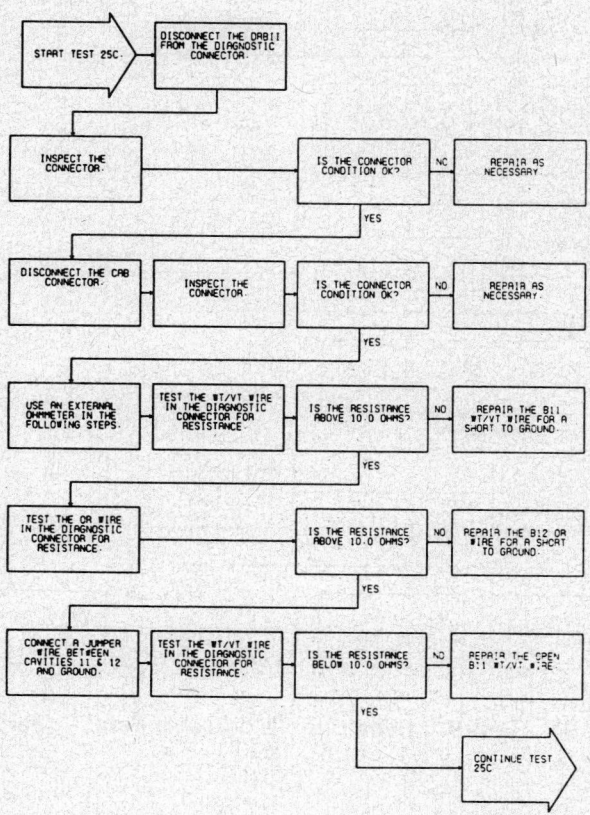

Fig. 88   Test 25C: DRB II Error Messages (Part 1 of 2). 1992

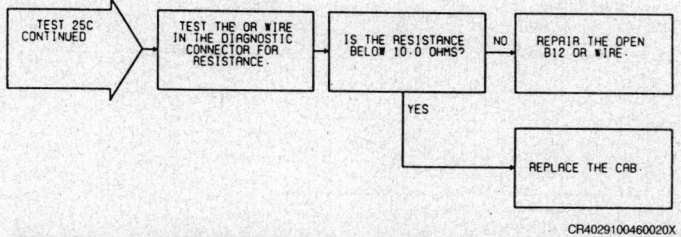

Fig. 88   Test 25C: DRB II Error Messages (Part 2 of 2). 1992

1. Your diagnostic test procedure must begin with a thorough visual inspection the ABS system components for damaged components or disconnected connectors.

2. Connect the DRBII to the data link connector.

AC AND AY BODIES

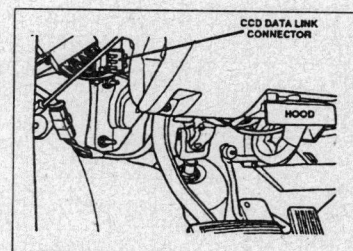

AS BODY

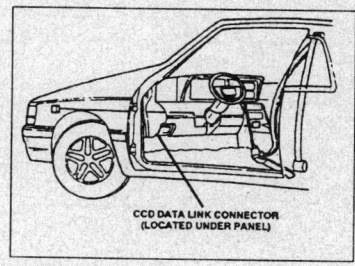

3. With the DRBII, read Bendix ABS fault codes and record. If you encounter a "No Response" message of the DRBII, perform **TEST 23A. NOTE:** The ignition key must be turned off to ensure that faults are properly erased inside the CAB.

4. Turn the ignition key on. With the DRBII, monitor the read fault code display for 4 minutes. If any faults are present, proceed to the appropriate diagnostic test. In some instances, the cause of one fault message may trigger the setting of an additional fault message. If multiple fault messages appear on the DRBII when reading faults, fault repairs must be performed in the order in which they are displayed in the chart below. If there is a customer related complaint, and no warning lamps have been illuminated nor any faults stored in the CAB's memory, perform the indicated test. If no fault codes are present at this time, perform **TEST VER-1A. CAUTION:** Before performing any road test, verify that braking capability is present.

Fig. 89   Test 1A: Checking System For Faults (Part 1 of 2). 1993

NOTE: When inspecting connectors look at both sides of the connector for any corrosion, pin push-outs or spread cavities. Ensure that the connector is properly wired by verifying the wire color in each against the appropriate pinout illustration.

DRBII MESSAGE	DIAGNOSTIC TEST
CAB FAULT	TEST 2A
MODULATOR FAULT	TEST 3A
SOLENOID UNDERVOLTAGE FAULT	TEST 4A
LOW FLUID/PARKING BRAKE FAULT	TEST 5A
SYSTEM RELAY FAULT	TEST 6A
LOW ACCUMULATOR FAULT	TEST 7A
PRIMARY PRESSURE/DELTA PRESSURE FAULT	TEST 17A
BOOST PRESSURE FAULT	TEST 8A
RIGHT REAR WHEEL SPEED SENSOR CONTINUITY FAULT	TEST 9A
LEFT REAR WHEEL SPEED SENSOR CONTINUITY FAULT	TEST 10A
RIGHT FRONTWHEEL SPEED SENSOR CONTINUITY FAULT	TEST 11A
LEFT FRONTWHEEL SPEED SENSOR CONTINUITY FAULT	TEST 12A
RIGHT REAR WHEEL SPEED SENSOR FAULT	TEST 13A
LEFT REAR WHEEL SPEED SENSOR FAULT	TEST 14A
RIGHT FRONT WHEEL SPEED SENSOR FAULT	TEST 15A
LEFT FRONT WHEEL SPEED SENSOR FAULT	TEST 16A
ANTILOCK LAMP FAULT	TEST 18A
ANTILOCK RELAY FAULT	TEST 19A
EXCESS DECAY FAULT	TEST 20A
DRBII "NO RESPONSE" MESSAGE	TEST 23A
Customer related complaints:	
HARD PEDAL/CLICKING NOISES	TEST 25A
NOISY PUMP/MOTOR OR EXCESSIVE RUN TIME	TEST 26A
SCRAPING/WHIRRING NOISE AT WHEELS	TEST 27A

Fig. 89   Test 1A: Checking System For Faults (Part 2 of 2). 1993

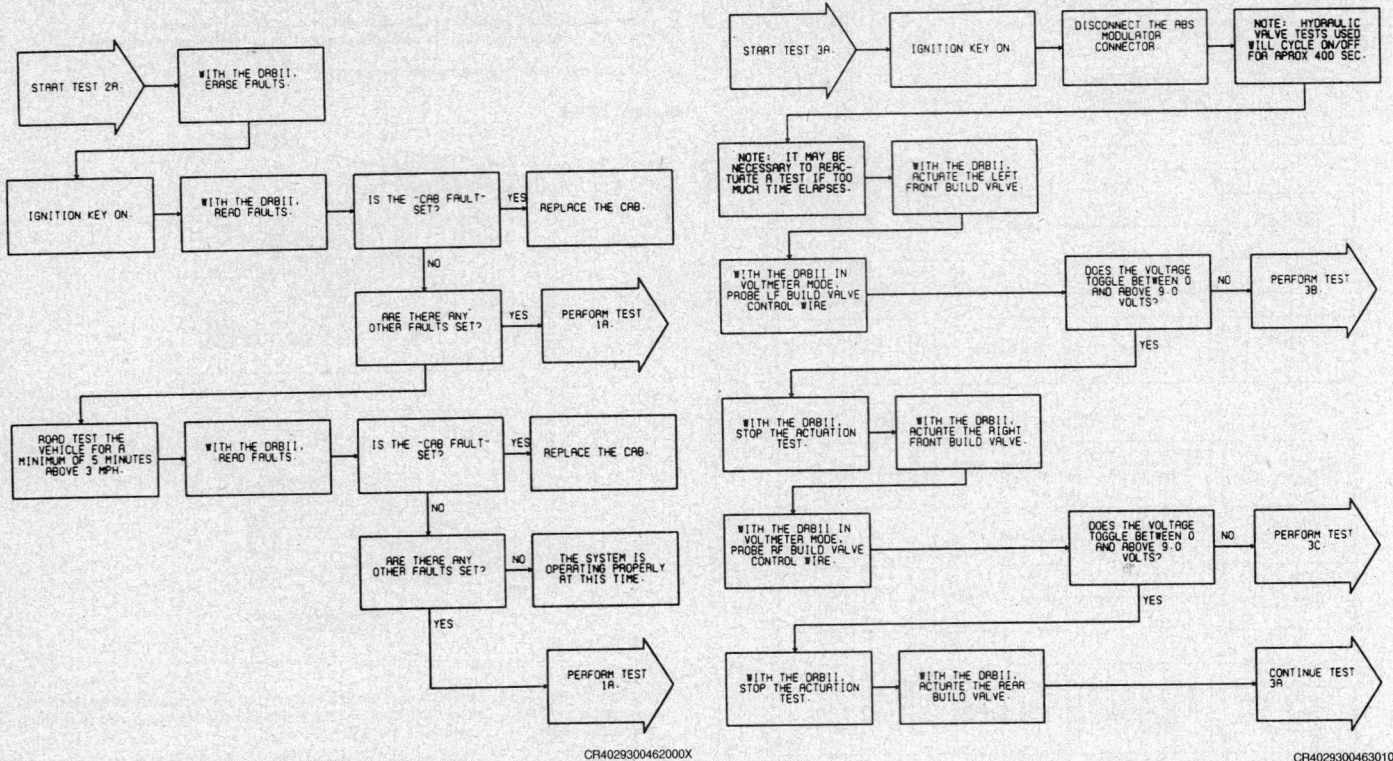

Fig. 90   Test 2A: Repairing "Cab Fault." 1993

Fig. 91   Test 3A: Repairing "Modulator Fault" (Part 1 of 4). 1993

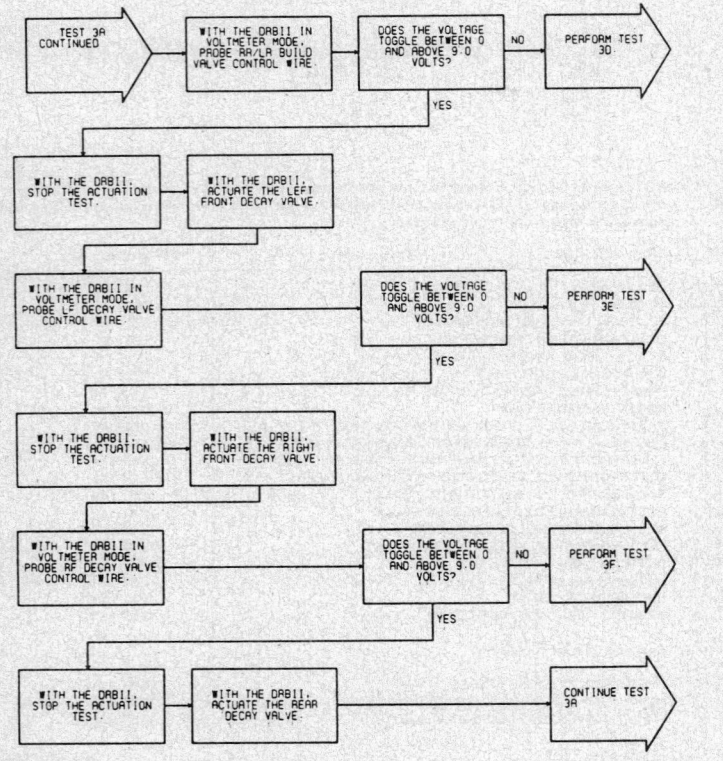

Fig. 91   Test 3A: Repairing "Modulator Fault" (Part 2 of 4). 1993

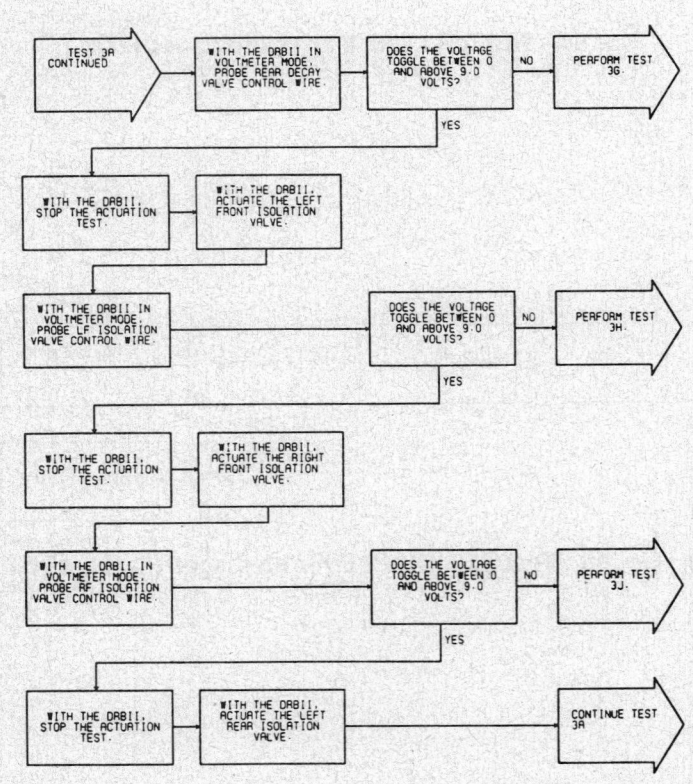

Fig. 91   Test 3A: Repairing "Modulator Fault" (Part 3 of 4). 1993

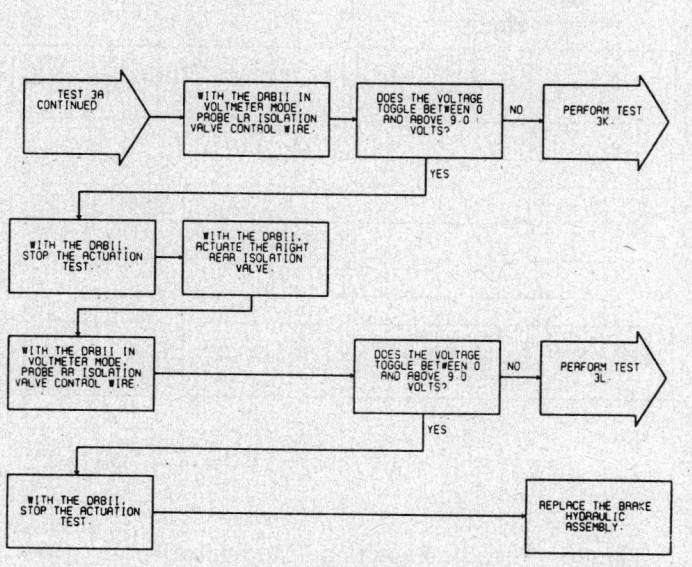

Fig. 91   Test 3A: Repairing "Modulator Fault" (Part 4 of 4). 1993

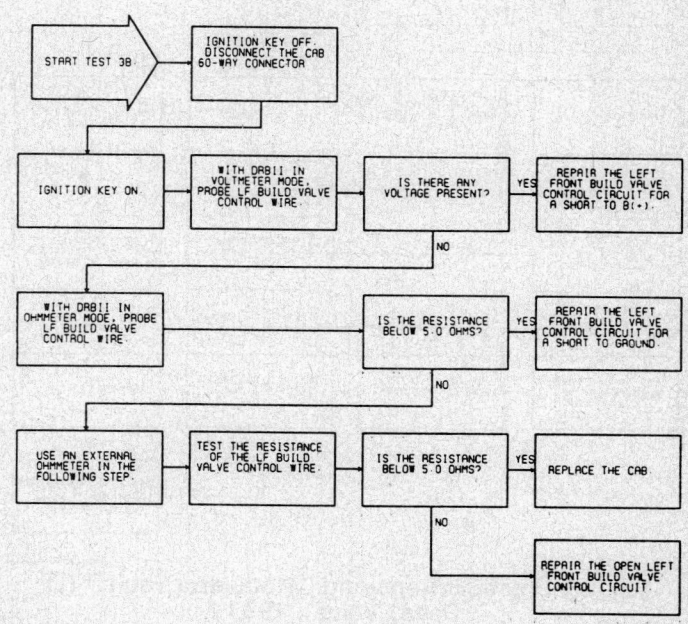

Fig. 92   Test 3B: Repairing "Modulator Fault" (LF Build Valve). 1993

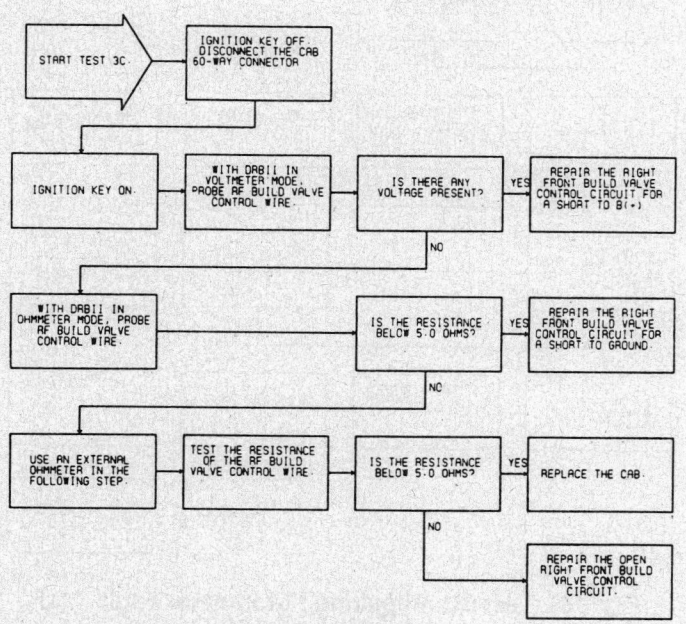

Fig. 93   Test 3C: Repairing "Modulator Fault" (RF Build Valve). 1993

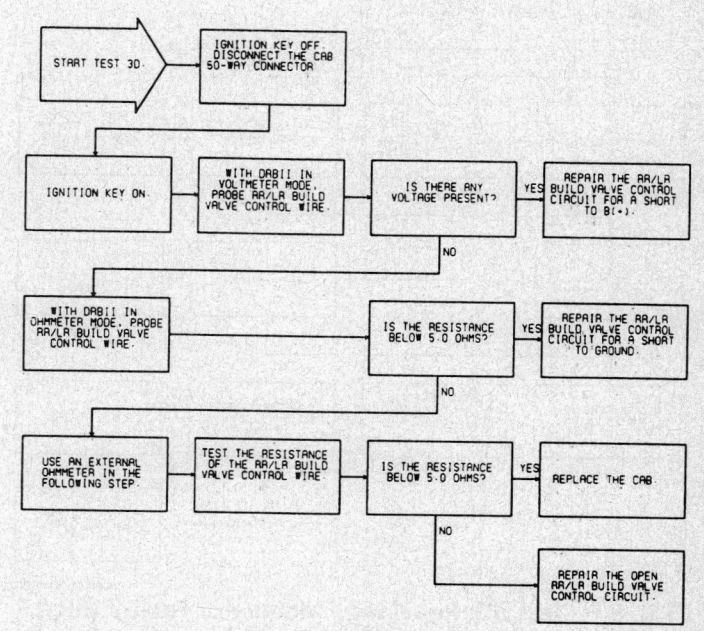

Fig. 94   Test 3D: Repairing "Modulator Fault" (RR/LR Build Valve). 1993

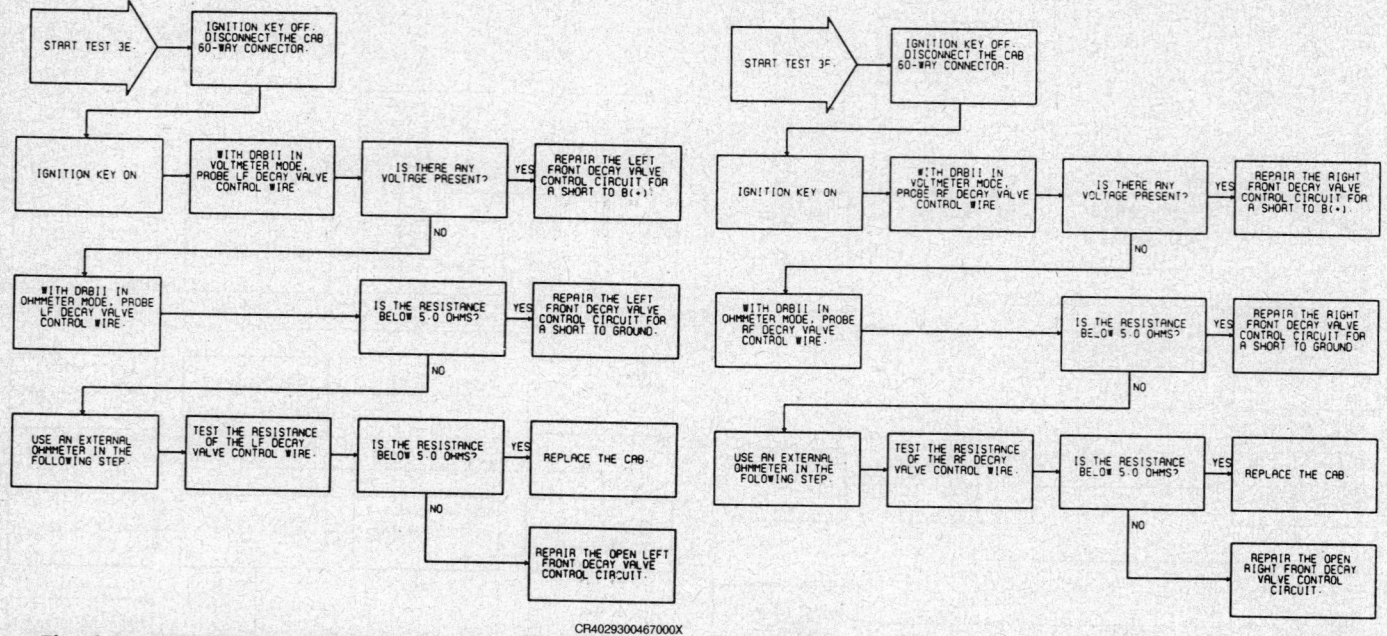

Fig. 95   Test 3E: Repairing "Modulator Fault " (LF Decay Valve). 1993

CR4029300467000X

Fig. 96   Test 3F: Repairing "Modulator Fault " (RF Decay Valve). 1993

CR4029300468000X

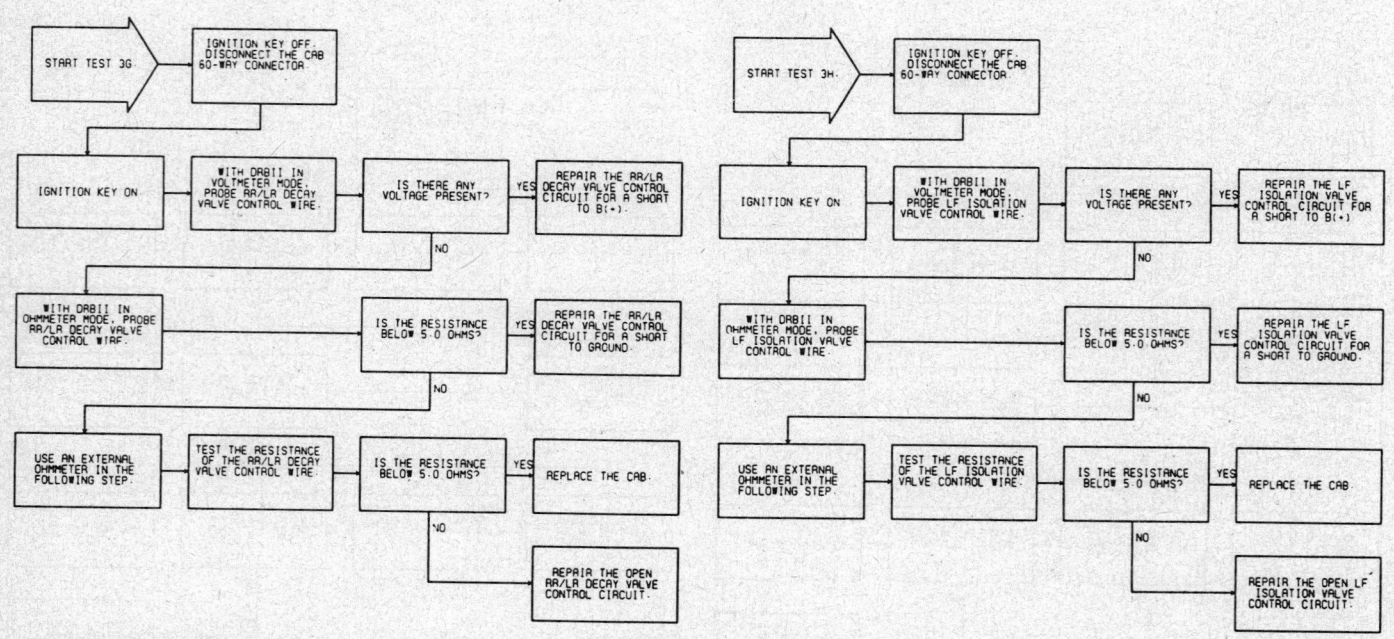

Fig. 97   Test 3G: Repairing "Modulator Fault " (RR/LR Decay Valve). 1993

CR4029300469000X

Fig. 98   Test 3H: Repairing "Modulator Fault " (LF Isolation Valve). 1993

CR4029300470000X

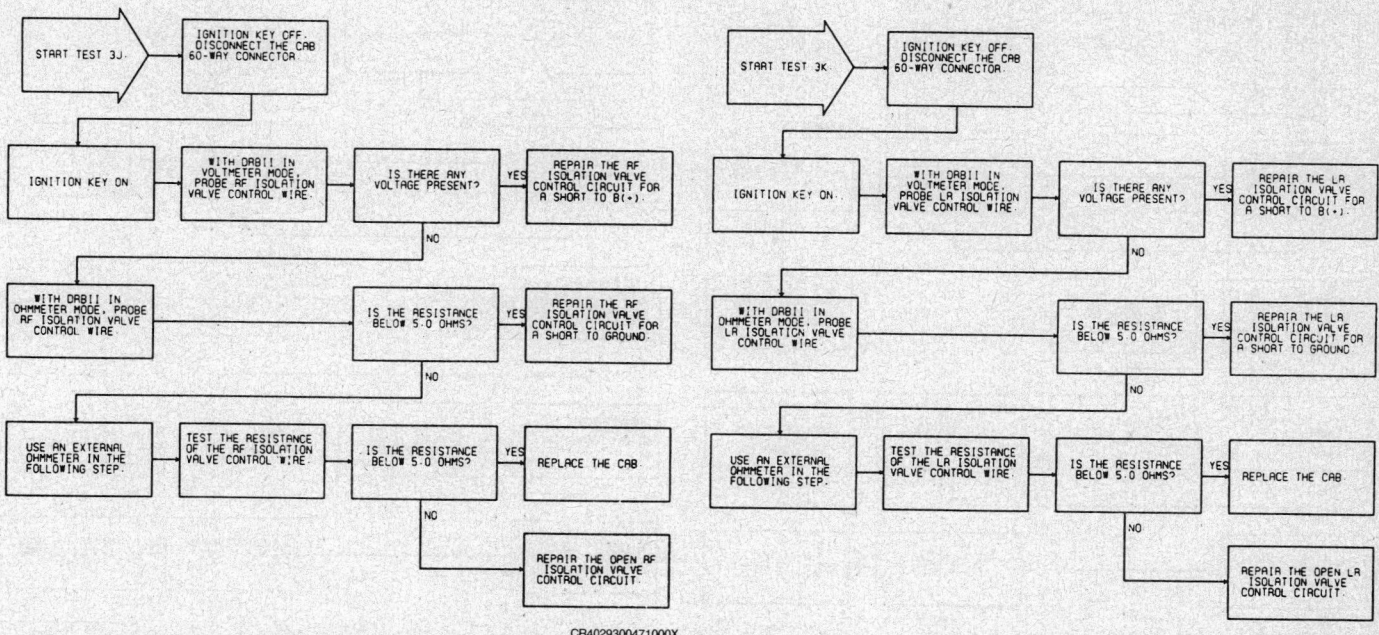

Fig. 99 Test 3J: Repairing "Modulator Fault" (RF Isolation Valve). 1993

CR4029300471000X

Fig. 100 Test 3K: Repairing "Modulator Fault" (LR Isolation Valve). 1993

CR4029300472000X

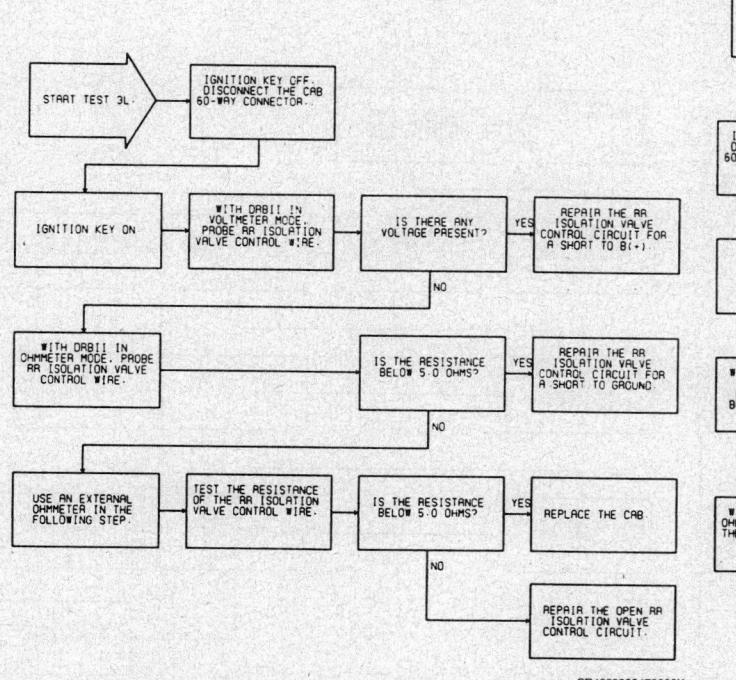

Fig. 101 Test 3L: Repairing "Modulator Fault" (RR Isolation Valve). 1993

CR4029300473000X

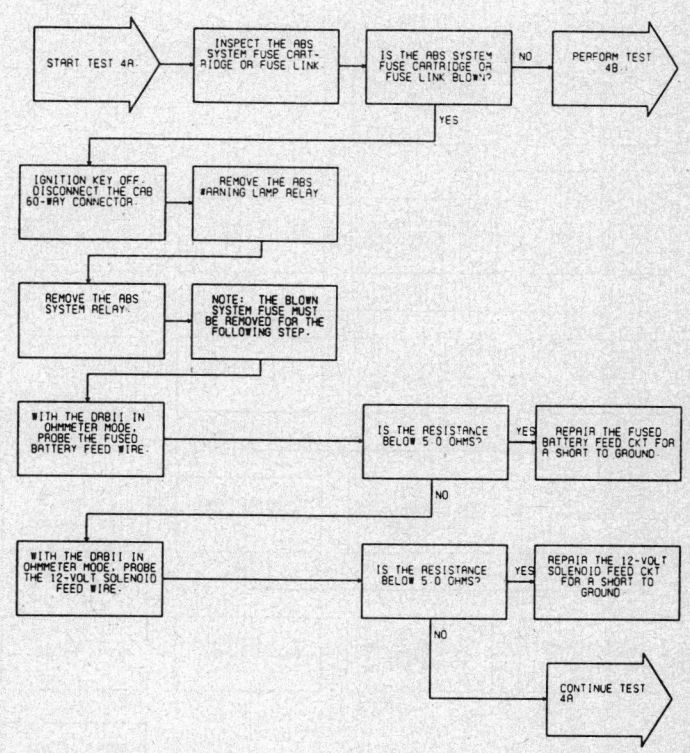

Fig. 102 Test 4A: Repairing "Solenoid Undervoltage Fault" (Part 1 of 2). 1993

CR4029300474010X

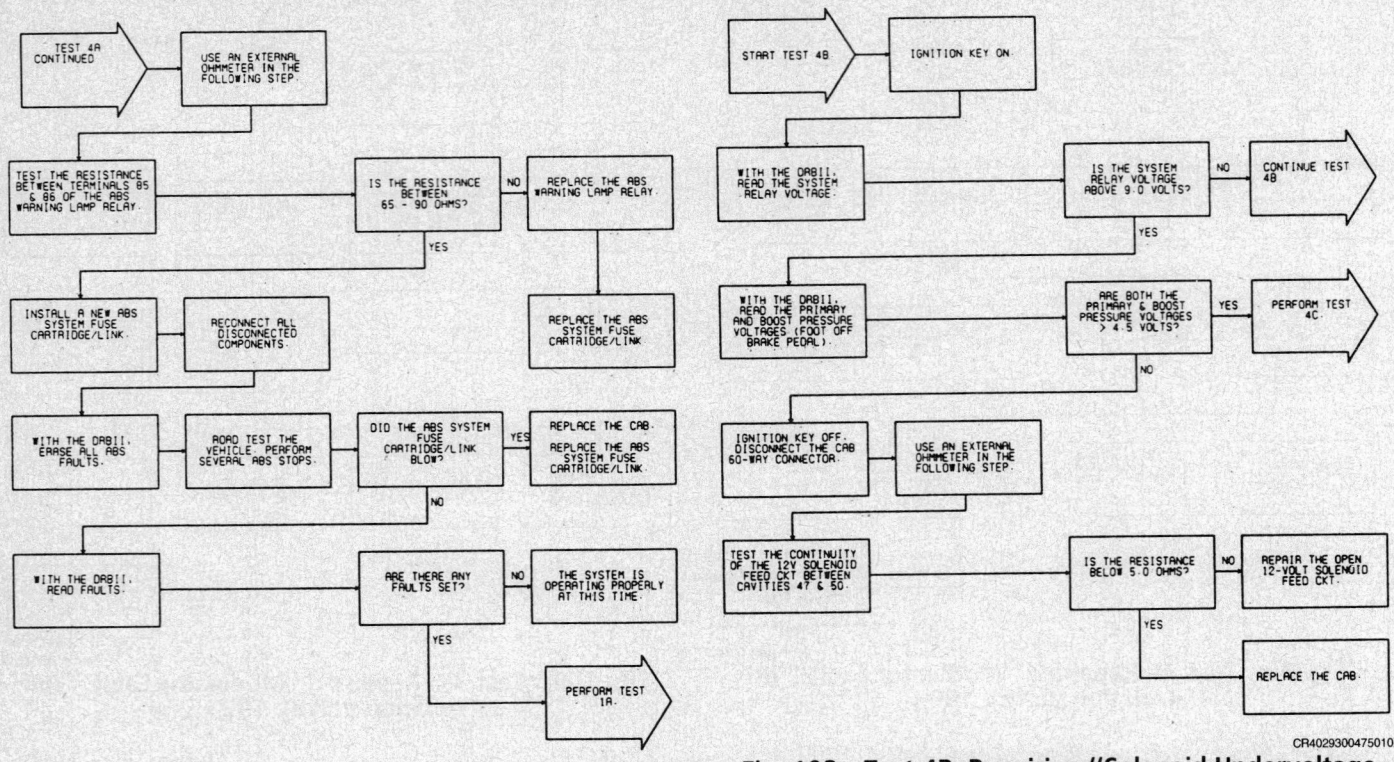

Fig. 102   Test 4A: Repairing "Solenoid Undervoltage Fault" (Part 2 of 2). 1993

Fig. 103   Test 4B: Repairing "Solenoid Undervoltage Fault" (Part 1 of 4). 1993

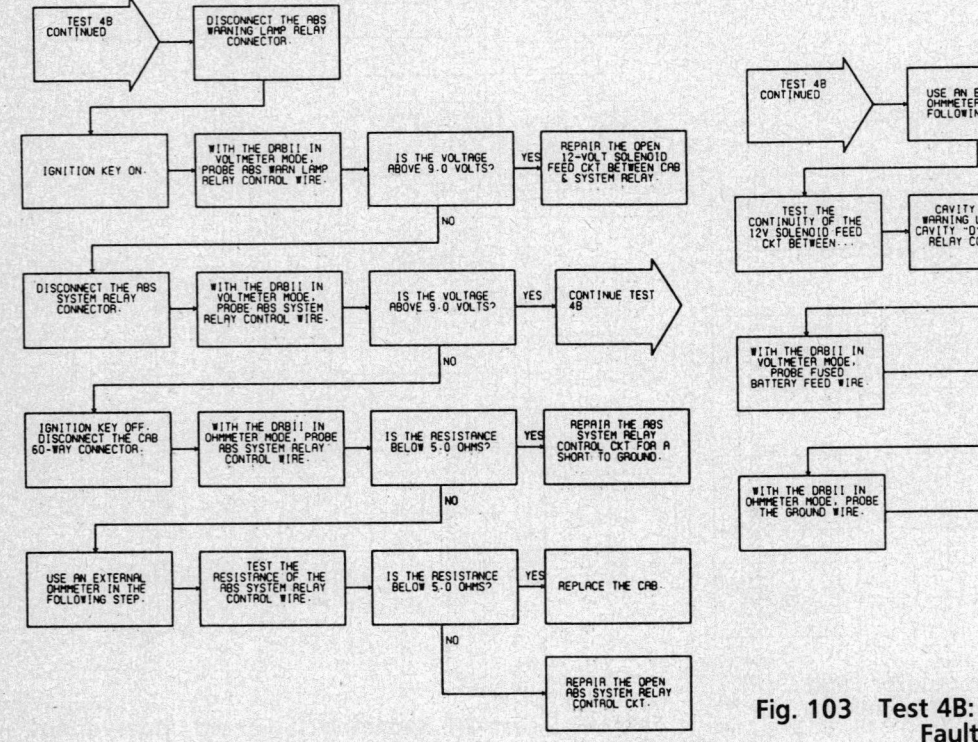

Fig. 103   Test 4B: Repairing "Solenoid Undervoltage Fault" (Part 2 of 4). 1993

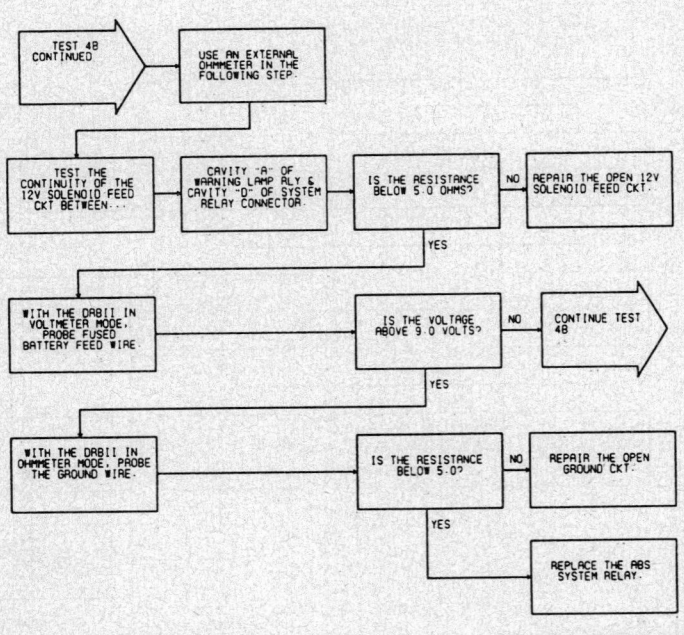

Fig. 103   Test 4B: Repairing "Solenoid Undervoltage Fault" (Part 3 of 4). 1993

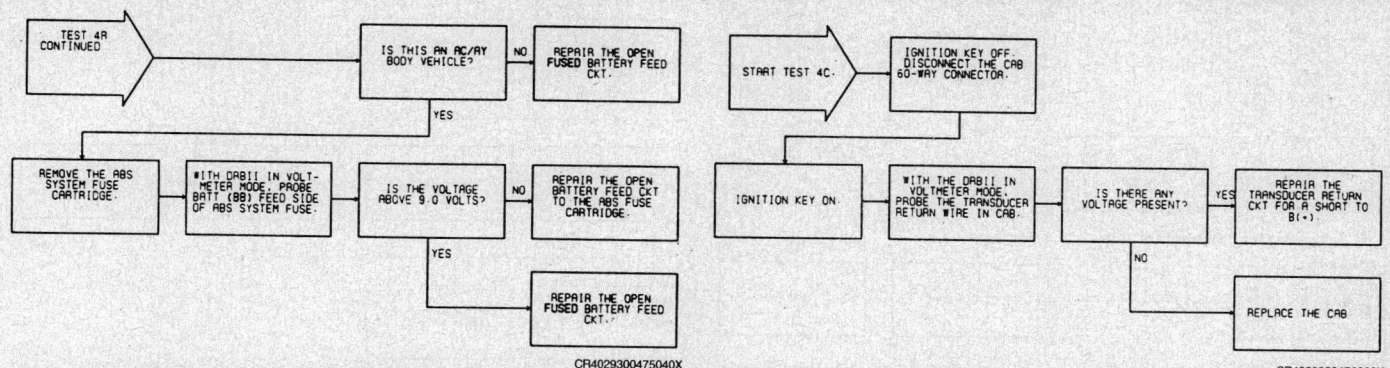

Fig. 103 Test 4B: Repairing "Solenoid Undervoltage Fault" (Part 4 of 4). 1993

CR4029300475040X

Fig. 104 Test 4C: Repairing "Solenoid Undervoltage Fault." 1993

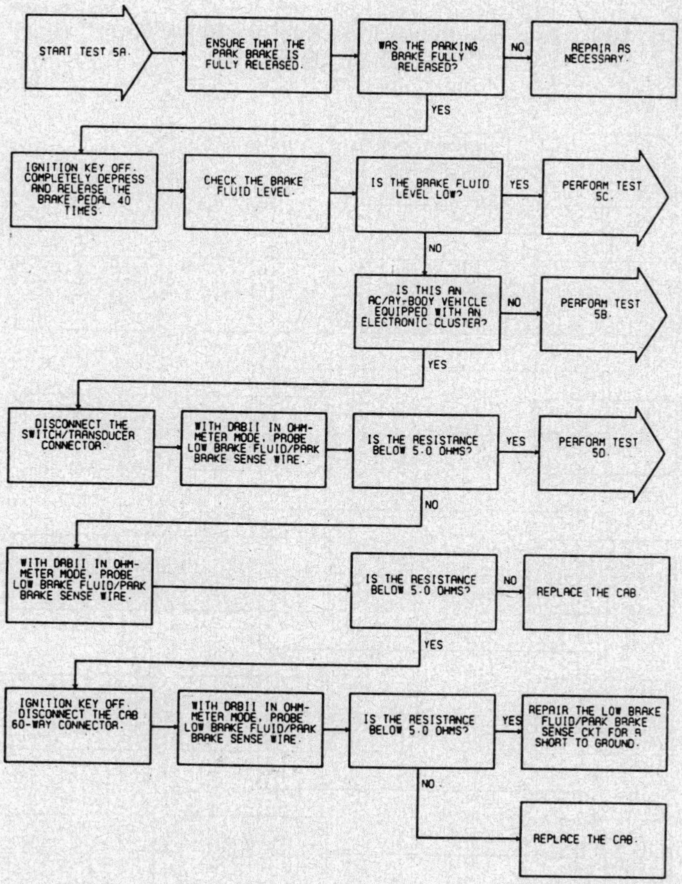

CR4029300476000X

Fig. 105 Test 5A: Repairing "Low Fluid/Parking Brake" Fault. 1993

CR4029300477000X

Fig. 106 Test 5B: Repairing "Low Fluid/Parking Brake" Fault. 1993

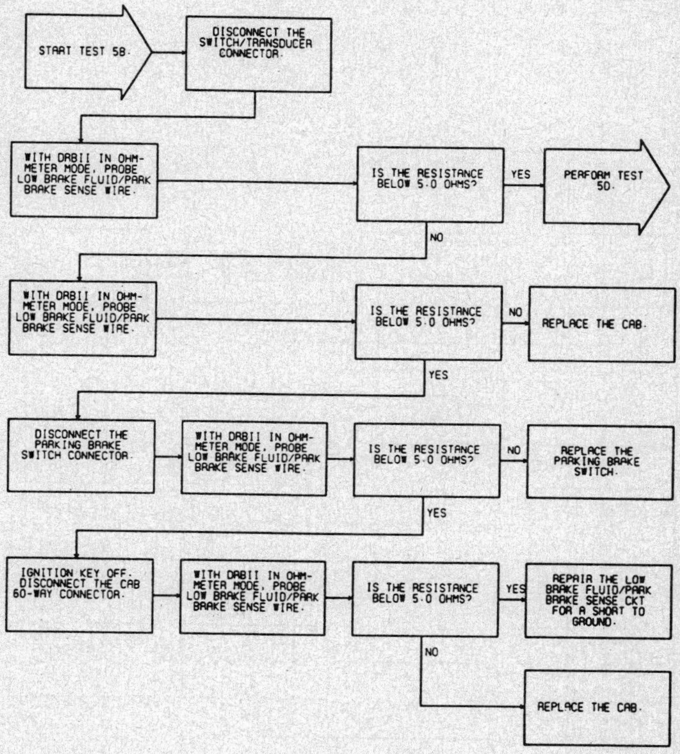

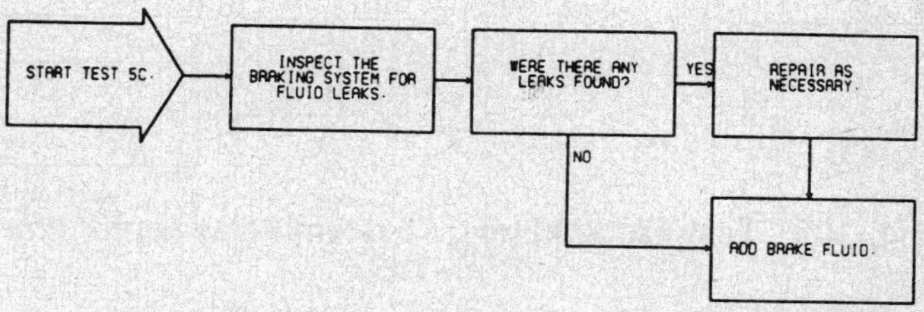

CR4029300478000X

Fig. 107 Test 5C: Repairing "Low Fluid/Parking Brake" Fault. 1993

CR4029300479000X

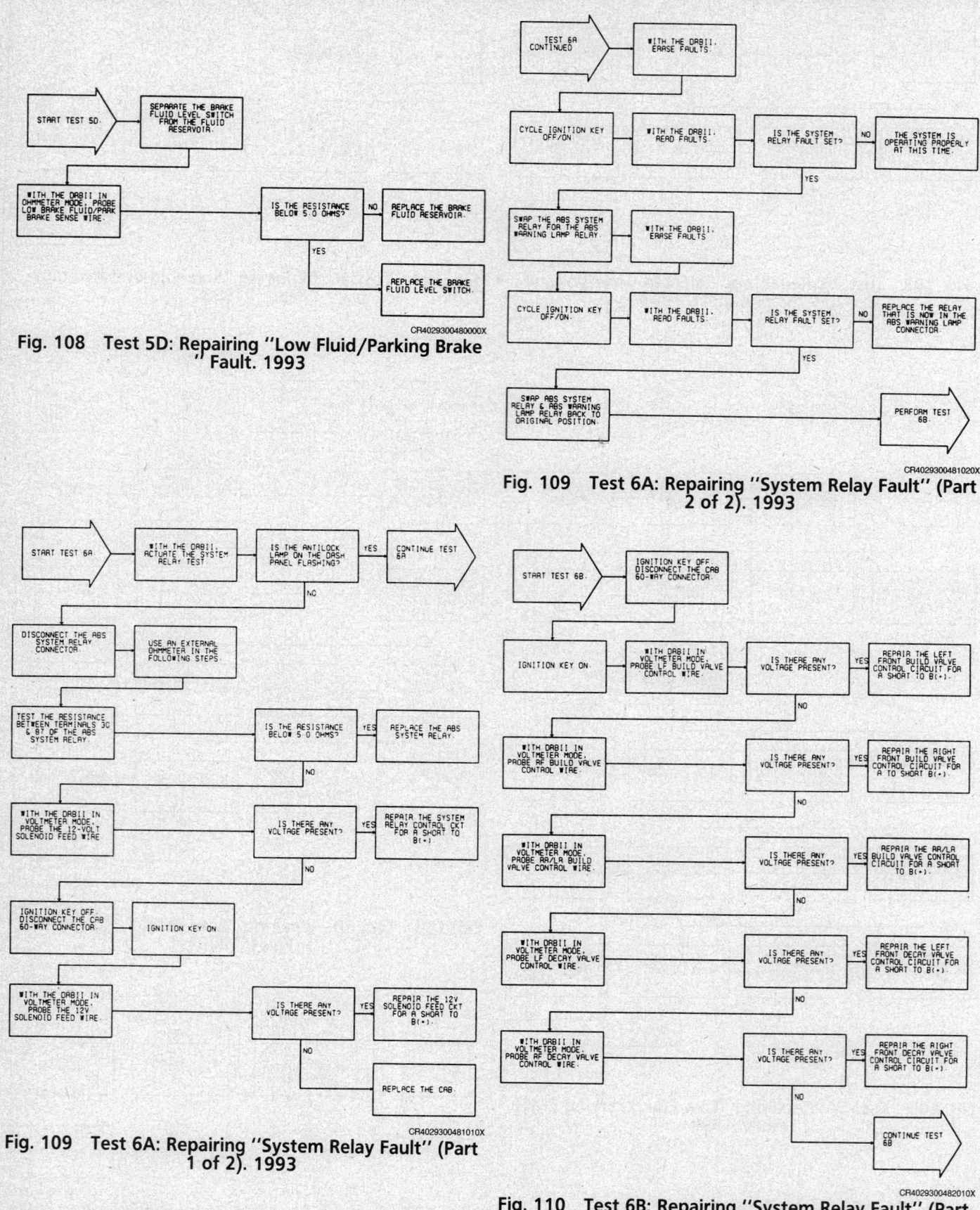

Fig. 108   Test 5D: Repairing "Low Fluid/Parking Brake Fault. 1993

Fig. 109   Test 6A: Repairing "System Relay Fault" (Part 2 of 2). 1993

Fig. 109   Test 6A: Repairing "System Relay Fault" (Part 1 of 2). 1993

Fig. 110   Test 6B: Repairing "System Relay Fault" (Part 1 of 2). 1993

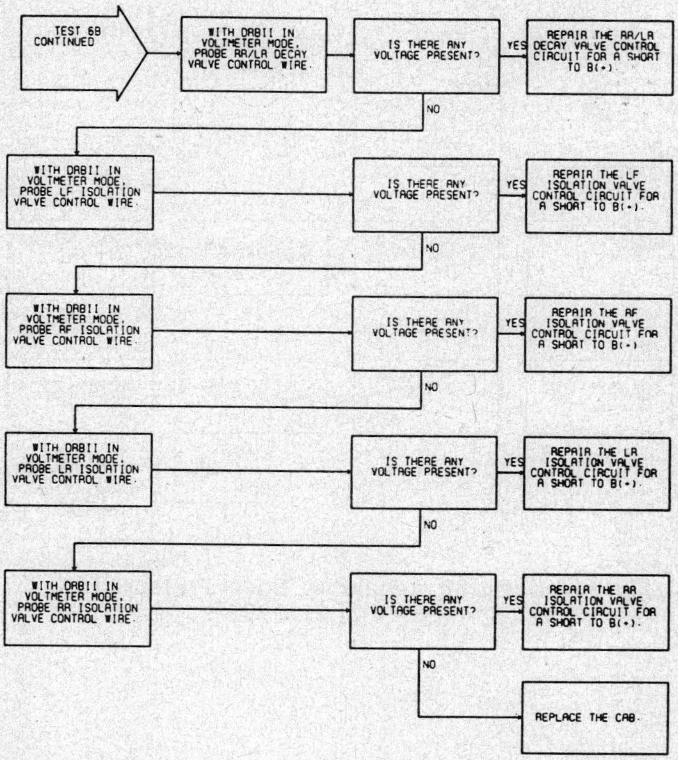

TEST 6B CONTINUED → WITH DRBII IN VOLTMETER MODE, PROBE RR/LR DECAY VALVE CONTROL WIRE. → IS THERE ANY VOLTAGE PRESENT? → YES → REPAIR THE RR/LR DECAY VALVE CONTROL CIRCUIT FOR A SHORT TO B(+).

NO → WITH DRBII IN VOLTMETER MODE, PROBE LF ISOLATION VALVE CONTROL WIRE. → IS THERE ANY VOLTAGE PRESENT? → YES → REPAIR THE LF ISOLATION VALVE CONTROL CIRCUIT FOR A SHORT TO B(+).

NO → WITH DRBII IN VOLTMETER MODE, PROBE RF ISOLATION VALVE CONTROL WIRE. → IS THERE ANY VOLTAGE PRESENT? → YES → REPAIR THE RF ISOLATION VALVE CONTROL CIRCUIT FOR A SHORT TO B(+).

NO → WITH DRBII IN VOLTMETER MODE, PROBE LR ISOLATION VALVE CONTROL WIRE. → IS THERE ANY VOLTAGE PRESENT? → YES → REPAIR THE LR ISOLATION VALVE CONTROL CIRCUIT FOR A SHORT TO B(+).

NO → WITH DRBII IN VOLTMETER MODE, PROBE RR ISOLATION VALVE CONTROL WIRE. → IS THERE ANY VOLTAGE PRESENT? → YES → REPAIR THE RR ISOLATION VALVE CONTROL CIRCUIT FOR A SHORT TO B(+).

NO → REPLACE THE CAB.

CR4029300482020X

Fig. 110 Test 6B: Repairing "System Relay Fault" (Part 2 of 2). 1993

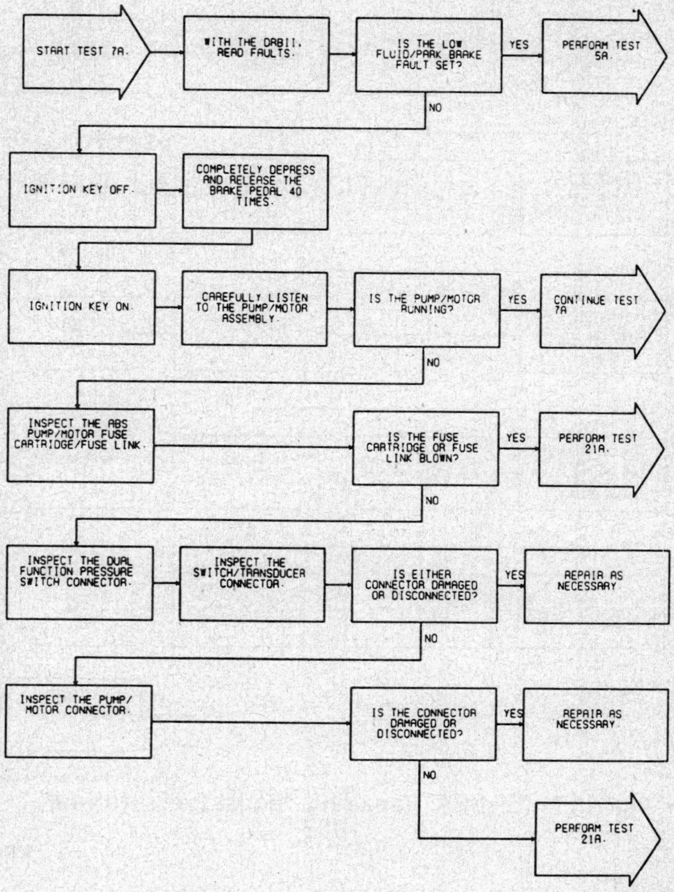

START TEST 7A. → WITH THE DRBII, READ FAULTS. → IS THE LOW FLUID/PARK BRAKE FAULT SET? → YES → PERFORM TEST 5A.

NO → IGNITION KEY OFF. → COMPLETELY DEPRESS AND RELEASE THE BRAKE PEDAL 40 TIMES.

IGNITION KEY ON. → CAREFULLY LISTEN TO THE PUMP/MOTOR ASSEMBLY. → IS THE PUMP/MOTOR RUNNING? → YES → CONTINUE TEST 7A

NO → INSPECT THE ABS PUMP/MOTOR FUSE CARTRIDGE/FUSE LINK. → IS THE FUSE CARTRIDGE OR FUSE LINK BLOWN? → YES → PERFORM TEST 21A.

NO → INSPECT THE DUAL FUNCTION PRESSURE SWITCH CONNECTOR. → INSPECT THE SWITCH/TRANSDUCER CONNECTOR. → IS EITHER CONNECTOR DAMAGED OR DISCONNECTED? → YES → REPAIR AS NECESSARY

NO → INSPECT THE PUMP/MOTOR CONNECTOR. → IS THE CONNECTOR DAMAGED OR DISCONNECTED? → YES → REPAIR AS NECESSARY

NO → PERFORM TEST 21A.

CR4029300483010X

Fig. 111 Test 7A: Repairing "Low Accumulator Fault" (Part 1 of 2). 1993

TEST 7A CONTINUED → DOES THE PUMP/MOTOR QUIT RUNNING WITHIN 2 MINUTES? → NO → PERFORM TEST 22A.

YES → DISCONNECT THE SWITCH/TRANSDUCER CONNECTOR. → WITH THE DRBII IN VOLTMETER MODE, PROBE LOW ACCUMULATOR SW SENSE WIRE. → IS THE VOLTAGE ABOVE 9.0 VOLTS? → YES → PERFORM TEST 7B.

NO → IGNITION KEY OFF. DISCONNECT THE CAB 60-WAY CONNECTOR. → USE AN EXTERNAL OHMMETER IN THE FOLLOWING STEP.

TEST THE CONTINUITY OF LOW ACCUMULATOR SWITCH SENSE WIRE. → IS THE RESISTANCE BELOW 5.0 OHMS? → YES → REPLACE THE CAB.

NO → REPAIR THE OPEN LOW ACCUMULATOR SWITCH SENSE CKT.

CR4029300483020X

Fig. 111 Test 7A: Repairing "Low Accumulator Fault" (Part 2 of 2). 1993

START TEST 7B. → COMPLETELY DEPRESS & RELEASE THE BRAKE PEDAL 40 TIMES.

WITH THE DRBII IN OHMMETER MODE, PROBE THE LOW ACCUMULATOR SWITCH SENSE WIRE. → IS THE RESISTANCE BELOW 5.0 OHMS? → YES → REPLACE THE DUAL FUNCTION PRESSURE SWITCH (DFPS).

NO → DISCONNECT THE DUAL FUNCTION PRESSURE SWITCH CONNECTOR. → USING AN EXTERNAL OHMMETER, MEASURE THE RESISTANCE OF ...

THE LOW ACCUMULATOR SWITCH SENSE WIRE. → IS THE RESISTANCE BELOW 5.0 OHMS? → NO → REPAIR THE OPEN LOW ACCUMULATOR SWITCH SENSE CKT.

YES → PERFORM TEST 22A.

CR4029300484000X

Fig. 112 Test 7B: Repairing "Low Accumulator Fault." 1993

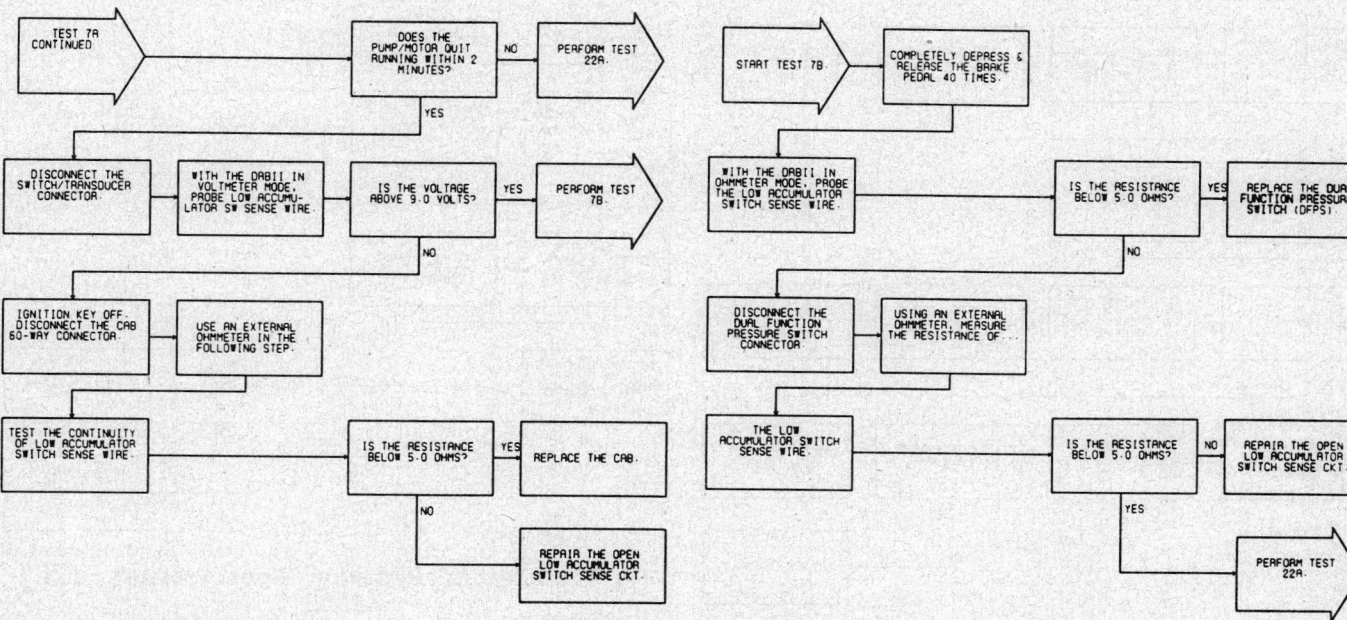

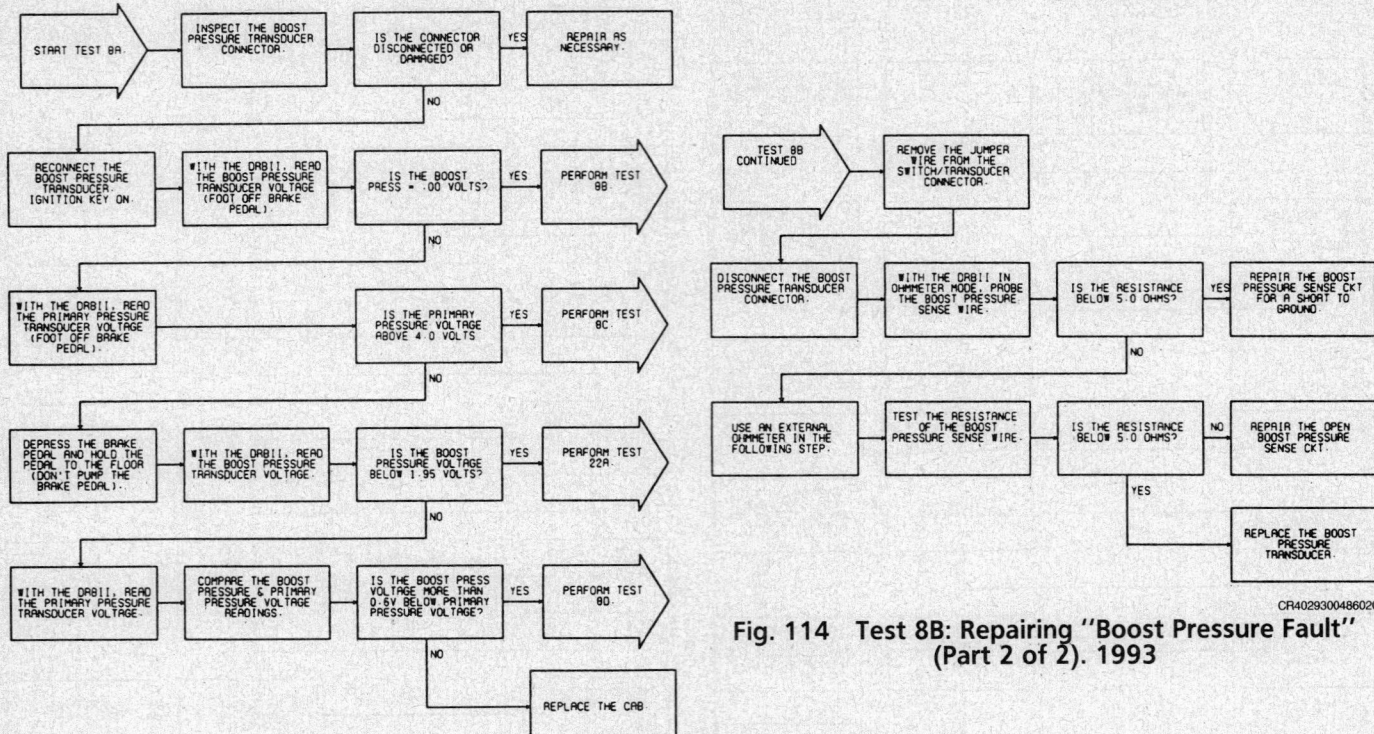

Fig. 113 Test 8A: Repairing "Boost Pressure Fault."
1993

Fig. 114 Test 8B: Repairing "Boost Pressure Fault"
(Part 2 of 2). 1993

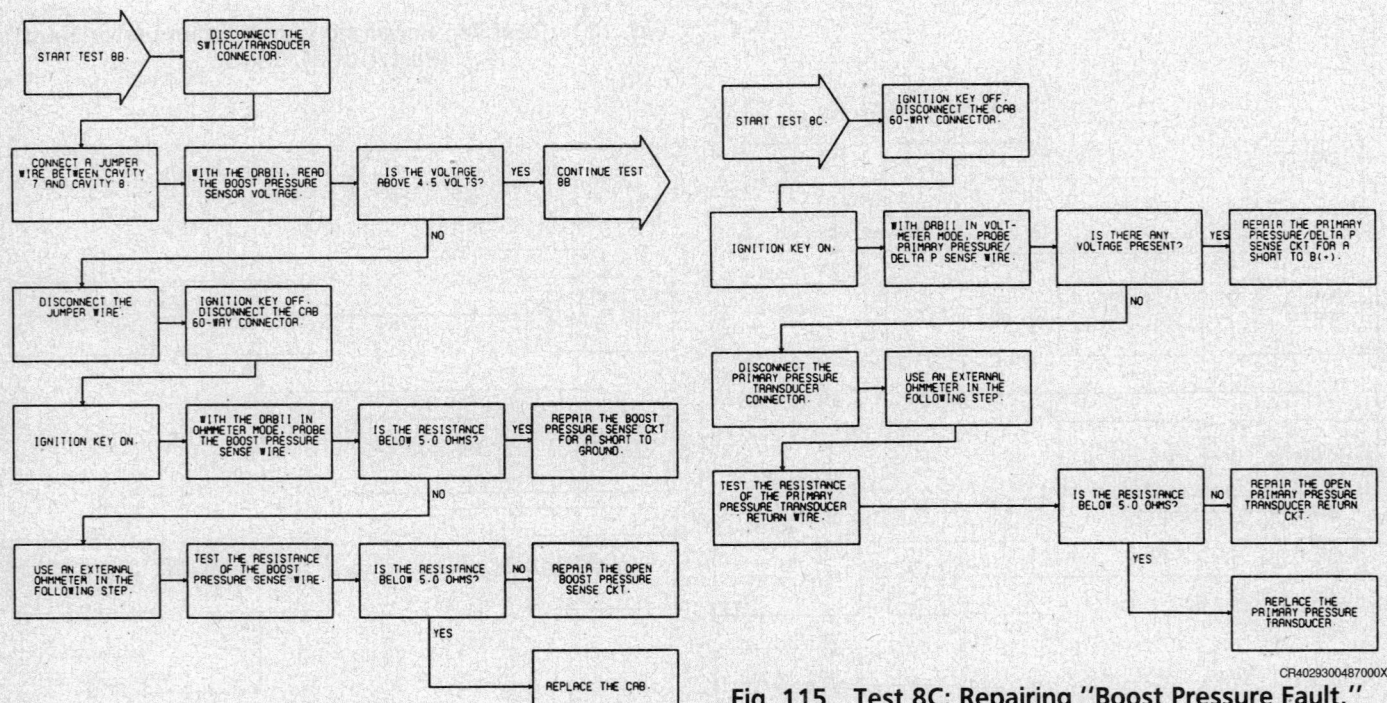

Fig. 114 Test 8B: Repairing "Boost Pressure Fault"
(Part 1 of 2). 1993

Fig. 115 Test 8C: Repairing "Boost Pressure Fault."
1993

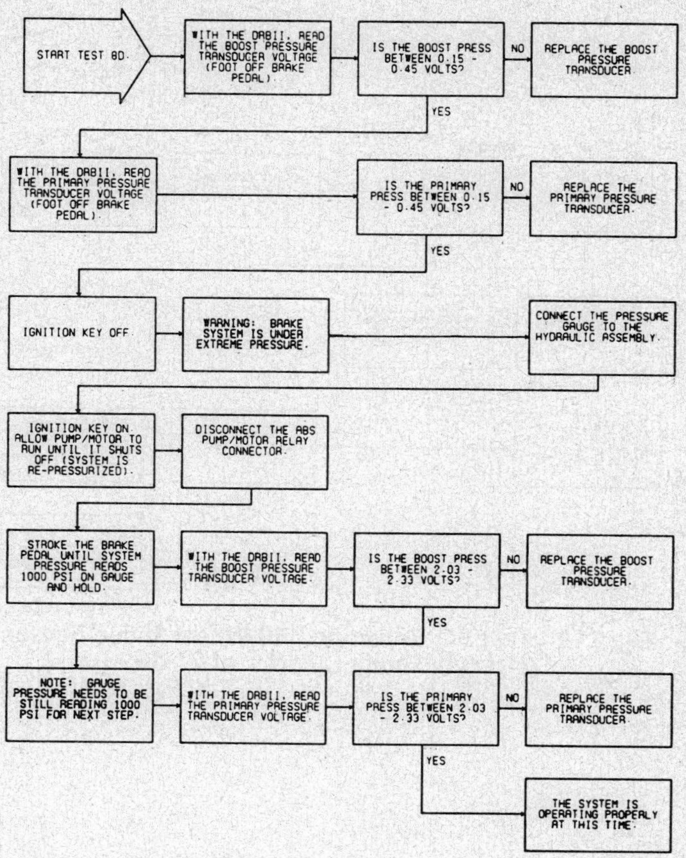

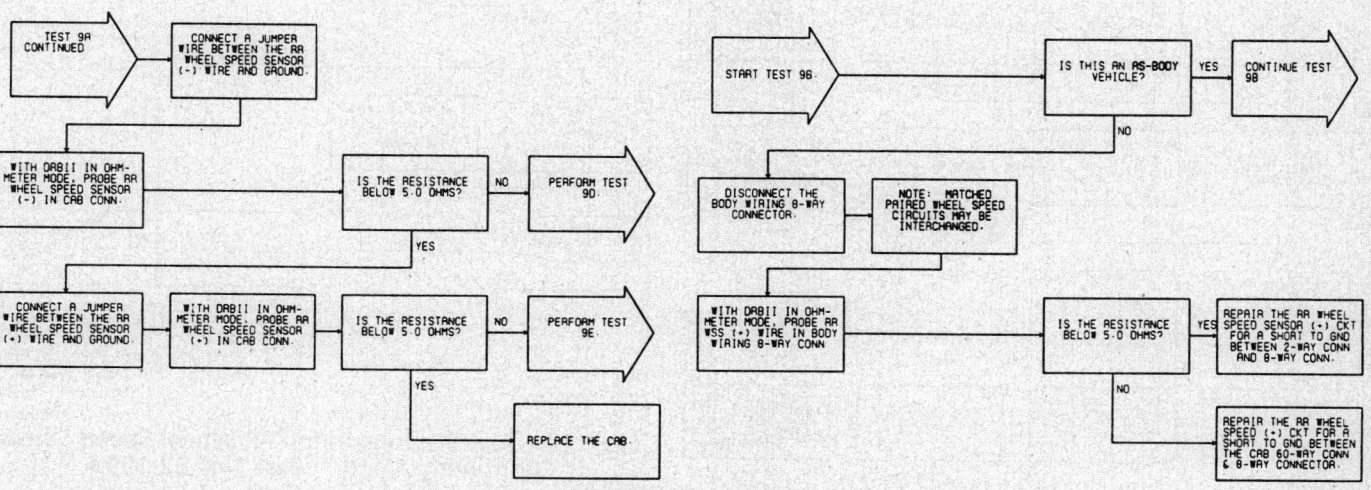

Fig. 116   Test 8D: Repairing "Boost Pressure Fault."
1993
CR4029300488000X

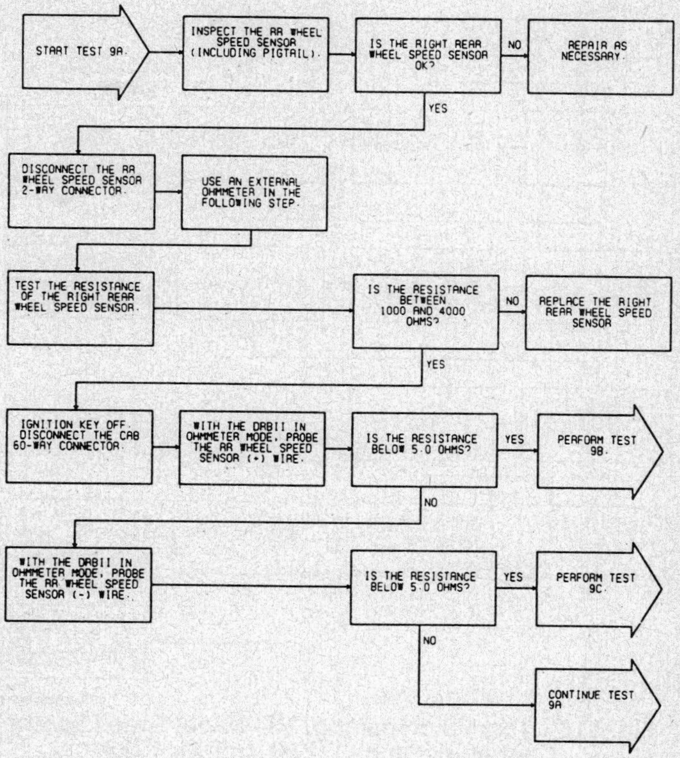

Fig. 117   Test 9A: Repairing "RR Wheel Speed Sensor
Continuity Faulty" (Part 1 of 2). 1993
CR4029300489010X

Fig. 117   Test 9A: Repairing "RR Wheel Speed Sensor
Continuity Faulty" (Part 2 of 2). 1993
CR4029300489020X

Fig. 118   Test 9B: Repairing "RR Wheel Speed Sensor
Continuity Faulty" (Part 1 of 2). 1993
CR4029300490010X

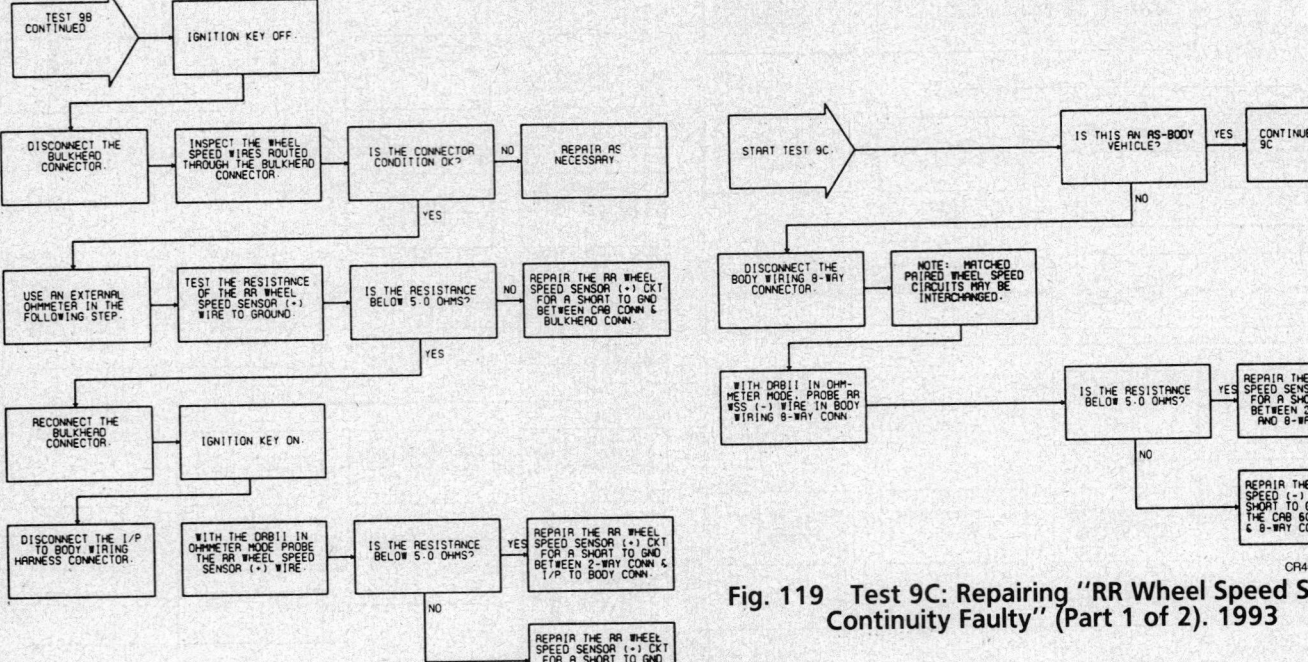

Fig. 118 Test 9B: Repairing "RR Wheel Speed Sensor Continuity Faulty" (Part 2 of 2). 1993

Fig. 119 Test 9C: Repairing "RR Wheel Speed Sensor Continuity Faulty" (Part 1 of 2). 1993

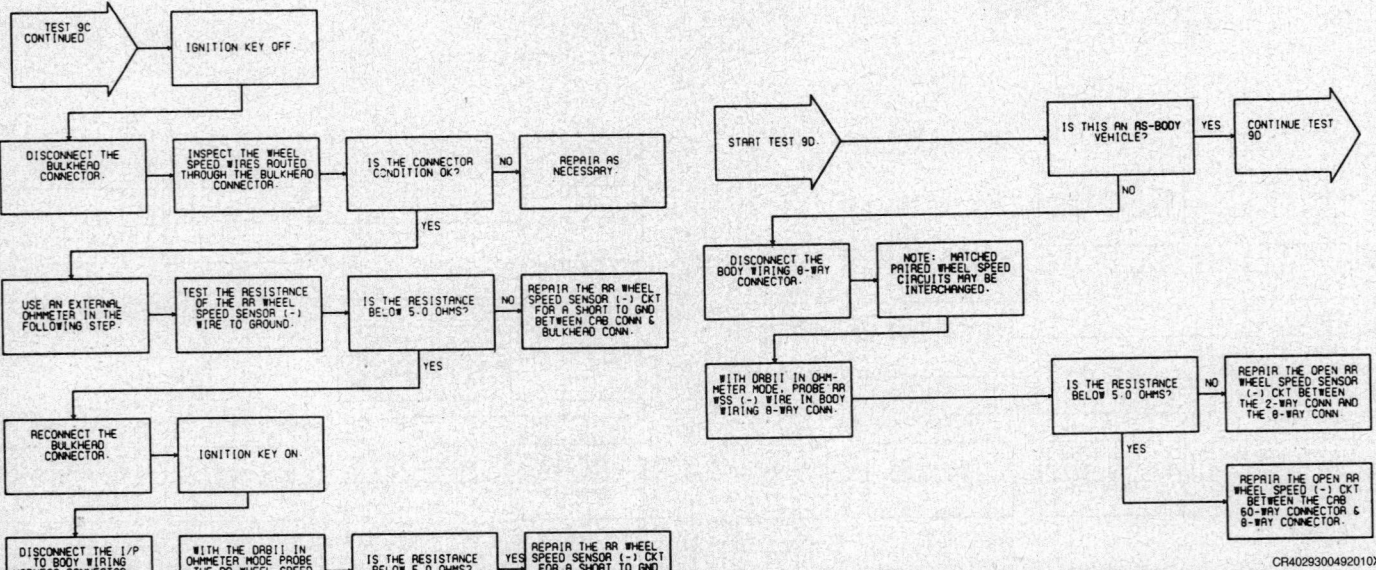

Fig. 119 Test 9C: Repairing "RR Wheel Speed Sensor Continuity Faulty" (Part 2 of 2). 1993

Fig. 120 Test 9D: Repairing "RR Wheel Speed Sensor Continuity Faulty" (Part 1 of 2). 1993

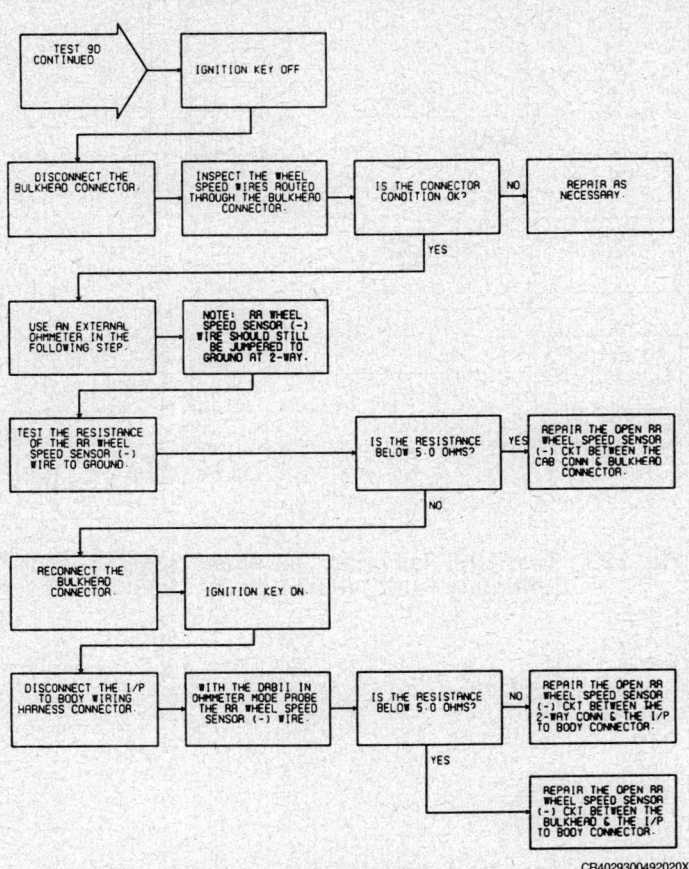

CR4029300492020X

Fig. 120   Test 9D: Repairing "RR Wheel Speed Sensor Continuity Faulty" (Part 2 of 2). 1993

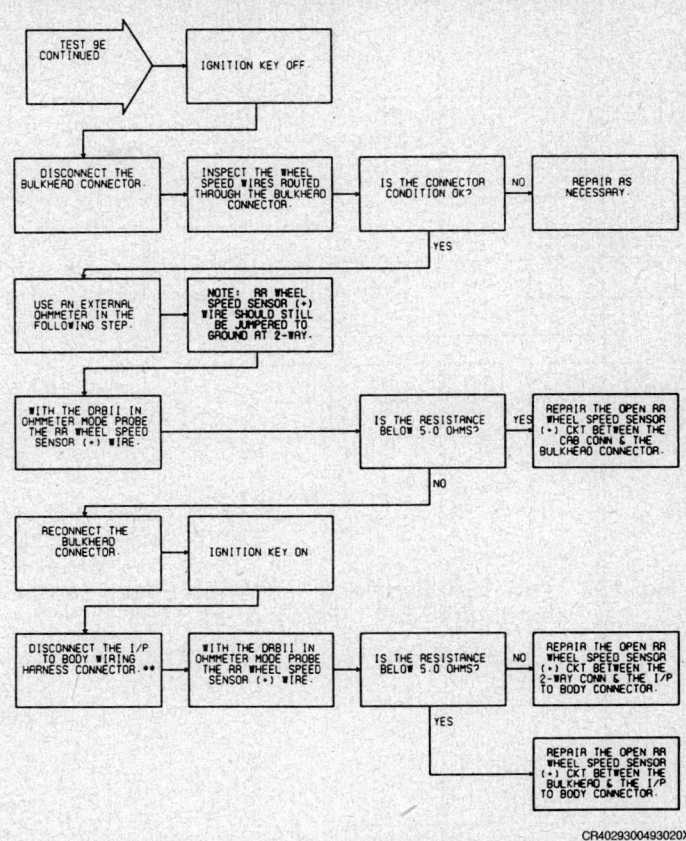

CR4029300493020X

Fig. 121   Test 9E: Repairing "RR Wheel Speed Sensor Continuity Faulty" (Part 2 of 2). 1993

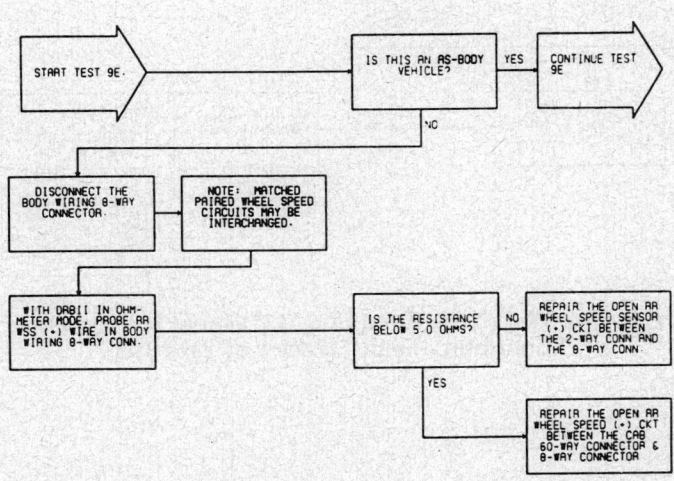

CR4029300493010X

Fig. 121   Test 9E: Repairing "RR Wheel Speed Sensor Continuity Faulty" (Part 1 of 2). 1993

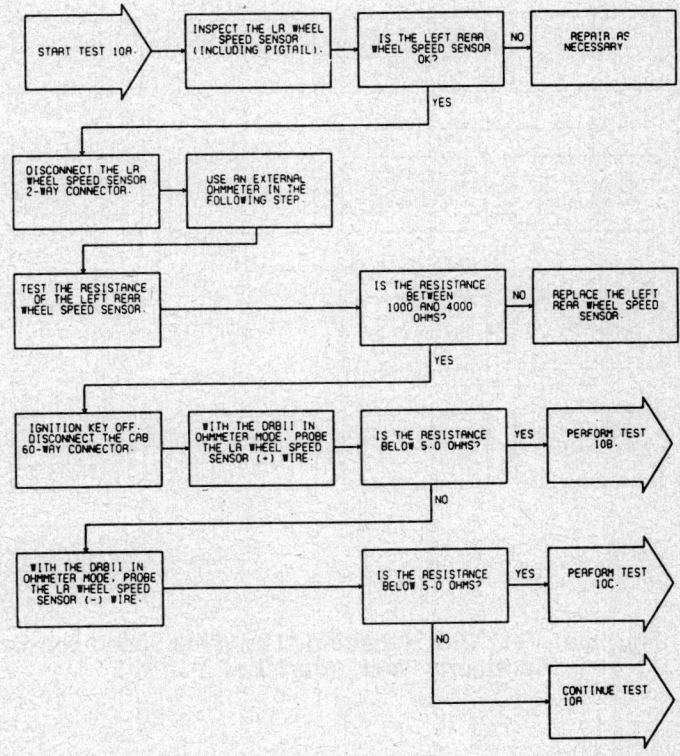

CR4029300494010X

Fig. 122   Test 10A: Repairing "LR Wheel Speed Sensor Continuity Fault" (Part 1 of 2). 1993

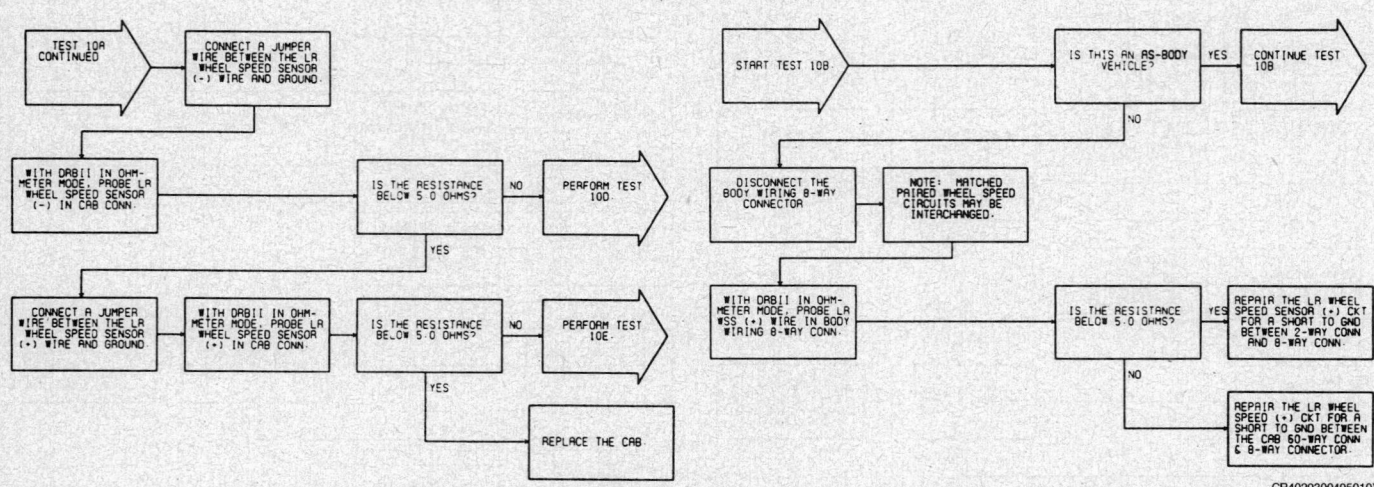

Fig. 122 Test 10A: Repairing "LR Wheel Speed Sensor Continuity Fault" (Part 2 of 2). 1993

Fig. 123 Test 10B: Repairing "LR Wheel Speed Sensor Continuity Fault" (Part 1 of 2). 1993

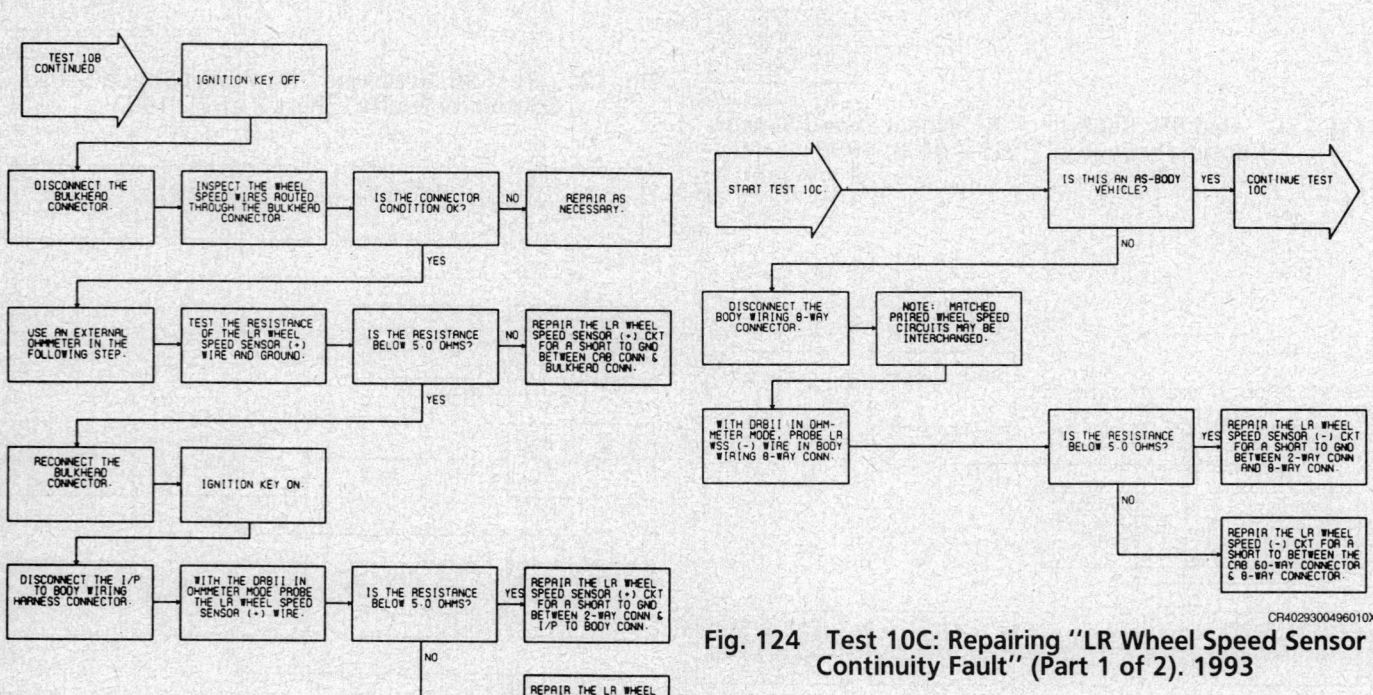

Fig. 123 Test 10B: Repairing "LR Wheel Speed Sensor Continuity Fault" (Part 2 of 2). 1993

Fig. 124 Test 10C: Repairing "LR Wheel Speed Sensor Continuity Fault" (Part 1 of 2). 1993

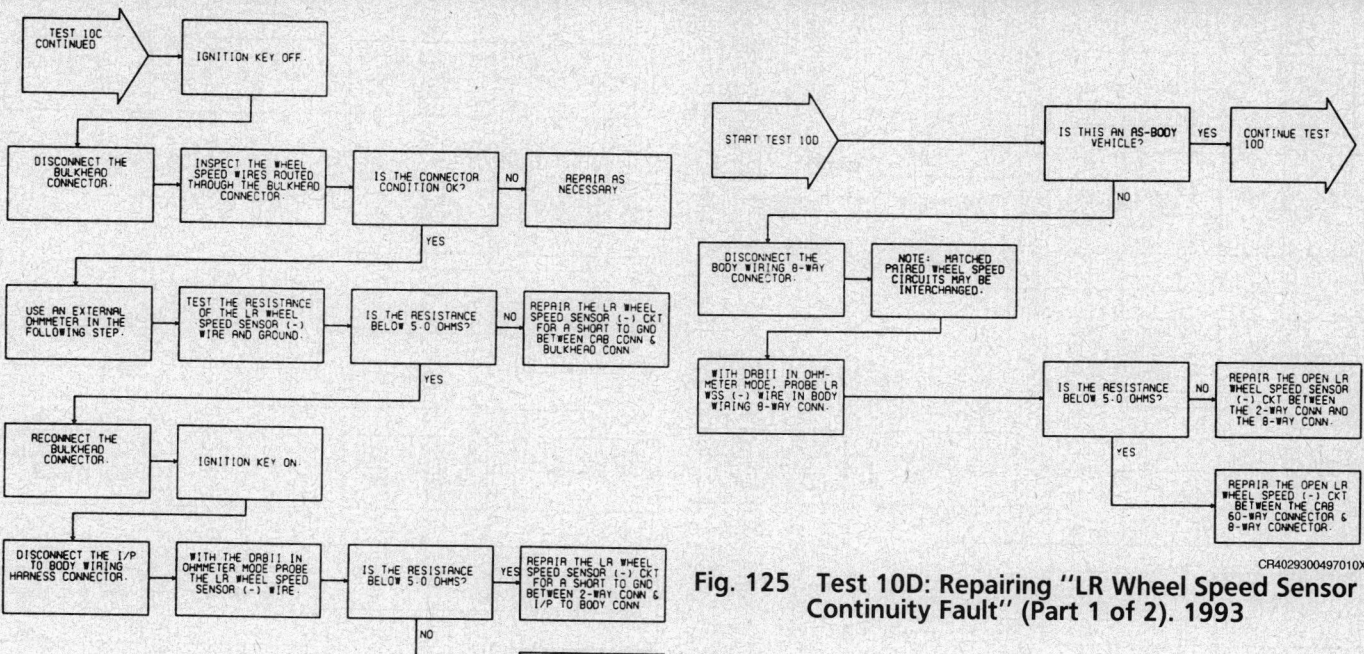

TEST 10C CONTINUED → IGNITION KEY OFF.

DISCONNECT THE BULKHEAD CONNECTOR. → INSPECT THE WHEEL SPEED WIRES ROUTED THROUGH THE BULKHEAD CONNECTOR. → IS THE CONNECTOR CONDITION OK? — NO → REPAIR AS NECESSARY.

YES

USE AN EXTERNAL OHMMETER IN THE FOLLOWING STEP. → TEST THE RESISTANCE OF THE LR WHEEL SPEED SENSOR (-) WIRE AND GROUND. → IS THE RESISTANCE BELOW 5.0 OHMS? — NO → REPAIR THE LR WHEEL SPEED SENSOR (-) CKT FOR A SHORT TO GND BETWEEN CAB CONN & BULKHEAD CONN

YES

RECONNECT THE BULKHEAD CONNECTOR. → IGNITION KEY ON.

DISCONNECT THE I/P TO BODY WIRING HARNESS CONNECTOR. → WITH THE DRBII IN OHMMETER MODE PROBE THE LR WHEEL SPEED SENSOR (-) WIRE. → IS THE RESISTANCE BELOW 5.0 OHMS? — YES → REPAIR THE LR WHEEL SPEED SENSOR (-) CKT FOR A SHORT TO GND BETWEEN 2-WAY CONN & I/P TO BODY CONN

NO

REPAIR THE LR WHEEL SPEED SENSOR (-) CKT FOR A SHORT TO GND BETWEEN THE BULKHEAD & I/P TO BODY CONN.

CR4029300496020X

Fig. 124   Test 10C: Repairing "LR Wheel Speed Sensor Continuity Fault" (Part 2 of 2). 1993

START TEST 10D → IS THIS AN AS-BODY VEHICLE? — YES → CONTINUE TEST 10D

NO

DISCONNECT THE BODY WIRING 8-WAY CONNECTOR. → NOTE: MATCHED PAIRED WHEEL SPEED CIRCUITS MAY BE INTERCHANGED.

WITH DRBII IN OHMMETER MODE, PROBE LR WSS (-) WIRE IN BODY WIRING 8-WAY CONN. → IS THE RESISTANCE BELOW 5.0 OHMS? — NO → REPAIR THE OPEN LR WHEEL SPEED SENSOR (-) CKT BETWEEN THE 2-WAY CONN AND THE 8-WAY CONN.

YES

REPAIR THE OPEN LR WHEEL SPEED (-) CKT BETWEEN THE CAB 60-WAY CONNECTOR & 8-WAY CONNECTOR.

CR4029300497010X

Fig. 125   Test 10D: Repairing "LR Wheel Speed Sensor Continuity Fault" (Part 1 of 2). 1993

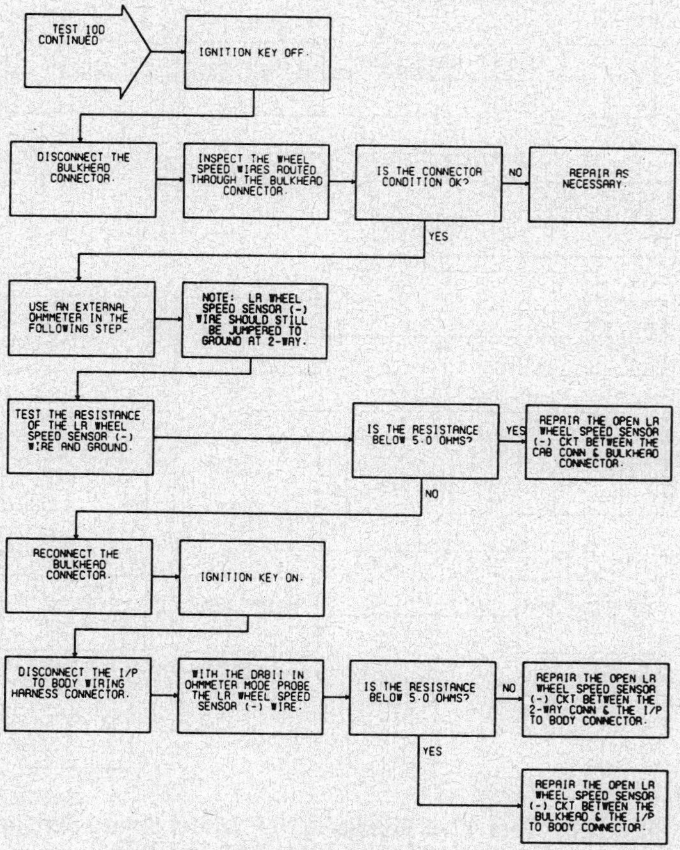

TEST 10D CONTINUED → IGNITION KEY OFF.

DISCONNECT THE BULKHEAD CONNECTOR. → INSPECT THE WHEEL SPEED WIRES ROUTED THROUGH THE BULKHEAD CONNECTOR. → IS THE CONNECTOR CONDITION OK? — NO → REPAIR AS NECESSARY.

YES

USE AN EXTERNAL OHMMETER IN THE FOLLOWING STEP. → NOTE: LR WHEEL SPEED SENSOR (-) WIRE SHOULD STILL BE JUMPERED TO GROUND AT 2-WAY.

TEST THE RESISTANCE OF THE LR WHEEL SPEED SENSOR (-) WIRE AND GROUND. → IS THE RESISTANCE BELOW 5.0 OHMS? — YES → REPAIR THE OPEN LR WHEEL SPEED SENSOR (-) CKT BETWEEN THE CAB CONN & BULKHEAD CONNECTOR.

NO

RECONNECT THE BULKHEAD CONNECTOR. → IGNITION KEY ON.

DISCONNECT THE I/P TO BODY WIRING HARNESS CONNECTOR. → WITH THE DRBII IN OHMMETER MODE PROBE THE LR WHEEL SPEED SENSOR (-) WIRE. → IS THE RESISTANCE BELOW 5.0 OHMS? — NO → REPAIR THE OPEN LR WHEEL SPEED SENSOR (-) CKT BETWEEN THE 2-WAY CONN & THE I/P TO BODY CONNECTOR.

YES

REPAIR THE OPEN LR WHEEL SPEED SENSOR (-) CKT BETWEEN THE BULKHEAD & THE I/P TO BODY CONNECTOR.

CR4029300497020X

Fig. 125   Test 10D: Repairing "LR Wheel Speed Sensor Continuity Fault" (Part 2 of 2). 1993

START TEST 10E → IS THIS AN AS-BODY VEHICLE? — YES → CONTINUE TEST 10E

NO

DISCONNECT THE BODY WIRING 8-WAY CONNECTOR. → NOTE: MATCHED PAIRED WHEEL SPEED CIRCUITS MAY BE INTERCHANGED.

WITH DRBII IN OHMMETER MODE, PROBE LR WSS (+) WIRE IN BODY WIRING 8-WAY CONN. → IS THE RESISTANCE BELOW 5.0 OHMS? — NO → REPAIR THE OPEN LR WHEEL SPEED SENSOR (+) CKT BETWEEN THE 2-WAY CONN AND THE 8-WAY CONN.

YES

REPAIR THE OPEN LR WHEEL SPEED (+) CKT BETWEEN THE CAB 60-WAY CONNECTOR & 8-WAY CONNECTOR.

CR4029300498010X

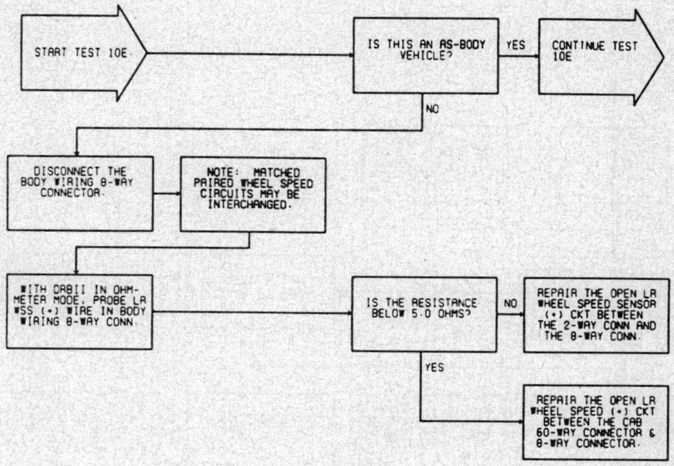

Fig. 126   Test 10E: Repairing "LR Wheel Speed Sensor Continuity Fault" (Part 1 of 2). 1993

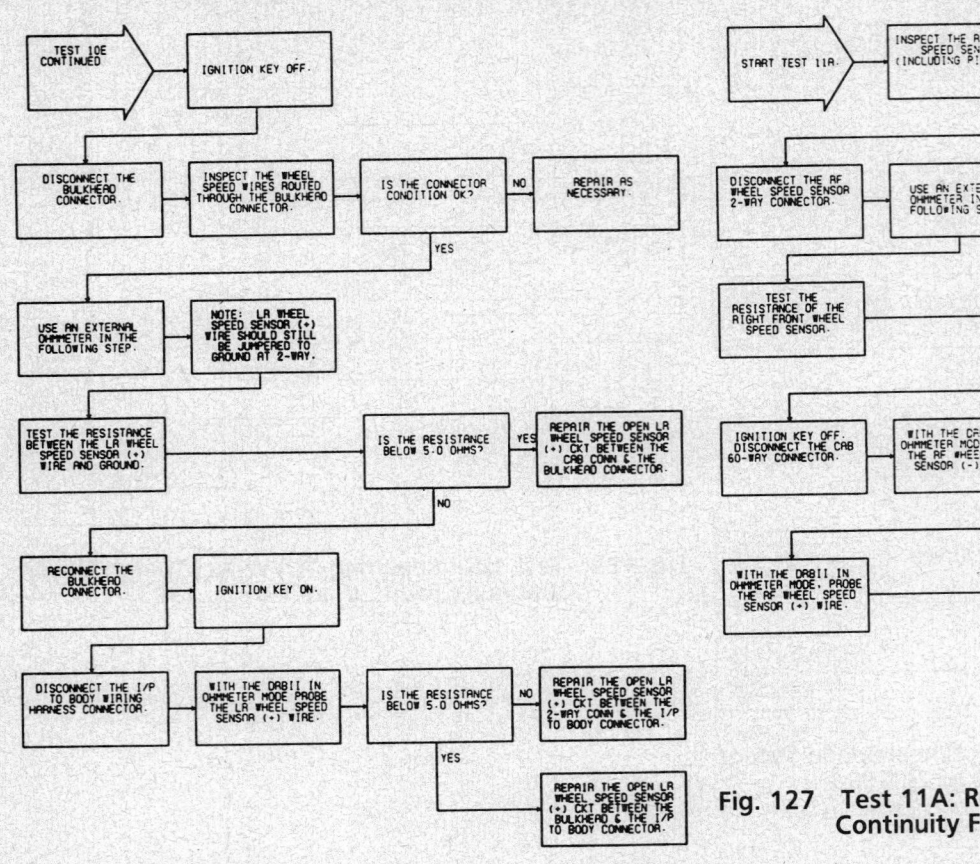

Fig. 126   Test 10E: Repairing "LR Wheel Speed Sensor Continuity Fault" (Part 2 of 2). 1993

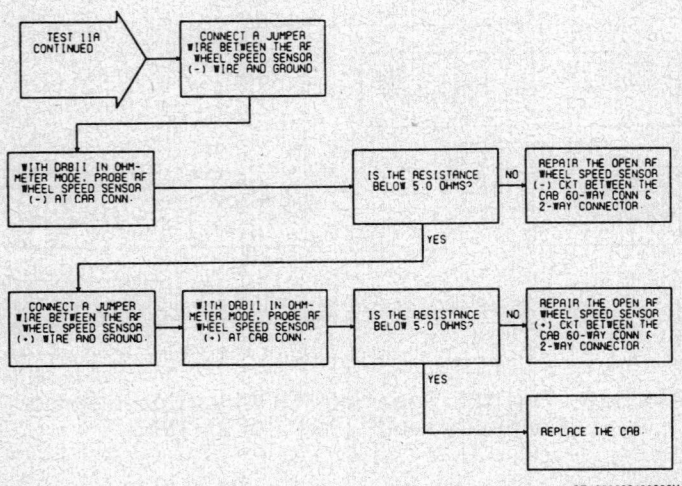

Fig. 127   Test 11A: Repairing "RF Wheel Speed, Sensor Continuity Fault" (Part 2 of 2). 1993

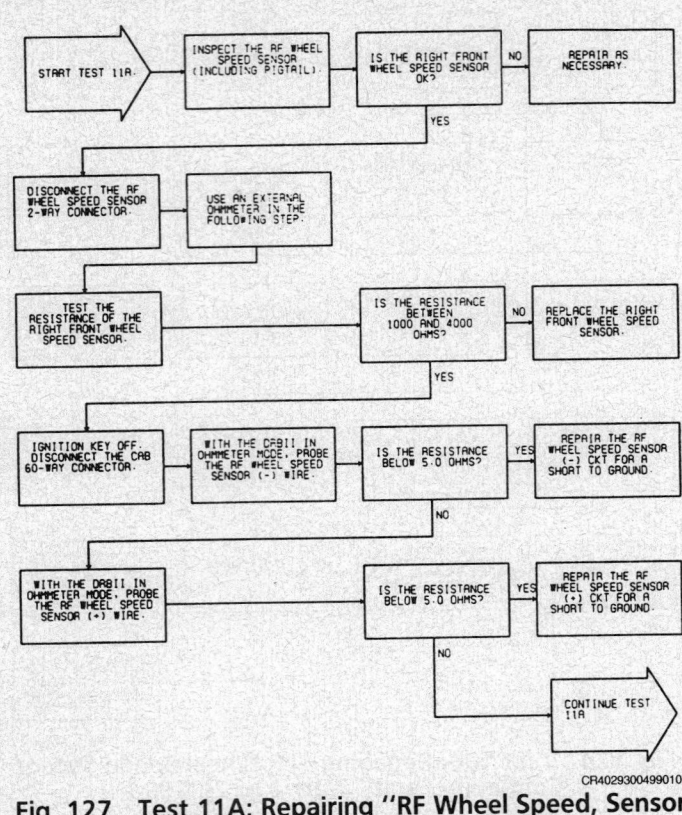

Fig. 127   Test 11A: Repairing "RF Wheel Speed, Sensor Continuity Fault" (Part 1 of 2). 1993

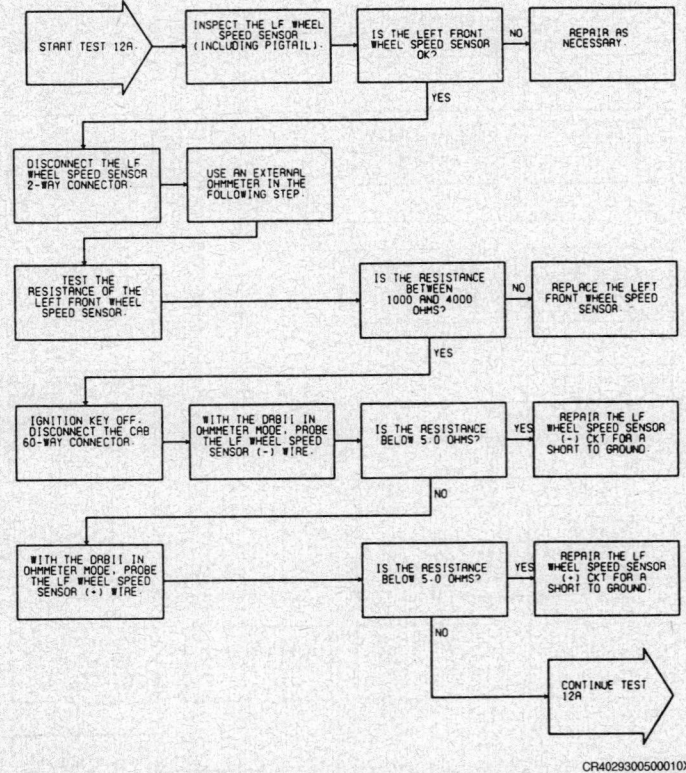

Fig. 128   Test 12A: Repairing "LF Wheel Speed Sensor Continuity Fault" (Part 1 of 2). 1993

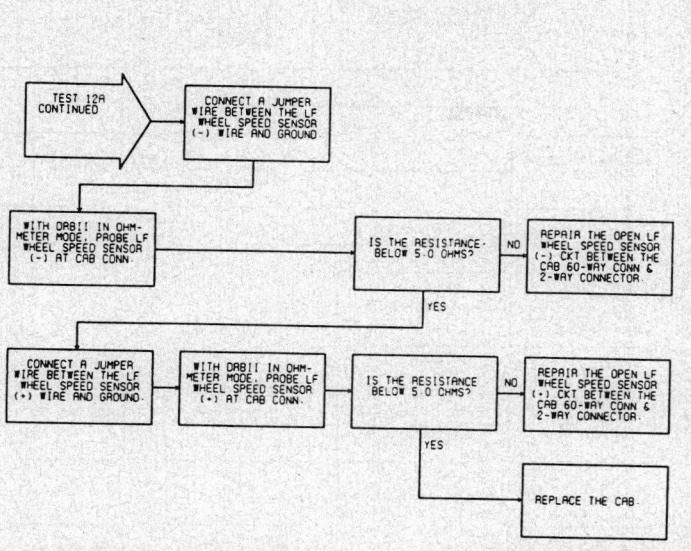

Fig. 128   Test 12A: Repairing "LF Wheel Speed Sensor Continuity Fault" (Part 2 of 2). 1993

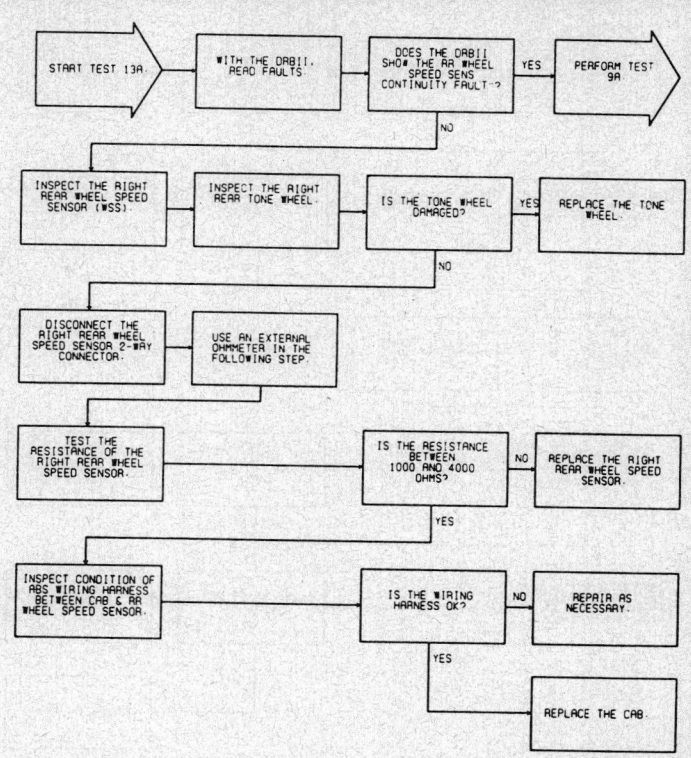

Fig. 129   Test 13A: Repairing "Right Rear Wheel Speed Sensor Fault." 1993

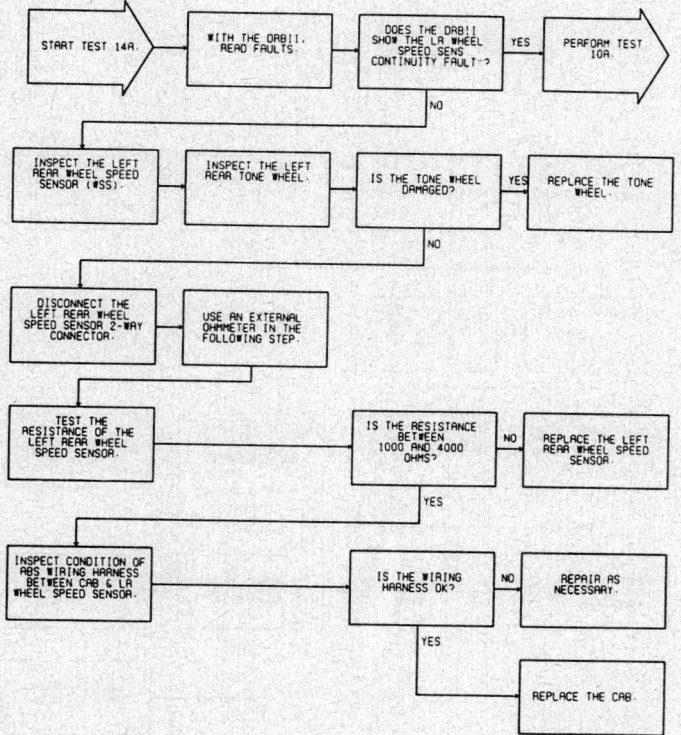

Fig. 130   Test 14A: Repairing "Left Rear Wheel Speed Sensor Fault." 1993

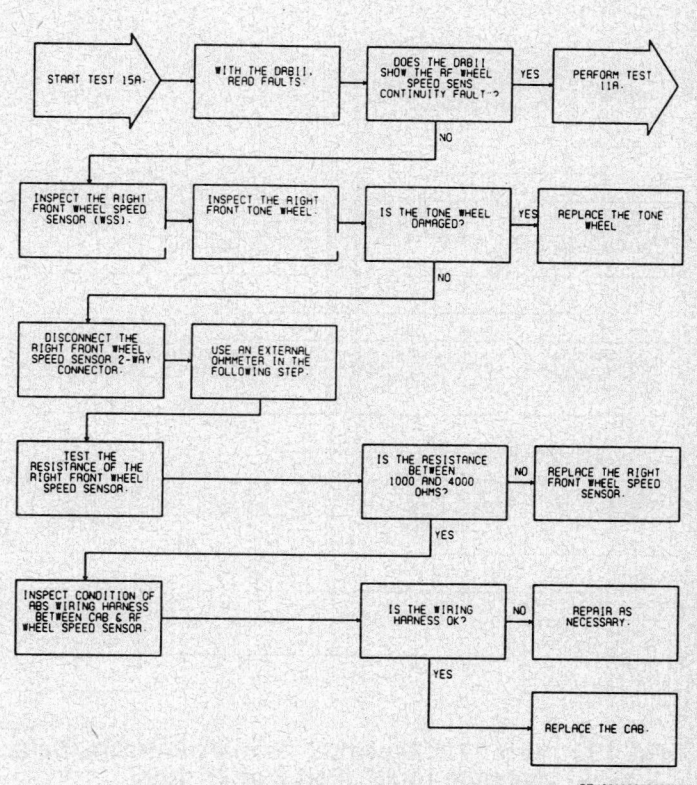

Fig. 131   Test 15A: Repairing "Right Front Wheel Speed Sensor Fault." 1993

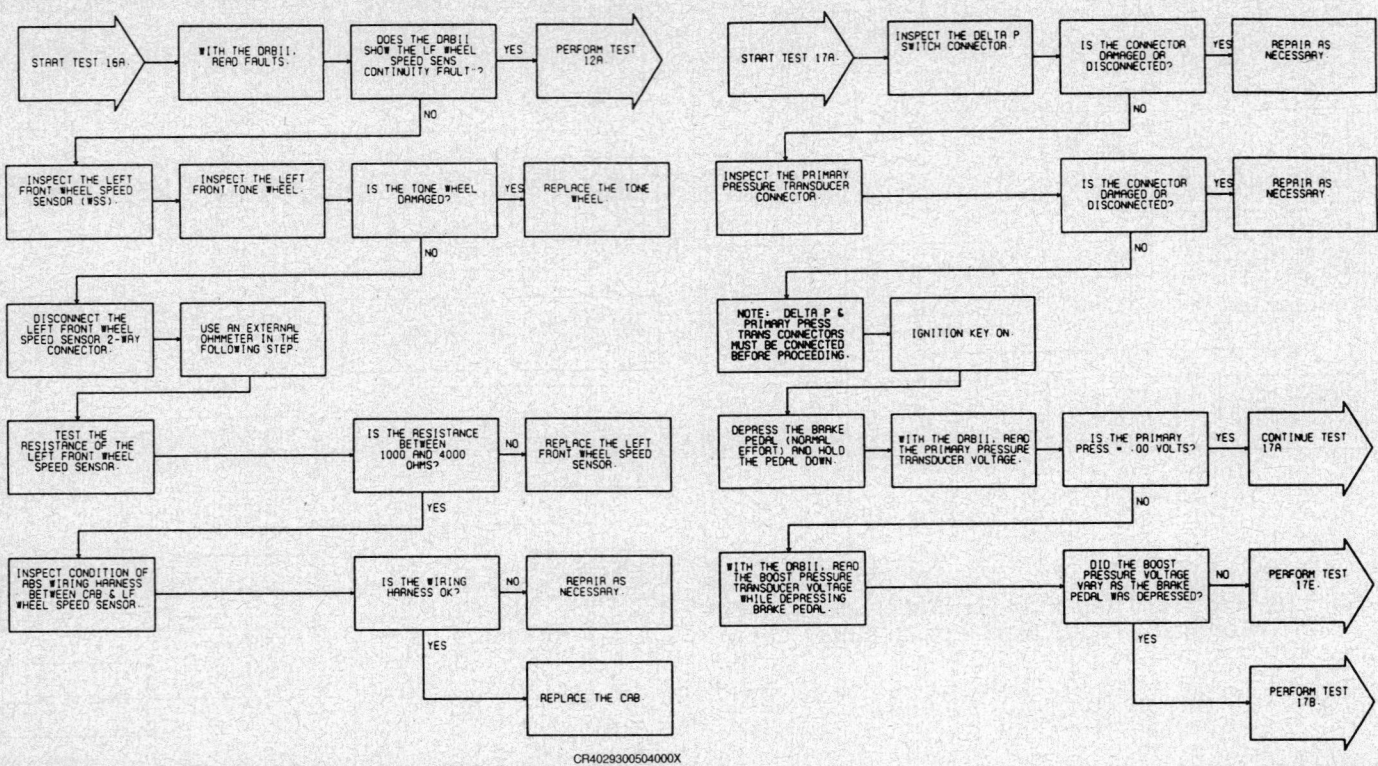

Fig. 132   Test 16A: Repairing "Left Front Speed Sensor Fault." 1993

Fig. 133   Test 17A: Repairing "Primary Pressure/Delta Pressure Fault" (Part 1 of 2). 1993

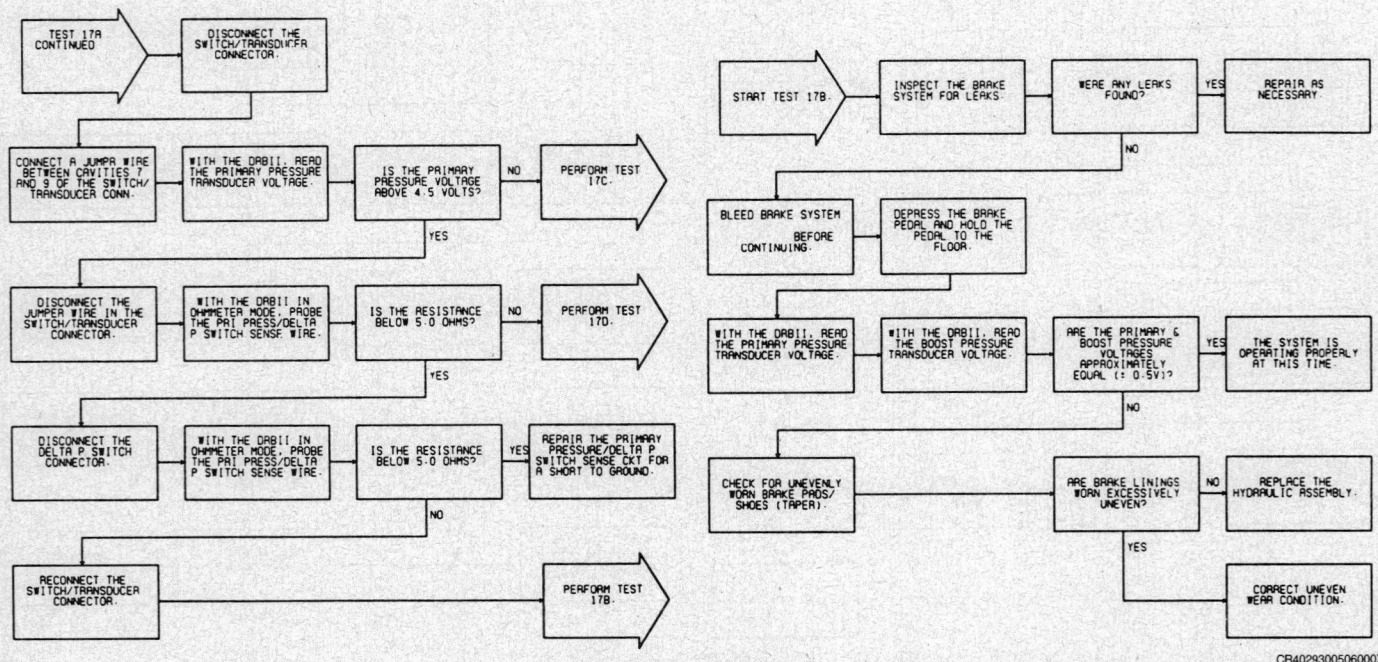

Fig. 133   Test 17A: Repairing "Primary Pressure/Delta Pressure Fault" (Part 2 of 2). 1993

Fig. 134   Test 17B: Repairing "Primary Pressure/Delta Pressure Fault." 1993

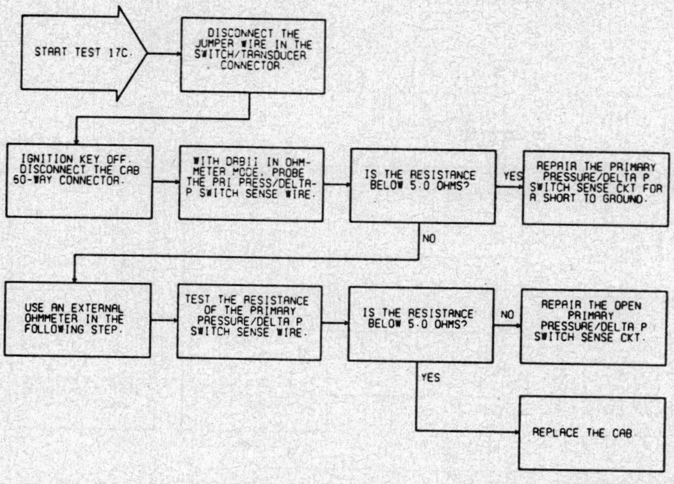

Fig. 135 — Test 17C flowchart:

START TEST 17C. → DISCONNECT THE JUMPER WIRE IN THE SWITCH/TRANSDUCER CONNECTOR.

IGNITION KEY OFF. DISCONNECT THE CAB 60-WAY CONNECTOR. → WITH DRBII IN OHMMETER MODE, PROBE THE PRI PRESS/DELTA-P SWITCH SENSE WIRE. → IS THE RESISTANCE BELOW 5.0 OHMS? — YES → REPAIR THE PRIMARY PRESSURE/DELTA P SWITCH SENSE CKT FOR A SHORT TO GROUND.

NO ↓

USE AN EXTERNAL OHMMETER IN THE FOLLOWING STEP. → TEST THE RESISTANCE OF THE PRIMARY PRESSURE/DELTA P SWITCH SENSE WIRE. → IS THE RESISTANCE BELOW 5.0 OHMS? — NO → REPAIR THE OPEN PRIMARY PRESSURE/DELTA P SWITCH SENSE CKT.

YES ↓ REPLACE THE CAB

Fig. 135 Test 17C: Repairing "Primary Pressure/Delta Pressure Fault." 1993

CR4029300507000X

Fig. 136 — Test 17D (Part 2 of 2) flowchart:

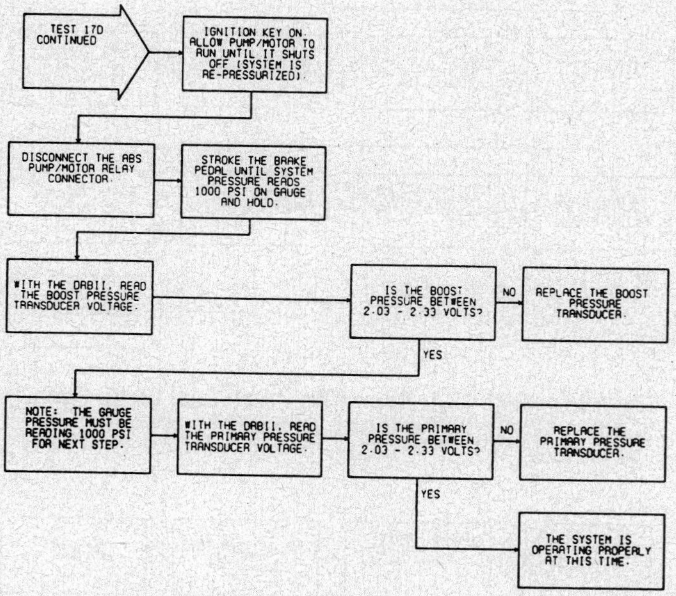

TEST 17D CONTINUED → IGNITION KEY ON. ALLOW PUMP/MOTOR TO RUN UNTIL IT SHUTS OFF (SYSTEM IS RE-PRESSURIZED).

DISCONNECT THE ABS PUMP/MOTOR RELAY CONNECTOR. → STROKE THE BRAKE PEDAL UNTIL SYSTEM PRESSURE READS 1000 PSI ON GAUGE AND HOLD.

WITH THE DRBII, READ THE BOOST PRESSURE TRANSDUCER VOLTAGE. → IS THE BOOST PRESSURE BETWEEN 2.03 - 2.33 VOLTS? — NO → REPLACE THE BOOST PRESSURE TRANSDUCER.

YES ↓

NOTE: THE GAUGE PRESSURE MUST BE READING 1000 PSI FOR NEXT STEP. → WITH THE DRBII, READ THE PRIMARY PRESSURE TRANSDUCER VOLTAGE. → IS THE PRIMARY PRESSURE BETWEEN 2.03 - 2.33 VOLTS? — NO → REPLACE THE PRIMARY PRESSURE TRANSDUCER.

YES ↓ THE SYSTEM IS OPERATING PROPERLY AT THIS TIME.

Fig. 136 Test 17D: Repairing "Primary Pressure/Delta Pressure Fault" (Part 2 of 2). 1993

CR4029300508020X

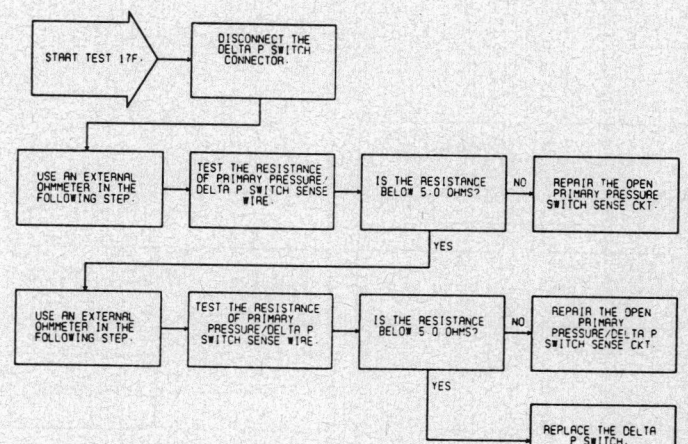

Fig. 136 — Test 17D (Part 1 of 2) flowchart:

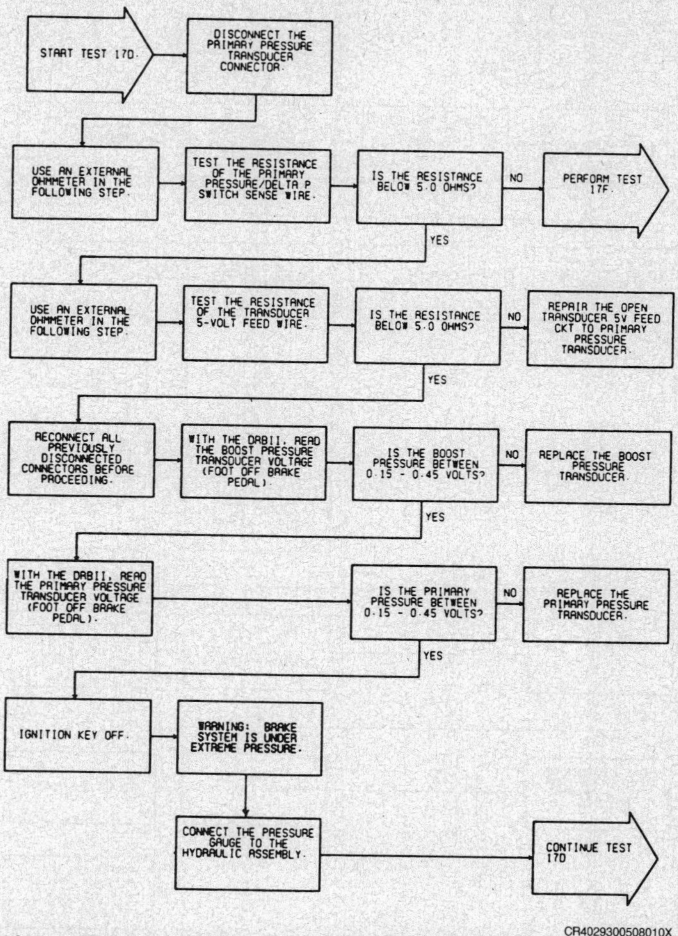

START TEST 17D. → DISCONNECT THE PRIMARY PRESSURE TRANSDUCER CONNECTOR.

USE AN EXTERNAL OHMMETER IN THE FOLLOWING STEP. → TEST THE RESISTANCE OF THE PRIMARY PRESSURE/DELTA P SWITCH SENSE WIRE. → IS THE RESISTANCE BELOW 5.0 OHMS? — NO → PERFORM TEST 17F.

YES ↓

USE AN EXTERNAL OHMMETER IN THE FOLLOWING STEP. → TEST THE RESISTANCE OF THE TRANSDUCER 5-VOLT FEED WIRE. → IS THE RESISTANCE BELOW 5.0 OHMS? — NO → REPAIR THE OPEN TRANSDUCER 5V FEED CKT TO PRIMARY PRESSURE TRANSDUCER.

RECONNECT ALL PREVIOUSLY DISCONNECTED CONNECTORS BEFORE PROCEEDING. → WITH THE DRBII, READ THE BOOST PRESSURE TRANSDUCER VOLTAGE (FOOT OFF BRAKE PEDAL). → IS THE BOOST PRESSURE BETWEEN 0.15 - 0.45 VOLTS? — NO → REPLACE THE BOOST PRESSURE TRANSDUCER.

YES ↓

WITH THE DRBII, READ THE PRIMARY PRESSURE TRANSDUCER VOLTAGE (FOOT OFF BRAKE PEDAL). → IS THE PRIMARY PRESSURE BETWEEN 0.15 - 0.45 VOLTS? — NO → REPLACE THE PRIMARY PRESSURE TRANSDUCER.

YES ↓

IGNITION KEY OFF. → WARNING: BRAKE SYSTEM IS UNDER EXTREME PRESSURE. → CONNECT THE PRESSURE GAUGE TO THE HYDRAULIC ASSEMBLY. → CONTINUE TEST 17D

CR4029300508010X

Fig. 136 Test 17D: Repairing "Primary Pressure/Delta Pressure Fault" (Part 1 of 2). 1993

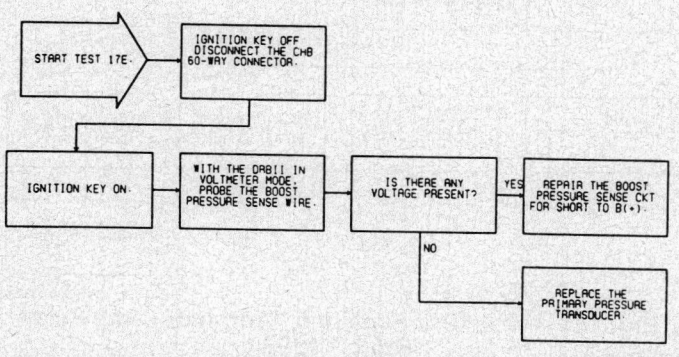

Fig. 137 — Test 17E flowchart:

START TEST 17E. → IGNITION KEY OFF. DISCONNECT THE CAB 60-WAY CONNECTOR.

IGNITION KEY ON. → WITH THE DRBII IN VOLTMETER MODE, PROBE THE BOOST PRESSURE SENSE WIRE. → IS THERE ANY VOLTAGE PRESENT? — YES → REPAIR THE BOOST PRESSURE SENSE CKT FOR SHORT TO B(+).

NO ↓ REPLACE THE PRIMARY PRESSURE TRANSDUCER.

CR4029300509000X

Fig. 137 Test 17E: Repairing "Primary Pressure/Delta Pressure Fault." 1993

Fig. 138 — Test 17F flowchart:

START TEST 17F. → DISCONNECT THE DELTA P SWITCH CONNECTOR.

USE AN EXTERNAL OHMMETER IN THE FOLLOWING STEP. → TEST THE RESISTANCE OF PRIMARY PRESSURE/DELTA P SWITCH SENSE WIRE. → IS THE RESISTANCE BELOW 5.0 OHMS? — NO → REPAIR THE OPEN PRIMARY PRESSURE SWITCH SENSE CKT.

YES ↓

USE AN EXTERNAL OHMMETER IN THE FOLLOWING STEP. → TEST THE RESISTANCE OF PRIMARY PRESSURE/DELTA P SWITCH SENSE WIRE. → IS THE RESISTANCE BELOW 5.0 OHMS? — NO → REPAIR THE OPEN PRIMARY PRESSURE/DELTA P SWITCH SENSE CKT.

YES ↓ REPLACE THE DELTA P SWITCH.

CR4029300510000X

Fig. 138 Test 17F: Repairing "Primary Pressure/Delta Pressure Fault." 1993

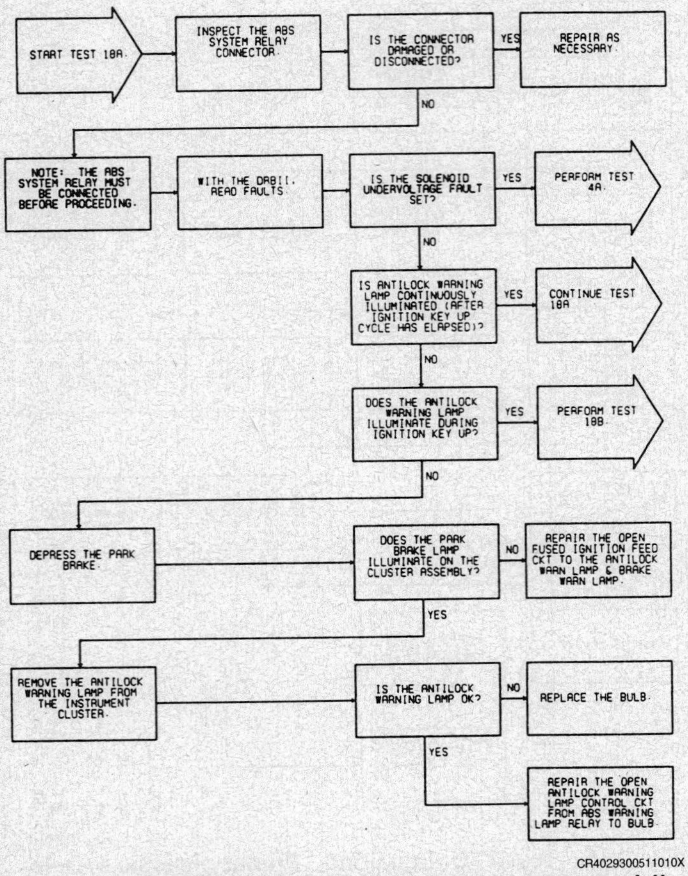

START TEST 18A.
INSPECT THE ABS SYSTEM RELAY CONNECTOR.
IS THE CONNECTOR DAMAGED OR DISCONNECTED?
YES
REPAIR AS NECESSARY.
NO
NOTE: THE ABS SYSTEM RELAY MUST BE CONNECTED BEFORE PROCEEDING.
WITH THE DRBII, READ FAULTS.
IS THE SOLENOID UNDERVOLTAGE FAULT SET?
YES
PERFORM TEST 4A.
NO
IS ANTILOCK WARNING LAMP CONTINUOUSLY ILLUMINATED (AFTER IGNITION KEY UP CYCLE HAS ELAPSED)?
YES
CONTINUE TEST 18A
NO
DOES THE ANTILOCK WARNING LAMP ILLUMINATE DURING IGNITION KEY UP?
YES
PERFORM TEST 18B.
NO
DEPRESS THE PARK BRAKE.
DOES THE PARK BRAKE LAMP ILLUMINATE ON THE CLUSTER ASSEMBLY?
NO
REPAIR THE OPEN FUSED IGNITION FEED CKT TO THE ANTILOCK WARN LAMP & BRAKE WARN LAMP.
YES
REMOVE THE ANTILOCK WARNING LAMP FROM THE INSTRUMENT CLUSTER.
IS THE ANTILOCK WARNING LAMP OK?
NO
REPLACE THE BULB.
YES
REPAIR THE OPEN ANTILOCK WARNING LAMP CONTROL CKT FROM ABS WARNING LAMP RELAY TO BULB.
CR4029300511010X

Fig. 139 Test 18A: Repairing "Anti-lock Lamp Fault" (Part 1 of 2). 1993

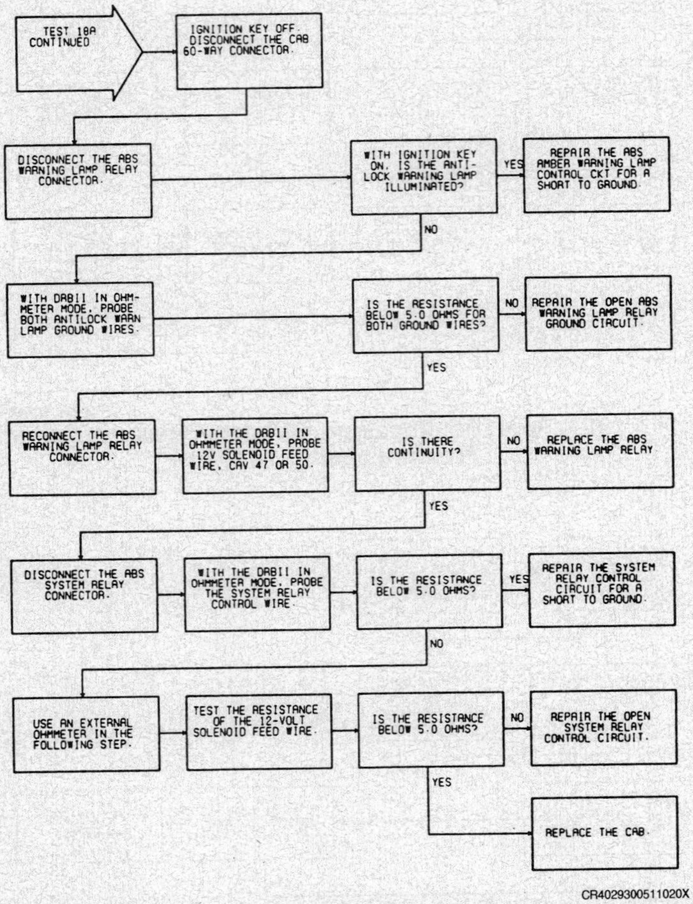

TEST 18A CONTINUED
IGNITION KEY OFF. DISCONNECT THE CAB 60-WAY CONNECTOR.
DISCONNECT THE ABS WARNING LAMP RELAY CONNECTOR.
WITH IGNITION KEY ON, IS THE ANTI-LOCK WARNING LAMP ILLUMINATED?
YES
REPAIR THE ABS AMBER WARNING LAMP CONTROL CKT FOR A SHORT TO GROUND.
NO
WITH DRBII IN OHM-METER MODE, PROBE BOTH ANTILOCK WARN LAMP GROUND WIRES.
IS THE RESISTANCE BELOW 5.0 OHMS FOR BOTH GROUND WIRES?
NO
REPAIR THE OPEN ABS WARNING LAMP RELAY GROUND CIRCUIT.
YES
RECONNECT THE ABS WARNING LAMP RELAY CONNECTOR.
WITH THE DRBII IN OHMMETER MODE, PROBE 12V SOLENOID FEED WIRE, CAV 47 OR 50.
IS THERE CONTINUITY?
NO
REPLACE THE ABS WARNING LAMP RELAY
YES
DISCONNECT THE ABS SYSTEM RELAY CONNECTOR.
WITH THE DRBII IN OHMMETER MODE, PROBE THE SYSTEM RELAY CONTROL WIRE.
IS THE RESISTANCE BELOW 5.0 OHMS?
YES
REPAIR THE SYSTEM RELAY CONTROL CIRCUIT FOR A SHORT TO GROUND.
NO
USE AN EXTERNAL OHMMETER IN THE FOLLOWING STEP.
TEST THE RESISTANCE OF THE 12-VOLT SOLENOID FEED WIRE.
IS THE RESISTANCE BELOW 5.0 OHMS?
NO
REPAIR THE OPEN SYSTEM RELAY CONTROL CIRCUIT.
YES
REPLACE THE CAB.
CR4029300511020X

Fig. 139 Test 18A: Repairing "Anti-lock Lamp Fault" (Part 2 of 2). 1993

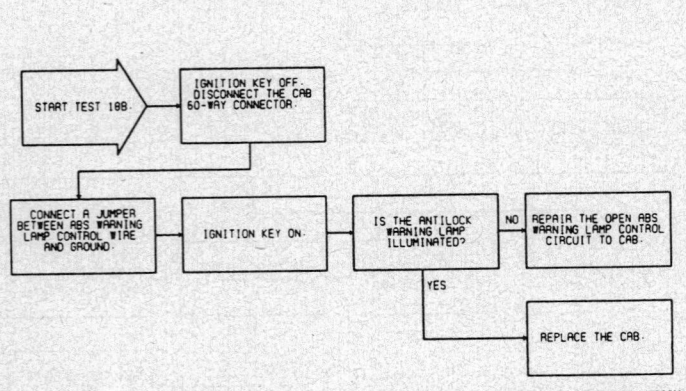

START TEST 18B.
IGNITION KEY OFF. DISCONNECT THE CAB 60-WAY CONNECTOR.
CONNECT A JUMPER BETWEEN ABS WARNING LAMP CONTROL WIRE AND GROUND.
IGNITION KEY ON.
IS THE ANTILOCK WARNING LAMP ILLUMINATED?
NO
REPAIR THE OPEN ABS WARNING LAMP CONTROL CIRCUIT TO CAB.
YES
REPLACE THE CAB.
CR4029300512000X

Fig. 140 Test 18B: Repairing "Anti-lock Lamp Fault." 1993

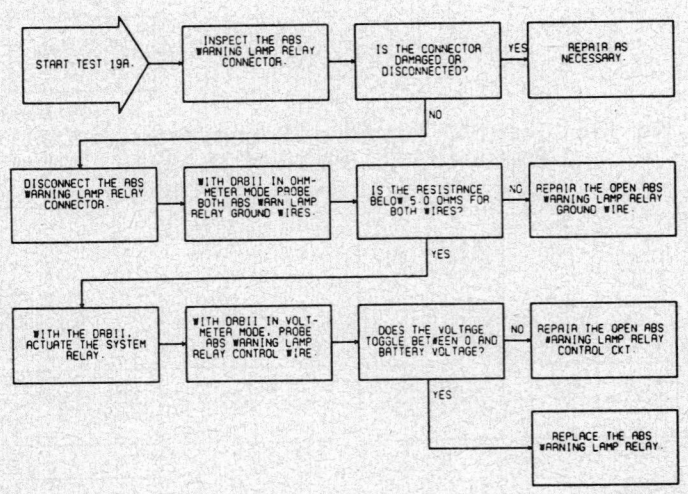

START TEST 19A.
INSPECT THE ABS WARNING LAMP RELAY CONNECTOR.
IS THE CONNECTOR DAMAGED OR DISCONNECTED?
YES
REPAIR AS NECESSARY.
NO
DISCONNECT THE ABS WARNING LAMP RELAY CONNECTOR.
WITH DRBII IN OHM-METER MODE PROBE BOTH ABS WARN LAMP RELAY GROUND WIRES.
IS THE RESISTANCE BELOW 5.0 OHMS FOR BOTH WIRES?
NO
REPAIR THE OPEN ABS WARNING LAMP RELAY GROUND WIRE.
YES
WITH THE DRBII, ACTUATE THE SYSTEM RELAY.
WITH DRBII IN VOLT-METER MODE, PROBE ABS WARNING LAMP RELAY CONTROL WIRE.
DOES THE VOLTAGE TOGGLE BETWEEN 0 AND BATTERY VOLTAGE?
NO
REPAIR THE OPEN ABS WARNING LAMP RELAY CONTROL CKT.
YES
REPLACE THE ABS WARNING LAMP RELAY.
CR4029300513000X

Fig. 141 Test 19A: Repairing "Anti-lock Lamp Relay Fault." 1993

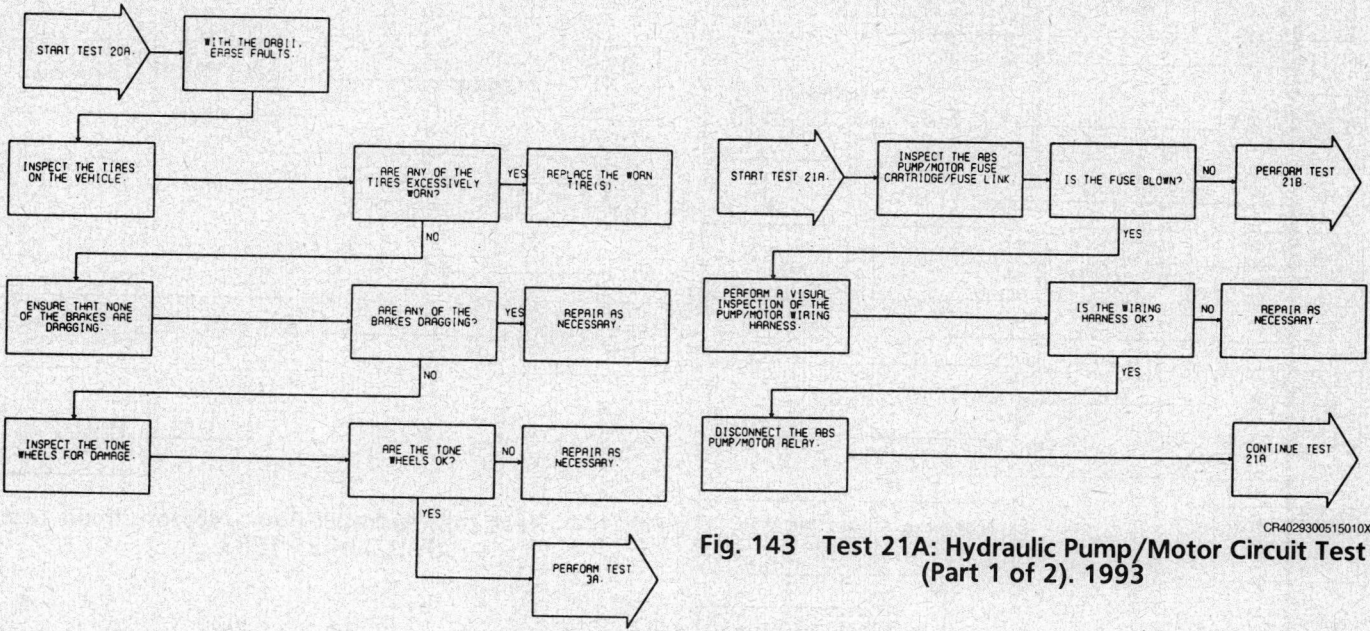

**Fig. 142   Test 20A: Repairing "Excess Decay Fault."
1993**

**Fig. 143   Test 21A: Hydraulic Pump/Motor Circuit Test
(Part 1 of 2). 1993**

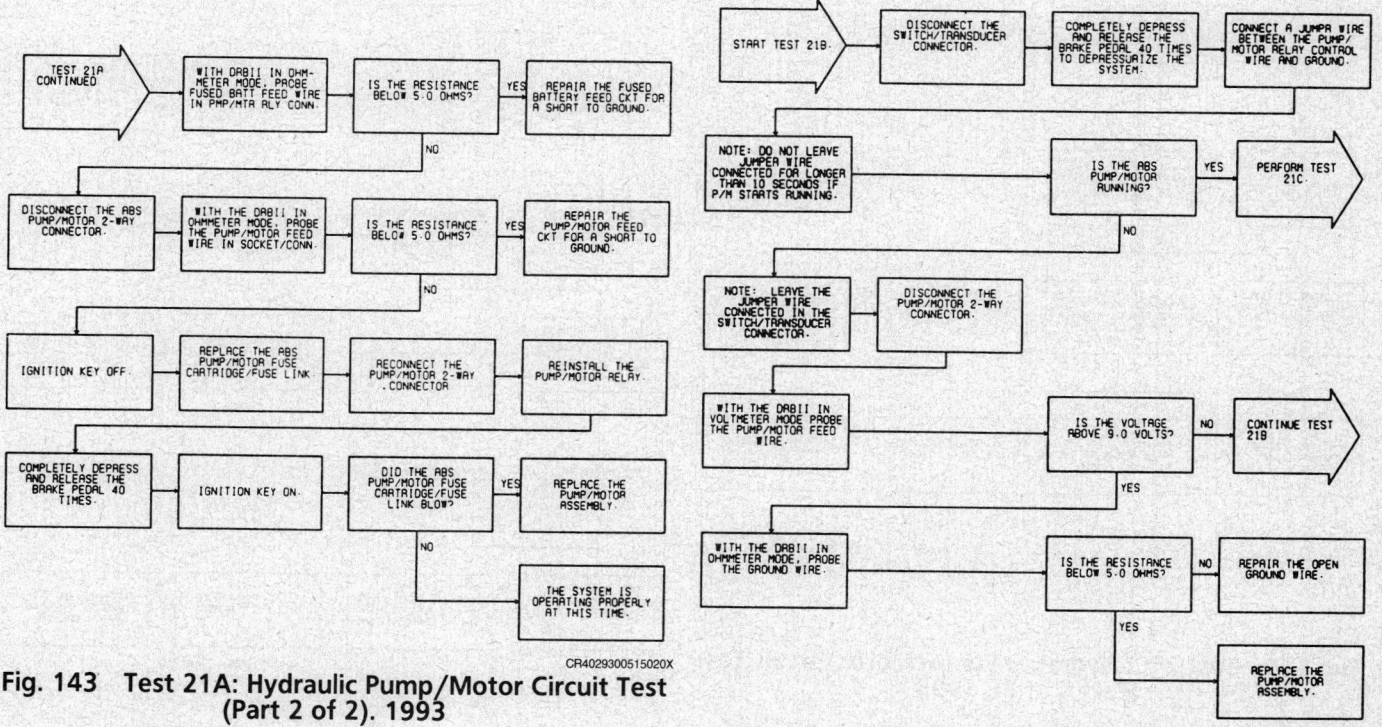

**Fig. 143   Test 21A: Hydraulic Pump/Motor Circuit Test
(Part 2 of 2). 1993**

**Fig. 144   Test 21B: Hydraulic Pump/Motor Circuit Test
(Part 1 of 3). 1993**

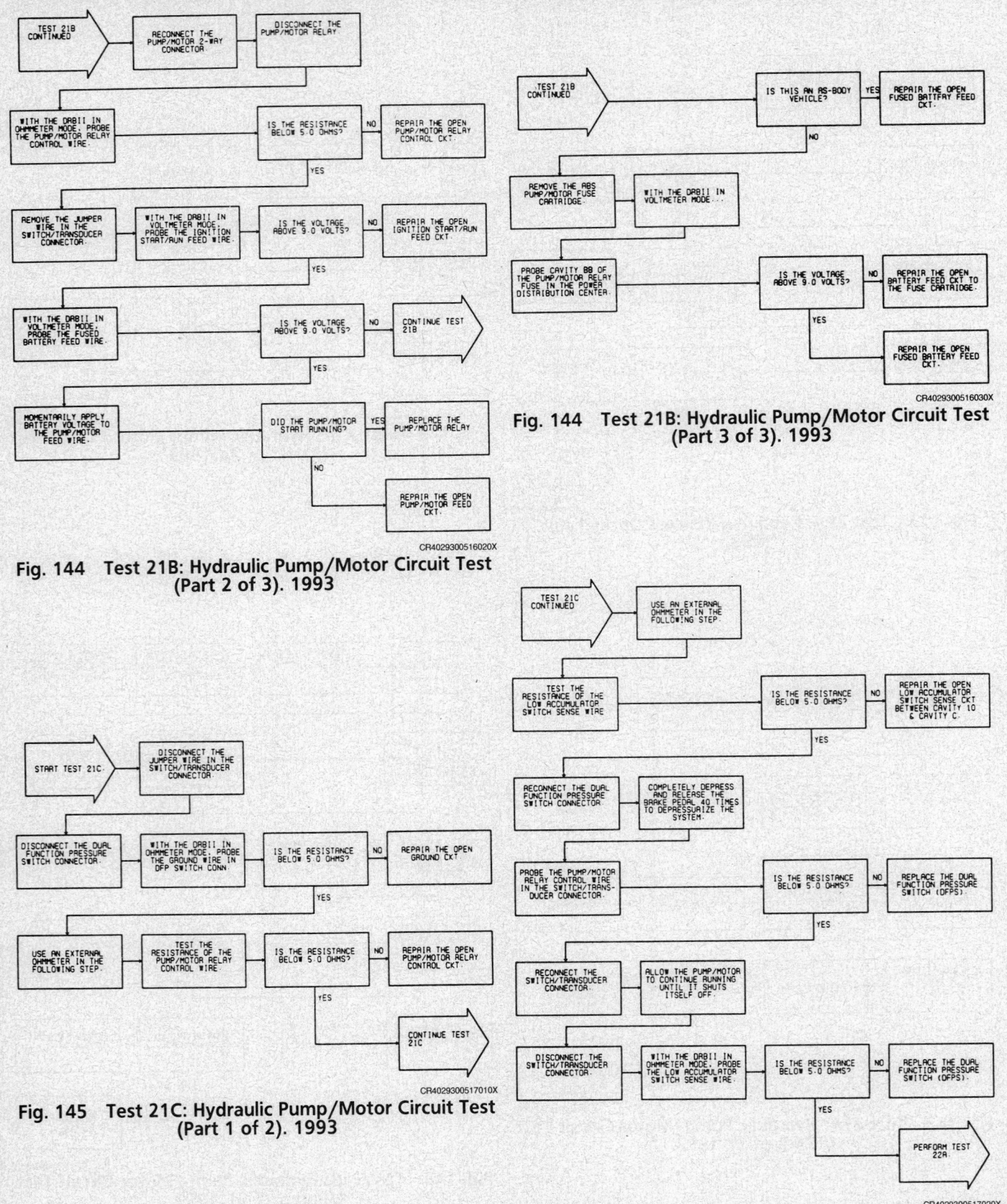

Fig. 144   Test 21B: Hydraulic Pump/Motor Circuit Test
(Part 3 of 3). 1993

Fig. 144   Test 21B: Hydraulic Pump/Motor Circuit Test
(Part 2 of 3). 1993

Fig. 145   Test 21C: Hydraulic Pump/Motor Circuit Test
(Part 1 of 2). 1993

Fig. 145   Test 21C: Hydraulic Pump/Motor Circuit Test
(Part 2 of 2). 1993

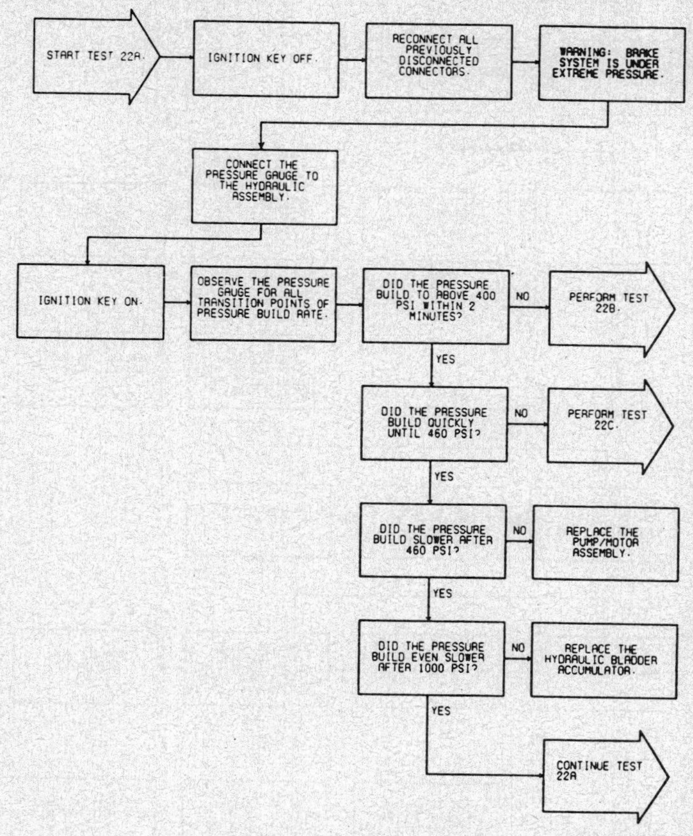

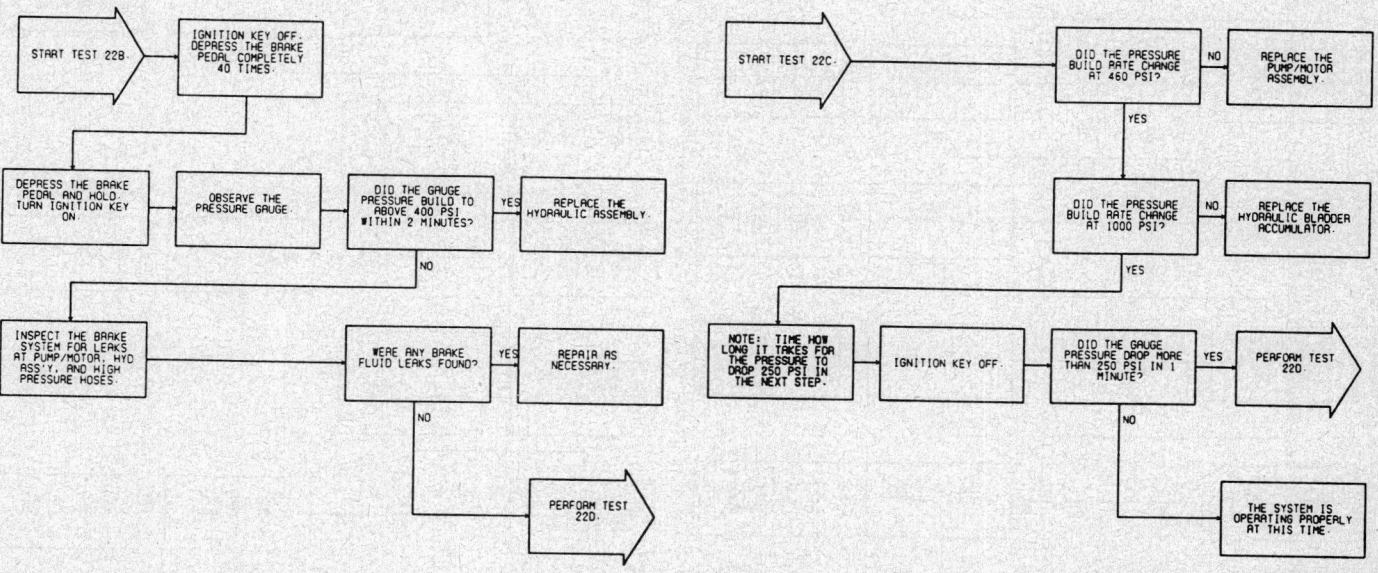

CR4029300518010X

Fig. 146 Test 22A: Hydraulic Pressure Performance Test (Part 1 of 2). 1993

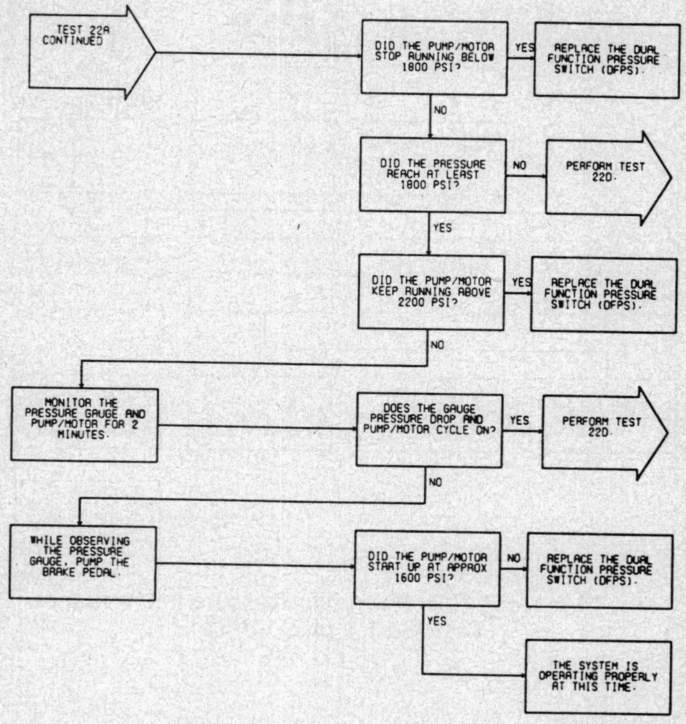

CR4029300518020X

Fig. 146 Test 22A: Hydraulic Pressure Performance Test (Part 2 of 2). 1993

CR4029300519000X

Fig. 147 Test 22B: Hydraulic Pressure Performance Test. 1993

CR4029300520000X

Fig. 148 Test 22C: Hydraulic Pressure Performance Test. 1993

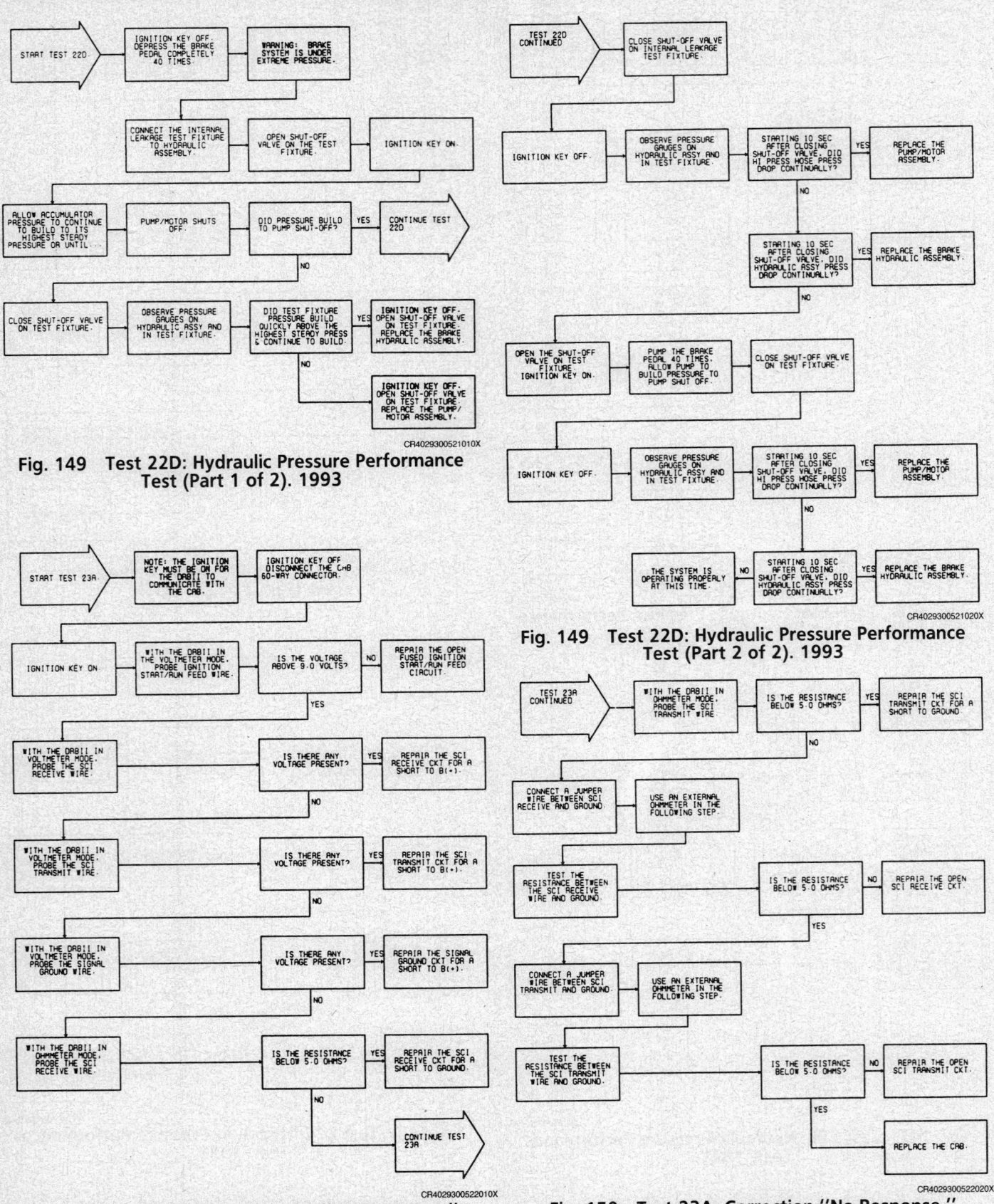

Fig. 149 Test 22D: Hydraulic Pressure Performance Test (Part 1 of 2). 1993

CR4029300521010X

Fig. 149 Test 22D: Hydraulic Pressure Performance Test (Part 2 of 2). 1993

CR4029300521020X

Fig. 150 Test 23A: Correction "No Response" Condition (Part 1 of 2). 1993

CR4029300522010X

Fig. 150 Test 23A: Correction "No Response" Condition (Part 2 of 2). 1993

CR4029300522020X

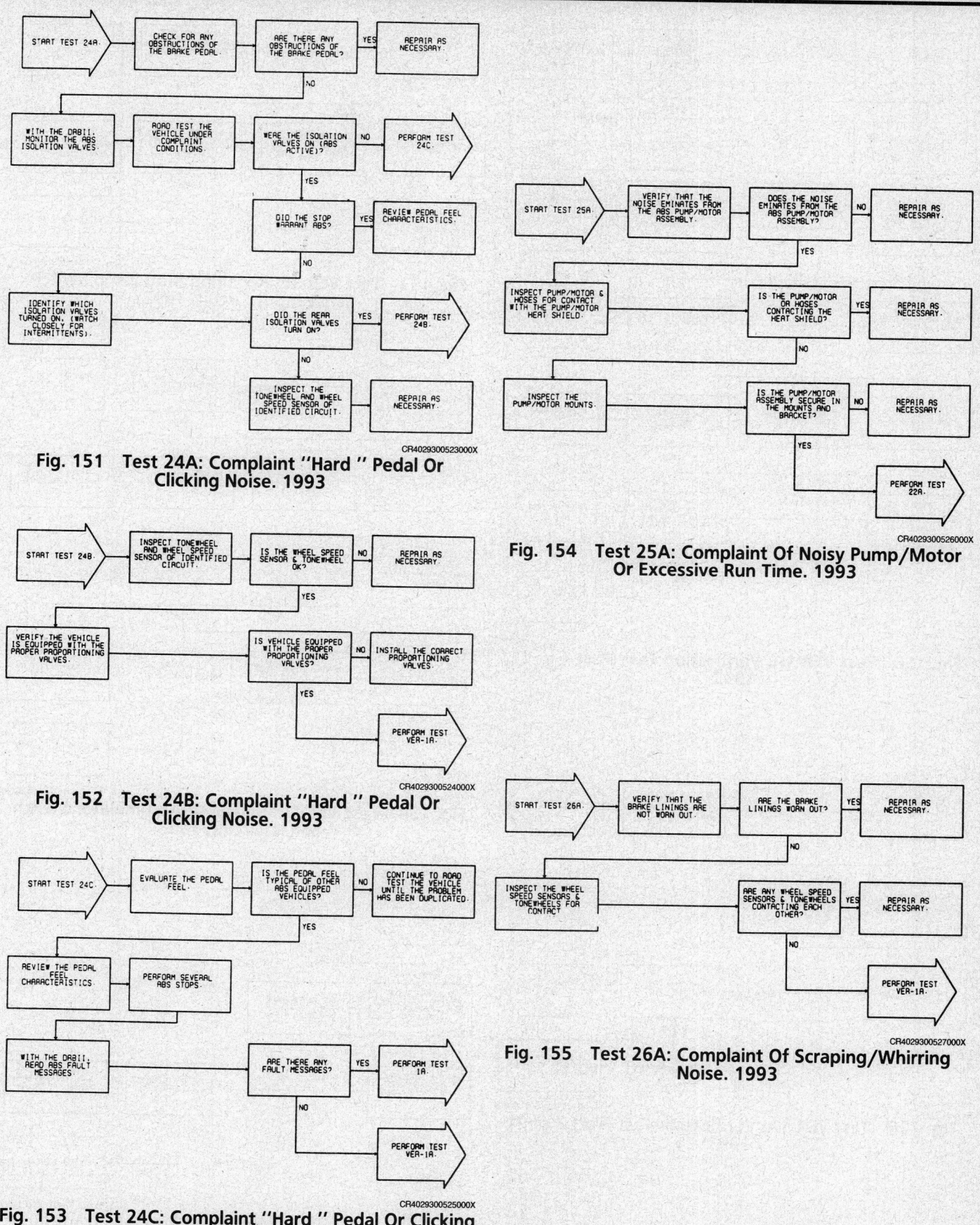

Fig. 151   Test 24A: Complaint "Hard" Pedal Or Clicking Noise. 1993

CR4029300523000X

Fig. 152   Test 24B: Complaint "Hard" Pedal Or Clicking Noise. 1993

CR4029300524000X

Fig. 153   Test 24C: Complaint "Hard" Pedal Or Clicking Noise. 1993

CR4029300525000X

Fig. 154   Test 25A: Complaint Of Noisy Pump/Motor Or Excessive Run Time. 1993

CR4029300526000X

Fig. 155   Test 26A: Complaint Of Scraping/Whirring Noise. 1993

CR4029300527000X

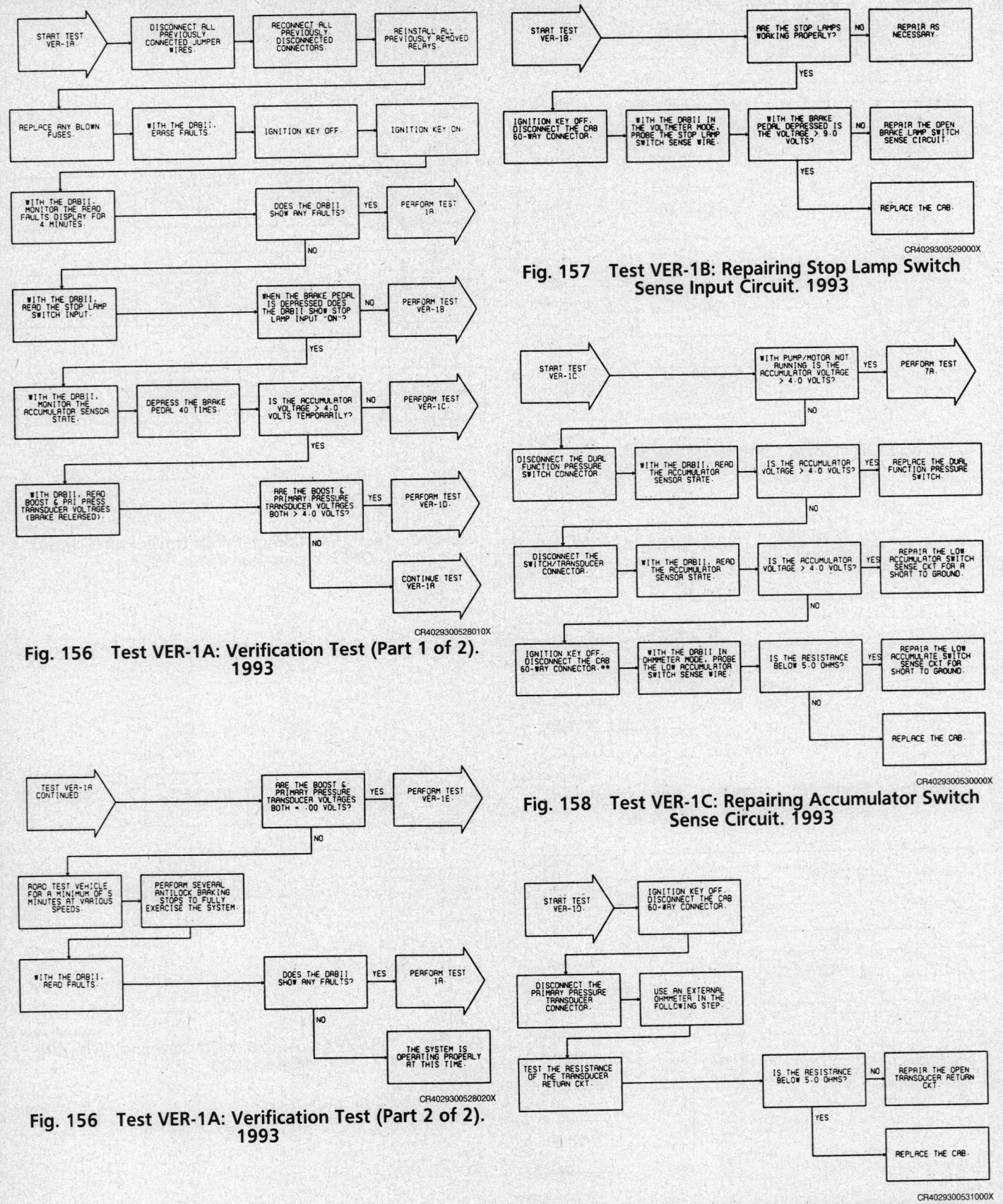

Fig. 156   Test VER-1A: Verification Test (Part 1 of 2). 1993

Fig. 156   Test VER-1A: Verification Test (Part 2 of 2). 1993

Fig. 157   Test VER-1B: Repairing Stop Lamp Switch Sense Input Circuit. 1993

Fig. 158   Test VER-1C: Repairing Accumulator Switch Sense Circuit. 1993

Fig. 159   Test VER-1D: Repairing Pressure Transducer Return Circuit. 1993

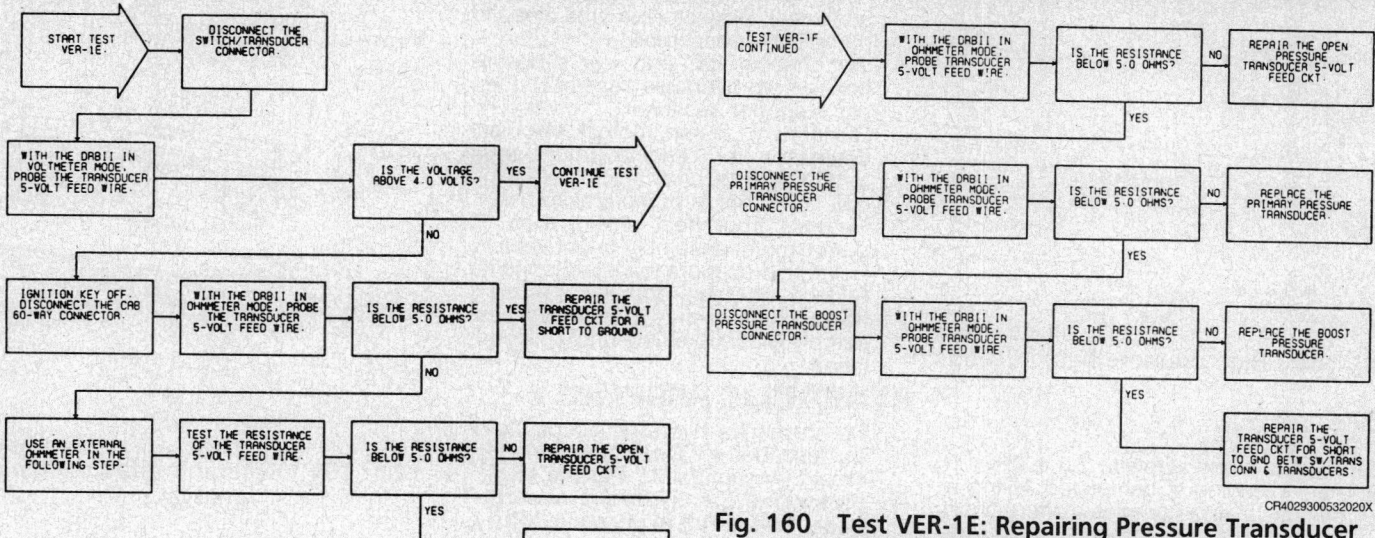

Fig. 160   Test VER-1E: Repairing Pressure Transducer
5-Volt Feed Circuit (Part 2 of 2). 1993

CR4029300532020X

Fig. 160   Test VER-1E: Repairing Pressure Transducer
5-Volt Feed Circuit (Part 1 of 2). 1993

CR4029300532010X

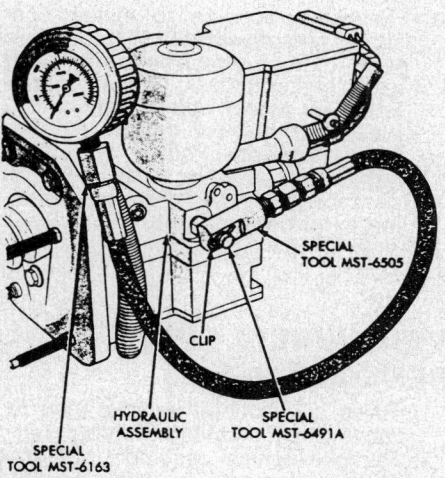

Fig. 161   Pressure gauge & adapter
installed on hydraulic assembly

CR4029100533000X

SYSTEM SERVICE

Certain components of the ABS system are not intended to be serviced individually. Attempting to remove or disconnect certain system components, may result in personal injury and/or improper system operation. Only the components with removal and installation procedures should be serviced.

Brake System Bleed

During bleeding procedures ensure brake fluid level remains close to the Full level in the reservoir.

PRESSURE BLEEDING

1. Turn ignition to the Off position.
2. De-pressurize the system as outlined in "De-Pressurizing Hydraulic Accumulator" under "Precautions."
3. Remove both reservoir caps.
4. Install pressure bleeder adapter on front reservoir port and a dummy cap on the rear port of the reservoir.
5. Attach bleeding equipment to bleeder adapter. Charge pressure bleeder to approximately 20 psi.
6. Connect a clear hose to bleed screw and place other end into a container partially filled with clean brake fluid.
7. With pressure bleeder turn On, open bleeder screw 3/4 to 1 full turn allowing fluid to flow into container.
8. Leave bleeder screw open until a clear, bubble-free flow is coming from hose in container. If the reservoir has been drained or the hydraulic assembly has been changed, slowly depress the brake pedal one or two times while the bleed screw is open. This will help purge the system of air.
9. **Torque** bleed screw to 7.5 ft. lbs.
10. Line bleeding should be performed in the following order:
    a. Left rear.
    b. Right rear.
    c. Left front.
    d. Right front.
11. After bleeding is completed, remove pressure bleeding equipment and adapter by closing pressure bleeder valve and slowly unscrewing bleeder adapter from hydraulic assembly.
12. Using a suitable syringe or equivalent remove excess fluid from reservoir or full reservoir to the Full level.
13. Install reservoir caps and turn on ignition to allow ABS pump to charge the accumulator.

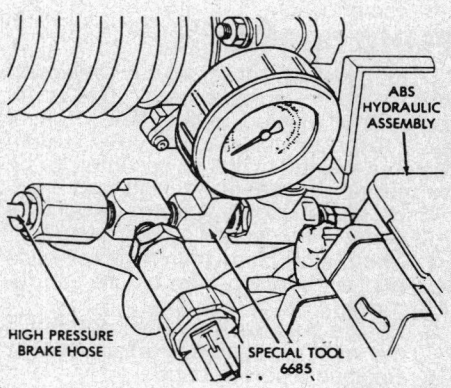

Fig. 162   Test gauge tool No. 6685
or equivalent installed

CR4029100534000X

MANUAL BLEEDING

1. Turn ignition to the Off position.
2. De-pressurize the system as outlined in "De-Pressurizing Hydraulic Accumulator" under "Precautions."
3. Connect a clear hose to bleed screw and place other end into a container partially filled with clean brake fluid.
4. Slowly pump brake pedal several times using full strokes, continue to hold pressure on the pedal at the bottom of it's travel.
5. With pressure on pedal, open bleeder screw 3/4 to 1 full turn allowing fluid to flow into container.
6. Leave bleeder screw open until fluid no longer flows from hose. Tighten bleed screw and release pedal. **Ensure bleeder screw is tight prior to releasing the brake pedal.**
7. Repeat bleeding steps until clear, bubble-free flows from the hose. Perform bleed procedure in the following order:
    a. Left rear.
    b. Right rear.

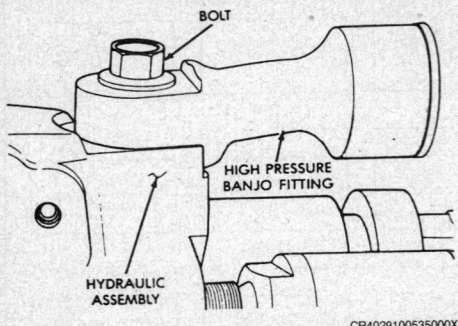

Fig. 163 High pressure banjo fitting

c. Left front.
d. Right front.
8. **Torque** bleed screw to 7.5 ft. lbs.
9. After bleeding is completed, Using a suitable syringe or equivalent remove excess fluid from reservoir or full reservoir to the Full level.
10. Install reservoir caps and turn on ignition to allow ABS pump to charge the accumulator.

FLUID CHECK

The hydraulic assembly is equipped with a plastic fluid reservoir and a filter/strainer located in the filler neck of each reservoir section. The ABS system requires that the hydraulic accumulator be de-pressurized when checking fluid level.
1. De-pressurize the system as outlined under "Precautions."
2. Thoroughly clean both reservoir caps and surrounding area before cap removal.
3. Ensure fluid level is at but not above the white screen on filter/strainer.
4. Replace reservoir caps.

DE-PRESSURIZING HYDRAULIC ACCUMULATOR

The ABS pump/motor assembly will keep the hydraulic accumulator charged to a pressure between 1600-2000 psi anytime the ignition switch is in the On position. The pump/motor cannot run if the ignition is off or either battery cable is disconnected.

The hydraulic accumulator should be depressurized before disassembling any portion of the hydraulic system. Refer to the "Precautions" section for proper de-pressurizing procedures.

Component Replace

PUMP/MOTOR ASSEMBLY

1. De-pressurize hydraulic accumulator as described in "De-Pressurizing Hydraulic Accumulator." **Failure to depressurize the hydraulic accumulator, may result in personal injury, or damage to painted surfaces.**
2. Remove fresh air intake ducts from engine induction system.
3. Disconnect electrical connectors from the pump/motor assembly and any

additional connectors in area close to pump/motor assembly.
4. Disconnect high and low pressure hoses from hydraulic assembly, then cap spigot on reservoir.
5. Disconnect pump/motor electrical connector from engine mount, then remove pump heat shield attaching bolt from front of pump bracket.
6. Remove front heat shield, then lift pump/motor assembly out of vehicle.
7. Reverse procedure to install, lubricate O-rings on high and low pressure hose connections to pump/motor assembly with brake fluid prior to installation.

HYDRAULIC ASSEMBLY

1. De-pressurize hydraulic accumulator as described in "De-Pressurizing Hydraulic Accumulator." **Failure to depressurize the hydraulic accumulator, may result in personal injury, or damage to painted surfaces.**
2. Remove fresh air intake ducts from engine induction system.
3. Disconnect all electrical connectors from hydraulic assembly.
4. Remove as much fluid as possible from the reservoir on hydraulic assembly.
5. Remove high pressure hose fitting from assembly.
6. Disconnect pump return hose from filter nipple, then cap spigot on filter.
7. Disconnect all brake tubes from hydraulic assembly.
8. Working under the instrument panel, position a small screwdriver between center tang on retainer clip and pin in brake pedal. Rotate screwdriver enough to allow retainer clip center tang to pass over end of brake pedal pin.
9. Remove four hydraulic assembly mounting nuts, then the hydraulic assembly from vehicle.
10. Reverse procedure to install.

CONTROLLER ANTI-LOCK BRAKE (CAB)

1. Turn ignition switch to the OFF position, then raise and support vehicle.
2. Remove transmission oil cooler line routing clip, then disconnect CAB 60-way connector. **Verify that ignition switch is in the OFF position before disconnecting connector.**
3. Remove CAB mounting bolts, the the CAB from the vehicle.
4. Reverse procedure to install.

FRONT WHEEL SPEED SENSORS

1. Raise and support vehicle, then remove wheel and tire assembly.
2. Remove screw from clip that attaches sensor assembly to fender shield.
3. Pull sensor assembly grommet from fender shield, then unplug sensor connector from harness.
4. Remove retainer clip from bracket on strut damper, then the three sensor assembly grommets from retainer brackets.

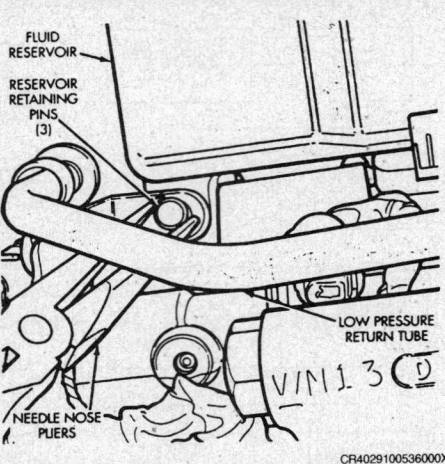

Fig. 164 Reservoir retaining pin removal

5. Remove sensor head screw, then remove sensor head from steering knuckle. **If sensor has seized, due to corrosion. Do not use pliers on sensor head. Use a hammer and a punch and tap edge of sensor ear, rocking sensor side to side until free.**
6. Reverse procedure to install, coat speed sensor with High Temperature Multi-Purpose grease before installing into steering knuckle. **Proper installation of wheel speed sensor cables is critical for continued system operation. Failure to install cables in retainers, may result in contact with moving parts, resulting in an open circuit.**

REAR WHEEL SPEED SENSORS

1. Raise and support vehicle, then remove wheel and tire assembly.
2. Remove sensor assembly grommet from underbody and pull harness through hole in underbody.
3. Unplug connector from harness, then remove sensor grommet bracket screw from body hose bracket, just forward of trailing arm bushing.
4. Remove sensor assembly clip, located on inboard side of trailing arm.
5. Remove rear sensor wire fastener from rear brake hose bracket, then the outboard sensor assembly retainer nut.
6. Remove sensor head screw, then remove sensor head from adapter assembly. **If sensor has seized, due to corrosion. Do not use pliers on sensor head. Use a hammer and a punch and tap edge of sensor ear, rocking sensor side to side until free.**
7. Reverse procedure to install, coat speed sensor with High Temperature Multi-Purpose grease before installing into steering knuckle and **torque** screw to 5 ft. lbs.

DUAL FUNCTION PRESSURE SWITCH

1. De-pressurize the system as outlined in "De-Pressurizing Hydraulic Accumulator" under "Precautions."
2. Raise and support vehicle.
3. Disconnect wiring harness from dual function switch and boost pressure transducer.
4. Remove dual function pressure switch using socket tool No. 6607 or equivalent.
5. Reverse procedure to install, noting the following:
   a. Clean area around dual function pressure switch port.
   b. **Torque** dual function pressure switch to 9 ft. lbs.
   c. With ignition switch in the On position, check for leaks at the dual function pressure switch.
   d. De-pressurize the system a second time as outlined in "De-Pressurizing Hydraulic Accumulator" under "Precautions." This will purge any air that may have entered the system when the switch was removed.
   e. Turn ignition switch to the On position to pressurize the system. Road test to ensure system is operating properly.

PRIMARY PRESSURE TRANSDUCER

1. De-pressurize the system as outlined in "De-Pressurizing Hydraulic Accumulator" under "Precautions."
2. Remove as much fluid from the reservoir as possible.
3. Using band wrench tool No. C-4065 or equivalent, loosen bladder accumulator then remove bladder and brake fluid spray shield.
4. Remove high pressure banjo fitting from hydraulic assembly.
5. Using suitable needle nose pliers, remove the three fluid reservoir retaining pins from the hydraulic assembly, **Fig. 164. Compress barb on opposite side of retaining pin to prevent pin from breaking.**

6. Remove brake fluid reservoir from hydraulic assembly by carefully prying between reservoir and hydraulic assembly using a suitable blunt pry bar. Use a rocking motion to help disengage reservoir from grommets.
7. Remove brake fluid level sensor from reservoir then the reservoir from the vehicle.
8. Disconnect hydraulic assembly wiring harness connector from the primary pressure transducer then remove the transducer using socket tool No. 6684 or equivalent.
9. Reverse procedure to install, noting the following:
   a. **Torque** primary pressure transducer to 106 inch lbs.
   b. Install new reservoir sealing grommets by lubricating them with brake fluid then placing them on reservoir outlets.
   c. Press reservoir into place by hand using a rocking motion to help seat reservoir. **Never pound on reservoir to install.**
   d. Ensure barbs on reservoir retaining pins are extending past reservoir on opposite side.
   e. **Torque** high pressure banjo fitting to 10 ft. lbs.
   f. **Torque** bladder accumulator to 35 ft. lbs.
   g. Bleed system as outlined under "Bleeding Brakes."

DIFFERENTIAL PRESSURE SWITCH

1. De-pressurize the system as outlined in "De-Pressurizing Hydraulic Accumulator" under "Precautions."
2. Disconnect hydraulic assembly wiring harness connector from the primary pressure transducer.
3. Disconnect differential pressure switch wiring harness connector from hydraulic assembly wiring harness. **Do not attempt to disconnect the harness connector from the differential pressure switch.**
4. Raise and support vehicle.
5. Remove differential pressure switch using socket tool No. 6684 or equivalent.

6. Reverse procedure to install, noting the following:
   a. **Torque** differential pressure switch to 13 inch lbs.
   b. Turn ignition switch to the On position to pressurize the system and check for leaks.
   c. De-pressurize the system check fluid level, then repressurize the system to purge any air out of the hydraulic assembly. Refer to procedure found in "De-Pressurizing Hydraulic Accumulator" under "Precautions" to properly de-pressurize the system.
   d. Road test the vehicle to ensure system is operating normally.

BOOST PRESSURE TRANSDUCER

1. De-pressurize the system as outlined in "De-Pressurizing Hydraulic Accumulator" under "Precautions."
2. Raise and support vehicle.
3. Disconnect hydraulic assembly wiring harness connectors from the dual function pressure switch and boost pressure transducer.
4. Remove dual function pressure switch using socket tool No. 6607 or equivalent.
5. Remove boost pressure transducer using socket tool No. 6684 or equivalent.
6. Reverse procedure to install, noting the following:
   a. **Torque** boost pressure transducer and dual function pressure switch to 106 inch lbs.
   b. Turn ignition switch to the On position to pressurize the system and check for leaks.
   c. De-pressurize the system check fluid level, then repressurize the system to purge any air out of the hydraulic assembly. Refer to "Precautions" to properly de-pressurize the system.
   d. Road test the vehicle to ensure system is operating normally.

Type 4—Anti-Lock Braking System

NOTE: On Air Bag Equipped Models, Refer To "Air Bag System Precautions" Located In The Front Of This Manual For System Disarming & Arming Procedures.

INDEX

PRECAUTIONS

AIR BAG SYSTEMS

Refer to "Air Bag System Precautions" in the front of this manual for system disarming and arming procedures.

DESCRIPTION

The Anti-Lock Braking System (ABS) prevents the wheels from locking up when braking, regardless of the surface conditions. This allows the car to stop in a shorter distance, and allows the driver to maintain directional control of the vehicle during heavy braking.

During normal braking conditions, the ABS operates like a conventional diagonally split, hydraulic power assist system. During heavy braking, however, each wheel's braking pressure is modulated according to its speed. To maintain vehicle stability, both rear wheels receive the same signal.

TROUBLESHOOTING

FWD MODELS

Refer to **Figs. 1 and 2** when troubleshooting the ABS system on FWD models.

AWD MODELS

Refer to **Fig. 3** when troubleshooting the ABS system on AWD models.

DIAGNOSIS & TESTING

Accessing Diagnostic Trouble Codes

1. Connect Diagnostic Readout Box (DRB II) per manufacturers instructions.
2. After DRB II has been connected, DRB II will display diagnostic trouble code(s).
3. After diagnostic trouble code(s) have been displayed, refer to the appropriate diagnostic charts that follow.

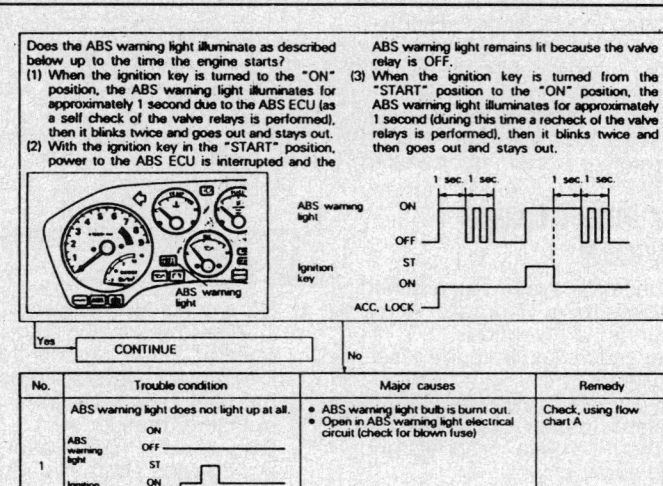

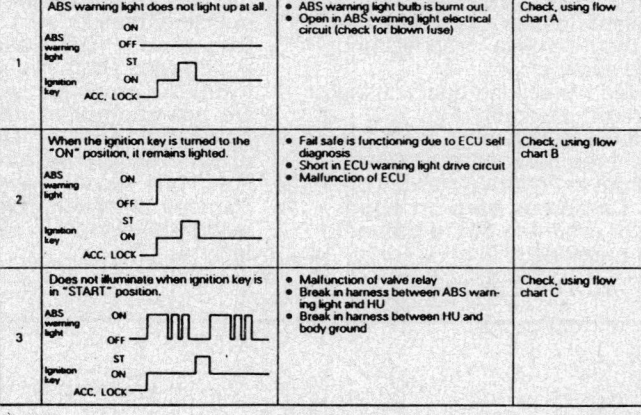

CR4029100537010X

Fig. 1   Anti-Lock brake system troubleshooting (Part 1 of 2). 1992 Laser & Talon FWD

DIAGNOSIS w/DRB II (DIAGNOSTIC READOUT BOX II)

FWD MODELS

Colt Vista & Summit Wagon

Locate the appropriate ABS diagnostic trouble code service procedure using the diagnostic trouble code reference chart, **Fig. 4**, and ABS diagnosis charts, **Figs. 5 through 14**.

Laser & Talon

Locate the appropriate ABS system diagnostic trouble code service procedures using the diagnostic trouble code reference chart, **Fig. 4**, and ABS diagnosis charts, **Fig. 5** and **Figs. 15 through 23**.

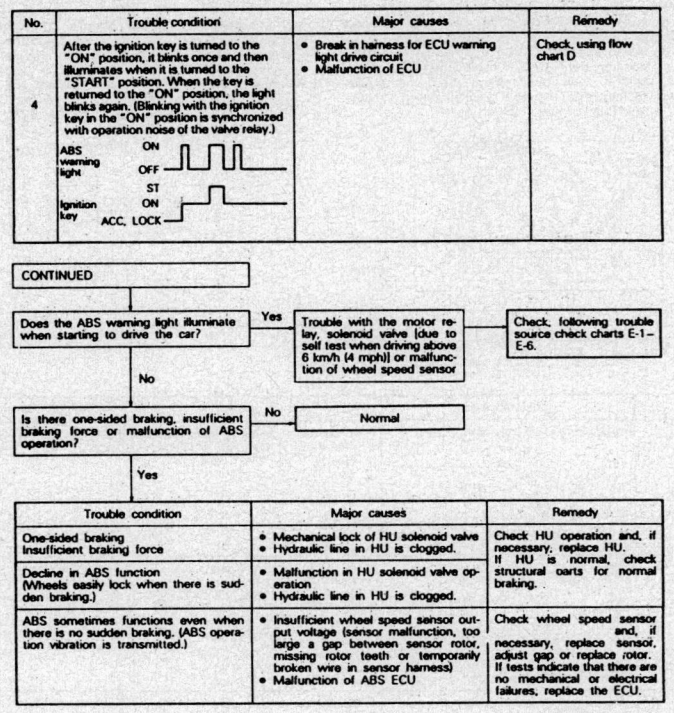

Fig. 1 Anti-Lock brake system troubleshooting (Part 2 of 2). 1992 Laser & Talon FWD

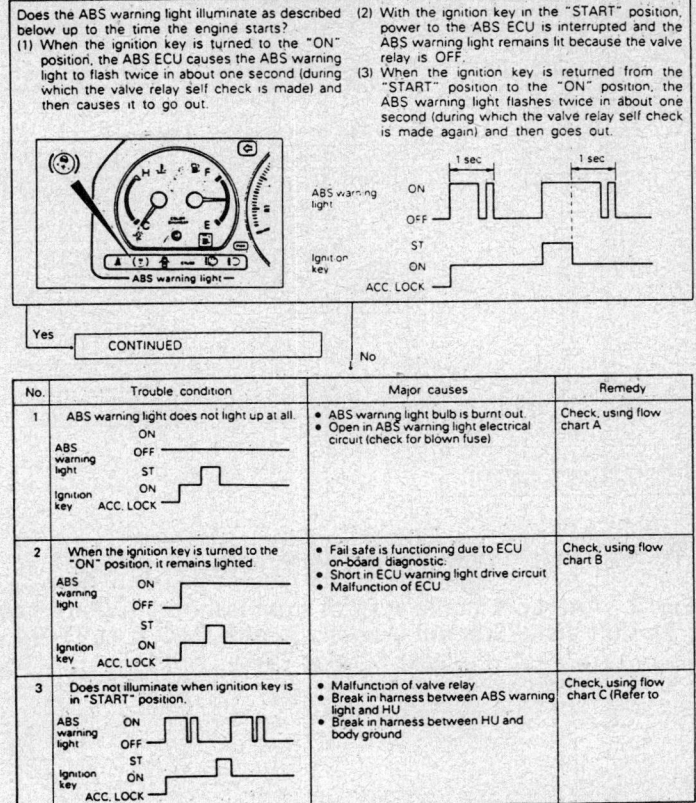

Fig. 2 Anti-Lock brake system troubleshooting (Part 1 of 3). Colt Vista/Summit Wagon, Stealth FWD & 1993–94 Laser & Talon FWD

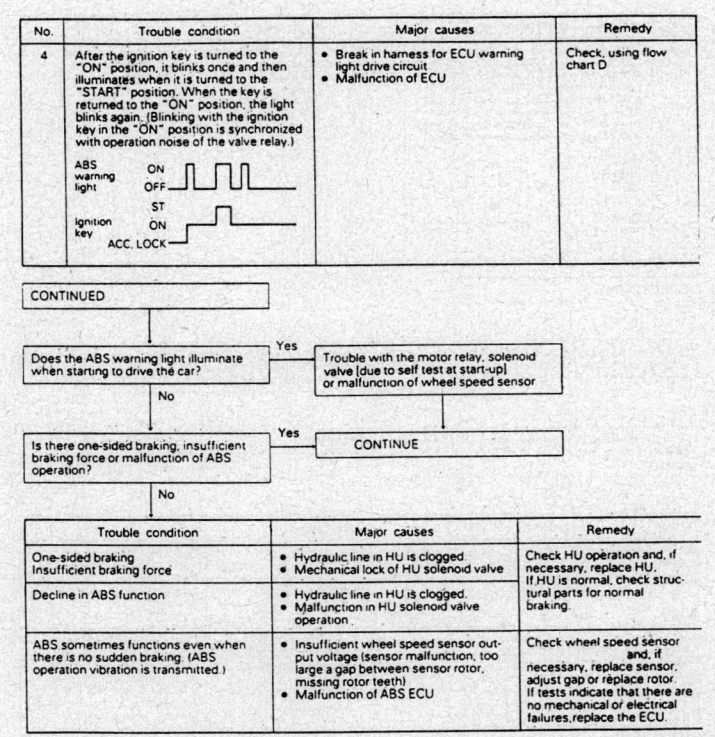

Fig. 2 Anti-Lock brake system troubleshooting (Part 2 of 3). Colt Vista/Summit Wagon, Stealth FWD & 1993–94 Laser & Talon FWD

Stealth

Locate the appropriate ABS system diagnostic trouble code service procedure using the diagnostic trouble code reference chart, **Fig. 4**, and ABS diagnosis charts, **Fig. 5** and **Figs. 24 through 32.**

AWD MODELS

Colt Vista & Summit Wagon

Locate the appropriate ABS system diagnostic trouble code service procedures using the diagnostic trouble code reference chart, **Fig. 33**, and ABS diagnosis charts, **Figs. 34 through 44.**

Laser & Talon

Locate the appropriate ABS system diagnostic trouble code service procedures using the diagnostic trouble code reference chart, **Fig. 33**, and ABS diagnosis charts, **Fig. 34** and **Figs. 45 through 54.**

Stealth

Locate the appropriate ABS system diagnostic trouble code service procedures using the diagnostic trouble code reference chart, **Fig. 33**, and ABS diagnosis charts, **Fig. 34** and **Figs. 55 through 64.**

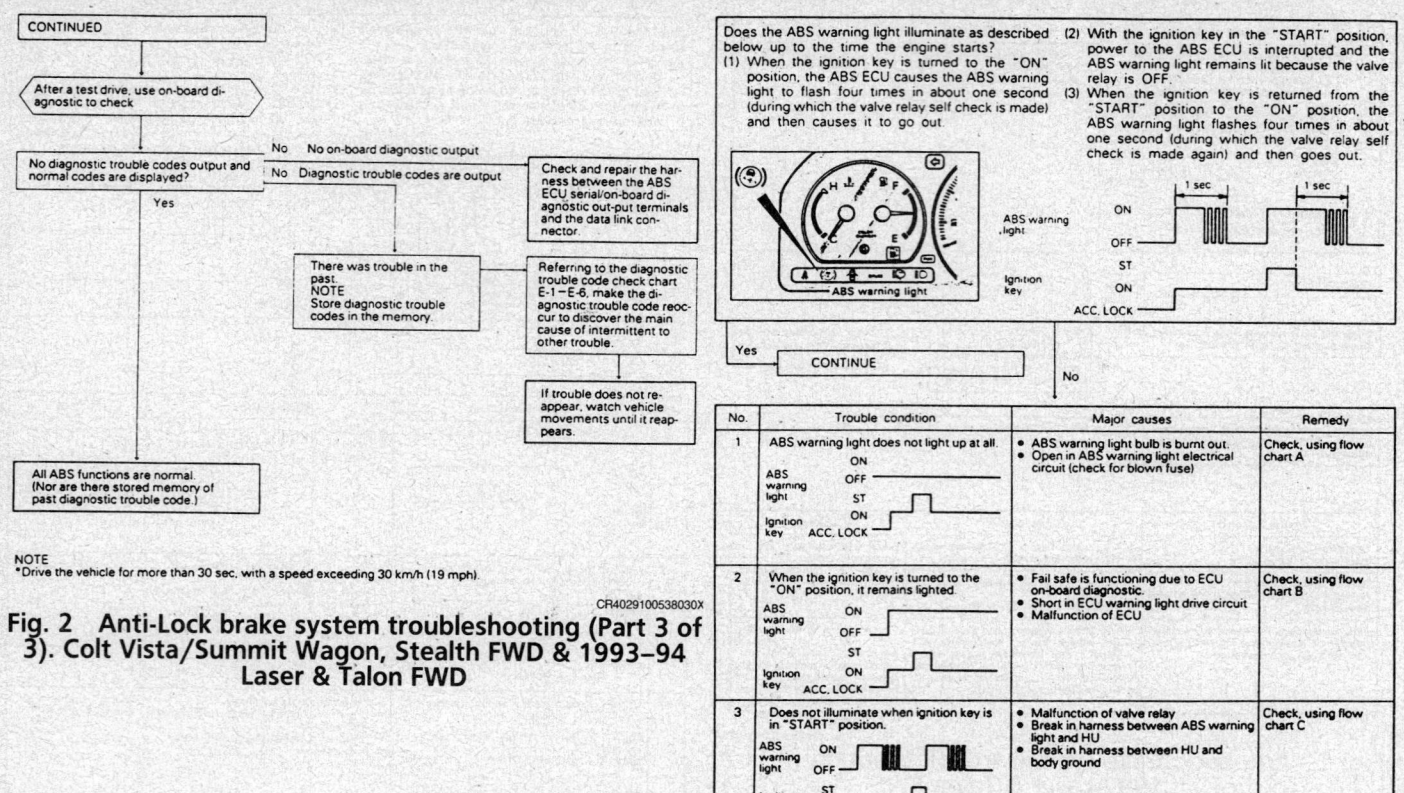

CONTINUED

After a test drive, use on-board diagnostic to check

No diagnostic trouble codes output and normal codes are displayed? — No → No on-board diagnostic output

— No → Diagnostic trouble codes are output → Check and repair the harness between the ABS ECU serial/on-board diagnostic out-put terminals and the data link connector.

Yes

There was trouble in the past.
NOTE
Store diagnostic trouble codes in the memory. → Referring to the diagnostic trouble code check chart E-1–E-6, make the diagnostic trouble code reoccur to discover the main cause of intermittent to other trouble.

If trouble does not re-appear, watch vehicle movements until it reappears.

All ABS functions are normal. (Nor are there stored memory of past diagnostic trouble code.)

NOTE
*Drive the vehicle for more than 30 sec. with a speed exceeding 30 km/h (19 mph).

CR4029100538030X

Fig. 2 Anti-Lock brake system troubleshooting (Part 3 of 3). Colt Vista/Summit Wagon, Stealth FWD & 1993–94 Laser & Talon FWD

Does the ABS warning light illuminate as described below up to the time the engine starts?
(1) When the ignition key is turned to the "ON" position, the ABS ECU causes the ABS warning light to flash four times in about one second (during which the valve relay self check is made) and then causes it to go out.

(2) With the ignition key in the "START" position, power to the ABS ECU is interrupted and the ABS warning light remains lit because the valve relay is OFF.
(3) When the ignition key is returned from the "START" position to the "ON" position, the ABS warning light flashes four times in about one second (during which the valve relay self check is made again) and then goes out.

Yes → CONTINUE   No

No.	Trouble condition	Major causes	Remedy
1	ABS warning light does not light up at all.	• ABS warning light bulb is burnt out. • Open in ABS warning light electrical circuit (check for blown fuse)	Check, using flow chart A
2	When the ignition key is turned to the "ON" position, it remains lighted.	• Fail safe is functioning due to ECU on-board diagnostic. • Short in ECU warning light drive circuit • Malfunction of ECU	Check, using flow chart B
3	Does not illuminate when ignition key is in "START" position.	• Malfunction of valve relay • Break in harness between ABS warning light and HU • Break in harness between HU and body ground	Check, using flow chart C

CR4029100539010X

Fig. 3 Anti-Lock brake system troubleshooting (Part 1 of 3). AWD models

DIAGNOSIS LESS DRB II (DIAGNOSTIC READOUT BOX II)

FWD Models

Refer to **Figs. 5 through 32** when diagnosing the ABS system on FWD models.

AWD Models

Refer to **Figs. 34 through 64** when diagnosing the ABS system on AWD models.

No.	Trouble condition	Major causes	Remedy
4	After the ignition key is turned to the "ON" position, it blinks once and then illuminates when it is turned to the "START" position. When the key is returned to the "ON" position, the light blinks again. (Blinking with the ignition key in the "ON" position is synchronized with operation noise of the valve relay.)	• Break in harness for ECU warning light drive circuit • Malfunction of ECU	Check, using flow chart D

CONTINUED

Does the ABS warning light illuminate when starting to drive the car? — Yes → Trouble with the motor relay, solenoid valve (due to self test at start-up or malfunction of wheel speed sensor)

No

Is there one-sided braking, insufficient braking force or malfunction of ABS operation? — Yes → CONTINUE

No

Trouble condition	Major causes	Remedy
One-sided braking Insufficient braking force	• Hydraulic line in HU is clogged. • Mechanical lock of HU solenoid valve	Check HU operation and, if necessary, replace HU. If HU is normal, check structural parts for normal braking.
Decline in ABS function	• Hydraulic line in HU is clogged. • Malfunction in HU solenoid valve operation	
ABS sometimes functions even when there is no sudden braking. (ABS operation vibration is transmitted.)	• Insufficient wheel speed sensor output voltage (sensor malfunction, too large a gap between sensor rotor, missing rotor teeth). • Malfunction of ABS ECU	Check wheel speed sensor and, if necessary, replace sensor, adjust gap or replace rotor. If tests indicate that there are no mechanical or electrical failures, replace the ECU.

CR4029100539020X

Fig. 3 Anti-Lock brake system troubleshooting (Part 2 of 3). AWD models

Clearing Diagnostic Trouble Codes

Diagnostic trouble codes (DTCs) can be cleared by either selecting the "Erase" mode on the DRB II or by disconnecting the battery ground cable for more than 5 minutes.

Continued on page 25-148

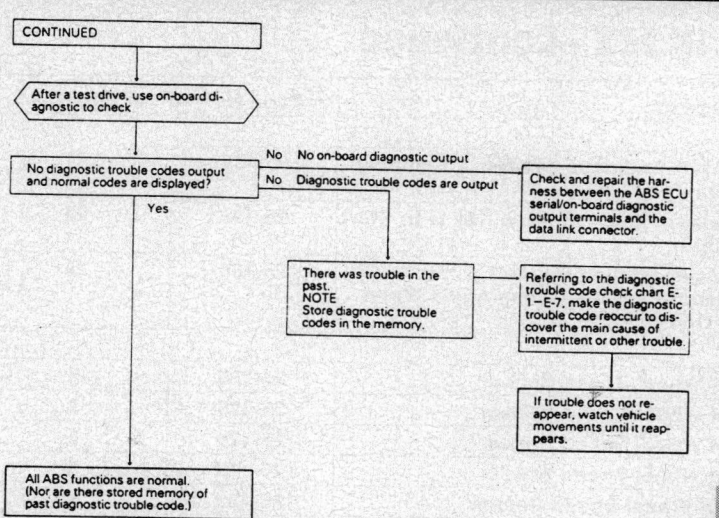

Fig. 3 Anti-Lock brake system troubleshooting (Part 3 of 3). AWD models

NOTE
*Drive the vehicle for more than 30 sec. with a speed exceeding 30 km/h (19 mph).

Diagnostic trouble code		Check chart name or remedy		Diagnostic trouble code		Check chart name or remedy
No	Scan tool display letters			No	Scan tool display letters	
11	FL SNSR. OPEN	E·1		41	FL SOL. VALVE	E·4
12	FR SNSR. OPEN			42	FR SOL. VALVE	
13	RR SNSR. OPEN			43	REAR SOL. V	
14	RL SNSR. OPEN			51	VALVE RELAY	E·5
15	VEH. SPD SNSR	E·2		52	MOTOR RELAY	E·6
22	STOP LAMP SW	E·3		55	CONT. UNIT	ECU replacement

CR4029200720000X

Fig. 4 Diagnostic trouble code reference chart. FWD models

DIAGNOSTIC CHART INDEX

Code	Chart	Description	Page No.	Fig. No.
COLT VISTA & SUMMIT WAGON FWD				
11	E1	Input Abnormality Of Wheel Speed Sensor	25-125	5
12	E1	Input Abnormality Of Wheel Speed Sensor	25-125	5
13	E1	Input Abnormality Of Wheel Speed Sensor	25-125	5
14	E1	Input Abnormality Of Wheel Speed Sensor	25-125	5
15	E2	Output Abnormality Of Wheel Speed Sensor	25-126	6
22	E3	Abnormality Of Stop Light Switch Circuit	25-126	7
41	E4	Abnormality Of Solenoid Valve Drive Circuit	25-127	8
42	E4	Abnormality Of Solenoid Valve Drive Circuit	25-127	8
43	E4	Abnormality Of Solenoid Valve Drive Circuit	25-127	8
51	E5	Abnormality Of Valve Relay Drive Circuit	25-127	9
52	E6	Abnormality Of Motor Drive Circuit	25-127	10
55	A	ABS Warning Light Does Not Light At All	25-127	11
55	B	ABS Warning Light Stays On When Ignition Key Is In On Position	25-128	12
55	C	ABS Warning Light Does Not Illuminate When Ignition Key Is In Start Position	25-129	13
55	D	ABS Warning Light Blinks Once After Ignition Key Is Turned To On Position, Iluminates In Start Position & Blinks Once Again When Turned To On Position	25-129	14
LASER & TALON FWD				
11	E1	Input Abnormality Of Wheel Speed Sensor	25-125	5
12	E1	Input Abnormality Of Wheel Speed Sensor	25-125	5
13	E1	Input Abnormality Of Wheel Speed Sensor	25-125	5
14	E1	Input Abnormality Of Wheel Speed Sensor	25-125	5
15	E2	Output Abnormality Of Wheel Speed Sensor	25-129	15
22	E3	Abnormality Of Stop Light Switch Circuit	25-130	16
41	E4	Abnormality Of Solenoid Valve Drive Circuit	25-130	17
42	E4	Abnormality Of Solenoid Valve Drive Circuit	25-130	17
43	E4	Abnormality Of Solenoid Valve Drive Circuit	25-130	17
51	E5	Abnormality Of Valve Relay Drive Circuit	25-131	18
52	E6	Abnormality Of Motor Drive Circuit	25-131	19
55	A	ABS Warning Light Does Not Light At All	25-131	20

Continued

DIAGNOSTIC CHART INDEX –Continued

Code	Chart	Description	Page No.	Fig. No.
LASER & TALON FWD -Continued				
55	B	ABS Warning Light Illuminated After Engine Is Started & Remains On	25-132	21
55	C	ABS Warning Light Does Not Illuminate When Ignition Key Is In Start Position	25-132	22
55	D	ABS Warning Light Blinks Once After Ignition Key Is Turned To On Position, Illuminates In Start Position & Blinks Once Again When Turned To On Position	25-133	23
STEALTH FWD				
11	E1	Input Abnormality Of Wheel Speed Sensor	25-125	5
12	E1	Input Abnormality Of Wheel Speed Sensor	25-125	5
13	E1	Input Abnormality Of Wheel Speed Sensor	25-125	5
14	E1	Input Abnormality Of Wheel Speed Sensor	25-125	5
15	E2	Output Abnormality Of Wheel Speed Sensor	25-133	24
22	E3	Abnormality Of Stop Light Switch Circuit	25-133	25
41	E4	Abnormality Of Solenoid Valve Drive Circuit	25-134	26
42	E4	Abnormality Of Solenoid Valve Drive Circuit	25-134	26
43	E4	Abnormality Of Solenoid Valve Drive Circuit	25-134	26
51	E5	Abnormality Of Valve Relay Drive Circuit	25-134	27
52	E6	Abnormality Of Motor Drive Circuit	25-134	28
55	A	ABS Warning Light Does Not Light At All	25-134	29
55	B	ABS Warning Light Stays On When Ignition Key Is In On Position	25-135	30
55	C	ABS Warning Light Does Not Illuminate When Ignition Key Is In Start Position	25-136	31
55	D	ABS Warning Light Blinks Once After Ignition Key Is Turned To On Position, Illuminates In Start Position & Blinks Once Again When Turned To On Position	25-136	32
COLT VISTA & SUMMIT WAGON AWD				
11	E1	Input Abnormality Of Wheel Speed Sensor	25-136	34
12	E1	Input Abnormality Of Wheel Speed Sensor	25-136	34
13	E1	Input Abnormality Of Wheel Speed Sensor	25-136	34
14	E1	Input Abnormality Of Wheel Speed Sensor	25-136	34
15	E2	Output Abnormality Of Wheel Speed Sensor	25-136	35
21	E3	Abnormality Of G Sensor Circuit	25-137	36
22	E4	Abnormality Of Stop Light Switch Circuit	25-137	37
41	E5	Abnormality Of Solenoid Valve Drive Circuit	25-138	38
42	E5	Abnormality Of Solenoid Valve Drive Circuit	25-138	38
43	E5	Abnormality Of Solenoid Valve Drive Circuit	25-138	38
51	E6	Abnormality Of Valve Relay Drive Circuit	25-138	39
52	E7	Abnormality Of Motor Drive Circuit	25-139	40
55	A	ABS Warning Light Does Not Light At All	25-139	41
55	B	ABS Warning Light Stays On When Ignition Key Is In On Position	25-140	42
55	C	ABS Warning Light Does Not Illuminate When Ignition Key Is In Start Position	25-141	43
55	D	ABS Warning Light Blinks Once After Ignition Key Is Turned To On Position, Illuminates In Start Position & Blinks Once Again When Turned To On Position	25-141	44
LASER & TALON AWD				
11	E1	Input Abnormality Of Wheel Speed Sensor	25-136	34
12	E1	Input Abnormality Of Wheel Speed Sensor	25-136	34
13	E1	Input Abnormality Of Wheel Speed Sensor	25-136	34
14	E1	Input Abnormality Of Wheel Speed Sensor	25-136	34
15	E2	Output Abnormality Of Wheel Speed Sensor	25-141	45
21	E3	Abnormality Of G Sensor Circuit	25-142	46
22	E4	Abnormality Of Stop Light Switch Circuit	25-142	47
41	E5	Abnormality Of Solenoid Valve Drive Circuit	25-142	48

Continued

DIAGNOSTIC CHART INDEX –Continued

Code	Chart	Description	Page No.	Fig. No.
LASER & TALON AWD -Continued				
42	E5	Abnormality Of Solenoid Valve Drive Circuit	25-142	48
43	E5	Abnormality Of Solenoid Valve Drive Circuit	25-142	48
51	E6	Abnormality Of Valve Relay Drive Circuit	25-142	49
52	E7	Abnormality Of Motor Drive Circuit	25-143	50
55	A	ABS Warning Light Does Not Light At All	25-143	51
55	B	ABS Warning Light Illuminated After Engine Is Started & Remains On	25-144	52
55	C	ABS Warning Light Does Not Illuminate When Ignition Key Is In Start Position	25-144	53
55	D	ABS Warning Light Blinks Once After Ignition Key Is Turned To On Position, Illuminates In Start Position & Blinks Once Again When Turned To On Position	25-144	54
STEALTH AWD				
11	E1	Input Abnormality Of Wheel Speed Sensor	25-136	34
12	E1	Input Abnormality Of Wheel Speed Sensor	25-136	34
13	E1	Input Abnormality Of Wheel Speed Sensor	25-136	34
14	E1	Input Abnormality Of Wheel Speed Sensor	25-136	34
15	E2	Output Abnormality Of Wheel Speed Sensor	25-145	55
21	E3	Abnormality Of G Sensor Circuit	25-145	56
22	E4	Abnormality Of Stop Light Switch Circuit	25-145	57
41	E5	Abnormality Of Solenoid Valve Drive Circuit	25-146	58
42	E5	Abnormality Of Solenoid Valve Drive Circuit	25-146	58
43	E5	Abnormality Of Solenoid Valve Drive Circuit	25-146	58
51	E6	Abnormality Of Valve Relay Drive Circuit	25-146	59
52	E7	Abnormality Of Motor Drive Circuit	25-146	60
55	A	ABS Warning Light Does Not Light At All	25-146	61
55	B	ABS Warning Light Stays On When Ignition Key Is In On Position	25-147	62
55	C	ABS Warning Light Does Not Illuminate When Ignition Key Is In Start Position	25-148	63
55	D	ABS Warning Light Blinks Once After Ignition Key Is Turned To On Position, Illuminates In Start Position & Blinks Once Again When Turned To On position	25-148	64

[Explanation]
The ABS ECU detects breaks in the wheel speed sensor wire. This diagnostic trouble code is output if the wheel speed sensor signal is not input (or short circuited) or if its output is low when starting to drive or while driving.

[Hint]
In addition to a broken wire/short circuit in the wheel speed sensor, also check whether the sensor gap is too large, sensor harness wire is broken, or sensor harness and body connector are not properly connected.

CR4029100540000X

Fig. 5 Codes 11, 12, 13 & 14: Input Abnormality Of Wheel Speed Sensor. FWD models

[Explanation]

This diagnostic trouble code is output when there is an abnormality (other than broken wire or short circuit) in any of the wheel speed sensor output signals while driving.

[Hint]

The following can be considered as the cause of the wheel speed sensor output abnormality.
- Distortion of rotor, teeth missing
- Low frequency noise interference when sensor harness wire is broken
- Noise interference in sensor signal
- Sensor output signal is below the standard value or amplitude modulation is over the standard value. Using an oscilloscope to measure the wave shape of the wheel speed sensor output signal is very effective.

- Broken sensor harness
- Poor connection of connector

NOTE
(1) If contact is poor, check the sensor cable by bending and lightly stretching it.
(2) Except for the case where a fault condition exists in the system, but the inspection results are normal; if an abnormality cannot be found in the sensor circuit displayed as abnormal, erase the diagnostic trouble code and turn the ignition switch to OFF once, and then test-drive again. If the same diagnostic trouble code is output, replace the ABS ECU. If the trouble does not occur anymore, the problem is likely to be with the ABS ECU.
(If the trouble is in the speed sensor circuit, but is difficult to recreate, it will recur even after the ABS ECU has been replaced.)

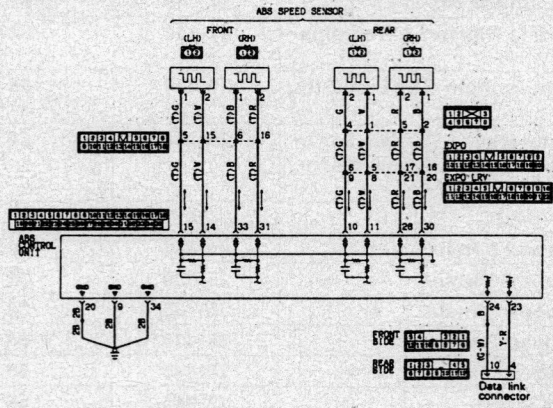

CR4029100541010X

Fig. 6   Code 15: ABS Chart E2, Output Abnormality Of Wheel Speed Sensor (Part 1 of 2). Colt Vista & Summit Wagon FWD

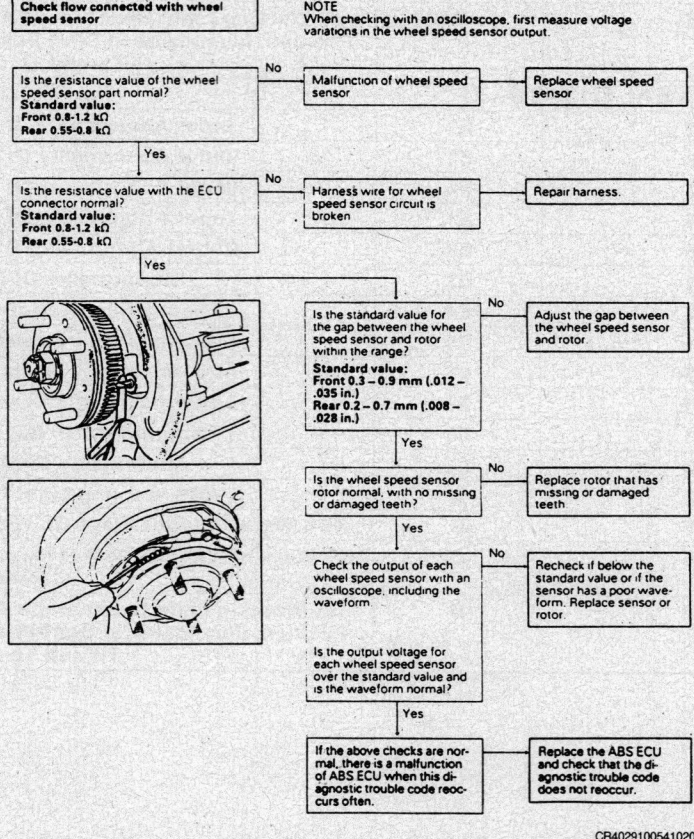

CR4029100541020X

Fig. 6   Code 15: ABS Chart E2, Output Abnormality Of Wheel Speed Sensor (Part 2 of 2). Colt Vista & Summit Wagon FWD

[Explanation]

The ABS ECU outputs this diagnostic trouble code in the following cases.
- Stop light switch may remain on for more than 15 minutes without ABS operation.
- The harness wire for the stop light switch may be open.

[Hint]

If the stop light operates normal, the harness for the stop light switch input circuit is broken or there is a malfunction in the ABS ECU.

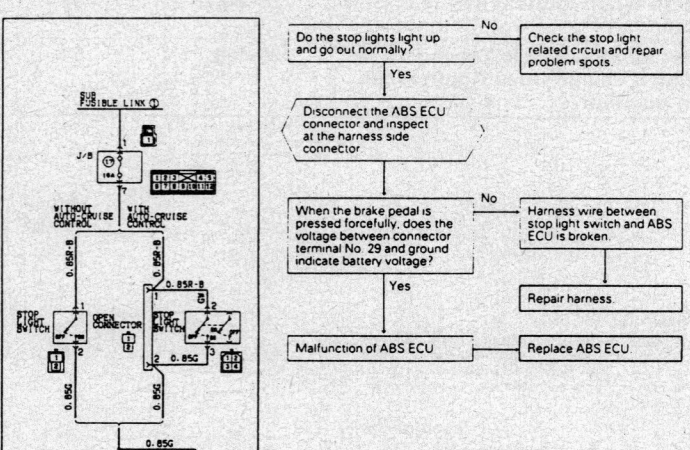

CR4029100542000X

Fig. 7   Code 22: ABS Chart E3, Abnormality Of Stop Light Switch Circuit. Colt Vista & Summit Wagon FWD

[Explanation]

The ABS ECU normally monitors the solenoid valve drive circuit.
If no current flows in the solenoid even if the ECU turns the solenoid ON or if it continues to flow even when turned OFF, the ECU determines the solenoid coil wire is broken/short-circuited or the harness is broken/short-circuited, and then these diagnostic trouble codes are output.

[Explanation]

When the ignition switch is turned ON, the ABS ECU switches the valve relay OFF and ON for an initial check, compares the voltage of the signal to the valve relay and valve power monitor line voltage to check whether the valve relay operation is normal. In addition, normally it monitors whether or not there is power in the valve power monitor line since the valve relay is normally ON. Then, if the supply of power to the valve power monitor line is interrupted, this diagnostic trouble code will be output.

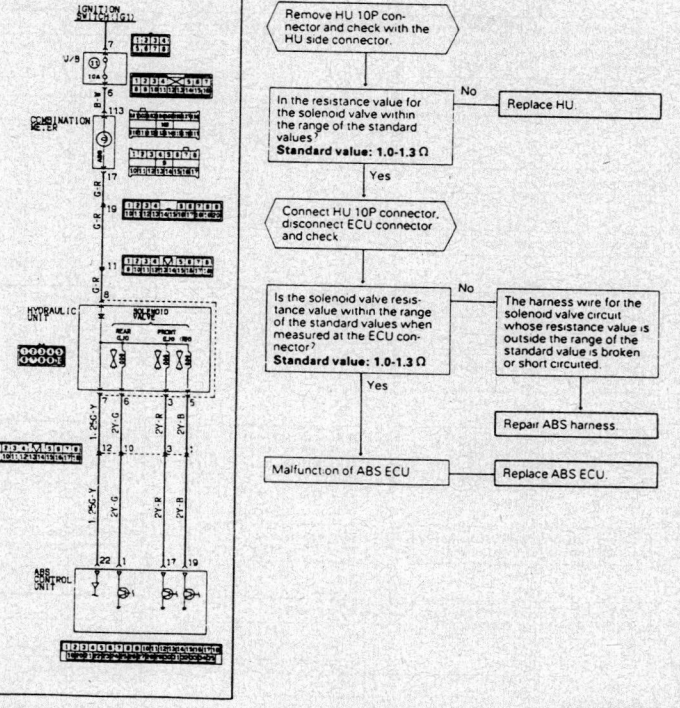

Fig. 8 Codes 41, 42 & 43: ABS Chart E4, Abnormality Of Solenoid Valve Drive Circuit. Colt Vista & Summit Wagon FWD

CR4029100543000X

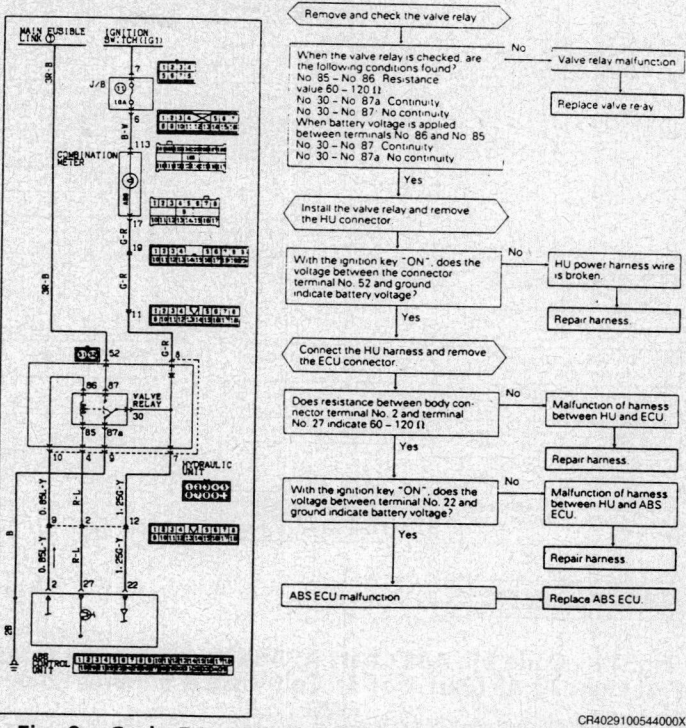

Fig. 9 Code 51: ABS Chart E5, Abnormality Of Valve Relay Drive Circuit. Colt Vista & Summit Wagon FWD

CR4029100544000X

[Explanation]

The ABC-ECU outputs this diagnostic trouble code when the motor relay and motor are as follows.
• When the motor relay is ON and no signal is input to the motor monitor line (motor does not operate, etc.)
• When the motor relay is OFF and signals enter the motor monitor line for a period of approximately 5 seconds or more (motor operates continuously, etc.)
• When motor does not operate

[Explanation]

When it does not light up at all, there is a strong possibility that there is trouble with ABS warning light or with power to the light.

[Hint]

If other warning lights do not light up either, fuse is probably blown.

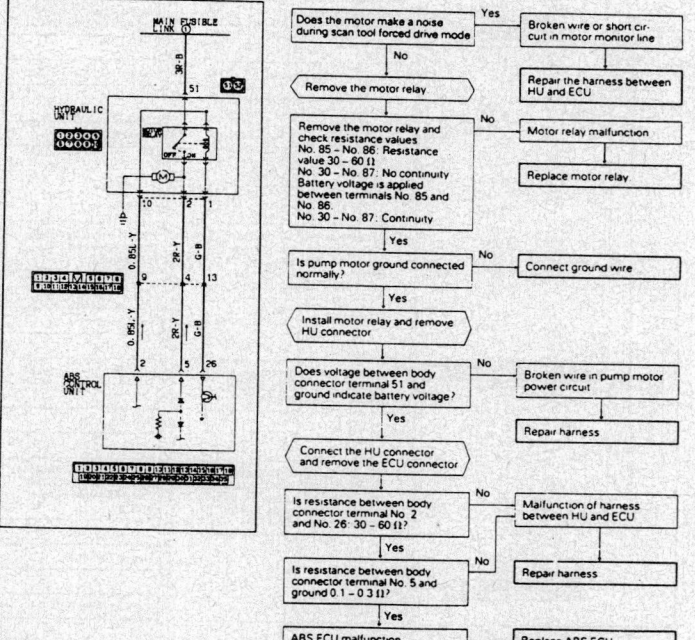

Fig. 10 Code 52: ABS Chart E6, Abnormality Of Motor Drive Circuit. Colt Vista & Summit Wagon FWD

CR4029100545000X

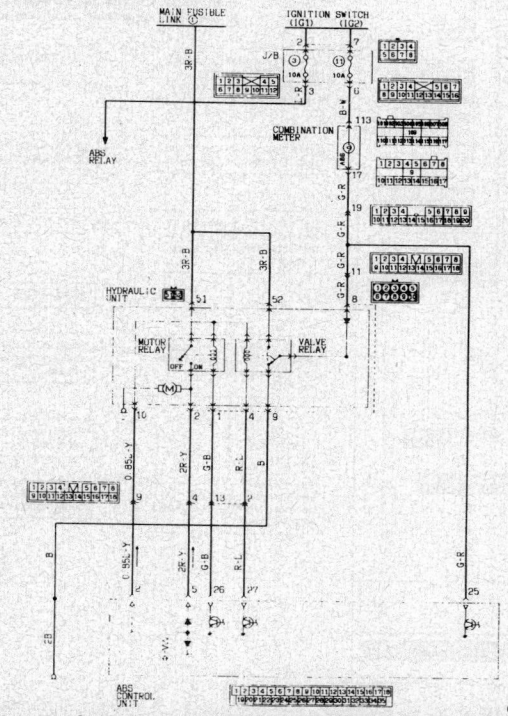

Fig. 11 Code 55: ABS Chart A, ABS Warning Light Does Not Light At All (Part 1 of 3). Colt Vista & Summit Wagon FWD

CR4029100546010X

TYPE 4-ANTI-LOCK BRAKING SYSTEM

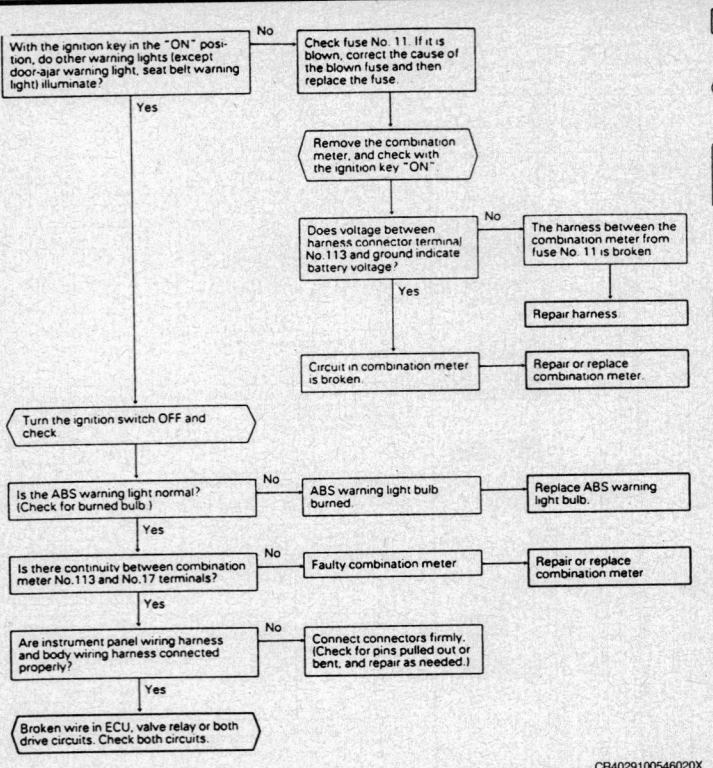

Top-left flowchart:

With the ignition key in the "ON" position, do other warning lights (except door-ajar warning light, seat belt warning light) illuminate? → **No** → Check fuse No. 11. If it is blown, correct the cause of the blown fuse and then replace the fuse.

↓ **Yes**

Remove the combination meter, and check with the ignition key "ON".

↓

Does voltage between harness connector terminal No.113 and ground indicate battery voltage? → **No** → The harness between the combination meter from fuse No. 11 is broken → Repair harness.

↓ **Yes**

Circuit in combination meter is broken. → Repair or replace combination meter.

Turn the ignition switch OFF and check.

↓

Is the ABS warning light normal? (Check for burned bulb.) → **No** → ABS warning light bulb burned. → Replace ABS warning light bulb.

↓ **Yes**

Is there continuity between combination meter No.113 and No.17 terminals? → **No** → Faulty combination meter → Repair or replace combination meter.

↓ **Yes**

Are instrument panel wiring harness and body wiring harness connected properly? → **No** → Connect connectors firmly. (Check for pins pulled out or bent, and repair as needed.)

↓ **Yes**

Broken wire in ECU, valve relay or both drive circuits. Check both circuits.

CR4029100546020X

Fig. 11 Code 55: ABS Chart A, ABS Warning Light Does Not Light At All (Part 2 of 3). Colt Vista & Summit Wagon FWD

[Explanation]
This is the symptom when the ABS ECU does not power up due to broken ECU power circuit, etc., when the fail safe function operates and isolates the system or when the warning light drive circuit is short circuited.

[Hint]
Check the on-board diagnostic output and if there is no output voltage or if the scan tool and ABS ECU cannot communicate, there is a good possibility that power is not flowing to the ECU.

Caution
• If the diagnostic trouble code is output, the system can be in the fail safe mode. In such a case, erase the diagnostic trouble code and then restart the engine to check if the system is currently in a fault condition.

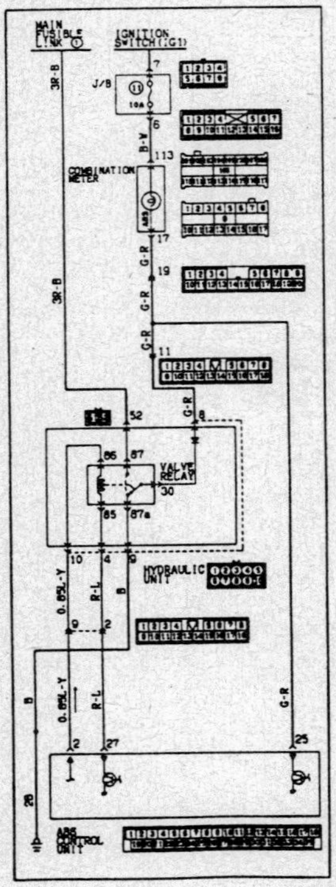

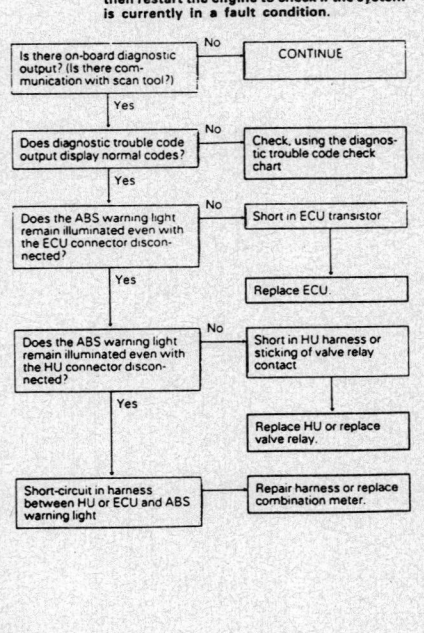

Is there on-board diagnostic output? (Is there communication with scan tool?) → **No** → CONTINUE

↓ **Yes**

Does diagnostic trouble code output display normal codes? → **No** → Check, using the diagnostic trouble code check chart.

↓ **Yes**

Does the ABS warning light remain illuminated even with the ECU connector disconnected? → **No** → Short in ECU transistor

↓ **Yes**

Replace ECU.

Does the ABS warning light remain illuminated even with the HU connector disconnected? → **No** → Short in HU harness or sticking of valve relay contact

↓ **Yes**

Replace HU or replace valve relay.

Short-circuit in harness between HU or ECU and ABS warning light → Repair harness or replace combination meter.

CR4029100547010X

Fig. 12 Code 55: ABS Chart B, ABS Warning Light Stays On When Ignition Key Is In On Position (Part 1 of 2). Colt Vista & Summit Wagon FWD

Top-right flowchart:

Check ABS ECU.

↓

Remove the ECU connector and check.

↓

Does the voltage between ECU harness connector terminal No. 25 and ground indicate battery voltage while the ignition key is in the "ON" position? → **No** → Broken wire between ABS warning light and ECU → Repair harness.

↓ **Yes**

ABS ECU malfunction → Replace ABS ECU.

Check valve relay.

↓

Remove valve relay and check.

↓

Is valve relay normal? → **No** → Valve relay malfunction → Replace valve relay

↓ **Yes**

Install the valve relay, remove the HU connector and check.

↓

Does voltage between the HU harness connector terminal No. 8 and ground indicate battery voltage while the ignition key is in the "ON" position? → **No** → Broken harness wire between ABS warning light and HU → Repair harness

↓ **Yes**

Is there continuity between HU harness connector terminal No. 9 and ground? → **No** → Broken harness wire between HU and ground → Repair harness

↓ **Yes**

Is there continuity between HU harness connector terminals No. 8 and No. 9? → **No** → HU malfunction → Replace HU

↓ **Yes**

Connector not connected securely → Replace connector.

NOTE
For inspection sections marked by *, pay attention to the polarity of the diodes.

CR4029100546030X

Fig. 11 Code 55: ABS Chart A, ABS Warning Light Does Not Light At All (Part 3 of 3). Colt Vista & Summit Wagon FWD

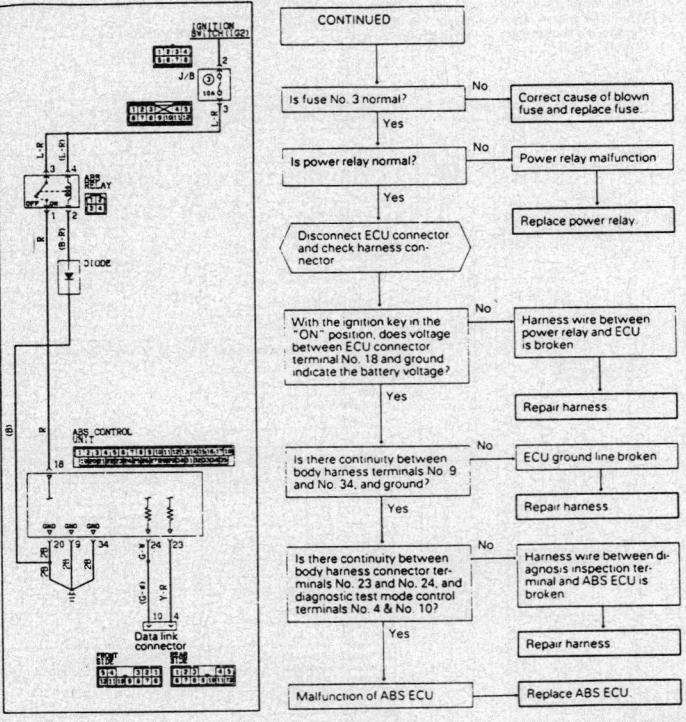

CONTINUED

↓

Is fuse No. 3 normal? → **No** → Correct cause of blown fuse and replace fuse.

↓ **Yes**

Is power relay normal? → **No** → Power relay malfunction → Replace power relay.

↓ **Yes**

Disconnect ECU connector and check harness connector.

↓

With the ignition key in the "ON" position, does voltage between ECU connector terminal No. 18 and ground indicate the battery voltage? → **No** → Harness wire between power relay and ECU is broken → Repair harness

↓ **Yes**

Is there continuity between body harness terminals No. 9 and No. 34, and ground? → **No** → ECU ground line broken → Repair harness

↓ **Yes**

Is there continuity between body harness connector terminals No. 23 and No. 24, and diagnostic test mode control terminals No. 4 & No. 10? → **No** → Harness wire between diagnosis inspection terminal and ABS ECU is broken → Repair harness

↓ **Yes**

Malfunction of ABS ECU → Replace ABS ECU.

CR4029100547020X

Fig. 12 Code 55: ABS Chart B, ABS Warning Light Stays On When Ignition Key Is In On Position (Part 2 of 2). Colt Vista & Summit Wagon FWD

TYPE 4-ANTI-LOCK BRAKING SYSTEM

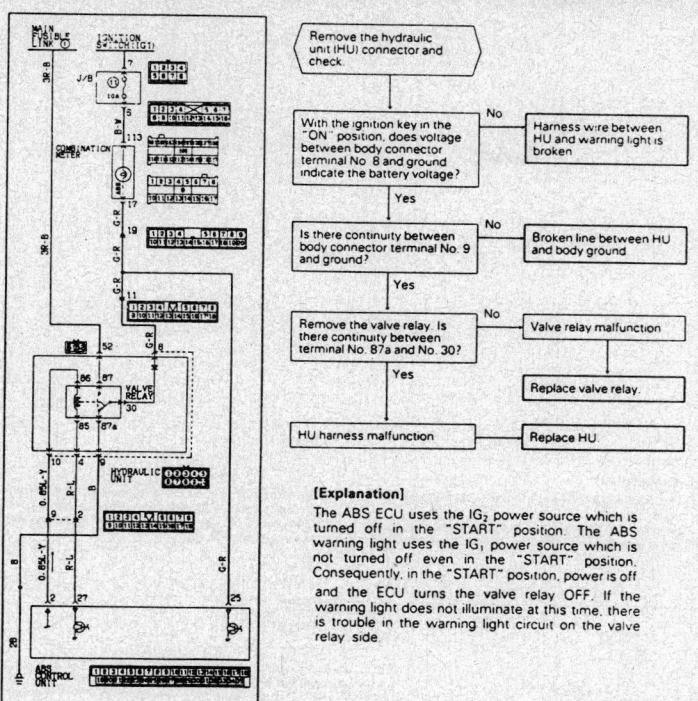

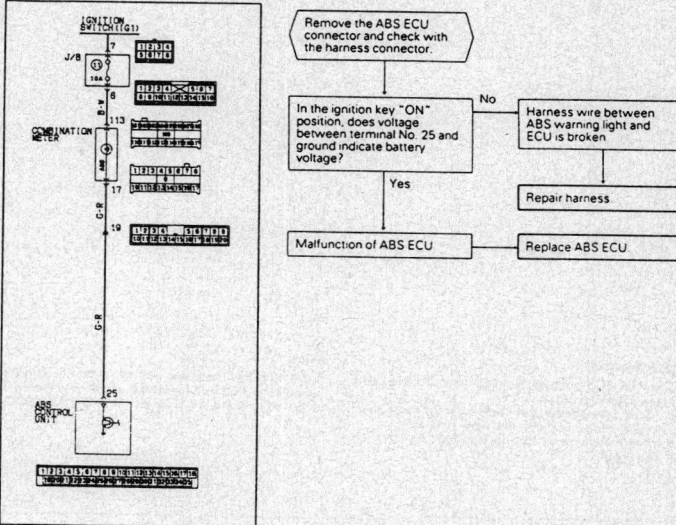

[Explanation]

When power flows, the ABS ECU turns on the warning light for approximately 1 sec. while it performs a valve relay test. If there is a break in the harness between the ECU and the warning light, the light illuminates only when the valve relay is off in the valve relay test, etc.

[Explanation]

The ABS ECU uses the IG_2 power source which is turned off in the "START" position. The ABS warning light uses the IG_1 power source which is not turned off even in the "START" position. Consequently, in the "START" position, power is off and the ECU turns the valve relay OFF. If the warning light does not illuminate at this time, there is trouble in the warning light circuit on the valve relay side.

Fig. 13 Code 55: ABS Chart C, ABS Warning Light Does Not Illuminate When Ignition Key Is In Start Position. Colt Vista & Summit Wagon FWD

Fig. 14 Code 55: ABS Chart D, ABS Warning Light Blinks Once After Ignition Key Is Turned To On Position, Illuminates In Start Position & Blinks Once Again When Turned To On Position. Colt Vista & Summit Wagon FWD

[Explanation]

This diagnostic trouble code is output when there is an abnormality (other than broken wire or short circuit) in the wheel speed sensor output signal while driving.

[Hint]

The following can be considered as the cause of the wheel speed sensor output abnormality.
• Distortion of rotor, teeth missing
• Low frequency noise interference when sensor harness wire is broken
• Noise interference in sensor signal
• When the sensor output signal is below the standard value or when amplitude modulation is over the standard value, using an oscilloscope to measure the wave shape of the wheel speed sensor output signal is very effective.
• Loose wheel bearing

• Temporarily broken wire in sensor harness
• Sensor harness and body connector are not properly inserted.

NOTE
(1) If contact is poor, check the sensor cable by bending and lightly stretching it.
(2) If there is currently no trouble and if abnormality in the displayed sensor circuit cannot be discovered since values are normal even when checked, turn the ignition switch OFF and re-execute the driving test. Try replacing the ABS ECU only if the same diagnostic trouble code is output at this time.

(If it is difficult to recreate the trouble, there is a possibility of speed sensor trouble recurring even if the ECU is replaced.)

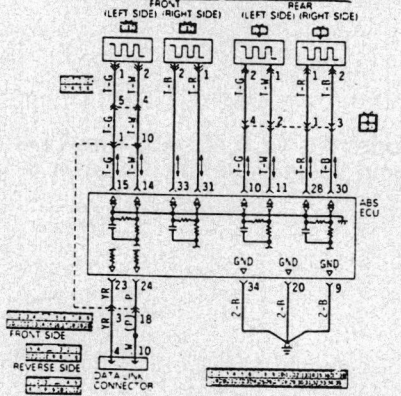

Fig. 15 Code 15: ABS Chart E2, Output Abnormality Of Wheel Speed Sensor (Part 1 of 2). Laser & Talon FWD

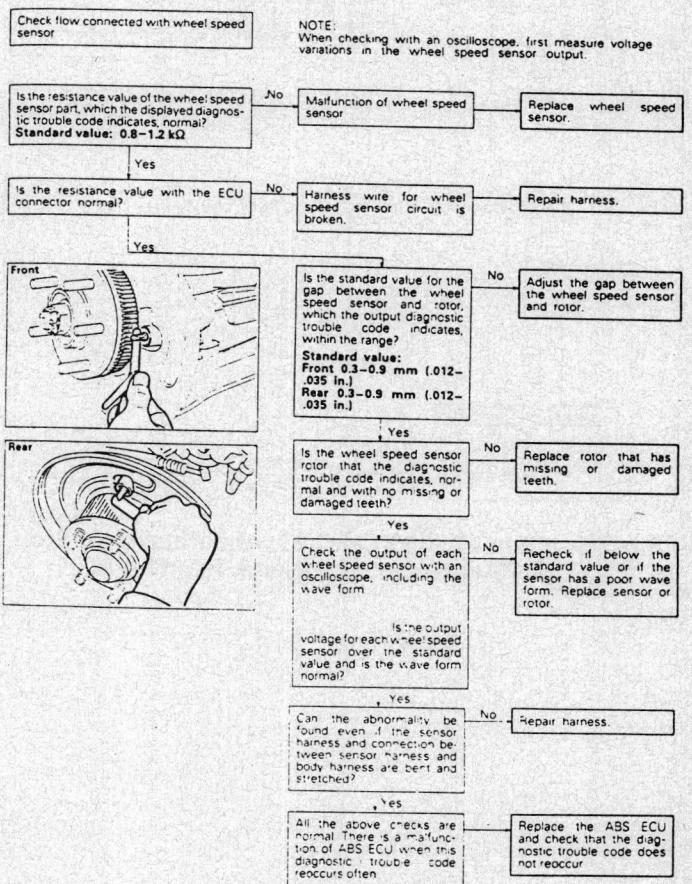

Fig. 15 Code 15: ABS Chart E2, Output Abnormality Of Wheel Speed Sensor (Part 2 of 2). Laser & Talon FWD

[Explanation]

The ABS ECU outputs this diagnostic trouble code in the following cases.

- Stop light switch may remain on for more than 15 minutes without the ABS functions.
- The harness wire for the stop light switch may be open.

[Hint]

If the stop light operates normal, the ABS harness wire for the stop light switch input circuit to the ECU is broken or there is a malfunction in the ABS ECU.

[Explanation]

The ABS ECU normally monitors the solenoid valve drive circuit.

If no current flows in the solenoid even if the ECU turns the solenoid ON or if it continues to flow even when turned OFF, the ECU determines the solenoid coil wire is broken/short circuited or the harness is broken short circuited and then these diagnostic trouble codes are output.

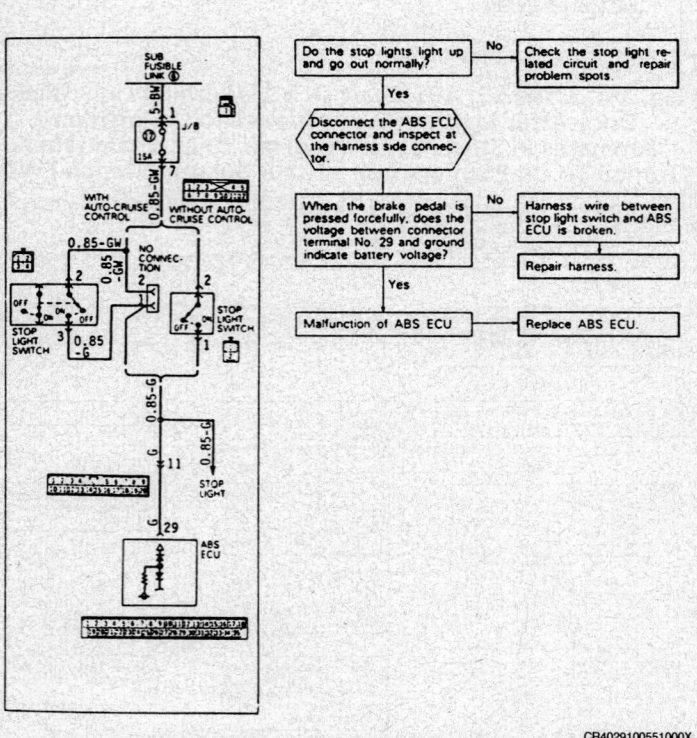

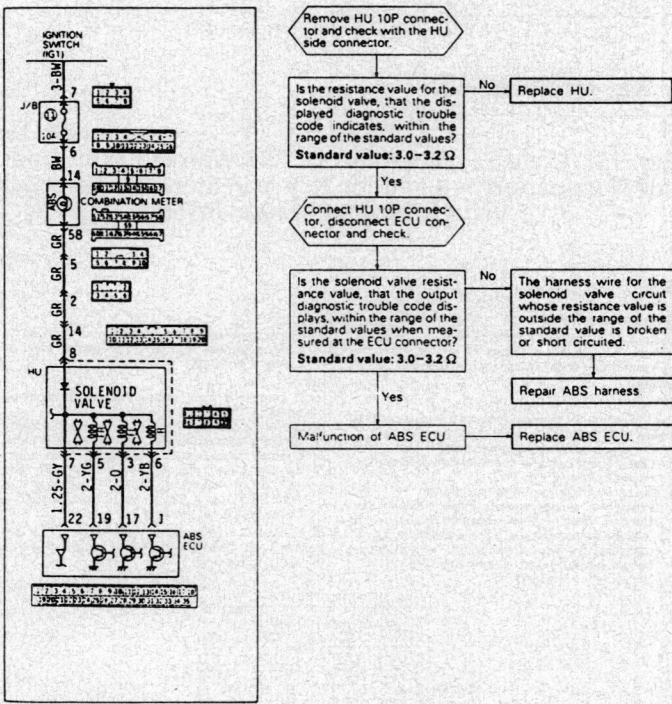

Fig. 16   Code 22: ABS Chart E3, Abnormality Of Stop Light Switch Circuit. Laser & Talon FWD

Fig. 17   Codes 41, 42 & 43: ABS Chart E4, Abnormality Of Solenoid Valve Drive Circuit. Laser & Talon FWD

[Explanation]

When the ignition switch is turned ON, the ABS ECU switches the valve relay OFF and ON for an initial check, compares the voltage of the signal to the valve relay and valve power monitor line voltage to check whether the valve relay operation is normal. In addition, normally it monitors whether or not there is power in the valve power monitor line since the valve relay is normally ON. Then, if the supply of power to the valve power monitor line is interrupted, this diagnostic trouble code will output.

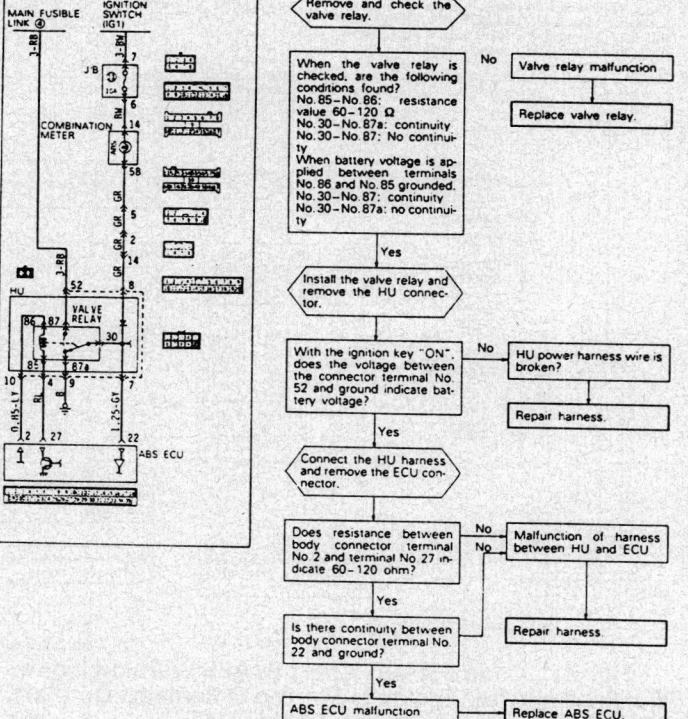

Fig. 18   Code 51: ABS Chart E5, Abnormality Of Valve Relay Drive Circuit. Laser & Talon FWD

[Explanation]

The ABS ECU outputs this diagnostic trouble code for the motor relay and motor in the following cases.
- When the motor relay does not function
- When there is trouble with the motor itself and it does not revolve
- When the motor ground line is disconnected and the motor does not revolve
- When the motor continues to revolve

[Hint]

If there is motor operation noise when wheel speed exceeds 6km/h (4mph) when starting up after the engine is started, or when there is forced scan tool (DRB-II) drive, there is a broken or short circuited motor monitor wire.

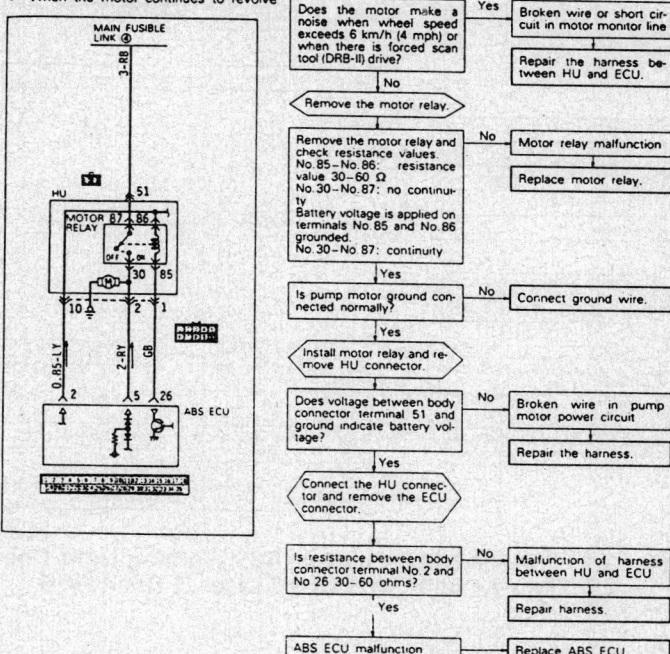

Fig. 19   Code 52: ABS Chart E6, Abnormality Of Motor Drive Circuit. Laser & Talon FWD

[Explanation]

When it does not light up at all, there is a strong possibility that there is trouble with ABS warning light or with power to the light.

[Hint]

If other warning lights do not light up either, fuse is probably blown.

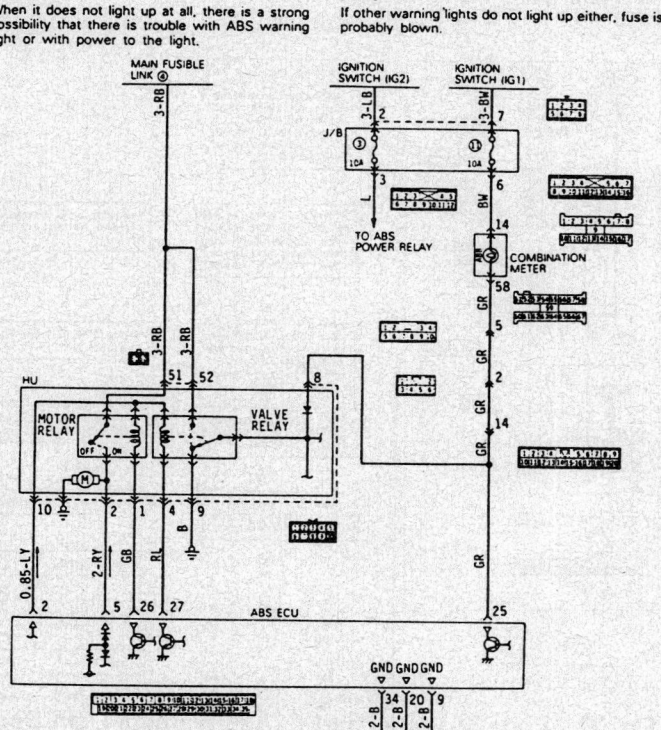

Fig. 20   Code 55: ABS Chart A, ABS Warning Light Does Not Light At All (Part 1 of 3). Laser & Talon FWD

Fig. 20   Code 55: ABS Chart A, ABS Warning Light Does Not Light At All (Part 2 of 3). Laser & Talon FWD

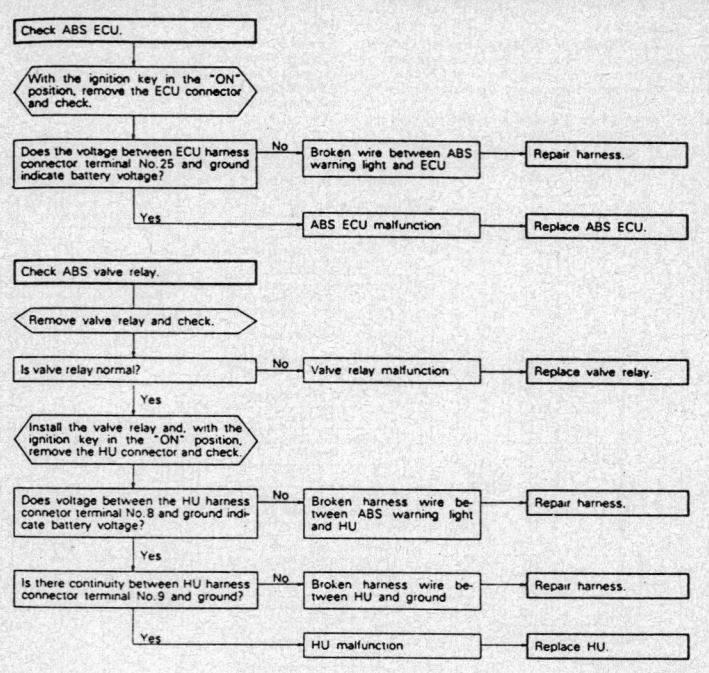

Check ABS ECU.

With the ignition key in the "ON" position, remove the ECU connector and check.

Does the voltage between ECU harness connector terminal No.25 and ground indicate battery voltage? — **No** → Broken wire between ABS warning light and ECU → Repair harness.

↓ **Yes**

ABS ECU malfunction → Replace ABS ECU.

Check ABS valve relay.

Remove valve relay and check.

Is valve relay normal? — **No** → Valve relay malfunction → Replace valve relay.

↓ **Yes**

Install the valve relay and, with the ignition key in the "ON" position, remove the HU connector and check.

Does voltage between the HU harness connector terminal No.8 and ground indicate battery voltage? — **No** → Broken harness wire between ABS warning light and HU → Repair harness.

↓ **Yes**

Is there continuity between HU harness connector terminal No.9 and ground? — **No** → Broken harness wire between HU and ground → Repair harness.

↓ **Yes**

HU malfunction → Replace HU.

CR4029100555030X

Fig. 20   Code 55: ABS Chart A, ABS Warning Light Does Not Light At All (Part 3 of 3). Laser & Talon FWD

[Explanation]

This is the symptom when the ABS ECU does not power up due to broken ECU power circuit, etc., when the fail safe function operates and isolates the system or when the warning light drive circuit is short circuited.

[Hint]

Check the on-board diagnostic output and if there is no output voltage or if the scan tool (DRB-II) and ABS ECU cannot communicate, there is a good possibility that power is not flowing to the ECU.

Caution
• If there is no output of diagnostic trouble codes, there is a good possibility that the fail safe is functioning.

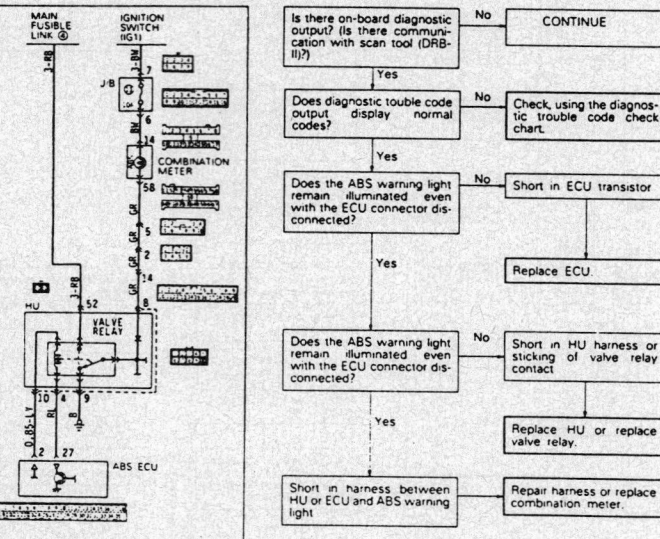

Is there on-board diagnostic output? (Is there communication with scan tool (DRB-II)?) — **No** → CONTINUE

↓ **Yes**

Does diagnostic trouble code output display normal codes? — **No** → Check, using the diagnostic trouble code check chart.

↓ **Yes**

Does the ABS warning light remain illuminated even with the ECU connector disconnected? — **No** → Short in ECU transistor

↓ **Yes** → Replace ECU.

Does the ABS warning light remain illuminated even with the ECU connector disconnected? — **No** → Short in HU harness or sticking of valve relay contact

↓ **Yes** → Replace HU or replace valve relay.

Short in harness between HU or ECU and ABS warning light → Repair harness or replace combination meter.

CR4029100556010X

Fig. 21   Code 55: ABS Chart B, ABS Warning Light Illuminated After Engine Is Started & Remains On (Part 1 of 2). Laser & Talon FWD

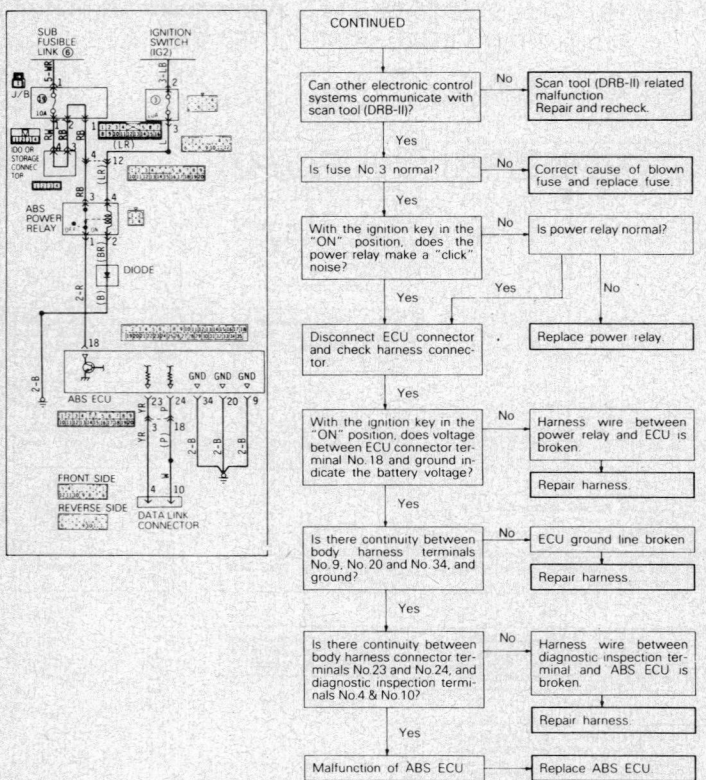

CONTINUED

Can other electronic control systems communicate with scan tool (DRB-II)? — **No** → Scan tool (DRB-II) related malfunction Repair and recheck.

↓ **Yes**

Is fuse No.3 normal? — **No** → Correct cause of blown fuse and replace fuse.

↓ **Yes**

With the ignition key in the "ON" position, does the power relay make a "click" noise? — **Yes** / **No** → Is power relay normal? — **No** → Replace power relay.

↓ **Yes**

Disconnect ECU connector and check harness connector.

↓ **Yes**

With the ignition key in the "ON" position, does voltage between ECU connector terminal No.18 and ground indicate the battery voltage? — **No** → Harness wire between power relay and ECU is broken. Repair harness.

↓ **Yes**

Is there continuity between body harness terminals No.9, No.20 and No.34, and ground? — **No** → ECU ground line broken Repair harness.

↓ **Yes**

Is there continuity between body harness connector terminals No.23 and No.24, and diagnostic inspection terminals No.4 & No.10? — **No** → Harness wire between diagnostic inspection terminal and ABS ECU is broken. Repair harness.

↓ **Yes**

Malfunction of ABS ECU → Replace ABS ECU.

CR4029100556020X

Fig. 21   Code 55: ABS Chart B, ABS Warning Light Illuminated After Engine Is Started & Remains On (Part 2 of 2). Laser & Talon FWD

[Explanation]

The ABS ECU uses the IG2 power source which is turned off in the "START" position. The ABS warning light uses the IG1 power source which is not turned off even in the "START" position. Consequently, in the "START" position, power is off and the ECU turns the valve relay OFF. If the warning light does not illuminate at this time, there is trouble in the warning light circuit on the valve relay side.

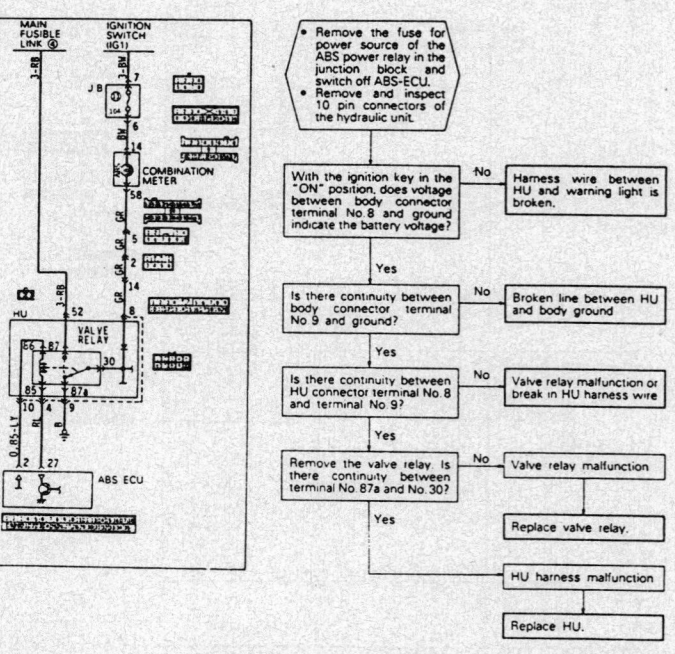

• Remove the fuse for power source of the ABS power relay in the junction block and switch off ABS-ECU.
• Remove and inspect 10 pin connectors of the hydraulic unit.

With the ignition key in the "ON" position, does voltage between body connector terminal No.8 and ground indicate the battery voltage? — **No** → Harness wire between HU and warning light is broken.

↓ **Yes**

Is there continuity between body connector terminal No.9 and ground? — **No** → Broken line between HU and body ground

↓ **Yes**

Is there continuity between HU connector terminal No.8 and terminal No.9? — **No** → Valve relay malfunction or break in HU harness wire

↓ **Yes**

Remove the valve relay. Is there continuity between terminal No.87a and No.30? — **No** → Valve relay malfunction

↓ **Yes** → Replace valve relay.

HU harness malfunction

Replace HU.

CR4029100557000X

Fig. 22   Code 55: ABS Chart C, ABS Warning Light Does Not Illuminate When Ignition Key Is In Start Position. Laser & Talon FWD

[Explanation]

When power flows, the ABS ECU turns on the warning light for approximately 1 sec. while it performs a valve relay test. If there is a break in the harness between the ECU and the warning light, the light illuminates only when the valve relay is off in the valve relay test, etc.

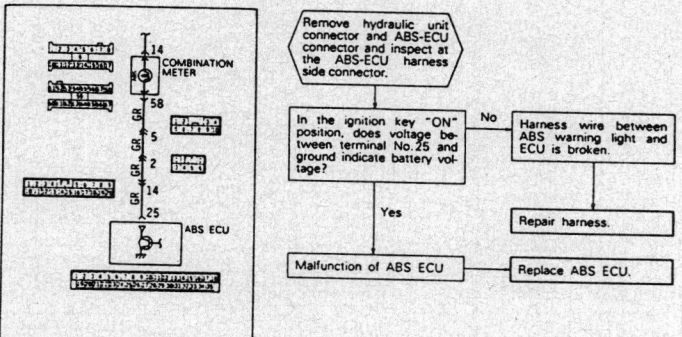

Fig. 23 Code 55: ABS Chart D, ABS Warning Light Blinks Once After Ignition Key Is Turned To On Position, Illuminates In Start Position & Blinks Once Again When Turned To On Position. Laser & Talon FWD

CR4029100558000X

[Explanation]

The warning light lights up when there is an abnormality (other than broken wire or short circuit) in any of the wheel speed sensor output signals while driving.

[Hint]

The following can be considered as the cause of the wheel speed sensor output abnormality.
- Distortion of rotor, teeth missing
- Low frequency noise interference when sensor harness wire is broken
- Noise interference in sensor signal
- The sensor output signal is below the standard value or amplitude modulation is over the standard value. Using an oscilloscope to measure the wave shape of the wheel speed sensor output signal is very effective.
- Broken sensor harness
- Poor connection of connector

NOTE
(1) If contact is poor, check the sensor cable by bending and lightly stretching it.
(2) Except for the case where a fault condition exists in the system, but the inspection results are normal; if an abnormality cannot be found in the sensor circuit displayed as abnormal, erase the diagnostic trouble code and turn the ignition switch to OFF once, and then test-drive* again. If the same diagnostic trouble code is output, replace the ABS ECU. If the trouble does not occur anymore, the problem is likely to be with the ABS ECU.
(If the trouble is in the speed sensor circuit, but is difficult to recreate, it will recur even after the ABS ECU has been replaced.)
(3) *: Drive at 19 mph or higher for more than 30 seconds.

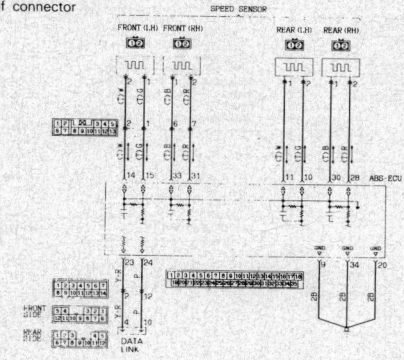

Fig. 24 Code 15: ABS Chart E2, Output Abnormality Of Wheel Speed Sensor (Part 1 of 2). Stealth FWD

CR4029100559010X

NOTE
When checking with an oscilloscope, first measure voltage variations in the wheel speed sensor output.

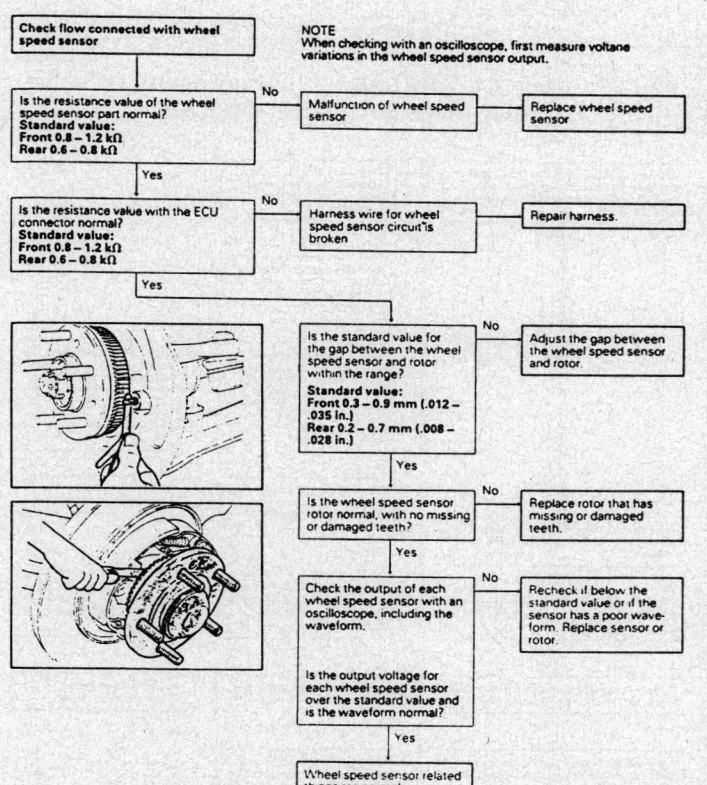

Fig. 24 Code 15: ABS Chart E2, Output Abnormality Of Wheel Speed Sensor (Part 2 of 2). Stealth FWD

CR4029100559020X

[Explanation]

The ABS ECU outputs this diagnostic trouble code in the following cases.
- Stop light switch may remain on for more than 15 minutes without ABS operation.
- The harness wire for the stop light switch may be open.

[Hint]

If the stop light operates normal, the harness for the stop light switch input circuit is broken or there is a malfunction in the ABS ECU.

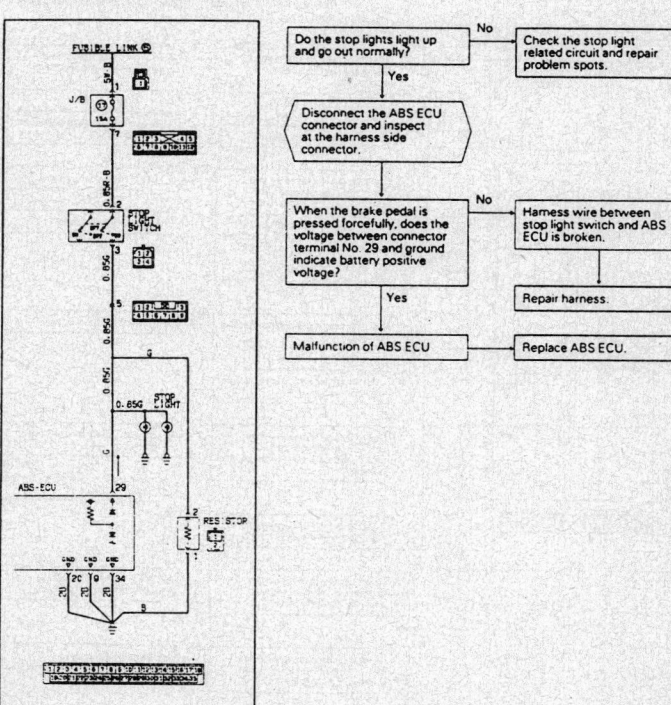

Fig. 25 Code 22: ABS Chart E3, Abnormality Of Stop Light Switch Circuit. Stealth FWD

CR4029100560000X

[Explanation]

The ABS ECU normally monitors the solenoid valve drive circuit.
If no current flows in the solenoid even if the ECU turns the solenoid ON or if it continues to flow even when turned OFF, the ECU determines the solenoid coil wire is broken/short-circuited or the harness is broken/short-circuited, and then these diagnostic trouble codes are output.

[Explanation]

When the ignition switch is turned ON, the ABS ECU switches the valve relay OFF and ON for an initial check, compares the voltage of the signal to the valve relay and valve power monitor line voltage to check whether the valve relay operation is normal. In addition, normally it monitors whether or not there is power in the valve power monitor line since the valve relay is normally ON. Then, if the supply of power to the valve power monitor line is interrupted, this diagnostic trouble code will be output.

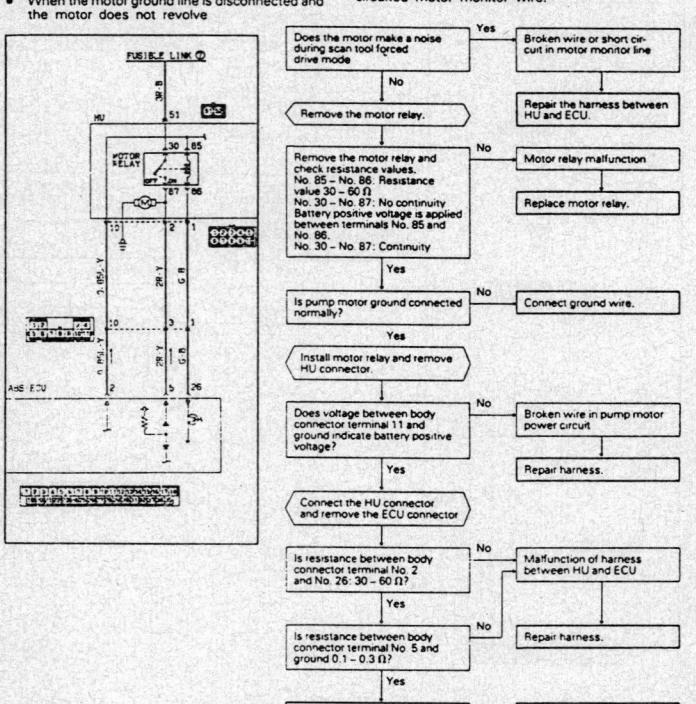

Fig. 26 Codes 41, 42 & 43: ABS Chart E4, Abnormality Of Solenoid Valve Drive Circuit. Stealth FWD

CR4029100561000X

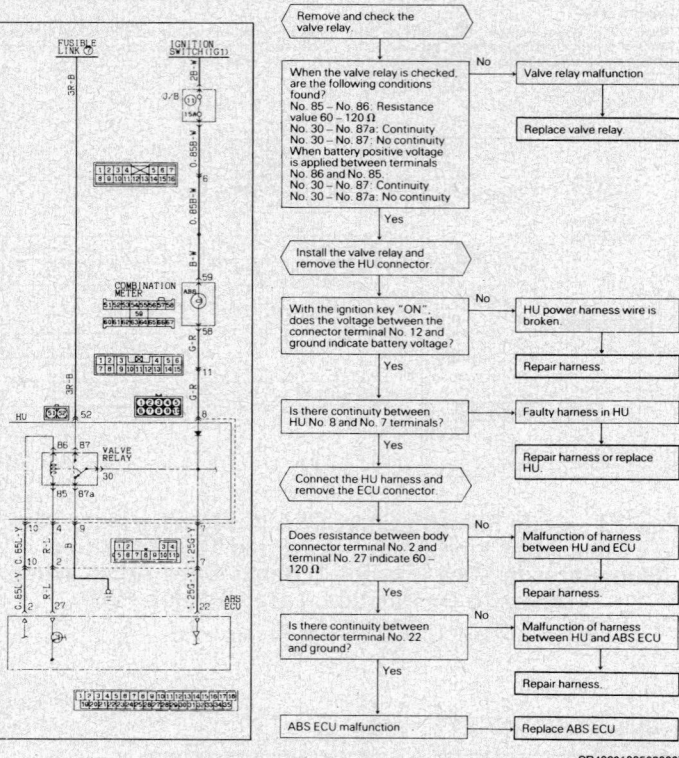

Fig. 27 Code 51: ABS Chart E5, Abnormality Of Valve Relay Drive Circuit. Stealth FWD

CR4029100562000X

[Explanation]

The ABS ECU outputs this diagnostic trouble code for the motor relay and motor in the following cases.
• When the motor relay does not function
• When there is trouble with the motor itself and it does not revolve
• When the motor ground line is disconnected and the motor does not revolve

• When the motor continues to revolve

[Hint]

If there is motor operation noise during scan tool forced drive mode, there is a broken or short circuited motor monitor wire.

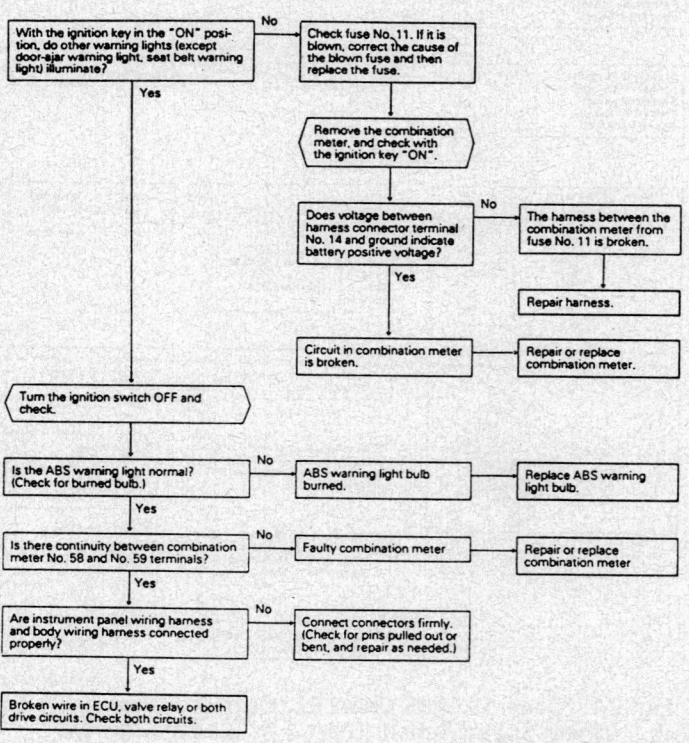

Fig. 28 Code 52: ABS Chart E6, Abnormality Of Motor Drive Circuit. Stealth FWD

CR4029100563000X

Fig. 29 Code 55: ABS Chart A, ABS Warning Light Does Not Light At All (Part 2 of 3). Stealth FWD

CR4029100564020X

[Explanation]
When it does not light up at all, there is a strong possibility that there is trouble with ABS warning light or with power to the light.

[Hint]
If other warning lights do not light up either, fuse is probably blown.

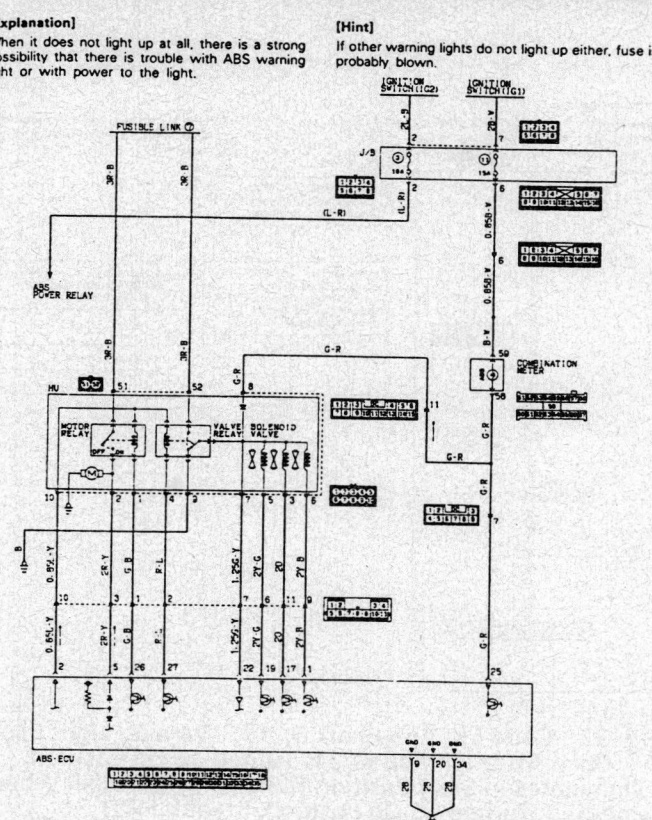

Fig. 29   Code 55: ABS Chart A, ABS Warning Light Does Not Light At All (Part 1 of 3). Stealth FWD

Check ABS ECU.

Remove the ECU connector and check.

Does the voltage between ECU harness connector terminal No. 25 and ground indicate battery positive voltage while the ignition key is in the "ON" position? — No → Broken wire between ABS warning light and ECU → Repair harness.

Yes → ABS ECU malfunction → Replace ABS ECU.

Check valve relay.

Remove valve relay and check.

Is valve relay normal? — No → Valve relay malfunction → Replace valve relay.

Yes

Install the valve relay, remove the HU connector and check.

Does positive voltage between the HU harness connector terminal No. 8 and ground indicate battery positive voltage while the ignition key is in the "ON" position? — No → Broken harness wire between ABS warning light and HU → Repair harness.

Yes

Is there continuity between HU harness connector terminal No. 9 and ground? — No → Broken harness wire between HU and ground → Repair harness.

Yes

Is there continuity between HU harness connector terminals No. 8 and No. 9? — No → HU malfunction → Replace HU.

Yes → Connector not connected securely. → Replace connector.

Fig. 29   Code 55: ABS Chart A, ABS Warning Light Does Not Light At All (Part 3 of 3). Stealth FWD

[Explanation]
This is the symptom when the ABS ECU does not power up due to broken ECU power circuit, etc., when the fail safe function operates and isolates the system or when the warning light drive circuit is short circuited.

[Hint]
Check the on-board diagnostic output and if there is no output voltage or if the scan tool and ABS ECU cannot communicate, there is a good possibility that power is not flowing to the ECU.

Caution
- If the diagnostic trouble code is output, the system can be in the fail safe mode. In such a case, erase the diagnostic trouble code and then restart the engine to check if the system is currently in a fault condition.

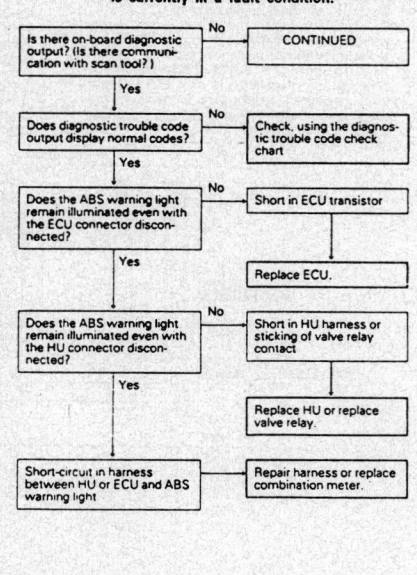

Is there on-board diagnostic output? (Is there communication with scan tool?) — No → CONTINUED

Yes

Does diagnostic trouble code output display normal codes? — No → Check, using the diagnostic trouble code check chart

Yes

Does the ABS warning light remain illuminated even with the ECU connector disconnected? — Yes → Short in ECU transistor → Replace ECU.

No

Does the ABS warning light remain illuminated even with the HU connector disconnected? — Yes → Short in HU harness or sticking of valve relay contact → Replace HU or replace valve relay.

No → Short-circuit in harness between HU or ECU and ABS warning light → Repair harness or replace combination meter.

Fig. 30   Code 55: ABS Chart B, ABS Warning Light On When Ignition Key Is In On Position (Part 1 of 2). Stealth FWD

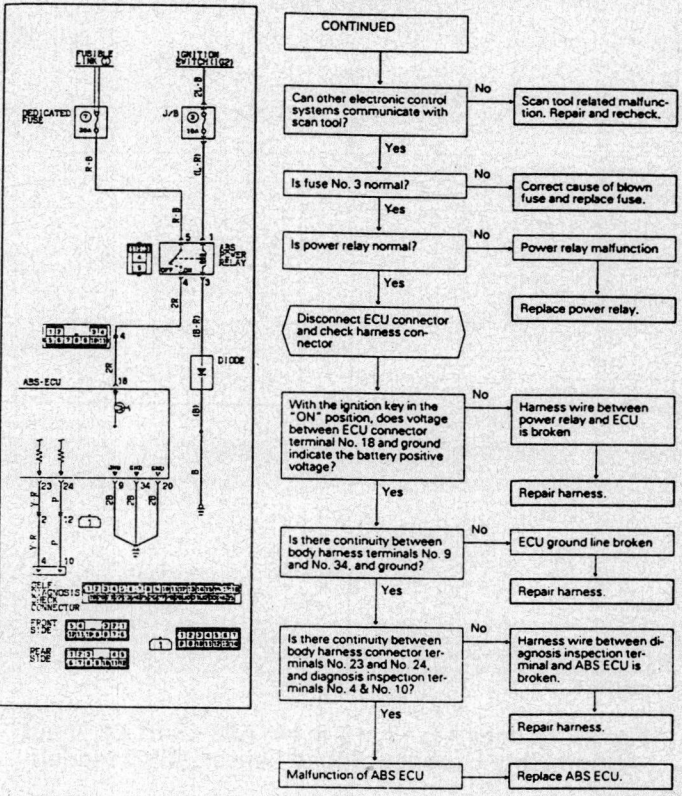

CONTINUED

Can other electronic control systems communicate with scan tool? — No → Scan tool related malfunction. Repair and recheck.

Yes

Is fuse No. 3 normal? — No → Correct cause of blown fuse and replace fuse.

Yes

Is power relay normal? — No → Power relay malfunction → Replace power relay.

Yes

Disconnect ECU connector and check harness connector

With the ignition key in the "ON" position, does voltage between ECU connector terminal No. 18 and ground indicate the battery positive voltage? — No → Harness wire between power relay and ECU is broken → Repair harness.

Yes

Is there continuity between body harness terminals No. 9 and No. 34, and ground? — No → ECU ground line broken → Repair harness.

Yes

Is there continuity between body harness connector terminals No. 23 and No. 24, and diagnosis inspection terminals No. 4 & No. 10? — No → Harness wire between diagnosis inspection terminal and ABS ECU is broken. → Repair harness.

Yes → Malfunction of ABS ECU → Replace ABS ECU.

Fig. 30   Code 55: ABS Chart B, ABS Warning Light Stays On When Ignition Key Is In On Position (Part 2 of 2). Stealth FWD

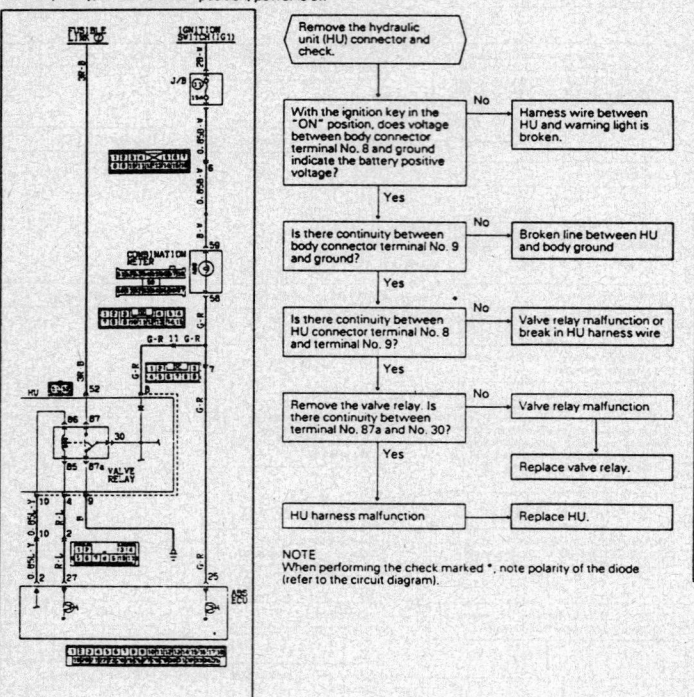

[Explanation]

The ABS ECU uses the IG₂ power source which is turned off in the "START" position. The ABS warning light uses the IG₁ power source which is not turned off even in the "START" position. Consequently, in the "START" position, power is off and the ECU turns the valve relay OFF. If the warning light does not illuminate at this time, there is trouble in the warning light circuit on the valve relay side.

NOTE
When performing the check marked *, note polarity of the diode (refer to the circuit diagram).

Fig. 31 Code 55: ABS Chart C, ABS Warning Light Does Not Illuminate When Ignition Key Is In Start Position. Stealth FWD

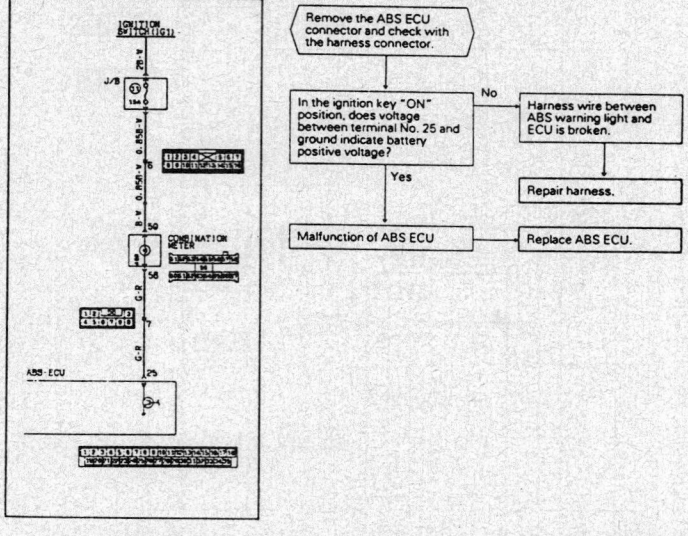

[Explanation]

When power flows, the ABS ECU turns on the warning light for approximately 1 sec. while it performs a valve relay test. If there is a break in the harness between the ECU and the warning light, the light illuminates only when the valve relay is off in the valve relay test, etc.

Fig. 32 Code 55: ABS Chart D, ABS Warning Light Blinks Once After Ignition Key Is Turned To On Position, Illuminates In Start Position & Blinks Once Again When Turned To On Position. Stealth FWD

Diagnostic trouble code		Check chart name or remedy		Diagnostic trouble code		Check chart name or remedy
No	Scan tool display letters			No	Scan tool display letters	
11	FL SNSR. OPEN	E-1		41	FL SOL VALVE	E-5
12	FR SNSR. OPEN			42	FR SOL VALVE	
13	RR SNSR. OPEN			43	VALVE DRIFT	
14	RL SNSR. OPEN			51	VALVE RELAY	E-6
15	VEH. SPD. SNSR	E-2		52	MOTOR RELAY	E-7
21	G SNSR	E-3		55	CONT UNIT	ECU replacement
22	STOP LAMP SW	E-4				

Fig. 33 Diagnostic trouble code reference chart. AWD models

[Explanation]

The ABS ECU detects breaks in the wheel speed sensor wire. This diagnostic trouble code is output if the wheel speed sensor signal is not input (or short circuited) or if its output is low when starting to drive or while driving.

[Hint]

In addition to a broken wire/short circuit in the wheel speed sensor, also check whether the sensor gap is too large, sensor harness wire is broken, or sensor harness and body connector are not properly connected.

Fig. 34 Codes 11, 12, 13 & 14: ABS Chart E1, Input Abnormality Of Wheel Speed Sensor. AWD models

[Explanation]

This diagnostic trouble code is output when there is an abnormality (other than broken wire or short circuit) in any of the wheel speed sensor output signals while driving.

[Hint]

The following can be considered as the cause of the wheel speed sensor output abnormality.
- Distortion of rotor, teeth missing
- Low frequency noise interference when sensor harness wire is broken
- Noise interference in sensor signal
- Sensor output signal is below the standard value or amplitude modulation is over the standard value. Using an oscilloscope to measure the wave shape of the wheel speed sensor output signal is very effective.

- Broken sensor harness
- Poor connection of connector

NOTE
(1) If contact is poor, check the sensor cable by bending and lightly stretching it.
(2) Except for the case where a fault condition exists in the system, but the inspection results are normal; if an abnormality cannot be found in the sensor circuit displayed as abnormal, erase the diagnostic trouble code and turn the ignition switch to OFF once, and then test-drive again. If the same diagnostic trouble code is output, replace the ABS ECU. If the trouble does not occur anymore, the problem is likely to be with the ABS ECU.
(If the trouble is in the speed sensor circuit, but is difficult to recreate, it will recur even after the ABS ECU has been replaced.)

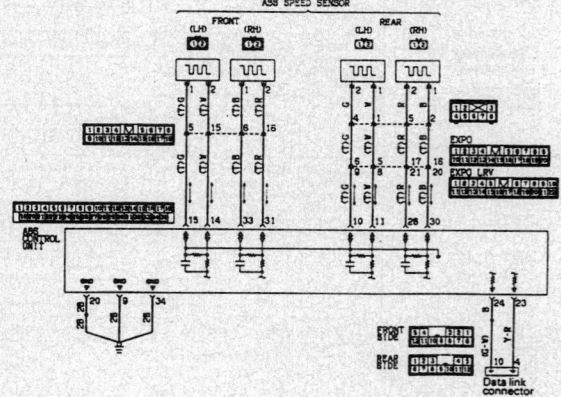

Fig. 35 Code 15: ABS Chart E2, Output Abnormality Of Wheel Speed Sensor (Part 1 of 2). Colt Vista & Summit Wagon AWD

Check flow connected with wheel speed sensor

NOTE
Check speed sensor harness and connector connection and then observe with oscilloscope.

Is the resistance value of the wheel speed sensor part normal? **Standard value: 0.8 – 1.2 kΩ** — No → Malfunction of wheel speed sensor → Replace wheel speed sensor

↓ Yes

Is the resistance value at the ECU connector normal? **Standard value: 0.8 – 1.2 kΩ** — No → Harness wire for wheel speed sensor circuit is broken → Repair harness.

↓ Yes

Is the front wheel speed sensor-to-rotor clearance normal? **Standard value: 0.3 – 0.9 mm (.012 – .035 in.)** — No → Adjust the gap between the wheel speed sensor and rotor.

↓ Yes

Are there any abnormalities such as a loose rear speed sensor mounting bolt? — No → Retighten or correct abnormalities

↓ Yes

Is the rear speed sensor mounting surface-to-rotor tooth flank (all around) distance normal? **Standard value: 0.3 – 0.9 mm (.012 – .035 in.)** — No → Adjust the gap between the wheel speed sensor and rotor.

↓ Yes

Is the wheel speed sensor rotor normal, with no missing or damaged teeth? — No → Replace rotor that has missing or damaged teeth

↓ Yes

Check the output of each wheel speed sensor with an oscilloscope, including the waveform. Is the output voltage for each wheel speed sensor over the standard value and is the waveform normal? — No → Recheck if below the standard value or if the sensor has a poor waveform. Replace sensor or rotor.

↓ Yes

If the above checks are normal, there is a malfunction of ABS ECU when this diagnostic trouble code reoccurs often. → Replace the ABS ECU and check that the diagnostic trouble code does not reoccur.

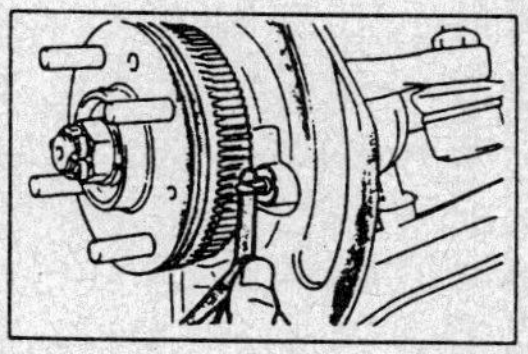

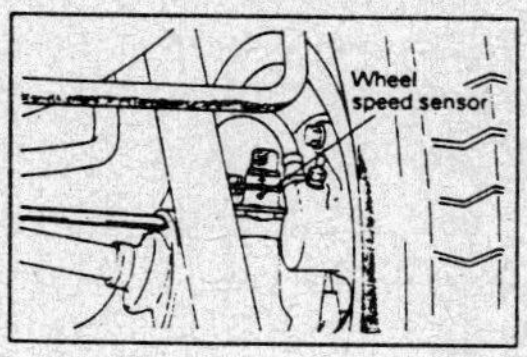

CR4029100569020X

Fig. 35 Code 15: ABS Chart E2, Output Abnormality Of Wheel Speed Sensor (Part 2 of 2). Colt Vista & Summit Wagon AWD

[Explanation]
The ABS-ECU outputs this diagnostic trouble code in the following cases.
• G sensor OFF trouble (It is judged that the G sensor continues to be OFF for more than approximately 13 seconds except when the vehicle is stopped or when there is stop light switch input.)
• When there is a broken wire or short circuit in the harness for the G sensor system

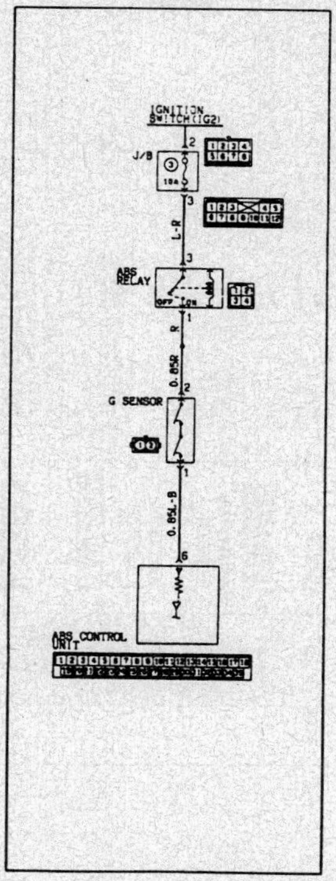

Is G sensor normal? — No → Replace G sensor

↓ Yes

Remove the ABS-ECU connector and check at the harness connector.

↓

With the ignition key "ON", does the voltage between terminal No. 6 and ground indicate battery voltage? — No → The harness between the G sensor and the ABS ECU is broken → Repair harness.

↓ Yes

ABS-ECU malfunction → Replace ABS-ECU.

CR4029100570000X

Fig. 36 Code 21: ABS Chart E3, Abnormality Of G Sensor Circuit. Colt Vista & Summit Wagon AWD

[Explanation]
The ABS-ECU outputs this diagnostic trouble code in the following cases.
• Stop light switch remains on for more than 15 minutes while the ABS is not functioning.
• The harness wire for the stop light switch may be open.

[Hint]
If the stop light operates normal, the harness for the stop light switch input circuit is broken or there is a malfunction in the ABS-ECU.

Do the stop lights light up and go out normally? — No → Check the stop light related circuit and repair problem spots

↓ Yes

Disconnect the ABS-ECU connector and inspect at the harness side connector

↓

When the brake pedal is pressed forcefully, does the voltage between connector terminal No. 29 and ground indicate battery voltage? — No → Harness wire between stop light switch and ABS-ECU is broken → Repair harness

↓ Yes

Malfunction of ABS-ECU → Replace ABS-ECU.

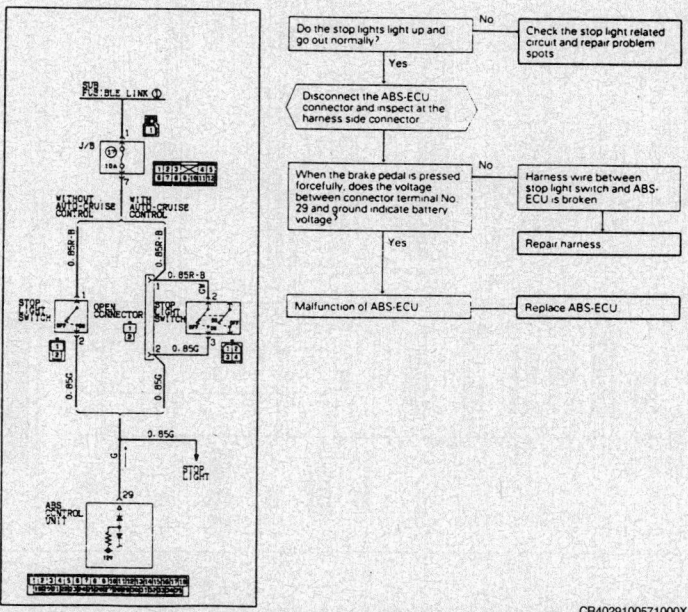

CR4029100571000X

Fig. 37 Code 22: ABS Chart E4, Abnormality Of Stop Light Switch Circuit. Colt Vista & Summit Wagon AWD

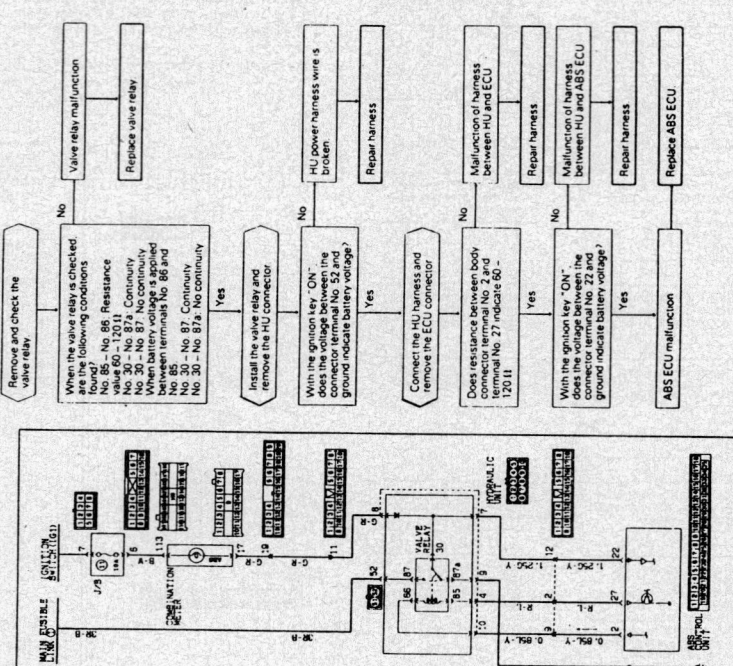

[Explanation]

When the ignition switch is turned ON, the ABS ECU switches the valve relay OFF and ON for an initial check, compares the voltage of the signal to the valve relay and valve power monitor line voltage to check whether the valve relay operation is normal. In addition, normally it monitors whether or not there is power in the valve power monitor line since the valve relay is normally ON. If the supply of power to the valve power monitor line voltage is interrupted, this diagnostic trouble code will be output.

CR402910057300X

Fig. 39 Code 51: ABS Chart E6, Abnormality Of Valve Relay Drive Circuit. Colt Vista & Summit Wagon AWD

[Explanation]

The ABS-ECU normally monitors the solenoid valve drive circuit. If no current flows in the solenoid even if the ECU turns the solenoid ON or if it continues to flow even when turned OFF, the ECU determines the solenoid coil wire is broken/short-circuited or the harness is broken/short-circuited, and then these diagnostic trouble codes are output. ABS-ECU controls the solenoid valve current and if the current value of the solenoid valves differs from each other in the same mode, solenoid valve drift error is produced and the ABS-ECU goes into the failsafe mode.

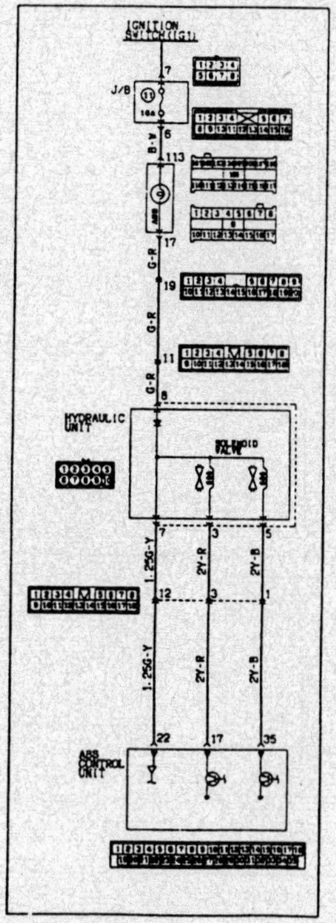

CR402910057200X

Fig. 38 Codes 41, 42 & 43: ABS Chart E5, Abnormality Of Solenoid Valve Drive Circuit. Colt Vista & Summit Wagon AWD

[Explanation]

When it does not light up at all, there is a strong possibility that there is trouble with ABS warning light or with power to the light.

[Hint]

If other warning lights do not light up either, fuse is probably blown.

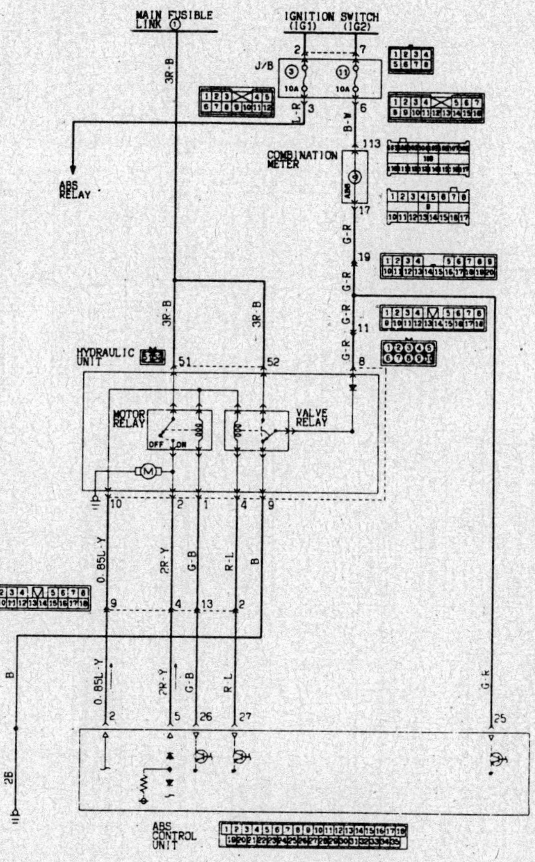

Fig. 41 Code 55: ABS Chart A, ABS Warning Light Does Not Light At All (Part 1 of 3). Colt Vista & Summit Wagon AWD

[Explanation]

The ABC-ECU outputs this diagnostic trouble code when the motor relay and motor are as follows.

- When the motor relay is ON and no signal is input to the motor monitor line (motor does not operate, etc.)
- When the motor relay is OFF and signals enter the motor monitor line for a period of approximately 5 seconds or more (motor operates continuously, etc.)
- When motor does not operate

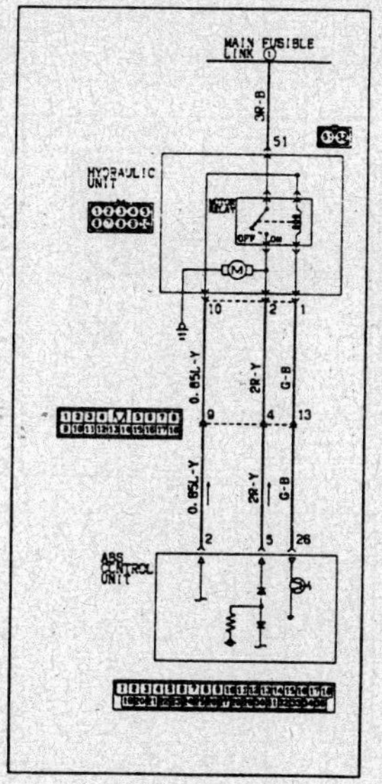

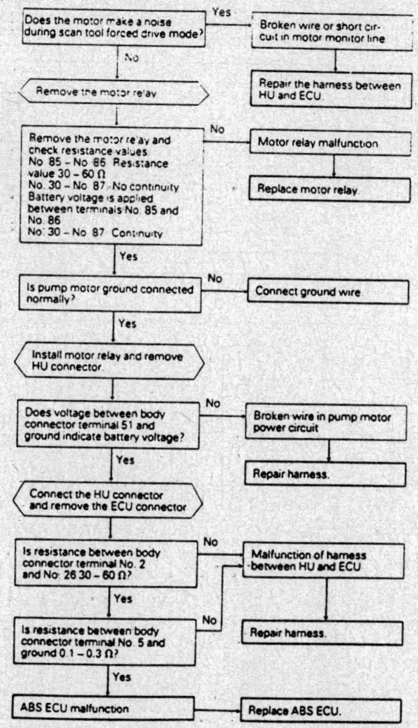

Fig. 40 Code 52: ABS Chart E7, Abnormality Of Motor Drive Circuit. Colt Vista & Summit Wagon AWD

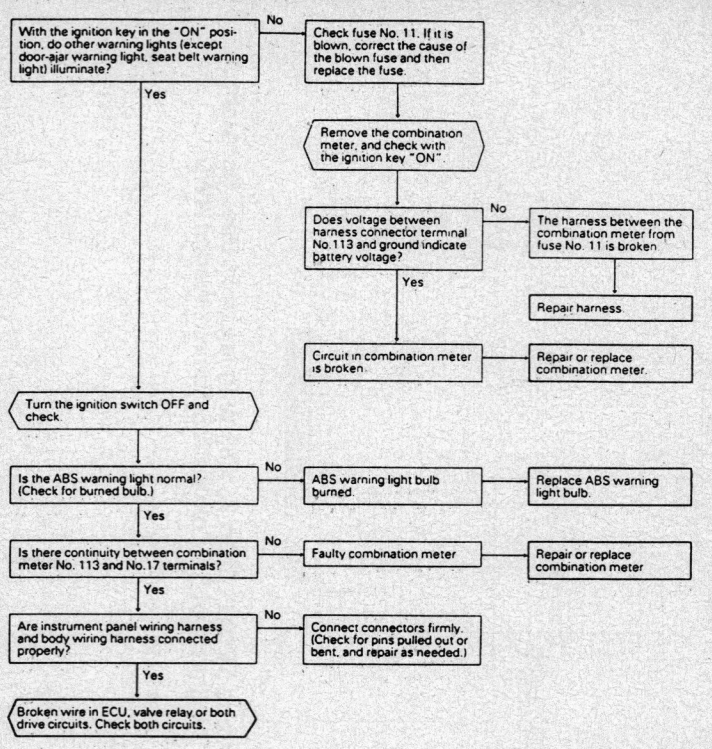

Flowchart (Fig. 41, Part 2 of 3):

- With the ignition key in the "ON" position, do other warning lights (except door-ajar warning light, seat belt warning light) illuminate? — **No** → Check fuse No. 11. If it is blown, correct the cause of the blown fuse and then replace the fuse.
  - → Remove the combination meter, and check with the ignition key "ON".
  - → Does voltage between harness connector terminal No. 113 and ground indicate battery voltage? — **No** → The harness between the combination meter from fuse No. 11 is broken. → Repair harness.
    - **Yes** → Circuit in combination meter is broken. → Repair or replace combination meter.
- **Yes** → Turn the ignition switch OFF and check.
  - → Is the ABS warning light normal? (Check for burned bulb.) — **No** → ABS warning light bulb burned. → Replace ABS warning light bulb.
  - **Yes** → Is there continuity between combination meter No. 113 and No.17 terminals? — **No** → Faulty combination meter → Repair or replace combination meter.
  - **Yes** → Are instrument panel wiring harness and body wiring harness connected properly? — **No** → Connect connectors firmly. (Check for pins pulled out or bent, and repair as needed.)
  - **Yes** → Broken wire in ECU, valve relay or both drive circuits. Check both circuits.

CR4029100575020)

Fig. 41   Code 55: ABS Chart A, ABS Warning Light Does Not Light At All (Part 2 of 3). Colt Vista & Summit Wagon AWD

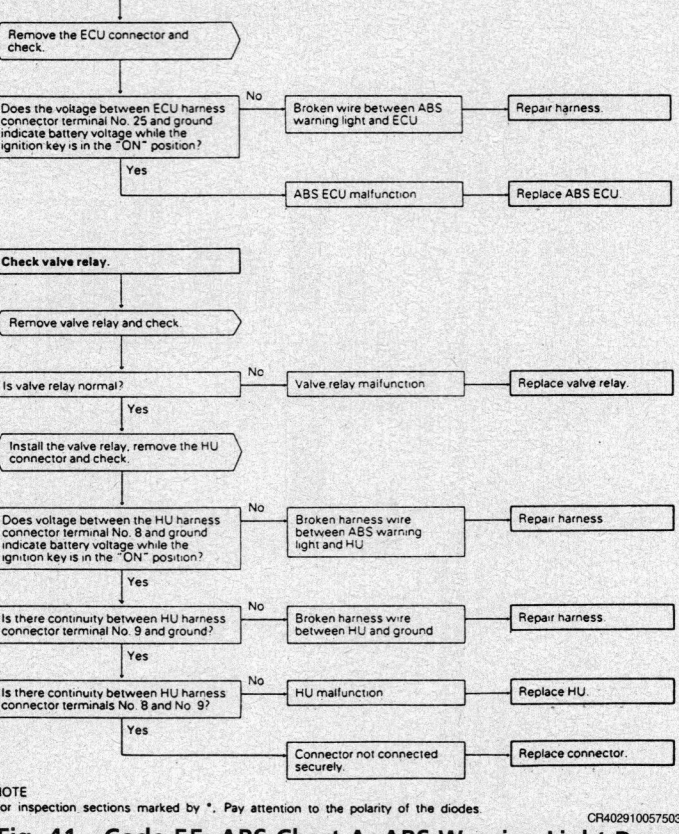

Flowchart (Fig. 41, Part 3 of 3):

- Check ABS ECU.
  - → Remove the ECU connector and check.
  - → Does the voltage between ECU harness connector terminal No. 25 and ground indicate battery voltage while the ignition key is in the "ON" position? — **No** → Broken wire between ABS warning light and ECU → Repair harness.
    - **Yes** → ABS ECU malfunction → Replace ABS ECU.
- Check valve relay.
  - → Remove valve relay and check.
  - → Is valve relay normal? — **No** → Valve relay malfunction → Replace valve relay.
  - **Yes** → Install the valve relay, remove the HU connector and check.
  - → Does voltage between the HU harness connector terminal No. 8 and ground indicate battery voltage while the ignition key is in the "ON" position? — **No** → Broken harness wire between ABS warning light and HU → Repair harness.
  - **Yes** → Is there continuity between HU harness connector terminal No. 9 and ground? — **No** → Broken harness wire between HU and ground → Repair harness.
  - **Yes** → · Is there continuity between HU harness connector terminals No. 8 and No. 9? — **No** → HU malfunction → Replace HU.
  - **Yes** → Connector not connected securely. → Replace connector.

NOTE
For inspection sections marked by *. Pay attention to the polarity of the diodes.

CR4029100575030X

Fig. 41   Code 55: ABS Chart A, ABS Warning Light Does Not Light At All (Part 3 of 3). Colt Vista & Summit Wagon AWD

[Explanation]
This is the symptom when the ABS ECU does not power up due to broken ECU power circuit, etc., when the fail safe function operates and isolates the system or when the warning light drive circuit is short circuited.

[Hint]
Check the on-board diagnostic output and if there is no output voltage or if the scan tool and ABS ECU cannot communicate, there is a good possibility that power is not flowing to the ECU.

Caution
- **If the diagnostic trouble code is output, the system can be in the fail safe mode. In such a case, erase the diagnostic trouble code and then restart the engine to check if the system is currently in a fault condition.**

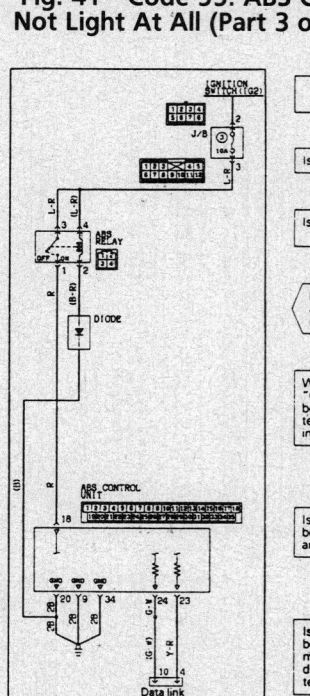

Flowchart (Fig. 42, Part 1 of 2):

- Is there on-board diagnostic output? (Is there communication with scan tool?) — **No** → CONTINUE
  - **Yes** → Does diagnostic trouble code output display normal codes? — **No** → Check using the diagnostic trouble code check chart
  - **Yes** → Does the ABS warning light remain illuminated even with the ECU connector disconnected? — **No** → Short in ECU transistor → Replace ECU.
  - **Yes** → Does the ABS warning light remain illuminated even with the HU connector disconnected? — **No** → Short in HU harness or sticking of valve relay contact → Replace HU or replace valve relay.
  - **Yes** → Short in harness between HU or ECU and ABS warning light → Repair harness or replace combination meter.

CR4029100576010X

Fig. 42   Code 55: ABS Chart B, ABS Warning Light Stays On When Ignition Key Is In On Position (Part 1 of 2). Colt Vista & Summit Wagon AWD

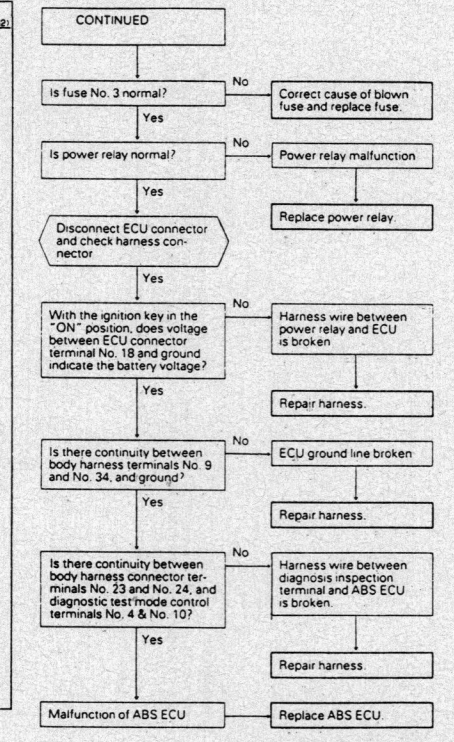

Flowchart (Fig. 42, Part 2 of 2):

- CONTINUED
  - → Is fuse No. 3 normal? — **No** → Correct cause of blown fuse and replace fuse.
  - **Yes** → Is power relay normal? — **No** → Power relay malfunction → Replace power relay.
  - **Yes** → Disconnect ECU connector and check harness connector
  - → With the ignition key in the "ON" position, does voltage between ECU connector terminal No. 18 and ground indicate the battery voltage? — **No** → Harness wire between power relay and ECU is broken → Repair harness.
  - **Yes** → Is there continuity between body harness terminals No. 9 and No. 34, and ground? — **No** → ECU ground line broken → Repair harness.
  - **Yes** → Is there continuity between body harness connector terminals No. 23 and No. 24, and diagnostic test mode control terminals No. 4 & No. 10? — **No** → Harness wire between diagnosis inspection terminal and ABS ECU is broken → Repair harness.
  - **Yes** → Malfunction of ABS ECU → Replace ABS ECU.

CR4029100576020X

Fig. 42   Code 55: ABS Chart B, ABS Warning Light Stays On When Ignition Key Is In On Position (Part 2 of 2). Colt Vista & Summit Wagon AWD

TYPE 4-ANTI-LOCK BRAKING SYSTEM

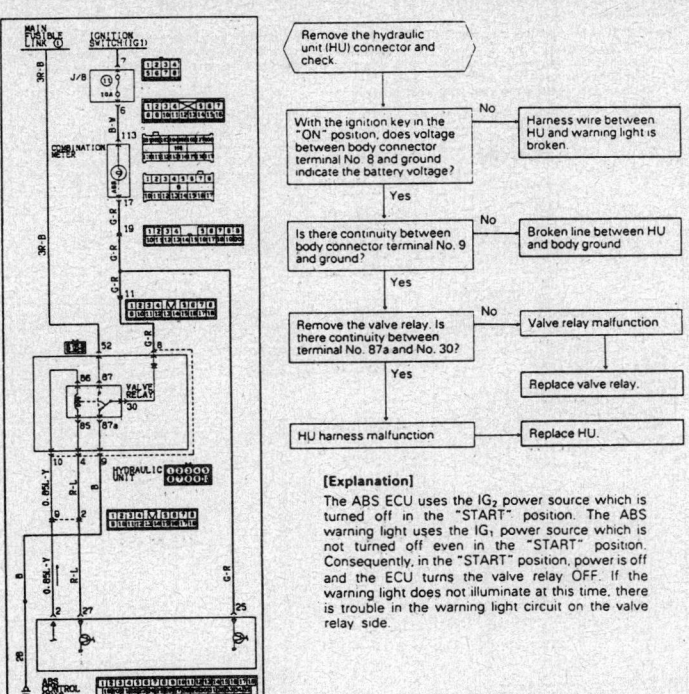

[Explanation]
The ABS ECU uses the IG$_2$ power source which is turned off in the "START" position. The ABS warning light uses the IG$_1$ power source which is not turned off even in the "START" position. Consequently, in the "START" position, power is off and the ECU turns the valve relay OFF. If the warning light does not illuminate at this time, there is trouble in the warning light circuit on the valve relay side.

CR4029100577000X

Fig. 43   Code 55: ABS Chart C, ABS Warning Light Does Not Illuminate When Ignition Key Is In Start Position. Colt Vista & Summit Wagon AWD

[Explanation]
When power flows, the ABS ECU turns on the warning light for approximately 1 sec. while it performs a valve relay test. If there is a break in the harness between the ECU and the warning light, the light illuminates only when the valve relay is off in the valve relay test, etc.

CR4029100578000X

Fig. 44   Code 55: ABS Chart D, ABS Warning Light Blinks Once After Ignition Key Is Turned To On Position, Illuminates In Start Position & Blinks Once Again When Turned To On Position. Colt Vista & Summit Wagon AWD

[Explanation]
This diagnostic trouble code is output when there is an abnormality (other than broken wire or short circuit) in the wheel speed sensor output signal while driving.

[Hint]
The following can be considered as the cause of the wheel speed sensor output abnormality.
- Distortion of rotor, teeth missing
- Low frequency noise interference when sensor harness wire is broken
- Noise interference in sensor signal
- When the sensor output signal is below the standard value or when amplitude modulation is over the standard value, using an oscilloscope to measure the wave shape of the wheel speed sensor output signal is very effective.
- Loose wheel bearing

- Temporarily broken wire in sensor harness
- Sensor harness and body connector are not properly inserted.

NOTE
(1) If contact is poor, check the sensor cable by bending and lightly stretching it.
(2) If there is currently no trouble and if abnormality in the displayed sensor circuit cannot be discovered since values are normal even when checked, turn the ignition switch OFF and re-execute the driving test. Try replacing the ABS ECU only if the same diagnostic trouble code is output at this time.

(If it is difficult to recreate the trouble, there is a possibility of speed sensor trouble recurring even if the ECU is replaced.)

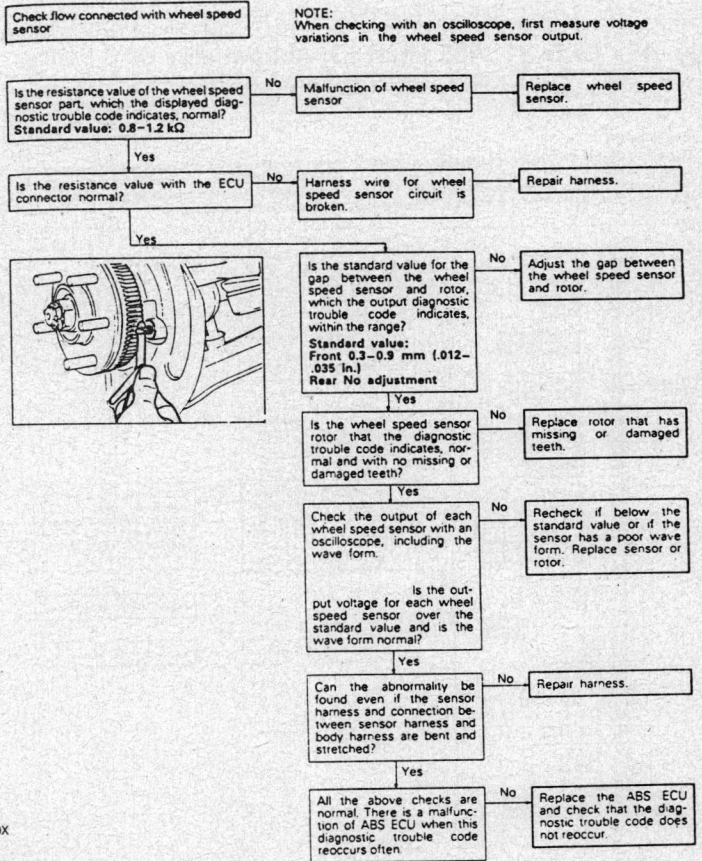

CR4029100579020X

Fig. 45   Code 15: ABS Chart E2, Output Abnormality Of Wheel Speed Sensor (Part 2 of 2). Laser & Talon AWD

CR4029100579010X

Fig. 45   Code 15: ABS Chart E2, Output Abnormality Of Wheel Speed Sensor (Part 1 of 2). Laser & Talon AWD

[Explanation]

The ABS ECU outputs this diagnostic trouble code in the following cases.
- OFF trouble turning G sensor OFF (It is judged that the G sensor continues to be OFF for more than approximately 13 seconds except when the vehicle is stopped or when there is stop light switch input.
- When there is a broken wire or short circuit in the harness for the G sensor system.

[Explanation]

The ABS ECU outputs this diagnostic trouble code in the following cases.
- Stop light switch may remain on for more than 15 minutes without the ABS functions.
- The harness wire for the stop light switch may be open.

[Hint]

If the stop light operates normal, the ABS harness wire for the stop light switch input circuit to the ECU is broken or there is a malfunction in the ABS ECU.

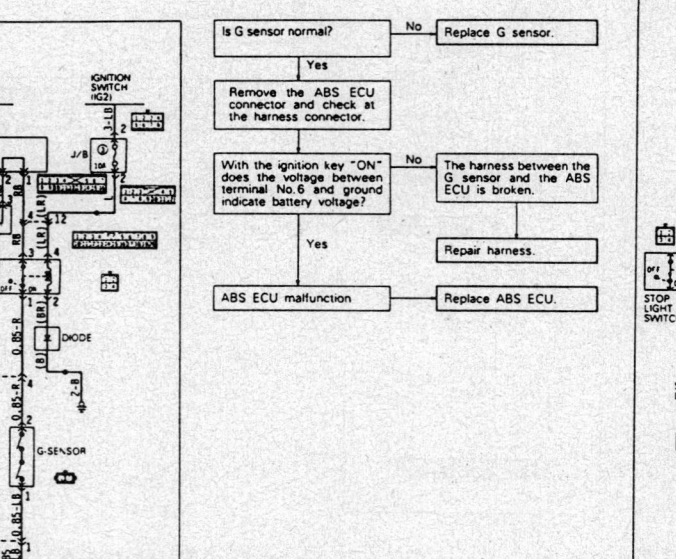

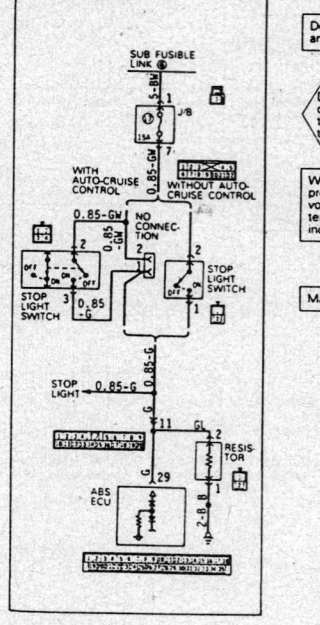

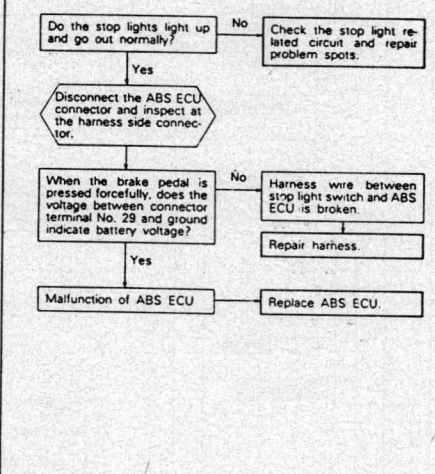

Fig. 47   Code 22: ABS Chart E4, Abnormality Of Stop Light Switch Circuit. Laser & Talon AWD

Fig. 46   Code 21: ABS Chart E3, Abnormality Of G Sensor Circuit. Laser & Talon AWD

[Explanation]

When the ignition switch is turned ON, the ABS ECU switches the valve relay OFF and ON for an initial check, compares the voltage of the signal to the valve relay and valve power monitor line voltage to check whether the valve relay operation is normal. In addition, normally it monitors whether or not there is power in the valve power monitor line since the valve relay is normally ON. Then, if the supply of power to the valve power monitor line is interrupted, this diagnostic trouble code will output.

[Explanation]

The ABS ECU normally monitors the solenoid valve drive circuit.
If no current flows in the solenoid even if the ECU turns the solenoid ON or if it continues to flow even when turned OFF, the ECU determines the solenoid coil wire is broken/short circuited or the harness is broken short circuited and then these diagnostic trouble codes are output.

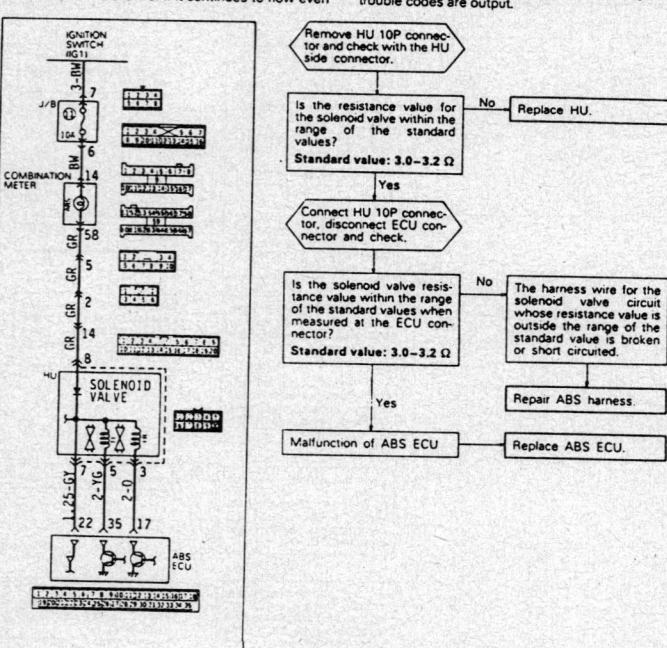

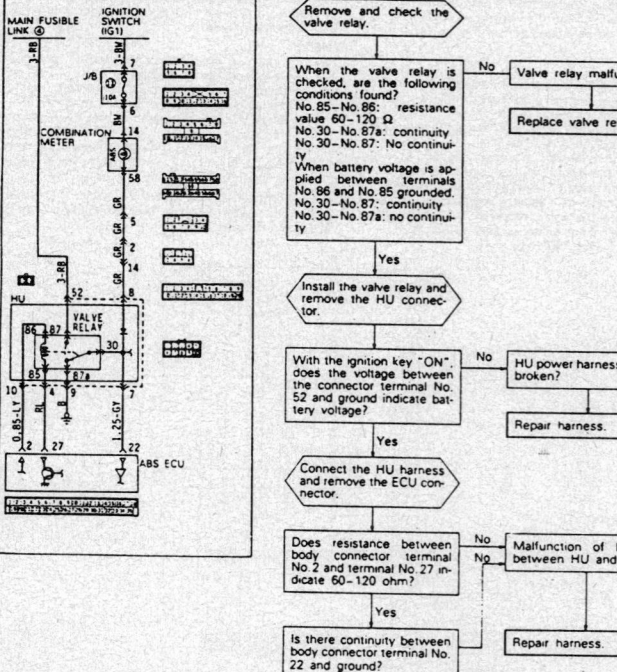

Fig. 48   Codes 41, 42 & 43: ABS Chart E5, Abnormality Of Solenoid Valve Drive Circuit. Laser & Talon AWD

Fig. 49   Code 51: ABS Chart E6, Abnormality Of Valve Relay Drive Circuit. Laser & Talon AWD

TYPE 4-ANTI-LOCK BRAKING SYSTEM

[Explanation]
The ABS ECU outputs this diagnostic trouble code for the motor relay and motor in the following cases.
• When the motor relay does not function
• When there is trouble with the motor itself and it the motor does not revolve
• When there is trouble with the motor itself and it the motor does not revolve
• When the motor continues to revolve

[Hint]
If there is motor operation noise when wheel speed exceeds 6km/h (4mph) when starting up after the engine is started, or when there is forced scan tool (DRB-II) drive, there is a broken or short circuited motor monitor wire.

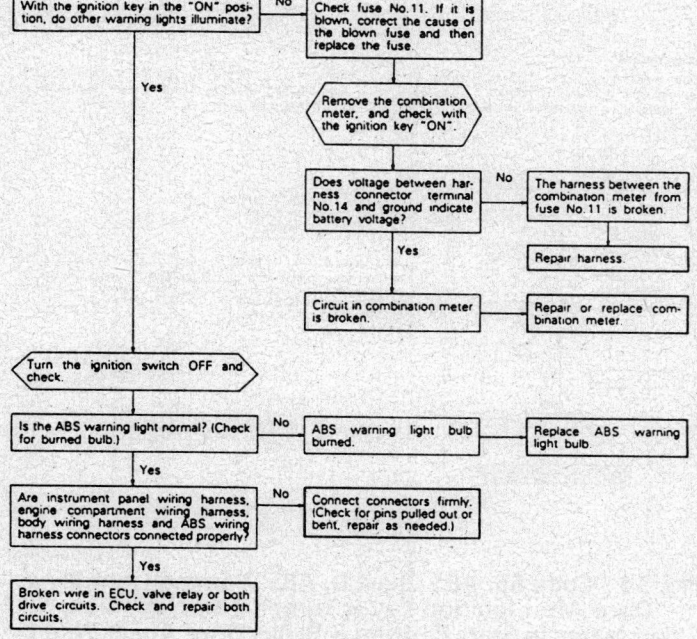

Fig. 50 Code 52: ABS Chart E7, Abnormality Of Motor Drive Circuit. Laser & Talon AWD

[Explanation]
When it does not light up at all, there is a strong possibility that there is trouble with ABS warning light or with power to the light.

[Hint]
If other warning lights do not light up either, fuse is probably blown.

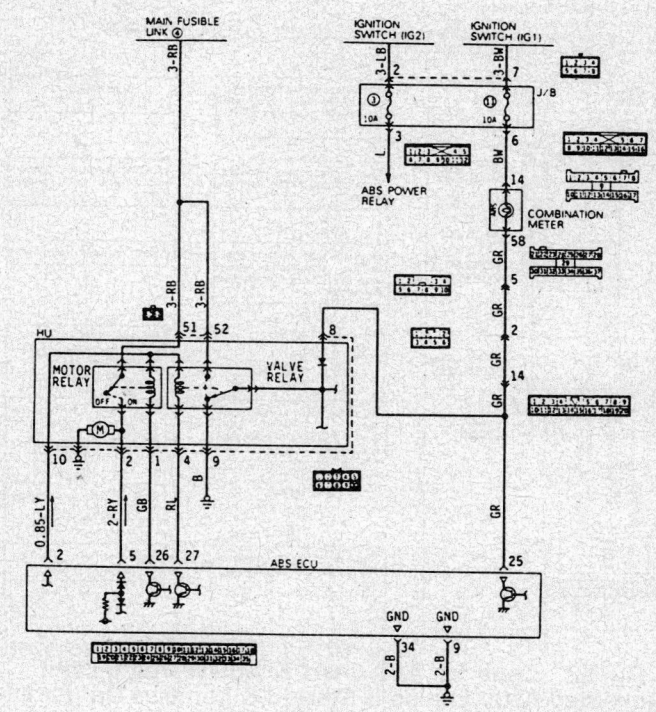

Fig. 51 Code 55: ABS Chart A, ABS Warning Light Does Not Light At All (Part 1 of 3). Laser & Talon AWD

Fig. 51 Code 55: ABS Chart A, ABS Warning Light Does Not Light At All (Part 2 of 3). Laser & Talon AWD

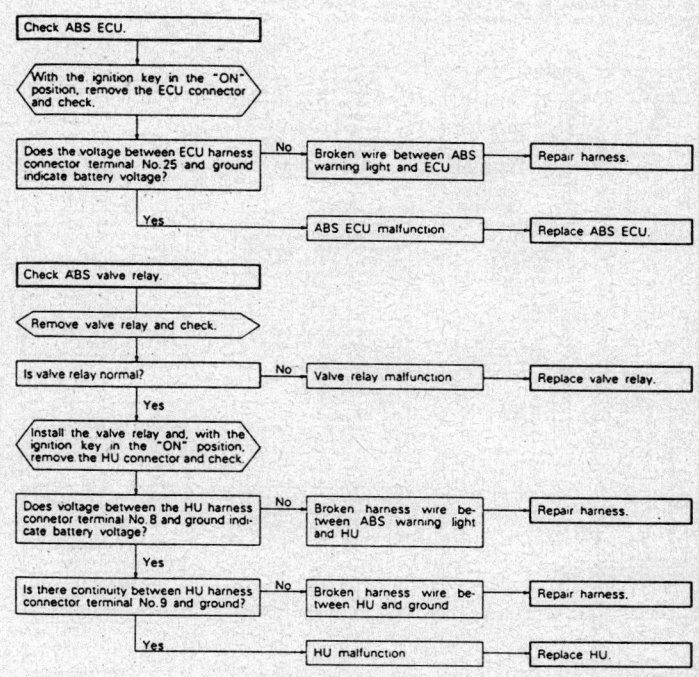

Fig. 51 Code 55: ABS Chart A, ABS Warning Light Does Not Light At All (Part 3 of 3). Laser & Talon AWD

[Explanation]

This is the symptom when the ABS ECU does not power up due to broken ECU power circuit, etc., when the fail safe function operates and isolates the system or when the warning light drive circuit is short circuited.

[Hint]

Check the on-board diagnostic output and if there is no output voltage or if the scan tool (DRB-II) and ABS ECU cannot communicate, there is a good possibility that power is not flowing to the ECU.

Caution
- If there is no output of diagnostic trouble codes, there is a good possibility that the fail safe is functioning.

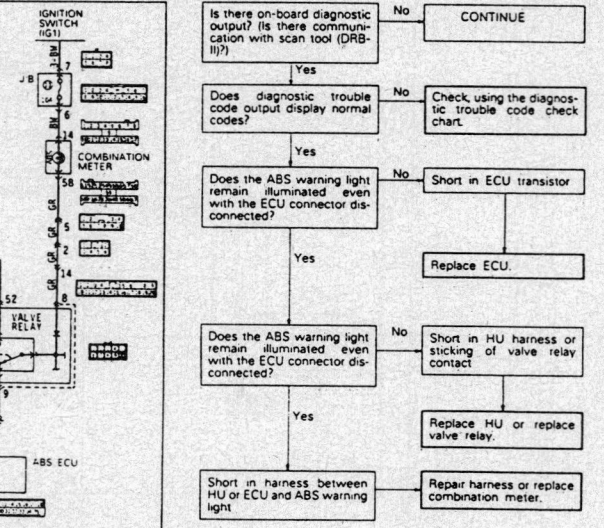

CR4029100586010X

Fig. 52 Code 55: ABS Chart B, ABS Warning Light Illuminated After Engine Is Started & Remains On (Part 1 of 2). Laser & Talon AWD

CR4029100586020X

Fig. 52 Code 55: ABS Chart B, ABS Warning Light Illuminated After Engine Is Started & Remains On (Part 2 of 2). Laser & Talon AWD

[Explanation]

The ABS ECU uses the IG2 power source which is turned off in the "START" position. The ABS warning light uses the IG1 power source which is not turned off even in the "START" position. Consequently, in the "START" position, power is off and the ECU turns the valve relay OFF. If the warning light does not illuminate at this time, there is trouble in the warning light circuit on the valve relay side.

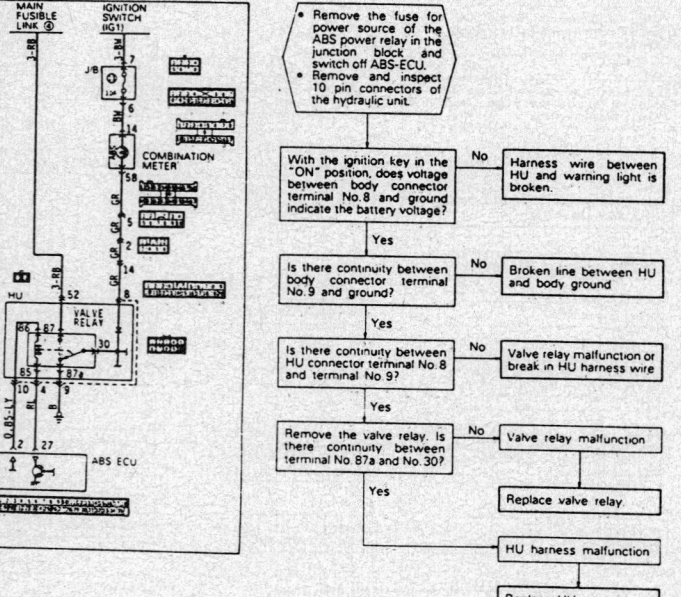

CR4029100587000X

Fig. 53 Code 55: ABS Chart C, ABS Warning Light Does Not Illuminate When Ignition Key Is In Start Position. Laser & Talon AWD

[Explanation]

When power flows, the ABS ECU turns on the warning light for approximately 1 sec. while it performs a valve relay test. If there is a break in the harness between the ECU and the warning light, the light illuminates only when the valve relay is off in the valve relay test, etc.

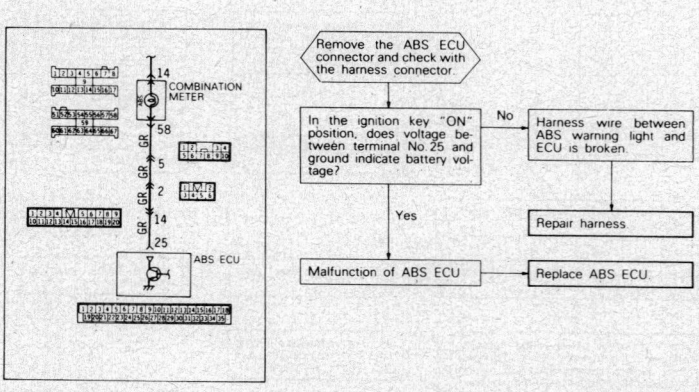

CR4029100588000X

Fig. 54 Code 55: ABS Chart D, ABS Warning Light Blinks Once After Ignition Key Is Turned To On Position, Illuminates In Start Position & Blinks Once Again When Turned To On Position. Laser & Talon AWD

[Explanation]

This diagnostic trouble code is output when there is an abnormality (other than broken wire or short circuit) in any of the wheel speed sensor output signals while driving.

[Hint]

The following can be considered as the cause of the wheel speed sensor output abnormality.
- Distortion of rotor, teeth missing
- Low frequency noise interference when sensor harness wire is broken
- Noise interference in sensor signal
- The sensor output signal is below the standard value or amplitude modulation is over the standard value. Using an oscilloscope to measure the wave shape of the wheel speed sensor output signal is very effective.

- Broken sensor harness
- Poor connection of connector

NOTE
(1) If contact is poor, check the sensor cable by bending and lightly stretching it.
(2) Except for the case where a fault condition exists in the system, but the inspection results are normal; if an abnormality cannot be found in the sensor circuit displayed as abnormal, erase the diagnostic trouble code and turn the ignition switch to OFF once, and then test-drive again. If the same diagnostic trouble code is output, replace the ABS ECU. If the trouble does not occur anymore, the problem is likely to be with the ABS ECU.
(If the trouble is in the speed sensor circuit, but is difficult to recreate, it will recur even after the ABS ECU has been replaced.)

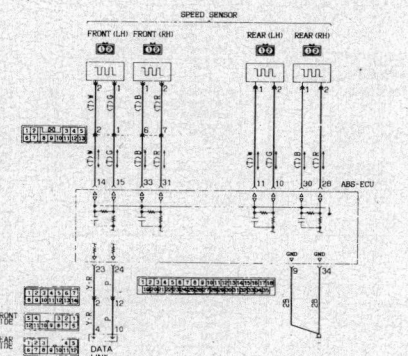

Fig. 55   Code 15: ABS Chart E2, Output Abnormality Of Wheel Speed Sensor (Part 1 of 2). Stealth AWD

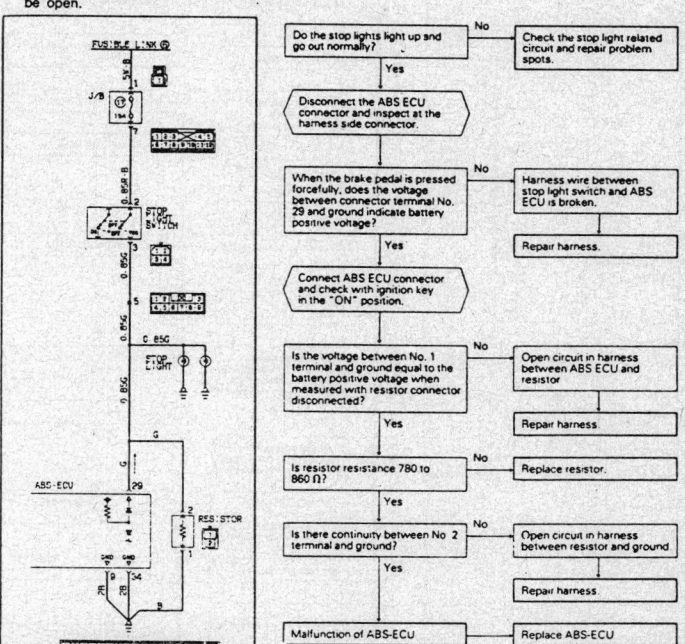

Fig. 55   Code 15: ABS Chart E2, Output Abnormality Of Wheel Speed Sensor (Part 2 of 2). Stealth AWD

[Explanation]

The ABS ECU outputs this diagnostic trouble code in the following cases.
- G sensor OFF trouble (It is judged that the G sensor continues to be OFF for more than approximately 13 seconds except when the vehicle is stopped or when there is stop light switch input.
- When there is a broken wire or short circuit in the harness for the G sensor system.

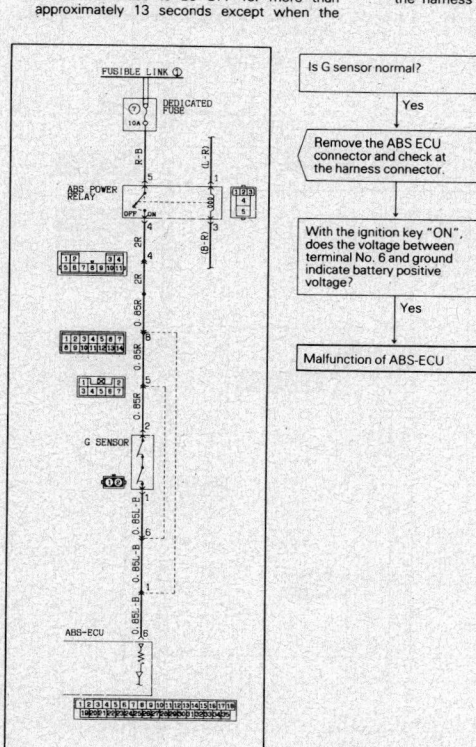

Fig. 56   Code 21: ABS Chart E3, Abnormality Of G Sensor Circuit. Stealth AWD

[Explanation]

The ABS ECU outputs this diagnostic trouble code in the following cases.
- Stop light switch may remain on for more than 15 minutes without ABS operation.
- The harness wire for the stop light switch may be open.

[Hint]

If the stop light operates normal, the harness for the stop light switch input circuit is broken or there is a malfunction in the ABS-ECU.

Fig. 57   Code 22: ABS Chart E4, Abnormality Of Stop Light Switch Circuit. Stealth AWD

[Explanation]

The ABS ECU normally monitors the solenoid valve drive circuit.
If no current flows in the solenoid even if the ECU turns the solenoid ON or if it continues to flow even when turned OFF, the ECU determines the solenoid coil wire is broken/short-circuited or the harness is broken/short-circuited, and then these diagnostic trouble codes are output. ABS ECU controls the solenoid valve current and if the current value of the solenoid valves differs from each other in the same mode, solenoid valve drift error is produced and the ABS ECU goes into the failsafe mode.

[Explanation]

When the ignition switch is turned ON, the ABS ECU switches the valve relay OFF and ON for an initial check, compares the voltage of the signal to the valve relay and valve power monitor line voltage to check whether the valve relay operation is normal. In addition, normally it monitors whether or not there is power in the valve power monitor line since the valve relay is normally ON. Then, if the supply of power to the valve power monitor line is interrupted, this diagnostic trouble code will be output.

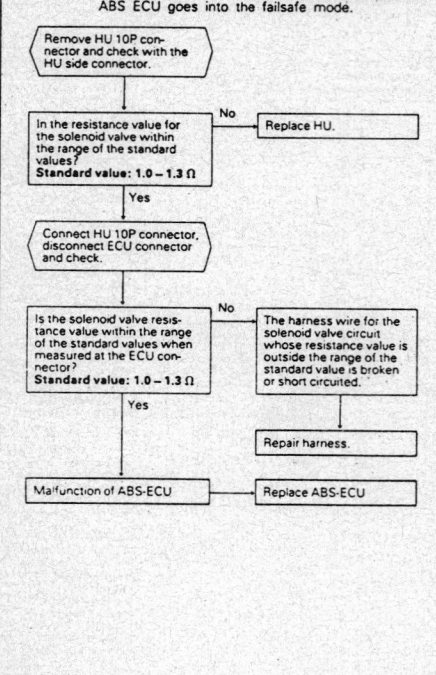

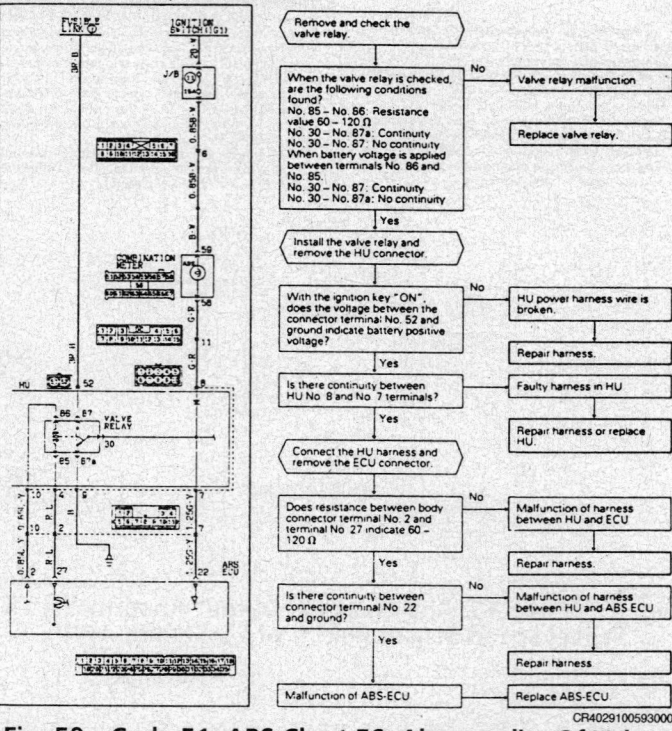

Fig. 58   Codes 41, 42 & 43: ABS Chart E5, Abnormality Of Solenoid Valve Drive Circuit. Stealth AWD

Fig. 59   Code 51: ABS Chart E6, Abnormality Of Valve Relay Drive Circuit. Stealth AWD

[Explanation]

The ABS ECU outputs this diagnostic trouble code for the motor relay and motor in the following cases.
• When the motor relay does not function
• When there is trouble with the motor itself and it does not revolve

• When the motor ground line is disconnected and the motor does not revolve
• When the motor continues to revolve

[Hint]

If there is motor operation noise during scan tool forced drive mode, there is a broken or short circuited motor monitor wire.

[Explanation]

When it does not light up at all, there is a strong possibility that there is trouble with ABS warning light or with power to the light.

[Hint]

If other warning lights do not light up either, fuse is probably blown.

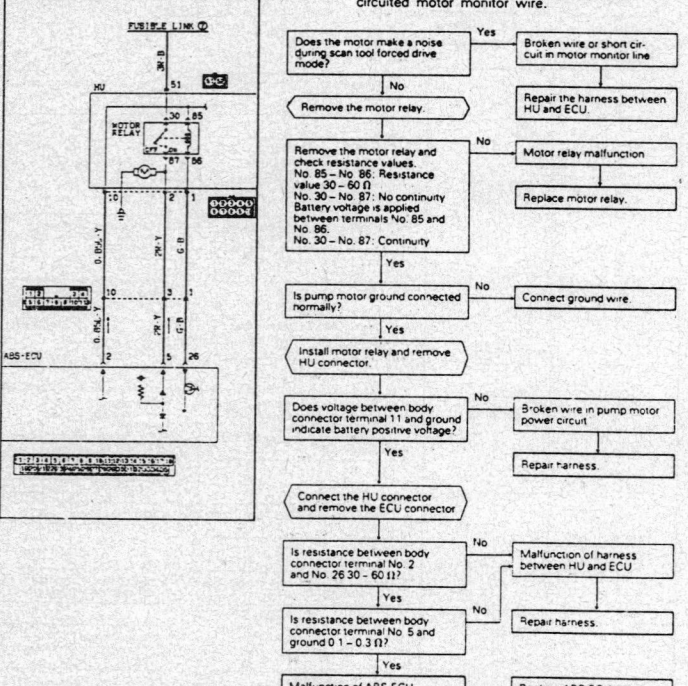

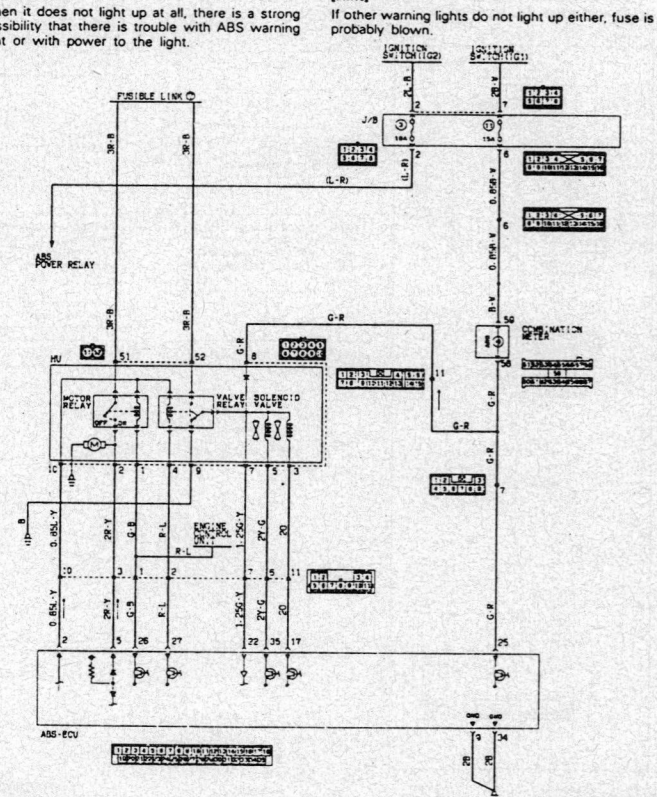

Fig. 60   Code 52: ABS Chart E7, Abnormality Of Motor Drive Circuit. Stealth AWD

Fig. 61   Code 55: ABS Chart A, ABS Warning Light Does Not Light At All (Part 1 of 3). Stealth AWD

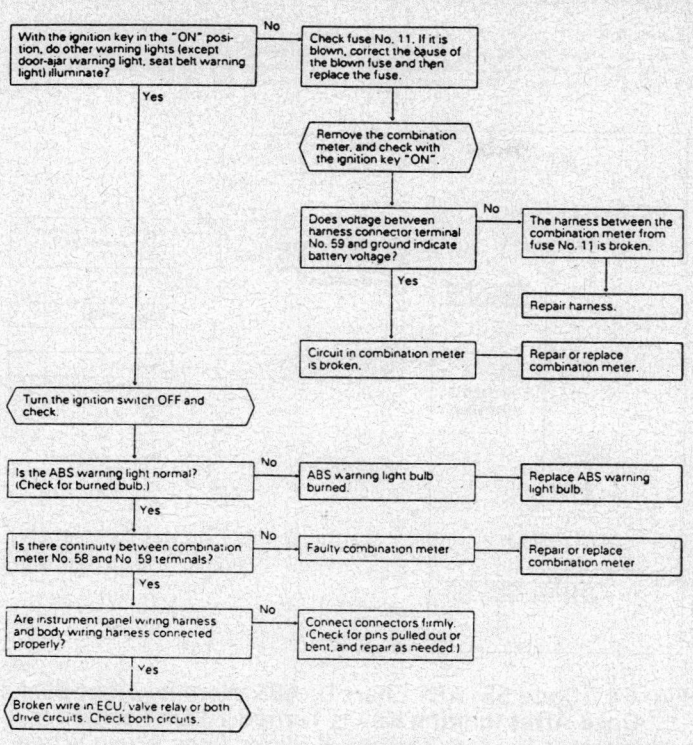

With the ignition key in the "ON" position, do other warning lights (except door-ajar warning light, seat belt warning light) illuminate? — No → Check fuse No. 11. If it is blown, correct the cause of the blown fuse and then replace the fuse.

↓ Yes

↓

Remove the combination meter, and check with the ignition key "ON".

↓

Does voltage between harness connector terminal No. 59 and ground indicate battery voltage? — No → The harness between the combination meter from fuse No. 11 is broken.
↓ → Repair harness.

↓ Yes

Circuit in combination meter is broken. → Repair or replace combination meter.

↓

Turn the ignition switch OFF and check.

↓

Is the ABS warning light normal? (Check for burned bulb.) — No → ABS warning light bulb burned. → Replace ABS warning light bulb.

↓ Yes

Is there continuity between combination meter No. 58 and No. 59 terminals? — No → Faulty combination meter → Repair or replace combination meter

↓ Yes

Are instrument panel wiring harness and body wiring harness connected properly? — No → Connect connectors firmly. (Check for pins pulled out or bent, and repair as needed.)

↓ Yes

Broken wire in ECU, valve relay or both drive circuits. Check both circuits.

CR4029100595020X

Fig. 61   Code 55: ABS Chart A, ABS Warning Light Does Not Light At All (Part 2 of 3). Stealth AWD

Check ABS ECU.

↓

Remove the ECU connector and check.

↓

Does the voltage between ECU harness connector terminal No. 25 and ground indicate battery positive voltage while the ignition key is in the "ON" position? — No → Broken wire between ABS warning light and ECU → Repair harness.

↓ Yes

ABS ECU malfunction → Replace ABS ECU.

Check valve relay.

↓

Remove valve relay and check.

↓

Is valve relay normal? — No → Valve relay malfunction → Replace valve relay.

↓ Yes

Install the valve relay, remove the HU connector and check.

↓

Does voltage between the HU harness connector terminal No. 8 and ground indicate battery positive voltage while the ignition key is in the "ON" position? — No → Broken harness wire between ABS warning light and HU → Repair harness.

↓ Yes

Is there continuity between HU harness connector terminal No. 9 and ground? — No → Broken harness wire between HU and ground → Repair harness.

↓ Yes

Is there continuity between HU harness connector terminals No. 8 and No. 9? — No → HU malfunction → Replace HU.

↓ Yes

Connector not connected securely. → Replace connector.

CR4029100595030X

Fig. 61   Code 55: ABS Chart A, ABS Warning Light Does Not Light At All (Part 3 of 3). Stealth AWD

[Explanation]
This is the symptom when the ABS ECU does not power up due to broken ECU power circuit, etc., when the fail safe function operates and isolates the system or when the warning light drive circuit is short circuited.

[Hint]
Check the on-board diagnostic output and if there is no output voltage or if the scan tool and ABS ECU cannot communicate, there is a good possibility that power is not flowing to the ECU.

Caution
• If the diagnostic trouble code is output, the system can be in the fail safe mode. In such a case, erase the diagnostic trouble code and then restart the engine to check if the system is currently in a fault condition.

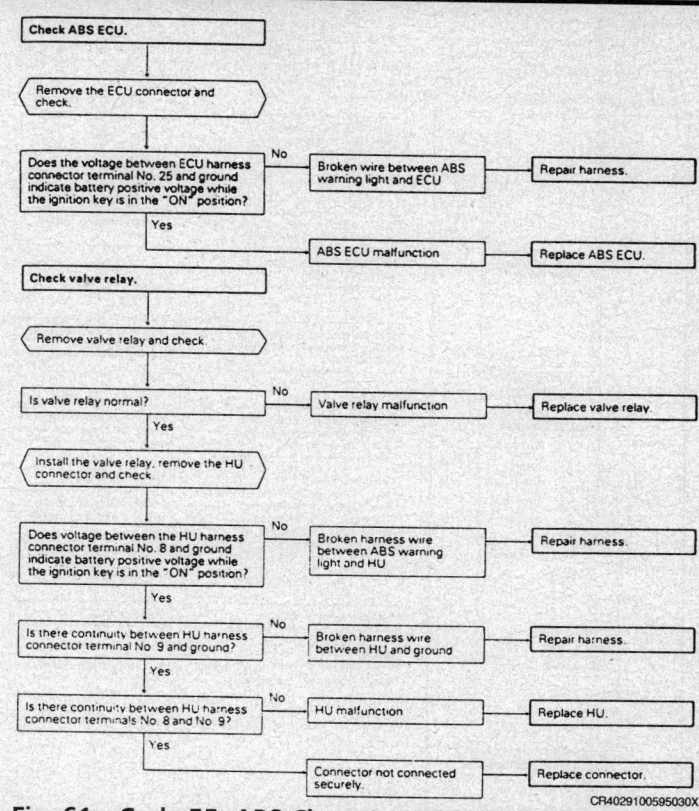

Is there diagnosis output? (Is there communication with scan tool?) — No → CONTINUE

↓ Yes

Does diagnostic trouble code output display normal codes? — No → Check, using the diagnostic trouble code check chart

↓ Yes

Does the ABS warning light remain illuminated even with the ECU connector disconnected? — No → Short in ECU transistor
↓ → Replace ECU.

↓ Yes

Does the ABS warning light remain illuminated even with the HU connector disconnected? — No → Short in HU harness or sticking of valve relay contact
↓ → Replace HU or replace valve relay.

↓ Yes

Short in harness between HU or ECU and ABS warning light → Repair harness or replace combination meter.

CR4029100596010X

Fig. 62   Code 55: ABS Chart B, ABS Warning Light Stays On When Ignition Key Is In On Position (Part 1 of 2). Stealth AWD

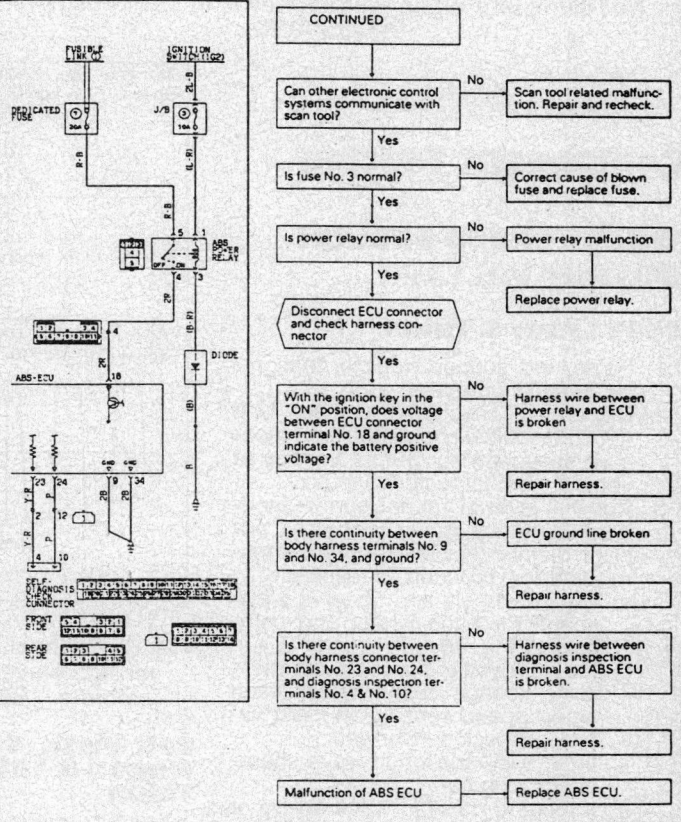

CONTINUED

↓

Can other electronic control systems communicate with scan tool? — No → Scan tool related malfunction. Repair and recheck.

↓ Yes

Is fuse No. 3 normal? — No → Correct cause of blown fuse and replace fuse.

↓ Yes

Is power relay normal? — No → Power relay malfunction
↓ → Replace power relay.

↓ Yes

Disconnect ECU connector and check harness connector

↓ Yes

With the ignition key in the "ON" position, does voltage between ECU connector terminal No. 18 and ground indicate the battery positive voltage? — No → Harness wire between power relay and ECU is broken
↓ → Repair harness.

↓ Yes

Is there continuity between body harness terminals No. 9 and No. 34, and ground? — No → ECU ground line broken
↓ → Repair harness.

↓ Yes

Is there continuity between body harness connector terminals No. 23 and No. 24, and diagnosis inspection terminals No. 4 & No. 10? — No → Harness wire between diagnosis inspection terminal and ABS ECU is broken
↓ → Repair harness.

↓ Yes

Malfunction of ABS ECU → Replace ABS ECU.

CR4029100596020X

Fig. 62   Code 55: ABS Chart B, ABS Warning Light Stays On When Ignition Key Is In On Position (Part 2 of 2). Stealth AWD

[Explanation]
The ABS ECU uses the IG₂ power source which is turned off in the "START" position. The ABS warning light uses the IG₁ power source which is not turned off even in the "START" position. Consequently, in the "START" position, power is off and the ECU turns the valve relay OFF. If the warning light does not illuminate at this time, there is trouble in the warning light circuit on the valve relay side.

[Explanation]
When power flows, the ABS ECU turns on the warning light for approximately 1 sec. while it performs a valve relay test. If there is a break in the harness between the ECU and the warning light, the light illuminates only when the valve relay is off in the valve relay test, etc.

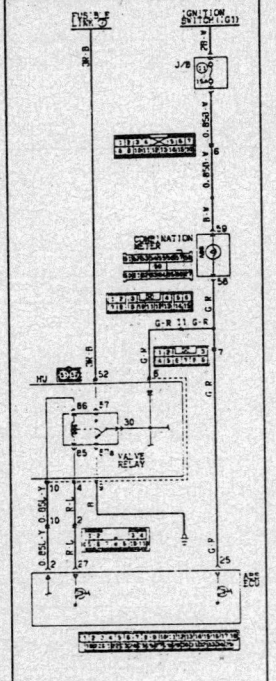

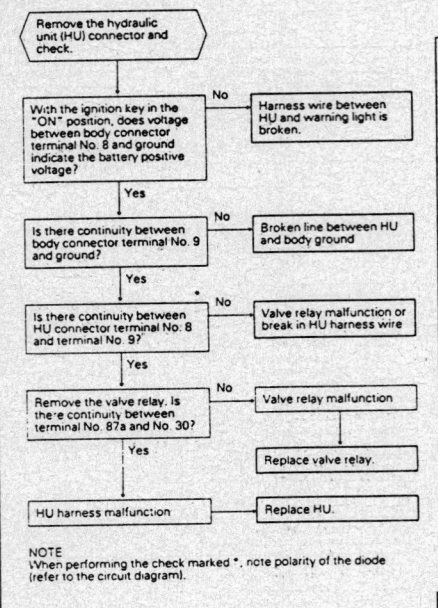

Remove the hydraulic unit (HU) connector and check.

With the ignition key in the "ON" position, does voltage between body connector terminal No. 8 and ground indicate the battery positive voltage? — No → Harness wire between HU and warning light is broken.

Yes ↓

Is there continuity between body connector terminal No. 9 and ground? — No → Broken line between HU and body ground

Yes ↓

Is there continuity between HU connector terminal No. 8 and terminal No. 9? — No → Valve relay malfunction or break in HU harness wire

Yes ↓

Remove the valve relay. Is there continuity between terminal No. 87a and No. 30? — No → Valve relay malfunction

Yes ↓ → Replace valve relay.

HU harness malfunction → Replace HU.

NOTE
When performing the check marked *, note polarity of the diode (refer to the circuit diagram).

CR4029100597000X

Fig. 63   Code 55: ABS Chart C, ABS Warning Light Does Not Illuminate When Ignition Key Is In Start Position. Stealth AWD

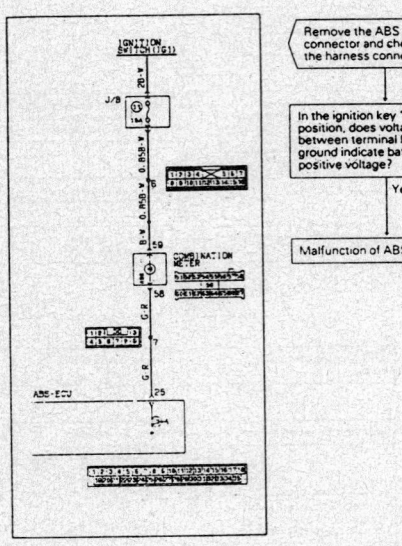

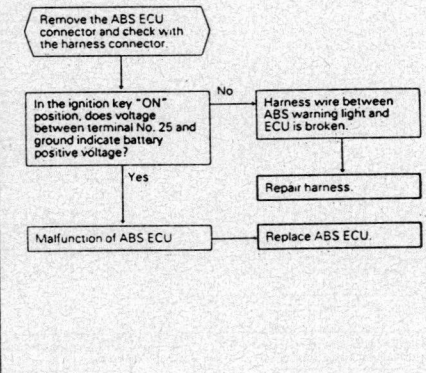

Remove the ABS ECU connector and check with the harness connector.

In the ignition key "ON" position, does voltage between terminal No. 25 and ground indicate battery positive voltage? — No → Harness wire between ABS warning light and ECU is broken.

Yes ↓ → Repair harness.

Malfunction of ABS ECU → Replace ABS ECU.

CR4029100598000X

Fig. 64   Code 55: ABS Chart D, ABS Warning Light Blinks Once After Ignition Key Is Turned To On Position, Illuminates In Start Position & Blinks Once Again When Turned To On position. Stealth AWD

Component Testing

WHEEL SPEED SENSOR OUTPUT VOLTAGE

1992 Laser & Talon

1. Raise and support vehicle, then release parking brake.
2. Disconnect Electronic Control Unit (ECU) electrical connector, then measure speed sensor output voltage at vehicle side harness connector.
3. Put shift lever in 1st position on models with manual transmission or L position on models with automatic transmission and proceed as follows:
   a. Rotate wheels and observe wave shape for each wheel and compare to **Fig. 65**.
   b. If output voltage is to low or there is no voltage output, check each wheel speed sensor. On FWD vehicles, check sensor gap.
   c. If there is variation in wave shape, check axle hub.
   d. If there is noise in wave shape or distortion, check for a broken or disconnected speed sensor wire, faulty wheel speed sensor, or missing teeth.

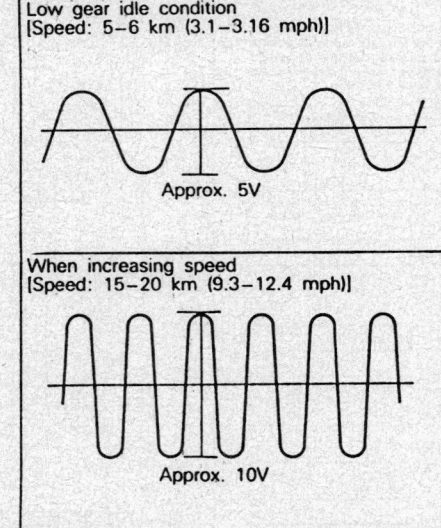

Low gear idle condition
[Speed: 5–6 km (3.1–3.16 mph)]

Approx. 5V

When increasing speed
[Speed: 15–20 km (9.3–12.4 mph)]

Approx. 10V

CR4029100599000X

Fig. 65   Wheel speed sensor output voltage wave shape monitoring points. 1992 Laser & Talon

Colt Vista, Stealth, Summit Wagon & 1993–94 Laser & Talon

1. Raise and support vehicle, then release parking brake.
2. Disconnect Electronic Control Unit (ECU) electrical connector, then mea-

sure speed sensor output voltage with adapter harness MB991356 or equivalent connected to harness side connector. **Never insert a probe into connector as it may result in poor contact later. Do not connect connector marked "" except when recording wave form on a driving test. If necessary, connect connector to ECU.**

3. Manually turn wheel to be measured by ½–1 turn per second, then measure output voltage with a circuit tester or oscilloscope, **Fig. 66 and 67**.
4. Output voltage when measured with a circuit tester should be 70 millivolts (mV) or more.
5. Output voltage when measured with an oscilloscope should be 100 mV or more.
6. Probable causes of low output voltage are: speed sensor pole piece to rotor clearance to great, or faulty speed sensor.
7. **On AWD models,** in order to observe output state of wheel speed sensors, shift into low gear and drive wheels.
8. **On FWD models,** in order to observe output state of wheel speed sensors on front wheels, shift into low gear and drive wheels. On rear wheels turn manually at a constant speed.
9. **On all models,** observe output voltage wave form of each wheel speed sensor with an oscilloscope, output voltage is low when wheel speed is low and increases as wheel speed increases.
3. If continuity is not as specified, replace power relay.

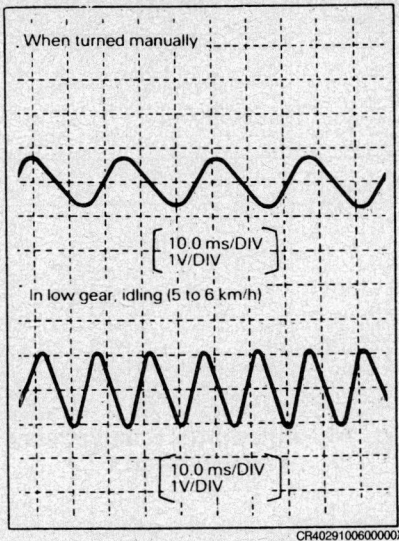

Fig. 66 Wheel speed sensor output voltage wave shape monitoring points. Colt Vista, Summit Wagon, Stealth & 1993–94 Laser & Talon

Terminal No. (same for AWD and FWD)			
FL	RR	FR	RL
4	24	21	8
5	26	23	9

CR4029100601000X

Fig. 67 Wheel speed sensor terminal output voltages. Colt Vista, Summit Wagon & Stealth

ABS VALVE RELAY & MOTOR RELAY

1. Remove right front splash shield, then the relay box cover by inserting a screwdriver between hydraulic unit and cover to pry off lock.
2. Remove relays, large one is motor relay and small one is valve relay.
3. Check continuity of relays both when energized and de-energized as shown in **Fig. 75 and 76.**
10. Refer to chart in **Fig. 68** to diagnose waveform measurement.

ABS POWER RELAY

Laser & Talon

1. Remove ABS power relay from ABS control unit bracket.
2. Connect terminal 2 of the power relay to battery voltage, then check continuity between terminals as shown in **Figs. 69 and 70** with terminal 4 grounded.
3. If continuity is not as specified, replace power relay.

Colt Vista, Stealth & Summit Wagon

1. Remove relay box cover in engine compartment, then the power relay.
2. Apply battery voltage to terminal 1 and check for continuity between terminals as shown in **Figs. 71 through 72** with terminal 3 short-circuited to ground.

Symptom	Probable causes	Remedy
Too small or zero waveform amplitude	Faulty wheel speed sensor	Replace sensor
	Incorrect pole piece-to-rotor clearance	Adjust clearance
Waveform amplitude fluctuates excessively (this is no problem if the minimum amplitude is 100 mV or more)	Axle hub eccentric or with large runout	Replace hub
Noisy or disturbed waveform	Open circuit in sensor	Replace sensor
	Open circuit in harness	Correct harness
	Incorrectly mounted wheel speed sensor	Mount correctly
	Rotor with missing or damaged teeth	Replace rotor

CR4029100602000X

Fig. 68 Wheel speed sensor output voltage waveform measurement diagnosis. Colt Vista, Summit Wagon, Stealth & 1993–94 Laser & Talon

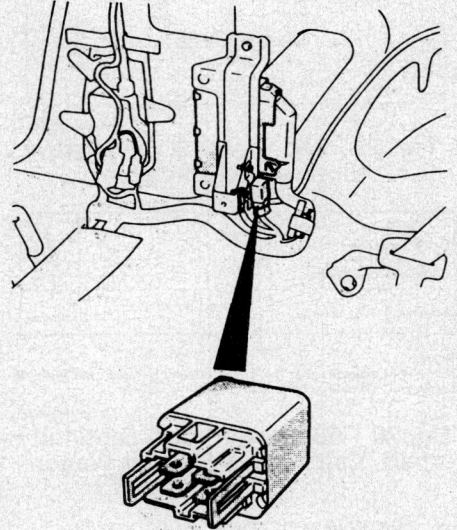

Power is supplied	1–3 terminals	Continuity
Power is not supplied	1–3 terminals	No continuity
	2–4 terminals	Continuity

CR4029100604000X

Fig. 70 ABS power relay continuity chart. Laser & Talon

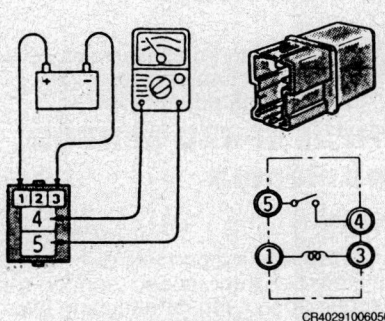

Power relay (ABS)

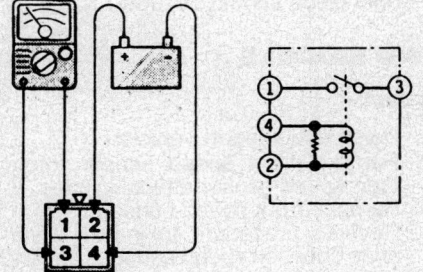

Fig. 69 ABS power relay inspection. Laser & Talon

4. If continuity is not as specified, replace valve or motor relay.

SYSTEM SERVICE

Brake System Bleed

1. If brake fluid has been drained from master cylinder, bleed as follows:
   a. Fill reservoir with DOT 3 brake fluid, then depress and hold brake pedal.
   b. With master cylinder outlet port plugged, release brake pedal.
   c. Repeat 3 to 4 times, refilling reservoir as necessary.
2. With engine running, bleed brake lines as follows:

CR4029100605000X

Fig. 71 ABS power relay inspection. Stealth

   a. Bleed line to wheel that is diagonally opposite master cylinder.
   b. Bleed line to wheel that is nearest to master cylinder.
   c. Bleed line to remaining rear wheel, then to remaining front wheel.
   d. Ensure master cylinder is kept full.
3. When adding brake fluid, fit filter to reserve tank.

Component Replace

HYDRAULIC UNIT

1. Remove splash shield, relay box, and air duct, if necessary.
2. Disconnect brake tube connections, then harness connections.
3. Remove bracket bolts.
4. Remove hydraulic unit bolts, then hydraulic unit.
5. Remove ground wire.

When energized	Between terminals 4 and 5	Continuity
When de-energized	Between terminals 4 and 5	No continuity
	Between terminals 1 and 3	Continuity

CR4029100606000X

Fig. 72　ABS power relay continuity chart. Stealth

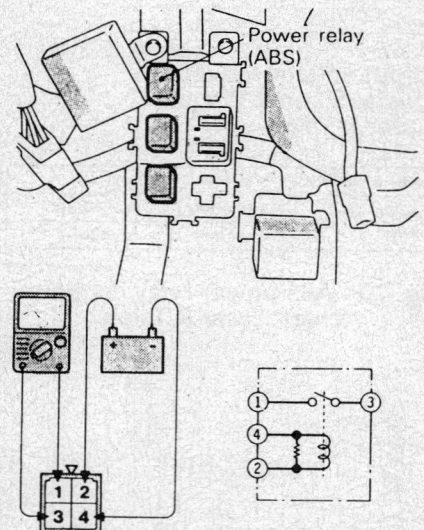

Fig. 75　ABS power relay inspection. Colt Vista & Summit Wagon

CR4029100607000X

6. This unit cannot be disassembled. Do not drop or turn upside down.
7. Reverse procedure to install.

WHEEL SPEED SENSOR

FWD MODELS

Front

1. Raise and support vehicle.
2. Remove front speed sensor rotors, then speed sensor attaching clips.
3. Remove front speed sensor and bracket.
4. Reverse procedure to install. Clearance between speed sensor rotor and pole piece should be .012-.035 inch.

Rear

1. Raise and support vehicle.
2. Remove rear speed sensor rotors, then speed sensor attaching clips.

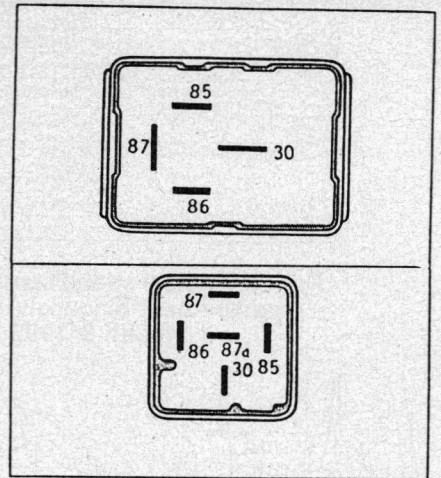

Fig. 73　ABS motor & valve relay terminal identification

Terminal / Battery voltage	1	2	3	4
Continuity no voltage		O—O		
Continuity with voltage	O—O	⊕- - -⊖		O—⊕

NOTE
(1) O—O indicates that there is continuity between the terminals
(2) ⊕- - -⊖ indicates connection of battery voltage.

CR4029100608000X

Fig. 76　ABS power relay continuity chart. Colt Vista & Summit Wagon

3. Remove rear speed sensors.
4. Reverse procedure to install. Clearance between speed sensor rotor and pole piece should be .008-.028 inch.

AWD MODELS

Front

1. Raise and support vehicle.
2. Remove front speed sensor rotors, then speed sensor attaching clips.
3. Remove front speed sensors.
4. Reverse procedure to install. Clearance between speed sensor rotor and pole piece should be .012-.035 inch.

Rear

1. Raise and support vehicle.
2. Remove rear speed sensor rotors, then speed sensor attaching clips.
3. Remove cable band.

Motor Relay

When de-energized	Between terminals 85 and 86	30 60Ω
	Between terminals 30 and 87	No continuity (×Ω)
When energized between terminals 85 and 86	Between terminals 30 and 87	Continuity (approx. 0Ω)

Valve Relay

When de-energized	Between terminals 85 and 86	60 120Ω
	Between terminals 30 and 87a	Continuity (approx. 0Ω)
	Between terminals 30 and 87	No continuity (×Ω)
When energized between terminals 85 and 86	Between terminals 30 and 87a	No continuity (×Ω)
	Between terminals 30 and 87	Continuity (approx. 0Ω)

CR4029100610000X

Fig. 74　ABS motor & valve relay continuity charts

4. Remove rear speed sensors, then O-rings.
5. Reverse procedure to install. Because rear speed sensor pole piece to rotor tooth surface clearance is not adjustable, sensor installation surface to rotor tooth surface clearance should be 1.11—1.12 inch.

G SENSOR
AWD Models

1. **On Laser, Talon and Stealth,** remove front and rear console assemblies.
2. **On Colt Vista and Summit Wagon,** remove center console assembly.
3. **On all models,** disconnect electrical connector.
4. Remove G sensor and bracket.
5. Reverse procedure to install.

ELECTRONIC CONTROL UNIT

1. **On Laser, Talon and Stealth,** remove rear seat cushion, rear seat back and right rear quarter panel trim.
2. **On Colt Vista and Summit Wagon,** remove cup holder box from in front of shifter assembly.
3. **On all models,** disconnect electrical connector.
4. Remove ECU attaching bolts, then remove ECU.
5. Reverse procedure to install.

Type 5—Anti-Lock Braking System

NOTE: On Air Bag Equipped Models, Refer To "Air Bag System Precautions" Located In The Front Of This Manual For System Disarming & Arming Procedures.

INDEX

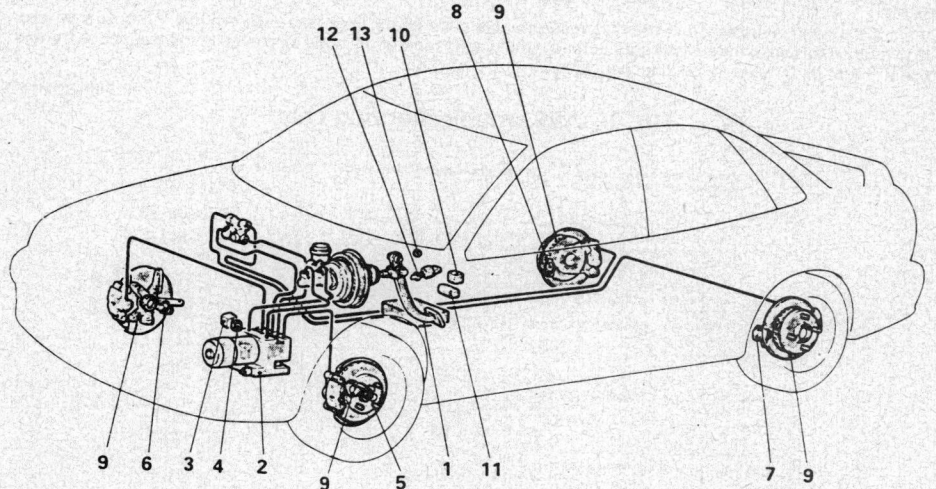

1. ABS-ECU
2. Hydraulic unit
3. ABS valve relay
4. ABS motor relay
5. Wheel speed sensor (front left)
6. Wheel speed sensor (front right)
7. Wheel speed sensor (rear left)
8. Wheel speed sensor (rear right)
9. Rotor
10. ABS power relay
11. Data link connector
12. Stop light switch
13. ABS warning light

CR4029100612000X

Fig. 1 ABS component locations

PRECAUTIONS

AIR BAG SYSTEMS

Refer to "Air Bag System Precautions" in the front of this manual for system disarming and arming procedures.

DESCRIPTION

The Anti-Lock Braking System (ABS) prevents the wheels from locking up when braking, regardless of the surface conditions. This allows the car to stop in a shorter distance, and allows the driver to maintain directional control of the vehicle during heavy braking.

During normal braking conditions, the ABS operates like a conventional diagonally split, hydraulic power assist system. During heavy braking, however, each wheel's braking pressure is modulated according to its speed. To maintain vehicle stability, both rear wheels receive the same signal.

Refer to **Fig. 1** for component locations.

TROUBLESHOOTING

Refer to **Fig. 2** when performing general troubleshooting procedures on the ABS system, or to **Figs. 3 through 10** when troubleshooting specific symptoms.

DIAGNOSIS & TESTING
Accessing Diagnostic Trouble Codes
USING SCAN TOOL

1. With ignition in Off position, connect scan tool then turn ignition On.
2. Select ABS system on scan tool. The ABS warning light illuminates indicating the the system in in the scan tool mode. **In the scan tool mode the ABS does not operate.**
3. Read and record on-board diagnostic trouble codes.
4. Erase diagnostic trouble code memory as outlined under "Clearing Diagnostic Trouble Codes." If memory cannot be erased, the function is being stopped by a problem that is currently displayed. If memory can be erased, then problem was only temporary or is a problem that can only be detected while driving.
5. If the diagnostic trouble code is not erased or if the ABS function is stopped by a repeated driving test and a diagnostic trouble code is output, inspect system according to **Fig. 11**.
6. Diagnostic Trouble Codes 16 (battery is dead) and 35 (engine is stopped) are output even when the ABS system is normal. These diagnostic trouble codes are output only for a current problem and, if the vehicle's condition returns to normal, then the diagnostic trouble codes will disappear.
7. After inspection, turn ignition switch to Off position and disconnect scan tool.

USING VOLTMETER

1. With vehicle stopped and engine idling, read and record pattern of output voltage between ground and ABS terminal of the data link connector, **Fig. 12**.
2. Output voltage is an indicator of diagnostic trouble codes as shown in **Fig. 13**.

3. Erase diagnostic trouble code memory as outlined under "Clearing Diagnostic Trouble Codes."
4. If memory cannot be erased, the function is being stopped by a problem that is currently displayed. If memory can be erased, then problem was only temporary or is a problem that can only be detected while driving.
5. If the diagnostic trouble code is not erased or if the ABS function is stopped by a repeated driving test and a diagnostic trouble code is output, inspect system according the diagnostic trouble symptom quick reference inspection chart, **Fig. 14.**
6. Diagnostic Trouble Codes 16 (battery is dead) and 35 (engine is stopped) are output even when the ABS system is normal. These diagnostic trouble codes are output only for a current problem and, if the vehicle's condition returns to normal, then the diagnostic trouble codes will disappear.

DIAGNOSTIC CHARTS

Proceed to the appropriate diagnostic trouble code chart, **Figs. 15 though 28,** as indicated by the diagnostic trouble code quick reference inspection chart, **Fig. 11.**

POINTS TO NOTE FOR TRANSIENT MALFUNCTIONS

Momentary problems can occur in electronic circuits and with input and output signals, which can result in temporary trouble symptoms or a diagnostic trouble code being recorded by means of ECU onboard diagnostics. If the cause of the problem is continuous, the location of the abnormality can be discovered through standard troubleshooting procedures. However, the symptoms of some transient problems may return to normal by themselves, so there is a possibility that the cause of the problem will be unclear.

The causes of problems in vehicles which are malfunctioning "temporarily" (when trouble symptoms do not reoccur) are mainly vibrations, heat and excess electrical resistance. By carrying out an inspection according to the simulation method given below, the trouble symptom can be made to reoccur.
1. When the main cause is probably vibration, proceed as follows:
   a. Gently shake connector up, down, right and left.
   b. Gently rock each sensor by hand.
   c. Gently shake other moving parts.
2. When the main cause is probably heat, heat the component under suspicion to no more than 176°F.
3. When the main cause is probably excessive electrical resistance, turn all electrical switches, including the headlight and rear defogger.
4. If the trouble symptom does not reoccur even after performing these inspections, do not continue attempts to simulate cause of symptom.

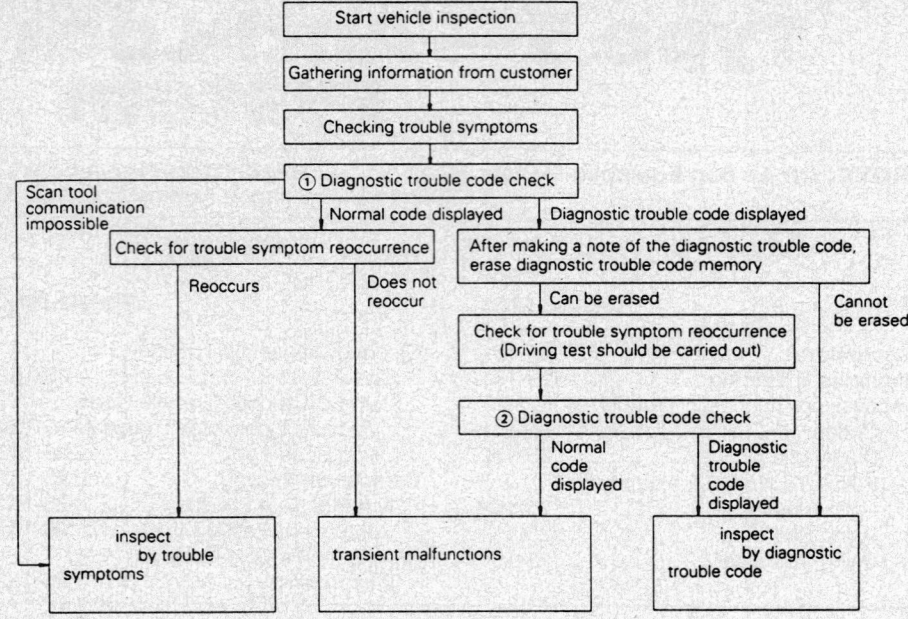

NOTE
If a normal code is displayed in the diagnostic trouble code check in ②, the problem may be only transient. However, in this case the related connector for the diagnostic trouble code displayed in the diagnostic trouble code check in ① should be checked first.

CR4029100611000X

Fig. 2   ABS troubleshooting chart

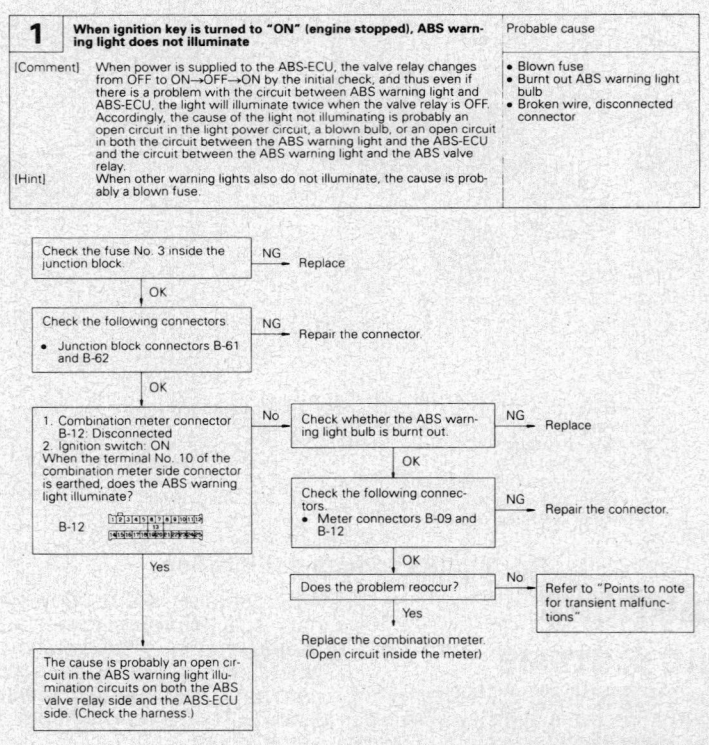

CR4029100634000X

Fig. 3   Symptom troubleshooting chart 1

Diagnostic Trouble Code Interpretation

Refer to **Fig. 11** for diagnostic trouble code interpretation.

Clearing Diagnostic Trouble Codes
USING SCAN TOOL

1. Erase memory with scan tool using tool manufacturer's instructions. After

Continued on page 25-161

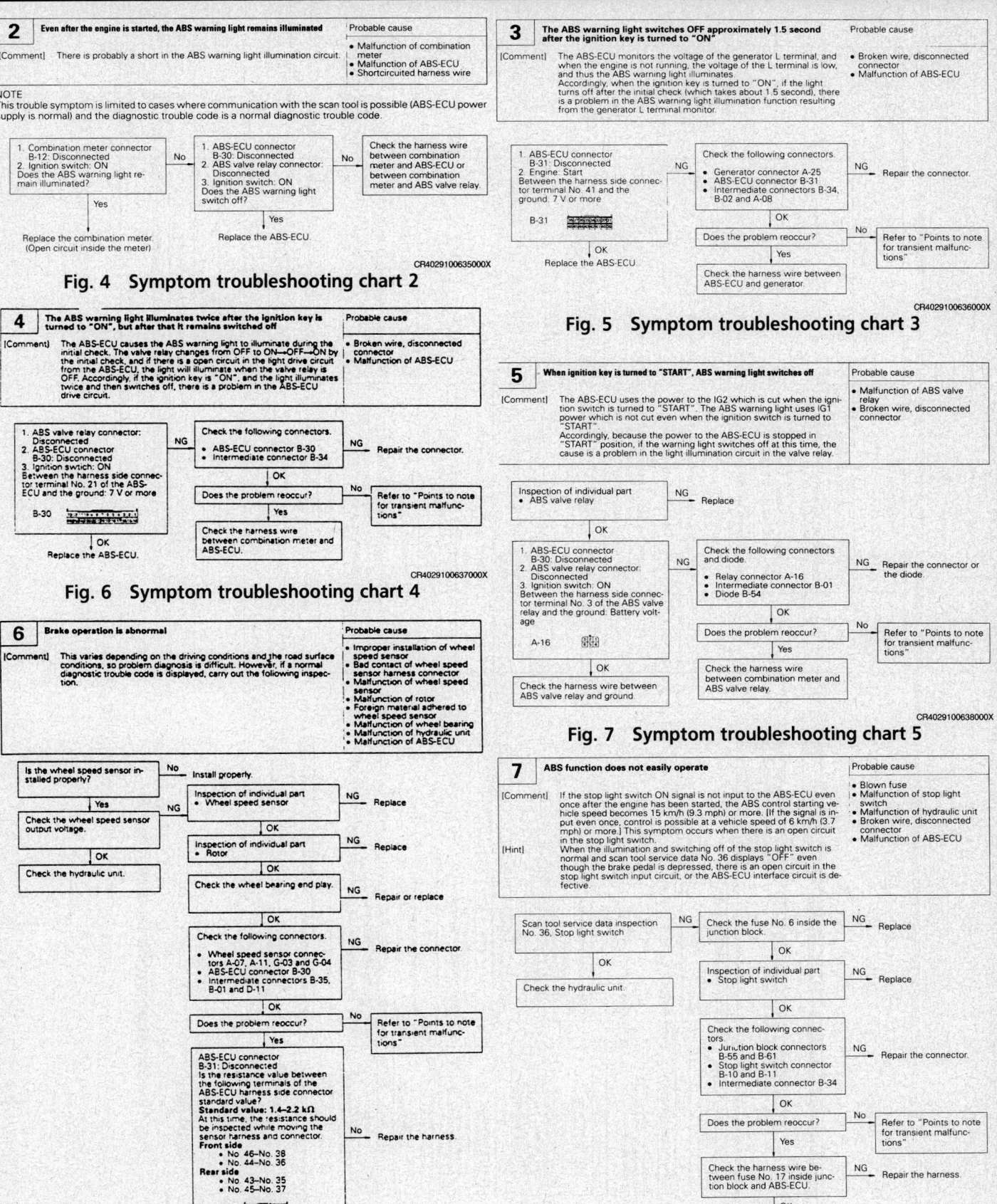

2 | Even after the engine is started, the ABS warning light remains illuminated | Probable cause

[Comment] There is probably a short in the ABS warning light illumination circuit.

- Malfunction of combination meter
- Malfunction of ABS-ECU
- Shortcircuited harness wire

NOTE
This trouble symptom is limited to cases where communication with the scan tool is possible (ABS-ECU power supply is normal) and the diagnostic trouble code is a normal diagnostic trouble code.

1. Combination meter connector B-12: Disconnected
2. Ignition switch: ON
Does the ABS warning light remain illuminated?

→ No → 1. ABS-ECU connector B-30: Disconnected
2. ABS valve relay connector: Disconnected
3. Ignition switch: ON
Does the ABS warning light switch off?

→ No → Check the harness wire between combination meter and ABS-ECU or between combination meter and ABS valve relay.

↓ Yes
Replace the combination meter. (Open circuit inside the meter)

↓ Yes
Replace the ABS-ECU.

CR4029100635000X

Fig. 4 Symptom troubleshooting chart 2

3 | The ABS warning light switches OFF approximately 1.5 second after the ignition key is turned to "ON" | Probable cause

[Comment] The ABS-ECU monitors the voltage of the generator L terminal, and when the engine is not running, the voltage of the L terminal is low, and thus the ABS warning light illuminates. Accordingly, when the ignition key is turned to "ON", if the light turns off after the initial check (which takes about 1.5 second), there is a problem in the ABS warning light illumination function resulting from the generator L terminal monitor.

- Broken wire, disconnected connector
- Malfunction of ABS-ECU

1. ABS-ECU connector B-31: Disconnected
2. Engine: Start
Between the harness side connector terminal No. 41 and the ground: 7 V or more

B-31

→ NG → Check the following connectors.
- Generator connector A-25
- ABS-ECU connector B-31
- Intermediate connectors B-34, B-02 and A-08

→ NG → Repair the connector.

↓ OK
Replace the ABS-ECU.

↓ OK
Does the problem reoccur? → No → Refer to "Points to note for transient malfunctions"

↓ Yes
Check the harness wire between ABS-ECU and generator.

CR4029100636000X

Fig. 5 Symptom troubleshooting chart 3

4 | The ABS warning light illuminates twice after the ignition key is turned to "ON", but after that it remains switched off | Probable cause

[Comment] The ABS-ECU causes the ABS warning light to illuminate during the initial check. The valve relay changes from OFF to ON→OFF→ON by the initial check, and if there is a open circuit in the light drive circuit from the ABS-ECU to the valve relay, the light will illuminate when the valve relay is OFF. Accordingly, if the ignition key is "ON", and the light illuminates twice and then switches off, there is a problem in the ABS light drive circuit.

- Broken wire, disconnected connector
- Malfunction of ABS-ECU

1. ABS valve relay connector: Disconnected
2. ABS-ECU connector B-30: Disconnected
3. Ignition switch: ON
Between the harness side connector terminal No. 21 of the ABS-ECU and the ground: 7 V or more

B-30

→ NG → Check the following connectors.
- ABS-ECU connector B-30
- Intermediate connector B-34

→ NG → Repair the connector.

↓ OK
Does the problem reoccur? → No → Refer to "Points to note for transient malfunctions"

↓ Yes
Check the harness wire between combination meter and ABS-ECU.

↓ OK
Replace the ABS-ECU.

CR4029100637000X

Fig. 6 Symptom troubleshooting chart 4

5 | When ignition key is turned to "START", ABS warning light switches off | Probable cause

[Comment] The ABS-ECU uses the power to the IG2 which is cut when the ignition switch is turned to "START". The ABS warning light uses IG1 power which is not cut even when the ignition switch is turned to "START".
Accordingly, because the power to the ABS-ECU is stopped in "START" position, if the warning light switches off at this time, the cause is a problem in the light illumination circuit in the valve relay.

- Malfunction of ABS valve relay
- Broken wire, disconnected connector

Inspection of individual part
- ABS valve relay

→ NG → Replace

↓ OK
1. ABS-ECU connector B-30: Disconnected
2. ABS valve relay connector: Disconnected
3. Ignition switch: ON
Between the harness side connector terminal No. 3 of the ABS valve relay and the ground: Battery voltage

A-16

→ NG → Check the following connectors and diode.
- Relay connector A-16
- Intermediate connector B-01
- Diode B-54

→ NG → Repair the connector or the diode.

↓ OK
Does the problem reoccur? → No → Refer to "Points to note for transient malfunctions"

↓ Yes
Check the harness wire between combination meter and ABS valve relay.

↓ OK
Check the harness wire between ABS valve relay and ground.

CR4029100638000X

Fig. 7 Symptom troubleshooting chart 5

6 | Brake operation is abnormal | Probable cause

[Comment] This varies depending on the driving conditions and the road surface conditions, so problem diagnosis is difficult. However, if a normal diagnostic trouble code is displayed, carry out the following inspection.

- Improper installation of wheel speed sensor
- Bad contact of wheel speed sensor harness connector
- Malfunction of wheel speed sensor
- Malfunction of rotor
- Foreign material adhered to wheel speed sensor
- Malfunction of wheel bearing
- Malfunction of hydraulic unit
- Malfunction of ABS-ECU

Is the wheel speed sensor installed properly? → No → Install properly.

↓ Yes
Check the wheel speed sensor output voltage.

→ Inspection of individual part
- Wheel speed sensor
→ NG → Replace

↓ OK
Check the hydraulic unit.

↓ OK
Inspection of individual part
- Rotor
→ NG → Replace

↓ OK
Check the wheel bearing end play. → NG → Repair or replace

↓ OK
Check the following connectors.
- Wheel speed sensor connectors A-07, A-11, G-03 and G-04
- ABS-ECU connector B-30
- Intermediate connectors B-35, B-01 and D-11
→ NG → Repair the connector.

↓ OK
Does the problem reoccur? → No → Refer to "Points to note for transient malfunctions"

↓ Yes
ABS-ECU connector B-31: Disconnected
Is the resistance value between the following terminals of the ABS-ECU harness side connector standard value?
Standard value: 1.4–2.2 kΩ
At this time, the resistance should be inspected while moving the sensor harness and connector.
Front side
- No. 46–No. 38
- No. 44–No. 36
Rear side
- No. 43–No. 35
- No. 45–No. 37

B-31

→ No → Repair the harness.

↓ Yes
Replace the ABS-ECU.

CR4029100639000X

Fig. 8 Symptom troubleshooting chart 6

7 | ABS function does not easily operate | Probable cause

[Comment] If the stop light switch ON signal is not input to the ABS-ECU even once after the engine has been started, the ABS control starting vehicle speed becomes 15 km/h (9.3 mph) or more. [If the signal is input even once, control is possible at a vehicle speed of 6 km/h (3.7 mph) or more.] This symptom occurs when there is an open circuit in the stop light switch.

[Hint] When the illumination and switching off of the stop light switch is normal and scan tool service data No. 36 displays "OFF" even though the brake pedal is depressed, there is an open circuit in the stop light switch input circuit, or the ABS-ECU interface circuit is defective.

- Blown fuse
- Malfunction of stop light switch
- Malfunction of hydraulic unit
- Broken wire, disconnected connector
- Malfunction of ABS-ECU

Scan tool service data inspection No. 36, Stop light switch → NG → Check the fuse No. 6 inside the junction block. → NG → Replace

↓ OK
Check the hydraulic unit.

↓ OK
Inspection of individual part
- Stop light switch
→ NG → Replace

↓ OK
Check the following connectors.
- Junction block connectors B-55 and B-61
- Stop light switch connector B-10 and B-11
- Intermediate connector B-34
→ NG → Repair the connector.

↓ OK
Does the problem reoccur? → No → Refer to "Points to note for transient malfunctions"

↓ Yes
Check the harness wire between fuse No. 17 inside junction block and ABS-ECU. → NG → Repair the harness.

↓ OK
Replace the ABS-ECU.

CR4029100640000X

Fig. 9 Symptom troubleshooting chart 7

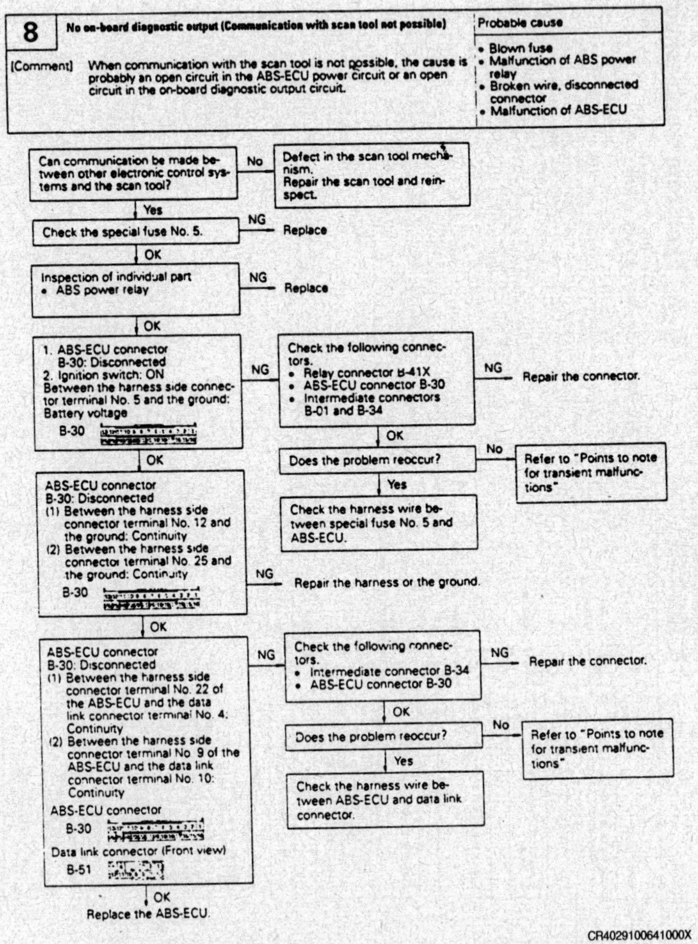

Diagnostic trouble code No.	Inspection item	Diagnosis content	Inspection chart No.
11	Front right wheel speed sensor	Open circuit	2
12	Front left wheel speed sensor		
13	Rear right wheel speed sensor		
14	Rear left wheel speed sensor		1
15	Open circuit in sensor	Open circuit in sensor	
16	Drop of battery voltage	Drop of ABS operation voltage	6
21	Front right wheel speed sensor	Short circuit	3
22	Front left wheel speed sensor		
23	Rear right wheel speed sensor		
24	Rear left wheel speed sensor		
25	Both rear wheel speed sensors	Open circuit in both rear wheel speed sensors, short circuit	4
31	Rotor of front right wheel speed sensor	Chipped tooth of rotor	5
32	Rotor of front left wheel speed sensor		
33	Rotor of rear right wheel speed sensor		
34	Rotor of rear left wheel speed sensor		
35	Generator	Drop of generator output voltage	7
41	Front right solenoid valve	No response to solenoid valve drive signal	8
42	Front left solenoid valve		
43	Rear right solenoid valve		
44	Rear left solenoid valve		
51	Valve relay 1	Detection impossible in OFF condition	9
52	Valve relay 2	Detection impossible in ON condition	10
53	Motor relay, motor 1	ON impossible	11
54	Motor relay, motor 2	OFF impossible	12
55	Sticking of motor	Motor operation impossible	13
62	Malfunction inside hydraulic unit	Hydraulic pressure reduction impossible	14
63	Malfunction inside ABS-ECU	Irregular program, etc.	Replace ABS-ECU

CR40291006130000X

Fig. 11 Diagnostic trouble code quick reference inspection chart

CR40291006410000X

Fig. 10 Symptom troubleshooting chart 8

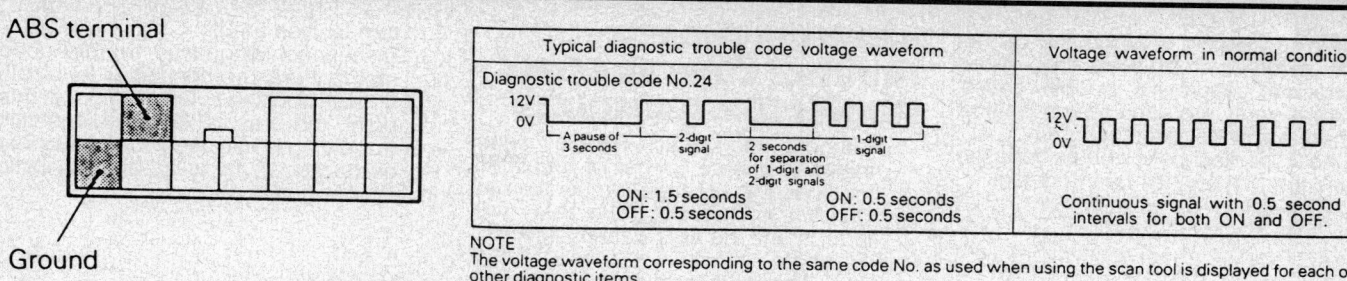

ABS terminal

Ground

CR4029100614000X

Fig. 12   Data link connector

Typical diagnostic trouble code voltage waveform	Voltage waveform in normal condition
Diagnostic trouble code No.24	

Diagnostic trouble code No.24

12V
0V
A pause of 3 seconds — 2-digit signal — 2 seconds for separation of 1-digit and 2-digit signals — 1-digit signal

ON: 1.5 seconds
OFF: 0.5 seconds

ON: 0.5 seconds
OFF: 0.5 seconds

12V
0V

Continuous signal with 0.5 second intervals for both ON and OFF.

NOTE
The voltage waveform corresponding to the same code No. as used when using the scan tool is displayed for each of the other diagnostic items.

Fig. 13   Voltmeter output voltage results   CR4029100615000X

Trouble symptom		Inspection chart No.
When the ignition key is turned to "ON" (engine stopped), the ABS warning light does not illuminate. 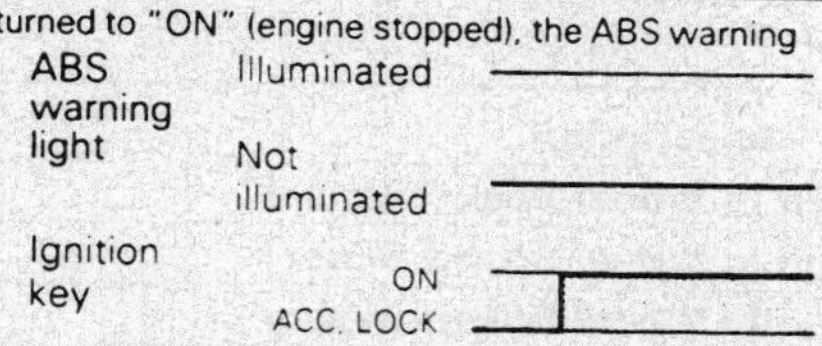	ABS warning light — Illuminated / Not illuminated; Ignition key — ON / ACC. LOCK	1
After the engine starts, the light remains illuminated. 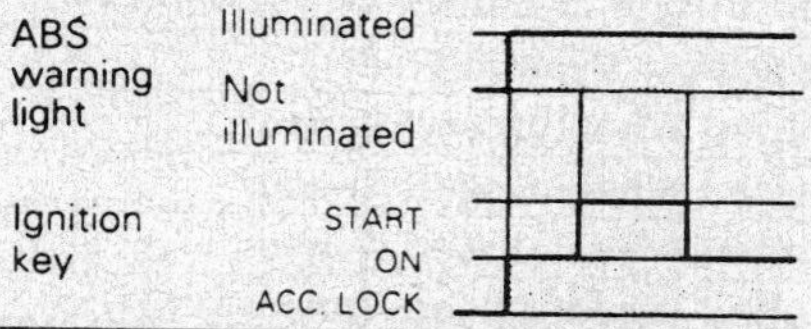	ABS warning light — Illuminated / Not illuminated; Ignition key — START / ON / ACC. LOCK	2
The ABS warning light switches off approximately 1.5 second after the ignition key is turned to "ON". 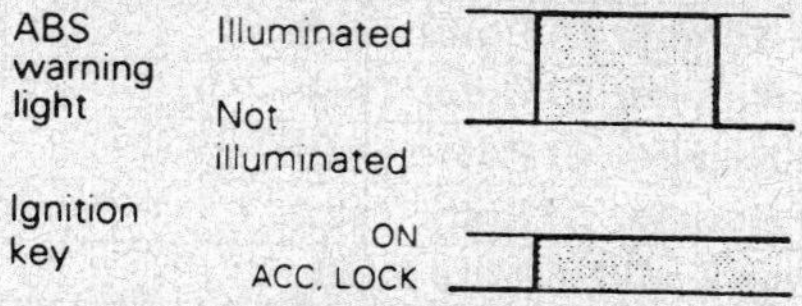	ABS warning light — Illuminated / Not illuminated; Ignition key — ON / ACC. LOCK	3
After the ignition key is turned to "ON", the ABS warning light illuminates twice, but after that it remains switched off. 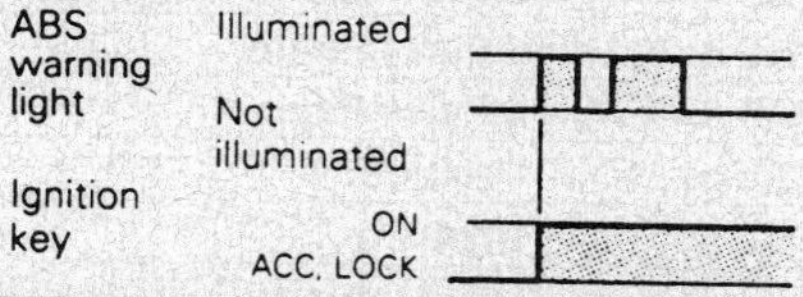	ABS warning light — Illuminated / Not illuminated; Ignition key — ON / ACC. LOCK	4
When the ignition key is turned to "START", the ABS warning light switches off. 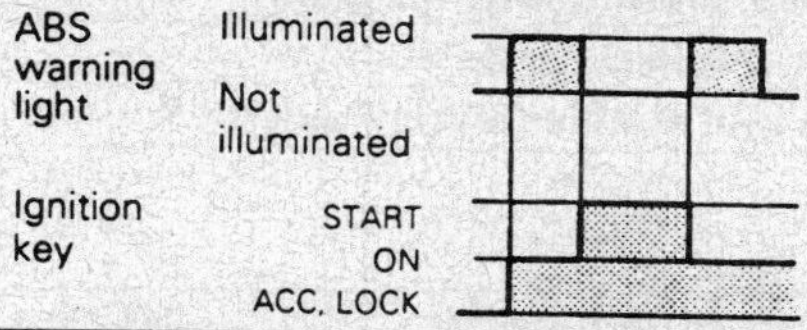	ABS warning light — Illuminated / Not illuminated; Ignition key — START / ON / ACC. LOCK	5
Faulty ABS operation	Unequal braking power on both sides	6
	Insufficient braking power	
	ABS operates under normal braking conditions	
	ABS operates before vehicle stops under normal braking conditions	
	Large brake pedal vibration when ABS operates	
	Large amount of skidding when ABS operates (ABS does not operate properly)	7
No on-board diagnostic output (no communication with scan tool)		8

CR4029100616000X

Fig. 14   Diagnostic trouble symptom quick reference inspection chart

erasing memory, a command cannot be received from scan tool. When checking diagnostic trouble codes, momentarily stop and restart engine, then reactivate scan tool.

2. Check for diagnostic trouble codes to ensure memory has been erased.

USING DIAGNOSTIC TROUBLE CODE ERASURE CONNECTOR TERMINALS

1. Connect diagnostic trouble code memory erasure connector terminals together, **Fig. 29** then turn ignition to On. At this time, the valve relay will turn Off and the ABS warning light will illuminate.
2. After 7 seconds or more has passed, turn ignition to Off.
3. Disconnect diagnostic trouble code memory erasure connector terminals and turn ignition to On position. At this point, the erasure of one diagnostic trouble code has been erased. Repeat as necessary to erase all diagnostic trouble codes.

DIAGNOSTIC CHART INDEX

Code	Description	Page No.	Fig. No.
11	Open Circuit In Wheel Speed Sensor	25-157	16
12	Open Circuit In Wheel Speed Sensor	25-157	16
13	Open Circuit In Wheel Speed Sensor	25-157	16
14	Open Circuit In Wheel Speed Sensor	25-157	16
15	Open Circuit In Sensor	25-156	15
16	Power Supply System Fault	25-158	20
21	Short Circuited Wheel Speed Sensor	25-157	17
22	Short Circuited Wheel Speed Sensor	25-157	17
23	Short Circuited Wheel Speed Sensor	25-157	17
24	Short Circuited Wheel Speed Sensor	25-157	17
25	Open Or Short Circuit In Both Rear Wheel Speed Sensors	25-157	18
31	Incorrect Number Of Rotor Teeth	25-157	19
32	Incorrect Number Of Rotor Teeth	25-157	19
33	Incorrect Number Of Rotor Teeth	25-157	19
34	Incorrect Number Of Rotor Teeth	25-157	19
35	Generator & Allied Parts Fault	25-158	21
41	Solenoid Valve & Allied Parts Fault	25-158	22
42	Solenoid Valve & Allied Parts Fault	25-158	22
43	Solenoid Valve & Allied Parts Fault	25-158	22
44	Solenoid Valve & Allied Parts Fault	25-158	22
51	Valve Relay " On" Problem	25-158	23
52	Valve Relay " Off" Problem	25-159	24
53	Motor Relay, Motor " Off" Problem	25-159	25
54	Motor Relay, Motor " On" Problem	25-159	26
55	Motor & Allied Parts Fault	25-159	27
62	Hydraulic Unit & Allied Parts Fault	25-160	28

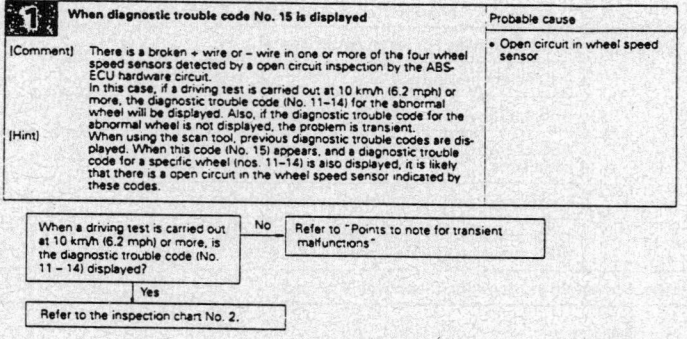

CR4029100620000X

Fig. 15   Code 15: Open Circuit In Sensor

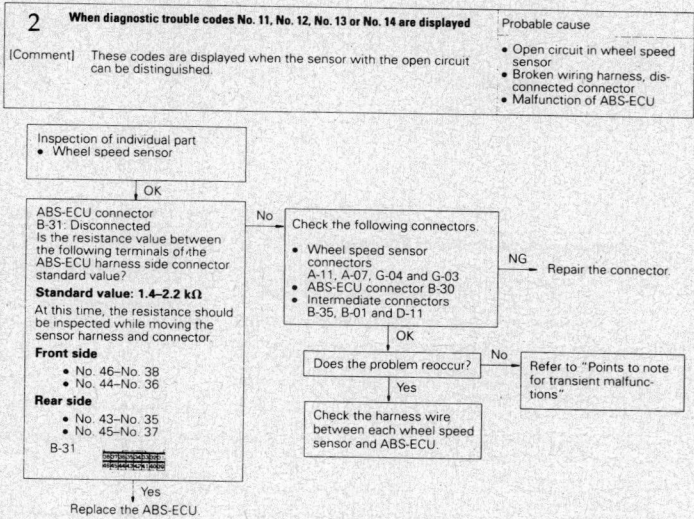

2 When diagnostic trouble codes No. 11, No. 12, No. 13 or No. 14 are displayed

[Comment] These codes are displayed when the sensor with the open circuit can be distinguished.

Probable cause
- Open circuit in wheel speed sensor
- Broken wiring harness, disconnected connector
- Malfunction of ABS-ECU

Fig. 16 Codes 11, 12, 13 & 14: Open Circuit In Wheel Speed Sensor

CR4029100621000X

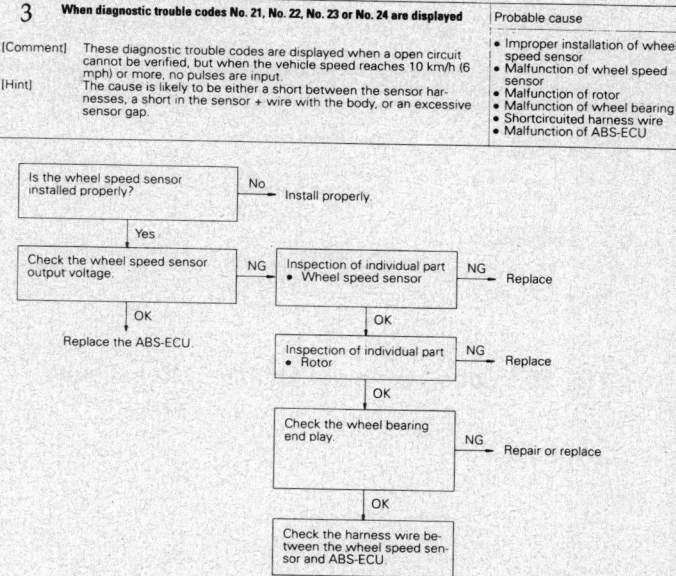

3 When diagnostic trouble codes No. 21, No. 22, No. 23 or No. 24 are displayed

[Comment] These diagnostic trouble codes are displayed when a open circuit cannot be verified, but when the vehicle speed reaches 10 km/h (6 mph) or more, no pulses are input.

[Hint] The cause is likely to be either a short between the sensor harnesses, a short in the sensor + wire with the body, or an excessive sensor gap.

Probable cause
- Improper installation of wheel speed sensor
- Malfunction of wheel speed sensor
- Malfunction of rotor
- Malfunction of wheel bearing
- Shortcircuited harness wire
- Malfunction of ABS-ECU

Fig. 17 Codes 21, 22, 23 & 24: Short Circuited Wheel Speed Sensor

CR4029100622000X

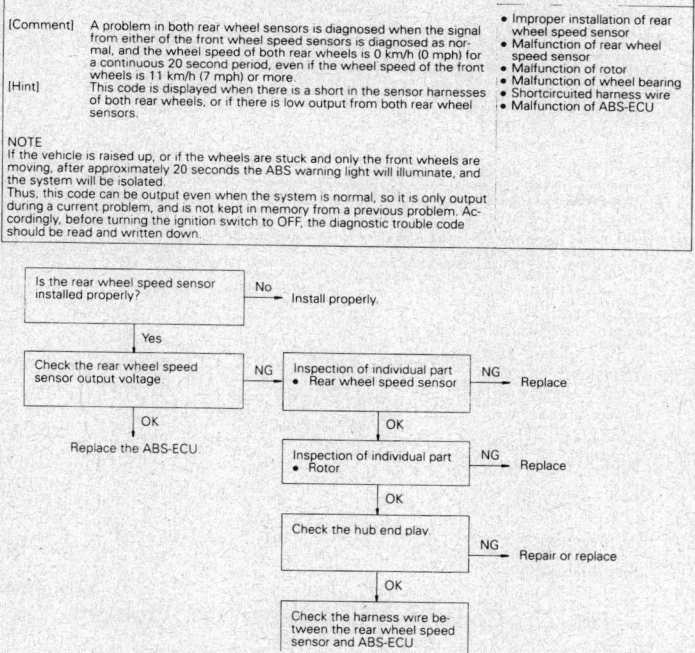

4 When diagnostic trouble code No. 25 is displayed

[Comment] A problem in both rear wheel sensors is diagnosed when the signal from either of the front wheel speed sensors is diagnosed as normal, and the wheel speed of both rear wheels is 0 km/h (0 mph) for a continuous 20 second period, even if the wheel speed of the front wheels is 11 km/h (7 mph) or more.

[Hint] This code is displayed when there is a short in the sensor harnesses of both rear wheels, or if there is low output from both rear wheel sensors.

NOTE
If the vehicle is raised up, or if the wheels are stuck and only the front wheels are moving, after approximately 20 seconds the ABS warning light will illuminate, and the system will be isolated.
Thus, this code can be output even when the system is normal, so it is only output during a current problem, and is not kept in memory from a previous problem. Accordingly, before turning the ignition switch to OFF, the diagnostic trouble code should be read and written down.

Probable cause
- Improper installation of rear wheel speed sensor
- Malfunction of rear wheel speed sensor
- Malfunction of rotor
- Malfunction of wheel bearing
- Shortcircuited harness wire
- Malfunction of ABS-ECU

Fig. 18 Code 25: Open Or Short Circuit In Both Rear Wheel Speed Sensors

CR4029100623000X

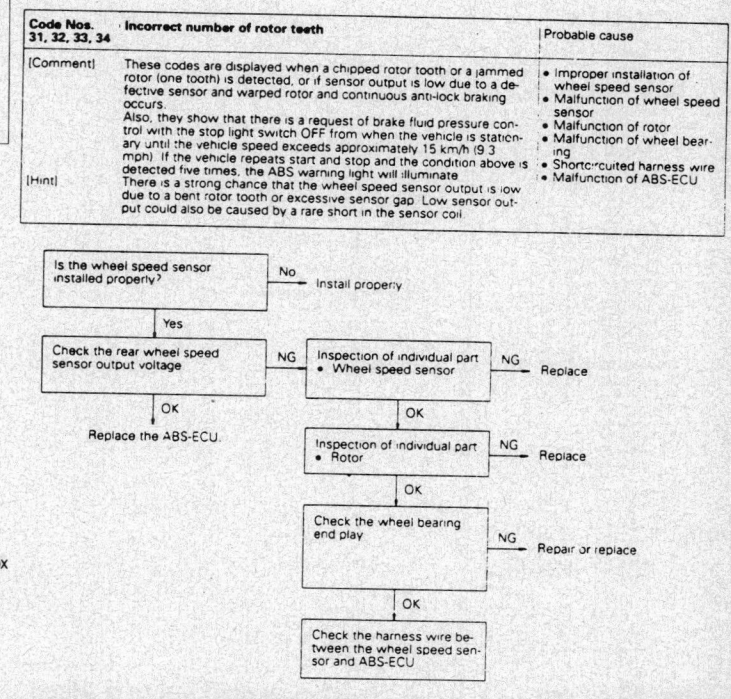

Code Nos. 31, 32, 33, 34	Incorrect number of rotor teeth	Probable cause
[Comment]	These codes are displayed when a chipped rotor tooth or a jammed rotor (one tooth) is detected, or if sensor output is low due to a defective sensor and warped rotor and continuous anti-lock braking occurs. Also, they show that there is a request of brake fluid pressure control with the stop light switch OFF from when the vehicle is stationary until the vehicle speed exceeds approximately 15 km/h (9.3 mph). If the vehicle repeats start and stop and the condition above is detected five times, the ABS warning light will illuminate.	• Improper installation of wheel speed sensor • Malfunction of wheel speed sensor • Malfunction of rotor • Malfunction of wheel bearing • Shortcircuited harness wire • Malfunction of ABS-ECU
[Hint]	There is a strong chance that the wheel speed sensor output is low due to a bent rotor tooth or excessive sensor gap. Low sensor output could also be caused by a rare short in the sensor coil.	

Fig. 19 Codes 31, 32, 33 & 34: Incorrect Number Of Rotor Teeth

CR4029200722000X

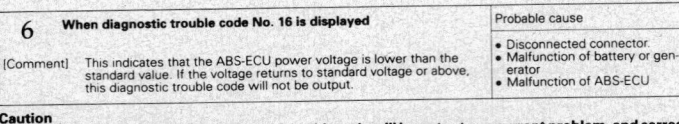

6 | **When diagnostic trouble code No. 16 is displayed** | **Probable cause**

[Comment] This indicates that the ABS-ECU power voltage is lower than the standard value. If the voltage returns to standard voltage or above, this diagnostic trouble code will not be output.

- Disconnected connector.
- Malfunction of battery or generator
- Malfunction of ABS-ECU

Caution
If the battery voltage drops during inspection, this code will be output as a current problem, and correct diagnosis of the problem cannot be made.
Before carrying out the following inspection, check the battery level, and refill it if necessary.

1. ABS-ECU connector
   B-30: Disconnected
2. Engine: Start
Between the connector terminal No. 5 and the ground: 10 V or more

B-30

→ NG →

Check the following connectors.
- Relay connector B-41X
- ABS-ECU connector B-30
- Intermediate connectors B-01 and B-34

→ NG → Repair the connector.

↓ OK

Does the problem reoccur? → No → Refer to "Points to note for transient malfunctions"

↓ Yes

Check the battery or the generator.

↓ OK

Replace the ABS-ECU.

CR4029100625000X

Fig. 20   Code 16: Power Supply System Fault

7 | **When diagnostic trouble code No. 35 is displayed** | **Probable cause**

[Comment] This indicates that the output voltage of the generator L terminal is low when the ignition key is turned to "ON" and the engine is stopped, or when the engine is running.
If the voltage returns to standard voltage or above, this problem code will not be output.

[Hint] When the output voltage of the generator L terminal is low, the charge warning light will illuminate. This code also appears when there is a short in the generator L terminal monitor circuit, but not if there is a open circuit in that circuit. If the scan tool service data displays No. 35, this diagnostic trouble code is output.

- Incorrectly connected connector, shortcircuited harness wire.
- Malfunction of generator
- Malfunction of ABS-ECU

NOTE
If the engine is stopped, this code will be output, even if the situation is normal, so the following inspection should only be carried out if the code is output while the engine is running.

1. ABS-ECU connector
   B-31: Disconnected
2. Engine: Start
Between the connector terminal No. 41 and the ground: 7 V or more

B-31

→ NG →

Check the following connectors.
- ABS-ECU connector B-31
- Generator connector A-25
- Intermediate connectors B-34, B-02 and A-08

→ NG → Repair the connector.

↓ OK

Does the problem reoccur? → No → Refer to "Points to note for transient malfunctions"

↓ Yes

Check the generator and the harness wire between ABS-ECU and generator.

↓ OK

Replace the ABS-ECU.

CR4029100626000X

Fig. 21   Code 35: Generator & Allied Parts Fault

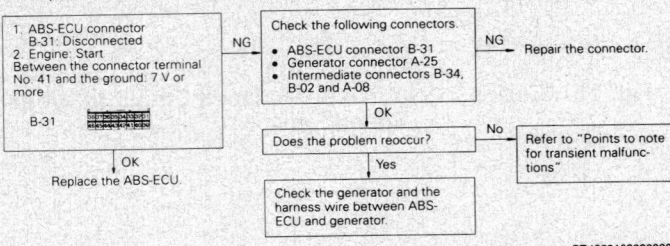

8 | **When diagnostic trouble codes No. 41, No. 42, No. 43 or No. 44 are displayed** | **Probable cause**

[Comment] The ABS-ECU normally monitors the solenoid valve drive circuit. If there is no current flowing to the solenoid even when the solenoid is ON, or the current continues to flow to the solenoid even when the solenoid is OFF, the ABS-ECU diagnoses a open circuit or short in the solenoid coil or a open circuit or short in the harness, and this diagnostic trouble code is output.

- Malfunction of hydraulic unit
- Broken wire, disconnected connector
- Shortcircuited harness wire
- Malfunction of ABS-ECU

Hydraulic unit connector
A-13: Disconnected
Is the resistance value between the following terminals of the hydraulic unit side connector standard value?

Standard value: 3.10–3.34 Ω
- No. 7–No. 5
- No. 3–No. 1
- No. 8–No. 6
- No. 4–No. 2

A-13

→ No → Replace the hydraulic unit.

↓ Yes

1. Hydraulic unit connector
   A-13: Disconnected
2. ABS-ECU connector
   B-30: Disconnected
Is the resistance value between the terminals of the hydraulic unit side connector and ABS-ECU harness side connector standard value?

Standard value: 3.10–3.34 Ω
Hydraulic – ABS-ECU side
unit
side
- No. 7–No. 15
- No. 3–No. 2
- No. 8–No. 14
- No. 4–No. 1

Hydraulic
unit
side   ABS-ECU side

A-13   B-30

→ NG →

Check the following connectors.
- Hydraulic unit connector A-13
- ABS-ECU connector B-30
- Intermediate connectors B-01 and B-35

→ NG → Repair the connector.

↓ OK

Does the problem reoccur? → No → Refer to "Points to note for transient malfunctions"

↓ Yes

Check the harness wire between hydraulic unit and ABS-ECU.

↓ Yes

Replace the ABS-ECU.

CR4029100627000X

Fig. 22   Codes 41, 42, 43 & 44: Solenoid Valve & Allied Parts Fault

9 | **When diagnostic trouble code No. 51 is displayed** | **Probable cause**

[Comment] During the initial check when the ignition switch is turned to "ON", if power is being supplied to the solenoid when the valve relay is OFF, the ABS-ECU diagnoses a melted relay contact or a short in the valve relay drive circuit, and this diagnostic trouble code is output.

- Malfunction of ABS valve relay
- Shortcircuited harness wire
- Malfunction of ABS-ECU

Inspection of individual part
- ABS valve relay

→ NG → Replace

↓ OK

1. ABS-ECU connector
   B-30: Disconnected
Between the harness side connector terminal No. 8 and the ground: No continuity

B-30

→ NG → Check the harness wire between ABS valve relay and ABS-ECU.

↓ OK

Replace the ABS-ECU.

CR4029100628000X

Fig. 23   Code 51: Valve Relay "On" Problem

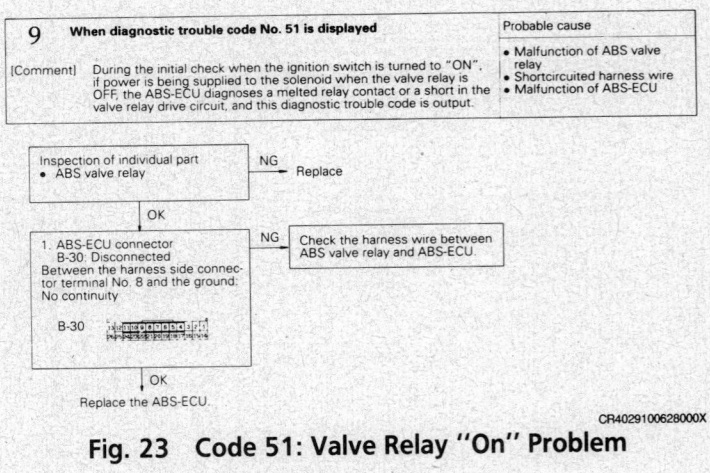

10 | When diagnostic trouble code No. 52 is displayed | Probable cause

[Comment] During the initial check when the ignition switch is turned to "ON", if power is not being supplied to the solenoid when the valve relay is ON, the ABS-ECU diagnoses an OFF problem in the valve relay (not turned ON), and outputs this diagnostic trouble code.

Probable cause
- Malfunction of ABS valve relay
- Broken wire, disconnected connector
- Malfunction of ABS-ECU

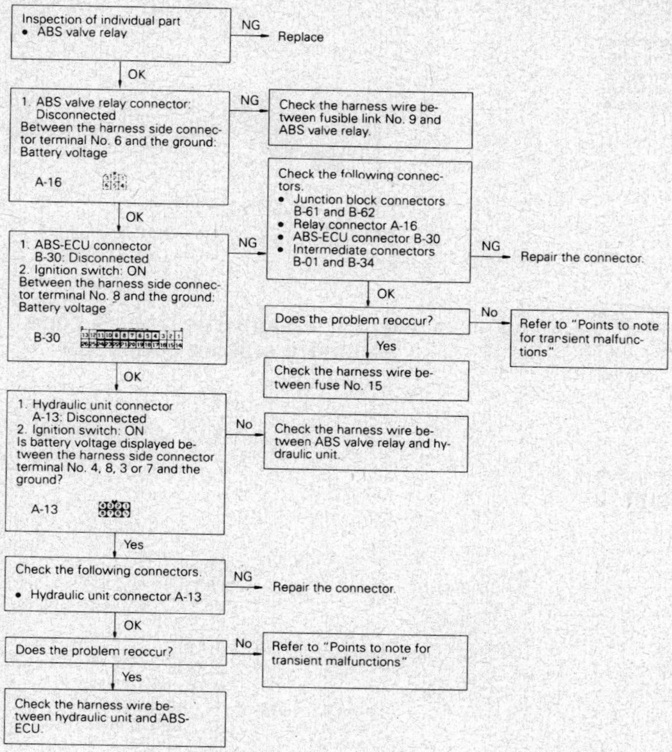

Inspection of individual part
- ABS valve relay
→ NG → Replace
↓ OK

1. ABS valve relay connector: Disconnected
Between the harness side connector terminal No. 6 and the ground: Battery voltage

A-16
→ NG → Check the harness wire between fusible link No. 9 and ABS valve relay.
↓ OK

1. ABS-ECU connector B-30: Disconnected
2. Ignition switch: ON
Between the harness side connector terminal No. 8 and the ground: Battery voltage

B-30
→ Check the following connectors.
- Junction block connectors B-61 and B-62
- Relay connector A-16
- ABS-ECU connector B-30
- Intermediate connectors B-01 and B-34
→ NG → Repair the connector.
↓ OK
Does the problem reoccur?
→ No → Refer to "Points to note for transient malfunctions"
↓ Yes
Check the harness wire between fuse No. 15
↓ OK

1. Hydraulic unit connector A-13: Disconnected
2. Ignition switch: ON
Is battery voltage displayed between the harness side connector terminal No. 4, 8, 3 or 7 and the ground?

A-13
→ No → Check the harness wire between ABS valve relay and hydraulic unit.
↓ Yes

Check the following connectors.
- Hydraulic unit connector A-13
→ NG → Repair the connector.
↓ OK
Does the problem reoccur?
→ No → Refer to "Points to note for transient malfunctions"
↓ Yes
Check the harness wire between hydraulic unit and ABS-ECU.

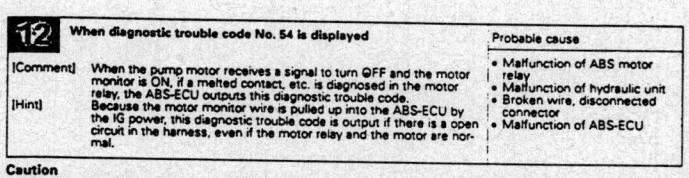

Fig. 24 Code 52: Valve Relay "Off" Problem

CR4029100629000X

---

11 | When diagnostic trouble code No. 53 is displayed | Probable cause

[Comment] When the motor pump receives a signal to turn ON and voltage at the motor monitor is LOW, the ABS-ECU outputs this diagnostic trouble code.
[Hint] If the sound of the motor relay operation can be heard when the No. 6 motor relay is driven by a scan tool actuator test, there is probably a short in the motor monitor wire.

Probable cause
- Malfunction of ABS motor relay
- Defective harness wire, disconnected connector
- Malfunction of ABS-ECU

Caution
In the case of actuator test No. 06, the engine should be started left running for a while after the test is completed to prevent the battery from being drained.

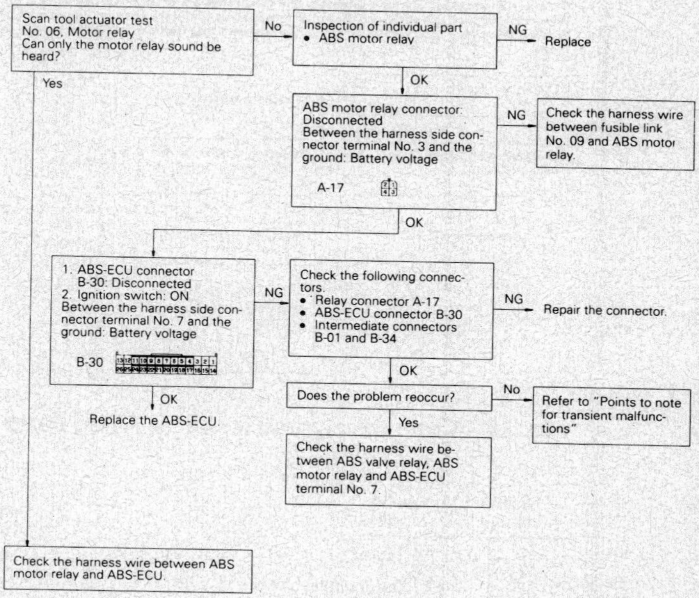

Scan tool actuator test No. 06, Motor relay
Can only the motor relay sound be heard?
→ No → Inspection of individual part
- ABS motor relay
→ NG → Replace
↓ OK
↓ Yes

ABS motor relay connector: Disconnected
Between the harness side connector terminal No. 3 and the ground: Battery voltage

A-17
→ NG → Check the harness wire between fusible link No. 09 and ABS motor relay.
↓ OK

1. ABS-ECU connector B-30: Disconnected
2. Ignition switch: ON
Between the harness side connector terminal No. 7 and the ground: Battery voltage

B-30
→ NG → Check the following connectors.
- Relay connector A-17
- ABS-ECU connector B-30
- Intermediate connectors B-01 and B-34
→ NG → Repair the connector.
↓ OK
Replace the ABS-ECU.

Does the problem reoccur?
→ No → Refer to "Points to note for transient malfunctions"
↓ Yes
Check the harness wire between ABS valve relay, ABS motor relay and ABS-ECU terminal No. 7.

Check the harness wire between ABS motor relay and ABS-ECU.

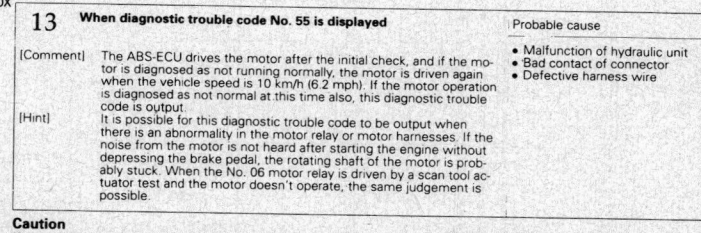

CR4029100630000X

Fig. 25 Code 53: Motor Relay, Motor "Off" Problem

---

12 | When diagnostic trouble code No. 54 is displayed | Probable cause

[Comment] When the pump motor receives a signal to turn OFF and the motor monitor is ON, if a melted contact, etc. is diagnosed in the motor relay, the ABS-ECU outputs this diagnostic trouble code.
[Hint] Because the motor monitor wire is pulled up into the ABS-ECU by the IG power, this diagnostic trouble code is output if there is a open circuit in the harness, even if the motor relay and the motor are normal.

Probable cause
- Malfunction of ABS motor relay
- Malfunction of hydraulic unit
- Broken wire, disconnected connector
- Malfunction of ABS-ECU

Caution
If there is a melted contact in the motor relay, the motor will keep turning, even if the ignition switch is turned to OFF. In such a case, immediately remove the fusible link (60 A) or disconnect the hydraulic unit A-12 connector. Excessive running of the motor will consume a battery.

When ignition switch is turned to "OFF", does the motor stop?
→ No → Inspection of individual part
- ABS motor relay
→ NG → Replace
↓ OK
Check the harness wire between ABS motor relay and ABS-ECU terminal No. 7.
↓ Yes

Check the following connectors.
- ABS-ECU connector B-30
- Intermediate connectors B-01 and B-35
→ NG → Repair the connector.
↓ OK

Check the harness wire between ABS motor relay and ABS-ECU terminal No. 13.
→ NG → Repair the connector.
↓ OK
Replace the ABS-ECU.

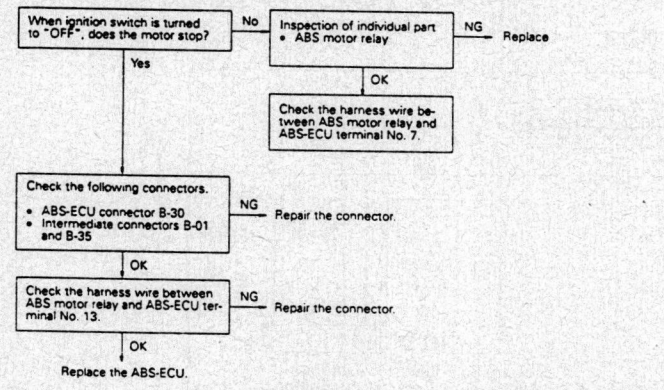

CR4029100631000X

Fig. 26 Code 54: Motor Relay, Motor "On" Problem

---

13 | When diagnostic trouble code No. 55 is displayed | Probable cause

[Comment] The ABS-ECU drives the motor after the initial check, and if the motor is diagnosed as not running normally, the motor is driven again when the vehicle speed is 10 km/h (6.2 mph). If the motor operation is diagnosed as not normal at this time also, this diagnostic trouble code is output.
[Hint] It is possible for this diagnostic trouble code to be output when there is an abnormality in the motor relay or motor harnesses. If the noise from the motor is not heard after starting the engine without depressing the brake pedal, the rotating shaft of the motor is probably stuck. When the No. 06 motor relay is driven by a scan tool actuator test and the motor doesn't operate, the same judgement is possible.

Probable cause
- Malfunction of hydraulic unit
- Bad contact of connector
- Defective harness wire

Caution
If the battery is depleted or if the generator L terminal voltage is low, the motor will not be driven, so when carrying out the motor drive check, check to be sure that these things are normal. Carry out the motor drive check while the vehicle is stationary.

Hydraulic unit connector A-12: Disconnected
When the battery is connected directly to the hydraulic unit motor terminal, does the motor operate?
→ No → Replace the hydraulic unit.
↓ Yes

Inspection of individual part
- ABS motor relay
→ NG → Replace
↓ OK

Check the following connectors.
- Relay connector A-17
- Hydraulic unit connector A-12
- ABS-ECU connector B-30
- Intermediate connectors B-01 and B-35
→ NG → Repair the harness.
↓ OK

Does the problem reoccur?
→ No → Refer to "Points to note for transient malfunctions"
↓ Yes
Check the harness wire between ABS-ECU and hydraulic unit, between ABS motor relay and hydraulic unit or between hydraulic unit and ground.

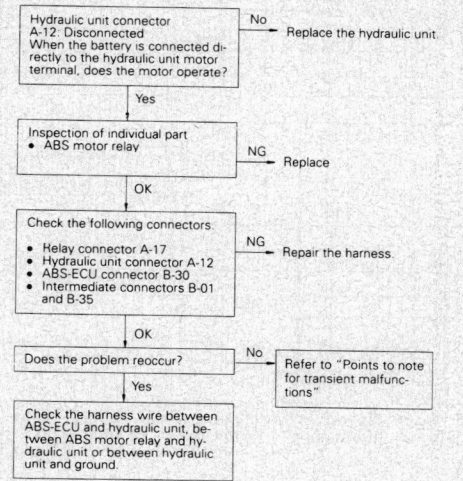

CR4029100632000X

Fig. 27 Code 55: Motor & Allied Parts Fault

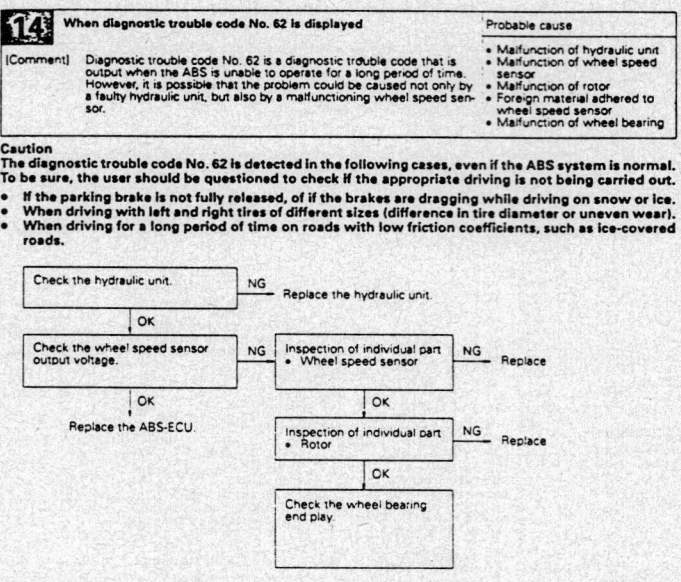

14. **When diagnostic trouble code No. 62 is displayed**

[Comment] Diagnostic trouble code No. 62 is a diagnostic trouble code that is output when the ABS is unable to operate for a long period of time. However, it is possible that the problem could be caused not only by a faulty hydraulic unit, but also by a malfunctioning wheel speed sensor.	**Probable cause** • Malfunction of hydraulic unit • Malfunction of wheel speed sensor • Malfunction of rotor • Foreign material adhered to wheel speed sensor • Malfunction of wheel bearing

Caution
The diagnostic trouble code No. 62 is detected in the following cases, even if the ABS system is normal. To be sure, the user should be questioned to check if the appropriate driving is not being carried out.

- If the parking brake is not fully released, or if the brakes are dragging while driving on snow or ice.
- When driving with left and right tires of different sizes (difference in tire diameter or uneven wear).
- When driving for a long period of time on roads with low friction coefficients, such as ice-covered roads.

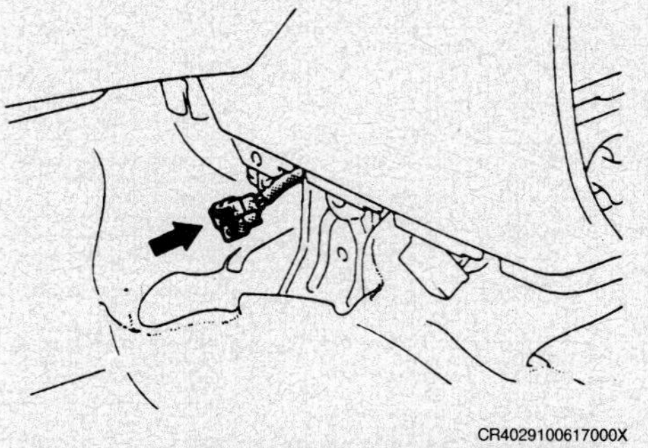

Fig. 29 Diagnostic trouble code memory erasure connector

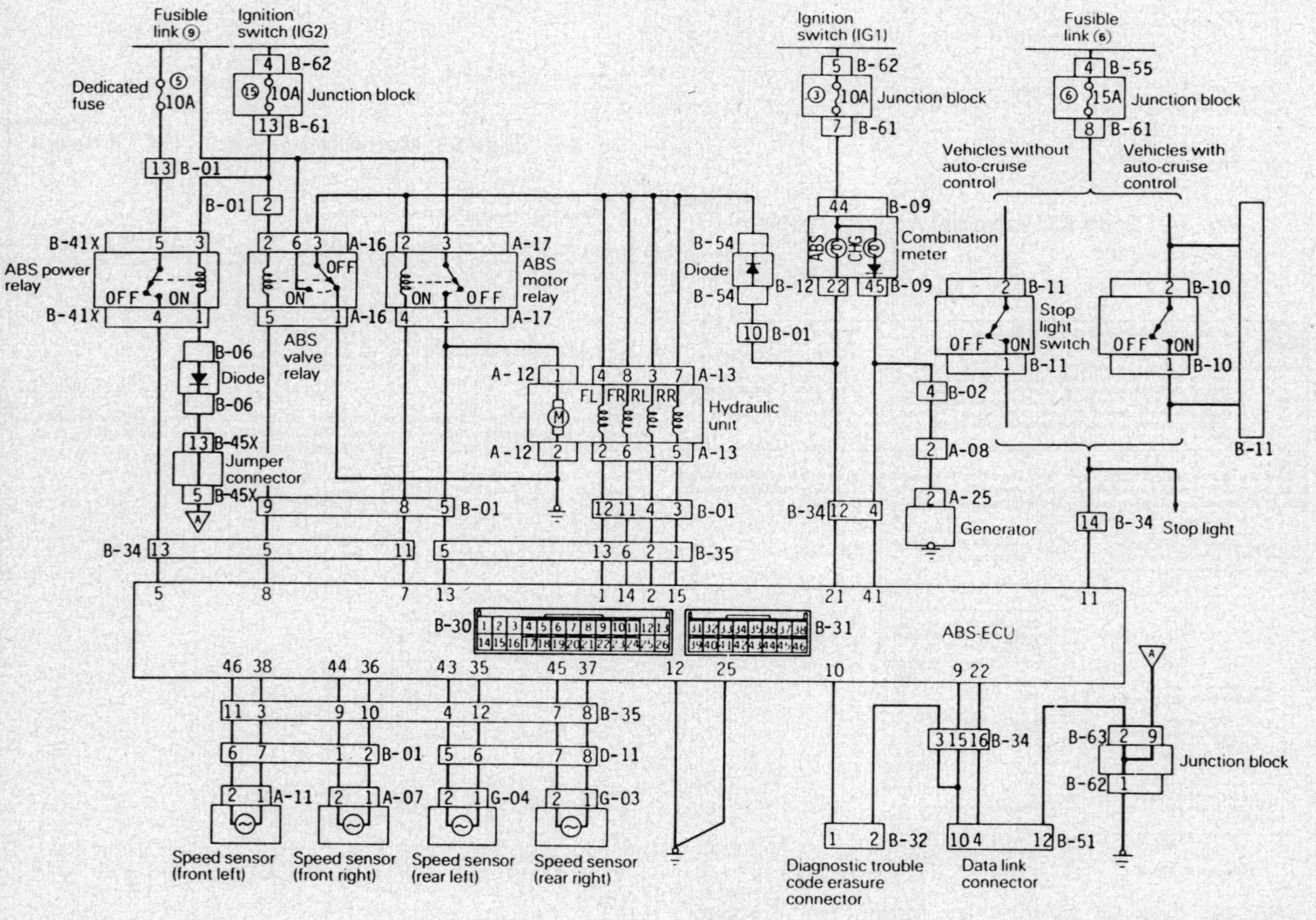

CR4029100617000X

CR4029100633000X

Fig. 28 Code 62: Hydraulic Unit & Allied Parts Fault

Fig. 30 ABS wiring diagram

CR4029100619000X

No.	Drive condition	Drive object	Drive specifications
01		Front right solenoid valve	Hydraulic pressure increase → hydraulic pressure decrease (2 sec) → hydraulic pressure increase (The motor turns ON at the same time as hydraulic pressure reduction, and then turns OFF 0.85 seconds after hydraulic pressure reduction is completed.)
02	A and B	Front left solenoid valve	
03		Rear right solenoid valve	
04		Rear left solenoid valve	
05	A	Valve relay and ABS warning light	Relay OFF signal is output for 2 seconds. For a six second period including 2 seconds before and after this, the ABS-ECU outputs and ABS warning light OFF signal. This checks the operation by illuminating the warning light when the relay is OFF.
06	A	Motor relay	Motor ON signal is output for 2 seconds.

Drive conditions:
- Condition A: Highest wheel speed is less than 10 km/h (6 mph).
- Condition B: Wheel speed of both front wheels or both rear wheels is 0 km/h (0 mph).

CR4029100618000X

Fig. 31   Actuator test specifications

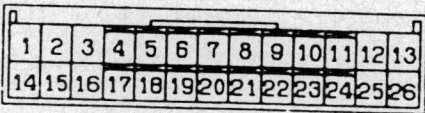

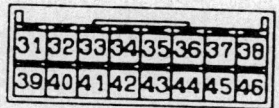

Terminal No.	Signal	Input or output	Item	Check condition		Diagnosis standard	Main abnormal location
1	Front left solenoid	Output	Voltage	Ignition switch: ON (When solenoid is OFF approx. 1 second after engine is started.)		Battery positive voltage	• ABS valve relay • Hydraulic unit
2	Rear left solenoid	Output	Voltage	Ignition switch: ON (When solenoid is OFF approx. 1 second after engine is started.)		Battery positive voltage	• ABS valve relay • Hydraulic unit
5	Ignition switch	Input	Voltage	Ignition switch: ON		Battery positive voltage	• ABS power relay
				Ignition switch: START		0V	
7	Motor relay coil	Output	Voltage	Ignition switch: ON (Approx. 1 second after engine is started.)	Motor: ON	Battery positive voltage	• ABS motor relay • ABS-ECU
					Motor: OFF	0–2V	
8	Valve relay coil	Output	Voltage	Ignition switch: ON	When idling	0–2V	• ABS valve relay • ABS-ECU
					When system abnormality is detected	Battery positive voltage	
9	Service data and actuator test	Input	Voltage	Scan tool: Disconnected		Approx. 12V	• Harness
				Scan tool: Connected		0V	
10	Diagnostic trouble	Output	Voltage	Scan tool: Disconnected		0 ↔ 12V (Displayed in intervals of 0.5 sec.)	
11	Stop light switch	Input	Voltage	Ignition switch: ON (Stop light switch: ON)		8V or more	• Stop light switch
				Ignition switch: ON (Stop light switch: OFF)		1.5V or less	
12	Ground	Input	Continuity	At any time		Continuity	• Body ground

CR4029100642010X

Fig. 32   ABS ECU Inspection, connector connected (Part 1 of 2)

Component Testing

Refer to **Fig. 30** when diagnosing the ABS system.

ACTUATOR TEST FUNCTION

The actuator test function is only available through the scan tool. Refer to manufacturer's instructions and the actuator test specification chart, **Fig. 31**.

COMPONENT TESTING

ABS ECU

1. Ensure battery voltage is normal.
2. With the ABS ECU connector connected, check voltage and continuity between each terminal and ground when ignition is the On position as shown in **Fig. 32**.
3. With the ABS ECU connector disconnected, check resistance and continuity between each terminal on the harness side of the connector as shown in **Fig. 33**.

Wheel Speed Sensor Output Voltage Check

1. Ensure clearance between wheel speed sensor and the rotor is .012–.035 inch.
2. Raise and support vehicle and release parking brake.
3. Disconnect ABS ECU harness connector and measure from the harness side of connector, **Fig. 34 & 35**.
4. Rotate wheel to be measured at approximately 1/2 to 1 rotation per second and check output voltage using a circuit tester. Ensure voltage indicated is 70 mV or more.
5. If voltage is lower than specified, inspect the following:
   a. Excessive clearance between wheel speed sensor pole piece and the rotor.
   b. Faulty wheel speed sensor.
6. Adjust or replace as necessary.

Hydraulic Unit (HU)

1. Raise and support vehicle.
2. Release parking brake and feel drag force on each wheel. When using the brake force tester, take a reading of the brake drag force.
3. Turn ignition key to Off position and set position scan tool as shown **Fig. 36**.
4. Ensure shift lever is in neutral, then start engine. At this time the ABS system will switch to the scan tool mode and the ABS warning lamp will light. When the ABS has been interrupted by the fail safe function, the scan tool actuator testing cannot be used.
5. Use scan tool to force drive the actuator.
6. Turn wheel by hand and check the change in braking force when pedal is applied. When using the brake force tester, depress brake pedal until braking force is at 397 lbs. for the front wheel and 143 lbs. for the rear and en-

Terminal No.	Signal	Input or output	Item	Check condition		Diagnosis standard	Main abnormal location
13	Motor monitor	Input	Voltage	Ignition switch: ON (Approx. 1 second after engine is started.)	Motor: ON	Battery positive voltage	• ABS motor relay • ABS-ECU • Hydraulic unit
					Motor: OFF	0–2V	
14	Front right solenoid	Output	Voltage	Ignition switch: ON (When solenoid is OFF approx. 1 second after engine is started.)		Battery positive voltage	• ABS valve relay • Hydraulic unit
15	Rear right solenoid						
21	ABS warning light	Output	Voltage	Ignition switch: ON	When light switches off	Battery positive voltage	• ABS warning light
					When light illuminates	0–2V	
22	Scan tool	Output/ Input	Voltage	Scan tool: Connected		Serial communication with scan tool	• Harness
				Scan tool: Disconnected		1V or less	
25	Ground	Input	Continuity	At any time		Continuity	• Body ground
35	Rear left wheel speed sensor (– wire)	Input	Continuity	At any time		Continuity	• Rear left wheel speed sensor • ABS-ECU
36	Front right wheel speed sensor (– wire)	Input	Continuity	At any time		Continuity	• Front right wheel speed sensor • ABS-ECU
37	Rear right wheel speed sensor (– wire)	Input	Continuity	At any time		Continuity	• Rear right wheel speed sensor • ABS-ECU
38	Front left wheel speed sensor (– wire)	Input	Continuity	At any time		Continuity	• Front left wheel speed sensor • ABS-ECU
41	Generator	Input	Voltage	Ignition switch: ON (During engine stopped)		2–5V	• Generator
				Ignition switch: ON (During engine running)		Approx. 12V	

CR4029100642020X

Fig. 32   ABS ECU Inspection, connector connected (Part 2 of 2)

sure braking force changes to the brake drag force measurement from step 2 when the actuator is force driven.

7. Results should be as shown in **Fig. 37.**
8. If results are not as specified, correct according to the diagnosis table, **Fig. 38.**

Power Relay

Remove in instrument undercover the the power relay and inspect as shown in **Fig. 39.**

Motor & Valve Relay

Inspect the motor and valve relays as shown in **Figs. 40 and 41.**

SYSTEM SERVICE

Brake System Bleed

1. If brake fluid has been drained from master cylinder, bleed as follows:
   a. Fill reservoir with DOT 3 brake fluid, then depress and hold brake pedal.
   b. With master cylinder outlet port

plugged, release brake pedal.
   c. Repeat 3 to 4 times, refilling reservoir as necessary.
2. With engine running, bleed brake lines as follows:
   a. Bleed line to wheel that is diagonally opposite master cylinder.
   b. Bleed line to wheel that is nearest to master cylinder.
   c. Bleed line to remaining rear wheel, then to remaining front wheel.
   d. Ensure master cylinder is kept full.
3. When adding brake fluid, fit filter to reserve tank.

Component Replace

HYDRAULIC UNIT (HU)

Replace the HU in numbered sequence shown in **Fig. 42**, noting the following:
1. Because the HU is quite heavy, caution should be exercised during removal and installation.
2. Do not disassemble the HU assembly.
3. Do not drop or otherwise subject the HU to impact shocks.
4. Never turn the HU upside down or lay it on it's side.
5. Install the HU brake pipe as shown in **Fig. 43.**

WHEEL SPEED SENSOR

Replace the wheel speed sensor in numbered sequence shown in **Fig. 44**, noting the following:
1. Use care when handling the pole piece at the tip of the sensor and toothed edge of the rotor.
2. Inspect the speed sensor as follows:
   a. Check for damage or for any metallic foreign material has adhered to the pole piece at the sensors tip.
   b. Measure resistance of sensor, and ensure it is within 1.4-2.2 kohms.
   c. Check sensor cable for breakage, damage or disconnection.
   d. Replace if necessary.
3. Inspect speed sensor insulation resistance by measuring between terminals 1 than 2 and the sensor body. Resistance should be 100 kohms or more. Replace if necessary.
4. Inspect rotor teeth and ensure none are broken or deformed. replace if necessary.
5. When installing rear speed sensor ensure a .012-.035 inch clearance is obtained.

ABS ECU

Replace the ABS ECU in numbered sequence shown in **Fig. 45** by removing the unit from the bottom of the center console.

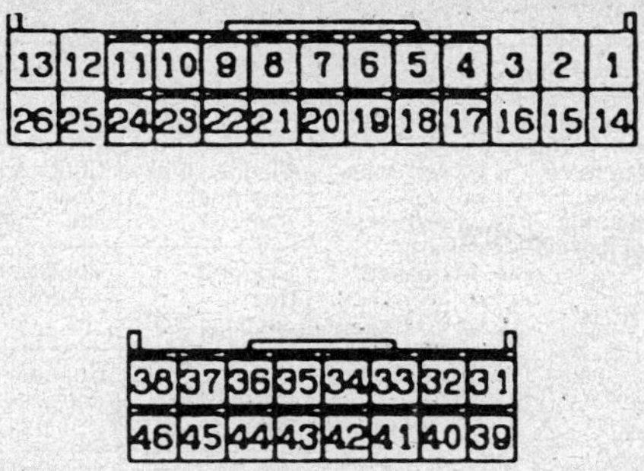

```
13 12 11 10 9 8 7 6 5 4 3 2 1
26 25 24 23 22 21 20 19 18 17 16 15 14
```

```
38 37 36 35 34 33 32 31
46 45 44 43 42 41 40 39
```

Terminal No.	Signal	Item	Check terminal	Check condition	Diagnosis standard	Main abnormal location
1	Front left solenoid	Resistance	Between terminal No. 1 and body ground	Ignition switch: OFF	3.10–3.34Ω	• Hydraulic unit • ABS valve relay
2	Rear left solenoid	Resistance	Between terminal No. 2 and body ground	Ignition switch: OFF	3.10–3.34Ω	• Hydraulic unit • ABS valve relay
13	Motor monitor	Continuity	Between terminal No. 13 and body ground	Ignition switch: OFF	Continuity	• Hydraulic unit
14	Front right solenoid	Resistance	Between terminal No. 14 and body ground	Ignition switch: OFF	3.10–3.34Ω	• Hydraulic unit • ABS valve relay
15	Rear right solenoid	Resistance	Between terminal No. 15 and body ground	Ignition switch: OFF	3.10–3.34Ω	• Hydraulic unit • ABS valve relay
43	Rear left wheel speed sensor (+ wire)	Resistance	Between terminals No. 35 and No. 43	Ignition switch: OFF	1.4–2.2 kΩ	• Rear left wheel speed sensor
44	Front right wheel speed sensor (+ wire)	Resistance	Between terminals No. 36 and No. 44	Ignition switch: OFF	1.4–2.2 kΩ	• Front right wheel speed sensor
45	Rear right wheel speed sensor (+ wire)	Resistance	Between terminals No. 37 and No. 45	Ignition switch: OFF	1.4–2.2 kΩ	• Rear right wheel speed sensor
46	Front left wheel speed sensor (+ wire)	Resistance	Between terminals No. 38 and No. 46	Ignition switch: OFF	1.4–2.2 kΩ	• Front left wheel speed sensor

CR4029100643000X

Fig. 33   ABS ECU Inspection, connector disconnected

```
38 37 36 35 34 33 32 31
46 45 44 43 42 41 40 39
```

CR4029100644000X

Fig. 34   ASB ECU Connector terminal identification

Terminal No.	Front left	Front right	Rear left	Rear right
	38	36	35	37
	46	44	43	45

CR4029100645000X

Fig. 35   ABS ECU wheel speed sensor terminal numbers

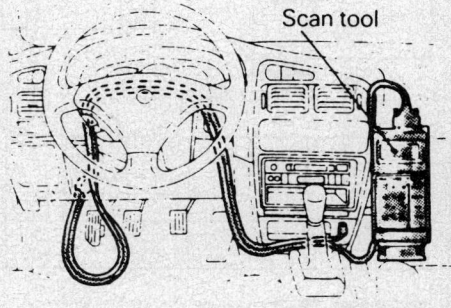

Scan tool

CR4029100646000X

Fig. 36   Scan tool connection for HU test

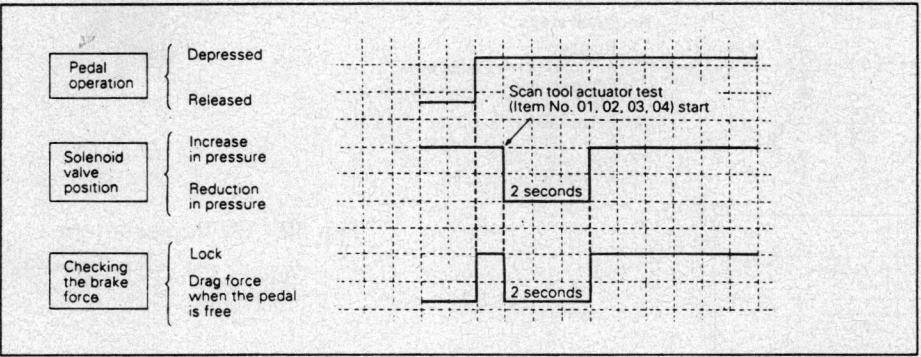

CR4029100647000X

Fig. 37   HU test results

No.	Scan tool display	Operation	Judgement		Probable cause	Remedy
			Normal	Abnormal		
01	FR VALVE M	(1) Depress brake pedal to lock wheel. (2) Using the scan tool, select the wheel to be checked and force the actuator to operate. (3) Turn the selected wheel manually to check the change of brake force.	Brake force released for 2 seconds after locking.	Wheel does not lock when brake pedal is depressed.	Clogged brake line other than HU	Check and clean brake line
02	FL VALVE M				Clogged hydraulic circuit in HU	Replace HU assembly
03	RR VALVE M			Brake force is not released.	Incorrect HU brake tube connection	Connect correctly
04	RL VALVE M				HU solenoid valve not functioning correctly	Replace HU assembly

CR4029100648000X

Fig. 38   HU diagnostic table

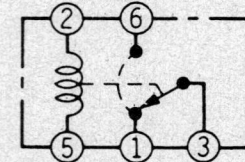

When no current flows	Between ② – ⑤ terminals	64–84Ω
	Between ① – ③ terminals	Continuity (approx. 0Ω)
	Between ③ – ⑥ terminals	No continuity (∞ Ω)
When current flows between terminals ② – ⑤	Between ① – ③ terminals	Continuity (∞ Ω)
	Between ③ – ⑥ terminals	Continuity (approx. 0Ω)

CR4029100651000X

Fig. 41   Valve relay inspection

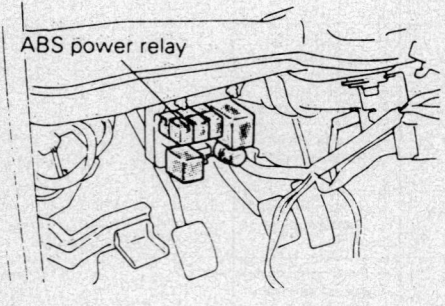

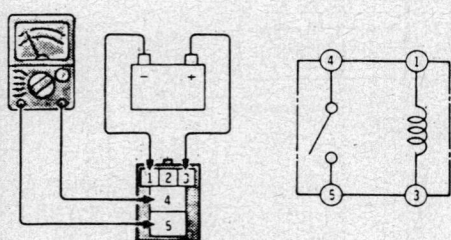

Terminal	1	2	3	5
Battery voltage				
Continuity no voltage		○—○		○—○
Continuity with voltage	○—○		○—○	
		⊕—○		○—⊖

NOTE
(1) ○—○ indicates that there is continuity between the terminals.
(2) ⊕—○ indicates connection of battery voltage.

Fig. 39   Power relay inspection

CR4029100649000X

 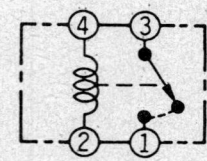

When no current flows	Between ② – ④ terminals	90–110Ω
	Between ① – ③ terminals	No continuity (∞ Ω)
When current flows between terminals ② – ④	Between ① – ③ terminals	Continuity (approx. 0Ω)

CR4029100650000X

Fig. 40   Motor relay inspection

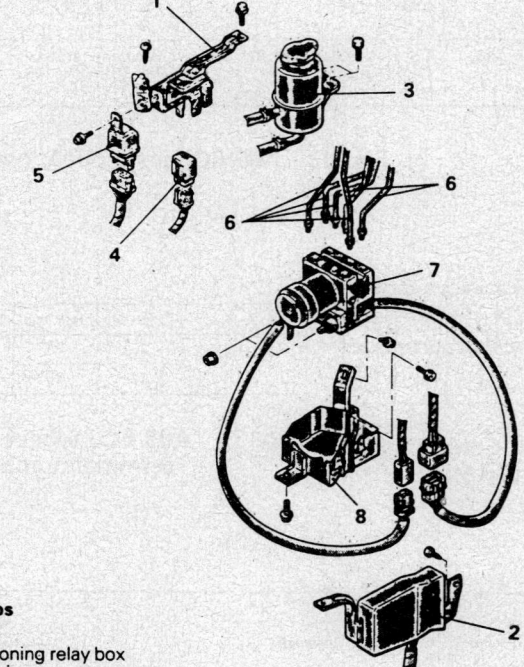

Removal steps
1. Bracket
2. Air conditioning relay box
3. Oil reservoir
4. Motor relay
5. Valve relay
6. Brake pipe
7. Hydraulic unit
8. Hydraulic unit bracket

CR4029100652000X

Fig. 42   HU Replacement

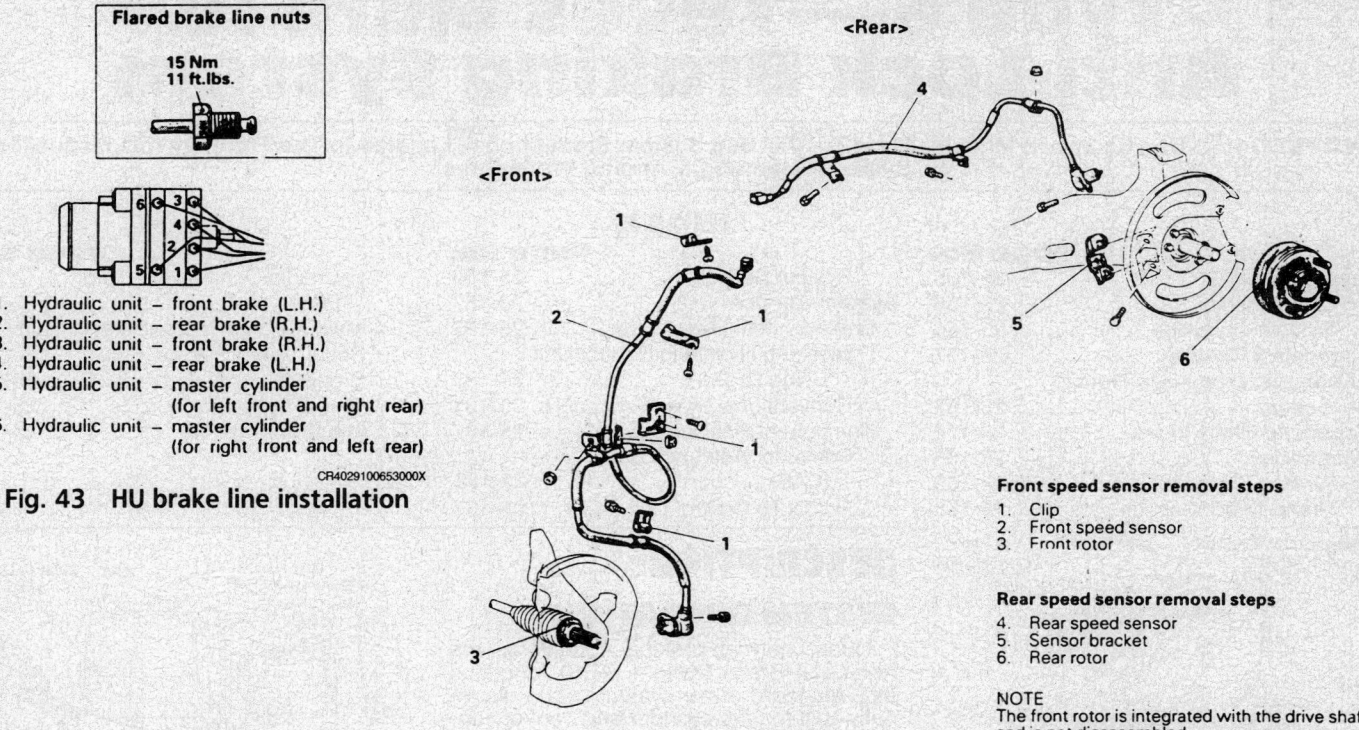

Flared brake line nuts

15 Nm
11 ft.lbs.

1. Hydraulic unit – front brake (L.H.)
2. Hydraulic unit – rear brake (R.H.)
3. Hydraulic unit – front brake (R.H.)
4. Hydraulic unit – rear brake (L.H.)
5. Hydraulic unit – master cylinder
   (for left front and right rear)
6. Hydraulic unit – master cylinder
   (for right front and left rear)

CR4029100653000X

Fig. 43   HU brake line installation

Front speed sensor removal steps

1. Clip
2. Front speed sensor
3. Front rotor

Rear speed sensor removal steps

4. Rear speed sensor
5. Sensor bracket
6. Rear rotor

NOTE
The front rotor is integrated with the drive shaft
and is not disassembled.

CR4029100654000X

Fig. 44   Wheel speed sensor replacement

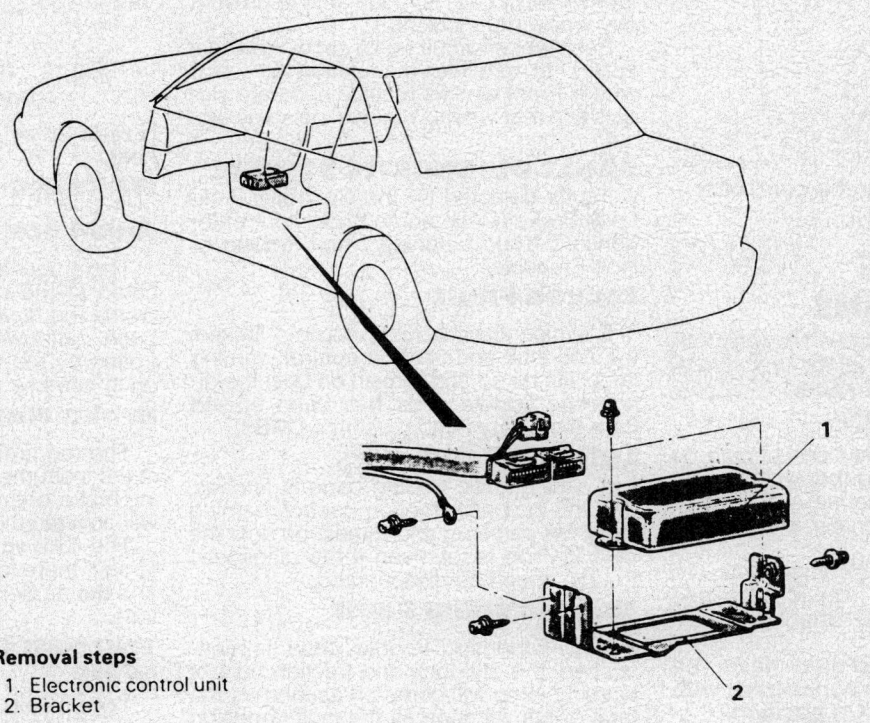

Removal steps

1. Electronic control unit
2. Bracket

CR4029100655000X

Fig. 45   ABS ECU replacement

Type 6—Teves Mark IV Anti-Lock Braking System

NOTE: On Air Bag Equipped Models, Refer To "Air Bag System Precautions" Located In The Front Of This Manual For System Disarming & Arming Procedures.

INDEX

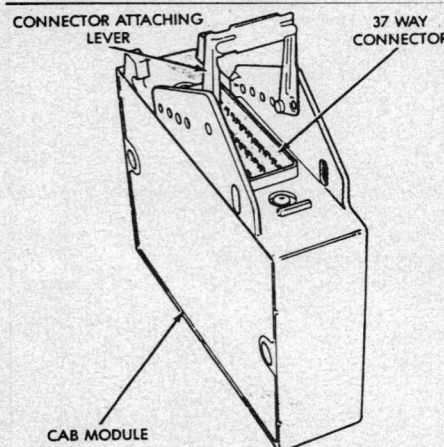

Fig. 1 Anti-lock brake controller (CAB)

PRECAUTIONS
AIR BAG SYSTEMS

Refer to "Air Bag System Precautions" in the front of this manual for system disarming and arming procedures.

SYSTEM SERVICE

General service precautions should be followed when servicing the ABS system. Failure to do so may cause ABS system component failure. Service precautions are as follows:

1. Many ABS system components are not independently serviceable and must be replaced with their respective assemblies.
2. **CAB connector should never be disconnected or connected with ignition switch in On position.**
3. **If arc welding is being performed on vehicle, disconnect CAB electrical connector during welding operation.**

PUMP/MOTOR SERVICE

The pump/motor assembly can only be serviced as part of the hydraulic control unit.

DESCRIPTION

SYSTEM OPERATION

Under normal braking conditions, the Anti-Lock Brake System (ABS) functions as a standard brake system with a diagonally split master cylinder and conventional brake booster.

If a wheel lock is detected during braking, the system will enter ABS mode. During ABS mode, hydraulic pressure in the four wheel circuits is modulated to prevent any wheel from locking.

Each wheel circuit has a set of electrical valves to provide modulation to each wheel. Front wheels receive separate signals and rear wheels receive the same signal.

FAULT DIAGNOSTIC SYSTEM

Faults detected by the Controller Anti-Lock Brake (CAB) come under four categories: Locked, Latching, Non-Latching, or Non-Erasable.

Locked Fault

If a diagnostic trouble code is locked, the anti-lock and traction control warning lamp will be on and remain on until the diagnostic trouble code has been erased from the CAB memory using a DRB II.

Latched Fault

If a diagnostic trouble code is latched, the anti-lock and traction control warning lamp will come on and remain on until the next ignition reset, even if the diagnostic trouble code has disappeared.

Non-Latching Fault

If a diagnostic trouble code is non-latched, the anti-lock and traction control warning lamp will come on as long as the fault exists. As soon as the fault condition goes away, the warning lamps are turned off, but the diagnostic trouble code will be stored.

Non-Erasable Fault

This type of fault cannot be erased with a DRB II tester or by cycling the ignition switch, the anti-lock and traction warning lamps will stay ON until system operation

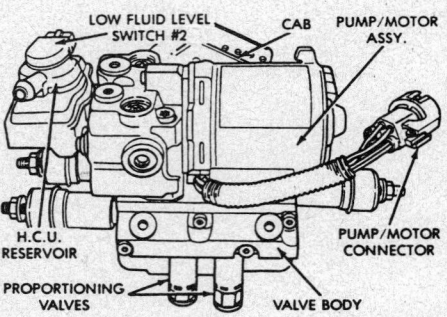

Fig. 2 Hydraulic control unit component locations

is restored by replacing defective components.

WARNING LAMP SYSTEMS
Anti-Lock Warning Lamp

The amber anti-lock warning lamp is located in the message center. The lamp warns the driver that ABS functions have been shutdown. The warning lamp is controlled by the CAB or main relay through an in harness diode.

Brake Warning Lamp

The red brake warning lamp is located in the instrument panel. Applying the parking brake, or low master cylinder fluid level will activate the lamp.

The CAB will also activate the warning lamp if there is a fault in the ABS system, and the amber anti-lock lamp fails to activate.

Traction Control Function Lamp

The green traction control function lamp is located in the message center. It informs the driver that system has entered traction control mode. The lamp is controlled by the CAB.

Traction Control Warning Lamp

The amber traction control warning lamp is located in the message center. It

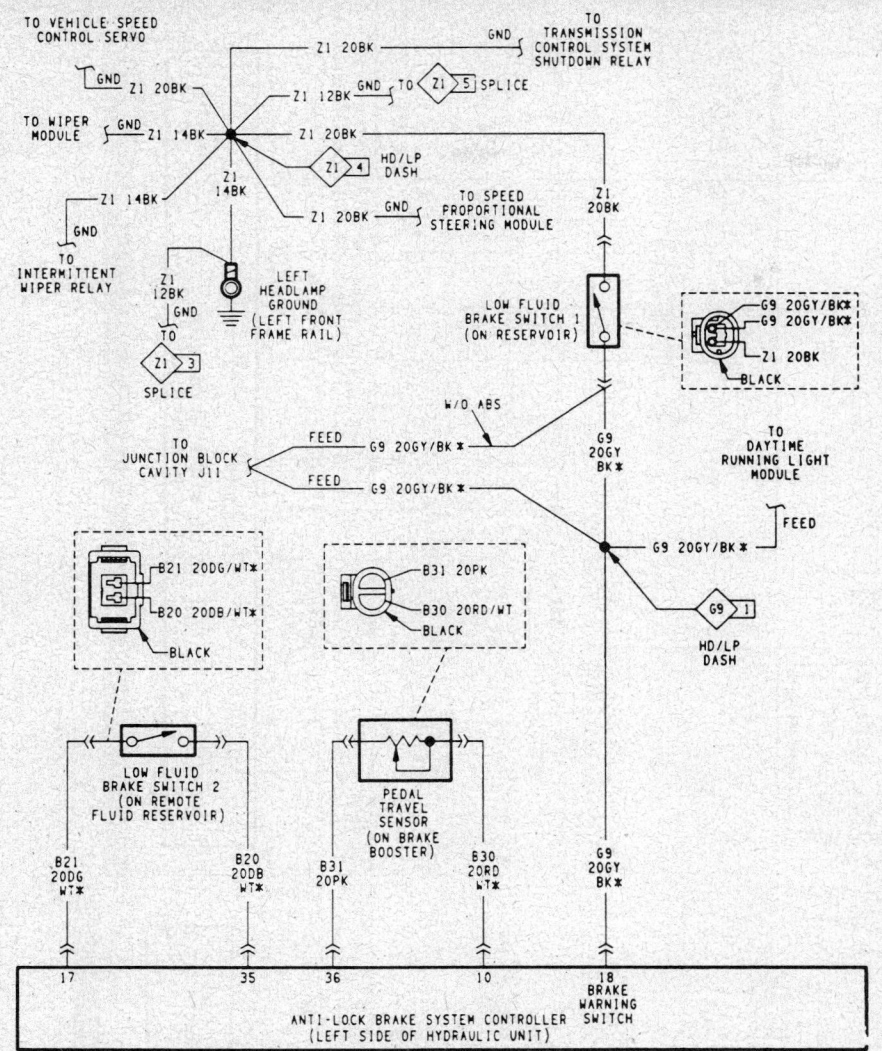

Fig. 3 ABS wiring diagram (Part 1 of 5)

will inform the driver that the traction control function has been turned Off by the CAB. The lamp will also come On when the traction control switch is turned Off with the ignition On.

Normal Operation Of Warning Lamp

When the engine is in the crank position the red brake warning lamp will be On, once engine is started the amber anti-lock and traction control lamp will come On for one to two seconds then go Off. Verification of system is then complete.

COMPONENTS
Controller Anti-Lock Brake System (CAB)

The CAB, **Fig. 1**, is a microprocessor device which monitors wheel speed and controls ABS and traction control functions. It contains two microprocessors which receive the same signals, then independently process that information. The two microprocessors then compare signals to make sure they agree with each other, if not the CAB will shutdown ABS and traction control functions and turn on warning lamps.

Vacuum Booster w/Integrated Pedal Travel Sensor

The Mark IV ABS system uses a special vacuum booster and master cylinder. The booster used with the Mark IV is a new "0 lost travel reaction disc type booster with the addition of a pedal travel sensor (PTS). The PTS is a linear variable displacement transducer with seven steps which provide brake pedal position information to the CAB.

Master Cylinder w/Center Valves & Fluid Level Switch—FLS–1

The master cylinder is a standard tandem design with the exception of central valves that are used in conjunction with existing compensation ports. The center valve is a spring loaded ball and seat design which is unseated by a stop in the master cylinder when brakes are released.

A fluid level switch is located in the master cylinder fluid reservoir. The switch closes when low fluid level is detected, and the FLS-1 turns on the warning lamp. This will not disable the ABS system.

Hydraulic Control Unit (HCU)

The HCU consists of a valve block assembly, pump/motor assembly, and a fluid reservoir with a fluid level switch. The HCU is located on the left frame rail forward of the master cylinder.

There are two Hydraulic Control Units. One for ABS only, and one for ABS and traction control combined. **If a new HCU unit is installed with the wrong type of CAB, the system will disable itself and a diagnostic trouble code will be stored.**

Wheel Speed Sensors

One wheel speed sensor (WSS) is located at each wheel and sends a AC signal to the CAB. The voltage is generated by magnetic induction when a tooth sensor ring passes by a stationary magnetic sensor. The CAB then converts the AC signal into digital signals for each wheel. The four wheel speed sensors are serviced individually. The front tone wheels are serviced as an assembly with the outer C.V joint housing. The rear tonewheels are serviced as an assembly with the rotor hub.

Pump/Motor Assembly

The pump/motor assembly consists of an electric motor with a rotation sensor and a dual piston pump, **Fig. 2**. The rotation sensor is an inductive pickup used by the CAB to monitor pump/motor operation.

TROUBLESHOOTING

Refer to Anti-Lock Brake System (ABS) wiring diagram, **Fig. 3**, and to flowcharts under "Diagnosis & Testing" when troubleshooting the anti-lock brake system.

DIAGNOSIS & TESTING
Accessing Diagnostic Trouble Codes

To enter diagnostic mode, vehicle speed must be below 10 mph. If vehicle speed is above 10 mph, a "No Response" message will be displayed on the DRB II. The following are characteristics of diagnostic mode.

1. The amber anti-lock warning lamp and brake warning lamp will flash.
2. If a hard fault, such as an inlet or outlet valve fault or main relay/power circuit failure fault, is present, these lamps will illuminate without blinking and no diagnostic operations will be available until the fault condition is cleared.
3. Anti-lock and traction control operation are disabled.
4. You will be unable to actuate the valves in the valve body when the vehicle speed is above 5 mph.
5. If valve actuation is attempted above 5 mph, a "vehicle in motion" message will be displayed through the DRB II.
6. Refer to test 1A and 1B, **Fig. 4 and 5** for checking the system for faults, then proceed as indicated to the remaining diagnostic charts shown in **Figs. 6 through 49**. After performing appropriate procedure, perform verification test shown in **Fig. 50** to verify system operation.

Continued on page 25-187

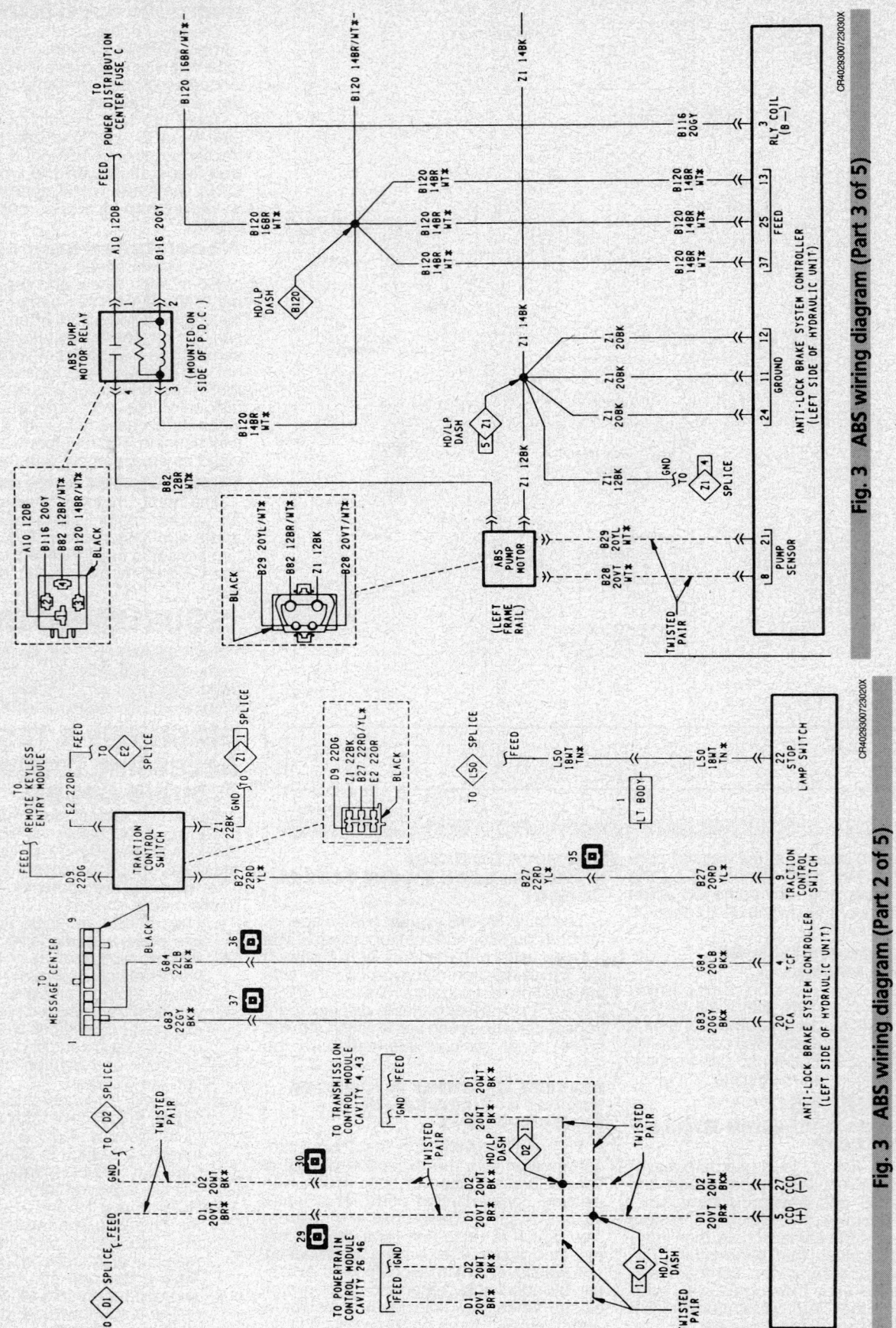

Fig. 3 ABS wiring diagram (Part 3 of 5)

Fig. 3 ABS wiring diagram (Part 2 of 5)

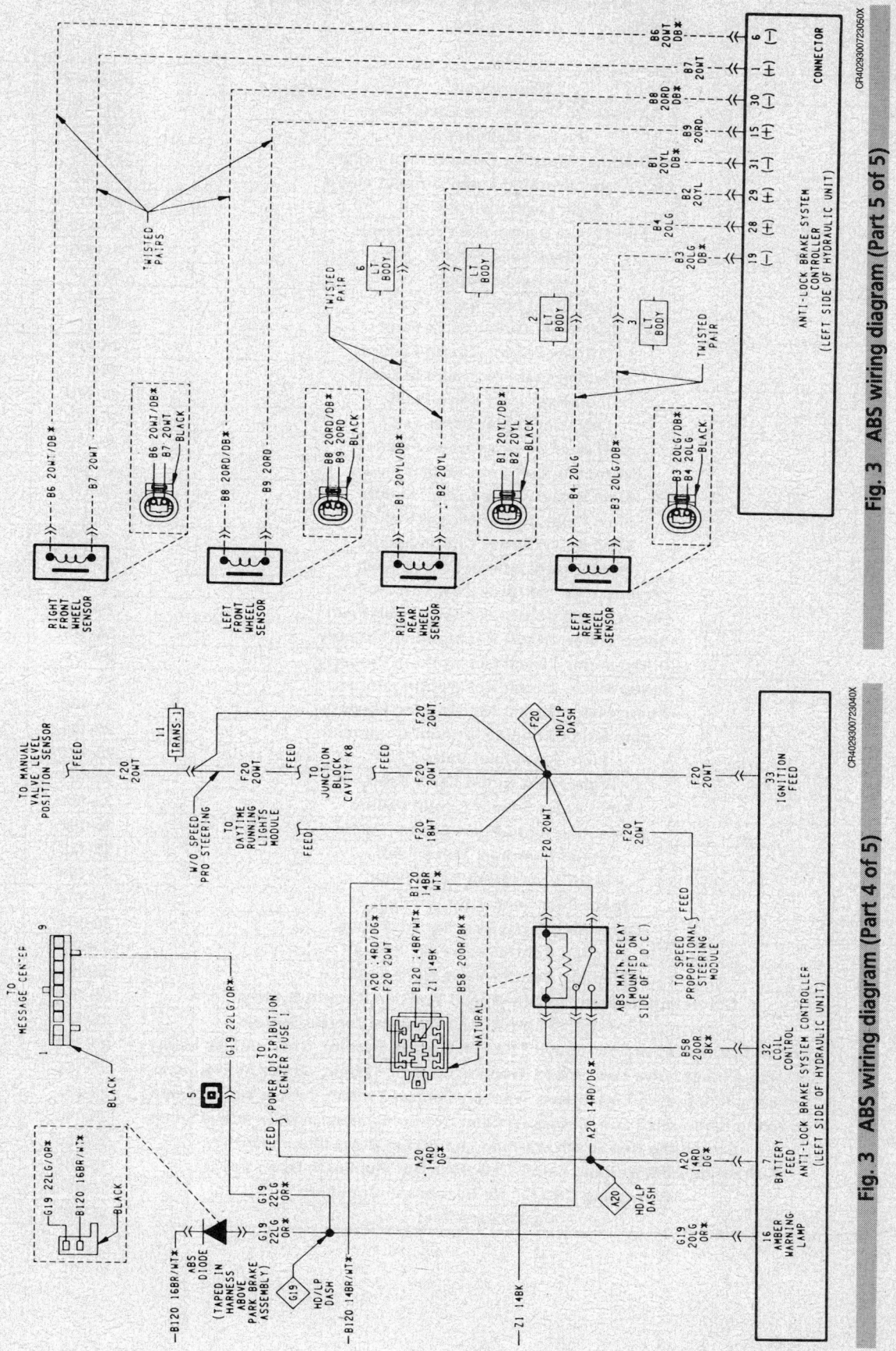

Fig. 3 ABS wiring diagram (Part 5 of 5)

Fig. 3 ABS wiring diagram (Part 4 of 5)

TYPE 6-TEVES MARK IV ANTI-LOCK BRAKING SYSTEM

DIAGNOSTIC CHART INDEX

Test	Description	Page No.	Fig. No.
1A	Checking System For Fault Codes	25-171	4
1B	System Malfunctions	25-171	5
2A	ABS Amber Warning Lamp Circuit Failure	25-172	6
2B	ABS Amber Warning Lamp Circuit Failure	25-172	7
3A	Fluid Level Switch Open	25-172	8
4A	Fluid Level Switch Not Processable	25-173	9
5A	Hydraulic Failure	25-173	10
5B	Hydraulic Failure	25-174	11
6A	Left Front Inlet Valve Fault	25-174	12
7A	Left Front Outlet Valve Fault	25-174	13
8A	Left Front Sensor Circuit Failure	25-174	14
9A	Correcting Left Front Sensor Faults	25-175	15
10A	Left Rear Inlet Valve Fault	25-175	16
11A	Left Rear Outlet Valve Fault	25-175	17
12A	Left Rear Sensor Circuit Failure	25-175	18
13A	Correcting Left Rear Sensor Faults	25-176	19
14A	Main Relay/Power Circuit Failure	25-177	20
14B	Main Relay/Power Circuit Failure	25-177	21
14C	Main Relay/Power Circuit Failure	25-178	22
15A	Pedal Travel Sensor Circuit Fault	25-178	23
16A	Pressure Switch/Brake SW Circuit Fault	25-178	24
16B	Pressure Switch/Brake SW Circuit Fault	25-179	25
17A	Pump Motor Circuit Not Working Properly	25-179	26
17B	Pump Motor Circuit Not Working Properly	25-179	27
17C	Pump Motor Circuit Not Working Properly	25-180	28
17D	Pump Motor Circuit Not Working Properly	25-180	29
18A	Pump Motor Running Without Command	25-181	30
19A	Right Front Inlet Valve Fault	25-181	31
20A	Right Front Outlet Valve Fault	25-181	32
21A	Right Front Sensor Circuit Failure	25-181	33
22A	Correcting Right Front Sensor Faults	25-182	34
23A	Right Rear Inlet Valve Fault	25-182	35
24A	Right Rear Outlet Valve Fault	25-182	36
25A	Right Rear Sensor Circuit Failure	25-183	37
26A	Correcting Right Rear Sensor Faults	25-183	38
27A	Traction Control Valve No. 1 Fault	25-183	39
28A	Traction Control Valve No. 2 Fault	25-184	40
29A	Correcting Inoperative Low-Speed Traction Control System	25-184	41
29B	Correcting Inoperative Low-Speed Traction Control System	25-184	42
30A	Correcting Inoperative Low-Speed Traction Control System, Green Active Lamp	25-184	43
30B	Correcting Inoperative Low-Speed Traction Control System, Green Active Lamp	25-185	44
31A	Correcting Inoperative Low-Speed Traction Control System, Amber Active Lamp	25-185	45
31B	Correcting Inoperative Low-Speed Traction Control System, Amber Active Lamp	25-186	46
32A	Correcting Red Brake Warning Lamp That Stays Illuminated	25-186	47
33A	Correcting ABS Warning Lamp That Does Not Illuminate Upon Key Up	25-186	48
34A	Correcting DRB II " No Response" Condition	25-186	49
35A	Verification Test	25-187	50

1. Your diagnostic test procedure must begin with a thorough visual inspection of the ABS system components for damaged components or disconnected connectors.

2. Connect the DRBII to the CCD bus data link connector.

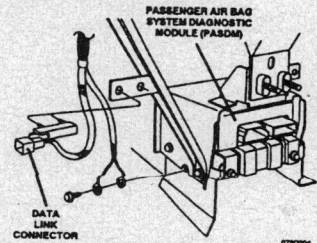

3. With the DRBII, read fault codes. If the "Controller Failure" fault is set, then replace the CAB. Otherwise, erase all fault codes using the DRBII. NOTE: The ignition key must be turned off to ensure that faults are properly erased inside the CAB.

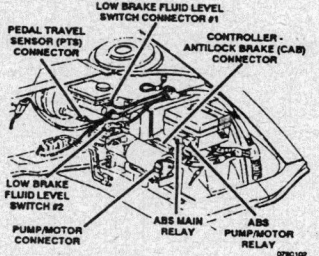

4. Turn the ignition key on. With the DRBII, read fault codes. If any faults are present, proceed to the appropriate diagnostic test. NOTE: If the "Main Relay/Power Circuit Failure" fault is set, this fault must be repaired prior to any other fault repairs. Before performing any road tests, verify that full braking capability is present.

5. If there are no faults present upon key up, road test vehicle and attempt several ABS stops and traction control starts. Again, with the DRBII, read fault codes. If any faults are present, proceed to the appropriate diagnostic test. NOTE: If the "Main Relay/Power Circuit Failure" fault is set, this fault must be repaired prior to any other fault repairs. NOTE: The DRBII must not be in Teves ABS diagnostic mode when performing any ABS stops or traction control starts. These systems are disabled when DRBII is in diagnostic mode.

6. If there are no fault codes present, proceed to TEST 1B for a list of system malfunctions and their appropriate diagnostic tests.

CR4029100658010X

Fig. 4   Test 1A: Checking System For Diagnostic Trouble Codes (Part 1 of 2)

DRBII FAULT DISPLAYED	DIAGNOSTIC TEST
ABS AMBER WARNING LAMP CIRCUIT FAILURE	2A
CONTROLLER FAILURE	Replace CAB
FLUID LEVEL SWITCH OPEN	3A
FLUID LEVEL SWITCH NOT PROCESSABLE	4A
HYDRAULIC FAILURE	5A
LEFT FRONT INLET VALVE	6A
LEFT FRONT OUTLET VALVE	7A
LEFT FRONT SENSOR CIRCUIT FAILURE	8A
LEFT FRONT SENSOR CONTINUITY > 25 MPH	8A
LEFT FRONT SENSOR CONTINUITY < 25 MPH	8A
LEFT FRONT SENSOR SIGNAL MISSING	8A
LEFT FRONT SENSOR SPEED COMPARISON	8A
LEFT REAR INLET VALVE	10A
LEFT REAR OUTLET VALVE	11A
LEFT REAR SENSOR CIRCUIT FAILURE	12A
LEFT REAR SENSOR CONTINUITY > 25 MPH	12A
LEFT REAR SENSOR CONTINUITY < 25 MPH	12A
LEFT REAR SENSOR SIGNAL MISSING	12A
LEFT REAR SENSOR SPEED COMPARISON	12A
MAIN RELAY/POWER CIRCUIT FAILURE	14A
PEDAL TRAVEL SENSOR CIRCUIT	15A
PRESSURE SWITCH/BRAKE SW CIRCUITS	16A
PUMP MOTOR CIRCUIT NOT WORKING PROPERLY	17A
PUMP MOTOR RUNNING WITHOUT COMMAND	18A
RIGHT FRONT INLET VALVE	19A
RIGHT FRONT OUTLET VALVE	20A
RIGHT FRONT SENSOR CIRCUIT FAILURE	21A
RIGHT FRONT SENSOR CONTINUITY > 25 MPH	21A
RIGHT FRONT SENSOR CONTINUITY < 25 MPH	21A
RIGHT FRONT SENSOR SIGNAL MISSING	21A
RIGHT FRONT SENSOR SPEED COMPARISON	21A
RIGHT REAR INLET VALVE	23A
RIGHT REAR OUTLET VALVE	24A
RIGHT REAR SENSOR CIRCUIT FAILURE	25A
RIGHT REAR SENSOR CONTINUITY > 25 MPH	25A
RIGHT REAR SENSOR CONTINUITY < 25 MPH	25A
RIGHT REAR SENSOR SIGNAL MISSING	25A
RIGHT REAR SENSOR SPEED COMPARISON	25A
TRACTION CONTROL VALVE #1	27A
TRACTION CONTROL VALVE #2	28A

CR4029100658020X

Fig. 4   Test 1A: Checking System For Diagnostic Trouble Codes (Part 2 of 2)

CR4029100659000X

Fig. 5   Test 1B: System Malfunctions

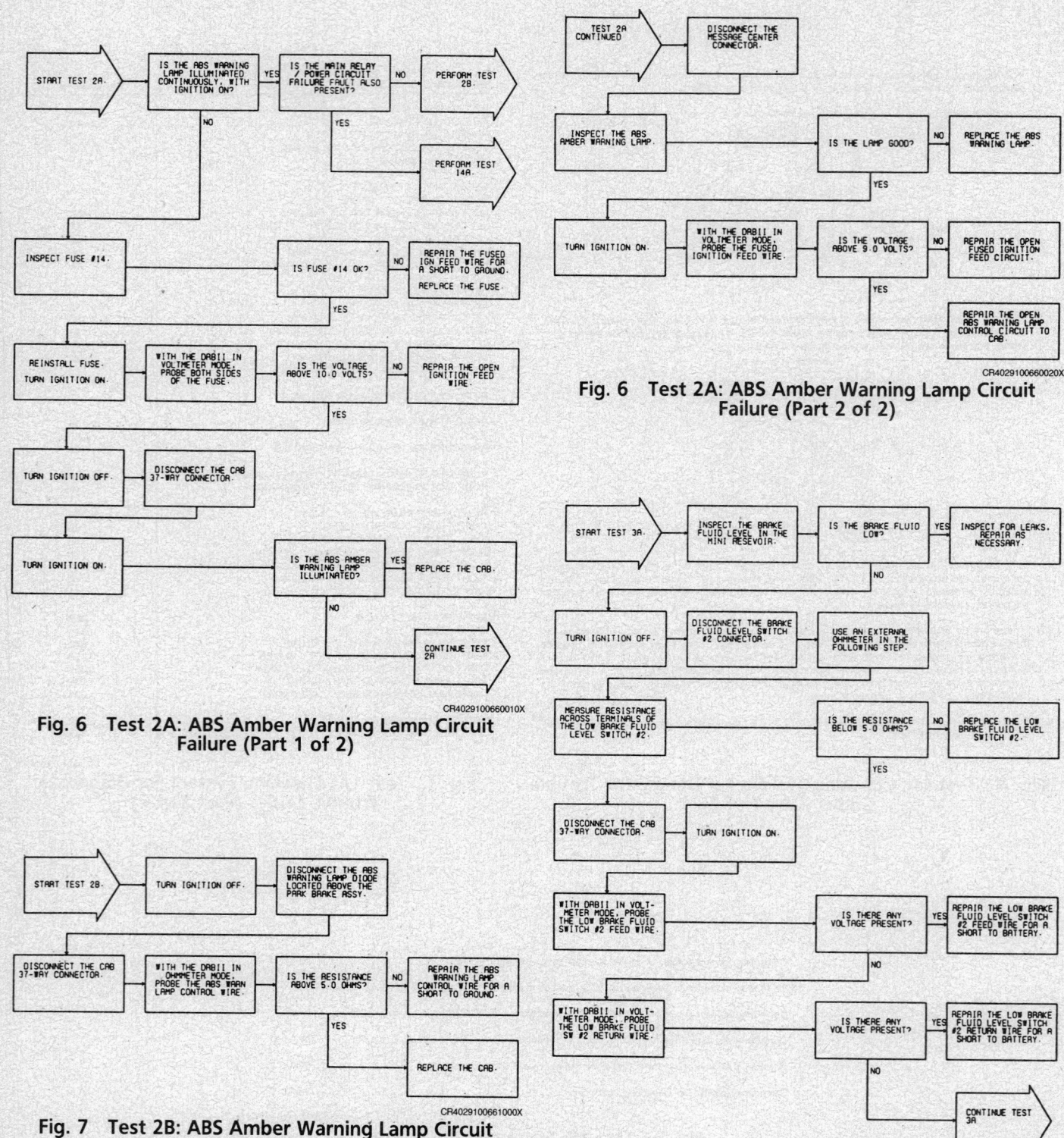

Fig. 6   Test 2A: ABS Amber Warning Lamp Circuit Failure (Part 1 of 2)

CR4029100660010X

Fig. 6   Test 2A: ABS Amber Warning Lamp Circuit Failure (Part 2 of 2)

CR4029100660020X

Fig. 7   Test 2B: ABS Amber Warning Lamp Circuit Failure

CR4029100661000X

Fig. 8   Test 3A: Fluid Level Switch Open (Part 1 of 2)

CR4029100662010X

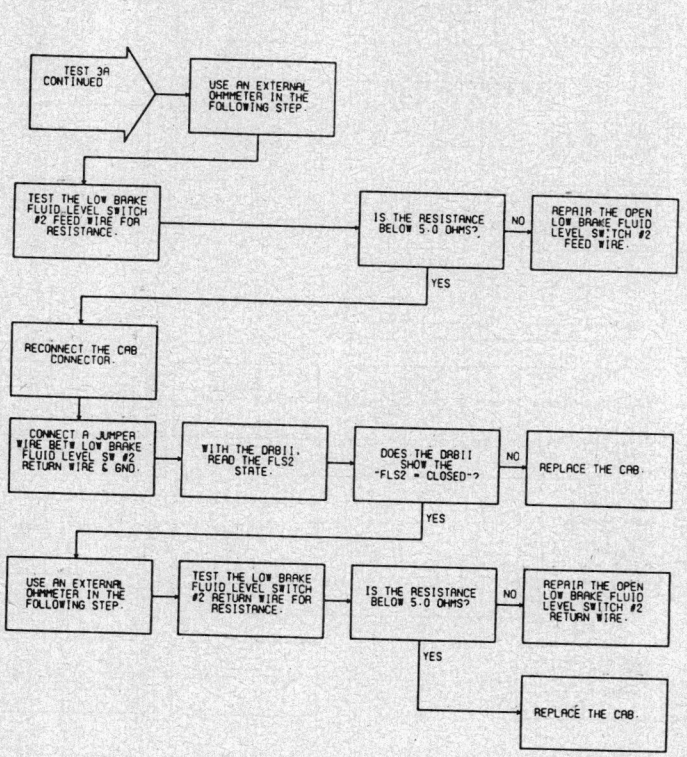

Fig. 8   Test 3A: Fluid Level Switch Open (Part 2 of 2)

CR4029100662020X

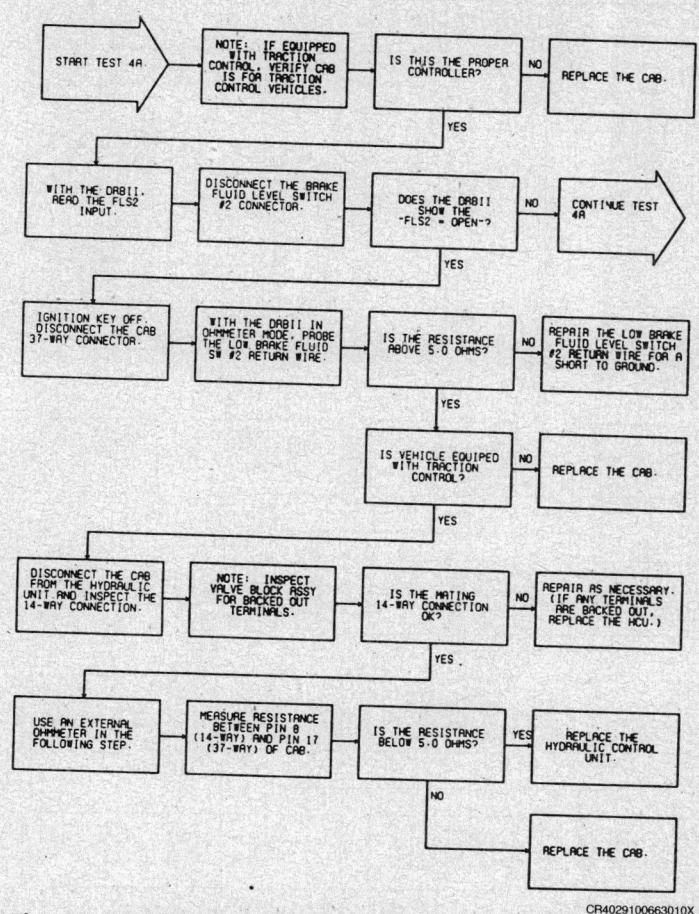

CR4029100663010X

Fig. 9   Test 4A: Fluid Level Switch Not Processable (Part 1 of 2)

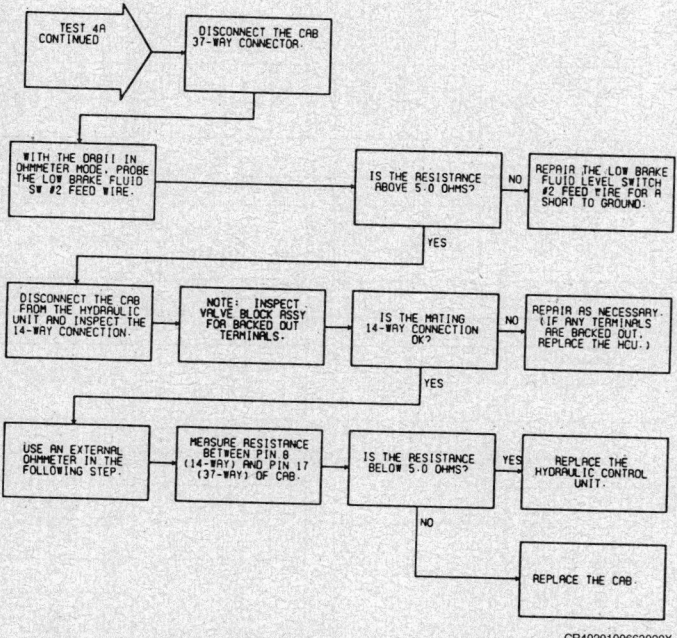

CR4029100663020X

Fig. 9   Test 4A: Fluid Level Switch Not Processable (Part 2 of 2)

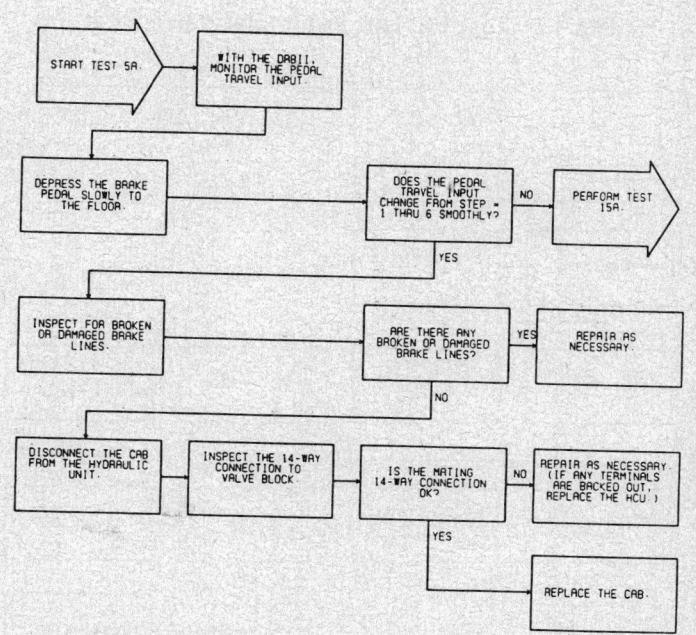

CR4029100664000X

Fig. 10   Test 5A: Hydraulic Failure

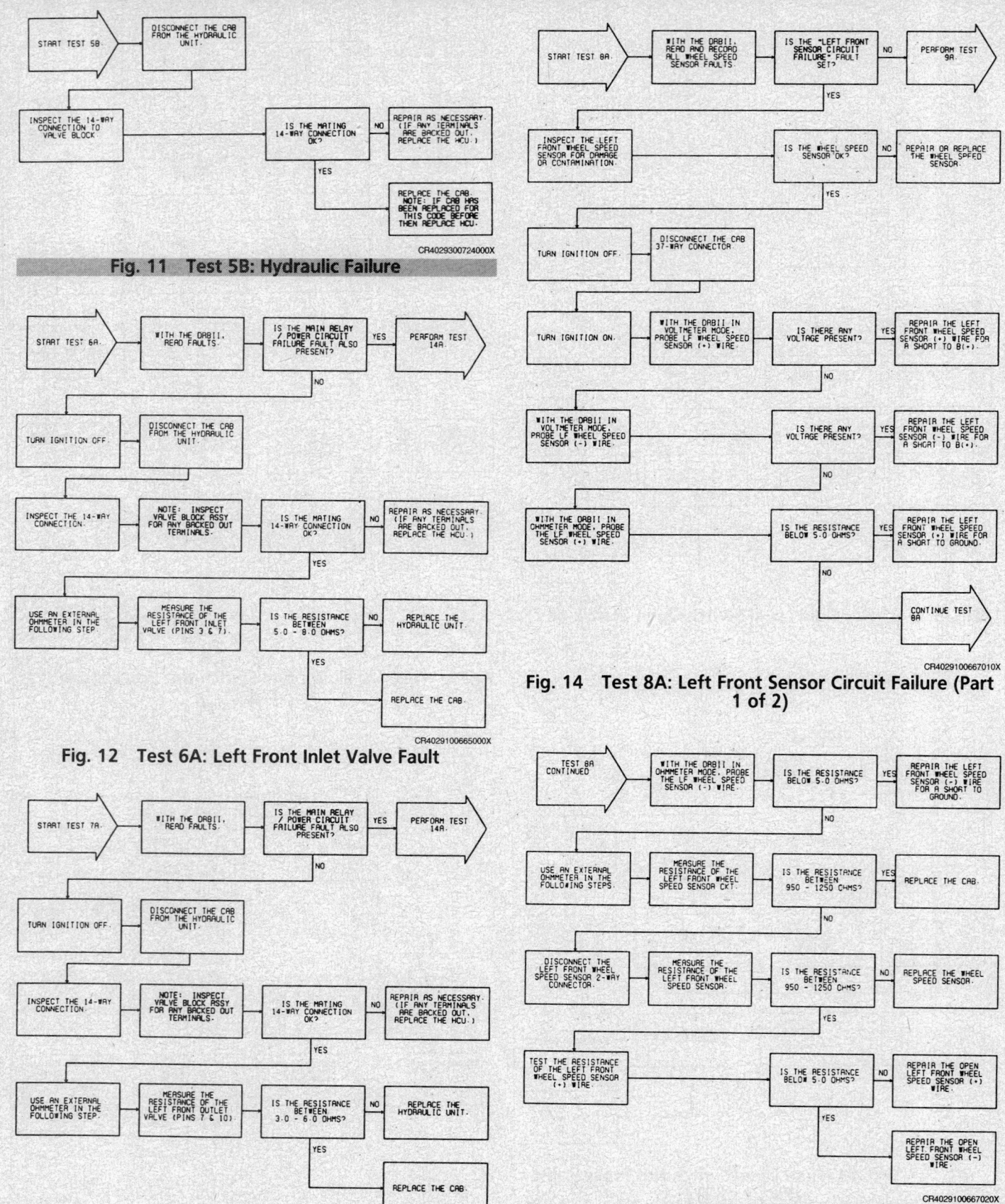

Fig. 11   Test 5B: Hydraulic Failure

Fig. 12   Test 6A: Left Front Inlet Valve Fault

Fig. 13   Test 7A: Left Front Outlet Valve Fault

Fig. 14   Test 8A: Left Front Sensor Circuit Failure (Part 1 of 2)

Fig. 14   Test 8A: Left Front Sensor Circuit Failure (Part 2 of 2)

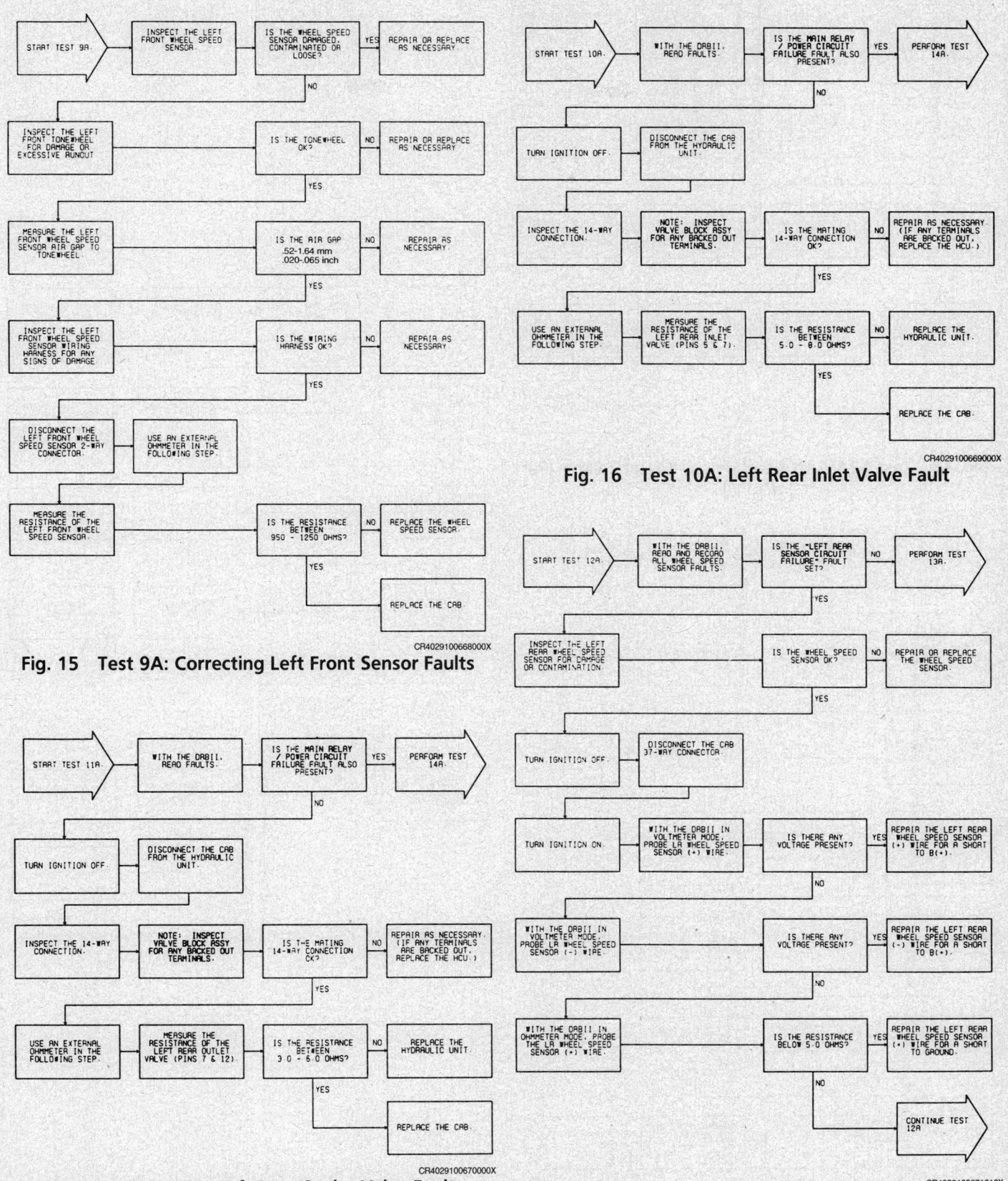

Fig. 15   Test 9A: Correcting Left Front Sensor Faults

CR4029100668000X

Fig. 16   Test 10A: Left Rear Inlet Valve Fault

CR4029100669000X

Fig. 17   Test 11A: Left Rear Outlet Valve Fault

CR4029100670000X

Fig. 18   Test 12A: Left Rear Sensor Circuit Failure (Part 1 of 2)

CR4029100671010X

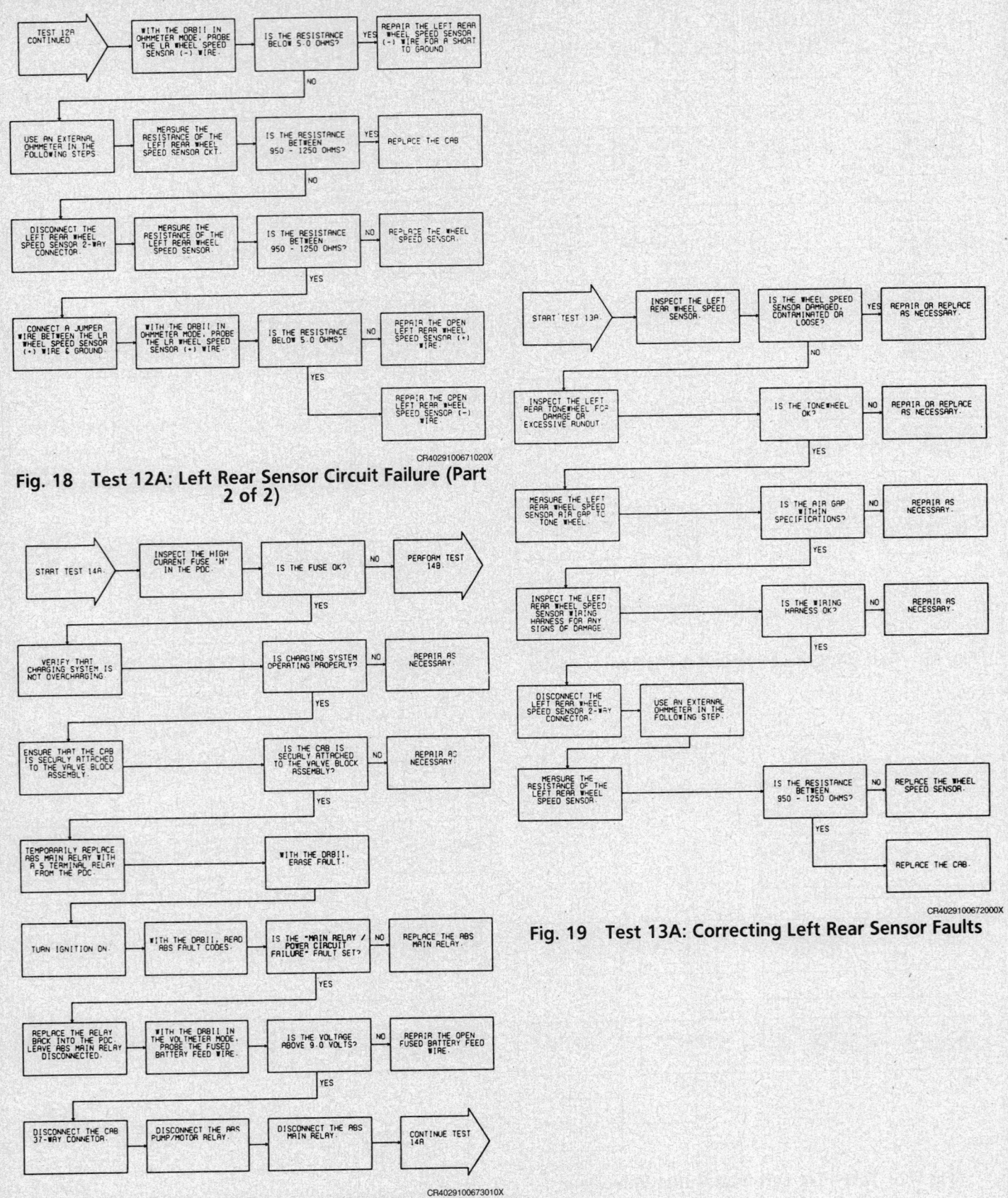

Fig. 18   Test 12A: Left Rear Sensor Circuit Failure (Part 2 of 2)

CR4029100671020X

Fig. 19   Test 13A: Correcting Left Rear Sensor Faults

CR4029100672000X

Fig. 20   Test 14A: Main Relay/Power Circuit Failure (Part 1 of 3)

CR4029100673010X

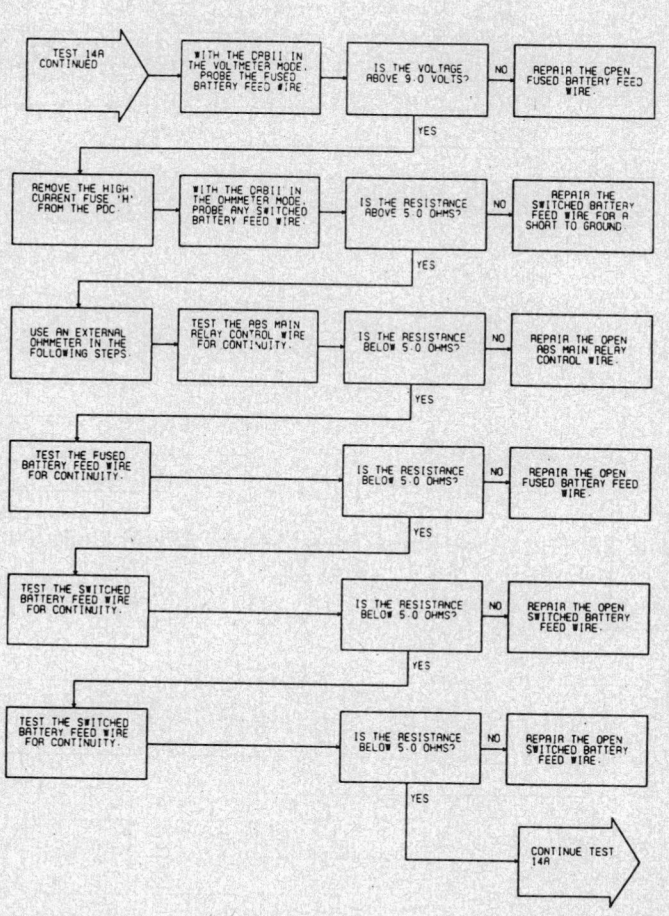

Fig. 20   Test 14A: Main Relay/Power Circuit Failure (Part 2 of 3)

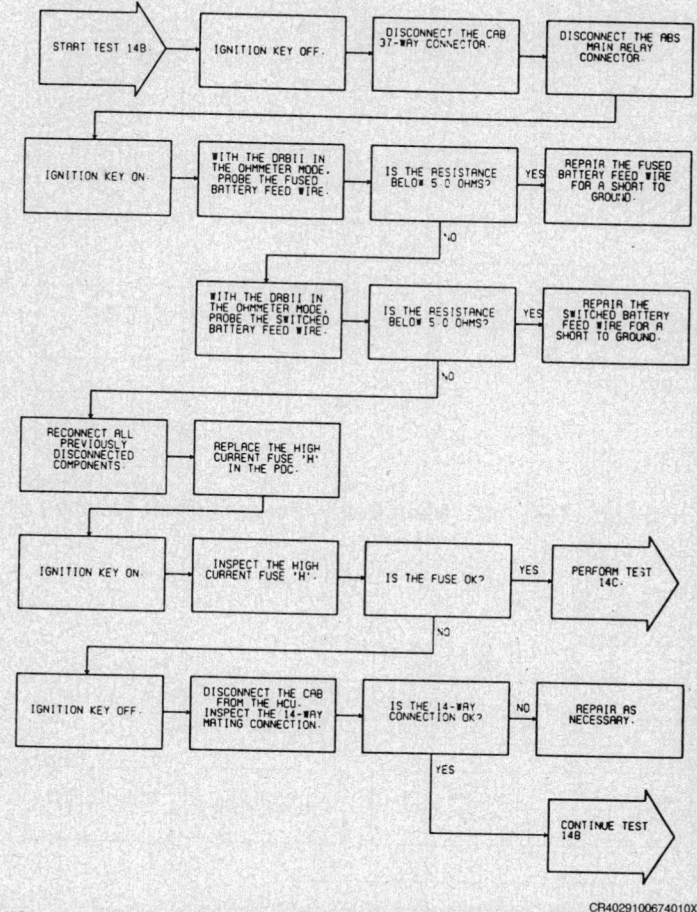

Fig. 21   Test 14B: Main Relay/Power Circuit Failure (Part 1 of 2)

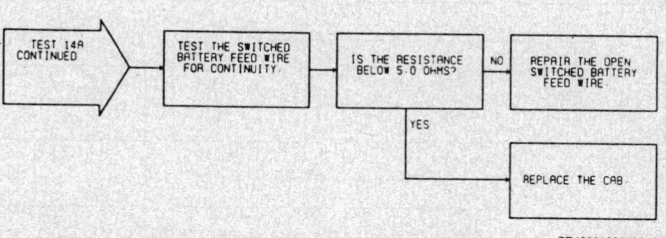

Fig. 20   Test 14A: Main Relay/Power Circuit Failure (Part 3 of 3)

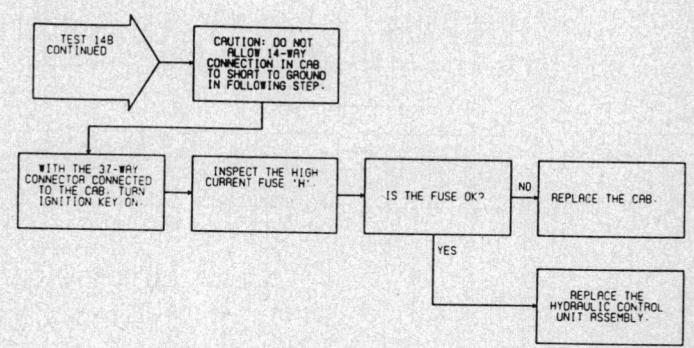

Fig. 21   Test 14B: Main Relay/Power Circuit Failure (Part 2 of 2)

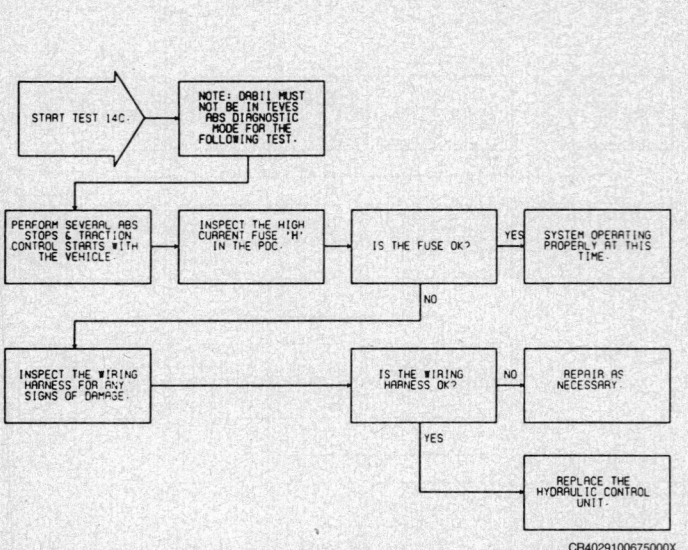

Fig. 22 Test 14C: Main Relay/Power Circuit Failure

CR4029100675000X

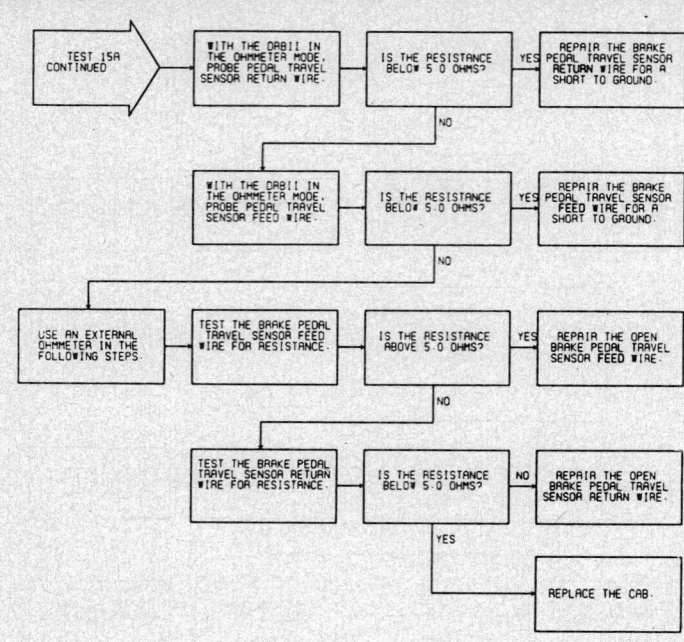

CR4029100676020X

Fig. 23 Test 15A: Pedal Travel Sensor Circuit Fault (Part 2 of 2)

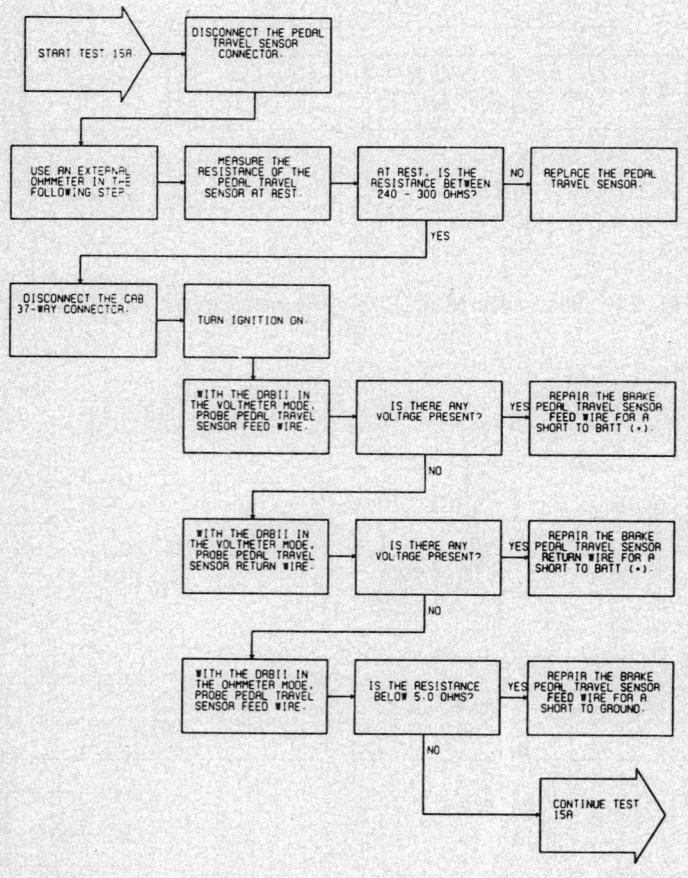

CR4029100676010X

Fig. 23 Test 15A: Pedal Travel Sensor Circuit Fault (Part 1 of 2)

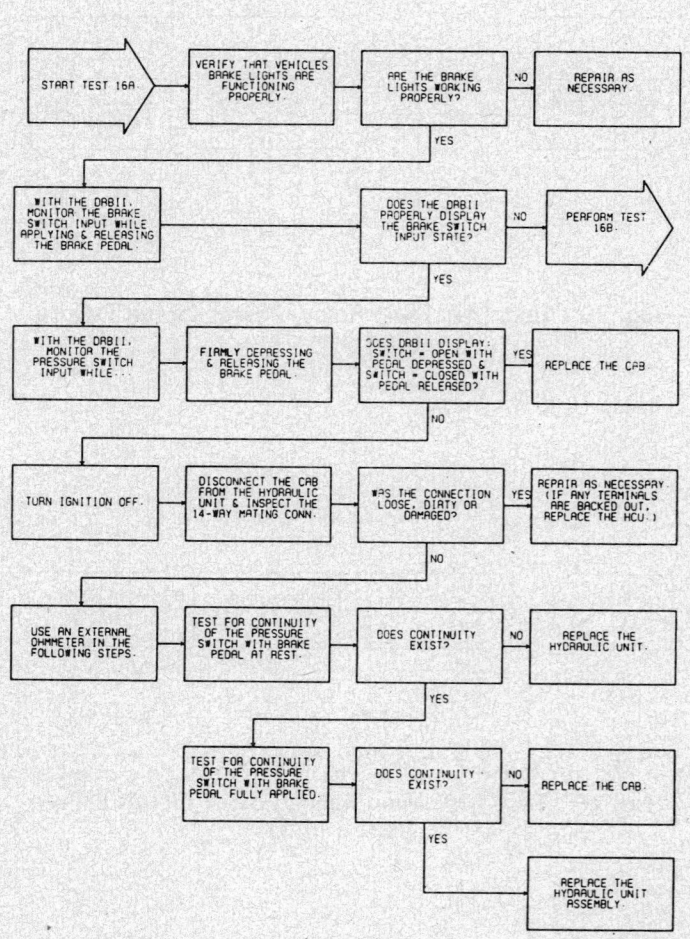

CR4029100677000X

Fig. 24 Test 16A: Pressure Switch/Brake SW Circuit Fault

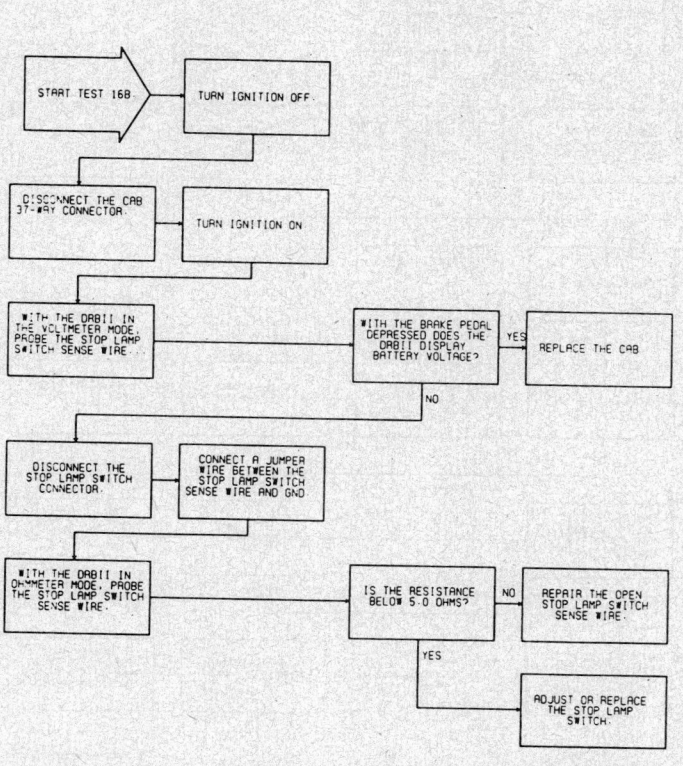

Fig. 25 Test 16B: Pressure Switch/Brake SW Circuit Fault

CR4029100678000X

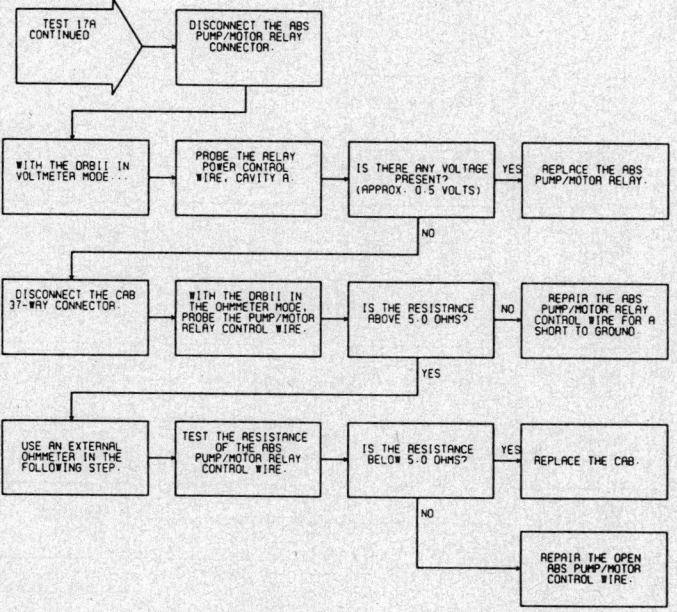

Fig. 26 Test 17A: Pump Motor Circuit Not Working Properly (Part 2 of 2)

CR4029100679020X

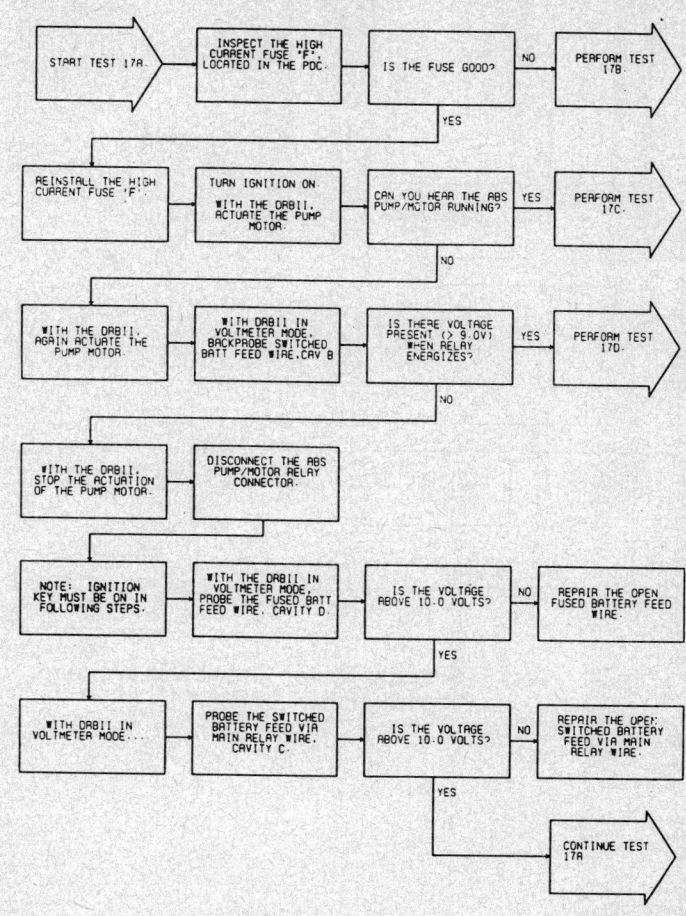

Fig. 26 Test 17A: Pump Motor Circuit Not Working Properly (Part 1 of 2)

CR4029100679010X

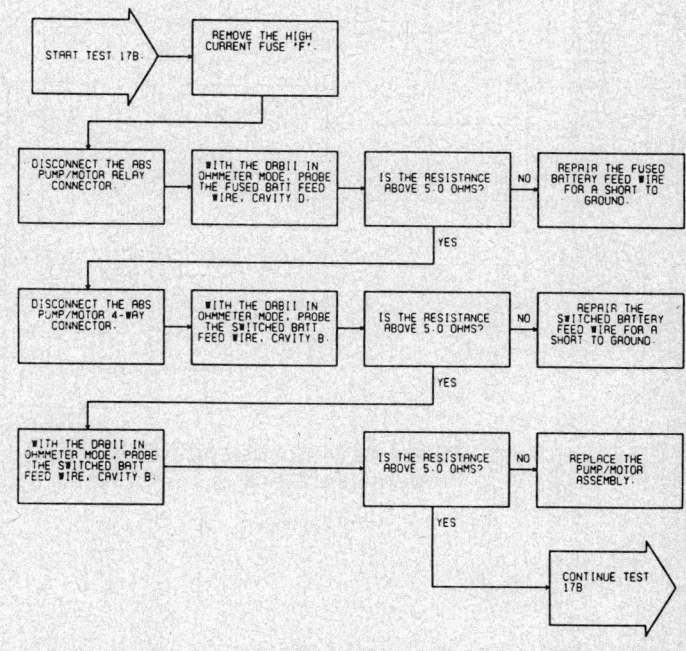

Fig. 27 Test 17B: Pump Motor Circuit Not Working Properly (Part 1 of 2)

CR4029100680010X

TYPE 6-TEVES MARK IV ANTI-LOCK BRAKING SYSTEM

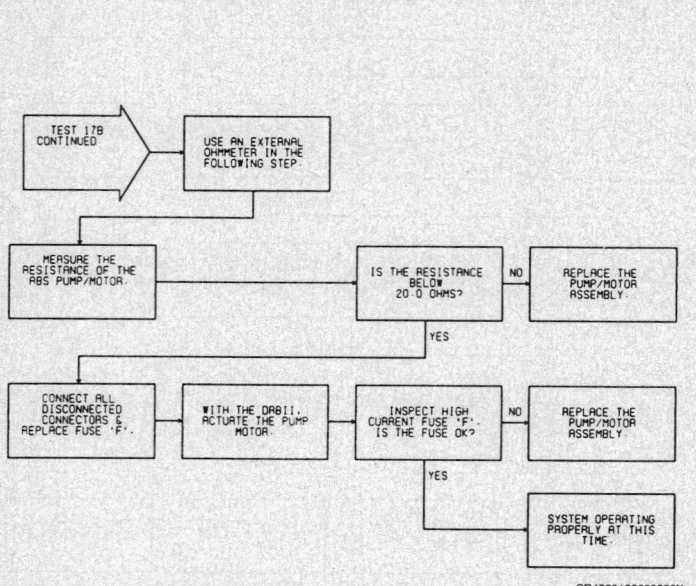

Fig. 27 Test 17B: Pump Motor Circuit Not Working Properly (Part 2 of 2)

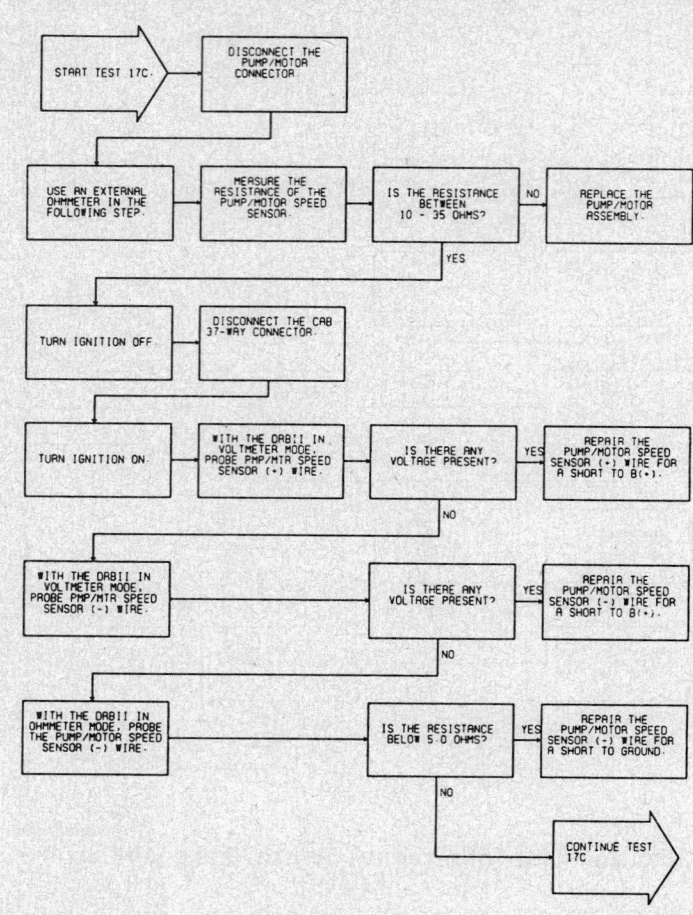

Fig. 28 Test 17C: Pump Motor Circuit Not Working Properly (Part 1 of 2)

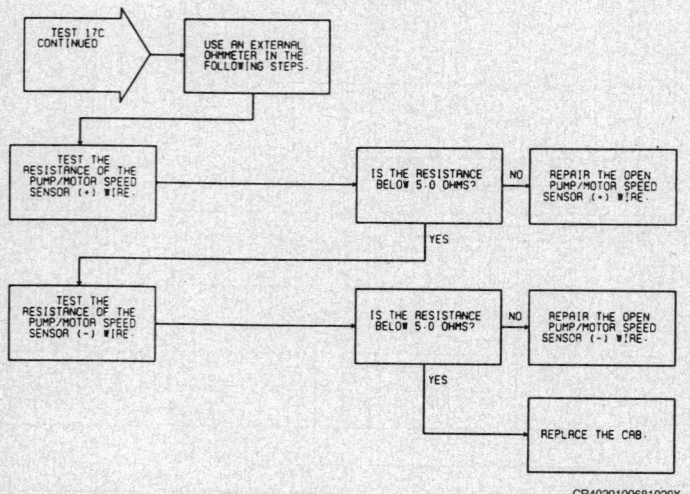

Fig. 28 Test 17C: Pump Motor Circuit Not Working Properly (Part 2 of 2)

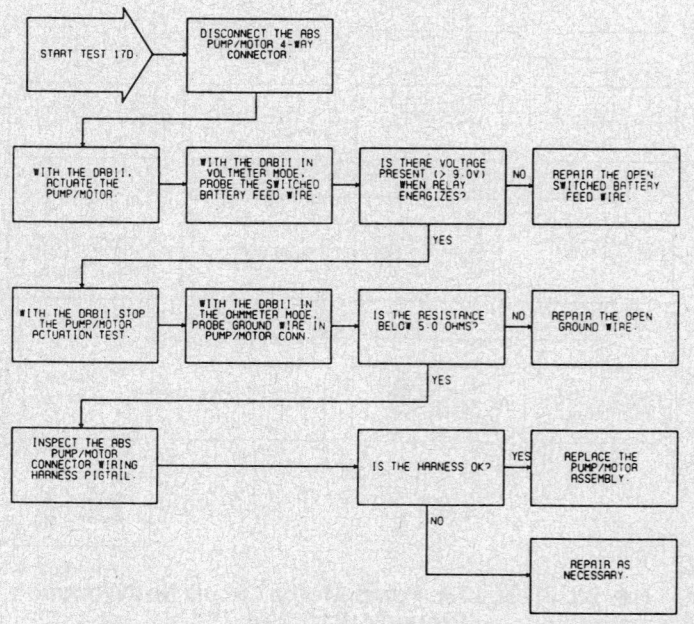

Fig. 29 Test 17D: Pump Motor Circuit Not Working Properly

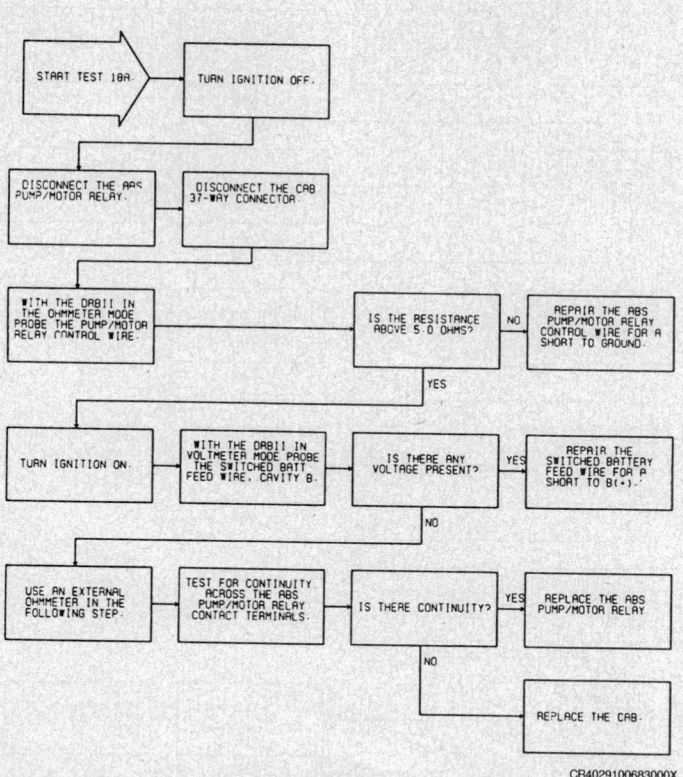

Fig. 30   Test 18A: Pump Motor Running Without Command

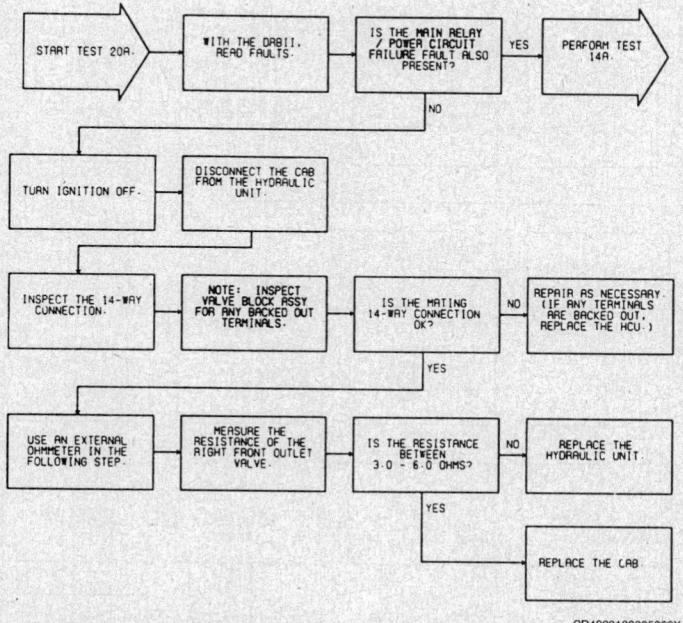

Fig. 32   Test 20A: Right Front Outlet Valve Fault

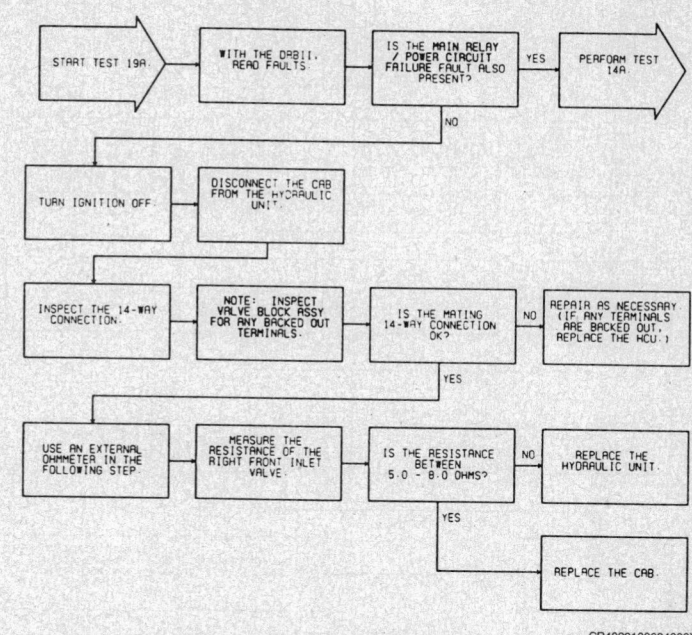

Fig. 31   Test 19A: Right Front Inlet Valve Fault

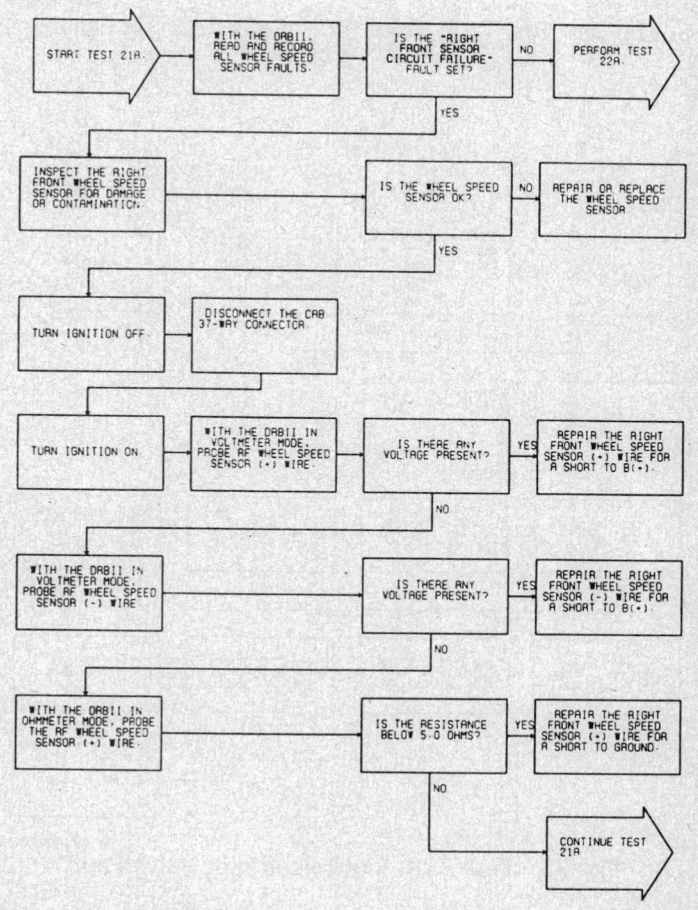

Fig. 33   Test 21A: Right Front Sensor Circuit Failure (Part 1 of 2)

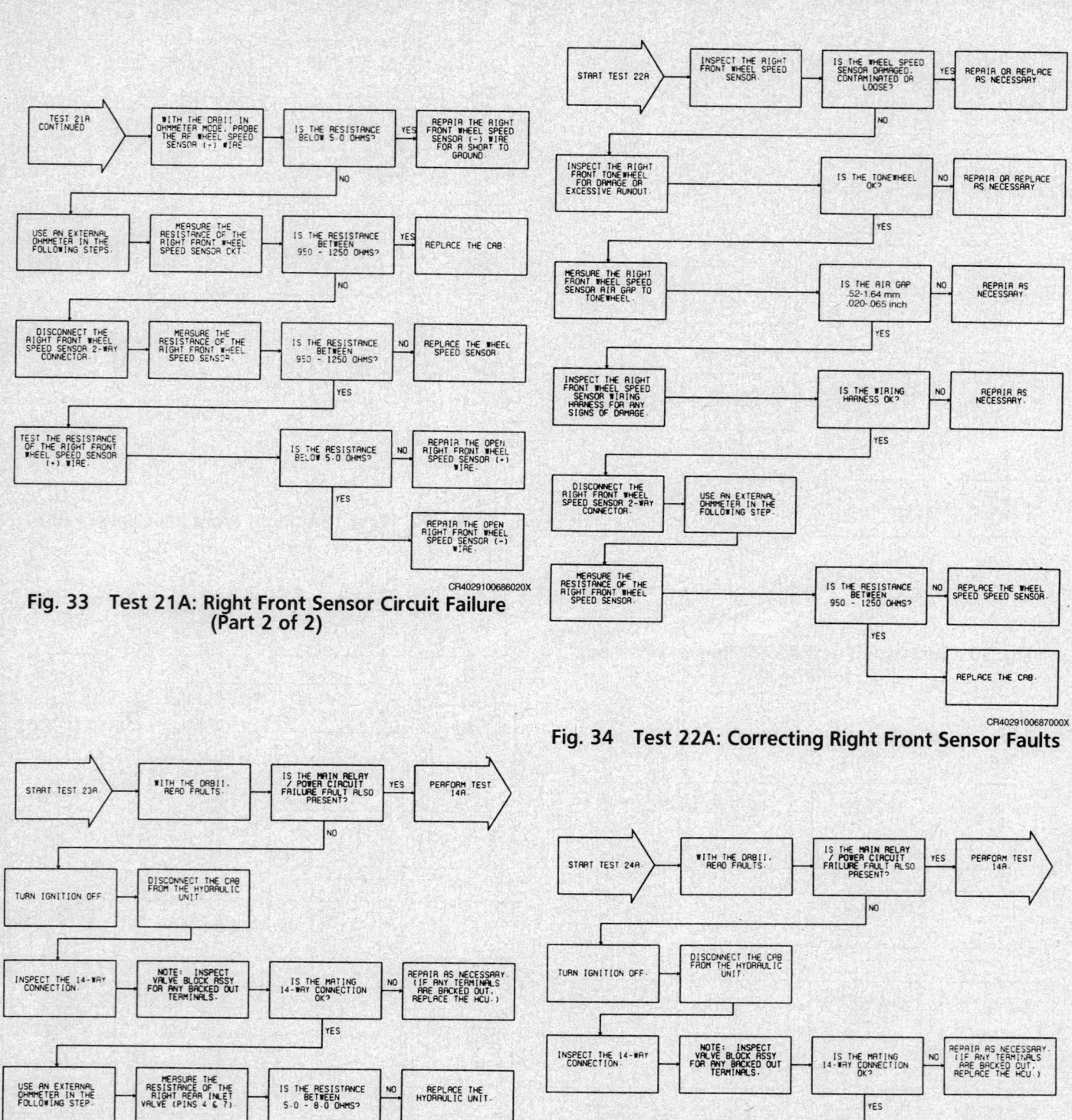

Fig. 33   Test 21A: Right Front Sensor Circuit Failure (Part 2 of 2)

CR4029100686020X

Fig. 34   Test 22A: Correcting Right Front Sensor Faults

CR4029100687000X

Fig. 35   Test 23A: Right Rear Inlet Valve Fault

CR4029100688000X

Fig. 36   Test 24A: Right Rear Outlet Valve Fault

CR4029100689000X

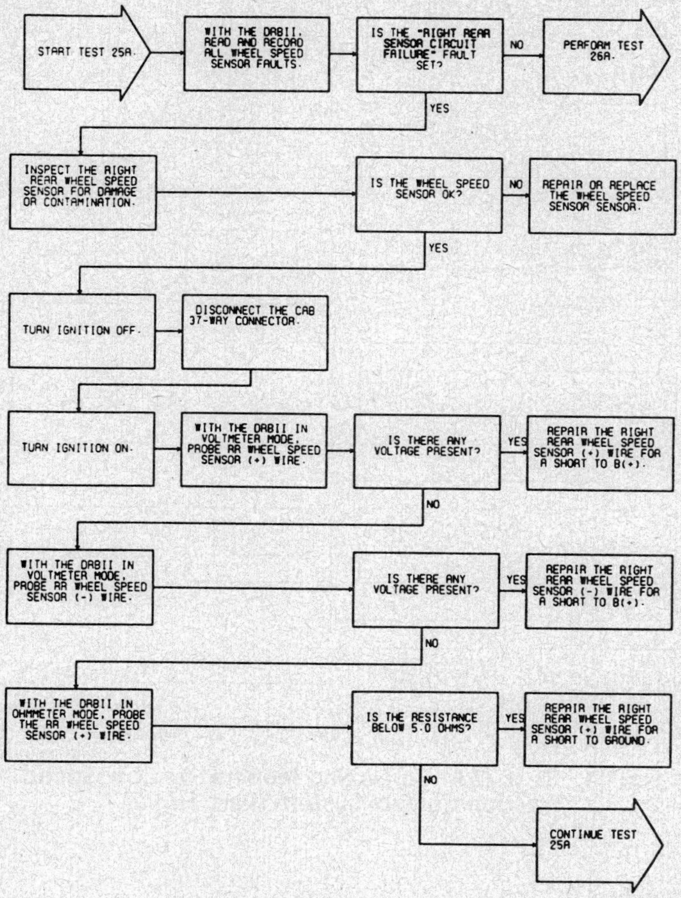

Fig. 37 Test 25A: Right Rear Sensor Circuit Failure (Part 1 of 2)

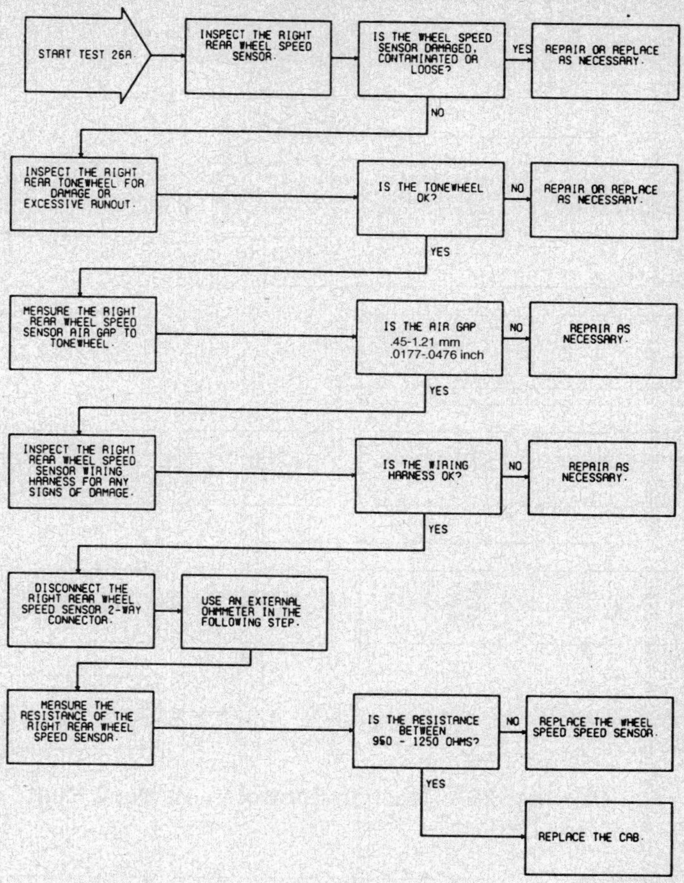

Fig. 38 Test 26A: Correcting Right Rear Sensor Faults

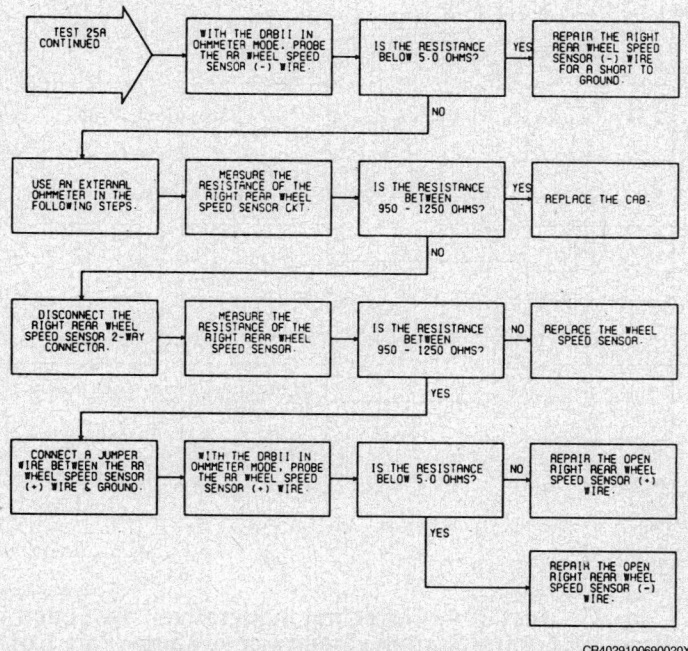

Fig. 37 Test 25A: Right Rear Sensor Circuit Failure (Part 2 of 2)

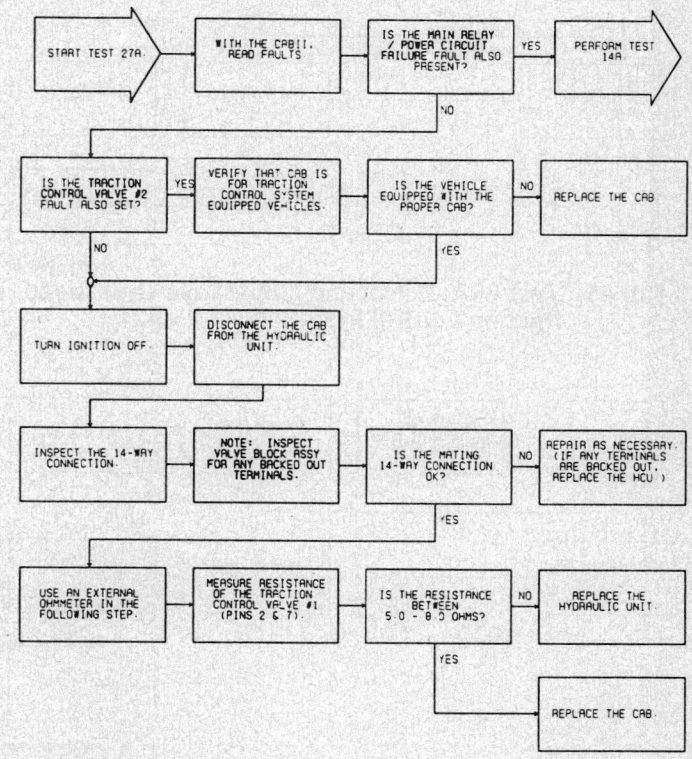

Fig. 39 Test 27A: Traction Control Valve No. 1 Fault

CR4029100693000X

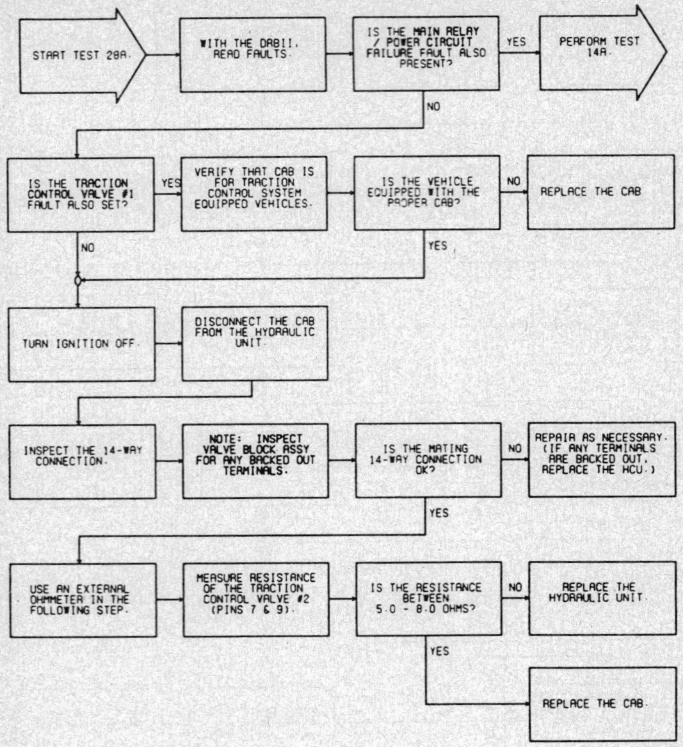

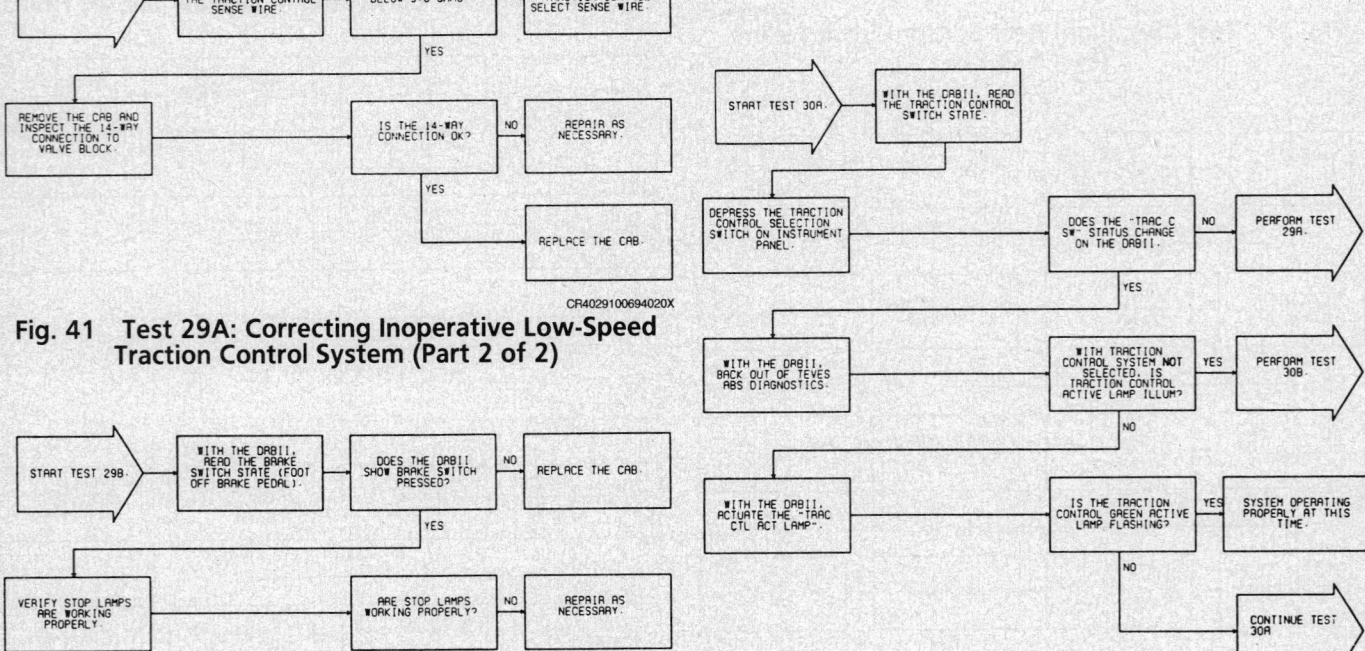

Fig. 40 Test 28A: Traction Control Valve No. 2 Fault

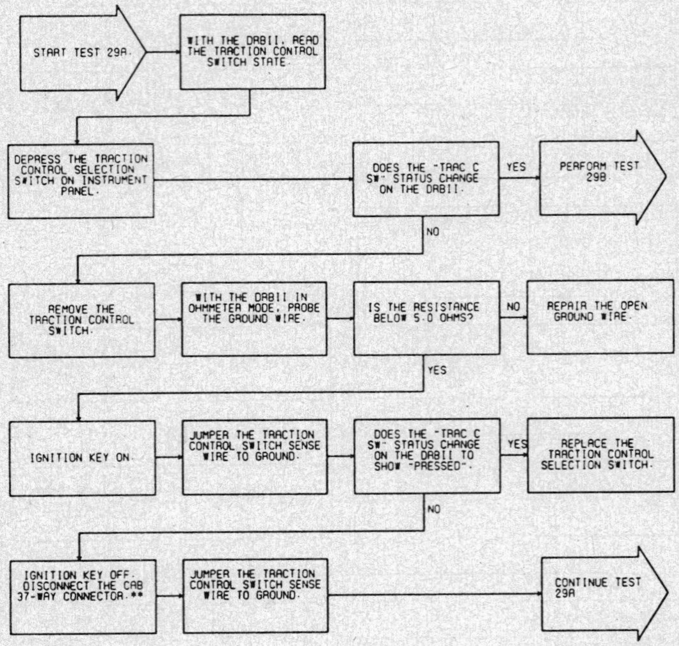

CR4029100694010X

Fig. 41 Test 29A: Correcting Inoperative Low-Speed Traction Control System (Part 1 of 2)

CR4029100694020X

Fig. 41 Test 29A: Correcting Inoperative Low-Speed Traction Control System (Part 2 of 2)

CR4029100695000X

Fig. 42 Test 29B: Correcting Inoperative Low-Speed Traction Control System

CR4029100696010X

Fig. 43 Test 30A: Correcting Inoperative Low-Speed Traction Control System, Green Active Lamp (Part 1 of 2)

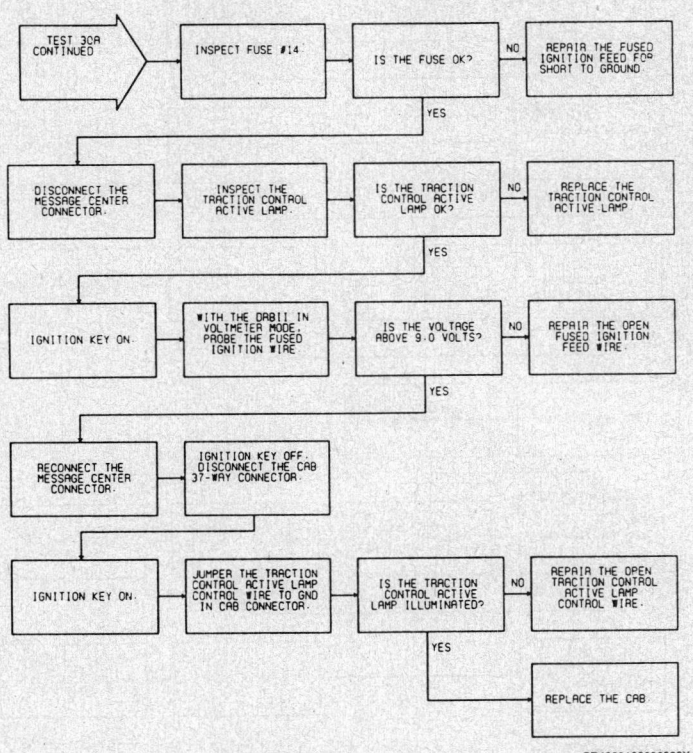

CR4029100696020X

Fig. 43   Test 30A: Correcting Inoperative Low-Speed Traction Control System, Green Active Lamp (Part 2 of 2)

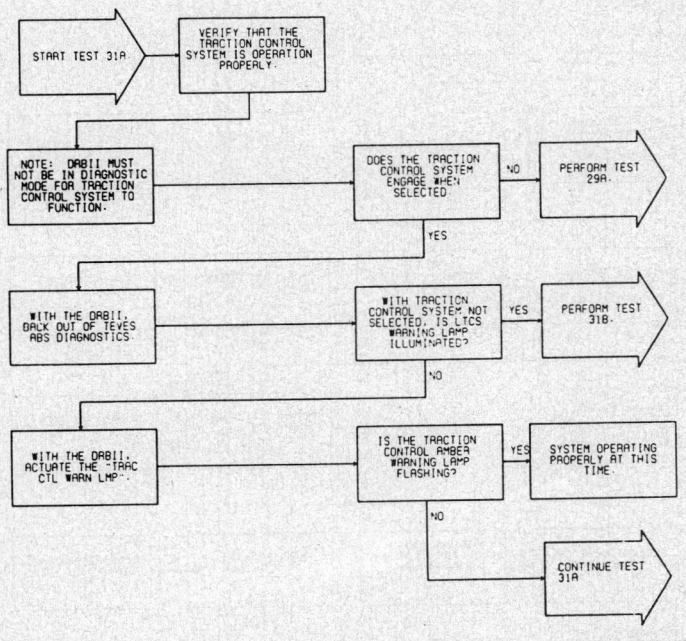

CR4029100698010X

Fig. 45   Test 31A: Correcting Inoperative Low-Speed Traction Control System, Amber Active Lamp (Part 1 of 2)

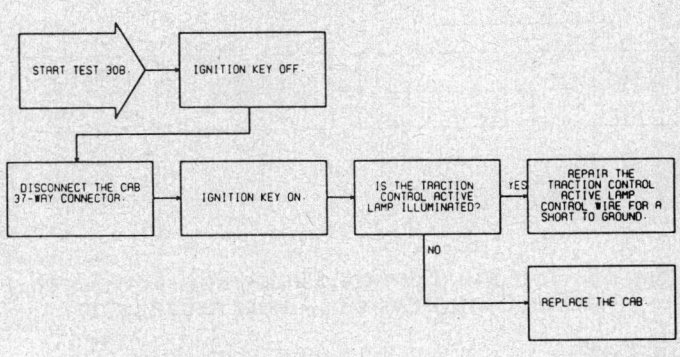

CR4029100697000X

Fig. 44   Test 30B: Correcting Inoperative Low-Speed Traction Control System, Green Active Lamp

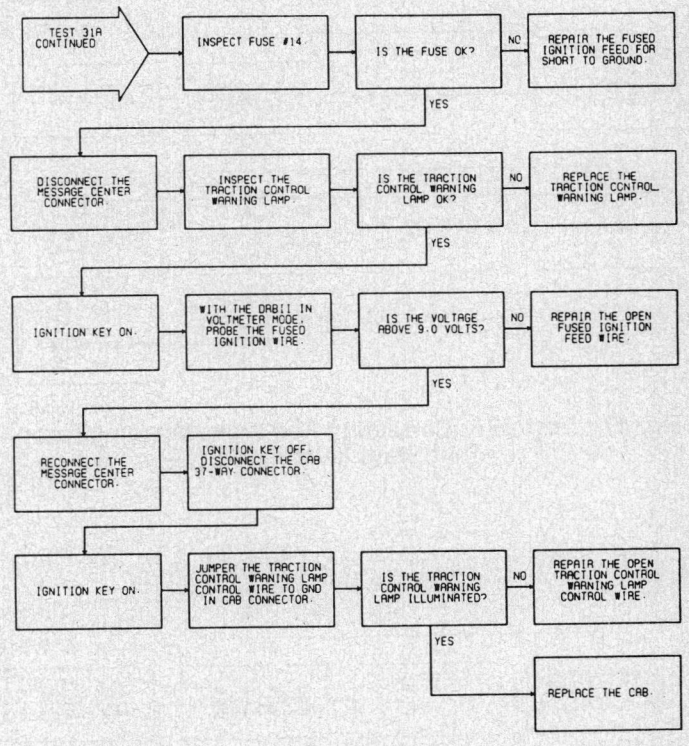

CR4029100698020X

Fig. 45   Test 31A: Correcting Inoperative Low-Speed Traction Control System, Amber Active Lamp (Part 2 of 2)

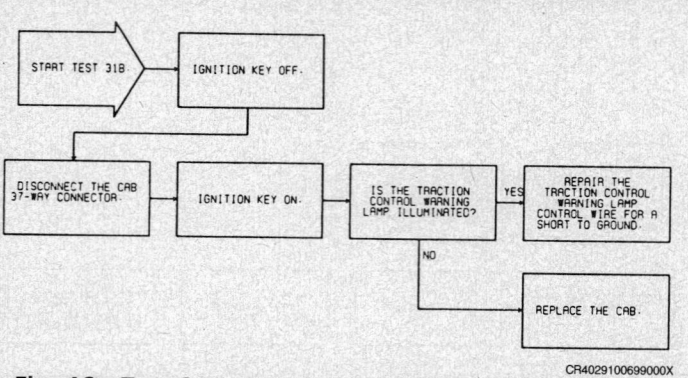

Fig. 46 Test 31B: Correcting Inoperative Low-Speed Traction Control System, Amber Active Lamp

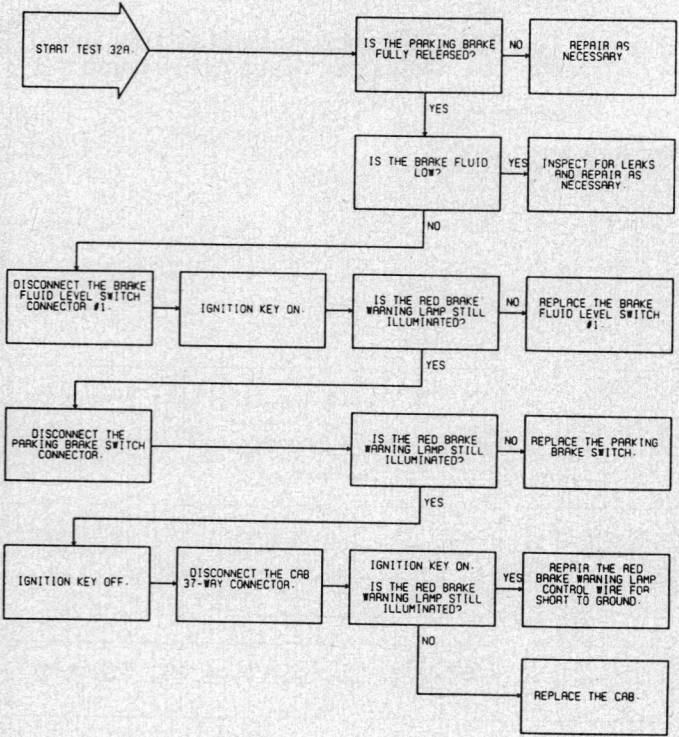

Fig. 47 Test 32A: Correcting Red Brake Warning Lamp That Stays Illuminated

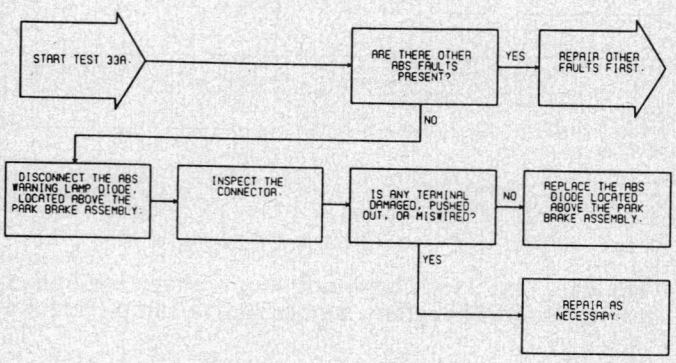

Fig. 48 Test 33A: Correcting ABS Warning Lamp That Does Not Illuminate Upon Key Up

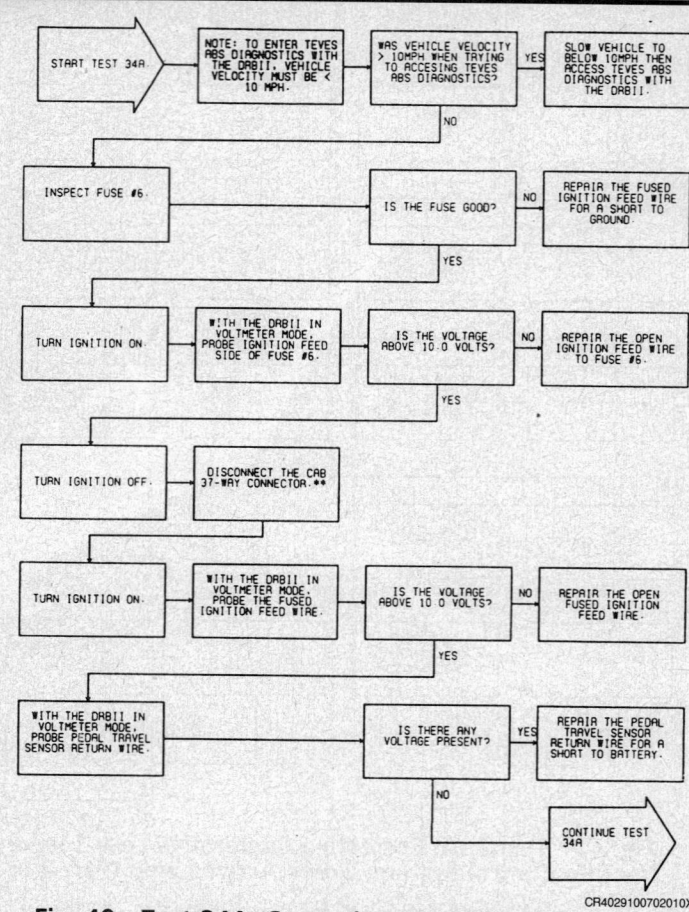

Fig. 49 Test 34A: Correcting DRB II "No Response" Condition (Part 1 of 2)

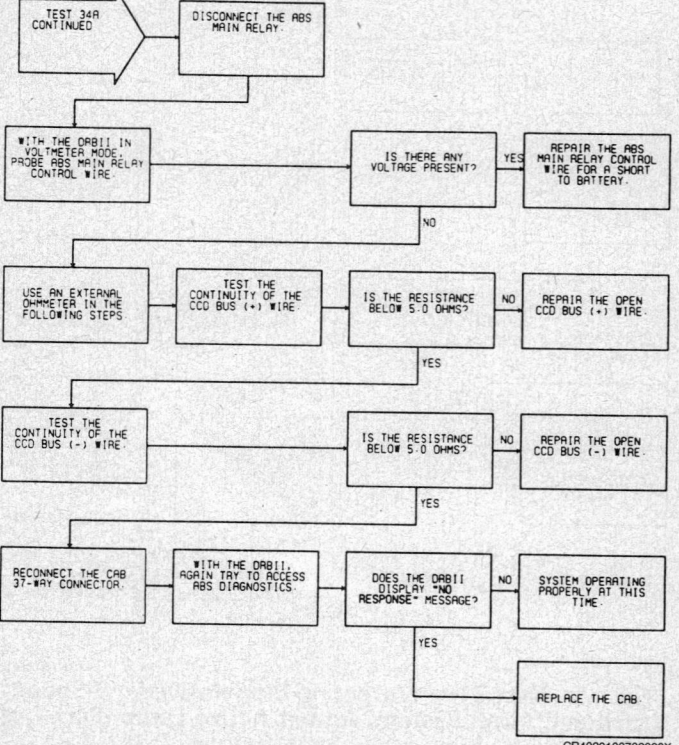

Fig. 49 Test 34A: Correcting DRB II "No Response" Condition (Part 2 of 2)

1. Connect all previously disconnected components and connectors.

2. With the DRBII erase all fault codes.

3. Turn the ignition key on. With the DRBII read fault codes; if any faults are present then repeat TEST 1A.

4. If there are no faults present upon key up, road test vehicle for at least 5 minutes. Perform several antilock braking stops and traction control starts if equipped. **CAUTION: Ensure braking capability is available before road testing vehicle. NOTE:** When the DRBII is in Teves ABS diagnostics then ABS system is disabled.

5. Again, with the DRBII read fault codes; if any faults are present then repeat TEST 1A.

6. If there are no fault codes present and the customers complaint can no longer be duplicated, repair is complete.

Fig. 50   Test 35A: Verification Test

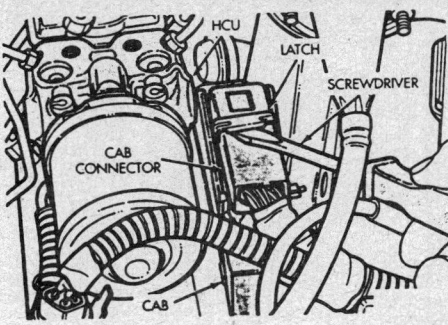

Fig. 51   Controller anti-lock brake system (CAB) connector locking latch

SYSTEM SERVICE

Brake System Bleed

The TEVES MARK IV anti-lock brake system should be bled in three steps: first, follow the Conventional Bleed Procedure; second, use the DRB II tester to bleed the Hydraulic Control Unit (HCU); finally, repeat the Conventional Bleed Procedure.

CONVENTIONAL BLEED PROCEDURE

Pressure Bleeding

1. Connect pressure bleeder tool No. C-3496-B or equivalent and adapter BB400-9A or equivalent to pressurize brake system. Follow manufactures instructions, for use of pressure bleeding equipment.
2. Attach clear hose to bleeder screw at one wheel, place other end into clear jar. Open bleeder screw one full turn, after four to eight ounces of fluid have been bled into jar close bleeder screw.
3. Repeat for all wheels in the following order: RR-LR-RF-LF, repeat procedure until no air bubbles appear and brake pedal travel is satisfactory.

Manual Bleeding

1. Connect a transparent hose to caliper bleed screw, and place the other end of hose in a transparent container partially filled with clean brake fluid.
2. Have an assistant pump brake pedal several times with full strokes of the brake pedal, then hold the pedal under pressure before opening bleeder screw.
3. Open the bleed screw 1 turn. Keep screw open until fluid no longer comes out from bleeder, then tighten bleeder screw and release brake pedal.
4. Repeat this procedure until air bubbles are no longer present in fluid coming from bleeder hose.
5. Repeat for all wheels in the following order: RR-LR-RF-LF.

BLEEDING HYDRAULIC CONTROL UNIT USING DRB II

1. Connect DRB II scan tool to vehicle diagnostics connector which is locat-

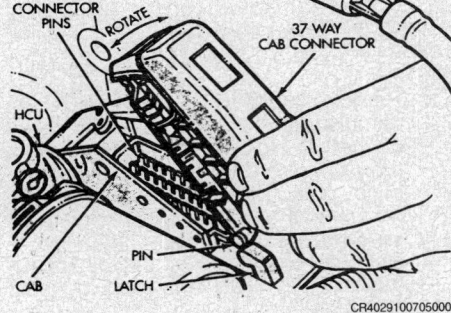

Fig. 52   Connector removal from controller anti-lock brake system (CAB)

ed under dash panel, right of steering column.
2. Install cartridge into DRB II containing correct software for bleeding Teves Anti-Lock system.
3. Perform procedure described in DRB II scan tool diagnostic manual.

Component Replace

HYDRAULIC CONTROL UNIT (HCU)

1. Raise and support vehicle, disconnect battery cables, then remove battery.
2. Remove battery tray attaching bolts, then tray.
3. Disconnect pump motor and fluid level sensor electrical connectors from HCU.
4. **Ensure ignition switch is in the OFF position,** then disconnect 37 way connector using a screwdriver. Lift connector latch away from connector, **Fig. 51,** then rotate connector latch until fully against CAB. This will lift CAB connector away from CAB terminal.
5. Grab connector and rotate rear of connector up until it clears connector pins on CAB **Fig. 52.** Remove CAB connector pin from latch on CAB and place off to side.
6. Disconnect the two brake tubes from proportioning valves, two brake fluid tubes from the master cylinder at HCU, two brake fluid output tubes from valve block on HCU, then brake fluid supply hose from master cylinder reservoir. Plug ends of supply hose so brake fluid will not drain out of master cylinder.

7. Remove HCU bracket to left inner fender attaching bolts, then two HCU bracket to left frame rail mounting bolts.
8. Remove HCU and mounting bracket from vehicle as an assembly.
9. Transfer CAB module from HCU to replacement HCU.
10. Reverse procedure to install noting the following:
    a. **Torque** two bracket to frame rail attaching bolts to 14 ft. lbs.
    b. **Torque** bracket to inner fender bolt to 18 inch lbs.
    c. **Prior to installing 37 way connector, ensure ignition switch is in the OFF position.**
    d. Bleed system as described under "Brake System Bleed."
    e. Heat shield must be installed when replacing HCU. Failure to do so could result in failure to CAB do to high temperatures.

HYDRAULIC CONTROL UNIT FLUID RESERVOIR

1. Remove HCU assembly as described in "Hydraulic Control Unit" found in "Component Replace" section.
2. Drain brake fluid from HCU fluid reservoir, then using a 1/8 inch pin punch, drive fluid reservoir retaining roll pin down until it is below hole in fluid reservoir, **Fig. 53.** If replacing reservoir with traction control, remove roll pin completely from housing.
3. Insert a screwdriver between reservoir and pump housing, then pry fluid reservoir from HCU assembly.
4. Reverse procedure to install noting the following:
    a. When replacing HCU reservoir with traction control, roll pin must be installed from the top.
    b. Bleed system as described under "Brake System Bleed."

PEDAL TRAVEL SENSOR

When removing pedal travel sensor, brake booster must be bled of vacuum. If not pedal travel sensor sealing O-ring may be sucked into the brake booster. If O-ring falls into booster, booster must be replaced.

1. Pump brake pedal 20 times to evacuate all stored vacuum from brake booster, then remove electrical connector from pedal travel sensor.

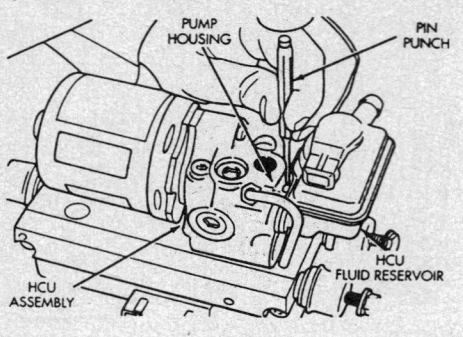

Fig. 53 Hydraulic control unit (HCU) reservoir retaining pin removal

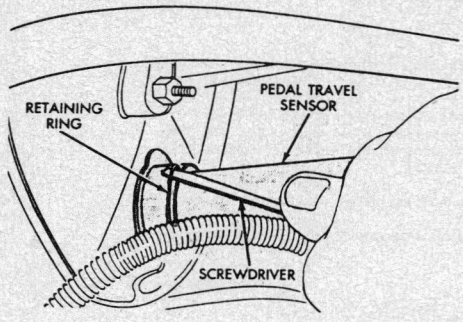

Fig. 54 Pedal travel sensor retaining ring removal

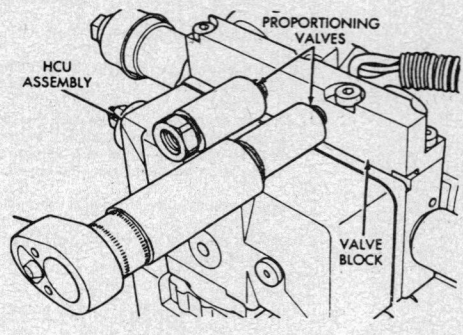

Fig. 55 Proportioning valve replacement

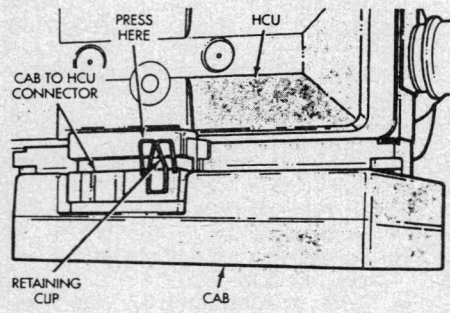

Fig. 56 Controller anti-lock brake system to hydraulic control unit retaining clip

2. Using a small screwdriver remove pedal travel sensor retaining ring, **Fig. 54.**
3. Pull pedal travel sensor straight out from booster, then remove pedal travel O-ring.
4. Reverse procedure to install noting the following:
   a. Tab of retaining ring should be located in top notch of mounting grommet.
   b. Lubricate O-ring with brake fluid before installing.
   c. Ensure travel sensor is inserted into grommet until tab on travel sensor is past retaining ring.

PROPORTIONING VALVES

Proportioning valves should never be disassembled.
1. Remove HCU as described under "Hydraulic Control Unit" found in section.
2. Remove required valve from HCU, **Fig. 55.**
3. Reverse procedure to install. **Torque** proportioning valve to 106 inch lbs.

CONTROLLER ANTI-LOCK BRAKE (CAB)

1. Ensure ignition switch is in Off position.
2. Remove HCU as described under "Hydraulic Control Unit" found in section.

3. Remove two CAB module to HCU assembly mounting bolts, press down on CAB to HCU retaining clip **Fig. 56,** then remove CAB from HCU assembly by pulling it straight out of the connector on the HCU. **Do not twist CAB when removing it from HCU.**
4. Reverse procedure to install, **torquing** CAB to HCU attaching bolts to 106 inch lbs.

WHEEL SPEED SENSOR

Inspect tonewheel for missing or broken teeth, ensure tonewheel has not made contact with wheel speed sensor. Replace tonewheel if runout exceeds .010 inch.

Front

1. Raise and support vehicle, then remove tire and wheel assembly.
2. Remove grommet retaining clip attaching screw, then pull sensor assembly grommet from fender shield.
3. Unplug speed sensor connector from vehicle wiring harness connector, then remove speed sensor cable routing bracket from front strut assembly.
4. Remove screw attaching speed sensor head to steering knuckle, then sensor from steering knuckle. **Do not use pliers on sensor head, use a hammer and punch to tap edge of sensor ear, rocking sensor side to side until free.**
5. Reverse procedure to install noting the following:
   a. Coat sensor head with high temperature multi-purpose E.P grease.
   b. **Torque** speed sensor head to 60 inch lbs.
   c. In two steps, **torque** wheel lug nuts to 95 ft. lbs.

Rear

1. Remove rear seat lower cushion and seat back from vehicle. Lift edge of sound insulation on rear bulkhead, then disconnect speed sensor cable from vehicle wiring harness.
2. Raise and support vehicle, then remove rear wheel and tires.
3. Remove grommet retaining clip attaching screw, then pull speed sensor assembly and grommet from hole in fenderwell.
4. Remove speed sensor head attaching

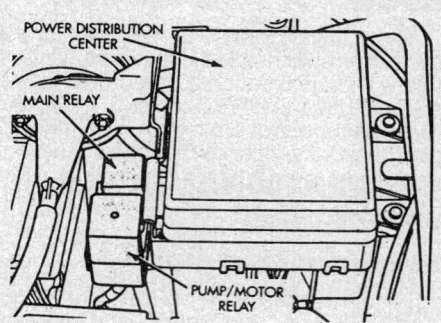

Fig. 57 System relay/warning lamp relay location

bolt from rear adapter, then remove rear speed sensor head from adapter. **Do not use pliers on speed sensor, use a hammer and punch to tap edge of sensor ear, rocking sensor from side to side until free.**
5. Remove screws attaching speed sensor cable mounting tube to inboard side of trailing arm, then speed sensor cable routing brackets at rear fenderwell and trailing arm bracket at rear knuckle.
6. Remove speed sensor from cable assembly from vehicle.
7. Reverse procedure to install noting the following:
   a. Coat sensor head with high temperature multi-purpose E.P grease.
   b. **Torque** speed sensor head to 60 inch lbs.
   c. In two steps, **torque** wheel lug nuts to 95 ft. lbs.

MAIN & PUMP/MOTOR RELAY

The main relay and pump motor relay are serviced as an assembly with the relay mounting bracket. The relay bracket is mounted to the side of the power distribution center (PDC), **Fig. 57.**
1. Remove relay electrical connector by pulling straight down on wiring harness.
2. Remove relays and bracket from side of PDC.
3. Reverse procedure to install.

AUTOMATIC TRANSMISSIONS/TRANSAXLES

TABLE OF CONTENTS

Torqueflite (31TH) Three Speed Automatic Transaxle

INDEX

IDENTIFICATION

A seven digit part number is stamped on a pad located at the rear of the transaxle on the transaxle oil pan flange. This number must be referred to when servicing the transaxle due to differences in some internal components.

DESCRIPTION

These transaxles combine a torque converter, three speed automatic transaxle, final drive gearing and differential combined into one unit. The torque converter, transaxle and differential assemblies are housed in an integral aluminum diecast housing, **Fig. 1. The differential oil sump is integral with the transaxle sump. Separate filling of the differential is not necessary.**

The torque converter is connected to the crankshaft through a flexible driveplate. Converter cooling is accomplished by an oil-to-water type cooler, located in the radiator side tank. The torque converter cannot be disassembled.

The transaxle consists of two multiple disc clutches, an overrunning clutch, two servos, a hydraulic accumulator, two bands and two planetary gear assemblies to provide three forward and one reverse gear. The sun gear is connected to the front clutch retainer. The hydraulic system consists of an oil pump, and a single valve body which contains all of the valves except the governor valves. Output torque from the main drive gears is transferred through helical gears to the transfer shaft. An integral ring gear on the transfer shaft drives the differential ring gear.

All vehicles except turbocharged models are equipped with a lock-up torque converter. The lock-up mode is activated only in direct drive (3rd gear) and is controlled by the engine control computer. A lock-up solenoid on the valve body transfer plate is powered by the computer to activate torque converter lock-up.

TROUBLESHOOTING

HARSH ENGAGEMENT FROM NEUTRAL TO DRIVE OR REVERSE

1. High idle speed.
2. Defective or leaking valve body.
3. High hydraulic pressure.
4. Worn or damaged rear clutch.
5. Worn low-reverse band.
6. Planetary gear sets seized or broken.
7. Insufficient clutch plate clearance.
8. Low-reverse band linkage improperly adjusted.

DELAYED ENGAGEMENT FROM NEUTRAL TO DRIVE OR REVERSE

1. Low hydraulic pressure.
2. Defective or leaking valve body.
3. Low-reverse servo, band or linkage malfunction.
4. Low fluid level.
5. Incorrect gearshift linkage adjustment.
6. Clogged transaxle oil filter.
7. Faulty oil pump.
8. Worn or damaged input shaft seal rings.
9. Aerated fluid.
10. Low idle speed.
11. Worn or damaged reaction shaft support seal rings.
12. Worn or defective front clutch.
13. Worn or defective rear clutch.
14. Overrunning clutch inner race damaged.
15. Insufficient clutch plate clearance.
16. Faulty cooling system.
17. High hydraulic pressure.
18. Governor malfunction.
19. Low-reverse band worn.

RUNAWAY UPSHIFTS

1. Low hydraulic pressure.
2. Defective or leaking valve body.
3. Low fluid level.
4. Clogged transaxle oil filter.
5. Aerated fluid.
6. Incorrect throttle linkage adjustment.
7. Worn or damaged reaction shaft support seal rings.
8. Kickdown servo, band or linkage malfunction.
9. Worn or faulty front clutch.
10. Insufficient clutch plate clearance.
11. High fluid level.
12. Governor malfunction.
13. Governor support seal rings worn or broken.
14. Input shaft seal rings worn or broken.
15. Faulty oil pump.

NO UPSHIFT

1. Low hydraulic pressure.
2. Defective or leaking valve body.
3. Low fluid level.
4. Incorrect gearshift linkage adjustment.
5. Incorrect throttle linkage adjustment.
6. Worn or damaged governor support seal rings.
7. Worn or damaged reaction shaft support seal rings.
8. Faulty governor.
9. Kickdown servo, band or linkage malfunction.
10. Worn or faulty front clutch.
11. Rear clutch dragging.
12. Insufficient clutch plate clearance.
13. High hydraulic pressure.
14. Aerated fluid.
15. Input shaft seal rings worn or broken.
16. Faulty oil pump.

3-2 KICKDOWN RUNAWAY

1. Low hydraulic pressure.
2. Defective or leaking valve body.
3. Low fluid level.
4. Aerated fluid.
5. Incorrect throttle linkage adjustment.

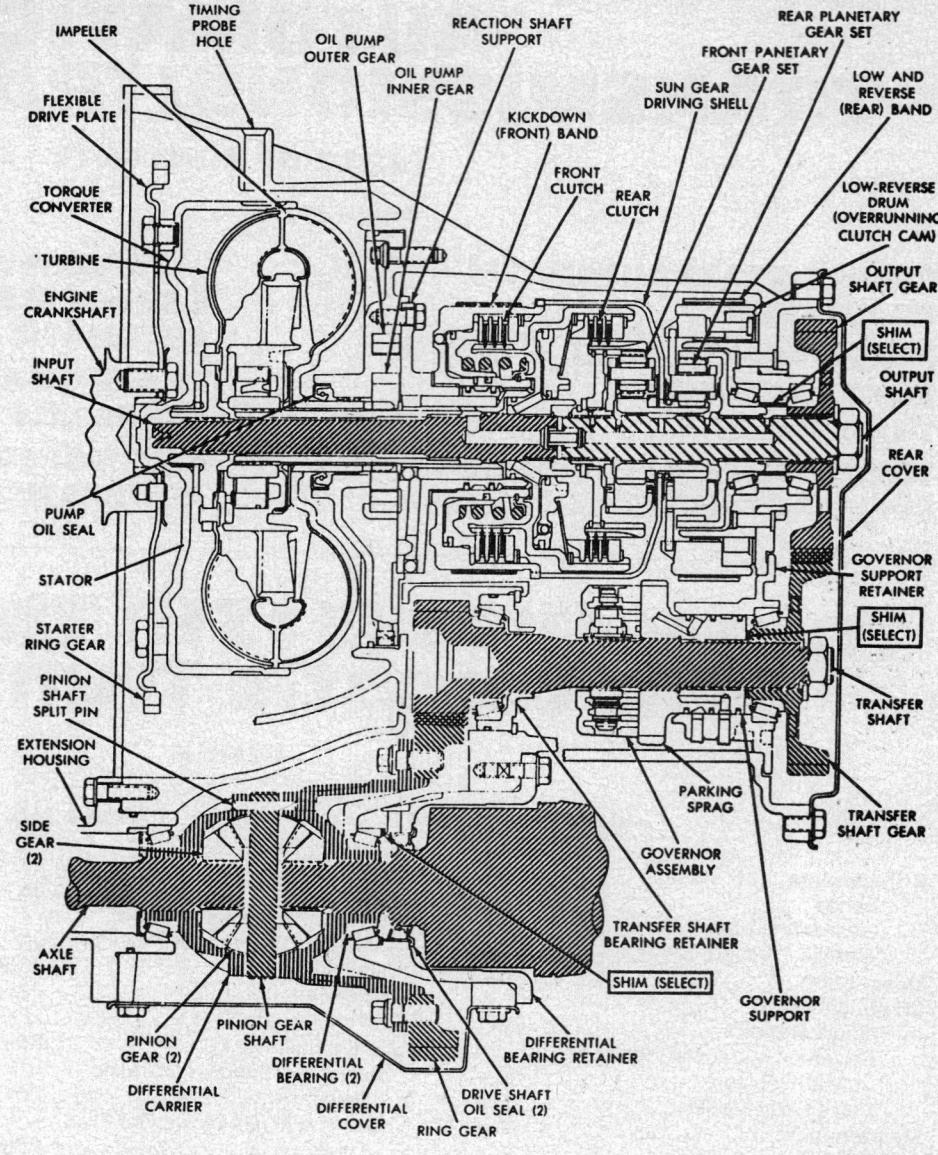

Fig. 1   Cross-sectional view of Torqueflite automatic transaxle

6. Kickdown band adjustment.
7. Worn or damaged governor support seal rings.
8. Kickdown servo, band or linkage malfunction.
9. Worn or faulty front clutch.
10. Rear clutch dragging.
11. Insufficient clutch plate clearance.
12. Governor malfunction.
13. Driveshaft(s) or bushing(s) damaged.
14. Input shaft seal rings worn or broken.
15. Faulty oil pump.

NO KICKDOWN OR NORMAL DOWNSHIFT

1. Defective or leaking valve body.
2. Incorrect throttle linkage adjustment.
3. Faulty governor.
4. Kickdown servo, band or linkage malfunction.
5. Insufficient clutch plate clearance.
6. Governor support seal rings worn or broken.
7. Aerated fluid.
8. Input shaft seal rings worn or broken.

ERRATIC SHIFTS

1. Low hydraulic pressure.
2. Defective or leaking valve body.
3. Low fluid level.
4. Incorrect gearshift linkage adjustment.
5. Clogged transaxle oil filter.
6. Faulty oil pump.
7. Aerated fluid.
8. Incorrect throttle linkage adjustment.
9. Worn or damaged governor support seal rings.
10. Worn or damaged reaction shaft support seal rings.
11. Faulty governor.
12. Kickdown servo, band or linkage malfunction.
13. Worn or faulty front clutch.
14. Rear clutch dragging.
15. Insufficient clutch plate clearance.
16. High hydraulic pressure.
17. High fluid level.

18. Governor support seal rings worn or broken.
19. Input shaft seal rings worn or broken.

SLIPS IN 1, 2 OR DRIVE

1. Low hydraulic pressure.
2. Defective or leaking valve body.
3. Low fluid level.
4. Incorrect gearshift linkage adjustment.
5. Clogged transaxle oil filter.
6. Faulty oil pump.
7. Worn or damaged input shaft seal rings.
8. Aerated fluid.
9. Incorrect throttle linkage adjustment.
10. Overrunning clutch not holding.
11. Worn or faulty rear clutch.
12. Overrunning clutch worn damaged or seized.
13. Insufficient clutch plate clearance.
14. Kickdown band adjustment too tight.
15. High hydraulic pressure.
16. High fluid level.
17. Worn or faulty front clutch.
18. Kickdown servo band or linkage malfunction.
19. Governor malfunction.
20. Governor support seal rings worn or broken.
21. Low-reverse band worn out.
22. Stuck switch valve.

SLIPS IN REVERSE ONLY

1. Low hydraulic pressure.
2. Low-reverse band adjustment.
3. Defective or leaking valve body.
4. Low-reverse servo, band or linkage malfunction.
5. Low fluid level.
6. Incorrect gearshift linkage adjustment.
7. Faulty oil pump.
8. Aerated fluid.
9. Worn or damaged reaction shaft seal rings.
10. Worn or faulty front clutch.
11. Overrunning clutch inner race damaged.
12. Rear clutch dragging.
13. Worn or faulty rear clutch.
14. Faulty cooling system.
15. Kickdown band adjustment too tight.
16. High hydraulic pressure.
17. Governor malfunction.

SLIPS IN ALL RANGES

1. Low hydraulic pressure.
2. Defective or leaking valve body.
3. Low fluid level.
4. Clogged transaxle oil filter.
5. Faulty oil pump.
6. Worn or damaged input shaft seal rings.
7. Aerated fluid.
8. Rear clutch dragging.
9. Kickdown band adjustment too tight.
10. High fluid level.
11. worn or faulty front clutch.
12. Governor malfunction.

NO DRIVE IN ANY RANGE

1. Low hydraulic pressure.
2. Defective or leaking valve body.
3. Low fluid level.
4. Clogged transaxle oil filter.
5. Faulty oil pump.
6. Planetary gear sets damaged or seized.

7. Rear clutch dragging.
8. Kickdown band adjustment too tight.
9. High fluid level.
10. Worn or faulty front clutch.
11. Engine idle speed too high.

NO DRIVE IN 1, 2 OR DRIVE

1. Low hydraulic pressure.
2. Defective or leaking valve body.
3. Low fluid level.
4. Worn or damaged input shaft seal rings.
5. Overrunning clutch not holding.
6. Worn or faulty rear clutch.
7. Planetary gear sets damaged or seized.
8. Overrunning clutch worn, damaged or seized.
9. Rear clutch dragging.
10. Kickdown band adjustment too tight.
11. Low-reverse band worn out.
12. Engine idle speed too high.
13. Stuck switch valve.

NO DRIVE IN REVERSE

1. Low hydraulic pressure.
2. Low-reverse band adjustment.
3. Defective or leaking valve body.
4. Low-reverse servo, band or linkage malfunction.
5. Incorrect gearshift linkage adjustment.
6. Worn or damaged reaction shaft support seal rings.
7. Worn or faulty front clutch.
8. Worn or faulty rear clutch.
9. Planetary gear sets damaged or seized.
10. Rear clutch dragging.
11. Faulty cooling system.
12. High hydraulic pressure.
13. Faulty oil pump.

DRIVE IN NEUTRAL

1. Defective or leaking valve body.
2. Incorrect gearshift linkage adjustment.
3. Insufficient clutch plate clearance.
4. Worn or faulty rear clutch.
5. Rear clutch dragging.
6. Hydraulic pressure too high.
7. Low-reverse band worn out.
8. Hydraulic pressure too low.

DRAGS OR LOCKS

1. Low-reverse band adjustment.
2. Kickdown band adjustment.
3. Planetary gear sets damaged or seized.
4. Overrunning clutch worn, damaged or seized.
5. Worn or faulty rear clutch.
6. Low fluid level.
7. Engine idle speed too high.
8. Stuck switch valve.

HARD TO FILL (OIL BLOWS OUT FILLER TUBE)

1. Clogged transaxle oil filter.
2. Aerated fluid.
3. High fluid level.
4. Breather clogged.

TRANSAXLE OVERHEATS

1. Stuck switch valve.
2. High idle speed.
3. Low hydraulic pressure.
4. Low fluid level.
5. Incorrect gearshift adjustment.
6. Faulty oil pump.
7. Kickdown band adjustment too tight.
8. Faulty cooling system.
9. Insufficient clutch plate clearance.
10. Overrunning clutch worn, broken or seized.
11. Planetary gear sets broken or seized.
12. Rear clutch dragging.
13. High hydraulic pressure.
14. Worn or faulty front clutch.
15. Low-reverse servo, band, or linkage malfunction.
16. Defective or leaking valve body.

HARSH UPSHIFTS

1. Low hydraulic pressure.
2. Incorrect throttle linkage adjustment.
3. Kickdown band adjustment.
4. High hydraulic pressure.
5. Rear clutch dragging.
6. Governor support seal rings worn broken.
7. Driveshaft(s) or bushing(s) damaged.

DELAYED UPSHIFT

1. Incorrect throttle linkage adjustment.
2. Kickdown band adjustment.
3. Worn or damaged governor support seal rings.
4. Worn or damaged reaction shaft support seal rings.
5. Faulty governor.
6. Kickdown servo, band or linkage malfunction.
7. Worn or faulty front clutch.
8. Driveshaft(s) or bushing(s) damaged.
9. Aerated fluid.
10. Faulty oil pump.

GRATING, SCRAPING OR GROWLING NOISE

1. Low-reverse band out of adjustment.
2. Kickdown band adjustment.
3. Output shaft bearing or bushing damaged.
4. Planetary gear sets damaged or seized.
5. Overrunning clutch worn, damaged or seized.
6. Worn or faulty rear clutch.
7. Stuck switch valve.

BUZZING NOISE

1. Defective or leaking valve body.
2. Low fluid level.
3. Aerated fluid.
4. Overrunning clutch inner race damaged.
5. Insufficient clutch plate clearance.
6. Kickdown band adjustment too tight.
7. Faulty governor.
8. Low-reverse band improperly adjusted.

NO LOCK UP

1. Stuck switch valve.
2. Low hydraulic pressure.
3. Defective or leaking valve body.
4. Low fluid level.
5. Faulty oil pump.

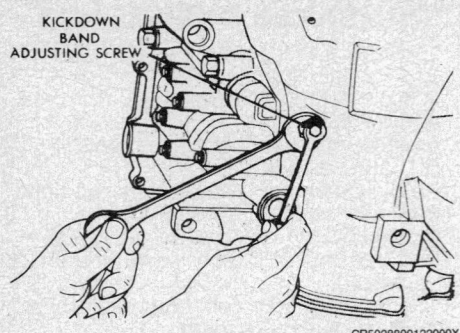

Fig. 2 Kickdown band adjustment

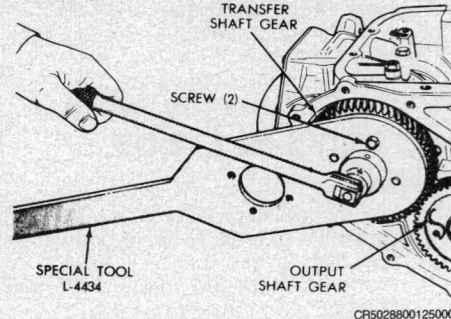

Fig. 3 Transfer shaft gear nut removal

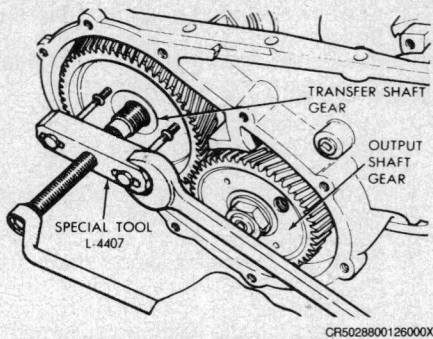

Fig. 4 Transfer shaft gear removal

6. Worn or broken input shaft seal rings.
7. Aerated fluid.

MAINTENANCE

FLUID CHECK

To check fluid level, apply the parking brake and operate engine at idle speed with transaxle in N or P position. Add fluid as necessary.

FLUID CHANGE

Fluid and filter changes are not required for average passenger car use. Severe usage such as commercial type usage or prolonged operation in city traffic, requires that fluid be changed and bands adjusted every 15,000 miles.

Whenever the factory fill fluid is changed, only fluids of the type labeled Mopar ATF Plus (Type 7176) should be used. Dexron II automatic transmission fluid should be used only if the recommended fluid is not available.

1. Raise vehicle and place a suitable drain pan under transaxle oil pan.
2. Loosen transaxle oil pan attaching bolts and allow fluid to drain, then remove oil pan.
3. Replace oil filter and adjust bands if necessary, then install oil pan and gasket.
4. Add four quarts of approved automatic transaxle fluid through the filler tube.
5. Start engine and allow to idle for at least two minutes, then with parking brake applied move selector lever momentarily to each position. Place selector lever in N or P and check fluid level. Add fluid to bring level to Add mark.
6. Recheck fluid level after transaxle has reached operating temperature. The level should be between Add and Full marks.

ADJUSTMENTS

BANDS

Kickdown Band

1. Loosen locknut and back off nut approximately five turns, **Fig. 2.**
2. Ensure adjusting screw turns freely in transaxle case.
3. Using wrench tool No. C-3880-A and

adapter tool No. C-3705 or equivalents, **torque** band adjusting screw to 47-50 inch lbs. If adapter tool No. C-3705 is not used, **torque** adjusting screw to 72 inch lbs.
4. Back off adjusting screw 2½ turns. **Torque** locknut to 35 ft. lbs. while preventing adjusting screw from turning.

Low-Reverse Band

1. Loosen locknut and back off nut approximately five turns.
2. **Torque** adjusting nut to 41 inch lbs.
3. Back off adjusting nut 3½ turns.
4. **Torque** locknut to 10 ft. lbs.

GEARSHIFT LINKAGE

When it is necessary to remove linkage cable from levers, plastic grommets must be replaced.
1. Set parking brake, then place selector lever in P position.
2. Loosen clamp bolt on gear shift cable bracket.
3. **On column shift models,** ensure preload adjustment spring engages fork on transaxle bracket.
4. **On all models,** pull shift lever by hand to front detent position (Park) and tighten lock. **Torque** screw to 100 inch lbs.
5. Check adjustment as follows:
   a. Detent position for neutral and drive should be within limits of hand lever gate stops.
   b. Key start must occur only when shift lever is in Park or Neutral position.

THROTTLE PRESSURE LINKAGE,

Cable Type

1. Perform adjustment with engine at operating temperature.
2. Loosen cable mounting bracket lock screw.
3. Position mounting bracket with both alignment tabs touching transaxle cast surface.
4. Release cross-lock on cable assembly by pulling the cross-lock upward. **To ensure proper adjustment, the cable must be free to slide all the way toward engine, against its stop, after the cross-lock is released.**
5. Move transaxle throttle control lever fully clockwise against its internal

stop, and press cross-lock downward into locked position.
6. Check cable for freedom of movement by moving throttle control lever.

Rod Type

1. Ensure engine is at operating temperature.
2. Loosen adjustment swivel lock screw. Swivel must slide freely along flat end of throttle rod.
3. Hold transaxle throttle lever firmly toward engine, against its internal stop. **Torque** swivel lock screw to 100 inch lbs.

IN-VEHICLE REPAIRS

VALVE BODY, REPLACE

1. Loosen transaxle oil pan attaching bolts and allow transaxle to drain, then remove oil pan.
2. Remove oil filter attaching screws and oil filter.
3. Using a screwdriver, remove E-clip, then remove parking rod.
4. Remove seven valve body attaching bolts, then remove valve body and governor oil tubes.
5. Reverse procedure to install. **Torque** valve body attaching bolts to 105 inch lbs.

GOVERNOR & TRANSFER SHAFT OIL SEAL, REPLACE

The governor assembly can be removed for reconditioning or replacement without removing the transfer gear cover, transfer gear and governor support. To remove governor, drain transmission fluid and remove transmission oil pan. Remove valve body, unbolt governor from governor support, then remove governor.

When cleaning or assembling the governor assembly, ensure governor valves move freely in governor body bores.
1. Remove rear cover attaching bolts and rear cover.
2. Using transfer shaft gear tool No. L-4434 or equivalent, remove transfer shaft gear retaining nut, **Fig. 3.**
3. Using transfer shaft gear puller tool No. L-4407 or equivalent, remove transfer shaft gear and shim, **Fig. 4.**
4. Remove governor support retainer, then remove low-reverse band anchor pin.
5. Remove governor assembly.

6. Remove transfer shaft retainer snap ring, then using transfer shaft and bearing retainer removal tool No.L-4512 or equivalent and a suitable puller, remove transfer shaft and retainer assembly.
7. Remove transfer shaft retainer from shaft.
8. Using a screwdriver, remove oil seal from transfer shaft retainer.
9. Using suitable tool, tap oil seal into shaft retainer.
10. Reverse procedure to install. **Torque** transfer shaft gear retaining nut to 200 ft. lbs.

TRANSAXLE
REPLACE

The transaxle and converter must be removed as an assembly to prevent damage to the torque converter driveplate, pump bushing and oil seal. **The driveplate will not support a load. Do not allow the weight of the transaxle to rest on the driveplate.**

1. Disconnect battery cables.
2. Disconnect transaxle shift control and throttle cables from transaxle and position aside. Unplug lockup toque converter plug, if equipped.
3. Disconnect upper and lower oil cooler lines.
4. **On models equipped with the lock-up torque converter**, unplug the lockup converter plug located near the dipstick.
5. **On all models**, install an engine support fixture across top of engine compartment.
6. Remove three upper bellhousing bolts.
7. Remove hub castle locks, nuts and cotter pins.
8. Raise and support vehicle, then remove front wheels.
9. Remove left splash shield.
10. Remove speedometer adapter, cable and pinion as an assembly.
11. Remove sway bar and both lower ball joint to steering knuckle bolts.
12. Pry lower ball joint from steering knuckle, then remove driveshaft from hub.
13. Remove both driveshafts, supporting both joints at housing.
14. Remove dust cover if equipped, then mark position of torque converter to driveplate and remove torque converter retaining bolts.
15. Remove access plug in right splash shield to rotate engine.
16. Disconnect neutral/park safety switch wire, then remove engine mount bracket from front crossmember.
17. Remove front engine mount insulator through bolt and bellhousing bolts.
18. Support transaxle with a suitable jack.
19. Remove left engine mount and long through bolt.
20. Remove starter.
21. Remove lower bellhousing bolts.
22. Move transaxle away from engine and lower from vehicle. **It may be necessary to pry transaxle away from vehicle between the extension housing and engine block for clearance.**
23. Reverse procedure to install, noting the following:
    a. **Torque** transaxle-to-engine bolts to 70 ft. lbs.
    b. **Torque** starter attaching bolts to 40 ft. lbs.
    c. **Torque** flex plate-to-torque converter bolts to 55 ft. lbs.
    d. **Torque** bellhousing cover bolts to 105 inch lbs.
    e. Fill transaxle to specifications with suitable lubricant, then adjust shift and throttle cables.

TIGHTENING SPECIFICATIONS

Component	Torque/Ft. Lbs.
Bellhousing Cover Bolt	105①
Connector Assembly Cooler Line	250①
Cooler Hose Connector To Radiator	110①
Differential Bearing Retainer To Case Bolt	250①
Differential Cover To Case Screw Assembly	165①
Differential Extension Housing To Case Bolt	250①
Differential Ring Gear Screw	70
Flexplate To Crankshaft Bolt	②
Flexplate To Torque Converter	③
Front Motor Mount Bolt	40
Governor Counterweight Screw Assembly	250①
Governor To Support Bolt	5
Kickdown Band Adjustment Locknut	35
Left Motor Mount Bolt	40
Lower Bellhousing Cover Screw Assembly	105①
Manual Cable To Transaxle Case Bolt	250①
Manual Control Lever Screw Assembly	105①
Neutral Safety Switch	25
Output Shaft Nut	200
Pressure Check Plug	45①
Pump To Case Bolt Assembly	275①

Component	Torque/Ft. Lbs.
Reaction Shaft Assembly Bolt	250①
Rear Cover To Case Screw Assembly	165①
Reverse Band Shaft Plug	5
Speedometer To Extension Screw Assembly	60①
Starter To Transaxle Bellhousing Bolt	40
Transfer Shaft Gear Retaining nut	200
Throttle Cable To Transaxle Case Bolt	105①
Throttle Lever To Transaxle Shaft Bolt	105①
Transaxle Oil Pan To Case	165①
Transaxle To Cylinder Block Screw Assembly	70
Transaxle To Engine Bolts	70
Transfer Shaft Nut	200
Valve Body Filter Screw Assembly	40①
Valve Body Reverse Band Adjusting Locknut	120①
Valve Body Screw Assembly	40①
Valve Body Sprag Retainer To Transfer Case Bolt	250①
Valve Body Transfer Plate Screw Assembly	40①
Valve Body Transfer Plate To Case Screw	105①

①—Inch lbs.
②—1992, 70 ft. lbs.; 1993–94, 55 ft. lbs.
③—1992, 55 ft. lbs.; 1993–94, 50 ft. lbs.

ZF-4HP-18 Automatic Transaxle

INDEX

IDENTIFICATION

A transaxle identification plate is located on the left side of the case above the oil pan. The information on this plate consists of the build sequence number, manufacturers part number and transaxle type. Refer to these numbers when servicing the transaxle.

DESCRIPTION

The ZF-4HP-18 automatic transaxle, **Fig. 1,** has four forward speeds and one reverse and is used on all Monaco and Premier models with 3.0L/V6-182 engines. Third gear ratio is 1:1. Fourth gear is an overdrive range providing an 0.74:1 gear ratio. **The transaxle and differential are not integral and require different lubricants.**

The transaxle consists of a three element torque converter, front mounted oil pump, planetary gear mechanism, roller and sprag clutches, clutch and brake mechanisms and a brake band. The brake band is applied in second and fourth gear ranges by the piston assembly. Transaxle shifting is controlled by a governor valve, a line pressure valve, a throttle pressure regulator valve and a modulator valve. Valve operation is dependent on shift lever position, vehicle speed and throttle position.

TROUBLESHOOTING

DOES NOT ENGAGE IN PARK

1. Shift cable incorrectly adjusted.
2. Excess clearance on detent plate.
3. Detent segment out of position.
4. Park pawl damaged.

NO REVERSE

1. Shift cable incorrectly adjusted.

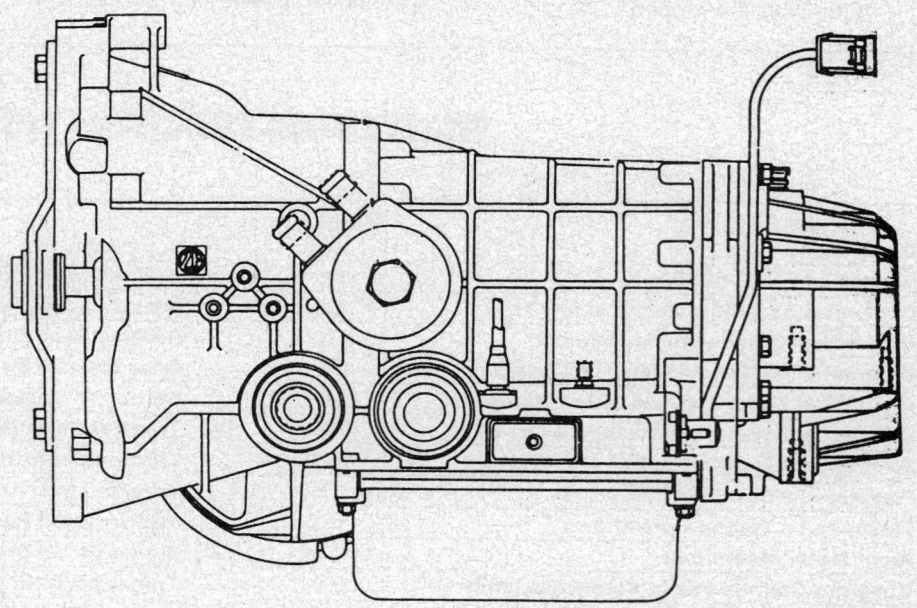

Fig. 1   ZF-4HP-18 automatic transaxle

CR5028800105000X

2. Oil screen plugged or contaminated.
3. Reverse clutch damaged.
4. First-reverse brake damaged.
5. Governor sticking.
6. Lock-up valve 1 and reverse gear sticking.

SLIPS ON ACCELERATION FROM STOP

1. 1-2-3 clutch damaged.
2. First-reverse brake damaged.
3. Turbine shaft O-ring or pump starter malfunction.
4. Oil leaking into reverse clutch or piston ring has scored center plate seat.

CREEPS IN NEUTRAL

1. Shift cable incorrectly adjusted.

SLUGGISH ACCELERATION, NO POWER

1. Converter valve open.
2. Oil screen plugged.
3. 1-2-3 clutch defective.
4. Roller clutch slips.
5. Shift cable incorrectly adjusted.
6. Throttle or shift valve slipping.

HARSH ENGAGEMENT FROM NEUTRAL TO DRIVE

1. Accumulator sticking or spring broken.
2. 1-2-3 clutch damaged.

HARSH ENGAGEMENT FROM PARK OR NEUTRAL TO REVERSE

1. Accumulator inoperative.

HARSH ENGAGEMENT AT IDLE SPEEDS

1. Accumulator malfunction.
2. Modulator pressure too high.
3. Clutch pack damage.

NO 1-2 OR 2-1 SHIFT IN DRIVE

1. Governor contaminated, sticking.
2. 1-2 shift valve slips.
3. Forward brake or 2-4 band malfunction.

NO 2-3 OR 3-2 SHIFT IN DRIVE

1. Governor contaminated, sticking.
2. 2-3 shift valve sticks.
3. 3-4 clutch damaged.
4. Oil supply for 3-4 clutch leaking.

NO 3-4 OR 4-3 SHIFT IN DRIVE

1. Governor contaminated, sticking.
2. 3-4 valve sticks.
3. Forward brake inoperative.
4. 2-4 band loose.
5. 2-3-4 upshift valve sticks.
6. Position 3 valve sticks.

NO 1ST GEAR

1. Governor piston sticks.
2. Leakage in governor assembly.
3. 1-2 shift valve sticks.
4. 2-4 band binds, drags.
5. 2-4 band will not release.

NO 1ST OR 2ND GEAR

1. Center rectangular ring of governor flange defective.
2. Governor piston sticking.
3. 1-2 and 2-3 shift valves sticking.
4. Closing cap in center plate leaking (reverse clutch always filled with oil).

SHIFTS 1-3 IN DRIVE, NO 2ND GEAR

1. 2-3 shift valve sticks.
2. 2-3-4 shift valve sticks.
3. 1-2-3 shift valve sticks.

NO KICKDOWN OR NORMAL DOWNSHIFT

1. Throttle valve cable incorrectly adjusted.
2. Governor sticking.

KICKDOWN SHIFTS TOO LONG OR HARSH

1. Accumulator malfunction.
2. Modulator pressure incorrect.
3. Clutch pack damage.

ENGINE OVERSPEED DURING 3-4 SHIFT

1. Orifice control valve sticking.
2. 3-4 traction valve binding.
3. 2-4 band slips.

ENGINE OVERSPEED DURING 4-3 SHIFT

1. Time control valve and 4-3 downshift valves not coordinated.
2. 1-2-3 clutch damaged.
3. Damper function of 1-2-3 clutch and 4-3 traction valve not functioning properly.

MANUAL 2ND GEAR DOWNSHIFT, DOWNSHIFT EARLY OR LATE

1. Lock-up valve 2 binding.
2. Governor piston binding.

NO OVERRUN BRAKING IN MANUAL 1ST GEAR (D1)

1. 2-4 band inoperative.
2. 2-4 band damaged.

MANUAL 2-1 DOWNSHIFT INCORRECT

Lock-up valve 1 prevents downshift to 1st gear when speed is 25 mph or more.

1. Lock-up valve 1 and reverse gear binding.
2. Governor piston binding.

NO OVERRUN BRAKING IN 1ST GEAR

1. First-reverse brake damaged.

THROTTLE VALVE CABLE STICKS

1. Cable not attached to cam.
2. Internal friction in cable.
3. Throttle pressure piston sticks.

NOISY & NO DRIVE OR REVERSE

1. Valve body oil screen plugged.
2. Converter driveplate damaged.
3. Oil pump gears worn or damaged.

OIL LEAKAGE

1. Oil leaking from converter housing—torque converter leaking at welded seam or pump seal leaking.
2. Leakage between transaxle and oil pan—Oil pan warped, bolts loose or gasket damaged.
3. Leakage between transaxle housing and differential cover—bolts loose.
4. Leakage at transaxle cooler—cooler cracked or split, attaching bolt loose or gasket damaged.
5. Leakage at 2-4 band piston cover—cover O-rings worn or damaged.
6. Leakage from 2-4 band retaining shaft—retaining shaft O-ring damaged.
7. Leakage at output shaft—bolts loose or seal rings damaged.
8. Oil leakage from throttle cable connection in case—cable connector O-ring damaged.
9. Leakage at differential—Output shaft seals or cover seal leaking.
10. Leakage at speedometer sensor—sensor or O-ring damaged.
11. Leakage at breather vents in transaxle or differential—transaxle or differential overfilled or incorrect fluids used.
12. Leakage at selector shaft—seal ring damaged.

NOISY IN ALL POSITIONS (OIL PUMP)

1. Fluid level too low.
2. Valve body leaking internally.
3. Oil screen plugged.

NOISY IN ALL POSITIONS

1. Differential or pinion gear bearing adjustment incorrectly set.

MAINTENANCE

FLUID CHECK

Check fluid with engine idling and vehicle on a level surface. Shift transaxle through all gear ranges and return to park, then check and correct fluid level to the "Full Cold" or "Full Hot" mark on dipstick, depending on present operating temperature.

FLUID CHANGE

The only fluid recommended for use in the ZF-4HP-18 transaxle is Mercon automatic transmission fluid. **Do not use any other type of fluid.**

1. Raise and support vehicle.
2. Remove underbody splash shield.
3. Loosen fill tube-to-oil pan attaching nut and drain fluid. Disconnect fill tube from pan.
4. Remove oil pan retaining clamp attaching nuts, then remove retaining clamps and oil pan.
5. Remove oil screen cover bolts, then the cover.
6. Remove oil screen and cover gasket. Clean oil pan, magnet and screen, replacing screen if necessary.
7. Install new O-ring on oil screen. Coat new oil screen cover gasket with petroleum jelly, then install on valve body. Install screen, pressing tabs (Q) into valve body as shown in **Fig. 2.**
8. Install oil screen cover, ensuring oil screen and cover gasket are aligned. Install cover bolts finger tight, referring to bolt length as shown in **Fig. 3,** then tighten to specifications.
9. Install magnet in oil pan, ensuring it is seated in indentation in pan.
10. Install new gasket on oil pan, then position pan on case. Install pan retaining clamps and attaching nuts on mounting studs. **Torque** clamp nuts to 54 inch lbs.
11. Connect fill tube and attaching nut to oil pan. **Torque** nut to 74 ft. lbs.
12. Install underbody splash shield and lower vehicle.
13. Remove transaxle dipstick and add

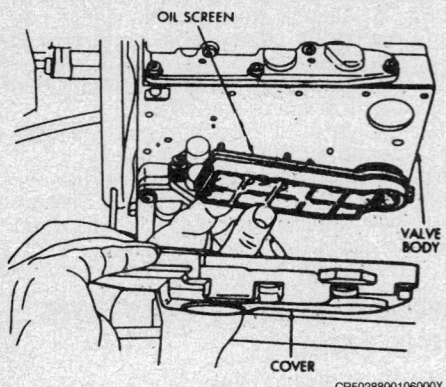

Fig. 2 Oil screen installation

2¼ quarts of Mercon automatic transmission fluid through fill tube. Check and adjust fluid level as necessary.

ADJUSTMENTS

BANDS

2-4 Band

1. Remove valve body as outlined under "Valve Body, Replace."
2. Remove band adjusting shim, then measure its thickness.
3. Using a feeler gauge, check clearance between band pin nut and case, **Fig. 4.** Install suitable shim to obtain .049-.059 inch (1.25-1.50 mm) clearance between nut and pin.
4. Install valve body as outlined under "Valve Body, Replace."

GEARSHIFT CABLE

1. Shift gear selector into P.
2. Raise and support vehicle.
3. Using screwdriver, release cable adjuster clamp.
4. Move gear shift lever into P detent position. P detent is last rearward position.
5. Ensure engagement of park lock by attempting to rotate driveshafts. Driveshafts will not turn when park lock is properly engaged.
6. Lock shift cable into position by pressing adjuster clamp down until it snaps.
7. Lower vehicle. Turn ignition key to L position, then ensure gear selector remains locked in P.
8. Turn ignition key to On position. Ensure engine starts only when shift lever engaged in P or N. **If engine starts in any other position, cable adjustment is incorrect.**
9. Shift gear selector into P. Ensure ignition key can be returned to L position.

THROTTLE VALVE CABLE

1. Loosen throttle valve cable locknuts, then lift threaded cable shank out of engine bracket.
2. Place throttle lever in idle position.
3. Pull cable wire forward, then place 1.50 inch gauge block on wire between cable connector and cable end, **Fig. 5.**
4. Pull cable shank rearward to detent

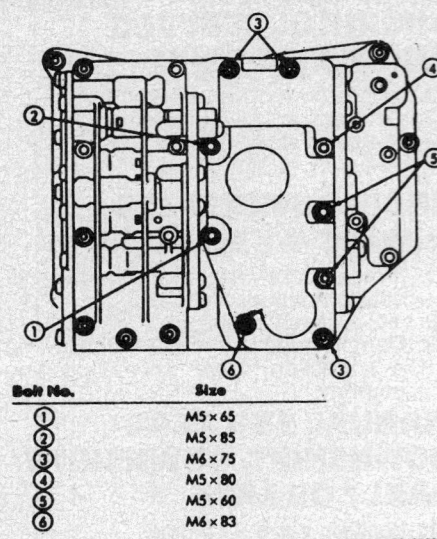

Bolt No.	Size
①	M5 × 65
②	M5 × 85
③	M6 × 75
④	M5 × 80
⑤	M5 × 60
⑥	M6 × 83

Fig. 3 Oil screen cover bolt installation

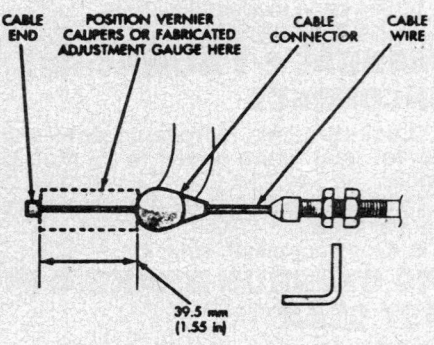

Fig. 5 Throttle valve cable adjustment

position, then insert shank into engine bracket. Tighten locknuts, locking shank into place. **Ensure cable is in detent position, not wide open throttle position.**
5. Remove gauge block and recheck adjustment. Cable detent position should be reached when cable wire travel is 1.50-1.54 inches.

IN-VEHICLE REPAIRS

VALVE BODY, REPLACE

1. Shift gear selector into manual first gear position (D1).
2. Raise and support vehicle.
3. Remove underbody splash shield.
4. Loosen fill tube-to-oil pan attaching nut, then drain fluid. Disconnect fill tube from pan.
5. Remove oil pan retaining clamp attaching nuts, then remove retaining clamps and oil pan. **Do not remove oil screen, as valve body is removed with oil screen in place.**
6. Remove valve body attaching bolts, then the valve body.
7. Reverse procedure to install, noting the following:

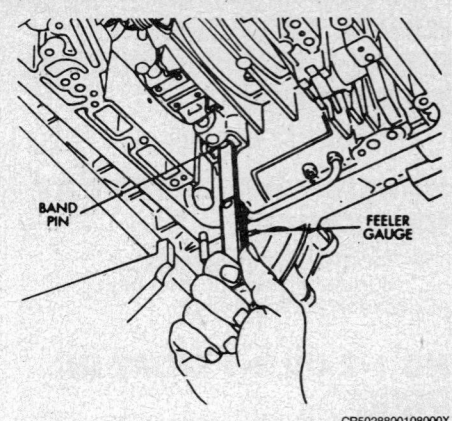

Fig. 4 2-4 band adjustment

a. Place gear shift lever into manual first gear detent (last detent in counterclockwise direction).
b. Pull throttle cable to wide open throttle position to avoid jamming the throttle cam and piston during valve body installation.
c. Push manual valve (D), **Fig. 6,** all the way into manual first gear position.
d. **Torque** valve body attaching bolts to 72 inch lbs.
e. **Torque** oil pan clamp nuts to 54 inch lbs., **torque** fill tube attaching nut to 74 ft. lbs.
f. Remove transaxle dipstick and add 2¼ quarts of Mercon automatic transmission fluid through fill tube. Check and adjust fluid level as necessary.
g. Adjust throttle valve cable as described under "Adjustments."

GOVERNOR, REPLACE

1. Raise and support vehicle.
2. Remove underbody splash shield.
3. Disconnect exhaust pipes.
4. Remove differential drain plug, then drain lubricant.
5. Remove reduction gear case to transaxle attaching bolts, then the reduction gear assembly. Remove gear case gasket.
6. Remove spring washers, **Fig. 7,** noting position for assembly reference.
7. Remove governor cover, then the governor.
8. Remove governor valve attaching bolts, then the valves, **Fig. 8.**
9. Remove one steel and two rubber seals from governor body.
10. Reverse procedure to install, noting the following:
   a. **Torque** governor valve attaching bolts to 8 ft. lbs.
   b. Install new steel and rubber governor seals.
   c. Coat new case-to-transaxle gasket with petroleum jelly and **torque** attaching bolts to 17 ft. lbs.
   d. **Torque** differential drain plug to 18 ft. lbs.
   e. Remove differential fill plug and fill with synthetic type, 75W-140 hy-

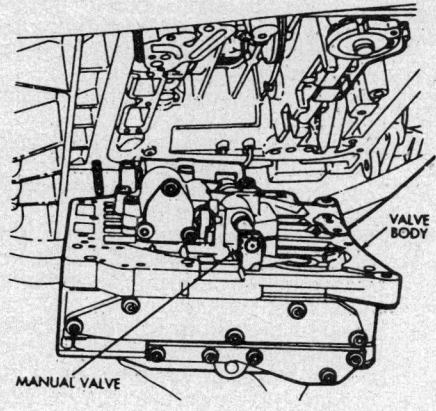

Fig. 6   Manual valve location

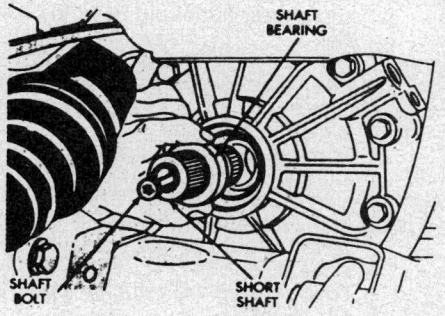

Fig. 9   Short output shaft removal

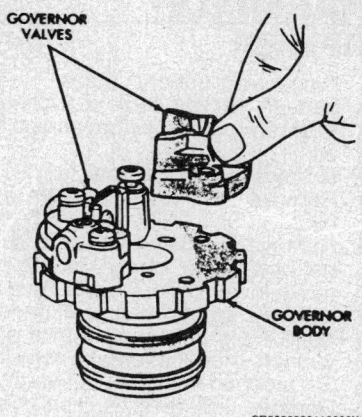

Fig. 8   Governor valves

Fig. 7   Governor spring washers

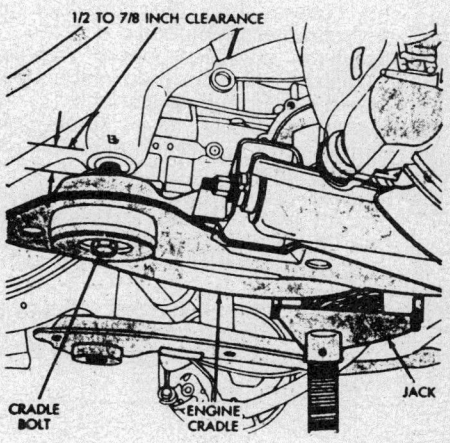

Fig. 10   Lowering engine cradle

poid gear lubricant. Add lubricant until it flows from fill hole, then install fill plug and **torque** to 37 ft. lbs.

OUTPUT SHAFT SEAL, REPLACE

Short Output Shaft

It is necessary to remove differential cover to replace short output shaft inner seal.

1. Raise and support vehicle.
2. Remove differential drain plug, then drain lubricant.
3. Using a suitable punch, remove roll pin attaching driveshaft to output shaft.
4. Using a screwdriver, remove output shaft dust cover.
5. Loosen retaining bolt (C), then pull output shaft and bearing (D) out of differential cover, **Fig. 9.**
6. Using a screwdriver, pry outer seal from cover.
7. Remove differential as follows:
   a. Remove differential fill plug, then the differential cover bolts.
   b. Using suitable jack, raise transaxle as far as possible.
   c. Loosen engine cradle bolts until there is a 1/2-7/8 inch space between cradle and side sill, as shown in **Fig. 10. Do not completely remove cradle bolts.**
   d. Disconnect oil filler tube, then remove differential cover and ring gear assembly from transaxle case.

8. Using a screwdriver, remove inner seal from case. **Do not damage seal bore with screwdriver when removing seal.**
9. Install new inner seal using seal installer tool No. 6174 and drive handle No. C-6091 or C-4171 or equivalents.
10. Install differential as follows:
    a. Install ring gear assembly.
    b. Install new seal on differential cover, then install cover on transaxle case. **Torque** cover attaching bolts to 17 ft. lbs.
    c. **Torque** engine cradle bolts to 44 ft. lbs., then remove jack from transaxle.
11. **Ensure output shaft bearing is packed full of suitable grease prior to shaft installation.** Install output shaft and bearing in cover, then install retaining nut and **torque** to 18 ft. lbs.
12. Using seal installer tool No. 6152 or equivalent, install outer seal.
13. Using dust cover installing tool No. 6156 or equivalent and a driver handle, install dust cover over outer seal.
14. Install differential drain plug and **torque** to 18 ft. lbs. Fill differential with synthetic type, 75W-140 hypoid gear lubricant. Add lubricant until it flows from fill hole, then install fill plug and **torque** to 37 ft. lbs.
15. Attach driveshaft to output shaft. Using suitable punch, install driveshaft roll pin.
16. Install underbody splash shield, then lower vehicle.

Long Output Shaft

1. Raise and support vehicle.
2. Remove differential drain plug, then drain lubricant.
3. Using a suitable punch, remove roll pin attaching driveshaft to output shaft.
4. Using a suitable screwdriver, remove output shaft dust cover.
5. Using seal removal tool No. 6159 and bolt from puller tool No. 6149 or equivalents, remove outer seal.

6. Using snap ring pliers, remove output shaft retaining ring. Remove output shaft and bearing from transaxle case.
7. Using a screwdriver, remove inner seal from case. **Do not damage seal bore with screwdriver when removing seal.**
8. Using seal installer tool No. 6154 or equivalent and a driver handle, install new inner seal.
9. **Ensure output shaft bearing is packed full of suitable grease prior to shaft installation.** Install output shaft and bearing, then the retaining ring.
10. Using seal installer tool No. 6152 or equivalent, install outer seal.
11. Using compressor tool No. 6156 or equivalent and a driver handle, install dust cover.
12. Install differential drain plug and **torque** to 18 ft. lbs. Fill differential with synthetic type, 75W-140 hypoid gear lubricant. Add lubricant until it flows from fill hole, then install fill plug and **torque** to 37 ft. lbs.
13. Attach driveshaft to output shaft. Using suitable punch, install driveshaft roll pin.
14. Install underbody splash shield, then lower vehicle.

TRANSAXLE
REPLACE

1. Disconnect battery cables.
2. Loosen throttle cable adjusting nuts, then remove cable from engine bracket.
3. Raise and support vehicle.
4. Remove front wheel and tire assemblies.
5. Remove steering knuckle-to-strut upper bolts, then loosen, but do not remove lower bolts. **Do not turn bolts,** as they are splined just under bolt head. Hold bolt head with a suitable wrench, then loosen and remove nut. Tilt steering knuckles outward.
6. Remove underbody splash shield.
7. Loosen fill tube-to-oil pan attaching nut and drain transmission fluid, then reinstall nut and **torque** to 74 ft. lbs.
8. Remove both torque converter housing covers, then the converter to driveplate attaching bolts.
9. Using a suitable punch, remove driveshaft roll pins, then disconnect driveshafts from output shafts.
10. Support transaxle with a suitable jack.
11. Remove crossmember-to-side sill attaching nuts.
12. Remove rear cushion to support bracket bolt, then the exhaust pipe bracket attaching bolts, **Fig. 11.**
13. Remove crossmember and rear cushion.
14. Remove support bracket attaching bolts, then the support bracket.
15. Disconnect front exhaust pipe from

TRANSAXLE SUPPORT BRACKET

BRACKET-TO-CUSHION BOLT

REAR CUSHION

EXHAUST PIPE BRACKET BOLTS (2)

EXHAUST PIPE BRACKET   CROSSMEMBER

CR5028800116000X

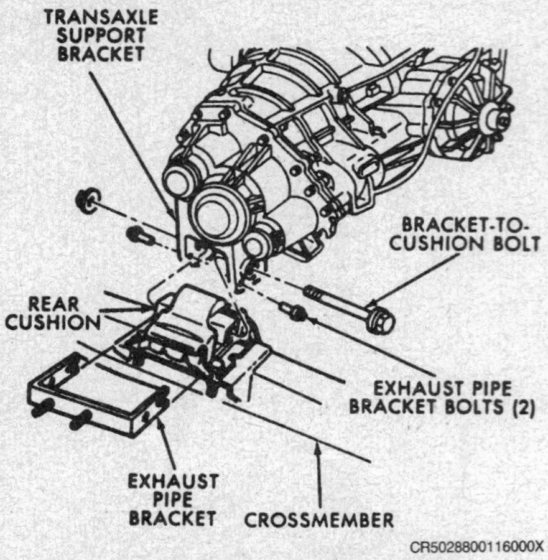

Fig. 11 Rear support bracket assembly

exhaust manifolds, then remove catalytic converter-to-front pipe attaching nuts. Remove front pipe bracket bolts and nuts.
16. Disconnect oxygen sensor electrical connector.
17. Loosen engine cradle bolts until there is a 1/2-7/8 inch space between cradle and side sill, as shown in **Fig. 10. Do not completely remove cradle bolts or lower cradle more than one inch.**
18. Remove front exhaust pipe.
19. Remove starter attaching bolts, then the starter, plate and dowel.
20. Disconnect shift cable from shift transaxle lever, then remove cable

bracket bolts and separate bracket from case. Remove bracket brace rod, then disconnect cable from bracket by squeezing lock tabs.
21. Remove engine timing sensor and attaching bolts.
22. Disconnect and plug transaxle cooler hoses from transaxle cooler.
23. Disconnect speedometer sensor electrical connector.
24. Remove engine-to-transaxle mounting stud nuts and attaching bolts. Pull transaxle away from engine and lower from under vehicle.
25. Reverse procedure to install, noting the following:
   a. Coat torque converter pilot hub with graphite grease prior to installation.
   b. **Torque** engine-to-transaxle attaching bolts, mounting stud nuts and starter attaching bolts to 31 ft. lbs.
   c. **Torque** support bracket to transaxle attaching bolts to 30 ft. lbs. and rear cushion-to-support bracket bolt to 49 ft. lbs.
   d. **Torque** crossmember-to-side sill attaching nuts to 44 ft. lbs. and engine cradle bolts to 92 ft. lbs.
   e. Apply Loctite to driveplate to converter attaching bolts and **torque** to 24 ft. lbs.
   f. **Torque** steering knuckle bolts to 148 ft. lbs.
   g. Fill transaxle with Mercon automatic transmission fluid.
   h. Adjust throttle valve cable as described under "Adjustments."

TIGHTENING SPECIFICATIONS

Component	Torque/Ft. Lbs.
Bellcrank Bracket Bolts	29–33
Cover Bolts	45 ①
Crossmember To Engine Cradle Bolts	29–33
Detent Plunger	170–184 ①
Differential Housing Cover Baffle Plate Bolt	84–96 ①
Differential Housing Cover Bolts	142–158 ①
Differential Housing Drain & Fill Plugs	170–184 ①
Driveplate To Crankshaft Bolt	②
Engine Timing Sensor Bolts	68–76 ①
Exhaust Bracket Bolts	29–33
Exhaust Pipe Flange To Catalytic Converter Nut	28–32
Exhaust Pipe Flange To Manifold Nuts	21–25
Fill Tube Attaching Nut	74
Fill Tube Bracket Bolt	12–13
Fluid Cooler Bolts	22–26
Manual Shaft Lock Plate Bolt	84–96 ①
Oil Screen Bolts	43–49 ①
Rear Coverplate Bolts	142–158 ①

Component	Torque/Ft. Lbs.
Road Speed Sensor Bracket Bolt	84–96 ①
Shift Cable Bracket Bolts	29–33
Shift Cable Bracket Brace Bolts	168–202 ①
Solenoid Connector Bolt	84–96 ①
Starter Bolts	22–26
Starter Shield Nuts	90–102 ①
Starter Wire Harness Nuts	75–85 ①
Steering Knuckle Bolts	140–156
TCU Speed Sensor Bracket Bolt	84–96 ①
Torque Convertor Bolts	24
Transaxle Bracket Bolts	28–30
Transaxle Bracket To Rear Mount Bolt	46–52
Transaxle Oil Pan Bolts	84–96 ①
Transaxle Shift Lever Bolt	96–124 ①
Valve Body Bolts	43–49 ①
Wheel Lug Nuts	59–65
Wiring Harness Clamp Bolt	150 ①

①—Inch lbs.
②—40 ft. lbs., then an additional 60°.

F3A21 & F3A22 Automatic Transaxles

INDEX

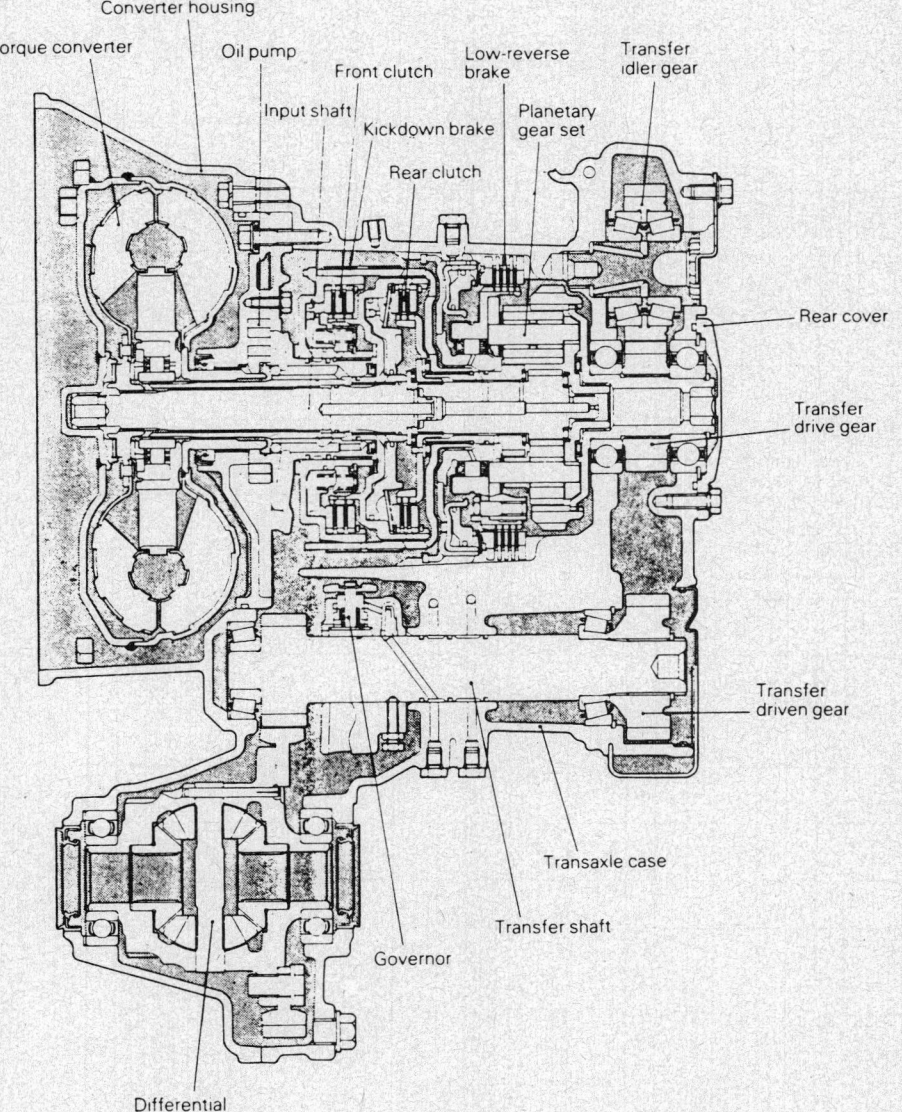

Fig. 1   F3A21 automatic transaxle. (F3A22 similar)

CR5028800561000X

DESCRIPTION

The F3A21 & F3A22 are fully automatic three speed transaxles with a lock-up torque converter **Fig. 1**. These transaxles are used on all Colt and Summit models with 1.5L/4-96 engines.

TROUBLESHOOTING

TRANSAXLE

Refer to **Fig. 2** when troubleshooting these transaxles.

SHIFT LOCK CONTROL SYSTEM

Refer to **Fig. 3,** when troubleshooting the shift lock system.

MAINTENANCE

CHECKING FLUID LEVEL

The vehicle on level surface, start engine and operate at idle speed. With parking brake applied, place selector lever in N, then remove dipstick and check fluid level. Transmission should be at operating temperature when checking fluid level (160-180°F). Fluid level should be between Add and Full lines on dipstick. If necessary, add Dexron II automatic transmission fluid to bring fluid level within Add and Full lines on dipstick.

CHANGING FLUID

The automatic transaxle fluid should be changed every 30,000 miles on these units. When refilling transaxle, add only Dexron II automatic transaxle fluid.
1. Raise and support front of vehicle, then position drain pan under transaxle and remove drain located at bottom of differential and allow transaxle to drain.
2. Install drain plug, then add 4.2 quarts of the specified automatic transaxle fluid through transaxle dipstick hole.
3. Start engine and check fluid level as outlined under "Checking Fluid Level.

IDENTIFICATION

The transaxle identification number is located on the vehicle information code plate, which is attached on the fender shield in the engine compartment. The plate indicates model, body code, engine and transaxle model number.

Fig. 2   Transaxle troubleshooting chart

Probable cause		Starter inoperative	Forward drive impossible	Reverse drive impossible	Engine stalls when shifting from "N" to "D", "R"	Clutch slips in "D" position (stall rpm too high)	Clutch slips in "R" position (stall rpm too high)	Stall rpm too low	Vehicle starts to move in "P" or "N" position	Vehicle starts to move in position midway of "N" and "R" or "N" and "D"	Parking mechanism does not work	Abnormal shock felt when selecting "D", "2", "L" or "R"	Shifting does not take place according to shift pattern	Unsmooth start	High creep and idle vibration	Large shock felt when shifting from 1st to 2nd	Large shock felt when shifting from 2nd to 3rd	Large shock felt when shifting down in "D" or "2"	Engine running up when shifting up	Large shock when shifting from 3rd to 2nd	Damper clutch inoperative	Converter housing whining with increasing engine rpm	Mechanical noise (rattling) from converter housing	Abnormal noise from transaxle case
Engine	1 Idling rpm abnormal		⊗		⊗							X		X	X									
	2 Performance failure		X	X	X	X	X	X				X	X	X	X	X	X	X		X				
Transaxle proper (power train)	3 Throttle control cable inadequately adjusted		X	X	⊗	X	X	X				⊗	X	X		X	X	X	X	X				
	4 Manual linkage inadequately adjusted	X	⊗	⊗		⊗	⊗	X	⊗	⊗	⊗			X										
	5 Torque converter failure		X	X	X	X	X	X						X							X	X		
	6 Oil pump failure		X			X	X																	
	7 One way clutch failure		X			X																		
	8 Damaged or worn gear or other rotating parts, shim preload inadequately adjusted			X					X	X	X						X							X
	9 Parking mechanism failure								⊗	⊗	X													
	10 Cracked drive plate or loose bolt																						X	
Hydraulic system (including friction elements)	11 Low fluid level		⊗	⊗		X	X					X	X	X		X	X		X	X	X			
	12 Low line pressure (broken seal, leaks, looseness, etc.)		⊗	⊗		⊗	⊗					X	X	X		X	X		⊗	⊗	X			
	13 Faulty valve body (valve sticking, poor machining, blowhole, poor adjustment, etc.)		⊗	⊗	X	X	X		X	X		X	X	X		X	X	X	X	X	X			
	14 Faulty front clutch, piston		⊗	X	X	X	X										X							
	15 Faulty rear clutch, piston		X			X										X								
	16 Faulty kickdown band or piston			X												X			X	X				
	17 Kickdown servo poorly adjusted			X								X				X	X	X	X	X				
	18 Faulty low reverse brake, piston			X									X											
	19 O-ring missing in low reverse brake circuit between valve body and case																							
Electrical control system	20 Governor failure									X														
	21 Faulty inhibitor switch, open wire, poor adjustment	X																						
	22 Faulty throttle position sensor, poor adjustment																				X			
	23 Pulse generator (A) open wire or shorting																				X			
	24 Pulse generator (B) open wire or shorting																				X			
	25 Faulty ignition signal system																				X			
	26 Damper clutch control solenoid valve open wire (valve closed)																				X			
	27 Damper clutch solenoid valve shorting, sticking (valve open)				⊗																X			
	28 Coolant temperature sensor faulty																				X			
	29 Faulty control unit																				X			

Remarks. ⊗ indicates items to be given high priority in inspection.

CR5028800564000X

Symptom	Probable cause	Remady
The selector lever can be operated from "P" to "R" without depressing the brake pedal when the ignition key is in the ACC position.	• Damaged shift lock lever, foreign matter caught in the mechanism • Poorly adjusted shift lock cable, broken or disconnected cable • Broken or fatigued return spring of shift lock cable (shift lock lever side)	• Check selector lever bracket assembly and replace if necessary. • Check, adjust or replace shift lock cable.
The selector lever cannot be moved from "P" to "R" when the brake pedal is depressed with the ignition key in the ACC position.	• Faulty selector lever assembly • Shift lock cable, key interlock cable, automatic transaxle control cable binding • Poor routing of shift lock cable, key interlock cable • Broken or fatigued return spring of shift lock cable (brake pedal side)	• Check selector lever bracket assembly and replace if necessary. • Check, adjust or replace shift lock cable and key interlock cable. • Check routing of cables. • Replace shift lock cable.
The selector lever can be moved from "P" to "R" when the brake pedal is depressed even though the ignition key is in the LOCK position.	• Deformed, damaged or worn interlock cam or interlock lever • Poorly adjusted, broken, stretched or disconnected key interlock cable	• Check interlock cam and interlock lever or replace selector lever bracket assembly. • Check, adjust or replace key interlock cable.
The selector lever cannot be moved smoothly from "P" to "R".	• Shift lock lever cannot be moved smoothly due to a large amount of play or friction of the fulcrum pin of the shift lock lever. • Poorly adjusted shift lock cable, considerable elongation of inner cable • Poorly adjusted key interlock cable • Broken or fatigued return spring of shift lock cable (brake pedal side) • Interlock cam and interlock lever not sliding smoothly	• Check and adjust shift lock lever, check and replace selector lever bracket assembly. • Check and adjust or replace shift lock cable and key interlock cable.
The selector lever cannot be moved from "R" to "P".	• Shift lock lever or interlock cam binding	• Check selector lever bracket assembly, apply grease or replace assembly.
The ignition key cannot be turned to LOCK when the selector lever is in the "P" position.	• Damaged interlock cam or interlock lever or foreign matter caught in the mechanism • Poorly adjusted key interlock cable, binding inner cable • Slide lever in key cylinder not sliding smoothly	• Check selector lever bracket assembly and replace if necessary. • Adjust or replace key interlock cable. • Check slide lever and replace if necessary.
The ignition key can be turned to LOCK even when the selector lever is at any position other than "P".	• Broken spring pin • Damaged interlock cam • Damaged interlock cover • Poorly adjusted or broken key interlock cable, stretched inner cable • Damaged slide lever	• Replace spring pin. • Check selector lever bracket assembly and replace if necessary. • Check and adjust or replace key interlock cable. • Replace slide lever.
The stop light stays ON.	• Poorly adjusted shift lock cable • Broken shift lock cable spring	• Check and adjust or replace shift lock cable.

Fig. 3 Shift lock control system troubleshooting

CR5028800567000X

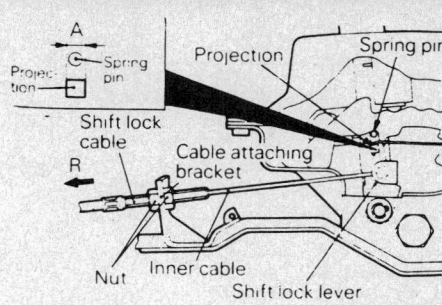

Fig. 4 Shift lock cable adjustment. 1992

CR5028800566000X

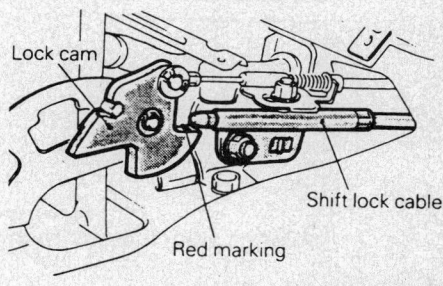

Fig. 5 Shift lock cable adjustment. 1993–94

CR5028800569000X

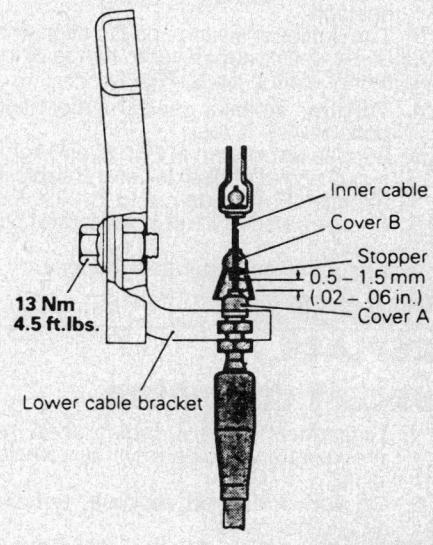

Fig. 6 Throttle control cable adjustment

CR5028800573000X

ADJUSTMENTS
SHIFT LOCK CABLE
1992

1. With selector lever in "P" position, install end of shift lock cable to shift lock lever.
2. Pull shift lock cable in direction indicated in **Fig. 2** until resistance is felt, then adjust so spring hook projection of shift lock lever is positioned within range "A" in **Fig. 4** relative to spring pin.

3. Move shift lock cable toward lower end of cable attaching bracket and tighten nut.
4. Ensure stop light comes on when brake pedal is depressed.

1993—94

1. Place selector lever in Park position.
2. Install cable so it is above red marking, **Fig. 5**.

THROTTLE CONTROL CABLE

1. Place throttle lever in curb idle position.

2. Raise throttle cable cover (B) upward, then loosen cable lower mounting bracket bolt, **Fig. 6**.
3. Move cable lower mounting bracket until clearance between nipple and top of cable cover (A) is .02–.06 inch, then **torque** cable lower mounting bracket bolt to 9 to 10.5 ft. lbs.
4. With throttle lever in wide open position, pull throttle cable upward to ensure cable has freedom of movement.

INHIBITOR SWITCH & CONTROL CABLE

1. Place selector lever in Neutral position.

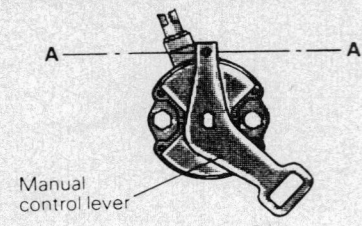

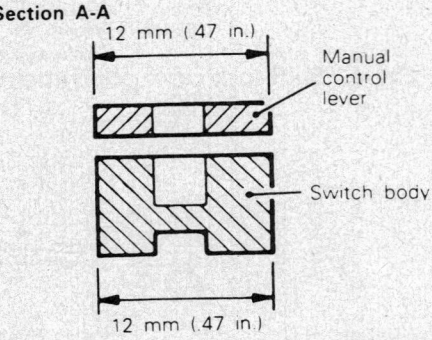

Fig. 7   Inhibitor switch adjustment

2. Place manual control lever in Neutral position.
3. Turn inhibitor switch body to align end of manual control lever to flange of inhibitor switch body, **Fig. 7.**
4. **Torque** inhibitor switch mounting bolts to 7-9 ft. lbs.
5. Loosen nut shown in **Fig. 8,** and lightly pull end of transaxle control cable in direction F. **Torque** nut to 7-10 ft. lbs.
6. Ensure selector lever is in Neutral position.
7. Ensure switch operates properly.

TRANSAXLE
REPLACE
EXCEPT COLT VISTA

1. Disconnect battery cables, then remove battery and battery tray from vehicle.
2. **On turbocharged models,** remove air cleaner case.
3. **On all models,** disconnect kickdown cable from engine and control cable from transaxle.
4. Disconnect inhibitor switch electrical connector, oil cooler lines and speed-

ometer cable from transaxle. **Plug oil cooler lines to prevent contamination.**
5. Disconnect starter motor wiring harness, then remove upper transaxle to engine attaching bolts from transaxle.
6. Remove starter motor attaching bolts and the starter motor.
7. Raise and support vehicle.
8. Remove undercover, then drain transaxle fluid into a suitable container.
9. Disconnect stabilizer bar from lower arm, then unfasten lower arm ball joint connection.
10. Remove right and left driveshafts from transaxle and position aside.
11. Remove bellhousing cover, then the torque converter to driveplate attaching bolts. Rotate crankshaft as necessary to gain access to all three bolts. **After removing attaching bolts, push torque converter into transaxle to avoid leaving the converter in the engine.**
12. Support transaxle with a suitable jack, then remove remaining engine to transaxle attaching bolts.
13. Remove transaxle mount insulator bolt, then the mount bracket from transaxle.
14. Slide transaxle to the right, then carefully lower assembly from vehicle.
15. Reverse procedure to install. Install torque converter first to the transaxle, then to the engine.

COLT VISTA

1. Drain transaxle fluid into a suitable container, then remove transaxle oil level gauge.
2. Disconnect battery cables, then remove battery and battery tray.
3. Remove air cleaner assembly and reservoir/windshield washer fluid tank if necessary.
4. Disconnect oil cooling lines from transaxle. Plug lines and openings to prevent contamination.
5. Disconnect throttle control cable, speedometer cable and all electrical connectors from transaxle.
6. Disconnect starter motor wiring and remove starter motor.
7. Raise and support vehicle.
8. Remove dust cover, then the stabilizer bar and strut bar.
9. Remove driveshafts from transaxle as follows:

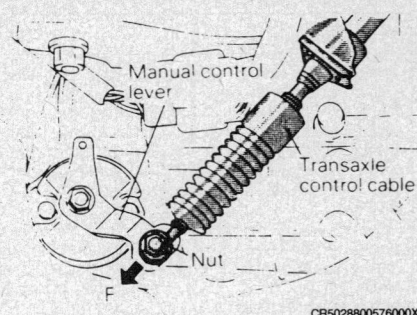

Fig. 8   Control cable adjustment

a. Loosen ball joint stud nut, then disconnect ball joint from steering knuckle using separating tool No. MB991113 or equivalent.
b. Loosen tie rod end stud nut, then disconnect tie rod from steering knuckle using separating tool No. MB991113 or equivalent.
c. Pry righthand driveshaft, then lefthand driveshaft out of transaxle case using two suitable screwdrivers. **Do not insert screwdrivers far enough to damage oil seal.**
10. Remove driveshaft circlips from transaxle case.
11. Remove bellhousing cover attaching bolts and the cover.
12. Remove three torque converter to driveplate attaching bolts, rotating flywheel as necessary. **After removing attaching bolts, push torque converter into transaxle to avoid leaving the converter in the engine.**
13. Remove transaxle mounting bracket as follows:
    a. Scribe hood hinge locations and remove hood.
    b. Lift engine slightly using suitable engine lifting equipment to relieve pressure from mount insulators.
    c. Support lower portion of transaxle with a suitable jack, then remove mounting bracket.
14. Remove transaxle attaching bolts, then slide transaxle to the right and carefully lower assembly from vehicle.
15. Reverse procedure to install, noting the following:
    a. Install torque converter first to transaxle and then to engine.
    b. Fill transaxle to specifications.
    c. Adjust throttle control cable and control cable.

TIGHTENING SPECIFICATIONS

Component	Torque/Ft. Lbs.
Air Cleaner Nut	6–7
Bearing Retainer Bolt	11–15
Bellhousing Cover To Transaxle	7–9
Control Cable To Body	7–10
Converter Housing Bolt	14–17
Differential Drive Gear Bolt	94–101
Driveplate	94–101
Driveplate To Converter Bolt	33–38
Governor Setscrew	6–7
Governor Bolt Locknut	3–4
Idler Shaft Lock Plate Bolt	15–19
Inhibitor Switch	7–9
Kickdown Servo Piston Plate Screw	4–6
Lever To Bracket Assembly	10–14
Lock Plate Bolt	10–12
Lower Arm Ball Joint To Knuckle	43–52
Manual Control Lever Nut	13–15
Manual Control Shaft Setscrew	6–7
Oil Cooler Connector	11–15
Oil Filter Bolt	4–5
Oil Pan Bolt	7–9

Component	Torque/Ft. Lbs.
Oil Pump Assembly Mounting Bolt	11–15
One-Way Clutch Outer Race Bolt	25–327
Planetary Carrier Bolt	11–15
Pressure Check Plug	6–7
Pulse Generator Mounting Bolt	7–9
Pump Housing To Reaction Shaft Support Bolt	7–9
Speedometer Sleeve Locking Plate Bolt	2–4
Sprag Rod Support Bolt	14–20
Starter Motor To Transaxle	20–25
Throttle Cam Bolt	6–7
Tie Rod End To Knuckle	11–25
Transaxle Bracket To Transaxle	43–58
Transaxle Drain Plug	22–25
Transaxle Mount Bolt	①
Transaxle Mount Bracket To Body	29–36
Transaxle Mount Bracket To Transaxle Bracket	65–80
Transaxle Mounting Bracket To Tension Rod	54–69
Valve Body Assembly Mounting Bolt	7–9
Valve Body Bolt	4–5

① —12 mm bolt, 31–40 ft. lbs.; 10 mm bolt, 22–25 ft. lbs.; 8 mm bolt, 7–8 ft. lbs.

F4A22, F4A23, F4A33, W4A32 & W4A33 Automatic Transaxles

INDEX

IDENTIFICATION

The transaxle identification number is located at the top of the bellhousing, Fig. 1.

DESCRIPTION

The Mitsubishi F4A22, F4A33, W4A33 is a fully automatic four-speed electronically controlled transaxle. This transaxle is used on Summit sedans with 1.6L/4-98 non-turbo engine, Laser, Talon and Stealth. The Mitsubishi F4A23 & W4A32 are a fully automatic four-speed electronically controlled transaxle. These transaxles are used on 1992 Colt Vista and Summit Wagon models.

TROUBLESHOOTING

TRANSAXLE

Refer to Fig. 2 when troubleshooting the transaxle.

SHIFT LOCK CONTROL SYSTEM

Refer to "F3A21 & F3A22" transaxle section shift lock control system troubleshooting.

MAINTENANCE

CHECKING FLUID LEVEL

With vehicle on level surface, start engine and operate at idle speed. With parking brake applied, move shift lever through each gear, then place selector lever in N. Remove dipstick and check fluid level. Transmission should be at operating temperature when checking fluid level (160–180°F). Fluid level should be within the Hot range on dipstick. If necessary, add Dexron II automatic transmission fluid to bring fluid level within the Hot range.

CHANGING FLUID

The automatic transaxle fluid should be changed every 30,000 miles on these units. When refilling transaxle, add only Dexron II automatic transaxle fluid.

1. Remove drain plug from bottom of differential and drain fluid into a suitable container.
2. Loosen transaxle oil pan attaching bolts, then tap pan at one corner to break loose and drain fluid into a suitable container.

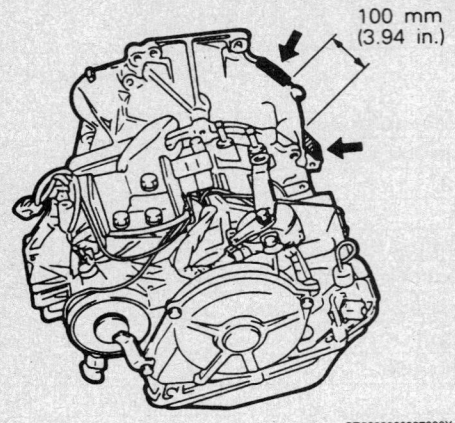

100 mm (3.94 in.)

CR5028800327000X

Fig. 1 Transaxle identification

3. Remove oil pan and drain residual fluid.
4. Inspect oil filter for damage or obstructions and replace if necessary.
5. Install drain plug with a new gasket and **torque** to 22-25 ft. lbs.
6. Clean transaxle case and oil pan mating surfaces, then install oil pan with a new gasket and **torque** attaching bolts to 7.5-8.5 ft. lbs.
7. Add 4.2 quarts Dexron II automatic transmission fluid to transaxle through dipstick hole.
8. Run engine at idle for at least two minutes, then shift transaxle through all ranges and recheck fluid level.
9. Add sufficient fluid to bring level to lower mark on dipstick, then run engine until normal operating temperature is reached. Recheck dipstick and ensure fluid level is within Hot range.

ADJUSTMENTS

INHIBITOR SWITCH & CONTROL CABLE

Refer to "F3A21 & F3A22 Automatic Transaxles" section for inhibitor switch and control cable adjustment.

KICKDOWN SERVO

1. Thoroughly clean area around kickdown servo cover.
2. Remove snap ring, then kickdown servo switch.
3. Install holding fixture No. MD998918 and adapter MD998915 as shown in **Fig. 3**. Ensure piston is not pushed in by tool. When installing adapter to brake pressure take-out port, tighten only by hand.
4. Loosen locknut past V channel in adjuster rod, then tighten tool No. MD998916 (inner) until there is contact with locknut **Fig. 4**.
5. Attach tool No. MD998916 (outer) to locknut. Turn outer tool to left and inner tool to right to lock locknut and inner tool.
6. Install torque wrench to inner tool. **Torque** locknut to 7.2 ft. lbs., then loosen locknut and **retorque** to 3.6 ft. lbs. Back off inner tool by 2-2¼ turns

on all models except F4A23, on F4A23 back off inner tool by 2½-2¾ turns.
7. Attach outer tool to locknut. Turn outer tool to right and inner tool to left to unlock locknut and inner tool.
8. Tighten locknut by hand until it contacts piston. Using torque wrench, **torque** locknut to 18-23 ft. lbs.
9. Remove holding fixture, then install a plug to outlet of low reverse pressure port.

SHIFT LOCK CONTROL

Colt Vista, Summit & Summit Wagon

Refer to "F3A21 & F3A22 Automatic Transaxles" section for shift lock control adjustment.

Laser & Talon

1. Move select lever to Reverse position, then clamp shift lock cable.
2. Connect shift lock cable to select lever assembly and temporarily tighten nut.

3. Slide shift lock cable so distance between select lever assembly's detent pin and end of shift lock cable (distance A) is .04-.15 inch, **Fig. 5**.

Stealth

1. Place selector lever in Park position, the disconnect key interlock cable from selector lever.
2. Turn lock cam B, **Fig. 6**, counterclockwise (arrow 1) to move set lever upward (arrow 2).
3. Fit cutout in set lever to lockpin of lock cam B.
4. Connect shift lock cable to lock cam B and temporarily tighten nut. Install spring and washer to shift lock cable, **Fig. 7**.
5. Press set lever to prevent lock cam B from moving, then lightly pull shift lock cable to remove slack. Tighten nut to secure shift lock cable in position. Ensure shift lock cable end is in contact with fixing pin of lock cam B, **Fig. 4**.
6. Connect key interlock cable to lock cam A, **Fig. 8**, then temporarily tighten nut. Install spring and washer to key interlock cable.

Driving impossible or abnormal (before start-off)

Presumed cause			Starter motor won't function	Forward/backward movement impossible	Forward movement impossible	Backward movement impossible	Engine stalls when N → D or R	Clutch slips at D (stall rpm too high)	Clutch slips at R (stall rpm too high)	Stall rpm too low	Vehicle moves at P or N	Engine starts, or vehicle moves between N-R or N-D	Parking doesn't hold	Abnormal vibration-shock when shift to D-2-L-R
Engine	1	Abnormal idling rpm					⊗							×
	2	Performance malfunction						×		×				
Transaxle (power train)	3	Improper adjustment of manual linkage	×	⊗	⊗	⊗		⊗	⊗		⊗	⊗	⊗	⊗
	4	Malfunction of torque convertor		×	×	×				×				
	5	Operation malfunction of oil pump		×	×	×		×	×					
	6	Malfunction of one-way clutch			×				×					
	7	Damaged or worn gear or other rotating part, or improper adjustment of the preload									×		×	
	8	Malfunction of parking mechanism											×	
	9	Cracked drive plate, or loose bolt		×										
	10	Worn inside diameter of front clutch retainer						×	×					
Oil pressure system (including friction elements)	11	Low fluid level		⊗	⊗	⊗		×	×					
	12	Line pressure too low (seal damaged, leakage, looseness etc.)		⊗	⊗	⊗		⊗	⊗					
	13	Malfunction of valve body (sticking valve, working cavity, adjustment etc.)		⊗	⊗	⊗	×	×	×		×	×		×
	14	Malfunction of front clutch or piston						×						×
	15	Malfunction of rear clutch or piston			×				×					
	16	Malfunction of kickdown band or piston												×
	17	Improper adjustment of kickdown servo												×
	18	Malfunction of low-reverse brake or piston		×		×			×					×
	19	O-ring of low-reverse brake circuit between valve body and case not installed				×			×					
	20	Malfunction of end clutch or piston (check ball hole, other)												×
Electronic control system	21	Malfunction of inhibitors switch, damaged or disconnected wiring or improper adjustment	×								×	×		×
	22	Malfunction of TPS, or improper adjustment												
	23	Pulse generator (A) damaged or disconnected wiring, or short-circuit												
	24	Pulse generator (B) damaged or disconnected wiring, or short-circuit							×					
	25	Malfunction of kickdown servo switch												
	26	SCSV-A or B damaged or disconnected wiring, or short-circuit or sticking (valve open)												
	27	Malfunction of ignition signal system												
	28	Incorrectly grounded ground strap												
	29	PCSV damaged or disconnected wiring, or short-circuit												
	30	PCSV damaged or disconnected wiring (valve open)		⊗	⊗	⊗		×	×					
	31	DCCSV damaged or disconnecting wiring (valve closed)												
	32	DCCSV short-circuit or sticking (valve open)					⊗							
	33	Malfunction of overdrive control switch												×
	34	Malfunction of accelerator switch, or improper adjustment												×
	35	Malfunction of oil-temperature sensor												
	36	Malfunction of lead switch												
	37	Poor contact of ignition system												
	38	Malfunction of transaxle control unit												×

NOTE: ⊗ indicates items of high priority during inspection.
Abbreviations: TPS = Throttle position sensor   SCSV = Shift control solenoid valve

CR5019000166010X

Fig. 2 Transaxle troubleshooting (Part 1 of 2)

	Transaxle malfunction of shift-shock (after start-off)																Abnormal noise, other			
	Won't shift from 2nd to 3rd	Won't shift to 4th	Overdrive control switch doesn't function	Doesn't shift according to shift pattern (shifting is possible)	Improper start-off (starts off from 2nd, etc.)	Excessive creeping or idling vibration	Excessive vibration-shock when shift 1-2 or 3-4	Excessive vibration-shock when shift 2-3 or 4-3	Excessive vibration-shock during upshift	Excessive vibration-shock during D-2 downshift	Sudden engine rpm increase during upshift	Sudden engine rpm increase during 3-2 shift, excessive vibration	Excessive vibration-shock only when cold	Excessive vibration-shock (other than already described)	Damper clutch won't function	Abnormal vibration in high-load region in low gear (approx. 1 Hz)	Abnormal noise from convertor housing together with engine rpm	Mechanical noise (clatter noise) from convertor housing	Abnormal noise inside transaxle case	3rd gear is held
1						×														
2					×		×	×	×	×			×	×		×				
3		×			×															×
4					×										×	×				
5												×					×			
6																				
7																			×	
8																				
9																		×		
10	×	×									×	×								×
11												×								×
12											⊗	⊗		×						×
13	×			×	×		×	×	×	×	×	×	×	×	×	×				×
14	×							×	×		×									×
15																				×
16							×				×	×								×
17							×				×	×		×						×
18										×										×
19																				×
20		⊗					×				×									×
21		×			×															×
22				⊗			×	×	⊗	×	⊗	×		×	×	×				
23							×	×	×	×	×	×		×	×	×				×
24				×											×	×				×
25							×					×								×
26																				×
27							×	×	×	×	×	×		×	×					
28																				×
29																				×
30	×	×									×	×								×
31															×					
32																×				×
33		×	×																	×
34					×	×									×					
35														×	×	×				
36																				×
37				×																×
38	×	×	×	×	×	×	×	×	×	×	×	×	×	×	×	×	×			×

PSCV = Pressure control solenoid valve
DCCSV = Damper clutch control solenoid valve

CR5019000166020X

Fig. 2 Transaxle troubleshooting (Part 2 of 2)

CR5028800334000X

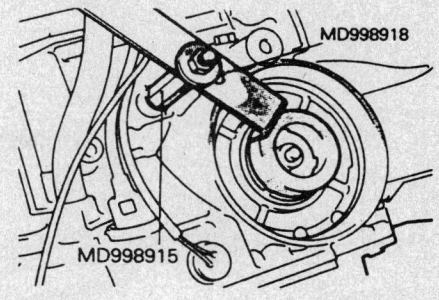

Fig. 3 Kickdown servo tools

CR5028800335000X

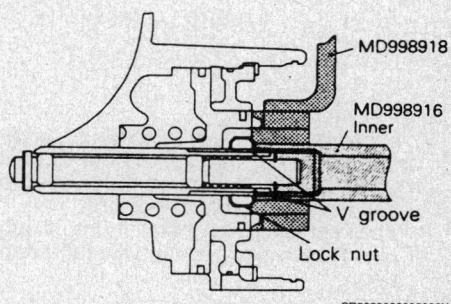

Fig. 4 Installing inner & outer adjustment tools

CR5028800579000X

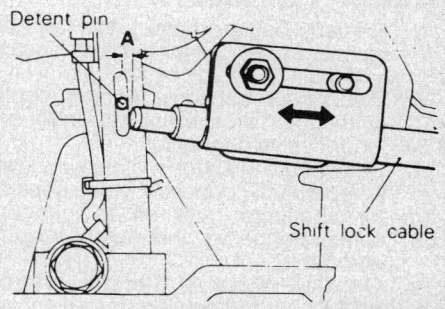

Fig. 5 Shift lock cable adjustment. Laser & Talon

CR5029000580000X

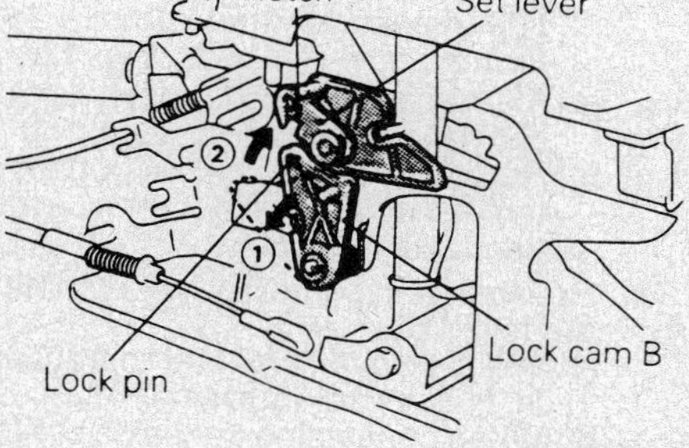

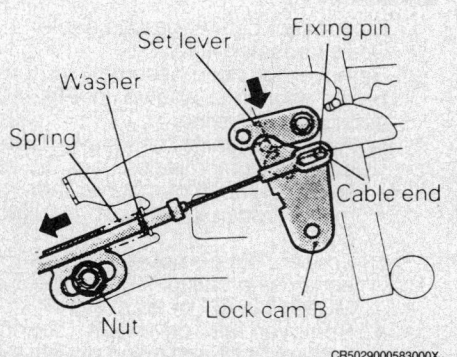

Fig. 6 Lock cam B location. Stealth

CR5029000583000X

Fig. 7 Lock cam B spring & washer location. Stealth

CR5029000586000X

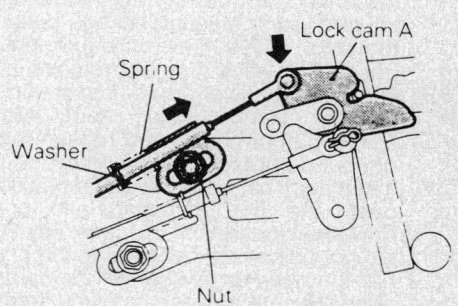

Fig. 8 Lock cam A location. Stealth

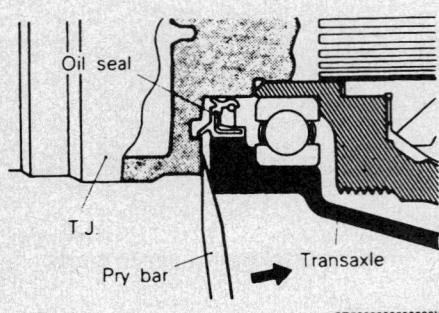

Fig. 9 Driveshaft removal. Except Stealth

7. Press lock cam A in direction of arrow and push key interlock cable to take up slack, **Fig. 1.** Tighten nut to secure key interlock cable in position.
8. Turn set lever and install it onto fixing pin of lock cam A, then install snap ring.

TRANSAXLE
REPLACE

EXCEPT STEALTH

1. Remove battery, battery tray and air cleaner assembly, then drain transaxle fluid.
2. Disconnect transaxle control cable, fluid cooler lines and shift control solenoid valve connector.
3. Disconnect inhibitor switch, kickdown servo switch connector, pulse generator connector and oil temperature sensor connector, then the speedometer cable.
4. **On Colt Vista & Summit Wagon w/1.8L/4-110 engine,** install engine support fixture No. MB9911191 or equivalent.
5. **On all models,** remove starter assembly, transaxle upper connecting bolt and transaxle mounting bracket.
6. Remove transaxle under-guard, then disconnect tie rod end from steering knuckle using steering linkage puller tool No. MB990635 or equivalent. Loosen the nut but do not remove it.
7. Remove the lower arm ball joint connection using puller tool No. MB990635 or equivalent. Loosen the nut but do not remove it.
8. Insert a pry bar between the transaxle case and the driveshaft and pry driveshaft loose from the case, **Fig. 9.** Do not pull on driveshaft or insert pry bar too deep or oil seal will be damaged. Secure driveshaft away from transaxle with rope or wire.
9. Remove bellhousing cover, driveplate connection and transaxle assembly lower connecting bolt.

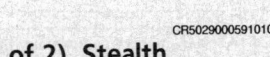

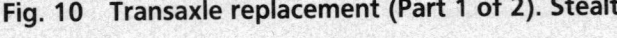

1. Side under cover
2. Battery
3. Battery seat. Washer tank
4. Volume air flow sensor connector
5. Air cleaner cover. Air intake hose
6. Clip
7. Connection for transaxle control cable
8. Connection for oil cooler hose
9. Park/neutral position switch connector
10. Kickdown servo switch connector, pulse generator connector and oil temperature sensor connector
11. Shift control solenoid valve connector
12. Connection for transaxle ground cable
13. Connection for speedometer cable
14. Connection for transaxle mount bracket

Fig. 10 Transaxle replacement (Part 1 of 2). Stealth

10. Support transaxle assembly using a suitable jack, move to the right and lower out of chassis.
11. Reverse procedure to install.

STEALTH

1. Disconnect battery ground cable.
2. Drain transaxle fluid.
3. Remove transaxle assembly in numbered sequence shown in **Fig. 10,** noting the following:
   a. Raise transaxle assembly using suitable transmission jack to relieve weight off of mounts, then remove transaxle mount insulator bolt.
   b. Loosen, but do not remove tie rod ends using ball joint puller tool No. MB991113-01 or equivalent.
   c. Remove left driveshaft bearing bracket bolts and insert pry bar between bearing bracket and cylinder block.
   d. Remove left driveshaft and inner shaft assembly from transaxle. Re-move driveshaft and inner shaft assembly together with hub and knuckle
   e. Remove right driveshaft by applying pry bar to protrusion, **Fig. 11. Remove driveshaft as an assembly together with hub and knuckle**
   f. Support transaxle assembly with a suitable transaxle stand, then rotate crankshaft and remove four torque converter bolts, **Fig. 12.**
   g. After removing bolts, push torque converter toward transaxle.
   h. Remove coupling bolt at bottom of transaxle assembly, then lower transaxle assembly.
4. Reverse procedure to install, noting the following:
   a. Install torque converter to transaxle, then install transaxle.
   b. When connecting transaxle control cable to manual control lever, tighten nut temporarily, then loosen nut and pull cable out slightly and tighten nut.

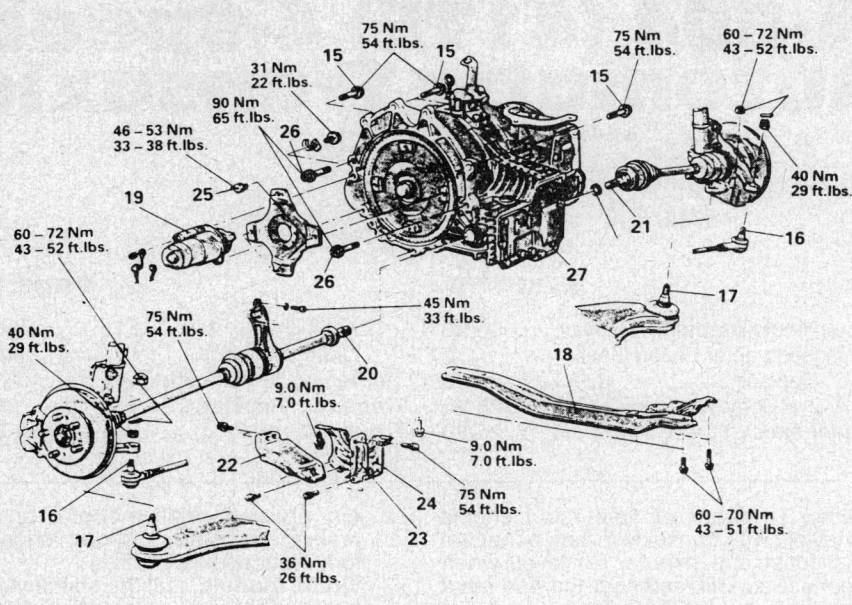

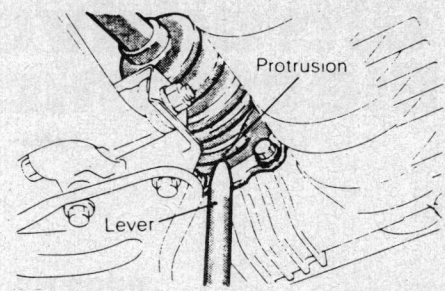

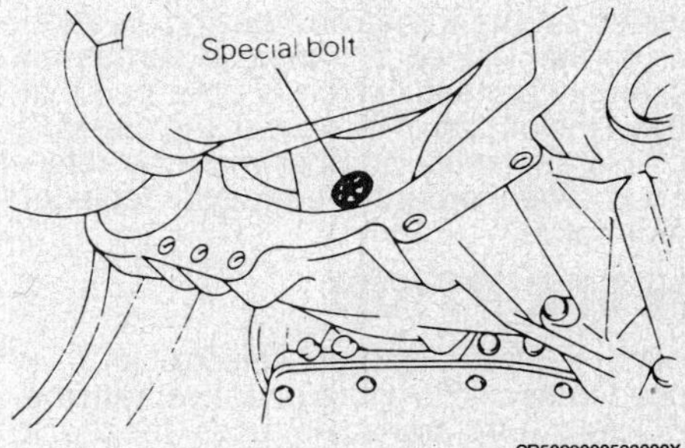

15 Transaxle assembly upper part coupling bolt
16 Connection for tie rod end
17 Connection for lower arm ball joint
18 Right member
19 Starter
20 Drive shaft (left side). Inner shaft assembly
21 Drive shaft (right side)
22 Transaxle stay (front bank side)
23 Transaxle stay (rear bank side)
24 Bell housing cover
25 Torque converter connecting bolt
26 Transaxle assembly lower part coupling bolt
27 Transaxle assembly

CR5029000591020X

Fig. 10 Transaxle replacement (Part 2 of 2). Stealth

CR5029000592000X

Fig. 11 Driveshaft removal. Stealth

CR5029000593000X

Fig. 12 Torque converter bolts removal. Stealth

TIGHTENING SPECIFICATIONS

Component	Torque/Ft. Lbs.
Automatic Seat belt Guide Ring	12–19
Ball Joint To Knuckle	43–52
Bearing Retainer	12–15
Bellhousing Cover To Engine	7–9
Clamp To Body	3–4
Converter Housing	14–16
Drain Plug	22–25
Driveplate To Convertor	34–38
End Clutch Cover	5–6
Hose Bracket	2–4
Inhibitor Switch	7–9
Lever Assembly To Bracket Assembly	10–14
Lock Plate	26–32
Manual Control Lever Nut	13–15
Manual Control Shaft Setscrew	6–7
Oil Cooler Hose Clamp	3–4
Oil Filter	4–5

Component	Torque/Ft. Lbs.
Oil Pan	7–9
Oil Pump Assembly	11–15
One-Way Clutch Outer Race	18–25
Pressure Check Plug	6–7
Pulse Generator	7–9
Pump Housing To Reaction Shaft Support	7–9
Selector Lever Assembly	7–10
Shift Lock Cable To Selector Lever Assembly	3–4
Speedometer Sleeve Locking Plate	2–4
Sprag Rod Support	15–19
Starter Motor	20–25
Tie Rod End To Knuckle	17–25
Torque Converter To Driveplate	53–55
Transaxle Control Cable Adjusting Nut	7–10
Transaxle Control Cable To Body	7–10
Transaxle Mount Bracket To Transaxle	43–58
Transfer Locknut	145–166

Ultradrive A-604 (41TE) 4-Speed Electronic Automatic Transaxle

INDEX

IDENTIFICATION

During production, the transaxle identification number (TIN) is stamped on a boss located on the transaxle housing. In addition to the TIN, each transaxle carries an assembly part No. which is on a pad just above the oil pan at the rear of the transaxle. This assembly number must be referenced when ordering transaxle replacement parts.

DESCRIPTION

The A-604 Ultradrive electronic four speed transaxle is a fully adaptive transaxle. The A-604 transaxle uses feedback sensors to adjust functions on a real time basis, similar to electronic anti-lock brake controls.

The A-604 transaxle provides four forward speeds with ratios of 2.84:1, 1.57:1, 1.00:1 and .069:1, and with torque converter lock-up available in second, direct, or overdrive gear. Reverse ratio is 2.21:1. The A-604, **Fig. 1,** consists of three multiple disc input clutches, two multiple disc grounded clutches, four hydraulic accumulators and two planetary gear sets to provide four forward speeds and reverse ratio. Electrical solenoids provide the transaxles shifting control. Sensors on the transaxle send control inputs to the electronic control unit located under the hood in a potted, diecast aluminum housing. The system can be diagnosed by accessing information from the electronic control unit memory. The transaxle and differential sump have a common oil sump with a communicating opening between the two.

TROUBLESHOOTING

Before attempting any repair on the A-604 EAT, general engine performance, transmission fluid level and shift linkage must first be checked and adjusted if necessary. For specific symptom diagnosis, refer to **Figs. 2 through 5.**

MAINTENANCE
ADDING OIL

Oil level should be checked every six months. To check oil level, start engine and let idle with transaxle in park or neutral for at least one minute. Oil level, when properly filled, will read near the Add mark when oil is cold, (70°F), and in the Hot zone when oil is at normal operating temperature (180°F). Add as necessary.

CHANGING OIL

Fluid and filter changes are not required for average passenger vehicle usage. If the vehicle is subjected to severe usage, the fluid and filter should be changed at 15,000 mile intervals. The magnet on the inside of the oil pan should also be cleaned with a clean, dry cloth at this time. Fluid and filter change procedure is as follows:

1. Raise vehicle on a suitable hoist and place a wide drain pan container under transaxle oil pan.
2. Loosen pan bolts and tap pan at one corner to break seal and allow fluid to drain, then remove pan.
3. Install new filter and O-ring an bottom of valve body, then clean the oil pan and magnet.
4. Reinstall pan using RTV sealant and **torque** pan bolts to 165 inch lbs.
5. Add four quarts of Mopar ATF Plus Type 7176 or Dexron II automatic transmission fluid through the fill tube.
6. Start engine and allow to idle for at least one minute, then with parking and service brakes applied, move selector lever through it's range, pausing momentarily at each position. Return lever to P or N position.
7. Add fluid to bring level 1/8 inch below the Add mark. Recheck fluid level after transaxle is at normal operating temperature.

ADJUSTMENTS
GEARSHIFT LINKAGE ADJUSTMENT

When it is necessary to disassemble linkage cable from levers, plastic grommet retainers should always be replaced with new grommets.

1. Place gearshift lever in P position, then loosen clamp bolt on gearshift cable bracket.
2. **On column shift models,** ensure preload adjustment spring engages fork on transaxle bracket.
3. **On all models,** pull the shift lever by hand all the way to the front detent position (P) and **torque** lock screw to 100 inch lbs.

IN-VEHICLE REPAIRS
SPEEDOMETER PINION GEAR, REPLACE

1. Disconnect speedometer cable, if equipped.
2. Remove electrical connector from sensor. **Weather seal must stay on connector.**
3. Remove distance sensor attaching bolt, then pull sensor and pinion gear assembly out of extension housing.
4. Remove pinion gear from sensor.
5. Reverse procedure to install, noting the following:
   a. Install new O-ring on distance sensor outside diameter.
   b. **Torque** distance sensor attaching bolt to 60 inch lbs.
   c. **Torque** speedometer cable to 35 inch lbs.

SOLENOID ASSEMBLY, REPLACE

1. Remove input speed sensor, **Fig. 6.**
2. Remove sound cover located under input speed sensor opening.
3. Remove solenoid assembly attaching screws, **Fig. 7,** and solenoid assembly.
4. Reverse procedure to install.

VALVE BODY, REPLACE

1. Raise and support vehicle.
2. Drain transmission fluid as described under "Maintenance."
3. Remove oil pan attaching bolts and oil pan.
4. Remove oil filter, then the valve body attaching bolts.
5. Push park rod rollers from guide bracket, **Fig. 8,** then remove valve body.

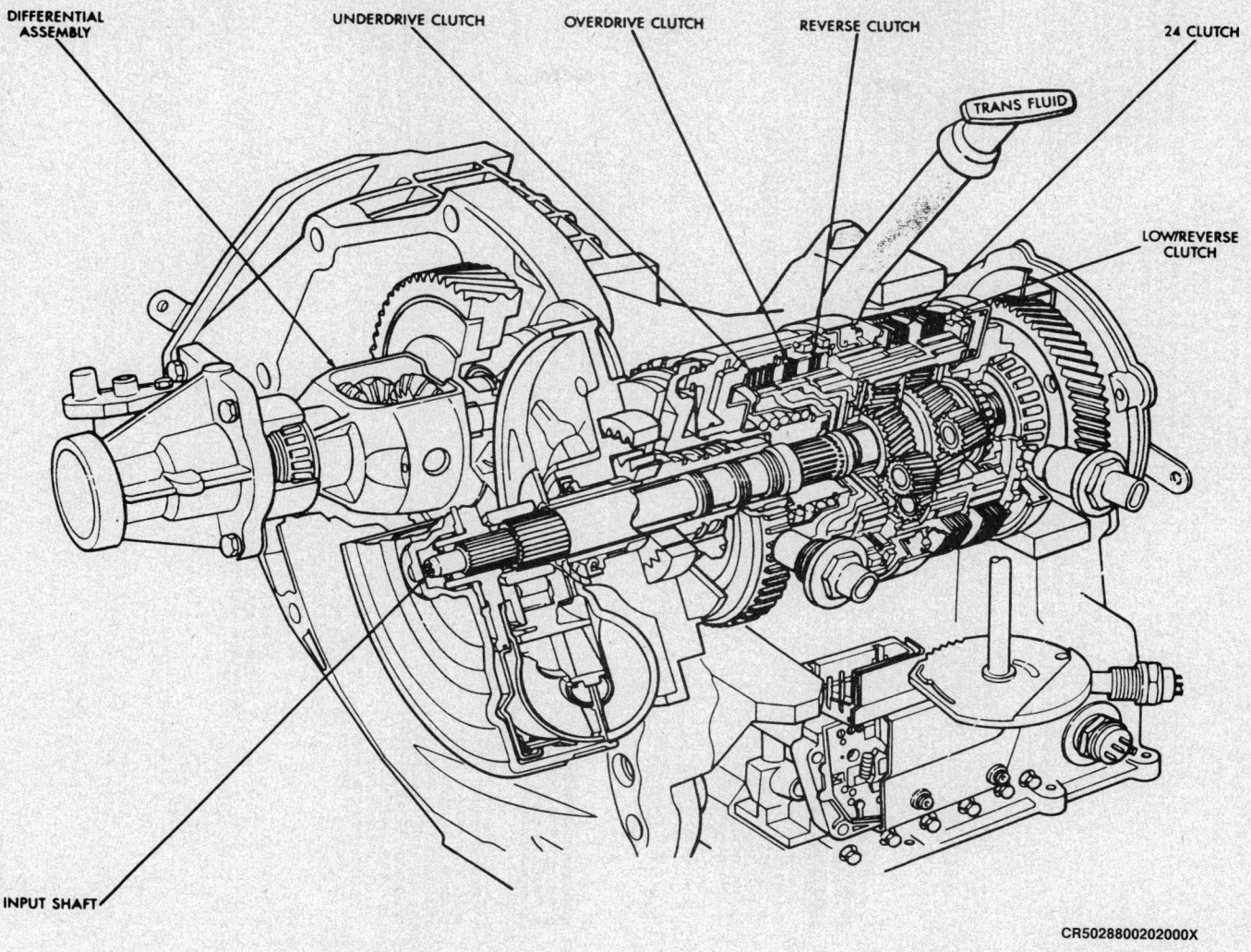

Fig. 1 Cross-sectional view of transaxle

6. Reverse procedure to install noting the following:
   a. Guide park rollers into guide bracket.
   b. **Torque** valve body attaching bolts to 40 inch lbs.
   c. **Torque** oil pan attaching bolts to 14 ft. lbs.

TRANSAXLE
REPLACE

Transaxle and torque converter must be removed as an assembly.
1. Disconnect battery ground cable, then the shift control linkage.
2. Support engine with suitable engine lifting equipment, then remove bellhousing upper attaching bolts.
3. Raise and support vehicle, then remove front wheels and left splash shield.
4. Remove wheel hub nut and driveshafts.
5. Remove torque converter dust cover, then mark torque converter and driveplate for reference during reassembly.
6. Remove torque converter mounting bolts, then disconnect electrical connectors at PRNDL and neutral safety switches.
7. Remove front engine mount insulator and bracket.
8. **On vehicles w/direct ignition system,** remove crankshaft position sensor from bellhousing.
9. **On all models,** disconnect and remove distance sensor, then the starter motor.
10. Position transaxle jack securely under transaxle, then remove left transaxle mount.
11. Lower transaxle assembly from vehicle.
12. Reverse procedure to install.

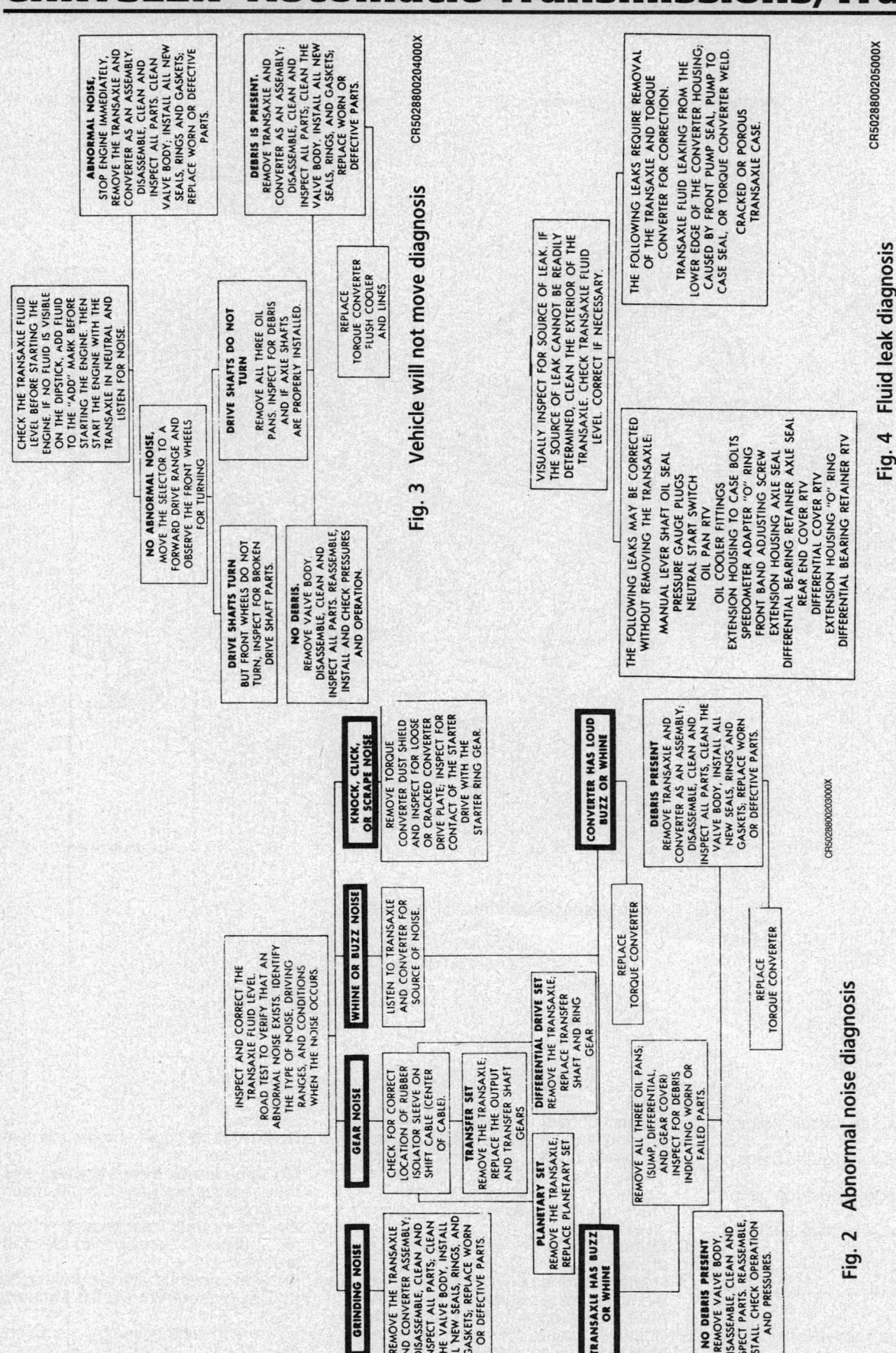

Fig. 2 Abnormal noise diagnosis

Fig. 3 Vehicle will not move diagnosis

Fig. 4 Fluid leak diagnosis

POSSIBLE CAUSE	HARSH ENGAGEMENT FROM NEUTRAL TO D	R	DELAYED ENGAGEMENT FROM NEUTRAL TO D	R	RUNAWAY UPSHIFT	NO UPSHIFT	3-2 KICKDOWN RUNAWAY	NO KICKDOWN OR NORMAL DOWNSHIFT	SHIFTS ERRATIC	SLIPS IN FORWARD DRIVE POSITIONS	SLIPS IN REVERSE ONLY	SLIPS IN ALL POSITIONS	NO DRIVE IN ANY POSITION	NO DRIVE IN FORWARD DRIVE POSITIONS	NO DRIVE IN REVERSE	DRIVES IN NEUTRAL	DRAGS OR LOCKS	GRATING, SCRAPING GROWLING NOISE	BUZZING NOISE	HARD TO FILL, OIL BLOWS OUT FILLER HOLE	TRANSAXLE OVERHEATS	HARSH UPSHIFT	DELAYED UPSHIFT	NO TORQUE CONVERTER CLUTCH APPLICATION
34 Engine performance.	X	X				X			X													X	X	
33 Overrunning clutch inner race damaged.																			X					
32 Overrunning clutch worn, broken or seized.										X				X			X	X						
31 Planetary gear sets broken or seized.													X	X	X		X	X						
30 Rear clutch dragging.																X								
29 Worn or faulty rear clutch.	X	X	X							X				X	X	X								
28 Insufficient clutch plate clearance.																X					X			
27 Faulty cooling system.																					X			
26 Kickdown band adjustment too tight.																	X				X			
25 Hydraulic pressure too high.	X	X																				X		
24 High fluid level.																				X				
23 Worn or faulty front clutch.				X	X	X	X		X		X				X								X	
22 Kickdown servo band or linkage malfunction.					X	X	X	X	X														X	
21 Governor malfunction.						X		X	X														X	
20 Worn or broken reaction shaft support seal rings.				X	X	X			X		X				X								X	
19 Governor support seal rings broken or worn.						X	X		X														X	
18 Driveshaft(s) bushing(s) damaged.																		X						
17 Overrunning clutch not holding.										X				X										
16 Kickdown band out of adjustment.							X											X				X	X	
15 Incorrect throttle linkage adjustment.					X	X	X	X	X	X												X	X	
14 Engine idle speed too low.			X	X																				
13 Aerated fluid.			X	X	X		X		X	X	X	X							X	X				X
12 Worn or broken input shaft seal rings.			X	X						X		X		X										X
11 Faulty oil pump.			X	X					X	X	X	X	X								X			X
10 Oil filter clogged.			X	X	X				X	X		X	X							X				
9 Incorrect gearshift control linkage adjustment.			X	X		X			X	X	X				X	X					X			
8 Low fluid level.			X	X	X	X	X		X	X	X	X	X	X					X		X			X
7 Low-reverse servo, band or linkage malfunction.		X		X							X				X									
6 Valve body malfunction or leakage.	X		X	X	X	X	X	X	X	X	X	X	X	X	X	X			X					X
5 Low-reverse band worn out.		X		X							X				X		X	X						
4 Hydraulic pressures too low.			X	X	X	X	X		X	X	X	X	X	X	X						X	X		X
3 Engine idle speed too high.	X	X																			X			
2 Stuck switch valve.																					X			X
1 Low-reverse band misadjusted.		X		X							X													

CONDITION

CR5028800594000X

Fig. 5 Symptom diagnosis chart

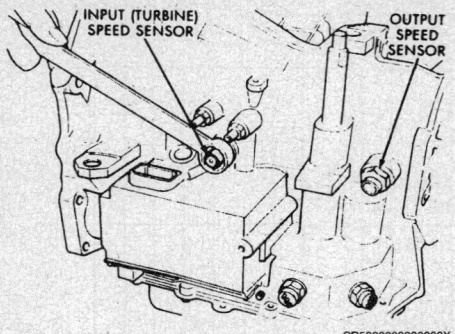

Fig. 6   Input speed sensor removal

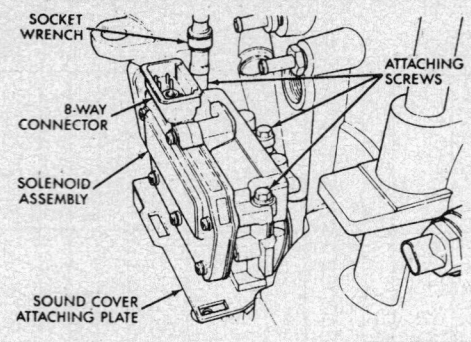

Fig. 7   Solenoid assembly removal

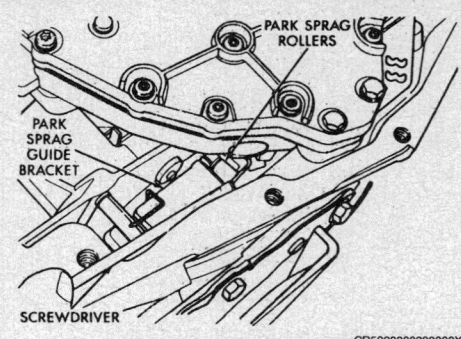

Fig. 8   Park rod rollers from guide bracket removal

TIGHTENING SPECIFICATIONS

Component	Torque/Ft. Lbs.	Component	Torque/Ft. Lbs.
Cooler Line Fittings	9	Pressure Taps	4
Differential Cover	13–14	PRNDL Switch	25
Differential Ring Cover	70	Pump To Case	23
Differential Bearing Retainer	21	Reaction Shaft To Pump	23
Extension Housing	21	Solenoid Assembly To Case	8–9
Input Speed Sensor	20	Transfer Plate To case	8–9
L/R Clutch Retainer	3–4	Valve Body & Transfer Plate	3–4
Neutral Safety Switch	25	Vent Assembly	9
Oil Pan To Case	14	8-Way Solenoid Connector	3
Output Gear Bolt	200	60-Way EATX Connector	3
Output Speed Sensor	20		

42LE 4-Speed Electronic Automatic Transaxle

INDEX

IDENTIFICATION

The 42LE four speed transaxle identification code is printed on a bar code label. This label is located on the transaxle case, **Fig. 1.**

DESCRIPTION

The 42LE transaxle provides forward ratios of 2.84, 1.57, 1.00 and .69 with torque converter clutch available in second, direct or overdrive gear. The reverse ratio is 2.21.

The shift lever is conventional with six positions. When overdrive is selected the transaxle shifts normally through all four speeds with the torque converter clutch operational in third and overdrive; this position is recommended for most driving. The third position is tailored for use in hilly or mountainous driving. When third is selected, the transaxle uses only first, second and direct gear with second-direct shift delayed to 40 MPH or greater. When operating in third or low positions, torque converter clutch application occurs in direct gear. If high engine coolant temperature occurs, the torque converter clutch will also engage in second gear.

TROUBLESHOOTING

Prior to attempting any repair on the 42LE transaxle, general engine performance, transaxle fluid level and shift linkage must first be checked and adjusted, if necessary. For specific symptom diagnosis, refer to **Figs. 2 through 5.**

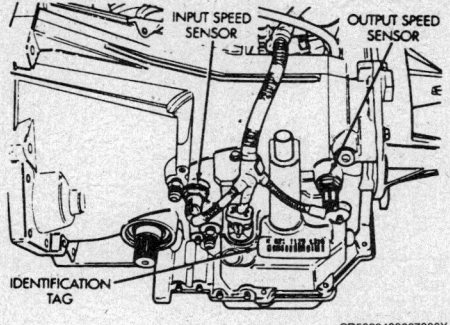

Fig. 1   Transaxle identification tag location

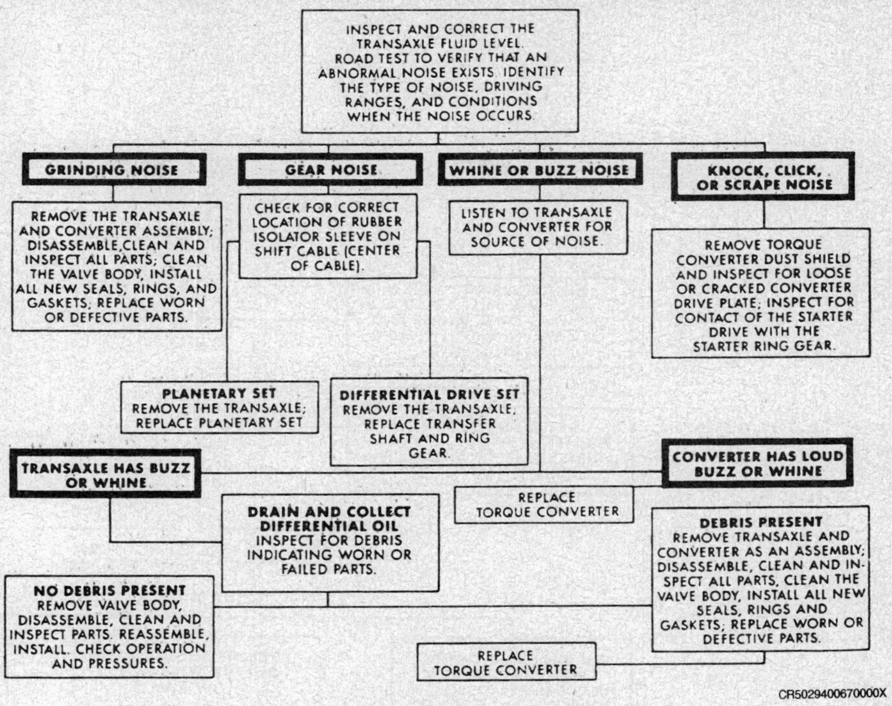

INSPECT AND CORRECT THE TRANSAXLE FLUID LEVEL. ROAD TEST TO VERIFY THAT AN ABNORMAL NOISE EXISTS. IDENTIFY THE TYPE OF NOISE, DRIVING RANGES, AND CONDITIONS WHEN THE NOISE OCCURS.

GRINDING NOISE
REMOVE THE TRANSAXLE AND CONVERTER ASSEMBLY; DISASSEMBLE, CLEAN AND INSPECT ALL PARTS; CLEAN THE VALVE BODY, INSTALL ALL NEW SEALS, RINGS, AND GASKETS; REPLACE WORN OR DEFECTIVE PARTS.

GEAR NOISE
CHECK FOR CORRECT LOCATION OF RUBBER ISOLATOR SLEEVE ON SHIFT CABLE (CENTER OF CABLE).

WHINE OR BUZZ NOISE
LISTEN TO TRANSAXLE AND CONVERTER FOR SOURCE OF NOISE.

KNOCK, CLICK, OR SCRAPE NOISE
REMOVE TORQUE CONVERTER DUST SHIELD AND INSPECT FOR LOOSE OR CRACKED CONVERTER DRIVE PLATE; INSPECT FOR CONTACT OF THE STARTER DRIVE WITH THE STARTER RING GEAR.

PLANETARY SET
REMOVE THE TRANSAXLE; REPLACE PLANETARY SET

DIFFERENTIAL DRIVE SET
REMOVE THE TRANSAXLE; REPLACE TRANSFER SHAFT AND RING GEAR.

TRANSAXLE HAS BUZZ OR WHINE

CONVERTER HAS LOUD BUZZ OR WHINE

REPLACE TORQUE CONVERTER

DRAIN AND COLLECT DIFFERENTIAL OIL INSPECT FOR DEBRIS INDICATING WORN OR FAILED PARTS.

DEBRIS PRESENT REMOVE TRANSAXLE AND CONVERTER AS AN ASSEMBLY; DISASSEMBLE, CLEAN AND INSPECT ALL PARTS, CLEAN THE VALVE BODY, INSTALL ALL NEW SEALS, RINGS AND GASKETS; REPLACE WORN OR DEFECTIVE PARTS.

NO DEBRIS PRESENT REMOVE VALVE BODY, DISASSEMBLE, CLEAN AND INSPECT PARTS. REASSEMBLE, INSTALL. CHECK OPERATION AND PRESSURES.

REPLACE TORQUE CONVERTER

Fig. 2   Abnormal noise diagnosis

MAINTENANCE
FLUID CHECK
Transaxle

With vehicle on level surface, start engine and operate at idle speed for a minimum of one minute. Place selector lever in Park position. Remove dipstick and check fluid level. Transaxle should be at operating temperature when checking fluid level (160-180°F). Fluid level should be within the Hot range on dipstick. If necessary, add Mopar ATF Plus (Type 7176) automatic transmission fluid to bring fluid level within the Hot range.

Differential

The differential sump is checked separately from the transaxle. A fill plug located on the side of the transaxle must be removed to check fluid level, **Fig. 6.** Fluid should be level with bottom of the fill hole. If necessary, add Mopar petroleum based hypoid gear lubricant 80W-90 to bring level to bottom of fill hole. Synthetic gear lubricants should not be used.

FLUID CHANGE
Transaxle Fluid & Filter

1. Raise and support vehicle, then place drain container under transaxle oil pan.
2. Loosen pan bolts and tap pan at one corner to break it loose allowing fluid to drain, then remove oil pan and filter.
3. Install new filter and O-ring on bottom of valve body. **Torque** filter mounting bolts to 40 inch lbs.
4. Clean and install oil pan and magnet. **Torque** oil pan bolts to 165 inch lbs.
5. Install four quarts of Mopar ATF Plus (Type 7176) automatic transmission fluid through dipstick opening.
6. Start engine and allow to idle for at least one minute. With parking and service brakes applied, move selector lever momentarily to each position, ending in Park or Neutral position.
7. Add fluid to bring level 1/4 inch above bottom hole of dipstick.
8. Recheck fluid level after transaxle has reached normal operating temperature.

Differential

1. Raise and support vehicle.
2. Remove differential drain plug located on the bottom of the differential housing. Allow fluid to drain into suitable container.
3. Remove differential fill plug located on differential side cover.
4. Install drain plug. **Torque** plug to 60 inch lbs.
5. Fill differential with Mopar petroleum based hypoid gear lubricant 80W-90. Fluid should be level with bottom of fill hole. Differential capacity is approximately 32 ounces.
6. Install fill plug. **Torque** plug to 35 inch lbs.

ADJUSTMENTS
GEARSHIFT LINKAGE
Column Shift

1. Remove upper steering column shroud, then rotate cable adjuster into unlock position.
2. Ensure transaxle shift lever (at transaxle) is in the Park position.
3. Tilt steering column to full up position, then place shifter in Park position with key removed.
4. Adjust by rotating adjuster to lock position.
5. Install upper steering column shroud.
6. Check shifter for proper operation. Vehicle should start in Park or Neutral only.

Floor Shift

1. Remove shifter handle and console bezel, then loosen nut on shifter cable adjuster.
2. Set shift lever assembly in Park (most rearward) position at transaxle.
3. Place shifter in Park position, then place ignition in lock with key removed.
4. Tighten adjuster nut at shifter.
5. Install console bezel and shifter handle.
6. Check shifter for proper operation. Vehicle should start in Park or Neutral only.

IN-VEHICLE REPAIRS
VALVE BODY, REPLACE

The solenoid pack and manual valve lever position sensor are mounted on top side of valve body. They will remain attached to the valve body when the valve body is removed.

1. Disconnect MVLPS wiring connector, then the shift cable from shift lever at transaxle.
2. Move shift lever clockwise as far as possible, then remove shift lever.
3. Remove transaxle pan bolts, then the oil pan.
4. Remove oil filter from valve body.
5. Remove valve body attaching bolts, then the valve body.
6. Reverse procedure to install.

SOLENOID PACK, REPLACE

1. Remove valve body as outlined under "Valve Body, Replace."
2. Remove solenoid pack retaining screw, then the solenoid pack and screen.
3. Reverse procedure to install.

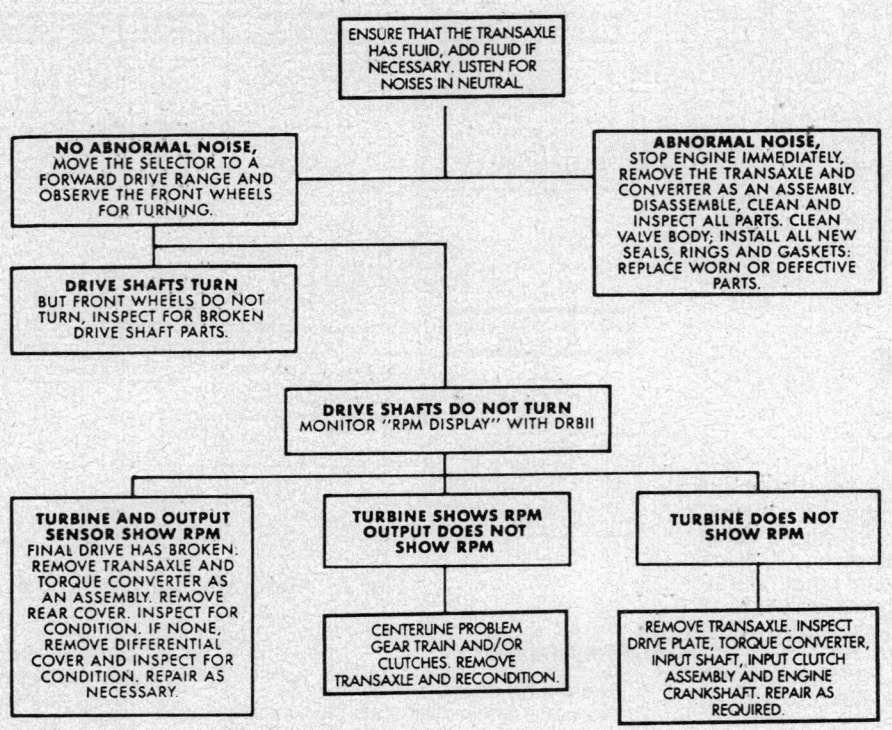

Fig. 3   Vehicle will not move diagnosis

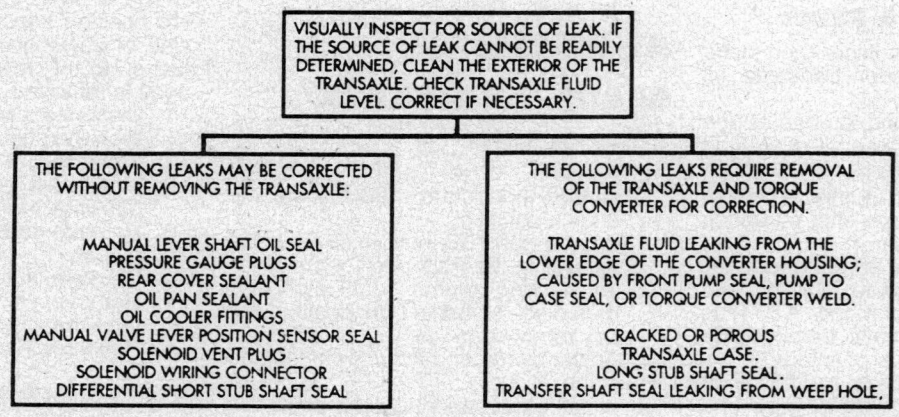

Fig. 4   Fluid leak diagnosis

POSSIBLE CAUSE

CONDITION	HARSH ENGAGEMENT FROM NEUTRAL TO D	R	DELAYED ENGAGEMENT FROM NEUTRAL TO D	R	POOR SHIFT QUALITY	SHIFTS ERRATIC	DRIVES IN NEUTRAL	DRAGS OR LOCKS	GRATING, SCRAPING, GROWLING NOISE	ENGINE MISFIRE	BUZZING NOISE	BUZZING NOISE DURING SHIFTS ONLY	HARD TO FILL OIL BLOWS OUT FILLER TUBE	TRANSAXLE OVERHEATS	HARSH UPSHIFT	NO UPSHIFT INTO OVERDRIVE	NO TORQUE CONVERTER CLUTCH	HARSH DOWNSHIFTS	HIGH SHIFT EFFORTS	HARSH CONVERTER CLUTCH
Engine Performance	X	X			X									X		X		X		
Worn or faulty clutch(es)	X	X	X	X	X	X	X							X	X	X				
— Underdrive clutch	X		X		X	X	X													
— Overdrive clutch					X	X	X								X	X				
— Reverse clutch		X		X	X	X									X	X				
— 2/4 clutch					X	X										X				
— Low/reverse clutch	X	X			X	X										X				
Clutch(es) dragging					X															
Insufficient clutch plate clearance					X								X							
Damaged clutch seals		X	X													X				
Worn or damaged accumulator seal ring(s)	X	X	X	X												X				
Faulty cooling system														X						
Engine coolant temp. too low																X	X			
Incorrect gearshift control linkage adjustment			X	X	X	X								X						
Shift linkage damaged																			X	
Chipped or damaged gear teeth								X	X											
Planetary gear sets broken or seized								X	X											
Bearings worn or damaged								X	X											
Driveshaft(s) bushing(s) worn or damaged									X											
Worn or broken reaction shaft support seal rings			X	X	X	X										X				
Worn or damaged input shaft seal rings			X	X												X				
Valve body malfunction or leakage	X	X	X	X	X	X	X				X					X	X	X	X	
Hydraulic pressures too low			X	X	X	X								X	X					
Hydraulic pressures too high	X	X												X		X				
Faulty oil pump			X	X										X		X				
Oil filter clogged			X	X	X	X						X								
Low fluid level			X	X	X	X					X			X		X	X			
High fluid level														X	X					
Aerated fluid			X	X	X	X					X			X	X	X	X			
Engine idle speed too low			X	X																
Engine idle speed too high	X	X																		
Normal solenoid operation												X								
Solenoid sound cover loose												X								
Sticking torque converter clutch position																				X
Torque Converter Failure	X													X		X				X
Drive Plate cracked or bent								X	X											

Fig. 5   Symptom diagnosis chart

CR5029400673000X

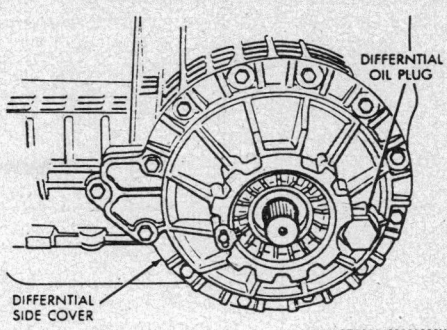

DIFFERNTIAL OIL PLUG

DIFFERNTIAL SIDE COVER

CR5029400669000X

Fig. 6   Differential oil fill plug location

tion. Remove adjuster.
5. Using press and seal remover No. 6558 or equivalent, replace oil seal.
6. Inspect stub shaft for corrosion.
7. Lubricate O-ring, threads on adjuster, seal protector and seal lips with gear oil.
8. Install outer adjuster into transaxle case. **Torque** adjuster to within 10 ft. lbs. of torque reading recorded in step 4.
9. Rotate ring gear four revolutions in both directions to seat differential bearings.
10. Continue tightening outer adjuster until alignment marks line up in there original location, then install adjuster lock.
11. Install new driveshaft retaining circlip and O-ring on stub shaft, then the driveshaft.
12. Check fluid level in differential. Adjust as necessary.

TRANSAXLE
REPLACE

1. Disconnect both battery cables, then remove air inlet tube.
2. Disconnect crankshaft position sensor connector, then remove sensor. Sensor is located on upper right side of transaxle bellhousing.
3. Disconnect transaxle wiring connector located on right shock tower.
4. Raise and support vehicle, then remove front wheels.
5. Remove strut to steering knuckle bolts on both sides of vehicle.
6. Remove ABS wheel speed sensor, if equipped.
7. Using pry bar, disconnect inner CV joint from transaxle.
8. Pull top of knuckle and driveshaft outward to allow clearance during removal. Do not allow inner CV joint to hang unsupported.
9. Remove engine to transaxle brackets, then the bellhousing cover.
10. Place alignment mark on torque converter and flex plate, then remove torque converter bolts.
11. Remove starter attaching bolts, then the starter and position aside.
12. Disconnect transaxle cooler lines at transaxle, then the gear selector cable from transaxle.

MANUAL VALVE LEVER POSITION SENSOR (MVLPS), REPLACE

1. Disconnect MVLPS electrical connector.
2. Remove valve body as outlined under "Valve Body, Replace."
3. Remove manual shaft retaining screw, then slide MVLPS off manual valve shaft.
4. Reverse procedure to install.

INPUT SPEED SENSOR, REPLACE

1. Disconnect electrical connector from input speed sensor. Ensure weather seal stays attached to connector.
2. Unscrew sensor from transaxle.
3. Reverse procedure to install, **torquing** sensor to 15-25 ft. lbs.

OUTPUT SPEED SENSOR, REPLACE

1. Disconnect electrical connector from output speed sensor. Ensure weather seal stays attached to connector.
2. Unscrew sensor from transaxle.
3. Reverse procedure to install, **torquing** sensor to 15-25 ft. lbs.

SHORT (RIGHT) STUB SHAFT SEAL, REPLACE

1. Place vehicle in Neutral position, then raise and support vehicle.
2. Remove short driveshaft, then place alignment mark on outer adjuster and housing.
3. Remove outer adjuster lock.
4. Using tool No. 6503 loosen outer adjuster, then retighten to alignment mark using a torque wrench. Record amount of torque required to return alignment marks to their original loca-

13. Disconnect exhaust system at manifolds, then remove exhaust system.
14. Place and secure transmission jack under transaxle, then slightly raise transaxle to relieve weight on rear transaxle mount.
15. Remove transaxle mount through bolt, then the rear crossmember mounting bolts.
16. Pry transaxle mount rearward to separate mount from transaxle.
17. Remove rear crossmember, then lower rear of transaxle to gain access to bellhousing bolts.
18. Remove bellhousing bolts, then the dipstick tube from transaxle.
19. Remove engine to transaxle bolts, then the transaxle from vehicle.
20. Reverse procedure to install. Adjust gear shift cable if necessary.

TIGHTENING SPECIFICATIONS

Component	Torque/Ft. Lbs.
Adjuster Lock Bracket Screws	40①
Cooler Line Connector	155①
Differential Cover To Case	250①
Differential Drain Plug	60①
Differential Fill Plug	35①
Driveplate To Crankshaft Bolts	75
End Cover To Case Screw	250①
Filter Retainer	40①
Input Sensor To Case	15–25
Manual Lever To Valve Body	40①
Oil Pan To Case Screw	165①
Output Sensor To Case	15–25
Output Shaft Stake Nut	200
Park Sprag Retention Screw	40①
Pressure Check Plug (Wet)	45①
Pump To Case Bolt	265①
Solenoid Assembly To Transfer Plate	50①
Solenoid Wiring Connector Retainer	50①
Torque Converter To Driveplate	60
Transfer Plate To Case	105①
Valve Body Screw	40①
Wiring Harness Tie Down Bolt	50①

①—Inch lbs.

FRONT WHEEL DRIVE AXLES

TABLE OF CONTENTS

Application Chart

Model	Type No.	Page No.
Acclaim & Spirit	1	27-1
Colt & Colt Vista	2	27-7
Concorde, Intrepid, LHS & Vision	4	27-16
Daytona	1	27-1
Dynasty	1	27-1
Imperial	1	27-1
Laser & Talon	3	27-12
LeBaron	1	27-1

Model	Type No.	Page No.
Monaco & Premier	3	27-12
Neon	1	27-1
New Yorker (1992-93)	1	27-1
New Yorker (1994)	4	27-16
Shadow & Sundance	1	27-1
Stealth	2	27-7
Summit & Summit Wagon	2	27-7

Type 1

INDEX

DRIVESHAFT IDENTIFICATION

Driveshafts are identified by manufacturer, **Figs. 1 and 2**. Two different driveshaft systems are used. Some models use an "equal length" system while all others use an "unequal length" system. The "equal length" system has short solid interconnecting shafts of equal length on the left and right sides. The "unequal length" system has a short solid interconnecting shaft on left side with a longer tubular interconnecting shaft on right.

Replacement procedures of driveshafts are essentially the same for all types of assemblies used.

DRIVESHAFT REPLACE

REMOVAL

Inboard C/V joints have stub shafts splined into differential side gears, or splined into the intermediate shaft on right side of an equal length system. Driveshafts are spring loaded and are retained to side gears by constant spring pressure provided by spring contained in C/V joints.

Do not move vehicle on it's wheels after hub nut is loosened, bearing damage will result.

1. Remove cotter pin, lock and spring washer, then the hub nut washer and wheel assembly.
2. Remove brake caliper and rotor as outlined under "Disc Brakes."
3. If removing the righthand driveshaft, speedometer pinion must be removed prior to driveshaft removal, **Fig. 3.**
4. **On models except Neon,** remove cotter pin and retaining nut from tie rod end, then using tie rod end removing tool No. C-3894-A or equivalent, remove tie rod end from steering knuckle.
5. **On Neon models,** remove retaining nut from tie rod end by holding ball shaft with an $^{11}/_{32}$ socket and using a suitable wrench to remove the nut, then using tie rod end removing tool No. MB-990635 or equivalent, remove tie rod end from steering knuckle.
6. **On all models,** remove clamp bolt securing ball joint clamp to steering knuckle, then separate ball joint stud from steering knuckle. **Do not damage ball joint or C/V joint boots.**

7. Separate outer C/V joint splined shaft from hub by holding C/V housing while moving knuckle/hub assembly away from C/V joint. **Do not damage slinger on outer C/V joint. Do not attempt to remove, repair or replace.**

8. Support axle assembly, then remove axle from differential by pulling outward on the inner C/V joint outer housing. **Do not pull on shaft as inner joint or boot damage may result.** If clearance between driveshaft assembly and differential case allows, removal may be aided by inserting a suitable pry bar between differential case and carefully prying against end face of stub.

9. Remove driveshaft assembly from vehicle.

INSTALLATION

1. Hold inner joint assembly at housing while aligning and guiding inner joint spline into transaxle. **On equal length systems, ensure rubber washer seal is in place on right inner C/V joint.**

2. **On all models,** push knuckle/hub assembly out and install splined outer C/V joint shaft into hub.

3. Install knuckle assembly on ball joint stud.

4. Install clamp bolt. **Torque** to 70 ft. lbs.

5. **On models except Neon,** install tie rod end into steering knuckle, then **torque** retaining nut to 35 ft. lbs. and install new cotter pin.

6. **On Neon,** install tie rod end into steering knuckle, then holding tie rod end ball shaft with an 11/32 socket wrench **torque** retaining nut to 45 ft. lbs. and install new cotter pin.

7. **On all models,** install brake caliper and rotor as outlined under "Disc Brakes."

8. Install speedometer pinion, **Fig. 3.**

9. Fill differential to bottom of filler plug hole with Dexron automatic transaxle fluid.

10. **On models except Neon,** install washer and hub nut. **Torque** hub nut to 180 ft. lbs. Install nut plate and cotter pin.

11. **On Neon,** install washer and hub nut. **Torque** hub nut to 150 ft. lbs. Install nut plate and cotter pin.

12. If, after attaching driveshaft assembly in vehicle, the inboard boot appears collapsed or deformed, vent the inner boot by inserting a round tipped, small diameter rod between boot and shaft. As venting occurs, the boot will return to normal shape.

13. **On models except Neon,** after installation of driveshaft, check driveshaft length as outlined under "Adjustments."

DRIVESHAFT SERVICE
ADJUSTMENT

Driveshaft Length except Neon

If the vertical bolts on both engine mounts have been loosened, or vehicle

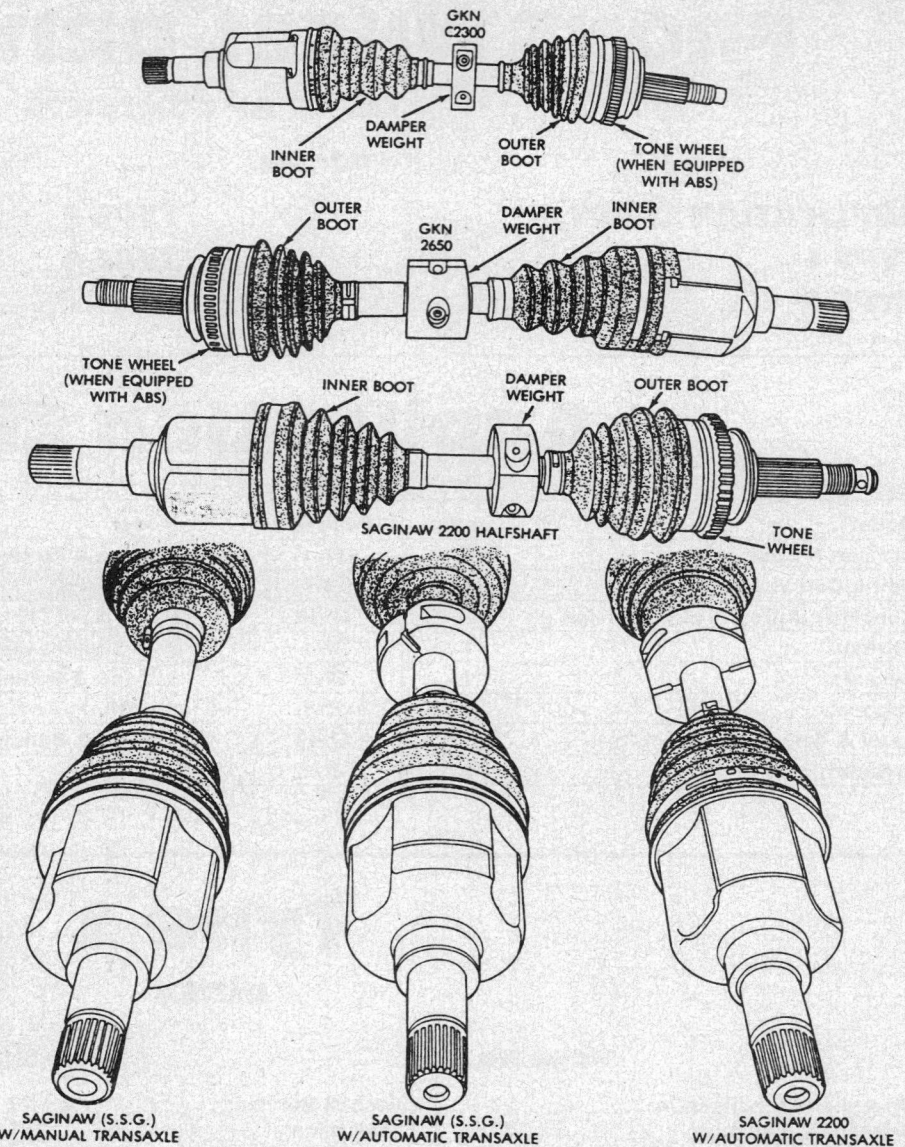

Fig. 1 Type 1 driveshaft identification. Except Neon

has experienced front structural damage, driveshaft lengths must be checked.

The engine mounts incorporate slotted bolt holes to permit side to side positioning of the engine, thereby affecting length of driveshafts. To check driveshaft length proceed as follows.

1. Position vehicle with wheels straight ahead and body weight distributed on all 4 tires.

2. Measure direct distance between inner edge of outboard boot to inner edge of inboard boot on both driveshafts, **Fig. 4.**

3. Driveshaft length must be within specifications in chart, **Fig. 5** If measurement is not within specifications, engine position must be corrected as follows:

   a. Remove load from engine mounts by carefully supporting engine and transaxle assembly with a suitable jack.

   b. Loosen right and left engine mount vertical bolts, then loosen only the right and front engine mount bracket to crossmember attaching bolts.

   c. Pry engine to right or left as necessary to bring driveshaft length within specifications. **Ensure left engine mount is sleeved over long support bolt and shaft, Fig. 6, to provide lateral adjustment whether or not engine weight is removed.**

   d. **Torque** engine mount vertical bolts to 27 ft. lbs. and front and center left engine mount bolts to 40 ft. lbs.

INNER CONSTANT VELOCITY JOINT SERVICE

Disassemble

1. Remove clamp and boot from joint and discard, **Fig. 7.**

2. **On GKN units,** Clamp interconnect-

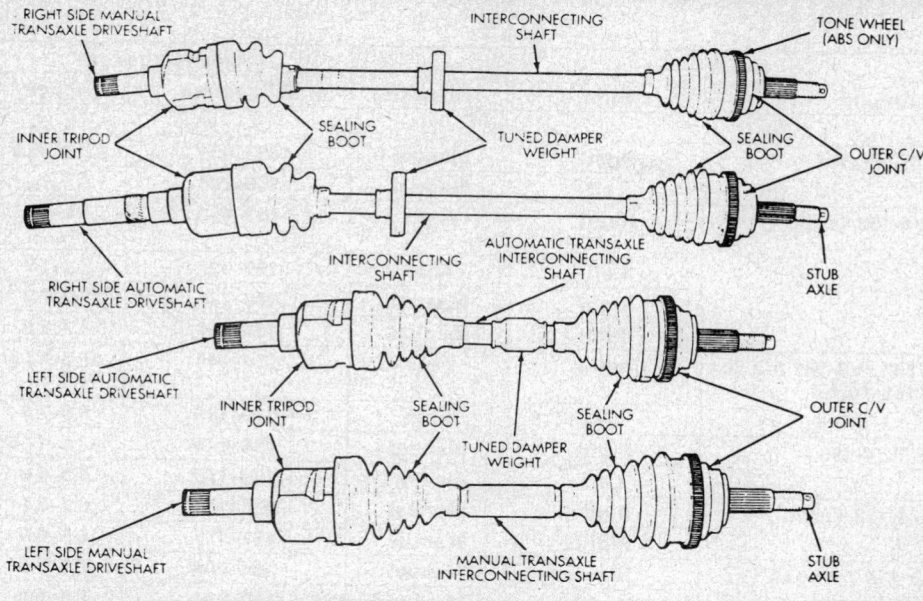

Fig. 2 Type 1 driveshaft identification. Neon

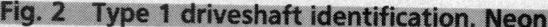

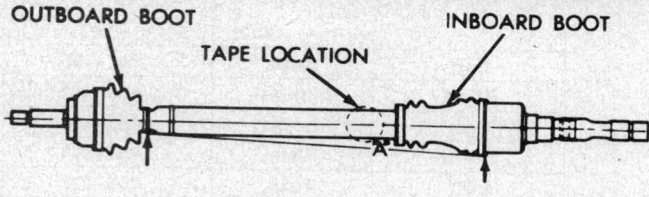

Fig. 4 Driveshaft measurement

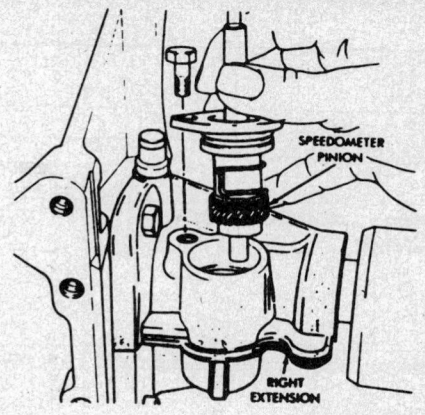

Fig. 3 Speedometer pinion replacement

OUTER CONSTANT VELOCITY JOINT SERVICE

Disassemble

1. Cut boot clamps from boot and discard boot and clamps, **Fig. 10.**
2. Clean grease from joint.
3. **On GKN units,** support shaft in a soft jawed vise, support outer joint and tap with a mallet to dislodge joint from internal circlip installed in a groove at outer end of shaft, **Fig. 11.** Do not remove slinger from housing.
4. **On SSG units,** loosen damper weight bolts and slide weight and boot toward inner joint, then expand circlip with suitable pliers, slide joint from shaft and reinstall damper weight.
5. **On all units,** remove circlip from shaft groove and discard, **Fig. 12.**
6. **On GKN units,** do not remove heavy lock ring from shaft, **Fig. 12,** unless shaft requires replacement.
7. **On all units,** if constant velocity joint was operating satisfactorily and grease does not appear contaminated, proceed to "Assembly" procedure, Step 8.
8. If constant velocity joint is noisy or badly worn, replace entire unit. The repair kit will include boot, clamps, circlip and lubricant. Clean and inspect joint as outlined in the following steps.
9. Clean surplus grease and mark relative position of inner cross, cage and housing with a dab of paint.
10. Hold joint vertically in a soft jawed vise.
11. Press downward on one side of inner race to tilt cage and remove ball from opposite side, **Fig. 13.** If joint is tight, use a hammer and a brass drift to tap inner race. Do not strike cage. Repeat this step until all six balls are removed. A screwdriver may be used to pry balls loose.
12. Tilt cage assembly vertically and position two opposing, elongated cage windows in area between ball grooves. Remove cage and inner race assembly by pulling upward from housing, **Fig. 14.**
13. Rotate inner cross 90° to cage and

ing bar in a vise and hold C/V joint housing on an angle. Gently pull on housing until one of the rollers is free. Continue to hold housing on an angle and continue to pull on the housing until all roller are free.

3. **On SSG units,** use a flathead screwdriver to pry wire ring out of groove and slide tripod from housing, **Fig. 8. When removing housing from tripod, hold rollers in place on the trunnion studs to prevent rollers and needle bearings from falling out. After tripod is out of housing, secure rollers in place with tape.**

4. Remove snap ring from end of shaft, then the tripod using a brass drift.

Inspection

Remove grease from assembly and inspect bearing race and tripod components for wear and damage and replace as necessary. On spring loaded joints inspect spring, spring cup and spherical end of connecting shaft for wear and damage and replace as necessary. **Components of spring loaded and non-spring loaded inner C/V joints cannot be interchanged.**

Assembly

Do not use the GKN boot clamps on the Saginaw hard plastic C/V boots, as these clamps do not have the load capacity to withhold the much greater force needed to clamp plastic boots.

1. **On right side of equal length systems,** slide rubber seal over stub shaft and into groove.
2. **On all models,** slide small end of boot over shaft. On Tubular type shafts, align boot lip with mark on shaft outer diameter. On solid type shafts, position small end of boot in groove on shaft.
3. Place rubber clamp over groove on boot, if equipped.
4. **On GKN units,** install tripod on shaft with non-chamfered face of tripod body facing shaft retainer groove.
5. **On SSG units,** place wire ring retainer over interconnecting shaft.
6. **On all models,** slide tripod on shaft.
7. Lock tripod assembly on shaft by installing snap ring in shaft groove.
8. Distribute ½ of grease provided into boot and remaining amount into housing.
9. Position spring, with spring cup attached to exposed end, into spring pocket, **Fig. 9.** Place a small amount of grease on spring cup, then position housing over tripod. Slip tripod into housing. On GKN units, bend retaining tabs down to original position. On SSG units, install tripod wire retaining ring into position. **On all spring units, ensure tripod is securely retained in housing and spring remains centered in housing spring pocket when tripod is installed and seated in spring cup.**
10. Position boot over boot retaining groove in housing, then install clamp.

Model	Engine	Side	Transaxle	Driveshaft Length	
				Millimeters	**Inches**
1992					
Daytona & LeBaron	3.0L/V6-181	Right	Manual	453–461	17.8–18.1
		Left	Manual	196–204	7.7–8.0
Daytona, LeBaron, Shadow & Sundance	2.5L/4-153 Turbo	Right	Auto	453–461	17.8–18.1
		Left	Auto	189–197	7.4–7.7
		Right	Manual	189–197	7.4–7.7
		Left	Manual	196–204	7.7–8.0
LeBaron Landau, Spirit & Acclaim	2.5L/4-153, 3.0L/V6-181 & 2.5L/4-153 Turbo	Right	Auto	434–444	17.0–17.5
		Left	Auto	176–186	6.9–7.3
	2.5L/4-153	Right	Manual	434–444	17.0–17.5
		Left	Manual	165–175	6.5–6.9
	2.5L/4-153 Turbo	Right	Manual	165–175	6.5–6.9
		Right	Manual	165–175	6.5–6.9
	2.2L/4-135 Turbo III	Right	Manual	194–204	7.6–8.0
		Left	Manual	194–204	7.6–8.0
New Yorker/Salon, Dynasty, Daytona, LeBaron, Shadow & Sundance	2.2L/4-135 & 2.5L/4-153	Right	Auto	452–460	17.8–18.1
		Left	Auto	188–196	7.4–7.7
		Right	Manual	453–461	17.8–18.1
		Left	Manual	196–204	7.7–8.0
	3.0L/V6-181	Right	Auto	453–461	17.8–18.1
		Left	Auto	189–197	7.4–7.7
New Yorker/Salon/Fifth Avenue, Dynasty & Imperial	3.3L/V6-203 & 3.8L/V6-231	Right	Auto	189–197	7.4–7.7
		Left	Auto	189–197	7.4–7.7
1993					
Daytona & LeBaron	3.0L/V6-181	Right	Manual	453–461	17.8–18.1
		Left	Manual	196–204	7.7–8.0
LeBaron/Landau, Spirit & Acclaim	2.5L/4-153	Right	Auto	442–452	17.4–17.8
		Left	Auto	166–176	6.5–6.9
		Right	Manual	442–452	17.4–17.8
		Left	Manual	①	①
	3.0L/V6-181	Right	Auto	171–181	6.7–7.1
		Left	Auto	442–452	17.4–17.8
New Yorker/Salon, Dynasty, Daytona, LeBaron, Shadow & Sundance	2.2L/4-135 & 2.5L/4-153	Right	Auto	452–460	17.8–18.1
		Left	Auto	188–196	7.4–7.7
		Right	Manual	453–461	17.8–18.1
		Left	Manual	196–204	7.7–8.0
	3.0L/V6-181	Right	Auto	453–461	17.8–18.1
		Left	Auto	189–197	7.4–7.7
New Yorker/Salon/Fifth Avenue, Dynasty & Imperial	3.3L/V6-203 & 3.8L/V6-231	Right	Auto	453–461	17.8–18.1
		Left	Auto	189–197	7.4–7.7
1994					
Acclaim & Spirit	2.5L/4-153	Right	Auto	442–452	17.4–17.8
		Left	Auto	166–176	6.5–6.9
		Right	Manual	442–452	17.4–17.8
		Left	Manual	①	①
	3.0L/V6-181	Right	Auto	171–181	6.7–7.1
		Left	Auto	442–452	17.4–17.8

Continued

TYPE 1

Model	Engine	Side	Transaxle	Driveshaft Length	
				Millimeters	Inches
1994-CONTINUED					
LeBaron, Shadow & Sundance	2.5L/4-153	Right	Auto	452–460	17.8–18.1
		Left	Auto	188–196	7.4–7.7
		Right	Manual	453–461	17.8–18.1
		Left	Manual	196–204	7.7–8.0
	3.0L/V6-181	Right	Manual	453–461	17.8–18.1
		Left	Manual	196–204	7.7–8.0
		Right	Auto	453–461	17.8–18.1
		Left	Auto	189–197	7.4–7.7

①—With SSG driveshaft, 6.5–6.9 inches
(165–175 mm); with GKN driveshaft,
6.8–7.0 inches (168–178 mm).

Fig. 5   Driveshaft length specifications. Except Neon

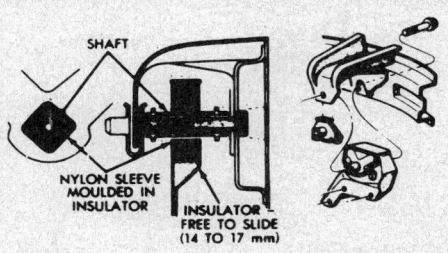

Fig. 6   Left engine mount adjustment

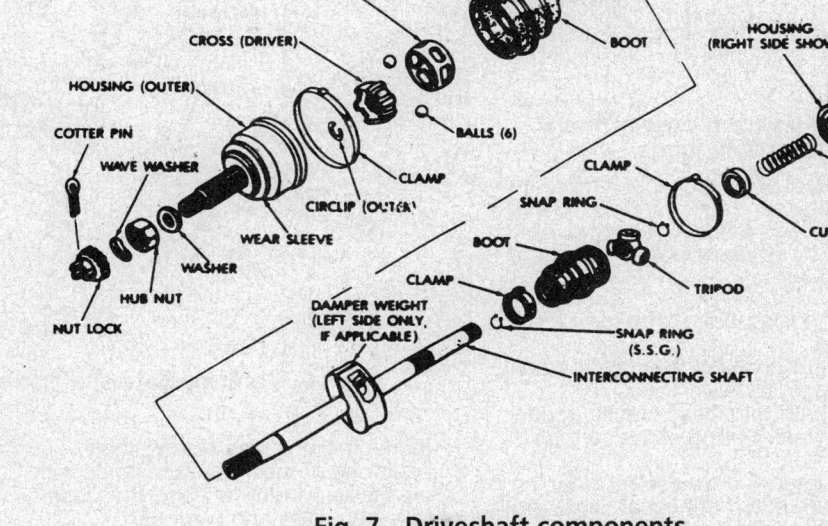

Fig. 7   Driveshaft components

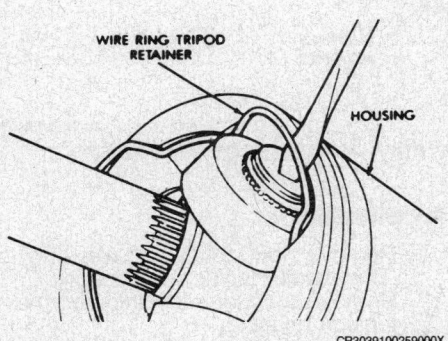

Fig. 8   Tripod from housing removal. SSG inner C/V joint

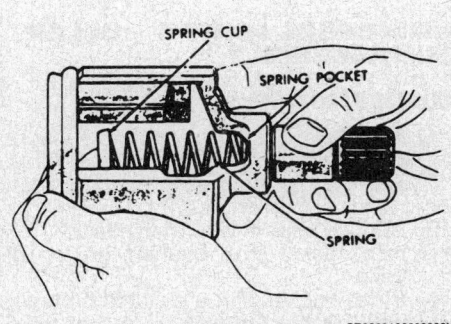

Fig. 9   C/V joint retention spring

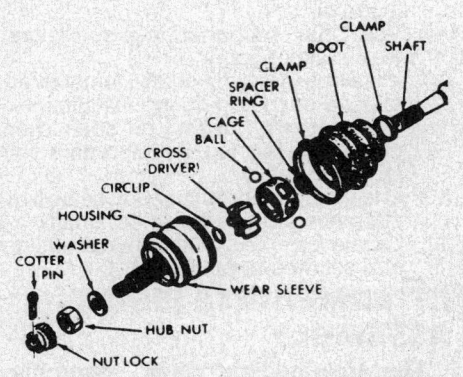

Fig. 10   Disassembled view of outer C/V joint

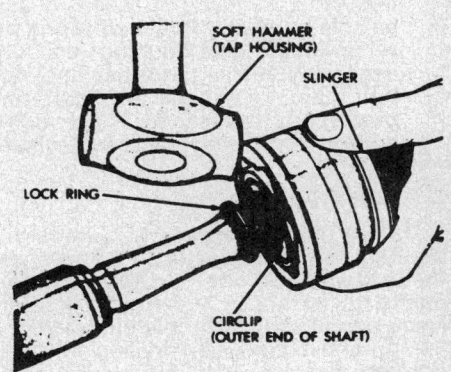

Fig. 11   Outer C/V joint removal from shaft. Except SSG units

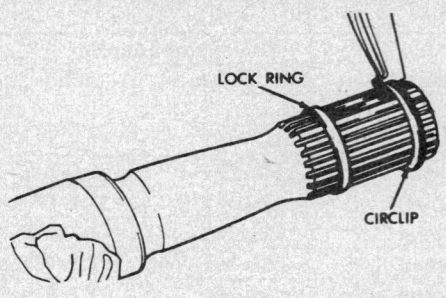

Fig. 12 Outer C/V joint circlip removal

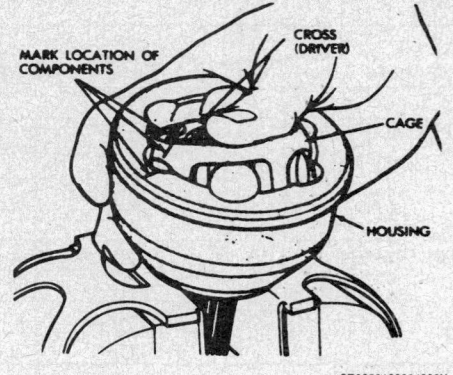

Fig. 13 Outer C/V joint ball removal

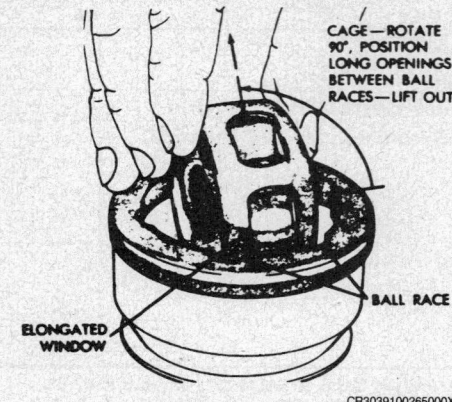

Fig. 14 Outer C/V joint cage & cross assembly removal

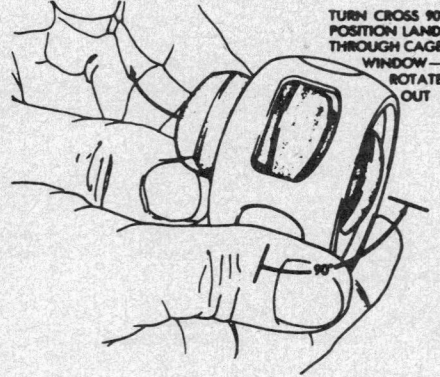

Fig. 15 Cross from cage removal. Outer C/V joints

align one of race spherical lands with an elongated cage window. Raise land into cage window and remove inner race by swinging outward, **Fig. 15.**

Inspection

1. Check housing ball races for excessive wear.
2. Check splined shaft and nut threads for damage.
3. Inspect balls for pitting, cracks, scouring and wear. Dulling of the surface is normal.
4. Inspect cage for excessive wear on inner and outer spherical surfaces, heavy brinnelling of cage, window cracks and chipping.
5. Inspect inner race (cross) for excessive wear or scouring of ball races.
6. If any of the defects listed in Steps 1 through 5, are found, replace C/V assembly as a unit. **Polished areas in races (cross and housing) and on cage spheres are normal and do not indicate a need for joint replacement unless they are suspected of causing noise and vibration.**

Assemble

Do not use the GKN boot clamps on the Saginaw hard plastic C/V boots, as these clamps do not have the load capacity to withhold the much greater force needed to clamp plastic boots.

1. If removed, position wear sleeve on joint housing, then tap sleeve onto housing using seal wear sleeve tool No. C-4698 or equivalent.
2. Lightly oil components, then align

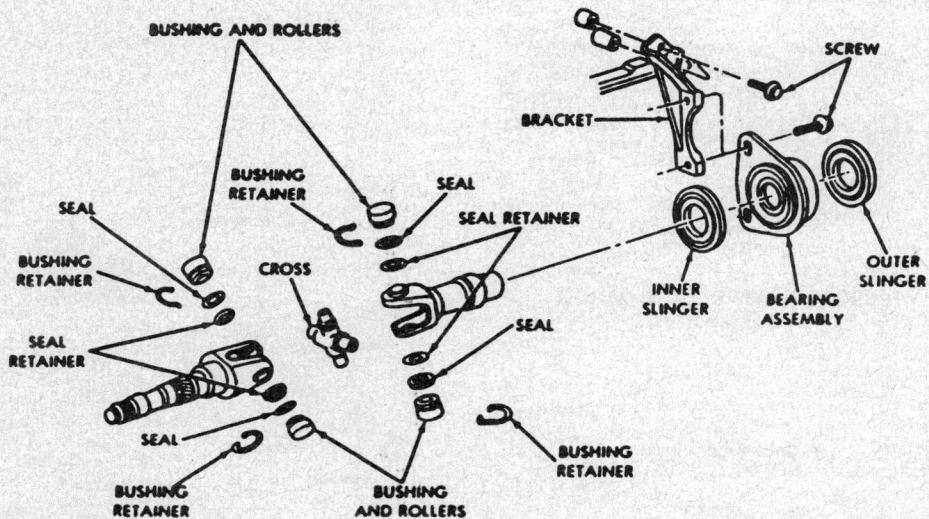

Fig. 16 Intermediate shaft assembly. Turbocharged models

marks made during disassembly.
3. Align one of the inner race lands with elongated window of cage, then insert race into cage and pivot 90°.
4. Align elongated cage windows with housing land, then pivot cage 90°.
5. Lubricate ball races with one packet of grease from kit.
6. Tilt cage and inner race assembly and insert balls.
7. With shaft supported in a soft jawed vise, install boot.
8. Install snap ring on shaft. Do not overexpand snap ring during installation.
9. Position joint housing on shaft, then engage by tapping sharply with a soft faced mallet.
10. Ensure snap ring is properly seated by attempting to pull joint from shaft.
11. Locate large end of boot over housing and secures boot clamps.

INTERMEDIATE SHAFT ASSEMBLY

The intermediate shaft assembly, Fig. 16, used on front wheel drive equal length systems is the same for manual and automatic transaxles.

REMOVAL

1. Remove right driveshaft, referring to "Driveshaft, Replace" procedure.
2. Remove speedometer pinion from extension housing.
3. Remove two screws from bearing assembly bracket to engine block.
4. Remove intermediate shaft assembly from transaxle extension by pulling yoke outward.

UNIVERSAL JOINT & ROLLER SUBASSEMBLY

Disassemble

1. Mark relationship of shafts to insure proper alignment during assembly. Apply penetrating oil to bushing, then remove snap rings.
2. Support yoke in vise, then position 1 1/8 inch socket over bushing on top of yoke.
3. Strike socket with a suitable hammer until bushing moves up out of yoke into socket.
4. Turn assembly in vise and remove remaining bushings in same manner.

Assemble

1. Hold cross in position between yoke ears with one hand and start one bushing assembly into yoke with other hand.
2. Hammer bushing assembly into yoke, then install snap ring.
3. Install remaining bushing assemblies in same manner.

BRACKET, BEARING & SLINGER ASSEMBLY

Disassemble

1. Remove two bearing assembly to support bracket attaching screws, then separate bearing from bracket.
2. Press intermediate shaft out of bearing assembly and outer slinger. **Do not dent or damage inner slinger or** end of stub shaft.
3. If either slinger is damaged, it should be replaced by carefully pressing shaft through slinger. **The bearing assembly is not serviceable and must be replaced as an assembly.**

Assemble

1. Place new slinger on stub shaft, then using a suitable tool, drive slinger down until it bottoms out on shoulder of shaft. Ensure slinger is properly seated.
2. Press bearing assembly onto shaft, leaving a minimum of 1/32 inch clearance between slinger and bearing assembly. **Apply pressure only to inner race of bearing assembly during installation.**
3. Press outer slinger into position using a suitable tool. The slinger must bottom out on shoulder of shaft.

INSTALLATION

1. Attach bracket to bearing assembly and **torque** screws to 21 ft. lbs.
2. Hold stub yoke and install spline into transaxle.
3. Attach bracket to engine, then loosely install attaching screws.
4. Push intermediate shaft assembly into transaxle as far as possible, then **torque** bracket to engine attaching screws to 40 ft. lbs.
5. Apply suitable grease inside spline and pilot bore on bearing end of intermediate shaft.
6. Install speedometer pinion, then the right driveshaft. Refer to "Driveshaft, Replace" procedure.

Type 2

INDEX

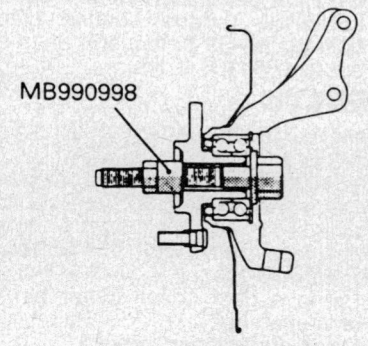

Fig. 1 Wheel bearing support tool installation

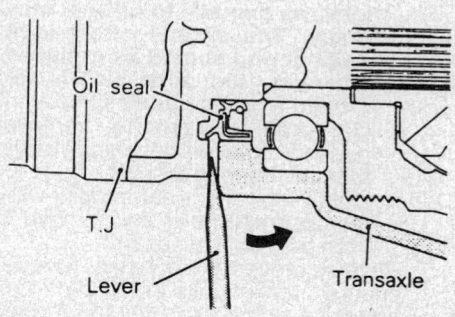

Fig. 2 Front drive axle removal from transaxle case

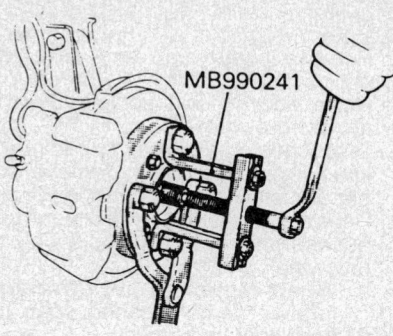

Fig. 3 Pressing front drive axle from hub

DRIVESHAFT
REPLACE

COLT VISTA & SUMMIT WAGON

Front Wheel Drive (FWD)

Do not apply vehicle load to the wheel bearing after removal of the driveshaft. If a load must be applied to the bearing in moving the vehicle, temporarily secure bearing with stub axle replacement tool No. MB990998 or equivalent, Fig. 1.

1. Remove hub dust cap and loosen drive axle nut, then raise and support front of vehicle and remove wheel and tire assembly.
2. Remove undercover, then remove strut bar and ball joint from lower control arm. **Use care not to damage ball joint dust boot.**
3. Drain transaxle fluid.
4. Insert a suitable pry bar between transaxle case and outer case of double offset joint, then withdraw drive axle, **Fig. 2.** Cover drive axle opening in transaxle. When removing drive axle, support at tripod or double offset joint and pull shaft straight out to prevent damage to boot or joint. After disconnecting drive axle from transaxle, support shaft in proper position. **Pry bar should not be inserted more than .28 inch between transaxle case and outer case of offset joint, as damage to oil seal may result. The double offset joint retainer ring should be replaced whenever the drive axle is removed from transaxle case.**
5. Press drive axle, from hub using axle shaft puller tool No. MB990241 or equivalent, **Fig. 3. When pressing drive axle from hub, use care to prevent the spacer from moving out of position.**
6. Reverse procedure to install. Position drive axle so that raised inner diameter of washer is facing nut, then install

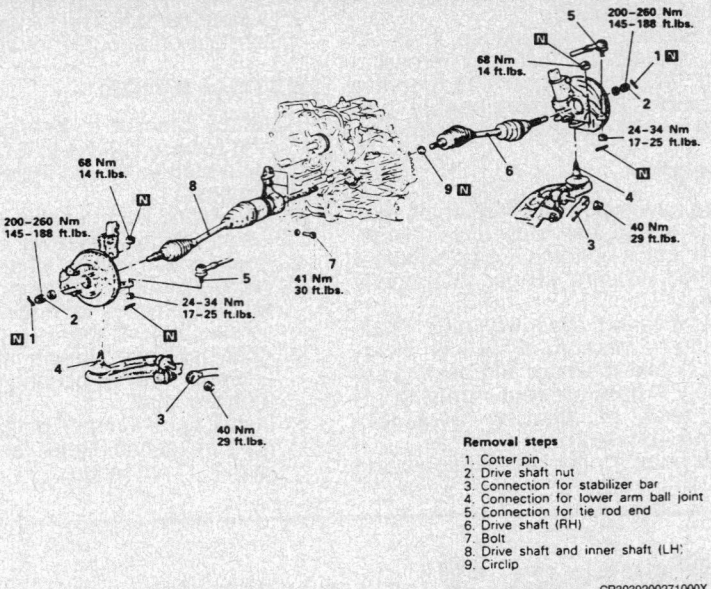

Fig. 4 Driveshaft removal. 1992 Colt Vista & Summit Wagon

Removal steps
1. Cotter pin
2. Drive shaft nut
3. Connection for stabilizer bar
4. Connection for lower arm ball joint
5. Connection for tie rod end
6. Drive shaft (RH)
7. Bolt
8. Drive shaft and inner shaft (LH)
9. Circlip

CR3039200271000X

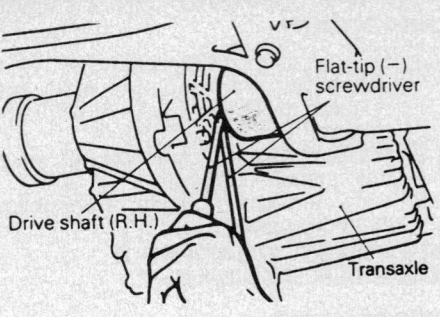

Fig. 5 RH driveshaft inner joint removal

CR3039100272000X

and **torque** drive axle nut to 145-188 ft. lbs.

All Wheel Drive (AWD)

Do not apply vehicle load to the wheel bearing after removal of the driveshaft. If a load must be applied to the bearing in moving the vehicle, temporarily secure bearing with stub axle replacement tool No. MB990998 or equivalent, Fig. 1.

1. Remove center cap and drive axle nut.
2. Raise and support vehicle, then remove front wheel.
3. Disconnect lower arm ball joint and knuckle coupling, then remove strut bar and stabilizer bar from lower arm.
4. Remove driveshaft in numbered sequence shown in **Fig. 4,** noting the following:
   a. **When removing LH driveshaft,** remove center bearing snap ring from bearing bracket.
   b. Lightly tap double offset joint outer race with a wooden hammer and disconnect drive axle from cardan joint assembly.
   c. Disconnect drive axle from bearing bracket.
   d. **On both driveshafts,** press drive axle from hub using axle shaft puller tool No. MB990241 or equivalent, **Fig. 3. When pressing drive axle from hub, use care to prevent the spacer from moving out of position.**
   e. **When removing RH driveshaft,** use two screwdrivers as shown in **Fig. 5.**
   f. **When removing LH driveshaft,** insert a suitable pry bar between transaxle case and outer case of double offset joint, then withdraw drive axle, **Fig. 2.** Cover drive axle opening in transaxle. When removing drive axle, support at tripod or double offset joint and pull shaft straight out to prevent damage to boot or joint. After disconnecting drive axle from transaxle, support shaft in proper position. **Pry bar should not be inserted more than .28 inch between transaxle case and outer case of offset joint, as damage to oil seal may result. The double offset joint retainer ring should be replaced whenever the drive axle is removed from transaxle case.**
   g. **On both driveshafts,** remove bearing bracket attaching bolts, then the bearing bracket.
   h. Lightly tap yoke of cardan joint with a wooden hammer and remove it from transaxle assembly.
5. Reverse procedure to install. **Torque** bearing bracket bolts to 29-39 ft. lbs. and drive axle nut to 145-188 ft. lbs.

COLT & SUMMIT

Do not apply vehicle load to the wheel bearing after removal of the driveshaft. If a load must be applied to the bearing in moving the vehicle, temporarily secure bearing with stub axle replacement tool No. MB990998 or equivalent, Fig. 1.

1. Remove hub nut cotter pin, hub nut and washer, then raise and support vehicle.
2. Remove undercover and center member from vehicle, if so equipped.
3. Remove lower ball joint from steering knuckle, using steering linkage puller No. MB991113 or equivalent.
4. Remove tie rod from steering knuckle using tool No. MB991113 or equivalent.
5. **On drive axles equipped with center bearing,** remove center bearing bracket mounting bolts.

6. **On drive axles not equipped with center bearing,** insert pry bar between transaxle case and driveshaft, then pry drive axle from transaxle case, **Fig. 2.** Remove drive axle from hub using axle shaft puller tool No. MB990241 or equivalent, **Fig. 3.** Do not pull on drive axle or joints will be damaged. Do not insert pry bar further than necessary or damage to oil seal will result.
7. **On drive axle equipped with center bearing,** remove driveshaft from hub using shaft remover tool No. MB990241 or equivalent. Remove driveshaft and innershaft from transaxle by lightly tapping tripod joint with plastic hammer. **Do not pull on drive axle or joints will be damaged.**
8. **On all driveaxles,** reverse procedure to install. **Torque** bearing bracket bolts to 29-39 ft. lbs. and drive axle nut to 145-188 ft. lbs.

STEALTH

Do not apply vehicle load to the wheel bearing after removal of the driveshaft. If a load must be applied to the bearing in moving the vehicle, temporarily secure bearing with stub axle replacement tool No. MB990998 or equivalent, Fig. 1.

1. Remove dust cover, cotter pin and driveshaft nut.
2. Raise and support vehicle.
3. Drain transmission oil.
4. Disconnect lower arm ball joint from knuckle, then remove stabilizer and strut bars from lower arm.
5. **On lefthand driveshaft,** remove bearing bracket attaching bolts.
6. **On righthand driveshaft,** insert suitable pry bar between transmission case and driveshaft, then pry driveshaft from transmission, **Fig. 2. Do not pull on driveshaft and do not insert pry bar deep enough to damage oil seal.**
7. **On lefthand driveshaft,** if innershaft is hard to remove from transaxle, strike center bearing bracket lightly with a plastic hammer.
8. **On all driveshafts,** using tool No. MB990241 or equivalent, remove driveshaft from hub, **Fig. 2.**
9. Reverse procedure to install, noting the following:

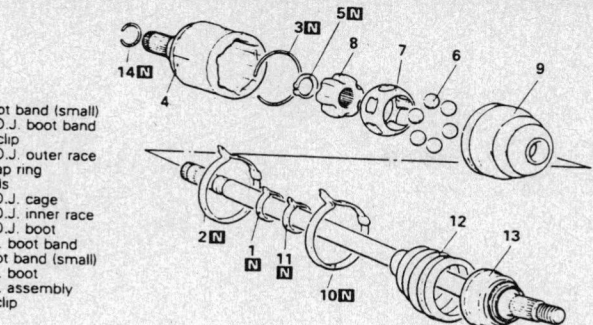

1. Boot band (small)
2. D.O.J. boot band
3. Circlip
4. D.O.J. outer race
5. Snap ring
6. Balls
7. D.O.J. cage
8. D.O.J. inner race
9. D.O.J. boot
10. B.J. boot band
11. Boot band (small)
12. B.J. boot
13. B.J. assembly
14. Circlip

N : Non-reusable parts
B.J. : Birfield Joint
D.O.J. : Double Offset Joint

CR3039100273000X

Fig. 6   Exploded view of double offset joint type front drive axle

a. Ensure driveshaft washer is correctly installed.
b. Lower vehicle to ground, then attach and adjust driveshaft nut, **torquing** to 144-188 ft. lbs.
c. If cotter pin holes do not line up, tighten bolt without exceeding **torque** of 188 ft. lbs., until holes line up.
d. Install cotter pin. Always use new cotter pins.
e. Refill transaxle to proper level.

DRIVESHAFT SERVICE

COLT/SUMMIT & COLT VISTA/SUMMIT WAGON W/TWO WHEEL DRIVE

DOUBLE OFFSET JOINT TYPE

When servicing the drive axle, do not disassemble the Birfield bell type constant velocity joint, as components on this type joint are precision fitted and are replaced only as a unit.

Disassemble

1. Remove Double Offset Joint (DOJ) boot bands, then remove circlip using a suitable screwdriver, **Fig. 6**.
2. Remove DOJ outer race from DOJ joint assembly.
3. Remove snap ring, then remove DOJ inner race, cage and balls as an assembly. Clean bearing assembly without disassembling them.
4. Wind tape around drive axle splines, then remove DOJ and Birfield joint boot band and slide boots from drive axle. When inspecting Birfield joint, note amount of grease removed for reassembly.

Assemble

A special grease containing Molybdenum is used to lubricate the drive axle double offset joint and the Birfield joint. This special grease is included in the drive axle repair kit and must be used.

1. Wrap tape around drive axle splines to prevent damage to boots, then install Birfield joint and DOJ boots.

2. Apply special grease to DOJ joint assembly.
3. Install DOJ joint assembly on drive axle with chamfered side of cage facing splined end of shaft, then install snap ring.
4. Apply 1.4-2.1 ounces of special Molybdenum grease to double offset joint outer race, then position outer race on drive axle.
5. Apply an additional .7-1.4 ounce of special Molybdenum grease to DOJ boot, then install clip.
6. Add amount of special Molybdenum grease to Birfield joint as removed during disassembly and inspection.
7. Install boots and boot bands for each joint. When installing boot bands for DOJ, position bands, **Fig. 7**, so that dimension A is 3.5 inches on two wheel drive models or 3.3 inches on four wheel drive models.

TRIPOD JOINT TYPE DRIVESHAFT

Disassemble

When servicing the drive axle, do not disassemble the Rzeppa type constant velocity joint, as components of this type joint are precision fitted and are replaced only as a unit.

1. Remove boot clamps, then remove boot from tripod joint housing and position on drive axle, **Fig. 8 and 9**.
2. Pull drive axle from tripod joint housing, then remove snap ring and lift tripod joint spider from housing. Clean tripod joint spider and check for wear and damage. Also check joint needle roller bearings for smooth operation. **Do not disassemble tripod joint spider.**
3. Wind tape around drive axle splines, then remove bands for Rzeppa type joint and remove boots from drive axle. If Rzeppa joint is to be reused, do not wipe away grease. Check grease for contamination and clean and replace grease only if necessary. Note amount of grease removed for use during reassembly.

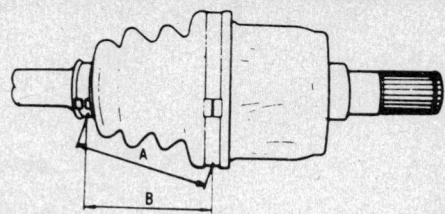

CR3039100274000X

Fig. 7   Double offset joint or tripod joint boot length measurement

4. **On models with innershaft,** continue disassembly as follows:
   a. Using press and support fixture No. MB991248 or equivalent, press innershaft and seal plate out of Tripod case.
   b. Using two inch steel pipe as support, **Fig. 10**, press innershaft from center bearing support.
   c. Using screwdriver, remove driveshaft side dust seal, then using same steel pipe press out center bearing and differential side dust seal.

Assemble

A special grease is used to lubricate the drive axle tripod joint and Rzeppa joint. This grease is included in the drive axle repair kit and must be used.

1. Press fit center bearing into center bearing support, then lubricate and press fit dust seals into center bearing.
2. Press fit innershaft into center bearing, then the innershaft assembly into Tripod case.
3. Apply grease to drive axle, then install boots.
4. Position tripod joint spider on drive axle, then install snap ring.
5. Apply 2.8-3.2 ounces of special grease to tripod joint housing, then insert drive axle and spider into housing.
6. Apply another 2.8-3.2 ounces of special grease to tripod joint boot.
7. Apply as much special grease as removed to Rzeppa joint, if necessary.
8. Install bands and boots for each joint. When installing boot bands for tripod joint, bands must be positioned 3.1 inches apart (dimension A), **Fig. 7**.

COLT VISTA & SUMMIT WAGON W/FOUR WHEEL DRIVE

Driveshafts are identical between two wheel drive and four wheel drive, except for the center bearing support assembly on the left side four wheel drive driveshaft.

The following procedures are only for the left side drive axle. Refer to "Colt/Summit & Colt Vista/Summit Wagon w/Two Wheel Drive" for service procedures not cover in this section.

Center Bearing, Replace

1. Remove double offset joint outer race from drive axle.

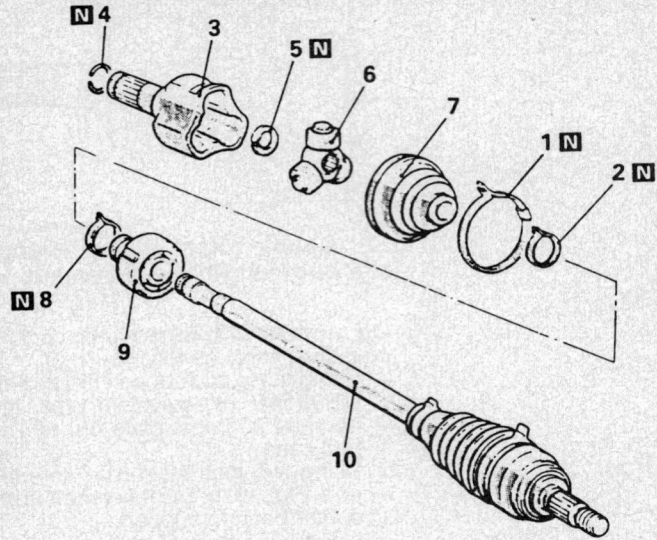

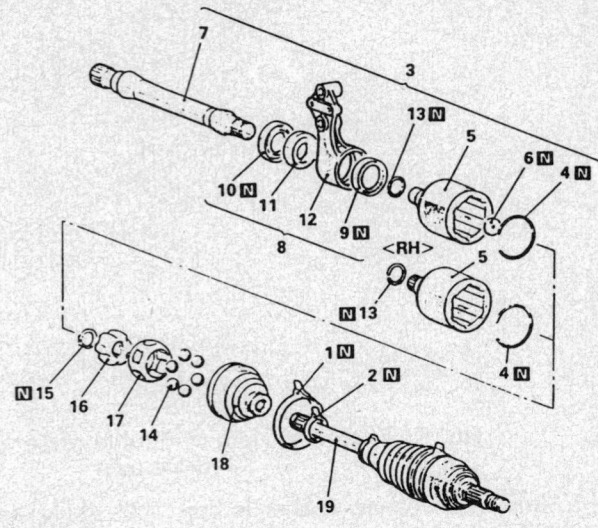

Disassembly steps

1. T.J. boot band (large)
2. T.J. boot band (small)
3. T.J. case
4. Circlip
5. Snap ring
6. Spider assembly
7. T.J. boot
8. Damper band
9. Dynamic damper
10. R.J. assembly <2.4L Engine>
    B.J. assembly <1.8L Engine>

Caution
Do not disassemble the B.J. or R.J. assembly.

CR3039100275000X

Fig. 8   Exploded view of tripod type front drive axle. Less innershaft

Disassembly steps

1. D.O.J. boot band (large)
2. D.O.J. boot band (small)
3. D.O.J. outer race and inner shaft assembly
4. Circlip
5. D.O.J. outer race
6. Seal plate
7. Inner shaft
8. Bracket assembly
9. Outer dust seal
10. Inner dust seal
11. Bearing
12. Bracket
13. Circlip
14. Balls
15. Snap ring
16. D.O.J. inner race
17. D.O.J. cage
18. D.O.J. boot
19. B.J. assembly

CR3039100276000X

Fig. 9   Exploded view of tripod type front drive axle. With innershaft

2. Using a suitable grinder, partially grind the certain point of the circumference of the bearing retainer to a thickness of .04–.06 inch.
3. Using a suitable hammer and chisel, break then remove bearing retainer. When the break is made in the bearing retainer, tap the chisel in between the bearing and bearing retainer and pry to remove the bearing retainer. **Do not damage the drive axle in any way.**
4. Remove center bearing assembly using bearing remover MB990560 or equivalent and a press.
5. To install proceed as follows:
   a. After passing the snap ring through the double offset joint outer race, use press tool MB990560 or equivalent and a press to install center bearing assembly onto the shaft of the double offset joint outer race.
   b. Face polished surface of the bearing retainer toward the bearing side and, after placing it onto the shaft of the double offset joint outer face, use the tool mentioned previously and the press to install bearing retainer.
   c. Install drive axle onto double offset joint outer race.

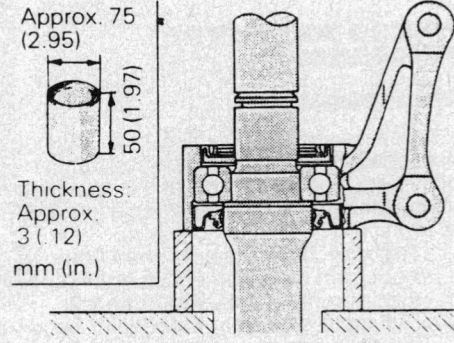

Approx. 75 (2.95)
50 (1.97)
Thickness: Approx. 3 (.12) mm (in.)

CR3039100277000X

Fig. 10   Innershaft removal

Center Bearing Dust Seal, Replace

1. Using a suitable screwdriver, remove dust seal from bearing bracket assembly.
2. Using a handle and adapter installer tools No. MB990938 and 990930 or equivalents and a mallet, press dust seal in until seal is flush with bearing bracket end.

3. Coat inside circumference of seal with suitable grease.

STEALTH

1. Refer to **Fig. 11**, for disassembly procedures noting the following:
   a. Remove inner shaft assembly, with seal plate, from the tripot joint case as shown in **Fig. 12**, using special tool MB991248 or equivalent.
   b. Use special tool MB990810-01 or equivalent, when removing inner shaft from center bearing bracket.
   c. Remove center bearing from center bracket using special tool MB990938-01, and MB990930-01 or equivalent, as shown in **Fig. 13**.
   d. Wrap splines on driveshaft with tape, so that the tripot joint and birfield joint boots are not damaged when removed. Remove tripot joint and birfield joint boots from shaft.
2. Reverse procedures to install noting the following:
   a. Apply grease to rear surface of dust seals.
   b. Press inner seal using pullers, special tool MB990890-01 or equivalent, and outer seal using MB990934-01, and MB990890-01 or equivalent, as shown in **Fig. 14**.
   c. Install tripot joint case and inner shaft assembly, applying multi purpose grease to the inner shaft spline.
   d. Press seal plate into tripot joint

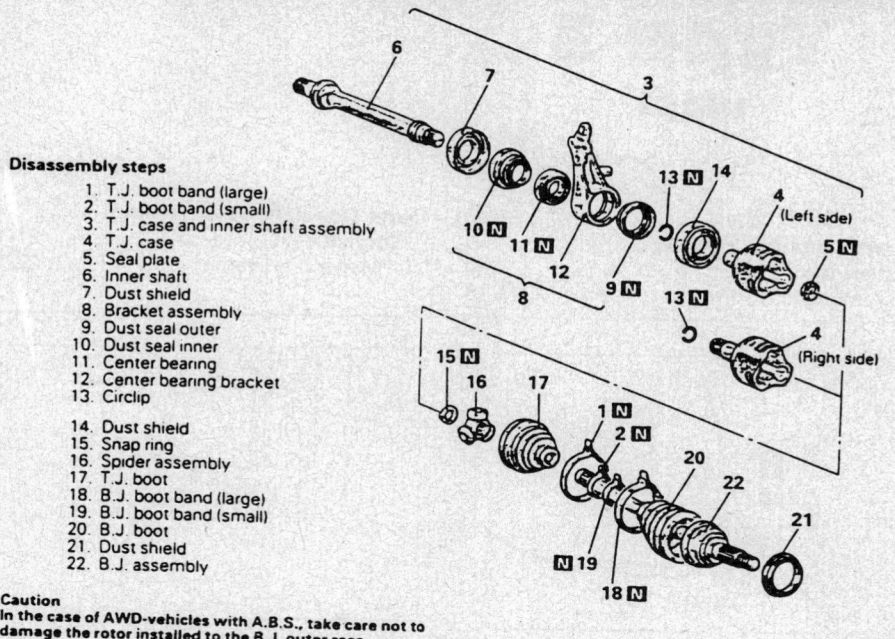

Disassembly steps

1. T.J. boot band (large)
2. T.J. boot band (small)
3. T.J. case and inner shaft assembly
4. T.J. case
5. Seal plate
6. Inner shaft
7. Dust shield
8. Bracket assembly
9. Dust seal outer
10. Dust seal inner
11. Center bearing
12. Center bearing bracket
13. Circlip
14. Dust shield
15. Snap ring
16. Spider assembly
17. T.J. boot
18. B.J. boot band (large)
19. B.J. boot band (small)
20. B.J. boot
21. Dust shield
22. B.J. assembly

Caution
In the case of AWD-vehicles with A.B.S., take care not to damage the rotor installed to the B.J. outer race.

Fig. 11   Exploded view of front drive axle. Stealth

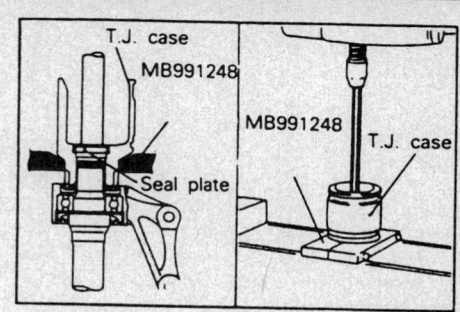

Fig. 12   Innershaft removal

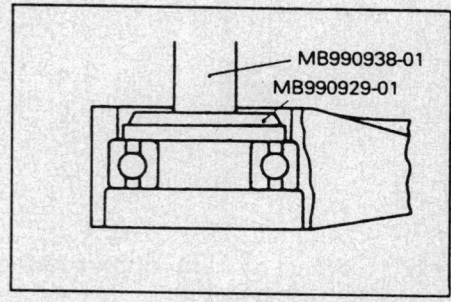

Fig. 13   Center bearing removal from bracket. Stealth

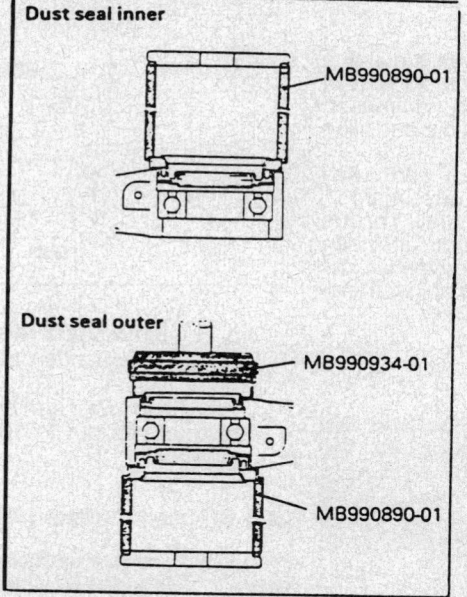

Fig. 14   Dust seals installation. Stealth

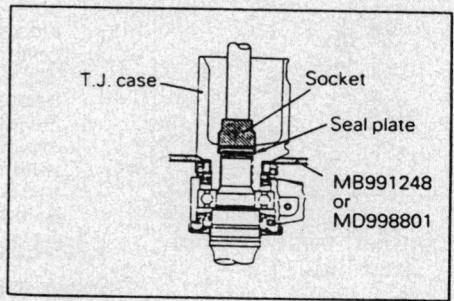

Fig. 15   Seal plate installation into tripot joint case. Stealth

case as shown in **Fig. 15,** using special tool MB9911248 or equivalent.
e. Set distance between tripot joint boot bands to 3.23-3.47 inch, then secure boot bands.

Type 3

INDEX

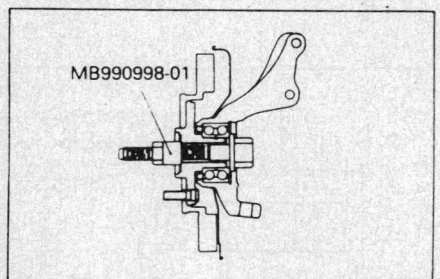

Fig. 1   Wheel bearing support tool installation

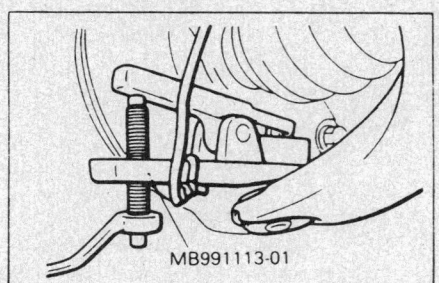

Fig. 2   Ball joint removal from steering knuckle

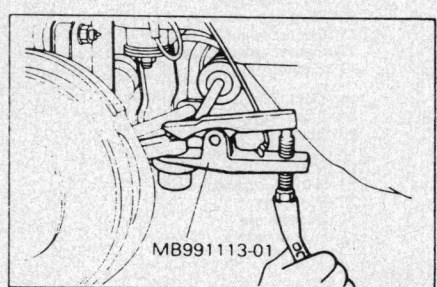

Fig. 3   Tie rod removal from steering knuckle

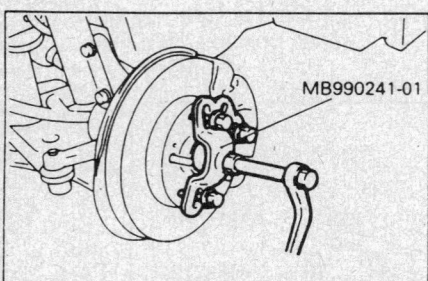

Fig. 4   Driveshaft removal from front hub

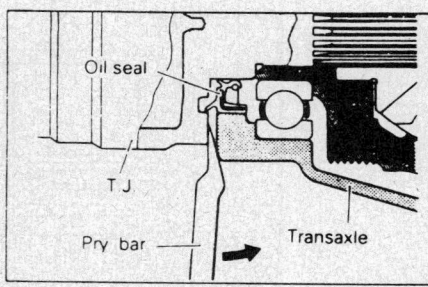

Fig. 5   Driveshaft removal from transaxle case

DRIVESHAFT
REPLACE

MONACO & PREMIER

Use caution when servicing driveshafts. Do not strike the end of the shaft or drop it. Inspect C/V boots and replace if damaged or worn.

1. Raise and support vehicle.
2. Remove tire and wheel assembly, then the brake caliper. Do not disconnect brake caliper hose or suspend caliper from hose.
3. Using suitable tool to hold wheel hub in place, remove driveshaft nut.
4. Loosen driveshaft in hub. If driveshaft does not come loose by hand, use hub puller No. T.Av. 1050 or equivalent. **Do not attempt to loosen driveshaft by striking it with a hammer.**
5. Using a punch, remove driveshaft roll pin.
6. Remove steering knuckle to strut attaching bolts. **Do not turn bolts, as they are splined just under bolt**

head. Hold bolt head with a suitable wrench, then unscrew nut to end of bolt. Tap nut with brass hammer to loosen bolt, then remove nut and slide bolt from knuckle.

7. Tilt steering knuckle out and away from strut, then remove driveshaft.
8. Reverse procedure to install. **Torque** steering knuckle to strut attaching nuts to 123 ft. lbs. and driveshaft nut to 181 ft. lbs. Check and adjust transaxle fluid level if necessary.

LASER & TALON
Two Wheel Drive

Do not apply vehicle load to the wheel bearing after removal of the driveshaft. If a load must be applied to the bearing in moving the vehicle, temporarily secure bearing with stub axle replacement tool No. MB990998-01 or equivalent, Fig. 1.

1. Loosen drive axle nut, then raise and support front of vehicle and remove wheel and tire assembly.
2. Using special tool No. MB991113-01, **Fig. 2,** disconnect lower arm ball joint from knuckle.
3. Using special tool No. MB991113-01, **Fig. 3,** disconnect tie rod end from knuckle.
4. Press driveshaft from hub using shaft puller No. MB990241-01, **Fig. 4.**
5. Insert a suitable pry bar between the transaxle case and the driveshaft, and pry the shaft from the transaxle, **Fig. 5. Do not pull on the shaft, as damage to the joint may result. Pry bar should not be inserted too deep, as damage to the oil seal may result.**
6. Reverse procedure to install. Lower vehicle to the ground and tighten

knuckle to lower arm ball joint nut, and **torque** axle nut to 188 ft. lbs. maximum.

All Wheel Drive (AWD)

Do not apply vehicle load to the wheel bearing after removal of the driveshaft. If a load must be applied to the bearing in moving the vehicle, temporarily secure bearing with stub axle replacement tool No. MB990998-01 or equivalent, Fig. 1.

The following procedure is only for the left side drive axle. Refer to "Two Wheel Drive" for right side drive axle replacement procedure.

1. Loosen drive axle nut, then raise and support front of vehicle and remove wheel and tire assembly.
2. Using special tool No. MB991113-01, **Fig. 2,** disconnect lower arm ball joint from knuckle.
3. Using special tool No. MB991113-01, **Fig. 3,** disconnect tie rod end from knuckle.
4. Press driveshaft and inner shaft as-

DISASSEMBLY AND REASSEMBLY

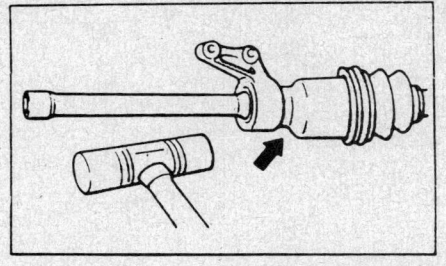

CR3039100291000X

Fig. 6   Driveshaft & inner shaft assembly removal from transaxle case.

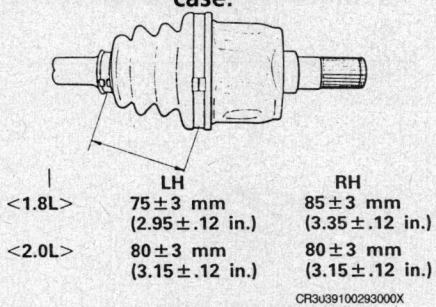

	LH	RH
<1.8L>	75±3 mm (2.95±.12 in.)	85±3 mm (3.35±.12 in.)
<2.0L>	80±3 mm (3.15±.12 in.)	80±3 mm (3.15±.12 in.)

CR3u39100293000X

Fig. 8   Tripod joint boot installation. Laser & Talon Except 4WD LH shaft

sembly from hub using shaft puller No. MB990241-01, **Fig. 4.**
5. Remove driveshaft and inner shaft assembly from transaxle by lightly tapping the tripod joint case with a plastic hammer, **Fig. 6.**
6. Reverse procedure to install. Lower vehicle to the ground, then tighten knuckle to lower arm ball joint nut, and **torque** axle nut to 188 ft. lbs. maximum.

DRIVESHAFT SERVICE

LASER & TALON

Two Wheel Drive

Disassemble shaft assembly components in order as they appear, **Fig. 7,** noting the following:
1. Remove snap ring from shaft using suitable snap ring pliers.
2. Remove spider assembly from shaft.
3. Clean spider assembly and check for wear or damage. Do not disassemble spider assembly, if the tripod joint case of the shaft assembly is bent, the joint may be damaged. Use care in handling the shaft.
4. Wrap vinyl tape around splines of the shaft to prevent damage to boots during removal.
5. Check driveshaft for damage, bending or corrosion.
6. Check spline for wear or damage.
7. Check for entry of water or foreign material into birfield joint.
8. Check spider assembly for roller rotation, wear, or corrosion.
9. Check the groove inside the tripod joint case for wear or corrosion.
10. Check boots for deterioration, damage, or cracking.

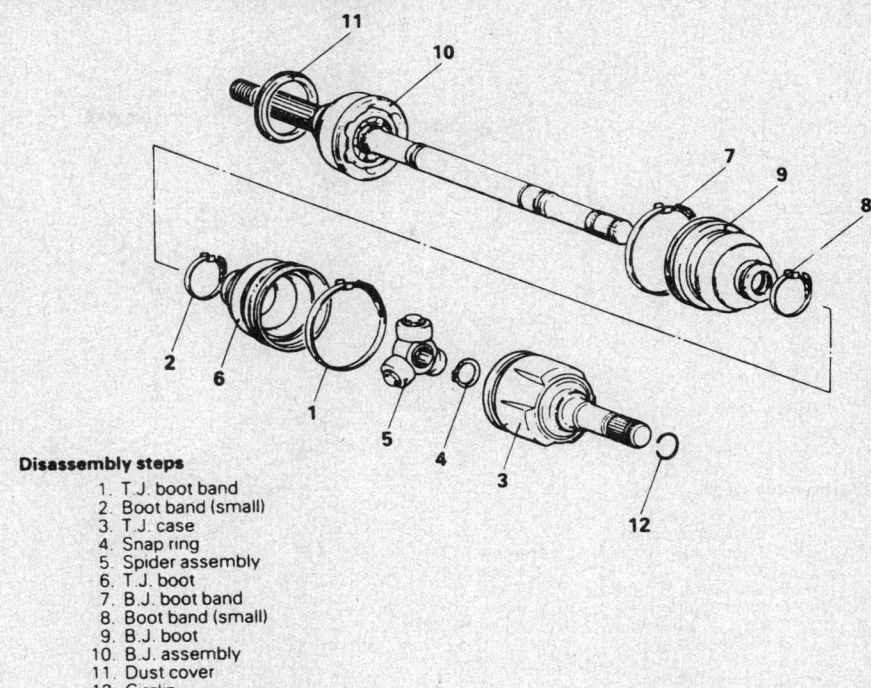

Disassembly steps
1. T.J. boot band
2. Boot band (small)
3. T.J. case
4. Snap ring
5. Spider assembly
6. T.J. boot
7. B.J. boot band
8. Boot band (small)
9. B.J. boot
10. B.J. assembly
11. Dust cover
12. Circlip

CR3039100292000X

Fig. 7   Exploded view of Birfield joint & tripod type driveshaft assembly. Laser & Talon Except 4WD LH shaft

11. Assemble in reverse order of disassembly. A special grease is used to lubricate the joint assemblies. Each joint requires 3.9 oz. of grease.
12. Install bands and boots for each joint. When installing boot bands for tripod joint, set bands at specified distance, **Fig. 8,** in order to adjust the amount of air inside the boot.

Four Wheel Drive

The following procedure is only for the left side drive axle. Refer to "Two Wheel Drive" for service procedure on right side drive axle.

Disassemble shaft assembly components in order as they appear, **Fig. 9,** noting the following:
1. Separate outer part of shaft from inner shaft assembly.
2. Remove snap ring from shaft using suitable snap ring pliers.
3. Remove spider assembly from shaft.
4. Clean spider assembly and check for wear or damage. Do not disassemble spider assembly, if the tripod joint case of the shaft assembly is bent, the joint may be damaged. Use care in handling the shaft.
5. Wrap vinyl tape around splines of the shaft to prevent damage to boots during removal.
6. Do not disassemble the birfield joint assembly, it is not serviceable.
7. Using special tool No. MB991248 or MD998801 or equivalent, **Fig. 10,** press inner shaft assembly along with seal plate from the tripod joint case.
8. Using special tool No. MB990810-01

or equivalent, **Fig. 11,** remove inner shaft from center bearing bracket.
9. Using special tools No. MB990938-01 and MB990929-01 or equivalent, **Fig. 12,** remove center bearing from bracket.
10. Check driveshaft for damage, bending, or corrosion.
11. Check inner shaft for damage, bending, or corrosion.
12. Check driveshaft spline for wear or damage.
13. Check inner shaft spline for wear or damage.
14. Check for entry of water or foreign material into birfield joint.
15. Check spider assembly for roller rotation, wear, or corrosion.
16. Check the groove inside the tripod joint case for wear or corrosion.
17. Check boots for deterioration, damage, or cracking.
18. Check the center bearing for seizure, discoloration, or roughness of rolling.
19. Check the dust cover for damage or deterioration.
20. Assemble in reverse order, noting the following:
a. Apply multipurpose grease to the center bearing and inside of the center bearing bracket.
b. Apply multipurpose grease to the inside lip of the bearing dust seals. Ensure that grease does not adhere to anything outside the lip.
c. When installing dust seals, ensure that seal surface is even with surface of bearing bracket.
d. Use a suitable pipe to support the inner race of the center bearing

DISASSEMBLY AND REASSEMBLY

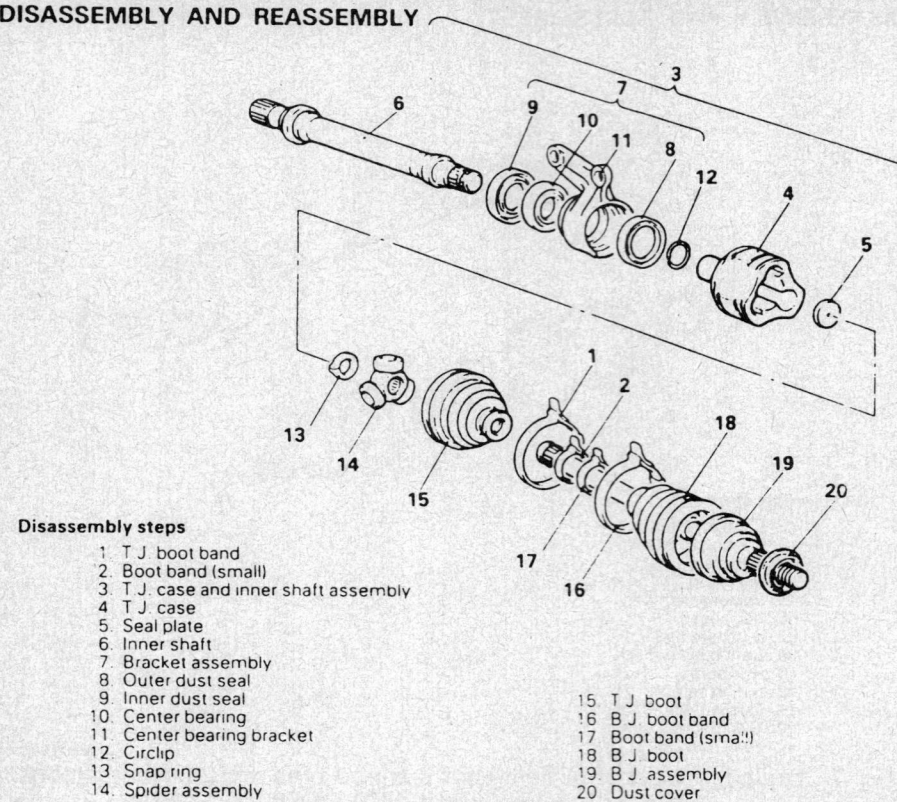

Disassembly steps

1. T.J. boot band
2. Boot band (small)
3. T.J. case and inner shaft assembly
4. T.J. case
5. Seal plate
6. Inner shaft
7. Bracket assembly
8. Outer dust seal
9. Inner dust seal
10. Center bearing
11. Center bearing bracket
12. Circlip
13. Snap ring
14. Spider assembly
15. T.J. boot
16. B.J. boot band
17. Boot band (small)
18. B.J. boot
19. B.J. assembly
20. Dust cover

Fig. 9 Exploded view of birfield joint, tripod type driveshaft & inner shaft assembly. Laser & Talon 4WD LH shaft

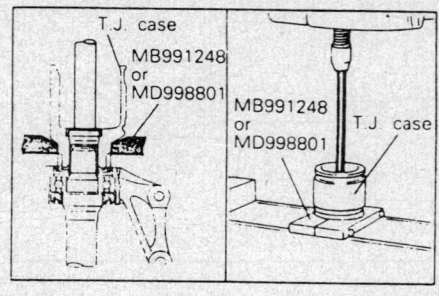

Fig. 10 Inner shaft assembly removal from tripod joint case

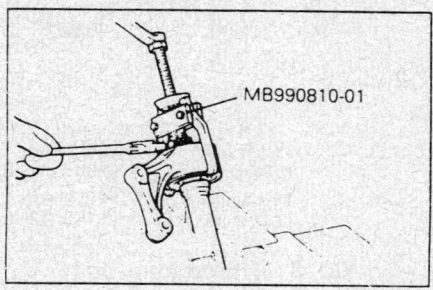

Fig. 11 Inner shaft removal from center bearing bracket

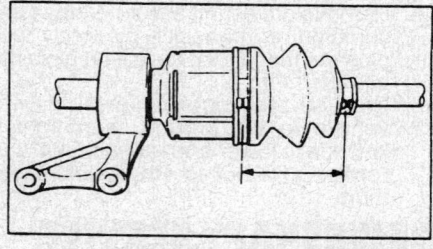

Fig. 14 Tripod joint boot installation. Laser & Talon 4WD LH shaft

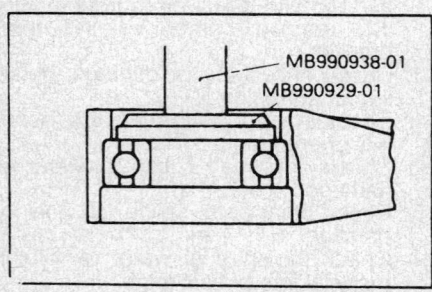

Fig. 12 Center bearing removal from center bearing bracket

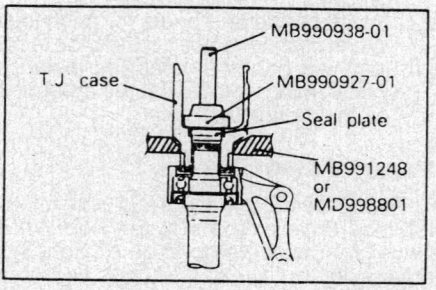

Fig. 13 Seal plate installation into tripod joint case

when pressing inner shaft into place.

e. Apply multipurpose grease to the spline of the inner shaft, then press into the tripod joint case.

f. Using special tools No. MB990938-01, MB990927-01, and MB991248 or MD998801 or equivalents, **Fig. 13**, press seal plate into tripod joint case.

g. A special grease is used to lubricate the joint assemblies, the tripod joint uses 3.9 oz., half at the joint and half in the boot. The birfield joint uses 3.2 oz., half at the joint half in the boot. The grease is supplied in the repair kit.

h. When installing boot bands on the tripod joint, set the bands at a dis-

tance of 3.23–3.47 inch, **Fig. 14**, to adjust the amount of air inside the boot.

INNER CONSTANT VELOCITY JOINT SERVICE
MONACO & PREMIER
Remove & Disassemble

1. Remove driveshaft as described under "Driveshaft, Replace."
2. Cut and remove boot clamps, then slide boot from C/V joint housing, **Fig. 15**. If boot is to be reused, avoid damaging boot when cutting clamps.
3. Remove C/V joint housing by pulling it straight off the tripod.

4. Using snap ring pliers, spread plastic retaining ring (D), then tap tripod off shaft with plastic mallet, **Fig. 16**.
5. Remove boot from shaft. Inspect C/V joint housing, boot, plastic retaining ring, tripod and tripod bearings. Replace worn or damaged components.

Assemble & Install

1. Install new retaining ring by pushing non-tapered end into tripod until it snaps into groove.
2. Install boot on driveshaft.
3. Tap tripod onto driveshaft until retaining ring seats in shaft groove.
4. Lubricate C/V joint housing, tripod bearings and the interior of boot with grease supplied in service kit, then slide housing onto tripod and bearings.
5. Seat boot on housing and driveshaft, then bleed air from boot by inserting a smooth rod (T) between boot and housing, **Fig. 17**. **Do not damage boot while purging air.**

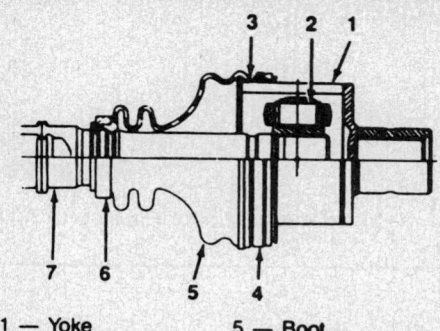

1 — Yoke
2 — Spider
3 — Metal Cover
4 — Retaining Clamp
5 — Boot
6 — Retaining Ring
7 — Driveshaft

CR3039100283000X

Fig. 15 Inner C/V joint assembly. Monaco & Premier

6. Using boot clamp pliers No. T.Av 1034 or equivalent, install and tighten boot clamps.
7. Install driveshaft as described under "Driveshaft, Replace."

OUTER CONSTANT VELOCITY JOINT SERVICE

MONACO & PREMIER
Removal & Disassembly

1. Remove driveshaft as described under "Driveshaft, Replace."

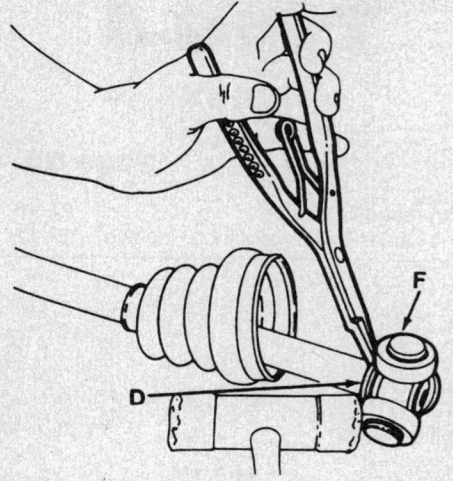

CR3039100284000X

Fig. 16 Trunnion from driveshaft removal. Monaco & Premier

2. Cut and remove boot clamps, then slide boot rearward for access to plastic retaining ring. If boot is to be reused, avoid damaging boot when cutting clamps.
3. Using snap ring pliers, spread plastic retaining ring, then tap C/V joint with plastic mallet to free shaft from retaining ring.
4. Remove C/V joint, then slide boot off shaft. Inspect retaining ring, and replace if necessary.

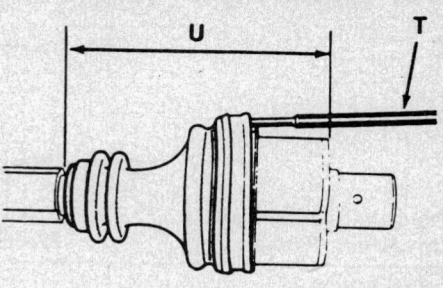

CR3039100285000X

Fig. 17 Inner C/V boot installation. Monaco & Premier

Installation

1. Install new retaining ring with tapered end into C/V joint and segmented end onto driveshaft.
2. Slide boot onto driveshaft.
3. Lubricate C/V joint with grease supplied in service kit. Align driveshaft with plastic retaining ring and C/V joint, then tap joint onto shaft until retaining ring snaps into place.
4. Position boot in clamp groves of C/V joint and driveshaft, then using boot clamps pliers No. T.Av 1034 or equivalent, install and tighten boot clamps.
5. Install driveshaft as described under "Driveshaft, Replace."

Type 4

INDEX

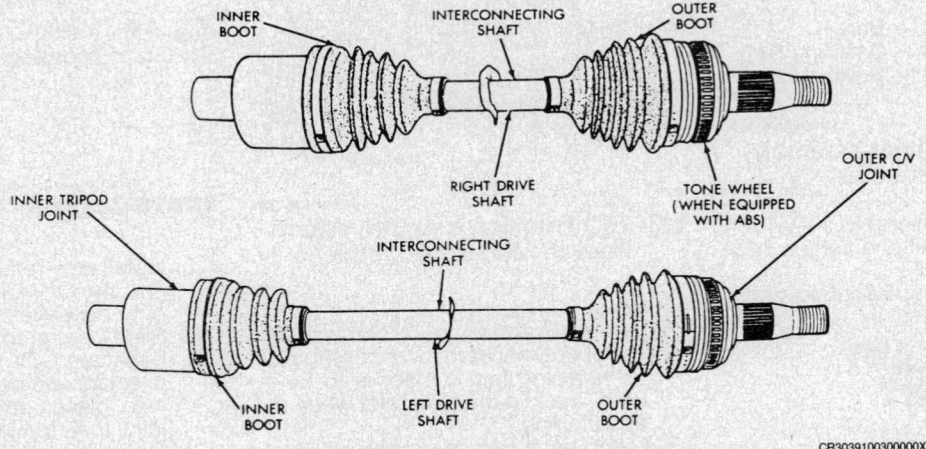

Fig. 1   Driveshaft identification

DRIVESHAFT IDENTIFICATION

These models use an "unequal length" system. The "unequal length" system has a short solid interconnecting shaft on right side with a longer tubular interconnecting shaft on right, **Fig. 1.**

DRIVESHAFT REPLACE

1. Raise and support vehicle.
2. Remove wheel and tire assemblies.
3. Remove brake caliper assembly as outlined under the "Disc Brake" section.
4. Remove brake rotor by pulling it straight off mounting studs.
5. Remove speed sensor cable routing bracket from strut assembly.
6. Remove stub axle and hub retaining nut.
7. Insert suitable pry bar between transmission case and driveshaft, then pry driveshaft from transmission, **Fig. 2. Do not pull on driveshaft and do not insert pry bar deep enough to damage oil seal. Only pry inner joint from retaining snap ring. Do not attempt to remove inner tripod joint from transaxle stub shaft.**
8. Support steering knuckle then disconnect and remove strut assembly from steering knuckle.
9. Hold outer CV joint assembly with one hand, grasp steering knuckle with the other hand and rotate it out and to the rear of the vehicle, until outer CV joint clears hub and bearing assembly.

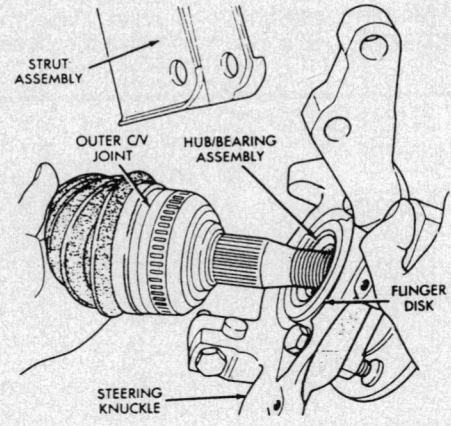

Fig. 2   Outer CV joint from hub removal/installation

10. Remove driveshaft inner tripod joint from transaxle stub shaft. **Do not pull on interconnecting shaft to remove inner tripod joint from stub shaft.**
11. Reverse procedure to install, noting the following:
    a. Install new O-ring seal and tripod joint retaining circlip.
    b. When installing outer CV joint into hub and bearing assembly, do not allow flinger disk, **Fig. 3**, to become damaged.
    c. **Torque** strut attaching bolts to 125 ft. lbs. **Strut bolts have a serrated shaft so do not turn bolts in steering knuckle. Turn nut on bolts do not turn bolts.**
    d. Apply vehicle brakes and **torque** new hub and bearing stub shaft nut to 70-90 ft. lbs. **Do not exceed the 90 ft. lbs. as damage to driveshaft may occur.**

DRIVESHAFT SERVICE

The driveshaft assembly, **Fig. 3**, is a non-serviceable item, except for the inner and outer driveshaft boots. If any failure of internal components is diagnosed during a road test or disassembly, the driveshaft will need to replaced as an assembly.

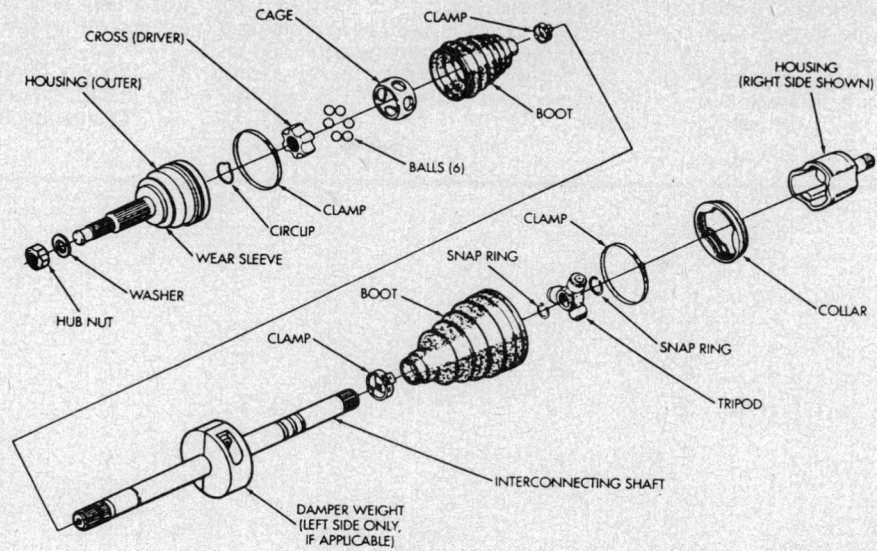

Fig. 3   Exploded view of driveshaft assembly

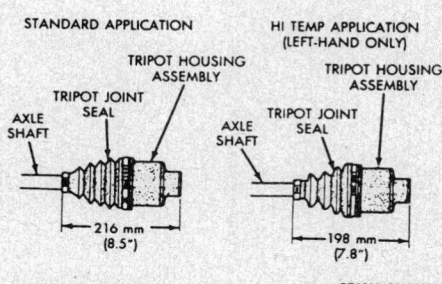

Fig. 4   Proper inner tripod joint stroke position

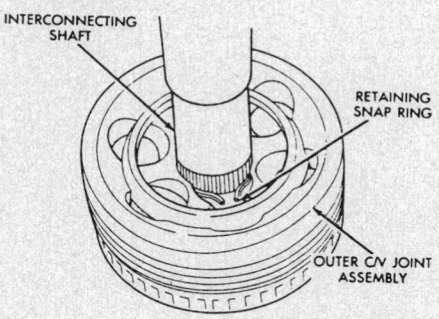

Fig. 5   Outer CV joint retaining snap ring location

INNER DRIVESHAFT BOOT, REPLACE

Removal

1. Remove driveshaft as outlined under "Driveshaft, Replace."
2. Remove inner joint boot clamps then slide boot down interconnecting shaft.
3. Remove interconnecting shaft and spider assembly out of joint housing.
4. Remove snap ring then spider assembly from interconnecting shaft using a brass drift if necessary. **Do not hit the outer tripod bearings when removing spider assembly.**
5. Remove joint boot from interconnecting shaft.
6. Clean and inspect spider assembly, tripod joint housing and interconnecting shaft for any signs of excessive wear. **If any excessive wear is present, replacement of entire driveshaft will be necessary.**

Installation

Two different types of boots are used on these models, a high temperature, soft and pliable type and a normal temperature, stiff and rigid type. The replacement boot must be the same type which was removed.

1. Install new boot clamps and boot onto interconnecting shaft.
2. Install spider assembly onto interconnecting shaft then the retaining snap ring. **Ensure retaining snap ring is fully installed.**
3. Distribute 1/2 the amount of grease provided in boot service package into tripod housing and the remaining amount into boot.
4. Install spider assembly into tripod housing.
5. Position boot over boot retaining groove on interconnecting shaft and install boot retaining clamp using Crimper tool No. C-4975 or equivalent.
6. Position boot into tripod housing retaining groove.
7. Prior to crimping boot clamp, the inner tripod joint must be at correct stroke position as shown in **Fig. 4.** This ensures proper amount of air is inside sealing boot before clamp is crimped. **Failure to perform this step will result in inner boot failure.**
8. After adjusting stroke position, crimp boot clamp using Crimper tool.
9. Install driveshaft as outlined under "Driveshaft, Replace."

OUTER DRIVESHAFT BOOT, REPLACE

Removal

1. Remove driveshaft as outlined under "Driveshaft, Replace."
2. Remove inner joint boot clamps then slide boot down interconnecting shaft.
3. Remove grease to expose outer CV joint retaining ring, **Fig. 5.**
4. Spread retaining ring and slide CV joint assembly off interconnecting shaft.
5. Remove and discard failed boot and clamps.
6. Clean and inspect spider assembly, CV joint and interconnecting shaft for any signs of excessive wear. **If any excessive wear is present, replacement of the entire driveshaft will be necessary.**

Installation

1. Install new boot clamps and boot onto interconnecting shaft.
2. Install CV joint onto interconnecting

shaft by pushing shaft into CV joint until retaining snap ring is seated in groove on shaft, **Fig. 5.**

3. Distribute $1/2$ the amount of grease provided in boot service package into CV joint assembly and remaining amount into boot.

4. Position boot over boot retaining grove on interconnecting shaft and install boot retaining clamp using Crimper tool No. C-4975 or equivalent.

5. Position boot over boot retaining grove on CV joint housing and install boot retaining clamp using Crimper tool No. C-4975 or equivalent.

6. Install driveshaft as outlined under "Driveshaft, Replace."

ALL WHEEL DRIVE SYSTEM

NOTE: Refer To "Front Drive Axles" For Procedures Not Found In This Section.

INDEX

Symptom	Probable cause	Remedy
AXLE SHAFT Noise while wheels are rotating	Brake drag Bent axle shaft Worn or scarred axle shaft bearing	Replace
Grease leakage	Worn or damaged oil seal Malfunction of bearing seal	Replace
DRIVE SHAFT Noise	Wear, play or seizure of ball joint Excessive drive shaft spline looseness	Replace
DIFFERENTIAL (CONVENTIONAL DIFFERENTIAL) Constant noise	Improper final drive gear tooth contact adjustment Loose or damaged side bearing Loose, worn or damaged drive pinion bearing	Correct or replace
	Worn drive gear, drive pinion Worn side gear spacer or pinion shaft Deformed drive gear or differential case Damaged gear	Replace
	Foreign material	Eliminate the foreign material and check; replace the parts if necessary
	Insufficient oil	Replenish
Gear noise while driving	Poor gear engagement Improper gear adjustment Improper drive pinion preload adjustment	Correct or replace
	Damaged gear	Replace
	Foreign material	Eliminate the foreign material and check; replace the parts if necessary
	Insufficient oil	Replenish
Gear noise while coasting	Improper drive pinion preload adjustment Damaged gear	Correct or replace Replace
Bearing noise while driving or coasting	Cracked or damaged drive pinion rear bearing	Replace
Noise while turning	Loose side bearing Damaged side gear, pinion gear or pinion shaft	Replace
Heat	Insufficient gear backlash Excessive preload	Adjust
	Insufficient oil	Replenish
Oil leakage	Clogged vent plug	Clean or replace
	Cover insufficiently tightened Seal malfunction	Retighten, apply sealant, or replace the gasket
	Worn or damaged oil seal	Replace
	Excessive oil	Adjust the oil level
DIFFERENTIAL (LIMITED SLIP DIFFERENTIAL) Abnormal noise during driving or gear changing	Excessive final drive gear backlash Insufficient drive pinion preload	Adjust
	Excessive differential gear backlash	Adjust or replace
	Worn spline of a side gear	Replace
	Loose companion flange self-locking nut	Retighten or replace

CR3039100178010X

Fig. 1   All Wheel Drive (AWD) troubleshooting chart (Part 1 of 2)

DESCRIPTION

This system used on Colt Vista, Laser, Stealth, Summit Wagon and Talon is a full time All Wheel Drive (AWD) system. It has an optional limited slip differential for increased traction. The main components used in this system are the transfer case, rear drive axle, axle shafts and driveshaft.

TROUBLESHOOTING

Refer to **Fig. 1** when troubleshooting system malfunctions.

AXLE SHAFT
REPLACE

LASER, STEALTH & TALON

1. Raise and support vehicle, then remove tire and wheel assembly.
2. **On models with Anti-lock Brake System (ABS),** remove ABS rear speed sensor and O-ring, **Fig. 2.** Exercise care when removing ABS sensor, do not allow sensor pole piece tip to come in contact with other parts.
3. **On all models,** remove brake caliper and suspend with wire.
4. Using end yoke holder tool No. MB990767, or equivalent, to secure axle shaft, remove companion shaft self-locking nut, **Fig. 3.**
5. Using slide hammer tool No. C-637 and axle puller tool No. CT-1003, or equivalents, remove axle shaft assembly.
6. Reverse procedure to install, on Laser and Talon, **torque** axle shaft self-locking nut to 116–159 ft. lbs. On Stealth, **torque** axle shaft self-locking nut to 188–217 ft. lbs.

COLT VISTA

Refer to "Axle Hub, Replace" for procedure.

Symptom	Probable cause	Remedy
NOTE In addition to a malfunction of the differential carrier components, abnormal noise can also be caused by the universal joint of the propeller shaft, the axle shafts, the wheel bearings, etc. Before disassembling any parts, take all possibilities into consideration and confirm the source of the noise.		
Abnormal noise when cornering	Damaged differential gears Damaged pinion shaft	Replace
	Insufficient gear oil quantity	Replenish
Gear noise	Improper final drive gear tooth contact adjustment	Adjust or replace
	Incorrect final drive gear backlash Improper drive pinion preload adjustment	Adjust
	Damaged, broken, and/or seized tooth surfaces of the drive gear and drive pinion Damaged, broken, and/or seized drive pinion bearings Damaged, broken, and/or seized side bearings Damaged differential case Inferior gear oil	Replace
	Insufficient gear oil quantity	Replenish
NOTE Noise from the engine, muffler vibration, transaxle, propeller shaft, wheel bearings, tires, body, etc., is easily mistaken as being caused by malfunctions in the differential carrier components. Be extremely careful and attentive when performing the driving test, etc. Test methods to confirm the source of the abnormal noise include: coasting acceleration, constant speed driving, raising the rear wheels on a jack, etc. Use the method most appropriate to the circumstances.		
Gear oil leakage	Worn or damaged front oil seal, or an improperly installed oil seal Damaged gasket	Replace
	Loose companion flange self-locking nut	Retighten or replace
	Loose filler or drain plug	Retighten or apply adhesive
	Clogged or damaged vent plug	Clean or replace
Seizure	Insufficient final drive gear backlash Excessive drive pinion preload Excessive side bearing preload Insufficient differential gear backlash Excessive clutch plate preload	Adjust
	Inferior gear oil	Replace
	Insufficient gear oil quantity	Replenish
NOTE In the event of seizure, disassemble and replace the parts involved, and also be sure to check all components for any irregularities and repair or replace as necessary.		
Break down	Incorrect final drive gear backlash Insufficient drive pinion preload Insufficient side bearing preload Excessive differential gear backlash	Adjust
	Loose drive gear clamping bolts	Retighten
NOTE In addition to disassembling and replacing the failed parts, be sure to check all components for irregularities and repair or replace as necessary.		
The limited slip differential does not function (on snow, mud, ice, etc.)	The limited slip device is damaged	Disassemble, check the functioning, and replace the damaged parts

CR3039100178020X

Fig. 1 All Wheel Drive (AWD) troubleshooting chart (Part 2 of 2)

AXLE SHAFT SERVICE

LASER, STEALTH & TALON

Disassemble

1. Using bearing removal tool No. MB990560, or equivalent, remove outer bearing and dust cover from axle shaft, **Fig. 4.**
2. Using installer handle tool No. C-4171 and bearing/oil seal removal tool No. MB990928, or equivalents, remove inner bearing and oil seal from axle shaft trailing arm.

Inspection

1. Check companion flange for wear or damage.
2. Check dust cover for deformation or damage.
3. Check wheel bearings for burning, discoloration or rough rotation.
4. Check oil seal and axle shaft for cracking, wear or damage.

Assemble

1. Using installer handle tool No. C-4171 and bearing installer tool No. MB990931, or equivalents, press inner bearing onto trailing arm.

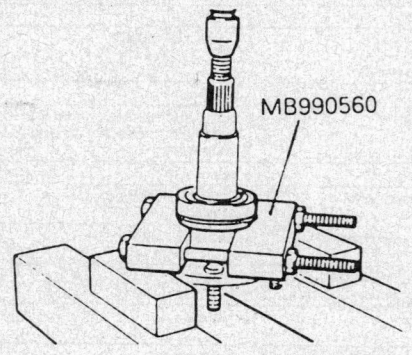

CR3039100192000X

Fig. 4 Outer bearing removal from axle shaft

2. Apply suitable multipurpose grease to lip of new oil seal. Using oil seal installation tool No. MB990799 and a plastic hammer, or equivalents, gradually and evenly press oil seal onto trailing arm with depression of oil seal facing upward, **Fig. 5,** until it contacts shoulder on inside of inner arm.
3. Position inner dust cover as shown in **Fig. 6.** With oil seal installation tool

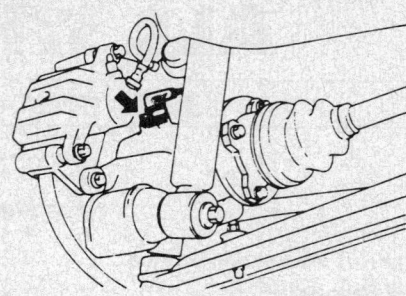

CR3039400353000X

Fig. 2 ABS rear speed sensor removal. Stealth

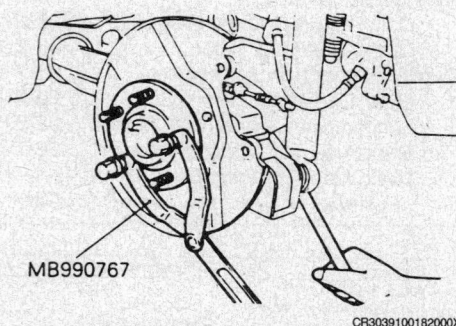

MB990767

CR3039100182000X

Fig. 3 Axle shaft self-locking nut removal

No. MB990799 and plastic hammer, or equivalents, gradually and evenly press fit dust cover until it contacts axle shaft shoulder.
4. Position outer dust cover with depression facing upward as shown in **Fig. 7.** With dust cover installation tool No. MB990799 and plastic hammer, or equivalents, gradually and evenly press fit dust cover onto axle shaft.
5. Apply multipurpose grease around entire circumference of inner side of outer bearing seal lip. Using bearing installation tool No. MB990560, or equivalent, press fit outer bearing to axle shaft so that the bearing lip surface is facing towards the axle shaft flange as shown in **Fig. 8.**

COLT VISTA & SUMMIT WAGON

Refer to "Axle Hub, Replace " for procedure.

DRIVESHAFT
REPLACE

EXCEPT COLT VISTA & SUMMIT WAGON

1. Raise and support vehicle.
2. Remove companion flange to driveshaft bolts.
3. Using a suitable prying tool, pry driveshaft out of differential carrier.

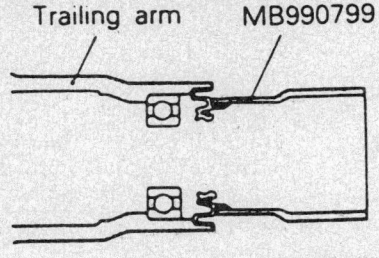

Fig. 5   Oil seal installation

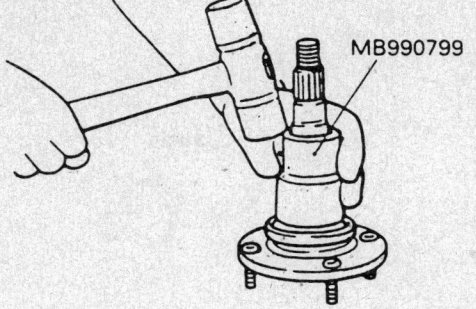

Fig. 6   Inner dust cover installation

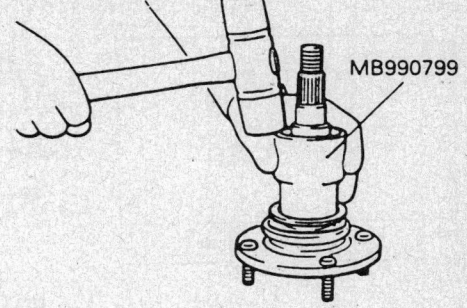

Fig. 7   Outer dust cover installation

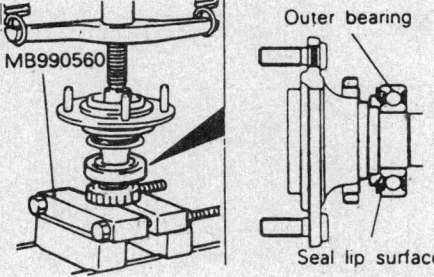

Fig. 8   Outer bearing installation

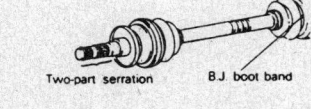

Item	Drive shaft (left)	Drive shaft (right)
B.J. boot band identification color	Yellow	Orange

Fig. 9   Driveshaft identification. Laser & Talon

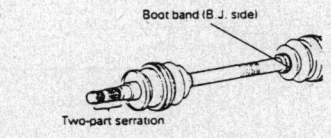

Item	Drive shaft	
	LH	RH
Boot band (B.J. side) identification color	White	Blue

Fig. 10   Driveshaft identification. Stealth

4. Remove circlip from driveshaft and oil seal from differential carrier.
5. Reverse procedure to install, noting the following:
   a. **Use caution to ensure differential carrier oil seal is not damaged by driveshaft spline.**
   b. **On Laser, Talon and Stealth models,** driveshafts are of different length. Driveshafts can be distinguished from each other by identification color of boot band C, **Figs. 9 and 10.**
   c. On all models, ensure there is no oil or grease on threaded portion of companion flange and driveshaft attaching bolt and nut. **Torque** driveshaft to companion flange bolts to 40–47 ft. lbs.

COLT VISTA & SUMMIT WAGON

1. Raise and support vehicle.
2. Use spanner wrench tool No. MB990767, or equivalent, to lock hub while removing driveshaft retaining nut. **Do not apply vehicle weight to the wheel bearing while loosening shaft nut. If vehicle is to be moved after removal of driveshaft, install bolt tool No. MB990998, or equivalent, to support bearing.**
3. Remove companion flange to differential carrier bolts. Support driveshaft and press driveshaft out of rear axle hub using rear axle puller and spanner wrench tool Nos. MB990241 and MB990767, or equivalents.
4. Inspect driveshaft boots for damage or deterioration.
5. Reverse procedure to install, **torquing** companion flange bolts to 40–47 ft. lbs. and driveshaft nut to 145–188 ft. lbs.

DRIVESHAFT SERVICE
COLT VISTA & SUMMIT WAGON
Disassemble

1. Remove circlip from end of driveshaft, **Fig. 11.**
2. Remove boot bands B and C, then the circlip and D.O.J. outer race.
3. Remove snap ring with suitable snap ring pliers as shown in **Fig. 12,** then D.O.J. inner race, cage and balls as a unit. **Be careful that balls do not drop out of cage. If balls do drop out, press them back into D.O.J. cage with D.O.J. inner race.**
4. Wipe any remaining grease off of driveshaft spline, then remove boot bands A and C.
5. Remove D.O.J. and B.J. boots. **If boots are to be reused, wrap splined portion of driveshaft with vinyl tape before removing boots.**
6. Remove dust cover, driveshaft and B.J. **Do not disassemble B.J.**

Inspection

1. Check driveshaft for damage, bending or corrosion.
2. Check driveshaft spline for wear or damage.
3. Check B.J. for entry of water or foreign material.
4. Check D.O.J outer race for damage or corrosion.
5. Check D.O.J. cage, balls and inner race for damage, corrosion or wear.

Assemble

1. Assemble driveshaft and B.J., then install dust cover.
2. Wrap vinyl tape around driveshaft spline, then insert driveshaft in B.J.

boot, boot bands A, C, C, B and D.O.J. boot in that sequence, **Fig. 13.**
3. Fill inside of B.J. and B.J. boot with grease included in the driveshaft repair kit. **The grease in the repair kit should be divided into two equal portions for the B.J. and B.J. boot. This is a special type of grease, ensure no other type of grease comes in contact with the joint.**
4. Secure B.J. boot with boot bands A and C to driveshaft and B.J. **Ensure B.J. is at a zero angle with driveshaft to ensure the boot contains the correct amount of air.**
5. Apply repair kit grease to D.O.J. cage, balls and inner race as shown in **Fig. 14.**
6. Install cage, balls and inner race onto driveshaft, then using snap ring pliers, fit snap ring securely into groove in shaft, **Fig. 12.**
7. Fill D.O.J. outer race with repair kit grease, then fit driveshaft into D.O.J. outer race.
8. Fill more grease into D.O.J. outer race after it is installed on driveshaft, then install circlip onto D.O.J. outer race.
9. Assemble D.O.J. boot to D.O.J. outer race, then secure boot to driveshaft with boot band C.
10. Place boot band B on D.O.J. boot. **Do not secure boot band B at this time.**
11. Set D.O.J. boot bands from 2¾–3¼ inches apart as shown in **Fig. 15,** then tighten boot band C securely.
12. Pull part of D.O.J. boot away from D.O.J. outer race to allow pressure to escape from boot, then tighten boot band B securely to D.O.J. outer race.

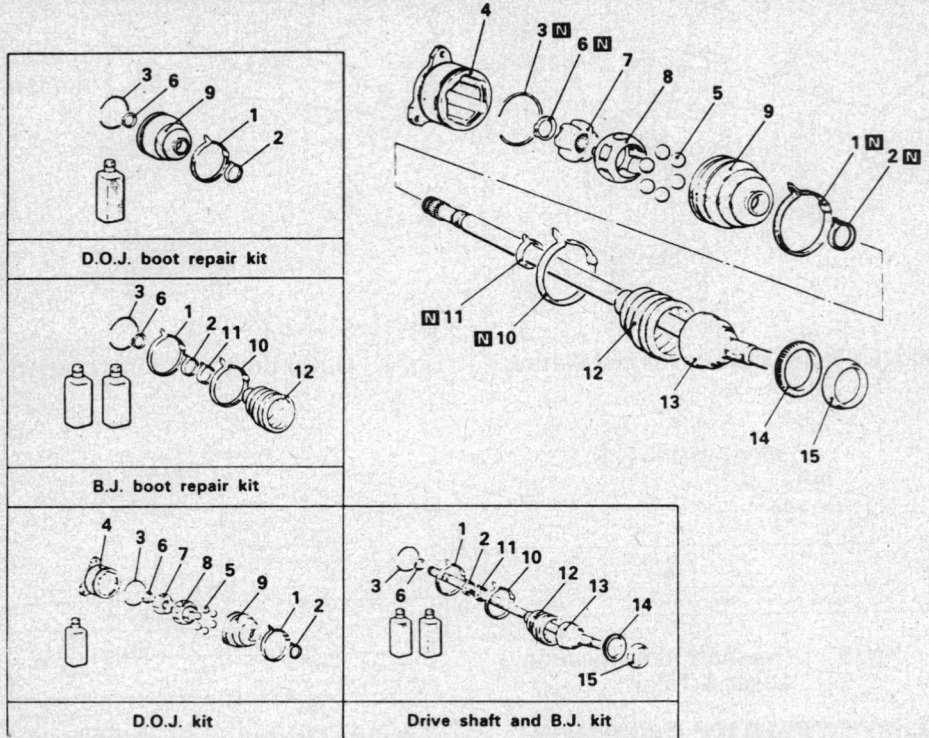

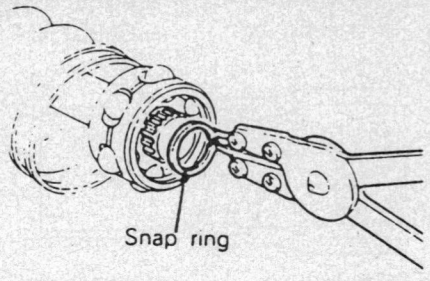

Fig. 12 Snap ring replacement & installation. Colt Vista

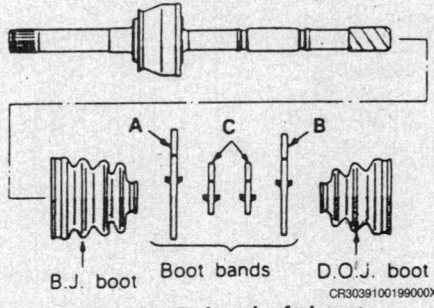

Fig. 13 Driveshaft boot installation. Colt Vista

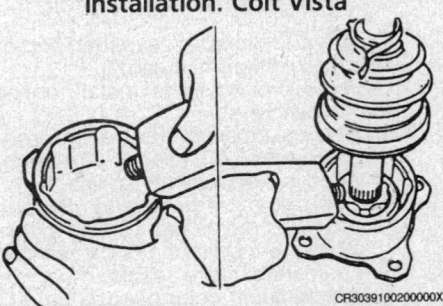

Fig. 14 Applying grease to D.O.J. cage, balls & inner race. Colt Vista

Disassembly steps
1. Boot band (B)
2. Boot band (C)
3. Circlip
4. D.O.J. outer race
5. Balls
6. Snap ring
7. D.O.J. inner race
8. D.O.J. cage
9. D.O.J. boot
10. Boot band (A)
11. Boot band (C)
12. B.J. boot
13. B.J. assembly
14. Rear rotor <Vehicles with ABS>
15. Dust cover

Reassembly steps
13. B.J. assembly
14. Rear rotor <Vehicles with ABS>
15. Dust cover
12. B.J. boot
10. Boot band (A)
11. Boot band (C)
2. Boot band (C)
1. Boot band (B)
9. D.O.J. boot
8. D.O.J. cage
7. D.O.J. inner race
6. Snap ring
5. Balls
4. D.O.J. outer race
3. Circlip

NOTE
(1) B.J.: Birfield Joint
(2) D.O.J.: Double Offset Joint

Caution
Do not disassemble the B.J. assembly.

Fig. 11 Exploded view of driveshaft. Colt Vista & Summit Wagon

STEALTH, LASER & TALON
Disassemble

1. Remove Tripod Joint (TJ) boot bands, **Fig. 16.**
2. Remove TJ case.
3. Remove snap ring off TJ end of driveshaft.
4. Remove spider assembly off driveshaft. **Do not disassemble spider assembly.**
5. Wrap vinyl tape around splines of driveshaft then remove TJ boot.
6. Remove Birfield Joint (BJ) bands.
7. Wrap vinyl tape around splines of driveshaft then remove BJ joint boot.
8. Remove BJ joint. **Do not disassemble BJ joint.**

Inspection

1. Check driveshaft for damage, bending or corrosion.
2. Check driveshaft spline for wear or damage.
3. Check B.J. for entry of water or foreign material.
4. Check spider assembly for roller rotation, wear or corrosion.
5. Check B.J. outer race for damage or corrosion.
6. Check boots for damage, cracking or wear.

Assemble

Reverse disassembly procedure to assemble, noting the following:
1. Wrap vinyl tape around spline on

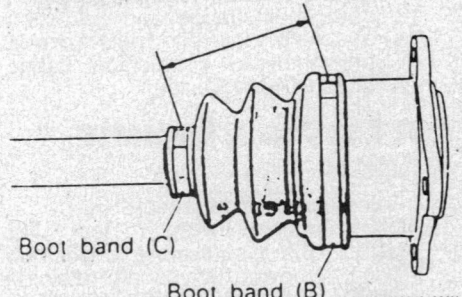

Fig. 15 Driveshaft boot band installation. Colt Vista

driveshaft then install BJ and TJ boots.
2. Fill inside of BJ and BJ boot with half of grease included in repair kit.
3. Secure boot bands with driveshaft at a 0° angle.
4. Apply grease to spider assembly then install spider assembly with chamfered spline end first.
5. Install TJ on driveshaft.
6. Set TJ boot bands 3.23-4.47 inches apart to adjust amount of air inside boot then tighten TJ boot band securely.

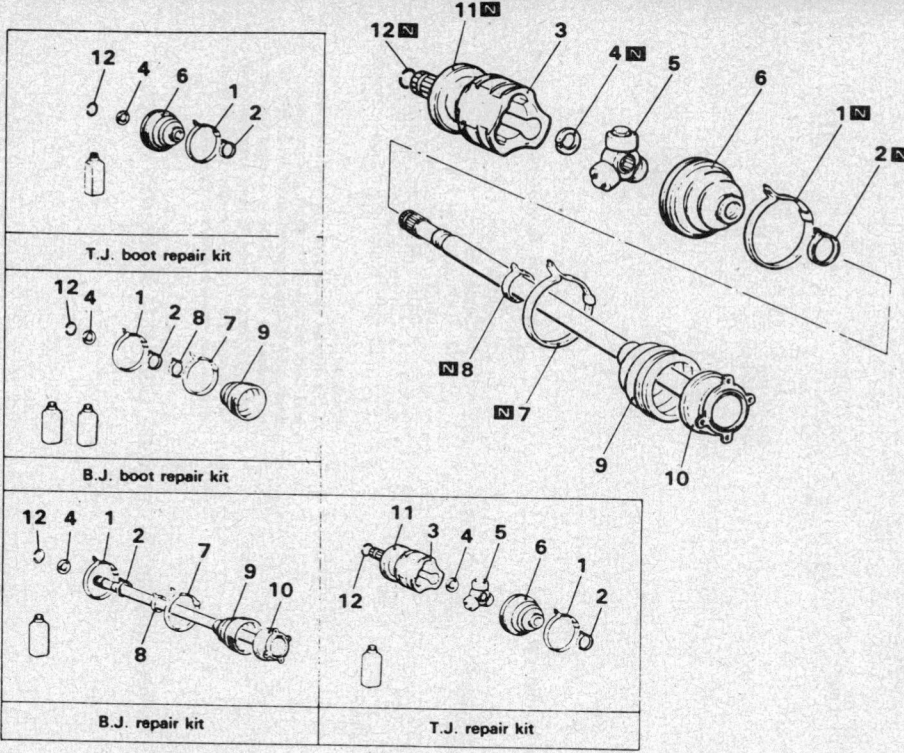

Disassembly steps

1 T.J. boot band (large)	7 B.J. boot band (large)
2 T.J. boot band (small)	8 B.J. boot band (small)
3 T.J. case	9 B.J. boot
4 Snap ring	10 B.J. assembly
5 Spider assembly	11 Dust cover
6 T.J. boot	12 Circlip

NOTE
Reverse the disassembly procedures to reassemble.

N : Non-reusable parts

CR3039100202000X

Fig. 16 Exploded view of driveshaft. Stealth, Laser & Talon

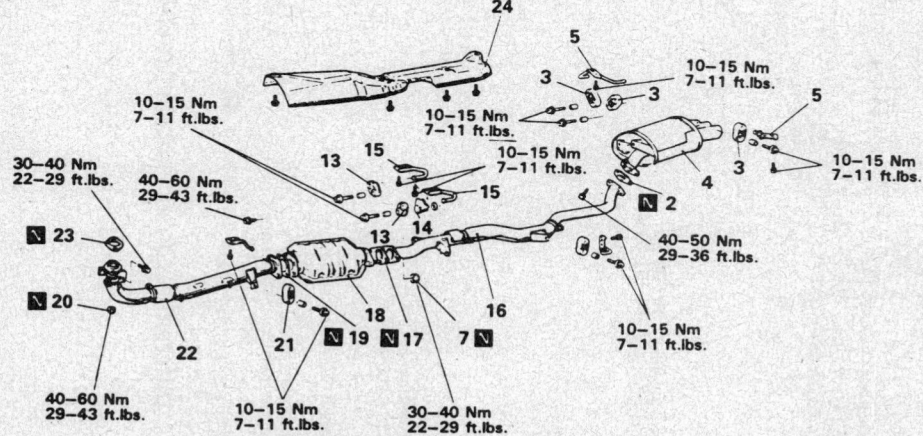

CR3039100187000X

Fig. 17 Exploded view of exhaust system. Laser & Talon

DIFFERENTIAL CARRIER
REPLACE
LASER & TALON

1. Remove driveshafts as described in "Driveshaft, Replace."
2. Position a suitable jack under rear axle assembly, then drain differential gear oil.
3. Remove center exhaust pipe as shown in **Fig. 17**.
4. Scribe mating marks on differential companion flange and flange yoke for assembly reference.
5. Remove differential to propeller shaft connection, then support propeller shaft with wire.
6. Remove dynamic damper to differential support member bolts.
7. Remove differential support member bolts, then the carrier, **Fig. 18**.
8. Reverse procedure to install, noting the following:
   a. **Torque** differential support member attaching bolts to 80-94 ft. lbs.
   b. **Torque** dynamic damper to differential support member attaching bolts to 58-72 ft. lbs.
   c. **Torque** propeller shaft to differential carrier attaching bolts to 22-25 ft. lbs.
   d. **Torque** driveshaft to companion flange attaching bolts to 40-47 ft. lbs.

COLT VISTA & SUMMIT WAGON

1. Remove driveshafts as described in "Driveshaft, Replace."
2. Position a suitable jack under rear axle assembly, then drain differential gear oil.
3. Scribe mating marks on differential companion flange, propeller shaft flange and flange yoke for assembly reference.
4. Remove differential to propeller shaft connection, then support propeller shaft with wire.
5. Remove companion flange using slide hammer and adapter tool Nos. MB990211 and MB991354, or equivalents.
6. Remove differential carrier rear mounting bolt, **Fig. 19**
7. Remove differential carrier front mounting bolt and nut.
8. Remove differential carrier.
9. Remove differential front support bracket.
10. Reverse procedure to install, do not interchange RH and LH companion flanges.

STEALTH

1. Remove driveshafts as outlined under "Driveshaft, Replace."
2. Position a suitable jack under rear axle assembly, then drain differential gear oil.
3. Scribe mating marks on differential companion flange and flange yoke for assembly reference.
4. Remove differential to propeller shaft connection, then support propeller shaft with wire.
5. Remove differential lower and rear support members, **Fig. 20**.
6. Remove rear wheel oil pump retaining bolt.

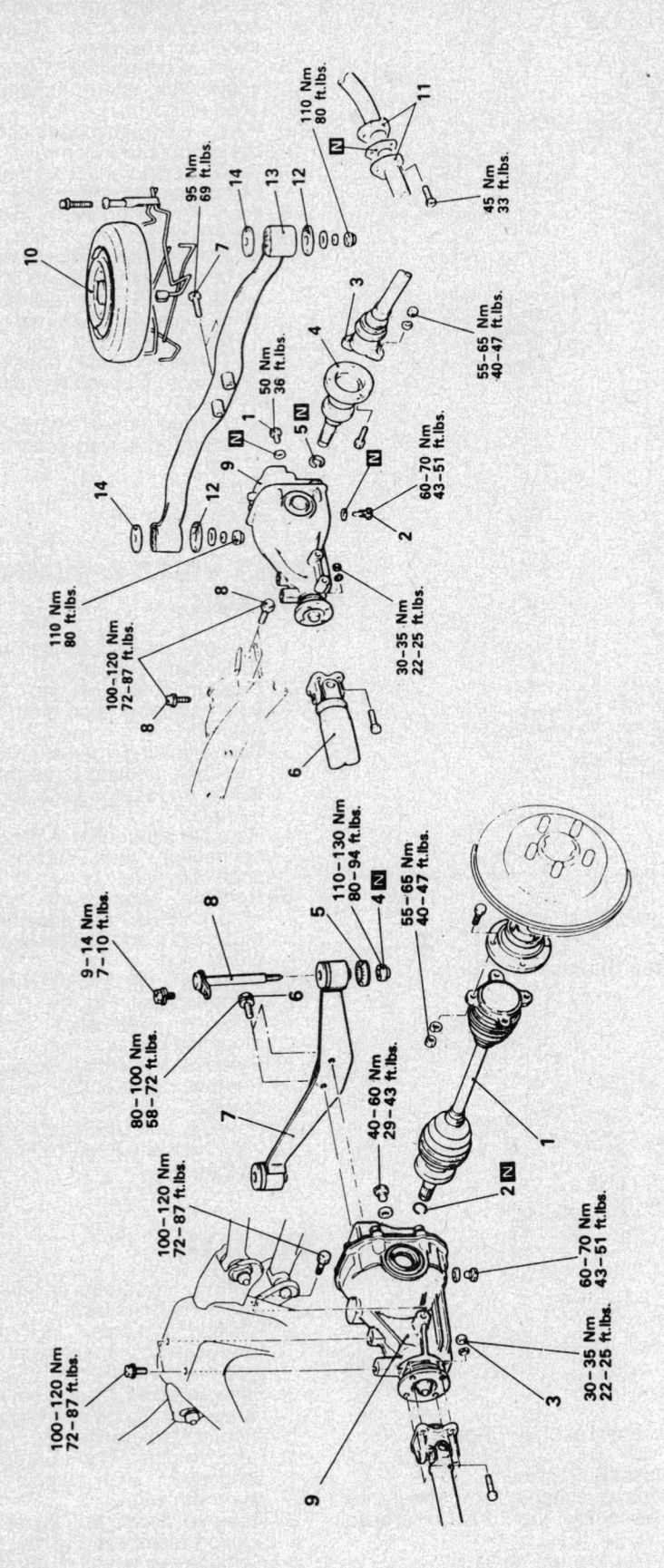

Differential support member removal steps

7. Bolts
10. Spare tire
11. Connection for main muffler and center exhaust pipe
12. Differential mount lower stopper
13. Differential support member
14. Differential mount upper stopper

Caution

If the thread section of the mounting bolts and nuts for the drive shaft and propeller shaft and the companion shaft have any oil or grease on them, there is a possibility that they may loosen, even if they are tightened to the specified torque, so the threads should always be cleaned before tightening.

Differential carrier removal steps

1. Filler plug
2. Drain plug
3. Drive shaft connection
4. Companion shaft
5. Circlip
6. Propeller shaft connection
7. Bolts
8. Bolts
9. Differential Carrier

Fig. 19 Differential carrier removal. Colt Vista & Summit Wagon

Fig. 18 Differential carrier removal. Laser & Talon

Removal steps

1. Drive shaft
2. Circlip
3. Propeller shaft connection
4. Differential support member nut
5. Stopper (lower)
6. Differential support member installation bolts
7. Differential support member
8. Differential support member installation bolts
9. Differential carrier

N : Non-reusable parts.

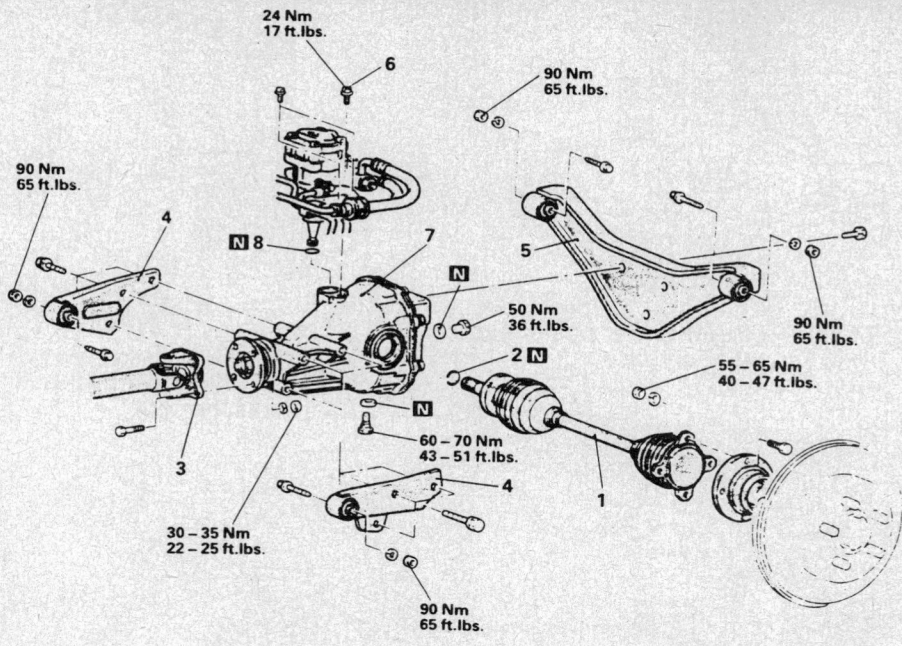

Removal steps
1. Drive shaft
2. Circlip
3. Propeller shaft connection
4. Differential support assembly
5. Differential support member assembly
6. Rear wheel oil pump installation bolt
7. Differential carrier
8. O-ring

Fig. 20 Differential carrier removal. Stealth

CR3039100190000X

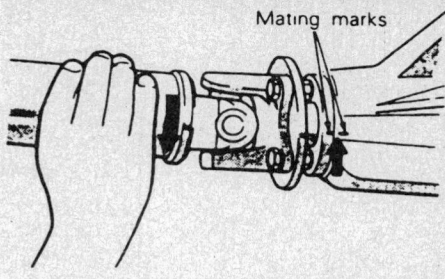

Fig. 21 Rear axle total backlash check

CR3039100179000X

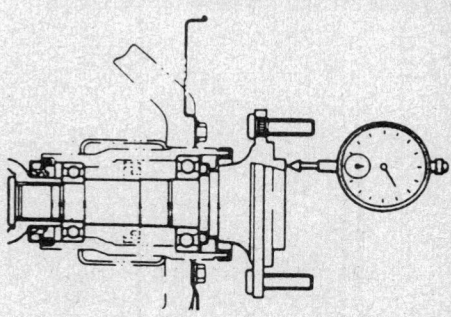

Fig. 22 Rear wheel bearing endplay check

CR3039100180000X

7. Remove and support rear wheel oil pump then lower differential carrier from vehicle. **Use care not to damage rear wheel oil pump gears.**
8. Reverse procedure to install.

CARRIER INSPECTION & SERVICE

REAR AXLE TOTAL BACKLASH

If vehicle vibrates and has a booming sound due to system driveline imbalance. Total axle backlash should be checked. To check backlash, proceed as follows:
1. Place gearshift in neutral, apply parking brake, then raise and support vehicle.
2. Manually turn propeller shaft clockwise as far as it will go and scribe mating mark on companion flange dust cover and differential carrier, **Fig. 21.**
3. Manually turn shaft counterclockwise as far as it will go and measure movement of mating marks.
4. If axle total backlash is less than .2 inch (5 mm), backlash is satisfactory.
5. If backlash is more than .2 inch (5 mm), adjust as necessary.

GEAR OIL LEVEL CHECK

1. Remove filler plug and check oil level.
2. If oil level reaches bottom of filler plug hole, oil level is satisfactory.
3. If level does not reach bottom of filler plug hole, fill differential with MOPAR Hypoid Gear Oil API classification GL-5 or equivalent.

REAR WHEEL BEARING ENDPLAY CHECK

1. Raise and support vehicle on axle stands.
2. Remove rear wheel and tire assembly, then disconnect parking brake cable from rear brake.
3. Remove caliper assembly and brake disc.
4. Position a dial indicator as shown in **Fig. 22,** and measure endplay when axle is moved in an axial direction.
5. **On all models except Colt Vista and Summit Wagon,** proceed as follows:
   a. If endplay is less than .031 inch (.8 mm), endplay is satisfactory.
   b. If endplay exceeds .031 inch (.8 mm), ensure **torque** of axle shaft companion flange is 116-159 ft. lbs. on except Stealth, 137 ft. lbs. on Stealth less turbo or 188-217 ft. lbs. on Stealth with turbo.

c. If torque is within specification, replace wheel bearing.
6. **On Colt Vista and Summit Wagon,** proceed as follows:
   a. If endplay is less than .002 inch, endplay is satisfactory.
   b. If endplay exceeds .002 inch, replace rear wheel bearing.

REAR WHEEL BEARING ROTATION SLIDING RESISTANCE CHECK
Laser, Stealth & Talon

1. Raise and support vehicle.
2. Disconnect driveshaft at companion flange, refer to "Driveshaft, Replace."
3. Remove caliper assembly and suspend with wire.
4. Attach a spring balance to hub bolt, then pull balance at a right angle to bolt, **Fig. 23.** Measure rotation starting torque.
5. If rotation starting torque is less than 6 inch lbs., bearing is satisfactory.
6. If rotation starting torque is more than 6 inch lbs., ensure tightening torque of axle shaft companion flange is as follows:
   a. Ensure **torque** is 116-159 ft. lbs. on Laser and Talon.
   b. Ensure **torque** is 137 ft. lbs. on Stealth less turbo.
   c. Ensure **torque** is 188-217 ft. lbs. on Stealth with turbo.
7. If torque is satisfactory, replace wheel bearing.

LIMITED-SLIP DIFFERENTIAL CHECK

1. Block front wheels and move shift lever to neutral.

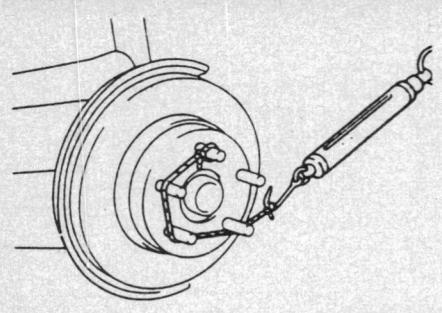

Fig. 23 Rear wheel bearing rotation sliding resistance check

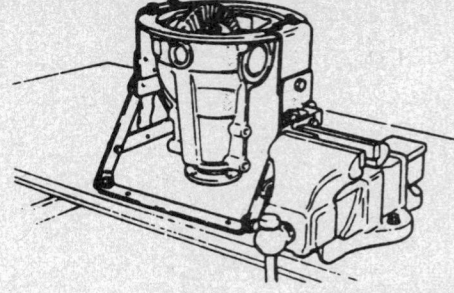

Fig. 24 Differential carrier positioned in working base

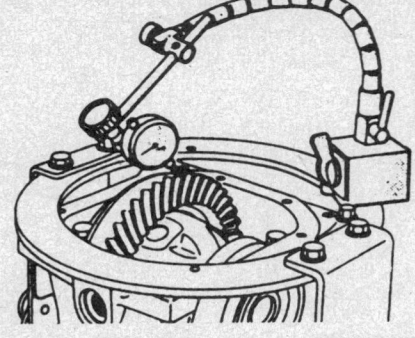

Fig. 25 Final drive gear backlash measurement

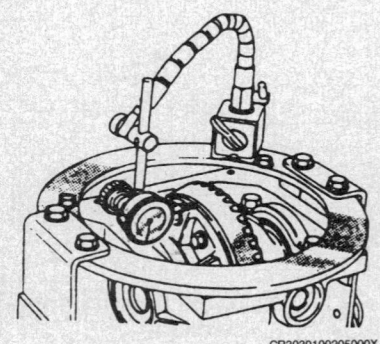

Fig. 26 Drive gear runout measurement

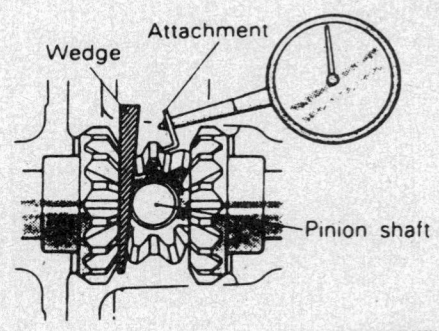

Fig. 27 Differential gear backlash measurement

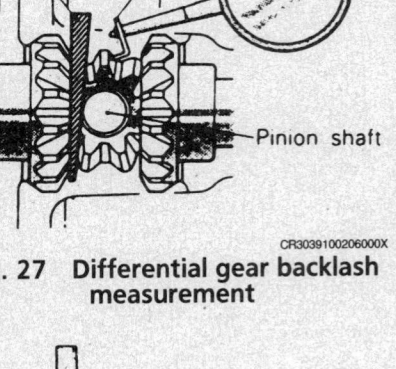

Fig. 28 Final drive gear to check tooth contact marking

2. Release parking brake completely, then raise rear wheels and support with rigid jack stand.
3. Disconnect coupling of differential and propeller shaft.
4. Rotate one wheel slowly, ensure wheel on opposite side turns in the same direction.
5. If wheel turns in the opposite direction, replace viscous unit.

DIFFERENTIAL CARRIER SERVICE

EXCEPT LIMITED SLIP

PRE-DISASSEMBLE INSPECTION

1. Support working base in a vise, and attach differential carrier to working base, **Fig. 24.**
2. Check final drive gear backlash as follows:
   a. Lock drive pinion in place, then mount dial indicator as shown in **Fig. 25.**
   b. Measure backlash at four points or more on the circumference of the drive gear. Backlash should be within .004–.006 inch.
3. Mount dial indicator as shown in **Fig. 26,** then measure drive gear runout at the shoulder on the reverse side of drive gear. Runout should not exceed .002 inch.
4. **On except Stealth models,** lock side gear with a wedge as shown in **Fig. 27,** then measure differential gear backlash with dial indicator on pinion

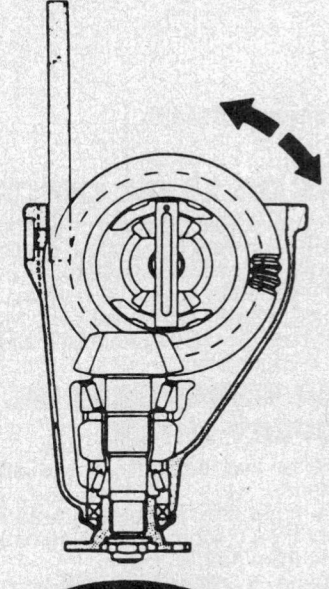

Fig. 29 Final drive gear rotation

gear. Differential gear backlash should not exceed .008 inch.
5. **On all models,** check final drive gear tooth contact as follows:
   a. Apply a thin, uniform coat of machine blue to both surfaces of drive gear teeth as shown in **Fig. 28.**

b. Insert a brass rod between differential carrier and differential case, then rotate companion flange by hand (once in normal direction, and once in reverse direction) while applying a load to drive gear, so that revolution torque applied to the drive pinion is approximately 28–33 inch lbs., **Fig. 29.**
c. Compare and adjust tooth contact pattern as shown in **Fig. 30.**
d. If correct tooth pattern cannot be obtained by adjustment, drive gear and drive pinion have exceeded their usage limit and both gears should be replaced as a set.

DISASSEMBLE

Colt Vista, Laser, Summit Wagon & Talon

1. Support working base in a vise, and attach differential carrier to working base.
2. Remove differential cover and vent plug, **Fig. 31.**
3. Using two hammer shafts or equivalent, slowly and carefully pry differential case assembly out of gear carrier. **Ensure side bearing outer race is not dropped when removing differential case assembly. Keep right and left side bearings separate, so that they do not become mixed at time of reassembly.**
4. Using side bearing puller tool No. MB990810 and side bearing cup tool No. MB990811, or equivalents, pull out side bearing inner races, **Fig. 32.**
5. Scribe mating marks on differential

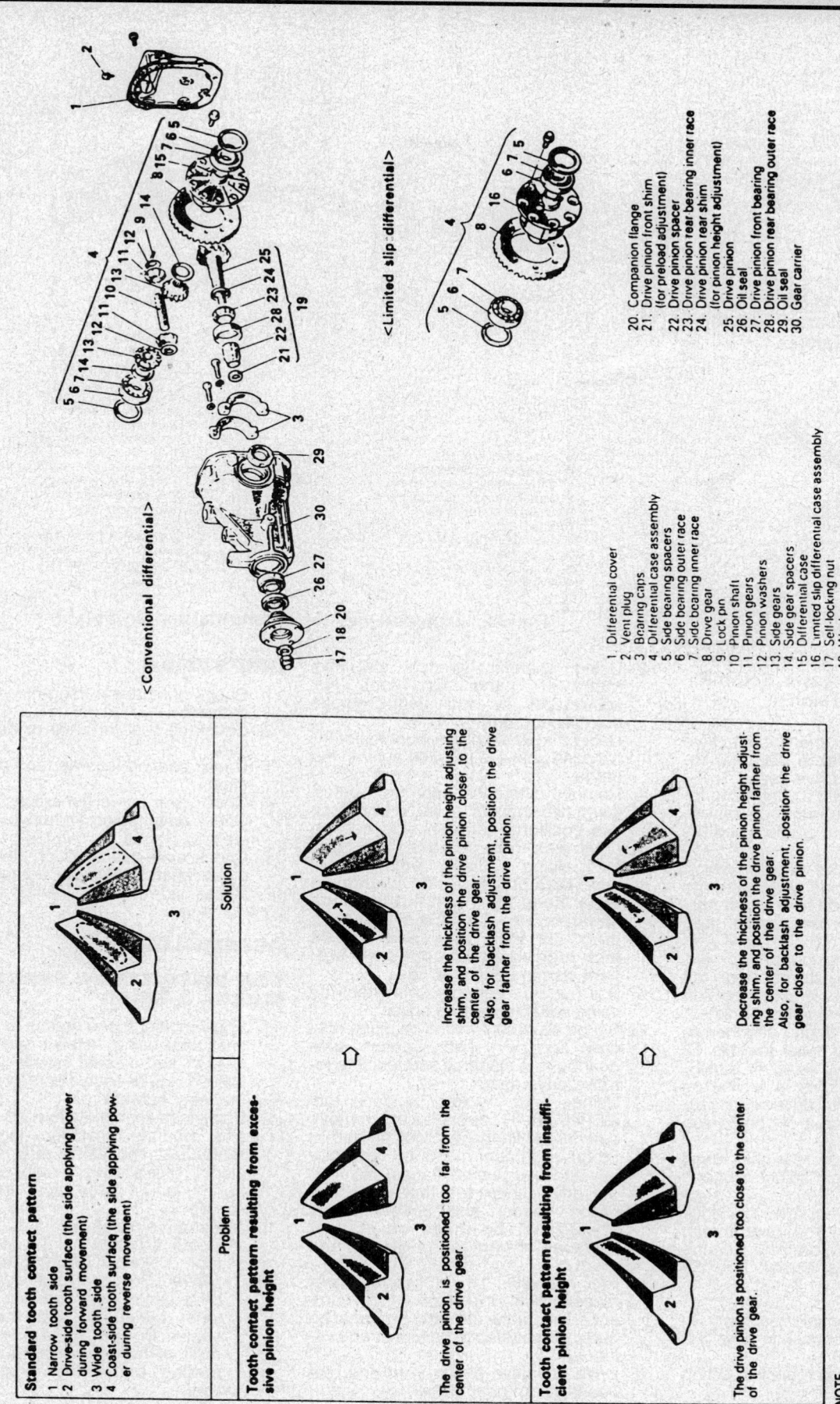

<Conventional differential>

<Limited slip differential>

1. Differential cover
2. Vent plug
3. Bearing caps
4. Differential case assembly
5. Side bearing spacers
6. Side bearing outer race
7. Side bearing inner race
8. Drive gear
9. Lock pin
10. Pinion shaft
11. Pinion gears
12. Pinion washers
13. Side gears
14. Side gear spacers
15. Differential case
16. Limited slip differential case assembly
17. Self-locking nut
18. Washer
19. Drive pinion assembly
20. Companion flange
21. Drive pinion front shim (for preload adjustment)
22. Drive pinion spacer
23. Drive pinion rear bearing inner race
24. Drive pinion rear shim (for pinion height adjustment)
25. Drive pinion
26. Oil seal
27. Drive pinion front bearing
28. Drive pinion rear bearing outer race
29. Oil seal
30. Gear carrier

Fig. 31 Exploded view of differential carrier. Colt Vista, Laser, Summit Wagon & Talon

CR303910021000X

Standard tooth contact pattern

1 Narrow tooth side
2 Drive-side tooth surface (the side applying power during forward movement)
3 Wide tooth side
4 Coast-side tooth surface (the side applying power during reverse movement)

Problem	Solution
Tooth contact pattern resulting from excessive pinion height	
The drive pinion is positioned too far from the center of the drive gear.	Increase the thickness of the pinion height adjusting shim, and position the drive pinion closer to the center of the drive gear. Also, for backlash adjustment, position the drive gear farther from the drive pinion.
Tooth contact pattern resulting from insufficient pinion height	
The drive pinion is positioned too close to the center of the drive gear.	Decrease the thickness of the pinion height adjusting shim, and position the drive pinion farther from the center of the drive gear. Also, for backlash adjustment, position the drive gear closer to the drive pinion.

NOTE
(1) Tooth contact pattern is a method for judging the result of the adjustment of drive pinion height and final drive gear backlash. The adjustment of drive pinion hight and final drive gear backlash should be repeated until tooth contact patterns bear a similarity to the standard tooth contact pattern.

CR303910020900X

Fig. 30 Final drive gear & drive pinion adjustment

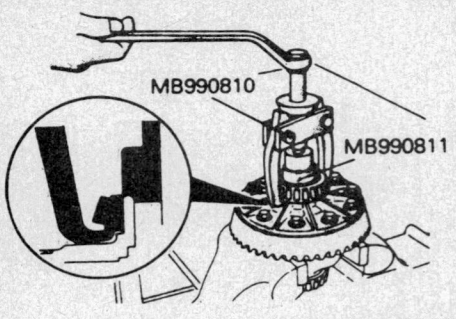

Fig. 32 Side bearing inner race removal. Colt Vista, Laser, Summit Wagon & Talon

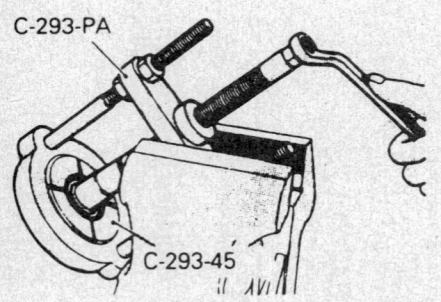

Fig. 33 Rear bearing inner race removal. Colt Vista, Laser, Summit Wagon & Talon

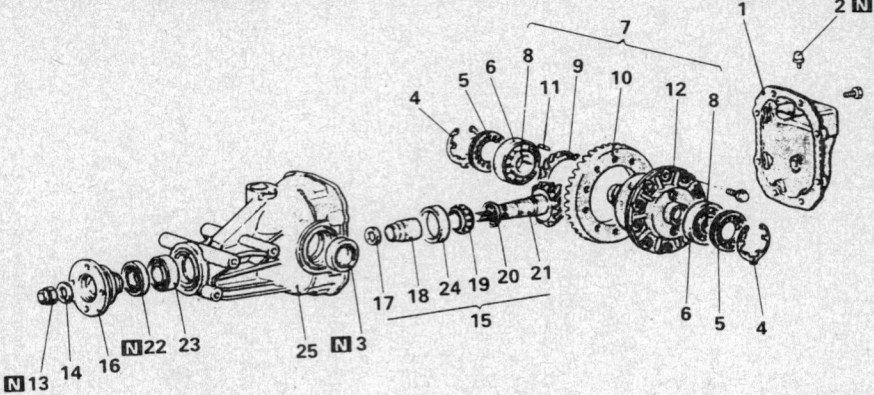

Disassembly steps

1. Differential cover assembly
2. Vent plug
3. Oil seal
4. Snap ring
5. Side bearing nut
6. Side bearing outer race
7. Differential case assembly
8. Side bearing inner race
9. Drive gear (for 4WS)
10. Drive gear
11. Spring pin (for 4WS)
12. LSD case
13. Self-locking nut
14. Washer
15. Drive pinion assembly
16. Companion flange
17. Drive pinion front shim (for preload adjustment)
18. Drive pinion spacer
19. Drive pinion rear bearing inner race
20. Drive pinion rear shim (for drive pinion height adjustment)
21. Drive pinion
22. Oil seal
23. Drive pinion front bearing
24. Drive pinion rear bearing outer race
25. Differential carrier

Fig. 34 Exploded view of differential carrier. Stealth

case and drive gear, then loosen drive gear attaching bolts in diagonal sequence to remove drive gear.

6. Drive out lockpin with a punch and remove pinion gears, pinion washers, side gears, side gear spacers and differential case.
7. Scribe mating marks on drive pinion and companion flange. **Mating marks should not be made to contact surfaces of companion flange and propeller shaft.**
8. Using side bearing puller tool No. MB990810, or equivalent, drive out drive pinion together with drive pinion spacer and drive pinion front shims.
9. Mount companion flange attached to taper roller bearing puller tool No. C-293-PA and bearing remover tool C-293-45, or equivalents in a vise as shown in **Fig. 33.** Pull drive pinion rear bearing inner race out of companion flange.
10. Remove drive pinion rear shim used for drive pinion height adjustment and drive pinion.
11. Remove oil seal, then drive out drive pinion front bearing from gear carrier.
12. Drive out drive pinion rear bearing outer race from gear carrier.

Stealth

Disassemble differential assembly in numbered sequence shown in **Fig. 34,** noting the following:

1. Refer to "Pre-Disassemble Inspection procedure.

2. Using spanner wrench tool No. MB991367 and pin tool No. MB991385, or equivalent, remove side bearing nut.
3. Using a suitable press, push differential case until it is pressed against the carrier.
4. Remove differential case from press. Insert two spacers in diagonally opposite positions between side bearing outer race to be removed and inner race. Using a press, remove outer race. **Do not allow side bearing to drop. Keep right and left bearings separate. Use a spacer 1.18 inches long, .39 inch wide and .04-.08 inch high made of copper to prevent damage to bearings.**
5. Pull out side bearing inner races by using suitable bearing puller.
6. Scribe alignment marks on differential case and drive gear. Loosen drive gear bolts in diagonal sequence to remove drive gear.
7. Using end yoke holder tool MB990767-01, or equivalent, remove companion flange self-locking nut.
8. Scribe alignment marks on drive pinion and companion flange. Remove out drive pinion together with drive pinion spacer and shims. **Marks should not be made on contact surfaces of companion flange and shaft.**
9. Pull out drive pinion bearing inner races by using insert tool, pinion carrier bearing puller tool, and side bearing cup remover step plate tool or equivalent.
10. Drive out drive pinion front and rear bearing from gear carrier.

INSPECTION

1. Check companion flange for wear or damage.
2. Check oil seal for wear or deterioration.
3. Check bearing for wear and discoloration.
4. Check gear carrier for cracks.
5. Check drive pinion and drive gear for wear or cracks.
6. Check side gears, pinion gears and pinion shaft for wear or damage.
7. Check side gear spline for wear or damage.

ASSEMBLE

Colt Vista, Laser, Summit Wagon & Talon

1. Apply multipurpose grease to lip of oil seal, then using installer bar tool No. C-4171 and oil seal installer tool No. MB991115, or equivalents, press seal into gear carrier.
2. Using installer handle tool No. C-4171 and bearing installer tool Nos. MB990932 and MB990935, or equivalents, press drive pinion rear and front bearing outer races into gear carrier.
3. Adjust drive pinion height as follows:
   a. Install a pinion height gauge set tool Nos. MB990835 and MB990836, or equivalent, and drive pinion front and rear bearing inner races on gear carrier as shown in **Fig. 35. Apply a thin coat of multipurpose grease to mating surface on washer of tool.**

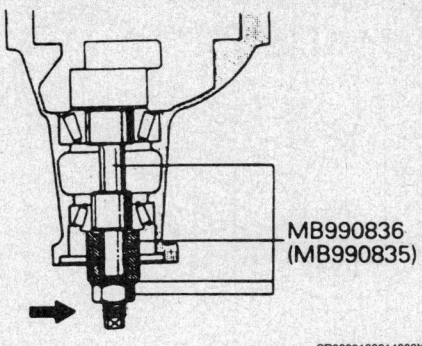

Fig. 35 Drive pinion height adjustment. Colt Vista, Laser, Summit Wagon & Talon

Bearing classification	Bearing lubrication	Rotation torque (starting friction torque) Nm (in.lbs.)
New	None (with rust-prevention oil)	0.9–1.2 (8–10)
New/reused	Oil application	0.4–0.5 (3–4)

NOTE
(1) Gradually tighten the nut of the special tool while checking the drive pinion turning torque.
(2) Because the special tool cannot be turned one turn, turn it several times within the range that it can be turned; then, after fitting to the bearing, measure the rotation torque.

Fig. 36 Drive pinion turning torque specifications (less oil seal installed). Laser, Summit Wagon & Talon

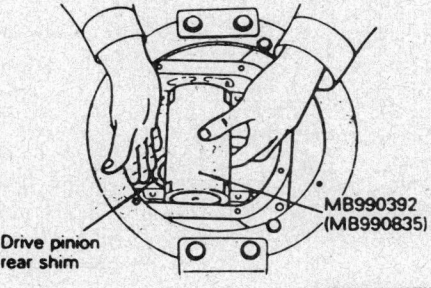

Fig. 37 Selecting drive pinion adjustment shims. Colt Vista, Laser, Summit Wagon & Talon

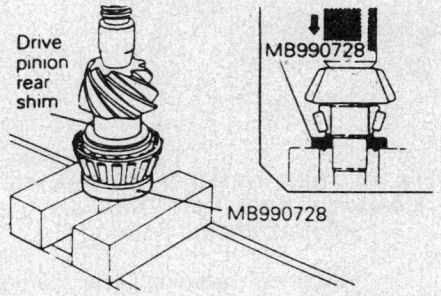

Fig. 38 Drive pinion inner race installation. Colt Vista, Laser, Summit Wagon & Talon

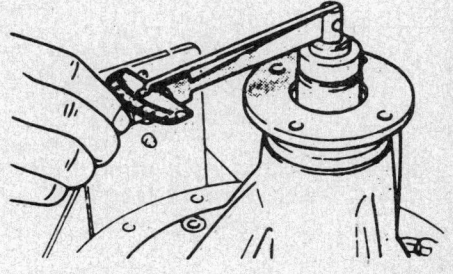

Fig. 39 Drive pinion turning torque check. Colt Vista, Laser, Summit Wagon & Talon

b. Tighten handle of special tool until standard value of drive pinion turning torque is obtained. On Colt Vista, specification is 6-9 inch lbs. and on Talon, refer to **Fig. 36.**
c. Measure drive pinion turning torque (without oil seal).
d. Position special tool No. MB990835, or equivalent, in side bearing seat of gear carrier as shown in **Fig. 37.** Select a drive pinion rear shim of a thickness which corresponds to the gap between special tools. **Clean side bearing seat thoroughly. When positioning special tool, ensure cutout sections of tool are in position shown in Fig. 37, and that special tool is in close contact with side bearing seat. When selecting drive pinion rear shims, keep number of drive shims to a minimum.**
e. Fit selected drive pinion rear shims to drive pinion, then using bearing installer tool No. MB990728, or equivalent, press rear bearing inner race onto drive pinion as shown in **Fig. 38.**
4. Adjust drive pinion preload as follows:
   a. Fit drive pinion front shims between drive pinion spacer and drive pinion front bearing inner race.
   b. **Torque** companion flange to 116-159 ft. lbs. using end yoke holder tool No. MB990767, or equivalent. **Do not install oil seal.**

c. Using a torque wrench, measure drive pinion turning torque as shown in **Fig. 39.**
d. Compare measurement. On Colt Vista, specification is 6-9 inch lbs. and on Talon, refer to **Fig. 36.** If turning torque is not within specification, adjust by replacing drive pinion front shims or drive pinion spacer. **If a number of shims will be required to bring preload within specified value, reduce the number of shims by replacing the spacer.**
e. Remove companion flange and drive pinion, then drive oil seal into gear carrier front lip. Apply a thin coat of multipurpose grease to the oil seal lip.
f. Apply a thin coat of multipurpose grease to companion flange washer contacting surface prior to installing drive pinion.
g. Install drive pinion assembly and companion flange with mating marks aligned, and **torque** companion flange self-locking nut to 116-159 ft. lbs.
h. Measure drive pinion turning torque, and compare with specified value. On Colt Vista, specification is 6-9 inch lbs. and Talon, refer to **Fig. 40.** If turning torque is not within specified value, ensure companion flange self-locking nut

is tightened within specification and oil seal is correctly installed.
5. **On except Laser and Talon models,** adjust differential gear backlash as follows:
   a. Assemble side gears, side gear spacers, pinion gears and pinion washers into differential case.
   b. Temporarily install pinion shaft. **Do not drive in lockpin at this time.**
   c. While locking side gear with wedge measure differential gear backlash with dial indicator as shown in **Fig. 41.** Measurement should be made for both gears individually.
   d. Gear backlash should not exceed .008 inch (.2 mm). If side gear exceeds limit, adjust by installing thicker side gear spacers.
   e. After adjustment, ensure differential gear rotates smoothly.
   f. If backlash cannot be adjusted, replace side gear and pinion gear as a set.
   g. Align pinion shaft lockpin hole with differential case lockpin hole, and drive in lockpin.
   h. Stake lockpin with punch at two points as shown in **Fig. 42.**
6. **On all models,** clean drive gear attaching bolts, then using a M10 X 1.25 tap, remove adhesive adhering to threaded holes of drive gear. Clean remaining material out of drive gear using compressed air.

Bearing classification	Bearing lubrication	Rotation torque (starting friction torque) Nm (in.lbs.)
New	None (with rust-prevention oil)	1.0–1.3 (9–11)
New/reused	Oil application	0.5–0.6 (4–5)

Fig. 40 Drive pinion turning torque specifications (w/oil seal installed). Laser, Summit Wagon & Talon

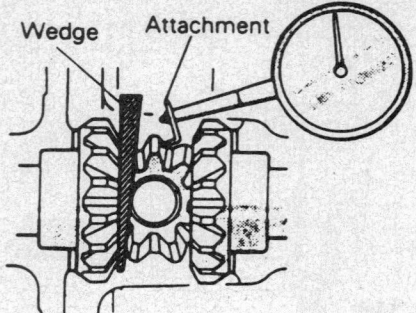

Fig. 41 Differential gear backlash check. Colt Vista, Laser, Summit Wagon & Talon

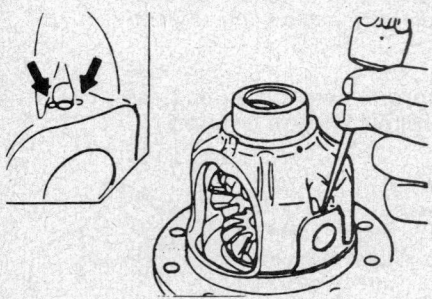

Fig. 42 Lockpin installation. Colt Vista, Laser, Summit Wagon & Talon

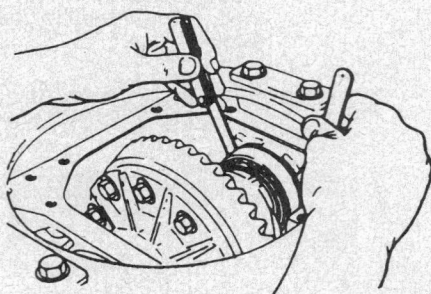

Fig. 43 Gear carrier & side bearing clearance check. Colt Vista, Laser, Summit Wagon & Talon

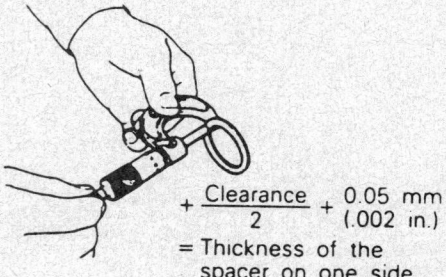

$$+ \frac{Clearance}{2} + \frac{0.05 \text{ mm}}{(.002 \text{ in.})}$$
= Thickness of the spacer on one side

Fig. 44 Side bearing spacers selection. Colt Vista, Laser, Summit Wagon & Talon

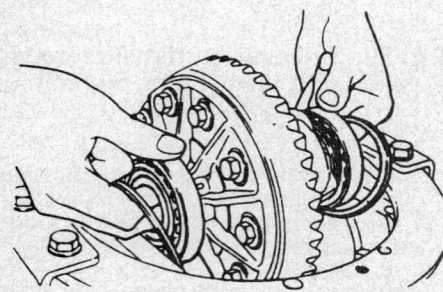

Fig. 45 Side bearing spacers & differential case assembly installation. Colt Vista, Laser, Summit Wagon & Talon

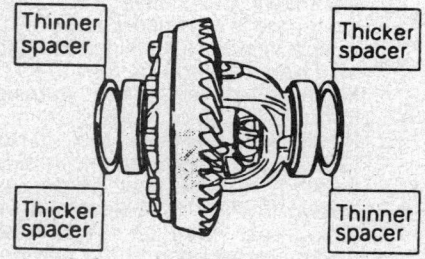

Fig. 46 Side bearing spacers change. Colt Vista, Laser, Summit Wagon & Talon

7. Apply multipurpose adhesive Mopar Loctite No. 271 or equivalent to threaded holes of drive gear.
8. Install drive gear onto differential case with mating marks aligned. **Torque** drive gear attaching bolts in a diagonal sequence to 58-65 ft. lbs.
9. Using bearing installer tool No. MB990728, or equivalent, press side bearing inner races to differential case.
10. Adjust final drive gear backlash as follows:
    a. Install side bearing spacers, which are thinner than those removed, to side bearing outer races and then mount differential case assembly into gear carrier. **Use side bearing spacers with the same thickness for both drive pinion and drive gear sides.**
    b. Push differential case to one side of the gear carrier and measure clearance between gear carrier and side bearing as shown in **Fig. 43**.
    c. Measure thickness of side bearing spacers on one side, then select two pairs of spacers which correspond to that thickness plus one half of clearance plus .002 inch, **Fig. 44.** Install one pair each to drive pinion side and drive gear side.
    d. Install side bearing spacers and differential case assembly to gear carrier as shown in **Fig. 45.**
    e. Tap side bearing spacers with a brass bar to fit them to side bearing outer race.
    f. Align mating marks on gear carrier and bearing cap, then tighten bearing cap.
    g. With drive pinion locked in place, measure final drive gear backlash with a dial indicator mounted on drive gear as shown in **Fig. 25.**
    h. Measure at four or more points around the circumference of the drive gear, backlash should be within .004-.006 inch (.11-.16 mm).
    i. Change side bearing spacers as shown in **Fig. 46,** and then adjust final drive gear backlash between drive gear and drive pinion. **When increasing number of side bearing spacers, use the same number of each, and as few as possible.**
    j. Check drive gear and drive pinion for proper tooth contact, refer to "Pre-Disassemble Inspection" for adjustment procedure.
    k. Measure drive gear runout at shoulder on reverse side of drive gear, **Fig. 26.** If drive gear runout exceeds .002 inch, reinstall by changing phase of drive gear and differential case, and measure.
11. **On Colt Vista and Talon models,** apply a semi-drying sealant to installation surface of differential cover and vent plug, **torque** cover bolts to 22-30 ft. lbs.

Stealth

Assemble differential carrier in numbered sequence shown in **Fig. 47,** noting the following:
1. **On models w/Four Wheel Steering (4WS),** tap spring pin into differential case to position shown in **Fig. 48,** be-

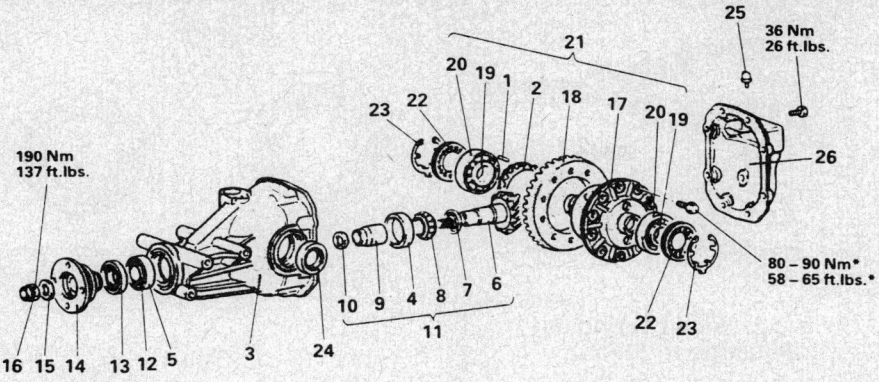

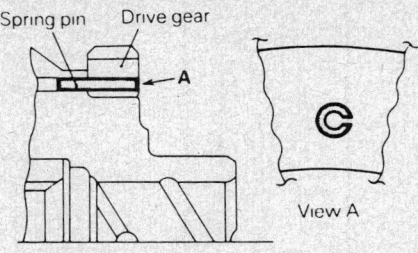

Fig. 48 Spring pin installation. Stealth

Fig. 47 Differential carrier assembly. Stealth

Reassembly steps

1. Spring pin (for 4WS)
2. Drive gear (for 4WS)
3. Differential carrier
4. Drive pinion rear bearing outer race
5. Drive pinion front bearing outer race
   Drive pinion height adjustment
6. Drive pinion
7. Drive pinion rear shim
   (for drive pinion height adjustment)
8. Drive pinion rear bearing inner race
9. Drive pinion spacer
   Drive pinion preload adjustment
10. Drive pinion front shim
11. Drive pinion assembly
12. Drive pinion front bearing inner race
13. Oil seal
14. Companion flange
15. Washer
16. Self-locking nut
17. LSD case
18. Drive gear
19. Side bearing inner race
20. Side bearing outer race
    Final drive gear backlash adjustment
21. Differential case assembly
22. Side bearing nut
23. Snap ring
24. Oil seal
25. Vent plug
26. Differential cover assembly

NOTE
* Tightening torque with oil applied.

Fig. 49 Drive pinion height adjustment. Stealth

Bearing classification	Bearing lubrication	Rotation torque Nm (in.lbs.)
New	None (with rust-prevention oil)	0.3 – 0.5 (3 – 4)
New/reused	Gear oil application	0.15 – 0.25 (1 – 2)

NOTE
(1) Gradually tighten the nut of the special tool while checking the drive pinion rotation torque.
(2) Because the special tool cannot be turned one turn, turn it several times within the range that it can be turned; then, after fitting to the bearing, measure the rotation torque.

Fig. 50 Rotation torque value. Stealth

fore press fitting rear wheel oil pump drive gear. Notch on spring should be in position shown.

2. **On all models,** with beveled part of rear wheel oil pump drive gear at inner side, press in drive gear, using rear suspension bushing base tool No. MB990890-01, or equivalent, until drive gear contacts end surface of differential case. Ensure drive gear and spring pin are flush.

3. Press fit drive pinion rear and front bearing outer races onto gear carrier using handle tool and bearing and oil seal installer tool set No. MB990925, or equivalent. **Use care not to press in outer race at an angle.**

4. Adjust pinion height as follows:
   a. Install special tools as shown in **Fig. 49.**
   b. Tighten handle of tool until the standard value shown in **Fig. 50,** of drive pinion turning torque is obtained.
   c. Measure drive pinion turning torque without oil seal installed.
   d. Position gauge tube tool No. MB990392-01, or equivalent, in side bearing beat of gear carrier then select a drive pinion rear shim of thickness which corresponds to gap between special tools.
   e. Install selected shim on drive pinion and press fit rear bearing inner race using bearing installer tool No. MT215013, or equivalent.

5. Adjust drive pinion preload as follows:
   a. Install drive pinion front shim(s) between pinion spacer and pinion front bearing inner race.
   b. Tighten companion flange to specification using end yoke holder tool. Do not install oil seal.
   c. Ensure drive pinion turning torque is as shown in **Fig. 50.**
   d. If drive pinion turning torque is not within specified range, adjust by replacing drive pinion front shims(s) or drive pinion spacer.
   e. Remove companion flange and drive pinion.
   f. Install oil seal using suitable oil seal installation tool.
   g. Install drive pinion and companion flange aligning marks made during disassembly then tighten companion flange self-locking nut to specification.

h. Measure pinion turning torque with oil seal installed and ensure turning torque is no more than one inch lb. greater than what is shown in **Fig. 50.**

6. Adjust differential gear backlash as follows:
   a. Assemble side gears and spacers, pinion gears and washers into differential case.
   b. Temporarily install pinion shaft.
   c. While locking side gear with wedge, measure differential gear backlash with a dial indicator on pinion gear. **The measurement should be made for both pinion gears individually.**
   d. If differential gear backlash exceeds .008 inch, adjust backlash by installing thicker side gear spacers.
   e. Measure differential gear backlash again and confirm it is within the specification.
   f. After adjustment, ensure backlash is less than limit and differential gear rotates smoothly.
   g. When adjustment is impossible, replace side gear pinion hears as a set.

7. Align pinion shaft lockpin hole with differential case and install lockpin.
8. Stake lockpin at two points.
9. Clean drive gear attaching bolts.
10. Use a 10mm x 1.25 tap to remove adhesive from threaded holes of drive gear.
11. Install drive gear onto differential case aligning marks made during disassembly. Tighten bolts in a diagonal sequence.

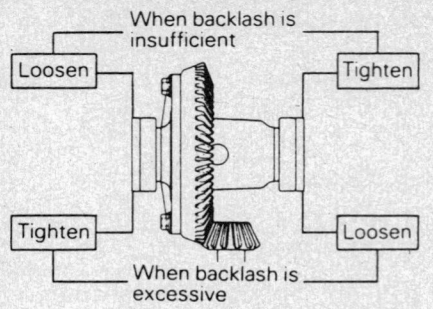

Fig. 51 Final gear backlash adjustment. Stealth

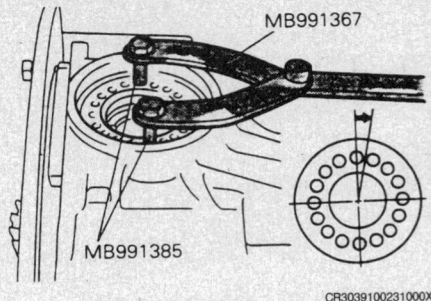

Fig. 52 Side bearing nut adjustment. Stealth

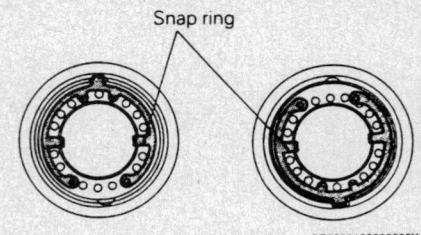

Fig. 53 Snap ring installation. Stealth

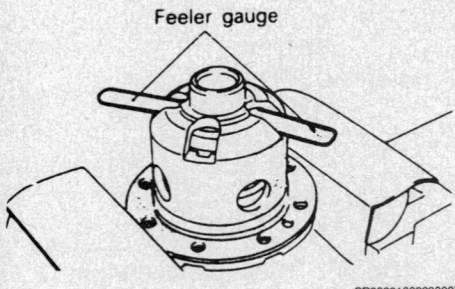

Fig. 54 Differential case assembly mounting in vise. Laser, Talon, Stealth & Colt Vista & Summit Wagon

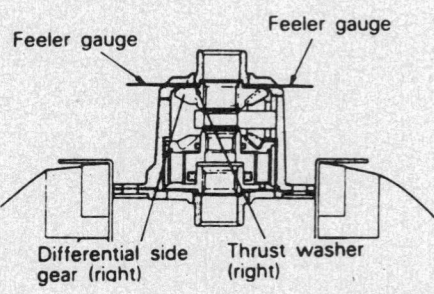

Fig. 55 Feeler gauge insertion into differential case. Laser, Talon, Stealth & Colt Vista & Summit Wagon

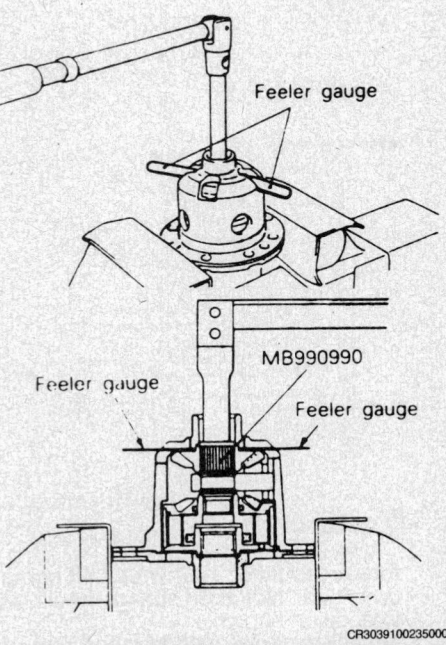

Fig. 56 Differential gear backlash check (w/limited slip differential). Laser, Talon, Stealth & Colt Vista & Summit Wagon

12. Press side bearing inner races onto differential case.
13. Adjust final drive gear backlash as follows:
    a. Using spanner wrench tool No. MB991367 and pin tool No. MB991385, or equivalent, temporarily tighten side bearing nut until just before preloading.
    b. Measure final drive gear backlash at four or more points on drive gear.
    c. Using spanner wrench and pin tools, adjust backlash until a .004-.006 inch value is reached by turning side bearing nut as shown, Fig. 51.
    d. Using the spanner wrench to apply preload, turn down both right and left side bearing nuts on half the distance between centers of two neighboring holes, Fig. 52.
    e. Install snap ring at either position shown to lock side bearing nut, Fig. 53.
    f. Check drive gear and pinion tooth contact as outlined under " Pre-Disassemble Inspection."
    g. Measure drive gear runout at shoulder on reverse side of drive gear.
    h. If runout exceeds .002 inch, reinstall by changing the phase of drive gear and differential case, and measure.
    i. Using suitable oil seal installer, install oil seal flush with gear carrier end face.

LIMITED SLIP

LASER, STEALTH, TALON & COLT VISTA & SUMMIT WAGON

Pre-Disassemble Inspection

1. Secure differential case assembly in a vise so that differential side gear (right) is facing upward as shown in Fig. 54.
2. Insert a .0012 inch (.03 mm) feeler gauge at two places (diagonally) between differential case B and thrust washer, Fig. 55. Do not insert feeler gauge in oil groove of differential case B.
3. Insert side gear holding tool No. MB990990, or equivalent, at spline part of differential case B (right) and ensure side gear rotates, Fig. 56.
4. Insert a .0035 inch (.09 mm) feeler gauge to replace .0012 inch (.03 mm) feeler gauge.
5. Insert side gear holding tool No. MB990990, or equivalent, at spline part of differential case B (right) and ensure side gear does not rotate, Fig. 56.
6. Differential gear backlash (clearance in thrust direction of side gear) should be within .0012-.0035 inch (.03 mm-.09 mm). If clearance in the thrust direction of the side gear is within standard value range, backlash of differential gear is normal.
7. If clearance in thrust direction of side gear is not within specification, remove differential case A and make

adjustment by adjusting thickness of the thrust washer (left).

Disassemble

1. Remove attaching screw from differential case A, Fig. 57.
2. Remove differential case B.
3. Remove left thrust washer. Since thrust washer from left side is of a different thickness than the right side, it will be necessary to mark the washer in some manner for assembly reference.
4. Remove viscous unit, pinion mate washer, differential pinion mate, pinion shaft and righthand differential side gear.
5. Remove right thrust washer. Since thrust washer from right side is of a different thickness than the left side, it will be necessary to mark the washer for assembly reference.

Inspection

1. Check gears and differential pinion shaft for unusual wear or damage.

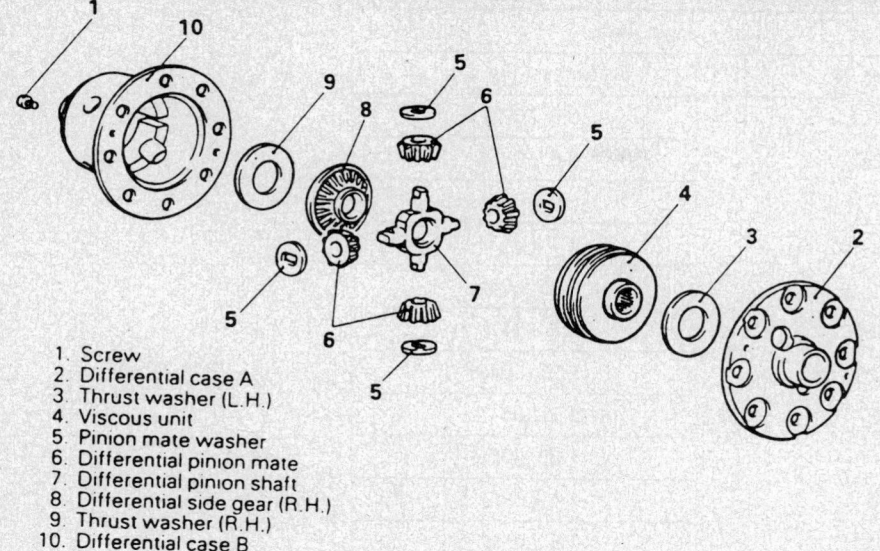

1. Screw
2. Differential case A
3. Thrust washer (L.H.)
4. Viscous unit
5. Pinion mate washer
6. Differential pinion mate
7. Differential pinion shaft
8. Differential side gear (R.H.)
9. Thrust washer (R.H.)
10. Differential case B

Fig. 57 Exploded view of differential carrier (with limited slip differential). Laser, Talon, Stealth & Colt Vista & Summit Wagon

2. Check spline part of right side differential gear for stepped wear or damage.
3. Check thrust washer and pinion mate washer for unusual wear of contact surfaces, heat damage or other damage.
4. Check contact surfaces of differential cases A and B for damage or wear, **Fig. 58.**
5. Check spline part of viscous unit for stepped wear or damage, and check contact surface with differential case B.
6. Check left side gear of viscous unit for unusual wear or damage.

Assemble

1. With pinion mate washer in position shown in **Fig. 59,** install to differential pinion mate to differential pinion shaft, and then install to differential case B.
2. If differential side gear and pinion mate gear have been replaced, select left side thrust washer as follows:
   a. Wash differential side gear and pinion mate gear in unleaded gasoline to remove all foreign material.
   b. Install previously used thrust washers (matching left and right sides), together with gears, viscous unit, pinion mate washer and pinion shaft to differential cases A and B. Using screws, secure temporarily.
   c. Secure differential case assembly in a vise so that right side differential side gear is facing upward, **Fig. 54. Do not hold differential case too tightly.**
   d. Insert a .0012 inch feeler gauge at two places (diagonally) between differential case B and right side thrust washer. **Do not insert feeler gauge in oil groove of differential case B.**

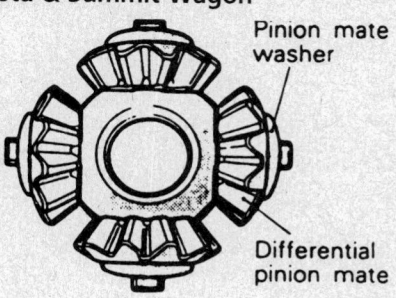

Pinion mate washer

Differential pinion mate

Fig. 59 Differential pinion mate installation. Laser, Talon, Stealth & Colt Vista & Summit Wagon

   e. Insert side gear holding tool No. MB990990, or equivalent, at spline part of differential case B (right) and ensure side gear does not rotate, **Fig. 56.**
   f. Differential gear backlash (clearance in thrust direction of side gear) should be within .0012-.0035 inch (.03 mm-.09 mm). If clearance in the thrust direction of the side gear is within standard value range, backlash of differential gear is normal.
   g. If clearance in thrust direction of side gear is not within specification, remove differential case A and make adjustment by selecting appropriate thrust washer from chart shown in **Fig. 60.**
3. After installing thrust washers, align mating marks of differential cases and reassemble.

POWER TRANSFER UNIT
REPLACE

LASER & TALON

1. Remove two front exhaust pipe at-

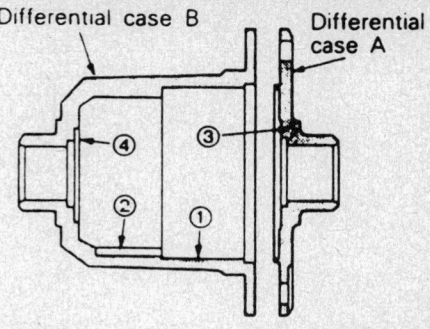

CR3039100237000X

Fig. 58 Differential case contact surfaces. Laser, Talon, Stealth & Colt Vista & Summit Wagon

taching nuts and lower exhaust pipe, **Fig. 61.**
2. Remove transfer assembly mounting bolts.
3. Remove driveshaft by moving transfer assembly to the left and lowering the front side. Suspend driveshaft with a piece of wire.
4. Reverse procedure to install, noting the following:
   a. **Torque** transfer assembly mounting bolts to 40-43 ft. lbs.
   b. **Torque** front exhaust pipe attaching nuts to 29-43 ft. lbs.

COLT VISTA & SUMMIT WAGON

1. Raise and support vehicle.
2. Remove transaxle and transfer case assembly as outlined in the "Colt, Colt Vista, Summit & Summit Wagon" section.
3. Separate transfer assembly from transaxle.
4. Reverse procedure to install.

STEALTH

1. Drain transaxle assembly.
2. Remove active front venturi skirt from vehicle.
3. Remove front exhaust pipe and main muffler assembly from vehicle.
4. Remove driveshaft retaining bolts then midship bearing retaining bolts and driveshaft from vehicle.
5. Remove five transfer case retaining bolts, then transfer assembly.
6. Reverse procedure to install. **Torque** transfer assembly bolts to 64 ft. lbs.

POWER TRANSFER UNIT SERVICE

LASER & TALON

DISASSEMBLE

1. Remove cover and cover gasket, **Fig. 62.**
2. Remove extension housing assembly and transfer case subassembly.
3. Remove spacer, O-ring and transfer case adapter subassembly.

Thrust washer (left)	
Part No.	Thickness mm (in.)
	0.8 (.031)
	0.9 (.035)
	1.0 (.039)
	1.1 (.043)
	1.15 (.045)
MB569243	1.2 (.047)
	1.25 (.049)
	1.3 (.051)
	1.35 (.053)
	1.4 (.055)
	1.5 (.059)

CR3039100239000X

Fig. 60 Thrust washer thickness chart. Laser, Talon, Stealth & Colt Vista & Summit Wagon

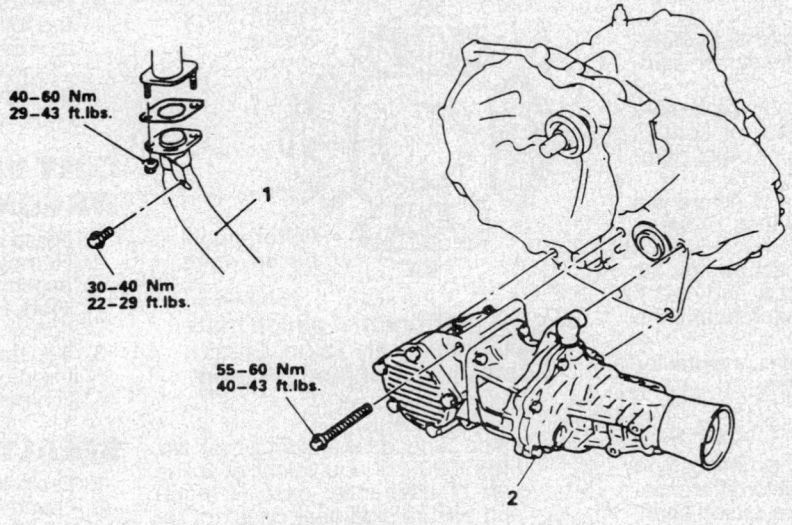

1. Front exhaust pipe connection
2. Transfer assembly

CR3039100191000X

Fig. 61 Transfer assembly removal. Laser & Talon

SUBASSEMBLY SERVICE

Extension Housing Assembly

1. Remove air breather, **Fig. 63.**
2. Remove dust shield guard and oil seal from extension housing assembly.
3. Reverse procedure to assemble, noting the following:
   a. Use oil seal installer MD998304 or equivalent when installing oil seal.
   b. Prior to installing air breather, apply 3M Super Weatherstrip No. 8001 or equivalent to air breather.

Transfer Case Subassembly

1. Remove transfer cover, **Fig. 64.**

2. Remove O-ring, spacer and outer race.
3. Remove drive bevel gear assembly spacer and oil seal.
4. Reverse procedure to assemble, noting the following:
   a. Use oil seal installer MD998323 or equivalent when installing oil seal.
   b. Using preload socket tool No. MB990326 and side gear holding tool No. MB990900, or equivalents, check turning torque of the drive bevel gear assembly as shown in **Fig. 65.** If turning torque is not within 1.23-1.81 ft. lbs., adjust by installing new spacers. Select spacers of nearly same thickness on both sides.

Transfer Case Adapter Subassembly

1. Unstake locknut and using special spanner tool No. MB991013, or equivalent, remove locknut, **Fig. 66.**
2. Using a press, remove driven gear bevel assembly.
3. Remove taper roller bearing, spacer, collar and outer races.
4. Reverse procedure to assemble, noting the following:
   a. When installing taper roller bearing, use installer cap tool No. MD998812, installer tube tool No. MD998814 and installer adapter tool No. MD998820, or equivalent, as shown in **Fig. 67.**

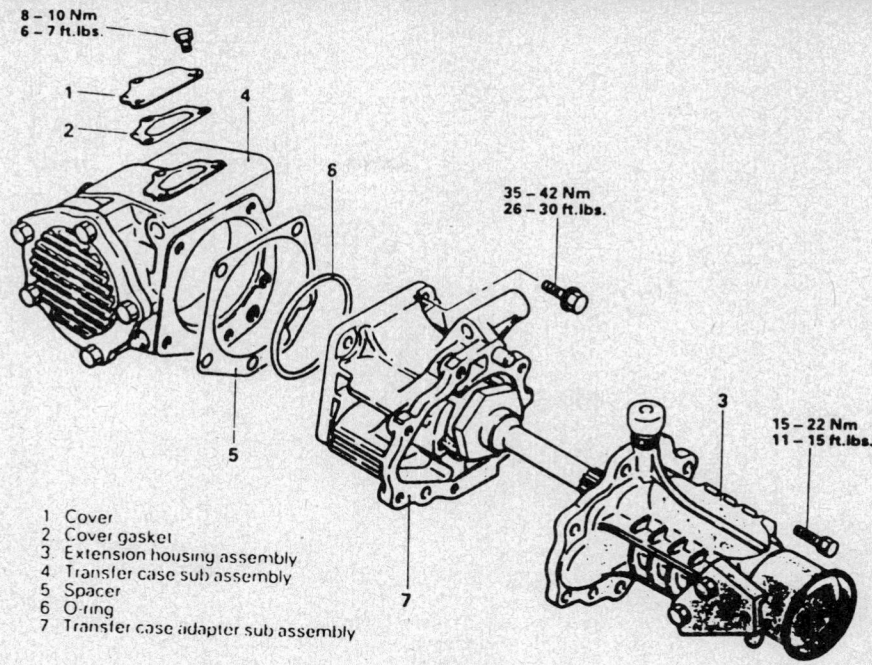

8 – 10 Nm
6 – 7 ft. lbs.

35 – 42 Nm
26 – 30 ft.lbs.

15 – 22 Nm
11 – 15 ft.lbs.

1 Cover
2 Cover gasket
3 Extension housing assembly
4 Transfer case sub assembly
5 Spacer
6 O-ring
7 Transfer case adapter sub assembly

CR3039100243000X

Fig. 62 Exploded view of transfer assembly. Laser, Talon & Colt Vista & Summit Wagon

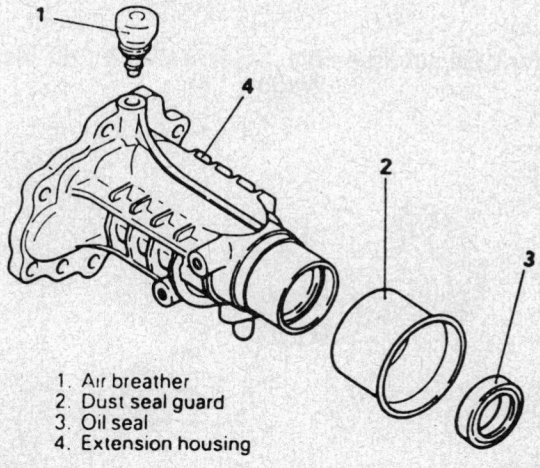

1. Air breather
2. Dust seal guard
3. Oil seal
4. Extension housing

CR3039100244000X

Fig. 63 Extension housing assembly. Laser, Talon & Colt Vista & Summit Wagon

b. **Torque** locknut to 102-115 ft. lbs., then stake locknut at two places.

c. Using wrench adapter tool No. MD998806 and suitable torque wrench, or equivalents, check turning torque of the driven bevel gear assembly as shown in **Fig. 68.** If turning torque is not within 0.72-1.23 ft. lbs., adjust with adjusting spacer.

Drive Bevel Gear Assembly

1. Using bearing removal tool No. MD998801, or equivalent, remove taper roller bearings and drive bevel gear as shown in **Fig. 69.**
2. Using installer cap tool No. MD998812 and installer adapter tool No. MD998827, or equivalent, install taper roller bearing above drive bevel gear, **Fig. 70.**
3. Using bearing installation tool No. MD998350, or equivalent, install taper roller bearing at opposite end drive bevel gear, **Fig. 70.**

Driven Bevel Gear Assembly

1. Using bearing removal tool No. MD998801, or equivalent, remove taper roller bearing from driven gear assembly, **Fig. 71.**
2. Use collar to install taper roller bearing onto driven bevel gear.

COLT VISTA & STEALTH

The transfer assembly used on these models cannot be serviced. If the transfer assembly, other than the extension housing, dust seal guard to rear oil seal, are found defective complete component replacement is required.

AXLE HUB
REPLACE
COLT VISTA & SUMMIT WAGON

1. Remove stabilizer bar assembly as outlined under "Stabilizer Bar, Re-

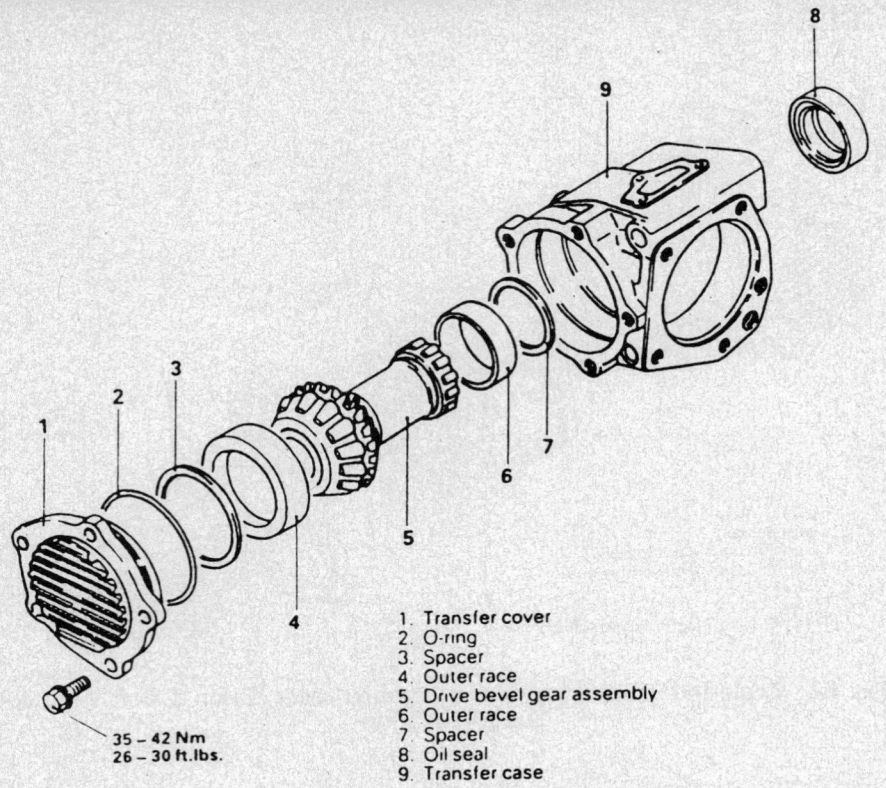

1. Transfer cover
2. O-ring
3. Spacer
4. Outer race
5. Drive bevel gear assembly
6. Outer race
7. Spacer
8. Oil seal
9. Transfer case

35 – 42 Nm
26 – 30 ft.lbs.

CR3039100245000X

Fig. 64   Transfer case subassembly. Laser, Talon & Colt Vista & Summit Wagon

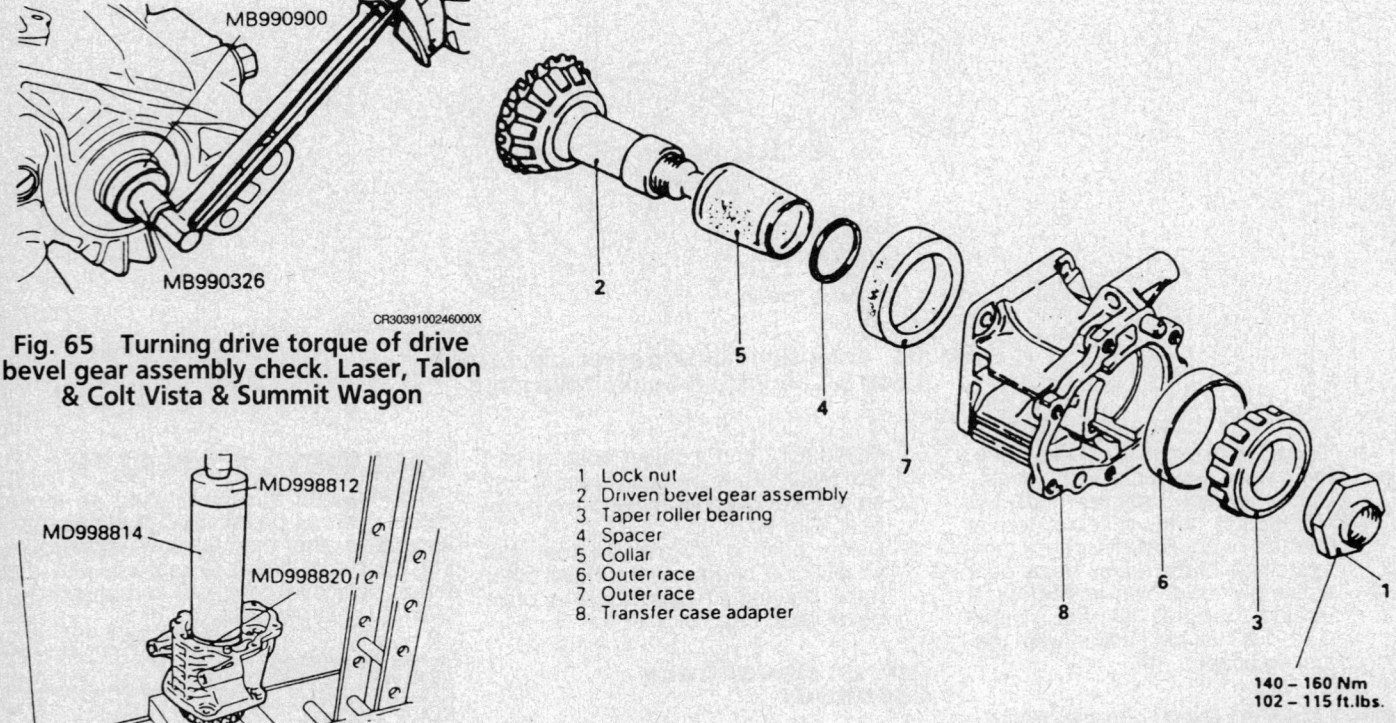

MB990900

MB990326

CR3039100246000X

Fig. 65   Turning drive torque of drive bevel gear assembly check. Laser, Talon & Colt Vista & Summit Wagon

MD998812

MD998814

MD998820

CR3039100248000X

Fig. 67   Taper roller bearing installation. Laser, Talon & Colt Vista & Summit Wagon

1. Lock nut
2. Driven bevel gear assembly
3. Taper roller bearing
4. Spacer
5. Collar
6. Outer race
7. Outer race
8. Transfer case adapter

140 – 160 Nm
102 – 115 ft.lbs.

CR3039100247000X

Fig. 66   Transfer case adapter subassembly. Laser, Talon & Colt Vista & Summit Wagon

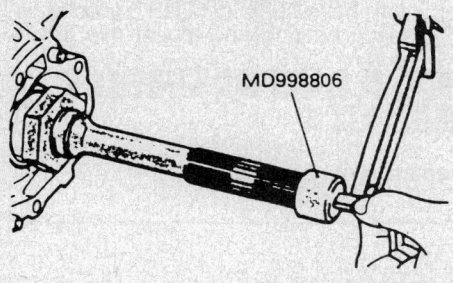

Fig. 68 Turning drive torque of driven bevel gear assembly check. Laser, Talon & Colt Vista & Summit Wagon

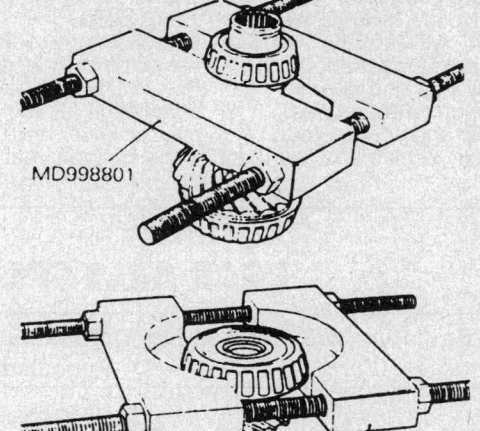

Fig. 69 Taper roller bearing removal from drive bevel gear assembly. Laser, Talon & Colt Vista & Summit Wagon

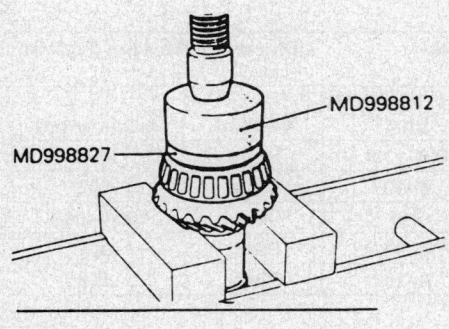

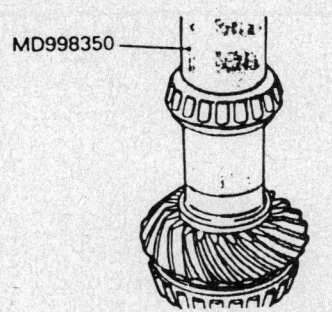

Fig. 70 Taper roller bearing installation on drive bevel gear assembly. Laser, Talon & Colt Vista & Summit Wagon

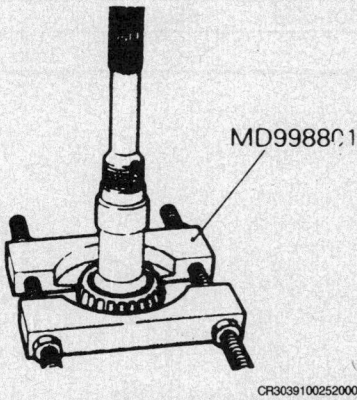

Fig. 71 Tapper roller bearing removal from driven bevel gear assembly. Laser, Talon & Colt Vista & Summit Wagon

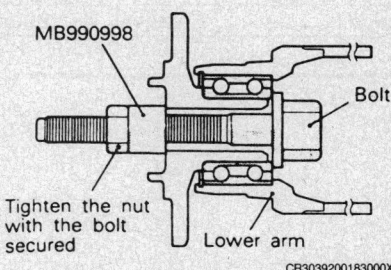

Fig. 72 Installing bolt tool. Colt Vista & Summit Wagon

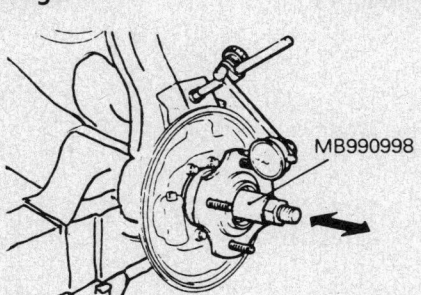

Fig. 73 Rear axle endplay inspection. Colt Vista & Summit Wagon

place" in the "Rear Suspension" section of the "Concorde, Intrepid, LHS, Vision & 1994-95 New Yorker."

2. Remove lower arm assembly as outlined under "Lower Arm, Replace" in the "Rear Suspension" section of the

"Concorde, Intrepid, LHS, Vision & 1994-95 New Yorker."

3. Mount lower arm assembly in a suitable vice then remove rear axle hub using a slide hammer and adapter tool Nos. MB990241 & MB990211, or

equivalents.

4. Remove wheel bearing snap ring then press wheel bearing race off of axle hub using bearing remover tool No. MB990560, or equivalent.

5. Using bearing removal tool Nos. MB990938 and MB990934, remove wheel bearing from lower arm.

6. Check rear hub spline for wear or damage and dust shield for deformation or damage.

7. Using a suitable press and bearing installation tool Nos. MB991400, MB991401 and MB991411, or equivalents, press rear wheel bearing into lower arm.

8. Using a suitable press and bearing installation tool Nos. MB991400, MB991401 and MB991411, or equivalents, press axle hub into bearing in lower arm.

9. Inspect wheel bearing starting torque and follows:

   a. Use bolt tool No. MB990998, or equivalent to mount rear hub onto lower arm as shown in **Fig. 72**.

   b. **Torque** nut of special bolt to 145-188 ft. lbs.

   c. Rotate rear hub to seat bearing.

   d. With bolt tool installed, measure wheel bearing starting torque using torque wrench, adapter and socket tool Nos. MB990998, MB990685 and MB990326, or equivalents. Starting torque should be 9 inch lbs. or less and bearing must not feel rough when rotated.

10. Install a dial indicator and adapter tool No. MB990998, or equivalent, as shown in **Fig. 73** to ensure endplay is .0020 inch.

11. If starting torque and rear hub endplay are not with in limits with nut **torqued** to 145-188 ft. lbs., check for correct installation of the bearing, rear hub and/or lower arm.

12. If the bearing, rear hub and/or lower arm have been installed correctly, replace bearing and repeat this procedure.

AXLE HUB ASSEMBLY SERVICE

Refer to "Axle Hub, Replace" for bearing replacement procedure.

REAR AXLE SPECIFICATIONS

NOTE: On Models Equipped With Limited Slip Differential, Refer To "Limited Slip Differential (LSD)" Section For Specifications.

Model	Carrier Type	Ring Gear & Pinion Backlash		Pinion Bearing Preload			Differential Bearing Preload	
		Method	Adjustment	Method	With Seal Inch Lbs.	Less Seal Inch Lbs.	Method	Adjustment
Colt Vista	Removal	Shim	.004–.006	Shim	6.1–8.6	8.6–11.3	Shim	.002
Laser	Removal	Shim	.004–.006	Shim	—	8–10	Shim	.002
Stealth	Removal	Shim	.004–.006	Shim	—	3–4	Nut	.004–.006
Summit Wagon	Removal	Shim	.004–.006	Shim	6.1–8.6	8.6–11.3	Shim	.002
Talon	Removal	Shim	.004–.006	Shim	—	8–10	Shim	.002

ACTIVE SUSPENSION SYSTEMS

TABLE OF CONTENTS

Automatic Level Control

NOTE: On Air Bag Equipped Models, Refer To "Air Bag System Precautions" Located In The Front Of This Manual For System Disarming & Arming Procedures.

INDEX

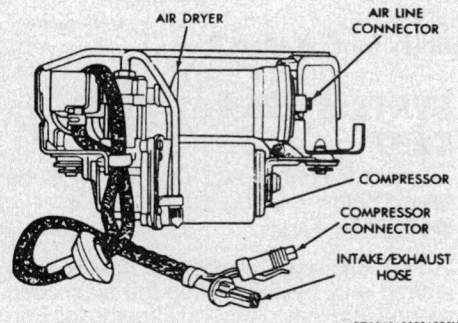

Fig. 1   Compressor assembly

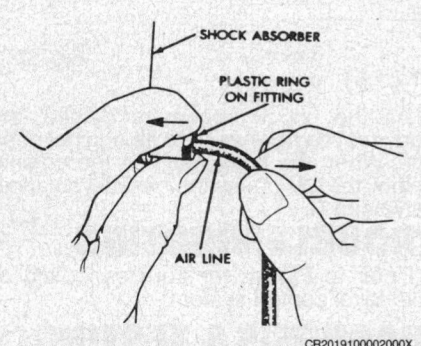

Fig. 2   Air line removal

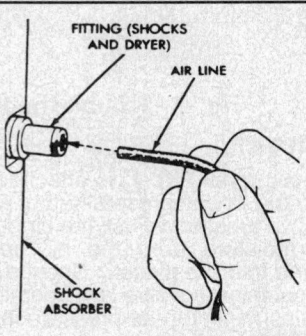

Fig. 3   Air line installation

PRECAUTIONS
AIR BAG SYSTEMS

Refer to "Air Bag System Precautions" in the front of this manual for system disarming and arming procedures.

DESCRIPTION

The Automatic Load Leveling System (ALLS) adjusts the carrying height of the vehicle when weight is added or removed from the vehicle. The ALLS system consists of an air compressor, electronic height sensor, compressor relay, manual switch, exhaust solenoid, an air dryer and air adjustable shock absorbers.

SYSTEM COMPONENTS

Air Compressor

The air compressor supplies air pressure between 170-220 psi to the rear shocks, the air compressor assembly, **Fig. 1** is located near the vehicle's rear axle. Air is also released from the system by way of an exhaust valve located in the compressor head.

Control Module (CM)

The Control Module (CM) is a device that controls the ground circuits for the compressor relay and the exhaust valve solenoid. A microprocessor within the CM limits the compressor pump operation time to 140 to 160 seconds to prevent damage to compressor motor.

In addition, there is an air regeneration cycle that is controlled by the CM, if the height sensor signal is the neutral or high position. When the ignition switch in turned to the ON position, after a 22 to 28 second delay the compressor will run from 2 to 6 seconds.

To prevent excessive cycling, a 12 to 18 second delay is incorporated in the microprocessor.

Height Sensor

This sensor switch is located in the RH rear shock absorber and monitors the height at rear of vehicle. The sensor sends signals to the Control Module as to the status of the height, low, trim or high.

Air Lines & Fittings

To release an air line from its fitting, pull back on plastic ring and pull air line from fitting, **Fig. 2**. The fitting has a unique push in feature. A brass type collet locks the air line in place. One rubber O-ring seals the air line. To attach air line, push line into fitting, **Fig. 3**.

Compressor Relay

The compressor relay completes the circuit to the compressor when energized by the height sensor. The relay is located either next to the compressor, in relay panel under instrument panel or in wiring harness above steering column.

Air Adjustable Shocks Absorbers

Air shock absorbers are essentially hydraulic shock absorbers with a neoprene bladder sealing the upper and lower sections together, forming an air cylinder.

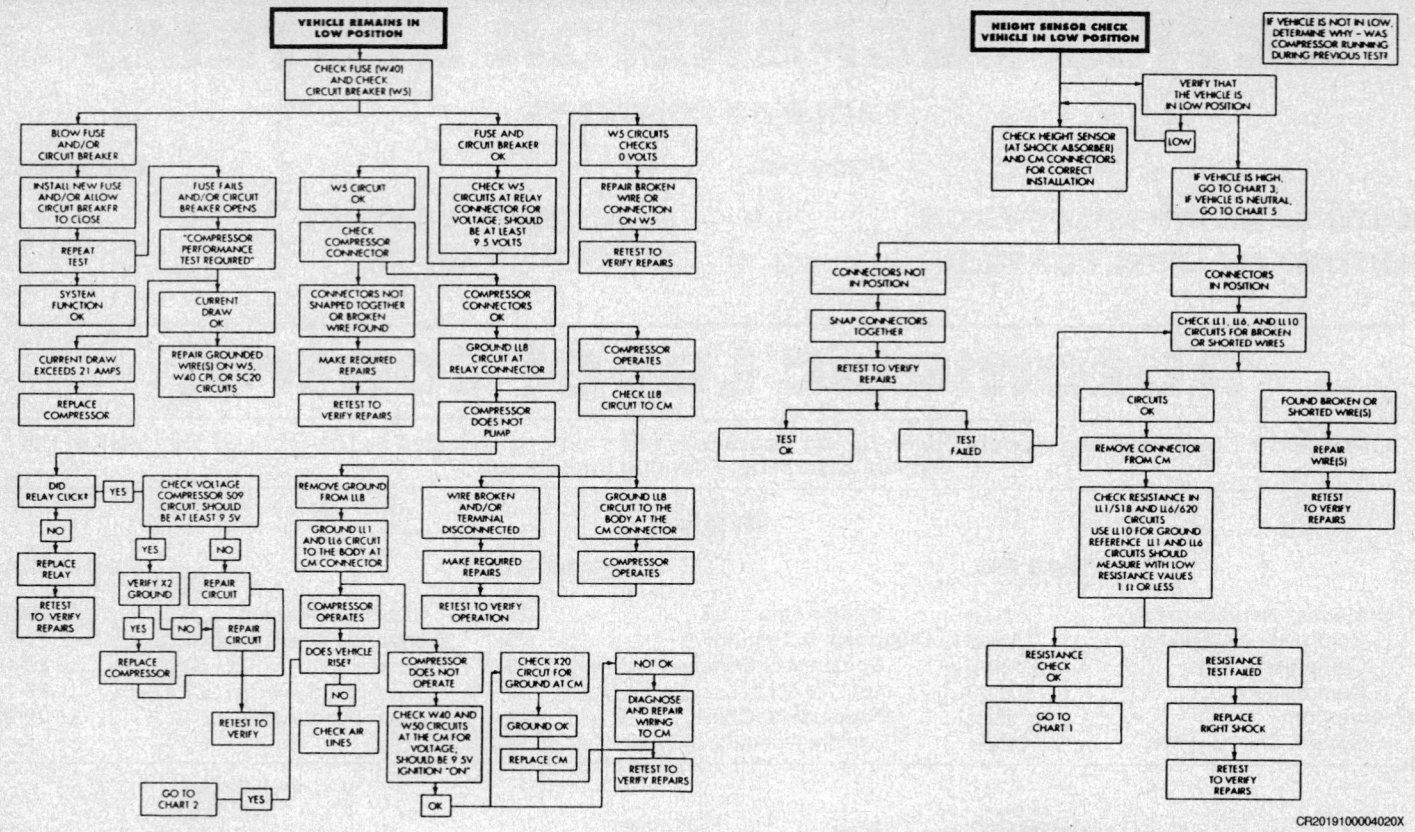

Fig. 4   Troubleshooting (Part 1 of 5)

Fig. 4   Troubleshooting (Part 2 of 5)

Air Dryer

The air dryer, **Fig. 1,** is attached externally to the air compressor output and performs two functions. First, the air dryer absorbs moisture from the air before is delivered into the system. Second, the air dryer contains a valve arrangement that maintains minimum air pressure in the air adjustable shock absorbers.

SYSTEM OPERATION

Raising The Vehicle

When weight is added to the rear suspension lowering the height sensor, this action will activate the internal time delay circuit. After a time delay of 12–18 seconds, the Control Module (CM) activates the ground circuit to the compressor relay.

With the relay grounded, the compressor motor runs and air is sent through the system. As the shock absorbers inflate, the body moves upward to a corrected position. When the body reaches the correct height, the CM stops the compressor operation.

Lowering The Vehicle

When weight is removed from the rear suspension raising the height sensor, this action will activate the internal time delay circuit. After a time delay of 12–18 seconds, the Control Module (CM) activates the ground circuit to the exhaust valve solenoid. Air is exhausted from the shock absorbers through the air dryer and exhaust solenoid into the atmosphere.

As the shock absorbers deflate, the body moves downward to its original position. When the body reaches the original height, the CM opens the exhaust solenoid valve circuit.

TROUBLESHOOTING

Refer to **Fig. 4,** for troubleshooting of auto level control system.

DIAGNOSIS & TESTING

Prior to performing diagnosis tests, check and ensure that all fuses and fuse links are in good condition. Check all connectors that link the system to the main body wiring harness. These include the compressor, height sensor, Control Module, relay and underbody to trunk and load leveling harness to main harness. Check all air lines, connectors and other components for correct installation.

Refer to **Fig. 5,** for system wiring circuits when performing diagnosis of system.

To properly perform the following diagnosis and testing the use of a DRBII readout tool or equivalent is required, follow tool manufacturers instructions for proper installation of the tool prior to testing speed control system.

Refer to **Figs. 6 through 14,** for diagnosis and testing of automatic load leveling system. After system testing has been completed, perform verification test shown in **Fig. 7.**

SYSTEM TESTING

Refer to **Fig. 5,** for system wiring circuits when performing testing of system.

SYSTEM OPERATIONAL TEST

A test weight of 275-300 lbs. must be added before starting diagnosis tests.

Preparation

The following system test operation is started only by connecting the diagnostic ground terminal to ground after the ignition switch is turned to the ON position. A monitor lamp must be connected between the Test lamp ground terminal, **Fig. 15,** to display the Control Module status.

1. Remove protective connector cover from diagnosis connector located behind the right rear quarter trim panel.
2. Insert a wire into diagnostic ground terminal, **Fig. 15,** then attach to compressor ground terminal or as an alternate, insert wire into diagnostic ground terminal. Ground other end of test wire to body ground or a Control Module fastener.

Operation

1. The compressor relay output, from the Control Module (CM), is activated until the vehicle is in the high position. The maximum relay output operation time is 140-160 seconds. If the expected position is not obtained, the CM ceases test and any further operation. The monitor lamp output is continuously activated until the ignition is cycled from OFF to ON or 1 hour has passed after the ignition switch was turned to the OFF position.

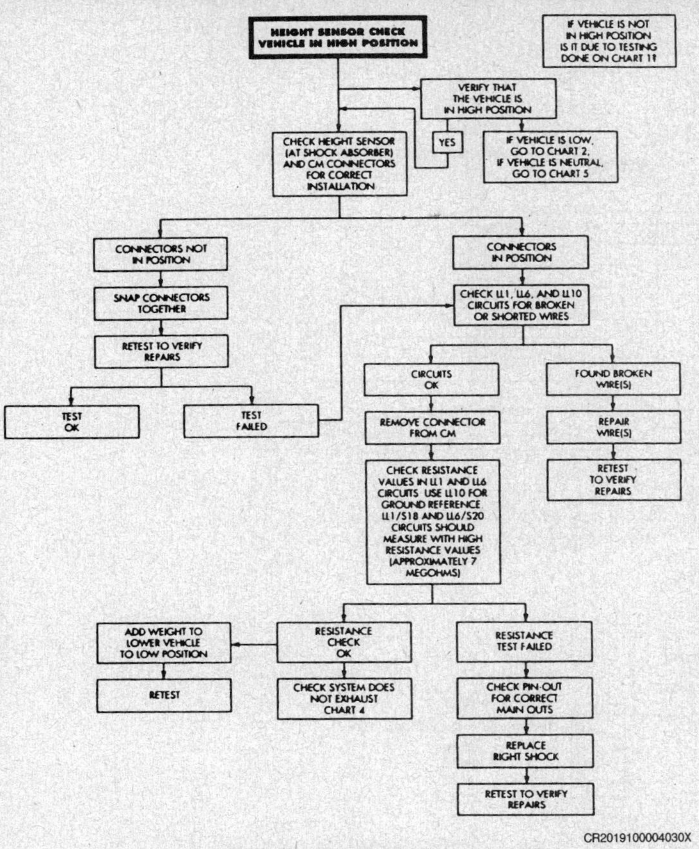

HEIGHT SENSOR CHECK VEHICLE IN HIGH POSITION

IF VEHICLE IS NOT IN HIGH POSITION IS IT DUE TO TESTING DONE ON CHART 1?

VERIFY THAT THE VEHICLE IS IN HIGH POSITION

CHECK HEIGHT SENSOR (AT SHOCK ABSORBER) AND CM CONNECTORS FOR CORRECT INSTALLATION

YES

IF VEHICLE IS LOW, GO TO CHART 2. IF VEHICLE IS NEUTRAL, GO TO CHART 5

CONNECTORS NOT IN POSITION

CONNECTORS IN POSITION

SNAP CONNECTORS TOGETHER

RETEST TO VERIFY REPAIRS

CHECK LL1, LL6, AND LL10 CIRCUITS FOR BROKEN OR SHORTED WIRES

TEST OK

TEST FAILED

CIRCUITS OK

FOUND BROKEN WIRE(S)

REMOVE CONNECTOR FROM CM

REPAIR WIRE(S)

CHECK RESISTANCE VALUES IN LL1 AND LL6 CIRCUITS USE LL10 FOR GROUND REFERENCE LL1/S18 AND LL6/S20 CIRCUITS SHOULD MEASURE WITH HIGH RESISTANCE VALUES (APPROXIMATELY 7 MEGOHMS)

RETEST TO VERIFY REPAIRS

ADD WEIGHT TO LOWER VEHICLE TO LOW POSITION

RESISTANCE CHECK OK

RESISTANCE TEST FAILED

RETEST

CHECK SYSTEM DOES NOT EXHAUST CHART 4

CHECK PIN-OUT FOR CORRECT MAIN OUTS

REPLACE RIGHT SHOCK

RETEST TO VERIFY REPAIRS

CR2019100004030X

Fig. 4 Troubleshooting (Part 3 of 5)

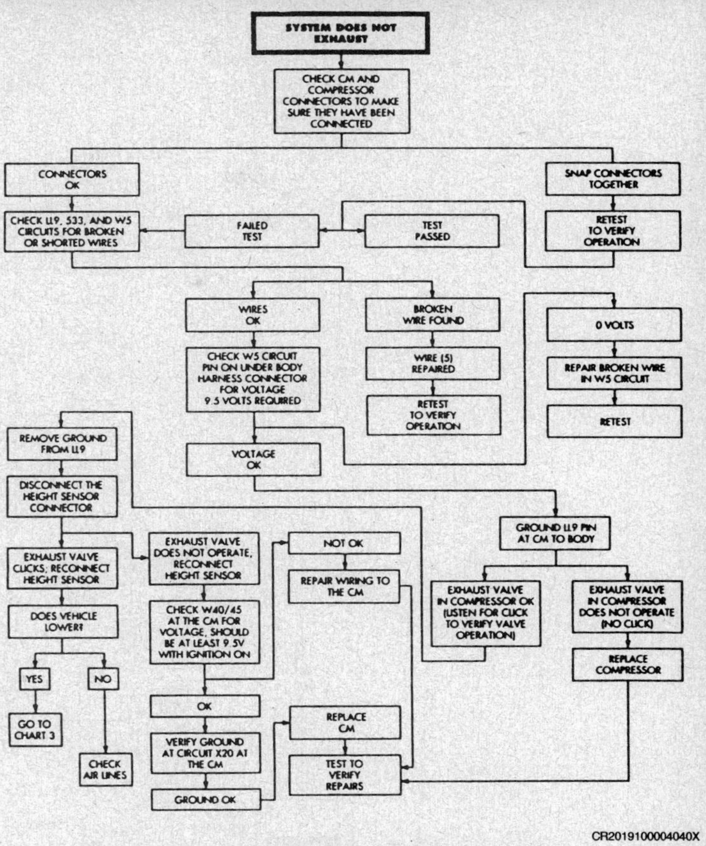

SYSTEM DOES NOT EXHAUST

CHECK CM AND COMPRESSOR CONNECTORS TO MAKE SURE THEY HAVE BEEN CONNECTED

CONNECTORS OK

SNAP CONNECTORS TOGETHER

CHECK LL9, S33, AND W5 CIRCUITS FOR BROKEN OR SHORTED WIRES

FAILED TEST

TEST PASSED

RETEST TO VERIFY OPERATION

WIRES OK

BROKEN WIRE FOUND

0 VOLTS

CHECK W5 CIRCUIT PIN ON UNDER BODY HARNESS CONNECTOR FOR VOLTAGE 9.5 VOLTS REQUIRED

WIRE (S) REPAIRED

REPAIR BROKEN WIRE IN W5 CIRCUIT

REMOVE GROUND FROM LL9

VOLTAGE OK

RETEST TO VERIFY OPERATION

RETEST

DISCONNECT THE HEIGHT SENSOR CONNECTOR

EXHAUST VALVE DOES NOT OPERATE, RECONNECT HEIGHT SENSOR

NOT OK

GROUND LL9 PIN AT CM TO BODY

EXHAUST VALVE CLICKS; RECONNECT HEIGHT SENSOR

REPAIR WIRING TO THE CM

CHECK W40/45 AT THE CM FOR VOLTAGE, SHOULD BE AT LEAST 9.5V WITH IGNITION ON

EXHAUST VALVE IN COMPRESSOR OK (LISTEN FOR CLICK TO VERIFY VALVE OPERATION)

EXHAUST VALVE IN COMPRESSOR DOES NOT OPERATE (NO CLICK)

DOES VEHICLE LOWER?

YES

NO

GO TO CHART 3

CHECK AIR LINES

OK

VERIFY GROUND AT CIRCUIT X20 AT THE CM

REPLACE CM

REPLACE COMPRESSOR

GROUND OK

TEST TO VERIFY REPAIRS

CR2019100004040X

Fig. 4 Troubleshooting (Part 4 of 5)

HEIGHT SENSOR CHECK VEHICLE IN MID POSITION

VERIFY THAT THE VEHICLE IS AT CORRECT HEIGHT

YES

NO

CHECK HEIGHT SENSOR (AT SHOCK ABSORBER) AND CM CONNECTORS FOR CORRECT INSTALLATION

IF VEHICLE IS HIGH, GO TO CHART 3. IF VEHICLE IS LOW, GO TO CHART 2.

CONNECTORS NOT IN POSITION

CONNECTORS IN POSITION

SNAP CONNECTORS TOGETHER

CHECK LL1, LL6, AND LL10 CIRCUITS FOR BROKEN OR SHORTED WIRES

RETEST TO VERIFY REPAIRS

TEST OK

TEST FAILED

CIRCUITS OK

FOUND BROKEN WIRE(S)

REMOVE CONNECTOR FROM CM

REPAIR WIRE(S)

CHECK RESISTANCE VALUES IN LL1 AND LL6 CIRCUITS. USE LL10 FOR GROUND REFERENCE. LL6 CIRCUIT SHOULD MEASURE APPROXIMATELY 7 MEGOHMS. LL1 CIRCUIT SHOULD MEASURE AT 1 Ω OR LESS

RETEST TO VERIFY REPAIRS

RESISTANCE CHECK OK

RESISTANCE TEST FAILED

REPLACE CM

REPLACE RIGHT SHOCK

RETEST TO VERIFY REPAIRS

RETEST TO VERIFY REPAIRS

CR2019100004050X

Fig. 4 Troubleshooting (Part 5 of 5)

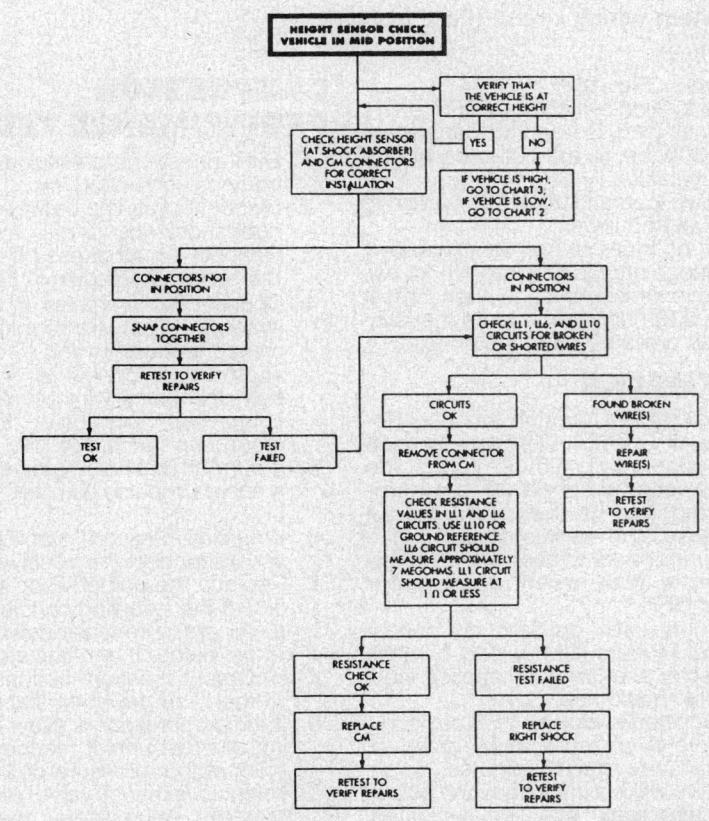

2. The monitor lamp output should flash to indicate the position of the height sensor. The sensor should be in the high position. A continuously lighted monitor lamp will indicate a failure.

3. Next the exhaust solenoid output is activated until the vehicle is in the low position. The maximum exhaust solenoid operation time is 110–130 seconds. If the expected position is not obtained, the CM ceases test and any further operation. The monitor lamp output is lighted continuously until the ignition is cycled from OFF to ON or 1 hour has passed after the ignition switch was turned to the OFF position.

4. The monitor lamp should flash to indicate the height sensor in the low position. A continuously lighted monitor lamp will indicate a failure.

5. The compressor relay output is activated to return the vehicle to the level position. The maximum operation time of the relay is 140–160 seconds. If the expected position is not obtained, the CM ceases test and any further operation. The monitor lamp is continuously lighted until the ignition is cycled from OFF to ON or 1 hour has passed after the ignition switch was turned to the OFF position.

6. Completion of test is when test successfully completed, the CM resumes normal operation. The test is now complete. throughout the testing, the vehicle load must be maintained, no

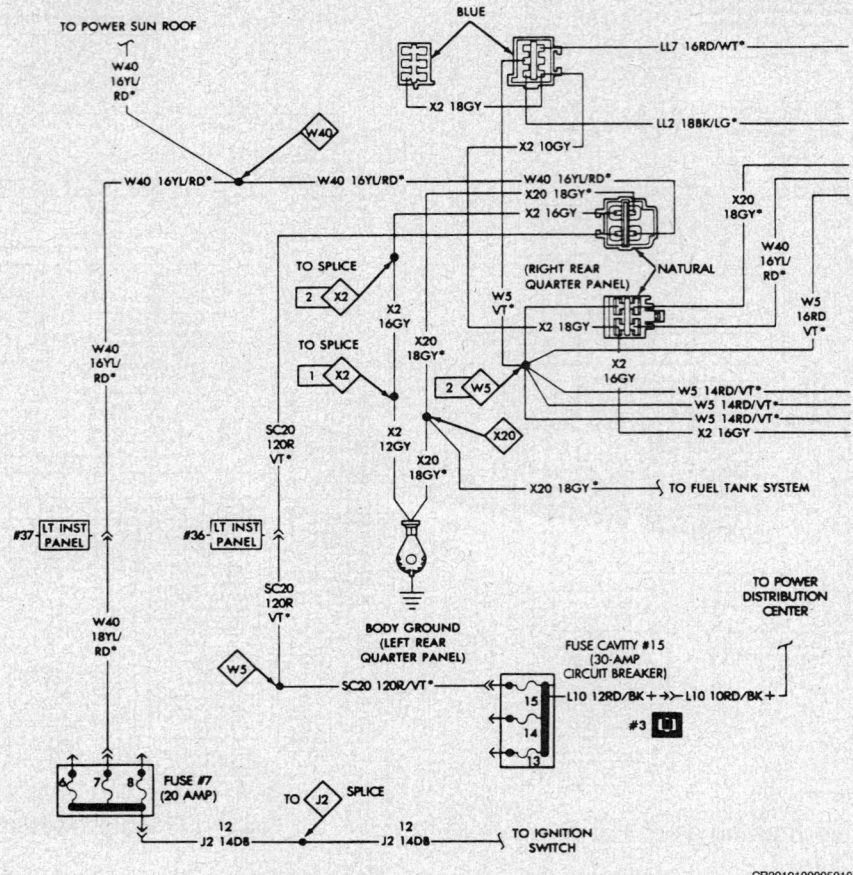

Fig. 5   System wiring circuit (Part 1 of 2)

CR2019100005010X

loads are allow to be added or removed to or from the vehicle once the test have been started.
7. If any of the tests fail, refer to the charts shown under "Troubleshooting."

Verification Test

To verify system operation test, disconnect test ground wire then reconnect and perform test again.

Termination Of Test

The test operation is terminated when any of the following takes place:
1. Disconnecting the diagnostic input from ground circuit.
2. Turning ignition switch to OFF position.

When test operation is terminated, the CM resumes normal operation unless it ceases operation due to it detecting a system malfunction.

RESIDUAL AIR CHECK

The air dryer has a valve arrangement which maintains a minimum pressure in the shocks to improve ride characteristics under light load conditions. To check this function, proceed as follows:
1. Remove air line from dryer fitting and right shock absorber. Install a suitable 0-300 psi pressure gauge in line as

shown in, **Fig. 16.**
2. Cycle ignition switch from OFF to ON.
3. Apply a load to rear suspension of 275-300 lbs. to run compressor and raise vehicle.
4. Remove load and allow the system to exhaust and lower.
5. When no more air can be exhausted, the gauge should indicate 10-22 psi.
6. Remove pressure gage then repeat steps 2 through 4 to ensure that system air pressure on in the shocks.

LEAK CHECKS

1. Repeat steps 1 through 3 under "Residual Air Check." Allow system to fill until gage reads 70-90 psi. **If the compressor is permitted to run until it reaches its maximum output pressure, the vent solenoid valve will function as a relief valve resulting in a leak when compressor shuts OFF.**
2. With load still applied, disconnect Control Module (CM) wiring harness connector, then remove applied load. Vehicle should rise.
3. Turn ignition switch to OFF position.
4. Observe if pressure leaks down or holds steady after 15 minutes.
5. If system will not inflate beyond 50 psi, a severe leak may be indicated. Check for pinched pressure line between compressor and shocks.

COMPRESSOR PERFORMANCE TEST

1. Disconnect compressor motor wiring harness connector.
2. Disconnect air line between dryer and right shock absorber.
3. Connect an air pressure gauge into the system as shown in **Fig. 17.**
4. Connect an ammeter in series between the red wire terminal in compressor connector and a 12 volt power source. Connect a ground wire from the black wire terminal on the compressor connector to a good ground on frame, **Fig. 17.**
5. If current draw to motor exceeds 21 amperes, replace compressor assembly.
6. When air pressure stabilizes at 120 psi, disconnect the positive wire lead.
7. Replace the compressor assembly if any of the following conditions exists:
   a. Air pressure leaks down below 90 psi before it remains steady.
   b. Output pressure builds up to less than 110 psi when stabilizes.
8. If the compressor is allow to run during this test until it reaches its maximum output pressure of 220 psi, the solenoid exhaust valve will act as a pressure relief valve. the resulting leak down, after the compressor is shut off will indicate a false leak.

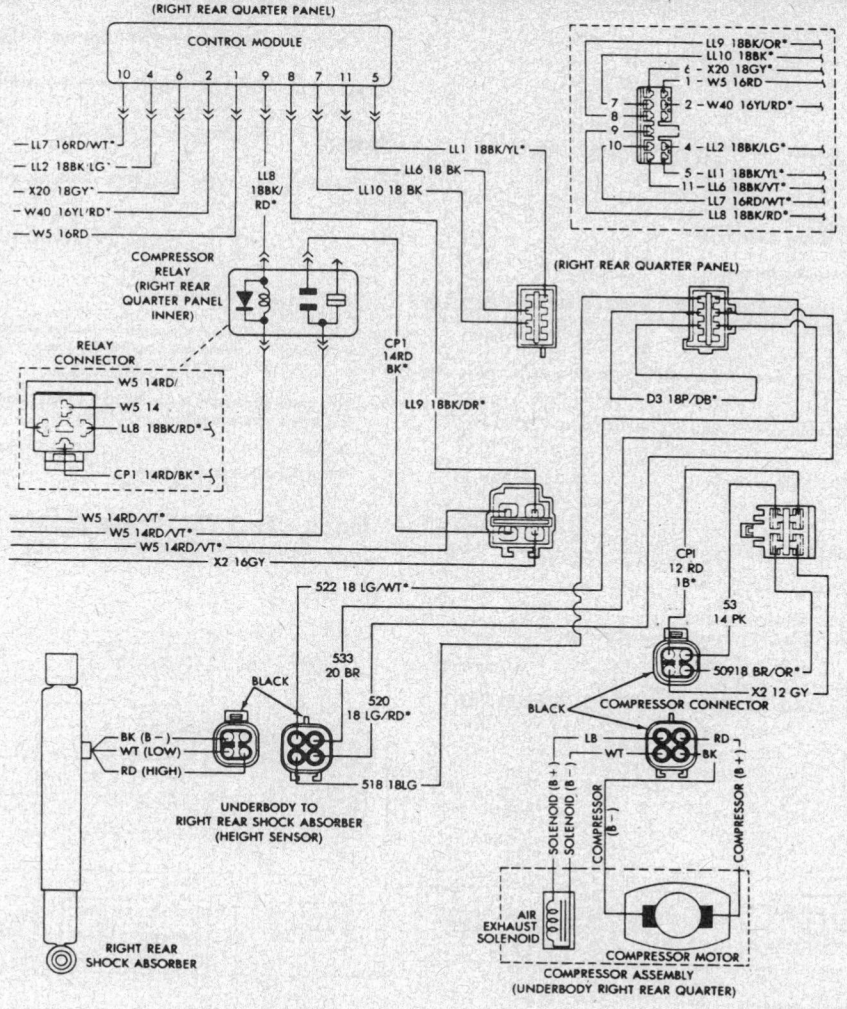

Fig. 5 System wiring circuit (Part 2 of 2)

CR2019100005020X

DIAGNOSTIC CHART INDEX

Test	Description	Page No.	Fig. No.
1A	Load Leveling System Inspection	29-6	6
2A	Repair Verification	29-6	7
2B	No Diagnostic Trouble Code Messages Test	29-6	8
3A	Compressor Inspection	29-6	9
4A	Battery To Module Voltage Supply Inspection	29-7	10
5A	Air Exhaust System Inspection	29-7	11
6A	Height Sensor "Trim" Input Inspection	29-7	12
7A	Height Sensor Ground Inspection	29-8	13
8A	Height Sensor Circuit Inspection	29-8	14

1. Perform a visual inspection.

2. Connect the DRBII to the load leveling diagnostic connector located near the LLCM.

3. Turn the ignition key on.

4. Using the DRBII, actuate the load leveler system test.

   >> Do not turn the ignition key off during the test.

   >> Sit on the trunk lid opening throughout the test. This must be done to force the vehicle to the the "low" position. Only 150 pounds are necessary, and more weight may cause the test to "time out."

5. Refer to the following message list for the correct diagnostic test to perform for each message that is displayed on the DRBII.

   "TESTING COMPLETE LOAD LEVELER PASSED ALL DIAGNOSTIC TESTS" .... Test 2B

   "TEST 1: TEST FAILED, FAILED TO LEVEL CAR" .... Test 3A

   "TEST 1: TEST FAILED, TIME OUT ERROR" .... Test 4A

   "TEST 2: TEST FAILED, FAILED TO LEVEL CAR" .... Test 5A

   "TEST 3: TEST FAILED, FAILED TO LEVEL CAR" .... Test 3A

   "ERROR FROM PREVIOUS LOAD LEVELER TEST"
   Turn the ignition off and retest system. If the message reappears, go to .... Test 8A

   CR2019100006000X

Fig. 6   Test 1A: Load Leveling System Inspection.

1. Reconnect all connectors that were disconnected during your repair.

2. Use the DRBII to re-perform the system test.

3. If any further fault messages appear, perform TEST 1A again.

4. Replace all covers and trim, and return vehicle to owner.

CR2019100007000X

Fig. 7   Test 2A: Repair Verification

1. Make sure that no leaks are present in the load leveling system. To do this, use a soap and water spray bottle to check and pinpoint any leaks.

2. If the owner's complaint is that the load leveling system does not level the vehicle, a compressor output test should be done.

3. Return the vehicle to the owner.

CR2019100008000X

Fig. 8   Test 2B: No Diagnostic Trouble Code Message Test

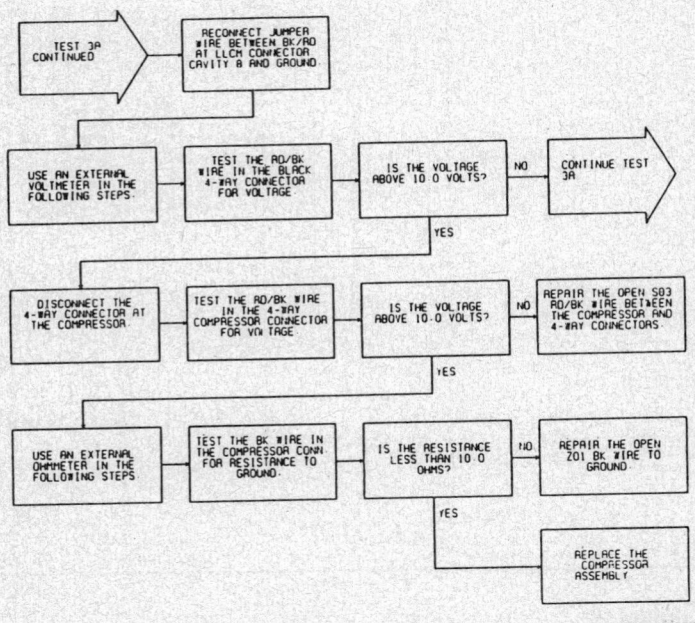

CR2019100009020X

Fig. 9   Test 3A: Compressor Inspection (Part 2 of 3)

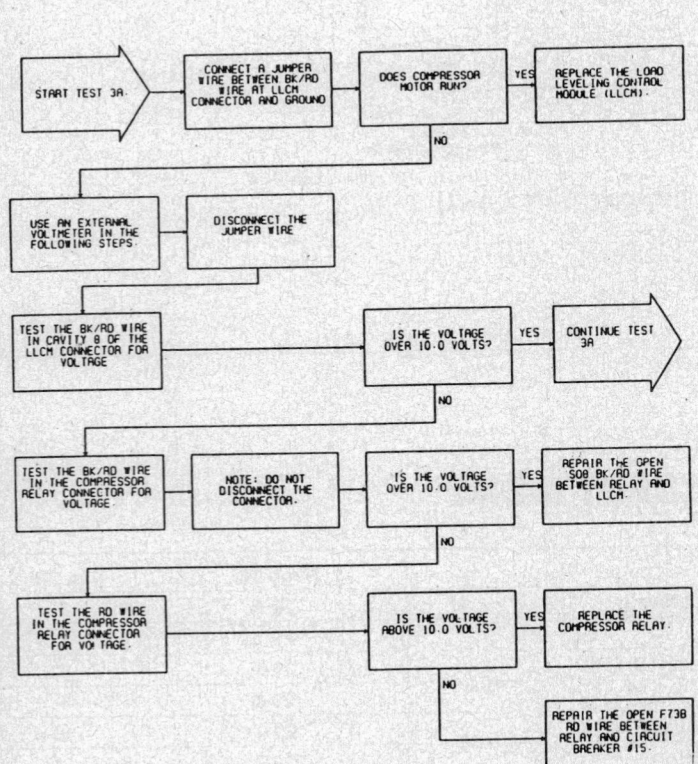

CR2019100009010X

Fig. 9   Test 3A: Compressor Inspection (Part 1 of 3)

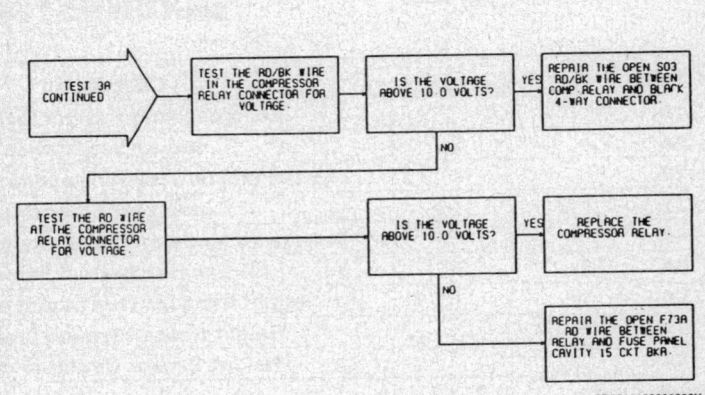

CR2019100009030X

Fig. 9   Test 3A: Compressor Inspection (Part 3 of 3)

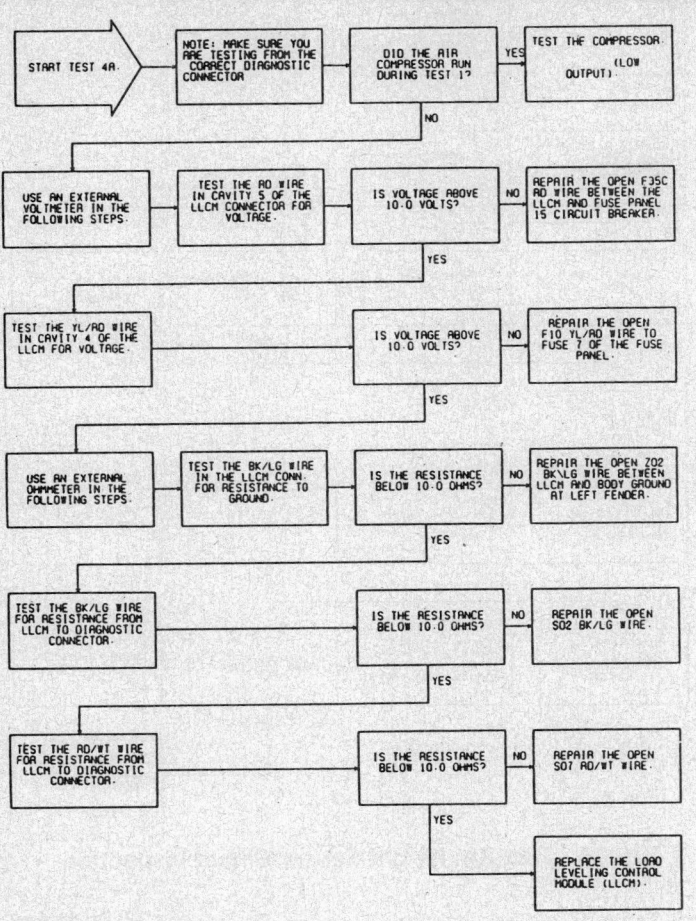

Fig. 10 Test 4A: Battery To Module Voltage Supply Inspection

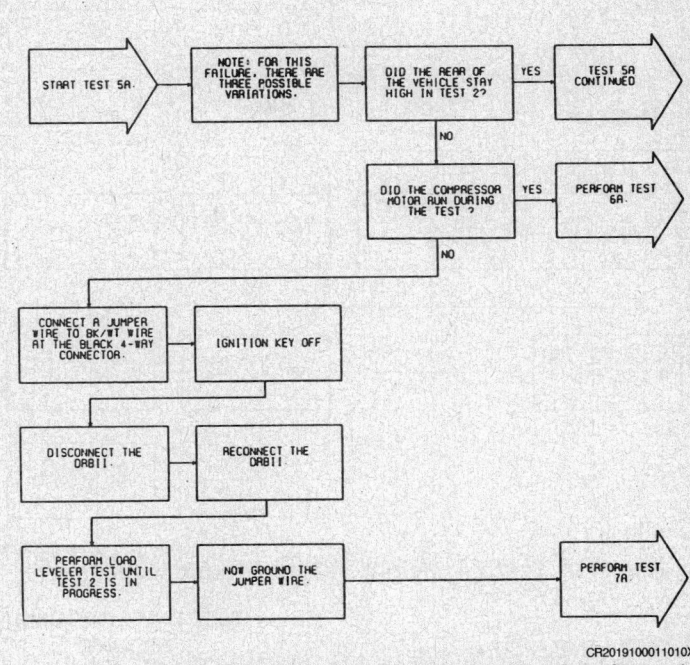

Fig. 11 Test 5A: Air Exhaust System Inspection (Part 1 of 2)

Fig. 11 Test 5A: Air Exhaust System Inspection (Part 2 of 2)

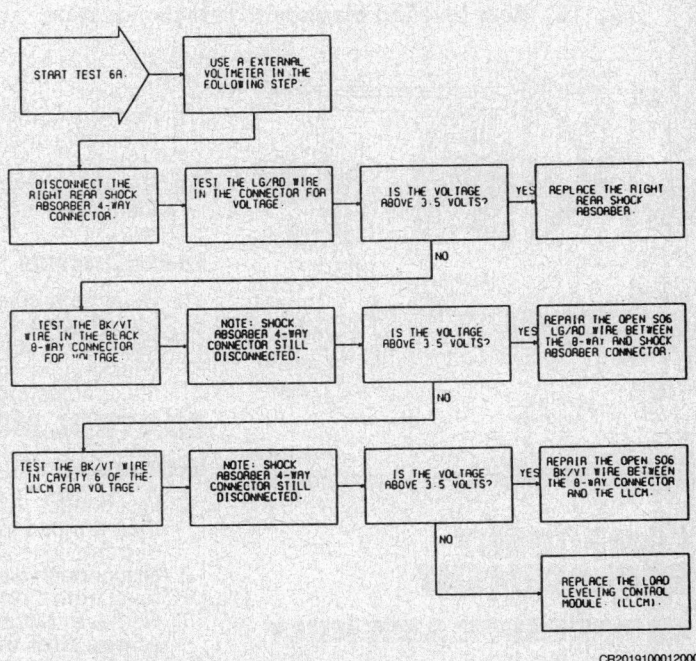

Fig. 12 Test 6A: Height Sensor "Trim" Input Inspection

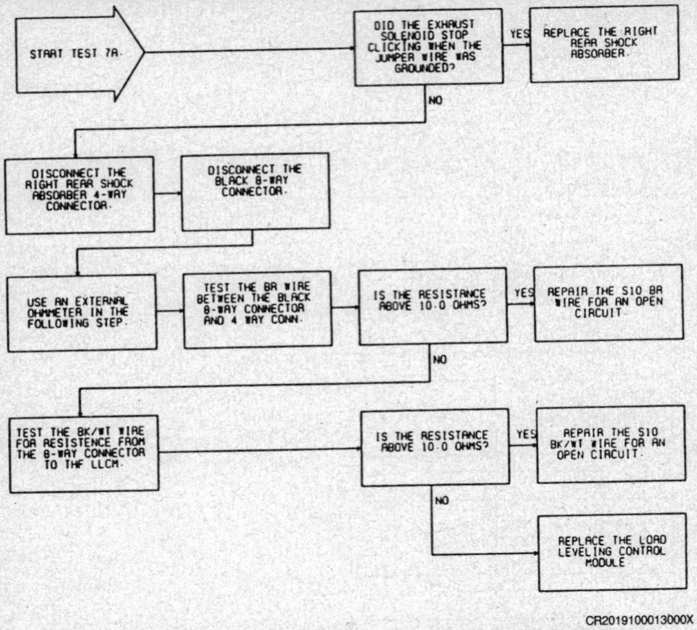

Test 7A (flowchart, Fig. 13)

START TEST 7A →

DID THE EXHAUST SOLENOID STOP CLICKING WHEN THE JUMPER WIRE WAS GROUNDED? — YES → REPLACE THE RIGHT REAR SHOCK ABSORBER.

NO ↓

DISCONNECT THE RIGHT REAR SHOCK ABSORBER 4-WAY CONNECTOR. → DISCONNECT THE BLACK 8-WAY CONNECTOR. ↓

USE AN EXTERNAL OHMMETER IN THE FOLLOWING STEP. → TEST THE BR WIRE BETWEEN THE BLACK 8-WAY CONNECTOR AND 4 WAY CONN. → IS THE RESISTANCE ABOVE 10.0 OHMS? — YES → REPAIR THE S10 BR WIRE FOR AN OPEN CIRCUIT.

NO ↓

TEST THE BK/WT WIRE FOR RESISTENCE FROM THE 8-WAY CONNECTOR TO THE LLCM. → IS THE RESISTANCE ABOVE 10.0 OHMS? — YES → REPAIR THE S10 BK/WT WIRE FOR AN OPEN CIRCUIT.

NO ↓

REPLACE THE LOAD LEVELING CONTROL MODULE.

CR2019100013000X

Fig. 13   Test 7A: Height Sensor Ground Inspection

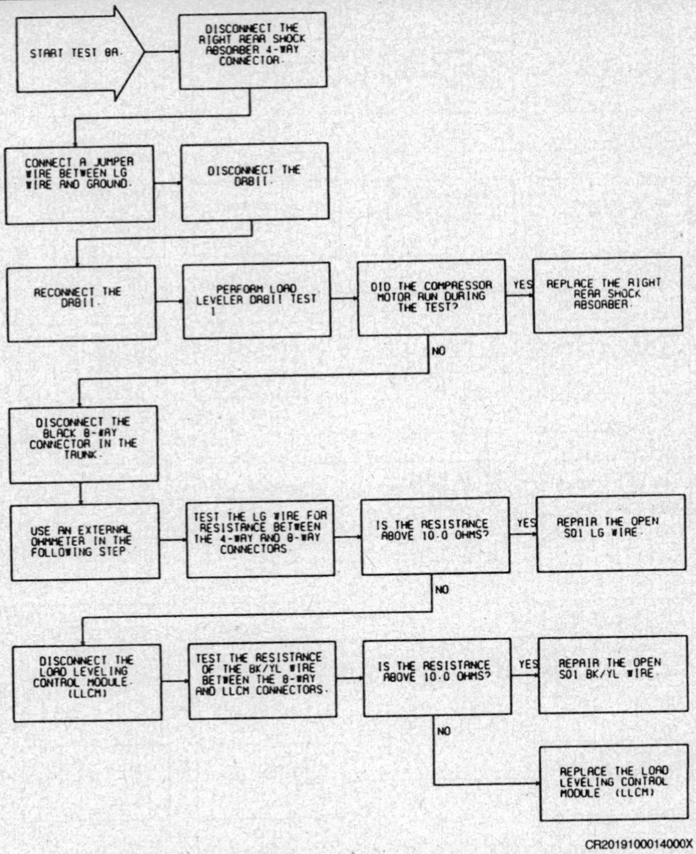

Test 8A (flowchart, Fig. 14)

START TEST 8A → DISCONNECT THE RIGHT REAR SHOCK ABSORBER 4-WAY CONNECTOR. ↓

CONNECT A JUMPER WIRE BETWEEN LG WIRE AND GROUND. → DISCONNECT THE DRBII. ↓

RECONNECT THE DRBII. → PERFORM LOAD LEVELER DRBII TEST. → DID THE COMPRESSOR MOTOR RUN DURING THE TEST? — YES → REPLACE THE RIGHT REAR SHOCK ABSORBER.

NO ↓

DISCONNECT THE BLACK 8-WAY CONNECTOR IN THE TRUNK. ↓

USE AN EXTERNAL OHMMETER IN THE FOLLOWING STEP. → TEST THE LG WIRE FOR RESISTANCE BETWEEN THE 4-WAY AND 8-WAY CONNECTORS. → IS THE RESISTANCE ABOVE 10.0 OHMS? — YES → REPAIR THE OPEN S01 LG WIRE.

NO ↓

DISCONNECT THE LOAD LEVELING CONTROL MODULE (LLCM). → TEST THE RESISTANCE OF THE BK/YL WIRE BETWEEN THE 8-WAY AND LLCM CONNECTORS. → IS THE RESISTANCE ABOVE 10.0 OHMS? — YES → REPAIR THE OPEN S01 BK/YL WIRE.

NO ↓

REPLACE THE LOAD LEVELING CONTROL MODULE (LLCM).

CR2019100014000X

Fig. 14   Test 8A: Height Sensor Circuit Inspection

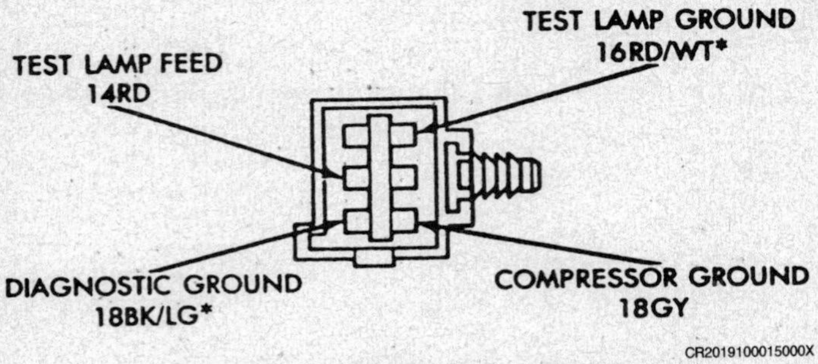

Fig. 15

TEST LAMP FEED 14RD

TEST LAMP GROUND 16RD/WT*

DIAGNOSTIC GROUND 18BK/LG*

COMPRESSOR GROUND 18GY

CR2019100015000X

Fig. 15   Rear leveling diagnostic test pin location

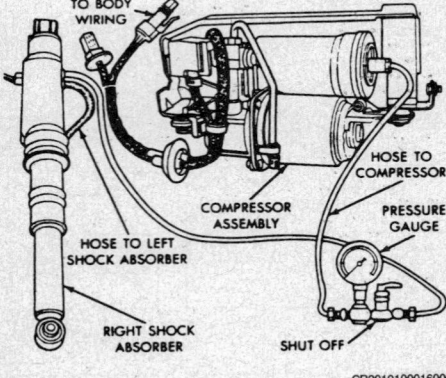

TO BODY WIRING — HOSE TO COMPRESSOR — COMPRESSOR ASSEMBLY — PRESSURE GAUGE — HOSE TO LEFT SHOCK ABSORBER — RIGHT SHOCK ABSORBER — SHUT OFF

CR2019100016000X

Fig. 16   Pressure gauge installation

COMPONENT REPLACEMENT

COMPRESSOR ASSEMBLY

Removal

1. Disconnect battery negative cable and raise vehicle.
2. Remove compressor cover, air hose and electrical connectors, **Fig. 18.**
3. Remove compressor mounting bracket screws, then lower assembly from vehicle.
4. Remove mounting bracket screws, then mounting bracket from compressor.

Installation

1. Reverse procedures to install, **torquing** all screws to 70 inch lbs.
2. Refer to "Diagnosis & Testing" while checking operation if necessary to make adjustments.

CONTROL MODULE

Removal

1. Disconnect battery negative cable, then remove trim panel from RH side of trunk.
2. Disconnect electrical connector and relay from Control Module, **Fig. 19.**
3. Remove Control Module mounting screws, then the assembly.

Installation

1. Install relay on Control Module bracket, then place Control Module on bracket and install screws. **Torque screws to 19-29 inch lbs.**
2. Connect relay and module electrical connectors, then replace trim panel.

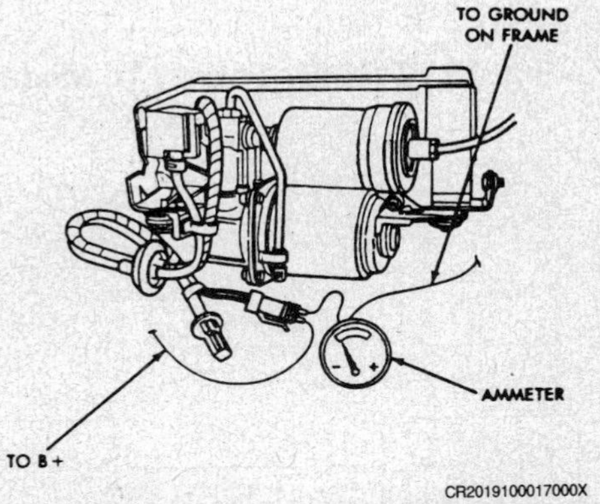

TO GROUND ON FRAME

AMMETER

TO B+

CR2019100017000X

Fig. 17   Compressor current draw test

COMPRESSOR RELAY

Right Shock Absorber w/Height Sensor

1. Disconnect battery negative cable and raise vehicle, then remove tire assembly.
2. Disconnect height sensor connector, located on RH frame rail, then remove air lines connected to Shock Absorber.
3. To remove Shock Absorber, refer to "Shock Absorber Removal" to replace Shocks.
4. Reverse procedure to install.

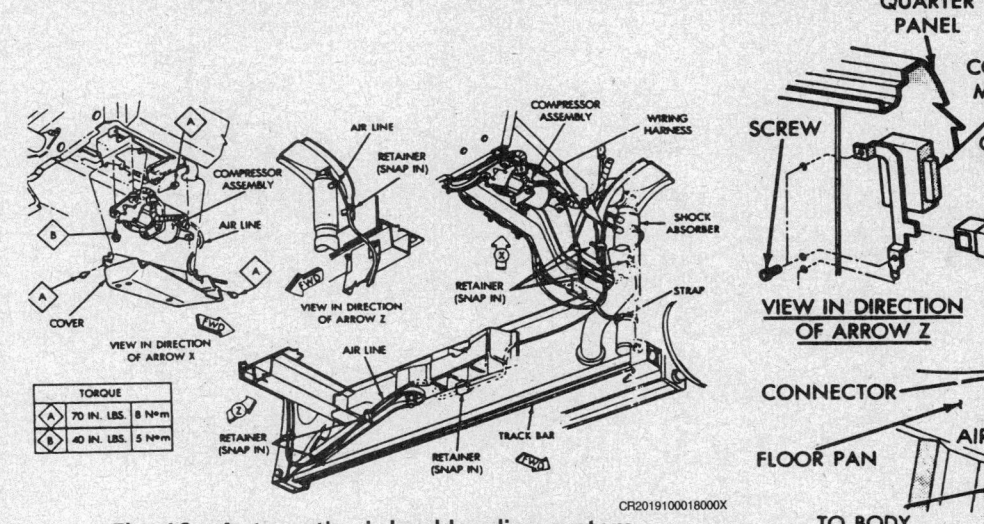

Fig. 18   Automatic air load leveling system

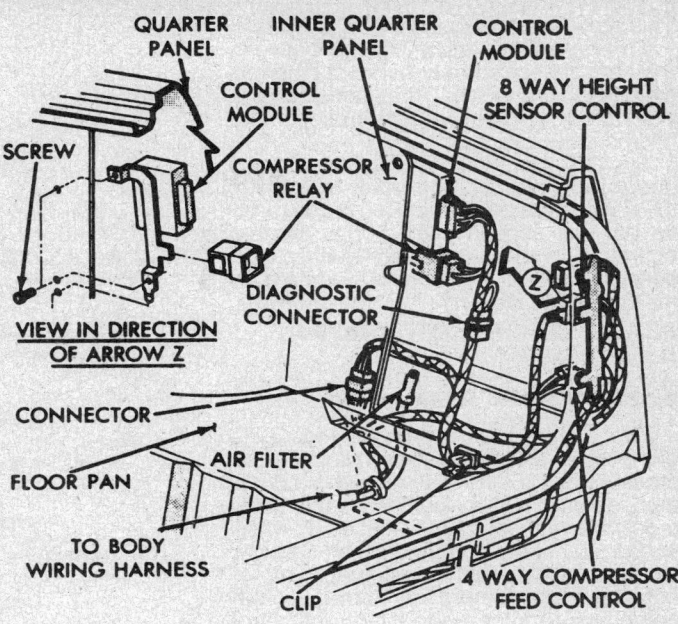

Fig. 19   Control module & compressor relay wiring

Automatic Air Suspension

NOTE: On Air Bag Equipped Models, Refer To "Air Bag System Precautions" Located In The Front Of This Manual For System Disarming & Arming Procedures.

INDEX

PRECAUTIONS

AIR BAG SYSTEMS

Refer to "Air Bag System Precautions" in the front of this manual for system disarming and arming procedures.

DESCRIPTION

The Automatic Air Suspension (AAS) system, **Fig. 1**, automatically controls vehicle ride height to provide optimum vehicle performance regardless of load conditions. The system's unique air springs offer spring rates lower than those of cars equipped with conventional coil springs. This combination of height control and reduced spring rates improves suspension performance.

The AAS system consists of an air compressor/dryer assembly, compressor relay, front struts, rear springs and shocks absorbers, a control module, rear height sensor and compressor cover.

Front springs and height sensors are integral parts of the strut assemblies. Rear ride height is measured by a height sensor in the right rear shock absorber. As pressurized air is discharged from the air compressor/dryer assembly and routed to each air spring by four separate air lines, a Control Module (CM) managing AAS system operation activates solenoids in the air springs to regulate system air pressure and volume.

SYSTEM COMPONENTS

AIR SPRINGS

The front and rear air springs, **Fig. 2**, are pneumatic cylinders that replace steel coil springs. The air springs allow suspension height to be adjusted for all load conditions. The air springs allow the reduction of spring rates to improve ride characteristics.

SPRING SOLENOIDS

The front and rear spring solenoids control air flow in and out of the front and rear air springs. The Air Suspension Control Module (ASCM) opens the solenoids when the system requires air to be added to or exhausted from the air springs. The solenoids operate at a current draw range of 0.6-1.5 amps.

HEIGHT SENSORS

The height sensor is a magnetic switch type sensor, located in the right rear shock absorber, left and right front struts, **Fig. 2**, which monitors vehicle height. The sensors transmit signals to the ASCM relating to vehicle status (low, trim, medium and high).

CONTROL MODULE

The Air Suspension Control Module (ASCM) is a device that controls the ground circuits for the compressor relay, compressor exhaust solenoid valve, front and rear solenoid valves. A microprocessor with in the ASCM controls compressor pump operation from 170-190 seconds.

This prevents damage to the AAS system.

To prevent excessive cycling between the compressor and the exhaust solenoid circuits during normal ride conditions, a 12-18 second delay is incorporated in the microprocessor logic.

System operation is inhibited when a door(s) are opened, the trunk is opened, the service brakes are applied or the throttle position sensor is 65-100%. System operation is also inhibited during high speed cornering. The Control Module is on the CCD bus system.

AIR COMPRESSOR/DRYER ASSEMBLY

Compressor Assembly

The compressor assembly, **Fig. 3**, is driven by an electric motor and supplies air pressure of 135-180 psi. A solenoid operated exhaust valve, located in the compressor head assembly, releases air when energized. A heat actuated circuit breaker, located inside the compressor motor housing, is used to prevent damage to the compressor motor in the event of Control Module failure.

Compressor Air Dryer

The air dryer is attached to the compressor. The air dryer has two functions; it absorbs moisture from the atmosphere before it enters the system, and with internal valves, maintains a residual pressure of 25-40 psi.

AIR LINES

Four nylon air lines, **Figs. 4 and 5,** are routed from the compressor air dryer to each strut/spring assembly. Right side strut and air spring air lines are routed with the fuel line. Left side strut and air spring air lines are routed across the vehicle in front of the fuel tank and forward with the fuel line.

SYSTEM OPERATION

Engine Run Operation

The AAS system will compensate for load addition or removal when the trunk and all doors are closed, engine speed exceeds 600 RPM, throttle angle is less than 65 degrees, the brake is not applied, the vehicle is not cornering above 10 MPH and the charging system is functioning normally.

Engine Off Operation

After passengers and/or load are removed from the vehicle, the AAS system will correct the vehicle attitude after the trunk and all doors are closed and the ignition switch is in the OFF position. **Opening a door or the trunk activates the body computer and the ASCM, AAS is then capable of leveling if required.**

Long Term Ignition Off Operation

With the ignition off, the AAS system is still capable of an additional leveling cycle up to two hours after each time a door or the trunk lid is closed. This feature is intended to prevent icing between the tire and the inner fender shield.

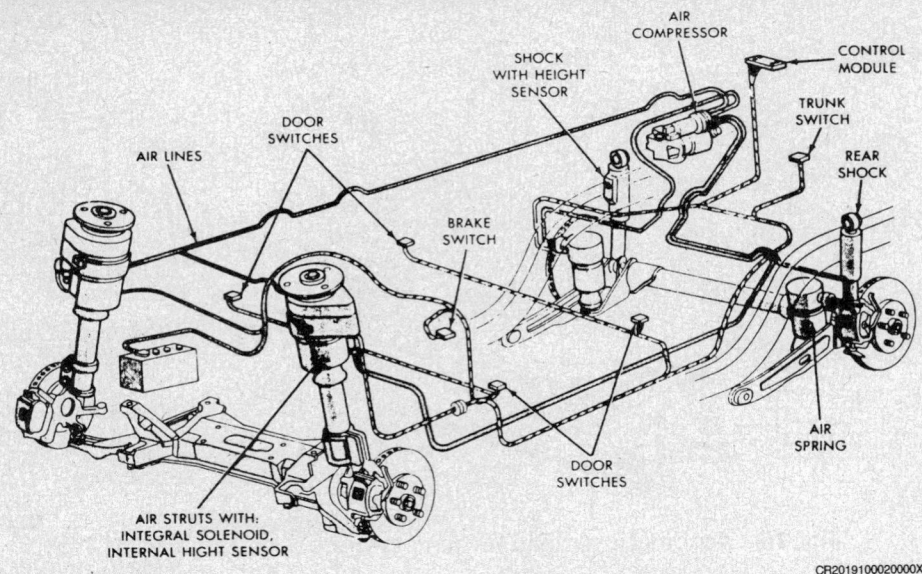

Fig. 1 Automatic Air Suspension (AAS) system

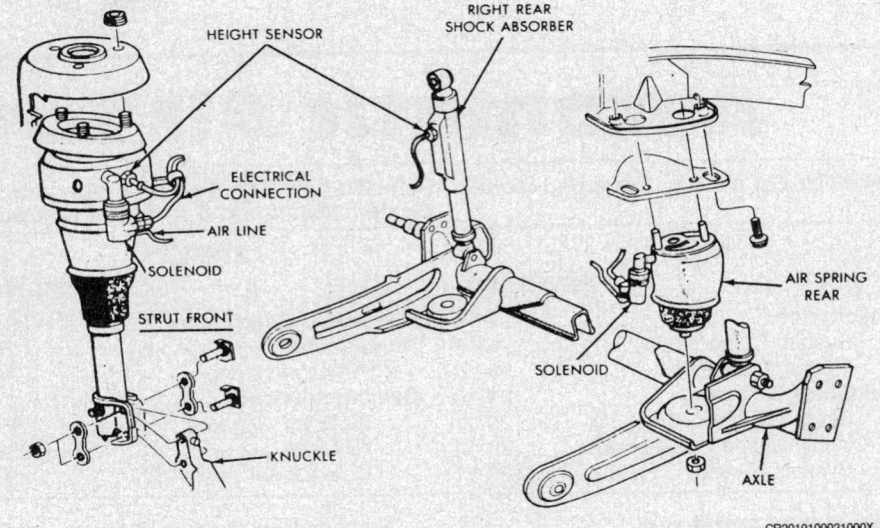

Fig. 2 Front & rear air springs

System Operation Inhibitors

AAS operation is inhibited when the trunk or a door is open, the service brakes are applied, the throttle is in the wide open position or the charging system fails. **The maximum compressor pump or exhaust time is three minutes.**

System Failures

Models equipped with air suspension and overhead console will alert the driver if an AAS system malfunction has occurred. The overhead console will display a "Check Air Suspension" warning when a malfunction has occurred.

TROUBLESHOOTING

Refer to **Figs. 6 through 9,** when troubleshooting this system.

DIAGNOSIS & TESTING

Refer to **Fig. 10,** for system wiring circuit diagram when diagnosing this system.

INITIAL DIAGNOSTIC CHECK

All doors and trunk must be closed for the system to function.
1. Check for blown or missing fuses.
2. Ensure all connector terminals are correctly installed.
3. Check pin 21 for a minimum of 9.5 volts.
4. Check pin 20 for a minimum of 9.5 volts with ignition key in ON position.
5. Check voltage at pins 5 and 16. Voltage indicated should exceed 0 volts.
6. Check pin 19 for continuity.
7. Ensure engine idle speed is above 680 RPM.

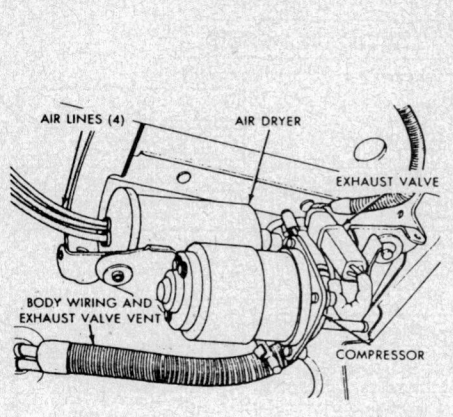

Fig. 3   Air compressor/dryer assembly

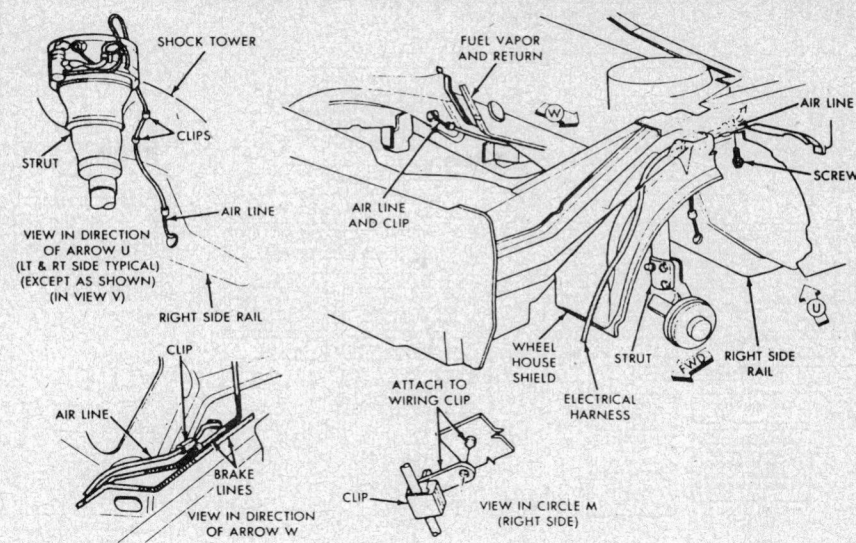

Fig. 4   Front air lines

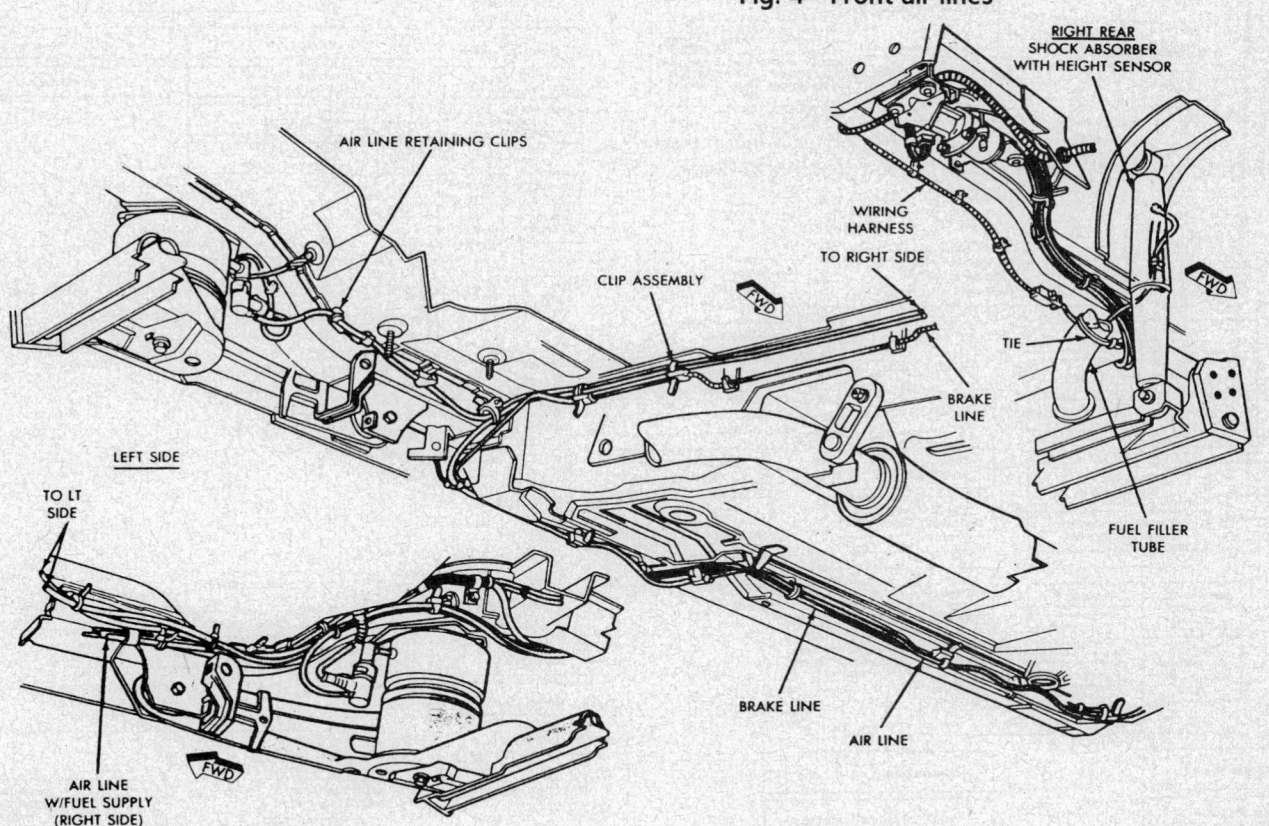

Fig. 5   Rear air lines & height sensor

DIAGNOSTIC PROCEDURE

Diagnosis of the AAS system requires use of the DRB II diagnostic readout tool and an air suspension software cartridge. A volt/ohmmeter can be used for some testing. Follow manufacturer's instructions for use of the DRB II.

1. Connect DRB II to diagnostic connector under drivers's side dash panel.

Once connected, the tester will conduct a complete check of AAS system status and list the steps to follow to access and diagnose the failure.

2. Perform diagnostic procedures as shown in **Figs. 11 through 26** on 1992 models or **Figs. 27 through 62** on 1993 models.

3. After procedure is completed, perform verification test as shown in **Fig. 12** for 1992 models.

SYSTEM TESTING

Refer to **Fig. 10**, for 1992 models and **Fig. 27** for 1993 models when performing system testing procedures.

Residual Air Check

The air dryer has a valve arrangement which maintains a minimum pressure of 25-40 psi. Check residual pressure as follows:

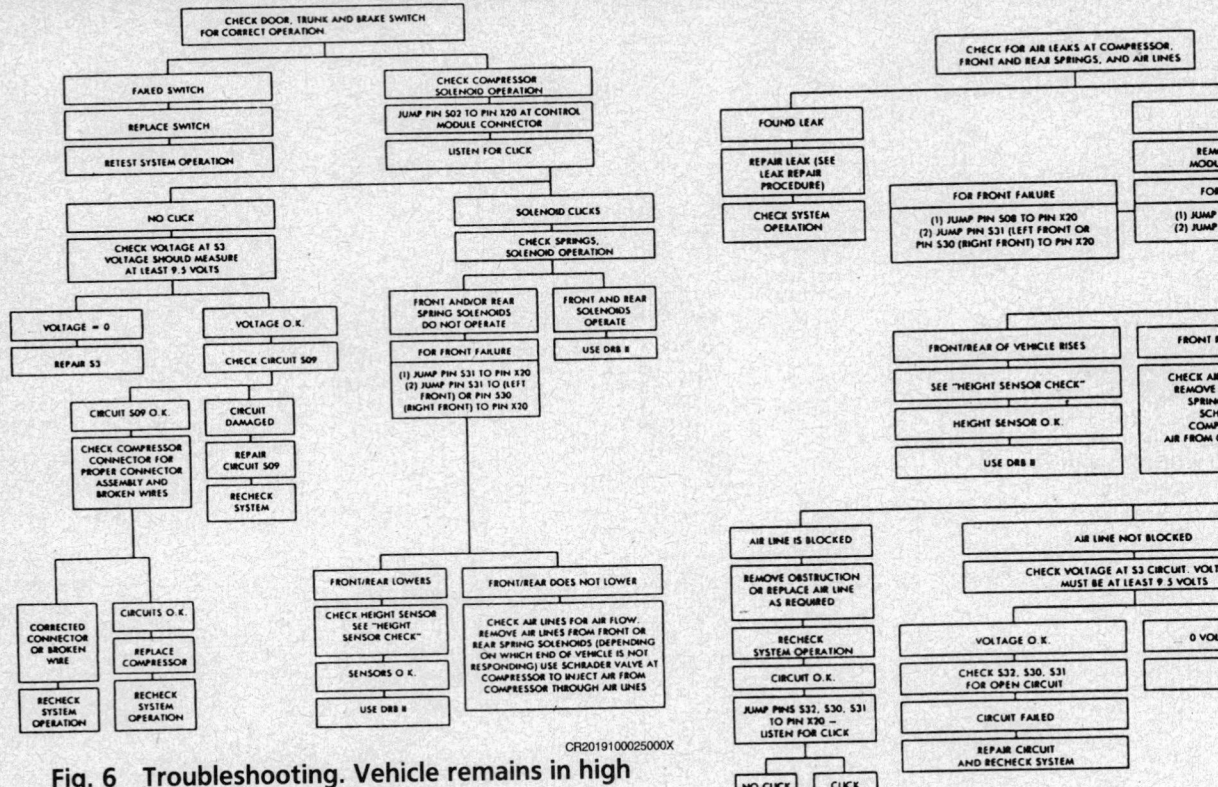

Fig. 6   Troubleshooting. Vehicle remains in high position

CR2019100025000X

Fig. 7   Troubleshooting. Vehicle remains low at front or rear, compressor operates

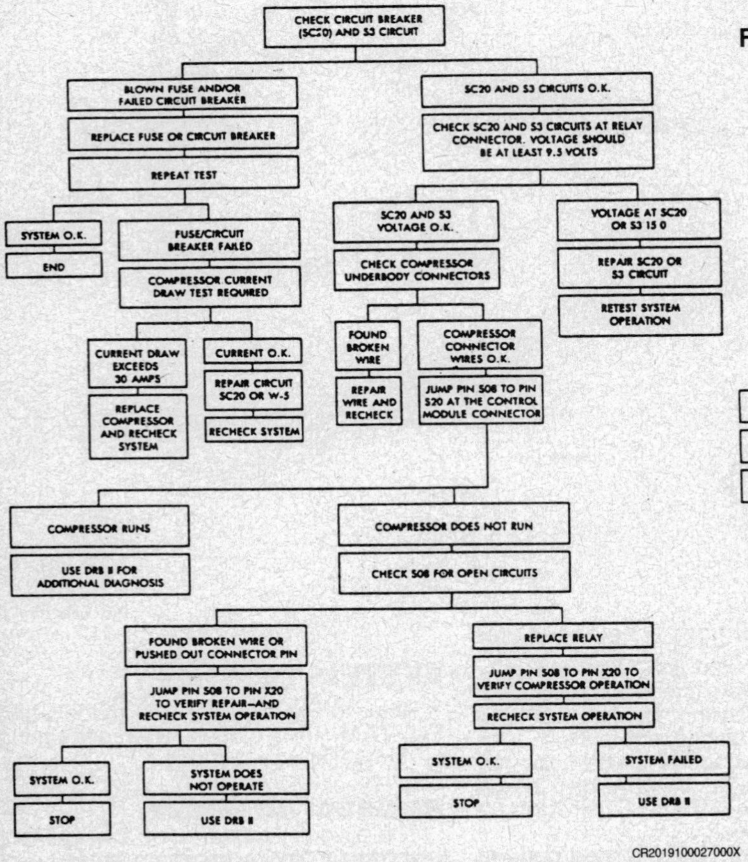

CR2019100026000X

Fig. 8   Troubleshooting. Vehicle remains low, compressor does not pump

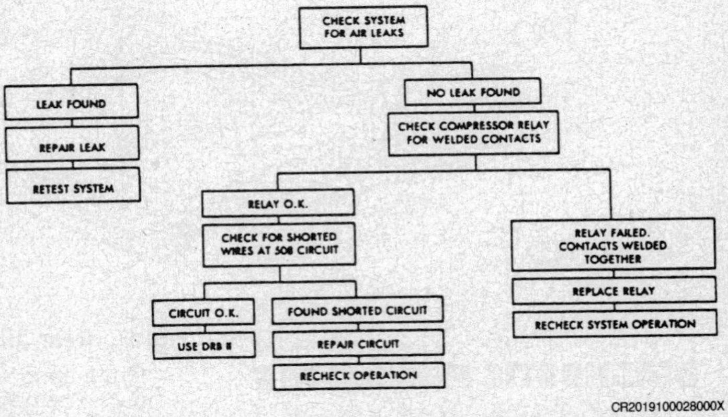

CR2019100027000X

Fig. 9   Troubleshooting compressor overrun

CR2019100028000X

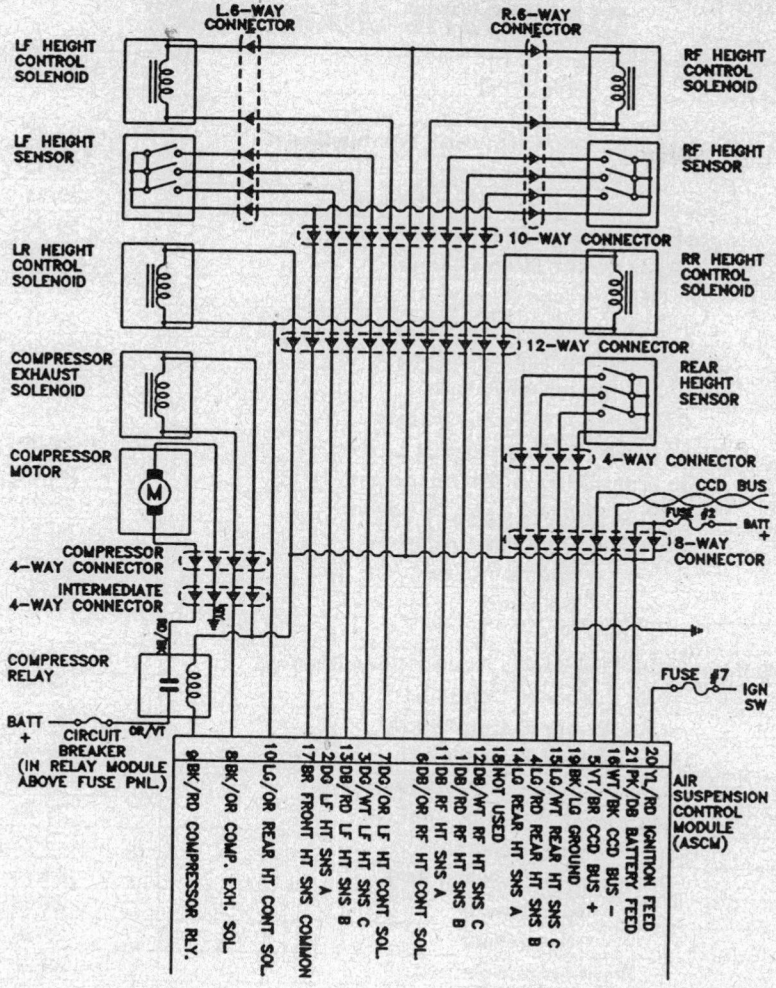

Fig. 10   Air suspension system wiring schematic

1. Remove air line from dryer fitting and strut or spring. Attach a piece of bulk nylon tubing to one side of a suitable 0-300 psi pressure gauge and to the strut or spring solenoid.
2. Attach another piece of nylon tubing from dryer to the other side of the pressure gauge. A compression ball sleeve nut and sleeve for 3/16 inch tubing with ball sleeve connector and an internal pipe T-fitting can be used to attach the tubing to the pressure gauge.
3. Activate compressor by grounding pin 508 to pin X20. Cycle unit and read actual air pressure. Pressure of 25-40 psi indicates that the system and the compressor are acceptable.

Compressor Performance Test

This test can be performed on the vehicle to evaluate compressor current draw, pressure output and leak down. To test compressor performance, proceed as follows:

1. Disconnect compressor motor wiring harness.
2. Disconnect air line between dryer and strut or spring solenoid.

3. Connect a suitable air pressure gauge to the AAS system. Refer to "Residual Air Check."
4. Connect an ammeter in series between compressor connector red wire terminal and a 12 volt power source. Also connect a ground wire from compressor connector black terminal to a known good ground on frame, **Fig. 63.**
5. If compressor motor current draw exceeds 30 amps, replace compressor assembly.

Air Leak Check

Use a soap and water solution or a liquid designed for leak detection.

1. Check all air line to connector joints:
   a. Air line to compressor connectors.
   b. Air line to solenoids.
2. Check front strut and rear spring rubber membranes.
3. Check solenoid to volume canister joint:
   a. Front strut to solenoid valve connections.
   b. Rear spring to solenoid valve connections.
4. Check air lines for ruptures, cuts, splits and heat damage.

Height Sensor Check

If sensor signal(s) are missing, proceed as follows:

1. Check ground circuit continuity as follows:
   a. Check front ground circuit for continuity.
   b. Check rear ground circuit for continuity.
2. If an open circuit is indicated, repair as necessary.
3. If continuity is indicated, replace the affected strut or the right rear shock absorber. **Complete circuit testing before replacing a strut or the right rear shock absorber.**
4. To measure resistance values, refer to "Initial Diagnostic Check" and **Fig. 64,** noting the following:
   a. Height sensor signals must be verified using an ohmmeter to measure resistance.
   b. Refer to **Fig. 64,** for sensor signal information.
   c. Measure resistance values by completing the circuit between the appropriate sensor pin and the appropriate ground pin.

Continued on page 29-35

DIAGNOSTIC CHART INDEX

Test	Description	Page No.	Fig. No.
1992			
Test 1A	DRB II Hook-Up/Reading Diagnostic Trouble Codes	29-15	11
Test 2A	Verification Test	29-15	12
Test 3A	Right Front Height Sensor Circuit	29-15	13
Test 4A	Left Front Height Sensor Circuit	29-16	14
Test 5A	Rear Height Sensor Circuit	29-18	15
Test 6A	"No Message Received "	29-19	16
Test 7A	"Compressor Overrun "	29-19	17
Test 8A	"Disabling Bus Message "	29-19	18
Test 9A	Compressor Failure	29-20	19
Test 9B	Compressor Fails To Operate	29-20	20
Test 10A	Right Front Will Not Raise Or Lower	29-20	21
Test 11A	Both Front Springs Will Not Lower	29-21	22
Test 12A	Left Front Will Not Raise Or Lower	29-21	23
Test 13A	Rear Will Not Raise Or Lower	29-21	24
Test 13B	Rear Will Not Raise	29-22	25
Test 14A	Solenoid	29-22	26
1993			
Test 1A	DRB II Hook-Up/ Diagnostic Trouble Code Reading	29-23	29
Test 2A	"No Response Condition"	29-23	30
Test 2A	"No Response Condition"	29-23	30
Test 3A	System Operation	29-24	31
Test 4A	Air Suspension Control Module Codes	29-24	32
Test 5A	Compressor Does Not Shut Off	29-24	33
Test 6A	Exhaust Solenoid	29-25	34
Test 7A	Compressor Does Not Start	29-25	35
Test 7B	Compressor	29-25	36
Test 7C	Compressor	29-26	37
Test 8A	Right Front Solenoid	29-26	38
Test 9A	Left Front Solenoid	29-26	39
Test 10A	Right Front Height Solenoid	29-27	40
Test 11A	Left Front Height Solenoid	29-27	41
Test 11B	Right Front Height Sensor	29-27	42
Test 11C	Right Front Height Sensor	29-28	43
Test 11D	Right Front Height Sensor	29-28	44
Test 12A	Left Front Height Sensor	29-28	45
Test 12B	Left Front Height Sensor	29-29	46
Test 12C	Left Front Height Sensor	29-29	47
Test 12D	Left Front Height Sensor	29-29	48
Test 13A	Rear Height Sensor	29-30	49
Test 13B	Rear Height Sensor	29-30	50
Test 13C	Rear Height Sensor	29-30	51
Test 13D	Rear Height Sensor	29-30	52
Test 14A	Compressor	29-31	53
Test 14B	Compressor Overrun	29-31	54
Test 14C	Compressor Overrun	29-32	55
Test 15A	ASCM Communications (No BCM Messages)	29-32	56
Test 16A	ASCM Communications (No PCM Messages)	29-32	57
Test 17A	Right Front Height Solenoid Staying Closed	29-32	58
Test 18A	Left Front Height Solenoid Staying Closed	29-33	59
Test 19A	Rear Height Solenoid Staying Closed	29-34	60
Test 19B	Rear Height Solenoid Staying Closed	29-34	61
Test 19C	Rear Height Solenoid Staying Closed	29-35	62

This test gives instructions for using the DRBII to read the air suspension system faults that have been recorded in the memory of the Air Suspension Control Module (ASCM). It then gives directions about what diagnostic test(s) must be performed.

1. Perform a visual inspection.

2. Connect the DRBII to the bus diagnostic connector.

3. Turn the ignition key on.

If the DRBII screen is blank, displays an error message, fails the bus test ("BUS TEST FAILS"), or displays "NO RESPONSE", there is a DRBII or bus failure.

NOTE: DRBII or bus problems must be corrected before proceeding with fault diagnosis testing.

4. Read faults with the DRBII and write them down.

5. Refer to the following list for the correct diagnostic test to perform for each fault that is displayed on the DRBII.

NOTE: Repairing one fault may sometimes correct other faults. If more than one fault is read, repair the faults in the order shown below. After the first fault is repaired, read faults again.

If no faults are read, go to	Test 2A
COMPRESSOR OVERRUN	Test 7A
R/F HEIGHT SENSOR	Test 3A
L/F HEIGHT SENSOR	Test 4A
REAR HEIGHT SENSOR	Test 5A
NO ENG MSGS RCVD	Test 6A

CR2019100030000X

Fig. 11   Test 1A: DRB II Hook-Up/Reading Diagnostic Trouble Codes. 1992

6. Turn the ignition key to the OFF position. Close all doors and the deck lid.

7. Allow the system to adjust the vehicle height until all sensors indicate "CUST" height.

NOTE: You will have to change the DRBII to "SENSOR STATE" to read "CUST" height.

NOTE: The compressor may stop running after 3 minutes. If the vehicle has not yet reached "CUST" height, open and close a door to reset the compressor.

If the system fails to adjust the vehicle height to "CUST" height, go to .... Test 8

If Steps 1 through 7 were performed without error, the air suspension system is working normally.

CR2019100031020X

Fig. 12   Test 2A: Verification Test (Part 2 of 2). 1992

This test verifies the correct operation of the air suspension system. It must be performed after reading faults with the DRBII and finding none, or after a vehicle repair has been made.

A. Reconnect all previously disconnected connectors.

B. As diagnostic tests are performed, watch the DRBII display. The term "ILL" may be displayed briefly or steadily. In either case, go to the test indicated in the procedure below for the "ILL" message.

C. The battery must be charged and at a rated capacity before performing any of these air suspension tests.

D. The vehicle must be on a flat surface during these tests.

E. The step numbers below must be followed in order.

F. The vehicle must be in "CUST" (customer) height mode, not in "SHIP" mode.

G. The deck lid or a door must be open to perform these tests.

H. Turn the ignition key to the ON position.

NOTE: Use the DRBII to raise and lower the vehicle as instructed in the following steps. During the tests, use the DRBII to read the state of the height sensors.

1. Raise the right front until the sensor reads "HIGH".
   If the compressor will not run, go to .... Test 9
   If the compressor runs but the right front will not raise, go to .... Test 10
   If the right front raises but the sensor indicates "ILL", go to .... Test 3

2. Raise the left front until the sensor indicates "HIGH".
   If the left front will not raise, go to .... Test 12
   If the left front raises but the sensor indicates "ILL", go to .... Test 4

3. Lower the left and right front until the sensor indicates "LOW".
   If neither side lowers, go to .... Test 10
   If the left front will not lower, go to .... Test 12
   If the right front will not lower, go to .... Test 10
   If the right front lowers but the sensor indicates "ILL", go to .... Test 3
   If the left front lowers but the sensor indicates "ILL", go to .... Test 4

4. Raise the rear until the sensor indicates "HIGH".
   If the rear will not raise, go to .... Test 13
   If the rear raises but the sensor indicates "ILL", go to .... Test 5

5. Lower the rear until the sensor indicates "LOW".
   If the rear lowers but the sensor indictates "ILL", go to .... Test 5

CR2019100031010X

Fig. 12   Test 2A: Verification Test (Part 1 of 2). 1992

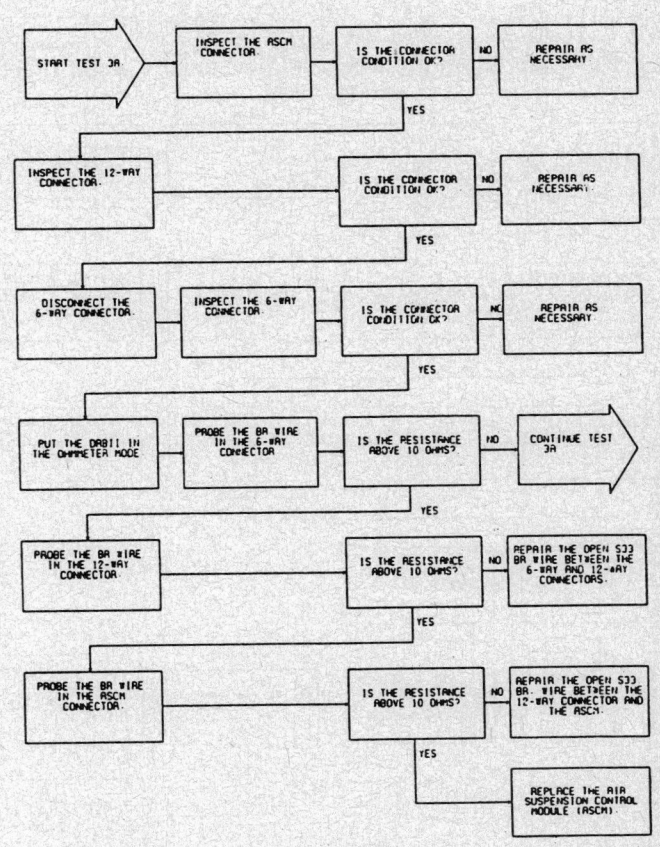

CR2019100032010X

Fig. 13   Test 3A: Right Front Height Sensor Circuit (Part 1 of 4). 1992

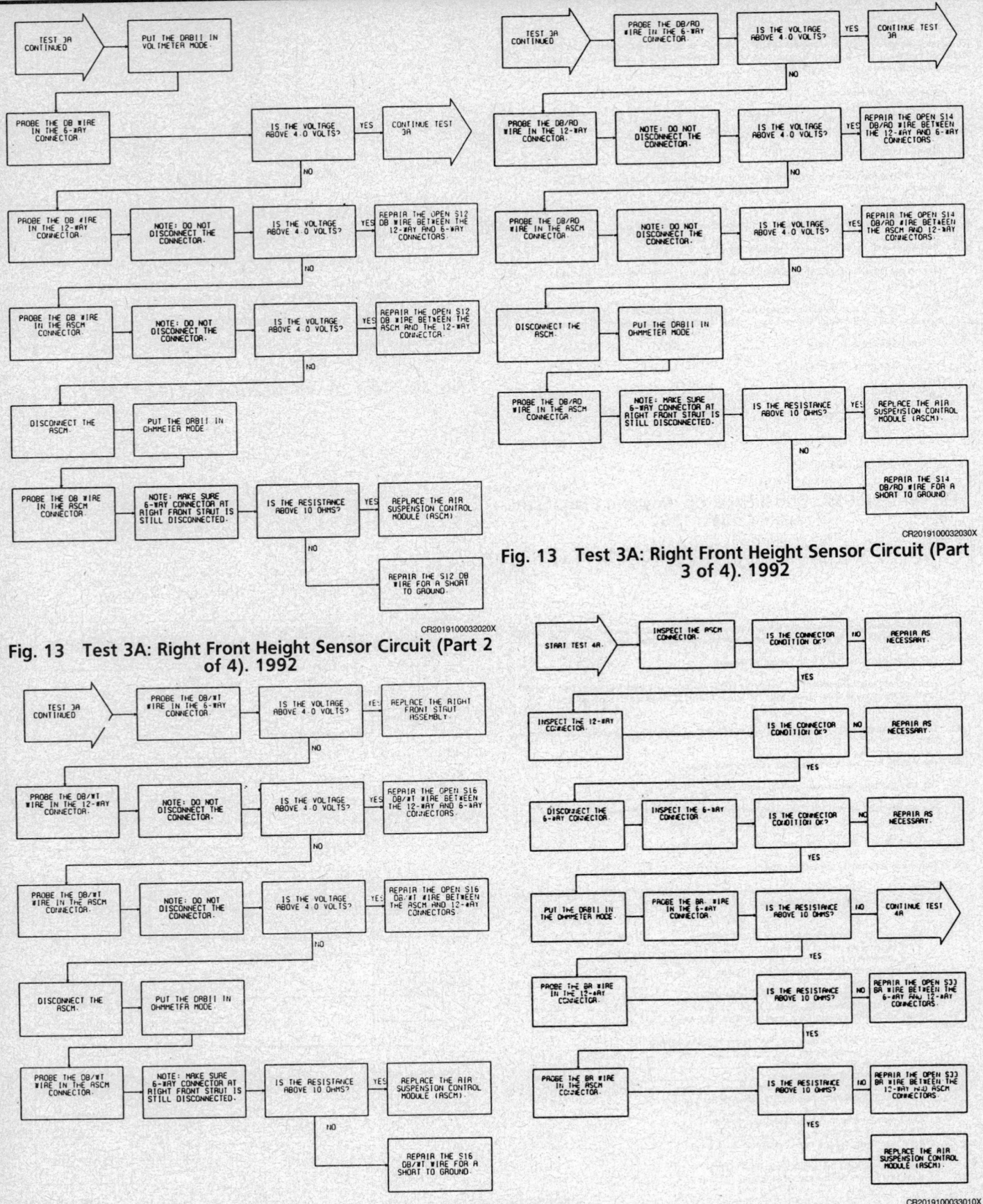

Fig. 13 Test 3A: Right Front Height Sensor Circuit (Part 2 of 4). 1992

CR2019100032020X

Fig. 13 Test 3A: Right Front Height Sensor Circuit (Part 3 of 4). 1992

CR2019100032030X

Fig. 13 Test 3A: Right Front Height Sensor Circuit (Part 4 of 4). 1992

CR2019100032040X

Fig. 14 Test 4A: Left Front Height Sensor Circuit (Part 1 of 4). 1992

CR2019100033010X

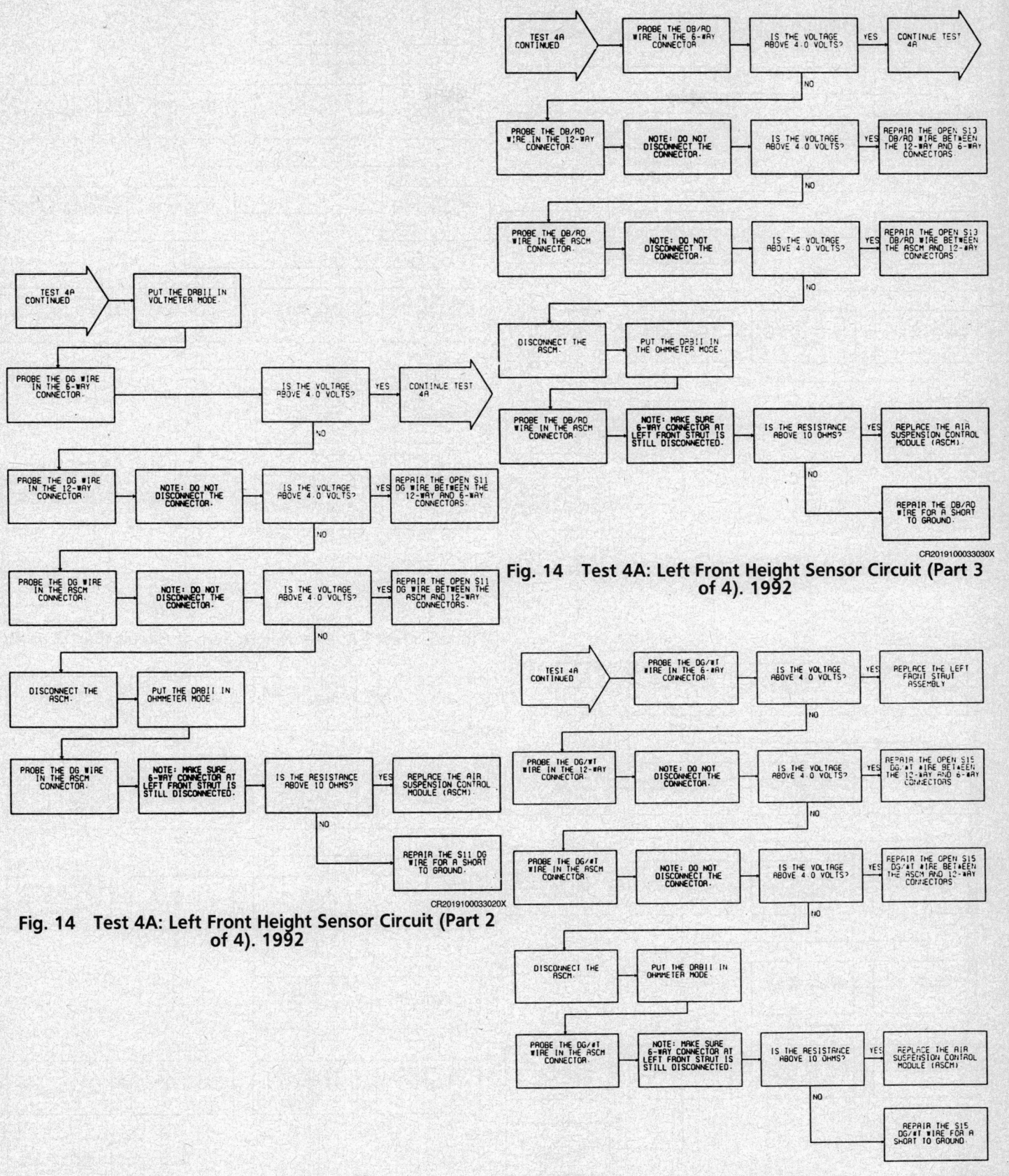

Fig. 14 Test 4A: Left Front Height Sensor Circuit (Part 3 of 4). 1992

Fig. 14 Test 4A: Left Front Height Sensor Circuit (Part 2 of 4). 1992

Fig. 14 Test 4A: Left Front Height Sensor Circuit (Part 4 of 4). 1992

CR2019100033030X

CR2019100033020X

CR2019100033040X

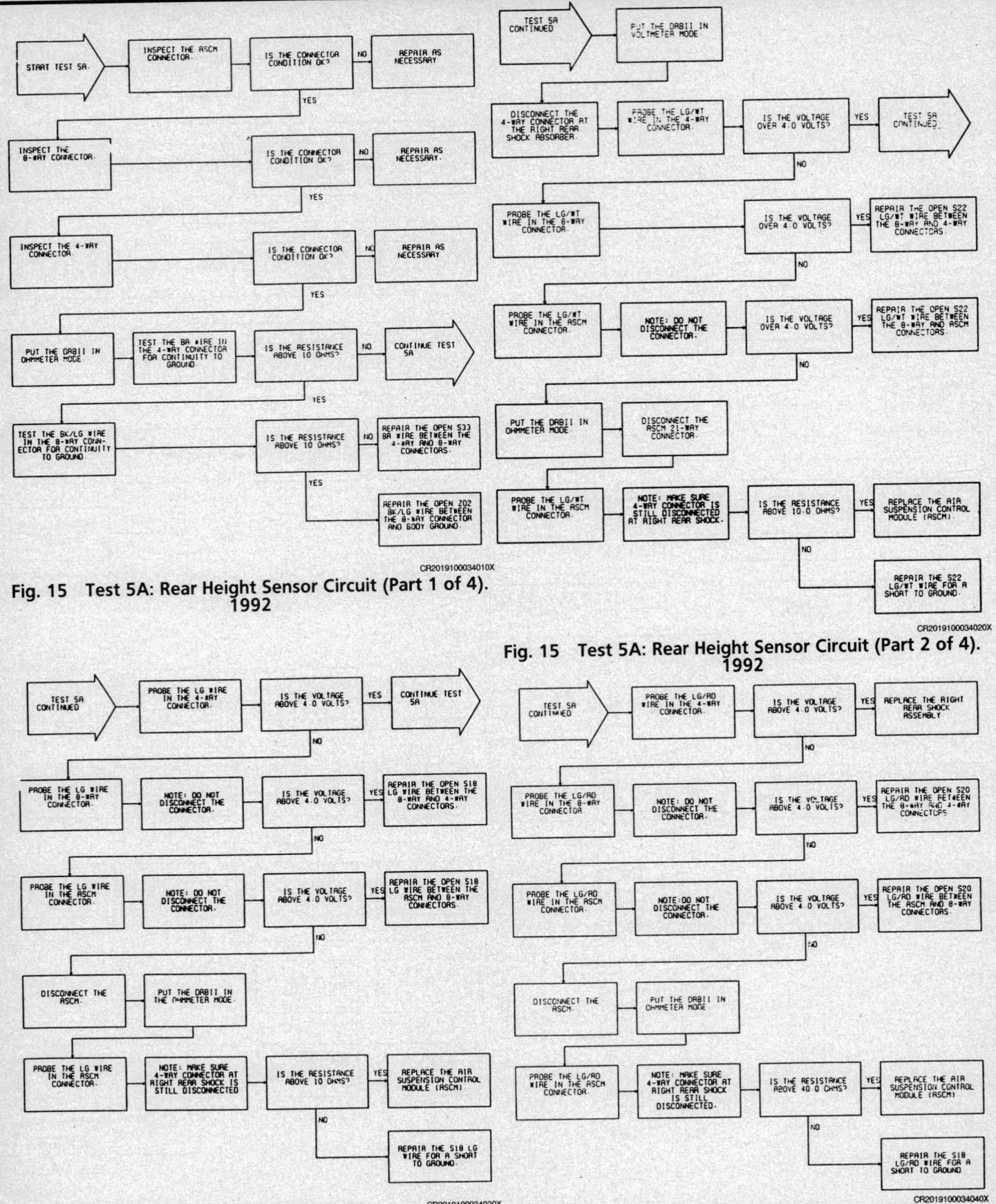

Fig. 15   Test 5A: Rear Height Sensor Circuit (Part 1 of 4). 1992

Fig. 15   Test 5A: Rear Height Sensor Circuit (Part 2 of 4). 1992

Fig. 15   Test 5A: Rear Height Sensor Circuit (Part 3 of 4). 1992

Fig. 15   Test 5A: Rear Height Sensor Circuit (Part 4 of 4). 1992

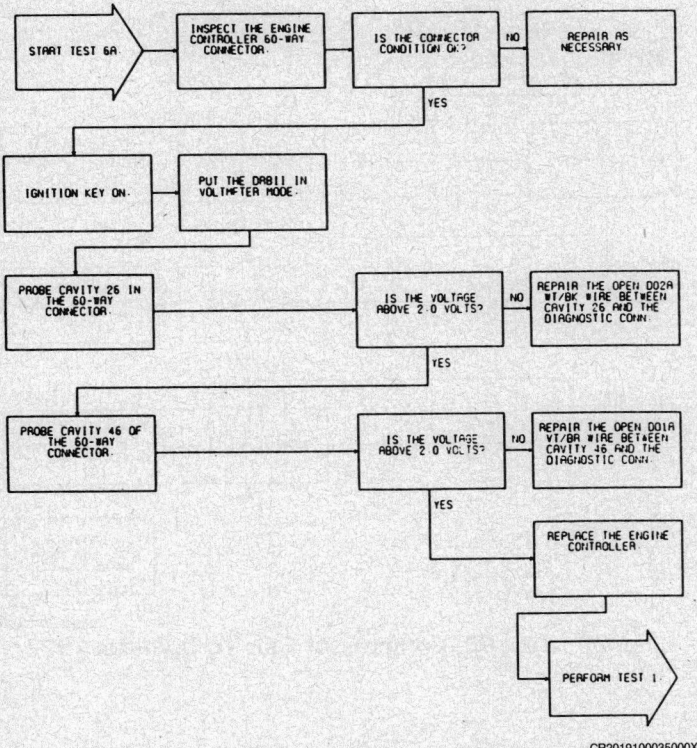

Fig. 16   Test 6A: "No Message Received". 1992

The fault message "COMPRESSOR OVERRUN" is generated by the Air Suspension Control Module (ASCM) when the compressor has run for longer than 180 seconds (three minutes).

The memory that the ASCM uses to hold fault messages is volatile. This means that the fault messages are lost when the key is turned off. Because of this, air suspension fault messages can only be seen while the fault is actually occurring.

However, the problem that causes the "COMPRESSOR OVERRUN" fault message can be easily detected by listening to the compressor run.

If the compressor does _not_ run for an unusual length of time (more than three minutes) when this fault is set, the ASCM is probably defective.

If the compressor _does run_ for an unusual length of time, the following problems may be the cause of the fault:

   – stuck relay contacts
   – shorted relay coil driver within the ASCM
   – possible air leak
   – defective ASCM
   – restricted air compressor intake
   – low air compressor capacity

Fig. 17   Test 7A: "Compressor Overrun". 1992

After successfully completing Step 6 of Test 2, the vehicle should be low at all four corners.

Step 7 of Test 2 asks the air suspension system to raise and level the vehicle to "CUST" (customer) height. NOTE: The doors and deck lid must be closed for the system to do this.

Failure of the system to level the vehicle to "CUST" height during Step 7 is likely because of a "disabling" message on the CCD bus. (The CCD bus is the information link between the on-board vehicle computers.)

To view the bus messages the Air Suspension Control Module (ASCM) is currently receiving, use the DRBII to select the "CCD Bus Monitor" test.

The figure below shows a normal DRBII display for a vehicle sitting in a flat stall with:

   – doors and deck lid closed
   – engine idling
   – throttle closed
   – key on (keeps the bus on and makes engine messages available)

NORMAL MESSAGES

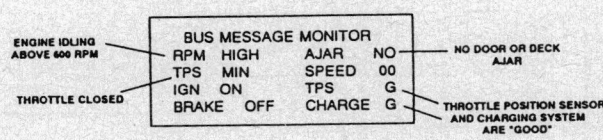

Fig. 18   Test 8A: "Disabling Bus Message" (Part 1 of 2). 1992

The figure below shows a DRBII display containing some bus messages that will cause the air suspension system to stop operating normally.

DISABLING MESSAGES

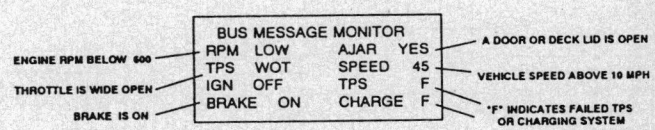

During any of the above conditions, the ASCM will decide to stop height correction. This is the normal program of the ASCM.

NOTE: None of these messages indicates a failure of any air suspension component.

The "AJAR" and "IGN" messages are from the vehicle's Body Controller. These messages represent what the Body Controller "thinks" the state of these switches is. For example, the brake message may say "ON" even though you are sure the brake pedal is not being depressed; or, the door ajar message may say "RR" (right rear door is ajar) even though you are sure it is not.

NOTE: Disabling messages on the bus must be corrected before proceeding with fault diagnosis testing.

Fig. 18   Test 8A: "Disabling Bus Message" (Part 2 of 2). 1992

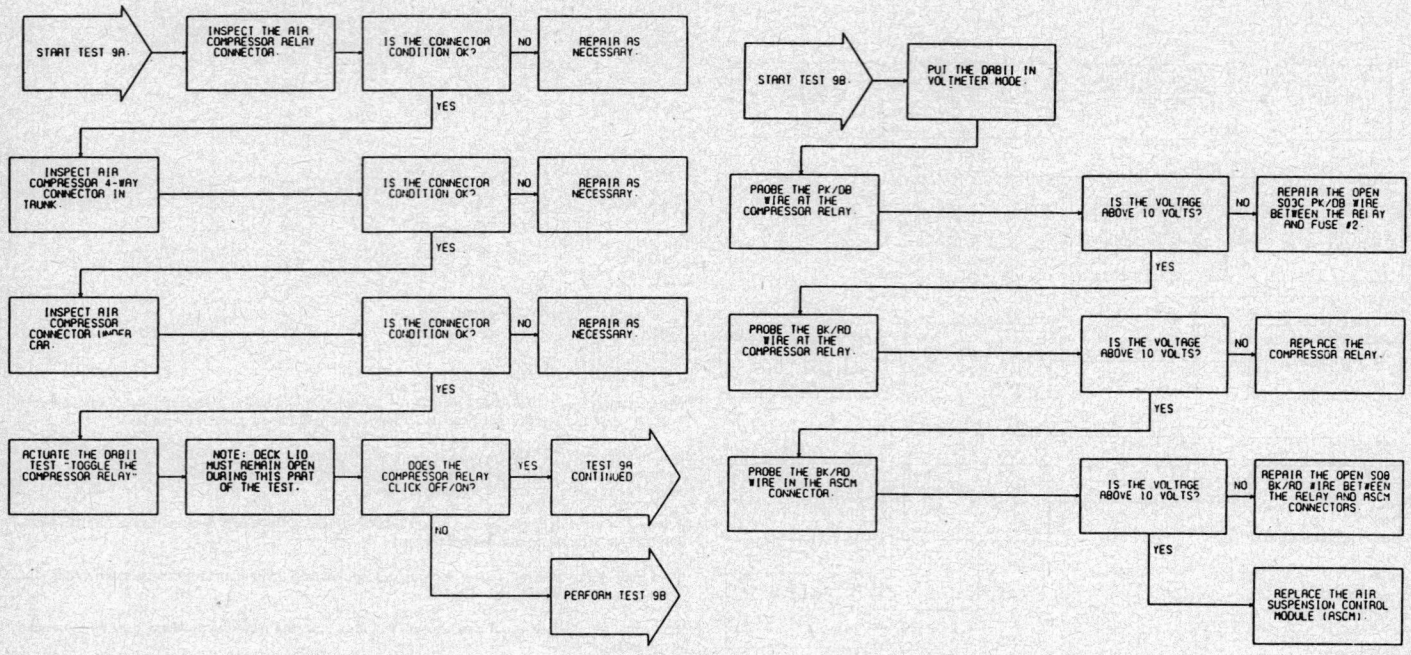

Fig. 19 Test 9A: Compressor Failure (Part 1 of 2). 1992

CR2019100038010X

Fig. 20 Test 9B: Compressor Fails To Operate. 1992

CR2019100039000X

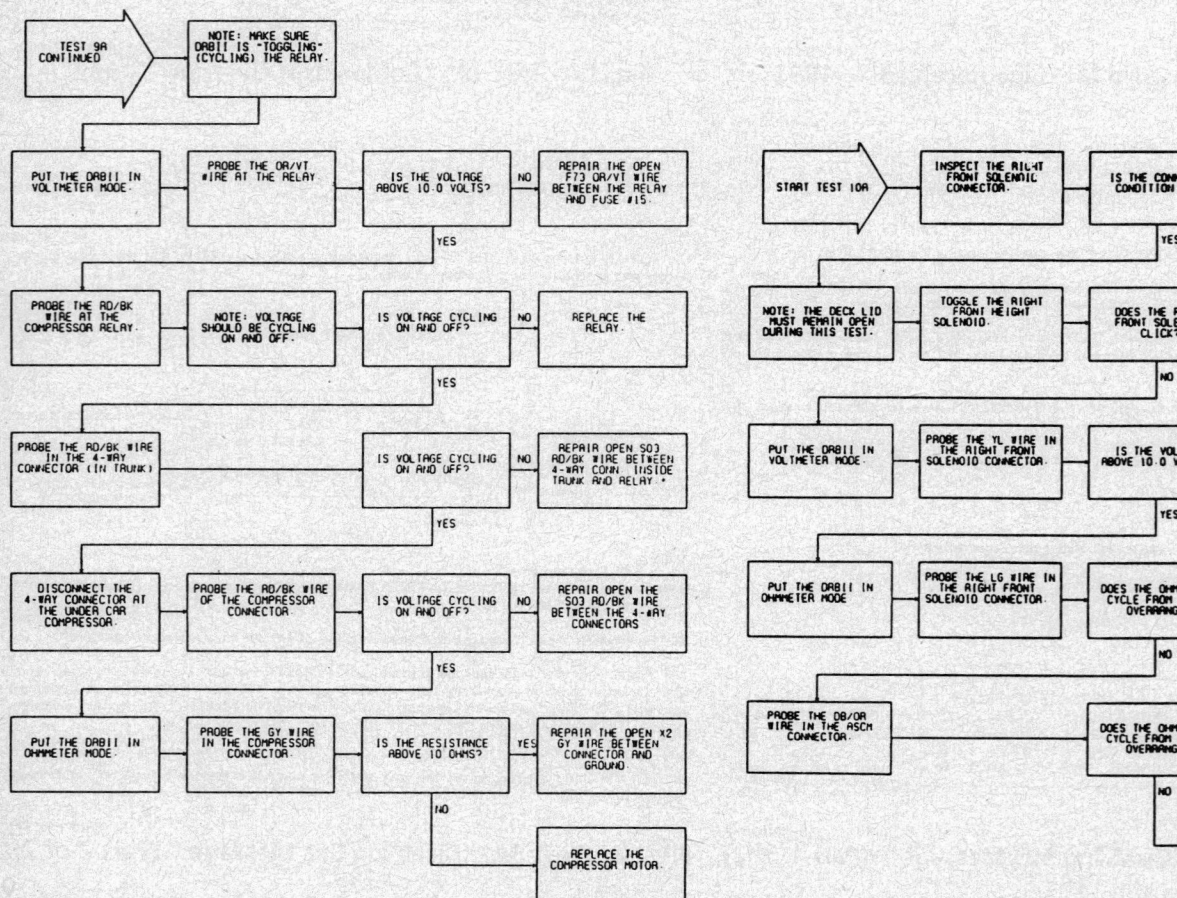

Fig. 19 Test 9A: Compressor Failure (Part 2 of 2). 1992

CR2019100038020X

Fig. 21 Test 10A: Right Front Will Not Raise Or Lower. 1992

CR2019100040000X

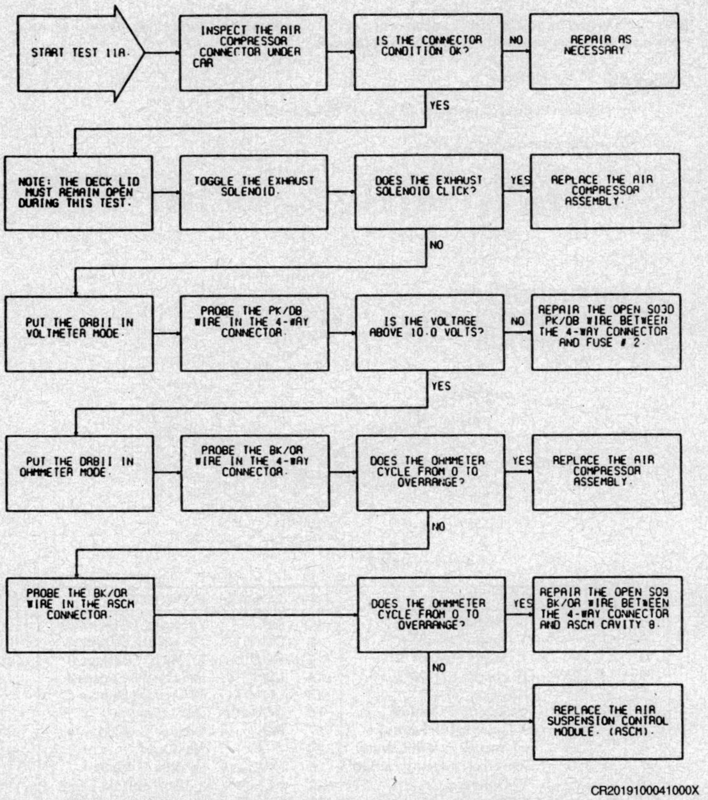

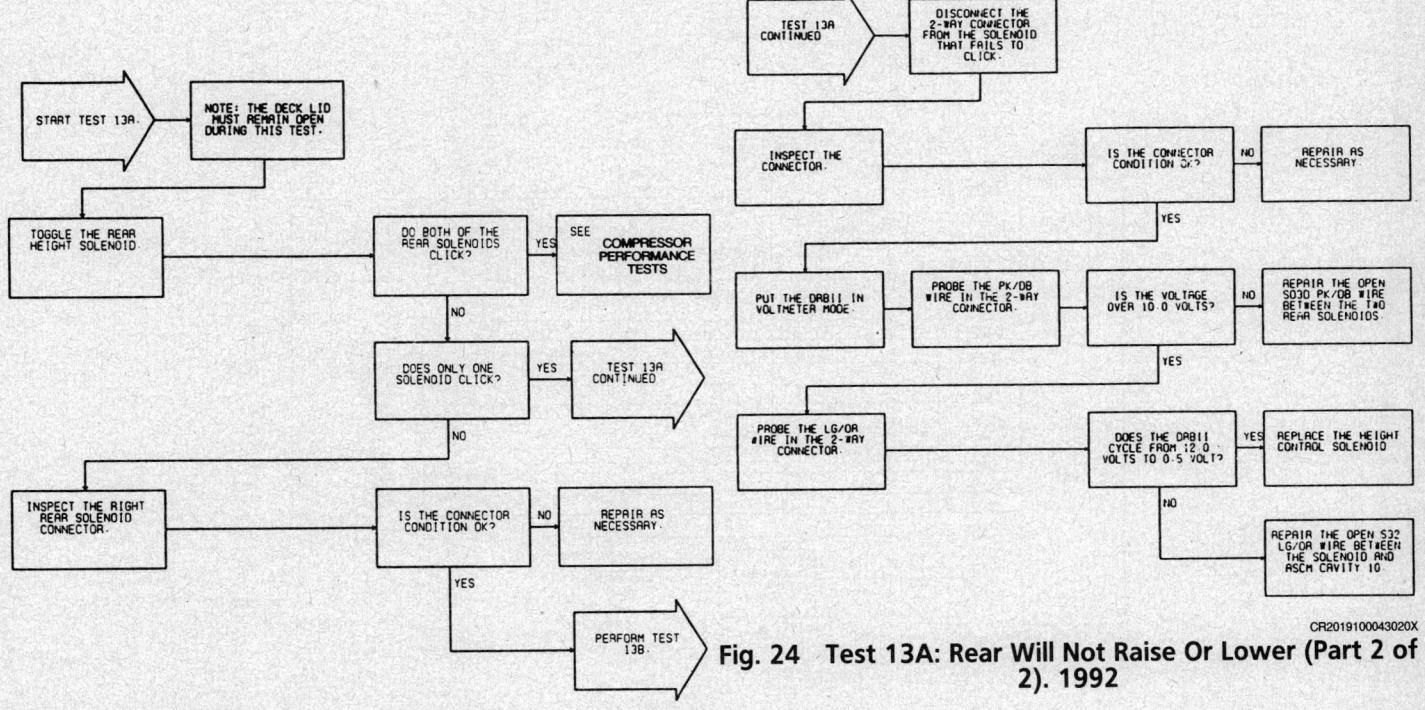

Fig. 22   Test 11A: Both Front Springs Will Not Lower. 1992

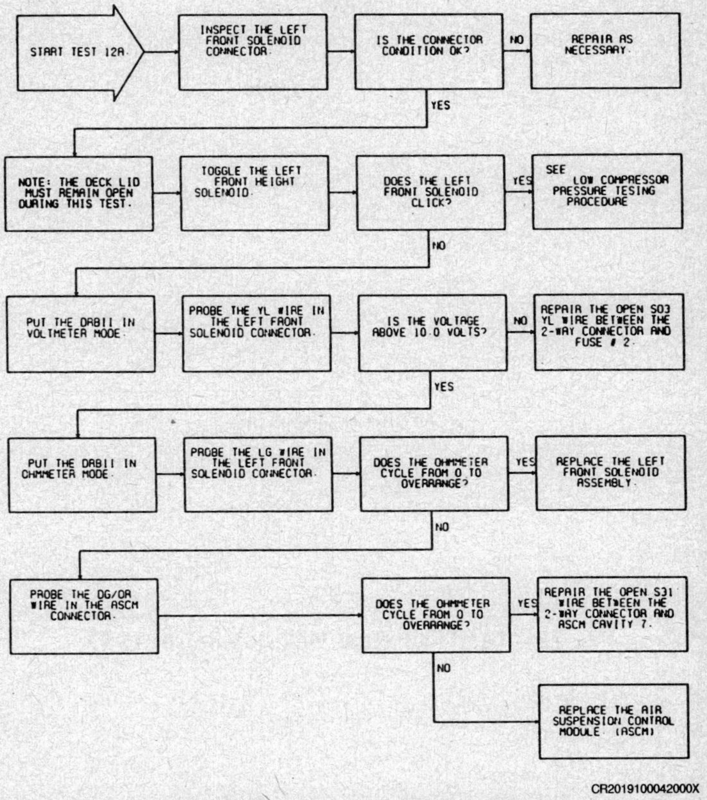

CR2019100041000X

Fig. 23   Test 12A: Left Front Will Not Raise Or Lower. 1992

CR2019100042000X

Fig. 24   Test 13A: Rear Will Not Raise Or Lower (Part 2 of 2). 1992

CR2019100043020X

Fig. 24   Test 13A: Rear Will Not Raise Or Lower (Part 1 of 2). 1992

CR2019100043010X

In Test 2, when you tried to raise either the front or rear of the car, the opposite end of the car also raised. This is a fault condition caused by one or both of the front solenoids allowing pressurized air to enter the air springs when they should be closed.

The solenoids may be stuck open by frozen water, dirt, or other foreign matter, or they may be held open electrically by the solenoid control wire shorted to ground.

Knowing this, do the following:

— Visually inspect the solenoids for foreign matter or seizure

— Inspect the solenoid control wires.

CR2019100045000X

Fig. 26   Test 14A: Solenoid. 1992

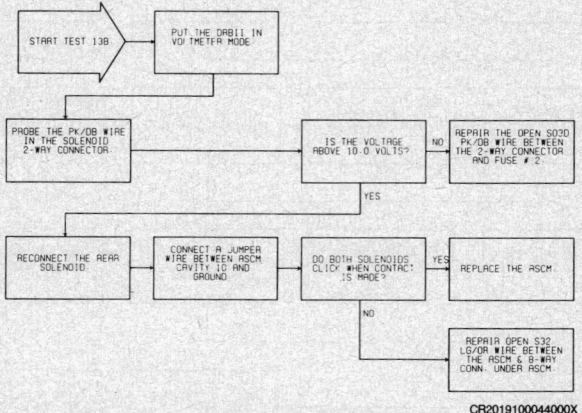

CR2019100044000X

Fig. 25   Test 13B: Rear Will Not Raise. 1992

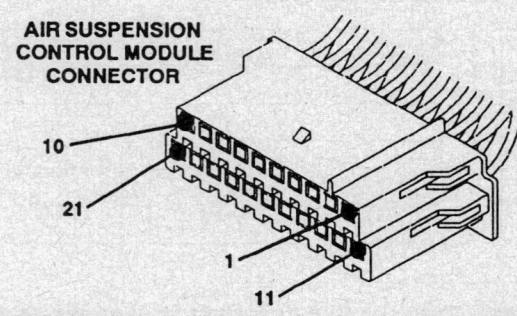

CAV	COLOR	FUNCTION	CAV	COLOR	FUNCTION
1	DB/RD	RF Height Sensor B	11	DB	RF Height Sensor A
2	DG	LF Height Sensor A	12	DB/WT	RF Height Sensor C
3	DG/WT	LF Height Sensor C	13	DG/RD	LF Height Sensor B
4	LG/RD	RR Height Sensor B	14	LG	RR Height Sensor A
5	VT/BR	CCD Bus (+)	15	LG/WT	RR Height Sensor C
6	DB/OR	RF Solenoid Control	16	WT/BK	CCD Bus (-)
7	DG/OR	LF Solenoid Control	17	BR	Sensor Ground
8	BK/OR	Exhaust Solenoid Control	18		Not Used
9	BK/RD	Compressor Relay Control	19	BK/LG	System Ground
10	LG/OR	RR Solenoid Control	20	YL/RD	Ignition 12-Volt Feed
			21	PK/WT	Fused Battery Feed

CR2019300046000X

Fig. 27   Air suspension control module connector identification. 1993

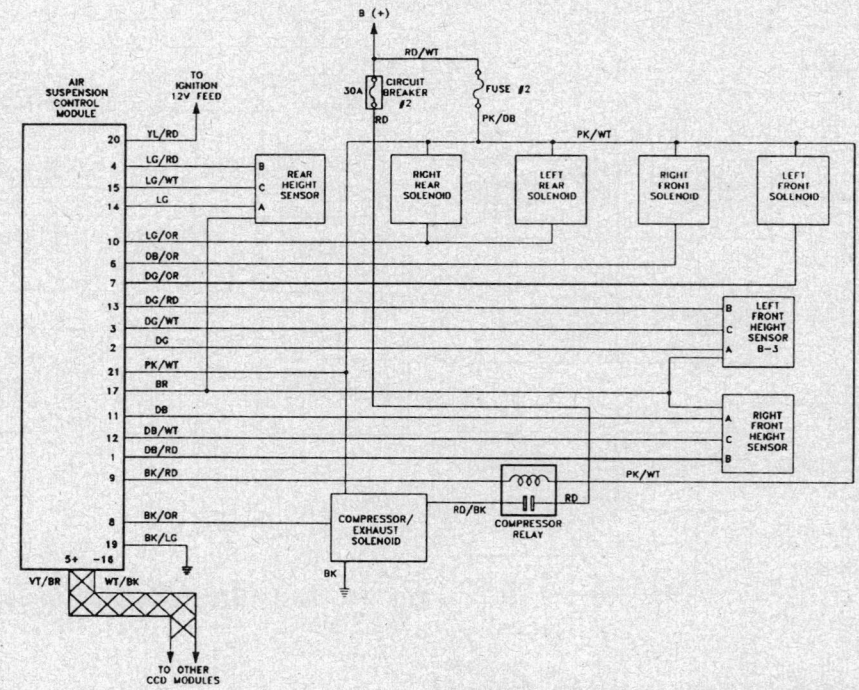

CR2019300047000X

Fig. 28   Air suspension system schematic. 1993

1. Your diagnostic test procedure must begin with a thorough visual inspection of the air suspension system for damaged components or disconnected connectors.

2. All testing should be performed on a level surface with all tires inflated to the proper pressure.

3. Connect the DRBII to the CCD bus data link connector.

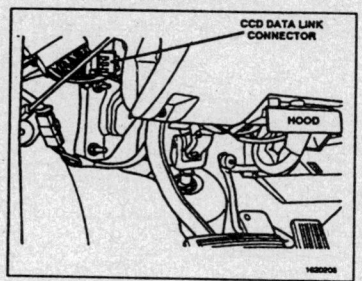

4. Start the engine and close all doors and trunk. Allow the car to run for 3 minutes. If the compressor is on continuously for more than 3 minutes, perform TEST 5A.

5. Select air suspension system.
   If the DRBII shows "No Response," Perform TEST 2A. Make sure the system is not in shipping mode.

6. If any fault codes are present, perform TEST 4A.

7. With the DRBII, select ASCM MONITORS, read the system status.

   If the DRBII shows,

   - "Stopped Due to Engine Not Running"
   - "Stopped Due to Charging System Failure"
   - "Stopped Due to Wide Open Throttle"

   - "Stopped Due to Bus Messages Not Received"
   - "Stopped Due to Doors and Trunk"

   - "Stopped Due to Brakes Applied"   Check brake switch adjustment

   - "Operational"   Perform TEST 3A.

CR2019300048000X

Fig. 29   Test 1A: DRB II Hook-Up/ Diagnostic Trouble Code Reading. 1993

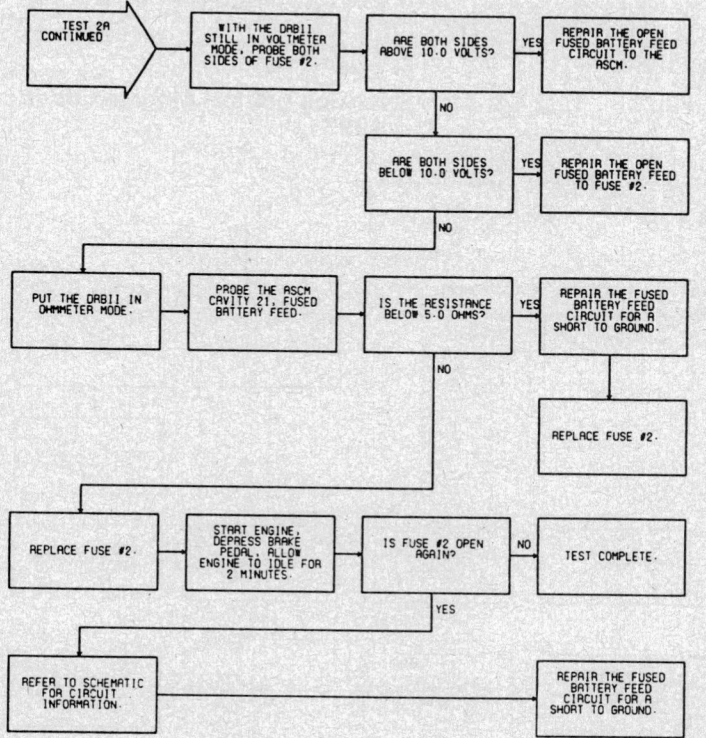

CR2019300049020X

Fig. 30   Test 2A: "No Response Condition" (Part 2 of 2). 1993

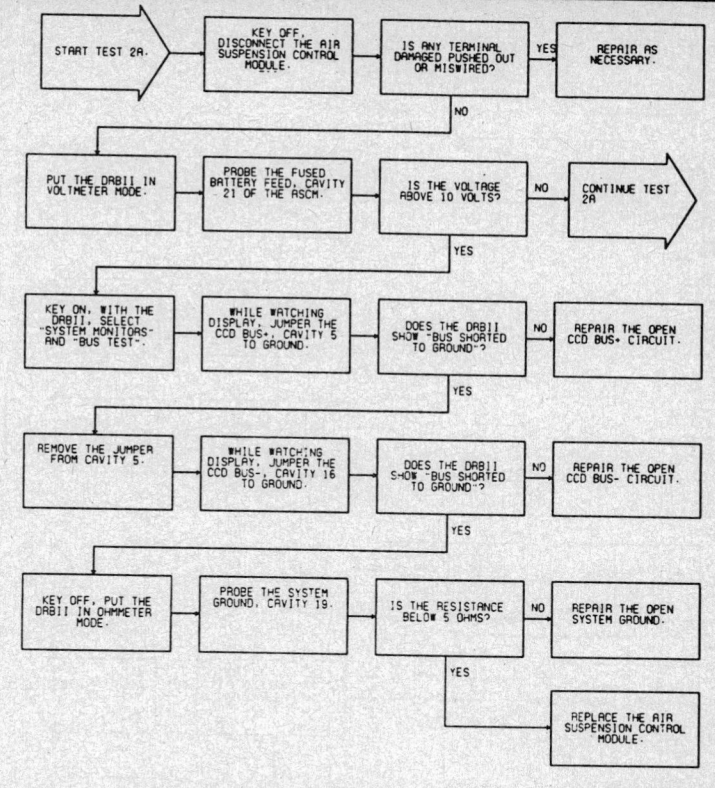

CR2019300049010X

Fig. 30   Test 2A: "No Response Condition" (Part 1 of 2). 1993

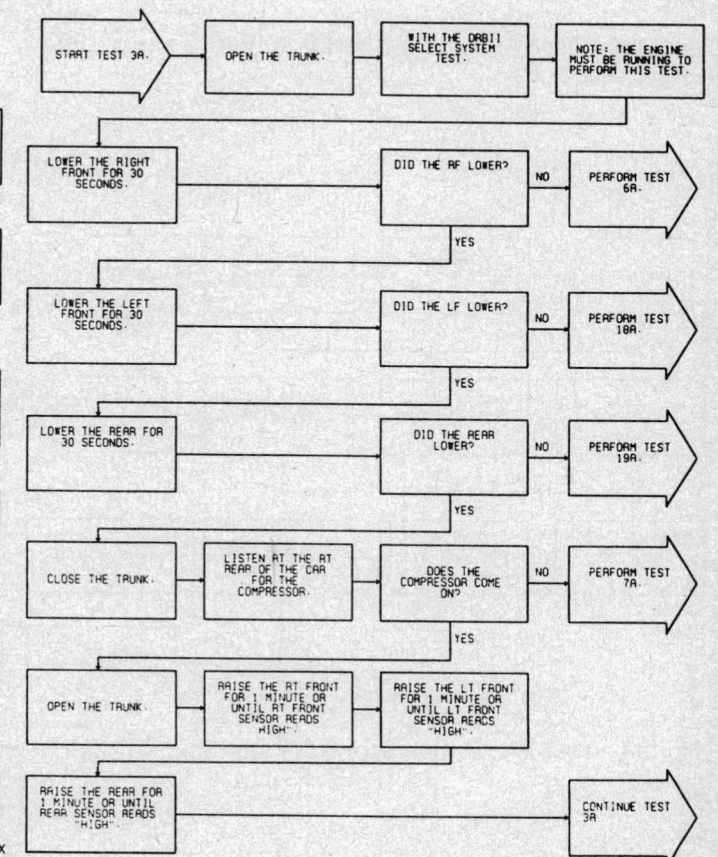

CR2019300050010X

Fig. 31   Test 3A: System Operation (Part 1 of 3). 1993

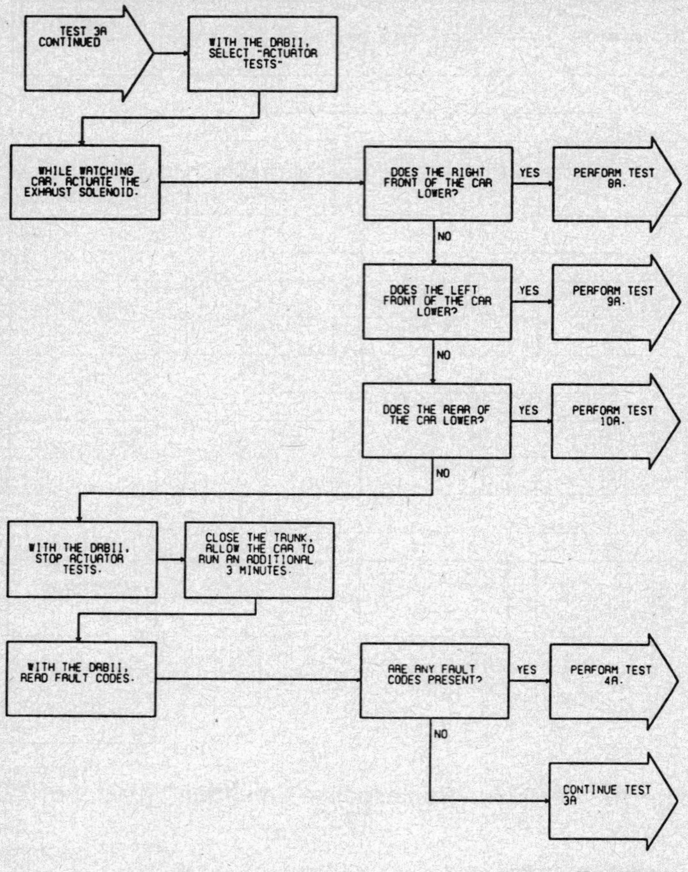

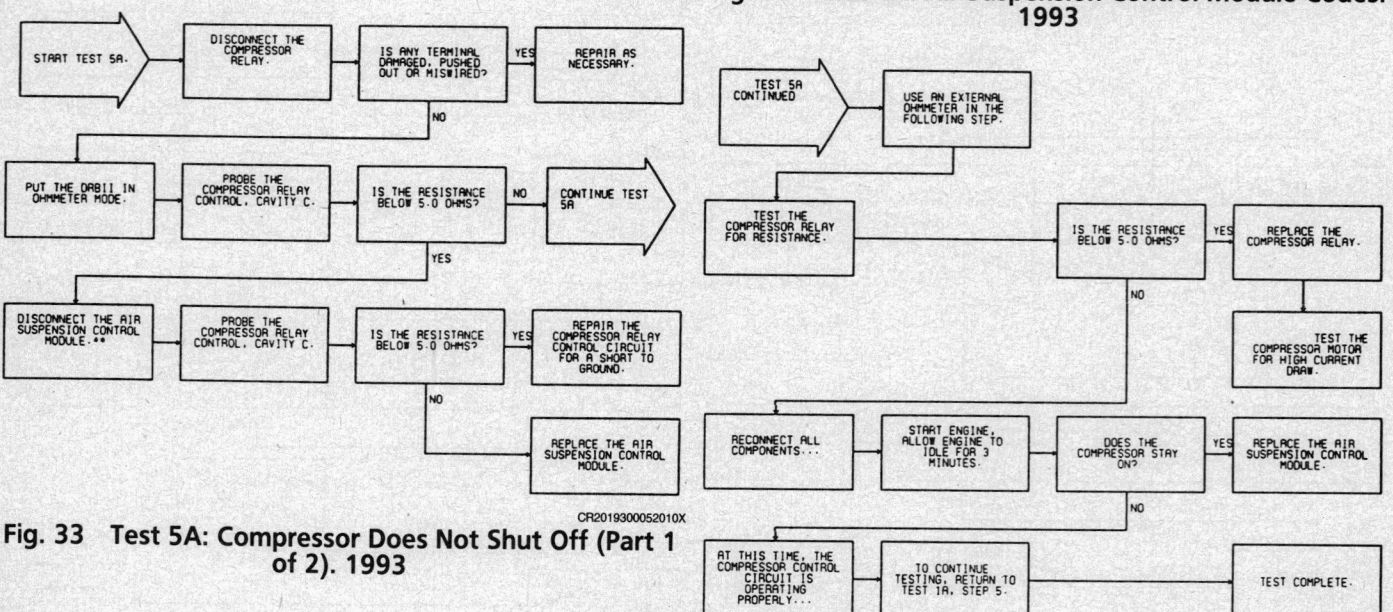

Fig. 31   Test 3A: System Operation (Part 3 of 3). 1993

CR2019300050030X

If more than one fault is present, repair the codes in the order shown below.

Compressor Overrun - compressor relay is activated more than 180 +/- 10 seconds continuously.

Perform TEST 14A.

Right Front Height Sensor Failure - illegal height sensor input is received for more than 3 +/- 1 seconds.

Perform TEST 11A.

Left Front Height Sensor Failure - illegal height sensor input is received for more than 3 +/- 1 seconds.

Perform TEST 12A.

Rear Height Sensor Failure - illegal height sensor input is received for more than 3 +/- 1 seconds.

Perform TEST 13A.

No BCM Messages Received - Body controller module messages are not received for 3 +/- 1 seconds while the CCD indicates the ignition is on.

Perform TEST 15A.

No PCM Messages Received - Powertrain control module messages are not received for 3 +/- 1 seconds while the CCD indicates the ignition is on.

Perform TEST 16A.

CR2019300051000X

Fig. 32   Test 4A: Air Suspension Control Module Codes. 1993

Fig. 31   Test 3A: System Operation (Part 2 of 3). 1993

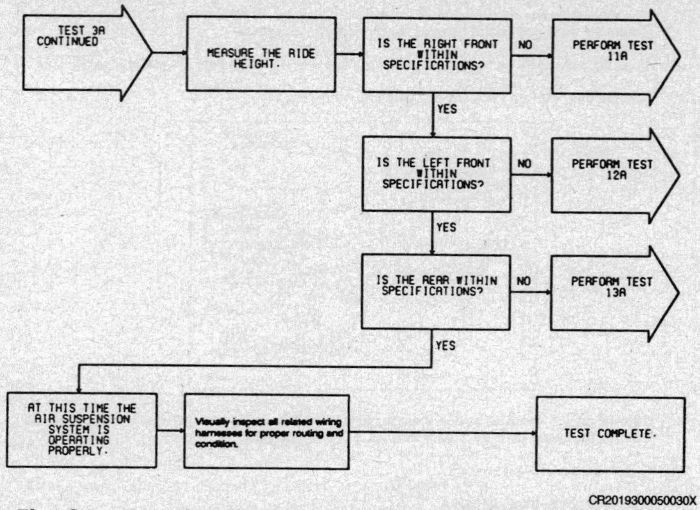

CR2019300050020X

Fig. 33   Test 5A: Compressor Does Not Shut Off (Part 1 of 2). 1993

CR2019300052010X

Fig. 33   Test 5A: Compressor Does Not Shut Off (Part 2 of 2). 1993

CR2019300052020X

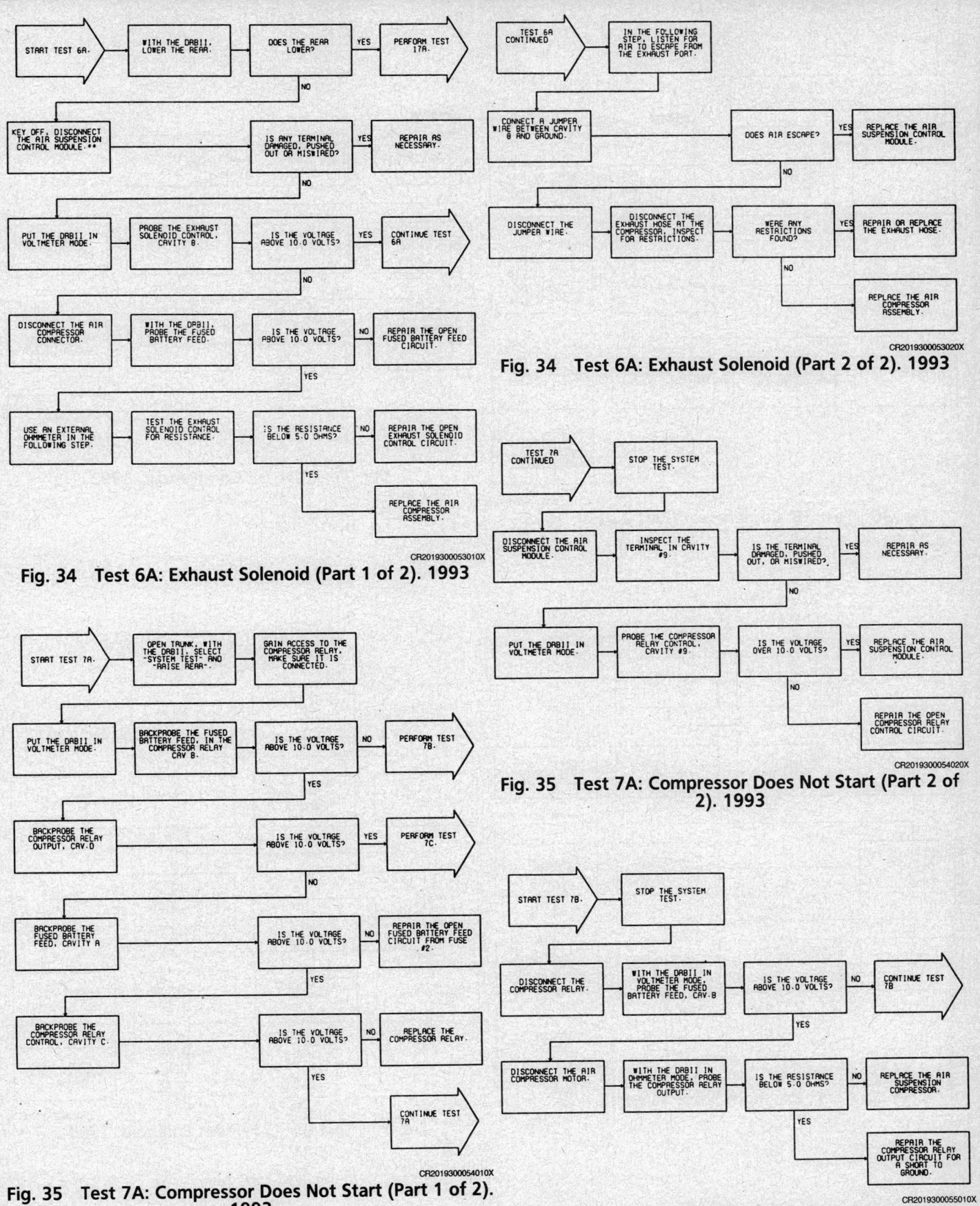

Fig. 34   Test 6A: Exhaust Solenoid (Part 1 of 2). 1993

CR2019300053010X

Fig. 34   Test 6A: Exhaust Solenoid (Part 2 of 2). 1993

CR2019300053020X

Fig. 35   Test 7A: Compressor Does Not Start (Part 2 of 2). 1993

CR2019300054020X

Fig. 35   Test 7A: Compressor Does Not Start (Part 1 of 2). 1993

CR2019300054010X

Fig. 36   Test 7B: Compressor (Part 1 of 2). 1993

CR2019300055010X

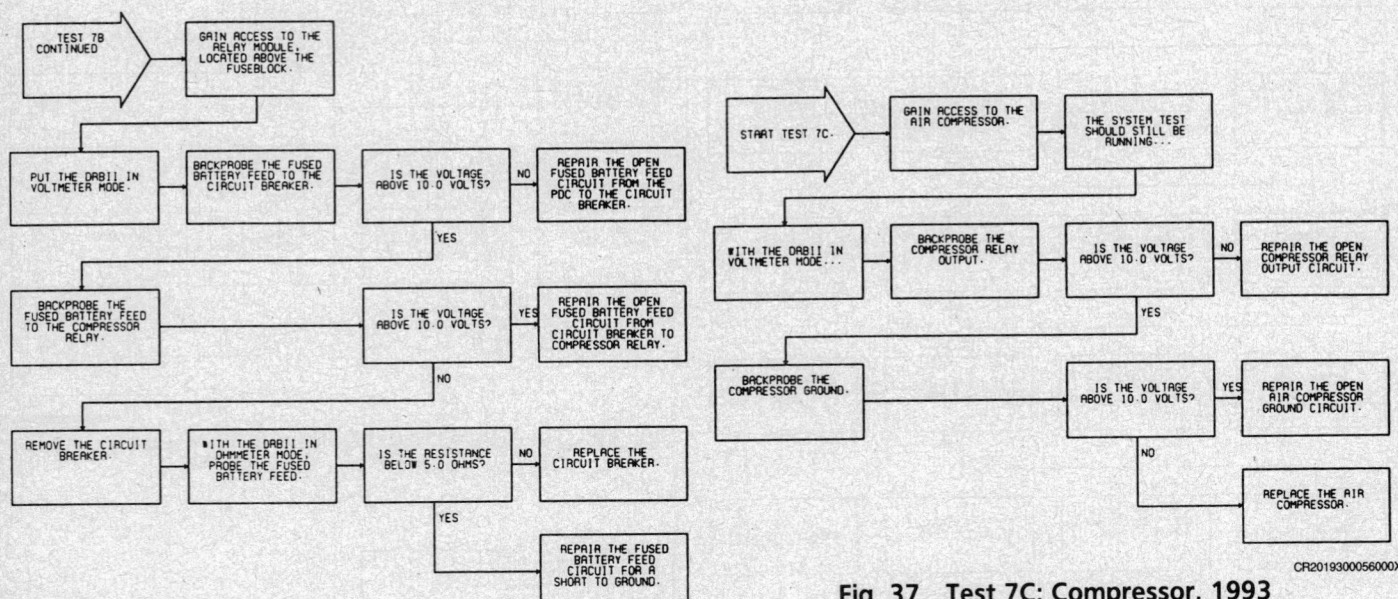

Fig. 36   Test 7B: Compressor (Part 2 of 2). 1993

CR2019300055020X

Fig. 37   Test 7C: Compressor. 1993

CR2019300056000X

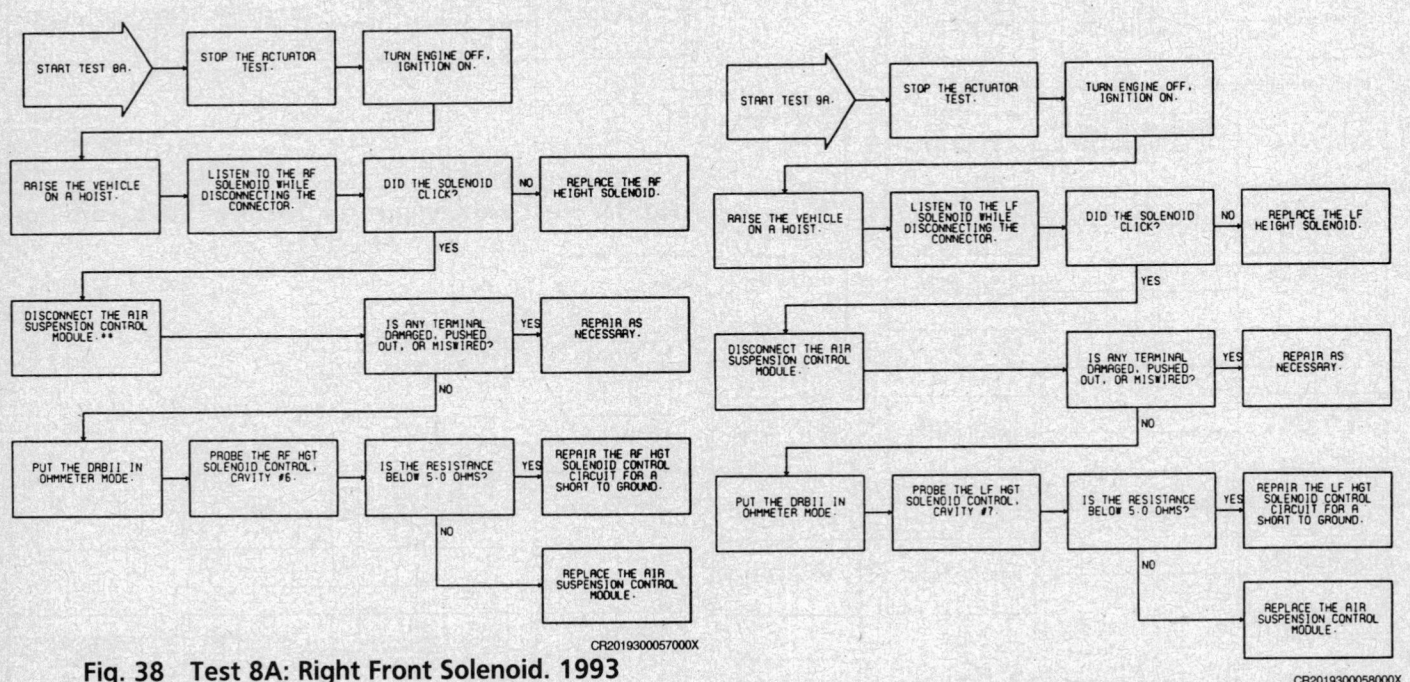

Fig. 38   Test 8A: Right Front Solenoid. 1993

CR2019300057000X

Fig. 39   Test 9A: Left Front Solenoid. 1993

CR2019300058000X

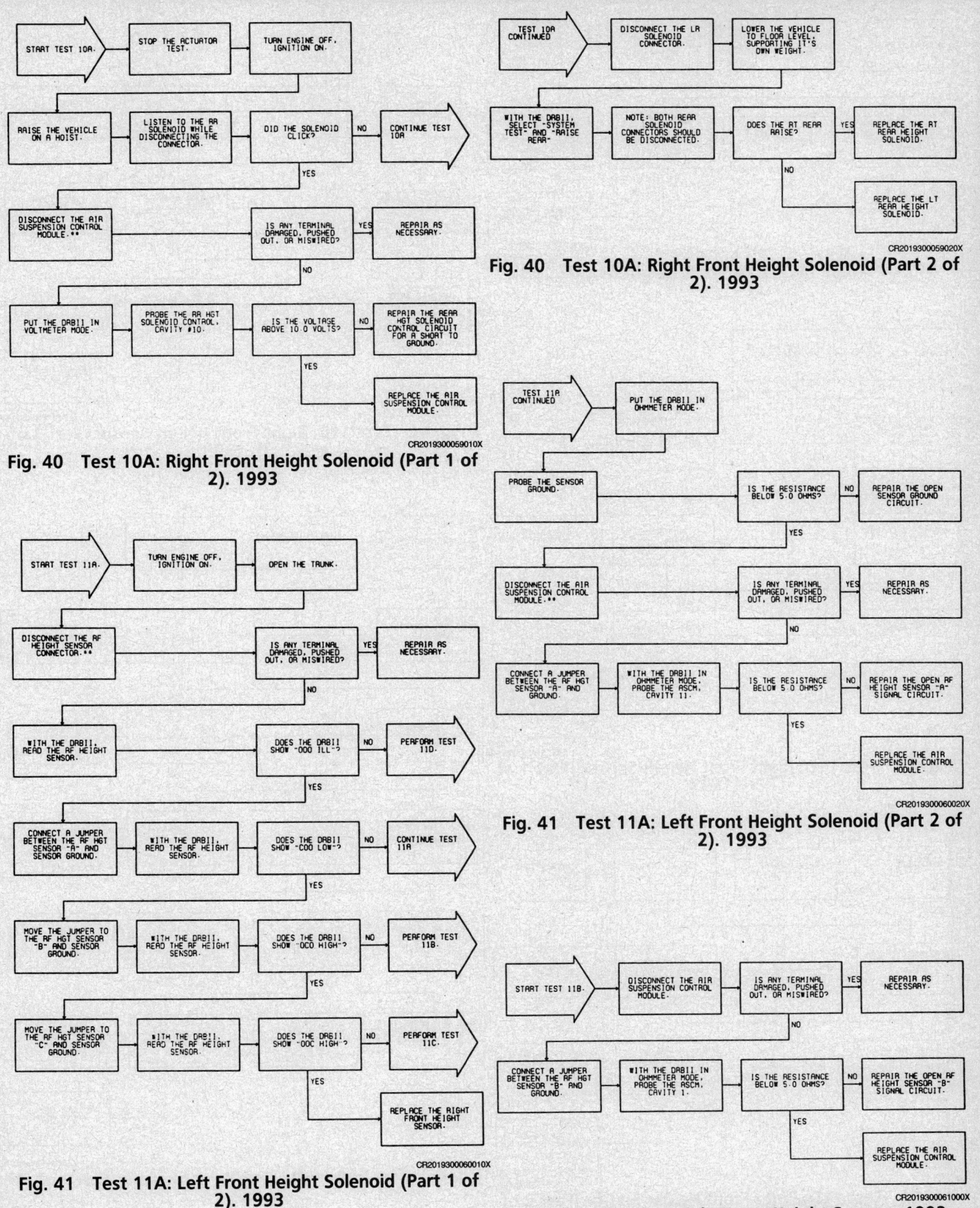

Fig. 40   Test 10A: Right Front Height Solenoid (Part 2 of 2). 1993

Fig. 40   Test 10A: Right Front Height Solenoid (Part 1 of 2). 1993

Fig. 41   Test 11A: Left Front Height Solenoid (Part 2 of 2). 1993

Fig. 41   Test 11A: Left Front Height Solenoid (Part 1 of 2). 1993

Fig. 42   Test 11B: Right Front Height Sensor . 1993

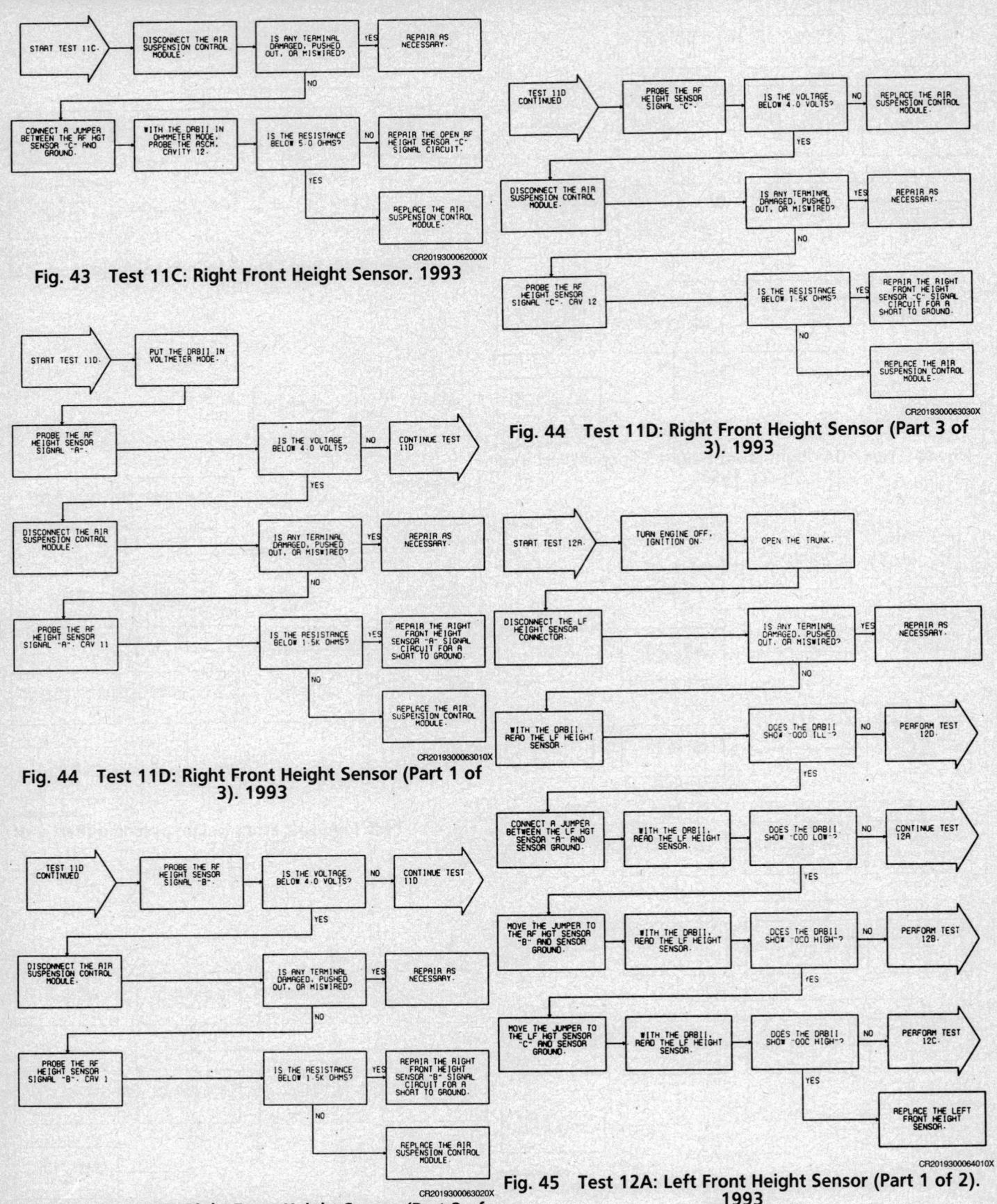

Fig. 43   Test 11C: Right Front Height Sensor. 1993

CR2019300062000X

Fig. 44   Test 11D: Right Front Height Sensor (Part 3 of 3). 1993

CR2019300063030X

Fig. 44   Test 11D: Right Front Height Sensor (Part 1 of 3). 1993

CR2019300063010X

Fig. 45   Test 12A: Left Front Height Sensor (Part 1 of 2). 1993

CR2019300064010X

Fig. 44   Test 11D: Right Front Height Sensor (Part 2 of 3). 1993

CR2019300063020X

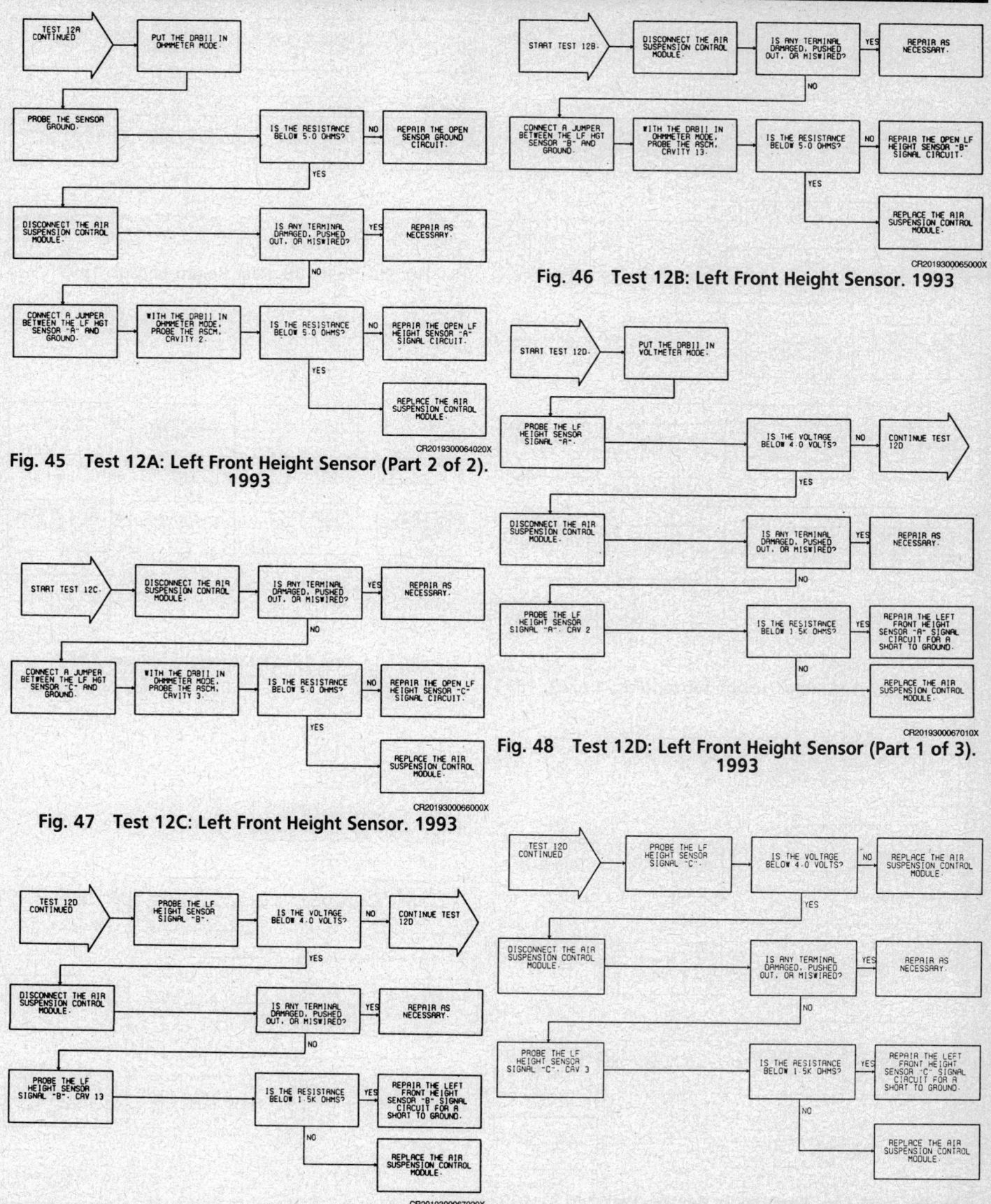

Fig. 45   Test 12A: Left Front Height Sensor (Part 2 of 2). 1993

Fig. 46   Test 12B: Left Front Height Sensor. 1993

Fig. 47   Test 12C: Left Front Height Sensor. 1993

Fig. 48   Test 12D: Left Front Height Sensor (Part 1 of 3). 1993

Fig. 48   Test 12D: Left Front Height Sensor (Part 2 of 3). 1993

Fig. 48   Test 12D: Left Front Height Sensor (Part 3 of 3). 1993

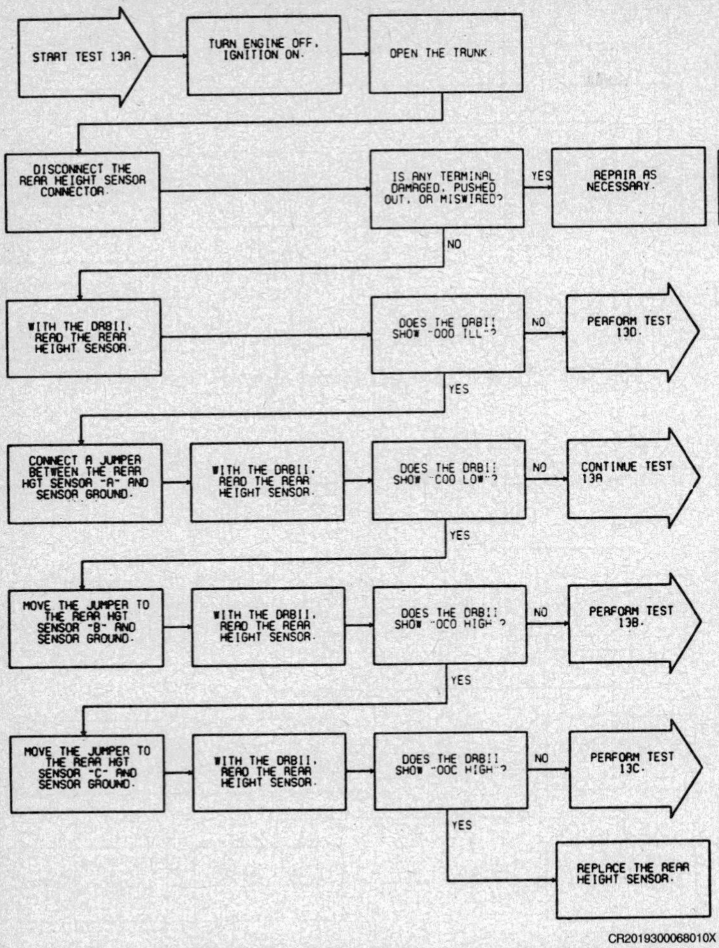

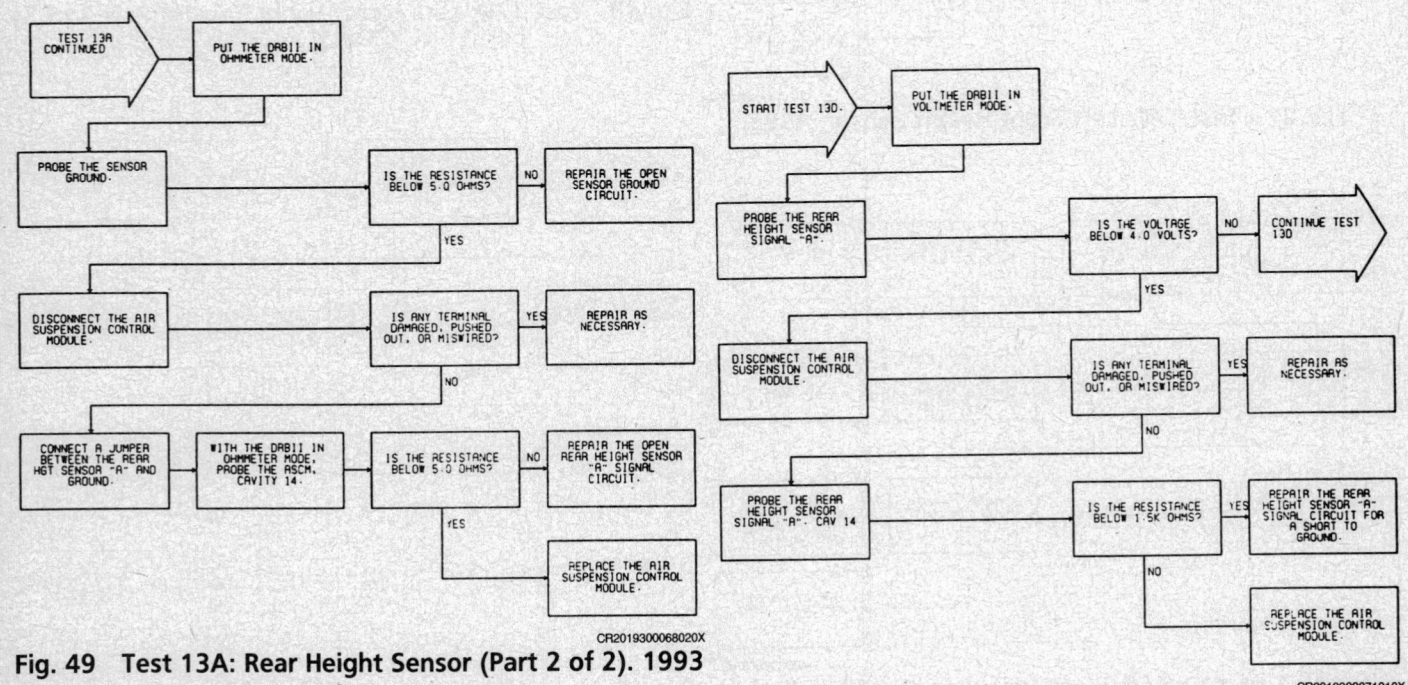

Fig. 49   Test 13A: Rear Height Sensor (Part 1 of 2). 1993

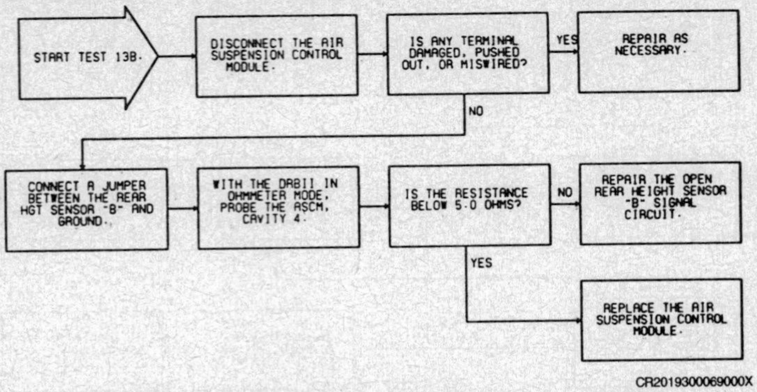

CR2019300068010X

Fig. 50   Test 13B: Rear Height Sensor. 1993

CR2019300069000X

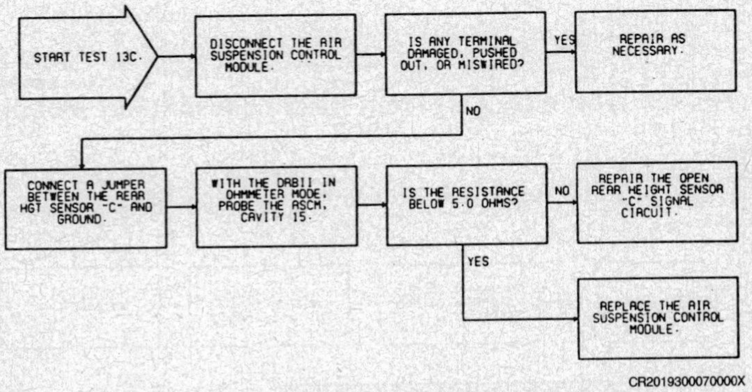

Fig. 51   Test 13C: Rear Height Sensor. 1993

CR2019300070000X

Fig. 49   Test 13A: Rear Height Sensor (Part 2 of 2). 1993

CR2019300068020X

Fig. 52   Test 13D: Rear Height Sensor (Part 1 of 3). 1993

CR2019300071010X

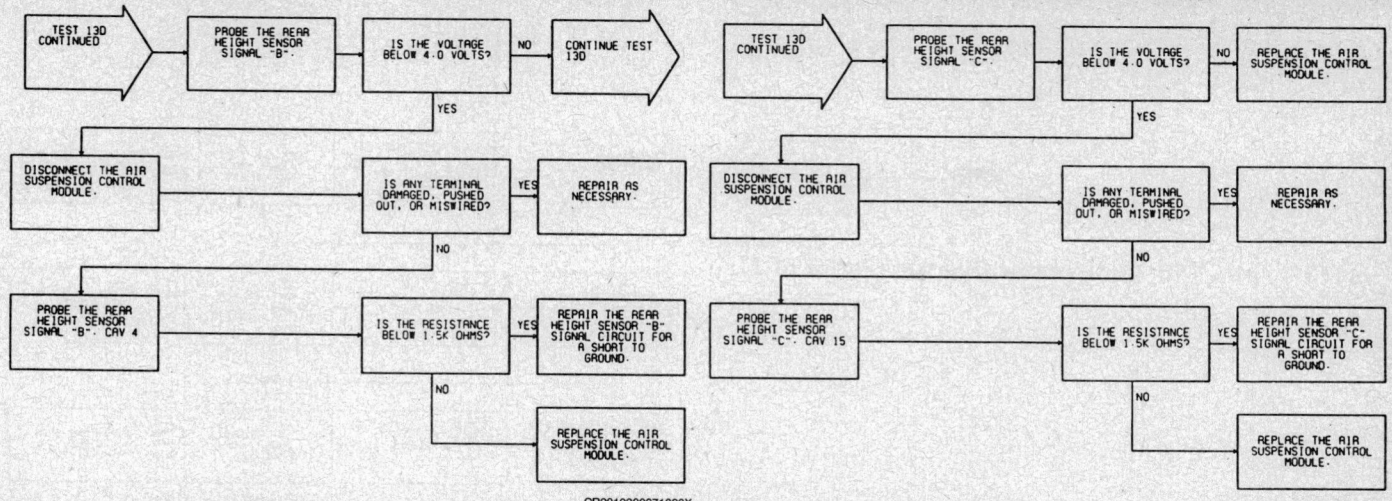

Fig. 52   Test 13D: Rear Height Sensor (Part 2 of 3). 1993

CR2019300071020X

Fig. 52   Test 13D: Rear Height Sensor (Part 3 of 3). 1993

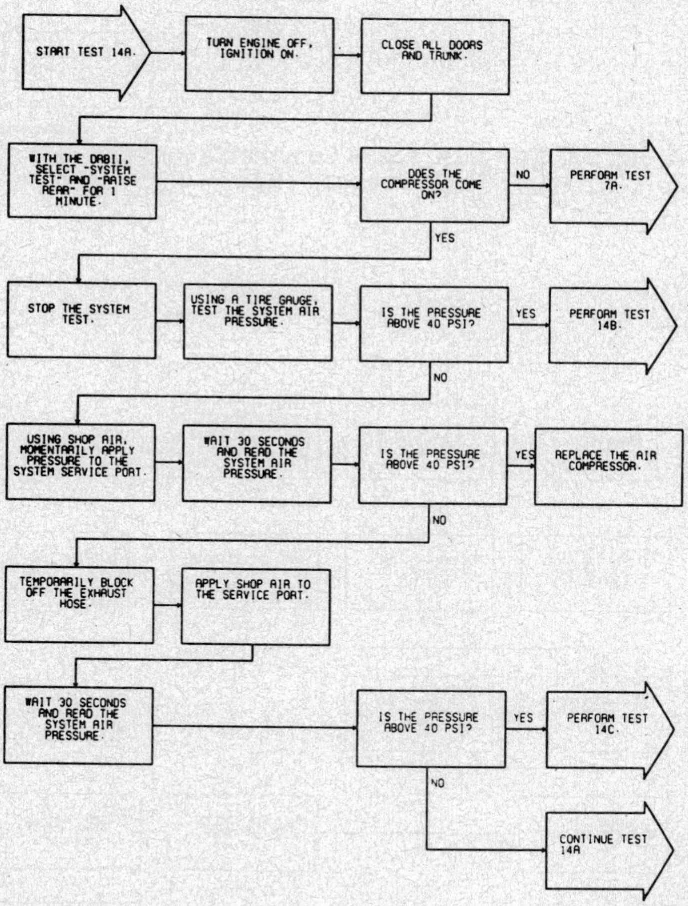

CR2019300071030X

Fig. 53   Test 14A: Compressor (Part 2 of 2). 1993

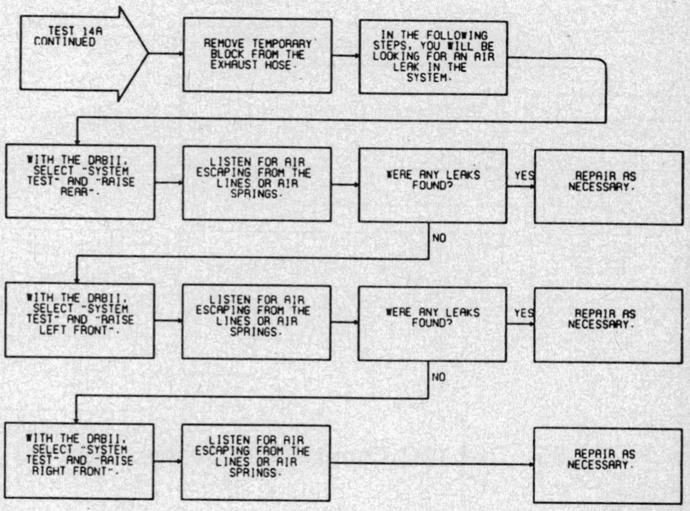

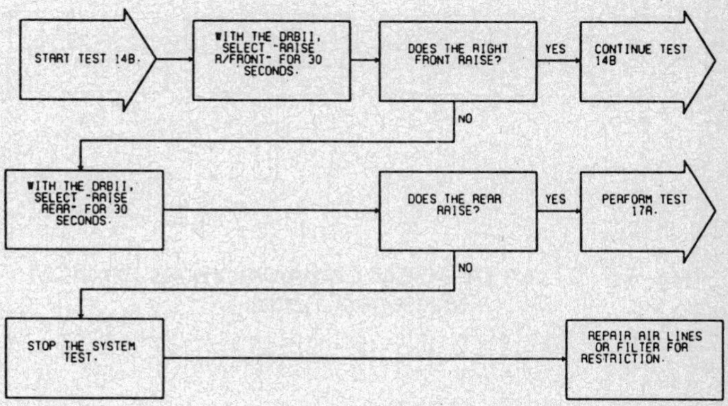

CR2019300072020X

Fig. 53   Test 14A: Compressor (Part 1 of 2). 1993

CR2019300072010X

Fig. 54   Test 14B: Compressor Overrun (Part 1 of 2). 1993

CR2019300073010X

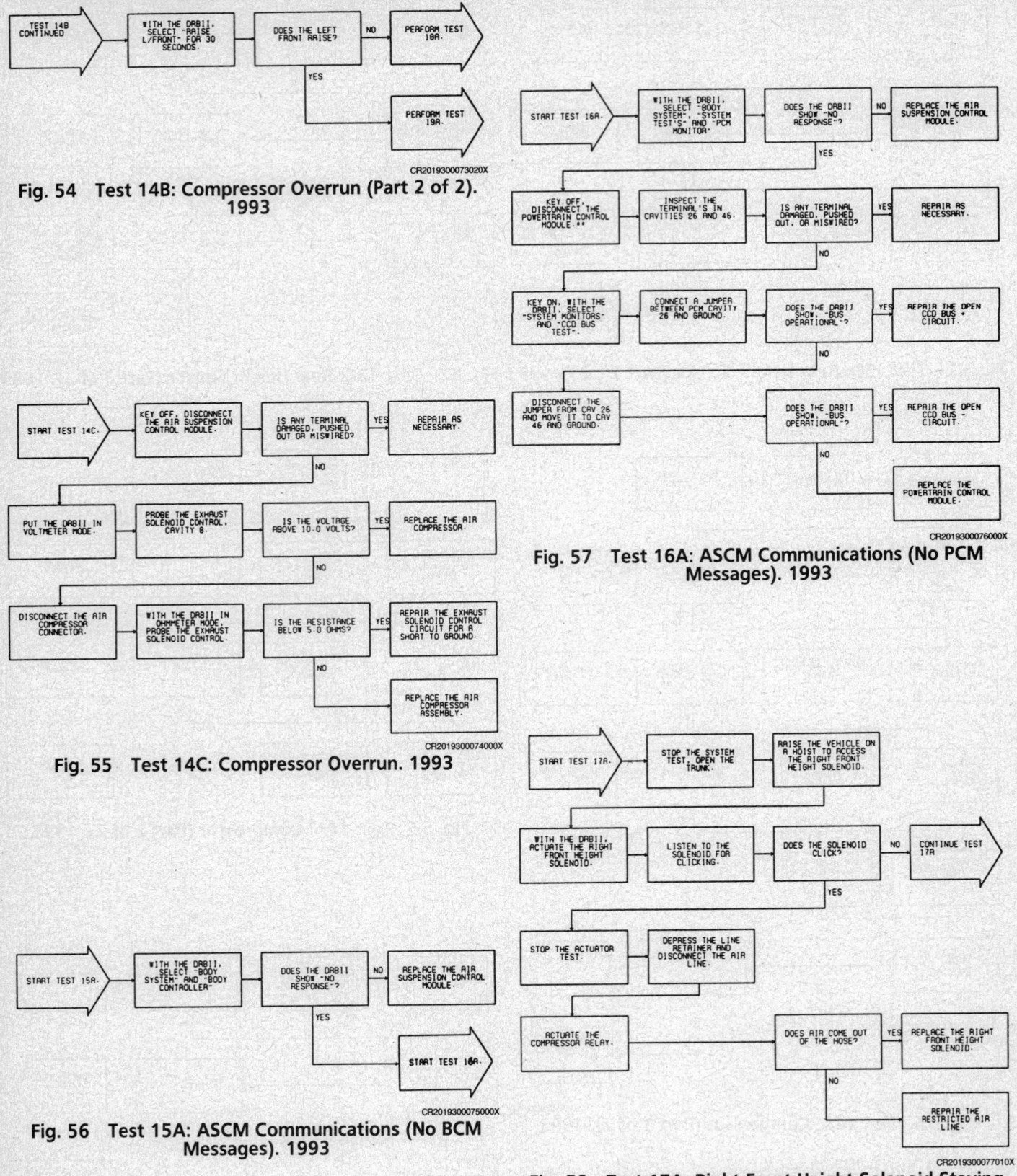

Fig. 54   Test 14B: Compressor Overrun (Part 2 of 2).
          1993

Fig. 55   Test 14C: Compressor Overrun. 1993

Fig. 56   Test 15A: ASCM Communications (No BCM
          Messages). 1993

Fig. 57   Test 16A: ASCM Communications (No PCM
          Messages). 1993

Fig. 58   Test 17A: Right Front Height Solenoid Staying
          Closed (Part 1 of 2). 1993

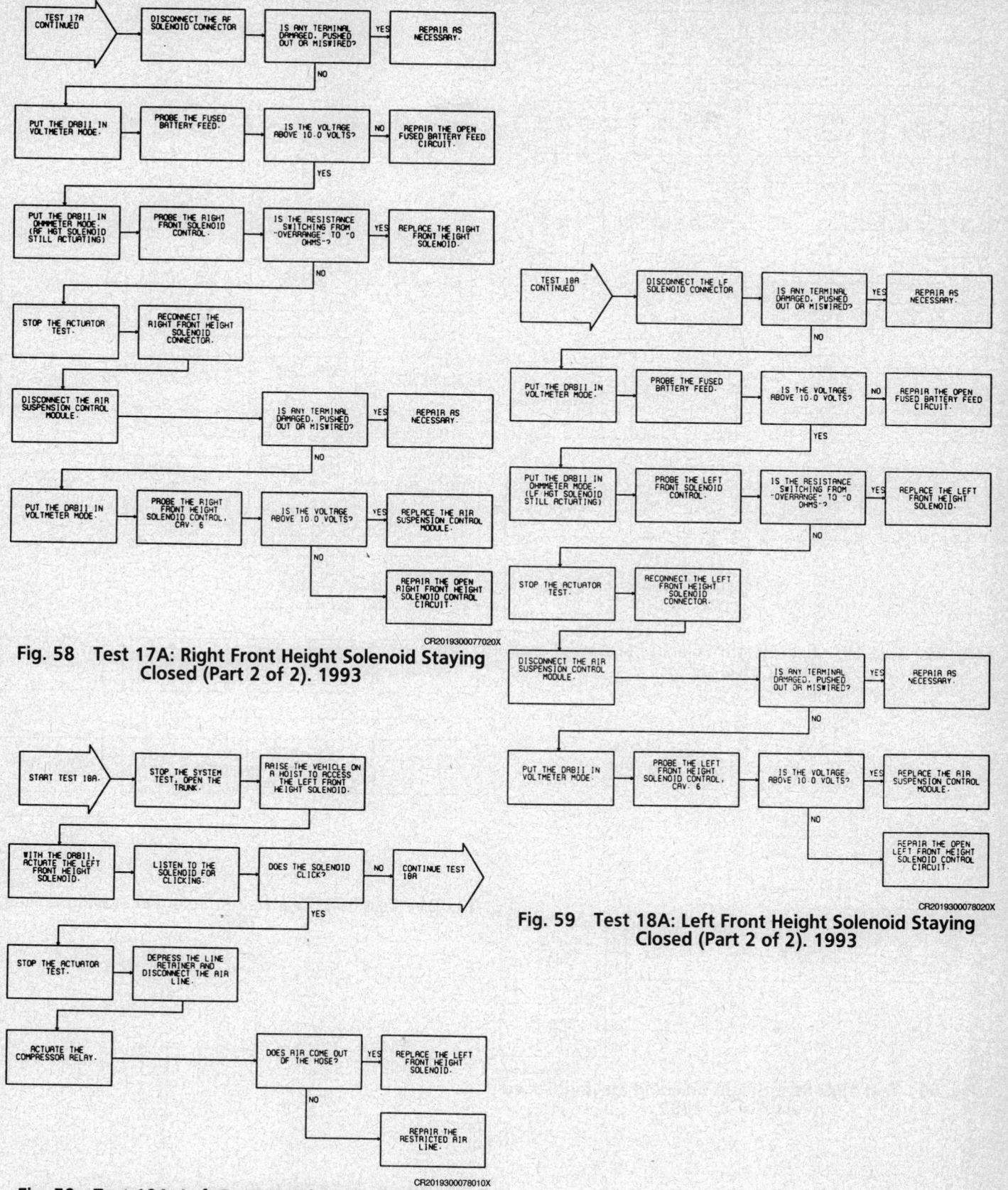

Fig. 58   Test 17A: Right Front Height Solenoid Staying Closed (Part 2 of 2). 1993

Fig. 59   Test 18A: Left Front Height Solenoid Staying Closed (Part 2 of 2). 1993

Fig. 59   Test 18A: Left Front Height Solenoid Staying Closed (Part 1 of 2). 1993

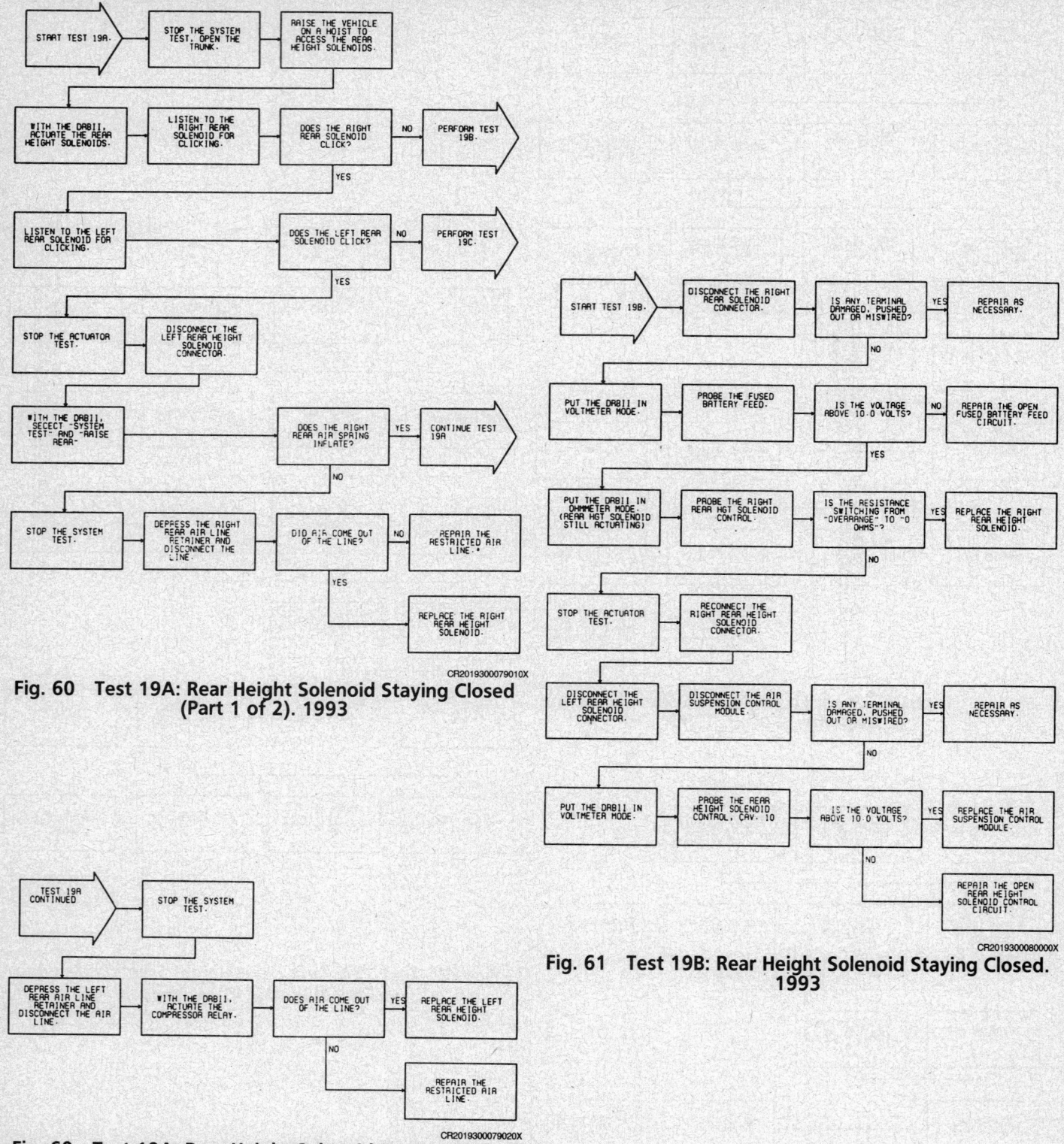

Fig. 60   Test 19A: Rear Height Solenoid Staying Closed (Part 1 of 2). 1993

Fig. 61   Test 19B: Rear Height Solenoid Staying Closed. 1993

Fig. 60   Test 19A: Rear Height Solenoid Staying Closed (Part 2 of 2). 1993

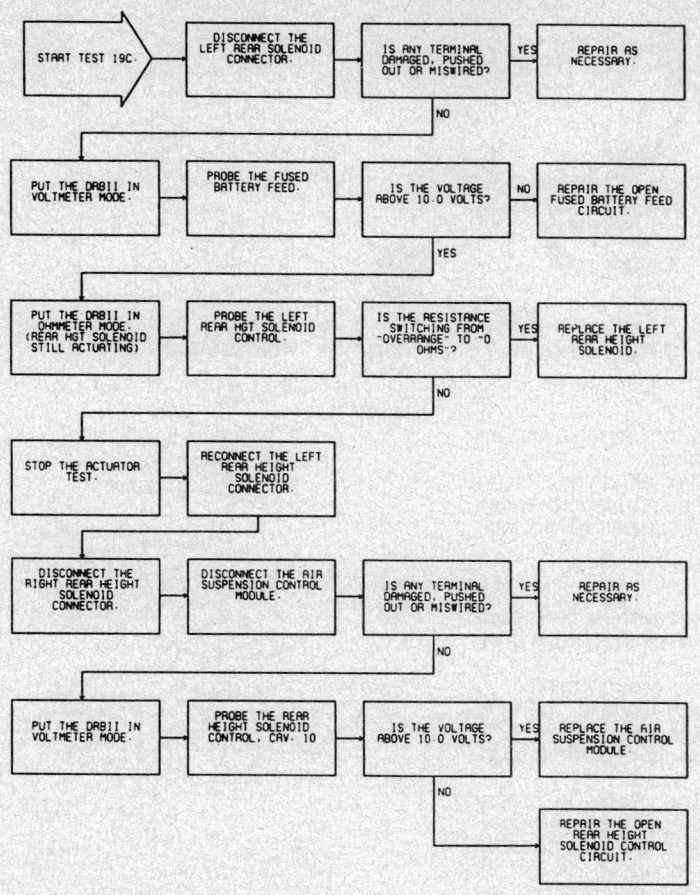

Fig. 62 Test 19C: Rear Height Solenoid Staying Closed. 1993

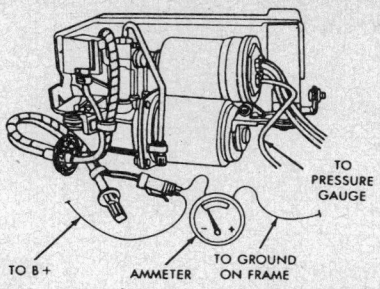

Fig. 63 Compressor current draw test

Fender Heights (Inches)	Mode Sensor Position	Sensor Signals		
		A	B	C
28.5–29.9	High	Open	Closed	Open
25.9–26.5	Trim	Closed	Open	Closed
24.0–24.5	Low	Closed	Open	Open

Fig. 64 Height sensor logic chart

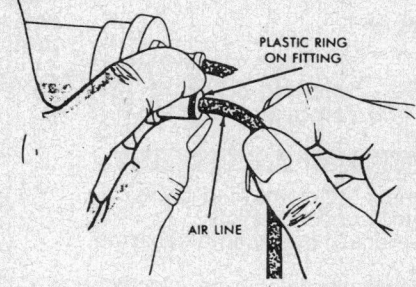

Fig. 65 Releasing air line

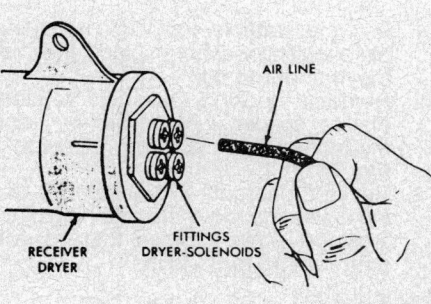

Fig. 66 Attaching air line

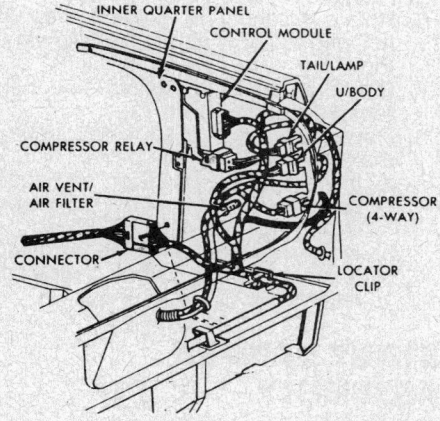

Fig. 67 Control module (ASCM) & relay removal

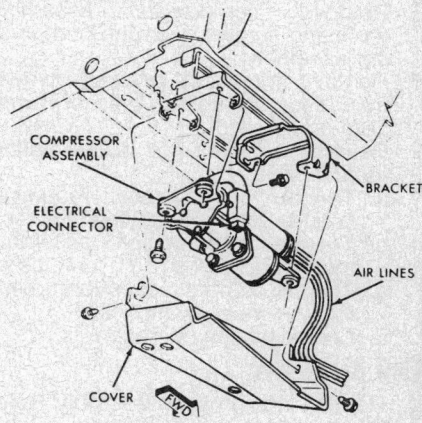

Fig. 68 Compressor assembly removal

SYSTEM SERVICE

Open trunk, door(s) or disconnect battery ground cable before raising vehicle. Rear air springs must be deflated before being removed from vehicle.

AIR LINES

1. To release an air line from fitting, pull back on plastic ring, then remove line from fitting, **Fig. 65.**
2. Air line fittings have a push-in feature. A brass type collet locks the air line in place. One rubber O-ring seals the air line to prevent leakage. To attach air line, push into fitting, **Fig. 66.**

CONTROL MODULE (ASCM)

1. Disconnect battery ground cable.
2. Remove right side trunk trim panel.
3. Disconnect Control Module and relay electrical connectors, **Fig. 67.**
4. Remove Control Module mounting screws, then the Control Module.
5. Reverse procedure to install, noting the following:

a. Install relay on Control Module mounting bracket, if required.
b. **Torque** Control Module mounting screws to 19-29 inch lbs.

COMPRESSOR RELAY

1. Remove right side trunk trim panel.
2. Disconnect relay electrical connector, **Fig. 67.**
3. Remove relay from Control Module mounting bracket by prying out on locating clip.
4. Reverse procedure to install.

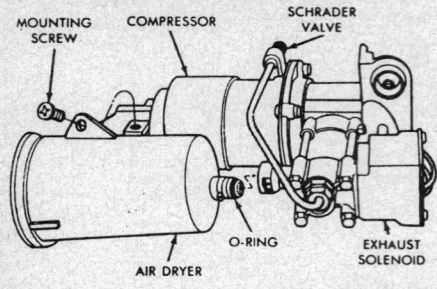

Fig. 69   Air dryer replacement

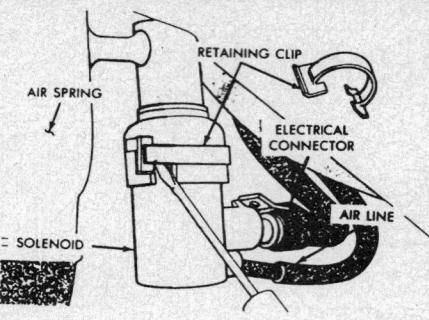

Fig. 70   Retaining clip removal

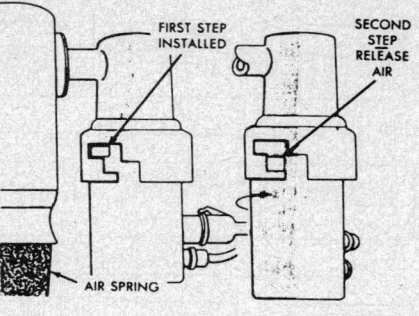

Fig. 71   Releasing air pressure

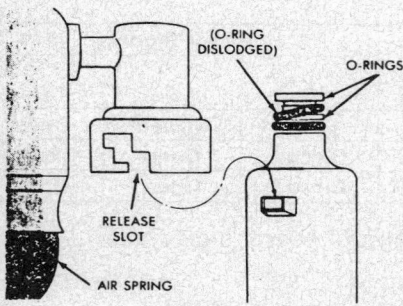

Fig. 72   Solenoid & O-ring removal

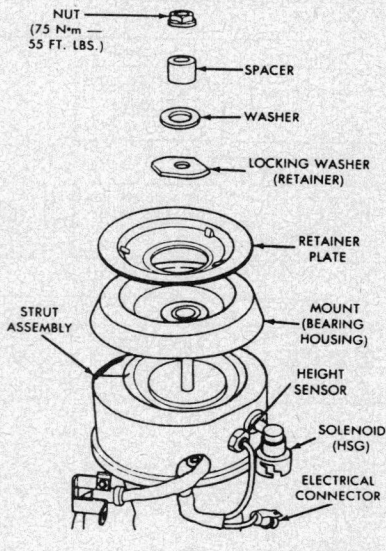

Fig. 73   Air strut upper mount assembly

COMPRESSOR ASSEMBLY

1. Disconnect battery ground cable.
2. Raise and support vehicle.
3. Remove cover from compressor assembly.
4. Disconnect air lines and electrical connectors. Refer to procedure outlined under "Air Lines" and **Fig. 68.**
5. Remove compressor assembly mounting screws, then the compressor assembly.
6. Remove mounting bracket screws, then slide mounting bracket away from compressor.
7. Reverse procedure to install, noting the following:
   a. **Torque** compressor mounting bracket screws to 70 inch lbs.
   b. **Torque** compressor assembly mounting screws to 70 inch lbs.
   c. **Torque** compressor cover mounting screws to 40 inch lbs.
   d. Check system operation.

AIR DRYER

1. Remove compressor assembly. Refer to procedure outlined under "Compressor Assembly."
2. Remove air dryer mounting screw.
3. Rotate air dryer assembly 90° to release retaining tangs from exhaust solenoid housing, then remove air dryer assembly, **Fig. 69.**
4. Reverse procedure to install, noting

the following:
   a. Inspect O-ring for damage and location on air dryer.
   b. Insert and index air dryer locking tangs into exhaust solenoid outlet.
   c. Rotate air dryer assembly to lock into position.

SOLENOIDS

Do not attempt to remove or install solenoids while the AAS system is supporting the vehicle.
1. Disconnect battery ground cable.
2. Raise and support vehicle, then remove wheel and tire.
3. Disconnect solenoid electrical connector.
4. Disconnect air line. Refer to procedure outlined under "Air Lines." Solenoids have molded square tangs that fit into stepped notches of the air spring housing. The notches provide an air relief position and a retaining position. The retaining position is locked with a retaining clip.
5. Remove retaining clip, **Fig. 70.**
6. Rotate solenoid to second step in housing to allow air pressure to vent, **Fig. 71.**
7. Rotate solenoid to release slot, then remove solenoid, **Fig. 72.**
8. Reverse procedure to install, noting the following:
   a. Inspect O-ring condition and position. O-ring can become dislodged during removal, **Fig. 72.**
   b. Install solenoid with tangs to top ledge of housing, then install retaining clip.

STRUT DAMPER ASSEMBLY

Disassemble & Assemble

Disassembly is limited to upper mount and bearing housing. The strut shock absorber, air spring with internal height sensor, solenoid and wiring harness are serviced as an assembly.

1. Using a suitable tool, hold retaining plate locking washer in place, then remove strut rod nut.
2. Remove locking washer retainer plate, spacer, flat washer and mount/bearing housing assembly, **Fig. 73.**
3. Reverse procedure to assemble. Using a suitable tool, hold retaining plate locking washer in place, then **torque** strut rod nut to 55 ft. lbs.

RECHARGING AIR SPRINGS

1. To activate compressor, ground pin S08 to pin X20.
2. To activate left front spring solenoid, ground pin S31 to pin X20.
3. To activate right front spring solenoid, ground pin S30 to pin X20.
4. To activate right rear spring solenoid, ground pin S32 to pin X20.

Electronic Control Suspension (ECS)

NOTE: On Air Bag Equipped Models, Refer To "Air Bag System Precautions" Located In The Front Of This Manual For System Disarming & Arming Procedures.

INDEX

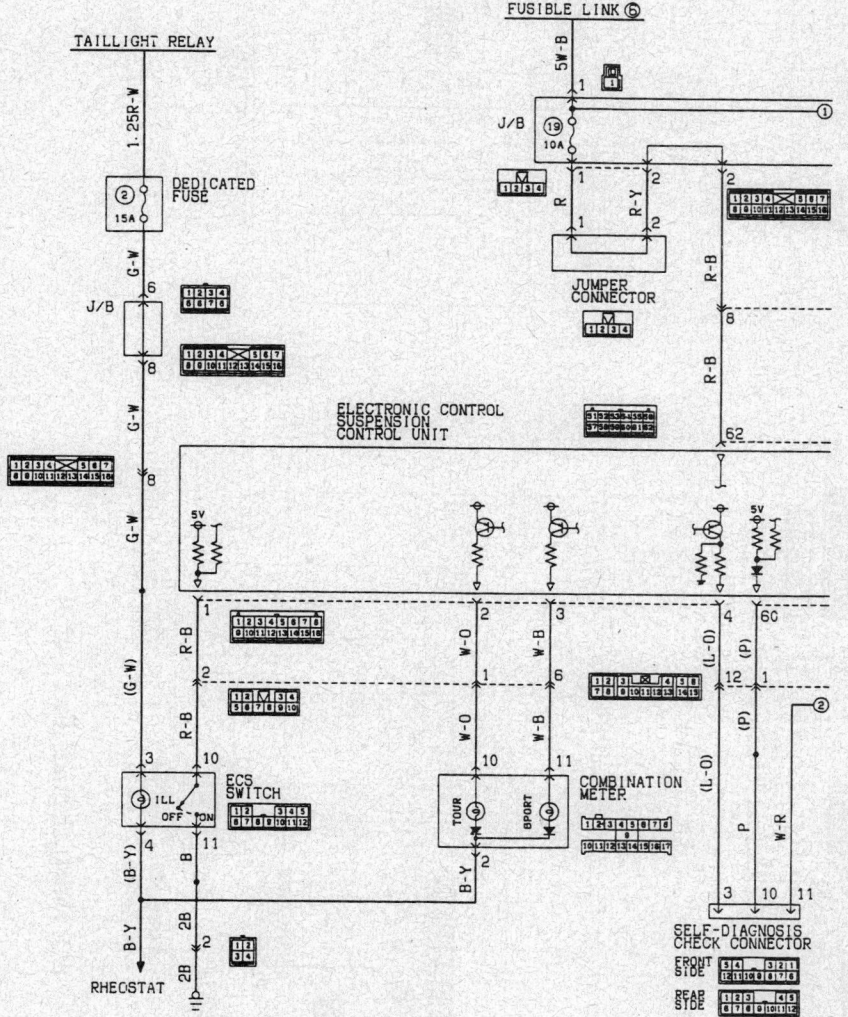

Fig. 1   ECS wiring diagram (Part 1 of 3)

CR2019100092010X

An ECS selector switch located on the righthand side of the instrument cluster provides a choice of Tour (soft) or Sport (hard) dampening. An ECS Indicator Light located on the lefthand side of the instrument cluster indicates which mode the system is in.

INSPECTION

If a problem associated with the following items occurs, the ECS indicator light (Tour Sport) in the combination light located to the left of the tachometer flashes at intervals of .5 seconds. At the same time, the self diagnosis code associated with the problem is output to the diagnosis connector. Warning indication items are G sensor, Steering angular velocity sensor, Vehicle speed sensor and Damping force changeover actuator (including position detection switch).

DIAGNOSIS & TESTING

Refer to **Fig. 1** for system wiring diagram when diagnosing the ECS system.

ACCESSING DIAGNOSTIC TROUBLE CODES

Using DRB II Scan Tool

1. Using DRB II Scan Tool No. MB991341, or equivalent, perform diagnostic tests shown in **Figs. 2 through 9**.
2. When diagnostic trouble codes (DTCs) have been located, repaired, and erased; retest system to ensure all problems have been corrected.

Using Voltmeter

1. Set ignition switch to OFF position.
2. Connect the positive lead of a voltmeter to No. 3 terminal of diagnostic connector and the negative lead to terminal No. 12, **Fig. 10**. The diagnostic connector is located beside the junction block.
3. Turn ignition switch to ON position.
4. Read Diagnostic Trouble Code on basis of deflection of pointer on voltmeter, **Fig. 11**.

PRECAUTIONS

AIR BAG SYSTEMS

Refer to Air Bag Systems Precautions in the front of this manual for system disarming and arming procedures.

DESCRIPTION

Electronic Control Suspension (ECS) detects pitching, bouncing and rough road conditions and automatically adjusts the dampening characteristics of the shock absorbers.

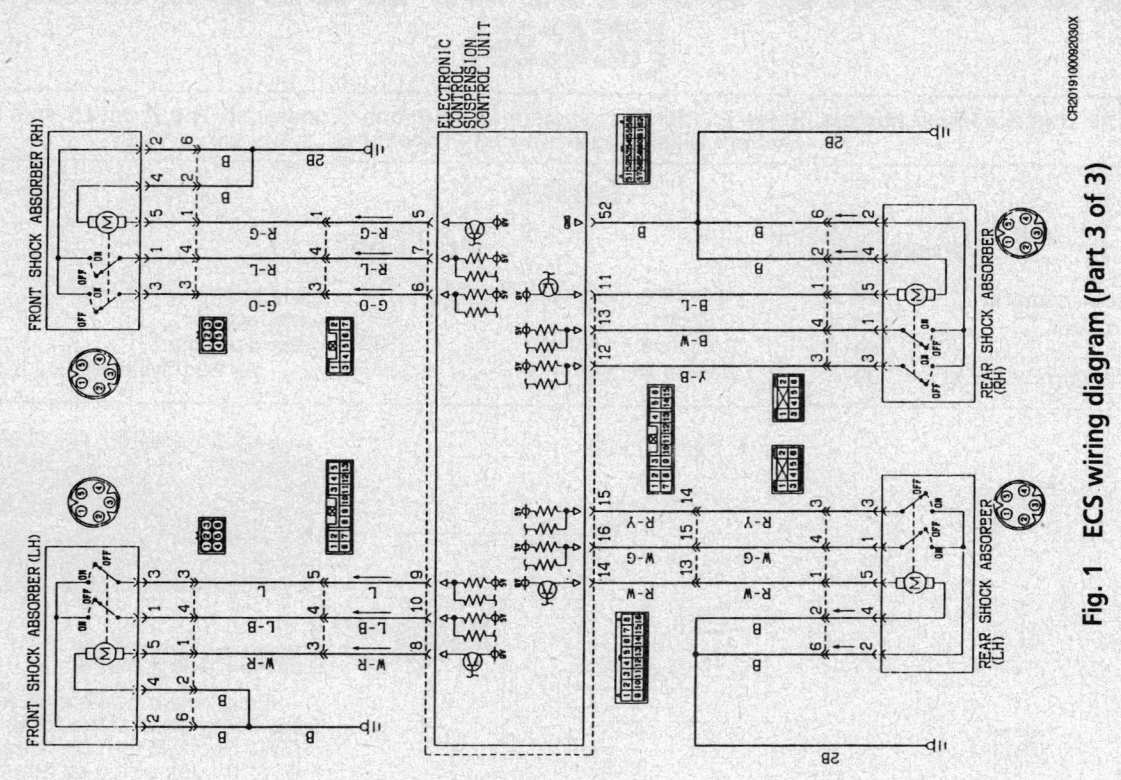

Fig. 1 ECS wiring diagram (Part 3 of 3)

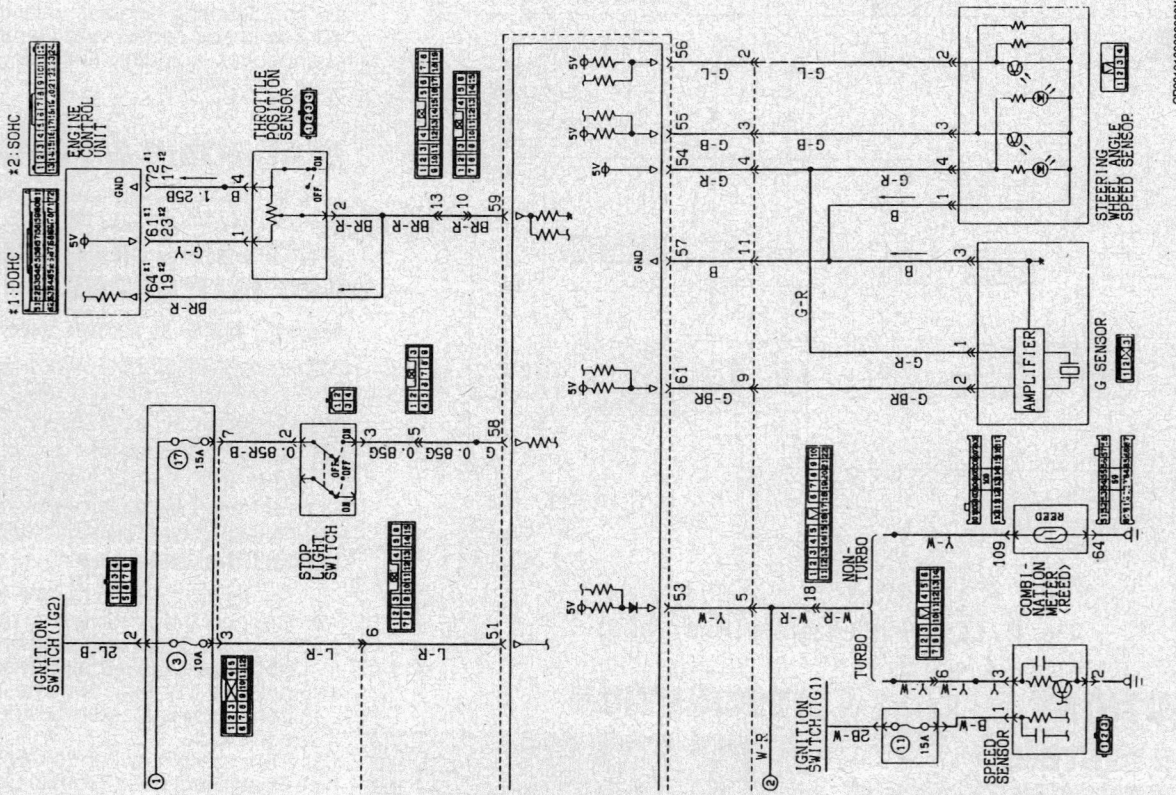

Fig. 1 ECS wiring diagram (Part 2 of 3)

5. Based on Diagnostic Trouble Code, repair the associated defective portion, **Fig. 12.**
6. Turn ignition switch to OFF position.
7. After repairs have been made, disconnect battery cables from battery then reconnect them after 10 seconds or more.
8. Turn ignition switch to ON position with voltmeter installed, then verify that a code zero is displayed. If code zero is not displayed, repeat steps 5 through 8 until code zero is displayed.

SYSTEM INSPECTION
Actuator Operating Sound

1. Turn ignition switch to ON position.

2. Check for actuator operating sound at top of shock tower each time control modes are changed.

Damping Force Check

1. Turn ignition switch to ON position.
2. Set ECS indicator on Tour.
3. Check damping force Soft state by shaking top mounting points of shock absorbers up and down.
4. Press ECS switch to change mode to Sport.
5. Repeat step 3 and ensure that damping force is harder than in the Soft mode.

COMPONENT TESTING
ECS Switch

Remove ECS switch then operate switch and ensure continuity exists as shown in **Fig. 13.**

COMPONENT REPLACEMENT
ECS CONTROL UNIT

1. Remove cargo floor righthand box.
2. Remove ECS control unit lid.
3. Disconnect ECS control unit electrical connector, then remove the ECS control unit.
4. Reverse procedure to install.

DIAGNOSTIC CHART INDEX

Code	Description	Page No.	Fig. No.
11	G Sensor	29-39	2
21	Anti-Roll Only Stops	29-39	3
24	Vehicle Speed Sensor	29-40	4
61	Dampening Actuator	29-40	5
62	Dampening Actuator	29-40	5
63	Dampening Actuator	29-40	5
64	Dampening Actuator	29-40	5
—	ECS Indicator Light Does Not Switch Modes	29-41	6
—	Anti-Dive Control Only Stops	29-41	7
—	Anti-Squat Control Only Stops	29-41	8
—	Diagnostic Trouble Code Verification Tests	29-41	9

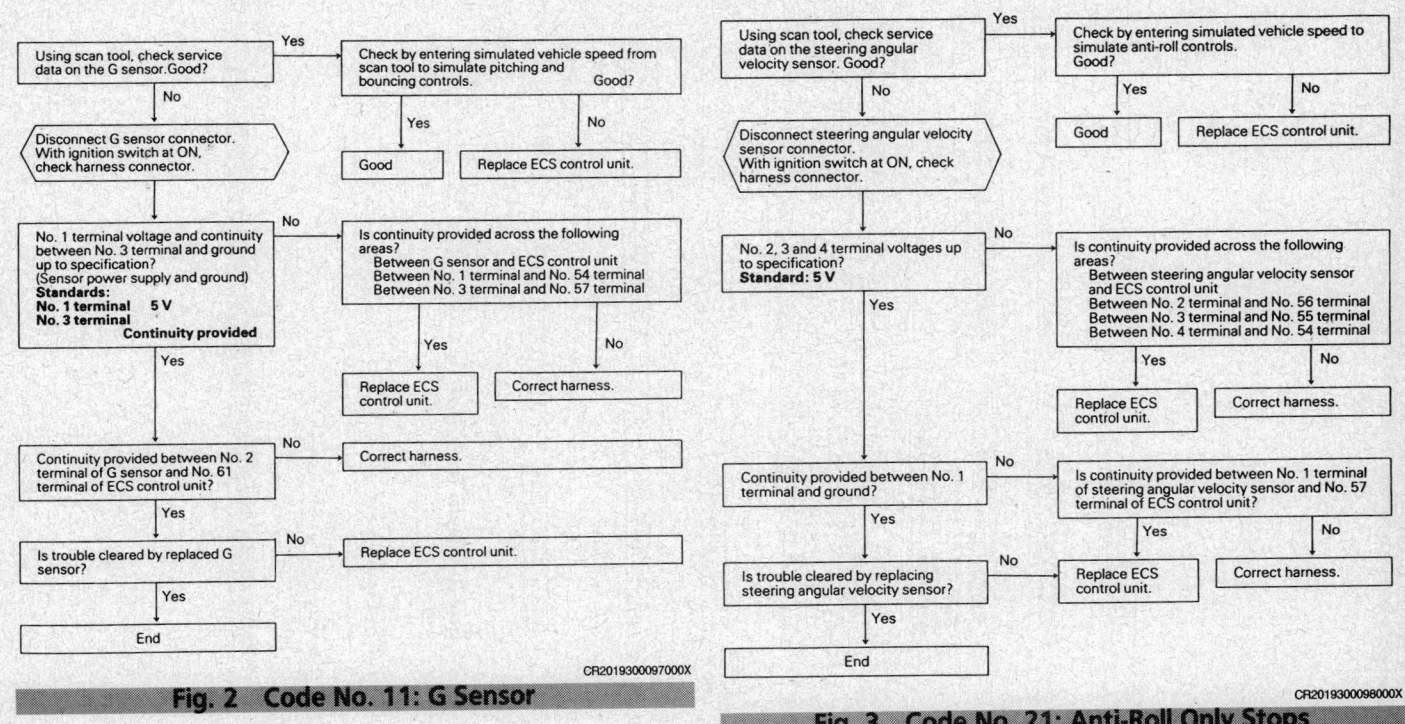

Fig. 2   Code No. 11: G Sensor

Fig. 3   Code No. 21: Anti-Roll Only Stops

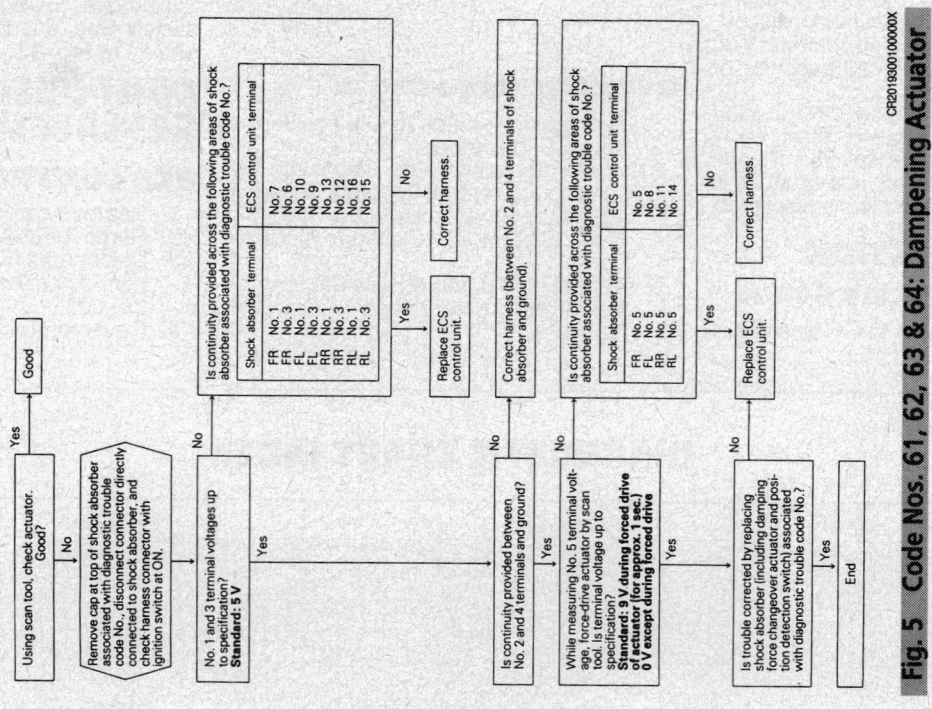

Fig. 5   Code Nos. 61, 62, 63 & 64: Dampening Actuator

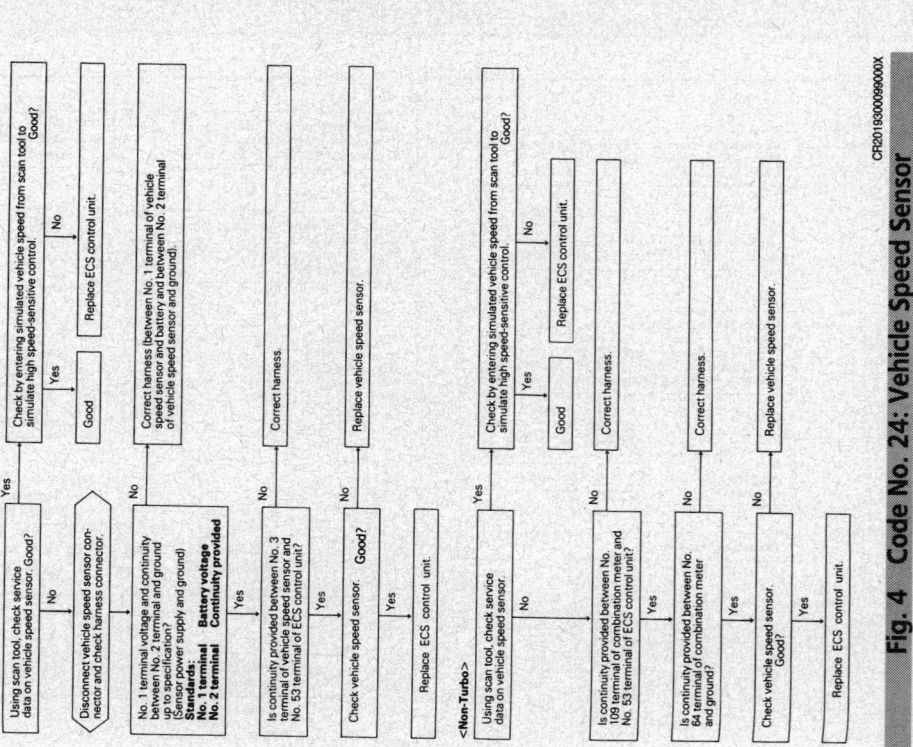

Fig. 4   Code No. 24: Vehicle Speed Sensor

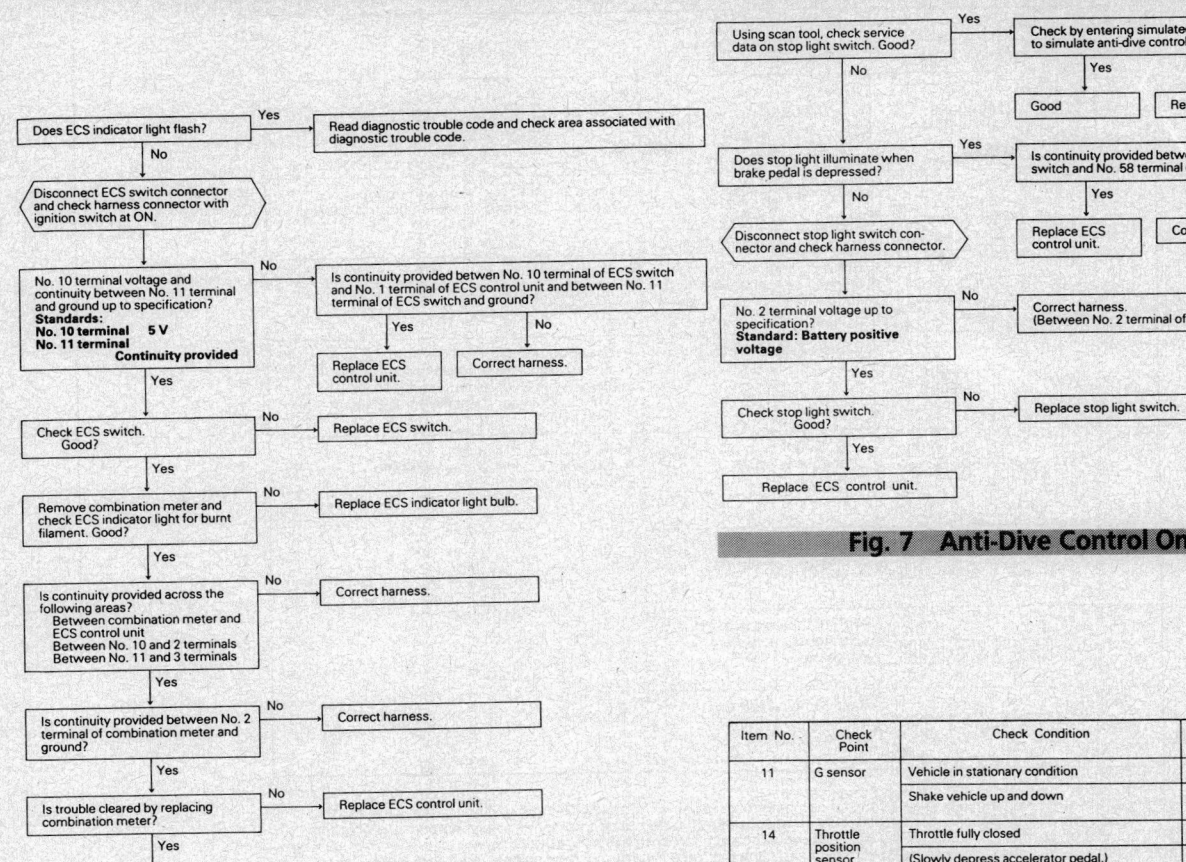

Fig. 6 — ECS Indicator Light Does Not Switch Modes (left column)

Does ECS indicator light flash? — Yes → Read diagnostic trouble code and check area associated with diagnostic trouble code.
- No ↓

Disconnect ECS switch connector and check harness connector with ignition switch at ON.
↓

No. 10 terminal voltage and continuity between No. 11 terminal and ground up to specification?
Standards:
No. 10 terminal   5 V
No. 11 terminal   Continuity provided
- No → Is continuity provided between No. 10 terminal of ECS switch and No. 1 terminal of ECS control unit and between No. 11 terminal of ECS switch and ground?
  - Yes → Replace ECS control unit.
  - No → Correct harness.
- Yes ↓

Check ECS switch. Good? — No → Replace ECS switch.
- Yes ↓

Remove combination meter and check ECS indicator light for burnt filament. Good? — No → Replace ECS indicator light bulb.
- Yes ↓

Is continuity provided across the following areas?
  Between combination meter and ECS control unit
  Between No. 10 and 2 terminals
  Between No. 11 and 3 terminals
- No → Correct harness.
- Yes ↓

Is continuity provided between No. 2 terminal of combination meter and ground? — No → Correct harness.
- Yes ↓

Is trouble cleared by replacing combination meter? — No → Replace ECS control unit.
- Yes ↓

End

CR2019300101000X

Fig. 6   ECS Indicator Light Does Not Switch Modes

Fig. 7 — Anti-Dive Control Only Stops (right column)

Using scan tool, check service data on stop light switch. Good? — Yes → Check by entering simulated vehicle speed from scan tool to simulate anti-dive control. Good?
  - Yes → Good
  - No → Replace ECS control unit.
- No ↓

Does stop light illuminate when brake pedal is depressed? — Yes → Is continuity provided between No. 3 terminal of stop light switch and No. 58 terminal of ECS control unit?
  - Yes → Replace ECS control unit.
  - No → Correct harness.
- No ↓

Disconnect stop light switch connector and check harness connector.
↓

No. 2 terminal voltage up to specification?
Standard: Battery positive voltage
- No → Correct harness. (Between No. 2 terminal of stop light switch and battery)
- Yes ↓

Check stop light switch. Good? — No → Replace stop light switch.
- Yes ↓

Replace ECS control unit.

CR2019300102000X

Fig. 7   Anti-Dive Control Only Stops

Fig. 9 — Diagnostic Trouble Code Verification Tests

Item No.	Check Point	Check Condition	Soundness Determination Value			
11	G sensor	Vehicle in stationary condition	2.0 – 3.0 V			
		Shake vehicle up and down	Indicated value increases or decreases from 2.5 V			
14	Throttle position sensor	Throttle fully closed	300 – 1,000 mV			
		(Slowly depress accelerator pedal.)	Smoothly increases.			
		Throttle fully opened	4,500 – 5,500 mV			
21	Steering angular velocity sensor	Slowly turn steering wheel counterclockwise	ST1 and ST2 indications change in the following combinations.			
			ST1	ON	ON	OFF	OFF
			ST2	ON	OFF	OFF	ON
		Slowly turn steering wheel clockwise.	ST1	ON	OFF	OFF	ON
			ST2	ON	ON	OFF	OFF

CR2019300104000X

Fig. 9   Diagnostic Trouble Code Verification Tests

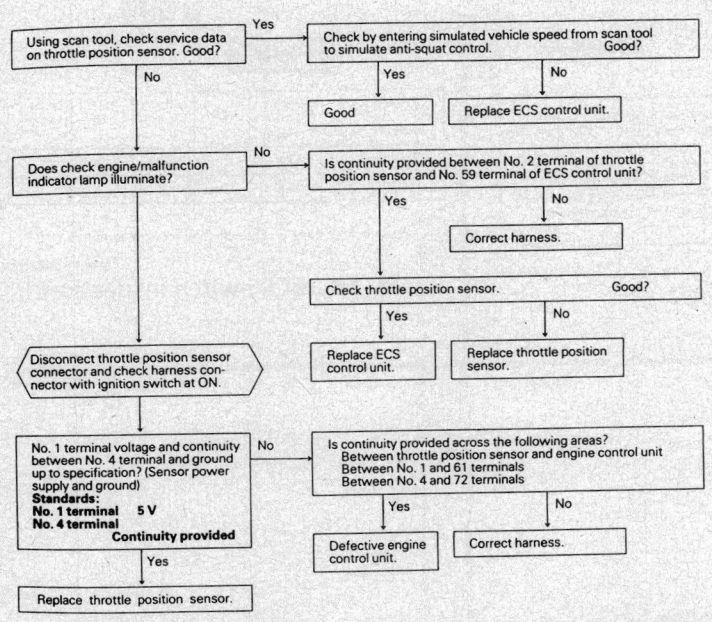

Fig. 8 — Anti-Squat Control Only Stops

Using scan tool, check service data on throttle position sensor. Good? — Yes → Check by entering simulated vehicle speed from scan tool to simulate anti-squat control. Good?
  - Yes → Good
  - No → Replace ECS control unit.
- No ↓

Does check engine/malfunction indicator lamp illuminate? — No → Is continuity provided between No. 2 terminal of throttle position sensor and No. 59 terminal of ECS control unit?
  - Yes ↓
    Check throttle position sensor. Good?
      - Yes → Replace ECS control unit.
      - No → Replace throttle position sensor.
  - No → Correct harness.
- No ↓

Disconnect throttle position sensor connector and check harness connector with ignition switch at ON.
↓

No. 1 terminal voltage and continuity between No. 4 terminal and ground up to specification? (Sensor power supply and ground)
Standards:
No. 1 terminal   5 V
No. 4 terminal   Continuity provided
- No → Is continuity provided across the following areas?
    Between throttle position sensor and engine control unit
    Between No. 1 and 61 terminals
    Between No. 4 and 72 terminals
  - Yes → Defective engine control unit.
  - No → Correct harness.
- Yes ↓

Replace throttle position sensor.

CR2019300103000X

Fig. 8   Anti-Squat Control Only Stops

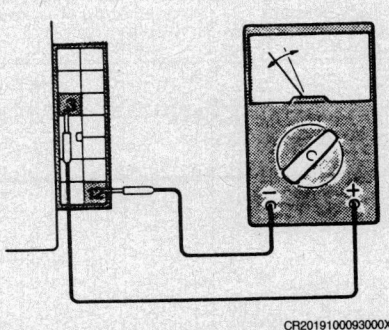

CR2019100093000X

Fig. 10   Diagnostic connector

Output Code		Diagnosis Item	Fail Safe
Code No.	Indication Pattern		
0		[Good]	[Good]
11		G sensor defective*	• Ride controls (pinching and bouncing control, bad road detection control) stop.
21		Steering angular velocity sensor open-circuited*	• Anti-roll control stops.
24		Vehicle speed sensor open-circuited*	• Steering stability controls (anti-roll, high speed sensitive controls) and attitude controls (anti-dive, anti-squat) stop. • Shock absorber damping force fixed at MEDIUM
61		F. R. damping force changeover actuator defective	• All ECS controls stop. • Normal shock absorber damping force fixed at HARD.
62	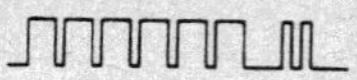	F. L. damping force changeover actuator defective	
63	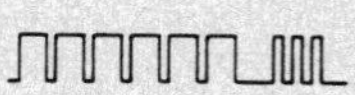	R. R. damping force changeover actuator defective	
64	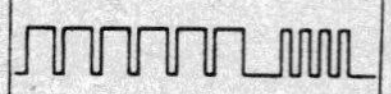	R. L. damping force changeover actuator defective	

NOTE
(1) Control stop, warning indication and fixed damping force return to normal when the ignition switch is set to OFF. When any of the problems marked* occurs, if no subsequent problem occurs (for example, when the problem is transient), normal operation will be restored even if the ignition switch is not set to OFF.
(2) Even if control stop, warning indication and fixed damping force return to normal as described above, the self-diagnosis code is stored in the memory in the ECS control unit.
(3) The self-diagnosis code can be cleared by stopping the power supply to the ECS control unit. In addition, it is automatically cleared if the ON/OFF control of the ignition switch is repeated 60 times after the self-diagnosis code has been output, provided that no new self-diagnosis code is output during the period.

CR2019100094000X

Fig. 11   Diagnostic Trouble Codes

Code No.	What is defective	Self-diagnosis determination conditions
11	G sensor defective	When sensor input of 0.5 or less or 4.5 V or more lasts for more than 10 seconds.
21	Steering angular velocity sensor open-circuited	Open circuit detected on the basis of difference in voltage level of sensor signal.
24	Vehicle speed sensor defective	When throttle opening of 30% (1.5 V) or more lasts for more than 60 seconds with the ignition switch at ON and if there is no input from the vehicle speed sensor during the period, it is regarded as a problem.
61 – 64	Damping force changeover actuator defective	If no damping force changeover is made in a second after actuator drive signal has been output (position detection switch output pattern does not change to that of target damping force), it is regarded as a problem.

CR2019100095000X

Fig. 12   Diagnostic Trouble Code conditions

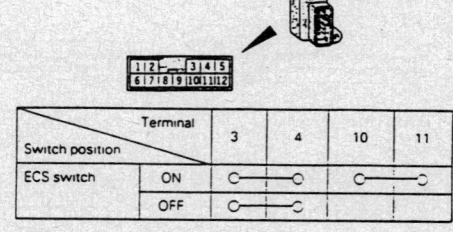

Terminal Switch position		3	4	10	11
ECS switch	ON	o—o		o—o	
	OFF	o—o			

NOTE
o—o indicates that there is continuity between the terminals.

CR2019100096000X

Fig. 13   ECS switch inspection

TROUBLESHOOTING SUPPLEMENT
INDEX

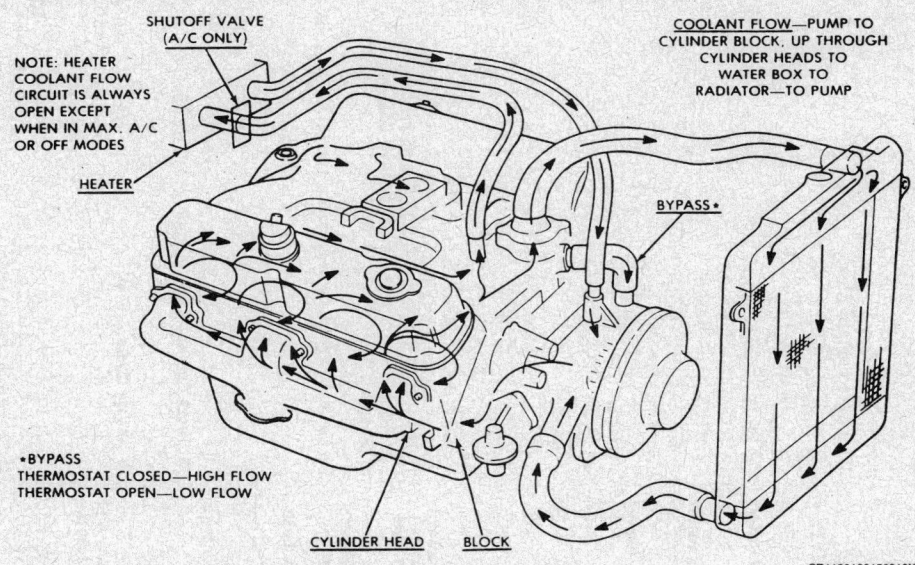

NOTE: HEATER COOLANT FLOW CIRCUIT IS ALWAYS OPEN EXCEPT WHEN IN MAX. A/C OR OFF MODES

SHUTOFF VALVE (A/C ONLY)

HEATER

COOLANT FLOW—PUMP TO CYLINDER BLOCK, UP THROUGH CYLINDER HEADS TO WATER BOX TO RADIATOR—TO PUMP

BYPASS *

*BYPASS
THERMOSTAT CLOSED—HIGH FLOW
THERMOSTAT OPEN—LOW FLOW

CYLINDER HEAD   BLOCK

CR1139100156010X

Fig. 1   Cooling (Part 1 of 7)

Symptom	Action
Blinking Engine Warning Light Or High Gage Indication— Without Coolant Loss	Normal with temporary operation with heavy load, towing a light trailer, high outdoor temperatures, and/or on a steep grade.
Coolant Loss	Improper refilling procedures can result in trapped air in the system. Subsequent operation of the pressure cap and coolant recovery system will deaereate the cooling system. A low coolant level will then result in the Coolant Reserve Tank. Add coolant.
Hot Vehicle (Not Engine) Heat Damage Hot Carpet, Seat, Trunk Hot Catalytic Converter Smoke, Burnt Odor	Check heat shielding, exhaust system, emission controls, ignition timing—fuel/air ratio, misfiring.
Hot Engine Crackling Sounds Hot Smell Severe Local Hot Spots	A moderate amount of sound of heating metal can be expected with any vehicle. However, a crackling sound from the thermostat housing, a hot smell and/or severe local hot spots on an engine can indicate blocked coolant passages. Inspect for plugged water passages, bad casting, core sand and plugging, a cracked block or head, or a blown head gasket. Usually accompanied with coolant loss.
Coolant Color	Coolant color is not necessarily an indication of adequate temperature or corrosion protection. Some oily discoloration of the coolant recovery system bottle will occur due to the production use of soluble oil (also called water pump lubricant) which has been added for corrosion protection.
Coolant Recovery Bottle —Level Changes	Level changes are to be expected as coolant volume changes with engine temperature. If the level in the bottle is between the Maximum and Minimum marks at normal engine operating temperature, the level should return to within that range after operation at elevated temperatures.
—Coolant NOT Returning	Coolant will not return to the radiator if the radiator cap vent valve does not function, if an air leak destroys vacuum, or if the overflow passage is blocked or restricted. Inspect all portions of the overflow passage, pressure cap, filler neck nipple, hose, and passages within the bottle for vacuum leak only. Coolant return failure will be evident by a low level in the radiator. Bottle level should increase during heat-up.

CR1139100156020X

Fig. 1   Cooling (Part 2 of 7)

CONDITION—AND CHECKS

THERMAL 60° GAUGE READS LOW

(1) Verify gauge. (Fig. 2) Is temperature really low?

(2) Does it read cold?

(3) Coolant level low in cold ambient. (Also poor heater performance)

(4) Coolant level O.K.

(5) Are above (1 thru 4) checks O.K.?

GAUGE READS HIGH—Without Pressure Cap Blow off without Coolant or Steam from CRS Tank and to Ground

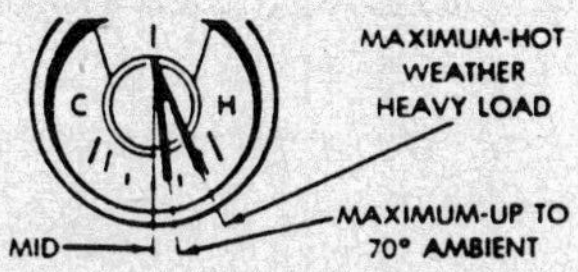

(1) Is it really reading high?

(2) If at "H" without other signs of boiling.

(3) Coolant Level low in Radiator and CRS

(4) Coolant level low in Radiator but not in CRS.

DIAGNOSIS

30 TO 40° GAUGE TRAVEL IS NORMAL

Fig. 2—Normal Gauge Travel

(1) Check temperature sending unit. Repair/Replace gauge or sending switch.

(2) Wiring disconnect or wrong sending unit for lite switch. not gauge.

(3) Check radiator and CRS for level—inspect for leaks.

(4) Check heater controls. doors.

(5) Replace thermostat.

(1) See Figure 3.

(2) Look for Grounded gauge, sending unit or wire.

(3) a—Fill full.
   b—Inspect for leaks. repair.
   c—Assure Pressure Cap was shut tight and seals at top and bottom of neck are functioning properly.

(4) a—Fill full.
   b—Inspect for leaks and repair.
   c—Inspect for leaks in CRS to radiator connection.
   d—Assure cap seals at top and bottom.

MAXIMUM-HOT WEATHER HEAVY LOAD

MAXIMUM-UP TO 70° AMBIENT

Fig. 3—Gauge Reading—Hot Weather—Heavy Load

Fig. 1 Cooling (Part 3 of 7)

CONDITION—AND CHECKS

(5) Check freeze point

(6) Assure Coolant Flow

(7) Other possible causes

TEMPERATURE GAUGE READS HOT, with Pressure Cap Blowoff and Steam and coolant to CRS and to Ground

(1) Coolant Level Low in Radiator and CRS

(2) Check Coolant Freeze point

(3) Assure Coolant Flow

(4) Thermostat failed shut

(5) Head Gasket Leak

DIAGNOSIS

(5) a—Adjust to 50/50 Glycol and water
   b—If no reading or below –50°F. mixture is too rich clean system before refilling

(6) a—Look for flow through filler neck with some coolant removed and thermostat open
   b—Repair water pump

(7) a—High speed only
   —Radiator or Condensor air side plugged
   —Radiator core tubes plugged
   —Add on A/C without proper radiator
   —Engine out of tune (specifications)
   —Brakes dragging
   —Bug screen
   —Trailer towing or hill climbing
   b—High and Low Speed
   —Thermostat failed partially shut particularly if ambient temperature is below 70F and vehicle has high mileage
   —Condensor or radiator air side plugged.
   —Add on A/C.
   c—Low Speed—NOT high speed
   —Check fan drive.

(1) a—Fill Cooling System Full and Air Vent.
   b—Inspect for Leaks—repair.
   c—Assure Pressure cap was shut and seals.
   d—If low in radiator but not in CRS. also check connection to filler neck and pressure cap sealing.

(2) Adjust to 50/50 Glycol and water. –35°F. Freeze Point.

(3) a—Look for flow through radiator filler neck with coolant lowered and thermostat open.
   b—When accompanied with "metal cracking sound"—consider core sand and/or bad head casting. Look for plugged core tubes.

(4) Especially in cold to medium ambient temperatures.

(5) Use block leak checker

CR11391001560040X

Fig. 1 Cooling (Part 4 of 7)

CR11391001560030X

CONDITION—AND CHECKS	DIAGNOSIS
TEMPERATURE GAUGE IS INCONSISTANT, Cycles—Irratic	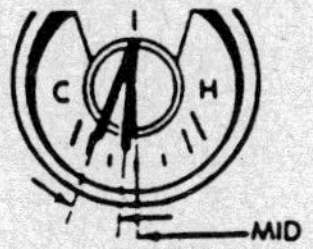
(1) Is cycle normal? See figures 4 and 5.	—Normal Thermostat Cycle (Fig. 4).

Fig. 4—Gauge Reaction to Thermostat

Fig. 5—Gauge Reaction—Stop after Heavy Use

—Hot water normal build up at stop after heavy use (Fig. 5).

CONDITION—AND CHECKS	DIAGNOSIS
(2) Is coolant level low in radiator (Low level can trap air in system which can put thermostat pellet in air and it opens late).	(2) Fill system and inspect for leaks.
(3) Is there a head gasket leak that puts exhaust gas in system? (This acts like trapped air with same effect as (2) above).	(3) Test with block leak checker and replace if necessary. b—Coolant in engine oil. c—White steam coming out of exhaust.
(4) Water pump impeller loose on shaft, slips sometimes.	(4) Replace.
(5) Air leak on suction side of water pump entraining Air; see 2 above.	(5) Find Leak and Repair.
PRESSURE CAP BLOW OFF, with steam to CRS and coolant to ground without high reading. Temperature Gauge above normal.	
(1) Check pressure cap relief pressure	(1) Replace if lower than 14 psi.
COOLANT LOSS TO GROUND without Pressure Cap Blow Off.	
(1) Leaks	(1) a—Pressure test sysstem while shaking hoses b—Water pump seal

Fig. 1 Cooling (Part 5 of 7)

CONDITION—AND CHECKS	DIAGNOSIS
COOLANT LOSS PAST PRESSURE CAP TOP SEAL—Glycol seen on Filler Neck	
(1) With normal gage reading	(1) a—Cap not on tight b—Top seal leaking c—Cap diaphragm "oil canned" d—Filler neck damaged e—Rubber seal out of position.
(2) With high gage reading or low gage reading on new vehicle.	(2) a—CRS Hose kinked. b—CRS tank and plastic tube plugged. c—Pressure Cap Rubber seal out of position.
DETONATION OR PRE-IGNITION When Nothing to Cause It In Engine or Ignition	
(1) Check coolant freeze point—If no reading on Vu-check or below -50°F. Freeze point be aware that 100% Glycol makes engine metal run hotter even without a hot gage reading.	(1) a—Adjust coolant to 50/50 Glycol and water (-35°F). b—If 100% glycol has been found in the system. Clean and flush the system before replacing with 50/50 glycol and water.
HOSES OBSERVED COLLAPSING ON COOL DOWN	
(1) Check pressure cap Vent Valve	(1) a—Must have stroke. Gasket swell can. prevent valve from opening. b—Replace cap.
(2) Check CRS hose for kinking or plugging.	(2) Repair as required.
(3) Inside of cap plugged with stop leak pellet. or green silica gel. or fiberglass.	(3) Clean cap.
FAN NOISY	
(1) Check for bent fan blades	(1) Repair as necessary
(2) Check for fan clearance to adjacent parts.	
(3) Check for air obstructions on radiator or condensor	
(4) Check for failed viscous fan drive.	
INADEQUATE AIR CONDITIONING PERFORMANCE—Cooling System Suspected	
(1) Check for plugged air side of condensor and radiator—front and rear	(1) Wash out with low velocity water.
(2) Check for missing air seals—recirculating air path	
(3) Assure correct cooling system parts	

Fig. 1 Cooling (Part 6 of 7)

CONDITION—AND CHECKS	DIAGNOSIS

HOT SMELL, Suspect Cooling System

(1) Was temperature gage high?

(2) Heat shields all in place?

(3) Heat exchanger air side plugged?

(4) Catalytic Converter—Engine missing or running rich.

(1) a—Yes, See "Gauge Reads High".
b—No, See 2, 3, and 4.

(2) a—Yes, See 3, 4 and 5.
b—No, Repair as required.

(3) Clean as required.

(4) Repair as required.

POOR HEATER PERFORMANCE—Suspect Failed Open Thermostat?

(1) Does gage read low?

(2) Check coolant level

(1) a—See "Thermal 60° Gauge Reads Low" Condition 3.

(2) a—See "Thermal 60° Gauge Reads Low" Condition 4.

CR1139100156070X

Fig. 1   Cooling (Part 7 of 7)

SERVICE DIAGNOSIS

Condition	Possible Cause	Correction
EXCESSIVE EXHAUST NOISE	(a) Leaks at pipe joints.	(a) Tighten clamps at leaking joints.
	(b) Burned or blown out muffler.	(b) Replace muffler assembly.
	(c) Burned or rusted out exhaust pipe.	(c) Replace exhaust pipe.
	(d) Exhaust pipe leaking at manifold flange.	(d) Tighten ball joint connection attaching bolts nuts to 24 ft. lb. (33 N·m), alternate tightening.
	(e) Exhaust manifold cracked or broken.	(e) Replace manifold.
	(f) Leak between manifold and cylinder head.	(f) Tighten manifold to cylinder head stud nuts or bolts to specifications.
	(g) Restriction in muffler or tail pipe.	(g) Remove restriction, if possible, or replace as necessary.
LEAKING EXHAUST GASES	(a) Leaks at pipe joints.	(a) Tighten U-bolt nuts at leaking joints to 150 in. lb. (17 N·m).
	(b) Damaged or improperly installed gaskets.	(b) Replace gaskets as necessary.
ENGINE HARD TO WARM UP OR WILL NOT RETURN TO NORMAL IDLE	(a) Heat control valve frozen in the open position.	(a) Free up manifold heat control valve using a suitable solvent.
	(b) Blocked crossover passage in intake manifold.	(b) Remove restriction or replace intake manifold.
HEAT CONTROL VALVE NOISY	(a) Thermostat broken.	(a) Replace thermostat.
	(b) Broken, weak or missing anti-rattle spring.	(b) Replace spring.

CR1139100157000X

Fig. 2   Exhaust

Condition	Possible Cause	Correction
NOISY VALVES	(a) Thin or diluted oil-low pressure.	(a) Change oil.
	(b) Worn valve guides.	(b) Ream and install new valves with O/S stems.
	(c) Excessive run-out of valve seats on valve faces.	(c) Grind valve seats and valves.
CONNECTING ROD NOISE	(a) Insufficient oil supply.	(a) Check engine oil level.
	(b) Low oil pressure.	(b) Check engine oil level. Inspect oil pump relief valve and spring.
	(c) Thin or diluted oil.	(c) Change oil to correct viscosity.
	(d) Excessive bearing clearance.	(d) Measure bearings for correct clearance.
	(e) Connecting rod journals out-of-round.	(e) Replace crankshaft or regrind journals.
	(f) Misaligned connecting rods.	(f) Replace bent connecting rods.
MAIN BEARING NOISE	(a) Insufficient oil supply.	(a) Check engine oil level.
	(b) Low oil pressure.	(b) Check engine oil level. Inspect oil pump relief valve and spring.
	(c) Thin or diluted oil.	(c) Change oil to correct viscosity.
	(d) Excessive bearing clearance.	(d) Measure bearings for correct clearances.
	(e) Excessive end play.	(e) Check No. 3 main bearing for wear on flanges.
	(f) Crankshaft journal out-of-round worn.	(f) Replace crankshaft or regrind journals.
	(g) Loose flywheel or torque converter.	(g) Tighten to correct torque.
OIL CONSUMPTION OR SPARK PLUGS OIL FOULED	(a) Worn, scuffed, or broken rings.	(a) Hone cylinder bores and install new rings.
	(b) Carbon in oil ring slot.	(b) Install new rings.
	(c) Rings fitted too tight in grooves.	(c) Remove the rings. Check grooves. If groove is not proper width, replace piston.
	(d) Worn valve guides.	(d) Ream guides and replace valves with oversize.
	(e) PCV system malfunction.	(e) Check system.
OIL PRESSURE DROP	(a) Low oil level.	(a) Check engine oil level.
	(b) Faulty oil pressure sending unit.	(b) Install new sending unit.
	(c) Clogged oil filter.	(c) Install new oil filter.
	(d) Worn parts in oil pump.	(d) Replace worn parts or pump.
	(e) Thin or diluted oil.	(e) Change oil to correct viscosity.
	(f) Excessive bearing clearance.	(f) Measure bearings for correct clearance.
	(g) Oil pump relief valve stuck.	(g) Remove valve and inspect, clean, and reinstall.
	(h) Oil pump cover bent or cracked.	(h) Install new oil pump.

CR1139100158020X

Fig. 3   Engine (Part 2 of 2)

ENGINE DIAGNOSIS

Condition	Possible Cause	Correction
ENGINE WILL NOT START	(a) Weak battery.	(a) Test battery specific gravity. Recharge or replace as necessary.
	(b) Corroded or loose battery connections.	(b) Clean and tighten battery connections. Apply a coat of light mineral grease to terminals.
	(c) Faulty starter.	(c)
	(d) Moisture on ignition wires and distributor cap.	(d) Wipe wires and cap clean and dry.
	(e) Faulty ignition cables.	(e) Replace any cracked or shorted cables.
	(f) Faulty coil or control unit.	(f) Test and replace if necessary.
	(g) Incorrect spark plug gap.	(g) Set gap.
	(h) Incorrect ignition timing.	(h)
	(i) Dirt or water in fuel system.	(i) Clean system.
	(j) Faulty fuel pump.	(j) Install new fuel pump.
ENGINE STALLS OR ROUGH IDLE	(a) Idle speed set too low.	(a) Electronic Fuel Injection.
	(b) Incorrect choke adjustment.	(b) Electronic Fuel Injection.
	(c) Idle mixture too lean or too rich.	(c) Electronic Fuel Injection.
	(d) Leak in intake manifold.	(d) Inspect intake manifold gasket and vacuum hoses replace if necessary.
	(e) Worn distributor rotor.	(e) Install new rotor.
	(f) Incorrect distributor wiring.	(f) Install correct wiring.
	(g) Faulty coil.	(g) Test and replace if necessary.
	(h) EGR valve leaking.	(h) Test and replace if necessary.
ENGINE LOSS OF POWER	(a) Incorrect ignition timing.	(a)
	(b) Worn distributor rotor.	(b) Install new rotor.
	(c) Worn distributor shaft.	(c) Remove and repair distributor.
	(d) Dirty or incorrectly gapped spark plugs.	(d) Clean plugs and set gap.
	(e) Dirt or water in fuel system.**	(e) Clean system.
	(f) Faulty fuel pump.	(f) Install new pump.
	(g) Incorrect valve timing.	(g) Check Valve Timing.
	(h) Blown cylinder head gasket.	(h) Install new head gasket.
	(i) Low compression.	(i) Test compression of each cylinder.
	(j) Burned, warped or pitted valves.	(j) Install new valves.
	(k) Plugged or restricted exhaust system.	(k) Install new parts as necessary.
	(l) Faulty ignition cables.	(l) Replace any cracked or shorted cables.
	(m) Faulty coil.	(m) Test and replace as necessary.
ENGINE MISSES ON ACCELERATION	(a) Dirty, or gap too wide in spark plugs.	(a) Clean spark plugs and set gap.
	(b) Incorrect ignition timing.	(b)
	(c) Dirt in fuel system.	(c) Clean fuel system.
	(d) Burned, warped or pitted valves.	(d) Install new valves.
	(e) Faulty coil.	(e) Test and replace if necessary.
ENGINE MISSES AT HIGH SPEED	(a) Dirty or gap set too wide in spark plug.	(a) Clean spark plugs and set gap.
	(b) Worn distributor shaft.	(b) Remove and repair distributor.
	(c) Worn distributor rotor.	(c) Install new rotor.
	(d) Faulty coil.	(d) Test and replace if necessary.
	(e) Incorrect ignition timing.	(e)
	(f) Dirt or water in fuel system or filter.	(f) Clean system and replace filter.

CR1139100158010X

Fig. 3   Engine (Part 1 of 2)

SUSPENSION/STEERING/DRIVE DIAGNOSIS (FRONT WHEEL DRIVE)

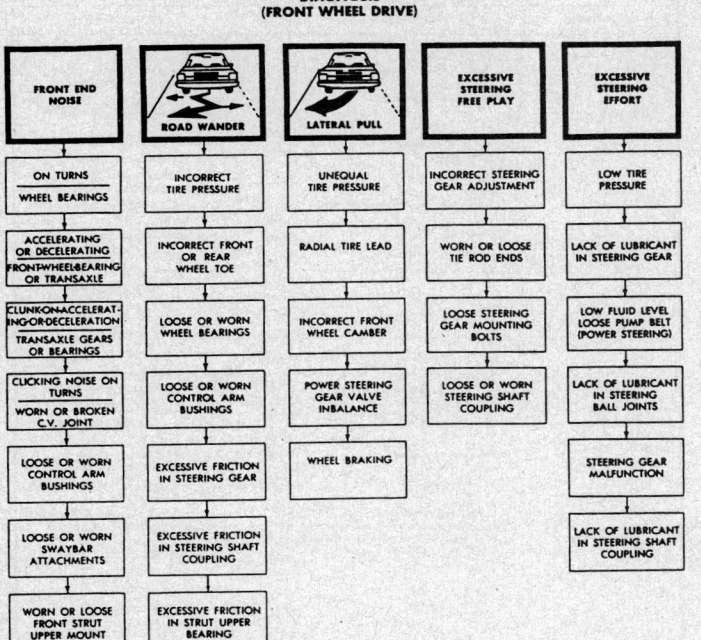

Fig. 4   Front Suspension & Steering Linkage, Front Wheel Drive

CR1139100159000X

STEERING NOISES

There is some noise in all power steering systems. One of the most common is a hissing sound evident at standstill parking. Hiss is a high frequency noise similar to that experienced while slowly closing a water tap. The noise is present in every valve and results from high velocity fluid passing valve orifice edges. There is no relationship between this noise and performance of the steering. Hiss may be expected when steering wheel is at end of travel or when slowly turning at standstill. --

CONDITION	POSSIBLE CAUSE	CORRECTION
OBJECTIONAL HISS OR WHISTLE	1. Noisy valve in gear	1. Check for proper seal between steering column coupling and dash seal.
		2. Ensure steering column lower coupling has no metal-to-metal contact within the coupling by performing an electrical continuity check. (Remove coupling for check.)
		3. If hiss is still extremely objectionable, replace steering gear.
RATTLE OR CLUNK	1. Gear loose on front crossmember	1. Check gear-to-crossmember mounting bolts. Tighten to specification.
	2. Crossmember-to-frame bolts or studs loose	2. Torque bolts and studs to specifications.
	3. Tie rod looseness (outer or inner)	3. Check tie rod pivot points for wear. Replace if necessary.
	4. Pressure hose touching other parts of vehicle	4. Adjust hose to proper position by loosening, repositioning, and retightening fitting. Do not bend tubing.
	5. Noise internal to gear	5. Replace gear.
CHIRP OR SQUEAL (IN THE AREA OF PUMP) PARTICULARLY NOTICEABLE AT FULL WHEEL TRAVEL AND DURING STANDSTILL PARKING	1. Loose belt	1. Adjust belt tension to specification.

CR1139100160010X

Fig. 5   Power Steering (Part 1 of 6)

STEERING NOISES (Continued)

There is some noise in all power steering systems. One of the most common is a hissing sound evident at standstill parking. Hiss is a high frequency noise similar to that experienced while slowly closing a water tap. The noise is present in every valve and results from high velocity fluid passing valve orifice edges. There is no relationship between this noise and performance of the steering. Hiss may be expected when steering wheel is at end of travel or when slowly turning at standstill.

CONDITION	POSSIBLE CAUSE	CORRECTION
Pump growl results from the development of high pressure fluid flow. Normally this noise should not be high enough to be objectionable. Abnormal situations, such as a low oil level causing aeration or hoses touching the vehicle body, can create a noise level that could bring complaints.		
WHINE OR GROWL (PUMP NOISE)	1. Low fluid level	1. Fill to proper level and perform leakage diagnosis. (Recheck after system is free of aeration.)
	2. Hose touching vehicle body or frame	2. Reposition hose. Replace hose if tube ends are bent.
	3. Extreme wear of pump internal parts	3. Replace pump and flush system.
SUCKING AIR SOUND	1. Loose return line clamp	1. Tighten or replace clamp.
	2. Missing O-ring on hose connection	2. Inspect connection and replace o-ring as required.
	3. Low fluid level	3. Fill to proper level and perform leakage diagnosis.
	4. Air leak between reservoir and pump	4. Inspect and replace reservoir as required.
SQUEAK OR RUB SOUND	1. Sound from steering column	1. Check for squeak in steering column. Inspect for contact between shroud intermediate shaft, column, and wheel. (Realign if necessary.)
		2. Check for sound of grease on steering column, dash to lower coupling seal.
	2. Sound internal to steering gear	1. Replace gear.
SCRUBBING/KNOCKING	1. Incorrect tire size	1. Verify tire size is the same as originally supplied.
	2. Check clearance between tires and other vehicle components, through full travel	2. Correct as necessary.
	3. Check for interference between steering gear and other components	3. Correct as necessary.
	4. Incorrect gear supplied	4. Replace gear.

CR1139100160020X

Fig. 5   Power Steering (Part 2 of 6)

BINDS STICKS SEIZED

CONDITION	POSSIBLE CAUSE	CORRECTION
CATCHES, STICKS IN CERTAIN POSITIONS OR DIFFICULT TO TURN	1. Low fluid level	1. Fill to proper level and perform leakage diagnosis.
	2. Tires not properly inflated	2. Inflate tires to proper pressure.
	3. Lack of lube in ball joints	3. Lubricate where possible.
	4. Lack of lube in outer tie rod ends	4. Lubricate where possible.
	5. Loose pump belt	5. Tighten or replace belt.
	6. Faulty pump flow control (Verify cause using Pump Test Procedure)	6. Replace pump.
	7. Excessive friction in steering column or intermediate shaft	7. Correct condition. (See Steering Column Service Procedure.)
	8. Steering column coupling binding	8. Realign as necessary.
	9. Excessive friction in gear	9. Replace gear.

SHAKE SHUDDER VIBRATION

CONDITION	POSSIBLE CAUSE	CORRECTION
VIBRATION OF THE STEERING WHEEL AND/ OR DASH DURING DRY PARK OR LOW SPEED STEERING MANEUVERS	1. Air in the power steering system	1. Steering shudder can be expected in new vehicles and vehicles with recent steering system repairs. Shudder should improve after the vehicle has been driven several weeks.
	2. Tires not properly inflated	2. Inflate tires to proper pressure.
	3. Excessive engine vibration	3. Make sure that engine is running properly.
	4. Loose tie rod end	4. Check inner and outer tie rod and jam nut for excessive free play.
	5. Faulty accessory drive belt tensioner (Poly-V belt systems only)	5. Check dynamic belt tensioner for abnormal vibration. (See Drive Belt Adjustments.)
	6. Overcharged air conditioner	6. Check air conditioning pump head pressure. (See Air Conditioning Refrigerant System Diagnosis.)

CR1139100160030X

Fig. 5   Power Steering (Part 3 of 6)

LOW ASSIST, NO ASSIST, OR HARD STEERING

CONDITION	POSSIBLE CAUSE	CORRECTION
STIFF, HARD TO TURN, SURGES, MOMENTARY INCREASE IN EFFORT WHEN TURNING	1. Tires not properly inflated	1. Inflate tires to proper pressure.
	2. Low fluid level	2. Add power steering fluid as required and perform leakage diagnosis.
	3. Loose belt	3. Tighten or replace belt.
	4. Lack of ball joint lubrication	4. Lubricate or replace as required.
	5. Low pressure pump (Verify using Pump Test Procedure)	5. Verify cause using Pump Test Procedure. Replace pump if necessary.
	6. High internal leak gear	6. Check steering system using test procedure. If steering gear is at fault, replace steering gear.

POOR RETURN TO CENTER

CONDITION	POSSIBLE CAUSE	CORRECTION
STEERING WHEEL DOES NOT WANT TO RETURN TO CENTER POSITION	1. Tires not properly inflated	1. Inflate tires to proper pressure.
	2. Improper front wheel alignment	2. Check and adjust as necessary.
	3. Lack of lubrication in ball joint	3. Replace as required or lubricate.
	4. Steering column U-joints misaligned	4. Realign steering column U-joints.
	5. Mispositioned dash cover	5. Reposition dash cover. To evaluate items 6 and 7, disconnect the intermediate steering shaft. Turn the steering wheel and listen for internal rubbing in column.
	6. Steering wheel rubbing	6. Adjust covers.
	7. Tight steering shaft bearings	7. Replace bearings.
	8. Excessive friction coupling universal joint	8. Replace U-joints.
	9. High friction in the steering gear	9. Replace steering gear.

CR1139100160040X

Fig. 5   Power Steering (Part 4 of 6)

LOOSE STEERING

CONDITION	POSSIBLE CAUSE	CORRECTION
EXCESSIVE WHEEL KICKBACK OR TOO MUCH STEERING WHEEL PLAY	1. Air in system	1. Add fluid.
	2. Gear loose on crossmember	2. Check gear to crossmember mounting bolts. Tighten to specification.
	3. Worn/broken intermediate shaft	3. Check for worn universal joint and broken isolator. Replace intermediate shaft if worn.
	4. Free play in steering column	4. Check and replace as required.
	5. Loose ball joints	5. Check and replace as required.
	6. Pinch bolt loose on ball joint	6. Check pinch bolts and tighten as required to specified torque.
	7. Front wheel bearings loose or worn	7. Tighten hub nut or replace with new parts as necessary.
	8. Loose outer tie rod ends	8. Check and replace as required.
	9. Loose inner tie rod ends	9. Replace gear.
	10. Defective steering gear rotary valve	10. Replace gear.

VEHICLE LEADS TO THE SIDE

CONDITION	POSSIBLE CAUSE	CORRECTION
WHEEL DOES NOT WANT TO RETURN TO CENTER POSITION	1. Radial tire lead	1. Rotate tires as recommended in Tire Service.
	2. Front end misaligned	2. Align front end as recommended in Wheel Alignment Service Procedure.
	3. Wheel braking	3. Check for dragging brakes as directed in Brake Service Procedure.
	4. Unbalanced steering gear valve. (If this is the cause, the steering efforts will be very light in direction of lead and heavier in the opposite direction)	4. Checking for pull with outer tie rod end disconnected. If verified, replace gear.

CR1139100160050X

Fig. 5   Power Steering (Part 5 of 6)

FLUID LEAK

CONDITION	POSSIBLE CAUSE	CORRECTION
LOW FLUID LEVEL WITH: • NO VISIBLE SIGNS OF LEAKS ON THE STEERING GEAR, PUMP, ON FLOOR, OR ANYWHERE ELSE LOW FLUID LEVEL WITH: • VISIBLE LEAK ON STEERING GEAR, PUMP, FLOOR, OR ANYWHERE ELSE	1. Overfilled reservoir	1. Adjust fill level.
	2. Hose connections at pump or gear	2. Check for loose fittings and tighten to specifications. If fittings are tight, examine for damaged or missing O-ring and replace as required.
	3. Pump or gear leak	3. Identify location of leak and repair or replace as indicated in Power Steering Pump and/or Gear sections of this service manual.

FOAMY OR MILKY FLUID

CONDITION	POSSIBLE CAUSE	CORRECTION
AERATION AND OVERFLOW OF FLUID	1. Air leaks	1. Check for air leak as described under sucking air and correct.
	2. Low fluid level	2. Extremely cold temperatures may cause system aeration if the oil level is low. Add fluid as required.
	3. Cracked pump housing	3. Remove pump from vehicle and separate reservoir from housing. Check expansion plug and housing for cracks. Replace pump as required.
	4. Water contamination	4. Drain and refill fluid if there is evidence of contamination.

CR1139100160060X

Fig. 5   Power Steering (Part 6 of 6)

CONDITION FOUND	CAUSE	CORRECTION
1. Clutch disc facing covered with oil or grease.	a) Oil leak at engine rear main or transaxle input shaft seal.	a) Correct leak and replace disc (do not clean and reuse the disc). Clean flywheel and clutch pressure plate. Clean inside of bell housing.
	b) Too much grease applied to splines or disc and input shaft.	b) Apply lighter grease coating to splines and replace disc (do not clean and reuse the disc).
2. Clutch disc and/or cover warped, or disc facings exhibit unusual wear or appear to be wrong type.	Incorrect or substandard parts.	Replace disc and/or cover with correct parts.
3. No fault found with clutch components.	a) Problem actually related to suspension or driveline component.	a) Further diagnosis required. Check engine/transmission mounts, suspension attaching parts and other driveline components as needed.
	b) Engine related problems.	b) Check EFI and ignition systems.
4. Partial engagement of clutch disc (one side worn-opposite side glazed and lightly worn).	a) Clutch cover, spring, or release fingers bent, distorted (rough handling, improper assembly).	a) Replace clutch cover and disc.
	b) Clutch disc damaged or distorted.	b) Replace disc.
	c) Clutch misalignment.	c) Check alignment and runout of flywheel, disc, or cover and/or clutch housing. Correct as necessary.

CR1139100161010X

Fig. 6   Clutch (Part 1 of 4)

CONDITION FOUND	CAUSE	CORRECTION
1. Disc facing worn out.	a) Normal wear. b) Driver frequently "rides" (slips) clutch. Results in rapid wear overheating. c) Insufficient clutch cover diaphragm spring tension.	Replace clutch disc. Also replace cover if pressure plate surface is damaged.
2. Clutch disc facing contaminated with oil or grease.	a) Leak at rear main seal or at transmission input shaft seal. b) Excessive amount of grease applied to input shaft splines. c) Road splash, water entering housing.	a), b), c), d) Replace leaking seals. Apply less grease to input shaft splines. Replace clutch disc (do not clean and reuse) and clutch cover.
3. Clutch is running partially disengaged.	a) Release bearing sticking-binding. Does not return to normal running position. b) Self-adjust mechanism sticking or binding.	a) Verify that bearing is actually binding, then replace bearing and transmission front bearing retainer if sleeve surface is damaged. b) Verify that self adjuster block in pedal is free to move up and down.
4. Flywheel height incorrect.	Flywheel surface improperly machined. Too much stock removed or surface is excessively tapered.	Replace flywheel.
5. Wrong disc or pressure plate installed.	Incorrect parts order or model number.	Replace with correct parts.
6. Clutch disc, cover and/or diaphragm spring, warped, distorted.	a) Rough handling (impact) bent cover, spring, or disc. b) Incorrect bolt tightening sequence and method caused warped cover.	Install new disc or cover as needed. Follow installation/tightening instructions.
7. Facing on flywheel side of disc torn, gouged, worn.	Flywheel surface scored and nicked.	Reduce scores and nicks by sanding or surface grinding. Replace flywheel if scores-nicks are deeper than .002-.004 inch.
8. Clutch disc facing burnt (charred). Flywheel and cover pressure plate surfaces heavily glazed.	a) Frequent operation under high loads or hard acceleration conditions. b) Driver frequently "rides" (slips) clutch. Results in rapid wear and overheating of disc and cover.	Scuff sand flywheel. Replace clutch cover and disc. Alert driver to problem cause.
9. One or both clutch disc facings have fractured into small pieces.	a) Driver performs a 5-1 downshift at vehicle speed in excess of 60 mph. b) Leak of rear main seal or transaxle input shaft seal. c) Excessive heat from slippage.	Alert driver to problem cause. Replace clutch cover and disc. Make sure flywheel surface is not damaged. If so, replace.

CR1139100161020X

Fig. 6   Clutch (Part 2 of 4)

CONDITION FOUND	CAUSE	CORRECTION
1. Clutch components damaged or worn out prematurely.	Incorrect or sub-standard clutch parts.	Replace with parts of correct type and quality.
2. Release shaft bushings in transaxle binding or seized.	a) Dirt or contamination. b) Corrosion.	a, b) Wipe shaft, replace or lube bushings.
3. Loose components.	Attaching bolts loose at flywheel, cover, or clutch housing.	Tighten bolts to specific torque. Replace any clutch bolts that are damaged.
4. Contact surface of release bearing damaged.	a) Clutch cover incorrect, or release fingers are bent or distorted causing damage. b) Release bearing defective.	a) Replace clutch cover and bearing. b) Replace bearing.
5. Release bearing is noisy.	Release bearing defective.	Replace bearing.
6. Clutch pedal squeak.	a) Pedal bushings worn out or cracked. b) Inadequate lubrication.	a) Replace bushings if worn or damaged. b) Lubricate bushings, adjuster and positioner.
7. Clutch pedal clicks loudly when pedal is depressed (may be an intermittent problem).	Auto-adjust clutch cable spring bent or missing.	Bend spring to dimension shown or replace spring.

CR1139100161030X

Fig. 6   Clutch (Part 3 of 4)

CONDITION FOUND	CAUSE	CORRECTION
1. Clutch components damaged or worn out prematurely.	Incorrect or sub-standard clutch parts.	Replace with parts of correct type and quality.
2. Release shaft bushings in transaxle binding or seized.	a) Dirt or contamination. b) Corrosion.	a, b) Wipe shaft, replace or lube bushings.
3. Loose components.	Attaching bolts loose at flywheel, cover, or clutch housing.	Tighten bolts to specific torque. Replace any clutch bolts that are damaged.
4. Contact surface of release bearing damaged.	a) Clutch cover incorrect, or release fingers are bent or distorted causing damage. b) Release bearing defective.	a) Replace clutch cover and bearing. b) Replace bearing.
5. Release bearing is noisy.	Release bearing defective.	Replace bearing.
6. Clutch pedal squeak.	a) Pedal bushings worn out or cracked. b) Inadequate lubrication.	a) Replace bushings if worn or damaged. b) Lubricate bushings, adjuster and positioner.
7. Clutch pedal clicks loudly when pedal is depressed (may be an intermittent problem).	Auto-adjust clutch cable spring bent or missing.	Bend spring to dimension shown or replace spring.

CR1139100161040X

Fig. 6   Clutch (Part 4 of 4)

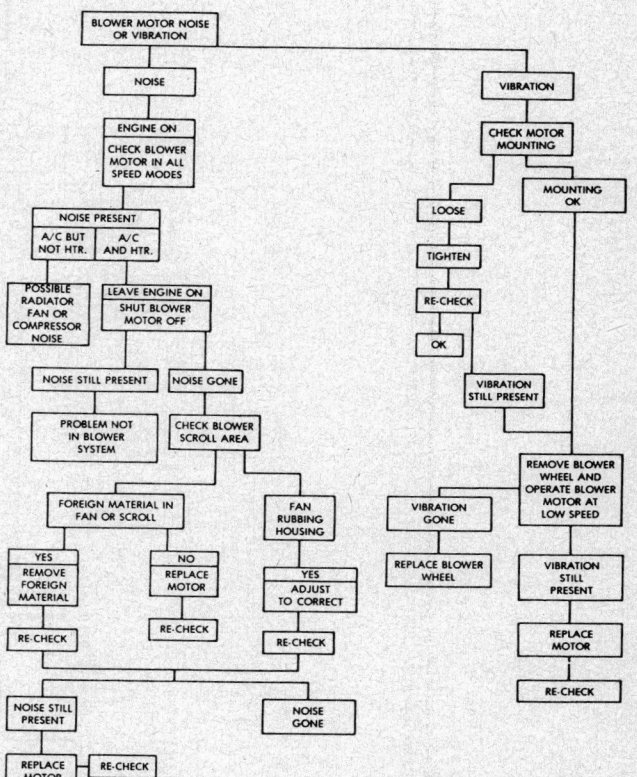

CR1139100162010X

Fig. 7   Blower Motor (Part 1 of 2)

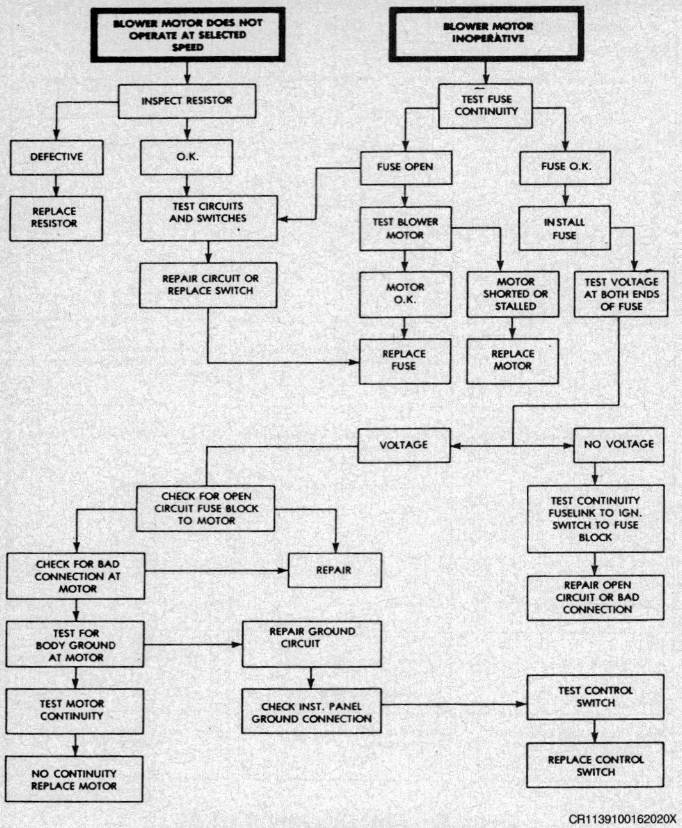

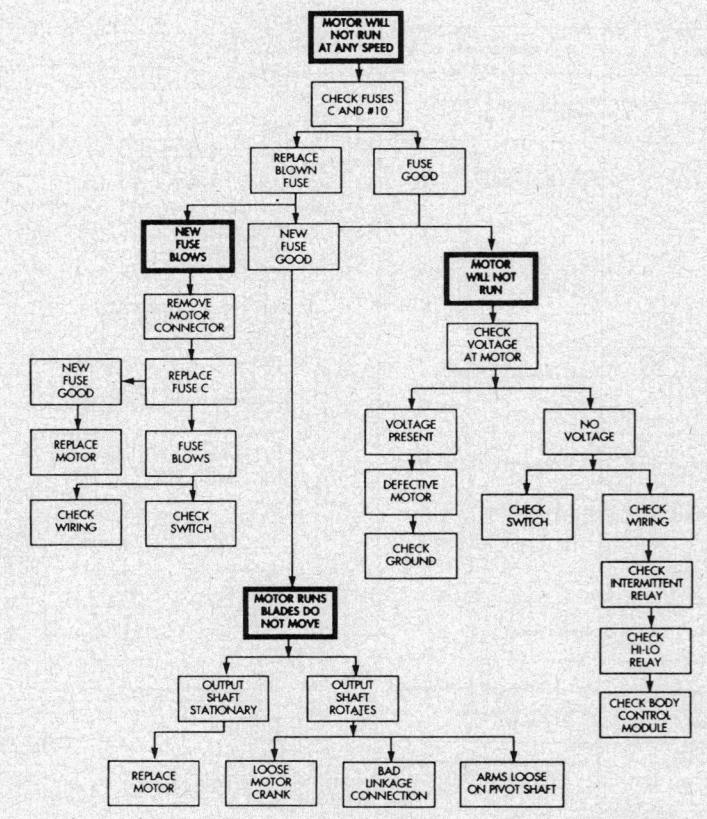

Fig. 7   Blower Motor (Part 2 of 2)

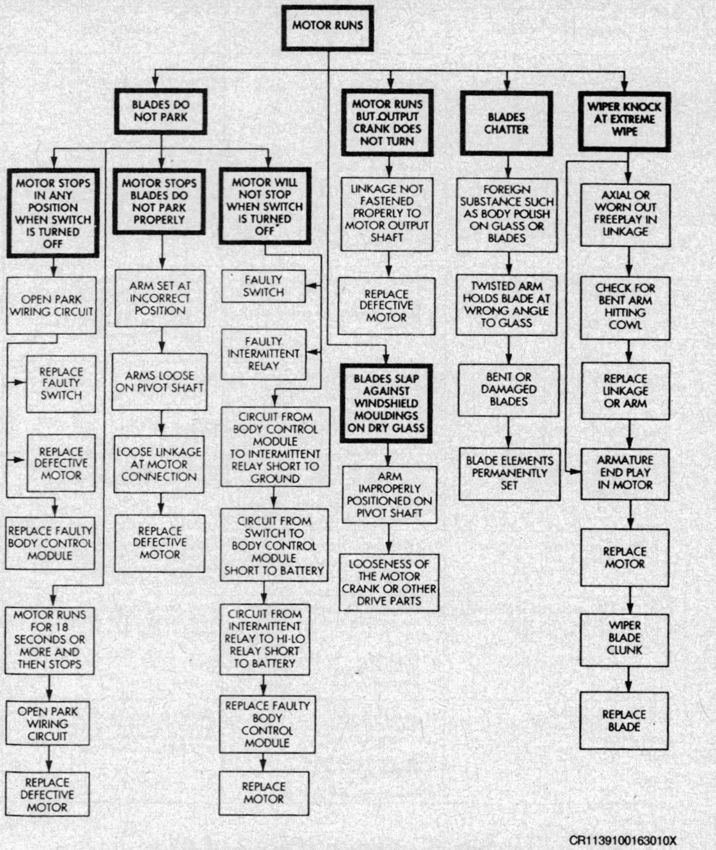

CR1139100162020X

Fig. 8   Windshield Wiper & Washer (Part 1 of 2)

CR1139100163010X

Fig. 8   Windshield Wiper & Washer (Part 2 of 2)

CR1139100163020X

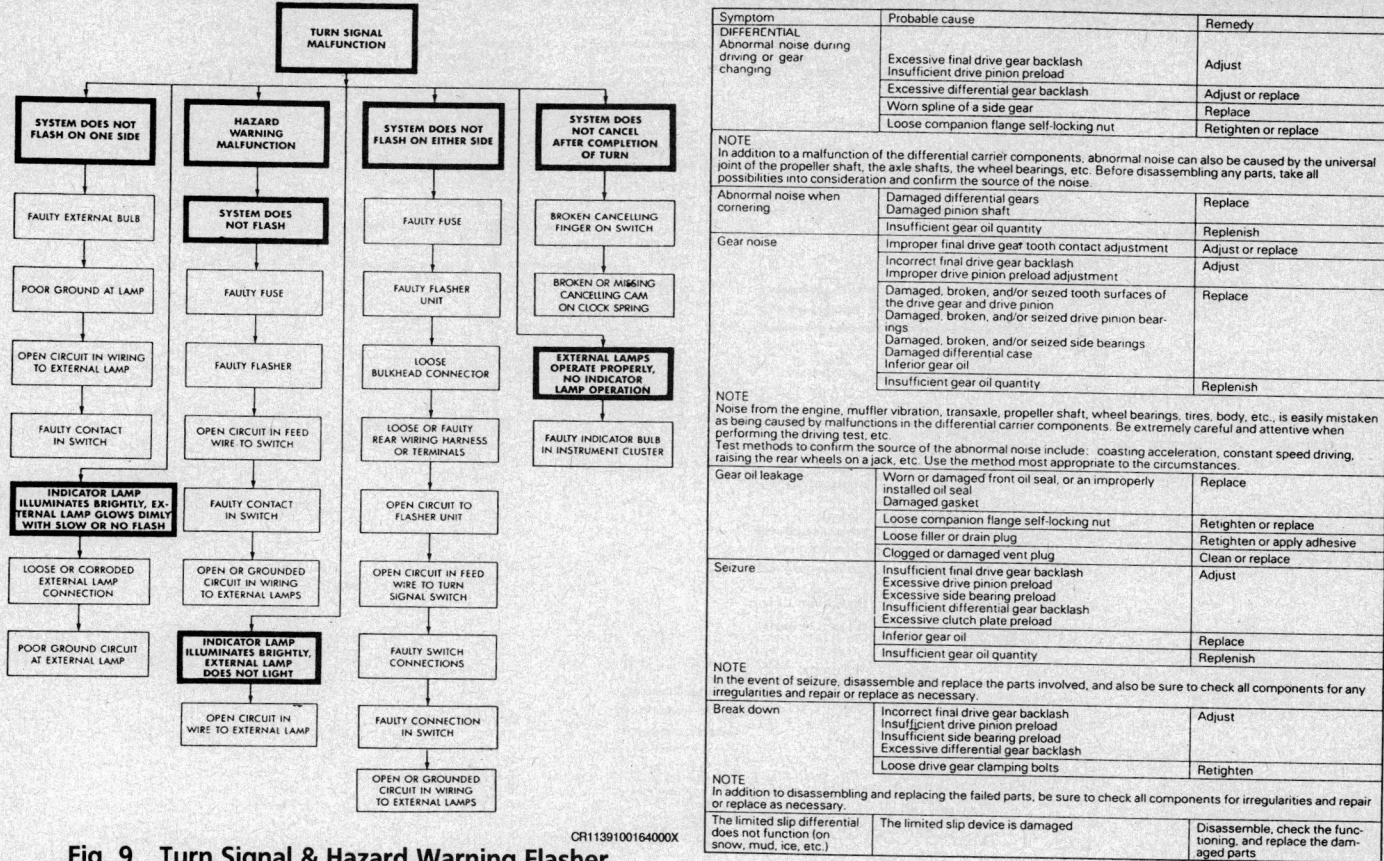

Fig. 9 Turn Signal & Hazard Warning Flasher

CR1139100164000X

Fig. 10 Rear Axle

Symptom	Probable cause	Remedy
DIFFERENTIAL Abnormal noise during driving or gear changing	Excessive final drive gear backlash Insufficient drive pinion preload	Adjust
	Excessive differential gear backlash	Adjust or replace
	Worn spline of a side gear	Replace
	Loose companion flange self-locking nut	Retighten or replace
NOTE In addition to a malfunction of the differential carrier components, abnormal noise can also be caused by the universal joint of the propeller shaft, the axle shafts, the wheel bearings, etc. Before disassembling any parts, take all possibilities into consideration and confirm the source of the noise.		
Abnormal noise when cornering	Damaged differential gears Damaged pinion shaft	Replace
	Insufficient gear oil quantity	Replenish
Gear noise	Improper final drive gear tooth contact adjustment	Adjust or replace
	Incorrect final drive gear backlash Improper drive pinion preload adjustment	Adjust
	Damaged, broken, and/or seized tooth surfaces of the drive gear and drive pinion Damaged, broken, and/or seized drive pinion bearings Damaged, broken, and/or seized side bearings Damaged differential case Inferior gear oil	Replace
	Insufficient gear oil quantity	Replenish
NOTE Noise from the engine, muffler vibration, transaxle, propeller shaft, wheel bearings, tires, body, etc., is easily mistaken as being caused by malfunctions in the differential carrier components. Be extremely careful and attentive when performing the driving test, etc. Test methods to confirm the source of the abnormal noise include: coasting acceleration, constant speed driving, raising the rear wheels on a jack, etc. Use the method most appropriate to the circumstances.		
Gear oil leakage	Worn or damaged front oil seal, or an improperly installed oil seal Damaged gasket	Replace
	Loose companion flange self-locking nut	Retighten or replace
	Loose filler or drain plug	Retighten or apply adhesive
	Clogged or damaged vent plug	Clean or replace
Seizure	Insufficient final drive gear backlash Excessive drive pinion preload Excessive side bearing preload Insufficient differential gear backlash Excessive clutch plate preload	Adjust
	Inferior gear oil	Replace
	Insufficient gear oil quantity	Replenish
NOTE In the event of seizure, disassemble and replace the parts involved, and also be sure to check all components for any irregularities and repair or replace as necessary.		
Break down	Incorrect final drive gear backlash Insufficient drive pinion preload Insufficient side bearing preload Excessive differential gear backlash	Adjust
	Loose drive gear clamping bolts	Retighten
NOTE In addition to disassembling and replacing the failed parts, be sure to check all components for irregularities and repair or replace as necessary.		
The limited slip differential does not function (on snow, mud, ice, etc.)	The limited slip device is damaged	Disassemble, check the functioning, and replace the damaged parts

CR1139100165000X

Fig. 11 A/C Compressor & Compressor Clutch

CR1139100166000X

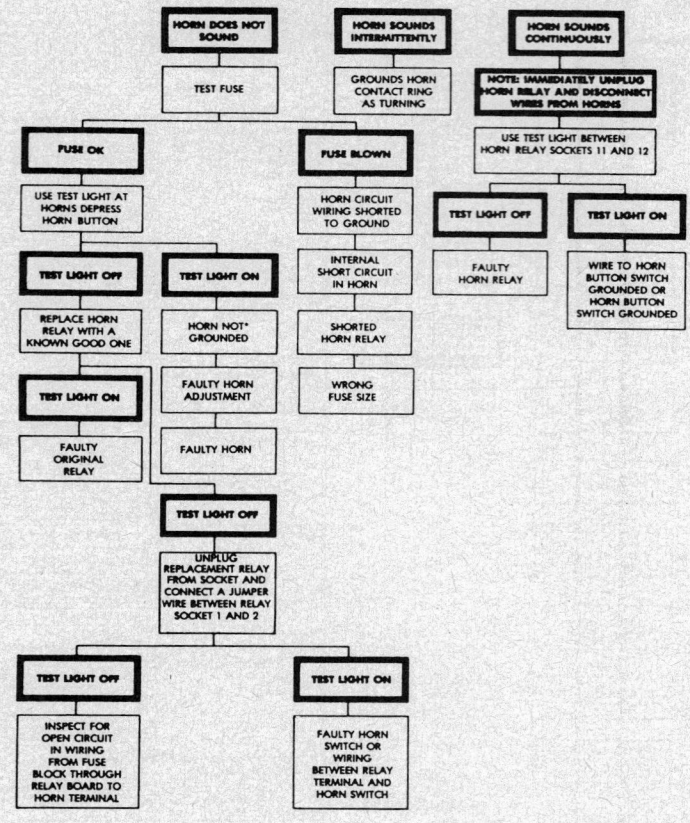

Fig. 12   Horn

CR1139100167000X

ENGINE REBUILDING SPECIFICATIONS

NOTE: For Engine Tightening Specifications, Refer To The Engine Section In The Appropriate Chassis Chapter Of This Manual.

INDEX

CYLINDER HEAD, VALVE GUIDE & VALVE SEATS

All measurements given in inches, unless otherwise specified.

Engine Liter/CID	Year	Cylinder Head Warpage Limit	Cylinder Head Overall Thickness	Valve Guides Inside Diameter (Standard)	Valve Guides Stem To Guide Clearance	Seat Angle	Valve Seats Seat Width Intake	Valve Seats Seat Width Exhaust	Runout
1.5L/4-90	1992-94	.008	4.209-4.217⑦	—	⑤	44.0°	.035-.051	.035-.051	—
1.8L/4-107③	1992-94	.008	3.484⑦	—	②	44.0-44.5°	.035-.051	.035-.051	—
1.8L/4-110④	1992	.008	4.720-4.728⑦	—	⑭	43.5-44.0°	.035-.051	.035-.051	—
1.8L/4-110⑱	1993-94	.008	4.720-4.728⑦	—	⑲	43.5-44.0°	.035-.051	.035-.051	—
2.0L/4-122⑩	1992-94	.008	5.197⑦	—	⑥	44.0-44.5°	.035-.051	.035-.051	—
2.0L/4-122㉑	1995	.002	—	.2350-.2360	㉒	45.0°	.035-.051	.035-.051	.002
2.2L/4-135 EFI	1992-94	.004	—	—	①	45.0°	.069-.088	.059-.078	.002
2.2L/4-135 Turbo III	1992-93	.004	—	—	⑮	45.0°	.069-.088	.059-.078	.002
2.4L/4-146	1992	.008	3.539-3.547⑦	—	②	44.0-45.5°	.035-.051	.035-.051	—
2.4L/4-146	1993-94	.008	4.720-4.728⑦	—	⑳	43.5-44.0°	.035-.051	.035-.051	—
2.5L/4-153	1992-94	.004	—	—	①	45.0°	.069-.088	.059-.078	.002
3.0L/V6-181⑫	1992-94	.002	—	.3140-.3150	⑯	44.0-44.3°	.035-.051	.035-.051	—
3.0L/V6-181⑪	1992	.002	4.363	.3150	—	45.0°	—	—	—
3.0L/V6-181⑨⑬	1992-94	.008	3.310⑦	—	②	44.0-44.5°	.035-.051	.035-.051	—
3.0L/V6-181⑩⑬	1992-94	.008	5.200⑦	—	⑤	44.0-44.5°	.035-.051	.035-.051	—
3.3L/V6-201	1992-94	.008	—	.3130-.3149	⑧	45.0-45.5°	.069-.088	.057-.078	.003
3.5L/V6-215	1993-94	.008	—	.3130-.3149	⑧	45.0-45.5°	.049-.069	.049-.069	.002
3.8L/V6-231	1992-93	.008	—	.2746-.2756	⑰	45.0-45.5°	.069-.088	.057-.078	.003

①—Exhaust, .0030-.0047 inch; intake, .0009-.0026 inch.

②—Exhaust: std., .0020-.0035 inch; service limit, .0060 inch. Intake: std., .0012-.0024 inch; service limit, .0040 inch.

③—Laser & Talon.

④—Colt Vista & Summit Wagon.

⑤—Exhaust, .0020-.0035 inch; intake, .0008-.0020 inch.

⑥—Exhaust, .0020-.0033 inch; intake, .0008-.0019 inch.

⑦—Minimum thickness is overall thickness, less warpage limit, combined w/amount of grinding of cylinder block gasket surface.

⑧—Maximum allowable by rocking method. Exhaust, .016 inch; intake, .010 inch.

⑨—Single overhead camshaft.

⑩—Dual overhead camshaft.

⑪—Monaco & Premier.

⑫—Except Monaco, Premier & Stealth.

⑬—Stealth.

⑭—Exhaust: std., .0020-.0035 inch; service limit, .0060 inch. Intake: std., .0008-.0020 inch; service limit, .0040 inch.

⑮—Exhaust, .0020-.0031 inch; intake, .0010-.0023 inch.

⑯—Exhaust: std., .0019-.0030 inch; service limit, .0060 inch. Intake: std., .0010-.0020 inch; service limit, .0040 inch.

⑰—Exhaust, .0020-.0037 inch; intake, .0009-.0026 inch.

⑱—Colt, Colt Vista, Summit & Summit Wagon.

⑲—Exhaust: std., .0012-.0024 inch; service limit, .0059 inch. Intake: std., .0008-.0016 inch; service limit, .0039 inch.

⑳—Exhaust: std., .0012-.0028 inch; service limit, .0059 inch. Intake: std., .0008-.0020 inch; service limit, .0039 inch.

㉑—Neon.

㉒—Exhaust: std., .0029-.0037 inch; service limit, .0040 inch. Intake: std., .0018-.0025 inch, service limit, .003 inch.

VALVE SPRINGS

All measurements given in inches, unless otherwise specified.

Engine Liter/CID	Year	Free Length	Installed Height	Spring Pressure, Pounds @ Inches	Maximum Straightness Deviation
1.5L/4-90	1992-94	⑪	1.575	⑫	4°
1.8L/4-107 ②	1992-94	1.937	1.469	68 @ 1.469	4°
1.8L/4-110 ③	1992-94	2.004	—	132 ⑩	4°
2.0L/4-122 ⑥	1992-94	1.902	—	66 ⑩	4°
2.0L/4-122 ⑮	1995	1.747	1.240-1.540	75 @ 1.540	—
2.2L/4-135 EFI	1992-94	2.390	1.220-1.650	108-120 @ 1.650	.079
2.2L/4-135 Turbo III	1992-93	2.094	1.730	115-127 @ 1.730	.065
2.4L/4-146	1992	1.961	—	73 ⑩	4°
	1993-94	2.008	1.740	60 @ 1.740	4°
2.5L/4-153 EFI	1992-94	2.390	1.620-1.680	108-120 @ 1.650	.079
2.5L/4-153 Turbo	1992-93	2.280	1.620-1.680	108-120 @ 1.650	.079
3.0L/V6-181 ⑧	1992-94	1.960	1.591	73 @ 1.591	4°
3.0L/V6-181 ⑦	1992	1.909	—	76 @ 1.575	—
3.0L/V6-181 ⑤ ⑨	1992-94	1.961	1.591	74 @ 1.591	4°
3.0L/V6-181 ⑥ ⑨	1992	1.846	1.492	62 @ 1.492	4°
	1993-94	1.827	1.492	53 @ 1.492	4°
3.3L/V6-201 ⑬	1992-94	1.909	1.539-1.598	90-100 @ 1.570	—
3.3L/V6-201 ⑭	1993	1.909	1.539-1.598	58-63 @ 1.570	—
3.5L/V6-215	1993-94	④	1.496	①	—
3.8L/V6-231	1992-93	1.909	1.539-1.598	90-100 @ 1.570	—

①—Exhaust, 80.7-89.3 lbs. @ 1.496 inches; Intake, 90.3-99.7 lbs. @ 1.496 inches.
②—Laser & Talon.
③—Colt Vista, Summit Wagon & 1993-94 Colt & Summit.
④—Exhaust, 1.799 inches; Intake, 1.781 inches.

⑤—Single overhead camshaft.
⑥—Dual overhead camshaft.
⑦—Monaco & Premier.
⑧—Except Monaco, Premier & Stealth.
⑨—Stealth.
⑩—At installed height.
⑪—Intake valve spring, 1.815 inches; Exhaust valve spring, 1.843 inches.

⑫—Intake, 51 lbs. at 1.575 inches; Exhaust, 64 lbs. at 1.575 inches.
⑬—Except 1993 Imperial & New Yorker Fifth Avenue.
⑭—1993 Imperial & New Yorker Fifth Avenue.
⑮—Neon.

VALVES

All measurements given in inches, unless otherwise specified.

Engine Liter/CID	Year	Stem Diameter		Clearance		Installed Height	Maximum Tip Refinish	Face Angle	Margin ①	
		Intake	Exhaust	Intake	Exhaust				Intake	Exhaust
1.5L/4-90	1992	.2585-.2591	.2571-.2579	⑤	⑥	—	—	45.0-45.5°	.020	.039
	1993-94	.2587-.2591	.2571-.2579	⑱	⑲	—	—	45.0-45.5°	.020	.039
1.8L/4-107 ⑮	1992-94	.3100	.3100	—	—	—	—	45.0-45.5°	.028	.039
1.8L/4-110 ⑯	1992	.2350-.2354	.2343-2350	—	—	—	—	45.0-45.5°	.020	.039
	1993-94	.2350-.2354	.2343-2350	⑦	⑫	—	—	45.0-45.5°	.020	⑬
2.0L/4-122 ⑨	1992-94	.2585-.2591	.2571-.2579	—	—	—	—	45.0-45.5°	.028	.040
2.0L/4-122 ⑳	1995	.2340	.2330	—	—	㉑	—	45.0-45.5°	.045	.058
2.2L/4-135 EFI	1992-94	.3124 ①	.3103 ①	—	—	1.960-2.009 ②	.020 ③	④	.030	.050
2.2L/4-135 Turbo III	1992-93	.3124 ①	.3103 ①	—	—	1.960-2.009 ②	.020 ③	④	.041	.042
2.4L/4-146	1992-94	.3100	.3100	—	—	—	—	45.0-45.5°	.028	.059
2.5L/4-153	1992-94	.3124 ①	.3103 ①	—	—	1.960-2.009 ②	.020 ③	④	.030	.050
3.0L/V6-181 ⑪	1992-94	.3130-.3140	.3120-.3125	—	—	—	—	45.0-45.5°	.027	.059
3.0L/V6-181 ⑩	1992	.3150	.3150	—	—	—	—	45.0°	.059	.067
3.0L/V6-181 ⑭ ⑧	1992-94	.3140	.3140	—	—	—	—	45.0-45.5°	.028	.059
3.0L/V6-181 ⑭ ⑨	1992-94	.2600	.2600	—	—	—	—	45.0-45.5°	.020	.039

Continued

VALVES -Continued

All measurements given in inches, unless otherwise specified.

Engine Liter/CID	Year	Stem Diameter		Clearance		Installed Height	Maximum Tip Refinish	Face Angle	Margin ①	
		Intake	Exhaust	Intake	Exhaust				Intake	Exhaust
3.3L/V6-201	1992-94	.3120-.3130	.3112-.3119	—	—	1.950-2.018	—	44.5-45.0°	.031	.047
3.5L/V6-215	1993-94	.2730-.2737	.2719-.2726	—	—	⑰	—	44.5-45.0°	.040	.057
3.8L/V6-231	1992-93	.3120-.3130	.3112-.3119	—	—	—	—	44.5-45.0°	.031	.047

① —Minimum.
② —Measured between tip of valve and top of seal boss.
③ —If more than .020 inch must be ground from valve stem, check clearance between rocker arm & valve spring retainer. If clearance is less than .050 inch, grind rocker arm ears.
④ —Exhaust, 44.5°; Intake, 45.0°.
⑤ —Hot, .0059 inch; cold, .0028 inch.
⑥ —Hot, .0098 inch; cold, .0067 inch.
⑦ —1992: no specification provided.

1993–94: hot engine, .0080 inch; cold engine, .0040 inch.
⑧ —Single overhead Camshaft.
⑨ —Dual overhead Camshaft.
⑩ —Monaco & Premier.
⑪ —Except Monaco, Premier & Stealth.
⑫ —1992: no specification provided. 1993–94: hot engine, .0120 inch; cold engine, .0080 inch.
⑬ —Colt & Summit, .031 inch; Colt Vista & Summit Wagon, .039 inch.
⑭ —Stealth.

⑮ —Laser & Talon.
⑯ —Colt Vista, Summit Wagon & 1993–94 Colt & Summit.
⑰ —Exhaust, 1.7600-1.8105 inches; Intake, 1.6680-1.7187 inches.
⑱ —Hot engine, .0080 inch; cold engine, .0040 inch.
⑲ —Hot engine, .0100 inch; cold engine, .0070 inch.
⑳ —Neon.
㉑ —Intake, 1.891 inches; exhaust, 1.889 inches.

CAMSHAFT

All measurements given in inches, unless otherwise specified.

Engine Liter/ CID	Year	Camshaft Journal Diameter	Camshaft Bearing Clearance	Camshaft Endplay	Lifter Bore Diameter	Lifter Diameter	Lifter To Bore Clearance
1.5L/4-90	1992-94	1.8110	.0024-.0039	—	—	—	—
1.8L/4-107 ③	1992-94	1.3360-1.3366	.0020-.0035	.0040-.0080	—	—	—
1.8L/4-110 ②	1992-94	1.7689-1.7693	.0020-.0035	—	—	—	—
2.0L/4-122	1992-94	1.0217-1.0224	.0020-.0035	.0040-.0080	—	—	—
2.0L/4-122 ⑪	1995	⑫	.0027-.0030	.0059	—	—	—
2.2L/4-135	1992-94	⑧	—	⑨	—	—	—
2.4L/4-146	1992	1.3362-1.3366	.0020-.0035	—	—	—	—
	1993-94	1.7689-1.7693	.0020-.0035	—	—	—	—
2.5L/4-153	1992-94	1.3950-1.3960	—	.0050-.0130	—	—	—
3.0L/V6-181 ⑦	1992-94	—	—	—	—	—	—
3.0L/V6-181 ⑥	1992	—	—	.0030-.0055	—	—	—
3.0L/V6-181 ⑩ ④	1992-94	1.3400	.0020-.0035	—	—	—	—
3.0L/V6-181 ⑩ ⑤	1992-94	1.0200	.0020-.0035	—	—	—	—
3.3L/V6-201	1992-94	①	.0010-.0040	.0050-.0120	.9051-.9059	.9035-.9040	.0011-.0024
3.5L/V6-215	1993-94	1.6944-1.6952	.0030-.0047	.0040-.0140	—	—	—
3.8L/V6-231	1992-93	①	.0010-.0040	.0050-.0120	.9051-.9059	.9035-.9040	.0011-.0024

① —No. 1, 1.997-1.999 inch; No. 2, 1.981-1.983 inch; No. 3, 1.966-1.968 inch; No. 4, 1.950-1.952 inch.
② —Colt Vista, Summit Wagon & 1993-94 Colt & Summit.
③ —Laser & Talon.
④ —Single overhead camshaft.
⑤ —Dual overhead camshaft.
⑥ —Monaco & Premier.
⑦ —Except Monaco, Premier & Stealth.
⑧ —Except 2.2L/4-135 turbo engine, 1.395-1.396 inch; 2.2L/4-135 turbo engine, 1.886-1.887 inch.
⑨ —Except 2.2L/4-135 turbo engines, .005-.013 inch; 2.2L/4-135 turbo engines, .001-.008 inch.
⑩ —Stealth.
⑪ —Neon.
⑫ —Bearing journal No. 1, 1.6190-1.6199 inch; No. 2, 1.6340-1.6350 inch; No. 3, 1.6500-1.6510 inch; No. 4, 1.6660-1.6680 inch; No. 5, 1.6820-1.6829 inch.

INTERMEDIATE SHAFT

All measurements given in inches, unless otherwise specified.

Engine Liter/ CID	Year	Journal Diameter		Bushing Bore Diameter		Oil Clearance	
		Outer	Inner	Outer	Inner	Outer	Inner
2.2L/4-135	1992-94	1.6799-1.6809	.7744-.7753	1.6823-1.6830	.7763-.7775	.0013-.0031	.0006-.0031
2.5L/4-153	1992-94	1.6799-1.6809	.7744-.7753	1.6823-1.6830	.7763-.7775	.0013-.0031	.0006-.0031

CRANKSHAFT, BEARINGS & RODS

All measurements given in inches, unless otherwise specified.

Engine Liter/CID	Year	Crankshaft Main Bearing Journal Diameter	Crankshaft Connecting Rod Journal Diameter	Crankshaft Maximum Out Of Round All	Crankshaft Maximum Taper All	Bearing Clearance Main Bearings	Bearing Clearance Connecting Rod Bearings	Connecting Rods Pin Bore Diameter	Connecting Rods Side Clearance	Crankshaft Endplay
1.5L/4-90	1992	1.8900	1.6500	.0006	.0006	.0008-.0024	.0008-.0024	—	.0039-.0098	.0020-.0071
	1993-94	1.8900	1.6500	.0002	.0002	.0008-.0020	.0008-.0020	—	.0039-.0098	.0020-.0071
1.8L/4-107 ⑦	1992-94	2.2400	1.7700	.0006	.0002	.0008-.0020	.0008-.0020	—	.0039-.0098	.0020-0070
1.8L/4-110 ⑥	1992	1.9678-1.9683	1.7709-1.7715	.0006	.0002	.0008-.0016	.0008-.0020	—	.0039-.0098	.0020-.0070
	1993-94	1.9678-1.9683	1.7709-1.7715	.0006	.0002	.0008-.0016	.0008-.0020	—	.0039-.0098	.0020-.0098
2.0L/4-122 ②	1992-93	2.2433-2.2439	1.7709-1.7715	.0006	.0002	.0008-.0020	.0008-.0020	—	.0040-.0098	.0020-.0070
	1994	2.2433-2.2439	1.7709-1.7715	.0006	.0002	.0008-.0016	.0008-.0020	—	.0040-.0098	.0020-.0070
2.0L/4-122 ⑧	1995	2.0469-2.0475	1.8894-1.8900	.0001	.0001	.0008-.0024	.0010-.0023	.8252-.8260	.0050-.0150	.0035-.0094
2.2L/4-135	1992-94	2.3620-2.3630	1.9680-1.9690	.0050	.0004	.0004-.0028	.0008-.0034	—	.0050-.0130	.0020-.0070
2.4L/4-146	1992	2.2433-2.2441	1.7709-1.7717	.0006	.0002	.0008-.0020	.0008-.0020	—	.0039-.0098	.0020-.0070
	1993-94	2.2433-2.2441	1.7709-1.7717	.0004	.0004	.0008-.0020	.0008-.0020	—	.0039-.0098	.0020-.0070
2.5L/4-153	1992-94	2.3620-2.3630	1.9680-1.9690	.0050	.0004	.0004-.0028	.0008-.0034	—	.0050-.0130	.0020-.0070
3.0L/V6-181 ④	1992-94	2.3610-2.3620	1.9680-1.9690	.0010	.0002	.0008-.0019	.0008-.0028	—	.0040-.0100	.0020-.0100
3.0L/V6-181 ③	1992	2.7576-2.7583	2.3611-2.3618	—	—	.0015-.0035	—	.9826-.9831	.0080-.0150	.0030-.0100
3.0L/V6-181 ① ⑤	1992-94	2.3580	1.9650	.0002	.0002	.0008-.0019	.0006-.0018	—	.0039-.0098	.0020-.0098
3.0L/V6-181 ② ⑤	1992	2.3580	1.9650	.0001	.0001	.0007-.0017	.0009-.0019	—	.0039-.0098	.0020-.0098
	1993-94	2.3580	1.9650	.0001	.0001	.0007-.0014	.0009-.0019	—	.0039-.0098	.0020-.0098
3.3L/V6-201	1992-94	2.5190	2.2830	.0010	.0010	.0007-.0022	.0007-.0030	—	.0050-.0150	.0030-.0090
3.5L/V6-215	1993-94	2.5190-2.5200	2.2820-2.2830	.0001	.0002	.0007-.0022	.0007-.0034	.9823-9451	.0050-.0150	.0040-.0120
3.8L/V6-231	1992-93	2.5190	2.2830	.0010	.0010	.0007-.0022	.0007-.0030	—	.0050-.0150	.0030-.0090

① —Single overhead camshaft.
② —Dual overhead camshaft.
③ —Monaco & Premier.
④ —Except Monaco, Premier & Stealth.
⑤ —Stealth.
⑥ —Colt Vista, Summit Wagon & 1993-94 Colt & Summit.
⑦ —Laser & Talon.
⑧ —Neon.

BALANCE SHAFT

All measurements given in inches, unless otherwise specified.

Engine Liter/CID	Year	Journal Diameter Front Left	Journal Diameter Front Right	Journal Diameter Rear Left	Journal Diameter Rear Right	Oil Clearance Front Left	Oil Clearance Front Right	Oil Clearance Rear Left	Oil Clearance Rear Right
1.8L/4-107	1992-94	.7270-.7276	1.5338-1.5344	1.4154-1.4160	1.4154-1.4160	.0008-.0021	.0008-.0024	.0020-.0036	.0020-.0036
2.0L/4-122 ①	1992-94	.7270-.7276	1.6519-1.6526	1.6126-1.6132	1.6122-1.6129	.0008-.0021	.0012-.0024	.0017-.0033	.0020-.0036
2.4L/4-146	1992-94	.7272-.7276	1.6512-1.6528	1.6122-1.6130	1.6122-1.6130	.0008-.0020	.0008-.0024	.0020-.0036	.0020-.0036

① —Dual overhead camshaft.

PISTONS, PINS & RINGS

All measurements given in inches, unless otherwise specified.

Engine Liter/ CID	Year	Piston Diameter (Std.)	Piston Clearance	Piston Pin Diameter	Piston Pin To Piston Clearance	Piston Ring End Gap ①		Piston Ring Side Clearance	
						Comp.	Oil	Comp.	Oil
1.5L/4-90	1992	2.9713-2.9724	.0008-.0016	—	—	㊵	.0079-.0276	⑱	—
	1993-94	2.9716-2.9724	.0008-.0016	—	—	㊵	.0079-.0276	⑱	—
1.8L/4-107 ⑭	1992-94	3.1730	.0008-.0016	—	—	㊶	.0079-.0276	㉗	—
1.8L/4-110 ⑮	1992-94	3.1882-3.1886	.0008-.0016	—	—	⑯	.0079-.0236	㉒	—
2.0L/4-122 ⑳	1992-94	3.3465	㉜	—	—	㊷	.0079-.276	.0012-.0028	—
2.0L/4-122 ㊹	1995	3.4434-3.4441	.0002-.0015 ㊺	.8267-.8269	.0002-.0007	㊻	.0090-.0260	.0010-.0026	.0002-.0070
2.2L/4-135 ③	1992-94	3.4430-3.4450 ⑤	.0005-.0015 ⑥	—	—	㉘	.0150-.0550	⑦	.0080 ②
2.2L/4-135 ④	1992-93	3.4410-3.4440 ㊸	.0018-.0028 ㉟	—	—	.0140-.0200	.0100-.0200	.0016-.0030	.0020 ②
2.4L/4-146	1992	3.4040-3.4055	.0004-.0012	—	—	㊴	.0079-.0276	㉒	—
	1993-94	3.4040-3.4055	.0004-.0012	—	—	㉓	.0039-.0157	.0012-.0028	—
2.5L/4-153 ③	1992-94	3.4430-3.4440 ㉚	.0010-.0020 ⑥	—	—	㉘	.0150-.0550	⑦	.0080 ②
2.5L/4-153 ④	1992-93	3.4430-3.4440 ㉛	.0006-.0016 ⑨	—	—	⑩	.0100-.0200	㉙	.0080 ②
3.0L/V6-181 ㉞	1992-93	3.5850-3.5860	.0012-.0020	—	—	⑪	.0120-.0350	⑫	⑬
	1994	3.5850-3.5860	.0012-.0020	—	—	㉖	.0080-.0240	㉜	—
3.0L/V6-181 ㉝	1992	—	—	.9839-.9843	.0015-.0085	.0160-.0220	—	.0010-.0020	.0015-.0035
3.0L/V6-181 ⑲ ㊱	1992-93	3.5866	.0012-.0020	—	—	㊲	.0118-.0354	⑰	—
3.0L/V6-181 ⑳ ㊱	1992-93	3.5866	.0012-.0020	—	—	㊳	.0079-.0236	㉒	—
3.0L/V6-181 ㊱	1994	3.5866	.0012-.0020	—	—	.0118-.0177	.0079-.0236	㉒	—
3.3L/V6-201	1992-94	3.6594-3.6602 ⑧	.0009-.0022	.9007-.9009	.0002-.0007	.0118-.0217	.0098-.0394	.0010-.0030	.0006-.0089
3.5L/V6-215	1993-94	3.7800-3.7778 ㉔	.0007-.0020	.9448-.9449	.0002-.0006	㉕	.0100-.0300	.0012-.0031	.0019-.0077
3.8L/V6-231	1992-93	3.7776-3.7783 ㉑	.0009-.0022	.9007-.9009	.0002-.0007	.0118-.0217	.0098-.0394	.0010-.0030	.0006-.0089

① —Minimum.
② —Maximum.
③ —Non-turbocharged engines.
④ —Turbocharged engines.
⑤ —Measured at right angle to piston pin, 1.14 inches from top of piston.
⑥ —Wear limit, .0027 inch.
⑦ —Top, .0015-.0031 inch; limit, .0040 inch. 2nd, .0015-.0037 inch; limit, .0040 inch.
⑧ —Measured at right angle to piston pin, 1.65 inches from top of piston.
⑨ —Wear limit, .0030 inch.
⑩ —Top, .010-.020 inch; 2nd, .009-.019 inch.
⑪ —Top, .012-.018 inch; 2nd, .010-.016 inch.
⑫ —Top, .0020-.0035 inch; limit, .0040 inch. 2nd, .0008-.0020 inch; limit, .0039 inch.
⑬ —Oil ring side rails must be free to rotate after assembly.
⑭ —Laser & Talon.
⑮ —Colt Vista & Summit Wagon.
⑯ —Top, .0098-.0157 inch; 2nd, .0157-.0217 inch.
⑰ —Top, .0020-.0035 inch; 2nd, .0008-.0024 inch.

⑱ —Top, .0012-.0028 inch; 2nd, .0008-.0024 inch.
⑲ —Single overhead camshaft.
⑳ —Dual overhead camshaft.
㉑ —Measured at right angle to piston pin, 1.41 inches from top of piston.
㉒ —Top, .0012-.0028; 2nd, .0008-.0024 inch.
㉓ —Top, .0098-.0138 inch; 2nd, .0157-.0217 inch.
㉔ —Measured at right angle to piston pin, .394 inches from bottom of piston.
㉕ —Top, .012-.018 inch; 2nd, .012-.022 inch.
㉖ —Top: .0120-.0180 inch; limit, .0310 inch. 2nd: .0180-.0240 inch; limit, .0310 inch.
㉗ —Top, .0018-.0033 inch; 2nd, .0008-.0024 inch.
㉘ —Top, .010-.020 inch; 2nd, .011-.021 inch.
㉙ —Top, .0016-.0030 inch; limit, .0040 inch. 2nd, .0016-.0035 inch; limit, .0040 inch.
㉚ —Measured at right angle to piston pin, 1.87 inches from top of piston.
㉛ —Measured at right angle to piston

pin, 1.48 inches from top of piston.
㉜ —Top: .0020-.0035 inch; limit, .0039 inch. 2nd: .0016-.0033 inch; limit, .0039 inch.
㉝ —Monaco & Premier.
㉞ —Except Monaco, Premier & Stealth.
㉟ —Wear limit, .0039 inch.
㊱ —Stealth.
㊲ —Top, .0118-.0177 inch; 2nd, .0098-.0157 inch.
㊳ —Top, .0118-.0177 inch; 2nd, .0177-.0236 inch.
㊴ —Top, .0098-.0157 inch; 2nd, .0079-.0157 inch.
㊵ —Top, .0079-.0157 inch; 2nd, .0079-.0138 inch.
㊶ —Top, .0118-.0177 inch; 2nd, .0079-.0217 inch.
㊷ —Top, .0098-.0157 inch; 2nd, .0177-.0236 inch.
㊸ —Measured at right angle to piston pin, 2.19 inches from top of piston.
㊹ —Neon.
㊺ —Measured 11/32 inch from bottom of skirt.
㊻ —Top, .009-.020 inch; 2nd, .019-.031 inch.

CYLINDER BLOCK

All measurements given in inches, unless otherwise specified.

Engine Liter/CID	Year	Cylinder Bore Diameter (Std.)	Cylinder Bore Taper (Max.)	Cylinder Bore Out Of Round (Max.)
1.5L/4-90	1992-94	2.9724-2.9736	.0008	.0008
1.8L/4-107 ⑥	1992-94	3.1730	.0004	.0004

Continued

CHRYSLER—Engine Rebuilding Specifications

CYLINDER BLOCK-Continued
All measurements given in inches, unless otherwise specified.

Engine Liter/CID	Year	Cylinder Bore Diameter (Std.)	Cylinder Bore Taper (Max.)	Cylinder Bore Out Of Round (Max.)
1.8L/4-110 [7]	1992-94	3.1894-3.1898	.0004	.0004
1.8L/4-110 [1]	1993-94	3.1890-3.1902	.0004	.0004
2.0L/4-122 [2]	1992-94	3.3465	.0004	.0004
2.0L/4-122 [8]	1995	3.4446-3.4452	.0020	.0020
2.2L/4-135	1992-94	3.4400-3.4500	.0050	.0020
2.4L/4-146	1992-94	3.4055-3.4067	.0004	.0004
2.5L/4-153	1992-94	3.4400-3.4500	.0050	.0020
3.0L/V6-181 [4]	1992-94	3.5860-3.5870	.0008	.0008
3.0L/V6-181 [3]	1992	[5]	[5]	[5]
3.3L/V6-201	1992-94	3.6600	.0020	.0030
3.5L/V6-215	1993-94	3.7800	.0020	.0030
3.8L/V6-231	1992-93	3.7790	.0020	.0030

[1]—Colt & Summit.
[2]—Dual overhead camshaft.
[3]—Monaco & Premier.
[4]—Except Monaco & Premier.
[5]—Cylinder liner.
[6]—Laser & Talon.
[7]—Colt Vista & Summit Wagon.
[8]—Neon.

CYLINDER LINER
All measurements given in inches, unless otherwise specified.

Engine Liter/CID	Year	Liner Inside Diameter	Liner Base Outside Diameter	Liner Height	Liner Protrusion Limits	Maximum Variation [1]
3.0L/V6-181 [3]	1992	[2]	3.8500	5.1600	.0020-.0050	.0016

[1]—Between adjacent cylinders.
[2]—One notch liner, 3.6614-3.6618 inches; two notch liner, 3.6618-3.6622 inches; three notch liner, 3.6622-3.6626 inches.
[3]—Monaco & Premier.

OIL PUMP
All measurements given in inches, unless otherwise specified.

Engine Liter/CID	Year	Rotor Backlash	Rotor To Body Clear.	Rotor Endplay [1]	Rotor Thickness (Minimum) Inner	Outer	Outer Rotor Diameter (Minimum)	Maximum Cover Flatness Variation	Relief Spring Free Length	Relief Spring Pressure Lbs. @ Inches
1.5L/4-90	1992-94	.0071 [2]	.0039-.0071	.0016-.0039	—	—	—	—	1.835	13.0 @ 1.579
1.8L/4-107 [13]	1992	—	[17]	[18]	—	—	—	—	1.835	13.4 @ 1.579
	1993-94	—	.0039-.0063	.0024-.0047	—	—	—	—	1.724	8.2 @ 1.579
1.8L/4-110 [14]	1992-94	.0071 [2]	.0039-.0071 [3]	.0016-.0039	—	—	—	—	1.835	13.4 @ 1.579
2.0L/4-122 [9]	1992-94	—	[7]	[8]	—	—	—	—	1.835	13.4 @ 1.579
2.0L/4-122 [19]	1995	.0080 [2]	.0150	—	.301	.301	3.148	—	2.390	18.0-19.0 @ 1.600
2.2L/4-135	1992-94	.0080 [2]	.0010-.0035 [3]	.0010-.0035	—	.944	2.469	.002	1.950	20.0 @ 1.340
2.4L/4-146	1992	—	[7]	[4]	—	—	—	—	1.834	13.4 @ 1.578
	1993-94	—	—	[8]	—	—	—	—	1.835	13.4 @ 1.579
2.5L/4-153	1992-94	.0080 [2]	.0010-.0035 [3]	.0010-.0035	—	.944	2.469	.002	1.950	20.0 @ 1.340
3.0L/V6-181 [11]	1992-94	[5]	.0040-.0070	.0015-.0035	—	—	—	—	—	[6]
3.0L/V6-181 [10]	1992	—	—	—	—	—	—	—	—	—
3.0L/V6-181 [12][15]	1992-94	—	.0039-.0071 [3]	.0016-.0037	—	—	—	—	1.724	8.3 @ 1.579
3.0L/V6-181 [12][16]	1992-94	—	.0039-.0071 [3]	.0016-.0037	—	—	—	—	1.823	15.2 @ 1.539
3.3L/V6-201	1992-94	.0080	.0220	—	.301	.301	3.141	.003	—	—
3.5L/V6-215	1993-94	.0007	.0070	—	.370	.370	3.149	.003	—	—
3.8L/V6-231	1992-93	.0080	.0220	—	.301	.301	3.141	.003	—	—

[1]—Measured between pump cover mounting surface and end of gear, using straightedge and feeler gauge.
[2]—Maximum inner & outer rotor tip clearance.
[3]—Maximum clearance between inner and outer rotors and body.
[4]—Drive gear, .0031-.0055 inch; driven gear, .0051-.0071 inch.
[5]—Inner rotor pilot to case, .006 inch maximum.
[6]—Relief valve opening pressure, 71.45-85.75 psi.
[7]—Drive gear, .0063-.0083 inch; driven gear, .0051-.0071 inch.
[8]—Drive gear, .0031-.0055 inch; driven gear, .0024-.0047 inch.
[9]—Dual overhead camshaft.
[10]—Monaco & Premier.
[11]—Except Monaco, Premier & Stealth.
[12]—Stealth.
[13]—Laser & Talon.
[14]—Colt Vista, Summit Wagon & 1993-94 Colt & Summit.
[15]—Non-Turbocharged.
[16]—Turbocharged.
[17]—Drive gear, .0024-.0047 inch; driven gear, .0039-.0079 inch.
[18]—Drive gear, .008 inch; driven gear, .006 inch.
[19]—Neon.

FORD MOTOR COMPANY

If You Want To Win Customers Over, Put Perfect Circle® Parts Under.

Customers will have confidence in you and your work when you install Perfect Circle® chassis parts.

Because all of our steering, suspension and driveline components come with a Lifetime Limited Warranty.

Perfect Circle people offer outstanding support in technical assistance and training.

- Hands-on training at our Center of Technology or chassis tech seminars held right in your place of business.
- Comprehensive service manuals, ride height and alignment specifications for easy reference.
- Videotape library–covering more than

We Help Provide The Quality And Expertise Your Customers Are Looking For.

20 service-related topics–for training at your convenience. What's more, Perfect Circle® provides full coverage to handle the range of import and domestic jobs. Which helps you win more customers over.

For details on the complete line of Perfect Circle chassis parts, write Perfect Circle Chassis Parts, P.O. Box 455, Toledo, Ohio 43697-0455.

People Finding A Better Way™

PERFECT CIRCLE®

DANA

FORD CROWN VICTORIA & THUNDERBIRD; MERCURY COUGAR & GRAND MARQUIS

NOTE: Refer To Rear Of This Manual For Vehicle Manufacturer's Special Service Tool Suppliers.

INDEX OF SERVICE OPERATIONS

NOTE: For Service Operations Not Listed Below, Refer To The Table Of Contents In The Front Of This Manual.

Specifications

GENERAL ENGINE SPECIFICATIONS

Year	Engine Liter/CID	VIN Code ②	Fuel System	Bore & Stroke	Compression Ratio	Net H.P. @ RPM ③	Maximum Torque Ft. Lbs. @ RPM	Normal Oil Pressure psi.
1992	3.8L/V6-232	4	SEFI	3.80 x 3.40	9.0	140 @ 3800	215 @ 2400	40-60 ④
	3.8L/V6-232 SC ⑤	C, R	SEFI	3.80 x 3.40	8.2	210 @ 4000	315 @ 2600	40-60 ④
	4.6L/V8-281 ⑥	W	SEFI	3.55 x 3.54	9.0	190 @ 4200	260 @ 3200	40-60 ⑦
	4.6L/V8-281 ⑧	W	SEFI	3.55 x 3.54	9.0	210 @ 4600	270 @ 3400	40-60 ⑦
	5.0L/V8-302 HO ①	T	SEFI	4.00 x 3.00	9.0	200 @ 4000	275 @ 3000	40-60 ⑦
1993	3.8L/V6-232	4	SEFI	3.80 x 3.40	9.0	140 @ 3800	215 @ 2400	40-60 ④
	3.8L/V6-232 SC ⑤	R	SEFI	3.80 x 3.40	8.2	210 @ 4000	315 @ 2600	40-60 ④
	4.6L/V8-281 ⑥	W	SEFI	3.55 x 3.54	9.0	190 @ 4200	260 @ 3200	40-60 ⑦
	4.6L/V8-281 ⑧	W	SEFI	3.55 x 3.54	9.0	210 @ 4600	270 @ 3400	40-60 ⑦
	5.0L/V8-302 HO ①	T	SEFI	4.00 x 3.00	9.0	200 @ 4000	275 @ 3000	40-60 ⑦
1994	3.8L/V6-232	4	SEFI	3.80 x 3.40	9.0	140 @ 3800	215 @ 2400	40-60 ④
	3.8L/V6-232 SC ⑤	R	SEFI	3.80 x 3.40	8.2	210 @ 4000	315 @ 2600	40-60 ④
	4.6L/V8-281 ⑥	W	SEFI	3.55 x 3.54	9.0	190 @ 4200	260 @ 3200	40-60 ⑦
	4.6L/V8-281 ⑧	W	SEFI	3.55 x 3.54	9.0	210 @ 4600	270 @ 3400	40-60 ⑦
1995	3.8L/V6-232	4	SEFI	3.80 x 3.40	9.0	140 @ 3800	215 @ 2400	40-60 ④
	3.8L/V6-232 SC ⑤	R	SEFI	3.80 x 3.40	8.2	210 @ 4000	315 @ 2600	40-60 ④
	4.6L/V8-281 ⑥	W	SEFI	3.55 x 3.54	9.0	190 @ 4200	260 @ 3200	40-60 ⑦
	4.6L/V8-281 ⑧	W	SEFI	3.55 x 3.54	9.0	210 @ 4600	270 @ 3400	40-60 ⑦

SEFI—Sequential Multi-Port Electronic Fuel Injection.
CID—Cubic Inch Displacement.
①—Cougar & Thunderbird.
②—The eighth digit of VIN denotes engine code.
③—Ratings are net-as installed in vehicle.
④—At 2500 RPM w/engine at operating temperature.
⑤—Supercharged engine.
⑥—Single exhaust.
⑦—At 2000 RPM w/engine at operating temperature.
⑧—Dual exhaust.

FORD CROWN VICTORIA & THUNDERBIRD, MERCURY COUGAR & GRAND MARQUIS

TUNE UP SPECIFICATIONS

Engine Liter/CID (VIN Code) ①	Spark Plug Gap	Ignition Timing BTDC				Curb Idle Speed RPM		Fast Idle Speed RPM		Fuel Pump Pressure, psi.
		Firing Order Fig. ③	Man. Trans.	Auto. Trans. ④	Mark Fig.	Man. Trans.	Auto. Trans.	Man. Trans.	Auto. Trans.	
1992										
3.8L/V6-232 (4)	.052-.056	A	—	⑤	—	—	⑥	—	⑥	35-40⑦
3.8L/V6-232 SC (C, R)	.054	B	⑤	⑤	②	700⑥	600⑥	⑥	⑥	35-40⑦
4.6L/V8-281 (W)	.054	1-3-7-2-6-5-4-8	—	⑤	②	640N⑥	—	⑥	35-40⑦	
5.0L/V8-302 HO (T)	.054	1-3-7-2-6-5-4-8	—	⑤	—	—	⑥	—	⑥	30-40⑦
1993										
3.8L/V6-232 (4)	.052-.056	A	—	⑤	—	—	⑥	—	⑥	35-40⑦
3.8L/V6-232 SC (R)	.054	B	⑤	⑤	②	700⑥	600⑥	⑥	⑥	35-40⑦
4.6L/V8-281 (W)	.054	1-3-7-2-6-5-4-8	—	⑤	②	—	640N⑥	—	⑥	35-40⑦
5.0L/V8-302 HO (T)	.054	1-3-7-2-6-5-4-8	—	⑤	—	—	—	—	⑥	30-40⑦
1994										
3.8L/V6-232 (4)	.052-.056	A	—	⑤	—	—	⑥	—	⑥	35-40⑦
3.8L/V6-232 SC (R)	.054	B	⑤	⑤	②	700⑥	600⑥	⑥	⑥	35-40⑦
4.6L/V8-281 (W)	.054	1-3-7-2-6-5-4-8	—	⑤	②	—	640N⑥	—	⑥	35-40⑦
1995										
3.8L/V6-232 (4)	.052-.056	A	—	⑤	—	—	⑥	—	⑥	35-40⑦
3.8L/V6-232 SC (R)	.054	B	⑤	⑤	②	700⑥	600⑥	⑥	⑥	35-40⑦
4.6L/V8-281 (W)	.054	1-3-7-2-6-5-4-8	—	⑤	②	—	640N⑥	—	⑥	35-40⑦

BTDC— Before Top Dead Center.

①—The eighth digit of Vehicle Identification Number (VIN) denotes engine code.

②—Equipped w/crankshaft sensor.

③—D:Drive. When checking idle speed, set parking brake & block drive wheels.

④—Before disconnecting wires from distributor cap, determine location of No. 1 wire in cap, as distributor position may have been altered from that shown at the end of this chart.

⑤—Non-adjustable.

⑥—Idle speed is controlled by an automatic idle speed control, no adjustment.

⑦—Wrap shop towel around fuel diagnostic valve to prevent fuel spillage. Connect suitable fuel pressure gauge to fuel diagnostic valve. Energize fuel pump & check pressure gauge reading.

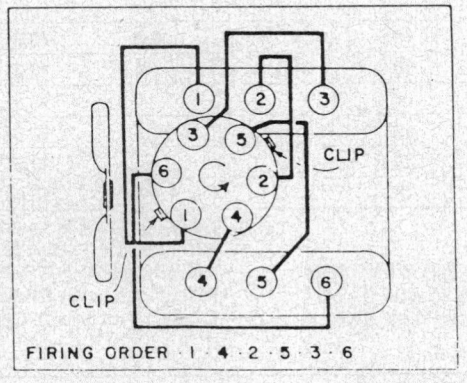

FIRING ORDER · 1 · 4 · 2 · 5 · 3 · 6

Fig. A

FM1139100104000X

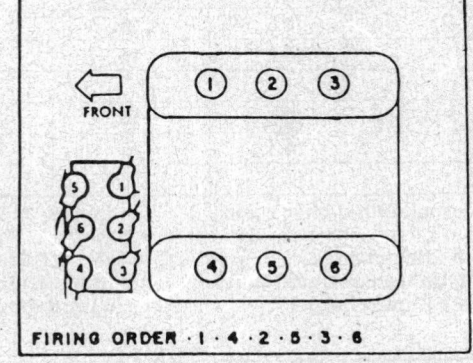

FRONT

FIRING ORDER · 1 · 4 · 2 · 5 · 3 · 6

Fig. B

FM1139100106000X

FRONT WHEEL ALIGNMENT SPECIFICATIONS

Year	Caster Angle, Degrees		Camber Angle, Degrees				Toe-In Inch	Toe Out on Turns, Deg.	
	Limits	Desired	Limits		Desired			Outer Wheel	Inner Wheel
			Left	Right	Left	Right			
COUGAR & THUNDERBIRD									
1992-95	+4.75 to +6.25	+5.5	-1.25 to +.25	-1.25 to +.25	-.5	-.5	1/8	19.73	20
CROWN VICTORIA & GRAND MARQUIS									
1992-95	+4.75 to +6.25	+5.5	-1.25 to +.25	-1.25 to +.25	-.5	-.5	1/8	18.51	20

REAR WHEEL ALIGNMENT SPECIFICATIONS

Year	Camber Angle, Degrees						Toe-In Inch
	Limits		Desired		Maximum Difference (Left Minus Right)		
	Left	Right	Left	Right	Limits	Desired	
COUGAR & THUNDERBIRD							
1992-94	-1 to 0	-1 to 0	-.5	-.5	-.5 to +.5	0	1/16
1995	-1.25 to +.25	-1.25 to +.25	-.5	-.5	-.75 to +.75	0	1/16

COOLING SYSTEM & CAPACITY DATA

Engine & VIN Code	Coolant Capacity, Qts.	Radiator Cap Relief Pressure, psi	Thermo. Opening Temp.	Fuel Tank Gals.	Engine Refill Qts.	Transmission Oil		Rear Axle Oil Pts.
						Man. Trans. Pts.	Auto. Trans. Qts. ①	
1992-93								
3.8L/V6-232 (4, C, R)	12.5	16	196	19	4⑧	6.3	12.3③	3.1④
4.6L/V8-281 (W)	13.6	16	196	18	5	—	12.3③	3.75
5.0L/V8-302 HO (T)	14.1	16	192	19	4②	—	12.3③	3.35
1994								
3.8L/V6-232 (4, C, R)	12.5	16	196	19	4⑧	6.3	12.3③	3.1④
4.6L/V8-281 (W)	13.6	16	196	18	5	—	12.3③	3.75
1995								
3.8L/V6-232 (4, C, R)	12.5	16	196	19	5	6.3	12.3③	3.1④
4.6L/V8-281 (W) ⑨	14.1	16	196	20	5	—	13.6③	3.75⑦
4.6L/V8-281 (W) ⑤	14.1	16	196	18	5	—	13.6③	⑥⑦

①—Approximate, make final check with dipstick.
②—Add 1 qt. with filter change.
③—Use Mercon type transmission fluid.
④—On 3.8L/V6-232 Supercharger engines, 3.50 Pts.
⑤—Cougar & Thunderbird.
⑥—Axle w/7.5 inch ring gear, 3 pts. Axle w/8.8 inch ring gear, 3.25 pts.
⑦—On models with Traction-Lok axle, add 2 oz. of friction modifier meeting Ford Motor Co. specification WSP-M2C196-A.
⑧—Add 1/2 qt. with filter change.
⑨—Crown Victoria & Grand Marquis.

LUBRICANT DATA

Year	Model	Lubricant Type				
		Transmission		Rear Axle	Power Steering	Brake System
		Manual	Automatic			
1992-95	All	Mercon	Mercon	XY-90-QL ①	②	DOT 3

① —Traction-Lok axles, add Friction Modifier C8AZ-19B546-A or equivalent.

② —Type F trans. fluid or premium power steering fluid.

Electrical

NOTE: On Air Bag Equipped Models, Refer To "Air Bag System Precautions" Located In The Front Of This Manual For System Disarming & Arming Procedures.

INDEX

PRECAUTIONS

AIR BAG SYSTEMS

Refer to "Air Bag System Precautions" in the front of this manual for system disarming and arming procedures.

FUSE PANEL & FLASHER LOCATION

COUGAR & THUNDERBIRD

Fuse panel is on left side of lower instrument panel.

Combination turn signal/hazard flasher is located to right side of steering column opening reinforcement, mounted on a bracket.

CROWN VICTORIA & GRAND MARQUIS

Fuse panel is located behind left side of instrument panel.

Flashers are located on fuse panel.

RELAY CENTER LOCATION

The relay center is located on the front lefthand side of the engine compartment.

STARTER
REPLACE

STARTER PROBLEMS: If starter is noisy or if it locks up, before condemning the starter, loosen three mounting bolts enough to hand fit the starter properly into pilot plate. Then tighten mounting bolts, starting with top bolt.

1. Disconnect battery ground cable.
2. Raise and support front of vehicle.
3. Remove starter shield, if equipped.
4. Disconnect starter cable and push on connector. **When disconnecting hard-shell connector at S-terminal, grasp the plastic shell and pull off. Do not pull on wire. Be careful to pull straight off to prevent damage to the connector and the S-terminal. If any part of the connection is damaged, replace the damaged components.**
5. **On Crown Victoria and Grand Marquis models, remove upper mounting bolt using a swivel socket and 22

inch extension. Access bolt from the front and along the side of right front engine mount.

6. **On all models,** remove mounting bolts and starter. **It may be necessary to turn wheels right or left to remove starter.**

7. Reverse procedure to install. **Torque** bolts to 15-20 ft. lbs.

DISTRIBUTOR
REPLACE
REMOVAL

1. Disconnect distributor from engine control sensor wiring.
2. Mark position of No. 1 cylinder distributor cap ignition wire tower on distributor base for installation reference.
3. Loosen distributor cap hold-down screws, then remove distributor cap and position aside with spark plug wires attached.
4. Remove distributor rotor.
5. Remove distributor hold-down clamp and retainer bolt.
6. Remove distributor by pulling straight upward. **Cover distributor opening in the engine front cover to prevent the entry of any foreign material or dirt into the engine.**

INSTALLATION

1. Prior to installing distributor, check the following:
   a. O-ring for a tight fit or any nicks, cuts or cracks.
   b. Turn distributor shaft manually and ensure it operates smoothly and freely, without binding.
2. Set No. 1 piston at TDC of its compression stroke, align timing pointer with TDC mark on crankshaft damper.
3. Align locating boss on distributor rotor with hole on armature.
4. Fully seat distributor rotor on distributor shaft.
5. Rotate distributor shaft so blade on distributor rotor is pointing toward reference mark on distributor base made during removal procedure.
6. While installing, continue rotating distributor rotor slightly so leading edge of armature vane is centered in distributor stator.
7. Rotate distributor in engine front cover to align leading edge of vane and distributor stator. **Verify distributor rotor is pointing at reference mark on distributor base. If vane and distributor stator cannot be aligned by rotating distributor in engine front cover, remove distributor enough to just disengage distributor gear from camshaft sprocket. Rotate distributor rotor enough to engage distributor gear on another tooth of the camshaft sprocket. Repeat step 2 if necessary.**
8. Install hold-down clamp and bolt, then tighten bolt, but leave it loose enough to rotate distributor.
9. Install distributor cap and ignition wires, **torque** distributor cap hold-down screws to 18-23 inch lbs.

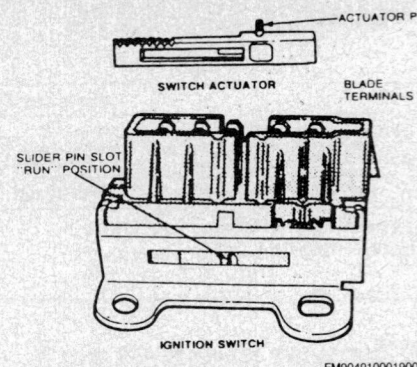

Fig. 1   Ignition switch replacement

10. Connect distributor to engine control sensor wiring.
11. Set ignition timing to specifications, then **torque** distributor hold-down bolt to 15-22 ft. lbs.
12. Recheck ignition timing. Adjust if necessary.

IGNITION LOCK
REPLACE
LOCK CYLINDER, FUNCTIONAL

The following procedures are for vehicles that have a functioning ignition switch lock cylinder, ignition key is available, or the lock cylinder key numbers are known and key can be made.

Cougar & Thunderbird

1. Disconnect battery ground cable.
2. **On models equipped with tilt column,** remove upper extension shroud by detaching from retaining clip at 9 o'clock position.
3. **On all models,** remove both trim shroud halves.
4. Disconnect key warning switch electrical connector.
5. Turn ignition key to "Run." Place gear selector lever in "Park" if equipped with column shift.
6. Insert a 1/8 inch diameter wire pin into hole in casting around lock cylinder. Remove lock cylinder while depressing retaining pin with wire.
7. Reverse procedure to install. Lock cylinder must be in "Run" and retaining pin depressed during installation. Following installation, turn key to check for correct operation in all positions.

Crown Victoria & Grand Marquis

1. Disconnect battery ground cable and turn lock cylinder to "RUN" position.
2. Insert a 1/8 inch diameter wire pin or small drift punch in hole in trim shroud under lock cylinder. Depress retaining pin while pulling out on lock cylinder to remove from column housing.
3. Install lock cylinder by turning to run position and depressing retaining pin. Insert lock cylinder into housing. En-

sure cylinder is fully seated and aligned in interlocking washer before turning key to "OFF." This will permit cylinder retaining pin to extend into cylinder housing hole.
4. Using key, rotate lock cylinder. Ensure correct mechanical operation in all positions. Connect battery ground cable.

LOCK CYLINDER, NON-FUNCTIONAL

The following procedure is for vehicles that have a inoperative ignition lock cylinder and the ignition switch cannot be rotated due to a lost or broken lock cylinder key, unknown key number, or an ignition switch cap that has been damaged to the extent that the key cannot be rotated.

1. Disconnect battery ground cable.
2. Remove steering wheel as described in "Steering Wheel, Replace."
3. Using channel lock or vise-grip type pliers, twist ignition cap or bezel until it separates from ignition switch.
4. Using a 3/8 inch diameter drill, drill down middle of key slot approximately 1 and 3/4 inches, until ignition switch lock cylinder breaks loose from breakaway base of ignition switch lock cylinder.
5. Remove lock cylinder and drill shavings from steering column tube flange.
6. Remove steering column upper bearing retainer, steering column lock housing bearing, ignition switch lock cylinder and steering column lock gear. Thoroughly clean all drill shavings and other foreign material from casting.
7. Install new ignition lock cylinder as described in "Lock Cylinder, Functional."

IGNITION SWITCH
REPLACE
COUGAR & THUNDERBIRD

1. Disconnect battery ground cable.
2. Remove steering column lower shroud, then remove four nuts holding column assembly to column mounting bracket.
3. Remove steering column shroud attaching screws, then the steering column shroud.
4. Disconnect ignition switch electrical connector, **Fig. 1,** then rotate ignition key lock cylinder to "Run" position.
5. Remove switch to lock cylinder attaching screws.
6. Remove ignition switch from actuator pin.
7. Adjust ignition switch by sliding carrier to "Run" position. **A new replacement switch assembly will be preset in "Run" position.**
8. Place ignition key lock cylinder in "Run" position by rotating cylinder approximately 90° from "Lock" position.
9. Install ignition switch on actuator pin. **Slightly move switch back and forth to align mounting holes with column lock housing threaded holes.**

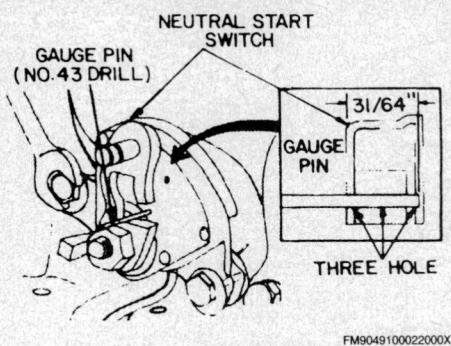

Fig. 2 Neutral safety switch replacement. Cougar & Thunderbird

10. Install switch to lock cylinder attaching bolts and **torque** bolts to 50-60 inch lbs.
11. Connect switch electrical connector.
12. Install steering column trim shrouds, then check ignition for proper operation.

CROWN VICTORIA & GRAND MARQUIS

1. Remove steering column shroud by removing self-tapping screws. Remove tilt lever if equipped.
2. Remove instrument panel lower steering column cover.
3. Disconnect ignition switch electrical connector.
4. Rotate ignition key lock cylinder to "RUN" position, then remove two screws retaining ignition switch.
5. Disconnect ignition switch from actuator.
6. Reverse procedure to install, noting the following:
   a. If necessary, move switch slightly back and forth to align mounting holes with column mounting holes.
   b. Ensure proper operation of ignition switch in all positions.

NEUTRAL SAFETY SWITCH
REPLACE

COUGAR & THUNDERBIRD

A4LD

1. Remove downshift linkage rod from transmission downshift lever.
2. Apply penetrating oil to downshift lever shaft and nut; then remove downshift outer lever.
3. Remove switch attaching bolts.
4. Disconnect multiple wire connector and remove switch from transmission.
5. Install new switch.
6. With transmission manual lever in neutral, rotate switch and install gauge pin (No. 43 drill) into gauge pin holes, **Fig. 2. Shank end of drill must be inserted approximately** 15/32 **inch into each of the gauge pin holes.**
7. Tighten switch attaching bolts and remove gauge pin.
8. Reverse remainder of procedure to install.

AOD

1. Disconnect battery ground cable.
2. Place transmission gear selector in manual Low position.
3. Raise and support vehicle.
4. Disconnect electrical connector from neutral start switch. Lift connector straight up off switch using a long screwdriver under rubber plug of connector.
5. Remove switch and O-ring using socket tool No. T74P-77247-A or equivalent. **Use of any tools other than those specified may result in damage to vehicle.**
6. Reverse procedure to install. **Torque** switch to 7-10 ft. lbs.

CROWN VICTORIA & GRAND MARQUIS

1. Disconnect battery ground cable.
2. Remove air cleaner assembly.
3. Place transmission selector lever in manual low position, then disconnect neutral safety switch electrical connector from switch. Lift connector straight off without any side-to-side motion.
4. Remove switch and O-ring using a 24 inch extension, universal adapter and socket tool No. T74P-77247-A. **Use of any tools other than those specified may result in damage to vehicle.**
5. Reverse procedure to install. **Torque** switch to 7-10 ft. lbs.

TRANSMISSION RANGE SENSOR
REPLACE

1. Disconnect battery ground cable.
2. Place manual control lever in neutral.
3. Raise and support vehicle.
4. Disconnect range sensor electrical connector.
5. Remove two range sensor to transmission attaching bolts, then the sensor from the transmission.
6. Reverse procedure to install, noting the following:
   a. Loosely install two attaching bolts.
   b. Align range sensor slots using Transmission Range Sensor Alignment Tool No. T92P-70010-AH or equivalent.
   c. **Torque** attaching bolts to 7-9 ft. lbs.

HEADLAMP SWITCH
REPLACE

COUGAR & THUNDERBIRD

1. Disconnect battery ground cable.
2. Remove two cluster trim panel retaining screws.
3. Pull off headlamp switch knob and snap off cluster trim panel.
4. Disconnect electrical connector to headlamp dimmer sensor assembly.
5. With headlamp switch in full On position, using opening in instrument panel, depress shaft release button on

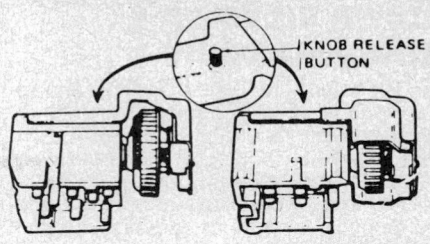

Fig. 3 Headlamp switch replacement. Crown Victoria & Grand Marquis

switch and remove shaft.
6. Remove headlamp switch retaining nut and pull switch through opening to disconnect wiring connector.
7. Reverse procedure to install.

CROWN VICTORIA & GRAND MARQUIS

1. Under instrument panel, depress light switch knob and shaft retainer button on side of switch and, while holding button in, pull knob and shaft assembly from switch, **Fig. 3.**
2. Unscrew trim bezel and remove locknut.
3. From under instrument panel, pull switch from panel while tilting downward, disconnect electrical connector and remove switch.
4. Reverse procedure to install.

STOP LIGHT SWITCH
REPLACE

1. Disconnect battery ground cable and disconnect wires at switch connector.
2. Remove hairpin retainer and slide stop light switch, pushrod, nylon washers and bushings away from brake pedal, and remove switch, **Fig. 4.**
3. Reverse procedure to install.

MULTI-FUNCTION SWITCH
REPLACE

COUGAR & THUNDERBIRD

1. Disconnect battery ground cable.
2. Remove lower left finish panel retaining bolts and carefully pull to disengage retaining clips.
3. Remove lower left reinforcement panel retaining bolts and remove panel.
4. Remove steering column lower shroud retaining screws and remove lower shroud.
5. Remove steering column retaining nuts, then remove column upper shroud.
6. Disconnect switch electrical connectors.
7. Remove switch retaining bolts, then remove switch.
8. Reverse procedure to install.

CROWN VICTORIA & GRAND MARQUIS

1. Tilt column to lowest position and remove tilt lever, if equipped.
2. Remove ignition lock cylinder.
3. Remove shroud screws, then remove upper and lower shrouds.
4. Remove two screws attaching multi-function switch to steering column casting. Disengage switch from casting.
5. Disconnect two electrical connectors.
6. Reverse procedure to install, **torque** retaining screws to 18-26 inch lbs.

TURN SIGNAL SWITCH
REPLACE

COUGAR & THUNDERBIRD

1. Disconnect battery ground cable.
2. Remove trim shroud or shroud halves.
3. Remove turn signal switch lever from switch. Grasp lever and use a pulling and twisting motion while pulling lever straight out from switch.
4. Peel back foam shield from turn signal switch, then disconnect two electrical connectors from switch.
5. Remove turn signal switch attaching screws, then remove switch.
6. Reverse procedure to install.

CROWN VICTORIA & GRAND MARQUIS

1. Disconnect battery ground cable.
2. **On models with tilt column,** unsnap extension shroud, located below steering wheel, from retaining clip.
3. **On all models,** remove attaching screws, then remove steering column trim shroud.
4. Remove turn signal switch lever by grasping lever and using a pulling twisting motion of the hand, while pulling lever straight out of switch.
5. Peel foam sight shield from switch, then disconnect two turn signal switch wire connectors.
6. Remove two screws attaching turn signal switch to lock cylinder housing, then disengage switch from housing.
7. Reverse procedure to install.

HORN SOUNDER
REPLACE

MODELS EQUIPPED W/TURN SIGNAL MOUNTED SWITCH

Horn sounder is located on the turn signal, headlight dimmer and horn lever. Refer to "Turn Signal Switch, Replace" when replacing switch.
1. Disconnect battery ground cable.
2. Pry switch cover off top. Use caution not to damage cover when removing.
3. Remove switch attaching screws, then lift switch from steering wheel. Use caution not to loose contact spring.

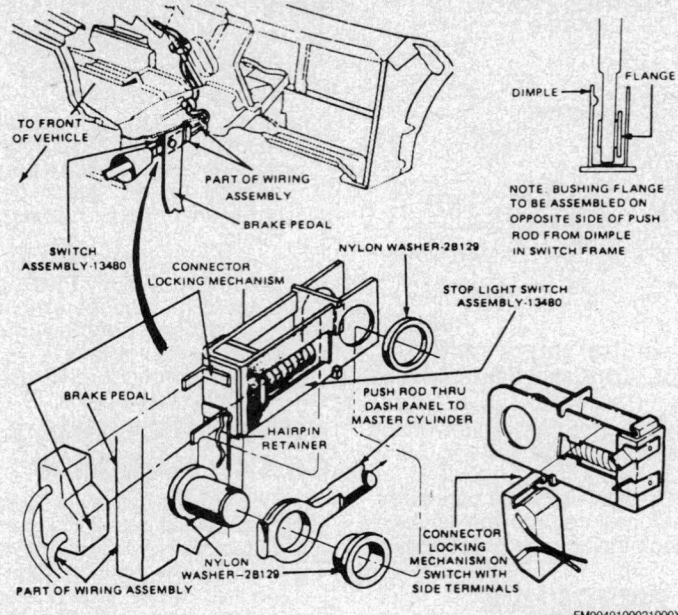

Fig. 4 Stop lamp switch replacement

4. Reverse procedure to install.

STEERING WHEEL
REPLACE

MODELS LESS PASSIVE RESTRAINT SYSTEM

1. Disconnect battery ground cable.
2. Remove horn pad and cover assembly.
3. Disconnect horn wire and speed control wiring, if equipped.
4. Remove and discard steering wheel nut.
5. Mark relationship between steering shaft and steering wheel hub for proper reinstallation.
6. Remove steering wheel with a suitable puller.
7. Reverse procedure to install. **Torque** new steering wheel bolt to 23-33 ft. lbs.

MODELS w/PASSIVE RESTRAINT SYSTEM

1. Center front wheels to straight ahead position.
2. Remove air bag module from steering wheel.
3. Disconnect speed control wire harness from steering wheel.
4. Remove and discard steering wheel retaining bolt, then install steering wheel puller tool No. T67L-3600-A or equivalent and remove steering wheel.
5. Route contact assembly wire harness through steering wheel as wheel is lifted off of shaft.
6. Reverse procedure to install, noting the following:

a. Route contact assembly wire harness through steering wheel opening at three o'clock position. Steering wheel and shaft alignment marks should be aligned.
b. Ensure air bag contact wire is not pinched and speed control wiring does not get trapped between steering wheel and contact assembly.
c. **Torque** steering wheel retaining bolt to 22-33 ft. lbs.
d. **Torque** air bag module retaining nuts to 36-47 inch lbs.

INSTRUMENT CLUSTER
REPLACE

COUGAR & THUNDERBIRD
1992—93

Standard Cluster

1. Disconnect battery ground cable.
2. Remove two retaining screws from cluster trim panel and remove trim panel.
3. Remove four cluster mounting screws, **Fig. 5,** then pull bottom of cluster towards steering wheel.
4. Reach behind cluster and disconnect two connectors.
5. **On 3.8L/V6-232 Supercharged engines,** disconnect vacuum lines for booster gauge.
6. **On all models,** swing bottom of cluster to clear top of steering column shroud and remove.
7. Reverse procedure to install.

Electronic Cluster

1. Disconnect battery ground cable.

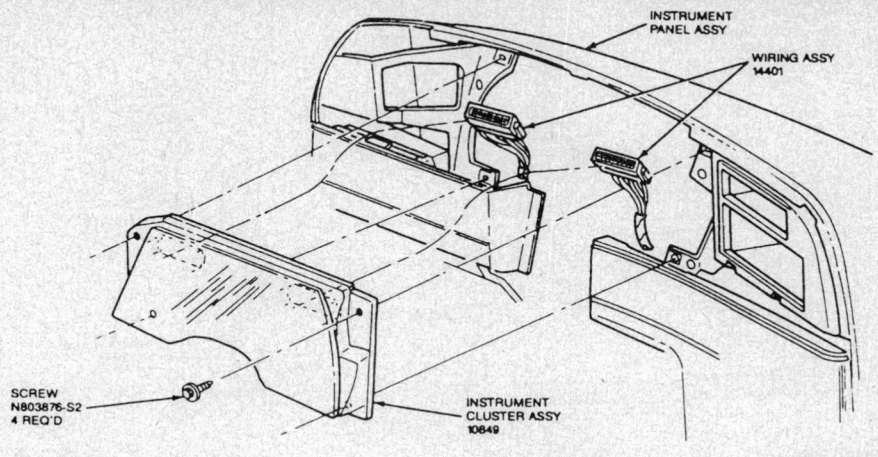

Fig. 5 Instrument cluster replacement. Cougar & Thunderbird

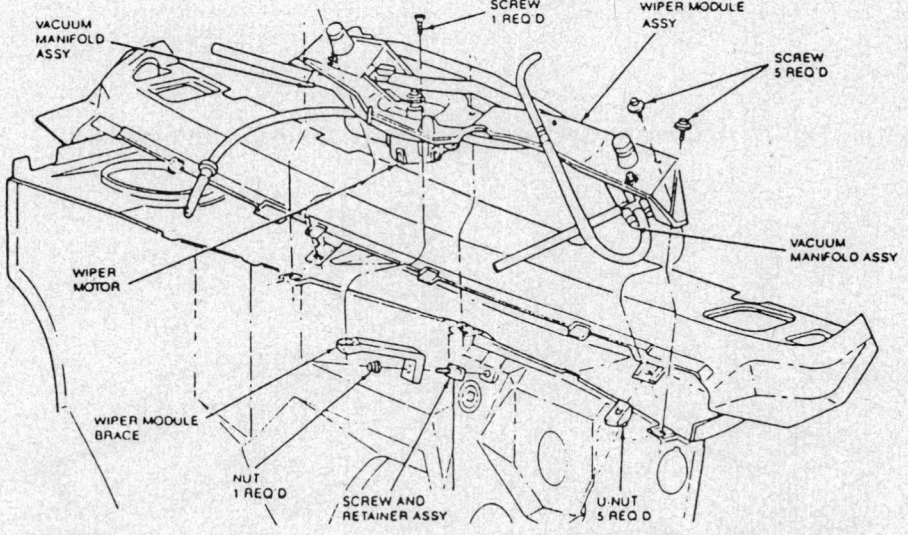

Fig. 6 Wiper motor replacement. Cougar & Thunderbird

8. Remove four screws retaining the instrument cluster to the instrument panel.
9. Pull instrument cluster out far enough to disconnect wiring and hoses.
10. Remove instrument cluster.
11. Reverse procedure to install.

CROWN VICTORIA & GRAND MARQUIS

Standard Cluster

1. Remove instrument cluster trim cover attaching screws and the trim cover.
2. Remove lower steering column cover attaching screws and the cover.
3. **On Grand Marquis models,** remove knee bolster.
4. **On all models,** remove steering column shroud lower half.
5. Remove screws securing transmission indicator column bracket to steering column. Detach cable loop from pin on shift lever and remove bracket from column.
6. Remove four instrument cluster attaching screws.
7. Disconnect cluster feed plug and remove cluster assembly from vehicle.
8. Reverse procedure to install.

Electronic Cluster

1. Set parking brake.
2. Unsnap center molding on left and right sides of instrument panel.
3. Remove steering column cover and column shroud.
4. Remove knobs from auto dim and auto lamp switches, if equipped.
5. Remove 13 screws retaining instrument panel and pull panel out.
6. Move shift lever to 1 position for access.
7. Disconnect electrical connectors from warning lamp module, switch module and center panel switches, if equipped.
8. Remove instrument panel carefully, using caution to not scratch cluster lens.
9. Disconnect electrical connector from front of cluster.
10. Disconnect PRNDL assembly from cluster by carefully bending bottom tab down and pulling PRNDL assembly forward.
11. Pull cluster out and disconnect electrical connectors on rear of cluster.
12. Remove instrument cluster.
13. Reverse procedure to install.

RADIO
REPLACE

When installing radio, adjust antenna trimmer for peak performance.
1. Disconnect battery ground cable.
2. Install radio removal tool No. T87P-19061-A or equivalent, into face plate. Push tools in approximately one inch to release retaining clips.
3. Slightly spread tools and pull radio from dash.
4. Disconnect power, antenna and speaker leads from radio.

---

2. Remove headlamp knob, then remove cluster finish panel by removing two screws located on upper inside surface.
3. Carefully pull away finish panel while detaching spring clips surrounding finish panel.
4. Disconnect connector on rear of switch assembly.
5. Disconnect autolamp module, if equipped.
6. Place clean soft cloth over steering column shroud to prevent damage, then remove four cluster retaining screws and pull bottom of cluster towards steering wheel.
7. Place clean soft cloth over lens, to prevent scratching.
8. Reach behind cluster and disconnect two electrical connectors.
9. Swing bottom of cluster out to clear top of cluster from crash pad and remove.
10. Reverse procedure to install.

1994–95

1. Disconnect battery ground cable.
2. Remove lower instrument panel steering column cover by removing three screws along bottom and pull on instrument panel steering column cover to unsnap three clips across top of instrument panel steering column cover.
3. Remove steering column shrouds.
4. Remove two screws retaining cluster finish panel above the instrument cluster face.
5. Pull cluster instrument panel finish panel to unsnap one retaining clip above the lefthand A/C register.
6. Pull cluster finish panel to unsnap three retaining clips on right side vertical edge.
7. Pull cluster finish panel away from instrument panel far enough to disconnect the wiring connectors. Remove the finish panel.

5. Reverse procedure to install. Ensure rear bracket is engaged on lower support rail.

WIPER MOTOR
REPLACE

COUGAR & THUNDERBIRD

1. Disconnect battery ground cable.
2. With wipers in Park position, remove arm and blade assemblies.
3. Remove left cowl vent screen.
4. Remove vacuum manifolds from wiper module, **Fig. 6.**
5. Disconnect wiring connectors, then remove five bolts and one nut from wiper module and remove module.
6. Remove crankpin clip, then disconnect linkage drive arm from motor crankpin.
7. Remove three motor attaching screws, pull motor from opening.
8. Reverse procedure to install, ensuring that wiper motor is in the park position prior to installation.

CROWN VICTORIA & GRAND MARQUIS

1. Disconnect battery ground cable.
2. Remove rear hood seal and wiper arm assemblies.
3. Remove cowl vent screens. Disconnect washer hoses from washer jets.
4. Remove wiper assembly retaining screws and lift assembly out. Disconnect washer hose.
5. Disconnect electrical connectors from wiper motor.
6. Reverse procedure to install.

WIPER SWITCH
REPLACE

COUGAR & THUNDERBIRD

1. Disconnect battery ground cable.
2. Remove four steering column shroud attaching screws, then grasp top and bottom of shroud and separate.
3. Using a screwdriver, disconnect wire connector from wiper switch.
4. Remove two wiper switch attaching screws, then remove switch.
5. Reverse procedure to install.

CROWN VICTORIA & GRAND MARQUIS

1. Disconnect battery ground cable.
2. Remove steering column cover screws and separate the two halves.
3. Remove wiper switch retaining screws, disconnect wiring connector and remove switch.
4. Reverse procedure to install.

WIPER TRANSMISSION
REPLACE

CROWN VICTORIA & GRAND MARQUIS

1. Disconnect battery ground cable.
2. Remove wiper arm and blade assemblies from pivot shafts. Remove rear hood seal.
3. Remove wiper motor and linkage cover for access to linkage.
4. Disconnect linkage drive arm from motor crank pin by removing retaining clip.
5. Remove six bolts retaining left and right pivot shafts to cowl, and remove the complete linkage assembly.
6. Reverse procedure to install.

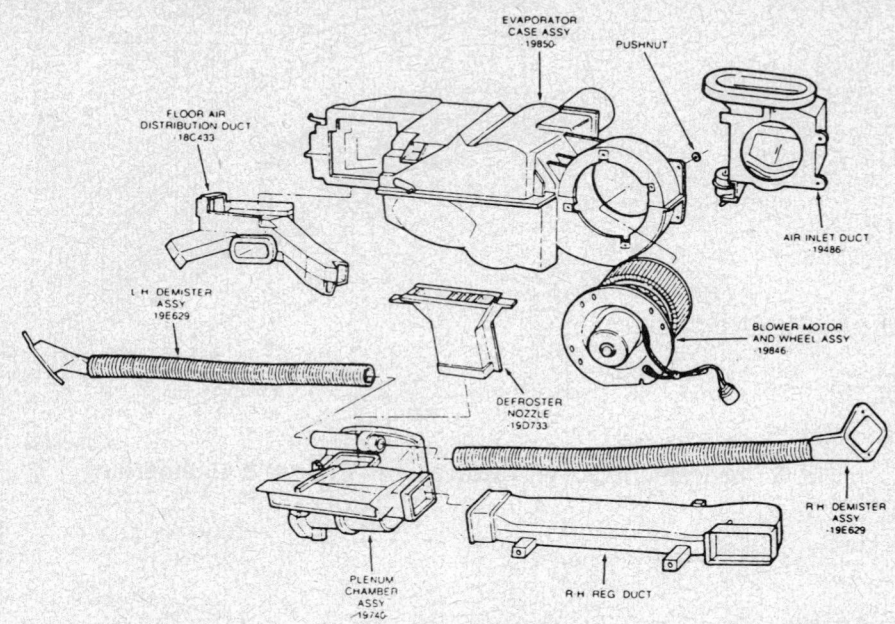

Fig. 7   A/C-heater system components. Cougar & Thunderbird

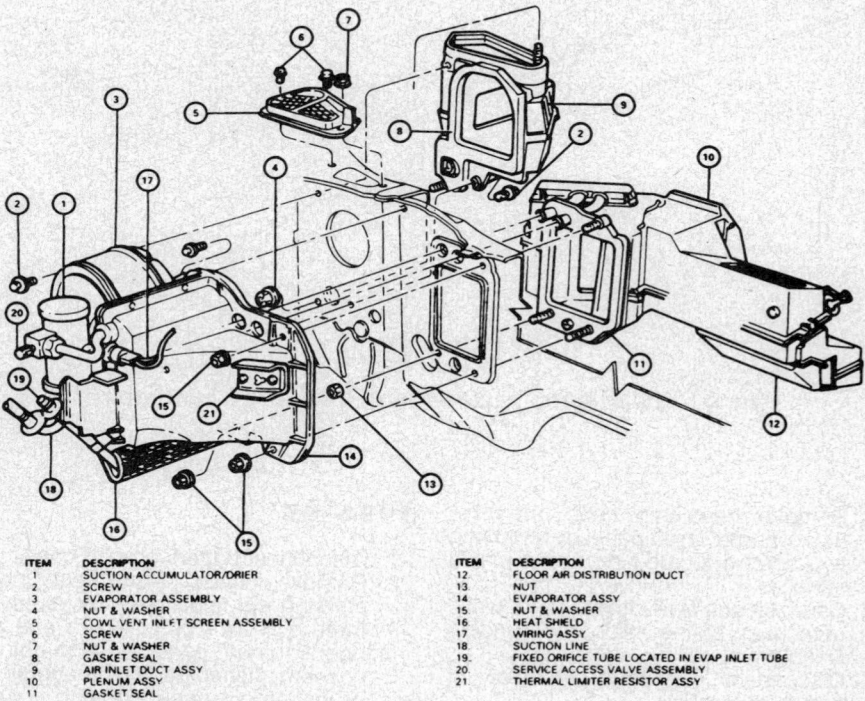

ITEM	DESCRIPTION	ITEM	DESCRIPTION
1	SUCTION ACCUMULATOR/DRIER	12	FLOOR AIR DISTRIBUTION DUCT
2	SCREW	13	NUT
3	EVAPORATOR ASSEMBLY	14	EVAPORATOR ASSY
4	NUT & WASHER	15	NUT & WASHER
5	COWL VENT INLET SCREEN ASSEMBLY	16	HEAT SHIELD
6	SCREW	17	WIRING ASSY
7	NUT & WASHER	18	SUCTION LINE
8	GASKET SEAL	19	FIXED ORIFICE TUBE LOCATED IN EVAP INLET TUBE
9	AIR INLET DUCT ASSY	20	SERVICE ACCESS VALVE ASSEMBLY
10	PLENUM ASSY	21	THERMAL LIMITER RESISTOR ASSY
11	GASKET SEAL		

FM7029100038000X

Fig. 8   A/C-heater system components. Crown Victoria & Grand Marquis

BLOWER MOTOR
REPLACE

COUGAR & THUNDERBIRD

1. Disconnect battery ground cable.
2. Remove glove compartment liner, then disconnect blower motor wire connector.

3. Remove four screws and pull blower motor outward, **Fig. 7.**
4. Remove push nuts from blower motor shaft and slide blower wheel off shaft.
5. Reverse procedure to install.

CROWN VICTORIA & GRAND MARQUIS

1. Disconnect battery ground cable.
2. Disconnect all blower motor electrical wires and connectors.
3. Remove blower motor cooling tube, then the mounting screws.
4. Rotate blower motor slightly to the right so bottom edge of mounting plate follows contour of wheelwell splash panel. Then, lift blower motor up and out of housing assembly.
5. Reverse procedure to install.

HEATER CORE
REPLACE
COUGAR & THUNDERBIRD

1. Disconnect battery ground cable.
2. Remove instrument panel as described in the "Dash Panel Service" section.
3. Remove right instrument panel brace located above heater case and attached to cowl.
4. Drain engine coolant and remove hoses from heater core, then plug hoses and the core.
5. Disconnect vacuum supply hose from in-line vacuum check valve in engine compartment.
6. Disconnect blower motor wire harness from resistor and motor lead.
7. Working under the hood, remove three heater assembly to dash panel retaining nuts.
8. In passenger compartment, remove heater assembly support bracket to cowl top panel attaching screw.
9. Remove one bracket to dash panel retaining screw below heater assembly.
10. Carefully remove heater assembly away from dash panel and remove heater assembly from vehicle, **Fig. 7.**
11. Remove four heater core access cover attaching screws, then the access cover from case.
12. Remove seal from heater core tubes, then remove heater core.
13. Reverse procedure to install.

CROWN VICTORIA & GRAND MARQUIS

1. Disconnect battery ground cable, then drain cooling system.
2. Disconnect heater hoses from heater core. Plug heater hoses and core fittings to prevent coolant spillage.
3. Remove bolt located below windshield wiper motor, attaching left end of plenum to dash panel.
4. Remove nut attaching upper left corner of evaporator or heater case to dash panel.

5. Disconnect vacuum control system supply hose from vacuum source, then push grommet and hose into passenger compartment.
6. Remove all instrument panel retaining screws and pull instrument panel back as far as possible without disconnecting any wire harnesses.
7. Loosen right door sill plate and remove side cowl trim panel.
8. Disengage temperature control cable housing from bracket on top of plenum. Disconnect cable from temperature blend door crank arm.
9. **On models w/automatic temperature control (ATC),** remove cross body brace and disconnect wiring harness from temperature blend door actuator and disconnect ATC sensor tube from evaporator case connector.
10. **On all models,** disconnect vacuum harness at vacuum connector near floor air distribution duct.
11. Disconnect white vacuum hose from outside recirculating air door vacuum motor.
12. Remove two hush panels.
13. Remove one plastic push fastener retaining floor air distribution duct to left end of plenum. Remove left screw and loosen right screw on rear face of plenum. Remove floor air distribution duct.
14. Remove two screws from rear side of floor air distribution duct to plenum, **Fig. 8.** To remove right screw, it may be necessary to remove the two screws attaching lower panel door vacuum motor to mounting bracket.
15. Remove push fastener attaching floor air distribution duct to left end of plenum, then remove floor air distribution duct.
16. Remove two nuts located along lower flange of plenum.
17. Carefully move plenum rearward, so that heater core tubes and plenum case upper stud clear openings in dash panel, then remove plenum from vehicle by rotating upper portion of the plenum forward, down and out from under instrument panel. It may be necessary to carefully pull lower edge of instrument panel rearward while plenum is being removed from behind instrument panel.
18. Remove retaining screws from heater core cover, then the cover from plenum assembly.
19. Remove retaining screw from heater core inlet and outlet tube bracket.
20. Pull heater core and seal assembly from plenum assembly.
21. Reverse procedure to install.

EVAPORATOR CORE
REPLACE

COUGAR & THUNDERBIRD

1. Disconnect battery ground cable.
2. Remove instrument panel as de-

scribed in "Dash Panel Service" section.
3. Discharge A/C refrigerant system.
4. Disconnect and cap high and lower pressure hoses.
5. Disconnect and cap refrigerant line from accumulator drier.
6. Drain engine coolant and remove hoses from heater core, then plug hoses and the core.
7. Disconnect blower motor wiring.
8. Working under the hood, remove three heater assembly to dash panel retaining nuts.
9. In passenger compartment, remove evaporator case assembly support bracket to cowl top panel attaching screw.
10. Remove one bracket to dash panel retaining screw below evaporator case assembly.
11. Carefully remove evaporator case assembly away from dash panel and remove heater assembly from vehicle, **Fig. 7.**
12. Using a small saw, cut top of evaporator case between dotted line, then remove evaporator core.
13. Reverse procedure to install. An evaporator core cover kit is available for installation.

CROWN VICTORIA & GRAND MARQUIS

1. Disconnect battery ground cable, then drain cooling system.
2. Disconnect and cap suction hose from accumulator drier.
3. Disconnect liquid line from evaporator inlet tube. Position liquid line away from evaporator assembly.
4. Disconnect 2 electrical connectors from de-ice switch in accumulator drier.
5. Disconnect heater hoses from heater core tubes.
6. Remove six right hand hood seal bracket assembly attaching screws, then remove ground strap and fold hood seal toward left hand side.
7. Disconnect and position aside all wiring and vacuum hoses attached to evaporator case.
8. Disconnect blower motor wiring.
9. From passenger side of dash panel, fold carpeting back on right hand side of floor, remove bottom left hand screw that supports inlet recirculation air duct.
10. From engine side of dash panel, one upper and two lower nuts from evaporator case mounting studs. Also remove two screws from blower motor portion of case.
11. Pull bottom of evaporator case assembly away from dash to disengage mounting studs, then pull top of case outward to disengage upper stud.
12. Remove evaporator case from vehicle, **Fig. 8.**
13. Separate evaporator case halves and remove evaporator core.
14. Reverse procedure to install.

3.8L/V6-232 Engine

INDEX

PRECAUTIONS

FUEL PRESSURE RELIEF

Release pressure from fuel system at the fuel pressure relief valve using tool No. T80L-9974-B or equivalent. When relieving fuel pressure, crank engine with fuel pump electrical connector disconnected.

ENGINE MOUNT
REPLACE

Whenever self-locking mounting bolts and nuts are removed, they must be replaced with new self-locking bolts and nuts.
1. Remove fan shroud attaching screws, then remove air tube from remote air cleaner.
2. Raise and support vehicle, then support engine using a jack and wood block placed below engine.
3. Remove insulator to front subframe through bolts, **Fig. 1.**
4. Disconnect shift linkage, then raise engine enough to clear clevis brackets.
5. Remove accessories and oil cooler line attaching clips from engine support brackets.
6. Remove bolts attaching insulator bracket assembly to engine, then remove insulator and bracket. **Left front engine mount removal on 3.8L/V6-232 Supercharged engine may require lowering front subframe.**
7. Reverse procedure to install. Tighten to specifications.

ENGINE
REPLACE

1. Disconnect battery ground cable and drain engine coolant.
2. Mark position of hood hinges and remove hood.
3. Remove left cowl vent screen and wiper module.

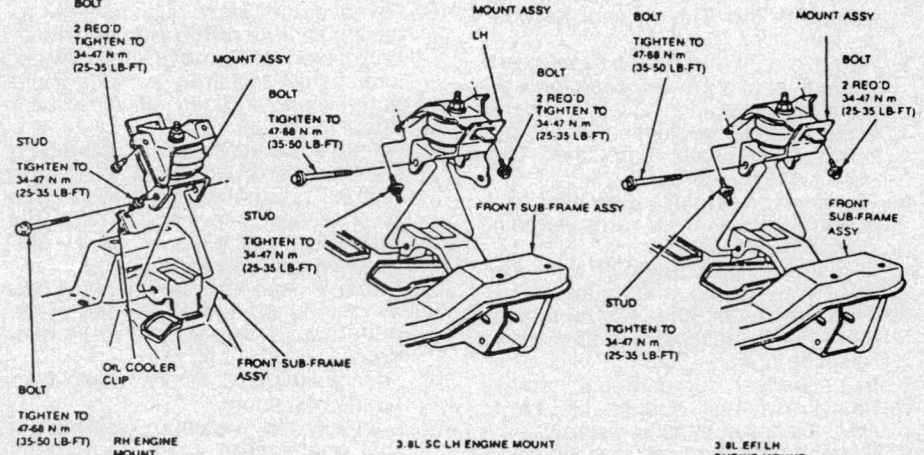

Fig. 1 Engine mount removal

4. Disconnect alternator to voltage regulator wiring harness.
5. **On 3.8L/V6-232 Supercharged engine,** remove upper intercooler tube from supercharger and cooler assemblies. Remove bolt retaining cooler tube to power steering bracket and remove tube.
6. **On all models,** remove radiator upper sight shield, release belt tension and remove belts.
7. Remove air cleaner to throttle body tube assembly, then disconnect cooling fan and motor assembly connector.
8. Remove fan shroud, fan assembly and upper radiator hose.
9. Disconnect automatic transmission oil cooler tubes from radiator, then disconnect heater hoses.
10. Disconnect lower radiator hose at water pump, then remove radiator retaining bolts and radiator assembly.
11. **On 3.8L/V6-232 Supercharged engines,** remove two push pins attaching intercooler to radiator.
12. **On all engines except 3.8L/V6-232 Supercharged,** disconnect power steering pump and bracket and position aside.
13. **On all models,** discharge A/C system as described in "Air Conditioning" section.
14. Disconnect A/C compressor clutch electrical connector and compressor lines. Cap or plug open A/C lines.
15. Remove A/C compressor retaining bolts, then the compressor.
16. Remove radiator coolant recovery reservoir.
17. Remove wiring shield, then the accelerator cable mounting bracket and position aside.
18. Release fuel system pressure, then disconnect fuel inlet & return hose.
19. Disconnect ECM electrical connector, engine feed harnesses and vacuum lines.

20. **On non-Supercharged engines,** disconnect ground wire assembly and coil wire.
21. **On 3.8L/V6-232 Supercharged models,** disconnect DIS module wiring, then remove coil pack retaining bolts and position aside.
22. Remove nuts attaching lower intercooler tube to supercharger elbow, then remove intercooler tube bolts at power steering bracket.
23. Remove alternator bracket bolts, then disconnect alternator wiring and remove alternator.
24. Remove power steering pump, then bracket assembly and position aside.
25. **On all models,** disconnect canister purge line.
26. Disconnect one end of throttle control valve cable.
27. Raise vehicle on hoist, then drain oil and remove oil filter.
28. **On 3.8L/V6-232 Supercharged models,** remove two nuts attaching lower intercooler tube to intercooler, then remove intercooler.
29. **On all models,** remove exhaust pipe-to-manifold nuts, then remove left exhaust shield.
30. Disconnect heated exhaust gas oxygen (HEGO) sensor assembly.
31. Remove inspection plug, then the torque converter bolts.
32. Remove engine to transmission bolts, then remove engine mount bolts.
33. **On 3.8L/V6-232 Supercharged models,** remove left mount retaining strap.
34. **On all models,** remove crankshaft pulley assembly.
35. Remove starter motor assembly, ground cable and starter harness retainers from left and right sides.
36. Disconnect oil level indicator sensor. Partially lower vehicle, then disconnect oil pressure sending unit gauge assembly.
37. Position floor jack under transmission.
38. Position engine lifting equipment and remove engine assembly from vehicle.
39. Reverse procedure to install. Tighten to specifications.

INTAKE MANIFOLD
REPLACE

The following procedure has been revised by a Technical Service Bulletin.
1. Disconnect battery ground cable and drain engine cooling system.
2. Remove air cleaner assembly including air intake duct and heat tube.
3. Disconnect accelerator cable at throttle body assembly, then speed control cable, if equipped.
4. Disconnect transmission linkage at upper intake manifold.
5. Remove bolts from accelerator cable mounting bracket and position cables aside.
6. Disconnect fuel lines at injector fuel rail assembly.
7. **On 3.8L/V6-232 Supercharged models,** remove supercharger.
8. **On all models,** disconnect radiator

hose at thermostat housing, then the coolant bypass hose from manifold.
9. Remove heater tube as follows:
   a. Disconnect heater tube from intake manifold.
   b. Remove tube support bracket retaining nuts, then remove heater hose from rear of heater tube.
   c. Loosen hose clamp at heater elbow, then remove heater tube with hose attached.
   d. Remove heater tube with lines attached and set assembly aside.
10. Disconnect vacuum lines at fuel rail assembly and intake manifold, then disconnect necessary electrical connectors.
11. Remove A/C compressor support bracket, if equipped. Disconnect one PCV line from upper intake manifold and valve. Remove second PCV line from left rocker cover.
12. Remove throttle body assembly, then the EGR valve assembly from upper manifold.
13. Remove wiring retainer bracket from left front side of intake manifold and position aside with spark plug wires.
14. Remove upper intake manifold bolts and studs, then the upper intake manifold.
15. Remove injectors and fuel rail assembly.
16. Remove heater water outlet hose, then the lower intake manifold attaching bolts and studs.
17. Remove lower intake manifold. **The manifold is sealed at each end with RTV-type sealer. To break seal, it may be necessary to pry on front of manifold with a screwdriver blade. Use care to prevent damage to machined surfaces when prying with screwdriver.**
18. Remove and discard manifold side gaskets and end seals.
19. Reverse procedure to install, noting the following:
   a. Clean all cylinder head/block to intake manifold contact areas.
   b. Apply a dab of gasket and trim adhesive part No. 19B508-AA or equivalent to each cylinder head mating surface. Press new intake manifold gasket into place over locating dowels.
   c. Apply a 1/8 inch bead of silicone sealer D6AZ-19562-B or equivalent at each corner where cylinder head joins the cylinder block.
   d. Install front and rear intake manifold end seals, then carefully lower intake manifold into position on cylinder block and cylinder heads. Use locating dowels as necessary to guide manifold.
   e. **On non-supercharged engines,** install attaching bolts and studs. **Torque** in two steps; first to 8 ft. lbs., then to 11 ft. lbs., in sequence shown in **Fig. 2.**
   f. **On 3.8L/V6-232 Supercharged engines,** install attaching bolts and studs. **Torque** to 8-11 ft. lbs. in sequence shown in **Fig. 3.**
   g. Tighten EGR valve assembly

mounting bolts, throttle body mounting bolts and A/C compressor support bracket bolts to specifications.

CYLINDER HEAD
REPLACE
REMOVAL

1. Disconnect battery ground cable and drain cooling system.
2. Remove air cleaner assembly, air intake duct and heat tube.
3. Loosen accessory drive belt idlers and remove drive belts.
4. If left cylinder head is being removed, proceed as follows:
   a. Remove intercooler and intercooler tubes.
   b. Remove oil filler cap and power steering pump front mounting bracket attaching bolts.
   c. Remove alternator assembly and accessory drive belt main idler.
   d. Remove power steering pump/alternator bracket attaching bolts.
5. If right cylinder head is being removed, proceed as follows:
   a. Remove A/C compressor belt and main drive belt.
   b. Remove mounting bracket retaining bolts. Leave hoses connected and position compressor aside.
   c. Remove PCV valve.
6. **On all models,** remove upper intake manifold.
7. **On 3.8L/V6-232 Supercharged models,** remove supercharger.
8. **On all models,** remove valve rocker arm cover attaching screws and injector fuel rail assembly.
9. Remove lower intake manifold and exhaust manifolds.
10. Loosen rocker arm fulcrum retaining bolts enough to allow rocker arm to be lifted off pushrod and rotate to one side.
11. Remove pushrods. Note position of each rod for installation. Pushrods must be installed in original position.
12. Remove and discard cylinder head retaining bolts, then remove cylinder head.

INSTALLATION

Always use new cylinder head bolts. Torque retention with used bolts can vary, which may result in coolant or compression leakage at cylinder head mating surface.
1. Position cylinder head and new gasket on dowels for alignment.
2. Apply a thin coating of Pipe Sealant w/Teflon part No. D8AZ-19554-A or equivalent to threads of short cylinder head bolts. **Do not apply to long bolts.**
3. Install cylinder head bolts in sequence shown in **Fig. 4. Torque** in five steps: first to 37 ft. lbs., then to 45 ft. lbs., 52 ft. lbs., 59 ft. lbs. and finally back off each bolt 2-3 turns.

4. **On 3.8L/V6-232 Supercharged engines,** final torque cylinder head bolts in sequence shown in **Fig. 4,** as follows:
   a. **Torque** to 48-55 ft. lbs.
   b. Rotate an additional 90-110°.
   c. Go to next bolt in sequence.
5. **On 3.8L/V6-232 non-supercharged engines,** final torque bolts in sequence shown in **Fig. 4,** as follows:
   a. **Torque** bolts to 11-18 ft. lbs.
   b. Rotate long bolts an additional 85-105°.
   c. Rotate short bolts an additional 65-85°.
   d. Go to next bolt in sequence.
6. Dip each pushrod end in Oil Conditioner D9AZ-19579-CA or equivalent, then install each pushrod in original position.
7. For each valve, rotate crankshaft until valve lifter rests on heel (base circle) of camshaft lobe. **Torque** fulcrum attaching bolts to initial value of 43 inch lbs.
8. Lubricate all rocker arm assemblies with Oil Conditioner D9AZ-19579-CA or equivalent heavy engine oil. Final **torque** fulcrum bolts to 19-25 ft. lbs.
9. Install exhaust manifolds and lower intake manifold. Tighten to specifications.
10. Install injector fuel rail assembly.
11. Install rocker cover and gasket. Tighten to specifications.
12. Install upper intake manifold and supercharger, if equipped. Tighten to specifications.
13. Reverse remainder of removal procedure to complete installation. Tighten to specifications.

VALVE ARRANGEMENT

FRONT TO REAR

Right Side .... I-E-I-E-I-E
Left Side .... E-I-E-I-E-I

VALVE LIFTERS

1. Disconnect secondary ignition wires from spark plugs using wire remover T74P-6666-A or equivalent. Remove ignition wire routing clips from rocker arm cover attaching bolt studs and position wires aside.
2. Remove intake manifold, refer to "Intake Manifold, Replace."
3. Remove rocker arm covers. On engines with stud mounted rocker arms, loosen stud nuts and rotate rocker arms to one side. On other engines, remove fulcrum bolt, fulcrum, rocker arm and fulcrum guide (if used).
4. Remove pushrods in sequence so they can be installed in their original bores.
5. Remove lifter guide retainer bolts, retainer and guide plate, if equipped.
6. Using a magnet rod, remove lifters and place in a numbered rack so they can be installed in their original bores. If lifters are stuck in bores by exces-

INSTALL BOLTS/STUD AS SHOWN AND TIGHTEN IN NUMERICAL SEQUENCE IN TWO SEPARATE STEPS AS FOLLOWS:

STEP 1 — 11 N·m (8 LB-FT)
STEP 2 — 15 N·m (11 LB-FT)

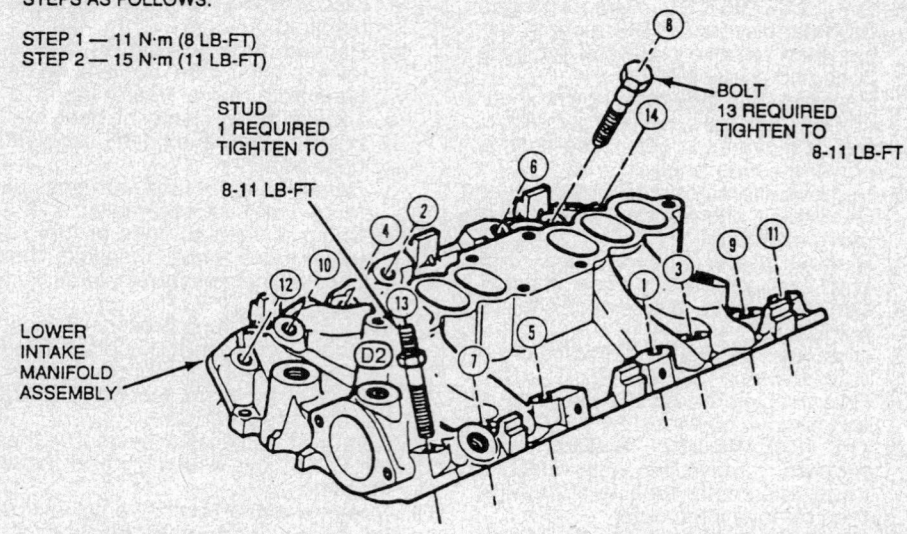

Fig. 2 Intake manifold tightening sequence. Except 3.8L/V6-232 Supercharged engines

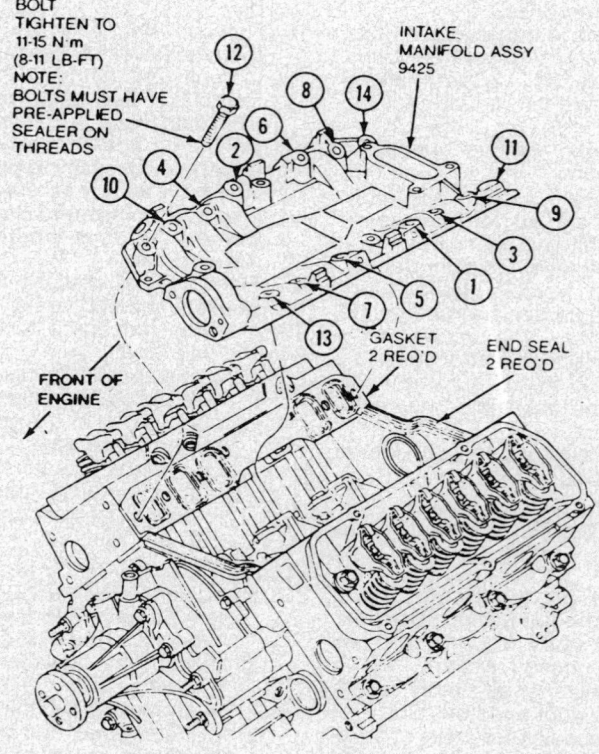

INSTALL BOLTS AS SHOWN AND TIGHTEN IN NUMERICAL SEQUENCE IN TWO SEPARATE STEPS AS FOLLOWS: 11 N·m (8 LB-FT) 15 N·m (11 LB-FT)

Fig. 3 Intake manifold tightening sequence. 3.8L/V6-232 Supercharged engines

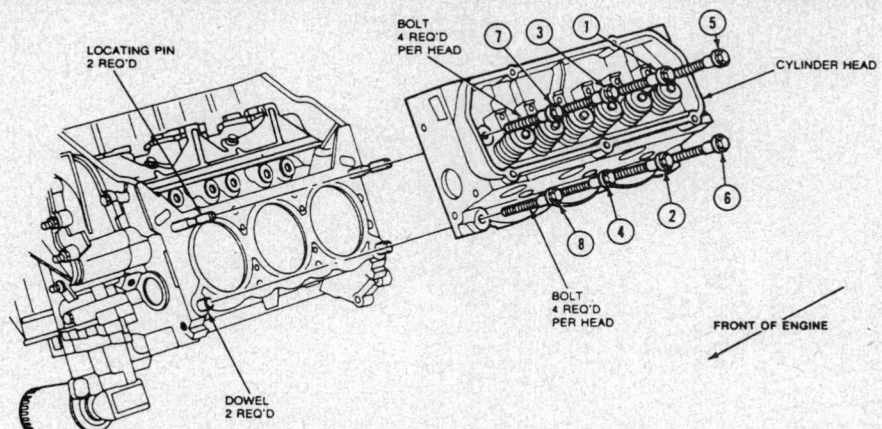

Fig. 4   Cylinder head tightening sequence

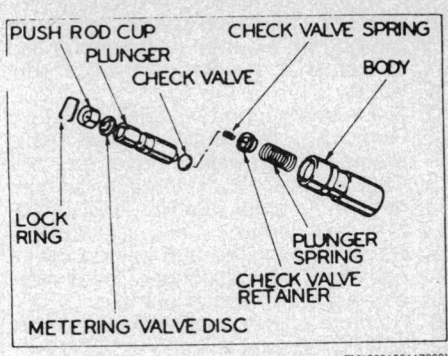

Fig. 5   Hydraulic valve lifter

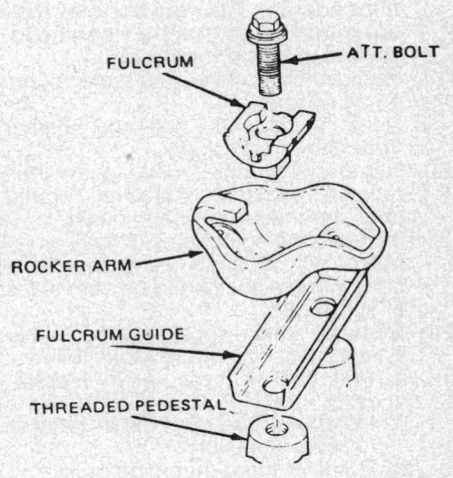

Fig. 7   Rocker arm assembly

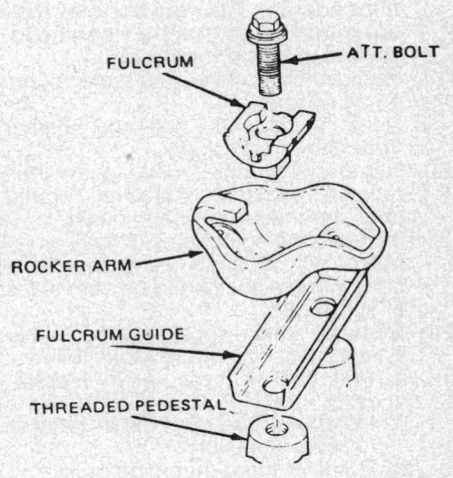

Fig. 6   Compressing lifter to check valve clearance

sive varnish, etc., it may be necessary to use a plier-type tool to remove. Rotate lifter back and forth to loosen from gum or varnish.

7. The internal parts of each lifter are matched sets. Do not intermix parts. Keep assemblies intact until they are to be cleaned, **Fig. 5**.

VALVE LIFT SPECIFICATIONS

Engine 3.8L/V6-232	Year 1992-95	Intake, Inch .424	Exhaust, Inch .447

CAMSHAFT LOBE LIFT SPECIFICATIONS

Engine 3.8L/V6-232	Year 1992-95	Intake, Inch .245	Exhaust, Inch .259

VALVE CLEARANCE SPECIFICATIONS

Correct valve clearance is .09-.19 inch.

VALVE ADJUSTMENT

A .060 inch longer or a .060 inch shorter pushrod is available to compensate for dimensional changes in the valve train. If clearance is less than specified, the .060 inch shorter pushrod should be used. If clearance is more than the maximum specified, the .060 inch longer pushrod should be used.

Using an auxiliary starter switch crankshaft until No. 1 cylinder is at TDC compression stroke, then compress valve lifter using tool T82C-6500-A or equivalent, **Fig. 6**. At this point, the following valves can be checked: intake Nos. 1, 3 and 6; exhaust Nos. 1, 2 and 4.

After clearance on these valves has been checked, rotate crankshaft until No. 5 cylinder is at TDC compression stroke (1 revolution of crankshaft), and then compress valve lifter using tool No. T82C-6500-A or equivalent, **Fig. 6**, and check the following valves: intake Nos. 2, 4 and 5; exhaust Nos. 3, 5 and 6.

ROCKER ARMS

These engines use stamped steel rocker arms retained by a fulcrum seat which bolts directly to the cylinder head and guides the rocker arm, **Fig. 7**. Torque fulcrum bolts in two steps as follows: For each valve rotate crankshaft until valve lifter rests on heel (base circle) of camshaft lobe and torque fulcrum bolt to 5-11 ft. lbs. After initial torquing of all fulcrum bolts, final torque to 19-25 ft. lbs. Final torque may be done with camshaft in any position.

VALVE GUIDES

Valve guides consist of holes bored in the cylinder head. For service the guide holes can be reamed oversize to accommodate valves with oversize stems of .015 and .030 inch.

FRONT COVER
REPLACE

To replace seal in timing gear cover, it is necessary to remove cover as outlined below.

1. Disconnect battery ground cable and drain cooling system.
2. Remove air cleaner and air intake duct.
3. **On 3.8L/V6-232 Supercharged engines**, remove electric cooling fan assembly.
4. **On non-supercharged engines**, remove fan/clutch assembly.
5. **On all models**, remove drive belts and water pump pulley.
6. Remove power steering pump mounting bracket bolts, if equipped. Leave hoses connected and position pump assembly aside.
7. Remove A/C compressor support bracket, if equipped. Leave compressor in place.
8. Disconnect coolant bypass hose and heater hoses at water pump and upper radiator hose at thermostat housing.
9. Disconnect ignition coil secondary wire from distributor cap, then remove distributor cap with ignition wires attached.
10. **On non-supercharged engines**, with No. 1 cylinder at TDC compression stroke, mark position of rotor to distributor housing and position of distributor housing to front cover.
11. Remove distributor hold-down clamp, then lift distributor from front cover.

12. **On 3.8L/V6-232 Supercharged engines,** remove hold-down clamp and lift camshaft synchronizer from front cover.
13. Raise and support vehicle.
14. Remove crankshaft pulley using crankshaft damper removal tool No. T85P-6316-D and vibration damper removal adapter tool No. T82L-6316-B or equivalents.
15. Remove oil filter and oil cooler, if equipped, then disconnect lower radiator hose from water pump.
16. Remove oil pan as described under "Oil Pan, Replace."
17. Lower vehicle and remove front cover attaching bolts, **Fig. 8. A front cover attaching bolt is located behind oil filter adapter. Also tag bolts as they are removed so that they can be installed at same location.**
18. Remove front cover and water pump as an assembly.
19. Remove camshaft bolt and washer from end of camshaft.
20. Remove distributor drive gear, then remove camshaft sprocket, crankshaft sprocket and timing chain.
21. If crankshaft sprocket is difficult to remove, pry off shaft using two large screwdrivers positioned on both sides of sprocket.
22. Remove chain tensioner assembly from front of cylinder block as follows:
    a. Pull back on ratcheting mechanism.
    b. Install pin through hole in bracket to relieve tension.
    c. Remove three mounting bolts.
23. Reverse procedure to install, noting the following:

    a. If a replacement front cover is to be installed, the water pump, oil pump, oil filter adapter and intermediate shaft must be removed from the front cover to be replaced and reinstalled on the replacement front cover. It may be necessary to rotate crankshaft 180° from the No. 1 cylinder TDC location to position fuel pump eccentric for fuel pump installation. When installing distributor, No. 1 cylinder must be at TDC position and marks made during removal must be aligned.
    b. Lightly oil all bolt and stud threads before installation, except those specifying special sealant.
    c. Rotate crankshaft as necessary to position piston No. 1 at TDC and crankshaft keyway at 12 o'clock position.
    d. Lubricate timing chain and front oil seal with new clean engine oil.
    e. Ensure timing marks are aligned across from each other.
    f. **On non-supercharged engines,** install distributor with rotor pointing at No. 1 cap tower.
    g. Tighten to specifications.

TIMING GEARS

Refer to "Front Cover, Replace" for timing gear replacement procedure.

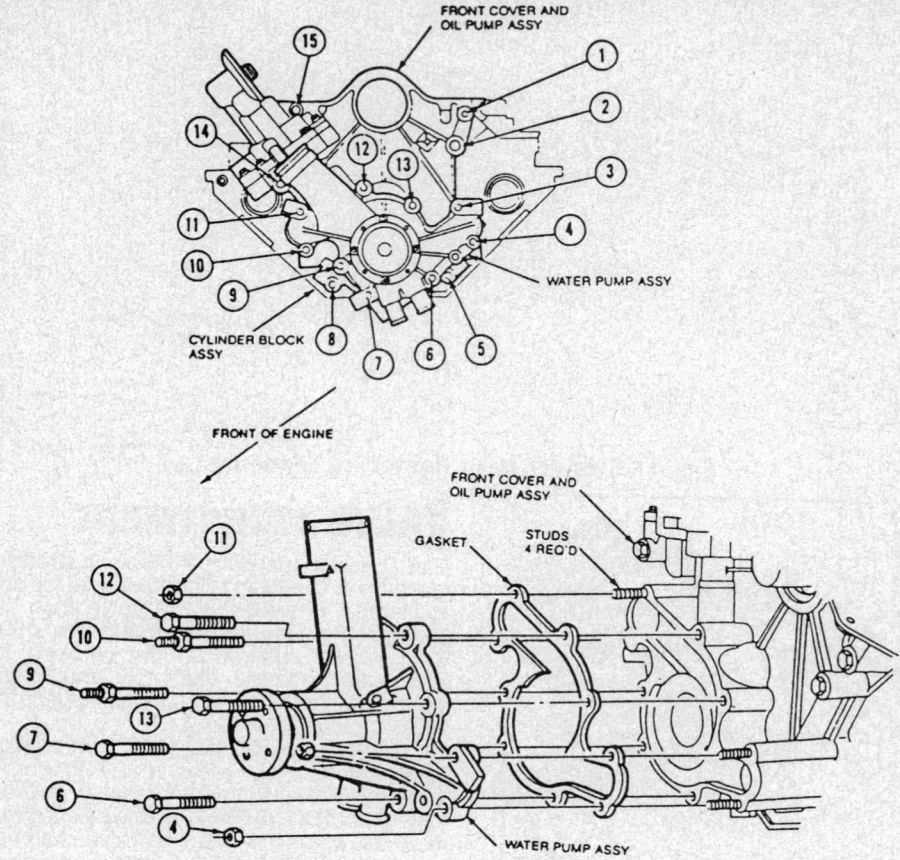

Fig. 8 Front cover & water pump bolt locations

TIMING CHAIN
REPLACE

Refer to "Front Cover, Replace" for timing chaing replacement procedure.

CAMSHAFT
REPLACE

1. Drain cooling system and remove radiator and grille.
2. **On engines equipped with air conditioning,** purge refrigerant from system and remove condenser.
3. **On all engines,** remove front cover, timing chain and sprockets.
4. Remove intake manifold.
5. Remove pushrods, lifters and oil pan.
6. Remove thrust plate, then carefully remove camshaft by pulling toward front of engine, **Fig. 9. Use care to avoid damaging camshaft bearings.**
7. Reverse procedure to install, noting the following:
   a. Lubricate cam lobes and bearing surfaces with Oil Conditioner D9AZ-19579-CA or equivalent.
   b. Tighten to specifications.

PISTON & ROD ASSEMBLY

When installed, piston and rod assembly should have the notch or arrow in piston head toward front of engine with connecting rod numbers positioned as shown in **Fig. 10.** Check side clearance between connecting rods at each crankshaft journal. Correct side clearance is .0047-.0114 Inch.

PISTONS, PINS & RINGS

Pistons are available in standard sizes and oversizes of .003, .020, .030 and .040 inch. Piston rings are available in standard sizes and oversizes of .020, .030 and .040 inch. Piston pins are available in standard size and oversizes of .001 and .002 inch.

MAIN & ROD BEARINGS

Main and rod bearings are available in standard sizes and undersizes of .001, .002, .010, .020 and .030 inch.

CRANKSHAFT REAR OIL SEAL
REPLACE

1. Using a sharp tool, punch one hole into seal metal surface between seal lip and engine block.
2. Remove seal using slide hammer tool No. T82L-9533-B or equivalent. Use care to prevent damage to sealing surface.
3. Lubricate new seal with clean engine

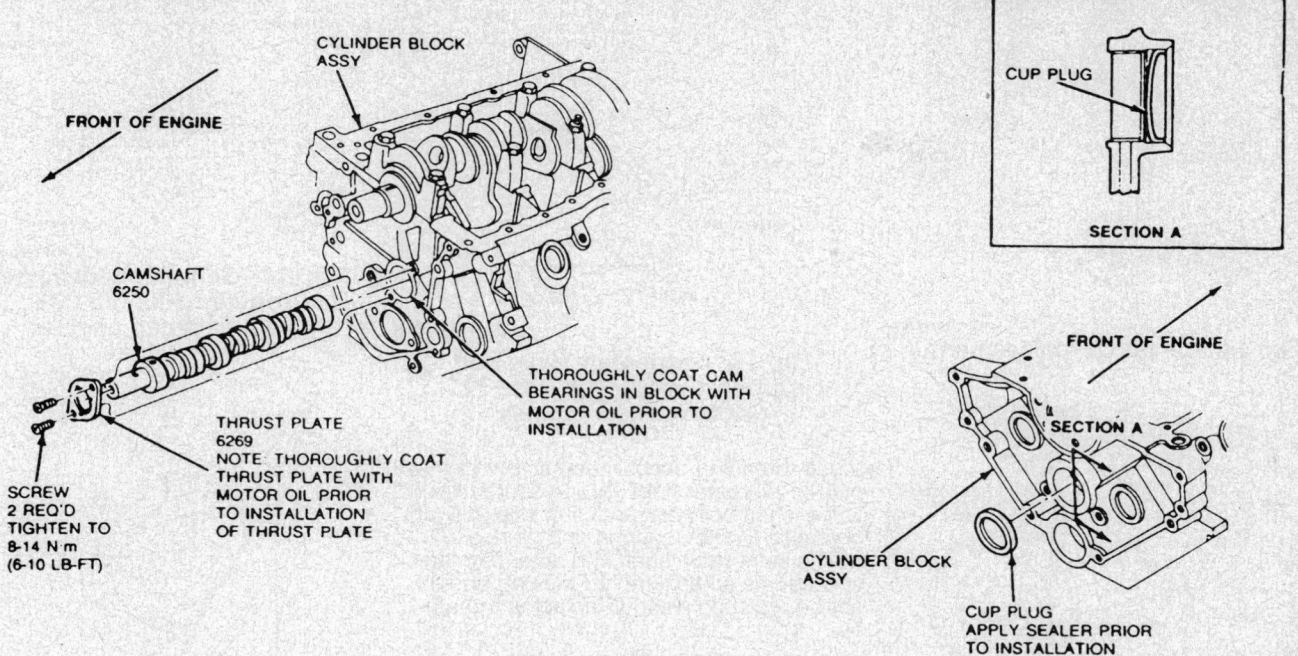

Fig. 9 Camshaft installation

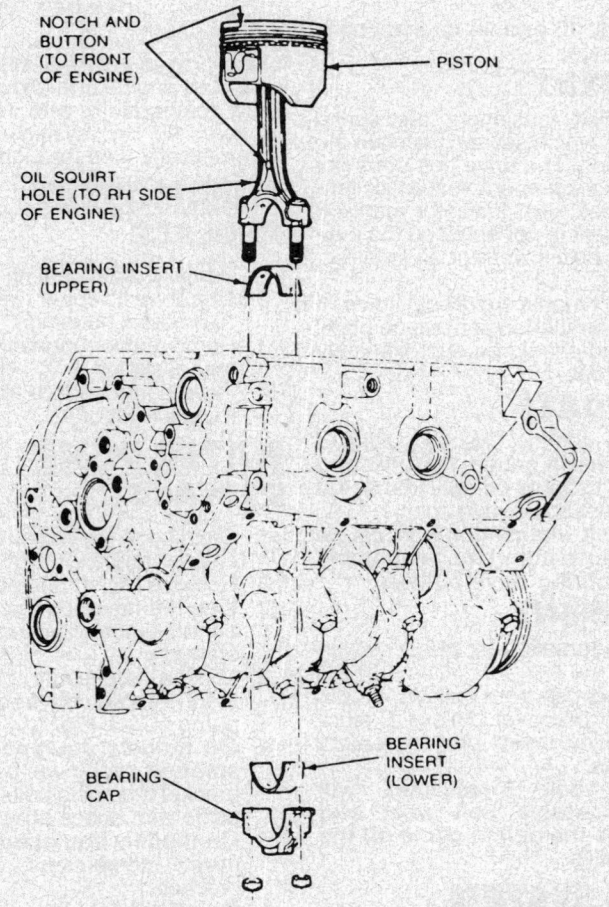

Fig. 10 Piston & rod assembly

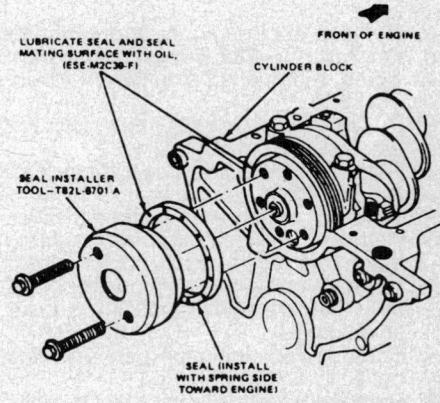

Fig. 11 Crankshaft rear seal installation

oil and install using seal installation tool No. T82L-6701-A or equivalent. Tighten bolts alternately to seat seal properly, **Fig. 11.**

OIL PAN
REPLACE

1. Disconnect battery ground cable, then remove air cleaner and air intake duct.
2. Remove two bolts attaching sight shield and position shield aside.
3. Remove hood weather seal and wiper assemblies.
4. Remove left cowl vent screen and wiper module.
5. **On 3.8L/V6-232 Supercharged engines,** remove supercharger.
6. **On all models,** install engine lifting eyes, then engine support fixture D88L-6000-A or equivalent.
7. Raise and support vehicle.

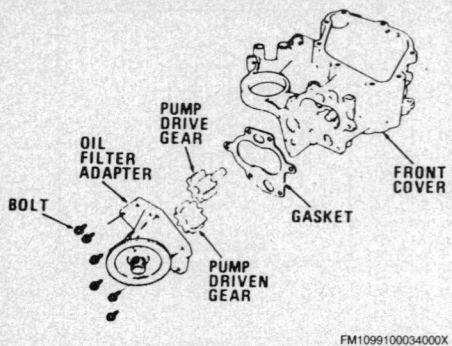

Fig. 12   Oil pump replacement

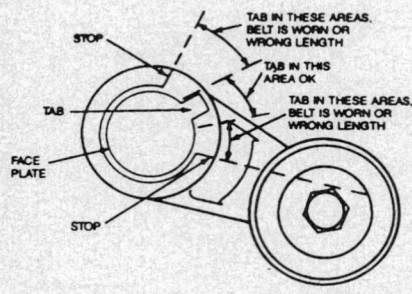

Fig. 15   Drive belt tensioner

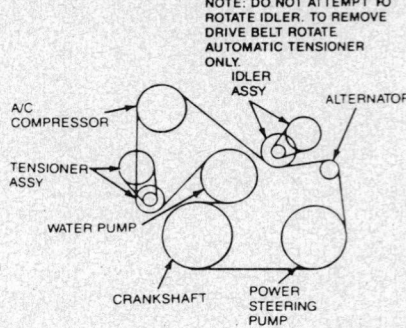

Fig. 13   Serpentine drive belt routing. Except 3.8L/V6-232 Supercharged engines

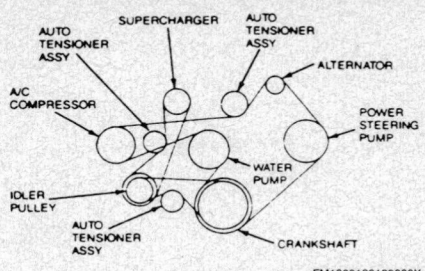

Fig. 14   Serpentine drive belt routing. 3.8L/V6-232 Supercharged engines

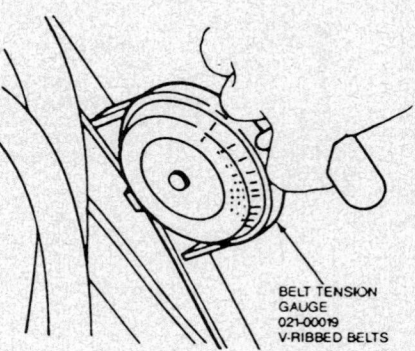

Fig. 16   Drive belt tension gauge

8. Remove engine mount through bolts.
9. **On 3.8L/V6-232 Supercharged engines,** remove left side mount retaining strap.
10. Partially lower vehicle, then raise engine at support fixture.
11. Raise vehicle and remove starter motor assembly.
12. Drain engine oil, then remove oil filter.
13. Remove wire loom, ground strap and automatic transmission cooler lines.
14. Remove oil pan-to-bellhousing bolts, then the crankshaft position sensor shield bolts.
15. Remove remaining oil pan retaining bolts.
16. Remove steering shaft pinch bolts and separate steering shaft.
17. Position a transmission jack under front of subframe.
18. Remove six rearward bolts on front of subframe, then loosen two front subframe bolts.
19. Remove lower strut to control arm bolts and nuts on both sides of vehicle.
20. Lower subframe, then remove oil pan.
21. Reverse procedure to install. Tighten to specifications.

OIL PUMP
REPLACE

On these engines, the oil pump is contained within the front cover, **Fig. 12.** To replace oil pump, remove front cover as described under "Front Cover, Timing Chain & Gears, Removal."

OIL PUMP SERVICE

Referring to **Fig. 12,** disassemble pump. To remove oil pressure relief valve, insert a self-threading sheet metal screw of the proper diameter into oil pressure relief valve chamber cap and pull cap out of chamber. Remove spring and plunger.

The inner rotor, shaft and outer race are serviced as an assembly. One part should not be replaced without replacing the other.

SERPENTINE DRIVE BELT
ROUTING

Refer to **Figs. 13 and 14** for serpentine drive belt routings.

ADJUSTMENT

Automatic belt tensioners are spring loaded devices which set and maintain the drive belt tension. The drive belt does not require tension adjustment. Automatic tensioners have belt wear indicator marks. If the indicator mark is not between the indicator lines, the belt is worn or an incorrect belt is installed.

If the indicator marks are difficult to view, locate the tab on the tensioner face plate, **Fig. 15.** The tab should be approximately between the stops.

TENSION DATA

Belt tension can be checked using a suitable belt tension gauge, **Figs. 16 and 17.** Belt tension should be checked at the middle of longest accessible span.

Incorrect belt installation will cause excessive belt wear and may cause the belt to come off the drive pulleys.

REPLACEMENT

1. Rotate automatic tensioner away from belt.
2. Remove old belt from pulleys.
3. Install new belt over pulleys. Ensure all V-grooves make proper contact with pulleys.
4. **Incorrect belt installation will cause excessive belt wear and may cause the belt to come off the drive pulleys.**

COOLING SYSTEM BLEED

These engines do not require a specific bleed procedure. After filling cooling system, start engine and allow to reach operating temperature with radiator cap removed. Air in system will then be automatically bled through cap opening.

THERMOSTAT
REPLACE

1. Partially drain cooling system.
2. Disconnect upper radiator hose at thermostat housing.
3. Remove two mounting bolts, housing and gaskets.
4. Reverse procedure to install. Tighten to specifications.

WATER PUMP
REPLACE

1. Drain cooling system, then remove air cleaner and air intake duct.
2. Remove fan shroud attaching screws then the fan and fan clutch attaching bolts. Remove fan and fan clutch and shroud.
3. Loosen accessory drive belt idler, then remove drive belt and water pump pulley, **Fig. 8.**
4. **On models equipped with power steering,** remove pump mounting bracket attaching bolts, position pump aside with hoses attached.
5. **On models equipped with A/C,** remove compressor front support bracket.
6. **On all models,** disconnect lower radiator hose, coolant bypass hose and heat hose from water pump.
7. **On models equipped with Trip-**

Application	Usage	Width x Length	Minimum Tension
3.8L EFI	Accessory	6K x 2510mm ± 6mm	74 LBS
3.8L S/C	Accessory	8K x 2280mm ± 6mm	135 LBS
3.8L S/C	Super Charger	8K x 996.5mm ± 6mm	69 LBS
3.8L S/C	Jackshaft	7K x 1080mm ± 6mm	56 LBS

FM1069100126000X

Fig. 17 Serpentine drive belt tension specifications

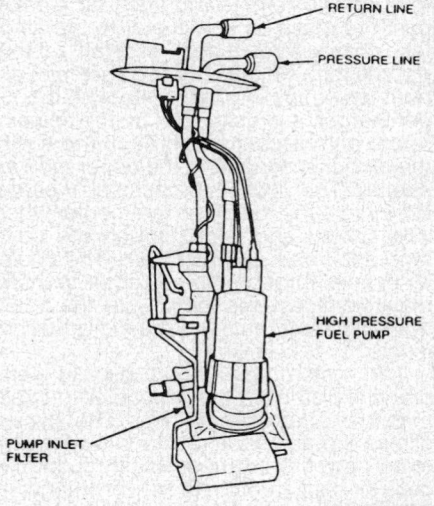

FM1029100137000X

Fig. 18 Fuel pump replacement

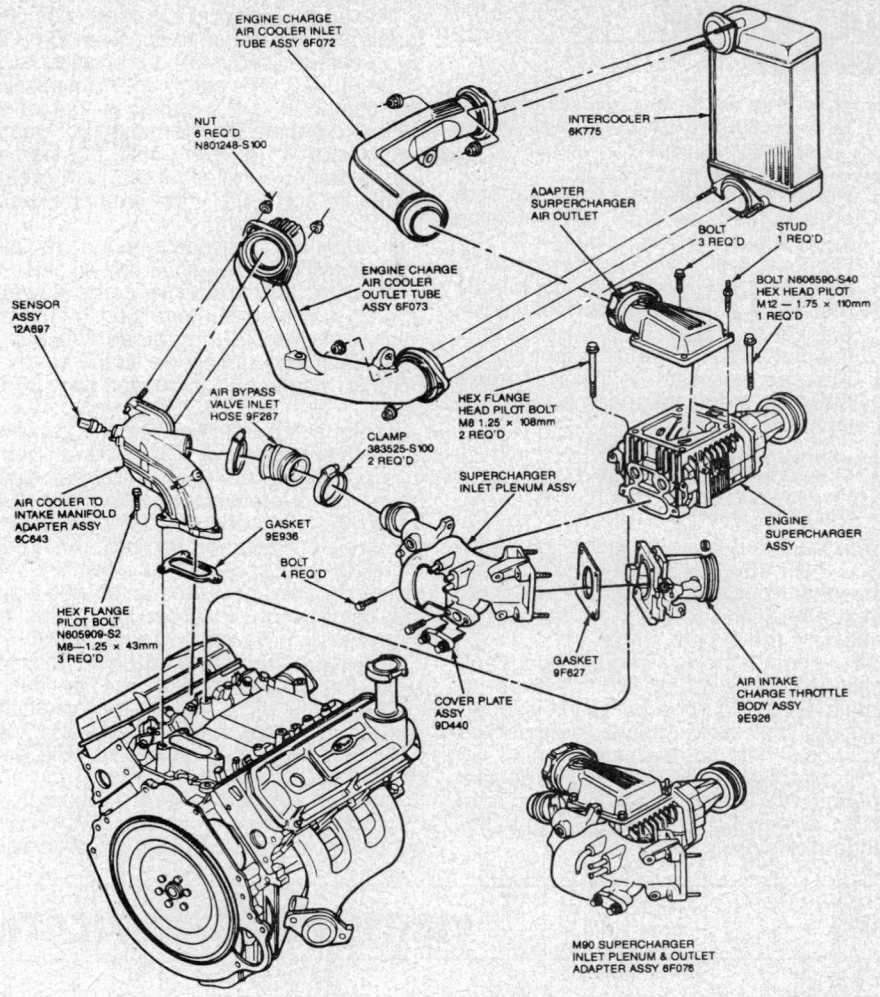

FM1059100032000X

Fig. 19 Supercharger operation & air flow

minder, remove fuel flow sensor support bracket. Do not disconnect fuel lines.
8. **On all models,** remove water pump attaching bolts, then remove water pump.
9. Reverse procedure to install.

RADIATOR
REPLACE

SUPERCHARGED ENGINE

1. Remove four nuts connecting upper and lower charge air cooler tubes to charge air cooler.
2. Slightly loosen upper charge air cooler inlet tube nut at alternator/power steering pump bracket.
3. Remove charge air cooler attaching screws and washers.
4. Push down slightly on charge air cooler to release retaining clips.
5. Remove charge air cooler from vehicle.
6. Drain cooling system.
7. Disconnect upper and lower radiator hoses.
8. **On models with automatic transmission,** disconnect transmission fluid cooler inlet and outlet lines from their intermediate fittings. **Cap both fittings to prevent contamination of the transmission oil cooling system.**
9. **On all models,** remove overflow hose from clip on fan shroud.
10. Remove wiring harness retaining clip from fan shroud.
11. Disengaging shroud from lower retaining clips, lift fan shroud and cooling fan assembly from radiator.
12. Remove two bolts attaching charge air cooler air duct to top of radiator.
13. Remove two radiator upper retaining bolts, then tilt radiator towards engine and lift out of vehicle.
14. Reverse procedure to install.

EXCEPT SUPERCHARGED ENGINE

1. Drain cooling system.
2. Disconnect upper, lower and overflow hose from radiator.
3. Disconnect automatic transmission fluid cooler inlet and outlet lines from radiator.
4. Remove two upper fan shroud to radiator support attaching bolts.
5. Lift fan shroud enough to disengage lower retaining clips and lay shroud back over fan.
6. Remove radiator upper support attaching bolts, then lift radiator from the vehicle.
7. Reverse procedure to install.

FUEL PUMP
REPLACE

1. Disconnect battery ground cable.
2. Relieve fuel pressure as described above.
3. Remove fuel tank from vehicle as follow:
   a. Drain fuel tank.
   b. Raise and support vehicle, then disconnect and cap fuel and vent lines from fuel tank. Tag lines so they can be installed in same locations. It may be necessary to remove exhaust pipe and shield to gain access to fuel tank.
   c. Disconnect electrical connectors from fuel sender and fuel pump. Tag electrical connections so they can be installed in same locations.
   d. Disconnect fuel filler tube.
   e. Remove fuel tank support straps, then lower fuel tank from vehicle.
4. Rotate fuel pump lock ring counterclockwise, **Fig. 18,** then remove fuel pump.
5. Reverse procedure to install.

FUEL FILTER
REPLACE

1. Turn engine off and relieve fuel system pressure as described under "Fuel Pressure Relief."
2. Raise and support vehicle.
3. Remove push connect fittings at both ends of the filter. Install new retaining in each push connect fitting.
4. Remove fuel filter from bracket by loosening worm gear clamp. Note direction of flow arrow as installed in bracket to ensure proper direction of fuel flow through replacement filter.
5. Reverse procedure to install. **Torque** fuel filter worm gear clamp to 16-24 inch lbs.

SUPERCHARGED 3.8L/V6-232

This engine is a modified version of the base 3.8L/V6-232. Modifications were necessary to enable the engine to handle added stress and to offset added weight created by the supercharger.

The engine block, cylinder head and crankshaft have been strengthened to contain the gas loads generating by supercharging. The cylinder head is constructed of a special heat treated aluminum.

The pistons are made out of a special hypereutectic alloy. The compression ratio is 8.2:1, compared to the 9.0:1 ratio in the standard engine.

The intake manifold is a newly designed plenum configuration to accommodate the supercharger and related components.

On models with automatic transmission, the camshaft is the same as that of the standard engine. The camshaft is a unique design with 8° greater intake duration, 4° less exhaust duration, .0122 inch greater intake lift and .0051 inch greater exhaust lift.

In addition to a conventional radiator, the supercharged engine uses an air-to-air intercooler. The intercooler cools air which is heated during compression by the supercharger before it is forced into the intake manifold. Cooling the air increases its density, resulting in increased power output.

The supercharger used on this engine is a Roots-type positive displacement pump. It is an engine driven compressor which uses two counter-rotating rotors to trap air inside the supercharger body where it is compressed and forced into the intake manifold and combustion chamber. The increased density of the fuel charge inside the combustion chamber generates the added engine power.

The supercharger is belt-driven indirectly off the engine crankshaft. The supercharger runs at 2.6 times the crankshaft's speed with a maximum speed of 15,600 RPM. Boost pressure is approximately 12 psi at 4,000 engine RPM.

The design of the system's rotors greatly contributes to a reduction in the noise generally associated with supercharged applications. Some Root's type systems use straight lobe rotors that result in uneven pressure pulses causing higher noise levels. This system uses a helical rotor design, which evens out the pressure pulses in the blower, reducing noise levels. The helical rotor design also increases efficiency by reducing the amount of air carried back to the inlet side of the supercharger through the space between the meshing rotors.

Air flows through the supercharged system as shown in **Fig. 19**. Air enters through the remote mounted air cleaner, past the mass air flow meter to the air intake charge throttle body assembly. It then passes through the supercharger inlet plenum assembly into the bottom of the supercharger, is pressurized by the spinning rotors and discharged through the top by the air outlet adapter to the upper tube assembly. The upper tube assembly carries the air into the top of the intercooler where it is cooled and sent through the outlet tube assembly at the bottom. The cooled air passes through the air cooler-to-intake manifold adapter assembly to the intake manifold, then routed to the individual cylinders.

The system also uses a bypass which branches off from the air cooler-to-intake manifold adapter assembly. The bypass allows the supercharger to idle when the extra power is not needed by routing excess air back through the supercharger inlet plenum assembly, allowing the engine to run normally aspirated.

TIGHTENING SPECIFICATIONS

Year	Component	Torque/ Ft. Lbs.
1992-95	A/C Compressor Mounting	30-45
	A/C Lower Mounting Bracket	30-45
	Alternator Pivot Bolt	45-57
	Camshaft Sprocket	30-37
	Camshaft Thrust Plate	6-10
	Connecting Rod	31-36
	Coolant Temperature Switch	8-12
	Crankshaft Dampner	103-132
	Crankshaft Pulley To Dampner	20-28
	Crankshaft Stud Bolt	6-8.5
	Cylinder Head	①
	Distributor Hold-Down	20-29
	ECT Sensor	6-9
	EGR Valve To Intake Manifold	15-22
	Fan Clutch Assembly	12-18
	Fan Shroud	24-48 ②
	Flywheel	54-64
	Front Cover	15-22
	Fuel Rail Assembly Bolt	6-8
	Fulcrum Bolt	①
	Heater Tube Support Bracket	15-22
	HEGO Sensor	28-33

Year	Component	Torque/ Ft. Lbs.
1992-95 –Cont'd	Intake Manifold (Except 3.8L/V6-232 Supercharged Engine)	①
	Intake Manifold (3.8L/V6-232 Supercharged Engine)	①
	Intake Manifold Retaining Strap	34-44
	Low Oil Level Sensor	20-30
	Main Bearing Cap	65-81
	Oil Drain Plug	15-25
	Oil Filter Adapter To Front Cover	18-22
	Oil Inlet Tube To Cylinder Block	15-22
	Oil Inlet Tube To Main Bearing Cap	30-40
	Oil Pan Bolts	80-106 ②
	Oil Pickup Tube	15-22
	Power Steering Lower Brace Bolt	18-24
	Power Steering Upper Brace Bolt	30-45
	Rocker Arm Cover	7-9
	Rocker Arm Fulcrum Bolt	①
	Spark Plug	5-11
	Thermostat Housing	15-22
	Throttle Body Nut	15-22
	Valve Lifter Guide Plate	7-10
	Water Pump	15-22

① —Refer To Text.
② —Inch Lbs.

4.6L/V8-281 Engine

NOTE: On Vehicles Equipped With Air Bags, Disarm Air Bag System As Described Under "Precautions" Before Any Diagnosis, Testing, Troubleshooting Or Repairs Are Performed. When Procedures Have Been Completed, Rearm Air Bag System As Outlined Under "Precautions."

INDEX

PRECAUTIONS

AIR BAG SYSTEMS

Refer to "Air Bag System Precautions" in the front of this manual for system disarming and arming procedures.

FUEL SYSTEM PRESSURE RELIEF

Cougar & Thunderbird

Fuel supply tubes will remain pressurized for long periods of time after engine shutdown. This pressure must be relieved before servicing any component of the fuel system. A valve is provided on the fuel injection supply manifold for this purpose.

1. Connect EFI and CFI fuel pressure gauge tool No. T80L-9974-B to fuel pressure relief valve cap on the fuel injection supply manifold.
2. Open manual valve on EFI and CFI fuel pressure gauge to relieve fuse system pressure.

Crown Victoria & Grand Marquis

Fuel supply lines, will remain pressurized after engine is shutoff. Pressure must be relieved prior to any fuel system servicing.

1. Remove fuel tank cap.
2. Using fuel pressure gauge tool No. T80L-9974-B or equivalent, relieve fuel system pressure at pressure relief

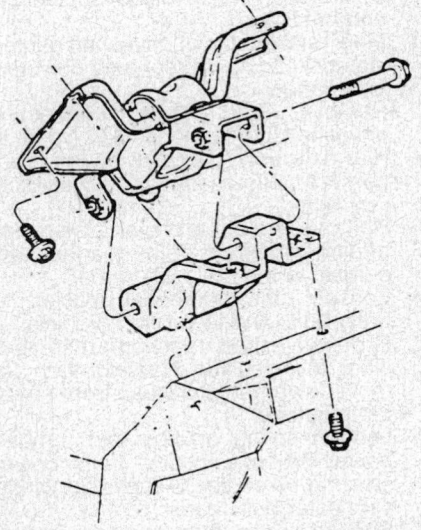

Fig. 1 Front engine mount removal

valve right rear fuel rail. **Pressure relief valve cap must be removed.**
3. Using suitable tool, remove pressure relief valve.
4. Reverse procedure to install. **Torque** fuel pressure relief valve to 48-84 inch lbs. **Torque** fuel pressure relief valve cap to 4-6 inch lbs.

ENGINE MOUNT
REPLACE

FRONT

1. Disconnect both battery cables and remove air inlet tube.
2. Drain cooling system, then remove cooling fan and shroud.
3. Relieve fuel system pressure as described under "Fuel System Pressure Relief."
4. Remove upper radiator hose, wiper module and support bracket.
5. Discharge A/C system and disconnect A/C compressor outlet hose, then remove bolt retaining hose assembly to right coil bracket.
6. Remove engine electrical harness 42-pin connector from bracket on brake vacuum booster.
7. Disconnect engine electrical connector and transmission harness electrical connector.
8. Disconnect throttle valve cable at throttle body, then remove heater outlet hose from right cylinder head.
9. Remove blower motor resistor.
10. Remove right engine mount to lower engine bracket attaching bolt. **Fig. 1.**
11. Disconnect EGR valve vacuum hoses and tube.
12. Remove EGR valve mounting bolts, then disconnect Heated Exhaust Gas Oxygen (HEGO) sensors.
13. Raise and support vehicle.
14. Remove engine mount through bolts.

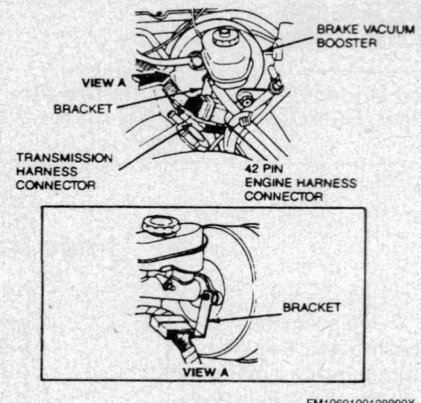

Fig. 2 Engine & transmission harness connectors

Right engine mount has one bolt; left mount has two bolts.

15. Remove EGR tube line attaching nut at right exhaust manifold, then remove EGR valve and tube assembly.
16. Disconnect exhaust pipes at manifolds, then lower and secure exhaust at crossmember.
17. Position a jack and wood block under oil pan, rearward of drain plug, then raise engine approximately 4 inches.
18. Install wood block under oil pan, then lower engine onto wood block.
19. Remove three engine mount attaching bolts from right and left engine mounts. Remove engine mounts.
20. Reverse procedure to install. Tighten to specifications.

REAR

1. Raise and support vehicle, then support transmission using a jack and a wood block.
2. Remove two bolts attaching mount to crossmember.
3. Raise transmission with jack and remove mount and retainer assembly.
4. Reverse procedure to install. Tighten to specifications.

ENGINE
REPLACE

COUGAR & THUNDERBIRD

1. Disconnect battery ground cable.
2. Drain cooling system, then remove air cleaner outlet tube and engine air cleaner.
3. Discharge air conditioning system, then remove fan blade and fan shroud.
4. Relieve fuel system pressure as described under "Fuel System Pressure Relief" and disconnect fuel lines.
5. Disconnect 42-pin connector and 8-pin connector and secure clear of engine.
6. Disconnect accelerator cable and speed control actuator with a screwdriver.
7. Disconnect throttle valve control actuating cable.
8. Disconnect electrical connector and vacuum hose from canister purge solenoid.
9. Disconnect power supply from power distribution box and starter relay.
10. Disconnect vacuum supply hose from throttle body adapter vacuum port.
11. Disconnect transmission oil cooler tubes from transmission oil cooler, then disconnect upper radiator hose from outlet tube.
12. Disconnect heater supply and return hoses.
13. Disconnect A/C compressor inlet and outlet hoses from A/C compressor using spring coupling disconnect tool No. T81P-19623-G1 and T81P-19623-G2 or equivalents.
14. Disconnect engine to frame wire and body ground strap from dash panel, then partially raise vehicle on a hoist and remove front wheels.
15. Disconnect right and left front antilock sensor and brackets wiring connectors.
16. Remove right and left front disc brake caliper bolts. Remove front disc brake calipers and secure to vehicle with wire. **Do not allow calipers to suspend from brake hoses.**
17. Disconnect right and left front suspension upper arms from front wheel spindles.
18. Disconnect front spring and shocks from front suspension lower arms.
19. Raise vehicle and drain engine oil, then disconnect dual converter Y pipe from exhaust manifolds and resonator.
20. Disconnect transmission shift cable and bracket.
21. Mark relationship of driveshaft centering socket yoke to rear axle universal joint flange.
22. Remove four bolts connecting driveshaft centering socket yoke to rear axle universal joint flange. Support rear axle assembly with suitable jack stand.
23. Remove two nut and bolt assemblies retaining the front of the rear axle assembly to the rear sub-frame.
24. Loosen rear differential bracket to body bolts and lower from vehicle.
25. Slide driveshaft rearward until it is clear of extension housing, then remove lower radiator hose from radiator inlet tube.
26. Loosen spring clamps and remove power steering hoses from power steering oil cooler. Disconnect wiring connector bulkhead.
27. Support front sub-frame using Rotunda Powertrain Lift Tool No. 014-00765 and Adapter tool No. 014-00341 or equivalents.
28. Remove rear engine support insulator retaining bolts, then disconnect steering coupling at pinch bolt joint.
29. Remove eight front sub-frame bolts.
30. Lower engine and transmission from vehicle.
31. Disconnect power steering pressure and return hoses from power steering pump.
32. Remove engine wire harness retainers from front sub-frame.

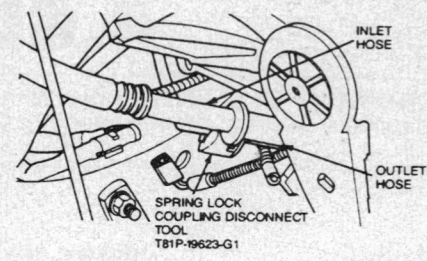

Fig. 3 A/C compressor lines removal

33. Remove left and right front engine support insulator through bolts.
34. Install Rotunda Engine Lift Bracket tool No. 014-00334 or equivalent, on side of LH cylinder head at front.
35. Attach Rotunda Engine Lift Brackets tool No. 014-00334 or equivalent, then install Rotunda Engine Lift Brackets on side of right cylinder head at rear.
36. Connect Rotunda Floor Crane tool No. 077-00043 or equivalent, to Engine Lift Brackets.
37. Remove starter motor, then the transmission oil cooler tubes.
38. Remove retaining nut from transmission line stud to cylinder block.
39. Remove transmission housing cover from cylinder block to access torque converter retaining nuts. Rotate crankshaft until each nut is accessible and remove nuts.
40. Lower engine and transmission assembly, then disconnect transmission wire harness connectors at transmission.
41. Remove six bolts retaining transmission to engine. Separate engine from transmission.
42. Reverse procedure to install, noting the following:
    a. Tighten to specifications.
    b. Align paint marks on flywheel and torque converter when connecting engine to transmission.
    c. Fill and bleed cooling system.
    d. Evacuate and recharge A/C system.
    e. Fill engine with new engine oil.
    f. Start engine and check for coolant, oil and fuel leaks.

CROWN VICTORIA & GRAND MARQUIS

1. Disconnect battery cables.
2. Mark position of hood hinges and remove hood.
3. Drain cooling system and discharge A/C system.
4. Relieve fuel system pressure as described under "Fuel System Pressure Relief," then disconnect fuel lines.
5. Remove engine cooling fan, shroud and radiator, then remove wiper module and bracket.
6. Remove air inlet tube and 42-pin electrical harness connector from bracket at brake vacuum booster, Fig. 2.
7. Disconnect 42-pin connector and

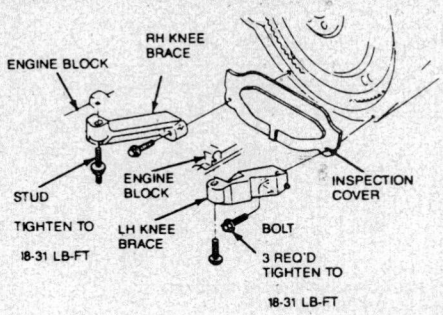

Fig. 4   Transmission line bracket assembly removal

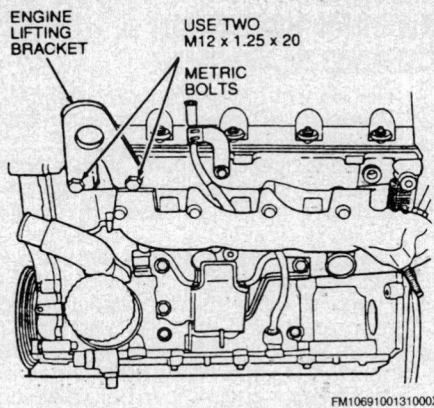

Fig. 5   Engine lift bracket installation

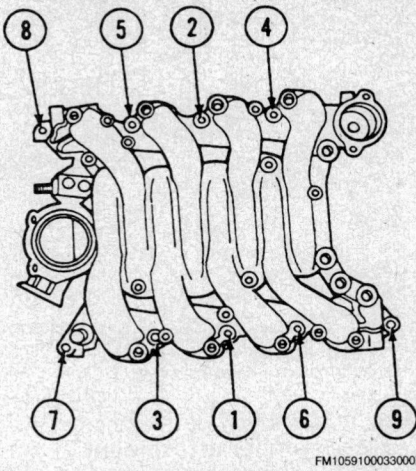

Fig. 6   Intake manifold tightening sequence

transmission harness electrical connector, then position connectors aside.

8. Disconnect accelerator, speed control cables and throttle valve cable.
9. Disconnect purge solenoid electrical connector and vacuum hose.
10. Disconnect power distribution and starter relay power supply.
11. Disconnect vacuum hose from throttle body port.
12. Disconnect heater hoses, then the alternator electrical harness at fender apron and junction box.
13. Using tool No. T81P-19623-G1, G2 or equivalent, remove A/C compressor inlet and outlet attaching hoses, **Fig. 3**.
14. Disconnect EVO sensor electrical connector from power steering pump.
15. Disconnect body ground strap at dash panel, then raise and support vehicle, then drain engine oil.
16. Disconnect exhaust pipes at manifolds, then lower exhaust system and suspend with wire from crossmember.
17. Remove transmission line bracket attaching nut, then remove engine to transmission knee braces attaching bolts and stud, **Fig. 4**.
18. Remove starter motor, then disconnect power steering pump from engine and position aside.
19. Remove plug to access torque converter attaching nuts, then rotate crankshaft to remove nuts (Four required).
20. Remove six engine to transmission attaching bolts.
21. Remove engine mount through bolts.
22. Lower vehicle and support transmission with suitable jack.
23. Install engine lift brackets, **Fig. 5**, then connect suitable lift equipment.
24. Carefully raise engine and separate from transmission, then remove engine from engine compartment.
25. Reverse procedure to install. Tighten to specifications.

INTAKE MANIFOLD
REPLACE

COUGAR & THUNDERBIRD

1. Disconnect battery ground cable, then drain cooling system.
2. Relieve fuel system pressure as described under "Fuel System Pressure Relief."
3. Remove air cleaner outlet tube, then release drive belt tensioner and remove drive belt.
4. Disconnect all ignition wires from spark plugs.
5. Disconnect ignition wire and brackets from camshaft cover studs.
6. Disconnect both ignition coils and camshaft position sensor.
7. Remove four bolts retaining ignition coil to ignition coil brackets.
8. Disconnect alternator wiring harness from junction block at front fender apron and from alternator.
9. Remove two bolts retaining alternator mounting bracket to intake manifold.
10. Remove two bolts retaining alternator to cylinder block, then remove alternator.
11. Raise and support vehicle.
12. Disconnect oil pressure sender and EVO harness sensor and reposition wiring for clearance.
13. Disconnect EGR valve to exhaust manifold tube from right exhaust manifold.
14. Lower vehicle, then disconnect accelerator cable and speed control actuator from throttle body.
15. Remove accelerator cable bracket from intake manifold and position clear of area.
16. Disconnect throttle valve control actuating cable from throttle body.
17. Disconnect vacuum hose from throttle body adapter vacuum port.
18. Disconnect heater supply hose.
19. Remove two bolts retaining thermostat housing to intake manifold and position upper radiator hose and thermostat housing clear of manifold.
20. Remove nine bolts retaining intake manifold to cylinder heads, then remove intake manifold and gaskets.
21. Reverse procedure to install, noting the following:
    a. Ensure alignment tabs on intake manifold gasket are aligned with holes in cylinder head.
    b. Install and tighten nine intake manifold retaining bolts in sequence shown in **Fig. 6** to 15-22 ft. lbs.
    c. Replace O-ring on thermostat housing.
    d. Tighten to specifications.
    e. Fill and bleed cooling system.

CROWN VICTORIA & GRAND MARQUIS

1. Disconnect battery ground cable and drain cooling system.
2. Relieve fuel system fuel pressure as described under "Fuel System Pressure Relief."
3. Remove wiper module and air inlet tube.
4. Release belt tensioner and remove accessory drive belt.
5. Disconnect spark plug wires from spark plugs and plug wire brackets from camshaft cover studs.
6. Disconnect both ignition coils, CID sensor and ignition wires from both coils.
7. Remove ignition wire tray and ignition wire assembly.
8. Disconnect alternator wiring harness from junction block, fender apron and alternator.
9. Remove alternator and mounting bracket.
10. Raise and support vehicle, then disconnect oil sending unit and EVO sensor. Position aside.
11. Disconnect EGR tube from right exhaust manifold, then lower vehicle.
12. Disconnect 42-pin connector, A/C compressor, HDR sensor and canister purge solenoid.
13. Remove PCV valve from camshaft cover, then disconnect canister purge vent hose from PCV valve.
14. Disconnect accelerator and speed control cables from throttle body, then remove accelerator cable bracket from intake manifold and position aside.
15. Disconnect throttle valve cable from throttle body.
16. Disconnect vacuum hose from throttle body adapter port.
17. Disconnect both HEGO sensors and heater supply hose.

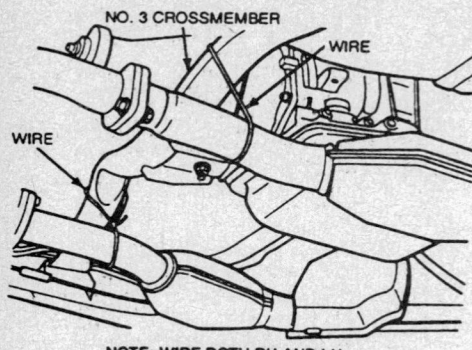

Fig. 7 Catalytic converter to crossmember attachment

NOTE: WIRE BOTH RH AND LH PIPE TO NO. 3 CROSSMEMBER

18. Remove thermostat housing, then disconnect upper hose and position aside.
19. Remove bolts attaching intake manifold, then the intake manifold and gaskets.
20. Reverse procedure to install, noting the following:
    a. Clean cylinder head and intake manifold surfaces.
    b. Install new intake manifold gaskets.
    c. **Torque** manifold bolts to 15-22 ft. lbs., in sequence shown, **Fig. 6.**

EXHAUST MANIFOLD
REPLACE
COUGAR & THUNDERBIRD

1. Disconnect battery ground cable.
2. Remove bolt retaining oil level indicator tube on left exhaust manifold.
3. Raise and support vehicle, then disconnect both heated oxygen sensors.
4. Remove EGR valve to exhaust manifold tube line nut from right exhaust manifold and remove EGR valve.
5. Disconnect three-way catalytic converter from exhaust manifolds.
6. Lower catalytic converter and wire to crossmember in positions shown in **Fig. 7.**
7. On left exhaust manifold, disconnect steering shaft and position clear of area. Remove eight bolts retaining exhaust manifold.
8. On right exhaust manifold, remove eight bolts retaining exhaust manifold to cylinder head, then remove manifold.
9. Reverse procedure to install, noting the following:
    a. **Torque** exhaust manifold retaining nuts in sequence shown in **Fig. 8,** to 15-22 ft. lbs.
    b. Loosen line nut at EGR valve prior to installing assembly into vehicle. This will allow enough movement to align EGR valve retaining bolts.
    c. Ensure exhaust system clears No. 3 crossmember. Adjust as necessary.
    d. Tighten all components to specifications.

CROWN VICTORIA & GRAND MARQUIS

1. Disconnect battery ground cables.
2. Remove air intake tube and drain cooling system.
3. Remove cooling fan and shroud, then relieve fuel system pressure as described under "Fuel System Pressure Relief."
4. Disconnect fuel lines and remove upper radiator hose.
5. Remove wiper module and support bracket.
6. Discharge A/C system, then disconnect A/C compressor outlet hose at compressor and remove bolt retaining hose assembly to right coil bracket.
7. Remove 42-pin engine electrical connector from bracket on brake booster.
8. Disconnect 42-pin electrical connector and transmission harness connector.
9. Disconnect throttle valve cable from throttle body, then disconnect heater outlet hose.
10. Remove ground strap at right cylinder head and position heater hose aside.
11. Remove blower motor resistor.
12. Remove right engine mount to lower engine bracket bolt.
13. Disconnect both heated exhaust gas oxygen (HEGO) sensors. Raise and support vehicle.
14. Remove engine mount through bolts.
15. Remove EGR tube line nut from right exhaust manifold.
16. Disconnect exhaust from manifolds. Lower exhaust and support with wire from crossmember.
17. **For left exhaust manifold,** remove engine mount from cylinder block and eight bolts retaining exhaust manifold.
18. Position a jack and a block of wood below oil pan, rearward of oil drain hole.
19. Raise engine approximately four inches.
20. **For right exhaust manifold,** remove eight mounting bolts and remove manifold.
21. Reverse procedure to install, noting the following:
    a. Position manifold to cylinder head and **torque** to 15-22 ft. lbs., in sequence shown in **Fig. 8.**
    b. Tighten to specifications.

CYLINDER HEAD
REPLACE
COUGAR & THUNDERBIRD
Removal

Cylinder head must not be set on head face. If valves are open, damage will occur.
1. Disconnect battery ground cable.
2. Drain cooling system and remove fan blade and fan shroud.
3. Relieve fuel system pressure as described under "Fuel System Pressure Relief."
4. Remove air cleaner outlet tube and the windshield wiper governor.

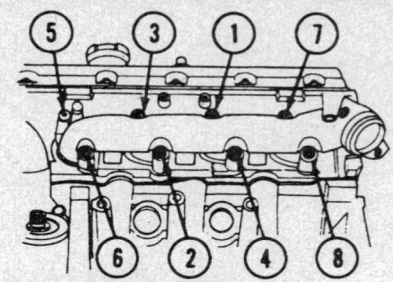

NOTE: ENGINE SHOWN REMOVED FOR CLARITY
NOTE: LH EXHAUST MANIFOLD SHOWN RH EXHAUST MANIFOLD TYPICAL

Fig. 8 Exhaust manifold tightening sequence

5. Release drive belt tensioner and remove drive belt. **Do not pull on ignition wires.**
6. Disconnect ignition wires from spark plugs.
7. Disconnect ignition wire and brackets from camshaft cover studs.
8. Remove bolts retaining power steering oil reservoir to the left ignition coil bracket and position clear of area.
9. Remove three nuts retaining right ignition coil bracket to engine front cover.
10. Remove left ignition coil and ignition wires as an assembly.
11. Remove four nuts retaining left ignition coil bracket to engine front cover.
12. Slide ignition coil brackets and ignition wire bracket assembly off mounting studs and remove from vehicle.
13. Remove water pump pulley.
14. Disconnect alternator wiring harness from junction block, front fender apron and alternator.
15. Remove two bolts retaining alternator mounting bracket to intake manifold.
16. Remove two bolts retaining alternator to cylinder block and remove alternator.
17. Disconnect and remove positive crankcase ventilation valve from camshaft cover.
18. Disconnect 42-pin engine harness connector and 8-pin connector leading to mass airflow sensor.
19. Remove nut retaining A/C liquid line to right strut tower.
20. Lift A/C liquid line and feed the 42-pin connector under the A/C liquid line. Position the 42-pin connector clear of area.
21. Disconnect crankshaft position sensor, A/C clutch and canister purge solenoid connectors.
22. Raise and support vehicle on a hoist, then remove bolts retaining power steering pump to cylinder block and engine front cover. **The front lower bolt on the power steering pump will not come all the way out.**
23. Secure power steering pump clear of area with suitable wire.
24. Remove four bolts retaining oil pan to front engine cover.
25. Remove crankshaft pulley bolt and crankshaft pulley retaining washer from crankshaft.

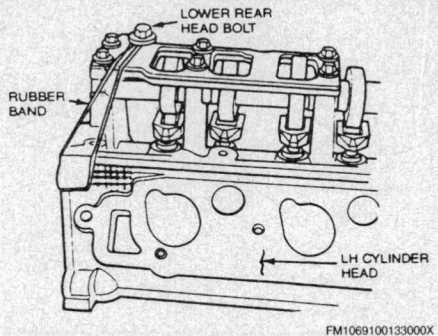

Fig. 9 LH lower rear head bolt removal

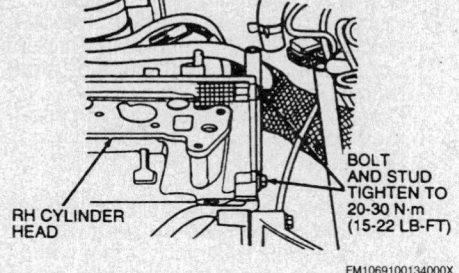

Fig. 10 Right cylinder head removal

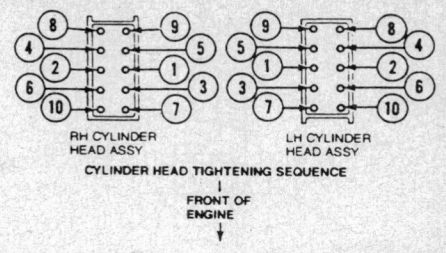

Fig. 11 Cylinder head bolt tightening sequence

26. Install crankshaft damper remover tool No. T58P-6316-D or equivalent, on crankshaft pulley and pull crankshaft pulley from crankshaft.
27. Disconnect EVO sensor and oil pressure sender.
28. Disconnect EGR valve to exhaust manifold tube from right exhaust manifold.
29. Disconnect three-way catalytic converter from right and left exhaust manifolds.
30. Lower exhaust and secure with wire to crossmember in positions shown in **Fig. 7.**
31. Remove bolt retaining starter wiring harness to rear of right cylinder head.
32. Remove bolts and stud bolts retaining right valve cover to cylinder head and remove valve cover.
33. Disconnect accelerator cable and speed control actuator.
34. Remove accelerator cable bracket from intake manifold and position clear of area.
35. Remove bolts and stud bolts retaining left valve cover to cylinder head and remove valve cover.
36. Disconnect throttle valve control actuating cable from throttle body.
37. Disconnect vacuum hose from throttle body adapter vacuum port.
38. Disconnect both heated oxygen sensors, then disconnect heater water hose.
39. Remove two bolts retaining thermostat housing to intake manifold and position upper radiator hose and thermostat housing out of the way.
40. Remove nine bolts retaining intake manifold to cylinder heads and remove intake manifold.
41. Remove intake manifold gaskets, then remove seven stud bolts and four bolts retaining engine front cover to engine and remove engine front cover.
42. Remove timing chains as described under "Timing Chains, Gears, Tensioners Guides, Replace" in the Lincoln chapter.
43. Remove 10 bolts retaining left cylinder head to cylinder block, noting the following:
    a. The lower rear bolt cannot be removed due to interference with the power brake booster.

b. Use a rubber band or similar item to retain the bolt away from the cylinder block as shown in **Fig. 9.**
44. Remove left cylinder head.
45. Remove ground strap, one stud and one bolt retaining water heater hose to right cylinder head.
46. Remove 10 bolts retaining the right cylinder head to the cylinder block, noting the following:
    a. The lower rear bolt cannot be removed due to interference with the A/C evaporator housing.
    b. Use a rubber band or similar item to hold bolt away from cylinder block as shown in **Fig. 10.**
47. Remove right cylinder head.
48. Clean cylinder head, intake manifold, camshaft cover and cylinder block sealing surfaces.
49. Inspect head face surface for scratches near coolant passage and combustion chamber.

Installation

1. **Cylinder head bolts must be replaced with new bolts.** They are torque-to-yield designed and cannot be reused.
2. Rotate crankshaft to a stable position where valves do not extend below cylinder head face.
3. Position new head gasket on cylinder block. Install lower rear cylinder head bolts and retain in position with rubber bands as described during removal procedure.
4. Position left cylinder head on cylinder block. Apply clean engine oil to all head bolt spot-faces.
5. Remove rubber band from lower rear bolt and install nine remaining bolts hand tight.
6. Tighten left cylinder head bolts as follows:
    a. **Torque** bolts in sequence shown in **Fig. 11,** to 25-30 ft. lbs.
    b. Rotate all bolts in same sequence 85-95°.
    c. Final tighten all bolts an additional 85-95° in same sequence.
7. Position right cylinder head on cylinder block dowels. Apply clean engine oil to all head bolt spot-faces.
8. Remove rubber band from lower rear bolt and install nine remaining bolts hand tight.
9. Tighten right cylinder head bolts as follows:
    a. **Torque** bolts in sequence shown

in **Fig. 11,** to 15-22 ft. lbs.
    b. Rotate all bolts in same sequence 85-95°.
    c. Final tighten all bolts an additional 85-95°.
10. Position heater water hose on cylinder head and install two bolts.
11. Rotate camshafts using flats matched at center of camshaft until both are in time and install Cam Positioning tool No. T92P-6256-A or equivalent on flats of camshaft. This will prevent camshafts from rotating.
12. Position crankshaft at No. 1 TDC by rotating crankshaft 45°. **Crankshaft must only be rotated in clockwise direction and only as far as TDC.**
13. Install timing chains as described under "Timing Chains, Gears, Tensioners & Guides."
14. Reverse remainder of removal procedure to complete cylinder head installation, noting the following:
    a. Tighten to specifications.
    b. Tighten intake manifold bolts to specifications in sequence shown in **Fig. 6.**
    c. Apply silicone gasket and sealant part No. F1AZ-19562-A or equivalent, at both places where the engine front cover meets the cylinder head.
    d. Ensure exhaust system clears the No. 3 crossmember. Adjust as necessary.
    e. Apply silicone gasket and sealant part No. F1AZ-19562-A or equivalent, in keyway of crankshaft pulley as shown in **Fig. 12.**

CROWN VICTORIA & GRAND MARQUIS

1. Disconnect battery ground cable and drain cooling system. Remove cooling fan and shroud.
2. Relieve fuel system fuel pressure a described under "Fuel System Pressure Relief."
3. Remove air inlet tube and wiper module.
4. Release belt tensioner and remove accessory drive belt.
5. Disconnect ignition wires from spark plugs and ignition wire brackets from camshaft cover studs.
6. Remove ignition wire tray from coil brackets.
7. Remove bolt securing A/C high pressure line to right coil bracket.

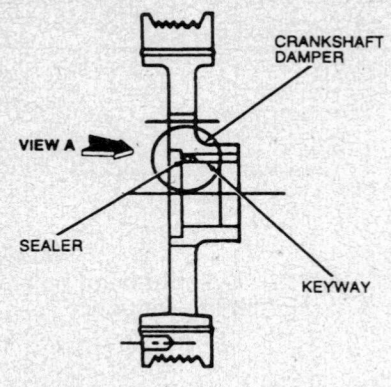

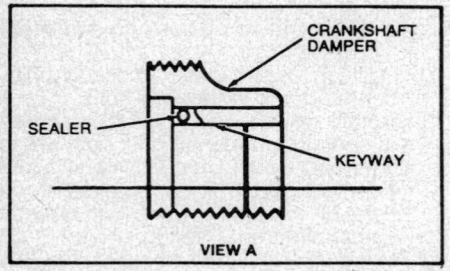

Fig. 12 Crankshaft pulley keyway silicone gasket sealant application locations

8. Disconnect both ignition coils and CID sensor, then remove nuts securing both coil brackets to front cover.
9. Slide ignition coil brackets and ignition wire assembly off mounting studs and remove.
10. Remove water pump pulley, then disconnect alternator wiring harness from junction block, fender apron and alternator.
11. Remove alternator and mounting bracket.
12. Disconnect positive battery cable at power distribution box, then remove attaching bolt from positive battery cable bracket located on right side of cylinder head.
13. Disconnect vent hose from canister purge solenoid, then place positive battery cable aside.
14. Disconnect canister purge solenoid vent hose from PCV valve, then remove PCV valve from camshaft cover.
15. Remove 42-pin engine harness connector from retaining bracket on brake vacuum booster, then disconnect and position aside.
16. Disconnect HDR sensor, A/C compressor clutch and canister purge solenoid electrical connectors.
17. Raise and support vehicle, then remove bolts retaining power steering pump to engine block and cylinder front cover. **Front lower bolt on power steering will not come out completely.**
18. Remove bolts attaching oil pan to front cover.
19. Remove crankshaft damper retaining

bolt and washer from crankshaft.
20. Install crankshaft damper remover tool No. T58P-6316-D or equivalent on damper, then pull damper from crankshaft.
21. Disconnect EVO sensor and oil sending unit and position aside.
22. Disconnect EGR tube from right exhaust manifold.
23. Disconnect exhaust for right and left manifolds, then suspend with wire.
24. Remove bolt retaining starter wiring harness to rear of right cylinder head, then lower vehicle.
25. Remove right and left camshaft cover to cylinder head.
26. Disconnect accelerator and speed control cables.
27. Remove accelerator bracket from intake manifold and position aside.
28. Disconnect throttle valve cable from throttle body, then the vacuum hose from throttle body elbow port.
29. Disconnect both HEGO sensor and heater supply hose.
30. Remove thermostat housing, then disconnect upper hose and position aside.
31. Remove intake manifold and gaskets.
32. Remove timing chain as described under "Timing Chains, Gears, Tensioners & Guides."
33. Remove bolts attaching left cylinder head. **The lower rear bolt cannot be removed due to interference with brake vacuum booster.** Use a rubber band or similar item to hold bolt away from engine as shown, **Fig. 9.**
34. Remove left cylinder head.
35. Remove ground strap retaining heater return line to right cylinder head.
36. Remove bolts attaching right cylinder head. **The lower rear bolt cannot be removed due to interference with evaporator housing.** Use a rubber band or similar item to hold bolt away from engine as shown, **Fig. 9.**
37. Remove right cylinder head.
38. Reverse procedure to install, noting the following:
   a. Rotate crankshaft counterclockwise 45°. This ensures that all pistons are below top of engine block deck face.
   b. **Torque** cylinder head bolts in three steps, in sequence shown in **Fig. 11.** First to 15-22 ft. lbs., then rotate in sequence 85-95°, then an additional 85-95°.
   c. Rotate crankshaft clockwise 45°. This will position crankshaft at TDC No. 1. **Crankshaft must only be rotated in clockwise direction and only as far as TDC.**
   d. Tighten remaining components to specifications.

VALVE LIFT SPECIFICATIONS

Year	Intake, Inch	Exhaust, Inch
1992-95	.472	.472

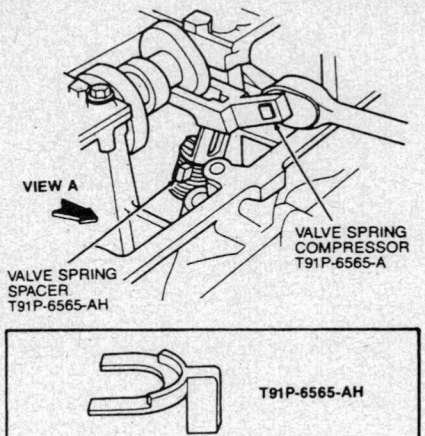

Fig. 13 Valve spring compression

VALVE ARRANGEMENT
FRONT TO REAR
Right Bank ....I-E-I-E-I-E-I-E
Left Bank ....E-I-E-I-E-I-E-I

CAMSHAFT LOBE LIFT SPECIFICATIONS

Year	Intake, Inch	Exhaust, Inch
1992-95	.2594	.2594

VALVE CLEARANCE SPECIFICATIONS

Correct clearance is .020-.069 inch at intake valves and .046-.095 inch at exhaust valves with hydraulic lash adjuster completely collapsed.

VALVE ADJUSTMENT

Valve clearance is maintained by a hydraulic lash adjuster and roller follower, and is not adjustable.

HYDRAULIC LASH ADJUSTER
REPLACE

1. Remove camshaft covers as described under "Camshaft Cover, Replace."
2. Position piston of cylinder at bottom of stroke and camshaft lobe at base circle.
3. Install valve spring spacer tool No. T91P-6565-AH or equivalent, between spring coils to prevent valve seal damage. **If spacer is not installed, retainer will hit valve stem seal and damage seal.**
4. Install Valve Spring Compressor tool No. T91P-6565-A or equivalent, under camshaft and on top of valve spring retainer, **Fig. 13.**

5. Compress valve spring and remove roller follower.
6. Remove valve spring compressor and spacer.
7. If necessary, remove hydraulic lash adjuster.
8. Repeat steps 2 through 7 for remaining cylinders as required.
9. Reverse procedure to install, noting the following:
   a. Valve lash adjuster must not exceed .059 inch (1.5mm) of plunger travel prior to installation.
   b. When installing roller follower, piston must be at bottom of stroke and camshaft at base circle.
   c. Tighten to specifications.

VALVE SPRING & VALVE STEM OIL SEAL
REPLACE
REMOVAL

If, during this procedure, air pressure has forced the piston to the bottom of the cylinder, any loss of air pressure will allow the valve to fall into the cylinder. A rubber band, tape or string wrapped around the end of the valve stem will prevent this and still allow enough travel to check the valve for binding and excess guide to valve stem clearance.

1. Remove camshaft covers as described under "Camshaft Cover, Replace."
2. Remove roller followers as described under "Hydraulic Lash Adjuster, Replace."
3. Remove spark plug, then position piston at top of stroke with both valves closed.
4. Install suitable air line with adapter in spark plug opening, then apply air pressure. Failure of air pressure to hold valves closed is an indication of valve or valve seat damage that may require cylinder head removal.
5. Install .40 inch shim between spring coils.
6. Using Valve Spring Compressor tool No. T91P-6565-A or equivalent, compress valve spring.
7. Remove keepers, retainer and valve spring.
8. Use suitable locking pliers, remove valve stem seal.
9. Repeat steps 3 through 8 as required.

INSTALLATION

1. **Piston must be at Top Dead Center (TDC) of cylinder being serviced.**
2. Remove air pressure, then inspect valve stem for damage. Rotate valve and check valve stem tip eccentric movement during rotation.
3. Position valve up and down through normal travel and check stem for binding. **If valve has been damaged. It will be necessary to remove cylinder head for service.**
4. If valve condition is good, apply engine oil to valve stem and hold valve closed, then apply air pressure in cyl-

inder.
5. Using Valve Stem Seal Replacer tool No. T88T-6571-A or equivalent, install valve stem seal.
6. Position valve spring and retainer over valve stem.
7. Install .40 inch shim between spring coils.
8. Compress valve spring, then install keepers.
9. Turn off air supply, then remove adapter from spark plug opening.
10. Install spark plug, then roller follower and camshaft cover.
11. Start engine and check for leaks.

CAMSHAFT COVER
REPLACE
RIGHT SIDE

1. Disconnect battery ground cable, then disconnect positive battery cable at power distribution box.
2. Remove positive battery cable bracket to cylinder head attaching bolt.
3. Disconnect High Data Rate (HDR) sensor, A/C compressor clutch and canister purge solenoid electrical connectors, then position aside.
4. Disconnect purge solenoid vent hose, then position positive battery cable aside.
5. Disconnect spark plug ignition wires. **Do not remove wires.**
6. Remove ignition wire brackets, then position wires aside.
7. Remove PCV valve and position aside.
8. Remove camshaft cover attaching bolts, then remove camshaft cover.
9. Reverse procedure to install. Tighten to specifications.

LEFT SIDE

1. Disconnect battery ground cable.
2. Remove air inlet tube.
3. Relieve fuel pressure as outlined under "Fuel System Pressure Relief," then disconnect fuel lines.
4. Raise and support vehicle.
5. Disconnect EVO sensor and oil pressure sending unit electrical connectors, then position electrical harness aside.
6. Lower vehicle, then remove 42-pin electrical harness connector from bracket at brake vacuum booster, **Fig. 2,** then disconnect and position aside.
7. Remove windshield wiper module.
8. Disconnect spark plug ignition wires. **Do not remove wires.**
9. Remove ignition wire brackets, then position wires aside.
10. Remove camshaft cover attaching bolts, then remove camshaft cover.
11. Reverse procedure to install. Tighten to specifications.

FRONT COVER
REPLACE

1. Disconnect battery ground cable and remove engine cooling fan and shroud.
2. Loosen water pump pulley bolts and

remove serpentine drive belt.
3. Remove water pump pulley.
4. Raise and support vehicle, then remove power steering pump attaching bolts. **Front lower power steering pump pull out completely.**
5. Support power steering pump and position aside.
6. Remove oil pan to front cover attaching bolts.
7. Remove crankshaft damper attaching bolt and washer, then remove damper using removal tool No. T58P-6316-D or equivalent.
8. Lower vehicle, then bolt securing A/C high pressure line to right coil bracket.
9. Remove camshaft covers front attaching bolts, then loosen remaining cover bolts.
10. Using plastic wedges or suitable tool, prop up camshaft covers.
11. Disconnect ignition coils and Crankshaft Identification (CID) sensor.
12. Remove right coil bracket attaching nuts, then position power steering hose aside.
13. Remove left coil bracket attaching nuts, then pull bracket and ignition wires from mounting studs and position aside.
14. Remove front cover attaching bolts and stub bolts, then remove front cover.
15. Reverse procedure to install, noting the following:
    a. Tighten to specifications.
    b. Apply silicone gasket and sealant E3AZ-19562-A or equivalent in damper keyway. Ensure crankshaft key and keyway are aligned, using Crankshaft Damper Replacer T47P-6316-B or equivalent, install crankshaft damper.

FRONT COVER SEAL
REPLACE

1. Disconnect battery ground cable.
2. Release belt tensioner and remove serpentine drive belt.
3. Raise and support vehicle, then remove crankshaft damper attaching bolt and washer.
4. Using crankshaft damper removal tool No. T58P-6316-D or equivalent, remove crankshaft damper.
5. Using front cover seal removal tool No. T74P-6700-A or equivalent, remove front cover seal.
6. Reverse procedure to install, noting the following:
   a. Install front cover seal using replacement tool No. T88T-6701-A1, A2 or equivalent.
   b. Apply silicone gasket and sealant part No. E3AZ-19562-A or equivalent in damper keyway. Ensure crankshaft key and keyway are aligned, using Crankshaft Damper Replacer tool No. T47P-6316-B or equivalent, install crankshaft.
   c. Tighten to specifications.

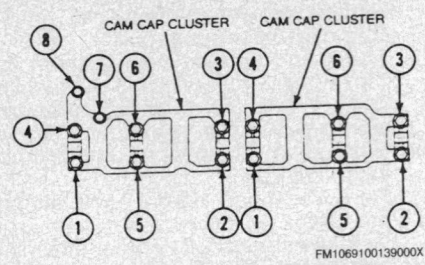

Fig. 14 Camshaft cap cluster assembly tightening sequence

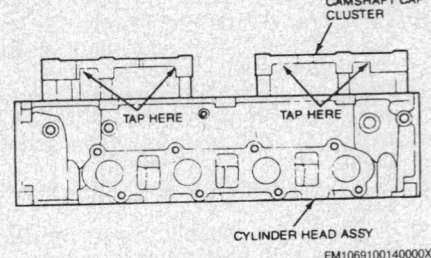

Fig. 15 Camshaft replacement

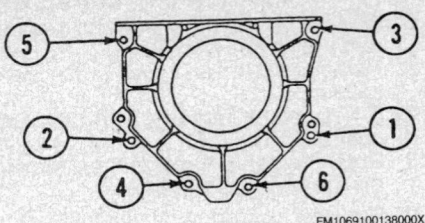

Fig. 16 Rear oil seal retainer tightening sequence

CAMSHAFT
REPLACE

1. Disconnect battery ground cable, then remove cooling fan and shroud.
2. Relieve fuel system pressure as described under "Fuel System Pressure Relief."
3. Remove camshaft covers as described under "Camshaft Cover, Replace."
4. Remove front cover as described under "Front Cover, Replace."
5. Remove timing chains as described under "Timing Chains, Gears, Tensioners & Guides."
6. Rotate crankshaft counterclockwise 45°. Ensure pistons are below top of engine deck face. **Crankshaft must be in position prior to rotating camshafts or piston and/or valve damage may result.**
7. Install Valve Spring Compressor tool No. T91P-6565-A or equivalent, under camshaft and on valve spring retainer.
8. Install .40 inch shim between spring coils and camshaft to prevent damage.
9. Camshaft must be at base circle before compressing valve spring, then rotate camshaft, as required, until roller followers are removed.
10. Compress valve spring, then remove roller follower.
11. Repeat steps 7 through 10 until all roller followers are removed.
12. Remove camshaft cap cluster assembly attaching bolts, **Fig. 14.**
13. Tap upward on camshaft cap, **Fig. 15**, then carefully remove camshaft cap and camshaft.
14. Reverse procedure to install, noting the following:
    a. Refer to **Fig. 14** for camshaft cap cluster bolt tightening sequence.
    b. Tighten attaching nuts and bolts to specifications.

PISTON & ROD ASSEMBLY

If old pistons are serviceable, ensure they are installed on original rods from which they were removed. Check side clearance between connecting rods and crankshaft journal. Correct clearance is .015-.040 inch.

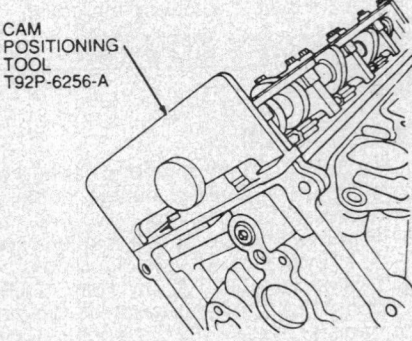

Fig. 17 Camshaft positioning tool

CRANKSHAFT REAR OIL SEAL
REPLACE

1. Using a suitable jack, lower transmission and support.
2. Remove flywheel.
3. Remove oil pan as described under "Oil Pan, Replace."
4. Remove rear oil seal retainer attaching bolts.
5. Reverse procedure to install. **Torque** seal retainer to 6.0-8.8 ft. lbs., in sequence shown in **Fig. 16.**

TIMING CHAINS, GEARS, TENSIONERS & GUIDES
REMOVAL

At no time, when the timing chains are removed and the cylinder heads are installed, may the crankshaft and/or camshaft be rotated. Rotation may result in valve and/or piston damage.

If engine has jumped time, cylinder heads must be removed to repair damage to valves and/or pistons.

1. Remove all necessary components to access timing chains.
2. Remove crankshaft position sensor tooth wheel and rotate engine to No. 1 cylinder TDC.
3. To prevent accidental rotation of camshafts, install cam positioning tools No. T92P-6256-A or equivalents, to flats on camshafts as shown in **Fig. 17.**
4. Remove two bolts retaining right tensioner to cylinder head and remove tensioner.
5. Remove right tensioner arm, then remove two bolts securing right chain guide to cylinder head and remove chain guide.
6. Remove right crankshaft gear.
7. Remove right camshaft sprocket retaining bolt, washer, gear and spacer, if necessary.
8. Remove two bolts securing left tensioner to cylinder head and remove tensioner.
9. Remove left tensioner arm, then the bolts securing left chain guide to cylinder head. Remove chain guide.
10. Remove left chain from camshaft and crankshaft gears.
11. Remove left crankshaft gear.
12. Remove left camshaft sprocket retaining bolt, washer, gear and spacer, if necessary.
13. **Do not rotate crankshaft and/or camshaft while timing chains are removed.**

INSTALLATION

If engine has jumped time, ensure all repairs to engine components and/or valve train are completed. Then rotate engine counterclockwise 45°. This will position all pistons below top of deck face. Install cylinder heads and begin with step 5.

1. Position left camshaft spacers and gears on camshaft, if removed.
2. Install washer and camshaft gear retaining bolt. Tighten to specifications.
3. Position right camshaft spacer and gear on camshaft, if removed.
4. Install washer and camshaft gear retaining bolt. Tighten to specifications. **Cam positioning tools No. T92P-6256-A or equivalent, must be installed on camshaft(s) to prevent from rotating.**
5. Install left crankshaft gear. Ensure tapered portion of gear faces away from engine block.
6. If copper links of timing chain are not visible, split chain in half and mark two opposing links as shown in **Fig. 18.**
7. Install left timing chain on camshaft gear. Ensure copper link is aligned with timing mark of camshaft gear. **Fig. 19.**
8. Install left timing chain on crankshaft gear. Ensure copper link is aligned with timing mark on crankshaft gear.
9. Install right crankshaft gear. Ensure tapered portion of gear faces toward engine block.
10. Install right timing chain on camshaft gear. Ensure copper link is aligned with timing mark of camshaft gear.
11. Install right timing chain on crankshaft

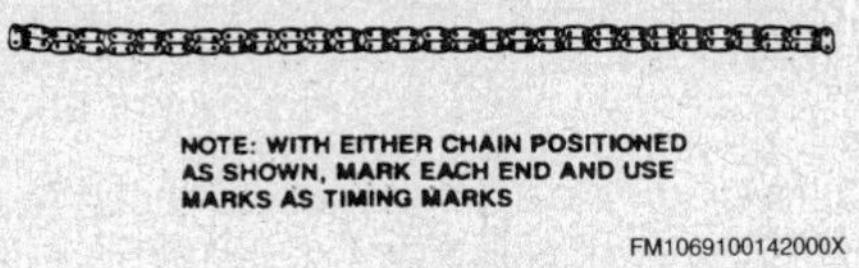

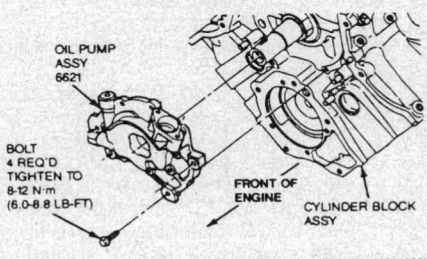

NOTE: WITH EITHER CHAIN POSITIONED AS SHOWN, MARK EACH END AND USE MARKS AS TIMING MARKS

FM1069100142000X

Fig. 18 Timing chain marks

OIL PUMP ASSY 6621

BOLT 4 REQ'D TIGHTEN TO 8-12 N·m (6.0-8.8 LB-FT)

FRONT OF ENGINE

CYLINDER BLOCK ASSY

FM1099100035000X

Fig. 21 Oil pump assembly

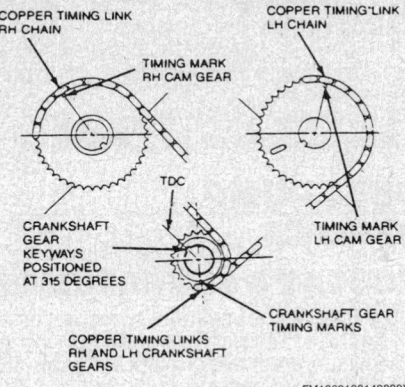

COPPER TIMING LINK RH CHAIN

COPPER TIMING LINK LH CHAIN

TIMING MARK RH CAM GEAR

TDC

CRANKSHAFT GEAR KEYWAYS POSITIONED AT 315 DEGREES

TIMING MARK LH CAM GEAR

CRANKSHAFT GEAR TIMING MARKS

COPPER TIMING LINKS RH AND LH CRANKSHAFT GEARS

FM1069100143000X

Fig. 19 LH timing chain installation

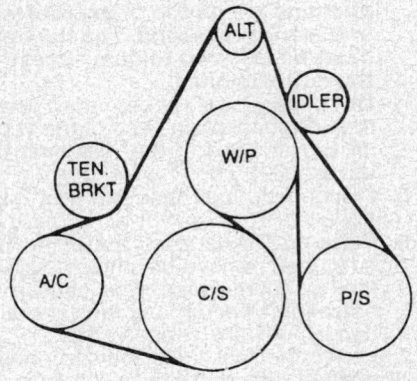

ALT

IDLER

W/P

TEN. BRKT

A/C

C/S

P/S

FM1069100145000X

Fig. 22 Serpentine drive belt routing

FRONT OF ENGINE

NOTE: DO NOT REMOVE TENSIONER LOCK PINS UNTIL CHAIN GUIDES HAVE BEEN INSTALLED

NOTE: LUBRICATE TENSIONER ARM CONTACT SURFACES WITH ENGINE OIL PRIOR TO ASSY

RH CYLINDER HEAD ASSY

RH TENSIONER ARM

RH CHAIN TENSIONER

LOCK PIN

BOLT 2 REQ'D TIGHTEN TO

15-22 LB-FT

LOCK PIN

BOLT 2 REQ'D TIGHTEN TO

15-22 LB-FT

LH CHAIN TENSIONER

DOWEL

LH TENSIONER ARM

LH CYLINDER HEAD ASSY

FM1069100144000X

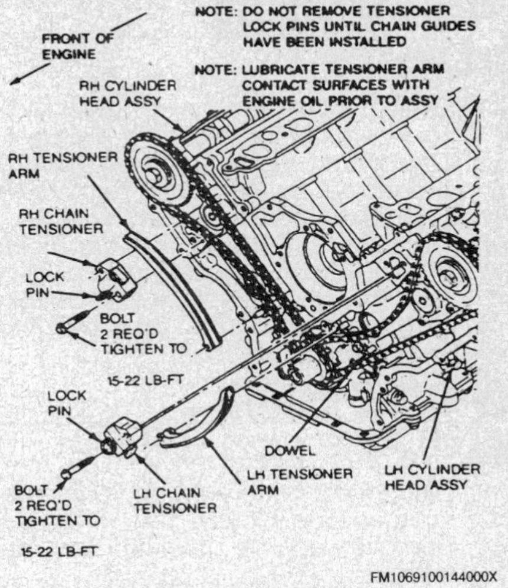

Fig. 20 Tensioner arm installation

a. Align oil pump inner rotor with flat of crankshaft.
b. **Torque** oil pump attaching bolts to 6.-8.8 ft. lbs.

BELT TENSION DATA

Automatic belt tensioners are spring loaded devices which set and maintain drive belt tension. The drive belt should not require tension adjustment for the life of belt. Automatic tensioners have belt wear indicator marks. If indicator mark is not between indicator lines, belt is worn or an incorrect belt is installed.

SERPENTINE DRIVE BELT

BELT ROUTING

Refer to **Fig. 22,** for drive belt routing.

ADJUSTMENT

Automatic belt tensioners are spring loaded devices which set and maintain the drive belt tension. The drive belt should not require tension adjustment.

REPLACEMENT

1. Rotate tensioner away from belt using a breaker bar installed in 1/2 inch square hole in tensioner arm.
2. Lift old belt over alternator pulley flange and remove.
3. When installing, position new belt over pulleys. Ensure all V-grooves make proper contact with pulley.
4. Ensure belt is properly installed on each pulley.

COOLING SYSTEM BLEED

1. Place heater temperature switch in maximum heat position.
2. Fill reservoir to below filler neck seat.
3. Leave pressure cap off and run engine until thermostat opens.
4. Stop engine and add coolant to reservoir as necessary to adjust level. Install pressure cap.

gear. Ensure copper link is aligned with crankshaft gear.

12. Lubricate tensioner arm contact surfaces with engine oil and install right and left tensioner arms on dowels. **Fig. 20.**
13. Install right and left timing chain tensioners. Tighten to specifications. **Do not remove lockpins until timing chain guides are installed.**
14. Install chain guides. Tighten to specifications.
15. Remove lockpins from timing chain tensioners and ensure all timing marks are aligned.
16. Remove cam positioning tools and install all components removed during removal procedure. Tighten to specifications.

OIL PAN
REPLACE

1. Disconnect ground and positive battery cables.
2. Remove air inlet tube and drain cooling system. Remove cooling fan and shroud.
3. Relieve fuel system pressure as described under "Fuel System Pressure Relief." Disconnect fuel lines.
4. Remove upper radiator hose, wiper module and support bracket.
5. Discharge A/C system, then disconnect A/C compressor outlet hose. Remove bolt securing hose assembly to right coil bracket.
6. Remove engine electrical harness 42-pin connector from bracket on brake vacuum booster.
7. Disconnect engine electrical connector, then disconnect transmission harness electrical connector.
8. Disconnect throttle valve cable at throttle body.
9. Disconnect heater outlet hose.
10. Remove right cylinder head ground strap attaching nut, then remove upper stud and lower bolt securing heater hose to cylinder head.
11. Remove blower motor resistor, then the right engine mount to lower engine bracket attaching bolt.

12. Disconnect exhaust system from manifolds.
13. Lower exhaust and secure to crossmember with wire.
14. Position a suitable jack and block of wood below oil pan, rearward of drain plug.
15. Raise engine approximately four inches, then insert two wood blocks, approximately 2.5-2.75 inches thick, under each engine mount.
16. Lower engine onto wood blocks and remove jack from below oil pan.
17. Loosen 16 retaining bolts and remove oil pan. **It may be necessary to loosen, without removing, the two nuts on rear transmission mount and raise extension housing of transmission slightly to remove oil pan.**
18. Reverse procedure to install. Tighten to specifications.

OIL PUMP
REPLACE

1. Remove camshaft covers, front cover and oil pan as previously described.
2. Remove timing chains as described under "Timing Chains, Gears, Tensioners & Guides, Replace."
3. Remove oil pump mounting bolts, then remove oil pump, **Fig. 21.**
4. Reverse procedure to install, noting the following:

THERMOSTAT
REPLACE

1. Drain coolant level below upper radiator hose and thermostat housing.
2. Disconnect upper radiator hose at thermostat housing, then remove two thermostat housing retaining bolts.
3. Remove O-ring seal and thermostat from intake manifold. Inspect O-ring for damage and replace if necessary.
4. Reverse procedure to install. Tighten bolts to specifications.

WATER PUMP
REPLACE

1. Disconnect battery ground cable and drain cooling system.
2. Remove engine cooling fan and shroud.
3. Release belt tensioner and remove accessory drive belt.
4. Remove water pump pulley mounting bolts, then remove water pump pulley.
5. Loosen mounting bolts and remove water pump.
6. Reverse procedure to install. Replace O-ring and tighten to specifications.

RADIATOR
REPLACE

COUGAR & THUNDERBIRD

1. Drain cooling system.
2. Disconnect upper, lower and overflow hose from radiator.
3. Disconnect automatic transmission fluid cooler inlet and outlet lines from radiator.
4. Remove two upper fan shroud to radiator support attaching bolts.
5. Lift fan shroud enough to disengage lower retaining clips and lay shroud back over fan.
6. Remove radiator upper support attaching bolts, then lift radiator from the vehicle.
7. Reverse procedure to install.

CROWN VICTORIA & GRAND MARQUIS

1. Turn lower fan shroud in upper fan shroud to allow clearance for fan shroud removal.
2. Disconnect cooling fan electrical connector at righthand side of fan shroud.
3. Remove radiator upper sight shield.
4. Loosen fan shroud from its radiator mounting, then remove lower radiator hose from supports on fan shroud.
5. Lift fan shroud and electric cooling fan assembly out of vehicle.
6. Disconnect transmission oil cooler inlet and outlet lines from radiator.
7. Drain engine cooling system.
8. Disconnect upper, lower and de-aeration hoses from radiator.
9. Remove two upper A/C condenser core to radiator attaching bolts.

10. Remove radiator support attaching bolts, then the supports.
11. Lift A/C condenser core enough to disengage lower retaining clips on radiator.
12. Remove radiator from vehicle.
13. Reverse procedure to install.

FUEL PUMP
REPLACE

COUGAR & THUNDERBIRD

1. Relieve fuel system pressure as described under "Precautions."
2. Disconnect battery ground cable, then raise and support vehicle.
3. Drain fuel from fuel tank, then remove the exhaust system as required for access. **The plastic fuel tube connections are on top of the fuel tank and are inaccessible. The fuel tank must be lowered to gain access to the connections.**
4. Disconnect fuel hoses and tubes, then disconnect one end of the vapor crossover hose at the rear over the driveshaft.
5. Disconnect fuel tank to filler pipe hose.
6. Place a safety support under the fuel tank, then remove bolts from the fuel tank support straps. Use caution to not deform the fuel tank, fuel tank support or fuel tank support straps.
7. Lower the fuel tank and disconnect the fuel lines and electrical connector from the fuel gauge sender, if required.
8. Remove any dirt that has accumulated around the fuel pump retaining flange so it will not enter the fuel tank during fuel pump removal and installation.
9. Turn fuel pump locking retainer ring counterclockwise using fuel tank sender wrench tool No. D84P-9275-A or equivalent, and remove fuel pump locking retainer ring.
10. Remove fuel pump assembly and the seal ring.
11. Reverse procedure to install, noting the following:
    a. Apply a light coating of Premium Long-Life Grease part No. XG-1 or XG-1-K or equivalent, on new fuel pump sealing ring to secure in position during installation.
    b. Ensure all locking tabs are under tabs before tightening locking ring.
    c. Tighten to specifications.

CROWN VICTORIA & GRAND MARQUIS

1. Relieve fuel system pressure as described under "Fuel System Pressure Relief."
2. Drain fuel tank, then raise and support vehicle.
3. Disconnect fuel supply and return line fittings and vent line.
4. Disconnect fuel pump and sender electrical connectors.

5. Remove fuel tank attaching support straps, then carefully lower fuel tank assembly. Ensure dirt does not enter tank or fuel system.
6. Using Fuel Tank Sender Wrench tool No. D74P-9275-A or equivalent, turn fuel pump locking ring counterclockwise, then remove locking ring.
7. Remove fuel pump assembly, then remove and discard seal ring.
8. Reverse procedure to install, noting the following:
   a. Once fuel pump is installed, using Fuel Pressure Gauge tool No. T80L-9974-B or equivalent on fuel charging assembly Schraeder valve, turn ignition from OFF to ON position for 3 seconds. Repeat OFF to ON switching 5 to 10 times until pressure gauge shows at least 35 psi.
   b. Tighten to specifications.

FUEL FILTER
REPLACE

COUGAR & THUNDERBIRD

1. Relieve fuel system pressure as described under "Fuel System Pressure Relief."
2. Disconnect battery ground cable.
3. Raise and support vehicle.
4. Remove push connect fittings at both ends of the fuel filter and base. Install new retainer clips in each push connect fitting.
5. Remove fuel filter and base from bracket by loosening worm gear clamp. Note direction of the flow arrow as installed in the bracket to ensure proper replacement.
6. Reverse procedure to install. Tighten to specifications.

CROWN VICTORIA & GRAND MARQUIS

1. Turn engine off and relieve fuel system pressure as described under "Fuel System Pressure Relief."
2. Raise and support vehicle.
3. Remove push connect fittings at both ends of the filter. Install new retainer clips in each push connect fitting.
4. Remove fuel filter and retainer from metal bracket by removing two retainer bolts.
5. Remove filter from retainer. Note direction of flow arrow points to open end of retainer.
6. Remove rubber insulator rings from filter.
7. Reverse procedure to install, noting the following:
   a. Replace insulator if filter moves freely after installation of retainer.
   b. **Torque** fuel filter retainer bolts to 27-44 inch lbs.
   c. Start engine and inspect for fuel leaks.

TIGHTENING SPECIFICATIONS
COUGAR & THUNDERBIRD

Component	Torque/Ft. Lbs.
Alternator Mounting Bolts	15-22
Alternator Rear Mounting Bracket To Intake Manifold	70-106 ①
Camshaft Sprocket Bolt	81-95
Crankshaft Pulley Bolt	114-121
Cylinder Head Bolts	②
ECT Sensor	12-17
EGR Valve Line Nut	26-33
EGR Valve Tube To Manifold Connector	33-48
Engine To Transmission Bolts	30-44
Exhaust Manifold Bolts	15-22
Exhaust Manifold Tube	26-33
Flywheel To Crankshaft Bolt	54-64
Front Cover	15-22
Front Engine Support Insulator Through Bolts	15-22
Front Sub-Frame To Body Bolts	73-100
Front Suspension Lower Arms To Spring & Shock Bolt	118-162
Front Suspension Upper Arms To Front Wheel Spindles	50-68
Fuel Filter Worm Gear Clamp	16-24 ①

Component	Torque/Ft. Lbs.
IAC Valve Bolts	70-106 ①
Intake Manifold Bolts	15-22
Oil Cooler Tube Bracket To Transmission Case	15-22
Oil Filter Adapter Bolt	15-22
Oil Pan Bolts	15-22
Oil Pan Drain Plug	8-12
Oxygen Sensors	27-3
Power Steering Pump Bolts	15-22
Rear Axle Assembly To Rear Sub-Frame	72-89
Rear Axle Differential Insulator Nuts	75-94
Rear Axle Universal Joint Flange	70-95
Rear Engine Support Insulator Retaining Bolts	15-2
Spark Plugs	80-106 ①
Thermostat Housing Bolts	15-22
Throttle Body & Adapter Bolts	73-100
Torque Converter Retaining Nuts	22-25
Transmission Case To Cylinder Block	18-31
Valve Cover Bolts	70-106 ①
Water Pump Pulley	15-22

①—Inch Lbs.
②—Refer to text.

CROWN VICTORIA & GRAND MARQUIS

Year	Component	Torque/Ft. Lbs.
1992-95	A/C Compressor Mounting Bolts	15-22
	Alternator To Cylinder Block	15-22
	Camshaft Cover Bolt	6-8.8
	Camshaft Gear Bolt	81-95
	Connecting Rod Bolt	①
	Coolant Temperature Switch	12-17
	Crankshaft Rear Oil Seal Retainer	①
	Cylinder Front Cover Bolt	15-22
	Cylinder Head Bolt	①
	Damper To Crankshaft Bolt	114-121
	ECT Sensor	12-17
	EGR Tube Connector	33-48
	EGR Valve Line Nut	26-33
	EGR Valve To Intake Manifold	15-22
	Engine Mount Attaching Bolts	45-59
	Engine Mount Through Bolts	15-22
	Engine To Transmission Bolts	30-44
	Engine To Transmission Braces	18-31
	Exhaust Manifold	①
	Exhaust Pipe To Exhaust Manifold	20-30
	Flywheel Bolts	54-64
	Front Cover	15-22
	Fuel Rail Retaining Bolts	6-8.8

Year	Component	Torque/Ft. Lbs.
1992-95 –Cont'd	Fuel Tank Strap	22-30
	HEGO Sensors	27-33
	Intake Manifold	①
	Main Bearing Cap	②
	Oil Filter Adapter	15-22
	Oil Inlet Tube To Main Bearing Cap	15-22
	Oil Inlet Tube To Oil Pump Bolt	6-8.8
	Oil Pan Drain Plug	8-12
	Oil Pan To Cylinder Block	15-22
	Oil Pump To Cylinder Block	6-8.8
	Power Steering Pump To Engine	15-22
	Rear Engine Mount Nuts	35-47
	Rear Engine Mount To Crossmember Bolts	51-67
	Rear Oil Seal Retainer	①
	Spark Plug	6.6-7.3
	Thermostat Mounting Bolts	15-22
	Throttle Body & Adapter Assembly	6-8.8
	Timing Chain Guides	6-8.8
	Timing Chain Tensioner Bolts	15-22
	Torque Converter Nuts	22-25
	Water Pump Mounting Bolts	15-22
	Water Pump Pulley Bolts	15-22

①–Refer to text.
②—Tighten in two steps, first to 22-25 ft. lbs., then an additional 85-95°.

5.0L/V8-302 Engine

NOTE: On Vehicles Equipped With Air Bags, Disarm Air Bag System As Described Under "Precautions" Before Any Diagnosis, Testing, Troubleshooting Or Repairs Are Performed. When Procedures Have Been Completed, Rearm Air Bag System As Outlined Under "Precautions."

INDEX

PRECAUTIONS

AIR BAG SYSTEMS

Refer to "Air Bag System Precautions" in the front of this manual for system disarming and arming procedures.

FUEL PRESSURE SYSTEM RELIEF

Fuel lines will remain pressurized for long periods of time after engine is turned off. This pressure must be relieved before servicing any fuel related component.

A valve on fuel charging assembly is used to relieve system pressure. Attach EFI and CFI fuel pressure gauge tool No. T80L-9974-B or equivalent, to Schraeder valve located on fuel rail. Pressure in fuel system may now be released.

ENGINE MOUNT

REPLACE

Whenever self-locking mounting bolts and nuts are removed, they must be replaced with new self-locking bolts and nuts.

1. Remove fan shroud attaching screws.
2. Support engine using a suitable jack with a wooden block placed under oil pan.
3. Remove nut and through bolt attaching insulator to frame crossmember.
4. Disconnect shift linkage, as required.
5. Raise engine slightly, then remove insulator and heat shield, if equipped, **Fig. 1**.
6. Reverse procedure to install. Tighten to specifications.

ENGINE

REPLACE

1. Disconnect battery ground cable and

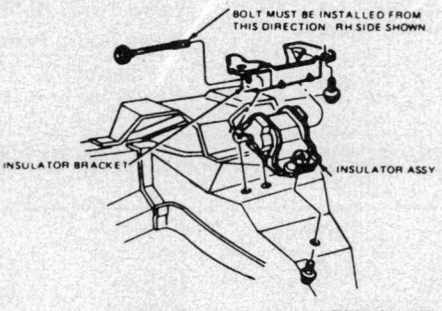

BOLT MUST BE INSTALLED FROM THIS DIRECTION. RH SIDE SHOWN

INSULATOR BRACKET

INSULATOR ASSY

FM1069100146000X

Fig. 1 Engine mount replacement

drain cooling system.
2. Disconnect engine compartment lamp connector and remove dipstick, then mark hinge positions and remove hood.
3. Discharge A/C system, then disconnect and plug A/C compressor lines.
4. Disconnect compressor clutch electrical connectors, power steering pressure switch and alternator wiring harness.
5. Remove fan shroud and fan assembly, then remove upper radiator hose.
6. Remove air cleaner to throttle body tube assembly. Disconnect transmission oil cooler lines.
7. Disconnect throttle and kickdown cables from throttle body and remove cable bracket retaining bolts. Position cable and bracket assembly clear of area.
8. Disconnect vacuum lines at upper intake manifold vacuum tee, A/C control panel vacuum supply hose, Thermactor valve and EGR valve.
9. Remove upper intake manifold, then disconnect main engine wiring har-

ness connectors at right side of dash panel.
10. Disconnect heater hoses at engine and position engine wiring harness sot it can be removed with engine.
11. Disconnect wiring harness from coil and distributor. Relieve fuel system pressure.
12. Disconnect fuel hoses from fuel supply manifold. Cap lines and fittings to prevent contamination.
13. Disconnect lower radiator hose from water pump. Remove radiator.
14. Raise and support vehicle, drain engine oil and remove filter.
15. Remove starter motor, then disconnect HEGO sensors from right and left catalytic converters.
16. Disconnect battery ground cable from left side of engine, then disconnect transmission cooler line brackets, ground straps and starter motor wiring harness from right side of engine.
17. Remove torque converter inspection cover and mark one of converter studs to flywheel for alignment during installation.
18. Remove torque converter retaining nuts, then the exhaust manifold heat shield at left manifold flange and disconnect exhaust pipe from flange.
19. Disconnect right exhaust manifold flange. Loosen transmission mount retaining nut.
20. Remove converter housing to engine bolts, then the motor mount through bolts.
21. Lower vehicle and remove power steering lines. Support transmission with suitable floor jack.
22. Install suitable engine lifting sling on engine lifting eyes. Lift engine assembly clear of engine mounts and remove assembly from vehicle.
23. Reverse procedure to install. Tighten to specifications.

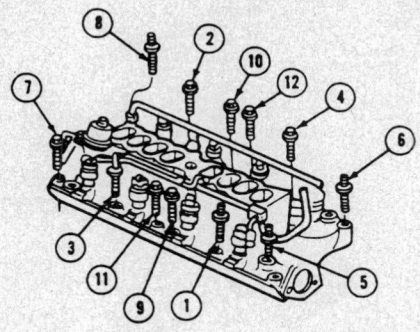

Fig. 2 Intake manifold tightening sequence

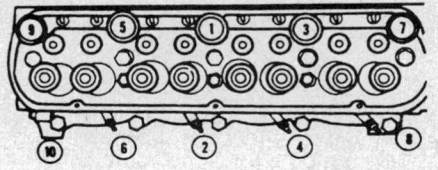

Fig. 3 Cylinder head tightening sequence

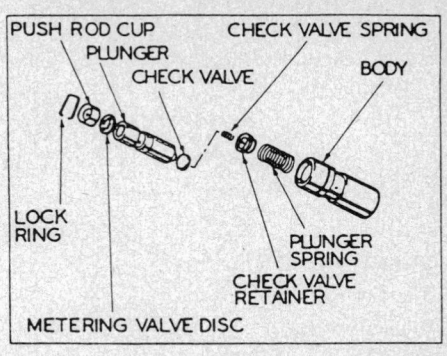

Fig. 4 Hydraulic valve lifter disassembled

INTAKE MANIFOLD
REPLACE

1. Disconnect battery ground cable and drain cooling system, then disconnect accelerator cable and speed control linkage from throttle body.
2. Disconnect transmission cable and remove accelerator cable bracket.
3. Disconnect vacuum lines at intake manifold fitting.
4. Disconnect spark plug wires. Remove wires and bracket assembly from rocker arm cover attaching stud. Remove distributor cap, adapter and spark plug wire assembly.
5. Relieve fuel system pressure, then disconnect fuel lines.
6. Disconnect distributor wiring connector, then remove distributor hold-down bolt. Remove distributor.
7. Disconnect upper radiator hose from coolant outlet housing and water temperature sending unit wire at sending unit.
8. Disconnect hose from intake manifold and two throttle body cooler hoses.
9. Loosen clamp on water pump bypass hose at coolant outlet housing and slide hose off of housing. Disconnect wires at ECT, ACT, TP, ISC solenoid and EGR sensors.
10. Disconnect injector wire connections and fuel charging assembly wiring.
11. Pull PCV valve out of grommet at rear of lower intake manifold. Disconnect fuel evaporative purge hose from plastic connector at front of upper intake manifold.
12. Remove upper intake manifold.
13. Remove heater tube assembly from lower intake manifold.
14. Remove lower intake manifold. It may be necessary to pry manifold away from cylinder head.
15. Avoid possible damage to gasket sealing surfaces. Remove intake manifold gaskets and seals.
16. Reverse procedure to install, noting the following:
   a. Apply a 1/16 inch bead of sealer to outer end of each intake manifold seal for the full width of seal (four places).
   b. **Torque** intake manifold bolts to 15-20 ft. lbs. in sequence shown in

Fig. 2.
   c. Following installation, fill and bleed cooling system, then adjust ignition timing.
   d. Operate engine at fast idle and check all hose connections and gaskets for leaks. When engine temperatures have stabilized, tighten intake manifold bolts to 23-25 ft. lbs.

EXHAUST MANIFOLD
REPLACE

1. Remove oil dipstick and tube assembly.
2. Remove thermactor hardware, if equipped.
3. Disconnect exhaust manifold from exhaust pipe. Remove spark plug wires and spark plugs.
4. Disconnect oxygen sensor (HEGO sensor).
5. Remove mounting bolts and washers, then remove exhaust manifolds.
6. Reverse procedure to install. Tighten to specifications.

CYLINDER HEAD
REPLACE

1. Disconnect battery ground cable and remove intake manifold.
2. Remove rocker arm cover.
3. Remove A/C compressor, if necessary.
4. **If removing left cylinder head,** disconnect power steering pump bracket from left cylinder head. Position pump clear of area. Disconnect oil lever indicator tube from exhaust manifold stud.
5. Remove thermactor crossover tube from rear of cylinder heads.
6. **If removing right cylinder head,** remove alternator mounting bracket from cylinder head.
7. Remove fuel line clip at front of right cylinder head.
8. Disconnect exhaust manifold from muffler intake pipe.
9. Loosen rocker arm stud nuts or bolts so that rocker arms can be rotated to the side.
10. Remove pushrods, keeping them in sequence so they may be installed in original locations. Remove exhaust valve stem caps.
11. Loosen cylinder head bolts and lift head off of block. If required, remove exhaust manifolds to gain access to lower attaching bolts. Remove and discard head gasket.

12. Reverse procedure to install, noting the following:
   a. Slightly tighten cylinder head bolts in a series of two steps in sequence shown in **Fig. 3**. Torque first step to 55-65 ft. lbs., then **torque** all cylinder head bolts again in sequence to 65-72 ft. lbs.
   b. It is not necessary to retighten bolts after extended operation. Bolts may be checked and retightened, if desired.
   c. Apply Multi-Purpose Grease D0AZ-19584-AA or equivalent, to both ends of pushrods and valve stem tips. Install pushrods in original positions.
   d. Install rocker arms and check valve clearance.
   e. Tighten all components to specifications.

VALVE ARRANGEMENT
FRONT TO REAR

Right .... I-E-I-E-I-E
Left .... E-I-E-I-E-I

VALVE LIFTERS

The internal parts of each hydraulic valve lifter assembly are a matched set. If these are mixed, improper valve operation may result. Therefore, disassemble, inspect and test each assembly separately to prevent mixing the parts.

Fig. 4 illustrates one type of hydraulic lifter used. On some late model engines, a roller type hydraulic lifter is used instead of conventional lifter.

1. Remove intake manifold and related parts.
2. Remove rocker arm covers.
3. Loosen rocker arm stud nuts or bolts and rotate rocker arms to the side.
4. Lift out pushrods, keeping them in sequence in a rack so they may be installed in their original location. **On some late model engines with roller type lifters, pushrods have a collar at upper end and can only be installed one way.**
5. On engines with roller type lifters, remove lifter guide retainer attaching bolts, then the guide retainer and guide plates. Ensure guide retainer and plates are marked so they may be

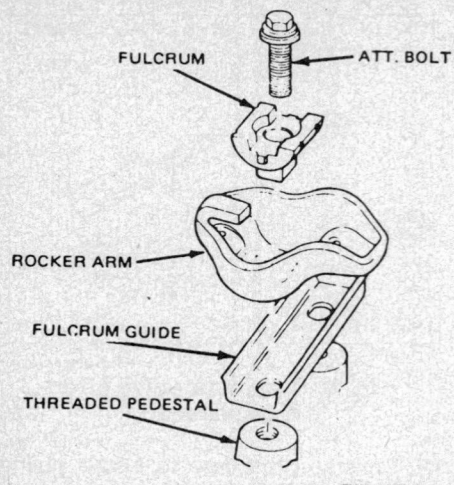

Fig. 5   Rocker arm

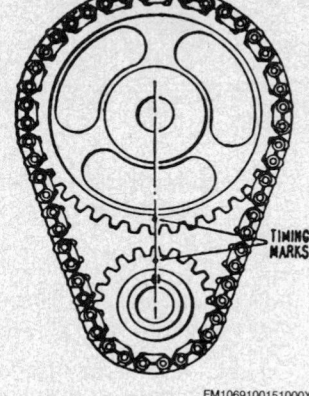

Fig. 6   Timing mark alignment

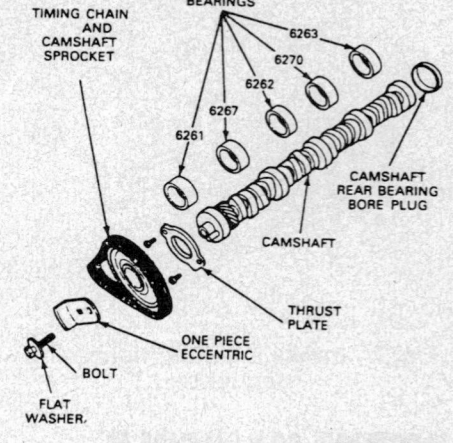

Fig. 7   Camshaft replacement

installed in their original location.
6. On all models, remove valve lifters, using a magnet rod, and place them in sequence in a rack so they may be installed in their original location.
7. Reverse procedure to install.

CAMSHAFT LOBE LIFT SPECIFICATIONS

Engine	Year	Intake, Inch	Exhaust, Inch
5.0L/V8-302 HO	1992–93	.278	.278

VALVE CLEARANCE SPECIFICATIONS

Valve clearance should be .098-.198 with the tappet fully collapsed.

VALVE ADJUSTMENT

1. With No. 1 piston at TDC at end of compression stroke, check following valves:
   a. Intake Nos. 1, 4 and 8; exhaust Nos. 1, 3 and 7.
2. Rotate crankshaft 360°. Check following valves:
   a. Intake Nos. 3 and 7; exhaust Nos. 2 and 6.
3. Rotate crankshaft 90°. Check following valves:
   a. Intake Nos. 2, 5 and 6; exhaust Nos. 4, 5 and 8.
4. If clearance is less than specified, install a shorter pushrod.
5. If clearance is greater than specified, install a longer pushrod.

ROCKER ARMS

These engines use a bolt and fulcrum attachment, **Fig. 5**. To replace, remove attaching bolt, then the fulcrum, rocker arm and fulcrum guide, if opposite rocker arm is being removed.

VALVE GUIDES

Valve guides in these engines are an in-tegral part of the head and, therefore, cannot be removed. For service, guides can be reamed oversize to accommodate one of three service valves with oversize stems (.003 inch, .015 inch and .030 inch).

Check valve stem clearance of each valve (after cleaning) in its respective valve guide. If clearance exceeds service limits of .0055 inch, ream valve guides to accommodate next oversize diameter valve.

FRONT COVER
REPLACE

1. Refer to "Water Pump, Replace" and perform all steps except removal of water pump. Leave water pump attached to front cover.
2. Drain oil crankcase, then remove crankshaft pulley from crankshaft vibration damper.
3. Remove damper attaching capscrew and washer. Install crankshaft damper removal tool No. T58P-6316-D or equivalent, on crankshaft vibration damper. Remove vibration damper.
4. Remove oil pan to front cover attaching bolts.
5. Carefully separate front cover from oil pan gasket.
6. Remove front cover and water pump as an assembly.
7. Reverse procedure to install, noting the following:
   a. Use care when installing cover to avoid seal damage or possible gasket mislocation.
   b. It may be necessary to force cover downward to slightly compress pan gasket. This can be accomplished by using front cover alignment tool No. T61P-6019-B or equivalent, at front cover attaching hole locations.
   c. Coat threads of attaching screws with oil resistant pipe sealant with Teflon D8AZ-19554-A or equivalent, and install screws. While pushing in on alignment tool, tighten oil pan to cover attaching screws to specifications.

   d. Tighten cover to block attaching screws to specifications, then remove pilot.
   e. Apply multi-purpose grease D0AZ-19584-AA or equivalent, to oil seal rubbing surface of vibration damper inner hub to prevent damage to seal. Apply silicone gasket and sealant E3AZ-19562-A or equivalent, to keyway before installing on crankshaft.
   f. Align crankshaft vibration damper keyway with key on crankshaft. Install vibration damper on crankshaft using crankshaft sprocket and damper replacement tool No. T52L-6306-AEE or equivalent. Install capscrew and washer and tighten to specifications. Install crankshaft pulley.
   g. Fill and bleed cooling system, then adjust ignition timing.

TIMING CHAIN
REPLACE

After removing front cover as outlined above, crank engine until timing marks are aligned as shown in **Fig. 6**. Remove camshaft sprocket retaining bolt, washer, fuel pump eccentric and spacer, if equipped. Slide both sprockets and chain forward and remove them as an assembly.

Reverse procedure to install chain and sprockets. Ensure timing marks are aligned.

CAMSHAFT
REPLACE

It may be necessary to remove or reposition radiator, A/C condenser and grille components to provide adequate clearance.

1. Remove front cover and timing chain as previously described.
2. Remove intake manifold and related components.
3. Remove EGR valve and rocker arm covers.
4. Loosen rocker arm stud nuts or bolts and rotate rocker arms to one side.

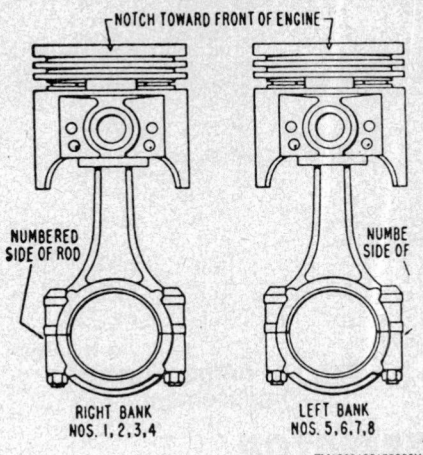

Fig. 8 Piston & rod assembly

5. Remove pushrods, keeping them in sequence in a rack so they may be installed in their original location.
6. Using a magnet, remove valve lifters and place them in a rack in sequence so they may be installed in their original location.
7. Remove camshaft thrust plate, **Fig. 7**, and carefully pull camshaft from engine, using care to avoid damaging camshaft bearings.
8. Reverse procedure to install, noting the following:

   a. Oil camshaft journals with heavy engine oil SG and apply Multi-Purpose Grease D0AZ-19584-AA or equivalent, to lobes and valve stem tips. Install camshaft thrust plate with groove toward cylinder block.
   b. Lubricate rocker arms and fulcrum seats with heavy engine oil SG.
   c. Tighten to specifications.
   d. Fill and bleed cooling system.

CAMSHAFT BEARINGS

When necessary to replace camshaft bearings, engine must be removed from vehicle and plug at the rear of the cylinder block must be removed in order to utilize the special camshaft bearing removal and installation tools required to do this job. If properly installed, camshaft bearings require no reaming—nor should this type bearing be reamed or altered in any manner in an attempt to fit bearings.

PISTON & ROD ASSEMBLY

Assemble pistons to rods so notch or arrow faces toward front of engine and numbered side of rod faces away from center of engine, **Fig. 8**. After installation, check side clearance between connecting rods at each crankshaft journal. Clearance should be .010-.020 inch.

PISTONS, PINS & RINGS

Pistons and rings are available in standard sizes and oversizes of .003, .020, .030 and .040 inch.

Oversize piston pins of .001 and .002 inch are available.

MAIN & ROD BEARINGS

Main and rod bearings are available in standard sizes and the following undersizes: .001, .002, .010, .020, .030, .040 inch.

CRANKSHAFT SEAL
REPLACE

A one piece crankshaft rear main oil seal must be used when replacement of seal is required.
1. Punch one hole into seal metal surface between seal lip and engine block using a suitable tool.
2. Screw threaded end of suitable slide hammer into hole and remove seal. Use caution not to damage oil seal surface.
3. Lubricate new seal with engine oil, then position seal on rear oil seal installer tool No. T82L-6701-A or equivalent.
4. Position tool and seal on rear of engine, then install tool attaching bolts. Tighten attaching bolts alternately until seal is properly seated.

OIL PAN
REPLACE

1. Disconnect battery ground cable and remove oil dipstick.
2. Disconnect air filter cover retaining clips to allow free movement when engine is raised.
3. Remove two bolts retaining radiator shroud to radiator and pull shroud loose from lower retaining clips.
4. Install engine support fixture tool No. D88L-6000-A or equivalent.
5. Raise and support vehicle, then drain engine oil and remove oil filter.
6. Remove engine mount through bolts, then loosen transmission mount nut to allow mount to move when engine is raised.
7. Partially lower vehicle, then raise engine approximately two inches, using support fixture tool.
8. Raise engine and remove power steering cooler line retaining clips. Remove bolt securing transmission lines to engine block.
9. Disconnect electrical connector from low oil level sensor located in oil pan, if equipped.
10. Remove oil pan retaining bolts, then remove steering shaft pinch bolt and separate steering shaft from power steering rack assembly.
11. Position two jack stands below engine support subframe. Remove lower strut-to-control arm bolts and nuts.
12. While supporting engine support subframe on jack stands, remove six rearward bolts on subframe. Loosen two forward bolts on subframe.
13. Lower subframe and remove oil pump/pick-up tube assembly and place it in oil pan.
14. Remove oil pan.
15. Reverse procedure to install, tighten to specifications.

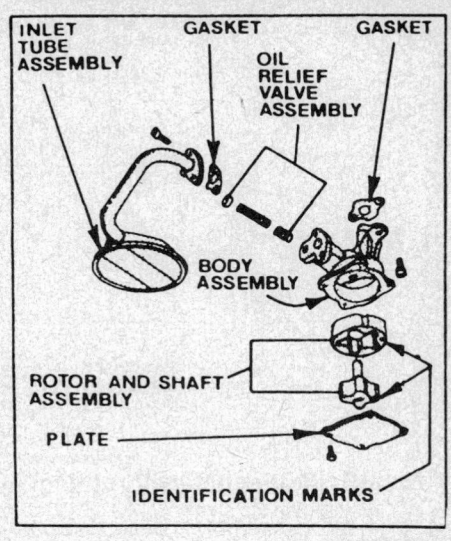

Fig. 9 Exploded view of oil pump

OIL PUMP
REPLACE

1. Remove oil pan as described under "Oil Pan, Replace" procedure.
2. Remove oil inlet pickup tube and screen assembly.
3. Remove oil pump attaching bolts, then the oil pump and intermediate driveshaft.
4. Reverse procedure to install, noting the following:
   a. Prime oil pump with engine oil before installing.
   b. Position intermediate driveshaft into distributor sprocket. With intermediate driveshaft firmly seated, the stop on the shaft should contact crankcase surface.
   c. Remove shaft and adjust as necessary. Position pump with intermediate driveshaft insert to cylinder block, then install and tighten attaching bolts to specification.
   d. **Do not force oil pump into position on cylinder block. If pump driveshaft is misaligned with distributor shaft, rotate driveshaft to a new position.**

OIL PUMP SERVICE

1. With all parts clean and dry, check inside of pump housing and outer race and rotor for damage or excessive wear, **Fig. 9**.
2. Check mating surface of pump cover for wear. Minor scuff marks are normal, but if cover, gears or housing surfaces are excessively worn, scored or grooved, replace pump. Inspect rotor for nicks, burrs or score marks. Remove minor imperfections with an oil stone.
3. Measure inner to outer rotor tip clearance. With rotor assembly removed from pump and resting on a flat surface, clearance must not exceed .012 inch.

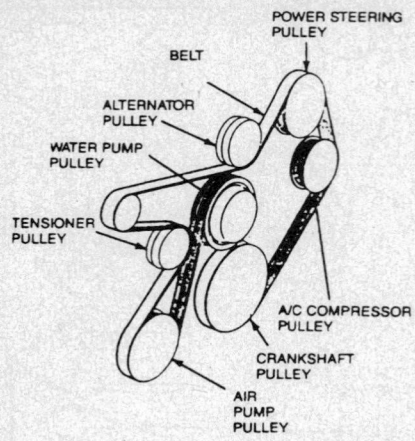

Fig. 10 Serpentine belt routing

4. With rotor assembly installed in housing, place a straightedge over rotor assembly and housing. Measure clearance between straightedge and inner rotor and outer race (rotor endplay). Clearance must not exceed .005 inch.
5. Inspect relief valve spring to see if it is collapsed or worn. Check relief valve spring tension. If spring is worn or damaged, replace pump. Check relief valve piston for free operation in the bore.
6. Internal components are not serviceable. If any component is out of specification, pump assembly must be replaced.

BELT TENSION DATA

Year	Model	Belt	New Lbs.	Used Lbs.
1992-93	Cougar & Thunderbird	6K ①	90	90

① —6 grooves with tensioner.

SERPENTINE DRIVE BELT

ADJUSTMENT

Automatic belt tensioners are spring loaded devices which set and maintain the drive belt tension. The drive belt should not require tension adjustment.

ROUTING

Refer to **Fig. 10** for serpentine drive belt routing.

REPLACEMENT

1. Rotate tensioner as shown in **Fig. 11**, and remove old belt.
2. Install new belt over pulleys. Ensure all V-grooves make proper contact with pulley.

COOLING SYSTEM BLEED

1. With engine off, add specified coolant

concentrate to radiator, then add water until it reaches radiator filler neck seat.
2. Remove vent plug on water bypass elbow (located on intake manifold behind water outlet connection). **Vent plug must be removed before radiator fill or engine may not fill completely. Do not turn plastic cap under vent plug or gasket may be damaged. Do not try to add coolant through vent plug hole. Install vent plug after filling radiator and before starting engine.**
3. Install radiator pressure cap to first notch.
4. Start and idle engine until upper radiator hose is warm.
5. Carefully remove cap and top off radiator with water.
6. Install cap on radiator. Fill coolant recovery reservoir to FULL COLD mark with coolant, then add water to FULL HOT mark. This will ensure a proper mixture in coolant recovery bottle.
7. Check for leaks at radiator draincock, block plug and vent plug.

THERMOSTAT
REPLACE

1. Partially drain coolant, until level is below thermostat.
2. Disconnect bypass hose from thermostat housing.
3. Mark location of distributor and loosen hold-down clamp.
4. Rotate distributor to gain access, if necessary.
5. Disconnect upper radiator hose and remove two thermostat housing bolts.
6. Remove thermostat, housing and gasket.
7. Reverse procedure to install. Tighten to specifications.

WATER PUMP
REPLACE

1. Drain cooling system, then remove upper radiator hose at engine.
2. Remove fan and clutch assembly from water pump shaft using fan clutch holding tool No. T84T-6312-C and fan clutch nut wrench tool No. T84T-6312-D or equivalents. Position fan and clutch in fan shroud.
3. Remove fan shroud and fan/clutch as one assembly.
4. Loosen water pump pulley bolts.
5. Remove accessory drive belt by rotating tensioner away from belt by using pulley retaining bolts only.
6. Remove water pump pulley, then disconnect radiator lower hose, heater hose and water pump bypass hose at water pump.
7. Remove bolts attaching pump to front cover. Remove pump.
8. Reverse procedure to install, noting the following:
   a. Tighten to specifications.
   b. Following installation, fill and bleed cooling system.

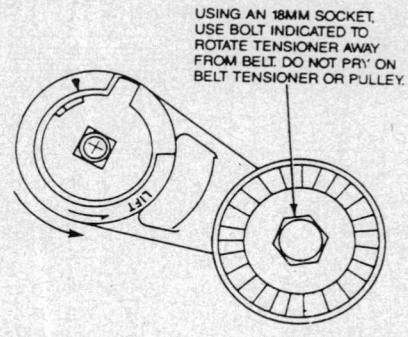

Fig. 11 Serpentine belt replacement

RADIATOR
REPLACE

1. Drain cooling system.
2. Disconnect upper, lower and overflow hose from radiator.
3. Disconnect automatic transmission fluid cooler inlet and outlet lines from radiator.
4. Remove two upper fan shroud to radiator support attaching bolts.
5. Lift fan shroud enough to disengage lower retaining clips and lay shroud back over fan.
6. Remove radiator upper support attaching bolts, then lift radiator from the vehicle.
7. Reverse procedure to install.

FUEL PUMP
REPLACE

1. Disconnect battery ground cable.
2. Release pressure from fuel system at fuel pressure relief valve using Fuel Pressure Gauge tool No. T80L-9974-B or equivalent. When relieving fuel pressure, crank engine with fuel pump electrical connector disconnected.
3. Drain fuel from tank through filler neck, then raise and support vehicle.
4. Remove exhaust pipe and exhaust shield, if necessary for access.
5. Disconnect fuel hoses and tubes. Disconnect one end of vapor crossover hose at rear of driveshaft. Disconnect filler hose. **Plastic fuel tube connections are on top of fuel tank and are inaccessible. Fuel tank must be lowered to gain access to connections.**
6. Place a support below fuel tank and remove bolts from fuel tank straps. Use caution not to damage fuel tank, fuel tank support or straps.
7. Lower fuel tank and disconnect fuel lines and electrical connector from fuel gauge sender. Clean fuel pump retaining flange to prevent fuel contamination.
8. Turn fuel pump locking ring counterclockwise using fuel tank sender wrench tool No. D84P-9275-A or equivalent, and remove locking ring.
9. Remove fuel pump, sender assembly and seal ring.
10. Reverse procedure to install, noting

the following:

a. Ensure locating keyways and seal ring remain in groove.

b. Hold pump assembly in place and install locking ring finger-tight. Ensure all locking tabs are under tank lock ring tabs.

c. Install EFI-CFI fuel pressure gauge tool No. T80L-9974-B or equivalent, on fuel charging assembly fuel diagnostic valve. Turn ignition switch from OFF to ON position for three seconds. Turn ignition switch for three seconds repeatedly until pressure gauge shows a minimum 35 psi.

FUEL FILTER
REPLACE

1. Turn engine off and relieve fuel system pressure as described under "Fuel Pressure Relief."
2. Raise and support vehicle.
3. Remove push connect fittings at both ends of the filter. Install new retaining in each push connect fitting.
4. Remove fuel filter from bracket by loosening worm gear clamp. Note direction of flow arrow as installed in bracket to ensure proper direction of fuel flow through replacement filter.
5. Reverse procedure to install. **Torque** fuel filter worm gear clamp to 16-24 inch lbs.

TIGHTENING SPECIFICATIONS

Year	Component	Torque/Ft. Lbs.
1992-93	Alternator Adjustment Arm To Water Pump Stud Nut	20-39
	Alternator Adjustment Arm To Alternator Bolt	24-40
	Camshaft Sprocket Bolt	40-45
	Camshaft Thrust Plate	9-12
	Connecting Rod Nut	19-24
	Crankshaft Damper Bolt	70-90
	Crankshaft Pulley To Damper	35-50
	Cylinder Head Bolts	①
	Distributor Hold-Down Bolt	18-26
	EGR Valve To Spacer	12-18
	Engine Insulator Assembly	26-38
	Engine Mount Through Bolts	45-65
	Exhaust Manifold	18-24
	Fan Clutch To Water Pump Hub	35-47
	Fan Shroud Attaching Screws	27-44 ②
	Flywheel to Crankshaft	75-85
	Front Cover	12-18
	Intake Manifold To Cylinder Head	①
	Main Bearing Cap Bolts	60-70
	Oil Filter Insert To Engine Adapter Bolt	20-30

Year	Component	Torque/Ft. Lbs.
1992-93 –Cont'd	Oil Inlet To Main Bearing Cap	22-32
	Oil Inlet Tube To Oil Pump	12-18
	Oil Pan Drain Plug	15-25
	Oil Pan To Engine	6-9
	Oil Pump To Engine	22-32
	Pulley To Damper Bolt	35-50
	Pump Bracket To Cylinder Head	40-55
	Rocker Arm Fulcrum Bolt	18-25
	Rocker Arm Cover	6-9
	Spark Plugs	5-10
	Steering Shaft Pinch Bolt	30-42
	Thermactor Pump Pivot Bolt	35-50
	Thermostat Housing	9-12
	Transmission Mount Nut	65-85
	Throttle Body Attaching Nut	12-18
	Throttle Body To EGR Spacer & Upper Intake Manifold	12-18
	Valve Lifter Guide Plate	71-106 ②
	Water Outlet Housing	12-18
	Water Pump	12-18

① —Refer to text.
② —Inch Lbs.

Clutch & Manual Transmission

INDEX

ADJUSTMENTS

HYDRAULIC SYSTEM SERVICE

SLAVE CYLINDER, REPLACE

1. Raise and support vehicle, then disconnect master cylinder pushrod from clutch pedal.
2. Disconnect clutch hydraulic line using clutch coupling tool No. T88T-70522-A or equivalent.
3. Remove transmission.
4. Loosen retaining bolts and remove clutch slave cylinder.
5. Reverse procedure to install, noting the following:
   a. Position slave cylinder over input shaft, aligning bleeder screw and line coupling with holes in transmission housing.
   b. Tighten to specifications and bleed system.

HYDRAULIC SYSTEM BLEEDING

1. Clean area around bleed valve at clutch actuating (slave) cylinder and clutch reservoir cap, **Fig. 1.**
2. Raise and support vehicle.
3. Attach a suitable length of hose to clutch actuating cylinder bleed valve.
4. While clutch pedal is being depressed, slightly open clutch actuating cylinder bleed valve.
5. Close bleed valve, then release clutch pedal.
6. Repeat procedure until air is removed from system. While performing procedure, maintain fluid level in clutch master cylinder. Add only DOT 3 type brake fluid to clutch master cylinder.

CLUTCH
REPLACE

1. Disconnect negative battery cable.
2. Disconnect clutch cylinder from clutch pedal and dash panel.
3. Raise and support vehicle, then remove starter.
4. Disconnect hydraulic coupling at transmission, using coupling disconnect tool No. T88T-70522-A or equivalent, by sliding white sleeve toward slave cylinder, and apply a slight tug

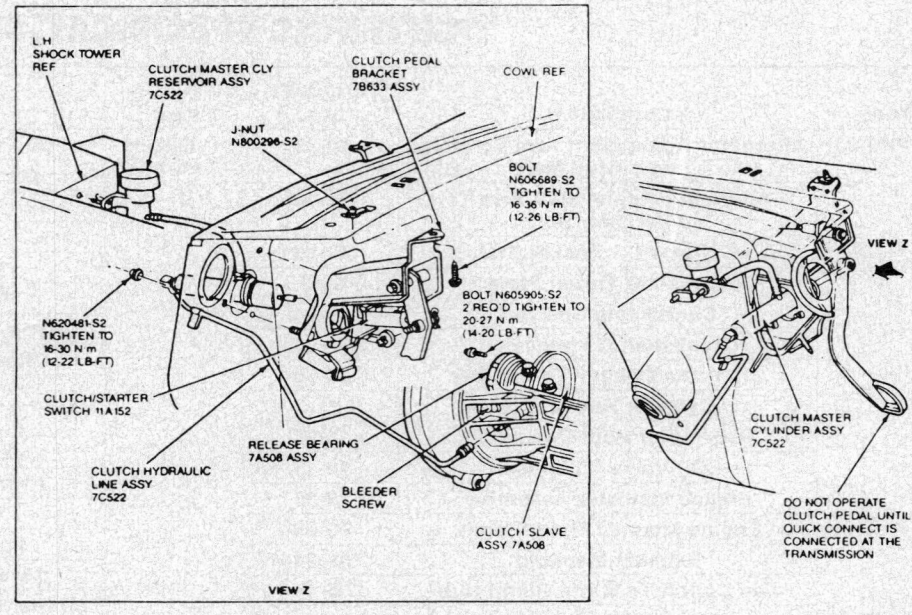

Fig. 1 Clutch hydraulic system

on tube.
5. Remove transmission as described under "Transmission, Replace."
6. Mark assembled position of pressure plate and cover to flywheel for reference during assembly.
7. Loosen pressure plate cover attaching bolts evenly, until pressure plate springs are expanded, then remove the bolts.
8. Remove pressure plate cover assembly, then the clutch disc from flywheel, **Fig. 2.**
9. Reverse procedure to install. Tighten pressure plate attaching bolts to specifications, in sequence shown in **Fig. 3.** Bleed clutch hydraulic system as necessary.

TRANSMISSION
REPLACE

1. Disconnect battery ground cable.
2. Place transmission shift lever in Neutral position, then remove shift lever knob.
3. Remove console upper cover, then remove shifter retaining bolts and shifter.
4. Raise and support vehicle, then drain

oil from transmission.
5. Remove body reinforcement in front axle.
6. Disconnect exhaust pipe from resonator.
7. Remove driveshaft to companion flange retaining bolts.
8. Position suitable axle stand under front axle, then remove forward and rearward retaining nuts and bolt plate.
9. Remove vent tube from hole in subframe, then lower front axle assembly and slide driveshaft from transmission. Position driveshaft on front driveshaft support.
10. Remove catalytic converter.
11. Disconnect clutch hydraulic line from actuating cylinder.
12. Remove starter motor assembly.
13. Position suitable transmission jack under transmission, then remove crossmember.
14. Remove flywheel housing to engine attaching bolts, then remove transmission from vehicle.
15. Reverse procedure to install. Lubricate driveshaft yoke splines with C1AZ-19590-BA or equivalent prior to installation. When installing driveshaft, align index marks on flange on yoke.

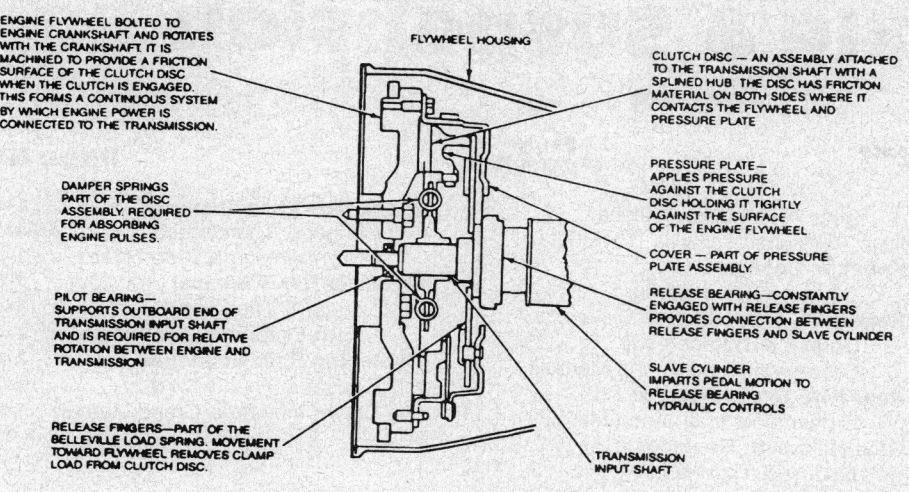

ENGINE FLYWHEEL BOLTED TO ENGINE CRANKSHAFT AND ROTATES WITH THE CRANKSHAFT IT IS MACHINED TO PROVIDE A FRICTION SURFACE OF THE CLUTCH DISC WHEN THE CLUTCH IS ENGAGED. THIS FORMS A CONTINUOUS SYSTEM BY WHICH ENGINE POWER IS CONNECTED TO THE TRANSMISSION.

FLYWHEEL HOUSING

DAMPER SPRINGS PART OF THE DISC ASSEMBLY. REQUIRED FOR ABSORBING ENGINE PULSES.

PILOT BEARING—SUPPORTS OUTBOARD END OF TRANSMISSION INPUT SHAFT AND IS REQUIRED FOR RELATIVE ROTATION BETWEEN ENGINE AND TRANSMISSION

RELEASE FINGERS—PART OF THE BELLEVILLE LOAD SPRING. MOVEMENT TOWARD FLYWHEEL REMOVES CLAMP LOAD FROM CLUTCH DISC.

CLUTCH DISC — AN ASSEMBLY ATTACHED TO THE TRANSMISSION SHAFT WITH A SPLINED HUB. THE DISC HAS FRICTION MATERIAL ON BOTH SIDES WHERE IT CONTACTS THE FLYWHEEL AND PRESSURE PLATE

PRESSURE PLATE—APPLIES PRESSURE AGAINST THE CLUTCH DISC HOLDING IT TIGHTLY AGAINST THE SURFACE OF THE ENGINE FLYWHEEL

COVER — PART OF PRESSURE PLATE ASSEMBLY.

RELEASE BEARING—CONSTANTLY ENGAGED WITH RELEASE FINGERS PROVIDES CONNECTION BETWEEN RELEASE FINGERS AND SLAVE CYLINDER

SLAVE CYLINDER IMPARTS PEDAL MOTION TO RELEASE BEARING HYDRAULIC CONTROLS

TRANSMISSION INPUT SHAFT

Fig. 2   Cross sectional view of clutch system

FM5049100030000X

Fig. 3   Clutch pressure plate tightening sequence

FM5049100031000X

TIGHTENING SPECIFICATIONS

Year	Component	Torque/Ft. Lbs.
1992-95	Axle Housing Bushing & Retaining Nuts	68-100
	Clutch Actuating Cylinder Bolts	14-20
	Clutch Pedal Assembly Retaining Bolts	16-22
	Clutch Pedal Assembly Retaining Nuts	12-22
	Clutch Pressure Plate To Flywheel Bolts	15-25
	Crossmember Attaching Bolts	35-50
	Driveshaft Yoke To Companion Flange	70-95
	Flywheel Housing To Engine Bolts	40-49
	Pressure Plate To Flywheel	20-28
	Transmission Drain & Filler Plugs	29-43
	Shifter Retaining Bolts	18-24
	Slave Cylinder	14-20

Rear Axle & Suspension

INDEX

DESCRIPTION

FORD INTEGRAL CARRIER w/BOLT-ON TYPE AXLE RETENTION

This rear axle, **Fig. 1**, is an integral design hypoid with the center line of the pinion set below the center line of the ring gear. The semi-floating axle shafts are retained in the housing by ball bearings and bearing retainers at axle ends.

The differential is mounted on two opposed tapered roller bearings which are retained in the housing by removable caps. Differential bearing preload and drive gear backlash is adjusted by nuts located behind each differential bearing cup.

The drive pinion assembly is mounted on two opposed tapered roller bearings. Pinion bearing preload is adjusted by a collapsible spacer on the pinion shaft. Pinion and ring gear tooth contact is adjusted by shims between the rear bearing cone and pinion gear.

FORD INTEGRAL CARRIER w/C-LOCK TYPE AXLE RETENTION

The gear set, **Fig. 2**, consist of a ring gear and an overhung drive pinion which is supported by two opposed tapered roller bearings. Pinion bearing preload is maintained by a collapsible spacer on the pinion shaft and adjusted by the pinion nut. The differential case is a one piece design with two openings to allow assembly of internal components and lubricant flow. The pinion shaft is retained with a threaded bolt assembled to the case. The differential case is mounted in the carrier between two opposed tapered roller bearings. The bearings are retained in the carrier by removable bearing caps. Differential bearing preload and ring gear backlash are adjusted by the use of shims located between the differential bearing cups and the carrier housing. Axle shafts are held in the housing by C-locks positioned in a slot on the axle shaft splined end, **Fig. 3**.

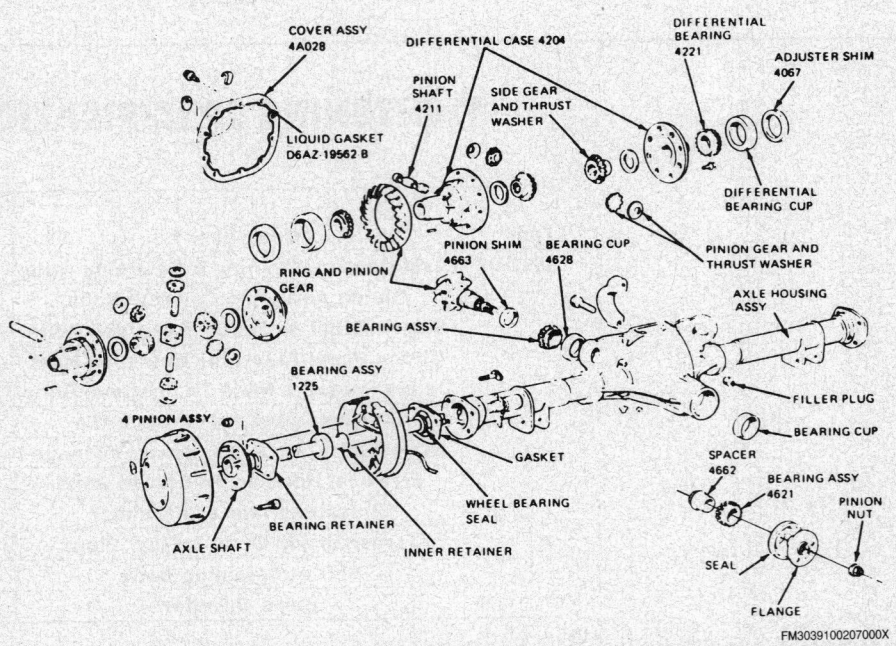

Fig. 1 Exploded view or Ford integral carrier type rear axle assembly w/bolt on type axle retention

REAR WHEEL DRIVE HALFSHAFT SYSTEM

This system shown in **Fig. 4**, employs constant velocity (CV) joints at both its inboard (differential) and outboard (wheel) ends for vehicle operating smoothness. The CV joints are connected by an interconnecting shaft which is splined at both ends and retained in the inboard and outboard CV joints by circlips.

The inboard CV joint stub shaft is splined and held in the differential side gear by circlip. The outboard CV joint stub shaft is pressed into the hub and secured with a free-spinning locknut. The CV joints are lube-for-life with a special CV joint grease and require no periodic lubrication. The CV boots should be periodically inspected and replaced immediately when damage or grease leakage is evident.

Halfshaft removal from the differential is accomplished by applying a load to the back face of the inboard CV joint assembly to overcome the circlip. The outboard joint end must be pressed from the hub.

The inboard tripod CV joints can be disassembled and serviced. Other then the CV boot, the outboard CV joint is serviced only as an assembly with the shaft.

REAR AXLE
REPLACE

CROWN VICTORIA & GRAND MARQUIS

1. Disconnect battery ground cable and

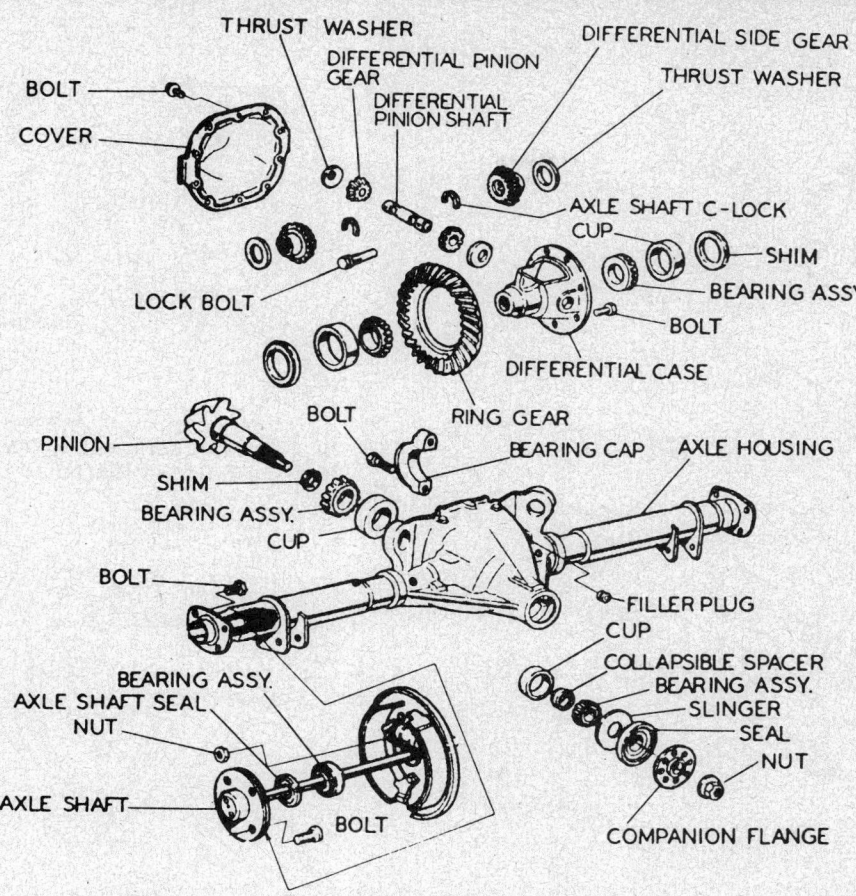

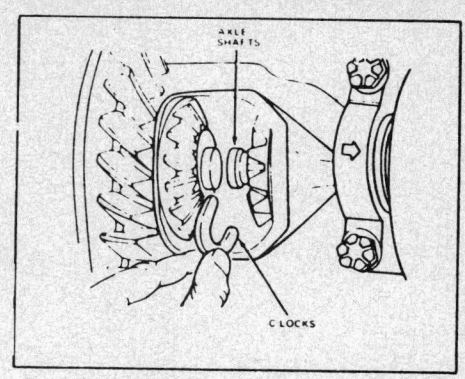

Fig. 3   Axle shaft C-lock. Crown Victoria & Grand Marquis

Fig. 2   Disassembled view of Ford integral carrier type rear axle assembly w/C-lock type axle retention

switch air suspension OFF.

2. Raise vehicle and position safety stands below rear frame crossmember.
3. Drain axle fluid by removing cover.
4. Remove wheels, rotors, calipers and ABS speed sensor.
5. Remove lock bolt from pinion shaft and remove shaft. **Fig. 5.**
6. Push axle shafts inward to remove C-locks.
7. Remove axle shafts, then remove right and left disc brake adapter brackets, bolts and J-nuts. **Fig. 6.**
8. Remove four retaining nuts from each disc brake adapter and support with wire from underbody.
9. Disconnect driveshaft at companion flange and support with wire.
10. Support axle housing with jackstands, then disengage brake line from clips that retain line to axle housing.
11. Release air spring pressure as described under "Air Suspension Pressure Relief." Remove air spring.
12. Disconnect vent from rear axle housing, then disconnect lower shock absorber studs from mounting brackets on axle housing.
13. Remove retaining nut and bolts and disconnect upper arms from mountings on axle housing ear brackets.
14. Lower axle housing assembly until

springs are released. Remove springs.
15. Disconnect lower arms from axle housing. Lower axle housing and remove from vehicle.
16. Reverse procedure to install. Tighten to specifications.

COUGAR & THUNDERBIRD

1. Remove right hand wheel cover, then loosen lug nuts.
2. Raise vehicle on a frame contact type hoist.
3. Remove wheel and tire assembly.
4. **On models with anti-lock brakes,** remove right and left hand brake sensors.
5. **On models with drum brakes,** remove right hand brake drum.
6. **On models with rear disc brakes,** proceed as follows:
   a. Disconnect parking brake cable from right hand caliper.
   b. Remove brake calipers with brake hoses attached. Suspend brake caliper from chassis with wire.
   c. Remove push nuts, then remove brake rotors.
7. **On all models,** Remove upper control arm bolt. Wire upper control arm to upper portion of shock to provide clearance for halfshaft removal.
8. Mark position of lower control arm to knuckle.

9. Remove right hand lower control arm to knuckle bolts and nuts.
10. Using tool No. T89P-3514-A or equivalent, remove right hand halfshaft from differential carrier. Use care not to damage differential oil seals or CV joint boots.
11. Remove halfshaft from knuckle.
12. Position differential plug No. T89P-4850-B or equivalent into differential housing to prevent fluid loss.
13. Mark position of driveshaft yoke to differential companion flange, then remove driveshaft retaining bolts.
14. Slide driveshaft forward and allow to rest on driveshaft hoop.
15. Using a suitable jack, support rear axle.
16. Remove rear axle mount retaining bolts, then remove rear mount.
17. Remove front axle retaining bolts and nuts.
18. Using tool No. T89P-3514-A or equivalent, remove left hand halfshaft inboard CV joint from differential carrier. Use care not to damage differential oil seals or CV joint boots.
19. While lowering rear axle assembly, move to right and disengage axle from left hand stub shaft.
20. Position differential plug T89P-4850-B or equivalent into differential housing to prevent fluid loss, then lower axle from vehicle.
21. Reverse procedure to install, noting the following:
    a. **New hub retainer nut, CV joint stub shaft circlips and differential seals must be installed.**
    b. Tighten to specifications.

REAR AXLE SHAFT
REPLACE

CROWN VICTORIA & GRAND MARQUIS
Removal

1. Disconnect battery ground cable and turn air suspension switch OFF.
2. Raise and support vehicle. Remove rear wheel and tire assembly.
3. Remove disc brake calipers and rotors.

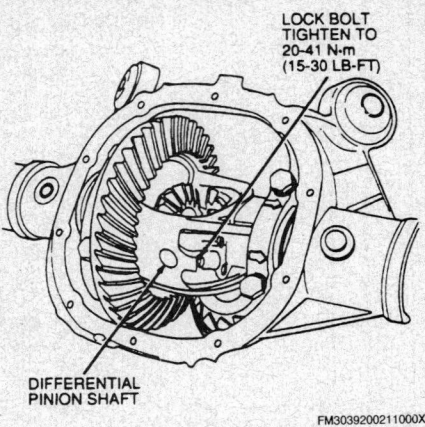

Fig. 5 Rear axle removal. Crown Victoria & Grand Marquis

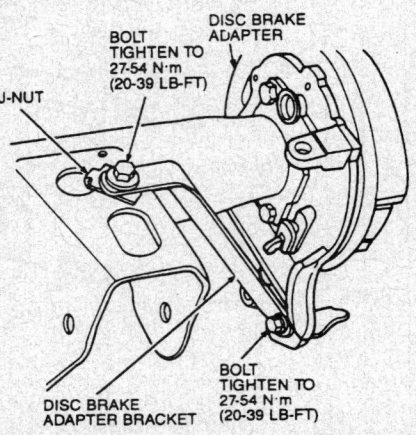

Fig. 6 Disc brake adapter removal. Crown Victoria & Grand Marquis

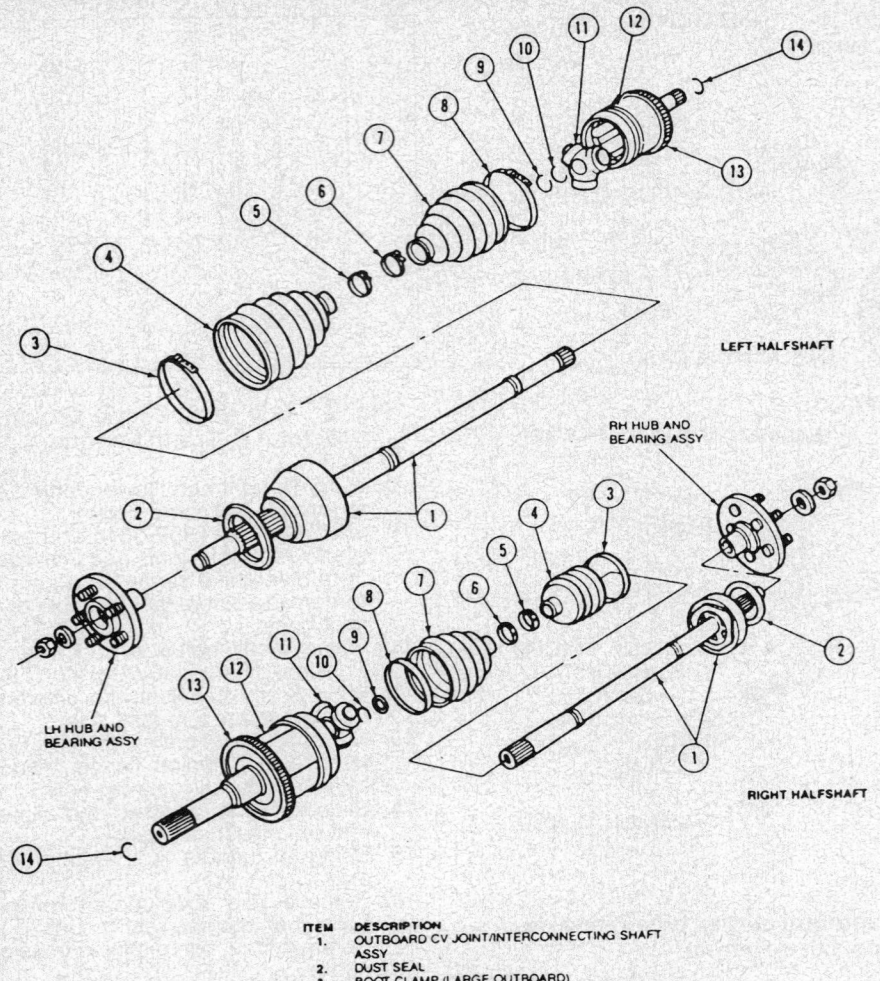

ITEM	DESCRIPTION
1.	OUTBOARD CV JOINT/INTERCONNECTING SHAFT ASSY
2.	DUST SEAL
3.	BOOT CLAMP (LARGE OUTBOARD)
4.	BOOT (OUTBOARD)
5.	BOOT CLAMP (SMALL OUTBOARD)
6.	BOOT CLAMP (SMALL INBOARD)
7.	BOOT (INBOARD)
8.	BOOT CLAMP (LARGE INBOARD)
9.	STOP RING
10.	CIRCLIP
11.	TRIPOD ASSY
12.	INBOARD JOINT OUTER RACE
13.	SENSOR RING (ANTI-SKID)
14.	CIRCLIP

Fig. 4 Rear wheel drive halfshaft system. Cougar & Thunderbird

4. Drain rear axle fluid by removing cover.
5. Remove differential pinion shaft lock bolt and differential pinion shaft. **Fig. 5.**
6. Push flanged end of axle shafts toward center of vehicle and remove C-lock from button end of axle shaft. **Fig. 3.**
7. Remove axle shaft from housing, use caution not to damage oil seal and ABS sensor ring.

Installation

1. Ensure O-ring is present on spline end of axle shaft.
2. Carefully slide axle shaft into axle housing. Use extreme caution to not damage bearing seal or ABS sensor ring.
3. Start splines into side gear and push firmly until button end of axle shaft can be seen in differential case.

4. Install C-lock on button end of axle shaft splines. Push shaft outboard until splines engage and the C-lock seats in counterbore of differential side gear.
5. Position differential pinion shaft through case and pinion gears, aligning hole in shaft with lock bolt hose. Apply rear axle lubricant E0AZ-19580-AA or equivalent, to pinion shaft lock bolt. Tighten to specifications.
6. Install cover and tighten to specifications.
7. Install ABS speed sensor, rotors and calipers. Tighten to specifications.

REAR HALFSHAFT
REPLACE

COUGAR & THUNDERBIRD

Do not begin this removal procedure unless following parts are available; new hub retainer nut; new inboard CV joint stub shaft circlip and new differential oil seal. Once removed, these parts must not be reused during assembly. Their torque holding ability is diminished during removal.

1. Remove wheel cover/hub cover and remove hub retainer nut, then loosen wheel nuts.
2. Raise and support vehicle on a frame contact hoist.
3. Remove rear wheel and tire assembly.
4. **On models with drum brakes,** remove brake drum.
5. **On models with disc brakes,** proceed as follows:
   a. Remove anti-lock brake sensors.
   b. Pull back on parking brake release lever and at same time pull on cable. This will slacken cable so cable end can be removed from brake caliper attachment.
   c. Remove upper and lower brake caliper attaching bolts.
   d. Remove caliper assembly from rotor, then carefully wire caliper to brake junction bracket.
   e. Remove brake rotor push nuts and remove rotor.

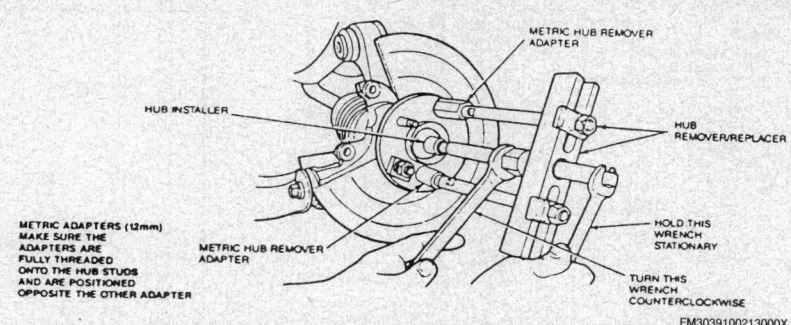

Fig. 7 Mounting hub removal tool. Cougar & Thunderbird

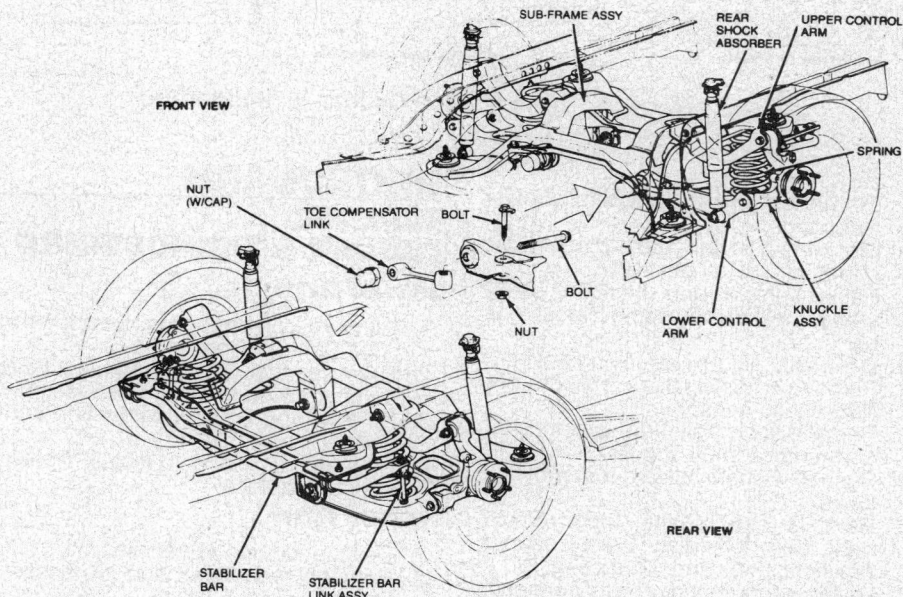

Fig. 8 Rear suspension. Cougar & Thunderbird

Fig. 9 Shock absorber replacement. Cougar & Thunderbird

6. **On all models,** remove upper control arm bolts and nuts, then wire upper control arm to upper shock absorber so that it does not damage CV joint boots when halfshaft is removed.
7. Using a paint marker, mark position of lower control arm in relation to knuckle with lower bushings in their relaxed position. When upper control arm bolt is removed from knuckle, lower bushings will return to their relaxed positions. **Failure to mark this position**

will result in bushing wind-up on assembly and incorrect ride height, causing misalignment and premature tire wear.

8. Install hub remover T81P-1104-C or equivalent to hub studs as shown in **Fig. 7.**
9. Turn wrench counterclockwise until halfshaft is free in hub.
10. Remove lower control arm attaching bolts.
11. Remove knuckle assembly while supporting outboard CV joint and boot. Carefully rest halfshaft on lower control arm.
12. Insert CV joint removal tool No. T89P-3514-A or equivalent between differential housing and CV joint. Push tool outward until CV joint becomes free from differential side gear. **Extreme care must be taken to prevent damage to the differential oil seal, differential housing, sensor ring and/or CV joint and boot.**
13. Remove halfshaft from vehicle, then plug differential housing to prevent loss of lubricant.
14. Reverse procedure to install, noting the following:
   a. Install new differential oil seal and circlip on inboard CV joint.
   b. Ensure to align reference marks on lower control arm to marks on knuckle/bushing assembly.
   c. If equipped with rear disc brakes, **torque** caliper retaining bolts to 80-100 ft. lbs.
   d. If equipped with anti-lock brakes, **torque** brake sensor retaining bolts to 14-20 ft. lbs.

SHOCK ABSORBER
REPLACE

COUGAR & THUNDERBIRD

These vehicles are equipped with gas pressurized rear shock absorbers which will extend unassisted. Do not apply heat or flame to shock tube during removal.

1. Position vehicle on drive-on hoist or alignment pit, so that rear suspension arms are supported during removal.
2. Remove all upper attaching parts from inside of luggage compartment, **Fig. 8 and 9.**
3. Remove attaching bolt and at lower arm, then remove shock absorber.
4. Reverse procedure to install. Tighten to specifications.

CROWN VICTORIA & GRAND MARQUIS

1. Disconnect battery ground cable and turn air suspension switch OFF.
2. Raise and support vehicle.
3. To assist in removing upper attachment on shock absorbers using a plastic dust tube, place an open end wrench on hex stamped into dust tube's metal cap. For shock absorbers with a steel dust tube, grasp tube to prevent stud rotation when loosening retaining nut.

4. Remove shock absorber retaining nut, washer and insulator assembly from stud on upper side of frame.
5. Compress shock absorber to clear hole in frame and remove inner insulator and washer from upper retaining stud.
6. Remove self-locking nut and disconnect chock absorber lower stud from mounting bracket on rear axle tube.
7. Reverse procedure to install. Tighten to specifications.

COIL SPRING
REPLACE

COUGAR & THUNDERBIRD

1. Raise and support vehicle.
2. Remove rear wheel and tire assembly.
3. Remove rear stabilizer bar link nuts at both ends of stabilizer bar. Rotate bar up and out of the way.
4. Disconnect parking brake cable at brake caliper.
5. Install three Spring Cages tool No. 086-00031 or equivalent, to rear springs as follows:
   a. Install one spring cage without an adjuster link to inboard side or innermost bend of spring, **Fig. 10.**
   b. Install two more spring cages, with adjusters, at 120° angles to the previously installed cage.
6. Place a transmission jack or suitable stand under lower rear control arm as far outboard as possible.
7. Support rear knuckle and caliper assembly by wiring upper control arm to body.
8. Remove lower shock absorber mounting bolt and nut.
9. Mark position of toe adjustment cam to subframe for reference. Loosen both inboard pivot bolts on lower control arm. **Control arm must not be lowered until pivot bolts are loose. Do not attempt to remove plastic cap on front of pivot nut.**
10. Remove two bolts and nuts attaching lower control arm to knuckle, **Fig. 11.**
11. Lower control arm by lowering jack. Ensure spring cages properly seat on spring as control arm is dropped.
12. Remove jack, pull control arm down fully by hand and remove rear spring with cages in place.
13. Using coil spring compressor tool No. D78P-5310-A or equivalent, compress spring and remove spring cages.
14. Remove upper and lower spring insulators from spring.
15. Reverse procedure to install, compress spring to approximately 10.5 inches overall length prior to installation.

CROWN VICTORIA & GRAND MARQUIS

1. Raise rear of vehicle and support at frame. Support rear axle with a suitable jack.
2. Remove rear stabilizer bar, if neces-

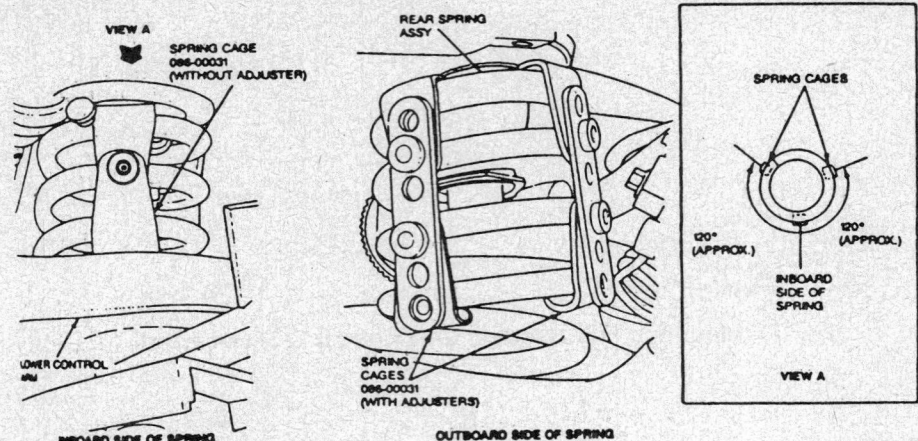

Fig. 10 Mounting spring cages. Cougar & Thunderbird

sary.
3. Disconnect shock absorbers at lower mountings.
4. Disconnect battery ground cable and switch air suspension OFF.
5. Raise vehicle and position safety stands below rear frame crossmember.
6. Drain axle fluid by removing cover.
7. Remove wheels, rotors, calipers and ABS speed sensor.
8. Remove lock bolt from pinion shaft and remove shaft. **Fig. 5.**
9. Push axle shafts inward to remove C-locks.
10. Remove axle shafts, then remove right and left disc brake adapter brackets, bolts and J-nuts. **Fig. 6.**
11. Remove four retaining nuts from each disc brake adapter and support with wire from underbody.
12. Disconnect driveshaft at companion flange and support with wire.
13. Support axle housing with jackstands, then disengage brake line from clips that retain line to axle housing.
14. Release air spring pressure as described under "Air Suspension Pressure Relief." Remove air spring.
15. Disconnect vent from rear axle housing, then disconnect lower shock absorber studs from mounting brackets on axle housing.
16. Remove retaining nut and bolts and disconnect upper arms from mountings on axle housing ear brackets.
17. Lower axle housing assembly until springs are released. Remove springs.
18. Disconnect lower arms from axle housing. Lower axle housing and remove from vehicle.
19. Reverse procedure to install. Tighten to specifications.
20. Lower axle to remove springs. **On some models, it may be necessary to disconnect right parking brake cable from right upper arm retainer prior to lowering axle.**
21. Reverse procedure to install. Install an insulator between upper seat and spring, if necessary. Tighten to specifications.

CONTROL ARM
REPLACE
COUGAR & THUNDERBIRD

Lower Arm

1. Remove coil spring as described in "Coil Spring, Replace."
2. Remove inner control arm pivot bolts and nuts, then remove arm assembly.
3. Remove toe compensating link from control arm.
4. Reverse procedure to install. Tighten to specifications.

Upper Arm

1. Raise and support vehicle.
2. Remove rear wheel and tire assembly.
3. Support knuckle and hub assembly so that it cannot swing outward.
4. Remove inner and outer pivot bolts and nuts at upper control arm, then remove upper control arm.
5. Reverse procedure to install, noting that inner pivot bolt used for camber adjustment has a specially-shaped washer under bolt head. Ensure fasteners are used in correct locations. Set camber adjustment as described in "Wheel Alignment." Tighten to specifications.

CROWN VICTORIA & GRAND MARQUIS

Control arms must be replaced in pairs.

If both upper control arms and both lower control arms are being removed at same time, remove both coil springs.

LOWER ARM

1. Disconnect battery ground cable and turn air suspension switch OFF.
2. Mark rear suspension shock tube relative to protective sleeve with vehicle on level ground.
3. Remove rear stabilizer bar, then raise and support vehicle and place jackstands below rear axle.
4. Lower vehicle until rear shocks are

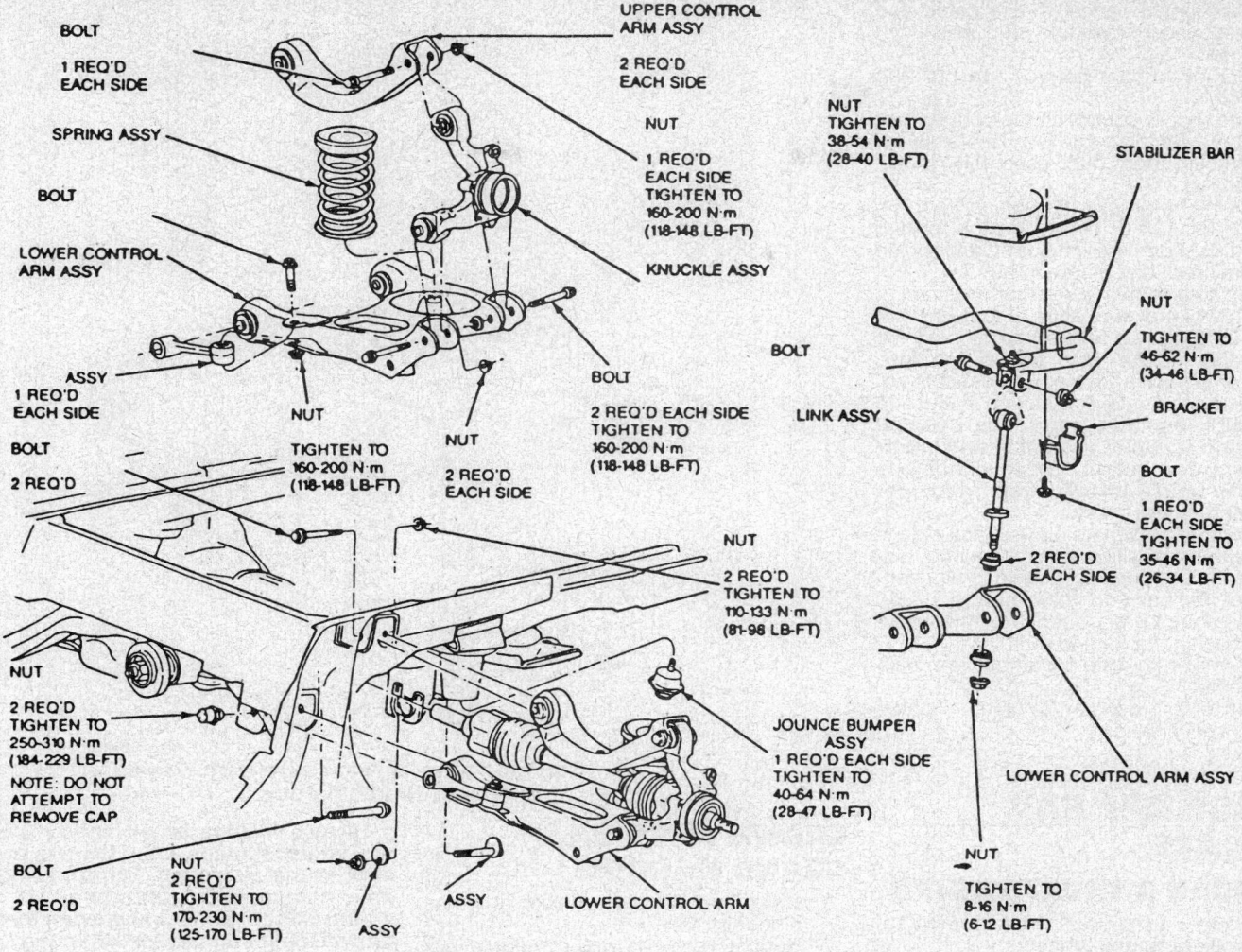

Fig. 11 Exploded view of rear suspension. Cougar & Thunderbird

FM2039100014000X

fully extended to relieve spring pressure.
5. Support axle below differential pinion nose as well as below axle.
6. Remove and discard lower arm pivot bolt and nut from axle bracket.
7. Disengage lower arm from bracket.
8. Remove and discard pivot bolt and nut from frame bracket. Remove lower control arm.
9. Reverse procedure to install. Tighten to specifications.

UPPER ARM

Control arms must be replaced in pairs. **Remove and replace one control at a time to prevent axle from rolling or slipping sideways.**

If both upper control arms and both lower control arms are being removed at same time, remove both coil springs.

Removal

1. Raise vehicle and support frame side rails with jackstands.
2. Support rear axle.
3. Lower axle and support below differential pinion nose.
4. Remove and discard nut and bolt se-

curing upper arm to axle housing. Disconnect arm from housing.
5. Remove and discard nut and bolt securing upper arm to frame bracket. Remove arm.

Installation

1. Hold upper arm in position on front arm bracket. Install new bolt and self-locking nut. Do not tighten.
2. Secure upper arm to axle housing with new nuts and bolts. **Bolts must be pointed toward front of vehicle.**
3. Raise suspension with hoist, until upper arm rear pivot hole is in position with hole in axle bushing. Install new pivot bolt and nut with nut facing inboard.
4. Tighten to specifications.

KNUCKLE
REPLACE

COUGAR & THUNDERBIRD

Do not begin this procedure unless a new hub retainer nut is available. Once removed, this part cannot be reused during assembly. Its torque holding

and/or retention capability is greatly diminished during removal.

1. Remove wheelcover/hub cover from wheel and tire assembly, then loosen wheel nuts.
2. Remove and discard hub nut and washer.
3. Raise and support vehicle, then remove wheel and tire assembly.
4. Pull back on parking brake cable release lever and at same time pull on cable. This action will relax cable so it can be removed from brake caliper or backing plate.
5. **On models with disc brakes,** proceed as follows:
   a. Remove parking brake cable from caliper.
   b. Remove upper and lower caliper attaching bolts and remove caliper assembly from rotor.
   c. Carefully wire caliper to brake junction bracket.
6. **On all models,** with push on nuts removed, remove brake rotor or drum assembly.
7. Remove three bolts retaining splash shield to knuckle and remove splash shield.

8. Disconnect parking brake cable and disconnect brake line from wheel cylinder.
9. Remove upper control arm nut and bolt.
10. Wire upper control arm to body to prevent damage to CV boots when knuckle and hub assembly is removed.
11. Install hub remover/replacer tool No. T81P-1104-C or equivalent to hub studs. Turn wrench counterclockwise until halfshaft is free in hub.
12. Using a paint marker, mark position of control arm in relation to knuckle with bushings in a relaxed position. When upper control arm bolt is removed from knuckle, lower arm bushings will return to a relaxed position. **Failure to mark position will cause bushing wind up upon assembly and incorrect ride height. These conditions can cause misalignment and premature tire wear.**
13. Note approximate angle of knuckle in relaxed position by measuring distance from upper bushing to any convenient point on vehicle body.
14. Remove lower control arm to knuckle attaching bolts and nuts.
15. Remove knuckle assembly from halfshaft.
16. Reverse procedure to install. Tighten to specifications.

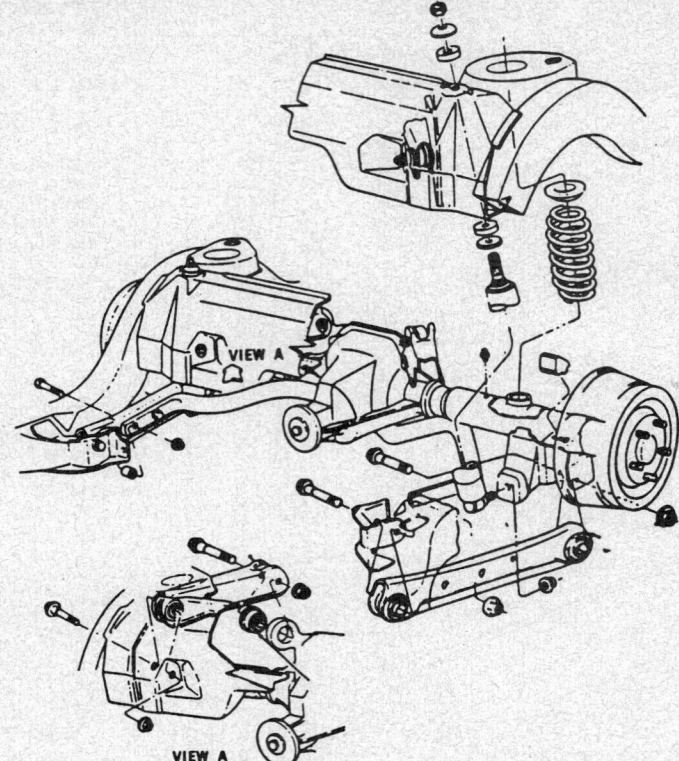

FM2039100012000X

Fig. 12 Exploded view of rear suspension. Crown Victoria & Grand Marquis

STABILIZER BAR
REPLACE
COUGAR & THUNDERBIRD

1. Raise and support vehicle, then remove both rear wheels.
2. Remove both stabilizer bar link upper retaining bolts and nuts.
3. Remove stabilizer bar bracket bolts.
4. Remove rear muffler hanger retaining nuts.
5. Remove stabilizer bar from vehicle.
6. Reverse procedure to install. Tighten to specifications.

CROWN VICTORIA & GRAND MARQUIS

1. Raise and support vehicle at frame side rails.
2. Support rear axle with a suitable jack and position axle so shock absorbers are fully extended.
3. Remove bolts, nuts and spacers attaching stabilizer bar to lower arms, **Fig. 12.**
4. Remove stabilizer bar from vehicle.
5. Reverse procedure to install. Tighten to specifications.

Do not remove an air spring under any circumstances when there is pressure in the air spring. Do not remove any component supporting an air spring without either exhausting the air or providing support for air spring.

AIR SUSPENSION PRESSURE RELIEF

Before servicing any air suspension components, disconnect power to system by turning air suspension switch OFF or by disconnect battery ground cable.

TIGHTENING SPECIFICATIONS
COUGAR & THUNDERBIRD

Year	Component	Torque/Ft. Lbs.	Year	Component	Torque/Ft. Lbs
1992-95	ABS Sensor Bolt	14-20	1992-95 –Cont'd	Lower Control Arm To Knuckle	118-148
	Axle Hub Nut	250		Lower Control Arm To Subframe (Front)	184-229
	Caliper Bolt	80-100		Lower Control Arm To Subframe (Rear)	125-170
	Caliper To Knuckle Bolts	44-60		Lower Control Arm To Toe Compensator Link Nut	118-148
	Crossmember bolt	12-17		Shock Absorber To Lower Control Arm	110-120
	Driveshaft Companion Flange Bolts	70-95		Shock Absorber Upper Mount	27-35
	Driveshaft Hoop Bolt	30-44		Splash Shield To Knuckle Bolts	45-59
	Exhaust Pipe To Muffler Bolt	21-29		Stabilizer Bar Link To Lower Control Arm	6-12
	Fuel Tank Strap Bolts	21-29		Stabilizer Bar U-Bracket To Subframe	26-34
	Hub Retainer Nut	188-254			
	Jounce Bumper To Body	28-47			

Continued

TIGHTENING SPECIFICATIONS-Continued
COUGAR & THUNDERBIRD-Continued

Year	Component	Torque/Ft. Lbs.	Year	Component	Torque/Ft. Lbs
1992-95 –Cont'd	Stabilizer Clevis To Stabilizer Bar	28-40	1992-95 –Cont'd	Upper Control Arm To Knuckle	118-148
	Stabilizer Link To Stabilizer Bar	34-46		Upper Control Arm To Subframe	81-98
				Wheel Lug Nut	80-106

CROWN VICTORIA & GRAND MARQUIS

Year	Component	Torque/Ft. Lbs.	Year	Component	Torque/Ft. Lbs.
1992-95	Driveshaft Flange Bolts	70-95	1992-95 –Cont'd	Speed Sensor Bolt	40-60 ①
	Disc Brake Adapter Bolts & Nuts	20-39		Stabilizer Bar	70-92
	Lower Arm To Axle	103-133		Stabilizer To Axle	16-21
	Lower Arm To Frame	120-150		Stabilizer Link To Frame	13-17
	Pinion Shaft Lock Bolt	15-29		Upper Arm To Axle	103-133
	Rear Cover Bolts	19-25		Upper Arm To Frame	120-150
	Shock Absorber To Axle Bracket	52-85		Wheel Lug Nuts	80-106
	Shock Absorber Upper Mount Nut	14-26			

①—Inch Lbs.

Front Suspension & Steering

NOTE: On Air Bag Equipped Models, Refer To "Air Bag System Precautions" Located In The Front Of This Manual For System Disarming & Arming Procedures.

INDEX

PRECAUTIONS

AIR BAG SYSTEMS

Refer to "Air Bag System Precautions" in the front of this manual for system disarming and arming procedures.

WHEEL BEARING

ADJUST

These models are equipped with sealed bearing units which do not require adjustment or maintenance. If the bearing is found to be defective, then the hub and bearing must be replaced as an assembly.

WHEEL BEARING

REPLACE

1. Raise and support front of vehicle, then remove wheel and tire assembly.
2. Remove grease cap from hub.
3. Remove disc brake caliper with brake hose attached. Suspend caliper from suspension with wire. Do not allow caliper to hang from brake hose.
4. Remove brake rotor.
5. Remove hub nut, then remove hub and bearing assembly, **Fig. 1.** If difficulty is encountered in hub removal, use hub removal tool No. T81P-1104-C or equivalent.

6. Reverse procedure to install. Use a new hub nut and tighten to specifications.

BALL JOINT INSPECTION

COUGAR & THUNDERBIRD

1. Raise front of vehicle and position jacks under sub-frame.
2. Position a suitable dial indicator to ball joint to be checked, in such a manner that lateral movement between spindle and arm can be measured.
3. Grasp tire at top and bottom, then slowly move tire inward and outward

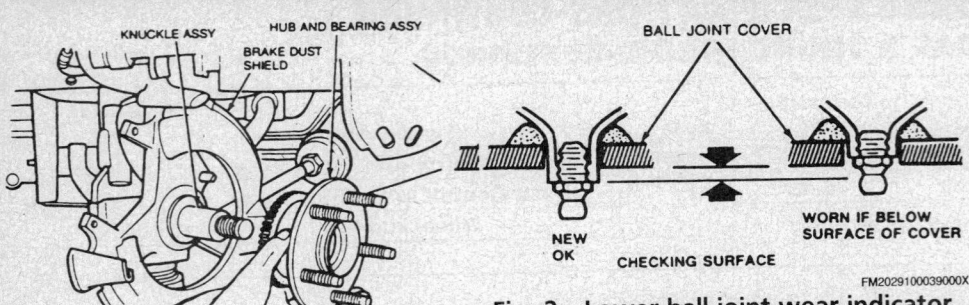

Fig. 1 Hub & wheel bearing assembly

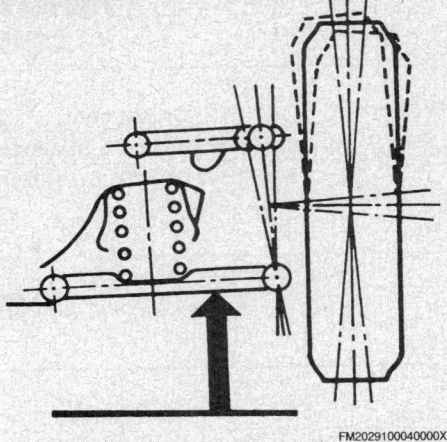

Fig. 2 Lower ball joint wear indicator. Crown Victoria & Grand Marquis

Fig. 3 Upper ball joint wear inspection. Crown Victoria & Grand Marquis

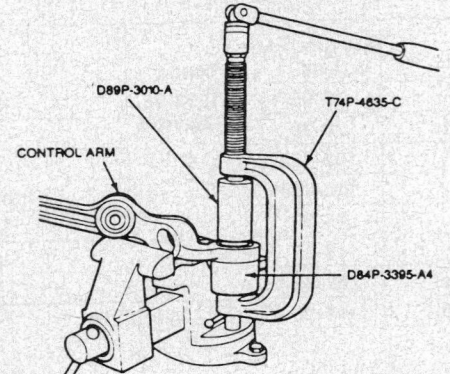

Fig. 4 Lower ball joint replacement. Cougar & Thunderbird

while noting indicator reading.
4. If dial indicator reading exceeds .015 inch, replace ball joint.

CROWN VICTORIA & GRAND MARQUIS

Lower Ball Joint

These models are equipped with lower ball joint wear indicators, **Fig. 2.** To check ball joint for wear, support vehicle in normal driving position with both ball joints loaded. Observe the checking surface of ball joint. If checking surface is inside the cover, **Fig. 2,** replace ball joint.

Upper Ball Joint

1. Raise car on floor jacks placed beneath lower control arms.
2. Grasp lower edge of tire and move wheel in and out, **Fig. 3.**
3. As wheel is being moved in and out, observe upper end of spindle and upper arm.
4. Any movement between upper end of spindle and upper arm indicates ball joint wear and loss of preload. If any such movement is observed, replace upper ball joint.

During the foregoing check, lower ball joint will be unloaded and may move. Disregard all such movement of lower ball joint. Also, do not mistake loose wheel bearings for a worn ball joint.

BALL JOINT
REPLACE

COUGAR & THUNDERBIRD

Upper Ball Joint

The upper ball joint and upper control arm must be replaced as an assembly. Refer to "Control Arm, Replace."

Lower Ball Joint

1. Remove lower control arm as described under "Control Arm, Replace."
2. Remove and discard ball joint boot seal, then position lower control arm in a vise.
3. Press ball joint from lower control arm using removal tools No. D89P-3010-A, D84P-3395-A4 and T74P-4635-C or equivalent, **Fig. 4.**
4. Reverse procedure to install. Do not remove protective cover from ball

joint until after it has been installed. Press ball joint into lower control arm until fully seated. After installing lower control arm, check and adjust wheel alignment as necessary. Tighten to specifications.

CROWN VICTORIA & GRAND MARQUIS

Upper Ball Joint

1. Raise and support front of vehicle. Remove wheel assembly.
2. Position jack below lower control arm at the ball joint.
3. Remove retaining nut and punch bolt from upper ball joint stud.
4. Mark position of alignment cams.
5. Remove ball joint retaining nuts.
6. Remove ball joint and spread slot with pry bar to separate ball joint stud from spindle.
7. Reverse procedure to install. Tighten to specifications.

Lower Ball Joint

The lower ball joint and lower control arm must be replaced as an assembly.

COIL SPRING
REPLACE
COUGAR & THUNDERBIRD

The upper shock mount cannot be rotated when the shock and spring are assembled. Mark position of upper mount to coil spring with chalk, paint or grease pencil, prior to disassembly, **Fig. 5.** If upper mount is not properly positioned during assembly it will not

install in vehicle. If installing new coil spring or upper mount transfer reference marks from removed parts to new parts.

1. Remove coil spring and shock strut assembly , **Fig. 6,** from vehicle as described under "Strut Assembly, Replace."
2. Position shock assembly in Spring Compressor tool No. 086-00029 or equivalent.
3. Compress spring and remove upper mount.
4. Release spring compressor to remove coil spring.
5. Position shock and coil assembly in Spring Compressor tool No. 086-00029 or equivalent and compress spring to install upper mount.
6. Install upper mount aligning reference marks.
7. Install nut and tighten to specification.
8. Release spring compressor, ensuring coil spring is properly seated.
9. Install coil spring and shock strut assembly from vehicle as described under "Strut Assembly, Replace."
10. Tighten to specifications.

CROWN VICTORIA & GRAND MARQUIS

1. Raise and support vehicle. Remove wheel assembly.
2. Disconnect stabilizer bar link from lower control arm.
3. Remove shock absorber, **Fig. 7.**
4. Remove steering center link from pitman arm.
5. Compress coil spring with a suitable spring compressor, tool D-78P-5310-A or equivalent.
6. Remove two lower control arm pivot bolts and disengage arm from crossmember.
7. Remove spring from vehicle.
8. Reverse procedure to install. Tighten to specifications.

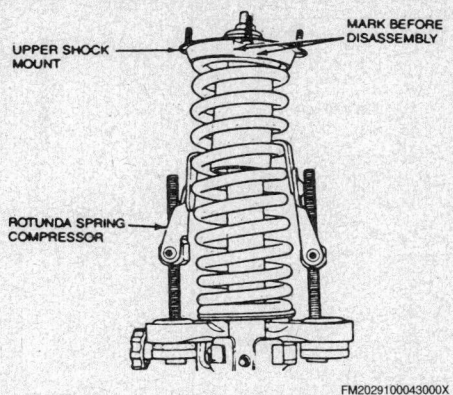

Fig. 5 Upper mount to spring alignment mark placement. Cougar & Thunderbird

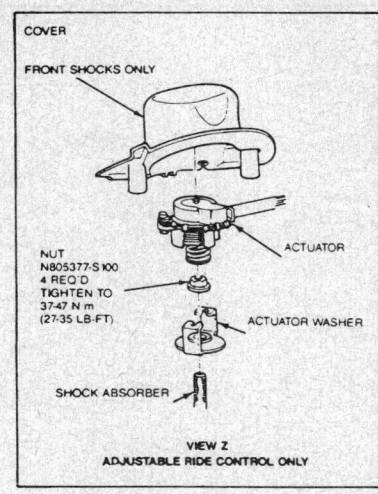

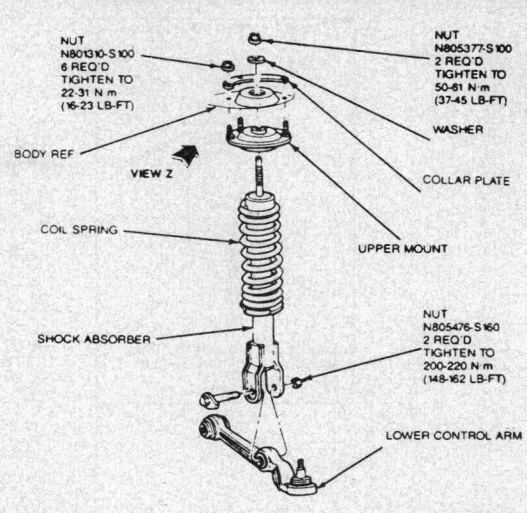

Fig. 6 Strut & coil spring replacement. Cougar & Thunderbird

STRUT
REPLACE

COUGAR & THUNDERBIRD

1. Remove plastic cover at upper shock mount.
2. Remove automatic ride actuator, if equipped.
3. Remove three upper mounting nuts and collar plate from studs in engine compartment.
4. Raise and support vehicle, then remove tire and wheel assemblies.
5. Remove lower shock mounting bolt and nut, **Fig. 6.**
6. Remove nut at stabilizer link upper mounting stud.
7. Separate link from spindle using joint separator tool No. D88L-3006-A or equivalent.
8. Support lower control arm assembly with transmission jack.
9. Raise control arm and spindle with jack until stabilizer link can be completely separated from spindle. Position link out of the way.
10. Remove spindle to upper control arm attaching nut and bolt. Discard nut and bolt.
11. Lower jack to separate spindle from upper control arm. Do not allow spindle to hang free, support with wire or other means.
12. Remove support from lower control arm and remove shock and coil spring assembly.
13. Reverse procedure to install. Tighten to specifications.

SHOCK ABSORBER
REPLACE

CROWN VICTORIA & GRAND MARQUIS

1. Remove nut, washer and bushing from shock absorber upper end.
2. Raise vehicle and install safety stands.
3. Remove two thread-cutting screws from lower end of shock absorber, then remove shock absorber.
4. Reverse procedure to install. **If**

threads in lower arm become damaged, reuse original thread-cutting screws along with 5/16-18 locknuts. Tighten to specifications.

CONTROL ARM
REPLACE

COUGAR & THUNDERBIRD

Upper Control Arm

1. Raise and support vehicle.
2. Remove tire and wheel assembly.
3. Remove and discard upper spindle to ball joint bolt and nut. Slightly spread spindle at slot and remove ball joint.
4. Lower vehicle, then brake off flags on upper control arm pivot bolt heads.
5. Remove upper control arm bolts, then upper control arm, **Fig. 8.**
6. Reverse procedure to install. Tighten to specifications.

Lower Control Arm

1. Raise and support vehicle.
2. Remove tire and wheel assembly.
3. Loosen lower ball joint nut three or four turns.
4. Rap spindle to separate ball joint. Leave nut attached.
5. Support spindle by wire to prevent excessive sagging of upper control arm.
6. Mark position of camber adjustment cam.
7. Remove nut attaching tension strut to control arm. hold strut by flats with wrench while turning nut. **Do not hold strut or damage surface in area shown in Fig. 9, damage to tension strut may result.**
8. Remove lower shock bolt and nut.
9. Remove pivot (camber) bolt and nut.
10. Remove nut at lower ball joint and remove control arm, **Fig. 8.**
11. Reverse procedure to install, after installation check front end alignment and adjust as necessary. Tighten to specifications.

CROWN VICTORIA & GRAND MARQUIS

Lower Control Arm

1. Raise and support front of vehicle, then remove front wheels.
2. Remove brake caliper, rotor, dust shield and ABS sensor, if equipped.
3. Remove jounce bumper, if equipped.
4. Remove shock absorber.
5. Disconnect stabilizer bar link from lower control arm.
6. Disconnect steering center link from pitman arm.
7. Remove lower ball joint attaching nut cotter pin, then loosen lower ball joint nut one or two turns. **Do not remove nut from stud at this time.**
8. Install ball joint press tool T57P-3006-B or equivalent between upper and lower ball joint studs.
9. Compress ball joint with tool, then tap spindle, near lower stud, to loosen stud in spindle.
10. Remove ball joint press tool, then position a suitable jack under lower control arm.
11. Install suitable coil spring compression tool, then remove coil spring.
12. Remove ball joint nut, then the lower control arm assembly, **Fig. 7.**
13. Reverse procedure to install, noting the following:
    a. Tighten to specifications.
    b. Ensure coil spring is properly aligned, **Fig. 7.**
    c. Check and adjust wheel alignment.

Upper Control Arm

1. Raise and support front of vehicle, then remove front wheels.
2. Remove upper ball joint attaching nut cotter pin, then loosen upper ball joint nut one or two turns. **Do not remove nut from stud at this time.**
3. Install ball joint press tool T57P-3006-B or equivalent between upper and lower ball joint studs.
4. Compress ball joint with tool, then tap spindle, near upper stud, to loosen stud in spindle.

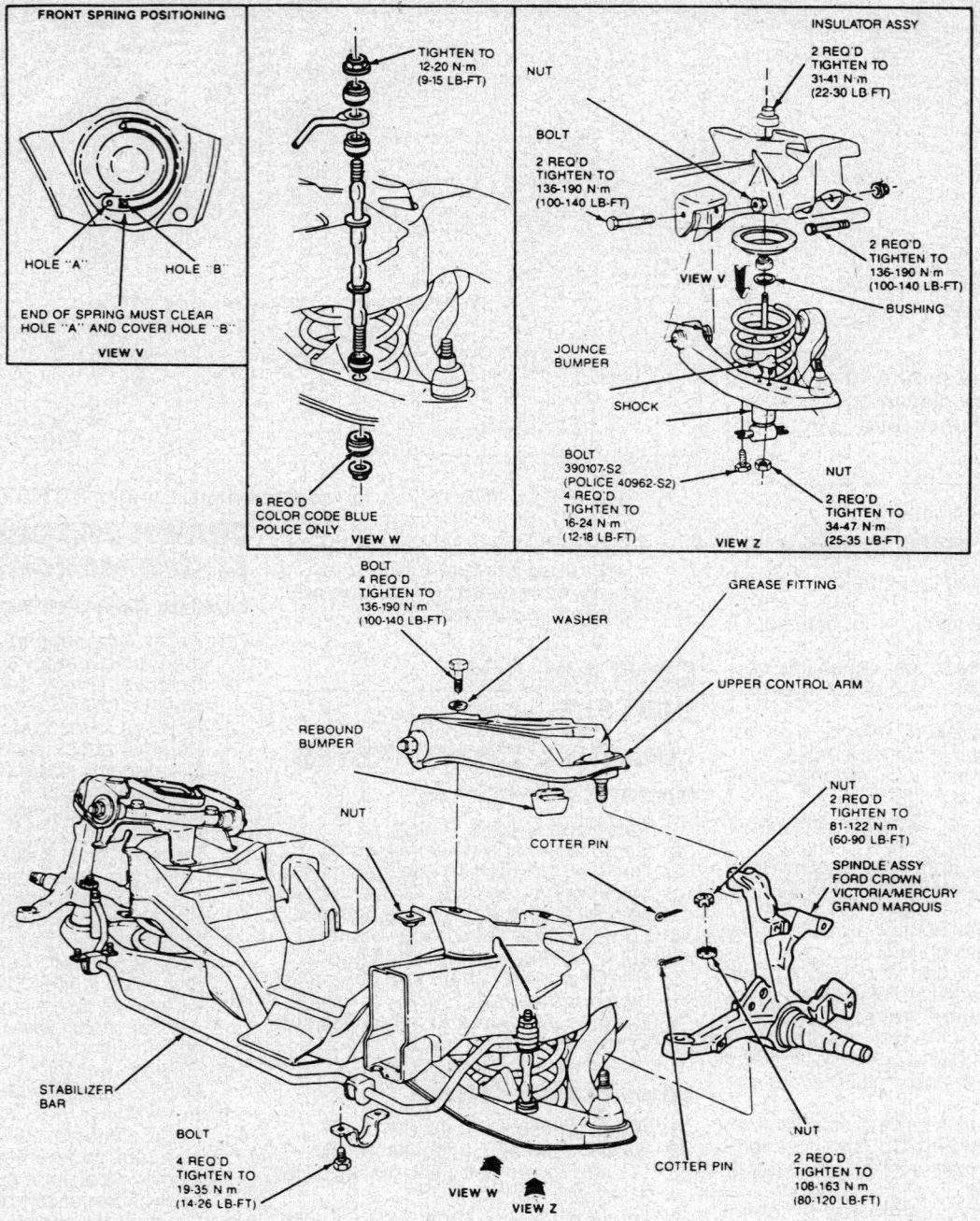

Fig. 7 Front suspension assembly. Crown Victoria & Grand Marquis

FM2029100044000X

5. Remove ball joint press tool, then position a suitable jack under lower control arm.

6. Remove upper control arm attaching bolts, then the upper control arm assembly, **Fig. 7.**

7. Reverse procedure to install. Tighten to specifications and check wheel alignment.

STABILIZER BAR
REPLACE

COUGAR & THUNDERBIRD

1. Remove air inlet tube, then remove stabilizer bar retaining bracket bolts and brackets.

2. Remove serpentine drive belt, then raise and support vehicle.

3. Remove front tire and wheel assemblies, then remove crankshaft vibration damper.

4. Remove cotter pins and castellated nuts at rod ends.

5. Separate tie rod ends from spindles using tie rod end removal tool No. 3290-D or equivalent.

6. Remove transmission oil cooler line bracket.

7. Remove stabilizer bar link from stabilizer bar using joint separator tool No. D88L-3006-A or equivalent.

8. Remove stabilizer bar from vehicles right side.

9. Remove stabilizer bar bushings from stabilizer bar.

10. Reverse procedure to install. Tighten to specifications.

CROWN VICTORIA & GRAND MARQUIS

1. Raise and support vehicle.

2. Remove nuts from pinch bolts at both spindles. Remove bolts.

3. Spread slots in spindles with a pry bar to free ball studs.

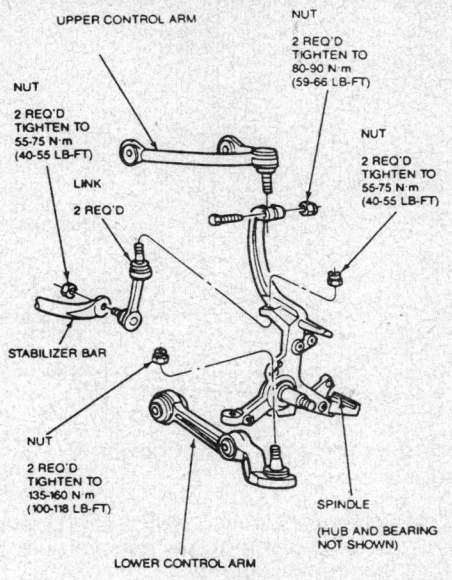

Fig. 8 Control arms & steering knuckle. Cougar & Thunderbird

4. Disconnect stabilizer bar brackets from frame. Pull bar forward until links can be removed from spindle attachments.
5. Reverse procedure to install. Tighten to specifications.

SPINDLE ASSEMBLY
REPLACE
COUGAR & THUNDERBIRD

1. Raise and support vehicle.
2. Remove tire and wheel assembly.
3. Remove brake caliper and rotor.
4. Remove hub and bearing assembly.
5. Remove anti-lock brake sensor and position out of the way.
6. Remove tie rod end cotter pin and loosen castellated nut. Separate tie rod end from spindle using tie rod end remover tool No. 3290-D, or equivalent.
7. Remove stabilizer bar link at spindle using joint separator tool No. D88L-3006-A, or equivalent.
8. Separate lower ball joint from spindle. Loosen nut and rap spindle with hammer. Remove nut.
9. Remove and discard upper spindle to upper control arm bolt and nut. Spread slot slightly and remove spindle from control arm and vehicle.
10. Reverse procedure to install. Tighten to specifications.

TENSION STRUT
REPLACE
COUGAR & THUNDERBIRD
Removal

1. Raise and support vehicle.
2. Remove tire and wheel assembly.
3. Hold tension strut on flats with wrench. Remove front sub-frame attaching nut and insulator. **Do not**

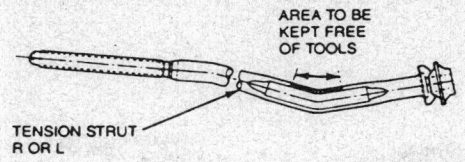

Fig. 9 Tension strut. Cougar & Thunderbird

hold strut or damage surface in area shown in Fig. 9, damage to tension strut may result.
4. Mark position, or note number of visible threads at tension strut rear sub-frame nut.
5. Back off tension strut rear sub-frame nut.
6. Remove tension strut to lower control arm attaching nut.
7. Remove lower shock bolt and nut.
8. Remove brake hose bracket to body attaching bolt.
9. Remove ABS sensor attaching bolt and position sensor out of the way.
10. Pry lower control arm rearward and remove tension strut.

Installation

1. If front tension strut insulators were removed, de-burr insulator sleeves before reassembly. If new sleeves are used, inner sleeve must be shorter than outer sleeve. Cut up to 1/4 inch off inner sleeve if necessary, **Fig. 10**.
2. Install tension strut retaining nut all the way down on threads. Install with nylon insert facing forward.
3. Install outer sleeve and rear washer. Word REAR must face outward.
4. Install rear insulator (without metal flange) with large end toward sub-frame.
5. Install tension strut in sub-frame.
6. Install front insulator, with the word FRONT toward front of vehicle and metal flange toward sub-frame.
7. Install front washer, with the words "THIS SIDE OUT" toward front of vehicle.
8. Install inner sleeve, loosely install front nut.
9. Install front washer and insulator on rear of tension strut, cup to face away from insulator.
10. Install tension strut into lower control arm.
11. Install rear insulator with small end toward control arm.
12. Install washer and cup facing rear of vehicle.
13. Return torsion strut-to-sub-frame nut to original position.
14. Install lower shock bolt and nut.
15. Holding tension strut with wrench, tighten strut to sub-frame to specification.
16. Tighten tension strut to lower control arm attaching nut to specification.
17. Install brake hose bracket, tighten to specifications.
18. Install ABS sensor, tighten to specifications.
19. Install tire and wheel assembly, check front wheel alignment.

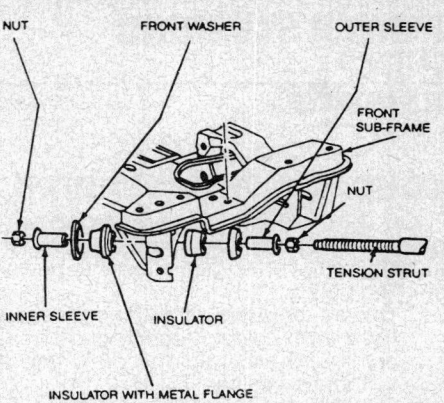

Fig. 10 Tension strut installation. Cougar & Thunderbird

POWER STEERING GEAR
REPLACE
COUGAR & THUNDERBIRD

1. Raise and support vehicle. Remove both front wheel and tire assemblies.
2. Remove cotter pins at outer tie rod ends and remove castellated nuts at each end. Discard cotter pins.
3. Separate tie rod ends from spindles, using tie rod end removal tool No. 3290-D or equivalent.
4. Disconnect and plug power steering return line hose.
5. Disconnect power steering pressure line at intermediate fitting and position out of the way.
6. Remove steering shaft retaining bolt.
7. Remove rack to sub-frame bolts and nuts, access nuts through hole in front crossmember, **Fig. 11**.
8. Lower rack as necessary, to remove pressure line inlet tube. Remove and discard plastic seal on inlet tube.
9. Cut tie strap securing pressure line to each tube.
10. Remove steering rack from vehicle.
11. Reverse procedure to install. Tighten to specifications.

CROWN VICTORIA & GRAND MARQUIS

1. Remove stone shield, if equipped.
2. Disconnect pressure and return lines from steering gear. Plug lines and ports in gear to prevent entry of dirt.
3. Remove two bolts that secure flex coupling to steering gear and to column.
4. Raise car and remove sector shaft nut.
5. Use a puller to remove pitman arm.
6. Support steering gear, then remove attaching bolts.
7. Work steering gear free of flex coupling and remove it from car.
8. Reverse procedure to install. Tighten to specifications.

POWER STEERING PUMP
REPLACE

COUGAR & THUNDERBIRD

On **3.8L/V6-232 Supercharged engines,** intercooler and intercooler tubes must be removed to gain access to power steering pump.

1. **On all engines,** disconnect return hose from power steering pump reservoir and allow fluid to drain into a suitable container.
2. Disconnect pressure hose from pump fitting, then remove pump mounting bracket and disconnect drive belt from pulley.
3. **On models w/fixed pump system,** remove pulley.
4. **On all models,** remove power steering pump.
5. Reverse procedure to install. Tighten to specifications.
6. **Do not overtighten pressure hose fitting.** Swivel and/or endplay of the fitting is normal and does not indicate a loose fitting.

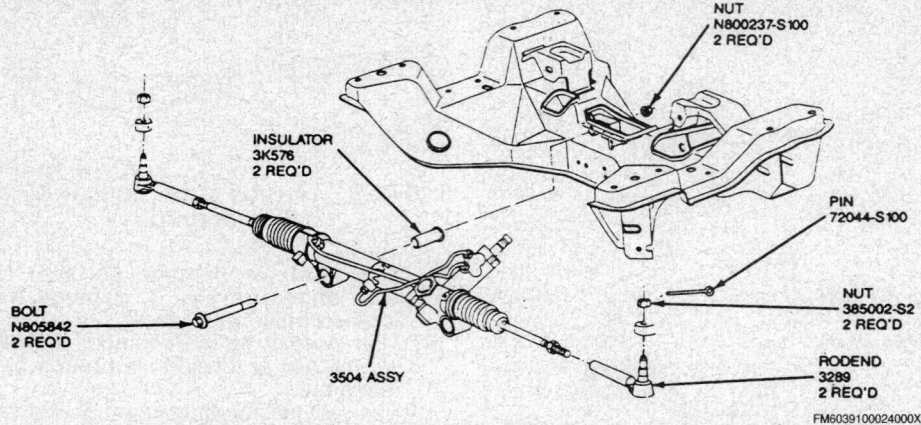

Fig. 11   Power rack & pinion steering gear installation. Cougar & Thunderbird

CROWN VICTORIA & GRAND MARQUIS

1. Disconnect power steering pump return line and allow power steering pump fluid to drain into a suitable container.
2. Disconnect power steering pump pressure hose from pump fitting.
3. Disconnect drive belt from power steering pump pulley, remove pulley, then remove pump.
4. Reverse procedure to install. Tighten to specifications.
5. **Do not overtighten pressure hose fitting.** Swivel and/or endplay of the fitting is normal and does not indicate a loose fitting.

TIGHTENING SPECIFICATIONS
COUGAR & THUNDERBIRD

Year	Component	Torque/Ft. Lbs	Year	Component	Torque/Ft. Lbs
1992-95	ABS Sensor Bolt	40-60 ①	1992-95 —Cont'd	Steering Flex Coupling Nut	20-30
	Brake Caliper Torx Bolts	25		Steering Gear To Crossmember	100-144
	Brake Hose Retaining Bolt	9-11		Shock To Upper Mount	37-45
	Hose Fittings At Gear	20-25		Tension Strut To Sub-frame	90-120
	Lower Control Arm To Shock	118-162		Tie Rod Ball Socket To Rack	55-65
	Lower Control Arm To Spindle (Ball Joint)	80-120		Tie Rod End To Jam Nut	35-50
	Lower Control Arm To Sub-frame	92-125		Tie Rod End To Spindle	39-54
	Lower Control Arm To Tension Strut	90-120		Upper Control Arm To Body	55-90
	Pressure Hose Fitting At Pump	10-15		Upper Control Arm To Spindle (Ball Joint)	50-65
	Pump Mounting Bracket	30-45		Upper Shock Mount To Body	16-23
	Stabilizer Bar Bracket	40-55		Wheel Hub Nut	189-254
	Stabilizer Bar Link To Spindle	40-55		Wheel Lug Nuts	85-106
	Stabilizer Bar Link To Stabilizer Bar	40-55			

① —Inch Lbs.

CROWN VICTORIA & GRAND MARQUIS

Year	Component	Torque/Ft. Lbs	Year	Component	Torque/Ft. Lbs
1992-95	Ball Joint To Lower Spindle	80-119	1992-95 —Cont'd	Pitman Arm Nut	44-46
	Ball Joint To Upper Spindle	51-67		Pitman Arm To Sector Shaft Retaining Nut	200-250
	Brake Caliper Torx Bolts	24		Pressure Hose To Gear	16-25
	Flex Coupling to Gear Input Shaft Bolt	20-30		Quick Connect Tube Nut	35-45
	Hub Nut	189-254		Return Hose To Gear	25-34
	Lower Arm To Crossmember	101-140		Sector Shaft Cover Bolts	55-70
	Lower Arm To Frame	101-140			
	Pinch Bolt & Nut	38-49			

TIGHTENING SPECIFICATIONS-Continued
CROWN VICTORIA & GRAND MARQUIS-Continued

Year	Component	Torque/Ft. Lbs	Year	Component	Torque/Ft. Lbs
1992-95 –Cont'd	Shock Absorber Top Stud Nut	16-20	1992-95 –Cont'd	Steering Gear To Side Rail Mounting Bolts	50-65
	Shock Absorber Upper Mount	19-27		Steering Pump To Engine	15-22
	Stabilizer Bar Link To Spindle	41-44		Upper Ball Joint To Upper Arm	107-129
	Stabilizer Link To Bar	30-40		Wheel Lug Nuts	85-104

Wheel Alignment

INDEX

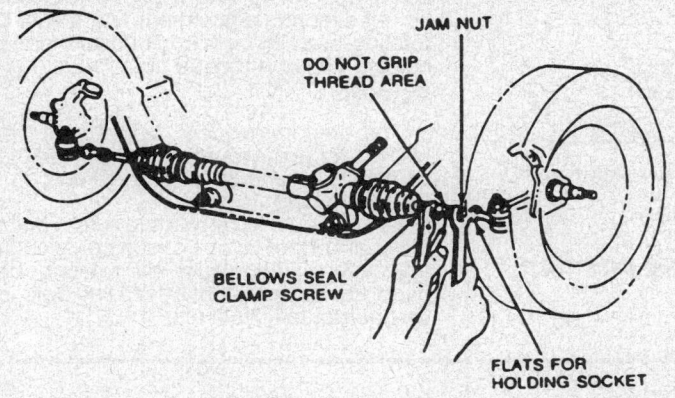

Fig. 1   Toe-in adjustment. Cougar & Thunderbird

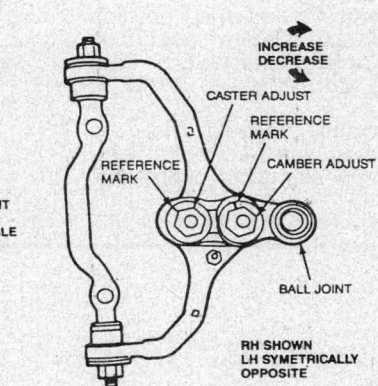

Fig. 2   Caster & camber adjustment. Crown Victoria & Grand Marquis

FRONT WHEEL ALIGNMENT

COUGAR & THUNDERBIRD

Caster

Caster is adjusted by moving the tension strut relative to the front sub-frame. Loosen nuts securing strut to sub-frame and adjust caster by running the nuts in appropriate direction until desired setting is achieved. The setting should be locked by holding adjusting nut and **torquing** locknut to 117 ft. lbs.

Camber

Camber is adjusted by rotating a cam bolt at lower control arm inner pivot. Loosen nut securing adjustment and adjust by rotating bolt head. Lock adjustment by holding bolt and **torque** nut to 125 ft. lbs.

Toe-In

1. Check to see that steering shaft and steering wheel marks are in alignment and in the top position.
2. Loosen clamp screw on tie rod bellows and free the seal on the rod to prevent twisting of bellows, **Fig. 1.**
3. Place opened end wrench on flats of tie rod socket to prevent socket from turning, then loosen tie rod jam nuts.
4. Use suitable pliers to turn tie rod inner end to correct the adjustment to specifications. Do not use pliers on tie rod threads. Turning to reduce number of threads showing will increase toe-in. Turning in opposite direction will reduce toe-in.
5. **Torque** tie rod jam nuts to 43-50 ft. lbs.

CROWN VICTORIA & GRAND MARQUIS

Caster & Camber

Camber and Caster adjustment tools No. T79P-3000-A are required to accurately adjust caster and camber.
1. Loosen two nuts on top of adjustment cams. **Fig. 2.**
2. Turn hex cams as required to obtain desired valve.
3. Adjust camber and caster on each wheel as determined by alignment specification.
4. If correct specification cannot be obtained, ensure upper control arm to frame retaining bolts are centered in slots. Loosen and reposition as required. **Torque** to 101-140 ft. lbs.
5. After proper settings have been obtained, hold each cam and **Torque** nuts to 107-129 ft. lbs.
6. Check toe-in and steering wheel spoke position.

Toe-In

Following adjustment of caster and camber, check steering wheel spoke position. If spokes are not in normal position, they can be properly adjusted while toe is being adjusted.

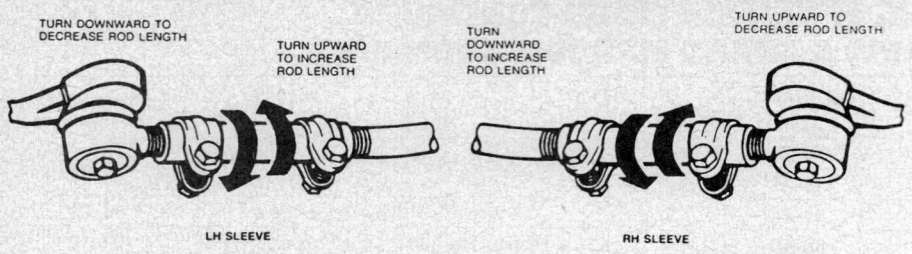

LH SLEEVE   RH SLEEVE

FM2049100028000X

Fig. 3   Toe-in adjustment. Crown Victoria & Grand Marquis

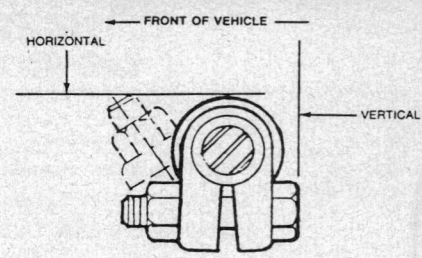

AFTER TOE SETTING, THE TWO CLAMP BOLTS ON EACH SIDE OF VEHICLE MUST BE POSITIONED WITHIN LIMITS SHOWN, WITH THREADED END OF BOLTS TOWARD FRONT OF VEHICLE.

Fig. 4   Sleeve position

1. Loosen two clamp bolts on each spindle connecting rod sleeve. **Fig. 3.**
2. Adjust toe. If steering wheel spokes are in normal position, lengthen or shorten both rods equally to obtain correct toe.
3. If steering wheel spokes are not correct, make necessary rod adjustments to obtain correct toe and steering wheel alignment.
4. When toe and steering wheel position are both correct, lubricate clamp, bolts and nuts. **Torque** clamp bolts on both connecting rod sleeves to 20-22 ft. lbs.
5. Sleeve position should not be changed when clamp bolts are tightened for proper clamp bolt orientation. **Fig. 4.**

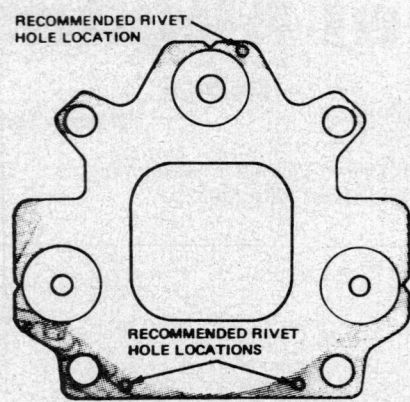

RECOMMENDED RIVET HOLE LOCATION

RECOMMENDED RIVET HOLE LOCATIONS

DRILL THREE (3) HOLES IN ALIGNMENT PLATE FOR 1/8 INCH RIVETS.

DRILL IN SHADED AREA ONLY.   FM2049100030000X

Fig. 5   Sleeve position

REAR WHEEL ALIGNMENT
COUGAR & THUNDERBIRD
Camber

Camber is adjusted by rotating a cam bolt at upper control arm inner pivot. Loosen nut securing adjustment and adjust by rotating head of bolt. Lock adjustment by holding bolt and **torque** nut to 98 ft. lbs.

Toe-In

The recommended adjustment sequence for rear alignment is to set toe then camber. Toe should be rechecked before final tightening.

Toe is adjusted by rotating a cam bolt at lower arm inner pivot. Loosen nut securing adjustment and adjust by rotating bolt head. Lock adjustment by holding bolt and **torque** nut to 170 ft. lbs.

NOTE: Refer To Rear Of This Manual For Vehicle Manufacturer's Special Service Tool Suppliers.

INDEX OF SERVICE OPERATIONS

NOTE: For Service Operations Not Listed Below, Refer To The Table Of Contents In The Front Of This Manual.

Specifications

GENERAL ENGINE SPECIFICATIONS

Year	Engine Liter/CID	VIN Code	Fuel System	Bore & Stroke	Comp. Ratio	Net H.P. @ RPM ①	Maximum Torque Ft. Lbs. @ RPM ①	Normal Oil Pressure, psi ④
1992	2.3L/4-140 ③	X	EFI	3.68 x 3.30	9.0	98 @ 4400	124 @ 2200	55-70
	3.0L/V6-182	U	SEFI	3.50 x 3.14	9.0	135 @ 5500	⑤	55-70
1993-94	2.3L/4-140 ③	X	HSC SFI	3.68 x 3.30	9.0	98 @ 4400	124 @ 2200	55-70
	3.0L/V6-182	U	OHV SFI	3.50 x 3.14	9.0	②	⑥	55-70

① —Ratings are net-as installed in vehicle.
② —Man. trans; 130 @ 4800, auto. trans; 135 @ 4800.
③ —High Swirl Combustion (HSC) engine.
④ —Pressure given is w/engine warm & operating at 2000 RPM.
⑤ —Man. trans; 150 @ 3250, auto. trans; 150 @ 4200.
⑥ —Man. trans; 150 @ 3000, auto. trans; 150 @ 4250.

TUNE UP SPECIFICATIONS

Year & Engine/VIN Code ①	Spark Plug Gap	Firing Order Fig. ③	Ignition Timing BTDC Man. Trans.	Ignition Timing BTDC Auto. Trans.	Timing Mark Fig.	Curb Idle Speed ② Man. Trans.	Curb Idle Speed ② Auto Trans.	Fast Idle Speed Man. Trans.	Fast Idle Speed Auto. Trans.	Fuel Pump Pressure, psi ⑥
1992-94										
2.3L/4-140/X	.054	A	15 ⑦	15 ⑦	⑧	⑤	⑤	⑤	⑤	50-60
3.0L/V6-182/U	.044	C	10 ⑦	10 ⑦	B	⑤	⑤	④	④	35-40

BTDC—Before Top Dead Center.
① —The eighth digit of the Vehicle Identification Number (VIN) denotes engine code.
② —D: Drive.
③ —Before disconnecting wires from distributor cap, determine location of No. 1 wire in cap, as distributor position may have been altered from that shown at the end of this chart.
④ —With throttle air bypass valve electrical connector disconnected.
⑤ —Idle speed controlled by an automatic idle speed control.
⑥ —Wrap shop towel around fuel diagnostic valve fitting to prevent fuel spillage. Connect a suitable fuel pressure gauge to fuel diagnostic valve. Energize fuel pump & check fuel pressure gauge reading.
⑦ —Disconnect inline spout connector, then start engine & adjust ignition timing as necessary. After completing adjustment, reconnect spout connector.
⑧ —Mark located on crankshaft pulley.

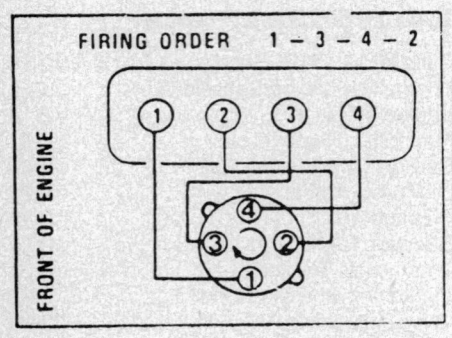

Fig. A

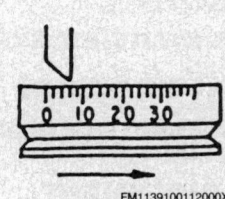

Fig. B

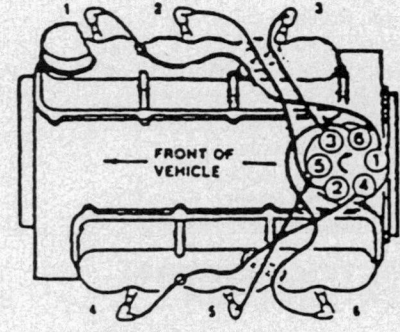

Fig. C

FRONT WHEEL ALIGNMENT SPECIFICATIONS

Year	Model	Caster Angle, Degrees		Camber Angle, Degrees				Toe-In. Inch	Toe Out on Turns, Deg.	
				Limits		Desired			Outer Wheel	Inner Wheel
		Limits	Desired	Left	Right	Left	Right			
1992-94	All	+1.69 to +3.19	+2.44	+0.66 to +2.16	+0.22 to +1.72	+1.41	+0.97	+.15	20	18.25

①—Toe-out, 0.10 inch.

REAR WHEEL ALIGNMENT SPECIFICATIONS

Year	Model	Camber Angle, Degrees				Toe-In. Inch
		Limits		Desired		
		Left	Right	Left	Right	
1992-94	All	-0.91 to +0.59	-0.91 to +0.59	-.16	-.16	0

COOLING SYSTEM & CAPACITY DATA

Year	Model or Engine/ VIN	Coolant Capacity, Qts.		Radiator Cap Relief Pressure, psi.	Thermo. Opening Temp.°F	Fuel Tank, Gals.	Engine Oil Refill, Qts. ②	Transaxle Oil ①	
		Less A/C Qts.	With A/C Qts.					Man. Trans., Pints	Auto Trans., Qts.
1992-94	2.3L/4-140/X	8.3	8.1	16	192	15.4	4.5	6.1	8.3
	3.0L/V6-182/U	8.3	8.1	16	192	15.4	4.5	6.1	8.3

①—Approximate. Make final check w/dipstick.
②—Includes filter.

LUBRICANT DATA

Year	Model	Lubricant Type					
		Transaxle		Transfer Case	Rear Axle	Power Steering	Brake System
		Manual	Automatic				
1992-94	All	Mercon	Mercon	ATF	90①	Type F	DOT 3

①—Hypoid Gear Lubricant.

Note: On Air Bag Equipped Models, Refer To "Air Bag System Precautions" Located In The Front Of This Manual For System Disarming & Arming Procedures.

INDEX

PRECAUTIONS

AIR BAG SYSTEMS

Refer to "Air Bag System Precautions" in the front of this manual for system disarming and arming procedures.

FUSE PANEL & FLASHER LOCATION

The fuse panel is located behind the lefthand side of the instrument panel.

The flashers are located on the fuse panel.

RELAY CENTER LOCATION

The relay center is located on the LH side of the engine compartment near the shock tower.

STARTER
REPLACE

1. Disconnect battery ground cable.
2. Raise and support vehicle.
3. Disconnect starter cable from starter motor terminal.
4. Remove upper and lower retaining bolts, then the starter.
5. Reverse procedure to install. **Torque** starter retaining bolts or nuts to 15-20 ft. lbs.

DISTRIBUTOR
REPLACE

REMOVAL

1. Disconnect distributor from wiring harness.
2. Mark position of No. 1 cylinder wire tower on distributor base for reference when installing distributor.
3. Loosen distributor cap hold-down screws, then remove cap. **Pull distributor cap straight off to prevent damage to rotor and spring.**

4. Position cap and wires aside, then remove distributor rotor.
5. Remove distributor hold-down bolts, then distributor.

INSTALLATION

1. Remove No. 1 cylinder spark plug, then rotate engine clockwise until No. 1 piston is on the compression stroke.
2. With No. 1 piston on compression stroke, align timing pointer with TDC mark on the crankshaft damper.
3. Align locating boss on rotor with hole on armature. Fully seat rotor on distributor shaft.
4. Rotate distributor shaft so blade on rotor is pointing toward mark on distributor base, that was previously made.
5. While installing distributor, continue rotating rotor slightly so leading edge of the vane is centered in vane switch stator assembly.
6. Rotate distributor in block to align leading of vane and vane switch stator assembly. Ensure rotor is pointing at No. 1 mark on distributor base. If vane and vane switch cannot be aligned by rotating distributor in cylinder block, remove distributor enough to just disengage distributor gear from camshaft gear, then rotate rotor enough to engage distributor gear on another tooth of camshaft gear.
7. Install distributor hold-down clamp and bolt.
8. Install distributor cap, No. 1 spark plug and ignition wires. Ensure that the ignition wires are securely connected to the distributor cap and spark plugs.
9. **Torque** distributor cap hold-down screws to 18-23 inch lbs.
10. Connect distributor electrical connector.
11. Adjust ignition timing to specifications, then **torque** distributor hold-down bolt to 17-25 ft. lbs.

IGNITION LOCK
REPLACE

1. Disconnect battery ground cable.

2. **On models equipped with tilt columns,** remove upper extension shroud by unsnapping shroud from retaining clip at 9 o'clock position.
3. **On all models,** remove five screws retaining the two trim shroud halves.
4. Disconnect key warning buzzer electrical connector, then turn the ignition key to the RUN position.
5. Place 1/8 diameter pin or small drift punch into hole in casting surrounding lock cylinder. Depress retaining pin while pulling out on lock cylinder to remove it from column housing.
6. Install lock cylinder by turning it to RUN position and depressing retaining pin. Insert lock cylinder into lock cylinder housing. **Ensure cylinder is fully seated and aligned in the interlocking washer before turning key to the OFF position. This will permit cylinder retaining pin to extend into cylinder housing hole.**
7. Rotate lock cylinder, using lock cylinder key, to ensure correct mechanical operation in all positions.
8. Connect key warning buzzer connector, then install shroud.
9. Connect battery ground cable and ensure proper operation. **Ensure vehicle cannot be started in drive and reverse.**

IGNITION SWITCH
REPLACE

1. Disconnect battery ground cable, then remove five steering column shroud attaching screws.
2. Remove two bolts and two nuts attaching steering column to column bracket, then lower steering column assembly to seat and remove column shrouds.
3. Disconnect ignition switch wire connector, then rotate ignition switch lock cylinder to the RUN position.
4. Remove the two retaining bolts attaching switch to lock cylinder housing.
5. Detach ignition switch from actuator pin, then remove switch.

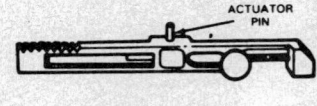

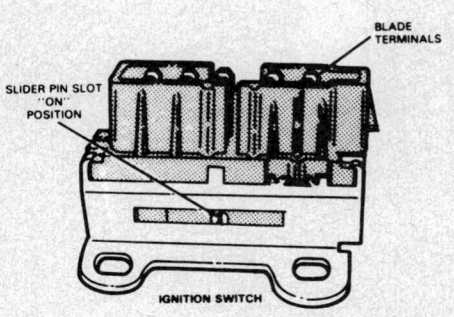

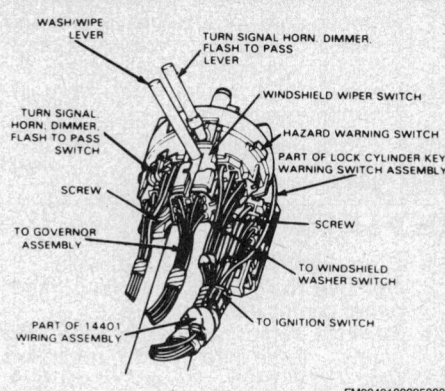

Fig. 2 Stop light switch

Fig. 3 Turn signal, hazard, horn, flash to pass & dimmer switch replacement

Fig. 1 Ignition switch replacement

6. Check to ensure that ignition switch actuator pin slot and ignition switch lock cylinder are in the Run position. **Replacement ignition switches are set in the Run position. The Run position on the ignition switch lock cylinder is located approximately 90° from the lock position.**
7. Position ignition switch on actuator pin. It may be necessary to move switch slightly to align switch to column mounting bolt holes, **Fig. 1.**
8. Install and tighten shear bolts until heads break off.
9. Connect wire connector to ignition switch, then connect battery ground cable and check ignition switch for proper operation.
10. Position upper shroud on column, then raise steering column and install column mounting bracket to instrument panel attaching bolts. **Torque** bolts to 15 to 25 ft. lbs.
11. Position lower shroud on column and install attaching bolts.

CLUTCH START SWITCH
REPLACE

1. Disconnect battery ground cable.
2. Remove trim panel above clutch pedal.
3. Disconnect electrical connector.
4. Remove clutch interlock retaining screw and hairpin clip, then remove switch. **Always install the switch with the self-adjusting clip one inch above end of the rod. The clutch pedal must be fully up (clutch engaged) or the switch may be improperly adjusted.**
5. Insert eyelet end of rod over pin on clutch pedal, then secure with hairpin clip.
6. Align mounting boss with corresponding hole in bracket, then install retaining screw.
7. Reset clutch interlock switch by depressing clutch pedal to floor.
8. Connect electrical connector, then install trim panel.

HEADLAMP SWITCH
REPLACE

1. Disconnect battery ground cable.
2. Remove two lefthand air vent control retaining screws, then place control aside.
3. Remove fuse panel bracket retaining screws, then move fuse panel assembly aside to gain access to headlamp switch.
4. Pull headlamp knob out to "On" position.
5. Depress headlamp knob and shaft retainer button on headlamp switch, then remove knob assembly.
6. Remove headlamp switch retaining bezel.
7. Disconnect multiple connector plug, then remove switch from instrument panel.
8. Reverse procedure to install.

STOP LIGHT SWITCH
REPLACE

1. Disconnect battery ground cable.
2. Remove retainer and outer white nylon washer from pedal pin. Slide switch off brake pedal pin far enough so that outer side of plate of switch clears pin. Remove switch, **Fig. 2.**
3. Reverse procedure to install.

TURN SIGNAL SWITCH
REPLACE

1. Disconnect battery ground cable.
2. Remove five shroud screws, then the lower shroud.
3. Remove upper shroud assembly.
4. Grasp switch lever and pull lever straight out from switch assembly, **Fig. 3.**
5. Peel back foam switch cover from turn signal switch.
6. Disconnect two electrical connectors.
7. Remove two self-tapping screws attaching switch assembly to lock cylinder housing, then disconnect switch from housing.
8. Reverse procedure to install.

DIMMER SWITCH
REPLACE

Refer to "Turn Signal Switch, Replace" for procedure.

STEERING WHEEL
REPLACE

1. Disconnect battery ground cable.
2. Remove horn pad retaining screws from rear of wheel, then pad assembly.
3. Remove air bag module assembly retaining screws, then air bag module.
4. Lift air bag module from wheel, then disconnect clockspring to module connector.
5. Remove energy absorbing foam from steering wheel assembly.
6. Disconnect horn pad wiring connector.
7. Loosen steering wheel attaching bolt four to six turns. Do not remove bolt.
8. Remove bolt completely to remove vibration damper, then reinstall bolt loosely on shaft.
9. Position steering wheel puller tool No. T67L-3600-A or equivalent on steering wheel.
10. Tighten bolt on removal tool until steering wheel is loose on shaft.
11. Reverse procedure to install, noting the following:
    a. **Torque** steering wheel retaining bolt to 23-33 ft. lbs.
    b. **Torque** air bag retaining bolts to 35-53 inch lbs.

INSTRUMENT CLUSTER
REPLACE

1. Disconnect battery ground cable.
2. Remove retaining screws from bottom of steering column opening and snap steering column cover out.
3. Remove steering column trim shroud, **Fig. 4.**
4. Remove lower cluster finish panels.
5. Remove cluster opening finish panel screws and pull panel rearward.
6. Disconnect speedometer cable from transaxle.

7. Remove screws retaining cluster and carefully pull cluster rearward enough to disengage speedometer cable.
8. Carefully pull cluster away from instrument panel.
9. Reverse procedure to install.

RADIO
REPLACE

1. Disconnect battery ground cable.
2. Remove radio knobs and instrument panel center trim panel.
3. Remove radio face plate mounting screws, then insert radio removing tool T87P-19061-A into radio face plate.
4. Pull radio outward by removal tool to disengage from rear mounting bracket.
5. Disconnect antenna and speaker leads from radio, then remove radio.
6. Remove nuts and washers from radio control shafts. Remove mounting plate.
7. Remove rear support retaining nut and support.
8. Reverse procedure to install.

WIPER MOTOR
REPLACE

1. Disconnect battery ground cable.
2. Lift passenger side water shield cover from cowl, then disconnect motor electrical connector.
3. Remove linkage retaining clip from motor arm, then the three bolts attaching motor to mounting bracket, **Fig. 5**.
4. Disconnect operating arm from motor, then separate motor from mounting bracket and remove from vehicle.
5. Reverse procedure to install.

WIPER SWITCH
REPLACE

The switch handle is an integral part of the switch and cannot be removed separately.
1. Disconnect battery ground cable.
2. Insert a small screwdriver into small slot on top of switch bezel.
3. While pushing down on screwdriver, work top part of switch bezel away from instrument panel.
4. Insert small screwdriver into small slot on bottom of switch bezel.
5. While pushing up on screwdriver, work bottom part of switch bezel away from instrument panel.
6. Remove switch from instrument panel, then remove connector.
7. Reverse procedure to install.

WIPER TRANSMISSION
REPLACE

1. Remove wiper arm and blade assemblies from pivot shaft.
2. Disconnect battery ground cable, then remove clip and disconnect linkage drive arm from motor crank pin.

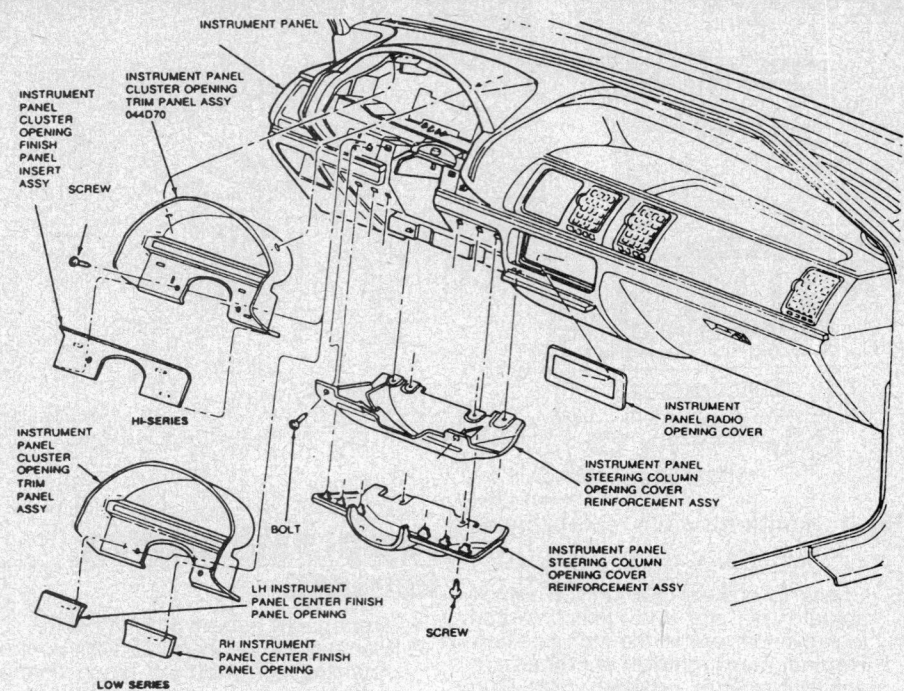

Fig. 4 Instrument cluster removal

FM9099100302000X

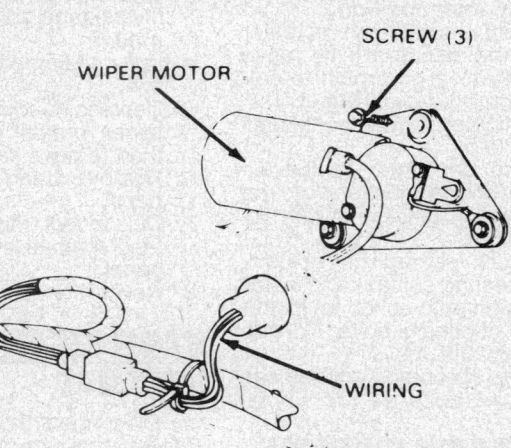

Fig. 5 Windshield wiper motor replacement

FM9029100159000X

3. Remove top grille from left and right cowl, then the pivot to cowl attaching screws.
4. Remove linkage and pivots from cowl chamber, **Fig. 6**.
5. Reverse procedure to install.

BLOWER MOTOR
REPLACE

1. Disconnect battery ground cable.
2. Remove screws securing right ventilator control cable to instrument panel.
3. Remove screw securing right register duct to lower right edge of instrument panel.
4. Remove glove box, then pull right register duct from installed position between air inlet duct and right register

opening, **Fig. 7**.
5.
6. Remove ventilator grille from bottom of ventilator assembly, then screws securing right ventilator assembly to blower housing.
7. Remove hub clamp spring from blower wheel hub, **Fig. 8**.
8. Pull blower wheel from blower shaft, then remove three blower motor flange attaching screws.
9. Pull blower motor from housing, disconnect electrical connector, then remove motor from vehicle.

HEATER CORE
REPLACE

1. Disconnect battery ground cable and drain engine coolant system.

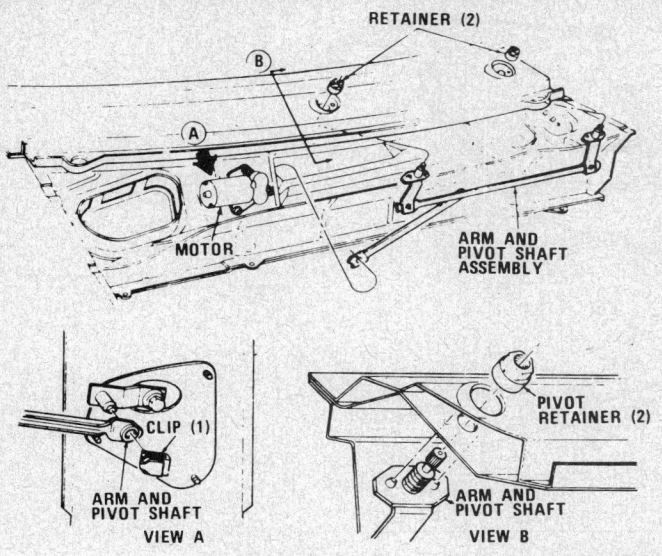

Fig. 6 Windshield wiper linkage replace

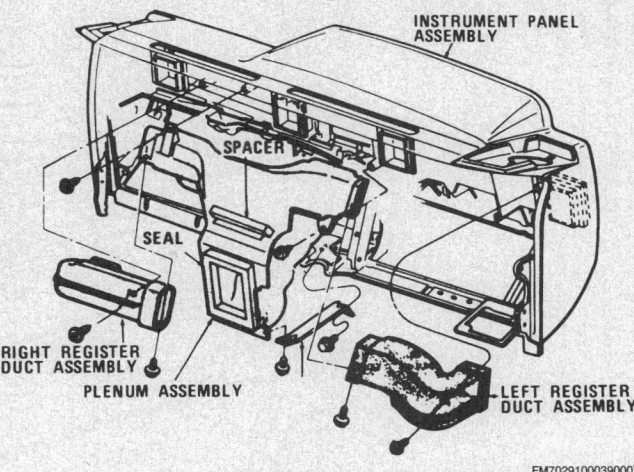

Fig. 7 Vent assembly removal

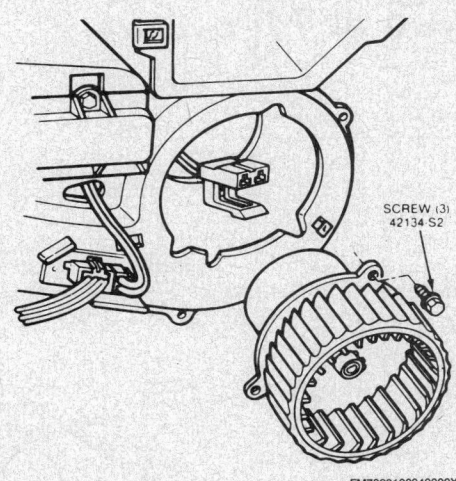

Fig. 8 Blower motor removal

2. Disconnect heater hoses from heater core and plug all lines and fittings.
3. Remove floor duct from plenum.
4. Remove screws attaching heater core cover to plenum, then the cover and heater core, **Fig. 9.**
5. Reverse procedure to install.

EVAPORATOR CORE
REPLACE

Whenever an evaporator core is replaced, it will be necessary to replace the suction accumulator/dryer.
1. Disconnect battery ground cable.
2. Drain coolant from radiator.
3. Discharge refrigerant from air conditioning system.
4. Working from inside engine compartment, disconnect heater hoses from heater core. Plug heater core tubes or blow any coolant from heater core with low pressure air.
5. Disconnect high pressure line and the accumulator/dryer inlet tubes from evaporator core at dash panel.

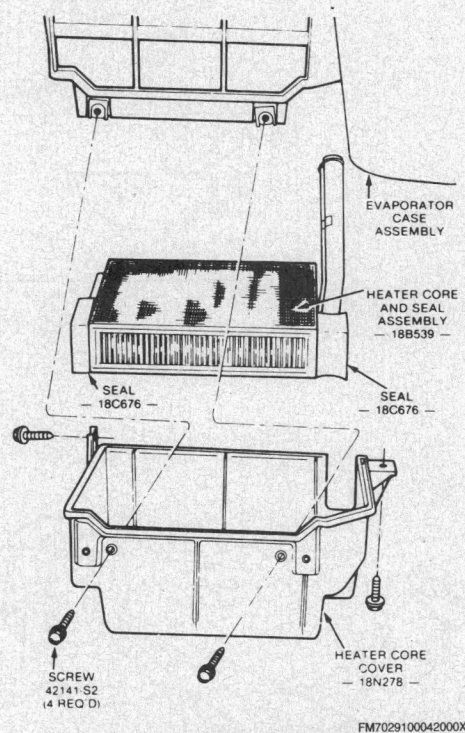

Fig. 9 Heater core removal

6. Cap refrigerant lines and evaporator core to prevent excess dirt and moisture from entering system.
7. Remove dash panel, refer to "Dash Panel Service" for procedure.
8. Disconnect wire harness connector from blower motor resistor.
9. Remove one screw attaching the bottom of evaporator case to dash panel.
10. Remove two nuts attaching evaporator case to dash panel in engine compartment.
11. Loosen sound insulation from the cowl top panel in the area around air inlet opening.
12. Remove two screws attaching support bracket and brace to cowl top panel, **Fig. 10.**
13. Remove air inlet duct from evaporator case (four screws).
14. Remove foam seal from evaporator core tubes.
15. Drill a 3/16 inch hole in both upright tabs on top of evaporator case, **Fig. 11.**
16. Using a small saw blade, cut the top of evaporator case between two raised outlines, **Figs. 12 through 14.**
17. Remove two blower motor resistor retaining screws, then blower motor resistor.
18. Fold cutout cover back from case,

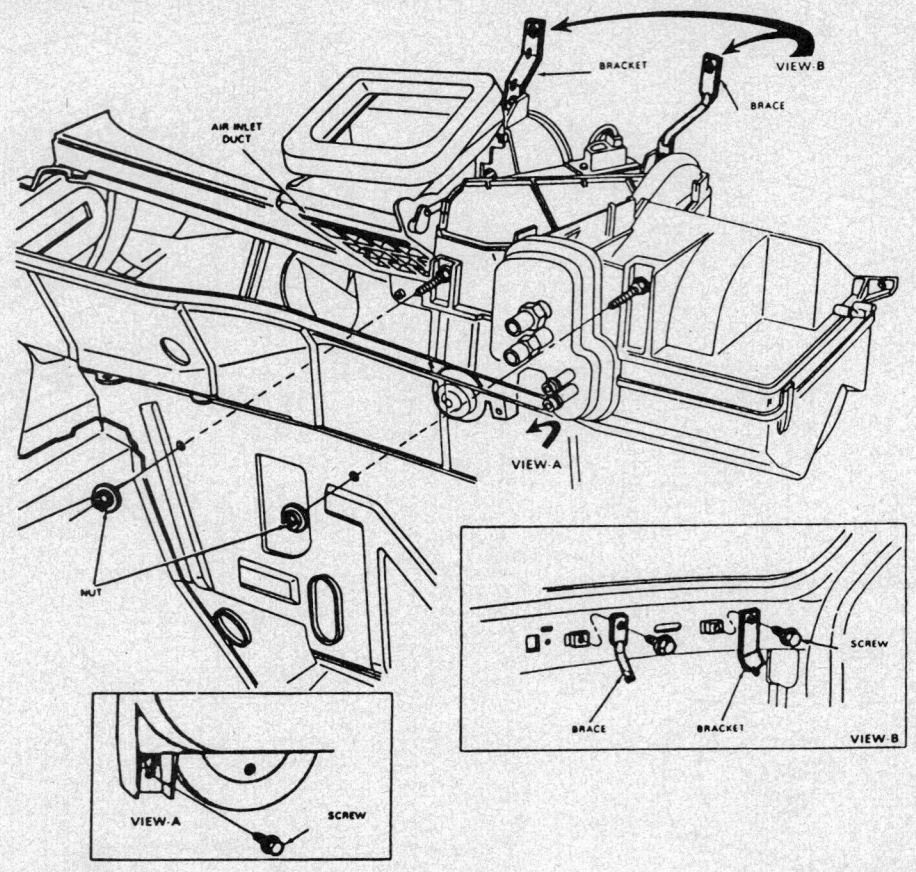

Fig. 10 Evaporator case

FM7029100043000X

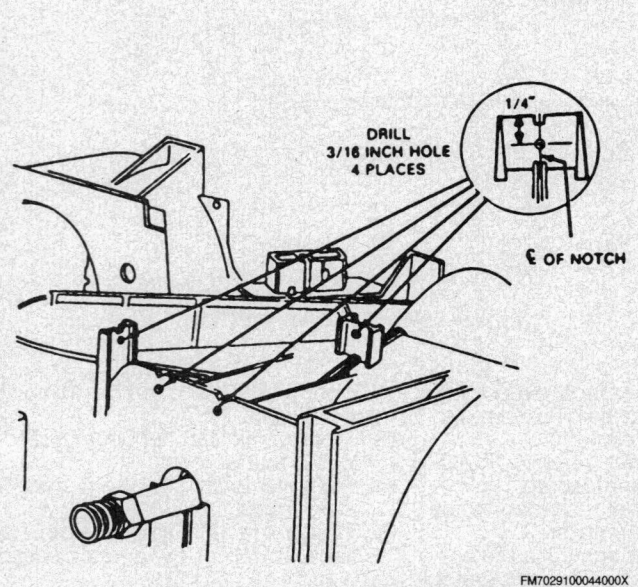

Fig. 11 Locations for drilling holes

FM7029100044000X

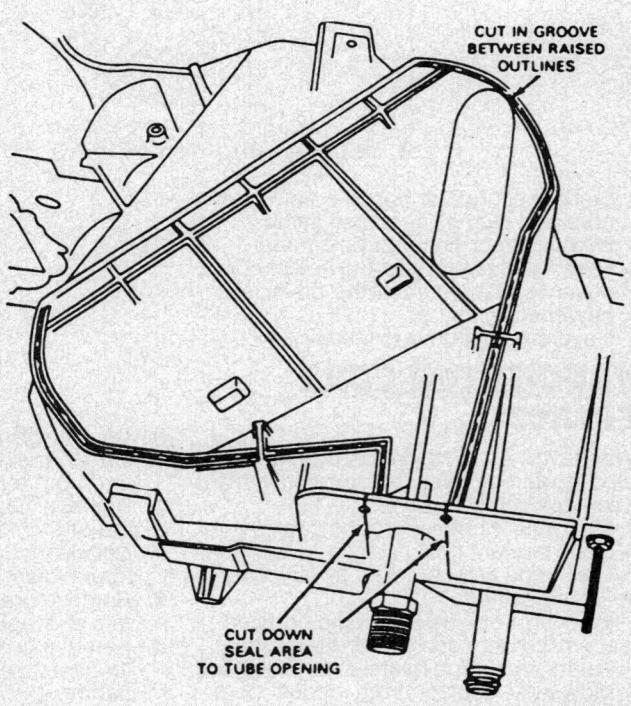

Fig. 12 Cutting outline locations. 1992

FM7029100045000X

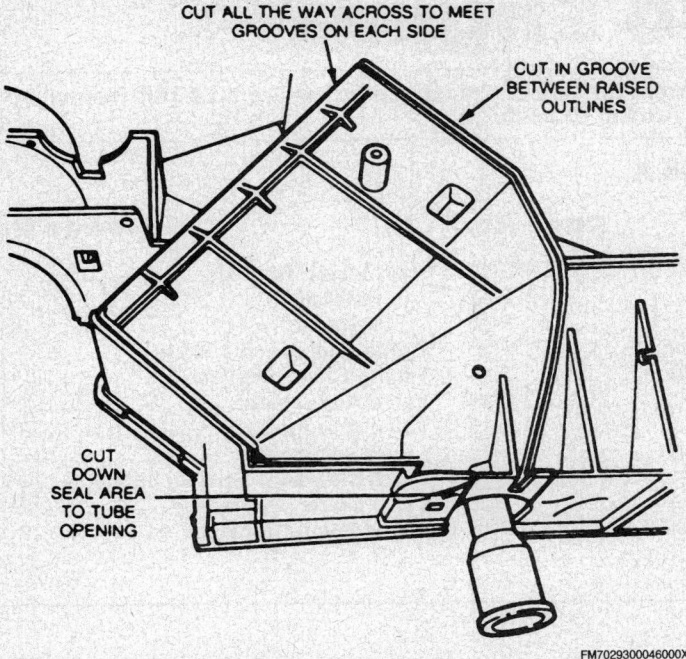

CUT ALL THE WAY ACROSS TO MEET GROOVES ON EACH SIDE

CUT IN GROOVE BETWEEN RAISED OUTLINES

CUT DOWN SEAL AREA TO TUBE OPENING

FM7029300046000X

Fig. 13   Cutting outline locations. 1993–94

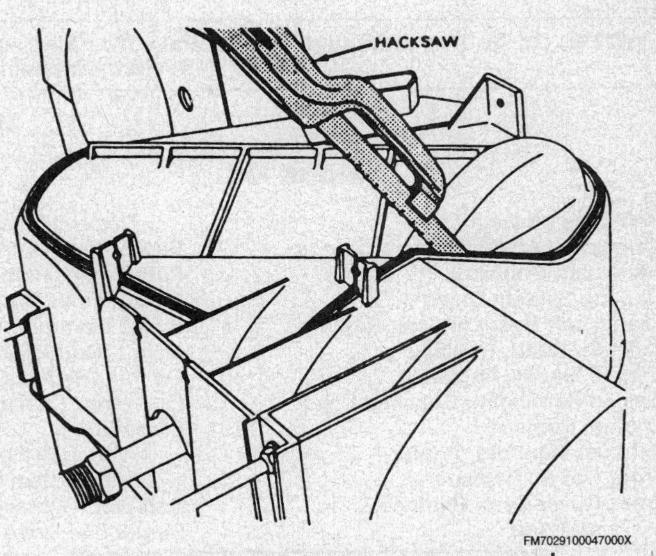

HACKSAW

FM7029100047000X

Fig. 14   Evaporator case cover removal

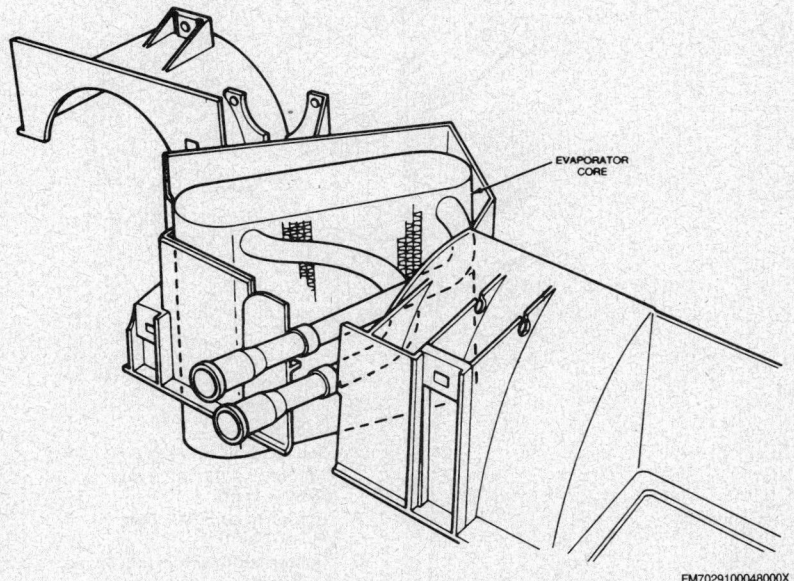

EVAPORATOR CORE

FM7029100048000X

Fig. 15   Evaporator core removal

Fig. 15.
19. Remove evaporator core.
20. Reverse procedure to install, noting the following:
   a. Install caulking cord (rope sealer) part No. D9AZ-19560-A or equivalent to seal evaporator case against leakage along cut line.
   b. Install a spring nut on each of the two upright tabs and with the two holes drilled in the front flange. Ensure hole in spring nut is aligned with the $3/16$ inch holes drilled in the tab and flange. Install and tighten screw in each spring nut (through the hole in the tab or flange) to secure the cutout cover in the closed position.

2.3L/4-140 Engine

NOTE: On Air Bag Equipped Models, Refer To "Air Bag System Precautions" Located In The Front Of This Manual For System Disarming & Arming Procedures.

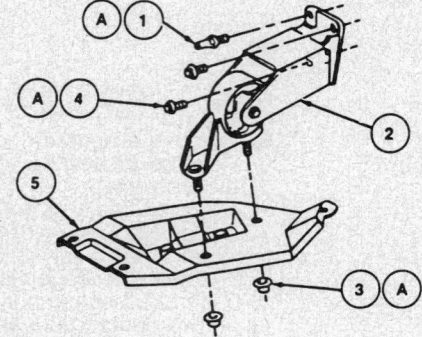

1A Stud Bolt
2 Insulator
3A Nut (2 Req'd)
4A Bolt (2 Req'd)
5 Stabilizer Bar Bracket Assy

FM1069400156000A

Fig. 1 LH front No. 1 insulator

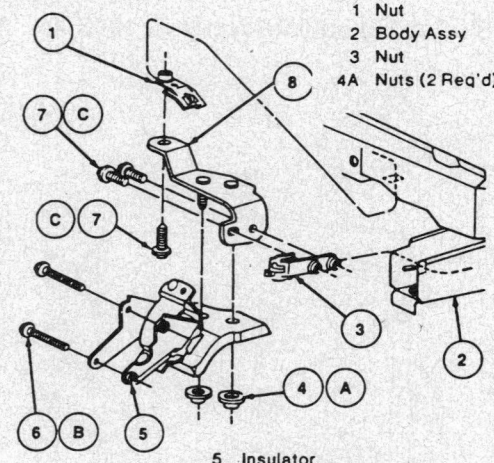

1 Nut
2 Body Assy
3 Nut
4A Nuts (2 Req'd)

5 Insulator
5B Bolt (2 Req'd)
7C Bolt (3 Req'd)
8 Support Bracket Assy
A Tighten to 97.7-132.3 N·m (73-97 Lb-Ft)
B Tighten to 40.3-54.7 N·m (30-40 Lb-Ft)
C Tighten to 68-92 N·m (51-67 Lb-Ft)

FM1069400157000A

Fig. 2 LH front No. 4 insulator

PRECAUTIONS

AIR BAG SYSTEMS

Refer to "Air Bag System Precautions" in the front of this manual for system disarming and arming procedures.

FUEL SYSTEM PRESSURE RELIEF

1. Remove air cleaner assembly.
2. Connect fuel pressure relief gauge tool No. T80L-9974-B, or equivalent, to fuel pressure relief valve at fuel supply manifold.
3. Open manual valve on fuel pressure relief gauge to relieve fuel pressure.
4. Remove fuel pressure relief gauge once fuel pressure has been relieved.

ENGINE MOUNT
REPLACE

Refer to **Figs. 1 through 4** when replacing engine mounts.

ENGINE
REPLACE

Engine and transaxle are removed as an assembly.
1. Mark position of hood hinges, then remove hood.
2. Relieve fuel pressure as outlined under "Precautions," then disconnect battery ground cable and remove air cleaner assembly.
3. Remove lower radiator hose and drain coolant from engine. Remove upper radiator hose from engine.

4. **On models equipped with automatic transaxle,** disconnect transaxle cooler lines from rubber hoses below radiator.
5. **On all models,** remove coil assembly from cylinder head. Disconnect coolant fan electrical connector.
6. Remove radiator shroud, engine cooling fan and radiator.
7. Carefully discharge refrigerant from air conditioning system, if equipped. Remove inlet and outlet lines from compressor.
8. Mark and disconnect all electrical and vacuum lines from engine.

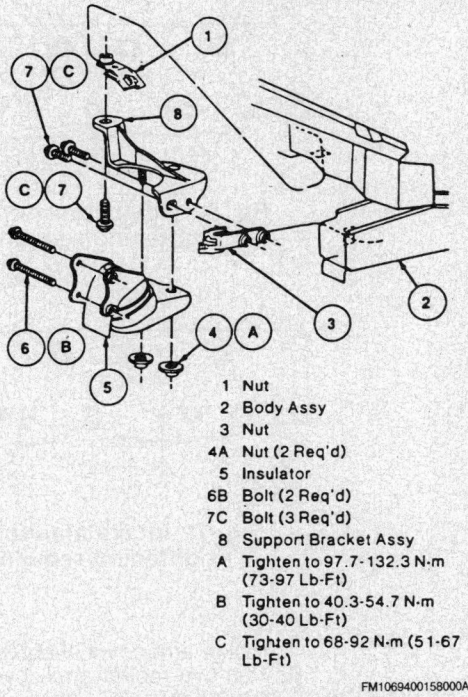

1 Nut
2 Body Assy
3 Nut
4A Nut (2 Req'd)
5 Insulator
6B Bolt (2 Req'd)
7C Bolt (3 Req'd)
8 Support Bracket Assy
A Tighten to 97.7-132.3 N·m (73-97 Lb-Ft)
B Tighten to 40.3-54.7 N·m (30-40 Lb-Ft)
C Tighten to 68-92 N·m (51-67 Lb-Ft)

FM1069400158000A

Fig. 3 LH rear support bracket

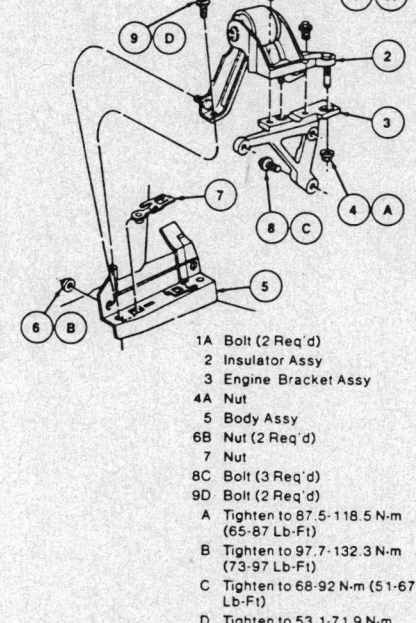

1A Bolt (2 Req'd)
2 Insulator Assy
3 Engine Bracket Assy
4A Nut
5 Body Assy
6B Nut (2 Req'd)
7 Nut
8C Bolt (3 Req'd)
9D Bolt (2 Req'd)
A Tighten to 87.5-118.5 N·m (65-87 Lb-Ft)
B Tighten to 97.7-132.3 N·m (73-97 Lb-Ft)
C Tighten to 68-92 N·m (51-67 Lb-Ft)
D Tighten to 53.1-71.9 N·m (40-53 Lb-Ft)

FM1069400159000A

Fig. 4 RH No. 3A insulator

9. **On models equipped with automatic transaxle,** disconnect TV linkage from transaxle.
10. **On models equipped with manual transaxle,** disconnect clutch cable from transaxle shift lever.
11. **On all models,** disconnect accelerator linkage, fuel supply and return lines from engine.
12. Disconnect thermactor pump discharge hose from pump.
13. Disconnect power steering pressure and return lines from pump, if equipped. Remove power steering line bracket from cylinder head.
14. Install engine support tool No. D79P-6000-A or equivalent, to engine lifting eye.
15. Raise and support vehicle.
16. Remove starter cable from starter.
17. Remove air hose from catalytic converter.
18. Remove bolt securing exhaust pipe bracket to oil pan. Remove two exhaust pipes to exhaust manifold nuts, then pull exhaust pipe out of rubber insulating grommets and position aside.
19. Disconnect speedometer cable from transaxle.
20. Remove water pump inlet hose from engine.
21. Remove bolts securing control arms to body. Remove stabilizer bar bracket bolts and brackets.
22. Remove halfshaft assemblies from transaxle.
23. **On models equipped with manual transaxle,** remove roll restrictor nuts from transaxle. Remove shift stabilizer bar to transaxle bolts. Remove shift mechanism to shift shaft nut and bolt from transaxle.
24. **On models equipped with automatic transaxle,** disconnect manual shift cable clip from transaxle shift lever. Remove manual shift linkage bracket bolts and bracket from transaxle.
25. **On all models,** remove nuts and left-hand rear No. 4 insulator mount bracket from body bracket.
26. Lower vehicle and install suitable lifting hoist to engine. **Do not allow front wheels to touch floor.**
27. Remove engine support tool No. D79L-6000-A or equivalent from engine.
28. Remove righthand No. 3 insulator intermediate bracket to engine bracket bolts and intermediate bracket to insulator nuts. Remove nut on the bottom of double ended stud which secures intermediate bracket to engine bracket. Remove bracket.
29. Carefully lower engine and transaxle assembly from vehicle.
30. Reverse procedure to install, noting the following:
    a. When installing engine/transaxle assembly, position assembly directly below engine compartment.
    b. Slowly lower vehicle over engine and transaxle. Do not allow front wheels to contact floor.

INTAKE MANIFOLD
REPLACE

1. Relieve fuel pressure as outlined under "Precautions," then disconnect battery ground cable and drain coolant from engine.
2. Disconnect accelerator cable.
3. Remove air cleaner assembly and heat stove duct from heat shield.
4. Disconnect all vacuum lines from intake manifold.
5. Remove thermactor belt from pulley, thermactor hose and thermactor pump from engine.
6. Remove exhaust pipe to exhaust manifold nuts and disconnect exhaust pipe from exhaust manifold.
7. Remove exhaust manifold heat shield.
8. Disconnect Exhaust Gas Oxygen (EGO) sensor electrical connector.
9. Disconnect thermactor check valve hose from tube assembly. Remove EGR valve bracket nuts and EGR valve bracket.
10. Disconnect water inlet hose from intake manifold.
11. Disconnect EGR hose from EGR valve.
12. Remove bolts, intake manifold and gasket from engine **Fig. 5.**
13. Remove bolts and exhaust manifold from engine.
14. Reverse procedure to install, noting the following:
    a. **Torque** exhaust manifold bolts in two steps and in sequence shown in **Fig. 6** first to 5-7 ft. lbs. then to 20-30 ft. lbs.
    b. **Torque** intake manifold bolts in two steps and in sequence shown in **Fig. 7** first to 5-7 ft. lbs. then to 15-22 ft. lbs.

EXHAUST MANIFOLD
REPLACE

Refer to "Intake Manifold, Replace" for exhaust manifold replacement.

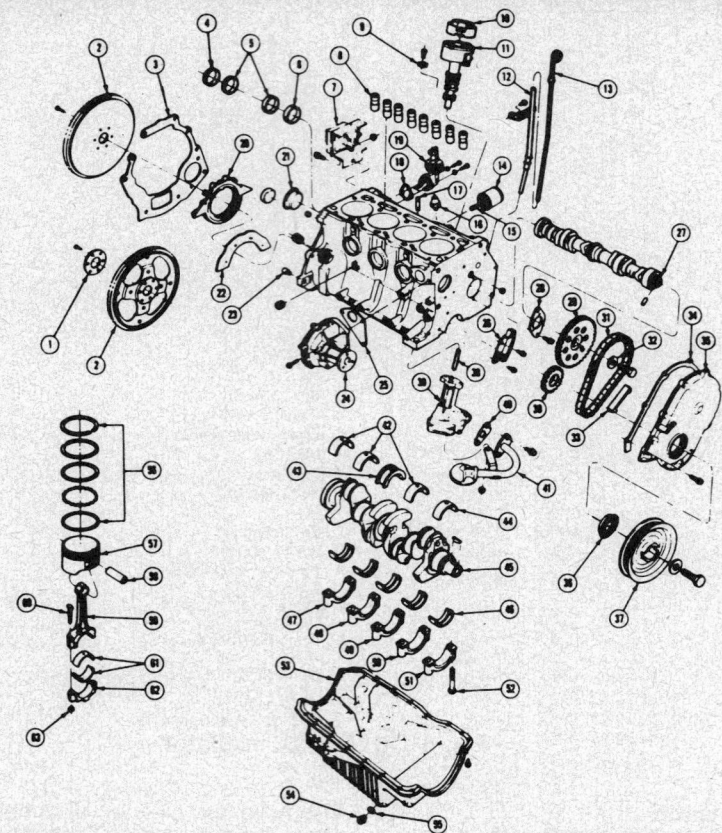

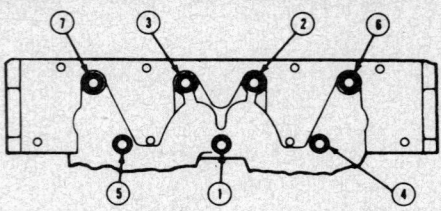

Fig. 6 Exhaust manifold bolt tightening sequence

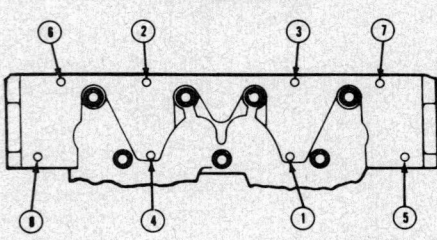

Fig. 7 Intake manifold bolt tightening sequence

1 REINFORCEMENT PLATE	17 FUEL PUMP PUSHROD	33 TIMING CHAIN DAMPER	49 MAIN BEARING CAP
2 FLYWHEEL	18 FUEL PUMP GASKET	34 FRONT COVER GASKET	50 MAIN BEARING CAP
3 REAR COVER PLATE	19 FUEL PUMP	35 FRONT COVER	51 MAIN BEARING CAP FRONT
4 CAMSHAFT BEARING	20 RETAINER ASSEMBLY	36 SEAL	52 BOLT
5 CAMSHAFT BEARING	21 COVER	37 CRANKSHAFT PULLEY ASSEMBLY	53 OIL PAN ASSEMBLY
6 CAMSHAFT BEARING	22 GASKET	38 INTERMEDIATE DRIVESHAFT	54 DRAIN PLUG
7 COIL	23 DOWEL	39 OIL PUMP ASSEMBLY	55 WASHER
8 TAPPET ASSEMBLY	24 WATER PUMP ASSEMBLY	40 PICK UP TUBE GASKET	56 PISTON RINGS
9 CLAMP	25 WATER PUMP GASKET	41 PICK UP TUBE ASSEMBLY	57 PISTON
10 ROTOR	26 TENSIONER ASSEMBLY	42 UPPER MAIN BEARING	58 PISTON PIN
11 DISTRIBUTOR ASSEMBLY	27 CAMSHAFT	43 UPPER THRUST BEARING	59 CONNECTING ROD
12 TUBE	28 THRUST PLATE	44 UPPER MAIN BEARING FRONT	60 STUD
13 OIL DIPSTICK	29 CAMSHAFT SPROCKET	45 CRANKSHAFT	61 ROD BEARINGS
14 OIL FILTER	30 CRANKSHAFT SPROCKET	46 LOWER MAIN BEARING	62 ROD CAP
15 INSERT	31 TIMING CHAIN ASSEMBLY	47 REAR MAIN BEARING CAP	63 NUT
16 OIL PRESSURE SWITCH	32 WASHER	48 MAIN BEARING CAP	

Fig. 5 Engine block assembly & components

CYLINDER HEAD
REPLACE

1. Relieve fuel pressure as outlined under "Precautions," then disconnect battery ground cable.
2. Remove lower radiator hose and drain coolant from engine.
3. Disconnect heater hose from fitting located under intake manifold.
4. Disconnect upper radiator hose from cylinder head.
5. Disconnect engine cooling fan switch from electrical connector.
6. Remove air cleaner assembly from engine.
7. Mark and disconnect all vacuum hoses from cylinder head.
8. Remove rocker arm cover.
9. Remove all accessory drive belts from engine.
10. Remove distributor cap and spark plug wires as an assembly.
11. Disconnect EGR tube from EGR valve. Disconnect choke cap wire.
12. Disconnect fuel supply and return lines from rubber connector, **Fig. 8.**
13. Disconnect accelerator cable and speed control cable, if equipped.
14. Raise and support vehicle.
15. Disconnect exhaust system from exhaust pipe. Lower vehicle.
16. Remove cylinder head bolts, cylinder head and gasket with thermactor pump, exhaust and intake manifolds attached. **Do not lay cylinder head flat. Damage to spark plugs or gasket surfaces may result.**
17. Reverse procedure to install. **Torque** cylinder head bolts in sequence shown in **Fig. 9**, in two steps. First to 51-59 ft. lbs., then to 70-76 ft. lbs.

VALVE COVER
REPLACE

The following procedure has been revised by a Technical Service Bulletin.
1. Disconnect battery ground cable.
2. Remove oil filler cap.
3. Disconnect PCV hose from PCV valve.
4. Disconnect throttle linkage cable from rocker arm cover.
5. Disconnect speed control cable from rocker arm cover, if equipped.
6. Remove rocker arm cover bolts and cover.
7. Reverse procedure to install, noting the following:
   a. If mold-in-place gasket is damaged by cuts longer than 1/8 inch, or by more than three nicks or cuts (any size), replace entire rocker cover assembly.
   b. If damaged, replace rubber isolators part No. E83Z-6C518-A or washer bolt and rubber isolator assembly part No. E93Z-6C519-A.
   c. Put one drop of adhesive tread lock part No. ESE-M2G260-AA on bolts if they are to be reused, failure to do so may result in oil leakage.
   d. Tighten rocker cover assembly to specifications.

VALVE ARRANGEMENT
FRONT TO REAR

2.3L/4-140 .... I-E-I-E-I-E-I

CAMSHAFT LOBE LIFT SPECIFICATIONS

Engine	Intake, Inch	Exhaust, Inch
2.3L/4-140 HSC	.249	.239

VALVE CLEARANCE SPECIFICATIONS

Engine	Valve Lash, Inch
2.3L/4-140 HSC	.070-.170①

①—With hydraulic valve lash adjuster completely collapsed.

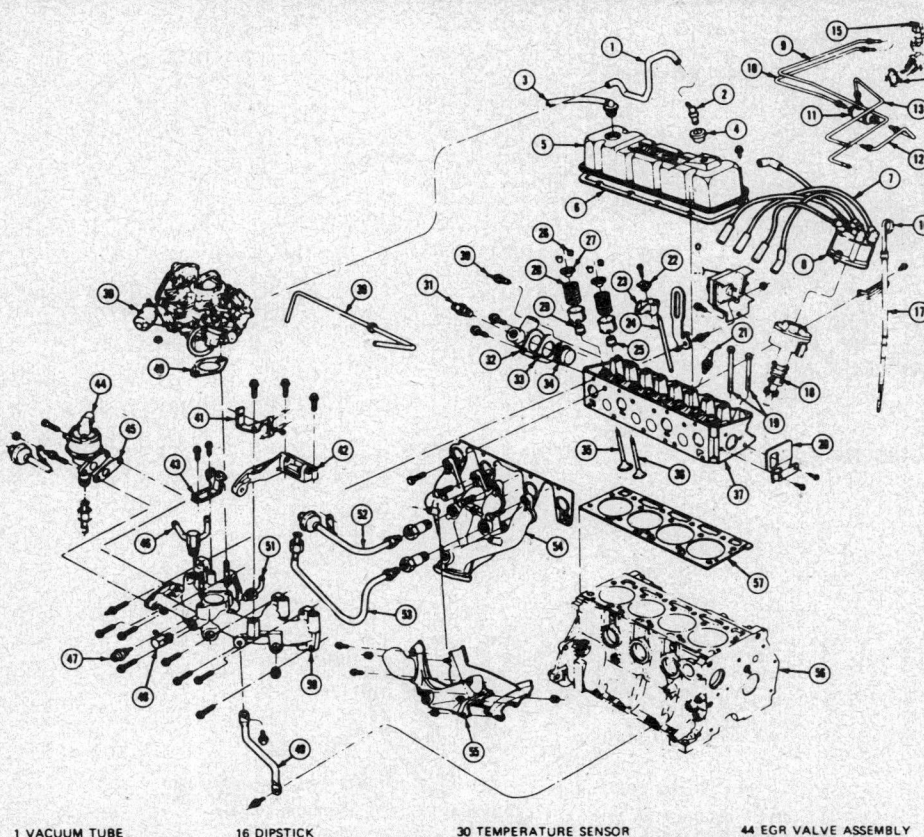

Fig. 9 Cylinder head bolt tightening sequence

M11 X 1.5 X 100.0 BOLT (5)
M11 X 1.5 X 80.0 BOLT (5)

FM1069100161000X

1 VACUUM TUBE	16 DIPSTICK	30 TEMPERATURE SENSOR	44 EGR VALVE ASSEMBLY
2 VENT VALVE ASSEMBLY	17 DIPSTICK TUBE ASSEMBLY	31 FAN SWITCH	45 EGR VALVE GASKET
3 TUBE ASSEMBLY	18 DISTRIBUTOR	32 WATER OUTLET CONNECTION	46 VACUUM FITTING
4 GROMMET	19 CYLINDER HEAD BOLTS	33 WATER OUTLET CONNECTION GASKET	47 SENSOR
5 ROCKER ARM COVER	20 ENGINE LIFTING EYE	34 THERMOSTAT ASSEMBLY	48 VACUUM FITTING
6 ROCKER ARM COVER GASKET	21 SPARK PLUG	35 INTAKE VALVE	49 BRACE
7 SPARK PLUG WIRES	22 ROCKER ARM FULCRUM	36 EXHAUST VALVE	50 INTAKE MANIFOLD ASSEMBLY
8 DISTRIBUTOR CAP	23 ROCKER ARM	37 CYLINDER HEAD	51 VACUUM FITTING
9 FUEL LINES	24 PUSHROD	38 CARBURETOR FUEL LINE	52 TUBE ASSEMBLY
10 FUEL LINES	25 EXHAUST VALVE STEM SEAL	39 CARBURETOR ASSEMBLY	53 TUBE ASSEMBLY
11 FUEL FILTER	26 KEY	40 CARBURETOR GASKET	54 EXHAUST MANIFOLD
12 FUEL FILTER LINES	27 SPRING RETAINER	41 BRACKET	55 HEAT SHIELD
13 FUEL FILTER LINES	28 SPRING	42 BRACKET	56 CYLINDER BLOCK
14 FUEL PUMP GASKET	29 INTAKE VALVE STEM SEAL	43 ACCELERATOR SHAFT BRACKET	57 CYLINDER HEAD GASKET
15 FUEL PUMP ASSEMBLY			

Fig. 8 Cylinder block assembly & components

FM1069100163000X

for noisy operation, ensure the noise is not caused by improper collapsed tappet gap, worn rocker arms, pushrods or valve tips. To check collapsed tappet gap, proceed as follows:

1. Rotate camshaft to position A as shown in **Fig. 10**.
2. Check intake and exhaust valves on compression stroke under camshaft position A. With camshaft in position A, tappet gap should be .072-.174 inch with tappet collapsed on base circle. Check No. 1 cylinder intake and exhaust valves. Check No. 2 cylinder intake valve. Check No. 3 cylinder exhaust valve. Tighten fulcrum bolts to specifications.
3. Rotate camshaft 180 degrees to position B as shown in **Fig. 10**. Check No. 2 cylinder exhaust valve. Check No. 3 cylinder intake valve. Check No. 4 cylinder intake and exhaust valve. Tighten fulcrum bolts to specification.

Remove lifters as follows:

1. Remove cylinder head as described previously.
2. Using a suitable magnet, remove lifters from lifter bores.
3. Place valve lifters in a rack so they can be installed in their original positions. **If the lifters are stuck in their bores by excessive varnish or gum buildup, use hydraulic lifter puller tool No. D81-6500-A or equivalent to remove valve lifters.**
4. Reverse procedure to install.

FRONT COVER
REPLACE

Refer to "Timing Chain, Replace" for front cover replacement procedure.

FRONT COVER SEAL
REPLACE
REMOVAL

The following removal and installation procedure can only be performed with the engine removed from the vehicle. Remove engine as described under "Engine, Replace."

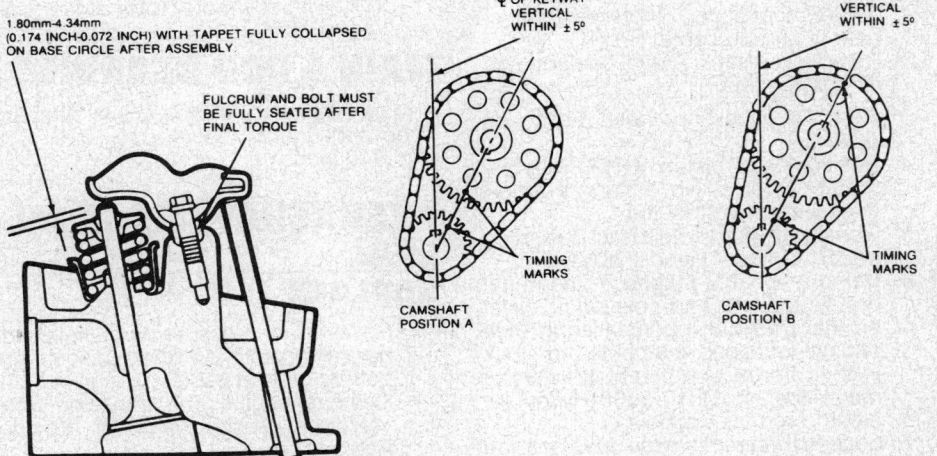

1.80mm-4.34mm (0.174 INCH-0.072 INCH) WITH TAPPET FULLY COLLAPSED ON BASE CIRCLE AFTER ASSEMBLY.

FULCRUM AND BOLT MUST BE FULLY SEATED AFTER FINAL TORQUE

Ç OF KEYWAY VERTICAL WITHIN ± 5°

TIMING MARKS

CAMSHAFT POSITION A

Ç OF KEYWAY VERTICAL WITHIN ± 5°

TIMING MARKS

CAMSHAFT POSITION B

FM1069100164000X

Fig. 10 Collapsed tappet gap inspection

VALVE ADJUSTMENT

This engine is equipped with hydraulic lifters and adjustment is not required.

HYDRAULIC LIFTERS
REPLACE

Before replacing a hydraulic valve lifter

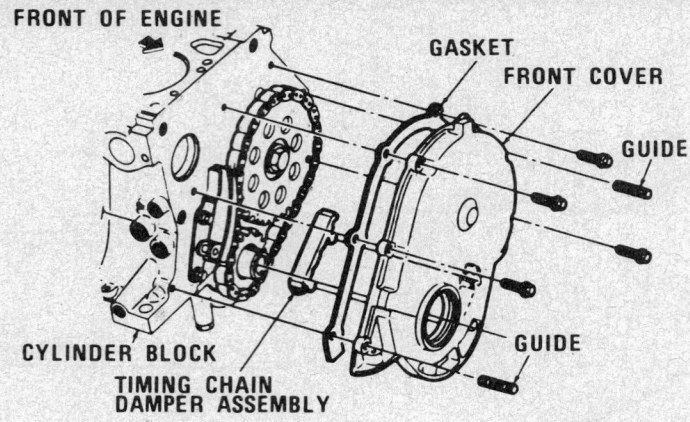

Fig. 11 Front cover removal

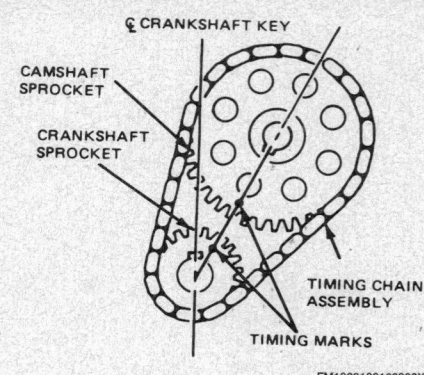

Fig. 12 Valve timing marks

1. Relieve fuel pressure as outlined under "Precautions," then disconnect battery ground cable.
2. Remove bolt and washer from crankshaft pulley.
3. Using bearing cone remover tool No. T77F-4220-B1 or equivalent, remove crankshaft pulley.
4. Using front cover seal remover tool No. T74P-6700-A or equivalent, remove front cover oil seal.

INSTALLATION

1. Coat new front cover oil seal with a suitable lubricant.
2. Using pinion oil seal installer tool No. T83T-4676-A or equivalent, install oil seal into front cover. Drive oil seal in until it is fully seated into front cover recess. Check oil seal after installation to ensure spring is properly positioned in oil seal.
3. Install crankshaft pulley, washer and bolt. Tighten crankshaft pulley bolt to specification.

TIMING CHAIN
REPLACE

The following procedure can only be performed with the engine removed from the vehicle. Remove engine as described under "Engine, Replace."

1. Relieve fuel pressure as outlined under "Precautions," then disconnect battery ground cable.
2. Remove dipstick, crankshaft pulley bolt, washer and pulley.
3. Remove front cover bolts and front cover, **Fig. 11.**
4. Align camshaft and crankshaft sprocket timing marks as shown in **Fig. 12.**
5. Remove camshaft sprocket bolt and washer.
6. Remove sprockets and timing chain from engine as an assembly, **Fig. 13.** Check timing chain vibration damper for wear. Replace if necessary.
7. Remove oil pan.
8. Reverse procedure to install. Ensure to align timing marks as shown in **Fig. 11.**

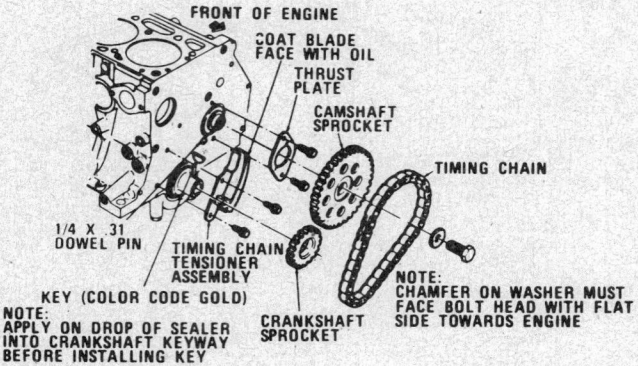

Fig. 13 Timing chain & sprockets removal

CAMSHAFT
REPLACE

The following procedure can only be performed with the engine removed from the vehicle. Remove engine as described under "Engine, Replace."

1. Relieve fuel pressure as outlined under "Precautions," then disconnect battery ground cable.
2. Remove dipstick. Drain coolant and oil from engine.
3. Remove accessory drive belts and pulleys.
4. Position No. 1 piston at TDC with distributor rotor at No. 1 firing position, then remove distributor.
5. Remove cylinder head as described under "Cylinder Head, Replace."
6. Using a suitable magnet, remove hydraulic tappets and position in order so that they can be installed in their original locations. If tappets are stuck in their bores, use hydraulic lifter remover tool No. D81L-6500A or equivalent to remove tappets.
7. Loosen then remove fan drive belt, fan and crankshaft pulley.
8. Remove front cover as described under "Front Cover, Timing Chain & Sprockets, Replace."
9. Remove fuel pump, gasket and fuel pump pushrod.
10. Remove timing chain, sprockets and timing chain tensioner as described under "Front Cover, Timing Chain & Sprockets, Replace."
11. Remove camshaft thrust plate. Carefully remove camshaft from engine to avoid damaging camshaft bearings, journals and lobes.
12. Reverse procedure to install. Lubricate camshaft with suitable oil before installing. Ensure No. 1 piston is at TDC with distributor rotor at No. 1 firing position.

MAIN & ROD BEARINGS

Main bearings are available in standard sizes and undersizes of .010, .020, .030 and .040 inch.

CRANKSHAFT REAR OIL SEAL
REPLACE

1. Relieve fuel pressure as outlined under "Precautions," then disconnect battery ground cable.
2. Remove engine and transaxle from vehicle as described under "Engine, Replace."
3. Remove transaxle from engine.
4. Remove rear cover plate.
5. Using a suitable tool, punch a hole into the seal metal surface between the lip and block. Using jet plug remover tool No. T77L-9533-B or equivalent, remove seal.
6. Reverse procedure to install.

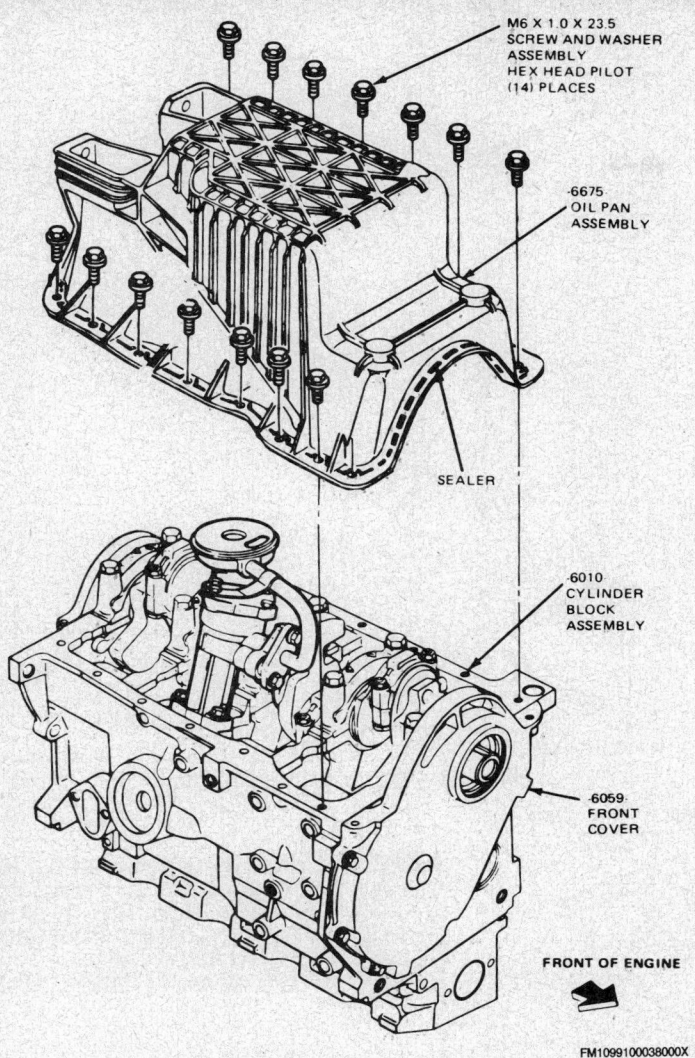

M6 X 1.0 X 23.5
SCREW AND WASHER
ASSEMBLY
HEX HEAD PILOT
(14) PLACES

-6675
OIL PAN
ASSEMBLY

SEALER

-6010
CYLINDER
BLOCK
ASSEMBLY

-6059
FRONT
COVER

FRONT OF ENGINE

FM1099100038000X

Fig. 14   Oil pan removal

6600
OIL PUMP
ASSEMBLY

M8 X 1.25 X 30.0
SCREW AND WASHER
ASSEMBLY (2)

6A605
INTERMEDIATE
DRIVESHAFT

APPLY OIL
TO SEALING
SURFACE

-6714
OIL FILTER
ASSEMBLY

6890
INSERT

FRONT OF ENGINE

FM1099100039000X

Fig. 15   Oil pump removal

OIL PAN
REPLACE

1. Disconnect battery ground cable.
2. Raise and support vehicle.
3. Drain coolant and oil from engine.
4. **On models equipped with manual transaxle,** remove roll restrictor.
5. **On all models,** remove starter from engine.
6. Disconnect exhaust pipe from oil pan.
7. Remove engine coolant tube located at the lower radiator hose, at the water pump and from tabs on oil pan.
8. Remove oil pan bolts and oil pan, **Fig. 14,** from engine.
9. Reverse procedure to install, noting the following:
   a. Remove all traces of RTV sealant from engine block and oil pan.
   b. Clean block rails, front cover, rear cover retainer and oil pan thoroughly with Dupont(R) Freon (TF) or equivalent solvent.
   c. Remove and clean oil pump pickup tube and screen assembly.
   d. Apply RTV part No. E8AZ-19652-A or equivalent, in oil pan groove. Completely fill the oil pan groove with sealer. Sealer Bead should be $3/16$ inch wide and $1/8$ inch rise above oil pan surface in all areas except half-rounds. The half-rounds should have $3/16$ wide bead and $3/16$ inch rise above oil pan surface. **Applying RTV in excess of the specified amount will not improve sealing of oil pan.**
   e. RTV sealant needs to cure completely before coming in contact with engine oil, about one hour at 65-75°F ambient temperature.

OIL PUMP
REPLACE

1. Disconnect battery ground cable.
2. Remove oil pan as described under "Oil Pan, Replace."
3. Remove oil pump bolts and oil pump, **Fig. 15,** from engine. Remove intermediate driveshaft from oil pump.
4. Reverse procedure to install.

BELT TENSION DATA

Belt	New, Lbs.	Used, Lbs.
A/C Compressor	50-90	40-60
Alternator	150-190	140-160
Power Steering	50-90	40-60

SERPENTINE DRIVE BELT

Refer to **Fig. 16,** for serpentine drive belt routing.

COOLING SYSTEM BLEED

This engine does not require a specified bleed procedure. After filling engine cooling system, run engine to operating temperature with radiator/pressure cap off and top up coolant as necessary.

THERMOSTAT
REPLACE
REMOVAL

1. Disconnect battery cable and wiring connector from thermo switch in thermostat housing.
2. Remove radiator cap, then attach a hose to drain tube and open draincock. Drain coolant level until its below water outlet connection. Close the draincock.
3. Loosen upper hose at radiator, then remove water outlet housing retaining bolts. Lift clear of engine and remove thermostat. Do not pry housing off.

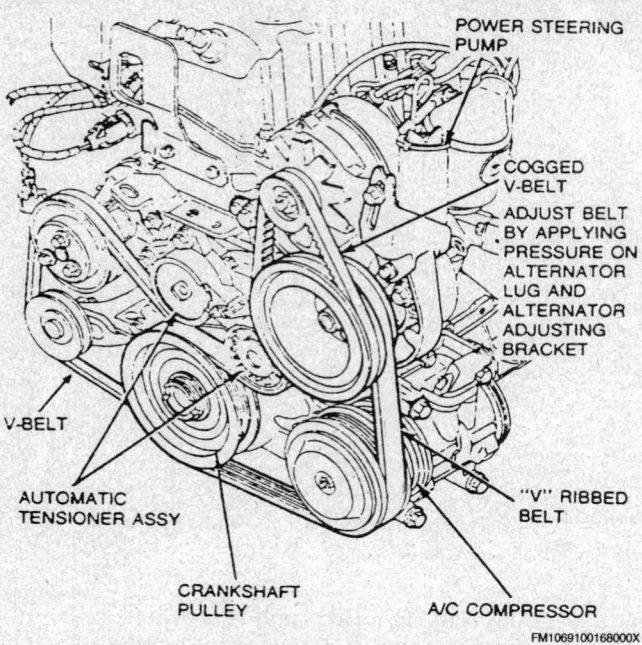

Fig. 16　Serpentine drive belt routing

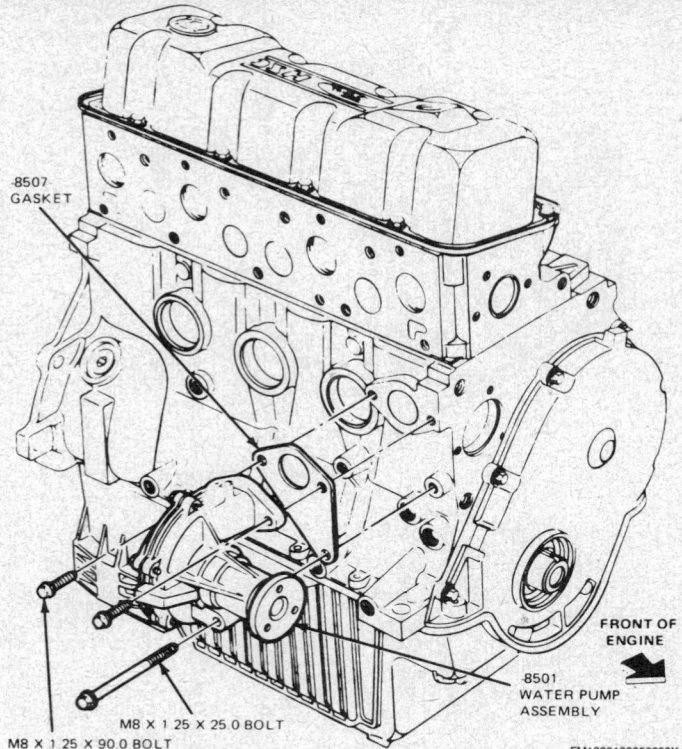

Fig. 17　Water pump removal

INSTALLATION

1. Clean outlet housing and cylinder head mating surfaces.
2. Position thermostat and seat so it will compress gasket. Position outlet to cylinder head, using a new gasket and install retaining bolts.
3. Connect top hose to radiator and tighten clamp. Ensure that draincock is closed.
4. Fill coolant system with coolant recommended by manufacturer as follows:
   a. Add 50 percent coolant, then add water until radiator is full. Allow coolant level to settle, then add more coolant until radiator remain full.
   b. Install radiator cap to first notch, connect battery cable and wire connector to thermo switch. Start engine and let idle until upper hose is warm, then carefully remove radiator cap and top off coolant level.
   c. Install cap securely and fill reservoir to FULL COLD mark with proper concentrate. Add water to FULL HOT mark. Check for leaks.

WATER PUMP
REPLACE

1. Disconnect battery ground cable and drain coolant from engine.
2. Loosen thermactor pump adjusting bolt and remove belt.
3. Remove thermactor air pump hose clamp, thermactor pump bracket bolts, pump and bracket assembly from engine.
4. Loosen water pump idler pulley bolt and remove belt from water pump pulley.
5. Remove water pump inlet tube.

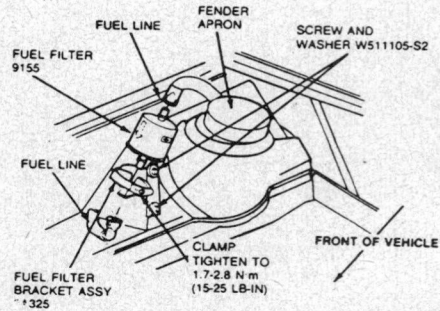

Fig. 18　Fuel filter removal

6. Remove water pump bolts and water pump, **Fig. 17.**
7. Reverse procedure to install.

RADIATOR
REPLACE

1. Disconnect battery ground cable, then drain engine coolant.
2. Disconnect upper radiator hose, then remove two fasteners retaining upper end of fan shroud to radiator end tank.
3. **On models equipped with air conditioning,** remove nut and screw retaining upper end of fan shroud to radiator at cross support, then nut and screw at end tank.
4. Disconnect air conditioning discharge line from shroud.
5. **On all models,** disconnect fan wiring and remove fan shroud from vehicle.
6. Disconnect lower radiator hose.
7. **On models equipped with automatic transaxle,** disconnect oil cooler lines.

8. **On all models,** remove two nut retaining top of radiator to crossmember, then tip radiator back to allow clearance with upper mounting stud and lift radiator from vehicle.
9. Reverse procedure to install.

FUEL PUMP
REPLACE

1. Relieve fuel pressure as outlined under "Precautions," then disconnect battery ground cable.
2. Remove fuel from fuel tank by pumping fuel out of fuel filler neck.
3. Raise and support vehicle.
4. Disconnect then remove fuel filler neck.
5. Support fuel tank, then remove tank support straps. Lower fuel tank partially and remove fuel lines, electrical connectors and vent lines from tank.
6. Turn fuel pump locking ring counterclockwise and remove locking ring.
7. Remove fuel pump, bracket and gasket assembly.
8. Reverse procedure to install. To pressurize fuel system, proceed as follows:
   a. Install pressure gauge tool No. T80L-9974-A or equivalent onto fuel rail pressure fitting.
   b. Turn ignition switch to ON position for 3 seconds, repeatedly 5 to 10 times until pressure gauge indicates 13 psi.

FUEL FILTER
REPLACE

1. Relieve fuel pressure as outlined under "Precautions," then disconnect battery ground cable.
2. Remove fuel filter push connectors, **Fig. 18.**
3. Install connector fitting retainer clips. Flow arrow direction should be positioned as installed to ensure proper fuel flow.
4. Loosen filter clip, then remove filter.
5. Reverse procedure to install.

TIGHTENING SPECIFICATIONS

Year	Component	Torque/Ft. Lbs.	Year	Component	Torque/Ft. Lbs.
1992-94	Accelerator Shaft Bracket Bolt	7-11	1992-94 —Cont'd	LH Front No. 1 Insulator To Transaxle Bolts	30-42
	Air Pump Bracket	15-22		LH Rear No. 4 Insulator To Body Bolts	75-100
	Camshaft Sprocket Bolt	41-56		LH Rear No. 4 Insulator To Transaxle	35-50
	Camshaft Tensioner Bolts	6-9		Main Bearing Cap Bolts	51-66
	Camshaft Thrust Plate Bolts	6-9		No. 4 Insulator Bracket To Body	45-65
	Connecting Rod Cap Bolts	6-9		Oil Pan Bolts	15-22
	Cooling Fan Switch	8-18		Oil Pan Drain Plug	15-25
	Crankshaft Pulley	21-26		Oil Pan To Transaxle	30-39
	Crankshaft Seal Retainer Bolts	140-170		Oil Pump Bolts	15-22
	Cylinder Head Bolts	①		Oil Sender	8-18
	Differential Valve Check Valve Connector	25-35		RH No. 3A Insulator Nuts	75-100
	Dipstick Tube	71-105②		RH No. 3A Intermediate Bracket Bolt	55-75
	Distributor Cap Screws	18-27②		Rocker Arm Bolts	71-106
	Distributor Hold-Down Bolt	17-25		Rocker Arm Cover	7-10
	EGR Tube Connector	25-35		Rocker Arm Shaft Bracket	20-26
	EGR Tube Nuts	25-35		Roller Restrictor Nuts	25-45
	EGR Valve Bolts	13-19		Shift Mechanism To Shift Shaft	7-10
	Engine Coolant Temperature Sensor	12-18		Shift Stabilizer Bar To Transaxle	25-35
	Exhaust Manifold	①		Spark Plugs	6-10
	Flywheel to Crankshaft	54-64		Support Brace-Intake Manifold	30-40
	Front Cover Bolts	6-9		Thermostat Studs	18-29
	Fuel Rack Bracket	15-22		Throttle Body Bolts	6-8
	Intake Manifold	①		Vacuum Fittings-Intake Manifold	71-101②
	Intermediate Bracket To Engine Bracket	60-70		Water Outlet Connection Bolts	15-22
	Intermediate Engine Bracket Bolt	52-70		Water Pump Bolts	15-22
	LH Front No. 1 Insulator To Bracket Nut	75-100		Water Pump Inlet Tube To Oil Pan	71-97②

①—Refer to text for tightening sequence.
②—Inch lbs.

3.0L/V6-182 Engine

NOTE: On Air Bag Equipped Models, Refer To "Air Bag System Precautions" Located In The Front Of This Manual For System Disarming & Arming Procedures.

NOTE: For Procedures Not Found In This Section, Refer to 3.0L/V6-182 Engine Section In The Ford Taurus & Mercury Sable Chapter.

INDEX

PRECAUTIONS
AIR BAG SYSTEMS

Refer to "Air Bag System Precautions" in the front of this manual for system disarming and arming procedures.

FUEL SYSTEM PRESSURE RELIEF

1. Remove air cleaner assembly.
2. Connect fuel pressure relief gauge tool No. T80L-9974-B, or equivalent, to fuel pressure relief valve at fuel supply manifold.
3. Open manual valve on fuel pressure relief gauge to relieve fuel pressure.
4. Remove fuel pressure relief gauge once fuel pressure has been relieved.

ENGINE
REPLACE

1. Relieve fuel pressure as outlined under "Precautions," then disconnect battery ground cable and remove air cleaner assembly.
2. Scribe hood hinge positions on hood for reference during assembly.
3. Discharge air conditioning system, if equipped. Cap all open lines.
4. Drain engine coolant system.
5. Locate Schraeder valve on fuel rail assembly, then remove protective cap.
6. Cover valve with shop towel, then using a small screwdriver, press inner valve stem inward slowly to release fuel system pressure. **Ensure all pressure is released.**
7. Disconnect all fuel lines from engine assembly, then position them aside.
8. Remove upper radiator hose.
9. Mark and record all electrical connector locations, then disconnect and set aside all wiring looms and connectors at junction blocks.
10. Mark and record all vacuum line connections, then disconnect all vacuum lines and crankcase ventilation hoses.
11. Disconnect power steering high pressure and return lines from power steering pump.
12. Remove power steering reservoir.
13. Disconnect air conditioning lines from condenser, leaving manifold lines attached to compressor.
14. Disconnect accelerator linkage, transaxle throttle valve linkage and speed control cable, if equipped.
15. Disconnect speedometer cable from transaxle.
16. **On models equipped with automatic transaxle,** disconnect transaxle cooler lines from radiator.
17. **On all models,** remove coolant overflow bottle, then lower radiator hose.
18. Remove power steering lines at rear of engine above transaxle.
19. Raise and support vehicle, then drain engine oil.
20. Disconnect heater hoses from engine, then position hoses aside.
21. Remove front wheel and tire assemblies.
22. Support center of exhaust system, then disconnect Y-pipe from engine exhaust manifolds.
23. Remove bolt retaining air conditioning line to engine block.
24. Disconnect tie rod ends from spindle assemblies.
25. Disconnect lower ball joints, then pull down on lower control arms to disengage ball joints from spindle.
26. Remove axle halfshaft assemblies from transaxle, then install plugs.
27. Lower vehicle, then remove ignition coil bracket retaining bolts. Position coil assembly out of the way.
28. Install engine lifting eyes part No. D81L-6001-D or equivalent, at front of righthand cylinder head and rear of lefthand cylinder head.
29. Remove through bolts from engine mounts.
30. Carefully lift engine out of vehicle, using universal load positioning sling tool No. 014-00036 or equivalent to tilt engine vertically to clear master cylinder.
31. Reverse procedure to install, noting the following:

   a. Fill and check transaxle fluid.
   b. Fill and check coolant system for leaks after engine warm up.
   c. If equipped, evacuate and recharge air conditioning system.
   d. Adjust ignition timing, if necessary.
   e. Road test vehicle. **When the battery has been disconnected, some abnormal drive symptoms may occur while the EEC-IV processor relearns its adaptive strategy. The vehicle may need to be driven 10 miles or more to relearn the strategy.**

CYLINDER HEAD
REPLACE

1. Rotate crankshaft to 0 degrees Top Dead Center (TDC) on the compression stroke.
2. Disconnect battery ground cable, then insulate cable end with electrical tape.
3. Drain engine coolant system.
4. Remove PCV closure hose and clean air flex tube.
5. Remove clean air flex tube from throttle body and mass air flow sensor (MAFS).
6. Locate Schraeder valve on fuel rail above intake manifold, then remove protective cap.
7. Cover valve with shop towel to prevent accidental fuel spray into eyes, then using a small screwdriver or equivalent, slowly release fuel system pressure. **Ensure all pressure is released.**
8. Mark location of vacuum lines, then remove vacuum lines from engine.
9. Disconnect TPS, idle air bypass valve, ECT, PFE, distributor, ignition coil and coolant temperature sending unit electrical connectors.
10. Disconnect upper radiator hose from thermostat housing.
11. Loosen EGR tube retaining nuts, then remove tube.
12. Remove air intake throttle body as follows:
   a. Loosen air cleaner air tube retaining clamps, then remove tube.

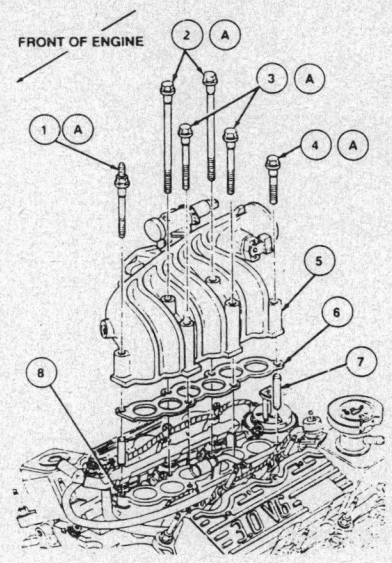

Item	Part Number	Description
1A	—	Stud Bolt
2A	—	Bolt—M8 x 1.25 x 130
3A	—	Bolt—M8 x 1.25 x 100
4A	—	Bolt—M8x 1.25 x 68
5	9E926	Air Intake Throttle Body
6	9H486	Air Intake Throttle Body Gasket
7	—	Guide Pin
8	—	Lower Intake Manifold
A		Tighten to 20-30 N·m (15-22 Lb-Ft)

FM1069100169000X

Fig. 1 Air intake throttle body bolt locations

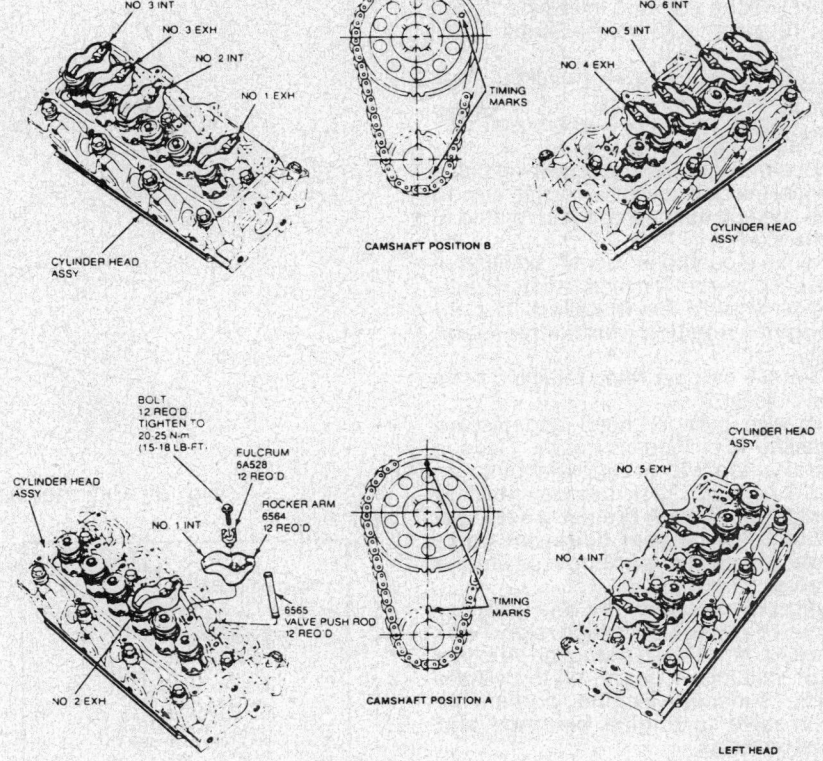

FM1069100170000X

Fig. 2 Rocker arm & valve locations

b. Remove air bypass valve solenoid (ISC) snowshield.

c. Disconnect throttle cable from throttle body lever.

d. Remove two throttle cable bracket retaining bolts from side of throttle body, then bracket assembly.

e. Loosen and remove five air intake throttle body retaining bolts and one stud bolt noting their locations, **Fig. 1.**

f. Remove air intake throttle body assembly from intake manifold. Discard old gasket.

13. Disconnect fuel injector harness retainers from inboard rocker arm cover studs, then electrical connectors at each injector. Remove fuel injector harness from engine.

14. Disconnect heater hose near thermostat housing.

15. Mark spark plug wires for reference during installation, then remove ignition wires from spark plugs.

16. Mark distributor housing to cylinder block and note rotor position in relation to distributor cap.

17. Remove distributor hold-down clamp and bolt, then distributor from engine.

18. Remove oil cooler tube assembly retaining bolt from ignition coil bracket.

19. Remove ignition coil from rear of left-hand cylinder head.

20. Remove rocker arm covers.

21. Loosen cylinder No. 3 intake valve rocker arm retaining nut, then rotate arm off of pushrod and away from top of valve stem, **Fig. 2.** Remove the pushrod.

22. Remove intake manifold retaining bolts. **Before attempting to remove intake manifold, break seal between the manifold and cylinder block. Wedge a large screwdriver between intake and cylinder block in the area between thermostat and transaxle.**

23. Remove intake manifold. **Intake manifold may be removed with fuel supply manifold and injectors in place.**

24. **If removing righthand cylinder head (rear of engine compartment),** proceed as follows:

a. Remove accessory drive belt. Using a socket, rotate tensioner away from belt.

b. Remove water pump to front cover hose.

c. Raise and support vehicle, then remove lower water pump tube.

d. Remove retaining nut from upper bracket, then bolt from lower bracket. Gently grasp tube at water pump end and pull tube out of water pump. Set assembly aside.

e. Remove exhaust inlet pipe flange retaining nuts from exhaust manifold studs.

f. Lower vehicle, then remove heater hose from rear of water pump.

g. Remove water pump pulley shield, then water pump from bracket.

h. Remove exhaust manifold heat shield, then exhaust manifold.

25. **If removing lefthand cylinder head (front of engine compartment),** proceed as follows:

a. Remove accessory drive belt. Using a 1/2 inch breaker bar, rotate tensioner away from drive belt.

b. Remove two power steering pulley shield retaining bolts, then shield.

c. Remove drive belt tensioner retaining bolt, then tensioner.

d. Remove three alternator bracket to cylinder head retaining bolts.

e. Remove upper alternator retaining bolt, then three air conditioning brace retaining bolts and remove brace.

f. Move assembly away from cylinder head slightly.
g. Remove exhaust inlet pipe flange retaining nuts from exhaust manifold studs.
h. Remove exhaust manifold heat shield.
i. Rotate or remove engine oil dipstick tube out of way.

26. Loosen rocker arm fulcrum retaining bolts enough to allow rocker arm to be lifted off the pushrod and rotated to one side.
27. Remove pushrods. Identify position of each pushrod for installation. **Pushrods should be installed in their original position during reassembly.**
28. Remove cylinder head retaining bolts and discard.
29. Remove cylinder head and discard gasket. If cylinder is stuck, place a heavy steel rod or equivalent into intake port and rock cylinder head to break seal. **When breaking seal, ensure removal tool does not damage machined surfaces or intake valve.**
30. Immediately wipe dry the cylinder bore of any coolant which might have leaked from head removal. Apply a light coating of engine oil to cylinder bore surfaces. **Engine coolant is corrosive to engine bearings and piston rings.**
31. Position new head gasket on cylinder block with V-cut toward front of engine.
32. Position cylinder head to engine block over dowels.
33. Install and hand tighten new cylinder head retaining bolts.
34. Tighten cylinder head bolts in sequence shown in **Fig. 3** as follows:
    a. **Torque** bolts to 52-66 ft. lbs., then back off all bolts one complete turn.
    b. **Torque** bolts in sequence to 33-41 ft. lbs.
    c. **Torque** bolts in sequence to 63-73 ft. lbs.
35. Apply a ¼ inch drop of silicone rubber part No. D6AZ-19562-AA or equivalent to intersection of cylinder block and cylinder head assembly at four corners as shown in **Fig. 4.**
36. Position intake gaskets onto cylinder heads, then front and rear intake manifold seals.
37. Carefully lower intake manifold into position aligning manifold bolt holes to those in cylinder heads.
38. Install bolt Nos. 1 through 4, **Fig. 5,** then hand tighten.
39. Install remaining bolts and tighten in two steps as follows:
    a. **Torque** in numerical sequence to 15-22 ft. lbs.
    b. **Torque** in sequence to 19-24 ft. lbs.
40. Completely coat distributor gear teeth with rear axle lubricant part No. XY-90-QL or equivalent, install retaining bolt and clamp and hand tighten.
41. Lubricate pushrods and rocker arms with oil conditioner part No. D9AZ-

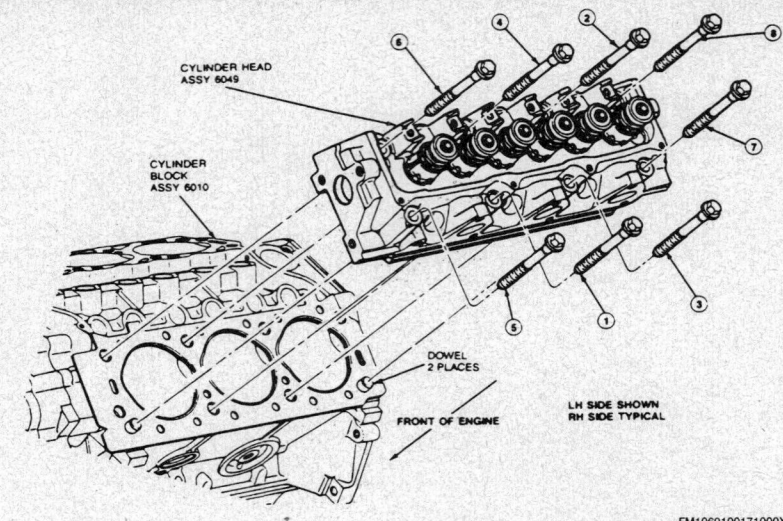

Fig. 3 Cylinder head bolt tightening sequence

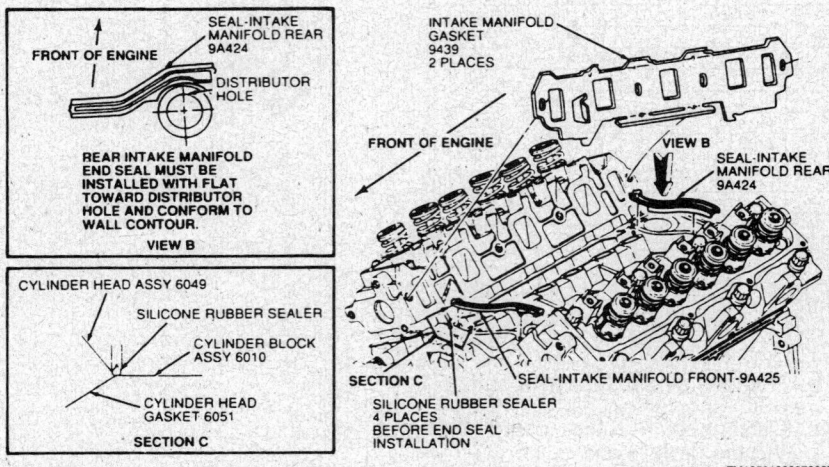

Fig. 4 Silicone rubber & intake seal installation

195579-CA or equivalent and install pushrods.
42. Move rocker arms into position with pushrods, then tighten retaining bolts.
43. Rotate crankshaft 360 degrees (one full turn) in a clockwise direction from 0 degrees TDC.
44. **Torque** rocker arm retaining bolts shown in camshaft position A, **Fig. 2** to 5-11 ft. lbs.
45. Rotate crankshaft 120 degrees in a clockwise direction. **Torque** remainder of rocker arms to 5-11 ft. lbs.
46. **Torque** rocker arm retaining bolts to 19-28 ft. lbs. **Fulcrum must be fully seated into cylinder head and pushrod must be fully seated in rocker arm and lifter sockets prior to final torque.**
47. Reverse remaining procedure to complete installation.

VALVE ADJUSTMENT

This engine is equipped with hydraulic lifters and adjustment is not required.

OIL PAN
REPLACE

1. Disconnect battery ground cable, then insulate cable end with electrical tape or equivalent.
2. Remove engine oil level dipstick, then raise and support vehicle.
3. If equipped with low oil level sensor, remove electrical connector retainer clip at sensor an disconnect connector.
4. Drain engine oil.
5. Remove starter motor as follows:
    a. Disconnect starter cable and push on connector from starter solenoid. **When disconnecting the plastic hard-shell connector at "S" terminal, grasp the plastic shell, depress the tab and pull lead off. Do not pull separately on wire. Be careful to pull straight off to prevent damage to the "S" solenoid terminal.**
    b. Remove upper starter retaining bolt, then lower bolt and starter assembly.

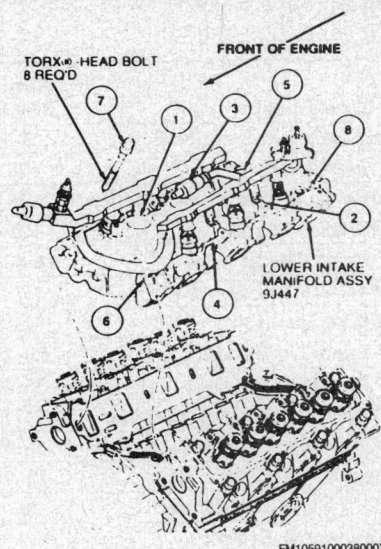

Fig. 5 Intake manifold tightening sequence

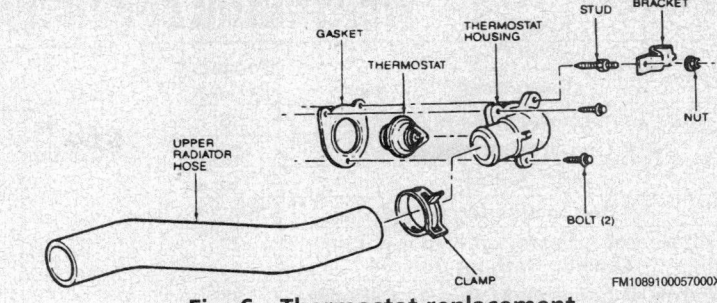

Fig. 6 Thermostat replacement

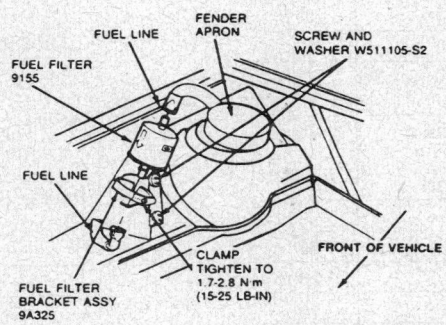

Fig. 7 Fuel filter replacement

6. Disconnect oxygen sensor electrical connectors.
7. Remove exhaust pipe and catalyst assembly from engine.
8. **On models equipped with automatic transaxle,** remove torque converter access cover from transaxle.
9. **On models equipped with manual transaxle,** remove left and right transaxle support plates.
10. **On all models,** remove oil pan retaining bolts. **Ensure internal pan baffle does not snag on oil pump pickup tube and screen when lowering pan.**
11. Remove oil pan gasket and discard.
12. Remove oil pump retaining bolt, then oil pump from main bearing cap. When oil pump is removed, the intermediate shaft which drives the distributor will remain in the pump. If replacing the pump, remove intermediate shaft by pulling it from the pump. Check retaining clip for damage, replace if necessary.
13. Insert oil pump intermediate shaft assembly into hex drive hole in oil pump assembly until retainer clicks into place.
14. Install oil pump assembly with intermediate shaft through intermediate shaft hole in rear main bearing cap, then position pump over locating pins.
15. Install oil pump retaining bolt, then **torque** to 30-40 ft. lbs.
16. Install a new oil pan gasket to cylinder block using retaining features and gasket & trim adhesive part No. D7AZ-19B508-AA or equivalent. Snug retaining bolts at all four corners and two places on cylinder block sealing rail to support unit until adhesive cures.
17. Apply a 3/16 inch bead of silicone sealer part No. E8AZ-19562-A or equivalent, to the junction of the rear main bearing cap and cylinder block.
18. Apply a 3/16 inch bead of silicone seal-

er part No. E8AZ-19562-A or equivalent, to the junction of the front cover assembly and cylinder block.
19. Remove bolts retaining gasket to cylinder block, then position oil pan and install retaining bolts and hand tighten.
20. **Torque** four corner bolts to 7-10 ft. lbs., then install and torque remaining bolts.
21. Install left and right transaxle plates on manual transaxles or access plate on automatic transaxles.
22. Install starter motor assembly. **Torque** retaining bolts to 16-19 ft. lbs.
23. Connect oil level sensor connector, then install retainer clip.
24. Fill crankcase with oil.
25. Replace oil level dipstick, then connect battery ground cable.
26. Check vehicle for leaks.

OIL PUMP
REPLACE

Refer to "Oil Pan, Replace" for procedure.

THERMOSTAT
REPLACE

1. Drain coolant from engine, then remove upper radiator hose from thermostat housing.
2. Remove three retaining bolts from housing, then remove housing and thermostat as an assembly.
3. Install thermostat into housing, **Fig. 6,** ensuring that jiggle valve in relation to housing.
4. Position gasket onto housing using bolts as holding device, then install housing assembly and retaining bolts. Tighten to specifications.

5. Install upper radiator hose, then fill coolant system as follows:
   a. Add 50 percent coolant, then add water until radiator is full. Allow coolant level to settle, then add more coolant until radiator remain full.
   b. Install radiator cap to first notch, connect battery cable and wire connector to thermo switch. Start engine and let idle until upper hose is warm, then carefully remove radiator cap and top off coolant level.
   c. Install cap securely and fill reservoir to FULL COLD mark with proper concentrate. Add water to FULL HOT mark. Check for leaks.

RADIATOR
REPLACE

1. Disconnect battery ground cable, then drain engine coolant.
2. Disconnect upper radiator hose, then remove two fasteners retaining upper end of fan shroud to radiator end tank.
3. **On models equipped with air conditioning,** remove nut and screw retaining upper end of fan shroud to radiator at cross support, then nut and screw at end tank.
4. Disconnect air conditioning discharge line from shroud.
5. **On all models,** disconnect fan wiring and remove fan shroud from vehicle.
6. Disconnect lower radiator hose.
7. **On models equipped with automatic transaxle,** disconnect oil cooler lines.
8. **On all models,** remove two nut retaining top of radiator to crossmember, then tip radiator back to allow clearance with upper mounting stud and lift radiator from vehicle.
9. Reverse procedure to install.

FUEL FILTER
REPLACE

1. Relieve fuel pressure as outlined under "Precautions," then disconnect battery ground cable.
2. Remove fuel filter push connectors, **Fig. 7.**
3. Install connector fitting retainer clips. Flow arrow direction should be positioned as installed to ensure proper fuel flow.
4. Loosen filter clip, then remove filter.
5. Reverse procedure to install.

TIGHTENING SPECIFICATIONS

Year	Component	Torque/Ft. Lbs.
1992–94	A/C Compressor Bracket To Block	35
	A/C Compressor Mounting	35
	ACT Sensor	15
	Air Bag to steering wheel	36-49 ①
	Alternator Adjustment Arm (Lock-In Tension Setting) Bolt	27
	Alternator Adjustment Arm To Cylinder Head Bolt	35
	Alternator Brace to Adjustment Arm & Throttle Body	12
	Alternator Pivot Bolt	43
	Auto Tensione & Power Steering Bracket To Cylinder Head	35
	Auto Tensioner To A/C Compressor Bracket Bolt	35
	Camshaft Sprocket To Camshaft	37-51
	Camshaft Thrust Plate Bolt	7
	Coil & Bracket Assembly To Cylinder Head	35
	Connecting Rod Nut	26
	Coolant Temperature Switch	15
	Crankshaft Pulley Nuts	30-44
	Crankshaft Vibration Damper To Crankshaft	93-121
	Cylinder Head	②
	Distributor Hold-Down Bolt	18
	ECT Sensor	12-17
	EGR To Throttle Body	15-22
	EGR Tube To EGR Valve & Exhaust Manifold	26-48
	Exhaust Heat Shield	12-15
	Exhaust Inlet Pipe To Manifold	25-34
	Exhaust Manifold	15-22
	Flywheel To Crankshaft	59

Year	Component	Torque/Ft. Lbs.
1992–94 —Cont'd	Fuel Rail To Intake Manifold	6-9
	Heater Elbow	18
	Heater Tube To Intake Manifold	26
	HEGO Sensor	30
	Hose Clamp	28-48 ①
	Idle Speed Control Solenoid	7
	Intake Manifold	②
	Low Level Oil Sensor	20-30
	Main Bearing Cap Bolt	55-63
	Oil Dipstick Tube To Exhaust Manifold	11-15
	Oil Drain Plug	9-12
	Oil Pressure Sending Unit	12–16
	Oil Pump To Cylinder Block	35
	PFE Sensor & Bracket	7
	Power Steering Bracket To Cylinder Head Bolt	29-41
	Rocker Arm bolt	②
	Rocker Arm Cover	8-10
	Spark Plug	5-11
	Thermostat Housing	8-10
	Throttle Body To Intake Manifold	19
	Throttle Cable Bracket	13
	Timing Cover To Cylinder Block	19
	TP Sensor	22 ①
	Water Pump Hose Clamps	19-37 ①
	Water Pump Pulley Shield	7-10
	Water Pump Pulley To Hub	15-22
	Water Pump To Front Cover	71-106 ①

①—Inch lbs.
②—Refer to text.

Clutch & Manual Transaxle

NOTE: On Air Bag Equipped Models, Refer To "Air Bag System Precautions" Located In The Front Of This Manual For System Disarming & Arming Procedures.

INDEX

PRECAUTIONS

AIR BAG SYSTEMS

Refer to "Air Bag System Precautions" in the front of this manual for system disarming and arming procedures.

ADJUSTMENTS

CLUTCH

Lift clutch pedal to the uppermost posi-tion when connecting or disconnecting the clutch cable. Whenever the clutch cable is disconnected for any reason, such as transmission removal or clutch, clutch pedal components, or clutch cable re-placement, it is important that the proper method for installing the clutch cable be followed. Under no circumstances should a prying instrument such as a screwdriver or a pry bar be used to install the cable into the quadrant.

The cable operated clutch control sys-tem, **Fig. 1**, is self adjusting and periodic adjustments are not required. If the clutch cable is replaced for any reason, an initial adjustment is performed by pulling the clutch pedal to its full upward position.

GEARSHIFT LINKAGE

Adjustment of the external gearshift link-age is not necessary and no provision is made for adjustment, **Fig. 2.**

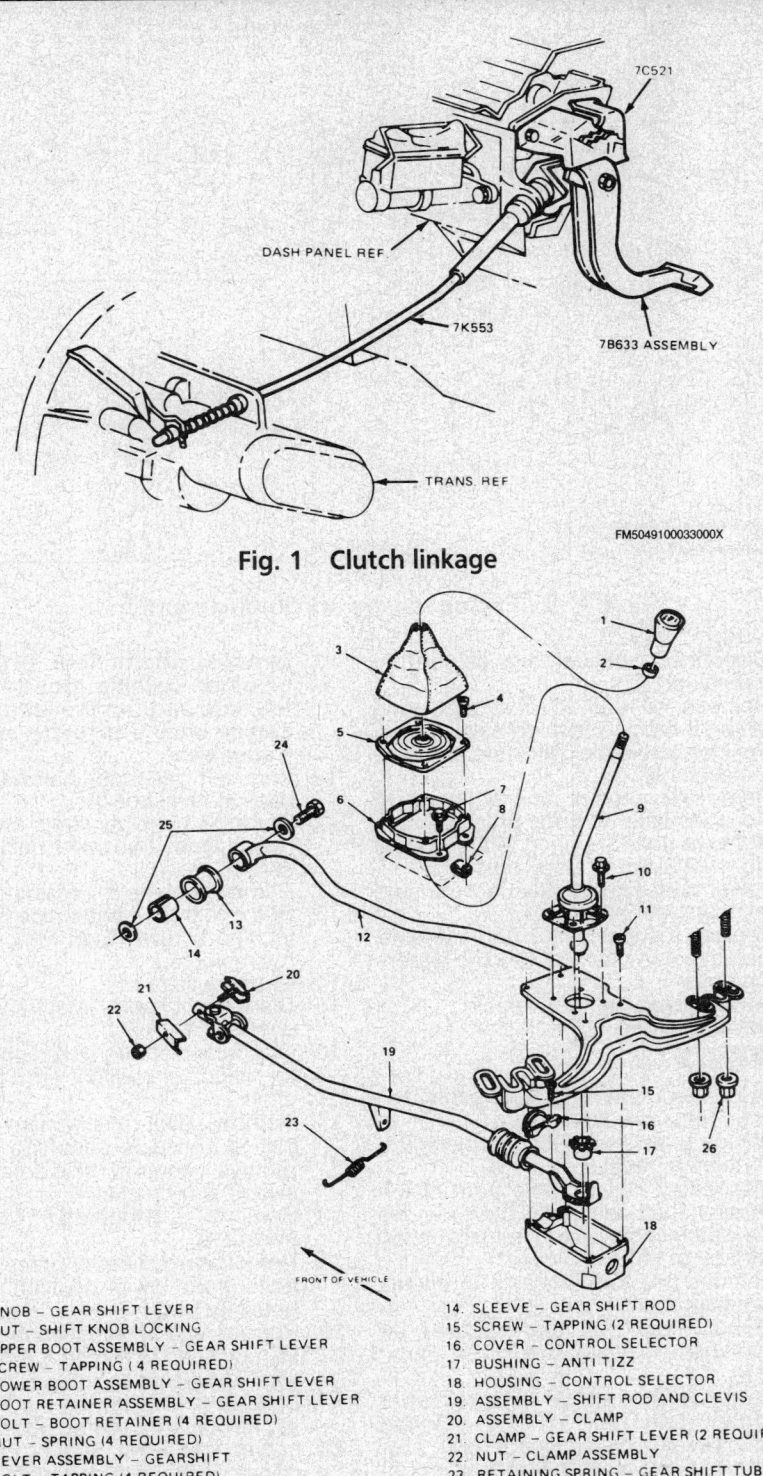

Fig. 1   Clutch linkage

Fig. 2   Exploded view of gearshift linkage

1. KNOB – GEAR SHIFT LEVER
2. NUT – SHIFT KNOB LOCKING
3. UPPER BOOT ASSEMBLY – GEAR SHIFT LEVER
4. SCREW – TAPPING (4 REQUIRED)
5. LOWER BOOT ASSEMBLY – GEAR SHIFT LEVER
6. BOOT RETAINER ASSEMBLY – GEAR SHIFT LEVER
7. BOLT – BOOT RETAINER (4 REQUIRED)
8. NUT – SPRING (4 REQUIRED)
9. LEVER ASSEMBLY – GEARSHIFT
10. BOLT – TAPPING (4 REQUIRED)
11. SCREW – TAPPING (4 REQUIRED)
12. SUPPORT ASSEMBLY (SHIFT STABILIZER BAR)
13. BUSHING – GEAR SHIFT STABILIZER BAR
14. SLEEVE – GEAR SHIFT ROD
15. SCREW – TAPPING (2 REQUIRED)
16. COVER – CONTROL SELECTOR
17. BUSHING – ANTI TIZZ
18. HOUSING – CONTROL SELECTOR
19. ASSEMBLY – SHIFT ROD AND CLEVIS
20. ASSEMBLY – CLAMP
21. CLAMP – GEAR SHIFT LEVER (2 REQUIRED)
22. NUT – CLAMP ASSEMBLY
23. RETAINING SPRING – GEAR SHIFT TUBE
24. BOLT - STABILIZER BAR ATTACHING
25. WASHER – FLAT (2 REQUIRED)
26. ASSEMBLY – NUT/WASHER (4 REQUIRED)

FM5049100034000X

CLUTCH
REPLACE

1. Remove manual transaxle as described under "Manual Transaxle, Replace" procedure.

2. Loosen pressure plate cover attaching bolts evenly to avoid distorting cover. If same pressure plate and cover are to be installed, mark cover and flywheel so pressure plate can be installed in original position.

3. Remove pressure plate and clutch

disc from flywheel, **Fig. 3.**

4. Position clutch disc and pressure plate onto flywheel with flatter side of clutch disc facing toward flywheel.

5. Ensure three dowel pins on flywheel are aligned with dowel pins on pressure plate.

6. Snug tighten cover attaching bolts, then align clutch disc using clutch aligner tool T81P-7550A or equivalent and tighten to specifications.

7. Remove alignment tool, then install transaxle and perform initial clutch adjustment.

SHIFT CABLE
REPLACE
REMOVAL

Whenever the clutch cable is disconnected for any reason, such as transaxle or clutch removal, clutch pedal components, or clutch cable replacement, it is imperative that the proper method for installing the clutch cable be followed.

1. Disconnect battery ground cable.

2. Prop up clutch pedal to lift pawl free of quadrant.

3. Remove air cleaner assembly to gain access to clutch cable.

4. Grasp the extended tip of the clutch cable with a pair of pliers, and unhook clutch cable from clutch bearing release lever. **Do not grasp wire strand portion of inner cable since this may cut wires and result in cable failure.**

5. Disconnect cable from insulator that is located on the rib of transaxle.

6. Remove panel above clutch pedal pad.

7. Position clutch shield away from brake pedal support bracket by removing the rear retaining screw.

8. Loosen front retaining screw located near toe board, and rotate shield out of the way.

9. With clutch pedal lifted up to release pawl, rotate gear quadrant forward. Unhook clutch cable from gear quadrant. Allow quadrant to swing rearward. **Do not allow quadrant to snap back.**

10. Pull cable through recess between clutch pedal and gear quadrant, and from insulator on pedal assembly.

11. Withdraw cable through engine compartment.

INSTALLATION

The clutch pedal must be lifted to disengage the adjusting mechanism during cable installation. Failure to do so will result in damage to the self-adjuster mechanism.

Do not use a prying instrument such as a screwdriver or a pry bar to install the cable into the quadrant.

1. Insert clutch cable assembly from then engine or passenger compartment through dash panel and dash panel grommet. **Ensure cable is routed under the brake lines and not trapped at the spring tower by**

the brake lines. If the vehicle is equipped with power steering, the clutch cable is to be routed inboard of the power steering hose.

2. Push clutch cable through insulator on stop bracket, then through recess between pedal and gear quadrant.
3. With clutch pedal lifted up to release pawl, rotate gear quadrant forward. Hook cable into gear quadrant.
4. Install clutch shield on brake pedal support bracket, then lower instrument trim panel.
5. Secure pedal in upper most position using wire, tape or equivalent.
6. Working inside engine compartment, insert clutch cable through insulator and hook cable into clutch release lever.
7. Remove device used to temporarily secure pedal against stop.
8. Adjust clutch pedal by depressing clutch pedal several times.
9. Install air cleaner assembly, then connect battery ground cable.

Fig. 3 Exploded view of clutch assembly

TRANSAXLE
REPLACE

4 SPEED

1. Disconnect battery ground cable.
2. Position a suitable block of wood approximately 7 inches of length under clutch pedal to hold clutch pedal up.
3. Grasp and pull clutch cable forward, disconnecting cable from clutch release shaft lever assembly.
4. Remove clutch casing from top rib of transaxle case.
5. Remove 2 top transaxle to engine attaching bolts.
6. Remove air cleaner assembly.
7. Raise and support vehicle, then remove front stabilizer bar to control arm attaching nut and washer.
8. Remove stabilizer bar mounting brackets.
9. Remove nut and bolt attaching lower control ball joint to steering knuckle assembly.
10. Using a suitable tool, pry lower control arm away from steering knuckle.
11. Using halfshaft remover tool D83P-4026-A or equivalent, pry left inboard CV joint assembly from transaxle. Remove inboard CV joint from transaxle by grasping the lefthand steering knuckle and swinging the knuckle and halfshaft outward from transaxle. **If the CV joint cannot be pried from transaxle, insert differential rotator tool T81P-4026-A or equivalent through right side of case and tap CV joint out.**
12. Wire halfshaft assembly in level position to prevent overextending CV joint.
13. Repeat steps 10 through 12 for other CV joint.
14. Remove back-up light switch electrical connector from transaxle.
15. Remove starter motor and position aside.
16. Remove engine roll restrictor.
17. Remove shift mechanism, shift indicator and bracket assembly.

18. Disconnect speedometer cable from transaxle.
19. Remove oil pan to clutch housing stiffener brace attaching bolts.
20. Position a suitable jack under transaxle assembly.
21. Remove 2 nuts securing lefthand rear No. 4 insulator to body bracket.
22. Remove bolts securing lefthand front No. 1 insulator to body bracket.
23. Lower transaxle slightly until transaxle clears rear mount.
24. Position a suitable jack under engine.
25. Remove 4 transaxle to engine attaching bolts.
26. Lower transaxle from vehicle.
27. Reverse procedure to install.

5 SPEED

1. Disconnect battery ground cable and drain transaxle fluid.
2. Wedge a seven inch wood block under clutch pedal.
3. Disconnect clutch cable from clutch release shaft assembly, then remove the clutch cable casing from rib on top surface of transaxle case.
4. Remove two top transaxle to engine mounting bolts.
5. Remove top bolt that secures air management valve bracket to transaxle.
6. Raise vehicle, then remove lower control arm ball joint to steering knuckle attaching nut and bolt. Discard nut and bolt and repeat procedure on opposite side.
7. Pry lower control arm from knuckle on both sides of vehicle using suitable pry bar. Use care not to damage or cut ball joint.
8. Pry left inboard CV joint assembly from transaxle using suitable pry bar. **Lubricant will drain from the seal at this time. Install two plugs.**
9. Remove inboard CV joint from transaxle. Repeat procedure on other side. **If the CV joint assembly cannot be pried from the transaxle, insert differential rotator tool T81P-4026-A or other suitable tool through the left side and tap the joint out. Tool can be used from either side of the transaxle.**
10. Wire left and right halfshaft assemblies in level position.
11. Remove back-up lamp switch connector from transaxle back-up lamp switch.
12. Remove engine roll restrictor bracket.
13. Remove three heater pipe bracket attaching screws, then remove engine roll restrictor.
14. Remove starter.
15. Disconnect shift mechanism from shaft.
16. Disconnect and remove control selector indicator switch arm from shift shaft.
17. Remove shift mechanism stabilizer bar to transaxle attaching bolt, then remove control selector indicator switch and bracket.
18. Remove speedometer cable from transaxle.
19. Remove two stiffener brace attaching bolts from lower position of clutch housing.
20. Position a jack under transaxle.
21. Remove two rear mount and air management valve to transaxle securing bolts, then remove three bolts attaching front mount to transaxle.
22. Lower transaxle support jack until transaxle clears rear mount and support engine with suitable jack. Use a suitable piece of wood between the jack and engine.
23. Remove remaining four engine-to-transaxle attaching bolts.
24. Remove transaxle from rear face of the engine and lower it from vehicle. **The transaxle case casting may have sharp edges. Wear protective gloves when handling the transaxle assembly.**
25. Reverse procedure to install, tightening to specifications.

TIGHTENING SPECIFICATIONS

Year	Component	Torque/ ft. Lbs.
1992–94	Back-up Lamp Switch	12–15
	Brake Hose Clip Bolt	8
	Control Selector Plate	6–8
	Control Arm To Knuckle Nut	30–45
	Clutch Cover Attaching Bolts	12–24
	Clutch Lever Cover Screws	1.5–2.0
	Detent Plunger Retaining Screw	6–8
	Engine Roll Restrictor Attaching Nuts	14–20
	Filler Plug	9–15
	Fork Interlock Sleeve Pin	12–15
	Front Hub Nut	180–200
	Front Stabilizer Bar Bracket Bolts	47–55
	Front Stabilizer Bar To Control Arm	107–125
	Lefthand Front No. 1 Insulator To Body Bracket	25–35
	Lefthand Rear No. 4 Insulator To Body Bracket	35–50
	Lower Control Arm Ball Joint To Steering Knuckle Nut	37–44

Year	Component	Torque/ ft. Lbs.
1992–94 —Cont'd	Oil Pan To Transaxle	28–38
	Pin To Release Fork	30–40
	Pressure Plate To Flywheel	12–24
	Reverse Shift Relay Lever Bracket	6–8
	Shift Lever Cover Screws	1.5–2.0
	Shift Mechanism To Shift Shaft	7–10
	Shift Mechanism Stabilizer To Transaxle Bolt	23–35
	Speedometer Cable	2–3
	Starter Cable	5.5–10
	Starter Nuts	25–30
	Starter Stud Bolts	30–40
	Transaxle Case To Clutch Housing	13–18
	Transaxle Front Mount Bolts	25–35
	Transaxle Rear Mount Bolts	40–51
	Transaxle To Engine Block	26–31
	Wheel Lug Nuts	80–105

Rear Axle & Suspension

INDEX

DESCRIPTION

These vehicles use a new MacPherson strut independent rear suspension, **Fig. 1.** Each side consists of a shock absorber strut assembly, two parallel control arms per side, tie rod, spindle and a jounce bumper and bracket.

The shock absorber strut assembly includes a rubber isolated top mount, upper spring seat, coil spring insulator, coil spring and a lower spring seat. the strut assembly is attached at the top by two studs, which retain the top mount of the strut to the inner body side panel. The lower end of the assembly is bolted to the spindle. The two control arms are attached to the underbody and spindle with nuts and bolts. The tie rod is attached to the underbody and the spindle. The jounce bumper bracket is bolted to the strut.

HUB & BEARING
REPLACE

1. Raise and support vehicle.
2. Remove grease cap from hub. Remove cotter pin, nut retainer, adjusting nut and flat washer from spindle, **Fig. 2.** Discard cotter pin.
3. Pull hub and drum assembly off spindle being careful not to drop outer bearing assembly.
4. Remove outer bearing assembly.
5. Using seal removal tool 1175-AC or equivalent, remove and discard grease seal. Remove inner bearing assembly from hub.
6. Reverse procedure to install.

WHEEL BEARING
ADJUST

1. Raise and support vehicle. Remove dust cover from hub. Remove wheel assembly, if necessary.
2. Remove cotter pin and nut retainer.
3. Back off adjusting nut 1 full turn.
4. Tighten adjusting nut, **Fig. 2,** to specifications, while rotating drum assembly.
5. Back off adjusting nut ½ turn, then re-tighten adjusting nut to 10-15 inch lbs. Position adjusting nut retainer over nut so slots are aligned with cotter pin hole, then install cotter pin.
6. Install dust cover, wheel assembly, if necessary and lower vehicle to ground.

SPINDLE KNUCKLE
REPLACE

1. Raise and support vehicle.
2. Remove wheel assembly.
3. Remove brake drum. Remove brake flex hose bracket to strut bolt.
4. Remove brake backing plate to spindle bolts, then the brake backing plate. **Care should be taken to ensure that brake flex hose is not stretched and brake tube is not bent.**
5. Remove lower control arm to spindle bolt, washer and nut.
6. Remove tie rod nut, bushing and washer.
7. Remove spindle to strut bolts, then the spindle.

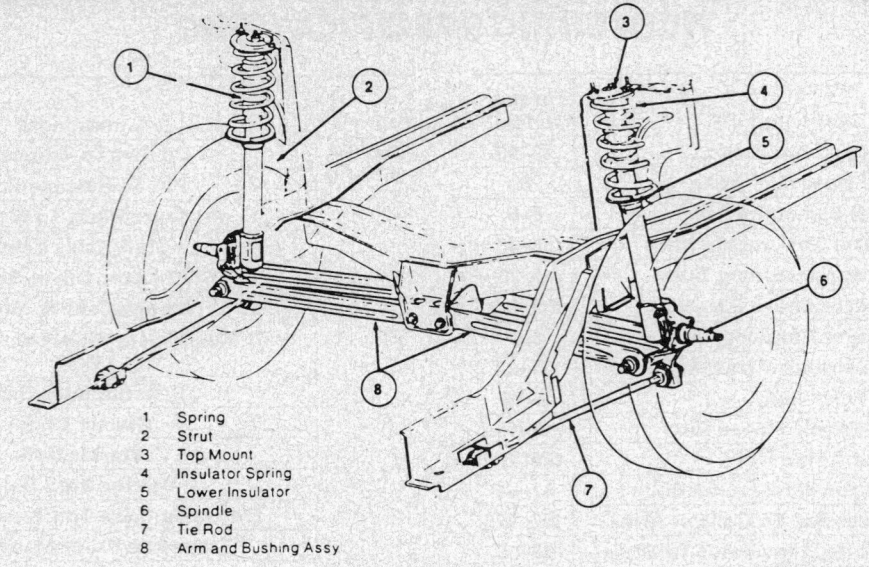

1 Spring
2 Strut
3 Top Mount
4 Insulator Spring
5 Lower Insulator
6 Spindle
7 Tie Rod
8 Arm and Bushing Assy

FM2039400015000A

Fig. 1 Rear suspension components

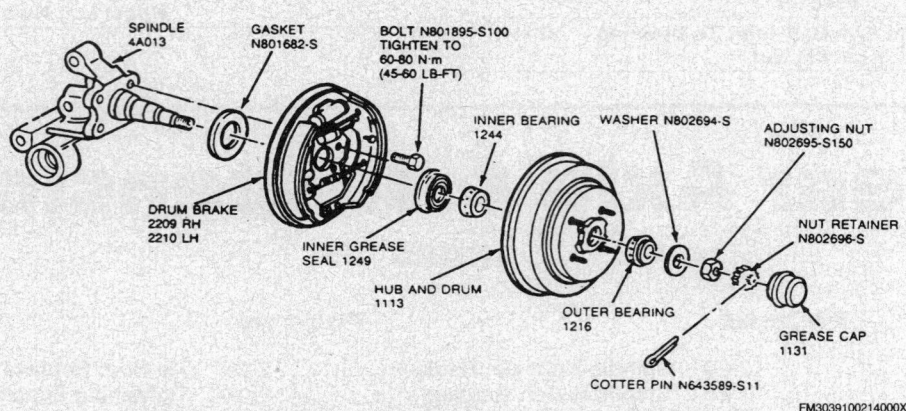

SPINDLE 4A013
GASKET N801682-S
BOLT N801895-S100 TIGHTEN TO 60-80 N·m (45-60 LB-FT)
INNER BEARING 1244
WASHER N802694-S
ADJUSTING NUT N802695-S150
DRUM BRAKE 2209 RH 2210 LH
INNER GREASE SEAL 1249
HUB AND DRUM 1113
OUTER BEARING 1216
NUT RETAINER N802696-S
GREASE CAP 1131
COTTER PIN N643589-S11

FM3039100214000X

Fig. 2 Exploded view of rear wheel bearing assembly

8. Reverse procedure to install. Tighten spindle to strut bolts, tie rod nut and lower control arm to spindle nut to specifications.

STRUT
REPLACE

1. Raise and support vehicle. Loosen upper strut mount to body nuts located in luggage compartment.
2. Remove wheel assembly.
3. Place a suitable jack under control arms.
4. Remove brake hose bracket to strut bolt and position brake hose bracket aside.
5. Remove jounce bumper bracket.
6. Remove two upper mount to body nuts, then the strut.
7. Place strut, spring and upper mount assembly into a suitable spring compressor tool. **Do not remove the spring from the strut without first compressing the spring.**
8. With spring compressed, remove strut shaft to mount nuts. Remove spring, strut and mount, **Fig. 3**, from spring compressor tool.

9. Reverse procedure to install. Tighten shaft nut, jounce bumper bracket to strut mount bolts and top mount to body nuts to specifications.

CONTROL ARM
REPLACE

1. Raise and support vehicle.
2. Remove wheel assembly.
3. Remove control arm to spindle nut and bolt.
4. Remove center mounting nut and bolt.
5. Remove control arm from vehicle.
6. Reverse procedure to install. Tighten control arm to body bolt and control arm to spindle nut to specifications. **When installing new control arms the bushing with the 10 mm hole is installed toward the center of the vehicle and the bushing with the 12 mm hole toward the spindle. The offset on the control arm must face up on the right side of the vehicle and down on the left side of the vehicle, Fig. 4. The flanged edge of the control arm stamping must face the rear of the vehicle.**

TIE ROD
REPLACE

1. Raise and support vehicle.
2. From inside of luggage compartment, loosen two strut top mount to body nuts.
3. Raise vehicle. Position a suitable jack under lower control arm with a piece of wood between jack and control arm.
4. Remove wheel assembly.
5. Remove two top mount studs, then tie rod to spindle retaining nut.
6. Remove tie rod to body retaining nut.
7. Lower jack until upper strut mount studs clear body mount holes.
8. Move spindle rearward until tie rod can be removed.
9. Place new washers and bushings on both ends of tie rod, **Fig. 5. Front and rear bushings are not interchangeable. The rear bushings have indentations incorporated in them.**
10. Insert tie rod into body bracket, then install new bushing, washer and nut. Do not tighten nut.

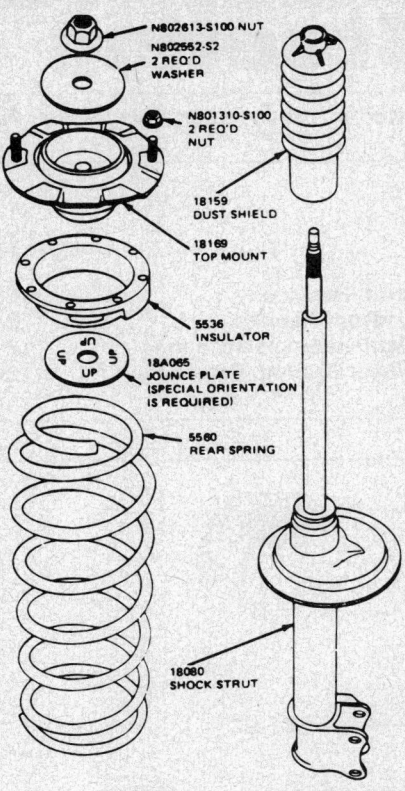

Fig. 3   Strut, spring & upper mount components

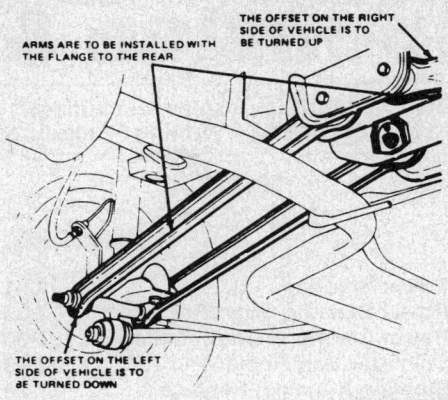

Fig. 4   Control arm installation

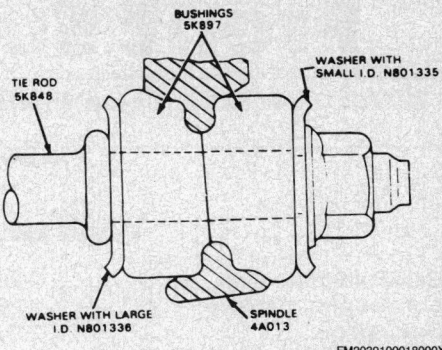

Fig. 5   Tie rod installation

11. Pull back on spindle until tie rod can be installed into the spindle. Install new bushing, washer and nut. Do not tighten nut.
12. Raise jack enough to secure the two strut mounting studs in place.
13. Install two strut to body mount nuts. Tighten nuts to specifications.
14. Using a suitable jack, raise lower control arm to curb height. Install tie rod nuts and tighten to specifications.
15. Remove jack and install wheel assembly. Lower vehicle.

STABILIZER BAR REPLACE

1. Raise and support vehicle.
2. Remove nut and washer assembly from attaching stud.
3. Remove washer assembly on stabilizer bar end.
4. Remove U-bracket to body bolts, then the stabilizer bar.
5. Reverse procedure to install.

TIGHTENING SPECIFICATIONS

Year	Component	Torque/Ft. Lbs.
1992-94	Bumper Bracket To Strut Mount	70-96
	Center Bearing & Attaching Bolts	23-30
	Control Arm To Body	30-40
	Control Arm To Spindle	60-80
	Inboard & Outboard U-joint Attaching Nuts	15-17
	Shaft Nut	35-50
	Stabilizer Bar Washer	6-17
	Stabilizer U-Bracket	18-22
	Strut Top Mount To Body	20-30
	Strut To Spindle	70-96
	Strut To Top Mount	35-50
	U-joint Retaining Caps & Bolts	15-17
	Wheel Bearing Adjusting Nut	17-25
	Wheel Lug Nut	80-105

Front Suspension & Steering

NOTE: On Air Bag Equipped Models, Refer To "Air Bag System Precautions" Located In The Front Of This Manual For System Disarming & Arming Procedures.

INDEX

DESCRIPTION

These vehicles use a MacPherson type front suspension with the vertical shock absorber struts attached to the upper fender reinforcements and the steering knuckle, **Fig. 1.** The lower control arms are attached inboard to a crossmember and outboard to the steering knuckle through a ball joint to provide lower steering knuckle position.

WHEEL BEARING
REPLACE

The front wheel bearings are cartridge design and are pre-greased, sealed and require no maintenance. The bearings are preset and cannot be adjusted.

1. Raise and support vehicle, then remove tire and wheel assembly.
2. Remove brake caliper and rotor.
3. Disconnect lower control arm and tie rod from knuckle (leave strut attached).
4. Loosen two strut top mount to apron attaching nuts.
5. Using suitable tools, remove hub bearing and knuckle assembly by pushing out constant velocity joint outer shaft until it is free of assembly.
6. Install hub removing tool D80L-1002-L and D80L-625-1 or equivalents, onto knuckle bosses and remove hub.
7. Remove snap ring retaining bearing in knuckle assembly. Discard snap ring.
8. Using a suitable press and bearing remover tools T83P-1104-AH3 and T83P-1104-AH2, press bearing from knuckle assembly. Discard bearing.
9. Remove halfshaft assembly. Place shaft into a suitable vise and remove bearing dust shield. Discard dust shield.
10. Reverse procedure to install.

BALL JOINT INSPECTION

1. Raise and support vehicle.
2. With suspension in full rebound position, grasp lower edge of tire and move wheel in and out, **Fig. 2.**
3. Observe lower end of knuckle and lower control arm as wheel is being moved in and out. Any movement between lower end of knuckle and lower arm indicates excessive ball joint wear.

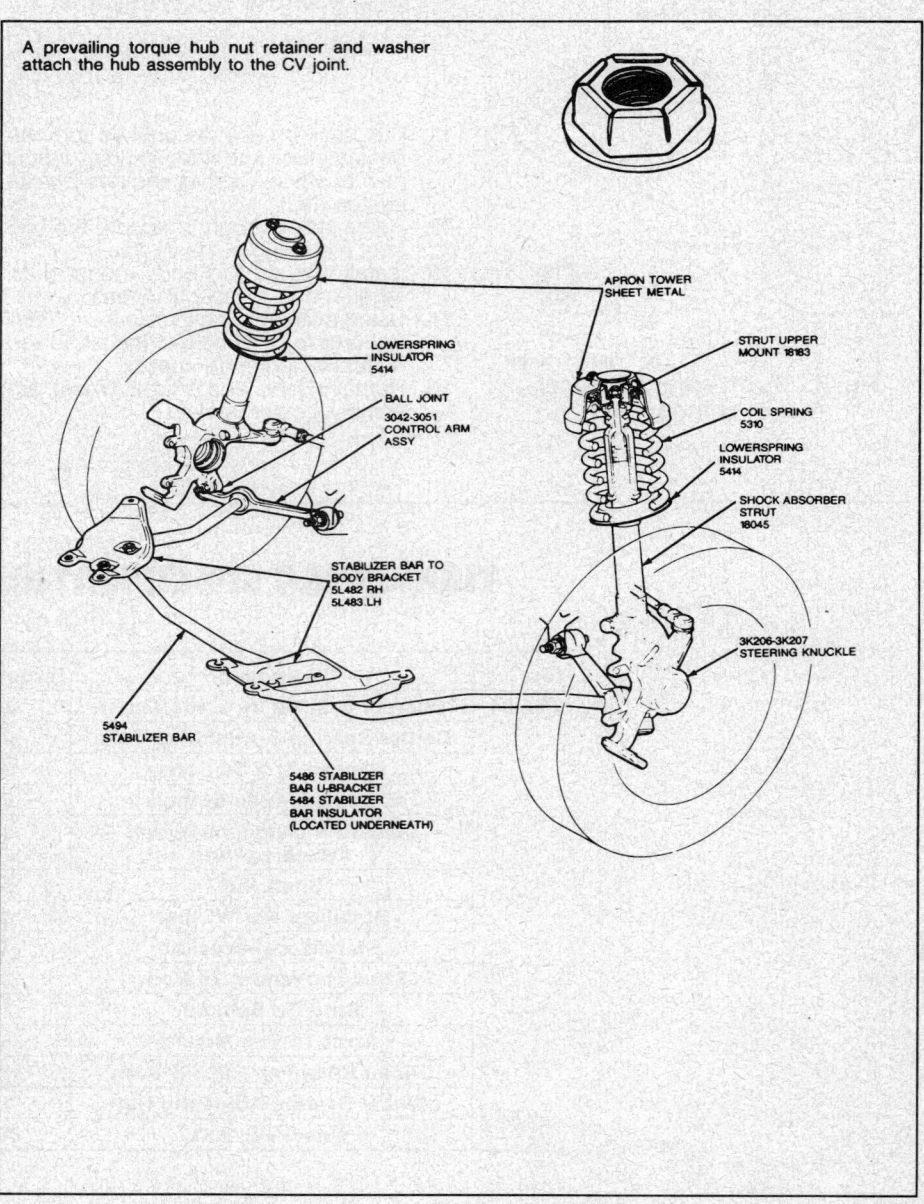

A prevailing torque hub nut retainer and washer attach the hub assembly to the CV joint.

LOWERSPRING INSULATOR 5414

BALL JOINT 3042-3051 CONTROL ARM ASSY

APRON TOWER SHEET METAL

STRUT UPPER MOUNT 18183

COIL SPRING 5310

LOWERSPRING INSULATOR 5414

SHOCK ABSORBER STRUT 18045

STABILIZER BAR TO BODY BRACKET 5L482 RH 5L483 LH

3K206-3K207 STEERING KNUCKLE

5494 STABILIZER BAR

5486 STABILIZER BAR U-BRACKET 5484 STABILIZER BAR INSULATOR (LOCATED UNDERNEATH)

FM2029100048000X

Fig. 1 Front suspension

4. If any movement is observed, install a new lower control arm assembly. The lower ball joint and control arm are serviced as an assembly only. Refer to "Control Arm, Replace" in this section.

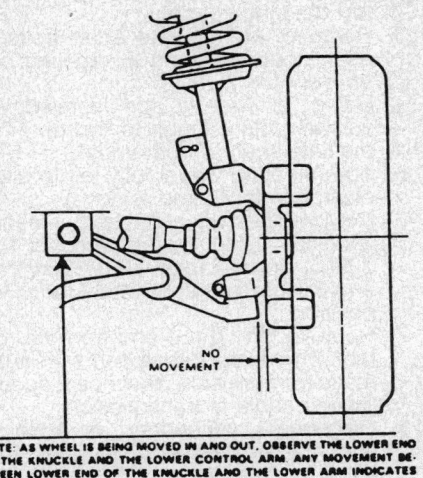

NOTE: AS WHEEL IS BEING MOVED IN AND OUT, OBSERVE THE LOWER END OF THE KNUCKLE AND THE LOWER CONTROL ARM. ANY MOVEMENT BETWEEN LOWER END OF THE KNUCKLE AND THE LOWER ARM INDICATES ABNORMAL BALL JOINT WEAR

FM2029100049000X

Fig. 2 Lower ball joint Check

STRUT
REPLACE

1. Raise and support vehicle, then remove tire and wheel assembly.
2. Loosen but do not remove, two top mount-to-shock tower nuts.
3. Remove brake hose retaining bracket from strut.
4. Remove strut-to-knuckle pinch bolt, then using a large screwdriver, slightly spread pinch joint.
5. Using a suitable pry bar, place top of bar under fender apron and pry down on knuckle until strut separates from knuckle. **Be careful not to pinch brake flex line.**
6. Remove two top mount-to-shock tower nuts, then strut from vehicle.
7. Install spring compressor in bench mount.
8. Compress spring with Rotunda spring compressor tool No. 086-00029 or equivalent.
9. Place 18 mm deep socket tool No. D81P-18045-A1 or equivalent, on strut shaft nut. Insert an 8 mm hex deep socket with 1/4-inch drive wrench. Remove top shaft mounting nut from shaft while holding 1/4 inch drive socket with a suitable extension. **Do not attempt to remove shaft nut by turning shaft and holding nut. The nut must be turned and the shaft held to avoid possible damage to shaft.**
10. Loosen spring compressor tool, then remove top mount bracket assembly, bearing insulator and spring.
11. reverse procedure to install. **Torque** strut shaft nut to 35-50 ft. lbs. Install new steering knuckle pinch nut and tighten to specifications. Tighten two top mount attaching nuts to specifications.

CONTROL ARM
REPLACE

1. Raise and support vehicle.

2. Remove nut from stabilizer bar, then the large dished washer.
3. Remove lower control arm inner pivot bolt and nut.
4. Remove lower control arm ball joint pinch bolt, then using a screwdriver, separate the control arm from the steering knuckle and remove from vehicle. **Ensure steering column is in unlocked position. Do not use a hammer to separate ball joint from knuckle.**
5. Reverse procedure to install, tightening to specifications.

STEERING KNUCKLE
REPLACE

1. Raise and support vehicle, then remove wheel assembly.
2. Remove cotter pin from tie rod end stud, then the slotted nut.
3. Using tie rod end remover tool 3290C and adapter T81P3504W, remove tie rod end from knuckle.
4. Remove brake caliper, then the hub from the driveshaft.
5. Loosen two top mount nuts. Do not remove nuts.
6. Remove pinch bolt and nut securing lower arm to steering knuckle, then using a screwdriver, separate lower arm from knuckle. **Ensure steering column is in unlocked position. Do not use a hammer to separate ball joint from knuckle.**
7. Remove shock absorber strut to steering knuckle pinch bolt, then using a screwdriver, slightly open knuckle to strut pinch joint.
8. Remove steering knuckle from shock absorber strut, **Fig. 3,** then from the vehicle.
9. Reverse procedure to install, tightening to specifications.

STABILIZER BAR
REPLACE

1. Raise and support vehicle.
2. Remove stabilizer insulator mounting bracket bolts.
3. Remove stabilizer bar to control arm attaching bolts, then the stabilizer bar assembly.
4. Remove worn insulators from stabilizer bar.
5. Reverse procedure to install. Tighten stabilizer bar to control arm attaching bolt and stabilizer insulator mounting bracket bolts to specifications.

TIE ROD
REPLACE

1. Unlock steering column by turning ignition key.
2. Engage parking brake, then raise and support vehicle.
3. Clean any loose dirt or oil from power steering gear and boot bellows.

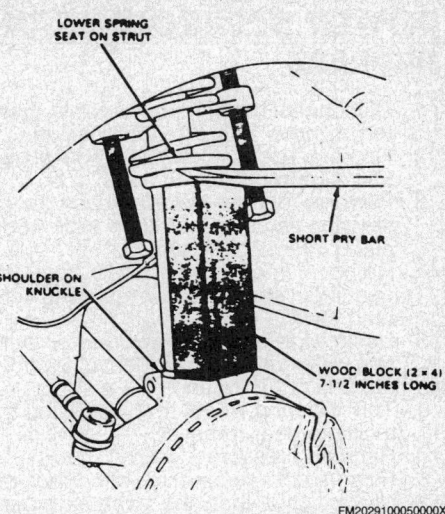

FM2029100050000X

Fig. 3 Separating shock absorber strut from knuckle

4. Disconnect outer tie rod end from steering knuckle.
5. Loosen jamb nut and keep flush with outer tie rod.
6. Remove cotter pin and castle nut, then disconnect outer tie rod from steering knuckle.
7. Mark threads at jamb nut location, then remove outer tie rod end from inner tie rod.
8. Remove jamb nut from inner tie rod spindle.
9. Remove left and right steering gear boot bellows along with breather tube.
10. Remove rollpin or rivet securing inner tie rod to steering rack, **Use a sharp chisel to gently pry up or rivet. Do not cut off.**
11. Use side cutters to remove rivet. **The rivet has a steel core which will deform the steering gear rack threads if it is not completely removed.**
12. If rivet is not accessible, unscrew inner tie rod (less than one full turn). **Have steering gear at or near full turn (lock) position. Use a wrench on rack teeth (flat) to resist rotation and prevent damage to pinion during removal and installation.**
13. Remove inner tie rod from steering gear rack using a wrench on rack teeth in combination Rotunda socket tool No. D90P-3290-A or equivalent.
14. Reverse procedure to install, noting the following:
    a. Replenish any grease which may have been removed from rack teeth.
    b. Install roll pin using channel locks.
    c. Check inner tie rod function by moving tie rod spindle. Handshake in various directions.
    d. Apply steering gear grease to inner tie rod groove where bellows attach to tie rod end. This allows for toe-in adjustment without twisting bellows.
    e. Tighten jamb nut to specifications.
    f. Tighten steering knuckle castle nut to specifications.
    g. Align front end to specification.

POWER STEERING GEAR
REPLACE

1. Disconnect battery ground cable, then turn ignition switch to On position.
2. Remove access panel from dash below steering column.
3. Remove four screws from dash panel steering column boot, then slide boot along intermediate shaft.
4. Remove intermediate shaft bolts at gear input shaft and from steering column shaft.
5. Using wide blade screwdriver, spread slot wide enough to loosen intermediate shaft at both ends.
6. Turn steering wheel to full left stop to facilitate gear removal.
7. Remove pressure switch.
8. Disconnect secondary air tube at check valve, then the exhaust pipes from exhaust manifold. Secure exhaust system to the side.
9. Remove exhaust hanger brackets from below steering gear and from side apron.
10. Disconnect pressure and return lines from intermediate connector and drain fluid.
11. Remove tie rod ends from steering knuckles using tie rod end remover tool 3290D and adapter T81P3504W. Turn right wheel to full left turn position.
12. **On models equipped with manual transmission,** remove left tie rod end from tie rod.
13. **On models equipped with automatic transmission,** disconnect speedometer cable from transmission.
14. Disconnect shift cable assembly from transmission.
15. **On all models,** remove gear mounting brackets and insulators.
16. Remove gear from intermediate shaft by pushing upward on shaft with bar while pulling gear downward.
17. Rotate gear downward and forward to clear input shaft.
18. Ensure input shaft is in full left turn position, then move gear through right side apron opening until left tie rod clears opening. Use caution to avoid damaging bellows.
19. Lower left side of gear and remove gear from vehicle.
20. Reverse procedure to install.

POWER STEERING PUMP
REPLACE

1. Remove alternator drive belt.
2. Place alternator in upper most position.
3. Remove radiator overflow bottle.
4. Remove power steering pump drive belt.
5. Disconnect return line from pump.
6. Completely back off power steering pump pressure line nut. The pressure line will separate when the pump bracket is removed.
7. Remove power steering pump mounting bolts and pump.
8. Reverse procedure to install.

MANUAL STEERING GEAR
REPLACE

1. Disconnect battery ground cable, then turn ignition switch to "On" position.
2. Remove access panel from dash below steering column.
3. Remove intermediate shaft bolts at gear input shaft and at steering column shaft.
4. Using a wide blade screwdriver, spread slots enough to loosen intermediate shaft at both ends.
5. Turn steering wheel fully left to allow clearance for tie rod removal.
6. Remove tie rod ends from steering knuckles using tie rod remover tool 3290D and adapter T81P3504W or equivalent. Turn right wheel to full left position.
7. Remove left tie rod end from tie rod, then on vehicles equipped with automatic transmission disconnect speedometer cable at transmission.
8. Disconnect secondary air tube at check valve, then exhaust pipes from exhaust manifold.
9. Remove exhaust hanger bracket from below steering gear. Wire exhaust system aside.
10. Remove gear mounting brackets and insulators, then separate gear from intermediate shaft while simultaneously pulling upward on shaft from inside vehicle. **Right and lefthand brackets and insulators are not interchangeable.**
11. Rotate gear forward and downward to clear input shaft.
12. Ensure input shaft is in full left turn position, then remove gear through right side apron opening until left tie rod clears shift linkage.
13. Lower left side of gear and remove gear from vehicle.
14. Reverse procedure to install. Ensure input shaft is at full left turn stop and right wheel assembly is in full left turn position. Use caution not to damage steering gear bellows.

TIGHTENING SPECIFICATIONS

Year	Component	Torque/Ft. Lbs.
1992-94	Control Arm To Body	48-55
	Control Arm To Knuckle	38-45
	Jamb Nut	42-50
	Pinch Bolt And Nut	38-45
	Lower Control Arm Inner Pivot Nut	98-115
	Stabilizer Bar Bracket Assembly To Body	48-55
	Stabilizer Bar Insulator U-Bracket Clamps To Bracket Assembly	85-100
	Stabilizer Bar To Control Arm	98-115
	Steering Knuckle Castle Nut	27-32
	Strut To Knuckle	55-81
	Strut Top Mount To Body	25-30
	Strut To Top Mount	35-50
	Tie Rod End To Steering Knuckle Slotted Nut	28-32
	Wheel Lug Nut	80-105

Wheel Alignment

INDEX

PRELIMINARY INSPECTION

1. Inspect tires for proper inflation and similar tread wear.
2. Inspect hub and bearing for excessive wear, repair as required.
3. Inspect ball joints.
4. Inspect tie rod ends for excessive looseness.
5. Check wheel and tire runout.
6. Inspect vehicle ride height.
7. Inspect rack and pinion for looseness at frame.
8. Ensure proper strut operation.
9. Check suspension and steering components for damage, replace as required.

FRONT WHEEL ALIGNMENT

CASTER & CAMBER

Caster and camber angles are preset at the factory and cannot be adjusted.

TOE-IN

To adjust toe-in, **Fig. 1**, lock steering wheel in the straight ahead position using suitable steering wheel holder. Remove small outer clamp from steering boot to prevent boot from twisting during adjustment procedure. Loosen tie rod adjusting nuts, then adjust left and right tie rods until each wheel has 1/2 the desired total toe specification. Tighten tie rod adjusting nuts, replace steering gear rubber boots and tighten clamp. Remove steering wheel holding tool.

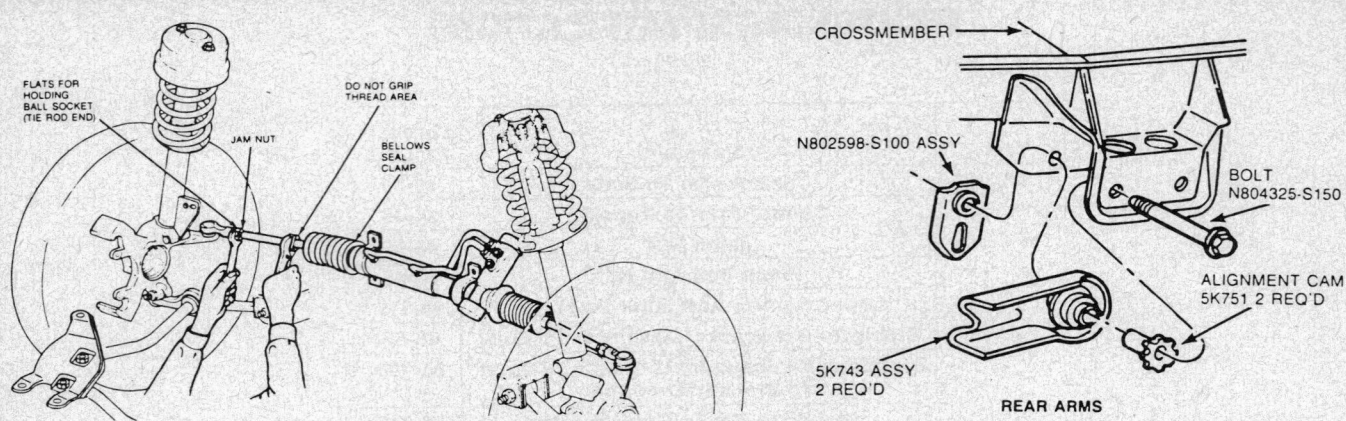

Fig. 1   Adjusting front wheel toe-in & toe-out   Fig. 2   Rear wheel toe-in & toe-out alignment cam

REAR WHEEL ALIGNMENT
CASTER & CAMBER

Caster and camber cannot be adjusted and factory set.

TOE-IN & TOE-OUT

Toe-in and toe-out can be adjusted if it is determined that the vehicle is not within alignment specifications. To adjust toe of either wheel, loosen bolt attaching rear control arm to body, **Fig. 2,** and rotate alignment cam until the required alignment setting is obtained. **Torque** control arm attaching bolt to 52-74 ft. lbs.

FORD CONTOUR & MERCURY MYSTIQUE

NOTE: Refer To Rear Of This Manual For Vehicle Manufacturer's Special Service Tool Suppliers.

INDEX OF SERVICE OPERATIONS

NOTE: For Service Operations Not Listed Below, Refer To The Table Of Contents In The Front Of This Manual.

Specifications
GENERAL ENGINE SPECIFICATIONS

Year	Engine Liter/CID	Engine VIN Code ①	Fuel System	Bore & Stroke	Compression Ratio	Net H.P. @ RPM ②	Maximum Torque Ft. Lbs. @ RPM	Normal Oil Pressure, psi ③
1995	2.0L/4-122	3	SEFI	3.34 X 3.46	9.6	125 @ 5500	130 @ 4000	20-45
1995	2.5L/V6-153	L	SEFI	3.25 X 3.13	9.7	170 @ 6200	165 @ 4200	20-45

CID—Cubic Inch Displacement.
①—The eighth digit denotes engine code.
②—Net rating, as installed on vehicle.
③—Engine hot, at 1500 RPM.

TUNE UP SPECIFICATIONS

Year & Engine (VIN Code) ①	Spark Plug Gap	Firing Order Fig.	Ignition Timing BTDC Man. Trans.	Ignition Timing BTDC Auto Trans.	Mark Fig.	Curb Idle Speed Man. Trans.	Curb Idle Speed Auto Trans.	Fast Idle Speed Man. Trans.	Fast Idle Speed Auto Trans.	Fuel Pump Pressure, psi. ③
1995										
2.0L/4-122 (3)	.048-.052	A	8-12 ④	8-12 ④	—	②	②	②	②	39
2.5/V6-153 (L)	.052-.056	B	8-12 ④	8-12 ④	—	②	②	②	②	40

BTDC—Before Top Dead Center.
②—Idle speed is controlled by Idle Air Control (IAC) valve.
②—D: Drive.
③—Wrap shop towel around diagnostic valve to prevent fuel spillage. Connect suitable fuel pressure gauge to fuel diagnostic valve. Place ignition switch in On position to energize fuel pump & check pressure gauge reading.
④—Non-adjustable.

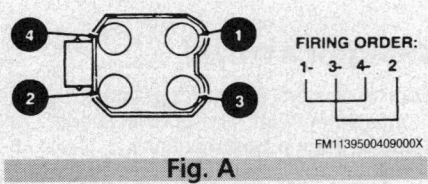

FIRING ORDER:
1- 3- 4- 2

FM1139500409000X

Fig. A

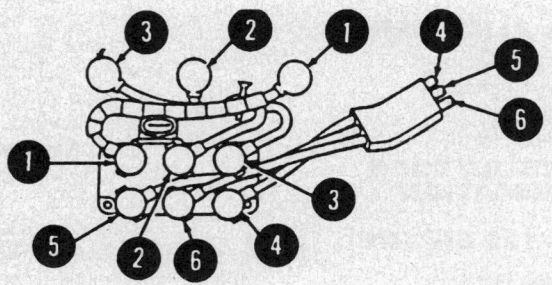

FIRING ORDER:
1-4-2-5-3-6

FM1139500410000X

Fig. B

FRONT WHEEL ALIGNMENT SPECIFICATIONS

| Year | Model | Caster Angle, Degrees | | Camber Angle, Degrees | | | | Toe-In, Degrees | Toe-Out On Turns, Degrees | |
| | | | | Limits | | Desired | | | | |
		Limits	Desired	Left	Right	Left	Right		Outer Wheel	Inner Wheel
1995	All	+2.8 to +4.8	+2.13	-1.1 to +.1	-1.1 to +.1	-.5	-.5	-.1	18.25	20

COOLING SYSTEM & CAPACITY DATA

| Year | Engine (VIN) ① | Coolant Capacity, Qts. | | Radiator Cap Relief Pressure, Lbs. | Thermo Opening Temp., Deg. F | Fuel Tank, Gals. | Engine Oil Refill, Qts. | Transaxle Oil | |
		Automatic Trans.	Manual Trans.					Manual Trans., Pts.	Auto. Trans., Qts. ②
1995	2.0L/4-122 (3)	7.5	7.0	16	187	14.5	4.5	5.5	9.0
	2.5L/V6-153 (L)	9.1	8.9	16	183	14.5	5.5	5.5	10.3

①—Eighth digit of Vehicle Identification Number (VIN) denotes engine code.
②—Approximate. Make final check with dipstick.

LUBRICANT DATA

| Year | Model | Lubricant Type | | | |
| | | Transaxle | | | |
		Manual	Automatic	Power Steering	Brake System
1995	All	Mercon	Mercon	Premium Power Steering Fluid①	DOT 3

①—Ford specification ESW-M2C33-F.

Electrical

NOTE: Refer To "Air Bag System Precautions" Located In The Front Of This Manual For System Disarming & Arming Procedures.

INDEX

PRECAUTIONS

AIR BAG SYSTEMS

Refer to "Air Bag System Precautions" in the front of this manual for system disarming and arming procedures.

FUSE PANEL & FLASHER LOCATION

The fuse junction panel is located to the left of the steering column and is attached to the instrument panel

The indicator flasher is located at the turn and emergency warning indicator switch at the steering column tube.

RELAY CENTER LOCATION

Relays are contained in the power distribution box, located in the engine compartment on the lefthand fender apron.

STARTER

REPLACE
2.0L/4-122

1. Disconnect battery ground cable, then raise and support vehicle.
2. Remove engine air intake resonators as described in "2.0L/4-122 Engine" section.
3. Lower vehicle, then remove upper starter motor bolt.

4. Raise and support vehicle, then remove B-terminal and S-terminal nuts from starter solenoid.
5. Remove lower starter motor bolts, then the motor from vehicle.
6. Reverse procedure to install, noting the following:
   a. When installing lower starter motor bolts, be sure to install ground cable.
   b. **Torque** lower starter motor bolts to 15-20 ft. lbs.
   c. **Torque** B-terminal nut to 80-124 inch lbs., then the S-terminal nut to 44-62 inch lbs.

2.5L/V6-153

1. Disconnect battery ground cable, then loosen engine air cleaner tube clamps on air cleaner outlet tube.
2. Disconnect crankcase ventilation hoses and IAC valve tube from air cleaner outlet tube fitting.
3. Remove air cleaner outlet tube from mass air flow sensor and throttle body.
4. Disconnect engine control sensor wiring connector from mass air flow sensor and intake air temperature sensor.
5. Remove engine air cleaner to body O-ring retainer.
6. Remove air cleaner body and engine air cleaner intake tube from bracket and engine cleaner intake tube and duct, as one piece.
7. Remove fuel supply and return lines from fuel line support bracket on accelerator cable bracket, then remove fuel line support bracket.
8. **On models equipped with automatic transaxle**, remove gear selector and gear shift cable bracket from transaxle.
9. **On all models**, remove engine air cleaner bracket from engine and transaxle support insulator.
10. Remove B- and S-terminal wiring nuts from starter solenoid.
11. Remove positive battery cable and S-terminal connector from starter solenoid and position connector and cable aside.
12. Remove starter motor bolts from top of starter motor.
13. Lifting starter motor, disengage alignment pins from transaxle case and carefully remove motor from vehicle.
14. Reverse procedure to install, noting the following:
    a. **Torque** starter motor bolts to 15-21 ft. lbs.
    b. **Torque** B-terminal nut to 80-124 inch lbs., then the S-terminal nut to 45-62 inch lbs.
    c. **Torque** engine air cleaner bracket to engine bolts and transaxle support insulator bolts to 15-22 ft. lbs.
    d. **Torque** engine air cleaner tube clamps to 24-48 inch lbs.

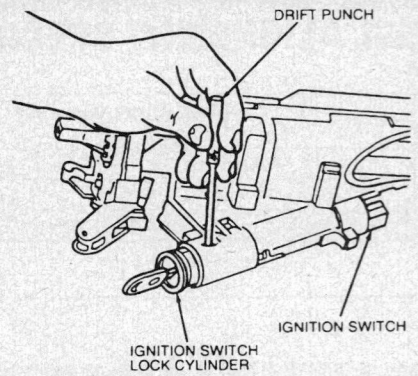

Fig. 1 Ignition lock cylinder removal w/functional lock

ALTERNATOR
REPLACE
2.0L/4-122

1. Disconnect battery ground cable, then remove engine air intake resonators as described in the "2.0L/4-122 Engine" section.
2. Disconnect engine control sensor wiring connector from mass air flow sensor, then the intake air temperature sensor.
3. Remove engine air cleaner to body O-ring retainer, then the air cleaner body and intake tube from bracket and engine air cleaner tube and duct.
4. Disconnect wire harness attachments to integral alternator/voltage regulator, then raise and support vehicle.
5. Remove alternator drive belt from alternator pulley, then remove alternator mounting bracket bolts and alternator bracket.
6. Lower vehicle, then remove power steering pressure hose bracket nut and bolt.
7. Remove power steering pressure hose bracket from engine lifting eye, then the alternator bolts and alternator.
8. Reverse procedure to install. **Torque** power steering pressure hose bracket nut and bolt to 70-106 inch lbs.

2.5L/V6-153

1. Disconnect battery ground cable, then disengage alternator drive belt form alternator pulley.
2. Raise and support vehicle, then remove righthand wheel and tire.
3. Remove righthand outer tie rod end from righthand spindle.
4. Remove exhaust system Y pipe as follows:
   a. Remove front and rear Y pipe flange fasteners from exhaust manifolds.
   b. Remove stud bolt and nut retainer from oil pan, then remove two remaining nuts and bolts from U pipe outlet connection.
   c. Discard exhaust converter inlet gasket, then remove Y pipe.
5. Disconnect wire harness attachments to integral alternator/voltage regulator, then remove alternator brace bolts and brace from alternator.
6. Remove righthand halfshaft as described in "Drive Axles" section.
7. Remove alternator bolts from bracket, then rotate alternator and remove through righthand side of vehicle.
8. Remove bracket bolts and bracket from cylinder block.
9. Reverse procedure to install, noting the following:
   a. **Torque** alternator bracket bolts to 15-22 ft. lbs.
   b. **Torque** alternator bolts to 29-40 ft. lbs.
   c. **Torque** alternator brace bolts to 15-22 ft. lbs.
   d. **Torque** output terminal nut to 80-97 inch lbs.
10.

IGNITION LOCK
REPLACE

FUNCTIONAL LOCK CYLINDER
Removal

The following procedure applies to vehicles with a functional ignition switch lock cylinder. Lock cylinder keys are available for these vehicles, or the lock cylinder key can be made. Place ignition key in lock cylinder.
1. Disconnect battery ground cable.
2. Remove three upper and lower steering column shroud screws, then the shrouds.
3. Turn ignition switch lock cylinder to accessory position.
4. Place 1/8- inch diameter wire pin or small drift punch in hole at top of lock cylinder housing, **Fig. 1**.
5. Press ignition switch lock cylinder pin while pulling lock cylinder from housing.

Installation

1. Install new ignition lock cylinder by turning it to accessory position and pressing in pin.
2. Insert lock cylinder into housing, then turn cylinder to Off position. This permits pin to extend into lock cylinder housing hole.
3. Rotate lock cylinder, using key, to check operation.
4. Install steering column shrouds, then the shroud screws.
5. Connect battery ground cable.

NON-FUNCTIONAL LOCK CYLINDER
Removal

The following procedure is for vehicles in which the ignition switch lock cylinder is inoperative and the ignition switch lock cylinder cannot be rotated due to a lost or broken lock cylinder key, unknown key number or with an ignition switch lock cylinder cap damaged and/or broken to the extent the key cannot be rotated.
1. Disconnect battery ground cable.
2. Remove upper and lower steering column shroud screws, then the shrouds.

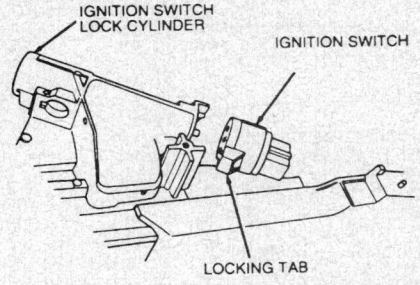

Fig. 2 Ignition switch replacement

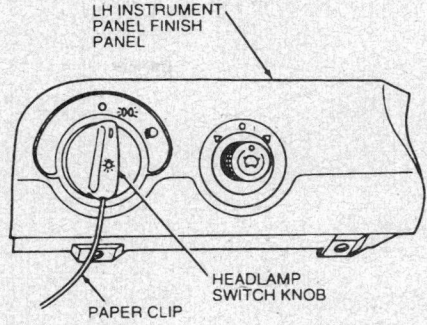

Fig. 3 Headlamp switch knob removal

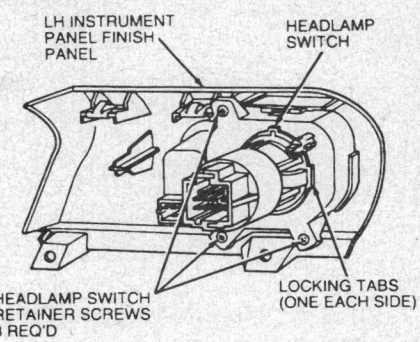

Fig. 4 Headlamp switch removal

3. Using 1/8-inch drill, drill out ignition switch lock cylinder pin.
4. Pull lock cylinder from steering column housing, then inspect housing for damage. If damaged, replace steering column as described in "Steering Columns" section.

Installation

1. Thoroughly clean all drill shavings and other foreign materials from steering column housing.
2. Install new lock cylinder by turning it to accessory position and pressing in pin.
3. Insert ignition switch lock cylinder into lock cylinder housing, then turn lock cylinder to OFF position. This permits pin to extend into lock cylinder housing hole.
4. Rotate lock cylinder, using key, to check for proper operation.
5. Install steering column shrouds, then the shroud screws.
6. Connect battery ground cable.

IGNITION SWITCH
REPLACE

1. Disconnect battery ground cable.
2. Remove steering column shroud screws, then the shrouds.
3. Disconnect ignition switch electrical connector, then depress locking tabs to remove switch, **Fig. 2.**
4. Reverse procedure to install.

CLUTCH START SWITCH
REPLACE

1. Disconnect battery ground cable.
2. Disconnect harness connector from clutch pedal position switch.
3. Rotate switch approximately 45 degrees and pull switch from bracket.
4. Reverse procedure to install.

NEUTRAL SAFETY SWITCH
REPLACE

1. Disconnect battery ground cable, then place manual control lever in NEUTRAL position.
2. Remove engine air intake resonators as described in "2.0L/4-122 Engine" section.
3. Lower vehicle, then remove Mass Air Flow (MAF) sensor as follows:

a. Loosen engine air cleaner tube clamps on air cleaner outlet tube.
b. **On models equipped with 2.5L/V6-153 engine,** disconnect crankcase ventilation hoses and Intake Air Control (IAC) valve tube from air cleaner outlet tube fitting.
c. **On all models,** remove outlet tube from MAF sensor and throttle body.
d. **On models equipped with 2.0L/4-122 engine,** remove outlet tube from engine air intake resonators.
e. **On all models,** disconnect engine control sensor wiring connector from MAF sensor.
f. Remove bolts or release clips from air cleaner cover.
g. Carefully remove mass air flow sensor.
h. **On models equipped with 2.0L/4-122 engine,** discard gasket.
i. **On models equipped with 2.5L/V6-153 engine,** inspect O-ring for wear or damage and replace as necessary.
4. Disconnect electrical harness from Transaxle Range (TR) sensor.
5. Remove TR sensor bolts, then the sensor.
6. Reverse procedure to install, noting the following:
a. Ensure manual control lever is in NEUTRAL position.
b. Align TR sensor slots using TR sensor tool No. T94P-70010-AH, or equivalent.
c. **Torque** TR sensor bolts to 7-9 ft. lbs.
d. **Torque** MAF sensor bolts to 25 inch lbs.
e. **Torque** engine air cleaner tube clamps to 24-48 inch lbs.

HEADLAMP SWITCH
REPLACE

1. Disconnect battery ground cable, then remove two lefthand finish panel to instrument panel screws.
2. Pull straight outward on lefthand finish panel to release finish panel clips.
3. Grasp headlamp switch knob and slide small pin into hole in bottom of headlamp switch knob to release locking tab, **Fig. 3.**

4. Pull knob straight away from headlamp switch, then remove three headlamp switch retainer to lefthand instrument panel finish panel screws.
5. Press locking tabs on headlamp switch retainer and separate retainer, **Fig. 4.**
6. Press locking tabs on headlamp switch and remove headlamp switch from headlamp switch retainer.
7. Reverse procedure to install.

STOP LIGHT SWITCH
REPLACE

1. Disconnect battery ground cable, then the wiring to stop light switch.
2. Remove switch by rotating 90 degrees counterclockwise and pulling toward rear of vehicle.
3. Reverse procedure to install.

COMBINATION SWITCH
REPLACE

1. Remove steering column upper shroud screws, then the upper shroud.
2. Press multi-function switch locking tab, then slide switch up and off of steering column.
3. Press locking tabs on multi-function switch electrical connector and remove connector from switch.
4. Reverse procedure to install.

STEERING WHEEL
REPLACE

1. Disconnect battery ground cable and air bag back-up power supply.
2. Remove air bag module screws, turning steering wheel 90 degrees one direction to remove first screw, then 180 degrees in opposite direction to remove second screw.
3. Disconnect air bag wire harness from driver side air bag module, then remove module from steering wheel.
4. Center front wheels to straight ahead position, then disconnect speed control wire harness from steering wheel.
5. Remove steering wheel bolt.
6. Route air bag sliding contact assembly wire harness through steering wheel opening while lifting steering wheel off shaft.

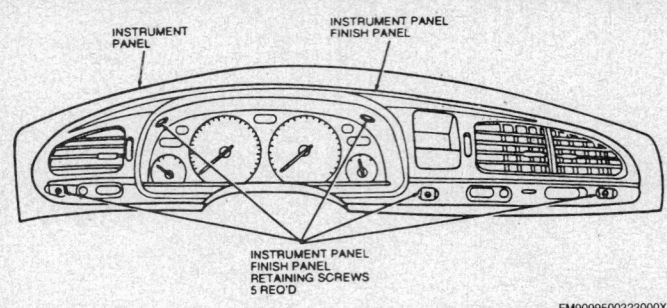

Fig. 5   Instrument panel finish panel removal

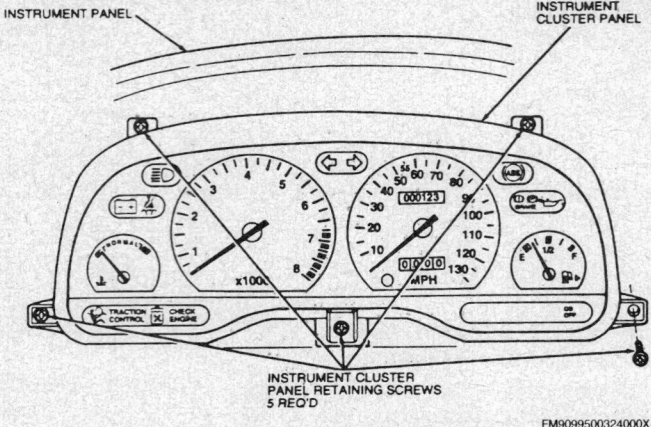

Fig. 6   Instrument cluster removal

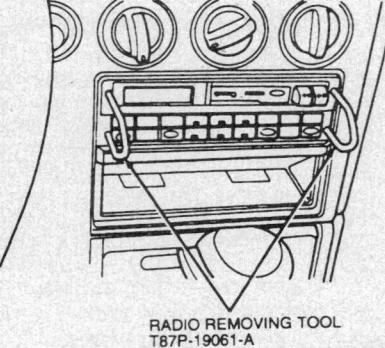

Fig. 7   Radio chassis removal

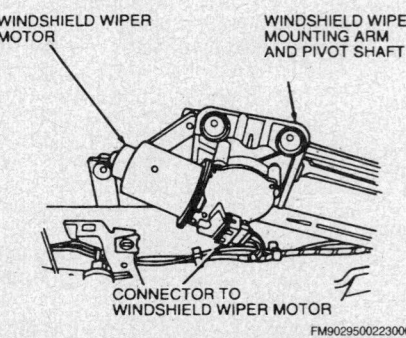

Fig. 8   Wiper motor removal

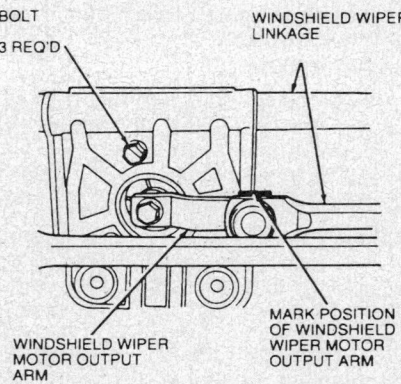

Fig. 9   Wiper pivot arm position marking

7. Reverse procedure to install, noting the following:
   a. Ensure front wheels are in straight-ahead position.
   b. Ensure steering wheel and steering shaft alignment marks are aligned and air bag contact wire is not pinched.
   c. **Torque** new steering wheel bolt to 37 ft. lbs.
   d. **Torque** air bag module screws to 8–10 ft. lbs.
   e. Verify air bag warning indicator.

INSTRUMENT CLUSTER
REPLACE

1. Disconnect battery ground cable.
2. Remove instrument panel finish panel as follows:
   a. Remove three instrument panel finish panel screw covers, then the screws, **Fig. 5.**
   b. Pull finish panel away from instrument panel, then disconnect wiring harness connectors from indicator lamps, heated back window switch and light and traction assist switch.
   c. Remove cluster instrument panel finish panel.
3. Remove instrument cluster panel screws, **Fig. 6.**
4. Pull instrument cluster away from instrument panel, then disconnect two cluster printed circuit connectors from instrument cluster back plate.
5. Reverse procedure to install.

RADIO
REPLACE

1. Record preset stations, then discon-

nect battery ground cable.
2. Install radio removing tool No. T87P-19061-A, or equivalent, into radio chassis, then push tools in approximately 1 inch to release retaining clips, **Fig. 7. Do not use excessive force when installing radio removing tool to avoid damaging retaining clips. Damaging clips will make removing radio chassis difficult and may cause damage.**
3. Apply light spreading force on tools and pull radio chassis out of instrument panel.
4. Disconnect wiring connectors and antenna cable.
5. Reverse procedure to install. Check radio chassis operation, then reset preset radio stations.

WIPER MOTOR
REPLACE

1. Disconnect battery ground cable.
2. Remove windshield wiper linkage from upper cowl panel as described under "Wiper Transmission, Replace."
3. Disconnect harness to wiper motor, **Fig. 8,** then the wiper motor output arm to wiper motor crankshaft bolt.
4. Remove wiper motor mounting plate bolts, then the motor.
5. Reverse procedure to install, noting the following:
   a. **Torque** wiper motor mounting plate bolts to 71–106 inch lbs.
   b. **Torque** wiper motor output arm bolt to 19 ft. lbs.

WIPER SWITCH
REPLACE

Refer to "Combination Switch, Replace" for replacing the wiper switch.

WIPER TRANSMISSION
REPLACE

1. Disconnect battery ground cable, then raise windshield wiper pivot arm nut covers.
2. Loosen windshield wiper pivot arm nuts approximately two turns, then lift pivot arms from wiper linkage.
3. Pull hood weatherstrip from cowl top extension, then remove upper fastener caps and screws.
4. Remove cowl vent screen lower screws.
5. Lift righthand cowl vent screen away from upper cowl panel, then remove vent screen.
6. Lift lefthand cowl vent screen away from upper cowl panel, then remove vent screen.
7. Mark position of wiper pivot arm in relation to wiper motor mounting bracket, **Fig. 9,** then remove windshield wiper linkage to upper cowl panel bolts, **Fig. 10.**
8. Remove wiper motor bolts, then the wiper linkage.

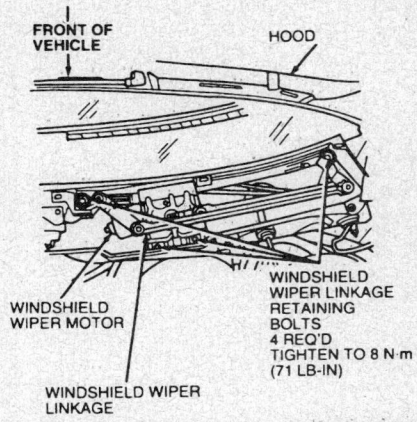

Fig. 10 Wiper linkage removal

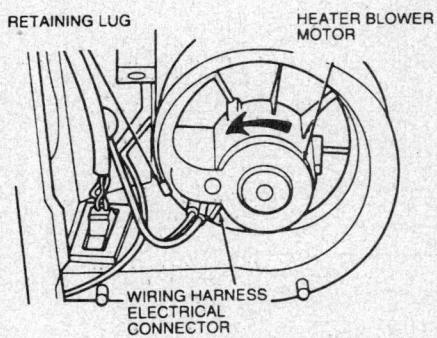

Fig. 11 Blower motor replacement

9. Reverse procedure to install, noting the following:
   a. **Torque** wiper linkage bolts to 71 inch lbs.
   b. **Torque** wiper pivot arm nuts to 18 ft. lbs.
   c. **Torque** wiper motor bolts to 71–106 inch lbs.

WIPER MODULE
REPLACE

1. Disconnect battery ground cable.
2. Pull central timer module straight away from fuse junction panel, then remove from vehicle.
3. Reverse procedure to install.

BLOWER MOTOR
REPLACE

1. Working from inside vehicle, remove push pins and upper footwell trim panel from passenger side.
2. Disconnect blower motor wire harness electrical connector.
3. Carefully lift retaining lug on A/C blower motor flange, **Fig. 11**, and rotate blower motor counterclockwise approximately 30 degrees to disengage it from A/C evaporator housing.
4. Pull blower motor out of A/C evaporator housing.
5. Reverse procedure to install. After in-serting blower motor into A/C evaporator housing, turn clockwise until retaining lug engages.

HEATER CORE
REPLACE

1. Disconnect battery ground cable, then remove front ash receptacle by pulling outward from console panel.
2. Remove transaxle control selector knob, then pry transaxle control lever plate away from console panel.
3. Remove front console panel to instrument panel screws, then, through ash receptacle opening, the console panel to instrument panel screws.
4. Open console glove compartment, then the console panel to front floor pan screws.
5. Raise console panel and ease parking brake handle boot over parking brake release handle.
6. Disconnect cigar lighter knob and element wires, then remove console panel.
7. Remove air bag diagnostic monitor, screws and bracket from heater outlet floor duct.
8. Remove air transfer duct to heater outlet floor duct screw, then push transfer duct up inside of heater outlet floor duct.
9. Remove heater outlet floor duct to heater core cover screws.
10. Release tab on each side of outlet floor duct, then remove duct from heater core cover.
11. Raise and support vehicle.
12. Disconnect heater water hoses from heater core inlet and outlet tubes. Plug heater water hoses and cap heater core tubes to prevent coolant loss during heater core removal.
13. Disconnect vacuum supply hose (black) from vacuum source in engine compartment.
14. Lower vehicle, then disconnect vacuum supply hose (black) from A/C vacuum reservoir tank and bracket inside vehicle.
15. Release four tabs, then remove heater core, cover and vacuum hose from evaporator housing, **Fig. 12**.
16. Remove heater dash panel seal and vacuum hose from heater core cover, **Fig. 13**.
17. Remove screw and heater core mounting bracket from heater core cover.
18. Remove heater core from heater core cover, then the heater core case seal from heater core.
19. Reverse procedure to install.

EVAPORATOR CASE
REPLACE
REMOVAL

1. Disconnect battery ground cable, then remove instrument panel as described under "Dash Panel Service."
2. Place drain pan or suitable container

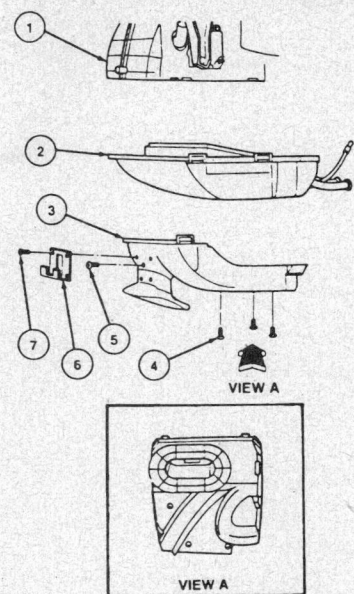

Item	Description
1	A C Evaporator Housing
2	Heater Core Cover
3	Heater Outlet Floor Duct
4	Screw (2 Req'd)
5	Screw (1 Req'd)
6	Air Bag Control Monitor Bracket
7	Screw (4 Req'd)

Fig. 12 Heater core removal from evaporator housing

under heater water hose connections at cowl panel.
3. Discharge refrigerant from A/C system as described under "Air Conditioning."
4. Raise and support vehicle.
5. Disconnect heater water hoses from heater core inlet and outlet tubes. Plug water hoses and cap heater core tubes to prevent coolant loss during evaporator housing removal.
6. Disconnect vacuum supply hose (black) from vacuum source in engine compartment.
7. Disconnect discharge line using spring lock coupling disconnect tool No. T81P-19623-G2, or equivalent.
8. Disconnect discharge line to jumper line from evaporator core inlet and outlet tubes at cowl panel using spring lock coupling disconnect tool No. T83P-19623-C, or equivalent.
9. Remove A/C evaporator housing to cowl panel nut, then, working from inside vehicle, remove nut from upper crossmember brace.
10. Remove bottom bracket bolt, then the crossmember brace.
11. Pull off A/C plenum demister adapter from righthand and lefthand sides of evaporator housing.
12. Remove two ram air intake duct to evaporator housing screws, then re-

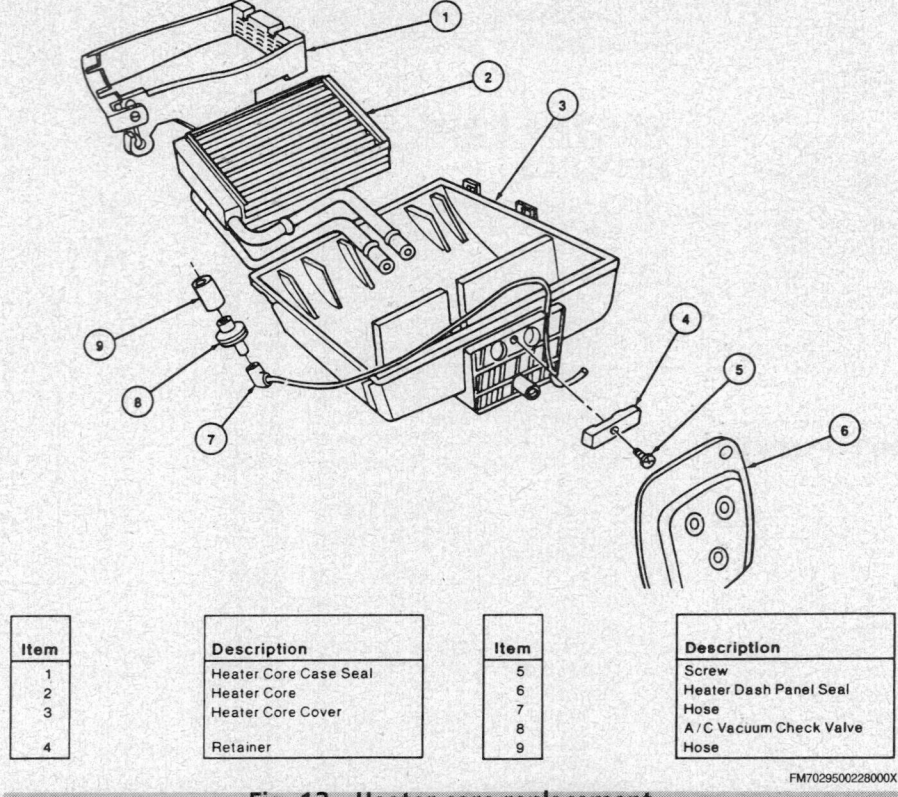

Item	Description
1	Heater Core Case Seal
2	Heater Core
3	Heater Core Cover
4	Retainer

Item	Description
5	Screw
6	Heater Dash Panel Seal
7	Hose
8	A/C Vacuum Check Valve
9	Hose

FM7029500228000X

Fig. 13 Heater core replacement

lease retaining clips and remove intake duct from evaporator housing.

13. Remove A/C vacuum reservoir tank and bracket to evaporator housing screw.
14. Disconnect vacuum hoses from vacuum reservoir tank and bracket and remove A/C vacuum reservoir tank and bracket from A/C evaporator housing.
15. Remove air bag diagnostic monitor bracket from heater outlet floor duct.
16. Remove air transfer duct to heater outlet floor duct screw, then push transfer duct up inside of heater outlet floor duct.
17. Remove heater outlet floor duct to heater core cover screws, then release tab on each side of heater outlet floor duct and remove floor duct from heater core cover.
18. Release tabs and remove heater core, cover and vacuum hose from A/C evaporator housing, **Fig. 12**.
19. Remove amplifier and power radio booster equalizer amplifier bracket from vehicle.
20. Remove A/C evaporator housing to instrument panel reinforcement screws, then rotate housing away from reinforcement, **Fig. 14**, and remove housing from vehicle.

INSTALLATION

1. Rotate housing into position on instrument panel reinforcement, then secure with screws.
2. Install heater core cover with heater core and vacuum hose to evaporator housing. Use additional metal service

INSTRUMENT PANEL REINFORCEMENT

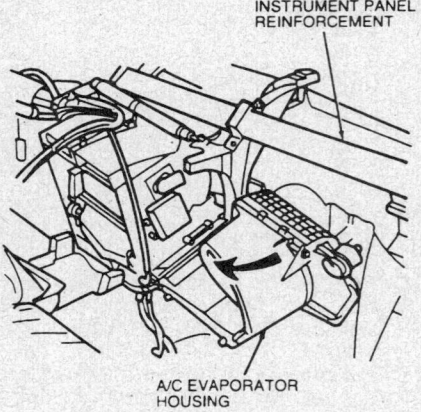

A/C EVAPORATOR HOUSING

FM7029500229000X

Fig. 14 Evaporator housing replacement

clips if necessary.
3. Install heater outlet floor duct to heater core cover. Use metal service clips if necessary.
4. Slide air transfer duct down to engage with rear seat air flow duct and secure with screw.
5. Install air bag diagnostic monitor bracket to heater outlet floor duct.
6. Install ram air intake duct to evaporator housing.
7. Install righthand and lefthand A/C plenum demister adapters to A/C evaporator housing.
8. Install A/C vacuum reservoir tank and bracket to evaporator housing, then connect two vacuum hoses and A/C

vacuum check valve to A/C vacuum reservoir tank and bracket.
9. Install radio power booster equalizer amplifier bracket.
10. Secure upper crossmember brace with nut, then the bottom mounting bracket with bolt.
11. Install instrument panel as described in "Dash Panel Service" section.
12. Working from inside engine compartment, install evaporator housing to cowl panel nut. Connect discharge line and evaporator to compressor suction line, or jumper line to evaporator core tubes at cowl panel.
13. Raise and support vehicle.
14. Connect heater water hoses to heater core tubes, then the vacuum source line.
15. Check and refill cooling system as necessary with recommended coolant mixture. Refer to "Cooling System Bleed."
16. Connect battery ground cable, then charge refrigerant system as described in "Air Conditioning" section.

EVAPORATOR CORE
REPLACE

When replacing an A/C evaporator core, replace suction accumulator/drier.

Before replacing an evaporator core, leak test core in vehicle to verify it is leaking. Refer to "Air Conditioning" section for leak test procedures.

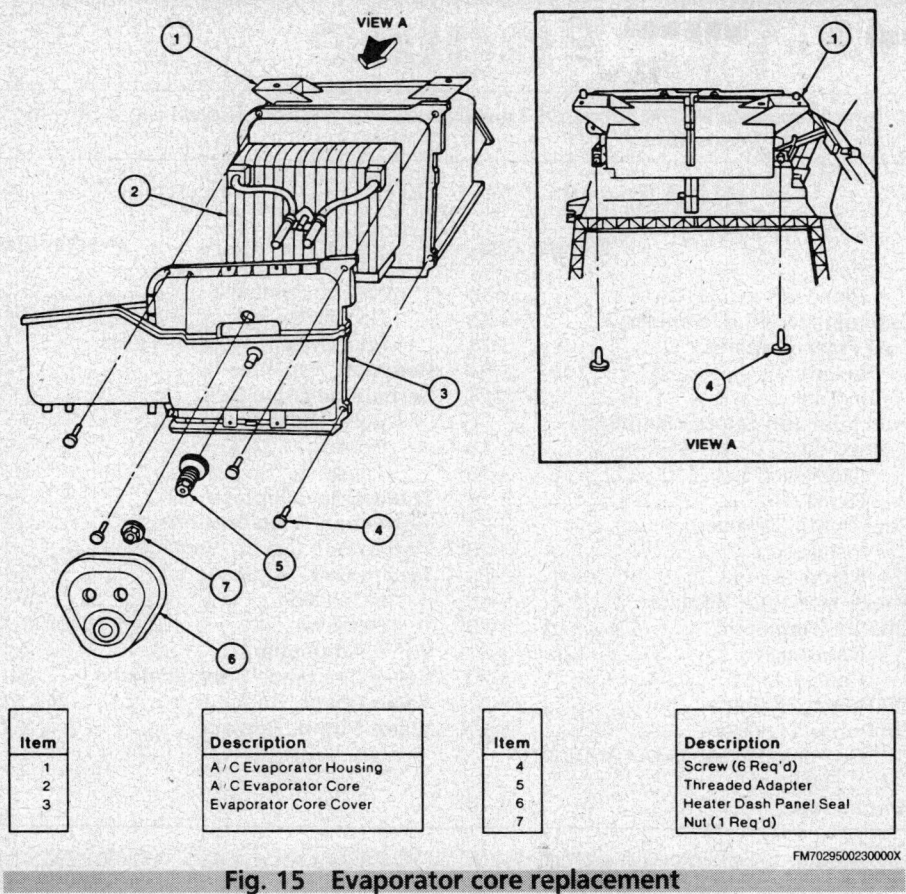

Item	Description
1	A/C Evaporator Housing
2	A/C Evaporator Core
3	Evaporator Core Cover

Item	Description
4	Screw (6 Req'd)
5	Threaded Adapter
6	Heater Dash Panel Seal
7	Nut (1 Req'd)

FM7029500230000X

Fig. 15 Evaporator core replacement

1. Remove evaporator housing as described under "Evaporator Case, Replace."
2. Remove vacuum line from vacuum control motor.
3. Remove metal clips and disengage lugs retaining A/C recirculating air duct to A/C evaporator housing.
4. Remove recirculating duct, then the heater dash panel seal and evaporator nut.
5. Remove rear A/C evaporator housing screws, then separate evaporator housing and remove evaporator core, **Fig. 15.**
6. Reverse procedure to install.

NOTE: Refer To "Air Bag System Precautions" Located In The Front Of This Manual For System Disarming & Arming Procedures.

INDEX

PRECAUTIONS
AIR BAG SYSTEMS

Refer to "Air Bag System Precautions" in the front of this manual for system disarming and arming procedures.

COOLING SYSTEM

This engine has an aluminum cylinder head and requires a special corrosion inhibiting coolant to avoid cooling system damage. Use only specified coolant in this engine.

FUEL SYSTEM PRESSURE RELIEF

Fuel supply lines will remain pressurized for long periods of time after engine shutdown. The pressure must be relieved before servicing the fuel system.

1. Remove engine air cleaner as follows:
   a. Remove engine air intake resonators as described under "Engine Air Intake Resonators, Replace."
   b. Disconnect engine control sensor wiring connectors from Mass Air Flow (MAF) sensor and Intake Air Temperature (IAT) sensor.
   c. Remove engine air cleaner to body O-ring retainer.
   d. Remove engine air cleaner body and intake tube from bracket and intake tube and duct.
2. Connect Multi-Port Fuel Injection (MFI) fuel pressure gauge tool No. T80L-9974-B, or equivalent, to fuel pressure relief valve cap on fuel injection supply manifold.

3. Open manual valve on gauge tool to relieve fuel system pressure.

ENGINE MOUNT
REPLACE
UPPER

Removal

1. Remove engine air intake resonators as described under "Engine Air Intake Resonators, Replace."
2. Install three bar engine support tool No. D88L-6000-A, or equivalent, to existing engine lifting eyes and support engine.
3. Remove front engine support self-locking nuts and discard nuts. **Engine support nuts are self-locking and must be replaced with new self-locking nuts when serviced.**
4. Remove upper front engine support bracket from vehicle.
5. Remove radiator coolant recovery reservoir bolts and position radiator coolant recovery reservoir aside to allow clearance for upper front engine support insulator removal.
6. Remove front engine support insulator bolts, then the insulator from righthand front fender apron, **Fig. 1.**

Installation

If the upper front engine support insulator or front engine support bracket has been removed, the engine and transaxle position MUST BE RE-ALIGNED to front subframe. Failure to realign engine and transaxle may result in possible component damage.

1. Raise and support vehicle, then remove two front subframe through bolt bolts and lefthand front engine support insulator.
2. Install powertrain alignment gauge tool No. T94P-6000-AH, or equivalent, to transaxle bracket and front subframe, **Fig. 2. Torque** vertical bolts and through bolt to 20 ft. lbs.
3. Loosen righthand front engine support insulator through bolt, then lower vehicle.
4. Position power steering hose bracket and return hose onto upper front support insulator, then install upper front engine support insulator and bolts to righthand front fender apron. Tighten bolts to specifications.
5. Position radiator coolant recovery reservoir. Tighten bolts to specifications.
6. Install upper front engine support bracket onto engine and upper front engine support insulator. **Torque** new self-locking upper front engine support bracket nuts to 7 ft. lbs. **Engine support nuts are self-locking and must be replaced with new self-locking nuts when serviced.**
7. Remove engine support tool, then **torque** upper front engine support bracket nuts to 52-70 ft. lbs.
8. Raise and support vehicle, then observe position of righthand front engine support insulator. Insulator must be centered in transaxle bracket and in perfect front-to-rear alignment.
9. Tighten righthand front engine support insulator through bolt to specifications.

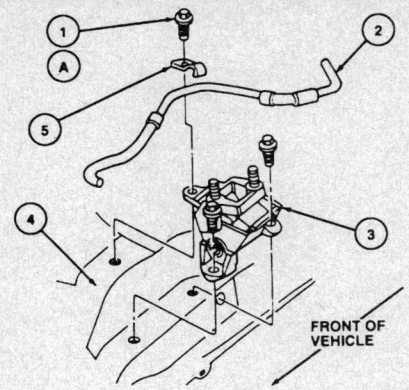

Item	Description
1	Bolt (3 Req'd)
2	Power Steering Return Hose
3	Front Engine Support Insulator (Upper)
4	Front Fender Apron (RH)
5	Power Steering Hose Bracket
A	Tighten to 70-95 N·m (52-70 Lb-Ft)

FM1069500380000X

Fig. 1 Upper front engine support insulator replacement

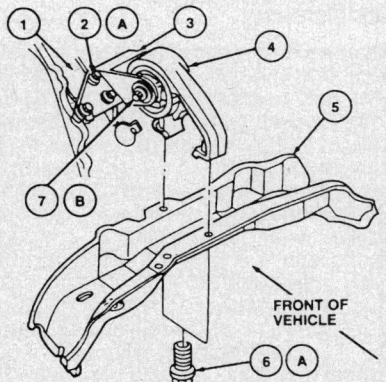

Item	Description
1	Transaxle
2	Bolt (3 Req'd)
3	Front Engine Support Bracket (RH)
4	Front Engine Support Insulator (RH)
5	Front Sub-Frame
6	Bolt (2 Req'd)
7	Through Bolt
A	Tighten to 41-55 N·m (30-40 Lb-Ft)
B	Tighten to 103-137 N·m (75-102 Lb-Ft)

FM1069500383000X

Fig. 4 Righthand front engine support insulator replacement. Automatic transaxle

10. Remove three gauge tool bolts and gauge tool.
11. Install lefthand front engine support insulator to front subframe with two bolts, then **torque** bolts to 7 ft. lbs. Observe insulator to ensure perfect front-to-rear alignment, then **torque** bolts to 30-40 ft. lbs.

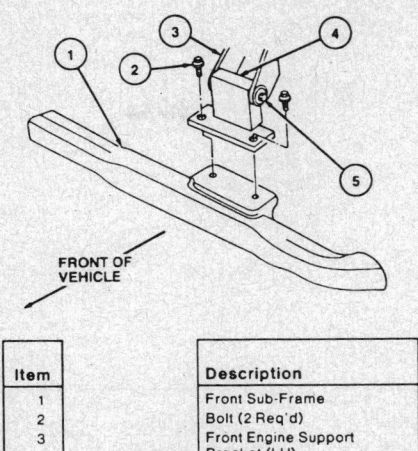

Item	Description
1	Front Sub-Frame
2	Bolt (2 Req'd)
3	Front Engine Support Bracket (LH)
4	Powertrain Alignment Gauge
5	Through Bolt

FM1069500381000X

Fig. 2 Powertrain alignment gauge tool installation

12. Install lefthand front engine support insulator through bolt and tighten to specifications.
13. Install engine air intake resonators as described under "Engine Air Intake Resonators, Replace."
14. Fill power steering system as described in "Power Steering" section.
15. Run engine and check for leaks.

LEFTHAND

Removal

1. Raise and support vehicle.
2. Remove lefthand front engine support insulator to front subframe bolts, **Fig. 3.**
3. Remove lefthand front engine support insulator through bolt, then the insulator.
4. If necessary, remove lefthand front engine support bracket bolts and lefthand front engine support bracket from transaxle case.

Installation

1. Install lefthand front engine support bracket to transaxle case. Tighten bracket bolts to specifications.
2. Install lefthand front engine support insulator onto front subframe. **Torque** bolts to 7 ft. lbs. Observe lefthand front engine support insulator to ensure perfect front-to-rear alignment, then **torque** bolts to 75-102 ft. lbs.
3. Lower vehicle.

RIGHTHAND

Removal

1. Disconnect battery ground cable, then raise and support vehicle.
2. Remove through bolt from righthand front engine support insulator, **Figs. 4 and 5.**
3. Remove righthand front engine support insulator to front subframe bolts, then the insulator, noting the following:

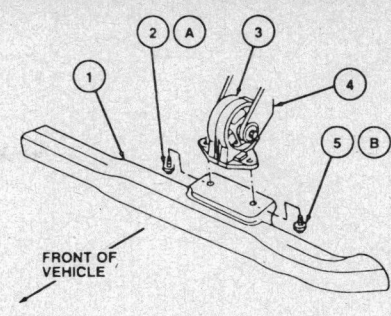

Item	Description
1	Front Sub-Frame
2	Bolt (2 Req'd)
3	Front Engine Support Insulator (LH)
4	Front Engine Support Bracket (LH)
5	Through Bolt
A	Tighten to 41-55 N·m (30-40 Lb-Ft)
B	Tighten to 103-137 N·m (75-102 Lb-Ft)

FM1069500382000X

Fig. 3 Lefthand front engine support insulator replacement

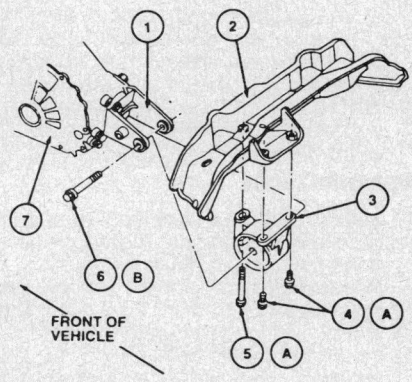

Item	Description
1	Front Engine Support Bracket (RH)
2	Front Sub-Frame
3	Front Engine Support Insulator (RH)
4	Bolt (2 Req'd)
5	Bolt
6	Through Bolt
7	Transaxle
A	Tighten to 41-55 N·m (30-40 Lb-Ft)
B	Tighten to 103-137 N·m (75-102 Lb-Ft)

FM1069500384000X

Fig. 5 Righthand front engine support insulator replacement. Manual transaxle

a. When removing righthand front engine support insulator, always disconnect battery ground cable prior to removal. Contact of righthand front engine support insulator to alternator output terminal with battery connected may short alternator and battery to ground, causing possible injury and damage to vehicle.

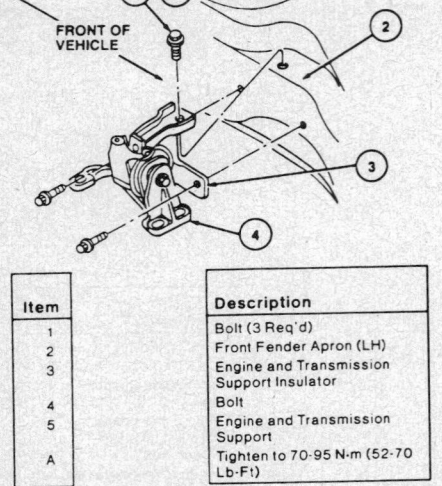

Item	Description
1	Bolt (3 Req'd)
2	Front Fender Apron (LH)
3	Engine and Transmission Support Insulator
4	Bolt
5	Engine and Transmission Support
A	Tighten to 70-95 N·m (52-70 Lb-Ft)

FM1069500385000X

Fig. 6 Engine & transaxle support insulator bolt removal. Automatic transaxle, manual transaxle similar

b. **On models equipped with 2.5L/V6-153 engine and automatic transaxle,** remove insulator through bottom of righthand side of front subframe, past righthand exhaust manifold and alternator.

4. **On all models,** if necessary, remove righthand front engine support bracket from transaxle.

Installation

1. Install righthand front engine support bracket to transaxle. Tighten nuts or bolts to specifications.
2. Position righthand front engine support insulator to front subframe, then install and loosely tighten bolts.
3. Install righthand front engine support insulator through bolt and loosely tighten.
4. Remove two front subframe through bolts and lefthand front engine support insulator bolt.
5. Install powertrain alignment gauge tool No. T94P-600-AH, or equivalent, **Fig. 2,** to transaxle bracket and front subframe, **Fig. 2. Torque** two vertical bolts, then the through bolt to 20 ft. lbs.
6. **Torque** righthand front engine support insulator bolts to front subframe to 7 ft. lbs. Observe position of righthand front engine support insulator. Insulator must be centered in transaxle bracket and in perfect front-to-rear alignment.
7. **Torque** righthand front engine support insulator through bolt to 75-102 ft. lbs.
8. Remove three gauge tool bolts and gauge tool.
9. Install lefthand front engine support insulator to front subframe with two bolts. **Torque** bolts to 7 ft. lbs. Observe position of lefthand front engine support insulator to ensure perfect front-to-rear alignment. **Torque lefthand front engine support insulator bolts to 30-40 ft. lbs.**

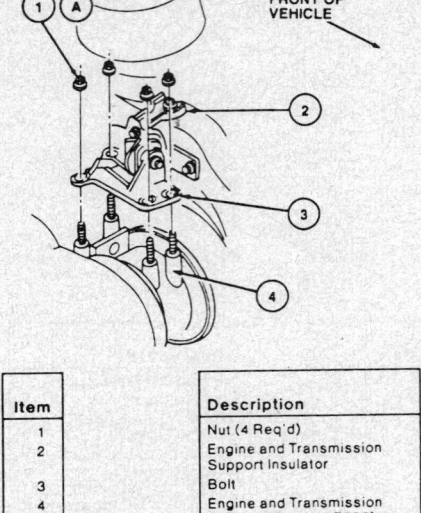

Item	Description
1	Nut (4 Req'd)
2	Engine and Transmission Support Insulator
3	Bolt
4	Engine and Transmission Support (Part of 6F063)
5	Transaxle
A	Tighten to 41-55 N·m (30-40 Lb-Ft)

FM1069500386000X

Fig. 7 Engine & transaxle support insulator replacement. Automatic transaxle

10. Install lefthand front engine support insulator through bolt. Tighten through bolt to specifications.
11. Lower vehicle, then connect battery ground cable.

ENGINE & TRANSAXLE SUPPORT INSULATOR

Removal

1. Disconnect battery ground cable, then remove engine air intake resonators as described under "Engine Air Intake Resonators, Replace."
2. Disconnect engine control sensor wiring connector from Mass Air Flow (MAF) sensor, then the engine control sensor wiring from Intake Air Temperature (IAT) sensor.
3. Remove engine air cleaner to body O-ring.
4. Remove engine air cleaner body and intake tube from bracket and intake tube and duct.
5. **On models equipped with 2.5L/V6-153 engine,** remove battery and battery tray.
6. **On all models,** remove air cleaner mounting bracket from engine and transaxle support insulator.
7. **On models equipped with 2.5L/V6-153 engine,** remove water pump pulley shield screws, then the shield.
8. **On all models,** install three bar engine support tool D88L-6000-A, or equivalent, to engine lifting eyes and support engine and transaxle.
9. Remove engine and transaxle support insulator to lefthand front fender apron bolts, **Fig. 6.**
10. Remove engine and transaxle support insulator nuts, then the insulator, **Figs. 7 and 8.** Discard nuts.

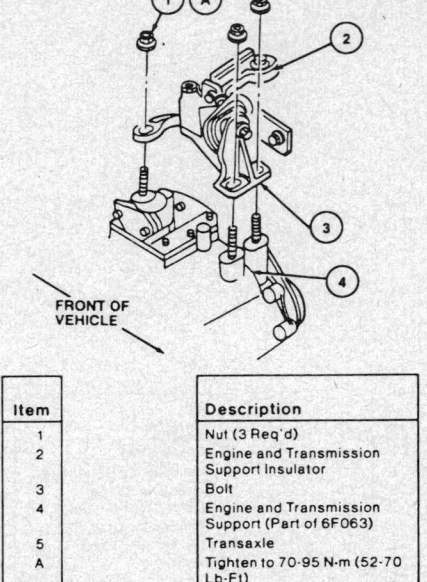

Item	Description
1	Nut (3 Req'd)
2	Engine and Transmission Support Insulator
3	Bolt
4	Engine and Transmission Support (Part of 6F063)
5	Transaxle
A	Tighten to 70-95 N·m (52-70 Lb-Ft)

FM1069500387000X

Fig. 8 Engine & transaxle support insulator replacement. Manual transaxle

Installation

If engine and transaxle support insulator or upper front engine support insulator has been removed, the engine and transaxle position must be realigned to the front subframe. Failure to realign the engine and transaxle may result in possible component damage.

1. Raise and support vehicle, then remove two front subframe, through bolts and lefthand front engine support insulator bolt.
2. Install powertrain alignment gauge tool No. T94P-6000-AH, or equivalent, to transaxle bracket and front subframe. **Torque** vertical bolts, then the through bolt to 20 ft. lbs.
3. Loosen righthand front engine support insulator through bolt, then lower vehicle.
4. Install engine and transaxle support insulator. Tighten bolts to specifications.
5. Install new engine and transaxle support insulator nuts. **Torque** nuts to 7 ft. lbs. **This vehicle uses self-locking nuts. These must be replaced with new self-locking nuts when servicing.**
6. Remove engine support, then **torque** engine and transaxle support insulator nuts to 52-70 ft. lbs.
7. Raise and support vehicle, then tighten righthand front engine support insulator through bolt to specifications. **Observe position of righthand front engine support insulator. It must be centered in transaxle bracket and in perfect front-to-rear alignment.**
8. Remove three bolts and gauge tool.
9. Install lefthand front engine support insulator to front subframe with two bolts. **Torque** bolts to 7 ft. lbs.

10. Observe lefthand front engine support insulator to ensure perfect front-to-rear alignment, then **torque** bolts to 30-40 ft. lbs.
11. Install lefthand front engine support insulator through bolt. Tighten through bolt to specifications.
12. Position air cleaner body and intake tube on bracket. Ensure mounting tabs are firmly seated in mounting bracket grommets.
13. Install O-ring retainer, then the air cleaner element.
14. Install air cleaner cover, then ensure rear of cover is fully engaged with body and close clamps.
15. Connect engine air control sensor wiring connector to Mass Air Flow (MAF) sensor.
16. Install air cleaner outlet tube.
17. Install engine air intake resonators as described under "Engine Air Intake Resonators, Replace."
18. Connect battery ground cable.

ENGINE
REPLACE

REMOVAL

1. Disconnect battery cables and wiring from battery.
2. Remove pinch bolt and disconnect steering shaft and joint at cowl in vehicle.
3. Remove engine air intake resonators as described under "Engine Air Intake Resonators, Replace."
4. Disconnect engine control sensor wiring connector from Mass Air Flow (MAF) sensor, then the engine control sensor wiring from Intake Air Temperature (IAT) sensor.
5. Remove engine air cleaner to body O-ring retainer.
6. Remove air cleaner body and intake tube from bracket and tube and duct.
7. Recover air conditioning system as described in "Air Conditioning" section.
8. Raise and support vehicle, then remove splash shield from front of subframe and body.
9. Remove three way catalytic converter as follows:
   a. Remove outlet flange nuts, then the muffler and exhaust converter outlet gasket from converter.
   b. Remove EGR valve to exhaust manifold tube, bracket and clamp from converter.
   c. Lower vehicle and remove heat shield and converter nuts from exhaust manifold.
   d. Remove converter and exhaust converter inlet gasket from exhaust manifold.
   e. Discard exhaust converter inlet gasket.
10. Drain cooling system as described under "Cooling System Bleed."
11. Remove lug nuts and front wheel and tire assemblies.
12. Remove cotter pins and nuts, then

separate lefthand and righthand stabilizer bar links from front stabilizer bar.
13. Remove lefthand and righthand tie rod end nuts, then separate ends from front wheel knuckles using tie rod end remover tool No. 3290-D, or equivalent.
14. Remove pinch bolts, then separate lefthand and righthand front suspension lower arms from front wheel knuckles at ball joint.
15. Remove lefthand and righthand front axle wheel hub retainer from halfshaft ends, then the halfshafts from knuckles.
16. Remove A/C accumulator screws from front subframe.
17. Disconnect vehicle speed sensor wiring harness at connector, then disconnect speedometer drive cable from transaxle.
18. **On models equipped with automatic transaxle**, proceed as follows:
   a. Remove righthand splash shield from front fender apron to access crankshaft pulley.
   b. Remove access plug from engine rear plate, then the torque converter nuts.
   c. Push torque converter into transaxle front pump support and gear.
19. **On all models,** disconnect engine control sensor wiring from knock sensor and oil pressure sensor located on righthand side of cylinder block.
20. Lower vehicle, then secure radiator and engine cooling fan motor, fan blade and fan shroud assembly to radiator support with safety wire.
21. Disconnect accelerator cable and speed control actuator from throttle body and accelerator cable bracket, then the engine control sensor wiring to fuel charging wiring at connector located near fuel pressure regulator.
22. Remove engine control sensor wiring screws from intake manifold.
23. Remove power steering pump auxiliary reservoir from bracket and position over engine assembly. Disconnect return hose from reservoir, then plug hose.
24. Disconnect power steering return hose from power steering pump.
25. Disconnect engine control sensor wiring from power steering pressure switch located on power steering pressure hose and from alternator.
26. Remove ground strap from alternator mounting bracket, then disconnect vacuum supply hose from intake manifold at fitting on rear of intake manifold.
27. Disconnect coolant hoses from radiator coolant reservoir, then the hoses from A/C compressor.
28. Disconnect fuel and supply lines from fuel injection supply manifold, then the vacuum supply hose from EGR valve.
29. Disconnect EGR pressure sensor vacuum hoses at exhaust manifold tube.
30. **On models equipped with automatic transaxle,**
   a. Pry shift cable from stud, then remove two bolts and shift cable and

bracket from transaxle.
   b. Disconnect engine control sensor wiring from Transaxle Range (TR) sensor, then remove shift cable, bracket and bolts from transaxle.
31. **On all models,** disconnect ground strap from transaxle case.
32. Disconnect engine control sensor wiring from ignition coil and radio ignition interference capacitor, then position wiring aside.
33. Remove vacuum supply line from power brake booster, then disconnect upper radiator hose from radiator.
34. Disconnect evaporative emission hose from connector located near radio interference capacitor, then the heater water hose near EGR valve.
35. Disconnect positive and negative battery cable retainer from battery tray.
36. **On models equipped with manual transaxle,** remove retainer and disconnect clutch hydraulic line from clutch actuator pipe at transaxle case.
37. **On all models,** disconnect block heater power supply wiring from lefthand side of radiator support, then raise and support vehicle.
38. Disconnect heater water hose at heater water tube located under engine.
39. **On models equipped with automatic transaxle,** remove transaxle oil cooler lines from transaxle, then the transaxle oil cooler lines from transaxle and oil cooler return line from bracket on lefthand side of transaxle.
40. **On models equipped with manual transaxle,** remove shift rod bolt and nut from stabilizer bar, then the bar.
41. **On all models,** disconnect lower radiator hose from radiator, then remove lower radiator support to front subframe bolts and rotate supports forward.
42. Disconnect A/C compressor wiring harness, then the engine control sensor wiring from heated oxygen sensor, engine coolant temperature sensor and crankshaft position sensor.
43. Remove bumper cover brace screws from lefthand and righthand sides of front subframe, then rotate braces forward.
44. Disconnect power steering oil cooler hoses at righthand front of front subframe, then drain power steering system.
45. Partially lower vehicle, then position and secure any hoses, lines and components to be removed with engine.
46. Install powertrain and subframe support bracket tool No. 134-00250, or equivalent, to Rotunda Powertrain Lift tool No. 134-00251, or equivalent.
47. Rotate transaxle adapters for transaxle removal, then position bracket and lift tools to provide proper contact at powertrain lift points.
48. Remove front subframe to body bolts. **Ensure engine is properly positioned and secure on lifting equipment. Damage to vehicle or personal injury may occur if engine is not secure.**

49. Remove upper front engine support bracket and engine and transaxle support insulator nuts. Discard nuts.
50. With assistant, lower engine and transaxle with front subframe as an assembly. Check for interference to body while lowering powertrain.
51. Support engine with Rotunda Floor Crane Positioning Sling tool No. 014-00036, and Rotunda Floor Crane tool No. 014-00071, or equivalents, from engine lifting eyes.
52. Remove lefthand and righthand halfshafts from transaxle as described in "Drive Axles" section.
53. Remove lefthand and righthand front engine support insulators from front subframe and transaxle as described under "Engine Mount, Replace."
54. Raise and support engine and transaxle assembly, then remove front subframe and lift tool.
55. Support transaxle with suitable transaxle jack
56. Remove starter motor bolts, then the starter motor.
57. Remove battery ground cable from engine to transaxle stud bolt.
58. Remove transaxle to engine bolts, then separate transaxle from engine.
59. **On models equipped with manual transaxle,** remove clutch pressure plate bolts, then the clutch pressure plate and clutch disc.
60. **On all models,** remove flywheel bolts and flywheel from crankshaft.
61. Remove engine rear plate, then install engine onto suitable engine stand, following manufacturer's instructions.

INSTALLATION

1. Remove engine from engine stand using Rotunda Floor Crane Positioning Sling tool No. 014-00036 and Rotunda Floor Crane tool No. 014-00071, or equivalent, attached to engine lifting eyes.
2. Install engine rear plate and flywheel. Tighten bolts in alternating sequence to specifications.
3. **On models equipped with manual transaxle,** install clutch disc and clutch pressure plate as described in "Clutch & Manual Transaxle" section.
4. **On all models,** align torque converter and flywheel and install transaxle to engine. Tighten transaxle to engine bolts to specifications.
5. If removed, place front subframe on powertrain and subframe support bracket tool No. 134-00250, or equivalent, then install engine and transaxle assembly onto bracket tool, **Fig. 9.**
6. Install powertrain alignment gauge tool No. T94P-6000-AH, or equivalent, to lefthand front engine support bracket and front subframe. Tighten bolts, then the through bolt to specifications.
7. Install righthand front engine support insulator bolts to front subframe and through bolt should be finger-tight.
8. Install battery ground cable to engine at transaxle stud bolt. Tighten nut to specifications.

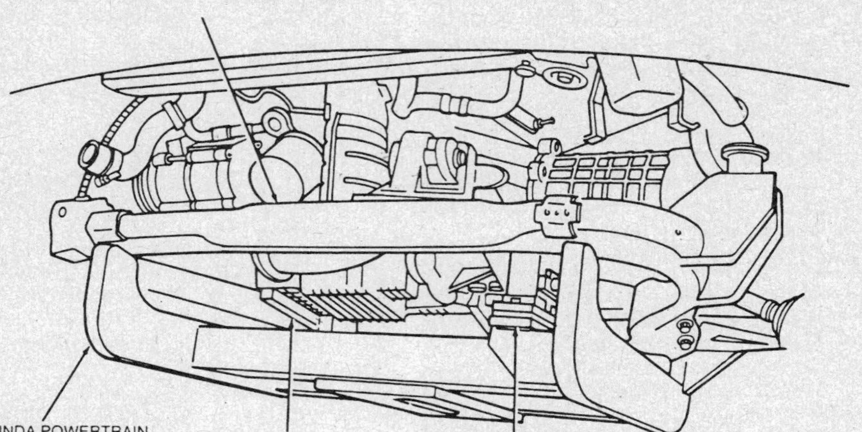

FRONT SUB-FRAME

ROTUNDA POWERTRAIN AND SUB-FRAME SUPPORT BRACKET 134-00250

ENGINE SUPPORT (PART OF 134-00250)

TRANSAXLE SUPPORT (PART OF 134-00250)

FM1069500388000X

Fig. 9   Powertrain & subframe support bracket tool installation

9. Install starter motor as described under "Electrical."
10. Install halfshafts as described in "Drive Axles."
11. Install subframe alignment pin set tool No. 94P-2100-AH, or equivalent, into front subframe, **Fig. 1.**
12. Partially lower vehicle, then install engine and transaxle assembly with front subframe to body.
13. Install front subframe bolts and tighten to specifications. Remove pin set tool.
14. Using new nuts, install upper front engine support bracket and engine and transaxle support insulator. Ensure engine and transaxle are firmly seated against front and rear brackets. **Torque** engine support bracket and transaxle support insulator nuts to 7 ft. lbs.
15. Remove powertrain lift and support bracket tools, then raise and support vehicle.
16. **Torque** front engine support bracket nuts to 52-70 ft. lbs.
17. Tighten engine and transaxle support insulator nuts, then the righthand front engine and support insulator through bolt to specifications.
18. Remove gauge tool, then install lefthand front engine support insulator to front subframe with bolts. **Torque** bolts to 7 ft. lbs. Observe lefthand front engine support insulator to ensure perfect front-to-rear alignment. **Torque** bolts to 30-41 ft. lbs.
19. Install lefthand front engine support insulator through bolt, then tighten to specifications.
20. Connect engine control sensor wiring to heated oxygen sensor, engine coolant temperature sensor and crankshaft position sensor.
21. Connect A/C wire harness, then install radiator supports to front subframe bolts. Tighten bolts to specifications.
22. Connect lower radiator hose to radiator.

23. **On vehicles equipped with manual transaxle,** install shift rod stabilizer to transaxle. Tighten shift rod bolt and stabilizer nut to specifications.
24. **On models equipped with automatic transaxle,** install transaxle oil cooler lines. Tighten nuts to specifications.
25. **On all models,** connect heater water hose at heater water tube located under engine, then lower vehicle.
26. Connect block heater power supply wiring to lefthand side of radiator support.
27. **On models equipped with manual transaxle,** connect clutch hydraulic line to clutch actuator pipe at transaxle case, then install retainer.
28. **On all models,** connect positive and negative battery cable retainer to battery tray.
29. Install heater water hose to connector tube located near EGR valve, then install heater hose in spring clamp securely.
30. Connect evaporative emission hose at connector located near radio ignition interference capacitor, then the upper radiator hoes to radiator.
31. Connect vacuum supply line to power brake booster, then the engine control sensor wiring to ignition coil and radio ignition interference capacitor.
32. Connect ground strap to transaxle case, then the engine control sensor wiring to Transaxle Range (TR) sensor.
33. **On models equipped with automatic transaxle,** install shift cable and bracket to transaxle. Tighten shift cable bracket bolts to specifications.
34. Connect vacuum hoses from EGR pressure sensor to EGR valve to exhaust manifold tube, then the vacuum supply hose to EGR valve.
35. Connect fuel supply and return lines to fuel injection supply manifold.
36. Connect A/C compressor hoses as described in "Air Conditioning" section.

37. Connect coolant hoses to radiator coolant recovery reservoir, then the vacuum supply hose for body to intake manifold at fitting on rear of intake manifold.
38. Install ground strap on alternator mounting bracket, then connect engine control sensor wiring to alternator.
39. Connect engine control sensor wiring to power steering pressure switch located on power steering pressure hose, then the return hose to pump. Tighten hose clamp securely.
40. Install power steering pump auxiliary reservoir to bracket.
41. Install engine control sensor wiring to intake manifold retainer screws. Tighten screws securely.
42. Connect engine control sensor wiring to fuel charging wiring at connector located near pressure regulator, then the accelerator cable and speed control actuator to accelerator cable bracket and throttle body.
43. Remove safety wire from radiator and radiator support, then raise and support vehicle.
44. Connect engine control sensor wiring to knock sensor and oil pressure sensor located on righthand side of cylinder block.
45. **On models equipped with automatic transaxle**, install torque converter to flywheel nuts, then the access plug onto engine rear plate. Tighten flywheel nuts to specifications, then the screws securely.
46. **On all models**, install righthand splash shield onto front fender apron and tighten screws securely.
47. Connect vehicle speed sensor wiring harness at connector, then install speedometer drive cable to transaxle.
48. Install A/C accumulator screws to front subframe and tighten screws securely.
49. Install driveshafts as described in "Drive Axles" section.
50. Install lefthand and righthand front wheel knuckles onto front suspension lower arms at ball joint. Tighten wheel knuckle to lower arm bolts to specifications.
51. Install lefthand and righthand tie rod ends to front wheel knuckle, using new nuts on tie rod end studs. **Torque** tie rod end stud nuts to 21 ft. lbs., then continue tightening nuts to align next castellation of nut with cotter pin hole in stud and install new cotter pins.
52. Connect lefthand and righthand front stabilizer bar link to front stabilizer bar. Tighten nuts to specifications.
53. Install front wheel and tire assemblies. Tighten lug nuts to specifications.
54. Install three-way catalytic converter as follows:
   a. Loosely install converter to exhaust manifold using new exhaust converter inlet gasket.
   b. Position muffler and exhaust converter outlet gasket onto converter and loosely install retainers onto outlet flange studs of converter.
   c. Align system and ensure muffler

FRONT OF ENGINE

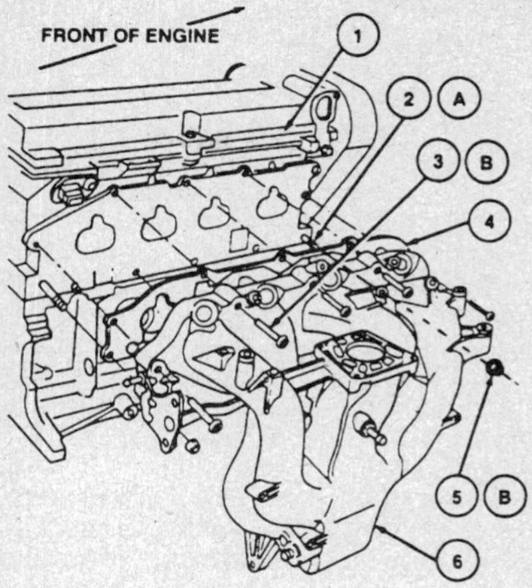

Item	Description
1	Cylinder Head
2	Stud (2 Req'd)
3	Bolt (8 Req'd)
4	Intake Manifold Gasket
5	Nut (2 Req'd)
6	Intake Manifold
A	Tighten to 0-10 N·m (0-89 Lb-In)
B	Tighten to 16-20 N·m (12-15 Lb-Ft)

FM1069500389000X

Fig. 10 Intake manifold replacement

and converter are fully engaged. Tighten all nuts and bolts to specifications, starting with front of system.
55. Install splash shield to front of subframe and body. Tighten screws securely.
56. Rotate front bumper cover braces rearward, then install two screws to front subframe and tighten securely.
57. Lower vehicle, then position engine air cleaner body and intake tube on mounting bracket. Ensure mounting tabs are firmly seated in mounting bracket grommets and intake tube is fully locked into air cleaner body opening.
58. Install air cleaner O-ring retainer, then the cover. Ensure rear of cover is fully engaged in body, then close retaining clamps.
59. Connect engine control sensor wiring connector to mass air flow sensor, then install air cleaner outlet tube.
60. Install engine air intake resonators as described under "Engine Air Intake Resonators, Replace."
61. Connect steering shaft and joint in vehicle. Tighten bolt to specifications.
62. Connect positive and battery ground cables and wiring to battery.
63. **On models equipped with automatic transaxle**, fill transaxle with approved fluid as described in "Automatic Transaxle/Transmission" section.
64. Fill power steering system with approved fluid as described in "Power Steering" section.

65. Fill engine cooling system with specified coolant as described under "Cooling System Bleed."
66. Recharge A/C system as described in "Air Conditioning" section.
67. Run engine and check for oil, coolant or fuel leaks. Verify proper operation of engine cooling fan and A/C system.

INTAKE MANIFOLD
REPLACE

1. Remove engine air intake resonators as described under "Engine Air Intake Resonators, Replace."
2. Depressurize fuel system as described under "Precautions."
3. Disconnect battery ground cable, then remove accelerator cable and speed control actuator from throttle body and accelerator cable bracket.
4. Remove fuel injection supply manifold as described under "Fuel Injection Supply Manifold, Replace."
5. Disconnect fuel charging wiring from engine coolant temperature sensor and engine control sensor wiring.
6. Remove crankcase ventilation tube from intake manifold fitting as follows:
   a. Raise and support vehicle, then drain cooling system as described under "Cooling System Bleed."
   b. Disconnect crankcase ventilation tube from positive crankcase ventilation valve.
   c. Disconnect upper radiator hose and radiator overflow hose from water hose connection.
   d. Remove water outlet connection bolts and water hose connection from water thermostat housing.
   e. Remove water thermostat and seals from water thermostat and water thermostat housing, then inspect seals for damage and replace if necessary.
   f. Remove crankcase ventilation tube bolt from rear of engine, then lower vehicle.
   g. Disconnect front vapor hose from crankcase ventilation tube at connector on crankcase ventilation tube.
   h. Disconnect crankcase ventilation tube from fitting on intake manifold, then remove tube.
7. Remove camshaft position sensor from cylinder head by disconnecting fuel charging wiring from sensor, then removing sensor screw and sensor.
8. Remove EGR valve, then the vacuum supply hose for body from fitting at rear of intake manifold and vacuum supply hose for power brake booster from bottom of intake manifold.
9. Remove bracket screws for electrical control sensor wiring from intake manifold
10. If necessary, remove fuel charging wiring from intake manifold.
11. Remove alternator and bracket, if necessary, as described under "Electrical. **Intake manifold can be removed without first removing alternator and bracket, but with some difficulty.**

12. Remove intake manifold bolts, nuts and studs, then the intake manifold and gasket from cylinder head, **Fig. 10.**
13. Remove throttle body and idle air control valve from intake manifold as necessary.
14. Reverse procedure to install. Tighten engine control sensor wiring bracket screws securely, then the accelerator cable bracket bolt to specifications.

EXHAUST MANIFOLD
REPLACE

1. Disconnect battery ground cable, then remove engine air intake resonators as described under "Engine Air Intake Resonators, Replace."
2. Disconnect heated oxygen sensor at wiring connector.
3. Remove oil level indicator tube bolt from cylinder head, then, using twisting motion, remove oil level indicator tube from cylinder block.
4. Remove lefthand exhaust manifold heat shield retainers, then the lefthand exhaust manifold heat shield from engine.
5. Raise and support vehicle, then remove heated oxygen sensor as follows:
   a. Disconnect engine control sensor wiring from oxygen sensor, then the oxygen sensor wiring lead from fan shroud retainer.
   b. Remove oxygen sensor from exhaust manifold using oxygen sensor wrench tool No. T94P-9472-A, or equivalent.
6. Remove three way catalytic converter as follows:
   a. Remove outlet flange nuts, then the muffler and exhaust converter outlet gasket from converter.
   b. Remove EGR valve to exhaust manifold tube bracket and clamp from converter.
   c. Lower vehicle, then remove heat shield and converter nuts from exhaust manifold.
   d. Remove converter and converter inlet gasket from exhaust manifold, then discard exhaust converter inlet gasket.
7. Lower vehicle, then remove exhaust manifold nuts from cylinder head studs.
8. Remove righthand exhaust manifold and gasket from engine.
9. Reverse procedure to install. Tighten components to specifications.

FUEL INJECTION SUPPLY MANIFOLD
REPLACE

REMOVAL

1. Disconnect battery ground cable, then remove fuel tank filler cap.

2. Relieve fuel pressure as described under "Precautions."
3. Remove engine air intake resonators as described under "Engine Air Intake Resonators, Replace."
4. Disconnect fuel charging wiring from fuel injectors and position wiring aside, then disconnect vacuum line at fuel pressure regulator.
5. Remove fuel line coupling retainer clip from fuel supply and return fittings, then disconnect fuel supply and return hoses using spring lock coupling disconnect tool No. D87L-9280-A (3/8 inch) or D87L-9280-B (1/2 inch), or equivalent.
6. Disconnect fuel supply and return hoses from intake manifold bracket.
7. Remove fuel injection supply manifold bolts.
8. Disengage fuel injection supply manifold with fuel injectors and remove fuel injection supply manifold. It may be easier to remove fuel injectors with fuel injection supply manifold as an assembly.
9. Use light, twisting motion to remove fuel injectors and clip from fuel injection supply manifold.

INSTALLATION

1. Install fuel injectors into fuel injection supply manifold, noting the following:
   a. Lubricate O-rings lightly with clean engine oil, then install fuel injector retainer clip to fuel injectors.
   b. Install fuel injectors to fuel injection manifold with light twisting and pushing motion.
   c. Push fuel injection supply manifold down to ensure all fuel injector O-rings are fully seated in fuel injection supply manifold cups and lower intake manifold.
   d. Ensure O-rings and washers are properly seated so no fuel leaks exist.
2. Install bolts while holding down fuel injection supply manifold. Tighten manifold bolts to specifications.
3. Connect fuel supply and return hoses to fuel injection supply manifold at connectors. Install clips over connectors securely.
4. Install fuel supply and return hoses to intake manifold bracket, then tighten screw securely.
5. Connect vacuum line to fuel pressure regulator, then the battery ground cable.
6. With fuel charging wiring disconnected, turn ignition switch to RUN position several times to allow fuel pump to pressurize fuel system.
7. Using clean towel, check for fuel leaks, then connect fuel charging wiring to fuel injectors.
8. Install engine air intake resonators as described under "Engine Air Intake Resonators, Replace."
9. Run vehicle at idle for two minutes, then turn engine off and inspect for leaks.

ENGINE AIR INTAKE RESONATORS
REPLACE

1. Remove air cleaner outlet tube as follows:
   a. Loosen air cleaner tube clamps on outlet tube, then remove outlet tube from mass air flow sensor and throttle body.
   b. Remove outlet tube from engine air intake resonators.
2. Disconnect engine control sensor wiring from intake air temperature sensor.
3. Loosen air cleaner tube clamp, then remove one engine air intake resonator from mass air flow sensor.
4. Remove nut and bolt for other resonator from throttle body and intake manifold, then the resonator from throttle body and intake manifold.
5. If necessary, remove intake air temperature sensor from resonator.
6. Reverse procedure to install. Tighten nuts, bolts and clamps to specifications.

CYLINDER HEAD
REPLACE

1. Drain engine coolant from radiator and cylinder block drain plugs.
2. Remove intake manifold as described under "Intake Manifold, Replace."
3. Remove exhaust manifold as described under "Exhaust Manifold, Replace."
4. Remove camshafts as described under "Camshaft, Replace."
5. Remove valve tappets from cylinder head, then support front of engine with wood block between crankshaft pulley and front subframe.
6. Remove righthand engine lifting eye bolt, then the righthand eye.
7. Remove power steering pump mounting bracket and cylinder head support bracket.
8. Remove camshaft timing belt tensioner pulley and front cover from front of cylinder head.
9. Remove water thermostat housing from cylinder head as follows:
   a. Raise and support vehicle.
   b. Disconnect crankcase ventilation tube from positive crankcase ventilation valve.
   c. Disconnect upper radiator hose and radiator overflow hose from water hose connection.
   d. Remove water outlet connection bolts and water hose connection from water thermostat housing.
   e. Remove water thermostat and seal from water thermostat, then the seal from water thermostat housing. Inspect seals for damage and replace if necessary.
10. Remove ignition coil bracket from cylinder head as follows:

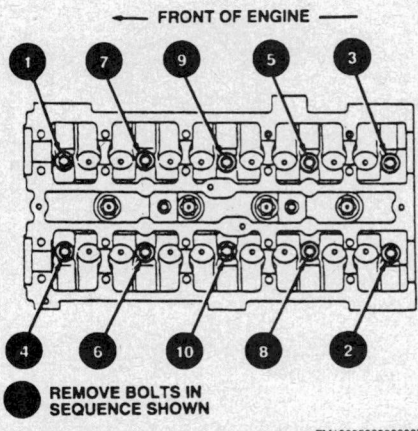

REMOVE BOLTS IN SEQUENCE SHOWN

FM1069500390000X

Fig. 11 Cylinder head bolt removal sequence

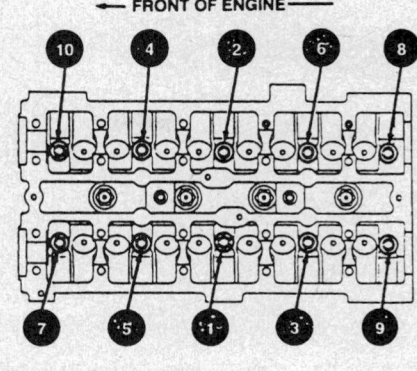

TIGHTEN BOLTS IN SEQUENCE SHOWN

FM1069500391000X

Fig. 12 Cylinder head bolt tightening sequence

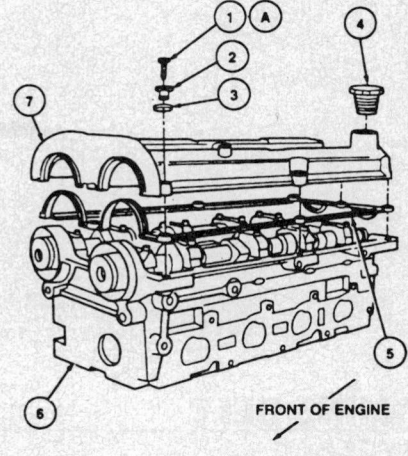

FRONT OF ENGINE

Item	Description
1	Bolt (10 Req'd)
2	Spacer (10 Req'd)
3	O-ring (10 Req'd)
4	Oil Filler Cap
5	Valve Cover Gasket
6	Cylinder Head
7	Valve Cover
A	Tighten to 6-8 N·m (53-71 Lb-In)

FM1069500399000X

Fig. 13 Valve cover replacement

a. Disconnect fuel charging wiring or engine control sensor wiring from ignition coil, then the ignition wires by squeezing locking tabs and twisting while pulling upward.
b. Remove ignition coil bolts or screws, then the coil.
c. Remove ignition coil bracket.
11. Remove spark plugs from cylinder head, then the cylinder head bolts in sequence, **Fig. 11. Discard cylinder head bolts.**
12. Remove cylinder head and head gasket from cylinder block.
13. If necessary, remove lefthand engine lifting eye from cylinder head.
14. Inspect cylinder head and cylinder block, then replace components as required.
15. Reverse procedure to install, noting the following:
   a. Clean cylinder head intake manifold, valve cover and cylinder head gasket surfaces. Ensure flatness of cylinder head and cylinder block gasket surfaces meets specifications.
   b. **Torque** new cylinder head bolts in sequence, **Fig. 12**, first to 15-22 ft. lbs., then to 30-37 ft. lbs. Final tighten all bolts an additional 90-120 degrees in same sequence.

VALVE COVER
REPLACE

1. Disconnect battery ground cable, then remove engine air intake resonators as described under "Engine Air Intake Resonators, Replace."
2. Disconnect crankcase ventilation tube from valve cover fitting.
3. Remove ignition wires and ignition wire separators from valve cover, then disconnect from spark plugs.
4. Remove power steering pressure hose bracket bolt and position pressure hose aside.

5. Remove upper camshaft timing belt cover and remove from engine cover.
6. Remove valve cover bolts, starting from outside of valve cover and working to inside of valve cover, then the valve cover with gasket from cylinder head, **Fig. 13.**
7. Inspect valve cover gasket and O-rings for damage or signs of leakage. Replace gasket and O-rings if necessary.
8. Reverse procedure to install, noting the following:
   a. **Torque** valve cover bolts, beginning in center of valve cover and working to outside of valve cover, to 53-71 inch lbs.
   b. Tighten upper camshaft timing belt cover bolts to specifications.
   c. Securely tighten power steering pressure hose bracket bolt and nut.

VALVE CLEARANCE SPECIFICATIONS

Valve clearance is automatically controlled and not adjustable.

VALVE ADJUSTMENT

The valve to camshaft lobe clearance is not adjustable. However, to measure valve clearance, it is important that all valve components be in a serviceable condition and installed and tightened properly.

If the valve face runout is excessive and/or it is necessary to remove pits and grooves, reface valves to a true 45 degree angle. Remove only enough stock to correct the runout or to clean up the pits and grooves. If the edges of the valve head are less than 1/32 inch thick after grinding, replace the valve as the valve will run too hot in the engine.

1. Inspect valve stem for bends and end of stem for grooves or scoring.
2. Inspect valve face and edge of valve head for pits, grooves or scores.

3. Check valve head for signs of burning or erosion, warpage and cracking. Minor pits, grooves, etc., may be removed. Replace severely damaged valves.
4. Inspect valve spring, valve spring retainers and valve spring retainer keys. Replace any visibly damaged parts.
5. Valve seat refacing should be closely coordinated with valve face refacing to ensure finished seat and valve face are concentric and to maintain specified interference angle. This is important so valve and seat will have compression-tight fit. Ensure refacer grinding wheels are properly dressed.
6. After seat has been refaced, measure seat contact width. Finished valve seat should contact approximate center of valve face. It is good practice to determine where valve seat contacts face.
7. Coat seat with Prussian Blue and set valve in place. Rotate valve with light pressure. If blue is transferred to center of valve face, contact is satisfactory. If blue is transferred to top edge of valve seat, lower valve seat. If blue is transferred to bottom edge of valve face, raise valve seat.
8. If valve seat width exceeds maximum limit, remove enough stock from top edge and/or bottom edge of seat to reduce width to specification.
9. On intake and exhaust seats, use 60 degree grinding wheel to remove stock from bottom of seat. A 30 degree angle wheel is used to remove stock from top of seats.

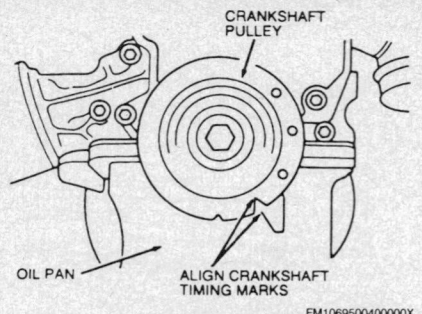

Fig. 14 Crankshaft alignment marks

FM1069500400000X

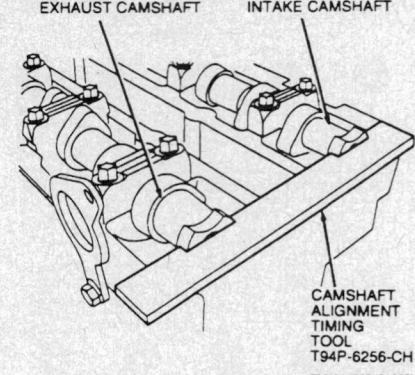

Fig. 15 Camshaft alignment

FM1069500401000X

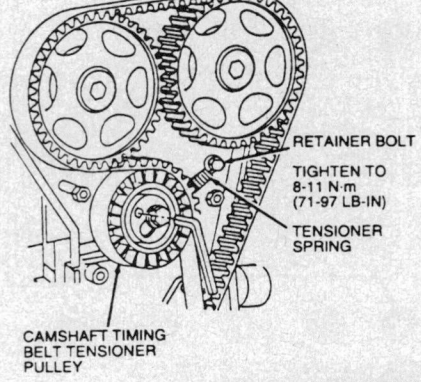

RETAINER BOLT
TIGHTEN TO
8-11 N·m
(71-97 LB-IN)
TENSIONER SPRING

CAMSHAFT TIMING BELT TENSIONER PULLEY

FM1069500402000X

Fig. 16 Timing belt installation

TIMING BELT
REPLACE
REMOVAL

1. Remove spark plugs, then rotate crankshaft to Top Dead Center (TDC) No. 1 cylinder. Position and align crankshaft timing marks to position all pistons below top of cylinder block deck face, **Fig. 14.**
2. Remove timing belt covers as described under "Timing Belt Cover, Replace."
3. Remove valve cover as described under "Valve Cover, Replace."
4. Using camshaft alignment timing tool No. T94P-6256-CH, or equivalent, align camshafts by installing tool into slots on camshafts at rear of engine, **Fig. 15.**
5. Loosen timing belt tensioner pulley bolt and move pulley to relieve tension on timing belt.
6. With tension relieved on timing belt, tighten tensioner pulley bolt securely while retaining position of pulley.
7. Mark direction of belt rotation, then remove belt.
8. Inspect belt for wear or damage. Replace as required.

INSTALLATION

1. Loosely install crankshaft pulley and verify crankshaft is at Top Dead Center (TDC) of No. 1 cylinder position, **Fig. 14.**
2. Verify camshafts are aligned using camshaft alignment timing tool No. T94P-6252-CH, or equivalent.
3. Install bolt and tensioner spring onto camshaft timing belt tensioner pulley and front of engine, **Fig. 16.** Tighten bolt to specifications. **Upon first service or replacement of camshaft timing belt, tensioner spring must be installed onto camshaft timing belt tensioner pulley (not supplied with engine, must be purchased separately) to obtain proper tension on camshaft timing belt. Failure to install tensioner spring may cause premature wear or failure of timing belt and possible damage to engine.**
4. Remove pulley and install belt onto

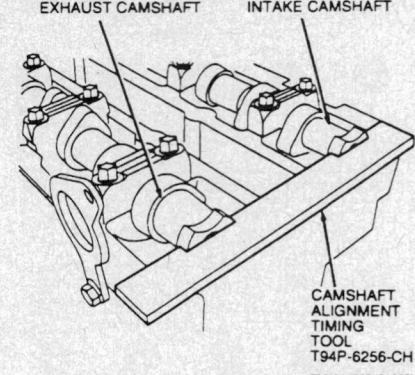

CYLINDER HEAD

CAMSHAFT SPROCKET HOLDING TOOL T74P-6256-B

CAMSHAFT SPROCKET

FM1069500403000X

Fig. 17 Camshaft sprocket holding tool installation

crankshaft sprocket and camshaft sprockets in counterclockwise direction.
5. Ensure span on belt from crankshaft sprocket to exhaust camshaft is not loose and timing belt is securely aligned on all sprockets.
6. Install lower timing belt cover and bolts. Tighten bolts to specifications.
7. Apply silicone gasket and sealer part No. F1AZ-19562-A or equivalent, to crankshaft keyway, then install crankshaft pulley and bolt. Tighten bolt to specifications.
8. Ensure crankshaft is at TDC No. 1 cylinder position, then loosen timing belt tensioner pulley bolt and allow spring attached to tensioner pulley to pull tensioner pulley against timing belt.
9. Remove camshaft alignment timing tool from camshafts, then turn crankshaft two revolutions in clockwise direction.
10. Tighten camshaft timing belt tensioner pulley bolt to specifications, then verify crankshaft is at TDC No. 1 cylinder and camshafts are aligned using timing tool, noting the following:
    a. If crankshaft and camshafts are slightly misaligned, the camshafts can be moved using camshaft sprocket holding tool No. T74P-6256-B, or equivalent, **Fig. 17,** so alignment timing tool can be installed. Crankshaft MUST remain at TDC No. 1 cylinder.
    b. Loosen camshaft sprocket to cam-

shaft bolt by holding camshaft sprocket in position with camshaft sprocket holding tool.
    c. Turn camshaft until timing tool can be installed.
11. Ensure crankshaft is at TDC position of No. 1 cylinder, then hold camshaft sprocket in position with holding tool, **Fig. 17,** then tighten camshaft sprocket bolt to specifications.
12. Remove tools and turn crankshaft clockwise two revolutions. Verify alignment of camshafts to crankshaft.
13. Install center and upper timing belt covers as described under "Timing Belt Cover, Replace."
14. Install valve cover as described under "Valve Cover, Replace."
15. Install spark plugs.

TIMING BELT COVER
REPLACE

Refer to **Fig. 18** when replacing timing belt cover.

1. Remove engine air intake resonators as described under "Engine Air Intake Resonators, Replace."
2. Disconnect power steering pressure hose bracket from engine lifting eye and position bracket aside.
3. Remove upper camshaft timing belt cover bolts, then the cover from engine.
4. Mark location of upper front engine support bracket, then remove bracket nuts and bracket from upper front engine support insulator.
5. Disconnect wire harness from low coolant level sensor connector at radiator coolant recovery reservoir.
6. Remove radiator coolant recovery reservoir retainers and position reservoir aside.
7. Remove upper front engine support insulator as described under "Engine Mount, Replace."
8. Set radiator coolant recovery reservoir into position, then loosely install bolt.
9. Loosen water pump pulley bolts. Do not remove bolts completely.

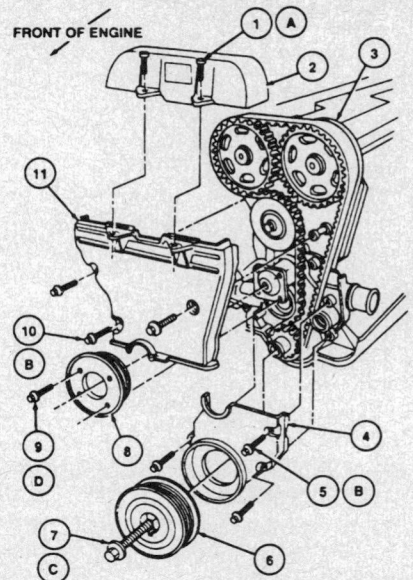

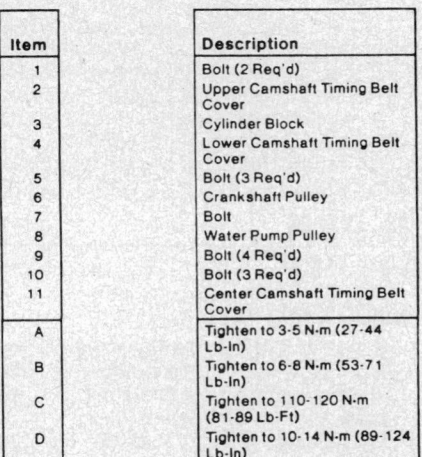

Item	Description
1	Bolt (2 Req'd)
2	Upper Camshaft Timing Belt Cover
3	Cylinder Block
4	Lower Camshaft Timing Belt Cover
5	Bolt (3 Req'd)
6	Crankshaft Pulley
7	Bolt
8	Water Pump Pulley
9	Bolt (4 Req'd)
10	Bolt (3 Req'd)
11	Center Camshaft Timing Belt Cover
A	Tighten to 3-5 N·m (27-44 Lb-In)
B	Tighten to 6-8 N·m (53-71 Lb-In)
C	Tighten to 110-120 N·m (81-89 Lb-Ft)
D	Tighten to 10-14 N·m (89-124 Lb-In)

FM1069500404000X

Fig. 18 Timing belt cover replacement

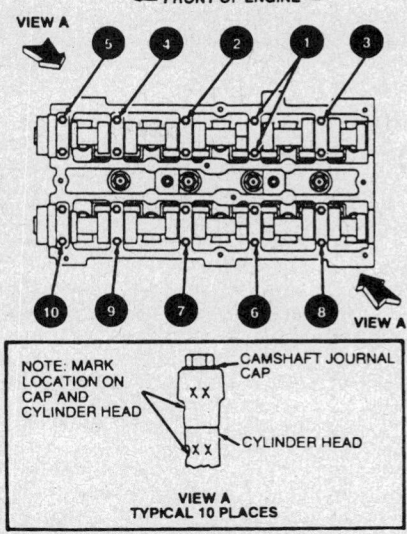

NOTE: MARK LOCATION ON CAP AND CYLINDER HEAD — CAMSHAFT JOURNAL CAP

CYLINDER HEAD

VIEW A
TYPICAL 10 PLACES

● LOOSEN BOLTS IN SEQUENCE SHOWN

FM1069500405000X

Fig. 19 Cylinder head camshaft journal cap removal sequence

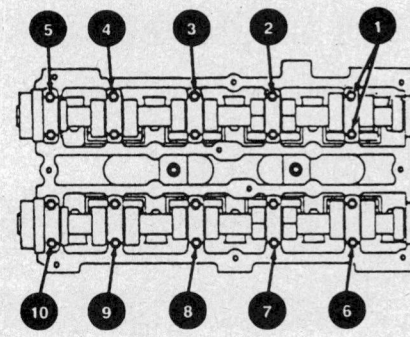

● TIGHTEN BOLTS IN SEQUENCE SHOWN

FM1069500407000X

Fig. 21 Cylinder head camshaft journal cap tightening sequence

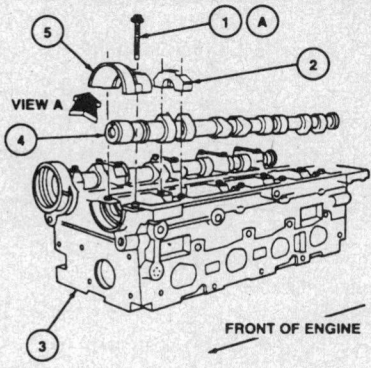

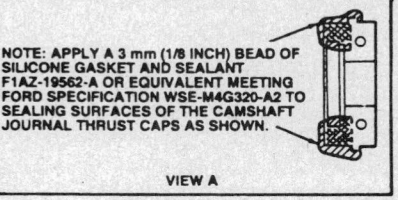

NOTE: APPLY A 3 mm (1/8 INCH) BEAD OF SILICONE GASKET AND SEALANT F1AZ-19562-A OR EQUIVALENT MEETING FORD SPECIFICATION WSE-M4G320-A2 TO SEALING SURFACES OF THE CAMSHAFT JOURNAL THRUST CAPS AS SHOWN.

VIEW A

Item	Description
1	Bolt (20 Req'd)
2	Camshaft Journal Cap (8 Req'd)
3	Cylinder Head
4	Camshaft
5	Camshaft Journal Thrust Cap (2 Req'd)
A	Tighten to 17-21 N·m (13-15 Lb-Ft)

FM1069500406000X

Fig. 20 Camshaft replacement

10. Remove serpentine drive belt as described under "Serpentine Drive Belt."
11. Remove drive belt idler pulley bolt and pulley from alternator bracket, then the water pump pulley from water pump.
12. Remove center timing belt cover bolts, then the cover from engine.
13. Raise and support vehicle, then remove crankshaft pulley.
14. Remove lower timing belt cover bolts and lower cover from engine.
15. Reverse procedure to install.

CAMSHAFT

REPLACE

REMOVAL

1. Remove timing belt as described under "Timing Belt, Replace."
2. Remove camshaft sprockets.
3. Remove valve cover as described under "Valve Cover, Replace."

4. Mark cylinder head camshaft journal cap number on outside edge of camshaft journal caps and cylinder head. **Cylinder head camshaft journal caps and cylinder head should be numbered to ensure they are assembled in original positions. Keep camshaft journal caps from cylinder head together. Do not mix with camshaft journal caps from another cylinder head. Failure to do so may result in engine damage.**
5. Remove cylinder head camshaft journal cap bolts in pairs, loosening one turn at a time, beginning at rear of cylinder head, **Fig. 19**, noting the following:
   a. Remove cylinder head camshaft journal thrust caps last to ensure proper camshaft position in cylinder head.
   b. Remove camshaft journal thrust cap last.
6. Remove intake and exhaust camshaft and camshaft front seals from cylinder head, **Fig. 20**.
7. Inspect camshafts and cylinder head for wear or damage. Replace components as required.

INSTALLATION

1. Ensure crankshaft is at Top Dead Center (TDC) No. 1 cylinder.
2. Lubricate camshafts with engine assembly lubricant part No. D9AZ-19579-D or equivalent.
3. Install camshafts into cylinder head. Camshafts are marked for identification. Intake camshaft also has additional cam lobe for camshaft position sensor.
4. Apply 1/8 inch bead of silicone gasket and sealant part No. F1AZ-19562-A or equivalent, to sealing surfaces of camshaft journal thrust caps and cylinder head.
5. Loosely install cylinder head camshaft journal caps and bolts. **Install camshaft journal thrust caps last.**
6. **Torque** cylinder head camshaft journal cap bolts in sequence, **Fig. 21**, in several steps, with final step to 13-15 ft. lbs.
7. Install valve cover as described under "Valve Cover, Replace."
8. Install camshaft front seals as de-

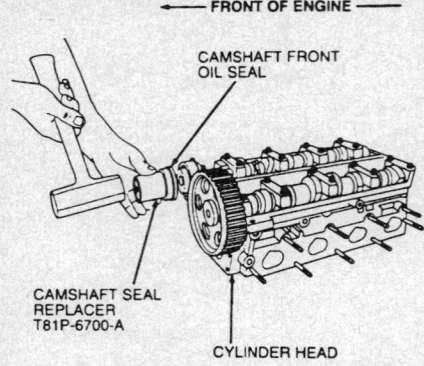

Fig. 22 Camshaft front seal installation

scribed under "Camshaft Front Seals, Replace."
9. Install camshaft sprockets.
10. Install timing belt as described under "Timing Belt, Replace."

CAMSHAFT FRONT SEALS
REPLACE

1. Remove timing belt as described under "Timing Belt, Replace."
2. Remove camshaft sprockets, then, using seal remover tool No. T92C-6700-CH, or equivalent, remove camshaft front oil seal from camshaft journal thrust caps.
3. Lubricate camshaft front oil seals with clean engine oil.
4. Using camshaft seal replacer tool No. T81P-6700-A, or equivalent, and rubber mallet, install camshaft front oil seals into camshaft journal thrust caps, **Fig. 22.**
5. Install camshaft sprockets.
6. Install timing belt as described under "Timing Belt, Replace."

CRANKSHAFT SEAL
REPLACE

1. Remove timing belt as described under "Timing Belt, Replace," then the camshaft sprocket.
2. Using seal remover tool No. T92C-6700-CH, or equivalent, remove crankshaft front seal from oil pump.
3. Clean and inspect oil pump crankshaft front seal bore.
4. Lubricate oil pump crankshaft front seal bore and crankshaft front seal with engine assembly lubricant D9AZ-19579-D or equivalent.
5. Using oil pump seal replacer tool No. T81P-6700-A, or equivalent, install crankshaft front seal into oil pump.
6. Install crankshaft timing sprocket, then the timing belt as described under "Timing Belt, Replace."

CRANKSHAFT REAR OIL SEAL
REPLACE

A one-piece crankshaft rear oil seal is used for replacement on all engines. If replacement is necessary, this type of crankshaft rear oil seal must be used. The complete crankshaft rear oil seal can be replaced without removing the crankshaft.

REMOVAL

1. Remove flywheel as follows:
    a. **On models equipped with automatic transaxle,** remove transaxle as described in "Automatic Transaxle/Transmission" section for automatic transaxle.
    b. **On models equipped with manual transaxle,** remove transaxle, then the clutch pressure plate and clutch disc as described under "Clutch & Manual Transaxle."
    c. **On all models,** observe position of flywheel on crankshaft flange, then remove flywheel bolts, flywheel and reinforcement plate.
2. Using sharp awl, punch hole in crankshaft rear oil seal metal surface between seal lip and seal retainer.
3. Screw in threaded end of jet plug remover tool No. T77L-9533-B, or equivalent, into oil seal and remove seal from retainer.
4. If necessary, remove crankshaft rear oil seal retainer, proceed as follows:
    a. Remove oil pan as described under "Oil Pan, Replace."
    b. Remove crankshaft rear oil seal retainer to cylinder block bolts, then the seal retainer and retainer gasket.

INSTALLATION

1. Clean and inspect crankshaft and cylinder block sealing surfaces, then clean and inspect seal retainer and cylinder block sealing surface. Remove gasket material with wire brush if necessary, using care to prevent damaging sealing surfaces.
2. Install seal retainer with new gasket flush to cylinder block at oil pan sealing surface using straight edge. Install and tighten bolts. Cylinder block oil pan sealing surface to crankshaft rear oil seal retainer oil pan sealing surface clearance should not exceed .012-.031 inch.
3. Lubricate crankshaft flange and crankshaft rear oil seal bore with engine assembly lubricant D9AZ-19579-D or equivalent.
4. Install seal using crankshaft rear seal replacer tool No. T88P-6701-B1 and rubber mallet, **Fig. 23.** Seat seal .02-0.0 inch flush to rear of retainer.
5. Install flywheel as follows:
    a. Coat flywheel bolt threads with oil resistant pipe sealant with Teflon part No. D8AZ-019554-A or equivalent, then position flywheel on crankshaft position.
    b. **On models equipped with automatic transaxle,** install flywheel reinforcement plate.
    c. **On all models,** install and tighten bolts to specifications in alternating sequence.

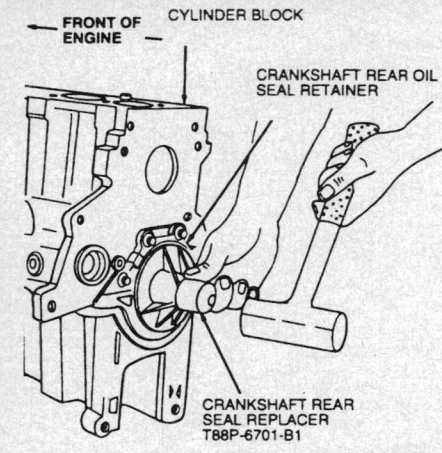

Fig. 23 Crankshaft rear oil seal installation

    d. Check flywheel runout.
    e. **On models equipped with manual transaxle,** install clutch disc and clutch pressure plate, then the transaxle as described under "Clutch & Manual Transaxle."
    f. **On models equipped with automatic transaxle,** install transaxle as described in "Automatic Transaxle/Transmission" section.
6. **On all models,** run engine and check for leaks.

OIL PAN
REPLACE

REMOVAL

1. Install three bar engine support tool No. D88L-6000-A, or equivalent, onto engine lifting eyes, then support engine.
2. Raise and support vehicle, then remove three way catalytic converter as follows:
    a. Remove outlet flange nuts, then the muffler and converter outlet gasket from converter.
    b. Remove EGR valve to exhaust manifold tube, bracket and clamp from converter.
    c. Lower vehicle, then remove heat shield and converter nuts from exhaust manifold.
    d. Remove converter and converter inlet gasket from exhaust manifold. Discard inlet gasket.
3. Disconnect engine control sensor wiring from low oil level sensor.
4. Remove heater water tube bolt from bottom of oil pan and position heater water tube aside.
5. Remove engine oil pan drain plug and drain oil from engine, then install drain plug with new gasket and tighten to specifications.
6. Remove oil pan bolts from transaxle housing, then the lower engine rear plate.
7. Remove lefthand and righthand front engine support insulator through bolts as described under "Engine Mount, Replace."
8. Lower vehicle.

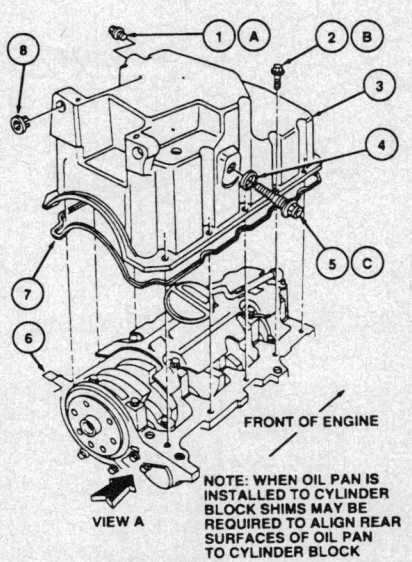

VIEW A

NOTE: WHEN OIL PAN IS INSTALLED TO CYLINDER BLOCK SHIMS MAY BE REQUIRED TO ALIGN REAR SURFACES OF OIL PAN TO CYLINDER BLOCK

3 mm (1/8 INCH)

SEALER

NOTE: APPLY A 3 mm (1/8 INCH) BEAD OF SILICONE GASKET AND SEALANT F1AZ-19562-A OR EQUIVALENT MEETING FORD SPECIFICATION WSE-M4G320-A2

VIEW A
TYPICAL 4 PLACES

Item	Description
1	Oil Pan Drain Plug
2	Bolt (10 Req'd)
3	Oil Pan
4	Low Oil Level Sensor Washer
5	Low Oil Level Sensor
6	Cylinder Block
7	Oil Pan Gasket
8	Oil Pan Spacer (As Req'd)
A	Tighten to 21-28 N·m (15-21 Lb-Ft)
B	Tighten to 20-24 N·m (15-18 Lb-Ft)
C	Tighten to 20-34 N·m (15-25 Lb-Ft)

FM1099500070000X

Fig. 24 Oil pan installation

9. Mark location of upper front engine support bracket, then remove bracket from upper front engine support insulator.
10. Raise engine to gain access for oil pan removal, supporting engine with engine support tool.
11. Raise and support vehicle, then remove oil pan bolts from cylinder block.
12. Remove oil pan and oil pan gasket.

INSTALLATION

1. Clean oil pan with suitable soap and water solution. Dry completely with compressed air and inspect oil pan for damage. Replace oil pan as necessary.
2. Clean oil pan to cylinder block sealing surfaces on oil pan and cylinder block with shop towel and metal brake parts cleaner part No. E6AZ-19579-BA or equivalent.
3. Apply 1/8 inch bead of silicone gasket and sealant part No. F1AZ-19562-A

or equivalent, to parting lines of oil pump and crankshaft rear main seal retainer on cylinder block at oil pan sealing surfaces, **Fig. 24.**
4. Install oil pan gasket, oil pan and bolts to cylinder, pushing oil pan flush against transaxle case. Tighten oil pan bolts to specifications.
5. Install lower engine rear plate. Tighten bolts to specifications.
6. Lower vehicle, then lower engine into position and support with three bar engine support tool No. D88L-6000-A, or equivalent.
7. Install lefthand and righthand front engine support insulator through bolts as described under "Engine Mount, Replace."
8. Connect engine control sensor wiring to low oil level sensor.
9. Install heater water tube and bolt to bottom of oil pan. Tighten bolt to specifications.
10. Install catalytic converter as follows:
    a. Loosely install converter to exhaust manifold using new converter inlet gasket.
    b. Position muffler and converter outlet gasket onto converter and loosely install retainers onto converter outlet flange studs.
    c. Align exhaust system, ensuring muffler and converter are fully engaged. Tighten all nuts and bolts, starting at front of system, to specifications.
    d. Install EGR valve to exhaust manifold tube to converter.
11. Lower vehicle, then remove engine support.
12. Fill crankcase to proper level with specified engine oil, then run engine and check for leaks.

OIL PUMP
REPLACE

1. Remove timing belt covers as described under "Timing Belt Cover, Replace."
2. Remove timing belt as described under "Timing Belt, Replace," then the crankshaft sprocket.
3. Remove oil pan as described under "Oil Pan, Replace," then the oil pump screen cover and tube as described under "Oil Pump Service."
4. Remove oil bypass filter.
5. Remove oil pump bolts, then the pump from cylinder block. Inspect pump and replace as necessary.
6. Reverse procedure to install, noting the following:
    a. Clean oil pump to cylinder block gasket sealing surfaces with wire brush. Use care to prevent damaging sealing surfaces.
    b. Rotate oil pump inner rotor to align with flats on crankshaft, then install pump with new gasket flush to cylinder block at oil pan sealing surface, using straight edge. Clearance between oil pan and oil pump sealing surfaces should not exceed .012-.031 inch.

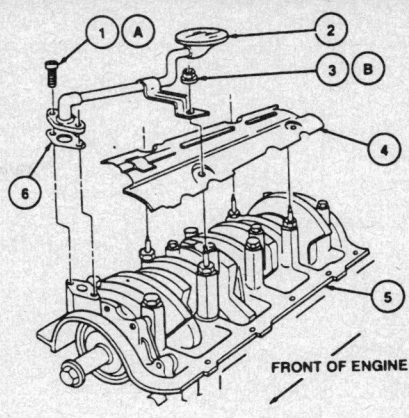

FRONT OF ENGINE

Item	Description
1	Bolt (2 Req'd)
2	Oil Pump Screen Cover and Tube
3	Nut (4 Req'd)
4	Oil Pan Baffle
5	Cylinder Block
6	Oil Pump Inlet Tube Gasket
A	Tighten to 8-11 N·m (71-97 Lb-In)
B	Tighten to 17-21 N·m (13-15 Lb-Ft)

FM1099500071000X

Fig. 25 Oil pump screen cover & tube replacement

c. Fill crankcase to proper level with specified engine oil, then run engine and check for leaks.

OIL PUMP SERVICE

OIL PUMP SCREEN COVER & TUBE, REPLACE

1. Remove oil pan as described under "Oil Pan, Replace."
2. Remove oil pump screen cover and tube nut from crankshaft main bearing cap stud bolt.
3. Remove oil pump screen cover and tube bolts from oil pump, then the screen cover and tube from engine, **Fig. 25.**
4. Inspect screen cover and tube and oil pump inlet tube gasket for damage and wear. Replace components as necessary.
5. Reverse procedure to install. Install new screen cover and tube support nut to crankshaft main bearing cap stud bolt, then tighten to specifications.

BELT TENSION DATA

Drive belts have an automatic drive belt tensioner and do not require adjustment.

The automatic belt tensioner is a spring loaded device which sets and maintains the drive belt tension. The drive belt should not require tension adjustment for the life of the drive belt.

The automatic belt tensioner has a drive belt wear indicator mark, **Fig. 26.** If the indicator mark is not approximately in the middle between the tabs on the front cover, the belt is worn or an incorrect belt is installed.

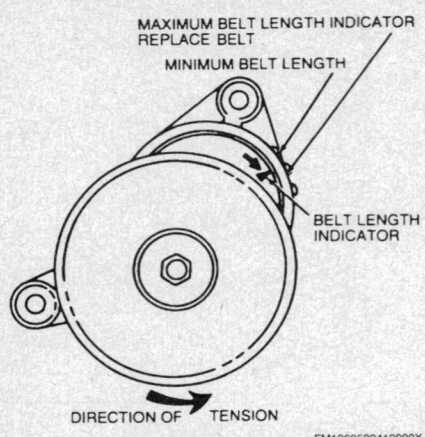

Fig. 26 Drive belt wear indicator mark

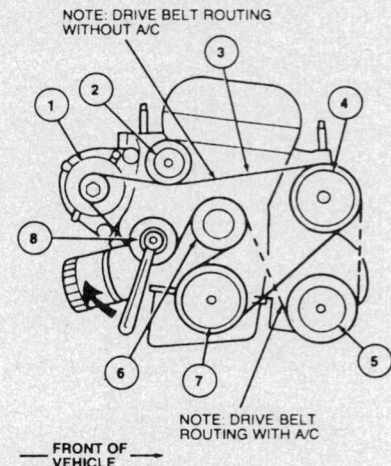

Item	Description
1	Generator
2	Drivebelt Idler Pulley
3	Accessory Drive Belt
4	Power Steering Pump Pulley
5	A/C Compressor
6	Water Pump Pulley
7	Crankshaft Pulley
8	Drive Belt Tensioner

Fig. 27 Drive belt routing

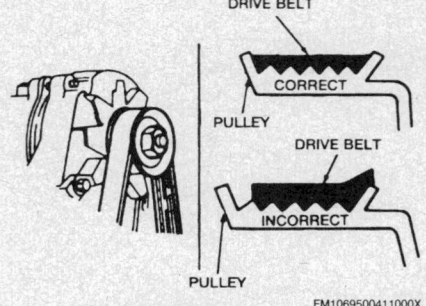

Fig. 28 Drive belt installation

SERPENTINE DRIVE BELT

ROUTING

Refer to **Fig. 27** for belt routing.

BELT, REPLACE

Minor cracks in the V-grooved portion of the drive belt are considered normal and acceptable. If the drive belt has chunks missing from the ribs, the drive belt should be replaced.

Conditions requiring drive belt replacement are rib chunk out, severe glazing, frayed cords, etc. Replace any drive belt exhibiting one of these conditions.
1. Raise and support vehicle.
2. Loosen drive belt tensioner with 13 mm wrench attached to pulley mounting bolt and rotate drive belt tensioner away from accessory drive belt.
3. Lift belt over pulley flanges and remove.
4. Position drive belt over top of tensioner pulley
5. Install drive belt onto rest of pulleys, then rotate drive belt tensioner clockwise and install drive belt on last pulley. Ensure drive belt is properly installed on each pulley, with all V-grooves making proper contact with each pulley, **Fig. 28.**

TENSIONER, REPLACE

1. Remove drive belt as described under "Belt Replacement."
2. Loosen belt tensioner bolts completely, then remove tensioner from front of engine.
3. Install tensioner and bolts to front of engine, then tighten bolts to specifications.
4. Install drive belt as described under "Belt Replacement."

COOLING SYSTEM BLEED

Never remove pressure relief cap under any conditions while engine is op- **erating. Failure to follow these instructions could result in personal injury and/or damage to the cooling system or engine.**

To avoid burns from scalding coolant or steam, use extreme care when removing the pressure relief cap.
1. Bring engine to normal operating temperature, then turn engine off.
2. Drain cooling system as follows:
   a. If cooling system is still hot, carefully wrap thick cloth around pressure relief cap and rotate slowly until pressure begins to release. Step back until pressure is released.
   b. Rotate pressure relief cap until free, then remove cap.
   c. Raise and support vehicle, then remove splash shield from front of front subframe.
   d. Open radiator draincock and drain coolant system, then remove inlet and outlet heater water hoses from heater core.
   e. Carefully use compressed air, blow regulated 10 psi of air pressure into heater core to ensure coolant is drained from core.
3. Fill cooling system as follows:
   a. Install all cooling system hoses previously removed, then check all hose clamps for proper tightness.
   b. Ensure radiator draincock is closed, then install splash shield onto front of front subframe and body.
   c. Lower vehicle, then add 50/50 mixture of specified coolant and

water into radiator coolant recovery reservoir fill neck until coolant mixture reaches MAX mark on radiator coolant recovery reservoir. **Some coolant/water will be retained in cylinder block if cylinder block drain plugs are not removed. When refilling cooling system after flushing, adjust coolant mix ratio to obtain 50/50 mixture. Be certain to account for approximately 1.06 quarts of water left in cylinder block when drain plugs are not removed.**
   d. Install pressure relief cap to radiator coolant recovery reservoir.
4. Bleed cooling system as follows:
   a. Select maximum heater temperature and blower motor speed settings, then position control to discharge air at A/C vents in instrument panel.
   b. Start engine and allow to idle. While engine is idling, feel for hot air at A/C vents.
   c. Start engine and allow to idle until normal operating temperature is reached. Hot air should discharge form A/C vents. Engine coolant temperature gauge should maintain a stabilized reading in middle of NORMAL range and upper radiator hose should feel hot to touch. **If air discharge remains cool and engine coolant temperature gauge does not move, engine coolant level is low in engine and must be filled. Stop engine, allow to cool and fill cooling system as outlined.**
   d. Check engine coolant level in radiator coolant recovery reservoir and fill as necessary. When engine coolant level indicator flashes, approximately 1-1.5 quarts of coolant mixture can be added to radiator coolant recovery reservoir after proper engine coolant system refill.

THERMOSTAT
REPLACE

1. Remove engine air intake resonators as described under "Engine Air Intake Resonators."
2. Drain engine cooling system so engine coolant level is below thermostat,

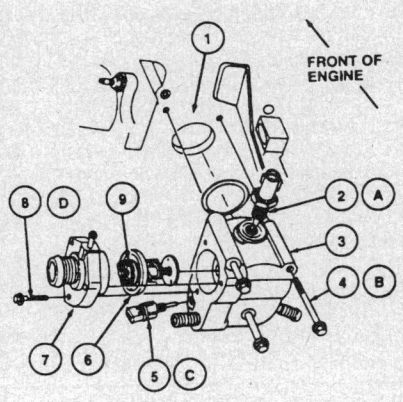

Item	Description
1	Cylinder Block
2	Engine Coolant Temperature Sensor
3	Water Thermostat Housing
4	Bolt (3 Req'd)
5	Water Temperature Indicator Sender Unit
6	O-Ring
7	Water Hose Connection
8	Bolt (3 Req'd)
9	Water Thermostat
A	Tighten to 10-14 N·m (89-124 Lb-In)
B	Tighten to 18-22 N·m (13-16 Lb-Ft)
C	Tighten to 7-10 N·m (62-89 Lb-In)
D	Tighten to 8-11 N·m (71-97 Lb-In)

FM1089500091000X

Fig. 29   Thermostat replacement

as described under "Cooling System Bleed," then disconnect upper radiator hose and radiator overflow hose from water hose connection.

3. Remove water outlet connection bolts, then the connection from thermostat housing, **Fig. 29.**
4. Remove thermostat and seal from housing. Inspect seal for damage and replace if necessary.
5. Reverse procedure to install, noting the following:
   a. Tighten water hose connection bolts to specifications.
   b. Fill cooling system with 50/50 mixture of water and specified coolant as described under "Cooling System Bleed."

WATER PUMP
REPLACE

1. Drain engine cooling system as described under "Cooling System Bleed," then raise and support vehicle.
2. Remove lower radiator hose form water pump, then lower vehicle.
3. Remove timing belt as described under "Timing Belt, Replace."
4. Remove water pump bolts, water pump housing gasket and water pump from cylinder block, **Fig. 30.** Inspect water pump and hoses for wear or damage and replace components as required.

5. Reverse procedure to install, noting the following:
   a. Clean water pump and cylinder block gasket sealing surfaces with wire brush.
   b. Install new water pump housing gasket.
   c. Lubricate lower radiator hose with silicone lubricant part No. D7AZ-19553-AA, or equivalent before installing hose to water pump.
   d. Fill engine cooling system with 50/50 mixture of water and specified coolant as described under "Cooling System Bleed," then run engine and check for coolant leaks.

RADIATOR
REPLACE

1. Drain engine cooling system as described under "Cooling System Bleed, then disconnect battery ground cable.
2. Remove upper radiator hose from radiator.
3. **On models equipped with 2.5L/V6-153 engine,** remove radiator overflow hose from radiator.
4. **On models equipped with automatic transaxle,** remove transaxle oil cooler tube from oil cooler inlet fitting.
5. **On all models,** remove fan shroud to radiator nut, then raise and support vehicle.
6. Remove lower radiator hose from radiator.
7. **On models equipped with automatic transaxle,** remove oil cooler tube from oil cooler outlet fitting on radiator by loosening tubes while holding connector with back-up wrench.
8. **On all models,** support fan shroud, radiator and A/C condenser core with suitable jack stand, then remove lower radiator supports from front subframe and radiator.
9. Position jack stands aside and carefully remove radiator.
10. Reverse procedure to install. Tighten bolts and fitting to specifications, then refill cooling system with 50/50 mixture of water and specified coolant as described under "Cooling System Bleed."

FUEL PUMP
REPLACE
REMOVAL

1. Relieve fuel system pressure as described under "Precautions."
2. Remove rear seat cushion.
3. Remove plastic grommet from floor pan, then disconnect fuel pump module electrical connector.
4. Disconnect fuel and vapor return tubes from fuel pump module. Disconnect fuel lines by compressing tabs on both sides of each nylon push con-

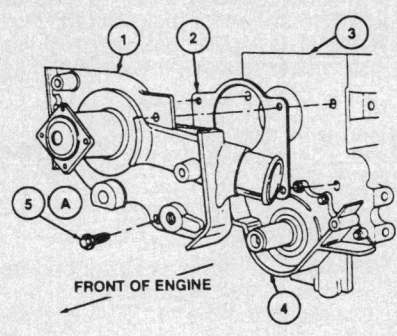

Item	Description
1	Water Pump
2	Water Pump Housing Gaskets
3	Cylinder Block
4	Oil Pump
5	Bolt (4 Req'd)
A	Tighten to 16-20 N·m (12-15 Lb-Ft)

FM1089500092000X

Fig. 30   Water pump replacement

nect fitting and ease fuel line out of module.
5. Turn pump locking retainer ring counterclockwise using fuel tank sender wrench tool No. D84P-9275-A, or equivalent.
6. Remove fuel pump module, then immediately cover opening in fuel tank in order to prevent fuel system contamination.
7. Remove fuel pump module O-ring seal and discard.

INSTALLATION

1. Clean fuel pump module mounting flange and mounting surface, then the O-ring seal groove on fuel tank. When cleaning module mounting surface on tank, use caution to prevent any foreign material from entering fuel system.
2. Apply light coat of premium long-life grease part No. XG-1-C,-K or equivalent, on new O-ring seal, then install seal to groove on fuel tank.
3. Install fuel pump module carefully to ensure filter is not damaged. Ensure locating keys are in keyways and O-ring seal remains in place.
4. Hold fuel pump module in place and install fuel pump locking retainer ring finger-tight. Ensure all locking tabs are under fuel tank lock ring tabs.
5. Secure fuel pump locking retainer ring by rotating clockwise, using wrench tool until fuel pump locking retainer ring rests against stops.
6. Connect fuel and vapor return tubes to fuel pump module, then the module electrical connector.
7. Install plastic grommet in floor pan, then the rear seat cushion.
8. Install multi-port fuel pressure gauge tool No. T80L-9974-B, or equivalent, to fuel pressure relief valve cap on fuel supply injection manifold.
9. Turn ignition switch to Run position for three seconds, five to 10 times un-

til pressure gauge reads at least 30 psi, then check for leaks at fittings.
10. Remove pressure gauge, then start engine and recheck for leaks.

FUEL FILTER
REPLACE

IN-TANK
1. Remove fuel pump as described under "Fuel Pump, Replace."
2. Remove filter mounted on fuel pump inlet.
3. Reverse procedure to install.

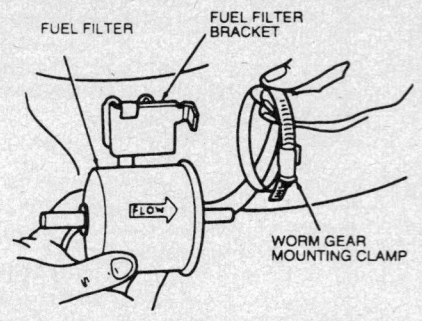

FM1029500156000X

Fig. 31 In-line fuel filter replacement

IN-LINE
1. Relieve fuel system pressure as described under "Precautions."
2. Remove push connect fittings at both ends of fuel filter, then install retainer clips in each connect fitting.
3. Remove fuel filter from bracket by loosening worm gear mounting clamp enough to allow filter to pass through, Fig. 31.
4. Reverse procedure to install, noting the following:
   a. Locate fuel filter against tab at lower end of bracket, ensuring proper direction of fuel flow, Fig. 31.
   b. Tighten worm gear mounting clamp to specifications.

TIGHTENING SPECIFICATIONS

Year	Component	Torque/Ft. Lbs.
1995	Accelerator Cable Bracket	71-106 ①
	Air Cleaner Bracket	15-22
	Battery Ground Cable To Engine At Transaxle Stud Bolt Nut	15-22
	Camshaft Sprocket Bolt	47-53
	Catalytic Converter Bracket Bolts	71-106 ①
	Catalytic Converter Clamp Bolt	15-22
	Center & Lower Timing Belt Cover Bolts	53-71 ①
	Crankshaft Pulley Bolt	81-89
	Cylinder Head Bolts	②
	Cylinder Head Camshaft Journal Cap	②
	Drive Belt Idler Pulley Bolt	35
	Drive Belt Tensioner Bolts	15-22
	EGR Valve To Exhaust Manifold Tube Nut	44
	Engine Air cleaner Tube Clamps	24-48 ①
	Engine & Transaxle Support Insulator Nuts	②
	Engine & Transaxle Support Insulator To Front Fender Apron Bolts	52-70
	Engine Lifting Eye	⑥
	Engine Rear Plate Bolts	79-86 ③
	Exhaust Manifold Heat Shield Nuts	71-106 ①
	Exhaust Manifold Nuts	13-16
	Exhaust Manifold Shield Retainers	71-106 ①
	Flywheel Bolts	④
	Flywheel Nuts	54-64 ③
	Front Engine Support Bracket To Front Sub-Frame Bolts	20
	Front Engine Support Bracket To Transaxle Bolts	⑤
	Front Engine Support Insulator Bolt	②
	Front Engine Support Insulator Through Bolt	75-102
	Front Stabilizer Bar Link To Stabilizer Bar Nuts	35
	Heated Oxygen Sensor	44
	Heater Water Tube Bolt	71-106 ①
	Lower Engine Rear Plate Bolts	71-106 ③
	Oil Level Indicator Tube Bolt	71-106 ①
	Oil Pan Drain Plug	15-21
	Oil Pan To Transaxle Case Bolts	15-18

Year	Component	Torque/Ft. Lbs.
1995	Oil Pan To Transaxle Housing Bolts	25-34
	Oil Pump Screen Cover & Tube Bolts	71-97 ①
	Power Steering Pump Mounting Bracket Support Bracket Bolts	29-41
	Radiator Coolant Recovery Reservoir Bolts	71-106 ①
	Radiator Supports To Front Sub-Frame Bolts	71-97 ①
	Righthand Front Engine Support Insulator Through Bolt	75-102
	Self-Locking Oil Pump Screen Cover & Tube Support Nut	13-15
	Shift Cable Bracket Bolts	15-19
	Shift Rod Bolt	17
	Stabilizer Nut	41
	Steering Shaft To Joint Bolt	18
	Three Way Catalytic Converter To Exhaust Manifold Nuts	26-33
	Throttle Body Bolts & Nuts	71-106 ①
	Tie Rod End Stud Nuts	②
	Timing Belt Pulley	26-30
	Timing Belt Tensioner Pulley	71-97 ①
	Transaxle Oil cooler Lines	18-22
	Transaxle To Engine Bolts	25-34
	Upper Front Engine Support Bolts	52-70
	Upper Front Engine Support Bracket Self-Locking Nuts	②
	Upper Timing Belt Cover Bolts	27-44 ①
	Valve Cover Bolts	②
	Water Hose Connection Bolts	71-97
	Water Pump Pulley Bolts	89-124
	Wheel Knuckle To Lower Arm Bolts	37-43
	Wheel Lug Nuts	95
	Worm Gear Mounting Clamp	15-25 ①

① —Inch lbs.
② —Refer to text.
③ —Tighten in alternating sequence.
④ —Automatic transaxle, 79–86 ft. lbs.; manual transaxle, 81–89 ft. lbs.
⑤ —Lefthand side, 30–40 ft. lbs.; righthand side, 40–55 ft. lbs.
⑥ —Lefthand side, 10–13 ft. lbs.; righthand side, 30–40 ft. lbs.

2.5L/V6-153 Engine

NOTE: Refer To "Air Bag System Precautions" Located In The Front Of This Manual For System Disarming & Arming Procedures.

INDEX

PRECAUTIONS

AIR BAG SYSTEMS

Refer to "Air Bag System Precautions" in the front of this manual for system disarming and arming procedures.

COOLING SYSTEM

This engine has an aluminum cylinder head and requires a special corrosion inhibiting coolant to avoid cooling system damage. Use only specified coolant in this engine.

FUEL SYSTEM PRESSURE RELIEF

Fuel supply lines will remain pressurized for long periods of time after engine shutdown. The pressure must be relieved before servicing the fuel system.
1. Remove engine air cleaner as follows:
   a. Remove engine air intake resonators as described under "Engine Air Intake Resonators, Replace."
   b. Disconnect engine control sensor wiring connectors from Mass Air Flow (MAF) sensor and Intake Air Temperature (IAT) sensor.
   c. Remove engine air cleaner to body O-ring retainer.
   d. Remove engine air cleaner body and intake tube from bracket and intake tube and duct.
2. Connect Multi-Port Fuel Injection (MFI) fuel pressure gauge tool No. T80L-9974-B, or equivalent, to fuel pressure relief valve cap on fuel injection supply manifold.
3. Open manual valve on gauge tool to relieve fuel system pressure.

ENGINE MOUNT
REPLACE
UPPER
Removal

1. Remove water pump pulley shield screws, then the shield.
2. Install three bar engine support tool No. D88L-6000-A, or equivalent, to existing engine lifting eyes and support engine.
3. Disconnect engine control sensor wiring from power steering pump switch connector, then remove power steering pressure hose bracket bolt from upper front engine support bracket.
4. Place towel below power steering pressure hose line to pump connection, then disconnect pressure hose from pump and position hose aside. **Do not allow power steering fluid to contact drive belt. Damage to drive belt may result.**
5. Position ignition wires away from upper front engine support bracket.
6. Remove front engine support self-locking nuts and discard nuts. **Engine support nuts are self-locking and must be replaced with new self-locking nuts when serviced.**
7. Remove upper front engine support bracket from vehicle.
8. Remove radiator coolant recovery reservoir bolts and position radiator coolant recovery reservoir aside to allow clearance for upper front engine support insulator removal.
9. Remove front engine support insulator bolts, then the insulator from righthand front fender apron, **Fig. 1.**

Installation

If the upper front engine support insulator or front engine support bracket has been removed, the engine and transaxle position must be realigned to front subframe. Failure to realign engine and transaxle may result in possible component damage.
1. Raise and support vehicle, then remove two front subframe through bolt bolts and lefthand front engine support insulator.
2. Install powertrain alignment gauge tool No. T94P-6000-AH, or equivalent, to transaxle bracket and front subframe, **Fig. 2. Torque vertical bolts and through bolt to 20 ft. lbs.**
3. Loosen righthand front engine support insulator through bolt, then lower vehicle.
4. Position power steering hose bracket and return hose onto upper front support insulator, then install upper front engine support insulator and bolts to righthand front fender apron. Tighten bolts to specifications.
5. Position radiator coolant recovery reservoir. Tighten bolts to specifications.
6. Install upper front engine support bracket onto engine and upper front engine support insulator. **Torque** new self-locking upper front engine support bracket nuts to 7 ft. lbs. **Engine support nuts are self-locking and must be replaced with new self-locking nuts when serviced.**
7. Remove engine support tool, then **torque upper front engine support bracket nuts to 52-70 ft. lbs.**
8. Raise and support vehicle, then observe position of righthand front engine support insulator. Insulator must

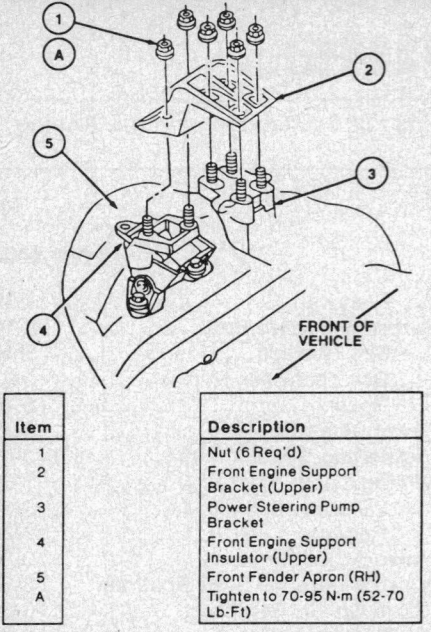

Item	Description
1	Nut (6 Req'd)
2	Front Engine Support Bracket (Upper)
3	Power Steering Pump Bracket
4	Front Engine Support Insulator (Upper)
5	Front Fender Apron (RH)
A	Tighten to 70-95 N·m (52-70 Lb-Ft)

FM1069500413000X

Fig. 1   Upper front engine support insulator replacement

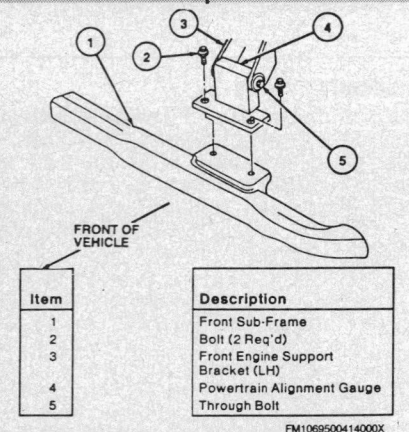

Item	Description
1	Front Sub-Frame
2	Bolt (2 Req'd)
3	Front Engine Support Bracket (LH)
4	Powertrain Alignment Gauge
5	Through Bolt

FM1069500414000X

Fig. 2   Powertrain alignment gauge tool installation

be centered in transaxle bracket and in perfect front-to-rear alignment.

9. Tighten righthand front engine support insulator through bolt to specifications.

10. Remove three gauge tool bolts and gauge tool.

11. Install lefthand front engine support insulator to front subframe with two bolts, then **torque** bolts to 7 ft. lbs. Observe insulator to ensure perfect front-to-rear alignment, then **torque** bolts to 30-40 ft. lbs.

12. Install lefthand front engine support insulator through bolt and tighten to specifications.

13. Install power steering pressure hose to pump, then position pressure hose bracket to upper front engine support bracket and install bolt. Tighten bolt to specifications.

14. Connect engine control sensor wiring to power steering pressure switch connector.

15. Position ignition wires and retainer

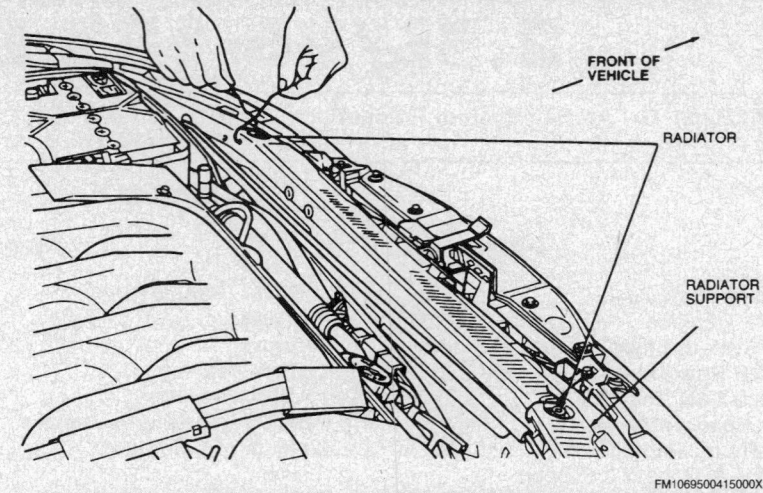

FM1069500415000X

Fig. 3   Radiator secured to radiator support

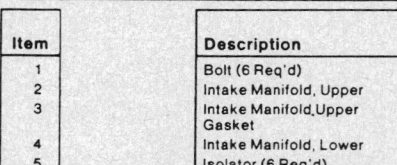

● REMOVE BOLTS IN SEQUENCE SHOWN

* HOLE LOCATION FOR GASKET LOCATING PINS

FRONT OF ENGINE

LOCATING PINS (2 EACH PER GASKET)

VIEW A

Item	Description
1	Bolt (6 Req'd)
2	Intake Manifold, Upper
3	Intake Manifold, Upper Gasket
4	Intake Manifold, Lower
5	Isolator (6 Req'd)

FM1059500070000X

Fig. 4   Upper intake manifold bolt removal sequence

onto upper front engine support bracket mounting studs.

16. Install water pump pulley shield and screws. Tighten screws securely.

17. Fill power steering system as described in "Power Steering" section.

18. Run engine and check for leaks.

LEFTHAND

Refer to "2.0L/4-122 Engine" section for lefthand front engine support insulator replacement.

RIGHTHAND

Refer to "2.0L/4-122 Engine" section for righthand front engine support insulator replacement.

ENGINE & TRANSAXLE SUPPORT INSULATOR

Refer to "2.0L/4-122 Engine" section for engine and transaxle support insulator replacement.

ENGINE
REPLACE
REMOVAL

1. Remove water pump pulley shield bolts from lefthand valve cover, then the shield.

2. Disconnect battery cables and wiring from battery.

3. Remove pinch bolt, then disconnect steering shaft and joint in vehicle.

4. Remove air cleaner as follows:
   a. Loosen engine air cleaner tube clamps on outlet tube, then disconnect crankcase ventilation hoses and IAC valve tube from air cleaner outlet tube fitting.
   b. Remove air cleaner outlet tube from Mass Air Flow (MAF) sensor and throttle body.
   c. Disconnect engine control sensor wiring connector form MAF and Intake Air Temperature (IAT) sensor.
   d. Remove engine air cleaner to body O-ring retainer, then the air cleaner body and intake tube from bracket.
   e. Remove engine air cleaner intake tube and duct.

5. **On models equipped with air conditioning,** recover air conditioning system as described in the "Air Conditioning" section.

6. **On all models,** raise and support vehicle.

7. Remove three way catalytic converter and Y pipe as follows:
   a. Remove converter outlet flange nuts, then the muffler and converter outlet gasket from converter. **Exhaust system normal operating temperature is very high. Never work around or attempt to**

service any or part of system until it has cooled. Use special care when working around three way catalytic converter. These units heat to a high temperature in only a short period of engine operation.

b. Remove converter nuts and exhaust pipe flange hold down springs.

c. Remove converter and inlet gasket from Y pipe, then discard gasket.

d. Remove front and rear Y pipe flange fasteners from exhaust manifolds.

e. Remove stud bolt and nut retainer from oil pan, then the Y pipe.

8. Drain engine cooling system as described under "Cooling System Bleed, then remove front wheel and tire assemblies.

9. Remove stabilizer bar link cotter pins and nuts, then separate stabilizer bar links from front stabilizer bar.

10. Remove front suspension lower arm pinch bolts, then separate front suspension lower arms from front wheel knuckles at ball joint.

11. Remove tie rod end cotter pins and nuts, then separate tie rod ends from front wheel knuckles with tie rod end remover tool No. 3290-D, or equivalent.

12. Remove axle wheel hub retainer from halfshaft ends, then the halfshafts.

13. Remove A/C accumulator screws from front subframe.

14. Disconnect speedometer drive cable from vehicle speed sensor on transaxle, then the sensor wiring harness at connector.

15. **If separating engine from automatic transaxle,** proceed as follows:

a. Remove engine rear plate access plug, then the torque converter nuts.

b. Push torque converter into transaxle front pump support and gear.

16. **On all models,** lower vehicle, then secure radiator and engine cooling fan motor, fan blade and fan shroud assembly to radiator support with safety wire, **Fig. 3.**

17. Disconnect accelerator cable and speed control actuator from throttle body, then remove accelerator cable bracket from throttle body.

18. Remove three engine control sensor wiring connectors from bracket on lefthand front fender apron, then disconnect wiring at connectors.

19. Remove engine control sensor wiring retainer from air cleaner bracket.

20. Disconnect ignition control module electrical connector by carefully lifting up on connector finger ends while grasping connector body and pulling away from module.

21. Remove ignition module screws, then the module from bracket.

22. Remove ignition control module bracket.

23. Remove power steering pump auxiliary reservoir from bracket and position over engine assembly.

24. Disconnect return hose from reservoir. Plug hose end.

25. Disconnect power steering pressure hose from power steering pump. **Do not allow power steering fluid to contact drive belt. Damage to drive belt may occur.**

26. Disconnect engine control sensor wiring from Powertrain Control Module (PCM) and retainer on righthand side of dash panel.

27. Remove engine control sensor wiring ground strap from righthand front fender apron.

28. Disconnect coolant hoses from radiator coolant recovery reservoir, then the fuel and supply lines from fuel injection supply manifold.

29. **On models equipped with automatic transaxle,** pry shift cable from stud, then remove shift cable bracket screws, bracket and cable.

30. **On all models,** disconnect ground strap from transaxle case.

31. Remove vacuum supply line from power brake booster, then the upper radiator hose from radiator.

32. Disconnect positive battery cable retainer from battery tray.

33. **On models equipped with manual transaxle,** remove clutch hydraulic retainer, then disconnect line from clutch actuator pipe at transaxle case.

34. **On models equipped with block heater,** disconnect block heater power supply wiring from righthand side of radiator support.

35. **On all models,** raise and support vehicle, then disconnect heater water hoses from heater core.

36. **On models equipped with air conditioning,** disconnect A/C suction hose from A/C condenser core, then the A/C discharge hose from A/C accumulator.

37. **On models equipped with manual transaxle,** proceed as follows:

a. Remove gearshift lever knob by grasping firmly with both hands and pulling up.

b. Unsnap console applique from console assembly and remove gearshift lever boot.

c. Remove gearshift stabilizer bar to case cover bolts, then raise and support vehicle.

d. Remove middle under body heat shield nuts, then the shield.

e. Remove transaxle gear shift rod and clevis from transaxle, then the stabilizer bar to bracket nut at righthand transaxle support insulator.

f. Remove gearshift stabilizer bar from vehicle.

38. **On models equipped with automatic transaxle,** remove transaxle oil cooler lines from transaxle, then the return line from bracket on lefthand side of transaxle.

39. **On all models,** disconnect lower radiator hose from radiator.

40. Remove lower radiator support to front subframe bolts, then rotate radiator supports forward.

41. **On models equipped with air conditioning,** disconnect A/C compressor wire harness at connectors.

42. **On all models,** remove two bumper cover brace to lefthand and righthand side of front subframe screws. Rotate bumper cover braces forward.

43. Partially lower vehicle, then position and secure any hoses, lines and components to be removed with engine.

44. Install powertrain and subframe support bracket tool No. 134-00250, or equivalent, to Rotunda Powertrain Lift tool No. 134-00251, or equivalent, then rotate transaxle adapters for transaxle removal.

45. Position bracket tool and adjust lift tool to provide proper contact at powertrain lift points.

46. Remove four subframe bolts. **Ensure engine is properly positioned and secure on lifting equipment. Damage to vehicle or personal injury may occur if engine is not secure.**

47. Remove upper front engine support bracket and engine and transaxle support insulator as described under "Engine Mount, Replace."

48. With assistance, lower engine and transaxle with front subframe as an assembly. Check for interference to body while lowering powertrain.

49. When powertrain is clear of body, raise and support vehicle.

50. Support engine with Rotunda Floor Crane Positioning Sling tool No. 014-00036 and Rotunda Floor Crane tool No. 014-00071, or equivalents, from engine lifting eyes.

51. Remove halfshafts from transaxle as described under "Front Wheel Drive Axles."

52. Remove front engine support insulators from subframe and transaxle as described under "Engine Mount, Replace."

53. Raise engine and transaxle assembly and remove front subframe and lift tool, then support transaxle with Rotunda Transmission Jack tool No. 066-00016, or equivalent.

54. Remove starter motor bolts, then the starter motor.

55. Disconnect engine control sensor wiring from transaxle at connectors, then remove engine control sensor wiring to transaxle case clips and position engine control sensor wiring aside.

56. Remove battery ground cable from engine to transaxle retaining stud bolt.

57. Remove transaxle to engine bolts and separate transaxle from engine.

58. **On models equipped with manual transaxle,** remove clutch pressure plate bolts, then the pressure plate and clutch disc.

59. **On all models,** remove flywheel bolts, then the flywheel from crankshaft.

60. Remove engine rear plate, then install engine onto suitable engine stand, following manufacturer's instructions.

INSTALLATION

1. Remove engine from engine stand using Rotunda Floor Crane Positioning Sling tool No. 014-00036 and Rotunda Floor Crane tool No. 014-00071, or equivalent, attached to en-

gine lifting eyes.

2. Install engine rear plate and flywheel. Tighten bolts to specifications.

3. **On models equipped with manual transaxle,** install transaxle to engine. Tighten bolts to specifications.

4. **On models equipped with automatic transaxle,** align torque converter and flywheel, then install transaxle to engine. Tighten transaxle bolts to specifications.

5. **On all models,** place front subframe on powertrain and subframe support bracket tool No. 134-00250, or equivalent, then install engine and transaxle assembly onto front subframe with bracket tool.

6. Install powertrain alignment gauge tool No. T-94P-6000-AH, or equivalent, to lefthand front engine support bracket and front subframe. **Torque** vertical bolts and through bolt to 20 ft. lbs.

7. Install battery ground cable to engine to transaxle stud bolt. Tighten nut to specifications.

8. Route engine control sensor wiring across transaxle and install clips for engine control sensor wiring onto transaxle.

9. Connect engine control sensor wiring to transaxle at all connectors.

10. Install starter motor as described under "Electrical."

11. Install halfshafts into transaxle as described in "Front Wheel Drive Axles" section.

12. Partially lower vehicle, then install engine and transaxle assembly into vehicle with front subframe, using powertrain and subframe support bracket tool No. 134-00250 and Rotunda Powertrain Lift tool No. 134-00251, or equivalent, with subframe alignment pin set tool No. T94P-2100-AH, or equivalent, installed onto front subframe. Ensure engine and transaxle are firmly seated against front and rear insulator brackets.

13. Using new nuts, install upper front engine support bracket and engine and transaxle support insulator. Tighten nuts to specifications.

14. Install front subframe to body, then remove alignment set tool, powertrain lift tool and support bracket tool.

15. Lower vehicle, then tighten front engine support bracket nuts to specifications.

16. Tighten engine and transaxle support insulator nuts to specifications, then raise and support vehicle.

17. **Torque** righthand front engine support insulator to subframe bolt to 7 ft. lbs. Ensure righthand front engine support insulator is centered in bracket and in perfect front-to-rear alignment. **Torque** insulator to subframe bolt to 30-40 ft. lbs.

18. Install lefthand front engine support insulator through bolt. Tighten to specifications.

19. **On models equipped with air conditioning,** connect wire harness to A/C compressor.

20. **On all models,** install front bumper cover braces to lefthand and righthand side of front subframe. Tighten bolts securely.

21. Install radiator supports to front subframe. Tighten radiator support bolts to specifications.

22. Connect lower radiator hose to radiator.

23. **On models equipped with automatic transaxle,** install transaxle oil cooler lines and brackets. Tighten bracket nuts and stabilizer bar nut to specifications.

24. **On models equipped with manual transaxle,** install shift rod and stabilizer bar to transaxle. Tighten shift rod bolt and stabilizer bar to specifications.

25. **On models equipped with air conditioning,** connect A/C suction hose to A/C condenser core, then the discharge hose to A/C accumulator.

26. **On all models,** install heater water hoses to heater core, installing hose spring clamp securely

27. Lower vehicle.

28. **On models equipped with block heater,** connect block heater power supply wiring to righthand side of radiator support.

29. **On models equipped with manual transaxle,** proceed as follows:
   a. Connect clutch hydraulic line to clutch actuator, then install retainer clip.
   b. Fill and bleed hydraulic system as described in "Hydraulic Brake Systems" section.

30. **On all models,** connect positive battery cable retainer to battery tray.

31. Connect upper radiator hose to radiator, then the vacuum supply line to power brake booster.

32. Connect ground strap to transaxle case.

33. **On models equipped with automatic transaxle,** install shift cable and bracket to transaxle. Tighten bolts to specifications.

34. **On all models,** connect fuel supply and return lines to fuel injection supply manifold, then the coolant hoses to radiator coolant recovery reservoir.

35. Install ground strap for engine control sensor wiring to righthand cylinder head. Tighten retainer securely.

36. Connect engine control sensor wiring to Powertrain Control Module (PCM), then position engine control sensor wiring into retainer bracket on righthand side of dash panel.

37. Connect power steering pressure hose to power steering pump, then install power steering pressure hose bracket to upper front engine support bracket. Tighten retainer securely.

38. Install power steering pump auxiliary reservoir to bracket.

39. Install ignition control module bracket, then the module and screws.

40. Connect ignition control module electrical connector.

41. Install engine control sensor wiring to air cleaner bracket retainer.

42. Connect three engine control sensor wiring connectors together, then to

bracket located on lefthand front fender apron.

43. Install accelerator cable bracket to throttle body, then connect cables to throttle body lever. Tighten accelerator cable bracket bolts to specifications.

44. Remove safety wire holding radiator to radiator support, then raise and support vehicle.

45. **On models equipped with automatic transaxle,** push torque converter into flywheel pilot and install torque converter to flywheel nuts. Tighten nuts to specifications.

46. Install access plug onto engine rear plate.

47. **On all models,** connect speedometer drive cable to vehicle speed sensor, then the speed sensor wiring harness at connector.

48. **On models equipped with air conditioning,** install A/C accumulator screws to front of subframe. Tighten screws securely.

49. **On all models,** install halfshafts into front wheel knuckles, then the front axle wheel hub retainers as described under "Front Wheel Drive Axles."

50. Install tie rod ends to front wheel knuckle. Install new nuts on tie rod end studs. **Torque** nuts to 21 ft. lbs. and continue tightening nuts to align next castellation of new nut with cotter pin hole in stud. Instal new cotter pins.

51. Install front wheel knuckles onto front suspension lower arms at ball joint. Tighten bolts to specifications.

52. Install front wheel and tire assemblies, then tighten lug nuts to specifications.

53. Install Y pipe and three way catalytic converter as follows:
   a. Install Y pipe, then the nut retainer and stud bolt to oil pan.
   b. Install front and rear Y pipe flange fasteners to exhaust manifolds.
   c. Install new converter and inlet gasket to Y pipe.
   d. Install exhaust pipe flange hold down springs and converter nuts.
   e. Install muffler and converter outlet gasket to converter, then the converter outlet flange nuts.

54. Install splash shield to front of subframe and body. Tighten shield screws securely.

55. Rotate front bumper cover braces rearward, then install two screws to front subframe. Tighten screws securely.

56. Lower vehicle, then install engine air cleaner as follows:
   a. Install engine air cleaner intake tube and duct.
   b. Install air cleaner body and intake tube to bracket, then the air cleaner to body O-ring retainer.
   c. Connect engine control sensor wiring connector to Mass Air Flow (MAF) and Intake Air Temperature (IAT) sensors.
   d. Install air cleaner outlet tube to MAF sensor and throttle body.
   e. Connect crankcase ventilation hoses and IAC valve tube to air

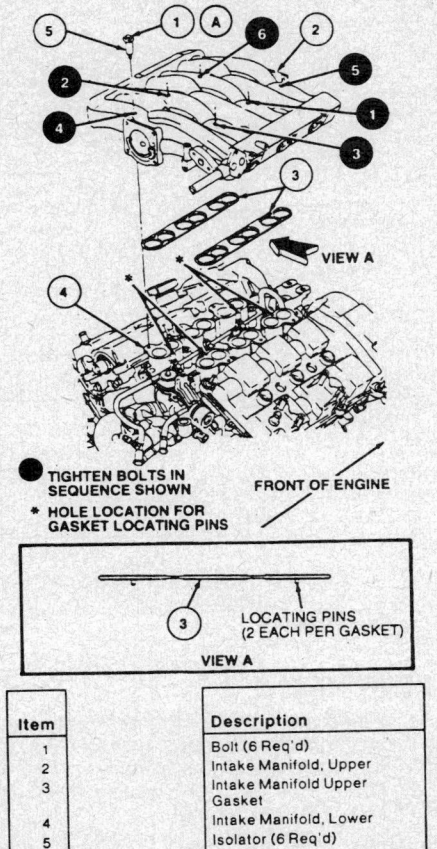

● TIGHTEN BOLTS IN SEQUENCE SHOWN

* HOLE LOCATION FOR GASKET LOCATING PINS

FRONT OF ENGINE

LOCATING PINS (2 EACH PER GASKET)

VIEW A

Item	Description
1	Bolt (6 Req'd)
2	Intake Manifold, Upper
3	Intake Manifold Upper Gasket
4	Intake Manifold, Lower
5	Isolator (6 Req'd)
A	Tighten to 8-12 N·m (71-106 Lb-In)

FM1059500071000X

Fig. 5 Upper intake manifold bolt tightening sequence

cleaner outlet tube fitting. Tighten engine air cleaner tube clamps to specifications.

57. Connect steering shaft and joint in vehicle and install pinch bolt. Tighten pinch bolt to specifications.
58. Install water pump pulley shield, then the bolts to lefthand cylinder head.
59. Connect battery cables and wiring to battery, then fill engine cooling system with specified coolant as described under "Cooling System Bleed."
60. **On models equipped with air conditioning,** recharge A/C system as described in "Air Conditioning" section.
61. **On all models,** run engine and check for oil, coolant or fuel leaks, then verify proper cooling fan motor and A/C system operation.

INTAKE MANIFOLD
REPLACE
UPPER

1. Disconnect battery ground cable.
2. Remove water pump pulley shield bolts, then the shield.
3. Press black retainer on upper intake manifold with screwdriver and disconnect main emission vacuum control connector and brake booster vacuum connector from manifold.

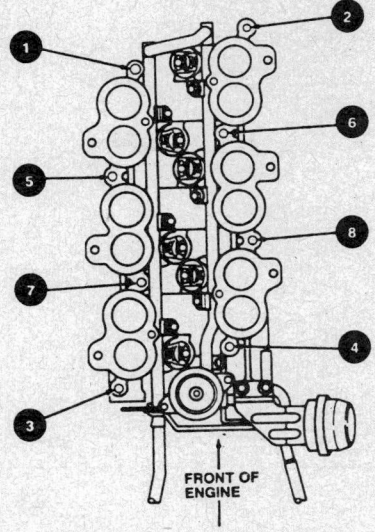

● REMOVE BOLTS IN SEQUENCE SHOWN

LOWER INTAKE MANIFOLD

FRONT OF ENGINE

FM1059500072000X

Fig. 6 Lower intake manifold bolt removal sequence

4. Loosen engine air cleaner tube clamps on air cleaner outlet tube.
5. Disconnect crankcase ventilation hoses and IAC valve tube from outlet tube fitting.
6. Remove outlet tube from Mass Air Flow (MAF) sensor and throttle body.
7. Remove accelerator cable and speed control actuator from throttle body, then the accelerator cable bracket from intake manifold. Position bracket aside.
8. Remove Idle Air Control (IAC) valve fresh air supply hose from upper intake manifold fitting.
9. Disconnect fuel charging wiring from Throttle Position (TP) sensor, IAC valve and EGR vacuum regulator control.
10. Remove vacuum supply hose from upper intake manifold to Positive Crankcase Ventilation (PCV) valve at upper intake manifold, then disconnect vacuum supply hoses to EGR vacuum regulator control and EGR valve.
11. Loosen and remove EGR valve to exhaust manifold tube nut from EGR valve, then position tube aside.
12. Remove intake manifold bolts in sequence, **Fig. 4. When removing engine components, always remove bolts in reverse order of tightening sequence or damage to engine components may occur.**
13. Remove upper intake manifold and lower intake manifold upper gaskets. Discard intake manifold upper gaskets.
14. Reverse procedure to install, noting the following:
    a. Install new intake manifold upper gaskets.
    b. **Torque** intake manifold bolts in sequence, **Fig. 5,** to 71-106 inch lbs.

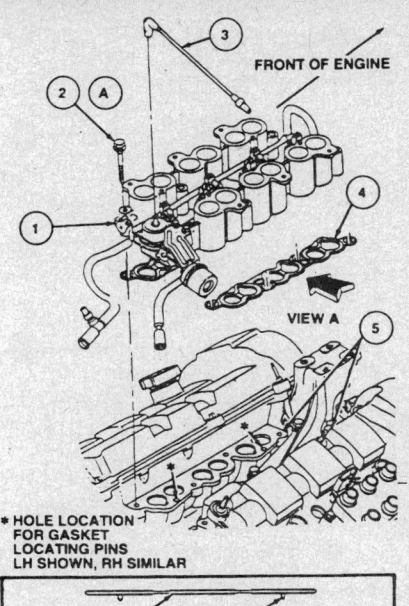

FRONT OF ENGINE

VIEW A

* HOLE LOCATION FOR GASKET LOCATING PINS LH SHOWN, RH SIMILAR

LOCATING PINS 2 EACH GASKET

VIEW A

Item	Description
1	Lower Intake Manifold
2	Bolt (8 Req'd)
3	Main Emission Vacuum Control Connector
4	Intake Manifold Gasket (2 Req'd)
5	Cylinder Head (2 Req'd)
A	Tighten to 8-12 N·m (71-106 Lb-In)

FM1059500073000X

Fig. 7 Lower intake manifold replacement

c. Tighten accelerator cable bracket bolts and EGR valve to exhaust manifold tube nut to specifications.

LOWER

1. Relieve fuel system pressure as described under "Precautions."
2. Disconnect battery ground cable, then remove upper intake manifold as previously described.
3. Disconnect fuel supply and return lines from fuel injection supply manifold.
4. Disconnect engine control sensor wiring from fuel injectors and valve cover studs. Position wiring aside.
5. Disconnect vacuum supply line from fuel pressure regulator and Intake Manifold Runner Control (IMRC) vacuum solenoid. Position line aside.
6. If necessary, remove fuel injection supply manifold and fuel injectors from lower intake manifold.
7. If necessary, remove IMRC vacuum solenoid from lower intake manifold.
8. Remove lower intake manifold to cylinder head bolts in sequence, **Fig. 6.**
9. Remove lower intake manifold from cylinder heads, then the intake manifold gaskets from cylinder heads, **Fig. 7.** Discard gaskets.
10. Reverse procedure to install, noting

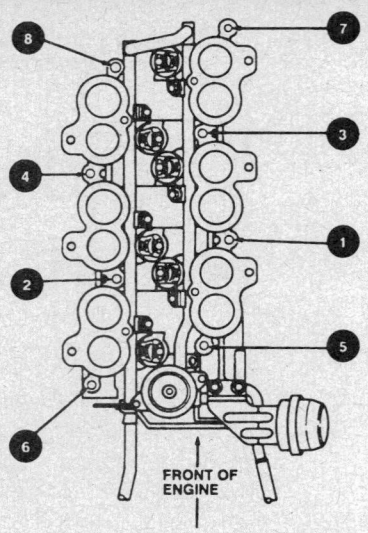

INSTALL BOLTS IN SEQUENCE SHOWN

LOWER INTAKE MANIFOLD

FM1059500074000X

Fig. 8   Intake manifold bolt tightening sequence

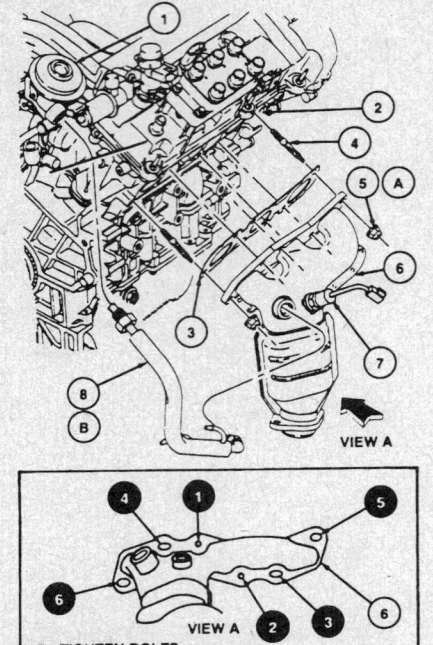

VIEW A

TIGHTEN BOLTS IN SEQUENCE SHOWN

Item	Description	
1	EGR Valve	
2	RH Cylinder Head	
3	Exhaust Manifold Gasket	
4	Stud Bolt (6 Req'd)	
5	Nut (6 Req'd)	
6	RH Exhaust Manifold	
7	Heated Oxygen Sensor	
8	EGR Valve to Exhaust Manifold Tube	
A	Tighten to 18-22 N-m (13-16 Lb-Ft)	
B	Tighten to 35-45 N-m (26-33 Lb-Ft)	

FM1079500016000X

Fig. 9   Exhaust manifold tightening sequence

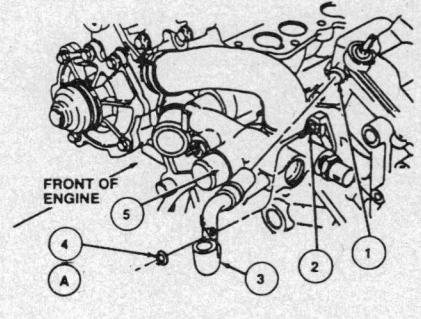

FRONT OF ENGINE

Item	Description
1	Oil Separator
2	Stud Bolt
3	Crankcase Ventilation Tube
4	Nut
5	Water Crossover
A	Tighten to 5-7 N-m (44-62 Lb-In)

FM1069500416000X

Fig. 10   Cylinder head replacement

the following:

a. Verify IMRC vacuum solenoid and plate operation using hand vacuum pump. Install new intake manifold gaskets.

b. **Torque** lower intake manifold bolts in sequence, **Fig. 8**, to 71-106 inch lbs.

c. Tighten IMRC vacuum solenoid bolts to specifications.

EXHAUST MANIFOLD
REPLACE

RIGHTHAND

1. Disconnect battery ground cable, then the engine control sensor extension wire from righthand heated oxygen sensor.

2. Raise and support vehicle, then remove alternator and bracket as described under "Electrical."

3. Remove three way catalytic converter and Y pipe as follows:

a. Remove converter outlet flange nuts, then the muffler and converter outlet gasket from converter. **Exhaust system normal operating temperature is very high. Never work around or attempt to service any or part of the system until it has cooled. Use special care when working around the three way catalytic converter. These units heat to high temperature in only a short period of engine operation.**

b. Remove converter nuts and exhaust pipe flange hold down springs.

c. Remove converter and inlet gasket from Y pipe, then discard gasket.

d. Remove front and rear Y pipe flange fasteners from exhaust manifolds.

e. Remove stud bolt and nut retainer from oil pan, then the Y pipe.

4. Remove righthand halfshaft support bearing bracket from support bearing and cylinder block as described in "Front Wheel Drive Axles" section.

5. Remove heated oxygen sensor from righthand exhaust manifold using oxygen sensor wrench tool No. T94P-9472-A, or equivalent. If excessive force is necessary to remove sensor, lubricate sensor with penetrating oil before removal.

6. Loosen EGR valve to exhaust manifold tube from righthand exhaust manifold.

7. Remove righthand exhaust manifold nuts from cylinder head studs, then the manifold and manifold gasket from engine.

8. Reverse procedure to install, noting the following:

a. **Torque** exhaust manifold nuts in sequence, **Fig. 1**, to 13-16 ft. lbs.

b. Tighten EGR valve to exhaust manifold tube nuts and heated oxygen sensor to specifications.

LEFTHAND

1. Disconnect battery ground cable, then the lefthand heated oxygen sensor from engine control sensor wiring.

2. Raise and support vehicle, then remove Y pipe as follows:

a. Remove front and rear flange pipe fasteners from exhaust manifolds, then the stud bolt and nut retainer from oil pan.

b. Remove two remaining nuts and bolts from pipe outlet connection, then discard exhaust converter inlet gasket.

c. Remove pipe.

3. Remove lower radiator hose tube bracket nuts from stud bolts, then the exhaust manifold nuts from lefthand cylinder head studs.

4. Position lower radiator hose tube to gain clearance for exhaust manifold removal, then remove lefthand exhaust manifold and exhaust manifold gasket from engine.

5. If necessary, remove heated oxygen sensor from lefthand exhaust manifold using oxygen sensor wrench tool No. T94P-9472-A, or equivalent. If excessive force is necessary to remove sensor, lubricate sensor with penetrating oil before removal.

6. Reverse procedure to install. **Torque** lefthand exhaust manifold nuts in sequence, **Fig. 9**, to 13-16 ft. lbs.

CYLINDER HEAD
REPLACE

1. Drain engine coolant from radiator and cylinder block drain plugs as described under "Cooling System Bleed."

2. Remove upper and lower intake manifolds as described under "Intake Manifold, Replace."

3. Remove oil pan as described under "Oil Pan, Replace."

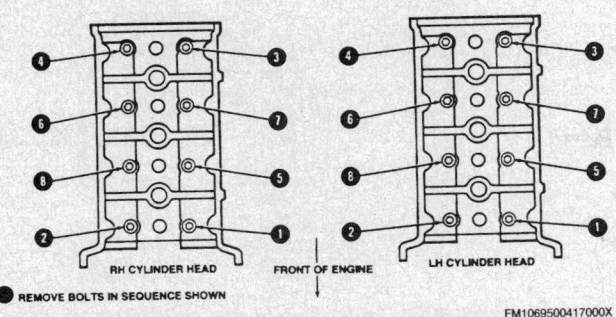

Fig. 11 Cylinder head bolt removal sequence

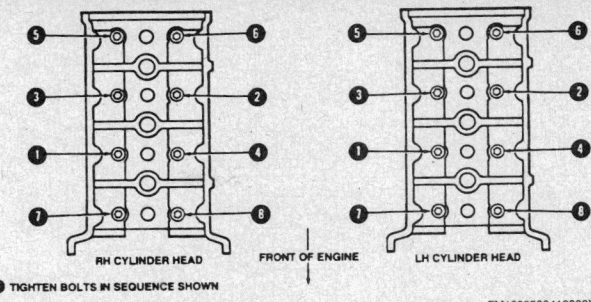

Fig. 12 Cylinder head bolt tightening sequence

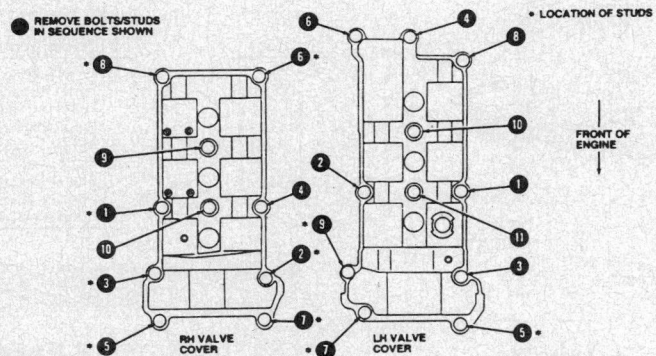

Fig. 13 Valve cover bolt removal sequence

4. Remove alternator and alternator bracket as described in the "Electrical."

5. Remove heated oxygen sensor from righthand exhaust manifold using oxygen sensor wrench tool No. T94P-9472-A, or equivalent. If excessive force is necessary to remove sensor, lubricate sensor with penetrating oil before removal.

6. **On lefthand cylinder head,** remove lefthand exhaust manifold as described under "Exhaust Manifold, Replace," then the water pump as described under "Water Pump, Replace."

7. **On both cylinder heads,** remove front cover as described under "Front Cover, Replace."

8. Remove camshafts as described under "Camshaft, Replace," then the valve tappets as described under "Valve Tappets, Replace."

9. Install upper front engine support insulator and front engine support bracket to front of engine and righthand front fender apron as described under "Engine Mount, Replace."

10. Remove three bar engine support tool No. D88L-6000-A, or equivalent.

11. **On righthand cylinder head,** proceed as follows:
    a. Disconnect hoses from EGR pressure sensor at EGR valve to exhaust manifold tube, then the pressure sensor electrical connector.
    b. Disconnect interior vacuum source hose from main emission vacuum harness, then the fuel vapor hose from Positive Crankcase Ventilation valve (PCV valve).

c. Disconnect EGR transducer electrical connector, then remove EGR valve to exhaust manifold tube from righthand exhaust manifold.
    d. Remove exhaust manifold tube from vehicle, then the fuel charging wiring bracket from EGR transducer bracket.

12. **On both cylinder heads,** remove air cleaner as follows:
    a. Loosen engine air cleaner tube clamps on outlet tube, then disconnect crankcase ventilation hoses and IAC valve tube from air cleaner outlet tube fitting.
    b. Remove air cleaner outlet tube from Mass Air Flow (MAF) sensor and throttle body.
    c. Disconnect engine control sensor wiring connector form MAF and Intake Air Temperature (IAT) sensor.
    d. Remove engine air cleaner to body O-ring retainer, then the air cleaner body and intake tube from bracket.
    e. Remove engine air cleaner intake tube and duct.

13. Remove crankcase ventilation tube from water crossover and oil separator, **Fig. 10.**

14. Remove water crossover bolt and stud bolt from righthand cylinder head, then the crossover and position aside.

15. **On lefthand cylinder head,** remove oil level dipstick.

16. **On both cylinder heads,** remove cylinder head bolts in sequence, **Fig. 11.**

17. Remove cylinder heads. Remove

righthand cylinder head with exhaust manifold and EGR transducer bracket attached.

18. Remove exhaust manifold and EGR transducer bracket from righthand cylinder head if necessary.

19. Inspect both cylinder heads and cylinder block for damage. Replace components as required.

20. Reverse procedure to install, noting the following:
    a. Clean cylinder heads, lower intake manifold valve cover and cylinder gasket surfaces. If cylinder heads were removed to replace cylinder gasket, check flatness of cylinder heads and cylinder block gasket surfaces.
    b. Install new head gaskets on cylinder block. Gaskets must be installed over cylinder head to block dowels.
    c. Ensure cylinder heads are installed in original positions. **Use care when positioning cylinder heads. Damage to cylinder block and/or cylinder heads may result.**
    d. **cylinder head bolts must be replaced with new bolts. They are torque-to-yield designed and cannot be reused. If reused, damage to engine may occur.**
    e. Install new "torque to yield" cylinder head bolts. **Torque** cylinder head bolts in sequence, **Fig. 12**, first to 27-32 ft. lbs., then rotate bolts 85-95 degrees. Next, rotate each bolt a one full turn, then **torque** to 27-32 ft. lbs in sequence. Finally, rotate each bolt 85-95 degrees, then, final tighten all bolts in sequence an additional 85-95 degrees.
    f. Inspect water crossover O-rings for wear or damage. Replace O-rings as necessary.
    g. Lubricate water crossover O-rings with specified engine coolant.

VALVE COVER
REPLACE
RIGHTHAND

1. Remove upper intake manifold as described under "Intake Manifold, Replace."

2. Remove ignition wires from ignition coils and spark plugs, then remove ignition coil as follows:

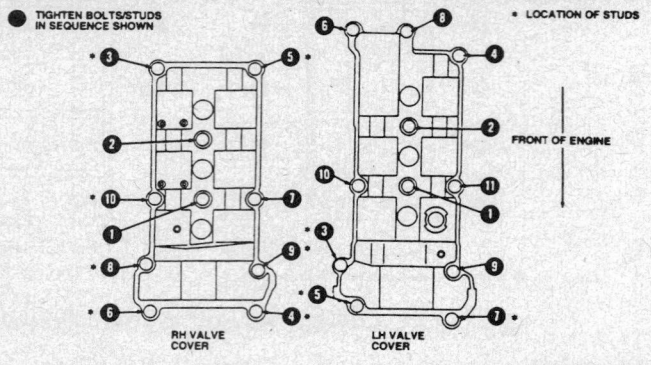

Fig. 14   Valve cover bolt tightening sequence

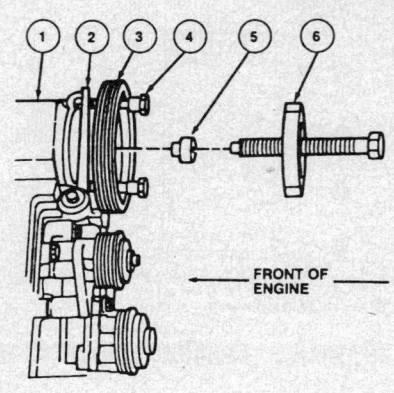

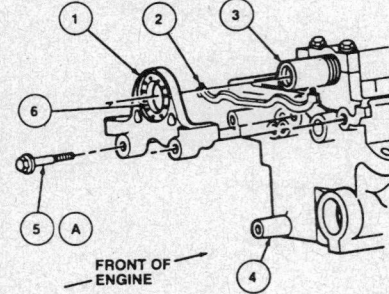

Item	Description
1	Camshaft Rear Oil Seal Retainer
2	Oil Seal Retainer Gasket
3	LH Intake Camshaft
4	LH Cylinder Head
5	Bolt (2 Req'd)
6	Camshaft Rear Oil Seal
A	Tighten to 8-12 N·m (71-106 Lb-In)

FM1069500422000X

Fig. 16   Rear camshaft rear oil seal retainer removal

Item	Description
1	Valve Cover
2	Water Pump Pulley Remover/Replacer
3	Water Pump Drive Pulley
4	Screw (2 Req'd)
5	Shaft Protector
6	Crankshaft Damper Remover

FM1069500421000X

Fig. 15   Water pump drive pulley removal

a. Disconnect battery ground cable, then the fuel charging wiring or engine control sensor wiring from ignition coil.
b. Disconnect fuel charging wiring from radio ignition interference capacitor.
c. Remove EGR vacuum regulator control from upper intake manifold.
d. Disconnect ignition wires by squeezing locking tabs and twisting while pulling upward, then remove ignition coil bolts or screws and ignition coil.
e. Remove radio ignition interference capacitor, then disconnect coil ground wire. Save radio ignition interference capacitor for installation with ignition coil.
3. Remove crankcase ventilation tube from righthand valve cover.
4. Remove fuel charging wiring retainer and in-line connector wiring bracket nuts and bracket from righthand valve cover stud bolts. Position bracket and fuel charging wiring aside.
5. Remove engine control sensor wiring nuts, then the wiring from righthand valve cover stud bolts. Position engine control sensor wiring aside.
6. Loosen valve cover bolts and stud bolts in sequence, **Fig. 13.**
7. Carefully remove valve cover from cylinder head, then the gaskets from cover.
8. Reverse procedure to install, noting the following:
   a. Clean valve cover sealing surfaces using shop towel and suitable metal cleaner. Apply .31 inch diameter bead of black silicone rubber sealant, part No. F4AZ-19562-B or equivalent, at two places on valve cover sealing surfaces where front cover and cylinder heads contact.
   b. Install new valve cover gaskets onto valve cover.
   c. **Torque** valve cover bolts and stud bolts in sequence, **Fig. 14,** to 71-106 inch lbs. within six minutes of applying sealer.

LEFTHAND

1. Remove upper intake manifold as described under "Intake Manifold, Replace."
2. Remove crankcase ventilation tube

from lefthand valve cover, then the fuel charging wiring brackets from lefthand valve cover stud bolts. Position fuel charging wiring aside.
3. Remove ignition wires from spark plugs and valve cover, then loosen valve cover bolts and stud bolts in sequence, **Fig. 13.**
4. Carefully remove valve cover from lefthand cylinder head, then the gaskets from cover.
5. Reverse procedure to install, noting the following:
   a. Clean valve cover sealing surfaces using shop towel and suitable metal cleaner. Apply .31 inch diameter bead of black silicone rubber sealant, part No. F4AZ-19562-B or equivalent, at two places on valve cover sealing surfaces where front cover and cylinder heads contact and two places on rear of cylinder head where camshaft seal retainer contacts cylinder head.
   b. Install new valve cover gaskets onto valve cover.
   c. **Torque** valve cover bolts in sequence, **Fig. 14,** to 71-106 inch lbs. within six minutes of applying sealer.

VALVE CLEARANCE SPECIFICATIONS

Valve clearance is hydraulically controlled and not adjustable.

VALVE ADJUSTMENT

Refer to "2.0L/4-122 Engine" section for valve adjustment information.

ROCKER ARMS
REPLACE
REMOVAL

1. Remove valve covers and gaskets as described under "Valve Cover, Replace."
2. Remove crankshaft pulley bolt from front of crankshaft, then rotate crankshaft to Top Dead Center (TDC) No. 1 cylinder. **Rotate crankshaft to position crankshaft keyway to 11 o'clock position and engine to TDC No. 1 cylinder before replacing camshafts and rocker arms, or damage to engine may occur.**
3. Verify alignment arrows on camshafts are aligned. If arrows are not aligned, rotate crankshaft one complete revolution.
4. Rotate crankshaft to position crankshaft keyway to 3 o'clock location. This will position righthand cylinder head camshafts to neutral position (base circle).
5. Rotate water pump drive belt tensioner clockwise to release water pump drive belt tension and remove water pump drive belt, then carefully release drive belt tensioner.

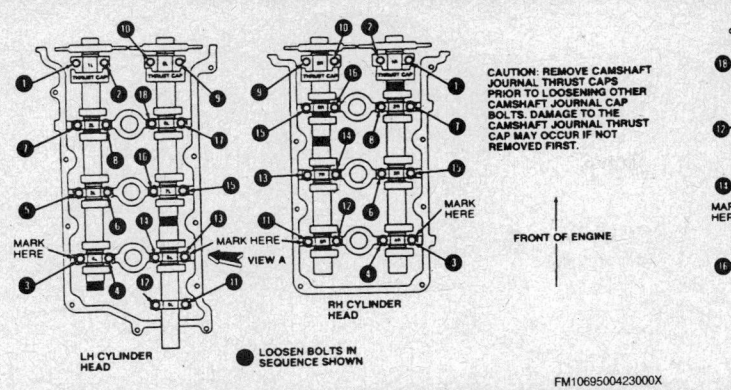

CAUTION: REMOVE CAMSHAFT JOURNAL THRUST CAPS PRIOR TO LOOSENING OTHER CAMSHAFT JOURNAL CAP BOLTS. DAMAGE TO THE CAMSHAFT JOURNAL THRUST CAP MAY OCCUR IF NOT REMOVED FIRST.

Fig. 17 Cylinder head camshaft journal cap bolt removal sequence

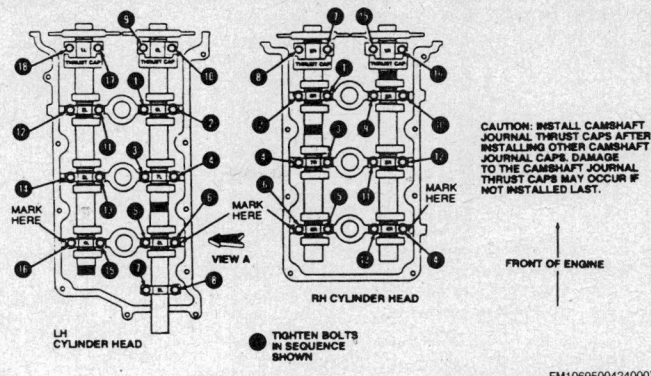

CAUTION: INSTALL CAMSHAFT JOURNAL THRUST CAPS AFTER INSTALLING OTHER CAMSHAFT JOURNAL CAPS. DAMAGE TO THE CAMSHAFT JOURNAL THRUST CAPS MAY OCCUR IF NOT INSTALLED LAST.

Fig. 18 Cylinder head camshaft journal cap bolt tightening sequence

6. Remove battery, then, using crankshaft damper remover tool No. T58P-6316-D and water pump pulley remover/replacer tool No. T94P-6312-AH, or equivalents, with shaft protector and screw, remove water pump drive pulley from lefthand intake camshaft, **Fig. 15.**
7. Remove camshaft rear oil seal bolts, then the retainer and gasket from lefthand cylinder head, **Fig. 16.**
8. Remove cylinder head camshaft journal thrust cap bolts and thrust caps from righthand cylinder head, noting the following:
   a. **Remove cylinder head camshaft journal thrust caps first to ensure damage to cylinder head camshaft journal thrust caps does not occur.**
   b. **Cylinder head camshaft journal caps and cylinder heads are numbered to ensure they are assembled in original position. When removed, keep camshaft journal caps from each cylinder head with head they were removed from. Do not mix with camshaft journal caps to ensure damage to cylinder head camshaft journal thrust caps does not occur.**
9. Loosen remaining righthand cylinder head camshaft journal cap bolts seven to eight turns in sequence, **Fig. 17,** in several passes (approximately one to two turns each pass) to allow camshafts to be raised from righthand cylinder head. Do not completely remove bolts.
10. With righthand cylinder head camshaft journal caps and camshafts loose on righthand cylinder head, remove rocker arms. **If roller rocker arms are to be reused, mark position or rocker arms to ensure they are assembled in original positions.**
11. Rotate crankshaft two revolutions and position crankshaft keyway to 11 o'clock location. This will position lefthand cylinder head camshafts to neutral position (base circle).
12. Verify alignment arrows on camshafts are aligned, then remove cylinder head camshaft journal thrust cap bolts and thrust caps from lefthand

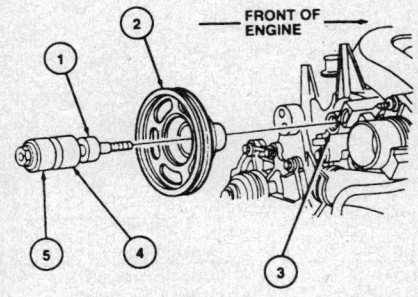

Item	Description
1	Screw
2	Water Pump Drive Pulley
3	LH Intake Camshaft
4	Replacer Cup
5	Power Steering Pump Pulley Replacer

Fig. 19 Water pump drive pulley installation

cylinder head, noting the following:
   a. Remove cylinder head camshaft journal thrust caps first to ensure damage to cylinder head camshaft journal thrust caps does not occur.
   b. **Cylinder head camshaft journal caps and cylinder heads are numbered to ensure they are assembled in original position When removed, keep camshaft journal caps from each cylinder head with head they were removed from. Do not mix with camshaft journal caps from another cylinder head.**
13. Loosen remaining lefthand cylinder head camshaft journal cap bolts seven to eight turns in sequence, **Fig. 17,** in several passes (approximately one to two turns each pass) to allow camshafts to be raised from lefthand cylinder head. Do not completely remove bolts.
14. With lefthand cylinder head camshaft journal caps and camshafts loose on lefthand cylinder head, remove rocker arms. **If roller rocker arms are to be reused, mark positions of rocker arms to ensure they are assembled in original positions.**

INSTALLATION

1. **Ensure rocker arms are installed in original locations. Crankshaft keyway must be at 11 o'clock position before installing rocker arms. Failure to do so may lead to engine damage.**
2. Lubricate rocker arms with suitable engine assembly lubricant, then install rocker arms onto lefthand cylinder head under camshafts.
3. With lefthand cylinder head rocker arms installed under camshafts, **torque** lefthand cylinder head camshaft journal cap bolts in sequence, **Fig. 18,** in several passes, to 71–106 inch lbs.
4. Align camshafts in lefthand cylinder head with thrust caps, then install lefthand cylinder head camshaft journal thrust caps. Tighten bolts to specifications.
5. Rotate crankshaft two revolutions and position crankshaft keyway to 3 o'clock position. This will position righthand cylinder head camshafts to neutral position (base circle).
6. **Ensure rocker arms are installed in original locations. Crankshaft keyway must be at 3 o'clock position before installing rocker arms. Failure to do so may lead to engine damage.**
7. Lubricate rocker arms with suitable engine assembly lubricant, then install rocker arms onto righthand cylinder head under camshafts.
8. With righthand cylinder head rocker arms installed under camshafts, **torque** righthand cylinder head camshaft journal cap bolts in sequence, **Fig. 18,** in several passes, to 71–106 inch lbs. Install cylinder head camshaft journal thrust cap last to ensure damage to No. 1 journal cap does not occur.
9. Align camshafts in righthand cylinder head with thrust caps, then install righthand cylinder head camshaft journal thrust caps. Tighten bolts to specifications.
10. Install camshaft rear oil seal and retainer and gasket onto lefthand cylinder head. Tighten rear oil seal retainer bolts to specifications.

11. Using power steering pump pulley re-placer tool No. T91P-3A733-A, screw tool No. T94P-6312-AH and replacer cup tool No. T94P-6312-AH, or equiv-alents, install water pump drive pulley on lefthand intake camshaft, **Fig. 19.**
12. Rotate water pump drive belt ten-sioner clockwise and install water pump drive belt, then carefully release drive belt tensioner.
13. Install battery.
14. Install crankshaft pulley bolt. **Torque** crankshaft pulley bolt first to 89 ft. lbs., then loosen a minimum of one full turn. Next, **torque** bolt to 35-39 ft. lbs., and, finally, rotate 85-95 degrees.
15. Install valve covers and valve cover gaskets as described under "Valve Cover, Replace."

HYDRAULIC VALVE LIFTERS
REPLACE

If valve tappets and roller rocker arms are to be reused, mark position of the rocker arms and valve tappets to ensure they are assembled in original positions.
1. Remove rocker arms as described under "Rocker Arms, Replace."
2. Remove valve tappets from cylinder heads, then inspect tappets. Replace tappets as necessary.
3. Lubricate valve tappets with suitable engine assembly lubricant, then install tappets to cylinder heads. Ensure valve tappets are installed in original positions.
4. Install rocker arms as described under "Rocker Arms, Replace."

FRONT COVER
REPLACE
REMOVAL

1. Disconnect battery ground cable, then remove lefthand and righthand valve covers as described under "Valve Cover, Replace."
2. Install three bar engine support tool No. D88L-6000-A, or equivalent, onto engine lifting eyes and support en-gine.
3. Remove power steering pressure hose bracket bolt from upper front en-gine support bracket.
4. Disconnect power steering pressure hose from power steering pump, then position hose aside.
5. Remove upper front engine support bracket nus and front engine support bracket from engine and upper front engine support insulator as described under "Engine Mount, Replace." Mark location of upper front engine support bracket before removing.
6. Disconnect low coolant level sensor connector from wire harness.
7. Remove radiator coolant recovery reservoir retainers and position radia-tor coolant recovery reservoir aside.
8. Remove front engine support insula-tor as described under "Engine Mount Replace."

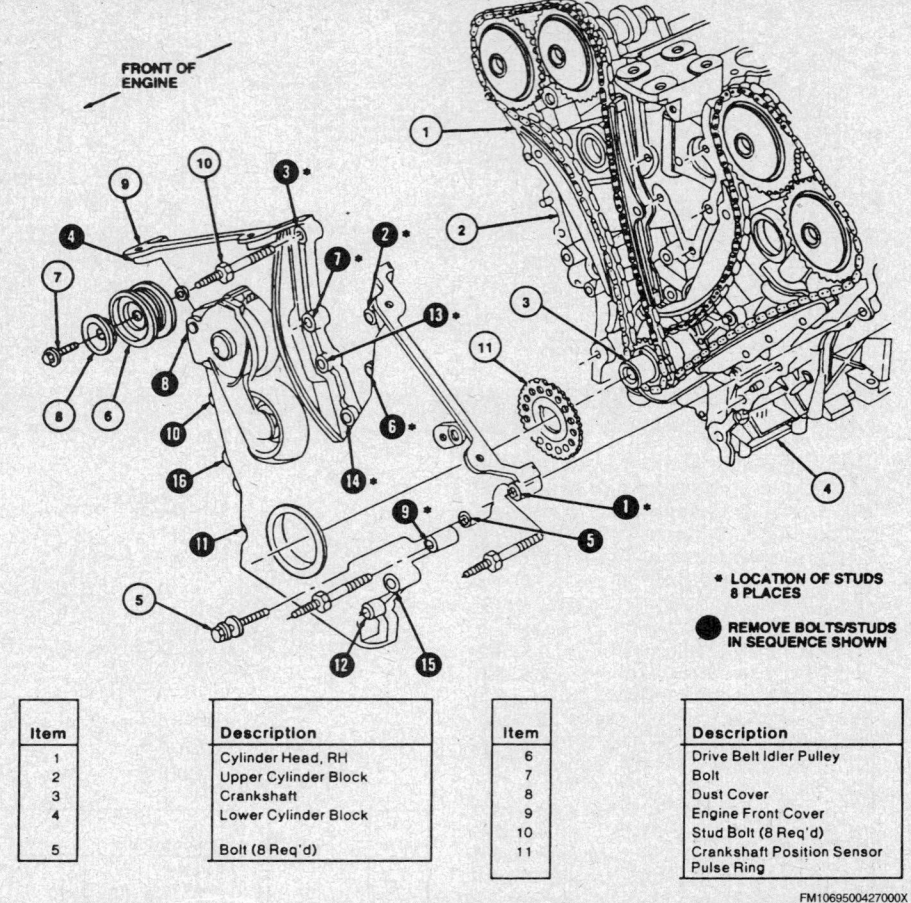

LOCATION OF STUDS 8 PLACES

REMOVE BOLTS/STUDS IN SEQUENCE SHOWN

Item	Description	Item	Description
1	Cylinder Head, RH	6	Drive Belt Idler Pulley
2	Upper Cylinder Block	7	Bolt
3	Crankshaft	8	Dust Cover
4	Lower Cylinder Block	9	Engine Front Cover
5	Bolt (8 Req'd)	10	Stud Bolt (8 Req'd)
		11	Crankshaft Position Sensor Pulse Ring

FM1069500427000X

Fig. 20 Front cover removal

9. Set radiator coolant recovery reser-voir into position, then disconnect fuel charging wiring at three connectors on in-line connector bracket at front of righthand cylinder head. Position wir-ing aside. Loosen power steering pump pulley bolts. Do not completely remove bolts.
10. Remove drive belt as described under "Serpentine Drive Belt."
11. Remove power steering pump pulley from pump.
12. Remove power steering pump and pump support nuts and bolts, then the pump and pump support.
13. Raise and support vehicle, then re-move oil pan drain plug and drain en-gine oil. Replace plug with new gasket and tighten to specifications.
14. Remove through bolt for front engine support insulators as described under "Engine Mount, Replace."
15. Lower vehicle, then raise engine to gain access for oil pan removal, then support engine with three bar engine support tool No. D88L-6000-A, or equivalent.
16. Position alternator aside, then remove alternator bracket from engine.
17. Remove crankshaft pulley, then dis-connect fuel charging wiring from CKP and CMP sensor electrical con-nectors.
18. Remove oil pan as described under "Oil Pan, Replace."

19. **On models equipped with air con-ditioning,** loosen A/C compressor bolts and position compressor to gain access to front cover bolt.
20. **On all models,** lower vehicle, then re-move fuel charging wiring bracket re-tainers and A/C hose bracket from front cover stud bolts. Position fuel charging wiring aside.
21. Remove front cover bolts in se-quence, **Fig. 20.** It may be necessary to raise and lower vehicle several times to follow bolt removal se-quence.
22. Remove front cover and cover gas-kets from vehicle. Discard gaskets.

INSTALLATION

1. Clean front cover to cylinder block and cylinder head sealing surfaces.
2. Apply .118 inch diameter bead, ap-proximately .472 inch long of black sil-icone rubber part No. F4AZ-19562-B or equivalent to cylinder block in six locations, **Fig. 21. Install front cover and front cover bolts and stud bolts in proper location and se-quence no more than six minutes after applying sealer.**
3. Install front cover with new cover gas-ket over alignment dowels to cylinder block and cylinder heads.
4. Install front cover bolts and stud bolts

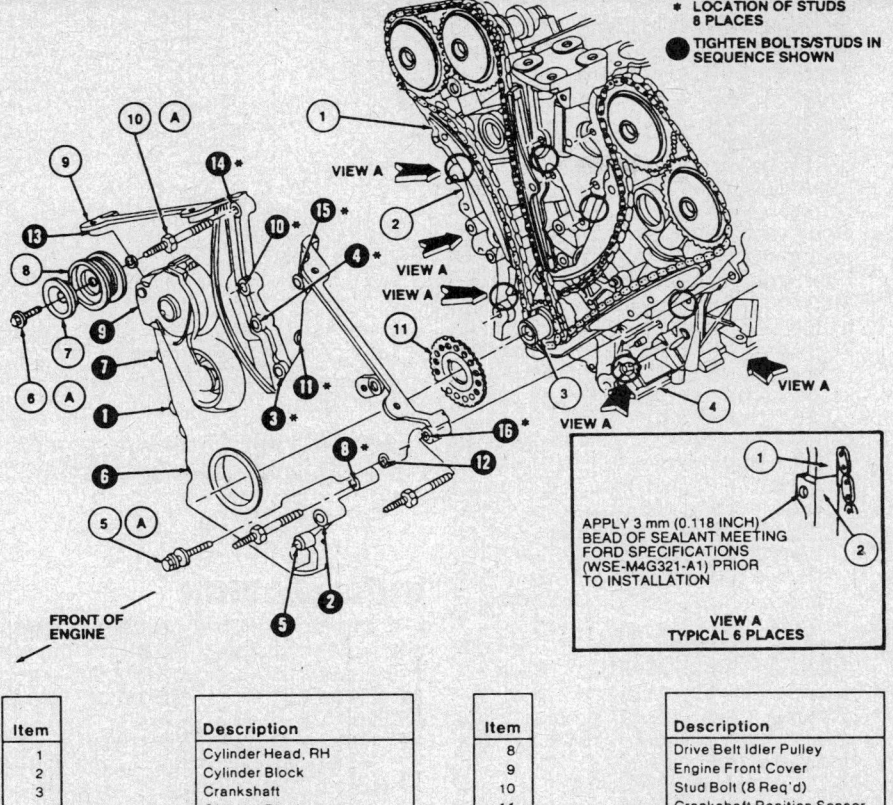

* LOCATION OF STUDS 8 PLACES
● TIGHTEN BOLTS/STUDS IN SEQUENCE SHOWN

VIEW A

APPLY 3 mm (0.118 INCH) BEAD OF SEALANT MEETING FORD SPECIFICATIONS (WSE-M4G321-A1) PRIOR TO INSTALLATION

VIEW A TYPICAL 6 PLACES

Item	Description
1	Cylinder Head, RH
2	Cylinder Block
3	Crankshaft
4	Cylinder Block
5	Bolt (8 Req'd)
6	Bolt
7	Dust Cover

Item	Description
8	Drive Belt Idler Pulley
9	Engine Front Cover
10	Stud Bolt (8 Req'd)
11	Crankshaft Position Sensor Pulse Ring
A	Tighten to 20-30 N·m (15-22 Lb-Ft)

FM1069500429000X

Fig. 21 Front cover installation

in proper locations and sequence, **Fig. 22**. Tighten cover bolts 1/4 turn after cover contacts cylinder block and cylinder heads. **Install bolts and stud bolts no more than six minutes after applying sealer.**

5. Install remaining front cover bolts and stud bolts, then **torque** all front cover bolts and stud bolts in sequence, **Fig. 21**, to 15-22 ft. lbs.

6. Install drive belt idler pulley onto righthand side of front cover. Tighten drive belt idler pulley bolt to specifications.

7. Position fuel charging wiring, then install lower fuel charging wiring bracket retainers and A/C hose bracket to front cover stud bolts. tighten bracket nut to specifications.

8. Raise and support vehicle.

9. **On models equipped with air conditioning,** position A/C compressor, then tighten compressor bolts to specifications.

10. Replace crankshaft front seal, if necessary, as described under "Crankshaft Seal, Replace."

11. Install oil pan as described under "Oil Pan, Replace."

12. Connect fuel charging wiring, CKP and CMP sensor electrical connectors.

13. Install crankshaft pulley.

14. Install alternator bracket and alternator to engine as described under "Electrical."

15. Install righthand front wheel and tire assembly, then lower vehicle.

16. Lower engine to installed position, then support engine with three bar engine support tool No. D88-6000-A, or equivalent.

17. Raise and support vehicle, then install front engine support insulator through bolts as described under "Engine Mount, Replace."

18. Lower vehicle, then install power steering pump support and pump to front of engine. Tighten pump support nuts and pump bolts to specifications.

19. Install power steering pump pulley onto pump, then loosely install bolts.

20. Install accessory drive belt as described under "Serpentine Drive Belt."

21. Tighten power steering pump pulley bolts to specifications.

22. Position and connect fuel charging wiring to three connectors on in-line connector bracket at front of righthand cylinder head.

23. Install upper front engine support insulator and upper front engine support bracket as described under "Engine Mount, Replace."

24. Remove engine support tool, then connect battery ground cable.

25. Fill crankcase to proper level with specified engine oil, then fill power steering system with specified steering fluid as described in "Power Steering" section.

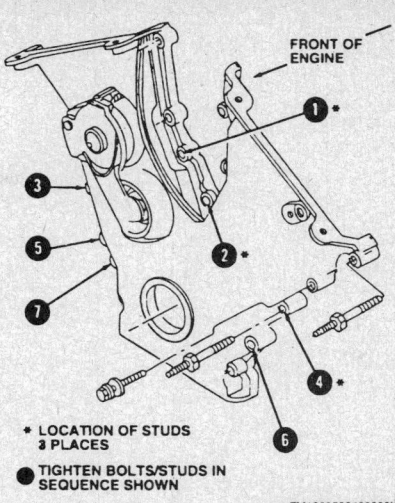

* LOCATION OF STUDS 2 PLACES
● TIGHTEN BOLTS/STUDS IN SEQUENCE SHOWN

FM1069500428000X

Fig. 22 Front cover bolt & stud bolt installation sequence

26. Run engine and check for leaks, then recheck fluid levels.

TIMING CHAIN
REPLACE
REMOVAL

If the timing chain guides, tensioner arms or the chains show premature wear or damage, also replace camshaft damper as described under "Camshaft Damper, Replace."

1. Remove front cover as described under "Front Cover, Replace."

2. Rotate crankshaft keyway to 11 o'clock location to position crankshaft at Top Dead Center (TDC) No. 1 cylinder.

3. Verify alignment arrows on camshafts are aligned. If arrows are not aligned, rotate crankshaft one complete revolution.

4. Rotate crankshaft to position crankshaft keyway to 3 o'clock position. This will position righthand cylinder head camshafts to neutral position (base circle).

5. Remove righthand timing chain tensioner bolts, then the tensioner.

6. Remove cylinder head camshaft journal thrust cap bolts and thrust caps from righthand cylinder head, noting the following:

   a. **Remove cylinder head camshaft journal thrust caps first to ensure damage to cylinder head camshaft journal thrust caps does not occur.**

   b. Cylinder head camshaft journal caps and cylinder heads are numbered to ensure they are assembled in original positions. If removed, keep camshaft journal caps from each cylinder head together. Do not mix with camshaft journal caps from another cylinder head.

7. Loosen remaining righthand cylinder head camshaft journal cap bolts in sequence, **Fig. 17**, seven to eight revo-

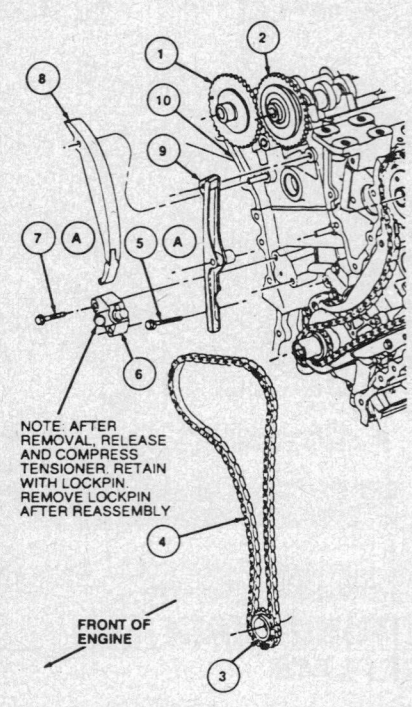

NOTE: AFTER REMOVAL, RELEASE AND COMPRESS TENSIONER. RETAIN WITH LOCKPIN. REMOVE LOCKPIN AFTER REASSEMBLY

FRONT OF ENGINE

Item	Part Number	Description
1	6250	RH Exhaust Camshaft
2	6250	RH Intake Camshaft
3		RH Timing Chain Crankshaft Sprocket
4		RH Timing Chain
5		Bolt (2 Req'd)
6		Timing Chain Tensioner
7		Bolt (2 Req'd)
8		Timing Chain Tensioner Arm
9		Timing Chain Guide
10		RH Cylinder Head
A		Tighten to 20-30 N·m (15-22 Lb-Ft)

FM1069500426000X

Fig. 23 Timing chain replacement. Righthand, Lefthand similar

lutions, in several passes, to allow camshafts to be raised from righthand cylinder head. Do not completely remove bolts.

8. With crankshaft keyway at 3 o'clock location and righthand cylinder head camshaft journal caps and camshafts loose on righthand cylinder head, remove rocker arms. If valve tappets and roller rocker arms are to be reused, mark position of rocker arms and valve tappets to ensure they are assembled in original positions.

9. Remove righthand timing chain tensioner arm and righthand timing chain. **If righthand tensioner arm and chain guide are to be reused, mark position of tensioner arm and chain guide to ensure they are assembled in original positions.**

10. Remove righthand timing chain guide bolts, then the guide, **Fig. 23.**

11. Remove righthand timing chain crankshaft sprocket, then rotate

crankshaft two revolutions and position crankshaft keyway to 11 o'clock location. This will position lefthand cylinder head camshafts to neutral position (base circle).

12. Verify alignment arrows on camshaft are aligned, then remove lefthand timing chain tensioner bolts and tensioner.

13. Remove cylinder head camshaft journal thrust cap bolts and caps from lefthand cylinder head, noting the following:
    a. **Remove cylinder head camshaft journal thrust caps first to ensure damage to cylinder head camshaft journal thrust caps does not occur.**
    b. Cylinder head camshaft journal caps and cylinder heads are numbered to ensure they are assembled in original positions. If removed, keep camshaft journal caps from each cylinder head together. Do not mix with camshaft journal caps from another cylinder head.

14. Loosen remaining lefthand cylinder head camshaft journal cap bolts in sequence, **Fig. 17,** in seven to eight revolutions, to allow camshafts to be raised from cylinder heads. Do not completely remove bolts.

15. With crankshaft keyway at 11 o'clock location and lefthand cylinder head camshaft journal caps and camshafts loose on lefthand cylinder head, remove rocker arms. If valve tappets and roller rocker arms are to be reused, mark position of rocker arms and valve tappets to ensure they are assembled in original positions.

16. Remove lefthand timing chain tensioner arm and lefthand timing chain. **If lefthand tensioner arm and chain guide are to be reused, mark position of tensioner arm and chain guide to ensure they are assembled in original positions.**

17. Remove lefthand timing chain guide bolts, then the guide.

18. Remove lefthand timing chain crankshaft sprocket, then inspect timing chain tensioners, tensioner arms, guides, crankshaft sprockets and timing chains for wear or damage. Replace components as necessary.

19. Using small screwdriver, release timing chain tensioner ratchet/pawl mechanism through access hole in tensioners.

20. Compress tensioner rack and piston into tensioner housing by inserting small wire into top of piston and gently unseat oil check ball, then compress tensioners by hand.

21. With tensioner rack and piston compressed, install .06 inch drill bit or wire into small hole above ratchet, engaging lock groove in rack of timing chain tensioners, **Fig. 24. Timing tensioners must be installed onto engine while compressed and locked. Failure to compress timing chain before installing may cause damage to engine.**

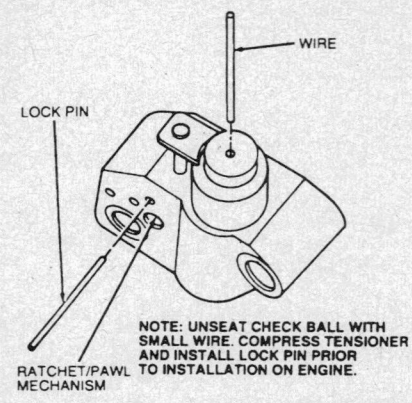

WIRE

LOCK PIN

RATCHET/PAWL MECHANISM

NOTE: UNSEAT CHECK BALL WITH SMALL WIRE. COMPRESS TENSIONER AND INSTALL LOCK PIN PRIOR TO INSTALLATION ON ENGINE.

FM1069500430000X

Fig. 24 Timing chain tensioner compression

INSTALLATION

If the timing chain guides, tensioner arms or the chains show premature wear or damage, also replace camshaft damper as described under "Camshaft Damper, Replace."

1. Ensure crankshaft keyway is at 11 o'clock location, then install lefthand timing chain crankshaft sprocket onto crankshaft, aligning key with keyway on sprocket. **Crankshaft keyway must be at 11 o'clock location before assembly. If not in this location, engine damage may result.**

2. Install lefthand timing chain guide and bolts to engine. Tighten guide bolts to specifications.

3. Verify alignment arrows on camshafts are aligned with each other, then install lefthand timing chain over lefthand crankshaft sprocket and lefthand camshaft sprockets.

4. Align timing index marks on lefthand timing chain with timing index marks on lefthand crankshaft sprocket and camshaft sprockets.

5. Install lefthand timing chain tensioner arm over alignment dowel on lefthand cylinder head, then install compressed lefthand timing chain tensioner and bolts onto cylinder block. Tighten lefthand timing chain tensioner bolts to specifications. **Timing chain tensioners must be installed onto engine while compressed and locked. Failure to compress tensioners before installation may cause damage to engine.**

6. Verify timing index marks on lefthand timing chain are in alignment with timing index marks on lefthand crankshaft sprocket and camshaft sprockets, **Fig. 25.**

7. Install righthand timing chain crankshaft sprocket onto crankshaft, then align crankshaft key with keyway on crankshaft sprocket.

8. Install righthand timing chain guide and bolts to engine. Tighten righthand timing chain guide bolts to specifications.

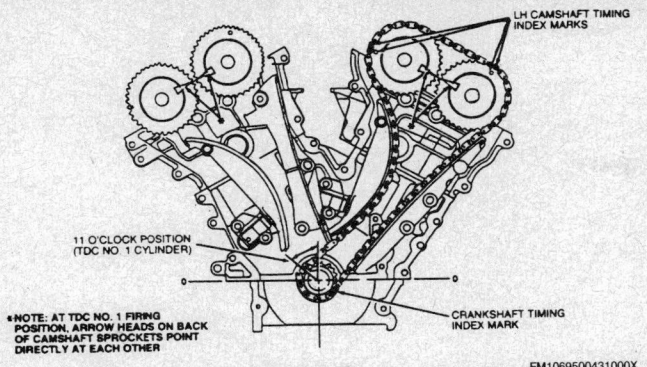

Fig. 25 Lefthand timing chain index mark alignment

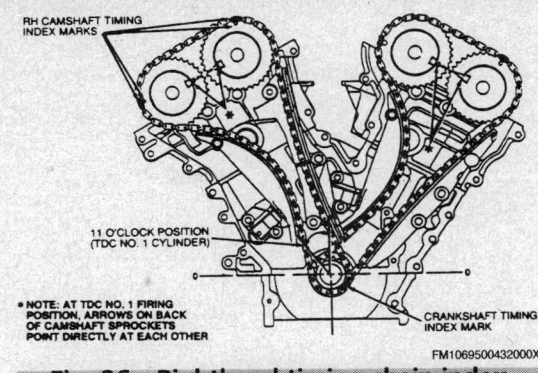

Fig. 26 Righthand timing chain index mark alignment

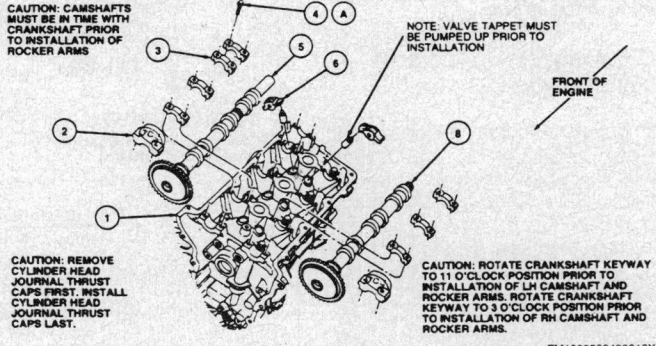

Fig. 27 Camshaft replacement (Part 1 of 2)

Item	Description	Item	Description
1	Cylinder Head	6	Rocker Arm (12 Req'd Each Side)
2	Camshaft Journal Thrust Cap (2 Req'd)	7	Valve Tappet (12 Req'd Each Side)
3	Camshaft Journal Thrust Cap (7 Req'd)	8	LH Exhaust Camshaft
4	Bolt (18 Req'd)	A	Tighten to 8-12 N·m (71-106 Lb-In)
5	LH Intake Camshaft		

FM1069500433020X

Fig. 27 Camshaft replacement (Part 2 of 2)

9. Verify alignment arrows on camshafts are aligned with each other, then install righthand timing chain over righthand crankshaft sprocket and righthand camshaft sprockets. Align timing index marks on righthand timing chain with timing index marks on righthand crankshaft sprocket and camshaft sprockets.
10. Install righthand timing chain tensioner arm over alignment dowel on righthand cylinder head.
11. Install compressed righthand timing chain tensioner and bolts onto cylinder block. Tighten tensioner bolts to specifications. **Timing chain tensioners must be installed onto engine while compressed and locked. Failure to compress tensioners before installation may cause damage to engine.**
12. Verify timing index marks on righthand timing chain are in alignment with timing index marks on righthand crankshaft sprocket and camshaft sprockets, **Fig. 26.**
13. Lubricate rocker arms with suitable engine assembly lubricant, then install rocker arms onto lefthand cylinder head under camshafts. Ensure rocker arms are installed in original locations. **Crankshaft keyway must be at 11 o'clock location before installing lefthand cylinder head rocker arms. Failure to do so may lead to engine damage.**
14. With lefthand cylinder head rocker arms installed, tighten lefthand cylinder head camshaft journal cap bolts in sequence, **Fig. 18**, in several passes, to 71-106 inch lbs. **Do not install cylinder head camshaft journal thrust caps until camshaft journal caps are installed or damage to thrust caps may occur.**
15. With lefthand cylinder camshaft journal caps installed and camshafts aligned with thrust caps, install thrust caps and tighten bolts to specifications.
16. Rotate crankshaft two revolutions and position crankshaft keyway to 3 o'clock location. This will position righthand cylinder head camshafts to neutral position (base circle).
17. Lubricate rocker arms with suitable engine assembly lubricant, then install rocker arms onto righthand cylinder head under camshafts. Ensure rocker arms are installed in original locations.

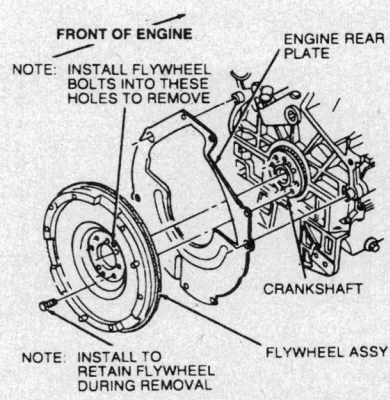

Fig. 28 Flywheel retaining bolt installation

Crankshaft keyway must be at 3 o'clock location before installing righthand cylinder head rocker arms. Failure to do so may lead to engine damage.

18. With righthand cylinder head rocker arms installed, tighten righthand cylinder head camshaft journal cap bolts in sequence, **Fig. 18,** in several passes, to 71-106 inch lbs. **Do not install cylinder head camshaft journal thrust caps until camshaft journal caps are installed or damage to thrust caps may occur.**
19. With righthand cylinder camshaft journal caps installed and camshafts aligned with thrust caps, install thrust caps and tighten bolts to specifications.
20. Remove lock pins from timing chain tensioners, then verify index timing marks on timing chains are in alignment with timing index marks on crankshaft and camshaft sprockets, **Figs. 25 and 26.**
21. Install front cover as described under "Front Cover, Replace."

CAMSHAFT
REPLACE

If timing chain guides, tensioner arms or chains show premature wear or damage, also replace camshaft damper as described under "Camshaft Damper, Replace."

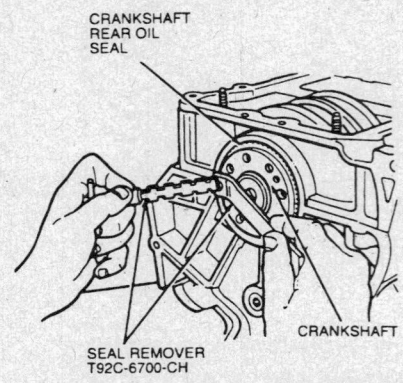

CRANKSHAFT REAR OIL SEAL

CRANKSHAFT

SEAL REMOVER T92C-6700-CH

CRANKSHAFT

Fig. 29 Crankshaft rear oil seal removal

1. Remove timing chains and rocker arms as described under "Timing Chain, Replace."
2. Remove intake and exhaust camshafts from cylinder heads, **Fig. 27.**
3. Inspect camshafts and cylinder heads for wear or damage. Replace components as necessary.
4. **Ensure camshaft keyway is at 11 o'clock position before installing. Failure to do so may lead to engine damage.**
5. Lubricate camshafts with engine assembly lubricant, then install camshafts into cylinder heads with timing marks on camshaft sprockets aligned.
6. Install timing chains and rocker arms as described under "Timing Chain, Replace."

CRANKSHAFT SEAL
REPLACE

1. Raise and support vehicle, then remove righthand front wheel and tire assembly.
2. Remove righthand splash shield from fender apron for access to crankshaft pulley.
3. Remove accessory drive belt as described under "Serpentine Drive Belt."
4. Remove crankshaft pulley bolt and washer from crankshaft, then, using crankshaft damper remover tool No. T58P-6316-D, or equivalent, remove crankshaft pulley from crankshaft.
5. Using seal remover tool No. T92C-6700-CH, or equivalent, remove crankshaft front seal from front cover.
6. Reverse procedure to install, noting the following:
   a. Lubricate seal sealing surfaces with suitable engine assembly lubricant, then, using crankshaft seal replacer tool No. T88T-6701-A and crankshaft damper replacer tool No. T74P-7316-B, or equivalents, install crankshaft front seal into front cover.
   b. Clean crankshaft pulley sealing surfaces with suitable metal cleaner to remove all residues which could interfere with sealer's ability to adhere.

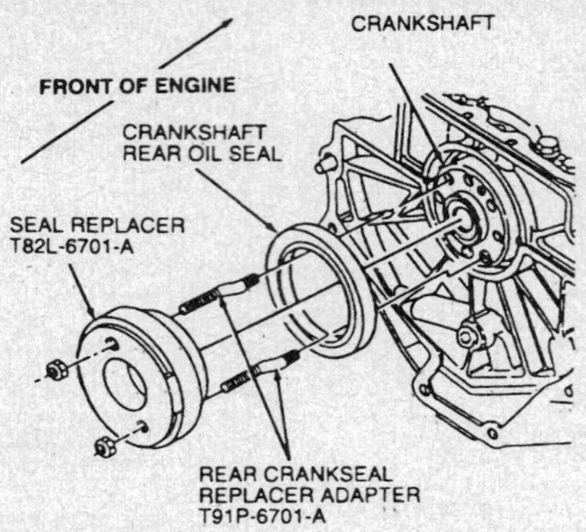

FRONT OF ENGINE

CRANKSHAFT

CRANKSHAFT REAR OIL SEAL

SEAL REPLACER T82L-6701-A

REAR CRANKSEAL REPLACER ADAPTER T91P-6701-A

NOTE: LUBRICATE CRANKSHAFT FLANGE AND REAR OIL SEAL BORE WITH ENGINE ASSY LUBRICANT D9AZ-19579-D OR EQUIVALENT MEETING FORD SPECIFICATION ESR-M99C80-A PRIOR TO INSTALLATION OF SEAL

FM1069500436000X

Fig. 30 Crankshaft rear oil seal installation

   c. Apply black silicone rubber part No. F4AZ-19562-B or equivalent, to front of crankshaft on inside diameter surface of pulley at keyway.
   d. Install crankshaft pulley using crankshaft damper replacer tool No. T74P-6316-B, or equivalent, and washer from bolt.
   e. **Torque** crankshaft pulley bolt to 89 ft. lbs., then loosen bolt a minimum of one full turn. Next, **torque** bolt to 35–39 ft. lbs., then rotate bolt an additional 85–95 degrees.

CRANKSHAFT REAR OIL SEAL
REPLACE

1. Remove flywheel as follows:
   a. Remove transaxle as described under "Clutch & Manual Transaxle for manual transaxle, or in "Automatic Transaxle/Transmission" section for automatic transaxle.
   b. **On models equipped with manual transaxle,** remove clutch pressure plate and clutch disc as described under "Clutch & Manual Transaxle."
   c. **On all models,** observe position of flywheel on crankshaft flange, then remove flywheel bolts.
   d. Install one flywheel bolt loosely to retain flywheel during removal, then install flywheel bolts into holes, **Fig. 28.**
   e. Tighten bolts to unseat flywheel from crankshaft, then remove bolt and flywheel from engine.
2. Using seal remover tool No. T92C-6700-CH, or equivalent, and piece of thin copper shim stock, .01 inch thick between crankshaft and seal remover tool, remove crankshaft rear oil seal from cylinder block, **Fig. 29.**
3. Clean and inspect crankshaft rear oil seal sealing surfaces on crankshaft and cylinder block, then lubricate crankshaft flange and crankshaft rear oil seal bore with suitable engine assembly lubricant.

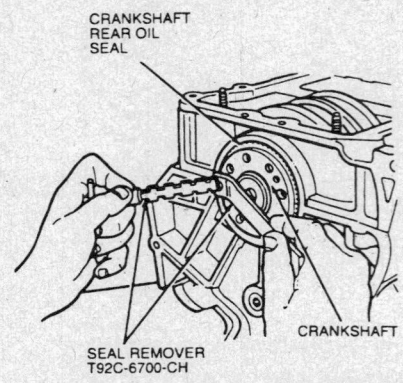

* LOCATION OF STUDS   FRONT OF ENGINE
● REMOVE BOLTS/STUDS IN SEQUENCE SHOWN

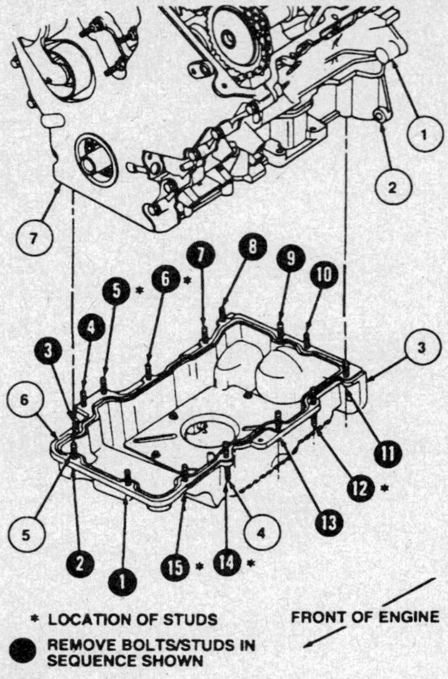

Item	Description
1	Upper Cylinder Block
2	Lower Cylinder Block
3	Oil Pan
4	Stud Bolt (5 Req'd)
5	Bolt (10 Req'd)
6	Oil Pan Gasket
7	Engine Front Cover

FM1099500072000X

Fig. 31 Oil pan bolt removal sequence

4. Install crankshaft rear oil seal using rear main seal replacer tool No. T82L-6701-A and rear crank seal replacer adapters tool No. T91P-6701-A, or equivalents, **Fig. 30.** Alternate bolt tightening to properly seat oil seal .02–0 inch flush to rear of cylinder block.
5. Install flywheel as follows:
   a. Position flywheel on crankshaft flange, then install and tighten bolts in alternating sequence to specifications.
   b. Check flywheel runout.
   c. **On models equipped with manual transaxle,** install clutch disc and clutch pressure plate.
   d. **On all models,** install transaxle as described under **Clutch & Manual Transaxle** for manual transaxle, or in "Automatic Transaxle/Transmission section for automatic transaxle."
6. Run engine and check for leaks.

OIL PAN
REPLACE

The normal operating temperature of the exhaust system is very high. Never work around or attempt to service any part of the exhaust system until it has cooled. Use special care when working around the three way catalytic converter. These units heat to a high tempera-

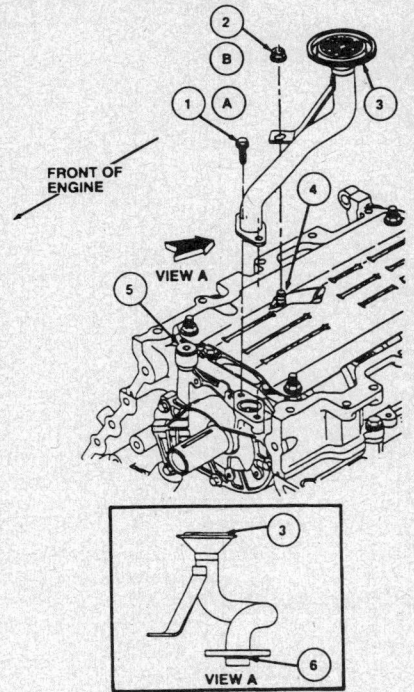

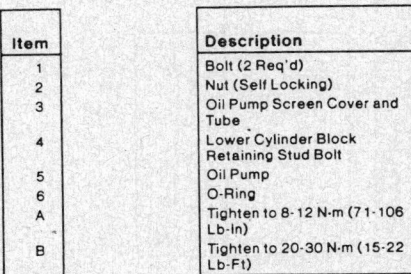

Item	Description
1	Bolt (2 Req'd)
2	Nut (Self Locking)
3	Oil Pump Screen Cover and Tube
4	Lower Cylinder Block Retaining Stud Bolt
5	Oil Pump
6	O-Ring
A	Tighten to 8-12 N·m (71-106 Lb-In)
B	Tighten to 20-30 N·m (15-22 Lb-Ft)

FM1099500073000X

Fig. 32 Oil pump screen cover and tube replacement

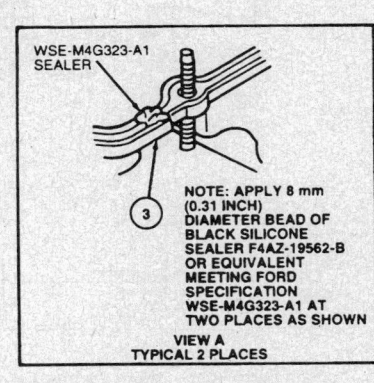

WSE-M4G323-A1 SEALER

NOTE: APPLY 8 mm (0.31 INCH) DIAMETER BEAD OF BLACK SILICONE SEALER F4AZ-19562-B OR EQUIVALENT MEETING FORD SPECIFICATION WSE-M4G323-A1 AT TWO PLACES AS SHOWN

VIEW A
TYPICAL 2 PLACES

Item	Description
1	Upper Cylinder Block
2	Lower Cylinder Block
3	Oil Pan
4	Stud Bolt (5 Req'd)

Item	Description
5	Bolt (10 Req'd)
6	Oil Pan Gasket
7	Engine Front Cover
A	Tighten to 20-30 N·m (15-22 Lb-Ft)

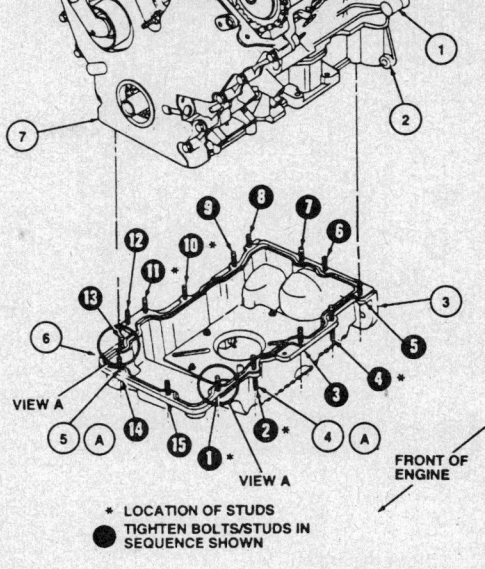

* LOCATION OF STUDS
● TIGHTEN BOLTS/STUDS IN SEQUENCE SHOWN

FM1099500074000X

Fig. 33 Oil pan installation

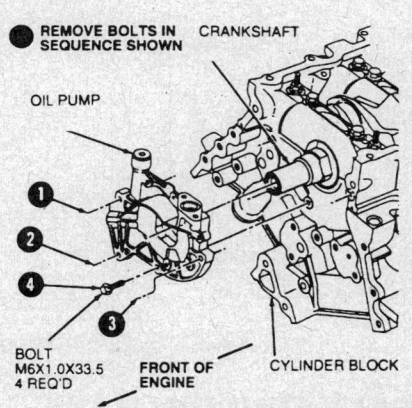

● REMOVE BOLTS IN SEQUENCE SHOWN

CRANKSHAFT

OIL PUMP

BOLT M6X1.0X33.5 4 REQ'D

FRONT OF ENGINE

CYLINDER BLOCK

FM1099500075000X

Fig. 34 Oil pump bolt removal sequence

ture after only a short period of engine operation.

1. Remove water pump pulley shield bolts from lefthand valve cover, then the water pump pulley shield from vehicle.
2. Install three bar engine support tool No. D88L-6000-A, or equivalent, onto engine lifting eyes and support engine.
3. Raise and support vehicle, then remove Y pipe as follows:
   a. Remove front and rear Y pipe flange fasteners from exhaust manifold, then the stud bolt and nut retainer from oil pan.
   b. Remove two remaining nuts and bolts from Y pipe outlet connection, then discard exhaust converter inlet gasket.
   c. Remove Y pipe.
4. Remove exhaust heat shield nuts, then the heat shields from lefthand side of oil pan.
5. Remove oil pan drain plug and drain engine oil from engine.
6. Install oil pan drain plug with new gasket and tighten to specifications.

7. Remove oil pan retaining bolts from transaxle housing.
8. **On models equipped with automatic transaxle,** remove engine rear plate access plug.
9. **On all models,** remove lefthand and righthand front engine support insulator through bolt as described under "Engine Mount, Replace."
10. Lower vehicle, then mark location of upper front engine support bracket.
11. Remove upper front engine support bracket nuts from upper front engine support insulator as described under "Engine Mount, Replace."
12. Raise engine to gain access for removal of oil pan. Support engine with engine support tool.

13. Raise and support vehicle, then remove oil pan retaining bolts, in sequence, from lower cylinder block, **Fig. 31.**
14. Remove oil pan and gasket, then discard gasket.
15. Remove oil pump screen cover and tube nut from lower cylinder block stud bolt.
16. Remove oil pump screen cover and tube bolts from oil pump, then the cover and tube from engine, **Fig. 32.**
17. Reverse procedure to install, noting the following:
   a. Inspect oil pump screen cover and tube O-ring for damage and wear. Replace O-ring as necessary.
   b. Install new self-locking oil pump screen cover and tube support nut to lower cylinder block stud. Tighten nut to specifications.
   c. Clean oil pan with suitable soap and water solution, then dry completely with compressed air. Inspect oil pan for damage and replace as necessary.
   d. Clean oil pan to lower cylinder block sealing surfaces with shop towel and suitable metal surface cleaner to remove all residues which may interfere with sealer's ability to adhere.
   e. Apply .31 inch diameter bead of suitable sealer on oil pan gasket, **Fig. 33,** then install new oil pan gasket.
   f. Tighten oil pan to transaxle bolts to specifications.
   g. **Torque** oil pan retaining bolts and studs in sequence, **Fig. 33,** to

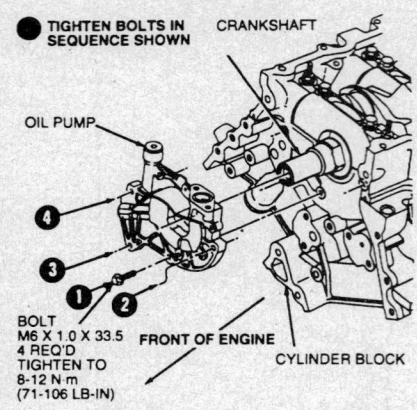

Fig. 35 Oil pump bolt tightening sequence

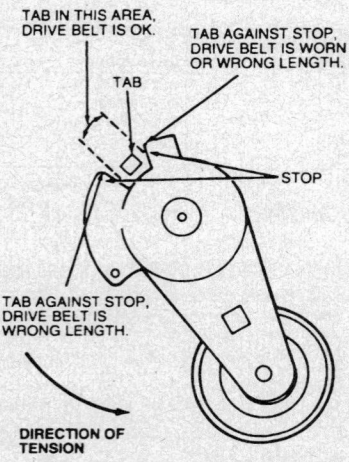

Fig. 36 Drive belt wear indicator mark

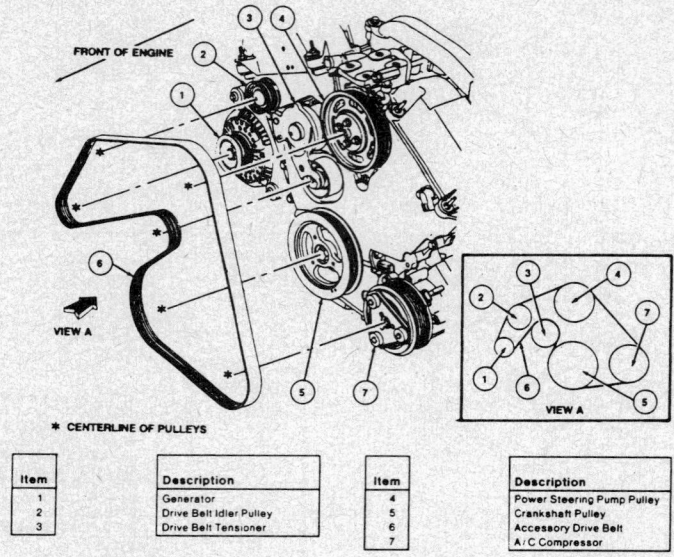

Fig. 37 Drive belt routing. Accessory with A/C

Item	Description	Item	Description
1	Generator	4	Power Steering Pump Pulley
2	Drive Belt Idler Pulley	5	Crankshaft Pulley
3	Drive Belt Tensioner	6	Accessory Drive Belt
		7	A/C Compressor

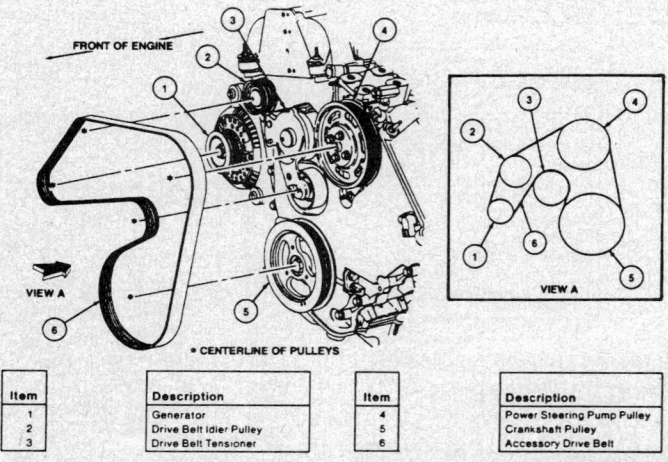

Fig. 38 Drive belt routing. Accessory less A/C

Item	Description	Item	Description
1	Generator	4	Power Steering Pump Pulley
2	Drive Belt Idler Pulley	5	Crankshaft Pulley
3	Drive Belt Tensioner	6	Accessory Drive Belt

15-22 ft. lbs.

h. Tighten oil pan to transaxle housing bolts to specifications.

OIL PUMP
REPLACE

1. Remove oil pan and oil pump screen cover and tube as described under "Oil Pan, Replace."
2. Remove front cover as described under "Front Cover, Replace."
3. Remove timing chains as described under "Timing Chain, Replace."
4. Remove crankshaft sprockets from crankshaft, then the oil pump bolts in sequence, **Fig. 34.**
5. Remove pump from cylinder block and inspect. Replace if necessary.
6. Reverse procedure to install, noting the following:
   a. **Torque** oil pump bolts in sequence, **Fig. 35,** to 71-106 inch lbs.
   b. Fill crankcase to proper level with specified engine oil, then run engine and check for leaks.

BELT TENSION DATA

Drive belts have an automatic drive belt tensioner and do not require adjustment.

The automatic belt tensioner is a spring loaded device which sets and maintains the drive belt tension. The drive belt should not require tension adjustment for the life of the drive belt.

The automatic belt tensioner has a drive belt wear indicator mark, **Fig. 36.** If the indicator mark is not approximately in the middle between the tabs on the front cover, the belt is worn or an incorrect belt is installed.

SERPENTINE DRIVE BELT
ROUTING

Refer to **Figs. 37 through 39** for belt routing.

BELT, REPLACE

Minor cracks in the V-grooved portion of the drive belt are considered normal and acceptable. If the drive belt has chunks missing from the ribs, the drive belt should be replaced.

Conditions requiring drive belt replacement are rib chunk out, severe glazing, frayed cords, etc. Replace any drive belt exhibiting one of these conditions.

1. **On water pump drive belt,** remove water pump pulley shield bolts from lefthand valve cover, then the shield from vehicle.
2. Remove water pump drive pulley, then rotate water pump belt tensioner clockwise by hand.
3. **On accessory drive belt,** rotate tensioner clockwise using breaker bar installed in 3/8-inch square hole in drive belt tensioner arm.
4. **On all drive belts,** lift belt over pulley flanges, then remove from vehicle.

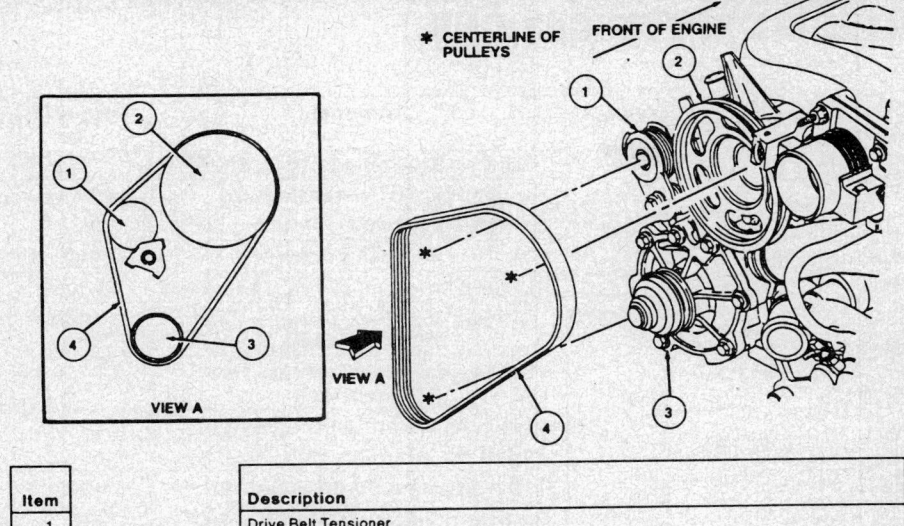

Fig. 39 Drive belt routing. Water pump

Item	Description
1	Drive Belt Tensioner
2	Water Pump Drive Pulley
3	Water Pump
4	Water Pump Drive Belt

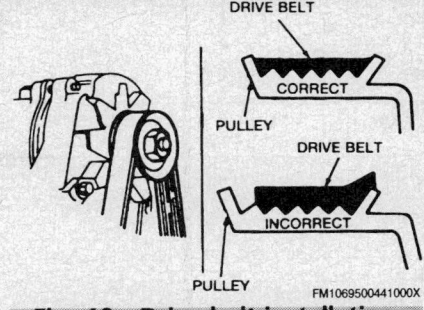

Fig. 40 Drive belt installation

5. **On accessory drive belt,** position belt under tensioner pulley into recess in front cover and up onto tensioner pulley.
6. **On water pump drive belt,** install belt by rotating tensioner clockwise by hand.
7. **On all drive belts,** install drive belt onto rest of pulleys, rotating tensioner clockwise to install belt on last pulley.
8. Ensure all V-grooves on belt make proper contact with pulley, **Fig. 40.**
9. **On water pump drive belt,** install water pump pulley shield, then the shield bolts to lefthand valve cover.

BELT TENSIONER, REPLACE

Accessory Drive

1. Remove drive belt as described under "Belt Replacement."
2. Loosen belt tensioner bolts completely, then remove tensioner from front of engine.
3. Align drive belt tensioner spring to slot in front cover, then install tensioner onto front cover. Tighten tensioner bolt to specifications.
4. Install drive belt as described under "Belt Replacement."

Water Pump

1. Remove water pump drive belt as described under "Belt Replacement."
2. Remove tensioner bolt and tensioner from water pump.
3. Align tab on tensioner with hole in mounting area on water pump, then install tensioner onto pump. Tighten bolts to specifications.
4. Install water pump drive belt as described under "Belt Replacement."

COOLING SYSTEM BLEED

Refer to "2.0L/4-122 Engine" for bleeding cooling system.

THERMOSTAT
REPLACE

Never remove the pressure relief cap under any conditions while the engine is operating. Failure to follow these instructions could result in damage to the cooling system or engine and/or personal injury. To avoid having scalding coolant or steam blow out of the cooling system or radiator coolant recovery reservoir, use extreme care when removing the pressure relief cap from a hot cooling system or radiator coolant recovery reservoir. Wait until the engine has cooled, then wrap a thick cloth around the pressure cap and turn it slowly until pressure begins to release. Step back while the pressure is released from the cooling system. When certain all pressure has been released, press down on the pressure cap (still with a cloth), turn and remove pressure relief cap.

1. Drain engine cooling system as described under "Cooling System Bleed" so engine coolant level is below water thermostat, then remove battery.
2. Disconnect radiator hoses from thermostat housing, then remove housing.
3. Remove housing bolts, then separate thermostat housings.
4. Remove O-ring seal and thermostat from housing. Inspect O-ring for damage and replace if necessary.
5. Reverse procedure to install. Fill cooling system with specified coolant mixture, then bleed system as described under "Cooling System Bleed."

WATER PUMP
REPLACE

1. Drain engine cooling system as described under "Cooling System Bleed."
2. Remove water pump pulley shield bolts from lefthand valve cover, then the shield from vehicle.
3. Rotate water pump drive belt tensioner clockwise to relieve tension on drive belt, then remove belt from pump and pump drive pulley.
4. Remove inlet and outlet hoses from pump.
5. Remove pump to lefthand cylinder head bolts, then the pump from engine.
6. Separate water pump housing and remove water pump drive belt tensioner if necessary.
7. Inspect pump and hoses for wear or damage. Replace components as necessary.
8. Reverse procedure to install, noting the following:
   a. Clean water pump to water pump housing gasket sealing surfaces using wire brush.
   b. Install new water pump to water pump housing gasket, if removed.
   c. Install new torque-to-yield water pump bolts onto lefthand cylinder head to 11-13 ft. lbs., then rotate bolts 85-95 degrees.
   d. Lubricate pump inlet and outlet hoses with suitable silicone lubricant.
   e. Rotate water pump drive belt tensioner clockwise when installing belt.
   f. Fill engine cooling system as described under "Cooling System Bleed," then run engine and check for coolant leaks.

RADIATOR
REPLACE

Refer to "2.0L/4-122 Engine" for radiator replacement.

FUEL PUMP
REPLACE

Refer to "2.0L/4-122 Engine" for fuel pump replacement.

FUEL FILTER
REPLACE

Refer to "2.0L/4-122 Engine" for fuel filter replacement.

TIGHTENING SPECIFICATIONS

Year	Component	Torque/Ft. Lbs.
1995	A/C Compressor Bolts	15-22
	A/C Condenser Core To Radiator Bolts	24-48 ①
	A/C Hose Bracket To Front Cover Nut	71-106 ①
	Accelerator Cable Bracket To Throttle Body Bolts	71-106 ①
	Accessory Drive Belt Tensioner Bolt	15-22
	Battery Ground Cable To Engine/ Transaxle Stud Nut	15-22
	Camshaft Journal Cap Bolts	②
	Camshaft Journal Thrust Cap Bolts	71-206 ①
	Camshaft Rear Oil Seal Retainer Bolts	71-106 ①
	Crankcase Ventilation Tube	44-62 ①
	Crankshaft Pulley Bolt	②
	Cylinder Head Bolts	②
	Drive Belt Idler Pulley Bolt	15-22
	EGR Valve To Exhaust Manifold Tube Nut	26-33
	Engine Air Cleaner Tube Clamps	24-48 ①
	Engine Rear Plate Bolts	54-64 ③
	Engine & Transaxle Support Insulator Nuts	④
	Exhaust Manifold Nuts	②
	Fan Shroud Nuts	24-48 ①
	Flywheel Bolts	54-64 ③
	Front Engine Support Bracket Nuts	52-70
	Front Engine Support Bracket To Sub-Frame Bolts	20
	Front Stabilizer Link To Front Stabilizer Bar Nuts	35
	Front Tie Rod End Nuts	②
	Front Wheel Knuckle To Front Suspension Lower Arm Bolts	37-43
	Heated Oxygen Sensor	26-34
	In-Line Fuel Filter Worm Gear Mounting Clamp	15-25 ①
	Lower Radiator Hose Tube Nuts	71-106 ①
	Lower Radiator Support Bolts	71-97 ①
	Muffler Inlet Flange Nuts	26-33
	Oil Pan Drain Plug	16-22

Year	Component	Torque/Ft. Lbs.
1995	Oil Pan Retaining Bolts & Studs	②
	Oil Pan To Transaxle Bolts	25-34
	Oil Pan To Transaxle Housing Bolts	25-34
	Oil Pump Bolts	②
	Oil Pump Screen Cover & Tube Bolts	71-106 ①
	Oil Pump Screen Cover & Tube Support Nut	15-22
	Power Steering Pressure Hose Bracket Bolt	71-106 ①
	Power Steering Pump Bolts	15-22
	Power Steering Pump Pulley Bolts	15-22
	Power Steering Pump Support Nuts	71-106 ①
	Radiator To Front Sub-Frame Bolts	71-97 ①
	Shift Cable Bracket Bolts	15-19
	Shift Rod Bolt	17
	Stabilizer Bar Nut	41
	Steering Shaft Pinch Bolt	18
	Thermostat Housing Bolts	15-22
	Three-Way Catalytic Converter Nuts	22-30
	Transaxle Oil Cooler Line Bracket Nuts	18-22
	Transaxle Oil Cooler Tube To Fitting	18-23
	Transaxle Stabilizer Bar Nut	41
	Transaxle To Engine Bolts	25-34
	Torque Converter To Flywheel Nuts	54-64
	Upper Intake Manifold Bolts	②
	Valve Cover Bolts	②
	Water Crossover Pipe To Cylinder Head Bolts	71-106 ①
	Water Pump Bolts	②
	Water Pump Drive Belt Tensioner Bolt	71-106 ①
	Water Pump To Water Pump Housing Bolts	16-18
	Wheel Lug Nuts	95

①—Inch lbs.
②—Refer to text.
③—Tighten in an alternating sequence.
④—Automatic transaxle, 30-41 ft. lbs.; manual transaxle, 52-70 ft. lbs.

Clutch & Manual Transaxle

INDEX

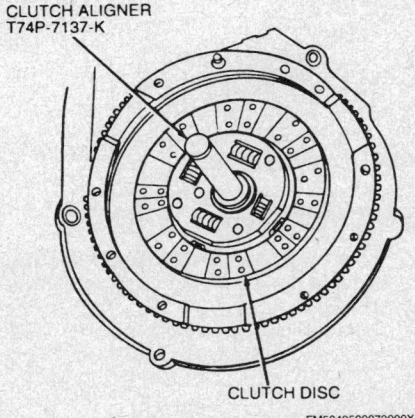

CLUTCH ALIGNER
T74P-7137-K

CLUTCH DISC

FM5049500073000X

Fig. 1 Flywheel removal

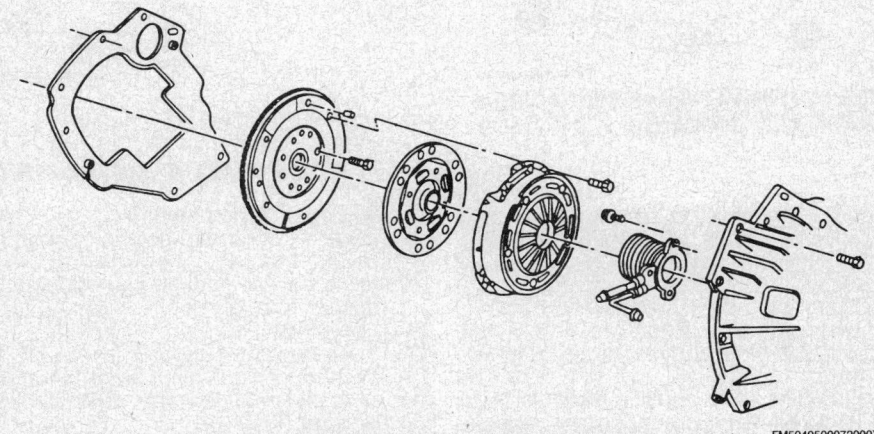

FM5049500072000X

Fig. 2 Exploded view of clutch assembly

ADJUSTMENTS

CLUTCH PEDAL

The clutch pedal mechanism is self-adjusting, not adjustment is required.

HYDRAULIC SYSTEM SERVICE

HYDRAULIC SYSTEM BLEED

Pump clutch pedal at least 30 times to ensure no air is in the system.

1. Clean top and side of fluid reservoir to avoid fluid contamination.
2. Remove air cleaner outlet tube and mass air flow sensor assembly.
3. Attach suitable hose to bleeder valve at clutch slave cylinder, then submerge other end in suitable container of clean brake fluid.
4. **Ensure clutch reservoir is full at all times.** While depressing clutch, slightly open bleeder valve, then observe air bubbles in clutch fluid at end of hose.
5. Close bleeder valve before releasing clutch pedal.
6. Repeat steps 3 and 4, until no bubbles are indicated.
7. Top off fluid in brake master cylinder reservoir, then install diaphragm and reservoir cap.
8. Replace air cleaner outlet tube and MAF sensor assembly.

CLUTCH SLAVE CYLINDER, REPLACE

1. Disconnect battery ground cable.

2. Disconnect slave cylinder to clutch master cylinder tube.
3. Remove transaxle as outlined under "Transaxle, Replace."
4. Remove three clutch slave cylinder attaching bolts, then cylinder.
5. Remove clutch slave cylinder bleed tube.
6. Reverse procedure to install. Bleed hydraulic system

CLUTCH
REPLACE

1. Remove transaxle as described under "Transaxle, Replace".
2. Flywheel housing to block dowels can be removed by using a suitable drift pin where the dowel is installed in a drilled hole **Fig. 1**, and suitable vise grip pliers where dowel is installed in a blind hole. They should be pulled or driven from their seat, ensuring to not damage the surface area around the dowel.
3. Remove clutch assembly, **Fig. 2**.
4. Reverse procedure to install, ensuring to use a suitable plastic or brass mallet to drive dowels into block. Do not damage surrounding block surface Tighten flywheel attaching bolts in sequence **Fig. 3** to specifications.

TRANSAXLE
REPLACE

1. Disconnect battery cables and remove battery.

2. Secure radiator and engine cooling fan motor, fan blade and shroud to radiator support using suitable wire, **Fig. 4.**
3. Loosen but do not remove upper shock absorber mounting nuts.
4. Remove mass air flow sensor and air cleaner outlet tube with resonator.
5. Remove engine air cleaner and lower bracket.
6. Install engine support tool No. D88L-6000-A, or equivalent.
7. Disconnect back-up lamp electrical connector.
8. Remove the bolt holding the ground strap to the transaxle.
9. Remove engine and transaxle support insulator
10. Disconnect hydraulic line and grommet from bracket.
11. Remove rubber inspection cover from transaxle clutch housing.
12. Disconnect hydraulic line fitting and position aside.
13. Remove upper transaxle to engine bolt.
14. Remove upper starter bolts and ground strap.
15. **On models with 2.0L/4-122 engine,** remove exhaust manifold heat shield and disconnect catalytic converter at exhaust manifold.
16. **On all models,** remove front tire and wheel assemblies.
17. Raise and properly support vehicle.
18. **On models with 2.0L/4-122 engine,** remove catalytic converter.
19. **On models with 2.5L/4-153 engine,** remove catalytic converter Y-pipe.

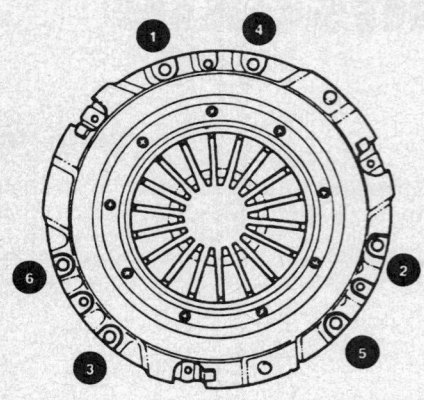

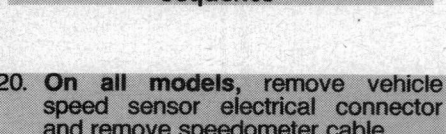

Fig. 3 Flywheel bolt tightening sequence

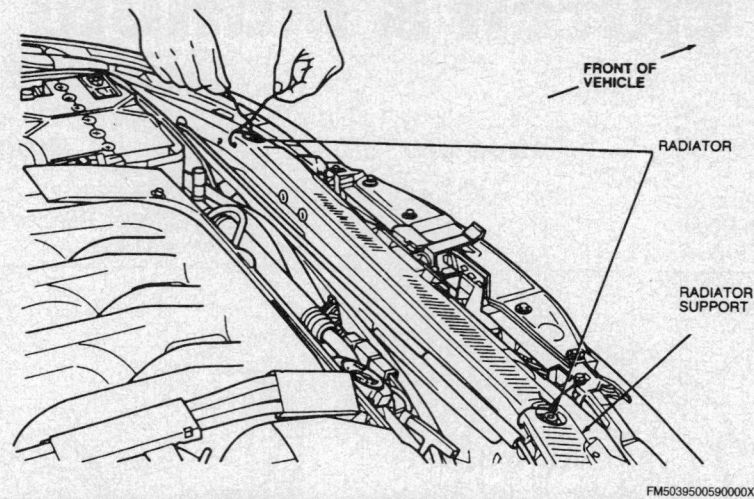

Fig. 4 Radiator & cooling fan wire support

20. **On all models,** remove vehicle speed sensor electrical connector and remove speedometer cable.
21. Remove lower radiator air deflector.
22. Push shift rod completely forward, and remove shift rod pinch bolt. Pull shift rod back and remove from transaxle.
23. Remove shift control stabilizer bar and bracket from righthand engine support insulator bracket.
24. Remove underbody heat shield beneath shift control.
25. Position and secure shift rod and stabilizer bar to allow transaxle removal.
26. Remove suction accumulator/drier from front subframe.
27. Remove left and right side halfshafts and intermediate shafts.
28. Remove righthand engine support insulator bracket.
29. Remove lefthand engine support insulator through-bolt.
30. Lower vehicle.
31. Adjust engine support tool No. D88L-6000-A, or equivalent, to remove tension at righthand front engine support bracket.
32. Remove righthand engine support bracket through-bolt.
33. Raise and properly support vehicle.
34. Remove front subframe.
35. Lower vehicle.
36. Loosen front mount nuts five turns.
37. Using suitable floor jack and wood block under transaxle, release tension from engine support tool. Lower transaxle to limits of front engine mount movement.
38. Adjust engine support tool No. D88L-6000-A, or equivalent, to hold engine.
39. Remove floor jack and wood block
40. Position transmission jack No. 014-002, or equivalent, to transmission. Secure transmission to jack.
41. Remove remaining starter bolts and position aside, supporting starter motor with suitable wire.
42. Remove engine oil pan to transaxle bolts.
43. Remove remaining bolts and separate transaxle from engine, then remove transaxle from vehicle.
44. Reverse procedure to install.

TIGHTENING SPECIFICATIONS

Year	Component	Torque/Ft. Lbs.
1995	Back-Up Lamp Switch	15-21
	Clutch Bleed Screw	10
	Clutch Bleed Tube Fitting	10.4
	Clutch Master Cylinder Nuts	7.4
	Clutch Pressure Plate To Flywheel	13-18
	Clutch Slave Cylinder Mounting	7-14
	Flywheel To Crankshaft	83
	Front Engine Support Bracket	61
	Front Shock Absorber Upper Mounting	34
	RH Engine Support Bracket	62
	Selector Housing	8
	Shift Stabilizer Bar	28-38
	Shift Rod	14-18
	Starter Motor Bolts	35
	Transaxle Case To Clutch Housing	28-38
	Transaxle to Engine	28-38
	Wheel Lug Nuts	63

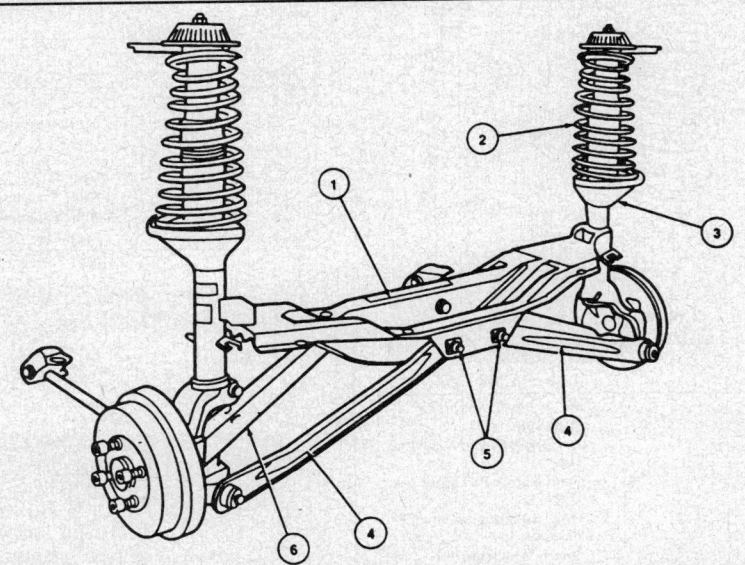

Item	Description
1	Rear Crossmember
2	Rear Spring
3	Rear Shock Absorber
4	Rear Rear Suspension Arm and Bushing

Item	Description
5	Rear Suspension Arm Adjusting Cam (2 Req'd)
6	Front Rear Suspension Arm and Bushing
7	Rear Suspension Tie Rod and Bushing

(Continued)

FM2039500044000X

Fig. 1 Rear suspension

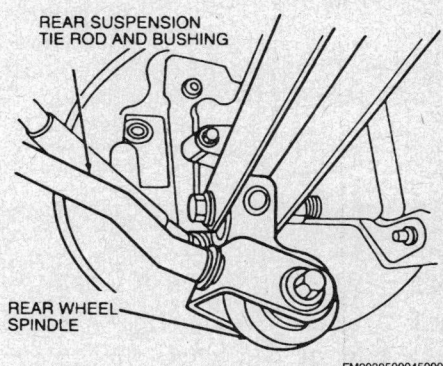

FM2039500045000X

Fig. 2 Rear spindle assembly

DESCRIPTION

The rear suspension, **Fig. 1,** is fully independent and utilizes McPherson struts for suspension damping under various conditions. A stamped rear suspension arm controls lateral wheel movement, while tie rods connected between the rear wheel spindles and forward mounted brackets control fore and aft wheel movement. The cartridge type rear wheel bearings are integrated into the hubs.

HUB & BEARING
REPLACE

1. Raise and support vehicle, then remove wheel.
2. **On models with rear disc brakes,** remove caliper and brake rotor. **It is not necessary to disconnect hydraulic line from caliper; support caliper aside to prevent hydraulic line damage.**
3. **On models with rear drum brakes,** remove brake drum retainer, then the drum.

4. **On all models,** remove and discard rear axle wheel hub retainer, then remove wheel hub. **Do not use an impact wrench to loosen retainer; spindle damage may result.**
5. Reverse procedure to install. Tighten new retainer and wheel lug nuts to specifications.

WHEEL BEARING
ADJUST

The wheel bearings are pre-greased and sealed; as a result, they require no periodic maintenance. Their cartridge design prohibits adjustment.

REAR WHEEL SPINDLE
REPLACE

1. Raise and support vehicle, then remove wheel and rear brake anti-lock sensor.
2. Remove rear wheel hub and bearing assembly as described under "Hub & Bearing, Replace." **On models with rear disc brakes,** remove disc brake shield.

4. **On models with rear drum brakes,** remove brake backing plate and position aside.
5. **On all models,** disconnect rear suspension tie rod and bushing at spindle, **Fig. 2.**
6. Disconnect rearward rear suspension arm with bushing and forward rear suspension arm with bushing at spindle, then remove strut to spindle pinch bolt.
7. Remove spindle from strut assembly.
8. Reverse procedure to install, noting the following:
   a. When installing rearward and forward rear suspension arms, tie rods and their respective bushings on spindle, tighten bolts snugly, but do not apply final torque until all other components have been installed and vehicle weight is upon wheels.
   b. Do not use an impact wrench to tighten new wheel hub retainer, as spindle damage may result.
   c. Tighten all bolts and nuts to specifications.

STRUT
REPLACE

1. Raise and support vehicle, then remove wheel.
2. Detach anti-lock brake sensor wiring from strut assembly, then remove sensor.
3. Disconnect rear brake hose from brake tube, then remove hose and retainer from strut assembly.
4. Remove parking brake cable and conduit tie strap from rear tie rod, then disconnect stabilizer bar link and bushing from forward rear suspension arm, **Fig. 3.**

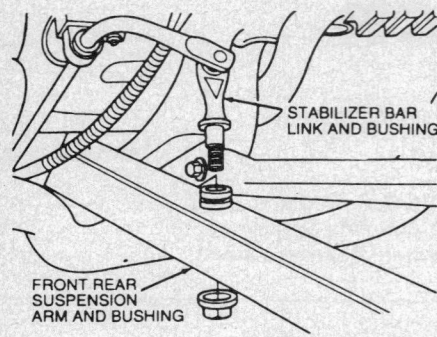

Fig. 3 Stabilizer bar link & forward rear suspension arm

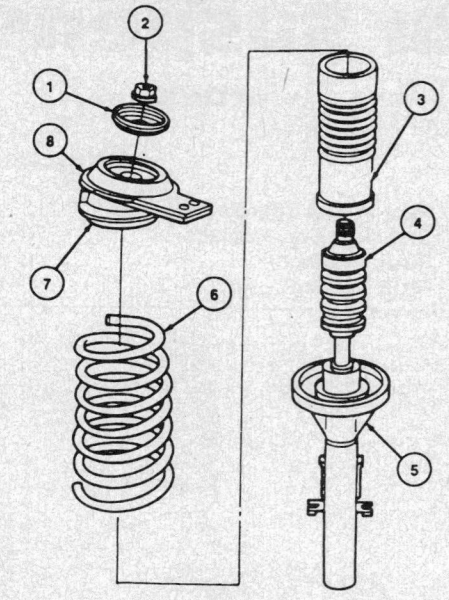

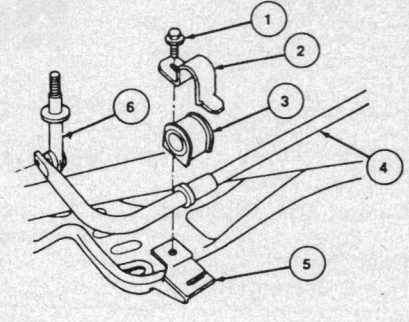

Item	Description
1	Bolt (4 Req'd)
2	Stabilizer Bar Bracket (2 Req'd)
3	Stabilizer Bar Insulator (2 Req'd)
4	Rear Stabilizer Bar
5	Rear Crossmember
6	Stabilizer Bar End

Fig. 5 Exploded view of stabilizer bar, insulator and bracket assembly

5. Disconnect rear tie rod and bushing assembly at spindle, **Fig. 2**, then place suitable jack stands beneath forward and rearward suspension arms.
6. Remove strut assembly to spindle pinch bolt, then tap on spindle to separate it from strut.
7. Compress spring using strut spring compressor tool No. T81P-5310-A or equivalent, then remove mounting bolts and strut assembly.
8. Reverse procedure to install, noting the following:
   a. When installing strut assembly, compress spring using strut spring compressor tool No. T81P-5310-A or equivalent.
   b. Tighten all bolts and nuts to specifications.
   c. Bleed brake system.

Item	Description
1	Rear Shock Absorber Bracket
2	Shock Absorber Mounting Nut
3	Rear Shock Absorber Dust Boot
4	Rear Suspension Jounce Bumper
5	Shock Absorber
6	Rear Spring
7	Spring Seat
8	Shock Absorber Bushing

Fig. 4 Exploded view of strut assembly

STRUT SERVICE

1. Position strut assembly in Rotunda strut spring compressor tool No. 014-00781 or equivalent, then compress spring.
2. Remove top nut, bracket, bushing and spring seat, **Fig. 4**, then slowly release spring compressor tool.
3. Remove spring, dust shield and jounce bumper.
4. Reverse procedure to assemble. Tighten top nut to specifications.

CONTROL ARM
REPLACE
LOWER
Forward Arm

1. Raise and support vehicle, then remove wheel.
2. Disconnect stabilizer bar end at forward suspension arm, then remove bolt and nut securing arm to rear wheel spindle.

3. Position suitable jack beneath subframe, then lower subframe until forward arm and bushing to crossmember bolt will clear fuel tank.
4. Remove forward arm from vehicle.
5. Reverse procedure to install, noting the following:
   a. When installing forward arm and bushing to crossmember bolt and nut, ensure bolt head faces fuel tank. Tighten bolt and nut snugly, but do not apply final torque until vehicle weight is resting upon rear wheels.
   b. Tighten all bolts and nuts to specifications.

Rearward Arm

1. Raise and support vehicle, then remove wheel and disconnect rearward arm from spindle.
2. Mark adjuster cam position for installation reference, then remove rearward arm and bushing assembly from crossmember.
3. Reverse procedure to install, noting the following:

a. When installing rearward arm, connect to spindle and tighten bolts and nuts snugly, but do not apply final torque until vehicle weight is resting upon rear wheels. **Tighten wheel lug nuts to specifications before lowering vehicle.**
b. After vehicle weight is resting on rear wheels, tighten rearward arm bolts and nuts to specifications.

TIE ROD
REPLACE

1. Raise and support vehicle, then remove wheel and disconnect parking brake cable and conduit from forward tie rod bracket.
2. Remove tie strap securing parking brake rear cable and conduit to rear suspension tie rod and bushing, then disconnect tie rod and bushing assembly at spindle.
3. Remove bolts, tie rod and bushing assembly and front bracket from vehicle.
4. Remove bolt and tie rod and bushing assembly from front bracket.
5. Reverse procedure to install. Tighten all bolts and nuts to specifications.

STABILIZER BAR
REPLACE

1. Raise and support vehicle, then remove wheel and disconnect stabilizer bar ends at lower arms, **Fig. 3**.
2. Remove stabilizer bar bracket, **Fig. 5**, then the stabilizer bar.
3. Remove lower suspension arm stabilizer bar insulators from stabilizer bar.
4. Reverse procedure to install. Tighten all bolts and nuts to specifications.

TIGHTENING SPECIFICATIONS

Year	Component	Torque/Ft. Lbs.	Year	Component	Torque/Ft. Lbs.
	Anti-Lock Sensor Bolt	7-8		Strut Mounting Bolts	17-22
	Drum Brake Backing Plate Bolts	33-40		Strut Top Nut	30-43
	Rearward Rear Suspension Arm To Crossmember Bolt	52-79		Strut To Spindle Pinch Bolt	52-72
	Spindle To Forward Rear Suspension Arm Bolt	52-79		Tie Rod Forward Bracket To Body Bolts	75-102
	Spindle To Rearward Rear Suspension Arm Bolt	75-102		Tie Rod To Spindle Bolt	75-102
	Stabilizer Bar Bracket Bolts	14-19		Wheel Hub Retainer	170-192
	Stabilizer Bar Link To Rear Suspension Arm	22-30		Wheel Lug Nuts	62

Front Suspension & Steering

NOTE: On Air Bag Equipped Models, Refer To "Air Bag System Precautions" Located In The Front Of This Manual For System Disarming & Arming Procedures.

INDEX

PRECAUTIONS

AIR BAG SYSTEMS

Refer to "Air Bag System Precautions" in the front of this manual for system disarming and arming procedures.

DESCRIPTION

The front suspension utilizes McPherson struts, a stabilizer bar, lower control arms and a tubular perimeter frame. Steering control is maintained by an integral power rack and pinion steering gear coupled with a belt driven, vane type power steering pump. Power steering fluid is contained in a remote reservoir.

WHEEL BEARING
ADJUST

The wheel bearings are pre-greased and sealed; as a result, they require no periodic maintenance. Their cartridge design prohibits adjustment.

HUB & BEARING
REPLACE

1. Raise and support vehicle, then remove wheel, caliper and rotor. **It is not**
necessary to disconnect brake hydraulic line to caliper, but it is necessary to prevent caliper from hanging on brake hose by supporting it from vehicle chassis.
2. Remove front brake anti-lock sensor and tie rod end cotter pin, then loosen tie rod end to knuckle nut.
3. Separate tie rod end from knuckle using the rod end remover tool No. TOOL-3290-D or equivalent, then separate halfshaft from wheel hub using special tools as shown in **Fig. 1. Support halfshaft during separation from wheel hub.**
4. Reverse procedure to install. Tighten bolts and nuts to specifications.

BALL JOINT
REPLACE
REMOVAL

1. Raise and support vehicle, then remove wheel and lower arm as described under "Control Arm, Replace."
2. Drill a .118 inch pilot hole through each rivet, **Fig. 2**, then drill a .354 inch hole in rivets to a depth of .472 inch.
3. Using a .275-.314 inch diameter punch, drive rivets out, then remove ball joint from vehicle.

INSTALLATION

1. Allow protective cover to remain on ball joint to protect seal, then position ball joint in lower arm.
2. Install 3 bolts and nuts in lower arm as shown, **Fig. 3**, to replace rivets.
3. Install lower arm as described under "Control Arm, Replace," then install wheel and lower vehicle.

STRUT
REPLACE

1. Raise and support vehicle, then remove wheel and, while holding piston rod with a hex wrench as shown in **Fig. 4**, remove strut top nut.
2. Disconnect stabilizer bar link from strut assembly, then disengage brake hose and anti-lock brake sensor wiring from strut brackets.
3. Remove strut to knuckle pinch bolt, then the strut assembly.
4. Reverse procedure to install, noting the following:
   a. Install strut top nut as shown in **Fig. 4** before tightening strut to knuckle pinch bolt.
   b. During stabilizer bar link installation, avoid damaging ball joint seal.
   c. Tighten bolts and nuts to specifications.

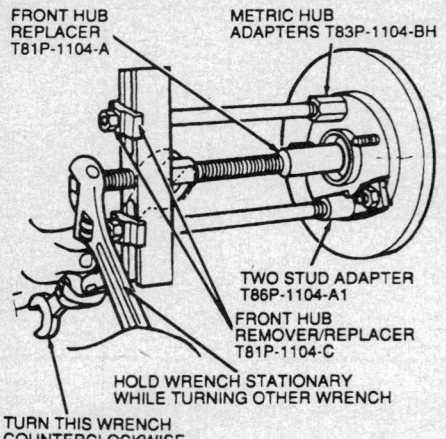

MAKE SURE THE HUB REMOVER ADAPTER IS FULLY THREADED ONTO THE HUB STUD AND IS POSITIONED OPPOSITE THE TWO STUD ADAPTER

FRONT HUB REPLACER T81P-1104-A

METRIC HUB ADAPTERS T83P-1104-BH

TWO STUD ADAPTER T86P-1104-A1

FRONT HUB REMOVER/REPLACER T81P-1104-C

HOLD WRENCH STATIONARY WHILE TURNING OTHER WRENCH

TURN THIS WRENCH COUNTERCLOCKWISE

FM2029500093000X

Fig. 1   Hub assembly removal

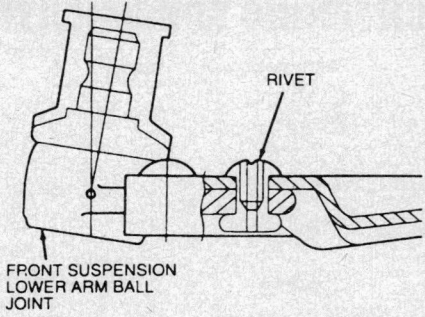

RIVET

FRONT SUSPENSION LOWER ARM BALL JOINT

FM2029500094000X

Fig. 2   Ball joint rivets

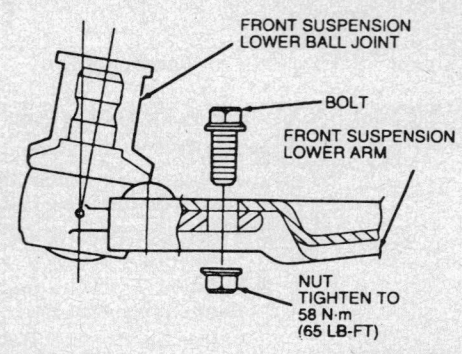

FRONT SUSPENSION LOWER BALL JOINT

BOLT

FRONT SUSPENSION LOWER ARM

NUT TIGHTEN TO 58 N·m (65 LB-FT)

FM2029500095000X

Fig. 3   Ball joint bolt installation

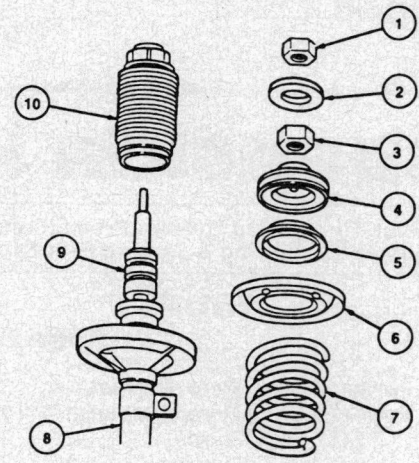

Item	Description
1	Nut
2	Retainer
3	Upper Mount Retainer Nut
4	Upper Mount
5	Bearing
6	Spring Seat
7	Front Coil Spring
8	Front Shock Absorber
9	Jounce Bumper
10	Dust Shield

FM2029500097000X

Fig. 5   Exploded view of strut assembly

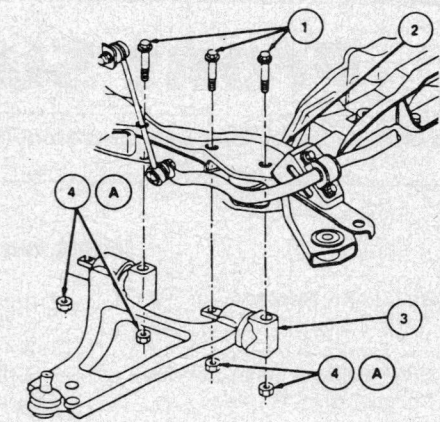

Item	Description
1	Bolts (4 Req'd)
2	Sub-frame
3	Front Suspension Lower Arm
4	Nuts (4 Req'd)
A	Tighten to 130 N·m (96 Lb-Ft)

FM2029500098000X

Fig. 6   Lower arm replacement

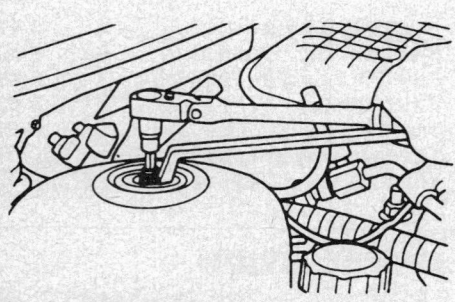

FM2029500096000X

Fig. 4   Strut top nut replacement

COIL SPRING & STRUT SERVICE

1. Remove strut assembly as described under "Strut, Replace," then position assembly in Rotunda spring compressor tool No. 086-00029 or equivalent.
2. Compress coil spring and remove thrust bearing retainer nut, thrust bearing, spring seat and dust shield, **Fig. 5.**
3. Release spring compressor tension and remove coil spring from strut assembly, then remove jounce bumper, **Fig. 5.**
4. Reverse procedure to assemble, noting the following:
   a. Compress coil spring for installation using Rotunda spring compressor tool No. 086-0029B or equivalent.
   b. Ensure coil spring seats properly in spring seat notch.
   c. Tighten thrust bearing nut to specifications.

CONTROL ARM
REPLACE
LOWER
Left Side

1. Disconnect battery ground cable, then support radiator assembly.
2. **On models with 2.0L/4-122 engine,** remove heat shield and catalytic converter retaining nuts from exhaust manifold.
3. **On all models,** raise and support vehicle, then remove 3-way catalytic converter, then disconnect steering column lower yoke.
4. **On models with manual transaxle,** disconnect gearshift rod and clevis.
5. **On all models,** remove lower front radiator cover, radiator supports and ball joint to knuckle pinch bolts.

6. Remove lower arm ball joints from knuckle, then disconnect power steering cooler lines at righthand front subframe and stabilizer bar link at front stabilizer bar.
7. Remove front and rear engine mount through bolts, then position Rotunda powertrain lift tool No. 014-00765 or equivalent under front subframe.
8. Remove lower arm bushing to subframe nuts, then lower subframe to gain access to lower suspension mounting bolts.
9. Remove 4 lower arm to subframe bolts and nuts, **Fig. 6,** then separate lower arm from subframe.
10. Reverse procedure to install, noting the following:
    a. Install lower arm bolts as shown, **Fig. 6.**
    b. Tighten all bolts and nuts to specifications.

Right Side

1. Raise and support vehicle, then re-

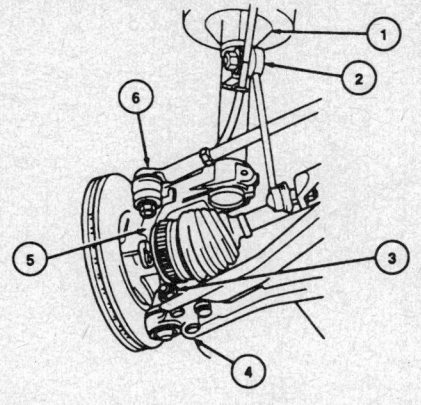

Item	Description
1	Front Shock Absorber
2	Stabilizer Bar Link
3	Lower Ball Joint-To-Knuckle Pinch Bolt
4	Front Suspension Lower Arm
5	Front Wheel Knuckle
6	Front Wheel Spindle Connecting Rod

FM2029500099000X

Fig. 7 Knuckle assembly

Item	Description
1	Front Sub-Frame
2	Stabilizer Bar
3	Stabilizer Bar Bracket
4	Stabilizer Bar Bracket Bolt (4 Req'd)
5	Stabilizer Bar Link

FM2029500100000X

Fig. 8 Stabilizer bar assembly

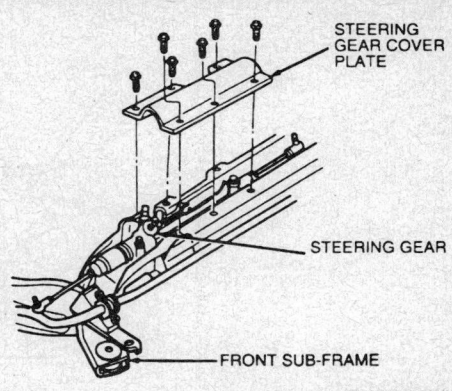

FM6029500193000X

Fig. 9 Steering gear cover plate removal

move wheel and ball joint to knuckle pinch bolt.

2. Separate lower arm ball joint from knuckle, then remove 4 lower arm bushing to subframe bolts, **Fig. 6.**
3. Reverse procedure to install, noting the following:
   a. Install lower arm bolts as shown, **Fig. 6.**
   b. Tighten all bolts and nuts to specifications.

STEERING KNUCKLE
REPLACE

1. Remove hub as described under "Hub & Bearing, Replace," then remove pinch bolt securing knuckle to lower arm ball joint.
2. Remove strut to knuckle pinch bolt, then the knuckle, **Fig. 7.**
3. Reverse procedure to install, noting the following:
   a. Install new pinch bolts and nuts on knuckle mounts.
   b. Tighten all bolts and nuts to specifications.

STABILIZER BAR
REPLACE

1. Raise and support vehicle, then remove both front wheels.
2. Remove stabilizer bar link from strut assembly, **Fig. 8,** then use ball joint remover tool No. D88L-3006-A or equivalent to remove link from stabilizer bar. **Avoid damaging stabilizer bar link ball joint seal during removal. Link assembly must be replaced if seal is damaged.**
3. Remove 4 stabilizer bar insulator bracket to subframe bolts, then the stabilizer bar.

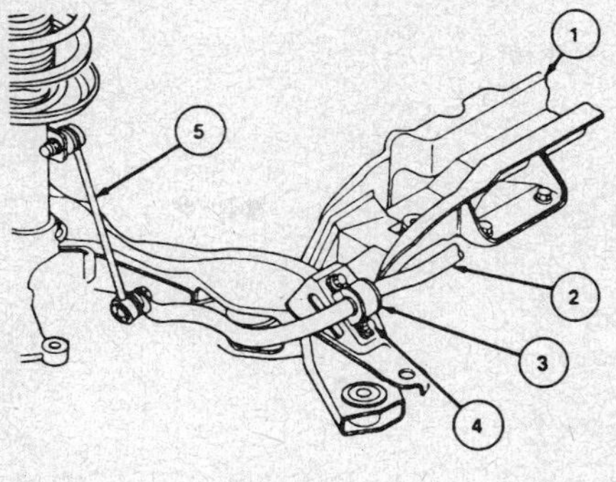

4. Reverse procedure to install, noting the following:
   a. **Avoid damaging stabilizer bar link ball joint seal during installation. Link assembly must be replaced if seal is damaged.**
   b. Tighten bolts and nuts to specifications.

TIE ROD END
REPLACE

1. Remove and discard cotter pin and nut from tie rod end, then use tie rod end remover tool No. TOOL-3290-D or equivalent to separate tie rod end from steering knuckle.
2. While holding tie rod end with a suitable wrench, loosen jam nut slightly. **Allow jam nut to remain as close to its original position as possible for tie rod end installation depth reference.**
3. Using suitable pliers, remove tie rod end from tie rod.
4. Reverse procedure to install, noting the following:
   a. Thread new tie rod end onto tie rod only until it reaches jam nut, then secure with jam nut until wheel alignment can be inspected and set.
   b. Install a new tie rod end stud nut and cotter pin.
   c. Tighten tie rod end to knuckle nut and tie rod end jam nut to specifications.
   d. Set front wheel toe to specifications as described in "Wheel Alignment" section.

POWER STEERING GEAR
REPLACE

1. Disconnect battery ground cable; then, working from inside passenger compartment, remove clamp plate bolt securing steering column shaft to flex coupling.

2. Rotate clamp plate to disengage from steering gear pinion shaft, then carefully remove floor seal.
3. Remove pinch bolt from flex coupling, then slide coupling from steering gear pinion shaft.
4. Using a suction gun or equivalent fluid suction tool, remove as much power steering fluid from pump auxiliary reservoir as possible.
5. Disconnect power steering return hose from pump auxiliary reservoir, then raise and support vehicle.
6. Remove front subframe assembly, then remove steering gear cover plate from subframe as shown, **Fig. 9.**
7. Disconnect pressure and return hose unions from power steering gear, then remove 2 bolts securing gear to subframe.
8. Separate steering gear from subframe. **Do not attempt to disassemble any part of steering gear. If any steering gear service is necessary, entire unit must be replaced.**
9. Remove spindle connecting rods and boots from steering gear assembly.
10. Reverse procedure to install, noting the following:
    a. Install new plastic seals on hydraulic lines.
    b. Tighten all bolts and nuts to specifications.
    c. Refill power steering fluid reservoir and bleed system as described under "Power Steering System Bleed."
    d. If tie rod ends were loosened during procedure, inspect and adjust wheel alignment as described in "Wheel Alignment" section.

POWER STEERING PUMP
REPLACE

2.0L/4-122 ENGINE

1. Disconnect battery ground cable, then remove exhaust manifold heat shield.
2. Disengage power steering pump reservoir hose from pump bracket and engine lifting bracket, then disconnect return hose and reservoir pump hose from pump.

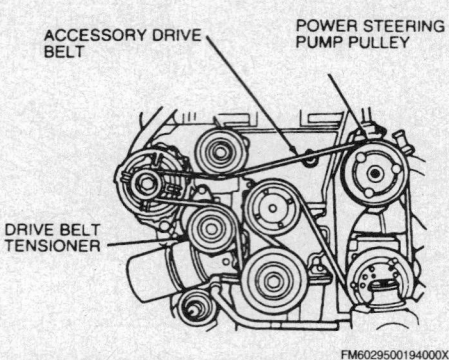

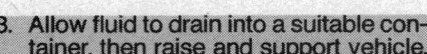

Fig. 10 Accessory drive belt & tensioner

FM6029500194000X

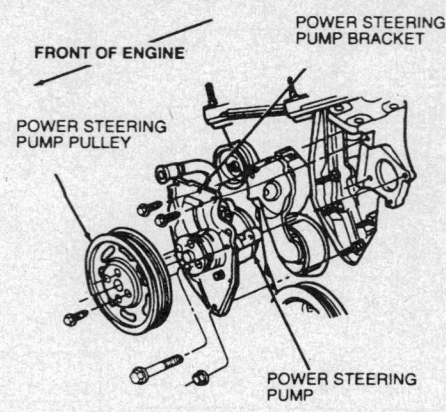

Fig. 11 Exploded view of power steering pump, pulley and bracket

FM6029500195000X

3. Allow fluid to drain into a suitable container, then raise and support vehicle.

4. Remove lower belt guard, then rotate drive belt tensioner clockwise as viewed from direction shown, **Fig. 10**, and remove accessory drive belt.

5. Lower vehicle, then remove traction assist module bolts and position module aside.

6. Rotate power steering pump pulley to gain access to each pump front mounting bolt, then remove 3 front bolts and 1 rear bolt and lift pump from vehicle.

7. If it is necessary to separate pulley from power steering pump, proceed as follows:

   a. Install power steering pump pulley remover tool No. T69L-10300-B or equivalent on pulley hub.

   b. Clamp hex head of tool in a suitable vise, then hold power steering pump in place while turning tool nut counterclockwise. **Do not apply inward or outward force on power steering pump shaft; internal pump damage may result.**

   c. Slide pulley from power steering pump shaft.

8. Reverse procedure to install, noting the following:

   a. If pulley and power steering pump were separated, install pulley on pump shaft using power steering pump pulley replacer tool No. T91P-3A733-A or equivalent. **Ensure threads on end of tool are fully engaged in power steering pump shaft; after pulley installation, ensure end of shaft is within .010 inch of being flush with pulley surface.**

   b. When placing pump in vehicle, install rear mounting bolt first, but do not tighten until three front bolts are in position.

   c. Rotate drive belt tensioner clockwise as viewed from direction shown in **Fig. 10** to install accessory drive belt.

   d. Tighten all bolts, nuts and fittings to specifications.

   e. Refill power steering fluid reservoir and bleed system as described under "Power Steering System Bleed.

2.5L/V6-153 ENGINE

1. Disconnect battery ground cable, then remove bolt securing power steering pressure hose to upper engine mount.

2. Disconnect power steering pressure hose from pump and allow fluid to drain into a suitable container, then position hose and ignition wire organizer aside.

3. Remove engine front support insulator, then loosen (but do not remove) power steering pump pulley bolts.

4. Rotate drive belt tensioner clockwise as viewed from drive belt side of engine, then remove accessory drive belt and power steering pump pulley.

5. Disconnect power steering reservoir pump hose from power steering pump, then remove pressure hose clamp from pump bracket.

6. Remove power steering pump bracket nuts and bolts, then the bracket and pump, **Fig. 11**. **Do not attempt to disassemble any part of power steering pump. If service is required, entire pump assembly must be replaced.**

7. Reverse procedure to install, noting the following:

   a. Do not tighten power steering pump pulley bolts to specifications until accessory drive belt has been installed.

   b. When installing accessory drive belt, rotate tensioner assembly clockwise as viewed from belt side of engine.

   c. Tighten all bolts, nuts and fittings to specifications.

   d. Refill power steering fluid reservoir and bleed system as described under "Power Steering System Bleed.

POWER STEERING SYSTEM BLEED

LESS AIR EVACUATOR TOOL

1. Raise and support front of vehicle, then fill power steering pump reservoir until fluid level is between MIN and MAX marks.

2. Disconnect Ignition Control Module (ICM) lead to prevent engine from starting, then crank engine for 30 seconds.

3. Check fluid level and add as necessary; then, while cranking engine again for 30 seconds, rotate steering wheel from lock to lock repeatedly. **Do not hold wheel at either lock more than 5 seconds; power steering pump damage may result.**

4. Check and add fluid as necessary, then reconnect ICM and lower vehicle.

WITH AIR EVACUATOR TOOL

1. Raise and support front of vehicle, then insert air evacuator rubber stopper securely into power steering pump reservoir opening.

2. Start engine, then apply 20-25 inches Hg vacuum for a minimum of 3 minutes with engine at idle.

3. Release vacuum and remove evacuator, then add fluid to reservoir until level is between MIN and MAX marks.

4. Install evacuator and again apply a vacuum of 20-25 inches Hg to system, then rotate steering wheel from lock to lock every 30 seconds for approximately 5 minutes. **Do not hold wheel at either lock; power steering pump damage may result.**

5. Stop engine, then release vacuum and remove air evacuator.

6. Lower front of vehicle to ground, then install power steering pump reservoir cap and start engine again.

7. Cycle steering wheel from lock to lock every 30 seconds for approximately 5 minutes.

8. If system has not yet been completely purged of air, repeat evacuation procedure.

9. Inspect all hose connections for fluid leakage and repair as necessary.

TIGHTENING SPECIFICATIONS

Year	Component	Torque/Ft. Lbs.
1995	Engine Mount Through Bolts	40-55
	Exhaust Manifold Heat Shield Bolts &Nuts	53①
	Lower Arm To Sub-Frame Bolts	96
	Lower Ball Joint Pinch Bolt	55-68
	Power Steering Hose To Bracket Bolts & Nut ②	53①
	Power Steering Hose To Engine Support Bracket Bolt ③	53①
	Power Steering Hose To Power Steering Pump Fittings	48
	Power Steering Hose Union To Steering Gear	23
	Power Steering Pump Mounting Bolts	18
	Power Steering Pump Pulley Bolts ③	8
	Stabilizer Bar Insulator Mounting Bracket To Sub-Frame Bolts	37
	Stabilizer Bar Link Nut	37
	Steering Gear Cover Plate To Sub-Frame	37
	Steering Gear To Sub-Frame Bolts	101
	Steering Shaft Clamp Plate Bolt	18
	Steering Shaft Flex Coupling Pinch Bolt	21
	Strut Thrust Bearing Nut	44
	Strut To Front Wheel Knuckle Pinch Bolt	40
	Strut Top Mounting Nut	34
	Tie Rod End Jam Nut	35-50
	Tie Rod End To Knuckle Nut	18-22
	Traction Assist Module Bolts	53①
	Wheel Hub Retainer	210
	Wheel Lug Nuts	63

①—Inch lbs.
②—2.0L/4-122 engine.
③—2.5L/V6-153 engine.

Wheel Alignment

INDEX

PRELIMINARY INSPECTION

1. Ensure all tires are inflated to proper pressure.
2. Inspect tire for wear patterns that may indicate improper wheel alignment, tire imbalance or damage due to bulges or separation.
3. Inspect suspension for modifications such as trailer towing equipment or heavy duty handling components.
4. Inspect vehicle for signs of overloading or sagging; ensure luggage compartment does not contain heavy objects.
5. Road test vehicle to isolate area of concern.

FRONT WHEEL ALIGNMENT

All wheel alignment inspections must be performed on an alignment rack leveled to within 1/16 inch side to side and front to rear. The alignment equipment must be capable of compensating for wheel runout and of measuring left and right front wheel toe independently.

CASTER & CAMBER

Front wheel caster and camber are preset by the manufacturer and are not adjustable. If caster and camber are not as indicated under "Front Wheel Alignment Specifications," inspect suspension components for damage, modification or excessive wear.

TOE

1. Start engine and rotate steering wheel back and forth several times, then place it in its centered position (wheels straight ahead).
2. Stop engine and lock steering wheel in position, then loosen steering ball stud dust seal outer clamp and slide off end of seal to prevent seal from twisting during adjustment.
3. Loosen tie rod end jam nuts, then adjust left and right tie rod ends until each wheel's toe measurement is 1/2 of total toe as specified under "Front Wheel Alignment Specifications."
4. **Torque** tie rod end jam nuts to 35-50 ft. lbs., then position steering ball stud dust seal outer clamp over seal and tighten securely. **Ensure seal is not twisted.**

VEHICLE RIDE HEIGHT

Vehicle ride height is preset by the manufacturer and is not adjustable. If vehicle ride height appears incorrect, check for damaged, modified or excessively worn suspension components.

LINCOLN

NOTE: Refer To Rear Of This Manual For Vehicle Manufacturer's Special Service Tool Suppliers.

INDEX OF SERVICE OPERATIONS

NOTE: For Service Operations Not Listed Below, Refer To The Table Of Contents In The Front Of This Manual.

Continued

Specifications
GENERAL ENGINE SPECIFICATIONS

Year	Engine Liter/CID ①	VIN Code ②	Fuel System	Bore & Stroke	Compression Ratio	Net HP @ RPM③	Maximum Torque, Ft. Lbs. @ RPM	Normal Oil Pressure, psi
1992	3.8L/V6-232	4	MPI	3.80 x 3.40	9.1	160 @ 4400	225 @ 3000	40-60
	4.6L/V8-281	W	SFI	3.55 x 3.54	9.0	④	⑤	20-45
	5.0L/V8-302 HO	E	SFI	4.00 x 3.00	9.1	225 @ 4200	300 @ 3200	40-60
1993–94	3.8L/V6-232	4	SFI	3.80 x 3.40	9.1	160 @ 4400	225 @ 3000	40-60
	4.6L/V8-281	W	SFI	3.55 x 3.54	9.0	④	⑤	20-45
	4.6L/V8-281	V	SFI	3.55 x 3.54	9.8	280 @ 5500	285 @ 4500	20-45
1995	3.8L/V6-232	4	SFI	3.80 x 3.40	9.1	160 @ 4400	225 @ 3000	40-60
	4.6L/V8-281 (2V)	W	SFI	3.55 x 3.54	9.0	⑥	⑦	20-45
	4.6L/V8-281 (4V)	V	SFI	3.55 x 3.54	9.8	280 @ 00	285 @ 4500	20-45

① —CID-cubic inch displacement.
② —The eighth digit of the VIN denotes engine code.
③ —Ratings are net (as installed in vehicle).

④ —Single exhaust, 190 @ 4200; dual exhaust, 210 @ 4600.
⑤ —Single exhaust, 260 @ 3200; dual exhaust, 270 @ 3400.

⑥ —Single exhaust. 190 @ 4250; dual exhaust, 210 @ 4250.
⑦ —Single exhaust. 260 @ 3250; dual exhaust, 270 @ 3250.

TUNE UP SPECIFICATIONS

Year & Engine/VIN Code ①	Spark Plug Gap, inch	Ignition Timing, °BTDC Firing Order, Fig. ④	Auto. Trans.	Timing Mark Fig.	Curb Idle Speed③	Fast Idle Speed	Fuel Pump Pressure, psi
1992							
3.8L/V6-232 (4)	.054	E	10⑨	D	⑥	⑥	35-40⑧
4.6L/V8-281 (W)	.054	A	10②	⑤	⑥	⑥	35-40⑦
5.0L/V8-302 (E) HO	.054	C	10⑨	B	⑥	⑥	35-40⑦
1993							
3.8L/V6-232 (4)	.054	E	10⑨	D	⑥	⑥	35-40⑧
4.6L/V8-281 (W) (2V) ⑩	.054	A ⑩	10②	⑤	⑥	⑥	35-40⑦
4.6L/V8-281 (V) (4V) ⑪	.054	F ⑪	10②	⑤	⑥	⑥	35-40⑦
1994							
3.8L/V6-232 (4)	.054	E	10⑨	D	⑥	⑥	35-40⑧
4.6L/V8-281 (W) (2V) ⑩	.054	A ⑩	10②	⑤	⑥	⑥	35-40⑦
4.6L/V8-281 (W) (4V) ⑪	.054	F ⑪	10②	⑤	⑥	⑥	35-40⑦
1995							
3.8L/V6-232 (4)	.054	E	10⑨	D	⑥	⑥	35-40⑧
4.6L/V8-281 (W) (2V)	.054	A	10②	⑤	⑥	⑥	35-40⑦
4.6L/V8-281 (V) (4V) ⑪	.054	F ⑪	10②	⑤	⑥	⑥	35-40⑦

BTDC—Before Top Dead Center.
① —The eighth digit of the Vehicle Identification Number (VIN) denotes engine code.
② —Non-adjustable.

③ —D: Drive.
④ —Before disconnecting wires from distributor cap, determine location of No. 1 wire in cap, as distributor position may have been altered from

that shown at the end of this chart.
⑤ —Equipped w/crankshaft sensor.
⑥ —Idle speeds are controlled by the automatic idle control.
⑦ —Wrap shop towel around fuel

diagnostic valve to prevent fuel spillage. Connect a suitable fuel pressure gauge to fuel diagnostic valve. Energize fuel pump & note fuel pressure gauge reading.
⑧—Wrap shop towel around fitting to prevent fuel spillage, then connect a suitable fuel pressure gauge to fuel

diagnostic valve on fuel rail assembly. Connect jumper wire to VIP self test connector FP terminal. The VIP connector is located at the right hand rear of the engine compartment at the electronic control assembly. Place ignition switch in On position, then connect

VIP jumper wire to ground & check fuel pressure gauge reading.
⑨—Disconnect in-line spout connector, then start engine & adjust ignition timing as necessary. After completing adjustment, reconnect spout connector.
⑩—2 valves per cylinder, Town Car.
⑪—4 valves per cylinder, Mark VIII.

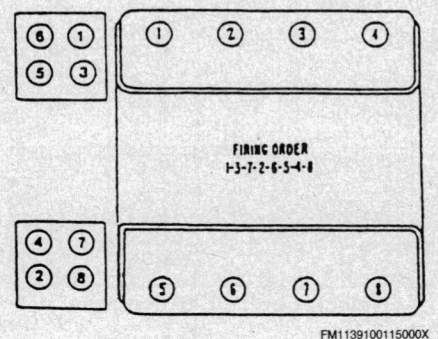

Fig. A

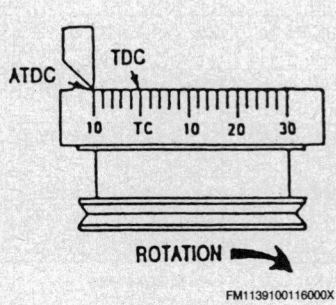

Fig. B

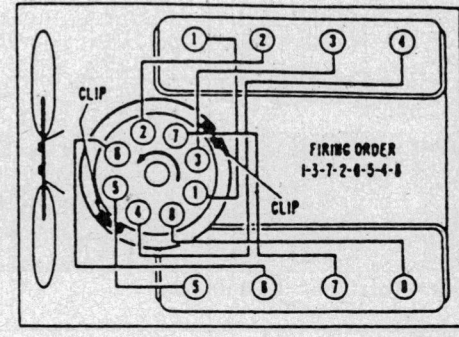

Fig. C

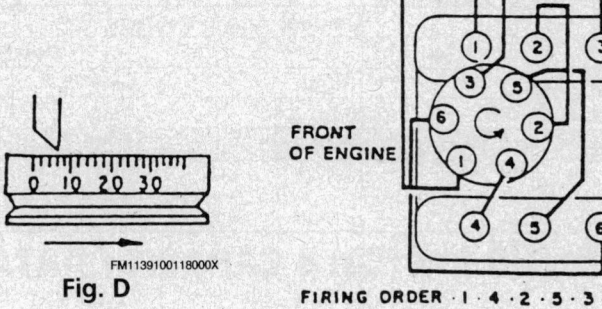

Fig. D

FIRING ORDER · 1 · 4 · 2 · 5 · 3 · 6

Fig. E

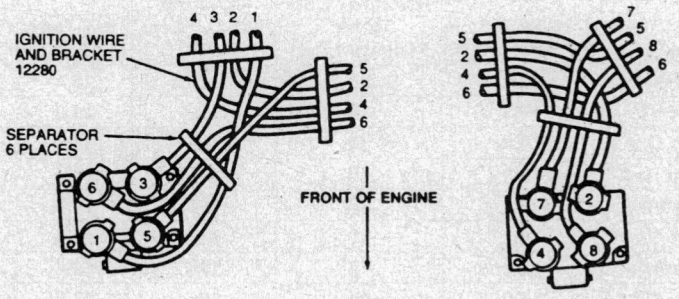

Fig. F

FRONT WHEEL ALIGNMENT SPECIFICATIONS

Year	Model	Caster Angle, Degrees		Camber Angle, Degrees				Toe-In, Inch	Toe Out On Turns, Degrees	
		Limits	Desired	Limits		Desired			Outer Wheel	Inner Wheel
				Left	Right	Left	Right			
1992-94	Town Car	+4.75 to +6.25	+5.50	-1.25 to +.25	-1.25 to +.25	-0.50	-0.50	1/16	18.51	20
	Mark VII	+0.60 to +2.70	+1.50	-.075 to +0.75	-.075 to +0.75	+0.00	+0.00	1/8	17.14	20
	Mark VIII	+4.75 to +6.25	+5.50	-1.25 to +.25	-1.25 to +.25	-0.50	-0.50	②	19.73	20
	Continental	+3.60 to +5.20	+4.40	-1.70 to -.50	-1.70 to -.50	-1.10	-1.10	①	18.21	20
1995	Continental	+3.60 to +5.20	+4.40	-1.70 to -.50	-1.70 to -.50	-1.10	-1.10	①	18.21	20
	Town Car	+5.25 to +6.75	+6.00	-1.25 to +0.25	-1.25 to +0.25	0.50	+0.50	③	18.51	20
	Mark VIII	+4.75 to 6.25	+5.50	-1.25 to +0.25	-1.25 to +0.25	-0.50	-0.50	5/64	19.73	20

①—Total toe, -.20 degrees. ②—Total toe, +.25 degrees. ③—Total toe out, -.0125 degrees.

REAR WHEEL ALIGNMENT SPECIFICATIONS

Year	Model	Camber Angle, Degrees				Toe-In, Degrees
		Limits		Desired		
		Left	Right	Left	Right	
1992-95	Continental	-2.00 to -0.60	-2.00 to -0.60	-1.30	-1.30	①
1993-95	Mark VIII	-1.00 to +0.00	-1.00 to 0.00	-0.50	-0.50	②

①—Total toe, +.20 degrees.
②—Total toe, +.12 degrees.

COOLING SYSTEM & CAPACITY DATA

Year	Engine/VIN & Model ①	Coolant Capacity, Qts.	Radiator Cap Relief Pressure, psi	Thermo. Opening Temp., Deg. F	Fuel Tank, Gal.	Engine Oil Refill, Qts.	Auto. Trans., Qts. ②	Rear Axle Oil, Pints
1992	3.8L/V6-232 (4) Continental	12.1	16	196	18.4	4⑤	12.8	⑥
	5.0L/V8-302 (E) Mark VII	14.1	16	192	21.0	4③④	12.3	3.75
	4.6L/V8-281 (W) Town Car	14.1	16	196	18.0	5③	12.3	3.75
1993	3.8L/V6-232 (4) Continental	12.1	16	196	18.4	4⑤	12.8	⑥
	4.6L/V8-281 (V) Mark VIII	14.1	16	196	18.0	5③	12.3	3.75
	4.6L/V8-281 (W) Town Car	14.1	16	196	18.0	5③	12.3	3.75
1994-95	3.8L/V6-232 (4) Continental	12.1	16	196	18.4	4⑤	12.2	⑥
	4.6L/V8-281 (V) Mark VIII	16.0	16	196	18.0	6②	14.0	3.0
	4.6L/V8-281 (W) Town Car	14.1	16	196	20.0⑦	5②	13.6	3.75

①—The eighth digit of Vehicle Identification Number (VIN) denotes engine code.
②—Approximate. Make final check with dipstick.
③—Add one quart w/filter change.
④—Dual sump oil pan. Remove both drain plugs to fully drain oil. One drain plug located at front of oil pan. Second drain plug located at left side of oil pan.
⑤—Add ½ qt. w/filter change.
⑥—Front wheel drive.
⑦—18.0 gal. depending on option content.

LUBRICANT DATA

Year	Model	Lubricant Type			
		Automatic Transaxle	Rear Axle	Power Steering	Brake System
1992-95	All	ATF	①	ATF②	DOT 3

①—Use ESP-M2C154-A (XY-80w90-QL) or equivalent plus four ounces of EST-M2C118-A (C8AZ-19B546-A) friction modifier or equivalent for

Traction-Lok axles.
②—Type F.
③—Use WSP-M2C197-A (XY-80w90-QL)

or equivalent plus two ounces of F3TZ-19B546–MA friction modifier or equivalent for Traction-Lok axles.

Electrical

NOTE: On Air Bag Equipped Models, Refer To "Air Bag System Precautions" Located In The Front Of This Manual For System Disarming & Arming Procedures.

INDEX

PRECAUTIONS

AIR BAG SYSTEMS

Refer to "Air Bag System Precautions" in the front of this manual for system disarming and arming procedures.

FUSE PANEL & FLASHER LOCATION

The fuse panel is located under the instrument panel to the lefthand side of the steering column.

The turn signal & hazard flashers are located on the fuse panel.

RELAY CENTER LOCATION

The relay center is located on the radiator support in the lower front center of the engine compartment.

STARTER

REPLACE

When servicing starter or performing any maintenance in the area of starter, note the heavy gauge input lead connected to the starter solenoid is hot at all times. Ensure protective cap is installed over terminal and is replaced after service. When battery has been disconnected and reconnected, some abnormal drive symptoms may occur while the EEC processor relearns its adaptive strategy. The vehicle may need to be driven 10 miles or more to relearn strategy.

1. Disconnect battery ground cable, then raise and support vehicle.
2. Disconnect starter cable and push-on connector at starter solenoid. **When disconnecting hard-shell connector at "S"terminal, pull plastic shell**

straight out, do not pull on wire.
3. Remove starter mounting bolts and the starter. It may be necessary to turn wheels to left or right to gain clearance for removal.
4. Reverse procedure to install, noting the following:
   a. **Torque** starter cable to starter terminal to 80–115 inch lbs.
   b. **Torque**starter mounting bolts 16–19 ft. lbs.
   c. Replace red solenoid cap.

DISTRIBUTOR

REPLACE

CONTINENTAL & MARK VII

1. Disconnect negative battery cable, then the distributor from wiring harness.
2. Mark position of No. 1 cylinder wire tower on distributor base, for installa-

tion reference.
3. Loosen distributor cap hold-down screws. Remove cap straight off distributor to prevent damage to rotor blade and spring.
4. Remove rotor from the distributor shaft and armature, by pulling upward.
5. Remove distributor hold-down clamp, then the distributor. **Cover distributor opening in cylinder block or head to prevent entry of foreign material.**
6. Reverse procedure to install, noting the following:
   a. No. 1 piston must be at TDC of compression stroke. Remove No. 1 cylinder spark plug and rotate engine clockwise until No. 1 piston is on the compression stroke.
   b. Align timing pointer with TDC on the crankshaft damper, then the locating boss on rotor with hole on armature. Fully seat rotor on distributor shaft.
   c. Rotate distributor shaft so blade on rotor is pointing toward mark that was previously made on distributor base.
   d. While installing distributor continue rotating rotor slightly so leading edge of vane is centered in vane switch stator assembly.
   e. Rotate distributor in block to align leading edge of vane and vane switch stator assembly. Verify rotor is pointing at No. 1 mark on distributor base.
   f. Install hold-down.

IGNITION LOCK
REPLACE
FUNCTIONAL LOCK
Town Car

1. Disconnect battery ground cable.
2. Turn lock cylinder key to Run position.
3. Place a 1/8 inch punch in hole in trim shroud under lock cylinder.
4. Depress retaining pin with punch and remove lock cylinder by pulling outward.
5. Install lock cylinder by turning it to Run position and depressing retaining pin. Ensure cylinder is fully seated and aligned with interlocking washer prior to turning key Off.
6. Rotate lock cylinder with key to ensure proper operation.

1993 Continental

1. Disconnect battery ground cable.
2. Turn lock cylinder key to Run position.
3. Using a 1/8 inch drift, depress lock cylinder retaining pin through access hole and remove lock cylinder, **Fig. 1. Carefully note position of bearing retainer prior to removal.**
4. Remove blue plastic bearing retainer by inserting screwdriver or similar tool with a 90° bend on its tip between bearing retainer and bearing, then prying upward.
5. Insert tip of screwdriver into double-D slot of bearing, then rotate 90°. Remove bearing.

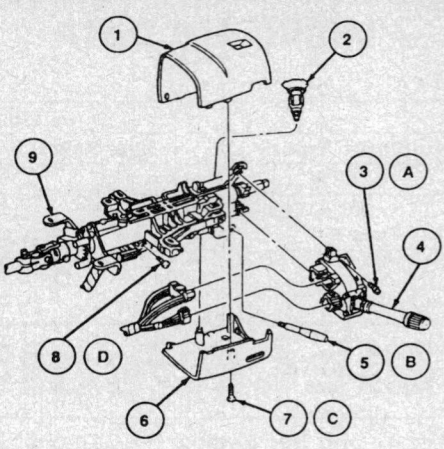

Item	Description
1	Steering Column Shroud
2	Ignition Lock Cylinder
3A	Screw
4	Turn Signal and Windshield Wiper Switch

FM9129100010000X

Fig. 1   Ignition lock removal

6. Remove lock drive gear. Note position of lock drive gear relative to rack teeth.
7. Reverse procedure to install.

Mark VII, Mark VIII & 1994—95 Continental

1. Disconnect battery ground cable.
2. Turn lock cylinder key to Run position.
3. Using a 1/8 inch drift, depress lock cylinder retaining pin through access hole and remove lock cylinder, **Carefully note position of bearing retainer prior to removal.**
4. Remove blue plastic bearing retainer by inserting screwdriver or similar tool with a 90° bend on its tip between bearing retainer and bearing, then prying upward.
5. Insert tip of screwdriver into double-d slot of bearing, then rotate 90°. Remove bearing.
6. Remove lock drive gear. Note position of lock drive gear relative to rack teeth.
7. Reverse procedure to install. Noting the following:
   a. Position of steering column lock gear is correct if last tooth on drive gear steering column lock gear is meshed with the last tooth on rack.
   b. Position steering column upper bearing retainer in lock cylinder housing and rotate double-d slot 90 degrees.
   c. Press blue plastic steering column upper bearing retainer into lock cylinder housing, ensuring original position.
   d. Line up flats of steering column lock gear with flats of washer by pulling down on the steering column lock cam.
   e. Install ignition switch assembly.
   f. Check for proper start in park and neutral, no start in drive and reverse and locked in lock position.

NON-FUNCTIONAL LOCK
Removal

1. Disconnect battery ground cable.
2. Remove steering wheel.
3. Disconnect key warning switch electrical connector. **On models equipped with ignition switch cap, use channel-lock or vise-grip type pliers to twist cap from lock cylinder.**
4. **On all models,** using a 1/8 inch drill, drill out retaining pin. **Do not drill deeper than 1/2 inch.**
5. Place a chisel at base of ignition lock cylinder cap, then strike chisel with sharp blows to break cap away from cylinder.
6. Using a 3/8 inch drill, drill down middle of ignition lock key slot 1 3/4 inches until lock cylinder breaks loose from breakaway base of lock cylinder.
7. Remove lock cylinder and drill shavings from lock cylinder housing.
8. Remove retainer, washer, ignition switch and actuator, then clean all drill shavings from casting.
9. Inspect lock cylinder housing; if any damage is present, replace housing.

Installation

1. Install actuator and ignition switch.
2. Install trim and electrical parts.
3. Install new ignition lock cylinder.
4. Install steering wheel.
5. Ensure lock operates properly.

IGNITION SWITCH
REPLACE

MARK VII, MARK VIII & TOWN CAR
Removal

1. Disconnect battery ground cable.
2. Remove steering column shroud.
3. **On models equipped with tilt steering column,** remove column lock lever.
4. Disconnect ignition switch electrical connector.
5. Rotate ignition key lock cylinder to the Run position.
6. Remove two ignition switch attaching bolts.
7. Disengage ignition switch from actuator pin.
8. Remove ignition switch.

Installation

1. Adjust ignition switch by sliding carrier to Run position.
2. Ensure ignition key lock cylinder is in Run position.
3. Install ignition switch pin into actuator hole in column.
4. Install switch attaching screws and **torque** to 50-70 inch lbs.
5. Connect ignition switch electrical connector, **Fig. 2.**
6. Connect battery ground cable.
7. Check ignition switch for proper operation.
8. Install steering column shrouds.

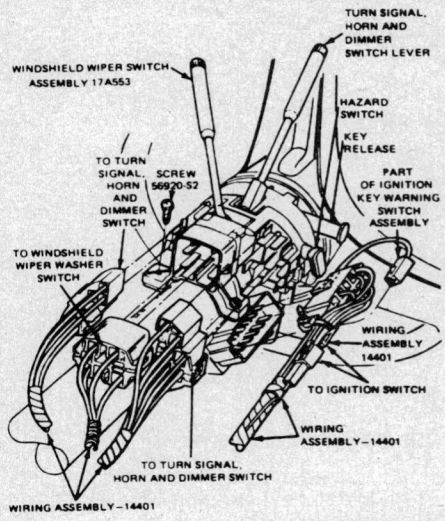

Fig. 2 Ignition switch installation

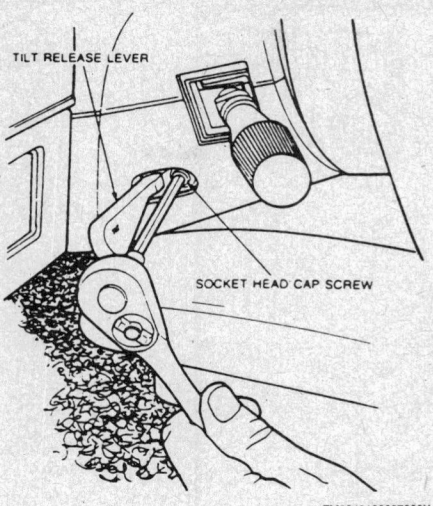

Fig. 3 Tilt release lever removal

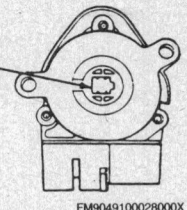

Fig. 4 Ignition switch adjustment

9. On tilt models install lock lever.

CONTINENTAL

Removal

1. Disconnect battery ground cable.
2. Turn lock cylinder key to Run position.
3. Place a ⅛ inch punch in hole in trim shroud under lock cylinder.
4. Depress retaining pin with punch and remove lock cylinder by pulling outward.
5. **On models with tilt column,** remove tilt release lever by removing one socket head capscrew, **Fig. 3.**
6. **On all models,** remove four instrument panel lower cover retaining screws, then the lower cover.
7. Remove three steering column shroud attaching screws, then the shroud.
8. Remove four steering column to support bracket retaining bolts, then lower column.
9. Remove three screws from diverter plate, then the diverter plate from column.
10. Disconnect ignition switch electrical connector.
11. Remove two tamper resistant Torx screws retaining ignition switch, then the switch.

Installation

1. Ensure ignition switch is in the Run position by rotating switch fully clockwise to start position and releasing slowly, **Fig. 4.**
2. Install ignition switch and cover assembly, then two Torx retaining screws. **Torque** screws to 30-48 inch lbs.
3. Connect ignition switch electrical connector.
4. Position diverter plate on column and install three attaching screws. **Torque** screw to 30-48 inch lbs.
5. Align steering column mounting holes with support bracket, install four nuts and **torque** to 15-25 ft. lbs.
6. Install steering column shrouds.

7. Install instrument panel lower cover.
8. **On models with tilt column,** install tilt release lever, then capscrew and **torque** to 6-8 ft. lbs.
9. Check operation of tilt column through its entire range and ensure there is no interference with instrument panel.
10. **On all models,** connect battery ground cable.
11. Check column functions as follows:
    a. With shift lever in Park position and ignition lock cylinder in Lock position, ensure steering wheel locks.
    b. With shift lever in Drive position and ignition lock cylinder in run position, rotate lock cylinder toward Lock position until it stops, ensure engine electrical is Off and steering wheel does not lock.
    c. Rotate ignition lock cylinder counterclockwise and check for accessory power.
    d. Place shift lever in Park position, then rotate ignition lock cylinder clockwise to the Start position and ensure starter is energized.

NEUTRAL SAFETY SWITCH
REPLACE

MARK VII & TOWN CAR

1. Disconnect battery ground cable.
2. Position transmission selector lever in "Lo" position.
3. Raise and support vehicle, then working from underneath vehicle, disconnect electrical harness from switch by lifting harness straight up off switch.
4. Using neutral start switch socket tool No. T74P-77247-A or equivalent, remove neutral start switch and O-ring seal by positioning tool over the extension housing area to gain access to switch.
5. Reverse procedure to install. **Torque** switch to 7-10 ft. lbs. using tool mentioned above.

CONTINENTAL w/AXOD TRANSAXLE

1. Disconnect battery ground cable.
2. Place shift lever in Neutral, then disconnect linkage from manual shift lever.
3. Disconnect switch wiring connector, then remove switch attaching bolts and switch.
4. Install switch and attaching bolts, but do not tighten bolts at this time.
5. Insert a No. 43 (.089 inch) drill bit through hole in switch, then **torque** attaching bolts to 7-9 inch lbs. and remove drill bit.
6. Reconnect switch connector and battery cable, then ensure that starter engages in Neutral or Park positions only.

HEADLAMP SWITCH
REPLACE

CONTINENTAL

1. Disconnect battery ground cable.
2. Remove headlamp switch knob and trim panel molding.
3. Remove trim panel retaining screw, then the trim panel.
4. Remove upper steering column cover, by unsnapping four tabs.
5. Remove headlamp switch-to-finish panel attaching screws, electrical connector and headlamp switch.
6. Reverse procedure to install.

MARK VII

1. Disconnect battery ground cable.
2. Remove center molding, then the headlamp switch knob.
3. Remove five cluster finish panel retaining screws.
4. Remove headlight switch lens by snapping out.
5. Remove two headlamp switch retaining screws.
6. Remove headlamp switch from instrument panel, then disconnect electrical connector.
7. Reverse procedure to install.

MARK VIII

1. Disconnect battery ground cable.
2. Remove headlamp switch knob by pulling it off.
3. Remove lamp switch knob applique by pulling at LH end to unsnap it from the finish panel and twist out bulb socket.
4. Remove two screws retaining LH end of finish panel to the instrument panel.

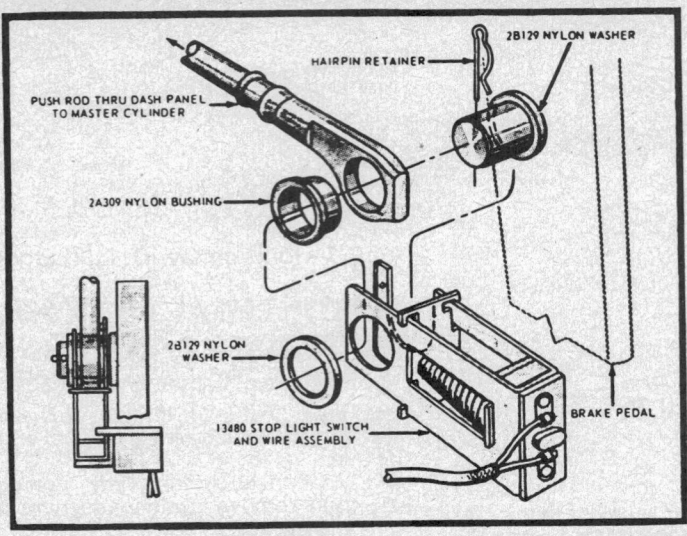

Fig. 5   Stop light switch

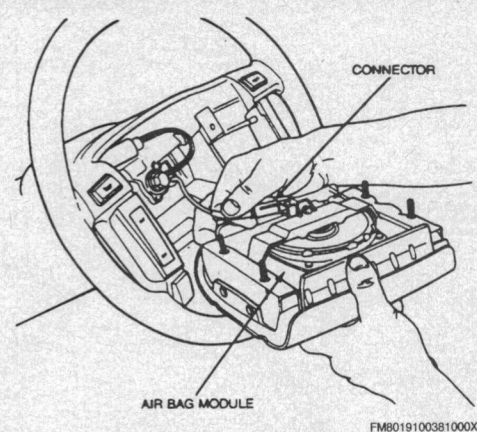

Fig. 6   Air bag module removal

5. Remove two screws at top of cluster opening retaining finish panel to the instrument panel.
6. Remove upper steering column cover by pulling up on forward edge to un-snap four snap-in tabs.
7. Pull LH end of finish panel rearward far enough to disconnect two wiring connectors.
8. Remove two screws retaining switch to center finish panel.
9. Reverse procedure to install.

TOWN CAR

1. Disconnect battery ground cable.
2. Insert a hooked tool into headlight switch knob slot and remove spring tension on knob, then pull off.
3. Remove headlamp auto dimmer switch knob, if equipped.
4. Remove righthand and lefthand moldings from instrument panel by pulling away from instrument panel and snapping out of retainers.
5. Remove 12 finish panel retaining screws.
6. Remove finish panel, then the headlamp switch bracket retaining screws and bracket.
7. Remove switch to bracket retaining nut, then disconnect electrical connector and remove switch.
8. Reverse procedure to install.

STOP LIGHT SWITCH
REPLACE

1. Disconnect wires at switch connector.
2. Remove hairpin retainer, then slide switch, pushrod and nylon washers and bushing away from brake pedal and remove switch, **Fig. 5.**
3. Reverse procedure to install.

MULTI-FUNCTION SWITCH
REPLACE
REMOVAL

1. Disconnect battery ground cable.

2. **On models with tilt column,** place tilt column to lowest position and remove tilt lever.
3. **On all models,** remove ignition lock cylinder.
4. Remove shroud attaching screws, then the upper and lower shroud.
5. Remove wiring harness retainer, then disconnect electrical connectors.
6. Remove multi-function switch to steering column attaching screws, then the multi-function switch.

INSTALLATION

1. Connect switch electrical connectors.
2. Install switch and retaining screws, **torque** screws to 18-27 inch lbs.
3. Install wiring harness retainer.
4. Install upper and lower trim shrouds. **Torque** screws to 6-10 inch lbs.
5. Install ignition lock cylinder.
6. Install tilt lever. **Torque** retaining bolt to 6-9 inch lbs.
7. Connect battery ground cable.
8. Check steering column and switch for proper operation.

STEERING WHEEL
REPLACE

MARK VII, TOWN CAR & CONTINENTAL

1. Center front wheels to straight ahead position.
2. Disconnect battery ground cable.
3. Disconnect back-up power supply.
4. Remove four air bag module retaining nuts, then lift module off steering wheel, **Fig. 6.**
5. Disconnect air bag wire harness from module, then remove module.
6. Disconnect speed control wire harness from steering wheel.
7. Remove steering wheel retaining bolt.
8. Using steering wheel puller tool No. T67L-3600-A or equivalent, remove steering wheel.
9. Reverse procedure to install, noting the following:

a. Ensure air bag wire is not pinched.
b. Install new steering wheel bolt and **torque** to 23-33 ft. lbs.
c. **Torque** air bag module retaining nuts to 3-4 ft. lbs.

INSTRUMENT CLUSTER
REPLACE

MARK VII

Less Electronic Cluster

1. Disconnect battery ground cable.
2. Remove instrument cluster finish panel, then disconnect warning lamp module connectors.
3. Remove instrument panel binnacle molding.
4. Remove five mask to backplate mounting screws. **Do not remove three top screws retaining lens to mask.**
5. Remove lens and mask assembly.
6. Lift main dial assembly from backplate. **Some effort may be required to pull quick connect terminals from clips.**
7. Install quick connect terminals to clips and position main dial assembly on backplate. **Ensure foam seal under indicator lamp baffle is correctly positioned.**
8. Install lens and mask assembly, then the five attaching screws.
9. Install instrument panel binnacle molding.
10. Connect warning lamp module connectors, then install instrument cluster finish panel.

With Electronic Cluster

1. Remove the four finish panel retaining screws, then rotate top of panel towards steering wheel and remove from vehicle, **Fig. 7.**
2. Remove the six instrument panel pad retaining screws, then rotate pad toward steering wheel and remove from vehicle.
3. Remove the four instrument cluster to instrument panel retaining screws, then pull cluster away from instrument panel.
4. Disconnect cluster electrical connector and remove cluster.

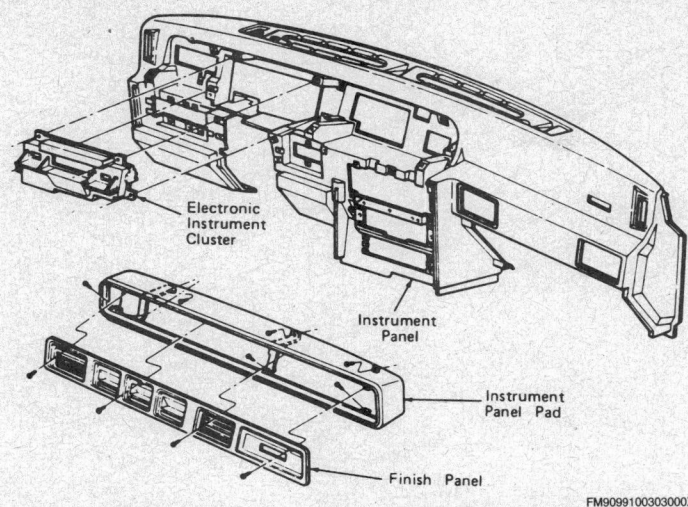

Electronic Instrument Cluster

Instrument Panel

Instrument Panel Pad

Finish Panel

FM9099100303000X

Fig. 7 Electronic instrument cluster. Mark VII

MARK VIII

1. Disconnect battery ground cable.
2. Remove instrument panel finish panel.
3. Remove four cluster to finish panel retaining screws. Do not remove screws securing lens and mask to backplate.
4. Rotate cluster face down and disconnect instrument cluster connector.
5. Slide cluster to right of I/P opening and unhook I/P harness from hook on back of instrument cluster.
6. Remove cluster assembly from panel.
7. Reverse procedure to install.

CONTINENTAL

1. Disconnect battery ground cable.
2. Position vehicle on a flat surface to prevent movement when gear shift selector is out of position.
3. Turn ignition switch to unlock shift lever, then move lever down from front of electronic instrument cluster (EIC).
4. Tilt steering column down, then remove right and left finish molding by pulling upward to unsnap clips.
5. Disconnect electrical connectors.
6. Remove five Torx screws below cluster that retain applique.
7. Unsnap applique along top, then pull applique away from panel.
8. Disconnect switch assembly electrical connectors.
9. Remove three attaching screws from bottom of steering column shroud.
10. Lift up top section of shroud and remove clip on left side near steering wheel. Separate upper section of shroud from side section near ignition switch. Slip upper section off shift lever.
11. Remove four Torx screws retaining cluster to instrument panel.
12. Place a soft cloth on steering column to prevent scratching front surface of cluster when removed.
13. Tilt top of cluster slightly toward rear of vehicle, then disconnect two snaps beneath cluster retaining PRNDL assembly.
14. Unplug three connectors behind cluster. **Connectors have locking tabs that must be pressed in to unplug connection.**
15. Loosen two clips retaining PRNDL assembly to cluster, then position aside.
16. Push bottom of cluster into instrument panel, then tilt top of cluster toward rear of vehicle and remove cluster.
17. Reverse procedure to install.

TOWN CAR
Analog Cluster

1. Disconnect battery ground cable.
2. Remove cluster trim cover retaining screws, then the trim cover.
3. Remove lower steering cover retaining screws, then the lower steering cover.
4. Remove lower half of steering column shroud.
5. Remove transmission indicator bracket retaining screw, then disconnect cable loop and bracket pin from steering column. Also remove column bracket from column.
6. Remove cluster retaining screws, then disconnect electrical feed plug from connector and remove cluster assembly.
7. Remove attaching screws from lens and mask assembly.
8. Remove temperature and fuel gauge from cluster.
9. Remove PRNDL retaining screws from speedometer.
10. Remove speedometer.

Digital Cluster

1. Disconnect battery ground cable.
2. Unsnap center molding on righthand and lefthand sides of instrument panel.
3. Remove steering column cover and shroud.
4. Remove knobs from auto dim and auto lamp, if equipped.
5. Remove 13 instrument panel retaining screws, then pull panel out.
6. Move shift lever to 1 position for easier access.
7. Disconnect electrical connectors from

warning module, switch module and center panel switches, if equipped.
8. Remove instrument panel.
9. Disconnect electrical connector from front of cluster.
10. Disconnect PRNDL assembly from cluster, by carefully bending bottom tab down and pulling assembly forward.
11. Pull cluster out and disconnect electrical connector.
12. Remove instrument cluster.
13. Reverse procedure to install.

RADIO
REPLACE

When installing radio, adjust antenna trimmer for peak performance.
1. Disconnect battery ground cable.
2. Install radio removal tool No. T87P-19061-A or equivalent into radio face plate, push tool in approximately one inch to release retaining clips.
3. Apply a light spreading force on tools and slowly pull radio from instrument panel.
4. Disconnect wiring connectors and antenna cable.
5. Reverse procedure to install.

WIPER MOTOR
REPLACE

MARK VII

1. Turn wipers on; then, with wiper blades straight up on windshield, turn ignition key to Off position.
2. Disconnect battery ground cable and remove arm and blade assemblies.
3. Remove left side cowl top grille.
4. Remove drive arm to motor crankpin retaining clip, then disconnect drive arm from crankpin.
5. Disconnect wiper motor electrical connector, then remove wiper motor retaining screws and the wiper motor from opening.

MARK VIII

1. Turn ignition switch to Run position. Turn on windshield wipers and cycle to mid-wipe position, then turn off ignition.
2. Disconnect battery ground cable.
3. Remove LH and RH wiper arms.
4. Remove cowl top to hood seal.
5. Remove LH and RH cowl vent screens.
6. Remove four retaining screws and washers, then the cowl top extension.
7. Disconnect two wiring connectors from motor.
8. Remove retaining bolts and washer assemblies from wiper module.
9. Lift module slightly to disengage support bracket from dash panel mounting stud. Move module sideways about 2 inches toward passenger side and remove module from vehicle.
10. Disconnect linkage drive arm from motor crankpin after removing clip.
11. Remove wiper motor's three retaining screws and remove motor from module.

12. Reverse procedure to install. **Before installing blade and arm assemblies to pivot shafts, cycle motor and turn off wiper switch to ensure wiper linkage is in park position.**

CONTINENTAL

1. Disconnect battery ground cable.
2. Disconnect power lead electrical connector from wiper motor.
3. Remove lefthand windshield wiper arm.
4. Remove linkage retaining clip from arm on motor by lifting locking tab up and pulling clip away from pin.
5. Remove motor and bracket assembly attaching bolts, then the motor.
6. Reverse procedure to install. **Torque motor attaching bolts to 60-85 inch lbs.**

TOWN CAR

1. Disconnect battery ground cable.
2. Remove rear hood seal, then the wiper arm assemblies.
3. Remove cowl vent screens and disconnect washer hoses from jets.
4. Disconnect electrical connectors from wiper motor.
5. Remove wiper assembly retaining screws, then lift assembly out of cowl, **Fig. 8.**
6. Unsnap and remove wiper linkage cover.
7. Remove linkage retaining clip from motor operating arm.
8. Remove motor retaining screws, then the motor.
9. Reverse procedure to install.

WIPER SWITCH
REPLACE

1. Disconnect battery ground cable.
2. Remove the steering column cover screws and separate the two halves.
3. Remove wiper switch retaining screws, disconnect wiring connector and remove switch.
4. Reverse procedure to install.

WIPER TRANSMISSION
REPLACE
MARK VII

The wiper transmission is mounted below the cowl top panel and can be reached by raising the hood. Because the pivot shaft and transmission assemblies are connected with unremovable plastic ball joints, the right and left pivot shafts and transmission are serviced as a unit.

1. Position wipers as outlined under "Wiper Motor, Replace."
2. Raise hood, then remove left and right cowl top grilles.
3. Remove drive arm to wiper motor crankpin retaining clip, then disconnect drive arm from crankpin.
4. Remove pivot shaft attaching screws, then guide transmission and pivots from cowl chamber.
5. Reverse procedure to install, ensuring wiper motor is in park position.

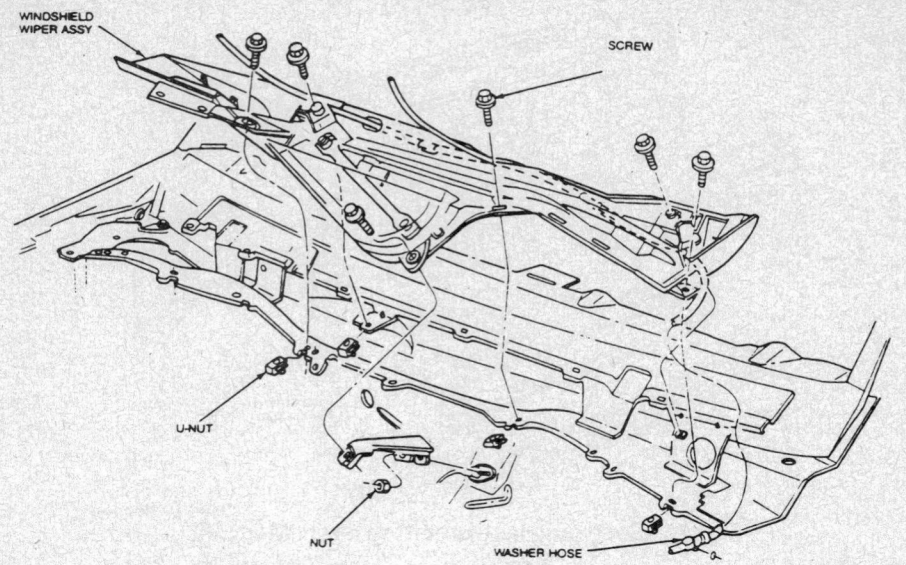

Fig. 8 Windshield wiper assembly. Town Car

CONTINENTAL

1. Disconnect battery ground cable.
2. Remove wiper arm and blade assembly from pivots shafts.
3. Remove leaf screens.
4. Remove motor crankpin clip, then disconnect linkage drive arm.
5. Remove pivot to cowl attaching screws, then the linkage and pivots from cowl chamber.
6. Reverse procedure to install.

TOWN CAR

Refer to "Wiper Motor, Replace" for wiper transmission replacement procedures.

BLOWER MOTOR
REPLACE
TOWN CAR

1. Disconnect battery ground cable.
2. Disconnect blower motor lead from wiring harness, then remove blower motor cooling tube from blower motor.
3. Remove the four blower motor retaining screws.
4. Rotate motor and wheel assembly slightly to the right so that bottom edge of mounting plate follows contour of wheelwell splash panel, then lift the motor and wheel assembly up and out of housing.
5. Reverse procedure to install.

MARK VII

1. Disconnect battery ground cable.
2. Remove glove compartment and shield, then disconnect wire connector from outside recirc actuator.
3. Remove side cowl panel, then instrument panel lower right-to-side attaching bolts.
4. Remove support bracket attaching screws at top of air recirc duct.
5. Remove five recirc duct attaching screws, then remove recirc duct.
6. Remove four blower motor plate attaching screws, then remove the blower motor and wheel assembly from blower housing.
7. Reverse procedure to install.

MARK VIII

1. Disconnect battery ground cable.
2. Lower glove compartment door to gain access to rear of evaporator case.
3. Disconnect blower motor electrical connector.
4. Remove A/C evaporator air control venturi and in-vehicle temperature sensor aspirator hose.
5. Remove pulse width modulator (blower motor speed controller).
6. Remove screw and pull blower motor assembly out of blower motor housing.
7. Pull push nut off blower motor shaft and remove blower wheel from shaft.
8. Reverse procedure to install.

CONTINENTAL

1. Remove release retainers and lower glove compartment door.
2. Remove recirc duct support bracket retaining screw.
3. Remove electrical connector retaining screw, then disconnect three connectors from bracket and remove bracket.
4. Remove vacuum connection to recirc door vacuum motor, then disconnect aspirator hoses from muffler.
5. Remove six recirc duct attaching screws.
6. Remove recirc duct from evaporator assembly from between instrument panel and evaporator case.
7. Disconnect blower motor electrical lead.
8. Remove blower motor wheel assembly attaching nut, then remove wheel.
9. Remove four blower motor attaching screws, then remove the motor from evaporator case.
10. Reverse procedure to install.

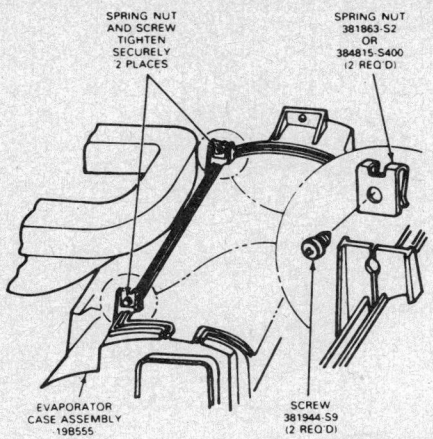

Fig. 9 Evaporator case tab drilling. Continental & Mark VII

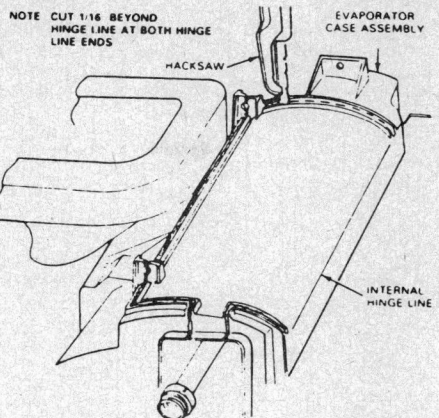

Fig. 10 Cutting evaporator case. Continental & Mark VII

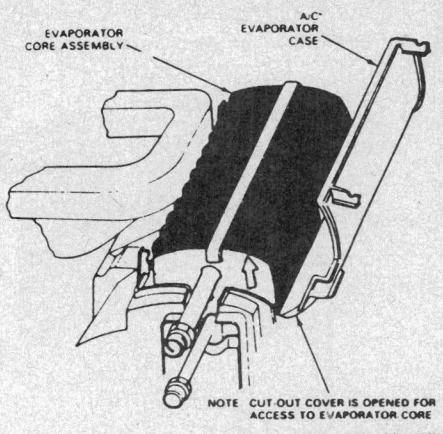

Fig. 11 Evaporator case from core removal. Continental & Mark VII

HEATER CORE
REPLACE
MARK VII

1. Remove instrument panel.
2. Discharge refrigerant from A/C system, then disconnect high and low pressure hoses. Cap hose ends to prevent entry of dirt and moisture.
3. Drain coolant and disconnect hoses from heater core. Plug hoses and core to prevent spillage.
4. Remove air inlet duct/blower housing assembly support brace to cowl top panel retaining screw.
5. Disconnect A/C wiring, if necessary, then working from engine compartment, remove the two evaporator case to dash panel retaining nuts.
6. Working from passenger compartment, remove evaporator case support bracket to cowl panel attaching screw.
7. Carefully pull evaporator case away from dash panel and remove from vehicle.
8. Remove heater core access cover to evaporator case attaching screws.
9. Remove heater core and seals from case, then remove seals from heater core tubes.

MARK VIII

1993–94

1. Disconnect battery ground cable.
2. Drain radiator coolant into suitable container.
3. Discharge refrigerant from A/C.
4. Disconnect heater hoses from heater tubes. Plug heater tubes and blow any coolant from heater core with low-pressure air.
5. Disconnect vacuum supply hose from in-line vacuum check valve in engine compartment.
6. Disconnect liquid line and accumulator from evaporator core at dash panel. Cap refrigerant lines and evaporator core to prevent entrance of dirt and moisture.
7. Remove instrument panel.

8. Remove floor register to bottom of evaporator case retaining screw.
9. Remove evaporator case to cowl top panel retaining screw.
10. Disconnect vacuum line, electrical connections and aspirator hose from evaporator case.
11. Remove evaporator case to dash panel retaining nuts.
12. Carefully pull evaporator assembly away from dash panel and remove evaporator case from vehicle.
13. Reverse procedure to install. **Ensure correct type O-rings are installed on A/C fittings.**

1995

1. Disconnect battery ground cable.
2. Drain radiator coolant into suitable container.
3. Remove instrument panel
4. Remove seal from heater core tubes.
5. Remove A/C electronic door actuator motor, three screws, from A/C evaporator housing.
6. Remove heater core cover and seal from A/C evaporator housing.
7. Disconnect heater hoses from heater tubes.
8. Carefully pull evaporator assembly away from dash panel and remove evaporator case from vehicle.
9. Reverse procedure to install.

CONTINENTAL

1. Remove instrument panel as described under "Dash Panel Service."
2. Remove evaporator case assembly.
3. Remove vacuum source from heater core tube.
4. Remove seal from heater core tubes.
5. Remove three blend door actuator to evaporator case screws, then remove actuator.
6. Remove four heater core access cover attaching screws, then remove cover and seal.
7. Remove heater core and seal.

TOWN CAR

1. Disconnect battery ground cable.

2. Disconnect heater hose from heater core tubes, then plug heater hoses and core tubes.
3. Remove three plenum to dash panel attaching nuts located below the windshield wiper motor.
4. Remove one nut retaining upper left-hand corner of evaporator case to dash panel.
5. Remove lefthand and righthand lower instrument panel insulators.
6. Disconnect two vacuum supply hoses from vacuum source, then push vacuum hoses and grommet into passenger compartment.
7. Remove instrument panel mounting screws, then pull instrument panel back as far as possible without disconnecting wiring harnesses.
8. Loosen righthand sill plate end, then remove righthand side cowl trim panel.
9. Remove cross body brace, then disconnect wiring harness from temperature blend door actuator.
10. Disconnect ATC sensor tube from evaporator case connector.
11. Disconnect the vacuum jumper harness at the multiple vacuum connector located near floor air distribution duct.
12. Disconnect white vacuum hose from outside-recirculating door vacuum motor.
13. Remove two hush panels, then the floor air distribution duct.
14. Remove two nuts along lower flange of plenum.
15. Carefully move plenum rearward to allow heater core tubes and stud at top of plenum to clear holes in dash panel. Remove plenum by rotating top of plenum forward, down and out from under instrument panel. Carefully pull lower edge of instrument panel rearward as necessary while rolling the plenum from behind the instrument panel.
16. Remove the four retaining screws from heater core cover and remove cover from plenum.
17. Remove heater core and seal assembly from plenum assembly.

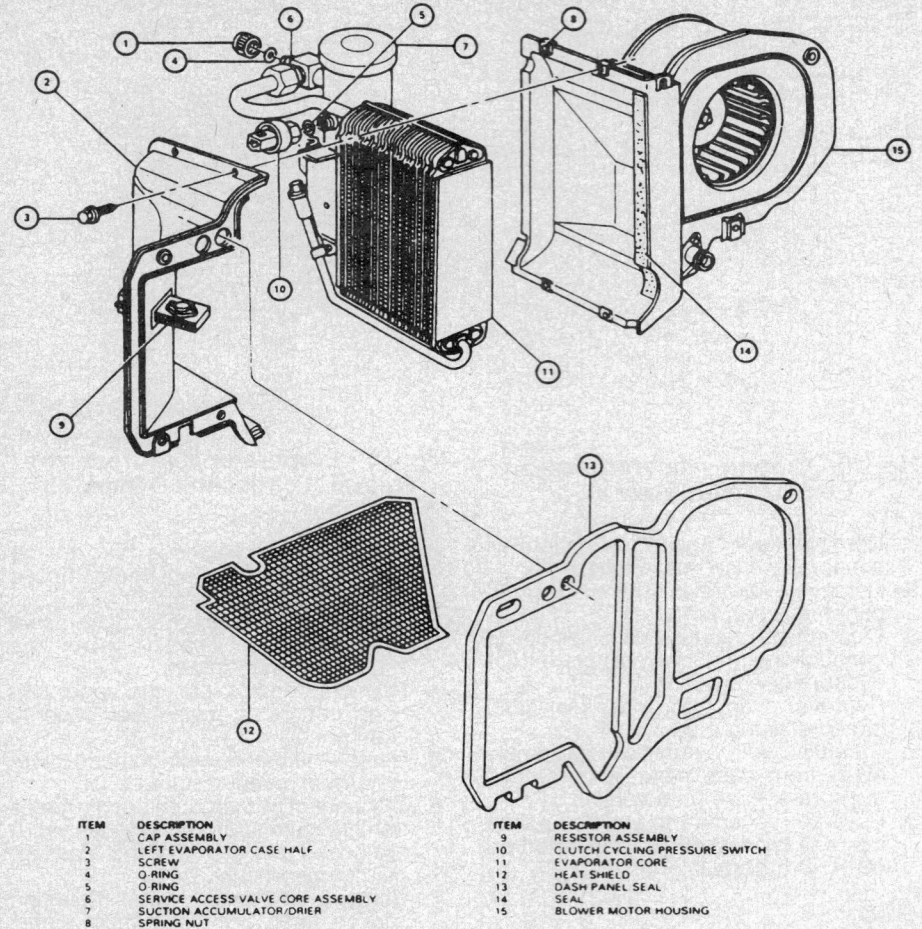

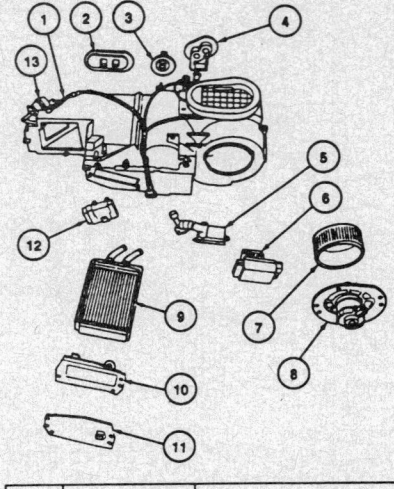

Item	Description
1	A / C Evaporator Housing
2	Heater Dash Panel Seal
3	A / C Evaporator Drain Tube Seal
4	A / C Evaporator Drain Tube Seal
5	A / C Evaporator Air Control Venturi
6	Pulse Width Modulator Assy (Blower Motor Speed Controller)
7	Blower Motor Wheel
8	A / C Blower Motor
9	Heater Core
10	Heater Core Cover Seal
11	Heater Core Cover
12	A / C Electronic Door Actuator Motor
13	Vacuum Control Motor

FM7029100053000A

ITEM	DESCRIPTION	ITEM	DESCRIPTION
1	CAP ASSEMBLY	9	RESISTOR ASSEMBLY
2	LEFT EVAPORATOR CASE HALF	10	CLUTCH CYCLING PRESSURE SWITCH
3	SCREW	11	EVAPORATOR CORE
4	O-RING	12	HEAT SHIELD
5	O-RING	13	DASH PANEL SEAL
6	SERVICE ACCESS VALVE CORE ASSEMBLY	14	SEAL
7	SUCTION ACCUMULATOR/DRIER	15	BLOWER MOTOR HOUSING
8	SPRING NUT		

FM7029100052000X

Fig. 12 Exploded view of evaporator case. Town Car

Fig. 13 Exploded view of evaporator case. Mark VIII

EVAPORATOR CORE
REPLACE
CONTINENTAL & MARK VII

1. Remove evaporator case as outlined under "Heater Core, Replace."
2. Disconnect and remove vacuum harness.
3. Remove six screws attaching recirculation duct, then remove duct.
4. Remove two screws from air inlet duct and remove duct from evaporator case.
5. Remove support bracket, then screws holding electronic connector bracket to recirculation duct.
6. Remove blend door actuator and cold engine lockout switch.
7. Remove molded seal from evaporator core tubes.
8. Drill a (3/16 inch) hole in both upright tabs on top of evaporator case, **Fig. 9.**
9. Using a hot knife or small saw blade, cut top of evaporator case between raised outline, **Fig. 10.**
10. Fold cutout cover back from opening and lift evaporator core from case, **Fig. 11.**
11. Reverse procedure to install, noting the following:
    a. Transfer four foam core seals to new evaporator core.
    b. Install caulking cord No. D9AZ-19560-A or equivalent to seal evaporator case against leakage along cut line.

TOWN CAR

1. Remove evaporator case as outlined under "Heater Core, Replace."
2. Remove dash panel seal, then the heat shield from bottom of evaporator case.
3. Remove six screws attaching two halves of case together.
4. Separate two halves of evaporator case, then remove evaporator core and mounting bracket.
5. Disconnect the suction accumulator/drier inlet from evaporator core outlet tube, **Fig. 12.**
6. Reverse procedure to install, noting the following:
   a. Install new O-rings to accumulator/drier.
   b. Apply caulking cord No. D9AZ-19560-A or equivalent to case flange and around evaporator core tubes.
   c. Install a new heat shield on bottom of evaporator case assembly with staples.

MARK VIII

1. Remove instrument panel.
2. Remove seal from heater core tubes, **Fig. 13.**
3. Remove blend door actuator to evaporator case retaining screws.
4. Remove actuator from case.
5. Remove access cover and seal from evaporator case.
6. Partially drain coolant from radiator and disconnect heater hoses from heater core.
7. Pull heater core and seals from evaporator case.
8. Reverse procedure to install. Fill radiator with specified coolant and check system operation.

3.8L/V6-232 Engine

NOTE: On Air Bag Equipped Models, Refer To "Air Bag System Precautions" Located In The Front Of This Manual For System Disarming & Arming Procedures.

INDEX

PRECAUTIONS

AIR BAG SYSTEMS

Refer to "Air Bag System Precautions" in the front of this manual for system disarming and arming procedures.

FUEL SYSTEM PRESSURE RELIEF

Fuel supply lines, on models equipped with fuel injected engines, will remain pressurized after the engine is shutoff. Pressure must be relieved prior to any fuel system servicing.
1. Remove fuel tank cap.
2. Using fuel pressure gauge tool No. T80L-9974-B or equivalent, relieve fuel system pressure at pressure relief valve righthand rear fuel rail. **Pressure relief valve cap must be removed.**
3. Using suitable tool, remove pressure relief valve.
4. Reverse procedure to install. **Torque** fuel pressure relief valve to 48-84 inch lbs. **Torque** fuel pressure relief valve cap to 4-6 inch lbs.

ENGINE MOUNT
REPLACE

This vehicle is equipped with two RH (front and rear) and one LH internally restrained hydraulic engine mounts. The two RH mounts are equipped with nylon heat shields. All mounts are located and attached to the front sub-frame assembly.

RH FRONT
1. Remove A/C compressor and position aside. It is not necessary to discharge A/C system.
2. Raise and support vehicle.
3. Remove engine mount-to-A/C compressor bracket attaching nut.
4. Temporarily attach A/C compressor to A/C bracket using two lower bolts.
5. Support engine using suitable jack and wood block.
6. Remove RH front and LH rear engine mount attaching nuts, **Fig. 1.**
7. Raise engine enough to relieve load, then remove mount.
8. Reverse procedure to install. **Torque** engine mount-to-A/C bracket attaching nut to 40-55 ft. lbs. and engine mount attaching nuts to 55-70 ft. lbs.

RH REAR
1. Raise and support vehicle.
2. Loosen RH front and LH engine mount attaching nuts, **Fig. 1.**
3. Support engine using suitable equipment, then raise engine approximately one inch.
4. Loosen RH rear engine mount and heat shield retaining nut.
5. Raise and support vehicle.
6. Loosen four sub-frame attaching bolts, then remove engine mount attaching nut and engine mount.
7. Reverse procedure to install. **Torque** engine mount attaching bolts to 55-75 ft. lbs.

LH MOUNT & SUPPORT ASSEMBLY
1. Raise and support vehicle.
2. Remove tire and wheel assembly.
3. Using a suitable jack support transmission.
4. Remove vertical restrictor assembly, then the nut retaining transaxle mount to support assembly.
5. Remove two through bolts retaining mount to frame.
6. Raise transmission, to release load on mount, then remove bolts retaining support assembly to transmission.
7. Remove mount.
8. Reverse procedure to install. **Torque** support assembly to transmission to 34-44 ft. lbs.

ENGINE
REPLACE
1. Drain cooling system and engine oil.
2. Mark position of hood hinges and remove hood.
3. Relieve fuel line pressure and discharge air conditioning system.
4. Disconnect the following:
   a. Alternator-to-voltage regulator wiring harness.
   b. Electric cooling fan and motor assembly.
   c. Transaxle oil cooler lines, then the transaxle pressure switch wiring.
   d. Heater hoses at engine block.
   e. Power steering hoses and hose routing brackets.
   f. A/C compressor clutch electrical connector, then the compressor discharge hose.
   g. Fuel lines.
   h. Power steering pump tube bracket.
   i. Electronic engine control (EEC-IV) wiring assembly.
   j. Vacuum lines and ground wires.
   k. Throttle cable at throttle valve.
5. Remove engine oil dipstick, then the upper radiator sight shield.
6. Remove integrated controller relay and position aside.
7. Remove air cleaner assembly, fan shroud, upper radiator hose and coolant recovery reservoir.
8. Remove wiring shield, then the accelerator cable mounting bracket.
9. Remove air suspension compressor and position aside.
10. Remove transaxle support assembly attaching bolts, then the support assembly.

11. Remove A/C compressor mounting bolts, then the compressor.
12. Raise and support vehicle.
13. Remove oil filter.
14. Disconnect exhaust gas oxygen sensor.
15. Release tension of drive belts, then remove crankshaft pulley and drive belt tensioner.
16. Remove starter motor.
17. Remove catalytic converter housing cover, then the converter and inlet pipe assembly.
18. Remove engine mount attaching nuts, then the torque converter-to-flywheel attaching nuts.
19. Remove oil level indicator sensor.
20. Disconnect lower radiator hose.
21. Loosen engine-to-transaxle attaching bolts, leaving bolts loosely installed.
22. Remove wheel and tire assemblies.
23. Remove drive belts.
24. Remove water pump pulley attaching bolts, then the pulley.
25. Remove radiator.
26. Remove distributor cap and position aside. Remove distributor rotor.
27. Remove exhaust manifold lock bolts.
28. Remove thermactor air pump attaching bolts, then the pump.
29. Disconnect oil pressure sending unit.
30. Remove engine-to-transaxle bolts.
31. Install suitable engine lifting device and position transmission jack under transaxle.
32. Raise transaxle assembly, then lift engine from vehicle.
33. Reverse procedure to install.

INTAKE MANIFOLD
REPLACE

1. Drain cooling system.
2. Remove air cleaner assembly.
3. Disconnect accelerator cable at throttle body. **On models with speed control,** disconnect speed control cable.
4. **On all models,** disconnect transaxle linkage at upper intake manifold, then remove accelerator cable mounting bracket attaching bolts and position cables aside.
5. Disconnect thermactor air supply hose from check valve.
6. Disconnect flexible fuel lines from steel lines over rocker cover, then the fuel lines at injector fuel rail assembly.
7. Disconnect upper radiator hose from thermostat housing, then the coolant bypass hose.
8. Disconnect heater tube from intake manifold, then remove tube support bracket attaching nut. Remove heater hose from rear of tube, then loosen hose clamp at heater elbow and remove tube with hose and fuel lines attached and set aside.
9. Disconnect vacuum lines and all necessary electrical connectors.
10. **On models equipped with A/C,** remove compressor support bracket.
11. **On all models,** disconnect PCV lines from upper intake manifold and left-hand rocker cover, then remove throttle body assembly.

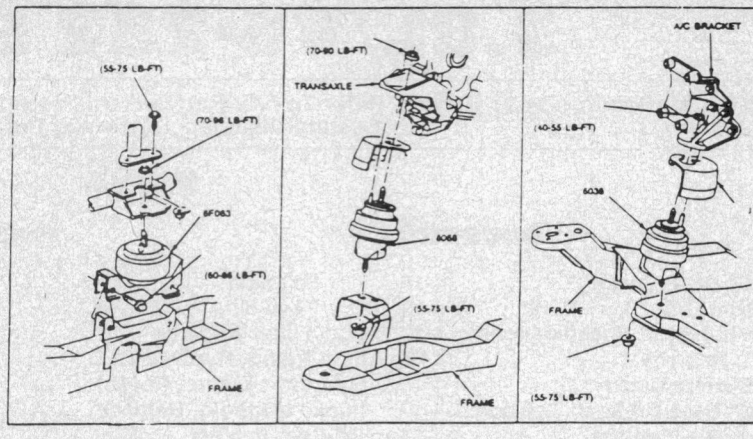

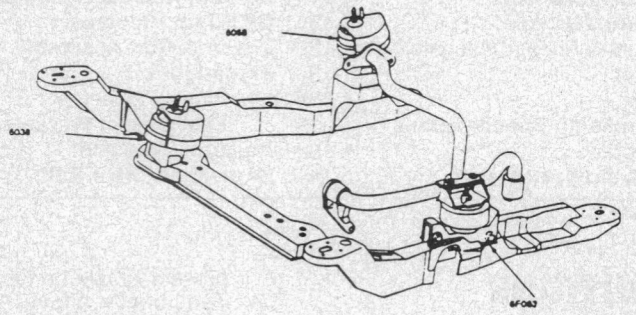

Fig. 1   Engine mount replacement

12. Remove EGR valve assembly from upper manifold.
13. Remove wiring retainer bracket and position aside.
14. Remove upper intake manifold attaching bolts, then the manifold, **Fig. 2.**
15. Remove fuel injectors and fuel rail assembly.
16. Remove heater outlet hose.
17. Remove lower manifold attaching bolts, the then lower manifold. **It may be necessary to pry on front of lower manifold to break the seal. Do not damage sealing surfaces.**
18. Reverse procedure to install, noting the following:
    a. Apply a 1/8 inch bead of silicone at each corner where cylinder head meets the block.
    b. Tighten manifold bolts to specifications in sequence as shown in **Fig. 3.**
    c. Tighten throttle body bolts to specifications in a cross pattern.
    d. **Torque** EGR attaching bolts to 15-22 ft. lbs.

EXHAUST MANIFOLD
REPLACE

LEFT SIDE

1. Remove oil dipstick tube support bracket.
2. Disconnect spark plug wires.
3. Raise and support vehicle.
4. Remove manifold-to-exhaust pipe attaching nuts.
5. Lower vehicle.

6. Remove exhaust manifold attaching bolts, then the manifold.
7. Reverse procedure to install. Tighten manifold attaching bolts to specifications.

RIGHT SIDE

1. Remove air cleaner outlet tube assembly.
2. Disconnect coil wire, then the spark plug wires.
3. Disconnect EGR tube.
4. Raise and support vehicle.
5. Remove manifold-to-exhaust pipe attaching nuts, then lower vehicle.
6. Remove exhaust manifold attaching bolts, then the manifold.
7. Reverse procedure to install. Tighten manifold attaching bolts to specifications.

CYLINDER HEAD
REPLACE

1. Drain cooling system
2. Disconnect negative battery cable.
3. Remove air cleaner assembly and drive belts.
4. If removing left cylinder head, proceed as follows:
    a. Remove oil fill cap.
    b. Remove power steering pump with hoses connected, positioning pump aside.
    c. **On models with A/C,** remove compressor mounting bracket bolts and position compressor aside.
    d. **On all models,** remove alternator and bracket.

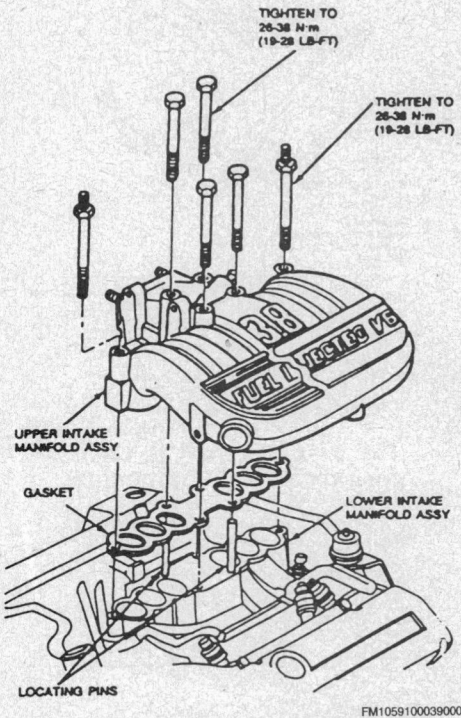

Fig. 2   Upper intake manifold replacement

TIGHTEN TO 26-38 N·m (19-28 LB-FT)

TIGHTEN TO 26-38 N·m (19-28 LB-FT)

UPPER INTAKE MANIFOLD ASSY

GASKET

LOWER INTAKE MANIFOLD ASSY

LOCATING PINS

FM1059100039000X

the following:

a. Apply suitable sealer to short cylinder head bolts, then lightly oil all other bolts.

b. Tighten rocker arm fulcrum attaching bolts, rocker arm cover bolts to specifications.

c. **Torque** cylinder head bolts in sequence shown, **Fig. 4,** in four steps; first to 37 ft. lbs., then 45 ft. lbs., 52 ft. lbs., and finally 59 ft. lbs., then back off all bolts in sequence 2-3 turns.

d. **Torque** long bolts to 11-18 ft. lbs., then an additional 85-105°.

e. **Torque** short bolts to 11-18 ft. lbs., then an additional 65-85°.

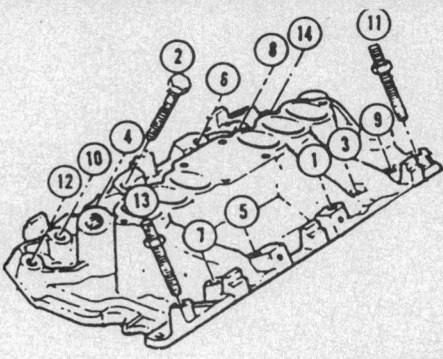

FM1059100040000X

Fig. 3   Intake manifold tightening sequence

VALVE COVER
REPLACE

1. Disconnect ignition wires from spark plugs and position aside.
2. Remove air cleaner assembly, oil fill cap and PCV valve.
3. Remove rocker arm cover attaching screws, then the covers.
4. Reverse procedure to install. Tighten attaching screws to specifications.

VALVE ARRANGEMENT
FRONT TO REAR

Right Side . . . . E-I-I-E-I-E
Left Side . . . . E-I-E-I-I-E

CAMSHAFT LOBE LIFT SPECIFICATIONS

Exhaust . . . . .259 inch
Intake . . . . .245 inch

VALVE CLEARANCE SPECIFICATIONS

Valve clearance should be 0.09-0.19 inch with tappet fully collapsed on base circle after assembly. Refer to "Valve Adjustment" for procedure.

VALVE ADJUSTMENT

This engine is equipped with non-adjustable hydraulic lifters (tappets). The following procedure relates to the measurement of valve clearance.

1. Position No.1 piston on top dead center (TDC), at the end of the compression stroke, **Fig. 5.**
2. Disconnect battery ground cable.
3. Remove valve cover.
4. Check clearance on the valves shown, refer to **Fig. 5**

5. Loosen rocker arm shaft assembly retaining bolts to allow removal of push rods.

6. Compress valve spring and remove push rods, ensuring piston in related cylinder is below TDC to avoid damage to piston or valve.

7. Using a tappet bleed down wrench or equivalent, apply pressure to valve rocker arm, then collapse lifter, **Fig. 6**

8. Measure valve clearance, follow crankshaft rotation procedure, refer to **Fig. 6**

9. Replace valve lifter if valve clearance is not within specifications.

HYDRAULIC LIFTERS
REPLACE

Before replacing hydraulic valve lifters for noisy operation, ensure the noise is not caused by improper rocker arm-to-stem clearance, worn rocker arms, pushrods or valve tips.

1. Disconnect ignition wires from spark plugs and position aside.
2. Remove upper intake manifold as described under "Intake Manifold, Replace."
3. Remove rocker arm cover attaching bolts, then the covers.
4. Remove lower intake manifold as described under "Intake Manifold, Replace."
5. Loosen rocker arm fulcrum attaching bolts, lift rocker arms off pushrods and rotate to side.
6. Remove pushrods, then the lifters. Keep lifters and pushrods in order, as they should be installed in their original position.
7. Reverse procedure to install. Lubricate lifters, pushrods and rocker arms with suitable lubricant. Torque rocker arm fulcrum bolts to specifications. **Ensure pushrods and rocker arms are fully seated prior to tightening bolts.**

SERVICE BULLETIN: A low medium pitch noise such as a squeak, chirp or knock that can be heard under the hood in the engine compartment may be caused

5. If removing right cylinder head, proceed as follows:
   a. Disconnect thermactor air control valve
   b. Disconnect thermactor tube support bracket from rear of cylinder head
   c. Remove accessory drive idler.
   d. Remove thermactor pump pulley, then the thermactor pump.
   e. Remove PCV valve.

6. Remove upper and lower intake manifolds as described under "Intake Manifold, Replace."

7. Remove rocker arm cover attaching screws, then the cover.

8. Remove injector fuel rail assembly.

9. Remove exhaust manifolds as described under "Exhaust Manifold, Replace."

10. Loosen rocker arm fulcrum attaching bolts and rotate rocker arm enough to allow removal of pushrods. Remove pushrods, noting their position. **Pushrods should be installed in their original position.**

11. Remove and discard cylinder head attaching bolts.

12. Remove cylinder head.

13. Reverse procedure to install, noting

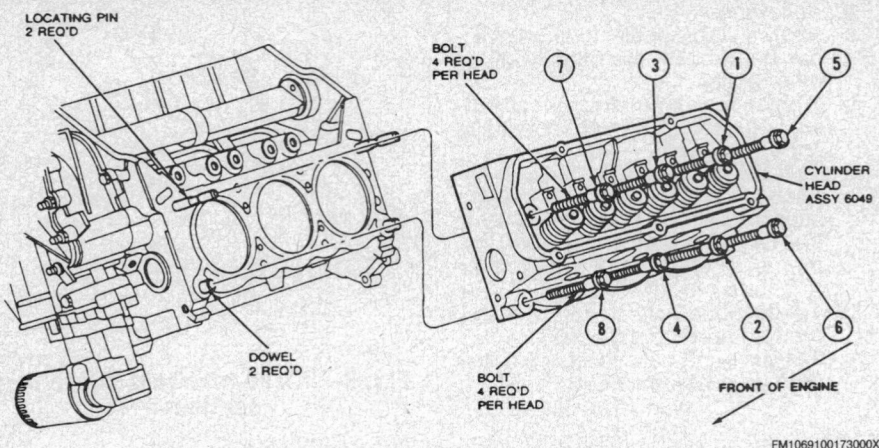

Fig. 4 Cylinder head tightening sequence

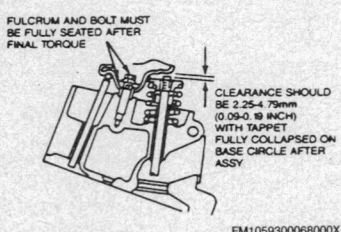

Fig. 6 Valve clearance measurement. Continental

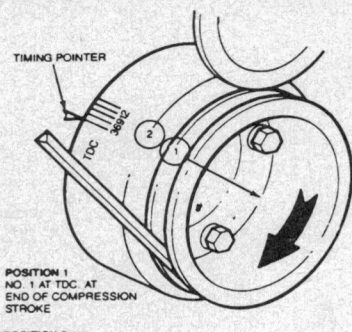

Fig. 5 Crankshaft to valve position at TDC. Continental

CYL. NO.	CRANKSHAFT POSITION	
	1	2
	SET GAP OF VALVES NOTED	
1	INT — EXH	NONE
2	EXH	INT
3	INT	EXH
4	EXH	INT
5	NONE	INT — EXH
6	INT	EXH

by the fulcrum and rocker assemblies. The noise is most noticeable at engine idle with engine at normal operating temperature.

Use the following diagnostic procedure to determine if a Break-In Additive will eliminate the noise or if a set of rocker arm assemblies are required.

1. Bring engine to normal operating temperature.
2. Using a stethoscope on the rocker arm cover, determine which rocker arms are noisy.
3. If noisy arms are present, add one container of Break-In Additive No. E9SZ-19579-A to the crankcase.
4. Continue to idle engine for ten minutes.
5. Test drive vehicle for no less than five minutes.
6. If noise persists rocker new rocker assemblies are required.

TIMING CHAIN
REPLACE

1. Drain cooling system.
2. Disconnect negative battery cable.
3. Loosen accessory drive belt idler, then remove drive belt and water pump pulley.
4. Remove power steering pump mounting bracket attaching bolts, then remove assembly with hoses connected, positioning pump aside.
5. **On models with A/C,** remove compressor front support bracket, leaving compressor in place.
6. **On all models,** disconnect coolant bypass hose and heater hose at water pump, then the upper radiator hose at thermostat housing.

7. Disconnect coil wire from distributor cap, then remove cap with plug wires attached. Remove distributor hold-down clamp and distributor.
8. Raise and support vehicle.
9. Remove crankshaft pulley and damper using suitable puller. If crankshaft pulley and damper have to be separated, mark damper and pulley for reassembly reference, as damper and pulley are balanced as a unit and should be installed back to their original position.
10. Remove oil filter and disconnect lower radiator hose.
11. Remove oil pan as described under "Oil Pan, Replace."
12. Lower vehicle.
13. Remove front cover attaching bolts, **Fig. 7. Ensure attaching bolt behind oil filter adapter is removed to avoid damaging cover upon removal.**
14. Remove ignition timing indicator.
15. Remove front cover and water pump as an assembly. Remove and discard cover gasket.
16. Remove camshaft bolt and washer from end of camshaft.
17. Remove distributor drive gear.
18. Remove camshaft sprocket, crankshaft sprocket and timing chain, **Fig. 8.**. If crankshaft sprocket is difficult to remove, pry it off the shaft using two large screwdrivers.
19. Reverse procedure to install. Align timing chain and sprockets by placing No. 1 cylinder at TDC and crankshaft keyway at 12 o'clock position.

CAMSHAFT
REPLACE

1. Remove engine from vehicle as described under "Engine, Replace."
2. Remove intake manifolds as described under "Intake Manifold, Replace."
3. Remove valve lifters as described under "Hydraulic Lifters, Replace."
4. Remove timing case cover and timing chain as described under "Timing Case Cover & Timing chain, Replace.

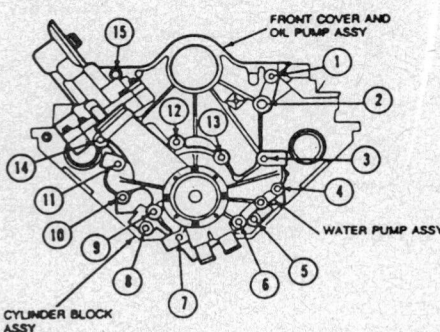

Fig. 7 Front cover bolt locations

5. Remove oil pan as described under "Oil Pan, Replace."
6. Remove camshaft through front of engine. **Do not damage bearing surfaces during removal.**
7. Reverse procedure to install. Lubricate cam lobes and bearings with suitable lubricant.

BALANCE SHAFT
REPLACE

A balance shaft system is used on 3.8L/V6-232 to provide increased engine smoothness. The counter-rotating shaft, driven by a gear mounted on the camshaft snout between the camshaft thrust plate and sprocket, is located above the camshaft in the cylinder block valley area. The balance shaft is retained in the cylinder block by a thrust plate, and rides on bearings very similar to that of the camshaft.

1. Remove engine from vehicle as described under "Engine, Replace."
2. Remove timing case cover and timing chain as described under "Timing Chain, Replace."
3. Remove oil pan as described under "Oil Pan, Replace."
4. Remove balance shaft thrust plate, **Fig. 9,** then the balance shaft. **Do not damage bearings during removal.**

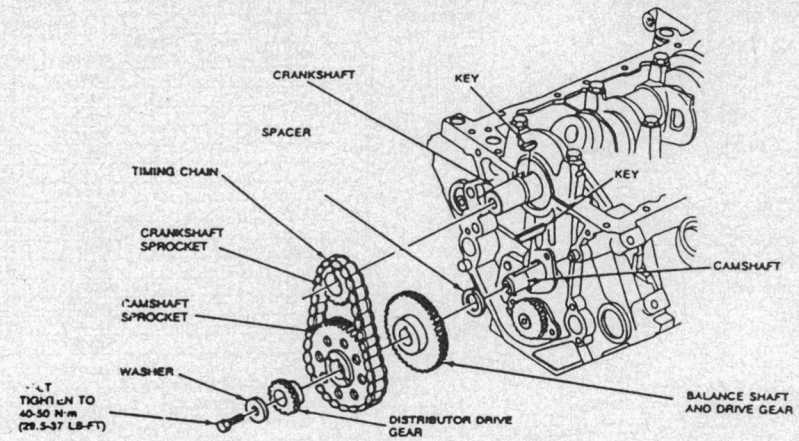

Fig. 8   Timing chain & sprocket removal

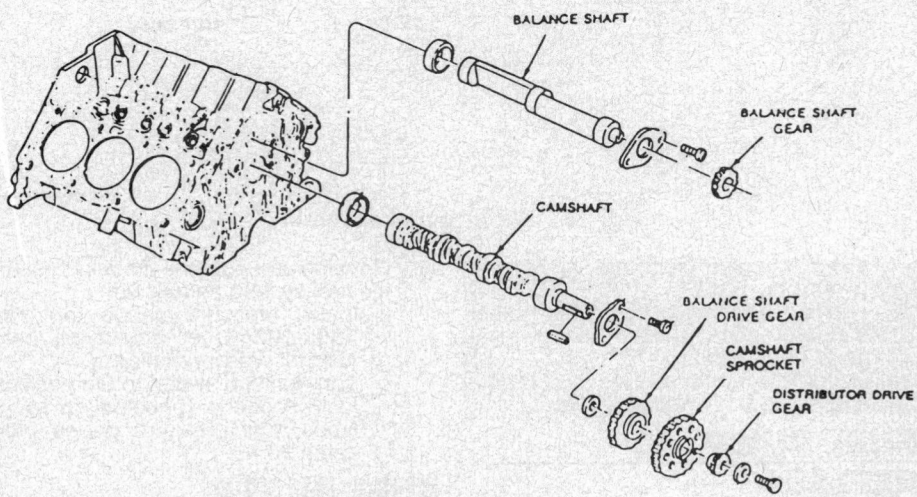

Fig. 9   Balance shaft assembly

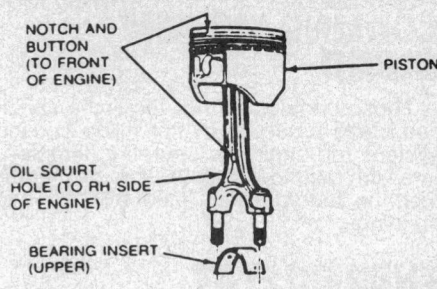

Fig. 10   Piston & rod assembly

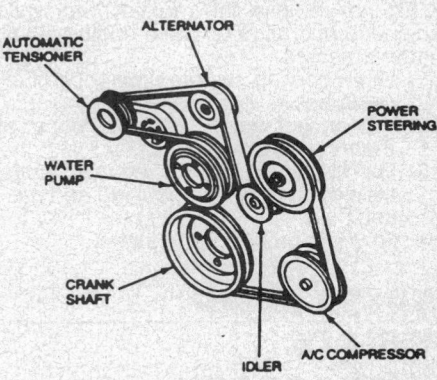

Fig. 11   Serpentine drive belt routing

a. **Torque** oil pump retaining bolts to 6-8 ft. lbs.
b. **Torque** four large engine front cover retaining bolts to 17-23 ft. lbs.
c. **Torque** oil pan drain plug to 15-25 ft. lbs.
d. Replace oil filter and fill engine oil.

5. Reverse procedure to install. Lubricate balance shaft bearing journals with suitable lubricant.

PISTON & ROD ASSEMBLY

Assemble rod to piston with notch on piston dome on same side as oil squirt hole on connecting rod, **Fig. 10.** Assemble piston and rod assembly in engine with notch in dome facing front of engine.

After installation, check connecting rod big end side clearance. Clearance should be .0047-.0114 inch.

CRANKSHAFT REAR OIL SEAL
REPLACE

1. Remove transaxle and flywheel as described under "Transaxle, Replace" in the "Automatic Transmissions/Transaxles" section.
2. Remove rear cover plate.
3. Using suitable tool, punch hole in seal metal between seal lip and cylinder block. Using suitable slide hammer remove seal.

4. Coat crankshaft seal area and seal lip with engine oil, then install seal using suitable driver.
5. Install rear cover plate, flywheel and transaxle.

OIL PAN
REPLACE

1. Disconnect negative battery cable.
2. Raise and support vehicle.
3. Drain engine oil and remove oil filter.
4. Remove catalytic convertor assembly, then the starter motor.
5. Remove torque convertor housing cover.
6. Remove oil pan attaching bolts, then the oil pan.
7. Reverse procedure to install.

OIL PUMP
REPLACE

1. Disconnect battery ground cable.
2. Drain engine oil and remove oil filter.
3. Remove oil pump retaining bolts (four) from engine front cover, then remove oil pump.
4. Reverse procedure to install, noting the following:

BELT TENSION DATA

Belt tension is automatically maintained on these models by an automatic tensioner. No adjustment is necessary.

SERPENTINE DRIVE BELT

BELT ROUTING

Refer to **Fig. 11,** for serpentine drive belt routing.

BELT REPLACEMENT

Using a breaker bar installed in 1/2 inch square hole in tensioner behind pulley, rotate tensioner clockwise and remove belt from pulley(s). **Use caution when removing or installing belts to ensure tool does not slip.**

ADJUSTMENT

Automatic belt tensioners are spring loaded devices which set and maintain the drive belt tension. The drive belt should not require tension adjustment for the life of the belt. Automatic tensioners have belt wear indicator marks. If the indicator mark is not between the MIN and MAX marks, the belt is worn or an incorrect belt is installed.

COOLING SYSTEM BLEED

These engines do not require a specified bleed procedure. After filling cooling system, run engine to operating temperature with radiator/pressure cap off. Air will then be automatically bled through cap opening.

THERMOSTAT
REPLACE

Do not remove the radiator cap while engine is operating or while engine is still under pressure.
1. Drain cooling system until coolant level is below thermostat.
2. Disconnect upper radiator hose at thermostat housing.
3. Remove two housing retaining bolts, then the thermostat housing and gasket.
4. Reverse procedure to install.

WATER PUMP
REPLACE

1. Drain cooling system.
2. Remove lower nut on both righthand engine mounts.
3. Raise and support vehicle.
4. Loosen accessory drive belt idler, then the drive belt and water pump pulley.
5. Remove air suspension pump.
6. Remove power steering pump bracket attaching bolts, then position bracket and pump aside.
7. **On models equipped with A/C,** remove compressor front support bracket, leaving compressor in place.
8. **On all models,** disconnect coolant bypass hose and heater hose from water pump.
9. Remove water pump attaching bolts, then the pump, **Fig. 12.** Discard old gasket.
10. Reverse procedure to install. **Torque** water pump attaching bolts to specifications and fan clutch attaching bolts to 12-18 ft. lbs. **Coat threads of No. 1 water pump bolt with suitable sealer.**

RADIATOR
REPLACE

1. Disconnect battery ground cable.
2. Drain engine coolant, then disconnect deareation hose and both radiator hoses.
3. Disconnect automatic transmission fluid inlet and outlet lines.
4. **On models equipped with fan shroud,** remove upper shroud mounting bolts at radiator support.
5. Lift fan shroud enough to disengage

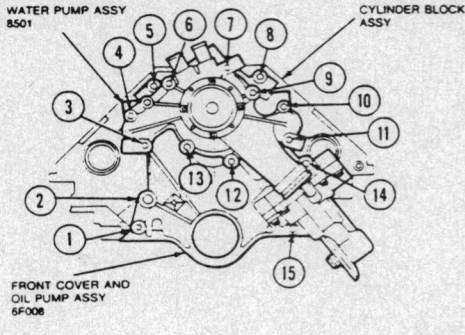
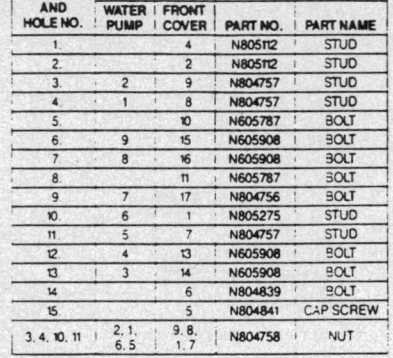

FASTENER AND HOLE NO.	HOLE NO. WATER PUMP	HOLE NO. FRONT COVER	FASTENERS PART NO.	FASTENERS PART NAME
1.		4	N805112	STUD
2.		2	N805112	STUD
3.	2	3	N804757	STUD
4.	1	8	N804757	STUD
5.		10	N605787	BOLT
6.	9	15	N605908	BOLT
7.	8	16	N605908	BOLT
8.		11	N605787	BOLT
9.	7	17	N804756	BOLT
10.	6	1	N805275	STUD
11.	5	7	N804757	STUD
12.	4	13	N605908	BOLT
13.	3	14	N605908	BOLT
14.		6	N804839	BOLT
15.			N804841	CAP SCREW
3, 4, 10, 11	2, 1, 6, 5	9, 8, 1, 7	N804758	NUT

NOTE TIGHTEN ALL FASTENERS TO 20-30 N·m (15-22 LB-FT)

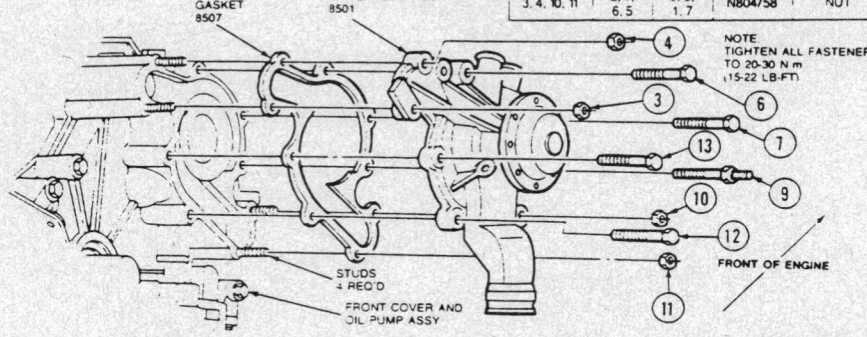

Fig. 12   Water pump assembly

FM1089100058000X

lower retaining clips and lay shroud over fan.
6. **On all models,** remove radiator upper support mounting bolts, then the supports and radiator.
7. Reverse procedure to install. Operate engine and check fluid levels.

FUEL PUMP
REPLACE

Fuel supply lines will remain pressurized for long periods of time after engine shutdown. This pressure must be relieved before any service is attempted. A valve is provided on the fuel rail assembly for this purpose. To relieve system pressure, remove air cleaner assembly and connect pressure gauge tool No. T80L-9974-B or equivalent onto fuel valve on fuel rail assembly.

1. Disconnect battery ground cable.
2. Relieve fuel system pressure as described previously.
3. Remove fuel from fuel tank by pumping fuel out of fuel filler neck.
4. Raise and support vehicle.
5. Disconnect and remove fuel filler neck.
6. Support fuel tank, then remove tank support straps. Lower fuel tank partially and remove fuel lines, electrical connectors and vent lines from tank. Remove tank.
7. Turn fuel pump locking ring counterclockwise and remove locking ring.
8. Remove fuel pump, bracket and gasket assembly.

9. Reverse procedure to install. Pressurize fuel system as follows:
   a. Install pressure gauge tool No. T80L-9974-B or equivalent onto fuel rail pressure fitting.
   b. Turn ignition switch to On position for 3 seconds, repeatedly 5 to 10 times until pressure gauge indicates 30 psi.

FUEL FILTER
REPLACE

Fuel supply lines will remain pressurized for long periods of time after engine shutdown. This pressure must be relieved before any service is attempted. A valve is provided on the fuel rail assembly for this purpose. To relieve system pressure, remove air cleaner assembly and connect pressure gauge tool No. T80L-9974-B or equivalent onto fuel valve on fuel rail assembly.

1. Turn engine off and relieve fuel system pressure.
2. Remove push connect fittings at both ends of the fuel filter. Note direction of flow arrow on filter.
3. Remove filter from bracket by loosening worm gear mounting clamp enough to allow filter to pass through.
4. Reverse procedure to install, noting the following:
   a. **Torque** worm gear mounting clamp to 15-25 inch lbs.
   b. Ensure flow arrow is pointed in correct direction, then start engine and inspect for leaks.

TIGHTENING SPECIFICATIONS

Year	Component	Torque/Ft. Lbs.
1992–95	Air Pump Brace To Bracket	52-70
	Air Pump Brace To Crankshaft Pulley Nut	15-22
	Air Pump Bracket To Engine	30-40
	Air Pump Pivot Bolt	30-40
	Air Pump Pulley	71-101 ③
	Alternator Brace To Alternator	30-44
	Alternator Brace To Intake Manifold Nut	15-22
	Alternator Brace To Water Pump	15-22
	Alternator Pivot Bolt	45-57
	Camshaft Sprocket Bolt	30-36
	Connecting Rod Nut	31-36
	Crankshaft Damper Bolt	104-132
	Crankshaft Pulley	20-28
	Cylinder Head Bolt	①
	Distributor Cap	18-23 ③
	Distributor Hold-Down	20-29
	ECT Sensor	6-9
	EGR Valve To Intake Manifold	15-22
	Flywheel Bolt	54-64
	Front Cover	15-22
	Fuel Injection To Intake Manifold Bolts	71-104 ③
	Heater Elbow	15-17
	Heater Tube To Intake Manifold Stud	8-10

Year	Component	Torque/Ft. Lbs.
1992–95 —Cont'd	Intake Manifold	②
	Low Level Oil Sensor	18-22
	Main Bearing Cap	65-74
	Oil Inlet Tube	15-22
	Oil Pan To Block	80-106 ③
	Oil Pan Drain Plug	15-25
	Rocker Arm Cover	80-106 ③
	Rocker Arm Fulcrum	④
	Spark Plugs	5-11
	Thermactor Check Valve To Intake Manifold	16-19
	Thermostat	15-22
	Throttle Body Nut	15-22
	Torque Converter To Flywheel	20-34
	Transmission To Engine Bolts	40-50
	Water Pump Pulley	71-101 ③
	Water Pump To Front Cover	15-22

① —Refer to text.
② —Torque bolts in three steps; first to 7 ft. lbs., then 15 ft. lbs., and finally 24 ft. lbs.
③ —Inch lbs.
④ —Torque in two steps; first to 44 inch lbs., then finally to 18-25 ft. lbs.

4.6L/V8-281 Engine

NOTE: On Air Bag Equipped Models, Refer To "Air Bag System Precautions" Located In The Front Of This Manual For System Disarming & Arming Procedures.

INDEX

PRECAUTIONS

AIR BAG SYSTEMS

Refer to "Air Bag System Precautions" in the front of this manual for system disarming and arming procedures.

FUEL SYSTEM PRESSURE RELIEF

Fuel supply lines, on models equipped with fuel injected engines, will remain pressurized after the engine is shutoff. Pressure must be relieved prior to any fuel system servicing.

1. Remove fuel tank cap.
2. Using fuel pressure gauge tool No. T80L-9974-B or equivalent, relieve fuel system pressure at pressure relief valve righthand rear fuel rail. **Pressure relief valve cap must be removed.**
3. Using suitable tool, remove pressure relief valve.
4. Reverse procedure to install. **Torque** fuel pressure relief valve to 48-84 inch lbs. **Torque** fuel pressure relief valve cap to 4-6 inch lbs.

ENGINE MOUNT
REPLACE

FRONT

1. Disconnect ground and positive battery cables.
2. Remove air inlet tube.
3. Drain cooling system, then remove cooling fan and shroud.
4. Relieve fuel system pressure as outlined under "Fuel System Pressure Relief."
5. Remove upper radiator hose.

6. Remove wiper module and support bracket.
7. Discharge A/C system.
8. Disconnect A/C compressor outlet hose, then remove hose assembly to righthand coil bracket attaching bolt.
9. Remove engine electrical harness 42-pin connector from bracket on brake vacuum booster.
10. Disconnect engine electrical connector, then disconnect transmission harness electrical connector.
11. Disconnect throttle valve cable at throttle body.
12. Disconnect heater outlet hose.
13. Remove heater outlet hose assembly to righthand cylinder head upper attaching stud, then loosen lower bolt and position aside.
14. Remove blower motor resistor.
15. Remove righthand engine mount to lower engine bracket attaching bolt.
16. Disconnect EGR valve vacuum hoses and tube.
17. Remove EGR valve to intake manifold attaching bolts.
18. Disconnect Heated Exhaust Gas Oxygen (HEGO) sensors.
19. Raise and support vehicle.
20. Remove righthand front engine mount two through bolts, then remove lefthand front engine mount through bolt, **Fig. 1.**
21. Remove EGR tube line attaching nut at righthand exhaust manifold, then remove EGR valve assembly.
22. Disconnect exhaust pipes at exhaust manifolds, then lower and support exhaust at crossmember.
23. Position suitable jack and wood block under oil pan, rearward of drain plug, then raise engine approximately 4 inches.

24. Install wood block under oil pan, then lower engine onto wood block.
25. Remove engine mount attaching bolts.
26. Reverse procedure to install, noting the following:
    a. **Torque** EGR valve and tube assembly to exhaust manifold line nut to 26-33 ft. lbs.
    b. **Torque** exhaust manifold to exhaust attaching bolts to 20-30 ft. lbs.
    c. **Torque** EGR valve to intake manifold attaching bolts to 15-22 ft. lbs.
    d. **Torque** heater outlet hose to righthand cylinder head attaching stud, bolt and ground strap to 15-22 ft. lbs.
    e. Refer to **Fig. 1,** for engine mount tightening specifications.

REAR

1. Raise and support vehicle, then using suitable jack and wood block support transmission.
2. Remove rear mount to crossmember attaching bolts.
3. Remove mount to transmission attaching bolt, **Fig. 2.**
4. Raise transmission with suitable jack, then remove mount assembly.
5. Reverse procedure to install. Refer to **Fig. 2,** for rear engine mount tightening specifications.

ENGINE
REPLACE

TOWN CAR

1. Disconnect both battery cables, then mark hood hinge positions for installation alignment.

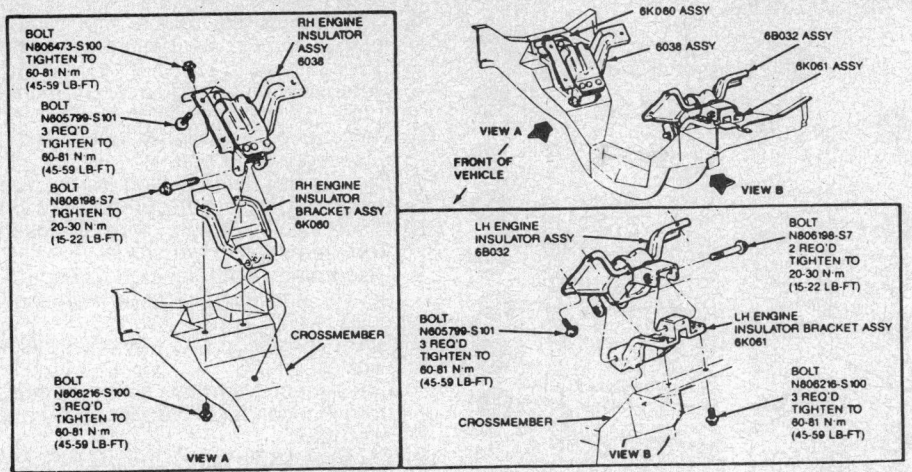

Fig. 1   Front engine mounts

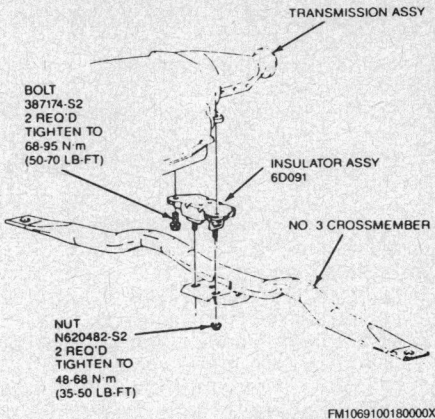

Fig. 2   Rear engine mount

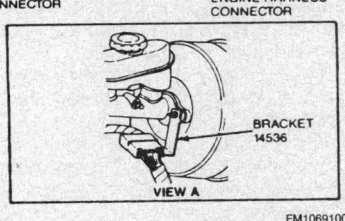

Fig. 3   Engine & transmission harness connectors

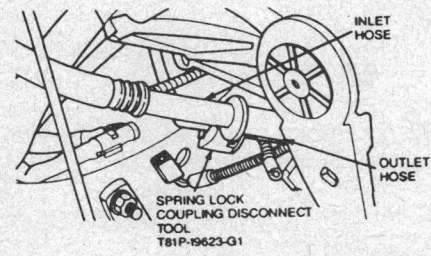

Fig. 4   A/C compressor lines

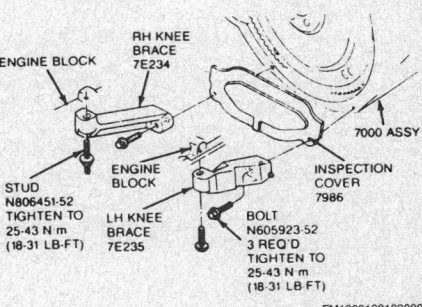

Fig. 5   Transmission line bracket assembly

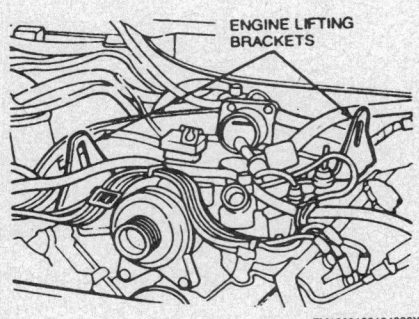

Fig. 6   Engine lift brackets

2. Remove hood, drain cooling system and discharge A/C system.
3. Relieve fuel system pressure as outlined under "Fuel System Pressure Relief," then disconnect fuel lines.
4. Remove engine cooling fan, shroud and radiator.
5. Remove wiper module and bracket.
6. Remove air inlet tube.
7. Remove 42-pin electrical harness connector from bracket at brake vacuum booster, **Fig. 3.**
8. Disconnect 42-pin connector and transmission harness electrical connector, then position connectors aside.
9. Using suitable tool, disconnect accelerator and speed control cables.
10. Disconnect throttle valve cable.
11. Disconnect purge solenoid electrical connector and vacuum hose.
12. Disconnect power distribution and starter relay power supply.
13. Disconnect throttle body elbow vacuum port supply hose.
14. Disconnect heater inlet and return hoses.
15. Disconnect alternator electrical harness at fender apron and junction box.
16. Using tool No. T81P-19623-G1, G2 or

equivalent, remove A/C compressor inlet and outlet attaching hoses, **Fig. 4.**
17. Disconnect EVO sensor electrical connector.
18. Disconnect body ground strap at dash panel.
19. Raise and support vehicle, then drain engine oil.
20. Disconnect exhaust pipes at exhaust manifolds, then lower and support exhaust at crossmember.
21. Remove transmission line bracket attaching nut, then remove engine to transmission knee braces attaching bolts and stud, **Fig. 5.**
22. Remove starter assembly.
23. Remove power steering pump attaching nuts and position pump aside.
24. Remove engine block plug to gain access to torque converter attaching nuts, then rotate crankshaft to remove attaching nuts.

25. Remove engine to transmission attaching bolts.
26. Remove righthand front engine mount two through bolts, then remove lefthand front engine mount through bolt.
27. Lower vehicle, using suitable jack, support transmission.
28. Install engine lift brackets, **Fig. 6,** then connect suitable lift equipment.
29. Carefully raise engine and separate from transmission, then remove engine.
30. Reverse procedure to install, noting the following:
   a. **Torque** engine to transmission attaching bolt to 30-44 ft. lbs.
   b. Refer to **Fig. 1,** for engine mount tightening specifications.
   c. **Torque** torque converter attaching nuts to 22-25 ft. lbs.
   d. **Torque** power steering pump attaching nuts to 15-22 ft. lbs.
   e. Refer to **Fig. 5,** for transmission brace tightening specifications.
   f. **Torque** exhaust to exhaust manifold attaching bolts to 20-30 ft. lbs.

MARK VIII

1. Disconnect both battery cables, then mark hood hinge positions for installation alignment.
2. Remove hood.
3. Remove engine appearance cover.
4. Remove IAT sensor electrical connector.
5. Remove air cleaner outlet tube and resonator.
6. Remove hood, drain cooling system and

7. Remove wiper module and bracket.
8. Discharge A/C system.
9. Remove engine cooling fan, shroud and radiator.
10. Relieve fuel system pressure as outlined under "Fuel System Pressure Relief," then disconnect fuel lines.
11. Disconnect 42-pin connector and transmission harness electrical connector, at left fender well, then position connectors aside.
12. Remove power distribution box and harness, then disconnect B+ wiring connector at distribution box.
13. Disconnect electrical connectors at EVAP canister purge valves.
14. Disconnect accelerator cable, speed control actuator from throttle body and cable brackets.
15. Disconnect canister purge vacuum line at throttle body.
16. Disconnect chassis supply vacuum line at cowl.
17. Disconnect heater inlet and outlet tubes at rear of righthand cylinder head.
18. Disconnect upper radiator hose at bypass tube and overflow hose at recovery reservoir.
19. Remove pressure and return hoses at power steering pump, then remove pump.
20. Remove upper cooling inlet hose from radiator.
21. Install engine lifting tool No. 014-00340 or equivalent.
22. Disconnect A/C refrigerant hoses at compressor. Refer to "Air Conditioning" section for procedure and precautions.
23. Raise vehicle and suitably support.
24. Remove front wheels.
25. Disconnect righthand and lefthand ride height sensor electrical connectors.
26. Remove right and left front brake calipers and suitably support.
27. Disconnect right and left front suspension upper control arms from steering knuckle.
28. Drain engine oil.
29. Remove converter Y pipe from lefthand and righthand exhaust manifolds.
30. Disconnect ground strap from right front fender.
31. Disconnect power steering pressure hose at steering gear.
32. Remove lower radiator hose.
33. Remove right and left strut at front suspension lower control arms.
34. Disconnect engine control sensor wiring and gear selector linkage.
35. Disconnect lower oil cooler tube from radiator.
36. Remove driveshaft retaining bolts at pinion flange.
37. Loosen rear differential bracket body bolts and lower.
38. Remove driveshaft.
39. Remove battery positive cable, then disconnect low oil sensor connector and wiring from oil pan.
40. Remove starter.
41. Support powertrain frame using powertrain lift tool No. 014-00765 and

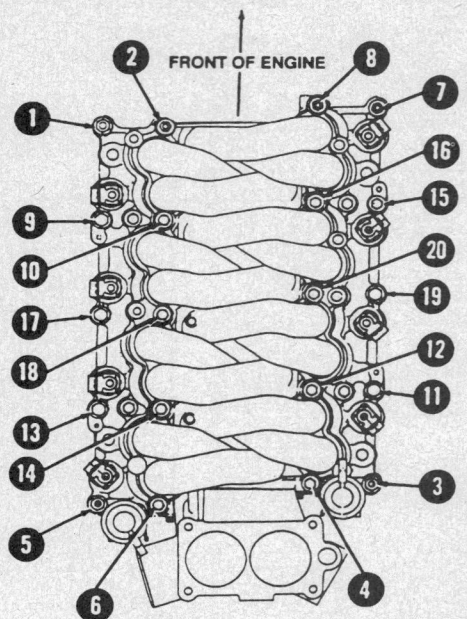

Fig. 7 Intake manifold bolt removal sequence. Mark VIII

FM1059500064000X

adapter tool No. 014-000341 or equivalents.
42. Remove rear engine support insulator, then disconnect steering coupling pinch bolt.
43. Remove powertrain frame retaining bolts, then lower engine and transmission from vehicle.
44. Reverse procedure to install, noting the following;
    a. **Torque** transmission mounting bolts to 30-44 ft. lbs.
45. **Torque** engine support insulator bolts to 15-22 ft. lbs.
46. **Torque** powertrain frame retaining bolts to 73-100 ft. lbs.
47. **Torque** rear engine support insulator bolts to 15-22 ft. lbs.
48. **Torque** rear axle assembly to rear sub-frame retaining bolts to 72-89 ft. lbs.
49. **Torque** rear axle differential nuts to 75-89 ft. lbs.
50. **Torque** driveshaft to pinion flange bolts to 70-96 ft. lbs.
51. **Torque** lower control arm to strut bolts to 118-162 ft. lbs.
52. **Torque** upper control arm to steering knuckle bolts 50-68 ft. lbs.
53. Refill and check, engine oil, transmission fluid, power steering fluid, and engine coolant.
54. Recharge A/C system as described in the "Air Conditioning" section.
55. Check front end alignment.

INTAKE MANIFOLD
REPLACE

1. Disconnect battery ground cable.
2. Drain cooling system.
3. **On Mark VIII models,** remove engine appearance cover, air cleaner outlet tube and air intake resonator.

4. **On all models,** relieve fuel system fuel pressure as described under "Precautions."
5. Remove wiper module and air inlet tube.
6. Release belt tensioner and remove accessory drive belt.
7. Disconnect ignition plug wires from spark plugs. **Do not pull on wire (s).**
8. Disconnect ignition wire brackets from camshaft cover studs.
9. Disconnect both ignition coils, CID sensor and ignition wires from both coils.
10. Remove ignition wire tray and ignition wire assembly.
11. Disconnect alternator wiring harness from junction block, fender apron and alternator.
12. **On Mark VIII models,** disconnect upper radiator hose and water bypass tube to the thermostat hose at the water bypass tube.
13. **On all models,** disconnect electrical connectors at ECT and engine temperature sending unit at bottom of coolant bypass tube.
14. Remove coolant bypass tube
15. Remove alternator and mounting bracket.
16. **On Mark VIII models,** disconnect accelerator cable and speed control actuator from throttle body.
17. **On all models,** disconnect the following vacuum lines:
    a. Chassis vacuum supply hose.
    b. Fuel pressure regulator vacuum harness.
    c. Righthand and lefthand intake manifold runner controls (IMRC).
    d. Intake manifold connection.
    e. Crankcase vent.
    f. Throttle body.
    g. PCV
18. Disconnect and remove upper engine wiring harness from intake manifold.
19. Disconnect eight fuel injector connectors.
20. Remove EGR valve.
21. Disconnect IAC and TPS electrical connectors.
22. Loosen and remove 20 intake manifold to cylinder head retaining bolts and studs in sequence shown in **Fig. 7**
23. Remove intake manifold.
24. **On Town Car,** raise and support vehicle.
25. **On all models,** disconnect oil sending unit and EVO sensor, then position aside.
26. Disconnect EGR tube from right exhaust manifold, then lower vehicle.
27. Disconnect 42-pin connector, A/C compressor, HDR sensor and canister purge solenoid.
28. Remove PCV valve from camshaft cover, then disconnect canister purge vent hose from PCV valve.
29. Disconnect accelerator and speed control cables from throttle body, then remove accelerator cable bracket from intake manifold and position aside.
30. Disconnect throttle valve cable from throttle body.

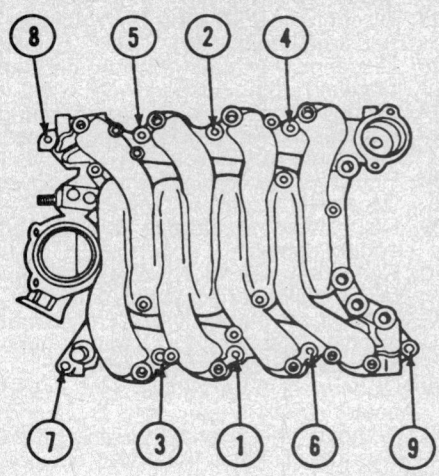

Fig. 8   Intake manifold tightening sequence. Town Car.

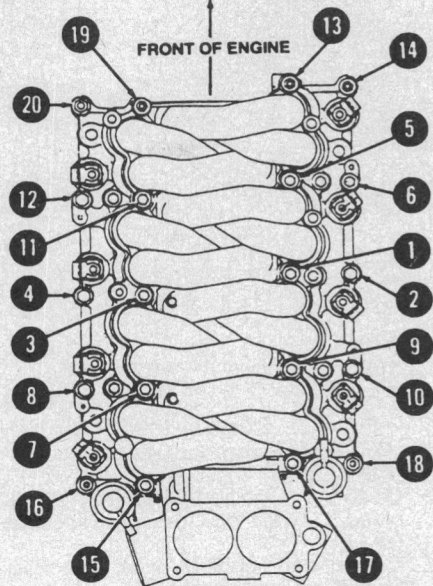

Fig. 9   Intake manifold tightening sequence. Mark VIII

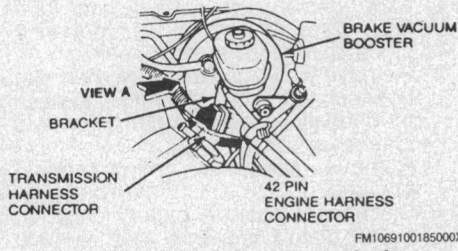

Fig. 11   Engine & transmission harness connectors

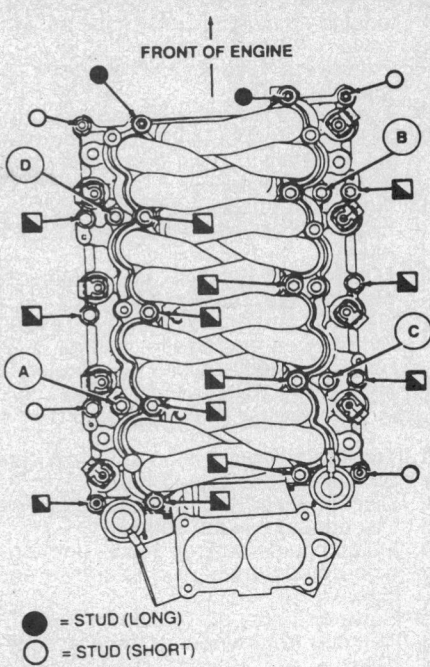

● = STUD (LONG)
○ = STUD (SHORT)
◼ = BOLT

Fig. 10   Intake manifold runner control (IMRC) tightening sequence. Mark VIII

31. Disconnect vacuum hose from throttle body adapter port.
32. Disconnect both HEGO sensors and heater supply hose.
33. Remove thermostat housing, then disconnect upper hose and position aside.
34. Remove bolts attaching intake manifold, then the intake manifold and gaskets.
35. Reverse procedure to install, noting the following:
   a. Clean cylinder head and intake manifold surfaces.
   b. Install new intake manifold gaskets.
   c. Tighten manifold bolts to specifications in sequence shown, Figs. 8 and 9
   d. **On Mark VIII models, tighten intake manifold runner control (IMRC) bolts, torque to 15-22 ft. lbs., in sequence shown, Fig. 10**

INTAKE MANIFOLD RUNNER CONTROL
REPLACE

Remove intake manifold runner control as described under "Intake Manifold, Replace."

EXHAUST MANIFOLD
REPLACE
TOWN CAR

1. Disconnect battery ground cable.
2. Remove air inlet tube.
3. Drain cooling system, then remove cooling fan and shroud.
4. Relieve fuel system fuel pressure. **Refer to "Precautions" in this section.**
5. Remove upper radiator hose.
6. Remove wiper module and support

bracket, then discharge refrigerant from system.
7. Disconnect A/C compressor outlet hose at compressor, then remove bolt retaining hose assembly to right coil bracket.
8. Remove 42-pin engine harness connector from retaining bracket on brake vacuum booster.
9. Disconnect 42-pin connector and transmission harness connector, **Fig. 11.**
10. Remove oil dipstick tube, on left exhaust manifold, then disconnect throttle valve cable from throttle body.
11. Disconnect heater outlet hose, then remove ground strap to right cylinder head.
12. Remove upper stud, then loosen lower bolt retaining heater outlet hose to right cylinder head and position aside.
13. Remove blower motor resistor.
14. Remove right engine insulator, then disconnect vacuum hoses from EGR valve and EGR tube.
15. Remove EGR valve assembly attaching bolts, then disconnect HEGO sensor.

16. Raise and support vehicle.
17. Remove two through bolts for left engine insulator and one through bolt for the right.
18. Remove EGR tube line nut from right manifold, then remove EGR assembly.
19. Disconnect exhaust from right and left manifolds, then suspend with wire.
20. Position a suitable jack and block of wood under oil pan, then raise engine approximately 4 inches.
21. If removing left manifold, remove engine insulator from cylinder block, then remove attaching bolts and manifold.
22. If removing right manifold, remove attaching bolts and manifold.
23. Reverse procedure to install. Tighten manifold bolts to specification in sequence shown in **Fig. 12.**

MARK VIII
Right Exhaust Manifold

1. Disconnect battery ground cable, then remove engine cover.
2. Disconnect air intake temperature sensor (IAT) connector and crankcase vent tube from air cleaner outlet tube.
3. Loosen air cleaner outlet to throttle body bolt.
4. Loosen clamp on engine air cleaner outlet tube assembly to engine air cleaner. Disconnect tube.
5. Remove retaining bolt from support bracket clamp on RH cam cover to

engine air cleaner outlet tube assembly.
6. Remove air cleaner and resonator assembly.
7. Disconnect RH oxygen sensor.
8. Remove four manifold to cylinder head retaining bolts from upper side of exhaust manifold.
9. Raise and support vehicle.
10. Disconnect exhaust pipe from LH catalyst.
11. Disconnect catalyst from exhaust manifold and remove catalyst.
12. Reverse procedure to install. Tighten RH exhaust manifold to cylinder head bolts to specifications in sequence shown, **Fig. 12.**

Left Exhaust Manifold

1. Turn off air suspension switch in cargo compartment.
2. Disconnect battery ground cable.
3. Disconnect oxygen sensor.
4. Install engine support tripod onto engine compartment and attach to engine.
5. Raise and support vehicle.
6. Remove front wheel and tire assemblies.
7. Disconnect EGR tube at LH catalyst.
8. Disconnect LH exhaust pipe at catalyst and RH catalyst at exhaust manifold.
9. Disconnect LH and RH ride height sensor wiring connectors and remove RH and LH brake caliper bolts. Remove calipers and support to vehicle using mechanic's wire.
10. Disconnect RH and LH upper control arms from spindles.
11. Disconnect steering shaft couple at rag joint.
12. Remove fastener attaching power steering lines to subframe.
13. Support subframe with engine jack.
14. Remove two motor mount through bolts.
15. Remove LH and RH lower strut to control arm bolts and nuts.
16. Remove eight subframe bolts, then lower subframe.
17. Remove LH manifold attaching bolts, then the manifold.
18. Remove and discard front and rear exhaust manifold gaskets.
19. Reverse procedure to install, noting the following
    a. Install new front and rear exhaust manifold gaskets.
    b. Tighten LH exhaust manifold to cylinder head bolts to specifications in sequence shown, **Fig. 12.**

CYLINDER HEAD
REPLACE

1. Disconnect battery ground cable.
2. Drain cooling system, then remove cooling fan and shroud.
3. Relieve fuel system fuel pressure. **Refer to "Precautions" in this section.**
4. Remove air inlet tube and wiper module.
5. Release belt tensioner, then remove accessory drive belt.

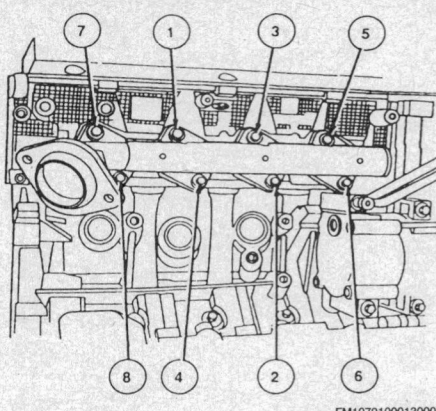

Fig. 12 Exhaust manifold tightening sequence

6. Disconnect ignition wires from spark plugs. **Do not pull on ignition wire (s).**
7. Disconnect ignition wire brackets from camshaft cover studs.
8. Remove bolt attaching A/C high pressure line to right coil bracket.
9. Disconnect both ignition coils and CID sensor.
10. Remove right and left coil bracket to front cover attaching nuts.
11. Slide ignition coil brackets and ignition wire assembly off mounting studs, then remove from vehicle.
12. Remove water pump pulley, then disconnect alternator wiring harness from junction block, fender apron and alternator.
13. Remove alternator and mounting bracket.
14. Disconnect positive battery cable at power distribution box, then remove attaching bolt from positive battery cable bracket located on right side of cylinder head.
15. Disconnect vent hose from canister purge solenoid, then place positive battery cable aside.
16. Disconnect canister purge solenoid vent hose from PCV valve, then remove PCV valve from camshaft cover.
17. Remove 42-pin engine harness connector from retaining bracket on brake vacuum booster, then disconnect and position aside.
18. Disconnect HDR sensor, A/C compressor clutch and canister purge solenoid electrical connectors.
19. Raise and support vehicle.
20. Remove bolts retaining power steering pump to engine block and cylinder front cover. **Front lower bolt on power steering will not come all the way out.**
21. Remove bolts attaching oil pan to front cover.
22. Remove crankshaft damper retaining bolt and washer from crankshaft.
23. Install crankshaft damper remover tool No. T58P-6316-D or equivalent on damper, then pull damper from crankshaft.
24. Disconnect EVO sensor and oil sending unit and position aside.

25. Disconnect EGR tube from right exhaust manifold.
26. Disconnect exhaust for right and left manifolds, then suspend with wire.
27. Remove bolt retaining starter wiring harness to rear of right cylinder head, then lower vehicle.
28. Remove right and left camshaft cover to cylinder head.
29. Disconnect accelerator and speed control cables.
30. Remove accelerator bracket from intake manifold and position aside.
31. Disconnect throttle valve cable from throttle body, then the vacuum hose from throttle body elbow port.
32. Disconnect both HEGO sensor and heater supply hose.
33. Remove thermostat housing, then disconnect upper hose and position aside.
34. Remove bolts attaching intake manifold, then the intake manifold and gaskets, **Fig. 13.**
35. Remove timing chain as described under "Timing Chain, Replace."
36. Remove bolts attaching left cylinder head. **The lower rear bolt cannot be removed due to interference with the brake vacuum booster. Use a rubber band or similar item to hold bolt away from engine as shown, Fig. 14.**
37. Remove left cylinder head.
38. Remove ground strap retaining heater return line to right cylinder head.
39. Remove bolts attaching right cylinder head. **The lower rear bolt cannot be removed due to interference with the evaporator housing. Use a rubber band or similar item to hold bolt away from engine as shown, Fig. 15.**
40. Remove right cylinder head.
41. Reverse procedure to install, noting the following:
    a. Rotate crankshaft counterclockwise 45°. This ensures that all pistons are below top of engine block deck face.
    b. **Torque** cylinder head bolts in sequence shown, **Fig. 16.** to 15-22 ft. lbs., then rotate in sequence 85-95°, then an additional 85-95°.
    c. Rotate crankshaft clockwise 45°. This will position crankshaft at TDC No. 1. **Crankshaft must only be rotated in the clockwise direction and only as far as TDC.**

VALVE ARRANGEMENT
FRONT TO REAR
Town Car

Right Side .... I-E-I-E-I-E-I-E
Left Side .... E-I-E-I-E-I-E-I

Mark VIII

Right
Side
. S-P-E-E-S-P-E-E-S-P-E-E-S-P-E-E①
Left
Side .. E-E-P-S-E-E-P-S-E-E-P-S-E-E-P-S
  ①—S = Secondary, P = Primary.

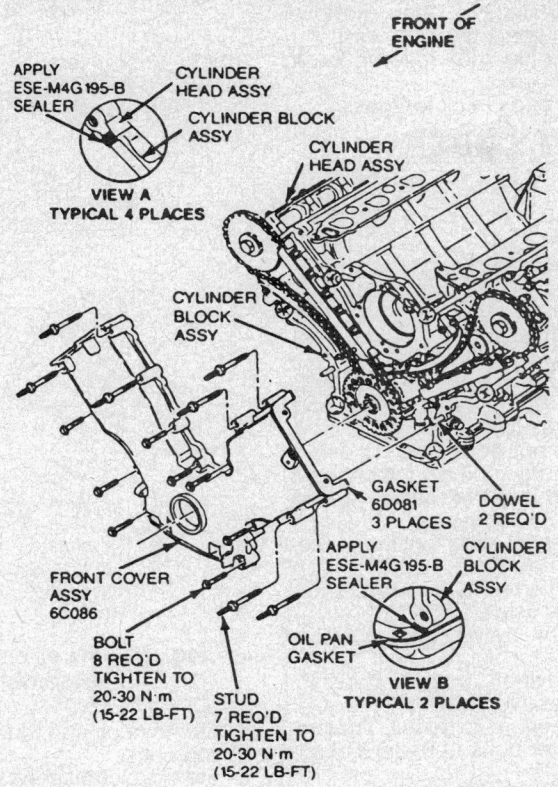

Fig. 13   Front cover removal

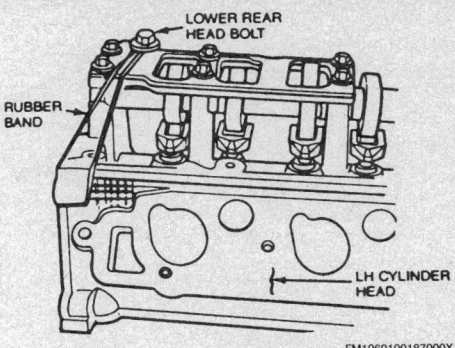

Fig. 14   LH lower rear head bolt removal

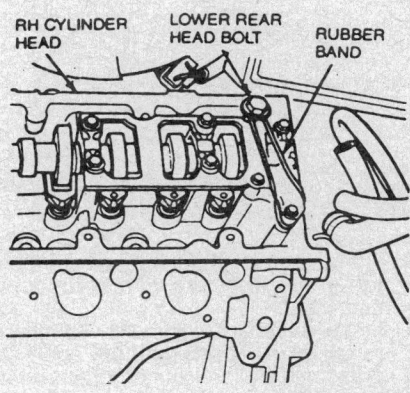

Fig. 15   RH lower rear head bolt removal

8. Repeat steps 2 through 7 as required.
9. Reverse procedure to install, noting the following:
   a. Valve lash adjuster must have no more than 1.5mm of plunger travel prior to installation.
   b. When installing roller follower, piston must be at bottom of stroke and camshaft at base circle.

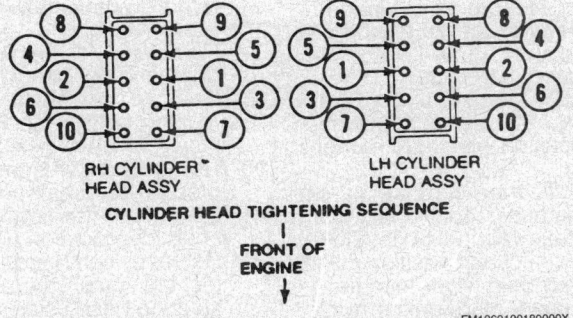

Fig. 16   Cylinder head tightening sequence

CAMSHAFT LOBE LIFT SPECIFICATIONS

Intake & Exhaust 2549

VALVE CLEARANCE SPECIFICATIONS

Valve lift should measure .020–.069 inch at intake valves and .046–.095 inch at exhaust valves with hydraulic lash adjuster completely collapsed.

VALVE ADJUSTMENT

This engine has automatic hydraulic lash adjusters. No valve adjustment is required.

HYDRAULIC LASH ADJUSTER
REPLACE

1. Remove camshaft covers as outlined under "Camshaft Cover, Replace."
2. Position piston of cylinder at bottom of stroke and camshaft lobe at base circle.
3. Install .40 inch shim between spring coils to prevent damage.
4. Install Valve Spring Compressor tool No. T91P-6565-A or equivalent, under camshaft and on valve spring retainer, **Fig. 17.**
5. Compress valve spring, then remove roller follower.
6. Remove valve spring compressor and shim.
7. Remove hydraulic lash adjuster, as required.

VALVE SPRING & VALVE STEM OIL SEAL
REPLACE

REMOVAL

If, during this procedure, air pressure has forced the piston to the bottom of the cylinder, any loss of air pressure will allow the valve to fall into the cylinder. A rubber band, tape or string wrapped around the end of the valve stem will prevent this and still allow enough travel to check the valve for binding and excess guide to valve stem clearance.

1. Remove camshaft covers as outlined under "Camshaft Cover, Replace."
2. Remove roller followers as outlined under "Hydraulic Lash Adjuster, Replace."

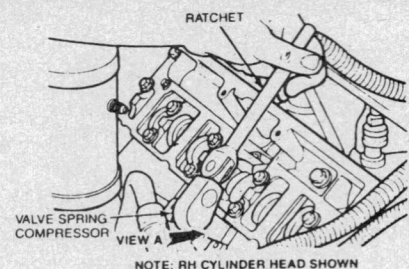

Fig. 17 Valve spring compressor

3. Remove spark plug, then position piston at top of stroke with both valves closed.
4. Install suitable air line with adapter in spark plug opening, then apply air pressure. Failure of air pressure to hold the valves closed is an indication of valve or valve seat damage that may require cylinder head removal.
5. Install .40 inch shim between spring coils.
6. Using Valve Spring Compressor tool No. T91P-6565-A or equivalent, compress valve spring.
7. Remove keepers, retainer and valve spring.
8. Use suitable locking pliers, remove valve stem seal.
9. Repeat steps 3 through 8 as required.

INSTALLATION

1. **Piston must be at Top Dead Center (TDC) of cylinder being serviced.**
2. Remove air pressure, then inspect valve stem for damage. Rotate valve and check valve stem tip eccentric movement during rotation.
3. Position valve up and down through normal travel and check the stem for binding. **If the valve has been damaged. It will be necessary to remove cylinder head for service.**
4. If valve condition is good, apply engine oil to valve stem and hold valve closed, then apply air pressure in cylinder.
5. Using Valve Stem Seal Replacer tool No. T88T-6571-A or equivalent, install valve stem seal.
6. Position valve spring and retainer over valve stem.
7. Install .40 inch shim between spring coils.
8. Compress valve spring, then install keepers.

9. Turn off air supply, then remove adapter from spark plug opening.
10. Install spark plug, then roller follower and camshaft cover.
11. Start engine and check for leaks.

CAMSHAFT COVER
REPLACE

RIGHT SIDE

1. Disconnect battery ground cable, then disconnect positive battery cable at power distribution box.
2. Remove positive battery cable bracket to cylinder head attaching bolt.
3. Disconnect High Data Rate (HDR) sensor, A/C compressor clutch and canister purge solenoid electrical connectors, then position aside.
4. Disconnect purge solenoid vent hose, then position positive battery cable aside.
5. Disconnect spark plug ignition wires. **Do not remove wires.**
6. Remove ignition wire brackets, then position wires aside.
7. Remove PCV valve and position aside.
8. Remove camshaft cover attaching bolts, then remove camshaft cover.
9. Reverse procedure to install. **Torque** camshaft cover bolts to 6-8.8 ft. lbs.

LEFT SIDE

1. Disconnect battery ground cable.
2. Remove air inlet tube.
3. Relieve fuel pressure as outlined under "Precautions," then disconnect fuel lines.
4. Raise and support vehicle.
5. Disconnect EVO sensor and oil pressure sending unit electrical connectors, then position electrical harness aside.
6. Lower vehicle, then remove 42-pin electrical harness connector from bracket at brake vacuum booster, **Fig. 3,** then disconnect and position aside.
7. Remove windshield wiper module.
8. Disconnect spark plug ignition wires. **Do not remove wires.**
9. Remove ignition wire brackets, then position wires aside.
10. Remove camshaft cover attaching bolts, then remove camshaft cover.
11. Reverse procedure to install. **Torque** camshaft cover bolts to 6-8.8 ft. lbs.

FRONT COVER
REPLACE

1. Remove engine cooling fan and shroud.
2. Loosen water pump pulley attaching bolts, then remove serpentine drive belt.
3. Remove water pump pulley attaching bolts, then remove pulley.
4. Raise and support vehicle.
5. Remove power steering pump attaching bolts. **Front lower power steering pump bolt will not come out.**
6. Support power steering pump and position aside.

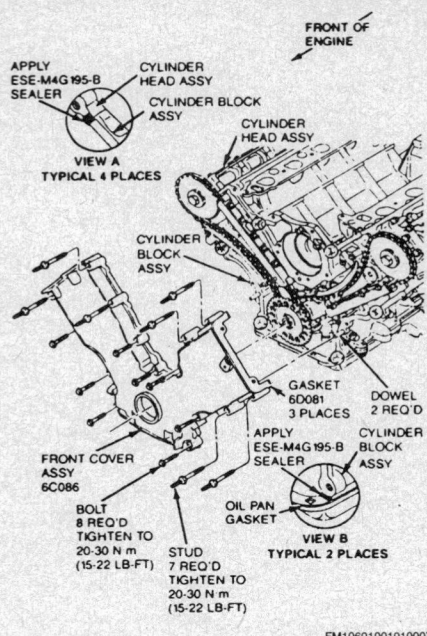

Fig. 18 Front engine cover assembly

7. Remove oil pan to front cover attaching bolts.
8. Remove crankshaft damper attaching bolt and washer.
9. Using crankshaft damper remover tool No T58P-6316-D or equivalent, remove crankshaft damper.
10. Lower vehicle.
11. Remove A/C high pressure line to righthand coil bracket attaching bolt.
12. Remove camshaft covers front attaching bolts, then loosen remaining cover bolts.
13. Using plastic wedges or suitable tool, prop up camshaft covers.
14. Disconnect ignition coils and Crankshaft Identification (CID) sensor.
15. Remove righthand coil bracket attaching nuts, then position power steering hose aside.
16. Remove lefthand coil bracket attaching nuts, then pull bracket and ignition wires from mounting studs and position aside.
17. Remove front cover attaching bolts and stub bolts, **Fig. 18,** then remove front cover.
18. Reverse procedure to install, noting the following:
    a. **Refer to Fig. 18,** for front cover tightening specifications.
    b. **Torque** coil bracket attaching nuts, oil pan attaching bolts, power steering pump attaching bolts and water pump pulley attaching bolts to 15-22 ft. lbs.
    c. **Torque** camshaft cover attaching bolts to 6-8.8 ft. lbs.
    d. Apply silicone gasket and sealant E3AZ-19562-A or equivalent in damper keyway. Ensure crankshaft key and keyway are aligned, using Crankshaft Damper Replacer T47P-6316-B or equivalent, install crankshaft damper.

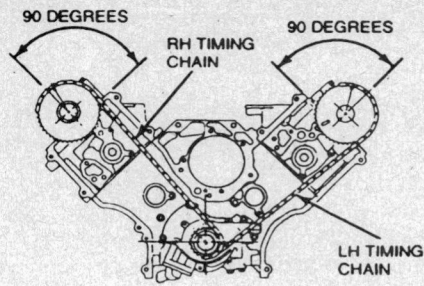

Fig. 19 Engine rotation to TDC

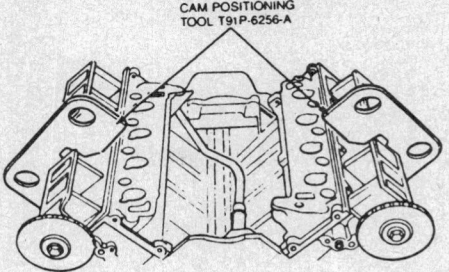

Fig. 20 Camshaft positioning tool

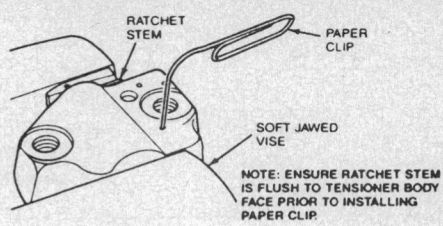

Fig. 21 Timing chain tensioner bleed

e. **Torque** crankshaft damper attaching bolt and washer to 114–121 ft. lbs.

FRONT COVER SEAL
REPLACE

1. Disconnect battery ground cable.
2. Release belt tensioner, then remove serpentine drive belt.
3. Raise and support vehicle.
4. Remove crankshaft damper attaching bolt and washer.
5. Using crankshaft damper remover tool No. T58P-6316-D or equivalent, remove crankshaft damper.
6. Using front cover seal remover tool No. T74P-6700-A or equivalent, remove front cover seal.
7. Reverse procedure to install, noting the following:
   a. Using front cover seal replacer tool No. T88T-6701-A1, A2 or equivalent, install front cover seal.
   b. Apply silicone gasket and sealant E3AZ-19562-A or equivalent in damper keyway. Ensure crankshaft key and keyway are aligned, using Crankshaft Damper Replacer T47P-6316-B or equivalent, install crankshaft.
   c. **Torque** crankshaft damper attaching bolt and washer to 114–121 ft. lbs.

TIMING CHAINS, GEARS, TENSIONERS & GUIDES
REPLACE

Note: This engine has an interference fit design. If engine has jumped time, then damage will result to cylinder, valve and piston assemblies.

At no time, when the timing chains are removed and the cylinder heads are installed, may the crankshaft and/or camshaft be rotated. Rotation may result in valve and/or piston damage.

1. Remove camshaft covers as outlined under "Camshaft Cover, Replace."
2. Remove front engine cover as outlined under "Front Cover, Replace."
3. Remove cylinder head as outlined under "Cylinder Head, Replace."
4. Remove High Data Rate (HDR) wheel, then rotate engine to No. 1 TDC, **Fig. 19.**

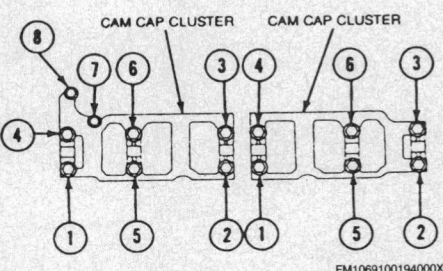

Fig. 22 Camshaft cap cluster assembly

5. Install Cam Positioning tool No. T91P-6256-A or equivalent on camshaft flats, **Fig. 20.**
6. Remove righthand tensioner attaching bolts, then remove tensioner and arm.
7. Remove righthand chain guide attaching bolts, then remove chain guide.
8. Remove righthand timing chain, then remove righthand crankshaft gear.
9. Remove righthand camshaft gear attaching bolt, washer, gear and spacer, if required.
10. Remove lefthand tensioner attaching bolts, then remove tensioner and arm.
11. Remove lefthand chain guide attaching bolts, then remove chain guide.
12. Remove lefthand timing chain, then remove lefthand crankshaft gear.
13. Remove lefthand camshaft gear attaching bolt, washer, gear and spacer, if required.
14. Reverse procedure to install, noting the following:
    a. If engine has jumped time, ensure all repairs to engine components and/or valve train are completed. Then rotate engine counterclockwise 45°. This will position all pistons below top of deck face.
    b. **Torque** camshaft and washer attaching bolt to 81–95 ft. lbs.
    c. Bleed timing chain tensioner as outlined under "Timing Chain Tensioner, Bleed."
    d. **Torque** timing chain tensioner attaching bolts to 15–22 ft. lbs.
    e. **Torque** timing chain guide attaching bolts to 6–8.8 ft. lbs.

TIMING CHAIN TENSIONER BLEED

1. Position timing chain tensioner in suitable soft-jawed vise.

2. Using suitable tool, position ratchet lock mechanism from ratchet stem, then slowly compress tensioner plunger by rotating vise handle. **Tensioner must be compressed slowly or internal seal damage may result.**
3. When tensioner plunger bottoms in tensioner bore, continue holding ratchet lock mechanism, then push ratchet mechanism down until flush with tensioner face.
4. While holding ratchet stem flush to tensioner face, release ratchet lock mechanism, then install paper clip or suitable tool to lock tensioner in collapsed position, **Fig. 21.**
5. **Do not remove paper clip or suitable tool until timing chain, tensioner, tensioner arm and timing chain guide are installed on engine.**

CAMSHAFT
REPLACE

1. Remove camshaft covers as outlined under "Camshaft Cover, Replace."
2. Remove engine front cover as outlined under "Front Cover, Replace."
3. Remove timing chains as outlined under "Timing Chains, Gears, Tensioners & Guides, Replace."
4. Rotate crankshaft counterclockwise 45°, ensuring pistons are below top of engine deck face. **Crankshaft must be in position prior to rotating camshafts or piston and/or valve damage may result.**
5. Install Valve Spring Compressor tool No. T91P-6565-A or equivalent, under camshaft and on valve spring retainer.
6. Install .40 inch shim between spring coils and camshaft to prevent damage.
7. Camshaft must be at base circle before compressing valve spring, then rotate camshaft, as required, until roller followers are removed.
8. Compress valve spring, then remove roller follower.
9. Repeat steps 5 through 8 until all roller followers are removed.
10. Remove camshaft cap cluster assembly attaching bolt, **Fig. 22.**
11. Tap upward on camshaft cap, **Fig. 23,** then carefully remove camshaft cap and camshaft.
12. Reverse procedure to install, noting the following:

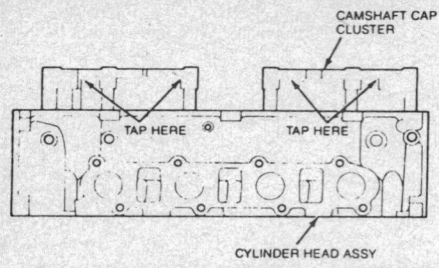

Fig. 23 Camshaft cap cluster

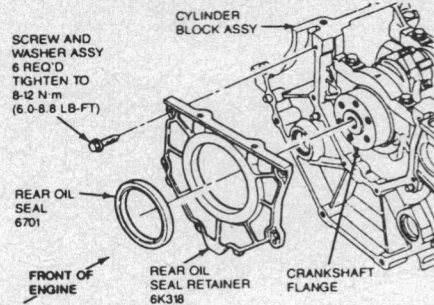

Fig. 24 Crankshaft rear oil seal

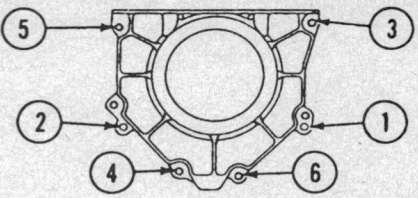

Fig. 25 Rear oil seal retainer tightening sequence

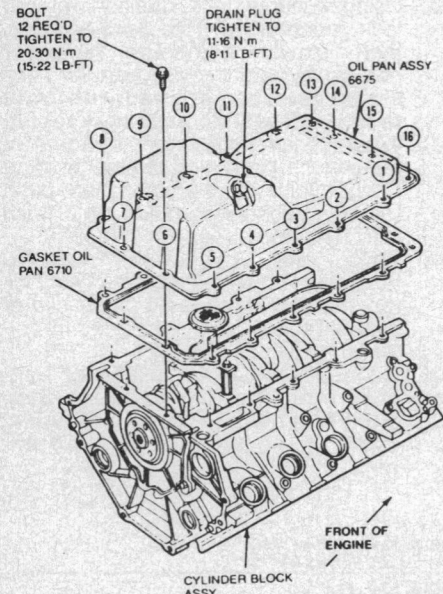

Fig. 26 Oil pan tightening sequence

a. Refer to **Fig. 22,** for camshaft cap cluster bolt tightening sequence.
b. Tighten attaching nuts and bolts to specifications.

PISTON & ROD ASSEMBLY

If the old pistons are serviceable, make certain that they are installed on the rods from which they were removed. Check side clearance between connecting rods and crankshaft journal. Clearance should be .015-.040 inch.

CRANKSHAFT REAR OIL SEAL
REPLACE

1. Using a suitable jack, lower transmission and support.
2. Remove flexplate assembly.
3. Remove oil pan as outlined under "Oil Pan, Replace."
4. Remove rear oil seal retainer attaching bolts, **Fig. 24.**
5. Reverse procedure to install. Refer to **Fig. 25,** for rear oil seal retainer attaching bolts tightening sequence.

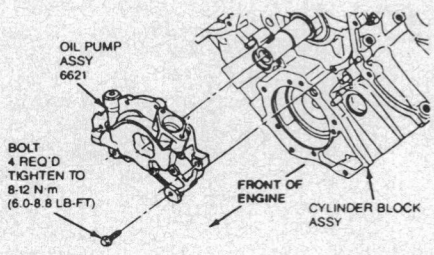

Fig. 27 Oil pump assembly

OIL PAN
REPLACE

1. Disconnect ground and positive battery cables.
2. Remove air inlet tube.
3. Drain cooling system, then remove cooling fan and shroud.
4. Relieve fuel system pressure as outlined under "Precautions," then disconnect fuel lines.
5. Remove upper radiator hose.
6. Remove wiper module and support bracket.
7. Discharge A/C system.
8. Disconnect A/C compressor outlet hose, then remove hose assembly to righthand coil bracket attaching bolt.
9. Remove engine electrical harness 42-pin connector from bracket on brake vacuum booster.
10. Disconnect engine electrical connector, then disconnect transmission harness electrical connector.
11. Disconnect throttle valve cable at throttle body.
12. Disconnect heater outlet hose.
13. Remove righthand cylinder head grounds strap attaching nut.
14. Remove heater outlet hose assembly to righthand cylinder head upper attaching stud, then loosen lower bolt and position aside.
15. Remove blower motor resistor.
16. Remove righthand engine mount to lower engine bracket attaching bolt.
17. Disconnect EGR valve vacuum hoses and tube.
18. Remove EGR valve to intake manifold attaching bolts.
19. Raise and support vehicle, then drain engine oil.
20. Remove righthand front engine mount two through bolts, then remove lefthand front engine mount through bolt.

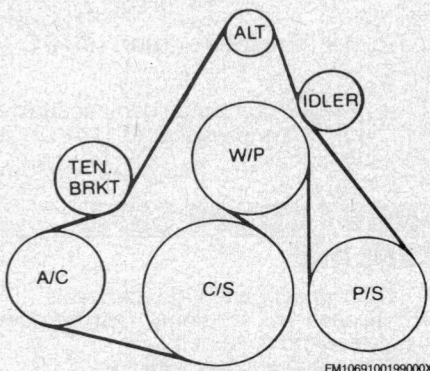

Fig. 28 Serpentine drive belt routing

21. Remove EGR tube line attaching nut at righthand exhaust manifold, then remove EGR valve assembly.
22. Disconnect exhaust pipes at exhaust manifolds, then lower and support exhaust at crossmember.
23. Position suitable jack and wood block under oil pan, rearward of drain plug, then raise engine approximately 4 inches.
24. Install two wood blocks approximately 2.5-2.75 inch thick under each engine mount.
25. Lower engine to wood blocks, then remove jack.
26. Remove oil pan attaching bolts. It may be necessary to loosen rear transmission mount attaching nuts and with suitable jack, raise extension housing slightly to remove oil pan.
27. Remove oil pan.
28. Reverse procedure to install. Refer to **Fig. 26,** for oil pan bolt tightening sequence and specification.

OIL PUMP
REPLACE

1. Remove camshaft covers as outlined under "Camshaft Covers, Replace."
2. Remove front cover as outlined under "Front Engine Cover, Replace."
3. Remove oil pan as outlined under "Oil Pan, Replace."
4. Remove timing chains as outlined under "Timing Chains, Gears, Tensioners & Guides, Replace."
5. Remove oil pump attaching bolts, then remove oil pump, **Fig. 27.**
6. Reverse procedure to install, noting the following:
   a. Align oil pump inner rotor with flat of crankshaft.
   b. **Torque** oil pump attaching bolts to 6.-8.8 ft. lbs.

BELT TENSION DATA

Automatic belt tensioners are spring loaded devices which set and maintain the drive belt tension. The drive belt should not require tension adjustment for the life of the belt. Automatic tensioners have belt wear indicator marks. If the indicator mark is not between the indicator lines, the belt is worn or an incorrect belt is installed.

SERPENTINE DRIVE BELT

BELT ROUTING

Refer to **Fig. 28**, for drive belt routing.

BELT REPLACEMENT

1. Rotate tensioner away from belt using a breaker bar installed in 1/2 inch square hole in tensioner arm.
2. Lift old belt over alternator pulley flange and remove.
3. When installing new belt over pulleys. Ensure all V-grooves make proper contact with pulley.
4. Ensure belt is properly installed on each pulley.

ADJUSTMENT

Automatic belt tensioners are spring loaded devices which set and maintain the drive belt tension. The drive belt should not require tension adjustment for the lift of the belt.

Automatic tensioners do not have to be removed to remove a belt. Rotate tensioner away from belt using a 1/2 inch breaker bar.

COOLING SYSTEM BLEED

A pressurized reservoir system is used which constantly separates the air from the cooling system. When the thermostat is open, coolant flows through a small hose from the top of the radiator outlet tank to the reservoir. The reservoir separates any entrapped air from the coolant and replenishes the system through the lower hose. The reservoir serves as the location for service fill, coolant expansion during warm up, system pressurization from the pressure cap and air separation during operation. The reservoir is designed to have approximately .5-1 liter of air when cold to allow for coolant expansion.

Add coolant to the minimum level on the reservoir.

THERMOSTAT

REPLACE

1. Drain coolant level below upper radiator hose and thermostat housing.
2. Disconnect upper radiator hose at thermostat housing, then remove two thermostat housing retaining bolts.
3. Remove O-ring seal and thermostat from intake manifold. Inspect O-ring for damage and replace if necessary.

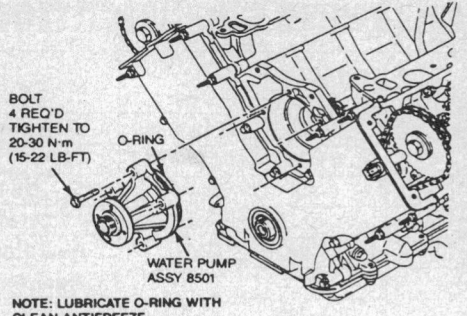

BOLT
4 REQ'D
TIGHTEN TO
20-30 N·m
(15-22 LB-FT)

O-RING

WATER PUMP
ASSY 8501

NOTE: LUBRICATE O-RING WITH
CLEAN ANTIFREEZE

FM1089100059000X

Fig. 29 Water pump replacement

4. Reverse procedure to install. Tighten to specifications.

WATER PUMP

REPLACE

1. Drain cooling system, then remove engine cooling fan and shroud.
2. Release belt tensioner, then remove accessory drive belt, **Fig. 29**.
3. Remove water pump pulley attaching bolts, then remove water pump pulley.
4. Remove water pump attaching bolts, then remove water pump.
5. Reverse procedure to install. **Torque** water pump and water pump pulley attaching bolts to 15-22 ft. lbs.

RADIATOR

REPLACE

1992-94

1. Disconnect battery ground cable.
2. Drain engine coolant, then disconnect deareation hose and both radiator hoses.
3. Disconnect automatic transmission fluid lines from radiator.
4. **On models equipped with fan shroud**, remove upper shroud mounting bolts at radiator support.
5. Lift fan shroud enough to disengage lower retaining clips and lay shroud over fan.
6. **On all models**,remove radiator upper support mounting bolts, then supports and radiator.
7. Reverse procedure to install, noting the following:
   a. Operate engine, check automatic transmission, radiator and coolant recovery tank for proper fluid level.

1995

1. Disconnect battery ground cable.
2. Drain engine coolant, then disconnect deareation hose and both radiator hoses.
3. Disconnect automatic transmission fluid inlet and outlet lines. Note, when removing transmission cooler lines, use a back-up wrench to hold fitting.
4. **On models equipped with fan shroud**, remove upper shroud mounting bolts at radiator support.

5. Remove upper A/C condenser core to radiator retaining bolts.
6. Lift fan shroud enough to disengage lower retaining clips and lay shroud over fan.
7. **On all models**,remove radiator upper support mounting bolts, then supports.
8. Reverse procedure to install, noting the following:
   a. Operate engine, check automatic transmission, radiator and coolant recovery tank for proper fluid level.

FUEL PUMP

REPLACE

1. Relieve fuel system pressure as outlined under "Precautions."
2. Using suitable tool, drain fuel tank at fuel filler neck.
3. Raise and support vehicle.
4. Disconnect fuel supply and return line fittings and vent line.
5. Disconnect fuel pump and sender electrical connectors.
6. Remove fuel tank attaching support straps, then carefully lower fuel tank assembly. Ensure dirt does not enter tank or fuel system.
7. Using Fuel Tank Sender Wrench No. D74P-9275-A or equivalent, turn fuel pump locking ring counterclockwise, then remove locking ring.
8. Remove fuel pump assembly, then remove and discard seal ring.
9. Reverse procedure to install, noting the following:
   a. Once fuel pump is installed, using Fuel Pressure Gauge tool No. T80L-9974-B or equivalent on the fuel charging assembly Schraeder valve, turn ignition from OFF to ON position for 3 seconds. Repeat OFF to ON switching 5 to 10 times until pressure gauge shows at least 35 psi.

FUEL FILTER

REPLACE

1. Turn engine off and relieve fuel system pressure as described under "Precautions."
2. Raise and support vehicle.
3. Remove push connect fittings at both ends of fuel filter. Install new retainer clips in each push connect fitting.
4. Remove fuel filter and retainer from metal bracket by removing two retainer bolts.
5. Remove filer from retainer. Note direction of flow arrow.
6. Remove rubber insulator rings from filter.
7. Reverse procedure to install, noting the following:
   a. Replace insulator (s) if filter moves freely after retainer installation.
   b. **Torque** retaining bolts to 27-44 inch lbs.
   c. Start engine and inspect for leaks.

TIGHTENING SPECIFICATIONS

Year	Component	Torque/Ft. Lbs.	Year	Component	Torque/Ft. Lbs.
1992–95	Alternator To Cylinder Block	15-22	1992–95 —Cont'd	Oil Inlet Tube To Oil Pump Bolt	6-8.8
	Camshaft Bolt	81-95		Oil Pan Drain Plug	8-12
	Camshaft Cover Bolt	6-8.8		Oil Pan To Cylinder Block	15-22
	Connecting Rod Bolt	①		Oil Pump To Cylinder Block	6-8.8
	Cylinder Front Cover Bolt	15-22		Rear Engine Mount Attaching Bolt	50-70
	Cylinder Head Bolt	②		Rear Engine Mount Attaching Nut	35-50
	Damper To Crankshaft Bolt	114-121		Spark Plug	6.6-7.3
	EGR Valve To Intake Manifold	15-22		Thermostat Housing	15-22
	Exhaust Manifold To Cylinder Head Bolt	15-22		Water Pump To Cylinder Block	15-22
	Exhaust Pipe To Exhaust Manifold	20-30		Water Pump To Pulley Bolt	15-22
	Front Engine Mount Attaching Bolts	45-59			
	Front Engine Mount Through Bolts	15-22			
	Intake Manifold To Cylinder Head Bolt	53-64 ③			
	Oil Inlet Tube To Main Bearing Cap	15-22			

① —Tighten in two steps; first to 18-25 ft. lbs., then finally rotate to 85-95°.
② —Tighten in three steps; first to 15-22 ft. lbs., then rotate 85-95°, and finally rotate again 85-95°.
③ —Retorque assembly w/engine hot.

5.0L/V8-302 Engine

NOTE: On Air Bag Equipped Models, Refer To "Air Bag System Precautions" Located In The Front Of This Manual For System Disarming & Arming Procedures.

INDEX

PRECAUTIONS

AIR BAG SYSTEMS

Refer to "Air Bag System Precautions" in the front of this manual for system disarming and arming procedures.

FUEL SYSTEM PRESSURE RELIEF

Fuel supply lines, on models equipped with fuel injected engines, will remain pressurized after the engine is shutoff. Pressure must be relieved prior to any fuel system servicing.
1. Remove fuel tank cap.
2. Using fuel pressure gauge tool No. T80L-9974-B or equivalent, relieve fuel system pressure at pressure relief valve righthand rear fuel rail. Pressure relief valve cap must be removed.
3. Using suitable tool, remove pressure relief valve.
4. Reverse procedure to install. **Torque** fuel pressure relief valve to 48-84 inch lbs. **Torque** fuel pressure relief valve cap to 4-6 inch lbs.

ENGINE MOUNT
REPLACE
MARK VII
1. Remove fan shroud attaching screws.
2. Raise and support engine using a jack and wood block placed under engine.
3. Remove insulator attaching nuts to No. 2 crossmember, **Fig. 1.**
4. Disconnect shift linkage.
5. Raise engine sufficiently with jack so insulator stud is remove from crossmember.
6. Remove transmission brace attached at righthand engine mount bracket.
7. Remove engine insulator attaching bolts from cylinder block, then remove insulator.
8. Reverse procedure to install.

ENGINE
REPLACE

On models equipped with Thermactor system, remove or disconnect components that will interfere with engine removal or installation.
1. Drain cooling system and crankcase.
2. Remove hood, then disconnect battery and alternator ground cables from cylinder block.

3. Remove air cleaner and duct assembly.
4. Disconnect upper and lower radiator hoses from engine block and transmission oil cooler lines from radiator.
5. Remove bolts attaching fan shroud to radiator.
6. Remove radiator, fan, spacer, pulley and fan shroud.
7. Remove alternator mounting bolts and position alternator aside.
8. Disconnect oil pressure sending unit wire connector and fuel line at fuel pump. Plug fuel tank line. On models equipped with electronic fuel injection, relieve pressure at the Schraeder type valve on the fuel charging valve before disconnecting fuel lines.
9. Disconnect accelerator cable from throttle and throttle valve vacuum line at intake manifold.
10. Disconnect transmission manual shift rod, then disconnect retracting spring at shift rod stud.
11. Disconnect transmission oil filler tube bracket from engine block.
12. **On models equipped with A/C,** isolate and remove compressor.
13. **On all models,** remove power steering pump bracket from cylinder head and position pump aside. Position pump so that fluid will not drain from reservoir.
14. Disconnect heater hoses from water pump and intake manifold and temperature sending unit wire connector.
15. Remove converter housing to engine upper attaching bolts.
16. Disconnect primary wire connector from ignition coil, then remove wiring harness from left rocker arm cover and position out of way. Disconnect ground strap from block. **On EEC-IV equipped vehicles,** disconnect wiring at sensors.
17. **On all models,** raise front of vehicle and remove starter.
18. Disconnect exhaust pipes from exhaust manifold, then remove engine support insulators from brackets on frame.
19. Disconnect transmission oil cooler lines from retainer and remove converter housing inspection cover.
20. Disconnect flywheel from converter, secure converter to converter housing.
21. Remove remaining converter housing to engine attaching bolts, then lower vehicle and support transmission using a suitable jack.
22. Attach engine lifting device to lifting brackets on intake manifold, then raise engine slightly and disconnect from transmission.
23. Carefully lift engine from engine compartment.
24. Reverse procedure to install.

INTAKE MANIFOLD
REPLACE

1. Disconnect battery ground cable and drain cooling system.
2. Remove air cleaner, PCV hose and air

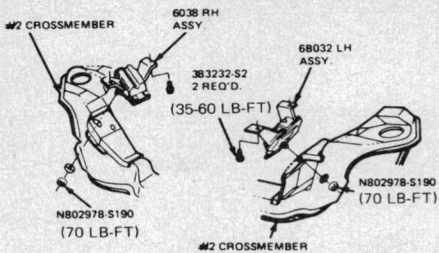

Fig. 1 Engine mounts. Mark VII

intake duct, then disconnect electric choke heater tube, if applicable.
3. Remove accelerator cable bracket, then disconnect speed control linkage, TV cable and all vacuum lines from manifold.
4. Disconnect high tension lead and primary wiring connector from ignition coil, then remove coil and support bracket from manifold.
5. Disconnect high tension leads from spark plugs, then remove distributor cap, adapter and high tension leads as an assembly.
6. Disconnect fuel return and supply lines. **Relieve fuel pressure at valve on metal fuel rail located at LH front corner of engine before disconnecting fuel lines.**
7. Disconnect electrical leads from distributor, then remove hold-down bolt and distributor. Mark position of rotor to aid installation.
8. Disconnect upper radiator hose, coolant temperature sending wire and throttle body cooler hoses at manifold.
9. Loosen hose clamp, then slide bypass hose off outlet housing.
10. Disconnect all remaining electrical connections that will interfere with manifold removal.
11. Disconnect crankcase vent hose assembly at rear of lower intake manifold, then the fuel evaporative purge tube, if so equipped.
12. Remove attaching bolts, then the upper intake manifold.
13. Remove lower intake manifold, together with fuel rails.
14. Reverse procedure to install, following tightening sequence **Fig. 2.**

CYLINDER HEAD
REPLACE

Before installing cylinder head, wipe off engine block gasket surface and be certain no foreign material has fallen into cylinder bores, bolt holes or in the valve lifter area. It is good practice to clean out bolt holes with compressed air.

Some cylinder head gaskets are coated with a special lacquer to provide a good seal once the parts have warmed up. Do not use any additional sealer on such gaskets. If the gasket does not have this lacquer coating, apply suitable sealer to both sides.

Tighten cylinder head bolts in three steps in sequence shown in **Fig. 3.** Final tightening should be to specifications.

Bolts should not be disturbed after tightening.
1. Remove intake manifold.
2. Disconnect battery ground cable at cylinder head.
3. **On Mark VII,** if left head is being removed, remove A/C compressor (if equipped). Also remove and wire power steering pump out of the way. If equipped with Thermactor System, disconnect hose from air manifold on left cylinder head.
4. **On Town Car,** if left head is being removed, remove power steering pump (if equipped).
5. **On Mark VII,** If right head is to be removed, remove alternator mounting bracket bolt and spacer, ground wire and air cleaner inlet duct, and A/C compressor bracket.
6. **On Town Car,** if right head is to be removed, remove air conditioning compressor and mounting bracket (if equipped).
7. **On all models,** if right head is to be removed on an engine with Thermactor System, remove air pump from bracket. Disconnect hose from air manifold.
8. Disconnect exhaust manifolds at exhaust pipes.
9. Remove rocker arm covers. If equipped with Thermactor System, remove check valve from air manifold.
10. Remove fulcrum bolts, oil deflectors (if used), fulcrums and rocker arms. On all engines, remove pushrods. Keep rocker arms and pushrods in order so they can be installed in the same position.
11. Remove head bolts and lift head off of block.
12. Reverse procedure to install. **Torque** cylinder head bolts in sequence shown in **Fig. 3.** first to 55-65 ft. lbs., then to 65-72 ft. lbs.

VALVE ARRANGEMENT
FRONT TO REAR

5.0L/V8-302, Right Bank .. I-E-I-E-I-E-I-E
5.0L/V8-302, Left Bank .... E-I-E-I-E-I-E-I

VALVE CLEARANCE SPECIFICATIONS

Engine	Int.	Exh.
5.0L/V8-302	.096-.146 ①	.096-.146 ①
5.0L/V8-302 H.O.	.123-.146 ①	.123-.146 ①

①—With hydraulic lifter fully collapsed.

VALVE ADJUSTMENT

To eliminate the need of adjusting valve lash, a positive stop nut fulcrum bolt and seat is used on these engines.

It is very important that the correct pushrod be used and all components be installed and torqued as follows:
1. Position the piston of the cylinder being worked on at TDC of its compression stroke.

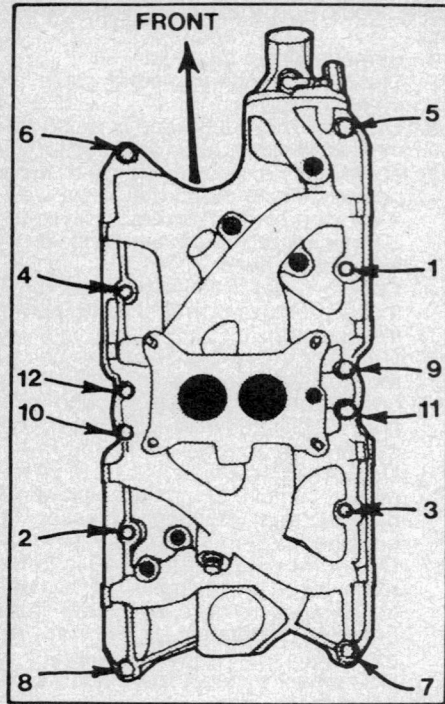

Fig. 2 Intake manifold tightening
sequence

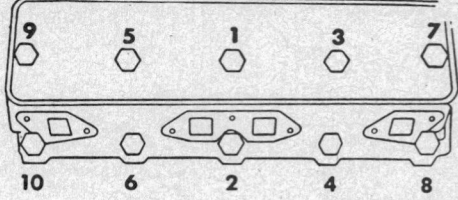

Fig. 3 Cylinder head tightening
sequence

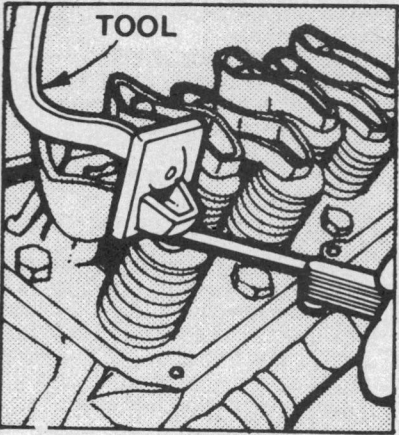

Fig. 4 Compressing lifter to
check valve clearance

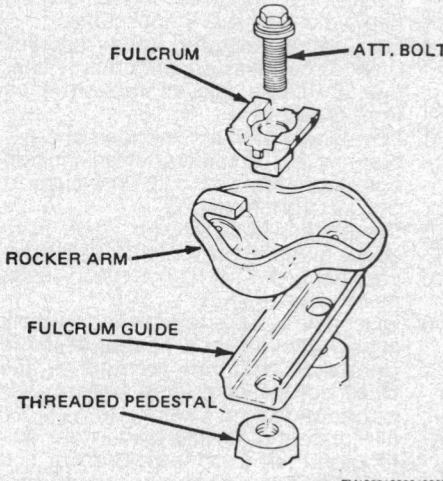

Fig. 5 Rocker arm & related parts

2. Install rocker arm, fulcrum seat and oil deflector. Install fulcrum bolt and tighten to specifications.

A .060 inch shorter pushrod or a .060 inch longer rod is available for service to provide a means of compensating for dimensional changes in the valve mechanism. Valve stem-to-rocker arm clearance should be as specified, with the hydraulic lifter completely collapsed, **Fig. 4.** Repeated valve grind jobs will decrease this clearance to the point that if not compensated for the lifters will cease to function.

When checking valve clearance, if the clearance is less than the minimum, the .060 inch shorter pushrod should be used. If clearance is more than the maximum, the .060 inch longer pushrod should be used. To check valve clearance, proceed as follows:

1. Mark crankshaft pulley at three locations, with number 1 location at TDC timing mark (end of compression stroke), number 2 location one half turn (180°) clockwise from TDC and number 3 location three quarter turn clockwise (270°) from number 2 location.
2. Turn the crankshaft to the number 1 location and check the clearance on the following valves:
   a. 5.0L/V8-302: intake Nos. 1, 7 and 8; exhaust Nos. 1, 4 and 5.
   b. 5.0L/V8-302 H.O.: intake Nos. 1, 4 and 8; exhaust Nos. 1, 3 and 7.
3. Turn the crankshaft to the number 2 location and check the clearance on the following valves:
   a. 5.0L/V8-302: intake Nos. 4 and 5; exhaust Nos. 2 and 6.

   b. 5.0L/V8-302 H.O.: intake Nos. 3 and 7; exhaust Nos. 2 and 6.
4. Turn the crankshaft to the number 3 location and check the clearance on the following valves:
   a. 5.0L/V8-302: intake Nos. 2, 3 and 6; exhaust Nos. 3, 7 and 8.
   b. 5.0L/V8-302 H.O.: intake Nos. 2, 5 and 6; exhaust Nos. 4, 5 and 8.

VALVE LIFT SPECIFICATIONS

Engine	Intake	Exhaust
5.0L/V8-302	.375	.390
5.0L/V8-302 H.O.	.442	.442

ROCKER ARMS
REPLACE

The rocker arm is supported by a fulcrum bolt which fits through the fulcrum seat and threads into the cylinder head. To disassemble, remove the bolt, fulcrum seat, fulcrum guide and rocker arm, **Fig. 5.**

VALVE GUIDES

Valve guides in these engines are an integral part of the head and, therefore, cannot be removed. For service, guides can

be reamed oversize to accommodate one of three service valves with oversize stems (.003 inch, .015 inch and .030 inch).

Check the valve stem clearance of each valve (after cleaning) in its respective valve guide. If the clearance exceeds the service limits of .0055 inch, ream the valve guides to accommodate the next oversize diameter valve.

HYDRAULIC LIFTERS
REPLACE

The internal parts of each hydraulic valve lifter assembly are a matched set. If these are mixed, improper valve operation may result. Therefore, disassemble, inspect and test each assembly separately to prevent mixing the parts.

All 5.0L/V8-302 engines are equipped with roller hydraulic lifters. Pushrods used on these engines have a collar at the upper end and must be installed in this position. To replace valve lifters, proceed as follows:

1. Remove intake manifold and related parts.
2. Remove rocker arm covers.
3. Loosen rocker arm stud nuts or bolts and rotate rocker arms to the side.
4. Lift out pushrods, keeping them in sequence in a rack so they may be installed in their original location.
5. Using a magnet rod, remove valve lifters and place them in sequence in a rack so they may be installed in their original location.
6. Reverse procedure to install.

FRONT COVER
REPLACE

If necessary to replace the front cover oil seal, the front cover must be removed first.
1. Drain cooling system and crankcase.
2. Remove fan shroud attaching bolts and position shroud over engine fan.
3. Remove engine fan, spacer and shroud.
4. Remove drive belts and A/C idler pulley bracket.

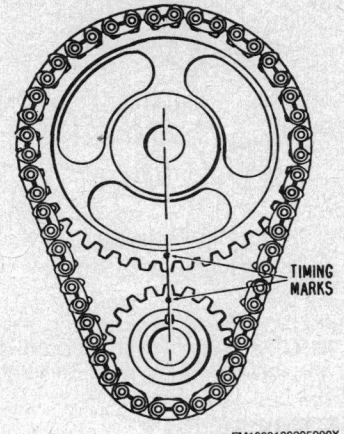

Fig. 6 Valve timing marks

5. Remove power steering pump and position aside.
6. Remove all accessory brackets attached to water pump, then remove water pump pulley.
7. Disconnect lower radiator hose, heater hose and bypass hose from water pump.
8. Remove crankshaft pulley from vibration damper.
9. Remove damper attaching screw and washer, then using a suitable puller, remove damper.
10. If applicable, disconnect fuel pump outlet line, then remove fuel pump attaching bolts and position pump aside.
11. Remove oil level dipstick.
12. Remove oil pan to front cover attaching bolts.
13. Remove front cover to engine block attaching bolts, then remove front cover and water pump as an assembly. **Use a thin blade knife to cut oil pan gasket flush with cylinder block face prior to separating front cover from cylinder block.**
14. Reverse procedure to install.

TIMING CHAIN
REPLACE

1. Remove timing case cover as outlined previously.
2. Crank the engine until the timing mark on the camshaft sprocket is adjacent to the timing mark on the crankshaft sprocket, **Fig. 6.**
3. Remove capscrews, lock plate and fuel pump eccentric from front of camshaft.
4. Place a screwdriver behind the camshaft sprocket and carefully pry the sprocket and chain off the camshaft.
5. Reverse the foregoing procedure to install the chain, being sure to align the timing marks as shown in **Fig. 6.**

CAMSHAFT
REPLACE

If it is necessary to replace the camshaft only, it may be accomplished without removing the engine from the chassis. How-

ever, if the camshaft bearings are to be replaced, the engine will have to be removed. To remove the camshaft, refer to the procedure outlined below. **It may be necessary to remove or reposition radiator, A/C compressor and grille components to provide adequate clearance.**

1. To remove camshaft, remove front cover and timing chain.
2. Remove distributor cap and spark plug wires, then remove distributor.
3. Disconnect automatic transmission oil cooler lines from radiator and remove radiator.
4. Remove intake manifold and TBI as an assembly.
5. Remove rocker arm covers.
6. Loosen rocker arm fulcrum or bolts and rotate rocker arms to one side.
7. Remove pushrods, keeping them in sequence in a rack so they may be installed in their original location.
8. Using a magnet, remove valve lifters and place them in a rack in sequence so they may be installed in their original location.
9. Remove camshaft thrust plate, and carefully pull camshaft from engine, using care to avoid damaging camshaft bearings.
10. Reverse procedure to install. **Prior to installation of the camshaft, lubricate pushrods and camshaft lobes with lubricant part No. D0AZ-19584-A or equivalent for 5.0L/V8-302 engines. Using engine oil SF, lubricate valve tappets & bores.**

PISTON & ROD ASSEMBLY

If the old pistons are serviceable, make certain that they are installed on the rods from which they were removed. The assembly must be assembled as shown in **Fig. 7.**
Check side clearance between connecting rods and crankshaft journal. Clearance should be .010–.020 inch.

PISTONS, PINS & RINGS

Pistons are available in oversizes of .003, .020, .030 and .040 inch.
Piston pins are available in oversizes of .001 and .002 inch.
Rings are available in oversizes of .020, .030 and .040 inch.

MAIN & ROD BEARINGS

Main and rod bearings are available in standard size and undersizes of .001, .002, .010, 020, .030 and .040 inch.

CRANKSHAFT REAR OIL SEAL
REPLACE

A one-piece rear oil seal is used on these engines. To replace seal, proceed as follows:

1. Using a sharp awl, punch one hole into seal metal surface between seal lip and engine block.

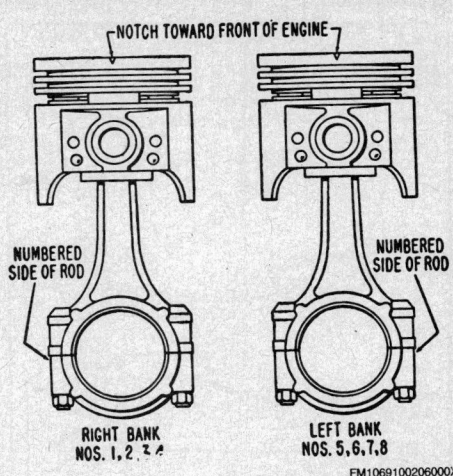

Fig. 7 Piston & rod assembly

2. Using slide hammer tool No. T82L-9533-B or equivalent, screw tool into hole in seal and remove seal by gently pulling rearward. Use caution to avoid damaging sealing surface.
3. Lubricate new seal with engine oil, then position seal on installer tool No. T82L-6701-A, or equivalent.
4. With spring end of seal facing towards engine, install tool, then alternately tighten bolts until rear face of seal is within .005 inch of the engine block.

OIL PAN
REPLACE

1. Disconnect battery ground cable and remove air cleaner assembly.
2. Disconnect accelerator cable and kickdown rod from throttle.
3. Remove accelerator mounting bracket bolts and bracket, then the EGR valve and cooler, if applicable.
4. Remove fan shroud attaching screws and position shroud over fan.
5. Disconnect wiper motor electrical connector and remove wiper motor.
6. Disconnect windshield washer hose.
7. Remove wiper motor mounting cover.
8. Remove oil level dipstick, then the dipstick tube retaining bolt from exhaust manifold.
9. If equipped with EGR cooler, remove Thermactor air dump tube retaining clamp, then the Thermactor crossover tube at rear of engine.
10. Raise and support vehicle, then drain engine oil.
11. Remove starter motor.
12. Disconnect fuel tank fuel line at fuel pump and plug line. **Vehicles equipped with electronic fuel injection have high pressure at the electric fuel pump. Pressure must be relieved at the Schraeder type valve on the fuel charging assembly (CFI), or at valve on metal fuel rail located at LH front corner of engine (SFI) before disconnecting fuel lines.**
13. Disconnect exhaust pipes from manifolds.

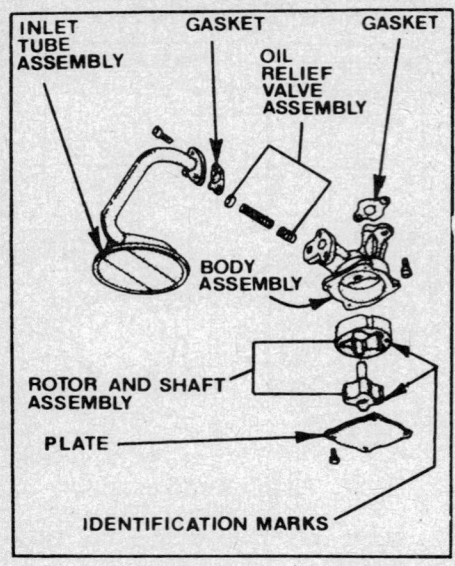

Fig. 8 Oil pump assembly

14. **If equipped with EGR cooler,** remove thermactor secondary air tube to converter housing clamps.
15. **On all models,** remove dipstick tube from oil pan.
16. Loosen transmission mount attaching nuts.
17. Remove engine mount through bolts.
18. Remove shift crossover bolts at transmission.
19. Disconnect transmission kickdown rod.
20. Remove brake line retainer from front crossmember.
21. With a suitable jack, raise engine as far as possible.
22. Place a block of wood between each engine mount and chassis bracket. When engine is secured in this position, remove jack, then the low oil level sensor, if equipped.
23. If equipped, remove stabilizer bar attaching bolts and lower stabilizer bar.
24. Remove transmission cooling line clamp retaining bolt, then position cooling lines aside.
25. Remove oil pan attaching bolts and lower pan to crossmember.
26. Remove oil pickup tube and oil pump retaining nuts and bolts, then lower tube and oil pump into oil pan.
27. Remove oil pan, together with pump, through front of vehicle.
28. Reverse procedure to install.

OIL PUMP
REPLACE

The oil pan must be removed to gain access to the oil pump. Refer to "Oil Pan, Replace" for procedure.

OIL PUMP SERVICE

To disassemble, remove the pump cover plate, **Fig. 8,** and lift out the rotor and shaft. Remove cotter pin that secures relief valve plug in pump housing. Drill a small

hole and insert a self-tapping screw into plug, then using pliers remove plug from pump housing. Then remove the retainer spring and relief valve from the pump housing. Inspect the pump as follows:

1. With all parts clean and dry, check the inside of the pump housing and the outer race and rotor for damage or excessive wear.
2. Check the mating surface of the pump cover for wear. If this surface is worn, scored or grooved, replace the cover.
3. Measure the clearance between the outer race and housing. This clearance should be .001–.013.
4. With the rotor assembly installed in the housing, place a straightedge over the rotor assembly and housing. Measure the clearance between the straightedge and the rotor and outer race. Recommended limits are .0016–.004 inch.
5. Check the driveshaft to housing bearing clearance by measuring the O.D. of the shaft and the I.D. of the housing bearing. The recommended clearance limits are .0015–.0030 inch.
6. Inspect the relief valve spring for a collapsed or worn condition.
7. Check the relief valve piston for scores and free operation in the bore. The specified clearance is .0015–.0030 inch.

BELT TENSION DATA

Belt	New	Used
Except ¼ inch	140	105
4 Ribs Except Air Pump	130	115
4 Ribs Air Pump	110	105
5 Ribs	150	135
6 Ribs ①	160	145
6 Ribs ②	113	110

① —w/tensioner.
② —w/absorber.

SERPENTINE DRIVE BELT
ROUTING

Refer to **Fig. 9,** for serpentine drive belt routing.

REPLACEMENT

1. Lift or rotate automatic tensioner.
2. Remove old belt.
3. Install new belt over pulleys. Ensure all V-grooves make proper contact with pulley.

ADJUSTMENT

Automatic belt tensioners are spring loaded devices which set and maintain the drive belt tension.

Automatic tensioners have belt wear indicator marks. If the indicator mark is not between the indicator lines, the belt is worn or an incorrect belt is installed.

COOLING SYSTEM BLEED

These engines do not require a specified bleed procedure. After filling cooling

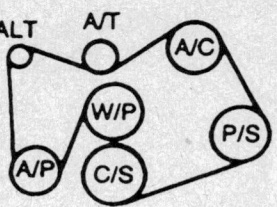

Fig. 9 Serpentine drive belt routing

system, run engine to operating temperature with radiator/pressure cap off. Air will then be automatically bled through cap opening.

THERMOSTAT
REPLACE

1. Drain cooling system until coolant level is below the thermostat.
2. Disconnect bypass hose at thermostat housing.
3. Mark location of distributor, then loosen hold-down clamp and rotate distributor to gain access.
4. Disconnect upper radiator hose at thermostat housing, then remove two housing retaining bolts.
5. Remove thermostat housing and gasket.
6. Reverse procedure to install. Tighten to specifications.

WATER PUMP
REPLACE

1. Drain cooling system, then remove fan shroud attaching bolts and position shroud over fan.
2. Remove fan, spacer and shroud.
3. Remove drive belts, then remove A/C idler pulley bracket.
4. Remove power steering pump and position aside.
5. Remove all accessory brackets which attach to water pump, then remove water pump pulley.
6. Remove lower radiator hose, heater hose and bypass hose from water pump.
7. Remove water pump to front cover attaching bolts, then remove water pump.
8. Reverse procedure to install.

RADIATOR
REPLACE

1. Disconnect battery ground cable.
2. Drain engine coolant, then disconnect overflow hose, upper and lower hoses from radiator.
3. Disconnect automatic transmission fluid inlet and outlet lines.
4. **On models equipped with fan shroud,** remove upper shroud mounting bolts at radiator support.
5. Lift fan shroud enough to disengage lower retaining clips and lay shroud over fan.
6. **On all models,** remove radiator upper

support mounting bolts, then supports and radiator.
7. Reverse procedure to install, noting the following:
   a. Operate engine, check automatic transmission, radiator and coolant recovery tank for proper fluid level.

FUEL PUMP
REPLACE
MECHANICAL

1. Disconnect fuel lines from fuel pump.
2. Remove fuel pump attaching bolts and the fuel pump and gasket.
3. Remove all gasket material from the pump and block gasket surfaces. Apply sealer to both sides of new gasket.
4. Position gasket on pump flange and hold pump in position against its mounting surface. Make sure rocker arm is riding on camshaft eccentric.
5. Press pump tight against its mounting. Install retaining screws and tighten them alternately.
6. Connect fuel lines. Then operate engine and check for leaks. **Before installing the pump, it is good practice to crank the engine so that the nose of the camshaft eccentric is out of the way of the fuel pump rocker arm when the pump is installed. In this way there will be the least amount of tension on the rocker arm, thereby easing the installation of the pump.**

ELECTRIC

When the electric fuel pump is removed from the fuel tank, all the rubber hoses, clamps and mounting gaskets should be replaced, as exposure to the air causes the hoses to become brittle and will lead to premature failure.

Removal

1. Remove air cleaner.
2. Relieve fuel system pressure as follows:
   a. **On CFI engines,** attach fuel pressure gauge tool No. T80L-9974-B or equivalent to fuel diagnostic valve on the fuel charging assembly, then slowly depressurize fuel system.
   b. **On EFI engines,** relieve fuel system pressure at valve, located in

fuel rail, on front left corner of engine.
3. **On all models,** siphon fuel from fuel tank, then raise and support vehicle.
4. Disconnect fuel supply, return and vent lines at the left and right side rear axle frame kickdowns.
5. Disconnect electrical connector in front of fuel tank.
6. Disconnect and remove fuel filler tube.
7. Remove fuel tank support straps, then the fuel tank.
8. Clean all dirt accumulated around fuel pump attaching flange, then disconnect supply and return line fittings and the electrical connector.
9. Turn fuel pump lock ring counterclockwise and remove lock ring.
10. Remove fuel pump and bracket assembly from fuel tank. Discard seal ring.

Installation

1. Clean fuel tank mounting surface and seal ring groove.
2. Lightly coat new seal ring with heavy grease to hold it in place, then install into fuel ring groove.
3. Carefully install fuel pump and bracket assembly into tank, ensuring filter is not damaged during installation. Ensure locating keys are positioned in keyways and seal ring remains in groove.
4. Holding pump assembly in place, install lock ring finger tight, ensuring all locking tabs are positioned under fuel tank ring tabs. Continue to turn lock ring clockwise until ring contacts stop.
5. Connect fuel pump electrical connector, then lubricate fittings and reconnect fuel lines.
6. Install fuel tank and tighten support straps.
7. Reconnect fuel sender and fuel pump wiring harness, then lower vehicle.
8. Install fuel filler tube and reconnect vent line.
9. Lubricate fittings at right and lefthand side of rear axle frame, reconnect finger tight, then tighten an additional 1/4 turn.
10. Fill fuel tank with at least 10 gallons of fuel and check for leaks.
11. Activate fuel pump until system is fully pressurized, then check all fittings for leakage. Repair leaks as necessary.

12. Start engine and recheck for leaks.

FUEL FILTER
REPLACE
MARK VII

1. Turn engine off, then relieve fuel system pressure as follows:
   a. **On CFI engines,** attach fuel pressure gauge tool No. T80L-9974-B or equivalent to fuel diagnostic valve on the fuel charging assembly, then slowly depressurize fuel system.
   b. **On EFI engines,** relieve fuel system pressure at valve, located in fuel rail, on front left corner of engine.
2. Raise and support vehicle.
3. Remove push connect fittings at both ends of filter. Install new retainer clips in each push connect fitting.
4. Remove fuel filter from bracket by loosening worm gear clamp. Note direction of flow arrow as installed in bracket to ensure proper direction of fuel flow through replacement filter.
5. Reverse procedure to install, noting the following:
   a. Install fuel filter into bracket, ensuring proper flow direction.
   b. **Torque** worm gear clamp to 15-25 inch lbs.
   c. Start engine and inspect for leaks.

TOWN CAR

1. Turn engine off and relieve fuel system pressure as described under "Fuel System Pressure Relief."
2. Raise and support vehicle.
3. Remove push connect fittings at both ends of fuel filter. Install new retainer clips in each push connect fitting.
4. Remove fuel filter and retainer from metal bracket by removing two retainer bolts.
5. Remove filer from retainer. Note direction of flow arrow.
6. Remove rubber insulator rings from filter.
7. Reverse procedure to install, noting the following:
   a. Replace insulator (s) if filter move freely after retainer installation.
   b. **Torque** retaining bolts to 27-44 inch lbs.
   c. Start engine and inspect for leaks.

TIGHTENING SPECIFICATIONS

Year	Component	Torque/Ft. Lbs.
1992	Alternator Adjustment Arm To Water Pump Stud Nut	20-39
	Alternator Adjustment Arm To Alternator Bolt	24-40
	Alternator And Thermactor Pump Bracket To Cylinder Head	③
	Camshaft Sprocket Gear Bolt	40-45
	Camshaft Thrust Plate	9-12
	Connecting Rod Nut	19-24

Year	Component	Torque/Ft. Lbs.
1992 —Cont'd	Crankshaft Damper Bolt	70-90
	Cylinder Head Bolt	①
	Distributor Hold-Down Bolt	18-26
	EGR Valve To Spacer Intake Manifold	12-18
	Exhaust Manifold	18-24
	Fan To Water Pump Hub Bolt	15-22
	Flywheel Bolt	75-85
	Front Cover Bolts	12-18

Continued

TIGHTENING SPECIFICATIONS-Continued

Year	Component	Torque/Ft. Lbs.
1992 —Cont'd	Intake Manifold Lower	12-18
	Intake Manifold To Cylinder Head	②
	Intake Manifold Upper	12-18
	Main Bearing Cap	60-70
	Oil Filter Insert To Cylinder Block Adapter Bolt	20-30
	Oil Inlet Tube To Oil Pump Bolt	12-18
	Oil Inlet Tube To Main Bearing Cap Nut	22-32
	Oil Pan To Block	6-9
	Oil Drain Plug	15-25
	Oil Pump To Cylinder Block	22-32
	Pulley To Damper Bolt	35-50
	Rocker Arm Cover	10-13
	Rocker Arm Fulcrum	18-25

Year	Component	Torque/Ft. Lbs.
1992 —Cont'd	Spark Plugs	5-10
	Thermactor Pump Pivot Bolt	35-50
	Thermactor Pump Adjustment Arm To Pump	22-32
	Thermactor Pump Pulley To Pump Hub	④
	Thermostat Housing	17-25
	Throttle Body Attaching Nut	12-18
	Vacuum fittings To Intake Manifold	10-13 ⑤
	Water Outlet Housing	12-18
	Water Pump To Cylinder Block Front Cover	12-18

①—Refer to text.
②—Torque in two steps; first 15-20 ft. lbs., then finally to 23-25 ft. lbs.
③—3/8 inch bolt 22-32 ft. lbs.; 7/16 inch bolt 40-55 ft. lbs.
④—Inch lbs.
⑤—Apply Teflon Tape.

Rear Axle & Suspension

INDEX

DESCRIPTION

CONTINENTAL

The Continental utilizes a fully independent rear suspension consisting of McPherson struts with integral air springs and dual-damping shock absorbers, counterbalancing torsion springs and a height sensor.

The air suspension and dual damping functions are controlled by a microcomputer based module which receives inputs for vehicle speed, door switch position, damping actuator feedback, steering wheel turning rate and angle, engine vacuum, throttle position, brake actuation, ignition switching, and vehicle ride height. The dual-damping function automatically switches from a soft to firm ride when the driving situation (hard cornering, acceleration or braking, etc.) dictates the need for increased damping effect.

The rear struts, **Fig. 1,** use a dual path mount which separates the strut and air spring mounting surfaces, to help provide for maximum isolation. The counterbalancing torsion springs, fitted between the strut and lower control arm, produce an outward force on the strut that tends to offset the binding forces induced by the rear wheels. The rotary design Hall effect type height sensor, **Fig. 2,** permits multiple height positions to be defined, resulting in specialized leveling during all types of driving and load characteristics.

MARK VII, MARK VIII & TOWN CAR

Fig. 3 illustrates the rear axle assembly used on these vehicles. When necessary to overhaul these units, refer to the rear axle specifications table at the beginning of this chapter.

The gear set consists of a ring gear and an overhung drive pinion which is supported by two opposed tapered roller bearings, **Fig. 3.** The differential case is a one-piece design with openings allowing assembly of the internal parts and lubricant flow. The differential pinion shaft is retained with a threaded bolt (lock) assembled to the case.

The roller type wheel bearings have no inner race, and the rollers directly contact the bearing journals of the axle shafts. The axle shafts do not use an inner and outer bearing retainer. Rather, they are held in the axle by means of C-locks. These C-locks also fit into a machined recess in the differential side gears within the differential case. There is no retainer bolt access hole in the axle shaft flange.

REAR AXLE
REPLACE

MARK VII, MARK VIII & TOWN CAR

1. Raise vehicle and position safety stands under the rear frame crossmember.
2. Disconnect driveshaft at companion flange and secure it to vehicle using wire.
3. Remove wheels and brake drums. If equipped with rear disc brakes, remove calipers from anchor plates and rotors from shafts.
4. **The rear anti-lock brake sensor ring must be removed before axle shafts are removed.** The sensor ring

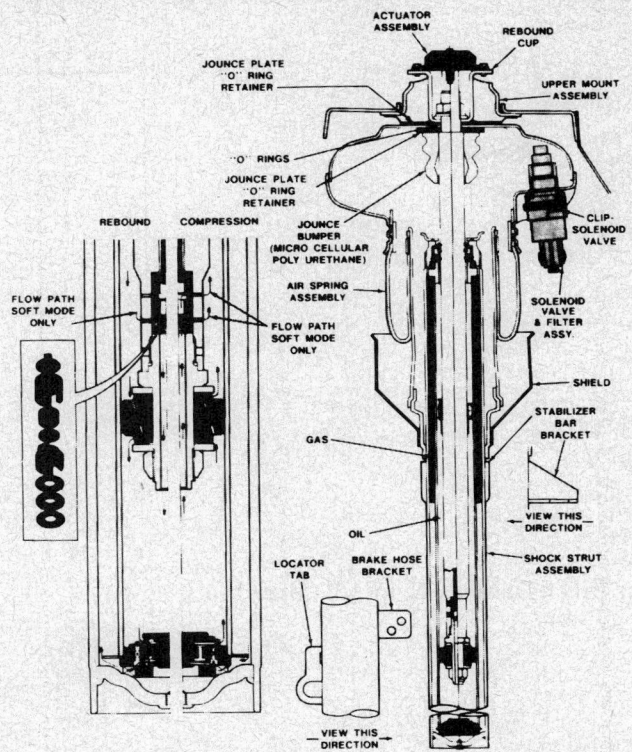

Fig. 1 Cross-sectional view of rear strut assembly. Continental

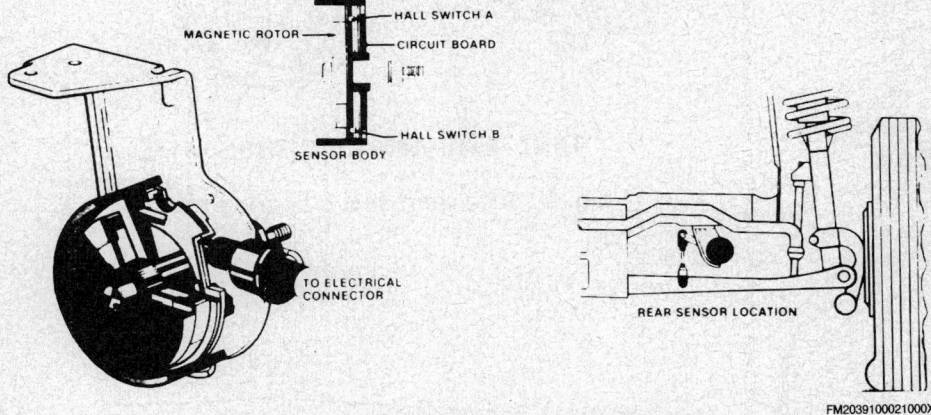

Fig. 2 Rotary height sensor. Continental

is located between the brake drum and axle shaft.

5. Support axle housing with floor jack.
6. Disconnect brake line from clips that retain line to axle housing, then disconnect vent from rear axle housing. Some axle vents may be secured to the housing assembly through the brake junction block. When reinstalling, apply thread locking compound E0AZ-19554-B or equivalent to ensure proper retention.
7. Disconnect shock absorbers from axle housing.
8. Disconnect upper control arms from mountings on axle housing.
9. Lower axle housing assembly until coils springs are released, then remove springs.
10. Disconnect lower control arms from mountings on axle housing, then lower the axle housing and remove it from vehicle.
11. Reverse procedure to install.

REAR AXLE SHAFT
REPLACE

MARK VII, MARK VIII & TOWN CAR

1. Raise car on hoist and remove wheels.
2. Drain differential lubricant.
3. Remove brake drums.
4. Remove differential housing cover.
5. Position safety stands under rear frame member and lower hoist to allow axle to lower as far as possible.
6. Working through differential case opening, remove pinion shaft lock bolt and pinion shaft.
7. Push axle shaft inward toward center of axle housing and remove C-lock (s) from housing, **Fig. 4.**
8. Remove axle shaft, using extreme care to avoid contact of shaft seal lip with any portion of axle shaft except seal journal.
9. Use a hook-type puller to remove seal and bearing, **Fig. 5.**
10. Reverse procedure to install, using suitable driving tools to install seal and bearing. Lubricate new bearing with rear axle lubricant and apply grease between the lips of the seal. Apply silicone sealant to carrier casting face as shown, **Fig. 6,** then install housing cover. **Torque** cover bolts to 30 ft. lbs.

PROPELLER SHAFT
REPLACE

MARK VII, MARK VIII & TOWN CAR

To maintain proper drive line balance, mark the driveshaft, universal joints, slip yoke and companion flange before removing the shaft assembly so it can be reinstalled in its original position.

1. Remove companion flange to drive pinion flange attaching bolts.
2. Pull driveshaft rearward until slip yoke clears transmission extension housing.
3. Reverse procedure to install.

STRUT
REPLACE

CONTINENTAL

1. Place the air suspension switch in the Off position before performing any work, or whenever raising the rear suspension.
2. Position suitable jack or hoist under vehicle, then raise just enough to contact body.
3. Disconnect air suspension electrical wiring and all related parts that will interfere with strut removal.
4. Loosen, but do not remove, the strut to inner body attaching nuts.
5. Raise and support vehicle, then remove wheel and tire assembly.
6. Remove brake hose to strut bracket attaching clip, then position hose aside.
7. If applicable, remove stabilizer bar attaching hardware and insulators, then separate stabilizer bar from link.
8. If applicable, remove tension strut to spindle attaching nut, washer and insulator, then move spindle rearward until it can be separated from tension strut.
9. Mark position of notch on toe adjustment cam, **Fig. 7.**
10. Remove strut to spindle pinch bolt,

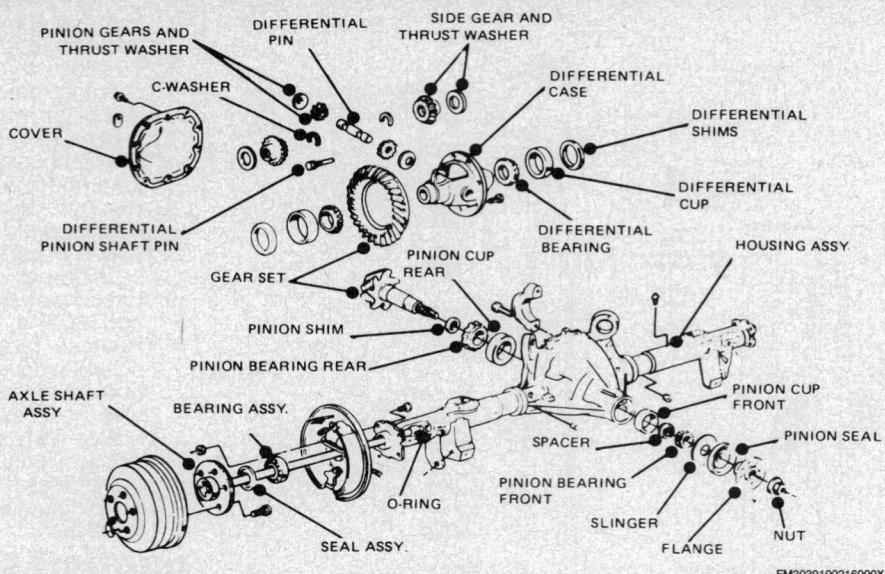

Fig. 3 Integral carrier type rear axle assembly. Mark VII, Mark VIII & Town Car

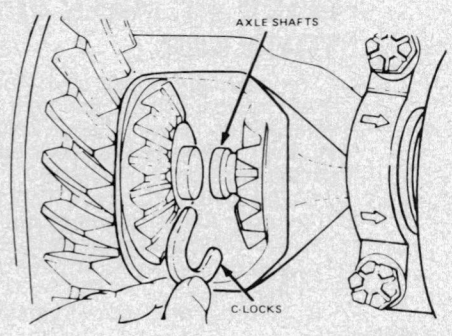

Fig. 4 Axle shaft "C" locks

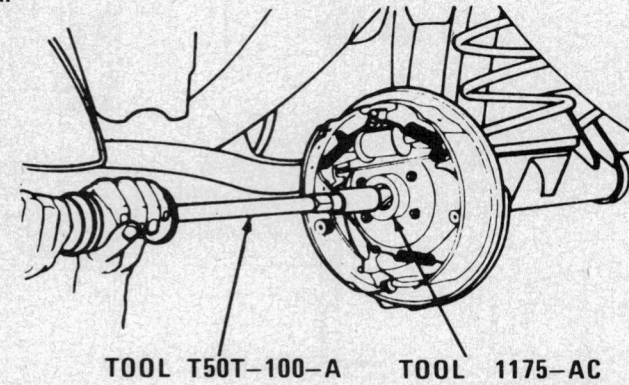

TOOL T50T-100-A   TOOL 1175-AC

Fig. 5 Axle shaft seal & bearing removal

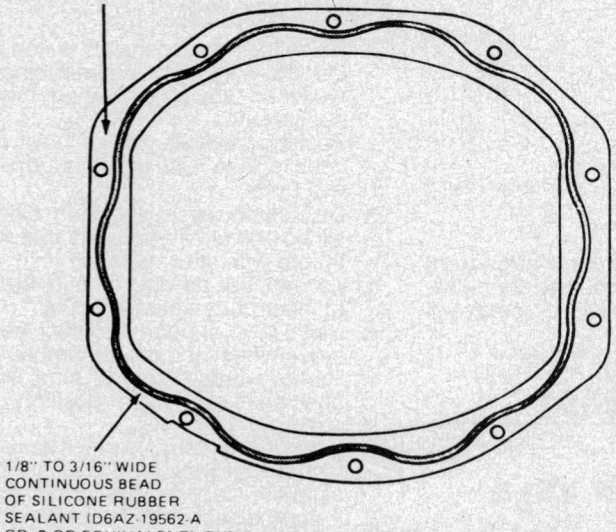

CARRIER CASTING FACE

1/8" TO 3/16" WIDE CONTINUOUS BEAD OF SILICONE RUBBER SEALANT (D6AZ-19562-A OR -B OR EQUIVALENT) TYPICAL BEAD INSTALLATION PARTS MUST BE ASSEMBLED WITHIN 1/4 HOUR AFTER APPLICATION OF SEALANT. GASKET SURFACE OF HOUSING AND CARRIER MUST BE FREE OF OIL.

Fig. 6 Applying sealant to carrier casting face

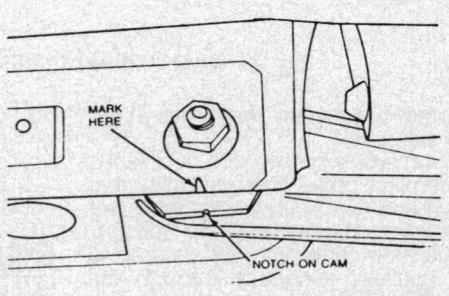

Fig. 7 Marking toe adjustment cam. Continental

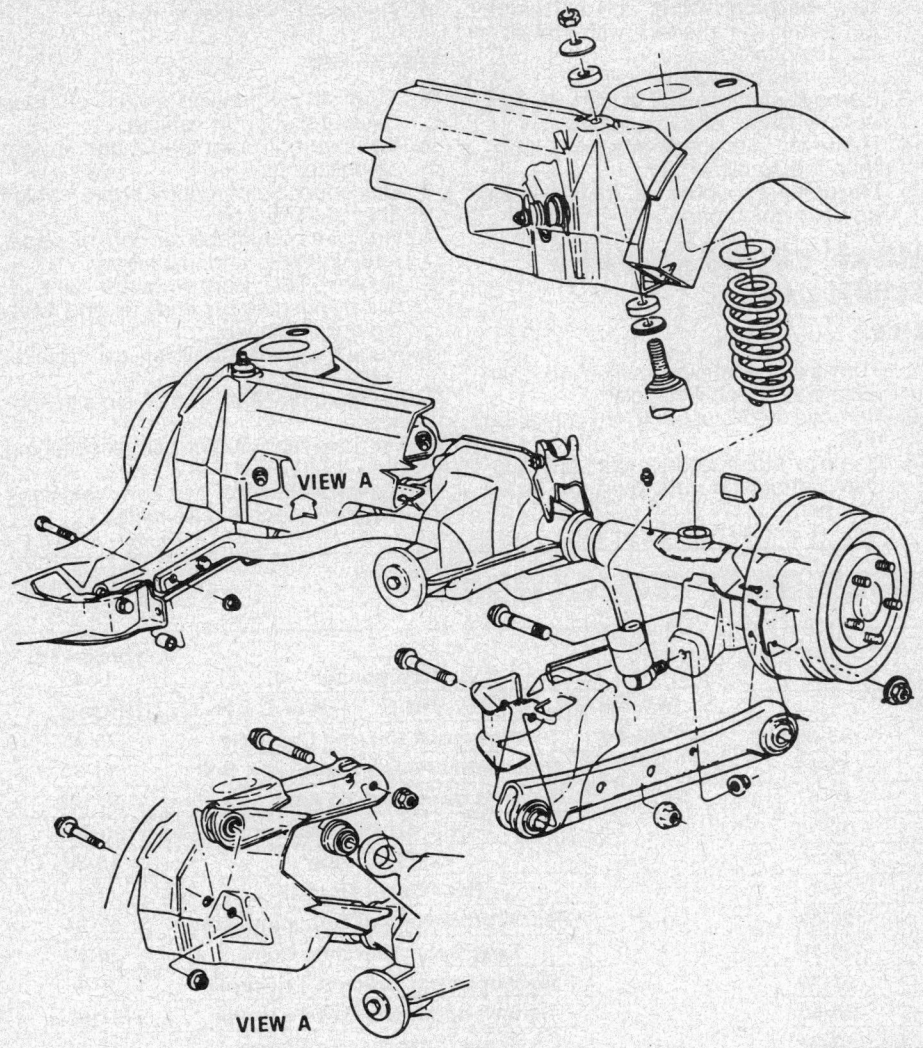

Fig. 8 Rear suspension components. Town Car

FM2039100019000X

and nut from lower shock absorber mounting bracket.

5. From underneath vehicle, compress shock absorber to clear hole in upper shock tower, then remove shock absorber. **These models are equipped with gas pressurized shock absorbers which extend unassisted during removal. Do not apply heat or flame to the shock absorber tube during removal.**

6. Reverse procedure to install. While holding shock absorber in position, **torque** lower cross bolt to 59 ft. lbs. Lower vehicle and install upper mounting nut, washer and insulator and **torque** nut to 24 to 26 ft. lbs.

COIL SPRING
REPLACE

TOWN CAR

1. Raise rear of vehicle and support at frame side sills. Support rear axle with a suitable jack.
2. Disconnect shock absorbers and stabilizer bar from axle housing, **Fig. 8.**
3. Disconnect righthand parking brake cable from righthand upper arm retainer.
4. Lower the axle housing until coil springs are released.
5. Remove springs and insulators, **Fig. 8.**
6. Reverse procedure to install.

CONTROL ARM
REPLACE

CONTINENTAL

1. If necessary, disconnect air suspension electrical wiring and all related parts that will interfere with control arm removal.
2. Raise and support vehicle.
3. Mark position of notch on toe adjustment cam, **Fig. 7.**
4. Remove control arm to spindle attaching bolt, nut, and washer.
5. Remove control arm to body attaching bolt and nut, then the control arm.
6. Reverse procedure to install, then check rear wheel alignment and adjust as necessary.

MARK VII, MARK VIII & TOWN CAR
Lower

1. Turn air suspension switch to off position, then raise and support vehicle and remove wheel assembly.
2. Vent air springs to atmosphere by removing air spring solenoid.
3. Remove the two air spring to lower control arm retaining bolts, and remove air spring from lower arm.
4. Remove control arm to frame and control arm to axle bracket pivot bolts and nuts.
5. Remove lower control arm.
6. Reverse procedure to install. **Torque** pivot bolts to 100 ft. lbs.

then using a pry bar or other suitable tool, separate pinch joint as necessary to allow for strut removal.

11. Disengage strut from pinch joint, then lower vehicle as necessary to allow removal of upper attaching nuts.
12. Remove strut from vehicle.
13. Reverse procedure to install.

TENSION STRUT
REPLACE

CONTINENTAL

1. If necessary, disconnect air suspension electrical wiring and all related parts that will interfere with tension strut removal.
2. Raise vehicle on frame contact hoist using lift pads located rearward of front wheels and forward of rear wheels. Raise hoist only enough to contact body.
3. Loosen, but do not remove, the upper strut to inner body attaching nuts, then raise and support vehicle.

4. Remove wheel and tire assembly.
5. Remove tension strut to spindle and tension strut to body attaching nuts.
6. While moving spindle rearward, remove tension strut from vehicle.
7. Reverse procedure to install, using new washers and bushings.

SHOCK ABSORBER
REPLACE

MARK VII, MARK VII & TOWN CAR

Turn air suspension switch off before replacing shock absorber.

1. Open luggage compartment to gain access to upper shock absorber attachment.
2. Remove rubber cap if equipped, from shock absorber stud, then remove nut, washer and insulator.
3. Raise vehicle and support rear axle.
4. Remove lower shock absorber protective cover, then remove cross bolt

LINCOLN

Upper

Always replace control arm in pairs. If one arm requires replacement, replace the same arm on the opposite side of the vehicle.

1. Turn air suspension switch off.
2. Raise and support vehicle, then disconnect rear height sensor from side arm. Note position of sensor adjustment bracket to aid in reassembly.
3. Remove upper arm to axle and upper arm to frame bracket pivot bolts and nuts.
4. Remove upper control arm.
5. Reverse procedure to install. **Torque** pivot bolts to 100 ft. lbs.

STABILIZER BAR
REPLACE
CONTINENTAL

1. If necessary, disconnect air suspension electrical wiring and all related parts that will interfere with stabilizer bar removal.
2. Raise and support vehicle.
3. Remove stabilizer bar to link attaching nuts, washers and insulators.
4. Remove U-bracket attaching bolts, then the stabilizer bar.
5. Reverse procedure to install, using new attaching parts.

MARK VII, MARK VIII & TOWN CAR
1992

1. Turn air suspension switch off, then raise and support vehicle.
2. Remove stabilizer bar to link attaching nuts.
3. Remove stabilizer bar to bushing U-clamp attaching nuts, then the stabilizer bar.

4. Reverse procedure to install.

1993—95

1. Turn air suspension switch off, then raise and support vehicle.
2. Remove both rear wheel and tire assemblies.
3. Disconnect emergency brake cables from stabilizer bar.
4. Remove both stabilizer bar link upper retaining nuts and insulators.
5. Remove links from stabilizer bar eyelets by pushing bar ends up and rotating out of the way.
6. Remove both stabilizer bar bracket bolts.
7. Remove brackets from T-slots in subframe.
8. Remove rear muffler hanger retaining nuts.
9. Remove stabilizer bar from vehicle.
10. Reverse procedure to install.

TIGHTENING SPECIFICATIONS

Year	Component	Torque/Ft. Lbs.
CONTINENTAL		
1992–94	**Arm Inner Pivot Retainer**	45-65
	Control Arm To Body	45-65
	Control Arm To Spindle	42-57
	Spring To Stud Nut	10-15
	Spring Clamp To Spindle Bolt	10-15
	Stabilizer Bar Link	5-7
	Stabilizer U-Bracket	25-37
	Strut Top Mount To Body	19-26
	Strut To Spindle	51-70
	Strut To Top Mount	35-50
	Stud To Arm Nut	17-24
	Tension Strut To Body	35-50
	Tension Strut To Spindle	35-50
	Wheel Lug Nuts	85-104
MARK VII, MARK VIII & TOWN CAR		
1992–95	**Air Spring To Lower Arm**	25-35
	Brake Backing Plate Bolts	20-40
	Clevis Bracket To Axle	55-70

Year	Component	Torque/Ft. Lbs.
MARK VII, MARK VIII & TOWN CAR -Continued		
1992–94 —Cont'd	**Differential Bearing Cap Bolt**	70-85
	Differential Pinion Shaft Lock Bolt	15-30
	Lower Arm To Axle	90-100
	Lower Arm To Frame	80-105
	Oil Filler Plug	15-30
	Rear Cover Screws	②
	Rear Muffler Hanger Retaining Nuts	17-24
	Ring Gear Attaching Bolts	70-85
	Sensor Lower Bracket To Frame	7-10
	Sensor Upper Bracket To Frame	110-150 ①
	Shock Absorber To Frame	17-27
	Shock Absorber To Clevis Bracket	45-60
	Stabilizer Bar Bracket To Subframe	25-34
	Stabilizer Bar To Axle	13-20
	Stabilizer Bar To Body	13-18
	Upper Arm To Axle	70-100
	Upper Arm To Frame	80-105
	Wheel Lug Nuts	85-104

①—Inch lbs.
②—Plastic cover 15-20 ft. lbs., metal cover 25-35 ft. lbs.

Front Suspension & Steering

NOTE: On Air Bag Equipped Models, Refer To "Air Bag System Precautions" Located In The Front Of This Manual For System Disarming & Arming Procedures.

INDEX

PRECAUTIONS

AIR BAG SYSTEMS

Refer to "Air Bag System Precautions" in the front of this manual for system disarming and arming procedures.

AIR SUSPENSION SYSTEM

Always place the air suspension switch in the Off position before performing any work, or whenever raising the front suspension.

WHEEL BEARING

ADJUST

MARK VII

1. With wheel rotating, **torque** adjusting nut to 17-25 ft. lbs., **Fig. 1.**
2. Back off adjusting nut 1/2 turn and **torque** nut to 10-15 inch lbs.
3. Place nut lock on nut so that castellations on lock are aligned with cotter pin hole in spindle and install cotter pin.
4. Check front wheel rotation, if it rotates noisily or rough, clean, inspect or replace wheel bearings as necessary.

MARK VIII & TOWN CAR

On these models the wheel bearings are preset and cannot be adjusted.

WHEEL BEARING

REPLACE

MARK VII

1. Raise car and remove front wheels.
2. Remove caliper mounting bolts. **It is not necessary to disconnect the brake line for this operation.**
3. Slide caliper off of the disc, inserting a spacer between the shoes to hold

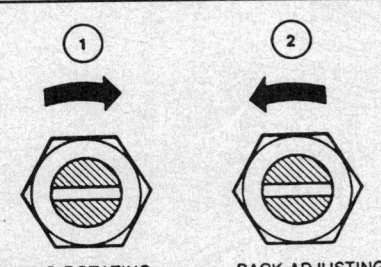

WITH HUB ROTATING, TIGHTEN ADJUSTMENT NUT, TO 23-34 N·m (17-25 LB-FT)

BACK ADJUSTING NUT OFF 1/2 TURN

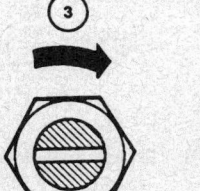

TIGHTEN ADJUSTING NUT TO 1.1-3.2 N·m (10-28 LB-IN)

INSTALL RETAINER AND A NEW COTTER PIN

FM3039100220000X

Fig. 1   Front wheel bearing adjustment. Mark VII

them in their bores after the caliper is removed. Position caliper assembly out of the way. **Do not allow caliper to hang by brake hose.**

4. Remove hub and disc. Grease retainer and inner bearing can now be removed.
5. Reverse procedure to install.

MARK VIII & TOWN CAR

1. Raise and support front of vehicle, then remove wheel and tire assembly.
2. Remove grease cap from hub.
3. Remove brake caliper and suspend from chassis with wire. Do not allow caliper to hang from brake hose.

4. Remove push clips, if equipped, then remove brake rotor, **Fig. 2.**
5. Remove hub nut, then remove hub and bearing assembly. If difficulty is encountered, use front hub remover tool No. T81P-1104-C or equivalent to remove hub and bearing assembly.
6. Reverse procedure to install. A new hub and bearing retaining nut should be installed. **Torque** hub bearing nut to 189-254 ft. lbs.

BALL JOINT INSPECTION

UPPER

Town Car

1. Raise car on floor jacks placed beneath lower control arms.
2. Grasp lower edge of tire and move wheel in and out.
3. As wheel is being moved in and out, observe upper end of spindle and upper arm.
4. Any movement between upper end of spindle and upper arm indicates ball joint wear and loss of preload. If such movement is observed, replace upper ball joint. **During the foregoing check, the lower ball joint will be unloaded and may move. Disregard all such movement of the lower joint. Also, do not mistake loose wheel bearings for a worn ball joint.**

LOWER

Mark VII

1. Support vehicle in normal driving position with both ball joints loaded.
2. Clean area around grease fitting and checking surface. **The checking surface is the round boss into which the grease fitting is installed.**
3. The checking surface should project

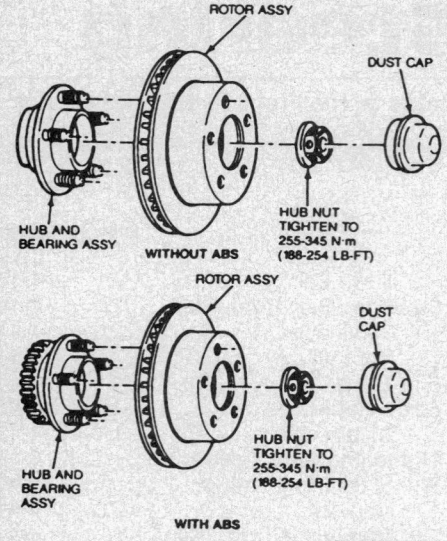

Fig. 2 Hub & bearing assembly.
Mark VIII & Town Car

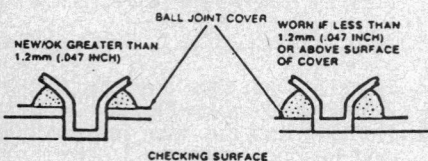

Fig. 3 Lower ball joint wear
indicator

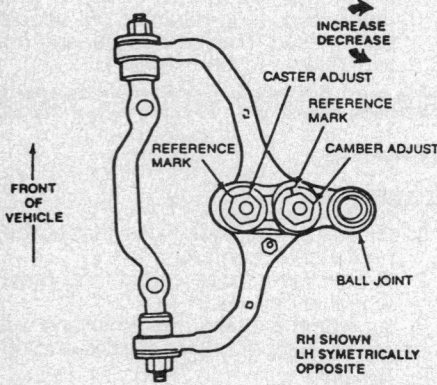

Fig. 4 Upper control assembly.
Town Car

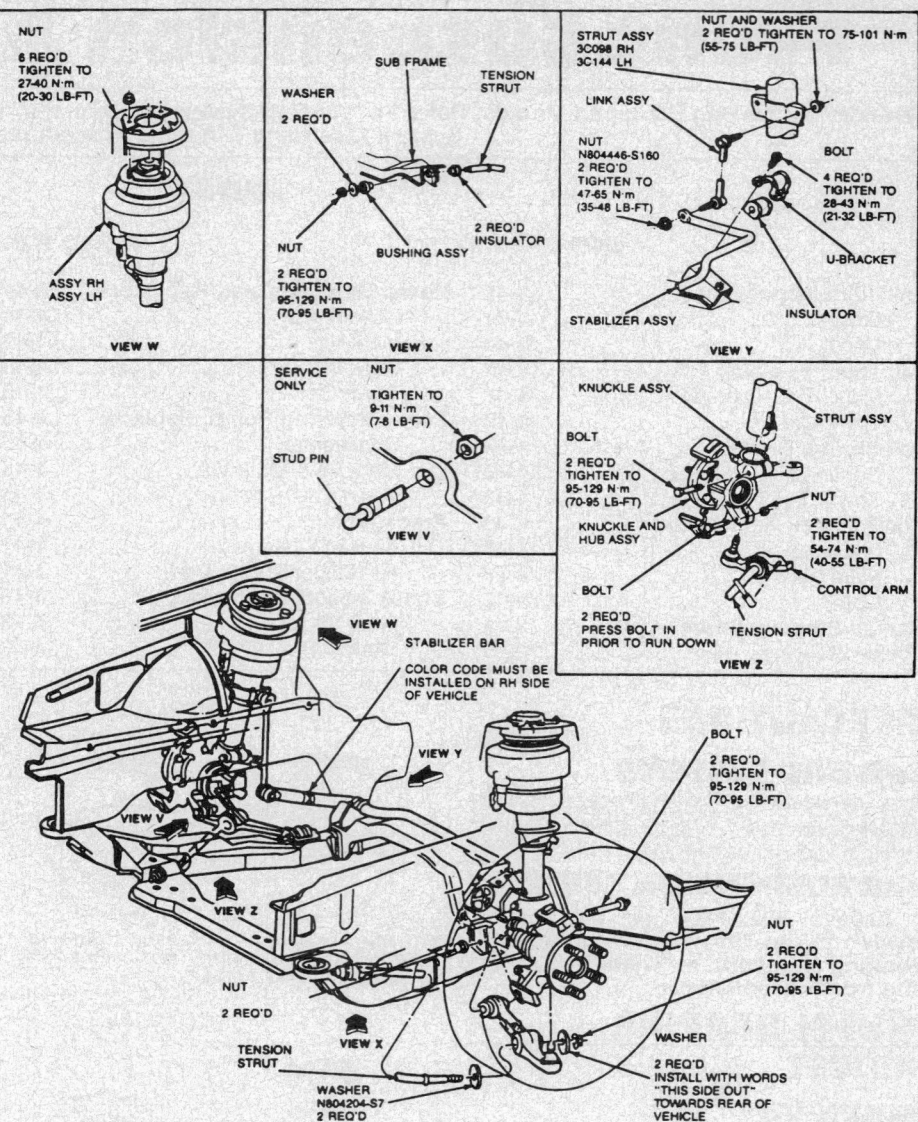

Fig. 5 Front suspension components. Continental

outside the cover, **Fig. 3.** If surface is inside cover replace lower arm assembly.

Mark VIII

1. Raise and support vehicle under sub-frame.
2. Attach dial indicator at ball joint to be checked so as to measure lateral movement between the spindle and the arm. Either upper or lower ball joint may be checked in this manner.
3. Hold tire at top and bottom and slowly move tire in and out. Note reading on dial indicator. If reading exceeds .015 inch, replace ball joint.

Town Car

These models are equipped with lower ball joint wear indicators, **Fig. 3.** To check ball joint for wear, support vehicle in normal driving position with both ball joints loaded. Observe the checking surface of the ball joint. If the checking surface is inside the cover, replace the ball joint.

BALL JOINT
REPLACE

MARK VII & MARK VIII

These ball joints are not serviceable. If they require replacement, the control arm and ball joint must be replaced as an assembly. Tighten ball joint stud to specifications

TOWN CAR

1. Raise and support vehicle, then remove wheel and tire assembly. Position jack stands under both sides of frame just to the rear of lower control arm.
2. Position a suitable jack under lower control arm.
3. Remove nut from upper ball joint to steering knuckle pinch bolt, then tap out pinch bolt.
4. Mark positions of caster and camber adjusting cams for use during installation, **Fig. 4.**
5. Remove two bolts attaching ball joint to upper control arm.
6. Using a suitable pry bar, spread slot to release ball joint from steering knuckle and remove.
7. Reverse procedure to install. Align caster and camber marks made during removal. After completing installation, check front wheel alignment.

COIL SPRING
REPLACE
CONTINENTAL

Refer to "Strut, Replace" for coil spring replacement procedure.

TOWN CAR

1. Raise and support vehicle.
2. Remove wheel and tire assembly.
3. Disconnect stabilizer bar link from lower control arm.
4. Remove shock absorber.
5. Remove steering center link from Pitman arm.
6. Compress coil spring with a suitable spring compressor.
7. Remove two lower control arm pivot bolts and disengage arm from crossmember.
8. Remove spring from vehicle.
9. Reverse procedure to install. Tighten stabilizer bar to lower control arm nuts and lower control arm to crossmember bolts to specifications.

STRUT
REPLACE
CONTINENTAL

1. Remove hub nut and loosen the upper strut attaching nuts, **Fig. 5.**
2. Raise and support vehicle. **Do not lift vehicle from lower control arm.**
3. Disconnect air suspension electrical wiring and all related parts that will interfere with strut removal.
4. Remove wheel and tire assembly.
5. Remove brake caliper and suspend with wire, then disconnect tie rod end.
6. Remove stabilizer bar link nut, then remove link from strut.
7. Remove lower control arm to steering knuckle pinch nut and bolt, then spread joint as necessary and disengage control arm from knuckle.
8. Using a suitable hub installation/removal tool, press axle from hub/rotor assembly. Wire axle shaft as necessary to maintain level position. **Do not permit axle shaft to move outward during disengagement from hub, since damage to CV joints could result.**
9. Remove strut to steering knuckle pinch bolt, then spread joint and remove steering knuckle and hub assembly.
10. Remove strut upper attaching nuts, then remove strut from vehicle.
11. Reverse procedure to install. Tighten to specifications.

SHOCK ABSORBER
REPLACE
MARK VII

Turn air suspension switch off before removing shock strut.
1. Place ignition switch in the Unlocked position so that front wheels are free to move.

2. From engine compartment, remove one strut to upper mounting nut. Use a screwdriver in rod slot to hold rod stationary when removing nut.
3. Raise front of vehicle by lower control arms, then place safety stands under frame jack pads located rearward of wheels.
4. Remove wheel and tire assembly, then remove brake caliper, rotor assembly and dust shield.
5. Remove two nuts and bolts attaching lower strut to spindle. **When removing the second lower strut to spindle nut, hold strut firmly as gas pressure will cause strut to fully extend.**
6. Lift strut upward from spindle to compress rod, then pull downward and remove strut.
7. Reverse procedure to install.

MARK VIII

These models are equipped with gas pressurized shock absorbers which extend unassisted during removal. Do not apply heat or flame during removal.
1. Raise and support vehicle.
2. Remove shock actuator.
3. Remove upper shock mount to body nuts from inside luggage compartment.
4. Remove bolt and nut at lower arm, then remove shock absorber.
5. Reverse procedure to install.

TOWN CAR

1. Remove nut, washer and bushing from upper end of shock absorber.
2. Raise and support vehicle.
3. Remove screws retaining shock absorber to lower control arm and remove shock absorber.
4. **These models are equipped with gas pressurized shock absorbers which extend unassisted during removal. Do not apply heat or flame during removal.**
5. Reverse procedure to install.

CONTROL ARM
REPLACE
LOWER
Continental

1. Raise and support vehicle.
2. Disconnect air suspension electrical wiring and all related parts that will interfere with control arm removal.
3. Remove wheel and tire assembly, then the tension strut nut and washer.
4. Remove lower control arm to steering knuckle pinch nut and bolt, then spread joint and separate ball joint from knuckle.
5. Remove lower control arm inner pivot bolt and nut, then the lower control arm.
6. Reverse procedure to install. Tighten to specifications.

Mark VIII

Do not begin procedure unless a new hub retainer nut is available. Once re-

moved, this part cannot be reused during assembly.
1. Raise and support front of vehicle, then remove rear knuckle/hub assembly.
2. Deflate rear air springs and disengage height sensor from lower arm ballstud attachment (LH only). Ensure the integral lower air spring clip is disengaged from lower arm.
3. Disconnect rear stabilizer bar straps from emergency brake cables (both sides).
4. Remove rear stabilizer bar link nuts at their lower arm attachment ends.
5. Remove link bushings and push link ends up and out of lower arm, then rotate bar and link assembly out of the way.
6. Mark toe adjustment cam-to-subframe position. Loosen both pivot attachment nuts at lower arm to subframe positions but do not remove bolts.
7. Remove shock absorber to lower control arm bolt.
8. Remove inner pivot bolts and nuts.
9. Remove lower control arm from vehicle.
10. Reverse procedure to install, noting the following:
    a. Tighten lower control arm to toe compensating link nut to specification.
    b. Ensure air spring assembly is fully seated and the spring is not kinked.

Town Car

1. Raise and support front of vehicle, then remove front wheels.
2. Remove brake caliper, rotor, dust shield and ABS sensor, if equipped.
3. Remove jounce bumper, if equipped.
4. Remove shock absorber.
5. Disconnect steering center link from pitman arm.
6. Remove lower ball joint attaching nut cotter pin, then loosen lower ball joint nut one or two times, **Fig. 6.** Do not remove nut from stud at this time.
7. Tap spindle boss sharply to relieve stud pressure, then tap near lower stud to loosen stud in spindle.
8. Position a suitable jack under lower control arm.
9. Install suitable coil spring compression tool, then remove coil spring.
10. Remove ball joint nut, then the lower control arm assembly.
11. Reverse procedure to install, noting the following:
    a. Tighten ball joint attaching nut specifications.
    b. Ensure coil spring is properly aligned, **Fig. 6.**
    c. Tighten control arm to crossmember attaching bolts and nuts to specifications.
    d. Check wheel alignment.

UPPER
Town Car

1. Raise and support vehicle, then remove wheel and tire assembly. Position jack stands under both side of

frame just to the rear of lower control arm.

2. Position a suitable jack under lower control arm.
3. Remove nut from upper ball joint to steering knuckle pinch bolt, then tap out pinch bolt.
4. Mark positions of caster and camber adjusting cams for use during installation, **Fig. 4.**
5. Using a suitable pry bar, spread slot to release ball joint from steering knuckle.
6. Remove upper control arm attaching bolts, then remove upper arm assembly, **Fig. 6.**
7. Reverse procedure to install. Align caster and camber marks made during removal. After completing installation, check front end alignment.

Mark VIII

1. Raise and support vehicle.
2. Remove wheel and tire assembly, **Fig. 7.**
3. Support knuckle and hub assembly.
4. Support knuckle and hub assembly so it cannot swing outward.
5. Remove inner and outer pivot bolts and nuts at upper control arm.
6. Reverse procedure to install. Tighten inner pivot nut to specification.

STABILIZER BAR
REPLACE

CONTINENTAL

1. Raise and support vehicle.
2. Remove stabilizer bar link to strut and link to bar attaching nuts.
3. Remove stabilizer bar mounting brackets, then the stabilizer bar. It may be necessary to move steering gear from sub-frame and lower rear of sub-frame to gain access to mounting brackets.
4. Reverse procedure to install. Tighten to specifications.

MARK VIII

1. Turn air suspension switch off, then raise and support vehicle.
2. Remove both rear wheel and tire assemblies.
3. Disconnect emergency brake cables from stabilizer bar.
4. Remove both stabilizer bar link upper retaining nuts and insulators.
5. Remove links from stabilizer bar eyelets by pushing bar ends up and rotating out of the way.
6. Remove both stabilizer bar bracket bolts.
7. Remove brackets from T-slots in subframe.
8. Remove rear muffler hanger retaining nuts.
9. Remove stabilizer bar from vehicle.
10. Reverse procedure to install.

TOWN CAR

1. Raise and support vehicle.
2. Remove stabilizer bar attaching clamps, then the stabilizer bar attaching bolts from each stabilizer link.

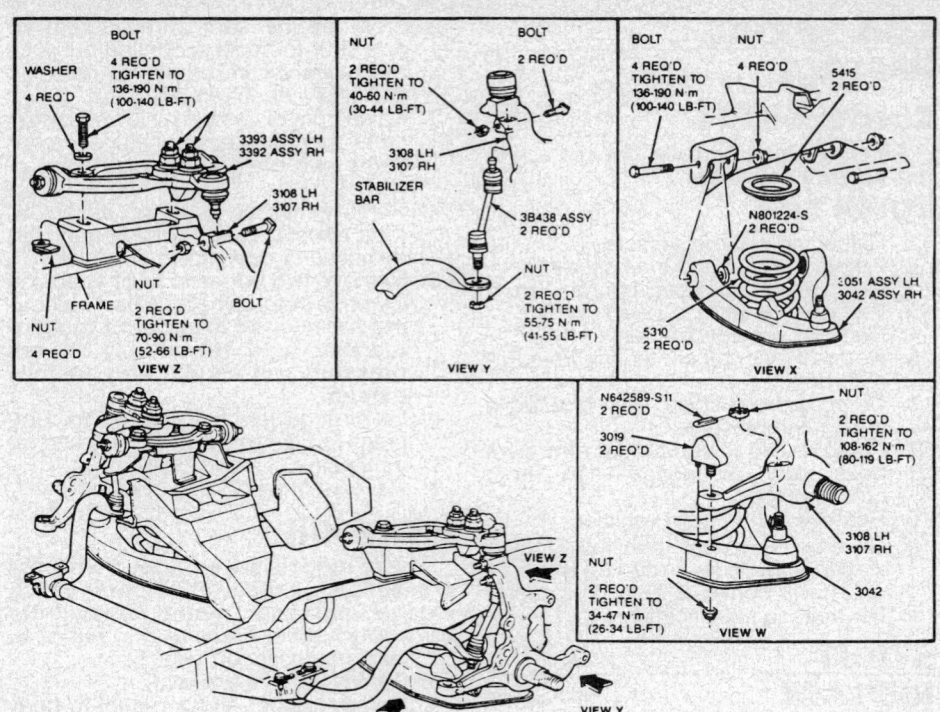

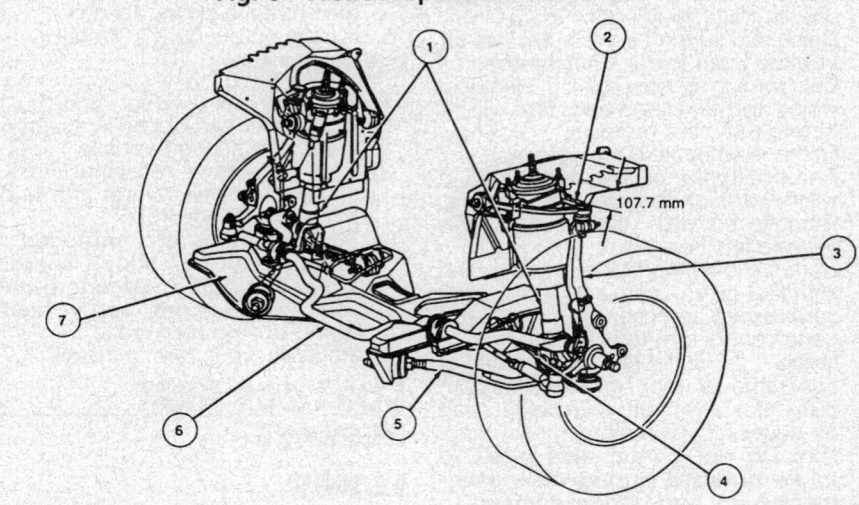

Fig. 6 Front suspension. Town Car

FM2029100053000X

Fig. 7 Front Suspension. Mark VIII

Item	Description	Item	Description
1	Spring / Shock Assy	4	Lower Control Arm
2	Upper Control Arm	5	Tension Strut (2 Req'd)
		6	Stabilizer Bar
3	Spindle	7	Front Subframe Assy

FM2029100054000X

3. Remove stabilizer bar assembly, **Fig. 6.**
4. Reverse procedure to install.

POWER STEERING GEAR
REPLACE

CONTINENTAL

1. Remove steering column boot attach-ments, then the intermediate shaft retaining bolts and shaft.
2. Remove secondary steering column boot from inside of passenger compartment.
3. Raise and support vehicle.
4. Remove tie rod ends from spindle, then gear to sub-frame attaching bolts.
5. Remove both height sensor attach-

ments, then both rear sub-frame to body attaching bolts.

6. Remove exhaust pipe to catalytic converter.
7. Carefully lower sub-frame assembly approximately four inches.
8. Remove heat shield band and fold down shield.
9. Rotate gear to clear bolts from sub-frame and pull left to allow room for line fitting removal.
10. Remove line fittings, then drain using a suitable pan.
11. Remove lefthand sway bar link, then gear assembly through lefthand wheel housing.
12. Reverse procedure to install.

TOWN CAR

1. Remove stone shield, if equipped.
2. Disconnect pressure and return lines from steering gear. Plug lines and ports in gear to prevent entry of dirt.
3. Remove two bolts that secure flex coupling to steering gear and to column.
4. Raise car and remove sector shaft nut.
5. Use a puller to remove pitman arm.
6. Support steering gear, then remove attaching bolts.
7. Work steering gear free of flex coupling and remove it from car.
8. Reverse procedure to install.

MARK VII
Integral Power Rack & Pinion

1. Disconnect battery ground cable.
2. Remove bolt retaining flexible coupling to input shaft.
3. Turn ignition switch on and raise vehicle.
4. Remove tie rod end retaining nuts, then separate studs from spindle arms.
5. Support gear and remove attaching bolts, then lower gear enough to gain access to pressure and return lines. Remove bolt attaching the hose bracket to the gear and bolts from the crossmember.

6. Disconnect and cap pressure and return lines, then remove steering gear.
7. Reverse procedure to install.

Integral Power Steering Gear

1. Disconnect lines from steering gear and plugs lines and ports.
2. Remove the two bolts securing flex coupling to steering gear and to column.
3. Raise vehicle and remove sector shaft nut and Pitman arm. **Do not damage the seals.**
4. Support steering gear and remove three attaching bolts. Remove flex coupling clamp bolt and work steering gear free of coupling, then remove steering gear.
5. Reverse procedure to install.

MARK VIII

1. Raise and support vehicle, then remove front wheel and tire assemblies.
2. Remove cotter pins at outer tie rod ends and castellated nuts at each end. Discard cotter pins.
3. Separate tie rod end studs from spindles using tie rod end remover, 3290-D or equivalent.
4. Place suitable container under vehicle, then disconnect and plug power steering return line hose.
5. Disconnect power steering pressure line at intermediate fitting.
6. Remove steering shaft retaining bolt.
7. Remove rack to subframe bolts and nuts.
8. Lower rack as necessary to remove pressure line inlet tube. Remove and discard plastic seal on inlet tube.
9. Cut tie strap securing pressure line to each tube.
10. Remove steering rack from vehicle.
11. Reverse procedure to install. Tighten steering rack retaining bolts and steering shaft retaining bolt to specifications.

POWER STEERING PUMP
REPLACE

CONTINENTAL

1. Disconnect battery ground cable.
2. Loosen tensioner assembly and rotate tensioner pulley clockwise.
3. Remove belt from alternator and power steering pulley.
4. Remove three bolts retaining pump to bracket and remove pump.
5. Reverse procedure to install.

TOWN CAR

1. Disconnect power steering pump return line and allow power steering pump fluid to drain into a suitable container.
2. Disconnect power steering pump pressure hose from pump fitting.
3. Disconnect drive belt from power steering pump pulley, remove pulley, then remove pump.
4. Reverse procedure to install. **Torque** pump to mounting bracket bolts to 30-45 ft. lbs. On Ford model CII power steering pump, **torque** pressure hose to pump fitting to 10-15 ft. lbs. Endplay on this fitting is normal and does not indicate a loose fitting.

MARK VII & MARK VIII

1. Disconnect fluid return hose from reservoir and drain power steering fluid into a container.
2. Remove pressure hose from pump fitting. Do not remove fitting from pump.
3. Disconnect belt from pulley. If necessary, remove pulley from pump installing pulley removal tool No. T75L-3733-A or equivalent so small diameter threads engage in pump shaft. While holding small hex head, rotate tool nut to remove pulley. Do not apply in and out pressure on pump shaft as this will damage the internal thrust areas.
4. Remove pump.
5. If pulley was removed, install tool and while holding small hex head, turn tool nut clockwise to install pulley. Pulley must be flush within .010 inch of the end of the pump. Do not apply in and out pressure on shaft. Remove tool.

TIGHTENING SPECIFICATIONS

Year	Component	Torque/Ft. Lbs.
CONTINENTAL		
1992-95	Control Arm To Knuckle	40-55
	Control Arm To Sub-Frame	70-95
	Front Bolts To Support Bracket	30-41
	Intermediate Shaft To Steering Column Nuts	15-25

Year	Component	Torque/Ft. Lbs.
CONTINENTAL		
1992-95 — Cont'd	Outlet Fitting To Valve Cover	25-34
	Pivot Bolt	45-57
	Pressure Hose Tube Nut To Pump Pressure Fitting	20-25
	Pump To Bracket	30-45
	Return Hose To Pump Hose Clamp	8-24
	Stabilizer Bar Bracket To Sub-Frame	21-32

Continued

TIGHTENING SPECIFICATIONS—Continued

Year	Component	Torque/Ft. Lbs.
CONTINENTAL		
1992-95 — Cont'd	Stabilizer Bar Link Assembly To Bar	35-48
	Stabilizer Bar Link Assembly To Strut	55-75
	Strut Top Mount To Body	22-32
	Strut To Knuckle	70-95
	Strut To Top Mount	35-50
	Support Bracket To Cylinder Head	15-22
	Tension Strut To Control Arm	70-95
	Tension Strut To Sub Frame	70-95
	Tie Rod Ball Socket Assembly To Rack	55-65
	Tie Rod End To Spindle Nut	35-47
	Tie Rod End To Steering Knuckle	23-25
	Wheel Lug Nuts	85-104
MARK VII, MARK VIII & TOWN CAR		
1992-95	Air Compressor To Bracket	30-40 ①
	Ball Joint To Spindle	100-120
	Compressor Bracket To Frame	30-40 ①
	Front Bolts To Support Bracket	30-45
	Inner Pivot Nut	50-68
	Lower Arm To No. 2 Crossmember	110-150
	Lower Control Arm To Toe Compensating Link Nut	83-113
	Pinion Bearing Plug	40-60
	Pinion Bearing Locknut	30-40
	Pivot Bolt	30-45
	Pressure Hose Fitting To Pump	10-15
	Pump Bracket To Rear Support	18-24
	Pump To Bracket	30-45
	Rear Support To Engine Head	30-45
	Return Hose To Pump	12-24 ①
	Sensor Lower Attachment To Arm	8-12
	Sensor Upper Attachment To Frame	26-34
	Shock Upper Mount To Body	62-75
	Shock Strut Upper Mount	55-92
	Spindle To Shock Strut	140-200
	Stabilizer Bar Mounting Clamp	40-55
	Stabilizer Bar To Lower Arm	9-12
	Steering Gear To No. 2 Crossmember	90-100
	Steering Rack Retaining Bolts	100-144
	Steering Shaft Retaining Bolt	20-30
	Support Bracket To Engine	30-45
	Support Bracket To Water Pump	30-45
	Tie Rod Ball Socket Assembly To Rack	55-65
	Tie Rod End To Jam Nut	35-50
	Tie Rod End To Spindle Nut	35-47
	Wheel Lug Nuts	85-104

①—Inch lbs.

Wheel Alignment

NOTE: On Air Bag Equipped Models, Refer To "Air Bag System Precautions" Located In The Front Of This Manual For System Disarming & Arming Procedures.

INDEX

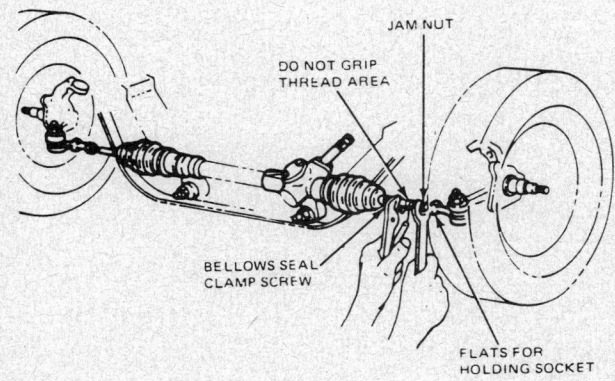

Fig. 1   Toe-in adjustment. Mark VII & Mark VIII

FM2049100028000X

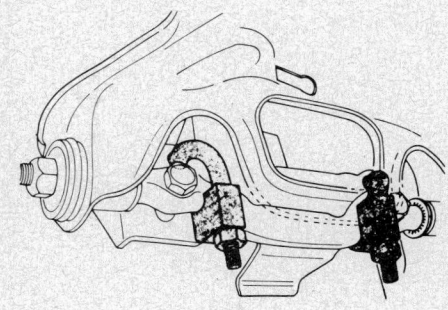

FM2049100029000X

Fig. 2   Caster & camber adjustment tools. Town Car

PRECAUTIONS

AIR BAG SYSTEMS

Refer to "Air Bag System Precautions" in the front of this manual for system disarming and arming procedures.

Preliminary Inspection

Prior to performing the front wheel alignment, a preliminary inspection should be made to determine the condition of the vehicle's suspension components. The following checks and procedures should be made prior to performing front wheel alignment:

1. Vehicle must be leveled by performing the air suspension system test.
2. Inflate tires to specified pressure (cold).
3. Check vehicle ride height.
4. Inspect all suspension and steering components for looseness.
5. Check existing caster, camber, and toe settings prior to alignment.
6. Check all suspension fasteners for proper torque.
7. Alignment equipment must be capable of four wheel alignment.

8. Alignment rack must be leveled to 1/16 of an inch, side to side and front to rear and be equipped with wheel run-out compensation.
Do not attempt to adjust alignment by heating or bending suspension or steering components.

FRONT WHEEL ALIGNMENT

MARK VII

Before performing wheel alignment check on these vehicles, ensure vehicle ride height is correct.

Caster & Camber

Caster is preset at the factory and is not adjustable.

To adjust camber, drill out pop rivet located on top of camber plate. Loosen the camber plate to body apron retaining nuts, then move the top of the shock strut to the desired location. Retighten the retaining nuts. It is not necessary to replace the pop rivet after the camber adjustment is completed.

Toe-In

1. Check to see that steering shaft and steering wheel marks are in alignment and in the top position.
2. Loosen clamp screw on the tie rod bellows and free the seal on the rod to prevent twisting of the bellows, **Fig. 1.**
3. Place open end wrench on flats of tie rod socket to prevent socket from turning, then loosen tie rod jam nuts.
4. Use suitable pliers to turn the tie rod inner end to correct the adjustment to specifications. Do not use pliers on tie rod threads. Turning to reduce number of threads showing will increase toe-in. Turning in the opposite direction will reduce toe-in.

MARK VIII & TOWN CAR

Caster and camber can be adjusted by loosening the bolts that attach the upper suspension arm to the shaft at the frame side rail, and moving the arm assembly in or out in the elongated bolt holes. Since any movement of the arm affects both caster and camber, both factors should be balanced against one another when making the adjustment.

LINCOLN

Caster

1. To adjust caster, install the adjusting tool as shown in **Fig. 2**.
2. Loosen both upper arm inner shaft retaining bolts and move either front or rear of the shaft in or out as necessary to increase or decrease caster angle. Then tighten bolt to retain adjustment.

Camber

1. Loosen both upper arm inner retaining bolts and move both front and rear ends of shaft inward or outward as necessary to increase or decrease camber angle.
2. Tighten bolts and recheck caster and readjust if necessary.

Toe-In

Position the front wheels in their straight-ahead position. Then turn both tie rod adjusting sleeves an equal amount until the desired toe-in setting is obtained.

CONTINENTAL

Toe-In

To adjust toe-in, lock steering wheel in straight ahead position using suitable steering wheel holder. Loosen, then slide off small outer clamps from steering boot to prevent boot from twisting during adjustment procedure. Loosen tie rod adjusting and jam nuts, then adjust length of left and right tie rods until each wheel has 1/2 the desired total toe specification. After adjustment is completed, tighten jam nuts, reinstall outer clamps and remove steering wheel holder.

REAR WHEEL ALIGNMENT

CONTINENTAL

Camber

Camber is factory set and cannot be adjusted.

Toe-In

Toe-In is adjusted by rotating the cams located inside the rear inner lower control arm bushings.

VEHICLE RIDE HEIGHT

Refer to the "Air Suspension" section for ride height adjustment procedures.

FORD MUSTANG

NOTE: Refer To The Rear Of This Manual For Vehicle Manufacturer's Special Service Tool Suppliers.

INDEX OF SERVICE OPERATIONS

NOTE: For Service Operations Not Listed Below, Refer To The Table Of Contents In The Front Of This Manual.

Specifications

GENERAL ENGINE SPECIFICATIONS

Year	Engine Liter/CID	Engine VIN Code [2]	Fuel System	Bore & Stroke	Compression Ratio	Net H.P. @ RPM [3]	Maximum Torque Ft. Lbs. @ RPM	Normal Oil Pressure, psi [1]
1992–93	2.3L/4-140	M	EFI	3.78 X 3.12	9.5	105 @ 4600	135 @ 2600	40–60
	5.0L/V8-302	E	SEFI	4.00 X 3.00	9.0	225 @ 4200	300 @ 3200	40–60
1994–95	3.8L/V6-232	4	SEFI	3.81 x 3.39	9.0	145 @ 4000	215 @ 2500	40–60
	5.0L/V8-302 HO	T	SEFI	4.00 x 3.00	9.0	215 @ 4200	285 @ 3400	40–60
	5.0L/V8-302 SHP	D	SEFI	4.00 x 3.00	9.0	240 @ 4800	285 @ 4000	40–60

CID—Cubic Inch Displacement
SEFI—Sequential Multi-Port Electronic
Fuel Injection
[1]—Engine hot, at 2000 RPM.
[2]—Eighth digit denotes engine code.
[3]—Net rating as installed on vehicle.

TUNE UP SPECIFICATIONS

Year & Engine/VIN Code [1]	Spark Plug Gap	Firing Order Fig. [4]	Ignition Timing BTDC Man. Trans.	Ignition Timing BTDC Auto. Trans.	Mark Fig.	Curb Idle Speed [3] Man. Trans.	Curb Idle Speed [3] Auto Trans.	Fast Idle Speed Man. Trans.	Fast Idle Speed Auto. Trans.	Fuel Pump Pressure, psi. [6]
1992–93										
2.3L/4-140/M	.032	E	10 [7]	10 [7]	B	[2]	[2]	[2]	[2]	35–40
5.0L/V8-302/E HO	.054	C	10 [5]	10 [5]	D	[2]	[2]	[2]	[2]	35–40
1994–95										
3.8L/V6-232	.054	F	14 [7]	14 [7]	G	720 [2]	650D [2]	[2]	[2]	35–40 [6]
5.0L/V8-302 HO	.504	C	10 [5]	10 [5]	A	675 [2]	625 [2]	[2]	[2]	35–40 [6]
5.0L/V8-302 SHP	.504	C	10 [5]	10 [5]	A	675 [2]	625 [2]	[2]	[2]	35–40 [6]

BTDC-Before Top Dead Center
[1]—Eighth digit of Vehicle Identification Number (VIN) denotes engine code.
[2]—Idle speed controlled by automatic idle speed control.
[3]—D: Drive. N: Neutral. When checking idle speed, set parking brake & block drive wheels.
[4]—Before disconnecting wires from distributor cap, determine location of No. 1 wire in cap, as distributor position may have been altered from that shown at end of this chart.
[5]—Disconnect in-line spout connector, then start engine & adjust ignition timing as necessary. After completing adjustment, reconnect spout connector.
[6]—Wrap shop towel around fuel diagnostic valve to prevent fuel spillage. Connect suitable fuel pressure gauge to fuel diagnostic valve. Place ignition switch in On position to energize fuel pump & check pressure gauge reading.
[7]—Non-adjustable.

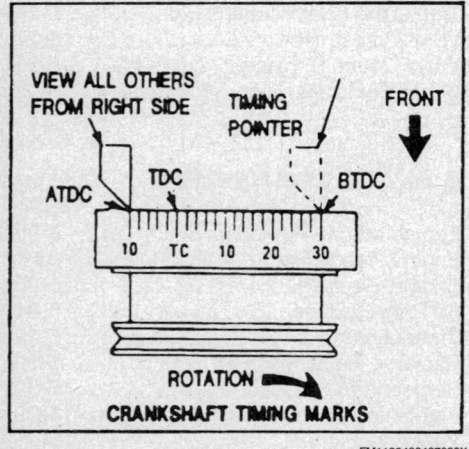

Fig. A

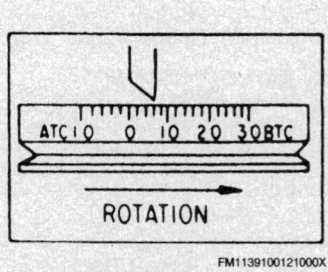

Fig. B

FM1139100121000X

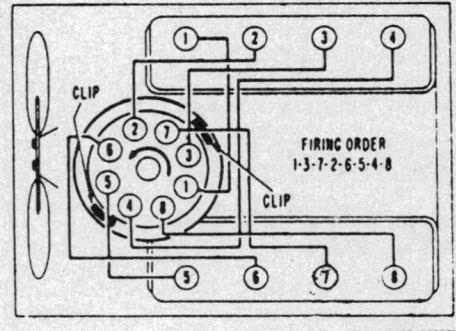

Fig. C

FM1139100122000X

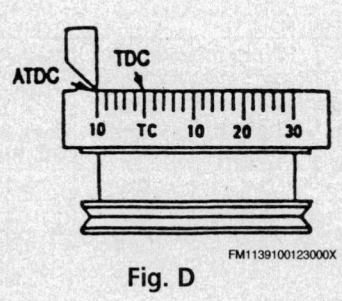

Fig. D

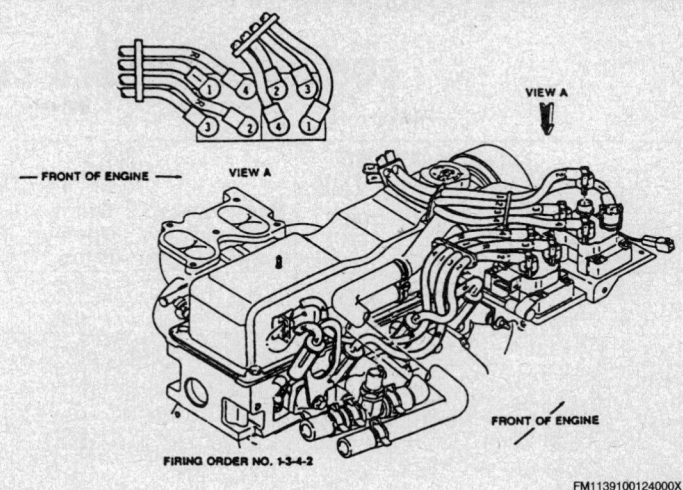

FIRING ORDER NO. 1-3-4-2

Fig. E

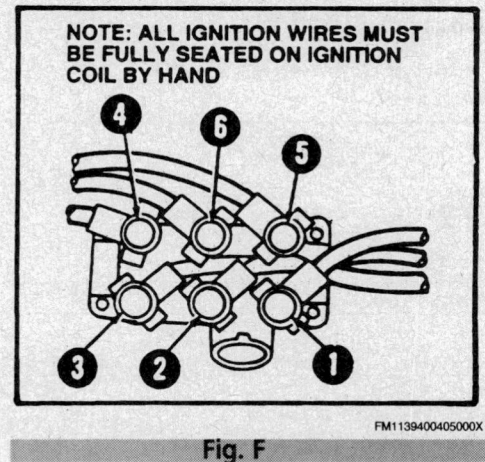

NOTE: ALL IGNITION WIRES MUST BE FULLY SEATED ON IGNITION COIL BY HAND

Fig. F

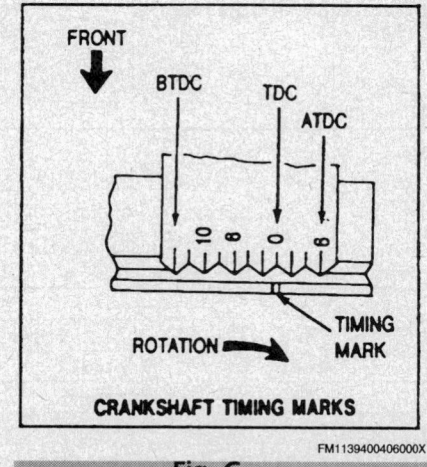

CRANKSHAFT TIMING MARKS

Fig. G

FRONT WHEEL ALIGNMENT SPECIFICATIONS

Year	Model	Caster Angle, Degrees		Camber Angle, Degrees					Toe-Out On Turns, Degrees	
		Limits	Desired	Limits		Desired		Toe-In, Inch	Outer Wheel	Inner Wheel
				Left	Right	Left	Right			
1992–93	2.3L/4-140	+1.15 to +2.65	+1.9	-1.25 to +.25	-1.25 to +.25	-.5	-.5	-.25 to 0	19.84	20
	5.0L/V8-302	+1.15 to +2.65	+1.9	-1.35 to +.15	-1.35 to +.15	-.6	-.6	-.25 to 0	19.84	20
1994	All	+2.85 to +4.35	+3.6	-1.35 to +.15	-1.35 to +.15	-.3	-.3	-.12	19.84	20
1995	Except Cobra & GT	+2.65 to +4.15	+3.4	-.75 to +.75	-.75 to +.75	-.6	-.6	-.12 to 0	19.84	20
	Cobra & GT	+2.65 to +4.15	+3.4	-.75 to +.75	-.75 to +.75	-.5	-.5	-.12 to +.01	19.84	20

COOLING SYSTEM & CAPACITY DATA

Year	Engine/VIN	Coolant Capacity, Qts.		Radiator Cap Relief Pressure, Lbs.	Thermo. Opening Temp,°F	Fuel Tank, Gals.	Engine Oil Refill, Qts. ①	Transmission Oil		Rear Axle Oil, Pints
		Less A/C	With A/C					5-Speed, Pints	Auto. Trans., Qts. ②	
1992–93	2.3L/4-140/M	9.9	9.9	16	192	15.4	5	5.6	10.0	3.3
	5.0L/V8-302/E	14.1	14.1	16	192	15.4	4 ③	5.6	10.0	3.3
1994	3.8L/V6-232/U	11.8	11.8	16	193	15.5	4	2.8	12.5	④
	5.0L/V8-502 (HO & SHP)/T & D	14.1	14.1	16	188	15.5	4	2.8	12.5	④
1995	3.8/V6-232/4	11.8	11.8	16	193	15.5	4	2.8	13.6	④
	5.0L/V8-502 (HO & SHP)/T & D	14.1	14.1	16	188	15.5	4	2.8	13.6	④

① —Add 1 qt. w/filter change unless otherwise noted.
② —Approximate. Make final check w/dipstick.
③ —Dual sump oil pan. Remove both drain plugs to fully drain oil. One drain plug is located at front of oil pan. Second drain plug located at left side of pan.
④ —7.5 inch axle, 3.5 pints; 8.8 inch axle, 3.75–4.00 pints.

LUBRICANT DATA

Year	Model	Lubricant Type				
		Transaxle		Rear Axle	Power Steering	Brake System
		Manual	Automatic			
1992–93	All	Mercon	Mercon	①	Type F	DOT 3
1994–95	All	Mercon	Mercon	②	Type F	DOT 3

① —XY-90-QL Gear Lubricant & 4 ounces of Friction Modifier.
② —XY-90-QL Gear Lubricant.

Electrical

NOTE: On Air Bag Equipped Models, Refer To "Air Bag System Precautions" Located In The Front Of This Manual For System Disarming & Arming Procedures.

INDEX

PRECAUTIONS

AIR BAG SYSTEMS

Refer to "Air Bag System Precautions" in the front of this manual for system disarming and arming procedures.

FUSE PANEL & FLASHER LOCATION

1992–93

The fuse panel is located on the left-hand side of the steering column, under the instrument panel.

The hazard and turn signal flashers are located on the fuse panel.

1994–95

The fuse panel is located on the left-hand side of the steering column, under the instrument panel. On models equipped with the 3.8L/V6-232 engine, the engine compartment fuse box is located in the lefthand side of the engine compartment, behind the radiator.

The combination turn signal and emergency warning indicator flasher is attached by a bracket to the lower lefthand instrument panel reinforcement, above the fuse holder.

RELAY CENTER LOCATION

1994–95

On models equipped with 3.8L/V6-232

engine, the engine compartment fuse box houses relays for the horn, starter and fog lamps. The engine compartment fuse box is located in the lefthand side of the engine compartment, behind the radiator.

STARTER

REPLACE

1. Disconnect battery ground cable.
2. Raise and support front of vehicle.
3. Disconnect starter cable from starter.
4. Remove starter motor bolts, then the starter.
5. Reverse procedure to install, noting the following:
6. **Torque** starter bolts to 15-20 ft. lbs.
7. **On 1994-95 models, torque** starter cable nut to 80-124 inch lbs.

DISTRIBUTOR

REPLACE

1992–93

Removal

1. Disconnect primary wire connector from distributor.
2. Using screwdriver, remove distributor cap, then position aside with wires attached.
3. Remove distributor rotor.
4. Note position of shaft plate, armature and rotor locating holes for assembly reference.
5. Remove distributor hold-down bolt and clamp and distributor.

Installation

1. Rotate distributor by hand to ensure free rotation.
2. Ensure base O-ring is in place, then position rotor locating holes in original locations.
3. Install distributor, ensuring TFI-IV module is in same position relative to engine as when it was removed.
4. Install hold-down bolt and tighten until distributor can just barely be rotated.
5. Press rotor on distributor shaft.
6. Connect wiring harness to distributor, then install distributor cap. **Torque** cap screws to 17-23 inch lbs.
7. Adjust ignition timing to specifications, then **torque** distributor hold-down bolt to 6-8.5 ft. lbs.

1994–95
Removal

1. Disconnect distributor from engine control sensor wiring.
2. Mark position of No. 1 cylinder distributor cap wire tower on distributor for reference when installing distributor.
3. Loosen distributor cap hold-down screws, then remove cap straight off to prevent damage to rotor blade and spring.
4. Position distributor cap and attached ignition wires aside, then remove rotor by pulling upward.
5. Remove distributor hold-down clamp and retainer bolt, then the distributor.
6. Cover distributor opening in cylinder block with clean shop towel to prevent foreign material or dirt from entering engine.

Installation

1. Inspect distributor as follows:
   a. O-ring should fit tightly and be free of cuts.
   b. Drive gear should be free of nicks, cracks and excessive wear.
   c. When rotated, distributor drive shaft should move freely, without binding.
2. Ensure No. 1 piston is at Top Dead Center (TDC) of compression stroke. If necessary, remove No. 1 cylinder spark plug and rotate engine clockwise until No. 1 piston is on compression stroke.
3. With No. 1 piston on compression stroke, align timing pointer with TDC on crankshaft damper.
4. Align locating boss on distributor rotor with hole on armature, then fully seat distributor rotor on distributor shaft.
5. Rotate distributor shaft on blade so distributor rotor blade is pointing toward mark on distributor base.
6. When installing distributor, rotate distributor rotor slightly so leading edge of vane is centered in vane switch stator assembly.
7. Rotate distributor in cylinder block to align by edge of vane and vane switch stator assembly. Verify distributor rotor is pointing at No. 1 mark on distributor base.
8. If vane and vane switch stator cannot be aligned by rotating distributor in cylinder block, proceed as follows:
   a. Remove distributor enough to disengage distributor gear from camshaft gear.
   b. Rotate distributor rotor enough to engage distributor gear on another tooth of camshaft gear.
   c. If necessary, reposition No. 1 piston at TDC as described previously.
9. Install distributor hold-down clamp and bolt, then tighten bolt loosely enough to rotate distributor.
10. Install distributor cap, No. 1 spark plug and ignition wires. Ensure ignition wires are securely connected to distributor cap and spark plugs.
11. **Torque** distributor cap hold-down screws to 18-23 inch lbs., then reconnect distributor to engine control sensor wiring.
12. Set engine ignition timing, then **torque** distributor hold-down bolt to 17-25 ft. lbs.
13. Recheck initial engine ignition timing and adjust if necessary.

IGNITION LOCK
REPLACE

1992-93

1. Disconnect battery ground cable and isolate with electrical tape.
2. **On models with tilt steering column,** remove upper extension shroud. Unsnap shroud from retaining clip located at 9 o'clock position.
3. **On all models,** remove trim shroud or shroud halves, then disconnect key

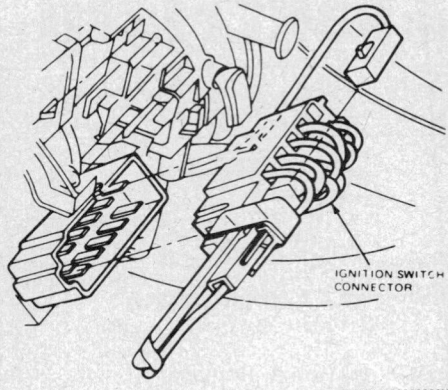

Fig. 1   Ignition switch

warning switch electrical connector.
4. **On models equipped with automatic transmission,** place gear shift lever in PARK.
5. **On models equipped with manual transmission,** place transmission in any gear.
6. **On all models,** insert a 1/8 inch diameter pin in hole in casting surrounding lock cylinder. Pull lock cylinder out of housing while depressing retaining pin.
7. To install, turn lock cylinder to RUN position and depress retaining pin.
8. Install lock cylinder into housing. Turn key to OFF position after ensuring cylinder is fully seated and aligned in interlocking washer.
9. Turn key to check for proper operation in all positions.
10. Install trim shroud and extension shroud.
11. Connect battery ground cable.

1994-95

1. Turn ignition switch to RUN position.
2. Using a 1/8 inch drift, press lock cylinder pin through access hole and remove ignition switch.
3. Remove blue plastic steering column upper bearing retainer by inserting screwdriver or similar tool, with 90 degree bend on tip, between steering column upper bearing retainer and steering column lock housing bearing, and prying upward.
4. Insert tip of screwdriver into double-d slot of steering column lock housing bearing, then rotate 90 degrees. Remove steering column lock housing bearing, then the steering column lock gear. Note relationship of steering column lock gear to position of rack teeth.
5. Position steering column lock gear in base of lock cylinder housing as noted previously. Last tooth on steering column lock gear should be meshed with last tooth on rack.
6. Position steering column upper bearing retainer into lock cylinder housing by inserting tip of screwdriver into double-d slot of lock housing bearing, then rotating 90 degrees.
7. Press blue plastic steering column upper bearing retainer into lock cylin-

der housing. Ensure steering column upper bearing retainer is in its original position.
8. Line up flats of steering column lock gear with flats of washer by pulling down on steering column lock cam.
9. Install ignition switch assembly as described under "Ignition Switch, Replace," then check for proper start in PARK and NEUTRAL. Ensure start circuit cannot be actuated in DRIVE or REVERSE positions and steering column tube is locked in LOCK position.

IGNITION SWITCH
REPLACE

REMOVAL

1. Disconnect battery ground cable and isolate cable end with electrical tape.
2. **On models equipped with tilt column,** remove upper extension shroud.
3. **On all models,** remove steering column trim shroud.
4. Remove electrical connector from switch, **Fig. 1.**
5. Rotate ignition key to On (Run) position.
6. Remove two ignition switch to lock cylinder housing screws.
7. Disengage switch from actuator pin.

INSTALLATION

1. Adjust switch by sliding carrier to switch On (Run) position.
2. Ensure ignition key lock cylinder is in On (Run) position by rotating key lock cylinder approximately 90 degrees from Lock position.
3. Install switch onto actuator pin.
4. **Torque** screws to 50-70 inch lbs.
5. Connect electrical connector to switch.
6. Install steering column trim shroud.
7. **On models equipped with tilt column,** install upper extension shroud.
8. **On all models,** connect battery ground cable.
9. Check for proper operation.

CLUTCH START SWITCH
REPLACE

The starter/clutch interlock switch is designed to prevent starting the engine unless the clutch pedal is fully depressed. The switch is connected between the ignition switch and the starter motor relay coil and maintains an open circuit with the clutch pedal in the up position (clutch engaged).

The switch is designed to automatically self-adjust the first time the clutch pedal is pressed to the floor. The self-adjuster consists of a two-piece clip snapped together over a serrated rod. When the plunger or rod is extended, the clip bottoms out on the serrations to a position determined by the clutch pedal travel. In this way, the switch is set to close the starter circuit when the clutch is pressed all the way to the floor (clutch disengaged). To replace clutch interlock switch, proceed as follows:

1992–93

1. Disconnect electrical connector.
2. Remove retaining pin from clutch pedal.
3. Remove switch bracket screw.
4. Lift switch and bracket assembly upward to disengage tab from pedal support.
5. Move switch outward to disengage actuating rod eyelet from clutch pedal pin, then remove switch from vehicle.
6. Place eyelet end of rod onto pivot pin. **Always install switch with self-adjusting clip about 1 inch from end of rod. Clutch pedal must be fully up (clutch engaged), otherwise switch may be misadjusted.**
7. Swing switch assembly around, engage tab in top of pedal support, and line up hole in mounting boss with hole in bracket.
8. Install attaching screw, then the retaining pin in pivot pin.
9. Connect connector.

1994

1. Disconnect wiring connector, then remove retaining pin from clutch pedal.
2. Remove clutch pedal position switch screw, then move switch inward to disengage actuating rod eyelet from clutch pedal pin and remove switch from vehicle.
3. Reverse procedure to install, noting the following:
   a. Always install clutch pedal position switch with self-adjusting clip about 1 inch from end of rod.
   b. Clutch pedal must be fully up (clutch engaged), otherwise clutch pedal position switch may be misadjusted.

1995

1. Disconnect battery ground cable, then disconnect harness connector from clutch pedal position switch.
2. Disconnect locating tab lock, then rotate switch about 90 degrees clockwise.
3. Remove switch lock plate, then pry switch off clutch push rod by hand.
4. Reverse procedure to install. An audible click will be heard when the clutch pedal position switch is mounted properly onto clutch push rod.

NEUTRAL SAFETY SWITCH
REPLACE

1992–93

5.0L/V8-302 w/AOD Transmission

1. Place selector lever in manual LOW position.
2. Disconnect battery ground cable and isolate cable end with electrical tape.
3. Raise and support vehicle.
4. Disconnect neutral safety switch electrical connector.

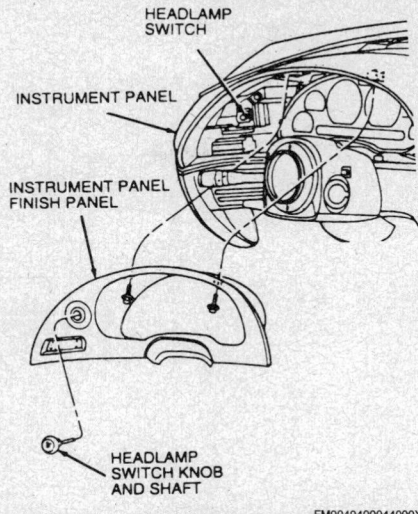

Fig. 2 Headlamp switch replacement. 1994–95

5. Using neutral start switch socket tool No. T74P-77247-A, or equivalent, and a ratchet, remove neutral start switch and O-ring.
6. Reverse procedure to install. **Torque** switch to 8–11 ft. lbs.

2.3L/4-140 w/A4LD Transmission

1. Disconnect battery ground cable and isolate cable end with electrical tape.
2. Disconnect electrical connector from neutral start switch.
3. Remove neutral start switch and O-ring using neutral start switch socket tool No. T74P-77247-A, or equivalent.
4. Reverse procedure to install, noting the following:
   a. **Torque** switch to 7-10 ft. lbs.
   b. Check operation of switch with parking brake engaged. Engine should start only in Neutral or Park positions.

1994–95

1. Disconnect battery ground cable, then place manual control lever in NEUTRAL position.
2. Raise and support vehicle, then disconnect electrical harness from Transmission Range (TR) sensor.
3. Remove two TR sensor bolts, then the sensor.
4. Ensure manual control lever is in NEUTRAL position.
5. Install TR sensor, then, loosely, the sensor bolts.
6. Align TR sensor slots using transmission range sensor alignment (MLPS alignment) tool No. T92P-70010-AH, or equivalent.

7. **Torque** sensor bolts to 7–9 ft. lbs., then remove tool.
8. Connect electrical harness to TR sensor, then lower vehicle.
9. Connect battery ground cable, then check for proper operation with parking brake control engaged. Engine should start only in PARK or NEUTRAL.

HEADLAMP SWITCH
REPLACE

1992–93

1. Disconnect battery ground cable.
2. While pulling out on switch assembly, push in on left side locking tabs with suitable tool until tabs release.
3. Pry right side of switch from dash panel.
4. Remove switch, then disconnect electrical connectors.
5. Reverse procedure to install.

1994–95

1. Disconnect battery ground cable, then pull headlamp switch to full ON position.
2. Reaching through opening in instrument panel, depress shaft release button on headlamp switch and remove headlamp switch knob and shaft, **Fig. 2.**
3. Remove cluster instrument panel finish panel as follows:
   a. Remove two screws above instrument cluster, then pull instrument panel finish panel to unsnap clip above lefthand register.
   b. Pull panel to unsnap three clips on righthand side vertical/horizontal edge, then remove panel.
4. Remove headlamp switch nut and pull switch through opening in instrument cluster.
5. Disconnect wiring to headlamp switch and remove headlamp switch.
6. Reverse procedure to install.

STOP LIGHT SWITCH
REPLACE

1. Disconnect wires at connector.
2. Remove hairpin retainer, then slide switch, pushrod and nylon washers and bushing away from pedal and remove switch, **Fig. 3.**
3. Position stop light switch so U-shaped side is nearest brake pedal and directly over/under pin.
4. Slide stoplight switch up/down, trapping master cylinder push rod and blade bushing between stoplight switch side plates.
5. Push stoplight switch and push rod assembly firmly toward brake pedal arm, then assemble outside white plastic washer to pin and install hairpin retainer to trap whole assembly.
6. Assemble wire harness connector to stop light switch and install wires in

retaining clip. **Stop light switch wire harness must have sufficient length to travel with switch during full stroke of brake pedal. If wire length is insufficient, reroute harness or service as required.**
7. Check stop light switch for proper operation.

MULTI-FUNCTION SWITCH
REPLACE

1. Disconnect battery ground cable and isolate cable end with electrical tape.
2. Remove steering column shroud retaining screws, then the upper and lower shrouds.
3. Remove electrical connectors.
4. Remove two multi-function switch to steering column self-tapping screws.
5. Remove switch from column.
6. Reverse procedure to install, noting the following:
   a. **Torque** multi-function switch to steering column self-tapping screws to 17-25 ft. lbs.
   b. **Torque** shroud screws to 6-10 inch lbs.
   c. Check switch for proper operation.

STEERING WHEEL
REPLACE

1992-93

1. Disconnect battery ground cable and isolate cable end with electrical tape.
2. Remove four air bag nuts.
3. Remove air bag module from steering wheel, then disconnect electrical connector.
4. Remove and discard steering wheel bolt.
5. Remove steering wheel from column.
6. Position steering wheel on column shaft.
7. Install new steering wheel bolt, then **torque** bolt to 23-32 ft. lbs.
8. Connect air bag electrical connector, then position module to wheel.
9. Install nuts, then **torque** nuts to 36-44 inch lbs.
10. Connect battery ground cable.

1994-95

1. Center front wheels to straight-ahead position, then disconnect battery ground cable and wait one minute for air bag diagnostic monitor to deplete its stored energy.
2. Remove two cover caps from steering wheel back cover to access driver side air bag module bolts.
3. Lift module off steering wheel and disconnect electrical connector, then remove module from steering wheel.
4. Disconnect horn and speed control wire harness from steering wheel.
5. Remove and discard steering wheel bolt.
6. Using steering wheel remover tool No.

T67L-3600-A, or equivalent, remove steering wheel from steering column and route air bag sliding contact assembly wire harness through steering wheel as steering wheel is lifted off steering column. **Be sure control assembly wire harness does not get caught on steering wheel when lifting steering wheel off steering column, to avoid damage to control assembly wire harness.**
7. Reverse procedure to install, noting the following:
8. **Ensure air bag sliding contact wire is not pinched or air bag monitor will detect a fault.**
9. Route air bag sliding contact assembly wire harness through steering wheel opening at three o'clock position, then position steering wheel on steering column. Steering wheel and steering column gear input shaft coupling alignment marks should be aligned.
10. **Torque** steering wheel bolt to 22-33 ft. lbs.
11. **Torque** air bag module bolts to 36-47 inch lbs.

INSTRUMENT CLUSTER
REPLACE

1992-93

1. Disconnect battery ground cable and isolate cable end with electrical tape.
2. Remove switch assemblies from righthand and lefthand sides of cluster assembly:
   a. While pulling out on switch assembly, push in on locking tabs with suitable tool until tabs release.
   b. Pull switch from dash panel.

c. Remove switch, then disconnect electrical connectors.
3. Remove two upper and three lower screws from instrument cluster trim cover, then the trim cover.
4. Pull cluster from panel slightly and disconnect speedometer cable and printed circuit electrical connectors.
5. Remove instrument cluster from instrument panel.
6. Reverse procedure to install.

1994-95

1. Disconnect battery ground cable, then remove light switch knob.
2. Remove two upper screws from instrument cluster bezel, then the instrument cluster bezel.
3. Remove four screws from instrument cluster panel, then pull instrument cluster away from instrument panel.
4. Disconnect two cluster printed circuit connectors from instrument cluster back plate, then remove cluster. **If gauges are being removed from cluster assembly, do not remove gauge pointer. Magnetic gauges cannot be recalibrated.**
5. Reverse procedure to install.

RADIO
REPLACE

1. Disconnect battery ground cable and isolate cable end with electrical tape.
2. Using radio removing tool No. T87P-19061, or equivalent, spread radio face plate, **Figs. 4 and 5.**
3. Remove radio, then disconnect antenna and electrical connectors.
4. **On 1994-95 models,** remove stereo tape cartridge container or digital audio compact disc player.

Item	Description
1	Master Cylinder Push Rod
2	Brake Pedal Arm Pin
3	Stoplight Switch
4	Stoplight Switch Actuating Pin
5	Stoplight Switch Contacts

Item	Description
6	Stoplight Switch Spring
7	Stoplight Switch Pressure Plate
8	Plastic Bushing
9	Push Rod Eye

FM9049400043000X

Fig. 3   Stop light switch replacement

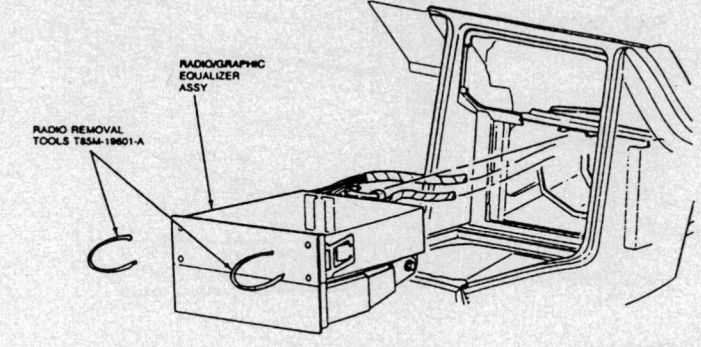

Fig. 4   Radio removal. 1992–93

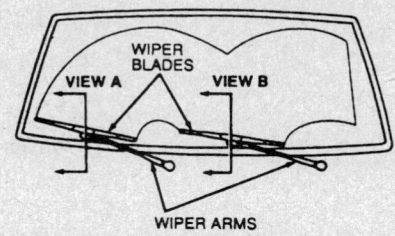

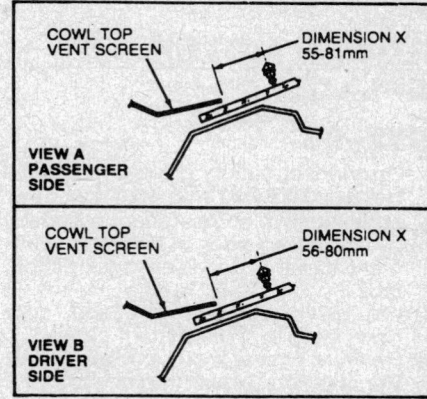

Fig. 6   Windshield wiper PARK position dimensions. 1994-95

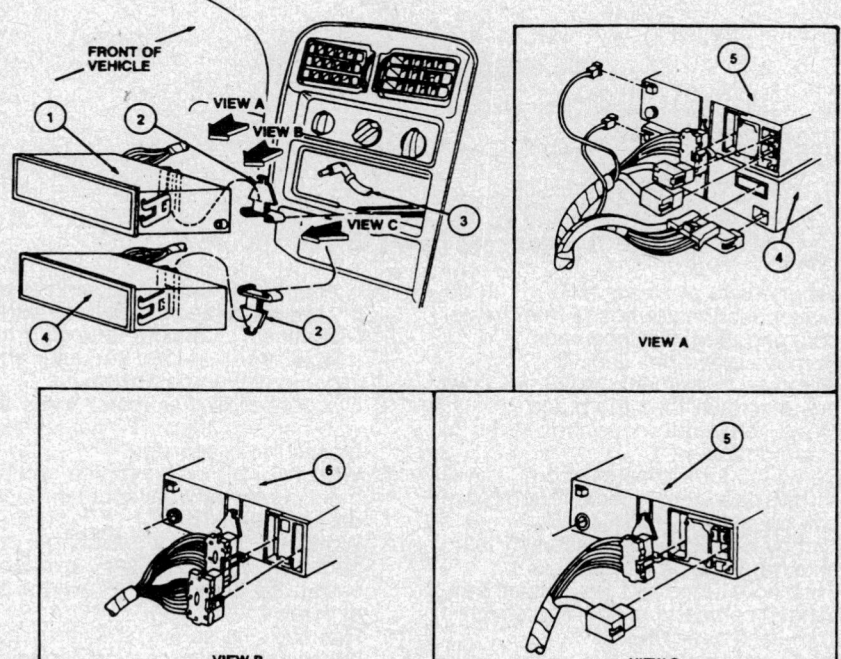

Item	Description
1	ESR Radio Chassis, ESC Radio Chassis and PAC Radio Chassis
2	Radio Chassis Support
3	Radio Antenna Lead In Cable
4	Digital Audio Compact Disc Player
5	ESC Radio Chassis, PAC Radio Chassis
6	ESR Radio Chassis

Fig. 5   Radio removal. 1994-95

WIPER MOTOR
REPLACE

1. Disconnect battery ground cable and isolate cable end with electrical tape.
2. Remove righthand wiper arm and blade assembly.
3. Remove cowl grill, then the clip and disconnect linkage drive arm from motor crank pin.
4. **On 1994-95 models,** remove plastic cowl extension from cowl.
5. **On all models,** disconnect wiper motor wire connector, then remove three motor screws and pull motor through opening.
6. Reverse procedure to install.

WIPER SWITCH
REPLACE

The wiper switch is part of the multi-function switch. For replacement procedure, refer to "Multi-Function Switch, Replace."

WIPER TRANSMISSION
REPLACE

1992–93

1. Disconnect battery ground cable and isolate cable end with electrical tape, then remove right wiper arm and blade assembly from pivot shaft.
2. Remove cowl top grille, then remove clip and disconnect linkage drive arm from wiper motor crank pin.
3. Remove two screws retaining right-hand pivot shaft to cowl and large nut and spacer from left pivot shaft, then remove linkage assembly.
4. Reverse procedure to install.

1994–95

1. Turn windshield wiper motors on. When windshield wiper blades are to full travel on windshield glass, turn key to OFF position.
2. Remove windshield wiper pivot arm and windshield wiper blade from windshield wiper mounting arm and pivot shaft.
3. Raise hood and disconnect battery ground cable.
4. Remove cowl vent screen, then the clip retaining windshield wiper mounting arm and pivot shaft to windshield wiper motor link.
5. Disconnect linkage drive arm from windshield wiper motor.
6. Remove mounting arm and pivot shaft screws, then guide mounting arm and pivot shafts from righthand

side of cowl chamber.

7. Reverse procedure to install, noting the following:
   a. Ensure wiper motor is in Park position before installing wiper pivot arm and wiper blade.
   b. Set windshield wiper blade to specified dimensions, **Fig. 6.**
   c. **Torque** windshield wiper mounting arm and pivot shaft screws to 115-150 inch lbs.

BLOWER MOTOR
REPLACE

1992-93

1. Disconnect battery ground cable and isolate cable end with electrical tape.
2. Loosen glove compartment assembly by squeezing sides of glove compartment together to disengage retainer tabs.
3. Let glove compartment and door hang in front of instrument panel.
4. Remove blower motor cooling hose.
5. Remove four blower motor assembly to blower motor housing screws.
6. Disconnect electrical connector from wiring harness.
7. Carefully pull blower motor assembly from housing.
8. Reverse procedure to install.

1994

1. Remove three blower motor screws, then the heater motor dash panel opening cover.
2. Disconnect electrical connector.
3. Pull heater blower motor and A/C blower wheel out of A/C evaporator housing.
4. Remove blower motor wheel retainer from heater blower motor and A/C blower wheel assembly, then the A/C blower wheel.
5. Reverse procedure to install. Install gasket material to new A/C blower motor.

1995

1. Disconnect jumper wire harness from main harness electrical connector, then the jumper wire harness from heater blower motor switch resistor.
2. Remove three blower motor screws, then pull blower motor out of A/C evaporator housing.
3. Remove heater blower motor cover and stiffener plate.
4. Disconnect jumper wire harness from blower motor.
5. Reverse procedure to install. Install gasket material to new A/C blower motor.

HEATER CORE
REPLACE

1992-93

Less Air Conditioning

1. Drain cooling system, then disconnect battery ground cable and isolate ca-

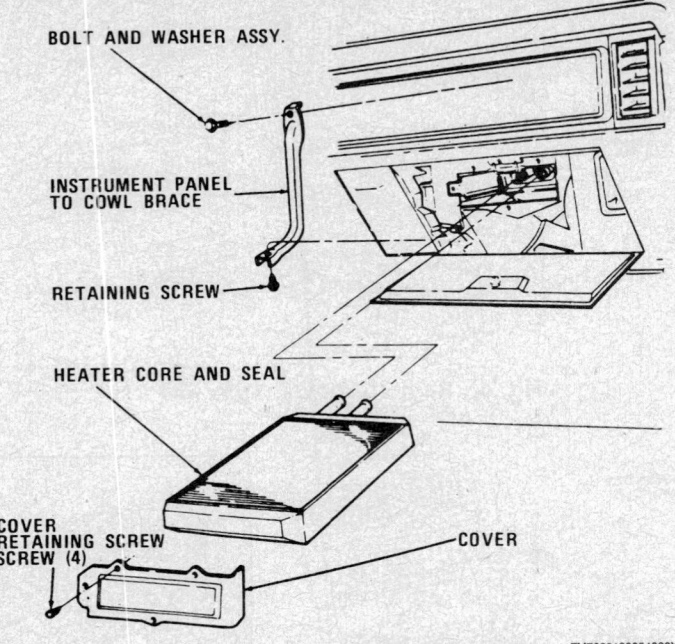

Fig. 7 Heater core replacement. Less A/C

ble end with electrical tape.
2. Disconnect heater hoses from heater core and plug core openings.
3. Remove glove box liner.
4. Remove instrument panel to cowl brace screws, then the brace.
5. Move temperature control lever to warm position.
6. Remove four heater core cover screws, then the cover, through glove box opening.
7. Remove heater core assembly stud nuts from engine compartment.
8. Push core tubes and seal toward passenger compartment to loosen core from case assembly.
9. Remove heater core from case through glove box opening, **Fig. 7.**
10. Reverse procedure to install.

With Air Conditioning

1. Remove instrument panel and lay it on front seat as outlined in "Dash Panel Service" section.
2. Discharge refrigerant from air conditioning system.
3. **On models equipped with 2.3L/4-140 engine,** remove speed control servo.
4. **On all models,** working from inside engine compartment, disconnect air conditioning lines from evaporator core at dash panel.
5. Remove low pressure line from accumulator/dryer, then cap all open lines to prevent system contamination.
6. Disconnect heater hoses from heater core tubes and plug hoses with suitable ⅝-inch and ¾-inch plugs.
7. Cap heater core tubes to prevent coolant loss from heater core during evaporator core removal.
8. Working from inside passenger compartment, remove screw attaching air

inlet duct and blower housing assembly support brace to cowl top panel.
9. Disconnect vacuum supply hose (black) from in-line vacuum check valve in engine compartment.
10. Disconnect blower motor wires from wire harness, then wire harness from blower motor resistor.
11. Working from inside engine compartment, remove two evaporator case to dash panel nuts.
12. Working from inside passenger compartment, remove two evaporator case support bracket to cowl top panel screws.
13. Remove one screw retaining bracket below evaporator case to dash panel.
14. Carefully pull evaporator case from dash panel, then remove case from vehicle.
15. Remove four heater core access cover attaching screws, then the cover from case.
16. Lift heater core from case.
17. Remove seal from heater core tubes.
18. Reverse procedure to install.

1994-95

1. Remove evaporator case as described under "Evaporator Case, Replace."
2. Remove four heater core access cover screws, then the cover from heater case.
3. Remove heater dash panel seal from heater inlet and outlet tubes, then pull heater core out of heater case.
4. Reverse procedure to install.

EVAPORATOR CASE
REPLACE

1994-95

Refer to **Fig. 8** when replacing the evaporator case.

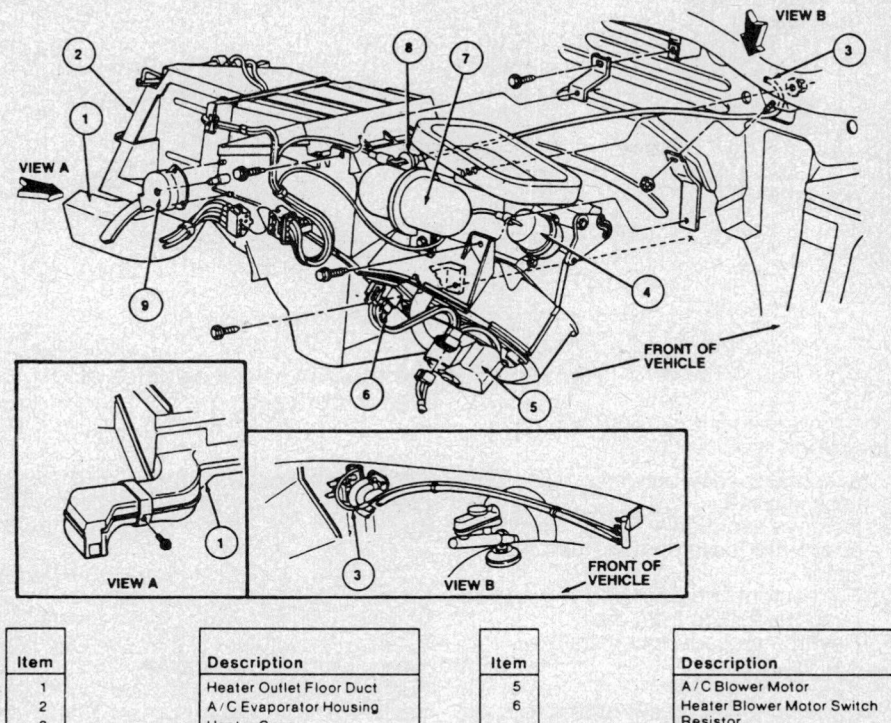

Item	Description
1	Heater Outlet Floor Duct
2	A/C Evaporator Housing
2	Heater Case
3	To Vacuum Source
4	Heater Air Inlet Duct Door

Item	Description
5	A/C Blower Motor
6	Heater Blower Motor Switch Resistor
7	Vacuum Tank
8	Check Valve
9	A/C Temperature Cable

FM7029400225000X

Fig. 8 Evaporator housing replacement. 1994-95

1. Disconnect battery ground cable.
2. Remove two console armrest mounting access covers at rear of console panel to access armrest bolts.
3. Remove four armrest to floor bracket bolts, then the armrest assembly.
4. Remove console panel gear shift plate, noting the following:
   a. **On models equipped with manual transmission,** shift boot is attached to bottom of finish panel.
   b. Remove shift knob and slide boot and console panel gear shift plate up shift lever to remove.
5. **On all models,** remove top finish panel as follows:
   a. Position emergency brake lever in UP position.
   b. Remove four screws and lift finish panel up.
   c. Disconnect necessary electrical connectors.
6. Remove console to rear floor bracket screws, then snap out front upper finish panel by inserting small screwdriver into notches at bottom of panel.
7. **On models equipped with radio chassis,** remove radio chassis as described under "Radio, Replace."
8. **On models without radio chassis,** pry radio cover finish panel out of console with small screwdriver.
9. **On all models,** flex glove compartment bin tabs inward, then drop down glove compartment assembly and remove two console to instrument panel screws.
10. Remove four console bracket screws, then the console panel from vehicle.
11. Remove three steering column opening cover to reinforcement panel bolts, then the cover.
12. Remove steering column opening reinforcement bolts and reinforcement.
13. Remove six steering column nuts, then lower steering column to floor.
14. Remove upper and lower steering column shrouds and disconnect wiring from turn signal and wiper switch.
15. Remove steering column through bolt and nut on engine compartment side of cowl panel, then the steering column from vehicle.
16. Remove brake pedal support nut.
17. Snap out instrument panel defroster opening grill.
18. Remove screws from speaker covers, then snap out covers.
19. Remove front screws retaining righthand and lefthand scuff plates at cowl side panels.
20. Remove righthand and lefthand cowl side trim panels, then disconnect wiring at righthand cowl side.
21. Remove cowl side bolts, then the five cowl top screw attachments.
22. Gently pull instrument panel away from righthand side of cowl panel, then disconnect speedometer cable, air conditioning controls and wire connectors.
23. Place drain pan or suitable container under heater water hose connections at cowl panel.

24. Disconnect heater water hoses from heater core tubes and plug heater water hoses with suitable $5/8$ inch and $3/4$ inch plugs. Cap tubes to prevent coolant loss from heater core during heater case removal.
25. Remove A/C evaporator case support bracket to cowl top panel screw, then disconnect vacuum supply hose (black) from A/C vacuum supply in engine compartment.
26. Working under hood, remove heater case to cowl panel nut, then, working inside passenger compartment, remove A/C evaporator case mounting bracket to cowl top panel screw.
27. Remove one screw retaining A/C evaporator case mounting bracket below heater case to cowl panel, then carefully pull heater case from cowl panel and remove heater case from vehicle.
28. Reverse procedure to install, noting the following:
   a. Check operation of all components.
   b. Check coolant level in radiator and coolant recovery reservoir. Fill as required with recommended coolant mixture.

EVAPORATOR CORE
REPLACE
1992-93

Whenever an evaporator core is replaced, it will be necessary to replace the suction/accumulator dryer.
1. Remove instrument panel and lay it on front seat as outlined in "Dash Panel Service" section.
2. Discharge refrigerant from air conditioning system as described in "Air Conditioning" section.
3. **On models equipped with 2.3L/4-140 engine,** remove speed control servo.
4. **On all models,** working from inside engine compartment, disconnect air conditioning lines from evaporator core at dash panel.
5. Remove low pressure line from accumulator/dryer, then cap all open lines to prevent contamination of system.
6. Disconnect heater hoses from heater core tubes and plug hoses with suitable $5/8$ inch and $3/4$ inch plugs.
7. Cap heater core tubes to prevent coolant loss from heater core during removal of evaporator core.
8. Working from inside passenger compartment, remove screw attaching air inlet duct and blower housing assembly support brace to cowl top panel.
9. Disconnect vacuum supply hose (black) from in-line vacuum check valve in engine compartment.
10. Disconnect blower motor wires from wire harness, then the wire harness from blower motor resistor.
11. Working from inside engine compartment, remove two evaporator case to dash panel nuts.
12. Working from inside passenger compartment, remove two evaporator case support bracket to cowl top pan-

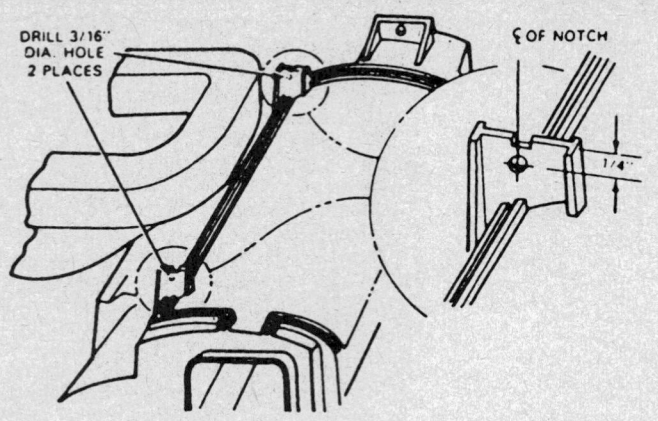

Fig. 9 Evaporator case tab hole locations

FM7029100055000X

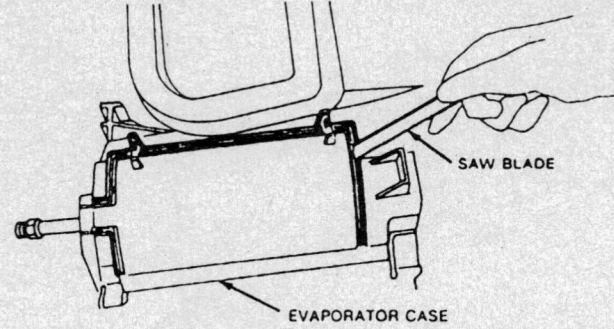

Fig. 10 Cutting between raised outlines of evaporator case

FM7029100056000X

el screws.
13. Remove one screw retaining bracket below evaporator case to dash panel.
14. Carefully pull evaporator case from dash panel, then remove case from vehicle.
15. Remove four air inlet duct to evaporator case screws, then the duct.
16. Remove foam seal from evaporator core tubes.
17. Drill 3/16 inch hole in both upright tabs, **Fig. 9.**
18. Using small saw blade, cut top of evaporator case between raised outlines, **Fig. 10.**
19. Remove two blower motor resistor to evaporator case screws, then the resistor.
20. Fold cutout flap from opening and lift evaporator core from case.
21. Reverse procedure to install.

1994–95

Whenever an A/C evaporator core is replaced, it is necessary to replace the suction accumulator/drier.

Before an A/C evaporator core is replaced, it must be leak tested in the vehicle. Refer to the "Air Conditioning" section for leak test procedures.

If it is necessary to replace an evaporator core, the new core is serviced with a service replacement A/C evaporator housing which has the new core. All vacuum control motors, vacuum lines and air ducts from the old evaporator housing must be transferred to the new evaporator housing. Refer to "Evaporator Case, Replace."

2.3L/4-140 Engine

NOTE: On Air Bag Equipped Models, Refer To "Air Bag System Precautions" Located In The Front Of This Manual For System Disarming & Arming Procedures.

INDEX

PRECAUTIONS

AIR BAG SYSTEMS

Refer to "Air Bag System Precautions" in the front of this manual for system disarming and arming procedures.

ENGINE MOUNT

REPLACE

1. Remove fan shroud.

2. Remove fuel pump shield to lefthand support bracket screw, if equipped.
3. Remove nut and washer assemblies attaching both insulators to crossmember, **Figs. 1 and 2.**
4. Disconnect transmission shift linkage.
5. Raise engine sufficiently to clear insulator studs from crossmember.
6. Remove bolts attaching insulator and bracket assembly from engine and remove insulator and bracket assembly.
7. Reverse procedure to install, noting the following:
   a. Tighten insulator and bracket assembly to specifications.
   b. Install crossmember nut assemblies onto insulator studs, then tighten to specifications.

ENGINE

REPLACE

1. Drain coolant from radiator and oil from crankcase.

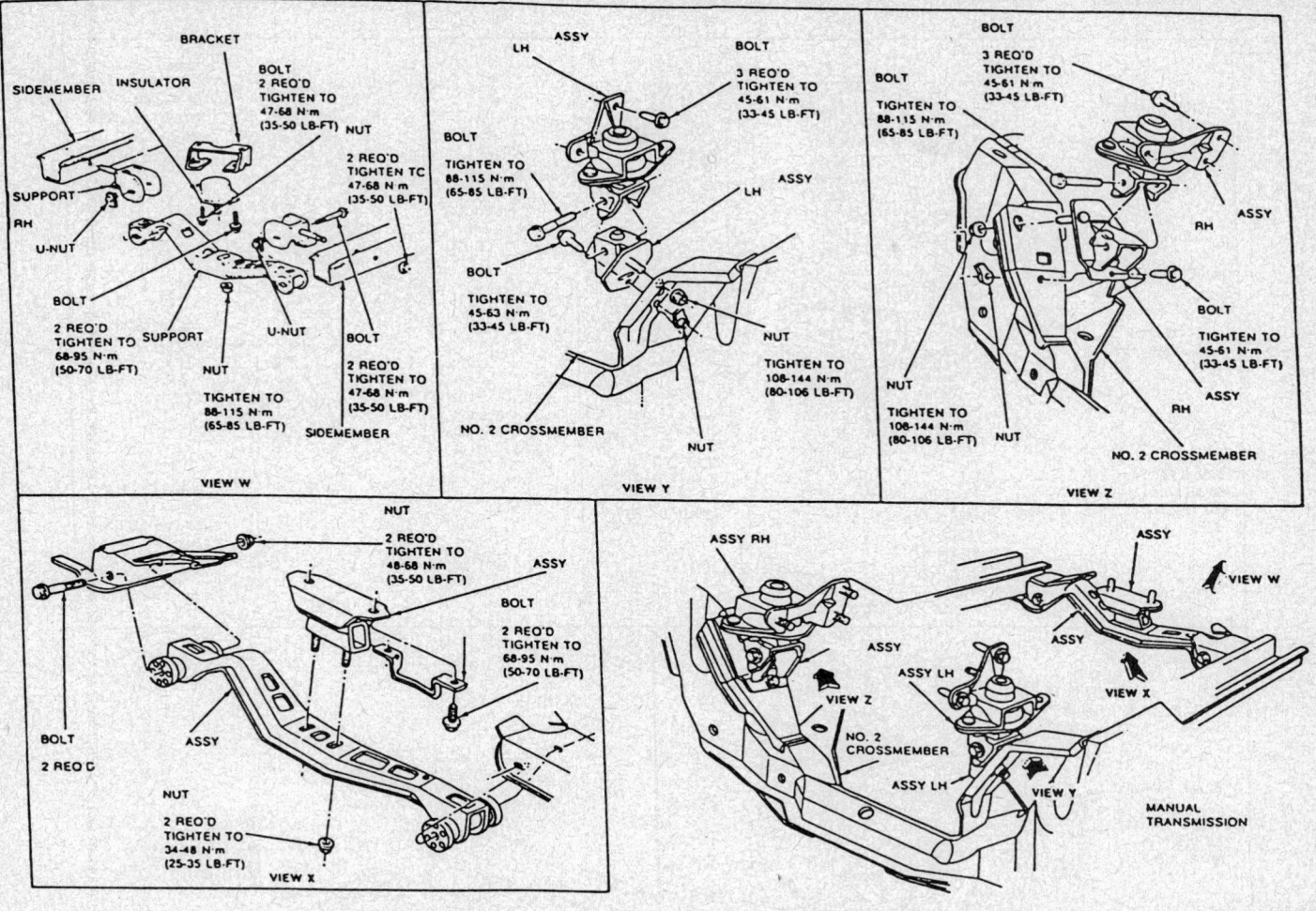

Fig. 1 Engine mount installation. Convertible models w/T5 transmission

2. Remove air cleaner and exhaust manifold shroud.
3. Disconnect battery ground cable.
4. Remove radiator hoses, then the radiator and fan.
5. Disconnect heater hoses from water pump and carburetor choke fitting.
6. Disconnect wires from alternator and starter and disconnect accelerator cable from carburetor.
7. **On models equipped with A/C,** remove compressor from bracket and position it aside with lines attached.
8. **On all models,** disconnect flex fuel line from tank line and plug tank line.
9. Disconnect primary wire at coil and disconnect oil pressure and temperature sending unit wires at sending units.
10. Remove starter and raise vehicle to remove flywheel or converter housing upper bolts.
11. Disconnect inlet pipe at exhaust manifold.
12. Disconnect engine mounts at underbody bracket and remove flywheel or converter housing cover.
13. **On models equipped with manual transmission,** remove flywheel housing lower bolts.
14. **On models equipped with automatic transmission,** disconnect converter from flywheel and remove converter housing lower bolts. Disconnect transmission oil cooler lines if attached to engine at pan rail.
15. **On all models,** lower vehicle and support transmission and flywheel or converter housing with jack.
16. Attach engine lifting hooks to brackets and carefully lift engine out of engine compartment.
17. Reverse procedure to install.

INTAKE MANIFOLD
REPLACE

UPPER INTAKE MANIFOLD & THROTTLE BODY ASSEMBLY

1. Label, then disconnect all electrical connectors and vacuum lines from manifold assembly.
2. Release pressure from fuel system at fuel pressure relief valve using fuel pressure gauge tool No. T80L-9974-B, or equivalent. The fuel pressure relief valve is located on fuel line in upper righthand corner of engine compartment.
3. Disconnect throttle linkage, cruise control and kickdown cables. Loosen, then position aside accelerator cable.
4. Disconnect air hose from crankcase vent hose.
5. Disconnect PCV system by disconnecting hose from upper intake manifold fitting.
6. Disconnect EGR tube from EGR valve.
7. Remove four upper intake manifold bolts, Fig. 3.
8. Remove upper intake manifold assembly.
9. Reverse procedure to install.

FUEL CHARGING ASSEMBLY
REPLACE

1. Remove fuel filler cap to relieve fuel tank pressure.
2. Drain coolant from radiator.
3. Release pressure from fuel system at relief valve using EFI pressure gauge tool No. T80L-9974-B, or equivalent. Fuel pressure relief valve is located

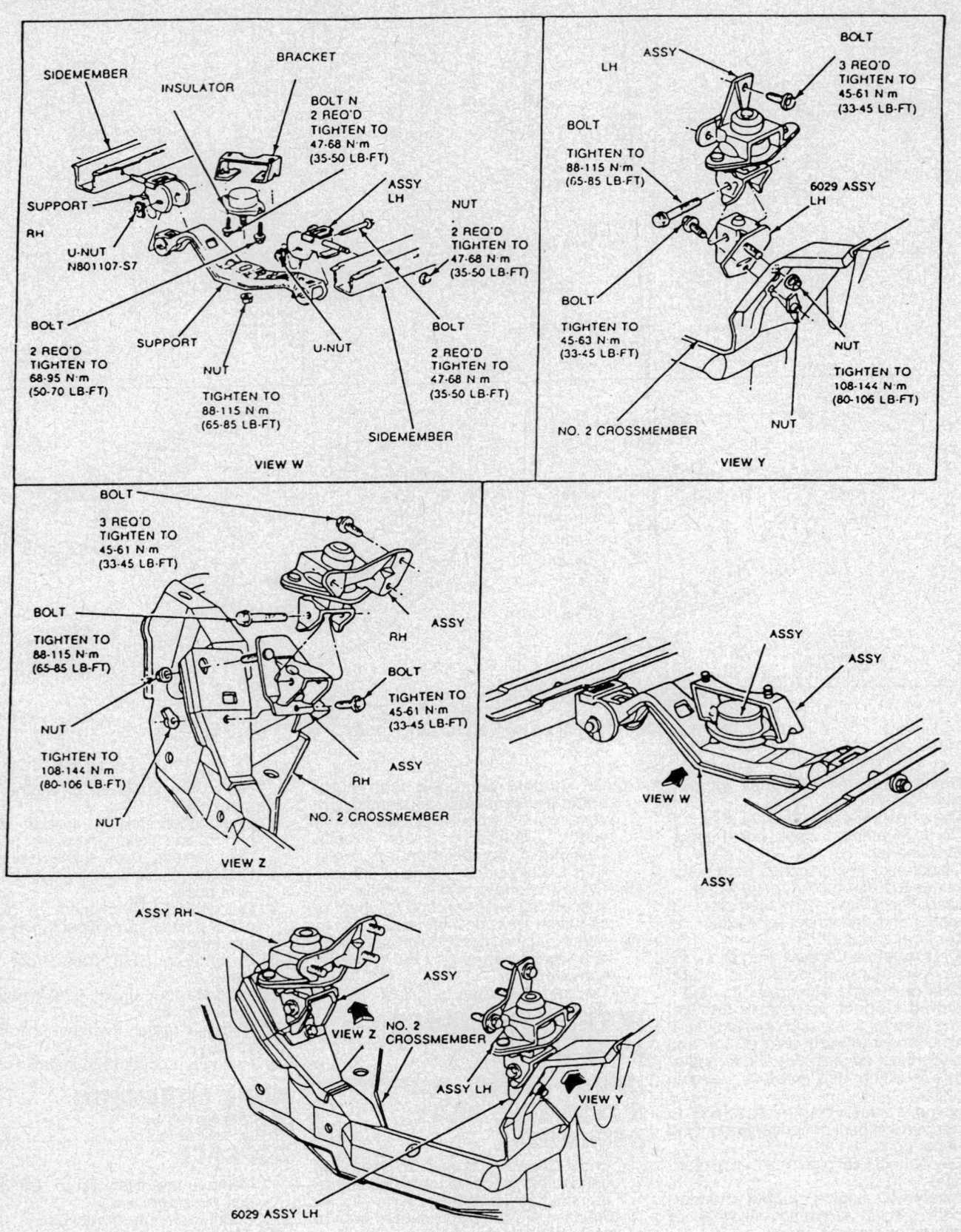

Fig. 2 Engine mount installation. Models w/A4LD transmission

FM1069100210000X

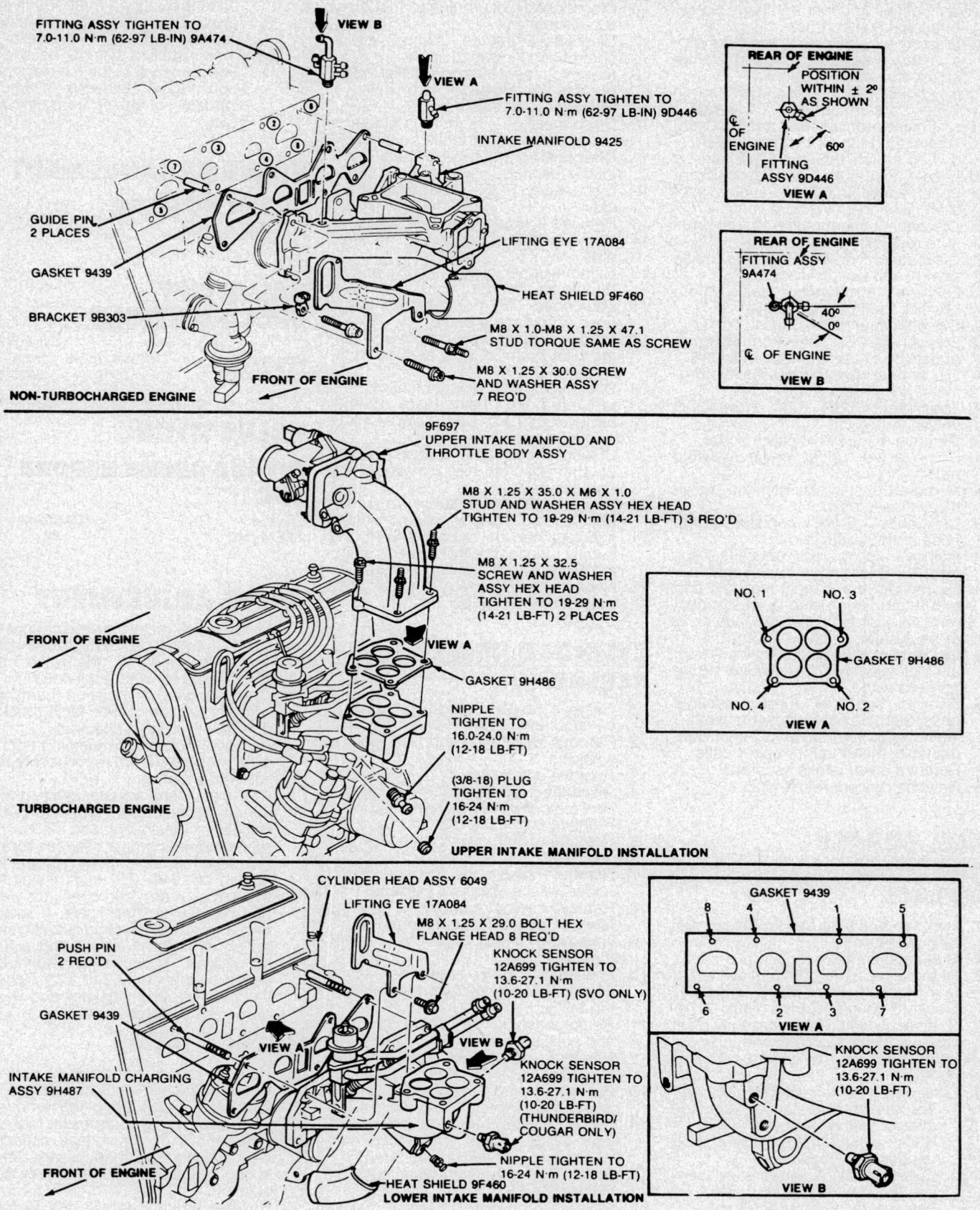

Fig. 3 Intake manifold assembly

on fuel line in upper righthand corner of engine compartment.

4. Disconnect electrical connectors at:
   a. Throttle position sensor, then the injector wiring harness.
   b. Knock sensor, then the air charge temperature sensor.
   c. Engine coolant temperature sensor, then the air bypass valve.
   d. Fan switch, then the EGR valve.
5. Label vacuum lines for installation at upper intake manifold vacuum tree, then disconnect vacuum lines.
6. Disconnect vacuum line to fuel pressure regulator.
7. Disconnect throttle linkage, cruise control and kickdown cable.
8. Remove accelerator cable from bracket, then position aside.
9. Disconnect air intake hose.
10. Disconnect PCV hose from fitting on underside of upper intake manifold.
11. Disconnect water bypass line at lower intake manifold.
12. Disconnect EGR tube from EGR valve.
13. Remove engine oil dipstick screw.
14. Remove four upper intake manifold nuts.
15. Remove upper intake manifold and air throttle assembly.
16. Disconnect EVAP canister purge hose from throttle body.
17. Remove spring lock coupling clips from fuel inlet and return fittings.
18. Disconnect fuel supply manifold and fuel return lines using quick connect removal tool No. D87L-9280-A or B, or equivalents.
19. Disconnect electrical connectors from all fuel injectors, then move wiring harness aside.
20. Remove two fuel supply manifold bolts, then the fuel supply manifold.
21. Remove four bottom bolts from intake manifold, then the four upper bolts.
22. Remove lower intake assembly.
23. Reverse procedure to install.

FUEL SUPPLY MANIFOLD
REPLACE

1. Remove fuel filler cap to relieve fuel tank pressure.
2. Drain coolant from radiator.
3. Release pressure from fuel system at fuel pressure relief valve using EFI pressure gauge tool No. T80L-9974-B, or equivalent. Fuel pressure relief valve is located on fuel line in upper righthand corner of engine compartment.
4. Disconnect electrical connectors at:
   a. Throttle position sensor, then the injector wiring harness.
   b. Knock sensor, then the air charge temperature sensor.
   c. Engine coolant temperature sensor, then the air bypass valve.
   d. Fan switch, then the EGR valve.
5. Label vacuum lines for installation at upper intake manifold vacuum tree, then disconnect vacuum lines.

6. Disconnect vacuum line to fuel pressure regulator.
7. Disconnect throttle linkage, cruise control and kickdown cable.
8. Remove accelerator cable from bracket, then position out of way.
9. Disconnect air intake hose.
10. Disconnect PCV hose from fitting on underside of upper intake manifold.
11. Disconnect water bypass line at lower intake manifold.
12. Disconnect EGR tube from EGR valve.
13. Remove engine oil dipstick screw.
14. Remove four upper intake manifold nuts.
15. Remove upper intake manifold and air throttle assembly.
16. Disconnect EVAP canister purge hose from throttle body.
17. Remove spring lock coupling retaining clips from fuel inlet and return fittings.
18. Disconnect fuel supply manifold and fuel return lines using quick connect removal tool No. D87L-9280-A or B, or equivalents.
19. Disconnect electrical connectors from all fuel injectors, then move wiring harness aside.
20. Remove two fuel supply manifold bolts, then the fuel supply manifold.
21. Injectors can be removed from fuel supply manifold at this time by exerting slight twisting/pulling motion.
22. Reverse procedure to install, tighten nuts and bolts to specification.

CYLINDER HEAD
REPLACE

1. Remove heater hose to rocker arm cover screw.
2. Remove distributor cap and ignition wires.
3. Remove spark plugs.
4. Disconnect all vacuum hoses necessary for cylinder head removal.
5. Remove engine oil dipstick.
6. Remove rocker arm cover bolts, then the cover.
7. Remove intake manifold as described under "Intake Manifold, Replace."
8. Remove alternator drive belt, then the alternator mounting bracket bolts.
9. Removing timing belt cover bolts, then the cover.
10. Loosen cam idler bolts, then move idler to unloaded position and retighten bolts.
11. Remove timing belt from camshaft and auxiliary sprockets.
12. Remove heat stove from exhaust manifold.
13. Remove exhaust manifold, then the timing belt idler and two bracket bolts.
14. Remove timing belt idler spring stop from cylinder head, then disconnect oil sending unit electrical connector.
15. Remove cylinder head bolts, then the cylinder head.
16. Reverse procedure to install, noting the following:
   a. **Torque** cylinder head bolts in sequence, **Fig. 4**, in two steps: first to

50-60 ft. lbs., then to 80-90 ft. lbs.
   b. **Torque** intake manifold bolts in sequence, **Fig. 5**, to 14-21 ft. lbs.
   c. When installing cylinder head, position camshaft in the 5 o'clock position, **Fig. 4**, allowing minimum protrusion of valves from cylinder head.

VALVE ARRANGEMENT
FRONT TO REAR

E-I-E-I-E-I-E-I

VALVE LIFT SPECIFICATIONS

Engine	Intake, Inch	Exhaust, Inch
2.3L/4-140	.3900	.3900

VALVE TIMING
INTAKE OPENS BEFORE TDC

Engine	Degrees
2.3L/4-140	22

VALVE ADJUSTMENT

The valve lash on this engine cannot be adjusted due to the use of hydraulic valve lash adjusters. However, the valve train can be checked for wear as follows:

1. Crank engine to position camshaft with flat section of lobe facing rocker arm of valve being checked.
2. Remove rocker arm retaining spring. **Late models do not incorporate the retaining spring.**
3. Collapse lash adjuster with valve spring compressor tool No. T74P-6565B, or equivalent, and insert correct size feeler gauge between rocker arm and camshaft lobe. Clearance should be .040-.050 inch. If not, remove rocker arm and check for wear and replace as necessary. If rocker arm is found satisfactory, check valve spring assembled height and adjust as needed. Valve spring assembled height should be 1.53 to 1.59 inches. If not, remove lash adjuster, and clean or replace parts as necessary.

ROCKER ARMS

1. Remove rocker arm cover.
2. Rotate camshaft until flat section of lobe faces rocker arm being removed.
3. With valve spring compressor tool No. 74P-6565B, or equivalent, collapse lash adjuster and, if necessary, valve spring and slide rocker arm over lash adjuster.
4. Reverse procedure to install. **Before rotating camshaft, ensure lash adjuster is collapsed to prevent valve train damage.**

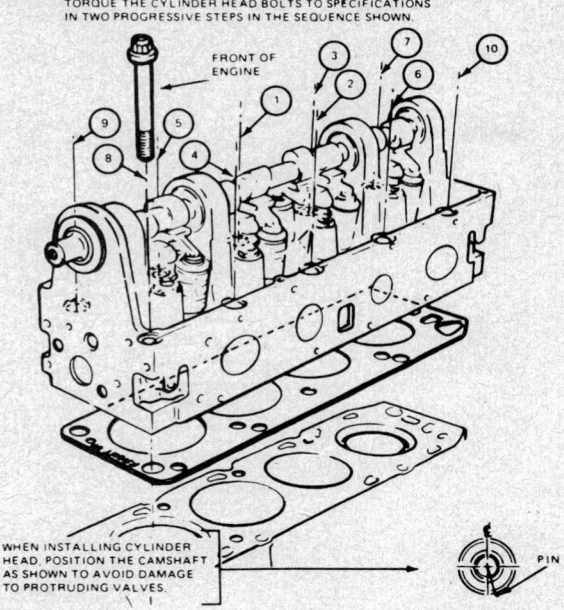

TORQUE THE CYLINDER HEAD BOLTS TO SPECIFICATIONS IN TWO PROGRESSIVE STEPS IN THE SEQUENCE SHOWN.

FRONT OF ENGINE

WHEN INSTALLING CYLINDER HEAD, POSITION THE CAMSHAFT AS SHOWN TO AVOID DAMAGE TO PROTRUDING VALVES.

PIN

FM1069100211000X

Fig. 4 Cylinder head bolt tightening sequence

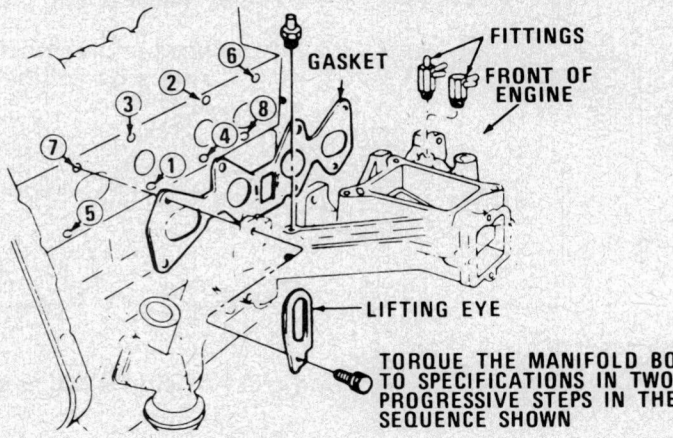

FITTINGS

GASKET

FRONT OF ENGINE

LIFTING EYE

TORQUE THE MANIFOLD BOLTS TO SPECIFICATIONS IN TWO PROGRESSIVE STEPS IN THE SEQUENCE SHOWN

FM1059100044000X

Fig. 5 Intake manifold tightening sequence. Except EFI models

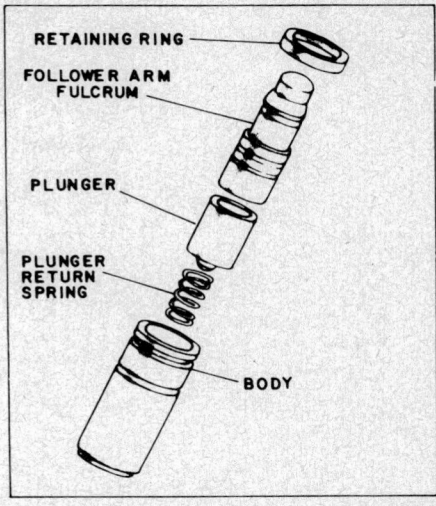

RETAINING RING
FOLLOWER ARM FULCRUM
PLUNGER
PLUNGER RETURN SPRING
BODY

FM1069100212000X

Fig. 6 Valve lash adjuster. Type I

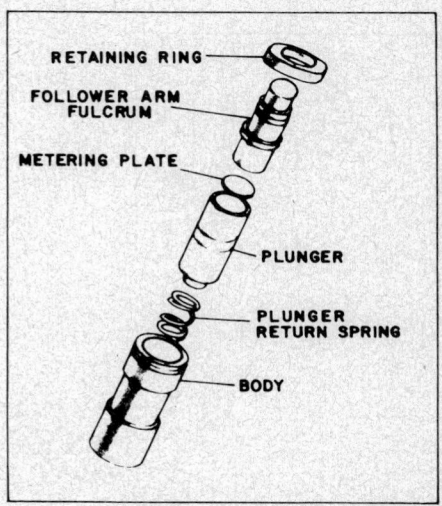

RETAINING RING
FOLLOWER ARM FULCRUM
METERING PLATE
PLUNGER
PLUNGER RETURN SPRING
BODY

FM1069100213000X

Fig. 7 Valve lash adjuster. Type II

VALVE GUIDES

Valve guides consist of holes bored in the cylinder head. For service, the guides can be reamed oversize to accommodate valves with oversize stems of .003, .015 and .030 inch.

LASH ADJUSTER
REPLACE

The hydraulic valve lash adjusters can be removed after rocker arm removal. There are two types of lash adjusters available, Type 1, being the standard lash adjuster, **Fig. 6**, and Type II, having a .020 inch oversize outside diameter, **Fig. 7**.

FRONT ENGINE SEALS
REPLACE

To gain access to the front engine seals,

remove the timing belt cover and proceed as follows:

CRANKSHAFT OIL SEAL

1. Without removing cylinder front cover, remove crankshaft sprocket with crankshaft sprocket remover tool No. T74P-6306A, or equivalent.
2. Remove crankshaft oil seal with front cover seal remover tool No. T74P-6700B, or equivalent.
3. Install new crankshaft oil seal with shaft seal installer tool No. T74P-6150A, or equivalent.
4. Install crankshaft sprocket with recess facing engine block.

CAMSHAFT & AUXILIARY SHAFT OIL SEALS

1. Remove camshaft or auxiliary shaft sprocket with camshaft sprocket remover/holding tool No. T74P-6256A, or equivalent.
2. Remove oil seal with front cover seal

remover tool No. T74P-6700B, or equivalent.
3. Install new oil seal with shaft seal installer tool No. T74P-6150A, or equivalent.
4. Install camshaft or auxiliary shaft sprocket with camshaft sprocket holding tool No. T74P-6256A, or equivalent, with center arbor removed.

TIMING BELT
REPLACE

1. Remove timing belt cover, then loosen belt tensioner and remove belt from sprockets, **Fig. 8**. Tighten tensioner bolt, holding tensioner in position. **Do not rotate crankshaft or camshaft after belt is removed. Rotating either component will result in improper valve timing.**
2. To install belt, ensure timing marks are aligned, **Fig. 9,** and place belt over sprockets.
3. Loosen tensioner bolt, allowing ten-

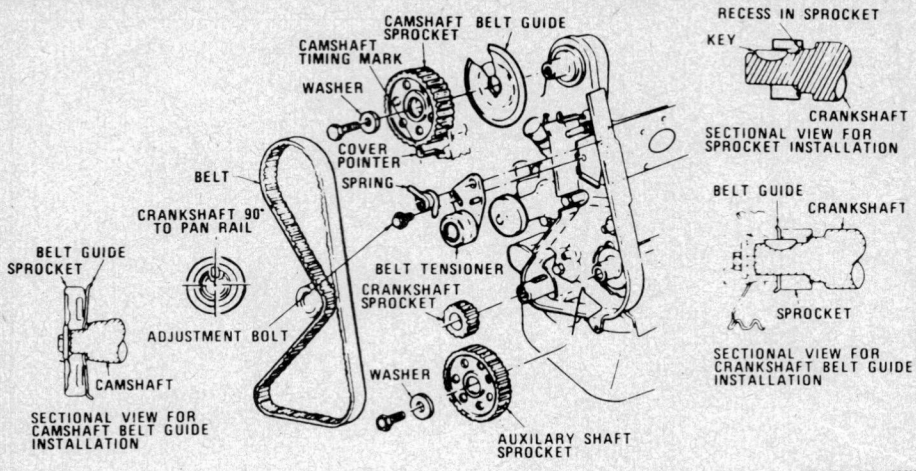

Fig. 8 Drive belt & sprocket installation

FM1069100214000X

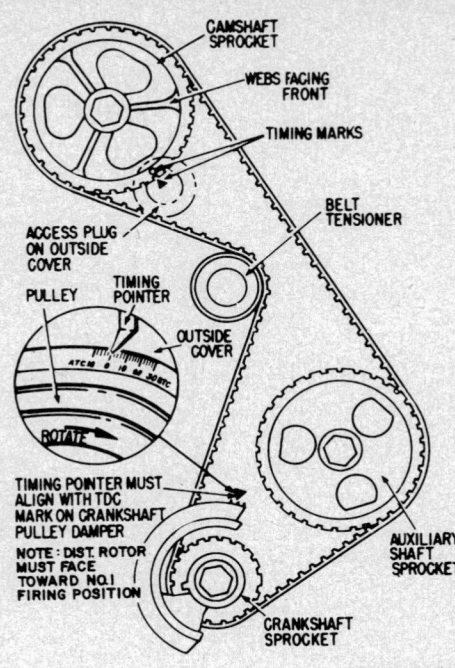

FM1069100215000X

Fig. 9 Valve timing marks

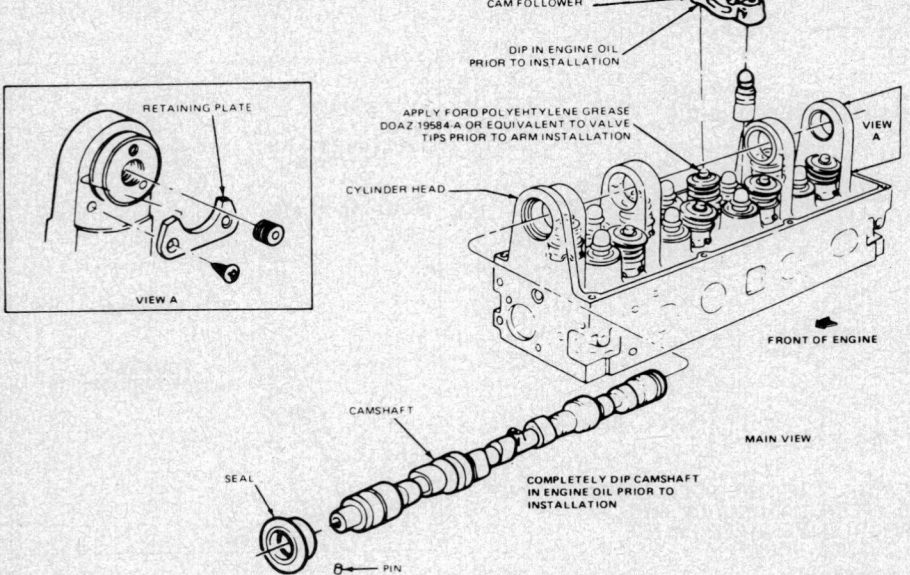

Fig. 10 Camshaft replacement

FM1069100216000X

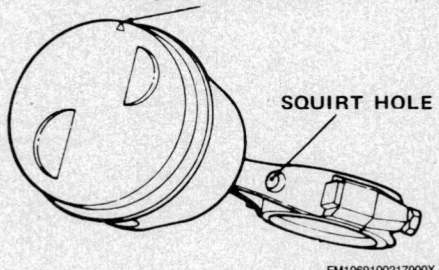

FM1069100217000X

Fig. 11 Piston & rod assembly

sioner to move against belt.
4. Rotate crankshaft two complete turns, removing slack from belt. Tighten tensioner adjustment and pivot bolts and check alignment of timing marks, **Fig. 9**.
5. Install timing belt cover.

CAMSHAFT
REPLACE

1. Disconnect ignition wires from spark plugs and rocker arm cover, then position aside.
2. Disconnect all vacuum hoses necessary for camshaft removal.
3. Remove rocker arm cover bolts and cover.
4. Remove alternator drive belt.
5. Remove alternator mounting bracket bolts and position bracket aside.
6. Remove upper radiator hose and disconnect lower hose.
7. Remove fan shroud. On models equipped with electric fan, remove fan and shroud as an assembly.
8. Remove timing belt cover bolts and cover.
9. Loosen cam idler bolts. Move idler to unloaded position and tighten bolts.
10. Remove timing belt from camshaft and auxiliary sprockets.
11. Raise and support vehicle.
12. Remove right and left engine mount nuts and washers.
13. Raise engine as far as possible using suitable transmission jack with block of wood positioned between jack and engine. Install wood blocks between No. 2 crossmember pedestals and engine mounts, then remove jack and lower vehicle.
14. Depress valve springs using valve spring compressor tool No. T74P-6565-A, or equivalent, and remove camshaft followers.
15. Remove camshaft sprocket bolt, then the sprocket using camshaft sprocket holding/removing tool No. T-74P-6256-B, or equivalent.
16. Remove seal using front cover seal remover tool No. T74P-6700-A, or equivalent.
17. Remove camshaft rear screws, then the retainer.
18. Remove camshaft from cylinder head, **Fig. 10**.
19. Reverse procedure to install. **Camshaft sprocket bolt should be replaced.** If new bolt is not available, coat threads of original bolt with pipe sealer D8AZ-19554-A, or equivalent.

PISTON & ROD ASSEMBLY

Assemble the rod to the piston with the arrow or notch on top of piston facing front of engine, **Fig. 11**.

Check side clearance between connecting rods at each connecting rod crankshaft journal. Clearance should be .0035-.0105 inch.

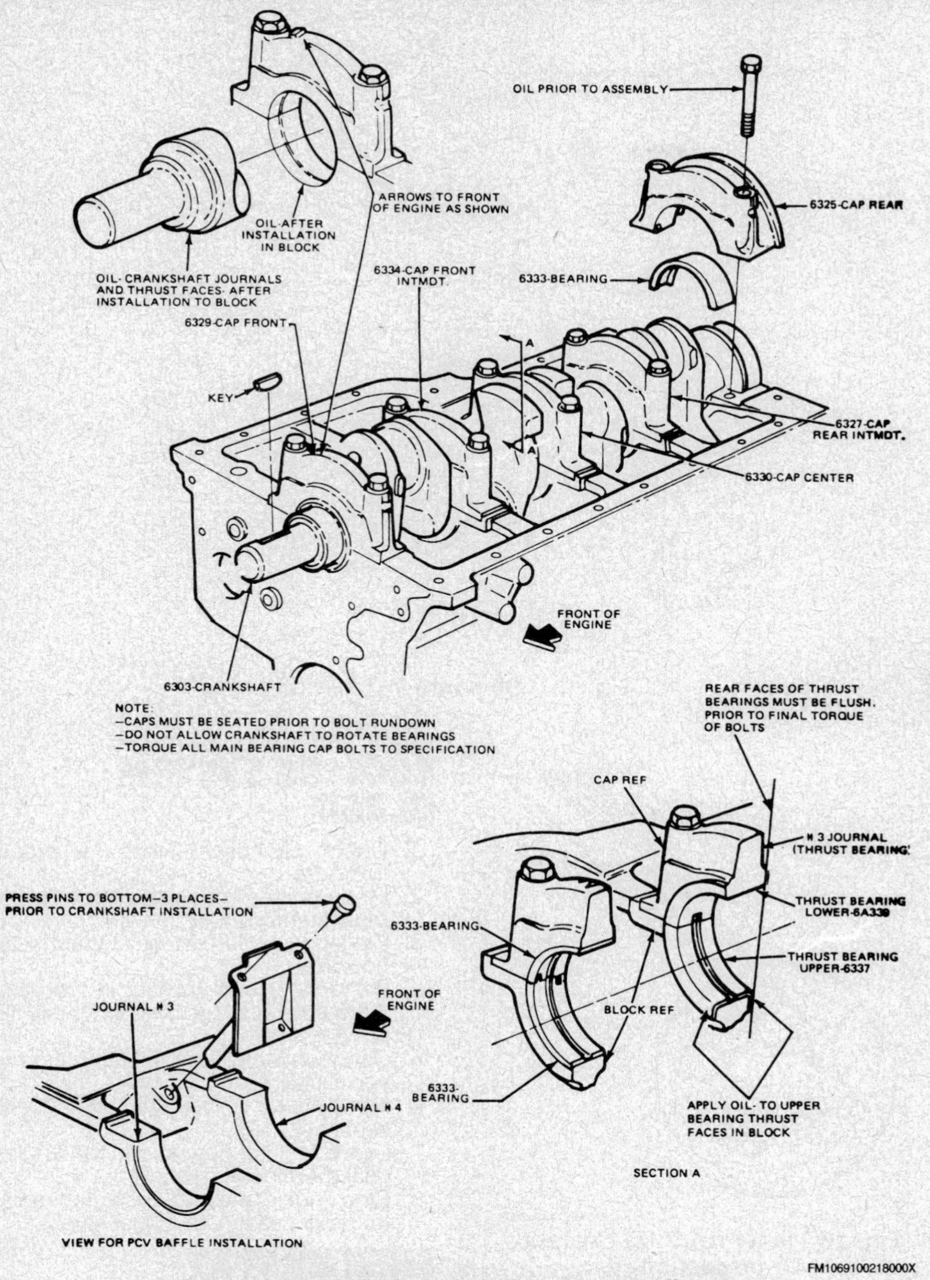

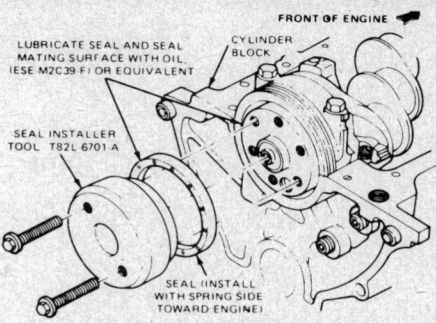

Fig. 13 Crankshaft rear oil seal installation

Fig. 12 Crankshaft & main bearing installation

PISTONS, PINS & RINGS

Oversize pistons are available in oversizes of .003 inch, .020 inch, .030 inch and .040 inch. Oversize rings are available in .020 inch, .030 inch and .040 inch oversizes. Oversize pins are not available.

MAIN & ROD BEARINGS

Undersize main bearings are available in .002 inch, .020 inch, .030 inch and .040 inch undersizes. Undersize rod bearings are available in undersizes of .002 inch, .010 inch, .020 inch, .030 inch and .040 inch.

The crankshaft and main bearings are installed with the arrows on the main bearing caps facing toward the front of the engine, **Fig. 12.** Install PCV baffle between bearing journals No. 3 and 4.

CRANKSHAFT REAR OIL SEAL

REPLACE

1. Remove oil pump, if necessary, as described under "Oil Pump, Replace."
2. Punch one hole into metal surface between seal and block using sharp awl.
3. Screw threaded end of slide hammer tool No. T77L-9533-B, or equivalent, into seal and remove seal. Use care to avoid damaging oil seal mating surface.

4. Apply suitable sealer to seal and block mating surfaces.
5. Position seal on crankshaft seal installer tool No. T82L-6701-A, or equivalent, **Fig. 13**, and install seal. Tighten bolts alternately to ensure proper seating of seal.
6. Install oil pump if previously removed.

OIL PAN
REPLACE

1. Remove air cleaner outlet tube at throttle body.
2. Remove engine oil dipstick.
3. Install suitable engine support equipment, then raise and support vehicle.
4. Remove engine mount through bolts.
5. Drain engine oil.
6. Remove starter cable and starter.
7. Disconnect exhaust manifold tube to inlet pipe bracket.
8. Disconnect catalytic converter at inlet pipe.
9. Remove transmission assembly.
10. Remove flywheel assembly.
11. **On models equipped with automatic transmission,** remove cooler lines from retainer at block.
12. **On all models,** lower vehicle and raise engine, then raise and support vehicle.
13. Remove oil pan bolts, then lower pan to chassis.
14. Remove oil pump drive and pickup tube assembly and lay in pan assembly.
15. Remove oil pan and pump assembly.
16. Reverse procedure to install.

OIL PUMP
REPLACE

The oil pump, **Fig. 14**, can be removed after oil pan removal, **Fig. 15.**

OIL PUMP SERVICE

1. Remove end plate and withdraw O-ring from groove in body.
2. Check clearance between inner rotor tip and outer rotor lobe, **Fig. 16.** This should not exceed .012 inch. Rotors are supplied only in a matched pair.
3. Check clearance between outer rotor and housing. This should not exceed .013 inch.

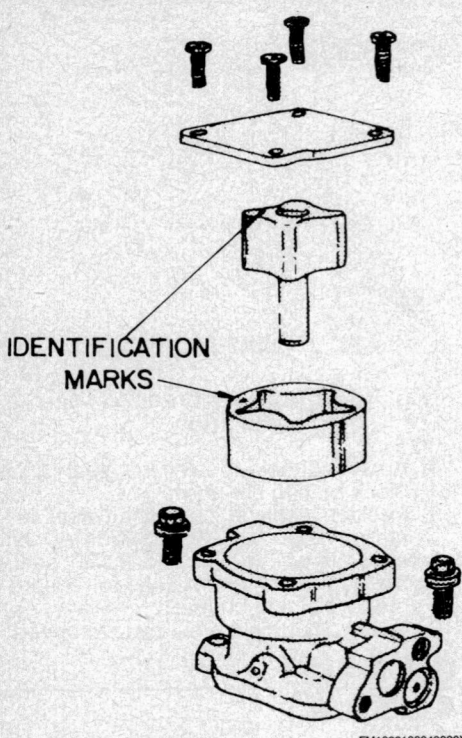

Fig. 14 Exploded view of oil pump

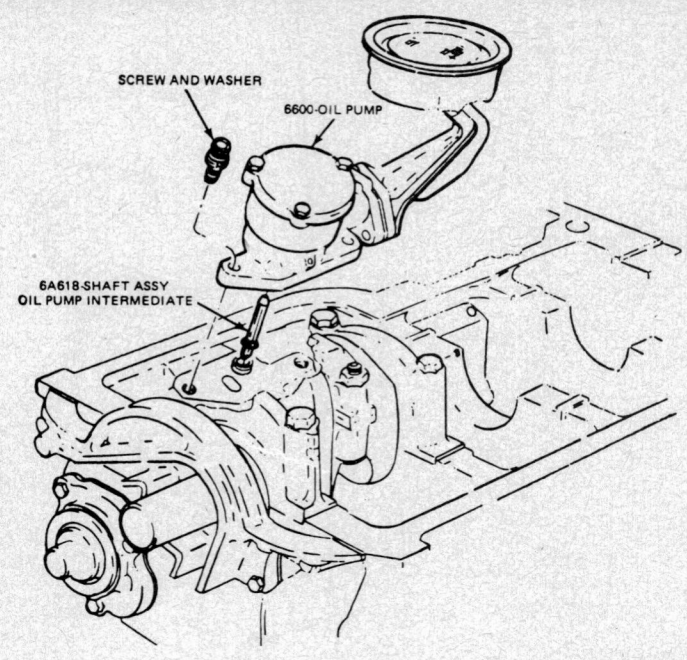

Fig. 15 Oil pump installation

FM1099100044000X

4. Place straightedge across face of pump body. Clearance between face of rotors and straightedge should not exceed .004 inch.
5. If necessary to replace rotor or driveshaft, remove outer rotor and then drive out retaining pin securing skew gear to driveshaft and pull off gear.
6. Withdraw inner rotor and driveshaft.

BELT TENSION DATA

Belt	New Lbs.	Used Lbs.
Except ¼ inch	140	110
¼ inch	65	40
4 Ribs Except Air Pump	130	115
4 Ribs Air Pump	110	105
5 Ribs	150	135
6 Ribs ①	113	110
6 Ribs ②	160	145

①—With automatic tensioner.
②—Fixed.

SERPENTINE DRIVE BELT

Conditions requiring belt replacement are excessive wear, rib chunk-out, severe glazing and frayed cords. Replace any belt exhibiting one of these conditions. Cracks on the rib side of a belt are considered acceptable.

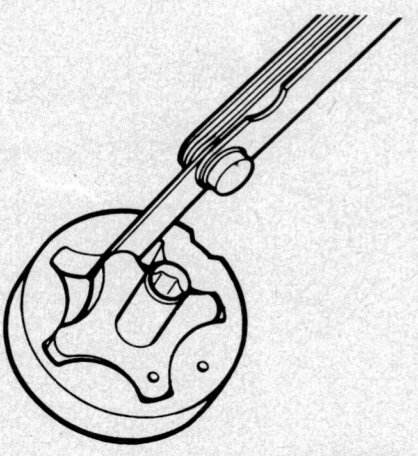

Fig. 16 Inner rotor tip clearance inspection

FM1099100045000X

If the belt has chunks missing from the ribs it should be replaced. If two or more adjacent ribs have lost sections a ½ inch or longer, or if the missing chunks are creating a noise or vibration condition. Replace the belt.

BELT ROUTING

Refer to **Fig. 17** for proper belt routing.

BELT REPLACEMENT

1. Lift or rotate automatic tensioner.
2. Remove belt(s).
3. Install new belt over pulleys. Ensure all V-grooves make proper contact with pulley.
4. Rotate tensioner over belt.

COOLING SYSTEM BLEED

1. Check all hose clamps for proper tightness.
2. Place heater temperature selector in maximum position.
3. Disconnect heater hose at thermostat housing.
4. Fill radiator until coolant is visible at thermostat housing or radiator cap filler neck seat.
5. Connect heater and tighten clamp to specifications.
6. Fill radiator to below radiator neck seat.
7. Leave radiator cap off and run engine until thermostat opens.
8. Stop engine and add coolant to radiator as necessary to adjust level.

THERMOSTAT
REPLACE

1. Disconnect battery cable, then the wiring connector from thermo switch in thermostat housing.
2. Remove radiator cap, then attach hose to drain tube and open draincock. Drain coolant until level is below water outlet connection, then close draincock.
3. Loosen upper hose at radiator, then remove water outlet housing bolts.
4. Remove thermostat housing, then the thermostat. Do not pry housing off.
5. Clean outlet housing and cylinder head mating surfaces.
6. Position thermostat and seat so it will compress gasket. Position outlet to cylinder head, using new gasket, then install bolts.
7. Connect top hose to radiator and

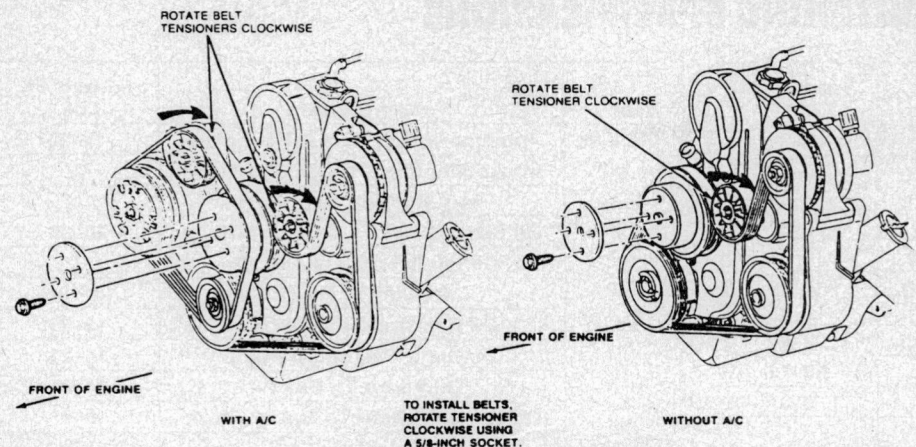

Fig. 17 Serpentine belt routing

ROTATE BELT TENSIONERS CLOCKWISE

ROTATE BELT TENSIONER CLOCKWISE

FRONT OF ENGINE

FRONT OF ENGINE

WITH A/C

TO INSTALL BELTS, ROTATE TENSIONER CLOCKWISE USING A 5/8-INCH SOCKET.

WITHOUT A/C

FM1069100220000X

12. Fill radiator with specified antifreeze and water mixture.
13. Operate engine and check for leaks at hose connections and at automatic transmission fluid cooler lines.
14. Check automatic transmission, radiator and coolant recovery reservoir fluid levels.

tighten clamp. Ensure draincock is closed.
8. Fill cooling system with coolant as follows:
  a. Add 50 percent coolant, then add water until radiator is full. Allow coolant level to settle, then add more coolant until radiator remains full.
  b. Install radiator cap to first notch, then connect battery cable and wire connector to thermo switch.
  c. Start engine and let idle until upper hose is warm, then carefully remove radiator cap and top off coolant level.
  d. Install cap securely and fill reservoir to FULL COLD mark with proper concentrate of coolant. Add water to FULL HOT mark.
  e. Check for leaks.

WATER PUMP
REPLACE

A provision for wrench clearance has been made in the timing belt inner cover, so only the outer cover must be removed in order to replace water pump.
1. Drain cooling system and disconnect hoses from pump.
2. Loosen alternator and remove drive belt.
3. Remove fan, spacer and pulley.
4. Remove drive belt cover.
5. Remove water pump bolts and water pump.
6. Reverse procedure to install.

RADIATOR
REPLACE

1. **On models equipped with automatic transmission,** disconnect automatic transmission fluid cooler inlet and outlet lines from radiator using disconnect tool No. T82L-9500-AH, or equivalent.
2. **On all models,** drain cooling system, then disconnect radiator upper and lower hoses and overflow hose from radiator.
3. Remove two upper shroud bolts at radiator support, then lift fan shroud enough to disengage lower clips and lay shroud back over fan.
4. Remove radiator upper support bolts, then the support.
5. Lift radiator from vehicle.
6. **On models equipped with automatic transmission,** if installing new radiator, transfer oil cooler line connectors to new radiator using pipe sealant with suitable oil resistant sealer.
7. **On all models,** position radiator assembly into vehicle, then install upper supports and bolts.
8. **On models equipped with automatic transmission,** connect oil cooler lines.
9. **On all models,** install fan assembly by attaching two lower legs to lower radiator rail with two bolts. Tighten bolts to specifications.
10. Install upper legs with two bolts. Tighten bolts to specifications.
11. Connect radiator upper, lower and overflow hoses, noting the following:
  a. Close draincock, then position hose clamps at least 2 inches from each end of hose.
  b. Slide hose on connections.
  c. **Ensure clamps are beyond bead and place in center of clamping surface of connections. New hose clamps must be installed inside hose alignment marks. Tighten clamp to specifications.**

FUEL PUMP
REPLACE

1. Disconnect battery ground cable.
2. Release pressure from fuel system at fuel pressure relief valve using fuel pressure gauge tool No. T80L-09974-B, or equivalent. Fuel pressure relief valve is located on fuel line in upper righthand corner of engine compartment.
3. Drain fuel tank through filler neck using Rotunda Fuel Storage Tanker tool No. 034-00002 and adapter hose tool No. 034-00011, or equivalents.
4. Raise and support vehicle.
5. Disconnect and remove fuel filler tube.
6. Remove fuel tank support straps and support fuel tank in vehicle.
7. Remove fuel lines and vent hose, then disconnect electrical connectors.
8. Remove fuel tank from vehicle.
9. Remove any dirt around fuel pump retaining flange, then turn fuel pump locking ring counterclockwise using fuel tank sender wrench tool No. D84P-9275-A, or equivalent.
10. Remove locking ring, then the fuel pump and bracket assembly.
11. Remove seal gasket and discard.
12. Reverse procedure to install.

FUEL FILTER
REPLACE

1. Release pressure from fuel system at fuel pressure relief valve using fuel pressure gauge tool No. T80L-09974-B, or equivalent. Fuel pressure relief valve is located on fuel line in upper righthand corner of engine compartment.
2. Raise and support vehicle.
3. Remove push connector fittings from fuel filter ends, then install new retainer clips in each fitting.
4. Loosen worm gear clamp, then remove filter from bracket. Note flow arrow as installed to ensure proper direction of fuel flow through filter.
5. Reverse procedure to install.

TIGHTENING SPECIFICATIONS

Year	Component	Torque/Ft. Lbs.
1992–93	Air Bag Module Attaching Nuts	24–32
	Air Cleaner Housing To Vane Air Meter	15–22
	Auxiliary Shaft Gear Bolt	28–40
	Auxiliary Shaft Thrust Plate Bolt	6–9
	Belt Tensioner (Timing Adjusting Bolt)	14–21
	Belt Tensioner (Timing Pivot Bolt)	28–40
	Camshaft Gear Bolt	50–71
	Camshaft Thrust Plate Bolt	6–9
	Connecting Rod Cap Bolts	④
	Crossmember Nut Assemblies	65–85
	Cylinder Front Cover Bolt	14–21
	Cylinder Head Bolts	①
	Distributor Clamp Bolt	14–21
	EGR Valve To Spacer Bolt	14–21
	EGR Tube Nut	9–12
	EGR Tube To Exhaust Manifold Connector	9–12
	Exhaust Manifold	③
	Engine Mount Insulator & Bracket Bolts	33–45
	Flywheel To Crankshaft	56–64
	Fuel Charging Assembly To Intake Manifold (Bolt)	12–15
	Fuel Charging Assembly To Intake Manifold (Stud)	5–7.5
	Fuel Charging Assembly To Intake Manifold (Nut)	12–15
	Fuel Charging Assembly To Cylinder Head	14–21
	Fuel Injector Manifold To Fuel Charging Assembly	15–22
	Heater Hose Clamps	12–18 ⑥

Year	Component	Torque/Ft. Lbs.
1992–93	Injector Wiring Harness Bracket	15–22
	Intake Manifold To Cylinder Head	①
	Main Bearing Cap Bolts	⑤
	Oil Filter Insert To Cylinder Block	20–35
	Oil Filter To Engine Block	②
	Oil Pan To Block	10–13.5
	Oil Pan Drain Plug to Pan	15–25
	Oil Pump Pickup To Pump	14–21
	Oil Pump To Block	14–21
	Oil Return Fitting To Upper Block	6–9
	Radiator Bolts	71–92 ⑥
	Radiator Hose Clamps	20–30 ⑥
	Rocker Arm Cover	5–8
	Spark Plugs	5–10
	Temperature Sending Unit To Block	8–18
	Throttle Body To Upper Intake Manifold	12–15
	Timing Belt Cover Bolt (Outer)	6–9
	Timing Belt Cover Stud (Inner)	14–21
	Vane Air Meter Mounting Screws	15–22
	Vibration Damper Or Pulley	114–151
	Water Bypass Line	12–20
	Water Jacket Drain Plug To Block	23–28
	Water Outlet Connection Bolt	14–21
	Water Pump To Block (Bolt)	14–21

① —Refer to text.
② —Torque in two steps: first to 5–7 ft. lbs., then to 14–21 ft. lbs.
③ —Torque in two steps: first to 14–17 ft. lbs., then to 20–30 ft. lbs.
④ —Torque in two steps: first to 25–30 ft. lbs., then to 30–36 ft. lbs.
⑤ —Torque in two steps: first to 50–60 ft. lbs., then to 75–85 ft. lbs.
⑥ —Inch lbs.

3.8L/V6–232 Engine

NOTE: On Air Bag Equipped Models, Refer To "Air Bag System Precautions" Located In The Front Of This Manual For System Disarming & Arming Procedures.

NOTE: For Procedures Not Found In This Section, Refer To The 3.8L/V6-232 Engine Section In The Cougar, Crown Victoria, Grand Marquis & Thunderbird Chapter.

INDEX

PRECAUTIONS

AIR BAG SYSTEMS

Refer to "Air Bag System Precautions" in the front of this manual for system disarming and arming procedures.

FUEL SYSTEM PRESSURE RELIEF

Fuel supply tubes will remain pressurized for long periods of time after engine shutdown. This pressure must be relieved before beginning fuel system service or personal injury or damage to vehicle may occur. A valve is provided on the fuel injection supply manifold for this purpose.

1. Remove engine air cleaner.
2. Connect EFI/CFI fuel pressure gauge tool No. T80L-9974-B, or equivalent, to fuel pressure relief valve on fuel injection supply manifold.
3. Open manual valve on fuel pressure gauge tool to relieve fuel system pressure.

ENGINE

REPLACE

REMOVAL

1. Drain engine cooling system.
2. Disconnect battery ground cable, then the underhood lamp electrical connector.
3. Mark Position of hood hinges, then remove hood.
4. Disconnect alternator to voltage regulator wiring assembly, then remove radiator upper sight shield.
5. Release drive belt tensioner and remove drive belt.
6. Remove air cleaner outlet tube as follows:
   a. Disconnect wire harness from intake air temperature sensor, then the crankcase ventilation tube from air cleaner outlet tube.
   b. Loosen air cleaner tube clamps on outlet tube, then disconnect outlet tube from throttle body.
   c. Disconnect outlet tube from mass airflow sensor, then remove tube.
7. Disconnect electric fan motor.
8. Disconnect constant control relay module at wiring connector, then remove radiator coolant recovery reservoir.
9. Remove radiator electrical motor, fan blade and fan shroud as an assembly.
10. Remove upper radiator hose.
11. **On models equipped with automatic transmission,** disconnect transmission oil cooler inlet and outlet tubes.
12. **On all models,** disconnect heater inlet and heater return tube hoses.
13. Disconnect lower radiator hose at water pump, then remove radiator bolts and radiator.
14. Disconnect power steering pressure hose, then remove power steering pump and bracket and position aside.
15. Remove mass airflow sensor, then disconnect power steering pressure switch at wiring connector.
16. **On models equipped with air conditioning,** proceed as follows:
    a. Disconnect A/C clutch from fuel charging wiring.
    b. Discharge A/C system as described in the "Air Conditioning" section.
    c. Disconnect A/C compressor lines. Cap or plug open lines.
    d. Remove A/C compressor bolts, then the compressor.
17. **On all models,** remove wiring shield, then disconnect accelerator cable and speed control actuator from throttle body.
18. Remove accelerator cable bracket and position aside with cables.
19. Relieve fuel system pressure as described under "Precautions."
20. Disconnect fuel supply hose, then the fuel return hose.
21. Disconnect fuel charging wiring from engine control sensor wiring at 40-pin connector.
22. Disconnect main vacuum source hose, then the direct ignition control module at wiring connector.
23. Disconnect fuel vapor hose.
24. **On models equipped with air conditioning,** remove A/C compressor mounting bracket with drive belt tensioner attached.
25. **On all models,** raise and support vehicle, then position drain pan beneath engine oil pan.
26. Drain engine oil, then remove oil filter and move drain pan away from vehicle.
27. Disconnect heated oxygen sensors.
28. Remove dual converter and pipe.
29. Remove inspection plug from engine rear plate.
30. **On models equipped with automatic transmission,** remove torque converter bolts.
31. **On all models,** remove engine to transmission bolts.
32. **On models equipped with automatic transmission,** remove transmission oil cooler line retainers from righthand front engine support insulator.
33. **On all models,** remove front engine support insulator to crossmember nuts.
34. Remove starter motor as described in the "Electrical" section.
35. Remove ground cable, then the starter motor wire harness retainers on both lefthand and righthand sides.
36. Partially lower vehicle, then position floor jack under transmission.
37. Position suitable engine lifting equipment, then remove engine assembly from vehicle and place on work stand.

INSTALLATION

Lightly oil all bolt and stud threads before installation, except those specifying special sealant.

1. Install suitable engine lifting equipment and remove engine assembly from work stand.
2. Position engine in engine compartment, then install two engine to transmission bolts.
3. Lower engine onto front engine support insulators, then remove lifting equipment. Seat lefthand side front engine support insulator locating pin before righthand side front engine support insulator.
4. Remove floor jack from under transmission, then tighten two engine to transmission bolts.
5. Raise and support vehicle, then install and tighten all remaining engine to transmission bolts.
6. **On models equipped with automatic transmission,** install torque converter bolts. Tighten bolts to specifications.
7. **On all models,** install inspection plug to engine rear plate, then the front engine support insulator nuts. Tighten insulator nuts to specifications.
8. Install starter motor as described in the "Electrical" section.
9. **On models equipped with automatic transmission,** install transmission oil cooler line bracket.
10. **On all models,** install dual converter and pipe.
11. Connect heated oxygen sensor.
12. Install oil filter, then lower vehicle.
13. **On models equipped with air conditioning,** install A/C compressor mounting bracket with drive belt tensioner attached.
14. **On all models,** connect fuel vapor hose.
15. Install radiator coolant recovery reservoir, then connect constant control relay module at wiring connector.
16. Connect main vacuum source hose, then the fuel charging wiring to engine control sensor wiring at 40-pin connector.
17. Connect ignition control module at wiring connector.
18. Remove plugs from fuel supply and return lines, then connect lines.
19. Install accelerator cable bracket, then connect accelerator cable and speed control actuator to throttle body.
20. Install wiring shield.
21. **On models equipped with air conditioning,** proceed as follows:
    a. Install A/C compressor, then the compressor bolts. Tighten bolts to specifications.
    b. Remove caps or plugs on A/C compressor lines, then connect lines to compressor.
    c. Connect A/C clutch to fuel charging wiring.
22. **On all models,** connect power steering pressure switch at wiring connector, then install mass airflow sensor.
23. Install power steering pump and

bracket, then connect power steering hoses.
24. Install radiator, then connect lower radiator hose to water pump.
25. Install heater inlet and heater return tube hoses.
26. **On models equipped with automatic transmission,** install transmission cooler lines.
27. **On all models,** install upper radiator hose.
28. Install radiator electric motor, fan blade and fan shroud as an assembly.
29. Connect electric fan motor to engine control sensor wiring.
30. Install radiator coolant recovery reservoir, then connect constant control relay module at wiring connector.
31. Position drive belt, then install radiator upper sight shield.
32. Install air cleaner outlet tube to throttle body as follows:
    a. Position air cleaner outlet tube to vehicle, then connect air cleaner outlet tube to mass air flow sensor.
    b. Connect air cleaner outlet tube to throttle body, then install tube clamps to tube. Tighten engine air cleaner tube clamps.
    c. Connect crankcase ventilation tube to air cleaner outlet tube.

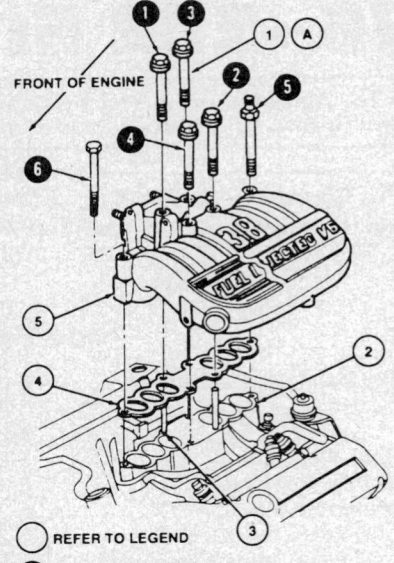

FRONT OF ENGINE

○ REFER TO LEGEND

● TIGHTEN IN SEQUENCE SHOWN

Item	Description
1A	Bolt (6 Req'd)
2	Lower Intake Manifold
3	Locating Pins (2 Req'd)
4	Intake Manifold Upper Gasket
5	Upper Intake Manifold
A	Tighten in sequence in three steps: ● 10 N·m (8 Lb-Ft) ● 20 N·m (15 Lb-Ft) ● 32 N·m (24 Lb-Ft)

FM1059400060000X

Fig. 1 Upper intake manifold bolt tightening sequence

d. Connect wire harness to intake air temperature sensor.
33. Install hood to original marked position.
34. Connect underhood lamp wiring, then the battery ground cable.
35. Refill crankcase to proper level with specified engine oil.
36. Refill engine cooling system.
37. **On models equipped with air conditioning,** drain, evacuate, pressure test and recharge A/C system as described in "Air Conditioning" section.
38. **On all models,** start engine and check for leaks.

INTAKE MANIFOLD
REPLACE
UPPER

1. Remove air cleaner outlet tube as follows:
   a. Disconnect wire harness from intake air temperature sensor, then the crankcase ventilation tube from air cleaner outlet tube.
   b. Loosen air cleaner tube clamps on outlet tube, then disconnect outlet tube from throttle body.
   c. Disconnect outlet tube from mass airflow sensor, then remove tube.
2. Disconnect accelerator cable at throttle body, then the speed control actuator.
3. Remove accelerator cable bracket bolts and position cable aside.
4. Disconnect vacuum lines at intake manifold, then the necessary electrical connectors.
5. Disconnect one crankcase ventilation tube at upper intake manifold and one at positive crankcase ventilation valve.
6. Remove throttle body if necessary, then the EGR valve from upper intake manifold.
7. Remove nut and bolt retaining engine support and wiring retainer bracket at lefthand front of intake manifold, then set aside with ignition wires.
8. Remove upper intake manifold bolts/studs, then the upper intake manifold and gasket.
9. Reverse procedure to install, noting the following:
   a. **Torque** upper intake manifold bolts in sequence, **Fig. 1,** first to 8, then to 15 and finally to 24 ft. lbs.
   b. Tightening remaining nuts and bolts.

LOWER

1. Drain engine cooling system.
2. Remove upper intake manifold as previously described.
3. Remove fuel injector and fuel injection supply manifold.
4. Remove heater water outlet hose.
5. Remove lower intake manifold bolts/studs, then the lower intake manifold. **Intake manifold is sealed at each end with RTV-type sealer. To break seal, it may be necessary to pry on front of manifold with screwdriver blade. If it is necessary to pry on intake manifold, use care**

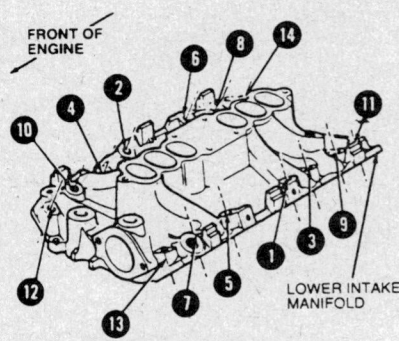

Fig. 2 Lower intake manifold bolt tightening sequence

TIGHTEN IN NUMERICAL SEQUENCE IN STEPS AS FOLLOWS:
STEP 1 — 11 N·m (8 LB-FT)
STEP 2 — 20 N·m (15 LB-FT)

FM1059400061000X

to prevent damage to machined surfaces.

6. Remove and discard intake manifold gasket and end seals.
7. If lower intake manifold is to be disassembled, proceed as follows:
   a. Remove water outlet connection and water thermostat, then the engine coolant temperature sensor. Water bypass tube is pressed-in and is not serviceable.
   b. Remove heater elbow.
   c. Remove all vacuum and electrical fittings.
8. Reverse procedure to install, noting the following:
   a. Lightly oil all bolt and stud threads before installation.
   b. When using silicone rubber sealer, assembly must occur within 15 minutes after sealer application. After this time, sealer may start to set and its effectiveness may be reduced.
   c. Ensure lower intake manifold, cylinder head and cylinder block mating surfaces are clean and free of old gasketing material. Clean with suitable solvent.
   d. **If intake manifold was disassembled,** apply coat of pipe sealant with Teflon part No. D8AZ-19554-A or equivalent, to all vacuum fittings, heater elbows and electrical fittings.
   e. Install lower intake manifold bolts and stud bolt in original locations.
   f. **Torque** lower intake manifold bolts and stud bolt in sequence, **Fig. 2,** first to 8, then to 15 ft. lbs.
   g. Tighten remaining nuts and bolts.
   h. Fill engine cooling system, then start engine and check for leaks.

EXHAUST MANIFOLD
REPLACE

LEFTHAND

1. Remove oil level indicator tube support bracket.
2. Disconnect heated oxygen sensor

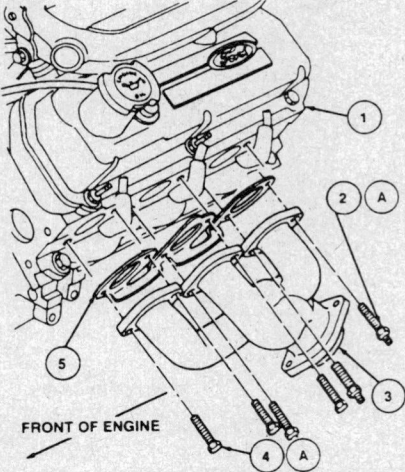

Item
1
2A
3
4A
5
A

Description
Cylinder Head
Stud (3 Req'd)
LH Exhaust Manifold
Bolt (3 Req'd)
Exhaust Manifold Gasket
Tighten to 20-33 N·m (15-22 Lb-Ft)

FM1059400062000X

Fig. 3 Lefthand exhaust manifold replacement

from fuel charging wiring, then the ignition wires from spark plugs.
3. Raise and support vehicle.
4. Remove exhaust manifold to converter and pipe nuts, then lower vehicle.
5. Remove exhaust manifold bolts, then the lefthand exhaust manifold and gasket, **Fig. 3.**
6. If installing new manifold, remove oxygen sensor.
7. Reverse procedure to install, noting the following:
   a. Lightly oil all bolt and stud threads before installation, except those specifying special sealant.
   b. Clean manifold, cylinder head and dual converter and Y pipe mating surfaces.
   c. Coat heated oxygen sensor threads with high temperature anti-seize compound. **Do not allow anti-seize compound to enter sensor flutes. Possible damage to heated oxygen sensor may occur.**
   d. Position exhaust manifold and exhaust manifold gasket on cylinder head, then install pilot bolt (lower front bolt hole on No. 5 cylinder). Slight warpage in exhaust manifold may cause misalignment between bolt holes in cylinder head and exhaust manifold. Elongate holes in exhaust manifold as necessary to correct misalignment. Do not elongate pilot hole.
   e. Tighten bolts and nuts to specifications, then start engine and check for exhaust leaks.

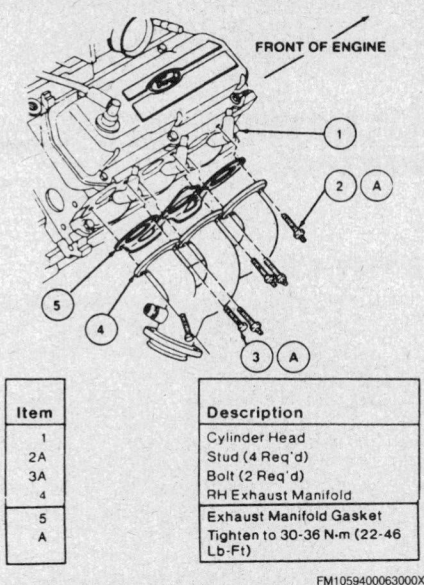

Fig. 4 Righthand exhaust manifold replacement

Item
1
2A
3A
4
5
A

Description
Cylinder Head
Stud (4 Req'd)
Bolt (2 Req'd)
RH Exhaust Manifold
Exhaust Manifold Gasket
Tighten to 30-36 N·m (22-46 Lb-Ft)

FM1059400063000X

RIGHTHAND

1. Disconnect coil ignition wire from ignition coil and ignition wires from spark plugs.
2. Remove spark plugs, then raise and support vehicle.
3. Disconnect EGR valve to exhaust manifold tube from exhaust manifold.
4. **On models equipped with automatic transmission,** remove transmission fluid level indicator tube.
5. **On all models,** remove heater inlet tube and hose.
6. Remove exhaust manifold to dual converter Y pipe nuts, then lower vehicle.
7. Remove exhaust manifold bolts, then the manifold and gasket, **Fig. 4.**
8. If installing new manifold, remove heated oxygen sensor.
9. Reverse procedure to install, noting the following:
   a. Lightly oil all bolt and stud threads before installation, except those specifying special sealant.
   b. Clean righthand exhaust manifold, cylinder head and dual converter and Y pipe mating surfaces.
   c. Coat heated oxygen sensor threads with high temperature anti-seize compound. **Do not allow anti-seize compound to enter sensor flutes. Possible damage to heated oxygen sensor may occur.**
   d. Position exhaust manifold and exhaust manifold gasket on cylinder head and start two bolts. Slight warpage in exhaust manifold may cause misalignment between bolt holes in cylinder head and exhaust manifold. Elongate holes in exhaust manifold as necessary to correct misalignment. Do not elongate pilot hole.
   e. Tighten bolts and nuts to specifica-

tions, then start engine and check for exhaust leaks.
f. Check transmission fluid level.

CYLINDER HEAD
REPLACE

REMOVAL

1. Drain engine cooling system, then disconnect battery ground cable.
2. Remove air cleaner outlet tube from throttle body as follows:
   a. Disconnect wire harness from intake air temperature sensor, then the crankcase ventilation tube from air cleaner outlet tube.
   b. Loosen air cleaner tube clamps on outlet tube, then disconnect outlet tube from throttle body.
   c. Disconnect outlet tube from mass airflow sensor, then remove tube.
3. Loosen drive belt tensioner, then remove drive belts.
4. **On lefthand cylinder head,** proceed as follows:
   a. Remove oil filler cap.
   b. Remove power steering pump front mounting bracket bolts.
   c. Remove alternator, then the belt idler pulley.
   d. Remove power steering pump/alternator bracket bolts, then place pump/bracket assembly aside, with hoses connected in position to prevent leakage.
5. **On righthand cylinder head,** proceed as follows:
   a. Remove drive belt.
   b. **On models equipped with air conditioning,** remove A/C mounting bracket bolts, then place A/C compressor aside with hoses connected.
   c. **On models without air conditioning,** remove A/C idler pulley.
   d. **On all models,** remove positive crankcase ventilation valve.
6. **On both cylinder heads,** remove upper intake manifold as described under "Intake Manifold, Replace."
7. Remove valve cover as described under "Valve Cover, Replace."
8. Remove fuel injection supply manifold.
9. Remove lower intake manifold as described under "Intake Manifold, Replace."
10. Remove exhaust manifolds as described under "Exhaust Manifold, Replace."
11. Loosen rocker arm fulcrum bolts enough to allow rocker arm to be lifted off push rod, and rotate to one side.
12. Remove push rods, then identify position of each push rod. Push rods should be installed in their original positions during assembly.
13. Remove cylinder head bolts, then the cylinder heads. Discard bolts.
14. Remove and discard old head gaskets.

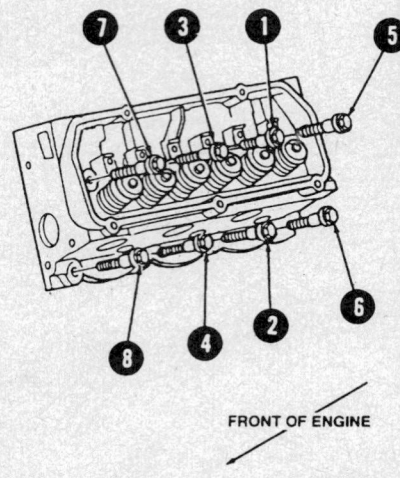

FRONT OF ENGINE

FM1069400378000X

Fig. 5   Cylinder head bolt tightening sequence

INSTALLATION

Always use new cylinder head bolts to ensure a leak-tight assembly. Torque retention with used bolts can vary, which may result in coolant or compression leakage at the cylinder head mating surface area.

1. Prepare cylinder head components as follows:
   a. Lightly oil all bolts and stud bolt threads before installation, except those specifying special sealant.
   b. Clean cylinder head, intake manifold, rocker arm cover and head gasket surfaces. If cylinder head was removed for head gasket replacement, check flatness of cylinder head and cylinder block gasket surfaces.
2. Position new head gasket(s) onto cylinder block using dowels for alignment, then position cylinder heads onto cylinder block.
3. **Torque** new cylinder head bolts in sequence, **Fig. 5,** first to 15, then to 29 and finally to 37 ft. lbs., then proceed as follows:
   a. Back off cylinder head bolts, one at a time, two to three revolutions. **Do not loosen all bolts at same time. Only work on one bolt at a time.**
   b. **Torque** long bolts, in sequence, **Fig. 5,** to 11-19 ft. lbs., then rotate an additional 85-95 degrees. Continue with next bolt in sequence.
   c. **Torque short bolts, in sequence, Fig. 5, to 7-15 ft. lbs., then rotate an additional 85-95 degrees. Continue with next bolt in sequence.**
4. Dip each push rod end in engine assembly lubricant D9AZ-19579-D or equivalent.
5. Install push rods in their original positions, then lubricate all rocker arms with engine assembly lubricant D9AZ-19579-D or equivalent.
6. Install rocker arms.
7. Install exhaust manifolds as de-

scribed under "Exhaust Manifold, Replace."
8. Install lower intake manifold as described under "Intake Manifold, Replace."
9. Install fuel injection supply manifold.
10. Position rocker arm and valve cover on cylinder head and install bolts. Note location of ignition wire routing clip stud bolts. Tighten rocker arm bolts to specifications.
11. Install upper intake manifold as described under "Intake Manifold, Replace."
12. Install spark plugs and tighten to specifications, then connect ignition wires to spark plugs.
13. **On lefthand cylinder head,** proceed as follows:
   a. Install oil filler cap.
   b. Install alternator/power steering pump mounting bracket, then the alternator.
   c. Install accessory drive belt tensioner.
   d. Install power steering pump, then the support bracket. Tighten to specifications.
14. **On righthand cylinder head,** proceed as follows:
   a. Install positive crankcase ventilation valve.
   b. **On models equipped with air conditioning,** install A/C compressor mounting and supporting brackets, then the compressor.
15. **On both cylinder heads,** install drive belt and tighten as described under "Serpentine Drive Belt."
16. Connect battery ground cable.
17. Install air cleaner outlet tube as follows:
   a. Install outlet tube, then connect tube to mass airflow sensor.
   b. Connect outlet tube to throttle body, then tighten air cleaner tube clamps on outlet tube.
   c. Connect crankcase ventilation tube to air cleaner outlet tube, then the wire harness to intake air temperature sensor.
18. Fill engine cooling system with specified coolant. **This engine has aluminum cylinder heads and requires a special corrosion inhibited coolant formulation to avoid cooling system damage.**
19. Start engine and check for coolant, fuel and oil leaks.

VALVE COVER
REPLACE

1. Disconnect ignition wires from spark plugs, then the ignition wire routing clips from valve cover bolt studs.
2. **On lefthand valve cover,** remove oil filler cap, then the crankcase ventilation hose.
3. **On righthand valve cover,** remove positive crankcase ventilation valve.
4. **On both valve covers,** remove valve cover screws, then the cover and gasket.

5. Reverse procedure to install, noting the following:
   a. Lightly oil bolt and stud threads before installation. Using solvent, clean cylinder head and valve cover sealing surfaces to remove all gasket material and dirt.
   b. Tighten valve cover bolts to specifications.

VALVE ADJUSTMENT

Valve clearance on this engine cannot be adjusted due to the use of hydraulic valve lash adjusters.

OIL PAN
REPLACE

1. Disconnect battery ground cable.
2. Remove air cleaner outlet as follows:
   a. Disconnect wire harness from intake air temperature sensor, then the crankcase ventilation tube from the air cleaner outlet tube.
   b. Loosen air cleaner tube clamps on outlet tube, then disconnect outlet tube from throttle body.
   c. Disconnect outlet tube from mass airflow sensor, then remove tube.
3. Remove two radiator upper sight shield bolts and position shield aside.
4. Remove hood weather seal.
5. Remove windshield wipers as described in the "Electrical" section.
6. Remove lefthand cowl vent screen and wiper module.
7. Install suitable engine support, then raise and support vehicle.
8. Remove front engine support insulator through bolts, then partially lower vehicle.
9. Raise engine with engine support, then raise and support vehicle.
10. Remove starter motor as described in the "Electrical" section.
11. Position drain pan under vehicle, then drain engine oil.
12. Remove oil filter, then the starter motor wire and ground strap.
13. **On models equipped with automatic transmission,** remove automatic transmission oil cooler lines.
14. **On all models,** remove oil pan to bell housing bolts and bolts at crankshaft position sensor lower shield.
15. Remove remaining oil pan bolts.
16. Remove steering shaft pinch bolt, then separate steering shaft.
17. Position transmission jack under front sub-frame, then remove six rearward bolts on front sub-frame and loosen two forward front sub-frame bolts.
18. Remove lower shock absorber to front suspension lower arm bolts and nuts.
19. Lower front sub-frame.
20. Remove oil pan, then empty any residual oil from pan.
21. Remove oil pump screen cover and tube bolts and support bracket nut.
22. Remove oil pump screen cover and tube, then discard oil pump inlet tube gasket.
23. Reverse procedure to install, noting the following:
    a. When using silicone rubber (RTV)

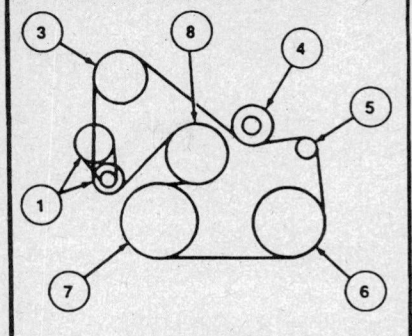

Fig. 6   Serpentine drive belt routing

FM1069400379000X

sealer, assembly must occur within 15 minutes after sealer application. After this time, sealer may start to set and its sealing effectiveness may be reduced.
   b. Apply silicone gasket and sealant F1AZ019652-A or equivalent to oil pan.
   c. Seat lefthand side locating pin before righthand side locating pin.
   d. Tighten nuts and bolts to specifications.
   e. Refill engine oil, then start engine and check for leaks.

OIL PUMP
REPLACE

1. Remove oil filter if necessary.
2. Remove oil pump and filter body to engine front cover bolts, then the oil pump and filter body from engine front cover.
3. Inspect O-ring for distortion and wear. Replace if necessary.
4. Reverse procedure to install. Tighten engine front cover bolts to specifications.

OIL PUMP SERVICE

1. Remove oil pump as described under "Oil Pump, Replace."
2. Lift pump gears out of pocket in oil pump and filter body, then remove oil pump body seal and discard.
3. Clean engine front cover and oil pump and filter body sealing surfaces.
4. Using straightedge and feeler gauge, measure across engine front cover mounting surface for wear or warpage.
5. If surface is out of flat by more than .0016 inch, replace front cover as described under "Engine Front Cover, Replace."
6. Lightly pack gear pockets with petroleum jelly or coat all gear surfaces with engine assembly lubricant D9AZ-19579-D. **Do not use chassis lubricants. Failure to properly coat oil pump gears may result in failure of pump to prime when engine is started.**
7. Install gears in oil pump and filter body pocket. Ensure petroleum jelly fills all voids between gears and pockets.

8. Position oil pump body seal and install oil pump and filter body to engine front cover using alignment dowels on engine front cover.
9. Tighten oil pump and filter body bolts to specifications.

OIL PRESSURE RELIEF VALVE

1. After drilling hole through valve plug, remove plug with slide hammer or by prying.
2. Remove spring and pressure relief valve from bore.
3. Thoroughly clean pressure relief valve bore and pressure relief valve to remove any metal chips which may have entered bore during drilling.
4. Inspect pressure relief valve and valve bore for wear, scoring or galling. If inspection determines part(s) to be unserviceable, replace pressure relief valve and/or oil pump and filter body.
5. Check clearance between pressure relief valve and bore. Valve should slip into bore without side play or binding.
6. Check spring for signs of fatigue or collapse.
7. Lubricate pressure relief valve with engine oil and install in bore. End with smaller diameter goes in first.
8. Position spring in bore, then install new plug. Plug can be tapped into bore using plastic tipped hammer. Ensure plug is .01 inch below machined surface.

OIL PUMP INTERMEDIATE SHAFT

1. Remove camshaft position sensor and housing.
2. Separate oil pump intermediate shaft from camshaft position sensor housing shaft.
3. Push lock ring end of oil pump intermediate shaft into camshaft position sensor housing shaft. Install oil pump intermediate shaft and camshaft position sensor. Install as assembly to ensure end of oil pump intermediate shaft is seated in oil pump drive gear.
4. Install hold-down clamp and tighten to specifications.

SERPENTINE DRIVE BELT

Conditions requiring belt replacement are excessive wear, rib chunk-out, severe glazing and frayed cords. Replace any belt exhibiting one of these conditions. Cracks on the rib side of a belt are considered acceptable.

If the belt has chunks missing from the ribs, it should be replaced. If two or more adjacent ribs have lost sections 1/2 inch or longer, or if the missing chunks are creating a noise or vibration condition, replace the belt.

BELT ROUTING

Refer to **Fig. 6** for serpentine drive belt routine.

BELT REPLACEMENT

1. Lift or rotate automatic tensioner.
2. Remove belt(s).
3. Install new belt over pulleys. Ensure all V-grooves make proper contact with pulley.
4. Rotate tensioner over belt.

WATER PUMP
REPLACE

1. Drain engine cooling system.
2. Remove radiator electrical motor, fan blade and fan shroud as an assembly.
3. Rotate drive belt tensioner, then remove drive belt.
4. Remove water pump pulley bolts, then the pulley.
5. Remove power steering pump pulley and water pump to power steering pump brace.
6. Remove heater water outlet tube bolts and heater water outlet tube from water pump.
7. Disconnect lower radiator hose from water pump.
8. Remove water pump bolts, stud bolts and nuts, then the water pump. Discard old water pump housing gasket. **If using prying device to assist in water pump removal, be careful not to damage mating surfaces.**
9. Reverse procedure to install, noting the following:
   a. Lightly oil all bolt and stud threads before installation, except those specifying special sealant.
   b. Apply gasket and trim adhesive D7AZ-19B508-B or equivalent, to water pump housing gasket to hold in position.
   c. Coat threads of No. 1 water pump bolt with pipe sealant with Teflon D8AZ-19554-A or equivalent, before installing.
   d. Fill engine cooling system with specified coolant. **This engine has aluminum cylinder heads and requires special corrosion inhibiting coolant formula to avoid cooling system damage.**
   e. Start engine and check for coolant leaks.

RADIATOR
REPLACE

1. **On models equipped with automatic transmission,** disconnect automatic transmission fluid cooler inlet and outlet lines from radiator using disconnect tool No. T82L-9500-AH, or equivalent.
2. **On all models,** drain cooling system, then disconnect radiator upper and lower hoses and overflow hose from radiator.
3. Remove two upper shroud bolts at radiator support, then lift fan shroud enough to disengage lower clips and lay shroud back over fan.
4. Remove radiator upper support bolts, then the support.
5. Lift radiator from vehicle.
6. **On models equipped with automatic transmission,** if installing new radiator, transfer oil cooler line connectors to new radiator using pipe sealant with suitable oil resistant sealer.
7. **On all models,** position radiator assembly into vehicle, then install upper supports and bolts.
8. **On models equipped with automatic transmission,** connect oil cooler lines.
9. **On all models,** install radiator electric motor, fan blade and fan shroud as an assembly by inserting two lower legs to radiator support with two bolts.
10. Install radiator support upper brackets and bolts. Tighten bolts to specifications.
11. Connect radiator upper, lower and overflow hoses, noting the following:
    a. Close draincock, then position hose clamps at least 2 inches from each end of hose.
    b. Slide hose on connections.
    c. **Ensure clamps are beyond bead and place in center of clamping surface of connections. New hose clamps must be installed inside hose alignment marks. Tighten clamp to specifications.**
12. Fill radiator with specified antifreeze and water mixture.
13. Operate engine and check for leaks at hose connections and at automatic transmission fluid cooler lines. **To avoid possible personal injury or vehicle damage, do not operate engine with hood open until fan blade has been first examined for cracks and separation.**
14. Check automatic transmission, radiator and coolant recovery reservoir fluid levels.

TIGHTENING SPECIFICATIONS

Year	Component	Torque/Ft. Lbs.
1992-95	A/C Compressor Bolts	30-45
	Connecting Rod Nuts	31-36
	Crankcase Ventilation Tube Mounting Bracket To Lower Intake Manifold Stud	15-22
	Cylinder Head Bolts	①
	Dual Converter & Pipe To Exhaust Manifold Nuts	16-23
	EGR Valve To Exhaust Manifold Bolt	25-35
	Engine Front Cover Bolts	③
	Engine Support & Wiring Bracket Bolt & Nut	15-22
	Engine Support Insulator Nuts	72-98
	Engine Support Insulator Through Bolts	35-50
	Engine To Transmission Bolts	⑤
	Exhaust Manifold Bolts	22-46
	Fuel Injection Supply Manifold Screws	6-8
	Heated Oxygen Sensor	28-33
	Heater Water Outlet Tube To Water Pump Bolts	71-106 ⑥
	Ignition Wire Routing Clip Stud Bolts	71-102 ⑥
	Lower Intake Manifold Bolts	①
	Lower Shock Absorber To Front Suspension Lower Arm Bolts	103-144
	Main Bearing Cap Bolts Or Stud	81-89
	Oil Level Indicator Tube Support Bracket Nut	15-22
	Oil Pan Bolts	80-106 ⑥

Year	Component	Torque/Ft. Lbs.
1992-95 — Cont'd	Oil Pump & Filter Body Bolts	④
	Oil Pump & Filter Body Bolts	④
	Oil Pump Intermediate Shaft Hold-Down Clamp	15-22
	Oil Pump Screen Cover & Tube Bolts	15-22
	Oil Pump Screen Cover & Tube Bracket Nut	30-40
	Radiator Bolts	71-92 ⑥
	Radiator Hose Clamps	20-30 ⑥
	Rocker Arm Bolts	7-9
	Spark Plugs	7-15
	Steering Shaft Pinch Bolt	30-42
	Throttle Body Nuts	②
	Torque Converter Bolts	20-34
	Upper Intake Manifold Bolts	①
	Water Outlet Connection Bolts	15-22
	Water Pump Bolts	15-22
	Water Pump Nuts	53-71 ⑥
	Water Pump Pulley Bolts	12-18
	Water Pump Stud Bolts	15-22

①—Refer to text.
②—Cross-tighten to 15-22 ft. lbs.
③—Smaller bolts, 118-22 ft. lbs.; larger bolts, 30-40 ft. lbs.
④—M8 bolts, 18-22 ft. lbs.; M6 bolts, 6-8 ft. lbs.
⑤—Automatic transmission, 40-50 ft. lbs.; manual transmission, 28-38 ft. lbs.
⑥—Inch lbs.

5.0L/V8-302 Engine

NOTE: On Air Bag Equipped Models, Refer To "Air Bag System Precautions" Located In The Front Of This Manual For System Disarming & Arming Procedures.

NOTE: For Procedures Not Found In This Section, Refer To 5.0L/V8-302 Engine Section In The Cougar, Crown Victoria, Grand Marquis & Thunderbird Chapter.

INDEX

PRECAUTIONS

AIR BAG SYSTEMS

Refer to "Air Bag System Precautions" in the front of this manual for system disarming and arming procedures.

FUEL SYSTEM PRESSURE RELIEF

Fuel supply tubes will remain pressurized for long periods of time after engine shutdown. This pressure must be relieved before beginning fuel system service or personal injury or damage to vehicle may occur. A valve is provided on the fuel injection supply manifold for this purpose.

1. On 1994-95 models, remove engine air cleaner.
2. On all models, connect EFI/CFI fuel

pressure gauge tool No. T80L-9974-B, or equivalent, to fuel pressure relief valve on fuel injection supply manifold.

3. Open manual valve on fuel pressure gauge tool to relieve fuel system pressure.

ENGINE MOUNT
REPLACE

1. Remove fan shroud screws, if necessary.
2. Remove insulators to lower bracket nuts, **Fig. 1**.
3. Raise engine with suitable jack and block of wood placed under oil pan.
4. Remove insulator to engine block bolts.
5. Remove insulator from vehicle.
6. Reverse procedure to install.

ENGINE
REPLACE

The engine replacement procedures are for the engine only without the transmission attached. Remove or disconnect parts of the secondary air injection system that will interfere with the removal or installation of the engine.

1992–93

Refer to the 5.0L/V8-302 Engine section in the Cougar, Crown Victoria, Grand Marquis & Thunderbird chapter for engine replacement procedures.

1994–95

Removal

1. Drain engine cooling system and crankcase.
2. Disconnect battery ground cable, then remove air cleaner outlet tube as follows:
   a. Disconnect wire harness from intake air temperature sensor, then the crankcase ventilation tube from the air cleaner outlet tube.
   b. Loosen air cleaner tube clamps on outlet tube, then disconnect outlet tube from throttle body.
   c. Disconnect outlet tube from mass airflow sensor, then remove tube.
3. Disconnect upper radiator hose from water outlet connection and lower radiator hose at water pump.
4. **On models equipped with automatic transmission,** disconnect transmission oil cooler lines.
5. **On all models,** remove radiator eletric motor, fan blade and fan as an assembly.
6. Remove radiator and drive belt.
7. Remove alternator/secondary air injection pump and alternator bracket as an assembly and position aside.
8. Disconnect engine control sensor wiring from oil pressure sender, then the low oil level sensor located on lefthand side of oil pan.
9. Relieve fuel pressure as described under "Precautions," then disconnect fuel supply and return lines.

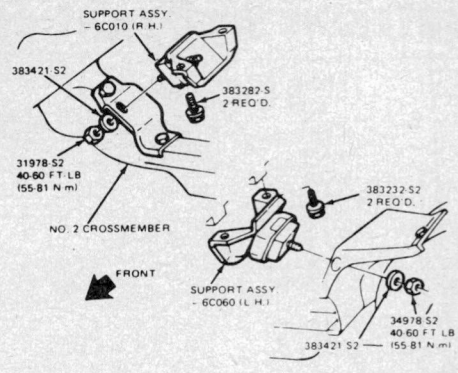

Fig. 1   Engine mounts

10. Disconnect accelerator cable from throttle body.
11. **On models equipped with automatic transmission,** disconnect throttle valve control actuating cable.
12. **On models equipped with speed control,** disconnect speed control linkage.
13. **On models equipped with automatic transmission,** disconnect transmission filler tube bracket from tube support bracket.
14. **On models equipped with air conditioning,** isolate and remove A/C compressor.
15. **On all models,** disconnect power steering pump bracket from cylinder block. Position pump aside and in position to prevent fluid from draining out.
16. Disconnect brake booster vacuum line from intake manifold.
17. Disconnect heater water hose from intake manifold heater inlet tube, then the engine control sensor wiring from water temperature indicator sender unit.
18. Remove flywheel or converter housing to engine upper bolts.
19. Disconnect fuel charging wiring at two 10-pin connectors.
20. Raise and support front of vehicle, then disconnect starter cable from starter motor and remove starter motor.
21. Disconnect dual converter and pipe from exhaust manifolds, then the front engine support insulators from front sub-frame.
22. Disconnect down-stream secondary air injection tubing and check valve from righthand exhaust manifold stud.
23. **On models equipped with automatic transmission,** proceed as follows:
   a. Disconnect transmission cooler lines from retainer, then remove converter housing inspection cover.
   b. Disconnect flywheel from torque converter, then secure converter in case.
   c. Remove remaining case to engine bolts.
24. **On all models,** lower vehicle and support transmission.
25. Attach engine lifting sling and hoist to engine lifting eyes on exhaust mani-

folds.
26. Raise engine slightly, then carefully pull from transmission. Carefully lift engine out of engine compartment, then install engine on work stand. **Avoid bending or damaging engine rear plate or other components.**

Installation

1. Attach engine lifting sling and engine lifting eyes to exhaust manifold, then hoist engine from work stand.
2. Lower engine carefully into engine compartment. Ensure exhaust manifolds are properly aligned with dual converter and pipe.
3. **On models equipped with automatic transmission,** start torque converter pilot into crankshaft. Align paint mark on flywheel to paint mark on torque converter.
4. **On models equipped with manual transmission,** start manual transmission input shaft pilot into crankshaft.
5. **On all models,** install flywheel or converter housing upper bolts. Ensure dowels in cylinder block engage housing.
6. Install front engine support insulators to front sub-frame attaching fasteners.
7. Raise and support front of vehicle, then connect dual converter and pipe to exhaust manifolds.
8. Install starter motor and starter wiring.
9. **On models equipped with automatic transmission,** remove retainer holding torque converter in case, then attach torque converter to flywheel and install converter housing inspection cover.
10. **On all models,** install remaining housing bolts.
11. Remove support from transmission and lower vehicle.
12. Connect fuel charging wiring at two 10-pin connectors.
13. Connect engine control sensor wiring to water temperature indicator sender unit, then the heater water hoses to intake manifold heater inlet tube.
14. Connect engine control sensor wiring to low oil level sensor.
15. **On models equipped with automatic transmission,** connect transmission filler tube support bracket.
16. **On all models,** connect accelerator cable and throttle valve control actuating cable.
17. **On models equipped with speed control,** connect speed control actuator.
18. **On all models,** connect fuel supply and return line.
19. Connect engine control sensor wiring to oil pressure sender.
20. Install alternator/air injection pump bracket and alternator bracket as an assembly, then the bolts.
21. Connect engine control sensor wiring.
22. **On models equipped with air conditioning,** install A/C compressor as described in the "Air Conditioning" section.
23. **On all models,** install drive belt, then the power steering pump bracket and bracket bolts.

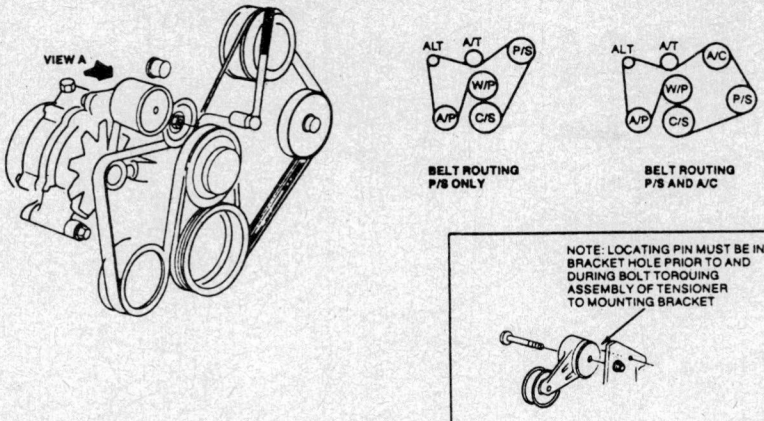

BELT ROUTING
P/S ONLY

BELT ROUTING
P/S AND A/C

NOTE: LOCATING PIN MUST BE IN BRACKET HOLE PRIOR TO AND DURING BOLT TORQUING ASSEMBLY OF TENSIONER TO MOUNTING BRACKET

VIEW A

FM1069100222000X

Fig. 2   Serpentine drive belt

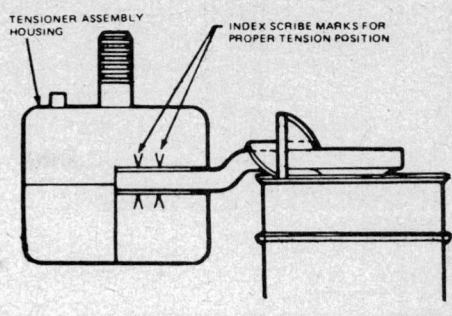

TENSIONER ASSEMBLY HOUSING

INDEX SCRIBE MARKS FOR PROPER TENSION POSITION

FM1069100223000X

Fig. 3   Serpentine drive belt tensioner alignment marks

24. Connect brake booster vacuum line.
25. Install radiator, then connect upper and lower radiator hoses.
26. **On models equipped with automatic transmission,** connect transmission oil cooler lines. Tighten bolts to specifications.
27. **On all models,** install radiator electric motor, fan blade and fan shroud as an assembly.
28. Fill and bleed cooling system, then fill crankcase with proper grade and quantity of oil.
29. **On models equipped with automatic transmission,** adjust throttle valve control actuating cable.
30. **On all models,** install air cleaner outlet tube.
31. Operate engine at fast idle and check all gaskets and hose connections for leaks.
32. Install and adjust hood as necessary.

VALVE CLEARANCE SPECIFICATIONS

Engine 5.0L/V8-302 HO	Valve Lash ①

①—With hydraulic lash adjuster completely collapsed, allowable measurement is .098–.198 inch, desired measurement is .123–.146 inch.

VALVE ADJUSTMENT

A .060 inch shorter pushrod or .060 inch longer pushrod is available for service to provide a means of compensating for dimensional changes in the valve mechanism. Valve stem to valve rocker arm clearance should be within specification with the hydraulic lifter completely collapsed.

Repeated valve reconditioning operations (valve seat and/or valve refacing) will decrease the valve opening clearance. The positive stop rocker arm bolt eliminates the necessity of adjusting the valve clearance. However, to obtain the specified valve clearance, it is important that all valve components be in a serviceable condition and tightened to specification.

If the clearance is less than specified, install a shorter pushrod. If the clearance is greater than specified, install a longer pushrod. To determine whether a shorter or longer pushrod is necessary, proceed as follows:
1. Disconnect brown lead (I terminal), then the red and blue lead (S terminal) at starter relay.
2. Install auxiliary starter switch between battery and S terminals of starter relay.
3. Crank engine with ignition switch (off) to position number 1 piston at TDC at end of compression stroke, then check the following valves:
   a. No. 1 intake, No. 1 exhaust.
   b. No. 4 intake, No. 3 exhaust.
   c. No. 8 intake, No. 7 exhaust.
4. Rotate crankshaft 360 degrees (one revolution) clockwise and check the following valves:
   a. No. 3 intake, No. 2 exhaust.
   b. No. 7 intake, No. 6 exhaust.
5. Rotate crankshaft 90 degrees (1/4 revolution) clockwise and check the following valves:
   a. No. 2 intake, No. 4 exhaust.
   b. No. 5 intake, No. 5 exhaust.
   c. No. 6 intake, No. 8 exhaust.
6. Replace pushrods as necessary.

OIL PAN
REPLACE
1992–93
1. Disconnect battery cables.
2. Remove fan shroud bolts and position fan shroud over fan.
3. Remove dipstick and tube assembly.

4. Raise and support vehicle, then drain crankcase. **Some oil pans have dual oil sumps. Make sure to remove both drain plugs to thoroughly drain oil.**
5. Remove two bolts steering gear to main crossmember bolts and allow steering gear to rest on frame away from oil pan.
6. Remove engine mount bolts, then raise engine and place 2 x 4 inch wooden block between each engine mount and vehicle frame.
7. Remove rear K-braces.
8. Remove oil pan bolts and lower oil pan onto frame.
9. Remove oil pump retaining bolts and inlet tube nut from No. 3 main bearing cap stud. Lower oil pump assembly into oil pan.
10. Remove oil pan. If necessary, rotate engine so crankshaft throws clear oil pan rail.
11. Reverse procedure to install.

1994–95
1. Disconnect battery ground cable, then remove oil level indicator tube from lefthand side of cylinder block.
2. Remove air cleaner outlet tube, then raise and support vehicle.
3. Drain crankcase, then disconnect low oil level sensor electrical connector.
4. Remove starter motor as described in the "Electrical" section.
5. Remove dual converter and pipe.
6. Remove front engine support insulator to front sub-frame nuts.
7. Remove rear engine support and rear engine support insulator.
8. Remove steering gear bolts and position steering gear forward out of way.
9. Raise and support engine in position allowing clearance for oil pan removal.
10. Remove oil pan bolts, then lower oil pan to front sub-frame.
11. Remove oil pump, oil pump screen cover and tube bolts. Allow oil pump and oil pump screen cover and tube to drop into oil pan.
12. Remove oil pan from vehicle.
13. Reverse procedure to install, noting the following:
   a. Clean oil pan and inspect for damage, then clean oil pan gasket surface on cylinder block.
   b. Tighten bolts and nuts to specifications.

c. Fill crankcase to proper level with specified engine oil.
d. Apply parking brake and, while holding foot on brake, start engine and allow to run for a few minutes.
e. Turn engine off and check for oil leaks.

SERPENTINE DRIVE BELT

1992–93

Some engines are equipped with a serpentine drive belt, **Fig. 2**, to drive the accessories in place of the usual arrangement. This "V" ribbed belt drives the fan/water pump, alternator, secondary air pump, optional A/C compressor and optional power steering pump.

The tensioner arm should be checked to ensure the top edge of the arm is located between the two index marks scribed on the circumference next to the slot of the tensioner housing, **Fig. 3**. If the tensioner arm is not properly aligned, the drive belt and pulleys should be inspected for wear and binding. If the drive belt and pulleys are satisfactory, the tensioner must be replaced as follows:

1. Insert 16-inch pry bar or equivalent in slot of tensioner bracket, then, using tensioner housing as fulcrum, push pry bar downward to force tensioner pulley upward, relieving tension on belt, **Fig. 2**.
2. Remove drive belt.
3. Remove bolt securing tensioner assembly to alternator bracket.
4. Remove tensioner assembly.
5. Position tensioner assembly so tang, located on rear of assembly, is placed to fit in hole or slot in alternator bracket.
6. Install tensioner assembly bolt through hole in alternator bracket and tighten bolt to specifications.
7. Install drive belt by inserting pry bar as previously described. Refer to decal located on top of windshield washer/coolant expansion reservoir for proper belt routing.
8. Remove pry bar.
9. The drive belt is automatically tensioned when the tensioner arm is located between the two index marks, **Fig. 3**.

1994–95

Some engines are equipped with a serpentine drive belt to drive the accessories in place of the usual arrangement. This "V ribbed belt drives the fan/water pump, alternator, secondary air pump, optional A/C compressor and optional power steering pump.

The tensioner can be checked with the engine running. Observe tensioner movement. The tensioner should move when the A/C compressor cycles or when the engine is accelerated rapidly. If the tensioner movement is constant and excessive, a pulley or shaft is probably bent or a pulley is out of round. In rare cases, excessive drive belt rideout (uneven depth of grooves in drive belt) can cause excessive

drive belt tensioner movement. To check this condition, replace belt with known good original equipment drive belt and repeat observation.

With engine off, check for proper drive belt routing, **Fig. 4**. Service as required.

Visually inspect tensioner wear indicator to ensure belt is within operating range. If necessary, replace drive belt.

Rotate tensioner and check for binding or frozen condition. If necessary, replace tensioner as follows:

1. Lift or rotate automatic drive belt tensioner away from drive belt, then remove drive belt. **Do not allow drive belt tensioner to snap back, as damage to tensioner could result.**
2. Remove tensioner bolt, then the tensioner.
3. Reverse procedure to install, noting the following:
   a. Install new tensioner locating pin in bracket prior to and during tightening of tensioner bolt.

b. **Incorrect drive belt installation will cause drive belt failure. Ensure belt is properly installed before starting engine, otherwise belt damage will occur.**

RADIATOR
REPLACE

1. **On models equipped with automatic transmission,** disconnect automatic transmission fluid cooler inlet and outlet lines from radiator using disconnect tool No. T82L-9500-AH, or equivalent.
2. **On all models,** drain cooling system, then disconnect radiator upper and lower hoses and overflow hose from radiator.
3. Remove two upper shroud bolts at radiator support, then lift fan shroud enough to disengage lower clips and lay shroud back over fan.
4. Remove radiator upper support bolts,

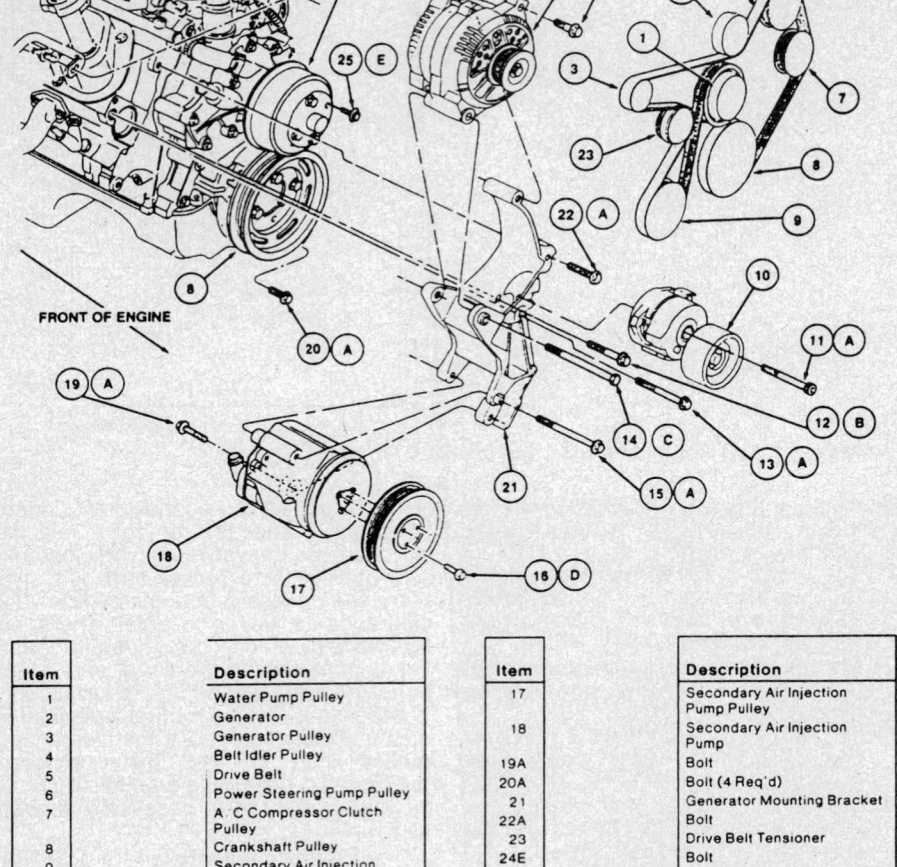

FRONT OF ENGINE

Fig. 4 Drive belt tensioner replacement. 1994-95

Item	Description
1	Water Pump Pulley
2	Generator
3	Generator Pulley
4	Belt Idler Pulley
5	Drive Belt
6	Power Steering Pump Pulley
7	A.C Compressor Clutch Pulley
8	Crankshaft Pulley
9	Secondary Air Injection Pump Pulley
10	Drive Belt Tensioner
11A	Bolt
12B	Bolt
13A	Bolt
14C	Bolt
15A	Bolt
16D	Bolt (3 Req'd)

Item	Description
17	Secondary Air Injection Pump Pulley
18	Secondary Air Injection Pump
19A	Bolt
20A	Bolt (4 Req'd)
21	Generator Mounting Bracket
22A	Bolt
23	Drive Belt Tensioner
24E	Bolt
25E	Bolt (4 Req'd)
A	Tighten to 29.7-40.3 N·m (22-30 Lb-Ft)
B	Tighten to 59.5-80.5 N·m (44-59 Lb-Ft)
C	Tighten to 40-55 N·m (30-41 Lb-Ft)
D	Tighten to 8.9-12.1 N·m (79-107 Lb-In)
E	Tighten to 21-29 N·m (15-21 Lb-Ft)

FM1069400377000X

then the support.

5. Lift radiator from vehicle.
6. **On models equipped with automatic transmission,** if installing new radiator, transfer oil cooler line connectors to new radiator using pipe sealant with suitable oil resistant sealer.
7. **On all models,** position radiator assembly into vehicle, then install upper supports and bolts.
8. **On models equipped with automatic transmission,** connect oil cooler lines.
9. **On 1992—93 models,** place fan shroud into clips on lower radiator support of radiator, then secure to upper support with two bolts.

10. Position shroud to maintain a minimum of .38 inch radial clearance to fan blade tips.
11. **On 1994—95 models,** install radiator electric motor, fan blade and fan shroud as an assembly by securing two lower legs to radiator support with two bolts.
12. Install radiator support upper brackets and bolts. Tighten bolts to specifications.
13. **On all models,** connect radiator upper, lower and overflow hoses, noting the following:
    a. Close draincock, then position hose clamps at least 2 inches from each end of hose.
    b. Slide hose on connections.

c. **Ensure clamps are beyond bead and place in center of clamping surface of connections. New hose clamps must be installed inside hose alignment marks. Tighten clamp to specifications.**
14. Fill radiator with specified antifreeze and water mixture.
15. Operate engine and check for leaks at hose connections and at automatic transmission fluid cooler lines. **To avoid possible personal injury or vehicle damage, do not operate engine with hood open until fan blade has been first examined for cracks and separation.**
16. Check automatic transmission, radiator and coolant recovery reservoir fluid levels.

TIGHTENING SPECIFICATIONS

Year	Component	Torque/Ft. Lbs.
1992-95	Air Bypass Valve To Throttle Body	6–8
	Alternator Adjustment Arm To Alternator Bolt	24–40
	Alternator Adjustment Arm To Cylinder Block Bolt	12–18
	Alternator Bracket To Cylinder Block	12–18
	Camshaft Sprocket Gear To Camshaft Bolt	40–45
	Camshaft Thrust Plate To Cylinder Block Bolt	9–12
	Connecting Rod Cap Bolts	19-24
	Cylinder Front Cover Bolt	12–18
	Cylinder Head To Engine Block	①
	Distributor Hold-Down Bolt	18–26
	EGR Valve To Intake Manifold Spacer	12–18
	Exhaust Manifold To Cylinder Head	18–24
	Fan To Water Pump Hub	12–18
	Flywheel To Crankshaft	75–85
	Front Engine Support Insulator Nuts ⑥	72–98
	Fuel Charging Assembly To Head	23–25
	Fuel Rail Assembly To Intake Manifold	6–8
	Intake Manifold	②
	Main Bearing Cap Bolts	60–70
	Oil Filter Insert To Cylinder Block Adapter Bolt	20–30

Year	Component	Torque/Ft. Lbs.
1992-95 -Cont'd	Oil Filter To Cylinder Block	③
	Oil Inlet Tube To Main Bearing Cap	22–32
	Oil Inlet Tube To Oil Pump Bolt	12–18
	Oil Pan Drain Plug	15–25
	Oil Pan To Cylinder Block ⑤	6-9
	Oil Pan To Cylinder Block Bolts ⑥	110–144 ⑦
	Oil Pump To Cylinder Block	22–32
	Pulley To Vibration Damper	35–50
	Radiator Bolts	71–92 ⑦
	Radiator Hose Clamps	20–30 ⑦
	Rocker Arm Cover	6-9
	Rocker Arm Fulcrum To Cylinder Head	18–25
	Rocker Arm Shaft Bracket	18–25
	Spark Plugs	5–10
	Tensioner Assembly Bolt	55–80
	Throttle Body To EGR Spacer And Upper Intake Manifold	12–18
	Throttle Cable To Manifold	8–10
	Timing Chain Front Cover	19–27
	Upper Intake To Fuel Charging Assembly	12–18
	Vacuum Fittings To Intake Manifold	6–10 ④
	Vibration Damper/Pulley	70–90
	Water Outlet Housing	9–12
	Water Pump To Cylinder Block Front Cover	12–18

①—Flanged hex bolts, torque to 25–35 ft. lbs., then to 45–55 ft. lbs., then advance each bolt an addition ¼ turn. Standard hex head bolts, torque to 55–65 ft. ;bs., then to 65–72 ft. lbs.

②—Torque in two steps: first to 11–15 ft. lbs., then to 20–25 ft. lbs. After assembly, retorque w/engine hot.

③—½ turn after gasket contacts sealing surface.
④—Install w/Teflon tape.
⑤—1992–93.
⑥—1994–95.
⑦—Inch lbs.

Clutch & Manual Transmission

INDEX

ADJUSTMENTS

CLUTCH PEDAL

A self-adjusting type clutch mechanism is used. The adjust mechanism consists of a spring-loaded ratchet quadrant attached to the clutch cable. To adjust the clutch pedal, grasp clutch pedal and pull upward, then slowly depress clutch pedal. If a click is heard during the procedure, an adjustment was necessary and has been accomplished. This procedure should be performed at least every 5000 miles.

CLUTCH

REPLACE

1992-93

2.3L/4-140 Engine

Before installing the throw-out bearing, apply a light film of lithium base lubricant part No. C1AZ-19590-B or equivalent, to the transmission front bearing retainer outside diameter, the clutch release fork and anti-rattle spring where they contact the release bearing hub and to the throw-out bearing where the bearing contacts the pressure plate release fingers. In addition, fill the throw-out bearing grease groove with the same lubricant. Wipe off all excess lubricant.

1. Lift clutch pedal to its uppermost position to disengage pawl and quadrant. Push quadrant forward, then unhook cable from quadrant and allow it to slowly swing rearward.
2. Raise and support vehicle.
3. Remove retainer pin and clevis pin from lower end of bellcrank.
4. Remove retaining clip, then the clutch cable from flywheel housing.
5. Remove starter electrical connectors, then starter motor from flywheel housing.
6. Remove transmission as described under "Transmission, Replace."
7. Remove flywheel housing to engine bolts, then the flywheel housing.
8. Disconnect short cable from release lever by pushing cable and releasing lever boot approximately 1/2 inch toward release bearing, then pulling cable rearward through hole in boot.
9. Remove release lever boot from flywheel housing.
10. Remove clutch release lever from housing by pulling it through window in housing until spring disengages from pivot.
11. Remove release bearing from release lever.
12. Loosen six pressure plate cover bolts evenly to gradually release spring tension and avoid distorting cover. If same pressure plate and cover is to be installed, mark cover and flywheel so pressure plate can be located in original position.
13. Remove pressure plate and clutch disc from flywheel.
14. Position clutch disc and pressure plate assembly on flywheel. Three dowel pins on flywheel must be properly aligned with pressure plate. Replace bent, damaged or missing dowel pins.
15. Start cover bolts but do not tighten.
16. Align clutch disc using suitable alignment tool inserted in pilot bearing. To avoid pressure distortion, alternately tighten bolts a few turns at a time until seated. Tighten pressure plate to specification.
17. Remove alignment tool.
18. Apply light film of long life lubricant part No. C1AZ-19590-BA or equivalent to:
    a. Outside diameter of transmission front bearing retainer.
    b. Release lever fork and anti-rattle spring where they contact release bearing hub.
    c. Release bearing surface contacting pressure plate release fingers.
    d. Release lever ball pivot and mating release lever pocket.
    e. Fill grease groove of release bearing hub. Clean all excess grease from inside bore of bearing hub or contamination of clutch disc will occur.
19. Attach clutch release bearing to release lever.
20. Attach release lever and release bearing to flywheel housing.
21. Install release lever boot in housing with hole toward transmission.
22. Install short cable in release lever boot, then into keyhole slot in release lever, by pushing boot toward release bearing.
23. Install flywheel housing to engine block and tighten to specification.
24. Install flywheel inspection plate.
25. Connect clutch cable to flywheel housing and connect retaining clip.
26. Place clevis over end fitting of cable, then install clevis pin and retaining pin.
27. Install starter motor, then transmission assembly.
28. Install clutch cable assembly by lifting clutch pedal to disengage pawl and quadrant. Then, push quadrant forward and hook end of cable over rear of quadrant.
29. Cycle clutch pedal several times to adjust cable.

5.0L/V8-302 Engine

1. Lift clutch pedal to its uppermost position to disengage pawl and quadrant. Push quadrant forward, unhook cable from quadrant and allow it to slowly swing rearward.
2. Raise and support vehicle.
3. Remove dust shield.
4. Remove retaining clip, then clutch cable from flywheel housing.
5. Remove flywheel inspection plate from front of clutch housing.
6. Remove transmission.
7. Remove clutch housing retaining bolts, then housing.
8. Remove clutch release lever from housing by pulling it through window in housing until retainer spring is disengaged from pivot.
9. Remove release bearing from release lever.
10. Loosen six pressure plate cover attaching bolts evenly to release spring tension gradually and avoid distorting cover. If same pressure plate and cover is to be installed, mark cover and flywheel so pressure plate can be located in original position.
11. Remove pressure plate and clutch disc from flywheel.
12. Reverse procedure to install. Tighten all components to specification.

1994-95

The clutch pedal must be lifted to disengage the adjusting mechanism during clutch release lever cable installation. Failure to do so will result in damage to the self-adjuster mechanism.

Under no circumstances should a prying instrument such as a screwdriver or a pry bar be used to install or remove the clutch release lever cable from clutch and brake pedal pivot shaft.

Refer to **Fig. 1** during clutch replacement.

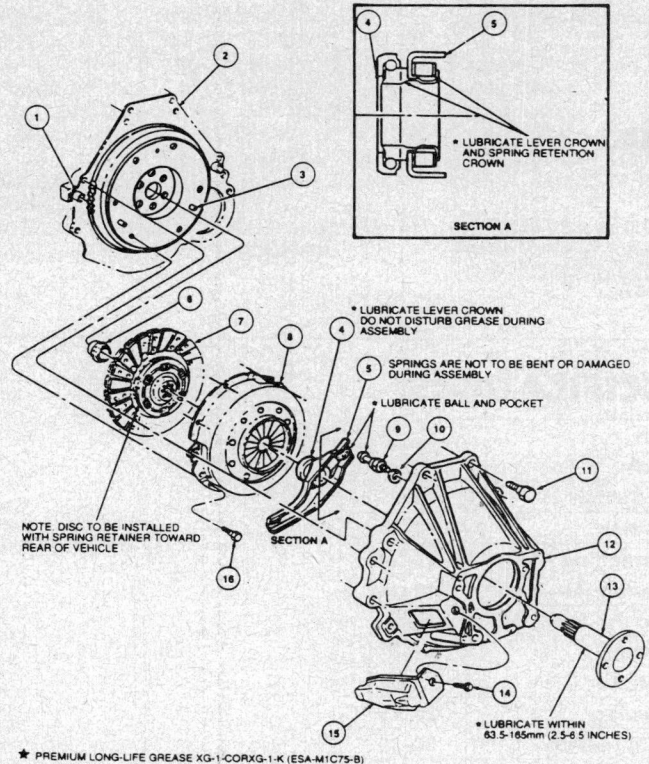

Item	Description	Item	Description
1	Flywheel Housing to Block Dowel (2 Req'd)	9	Clutch Release Lever Stud Washer
2	Rear Face of Block and Flywheel	10	Bolt (6 Req'd) (3.8L)
3	Flywheel Housing to Block Dowel (3 Req'd)	11	Bolt (6 Req'd) (5.0L)
4	Clutch Release Hub and Bearing	12	Flywheel Housing
5	Clutch Release Shaft	13	Main Drive Gear Bearing Retainer
6	Pilot Bearing (Install with Seal Toward Rear of Vehicle)	14	Bolt
7	Clutch Disc	15	Clutch Release Lever Dust Shield (Installed After Cable Assy)
8	Clutch Pressure Plate	16	Screw and Washer Assy (6 Req'd) (3.8L)
			Screw and Washer Assy (6 Req'd) (5.0L)

FM5049400071020X

Fig. 1 Clutch disc & pressure plate replacement (Part 2 of 2). 1994-95

★ PREMIUM LONG-LIFE GREASE XG-1-CORXG-1-K (ESA-M1C75-B)

FM5049400071010X

Fig. 1 Clutch disc & pressure plate replacement (Part 1 of 2). 1994-95

Removal

1. Lift clutch pedal to upper most position to disengage clutch and brake pedal pivot shaft.
2. Push clutch and brake pedal pivot shaft forward and unhook clutch release lever cable from clutch and brake pedal pivot shaft and allow it to slowly swing rearward.
3. Raise and support vehicle, then remove clutch release lever dust shield.
4. Disconnect clutch release lever cable from clutch release shaft.
5. Remove retaining clip, then the clutch release lever cable from flywheel housing.
6. Remove starter motor from flywheel housing, then the engine rear plate to front lower flywheel housing bolts.
7. Remove transmission as described under "Transmission, Replace."
8. Remove flywheel housing back just far enough to clear clutch pressure plate, then remove housing.
9. Remove clutch release shaft from flywheel housing by pulling it through window in flywheel housing until retainer spring disengages from pivot.
10. Remove clutch release hub and bearing from clutch release shaft.
11. Loosen six clutch pressure plate bolts evenly to release spring tension gradually and avoid distorting clutch pressure plate. If same clutch pressure plate is to be installed, mark plate and flywheel so pressure plate can be installed in its original position.
12. Remove clutch pressure plate and clutch disc from flywheel.

Installation

1. Position clutch disc and pressure plate assembly on flywheel, noting the following:
   a. Three flywheel housing to block dowels on flywheel must be properly aligned with clutch pressure plate.
   b. Bent, damaged or missing flywheel housing to block dowels must be replaced.
   c. Start clutch pressure plate bolts but do not tighten.
   d. Avoid touching clutch disc face, dropping parts or contaminating parts with oil or grease.
2. Align clutch disc using suitable alignment tool inserted in pilot bearing.
3. To avoid clutch pressure plate distortion, alternately tighten bolts a few turns at a time, until they are all tight, then tighten bolts to specifications.
4. Install transmission to flywheel housing.
5. Install engine rear plate to flywheel front lower housing bolts, then connect clutch release cable to flywheel housing and connect retaining clip.
6. Connect clutch release lever cable to clutch release shaft, then install clutch release lever dust shield.
7. Install starter motor as described in the "Electrical" section.
8. Lower vehicle, then install clutch release lever cable as follows:
   a. Lift clutch pedal to disengage clutch and brake pedal pivot shaft.
   b. Push clutch and brake pedal pivot shaft forward and hook end of clutch release lever cable over rear of clutch and brake pedal pivot shaft.
9. Cycle clutch pedal several times to adjust clutch release lever cable.

TRANSMISSION
REPLACE

1992-93

1. Raise and support vehicle.
2. Remove four bolts retaining catalytic converter, then converter.
3. Mark driveshaft so that it may be installed in the same relative position, then remove driveshaft. Cover extension housing to prevent leakage.
4. Disconnect electrical leads and speedometer cable from transmission.
5. Support rear of engine and transmission, then remove crossmember.
6. Lower transmission assembly to expose two bolts securing shift handle to shift tower, then remove bolts and handle assembly.
7. Disconnect wiring harness from back-up lamp switch.
8. **On 5.0L/V8-302 engines,** disconnect neutral sensing switch.
9. **On all models,** remove bolt from speedometer cable retainer, then speedometer driven gear from transmission.
10. Move transmission and jack rearward until transmission input shaft clears flywheel housing. If necessary, lower the engine enough to obtain clearance for transmission removal.
11. Reverse procedure to install.

1994-95

1. Raise and support vehicle, then mark driveshaft for installation reference.
2. Disconnect driveshaft from rear axle universal joint flange, then slide driveshaft off transmission output and fifth gear drive shaft and install extension housing seal replacer tool No. T61L-7657-A, or equivalent, into extension housing to prevent lubricant leakage.
3. Remove four dual converter Y pipe bolts, then the pipe.
4. Remove two rear transmission support to rear engine support nuts, then the bolts.
5. Support engine and transmission with transmission jack.
6. Remove two rear engine support bolt nuts.

7. Remove rear engine support bolts, then raise jack slightly and remove rear engine support.
8. Lower transmission to expose two bolts securing shift control selector lever and housing, then, using socket, remove two nuts and bolts.
9. Remove shift control selector lever and housing, then disconnect wiring harness from back-up lamp switch.
10. Remove speedometer cable bolt, then the speedometer drive gear from transmission.

11. Remove four transmission to flywheel housing bolts.
12. Move transmission and jack rearward until transmission input shaft clears flywheel housing. If necessary, lower engine enough to obtain clearance for transmission removal.
13. Reverse procedure to install, noting the following:
   a. Ensure transmission and flywheel housing mounting surfaces are free of dirt, paint and burrs.

   b. Fill transmission with specified transmission fluid. Apply pipe sealant with Teflon D8AZ-19554-A or equivalent, to transmission case plug in a clockwise direction prior to installation.
   c. Tighten nuts and bolts.
   d. Lower vehicle, then check shift and crossover motion for full shift engagement and smooth crossover operation.

TIGHTENING SPECIFICATIONS

Year	Component	Torque/Ft. Lbs.
1992–95	Back-Up Lamp Switch	20–35
	Bearing Retainer	11–20
	Catalytic Converter Attaching Bolts	20–30
	Cluster Gear Rear bearing Retainer	11–15
	Drain Plug	15–30
	Driveshaft Bolts ①	42–57
	Driveshaft Bolts ②	71–95
	Extension Housing	20–45
	Flywheel Bolts (2.3L/4-140)	56–64
	Flywheel Bolts (5.0L/V8-302)	75–85
	Flywheel Housing To Engine ③	28–38
	Flywheel Housing To Engine ④	39–54
	Neutral Sensing Switch	20–35
	Pressure Plate To Flywheel	12–24
	Shift Boot To Floor Pan	3–7
	Shift Cover	6–11
	Shift Lever To Transmission	23–32
	Speedometer Cable Retaining Screw	3–5
	Top Gear Sensing Switch	20–35
	Transmission Extension Housing Bolts	25–35
	Transmission Support ①	36–50
	Transmission Support ②	51–70
	Transmission To Flywheel Housing	45–65
	Turret Cover	11–15
1994-95	Dual Converter Y Pipe Bolts	20–30
	Flywheel Housing to Engine (3.8L/V6-232)	28–38
	Flywheel Housing to Engine (5.0L/V8-302)	38–55
	Pressure Plate to Flywheel (3.8L/V6-232)	30–37
	Pressure Plate to Flywheel (3.8L/V6-232)	18–24
	Speedometer Driven Gear Retainer Screw	54-115 ⑤
	Transmission Extension Housing Support Nut	26–35
	Transmission Shift Control Selector Lever & Housing Bolts	23–32
	Transmission to Flywheel Housing	45–65

① —1992–93.
② —1994–95.
③ —2.3L/4-140 engine.
④ —3.8L/V6-232 & 5.0L/V8-302 engines.
⑤ —Inch lbs.

Rear Axle & Suspension

INDEX

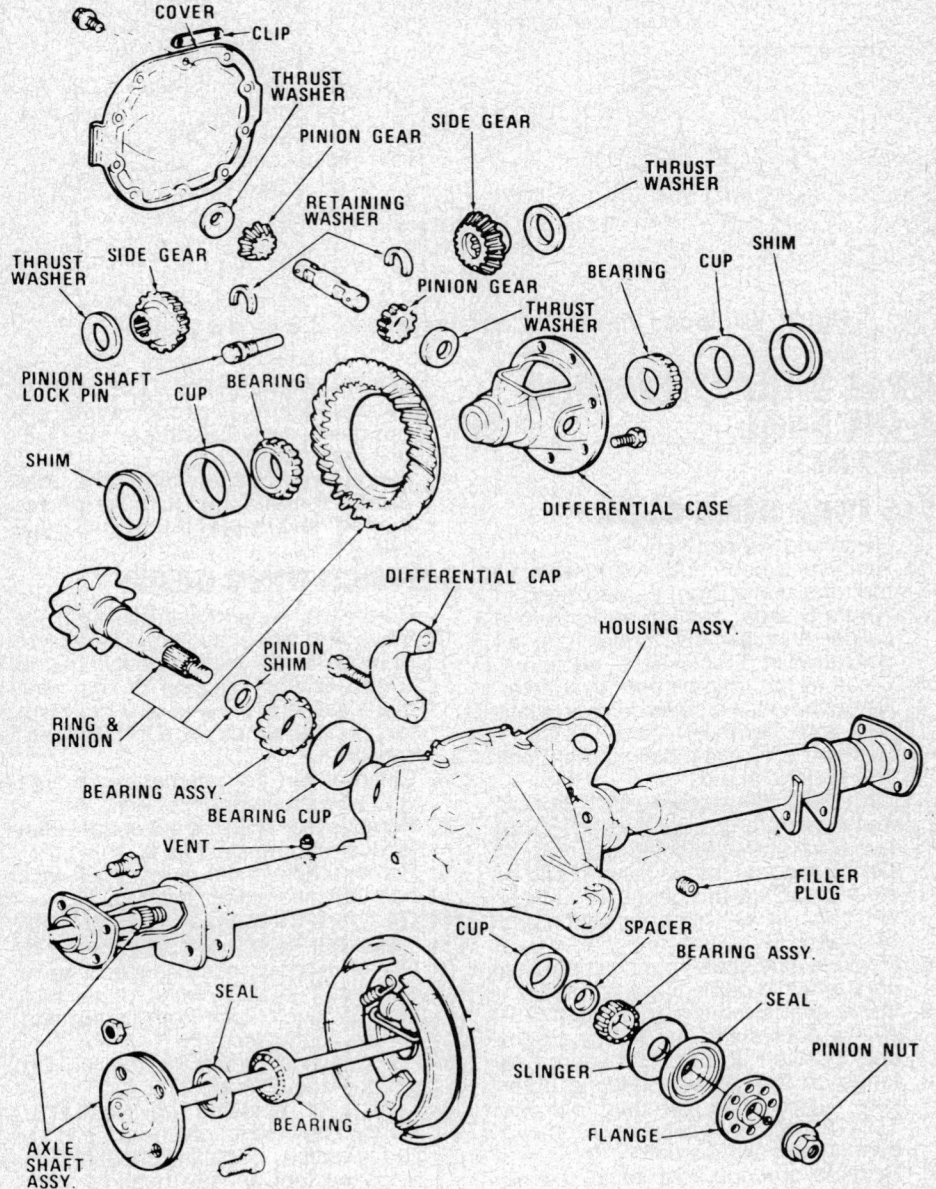

Fig. 1   Exploded view of integral rear axle. 7½ inch ring gear

The differential is mounted on two opposed tapered roller bearings which are retained in the housing by removable caps. Differential bearing preload and drive gear backlash is adjusted by nuts located behind each differential bearing cup.

The drive pinion assembly is mounted on two opposed tapered roller bearings. Pinion bearing preload is adjusted by a collapsible spacer on the pinion shaft. Pinion and ring gear tooth contact is adjusted by shims between the rear bearing cone and pinion gear.

REAR AXLE
REPLACE

1993-94

1. Raise and support vehicle, then position safety stands at rear frame members.
2. Drain lubricant from axle.
3. Mark driveshaft and pinion flanges for reassembly, then disconnect driveshaft at rear axle U-joint and remove driveshaft from transmission extension housing. Install seal replacer tool in extension housing to prevent leakage.
4. Disconnect shock absorbers at lower mountings.
5. Remove rear wheels and brake drums, then disconnect brake lines at wheel cylinders.
6. Disconnect vent hose from vent tube, then remove vent tube from brake junction and axle housing.
7. Remove clips retaining brake lines to axle housing.
8. Support rear axle housing using a suitable jack.
9. Disconnect upper control arms from mountings on axle housing, then carefully lower axle assembly until spring tension is relieved and remove coil springs. Disconnect lower control arms from axle housing.
10. Lower rear axle and remove from vehicle.
11. Reverse procedure to install.

1994-95

1. Raise and support vehicle, then position safety stands under rear frame crossmember.

FM3039100222000X

DESCRIPTION

This rear axle, **Fig. 1**, is an integral design hypoid with the center line of the pinion set below the center line of the ring gear. The semi-floating axle shafts are retained in the housing by ball bearings and bearing retainers at axle ends.

2. Drain lubricant from axle by removing axle housing cover.
3. Remove wheels, rear disc brake calipers and rear disc brake rotors as described in "Disc Brakes" section.
4. Remove differential pinion shaft lock pin from differential pinion shaft, then the differential pinion shaft.
5. Carefully remove rear brake anti-lock sensor. **Damage to rear brake anti-lock sensor may occur if sensor is not removed before axle shaft.**
6. Push axle shafts inward to remove rear axle shaft U-washers, then remove axle shafts.
7. Remove brake junction block to axle housing cover bolt, then the brake hose support bracket from clips and position aside.
8. Disconnect driveshaft at rear axle universal joint flange and wire it to underbody. Mark driveshaft centering socket yoke and rear axle universal joint flange.
9. Support rear axle housing with jackstands or hoist, then disengage rear brake hose from rear brake hose to rear axle housing clips.
10. Disconnect rear axle housing vent from rear axle housing. Some rear axle housing vents may be secured to rear axle housing through brake junction block. At assembly apply threadlock and sealer E0AZ-19554-AA or equivalent, to thread to ensure retention.
11. Disconnect lower shock absorber studs from rear shock absorber lower mounting bracket on rear axle housing, then remove rear suspension arm and bushing nuts and bolts from axle housing rear bracket mountings.
12. Lower rear axle housing assembly until rear springs are released, then lift out rear springs.
13. Remove rear suspension lower arm to rear axle housing nuts and bolts, then disconnect both rear suspension lower arms from rear axle housing.
14. Lower rear axle housing and remove it from vehicle.
15. Reverse procedure to install, noting the following:
    a. Installing rear wheel bearing or inner wheel bearing oil seal without proper tool may result in an early rear wheel bearing or inner wheel bearing oil seal failure. If inner wheel bearing oil seal becomes cocked in bore during installation, remove it and install a new one.
    b. Differential pinion shaft lock pin must be tightened to specification using stud and bearing mount tool No. E0AZ-19554-BA, or equivalent.
    c. Ensure machined surfaces on both axle housing cover and rear axle housing are clean before installing new silicone sealant. Inside of axle must be covered when cleaning machined surface to prevent axle contamination. Tighten axle housing cover bolt in crosswise pattern to ensure uniform draw on axle housing cover.

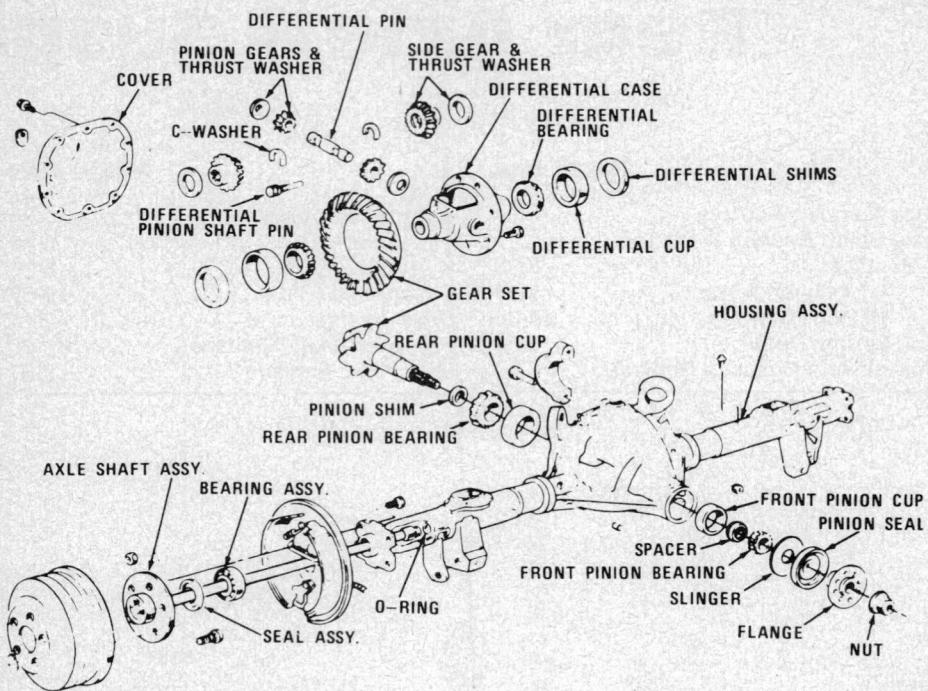

Fig. 2 Exploded view of integral rear axle. 8.8 inch ring gear

AXLE SHAFT, BEARING & OIL SEAL
REPLACE

7½ INCH RING GEAR

1. Raise and support vehicle.
2. Remove wheel and tire assembly, then the brake drum as described in "Drum Brakes" section or disc brake caliper and rear disc brake rotor as described in "Disc Brakes" section.
3. Clean all dirt from carrier cover area.
4. Remove housing cover to drain lubricant from rear axle.
5. Remove differential pinion shaft lock bolt and the shaft.
6. **On 1994-95 models,** carefully remove rear brake anti-lock sensor before removing axle shaft.
7. **On all models,** move flanged end of axle shafts toward center of vehicle and remove "C" clip from button end of shaft.
8. Remove axle shaft from housing. Use care to avoid damaging the oil seal.
9. Insert seal removing tool No. 1175-AC, or equivalent, into housing bore and position it behind bearing so tangs on tool engage bearing outer race. Using slide hammer tool No. T50T-100-A, or equivalent, remove bearing and seal as unit.
10. Reverse procedure to install, noting the following:
11. Lubricate new bearing with rear axle lubricant before installing. Apply suitable grease between lips of oil seal.
12. **Install bearing using wheel bearing installer tool No. T78P-1225-A, or equivalent, and seal using wheel**

seal installer tool No. T78P-1177-A, or equivalent. If proper tools are not used, early bearing or seal failure may result.
13. **If seal becomes cocked in the bore during installation, it must be removed and replaced with a new one.**

8.8 INCH RING GEAR

1. Raise and support vehicle, then remove rear wheel and tire assembly.
2. Remove brake drum as described in "Drum Brakes" section or rear disc brake calipers and rear disc brake rotors as described in "Disc Brakes" section.
3. Clean all dirt from carrier cover area with wire brush and/or cloth.
4. Remove axle housing cover and drain lubricant from axle, **Fig. 2.**
5. Remove differential pinion shaft lock bolt and differential pinion shaft.
6. **On 1994-95 models,** carefully remove rear brake anti-lock sensor.
7. **On all models,** push flanged end of axle shaft toward center of vehicle, then remove C-lock from button end of axle shaft assembly.
8. Remove axle shaft from housing. Do not damage oil seal.
9. Insert seal removing tool No. 1175-AC, or equivalent, into housing bore and position it behind bearing so tangs on tool engage bearing outer race. Using slide hammer tool No. T50T-100-A, or equivalent, remove bearing and seal as unit.
10. Reverse procedure to install, noting the following:
    a. Lubricate new bearing with lubricant E0AZ-19580-A or equivalent,

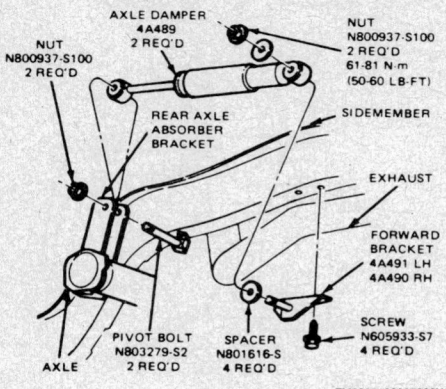

Fig. 3   Axle damper assembly

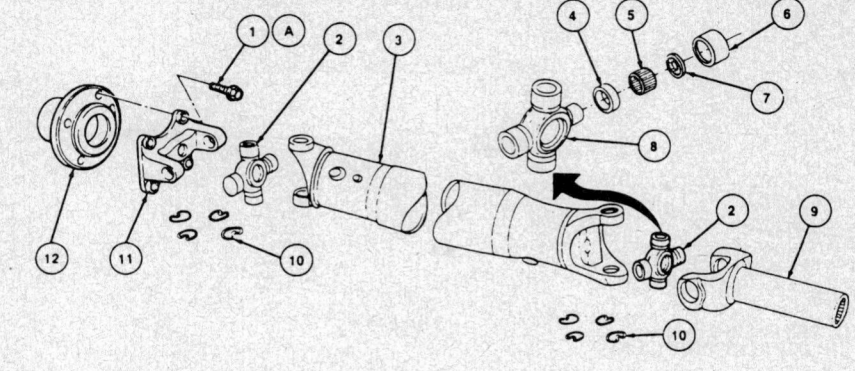

Item	Description	Item	Description
1A	Bolt (4 Req'd)	8	Spider
2	Rear Axle Shaft Universal Joint	9	Driveshaft Slip Yoke
3	Driveshaft	10	Snap Ring (4 Req'd)
4	Grease Seal	11	Driveshaft Centering Socket Yoke
5	Needle Rollers	12	Rear Axle Universal Joint Flange
6	Bearing Cup	A	Tighten to 95-130 N·m (71-95 Lb-Ft)
7	Thrust Washer		

Fig. 4   Driveshaft & universal joint components. Single Cardan type U-joint

and install bearing into housing bore using wheel bearing installing tool No. T78P-1225-A, or equivalent.

b. Install axle shaft seal using wheel seal installer tool No. T78P-1177-A, or equivalent. Apply lubricant C1AZ-19590-B or equivalent, between seal lips. **Installing bearing or seal assembly without proper tool may result in an early bearing or seal failure. If seal becomes cocked in bore during installation, remove it and install new one.**

c. Check for presence of axle shaft O-ring on shaft spline end and install if not present.

AXLE DAMPER
REPLACE

1. Raise vehicle and support rear axle.
2. Remove rear wheel, then the axle damper rear nut and pivot bolt, **Fig. 3.**
3. Remove axle damper forward nut, then the axle damper and spacer.
4. Reverse procedure to install.

PROPELLER SHAFT
REPLACE

1. To maintain balance, mark relationship of rear driveshaft yoke and the drive pinion flange of the axle if alignment marks are not visible.
2. Disconnect rear U-joint from companion flange, **Fig. 4.** Wrap tape around loose bearing caps to prevent them from falling off spider. Pull driveshaft toward rear of car until slip yoke clears transmission extension housing and the seal. Install suitable plug into extension housing to prevent lubricant leakage.
3. Lubricate slip yoke splines with suitable grease, then remove plug from transmission extension.
4. Inspect housing seal for damage and replace if necessary.
5. Align slip yoke index mark with transmission output shaft mark and install driveshaft assembly. Do not allow slip yoke assembly to bottom on output shaft with excessive force.
6. Install driveshaft so index mark on

rear flange is aligned with index mark on axle companion flange to ensure original driveline balance. When installing new driveshaft assembly, align factory made yellow paint mark at rear of driveshaft tube with factory made yellow paint mark on axle companion flange.

7. Tighten all flange bolts to specifications.

SHOCK ABSORBER
REPLACE

On all models except Mustang 3-door, open the luggage compartment to gain access to the upper shock stud. On Mustang 3-door models, entry to the upper shock attachment is made by opening the hatch door and removing the trim panel access door.

These vehicles are equipped with gas pressurized shock absorbers which will extend unassisted. Do not apply heat or flame to the shock absorber tube during removal.

1. From inside luggage compartment, remove rubber cap, if so equipped.
2. Remove nut, washer and insulator assembly from shock absorber upper stud.
3. Raise and support vehicle, then support rear axle.
4. Remove nut, washer and insulator assembly from shock absorber lower stud.
5. From underside of vehicle, compress shock absorber to clear it from hole in upper shock tower.
6. Remove shock absorber.
7. Reverse procedure to install, tighten bolts to specification.

COIL SPRING
REPLACE

1. Raise rear of vehicle and support at rear body crossmember.
2. Remove stabilizer bar, if equipped, **Fig. 5.**
3. Lower axle housing until shock absorbers are fully extended. **Axle housing must be supported with suitable jack.**
4. Position suitable jack under lower control arm rear pivot bolt to support control arm, then remove pivot bolt.
5. Carefully lower the lower control arm until spring tension is relieved, then remove coil spring and insulator.
6. Reverse procedure to install. Tighten lower control arm pivot bolt to specifications, with suspension at curb height.

CONTROL ARM
REPLACE

UPPER

1. Raise rear of vehicle and support at rear body crossmember.
2. Remove upper control arm rear and front pivot bolts, then the control arm.
3. If control arm axle bracket bushings are to be replaced, refer to **Figs. 6 and 7.**
4. Position upper control arm into side rail bracket, then install front pivot bolt. Do not tighten bolt at this time.
5. Raise rear axle until upper control arm rear pivot bolt hole is aligned with hole in axle housing, then install rear pivot bolt. Do not tighten bolt at this time.

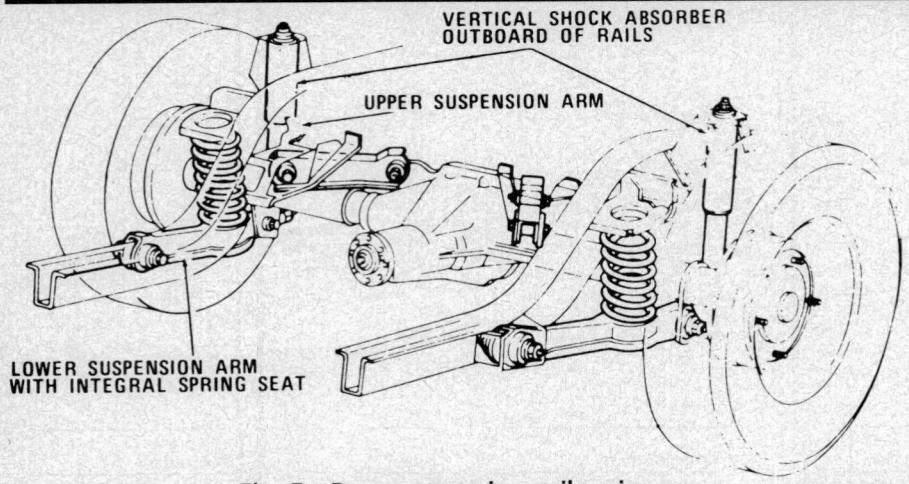

Fig. 5 Rear suspension coil spring

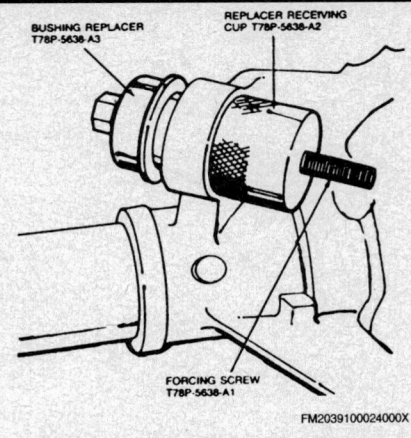

Fig. 7 Upper control arm axle bracket busing installation

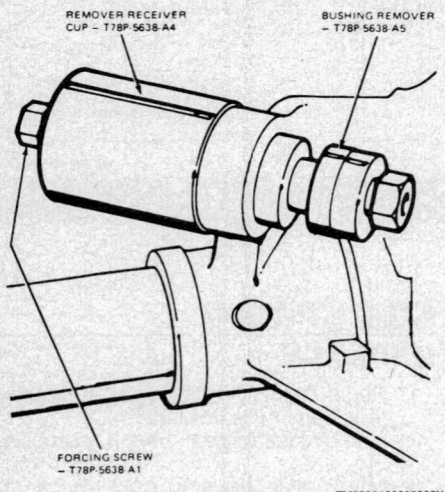

Fig. 6 Upper control arm axle bracket busing removal

6. Position suspension at curb height. Tighten front pivot bolt to specifications.

LOWER

1. Raise and support vehicle, then support body at rear crossmember.
2. Lower hoist until rear shock absorbers are fully extended, then place transmission jack under lower arm to axle pivot bolt. **Rear axle housing must be supported by hoist, transmission jack or jackstands.**
3. Remove and discard lower control arm front pivot bolt and nut, then remove control arm, **Fig. 8.**
4. Reverse procedure to install. Tighten front and rear pivot bolts to specifications.

CONTROL ARM BUSHING
REPLACE

1. Remove control arm as described under "Control Arm, Replace."
2. Place bushing remover and installer

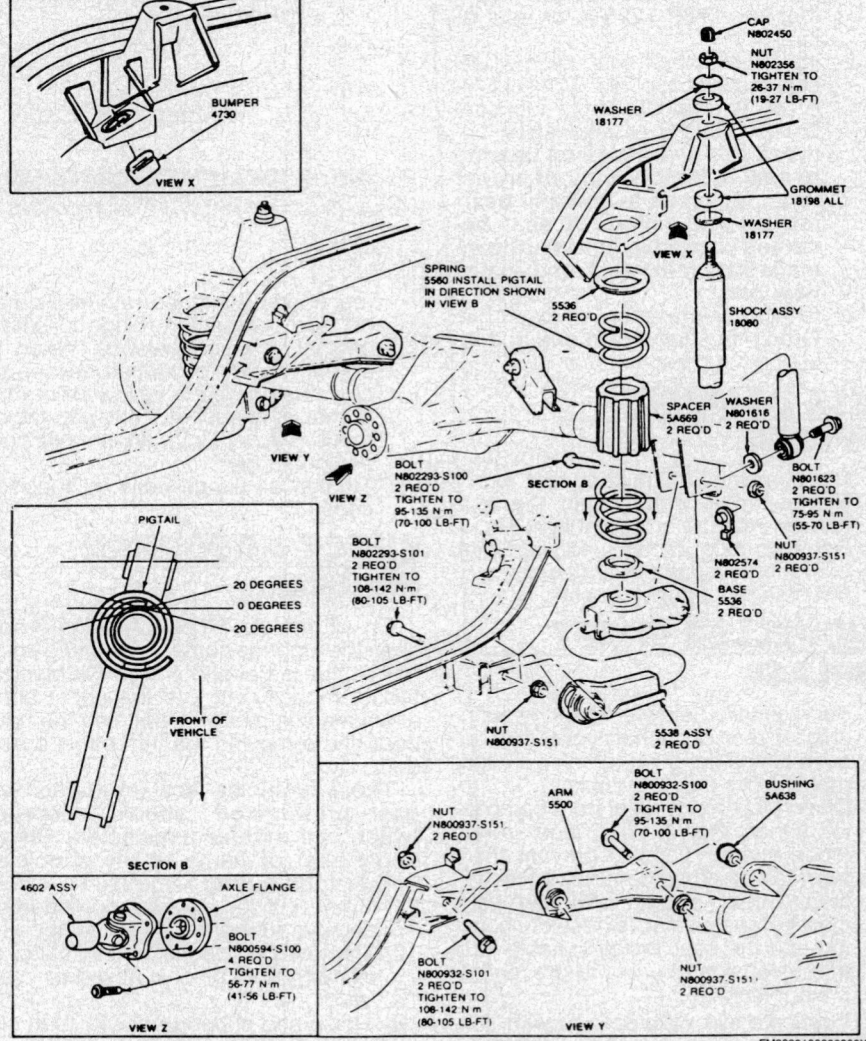

Fig. 8 Exploded view of rear suspension

set tool No. T78P-5638-A, or equivalent, as shown, **Fig. 6,** and remove bushing.
3. Using installer tool, install bushing into control arm bushing ear of rear axle housing, **Fig. 7.**
4. Install control arm as described under "Control Arm, Replace."

STABILIZER BAR
REPLACE

1. Raise and support rear of vehicle.
2. Remove four bolts attaching stabilizer bar to brackets on lower control arms.
3. Remove stabilizer bar from vehicle.
4. Reverse procedure to install.

TIGHTENING SPECIFICATIONS

Year	Component	Torque/Ft. Lbs.	Year	Component	Torque/Ft. Lbs.
1992-93	Axle Damper Front Bolt	57–75	1994-95	Axle Damper Front Bolt	57–75
	Axle Damper Rear Nut	57–75		Axle Damper Rear Nut	57–75
	Axle Flange Bolt	41–56		Clevis Bracket to Axle Nut	67–80
	Bracket Retaining Bolt	7–12		J-Nut	31–39
	Bumper To Bracket Nut	12–20		Lower Arm to Axle Pivot Bolt	71–97
	Clevis Bracket To Axle	55–70		Lower Arm to Frame Bolt	71–97
	Lower Arm To Axle	70–100		Rear Axle U-Joint Flange Bolt	41–56
	Lower Arm To Frame	80–105		Rear Axle Bumper To Bracket Nut	12–20
	Shock Absorber (Lower Attachment)	57–75		Rear Axle Bumper Bracket Retaining Bolt	8–11
	Shock Absorber (Upper Attachment)	20–27		Shock Absorber Upper Attachment	25–34
	Shock Absorber To Clevis Bracket ①	45–60		Shock Absorber Lower Attachment	57–75
	Stabilizer Bar To Lower Arm	33–51		Shock Absorber to Clevis Bracket Bolt	57–75
	Torx Drive Bolt	31–39		Upper Arm to Axle Bolt	70–100
	Upper Arm To Axle	70–100		Upper Arm to Frame Bolt	77–105
	Upper Arm To Frame	80–105		Wheel Lug Nuts	85–105
	Wheel Lug Nuts	85–104			

①—Vehicle equipped w/handling package.

Front Suspension & Steering

INDEX

DESCRIPTION

The front suspension, **Fig. 1,** is of the modified McPherson strut design, which uses shock struts and coil springs. The springs are mounted between the lower control and a spring pocket in the crossmember.

WHEEL BEARING
ADJUST

1993–94

1. Raise vehicle until wheel and tire clear floor.
2. Remove wheel cover and dust cap from hub.
3. Remove cotter pin and locknut.
4. Loosen adjusting nut 3 turns, then rock wheel, hub and rotor assembly in and out several times to move shoe and linings away from rotor.
5. While rotating wheel assembly, tighten adjusting nut to seat bearings. **Fig. 2.**
6. Back off adjusting nut one half turn. Tighten nut to specifications with suitable torque wrench or finger tight.

7. Locate nut lock on adjusting nut so castellations on lock are aligned with cotter pin hole in spindle.
8. Install new cotter pin and replace dust cap and wheel cover.

1994–95

The wheel bearings in these models are not adjustable.

WHEEL BEARING
REPLACE

1992–93

1. Raise vehicle and remove front wheels.
2. Remove caliper mounting bolts. **It is not necessary to disconnect brake lines for this operation.**
3. Slide caliper off of disc, inserting clean spacer between shoes to hold them in their bores after caliper is removed. Position caliper out of way. **Do not allow caliper to hang by brake hose.**
4. Remove hub and disc assembly. Grease retainer and inner bearing can now be removed, **Fig. 3.**
5. Reverse procedure to install.

1994–95

On these models, the wheel bearing and wheel hub must be replaced as an assembly.

1. Raise and support vehicle, then remove wheel and tire assembly.
2. Remove front hub cap grease seal from wheel hub and discard seal.
3. Remove two front disc brake caliper assembly bolts, then the caliper assembly and suspend with suitable wire. **Do not let front disc brake caliper assembly hang by front brake hose.**
4. Remove front disc brake rotor, then the factory push on nuts.
5. Remove front axle wheel hub retainer and discard.
6. Remove wheel hub and bearing. If assembly cannot be removed by hand, use front hub remover/replacer tool No. T81P-1104-C, or equivalent.
7. Reverse procedure to install.

BALL JOINT INSPECTION

Support vehicle in normal driving position with both ball joints loaded. Clean area around grease fitting and checking sur-

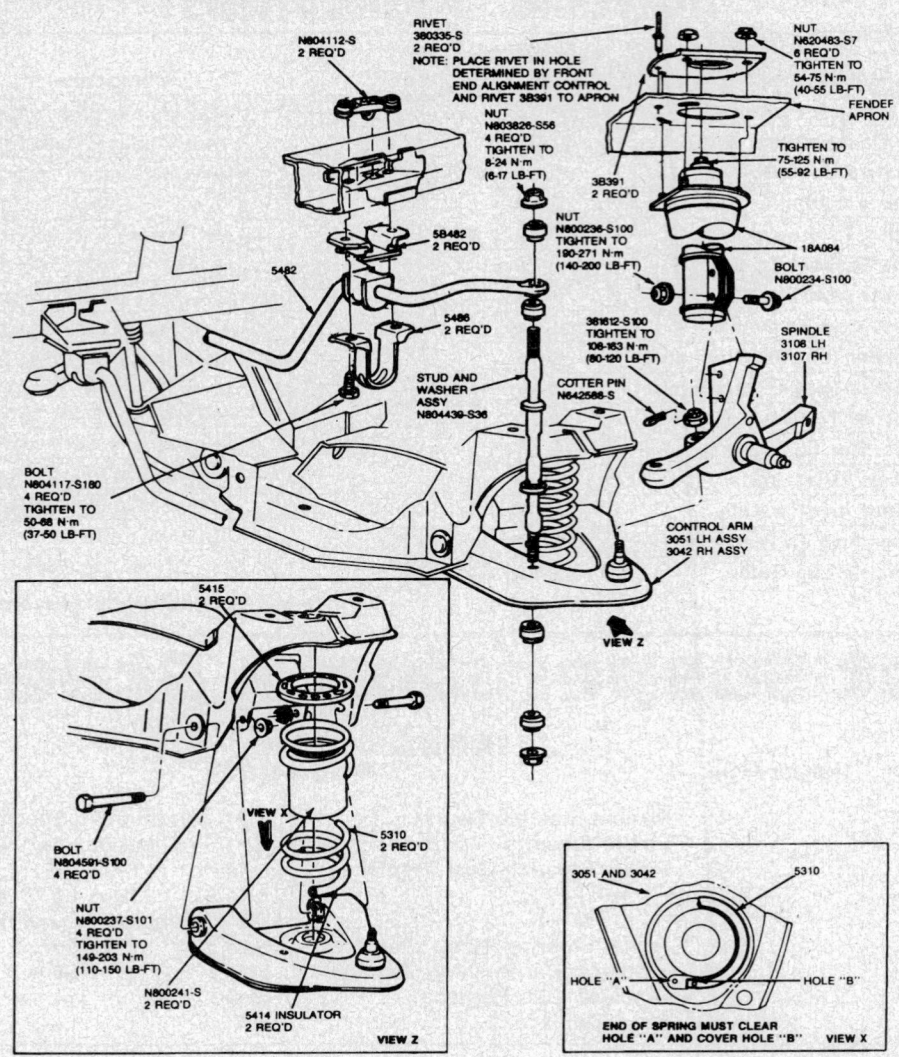

Fig. 1 Front suspension assembly

FM2029100057000X

face. The checking surface is the round boss into which the grease fitting is installed. The checking surface should project outside the ball joint cover, **Fig. 4.** If checking surface is inside the cover replace the lower control arm assembly.

BALL JOINT
REPLACE

1992-93

The lower ball joint and lower control arm must be replaced as an assembly.

1994-95

1. Remove lower control arm as described under "Control Arm, Replace."
2. Clamp front suspension lower arm in vise, then remove and discard joint boot seal.
3. Press out front suspension arm ball joint using C-frame tool No. T74P-4635-C, ball joint remover tool No. D89P-3010-A and cup tool No. D84P-3395-A4, or equivalents, **Fig. 5.**
4. When installing new front ball joint,

protective cover must be left in place during installation to protect ball joint seal. It may be necessary to cut off end of cover to allow it to pass through receiving cup.
5. Install ball joint with ball joint replacer tool No. D89P-3010-B, cup tool No. D84P-3395-A4 and C-frame tool No. T74P-4635C, or equivalents, **Fig. 6.**
6. Install lower control arm as described under "Control Arm, Replace."

COIL SPRING
REPLACE

1. Raise front of vehicle and place safety stands under jack pads located rearward of wheels, then remove wheel and tire assembly.
2. Remove the brake caliper and wire it out of the way.
3. Disconnect stabilizer bar link from lower control arm.
4. Remove steering gear retaining bolts if necessary, then position the gear so that the suspension arm bolt may be removed.

5. Using tie rod end remover tool No. 3290-D, or equivalent, disconnect tie rod from spindle.
6. Install spring compressor tool No. T82P-5310-A, or equivalent, on models equipped with 2.3L/4-140 engine, or tool No. D78P-5310-A, or equivalent, on models with 5.0L/V8-302 engine, then compress coil spring until it is free of the spring seat. **Ensure spring compressor is properly installed before compressing spring. Also ensure spring is sufficiently compressed to permit removal of lower control arm pivot bolts.**
7. Remove two lower control arm pivot bolts, then disengage lower control arm and remove spring assembly, **Fig. 1. Measure compressed length of spring and amount of curvature to aid in compressing and installing spring.**
8. Reverse procedure to install, noting the following:
   a. Ensure lower spring end is positioned between two holes in lower control arm spring pocket.

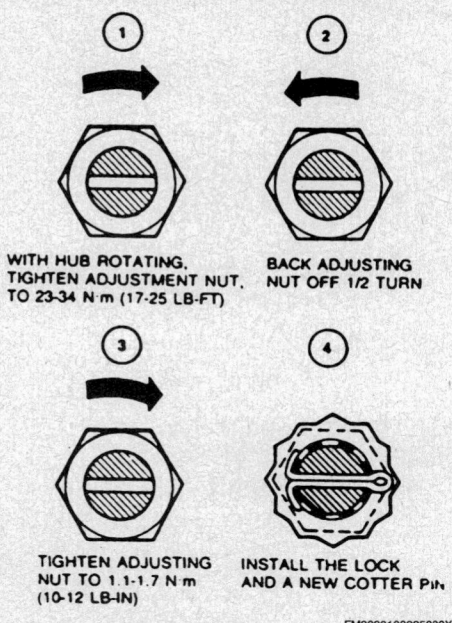

Fig. 2 Wheel bearing adjustment

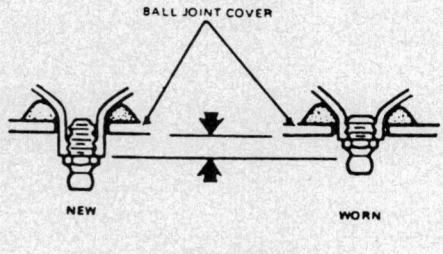

Fig. 4 Lower ball joint wear check

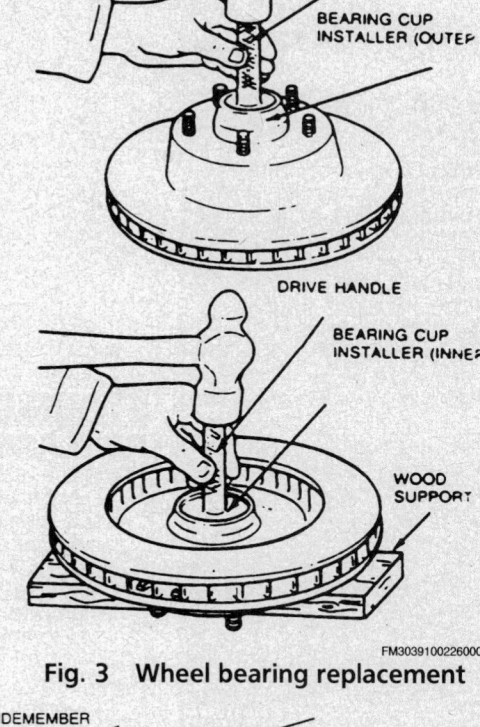

Fig. 3 Wheel bearing replacement

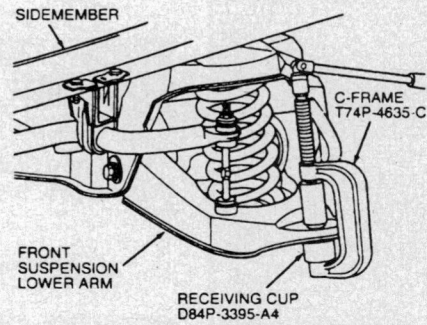

Fig. 5 Control arm ball joint removal. 1994-95

b. Tighten stabilizer bar and steering gear to No. 2 crossmember to specifications.
c. Tighten tie rod to steering spindle to specification.

STRUT
REPLACE

Due to the preload pressure in the strut assembly, it will take up to 50 lbs. of force to push the strut rod down into the cylinder assembly (lower can). **This is normal and does not indicate a binding condition.**

The bolts used in this installation are made to metric specification and require use of metric tools.

1. Place ignition switch in unlocked position to permit free movement of front wheels.
2. From engine compartment, remove upper shock absorber mounting nut.
3. Raise front of vehicle and support lower control arms. Position safety stands under frame jacking pads located rearward of wheels.
4. Remove wheel and tire assembly.
5. Remove caliper, rotor and dust shield.
6. Remove two bolts attaching shock absorber to spindle.
7. Lift strut upward from spindle to compress rod, then pull downward and re-

move shock absorber.
8. Remove jounce bumper, if equipped.
9. Reverse procedure to install. Tighten upper and lower mounting nuts to specifications.

CONTROL ARM
REPLACE

1992–93

1. Raise and support vehicle, allowing control arm to hang freely.
2. Remove wheel and tire assembly.
3. Remove brake caliper, rotor and dust shield, then disconnect tie rod from spindle using suitable tool.
4. If necessary, remove steering gear bolts and position gear as necessary to gain access to control arm bolts.
5. Remove cotter pin, then loosen ball joint stud nut approximately two turns. **Do not remove stud nut at this**

time.
6. Tap spindle boss with suitable mallet to disengage ball joint stud from spindle.
7. Using spring compressor tool No. T82P-5310-A, or equivalent, on models with 2.3L/4-140 engine, or tool No. D78P-5310-A, or equivalent, on 5.0L/V8-302 models, compress coil spring slightly.
8. Remove ball joint stud nut, then raise strut and spindle assembly and wire in place to gain increased working area for control arm removal.
9. Remove control arm to crossmember pivot bolts and nuts, then the control arm.
10. Reverse procedure to install, noting the following:
   a. When installing coil spring, ensure lower spring end is positioned between two holes in control arm spring pocket, **Fig. 1.**

b. Tighten control arm nuts, steering gear to crossmember nuts, ball joint stud nut and tie rod to spindle nut to specification.

1994–95

1. Raise and support vehicle, allowing front suspension lower arms to hang free.
2. Remove wheel and tire assembly.
3. If necessary to obtain more working room, remove front disc brake caliper, then wire it aside.
4. Remove front disc brake rotor and front disc brake rotor shield as described in "Disc Brakes" section.
5. Disconnect front wheel spindle connecting rod or end assembly from front wheel spindle using tie rod end remover tool No. 3290-D, or equivalent.
6. Remove steering gear bolts and position gear so front suspension lower arm bolt may be removed.
7. Disconnect front stabilizer link from front suspension lower arm.
8. Loosen ball joint nut one or two turns, then tap spindle boss sharply to relieve stud pressure. **Do not remove ball joint nut at this time.**
9. **On models equipped with 3.8L/V6-232 engine**, use spring compressor tool No. T82P-5310-A, or equivalent, to place upper plate in position into spring pocket cavity on crossmember. Hooks on plate should be facing toward center of vehicle.
10. **On models equipped with 5.0L/V8-302 engine**, use spring compressor tool No. D78P-5310-A, or equivalent, to install plate between coils near top of front coil spring. Mark location of plate on coils for installation and use care not to nick spring coils when installing upper plate.
11. **On all models**, install compression rod into front suspension lower arm spring pocket hole, through front coil spring, into upper plate.
12. Install lower plate, lower ball nut, thrust washer and bearing and forcing nut onto compression rod, then tighten forcing nut until drag on nut is felt.
13. Remove and discard ball joint stud nut and rasae entire front shock absorber and front wheel spindle assembly. Wire aside to obtain working room.
14. Remove and discard front suspension lower arm to crossmember nuts and bolts. Compressor tool forcing nut may need to be tightened or loosened for easy bolt removal.
15. Loosen compression rod forcing nut until spring tension is relieved, then remove forcing nut, front suspension lower arm and front coil spring.
16. Reverse procedure to install, noting the following:
17. Ensure spring pigtail is positioned between two holes in front suspension lower arm pocket.
18. Check front wheel alignment and adjust if out of specifications.

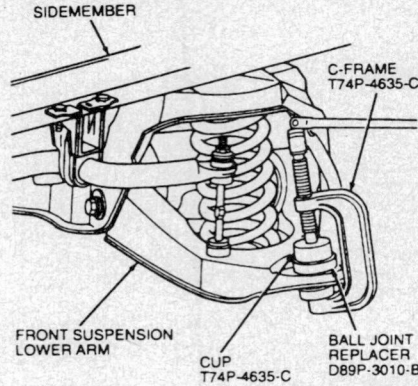

Fig. 6 Control arm ball joint installation. 1994-95

STABILIZER BAR
REPLACE

1. Raise and support vehicle.
2. Disconnect stabilizer bar from each link, then remove insulator clamps, insulators and stabilizer bar from vehicle.
3. Reverse procedure to install. Tighten clamp to side rail bolts and stabilizer bar to link nuts to specifications.

STABILIZER BAR BUSHING
REPLACE

Refer to "Stabilizer Bar, Replace," for stabilizer bar bushing replacement procedure.

POWER STEERING GEAR
REPLACE

1992–93

1. Disconnect battery ground cable.
2. Remove flexible coupling to input shaft bolt.
3. Place ignition switch in On position, then raise and support front of vehicle.
4. Remove cotter pins and nuts from tie rod ends, then, using suitable tool, separate tie rods from spindle arms.
5. Support steering gear, then remove two steering gear to crossmember nuts, bolts and washers. On power steering gears, lower gear slightly and disconnect pressure and return lines. Cap lines and fittings to prevent entry of dirt.
6. Remove steering gear from vehicle.
7. Reverse procedure to install. Tighten flexible coupling to input shaft bolt, tie rod to spindle arm nuts and steering gear to crossmember bolts to specifications. Tighten pressure line fitting at gear housing to specifications.

1994–95

1. Disconnect battery ground cable, then turn ignition switch to Run position.
2. Raise and support vehicle, then position drain pan to catch fluid from power steering lines.
3. Remove flexible coupling to power steering gear input shaft and control bolt.
4. Remove two front wheel spindle connecting end cotter pins and nuts, then separate studs from spindle arms using tie rod end remover tool No. 3290-D, or equivalent.
5. Remove two steering gear to No. 2 front crossmember nuts, insulator washers and bolts.
6. Remove front rubber insulators, then position steering gear to allow access to hydraulic lines.
7. Disconnect hydraulic lines, then remove steering gear.
8. Reverse procedure to install, noting the following:
   a. **Hydraulic lines are designed to swivel when properly tightened. Do not attempt to eliminate looseness by overtightening fittings, or plastic seals may be damaged.**
   b. Ensure all rubber insulators are pushed completely inside steering gear housing before installing bolts.
   c. Fill power steering system with specified steering fluid.
   d. If front wheel spindle connecting rod or ends were loosened, check and adjust front end alignment.

POWER STEERING PUMP
REPLACE

1. Disconnect return hose from power steering pump reservoir and allow fluid to drain into suitable container.
2. Disconnect pressure hose from power steering pump fitting, then remove pump mounting bracket and disconnect drive belt from pulley.
3. Remove belt from pulley, then the pulley.
4. Remove power steering pump.

5. Reverse procedure to install, noting the following:
6. Tighten pump to mounting bracket bolts and pressure hose to pump tube nut to specifications.
7. **Endplay of pressure hose to pump** fitting is normal and does not indicate a loose fitting. Do not overtighten.

TIGHTENING SPECIFICATIONS

Year	Component	Torque/Ft. Lbs.
1992-93	**Ball Joint To Spindle**	80-120
	Flexible Coupling To Input Shaft Bolt	20-30
	Lower Arm To No. 2 Crossmember	110-150
	Pressure Hose To Pump Tube Nut	10-15
	Pressure Line Fitting At Gear Housing	10-15
	Pump To Mounting Bracket Bolts	30-45
	Shock Strut To Upper Mount	50-75
	Shock Upper Mount To Body	50-75
	Spindle To Shock Strut	140-200
	Stabilizer Bar Mounting Clamp To Bracket	37-50
	Steering Gear To No. 2 Crossmember	90-100
	Stud & Washer Assembly To Stabilizer Bar & Lower Arm	6-12
	Tie Rod End To Spindle	35-47
	Tie Rod To Spindle Arm Nuts To	35-47
	Wheel Bearing Adjusting Nut	17-25
	Wheel Lug Nuts	85-104
1994-95	**Ball Joint to Spindle**	109-149
	Front Axle Wheel Hub Retainer	189-254
	Front Suspensoin Lower Arm to No. 2 Crossmember	141-191
	Stabilizer Bar Mounting Clamp to Bracket	44-59
	Stablilzer Bar Link	11-16
	Strut to Upper Mounting Bracket Nut	55-92
	Strut Upper Mount to Body	25-34
	Strut Lower Mounting to Spindle	141-199
	Tie Rod End to Spindle	35-47
	Wheel Lug Nuts	85-105

Wheel Alignment

INDEX

PRELIMINARY INSPECTION

1. Inspect tires for proper inflation and similar tread wear.
2. Inspect hub and bearing for excessive wear. Repair as necessary.
3. Inspect ball joints.
4. Inspect tie rod ends for excessive looseness.
5. Check wheel and tire runout.
6. Inspect vehicle ride height.
7. Inspect rack and pinion for looseness at frame.
8. Ensure proper strut operation.
9. Check suspension and steering components for damage. Replace as necessary.

FRONT WHEEL ALIGNMENT

Check the front wheel alignment under the following curb load conditions:

1. Spare tire, wheel, jack and jack handle in position.
2. Front seats in rearmost position.
3. All other loading removed.
4. All tires inflated to specified pressure (cold)
5. All excessive mud, dirt and road deposit accumulation removed from chassis and underbody.

CASTER

The caster angle is preset during production and not adjustable.

CAMBER

1. Remove pop rivet from camber plate.
2. **On 1992-93 models,** loosen three camber plate to body apron nuts.
3. **On 1994-95 models,** loosen two strut mount to body apron nuts and one strut mount to body apron bolt.
4. **On all models,** move top of shock strut as needed to bring camber angle within specifications, then tighten nuts. **It is not necessary to replace pop rivet.**

TOE-IN, ADJUST

1. Check to see if steering shaft and steering wheel marks are in alignment and in top position.
2. Loosen clamp screw on tie rod bellows and free seal on rod to prevent bellows from twisting.
3. Loosen tie rod jam nut.
4. Use suitable pliers to turn tie rod inner end to correct adjustment to specifications. Do not use pliers on tie rod threads. Turning to reduce number of threads showing will increase toe-in. Turning in the opposite direction will reduce toe-in. **Torque** to 43-50 ft. lbs. for 1992-93 models, or 35-50 ft. lbs. for 1994-95 models.

NOTE: Refer To The Rear Of This Manual For Vehicle Manufacturer's Special Service Tools.

INDEX OF SERVICE OPERATIONS

NOTE: For Service Operations Not Listed Below, Refer To The Table Of Contents In The Front Of This Manual.

Continued

INDEX OF SERVICE OPERATIONS—CONTINUED

Specifications

GENERAL ENGINE SPECIFICATIONS

	Engine							
Year	Liter/CID	VIN Code ②	Fuel System	Bore & Stroke	Comp. Ratio	Net H.P. @ RPM ③	Maximum Torque/Ft. Lbs. @ RPM	Normal Oil Pressure psi ①
1992	3 .0L/V6-182	U	SEFI	3.5 x 3.14	9.3	140 @ 4800	160 @ 3000	55-60
	3 .0L/V6-182 ④	Y	SEFI	3.5 x 3.15	9.8	220 @ 6200	200 @ 4800	—
	3.8L/V6-232	4	SEFI	3.8 x 3.4	9 .0	140 @ 3800	215 @ 2200	40-60
1993	3 .0L/V6-182	U	SEFI	3.5 x 3.1	9.3	135 @ 4800	165 @ 3000	55-60
	3 .0L/V6-182 ④	Y	SEFI	3.5 x 3.15	9.8	220 @ 6200	200 @ 4800	—
	3.2L/V6-195 ④	P	SEFI	3.6 x 3.15	9.8	220 @ 6200	200 @ 4800	—
	3.8L/V6-232	4	SEFI	3.8 x 3.4	9 .0	140 @ 3800	215 @ 2200	40-60
1994	3 .0L/V6-182	U	SEFI	3.5 x 3.1	9.3	135 @ 4800	165 @ 3000	55-60
	3 .0/LV6-182	U	SEFI ⑤	3.5 x 3.1	9.3	135 @ 4800	165 @ 3000	55-60
	3 .0L/V6-182 ④	Y	SEFI	3.5 x 3.15	9.8	220 @ 6200	200 @ 4800	—
	3.2L/V6-195 ④	P	SEFI	3.6 x 3.15	9.8	220 @ 6200	200 @ 4800	—
	3.8L/V6-232	4	SEFI	3.8 x 3.4	9 .0	140 @ 3800	215 @ 2200	40-60
1995	3 .0L/V6-182	U	SEFI	3.5 x 3.1	9.3	140 @ 4800	165 @ 3000	55-60
	3 .0L/V6-182	U	SEFI ⑤	3.5 x 3.1	9.3	140@ 4800	165 @ 3000	55-60
	3 .0L/V6-182 ④	Y	SEFI	3.5 x 3.15	9.8	220 @ 6200	200 @ 4800	—
	3.2L/V6-195 ④	P	SEFI	3.6 x 3.15	9.8	220 @ 6200	215 @ 4800	—
	3.8L/V6-232	4	SEFI	3.8 x 3.4	9 .0	140 @ 3800	215 @ 2200	40-60

CID-Cubic inch displacement.
①—At 2000 RPM.
②—The eighth digit of the VIN denotes engine code.
③—Ratings are net-as installed in vehicle.
④—SHO w/double overhead cam engine.
⑤Flexible fuel vehicle (FFV).

TUNE UP SPECIFICATIONS

		Ignition Timing BTDC, Degrees				Curb Idle Speed ③		Fast Idle Speed		
Liter/CID (VIN Code) ①	Spark Plug Gap	Firing Order Fig. ②	Man. Trans.	Auto. Trans.	Mark Fig.	Man. Trans.	Auto. Trans.	Man. Trans.	Auto. Trans.	Fuel Pump Pressure, Psi
1992										
3 .0L/V6-182 (U)	.044	D	—	10⑤	C	—	④	—	④	35-45⑥
3 .0L/V6-182 (Y)	.044	A	10⑦	—	⑧	760-830④	—	④	—	35-45⑥
3.8L/V6-238 (4)	.054	B	—	10⑤	C	—	650-750④	—	④	35-45⑥
1993-95										
3 .0L/V6-182 (U)	.044	D	—	10⑤	C	—	④	—	④	35-45⑥
3 .0L/V6-182 (U) ⑨	.044	D	—	10⑦	C⑧	—	④	—	④	35-45⑥

Continued

TUNE UP SPECIFICATIONS-Continued

Liter/CID (VIN Code) ①	Spark Plug Gap	Ignition Timing BTDC, Degrees				Curb Idle Speed ③		Fast Idle Speed		Fuel Pump Pressure, Psi
		Firing Order Fig. ②	Man. Trans.	Auto. Trans.	Mark Fig.	Man. Trans.	Auto. Trans.	Man. Trans.	Auto. Trans.	
1992										
3 .0L/V6-182 (Y)	.044	A	10⑦	—	⑧	760–830④	—	④	—	35–45⑥
3.2L/V6-195 (P)	.044	A	10⑦	—	⑧	—	④	—	④	35–45⑥
3.8L/V6-238 (4)	.054	B	—	10⑤	C	—	650–750④	—	④	35–45⑥

BTDC–Before Top Dead Center.

① —The eighth digit of the VIN denotes engine code.

② —Before disconnecting wires from distributor cap, determine location of No. 1 wire in cap, as distributor position may have been altered from that shown at the end of this chart.

③ —D: Drive.

④ —Idle speed is controlled by an automatic idle control system.

⑤ —Disconnect in-line spout connector, then start engine & adjust ignition timing as necessary. After completing adjustment, reconnect spout connector.

⑥ —Wrap shop towel around fitting to prevent fuel spillage, then connect a suitable fuel pressure gauge to fuel diagnostic valve on fuel rail assembly. Connect jumper wire to VIP self test connector FP terminal. The VIP connector is located at the right hand rear of the engine compartment at the electronic control assembly. Place ignition switch in On position, then connect VIP jumper wire to ground and check fuel pressure gauge reading.

⑦ —Non-adjustable.

⑧ —Equipped w/crankshaft position sensor.

⑨ —Flexible fuel vehicle (FFV).

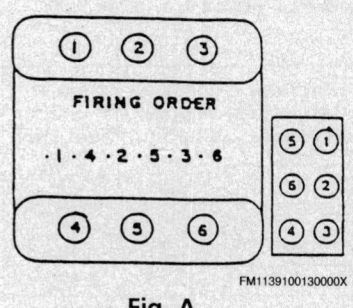

FM1139100130000X

Fig. A

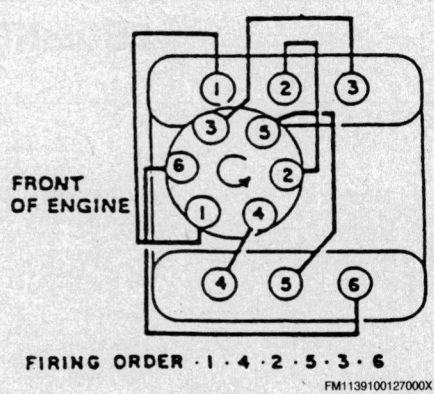

FRONT OF ENGINE

FIRING ORDER · 1 · 4 · 2 · 5 · 3 · 6

FM1139100127000X

Fig. B

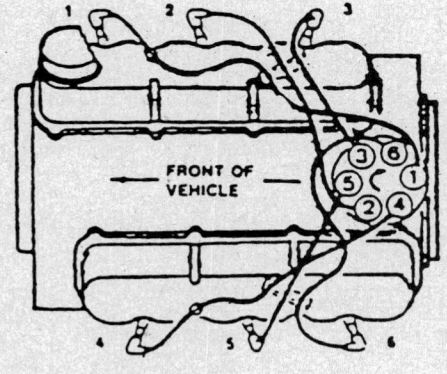

FRONT OF VEHICLE

FIRING ORDER: 1-4-2-5-3-6

FM1139100129000X

Fig. C

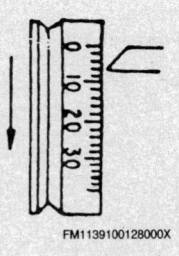

FM1139100128000X

Fig. D

FRONT WHEEL ALIGNMENT SPECIFICATIONS

Year	Model	Caster Angle, Degrees		Camber Angle, Degrees				Toe-In Inch	Toe Out on Turns, Degrees	
				Limits		Desired				
		Limits	Desired	Left	Right	Left	Right		Outer Wheel	Inner Wheel
1992-95	Taurus Sedan	+2.8 to +5.8	+3.8	-1.1 to +.1	-1.1 to +.1	-.5	-.5	①	18.25	20
	Sable Sedan	+2.7 to +5.7	+3.7	-1.1 to +.1	-1.1 to +.1	-.5	-.5	①	18.25	20
	All Sta. Wag.	+2.7 to +5.7	+3.7	-1 to +.2	-1 to +.2	-.4	-.4	①	18.25	20

①—Total toe, -.10 inch.

REAR WHEEL ALIGNMENT SPECIFICATIONS

Year	Model	Camber Angle, Degrees		Toe-In Inch
		Limits	Desired	
1992-95	Sedan	-1.6 to -.2	-.9	+.06
	Wagon	-1.9 to +.1	-.9	+.06

COOLING SYSTEM & CAPACITY DATA

Year	Model	Engine Liter/CID (VIN)	Coolant Capacity, Qts.		Radiator Cap Relief Pressure, Lbs.	Thermo. Opening Temp.	Fuel Tank Gals.	Engine Oil Refill, Qts. ②	Transaxle Capacity	
			Less A/C	With A/C					Manual Pts.	Automatic Qts. ①
1992	Sedan	3.0L/V6-182 (U)	11	11	16	197	④	4.5	—	12.8
	Wagon	3.0L/V6-182 (U)	11.8	11.8	16	197	④	4.5	—	12.8
	Sedan	3.0L/V6-182 (Y) ③	11.6	11.6	16	192	18.4	5	6.2	—
	Sedan	3.8L/V6-232 (4)	12.1	12.1	16	197	④	4.5	—	13.1
	Wagon	3.8L/V6-232 (4)	12.1	12.1	16	197	④	4.5	—	13.1
1993	Sedan	3.0L/V6-182 (U)	11	11	16	197	④	4.5	—	12.8
	Wagon	3.0L/V6-182 (U)	11.8	11.8	16	197	④	4.5	—	12.8
	Sedan	3.0L/V6-182 (Y) ③	11.6	11.6	16	192	18.4	5	6.2	—
	Sedan	3.2L/V6-195 (P) ③	11.6	11.6	16	192	18.4	5	—	13.1
	Sedan	3.8L/V6-232 (4)	12.1	12.1	16	197	④	4.5	—	13.1
	Wagon	3.8L/V6-232 (4)	12.1	12.1	16	197	④	4.5	—	13.1
1994	Sedan	3.0L/V6-182 (U)	11	11	16	197	④	4.5	—	12.25
	Wagon	3.0L/V6-182 (U)	11.8	11.8	16	197	④	4.5	—	12.25
	Sedan	3.0L/V6-182 (Y) ③	11.6	11.6	16	192	18.4	5	6.2	—
	Sedan	3.2L/V6-195 (P) ③	11.6	11.6	16	192	18.4	5	—	12.25
	Sedan	3.8L/V6-232 (4)	12.1	12.1	16	197	④	4.5	—	12.25
	Wagon	3.8L/V6-232 (4)	12.1	12.1	16	197	④	4.5	—	12.25
1995	Sedan	3.0L/V6-182 (U)	11	11	16	197	④	4.5	—	⑤
	Wagon	3.0L/V6-182 (U)	11.8	11.8	16	197	④	4.5	—	⑤
	Sedan	3.0L/V6-182 (Y) ③	11.6	11.6	16	192	18.4	5	6.2	—
	Sedan	3.2L/V6-195 (P) ③	11.6	11.6	16	192	18.4	5	—	⑤
	Sedan	3.8L/V6-232 (4)	12.1	12.1	16	197	④	4.5	—	⑤
	Wagon	3.8L/V6-232 (4)	12.1	12.1	16	197	④	4.5	—	⑤

①—Approximate, make final check w/dipstick.
②—Includes filter.
③—SHO w/double overhead cam engine.
④—Standard tank, 16.0 gals.; optional extended range tank, 18.6 gals.
⑤—Models with AXOD stamped on main control cover 12.25 qts.; models with AX4N stamped on main control cover 14 qts.

LUBRICANT DATA

Year	Model	Transmission		Power Steering	Brake System
		Manual	Automatic		
1992–95	All	MERCON ATF	MERCON ATF	Type F ATF	DOT 3

Electrical

NOTE: On Air Bag Equipped Models, Refer To "Air Bag System Precautions" Located In The Front Of This Manual For System Disarming & Arming Procedures.

INDEX

PRECAUTIONS

ADAPTIVE STRATEGIES RELEARN PROCEDURES

Vehicle specific information about operation, stored in PCM using battery backed up memory, may be lost when battery is disconnected. If this occurs poor engine performance, stalling and other driveability problems may occur. It may be necessary to drive the vehicle for up to 10 miles to allow the PCM to relearn this information

AIR BAG SYSTEMS

Refer to "Air Bag System Precautions" in the front of this manual for system disarming and arming procedures.

FUSE PANEL & FLASHER LOCATION

The fuse panel is located under the instrument panel left of the steering column. The combination turn signal/hazard flasher is located behind on the lefthand side instrument panel reinforcement above the fuse panel.

RELAY CENTER LOCATION

The relay panel is located at the front center of the engine compartment, at-

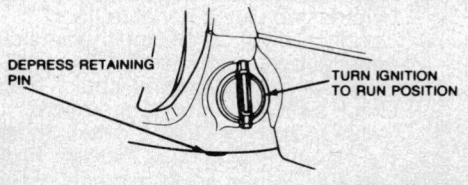

FM9129100011000X

Fig. 1 Ignition lock cylinder removal

tached to the radiator support. This panel contains the PCM relay, fuel pump relay, low fan control relay, high fan control relay and A/C WAC relay.

STARTER

REPLACE

If the starter motor is noisy or if it locks up, before replacing the starter, loosen the mounting bolts enough to hand fit the starter properly into the pilot plate. Tighten the mounting bolts, starting with the top one.

1. Disconnect battery ground cable, then the starter electrical cable.
2. Remove cable support and ground cable connection from upper starter stud bolt.
3. Remove starter brace from cylinder block and starter.
4. Remove starter mounting bolts.
5. **On models with automatic trans-**

mission, remove starter from between subframe and radiator.
6. **On models with manual transmission,** remove starter from between subframe and engine.
7. **On all models,** reverse procedure to install. Connect battery ground cable and refer to "Adaptive Strategies Relearn Procedures" under "Precautions."

IGNITION LOCK
REPLACE

1. Disconnect battery ground cable.
2. Rotate ignition switch to the RUN position, then working through steering column lower shroud, **Fig. 1,** depress lock cylinder retaining pin with suitable 1/8 inch drill.
3. Pull ignition lock cylinder from housing.
4. Rotate replacement lock cylinder to the Run position, then while depressing retaining pin, insert lock cylinder into housing. To ensure proper installation, rotate ignition switch through travel.
5. Install battery ground cable, then ensure ignition lock operates properly.
6. Connect battery ground cable. Refer to "Adaptive Strategies Relearn Procedures" under "Precautions."

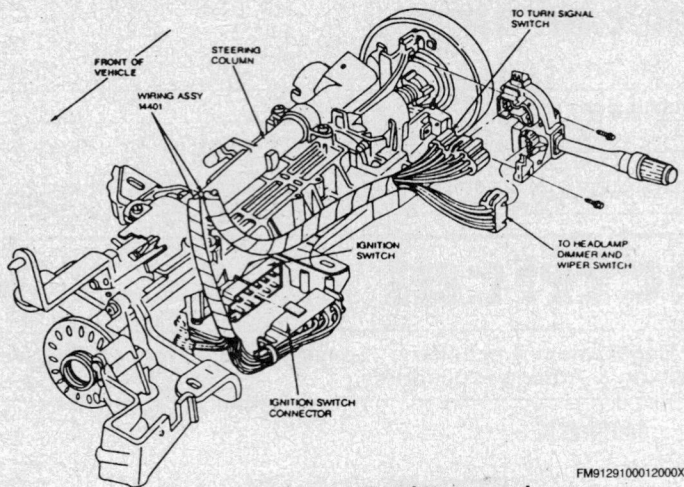

Fig. 2 Ignition switch removal

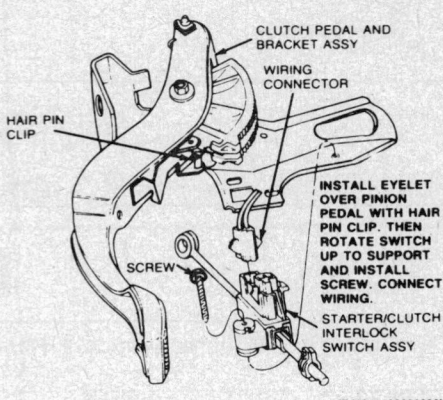

Fig. 3 Starter/clutch interlock switch removal

IGNITION SWITCH
REPLACE
REMOVAL

1. Disconnect battery ground cable.
2. Remove four or five steering column shroud attaching screws, then the shroud.
3. **On models with tilt steering,** remove tilt lever.
4. **On all models,** remove instrument panel lower steering column cover.
5. Disconnect ignition switch electrical connector **Fig. 2.**
6. Rotate lock cylinder to RUN position, then remove two ignition switch attaching screws.
7. Disengage ignition switch from actuator pin.

INSTALLATION

1. Set ignition lock and switch to their RUN positions, then install ignition switch onto the actuator pin.
2. Install switch attaching screws, moving switch slightly back and forth to align switch mounting holes with column lock housing threaded holes. **Torque** screws to 50-70 inch lbs.
3. Connect electrical connector and battery ground cable.
4. Check switch for proper function, including START and ACC positions. Ensure steering column locks with switch in LOCK position.
5. Install instrument panel lower steering column cover, trim shrouds and tilt lever.
6. Connect battery ground cable. Refer to "Adaptive Strategies Relearn Procedures" under "Precautions."

CLUTCH START SWITCH
REPLACE

1. Disconnect battery ground cable.
2. Remove panel above clutch pedal, then disconnect starter/clutch interlock switch wiring.

3. Remove starter/clutch interlock switch attaching screw and hairpin clip, then remove switch.
4. Depress barb at end of rod, then pull rod from clutch pedal.
5. Install switch with self-adjusting clip about one inch from end of rod. **During installation of switch, the clutch pedal must be fully up, otherwise the switch may become misadjusted.**
6. Insert eyelet end of rod over clutch pedal pin, then install hairpin clip, **Fig. 3.**
7. Align switch mounting hole with mounting bracket hole, then install and tighten attaching screw.
8. Adjust starter/clutch interlock switch by pressing clutch pedal to floor.
9. Connect wiring connector, then install panel above clutch pedal.
10. Connect battery ground cable, then check switch for proper operation.
11. Connect battery ground cable. Refer to "Adaptive Strategies Relearn Procedures" under "Precautions."

NEUTRAL SAFETY SWITCH
REPLACE

1. Disconnect battery ground cable.
2. Set shift lever in Neutral position.
3. Remove linkage from transmission manual shift lever.
4. Disconnect neutral safety switch wiring connector.
5. Remove neutral safety switch attaching bolts, then the switch.
6. Install replacement switch on manual shaft.
7. Install neutral safety switch attaching bolts. Do not tighten at this time.
8. Insert a No. 43 (.089 inch) drill bit through hole provided in switch.
9. **Torque** attaching bolts to 7-9 inch lbs., then remove drill bit.
10. Connect neutral safety switch wiring connector, then battery negative terminal.
11. Ensure starter operates in Neutral and Park positions only.

12. Connect battery ground cable. Refer to "Adaptive Strategies Relearn Procedures" under "Precautions."

HEADLAMP SWITCH
REPLACE

1. Disconnect battery ground cable.
2. Pull off headlamp switch knob and remove retaining nut.
3. Remove instrument cluster finish panel as follows:
   a. Engage parking brake and remove ignition lock cylinder as described under"Ignition Lock, Replace."
   b. **On models with tilt column,** set tilt column lever to full down position and remove tilt lever.
   c. **On all models,** remove four bolts, then cover and reinforcement assembly from under steering column.
   d. Remove steering column trim shrouds, then disconnect all electrical connections from steering column multi-function switch.
   e. Remove two multi-function switch retaining screws, then the switch.
   f. Pull gear shift lever to its lowest down position.
   g. Remove four cluster opening finish panel retaining screws.
   h. Pull finish panel away from instrument panel, then disconnect wiring from switches, clock and warning lamps.
4. Remove two headlamp switch to instrument panel retaining screws.
5. Pull switch out of instrument panel, then disconnect electrical connector and remove switch.
6. Reverse procedure to install. Connect battery ground cable and refer to "Adaptive Strategies Relearn Procedures" under "Precautions."

STOP LIGHT SWITCH
REPLACE

1. Lift stop lamp switch wire harness connector locking tab, remove wire connector.
2. Remove hairpin retainer and white ny-

lon washer, then slide switch and pushrod assembly away from brake pedal. Remove switch by sliding up and/or down. **Since switch side plate nearest switch is slotted, it is not necessary to remove master cylinder pushrod, black bushing or one white bushing, nearest the brake pedal from brake pedal pin, Fig. 4.**

3. Position switch so U-shaped side is nearest brake pedal and directly over brake pedal pin. **The black bushing must be in position in pushrod eyelet with washer face on side away from pedal arm.**
4. Slide switch up and down as necessary to trap black plastic bushing and pushrod between the two side plates of the switch, then push switch and pushrod assembly towards brake pedal arm.
5. Install white nylon washer on pedal pin, then the hairpin retainer. **Do not substitute other types of pin retainers. Replace only with production type hairpin retainer.**
6. Connect wire harness connector to switch, then check stop lamps for proper operation. The brake lamps should illuminate with less than 6 lbs. of force applied at the brake pedal pad.

MULTI-FUNCTION SWITCH
REPLACE

1. Disconnect battery ground cable.
2. **On models with tilt steering column,** move column to lowest position and remove tilt lever attaching screw and the lever.
3. **On all models,** remove ignition lock as described under "Ignition Lock, Replace."
4. Remove upper and lower steering column shrouds.
5. Remove wiring harness retainer, then the three multi-function switch wiring connectors.
6. Remove multi-function switch attaching screws, then disengage switch from casting and remove.
7. Reverse procedure to install, noting the following:
   a. **Torque** multi-function attaching screws to 18-27 inch lbs.
   b. **Torque** tilt lever attaching screw (if equipped) to 6-8.5 inch lbs.
   c. Connect battery ground cable. Refer to "Adaptive Strategies Relearn Procedures" under "Precautions."

STEERING WHEEL
REPLACE

1. Center front wheels to straight-ahead position.
2. Disconnect speed control wire harness from steering wheel.
3. Remove steering wheel retaining bolt.
4. Using steering wheel puller tool No. T67L-3600-A or equivalent, remove

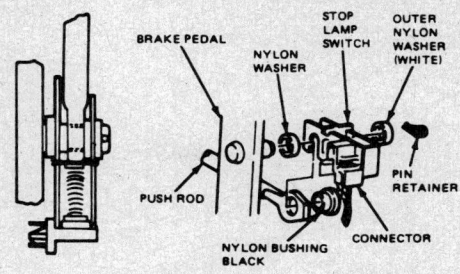

FM9049100033000X

Fig. 4 Brake lamp switch installation

steering wheel. Route contact assembly wire harness through steering wheel as wheel is lifted off shaft.

5. Reverse procedure to install, noting the following:
   a. Ensure vehicle front wheels are in straight-ahead position.
   b. Route contact assembly wire harness through steering column opening at the three o'clock position.
   c. Align steering shaft alignment marks.
   d. **Torque** steering wheel retaining nut to 23-33 ft. lbs.

INSTRUMENT CLUSTER
REPLACE

CONVENTIONAL

1. Disconnect battery ground cable.
2. Remove ignition lock assembly as outlined under "Ignition Lock, Replace."
3. Remove steering column trim shrouds.
4. Remove lower lefthand and radio trim panel attaching screws, then pull rearward to unclip.
5. **On Taurus models,** remove clock assembly.
6. **On all models,** remove cluster finish panel attaching screws and jam nut located behind headlamp switch, then rock finish panel outer edge rearward to remove.
7. **On models equipped with column shift,** disconnect PRNDL indicator from column.
8. Disconnect upper speedometer cable from lower cable in engine compartment.
9. Remove four instrument cluster attaching screws, then pull cluster rearward.
10. Disconnect cluster electrical connectors, then depress cable latch to disengage speedometer cable while pulling cable from cluster.
11. Remove instrument cluster.
12. Reverse procedure to install. Connect battery ground cable and refer to "Adaptive Strategies Relearn Procedures" under "Precautions."

ELECTRONIC

1. Disconnect battery ground cable.
2. Remove two lower trim panels.

3. Remove steering column cover, then PRNDL cable to cluster attaching screws.
4. Pull cluster trim panel rearward, disconnect switch module, then remove trim panel.
5. Remove four cluster attaching screws, then pull cluster bottom rearward.
6. Reach behind and underneath cluster, then disconnect electrical connectors.
7. Pull cluster bottom rearward to remove.
8. Reverse procedure to install. Connect battery ground cable and refer to "Adaptive Strategies Relearn Procedures" under "Precautions."

RADIO
REPLACE

1. Disconnect battery ground cable.
2. Install radio removal tool No. T87P-19061-A or equivalent, to radio face plate, push tool inward about one inch to release radio clips. **Do not push tool with excessive force or radio damage may result.**
3. Apply light even force on tool, then pull radio from instrument panel.
4. Disconnect radio electrical connector and antenna lead.
5. Reverse procedure to install. Connect battery ground cable and refer to "Adaptive Strategies Relearn Procedures" under "Precautions."

WIPER MOTOR
REPLACE

FRONT

1. Disconnect battery ground cable.
2. Disconnect wiper motor electrical connector.
3. Remove left side wiper arm. Lift water shield cover from passenger side cowl.
4. Remove linkage retaining clip from wiper motor arm.
5. Remove wiper motor attaching bolts, then the wiper motor.
6. Reverse procedure to install, noting the following:
   a. **Torque** wiper motor attaching bolts to 60-80 inch lbs.
   b. Connect battery ground cable. Refer to "Adaptive Strategies Relearn Procedures" under "Precautions."

REAR

1. Disconnect battery ground cable, then remove wiper arm and blade.
2. Remove pivot shaft attaching nut and washers, then disconnect wiper motor electrical connector. **Pull connector only. Do not pull wires.**
3. Remove wiper motor attaching nut, then the motor.
4. Reverse procedure to install. Connect battery ground cable and refer to "Adaptive Strategies Relearn Procedures" under "Precautions."

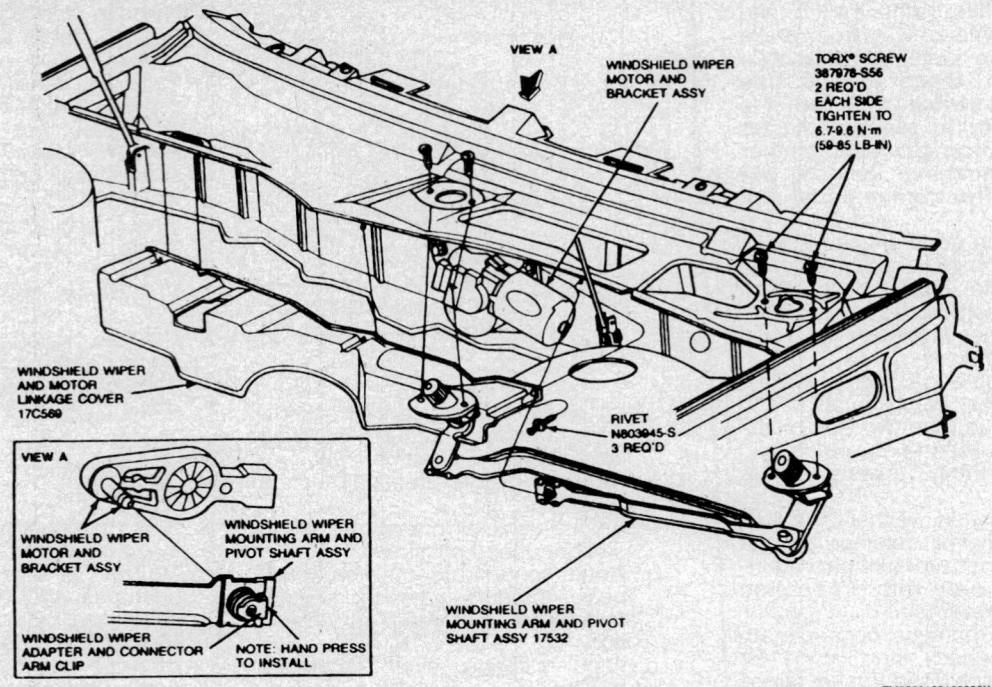

Fig. 5   Windshield wiper transmission removal

WIPER SWITCH
REPLACE
FRONT

The Windshield wiper switch is an integral part of the multi-function switch. For replacement procedures, refer to "Multi-Function Switch, Replace."

REAR

1. Remove four instrument cluster finish panel attaching screws, then remove by rocking upper edge of finish panel towards drivers seat.
2. Disconnect rear washer switch wiring connector.
3. Remove washer switch from instrument panel.
4. Reverse procedure to install.

WIPER TRANSMISSION
REPLACE

1. Disconnect battery ground cable.
2. Remove wiper arm and blade assemblies from windshield wiper pivot arms.
3. Remove leaf screens from both sides of cowl.
4. Remove linkage drive arm to motor crank arm retaining clip, then separate linkage drive arm from motor crank arm, **Fig. 5.**
5. Remove pivot arm to cowl attaching screws, then withdraw windshield wiper transmission from cowl chamber.
6. Reverse procedure to install, noting the following:
   a. **Torque** pivot arm attaching screws to 60-84 inch lbs.

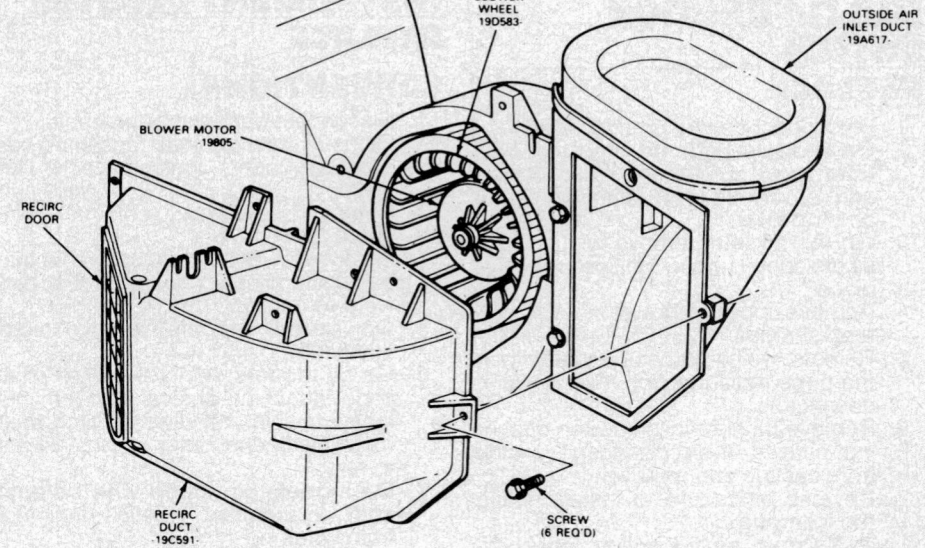

Fig. 6   Blower motor removal

   b. Connect battery ground cable. Refer to "Adaptive Strategies Relearn Procedures" under "Precautions."

BLOWER MOTOR
REPLACE

1. Disconnect battery ground cable.
2. Open glove compartment door, then release retainers and allow glove box door to swing downward. Remove recirculation duct support bracket to cowl attaching screw, then the recirculation door motor vacuum connection.
3. Remove six recirculation duct to heater case attaching screws, **Fig. 6,** then lower duct from between instrument panel and heater case and remove.
4. Disconnect blower motor electrical connection.
5. Remove blower wheel attaching clip and the blower wheel.
6. Remove blower motor attaching bolts, then the blower motor from the evaporator case.
7. Reverse procedure to install. Connect battery ground cable and refer to "Adaptive Strategies Relearn Procedures" under "Precautions."

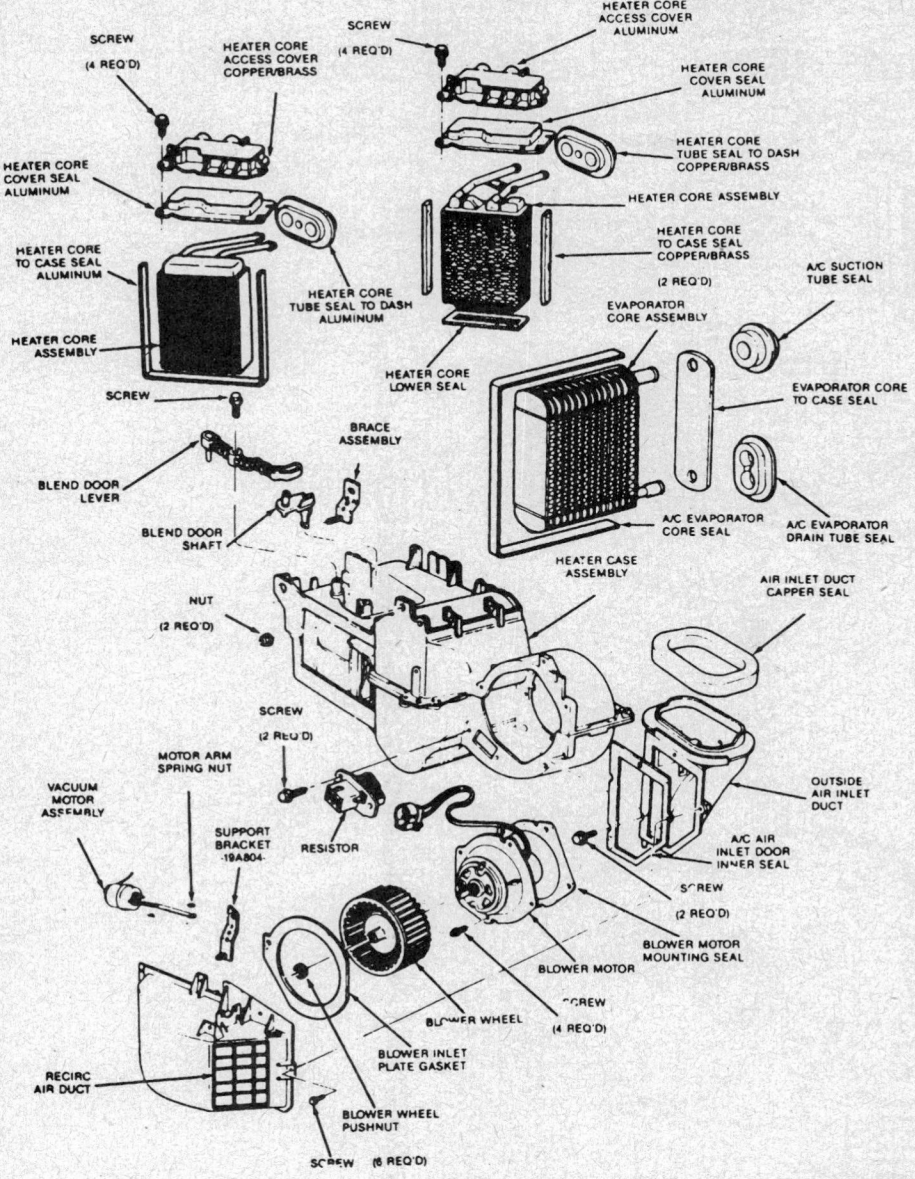

Fig. 7 Heater & evaporator case assembly. Less ATC

FM7029100058000X

WITH A/C

1. Remove instrument panel as described under "Dash Panel Service."
2. Remove evaporator case as described under "Evaporator Core, Replace."
3. Remove vacuum source line from heater core tube seal, then the seal from heater core tubes, **Fig. 7 and 8.**
4. Remove four heater core access cover attaching screws, then the access cover and seal from evaporator case.
5. Lift heater core and seals from evaporator case.
6. Reverse procedure to install.

EVAPORATOR CORE
REPLACE

1. Drain coolant from radiator and discharge A/C system.
2. Disconnect heater hoses from heater core, then plug heater core tubes.
3. Disconnect vacuum supply hose from in-line vacuum check valve in engine compartment.
4. Disconnect liquid line and accumulator from evaporator core at dash panel, then cap refrigerant lines and evaporator core to prevent entrance of dirt and excess moisture.
5. Remove instrument panel as described under "Dash Panel Service" section.
6. Remove evaporator case to instrument panel shake brace attaching screw, then the shake brace.
7. Remove two screws holding floor register and floor ducts to bottom of evaporator case.
8. Remove three evaporator case to dash panel retaining nuts, located in engine compartment.
9. Remove two support brackets to cowl top panel attaching screws, **Fig. 7.**
10. Carefully pull evaporator case assembly away from dash panel and remove it from vehicle. **Whenever the evaporator case is removed from the vehicle it will be necessary to replace the suction accumulator/drier.**
11. Disconnect and remove vacuum harness from vacuum motor.
12. Remove six recirc duct screws from evaporator, then the recirc duct.
13. Remove two air inlet to evaporator attaching screws.
14. Remove support bracket from evaporator case, then the molded seals from evaporator tubes.
15. **On models with automatic temperature control,** remove screws holding electronic connector bracket to recirc duct, **Fig. 8.**
16. Disconnect engine harness 14401 from blower speed control connector, then release three connectors from bracket and remove bracket.
17. Disconnect aspirator hose and remove blend door actuator.
18. **On all models,** drill a $3/16$ inch hole in each of two upright tabs on top of evaporator case as shown in **Fig. 9.**

HEATER CORE
REPLACE
LESS A/C

1. Disconnect battery ground cable.
2. Drain cooling system into suitable container.
3. Disconnect heater hoses from heater core, then plug heater core tubes.
4. Disconnect vacuum supply hose from inline check valve located in engine compartment.
5. Remove instrument panel as described under "Dash Panel Service."
6. Remove instrument panel to heater case shake brace attaching screw, then the instrument panel shake brace.
7. Remove floor register to heater case attaching bolts, then floor register.
8. Remove heater case to dash panel attaching nuts located in engine compartment.
9. Remove screws attaching top brackets to cowl top panel, then carefully pull heater assembly from dash panel and remove from vehicle.
10. Remove vacuum source line from heater core tube seal, then remove heater core tube seal.
11. Remove heater core access cover attaching screws, then the access cover.
12. Remove heater core and seals from heater case.
13. Reverse procedure to install. Connect battery ground cable and refer to "Adaptive Strategies Relearn Procedures" under "Precautions."

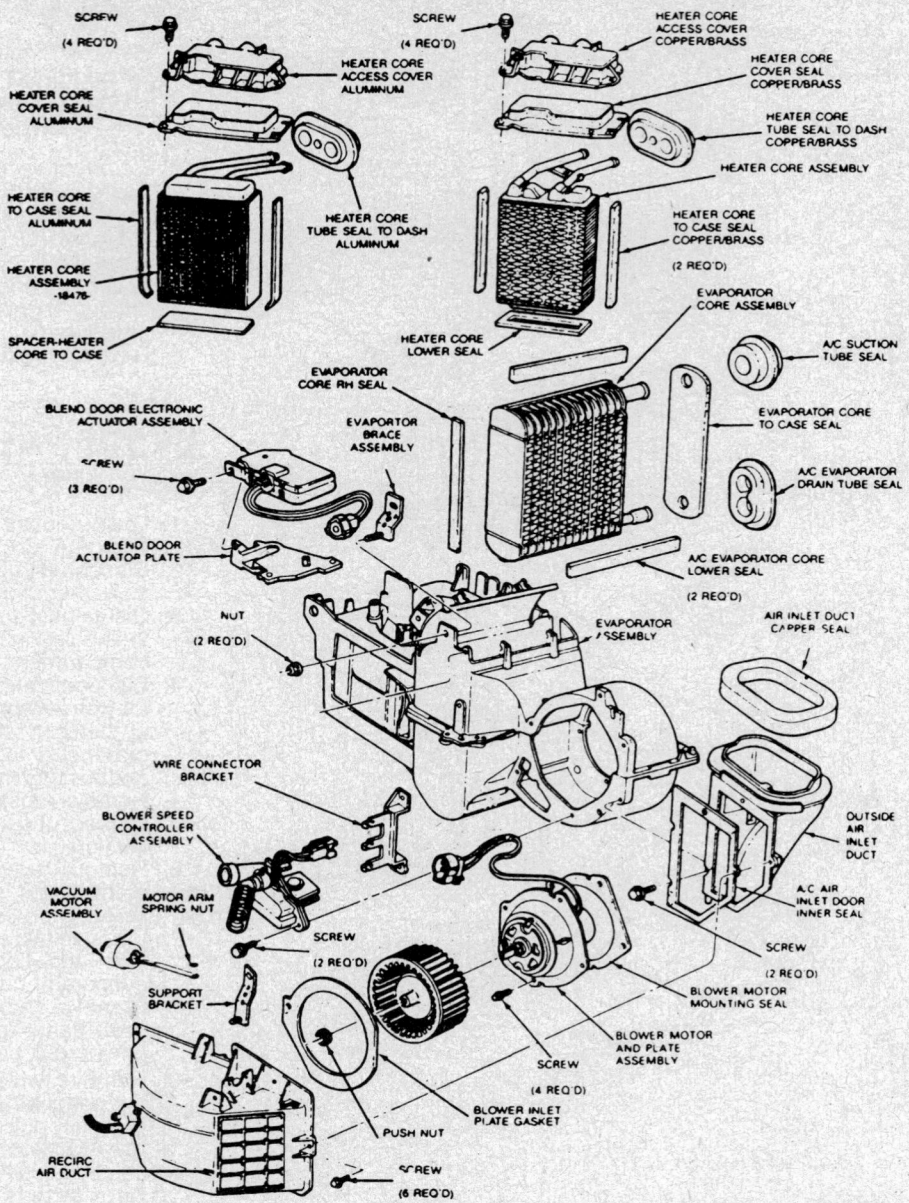

Fig. 8 Heater & evaporator case assembly. With ATC

FM7029100059000X

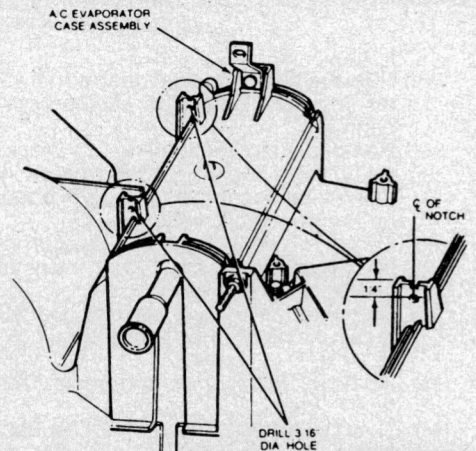

Fig. 9 Evaporator case tab drilling holes

FM7029100060000X

19. Using a small saw blade or equivalent, cut top of evaporator case between raised outlines as shown in **Fig. 10.**
20. Fold cutout cover back from opening and lift out evaporator core from case.
21. Reverse procedure to install, noting the following:
    a. Transfer two foam core seals to new evaporator core.
    b. Install spring nut on each of two

upright tabs and adjacent holes drilled in front flange. Align hole in spring nuts with $3/16$ inch holes drilled in tab and flange. Install screw in each spring nut to secure cutout cover in closed position, **Fig. 11.**
    c. Using caulking cord No. D9AZ-19560-A or equivalent, seal evaporator case along cut line as shown in **Fig. 11.**

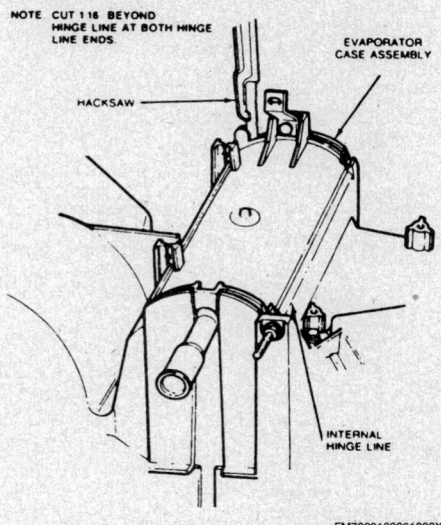

Fig. 10   Cutting evaporator case

FM7029100061000X

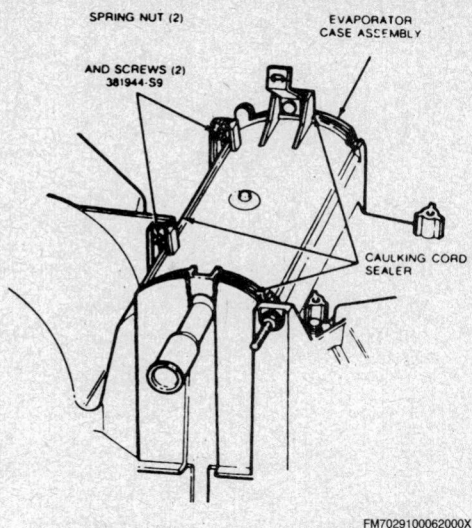

Fig. 11   Evaporator case cover securing & caulking

FM7029100062000X

3.0L/V6-182 Engine, Except SHO

NOTE: On Air Bag Equipped Models, Refer To "Air Bag System Precautions" Located In The Front Of This Manual For System Disarming & Arming Procedures.

PRECAUTIONS
AIR BAG SYSTEMS

Refer to "Air Bag System Precautions" in the front of this manual for system disarming and arming procedures.

ADAPTIVE STRATEGIES RELEARN PROCEDURES

Vehicle specific information about operation, stored in PCM using battery backed up memory, may be lost when battery is disconnected. If this occurs poor engine performance, stalling and other driveability problems may occur. It may be necessary to drive the vehicle for up to 10 miles to allow the PCM to relearn this information

FLEXIBLE FUEL MODELS

Flexible Fuel vehicles (FF) use unique methanol-compatible components. Certain gasoline only components may appear identical to these FF vehicle components. Under no circumstances should these components be interchanged.

FUEL SYSTEM PRESSURE RELIEF

When releasing fuel pressure on flexible fuel vehicles, use methanol resistant gloves and eye protection. Avoid prolonged skin contact with liquid or breathing of vapors.

If fuel methanol should be spilled on paint, flush immediately with cold water. Do not wipe, paint damage may occur.

Fuel supply lines will remain pressurized for long periods of time after engine shutdown. This pressure must be relieved before any service is attempted. A valve is provided on the fuel rail assembly for this purpose. To relieve system pressure, remove air cleaner assembly and connect pressure gauge tool No. T80L-9974-A or T80L-9974-B or equivalent, onto fuel valve on fuel rail assembly. To pressurize fuel system, proceed as follows:
1. Install pressure gauge tool No. T80L-9974-A or T80L-9974-B equivalent onto fuel rail pressure fitting.

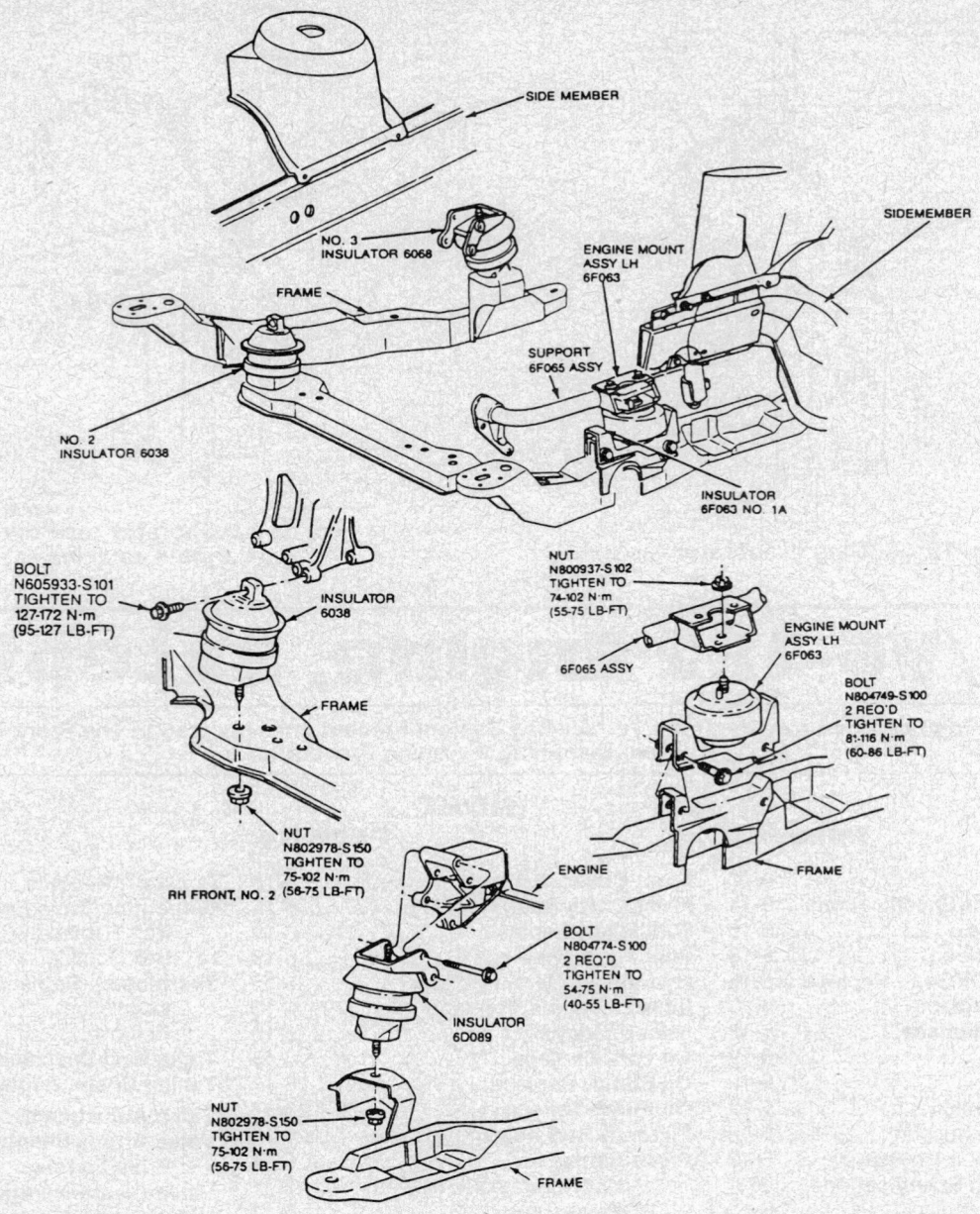

Fig. 1 Engine mounts

FM1069100232000X

2. Turn ignition switch to On position for 3 seconds, 5-10 times until pressure gauge indicates 13 psi.

ENGINE MOUNT
REPLACE
LH INSULATOR & SUPPORT

1. Raise and support vehicle.
2. Remove left front tire and wheel assembly, then support transaxle using suitable jack and block of wood.
3. Remove insulator to support attaching nuts, **Fig. 1.**
4. Remove insulator to frame through bolts, then raise transaxle enough to unload insulator.

5. Remove support assembly to transaxle attaching bolts.
6. Rotate support assembly counterclockwise to remove from upper stud.
7. Reverse procedure to install.

RH FRONT NO. 2 & RH REAR NO. 3

1. Raise and support vehicle.
2. Place jack and wood block under engine block.
3. Remove nuts retaining righthand front and righthand rear insulators to frame, **Fig. 1.**
4. Raise engine enough to unload insulator, then remove through bolts and engine mounts.
5. Reverse procedure to install.

ENGINE DAMPER
REPLACE
RH SIDE

Do not clamp damper tube or piston rod.

1. Remove bolt attaching lower end of damper to engine bracket, **Fig. 2.**
2. Remove upper end of damper to engine bracket attaching bolt.
3. Remove engine damper.
4. Reverse procedure to install.

LH SIDE

Do not clamp damper tube or piston rod.

1. Remove speed control servo and bracket assembly.

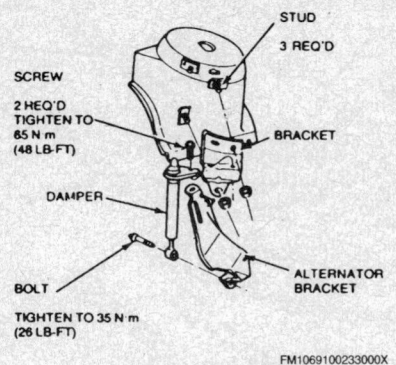

Fig. 2 RH engine damper assembly

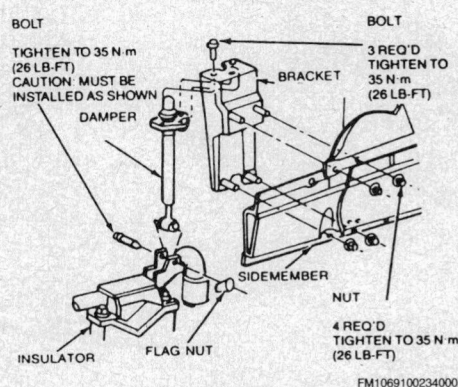

Fig. 3 LH engine damper assembly

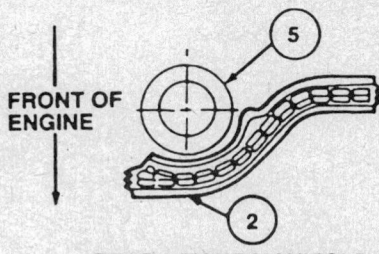

REAR INTAKE MANIFOLD END SEAL MUST BE INSTALLED WITH FLAT TOWARD DISTRIBUTOR HOLE AND CONFORM TO WALL CONTOUR.

Fig. 4 Rear intake manifold seal position

2. Remove bolt and flag nut attaching lower end of damper to engine mount attaching bracket, **Fig. 3.**
3. Remove bolts attaching upper damper bracket to side rail bracket.
4. Remove engine damper.
5. Reverse procedure to install.

ENGINE
REPLACE

1. Relieve fuel system pressure as outlined under "Precautions."
2. Disconnect battery ground cable, then drain engine coolant and oil into suitable containers.
3. Discharge A/C system (if equipped).
4. Remove air cleaner assembly, battery, battery tray, integrated relay controller, cooling fan assembly and bounce damper bracket.
5. Disconnect hoses from radiator, then remove radiator assembly.
6. Disconnect evaporative emission control hose.
7. Disconnect starter brace, then the exhaust pipes from manifolds.
8. Disconnect power steering hoses, fuel lines and vacuum hoses.
9. Disconnect engine ground strap, heater hoses, accelerator cable linkage, throttle valve linkage and speed control linkage (if equipped).
10. Remove engine mount through bolts, **Fig. 1.**
11. Disconnect the following electrical connectors:
    a. Ignition coil.
    b. Radio frequency suppressor.
    c. Cooling fan voltage resistor.
    d. Engine coolant temperature sensor.
    e. TFI module.
    f. Fuel injector wiring harness.
    g. Oil pressure sending switch.
    h. Ground wire.
    i. Block heater (if equipped).
    j. Knock sensor.
    k. EGO sensor.
    l. Oil level sensor.
    m. Alternator harness.
    n. A/C compressor (if equipped).
12. Install suitable engine lifting equipment and remove engine assembly.
13. Reverse procedure to install, noting the following:
    a. Tighten bolts and nuts to specifica-

tions.
    b. Connect battery ground cable. Refer to "Adaptive Strategies Relearn Procedures" under "Precautions."

INTAKE MANIFOLD
REPLACE

1. Relieve fuel system pressure as outlined under "Precautions."
2. Disconnect battery ground cable, then drain engine cooling system into suitable container.
3. Remove throttle body, then disconnect fuel lines.
4. Mark and disconnect vacuum lines and sensor connections, then remove fuel injector wiring harness.
5. Remove ignition coil and bracket and set aside.
6. Remove valve covers as described under "Valve Cover, Replace."
7. Loosen cylinder No. 3 rocker arms enough so rocker arms may be turned, then remove cylinder No. 3 push rods.
8. Disconnect upper radiator hose, then the heater hose from water outlet.
9. **On gasoline engines,** mark distributor rotor and body with reference marks, then remove distributor assembly.
10. **On flexible fuel engines,** remove camshaft position sensor assembly.
11. **On all models,** remove intake manifold attaching bolts, then using a suitable pry bar if necessary to break the adhesion of sealers, remove the intake manifold.
12. Reverse procedure to install, noting the following:
    a. Apply a ¼ inch drop of a suitable sealer to the junction of cylinder block to cylinder head at each corner.
    b. Refer to **Fig. 4** when installing rear intake manifold seal.
    c. **Torque** intake manifold bolts in sequence shown in **Fig. 5**, in two steps, first to 15-22 ft. lbs., then to 19-24 ft. lbs.
    d. Connect battery ground cable. Refer to "Adaptive Strategies Relearn Procedures" under "Precautions."

EXHAUST MANIFOLD
REPLACE
LEFT SIDE

1. Relieve fuel system pressure as outlined under "Precautions."
2. Remove dipstick tube support bracket, then remove exhaust pipe to manifold attaching nuts.
3. Remove exhaust manifold to cylinder head attaching bolts, then the manifold.
4. Reverse procedure to install, lightly lubricate nuts and bolts with engine oil, then tighten to specifications.

RIGHT SIDE

1. Relieve fuel system pressure as outlined under "Precautions."
2. Using suitable back-up wrench on EGR tube lower adapter, remove EGR tube from exhaust manifold.
3. Remove coolant bypass tube.
4. Remove exhaust pipe to manifold attaching nuts.
5. Remove exhaust manifold to cylinder head attaching bolts, then the manifold.
6. Reverse procedure to install, noting the following.
    a. Lightly lubricate nuts and bolts with engine oil.
    b. Tighten manifold attaching bolts to specifications.
    c. Tighten exhaust pipe to manifold attaching nuts to specifications.
    d. Tighten EGR tube to specifications.

CYLINDER HEAD
REPLACE

1. Relieve fuel system pressure as outlined under "Precautions."
2. Rotate crankshaft to 0° TDC of the compression stroke.
3. Disconnect battery ground cable, then drain cooling system.
4. Remove air cleaner outlet tube.
5. Remove intake manifold as described under "Intake Manifold, Replace."

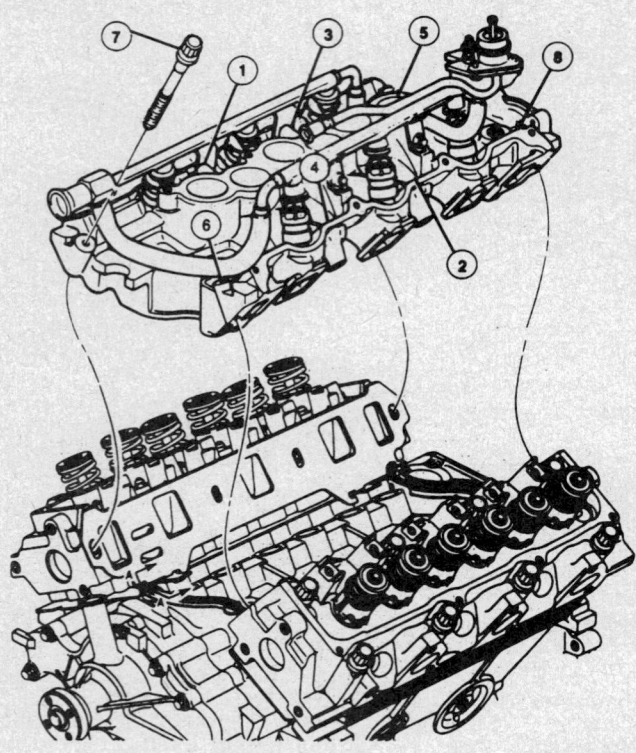

Fig. 5   Intake manifold bolt tightening sequence

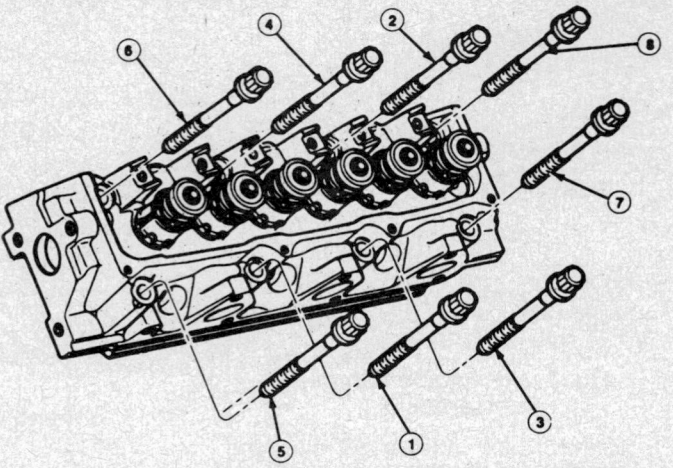

Fig. 6   Cylinder head bolt tightening sequence

VALVE COVER
REPLACE

1. Relieve fuel system pressure as outlined under "Precautions."
2. Disconnect battery ground cable, then disconnect spark plug wires from spark plugs.
3. Remove spark plug wire separators from valve cover attaching bolt studs.
4. If left side valve cover is being removed, performing the following:
   a. Disconnect crankcase breather hose and remove oil filler cap.
   b. Remove fuel injector harness stand-offs from inboard rocker arm cover studs and position harness out of the way.
5. If right side rocker arm cover is removed, perform the following:
   a. Remove throttle body assembly.
   b. Disconnect EGR tube and heater hoses.
   c. Remove PCV valve and move fuel injector harness out of the way.
6. Remove rocker arm cover attaching bolts, then the cover.
7. Reverse procedure to install, noting the following:
   a. Lightly oil bolt and stud threads prior to installation.
   b. Apply bead of RTV sealant at cylinder head to intake manifold rail step.
   c. Tighten rocker arm cover attaching bolts and EGR tube to specifications.
   d. Connect battery ground cable. Refer to "Adaptive Strategies Relearn Procedures" under "Precautions."

VALVE ARRANGEMENT
FRONT TO REAR

Right Side .... I-E-I-E-I-E
Left Side .... E-I-E-I-E-I

CAMSHAFT LOBE LIFT SPECIFICATIONS

Exhaust .... .260 inch
Intake .... .260 inch

6. **On 1992 models** remove accessory drive belt. If right side head is being removed, remove accessory belt idler. If left side head is being removed, remove alternator adjusting arm.
7. **On 1993-95 models,** using a 1/2 inch drive breaker bar inserted into the automatic belt tensioner, rotate and relax tension on the serpentine belt, then remove belt. Remove generator if left side head is being removed.
8. **On all models,** remove power steering pump bracket attaching bolts, then the pump and bracket as an assembly with hoses attached. Position pump and bracket assembly aside in an upright position to prevent leakage of fluid.
9. If left side cylinder head is being removed, remove coil bracket and dipstick tube. If right side cylinder head is being removed, remove ground strap and throttle cable support bracket.
10. Remove exhaust manifolds, then the PCV valve and valve covers.
11. Loosen remaining rocker arm fulcrum bolts enough to allow the rocker arms to be swung aside and the pushrods removed. Keep pushrods in order so they can be installed in original position.
12. Remove cylinder head attaching bolts, then the cylinder head(s) and gasket(s). Discard gaskets(s) and bolts.
13. Reverse procedure to install, noting the following:
   a. **Using new cylinder head bolts,** lightly oil bolt threads prior to installation.

   b. Replace any damaged gasket alignment dowels.
   c. **Torque** cylinder head bolts in sequence shown in **Fig. 6** to 59 ft. lbs.; **then loosen bolts in sequence one full turn.**
   d. Final **torque** cylinder head bolts, in sequence shown, in two steps, first to 37 ft. lbs., then to 68 ft. lbs.
   e. Prior to installation, lubricate rocker arm assemblies and dip each pushrod end in oil conditioner D9AZ-19579-C or other suitable heavy engine oil.
   f. Starting with engine at TDC compression No. 1 cylinder, rotate crankshaft 1 full turn clockwise, then install No. 2 and No. 5 exhaust and No. 1 and No. 4 intake push rod and rocker arm assembly.
   g. **Torque** rocker arm bolts in two steps, first to 5 - 11 ft. lbs., then to 19 - 28 ft. lbs.
   h. Rotate crankshaft 1/3 turn clockwise, then install remaining push rod and rocker arm assemblies.
   i. **Torque** rocker arm bolts in two steps, first to 5 - 11 ft. lbs., then to 19 - 28 ft. lbs.
   j. Ensure all rocker arm bolts are fully seated to their shoulder after tightening.
   k. If any valve train components were replaced or intermixed, check valve clearance as outlined under "Valve Clearance Specifications."
   l. Connect battery ground cable. Refer to "Adaptive Strategies Relearn Procedures" under "Precautions."

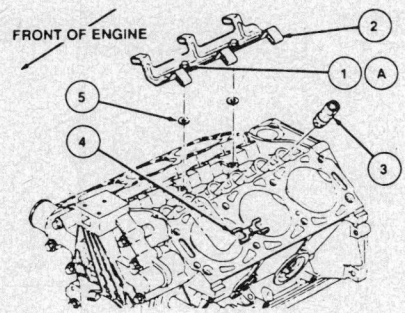

Item	Description
1A	Bolt (2 Req'd) (Part of 6K654)
2	Tappet Guide Plate and Retainer
3	Valve Tappet (12 Req'd)
4	Valve Tappet Guide Plate (6 Req'd)
5	Washer (2 Req'd) (Part of 6K564)
A	Tighten to 10-14 N·m (8-10 Lb-Ft)

FM1069500392000X

Fig. 7 Roller tappet removal

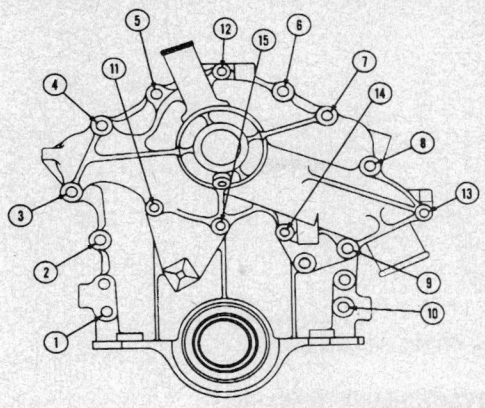

FASTENER AND HOLE NO.	FASTENERS		
	PART NO.	SIZE	FASTENER APPLICATION
1	N804113-S8	M8 x 1.25 x 43.5	F/C TO BLOCK
2	N804113-S100	M8 x 1.25 x 43.5	F/C TO BLOCK
3	N804811-S100	M8 x 1.25 x 70	W/P & F/C TO BLOCK
4	N804811-S8	M8 x 1.25 x 70	W/P & F/C TO BLOCK
5	N605909-S8	M6 x 1.25 x 42	F/C TO BLOCK
6	N804811-S8	M8 x 1.25 x 70	W/P & F/C TO BLOCK
7	N804811-S8	M8 x 1.25 x 70	W/P & F/C TO BLOCK
8	N804811-S8	M8 x 1.25 x 70	W/P & F/C TO BLOCK
9	N804811-S8	M8 x 1.25 x 70	W/P & F/C TO BLOCK
10	N605909-S8	M8 x 1.25 x 42	F/C TO BLOCK
11	N804168-S8	M6 x 1 x 25	W/P TO F/C
12	N804168-S8	M6 x 1 x 25	W/P TO F/C
13	N804168-S8	M6 x 1 x 25	W/P TO F/C
14	N804168-S8	M6 x 1 x 25	W/P TO F/C
15	N804168-S8	M6 x 1 x 25	W/P TO F/C

W/P — Water Pump Assy
F/C — Front Cover Assy
T/P — Timing Pointer

FM1069100236000X

Fig. 8 Timing cover & water pump removal

VALVE CLEARANCE SPECIFICATIONS

If any valve train component is replaced or if valve train components become intermixed, valve clearance will have to be checked on those valves.
1. Using a suitable pry bar, apply pressure to the push rod side of the rocker arm until hydraulic lifter has bled down and bottomed out.
2. Ensure clearance between valve stem and rocker arm is .085 and .185 inch.

VALVE ADJUSTMENT

Hydraulic valve lifters are used in this engine. No adjustment is required.

HYDRAULIC LIFTERS
REPLACE

Before replacing a hydraulic valve lifter for noisy operation, ensure the noise is not caused by improper rocker arm to stem clearance, worn rocker arms, pushrods or valve tips.
1. Set engine to TDC compression No. 1 cylinder.
2. Remove intake manifold as described under "Intake Manifold, Replace."
3. Loosen remaining rocker arm fulcrum attaching bolt(s) enough to swing rocker arm aside to allow pushrod(s) to be removed, then remove pushrod(s). Keep pushrods in order so they can be returned to original position.
4. Remove bolts from roller tappet guide retainer plate **Fig. 7**, then lift retainer plate from engine.
5. Remove roller tappet guide from tappet pair by lifting straight up.
6. **If the lifters are stuck in their bores by excessive varnish or gum build-up, use a suitable claw type puller** to remove roller tappets using a rocking and twisting motion.
7. Place roller tappet lifters in a rack so they can be installed in original positions.
8. Reverse procedure to install, noting the following:
   a. Ensure the word UP and/or button is facing up when installing roller tappet guide plates.
   b. Lubricate lifter(s), lifter bores, rocker arms and pushrod(s) with oil conditioner D9AZ-19579-A or suitable heavy engine oil.
   c. Starting with engine at TDC compression No. 1 cylinder, rotate crankshaft 1 full turn clockwise, then install No. 2 and No. 5 exhaust and No. 1 and No. 4 intake push rod and rocker arm assembly.
   d. **Torque** rocker arm bolts in two steps, first to 5-11 ft. lbs., then to 19-28 ft. lbs.
   e. Rotate crankshaft ⅓ turn clockwise, then install remaining push rod and rocker arm assemblies.
   f. **Torque** rocker arm bolts in two steps, first to 5-11 ft. lbs., then to 19-28 ft. lbs.
   g. Ensure all rocker arm bolts are fully seated to their shoulder after tightening.
   h. If any valve train components were replaced or intermixed, check valve clearance as described under "Valve Clearance Specifications."
   i. Connect battery ground cable. Refer to "Adaptive Strategies Relearn Procedures" under "Precautions."

FRONT COVER
REPLACE

1. Relieve fuel system pressure as outlined under "Precautions."
2. Disconnect battery ground cable, then loosen four water pump pulley bolts with drive belt in place.
3. **On 1992 models** loosen alternator belt-adjuster jackscrew to provide sufficient slack in belt for removal.
4. **On 1993-95 models,** using a ½ inch drive breaker bar inserted into serpentine belt auto tensioner, rotate tensioner to relieve tension until belt may be removed, then remove belt.
5. Drain cooling system, then remove lower radiator hose and heater hose from water pump.
6. Remove crankshaft pulley and damper as described under "Front Cover Seal, Replace."
7. Drain and remove oil pan as described under "Oil Pan, Replace."
8. Remove timing cover to block retaining bolts. Timing cover and water pump may be removed as an assembly by not removing bolts Nos. 11-15 as shown in **Fig. 8.**
9. After cover is pulled away from block, remove water pump pulley and bolts.
10. Check timing chain deflection for excessive wear.
11. Reverse procedure to install, noting the following:
    a. Carefully clean all gasket material from timing cover and cylinder block. The aluminum timing cov-

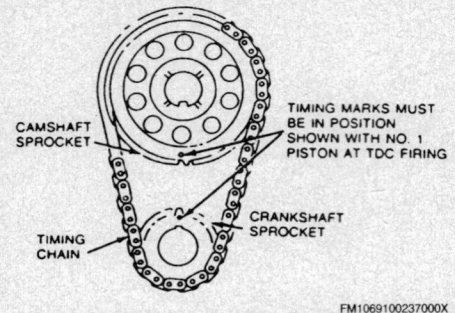

CAMSHAFT SPROCKET

TIMING MARKS MUST BE IN POSITION SHOWN WITH NO. 1 PISTON AT TDC FIRING

CRANKSHAFT SPROCKET

TIMING CHAIN

FM1069100237000X

Fig. 9   Timing chain alignment

FRONT OF ENGINE

Fig. 10   Timing chain installation

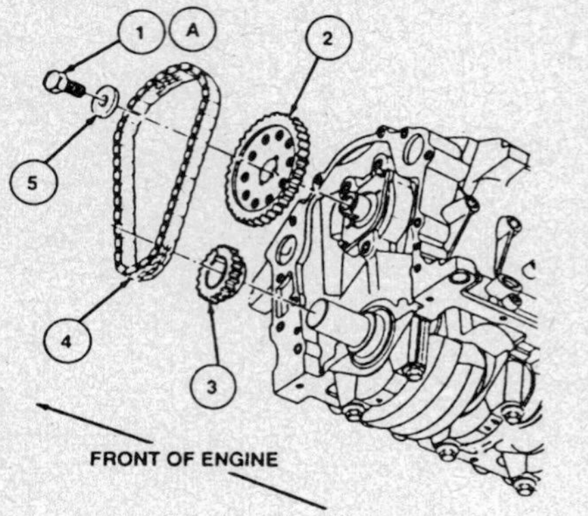

Item	Part Number	Description
1A	6279	Bolt
2	6256	Camshaft Sprocket
3	6306	Crankshaft Sprocket
4	6268	Timing Chain Lubricate With Oil
5	6278	Washer-Cam Sprocket
A		Tighten to 50-70 N-m (37-51 Lb-Ft)

FM1069100238000X

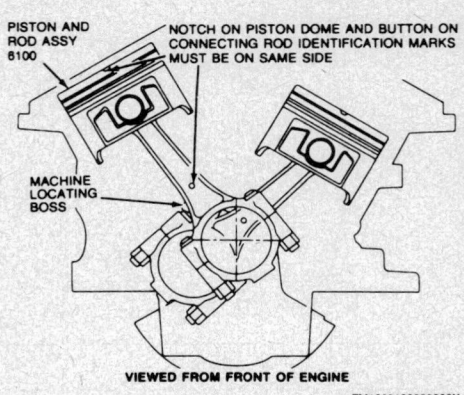

PISTON AND ROD ASSY 6100

NOTCH ON PISTON DOME AND BUTTON ON CONNECTING ROD IDENTIFICATION MARKS MUST BE ON SAME SIDE

MACHINE LOCATING BOSS

VIEWED FROM FRONT OF ENGINE

FM1069100239000X

Fig. 11   Piston & rod assembly

er gouges easily, use care when scraping gasket.

b. Inspect timing cover crankshaft seal, replace if necessary.
c. Before installing bolt Nos. 1, 2 and 3, apply pipe sealant No. D6AZ-19558-A or equivalent.
d. Tighten front cover bolts in sequence shown in **Fig. 8.**
e. **Torque** bolts 1 through 10 to 15-22 ft. lbs., then bolts 11 through 15 to 71-106 inch lbs.
f. Connect battery ground cable. Refer to "Adaptive Strategies Relearn Procedures" under "Precautions."

FRONT COVER SEAL
REPLACE

1. Loosen accessory drive belts, then remove right front wheel.
2. Remove four crankshaft pulley to damper attaching bolts, then remove accessory drive belt and pulley.
3. Remove vibration damper attaching bolt, then using suitable puller, remove vibration damper.
4. Using flat bladed screwdriver or other suitable tool, pry seal from front timing cover. **Use caution not to damage front cover or crankshaft.**
5. Lubricate replacement seal lip with clean engine oil, then install seal with suitable seal installer.
6. Lubricate inner hub surface of vibration damper with clean engine oil, then apply RTV sealant to keyway of inner hub surface of vibration damper.
7. Install vibration damper and tighten attaching bolt to specification.
8. Install crankshaft pulley, then tighten bolts to specifications.
9. Install accessory drive belts, then the right front wheel.
10. Start engine and check for oil leaks.

TIMING CHAIN
REPLACE

1. Remove front engine cover as described under "Front Cover, Replace"
2. Rotate crankshaft until No. 1 piston is at TDC and timing marks are aligned, **Fig. 9.**
3. Remove camshaft sprocket retaining bolt and washer.
4. Check timing chain deflection for excessive wear.
5. Slide sprockets and timing chain for-

ward and remove as an assembly.
6. Reverse procedure to install, noting the following:
   a. Slide timing chain and sprockets on with timing marks aligned, **Fig. 10.**
   b. The camshaft bolt is a special oil transferring part, **do not replace with a standard bolt.**
   c. Tighten to specifications.

CAMSHAFT
REPLACE

1. Remove engine from vehicle and mount in suitable work stand.
2. Remove front cover and timing chain as described under "Timing Chain, Replace."
3. Remove intake manifold and hydraulic valve lifters as described under "Hydraulic Valve Lifters, Replace."
4. Remove camshaft thrust plate, then carefully pull camshaft from cylinder block. Use caution to avoid damaging bearings, journals and lobes.
5. Reverse procedure to install, noting the following:
   a. Tighten camshaft thrust plate attaching screws to specification.
   b. Lubricate lifters, lifter bores, rocker arms and pushrods with oil conditioner D9AZ-19579-A or suitable heavy engine oil.

MAIN BEARINGS

Main bearings are available in standard sizes and undersizes of .001, .002, .010, .020, .030 and .040 inch.

PISTON & ROD ASSEMBLY

Assemble the rod to the piston with the notch on the piston dome on the same side as the button on the connecting rod identification marks. Assemble piston and rod assembly in engine with notch in dome facing front of engine, **Fig. 11.**

After installation, check connecting rod big end side clearance. Clearance should be .006- .014 inch.

CRANKSHAFT REAR OIL SEAL
REPLACE

1. Remove transaxle, then the flywheel.
2. Remove rear cover plate.
3. Using a suitable tool, punch a hole into the seal metal surface between the lip and block. Using slide hammer, Tool No. T77L-9533-B or equivalent, remove seal.
4. Coat crankshaft seal area and seal lip with engine oil, then using tool No. T82L-6701-A or equivalent, install seal.
5. Install rear cover plate and two dowels.
6. Install flywheel, then tighten bolts to specifications.

OIL PAN
REPLACE

1. Relieve fuel system pressure as outlined under "Precautions."
2. Disconnect battery ground cable, then remove oil dipstick, then raise and support vehicle.
3. **On models with low oil level sensor,** remove retainer clip at sensor and disconnect sensor electrical connector.
4. **On all models,** drain crankcase.
5. Remove starter motor, then disconnect Exhaust Gas Oxygen (EGO) sensor electrical connector.
6. Remove head pipe and catalytic converter assembly.
7. Remove lower engine/flywheel dust cover from converter/flywheel housing.

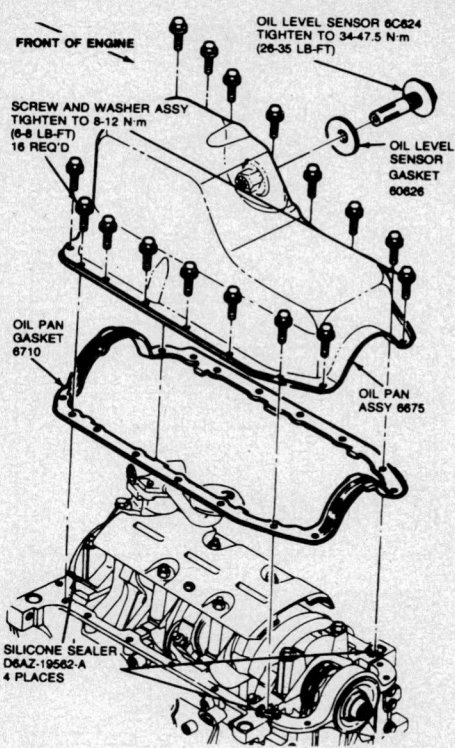

Fig. 12   Oil pan

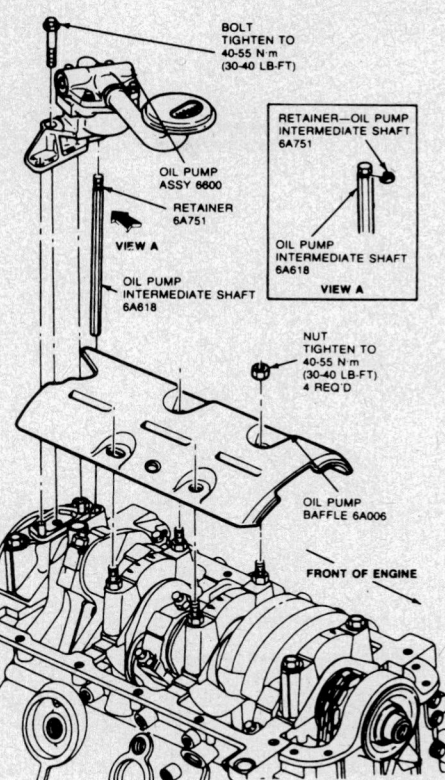

Fig. 13   Oil pump removal

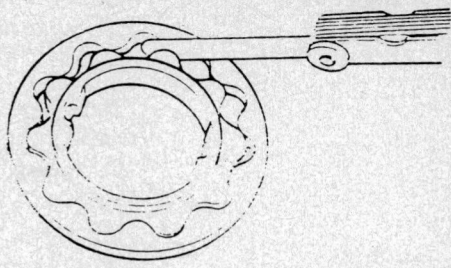

Fig. 14   Oil pump tip clearance

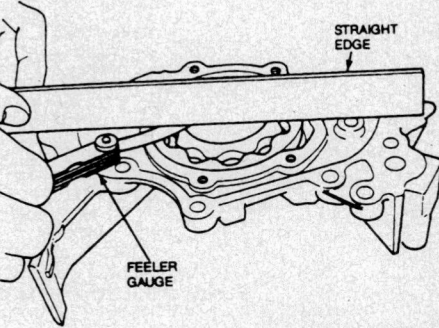

Fig. 15   Oil pump rotor endplay

8. Remove oil pan to cylinder block and front cover attaching screws, **Fig. 12**, then the oil pan and gasket.
9. Reverse procedure to install, noting the following:
   a. Clean all sealing surfaces using metal surface cleaner F4AZ-19A536-RA or equivalent.
   b. Apply ¼ inch bead of suitable silicone sealer to junction of front and rear main bearing caps with cylinder block, prior to installing new gasket. **Install pan within 5 minutes of sealant application.**
   c. Locate gasket to oil pan using a suitable gasket adhesive
   d. Tighten oil pan bolts to specifications, then loosen 1 full turn and retighten to specifications.
   e. Tighten low oil sensor to specifications (if equipped).
   f. Connect battery ground cable. Refer to "Adaptive Strategies Relearn Procedures" under "Precautions."

OIL PUMP
REPLACE

1. Remove oil pan as described under "Oil Pan, Replace."
2. Remove oil pump attaching bolts, **Fig. 13.**
3. Remove oil pump and intermediate shaft.
4. If necessary, pull intermediate shaft from oil pump.
5. Reverse procedure to install. When installing intermediate shaft into replacement pump, ensure shaft retainer clicks into position.

OIL PUMP SERVICE

1. Wash all parts in suitable solvent, then dry with compressed air.
2. Ensure all dirt and particles are removed.
3. Inspect inner pump housing for wear or damage.
4. Inspect pump cover mating surface for wear, scuff marks are normal, if surface is worn or grooved, replace pump assembly.
5. Inspect rotor for nicks, burrs or score marks, remove imperfections with suitable oil stone.
6. Using suitable feeler gauge, measure inner tip to outer rotor tip clearance, **Fig. 14,** clearance should be .0024-.0071 inch.
7. Install suitable straightedge, then using feeler gauge, measure rotor endplay, **Fig. 15,** clearance should be .0012-.0035 inch.
8. If any inspection is not as indicated, replace oil pump assembly.

BELT TENSION DATA

Belt	New, Lbs.	Used, Lbs.
5-Rib	140-160	110-130
6-Rib	①	①

①—Auto tensioner.

SERPENTINE DRIVE BELT

BELT ROUTING

Refer to **Figs. 16. and 17** for serpentine drive belt routing.

BELT, REPLACE

1992

Alternator Belt

1. Disconnect battery ground cable.
2. Loosen adjusting arm and pivot bolts.
3. Turn alternator belt adjusting screw counterclockwise, until belt can be removed.
4. Reverse procedure to install.
5. Connect battery ground cable. Refer to "Adaptive Strategies Relearn Procedures" under "Precautions."

Drive Belt

1. Disconnect battery ground cable.
2. Install suitable ½ inch drive flex handle in square hole in automatic tensioner.
3. Rotate and hold tensioner counterclockwise, then remove belt.
4. Reverse procedure to install.
5. Connect battery ground cable. Refer to "Adaptive Strategies Relearn Procedures" under "Precautions."

1993-95

Serpentine Belt

1. Disconnect battery ground cable.
2. Install suitable ½ inch drive flex handle in square hole in automatic tensioner.
3. Rotate and hold tensioner counterclockwise, then remove belt.

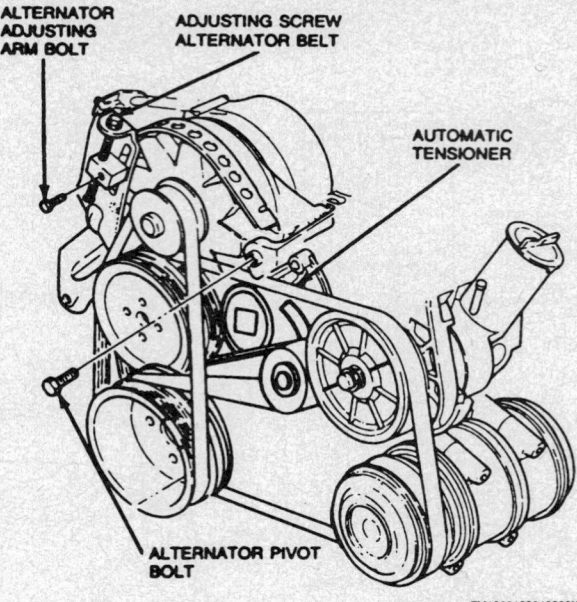

Fig. 16 Serpentine drive belt routing, 1992

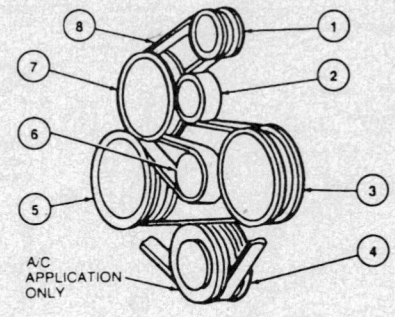

Item	Description
1	Generator
2	Drive Belt Tensioner
3	Power Steering Pump
4	A C Compressor
5	Crankshaft Pulley
6	Idler Pulley
7	Water Pump
8	Drive Belt

Fig. 17 Serpentine belt routing, 1993-95

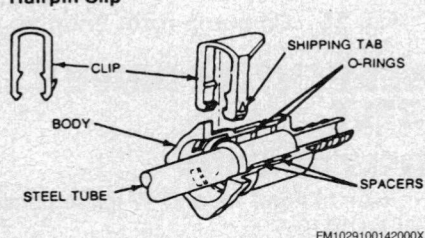

Fig. 18 Push connect fitting removal

4. Reverse procedure to install. Connect battery ground cable and refer to "Adaptive Strategies Relearn Procedures" under "Precautions."

COOLING SYSTEM BLEED

These engine do not require a specific bleed procedure. After filling cooling system, run engine to operating temperature with radiator/pressure cap off. Air will then be automatically bled through cap opening.

THERMOSTAT
REPLACE

REMOVAL

1. Drain cooling system below level of upper radiator hose.
2. Remove upper radiator hose, then three retaining bolts from thermostat housing.
3. Remove housing and thermostat as an assembly, discarding old gasket. Clean sealing surfaces with gasket scraper. Ensure not to gouge aluminum surfaces as these gouges may form leaks.

INSTALLATION

1. Install thermostat into housing, ensuring jiggle valve is at up in relation to housing.
2. Position gasket onto housing using bolts as holding device, then install housing assembly and retaining bolts.
3. Install upper radiator hose. Refer to "Cooling System, Bleed" fill and bleed cooling system with recommended amount and mixture.
4. Start engine and check for leaks.

WATER PUMP
REPLACE

1. Disconnect battery ground cable, then drain cooling system.
2. **On 1992 models** loosen accessory drive belt idler, then remove drive belt, then remove accessory drive belt idler bracket from engine.
3. **On all models** disconnect heater hose from water pump.
4. With drive belt still tight, loosen water pump pulley to pump hub attaching bolts.
5. Remove drive belt as outlined under "Serpentine Drive Belts." **The pump pulley cannot be removed at this time due to insufficient clearance between body and pump.**
6. Remove drive belt tensioner.
7. Remove 11 water pump attaching bolts, **Fig. 8,** then lift the water pump and pulley assembly up and out of vehicle and remove pulley.
8. Lightly lubricate all bolts and stud threads with oil.
9. Position pulley on replacement pump, then install pump/pulley assembly. Tighten attaching bolts in sequence shown in **Fig. 8**, to specifications as outlined under "Front Cover, Replace."
10. Install water pump pulley to pump hub attaching bolts and tighten to specifications.

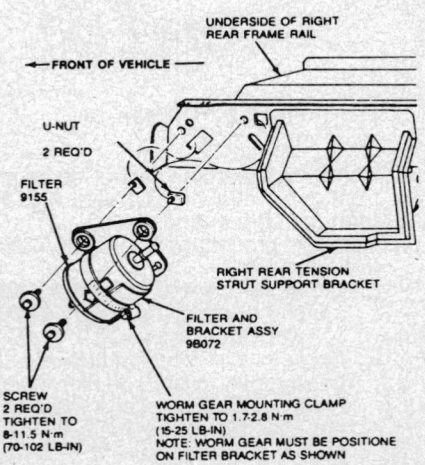

Fig. 19 Fuel filter removal & installation

11. Reverse procedure to install. Connect battery ground cable and refer to "Adaptive Strategies Relearn Procedures" under "Precautions.".

RADIATOR
REPLACE

1. Drain cooling system into a suitable container.
2. Disconnect radiator overflow hose.
3. **On SHO models**, remove coolant recovery tank.
4. **On all models**, disconnect battery ground cable.
5. Remove fan shroud mounting screws, then disconnect cooling fan wiring and remove fan and shroud.
6. Loosen clamps, then remove radiator hoses.
7. **On models with automatic transaxle,** disconnect oil cooler lines.

8. **On all models,** remove upper radiator retaining screws and brackets.
9. Tilt radiator rearward until it clears radiator support, then lift radiator from vehicle.
10. Reverse procedure to install, noting the following:
    a. Ensure radiator is seated in lower rubber mounts.
    b. Ensure radiator hose alignment mark is aligned with rib or notch on radiator.
    c. **On models with screw type clamps,** torque clamps to 20-30 inch lbs.
    d. **On models with tab type upper radiator mounts,** torque screws to 45-61 inch lbs.
    e. **On models with bracket type upper radiator mounts,** torque bolts to 9-17 ft. lbs.
    f. **On models with automatic transaxles,** use a suitable sealer or Teflon tape when connecting oil cooler lines.
    g. **On all models, torque** fan shroud mounting screws to 36 inch lbs.
    h. Connect battery ground cable. Refer to "Adaptive Strategies Relearn Procedures" under "Precautions."

FUEL PUMP
REPLACE

This procedure has been modified by a Technical Service Bulletin.
1. Relieve fuel system pressure as outlined under "Precautions."
2. Disconnect battery ground cable.
3. **On flexible fuel models,** remove fuel from tank as follows:
    a. Remove foam and rubber protective cover from special quick disconnect fitting on fuel drain tube found on right side of fuel tank.
    b. Attach adapter hose tool No. 034-00020 or equivalent, connected to a methanol fuel suitable fuel storage tanker to quick disconnect fitting.
    c. Pump fuel from tank.
4. **On non flexible fuel models** remove fuel from fuel tank by pumping fuel out of fuel filler neck using a suitable fuel storage tanker.
5. **On all models** raise and support vehicle.
6. Disconnect then remove fuel filler neck.
7. Support fuel tank, then remove tank support straps. Lower fuel tank partially and remove fuel lines, electrical connectors and vent lines from tank.

Remove tank and place on suitable workbench.
8. Turn fuel pump locking ring counterclockwise and remove locking ring.
9. Remove fuel pump, bracket and gasket assembly.
10. Reverse procedure to install. Connect battery ground cable and refer to "Adaptive Strategies Relearn Procedures" under "Precautions."

FUEL FILTER
REPLACE

1. Relieve fuel system pressure as outlined under "Precautions."
2. Twist push connect fittings at each end of the filter until they move freely on the tube.
3. Bend and break shipping tab from hairpin clip, then spread two clip legs approximately 1/8 inch, **Fig. 18.**
4. Remove clip from tube and fitting by pulling gently on its' triangular end.
5. Separate fitting and hose assembly from fuel filter.
6. Install retainer clips in each connect fitting.
7. Loosen worm gear mounting clip, then remove filter from bracket, **Fig. 19.**
8. Reverse procedure to install.

TIGHTENING SPECIFICATIONS

Year	Component	Torque/Ft. Lbs.
1992-95	A/C Compressor to Block	35
	A/C Compressor Mounting	35
	Alternator Adjustment Arm	27
	Alternator Adjustment Arm To Cylinder Head Bolt	35
	Alternator Pivot Bolt	43
	Auto Tensioner/Power Steering Bracket To Cylinder Head	35
	Camshaft Sprocket To Camshaft	46
	Camshaft Thrust Plate	7
	Coil & Bracket Assembly To Cylinder Head	35
	Connecting Rod Nut	26
	Crankshaft Damper To Crankshaft	93-121
	Crankshaft Pulley To Damper Bolts	37
	Cylinder Head Bolt	①
	Distributor Hold-Down Bolt	18
	ECT Sensor	12-17
	EGR Spacer To Intake Manifold Bolt	18
	EGR Tube To EGR Valve & Exhaust Manifold	26-48
	EGR Valve To Throttle Body	18
	Engine Mounts	①
	Exhaust Manifold	19
	Flywheel To Crankshaft	59
	Fuel Rail To Intake Manifold	7

Year	Component	Torque/Ft. Lbs.
1992-95 —Cont'd	Front Cover	①
	Intake Manifold To Cylinder Head	①
	Low Level Oil Sensor	20-30
	Main Bearing Cap	55-63
	Oil Drain Plug	10
	Oil Indicator Tube To Exhaust Manifold	13
	Oil Inlet Tube To Cylinder Block	15-22
	Oil Inlet To Main Bearing Cap	30-40
	Oil Insert To Cylinder Block	25
	Oil Pan To Cylinder Block	8-10
	Power Steering Bracket To Cylinder Head Bolt	29-41
	Valve Cover To Cylinder Head Bolt	8-10
	Rocker Arm Fulcrum To Cylinder Head Bolt	③
	Spark Knock Sensor	29-40
	Spark Plug To Cylinder Head	5-11
	Tensioner Locknut	25-37
	Thermostat Housing	6-9
	Throttle Body To Intake Manifold	19
	Timing Cover To Cylinder Block	19
	Water Pump Pulley To Hub	15-22
	Water Pump To Front Cover	71-106 ②

①—Refer to text.
②—Inch lbs.
③—First step, tighten to 5-11 ft. lbs.; second step, tighten to 19-28 ft. lbs.

3.0L/V6-182 & 3.2L/V6-195 SHO Engines

NOTE: On Air Bag Equipped Models, Refer To "Air Bag System Precautions" Located In The Front Of This Manual For System Disarming & Arming Procedures.

INDEX

PRECAUTIONS

AIR BAG SYSTEMS

Refer to "Air Bag System Precautions" in the front of this manual for system disarming and arming procedures.

ADAPTIVE STRATEGIES RELEARN PROCEDURES

Vehicle specific information about operation, stored in PCM using battery backed up memory, may be lost when battery is disconnected. If this occurs poor engine performance, stalling and other driveability problems may occur. It may be necessary to drive the vehicle for up to 10 miles to allow the PCM to relearn this information

FUEL SYSTEM PRESSURE RELIEF

Fuel supply lines will remain pressurized for long periods of time after engine shut-down. This pressure must be relieved before any service is attempted. A valve is provided on the fuel rail assembly for this purpose. To relieve system pressure, remove air cleaner assembly and connect pressure gauge tool No. T80L-9974-A or T80L-9974-B or equivalent onto fuel valve on fuel rail assembly. To pressurize fuel system, proceed as follows:

1. Install pressure gauge tool No. T80L-9974-A or T80L-9974-B equivalent onto fuel rail pressure fitting.
2. Turn ignition switch to On position for 3 seconds, repeatedly 5 to 10 times until pressure gauge indicates 13 psi.

ENGINE MOUNT

REPLACE

LH INSULATOR & SUPPORT ASSEMBLY

1. Remove bolt attaching roll damper, then position aside.
2. Remove back-up lamp switch, then the energy management bracket.
3. Raise and support vehicle.
4. Remove left front tire and wheel assembly, then support transaxle using suitable jack and block of wood.
5. Remove nuts attaching lower damper bracket to engine mount, **Fig. 1.**
6. Remove insulator to subframe through bolts, then raise transaxle enough to unload insulator.
7. Remove insulator and lower damper bracket.
8. Reverse procedure to install.

RH FRONT OR REAR INSULATOR

1. Remove lower damper attaching bolt from RH side of engine, **Fig. 1.**
2. Raise and support vehicle, then place suitable jack and block of wood under engine.
3. Remove nuts attaching roll damper to engine mount, then the roll damper.
4. Raise engine enough to unload insulator.
5. Remove two attaching bolts, then insulator from engine bracket.
6. Reverse procedure to install.

ENGINE DAMPER

REPLACE
RIGHT SIDE

Do not clamp damper tube or piston rod.

1. Remove nuts retaining lower end of damper to engine bracket.
2. Remove bolts retaining upper damper bracket to shock tower bracket.
3. Remove engine damper.
4. Position engine damper lower sleeve to line up with engine bracket notch, secure with new nut. **Torque** to 21-30 ft. lbs.
5. Position engine damper with upper bracket to shock tower bracket, secure with new nut. **Torque** to 40-55 ft. lbs.

LEFT SIDE

Do not clamp damper tube or piston rod.

1. Remove speed control servo and bracket assembly.
2. Remove bolt and flag nut retaining lower end of damper to No. 1A engine mount retaining bracket.
3. Remove bolts retaining upper damper bracket to side rail bracket.
4. Remove engine damper.
5. Insert lower end of damper into engine mount retaining bracket, **align groove in damper sleeve with notch in bracket.**
6. Insert bolt with bolt head toward engine through bracket and damper, then hand start new flag nut. **Torque** bolt to 21-30 ft. lbs.
7. Pull damper into position against shock tower mounting bracket.

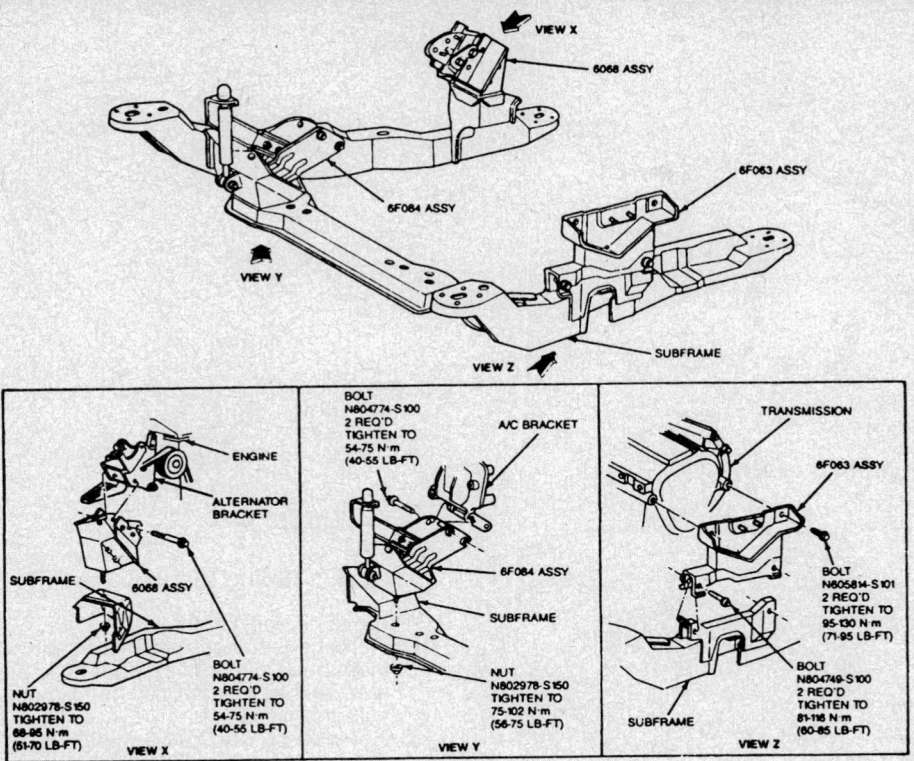

Fig. 1   Engine mounts

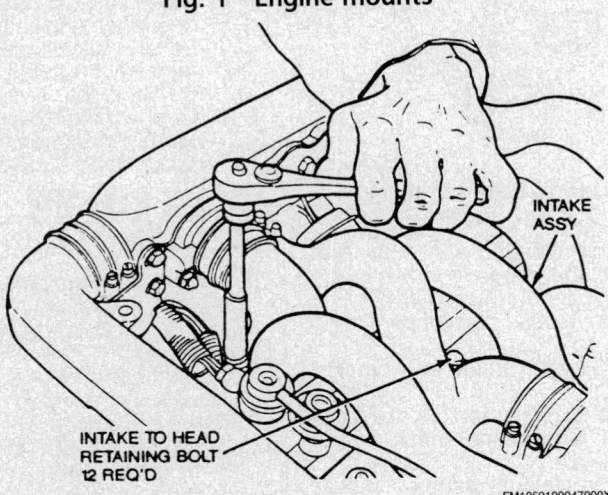

Fig. 2   Intake manifold bolt removal

harness on rear of engine.

15. **On 3 .0L/V6-182 engine,** remove belts from A/C compressor, alternator and power steering pump.
16. **On 3.2L/V6-195 engine,** remove accessory drive belt.
17. **On all engines,** disconnect cycling switch on top of suction accumulator/drier.
18. Disconnect A/C line at dash panel, then remove accumulator and bracket assembly.
19. Remove alternator assembly, then disconnect A/C discharge hose.
20. Remove A/C compressor and bracket assembly.
21. Raise and support vehicle.
22. Drain engine oil and remove oil filter.
23. Remove wheel and tires assemblies, then disconnect oil level sensor electrical connector.
24. Remove RH lower ball joint, tie rod end and stabilizer bar.
25. Remove center support bearing bracket, then RH CV joint from transaxle.
26. Disconnect heater exhaust gas oxygen sensor assembly.
27. Remove four exhaust catalyst to engine retaining bolts.
28. Remove starter mounting bolts, then starter assembly.
29. Remove lower transaxle mounting bolts, then engine mount to subframe attaching nuts.
30. Remove crankshaft pulley assembly, then lower vehicle.
31. Remove upper transaxle mounting bolts.
32. Install suitable engine lifting equipment.
33. Remove engine assembly.
34. Reverse procedure to install, Connect battery ground cable and refer to "Adaptive Strategies Relearn Procedures" under "Precautions.".

INTAKE MANIFOLD
REPLACE

1. Relieve fuel system pressure as outlined under "Precautions."
2. Drain cooling system, then disconnect battery ground cable.
3. Disconnect electrical connectors and vacuum lines from intake assembly, then remove air cleaner tube, then disconnect coolant lines and cables from throttle body.
4. Remove upper intake attaching bolts and upper intake brackets, then loosen four lower bolts and remove brackets.
5. Remove 12 intake manifold attaching bolts, **Fig. 2.**
6. Remove intake assembly and gaskets.
7. Reverse procedure to install, noting the following:
   a. Intake gasket is reuseable.
   b. Tighten 12 manifold retaining bolts to specification.
   c. When installing manifold brackets, bracket with stud must be installed in same location from which it was removed, **Fig. 3.**

8. Install speed control servo and bracket assembly.

ENGINE
REPLACE

1. Relieve fuel system pressure as outlined under "Precautions."
2. Disconnect battery ground cable, then drain cooling system.
3. Remove battery and battery tray assembly.
4. Disconnect under hood lamp electrical connector, then mark position of hood hinges and remove hood.
5. Remove oil dipstick tube, then disconnect alternator to voltage regulator wiring harness.

6. Remove radiator upper sight shield, discharge A/C system, then remove radiator coolant reservoir assembly.
7. Remove integrated relay controller.
8. Remove air cleaner hose assembly and upper radiator hose.
9. Disconnect electric fan and shroud, then remove lower radiator hose and radiator assembly.
10. Bleed fuel system, then disconnect fuel hoses.
11. Remove power steering reservoir and position aside.
12. Disconnect reservoir hose from power steering pump.
13. Disconnect throttle linkage, then vacuum and heater hoses.
14. Disconnect electrical connector from

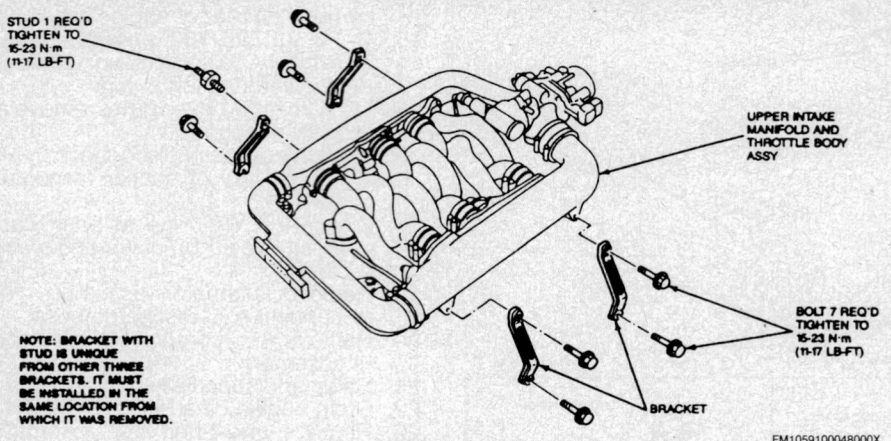

STUD 1 REQ'D TIGHTEN TO 15-23 N·m (11-17 LB-FT)

UPPER INTAKE MANIFOLD AND THROTTLE BODY ASSY

BOLT 7 REQ'D TIGHTEN TO 15-23 N·m (11-17 LB-FT)

BRACKET

NOTE: BRACKET WITH STUD IS UNIQUE FROM OTHER THREE BRACKETS. IT MUST BE INSTALLED IN THE SAME LOCATION FROM WHICH IT WAS REMOVED.

FM1059100048000X

Fig. 3 Upper intake manifold assembly

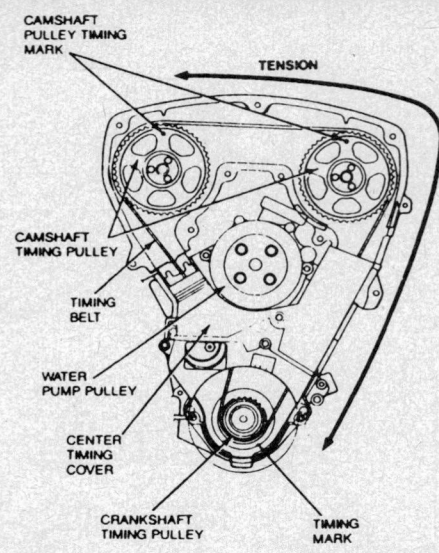

CAMSHAFT PULLEY TIMING MARK

TENSION

CAMSHAFT TIMING PULLEY

TIMING BELT

WATER PUMP PULLEY

CENTER TIMING COVER

CRANKSHAFT TIMING PULLEY

TIMING MARK

FM1069100242000X

Fig. 4 Timing mark alignment

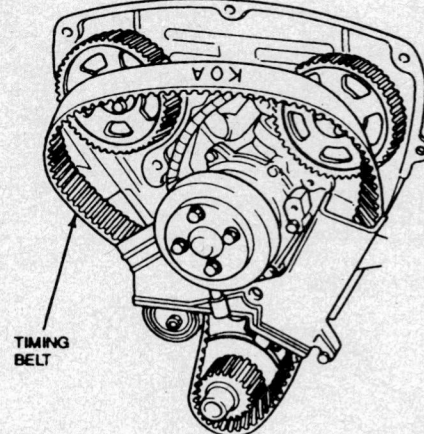

TIMING BELT

FM1069100243000X

Fig. 5 Timing belt installation

d. Connect battery ground cable. Refer to "Adaptive Strategies Relearn Procedures" under "Precautions."

EXHAUST MANIFOLD
REPLACE

LEFT SIDE

1. Relieve fuel system pressure as outlined under "Precautions."
2. Remove oil dipstick tube support bracket and power steering pressure and return hoses.
3. Remove exhaust pipe to manifold attaching nuts, then heat shield attaching bolts.
4. Remove exhaust manifold attaching nuts, then the manifold.
5. Reverse procedure to install, noting the following:
   a. Lightly lubricate bolts and nuts with oil.
   b. Tighten manifold attaching nuts to specifications.
   c. Tighten heat shield attaching bolts to specifications.
   d. Tighten exhaust pipe attaching nuts to specifications.

RIGHT SIDE

1. Remove right cylinder head as described under "Cylinder Head, Replace."
2. Remove heat shield attaching bolts.
3. Remove exhaust manifold attaching nuts, then the manifold.
4. Reverse procedure to install, noting the following:
   a. Lightly lubricate bolts and nuts with oil.
   b. Tighten manifold attaching nuts to specifications.
   c. Tighten heat shield attaching bolts to specifications.
   d. Install right cylinder as described under "Cylinder Head, Replace."

CYLINDER HEAD
REPLACE

1. Relieve fuel system pressure as outlined under "Precautions."
2. Disconnect battery ground cable, then drain cooling system.

3. Remove air cleaner assembly and outlet tube, then remove intake manifold as described previously.
4. Remove drive belts, then upper timing belt cover.
5. Remove LH idler pulley and bracket assembly.
6. Raise and support vehicle, then remove RH wheel and inner fender splash shield.
7. Remove crankshaft damper pulley, then lower timing belt cover.
8. Align timing marks as shown, **Fig. 4**.
9. Release tension on timing belt by loosening tensioner attaching nut, then rotate tensioner with a hex head wrench.
10. Lower vehicle until wheels touch and keep supported on hoist.
11. Disconnect crankshaft sensor wiring assembly, then the center cover.
12. Remove timing belt, ensure location of KOA or KOB on timing belt for proper installation, **Fig. 5**.
13. Remove cylinder head covers.
14. Remove camshaft timing pulleys.
15. Remove upper rear and center timing belt covers.
16. If left side head is being removed, remove coil bracket and dipstick tube. If right side head is being removed, re-

move coolant outlet hose.
17. Remove exhaust manifold on left cylinder head. On right cylinder head, ensure exhaust manifold is removed with the head.
18. Reverse procedure to install, noting the following:
   a. Lightly oil all bolts and nuts with oil.
   b. Using cylinder head bolt tightening sequence shown in **Fig. 6. Torque** bolts in two steps as follows; first step 37-50 ft. lbs., second step to 62-68 ft. lbs.
   c. Connect battery ground cable. Refer to "Adaptive Strategies Relearn Procedures" under "Precautions."

VALVE COVER
REPLACE

1. Relieve fuel pressure as outlined under "Precautions."
2. Remove upper intake manifold as outlined under "Intake Manifold, Replace."
3. Disconnect necessary vacuum, electrical and spark plug connectors.
4. Remove right valve cover as follows:
   a. **On 3.2L/V6-195 engines,** remove the right exhaust manifold to EGR valve tube.
   b. **On all engines,** remove fuel lines.
   c. Remove bolts, then lift off valve cover.
5. Remove left valve cover as follows:
   a. Remove oil filler cap
   b. Remove ignition coil cover.
   c. Remove bolts, then lift off valve cover.
6. Reverse procedure to install, noting the following:
   a. Inspect valve cover and spark plug hole gaskets and replace if damaged.
   b. Tighten bolts to specifications.

CAMSHAFT LOBE LIFT SPECIFICATIONS

Exhaust .... .315 inch
Intake .... .335 inch

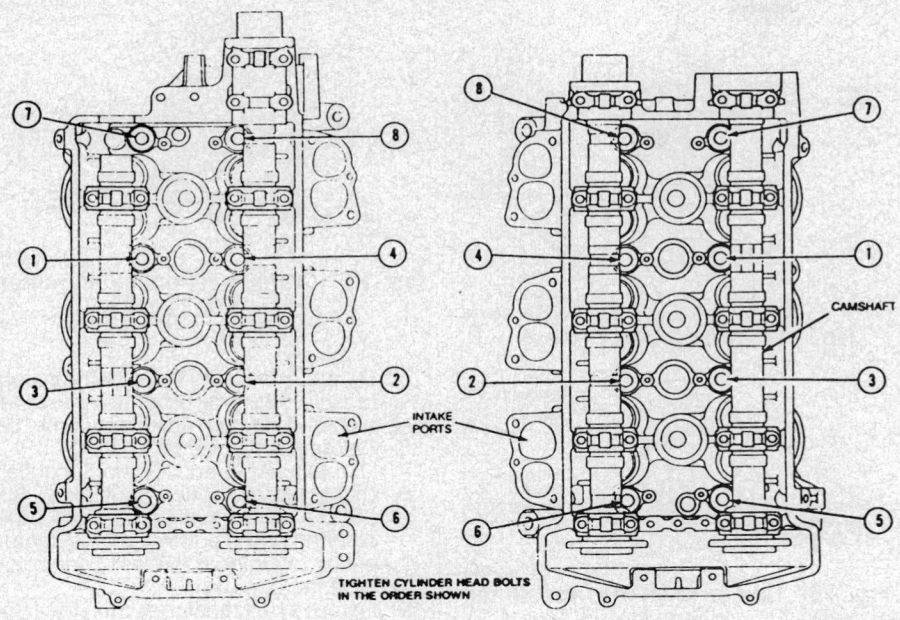

Fig. 6 Cylinder head bolt tightening sequence

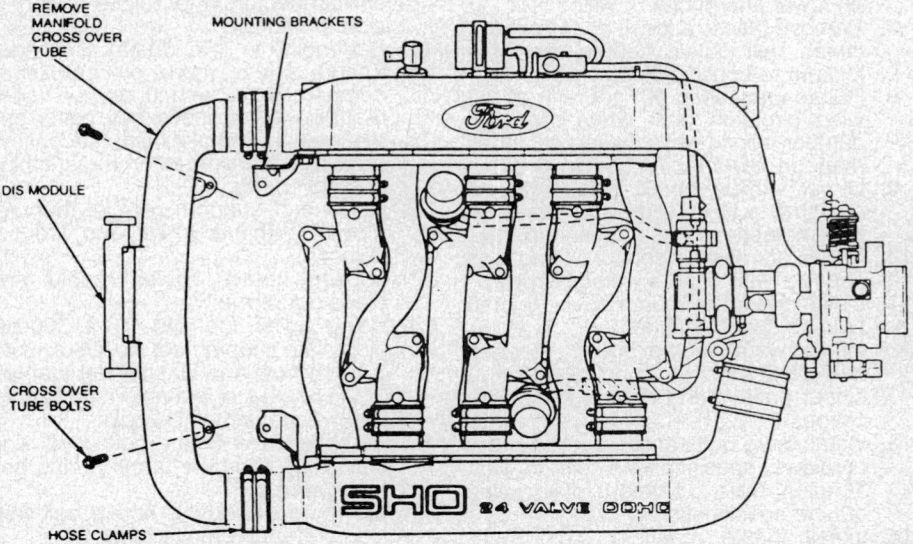

Fig. 9 Intake manifold assembly

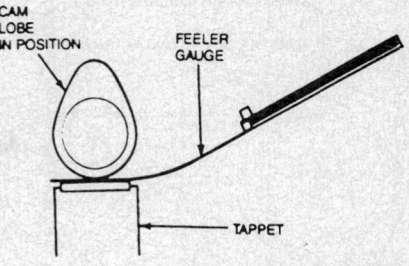

Fig. 7 Valve clearance checking

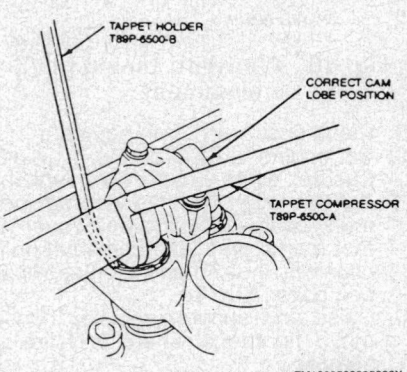

Fig. 8 Valve shim replacing

VALVE CLEARANCE SPECIFICATIONS

The cold valve clearance specification for intake valves is .006-.010 inch and for exhaust valves is .010-.014 inch.

VALVE ADJUSTMENT

The valves are adjusted by the use of shims placed between the camshaft and valve spring retainer.

Valves must be adjusted with engine cold.

1. Disconnect battery ground cable.
2. Remove upper intake manifold and valve covers as outlined under "Valve Cover, Replace."
3. Position cylinder for valves being checked at TDC compression.

4. Using a suitable feeler gauge, check clearance **Fig. 7**, record clearance of any valve not within specifications. "Refer to Valve Clearance Specifications."
5. Repeat procedure for each cylinder.
6. For each valve that requires adjustment, proceed as follows:
   a. Ensure cam lobe is pointing directly away from lifter **Fig. 8**, then using tappet compressing tool No. T89P-6500-A and tappet holding tool No. T89P-6500-B or equivalents, compress valve tappet.
   b. Using a suitable pick tool or magnet, remove tappet shim from tappet.
   c. Determine thickness of removed shim, then using previously recorded clearance determine the correct replacement shim size.
   d. Install replacement shim with size marking down
   e. Repeat above procedure for each valve requiring adjustment.
7. Install valve cover and intake manifold, noting the following:
   a. Ensure all replaced shims are fully seated into tappets.
   b. Tighten bolts to specifications.
   c. Connect battery ground cable. Refer to "Adaptive Strategies Relearn Procedures" under "Precautions."

TIMING BELT
REPLACE
3 .0L/V6-182
Removal

1. Relieve fuel system pressure as outlined under "Precautions."
2. Disconnect battery ground cable, then remove battery.
3. Remove engine roll damper, then disconnect wiring to DIS module, **Fig. 9**.
4. Loosen intake manifold crossover tube hose clamps.
5. Remove alternator/air conditioning and water pump/power steering belts by backing out tensioner pulley adjustment screws.
6. Remove water pump/power steering tensioner pulley and alternator/air conditioning tensioner pulley and bracket.
7. Remove upper timing belt cover, then disconnect crankshaft sensor connectors.

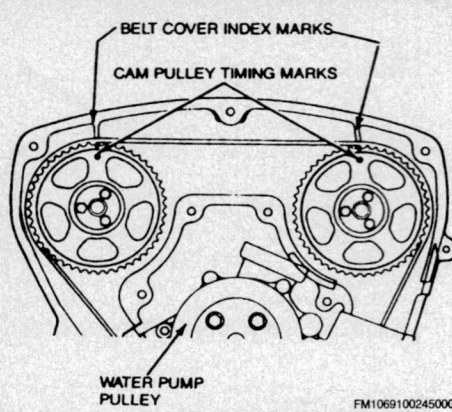

Fig. 10   Camshaft timing mark alignment

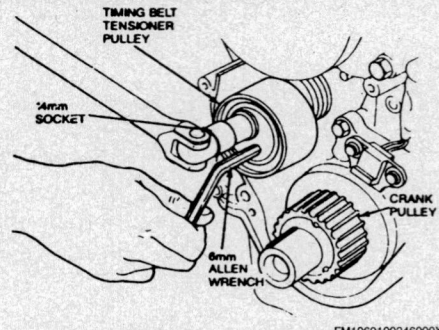

Fig. 11   Timing belt removal

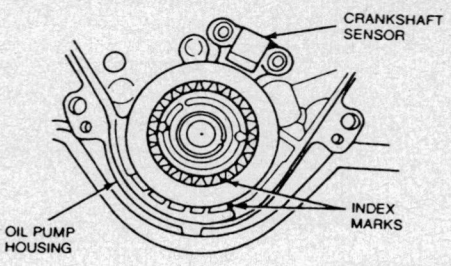

Fig. 12   Crankshaft pulley alignment marks

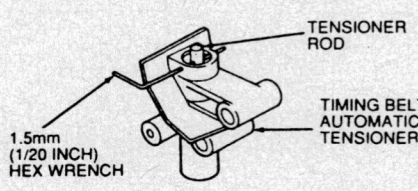

Fig. 13   Hex wrench into tensioner insertion

8. Place gear selector in neutral.
9. Set engine to TDC on No. 1 cylinder. Ensure white mark on crankshaft damper aligns with 0 degree index mark on lower timing belt cover and that marks on intake camshaft pulley align with index marks on metal timing belt cover, **Fig. 10.**
10. Raise and support vehicle, then remove righthand wheel and tire assembly.
11. Loosen fender splash shield and position out of the way.
12. Using puller tool No. T67L-3600-A, adapter tool No. D80L-630-3 and screws tool No. T89P-6701-A or equivalent, remove crankshaft damper.
13. Remove lower and center timing belt covers, then disconnect crankshaft sensor wire and grommet from slot in cover and stud on water pump.
14. Loosen timing belt tensioner, rotate pulley 180° clockwise and tighten tensioner nut to hold pulley in "unload" position, **Fig. 11.**
15. Lower vehicle and remove timing belt.

Installation

Do not let new timing belt come in contact with gasoline, oil, water or coolant prior to installation.
1. Ensure engine is at TDC on No. 1 cylinder. Check that camshaft pulley marks line up with index marks on upper steel belt cover and that crankshaft pulley aligns with index mark on oil pump housing, **Fig. 12.**
2. Install timing belt on crankshaft pulley and route to camshaft pulley as shown in **Fig. 5.** Ensure yellow lines on belt are aligned with index marks on pulleys.
3. Release tensioner locknut and leave nut loose, then raise and support vehicle.
4. Install center timing belt cover, connect crankshaft sensor wire and install grommet in slot. Ensure wire is routed properly, tighten bolts to specifications.
5. Install lower timing belt cover, tighten bolts to specifications.
6. Install crankshaft damper, then rotate crankshaft two revolutions in the clockwise direction until yellow mark

on damper aligns with 0 degree mark on lower timing belt cover.
7. Remove plastic access door on lower timing belt cover, tighten tensioner locknut to specification.
8. Rotate crankshaft 60° more in clockwise direction until white mark on damper aligns with 0 degree index mark on lower timing cover.
9. Lower vehicle, check that marks on camshaft pulleys align with marks on rear metal timing cover, **Fig. 10.**
10. Route crankshaft sensor wiring and connect with engine wiring harness.
11. Install upper timing belt cover, tighten bolts to specifications.
12. Install water pump/power steering and alternator/air conditioning tensioner pulleys and tighten to specifications.
13. Install drive belts and set tension according to specifications, refer to "Belt Tension Data." Tighten idler pulley nuts to specification.
14. Install intake manifold cross over tube, tighten bolts to specification.
15. Install engine roll damper and battery, then connect battery cables and raise vehicle.
16. Install splash shield, tire and wheel assembly, then lower vehicle.
17. Connect battery ground cable. Refer to "Adaptive Strategies Relearn Procedures" under "Precautions."

3.2L/V6-195
Removal

1. Relieve fuel system pressure as outlined under "Precautions."
2. Disconnect battery ground cable, then remove battery.
3. Remove engine roll damper, then disconnect wiring to ignition control module.
4. Loosen intake manifold crossover tube hose clamps, then remove intake manifold crossover tube.

5. Rotate accessory drive belt tensioner in a clockwise direction to relieve tension and remove accessory drive belt.
6. Disconnect surge tank fitting.
7. Remove upper and lower idler pulleys.
8. Using strap wrench tool No. D85L-6000-A or equivalent to hold power steering pump pulley in place, remove pulley retaining nut, washer and power steering pump.
9. Remove belt tensioner, then the upper and center timing belt covers.
10. Disconnect crankshaft position sensor connectors, then place transmission in neutral.
11. Set engine to TDC on No. 1 cylinder. Ensure white mark on crankshaft damper aligns with 0 degree index mark on lower timing belt cover and that marks on intake camshaft pulleys align with index mark on metal timing belt cover, **Fig. 10.**
12. Raise and support vehicle, then remove righthand wheel and tire assembly.
13. Loosen fender splash shield and place out of the way.
14. Using puller tool No. T67L-3600-A, step plate adapter tool No. D80L-630-3 and screw and washer set tool No. T89P-6701-A or suitable equivalents, remove crankshaft damper.
15. Remove lower timing belt cover and belt guide, then the upper timing belt tensioner bolt.
16. Slowly loosen lower timing belt tension bolt and remove tensioner.
17. Lower vehicle and remove timing belt.

Installation

Do not let new timing belt come in contact with gasoline, oil, water or coolant prior to installation.
1. Slowly compress timing belt tensioner in a soft jawed vise until hole in tensioner housing aligns with hole in tensioner rod.
2. Insert a 1/20 inch (1.5mm) hex wrench through holes as shown in **Fig. 13,** then release tensioner from vise.
3. Loosen timing belt idler bolt and ensure engine is at TDC on No. 1 cylinder. Check that camshaft pulley marks line up with index marks on upper steel belt cover and that crankshaft pulley aligns with index mark on oil pump housing, **Fig. 11.**
4. Install timing belt on crankshaft pulley and route to camshaft pulley as shown in **Fig. 5.** Ensure yellow lines

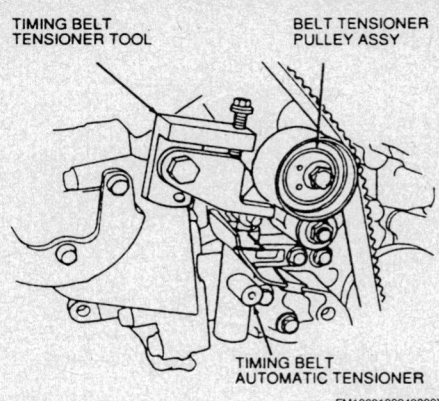

Fig. 14 Timing belt tensioner tool mounting

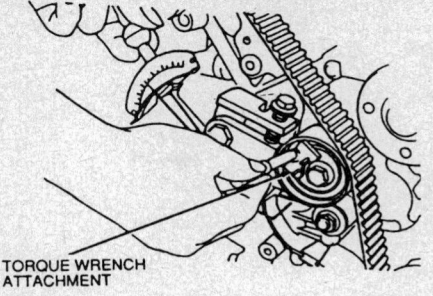

FM1069100250000X

Fig. 15 Timing belt tensioner tightening

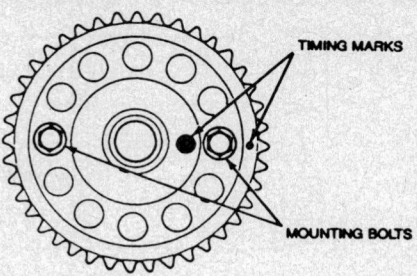

FM1069100251000X

Fig. 16 Chain sprocket alignment marks

on belt are aligned with index marks on pulleys. Lettering on belt "KOB" should be readable from rear of engine (top of lettering to front of engine). **Do not install timing belt tensioner with rod extended.**

5. Install timing belt tensioner on cylinder block while pushing timing belt idler toward belt, tighten tensioner bolt to specifications.
6. Install grommets between timing belt tensioner and oil pump.
7. Remove 1/20 inch hex wrench from tensioner, then position timing belt tensioner tool No. T93P-6254-B or equivalent using power steering bracket holes, **Fig. 14.**
8. Hand-tighten timing belt idler bolt.
9. Using an inch lb. torque wrench and torque wrench attachment tool No. T93P-6254-A or equivalent, rotate torque wrench attachment clockwise 4.3 inch lbs., **Fig. 15.**
10. Tighten timing belt tensioner to specifications, then remove belt tensioning tool No. T93P-6254-B.
11. Raise and support vehicle, then install belt guide and lower timing belt cover.
12. Using crankshaft seal installer/cover aligner tool No. T88T-6701-A with forcing screw from vibration damper and seal installer tool No. T82L-6316-A or equivalents, install crankshaft damper.
13. Rotate crankshaft two revolutions in a clockwise direction until yellow mark on damper aligns with 0 degree mark on lower timing belt cover.
14. Lower vehicle and ensure index marks on camshaft pulleys align with marks on rear metal timing belt cover, **Fig. 10.**
15. Route crankshaft sensor wiring and connect with engine wiring harness.
16. Install center timing belt cover, then the upper timing belt cover.
17. Install water pump pulley and accessory drive belt.
18. Connect surge tank fitting, then install intake manifold crossover tube.
19. Install engine roll damper and connect wiring to ignition control module.
20. Install and connect battery, then raise and support vehicle.

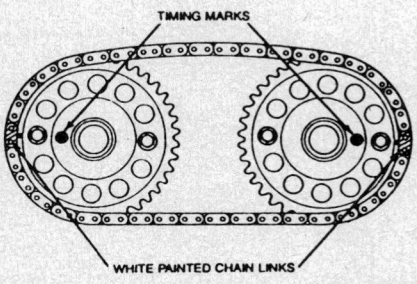

FM1069100252000X

Fig. 17 Timing chain & sprocket installation

21. Install splash shield, then tire and wheel assembly.
22. Connect battery ground cable. Refer to "Adaptive Strategies Relearn Procedures" under "Precautions."

CAMSHAFT
REPLACE

1. Place engine to TDC on No. 1 cylinder.
2. Remove valve covers as outlined under "Valve Cover, Replace."
3. Remove timing belt as described under "Timing Belt, Replace."
4. Remove camshaft pulleys, noting location of dowel pins.
5. Remove upper rear timing belt cover.
6. Loosen camshaft bearing caps uniformly. **If camshaft bearing caps are not loosened uniformly camshaft damage may result.**
7. Remove bearing caps, noting their position for proper installation.
8. Remove camshaft chain tensioner attaching bolts, then remove camshaft together with chain and tensioner.
9. Remove and discard oil seal.
10. Remove chain sprocket from camshaft.
11. Reverse procedure to install, noting the following:
   a. When installing chain sprockets, align timing marks on sprockets with camshaft as shown in **Fig. 16.** Tighten attaching bolts to specifications.
   b. Align white painted link with timing mark on sprocket, **Fig. 17.**
   c. Rotate camshaft approximately 60 degrees counterclockwise and install chain tensioners. **LH and RH**

chain tensioners are not interchangeable.
d. Lubricate camshaft journals with suitable lubricant.
e. Using tightening sequence shown in **Fig. 18,** tighten bearing caps in two steps to specification.
f. Tighten chain tensioner to specifications, then rotate camshafts 60° clockwise to ensure proper alignment of timing marks. Marks on camshaft sprockets should align with cylinder mating surfaces as shown in **Fig. 19.**
g. Set camshaft positioning tool No. T89P-6256-C or equivalent on camshafts to check for correct positioning as shown in **Fig. 20.** Flats on tool should align with flats on camshaft. If tool does not line up, repeat installation procedure.

CAMSHAFT SEAL
REPLACE

1. Set engine to TDC on No. 1 cylinder.
2. Remove timing belt upper cover as described under "Timing Belt, Replace."
3. Remove timing belt from camshaft pulleys.
4. Remove crankshaft pulleys, noting location of dowel pins.
5. Using seal puller tool No. T78P-3504-N or equivalent, remove camshaft seal.
6. Reverse procedure to install, applying silicone sealer D6AZ-19562-A or equivalent to new seal outer diameter and seal seating surface prior to installation.

PISTON & ROD ASSEMBLY

Refer to **Fig. 21.** for piston and rod assemble.

CRANKSHAFT & FRONT OIL SEAL
REPLACE

1. Loosen accessory drive belts, then remove RH front wheel.
2. Remove damper attaching bolt.
3. Remove drive belts from crankshaft damper.

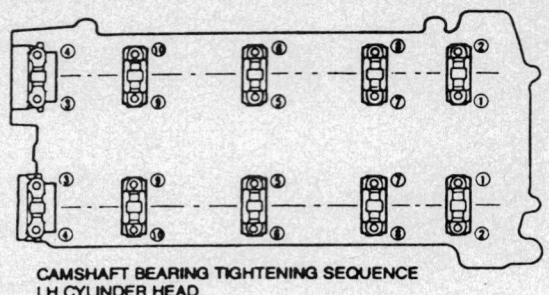

CAMSHAFT BEARING TIGHTENING SEQUENCE
LH CYLINDER HEAD

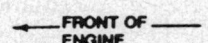

← FRONT OF ——
ENGINE

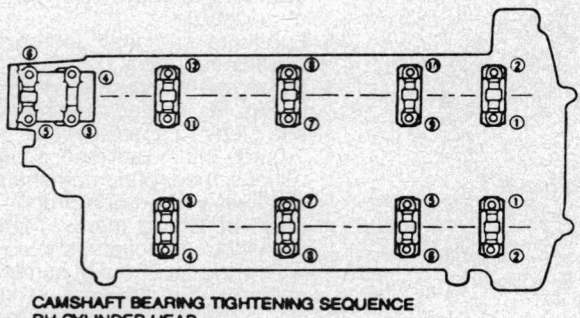

CAMSHAFT BEARING TIGHTENING SEQUENCE
RH CYLINDER HEAD

FM1069100253000X

Fig. 18   Camshaft bearing tightening sequence

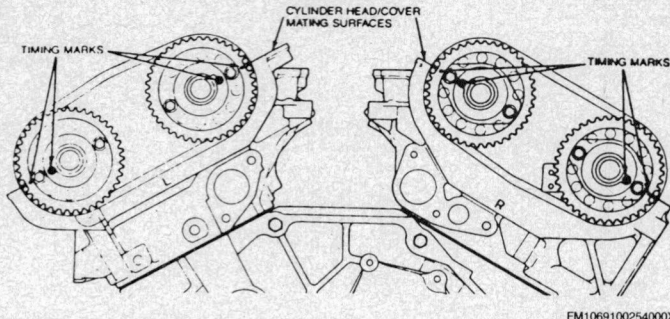

FM1069100254000X

Fig. 19   Timing marks w/cylinder head mating surface alignment

CAM POSITION TOOL

FLATS ON CAMS
MUST ALIGN WITH
FLATS ON TOOL

FM1069100255000X

Fig. 20   Cam position inspection

4. Using suitable puller tool No. T67L-3600-A or equivalent, remove crankshaft damper from crankshaft.
5. Remove timing belt as described under "Timing Belt, Replace."
6. Using suitable puller or equivalent, remove crankshaft timing gear. **Ensure not to damage crankshaft sensor or shutter.**
7. Using seal puller tool No. T78P-3504-N or equivalent, remove front oil seal.
8. Reverse procedure to install.

OIL PAN
REPLACE

1. Relieve fuel system pressure as outlined under "Precautions."
2. Disconnect battery ground cable, then remove oil dipstick.
3. Remove accessory drive belts, then timing belt as described under "Timing Belt, Replace."
4. Raise and support vehicle.
5. **On models with low oil sensor,** remove retainer clip at sensor, then disconnect sensor electrical connector, **Fig. 22.**
6. **On all models,** drain crankcase.
7. Remove starter motor, then disconnect Heater Exhaust Gas Oxygen (HEGO) sensor electrical connector.
8. Remove catalyst and pipe assembly.
9. Remove lower engine/flywheel dust cover from converter housing.
10. Remove oil pan and gasket.
11. Reverse procedure to install, noting the following,

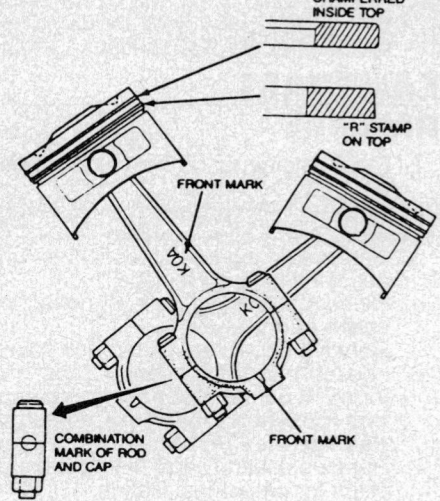

CHAMFERRED
INSIDE TOP

"R" STAMP
ON TOP

FRONT MARK

COMBINATION
MARK OF ROD
AND CAP

FRONT MARK

FM1069100256000X

Fig. 21   Piston & rod assembly

a. Tighten oil pan bolts to specifications, in sequence, **Fig. 23.**
b. Connect battery ground cable. Refer to "Adaptive Strategies Relearn Procedures" under "Precautions."

OIL PUMP
REPLACE

1. Remove oil pan as outlined under "Oil Pan, Replace."
2. Remove timing belt pulley as described under "Timing Belt, Replace."
3. Remove sump pickup tube to oil pump attaching bolts.

4. Remove oil pump to block attaching bolts, then remove pump.
5. Reverse procedure to install. Tighten bolts to specifications.

OIL PUMP SERVICE

1. Wash all parts in suitable solvent, then dry with compressed air.
2. Ensure all dirt and particles are removed.
3. Inspect inner pump housing for wear or damage.
4. Inspect pump cover mating surface for wear, scuff marks are normal, if surface is worn or grooved, replace pump assembly.
5. Inspect rotor for nicks, burrs or score marks, remove imperfections with suitable oil stone.
6. Using suitable feeler gauge, measure inner tip to outer rotor tip clearance, **Fig. 24,** clearance should be .0024-.0071 inch.
7. Install suitable straightedge, then using feeler gauge, measure rotor endplay, **Fig. 25,** clearance should be .0012-.0035 inch.
8. If any inspection is not as indicated, replace oil pump assembly.

BELT TENSION DATA

3.0L/V6—182

Belt	New	Used
A/C & Alternator	220-265	148-192
Power Steer. & Water Pump	154-198	112-157

3.2L/V6—195

Belt tension is maintained by an automatic belt tensioner.

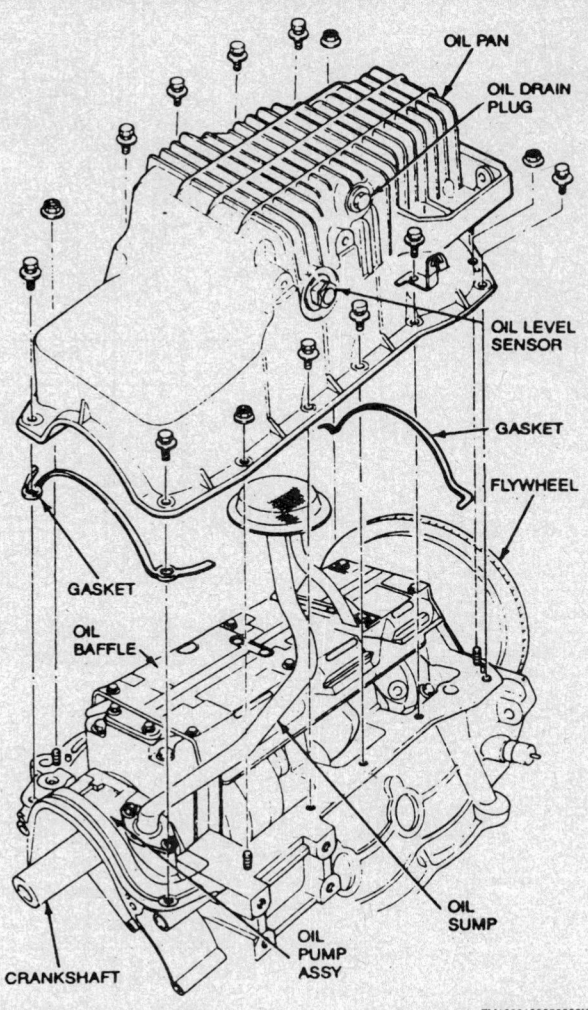

Fig. 22 Oil pan & pump removal

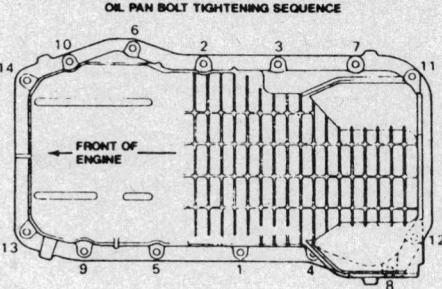

Fig. 23 Oil pan tightening sequence

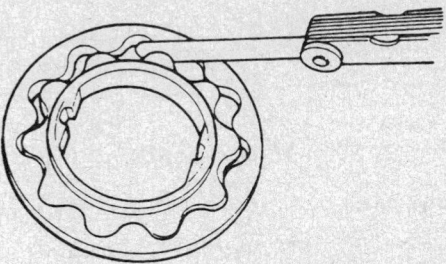

Fig. 24 Oil pump tip clearance

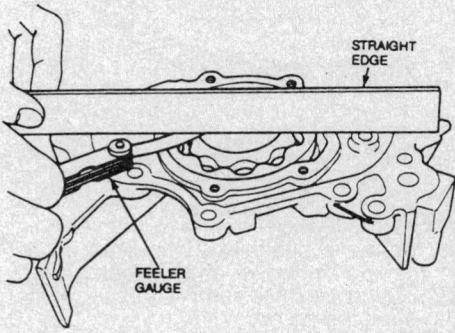

Fig. 25 Oil pump rotor endplay

SERPENTINE DRIVE BELT

BELT ROUTING

Refer to **Figs. 26. and 27** for serpentine drive belt routing.

BELT, REPLACE

3.0L/V6-182 Engine

1. Disconnect battery ground cable.
2. Loosen idler pulley nut.
3. Loosen idler adjusting screw until belt can be removed.
4. Reverse procedure to install.

3.2L/V6-195 Engine

1. Using a suitable 14 mm socket and wrench, rotate tensioner clockwise to release tension on belt.
2. While holding tensioner remove belt.
3. Reverse procedure to install.

COOLING SYSTEM BLEED

These engine do not require a specific bleed procedure. After filling cooling system, run engine to operating temperature with radiator/pressure cap off. Air will then be automatically bled through cap opening.

THERMOSTAT
REPLACE

REMOVAL

1. Drain cooling system below level of upper radiator hose.
2. Remove upper radiator hose, then three retaining bolts from thermostat housing.
3. Remove housing and thermostat as an assembly, discarding old gasket. Clean sealing surfaces with gasket scraper. Ensure not to damage aluminum surfaces as leak may form.

INSTALLATION

1. Install thermostat into housing. Ensure jiggle valve in relation to housing.
2. Position gasket onto housing using bolts as holding device, then install housing assembly and retaining bolts.
3. Install upper radiator hose. Refer to "Cooling System Bleed" fill and bleed cooling system with recommended amount and mixture.
4. Start engine and check for leaks.

WATER PUMP
REPLACE

1. Relieve fuel system pressure as outlined under "Precautions."
2. Drain cooling system, then disconnect battery cable.
3. Remove battery and battery tray, then drive belt and accessory belts.
4. Remove attaching bolts, retaining A/C, alternator idler pulley and bracket.
5. Disconnect electrical connector from ignition module and ground strap.
6. Loosen four clamps on upper intake connector tube, then remove two retaining bolts.
7. Remove upper intake connector tube.
8. Remove RH tire and wheel assembly and splash panel.
9. Remove upper timing belt cover, then the crankshaft pulley.

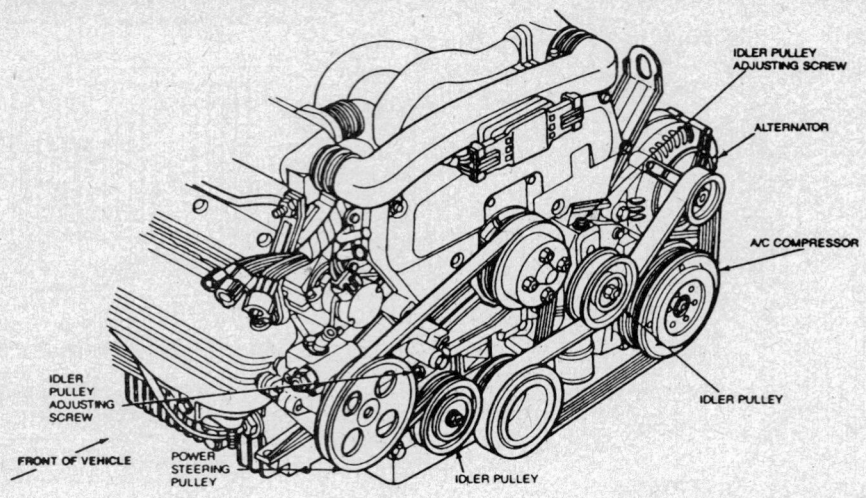

Fig. 26 Serpentine drive belt routing 3.0L/V6-182 SHO

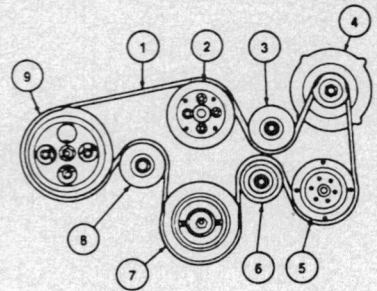

Item		Description
1		Drive Belt
2		Water Pump
3		Idler Pulley
4		Generator
5		A C Compressor
6		Idler Pulley/
7		Crankshaft Vibration Damper and Pulley
8		Drive Belt Tensioner
9		Power Steering Pump

FM1069500396000X

Fig. 27 Serpentine belt routing, 3.2L/V6-195 SHO

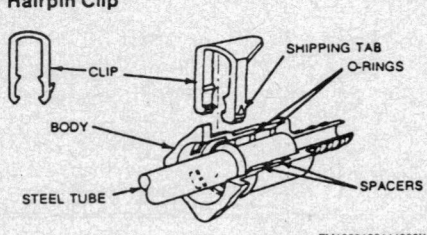

Fig. 28 Push connect fitting removal

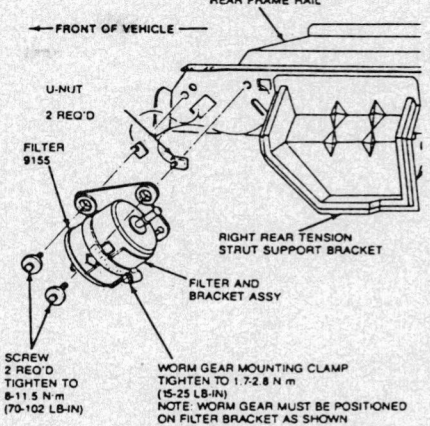

Fig. 29 Fuel filter removal

10. Remove lower timing belt cover.
11. Remove attaching bolts from center timing belt cover and position aside.
12. Remove water pump attaching bolts, then the pump.
13. Reverse procedure to install. Connect battery ground cable and refer to "Adaptive Strategies Relearn Procedures" under "Precautions."

RADIATOR
REPLACE

Refer to "Radiator, Replace" in the "3.0L/V6-182 Engine, Except SHO" section for radiator replacement procedure.

FUEL PUMP
REPLACE

1. Relieve fuel system pressure as outlined under "Precautions."
2. Disconnect battery ground cable.
3. Remove fuel from fuel tank by pumping fuel out of fuel filler neck.
4. Raise and support vehicle.
5. Disconnect then remove fuel filler neck.
6. Support fuel tank, then remove tank support straps. Lower fuel tank partially and remove fuel lines, electrical connector and vent lines from tank. Remove tank and place on suitable workbench.
7. Turn fuel pump locking ring counter-clockwise and remove locking ring.
8. Remove fuel pump, bracket and gasket assembly.
9. Reverse procedure to install. Connect battery ground cable and refer to "Adaptive Strategies Relearn Procedures" under "Precautions."

FUEL FILTER
REPLACE

1. Relieve fuel system pressure as outlined under "Precautions."
2. Twist push connect fittings at each end of the filter until they move freely on the tube.
3. Bend and break shipping tab from hairpin clip, then spread two clip legs approximately 1/8 inch, Fig. 28.
4. Remove clip from tube and fitting by pulling gently on its' triangular end.
5. Separate fitting and hose assembly from fuel filter.
6. Install retainer clips in each connect fitting.
7. Loosen worm gear mounting clip, then remove filter from bracket, Fig. 29.
8. Reverse procedure to install.

TIGHTENING SPECIFICATIONS

Year	Component	Torque/Ft. Lbs.
1992-95	A/C Compressor Bracket Bolts	27-40
	Alternator	25-36
	Alternator & A/C Pulley & Bracket	11-16
	Camshaft Bearing Caps	③
	Camshaft Pulley	15-18
	Camshaft Sensor	6-8
	Camshaft Sprocket Bolts	10-13
	Chain Tensioner	11-14
	Connecting Rod Nuts	④
	Converter To Engine	19-34
	Crankshaft Pulley Bolt	113-126
	Crankshaft Sensor Bolts	13-22 ②
	Cylinder Head Bolts	①
	EGR Tube To Exhaust Manifold	11-16
	Engine Coolant Temperature Sensor	12-17
	Engine Mount	①
	Exhaust Manifold To Cylinder Head	26-38
	Exhaust Pipe To Manifold	16-24
	Flywheel	⑥
	Front Cover Bolts	60-90 ②
	Fuel Rail	11-16
	Heat Shield	11-16
	Idler Pulley Nut	25-36
	Ignition Coil Pack Bracket	21-31
	Ignition Coil Pack Screws	3.3-5.2
	Intake Manifold	11-16
	Intake Manifold Crossover Tube	11-16
	Knock Sensor	22-28
	Main Bearing Caps	⑤

Year	Component	Torque/Ft. Lbs.
1992-95 —Cont'd	Main Bearing Support Beam	15-24
	Oil Drain Plug	15-24
	Oil Level Sensor	16-24
	Oil Pick Up Tube	60-90 ②
	Oil Pressure Sending Switch	12-17
	Oil Pump	11-16
	Oil Screen	6-8
	Oil Seal Carrier Bolts	55-82 ②
	Oil Sump To Oil Pump	6-8
	Power Steering Pump Pulley	40-50
	Pressure Plate	12-24
	Rocker Arm Cover Bolts	8-11
	Spark Plugs	17-19
	Tension Locknut	25-37
	Thermostat Housing	5-8
	Throttle Body Bolts	12-16
	Throttle Position Sensor	18-26 ②
	Timing Belt Rear Cover	70 ②
	Transaxle To Engine	25-35
	Upper Oil Baffle	11-16
	Water Pump Pulley	11-16

① —Refer to text.
② —Inch lbs.
③ —Tighten in two steps, first to 71–106 inch lbs., then to 12–16 ft. lbs.
④ —Tighten in two steps, first to 22–26 ft. lbs., then to 33–36 ft. lbs.
⑤ —Tighten in two steps, first to 34–50 ft. lbs., then to 58–65 ft. lbs.
⑥ —Tighten in two steps, first to 29–43 ft. lbs., then to 51–58 ft. lbs.

3.8L/V6-232 Engine

NOTE: On Air Bag Equipped Models, Refer To "Air Bag System Precautions" Located In The Front Of This Manual For System Disarming & Arming Procedures.

INDEX

PRECAUTIONS

AIR BAG SYSTEMS

Refer to "Air Bag System Precautions" in the front of this manual for system disarming and arming procedures.

ADAPTIVE STRATEGIES RELEARN PROCEDURES

Vehicle specific information about operation, stored in PCM using battery backed up memory, may be lost when battery is disconnected. If this occurs poor engine performance, stalling and other driveability problems may occur. It may be necessary to drive the vehicle for up to 10 miles to allow the PCM to relearn this information

FUEL SYSTEM PRESSURE RELIEF

Fuel supply lines will remain pressurized for long periods of time after engine shut-down. This pressure must be relieved before any service is attempted. A valve is provided on the fuel rail assembly for this purpose. To relieve system pressure, remove air cleaner assembly and connect pressure gauge tool No. T80L-9974-A or T80L-9974-B or equivalent onto fuel valve on fuel rail assembly. To pressurize fuel system, proceed as follows:

1. Install pressure gauge tool No. T80L-9974-A or T80L-9974-B equivalent onto fuel rail pressure fitting.
2. Turn ignition switch to On position for 3 seconds, repeatedly 5 to 10 times until pressure gauge indicates 13 psi.

ENGINE MOUNT
REPLACE

LH INSULATOR & SUPPORT ASSEMBLY

1. Raise and support vehicle.
2. Remove left front tire and wheel assembly, then support transaxle using suitable jack and block of wood.
3. Remove insulator to support attaching nuts, **Fig. 1.**
4. Remove insulator to frame through bolts, then raise transaxle enough to unload insulator.
5. Remove support assembly to transaxle attaching bolts, then the insulator and/or support assembly.
6. Reverse procedure to install.

RH FRONT

The following procedure has been revised per a Technical Service Bulletin.
1. Relieve fuel system pressure as outlined under "Precautions."
2. Using suitable 18mm swivel socket and long extension, remove mount upper attaching nut through engine compartment.
3. Raise and support vehicle.
4. Loosen, but do not remove, RH rear lower mount attaching nut.
5. Loosen, but do not remove, RH front lower mount attaching nut.
6. Lower vehicle.
7. Install suitable engine lifting equipment, then lift engine about one inch.
8. Raise and support vehicle, then remove engine mount.
9. Reverse procedure to install.

RH REAR

1. Raise and support vehicle.
2. Loosen RH front and RH rear insulator attaching nuts, **Fig. 1.**

3. Remove catalytic converter, then lower vehicle.
4. Using suitable engine support equipment, raise engine one inch and support.
5. Raise and support vehicle.
6. Loosen four subframe attaching bolts, then remove insulator attaching nut and insulator.
7. Reverse procedure to install.

ENGINE
REPLACE

1. Relieve fuel system pressure as outlined under "Precautions."
2. Disconnect battery ground cable, then drain cooling system.
3. Disconnect underhood lamp electrical connector, then mark position of hood hinges and remove hood.
4. Remove oil dipstick tube, then disconnect alternator to voltage regulator wiring harness.
5. Remove radiator upper sight shield, then cooling fan motor relay attaching bolts, then position relay aside.
6. Remove air cleaner assembly.
7. Disconnect engine cooling fan.
8. Remove fan shroud, then the upper radiator hose.
9. Disconnect transaxle oil cooler tubes, then the heater hoses.
10. Disconnect power steering pump pressure hose, then the A/C compressor electrical connector.
11. Discharge A/C system, then disconnect compressor to condenser line.
12. Remove coolant recovery reservoir.
13. Remove wiring shield and accelerator cable mounting bracket.
14. Disconnect fuel hoses, then the power steering pump pressure and return tube bracket.
15. Disconnect engine control sensor

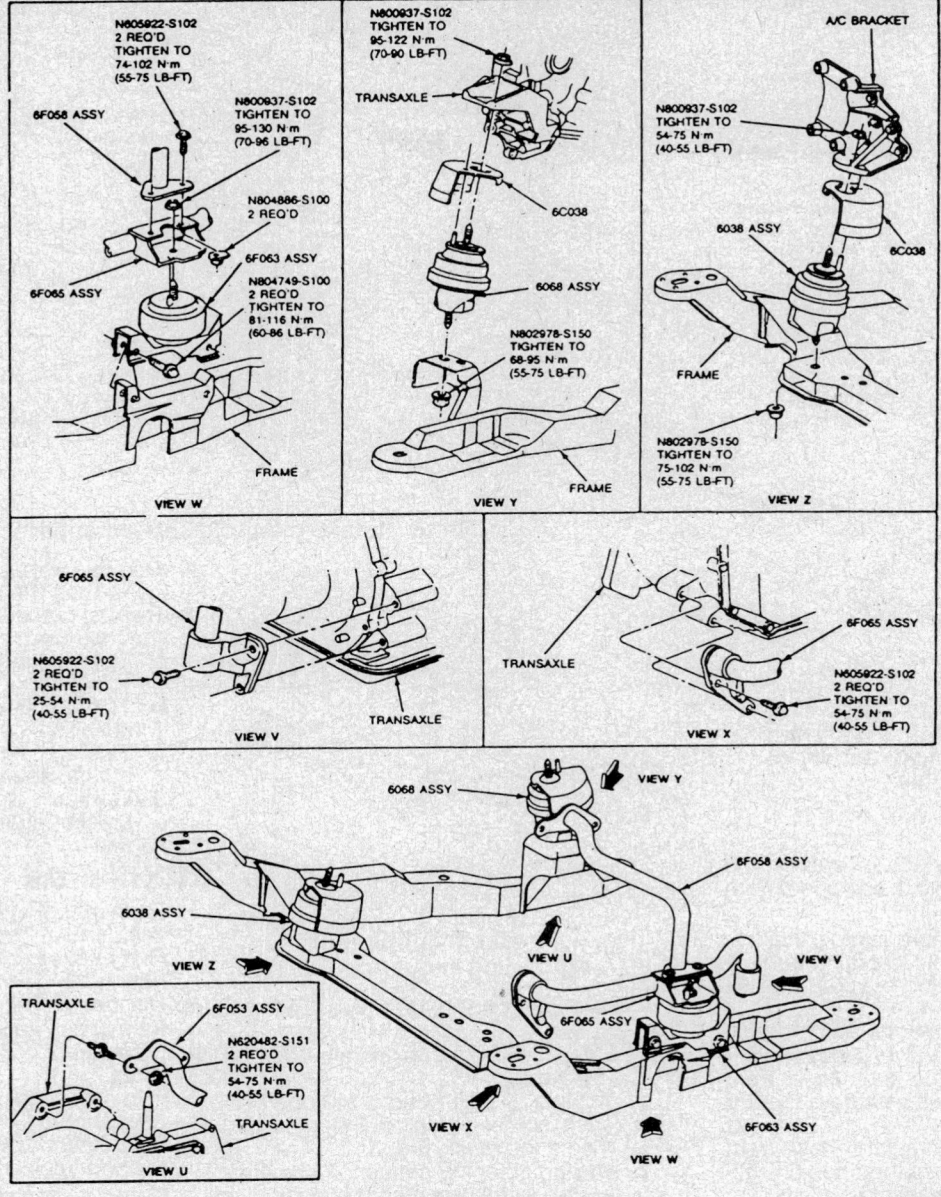

Fig. 1 Engine mounts

electrical connector.

16. Disconnect vacuum hoses and ground wire assembly.
17. Remove duct assembly, then disconnect throttle control valve cable.
18. Disconnect bulkhead electrical connector, then transaxle pressure switches.
19. Remove transaxle support assembly attaching bolts.
20. Remove transaxle support assembly.
21. Raise and support vehicle.
22. Drain engine oil and remove oil filter, then disconnect exhaust gas oxygen sensor.
23. Remove drive belt, then the crankshaft pulley.
24. Remove drive belt tensioner, then the starter motor.
25. Remove converter housing assembly,

then the inlet pipe converter assembly.

26. Remove engine support insulator retaining nuts.
27. Remove converter to flywheel attaching nuts.
28. Disconnect oil level sensor electrical connector.
29. Disconnect lower radiator hose, then remove engine to transaxle attaching bolts.
30. Remove wheel and tire assemblies.
31. Remove water pump pulley attaching bolts.
32. Remove water pump, then the distributor cap and position aside.
33. Remove distributor rotor, then the exhaust manifold bolt lock retaining bolts.
34. Remove thermactor air pump attach-

ing bolts and the pump, if equipped.

35. Disconnect oil pressure sender electrical connector.
36. Install suitable engine lifting equipment.
37. Remove engine assembly.
38. Reverse procedure to install, noting the following:
    a. Tighten to specifications.
    b. Connect battery ground cable. Refer to "Adaptive Strategies Relearn Procedures" under "Precautions."

INTAKE MANIFOLD
REPLACE

1. Relieve fuel system pressure as outlined under "Precautions."
2. Drain cooling system, then remove air cleaner assembly, intake duct and

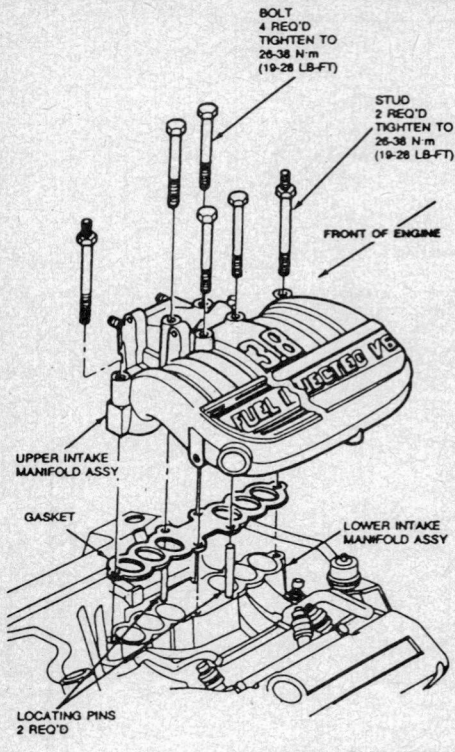

Fig. 2 Upper intake manifold assembly

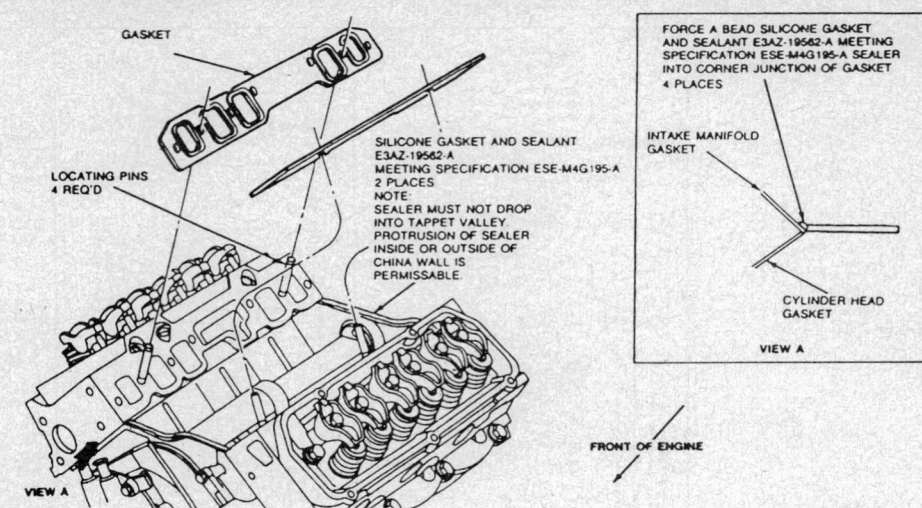

Fig. 3 Intake manifold sealant application

heat tube.
3. Disconnect accelerator cable and speed control cable (if equipped) from throttle body.
4. Disconnect transaxle linkage, then remove accelerator cable mounting bracket and position bracket and cables aside.
5. Disconnect thermactor air supply hose from check valve, if equipped.
6. Disconnect flexible fuel lines from steel lines, then fuel lines from injector fuel rail.
7. Disconnect upper radiator hose from thermostat housing, then coolant by-pass hose from manifold.
8. Disconnect heater tube from intake manifold, then remove tube support bracket attaching nut.
9. Disconnect heater hose from rear of tube, then remove tube.
10. Disconnect vacuum lines, then all necessary electrical connectors.
11. Remove A/C compressor support bracket, if equipped.
12. Disconnect PCV lines, then remove throttle body assembly.
13. Remove EGR valve, then the wiring retainer bracket and position aside.
14. Remove upper intake manifold attaching bolts, **Fig. 2,** then the upper manifold.
15. Remove injectors and fuel rail assembly.
16. Remove heater outlet hose.
17. Remove lower manifold attaching bolts and lower manifold. **It may be necessary to pry on front of lower manifold to break the seal. Ensure**

Fig. 4 Intake manifold bolt tightening sequence

care is taken not to damage sealing surfaces.
18. Reverse procedure to install, noting the following:
   a. Apply a 1/8 inch bead of silicone at each corner where cylinder head meets the block, **Fig. 3.**
   b. Using tightening sequence shown in **Fig. 4, torque** manifold bolts in two steps as follows: first step 8 ft. lbs. and second step 11 ft. lbs. As revised per Technical Service Bulletin.
   c. Tighten throttle body attaching bolts to specification in a criss-cross pattern.
   d. Tighten EGR attaching bolts to specifications.

EXHAUST MANIFOLD
REPLACE

LEFT SIDE

1. Relieve fuel system pressure as outlined under "Precautions."
2. Remove oil dipstick tube support bracket, then disconnect spark plug wires.
3. Raise and support vehicle, then remove exhaust pipe to manifold attaching nuts, then lower vehicle.

4. Remove exhaust manifold attaching bolts, then the manifold.
5. Reverse procedure to install, noting the following:
   a. Lightly lubricate bolts and nuts with oil.
   b. Tighten manifold attaching bolts to specification.
   c. Tighten exhaust pipe attaching nuts to specification.
   d. Tighten dipstick tube support bracket attaching nut to specification.

RIGHT SIDE

1. Relieve fuel system pressure as outlined under "Precautions."
2. Remove air cleaner assembly and heat tube.
3. Disconnect thermactor hose from air tube check valve, if equipped.
4. Disconnect coil wire, then spark plug wires.
5. Remove spark plugs, then the outer heat shroud.
6. Disconnect EGR tube, then raise and support vehicle.
7. Remove transmission dipstick tube and the thermactor downstream air tube.
8. Remove exhaust pipe to manifold attaching nuts, then lower vehicle.
9. Remove exhaust manifold attaching bolts, then the manifold and inner heat shroud.
10. Reverse procedure to install, noting the following:
   a. Lightly lubricate bolts and nuts with oil.
   b. Tighten manifold attaching bolts to specifications.
   c. Tighten exhaust pipe attaching nuts to specifications.
   d. Tighten outer heat shroud attaching screws specification.

CYLINDER HEAD
REPLACE

1. Relieve fuel system pressure as outlined under "Precautions."

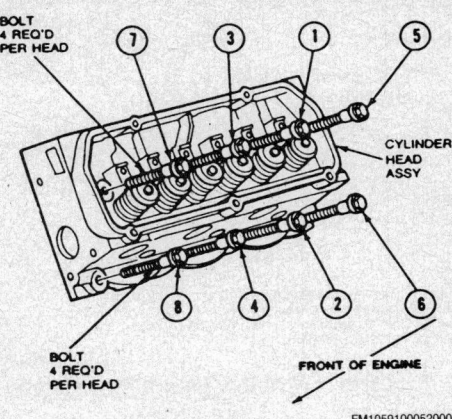

Fig. 5 Cylinder head bolt tightening sequence

FM10591000052000X

2. Disconnect battery ground cable, then drain cooling system.
3. Remove air cleaner assembly, intake duct and heat tube.
4. Remove drive belt, then if removing left cylinder head, proceed as follows:
    a. Remove power steering pump and position aside, then remove oil fill cap.
    b. Remove A/C compressor mounting bracket and position aside, if equipped.
    c. Remove alternator and bracket.
5. If removing right cylinder head, proceed as follows:
    a. Disconnect thermactor air control valve, if equipped.
    b. Disconnect thermactor tube support bracket from rear of cylinder head, if equipped.
    c. Remove accessory drive idler.
    d. Remove thermactor pump pulley and thermactor pump, if equipped.
    e. Remove PCV valve.
6. Remove intake manifold as described under "Intake Manifold, Replace."
7. Remove exhaust manifolds as described under "Exhaust Manifold, Replace."
8. Remove rocker arm cover attaching bolts and the cover.
9. Loosen rocker arm fulcrum attaching bolts enough to rotate rocker arm so pushrod can be removed. **Keep pushrods in order so they can be installed in original position.**
10. Remove and discard cylinder head attaching bolts.
11. Remove cylinder head.
12. Reverse procedure to install, noting the following:
    a. Lightly oil all bolts except short ones.
    b. Apply suitable sealer to short cylinder head bolts.
    c. Using tightening sequence shown in **Fig. 5,** tighten cylinder head attaching bolts in six steps as follows: **torque** bolts to 37 ft. lbs.; **torque** bolts to 45 ft. lbs.; **torque** bolts to 52 ft. lbs.; **torque** bolts to 59 ft. lbs.; back attaching bolts off 2-3 turns; **retorque** long bolts to

11-18 ft. lbs., then an additional 85-105°; **retorque** short bolts to 11-18 ft. lbs., then an additional 65-85°.
    d. Tighten rocker arm fulcrum attaching bolts to specifications.
    e. Tighten valve cover bolts to specifications.
    f. Connect battery ground cable. Refer to "Adaptive Strategies Relearn Procedures" under "Precautions."

VALVE COVER
REPLACE

1. Disconnect spark plug wires from spark plugs and position aside.
2. Remove air cleaner assembly, oil fill cap and PCV valve.
3. Remove rocker arm cover attaching bolts and the covers.
4. Reverse procedure to install. Tighten cover attaching bolts to specifications.

VALVE ARRANGEMENT
FRONT TO REAR

Right Side .... E-I-I-E-I-E
Left Side .... E-I-E-I-I-E

CAMSHAFT LOBE LIFT SPECIFICATIONS

Exhaust .... .241 inch
Intake .... .240 inch

VALVE CLEARANCE SPECIFICATIONS

If any valve train component is replaced or if valve train components become intermixed, valve clearance will have to be checked.
1. Using a suitable pry bar, apply pressure to the push rod side of the rocker arm until hydraulic lifter has bled down and bottomed out.
2. Ensure clearance between valve stem and rocker arm is .085 and .185 inch.

VALVE ADJUSTMENT

This engine is equipped with hydraulic lifters. No adjustments are required.

HYDRAULIC LIFTERS
REPLACE

Before replacing hydraulic valve lifters for noisy operation, ensure the noise is not caused by improper rocker arm to stem clearance, worn rocker arms, pushrods or valve tips.
1. Disconnect spark plug wires from spark plugs and position aside.
2. Remove intake manifolds as described under "Intake Manifold, Replace."
3. Remove valve cover attaching bolts and the covers.
4. Loosen rocker arm fulcrum attaching bolts enough so rocker arm can be lifted of pushrod and rotated aside.

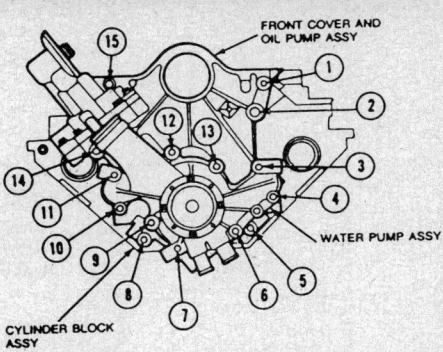

FM1069100260000X

Fig. 6 Front cover attaching bolt locations

5. Remove pushrods, then the lifters. Keep lifters and pushrods in order, so they can be installed in their original position.
6. Reverse procedure to install, noting the following:
    a. Lubricate lifters, pushrods and rocker arms with suitable lubricant.
    b. Tighten rocker arm fulcrum bolts to specifications. **Prior to torquing bolts, ensure pushrods and rocker arms are fully seated.**

FRONT COVER
REPLACE

1. Relieve fuel system pressure as outlined under "Precautions."
2. Disconnect battery ground cable, then drain cooling system.
3. Remove air cleaner assembly and air intake duct.
4. Remove cooling fan shroud attaching bolts, cooling fan clutch attaching bolts, then cooling fan clutch assembly and the fan shroud.
5. Remove drive belt, then the water pump pulley.
6. Remove power steering pump bracket attaching bolts, then position bracket and pump aside.
7. Remove A/C compressor front support bracket, if equipped.
8. Disconnect coolant bypass hose and heater hose from water pump.
9. Disconnect upper radiator hose from thermostat housing.
10. Disconnect coil wire from distributor cap, then remove cap and plug wires.
11. Remove distributor hold-down clamp, then the distributor.
12. Raise and support vehicle.
13. Remove crankshaft pulley and damper using suitable puller.
14. Remove oil filter, then disconnect lower radiator hose from water pump.
15. Remove oil pan as described under "Oil Pan, Replace."
16. Lower vehicle, then remove front cover attaching bolts, **Fig. 6.** Be sure to **remove attaching bolt located behind oil filter adapter. Cover will be damaged if pried on prior to bolt removal.**
17. Remove ignition timing indicator, then front cover and water pump as an assembly.

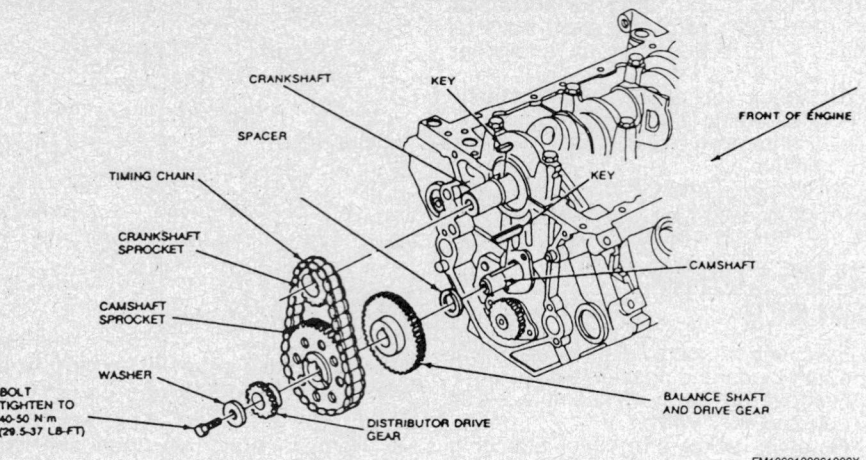

Fig. 7 Timing chains & sprocket removal

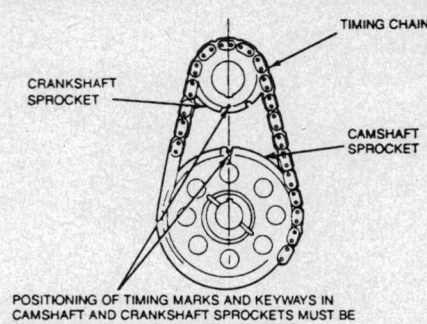

POSITIONING OF TIMING MARKS AND KEYWAYS IN CAMSHAFT AND CRANKSHAFT SPROCKETS MUST BE IN LINE AS SHOWN WITH NO. 1 PISTON AT TOP DEAD CENTER FIRING.

Fig. 8 Timing chain alignment

18. Separate water pump from front cover.
19. Reverse procedure to install. Connect battery ground cable and refer to "Adaptive Strategies Relearn Procedures" under "Precautions."

TIMING CHAIN
REPLACE

1. Remove front engine cover as outlined under "Front Cover, Replace."
2. Remove camshaft bolt and washer from end of camshaft.
3. Remove distributor drive gear, then camshaft sprocket, crankshaft sprocket and timing chain, **Fig. 7**.
4. Reverse procedure to install, noting the following:
    a. Ensure balance shaft timing is correct as outlined under "Balance Shaft, Replace."
    b. Tighten bolts to specifications.
    c. Do not replace camshaft bolt with a standard bolt.
    d. Align timing chain and sprockets by placing No. 1 cylinder at TDC and crankshaft keyway to 12 o'clock position. Ensure timing marks on sprockets are positioned across from each other, **Fig. 8**.

CAMSHAFT
REPLACE

1. Disconnect battery ground cable, then drain cooling system.
2. Remove radiator, then A/C condenser (if equipped).
3. Remove grille.
4. Remove lifters as described under "Hydraulic Valve Lifters, Replace."
5. Remove front cover and timing chain as described under "Timing Chain, Replace."
6. Remove camshaft from front of engine, ensuring not to damage bearings or lobes.
7. Reverse procedure to install, noting the following:
    a. Lubricate cam lobes and bearings with suitable lubricant.

b. Ensure balance shaft timing is correct as outlined under "Balance Shaft, Replace."
c. Tighten bolts to specifications.
d. Connect battery ground cable. Refer to "Adaptive Strategies Relearn Procedures" under "Precautions."

BALANCE SHAFT
REPLACE

1. Disconnect battery ground cable, then drain cooling system.
2. Remove radiator, then A/C condenser (if equipped).
3. Remove grille.
4. Remove front cover and timing chain as described under "Timing Chain, Replace."
5. Remove balance shaft thrust plate, **Fig. 9**, then balance shaft from front of engine, ensuring not to damage bearings.
6. Reverse procedure to install, noting the following:
    a. Lubricate balance shaft bearing journals with suitable lubricant.
    b. Ensure balance shaft timing marks are aligned, **Fig. 10**.
    c. Tighten to specifications.
    d. Connect battery ground cable. Refer to "Adaptive Strategies Relearn Procedures" under "Precautions."

PISTON & ROD ASSEMBLY

Assemble rod to piston with notch on piston dome on the same side as oil squirt hole on connecting rod. Assemble piston and rod assembly in engine with notch in dome facing front of engine, **Fig. 11**.
Police model engines contain pistons with a special hi silicone alloy. They are identified with two notches on top of the piston **Fig. 12**.

CRANKSHAFT REAR OIL SEAL
REPLACE

1. Remove transaxle, flywheel and rear

cover plate.
2. Using suitable tool, punch hole in seal metal between seal lip and cylinder block. Using suitable slide hammer remove seal.
3. Coat crankshaft seal area and seal lip with engine oil, then install seal using suitable driver.
4. Install rear cover plate, then the flywheel and transaxle. Tighten all bolts to specifications.

OIL PAN
REPLACE

1. Relieve fuel system pressure as outlined under "Precautions."
2. Disconnect battery ground cable then, raise and support vehicle.
3. Drain crankcase, then remove oil filter.
4. Remove catalytic converter assembly.
5. Remove starter motor, then torque converter housing cover.
6. Remove oil pan attaching bolts and oil pan.
7. Reverse procedure to install. Connect battery ground cable and refer to "Adaptive Strategies Relearn Procedures" under "Precautions."

OIL PUMP
REPLACE

1. Remove bolts holding oil pump and filter assembly to front engine cover.
2. Disengage pump from front engine cover and pump drive shaft.
3. Reverse procedure to install, noting the following:
    a. Ensure proper engagement of oil pump drive shaft into pump.
    b. **Torque** four large oil pump to front cover bolts to 17-23 ft. lbs.
    c. **Torque** two smaller bolts to 6-8 ft. lbs.

OIL PUMP SERVICE

1. Wash all parts in suitable solvent, then dry with compressed air.
2. Ensure all dirt and particles are removed.
3. Inspect inner pump housing for wear or damage.
4. Inspect pump cover mating surface for wear, scuff marks are normal, if surface is worn or grooved, replace pump assembly.

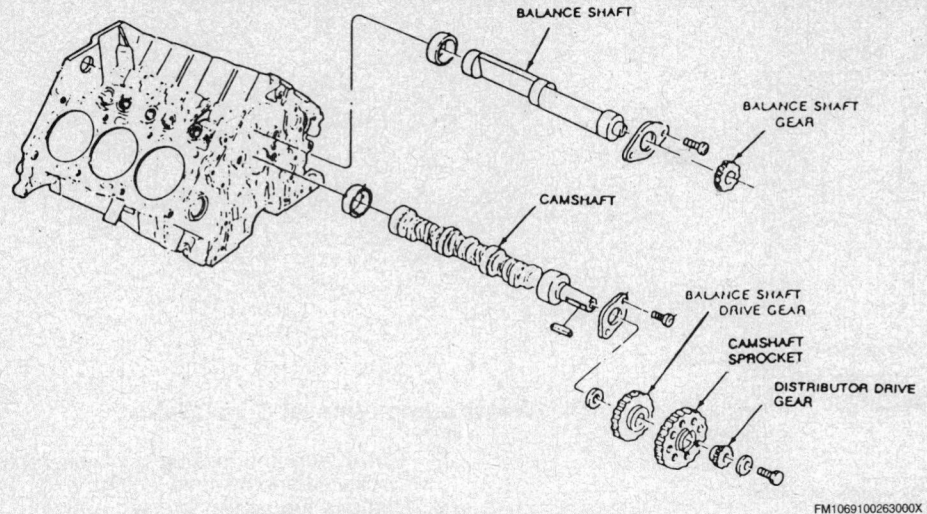

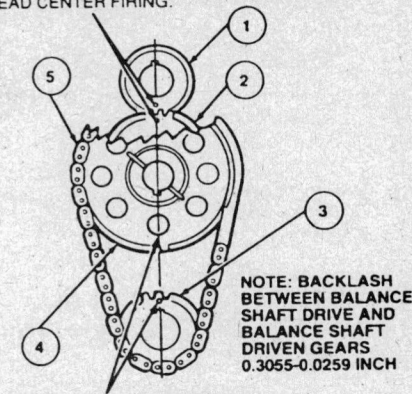

Fig. 9 Balance shaft assembly

FM1069100263000X

POSITIONING OF TIMING MARKS IN BALANCE SHAFT DRIVE GEAR AND BALANCE SHAFT DRIVEN GEAR MUST BE IN LINE AS SHOWN WITH NO. 1 PISTON AT TOP DEAD CENTER FIRING.

NOTE: BACKLASH BETWEEN BALANCE SHAFT DRIVE AND BALANCE SHAFT DRIVEN GEARS 0.3055-0.0259 INCH

POSITIONING OF TIMING MARKS AND KEYWAY IN CAMSHAFT AND CRANKSHAFT SPROCKET MUST BE IN LINE AS SHOWN WITH NO. 1 PISTON AT TOP DEAD CENTER FIRING.

FM1069500397000X

Fig. 10 Balance shaft timing

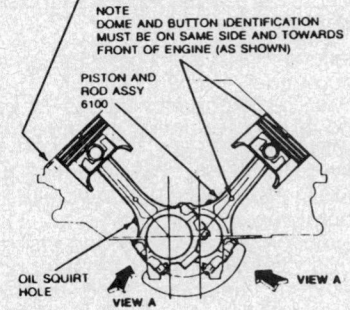

NOTE:
PISTON TO DECK CLEARANCE TO BE 0 27 BELOW DECK TO 0 25 ABOVE DECK WHEN MEASURED AT PISTON T D C PARALLEL TO CRANKSHAFT ON TRUE CENTERLINE OF PISTON (AVERAGE OF TWO READINGS)

NOTE
DOME AND BUTTON IDENTIFICATION MUST BE ON SAME SIDE AND TOWARDS FRONT OF ENGINE (AS SHOWN)

PISTON AND ROD ASSY 6100

OIL SQUIRT HOLE   VIEW A   VIEW A

NOTE:
TO PREVENT DAMAGE TO PISTONS AFTER ASSEMBLY, POSITION CRANKSHAFT KEYWAY SO ALL PISTONS ARE BELOW DECK

CONNECTING ROD BEARING 6211 VERTICAL ASSEMBLED CLEARANCE TO BE 0.022-0.060

FM1069100264000X

Fig. 11 Piston & rod assembly

5. Inspect rotor for nicks, burrs or score marks, remove imperfections with suitable oil stone.

BELT TENSION DATA

Belt tension is automatically maintained on this engine by an automatic tensioner. Therefore, no adjustment is necessary.

SERPENTINE DRIVE BELT

BELT ROUTING

Refer to **Fig. 13.** for serpentine drive belt routing.

BELT, REPLACE

1. Disconnect battery ground cable.
2. Install suitable 1/2 inch flex handle in square hole in tensioner.
3. Rotate tensioner counterclockwise, then remove belt.
4. Reverse procedure to install. Connect battery ground cable and refer to "Adaptive Strategies Relearn Procedures" under "Precautions."

COOLING SYSTEM BLEED

These engine do not require a specific bleed procedure. After filling cooling system, run engine to operating temperature with radiator/pressure cap off. Air will then be automatically bled through cap opening.

THERMOSTAT
REPLACE
REMOVAL

Do not remove the radiator cap while engine is operating or while engine is still under pressure.

1. Drain cooling system until coolant level is below thermostat.
2. Disconnect upper radiator hose at thermostat housing.
3. Remove two housing retaining bolts, then the thermostat housing and gasket.

INSTALLATION

So that the thermostat is correctly installed, the water outlet casting on all engines contains a locking recess into which the thermostat is turned and locked.

1. Clean gasket surface on thermostat housing and intake manifold, then position the thermostat in the housing, with the bridge section in the outlet casting. Turn the thermostat clockwise to lock it in position.
2. Position new gasket and thermostat housing on the manifold, then install two retaining bolts.
3. Connect upper hose to housing, then fill cooling system with recommended coolant.
4. Start engine and check for leaks.

TOP VIEW OF PISTONS

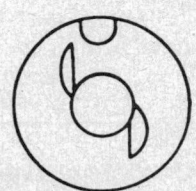

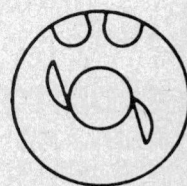

TAURUS/SABLE SINGLE NOTCH

TAURUS POLICE DUAL NOTCH

FM1069500398000X

Fig. 12 Piston types

WATER PUMP
REPLACE

1. Relieve fuel system pressure as outlined under "Precautions."
2. Drain cooling system.
3. Support engine using support bar tool No. D88L-6000-A or equivalent, then remove lower nut on both front engine supports.
4. Raise engine, then remove drive belt as outlined under "Serpentine Drive Belts."
5. Remove water pump pulley.
6. Remove power steering pump bracket attaching bolts, then position bracket and pump aside.
7. **On models with A/C remove A/C compressor support brackets, leave A/C compressor in place.**
8. Disconnect coolant hoses from water pump.
9. Remove water pump attaching bolts and pump Fig. 14..
10. Reverse procedure to install, noting the following:
    a. Use a suitable gasket adhesive to hold water pump gasket in place during assembly.
    b. **Coat threads of No. 1 water pump bolt with suitable sealer.**
    c. **Torque** water pump retaining bolts to 15-22 ft. lbs.

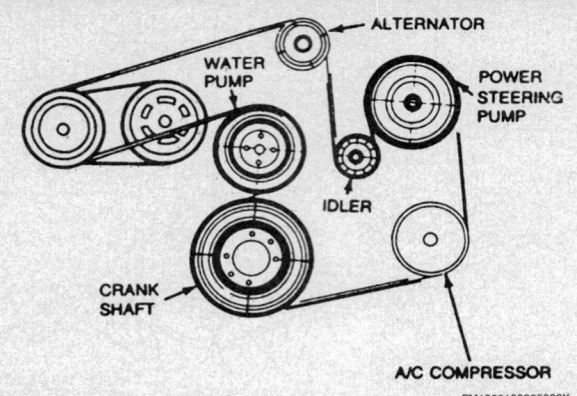

Fig. 13 Serpentine drive belt routing

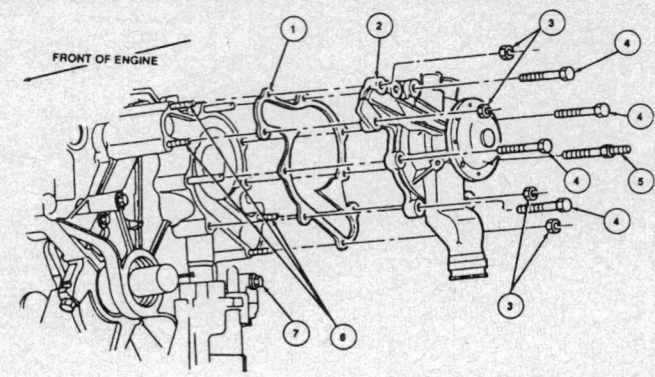

Fig. 14 Water pump removal & installation

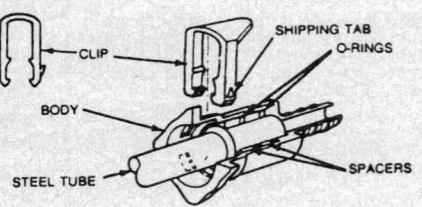

Fig. 15 Push connect fitting removal

RADIATOR
REPLACE

Refer to "Radiator, Replace" in the "3.0L/V6-182 Engine, Except SHO" section for procedures.

FUEL PUMP
REPLACE

1. Relieve fuel system pressure as outlined under "Precautions."
2. Disconnect battery ground cable.
3. Remove fuel from fuel tank by pumping fuel out of fuel filler neck.
4. Raise and support vehicle.
5. Disconnect and remove fuel filler

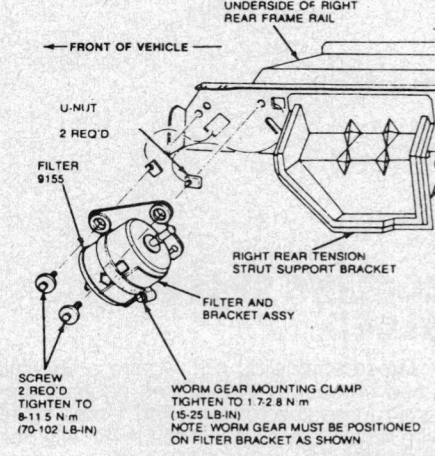

Fig. 16 Fuel filter removal & installation

neck.
6. Support fuel tank, then remove tank support straps. Lower fuel tank partially and remove fuel lines, electrical connectors and vent lines from tank. Remove tank and place on suitable workbench.
7. Turn fuel pump locking ring counterclockwise and remove locking ring.
8. Remove fuel pump, bracket and gasket assembly.
9. Reverse procedure to install. Connect battery ground cable and refer to "Adaptive Strategies Relearn Procedures" under "Precautions."

FUEL FILTER
REPLACE

1. Relieve fuel system pressure as outlined under "Precautions."
2. Twist push connect fittings at each end of the filter until they move freely on the tube.
3. Bend and break shipping tab from hairpin clip, then spread two clip legs approximately 1/8 inch, **Fig. 15.**
4. Remove clip from tube and fitting by pulling gently on its' triangular end.
5. Separate fitting and hose assembly from fuel filter.
6. Install retainer clips in each connect fitting.
7. Loosen worm gear mounting clamp, then remove filter from bracket, **Fig. 16.**
8. Reverse procedure to install.

TIGHTENING SPECIFICATIONS

Year	Component	Torque/Ft. Lbs.	Year	Component	Torque/Ft. Lbs.
1992-95	Alternator Bracket	30-40	1992-95 —Cont'd	Heater Tube To Intake Manifold	8-10
	Balance Shaft Thrust Plate	6-10		Intake Manifold To Cylinder Head	①
	Camshaft Sprocket To Camshaft	30-37		Low Level Oil Sensor	20-30
	Camshaft Thrust Plate	6-10		Main Bearing Cap	65-81
	Connecting Rod	31-36		Oil Inlet Tube Main Bearing	30-40
	Crankshaft Damper To Crankshaft	103-132		Oil Inlet Tube To Cylinder Block	15-22
	Crankshaft Pulley To Damper	20-28		Oil Pan To Cylinder Block	80-106 ②
	Cylinder Head Bolts	①		Oil Pump Cover	18-22
	Distributor Hold-Down Bolt	20-29		Rocker Arm Cover To Cylinder Head	80-106 ②
	EGR Valve To Intake Manifold	15-22		Rocker Arm Fulcrum To Cylinder Head	③
	Engine Mounts	①		Spark Plug To Cylinder Head	62-132 ②
	Exhaust Manifold	15-22		Throttle Body	15-22
	Fan Clutch Assembly	12-18		Water Pump Front Cover	15-22
	Flywheel To Crankshaft	54-64			
	Front Cover To Cylinder Block	15-22			
	Fuel Pump To Front Cover	15-22			

①—Refer to text.
②—Inch pounds.
③—First step, tighten to 44 inch lbs.; second step, tighten to 25 ft. lbs.

Clutch & Manual Transaxle

INDEX

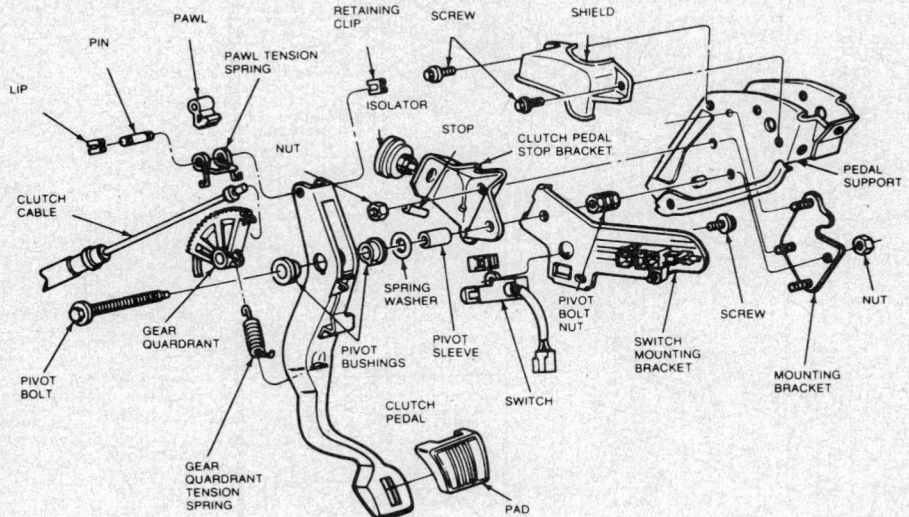

Fig. 1 Exploded view of clutch pedal & self-adjusting mechanism

FM5049100036000X

ADJUSTMENTS

CLUTCH

These models incorporate a self-adjusting clutch mechanism, **Fig. 1**. The self-adjust mechanism consists of a spring loaded ratchet quadrant attached to the clutch cable. During clutch cable replacement or whenever clutch adjustment is necessary, grasp the clutch pedal and pull upwards, then slowly depress clutch pedal several times.

Whenever the clutch cable is disconnected for any reason, the clutch pedal assembly must be restrained in the uppermost position during both removal and replacement of the components. After the clutch cable is installed and the clutch allowed to rest in its normal position, adjust clutch by slowly depressing clutch several times.

GEARSHIFT LINKAGE

Adjustment of the gearshift linkage is not necessary and no provision for adjustment is provided, **Fig. 2**.

CLUTCH

REPLACE

1. Remove transaxle as described under "Transaxle, Replace."
2. Loosen pressure plate attaching bolts evenly to avoid distortion. If pressure plate is to be reused, scribe reference marks between plate and flywheel for reference during assembly.
3. Remove pressure plate and clutch disc from flywheel, **Fig. 3. These models do not use a pilot bearing.**
4. Position clutch disc and pressure plate onto flywheel with flatter side of clutch disc facing toward flywheel.
5. Ensure three dowel pins on flywheel are aligned with holes in pressure plate, then install mounting bolts. Do not tighten at this time.
6. Using clutch alignment tool T81P-7550-A or equivalent, align clutch disc with flywheel. Alternately tighten pressure plate mounting screws until fully seated, then tighten bolts to specifications.
7. Remove alignment tool, than install transaxle.

TRANSAXLE

REPLACE

1. Disconnect battery ground cable.
2. Wedge a block of wood approximately seven inches in length under clutch pedal to hold pedal up slightly higher than it normal position.
3. Remove air cleaner hose.
4. Grasp clutch cable end with fingers and pull forward, disconnect end from clutch release shaft assembly.
5. Remove clutch cable casing from rib on top surface of transaxle case.
6. Install engine lifting eyes, then tie up wiring harness and power steering cooler hoses.
7. Disconnect speedometer cable and speed sensor wire.
8. Using engine support fixture tool No. 014-00750 or equivalent, support engine.
9. Raise and support vehicle, then remove tire and wheel assemblies.
10. Remove nut and bolt attaching lower control arm ball joint to steering knuckle. Discard removed nut and bolt, then repeat procedure on opposite side.
11. Using halfshaft remover tool No. D83P-4026-A or equivalent, pry lower control arm away from steering knuckle as shown in **Fig. 4**. Repeat procedure on opposite side. **Use care not to damage or cut ball joint boot. Pry bar must not contact the lower arm.**
12. Remove upper nut from stabilizer bar and separate stabilizer from knuckle.
13. Remove tie rod nut and separate tie rod end from knuckle.
14. Disconnect Heated Exhaust Gas Oxygen (HEGO) sensor, then remove exhaust catalyst assembly.
15. Disconnect power steering cooler from subframe and position out of the way.
16. Disconnect battery cable bracket from subframe.
17. Using a large pry bar, pry lefthand inboard CV joint assembly from transaxle. To prevent lubricant leaking from the seal, install transaxle plugs part No. T81P-1177-B or equivalent into transaxle. Repeat procedure on righthand side. **Use care when prying CV joint assembly so as not to damage the differential oil seal.**
18. Remove inboard CV joint from transaxle by grasping lefthand steering knuckle and swinging knuckle and halfshaft outward from the transaxle. Repeat procedure on righthand side. **If CV joint assembly cannot be pried out of transaxle, insert differential rotator tool No. T81P-4026-A or equivalent through side of transaxle and tap joint out, Fig. 5.**
19. Wire halfshaft assemblies in a near level position to prevent damage to assembly during remaining operations.
20. Remove center support bearing retaining bolts, then the righthand halfshaft from transaxle.
21. Remove two steering gear retaining nuts from sub-frame. Support steering gear by wiring up tie rod ends to coil springs.

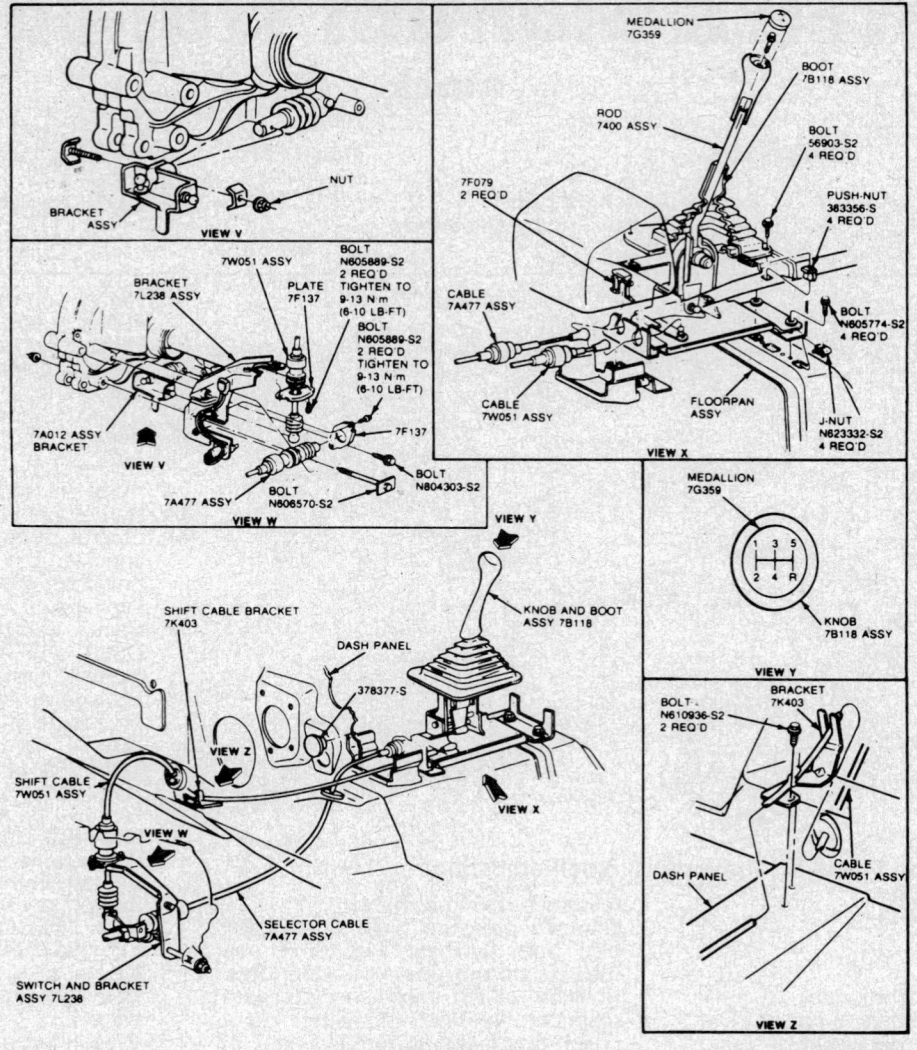

Fig. 2 Gearshift linkage

22. Remove transaxle to engine retaining bolts, then disconnect two shift cables from transaxle.
23. Remove engine mount bolts, then position jacks underbody mount positions and remove four bolts.
24. Lower sub-frame and position out of the way, then remove starter motor assembly.
25. Remove lefthand engine vibration dampener lower bracket.
26. Using a small screwdriver, disconnect back-up lamp switch connector and remove back-up lamp switch.
27. Position a suitable transmission jack under transaxle, then lower transaxle and remove it from engine. **Transaxle case castings may have sharp edges, wear protective gloves when handling transaxle assembly.**
28. Reverse procedure to install. Connect battery ground cable and refer to "Adaptive Strategies Relearn Procedures" under "Precautions."

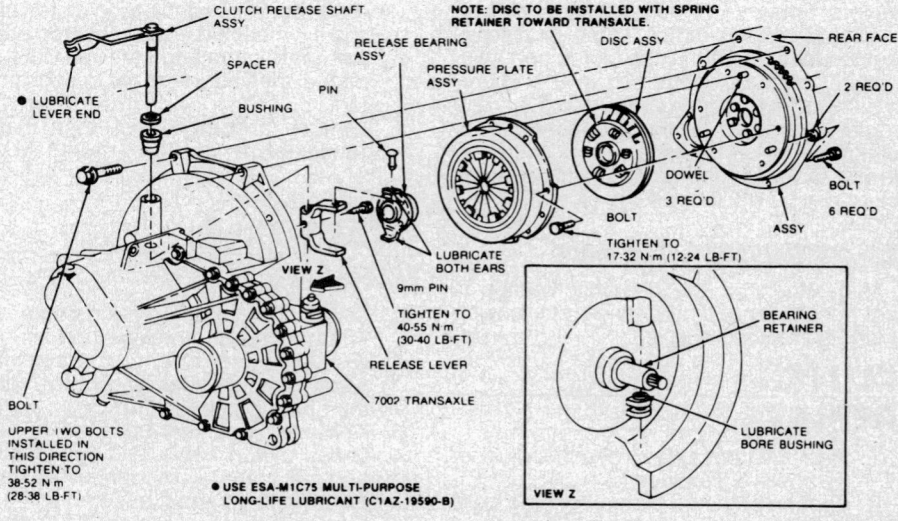

Fig. 3 Exploded view of clutch assembly

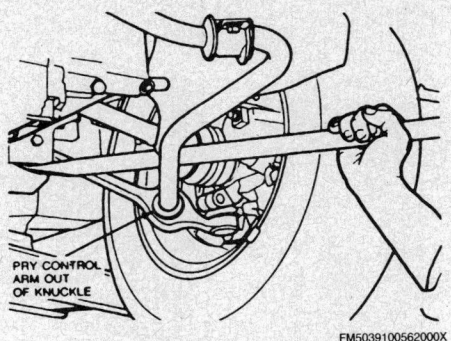

Fig. 4 Control arm & steering knuckle separation

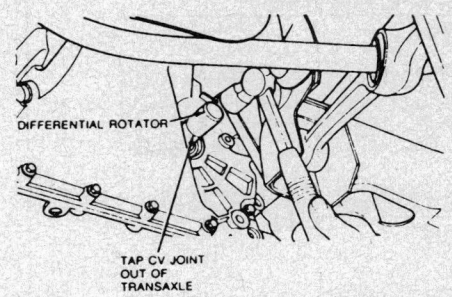

Fig. 5 CV joint from transaxle removal

TIGHTENING SPECIFICATIONS

Year	Component	Torque/Ft. Lbs.
1992-95	Air Manage Valve Bracket Bolt To Transaxle	28-31
	Ball Joint Nut	37-44
	Center Support Bearing Bolts	85-100
	Clutch Housing To Engine	31-39
	Clutch Pedal To Brake Support	15-25
	Control Arm To Steering Knuckle	37-44
	Engine Mount Bolts	40-55
	Front Mounting Bracket Bolts	25-35
	Lower Mount Bracket To Inner Bracket	45-61
	Pressure Plate Mounting Screws	12-24
	Rear Mount Bracket To Lower Bracket	45-61
	Rear Mounting Bolts	35-50

Year	Component	Torque/Ft. Lbs.
1992-95 —Cont'd	Roll Restrictor Nuts	25-30
	Shift Stabilizer Bar To Transaxle Case	35-46
	Speedometer	3-4
	Starter Stud Bolts	30-40
	Steering Gear Nuts	85-100
	Stiffener Brace Bolts	28-38
	Stop Mount Bracket To Clutch Pedal	26-29
	Sub-Frame Bolts	65-85
	Switch Actuator Bracket Bolt	7-10
	Tie Rod Nut	35-47
	Transaxle Mounting Stud	38-41
	Transaxle To Engine	28-31
	Wheel Lug Nuts	85-105

Rear Suspension

INDEX

DESCRIPTION

SEDAN

These models utilize an independent rear suspension. Each side consists of a McPherson strut, an upper mount and washers, two parallel lower control arms, a tension strut, a spindle and a stabilizer bar mounted on the strut.

The top of the McPherson strut is attached to the inner body side panel, while the lower end of the strut is attached to the spindle with a pinch clamp and bolt. The parallel lower control arms attach to the underbody with nuts and bolts. The tension strut attaches to the lower part of the spindle and to the underbody, **Fig. 1.**

WAGON

These models also utilize an independent rear suspension. Each side consists of an upper and lower control arm, a shock absorber, a two piece spindle tension control strut and a coil spring.

The top of the shock absorber is attached to the body side panel by a rubber insulated top mount assembly and to the lower control arms by two nuts. The upper control arm attaches to the crossmember and the upper part of the spindle. The lower control arm attaches to the underbody and lower part of the spindle. The coil spring operates against the lower control arm and is located inboard of the shock absorber, **Fig. 2.**

WHEEL BEARING
ADJUST

The rear wheel bearings are of a sealed cartridge design and are not adjustable. **Torque** rear wheel bearing retaining nut to 188-254 ft. lbs.

REAR WHEEL SPINDLE
REPLACE

SEDAN

1. Raise and support vehicle, then remove tire and wheel assembly.
2. Remove brake drum, then the brake hose to strut retaining clip.
3. Remove brake backing plate attaching bolts, then the plate. Wire backing plate out of the way.
4. Remove control arm to spindle attaching bolts, washers and nuts, then the tension strut nut, washer and bushing.
5. Remove spindle to strut pinch bolt, then the spindle.
6. Position replacement spindle onto tension strut, then onto shock strut.
7. Install new strut to spindle pinch bolt. Do not tighten at this time.
8. Install tension strut bushing, washer and new nut. Do not tighten at this time.
9. Install new control arm to spindle attaching bolts.
10. Using suitable jack, raise lower control arm to normal curb height, then tighten nuts and bolts as follows:
    a. Tighten spindle to strut bolt to specification.
    b. Tighten tension strut nut to specification.
    c. Tighten control arm to spindle attaching nuts to specification.
11. Install brake backing plate and brake hose to strut retaining clip.
12. Install brake drum and wheel and tire assembly.
13. Lower vehicle.

WAGON

1. Raise and support vehicle, then remove tire and wheel assembly. **If vehicle is raised on frame contact hoist, position suitable jack under lower control arm to raise arm to normal curb height.**
2. Remove brake drum and wheel bearings, then the brake backing plate.
3. Remove upper control arms to crossmember attaching nuts and bolts.
4. Remove bolt, one washer, adjusting cam and nut attaching spindle to lower control arm.
5. Remove spindle and upper control arm as an assembly, then remove upper control arm to spindle attaching nut and the spindle.
6. Install upper control arms to spindle using a new nut. Do not tighten at this time.
7. Position spindle and upper control arm assembly on lower control arm. Install new nut and washer, existing

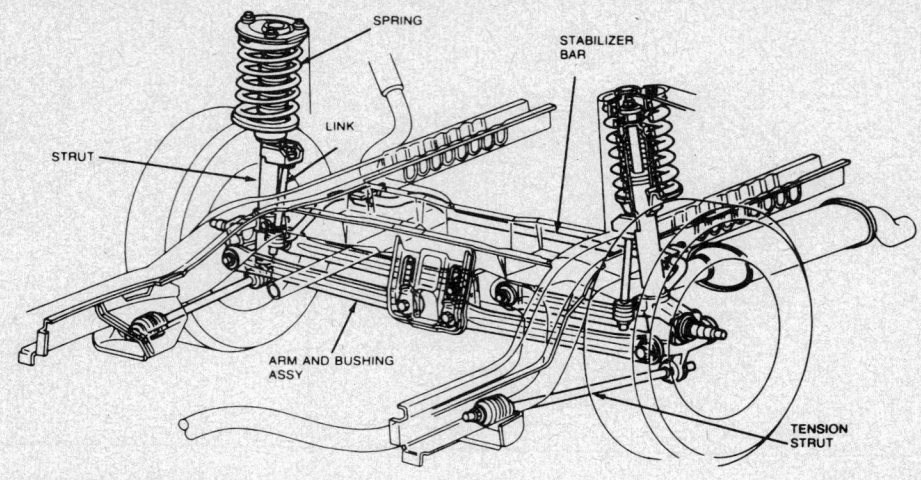

Fig. 1   Rear suspension. Sedan

FM2039100028000X

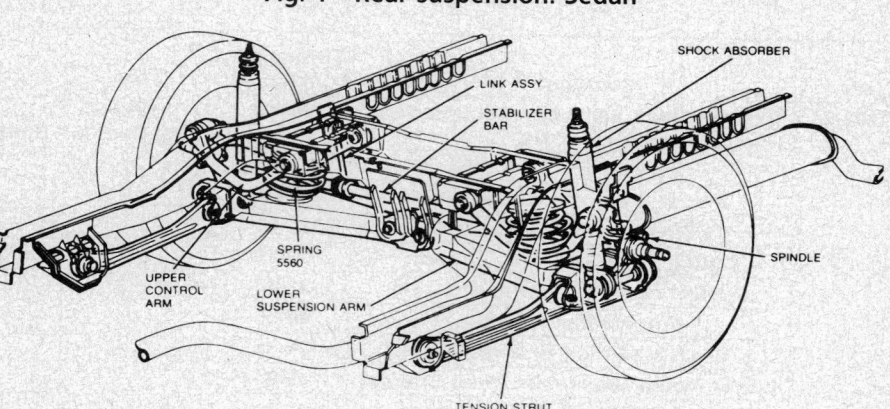

Fig. 2   Rear suspension. Wagon

FM2039100029000X

adjusting cam and new nut. Do not tighten at this time.
8. Position front and rear upper control arms to body bracket, then install new nuts and bolts. Do not tighten at this time.
9. Ensure lower control arm is at normal curb height, then proceed as follows:
    a. Tighten upper control arms to body bracket attaching bolts to specifications.
    b. Tighten upper control arms to spindle attaching nut to specifications.
    c. Tighten spindle to lower control arm attaching nut to specifications.
    d. Install brake backing plate, brake drum and wheel bearings.
    e. Install tire and wheel assembly, then remove jack assembly and lower vehicle.

STRUT
REPLACE

SEDAN

1. Position suitable jack or hoist under vehicle, then raise just enough to contact body.
2. Working in trunk, loosen, but do not remove, the three strut to inner body attaching nuts.

3. Raise and support vehicle, then remove tire and wheel assembly from side being worked on.
4. Remove brake differential valve to control arm attaching bolt.
5. Using suitable wire suspend control arm to body to ensure proper support after strut removal.
6. Remove brake hose to shock strut bracket attaching clip and position hose aside.
7. If equipped with stabilizer bar, remove U-bracket from body, then the stabilizer bar attaching nut, washer and insulator. Separate stabilizer bar from link.
8. Remove tension strut to spindle attaching nut, washer and insulator, then move spindle rearward enough to separate it from tension strut.
9. Remove strut to spindle pinch bolt, then using a pry bar or other suitable tool, separate pinch joint as necessary to allow for strut removal.
10. Remove strut from pinch joint, then lower vehicle as necessary to allow removal of bolts loosened in step 2. Remove strut from vehicle. **During strut removal, use care not to stretch the rear brake hose or kink the steel brake line.**
11. Remove link attaching nut, washer and insulator, then the link from the strut.

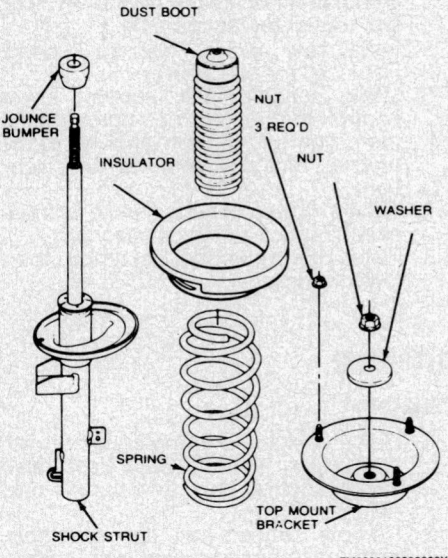

Fig. 3 McPherson strut components. Sedan

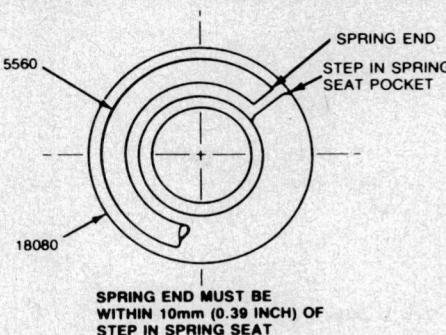

SPRING END MUST BE WITHIN 10mm (0.39 INCH) OF STEP IN SPRING SEAT

Fig. 4 Coil spring installation

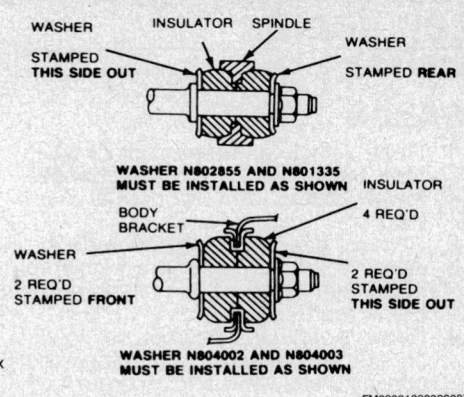

Fig. 5 Tension strut bushing installation. Sedan

12. Mark location of insulator to top mount, then place strut, spring and upper mount assembly in suitable spring compressor and compress spring.
13. While restraining strut shaft from turning, remove strut upper shaft mounting nut. **If strut is to be reused, do not use vise grips or pliers to hold strut shaft as damage will result.**
14. Carefully loosen spring compressor tool, then remove top mount bracket assembly, spring insulator and spring, **Fig. 3.**
15. Using new attaching parts, reverse procedure to install, noting the following:
    a. When installing spring on strut, ensure spring is properly located in upper and lower spring seats. Refer to **Fig. 4,** for spring end placement.
    b. When tightening strut nut, restrain strut shaft from turning. Tighten strut nut to specification.
    c. Tighten stabilizer link to strut attaching nut to specifications.
    d. Tighten strut pinch bolt to specifications.
    e. Tighten tension strut to spindle attaching nut to specifications.
    f. Tighten stabilizer link to stabilizer bar attaching nut to specifications.
    g. Tighten stabilizer bar U-bracket attaching bolt to specifications.
    h. Tighten strut top mount to body attaching nuts to specification.

TENSION STRUT
REPLACE
SEDAN

1. Raise vehicle on frame contact hoist using lift pads located rearward of front wheels and forward of rear

wheels. Raise hoist only enough to contact body.
2. Working inside trunk, loosen, but do not remove, three strut to inner body attaching nuts.
3. Raise vehicle, then remove tire and wheel assembly.
4. Remove tension strut to spindle attaching nut.
5. Remove tension strut to body attaching nut.
6. While moving spindle rearward, remove tension strut.
7. Install new inner washers and bushings on both ends of tension strut. Refer to **Fig. 5,** for bushing and washer identification.
8. Install tension strut end into body bracket, then install outer bushing, washers and nut. Do not tighten nut at this time.
9. While moving spindle rearward, install tension strut in spindle, then install outer bushing, washer and nut.
10. Ensure bushings are correctly seated in mountings, **Fig. 5.**
11. Support spindle with suitable jack stand, then working inside trunk, remove three strut to inner body attaching nuts. Install new nuts and tighten to specifications.
12. Remove jack stand, then install tire and wheel assembly.
13. Lower vehicle.

WAGON

1. Raise vehicle on frame contact hoist, then position suitable jack under lower control arm and raise arm to normal curb height.
2. Remove wheel and tire assembly, then tension strut to lower control arm attaching nut and bolt.
3. Remove tension strut to body bracket attaching nut and bolt, then the tension strut.
4. Insert front end of replacement torsion strut in body bracket, then install new attaching nut and bolt. Do not tighten at this time.
5. Position rear end of torsion strut in lower control arm, then install new attaching nut and bolt.
6. Tighten torsion strut to body bracket attaching nut and bolt to specifications.
7. Install wheel and tire assembly, then remove jack and lower vehicle.

SHOCK ABSORBER
REPLACE
WAGON

These models use gas filled shock absorbers.
1. Remove rear compartment access panels.
2. While restraining shock absorber shaft, loosen, but do not remove top mounting nut. **If shock absorber is to be reused, do not use vise grips or pliers to hold shock absorber shaft as damage will result.**
3. Raise and support rear of vehicle, then remove tire and wheel assembly. **If a frame contact hoist is used, support lower control arm with floor jack. If a twin post lift is used, support body with floor jacks on lifting pads forward of tension strut body bracket.**
4. Loosen shock absorber to lower control arm attaching nuts. Do not remove nuts at this time.
5. Lower vehicle, then remove shock absorber top mounting nut, washer and insulator.
6. Raise and support rear of vehicle. **If a frame contact hoist is used, support lower control arm with floor jack. If a twin post lift is used, support body with floor jacks on lifting pads forward of tension strut body bracket.**
7. Remove shock absorber to lower control arm attaching nuts, then remove shock absorber from vehicle. **The shock absorbers are gas filled and will require an effort to collapse them for removal.**
8. Reverse procedure to install, noting the following:
    a. Tighten shock absorber top mounting nut to specifications.
    b. Tighten shock absorber to lower control arm mounting nuts to specifications.

COIL SPRING
REPLACE

WAGON

1. Raise vehicle on frame contact hoist, then using suitable floor jack, raise lower control arm to normal curb height.
2. Remove tire and wheel assembly.
3. Remove brake hose bracket from body, then the stabilizer bar U-bracket from lower control arm.
4. Remove shock absorber to lower control arm attaching nuts, then the parking brake cable and clip from lower control arm.
5. Remove tension strut to lower control arm attaching nut and bolt, then wire upper control arms and spindle to keep them from dropping down.
6. Remove lower control arm to spindle attaching nut, bolt and toe adjusting cam.
7. Carefully lower control arm with floor jack until spring can be removed.
8. Remove spring and insulators.
9. Install lower spring insulator on control arm. Ensure insulator is seated properly.
10. Position upper insulator on spring, then install spring on lower control arm. Ensure spring is properly seated.
11. Using floor jack, raise lower control arm and spring while guiding upper spring insulator onto upper spring seat.
12. Position spindle in lower control arm and install new bolt, nut and existing toe adjusting cam. Install bolt with head facing front of vehicle. Do not tighten at this time.
13. Remove wire from upper control arms and spindle assembly, then position tension strut in lower control arm and install new nut and bolt. Do not tighten at this time.
14. Install parking brake cable and clip to lower control arm, then install lower end of shock absorber. Tighten nuts to specifications.
15. Install stabilizer bar and U-bracket. Install new bolt and tighten to specifications.
16. Install brake hose bracket. Tighten attaching bolt to specifications.
17. Using floor jack, raise lower control arm to normal curb height, then tighten lower control arm to spindle nut and tension strut to body bracket bolt to specifications.
18. Install tire and wheel assembly, then remove floor jack and lower vehicle.
19. Check rear end alignment.

CONTROL ARM
REPLACE

LOWER
Sedan

1. Raise and support vehicle.
2. Disconnect brake proportioning valve from left side front control arm, then

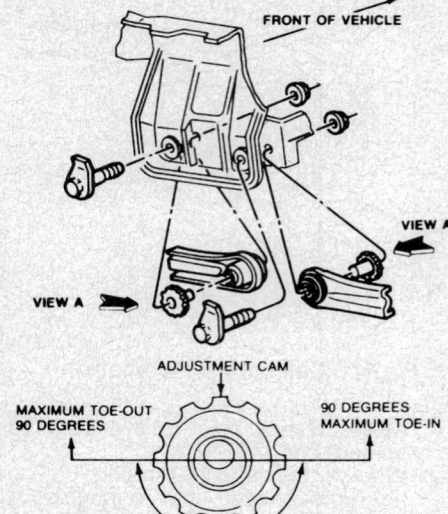

Fig. 6 Lower control arm bushing & cam installation. Sedan

the parking brake cable from control arms.
3. Remove control arm to spindle attaching bolt, nut and washer.
4. Remove control arm to body bracket attaching bolt and nut, then the control arm.
5. Position control arm (and cam where required, **Fig. 6**), at body bracket, then install new nut and bolt. Do not tighten at this time. **When installing control arms, the offset must face up (the arms are stamped "bottom" on lower edge). The flange edge of the right side rear arm stamping must face the front of the vehicle. The other three must face the rear of the vehicle. During installation, note that the control arms have two adjustment cams that fit inside the bushings at the control arm to body attachment. The cam is installed from the rear on the left arm and from the front on the right arm, Fig. 6.**
6. Position outer end of arm at spindle, then install new bolt, washer and nut. Tighten nut to specifications.
7. Tighten control arm to body bracket attaching nut to specifications.
8. Attach parking brake cables and brake proportioning valve to control arms.
9. Lower vehicle, then check rear toe and reset as necessary.

Wagon

1. Raise and support rear of vehicle, then remove tire and wheel assembly.
2. Remove rear spring. Refer to "Spring, Replace" for procedure.
3. Remove lower control arm to body bracket attaching bolt, then the control arm.
4. Position lower control arm in body bracket, then install new nut and bolt

with bolt head toward front of vehicle. Do not tighten at this time.
5. Install rear spring. Refer to "Spring, Replace" for procedure.
6. Using suitable jack, support lower control arm at normal curb height, then tighten control arm to body bracket attaching bolt to specifications.
7. Tighten lower control arm to spindle attaching bolt to specifications.
8. Install tire and wheel assembly, then lower vehicle.

UPPER
Wagon

1. Raise vehicle on frame contact hoist, then using suitable floor jack, raise lower control arm to normal curb height.
2. Remove wheel and tire assembly, then brake hose bracket from body.
3. Loosen spindle to upper control arms attaching nut.
4. Loosen spindle to lower control arm attaching nut.
5. Remove upper control arms to body brackets attaching nuts and bolts. Ensure spindle does not fall outward.
6. Carefully tilt upper part of spindle outward until upper control arms are clear of body brackets. Wire spindle in this position.
7. Remove spindle to upper control arms attaching nut, then the upper control arms.
8. Install upper control arms on spindle and install new nut. Do not tighten at this time.
9. Position upper control arms in body brackets, then install new nuts and bolts. Tighten to specifications. Remove wire from spindle.
10. Tighten upper control arms to spindle attaching nut to specification.
11. Tighten lower control arm to spindle attaching nut to specification.
12. Install brake hose bracket on body, then the tire and wheel assembly.
13. Remove floor jack and lower vehicle.
14. Check rear wheel alignment and correct as necessary.

STABILIZER BAR
REPLACE

SEDAN

1. Raise and support vehicle.
2. Remove stabilizer bar to link attaching nuts, washers and insulators from both sides. Remove U-bracket attaching bolts, then the stabilizer bar.
3. Remove link to strut attaching nuts, washers and insulators.
4. Inspect attaching parts for damage and replace as necessary.
5. Using new attaching parts, reverse procedure to install, noting the following:
   a. Tighten link to strut attaching nuts

b. Tighten U-bracket attaching bolts to specifications.

c. Tighten stabilizer bar to link attaching nuts to specifications.

WAGON

1. Raise and support vehicle.
2. Remove U-bracket retaining nuts and

bolts from either side, then slide U-brackets and insulators from stabilizer bar.

3. Remove link to body bracket attaching nuts and bolts, then the stabilizer and link assemblies.
4. Slide link assemblies from stabilizer bar.
5. Inspect attaching parts for damage

and replace as necessary.

6. Reverse procedure to install, noting the following:
   a. Install new nuts and bolts, then tighten link to body bracket attaching nuts and bolts to specifications.
   b. Install new nuts and bolts, then tighten U-bracket attaching nuts and bolts to specifications.

TIGHTENING SPECIFICATIONS

Year SEDAN	Component	Torque/Ft. Lbs.
1992-95	Control Arm To Spindle	42-57
	Control Arm To Body	45-65
	Stabilizer Bar Link To Stabilizer Bar	5-7
	Stabilizer Bar Link To Strut	5-7
	Stabilizer U-Bracket To Body	25-34
	Strut Top Mount To Body	19-26
	Strut To Top Mount	35-50
	Strut To Spindle	50-67
	Tension Strut To Spindle	35-50
	Tension Strut To Body	35-50
	Wheel Lug Nut	85-105
WAGON		
1992-95	Brake Hose Bracket	8-12

Year WAGON	Component	Torque/Ft. Lbs.
1992-95 —Cont'd	Lower Control Arm To Body	40-52
	Shock Absorber To Body	19-27
	Shock Absorber To Lower Suspension Arm	12-20
	Spindle To Lower Control Arm	40-55
	Stabilizer Bar U-Bracket To Lower Suspension Arm	20-30
	Stabilizer Link Assembly To Body	40-52
	Tension Strut To Body	40-52
	Tension Strut To Lower Suspension Arm	40-52
	Upper Control Arms To Body	70-95
	Upper Control Arms To Spindle	150-190
	Upper Suspension Arm To Spindle	40-55
	Wheel Lug Nuts	85-105

Front Suspension & Steering

INDEX

DESCRIPTION

This suspension is of the gas filled McPherson strut type, **Fig. 1**. The strut top mount consists of a rubber insulated bearing and seat and coil spring insulator. The top mount is attached to the body side apron by three bolts. The lower part of the strut is mounted in the steering knuckle and is retained by a pinch bolt. A forged lower control arm is attached to the subframe and to the steering knuckle. A tension strut is connected to the lower control arm and to the forward part of the subframe.

WHEEL BEARING
REPLACE
REMOVAL

1. Raise and support vehicle, then remove wheel and tire.

2. Remove and discard front axle retainer nut.
3. Remove front brake rotor as described under "Front Disc Brakes" section, then remove rotor shield.
4. Disconnect steering knuckle from ball joint and tie rod.
5. Loosen but do not remove front strut assembly top mounting nuts.
6. Using front hub installer, tool No. T81P-1004-A, with hub remover/replacer, tool No. T81P-004-C, metric hub remover adapters, tool No. T83P-1004-BH1 and a two stud adapter, tool No. T86P-1004-A1 or equivalents, push front axle from hub **Fig. 2**.
7. Suitably support front knuckle, then remove bolt retaining knuckle to strut.
8. Remove knuckle from vehicle, then place knuckle assembly on a suitable workbench.

9. Using hub puller, tool No. D80L-002-L and hub protector, tool No. D80L-625-1 or equivalents remove hub from bearing **Fig. 3**.
10. Remove and discard bearing retainer snap ring.
11. Place hub in a suitable press, then using front bearing spacer, tool No. T86P-1004-A2 (stepped side up) and bearing remover, tool No. T83P-1004-AH2 or equivalents, press bearing from knuckle **Fig. 4**.

INSTALLATION

1. Ensure journal area of knuckle is clean and free from damage.
2. Place knuckle supported on front bearing spacer, tool No. T86P-1004-A2 or equivalent (stepped side down) in a suitable press, then place new wheel bearing and bearing installer, tool No. T86P-1104-A3 or equivalent

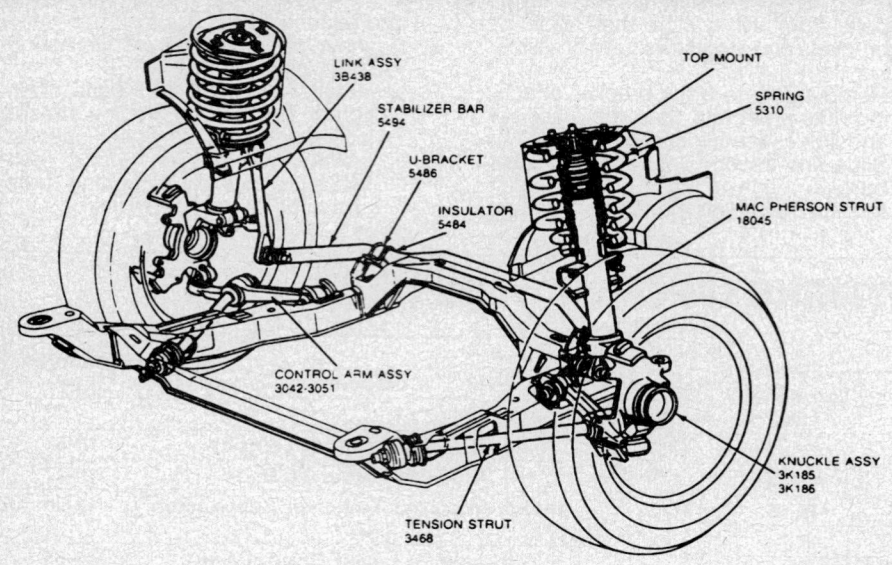

Fig. 1 Front suspension assembly

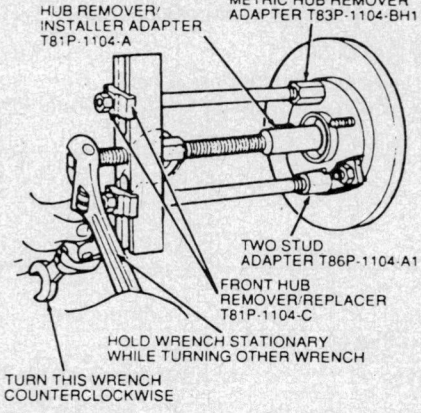

MAKE SURE THE HUB REMOVER ADAPTER IS FULLY THREADED ONTO THE HUB STUD AND IS POSITIONED OPPOSITE THE TWO STUD ADAPTER

Fig. 2 Axle shaft removal from hub

Fig. 3 Hub removal from bearing

into knuckle Fig. 5.

3. Press bearing fully into knuckle, then install new retaining snap ring.
4. Support front wheel hub on front bearing spacer, tool No. T86P-1004-A2 or equivalent (stepped side up) in a suitable press, then place knuckle and bearing assembly with bearing remover tool T83P-1004-AH2 or equivalent (flat side down) centered on inner race of bearing onto hub Fig. 6.
5. Press knuckle and bearing assembly fully onto hub, ensure hub rotates freely after installation.
6. Loosely install knuckle onto strut, then lubricate front axle splines and using hand pressure only, install into hub.
7. Install washer and new hub retainer nut.
8. Install knuckle onto ball joint and connect tie rod end.
9. Temporally install brake rotor to hub using suitable spacers and wheel nuts.
10. Install a suitable steel bar into cooling fins of rotor then rotate clockwise until steel bar rests against brake caliper support, then **torque hub retainer nut to 170-202 ft. lbs.**
11. Tighten remaining suspension component nuts and bolts to specifications, then remove temporally installed brake rotor.

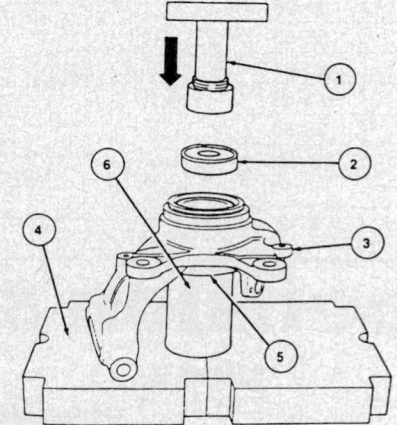

Item	Part Number	Description
1	—	Arbor Press
2	T83P-1104-AH2	Front Bearing Remover Tool
3	—	Front Wheel Knuckle and Bearing Assembly
4	—	Face Plate
5	—	Step Side Up
6	T86P-1104-A2	Front Bearing Spacer Tool

Fig. 4 Bearing removal from knuckle

12. Install disc brake rotor shield, then install rotor and caliper as outlined under "Front Disc Brakes."
13. Install wheel and tire, then lower vehicle. **Torque** wheel nuts to 85-105 ft. lbs.

BALL JOINT INSPECTION

1. Raise vehicle until wheels fall to a full down position.
2. Grasp lower edge of tire and move wheel assembly in and out.
3. As wheel is being moved, observe lower end of knuckle and lower control arm. Any movement would indicate abnormal ball joint wear.
4. If movement is observed, replace lower control arm assembly.

Item	Part Number	Description
1		Arbor Press
2	T86P-1104-A3	Bearing Installer Tool (Must be Positioned with Undercut Side Facing Bearing)
3		Front Wheel Knuckle-Outboard Side Down
4		Face Plate
5	T86P-1104-A2	Step Side Down
6		Front Bearing Spacer Tool
7		Front Wheel Bearing

Fig. 5 Bearing installation into knuckle

BALL JOINT
REPLACE

The ball joint must be replaced with the control arm as an assembly.

STRUT
REPLACE

1. Place ignition switch in Off position and ensure steering wheel is not locked.

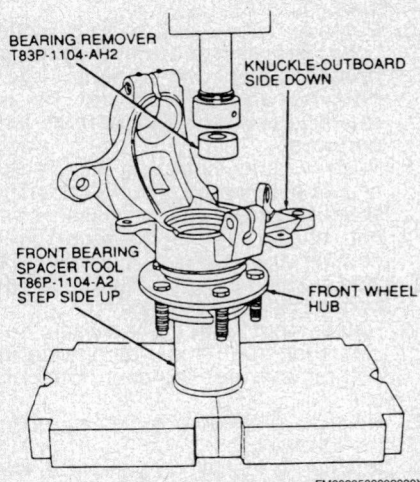

Fig. 6 Hub installation into bearing

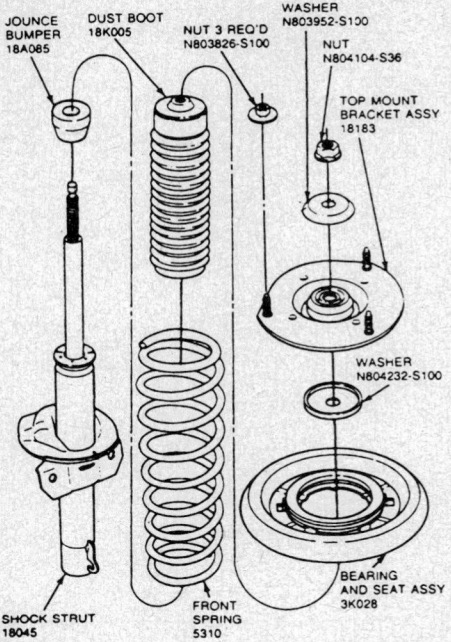

Fig. 7 McPherson strut assembly, 1992–93

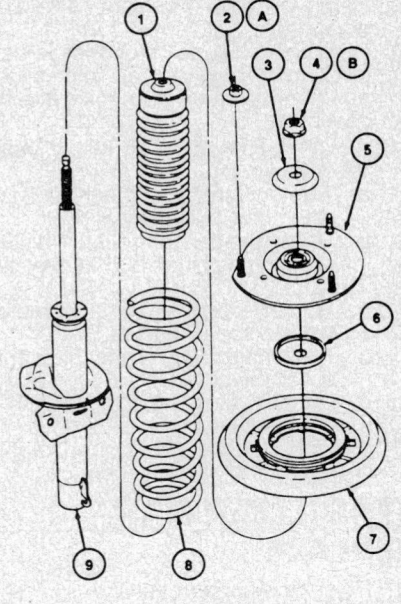

Item	Description
1	Dust Boot (Part of 3C198)
2A	Nut (3 Req'd)
3	Washer
4B	Nut
5	Front Shock Absorber Mounting Bracket
6	Washer
7	Front Suspension Bearing and Seal
8	Front Coil Spring
9	Front Spring and Shock
A	Tighten to 29.7-40.3 N·m (21.9-29.73 Lb-Ft)
B	Tighten to 53.1-72.9 N·m (39.2-53.8 Lb-Ft)

Fig. 8 McPherson strut assembly, 1994

2. Remove hub nut and loosen three strut attaching nuts, then raise and support vehicle. Do nut raise vehicle with lower control arm.
3. Remove wheel and tire assembly.
4. Remove brake caliper and wire it aside.
5. Remove brake rotor and tie rod end.
6. Remove stabilizer bar link nut, then remove link from strut.
7. Remove lower control arm to steering knuckle pinch nut and bolt, then slightly spread joint and remove lower control arm.
8. Using suitable hub remover/installer, press axle from hub. Wire axle shaft to body to maintain level position. **Do not allow axle shaft to move outward. Over extension of the constant velocity (CV) joint could result in separation of internal parts, which could cause CV joint failure.**
9. Remove strut to steering knuckle pinch bolt, then spread joint slightly and remove steering knuckle and hub assembly.
10. Remove strut attaching nuts, then remove strut assembly from vehicle.
11. Reverse procedure to install, noting the following:
   a. Tighten strut to steering knuckle pinch bolt to specification.
   b. Tighten lower control arm to steering knuckle pinch bolt to specifications.
   c. Tighten stabilizer bar assembly to strut to specifications.
   d. Tighten tie rod end attaching nut to specification.
   e. Tighten strut attaching nuts to specifications.
   f. With vehicle on ground, tighten hub nut to specification.

COIL SPRING & STRUT SERVICE

1. Compress strut spring with coil spring compressor D85P-7178-A or equivalent.

2. Using a 10 mm box wrench, restrain strut shaft, then remove strut mounting nut with suitable 21 mm crow foot socket. **Do not allow strut shaft to rotate.**
3. Loosen compressor tool, then remove strut top mount bracket assembly, bearing and seat assembly and spring, **Figs. 7 through 9**.
4. Reverse procedure to install.

CONTROL ARM
REPLACE

1. Place ignition switch in Off position and ensure steering wheel is not locked.
2. Raise and support vehicle.
3. Remove wheel and tire assembly.
4. Remove tension strut nut, then the dished washer.
5. Remove lower control arm to steering knuckle pinch nut and bolt, then slightly spread joint and separate ball joint from steering knuckle. **Do not use a hammer to separate suspension pieces.**
6. Remove lower control arm inner pivot bolt and nut, then the control arm.
7. Reverse procedure to install, noting the following:
   a. Tighten lower control arm pivot bolt to specification.
   b. Tighten lower control arm to steering knuckle attaching bolt to specifications.
   c. Tighten tension strut nut to specification.

STEERING KNUCKLE
REPLACE

1. Place ignition switch in Off position and ensure steering wheel is not locked.
2. Remove hub nut and loosen three strut attaching nuts, then raise and support vehicle. Do not raise vehicle with lower control arm.
3. Remove wheel and tire assembly.
4. Remove brake caliper and wire it aside.
5. Remove brake rotor and tie rod end.
6. Remove stabilizer bar link nut, then remove link from strut.
7. Remove lower control arm to steering knuckle pinch nut and bolt, then slightly spread joint and remove lower control arm.
8. Using suitable hub remover/installer, press axle from hub. Wire axle shaft to body to maintain level position. **Do not allow axle shaft to move outward. Over extension of the constant velocity (CV) joint could result in separation of internal parts, which could cause CV joint failure.**

9. Remove rotor splash shield (if equipped).
10. Remove strut to steering knuckle pinch bolt, then spread joint slightly and remove steering knuckle and hub assembly.
11. Reverse procedure to install, noting the following:
    a. Tighten strut to steering knuckle pinch bolt to specification.
    b. Tighten lower control arm to steering knuckle pinch bolt to specification.
    c. Tighten stabilizer bar assembly to strut to specifications.
    d. Tighten tie rod end attaching nut to specification.
    e. Tighten strut attaching nuts to specifications.
    f. With vehicle on ground, tighten hub nut to specification.

STABILIZER BAR
REPLACE

1. Raise and support vehicle.
2. Remove stabilizer bar link to strut attaching nuts.
3. Remove stabilizer bar link to stabilizer bar attaching nuts.
4. Remove steering gear to sub-frame attaching bolts, then move steering gear off sub-frame.
5. Support sub-frame with suitable safety stands, then remove rear sub-frame attaching bolts. Lower rear part of sub-frame to gain access to stabilizer bar mounting brackets.
6. Remove mounting brackets, then the stabilizer bar.
7. Reverse procedure to install, noting the following:
    a. Tighten stabilizer bar mounting brackets to specifications.
    b. Tighten sub-frame attaching bolts to specification.
    c. Tighten stabilizer bar link attaching nuts to specification.

POWER STEERING GEAR
REPLACE

1. Disconnect battery ground cable.
2. Remove steering shaft weather boot to dash panel attaching bolts.
3. Remove intermediate shaft to steering column shaft attaching bolts.
4. Move weather boot aside, then remove steering gear input shaft pinch bolt and remove intermediate shaft.

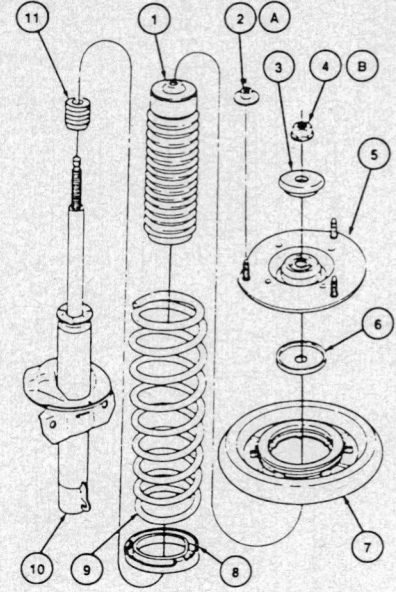

Item	Description
1	Dust Boot (Part of 3C 198)
2	Nut (3 Req'd)
3	Washer
4	Nut
5	Front Shock Absorber Mounting Bracket
6	Washer
7	Front Suspension Bearing and Seal
8	Front Spring Insulator
9	Front Coil Spring
10	Front Spring and Shock
11	Jounce Bumper
A	Tighten to 30-40 N·m (23-29 Lb·Ft)
B	Tighten to 53-72 N·m (40-53 Lb·Ft)

FM2029500087000X

Fig. 9   McPherson strut assembly, 1995

5. Raise and support vehicle.
6. Remove left front wheel and heat shield.
7. Remove bundling strap retaining lines to gear.
8. Remove tie rod ends from steering knuckles.
9. Place suitable drain pan under steering gear, then remove pressure and return lines from gear and allow to drain into pan.
10. Remove nuts from gear mounting bolts. **The gear mounting bolts are pressed into the steering gear housing and should not be removed during normal service procedures.**
11. Push weather boot end into vehicle and lift steering gear out of mounting holes. Rotate gear as necessary so input shaft passes between brake booster and floorpan. Carefully start working steering gear out through left front fender apron opening.
12. Rotate input shaft as necessary so it clears left front fender apron opening and remove steering gear from vehicle.
13. Reverse procedure to install, noting the following:
    a. Prior to installing hydraulic hoses, install new plastic seals on fittings.
    b. Tighten steering gear attaching nuts to specification.
    c. Tighten hydraulic pressure hose and hydraulic return hose fittings to specifications. **When hydraulic fittings are properly installed, the hoses are free to swivel.**
    d. Fill power steering system with automatic transmission fluid type F.
    e. Set toe-in to specifications.
    f. Connect battery ground cable. Refer to "Adaptive Strategies Relearn Procedures" under "Precautions."

POWER STEERING PUMP
REPLACE

1. Disconnect battery ground cable.
2. Loosen idler pulley, then remove power steering belt.
3. Using hub puller T69L-10300-B or equivalent, remove pulley from shaft.
4. Position suitable drain pan under pump, then disconnect return line and allow fluid to drain.
5. Completely back off pressure line fitting. Line will separate during pump removal.
6. Remove three pump to bracket attaching bolts, then the pump.
7. Reverse procedure to install.
    a. Tighten bolts and nuts to specifications.
    b. Connect battery ground cable. Refer to "Adaptive Strategies Relearn Procedures" under "Precautions."

TIGHTENING SPECIFICATIONS

Year	Component	Torque/Ft. Lbs.
1992-95	Control Arm Pivot Bolt	70-95
	Control Arm To Knuckle	40-55
	Control Arm To Sub-Frame	70-95
	Hub Nut	180-200
	Power Steering High Pressure Hose	20-25
	Power Steering Return Hose	15-20
	Stabilizer Bar Bracket To Sub-Frame	22-39
	Stabilizer Bar Link Assembly To Stabilizer Bar	35-48
	Stabilizer Bar Link Assembly To Shock Strut	55-75

Year	Component	Torque/Ft. Lbs.
1992-95 —Cont'd	Stabilizer Bar Mounting Brackets	85-100
	Steering Gear Attaching Nuts	85-100
	Strut Top Mount To Body	22-32
	Strut To Top Mount	35-50
	Strut To Knuckle	70-95
	Tension Strut To Control Arm	70-95
	Tension Strut To Sub-Frame	70-95
	Tie Rod End To Steering Knuckle	23-36
	Wheel Lug Nuts	85-105

Wheel Alignment

INDEX

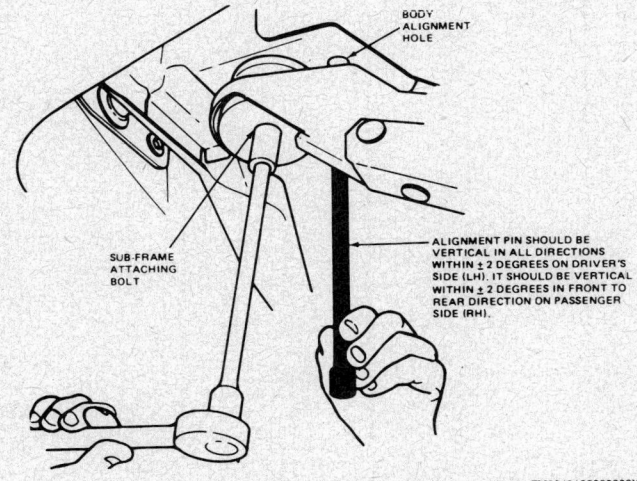

Fig. 1 Front suspension alignment

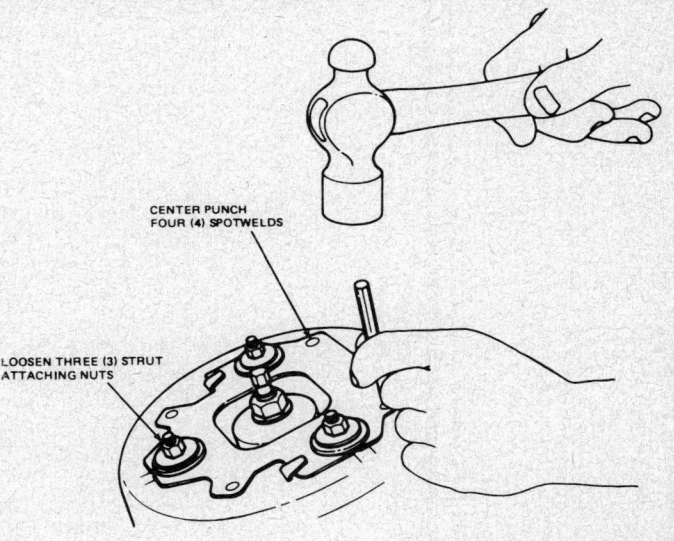

Fig. 2 Alignment plate loosening

FRONT WHEEL ALIGNMENT

CASTER & CAMBER

1. Prior to aligning the front end, the sub-frame alignment must be checked using the following procedure.
   a. Loosen sub-frame to body attaching bolts.
   b. Install a 3/4 inch outside diameter pipe or similar tool into left front sub-frame and body alignment holes, **Fig. 1.**
   c. Align left front sub-frame and body alignment holes, then slightly tighten left front sub-frame attaching bolt.
   d. Repeat steps b and c on right front alignment holes, then recheck left front alignment.
   e. Tighten sub-frame attaching bolts to specifications.
2. Center punch spot welds on both strut alignment plates, then loosen strut attaching nuts, **Fig. 2.**
3. Using Rotunda Spot-Eze or equivalent, remove spot welds. **Do not drill deeper than thickness of alignment plates.**
4. Remove strut attaching nuts, then the alignment plates.
5. Remove burrs from strut towers and alignment plates, then paint all exposed metal on strut towers and alignment plates.
6. Install alignment plates, then loosely install strut attaching nuts.
7. Align front end, then tighten strut attaching nuts to specifications.
8. Drill three 1/8 inch holes as indicated in **Fig. 3,** through alignment plates and strut towers, then paint exposed metal. **Do not drill deeper than 3/8 inch**

into strut tower.

9. Install three ⅛ inch diameter pop rivets with a grip range of ¼ inch into alignment plate/strut tower.

TOE-IN

To adjust toe-in, lock steering wheel in straight ahead position using suitable steering wheel holder. Loosen and slide off small outer clamps from steering boot to prevent boot from twisting during adjustment procedure. Loosen tie rod adjusting, then adjust left and right tie rods until each wheel has ½ the desired total toe specification. Tighten tie rod adjusting nuts and install clamps. Remove steering wheel holding tool.

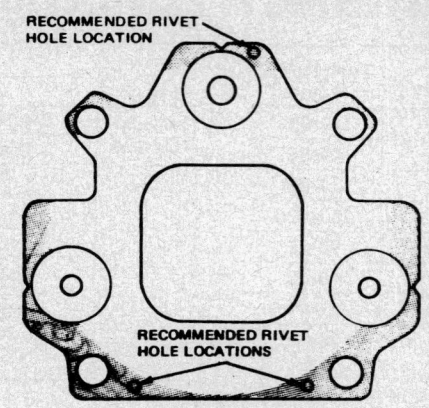

RECOMMENDED RIVET HOLE LOCATION

RECOMMENDED RIVET HOLE LOCATIONS

DRILL THREE (3) HOLES IN ALIGNMENT PLATE FOR 1/8 INCH RIVETS.

DRILL IN SHADED AREA ONLY.

FM2049100030000X

Fig. 3   Rivet hole location

REAR WHEEL ALIGNMENT

CASTER & CAMBER

The caster and camber angles are factory set and cannot be adjusted.

TOE-IN

On sedan models, toe-in is adjusted by rotating the cams located inside the rear inner lower control arm bushings.

On wagon models, toe-in is adjusted by rotating the cams located inside the outer lower control arm bushings.

FORD PROBE

NOTE: Refer To Rear Of This Manual For Vehicle Manufacturer's Special Service Tool Suppliers.

INDEX OF SERVICE OPERATIONS

NOTE: For Service Operations Not Listed Below, Refer To The Table Of Contents In The Front Of This Manual.

INDEX OF SERVICE OPERATIONS—CONTINUED

Specifications

GENERAL ENGINE SPECIFICATIONS

Year	Engine Liter/CID	VIN Code ②	Fuel System	Bore & Stroke	Compression Ratio	Net H.P. @ RPM	Maximum Torque Ft. Lbs. @ RPM	Normal Oil Pressure psi
1992	2.2L/4-133	C	EFI	3.39 x 3.70	8.6	110 @ 4700	130 @ 3000	43-57
	2.2L/4-133 Turbo	L	EFI	3.39 x 3.70	7.8	145 @ 4300	190 @ 3500	43-57
	3.0L/V6-182	U	EFI	3.50 x 3.14	9.3	145 @ 4800	165 @ 3400	43-57
1993–94	2.0L/4-121	A	EFI	3.27 x 3.62	9.0	115 @ 5500	124 @ 3500	57-71③
	2.5L/V6-152	B	EFI	3.33 x 2.92	9.2	164 @ 6000	156 @ 4000	57-71①
1995	2.0L/4-121	A	EFI	3.27 x 3.62	9.0	118 @ 5500	127 @ 3500	57-71③
	2.5L/V6-152	B	EFI	3.33 x 2.92	9.2	164 @ 6000	160 @ 4000	57-71①

①—With engine warm and operating at 4000 RPM.　　②—The eighth digit denotes engine code.　　③—With engine warm and operating at 3000 RPM.

TUNE UP SPECIFICATIONS

Year & Engine/VIN Code ①	Spark Plug Gap	Firing Order Fig. ④	Ignition Timing BTDC Man. Trans.	Ignition Timing BTDC Auto. Trans.	Mark Fig.	Curb Idle Speed Man. Trans.	Curb Idle Speed Auto. Trans.	Fast Idle Speed Man. Trans.	Fast Idle Speed Auto Trans.	Fuel Pump Pressure, psi.
1992										
2.2L/4-133/C	.041	⑥	6⑦	6⑦	⑧	750	750N	⑤	⑤	27–40⑨
2.2L/4-133/L Turbo	.041	⑥	9⑩	9⑩	⑧	750	750N	⑤	⑤	27–40⑨
3.0L/V6-182/U	.041	A	10⑪	10⑪	B	②	②	②	②	30–40③
1993–95										
2.0L/4-121/A	.040-.043	C	9-11	11-13	D	700	700	—	—	30–38
2.5L/V6-152	.040-.043	E	9-11	9-11	F	650	650	—	—	37–46

BTDC—Before Top Dead Center　　①—The eighth digit of the Vehicle Identification Number (VIN) denotes engine code.
N—Neutral　　②—Idle speed is controlled by an

Continued
SPECIFICATIONS

TUNE UP SPECIFICATIONS —Continued

automatic idle control system.

③ —Wrap shop towel around fitting to prevent fuel spillage, then connect a suitable fuel pressure gauge to fuel diagnostic valve on fuel rail assembly. Place ignition switch in On position & check fuel pressure gauge reading.

④ —Before disconnecting wires from distributor cap, determine location of No. 1 wire in cap, as distributor position may have been altered from that shown at the end of this chart.

⑤ —Computer controlled, non-adjustable.

⑥ —Timed at No. 1 cylinder, front of engine. Firing order, 1-3-4-2.

⑦ —With distributor vacuum hoses disconnected & plugged.

⑧ —Timing mark located on crankshaft pulley.

⑨ —Prior to disconnecting fuel lines, start engine, then disconnect fuel pump relay. After engine has stalled, turn ignition switch to off position. Disconnect fuel line located between fuel filter & fuel rail, install

a suitable fuel pressure gauge. After connecting fuel pressure gauge, install fuel pump relay & check fuel system pressure at various engine speeds.

⑩ —With test connector grounded. The test connector is located near the left hand strut tower above the brake master cylinder.

⑪ —Disconnect in-line spout connector, then start engine & adjust ignition timing as necessary. After completing adjustment, reconnect spout connector.

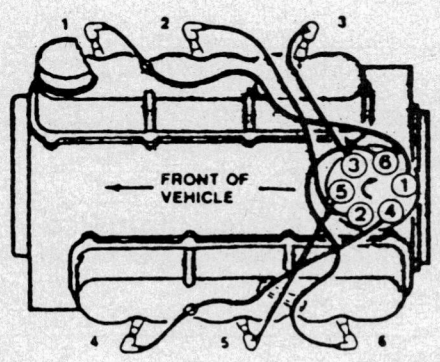

FIRING ORDER: 1-4-2-5-3-6

FM1139100131000X

Fig. A

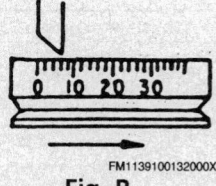

FM1139100132000X

Fig. B

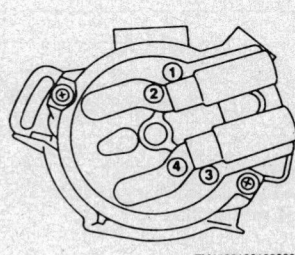

FM1139100133000X

Fig. C

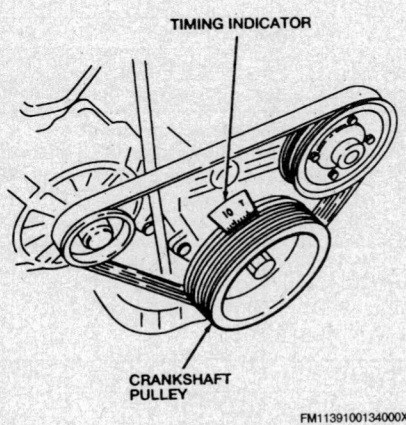

TIMING INDICATOR

CRANKSHAFT PULLEY

FM1139100134000X

Fig. D

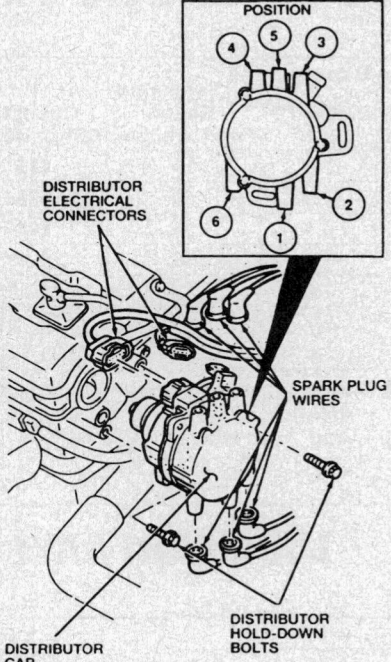

POSITION

DISTRIBUTOR ELECTRICAL CONNECTORS

SPARK PLUG WIRES

DISTRIBUTOR CAP

DISTRIBUTOR HOLD-DOWN BOLTS

FM1139100135000X

Fig. E

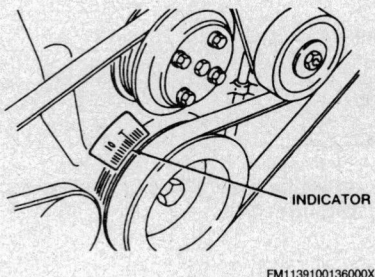

INDICATOR

FM1139100136000X

Fig. F

FRONT WHEEL ALIGNMENT SPECIFICATIONS

Year	Caster Angle, ③		Camber Angle, ③					Toe-In, Inch
	Limits	Desired	Limits		Desired			
			Left	Right	Left	Right		
1992	$+1^{3}/_{20}$ to $+2^{13}/_{20}$	$+1^{9}/_{10}$	$-^{29}/_{60}$ to $+1^{1}/_{60}$	$-^{29}/_{60}$ to $+1^{1}/_{60}$	$+^{4}/_{15}$	$+^{4}/_{15}$		.12
1993–94	$+3^{23}/_{30}$ to $+2^{11}/_{15}$	$+3^{1}/_{60}$	①	①	②	②		.12
1995	$+4^{1}/_{60}$ to $+2^{1}/_{60}$	$3^{1}/_{60}$	④	④	②	②		.12

① —2.0L/ 4-122 engine, -1 9/20 to +1/20;
2.5L/V6-152 engine, -1 13/20 to -3/20.

② —2.0L/4-122 engine, -7/10;
2.5L/V6-152 engine, -9/10

③ —Degrees.

④ —2.0L/4-122 engine, -1 7/10 to + 3/10;
2.5L/V6-152 engine, -1 9/10 to +1/10

REAR WHEEL ALIGNMENT SPECIFICATIONS

Year	Camber Angle, ②				Toe-In, Inch
	Limits		Desired		
	Left	Right	Left	Right	
1992	$-1^{11}/_{60}$ to $+^{19}/_{60}$	$-1^{11}/_{60}$ to $+^{19}/_{60}$	$-^{13}/_{60}$	$-^{13}/_{60}$	.12
1993–94	$-1^{1}/_{16}$ to $+^{5}/_{12}$ ①	$-1^{1}/_{16}$ to $+^{5}/_{12}$ ①	$-^{1}/_{3}$	$-^{1}/_{3}$	0.12
1995	①	①	③	③	0.12

① —Not adjustable.

② —Degrees.

③ —2.0L/4-122 engine, $-^{11}/_{30}$; 2.5L/V6-152 engine, $-^{9}/_{20}$.

COOLING SYSTEM & CAPACITY DATA

Year	Engine/VIN ①	Coolant Capacity		Radiator Cap Relief Pressure, psi.	Thermo. Opening Temp. Deg. F	Fuel Tank Gals.	Engine Oil Refill Qts.	Transaxle Oil ②	
		Less A/C Qts.	With A/C Qts.					5 Speed Pts.	Auto. Trans. Qts.
1992	2.2L/4-133/C	7.9	7.9	13	185	15.1	4.5③	7.2	8.3
	2.2L/4-133/L Turbo	7.9	7.9	13	185	15.1	4.5③	7.8	8.3
	3.0L/V6-182/U	9.9	9.9	13	185	15.1	4③	7.1	8.3
1993–94	2.0L/4-121/A	7.4	7.4	16	176–183	15.5	3.7	5.7	9.3
	2.5L/V6-152/B	7.9	7.9	13	176–183	15.5	4.2	5.7	9.3
1995	2.0L/4-121/A	7.4	7.4	16	176–183	15.5	3.7	5.7	④
	2.5L/V6-152/B	7.9	7.9	13	176–183	15.5	4.2	5.7	④

① —The eighth digit of Vehicle Identification Number (VIN) denotes engine code.

② —Approximate. Make final check with dipstick.

③ —Add ½ qt. with filter change.

④ —w/CD4E transaxle w/torque converter drained 8.8 qts., without converter drained 6.0 qts. or w/4EAT transaxle 7.2 qts.

LUBRICANT DATA

Year	Model	Lubricant Type			
		Transaxle		Power Steering	Brake System
		Manual	Automatic		
1992	All	Mercon	Mercon	Mercon	DOT 3
1993–95	All	GL-4 or GL-5	Mercon	Mercon	DOT 3

Electrical

NOTE: On Air Bag Equipped Models, Refer To "Air Bag System Precautions" Located In The Front Of This Manual For System Disarming & Arming Procedures.

INDEX

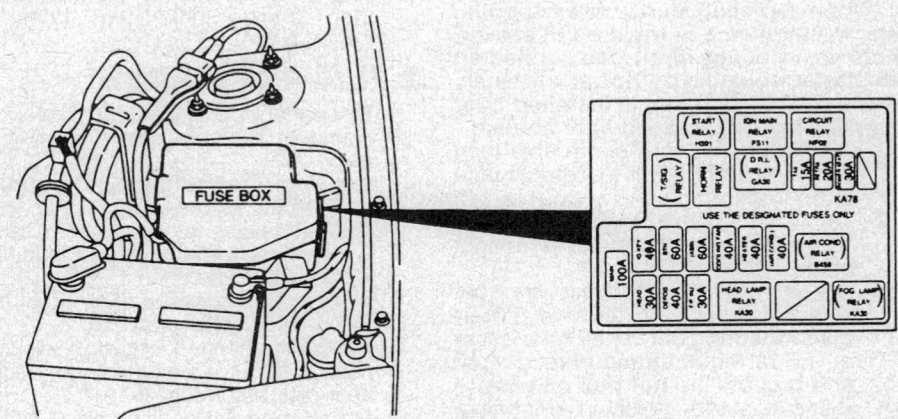

FM1039500208000X

Fig. 1 Relay center location

PRECAUTIONS

AIR BAG SYSTEMS

Refer to "Air Bag System Precautions" in the front of this manual for system disarming and arming procedures.

FUSE PANEL & FLASHER LOCATION

1992

The main fuse panel is located on the lefthand side of the engine compartment, near the battery. The interior fuse panel is located just above the lefthand side kick panel.

The flasher relay box is mounted below the lefthand side of the instrument panel, on the bulkhead.

1993-95

The main fuse panel is located on the lefthand side of the engine compartment, near the strut tower. The interior fuse panel is located behind the lefthand side kick panel.

The flasher relay box is located below the instrument cluster, near the lefthand kick panel.

RELAY CENTER LOCATION

The relay center is located on the left front inner fender in the engine compartment near the battery, **Fig. 1.**

STARTER

REPLACE

2.0L/4-122 ENGINE

When servicing starter or performing any maintenance in the area of starter, note heavy gauge input lead connected to starter solenoid is Hot at all times.

1. Disconnect battery ground cable, then isolate cable end with electrical tape or equivalent.
2. Remove air cleaner assembly, then the air cleaner duct.
3. Remove upper starter motor retaining bolts.
4. Raise and support vehicle, then remove intake manifold support bracket retaining bolts and bracket.
5. Disconnect wiring from starter assembly.
6. Remove lower starter motor retaining bolt, then the starter motor from vehicle.
7. Reverse procedure to install, noting the following:

a. Install upper starter motor retaining bolts first.
b. **Torque** starter motor retaining bolts to 23–34 ft. lbs.
c. **Torque** starter solenoid B-terminal nut to 80–120 in. lbs.
d. **Torque** intake manifold support bracket retaining bolts to 28–38 ft. lbs.

2.2L/4-133 ENGINE

When servicing starter or performing any maintenance in the area of starter, note heavy gauge input lead connected to starter solenoid is Hot at all times. Ensure protective cap is installed over terminal and is replaced after service.

1. Disconnect battery ground cable, then isolate cable end with electrical tape or equivalent.
2. Raise and support vehicle.
3. **On models with manual transaxles,** remove exhaust pipe bracket.
4. **On all models,** remove transaxle to engine bracket, then the intake manifold to engine bracket.
5. Disconnect wiring from starter motor.
6. Remove three starter motor retaining bolts, then the starter motor from vehicle.
7. Reverse procedure to install, noting the following:
   a. **Torque** starter motor retaining bolts to 27–38 ft. lbs.
   b. **Torque** starter solenoid B-terminal nut to 87—104 in. lbs.
   c. **Torque** intake manifold to engine bracket bolts to 14–22 ft. lbs.
   d. **On automatic transaxle models,** when installing transaxle to engine bracket, **torque** bellhousing bolt to 66–86 ft. lbs., then the remaining three bracket bolts to 27–38 ft. lbs.
   e. **On manual transaxle models,** when installing transaxle to engine bracket, **torque** bracket bolts to 32–45 ft. lbs.

2.5L/V6-152 ENGINE
Manual Transaxle

When servicing starter or performing any maintenance in the area of starter, note heavy gauge input lead connected to starter solenoid is Hot at all times.

1. Disconnect battery ground cable, then isolate cable end with electrical tape or equivalent.
2. Remove fresh air duct and the air cleaner assembly.
3. Disconnect wiring electrical connections from starter motor assembly.
4. Remove three starter motor retaining bolts, then the starter motor assembly.
5. Reverse procedure to install, noting the following:
   a. **Torque** starter motor retaining bolts to 24–33 ft. lbs.
   b. **Torque** starter solenoid B-terminal nut to 12–16 ft. lbs.

Automatic Transaxle

When servicing starter or performing any maintenance in the area of starter, note heavy gauge input lead connected to starter solenoid is Hot at all times.

1. Disconnect battery ground cable, then isolate cable end with electrical tape or equivalent.
2. Remove fresh air duct and the air cleaner assembly.
3. Using screwdriver or equivalent, disconnect shift cable from selector lever by prying cable from lever.
4. Squeeze lock tabs on shift cable, then remove shift cable from cable bracket.
5. Mark positions of wiring harness connectors, then disconnect engine wiring harness from the following components:
   a. Knock sensor.
   b. Throttle position sensor.
   c. Two fuel rail connectors.
   d. Distributor.
   e. Manual lever position (MLP) switch.
   f. Automatic transaxle.
   g. Two wire harness connectors.
6. Position engine wiring harness aside.
7. Remove two selector cable bracket mounting bolts, then the bracket.
8. Remove starter motor support bracket, then disconnect starter motor electrical connectors.
9. Remove three starter motor retaining bolts, then the starter motor from vehicle.
10. Reverse procedure to install, noting the following:
    a. **Torque** starter motor retaining bolts to 24–33 ft. lbs.
    b. **Torque** starter solenoid B-terminal nut to 12–16 ft. lbs.
    c. **Torque** selector cable bracket mounting bolts to 5–7 ft. lbs.

3.0L/V6-182 ENGINE

When servicing starter or performing any maintenance in the area of starter, note heavy gauge input lead connected to starter solenoid is Hot at all times. Ensure protective cap is installed over terminal and is replaced after service.

1. Disconnect battery ground cable, then isolate cable end with electrical tape or equivalent.
2. **On models with automatic transaxle,** remove kickdown cable routing bracket from engine block.
3. **On all models,** disconnect wire from starter solenoid "S" terminal. **When disconnecting hardshell connector at "S" terminal, grasp plastic shell and pull off. Do not pull on wire.**
4. Remove starter solenoid B-terminal nut, then disconnect cable from terminal.
5. Remove starter motor retaining bolts, then the starter motor.
6. Reverse procedure to install, noting the following:
   a. **Torque** starter motor retaining bolts to 15–20 ft. lbs.
   b. **Torque** starter solenoid B-terminal nut to 80–120 in. lbs.

DISTRIBUTOR
REPLACE
2.0L/4-122 ENGINE
Removal

1. Disconnect battery ground cable, then

isolate cable end with electrical tape or equivalent.
2. **On vehicles equipped with automatic transaxle,** disconnect coil electrical connector.
3. **On all vehicles,** disconnect distributor electrical connector.
4. Remove two distributor cap retaining screws, then position cap and wires aside.
5. Rotate engine until the No. 1 piston is at Top Dead Center (TDC) on the compression stroke. **It may be necessary to remove the No. 1 spark plug to confirm compression stroke.**
6. Remove two distributor hold-down bolts, then the distributor from vehicle.

Installation

1. Match alignment marks (dots) on distributor shaft and distributor housing.
2. Apply clean engine oil to O-ring on distributor.
3. Install distributor. **Ensure rotor points to the No. 1 wire tower. If rotor is misaligned, pull distributor out and rotate distributor shaft to the next tooth. Repeat this step until rotor alignment is correct.**
4. Install distributor cap and two retaining screws.
5. Connect distributor electrical connector.
6. **On vehicles with automatic transaxle,** connect coil electrical connector.
7. Hand tighten distributor hold-down bolts, then connect battery ground cable.
8. Adjust ignition timing as necessary, then **torque** hold-down bolts to 14–18 ft. lbs.

2.2L/4-133 ENGINE

1. Disconnect battery ground cable.
2. Remove distributor cap and position aside.
3. **On non-turbocharged engines,** perform the following:
   a. Mark positions of distributor vacuum hoses, noting location for installation reference, **Fig. 2**
   b. Disconnect distributor electrical connector from coil, **Fig. 3.**
4. **On turbocharged engines,** disconnect distributor electrical connector near distributor, **Fig. 4.**
5. **On all models,** position No. 1 piston at TDC on compression stroke.
6. Mark position of distributor in engine and the position of rotor on distributor housing for installation reference.
7. Remove distributor hold-down bolts, then lift distributor out of engine. **Do not crank engine after distributor has been removed.**
8. Reverse procedure to install, noting the following:
   a. Ensure No. 1 piston is at TDC on compression stroke.
   b. Install new O-ring onto distributor shaft and lubricate O-ring with engine oil.
   c. Install distributor, ensuring to engage drive gear into camshaft slot.

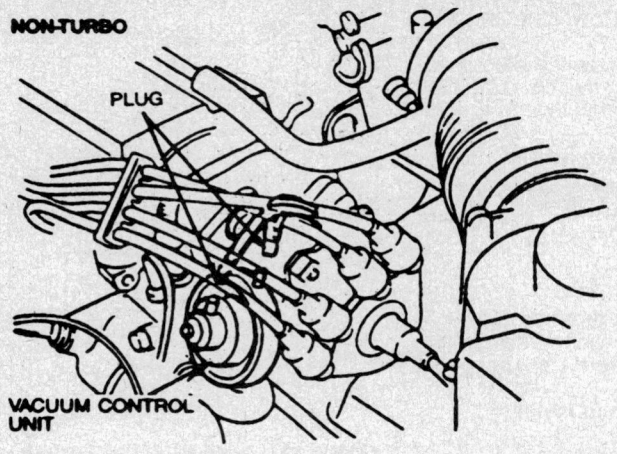

Fig. 2 Distributor vacuum hose location

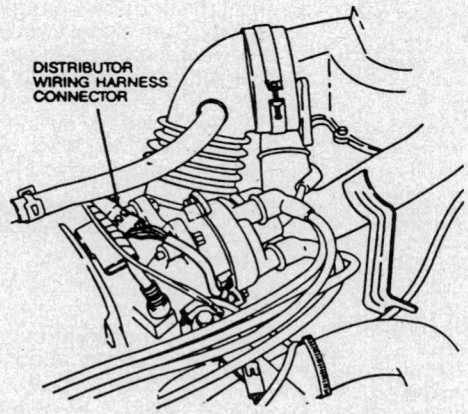

Fig. 4 Distributor wiring harness connector location. Turbocharged engines

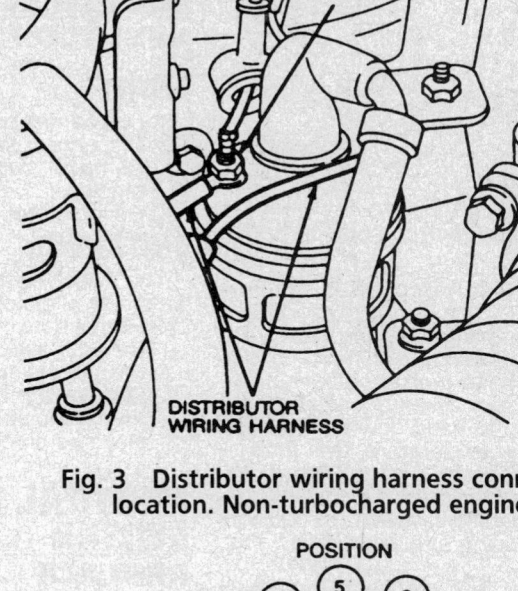

Fig. 3 Distributor wiring harness connector location. Non-turbocharged engines

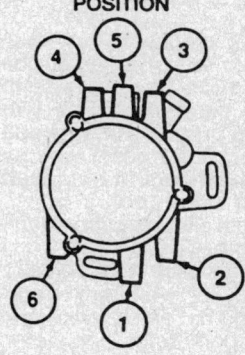

Fig. 5 Spark plug wire positions. 2.5L/V6-152 engine

2.5L/V6-152 ENGINE

1. Disconnect battery ground cable, then isolate cable end with electrical tape or equivalent.
2. Disconnect Volume Air Flow (VAF) meter electrical connector from left-hand side of air cleaner assembly.
3. Remove Fuel Pressure Regulator Control (FPRC) solenoid retaining screw from righthand side of air cleaner assembly, then position solenoid aside.
4. Remove air cleaner fresh air duct, then the air cleaner assembly from vehicle.
5. Mark position of spark plug wires for installation reference, then disconnect spark plug wires from distributor cap, **Fig. 5.**
6. Disconnect two distributor electrical connectors from top of distributor.
7. Remove distributor hold-down bolts, then the distributor assembly from vehicle.
8. Reverse procedure to install, noting the following:
   a. One of the tangs on the distributor shaft is larger than the other. This ensures only one installation posi-

tion.
   b. Hand tighten distributor hold-down bolts.
   c. **Torque** air cleaner assembly nuts and bolts to 14-18 ft. lbs.
   d. **Torque** fresh air duct nuts and three bolts to 71-88 in. lbs.
   e. Check and adjust engine timing.
   f. **Torque** distributor hold-down bolts to 19-25 ft. lbs.

3.0L/V6-182 ENGINE

1. Disconnect battery ground cable.
2. Disconnect primary wiring connector from distributor.
3. Remove distributor cap and position aside. **When removing distributor cap, mark position of the No. 1 wire tower on distributor base for installation reference.**
4. Rotate crankshaft pulley until rotor points to No. 1 wire tower TDC on distributor.

5. Disconnect TFI-IV harness connector.
6. Use Distributor wrench tool No. T82L-12270-A or equivalent to remove distributor hold-down bolt and clamp.
7. Lift distributor from engine.
8. Reverse procedure to install, noting the following:
   a. Ensure No. 1 piston is at TDC on the compression stroke.
   b. Ensure timing marks are aligned.
   c. **Torque** distributor cap hold-down screws to 17-25 ft. lbs.
   d. Tighten distributor hold-down bolt to 17-25 ft. lbs.
   e. Check initial timing. Adjust if necessary.

IGNITION SWITCH
REPLACE

1992

It is not necessary to remove the

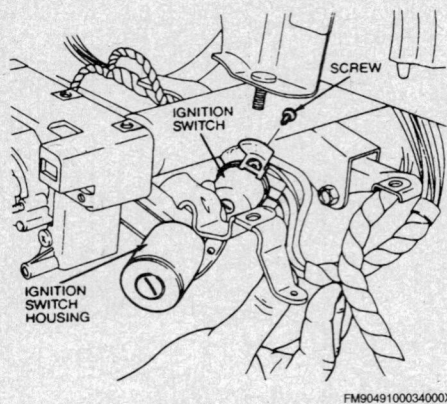

Fig. 6   Ignition switch replacement

steering wheel to remove the ignition switch.
1. Disconnect battery ground cable.
2. Remove steering column upper mounting bolts, then the steering column pivot lock assembly. Allow steering column to hang down. **It may be necessary to remove the instrument panel lower panel, lap duct, then defroster duct for access.**
3. Remove ignition switch to ignition switch housing attaching screw, **Fig. 6.**
4. Disconnect four ignition switch snap connectors from left of steering column. **Note location of each wire in the four wire connector. The two key-in warning buzzer wires (green and the red/orange tracer) may be removed by disengaging tang with a paper clip or other tool.**
5. Remove protective looming from ignition switch wiring.
6. Remove ignition switch from vehicle.
7. Install two key-in warning buzzer wires by aligning flat side of wire end with grooved portion of connector, then pushing wire into connector until locking tang engages wire end. Connect the other two ignition switch wires.
8. Install protective looming around ignition switch wiring.
9. Connect the four snap electrical connectors by pushing together until locking tangs engage.
10. Install ignition switch to ignition switch housing attaching screw.
11. Install upper steering column mounting bolts. Install instrument panel lower panel, lap duct, then defroster duct, if removed.

1993-95

It is not necessary to remove the steering wheel to remove the ignition switch.
1. Disconnect battery ground cable, then isolate cable end with electrical tape or equivalent.
2. Remove four lower steering column panel screws, then separate upper and lower steering column panels.
3. Remove lock cylinder illumination bulb from lower steering column panel.

4. Remove upper and lower steering column panels.
5. Disconnect ignition switch electrical.
6. Remove ignition switch retaining screw, then the ignition switch assembly from vehicle.
7. Reverse procedure to install.

CLUTCH START SWITCH
REPLACE

1992
1. Disconnect battery ground cable.
2. Disconnect switch wiring from switch.
3. Remove switch from clutch pedal bracket.
4. Reverse procedure to install.

1993-95
The switch assembly is located on left-hand side of clutch pedal support bracket.
1. Remove two switch retaining nuts, then pull switch downward to gain access to electrical connector.
2. Disconnect connector from switch, then remove switch.
3. Reverse procedure to install.

NEUTRAL SAFETY SWITCH
REPLACE

1992
1. **On turbocharged models,** remove intercooler inlet and outlet hoses.
2. Disconnect battery ground cable.
3. Set shift lever in Neutral position.
4. Disconnect neutral safety switch wiring connector.
5. Remove neutral safety switch from transaxle.
6. Install replacement switch.
7. Install neutral safety switch attaching bolts. Do not tighten at this time.
8. Insert a .079 inch drill bit through hole provided in switch, **Fig. 7.**
9. **Torque** neutral safety switch attaching bolts to 69-95 inch lbs., then remove drill bit.
10. Connect neutral safety switch wiring connector, then battery negative terminal.
11. Ensure starter operates in Neutral and Park positions only.

1993-95
1. Disconnect battery ground cable, then isolate cable end with electrical tape or equivalent.
2. Remove air cleaner assembly.
3. Using a screwdriver or equivalent, pry shift cable from transaxle shift lever.
4. Disconnect neutral position switch electrical connector.
5. Remove switch retaining bolts, then remove switch.
6. Reverse procedure to install, noting the following:
   a. Align neutral mark on top of switch (center line) with flats of switch shaft.
   b. **Torque** switch retaining bolts to 71-88 inch lbs.

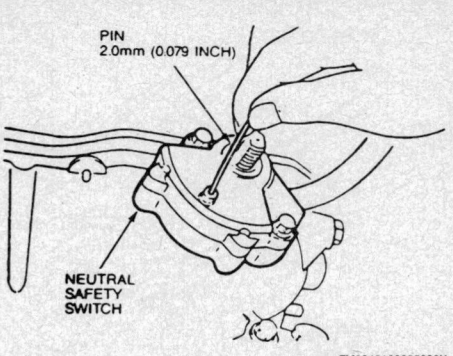

Fig. 7   Neutral safety switch adjustment

HEADLAMP SWITCH
REPLACE

1. Disconnect battery ground cable.
2. Remove turn signal switch as outlined elsewhere in this section.
3. Pull rotary switch knob from switch stem.
4. Remove light switch attaching screws, then the switch, **Fig. 8.**
5. Reverse procedure to install.

STOP LIGHT SWITCH
REPLACE

1992
1. Disconnect battery ground cable.
2. Disconnect electrical connector from stop light switch, **Fig. 9.**
3. Loosen locknut securing stop light switch, then rotate switch counterclockwise to remove.
4. Install nuts securing stop light switch to bracket. Do not tighten nuts at this time.
5. Connect electrical connector to switch.
6. Adjust switch for proper operation by rotating switch to obtain a brake pedal height of 8.54-8.74 inches as measured from firewall.

1993-95
1. Disconnect battery ground cable.
2. Remove lower steering column trim.
3. Disconnect brake switch electrical connector.
4. Remove brake switch, pulling it straight out from brake pedal.
5. Reverse procedure to install, noting the following:
   a. Ensure switch is correctly installed by pushing switch in until it bottoms out against brake pedal.

COMBINATION SWITCH
REPLACE

1. Disconnect battery ground cable.
2. Remove steering wheel as described under "Steering Wheel, Replace."
3. Remove four lower steering column panel retaining screws.
4. Separate upper and lower steering column panels, then remove lock cyl-

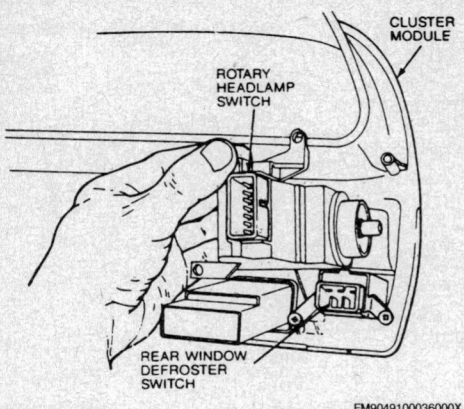

Fig. 8 Rotary light switch replacement

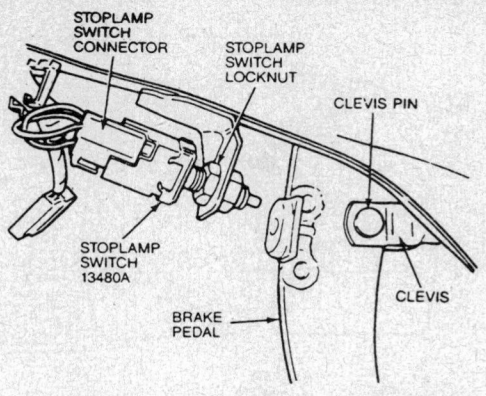

Fig. 9 Stop lamp switch replacement/adjustment

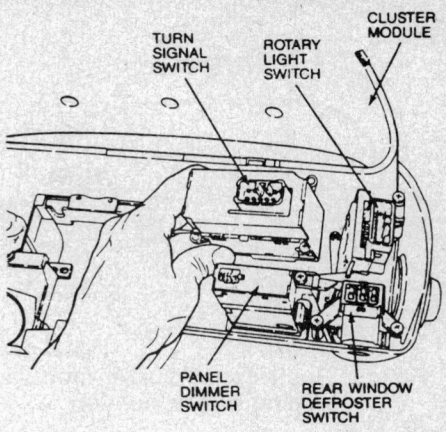

Fig. 10 Turn signal switch replacement

inder illumination bulb from lower panel.

5. Remove upper and lower steering column panels.
6. Apply two strips of tape across clockspring and housing to prevent accidental rotation.
7. Remove three clockspring retaining screws, then lift clockspring off steering column.
8. Remove clockspring ground screw, then disconnect electrical connector.
9. Remove clockspring assembly from steering column.
10. Remove cancel cam and spring from steering shaft, then the three combination switch retaining screws.
11. Disconnect combination switch electrical connectors.
12. Slide combination switch off steering column shaft.
13. Reverse procedure to install, noting the following:

TURN SIGNAL SWITCH
REPLACE

1992

1. Disconnect battery ground cable.
2. Remove steering wheel as outlined elsewhere in this section.
3. Remove two center cover attaching screws, then the cover.
4. Remove cluster module attaching screws, then disconnect electrical connectors from cluster module.
5. Remove cluster module by pulling away from instrument cluster.
6. Remove turn signal arm attaching screw, then the arm.
7. Remove two turn signal switch attaching screws, then the switch from rear of cluster module, **Fig. 10**.
8. Reverse procedure to install.

1993-95

Refer to "Combination Switch, Replace" procedure for turn signal switch replacement.

STEERING WHEEL
REPLACE

1992

1. Disconnect battery ground cable.
2. Remove two screws from back of steering wheel.
3. Pull steering wheel cover pad from steering wheel, then disconnect horn wire from pad.
4. Remove steering wheel hub cover, then the horn switch assembly.
5. Loosen steering wheel attaching nut.
6. Place an alignment mark between steering wheel and steering shaft.
7. Pull steering wheel to loosen. **Do not use steering wheel puller to remove steering wheel.**
8. Remove steering wheel attaching nut, then the steering wheel.
9. Reverse procedure to install. **Torque** steering wheel attaching nut to 29-36 ft. lbs.

1993-95

1. Disconnect battery ground cable.
2. Center front wheels to straight ahead position.
3. Disconnect speed control electrical connector, if equipped.
4. Make an alignment mark on steering wheel and steering shaft for correct alignment during assembly.
5. Remove steering wheel retaining nut. **Do not attempt to remove the steering wheel by hitting the steering shaft with a hammer. The steering shaft will collapse, causing the steering wheel to bind.**
6. Install steering wheel puller tool No. T67L-3600-A or equivalent to steering wheel.
7. Remove steering wheel assembly from column, routing wire harness through steering wheel as steering wheel is lifted off the shaft.
8. Apply two strips of tape across clockspring and housing to prevent accidental rotation. If clockspring rotates, adjust as follows:
   a. Turn clockspring clockwise until it stops. **Do not apply excessive force to clockspring.**

b. Rotate clockspring counterclockwise 2.75 turns.
c. Align marks on clockspring and housing.
9. Reverse procedure to install, noting the following:
   a. **Torque** steering wheel retaining nut to 29-36 ft. lbs.

INSTRUMENT CLUSTER
REPLACE

1992

Less Electronic Cluster

1. Disconnect battery ground cable.
2. Remove steering wheel as outlined elsewhere in this section.
3. Remove two column cover screws, then the cover.
4. Remove nine cluster module attaching screws, **Fig. 11**.
5. Gently pull cluster module outward, then disconnect seven electrical connectors from cluster cover.
6. Remove ignition switch illumination bulb.
7. Remove cluster module.
8. Loosen two cover hinge screws.
9. Remove six upper cluster cover attaching screws, then the cover. **Use caution not to tear rubber seal that joins upper and lower portions of cluster cover panels.**
10. Remove lower cluster cover panel.
11. Remove four cluster mounting screws, then disconnect two electrical connectors from rear of cluster.
12. Disconnect speedometer cable, then remove cluster from vehicle.
13. Reverse procedure to install.

With Electronic Cluster

1. Disconnect battery ground cable.
2. Remove steering wheel as outlined elsewhere in this section.
3. Remove two steering column cover screws, then the cover.
4. Remove nine cluster module attaching screws, **Fig. 12**.
5. Gently pull cluster module outward, then disconnect electrical connectors from cluster.

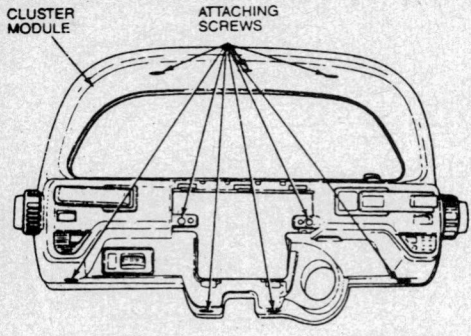

Fig. 11 Instrument cluster module attaching screw location

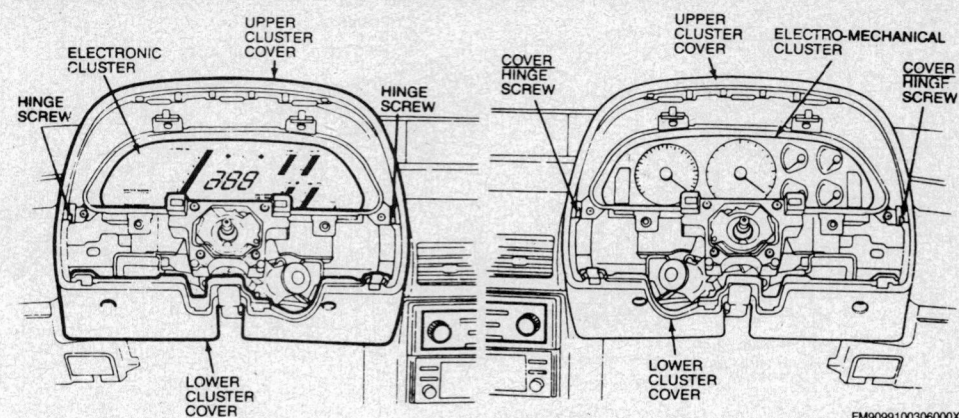

Fig. 12 Instrument cluster covers. Electronic cluster

Fig. 13 Instrument cluster covers. Electro-mechanical cluster

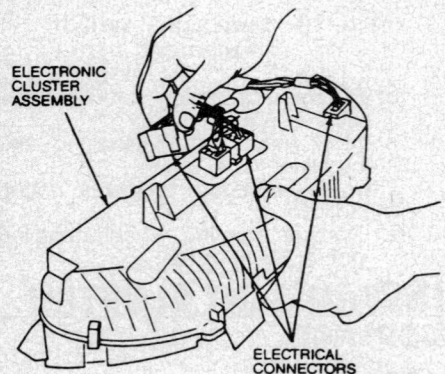

Fig. 14 Instrument cluster electrical connector disconnect. Electronic cluster

6. Disconnect resistor panel lamp dimmer switch electrical connector.
7. Remove instrument cluster bezel.
8. Remove two upper steering column retaining bolts and lower steering column.
9. Remove four instrument cluster retaining screws.
10. Disconnect instrument cluster from electrical connectors, then remove cluster from vehicle.
11. Reverse procedure to install, noting the following:

RADIO
REPLACE
1992

1. Disconnect battery ground cable.
2. Remove ash tray.
3. **On manual transaxle models,** remove gearshift and boot trim panel.
4. **On automatic transaxle models,** remove selector trim panel.
5. **On all models,** remove cigar lighter assembly.
6. Disconnect cigar lighter lamp by twisting the socket.
7. Remove two radio to instrument panel screws.
8. Insert radio removal tools No. T87P-19061-A or equivalent, into the face plate holes until tension of tools locking into place can be felt.
9. Flex outward on both sides of radio simultaneously, then pull radio outward using tools as handles.
10. Disconnect electrical connectors and antenna lead-in cable from back of radio.
11. Reverse procedure to install.

1993–95
Compact Disc Radio (CDR) & Graphic Equalizer (GEQ)

1. Disconnect battery ground cable.
2. Remove two armrest compartment retaining screws, then the armrest compartment, if equipped.
3. **On manual transaxle models,** unscrew shifter knob.
4. **On automatic transaxle models,** re-

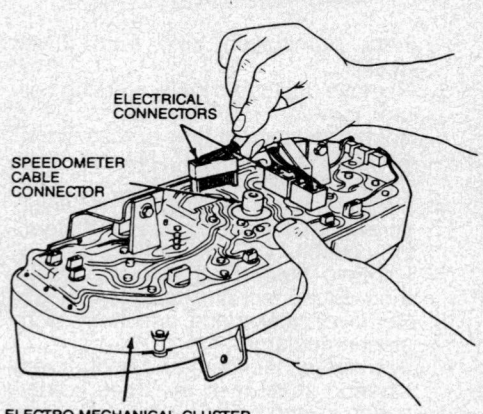

Fig. 15 Instrument cluster electrical connectors disconnect. Electro-mechanical cluster

move emergency override key switch cover from top of floor console.
5. **On all models,** engage parking brake, then gently pull up on upper half of floor console to separate it from the lower half.
6. Disconnect cigar lighter and cigar lighter element electrical connectors.
7. Remove ashtray illumination bulb from upper half of console.
8. Remove two dash panel control console bezel screws.
9. Remove four equalizer retaining screws, then the equalizer, if necessary.
10. Insert radio removal tools No. T87P-19061-A or equivalent, into face plate holes until the tension of the tools locking into place can be felt.
11. Flex outward on both sides of radio simultaneously, then pull radio outward using tools as handles.
12. Disconnect electrical connectors and antenna lead-in cable from back of radio.
13. Reverse procedure to install, noting the following:

Sub-Woofer Amplifier

The sub-woofer amplifier is located behind the lefthand quarter trim panel, near the B-pillar.

6. Remove ignition illumination bulb.
7. **On models with electro-mechanical cluster,** disconnect speedometer cable.
8. **On all models,** remove cluster module.
9. Loosen two cover hinge screws, **Fig. 12 and 13.**
10. Remove six screws from instrument cluster cover, then the cover.
11. Remove lower cluster cover panel. **Use caution not to rip the rubber seal that joins the upper and lower sections of the cluster cover panel.**
12. Remove four instrument cluster attaching screws, then disconnect electrical connectors from rear of cluster, **Figs. 14 and 15.**
13. Remove cluster from vehicle.
14. Reverse procedure to install.

1993–95

1. Disconnect battery ground cable then isolate cable.
2. Loosen hood release handle mounting nut.
3. Remove lower instrument panel cover screw.
4. Remove courtesy lamp from lower instrument panel cover by turning bulb 1/4 turn counterclockwise, then pulling bulb straight out.
5. Remove lower instrument panel cover, then the five instrument cluster bezel screws.

1. Disconnect battery ground cable, then isolate cable end with electrical tape or equivalent.
2. Remove package tray.
3. Remove trunk end screws, then the trunk end trim.
4. Remove lefthand lower trunk side trim as follows:
   a. Remove three push tabs.
   b. Remove two screws.
5. Remove lefthand quarter trim panel.
6. Remove sub-woofer amplifier assembly as follows:
   a. Remove two amplifier attaching nuts.
   b. Disconnect electrical connector.
   c. Remove sub-woofer amplifier assembly.
7. Reverse procedure to install. **Torque** sub-woofer amplifier assembly attaching nuts to 5 ft. lbs.

Premium Sound Amplifier

The premium sound amplifier is located behind the righthand quarter trim panel, near the B-pillar.

1. Disconnect battery ground cable, then isolate cable end with electrical tape or equivalent.
2. Remove package tray.
3. Remove trunk end screws, then the trunk end trim.
4. Remove righthand lower trunk side trim as follows:
   a. Remove three push tabs.
   b. Remove two screws.
5. Remove righthand quarter trim panel.
6. Remove premium sound amplifier assembly as follows:
   a. Remove three amplifier attaching nuts.
   b. Disconnect two amplifier electrical connectors.
   c. Remove premium sound amplifier assembly.
7. Reverse procedure to install. **Torque** amplifier attaching nuts to 5 ft. lbs.

WIPER MOTOR
REPLACE

1992

Front

1. Disconnect battery ground cable.
2. Remove arm and blade assemblies.
3. Disconnect hose from washer jet.
4. Remove lower molding, then the wiper linkage cover.
5. Pull wiper linkage from wiper motor output arm.
6. Disconnect electrical connectors from wiper motor.
7. Remove wiper motor attaching bolts, then the wiper motor.
8. Reverse procedure to install.

Rear

1. Disconnect battery ground cable.
2. Remove wiper arm and blade.
3. Remove pivot shaft boot, then the attaching nut and mount.
4. Pry off liftgate interior trim panel.
5. Disconnect wiper motor electrical connector.

6. Remove wiper motor attaching bolts, then the wiper motor.
7. Reverse procedure to install.

1993–95
Front

1. Disconnect battery ground cable, then isolate cable end with electrical tape or equivalent.
2. Remove wiper arm retaining nut covers, then retaining nuts.
3. Remove wiper arm assemblies from vehicle.
4. Remove lower windshield molding.
5. Disconnect wiper linkage from wiper motor output arm.
6. Remove wiring harness mounting bracket from wiper motor mounting bracket.
7. Remove four wiper motor mounting bracket retaining bolts, then disconnect wiper motor ground.
8. Disconnect wiper motor electrical connector, then remove wiper motor assembly from vehicle.
9. Reverse procedure to install, noting the following:
   a. The driver side wiper arm is marked D. The passenger wiper arm is marked PL.
   b. **Torque** wiper motor mounting bracket retaining bolts to 5-7 ft. lbs.
   c. **Torque** wiper arm retaining nuts to 7-10 ft. lbs.

Rear

1. Disconnect battery ground cable, then isolate cable end with electrical tape or equivalent.
2. Remove wiper arm and blade assembly.
3. Remove wiper motor shaft support nut cover, then support nut.
4. Remove liftgate side trim, then the liftgate lower trim
5. Disconnect wiper motor electrical connector.
6. Remove three wiper motor retaining bolts, then disconnect ground wire.
7. Remove wiper motor assembly from vehicle.
8. Reverse procedure to install, noting the following:
   a. **Torque** wiper motor retaining bolts to 5-7 ft. lbs.
   b. **Torque** wiper motor shaft support nut to 2-4 ft. lbs.

WIPER SWITCH
REPLACE

FRONT

1992

1. Disconnect battery ground cable.
2. Remove cluster module as outlined under "Instrument Cluster, Replace."
3. Remove front washer/interval rate control switch.
4. Remove front wiper control switch.
5. Remove front wiper/washer switch retaining screws, then the switch.
6. Reverse procedure to install.

1993–95

Refer to "Combination Switch, Replace" procedure for windshield wiper switch replacement.

REAR

1992

1. Disconnect battery ground cable.
2. Remove cluster module as outlined under "Instrument Cluster, Replace."
3. Remove front wiper/washer switch as outlined previously.
4. Remove rear wiper/washer switch retaining screws.
5. Remove control switch button by releasing the tangs.
6. Remove rear wiper/washer switch.
7. Reverse procedure to install.

1993–95

1. Disconnect battery ground cable, then isolate cable end with electrical tape or equivalent.
2. Remove two armrest retaining screws, then the armrest, if equipped.
3. **On manual transaxle models,** unscrew shifter knob.
4. **On automatic transaxle models,** remove emergency override key switch cover from top of floor console.
5. **On all models,** engage parking brake, then gently pull up on upper half of floor console to separate it from the lower half.
6. Disconnect cigar lighter and cigar lighter element electrical connectors from wiring harness.
7. Remove ashtray illumination bulb from upper half of console.
8. Remove two dash panel control console bezel screws, then bezel.
9. Disconnect wiper switch electrical connector, then squeeze the attaching tabs of switch assembly to remove wiper switch from control bezel.
10. Reverse procedure to install.

WIPER TRANSMISSION
REPLACE
FRONT

1. Disconnect battery ground cable.
2. Remove wiper arm and blade assemblies.
3. Remove lower molding, then the wiper linkage cover.
4. Pull wiper linkage from wiper motor output arm.
5. Remove pivot shaft retaining caps.
6. Remove pivot shafts and linkage.
7. Reverse procedure to install.

BLOWER MOTOR
REPLACE
1992

1. Disconnect battery ground cable.
2. Remove passenger side sound deadening panel.
3. Remove glove box and brace.
4. Remove blower motor cooling hose from blower motor.
5. Disconnect blower motor electrical connector from blower housing.

6. Remove three blower motor housing attaching screws, then the blower motor from vehicle.
7. Remove blower wheel retaining clip, then pull wheel from blower motor shaft.
8. Reverse procedure to install.

1993–95

1. Disconnect battery ground cable, then isolate cable end with electrical tape or equivalent.
2. Remove two hush panel retaining screws from below instrument panel.
3. Disconnect courtesy lamp electrical connector, then remove hush panel.
4. Disconnect blower motor electrical connector, then remove three blower motor retaining screws.
5. Remove blower motor assembly.
6. Reverse procedure to install.

HEATER CORE
REPLACE
1992
Less Air Conditioning

To replace the heater core, it will be necessary to remove the entire instrument panel, **Fig. 16.**
1. Disconnect battery ground cable.
2. Remove steering column.
3. Remove instrument cluster.
4. Remove floor console.
5. Remove hood release handle.
6. Remove ash tray and the cigar lighter assembly.
7. Remove left and right console kick panels.
8. Remove right and left instrument panel dash side covers.
9. Remove heater or A/C control panel.
10. Remove radio.
11. Remove trip computer.
12. Remove access cover to reach the center instrument panel dash mounting nut, then the nut, **Fig. 17.**
13. Remove eight remaining instrument panel mounting bolts, then the instrument panel, **Fig. 17** .
14. Drain cooling system.
15. Disconnect heater hoses from heater core extension tubes. Plug extension tubes and heater hoses to prevent coolant spillage into passenger compartment.
16. Remove main air duct, **Fig. 18.**
17. Remove heater case mounting nuts, **Fig. 18**, then pull heater case straight out. **Use caution not to bend core tubes.**
18. Remove two heater core tube braces to heater case attaching screws, then the braces.
19. Remove heater core from case by lifting straight up.
20. Reverse procedure to install.

With Air Conditioning

To replace the heater core, it will be necessary to remove the entire instrument panel, **Fig. 18.**
1. Perform steps 1 through 15 as outlined for models "Less Air Conditioning."

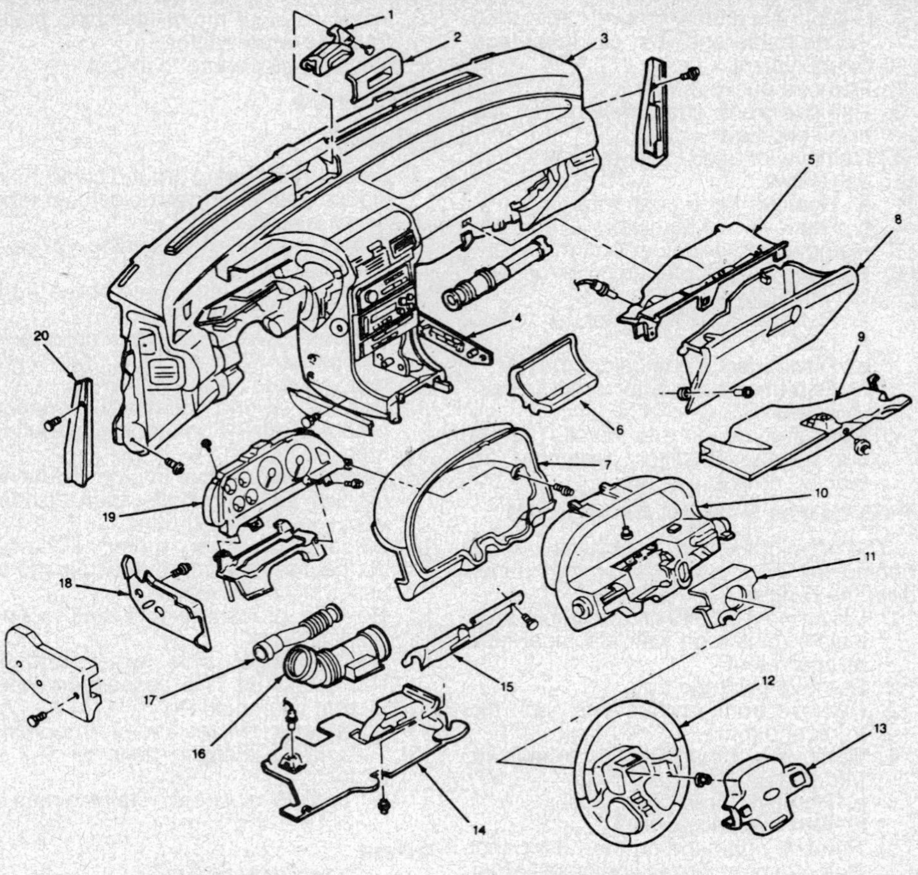

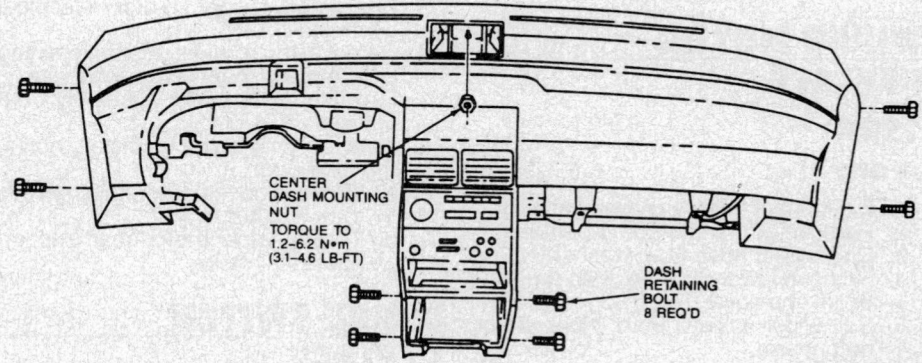

1.	TRIP COMPUTER	11.	COLUMN COVER
2.	TRIP COMPUTER COVER	12.	STEERING WHEEL
3.	INSTRUMENT PANEL	13.	STEERING WHEEL COVER
4.	DASH SIDE COVER	14.	LEFT SOUND DEADENING PANEL
5.	GLOVE COMPARTMENT PANEL	15.	LOWER PANEL
6.	LAP DUCT	16.	LAP DUCT
7.	CLUSTER COVER	17.	DEFROST DUCT
8.	GLOVE COMPARTMENT	18.	DASH SIDE WALL
9.	RIGHT SOUND DEADENING PANEL	19.	INSTRUMENT CLUSTER
10.	SWITCH MODULE	20.	DASH SIDE COVER

FM9099100309000X

Fig. 16 Instrument panel assembly

CENTER
DASH MOUNTING
NUT
TORQUE TO
1.2–6.2 N•m
(3.1–4.6 LB-FT)

DASH
RETAINING
BOLT
8 REQ'D

FM9099100310000X

Fig. 17 Instrument panel attachments

2. Discharge refrigerant from A/C system.
3. Remove charcoal canister from vehicle.
4. Disconnect refrigerant lines from evaporator. Plug evaporator and lines to prevent entry of dirt and moisture.
5. Disconnect A/C relay electrical connectors from top of evaporator case.
6. Remove air duct bands, **Fig. 19.**
7. Remove evaporator case attaching nuts, **Fig. 19**, then the evaporator case from vehicle.
8. Remove three heater case mounting nuts, **Fig. 20**, then pull heater case straight out. **Use caution not to bend core tubes.**
9. Remove two heater core tube braces

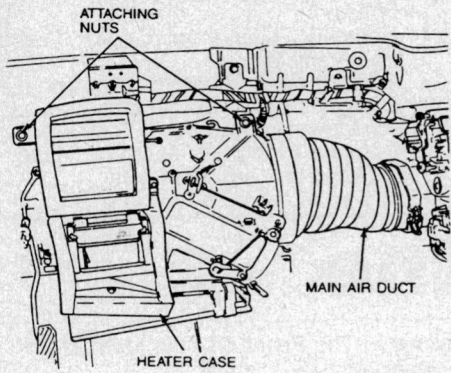

Fig. 18 Main air duct & heater case attachments. Less A/C

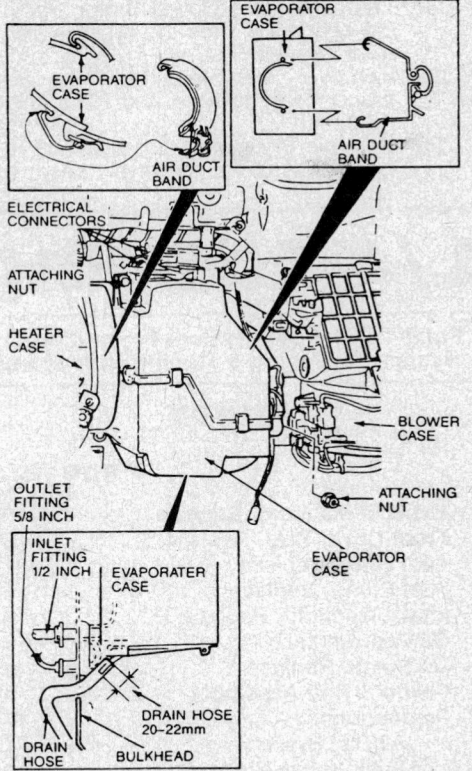

Fig. 19 Evaporator case assembly

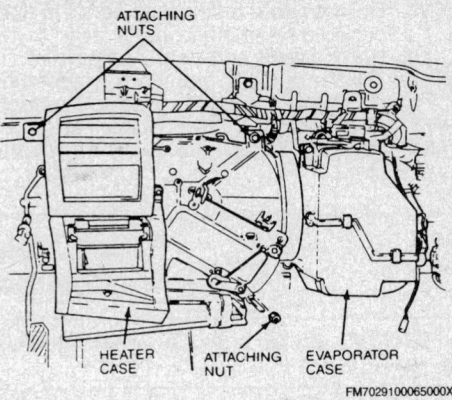

Fig. 20 Heater case attachments. Models w/air conditioning

to heater case attaching screws, then the braces.

10. Remove heater core from case by lifting straight up.
11. Reverse procedure to install.

1993–95

1. Disconnect the battery ground cable, then isolate cable end with electrical tape or equivalent.
2. Partially drain engine cooling system, then disconnect heater hoses at bulkhead in engine compartment.
3. Remove instrument cluster as described under "Instrument Cluster, Replace."
4. Open glove compartment door, then push in on sides of the compartment to release stoppers.
5. Remove two glove compartment retaining screws, then the glove compartment.
6. Remove lower hush panels from instrument panel.
7. Remove two armrest console retaining screws, then the armrest console, if equipped.
8. **On manual transaxle models,** unscrew shifter knob.
9. **On automatic transaxle models,** remove emergency override key switch cover from top of floor console.
10. **On all models,** engage parking brake, then gently pull up on upper half of floor console to separate it from the lower half.
11. Disconnect cigar lighter and cigar lighter element electrical connectors.
12. Then remove the ashtray illumination bulb from the upper half of console.
13. Remove two dash panel control console bezel screws, then the bezel.
14. Remove climate control assembly.
15. Remove left and right instrument panel side covers, then four side instrument panel retaining bolts.
16. Remove upper instrument panel bolt.
17. Remove four instrument panel to floor console retaining bolts.
18. Remove left and right A-pillar trim.
19. Tip instrument panel forward, then disconnect the necessary electrical connectors.
20. Remove instrument panel from vehicle.

21. Loosen upper left evaporator/blower unit nut to allow for removal of heater unit.
22. Remove three heater unit retaining screws, then the heater unit from vehicle.
23. Remove four brace screws then the brace from the heater unit.
24. Remove heater core from heater unit.
25. Reverse procedure to install.

EVAPORATOR CORE
REPLACE

1992

1. Remove instrument panel **Fig. 16,** as outlined under "Dash Panel Service" section.
2. Disconnect battery ground cable.
3. Discharge refrigerant from system, then remove carbon canister from vehicle.
4. Disconnect A/C lines from evaporator, then plug ends to prevent dirt and moisture from entering system, **Fig. 19.**
5. Fit Spring Lock Coupling tools No. T81P-19623-G2 1/2 inch or tool No. T83P-19623-C 5/8 inch to coupling.
6. Close tool and push into open side of cage to expand garter spring and release female fitting. Garter spring may not release if tool is cocked while pushing into cage opening.
7. After garter spring is expanded, pull fitting apart and remove tool from coupling.
8. Disconnect electrical connectors from

A/C relays at top of evaporator core.
9. Remove air duct bands and drain hose.
10. Remove evaporator case attaching nuts, then the evaporator case from vehicle.
11. Carefully remove evaporator case from vehicle.
12. Remove foam seals at inlet and outlet of the cooling unit by peeling them away from evaporator case.
13. Remove seven retaining clips from housing, then separate case halves and remove evaporator core.

1993–95

1. Discharge air conditioning system into a proper recovery system.
2. Disconnect high and low pressure lines from bulkhead, then the vacuum line.
3. Remove instrument cluster as described under "Instrument Cluster, Replace."
4. Open glove compartment door, then push in on compartment sides to release stoppers.
5. Remove two glove compartment retaining screws, then the glove compartment.
6. Remove lower hush panels from instrument panel.
7. Remove two armrest console retaining screws, then the armrest console, if equipped.
8. **On manual transaxle models,** unscrew shifter knob.
9. **On automatic transaxle models,** remove emergency override key switch cover from top of floor console.
10. **On all models,** engage parking brake, then gently pull up on upper half of floor console to separate it from the lower half.
11. Disconnect cigar lighter and cigar lighter element electrical connectors.
12. Remove ashtray illumination bulb from upper half of console.
13. Remove two dash panel control console bezel screws, then the bezel.
14. Remove climate control assembly.
15. Remove left and right instrument panel side covers, then the four side instrument panel retaining bolts.
16. Remove upper instrument panel bolt.

17. Remove four instrument panel to floor console retaining bolts.
18. Remove left and right A-pillar trim.
19. Tip instrument panel forward, then disconnect the necessary electrical connectors.
20. Remove instrument panel from vehicle.

21. Disconnect the blower motor electrical connector, then the resistor electrical connector.
22. Remove evaporator/blower case brace retaining nuts and bolts, then the brace.
23. Remove three nuts and one bolt retaining evaporator/blower case to

bulkhead.
24. Remove evaporator/blower case from vehicle.
25. Remove five evaporator/blower case screws, then separate evaporator/blower case halves.
26. Remove evaporator core from case.
27. Reverse procedure to install.

2.0L/4-122 Engine

NOTE: On Air Bag Equipped Models, Refer To "Air Bag System Precautions" Located In The Front Of This Manual For System Disarming & Arming Procedures.

INDEX

PRECAUTIONS

AIR BAG SYSTEMS

Refer to "Air Bag System Precautions" in the front of this manual for system disarming and arming procedures.

FUEL SYSTEM PRESSURE RELIEF

1. Start engine, then remove fuel pump relay from fuse box, **Fig. 1.**
2. After engine stalls, turn ignition off.
3. Install fuel pump relay.
4. When disconnecting fuel lines use rag as protection from fuel spray. **Plug hoses after they are disconnected.**

ENGINE MOUNT
REPLACE

Refer to **Fig. 2** when replacing engine mounts.

ENGINE
REPLACE

Exhaust gas sensors (EGO) can be contaminated by high volatility type silicones. This type of silicone can be found in sealants and gasket material. When volatile silicones migrate and come in contact with the EGO, contamination can occur rendering the EGO defective.

When performing service on the engine use only low volatility type silicone sealant. Replace the EGO if contaminated. **Do not use conventional silicone rubber sealants when low volatility silicone sealant is specified.**

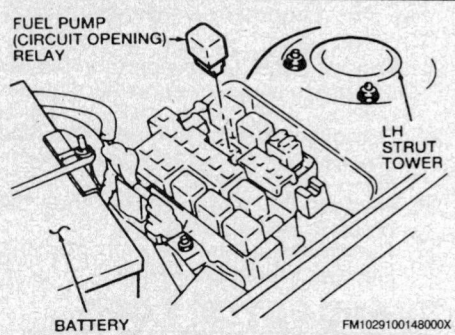

Fig. 1   Fuel pump relay removal

Use Ford part number F1AZ-19662-A Low Volatility RTV sealant or equivalent where specified.

AUTOMATIC TRANSAXLE

1. Relieve fuel system pressure as described under "Precautions."
2. Disconnect battery cables, then remove battery and battery tray from vehicle.
3. Disconnect engine compartment lamp electrical connector, then carefully remove hood assembly.
4. Drain engine oil and the cooling system.
5. Remove air intake system.
6. Remove A/C compressor mounting bolts if equipped, and position compressor aside. Support compressor assembly with wire.
7. Disconnect fuel lines from fuel rail assembly and position aside. **Plug disconnected fuel lines to prevent any fuel leakage. Label fuel lines for installation reference.**

8. Disconnect all engine wiring connectors and position aside. **Label connectors for installation reference.**
9. Remove power steering pump belt shield, then loosen power steering pump adjustment bolt.
10. Loosen power steering pump lock bolt and through bolt, then remove power steering belt.
11. Remove power steering hose hold-down bracket mounting bolts and brackets from cylinder head cover.
12. Remove power steering belt adjuster, then disconnect power steering pressure switch connector.
13. Remove power steering pump through bolt and position pump aside.
14. Loosen alternator adjusting bolt, then remove alternator upper mounting bolt and alternator belt.
15. Remove both radiator hoses.
16. Disconnect speed control vacuum line from back righthand side of intake manifold, if necessary.
17. Disconnect vacuum line connecting carbon canister to metal EGR vacuum line.
18. Disconnect EGR temperature sensor connector, if necessary.
19. Disconnect the accelerator cable, then the brake booster vacuum line from back lefthand side of intake manifold.
20. Disconnect heater hoses and remove starter motor upper mounting bolts.
21. Raise and support vehicle, then remove splash shield bolts and splash shields.
22. Disconnect starter motor electrical connector, then remove starter motor.

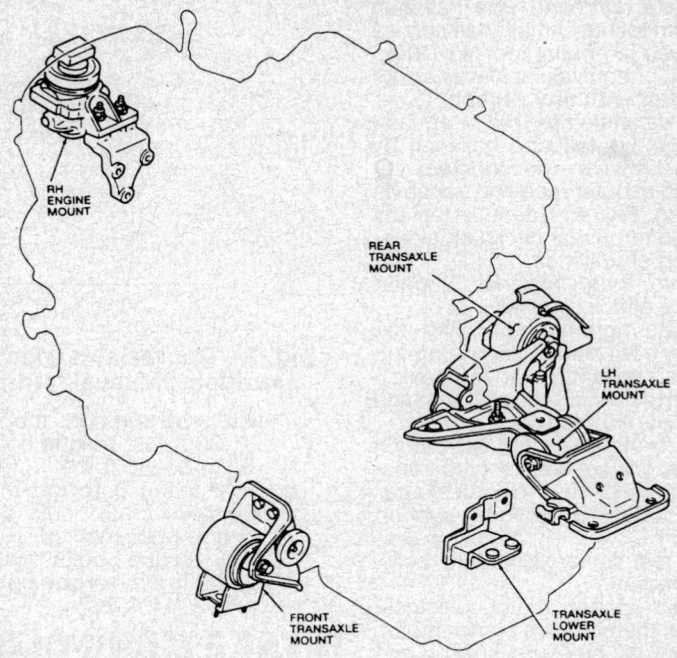

Fig. 2   Engine mount locations

FM1069100266000X

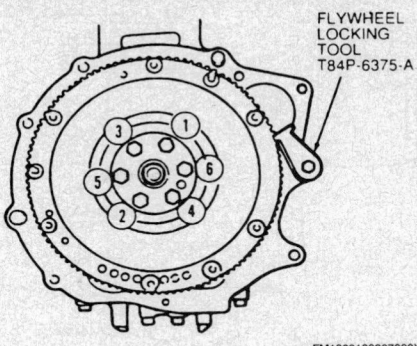

Fig. 3   Flex plate tightening sequence

FM1069100267000X

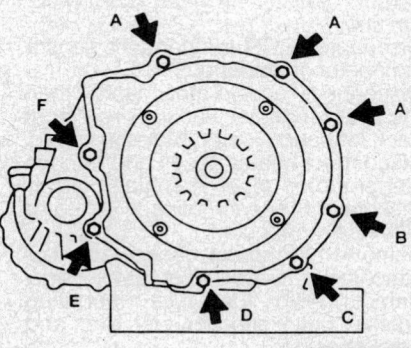

Fig. 4   Transaxle to engine bolt locations. Automatic transaxle

FM1069100268000X

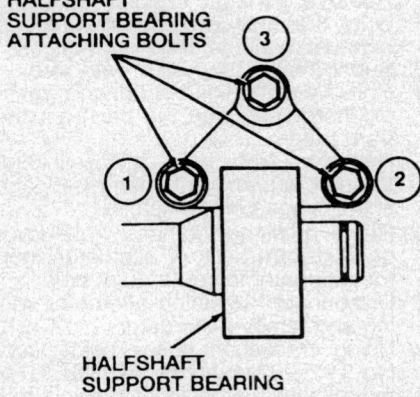

Fig. 5   Halfshaft support tightening sequence

FM1069100269000X

23. Remove intake manifold support bracket.
24. Remove halfshaft support bearing attaching bolts.
25. Disconnect oil pressure sensor connector.
26. Remove torque converter to flexplate attaching nuts.
27. Remove three engine to transaxle mounting bolts, then the transaxle to engine mounting bolts.
28. Disconnect oxygen sensor electrical connector.
29. Remove converter inlet pipe to catalytic converter attaching nuts.
30. Remove exhaust support attaching bolts, then the converter inlet pipe to exhaust manifold attaching nuts.
31. Support exhaust system with wire, then disconnect remaining alternator wiring.
32. Remove wiring harness hold-down bracket from back of alternator.
33. Remove alternator lower through bolt, then alternator from vehicle.
34. Using crankshaft pulley holder tool No. T92C-6316-AH or equivalent, remove crankshaft pulley.
35. Lower vehicle.
36. Slowly raise engine with a jack and remove righthand engine mount.
37. Attach an engine hoist to lifting eyes on engine, then remove remaining transaxle to engine mounting bolts.
38. Remove engine from vehicle.
39. Reverse procedure to install, noting the following:
   a. Install flywheel locking tool No. T84P-6375-A or equivalent, then using sequence shown in **Fig. 3**, **torque** flex plate mounting bolts in two or three steps to 70-75 ft. lbs.
   b. Refer to **Fig. 4**, then tighten transaxle to engine mounting bolts as

follows; **torque** bolts marked "A" to 50-73 ft. lbs., **torque** bolts marked "B" to 50-73 ft. lbs., **torque** bolts marked "C" to 28-38 ft. lbs., **torque** bolts marked "D" to 14-18 ft. lbs., **torque** bolts marked "E" to 28-38 ft. lbs., **torque** bolts marked "F" to 50-73 ft. lbs.
   c. Using sequence shown in **Fig. 5**, **torque** halfshaft support bearing attaching bolts to 32-45 ft. lbs.

MANUAL TRANSAXLE

1. Relieve fuel system pressure as described under "Precautions."
2. Disconnect battery cables, then remove battery and battery tray from vehicle.
3. Disconnect engine compartment lamp electrical connector, then carefully remove and set aside hood assembly.

4. Remove air intake system.
5. Drain engine coolant, then remove radiator and radiator hoses.
6. Drain engine oil.
7. Remove A/C compressor mounting bolts, if equipped, and position compressor aside. Support compressor assembly with wire.
8. Disconnect fuel lines from fuel rail assembly and position aside. **Plug disconnected fuel lines to prevent any fuel leakage. Label fuel lines for installation reference.**
9. Disconnect all engine wiring connectors and position aside. **Label connectors for installation reference.**
10. Remove power steering pump belt shield, then loosen power steering pump adjustment bolt.
11. Loosen power steering pump lock bolt and through bolt, then remove power steering belt.
12. Remove power steering hose hold-down bracket mounting bolts and brackets from cylinder head cover.
13. Remove power steering belt adjuster, then disconnect power steering pressure switch connector.
14. Remove power steering pump through bolt and position pump aside.
15. Loosen alternator adjusting bolt, then remove alternator upper mounting bolt and alternator belt.
16. Drain engine coolant and remove both radiator hoses.
17. Disconnect speed control vacuum line from back righthand side of intake manifold, if necessary.

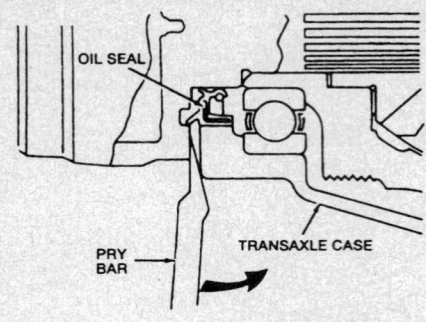

Fig. 6 Lefthand halfshaft removal

18. Disconnect vacuum line connecting carbon canister to metal EGR vacuum line.
19. Disconnect EGR temperature sensor connector, if equipped.
20. Disconnect accelerator cable, then the brake booster vacuum line from back lefthand side of intake manifold.
21. Disconnect heater hoses and remove starter motor upper attaching bolts.
22. Disconnect speed control actuator electrical connector.
23. Remove two speed control actuator attaching nuts and set actuator aside.
24. Remove two fuel filter mounting bracket bolts and set fuel filter and bracket aside.
25. Remove ignition control module.
26. Remove ground wire bracket mounted between transaxle and rear transaxle mount.
27. Remove rear transaxle mount through bolt, then the transaxle ground located at the top rear of the transaxle.
28. Disconnect Brake On/Off (BOO) switch and Vehicle Speed Sensor (VSS) connectors from rear of transaxle.
29. Remove slave cylinder line fitting from slave cylinder. **Plug metal line to prevent fluid leakage.**
30. Pull spring clips from slave cylinder line mounting brackets, then remove rubber line from metal line.
31. Disconnect Park/Neutral Position (PNP) switch from front of transaxle.
32. Raise and support vehicle, then remove front wheels and splash shields.
33. Remove six transverse member attaching bolts, then the transverse member.
34. Remove six transaxle cradle nuts and two bolts, then the transaxle cradle.
35. Remove two transaxle lower mount bolts and the transaxle lower mount.
36. Remove halfshafts as follows:
    a. Using hammer and chisel, carefully raise staked portion of halfshaft attaching nut.
    b. Apply brakes, then remove halfshaft attaching nut. **Discard nut after removal, never reuse nut.**
    c. Remove righthand stabilizer control link from lower control arm attaching bracket.
    d. Remove righthand side ball joint clamp bolt, then pry lower control arm from ball joint clamp.

e. Separate righthand side halfshaft from wheel hub. If halfshaft splines bind, use jaw puller tool No. D80L-1002-L or equivalent. **Never strike halfshaft with any object.**
f. Using an angled pry bar or equivalent, remove lefthand halfshaft by prying between the constant velocity joint outer race and transaxle housing, **Fig. 6.** Carefully tap pry bar end to unseat circlip on sidegear end of halfshaft.
g. Remove three halfshaft support bearing attaching bolts.
h. Separate righthand halfshaft assembly from differential by carefully prying halfshaft from transaxle.
i. Support halfshaft assemblies and slide out of transaxle.
j. Using transaxle plug set T88C-7025-AH or equivalent, plug transaxle openings to prevent leakage.
37. Remove intake manifold support bracket.
38. Remove rear transaxle mount bolts, then the mount.
39. Disconnect starter motor electrical connector, then remove starter motor.
40. Disconnect oil pressure sensor and oxygen sensor electrical connectors.
41. Remove converter inlet pipe to catalytic converter attaching nuts.
42. Remove exhaust support attaching bolts, then the converter inlet pipe to exhaust manifold attaching nuts.
43. Support exhaust system with wire.
44. Remove extension bar nut and washer, then disengage the bar from the transaxle.
45. Remove transaxle shift linkage through bolt and nut, then disengage shift linkage from transaxle.
46. Remove wiring harness hold-down bracket from back of alternator, then the alternator lower through bolt.
47. Disconnect remaining alternator wiring and remove alternator.
48. Using crankshaft pulley holder tool No. T92C-6316-AH or equivalent, remove crankshaft pulley attaching bolt.
49. Remove crankshaft pulley and guide plate.
50. Lower vehicle, then slightly raise engine with a jack and remove righthand engine mount.
51. Attach an engine hoist to lifting eyes on engine, then remove lefthand transaxle mount nuts and bolts.
52. Remove lefthand transaxle mount through bolt, then the mount.
53. Remove engine and transaxle assembly from vehicle.
54. Remove transaxle to engine mounting bolts and separate engine from transaxle.
55. Remove clutch and flywheel.
56. Remove crankshaft rear cover plate bolt and plate.
57. Reverse procedure to install, noting the following:
    a. Refer to **Fig. 7**, then tighten transaxle to engine mounting bolts as follows; **torque** bolts marked "A" to 66-86 ft. lbs., **torque** bolts marked "B" to 28-38 ft. lbs., **torque** bolts marked "C" to 14-18

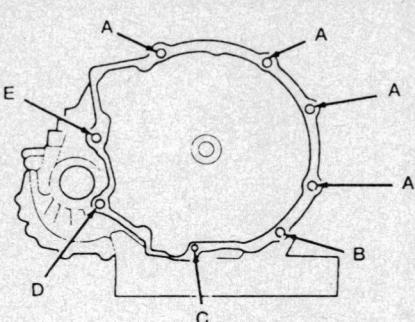

Fig. 7 Transaxle to engine bolt locations. Manual transaxle

ft. lbs., **torque** bolts marked "D" to 28-38 ft. lbs., **torque** bolts marked "E" to 66-86 ft. lbs.
    b. Refer to **Fig. 8, torque** then tighten transaxle cradle nuts as follows; **torque** bolts marked "A" 55-77 ft. lbs., **torque** bolts marked "B" 50-68 ft. lbs., **torque** bolts marked "C" 32-44 ft. lbs.

INTAKE MANIFOLD
REPLACE

1. Disconnect battery ground cable, then isolate cable end with electrical tape or equivalent.
2. Remove air intake system and fuel line mounting bracket.
3. Disconnect throttle cable.
4. Disconnect coolant line from idle air bypass air valve.
5. Disconnect coolant and vacuum lines from throttle body. **Mark vacuum lines for installation reference.**
6. Disconnect throttle position sensor connector.
7. **On models with automatic transaxle,** disconnect idle switch connector.
8. **On all models,** disconnect brake booster vacuum line from back lefthand side of intake manifold.
9. Disconnect EGR temperature sensor connector, if equipped.
10. Disconnect speed control vacuum line from back righthand side of intake manifold.
11. Disconnect EGR solenoid connectors.
12. Remove PCV valve from cylinder head cover.
13. Raise and support vehicle.
14. Remove intake manifold support bracket, then the EGR pipe from intake manifold.
15. Lower vehicle and remove intake manifold attaching bolts and nuts.
16. Remove intake manifold and discard gasket.
17. Reverse procedure to install. Refer to **Fig. 9** for manifold tightening sequence, then **torque** bolts and nuts to 14-19 ft. lbs.

EXHAUST MANIFOLD
REPLACE

Exhaust gas sensors (EGO) can be contaminated by high volatility type sili-

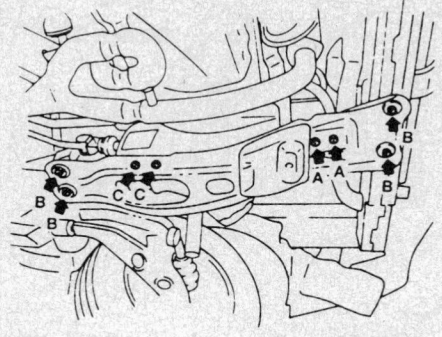

Fig. 8   Transaxle cradle bolt locations

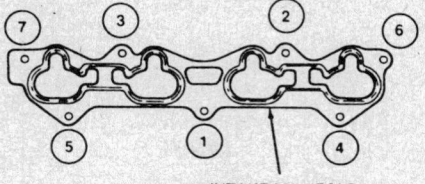

Fig. 9   Intake manifold tightening sequence

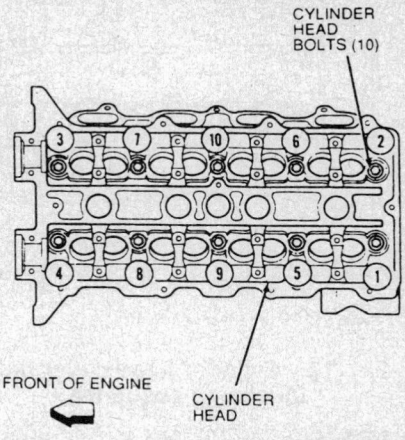

Fig. 10   Cylinder head bolt loosening sequence

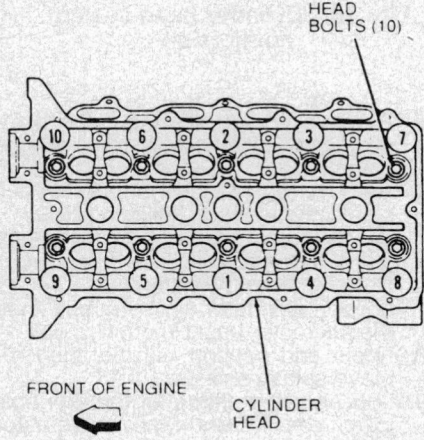

Fig. 11   Cylinder head bolt tightening sequence

cones. This type of silicone can be found in sealants and gasket material. When volatile silicones migrate and come in contact with the EGO, contamination can occur rendering the EGO defective.

When performing service on the engine use only low volatility type silicone sealant. Replace the EGO if contaminated. **Do not use conventional silicone rubber sealants when low volatility silicone sealant is specified.**

Use Ford part number F1AZ-19662-A Low Volatility RTV sealant or equivalent where specified.

1. Disconnect battery ground cable, then isolate cable end with electrical tape or equivalent.
2. Remove seven exhaust manifold heat shield bolts, then the heat shield.
3. Disconnect oxygen sensor connector, then using EGO sensor wrench tool No. T79P-9472-A or equivalent, remove sensor.
4. Raise and support vehicle.
5. Support exhaust system with wire, then remove three converter inlet pipe to exhaust manifold attaching nuts. Discard nuts.
6. Remove EGR pipe from back of exhaust manifold.
7. Lower vehicle.
8. Remove exhaust manifold mounting nuts, bolts and gasket. Discard nuts and manifold gasket.
9. Reverse procedure to install, noting the following:
   a. Tighten exhaust manifold mounting bolts to 12-17 ft. lbs.
   b. Tighten new exhaust manifold mounting nuts to 14-21 ft. lbs.

CYLINDER HEAD
REPLACE

Exhaust gas sensors (EGO) can be contaminated by high volatility type silicones. This type of silicone can be found in sealants and gasket material. When volatile silicones migrate and come in contact with the EGO, contamination can occur rendering the EGO defective.

When performing service on the engine use only low volatility type silicone sealant. Replace the EGO if contaminated. **Do not use conventional silicone rubber sealants when low volatility silicone sealant is specified.**

Use Ford part number F1AZ-19662-A Low Volatility RTV sealant or equivalent where specified.

1. Disconnect battery ground cable, then isolate cable end with electrical tape or equivalent.
2. Drain cooling system, then remove air intake system.
3. Remove power steering hose holddown bracket bolts from cylinder head cover.
4. Remove power steering pump belt shield, then loosen adjusting bolt.
5. Loosen lock bolt and power steering pump through bolt.
6. Remove power steering belt.
7. Loosen alternator adjusting bolt, then loosen alternator upper mounting bolt.
8. Raise and support vehicle, then remove righthand splash shield.
9. Loosen lower alternator through bolt, lower vehicle and remove alternator belt.
10. Remove power steering pump through bolt and lock bolt, then position pump aside.
11. Remove alternator bracket nut and bolt, then position bracket aside.
12. Remove exhaust manifold as described under "Exhaust Manifold, Replace."
13. Carefully remove cylinder head cover as described under "Cylinder Head Cover, Replace."
14. Remove timing belt as described under "Timing Belt, Replace."
15. Disconnect distributor/coil connectors, then all connectors at coolant temperature sensor housing.
16. Remove coolant temperature sensor housing from cylinder head and discard gasket.
17. Remove two distributor cap attaching screws, then the distributor cap. Position cap and wires aside.
18. Rotate engine until No. 1 piston is at TDC on compression stroke.
19. Remove two distributor hold-down bolts, then the distributor.
20. Remove camshafts as described under "Camshaft, Replace."
21. Remove cylinder head bolts in sequence shown in **Fig. 10**. Discard bolts.
22. Remove cylinder head and gasket from engine, then discard gasket.
23. Reverse procedure to install, noting the following:
   a. Ensure cylinder head and cylinder block mating surfaces are clean.
   b. **Do not reuse cylinder head bolts.**
   c. Refer to **Fig. 11** for bolt tightening sequence, then **torque** cylinder head bolts in two steps to 13-16 ft. lbs. After initial tightening, apply a paint mark to cylinder head bolts, then tighten bolts an additional 85-95° turn in sequence. Final tighten all bolts an additional 85-95°.
   d. Ensure timing marks are aligned on distributor shaft and distributor housing.

VALVE COVER
REPLACE

Exhaust gas sensors (EGO) can be contaminated by high volatility type silicones. This type of silicone can be found in sealants and gasket material. When volatile silicones migrate and come in contact with the EGO, contamination can occur rendering the EGO defective.

When performing service on the engine use only low volatility type silicone sealant. Replace the EGO if contaminated. **Do not use conventional silicone rubber sealants when low volatility silicone sealant is specified.**

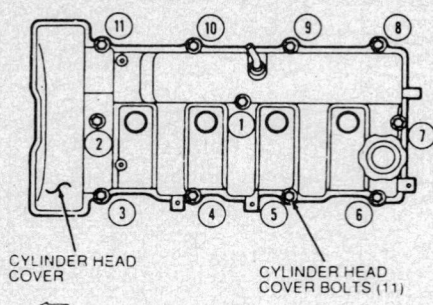

CYLINDER HEAD COVER

CYLINDER HEAD COVER BOLTS (11)

FRONT OF ENGINE

Fig. 12 Cylinder head cover bolt loosening sequence

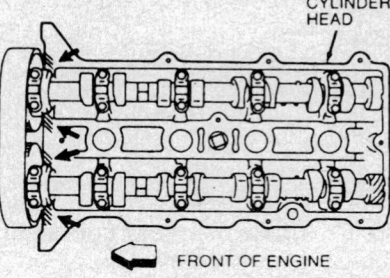

CYLINDER HEAD

FRONT OF ENGINE

Fig. 13 Cylinder head sealant application

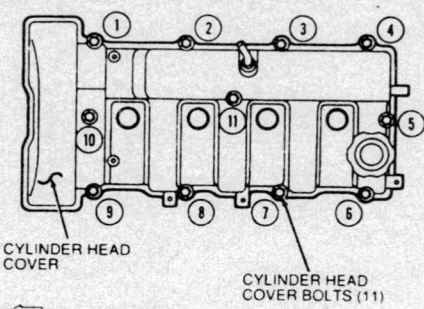

CYLINDER HEAD COVER

CYLINDER HEAD COVER BOLTS (11)

FRONT OF ENGINE

Fig. 14 Cylinder head cover bolt tightening sequence

Use Ford part number F1AZ-19662-A Low Volatility RTV sealant or equivalent where specified.

1. Disconnect battery ground cable, then isolate cable end with electrical tape or equivalent.
2. Remove power steering hose hold-down brackets.
3. Disconnect spark plug wires and wire clips. **Mark wires for installation reference.**
4. Disconnect breather tube from cover, then the PCV valve.
5. Using bolt loosening sequence shown in **Fig. 12**, remove cylinder head cover bolts in two steps.
6. Carefully pry cylinder head cover from cylinder head.
7. Remove cylinder head cover gasket, then discard.
8. Reverse procedure to install, noting the following:
   a. Apply a coat of silicone sealant to new cylinder head cover gasket.
   b. Apply silicone sealant to cylinder head as shown in **Fig. 13.**
   c. Refer to **Fig. 14** for bolt tightening sequence, then **torque** cylinder head cover bolts in two steps to 52-69 inch lbs.

CAMSHAFT LOBE LIFT SPECIFICATIONS

Intake: 1.6859-1.6918 inch
Exhaust: 1.7003-1.7062 inch

VALVE CLEARANCE SPECIFICATIONS

Hydraulic valve lash adjusters provide automatic lash adjustment which maintains a zero inch clearance between the camshaft lobes and the valve stems.

VALVE ADJUSTMENT

This engine uses hydraulic valve lifters. No adjustment is required.

FRONT COVER SEAL
REPLACE

1. Disconnect battery ground cable, then isolate cable end with electrical tape or equivalent.
2. Drain cooling system, then remove air intake system.

3. Remove power steering hose hold-down bracket bolts from cylinder head cover.
4. Remove power steering pump belt shield, then loosen adjusting bolt.
5. Loosen lock bolt and power steering pump through bolt.
6. Remove power steering belt.
7. Loosen alternator adjusting bolt, then the alternator upper mounting bolt.
8. Raise and support vehicle, then remove splash shields.
9. Loosen lower alternator through bolt, lower vehicle and remove alternator belt.
10. Using crankshaft pulley holder tool No. T92C-6316-AH or equivalent, remove crankshaft pulley attaching bolt.
11. Remove crankshaft pulley, sprocket and guide plate.
12. Using seal remover tool No. T92C-6700 or equivalent, remove front oil seal.
13. Reverse procedure to install.

TIMING BELT
REPLACE

Refer to **Fig. 15**, when performing the following procedure.

1. Disconnect battery ground cable, then isolate cable end with electrical tape or equivalent.
2. Remove cylinder head cover as described under "Cylinder Head Cover, Replace."
3. Remove power steering pump belt shield, then loosen adjusting bolt.
4. Loosen lock bolt and power steering pump through bolt, then remove power steering belt.
5. Loosen alternator adjusting bolt and alternator upper mounting bolt, then remove alternator belt.
6. Support engine using three bar engine support No. 014-00750 or equivalent.
7. Using suitable jack, raise engine slightly and remove righthand engine mount.
8. Remove timing belt upper cover.
9. Raise and support vehicle, then remove splash shields.
10. Using crankshaft pulley holder tool No. T92C-6316-AH or equivalent, remove crankshaft pulley attaching bolt.
11. Remove crankshaft pulley, sprocket and guide plate.

12. Remove timing belt lower cover bolts, then the cover.
13. Temporarily install crankshaft pulley attaching bolt.
14. Turn crankshaft until timing mark on crankshaft sprocket lines up with timing mark on oil pump and camshaft sprocket timing marks (E and I) line up as shown in **Fig. 16.**
15. Lower vehicle and insert camshaft pulley holding tool No. T92C-6256-AH or equivalent, **Fig. 17.**
16. Use an Allen wrench to turn timing belt tensioner and remove timing belt tensioner spring from hook pin.
17. Remove timing belt. **If reusing old timing belt, mark direction of belt for installation reference.**
18. Reverse procedure to install, noting the following
    a. Ensure all timing marks are aligned as shown in **Fig. 16.**
    b. Tighten to specifications.

CAMSHAFT
REPLACE

1. Disconnect battery ground cable, then isolate cable end with electrical tape or equivalent.
2. Remove cylinder head cover as described under "Cylinder Head Cover, Replace."
3. Remove power steering pump belt shield, then loosen adjusting bolt.
4. Loosen lock bolt and power steering pump through bolt, then remove power steering belt.
5. Loosen alternator adjusting bolt and alternator upper mounting bolt, then remove alternator belt.
6. Remove timing belt as described under "Timing Belt, Replace."
7. Holding camshaft with a suitable wrench, remove camshaft sprockets.
8. Using sequence shown in **Fig. 18,** remove camshaft bearing cap bolts two steps. **Camshaft bearing caps are marked for installation reference, ensure caps are installed in their correct position.**
9. Remove camshafts.
10. Reverse procedure to install. Using sequence shown in **Fig. 19. Torque** camshaft bearing cap bolts in three steps as follows:
    a. **Torque** to 35 inch lbs.
    b. **Torque** to 71 inch lbs.

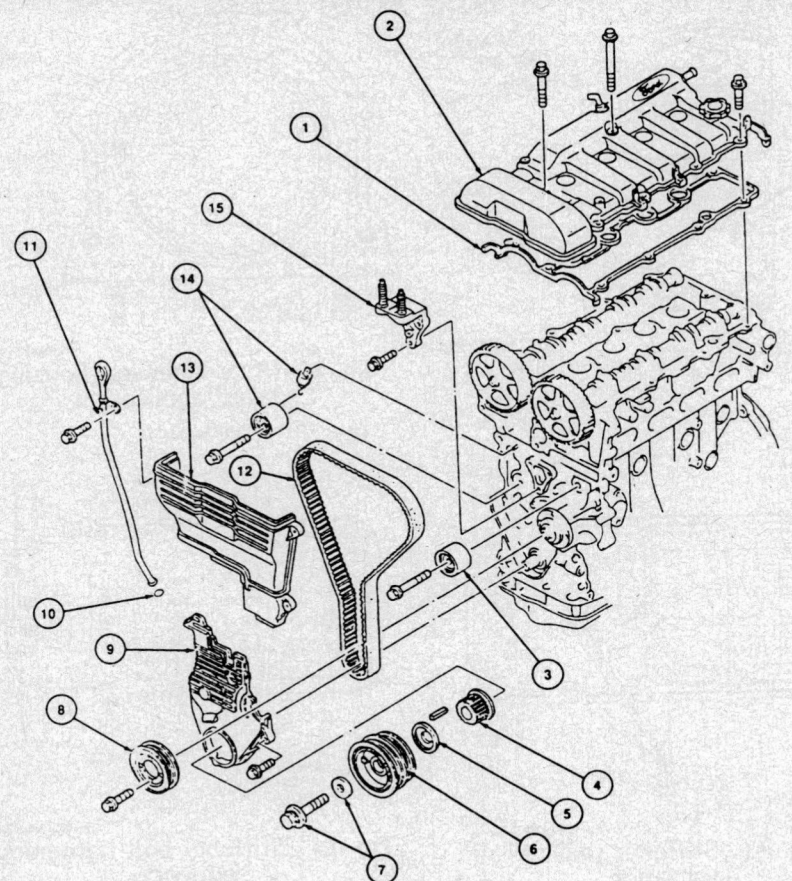

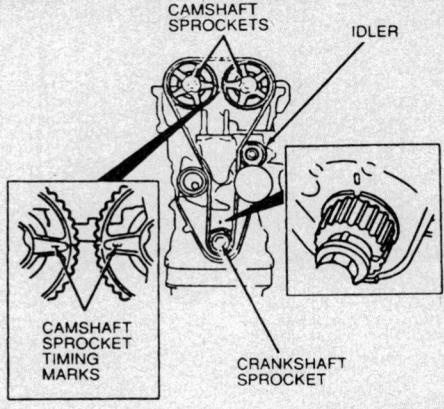

Fig. 16 Timing mark alignment

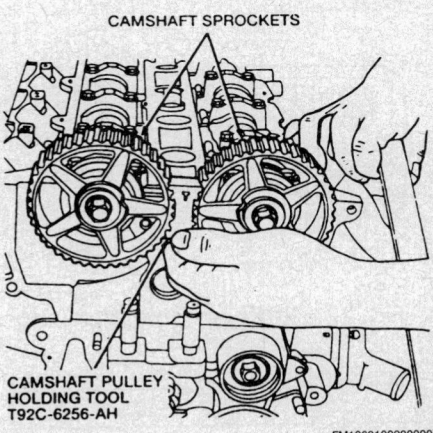

Fig. 17 Camshaft pulley holding tool positioning

Item	Description
1	Cylinder Head Cover Gasket
2	Cylinder Head Cover
3	Idler
4	Crankshaft Sprocket
5	Guide Plate
6	Crankshaft Pulley

Item	Description
7	Crankshaft Pulley Bolt and Washer
8	Water Pump Pulley
9	Timing Belt Lower Cover
10	Engine Oil Dipstick O-Ring
11	Engine Oil Dipstick
12	Timing Belt
13	Timing Belt Upper Cover

FM1069100278000X

Fig. 15 Timing belt assembly

c. **Torque** to 100-126 inch lbs.

PISTON & ROD ASSEMBLY

Refer to **Fig. 20** for piston and rod assembly installation direction.

CRANKSHAFT REAR OIL SEAL
REPLACE

1. Remove transaxle as described under "Engine, Replace."
2. Remove flywheel or flex plate as described under "Engine, Replace."
3. Remove rear main seal housing to stiffener attaching nuts.
4. Remove six rear main seal housing to block attaching bolts, then the seal housing from the block.
5. Using seal removal tool No. T92C-6700-CH or equivalent, remove seal from housing.
6. Reverse procedure to install, noting

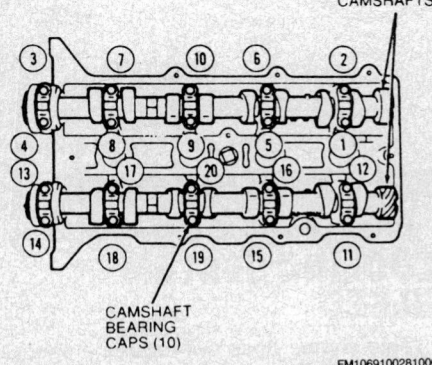

Fig. 18 Camshaft bearing cap loosening sequence

the following:
a. Apply a bead of silicone sealant to rear main seal housing as shown in **Fig. 21**.
b. Tighten to specifications.

OIL PAN
REPLACE

1. Raise and support vehicle.
2. Remove righthand splash shield, the drain oil from engine.
3. Disconnect oxygen sensor connector, then support exhaust system using a screw type jack.
4. Remove converter inlet pipe to exhaust manifold attaching nuts and position pipe aside.
5. Remove oil pan mounting bolts and carefully pry pan from stiffener.
6. Reverse procedure to install, applying a continuous bead of sealant around oil pan. Tighten to specifications.

OIL PUMP
REPLACE

1. Disconnect battery ground cable, then isolate cable end with electrical tape or equivalent.
2. Remove power steering pump belt shield, then loosen adjusting bolt.
3. Loosen lock bolt and power steering pump through bolt, then remove power steering belt.
4. Loosen alternator adjusting bolt, then loosen alternator upper mounting bolt and remove alternator belt.

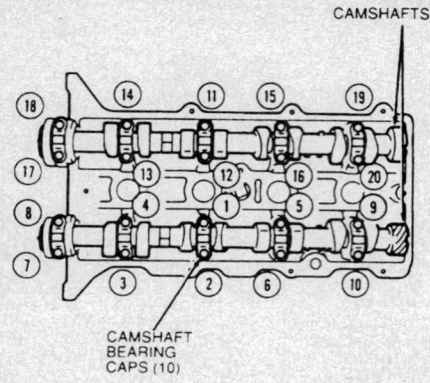

Fig. 19 Camshaft bearing cap tightening sequence

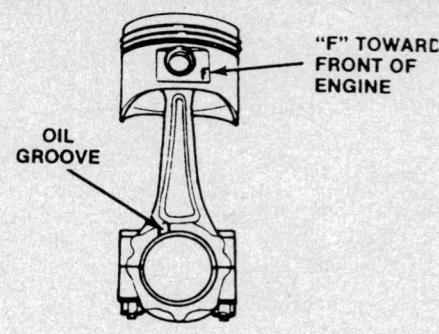

Fig. 20 Piston & rod assembly

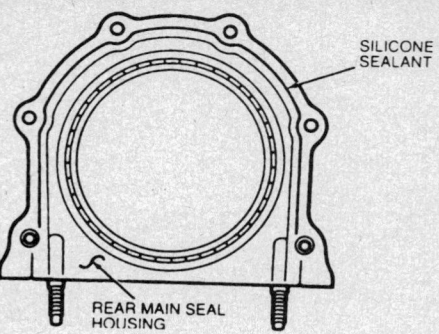

Fig. 21 Rear main seal housing sealant application

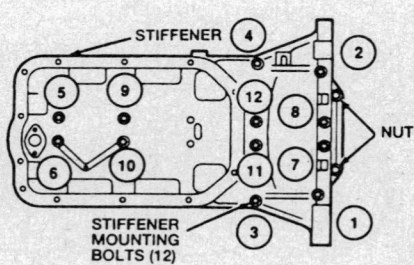

Fig. 22 Stiffener bolt loosening sequence

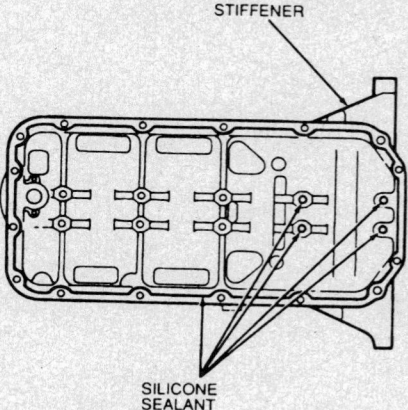

Fig. 23 Stiffener sealant application

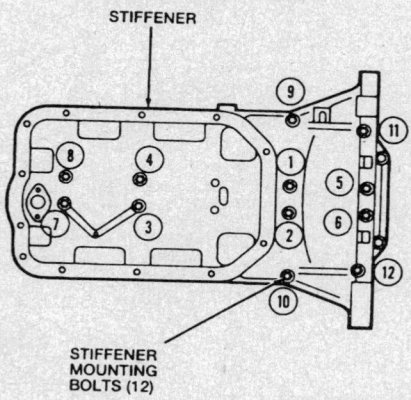

Fig. 24 Stiffener bolt tightening sequence

Drive Belt	New N (lb)	Used N (lb)	Limit N (lb)
GENERATOR	740-830 (170-180)	500-680 (110-150)	390 (88)
P/S, P/S + A/C	590-780 (140-170)	500-680 (110-150)	390 (88)

Fig. 25 Belt tension specifications

5. Raise and support vehicle, then remove righthand splash shield.
6. Using crankshaft pulley holder tool No. T92C-6316-AH or equivalent, remove crankshaft pulley attaching bolt.
7. Remove crankshaft pulley, sprocket and guide plate.
8. Remove A/C compressor and position aside, then the compressor mounting bracket.
9. Remove oil pan as described under "Oil Pan, Replace."
10. Remove oil pickup tube and discard gasket.
11. Remove rear main seal housing to stiffener attaching bolts.
12. Remove stiffener mounting bolts in two steps using sequence shown in **Fig. 22.**
13. Remove seven oil pump attaching bolts, then the pump.
14. Reverse procedure to install, noting the following:
    a. Apply a bead of silicone sealer to pump as shown in **Fig. 23.**
    b. **Torque** stiffener mounting bolts in sequence shown **Fig. 24,** to 14-19 ft. lbs.

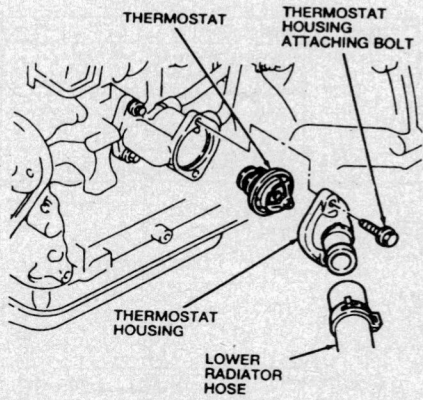

Fig. 26 Thermostat replacement

BELT TENSION DATA

Refer to **Fig. 25** for correct belt tension.

COOLING SYSTEM BLEED

This engine does not require a specific bleed procedure. After filling cooling system, run engine to operating temperature with radiator/pressure cap off. Air will automatically bleed through cap opening.

THERMOSTAT
REPLACE

1. Disconnect battery ground cable, then isolate cable end with electrical tape or equivalent.
2. Drain cooling system, then remove lower radiator hose from thermostat housing, **Fig. 26.**
3. Remove two thermostat housing attaching bolts, then the housing.
4. Remove thermostat from housing.
5. Reverse procedure to install. Tighten to specifications.

WATER PUMP
REPLACE

1. Disconnect battery ground cable, then isolate cable end with electrical tape or equivalent.
2. Drain cooling system.
3. Remove power steering pump belt shield, then loosen adjusting bolt.
4. Loosen lock bolt and power steering pump through bolt, then remove power steering belt.
5. Loosen alternator adjusting bolt, then loosen alternator upper mounting bolt and remove alternator belt.
6. Remove cylinder head cover as described under "Cylinder Head Cover, Replace."
7. Raise and support vehicle.
8. Using water pump pulley tool No. T92C-6312-AH or equivalent, remove water pump pulley.
9. Remove splash shields, then the timing belt as described under "Timing Belt, Replace."

10. Remove five water pump attaching bolts, then the water pump.
11. Reverse procedure to install. Tighten to specifications.

RADIATOR
REPLACE

Allow radiator to cool prior to beginning the following procedure. Slowly remove radiator cap to release system pressure. **Caution must be used as system contains scalding hot fluid which when under pressure can blow out of the radiator fill neck, causing personal injury.**
1. Disconnect battery ground cable.
2. Slowly remove radiator cap, then open drain valve at bottom of radiator and drain system.
3. Remove fresh air duct.
4. Remove upper and lower radiator hoses.
5. Disconnect overflow hose.
6. Disconnect cooling fan motor electrical connector.
7. **On models equipped with automatic transaxle,** disconnect transaxle oil cooler lines at radiator and plug hose ends to prevent leakage.
8. **On all models,** Remove radiator mounting brackets.
9. Remove radiator and cooling fan assembly from vehicle.
10. Reverse procedure to install, noting the following:
   a. **Torque** radiator mounting bracket bolts to 14–18 ft. lbs.
   b. Check and fill cooling system and transaxle fluid levels.

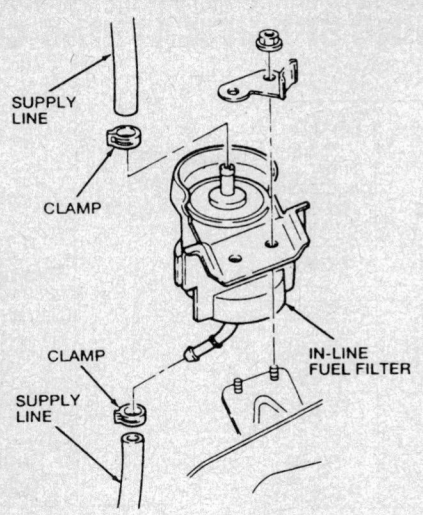

FM1029100149000X

Fig. 27 Fuel filter replacement

c. Operate engine until normal engine coolant temperature is reached and check for leaks.

FUEL PUMP
REPLACE

1. Relieve fuel system pressure as described under "Fuel Pressure Relief."
2. Disconnect battery ground cable.
3. Drain fuel from fuel tank, then raise and support vehicle.
4. Loosen filler neck hose clamp and remove hose.
5. Loosen overflow hose clamp and remove hose.

6. Loosen fuel supply and return line clamps and remove hoses.
7. Loosen two fuel tank vapor line clamps and remove hoses.
8. Disconnect fuel pump sender electrical connector from body harness mating connector.
9. Remove four attaching nuts on exhaust heat shield.
10. Remove one attaching nut on fuel tank shield.
11. Support fuel tank and remove center fuel tank strap.
12. Remove righthand fuel tank strap, then the fuel tank shield.
13. Remove lefthand fuel tank strap, then the tank.
14. Using a hammer and chisel, remove fuel pump lock ring.
15. Remove fuel pump assembly from tank.
16. Reverse procedure to install.

FUEL FILTER
REPLACE

1. Relieve fuel system pressure as described under "Fuel Pressure Relief."
2. Disconnect battery ground cable.
3. Remove two fuel filter mounting nuts on fuel filter bracket, **Fig. 27.**
4. Remove supply line clamps, then disconnect supply lines from both ends of the filter. **Plug lines to prevent leakage.**
5. Remove fuel filter from mounting bracket.
6. Reverse procedure to install. Tighten to specifications.

TIGHTENING SPECIFICATIONS

Year	Component	Torque/Ft. Lbs.
1993–95	A/C Compressor Mounting Bolts	18–26
	A/C Compressor Mounting Bracket	27–38
	Alternator Bracket	14–19
	Alternator Lower Through Bolt	27–38
	Alternator Upper Mounting Bolt	14–18
	Battery Tray Mounting Bolt	71–88 ①
	Camshaft Bearing Cap Bolts	②
	Camshaft Sprocket	36–45
	Coolant Return Pipe Mounting Bracket	14–19
	Coolant Temperature Sensor Housing	14–19
	Connecting Rod Bearing Cap Bolts	③
	Converter Inlet Pipe To Exhaust Manifold	27–38
	Crankshaft Pulley Attaching Bolt	116–123
	Crankshaft Rear Cover	71–88 ①
	Cylinder Head Bolts	②
	Cylinder Head Cover	②
	Distributor	14–19
	EGR Pipe To Exhaust Manifold	24–34
	Engine Mount Bracket Attaching Bolt	32–45

Year	Component	Torque/Ft. Lbs.
1993–95 —Cont'd	Engine Mount Attaching Nuts	54–75
	Engine Mount Through Bolts	63–86
	Exhaust Manifold Bolts	12–17
	Exhaust Manifold Heat Shield	71–88 ①
	Exhaust Manifold Nuts	14–21
	Exhaust Support Attaching Bolt	27–38
	Extension Bar Nut	28–38
	Flex Plate	70–75
	Flywheel	70–75
	Fuel Filter Bracket	71–97 ①
	Idler Bolt	27–38
	Intake Manifold Support Bracket	27–38
	LH Transaxle Mount Nuts	50–68
	LH Transaxle Mount Through Bolt	63–86
	Main Bearing Cap Bolts	④
	Oil Drain Plug	22–30
	Oil Pan Mounting Bolts	14–19
	Oil Pickup Tube Mounting Bolts	71–88 ①
	Oil Pressure Sensor	105–156 ①
	Oil Pump Attaching Bolts	14–19

Continued

TIGHTENING SPECIFICATIONS-Continued

Year	Component	Torque/Ft. Lbs.
1993-95 —Cont'd	Oxygen Sensor	22-36
	Power Steering Pump Belt Shield Attaching Bolts	61-86 ①
	Power Steering Hose Hold-Down Bracket Mounting Bolt	71-88 ①
	Power Steering Pump Lock Bolt	23-34
	Power Steering Pump Through Bolt	32-45
	Rear Main Seal Housing To Block	71-88 ①
	Rear Main Seal Housing To Stiffener Attaching Nuts	71-88 ①
	Rear Transaxle Mount Bolts	50-68
	Splash Shield Bolts	71-881 ①
	Starter	23-34
	Stiffener Mounting Bolts	②
	Thermostat Housing	14-19
	Timing Belt Tensioner Bolt	27-38

Year	Component	Torque/Ft. Lbs.
1993-95 —Cont'd	Timing Cover Bolts	71-88 ①
	Transaxle Cradle Nuts	②
	Transaxle Lower Mount Bolts	50-68
	Transaxle Shift Linkage Through Bolt	14-18
	Transaxle To Engine Block	②
	Transverse Member Bolts	68-96
	Water Pump Attaching Bolts	14-19
	Water Pump Pulley Attaching Bolts	71-88 ①
	Wheel Lug Nuts	65-86
	Engine Lifting Eye Attaching Bolts	27-38
	Water Bypass Pipe Mounting Bolt	14-19

①—Inch lbs.
②—Refer to text.
③—16–19 ft. lbs., then tighten an additional 85–95°.
④—13–16 ft. lbs.; then tighten an additional 90°.

2.2L/4-133 Engine

INDEX

PRECAUTIONS

FUEL SYSTEM PRESSURE RELIEF

On this engine, it is necessary to relieve the fuel system pressure before disconnecting any fuel lines or hoses.
1. Start engine.
2. Disconnect fuel pump relay, **Fig. 1.**
3. After the engine stalls, turn ignition switch OFF.
4. Reconnect fuel pump relay.

ENGINE MOUNT
REPLACE

Refer to "3.0L/V6-182 engine" section for engine mount replacement.

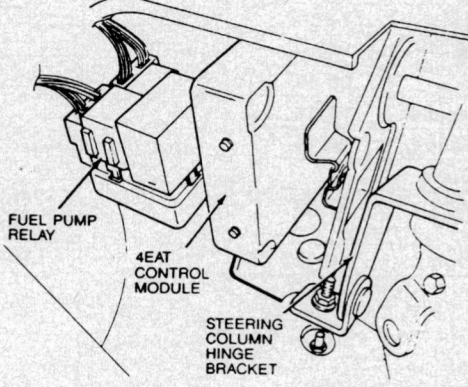

FUEL PUMP RELAY

4EAT CONTROL MODULE

STEERING COLUMN HINGE BRACKET

FM1029100150000X

Fig. 1   Fuel pump relay location

ENGINE
REPLACE

1. Relieve fuel system pressure as described under "Precautions."
2. Disconnect battery cables, then remove battery.
3. Mark hood hinge locations, then remove hood.
4. Drain cooling system, engine oil, automatic transaxle fluid and power steering fluid.
5. Disconnect or remove the following, **Fig. 2 and 3:**
   a. Battery carrier and fuse holder.
   b. Air filter assembly and duct.
   c. Accelerator cable, throttle valve cable and cruise control cable, if equipped.
   d. Engine and EFI wiring harnesses.

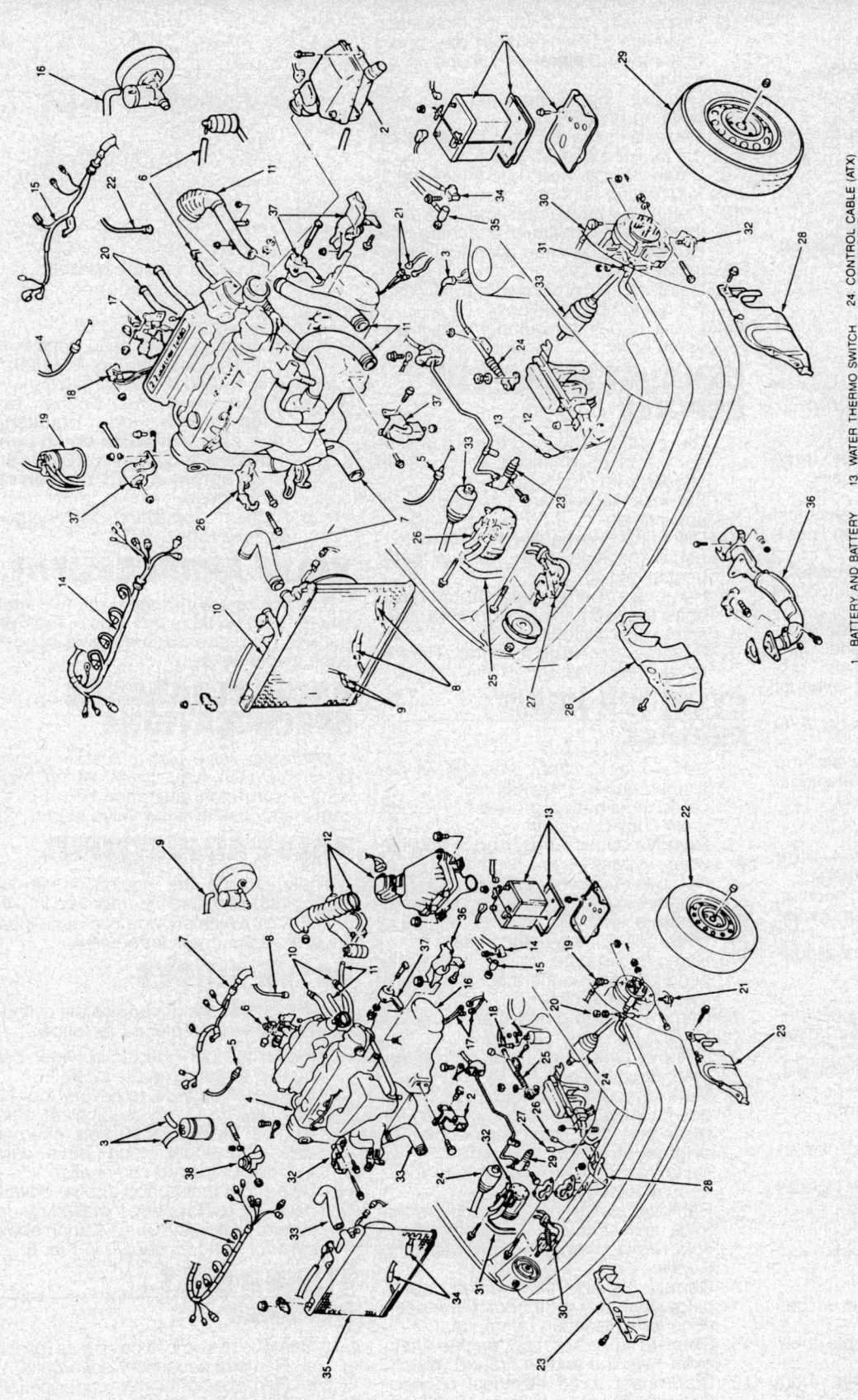

Fig. 3   Engine compartment component location. With turbo

1. BATTERY AND BATTERY CARRIER
2. AIR CLEANER ASSEMBLY
3. HIGH TENSION LEAD
4. ACCELERATOR CABLE
5. THROTTLE CABLE (ATX)
6. FUEL HOSE
7. RADIATOR HOSE
8. ATF HOSE (ATX)
9. RADIATOR HARNESS
10. RADIATOR AND ELEC-TRIC FAN
11. INTERCOOLER PIPE AND HOSE (TURBO)
12. HEAT GAUGE UNIT CONNECTOR
13. WATER THERMO SWITCH CONNECTOR
14. EGI HARNESS
15. BRAKE VACUUM HOSE
16. THREE-WAY SOLENOID ASSEMBLY
17. ASSEMBLY
18. EGR SOLENOID
19. CANISTER (TURBO)
20. HEATER HOSE
21. TRANSAXLE HARNESS
22. SPEEDOMETER CABLE
23. CLUTCH RELEASE CYLINDER (MTX)
24. CONTROL CABLE (ATX)
25. DRIVE BELT
26. A/C COMPRESSOR AND BRACKET
27. P/S OIL PUMP
28. INNER FENDER SPLASH GUARDS
29. FRONT WHEEL
30. TIE ROD END
31. STABILIZER CONTROL ROD
32. LOWER ARM BUSHING
33. DRIVESHAFT
34. CHANGE ROD (MTX)
35. EXTENSION BAR (MTX)
36. EXHAUST PIPE
37. ENGINE MOUNT

Fig. 2   Engine compartment component location. Less turbo

1. EFI HARNESS
2. ENGINE MOUNT #2
3. CANISTER HOSE
4. ENGINE AND TRANSAXLE
5. ACCELERATOR CABLE
6. THREE-WAY SOLENOID ASSEMBLY
7. EGI HARNESS
8. SPEEDOMETER CABLE
9. BRAKE VACUUM HOSE
10. HEATER HOSE
11. FUEL HOSE
12. AIR CLEANER ASSEMBLY
13. BATTERY AND BATTERY CARRIER
14. CHANGE ROD (MTX)
15. EXTENSION BAR (MTX)
16. TRANSAXLE
17. TRANSAXLE HARNESS
18. HIGH TENSION LEAD
19. STABILIZER CONTROL ROD
20. ROD
21. LOWER ARM BUSHING
22. FRONT WHEEL
23. ENGINE SIDE COVER
24. HALFSHAFT
25. CONTROL CABLE (ATX)
26. HEAT GAUGE UNIT CONNECTOR
27. RADIATOR TEMPERATURE SWITCH
28. EXHAUST PIPE
29. CLUTCH RELEASE CYLINDER (MTX)
30. POWER STEERING OIL PUMP
31. DRIVE BELT
32. A/C COMPRESSOR AND BRACKET
33. RADIATOR HOSE
34. ATF HOSE (ATX)
35. RADIATOR AND COOLING FAN
36. ENGINE MOUNT #4
37. ENGINE MOUNT #1
38. ENGINE MOUNT #3

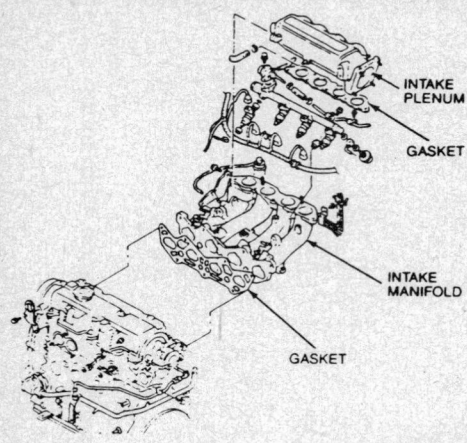

Fig. 4   Intake manifold & plenum

e. Distributor wiring at coil and three sensors at thermostat housing
f. Oxygen sensor.
g. Radiator and cooling fan electrical connectors, then radiator and cooling fan from vehicle.
h. **On automatic transaxle models,** disconnect transaxle oil cooler lines.
i. **On manual transaxle models,** remove clutch release cylinder.
j. **On turbocharged models,** disconnect front section of exhaust pipe.
k. **On all models,** discharge A/C system.
l. A/C lines on compressor and the A/C compressor clutch electrical connector.
m. Power steering lines.
n. Engine ground strap.
o. Heater hoses and fuel lines. **Plug fuel lines to prevent leakage.**
p. Vacuum lines to brake booster, charcoal canister, firewall mounted solenoids and distributor.
q. Automatic transaxle electrical connectors.
r. Speedometer cable.
6. **On turbocharged models,** disconnect and remove turbocharger hoses and pipe.
7. **On all models,** remove driveshafts, then the transaxle shift cable or rod.
8. Install engine lifting equipment.
9. Remove engine mounts.
10. Remove engine and transaxle as an assembly from vehicle.
11. Reverse procedure to install. Tighten to specifications.

INTAKE MANIFOLD
REPLACE

1. Relieve fuel system pressure as described under "Precautions."
2. Disconnect battery ground cable, then drain cooling system.
3. Remove air cleaner assembly, then the accelerator cable.
4. Remove water hose from bottom of intake manifold.
5. Remove intake plenum, **Fig. 4.**

6. Disconnect and mark for installation reference EGR pipe, then any hoses that may interfere with manifold removal.
7. Remove intake manifold attaching bolts and nuts.
8. Remove intake manifold bracket, then the intake manifold, **Fig. 4.**
9. Clean cylinder head and intake manifold mating surfaces.
10. Install new intake manifold gasket.
11. Install intake manifold, attaching nuts and bolts. Tighten to specifications.
12. Install intake plenum.
13. Install intake manifold bracket, then tighten to specifications.
14. Install remaining components in reverse order.

EXHAUST MANIFOLD
REPLACE

1. Disconnect exhaust gas oxygen sensor electrical connector, then remove sensor from manifold.
2. Remove turbocharger assembly, if applicable.
3. Disconnect exhaust pipe from exhaust manifold, then remove outer heat shield.
4. Remove exhaust manifold attaching bolts, the exhaust manifold, inner heat shield and gaskets.
5. Reverse procedure to install. Tighten to specifications.

CYLINDER HEAD
REPLACE

1. Relieve fuel system pressure as described under "Precautions."
2. Disconnect battery ground cable, then drain cooling system.
3. Remove upper radiator hose and the water bypass hose.
4. Remove accessory drive belts.
5. Remove righthand inner fender panel.
6. Remove crankshaft pulley attaching bolts, pulley, then baffle plate.
7. Remove two nuts, dowels from right-hand engine mount, then the engine mount from vehicle.
8. Remove seven timing belt cover attaching bolts, then the cover.
9. Remove timing belt tensioner, spring, then attaching bolt.
10. Mark direction of rotation on timing belt for installation reference, then remove belt. **Belt must be installed in original direction of rotation.**
11. Remove rocker arm cover, then rocker shaft assembly.
12. Remove intake and exhaust manifolds as described under "Intake Manifold, Replace" and "Exhaust Manifold, Replace."
13. Remove spark plug wires, spark plugs, then the distributor. Mark positions for installation reference.
14. Remove front and rear engine lifting eyes, then the engine ground wire.
15. Disconnect three electrical connectors from thermostat housing.
16. Remove cylinder head attaching bolts, cylinder head and the gasket.
17. Reverse procedure to install, noting

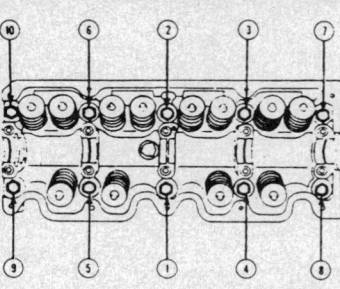

Fig. 5   Cylinder head bolt tightening sequence

the following
a. **Torque** cylinder head bolts in sequence shown in **Fig. 5**, to 29-32 ft. lbs., then to 59-64 ft. lbs.
b. **When installing timing belt, align mark on crankshaft sprocket with mark on oil pump housing and align mark on camshaft sprocket with mark on cylinder head.**
c. Tighten remaining fasteners to specifications.

VALVE ARRANGEMENT

The valves are arranged with two intake valves, both on the same side of the cylinder head and one exhaust valve, opposite each intake valve.

VALVE CLEARANCE SPECIFICATIONS

Hydraulic valve lash adjusters provide automatic lash adjustment which maintains a zero inch clearance between the camshaft lobes and the valve stems.

VALVE ADJUSTMENT

These engine are equipped with hydraulic lash adjusters incorporated into the rocker arm, which provide zero lash clearance. No adjustment is required.

VALVE GUIDES

Valve guides are driven into the cylinder head and can be replaced as follows.

1. Place cylinder head in a water bath heated to approximately 190°F.
2. Using valve guide removing tool No. T87C-6510-A or equivalent, and working from combustion chamber side of cylinder head, drive valve guides out toward camshaft.
3. Using tool mentioned above, drive in new guides. Properly installed guides should protrude .752-.772 inch above cylinder head as shown in **Fig. 6.**

TIMING BELT
REPLACE

1. Remove timing belt covers as follows:
   a. Remove accessory drive belts.
   b. Remove right inner fender panel.
   c. Remove bolts, the crankshaft pulley, then the baffle plate.
   d. Support engine.
   e. Remove attaching nuts and dow-

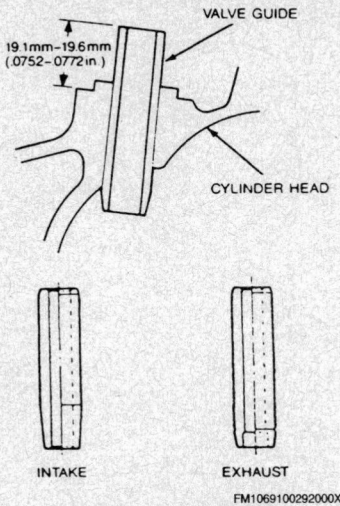

Fig. 6 Valve guide installation

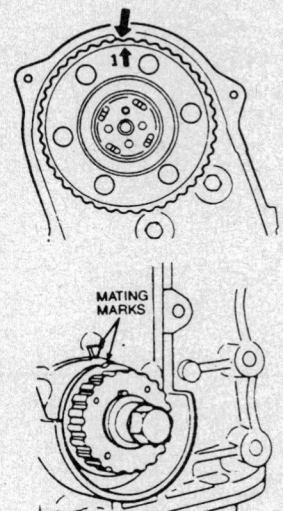

Fig. 7 Valve timing mark alignment

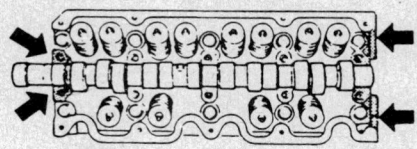

Fig. 8 Cylinder head sealant application

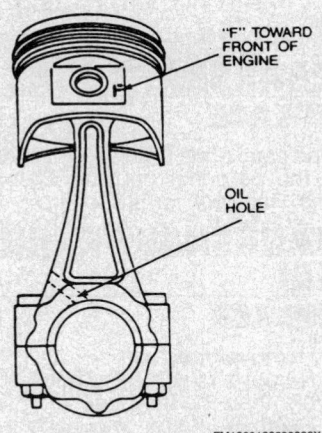

Fig. 10 Piston to connecting rod assembly

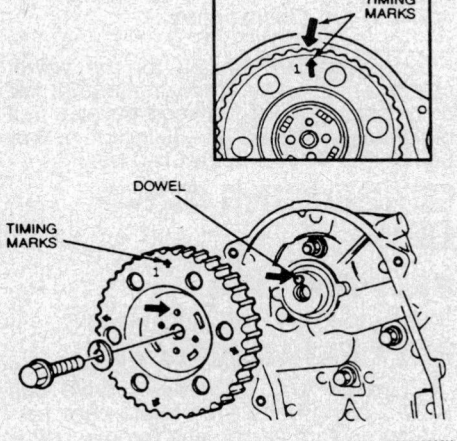

Fig. 9 Camshaft sprocket installation

els from right engine mount, then remove mount from engine.

f. Remove attaching bolts and upper and lower covers as needed.

2. Remove timing belt tensioner spring, retaining bolt, then the tensioner.
3. Mark direction of rotation on timing belt, then remove timing belt from engine. **Belt must be installed in original direction.**
4. Align camshaft sprocket timing mark with mark on cylinder head and crankshaft sprocket timing mark with mark on oil pump housing, **Fig. 1.**
5. Install timing belt. If reusing old belt, ensure belt is installed with rotation mark in same direction as noted in step 3.
6. Place timing belt tensioner and spring in position, then temporarily secure tensioner with spring fully extended.
7. With timing belt securely positioned

against idler pulley side, loosen tensioner bolt and allow tensioner to retract.
8. Turn crankshaft two revolutions in normal direction of rotation, then ensure timing marks are still aligned, **Fig. 1.**
9. Tighten tensioner retaining bolt to specifications, then apply 22 lbs. of pressure to belt. Measure belt deflection between idler pulley and camshaft sprocket. Belt deflection should be .30-.33 inch.
10. If belt deflection is not as specified, repeat steps 6 through 9. If deflection is still not as specified, replace tensioner.
11. Reverse procedure to install.

CAMSHAFT
REPLACE

1. Remove timing belt as described under "Timing Belt, Replace."
2. Remove rocker cover and the front and rear housings.
3. Prevent camshaft sprocket from rotating using a screwdriver, remove retaining bolt, then sprocket.
4. Remove rocker arm shaft assembly retaining bolts and the rocker shaft, then camshaft bearing caps.
5. Lift camshaft upward, then remove from cylinder head.
6. Clean camshaft journals, then position camshaft into cylinder head.
7. Position plasti-gauge on camshaft

journals and install bearing caps, then rocker shaft assembly. **Torque** rocker shaft retaining bolts in two steps to 13-20 ft. lbs., remove shaft, bearing caps, then measure bearing clearance. Bearing clearance should be .0014-.0033 inch for front and rear journals, or .0026-.0045 inch for the three center journals. Maximum clearance should not exceed .0059 inch. If bearing clearance is not as specified, replace cylinder head and/or camshaft.
8. Apply silicone sealant to areas shown, **Fig. 8,** then reinstall bearing caps, rocker shaft, then **torque** shaft retaining bolts in two steps to 13-20 ft. lbs. Install front and rear housings.
9. Install camshaft sprocket, aligning No. 1 mark on sprocket with dowel on camshaft, **Fig. 9.**
10. Install sprocket retaining bolt, prevent sprocket from rotating, then tighten retaining bolt to specifications.
11. Install timing belt, then rocker cover to complete installation.

PISTON & ROD ASSEMBLY

Assemble piston to connecting rod with F mark on piston and oil hole in connecting rod positioned as shown, **Fig. 10.**

PISTONS, PINS & RINGS

Pistons and rings are available in standard sizes, then .010 and .020 inch oversizes. Piston pins are available in standard size only. Maximum piston to bore clearance should not exceed .006 inch.

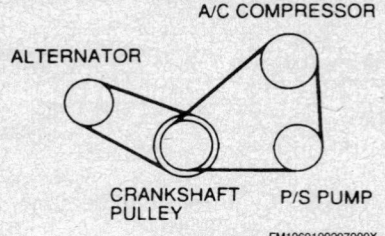

Fig. 11   Belt routing

CRANKSHAFT SEAL
REPLACE

The crankshaft front seal is incorporated into the oil pump housing. Refer to "Oil Pump, Replace" for procedure.

CRANKSHAFT REAR OIL SEAL
REPLACE

1. Remove transaxle.
2. Remove clutch assembly, if applicable, then the flywheel.
3. Remove starter mounting plate as necessary.
4. Remove crankshaft rear oil seal retainer, then press seal from retainer.
5. Clean seal retainer surface, then coat new seal with engine oil.
6. Position seal into retainer with hollow side of seal facing engine, then drive seal into retainer using rear crank seal replacer tool No. T88C-6701-BH or equivalent.
7. Install seal retainer using new gasket, then tighten retainer attaching bolts to specifications.
8. Trim excess gasket material from retainer.
9. Install starter mounting plate, then **torque** retaining bolts to 14-22 ft. lbs.
10. Install clutch assembly, if applicable, then the flywheel.
11. Install transaxle.

OIL PAN
REPLACE

1. Disconnect battery ground cable, then raise and support vehicle.
2. Remove splash shield from right inner fenderwell, then drain engine oil.
3. Remove engine to flywheel housing support bracket.
4. Disconnect front section of exhaust pipe, then remove exhaust pipe support.
5. Remove flywheel housing dust cover.
6. Remove oil pan attaching bolts and lower pan.
7. Disconnect oil strainer from pump, then drop into pan.
8. Remove oil pan with oil strainer, then the stiffener.
9. Clean mounting surfaces on cylinder block, oil pan, and stiffener.
10. Apply continuous bead of silicone sealer to both sides of stiffener on inside edge of bolt holes.
11. Install stiffener, oil strainer, then the oil

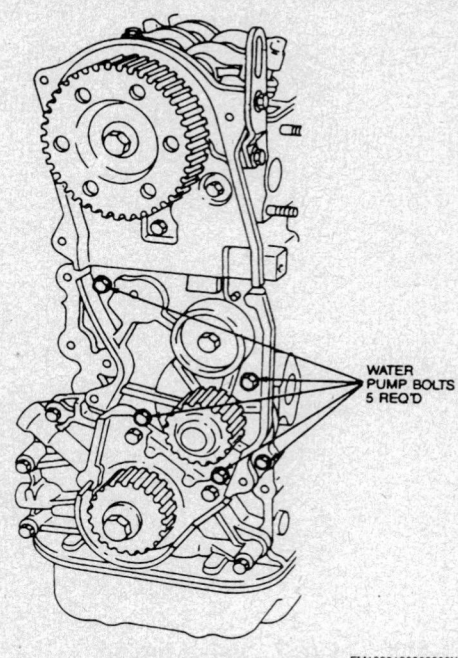

Fig. 12   Water pump mounting bolt location

pan. Tighten pan attaching bolts to specifications.
12. Perform steps 1 through 4 in reverse order to complete installation.

OIL PUMP
REPLACE

1. Remove timing belt as described under "Timing Belt, Replace."
2. Remove crankshaft sprocket retaining bolt, then the sprocket and key.
3. Remove oil pan as described under "Oil Pan, Replace."
4. With oil strainer disconnected from pump, remove pump to cylinder block bolts and pump, then the gasket.
5. Pry front crankshaft seal from pump using screwdriver, then clean seal bore.
6. Using front crank seal replacer tool No. T88C-6701-AH or equivalent, install new seal.
7. If reusing old pump, install new O-ring into pump body.
8. Apply continuous bead of silicone sealer to contact surface of oil pump. **Ensure sealer does not enter into outlet hole in pump or cylinder block.**
9. Install oil pump and gasket, tightening to specifications.
10. Perform steps 1 through 4 in reverse order to complete installation. Tightening crankshaft sprocket retaining bolt to specifications.

BELT TENSION DATA

To check belt tension for the alternator belt, apply approximately 22 lbs. of pressure to belt. Belt deflection should be .27-.35 inch for a used belt or .27-.35 inch for a new belt.

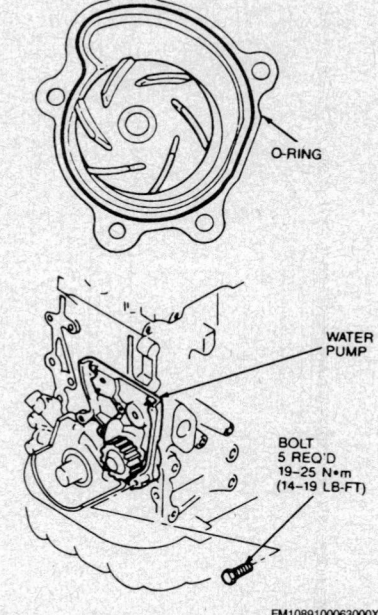

Fig. 13   Water pump O-ring positioning

To check belt tension for the power steering belt, apply approximately 22 lbs. of pressure to belt between pulleys. Belt deflection should be .31-.39 inch for a new belt or .35-.43 inch for a used belt.

SERPENTINE DRIVE BELT

BELT ROUTING

Refer to **Fig. 11.** for belt routing.

BELT REPLACEMENT

1. Loosen A/C compressor drive belt adjusting bolts, then rotate compressor toward engine and remove belt.
2. Loosen alternator pivot bolt and adjuster bolt, then rotate alternator toward engine and remove drive belt(s).
3. Reverse procedure to install.

COOLING SYSTEM BLEED

This engine does not require a specified bleed procedure. After filling cooling system, run engine to operating temperature with radiator/pressure cap off. Air will then be automatically bled through the cap opening.

THERMOSTAT
REPLACE

1. Drain radiator to below level of thermostat.
2. Disconnect coolant temperature switch at thermostat housing.
3. Using pliers, clamp hose clamps, then slide toward center of hose.
4. Remove upper radiator hose.
5. Remove two attaching nuts, thermostat housing, thermostat and gasket.

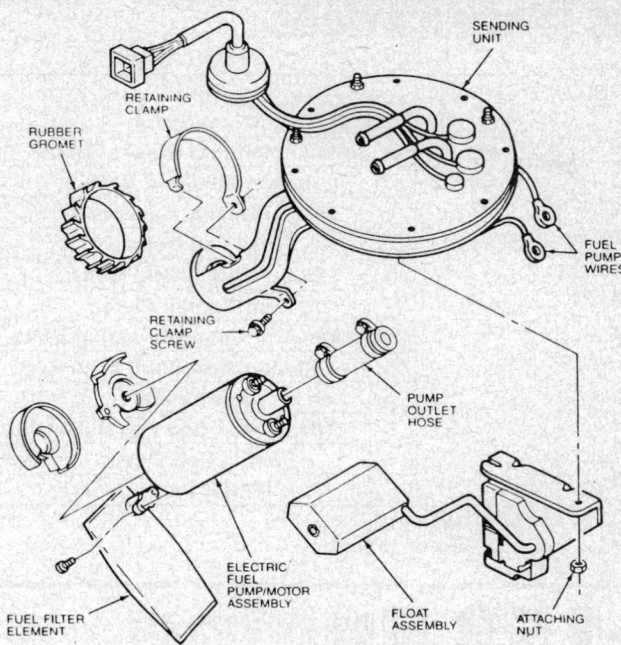

Fig. 14   Fuel sending unit & pump

FM1029100151000X

Do not pry housing off.

6. Reverse procedure to install, noting the following:
   a. Install new thermostat gasket.
   b. Tighten to specifications.

WATER PUMP
REPLACE

1. Drain cooling system.
2. Remove timing belt as described under "Timing Belt, Replace."
3. Remove water pump attaching bolts, then the water pump and O-ring, **Fig. 12.**
4. Clean water pump, then the cylinder block mating surface.
5. Position new O-ring on water pump as shown, **Fig. 13.**
6. Install water pump and attaching bolts. Tighten bolts to specifications.
7. Install timing belt and covers, then fill cooling system.

RADIATOR
REPLACE

Allow radiator to cool prior to beginning the following procedure. Slowly remove radiator cap to release system pressure. **Caution must be used as system contains scalding hot fluid which when under pressure can blow out of the radiator fill neck, causing personal injury.**

1. Disconnect battery ground cable.
2. Slowly remove radiator cap, then open drain valve at bottom of radiator and drain system.
3. Remove fresh air duct.
4. Remove upper and lower radiator hoses.
5. Remove radiator overflow hose.
6. Remove coolant expansion tank.

7. Disconnect cooling fan motor and A/C condenser cooling fan motor electrical connectors.
8. **On models equipped with automatic transaxle,** disconnect transaxle oil cooler lines at radiator and plug hose ends to prevent leakage.
9. **On all models,** remove radiator mounting brackets.
10. Move the air bag electrical wiring harness to allow clearance for radiator removal.
11. Remove radiator, engine cooling fan, and A/C cooling fan from the vehicle as an assembly.
12. Reverse procedure to install, noting the following:
    a. **Torque** radiator mounting bracket bolts to 14–18 ft. lbs.
    b. Check and fill cooling system and transaxle fluid levels.
    c. **Torque** fan shroud bolts to 71–88 inch lbs.
    d. Operate engine until normal engine coolant temperature is reached and check for leaks.

FUEL PUMP
REPLACE

The electric fuel pump is located in the fuel tank and is integral with the fuel sending unit.

1. Relieve fuel system pressure as outlined at the beginning of this section.
2. Disconnect battery ground cable.
3. Remove rear seat cushion.
4. Disconnect fuel sending unit electrical connector.
5. Remove sending unit access cover attaching screws, then the access cover.
6. Remove clamps, disconnect fuel supply, then return hoses from sending

unit.
7. Remove sending unit attaching screws, then the sending unit.
8. Disassemble sending unit to remove pump as shown in **Fig. 14.**
9. Reverse procedure to install.

FUEL FILTER
REPLACE

The in-line fuel filter is located in the engine compartment, in the fuel rail supply line.

1. Relieve fuel system pressure, refer to "Relieving Fuel System Pressure" procedure at the front of this section.
2. Remove supply clamps, then the fuel lines from both ends of filter assembly.
3. Remove filter from mounting bracket.
4. Reverse procedure to install.

TURBOCHARGER
REPLACE

1. Disconnect battery ground cable, then drain cooling system.
2. Remove inlet and outlet air hoses from turbocharger assembly.
3. Remove heat shields from exhaust manifold and turbocharger assembly. **It may be necessary to disconnect EGO sensor electrical connector to remove heat shield from turbocharger.**
4. Disconnect oil feed and return lines, the coolant inlet, then outlet hoses from turbocharger assembly.
5. Remove EGR tube from exhaust manifold.
6. Disconnect turbo boost control solenoid valve electrical connector, then remove air tube from solenoid valve at turbocharger outlet air hose.
7. Remove mounting bolt from retaining bracket under turbocharger assembly.
8. Discharge A/C system, if applicable, then disconnect refrigerant lines from compressor.
9. Remove EGO sensor from exhaust manifold.
10. Disconnect converter inlet pipe from turbocharger joint pipe.
11. Remove exhaust manifold attaching bolts, then the exhaust manifold and turbocharger as an assembly.
12. Reverse procedure to install, noting the following:
    a. Before connecting oil feed line, fill turbocharger inlet fitting with approximately 1 ounce of engine oil.
    b. Before starting engine, disconnect electrical connector from ignition coil, then crank engine for 20 seconds. Reconnect connector to coil and start engine, then allow to idle for approximately 30 seconds. Stop engine, disconnect battery ground cable, then depress brake pedal for at least 5 seconds before reconnecting cable. **The preceding procedure must be performed to cancel the malfunction code that will be stored in the computer memory.**

TIGHTENING SPECIFICATIONS

Year	Component	Torque/Ft. Lbs.
1992	Camshaft Sprocket Bolt	35–48
	Connecting Rod Nuts	48–51
	Crankshaft Pulley Bolts	109–152 ①
	Crankshaft Seal Retainer Bolts	69–104 ①
	Crankshaft Sprocket	108–116
	Crankshaft To Flywheel Bolts	71–76
	Crankshaft To Flywheel Support Bracket Bolts	27–38
	Cylinder Head Bolts	②
	Exhaust Manifold Bolts	16–21
	Exhaust Pipe To Exhaust Manifold Bolts	23–34
	Front/Rear Housing	14–19
	Flywheel Housing Dust Cover Bolts	49–95 ①
	Flywheel Housing Support Bracket Bolts	27–38

Year	Component	Torque/Ft. Lbs.
1992 —Cont'd	Intake Manifold Bracket Bolts	14–22
	Intake Manifold Bolts	14–22
	Main Bearing Cap Bolts	61–65
	Oil Pan Bolts	69–104 ①
	Outer Heat Shield Bolts	14–22
	Rear Engine Plate	14–22
	Rocker Arm Cover Retaining Bolts	52–69 ①
	Rocker Arm Shaft Bolt	13–20
	Spark Plug	11–17
	Thermostat Housing Bolts	14–22
	Timing Belt Cover	61–87 ①
	Water Pump	14–19

①—Inch lbs.
②—Refer to text.

2.5L/V6-152 Engine

NOTE: On Air Bag Equipped Models, Refer To "Air Bag System Precautions" Located In The Front Of This Manual For System Disarming & Arming Procedures.

INDEX

PRECAUTIONS
AIR BAG SYSTEMS

Refer to "Air Bag System Precautions" in the front of this manual for system disarming and arming procedures.

FUEL SYSTEM PRESSURE RELIEF

1. Start engine, then remove fuel pump relay from fuse box.
2. After engine stalls, turn ignition off and replace fuel pump relay.

ENGINE MOUNT
REPLACE

Refer to "Engine, Replace" procedure for engine mount replacement.

ENGINE
REPLACE
REMOVAL

1. Relieve fuel system pressure as described under "Precautions."
2. Remove battery and battery tray.
3. Remove fresh air duct and air cleaner assembly.
4. Raise and support vehicle.
5. Remove front tires and lower splash shields.
6. Remove six transverse member mounting bolts, then the transverse member.
7. Remove transaxle cradle attaching bolts and nuts, then the cradle.
8. Disconnect electrical connector from front oxygen sensor.
9. Remove three nuts from lefthand converter inlet pipe, then disconnect electrical connector from rear oxygen sensor.
10. Remove three nuts from rear exhaust manifold-to-converter inlet pipe flange.
11. **On models with manual transaxle,** remove nut and washer, then remove extension bar from transaxle.
12. Remove transaxle shift linkage through-bolt and nut, then disconnect linkage from transaxle.
13. **On all models,** disconnect A/C and oil pressure switch electrical connectors.
14. **On models with manual transaxle,** remove slave cylinder hydraulic line from cylinder, then the spring clips from the line.

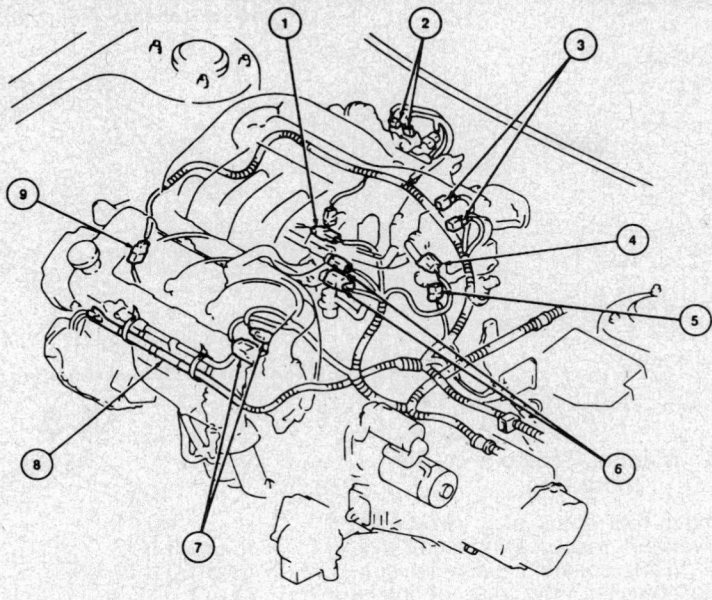

Item	Description
1	Knock Sensor
2	Variable Resonance Induction System (VRIS) Solenoids
3	EGR Control and Vent Solenoids
4	Throttle Position (TP) Sensor
5	Idle Air Control Bypass Air (IAC BPA)
6	Injector
7	Distributor
8	A/C and Generator Wiring Harness
9	Crankshaft Position (CKP) Sensor

FM1069100298000X

Fig. 1 Engine electrical connectors

15. Remove halfshafts as described in "Front Wheel Drive Axles" section.
16. Remove rear transaxle mount.
17. **On all models,** loosen center locknut on power steering/water pump belt tensioner, then loosen tensioner adjusting bolt and remove belt. Working through the pump pulley, remove three steering pump mounting bolts.
18. Separate steering pump from rear bracket, then position pump aside.
19. Remove A/C compressor from mounting bracket and position aside. **Leave refrigerant lines connected, but do not allow compressor to hang by them.**
20. Lower vehicle.
21. **On models with manual transaxle,** separate power steering hose bracket from steering pump, loosen generator and A/C belt tensioner locknut and adjusting bolt, then remove belt.
22. **On all models,** drain cooling system.
23. Disconnect coolant overflow hose from engine coolant overflow reservoir, then remove outlet (upper) hose from engine coolant elbow and disconnect radiator cooling fan connector.
24. Remove inlet (lower) hose from thermostat housing and the two radiator hold-down bolts.

25. Remove radiator and cooling fans.
26. Disconnect generator electrical connections. Label for installation reference.
27. Disconnect engine electrical and vacuum connections, **Fig. 1.** Label for installation reference.
28. Disconnect heater hoses from engine block, then the fuel supply line from fuel rails.
29. Disconnect accelerator cable from throttle body; then, with fuel lines connected, remove fuel filter and position aside.
30. Attach lifting cables to engine eye hooks and lift engine to tighten cables.
31. Remove left side transaxle mount nuts and through-bolt.
32. Remove both front transaxle mount nuts.
33. Remove two nuts and through bolt from righthand side engine mount, then the mount.
34. Remove engine and transaxle from vehicle. If necessary, separate engine from transaxle.

INSTALLATION
Manual Transaxle

1. Tighten engine to transaxle attaching bolts to specifications in sequence

shown in **Fig. 2.**
2. Lower engine and transaxle into engine compartment.
3. Install rear transaxle mount and tighten three nuts to specifications.
4. Install front and lefthand side transaxle mounts, then tighten mount nuts to specifications.
5. Install righthand engine mount and tighten nuts and through bolt to specifications.
6. Remove lift chains from engine eye hooks, then raise and support vehicle.
7. Install power steering pump and tighten mounting bolts to specifications.
8. Install drive belt over power steering and water pump pulleys, then tighten belt tensioner and center nut.
9. Install A/C compressor, tightening its mounting bolts to specifications, then position drive belt on A/C, crankshaft and generator pulleys. Tighten belt tensioner and center nut.
10. Align extension bar and **torque** nut to 23-33 ft. lbs., then install transaxle shift linkage and tighten bolt to specifications.
11. Install halfshafts as described in "Front Wheel Drive Axle" section.
12. Install transaxle cradle, then the attaching nuts and bolts as shown in **Fig. 3.** Tighten to specifications.
13. Install converter inlet pipes, tightening nuts to specifications.
14. Install transverse member and tighten mounting bolts to specifications.
15. Install splash shields and wheels, then lower vehicle.
16. Install power steering hose bracket retaining bolt at top of pump.
17. Connect electrical connectors and vacuum hoses, then install battery tray.
18. Connect throttle cable to throttle body, then the slave cylinder line to slave cylinder. Install slave cylinder line into two spring clips on bracket.
19. Install radiator and cooling fan assembly, then the radiator hoses.
20. Install battery tray and battery, then bleed clutch system.
21. Refill fluids, then check engine operation. Check for fluid loss.

Automatic Transaxle

1. **Torque** engine to transaxle attaching bolts to 50-73 ft. lbs. in sequence shown in **Fig. 4,** then lower engine and transaxle into vehicle.
2. Install righthand engine mount and tighten bolts and nuts to specifications.
3. Tighten lefthand transaxle mount through-bolt to specifications.
4. Remove lifting device, then raise and support vehicle.
5. Install front and rear transaxle mount through-bolts and tighten to specifications.
6. Lower vehicle, then align cooling fan relay bracket and install two bolts.
7. Connect shift cable to Manual Lever Position (MLP) switch and install spring clip.
8. Install fuel filter, then connect throttle cable to throttle body. Using a new

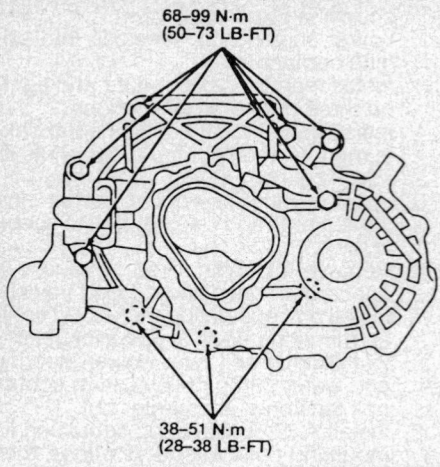

68–99 N·m
(50–73 LB-FT)

38–51 N·m
(28–38 LB-FT)

FM1069100299000X

**Fig. 2 Transaxle to engine
mounting bolts. Models w/manual
transaxle**

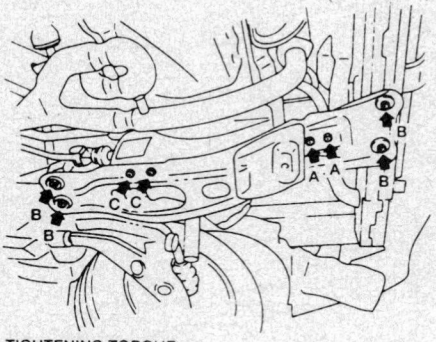

TIGHTENING TORQUE
A: 75 – 104 N·m (55 – 77 LB-FT)
B: 67 – 93 N·m (50 – 68 LB-FT)
C: 44 – 60 N·m (32 – 44 LB-FT)

FM1069100300000X

**Fig. 3 Manual transaxle cradle
mounting**

Transaxle-To-Engine Mounting Bolts

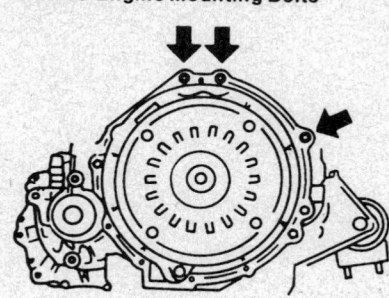

FM1069100301000X

**Fig. 4 Transaxle to engine
mounting. Models w/automatic
transaxle**

copper crush washer, install fuel rail supply line and **torque** line fitting to 18-25 ft. lbs.

9. Attach heater hoses to thermostat housing, then reconnect all disconnected electrical and vacuum connections.

10. Install radiator and cooling fan assembly, then the radiator hoses.

11. Install A/C compressor. Tighten bolts to specifications.

12. **Torque** power steering hose bracket-to-pump bolt to 23-34 ft. lbs., then working through the pump pulley install the three steering pump bolts and **torque** to 23-34 ft. lbs.

13. Install power steering/water pump belt, then raise and support vehicle and install halfshafts.

14. Connect converter inlet pipes to the exhaust manifolds and tighten attaching nuts to specifications.

15. Install transverse member and tighten bolts to specifications.

16. Install front splash shields and wheels, then lower vehicle.

17. Install generator/A/C belt and air cleaner case.

18. Install battery tray and battery, then refill fluids and check engine operation. Check for fluid loss.

INTAKE MANIFOLD
REPLACE

Refer to **Fig. 5** when replacing the intake manifold.

1. Relieve fuel system pressure as described under "Fuel System Pressure Relief", then disconnect battery ground cable and drain cooling system.

2. Disconnect vacuum hoses and electrical connectors from air cleaner assembly, then remove assembly.

3. Disconnect knock sensor electrical connector, then remove sensor bracket from intake manifold.

4. Remove crankshaft position sensor bracket from righthand side of intake manifold.

5. Remove rear spark plug wires, then the variable resource induction system (VRIS) solenoid electrical connector bracket from rear of intake manifold, **Fig. 6**.

6. Disconnect PCV valve vacuum hose from intake manifold, then the throttle position sensor and fuel rail electrical connectors.

7. Disconnect throttle cable from throttle body, then remove vacuum hose from fuel vapor canister.

8. Disconnect fuel supply line at fuel rails and discard copper crush washers, then remove vacuum and fuel lines from fuel pressure regulator.

9. Remove EGR breather tube, then the intake manifold bolts and nuts in two or three steps.

10. Reverse procedure to install, noting the following:
    a. Use two new copper crush washers when installing fuel rail supply line.
    b. Use new intake manifold gaskets.
    c. Tighten all bolts and nuts to specifications.

EXHAUST MANIFOLD
REPLACE

1. Disconnect battery ground cable, then raise and support vehicle.

2. Disconnect two oxygen sensor connectors, then remove three nuts at each exhaust manifold and lower exhaust system.

3. Remove three exhaust manifold insulator bolts, then the insulator.

4. Remove manifold retaining nuts and attaching bolts.

5. Reverse procedure to install, noting the following:
    a. Use a new gasket when installing manifold.
    b. **Torque** exhaust manifold insulator bolts to 71-88 inch lbs., then tighten manifold nuts and bolts to specifications.

CYLINDER HEAD
REPLACE

1. Drain cooling system, then remove timing belt covers and timing belt as described under "Timing Belt, Replace."

2. Remove intake manifold as described under "Intake Manifold, Replace."

3. Remove cylinder head covers as described under "Cylinder Head Cover, Replace."

4. Remove camshafts as described under "Camshaft, Replace."

5. Remove three seal plate bolts, then the seal plate, **Fig. 7**.

6. Remove coolant elbow, then raise and support vehicle.

7. Disconnect oxygen sensor connectors and lower catalytic converter inlet pipes, then lower the vehicle.

8. Remove hydraulic lash adjusters from cylinder head and mark them for installation reference. **Adjuster failure may result if reused adjusters are not returned to the bores from which they were removed.** Store adjusters intended for reuse upside-down in an oil-filled container.

9. Using sequence shown in **Fig. 8**, remove cylinder head bolts in two or three steps and **discard bolts**.

10. Remove cylinder head and discard gasket.

11. Reverse procedure to install, noting the following:
    a. Because left and right head gaskets are not interchangeable, ensure gasket identifying mark faces up when gasket is installed.
    b. Clean engine oil should be applied to lash adjuster friction surfaces.
    c. Adjusters to be reused must return to their original bores.
    d. Apply clean engine oil to threads of new cylinder head bolts.

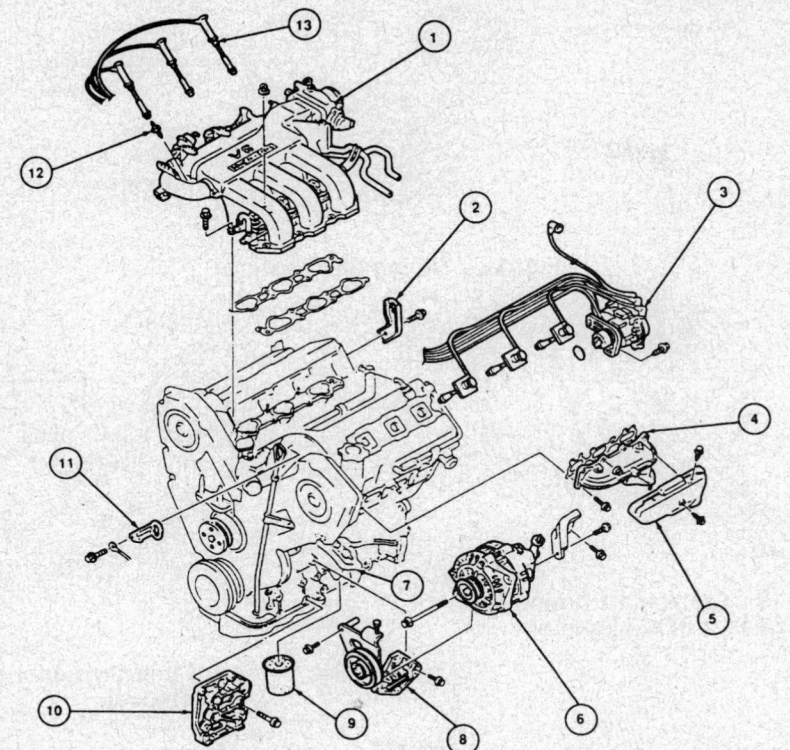

Item	Description
1	Throttle Body Assembly
2	Rear Engine Lifting Eye
3	Distributor and Spark Plug Wires
4	Front (LH) Exhaust Manifold
5	Front (LH) Exhaust Manifold Insulator
6	Generator
7	Oil Cooler Assembly
8	Bracket and Tensioner
9	Oil Filter
10	A / C Compressor Bracket
11	Front Engine Lifting Eye
12	Spark Plugs
13	Spark Plug Wires

FM1059100055000X

Fig. 5   Intake manifold

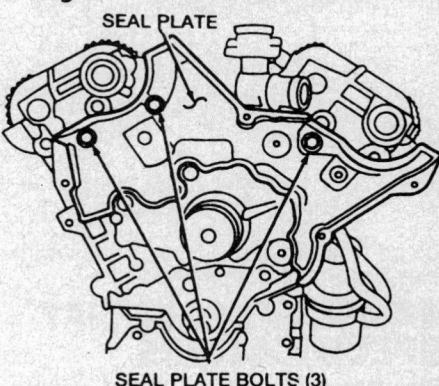

Fig. 6   VRIS bracket removal

FM1069100302000X

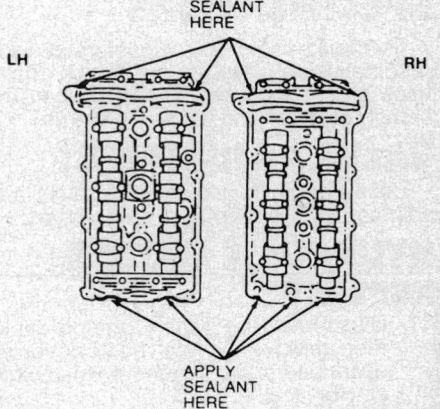

FM1069100305000X

Fig. 7   Seal plate bolt removal

FM1069100303000X

Fig. 10   Cylinder head sealant application

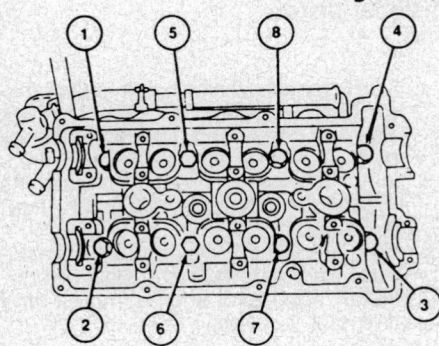

FM1069100306000X

Fig. 8   Cylinder head bolt removal

e. **Torque** cylinder head bolts in sequence shown in **Fig. 9** to 17-19 ft. lbs. in two or three steps, then place a small paint mark anywhere along the circumference of each bolt head and tighten bolts 85-95°. Final tighten all bolts an additional 85-95° in same sequence.

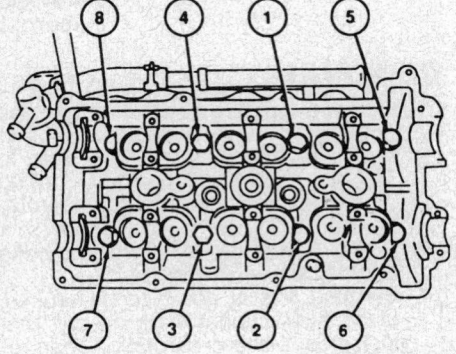

FM1069100307000X

Fig. 9   Cylinder head bolt tightening sequence

VALVE COVER
REPLACE

1. Remove intake manifold as described under "Intake Manifold, Replace."
2. Remove upper timing belt cover bolts.
3. Remove cylinder head cover bolts,

then the ventilation pipe from front cover.
4. Remove cylinder head cover and any remaining sealant or gasket material.
5. Reverse procedure to install, noting the following:
   a. Apply silicone sealant to areas shown in **Fig. 10**.
   b. Using sequence shown in **Fig. 11**, **torque** cover bolts in two steps to 43-78 inch lbs.
   c. Tighten upper timing belt cover bolts to 71-88 inch lbs.

VALVE ARRANGEMENT

The intake valves are situated on the in-

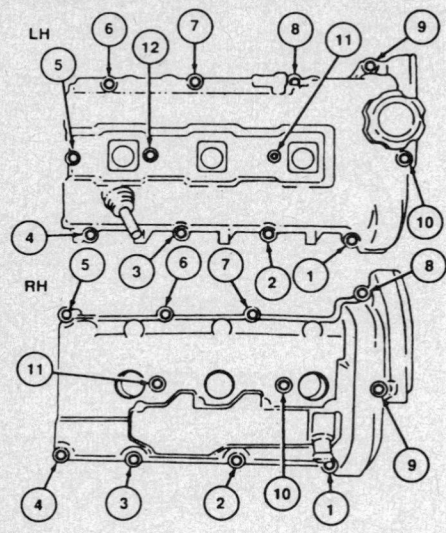

Fig. 11 Cylinder head cover bolt tightening sequence

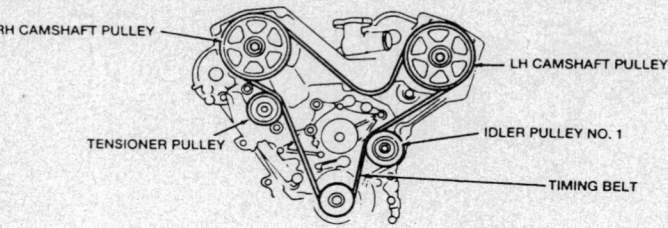

Fig. 12 Timing belt routing

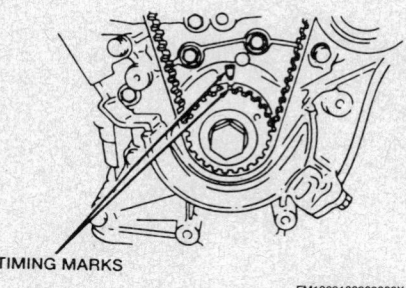

Fig. 13 Crankshaft timing belt gear to TDC alignment

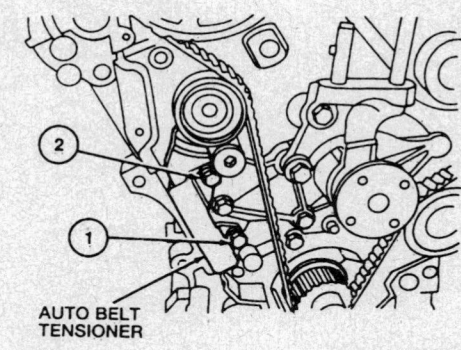

Fig. 14 Auto belt tensioner bolt removal

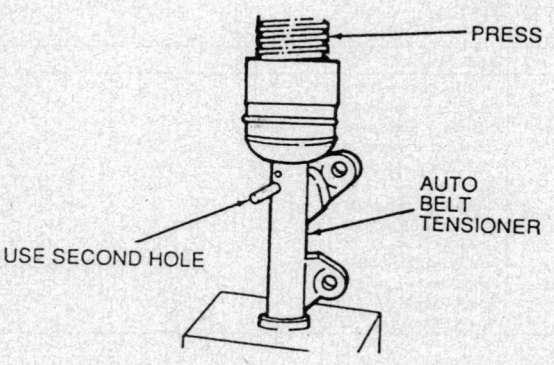

Fig. 15 Auto belt tensioner piston compressing

board side of each cylinder head and the exhaust on the outboard side.

CAMSHAFT LOBE LIFT SPECIFICATIONS

Standard	Wear Limit
1.7145	1.7067

VALVE CLEARANCE SPECIFICATIONS

Hydraulic valve lash adjusters provide automatic lash adjustment which maintains a zero inch clearance between the camshaft lobes and the valve stems.

VALVE ADJUSTMENT

Because this engine uses hydraulic lash adjusters, adjustment is not necessary.

HYDRAULIC LIFTERS
REPLACE

1. Disconnect the battery ground cable, then remove cylinder head cover as described under "Cylinder Head Cover, Replace."
2. Remove accessory drive belts, then the timing belt as described under "Timing Belt, Replace."
3. Remove camshafts as described under "Camshaft, Replace."
4. Remove hydraulic lash adjusters from cylinder head and, if any are to be reused, mark those for installation reference. **Adjuster failure may result if reused adjusters are not returned to the bores from which they were removed.**
5. Reverse procedure to install. **Coat friction surfaces with clean engine oil.**

TIMING BELT
REPLACE

Refer to **Fig. 12** when replacing timing belt.

REMOVAL

1. Remove timing belt covers, then the righthand engine mount.
2. Align crankshaft timing belt gear to TDC as shown in **Fig. 13** by turning crankshaft in direction of normal rotation.
3. Remove two auto belt tensioner bolts in order shown in **Fig. 14.**
4. If timing belt is going to be reused, place a directional mark on belt that indicates direction of rotation, then remove belt.

INSTALLATION

1. Compress auto belt tensioner until hole in piston is aligned with second hole in case. Insert a 0.06 inch diameter wire or pin through second hole to keep piston compressed, **Fig. 15.**
2. Align camshafts to TDC.
3. Turn crankshaft counterclockwise until timing gear is offset from TDC by one tooth, then install timing belt.

4. Turn crankshaft clockwise until crankshaft timing mark is again at TDC. Turning crankshaft should place all belt slack at or near tensioner.
5. Install tensioner and **torque** its mounting bolts to 14-18 ft. lbs., then remove pin.
6. Turn crankshaft two complete revolutions to ensure timing is still correct.
7. Install righthand engine mount and timing belt covers.

CAMSHAFT
REPLACE

Refer to **Fig. 16** when replacing camshaft.

REMOVAL

1. Remove intake manifold as described under "Intake Manifold, Replace."
2. Remove cylinder head covers as described under "Cylinder Head Cover, Replace."

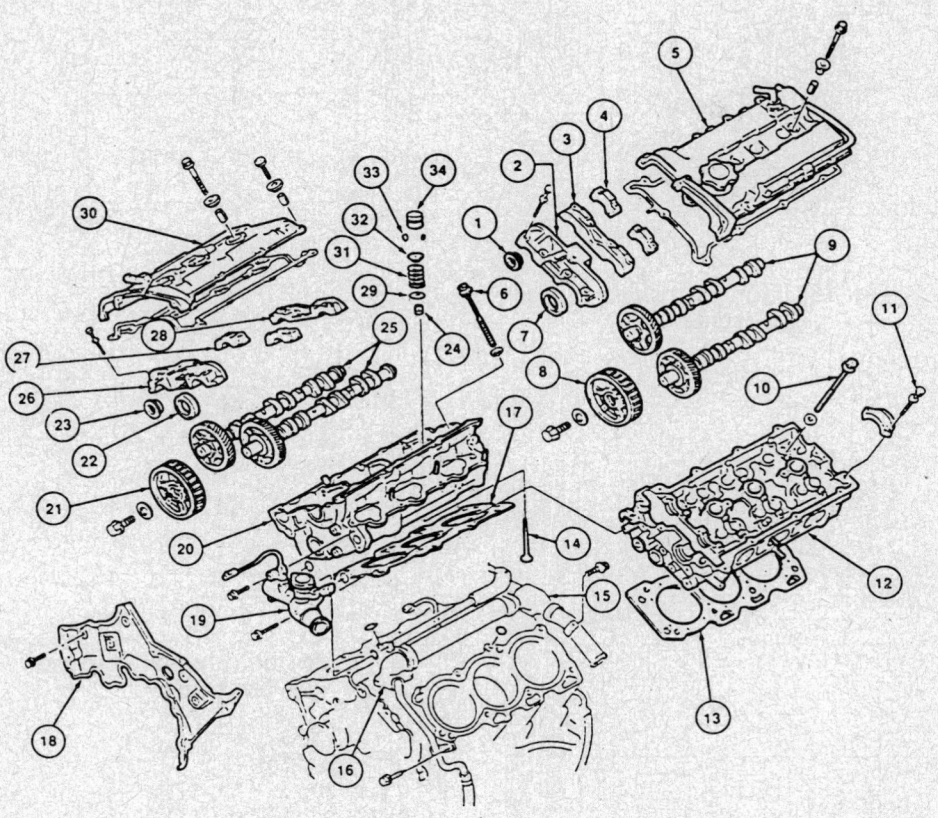

Item	Description
1	Blind Cap, Front (LH)
2	End Cap, Front (LH)
3	Thrust Cap, Front (LH)
4	Camshaft Caps, Front (LH)
5	Cylinder Head Cover, Front (LH)
6	Cylinder Head Bolt, Rear (RH)
7	Oil Seal, Front (LH)
8	Camshaft Pulley, Front (LH)
9	Camshafts, Front (LH)
10	Cylinder Head Bolt, Front (LH)
11	Camshaft Distributor Cap
12	Cylinder Head, Front (LH)
13	Cylinder Head Gasket, Front (LH)
14	Valve
15	Thermostat Housing
16	Coolant Elbow
17	Cylinder Head Gasket, Rear (RH)
18	Seal Plate
19	Coolant Elbow
20	Cylinder Head, Rear (RH)
21	Camshaft Pulley, Rear (RH)
22	Oil Seal, Rear (RH)
23	Blind Cap, Rear (RH)
24	Valve Guide
25	Camshafts, Rear (RH)
26	End Cap, Rear (RH)
27	Camshaft Caps, Rear (RH)
28	Thrust Cap, Rear (RH)
29	Lower Valve Seat
30	Cylinder Head Cover, Rear (RH)
31	Valve Spring
32	Upper Valve Seat
33	Valve Keeper
34	Hydraulic Lash Adjuster (HLA)

FM1069100312000X

Fig. 16 Camshafts replacement

3. Remove timing belt as described under "Timing Belt, Replace."
4. Remove camshaft pulley lock bolts, then the pulleys.
5. Turn camshafts until knock pins are aligned with marks on camshaft caps, **Fig. 17.** This will reduce pressure on hydraulic lash adjusters. **Do not remove camshaft when lobes are depressing any adjusters, as damage to camshaft or thrust journal support may result.**
6. **Camshaft caps are identified on righthand bank (rear) by numbers and on lefthand bank (front) by letters.** Loosen lefthand (front) camshaft cap bolts in five or six steps as shown in **Fig. 18.**
7. After removing left (front) camshaft caps, remove remaining camshaft cap bolts in sequence shown in **Fig. 19.**
8. Remove camshaft caps and camshafts, then the oil seals from camshafts. **To avoid damaging cylinder head thrust bearing support, remove thrust caps last.**

INSTALLATION

1. Install new oil seals on camshafts, then apply clean engine oil to camshaft journals and supports.
2. Install camshafts so gear marks align.
3. Apply a light coat of sealant to areas shown in **Fig. 20. Do not allow sealant to contact the camshafts.**
4. Install thrust caps and tighten bolts until they are fully seated against cylinder head.
5. Install remaining camshaft caps, noting the following:
   a. Right (rear) bank caps are numbered and left (front) are lettered.
   b. **Torque** camshaft cap bolts to 8-10 ft. lbs. in five equal steps, following sequence shown in **Fig. 21.**
6. Holding camshafts in place with a suitable wrench, install camshaft pulley and pulley lock bolts, then tighten lock bolts to specifications.
7. Install timing belt, cylinder head covers and intake manifold.

CRANKSHAFT REAR OIL SEAL
REPLACE
REMOVAL

1. **On models with manual transaxle,** proceed as follows:
   a. Remove transaxle, then secure flywheel by installing holding tool T74P-6375-A or equivalent.
   b. Loosen pressure plate bolts in two or three steps, then remove bolts and pressure plate.
   c. Remove flywheel attaching bolts using sequence shown in **Fig. 22.**
2. **On models with automatic transaxle,** proceed as follows:
   a. Remove transaxle.
   b. Use holding tool T74P-6375-A or equivalent, hold flex plate in position.
   c. Remove flex plate attaching bolts

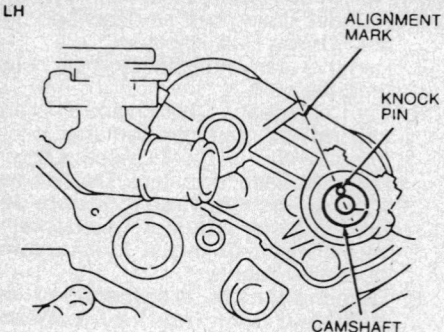

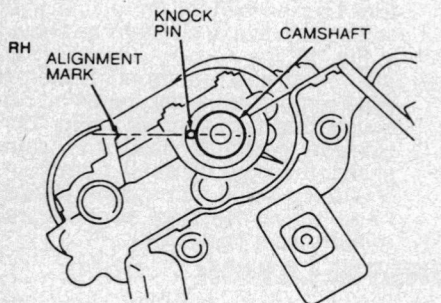

Fig. 17 Camshaft knock pin and cap mark alignment

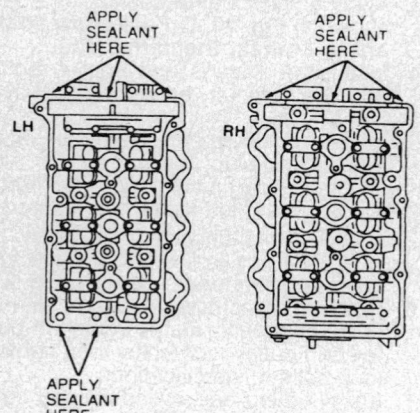

Fig. 20 Sealant application areas

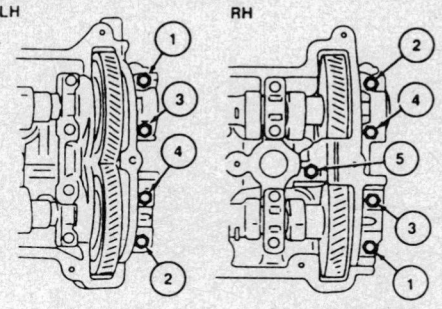

Fig. 18 Front camshaft cap bolt removal

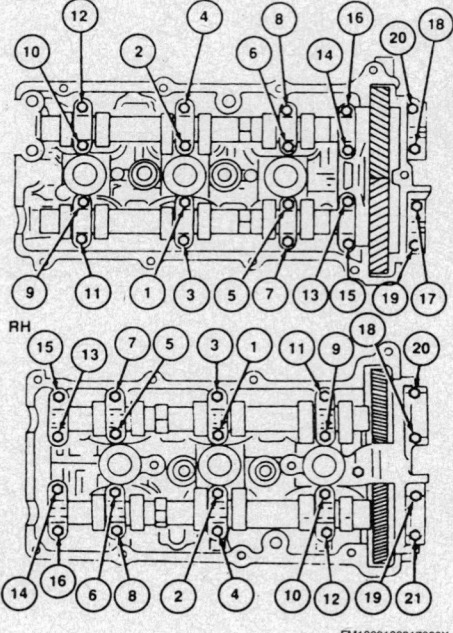

Fig. 21 Camshaft cap bolt tightening sequence

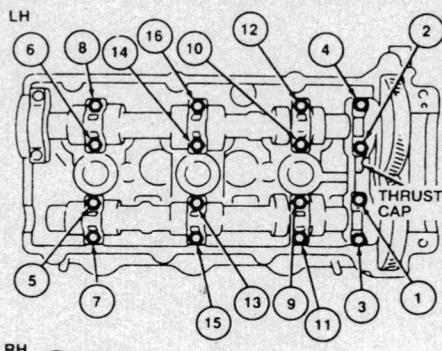

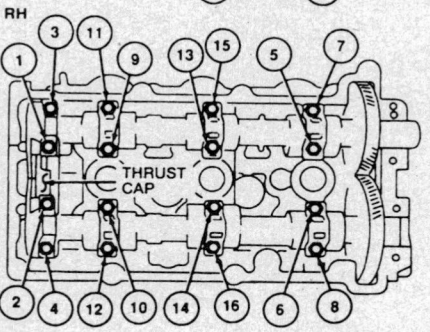

Fig. 19 Inside camshaft cap bolt removal

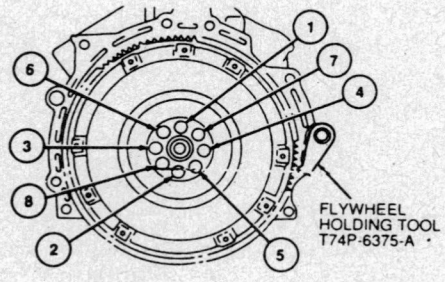

Fig. 22 Flywheel bolt removal sequence

using sequence shown in **Fig. 23.** Mark bolts for installation reference.

d. Remove backing plate, flex plate and adapter.

3. Using seal remover tool No. T92C-6700-CH or equivalent, remove rear main seal.

INSTALLATION

1. Apply clean engine oil to outer lips of rear main seal.
2. Position seal on Crankshaft Seal Replacer tool No. T92C-6701-BH or equivalent.
3. Install seal, then the flywheel or flex plate as follows:
   a. **On models with manual transaxle,** align flywheel to crankshaft, then loosely install flywheel bolts.
   b. Install holding tool No. T74P-6375-A or equivalent; then, using se-

quence shown in **Fig. 24,** torque flywheel bolts in two passes to 45–49 ft. lbs.

c. Using Clutch Aligning tool No. T74P-7137-K or equivalent, install clutch disc and pressure plate.

d. **On models with automatic transaxle,** align adapter, flex plate and backing plate, then loosely install flex plate bolts.

e. Install holding tool No. T74P-6375-A or equivalent; then, using sequence shown in **Fig. 25,** torque flex plate bolts to 45–50 ft. lbs.

4. Install transaxle and check for leaks.

OIL PAN
REPLACE

1. Drain engine oil, then disconnect both oxygen sensor connectors and lower exhaust system to gain access to oil pan bolts.
2. Remove oil pan bolts, then the pan.
3. Remove any remaining sealant from mating surfaces. **Failure to fully remove old sealant may cause en-**

gine block to crack.

4. Reverse procedure to install, noting the following:
   a. Apply a continuous bead of sealant inside bolt holes and overlap ends.
   b. Install pan within five minutes of applying sealant.
   c. **Torque** short pan retaining bolts to 14–18 ft. lbs. and long pan retaining bolts to 71–88 inch lbs.

OIL PUMP
REPLACE

REMOVAL

1. Remove timing belt as described under "Timing Belt, Replace."
2. Remove oil pan as described under "Oil Pan, Replace."
3. Discharge refrigerant from A/C system, then remove A/C compressor and mounting bracket.
4. Remove power steering pump and tensioner.
5. Using Crankshaft Damper Remover tool No. T74P-6316-A or equivalent,

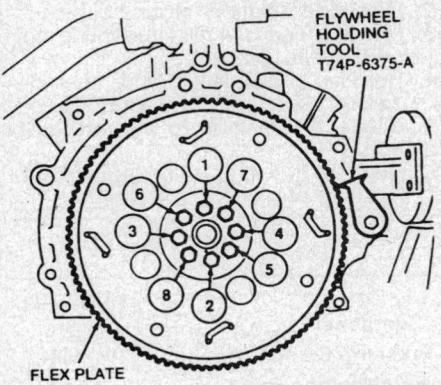

Fig. 23 Flex plate bolt removal sequence

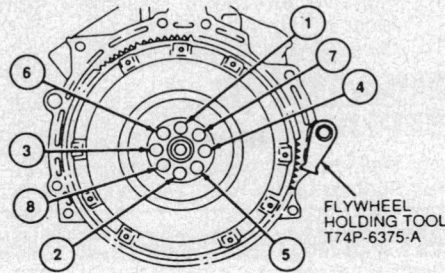

Fig. 24 Flywheel bolt tightening sequence

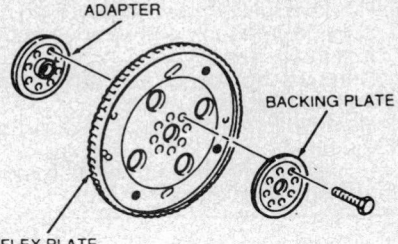

Fig. 25 Flex plate bolt tightening sequence

remove crankshaft timing gear from crankshaft.

6. Remove nine oil pump attaching bolts, then the two oil strainer to oil pump bolts.
7. Remove oil pump and housing from engine block.
8. Remove O-ring, then any sealant from oil pump mating surfaces.
9. Using a press and Front Seals Replacer tool No. T74P-6150-A or equivalent, remove oil seal from oil pump housing.

INSTALLATION

1. Using a press and Front Seals Replacer tool No. T74P-6150-A or equivalent, install a new oil seal.
2. Fit oil pump with a new O-ring.
3. Apply a continuous bead of silicone sealant to mating surface of oil pump. **Prevent sealant from entering oil hole.** Install pump within five minutes of sealant application, then tighten pump retaining bolts to specifications.
4. Install crankshaft timing gear and key.
5. Install power steering pump and tensioner. Tighten to specifications.
6. Attach A/C compressor bracket to engine block and tighten to specifications.
7. Attach A/C compressor to its mounting bracket and tighten to specifications.
8. Install oil strainer to oil pump and **torque** bolts to 71-88 inch lbs. Then, install oil pan as described under "Oil Pan, Replace."
9. Install timing belt as described under "Timing Belt, Replace."
10. Evacuate and recharge A/C system.

BELT TENSION DATA

Refer to **Fig. 26** for drive belt tension and torque specifications.

SERPENTINE DRIVE BELT

1. Loosen tensioner locknut.
2. Loosen tensioner adjusting bolt until there is enough slack to remove belt. Reverse procedure to install.

Drive Belt Tension	New N (lb)	Used N (lb)	Limit N (lb)
Generator	690-880 (160-190)	500-680 (110-150)	440 (99)
Generator + A/C	690-880 (160-190)	500-680 (110-150)	440 (99)
P/S	550-680 (130-150)	400-530 (88-120)	340 (77)

Fig. 26 Drive belt tension

COOLING SYSTEM BLEED

These engines do not require a specific bleed procedure. After filling cooling system, run engine to operating temperature with radiator/pressure cap off. Air will then be automatically bled through cap opening.

THERMOSTAT
REPLACE

1. Disconnect battery ground cable.
2. Drain cooling system, then remove fresh air duct and air cleaner assembly.
3. Disconnect lower radiator hose at coolant inlet pipe.
4. Remove coolant inlet pipe, then the thermostat housing. **Discard O-ring seal.**
5. Remove thermostat from housing.
6. Reverse procedure to install, using a new thermostat housing O-ring seal.

WATER PUMP
REPLACE

1. Drain cooling system, then remove timing belt as described under "Timing Belt, Replace."
2. Using Water Pump Pulley Remover tool No. T92C-6312-AH or equivalent, remove four water pump pulley bolts, then the pulley.
3. Remove five water pump mounting bolts, then the pump.
4. Reverse procedure to install, noting the following:
   a. Use a new water pump O-ring seal.
   b. Tighten all bolts to specifications.

RADIATOR
REPLACE

Allow radiator to cool prior to beginning the following procedure. Slowly remove radiator cap to release system pressure. **Caution must be used as system contains scalding hot fluid which when under pressure can blow out of the radiator fill neck, causing personal injury.**

1. Disconnect battery ground cable.
2. Slowly remove radiator cap, then open drain valve at bottom of radiator and drain system.
3. Remove fresh air duct.
4. Remove upper and lower radiator hoses.
5. Remove radiator overflow hose.
6. Remove coolant expansion tank.
7. Disconnect cooling fan motor and A/C condenser cooling fan motor electrical connectors.
8. **On models equipped with automatic transaxle**, disconnect transaxle oil cooler lines at radiator and plug hose ends to prevent leakage.
9. **On all models**, remove radiator mounting brackets.
10. Move the air bag electrical wiring harness to allow clearance for radiator removal.
11. Remove radiator, engine cooling fan, and A/C cooling fan from the vehicle as an assembly.
12. Reverse procedure to install, noting the following:
   a. **Torque** radiator mounting bracket bolts to 14-18 ft. lbs.
   b. Check and fill cooling system and transaxle fluid levels.
   c. **Torque** fan shroud bolts to 71-88 inch lbs.
   d. Operate engine until normal engine coolant temperature is reached and check for leaks.

FUEL PUMP
REPLACE

1. Relieve fuel system pressure as described under "Precautions."
2. Disconnect battery ground cable.
3. Drain fuel from fuel tank, then raise and support vehicle.
4. Loosen filler neck hose clamp and remove hose.
5. Loosen overflow hose clamp and remove hose.
6. Loosen fuel supply and return line clamps and remove hoses.
7. Loosen two fuel tank vapor line clamps and remove hoses.
8. Disconnect fuel pump sender electrical connector.
9. Remove four attaching nuts on exhaust heat shield.

10. Remove fuel tank shield attaching nut.
11. Support fuel tank and remove center fuel tank strap.
12. Remove righthand fuel tank strap, then the fuel tank shield.
13. Remove lefthand fuel tank strap, then the tank.
14. Using a hammer and chisel, remove fuel pump lock ring.
15. Remove fuel pump assembly from tank.
16. Reverse procedure to install.

FUEL FILTER
REPLACE

1. Relieve fuel system pressure as described under "Fuel Pressure Relief."
2. Disconnect battery ground cable.
3. Remove two fuel filter mounting nuts on fuel filter bracket.
4. Remove supply line clamps, then disconnect supply lines from both ends of filter. **Plug lines to prevent leakage.**
5. Remove fuel filter mounting bracket.
6. Reverse procedure to install.

TIGHTENING SPECIFICATIONS

Year	Component	Torque/Ft. Lbs.
1993–95	A/C Compressor Mounting Bolts	28-38
	A/C Compressor Mounting Bracket	28-38
	Battery Tray Mounting Bolt	71-88 ①
	Camshaft Bearing Cap Bolts	②
	Camshaft Pulley Lockbolts	90-103
	Coolant Elbow Bolts	14-18
	Converter Inlet Pipes	30-41
	Crankshaft Pulley Bolt	116-122
	Cylinder Head	②
	Cylinder Head Cover	②
	Engine Mount Bracket Attaching Bolt	32-45
	Engine Mount Attaching Nuts	54-77
	Engine Mount (RH) Through Bolts	50-68
	Engine Mount (LH) Through Bolts	63-86
	Exhaust Manifold Bolts	14-18
	Exhaust Manifold Nuts	14-18
	Extension Bar Nut	22-33
	Flex Plate	45-50
	Flywheel	45-49
	Front Engine Lifting Eye Attaching Bolts	14-18
	Front Engine Mount Nuts	55-75
	Front Engine Mount Through Bolt	63-86
	Fuel Filter Bracket	71-97 ①
	Generator Bolts	27-38
	Oil Drain Plug	22-30
	Oil Pan Mounting Bolts	②

Year	Component	Torque/Ft. Lbs.
1993–95 —Cont'd	Oil Pressure Switch	104-156 ①
	Oil Pump Attaching Bolts	14-18
	Power Steering Pump Belt Tensioner Lower Bolt	14-18 ①
	Power Steering Pump Belt Tensioner Upper Bolt	24-33 ①
	Power Steering Pump Rear Bracket Bolt	24-33
	Rear Engine Lifting Eye Attaching Bolts	27-38
	Rear Engine Mount Nuts	50-68
	Rear Engine Mount Through Bolt	63-86
	Splash Shield Bolts	71-88 ①
	Tensioner Locknut	24-34
	Thermostat Housing	14-18
	Timing Cover Bolts	71-88 ①
	Transaxle Cradle Nuts	②
	Transaxle Mount Nuts (Automatic Trans.)	50-68
	Transaxle Mount Nuts (Manual Trans.)	32-44
	Transaxle Mount Through Bolt	63-86
	Transaxle Shift Linkage Through Bolt	12-16
	Transaxle To Engine Block	②
	Transverse Member Bolts	69-93
	Water Pump Attaching Bolts	14-18
	Water Pump Pulley Attaching Bolts	71-88 ①
	Wheel Lug Nuts	66-86
	Water Pipe Mounting Bolt	14-18

①—Inch lbs.
②—Refer to text.

3.0L/V6-182 Engine
INDEX

PRECAUTIONS
FUEL SYSTEM PRESSURE RELIEF

On this engine, it is necessary to relieve fuel system pressure before disconnecting any fuel lines or hoses.
1. Start engine.
2. Disconnect fuel pump relay.
3. After engine stalls, turn ignition switch to "OFF" position.
4. Reconnect fuel pump relay.

ENGINE MOUNT
REPLACE

Refer to **Fig. 1** when replacing engine

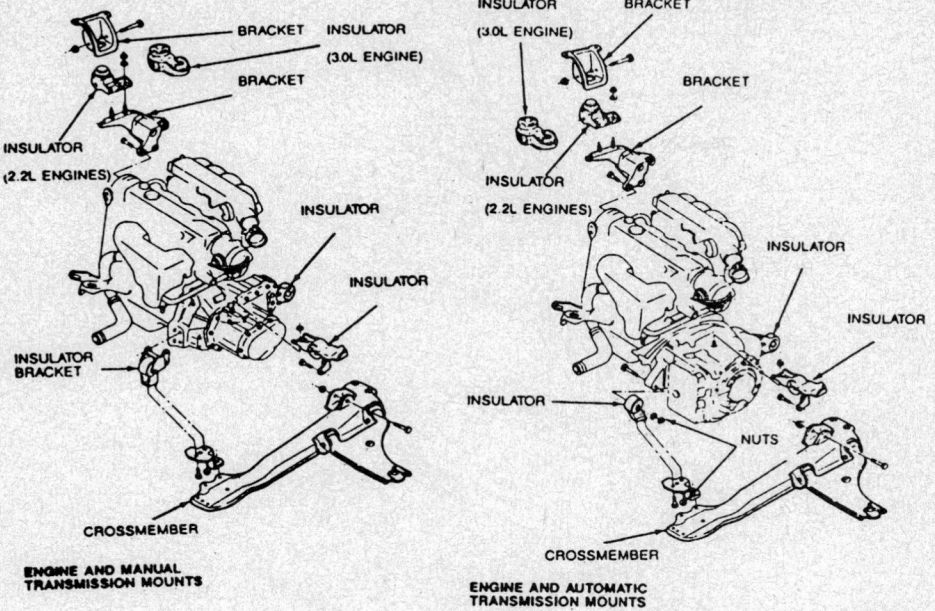

Fig. 1   Engine mounts

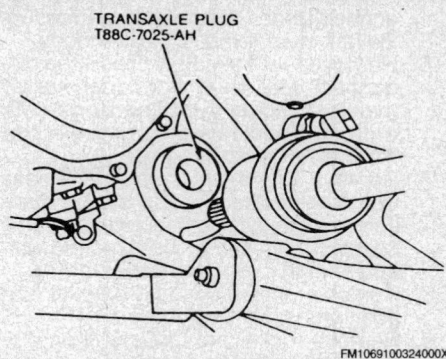

Fig. 2   Transaxle plug location

mounts.

ENGINE
REPLACE

Engine and transaxle are removed as an assembly.

1. Disconnect battery ground cable.
2. Mark hood hinge locations, then remove hood.
3. Drain cooling system and discharge A/C system.
4. Remove air cleaner assembly.
5. Remove vacuum valve assembly from righthand shock tower.
6. Disconnect fuel lines and position aside.
7. Relieve fuel system pressure as described under "Fuel System Pressure Relief"
8. Remove upper radiator hose.
9. Disconnect all electrical connectors and looms and position aside.
10. Disconnect or remove the following:
    a. Alternator.
    b. A/C compressor clutch.
    c. Ignition coil.
    d. Engine coolant temperature sensor.
    e. Injector wiring harness including six injector connectors.
    f. Air charge temperature sensor and throttle position sensor.
    g. Oil pressure sending switch.
    h. Engine ground straps.
    i. Block heater (if equipped).
    j. Knock sensor and EGR sensor.
    k. Oil level sensor.
    l. Vacuum lines and crankcase ventilation hoses.
    m. Heater hoses and power steering pump return lines.
11. Disconnect A/C lines from condenser and chassis, leaving manifold lines attached to compressor.
12. Disconnect accelerator linkage, trans-

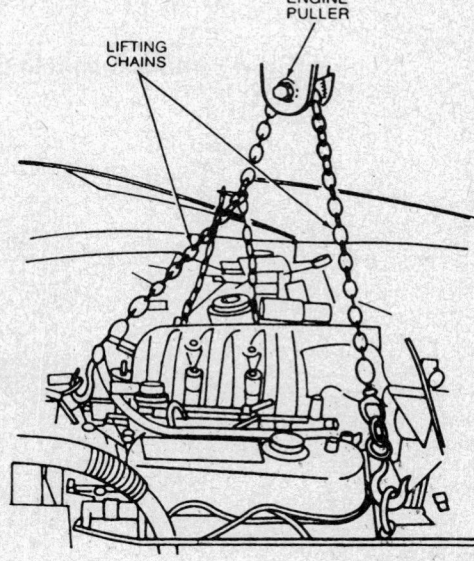

Fig. 3   Engine removal

mission throttle valve linkage and speed control cable (if equipped).
13. Remove battery and tray.
14. Remove fuse box and position aside.
15. Disconnect speed control servo and position aside.
16. **On models with automatic transaxle,** disconnect shift cable and electrical connectors and position aside.
17. **On models with analog cluster,** disconnect speedometer.
18. **On models with electronic cluster,** disconnect vehicle speed sensor connector.
19. **On models with manual transaxle,** remove clutch release cylinder with hose still attached and position aside.
20. **On all models,** remove radiator, cooling fan and shroud.

21. Raise and support vehicle.
22. Remove wheel and tire assemblies.
23. Remove lower radiator hose and front exhaust pipe.
24. Remove starter motor.
25. **On models with automatic transaxle,** remove torque converter nuts.
26. **On models with manual transmission,** remove shift control rod and extension bar.
27. **On all models,** remove stabilizer links and tie rod ends from lower control arms.
28. Disconnect lower ball joints, then pull down on control arms to disengage them from spindle.
29. Remove three bolts from dynamic damper bracket on righthand halfshaft assembly. Pulling outward on righthand brake and spindle assembly, disengage right halfshaft from transaxle.
30. Pulling outward on lefthand brake and spindle assembly, disengage left halfshaft assembly.
31. Install two transaxle plugs T88C-7025-AH or equivalent into differential side gears, **Fig. 2. Failure to install transaxle plugs may allow differential side gears to become improperly positioned.**
32. Disconnect lower rear transmission mount.
33. Lower vehicle and attach a suitable lifting device to engine lift points, **Fig. 3.**
34. Disconnect lower front engine mount and righthand upper engine mount at timing cover.
35. Disconnect lefthand upper engine mount at transaxle case.
36. Carefully lift engine and transaxle assembly from vehicle.
37. Reverse procedure to install.

INTAKE MANIFOLD
REPLACE

1. Disconnect battery ground cable, then drain cooling system.
2. Remove air cleaner outlet to throttle body flex hose.
3. Mark vacuum lines for reference, then remove at throttle body.
4. Remove ignition wires from spark plugs, then the harnesses from rocker cover retaining studs.
5. Relieve fuel system pressure as de-

scribed under "Fuel System Pressure Relief", then remove throttle body.

6. Remove fuel line safety clips, then disconnect fuel lines from fuel supply manifold. **Cover fuel line ends with a clean shop towel to prevent dirt from entering opening.**

7. Remove fuel injector wiring harness from engine, then the fuel supply manifold and injectors. Injectors and fuel supply manifold may be removed with intake manifold as an assembly.

8. Remove ignition coil and bracket and position aside.

9. Remove rocker arm covers, then disconnect upper radiator and heater hoses.

10. Disconnect EGR tube attaching nut from EGR valve (if equipped).

11. Disconnect PFE sensor hose from EGR tube nipple. Loosen lower tube attaching nut and rotate tube away from valve.

12. Mark and remove distributor assembly, then disconnect engine coolant temperature sensor connector.

13. Remove intake manifold retaining bolts. It may be necessary to pry intake manifold upward to break silicone seal.

14. Reverse procedure to install, noting the following:

   a. Ensure manifold mating surfaces are clean and free of old silicone sealer.

   b. Manifold must be installed within 15 minutes after sealer application.

   c. **Torque** manifold bolts in two passes, first to 11 ft. lbs., then to 18 ft. lbs., in sequence shown in **Fig. 4**.

EXHAUST MANIFOLD
REPLACE

LEFT SIDE

1. Remove dipstick tube support bracket and heat shield retaining nuts.
2. Raise and support vehicle.
3. Remove exhaust manifold to front exhaust pipe attaching nuts, then lower vehicle.
4. Remove exhaust manifold attaching nuts, then the manifold.
5. Reverse procedure to install, noting the following:
   a. Lubricate bolts lightly with clean oil.
   b. Tighten all bolts to specifications.

RIGHT SIDE

1. Raise and support vehicle.
2. Using back-up wrench on EGR tube lower adapter, remove EGR supply tube from exhaust manifold (if equipped).
3. Remove spark plugs and heat shield retaining nuts.
4. Remove manifold to exhaust pipe attaching nuts.
5. Remove exhaust manifold attaching bolts, then the manifold.
6. Reverse procedure to install, noting the following:
   a. Lubricate nuts and bolts lightly with clean oil.

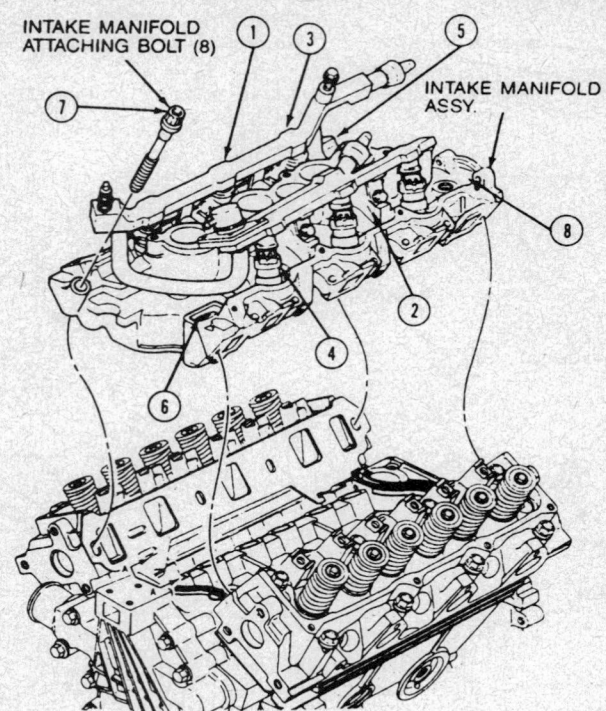

Fig. 4 Intake manifold bolt tightening sequence

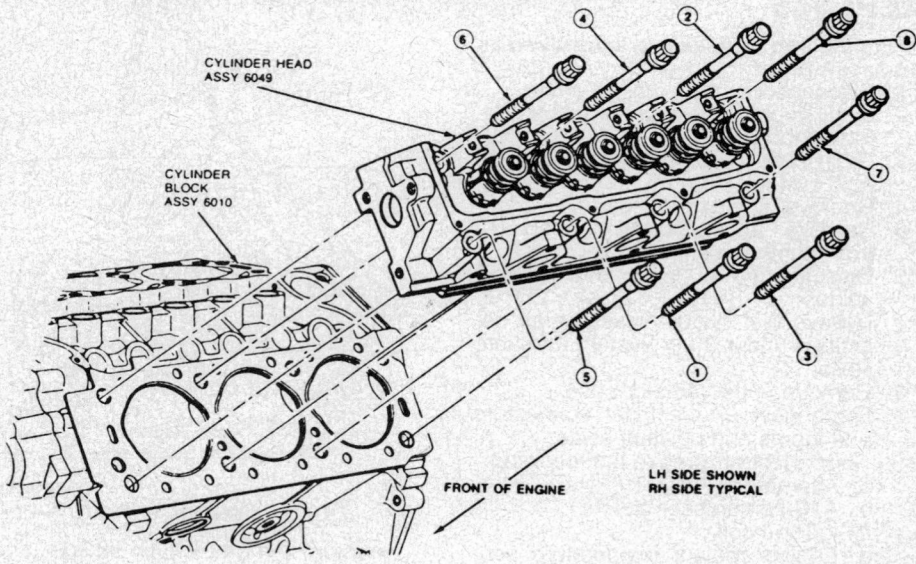

Fig. 5 Cylinder head bolt tightening sequence

   b. Tighten all bolts to specifications.

CYLINDER HEAD
REPLACE

1. Disconnect battery ground cable, then drain cooling system.
2. Remove air cleaner duct tube, then the intake manifold as described under "Intake Manifold, Replace".
3. Remove accessory drive belts. If front cylinder head is being removed, remove power steering pump.
4. Remove alternator/accessory support brackets, then the oil level dipstick and tube.
5. Remove ignition coil and bracket.
6. Remove exhaust manifold as described under "Exhaust Manifold, Replace".
7. Loosen rocker arm fulcrum attaching bolt enough to rotate rocker arm and remove pushrod. **Mark pushrods for installation reference.**
8. Remove cylinder head attaching bolts, then the cylinder head.
9. Remove and discard cylinder head gasket.
10. Reverse procedure to install, noting the following:

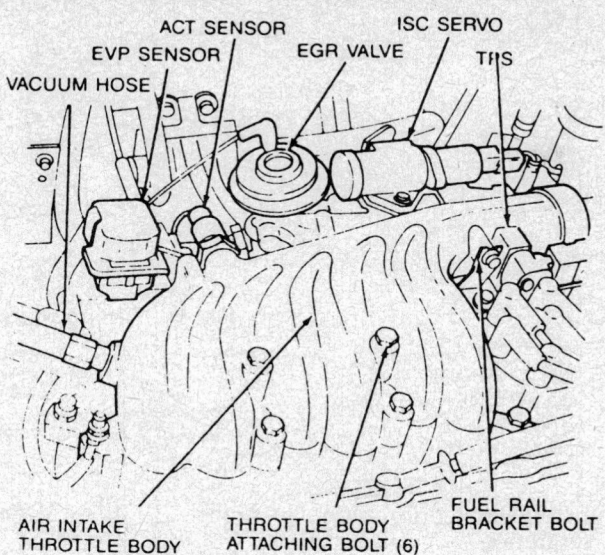

VACUUM HOSE — EVP SENSOR — ACT SENSOR — EGR VALVE — ISC SERVO — TPS

AIR INTAKE THROTTLE BODY — THROTTLE BODY ATTACHING BOLT (6) — FUEL RAIL BRACKET BOLT

FM1069100327000X

Fig. 6   Rocker arm cover removal

a. Lubricate bolts lightly with clean oil.
b. **Torque** cylinder head bolts in two passes, first to 33-41 ft. lbs., then to 63-73 ft. lbs., in sequence shown in **Fig. 5.**

VALVE COVER
REPLACE

LEFT SIDE

1. Disconnect spark plug wires from spark plugs.
2. Remove spark plug wire loom brackets from attaching bolt studs.
3. Disconnect crankcase hose from rocker cover.
4. Disconnect alternator harness loom retainers from rocker arm cover studs, then remove injector harness and position aside.
5. Remove two attaching bolts and six studs from rocker arm cover.
6. Remove rocker arm cover and gasket.
7. Reverse procedure to install, noting the following:
   a. Lubricate bolt and stud threads lightly prior to installation.
   b. Apply bead of Silicone Sealer or equivalent at cylinder head intake manifold rail step.
   c. Tighten rocker arm cover bolts to specifications.

RIGHT SIDE

1. Disconnect battery ground cable.
2. Disconnect air cleaner tube from throttle body, then remove plastic shield from throttle body.
3. Disconnect EGR supply tube and all vacuum hoses from air intake throttle body.
4. Disconnect ACT sensor, ISC servo, and TPS, **Fig. 6.**
5. Remove EVP sensor (if equipped), **Fig. 6.**
6. **On models with manual transaxle,** disconnect throttle cable.
7. **On models with automatic transaxle,** disconnect throttle valve control cable.
8. **On all models,** remove fuel rail bracket bolt from throttle body.
9. Remove air intake attaching bolts, then lift off throttle body.
10. Disconnect spark plug wires, then position injector harness aside.
11. Remove rocker arm cover attaching bolts, then the cover.
12. Reverse procedure to install, noting the following:
    a. Lubricate bolt and stud threads lightly prior to installation.
    b. Apply bead of Silicone Sealer or equivalent at cylinder head intake manifold rail step.
    c. Tighten rocker arm cover bolts to specifications.
    d. **Torque** EGR supply tube 37 ft. lbs.

VALVE CLEARANCE SPECIFICATIONS

Hydraulic valve lash adjusters provide automatic lash adjustment which maintains a zero inch clearance between the camshaft lobes and the valve stems.

VALVE ADJUSTMENT

This engine is equipped with hydraulic lifters. No adjustment is required.

HYDRAULIC LIFTERS
REPLACE

Before replacing hydraulic valve tappets due to noisy operation, ensure the noise is not caused by improper valve-to-rocker arm clearance, worn rocker arms, pushrods or rocker arm cover baffle clearance.

1. Disconnect battery ground cable, then drain cooling system.
2. Remove air intake throttle body.
3. Remove rocker arm covers and intake manifold assembly. Refer to "Intake Manifold, Replace" for procedure.

4. Loosen rocker arm fulcrum attaching bolts enough to lift rocker arm off pushrod and rotate aside.
5. Remove pushrods and **mark for installation reference.**
6. Using a magnet, remove tappets. **Mark tappets for installation reference. If tappets are stuck in their bores by excessive varnish or gum buildup, use hydraulic tappet puller or equivalent.**
7. Reverse procedure to install, noting the following:
   a. Lubricate each tappet and bore with suitable lubricant.
   b. Ensure pushrods and rocker arms are fully seated.
   c. **Torque** rocker arm fulcrum bolts in two passes, first to 5.1-11 ft. lbs., then to 20-28 ft. lbs.

CRANKSHAFT DAMPER
REPLACE

1. Remove accessory drive belts.
2. Raise and support vehicle, then remove right front wheel and plastic inner fender shield.
3. Remove water pump belt, then lower vehicle.
4. Support engine with suitable jack.
5. **On models with manual transaxle,** remove righthand engine mount.
6. **On models with automatic transaxle,** remove spacer from water pump bracket.
7. **On all models,** remove right upper engine mount at timing cover.
8. Lower jack carefully, allowing engine to rest on remaining mounts.
9. Raise and support vehicle.
10. Remove crankshaft damper bolt and flat washer; then, using Crankshaft Damper Remover tool No. T58P-6316-D or equivalent, remove damper from crankshaft end.
11. Remove three nuts and one bolt attaching right side of subframe to body. Pull down slightly to provide clearance for crankshaft damper removal.
12. Reverse procedure to install, noting the following:
    a. Lubricate crankshaft damper sealing surface with clean engine oil.
    b. Apply sealer to keyway of damper.
    c. Tighten damper to specifications.

FRONT COVER
REPLACE

1. Disconnect battery ground cable, then raise and support vehicle.
2. Remove crankshaft damper as described under "Crankshaft Damper, Replace."
3. Drain engine oil, then remove oil pan.
4. Remove timing cover bottom bolts, then lower vehicle.
5. Remove remaining timing cover bolts.
6. Carefully insert a flat-bladed screwdriver between timing cover and cylinder block. Pry timing cover from block.
7. Pull timing cover over end of crankshaft, then lower it from engine compartment. **Timing cover may be re-**

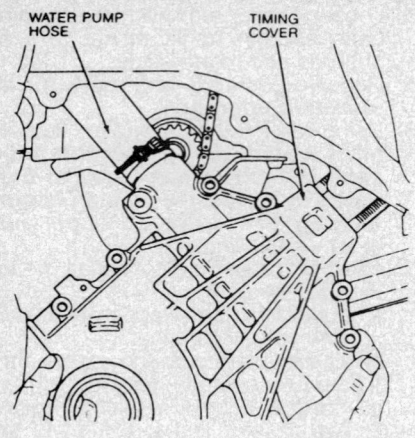

Fig. 7   Timing cover removal

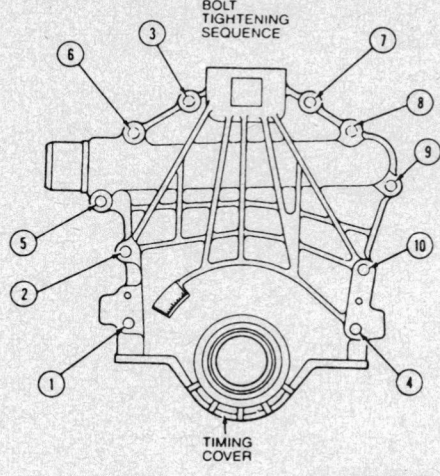

Fig. 8   Timing cover bolt tightening sequence

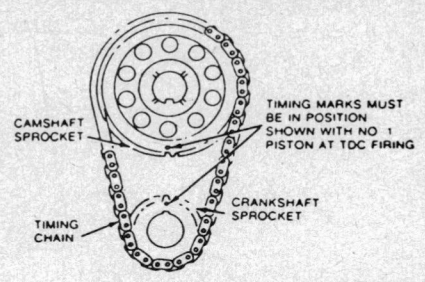

Fig. 9   Timing mark alignment

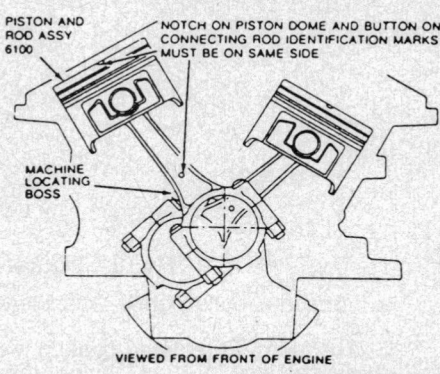

Fig. 11   Piston & rod assembly

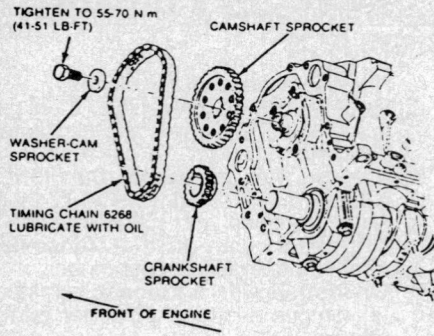

Fig. 10   Timing chain & sprockets installation

moved with water pump upper hose attached, Fig. 7.

8. Reverse procedure to install, noting the following:
   a. Clean gasket mating surfaces on cylinder block and timing cover.
   b. Ensure cover is correctly seated on dowels.
   c. Apply D6AZ-19558-A sealant or equivalent to timing cover bolt threads.
   d. Refer to **Fig. 8.** for bolt tightening sequence. Tighten to specifications.

FRONT COVER SEAL
REPLACE

1. Remove crankshaft damper as described under "Crankshaft Damper, Replace".
2. Using Front Cover Seal Remover tool No. T70P-6B070-B or equivalent, remove oil seal.
3. Reverse procedure to install.

TIMING GEARS

Refer to "Timing Chain, Replace" in this section for timing gear replacement.

TIMING CHAIN
REPLACE

1. Disconnect battery ground cable, then drain cooling system.

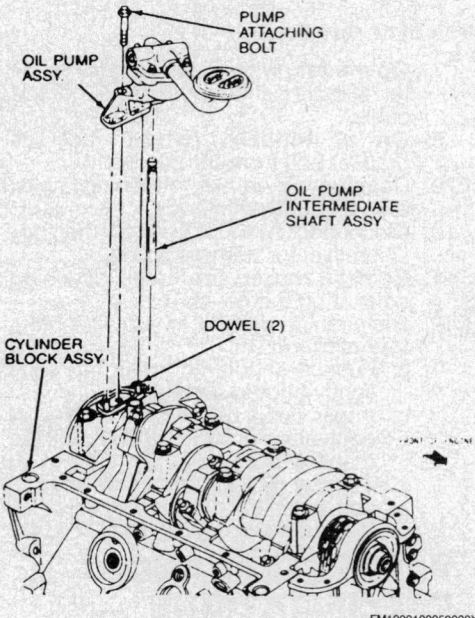

Fig. 12   Oil pump removal

2. Drain crankcase, then remove crankshaft pulley and damper as described under "Crankshaft Damper, Replace."
3. Remove timing cover as described under "Timing Cover, Replace."
4. Rotate crankshaft until No. 1 piston is at TDC on compression stroke and timing marks are aligned as shown, **Fig. 9.**
5. Remove camshaft sprocket attaching bolt and washer, then slide crankshaft sprocket, timing chain and camshaft sprocket from engine as an assembly.
6. Reverse procedure to install, noting the following:
   a. Clean and inspect parts before installation.
   b. Install replacement sprockets and timing chain as an assembly with timing marks aligned, **Fig. 10.**
   c. **Camshaft retaining bolt has a drilled oil passage for timing chain lubrication. If damaged,**

replace only with original equipment type bolt. Clean oil passage with solvent.

CAMSHAFT
REPLACE

1. Remove engine from vehicle as described under "Engine, Replace." Mount on suitable work stand.
2. Remove timing cover as described under "Timing Cover, Replace."
3. Remove rocker arm covers as described under "Rocker Arm, Replace" and the intake manifold as described under "Intake Manifold, Replace".
4. Remove hydraulic valve tappets as described under "Hydraulic Valve Tappets, Replace". **Mark for installation reference.**
5. Check camshaft endplay. If endplay is greater than .005 inch, replace thrust plate.
6. Remove timing chain and sprockets as described under "Timing Chain & Sprockets, Replace".
7. Remove camshaft thrust plate, then carefully pull camshaft from front of engine. Use caution to avoid damaging bearings, journals and lobes.
8. Reverse procedure to install, noting the following:
   a. Lubricate camshaft lobes and journals with SAE 50 weight oil.
   b. Tighten camshaft thrust plate to specifications.
   c. Lubricate tappets and tappet bores with heavy engine oil.

PISTON & ROD ASSEMBLY

Ensure notch in piston dome faces front

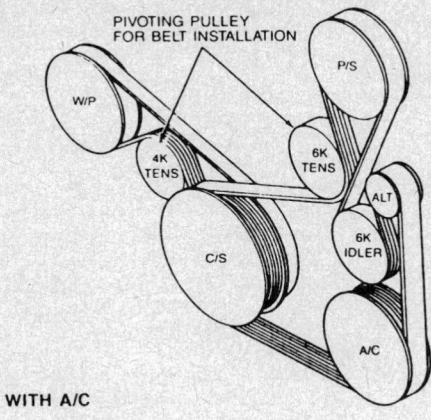

WITH A/C

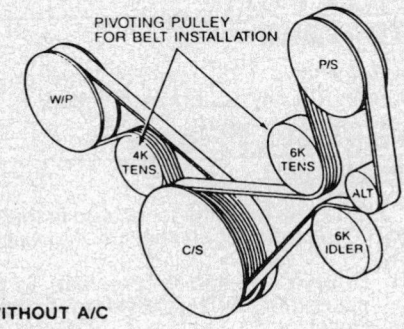

WITHOUT A/C

FM1069100333000X

Fig. 13 Belt routing

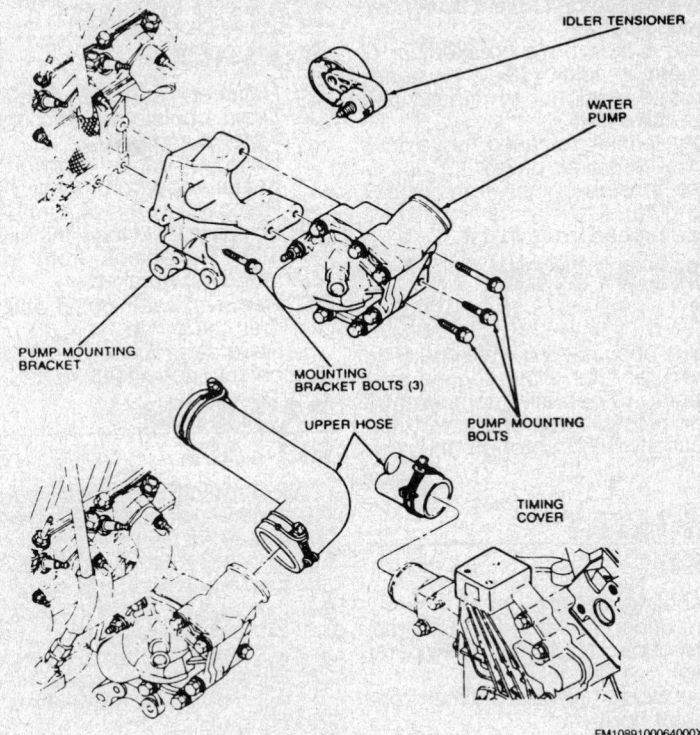

Fig. 14 Water pump removal

FM1089100064000X

of engine and machine locating boss faces righthand side of engine as shown, **Fig. 11.**

PISTONS, PINS & RINGS

Pistons and rings are available in standard sizes and in oversizes. Standard sizes are color-coded red or blue or have .0003 OS stamped on the dome. Piston to bore clearance should not exceed 0.0032 inch.

CRANKSHAFT REAR OIL SEAL

REPLACE

1. Using suitable tool, punch hole in seal metal between seal lip and cylinder block.
2. Screw in threaded end of Jet Plug Remover tool No. T77L-9533-B or equivalent; then, using slide hammer, remove seal. **Use care to avoid damaging oil seal surface.**
3. Lubricate outer lips and inner edge of new rear main seal with clean engine oil.
4. Place new seal on Rear Main Seal Installer tool No. T82L-6701-A or equivalent, then position tool and seal at seal bore.
5. Install and tighten bolts supplied with tool. **Engine flywheel bolts may be used if necessary.** Alternate tightening to ensure proper seating of seal.
6. Remove seal installer tool.

OIL PAN
REPLACE

1. Disconnect battery ground cable.
2. Raise and support vehicle, then drain crankcase.
3. Remove starter motor.
4. Remove front and rear transaxle to engine braces, then disconnect low oil level sensor electrical connector.
5. Remove exhaust inlet pipe from manifolds and position aside.
6. Drain cooling system, then remove water pump as described under "Water Pump, Replace."
7. Remove water pump bracket and idler pulley.
8. Remove attaching bolts from front of righthand crossmember.
9. Loosen, but do not remove, attaching bolts from rear of righthand crossmember. **Allow crossmember to drop as low as possible to permit removal of oil pan.**
10. Remove oil pan attaching bolts and the oil pan. Clean mating surfaces thoroughly.
11. Reverse procedure to install, noting the following:
    a. Apply a $1/5$ inch bead of Silicone Sealer D6AZ-19562-AA or equivalent to area between rear main bearing cap and cylinder block and between front cover assembly and cylinder block.
    b. Install oil pan within 15 minutes of silicone sealer application.
    c. Place oil pan gasket on oil pan with bend against pan surface. Adhere with Gasket and Seal Contact Adhesive D7AZ-19B508-AA or equiv-

alent.
d. Tighten all bolts to specifications.

OIL PUMP
REPLACE

1. Remove oil pan as described under "Oil Pan, Replace".
2. Remove oil pump mounting bolt, **Fig. 12.**
3. Remove oil pump and intermediate shaft from rear main bearing cap.
4. Pull intermediate shaft out of oil pump.
5. Reverse procedure to install, noting the following:
    a. Slide intermediate shaft into drive hole in pump assembly until a "click" is felt.
    b. Pour a small amount of clean engine oil into oil pump body outlet hole.
    c. Tighten all bolts to specifications.

BELT TENSION DATA

Belt tension is automatically maintained on these models by an automatic tensioner. Therefore, no adjustment is necessary.

SERPENTINE DRIVE BELT

BELT ROUTING

Refer to **Fig. 13** for belt routing.

BELT REPLACEMENT

If the serpentine belt is to be reused, mark rotation direction on belt for installation reference. **Failure to do so may result in belt noise.**

1. Remove plastic belt shield from power steering pump.
2. Insert a ½ inch drive breaker bar or equivalent in idler pulley tensioner, then rotate tensioner to release tension on drive belt.
3. With belt tension released, move drive belt off of tensioner pulley.
4. Release tensioner, then remove belt from engine.
5. Reverse procedure to install.

COOLING SYSTEM BLEED

This engine does not require a specified bleed procedure. After filling cooling system, run engine to operating temperature with radiator/pressure cap off. Air will then be automatically bled through the cap opening.

THERMOSTAT
REPLACE

1. Drain cooling system.
2. Loosen upper radiator hose clamp, then disconnect hose from thermostat housing.
3. Remove wiring harness bracket from thermostat housing.
4. Remove upper radiator hose.
5. Remove thermostat housing, thermostat and gasket. **Do not pry housing off.**
6. Reverse procedure to install, noting the following:
   a. Install a new thermostat gasket.
   b. Tighten bolts to specifications.

WATER PUMP
REPLACE

1. Raise and support vehicle.
2. Drain cooling system, then remove water pump belt.
3. Remove upper radiator hose and heater hose from pump, **Fig. 14.**
4. Remove lower radiator hose from water pump steel tube, then remove steel tube brace bolt from water pump mounting bracket.
5. Remove water pump attaching bolts, then the pump.
6. Reverse procedure to install. Tighten bolts to specifications.

RADIATOR
REPLACE

Allow radiator to cool prior to beginning the following procedure. Slowly remove radiator cap to release system pressure. **Caution must be used as system contains scalding hot fluid which when under pressure can blow out of the radiator fill neck, causing personal injury.**

1. Disconnect battery ground cable.
2. Slowly remove radiator cap, then open drain valve at bottom of radiator and drain system.
3. Remove fresh air duct.
4. Remove upper and lower radiator hoses.
5. Remove radiator overflow hose.
6. Disconnect cooling fan motor and A/C condenser cooling fan motor electrical connectors.
7. **On models equipped with auto-**matic transaxle, disconnect transaxle oil cooler lines at radiator and plug hose ends to prevent leakage.
8. **On all models, Remove radiator mounting brackets.**
9. Remove radiator, engine cooling fan, and A/C cooling fan from the vehicle as an assembly.
10. Reverse procedure to install, noting the following:
   a. **Torque** radiator mounting bracket bolts to 69-95 inch lbs.
   b. Check and fill cooling system and transaxle fluid levels.
   c. **Torque** fan shroud bolts to 61-87 inch lbs.
   d. Operate engine until normal engine coolant temperature is reached and check for leaks.

FUEL PUMP
REPLACE

Refer to "Fuel Pump, Replace" procedure in 2.2L/4-133 Engine section.

FUEL FILTER
REPLACE

The in-line fuel filter is located in the engine compartment, in the fuel rail supply line.

1. Relieve fuel system pressure as described under "Fuel System Pressure Relief".
2. Remove the supply clamps, then the fuel lines from both ends of the filter assembly.
3. Remove filter from mounting bracket.
4. Reverse procedure to install.

TIGHTENING SPECIFICATIONS

Year	Component	Torque/Ft. Lbs.
1992	Camshaft Sprocket to Camshaft	40-51
	Camshaft Thrust Plate	6-8
	Connecting Rod Nut	23-39
	Coolant Temp. Switch	12-18
	Crankshaft Damper	92-122
	Cylinder Head	①
	EGR Supply Tube to Exhaust Manifold	25-48
	EGR Tube Fitting to Exhaust Manifold	25-48
	EGR Valve to Throttle Body	15-22
	Exhaust Manifold	15-22
	Flywheel to Crankshaft Bolt	54-64
	Fuel Rail to Intake Manifold	6-8
	Intake Manifold to Cylinder Head	①
	Low Level Oil Sensor	20-30
	Main Bearing Cap Bolt	55-63

Year	Component	Torque/Ft. Lbs.
1992 —Cont'd	Oil Filter to Adapter	89-132 ②
	Oil Indicator Tube to Exhaust Manifold	11-15
	Oil Pan to Cylinder Block	7-10
	Oil Pan Drain Plug	8-12
	Oil Pressure Sending Unit	12-16
	Oil Pump to Main Cap Bolt	30-40
	Rocker Arm Fulcrum to Cylinder Head	①
	Spark Plug to Cylinder Head	5-11
	Thermostat Housing	8-10
	Timing Cover to Cylinder Block	15-22
	Water Pump Bracket	30-40
	Water Pump Idler Pulley	30-40
	Water Pump	15-22

① —Refer to text
② —Inch lbs.

Clutch & Manual Transaxle

INDEX

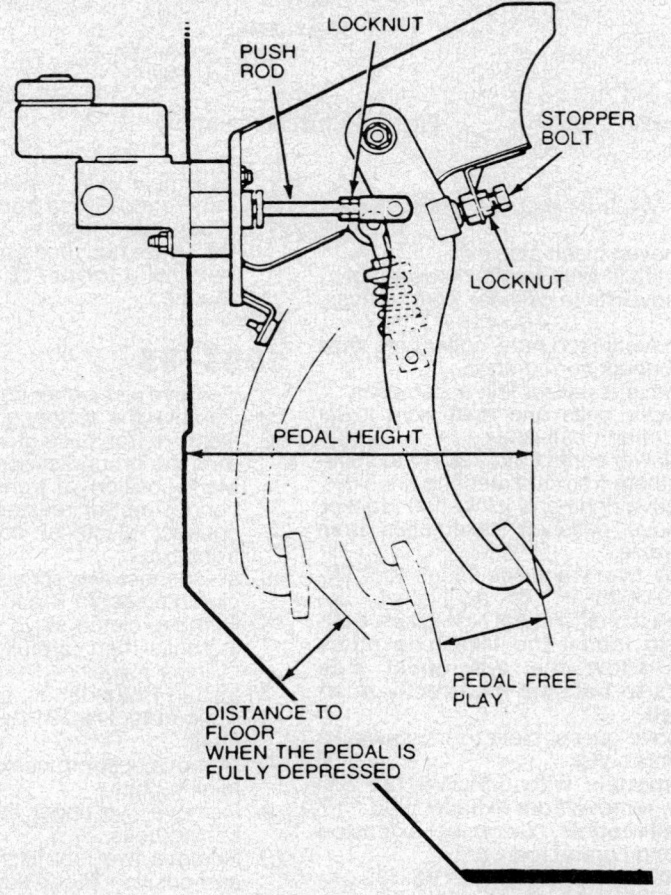

FM5049100039000X

Fig. 1 Clutch adjustment

ADJUSTMENTS

CLUTCH PEDAL HEIGHT

1. Measure distance from the bulkhead to the upper center of the pedal pad, **Fig. 1.**
2. **On 1992 models,** distance should be 8.5-8.7 inches.
3. **On 1993-95 models,** distance should be 7.32-8.31 inches.
4. It adjustment is required, remove lower dash panel, then the air ducts.
5. Loosen locknut, then turn stopper bolt until pedal height is within specifications.
6. After adjustment, tighten locknut **torque** to 122-156 inch lbs., then install air ducts and lower dash panel.

7. Depress clutch pedal repeatedly, then measure pedal height. Readjust as necessary.

CLUTCH PEDAL FREEPLAY

1. Measure clutch pedal freeplay distance, **Fig. 1.**
2. **On 1992 models,** freeplay should be .20-.51 inch.
3. **On 1993-95 models,** freeplay should measure 0.04-0.12 inch.
4. If adjustment is required, remove lower dash panel, then the air ducts.
5. Loosen locknut, then turn pushrod until pedal freeplay is within specifications.
6. Measure distance from the floor to center of pedal pad when pedal is fully depressed. The distance should be 2.64 inches.

7. Tighten locknut **torque**, 105-147 inch lbs.
8. Install air ducts, then the lower dash panel.

HYDRAULIC SYSTEM SERVICE

SLAVE CYLINDER, REPLACE

1. Disconnect pressure line from slave cylinder, then plug line to prevent leakage. **Avoid twisting pressure line during removal.**
2. Remove slave cylinder attaching bolts, then the cylinder.
3. Reverse procedure to install. Tighten bolts to specifications.

CLUTCH BLEED

The clutch hydraulic system must be bled whenever the pressure line is disconnected.

The fluid in the reservoir must be maintained at the 3/4 level or higher during air bleeding.

1. Remove bleeder cap from slave cylinder and attach vinyl hose to bleeder screw.
2. Place other end of hose in clear container partially filled with hydraulic fluid.
3. Slowly pump clutch pedal several times.
4. With clutch pedal depressed, loosen bleeder screw to release trapped air.
5. Tighten bleeder screw. **Pedal must remain depressed until bleeder screw has been tightened.**
6. Repeat steps 3 through 5 until no air bubbles appear in fluid.

CLUTCH MASTER CYLINDER

1992

1. Remove ABS relay box, if equipped.
2. Disconnect clutch pressure line from master cylinder.
3. Remove mounting nuts, then master cylinder.
4. Reverse procedure to install, noting the following:
   a. Tighten slave cylinder mounting nuts to specifications.
   b. Bleed air from system.

1993–95

1. Disconnect reservoir hose from clutch master cylinder, then plug hose.
2. Disconnect pressure line from clutch master cylinder. **Avoid twisting line during removal.**
3. Working from passenger compartment, remove clutch master cylinder upper retaining nut.
4. Working from engine compartment, remove clutch master cylinder lower retaining nut.
5. Carefully pull clutch master cylinder and gasket from bulkhead.
6. Reverse procedure to install, noting the following:
   a. Install new gasket.
   b. Tighten clutch master cylinder retaining nuts to specifications.
   c. **Torque** pressure line flare fitting to 10–15 ft. lbs.
   d. Bleed air from system.

CLUTCH
REPLACE

1. Disconnect battery ground cable.
2. Remove transaxle from vehicle.
3. Install Flywheel Lock tool No. T74P-6375-A or equivalent into transaxle mounting hole on engine, then engage tooth of locking tool into flywheel ring gear.
4. **To avoid dropping clutch disc when bolts are removed, use Clutch Aligning tool No. T71P-7137-H for 2.2L/4-133 turbo and 3.0L/V6-182 models or No. T74P-7137-K on 1992 non-turbocharged or 1993 models.**
5. Remove bolts attaching pressure plate assembly to flywheel, then the pressure plate assembly, **Fig. 2.**
6. Remove clutch disc and aligning tool.
7. Reverse procedure to install. Tighten to specifications.

TRANSAXLE
REPLACE

1992

1. Disconnect battery ground cable.
2. Disconnect or isolate main fuse block assembly.
3. Disconnect center lead from distributor terminal.
4. Disconnect airflow meter electrical connector from air cleaner assembly.
5. **On non-turbocharged models,** remove resonance chamber, then bracket. On turbocharged models, remove throttle body to intercooler air hose, then the air cleaner to turbocharger air hose.
6. Disconnect speedometer cable (analog cluster) or harness (digital cluster).
7. **On models with 3.0L/V6-182 engine,** position pan under radiator and drain coolant, then close valve.
8. Remove upper radiator hose.
9. Disconnect two ground wires from transaxle case.
10. **On all models,** raise and support vehicle.

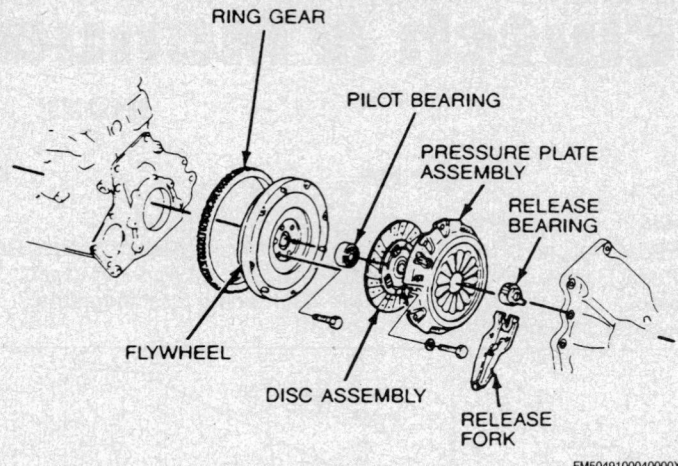

Fig. 2   Clutch assembly

RING GEAR
PILOT BEARING
PRESSURE PLATE ASSEMBLY
RELEASE BEARING
RELEASE FORK
DISC ASSEMBLY
FLYWHEEL

FM5049100040000X

11. Remove front tire and wheel assembly.
12. Remove splash shields.
13. Drain fluid from transaxle assembly.
14. Remove slave cylinder from transaxle.
15. Remove tie rod nuts, cotter pins, then disconnect tie rod ends.
16. Remove stabilizer link assemblies.
17. Remove bolts and nuts from lower control arm ball joints.
18. Pull lower control arms down to separate them from the steering knuckles.
19. Remove righthand joint shaft bracket.
20. Remove halfshaft assemblies from transaxle.
21. Install two Transaxle Plugs tool No. T88C-7025-AH or equivalent, between the differential side gears. **Failure to install the transaxle plugs may allow the differential side gears to become incorrectly positioned.**
22. Remove gusset plate to transaxle attaching bolts.
23. **On models with 3.0L/V6-182 engine,** remove front exhaust pipe.
24. **On all models,** disconnect extension bar and control rod.
25. **On models except 3.0L/V6-182 engine,** remove flywheel inspection cover.
26. **On all models,** remove starter motor, then access brackets.
27. Install Engine Support Bar tool No. D87L-6000-A or equivalent, then attach it to the engine hanger.
28. Remove center transaxle mount, then bracket.
29. Remove left transaxle mount.
30. Remove nut and bolt attaching right transaxle mount to vehicle frame.
31. Remove crossmember and left side lower control arm as an assembly.
32. Position jack under transaxle, then secure transaxle to jack.
33. Remove engine to transaxle attaching bolts.
34. Lower transaxle from vehicle.
35. Reverse procedure to install. Noting that during installation of the stabilizer link assemblies, turn the nuts on each

assembly until 1 inch of bolt thread can be measured from the upper nut. When this length is obtained, secure the upper nut, then back off the lower nut until a **torque** of 12–17 ft. lbs. is reached.

1993–95

1. Remove air cleaner and fresh air duct.
2. Remove the battery and battery tray.
3. Remove transaxle ground strap bolts, then the ground straps.
4. Mark position of transaxle electrical connectors for reassembly, then disconnect electrical connectors from transaxle.
5. Disconnect two spring clips retaining clutch pressure line to transaxle.
6. Remove clutch slave cylinder retaining bolts, then carefully position slave cylinder aside.
7. Install Rotunda Three Bar Engine Support tool No. 014-00750 or equivalent.
8. Remove upper transaxle to engine retaining bolts.
9. Remove two upper starter motor retaining bolts.
10. Remove two fuel filter retaining nuts and position filter aside. It is not necessary to disconnect fuel filter.
11. Remove two nuts and one through bolt from lefthand transaxle mount.
12. Raise and support vehicle.
13. **On 2.0L/4-122 models,** remove intake manifold support bracket.
14. **On all models,** disconnect starter motor from wiring harness.
15. Remove starter motor lower retaining bolt, then the starter motor.
16. Drain transaxle fluid from transaxle assembly, then discard drain plug washer.
17. Remove front tire and wheel assemblies.
18. Unstake halfshaft retaining nuts, then remove and discard retaining nuts.
19. Remove lower splash shields, then six transverse member retaining bolts.
20. Lower transverse member from vehicle.
21. Remove lefthand lower ball joint pinch

22. bolt, then pry the lower arm downward to separate the ball joint from spindle.
22. Pull lower edge of spindle outward to separate from end of halfshaft.
23. Using a pry bar, remove lefthand halfshaft from the transaxle case, then install Transaxle Plug tool No. T88C-7025-AH into side gear. **Failure to install transaxle plugs may allow side gears to become improperly positioned.**
24. Disconnect lefthand halfshaft at steering knuckle, then remove from vehicle.
25. **On models equipped with anti-lock brakes,** remove the clips from the lefthand wheel speed sensor, then the sensor wiring harness mounting nuts from strut assembly.

26. **On 2.5L/V6-152 models,** disconnect the lefthand and righthand Heated Oxygen Sensor electrical connectors.
27. Disconnect converter inlet pipes from exhaust manifolds, then discard retaining nuts.
28. Lower exhaust system far enough to gain access to righthand halfshaft support bearing.
29. Remove three righthand halfshaft support bearing retaining bolts.
30. **On models equipped with anti-lock brakes,** repeat Steps 21 through 25 for righthand halfshaft removal.
31. **On all models,** remove six nuts and two bolts from transaxle cradle.
32. Disconnect transaxle shift linkage from transaxle assembly.

33. Disconnect extension bar nut from transaxle.
34. Remove three rear transaxle mount to transaxle bolts, then the rear mount.
35. Remove lower transaxle to engine retaining bolts.
36. Separate transaxle from engine assembly, then lower transaxle from vehicle.
37. Reverse procedure to install, noting the following:
    a. Apply a thin coating of clutch grease or equivalent to the spline of the input shaft.
    b. Install a new washer on transaxle drain plug.
    c. Install new halfshaft retaining nuts.
    d. Tighten all components to specifications.

TIGHTENING SPECIFICATIONS

Year	Component	Torque/Ft. Lbs.
1992	Clutch Master Cylinder Nuts	14–19
	Extension Bar to Transaxle	40–51
	Center Transaxle Mount Bolts	27–40
	Center Transaxle Mount Nuts	47–66
	Crossmember Bolts	27–40
	Crossmember Nuts	55–69
	Flywheel	[5]
	Flywheel Inspection Cover	69–95 [4]
	Gusset Plate to Transaxle	27–38
	Left Mount to Bracket	49–69 [1]
	Pressure Plate	13–20
	Right Transaxle Mount	63–86
	Slave Cylinder	14–19
	Transaxle Case to Clutch Housing	13–14
	Transaxle Case to Clutch Housing	37–52 [1]
	Transaxle to Engine	66–86 [3]
	Transaxle to Engine	47–66 [2]
	Transaxle to Left Mount	27–38
	Transaxle to Left Mount	49–69 [1]
1993–95	Back-up Lamp Switch	15–21
	Clutch Master Cylinder Nuts	14–18
	Converter Inlet Pipe To Exhaust Manifold	30–41
	Extension Bar Nut	28–38
	Halfshaft Nuts	174–235 [8]
	Halfshaft Support Bearing Bolts	32–45
	Intake Manifold Bracket Bolts	27–38
	Lefthand Transaxle Mount Nuts	32–44

Year	Component	Torque/Ft. Lbs.
1993–95 —Cont'd	Lefthand Transaxle Mount Through Bolt	63–86
	Lower Engine To Transaxle Mounting Bolts [6]	28–38
	Lower Engine To Transaxle Mounting Bolts [7]	28–38
	Oil Level Plug	29–43
	Neutral Position Switch	15–21
	Pinch Bolt (Lower Ball Joint)	26–41
	Pressure Plate	13–18
	Rear Transaxle Mount To Transaxle Bolts	50–68
	Shift Rod Bolt	8–10
	Slave Cylinder	12–16
	Splash Shield Bolts	6–8
	Starter Motor Bolts	28–38
	Transaxle Cradle Nuts & Bolts	50–77
	Transaxle Shift Linkage Nut	14–18
	Transverse Member Bolts	69–96
	Upper Engine To Transaxle Mounting Bolts [6]	66–86
	Upper Engine To Transaxle Mounting Bolts [7]	50–73
	Wheel Lug Nuts	65–87

① —2.2L/4-133 turbo & 3.0L/V6-182 engine.
② —3.0L/V6-182 engine.
③ —Except 3.0L/V6-182 engine.
④ —Inch lbs.
⑤ —Except 2.5L/V6-152; 71–75 ft. lbs., 2.5L/V6-152; 45–49 ft. lbs.
⑥ —2.0L/4-122 Engine.
⑦ —2.5L/V6-152 Engine.
⑧ —Nut must be staked after tightening.

Rear Axle & Suspension

INDEX

DESCRIPTION

The rear suspension, **Fig. 1**, is fully independent and utilizes McPherson struts at each rear wheel. If the vehicle is equipped with the programmed ride control system, the rear strut towers locate the programmed ride control actuators and the strut assemblies. A forged rear spindle bolts to the shock absorber, double rear lateral links and a single trailing arm.

WHEEL BEARING
ADJUST
1992

1. Ensure parking brake is fully released.
2. Remove wheel and tire assembly.
3. Rotate brake drum to ensure no brake drag.
4. Using a dial indicator, check wheel bearing endplay. Endplay should not exceed .008 inch.
5. If measurement exceeds specification, replace bearing.

1993-95

1. Raise and support vehicle, then remove rear wheel.
2. **On models equipped with disc brakes,** remove rear disc brake caliper assembly.
3. **On all models,** install wheel lug nuts, then position Dial Indicator tool No. TOOL-4201-C or equivalent, against center of wheel hub.
4. Push and pull brake drum or rotor by hand, measuring wheel bearing endplay.
5. If bearing endplay exceeds .002 inch, check and adjust spindle retaining nut torque. Replace hub/wheel bearing if necessary.

WHEEL BEARING
REPLACE
1992

1. Remove rear brake drum or rotor from vehicle.
2. Remove dust seal and rear bearing.
3. Reverse procedure to install.
4. **Torque** wheel bearing locknut to 73-131 ft. lbs.

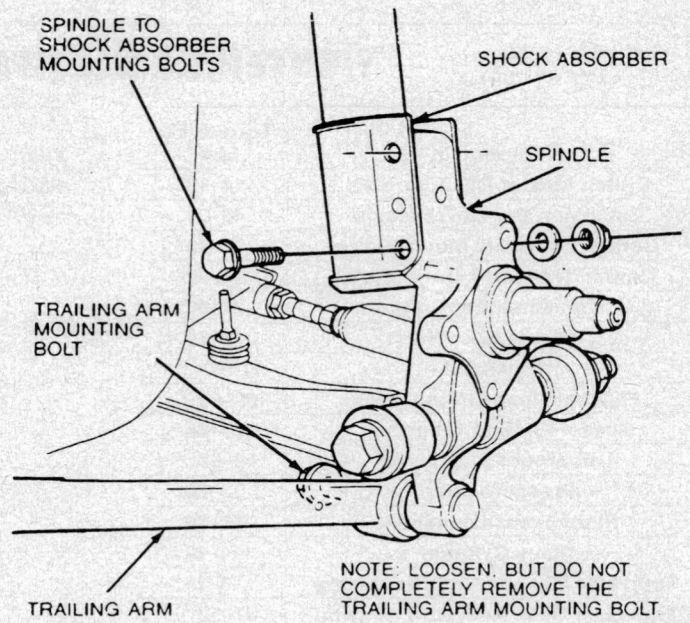

Fig. 1 Rear suspension components

1993-95

The hub/wheel bearing is not serviceable and must be replaced as an assembly.
1. Raise and support vehicle.
2. Remove rear wheel, then carefully raise staked portion of spindle locknut.
3. Remove and discard spindle locknut. **The retaining nut must not be reused. When loosening locknut, lock hub by applying service brakes.**
4. Remove brake drum or disc brake caliper and rotor.
5. Remove hub/wheel bearing assembly from vehicle.
6. Reverse procedure to install, noting the following:
   a. **Torque** the new spindle locknut to 130-174 ft. lbs.
   b. Stake spindle locknut at spindle indentation.

STRUT
REPLACE
1992

1. Disconnect battery ground cable, then raise and support vehicle.
2. Remove tire and wheel assembly.
3. Remove upper trunk side garnish, then the lower trunk side trim to gain access to strut assembly.
4. Disconnect programmed ride control module electrical connector from top of strut assembly, if equipped.
5. Remove programmed ride control module, if equipped.
6. Remove ABS harness and bracket, if equipped.
7. Remove rear brake drum and backing plate assembly or rear disc brake caliper, then the rotor assembly.
8. Remove brake line U-clip from strut housing.

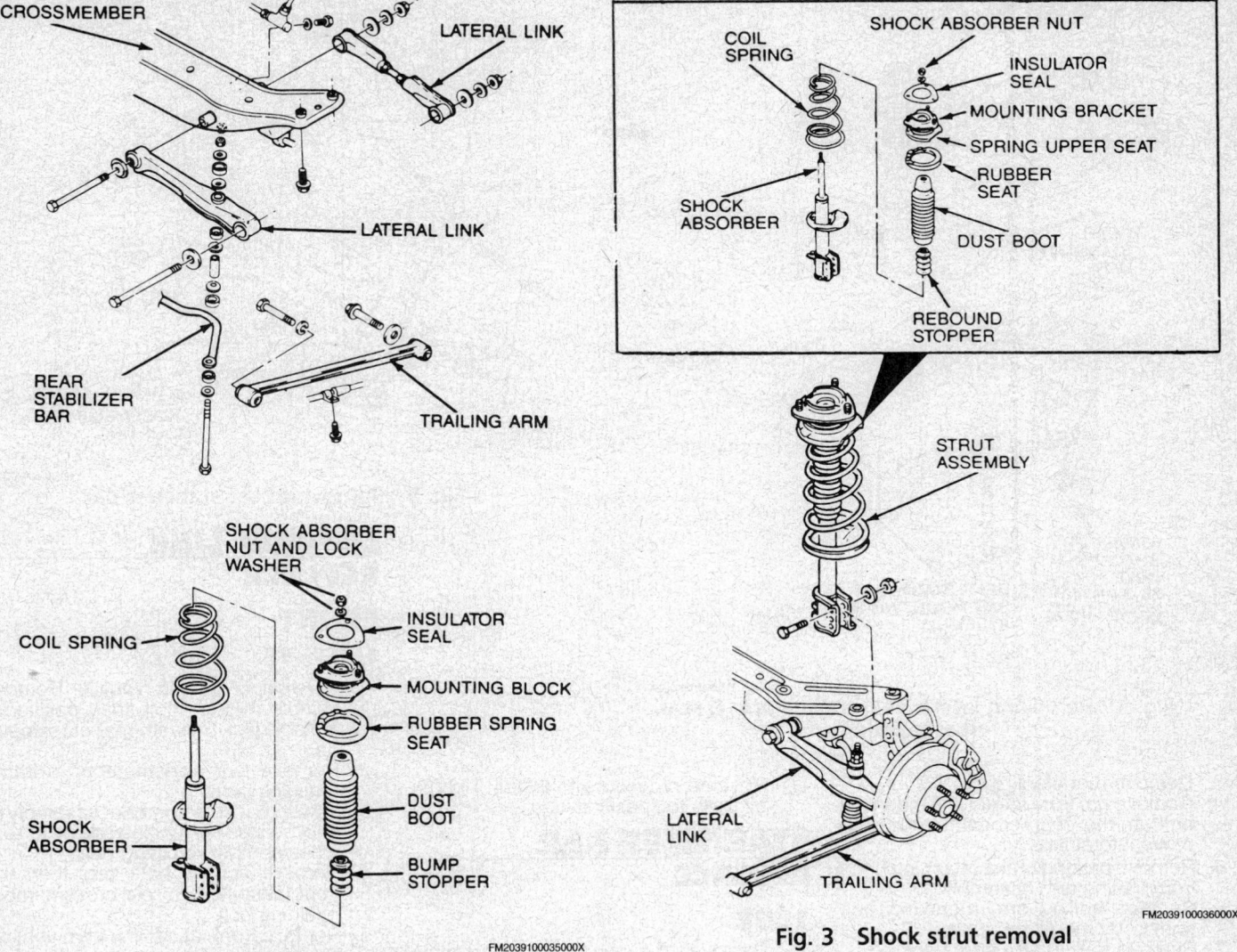

Fig. 2 Spindle removal

FM20391000035000X

Fig. 3 Shock strut removal

FM20391000036000X

9. Loosen trailing arm bolt, **Fig. 2.** Remove spindle to shock absorber attaching bolts.
10. Remove strut attaching nuts from inside the vehicle. Remove strut assembly, **Fig. 3.**
11. Reverse procedure to install. Tighten bolts to specifications.

1993—95

1. Raise and support vehicle, then remove rear wheels.
2. **On models equipped with anti-lock brakes,** remove speed sensor routing bracket.
3. **On all models,** remove brake line U-clip from strut assembly.
4. Remove two spindle to strut retaining bolts.
5. Remove trunk side panel to gain access to strut assembly.
6. Remove three upper strut retaining nuts, then the strut assembly.
7. Reverse procedure to install, tightening retaining nuts and bolts to specifications.

REAR CROSSMEMBER
REPLACE

1992

1. Disconnect battery ground cable.
2. Remove spindle from vehicle.
3. Remove rear stabilizer.
4. Remove nut from lateral link mounting bolt at the rear crossmember. Remove lateral link.
5. Remove parking brake attaching bolts from trailing arm assembly.
6. Remove trailing arm mounting bolt from body mounting bracket.
7. Remove trailing arm from vehicle.
8. Remove exhaust mounting bolts and brake line retaining bracket from rear crossmember.
9. Remove mounting bolts from end of the crossmember.
10. Remove rear crossmember and front lateral link as an assembly.
11. Remove common lateral link mounting bolt from rear crossmember.

12. Remove front lateral link from rear crossmember, **Fig. 4.**
13. Reverse procedure to install. Tighten bolts to specifications.

1993—95

1. Raise and support vehicle.
2. Remove spindle through bolts.
3. Remove stabilizer bar as described under "Stabilizer Bar, Replace."
4. Remove rear lateral link as described under "Rear Lateral Link, Replace."
5. Remove four rear crossmember to frame retaining bolts, then the rear crossmember.
6. Remove front lateral link.
7. Reverse procedure to install. Tighten all bolts to specifications.

TRAILING ARM
REPLACE

1992

1. Disconnect battery ground cable.
2. Remove spindle from vehicle.

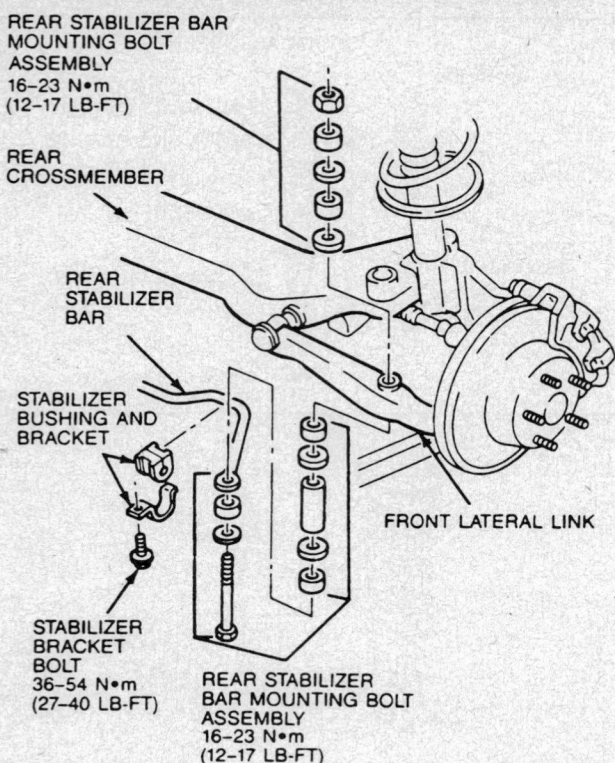

Fig. 4 Removing lateral link, trailing arm & rear crossmember

Fig. 5 Removing rear stabilizer bar

3. Remove rear stabilizer.
4. Remove nut from lateral link mounting bolt at the rear crossmember. Remove lateral link.
5. Remove parking brake attaching bolts from trailing arm assembly.
6. Remove trailing arm mounting bolt from body mounting bracket.
7. Remove trailing arm from vehicle.
8. Remove exhaust mounting bolts and brake line retaining bracket from rear crossmember.
9. Remove mounting bolts from end of the crossmember.
10. Remove rear crossmember and front lateral link as an assembly.
11. Remove common lateral link mounting bolt from rear crossmember.
12. Remove front lateral link from rear crossmember, **Fig. 4.**
13. Reverse procedure to install. Tighten bolts to specifications.

1993–95

1. Raise and support the vehicle.
2. Disconnect parking brake cable bracket from trailing arm.
3. Remove trailing arm to spindle bolt.
4. Remove the trailing arm to frame bolt, then trailing arm from vehicle.

5. Reverse procedure to install. Tighten all bolts to specifications.

STABILIZER BAR
REPLACE
1992

1. Remove mounting bolt assembly from front lateral link, **Fig. 5.**
2. Remove stabilizer bushing, then the bracket from rear crossmember.
3. Reverse procedure to install. Tighten bolts to specifications.

1993–95

1. Raise and support vehicle.
2. Remove two stabilizer bar to stabilizer control link retaining nuts.
3. Remove two stabilizer bracket retaining nuts, then stabilizer bracket retaining bolts.
4. Remove stabilizer bar from vehicle.
5. Reverse procedure to install, noting the following:
   a. Apply rubber grease to inside surface of stabilizer bar bushings.
   b. Align bushing with installation mark on stabilizer bar during installation.
   c. Tighten all bolts to specifications.

LATERAL LINK
REPLACE
FRONT
1993–95

1. Raise and support vehicle. Remove spindle through bolt, then position a suitable jack beneath rear crossmember.
2. Remove four crossmember to frame retaining bolts.
3. Lower rear crossmember assembly to gain access to front lateral link to rear crossmember retaining bolt.
4. Remove access hole cap, then the front lateral link to rear crossmember retaining bolt.
5. Remove front lateral link from vehicle.
6. Reverse procedure to install, noting the following:
   a. Tighten all bolts to specifications.
   b. Check wheel alignment.

REAR
1993–95

1. Raise and support vehicle.
2. Remove spindle through bolt.
3. Remove the stabilizer control link as described under "Stabilizer Control Link, Replace".
4. **Before removing adjusting cam bolt, scribe a mark on cam plate and crossmember for reference during installation.** Remove adjusting cam bolt.
5. Remove rear lateral link from vehicle.
6. Reverse procedure to install, noting the following:
   a. Tighten all bolts to specifications.
   b. Check wheel alignment.

TIGHTENING SPECIFICATIONS

Year	Component	Torque/Ft. Lbs.	Year	Component	Torque/Ft. Lbs.
1992	Crossmember Mounting Bolts	27–40	1993–95 —Cont'd	Rear Crossmember To Frame Bolts	27–40
	Hub Spindle To Back Plate	33–43		Rear Lateral Link To Stabilizer Control Link Nuts	27–40
	Hub Spindle To Shock Absorber	69–86		Speed Sensor Retaining Bolt	3–5
	Lateral Link Mounting Bolt	64–86		Wheel Bearing Locknut	130–174
	Wheel Bearing Locknut	73–131		Spindle Through Bolt	64–86
	Shock Absorber Tower Nut	47–67		Spindle To Strut Mounting Bolts	69–87
	Stabilizer Bar Mounting Bolt	12–17		Stabilizer Bar To Stabilizer Control Link Nuts	27–40
	Stabilizer Bracket Attaching Bolt	27–40		Stabilizer Bracket Bolts	27–40
	Strut Attaching Nuts	34–46		Stabilizer Bracket Nuts	27–40
	Trailing Arm Mounting Bolt (Front)	46–69		Trailing Arm To Frame Bolt	58–86
	Trailing Arm Mounting Bolt (Rear)	64–86		Trailing Arm To Spindle Bolt	64–86
	Wheel Lug Nuts	65–87		Upper Strut Retaining Nuts	34–46
1993–95	Adjusting Cam Bolt	58–86		Wheel Lug Nuts	65–87
	Front Lateral Link To Rear Crossmember Bolt	58–86			

Front Suspension & Steering

INDEX

DESCRIPTION

1992

This suspension is of the McPherson strut type, **Fig. 1**. The strut towers are located in the wheel wells and position the upper ends of the struts. If the vehicle is equipped with the optional Programmed Ride Control system, the ride control actuator bolts to the top of the strut mounting block that houses a rubber mounted strut bearing. The upper end of the coil spring rides in a rubber spring seat. A forged steering knuckle is bolted to the shock absorber.

If the vehicle is not equipped with the Programmed Ride Control System, the struts used are the conventional non-adjustable type. These struts are not interchangeable.

The lower ball joints are pressed into the lower control arm that is attached to the steering knuckle. The control arms are supported by rubber bushings at each end. A hollow stabilizer bar is connected to the control arms.

1993–95

The front suspension consists of Mc-Pherson struts and a single wishbone low-

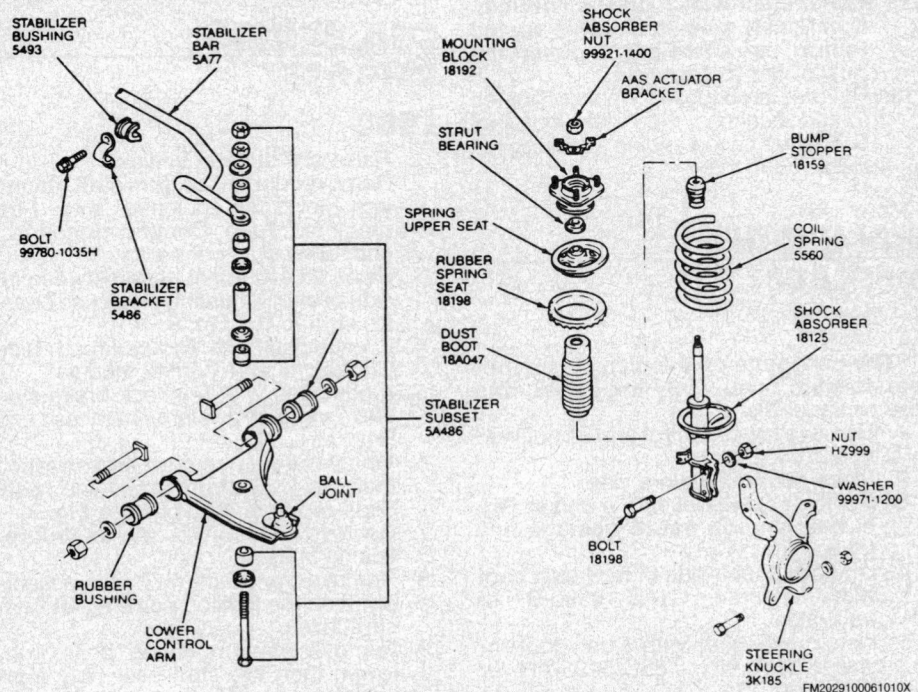

Fig. 1   Front suspension (Part 1 of 2)

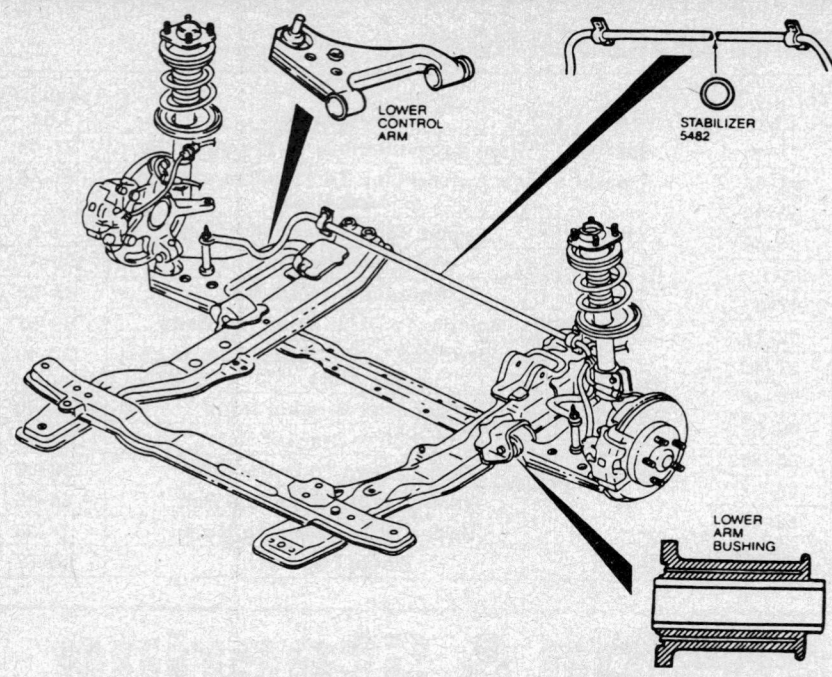

Fig. 1   Front suspension (Part 2 of 2)

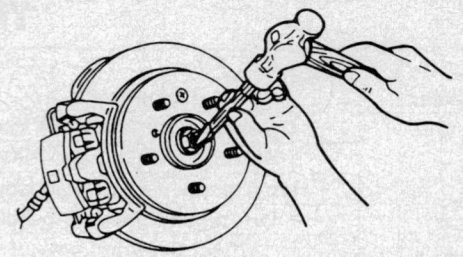

Fig. 2   Halfshaft attaching nut stake removal

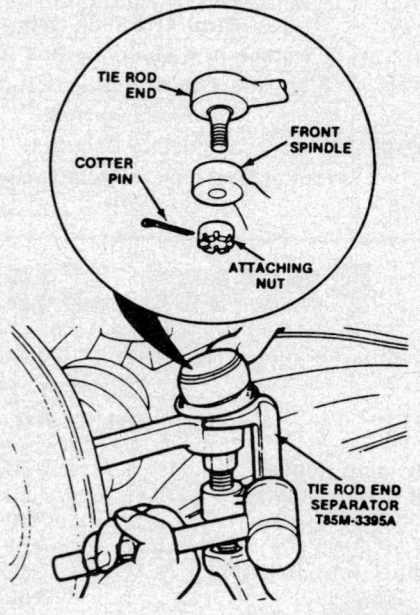

Fig. 3   Separating tie rod end from steering knuckle

er control arm. The upper end of the coil spring rides in a heavy rubber spring seat. A forged steering knuckle is bolted to the shock absorber.

The wide stance control arms are supported by rubber bushings at each end. Body lean on turns is controlled by a hollow stabilizer bar that connects both lower control arms. The front hub and rotor assemblies are supported by one piece roller bearings mounted in the steering knuckle. The wheel bearing is pressed into the steering knuckle. The hub assembly is pressed into the wheel bearing assembly.

WHEEL HUB & STEERING KNUCKLE
REPLACE

1. Raise and support vehicle.
2. Remove tire and wheel assembly.
3. Carefully raise the staked portion of the halfshaft attaching nut using a small cape chisel, **Fig. 2.**
4. Remove halfshaft attaching nut. When loosening the nut, lock the hub in position by having a helper lock the brakes. **Discard the nut, it should not be reused.**
5. Remove stabilizer bar link bolts.
6. Separate tie rod end from steering knuckle, **Fig. 3.**
7. Remove caliper, then anchor bracket assembly. Suspend caliper from coil spring. **Do not allow to hang from brake line.**
8. Remove brake rotor, **Fig. 4.**
9. **On models equipped with anti-lock brakes,** remove two wheel speed sensor retaining bolts, then the speed sensor.
10. Remove wheel speed sensor routing bracket.
11. **On all models,** use Tie Rod End Re-

mover tool No. TOOL-3290-D or equivalent to separate tie rod end from steering knuckle arm.
12. Remove lower ball joint clamp bolt, then separate ball joint from steering knuckle.
13. Remove steering knuckle to strut attaching bolts.
14. Slide front hub/steering knuckle assembly from strut bracket and halfshaft, **Fig. 4. Use caution not to damage grease seals. If hub binds on halfshaft splines, lightly tap end of halfshaft with a plastic hammer. If halfshaft splines become rusted to hub, use a two-jawed puller or a hub puller to separate.**
15. Reverse procedure to install. Tighten to specifications, then stake nut, **Fig. 5. Torque** tie rod ending attaching nut to 22–33 ft. lbs.

BALL JOINT
REPLACE

The ball joints on this vehicle are not serviceable parts. Only the dust boots are replaceable.
1. Remove lower control arm as outlined in this section.
2. Place control arm in a vise.
3. Remove dust boot with a chisel, **Fig. 6. Use caution not to damage ball joint.**
4. Liberally coat inside of new dust boot with lubricant C1AZ-19590-B or equivalent.
5. Install dust boot with Dust Boot Installer tool No. T88C-5493-AH or equivalent, **Fig. 7.**
6. Install lower control arm.

COIL SPRING
REPLACE
1992

1. Raise and support vehicle.
2. Remove rubber cap from strut mounting block. If equipped with Programmed Ride Control, disconnect control module connector.
3. Place an alignment mark between inside of strut mounting block and chassis strut tower, **Fig. 8.**
4. If equipped with Programmed Ride Control, remove control module.
5. If equipped with anti-lock brake system, remove system harness and bracket.
6. **On all models,** remove brake caliper, then the U-clip from brake line hose. Slide clip from strut bracket, **Fig. 9.**
7. Remove steering knuckle to strut retaining bolts.
8. Remove vane airflow meter assembly, then the ignition coil bracket from strut tower.
9. Remove strut mounting bolts from tower, then the strut assembly from vehicle.
10. Place strut assembly in a vise.

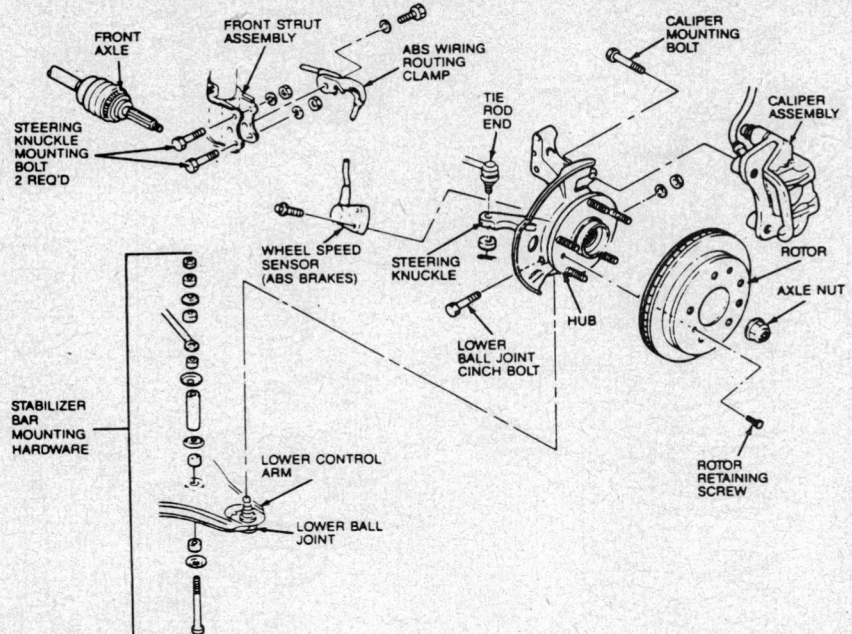

Fig. 4 Steering knuckle, hub & rotor installation

FM2029100064000X

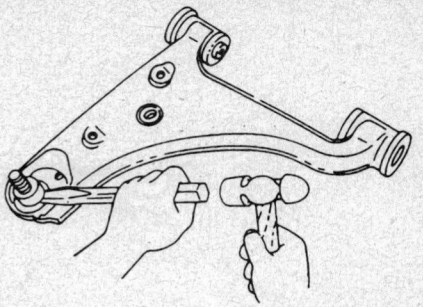

FM2029100066000X

Fig. 6 Ball joint dust boot removal

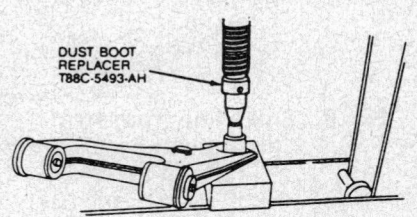

FM2029100067000X

Fig. 7 Ball joint dust boot installation

Fig. 5 Staking halfshaft attaching nut

RADIUS 1.5mm ± .25 (0.6 ± .01 INCH)

3/4 INCH APPROX.

6 1/2 INCH APPROX.

2mm (0.08 INCH) OR MORE

COLD CHISEL

ATTACHING NUT

THE STAKING TOOL CAN BE FABRICATED FROM AN EXISTING HARDENED CHISEL. THE CORRECT RADIUS ON THE CHISEL TIP WILL PREVENT IMPROPER STAKING. DO NOT ATTEMPT TO STAKE WITH A SHARPED EDGED TOOL.

FM2029100065000X

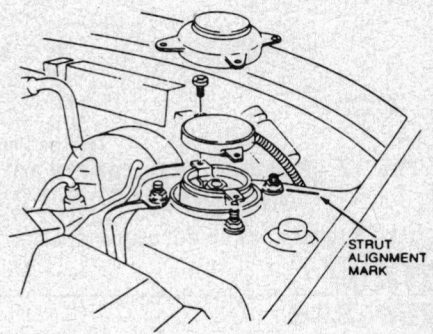

FM2029100068000X

Fig. 8 Placing strut alignment mark

11. Loosen, but do not remove shock absorber nut, **Fig. 10.**
12. Remove strut assembly from vise, then compress coil spring, using a Spring Compressor or tool No. D85P-7178-A.
13. Remove shock absorber nut, gradually releasing spring tension.
14. If equipped with Programmed Ride Control, remove control module bracket.
15. **On all models,** remove strut mounting block, upper rubber spring seat, dust boot, bump stopper, then coil spring from strut, **Fig. 11.**
16. Reverse procedure to assemble, then install. When installing the strut mounting block, ensure notch on mounting block is 180 degrees from the steering knuckle mounting bracket on the strut. Tighten to specifications.

1993–95

1. Raise and support vehicle, then remove front wheels.
2. **On models equipped with anti-lock brakes,** remove wheel speed sensor routing bracket.
3. **On all models,** remove brake line U-clip from strut housing.
4. Remove two steering knuckle to strut mounting bolts.
5. Remove four upper strut retaining nuts.
6. Remove strut assembly from vehicle.
7. Secure strut assembly in McPherson Strut Spring Compressor tool No. D85P-7178-A or equivalent.
8. Compress coil spring, then remove strut retaining nut.
9. Remove strut assembly from spring compressor.
10. Release spring compressor, then remove coil spring, upper rubber spring seat, upper spring seat, thrust bearing and strut mounting block.
11. Install strut mounting block, thrust bearing, upper spring seat, upper rubber spring seat and coil spring in the spring compressor. **Face direction indicator on strut mounting block toward rear outboard position during reassembly.**
12. Compress coil spring. **Ensure lower coil of spring is seated on step of lower seat.**
13. Position new strut in compressed coil spring.
14. Install strut retaining nut, then **torque to 66–86 ft. lbs.**
15. Release spring compressor, then remove strut assembly.
16. Reverse Steps 1 through 6 to install strut assembly in vehicle, noting the following:
   a. Tighten all bolts to specifications.

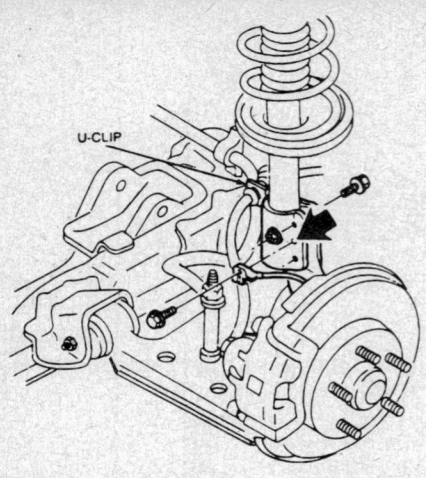

Fig. 9 Brake line from strut disconnect

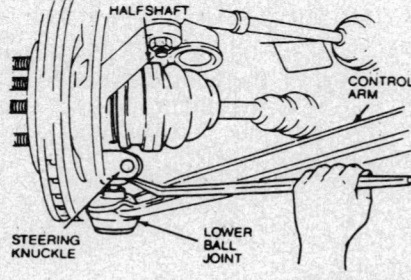

Fig. 12 Ball joint from control arm separation

   b. Check front wheel alignment.

STRUT
REPLACE

Refer to "Coil Spring, Replace" for procedure.

CONTROL ARM
REPLACE

LOWER

1992

1. Raise and support vehicle.
2. Remove wheel and tire assembly.
3. Remove brake caliper, then secure to coil spring. **Do not allow caliper to hang by brake hose.**
4. Remove stabilizer bar as outlined in this section.
5. Remove ball joint clamp bolt, then separate ball joint from steering knuckle, **Fig. 12.**
6. **On vehicles equipped with automatic transaxle,** remove harmonic damper from chassis subframe, left-hand side, **Fig. 13.**
7. Remove lower control arm mounting bolts, then the control arm, **Fig. 14.**
8. Reverse procedure to install. Tighten to specifications.

1993—95

1. Raise and support vehicle, then re-

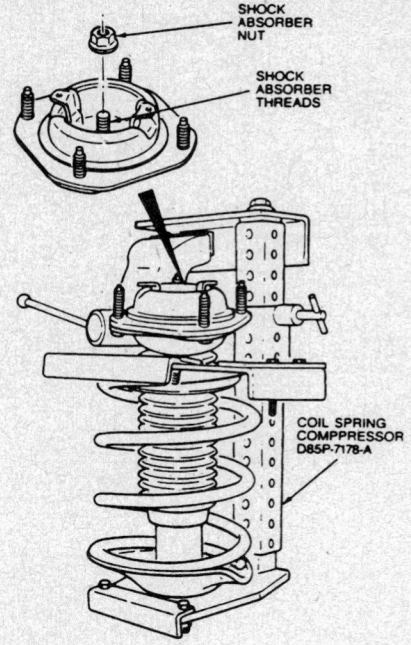

Fig. 10 Spring compressor installation

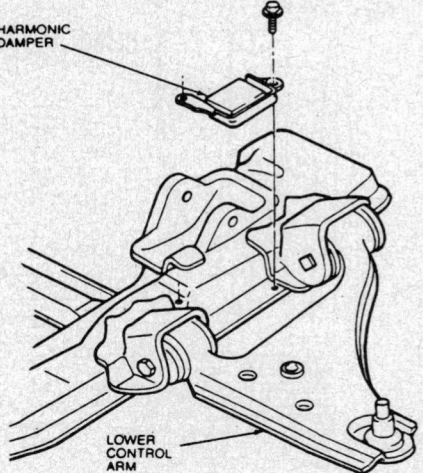

Fig. 13 Harmonic damper installation

move front wheels.
2. Remove lower ball joint pinch bolt.
3. Remove stabilizer control link to lower control arm retaining nut.
4. Separate ball joint stud from steering knuckle.
5. Remove two lower control arm bushing retaining bolts.
6. Remove lower control arm from vehicle.
7. Position new control arm against vehicle underbody.
8. Install lower control arm rear bushing bolt. **Torque** retaining bolt to 69-96 ft. lbs.
9. Install lower control arm front bushing bolt. **Torque** retaining bolt to 58-78 ft. lbs.
10. Install ball joint stud into steering knuckle.

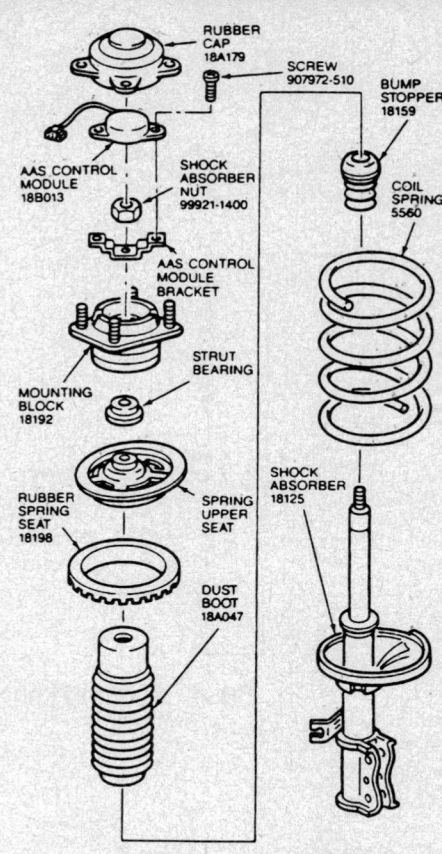

Fig. 11 Strut disassembled

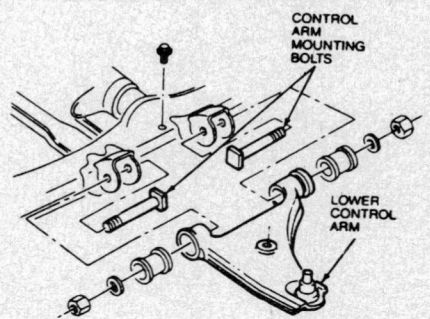

Fig. 14 Lower control arm installation

11. Install ball joint pinch bolt. **Torque** bolt to 25-42 ft. lbs.
12. Install stabilizer control link to lower control arm nut. **Torque** retaining nut to 27-40 ft. lbs.
13. Install front wheels, then **torque** wheel lug nuts to 65-87 ft. lbs.

STABILIZER BAR
REPLACE

1992

1. Raise and support vehicle.
2. Remove wheel and tire assembly.
3. Remove stabilizer bar link assembly from lower control arm, **Fig. 15.**
4. Remove mount bolt from stabilizer bar bushing.
5. Remove stabilizer bar from vehicle.

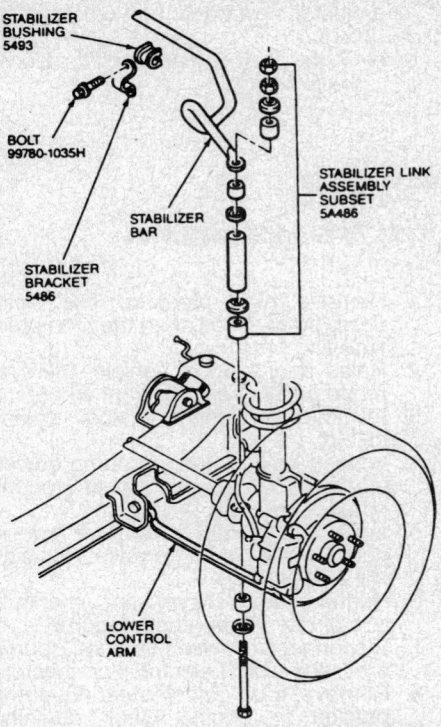

Fig. 15 Stabilizer bar installation

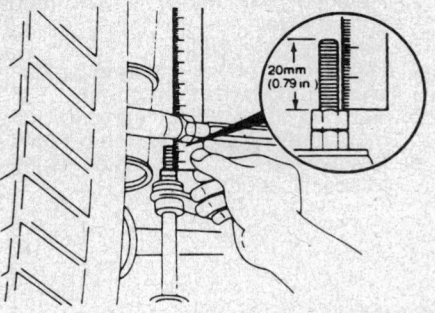

Fig. 16 Stabilizer bar link installation

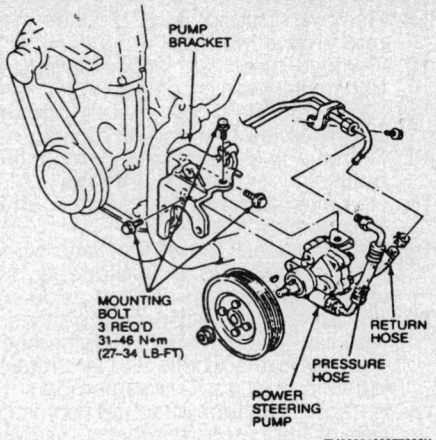

Fig. 17 Power steering pump installation

6. Reverse procedure to install. Tighten to specifications, and tighten stabilizer bar link nut until 0.79 inch of threads protrude above nut, **Fig. 16.**

1993–95

1. Raise and support vehicle, then remove front wheel.
2. Remove six transverse member retaining bolts, then the transverse member.
3. Remove two bolts and six nuts from transaxle cradle, then the cradle.
4. Disconnect Heated Oxygen Sensor electrical connectors.
5. Disconnect converter inlet pipe(s) at exhaust manifold(s) and position aside.
6. **On models equipped with manual transaxle,** remove extension bar nut, then the transaxle shift linkage bolt.
7. **On all models,** position a jack under front crossmember, then remove four bolts and two nuts retaining crossmember to body.
8. Remove stabilizer bar to stabilizer control link retaining nuts, then the four stabilizer bar bracket bolts.
9. Lower front crossmember to allow for removal of stabilizer bar.
10. Remove stabilizer bar from right side of vehicle.
11. Reverse procedure to install, noting the following:
    a. Tighten all bolts to specifications.
    b. Apply rubber grease to inside surfaces of stabilizer bushings.
    c. Align bushing with installation mark on stabilizer bar.

POWER STEERING GEAR
REPLACE

1992

Standard Power Steering Gear

1. Disconnect battery ground cable.
2. Raise and support vehicle.
3. Remove wheel and tire assemblies.
4. Separate tie rods from steering knuckles.
5. Remove plastic dust shield from both sides of lower inner fender.
6. Pull back dust boot and have a helper rotate steering column shaft until clamp bolt becomes accessible, then lock steering column.
7. Place an alignment mark between steering column pinion shaft and intermediate shaft lower universal joint.
8. Remove clamp bolt from steering column intermediate shaft lower universal joint.
9. Disconnect two hydraulic lines from steering gear. Position hydraulic lines aside.
10. Remove steering gear mount bolts, then lower steering gear until it clears bulkhead. Slide steering gear toward right until lefthand tie rod clears left lower control arm.
11. Slide steering gear toward left, then remove from vehicle.
12. Reverse procedure to install. Tighten to specifications.

Electronic Power Steering Gear

1. Disconnect battery ground cable.
2. Raise and support vehicle.
3. Remove wheel and tire assemblies.
4. Separate tie rods from steering knuckles.
5. Remove plastic dust shield from both sides of lower inner fender.
6. Pull back dust boot and have a helper rotate steering column shaft until clamp bolt becomes accessible, then lock steering column.
7. Place an alignment mark between steering column pinion shaft and intermediate shaft lower universal joint.
8. Remove clamp bolt from steering column intermediate shaft lower universal joint.

9. Disconnect solenoid valve, then the power steering pressure switch electrical connectors.
10. Disconnect three hydraulic lines from steering gear, and discard two copper washers from each fitting. Position hydraulic lines aside.
11. Remove steering gear mount bolts, then lower steering gear until it clears bulkhead. Slide steering gear toward right until lefthand tie rod clears left lower control arm. Then, slide steering gear toward left and remove from vehicle.
12. Reverse procedure to install, noting the following:
    a. Tighten steering gear mount bolts to specifications.
    b. **Torque** steering column intermediate shaft lower universal joint clamp bolt to 13-20 ft. lbs.
    c. Install new copper washers when connecting hydraulic lines to steering gear.

1993–95

1. Install Three Bar Engine Support tool No. D88L-6000-A or equivalent.
2. Raise and support vehicle, then remove front wheels.
3. Using Tie Rod End Remover tool No. TOOL-3290-D or equivalent, separate tie rod ends from left and right steering knuckles.
4. Remove left and right lower splash shields.
5. Remove six transverse member retaining bolts, then the transverse member.
6. Remove two bolts and six retaining nuts from transaxle cradle, then the cradle.
7. **On models equipped with 2.5L/V6-152 engine,** disconnect two Heated Oxygen Sensor electrical connectors.
8. Remove converter inlet pipes from exhaust manifolds, then position aside.
9. **On all models,** using two line wrenches, disconnect high pressure line from steering gear. Plug open lines.
10. Disconnect return line from steering gear, then plug line.

11. Remove ground wire bracket from rear engine mount.
12. Remove three rear engine mount to transaxle retaining bolts.
13. Remove rear motor mount through bolt, then the rear engine mount.
14. Remove two steering gear mounting brackets.
15. Remove steering intermediate shaft to pinion shaft pinch bolt.
16. **On manual transaxle equipped models,** remove extension bar retaining nut and position bar aside.
17. **On all models,** , position transmission jack under front crossmember, then remove six bolts and two retaining nuts from front crossmember.
18. Remove vent tube attached to driver's side of front crossmember.
19. Remove stabilizer bar to stabilizer control link retaining nuts.
20. Lower front crossmember to allow for removal of steering gear.
21. Remove steering gear from driver's side of vehicle.
22. Reverse procedure to install, noting the following:
    a. Tighten all components to specifications.
    b. Fill power steering fluid to correct level and check for leaks.
    c. Check front wheel alignment.

POWER STEERING PUMP
REPLACE

1992

1. Disconnect battery ground cable.

2. Remove righthand inner fender splash shield.
3. Remove drive belt.
4. Disconnect power steering pressure and return hoses from pump.
5. Remove three power steering pump mounting bolts and the pump, **Fig. 17.**
6. Reverse procedure to install. Tighten to specifications.

1993–95
2.0L/4-122 Engine

1. Remove two power steering pump belt shield retaining bolts, then the shield.
2. Remove pump adjustment bolt, then the pump retaining bolt.
3. Remove power steering pump drive belt.
4. Insert a screwdriver through hole in pump pulley, then remove retaining nut and pulley.
5. Remove two supply line manifold bolts.
6. Remove high pressure line banjo bolt, then disconnect pump pressure switch electrical connector.
7. Remove power steering pump through bolt, then the pump assembly.
8. If necessary, remove power steering pump brackets.
9. Reverse procedure to install, noting the following:

a. Install new banjo bolt crush washers.
b. Tighten all components to specifications.

2.5L/V6-152 Engine

1. Remove high pressure line holddown bracket bolt, then the high pressure line banjo bolt.
2. Raise and support vehicle, then remove passenger side front wheel.
3. Remove passenger side splash shield.
4. Loosen power steering pump adjusting bolt, then remove power steering pump drive belt.
5. Insert a screwdriver through hole in pump pulley, then remove retaining nut and pulley.
6. Remove two supply line manifold bolts from power steering pump.
7. Disconnect power steering pump pressure switch electrical connector.
8. Remove four power steering pump bracket to engine block retaining bolts.
9. Remove power steering pump from vehicle.
10. Reverse procedure to install, noting the following:
    a. Install new banjo bolt crush washers.
    b. Tighten all components to specifications.

TIGHTENING SPECIFICATIONS

Year	Component	Torque/Ft. Lbs.
1992	Ball Joint Clamp Bolt	32–40
	Control Arm Rod Jam Nuts	41–59
	Dynamic Damper Mounting Bolts	31–46
	Halfshaft Attaching Nut	116–174
	Lower Control Arm Mounting Bolts	69–93
	Power Steering Pump Mounting Bolts	27–34
	Stabilizer Bar Bushing	27–40
	Steering Gear Mount Bolts	27–40
	Steering Knuckle To Strut	69–86
	Strut Attaching Nuts	34–46
	Strut Tower Nut	47–69
	Tie Rod End Jam Nuts	51–72
	Wheel Lug Nuts	65–87
1993–95	Ball Joint Clamp Bolt	25–42
	Extension Bar Nut	28–38
	Front Crossmember	68–96
	Halfshaft Attaching Nut	174–235
	Intermediate Shaft to Pinion Shaft Bolt	13–20
	Lower Control Arm Front Bushing Bolt	58–78
	Lower Control Arm Rear Bushing Bolts	69–96

Year	Component	Torque/Ft. Lbs.
1993–95 —Cont'd	Lower Control Arm Rear Bushing Nut	66–86
	Power Steering Pump Through Bolt (2.0L/4-121)	32–45
	Power Steering Pump To Engine Block (2.5L/V6-152)	23–34
	Pulley Nut	36–43
	Rear Engine Mount Through Bolt	63–86
	Rear Engine Mount To Transaxle Bolts	50–68
	Speed Sensor Retaining Bolts	12–17
	Stabilizer Bar To Stabilizer Control Link Nuts	27–40
	Stabilizer Control Link To Lower Control Arm Nut	27–40
	Steering Gear Mounting Bracket Bolts	27–40
	Steering Knuckle To Strut	68–86
	Supply Line Manifold Bolts	10–13
	Transaxle Cradle Nuts & Bolts	50–77
	Transaxle Shift Linkage Bolt	14–18
	Transverse Member Bolts	68–96
	Wheel Lug Nuts	65–87

Wheel Alignment

INDEX

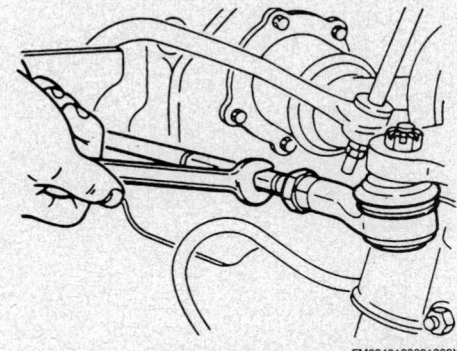

Fig. 1 Front toe-in adjustment

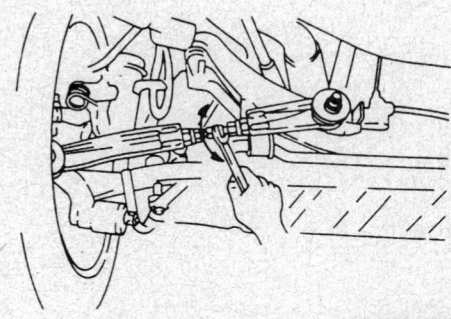

Fig. 2 Rear toe-in adjustment

PRELIMINARY INSPECTION

Before measuring and setting front wheel alignment, rest front wheels on turn plates.

Before setting rear toe, rest rear wheels on slider plates or turn plates. Before setting any alignment angle, jounce the vehicle three times at each end to establish trim height.

Special adapters are available for using a magnetic hub gauge at rear wheels. Depending on type of equipment used, these may not be necessary. Hub gauge will snap into place on brake drum after hub cap and bearing cap are removed. Magnetic mounting toe gauges may also be installed in the same manner.

Always perform wheel alignment on a level alignment rack. Do not attempt to check or adjust front wheel alignment without first inspecting front end components.

Check all factors of front wheel alignment except turning angle before making any adjustments. Check the turning angle only after camber and toe have been adjusted to specification. Check front wheel alignment under following curb load conditions:

1. Establish standing curb height.
2. Remove heavy weights from trunk.
3. Ensure all tires are inflated to specification (cold).
4. Ensure Fuel tank, oil reservoir and radiator are filled to specification. If necessary, add six pounds of weight to trunk for each gallon of gasoline missing from tank.
5. Place front seats in full rear position.
6. Check rear toe adjustment.
7. Always road test vehicle after adjusting alignment. If vehicle still pulls, switch front tires. If vehicle still pulls in same direction, recheck alignment and rear tracking. If vehicle pulls in opposite direction, rotate tires, then road test again.

FRONT WHEEL ALIGNMENT

Always adjust rear toe before setting front alignment angles.

CASTER

Front caster adjustment is not a separate procedure on this vehicle. Front caster should fall within specification when front camber is adjusted. If caster does not fall within specification, check control arms, stabilizers and bushings. If these components are satisfactory, check vehicle body for distortion at suspension mounting points.

CAMBER

1. Raise vehicle and support at body so that front suspension is unloaded.
2. Remove tire and wheel assembly.
3. Remove upper strut attaching nuts.
4. Lower strut, then rotate strut mounting block until camber is within specification.
5. Reinstall strut in strut tower.
6. **Torque** strut attaching nuts to 34-46 ft. lbs., then recheck camber adjustment.

TOE-IN

1. Loosen jam nuts at tie rod ends, then release clips at small ends of steering gear boots. **Ensure boots are free on tie rod ends so that they will not be twisted when tie rods are turned.**
2. Turn tie rods into or out of tie rod ends an equal amount on each side, **Fig. 1**. To increase toe-in, turn right tie rod toward front of vehicle, and turn left tie rod toward read of vehicle. To decrease toe-in, turn tie rods in opposite direction. One turn of each side tie rod changes toe-in by approximately 0.28 inch.
3. Check front tracking. **Always set tracking immediately after setting toe.** Set tracking by using rear wheels as a reference point. Follow equipment manufacturer's instructions to check tracking. The angle of each front wheel in relationship to rear wheels must be the same.
4. Ensure toe-in is still within specifications, then **torque** jam nuts to 51-72 ft. lbs. Ensure steering gear boot ends are correctly positioned on appropriate sections of tie rods, then install boot clips.
5. Measure turning angle by placing front wheels on a turning-radius gauge and fully turning wheels to the left, then right. On 1992 models, inner turning angle should be 36.44° and outer turning angle should be 30.99°. On 1993 models, inner turning angle should be 35-39° and outer turning angle should be 30-34°.

REAR WHEEL ALIGNMENT

TOE-IN

1992

1. Loosen jam nuts clockwise on right control arm, then loosen jam nuts counterclockwise on left control arm.
2. To increase toe-in, turn right control arm rod counterclockwise and turn left control arm rod clockwise, **Fig. 2.**
3. To decrease toe-in, turn right control

arm clockwise and turn left control arm counterclockwise. **Turn control arm rods into or out of control arm ends an equal amount on each side.** One turn of each control arm rod changes toe by .46 inch.

4. **Torque** control arm jam nuts to 41-59 ft. lbs.

1993—95

1. Loosen cam nut on rear lateral link.
2. Turning adjusting cam bolt one graduation mark changes toe-in about 0.13 inch. **Turning the left cam bolt counterclockwise increases toe-in, turning the cam bolt clockwise increases toe-out. Turning the right cam bolt clockwise increases toe-in, turning the cam bolt counterclockwise increases toe-out.**
3. Adjust toe-in to correct setting.
4. **Torque** the cam nut to 58-86 ft. lbs.

MERCURY CAPRI

NOTE: Refer To Rear Of This Manual For Vehicle Manufacturer's Special Service Tool Suppliers.

INDEX OF SERVICE OPERATIONS

NOTE: For Service Operations Not Listed Below, Refer To The Table Of Contents In The Front Of This Manual.

Specifications

GENERAL ENGINE SPECIFICATIONS

Year	Engine Liter/CID	Engine VIN Code	Fuel System	Bore and Stroke	Compression Ratio	Net H.P. @ RPM	Maximum Torque Ft. Lbs. @ RPM	Normal Oil Pressure psi
1992-94	1.6L/4-98 ②	Z	MPI	3.07 x 3.29	9.4	100 @ 5750	95 @ 5500	①
	1.6L/4-98 ③	6	MPI	3.07 x 3.29	7.9	132 @ 6000	136 @ 3000	①

① —25–31 psi. at 1000 RPM, 43–48 psi. at 3000 RPM as revised per Technical Service Bulletin No. 91-11B-7.

② —DOHC.
③ —Turbocharged engine.

TUNE UP SPECIFICATIONS

Year & Engine (VIN Code) ①	Spark Plug Gap	Ignition Timing @ BTDC				Curb Idle Speed, RPM ③		Fast Idle Speed, RPM		Fuel Pump Pressure, psi
		Firing Order	Man. Trans.	Auto. Trans.	Mark Fig.	Man. Trans.	Auto. Trans.	Man. Trans.	Auto. Trans.	
1992–94										
1.6L/4-98(Z) DOHC	.041	1-3-4-2	2 ⑤	2 ⑤	A	800–900	800–900N	②	②	64–85 ④
1.6L/4-98(6) Turbo	.041	1-3-4-2	12 ⑤	12 ⑤	A	800–900	800–900N	②	②	64–85 ④

BTDC–Before Top Dead Center.
① —The eighth digit of the Vehicle Identification Number (VIN) denotes engine code.
② —Controlled by ECA (Electronic Control Assembly).
③ —N: Neutral.
④ —Start engine. On 1992 models, disconnect vane airflow meter electrical connector. On 1993–94 models, remove fuel pump relay, located at center of instrument panel below PCM. On all models, after engine stalls, place ignition switch in Off position. Connect suitable fuel pressure test gauge between fuel filter & fuel rail. On 1992 models, connect vane airflow electrical connector. On 1993–94 models, install fuel pump relay. On all models, connect a jumper wire between fuel pump test connector terminals. Place ignition switch in On position & note fuel pressure.
⑤ —With distributor vacuum advance hose disconnected & plugged.

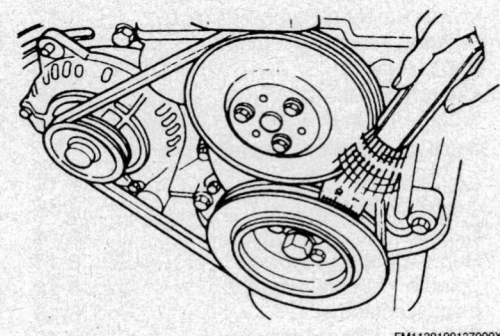

FM1139100137000X

Fig. A

FRONT WHEEL ALIGNMENT SPECIFICATIONS

Year	Caster Angle, Degrees		Camber Angle, Degrees		Toe-In Inch	King Pin Inclination Degrees
	Limits	Desired	Limits	Desired		
1992-94	-.15 to +2.35	+1.6	+.05 to +1.55	+.8	0 to .6	+12.3

REAR WHEEL ALIGNMENT SPECIFICATIONS

Year	Camber Angle, Degrees		Toe-In Degrees
	Limits	Desired	
1992-94	-¾ to +¾	0	0 to +.6

COOLING SYSTEM & CAPACITY DATA

Year	Model or Engine/VIN ①	Coolant Capacity, Qts.		Radiator Cap Relief Pressure, Lbs.	Thermo. Opening Temp.	Fuel Tank Gals.	Engine Oil Refill Qts.	Transaxle Oil	
		Man. Trans.	Auto. Trans.					Manual Transaxle Qts.	Auto. Transaxle Qts. ②
1992-94	1.6L/4-98(Z)	5.3	6.3	16	③	11.1	3.5 ④	3.4	7.2
	1.6L/4-98(6)	6.3	6.3	16	③	11.1	3.7 ④	3.5	7.2

① —The eighth digit of Vehicle Identification Number (VIN) denotes engine code.
② —Approximately. Make final check w/dipstick.
③ —Thermostat sub valve at 190.5°–193.5° and main valve at 196.5°–199.5°.
④ —Includes filter.

LUBRICANT DATA

Yea	Model	Lubricant Type			
		Transaxle		Power Steering	Brake System
		Manual	Automatic		
1992–94	All	①	Mercon	Mercon	DOT 3

① —Except turbo, 75W-90 GL-4/GL-5; Turbo, Mercon.

Electrical

NOTE: On Air Bag Equipped Models, Refer To "Air Bag System Precautions" Located In The Front Of This Manual For System Disarming & Arming Procedures.

INDEX

PRECAUTIONS

AIR BAG SYSTEMS

Refer to "Air Bag System Precautions" in the front of this manual for system disarming and arming procedures.

FUSE PANEL & FLASHER LOCATION

The fuse panel is located under the left side of the instrument panel. The hazard flasher is located inside the lefthand bottom edge of the instrument panel. The turn signal flasher is located on the relay panel above the fuse panel.

STARTER
REPLACE

1. Disconnect battery ground cable, then isolate cable end with electrical tape.
2. Disconnect starter electrical connectors, then remove starter motor upper attaching bolts.
3. Remove intake manifold upper support bracket attaching bolts.
4. Raise and support vehicle, then remove starter support bracket to intake manifold support bracket attaching bolt.
5. Remove intake manifold lower support bracket attaching bolts.
6. Loosen exhaust hangers, if necessary, then remove starter attaching bolts.
7. Reverse procedure to install noting the following:
   a. **Torque** starter to support bracket attaching nuts to 54–70 inch lbs.
   b. **Torque** starter support bracket to manifold support bracket attaching bolt to 14–19 ft. lbs.

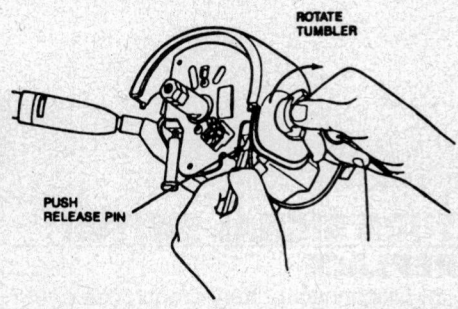

ROTATE TUMBLER

PUSH RELEASE PIN

FM9129100013000X

Fig. 1   Ignition lock replacement

c. **Torque** upper and lower starter attaching bolts to 23-30 ft. lbs.
d. **Torque** upper and lower intake manifold bracket attaching bolts to 22-34 ft. lbs.

DISTRIBUTOR
REPLACE

1. Disconnect battery ground cable, then isolate cable end with electrical tape.
2. Disconnect distributor high tension cable and mark for installation.
3. Disconnect remaining electrical connectors.
4. Remove distributor attaching bolt, then remove distributor.
5. Reverse procedure to install

IGNITION LOCK
REPLACE

1. Disconnect battery ground cable.
2. Remove steering wheel as outlined under "Steering Wheel, Replace."
3. Remove steering column lower shroud.

4. Install ignition key, then rotate tumbler while pushing release pin with 0.125 inch drift **Fig. 1.**
5. Remove lock from housing.
6. Reverse procedure to install.

IGNITION SWITCH
REPLACE

1. Disconnect battery ground cable.
2. Remove steering column lower shroud.
3. Remove center access panel and lower steering column trim panel.
4. Remove lefthand defroster connector tube.
5. Remove upper steering column attaching bolts, then lower steering column to rest on instrument panel brace. **Ensure wires are not pinched when steering column is lowered.**
6. Remove ignition lock as outlined under "Ignition Lock, Replace."
7. Remove upper steering column cover.
8. Remove column lock shield.
9. Disconnect ignition switch electrical connector.
10. Remove switch attaching screws, then remove switch.
11. Reverse procedure to install. **Torque** ignition switch attaching screws to 50-70 inch lbs. **Torque** steering column lock shield attaching screws to 11-14 ft. lbs. **Torque** upper steering column attaching bolts to 17-23 ft. lbs.

NEUTRAL SAFETY SWITCH
REPLACE

1. Disconnect battery ground cable.

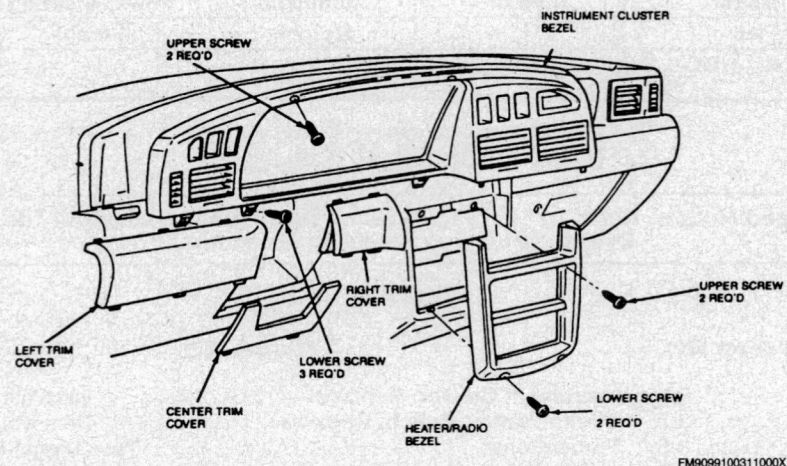

Fig. 2 Instrument cluster replacement

HEADLAMP SWITCH
REPLACE

1. Disconnect battery ground cable.
2. Remove instrument cluster bezel.
3. Disconnect headlamp switch electrical connectors.
4. Depress switch tangs, then remove switch from bezel.
5. Reverse to install.

STOP LIGHT SWITCH
REPLACE
REMOVAL

1. Disconnect stop lamp switch electrical connectors.
2. Remove stop lamp switch attaching nut, then remove switch.

INSTALLATION

1. Install switch, then finger tighten attaching nut.
2. Ensure distance from brake pedal to stop lamp switch is .078 inch. If distance is not as indicated, adjust by rotating stop lamp switch.
3. Tighten locknut, then reconnect electrical connectors.

TURN SIGNAL SWITCH
REPLACE

1. Disconnect battery ground cable.
2. Remove center trim panel and steering column lower access cover.
3. Remove steering column lower shroud.
4. Remove upper steering column attaching bolts, then lower steering column to rest on instrument panel brace. **Ensure wires are not pinched when lowering steering column.**
5. Remove turn signal switch attaching screws, then remove switch assembly.
6. Carefully pull multi-function lever out of switch, then disconnect switch electrical connectors.
7. Reverse procedure to install. **Torque** steering column attaching bolts to 17–23 ft. lbs.

STEERING WHEEL
REPLACE

1. Remove air bag module attaching nuts at rear of steering wheel.
2. Disconnect air bag module electrical connector.
3. Loosen steering wheel attaching bolt four to six turns.
4. Install steering wheel puller tool No. T67L-3600-A or equivalent, then remove steering wheel attaching bolt.
5. Remove steering wheel. **Ensure not to damage air bag clockspring or module when removing steering wheel.**
6. Reverse procedure to install. **Torque** steering wheel attaching bolt to 23–33 ft. lbs. **Torque** air bag module attaching screws to 17–26 inch lbs.

INSTRUMENT CLUSTER
REPLACE

1. Disconnect battery ground cable.
2. Remove radio/heater control bezel, steering column covers and instrument panel bezel attaching screws, **Fig. 2.**
3. Disconnect speedometer cable at transaxle.
4. Remove instrument cluster attaching screws.
5. Pull instrument cluster rearward, then disconnect speedometer cable from cluster.
6. Disconnect attaching electrical connectors, then remove instrument cluster.
7. Reverse procedure to install. **Torque** instrument cluster attaching screws to 2–3 ft. lbs.

RADIO
REPLACE

1. Disconnect battery ground cable.
2. Remove radio/heater control bezel.
3. Install radio removal tool No. T87P-19061-A or equivalent, **Fig. 3.**
4. Slide radio rearward to gain access.
5. Disconnect radio electrical connectors, then disconnect antenna.
6. Remove radio rear support attaching nut, then remove rear radio support.
7. Reverse procedure to install.

WIPER MOTOR
REPLACE

1. Disconnect battery ground cable.
2. Gently pry windshield wiper linkage from ball socket at motor.
3. Disconnect motor electrical connectors.
4. Remove motor to dash panel attaching bolts and rubber insulators, then remove wiper motor.
5. Reverse procedure to install. **Torque** motor to dash panel attaching bolts and insulators to 5-7 ft. lbs.

WIPER SWITCH
REPLACE

1. Remove center trim panel and lower steering column access panel.
2. Remove steering column lower shroud attaching screws, then remove lower shroud.
3. Disconnect wiper switch electrical connector and pull wiring out of routing clip.
4. Pull switch and lever assembly to remove.
5. Reverse procedure to install.

WIPER TRANSMISSION
REPLACE

1. Remove wiper arms as follows:
   a. Lift cover, then remove wiper arm attaching nut from shaft.
   b. Carefully pry arm from shaft.
2. Remove lower windshield molding.
3. Gently pry linkage from ball socket at windshield wiper motor.
4. Remove attaching caps and bolts from pivot shafts.

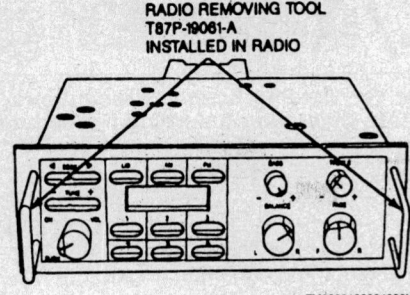

RADIO REMOVING TOOL
T87P-19061-A
INSTALLED IN RADIO

FM9039100004000X

Fig. 3   Radio replacement

5. Remove windshield wiper linkage.
6. Reverse procedure to install. **Torque** pivot shaft attaching bolts to 7-9 ft. lbs.

BLOWER MOTOR
REPLACE

1. Disconnect battery ground cable.
2. Disconnect blower motor electrical connector.
3. Remove blower motor and cover to lower case attaching screws.
4. Remove cover, cooling tube and blower motor.
5. Remove blower wheel to blower motor attaching nut, then remove blower wheel.
6. Remove blower motor gasket.
7. Reverse procedure to install.

HEATER CORE
REPLACE

1. Remove floor console and instrument panel assembly.
2. Drain cooling system.
3. Disconnect and plug heater hoses from heater core extension tubes.
4. Remove defroster hoses and plastic rivets.
5. Remove main air duct connecting heater case to blower case or air conditioning unit, if equipped.
6. Roll back carpet to gain access to lower duct and heater case mounting bolts, then disconnect lower duct from heater case.
7. Remove cable ends from heater case, then disconnect heater case wiring harness.
8. Remove heater case nuts and bolts, then remove heater case.
9. Remove heater core cover to heater case attaching screws, then remove heater core cover.
10. Remove tube brace attaching screws.
11. Loosen clamps and remove extension tubes from heater core, then remove O-ring from outlet tube.
12. Pull heater core outward, then remove any remaining extension tubes and grommets.
13. Reverse procedure to install. **Torque** heater case upper, lower and center attaching nuts and bolts to 5-7 ft. lbs. **Torque** heater hose clamps to 3-4 ft. lbs.

EVAPORATOR CORE
REPLACE

1. Disconnect battery ground cable, then discharge air conditioning system.
2. Remove air cleaner assembly, then remove front mounting bracket.
3. Disconnect and plug A/C lines from evaporator assembly.
4. Remove glove compartment assembly and upper panel.
5. Remove upper panel bracket.
6. Remove evaporator assembly electrical connectors, then release harness retainers.
7. Remove defroster tube, then remove air duct bands.
8. Remove evaporator assembly drain hose.
9. Remove evaporator assembly attaching nuts and bolts, then remove evaporator assembly.
10. Remove evaporator cover attaching clips, then separate case halves and remove evaporator.
11. Remove de-ice thermostat, then disconnect liquid tube from expansion valve inlet fitting.
12. Remove capillary tube from evaporator outlet, then remove expansion valve from evaporator inlet fitting.
13. Remove evaporator core.
14. Reverse procedure to install. **Torque** expansion valve to inlet fitting and liquid tube to expansion valve inlet fitting to 9-11 ft. lbs. **Torque** suction line to evaporator outlet fitting to 22-25 ft. lbs.

NOTE: On Air Bag Equipped Models, Refer To "Air Bag System Precautions" Located In The Front Of This Manual For System Disarming & Arming Procedures.

INDEX

PRECAUTIONS

AIR BAG SYSTEMS

Refer to "Air Bag System Precautions" in the front of this manual for system disarming and arming procedures.

FUEL SYSTEM PRESSURE RELIEF

Fuel pressure must be relieved prior to servicing any fuel system component.
1. Remove back seat cushion.
2. Disconnect fuel pump connector.
3. Run engine until engine stalls.
4. Connect fuel pump connector and install back seat cushion.

ENGINE MOUNT
REPLACE

RIGHTHAND
1. Support engine assembly with a suitable floor jack.
2. Remove mount to engine bracket nuts, **Fig. 1.**
3. Remove mount through bolt.
4. Remove bracket to body bolts.
5. Remove mount.
6. Reverse procedure to install.

FRONT
1. Support engine with engine support fixture tool No. D88l-6000-a, or equivalent.
2. Raise and support vehicle.
3. Remove engine mount nuts from crossmember, **Fig. 2.**
4. Remove engine mount bolts from transaxle.
5. Remove mount.
6. Reverse procedure to install.

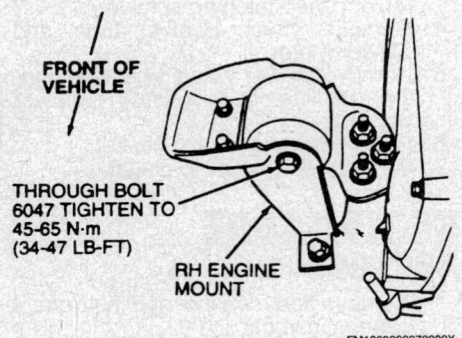

FRONT OF VEHICLE

THROUGH BOLT 6047 TIGHTEN TO 45-65 N·m (34-47 LB-FT)

RH ENGINE MOUNT

FM1069200372000X

Fig. 1 Righthand engine mount

REAR
1. Support engine with engine support fixture tool No. D88l-6000-a, or equivalent.
2. Raise and support vehicle.
3. Remove engine mount to crossmember nuts, **Fig. 3.**
4. Remove lefthand A-arm bolts. Remove engine support crossmember nuts and bolts.
5. Remove rear engine mount bolts and mount.
6. Reverse procedure to install.

ENGINE
REPLACE
1. Disconnect and remove battery, battery tray and battery tray support bracket.
2. Discharge A/C system.
3. Disconnect windshield washer hose at hood. Mark then remove hood assembly.
4. Disconnect intake air tube and wiring to ignition coil and vane air flow meter.

5. Remove air cleaner and air flow meter assembly.
6. Disconnect intercooler hoses from turbocharger, if equipped.
7. Drain cooling system and remove radiator assembly.
8. Disconnect accelerator cable and remove retaining bracket.
9. Disconnect speedometer cable at connection located under hood.
10. Disconnect and plug fuel lines at fuel filter and pressure regulator.
11. Disconnect power brake booster vacuum hose and disconnect heater hoses at heater core.
12. Mark then disconnect all necessary vacuum hoses.
13. **On models with manual transaxle turbocharged engines,** disconnect clutch cable and remove support bracket and cable from transaxle.
14. **On models with manual transaxle naturally aspirated engines,** disconnect clutch slave cylinder hydraulic line.
15. **On models with automatic transaxles,** remove transaxle cooler lines.
16. **On all models,** disconnect starter and alternator wiring connectors.
17. Disconnect engine coolant sensors located at the rear of engine block.
18. remove ground strap connection at thermostat cover.
19. Disconnect EGO sensor wire, main wiring harness, throttle position and knock sensor connector, distributor wiring and transaxle wiring.
20. Disconnect ground wire and strap at front of engine.
21. Install lifting eye on engine.
22. Remove engine oil dipstick tube.
23. Remove power steering pump and mounting bracket assembly and position aside.
24. **On models with A/C,** remove upper A/C compressor mounting bolts.
25. **On all models,** raise and support vehicle and drain engine oil.

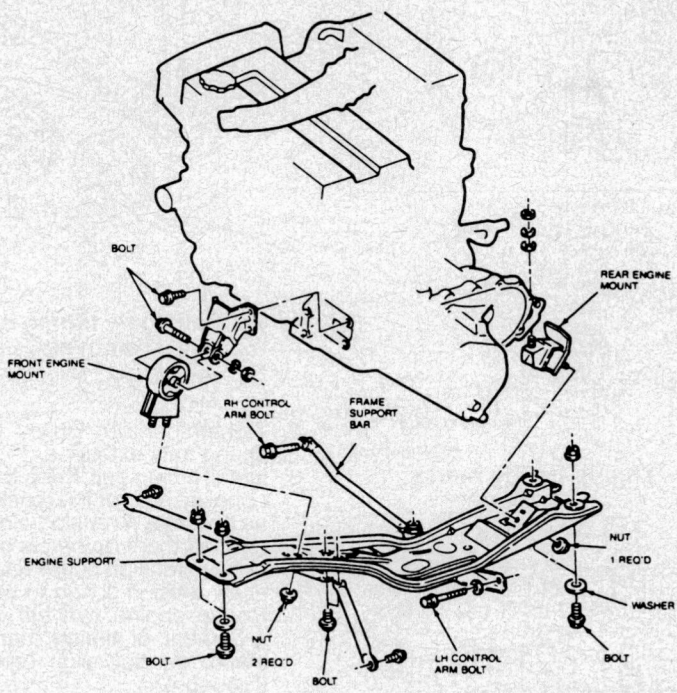

Fig. 2   Front engine mount

FM1069200373000X

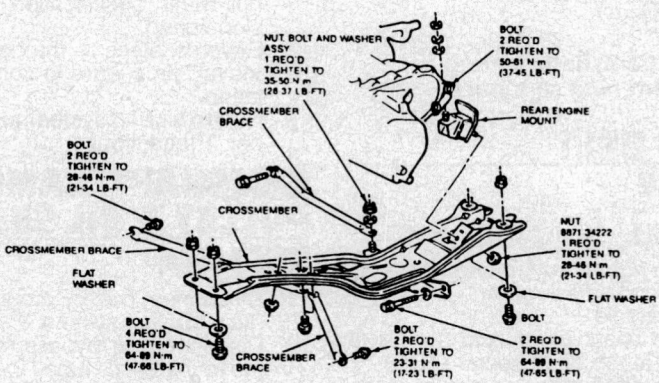

Fig. 3   Rear engine mount

FM1069100335000X

26. **On models with A/C,** remove lower A/C compressor mounting bolts and position compressor aside.
27. **On all models,** remove front tire and wheel assemblies.
28. Separate ball joints from steering knuckles.
29. Remove splash shields and drain transaxle oil.
30. Remove driveshafts as outlined under "Driveshaft, Replace" in the "Front Drive Axle" section.
31. Disconnect front exhaust pipe from engine.
32. Remove frame support bar to engine support bolt.

33. Loosen right control arm bolt and pivot support bar downward.
34. Remove exhaust hangers and allow exhaust system to hand down six inches and support with mechanic's wire.
35. Disconnect transaxle shift linkage and stabilizer bar at transaxle.
36. Remove nuts from front and rear engine mounts.
37. Lower vehicle.
38. Position engine lifting crane tool No. 077-00043, or equivalent. Attach chains onto eyes located on sides of cylinder head.
39. Support engine with crane and re-

move righthand engine mount through bolt.
40. Raise engine off mounts and slightly pivot engine/transaxle assembly.
41. disconnect oil pressure sensor and route starter/alternator wiring harness from engine.
42. Lift engine out of vehicle by turning assembly to clear brake master cylinder, shift linkage, radiator support and A/C lines.
43. Remove intake manifold support bracket and starter assembly.
44. Mark location and remove transaxle to engine retaining bolts.
45. Separate transaxle from engine.
46. Reverse procedure to install.

INTAKE MANIFOLD
REPLACE

1. Relieve fuel system pressure as outlined under "Precautions"
2. Disconnect battery ground cable and drain cooling system.
3. Disconnect intercooler tube and/or air intake tube and air bypass hoses.
4. Disconnect main engine harness connection and TPS connector.
5. Disconnect necessary vacuum hoses from throttle body.
6. Disconnect fuel lines at fuel filter and pressure regulator.
7. Disconnect throttle cable and hoses from BCA valve.
8. remove BCA valve nut and bolt.
9. Remove intake manifold bolts and nuts from support bracket and cylinder head.
10. Remove intake manifold and throttle body assembly.
11. Reverse procedure to install.

EXHAUST MANIFOLD
REPLACE

EXCEPT TURBOCHARGED ENGINE

1. Remove front exhaust pipe to exhaust manifold nuts.
2. Remove exhaust support bracket.
3. Disconnect EGO sensor.
4. Remove exhaust manifold nuts and manifold.
5. Reverse procedure to install.

TURBOCHARGED ENGINE

Refer to "Turbocharger, Replace" for exhaust manifold replacement procedures.

CYLINDER HEAD
REPLACE

1. Relieve fuel system pressure as outlined under "Precautions"
2. Disconnect battery ground cable and drain cooling system.
3. Remove air intake tube from throttle body.
4. Remove spark plug wires and retainers.

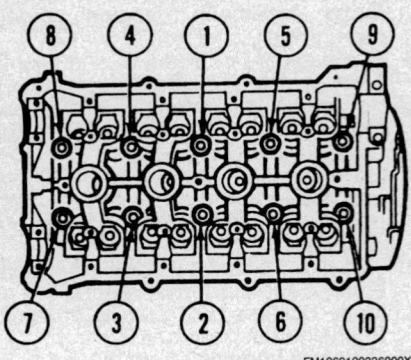

Fig. 4 Cylinder head tightening sequence

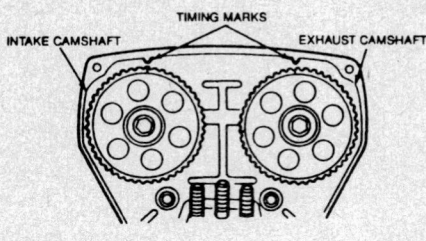

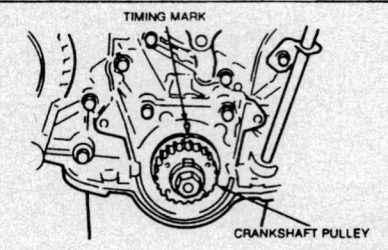

Fig. 5 Engine timing marks

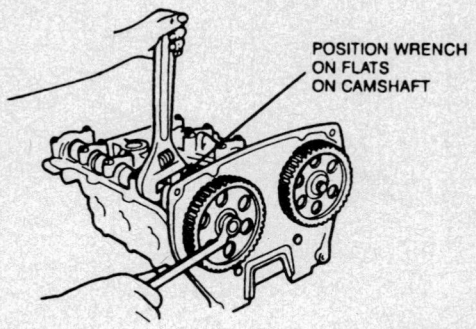

Fig. 6 Camshaft timing belt pulley removal

5. Remove air intake tube from air cleaner.
6. Disconnect cooling hose from thermostat cover.
7. Disconnect vacuum hoses and cooling hoses from throttle body and intake manifold.
8. Disconnect throttle cable.
9. Disconnect fuel lines at fuel filter and pressure regulator.
10. Disconnect main harness connector.
11. Disconnect EGO sensor connector and remove ground.
12. Disconnect intercooler tubes from turbocharger, if equipped.
13. Disconnect ground wire and straps from cylinder head.
14. Remove timing belt covers and timing belt as outlined under "Timing Belt and Covers."
15. **On turbocharged engines,** remove exhaust manifold and turbocharger assembly as outlined under "Turbocharger, Replace."
16. **On non-turbocharged engines,** disconnect front exhaust pipe from exhaust manifold.
17. **On all models,** remove intake manifold support upper bolts.
18. Remove cylinder head cover.
19. Remove cylinder head and intake manifold as an assembly.
20. Reverse procedure to install noting the following:
    a. Ensure coolant passage opening in intake manifold gasket align with manifold and cylinder head.
    b. Tighten cylinder head bolts in sequence shown in **Fig. 4** in two steps. First **torque** bolts to 14-25 ft. lbs. then repeat sequence and **torque** bolts to 56-60 ft. lbs.

VALVE ADJUSTMENT

These engines use hydraulic lash adjusters. No adjustments are required.

FRONT COVER
REPLACE

Refer to "Timing Belt, Replace," for timing belt cover replacement procedure.

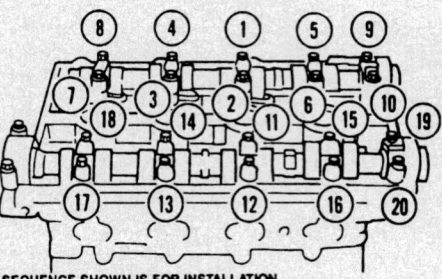

Fig. 7 Camshaft bearing cap tightening sequence

TIMING BELT
REPLACE
REMOVAL

1. Remove right front tire and wheel assembly and splash guard.
2. Lower vehicle.
3. Remove spark plugs and set No. 1 cylinder at top dead center (TDC).
4. Remove alternator and power steering belts.
5. Remove oil dipstick.
6. Remove water pump and crankshaft pulleys.
7. Remove crankshaft damper and baffle.
8. Remove upper, center and lower timing belt covers.
9. Remove timing belt tension spring.
10. Mark timing belt rotation direction.
11. Loosen timing belt tension pulley.
12. Support engine with a suitable floor jack and remove right engine mount as outlined under "Engine Mounts, Replace."
13. Remove timing belt.

INSTALLATION

1. Ensure timing marks are properly positioned on camshafts and crankshaft as shown, **Fig. 5.**

2. Tighten tension pulley with tension spring fully extended.
3. Install timing belt. Keep tension on the opposite side of the tensioner as tight as possible. If reusing old belt, ensure rotation mark on belt is correct.
4. Loosen tension pulley retaining bolt to allow tension spring to tighten belt.
5. Rotate engine two full turns. Check alignment of timing marks. If timing marks do not align repeat steps 1 through 4.
6. Tighten tension pulley retaining bolt and repeat step 5.
7. Measure timing belt tension between camshaft pulleys. Belt deflection should be .33-.45 inch. If deflection is not within specification, replace tension spring.
8. Reverse steps 1 through 9 of "Removal" procedure to complete installation.
9. Rearm air bag system as outlined under "Precautions."

CAMSHAFT, CAMSHAFT PULLEY & OIL SEAL
REPLACE

1. Disconnect battery ground cable and drain cooling system.
2. Disconnect air bypass hoses and remove intake air tube.
3. Disconnect throttle cable and remove retaining bracket.
4. Remove cylinder head cover.
5. Remove timing belt as outlined under Timing Belt & Covers, Replace."
6. Remove camshaft pulleys by holding camshaft with wrench then remove retaining bolt, **Fig. 6.**
7. Remove seal plate then camshaft seal using seal removing tool No. T78P-3504-N, or equivalent.
8. If removing intake camshaft, remove distributor as outlined under "Distributor, Replace" in the "Electrical" section.
9. Note cylinder number and rotation direction of each camshaft bearing cap, then remove camshaft bearing cap bolts alternator and gradually.
10. Remove the camshaft.
11. Reverse procedure to install noting the following:

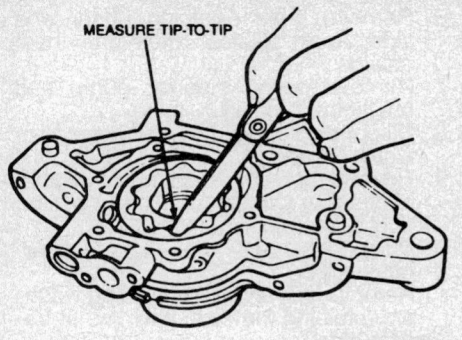

Fig. 8 Inner to outer rotor clearance measurement

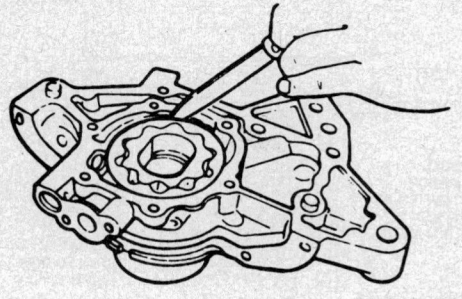

Fig. 9 Outer rotor to body clearance measurement

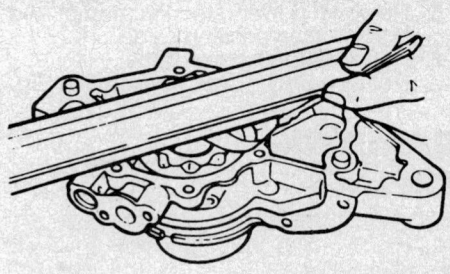

Fig. 10 Rotor to pump cover clearance measurement

a. Align timing marks on camshaft as outlined under "Timing Belt & Covers, Replace."
b. Tighten bearing caps is sequence shown in **Fig. 7** to specification.
c. Install new camshaft seals using seal installation tool Nos. T90P-6256-BH and T90P-6256-AH or equivalent.

CRANKSHAFT SEAL
REPLACE
FRONT

1. Remove timing belt as outlined under "Timing Belt & Covers, Replace."
2. Remove crankshaft timing belt pulley.
3. remove crankshaft seal using seal remover tool No. T78P-3504-N, or equivalent.
4. Coat seal with oil and install seal using seal installation tool No. T87P-6019-A.
5. Reverse procedure to install.

REAR

1. Remove transaxle assembly.
2. Remove clutch cover and disc, if equipped.
3. Remove flywheel.
4. Remove seal using seal remover tool No. T78P-3504-N, or equivalent.
5. Coat seal with oil and install seal using seal installation tool Nos. T87C-6701-A and T90P- 6701-AH.
6. Reverse procedure to install.

OIL PAN
REPLACE

1. Raise and support vehicle.
2. Drain engine oil into a suitable container.
3. Remove frame brace bolt. Loosen righthand A-arm front bolt and pivot brace downward.
4. Disconnect front exhaust pipe from engine.
5. Remove exhaust hangers and allow exhaust system to hang supported by mechanic's wire.
6. **On turbocharged models,** disconnect turbocharger oil return hose.
7. **On all models,** remove oil pan bolts.
8. Pry oil pan loose from cylinder block.

OIL PUMP SERVICE
REMOVAL

1. Remove timing belt as outlined under "Timing Belt & Covers, Replace."
2. Remove oil pan as outlined under "Oil Pan, Replace."
3. Remove crankshaft timing belt pulley.
4. Remove oil strainer/pickup tube.
5. Remove oil pump bolts and oil pump.

DISASSEMBLY

1. Remove oil pump cover.
2. Remove outer and inner rotors.
3. Remove cotter pin and remove pressure piston, cap and spring.
4. Remove oil seal using seal remover tool No. T78P-3504-N, or equivalent.

INSPECTION

1. Inspect pressure spring for weakness or breakage.
2. Pressure spring free length should be 1.791 inch.
3. Inner to outer rotor clearance should not exceed .0079 inch, **Fig. 8.**
4. Outer rotor to pump body clearance should not exceed .0087 inch, **Fig. 9.**
5. Rotor to pump body clearance should not exceed .0055 inch, **Fig. 10.**

ASSEMBLY

1. Install oil seal flush with pump body.
2. Install pressure piston, cap and spring with a new cotter pin.
3. install inner and outer rotors.
4. Install oil pump cover.

INSTALLATION

1. Clean gasket surface.
2. Install oil pump with new gasket.
3. Install oil pump bolts and tighten to specification.
4. Install crankshaft timing pulley, oil pan and timing belt and covers as outlined.

BELT TENSION DATA

New belts (no run time) should measure 0.31-.035 inch deflection with 22 lbs. of applied force, or 110-132 lbs., using a gauge.

Used belts (more that 10 minutes of run time) should measure 0.35-.039 inch deflection with 22 lbs. of applied force, or 110-132 lbs., using a gauge.

COOLING SYSTEM BLEED

These engines do not require a specified bleed procedure. After filling cooling system, run engine to operating temperature with radiator/pressure cap off. Air will then be automatically bled through cap opening.

THERMOSTAT
REPLACE

1. Disconnect cooling fan switch connector from switch on thermostat housing.
2. Remove radiator pressure cap. **Ensure engine is cool prior to servicing.**
3. Drain cooling system to a level below thermostat housing.
4. Disconnect upper radiator hose from thermostat housing, then remove housing retaining bolts.
5. Remove thermostat and gasket.
6. Clean mating surfaces of housing and cylinder head, then install thermostat in cylinder head, valve end first with jiggle valve at the top.
7. Coat new gasket with water resistant sealer B5A-19554-A or equivalent, and position it on cylinder head. The painted side of the gasket must face the thermostat. Ensure bolt holes are correctly aligned.
8. Install thermostat housing, ensuring that the gasket does not shift. Install two retaining bolts and **Torque to 14-22 ft. lbs.**
9. Connect upper radiator hose to thermostat housing, then fill system with recommended coolant mixture and install pressure cap.
10. Connect cooling fan switch connector, then start engine and allow to run until warm.
11. Ensure system is pressurized, then check for leaks.

WATER PUMP
REPLACE

1. Remove timing belt as outlined under "Timing Belt & Covers, Replace."
2. Drain cooling system.
3. Remove timing belt tensioner and idler pulleys.
4. Remove engine oil dipstick.

5. Remove power steering pump and bracket then position aside.
6. Remove water pump outlet.
7. Remove water pump assembly, **Fig. 11.**

RADIATOR
REPLACE

1. Disconnect battery ground cable.
2. Remove radiator pressure cap from filler neck.
3. Drain coolant.
4. Disconnect radiator upper and lower hoses from radiator inlet and outlet.
5. Disconnect overflow tube from filler neck.
6. Disconnect cooling fan wiring harness connector.
7. **On models with automatic transaxle,** disconnect and plug cooler lines.
8. **On all models,** remove radiator and cooling fan.
9. Remove fan shroud assembly.
10. Reverse procedure to install, noting the following:
    a. Torque fan and shroud retaining bolts to 48-60 inch lbs.
    b. Torque radiator retaining bolts to 80-115 inch lbs.
    c. Warm up engine to pressurize system, then check for leaks.

FUEL PUMP
REPLACE

1. Relieve fuel system pressure as outlined under "Precautions."
2. Disconnect battery ground cable.
3. Remove fuel tank sending unit.
4. Disconnect fuel pump wires from sending unit.
5. Remove clamp screw, clamp and rubber retaining band.
6. Remove fuel pump from sending unit.
7. Reverse procedure to install.

FUEL FILTER
REPLACE
INLINE

1. Relieve fuel system pressure as outlined under "Precautions."

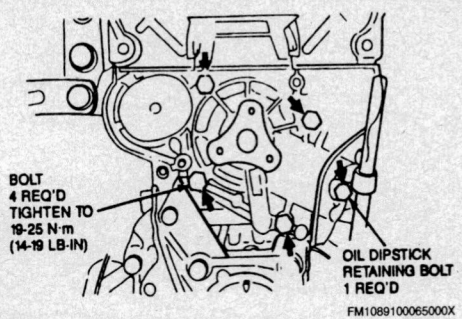

BOLT
4 REQ'D
TIGHTEN TO
19-25 N·m
(14-19 LB-IN)

OIL DIPSTICK
RETAINING BOLT
1 REQ'D

FM1089100065000X

Fig. 11   Water pump removal

2. Remove filter lower clamp and supply line, then plug supply line.
3. Remove filter upper clamp and outlet line.
4. Remove fuel filter from bracket.
5. Reverse procedure to install.

INTANK

1. Relieve fuel system pressure as outlined under "Precautions."
2. Remove fuel pump as outlined previously.
3. Remove fuel filter from fuel pump assembly.
4. Reverse procedure to install.

TURBOCHARGER
REPLACE

1. Relieve fuel system pressure as outlined under "Precautions," then disconnect battery ground cable and drain cooling system.
2. Remove throttle body air intake tube.
3. Disconnect intercooler hose from turbocharger assembly and position out of the way.
4. Disconnect the EGO sensor.
5. Remove bolts retaining lower heat shield to turbocharger and remove heat shield.

6. Remove bolts retaining upper and side heat shields, then the heat shields.
7. Remove power steering pump and bracket and position aside.
8. Disconnect lower radiator hose from water pump.
9. Remove screws retaining air cleaner duct tube, loosen tube and position duct tube aside.
10. Disconnect coolant return hose at turbocharger.
11. Remove bolt and brass sealing washers retaining the oil supply line at engine block.
12. Raise and support vehicle.
13. Disconnect front exhaust pipe from turbocharger.
14. Remove exhaust hangers and pull down and left on exhaust pipe.
15. Disconnect oil return hose at turbocharger.
16. Disconnect coolant return hose at turbocharger.
17. Remove turbocharger support bracket bolts.
18. Remove coolant bypass tube bolts from water pump.
19. Lower vehicle.
20. Loosen retaining clamp on coolant bypass tube at rear of cylinder head.
21. Remove 11 nuts from exhaust manifold.
22. Pull coolant bypass tube bracket from exhaust stud and position aside.
23. Pull exhaust manifold off stud and move assembly slightly to the right-hand side of engine compartment to clear cooling fan. Remove turbocharger and exhaust manifold assembly from vehicle.
24. Working on bench, remove four nuts retaining turbocharger to exhaust manifold, separate assembly and discard gasket.
25. Reverse procedure to install. If turbocharger was replaced proceed as follows:
    a. Disconnect ignition coil.
    b. Crank engine for 20 seconds.
    c. Connect ignition coil.
    d. Start engine and run at idle for 30 seconds.
    e. Check for leaks.

TIGHTENING SPECIFICATIONS

Year	Component	Torque/ Ft. Lbs.
1992-94	A-Arm Front Bolt	69–86
	A/C Compressor Bolt	30–40
	Ball Joint	32–40
	Camshaft Bearing Bolt	100–126 ①
	Camshaft Pulley	36–45
	Chassis Cross Brace Bolt	26–37
	Clutch Pressure Plate Bolt	13–19
	Connecting Rod Bearing Nut	35–38
	Crankshaft Main Bearing Bolt	40–43
	Crankshaft Pulley Bolt	109–152 ①
	Crankshaft Rear Seal Flange Bolt	69–95 ①
	Crankshaft Timing Pulley	80–87
	Cylinder Head Bolt	④
	Cylinder Head Cover Bolt	69–95 ①
	Engine End Plate	69–95 ①
	Exhaust Manifold Nut	29–42
	Exhaust Pipe To Manifold Nut	29–42
	Flywheel Bolt	71–76
	Front Engine Mount Nut	47–66
	Front Engine Mount Through Bolt	33–48
	Front Engine To Transaxle Bolt	27–38
	Front Exhaust Pipe To Support Bracket Bolt	32–45
	Fuel Tank Drain Plug	9—13
	Fuel Tank Sending Unit	5.3–8.8 ①
	Gusset Plate Bolt	27–38
	Intake Manifold	14–19
	Intake Manifold Support Bracket Bolt	23–34
	Intermediate Axle Shaft Bearing Support Bolt	27–38
	Knock Sensor	14–25
	Oil Cooler Nut	22–29
	Oil Pan Bolt	69–95 ①

Year	Component	Torque/ Ft. Lbs.
1992-94 —Cont'd	Oil Pressure Sensor	104–156 ①
	Oil Pump Assembly Bolt	14–19
	Oil Pump Cover	14–19
	Oil Pump Pickup Bolt	69–95 ①
	Oil Spray Nozzle Bolt	104–156 ①
	Power Steering Pivot Bolt	23–34
	Power Steering Pump Bracket Bolt	35–48
	Power Steering Pump Bracket Nut	35–48
	Power Steering Adjusting Nut	27–38
	Radiator Bracket Bolt	69–95 ①
	Rear Engine Mount Bolt	27–38
	Rear Engine Mount Nut	47–66
	Seal Plate Bolt	69–95 ①
	Shift Cable Pivot Nut ③	33–47
	Shift Cable Retaining Bolt	69–95 ①
	Shift Linkage Rod Nut	12–17
	Shifter Stabilizer nut	23–34
	Starter Bolt	25–34
	Starter Bracket To Support Bracket Bolt	14–19
	Timing Belt Cover Bolts	69–95 ①
	Timing Belt Pulley Bolt	27–38
	Torque Converter Bolt	25–36
	Torque Convertor Cover Plate Bolt	61–87 ①
	Transaxle To Engine Bolt	②
	Water Pump Outlet Bolt	14–19
	Water Pump Pulley Bolt	69–95 ①
	Wheel Lug Nuts	67–88

①—Inch lbs.
②—Manual transaxle, upper 66–86 ft. lbs., lower 27–38 ft. lbs.; automatic transaxle, upper, 41–59 ft. lbs.
③—Automatic transaxle.
④—See text.

Clutch & Manual Transaxle

INDEX

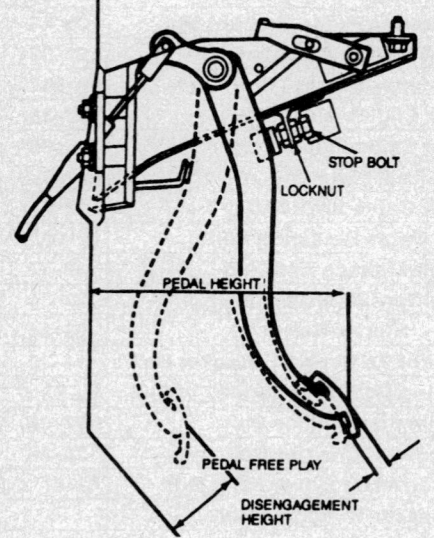

Fig. 1 Clutch adjustment.
Turbocharged models

ADJUSTMENTS

CLUTCH PEDAL HEIGHT

1. Measure distance from upper center of the pedal pad to dash panel, **Figs. 1 and 2.**
2. Distance should be 8.4-8.6 inches on turbocharged models and 9.02-9.22 inches on non-turbocharged models.
3. Loosen locknut, then turn stopper bolt until pedal height is within specifications.
4. Tighten locknut.

CLUTCH PEDAL FREEPLAY

1. Lightly depress pedal and measure freeplay, **Figs. 1 and 2.**
2. Freeplay should measure .350-.590 inches on turbocharged models and 0.02-1.2 inches on non-turbocharged models.
3. **On non-turbocharged models,** loosen locknut, then turn pushrod until pedal freeplay is within specification, **Fig. 2.**
4. Tighten locknut to 17-25 ft. lbs. Ensure pedal height is 9.02-9.22 inch.
5. **On turbocharged models,** if clutch pedal freeplay is not within specification, depress clutch release lever and pull pin away from lever.

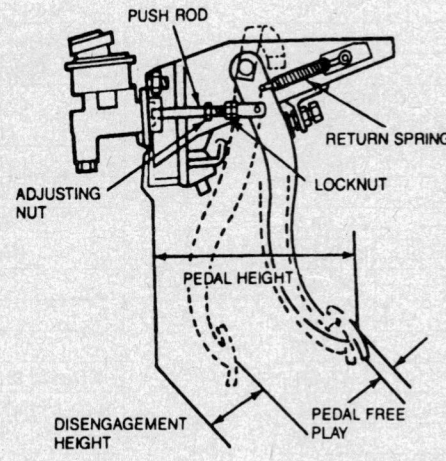

Fig. 2 Clutch adjustment.
Non-turbocharged models

6. Rotate adjusting nut (B), until a clearance 0.06-0.100 inch is obtained, **Fig. 3.**
7. Measure distance from floor and upper center of pedal pad when the pedal is fully depressed. Distance should be 3.3 inches.

HYDRAULIC SYSTEM SERVICE

SLAVE CYLINDER, REPLACE

This vehicle uses two types of clutch release systems. Turbocharged vehicles with type G transaxles use a mechanical cable system. Non-turbocharged vehicles with type F2 transaxles use a hydraulic clutch system.

1. Disconnect hydraulic line from slave cylinder and plug to prevent fluid loss.
2. Remove two retaining bolts, then slave cylinder.
3. Reverse procedure to install, noting the following:
   a. **Torque** retaining bolts to 12-16 ft. lbs.
   b. Fill reservoir and bleed clutch system.

CLUTCH SYSTEM BLEED

1. Raise and support vehicle.

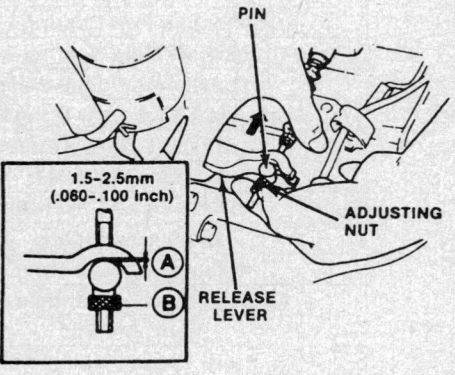

Fig. 3 Clutch pedal freeplay adjustment. Turbocharged models

2. Attach a hose to bleeder valve on clutch slave cylinder.
3. Depress clutch pedal to floor and hold.
4. Open bleeder valve 1/2 turn.
5. Watch for air bubbles in brake fluid while bleeding. **Keep reservoir full of fluid while bleeding.**
6. Close bleeder screw, then release clutch pedal.
7. Open bleeder valve 1/4 turn, then push pedal down as far as it will go. Close valve and release pedal.
8. Fill reservoir, then check clutch for proper operation. Repeat procedure as necessary.

CLUTCH MASTER CYLINDER, REPLACE

1. Remove battery, then windshield wiper motor.
2. Disconnect hydraulic line fitting at retaining bracket on transaxle case, then drain fluid from clutch master cylinder. Reconnect fitting after draining fluid.
3. Disconnect hydraulic line from master cylinder.
4. Remove master cylinder retaining nuts, then clutch master cylinder.
5. Reverse procedure to install, noting the following:
   a. **Torque** clutch master cylinder retaining nuts to 14-19 ft. lbs.
   b. Bleed hydraulic clutch system.

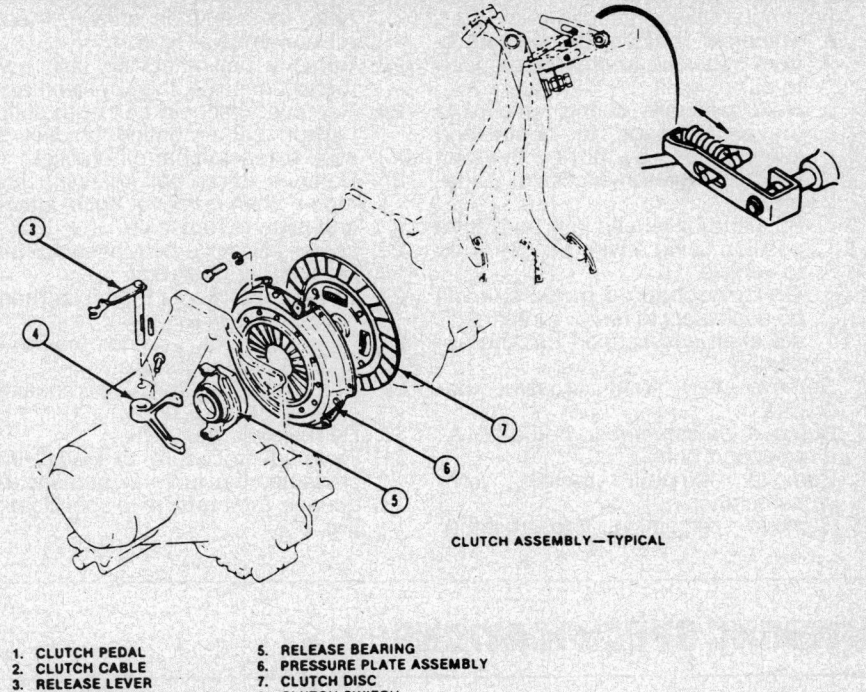

Fig. 4 Clutch assembly

1. CLUTCH PEDAL
2. CLUTCH CABLE
3. RELEASE LEVER
4. RELEASE FORK
5. RELEASE BEARING
6. PRESSURE PLATE ASSEMBLY
7. CLUTCH DISC
8. CLUTCH SWITCH

CLUTCH ASSEMBLY—TYPICAL

FM5049100044000X

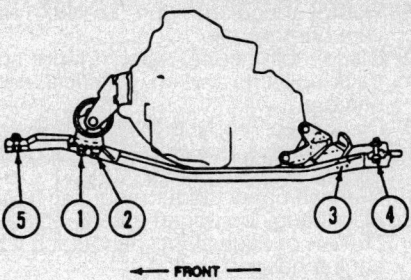

← FRONT →

FM5049100045000X

Fig. 5 Crossmember bolt removal

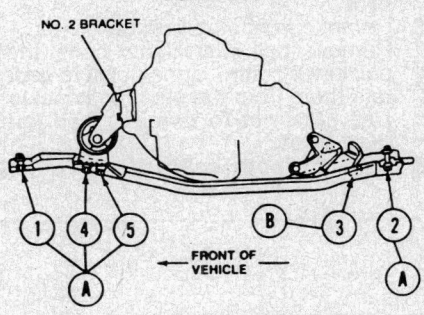

NO. 2 BRACKET

FRONT OF VEHICLE

A: TIGHTEN TO 64-89 N·m (47-66 LB-FT)
B: TIGHTEN TO 28-46 N·m (20-34 LB-FT)

FM5049100046000X

Fig. 6 Crossmember bolt installation

CLUTCH
REPLACE

1. Disconnect battery ground cable.
2. Remove transaxle from vehicle.
3. Install flywheel lock tool T74P-6375-A or equivalent, into transaxle mounting hole on engine, then engage tooth of locking tool into flywheel ring gear. **To avoid dropping clutch disc when bolts are removed, use clutch aligning tool T87C-7137-A or equivalent.**
4. Remove bolts attaching pressure plate to flywheel, then remove pressure plate assembly, **Fig. 4.**
5. Remove clutch disc and clutch aligning tool. **Use care when removing the last bolt to prevent dropping flywheel.**
6. Reverse procedure to install. **Torque** pressure plate assembly attaching bolts to 13-20 ft. lbs.

TRANSAXLE
REPLACE
NON-TURBOCHARGED MODELS

1. Disconnect battery ground cable.
2. Remove air cleaner assembly, then loosen both front wheel lug nuts.
3. Disconnect speedometer cable from transaxle.
4. Remove clutch slave hydraulic line retaining bracket and nut.
5. Remove bolts retaining ground wire and engine harness bracket to transaxle. Pull harness out of routing clip.
6. Disconnect ground strap at front of transaxle.
7. Install engine support bar tool D88L-6000-A or equivalent, then remove upper transaxle to engine retaining bolts.
8. Remove upper starter retaining bolts, then disconnect neutral safety switch and back-up lamp switch electrical connectors.
9. Raise and support vehicle, then remove front tire and wheel assemblies.
10. Remove splash shields.
11. Drain fluid from transaxle assembly.
12. Remove front stabilizer bar.
13. Remove bolts and nuts from lower control arm ball joints.
14. Pull lower control arms down to separate them from the steering knuckles. **Use care not to damage ball joint dust boot.**
15. Remove inner left fender splash shield.
16. Separate both halfshafts by pulling front hub outward as follows:
    a. Withdraw halfshafts horizontally from transaxle to prevent damage to oil lip seals.
    b. Hold halfshafts during removal to prevent damage to boots and joints caused by moving the joint through angles in excess of 20°.
    c. Suspend halfshafts in a horizontal position using a wire hanger or tie to vehicle.
17. Remove two crossmember braces, then remove crossmember brace to control arm support bolts.
18. Remove left control arm through bolt, then exhaust hanger from crossmember.
19. Remove remaining crossmember bolts in sequence shown, then the crossmember, **Fig. 5.**
20. Remove bolt attaching shift control rod to transaxle, then position aside.
21. Remove nut attaching shift extension bar mounting bracket, then slide extension bar off stud.
22. Remove bolts retaining clutch slave cylinder and set wire aside.
23. Remove lower bolt retaining starter motor, then remove bolts attaching end plate to transaxle.
24. Remove nut and washer retaining support bracket to exhaust manifold.
25. Remove gusset plate to transaxle attaching bolt.
26. Position jack under transaxle, then secure transaxle to jack.
27. Remove front engine mount and bracket from transaxle.
28. Remove bolts attaching transaxle to engine.
29. Remove the transaxle.
30. Reverse procedure to install. Install crossmember bolts in numerical sequence, then **torque** to specifications, **Fig. 6.**

TURBOCHARGED MODELS

1. Disconnect battery ground cable.
2. Remove air cleaner assembly, then loosen both front wheel lug nuts.
3. Disconnect speedometer cable from transaxle.
4. Remove clutch cable from release lever by removing adjusting nut and pin.
5. Remove intake air bypass valve mounting nut.
6. Remove clutch cable mounting bracket from transaxle.
7. Remove ground wire retaining bolt, then the ground wire.

8. Remove coolant pipe bracket and wire harness clip.
9. Disconnect neutral safety switch and back-up lamp switch electrical connectors.
10. Disconnect body ground connector, then remove two upper transaxle to engine attaching bolts.
11. Remove upper starter mounting bolts.
12. Install engine support bar tool D89L-6000-A or equivalent, then attach it to engine hanger.
13. Raise and support vehicle.
14. Drain fluid from transaxle assembly.
15. Remove front tire and wheel assemblies.
16. Remove front stabilizer bar.
17. Remove ball joint clamp bolts, then pull lower control arms down to separate them from the steering knuckles. **Use care not to damage ball joint dust boot.**
18. Separate both halfshafts by pulling

front hub outward as follows:
   a. Withdraw halfshafts horizontally from transaxle to prevent damage to oil lip seals.
   b. Hold halfshafts during removal to prevent damage to boots and joints caused by moving the joint through angles in excess of 20 degrees.
   c. Suspend halfshafts in a horizontal position using a wire hanger or tie to vehicle.
   d. **On turbocharged models,** it will be necessary to remove intermediate shaft and support bearing assembly.
19. Remove two front crossmember braces.
20. Remove crossmember brace to A-arm support bolts.
21. Remove exhaust hanger from crossmember.
22. Remove remaining crossmember

bolts in sequence shown, then the crossmember, **Fig. 5.**
23. Remove bolt attaching shift control rod to transaxle, then position aside.
24. Remove attaching bolt from shift extension bar mounting bracket, then slide extension bar off bracket.
25. Remove lower bolt retaining starter motor, then remove bolts attaching end plate to transaxle.
26. Lower transaxle by loosening engine bracket bar hook bolt.
27. Position jack under transaxle, then secure transaxle to jack.
28. Remove front engine mount and bracket from transaxle.
29. Remove bolts attaching transaxle to engine.
30. Remove the transaxle.
31. Reverse procedure to install. Install crossmember bolts in numerical sequence, then **torque** to specifications, **Fig. 6.**

TIGHTENING SPECIFICATIONS

Year	Component	Torque/Ft. Lbs.
1992-94	Back-Up Lamp Switch	14-18
	Ball Joint Clamp Bolt	32-40
	Clutch Cover to Flywheel	13-20
	Clutch Housing to Transaxle Housing	27-38
	Control Rod to Transaxle Nut	12-17
	Crossmember Brace to Control Arm	69-86
	Crossmember Front Braces	23-43
	Engine to Transaxle	47-66
	Extension Bar	23-34

Year	Component	Torque/Ft. Lbs.
1992-94 —Cont'd	Flywheel	60-65
	Front Engine Mounts	27-38
	Gusset to Transaxle	47-66
	Left Control Arm Through Bolt	93-117
	Neutral Switch	14-18
	Stabilizer Bar	23-33
	Starter Bolts	23-34
	Wheel Lug Nuts	67-88

Rear Suspension

INDEX

DESCRIPTION

The rear suspension is fully independent utilizing rear MacPherson struts at each wheel. Rear strut towers locate the spring and strut. Forged rear spindle bolts to the strut double lower control arms and a single trailing arm locate the rear suspension, **Fig. 1.**

Both of the control arms and the trailing arms have rubber bushings at each end. The control arms are attached to the rear crossmember and also to the spindle with a common bolt at each end. The trailing arm bolts to the strut and a bracket on the floorpan.

HUB & BEARING
REPLACE

1. Ensure parking brake is fully released.
2. Raise and support vehicle, then remove wheel and tire assembly.
3. Remove two caliper guide pin bolts, then lift caliper of disc with hose and cable attached, then tie caliper assembly to strut spring.
4. Remove grease cap, **Fig. 2.**
5. Raise staked portion of locknut using suitable tool.
6. Remove and discard locknut. **Locknuts are threaded left and right.**

The lefthand threaded locknut is located on the righthand side of the vehicle. Turn this locknut clockwise to loosen. The righthand threaded locknut is turned counterclockwise to loosen.

7. Remove washer and outer bearing from bearing hub.
8. Remove brake rotor/bearing hub assembly.
9. Remove bearing grease seal using suitable tool.
10. Remove inner bearing from bearing hub. **If bearings are to be reused, they should be tagged to be installed in their original position.**

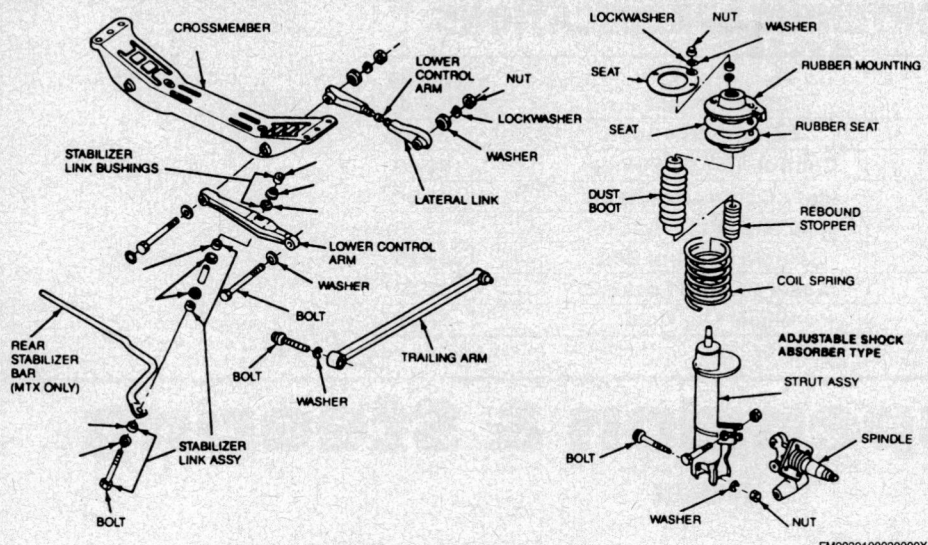

Fig. 1 Rear suspension

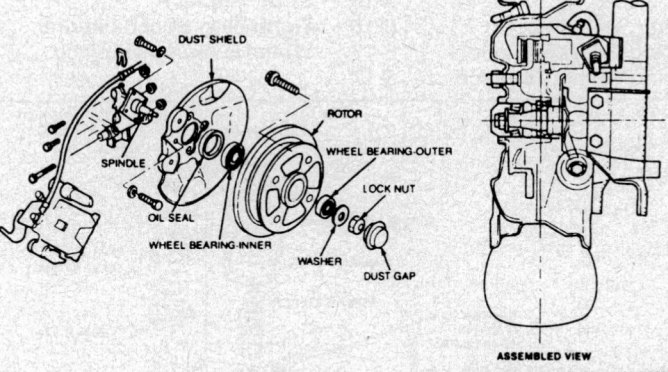

Fig. 2 Rear hub & bearing assembly

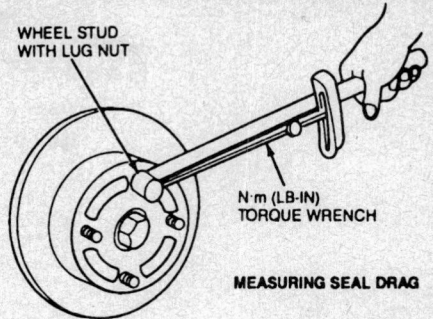

Fig. 3 Rear wheel bearing preload measurement

4. Remove trailing arm and spindle attaching bolts.
5. Mark alignment on strut rubber mounting bracket.
6. Inside trunk, remove upper strut attaching nuts.
7. Compress coil spring using tool No. T81P-5310-A or equivalent.
8. With spring compressed, remove strut rod attaching nut, rubber mounting bracket, spring upper and lower seat, then the rubber spring seat.
9. Release coil spring and remove spring compressor tool.
10. Remove coil spring, dust boot and rebound bumpers.
11. Reverse procedure to install. Torque attaching nuts and bolts to specifications.

COIL SPRING
REPLACE

Refer to "Strut, Replace," for coil spring replacement procedure.

CONTROL ARM
REPLACE

1. Remove rear wheel and tire assemblies.
2. Remove rear disc brake caliper and rotor assemblies.
3. Mark control arm and control arm bushings for alignment at installation.
4. Mark trailing arm and crossmember for alignment at installation.
5. Remove stabilizer link assembly.
6. Remove stabilizer bar and bushings.
7. Loosen inner and outer lower control arm attaching bolts.
8. Loosen spindle to strut attaching bolts.
9. Remove parking brake to rear trailing assembly attaching bolt.
10. Loosen trailing arm to strut attaching bolts.
11. Once all control arm and trailing arm attaching bolts are loosen, then remove all bolts and remove control arms and trailing arm.
12. Reverse procedure to install. Torque all attaching nuts and bolts to specifications.

TRAILING ARM
REPLACE

Refer to "Control Arm, Replace," for trailing arm replacement procedure.

---

11. Reverse procedure to install, noting the following:
    a. Install new grease seal using tool No. T87C-1175-A or equivalent.
    b. Torque all attaching nuts and bolts to specifications.
    c. **Torque** locknut to 18.1-21.7 ft. lbs. to seat bearings.
    d. Adjust bearing preload as outlined under "Wheel Bearing Preload, Adjust."

WHEEL BEARING
ADJUST

1. Loosen bearing hub locknut.
2. Measure seal drag, place a torque wrench on a lug nut positioned at twelve o'clock and measure amount of force required to turn the brake rotor, note torque wrench reading when rotation starts, **Fig. 3**.
3. Add amount of seal drag to required preload which is 1.3-4.3 inch lbs.
4. Finger tighten wheel bearing locknut, then place torque wrench on lug nut positioned at twelve o'clock, continue tightening locknut until indicated preload is with specifications.

SPINDLE KNUCKLE
REPLACE

1. Remove rear wheel and tire assemblies.
2. Remove rear disc brake caliper and rotor assemblies.
3. Loosen spindle to strut attaching bolts.
4. Loosen outer rear control arm nut and bolt.
5. Remove spindle to strut mount attaching bolt, then remove outer control arm bolt and nut.
6. Remove spindle assembly from strut.
7. Reverse procedure to install. Torque attaching nuts and bolts to specifications.

STRUT
REPLACE

1. Remove rear wheel and tire assemblies.
2. Remove rear disc brake caliper and rotor assemblies.
3. Loosen trailing arm attaching bolt, then loosen spindle to shock absorber attaching bolts.

TIGHTENING SPECIFICATIONS

Year	Component	Torque/ Ft. Lbs.
1992-94	Control Arm Bolt	69-86
	Control Arm To Spindle	69-86
	Inner Control Arm Bolts	69-86
	Rear Stabilizer Bracket	32-39
	Spindle To Strut Bolt	69-86
	Wheel Bearing Locknut	67-88
	Wheel Lug Nuts	67-88

Front Suspension & Steering

INDEX

DESCRIPTION

The front suspension consists of MacPherson struts, coil springs and single control arms, **Fig. 1.** Strut towers located in the wheelwells locate the upper ends of the struts. The strut mounting blocks house rubber mounted strut bearings. Both the upper and lower end of the coil springs ride in heavy rubber spring seats. A forged steering knuckle bolts to each strut assembly.

Ball joints connect the control arms to the steering knuckles. The wide control arms are supported by rubber bushings at each end. Body lean on turns is controlled by a hollow stabilizer bar that connects to both lower control arms.

WHEEL BEARING
REPLACE

1. Remove steering knuckle and hub assembly as outlined under "Steering Knuckle, Replace."
2. Remove hub and brake rotor assembly from steering knuckle using tool No. T87C-1104-A or equivalent.
3. Remove front bearing preload spacer, **Fig. 2. The spacer between bearings determines preload, do not discard.**
4. Mark hub and rotor assembly for installation alignment.
5. Place hub and rotor assembly in soft-jawed vise or equivalent, then remove hub and rotor attaching bolts.
6. Remove wheel hub bearing using tool Nos. D84L-1123-A and D80L-927-A or equivalents.
7. Remove hub outer grease seal, then remove inner grease seal from steering knuckle with suitable tool.

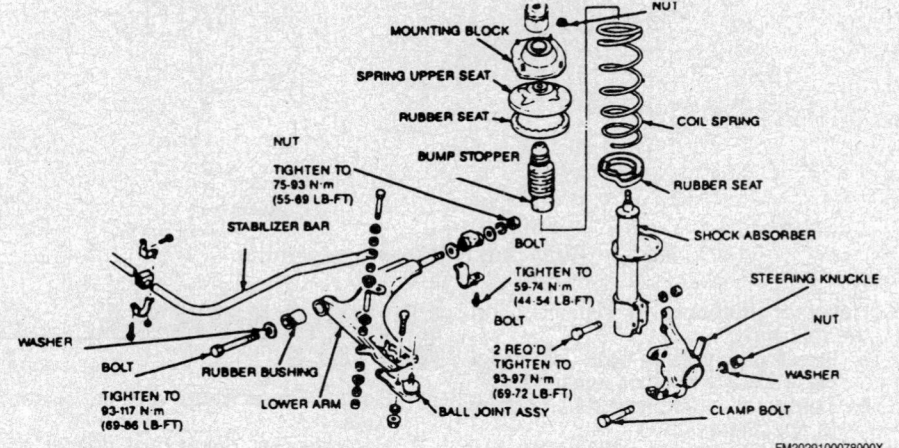

Fig. 1   Front suspension

8. Remove steering knuckle bearing.
9. Reverse procedure to install. Torque all attaching nuts and bolts to specifications.

HUB & BEARING
REPLACE

Refer to "Steering Knuckle, Replace" for hub and bearing replacement procedure.

BALL JOINT INSPECTION

1. Raise and support vehicle.
2. Move front wheel and tire assembly vertically while observing ball joint in lower control arm at bottom of steering knuckle.
3. If movement is detected between steering knuckle and control arm, ball joint should be replaced.

BALL JOINT
REPLACE

LOWER

1. Raise and support vehicle, then remove wheel and tire assembly.
2. Remove ball joint clamp attaching bolt from steering knuckle.
3. Using a small pry bar or equivalent, pull lower control arm downward to separate from steering knuckle.
4. Remove lower ball joint attaching blots.
5. Using a small pry bar or equivalent, pull ball joint from control arm.
6. Reverse procedure to install. Torque all attaching bolts to specifications.

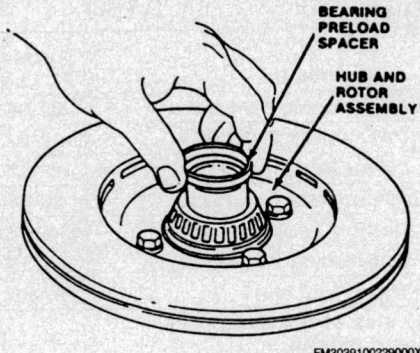

Fig. 2 Front wheel bearing preload spacer

FM3039100229000X

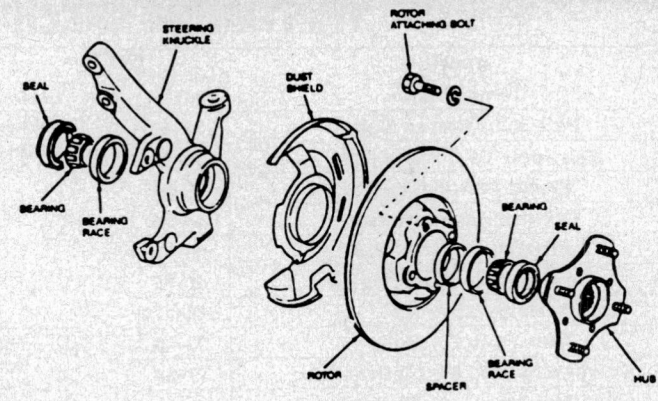

Fig. 3 Front wheel bearing

FM3039100230000X

COIL SPRING
REPLACE

Refer to "Strut, Replace," for coil spring replacement procedure.

STRUT
REPLACE

1. Raise and support vehicle, then remove wheel and tire assembly.
2. Remove brake caliper, then support and position aside.
3. Mark inside strut mounting block for installation alignment.
4. Remove steering knuckle to strut attaching nuts and bolts.
5. Remove brake line hose to strut attaching clip, then position brake line hose aside.
6. Remove strut mount to strut tower attaching nuts.
7. Remove strut and spring assembly, then compress spring using Rotunda Spring Compressor tool No. 086-00029 or equivalent.
8. Remove strut rod nut, then carefully release spring compressor.
9. Remove strut mounting block, upper spring seat, bump stopper, coil spring and lower spring seat from strut.
10. Reverse procedure to install.

CONTROL ARM
REPLACE

LOWER

1. Raise and support vehicle, then remove wheel and tire assembly.
2. Disconnect stabilizer bar from control arm, if equipped, **Fig. 1.**
3. Remove ball joint clamp attaching bolt.
4. Remove control arm front attaching bolt.
5. Remove control arm rear bracket and attaching bolts, then remove control arm.
6. Reverse procedure to install.

STEERING KNUCKLE
REPLACE

1. Raise and support vehicle, then remove wheel and tire assembly.

2. Carefully raise the staked portion of the halfshaft attaching nut using a suitable tool.
3. Remove halfshaft attaching nut, then discard nut. **When loosening the nut, apply brakes to lock hub.**
4. Remove stabilizer bar to control arm attaching nut, bolt, washer and bushings.
5. Remove tie rod end cotter pin, then remove attaching nut.
6. Separate tie rod end from steering knuckle using tool No. T85M-3395-A or equivalent.
7. Remove attaching clip at center of brake caliper flex hose.
8. Remove brake caliper attaching bolts, then support and position aside.
9. Remove lower ball joint clamp attaching nut and bolt.
10. Using suitable tool, pry control arm downward to separate ball joint from steering knuckle.
11. Remove steering knuckle to strut attaching bolts.
12. Remove steering knuckle and hub assembly from halfshaft, **Fig. 3. Use caution not to damage seals. If hub binds on halfshaft splines, loosen by lightly tapping end of halfshaft with plastic face hammer. Do not use metal faced hammer as constant velocity joint internal damage may result.**
13. Reverse procedure to install. Torque attaching nuts and bolts to specifications.

POWER STEERING GEAR
REPLACE

1. Remove battery assembly.
2. Raise and support vehicle, then remove front tire and wheel assemblies.
3. Separate tie rod ends from steering knuckle as follows:
   a. Remove tie rod end cotter pin and attaching nut.
   b. Using tool No. T85M-3395-A or equivalent separate tie rod end from steering knuckle.
   c. Mark tie rod end, jamb nut and tie rod for installation alignment.
   d. Loosen tie rod end jamb nut, then remove tie rod end.
4. Remove righthand lower inner fender dust shield.

5. Lower vehicle. **Do not allow anything but rear wheels to touch ground.**
6. Using suitable cutters, cut plastic wire tie clamping steering column dust boot to steering gear.
7. Pull dust boot back, then rotate steering column shaft until clamp bolt is accessible, then lock steering column.
8. Mark steering column pinion shaft and intermediate shaft lower universal joint for installation alignment.
9. Remove intermediate shaft lower universal joint attaching clamp bolt.
10. Disconnect power steering gear return line.
11. Remove power steering gear pressure hose banjo bolt, then position hose aside. **Do not reuse copper washers from fitting.**
12. Remove steering gear attaching bolts.
13. Carefully lower steering gear, then remove steering gear through righthand fenderwell.
14. Reverse procedure to install. Torque all attaching nuts and bolts to specifications.

POWER STEERING PUMP
REPLACE

1. Disconnect battery ground cable.
2. Remove righthand radiator support and brace.
3. Disconnect intercooler outlet hose at throttle inlet and position aside, if equipped.
4. Remove engine lifting eye ground wire.
5. Place drain pan below power steering pump, then disconnect power steering pump inlet and return lines, then plug lines.
6. Remove power steering pressure switch electrical connector.
7. Remove pump bracket adjusting screw, nut and block, then remove pivot bolt.
8. Position pump below bracket, then remove bracket attaching nut and bolts.
9. Remove pump bracket, then remove pump assembly.
10. Reverse procedure to install. Torque all attaching nuts and bolts to specifications.

TIGHTENING SPECIFICATIONS

Year	Component	Torque/Ft. Lbs.
1992-94	Ball Joint Clamp Bolt	32-40
	Ball Joint To Control Arm	69-86
	Brake Caliper Bolts	29-36
	Control Arm Bracket	44-54
	Control Arm (Front Bolt)	69-86
	Control Arm (Rear Nut)	55-69
	Halfshaft Nuts	116-174
	Hub To Rotor Bolts	33-40
	Power Steering Pump Bracket	27-38
	Stabilizer Link Bolts	①

Year	Component	Torque/Ft. Lbs.
1992-94 —Cont'd	Steering Knuckle To Strut	69-86
	Strut Assembly To Body	17-22
	Strut Rod Nut	22-27
	Tie Rod End Attaching Nut	26-29
	Tie Rod To Rack	43.4-57.9
	Tie Rod To Steering Knuckle Nut	22-33 ②
	Wheel Lug Nuts	67-88

① —Tighten nut until .43 inch of the bolt threads extend beyond the nut.
② —Torque to specifications, then continue to tighten to nearest cotter pi.

Wheel Alignment

INDEX

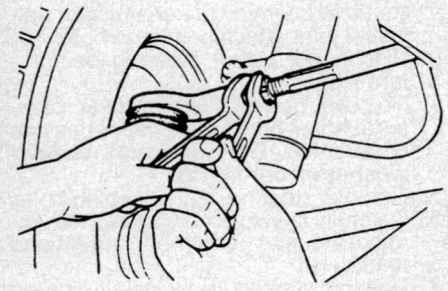

Fig. 1   Front toe-in adjustment

PRELIMINARY INSPECTION

Before measuring and setting front wheel alignment, rest front wheels on turn plates.

Before setting rear toe, rest rear wheels on slider plates or turn plates. Before setting any alignment angle, jounce the vehicle three times at each end to establish trim height.

Special adapters are available for using a magnetic hub gauge at rear wheels. Depending on type of equipment used, these may not be necessary. After removing hub cap and bearing cap, hub gauge will snap into place on brake drum. Magnetic mounting toe gauges may also be installed in the same manner.

Always perform wheel alignment on a level alignment rack. Before doing alignment, check the following.
1. Worn suspension parts.
2. Standing curb height.
3. Remove heavy weights from trunk.
4. Wheel bearings.
5. Full tank of gas.
6. Place front seats in full rear position.

7. Check rear toe adjustment.
8. Always road test vehicle after adjusting alignment. If vehicle still pulls, switch front tires. If vehicle still pulls in same direction, check alignment and rear tracking. If vehicle pulls in opposite direction, rotate tires, then road test again.

FRONT WHEEL ALIGNMENT

CASTER

While caster is pre-set at the factory and not adjustable, it should be checked as a possible cause of suspension complaints. When checking caster ensure tires are properly inflated. If caster does not fall within specification, check control arms, stabilizers and bushings. If these components are satisfactory, check vehicle body for distortion at suspension mounting points.

CAMBER

1. Raise vehicle and support at body so that front suspension is unloaded.
2. Remove tire and wheel assembly.
3. Loosen and remove four top strut attaching nuts from mounting studs.
4. Lower strut, then rotate strut and rotate bearing 180°.
5. Install strut in strut tower.
6. Install and tighten four attaching nuts.
7. Check camber is set correctly.

TOE-IN

1. Loosen jam nuts at tie rod ends, then release clips at small ends of steering gear boots. Ensure boots are free on tie rod ends so that they will not be twisted when tie rods are turned.
2. Turn tie rods into or out of tie rod ends

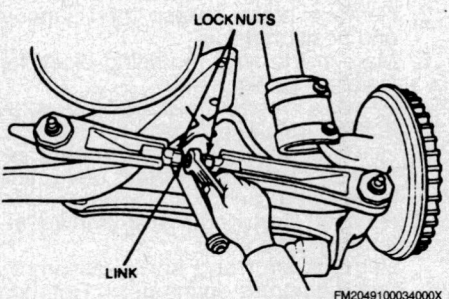

Fig. 2   Rear toe adjustment

an equal amount on each side, Fig. 1. to keep steering wheel centered.
3. Check front tracking. Always set tracking immediately after setting toe. Set tracking by using rear wheels as a reference point. Follow equipment manufacture's instructions to check tracking. The angle of each front wheel in relationship to rear wheels must be the same.
4. Check toe setting after setting tracking.
5. When toe is correct, tighten tie rod end locknuts to 26-28 ft. lbs. Verity that steering gear boot ends are positioned in the reduced diameter sections of tie rods and install boot clips.

REAR WHEEL ALIGNMENT

TOE ADJUSTMENT

Rear toe should always be checked whenever an alignment on the front wheels is required. Rear toe should be adjusted prior to setting the front alignment angles. Rear toe is adjusted by loosening the locknuts and rotating the adjustment link on the rear control arms, Fig. 2. One turn of the link will change toe .044 inch.

FORD ESCORT & MERCURY TRACER

NOTE: Refer To Rear Of This Manual For Vehicle Manufacturer's Special Service Tool Suppliers.

INDEX OF SERVICE OPERATIONS

NOTE: For Service Operations Not Listed Below, Refer To The Table Of Contents In The Front Of This Manual.

Specifications

GENERAL ENGINE SPECIFICATIONS

Year	Engine Liter/CID	Engine VIN Code	Fuel System	Bore & Stroke	Compression Ratio	Net H.P. @ RPM	Maximum Torque Ft. Lbs. @ RPM	Normal Oil Pressure, psi
1992-95	1.8L/4-112	8	EFI	3.27 x 3.35	9.0	127 @ 6500	114 @ 4500	②
	1.9L/4-116	J	SEFI	3.23 x 3.46	9.0	88 @ 4400	108 @ 3800	35-65①

①—Engine at normal operating temperature & 2000 RPM.
②—Engine at normal operating temperature, 28-43 psi at 1000 RPM and 43-57 psi at 3000 RPM.

TUNE UP SPECIFICATIONS

Engine (VIN Code)①	Spark Plug Gap	Ignition Timing,°BTDC Firing Order Fig.④	Ignition Timing,°BTDC Man. Trans.	Ignition Timing,°BTDC Auto. Trans.	Timing Mark Fig.	Curb Idle Speed③ Man. Trans.	Curb Idle Speed③ Auto. Trans.	Fast Idle Speed Man. Trans.	Fast Idle Speed Auto Trans.	Fuel Pump Pressure, psi⑧
1992–94										
1.8L/4-112	.041	⑦	10⑤	10⑤	B	750	750N	⑥	⑥	38-46
1.9L/4-116	.044	②	10②	10②	⑨	730-830⑩	730-830N⑩	⑩	⑩	35-40
1995										
1.8L/4-112	.041	⑦	10⑤	10⑤	B	700-800	700-800N	⑧	⑧	38-46
1.9L/4-116	.044	②	10②	10②	⑨	450-750	450-750	⑩	⑩	35-40

BTDC–Before Top Dead Center.
①—The eighth digit of the Vehicle Identification Number (VIN) denotes engine code.
②—Firing order, 1-3-4-2. Refer to Fig. C for spark plug wire connections at distributor cap.
③—N: Neutral.
④—Before disconnecting wires from distributor cap, determine location of No. 1 wire in cap, as distributor position may have been altered from that shown at the end of this chart.
⑤—With STI connector grounded, refer to Fig. D.
⑥—Computer controlled, non-adjustable.
⑦—Firing order, 1-3-4-2. Refer to Fig. A for spark plug wire connections at distributor cap.
⑧—Wrap shop towel around fitting to prevent fuel spillage, then connect a suitable fuel pressure gauge to fuel diagnostic valve on fuel rail assembly. Place ignition switch in On position & check fuel pressure gauge reading.
⑨—Equipped with a crankshaft position sensor.
⑩—Idle speed controlled by an automatic idle speed control.

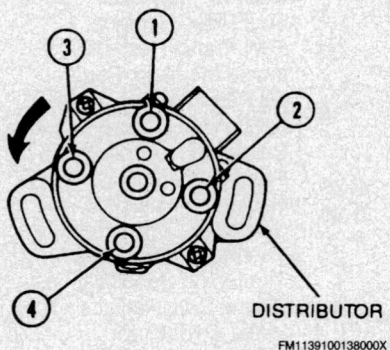

Fig. A

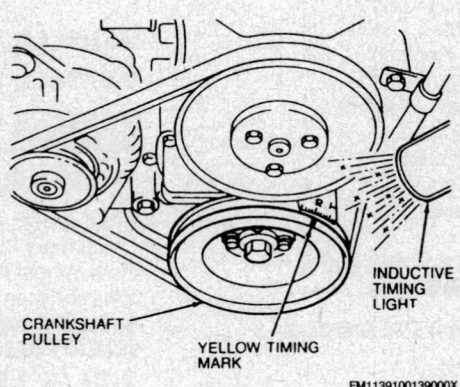

Fig. B

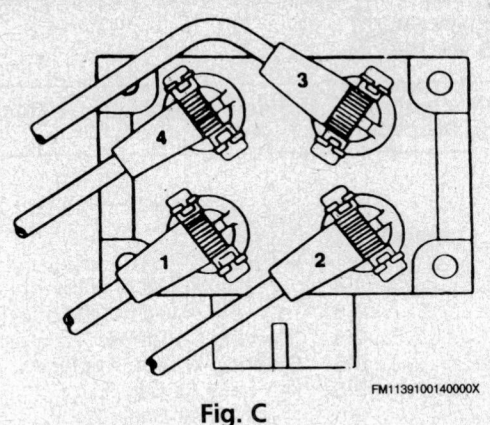

Fig. C

FM1139100140000X

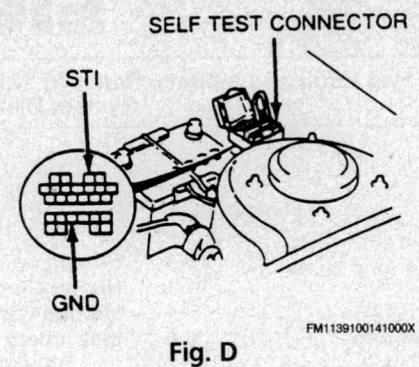

Fig. D

FM1139100141000X

FRONT WHEEL ALIGNMENT SPECIFICATIONS

Year	Caster Angle, Degrees		Camber Angle, Degrees		Toe-In Inch
	Limits	Desired	Limits	Desired	
1992-95	+1 to +2⁵/₆	+1¹¹/₁₂	-⁵/₁₆ to +²/₃	-¹/₁₂	.08

REAR WHEEL ALIGNMENT SPECIFICATIONS

Year	Caster Angle, Degrees		Camber Angle, Degrees		Toe-In Inch
	Limits	Desired	Limits	Desired	
1992-95	—	—	-1¹/₁₂ to +⁵/₁₂	-¹/₃	.08

COOLING SYSTEM & CAPACITY DATA

Year	Engine/VIN	Coolant Capacity, Qts.		Radiator Cap Relief Pressure, Lbs.	Thermo. Opening Temp.	Fuel Tank Gals.	Engine Oil Refill Qts.①	Transaxle Oil	
		Manual Transaxle	Automatic Transaxle					Manual Transaxle Pints	Auto. Transaxle Qts.②
1992-94	1.8L/4-112/8	5.3	6.3	13	192	13.2	4.0	7.1	6.1
	1.9L/4-116/J	5.3	6.3	16	192	11.9	4.0	5.66	6.1
1995	1.8L/4-112/8	5.3	6.3	13	192	13.2	4.0	7.1	6.7
	1.9L/4-116/J	5.3	6.3	16	192	11.9	4.0	5.66	6.7

① —Includes filter.
② —Approximate. Make final inspection
   w/dipstick.

LUBRICANT DATA

Year	Model	Lubricant Type					
		Transaxle		Transfer Case	Rear Axle	Power Steering	Brake System
		Manual	Automatic				
1992-95	All	Mercon	Mercon	—	—	Mercon	DOT 3

NOTE: On Air Bag Equipped Models, Refer To "Air Bag System Precautions" Located In The Front Of This Manual For System Disarming & Arming Procedures.

INDEX

PRECAUTIONS

AIR BAG SYSTEMS

Refer to "Air Bag System Precautions" in the front of this manual for system disarming and arming procedures.

FUSE PANEL & FLASHER LOCATION

These vehicles use two fuse panels. The passenger compartment fuse panel is located below the instrument panel, to the left of the steering wheel. The engine compartment fuse panel is located on the left side of the engine compartment.

The flasher unit is located below the lefthand side of the instrument panel.

RELAY CENTER LOCATION

The relay center is located at the rear lefthand side of the engine compartment.

STARTER
REPLACE

1.8L/4-112 ENGINE

1. Disconnect battery ground cable, then remove air duct from throttle body to resonance chamber.
2. Remove starter motor upper mount bolts, then raise and support vehicle.
3. Remove intake plenum support bracket, then disconnect "S" terminal connector from starter solenoid. When disconnecting connector from "S" terminal, grasp connector and depress plastic tab to remove.
4. Remove "B" terminal attaching nut and disconnect cable from terminal.
5. Remove starter motor lower mounting bolt, then the starter motor.

6. Reverse procedure to install. **Torque** upper and lower mounting bolts to 15-20 ft. lbs. and "B" terminal attaching nut to 7-12 ft. lbs.

1.9L/4-116 ENGINE

1. Disconnect battery ground cable.
2. **On models equipped with automatic transaxle,** remove kickdown cable routing bracket from engine block.
3. **On all models,** disconnect wire from starter solenoid "S" terminal. When disconnecting connector from "S" terminal, grasp connector and depress plastic tab to remove.
4. Remove "B" terminal attaching nut and disconnect cable from terminal.
5. Remove starter motor mounting bolts, then the starter motor.
6. Reverse procedure to install. **Torque** mounting bolts to 15-20 ft. lbs. and "B" terminal attaching nut to 7-12 ft. lbs.

DISTRIBUTOR
REPLACE

1.8L/4-112 ENGINE

1. Disconnect battery ground cable, then disconnect coil wire from distributor.
2. Remove distributor cap screws, then pull off cap and swing it aside.
3. Disconnect distributor electrical connector.
4. If distributor unit is not being replaced, scribe a reference mark across distributor base flange and cylinder head. This reference mark will allow installation without changing timing.
5. Remove distributor mounting bolts, then the distributor.
6. Reverse procedure to install noting the following:
   a. Ensure that drive tangs engage with camshaft slots.
   b. **Torque** distributor mounting bolts

to 14-19 ft. lbs.
   c. If a new distributor has been installed, ignition timing should be checked and adjusted.

1.9L/4-116 ENGINE

This engine uses a distributorless ignition.

IGNITION SWITCH
REPLACE

1. Remove multi-function switch as described under "Multi-Function Switch, Replace."
2. Disconnect ignition switch electrical connector.
3. Remove three mounting screws, then the ignition switch.
4. Reverse procedure to install.

HEADLAMP SWITCH
REPLACE

The headlamp and turn signal switches are serviced with the multi-function switch as a unit. Refer to "Multi-Function Switch, Replace" for procedure.

FOG LAMP SWITCH
REPLACE

1. Disconnect battery ground cable.
2. Detach hood release cable from left lower dash trim panel, then remove four retaining screws and left lower dash trim panel.
3. Disconnect electrical connector from fog lamp switch, then squeeze two lock tabs and remove fog lamp switch through front of trim panel.
4. Reverse procedure to install.

STOP LIGHT SWITCH
REPLACE

1. Disconnect battery ground cable, then disconnect stop lamp switch electrical connector.
2. Remove stop lamp locknut, then the stop lamp switch.
3. Reverse procedure to install, adjust stop lamp switch by turning the switch until it contacts the brake pedal, then turn an additional half turn.

MULTI-FUNCTION SWITCH
REPLACE

1. Disconnect battery ground cable, then remove steering wheel as described under "Steering Wheel, Replace."
2. Remove four retaining screws from steering column lower cover, then remove lower cover.
3. Remove steering column upper cover, then disconnect three multi-function switch electrical connectors.
4. Remove multi-function switch retaining screw, then pull electrical connectors from retaining brackets and remove switch.
5. Reverse procedure to install.

TURN SIGNAL SWITCH
REPLACE

Refer to "Headlamp Switch, Replace" for procedure.

DIMMER SWITCH
REPLACE

1. Disconnect battery ground cable.
2. Detach hood release cable from left lower dash trim panel, then remove four retaining screws and left lower dash trim panel.
3. Disconnect electrical connector from dimmer switch, then squeeze two lock tabs and remove dimmer switch through front of trim panel.
4. Reverse procedure to install.

STEERING WHEEL
REPLACE

LESS AIR BAG

1. Disconnect battery ground cable.
2. Remove steering wheel cover retaining screws from back side of wheel, then remove cover.
3. Disconnect horn and speed control electrical connectors.
4. Remove steering wheel mounting nut, then steering wheel using puller No. T67L-3600-A or equivalent.
5. Reverse procedure to install. **Torque** steering wheel mounting nut to 29-36 ft. lbs.

WITH AIR BAG

1. Ensure front wheels are in straight-ahead position.

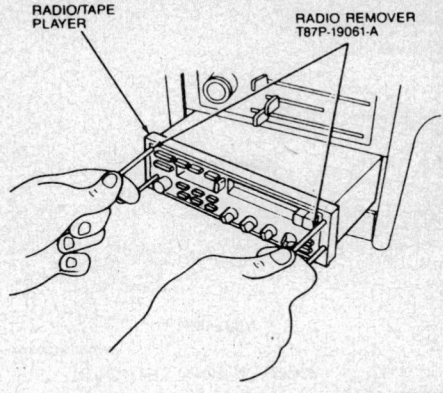

Fig. 1   Radio removal

FM9039100005000X

2. Disconnect battery ground cable, then wait at least one minute for back-up power supply to deplete.
3. Remove two driver side air bag module bolts from rear of steering wheel.
4. Pull driver side air bag module up and away from steering wheel and disconnect air bag module electrical connector from air bag sliding contact.
5. Remove air bag module.
6. Remove steering wheel bolt.
7. Using steering wheel puller tool, remove steering wheel.
8. Reverse procedure to install. **Torque** steering wheel mounting bolt to 34-46 ft. lbs.

INSTRUMENT CLUSTER
REPLACE

1992-94

1. Disconnect battery ground cable.
2. Remove four bolts securing steering column to instrument panel frame, then lower steering column.
3. Remove cap screws securing instrument cluster bezel to instrument panel, then the instrument cluster bezel.
4. Disconnect speedometer cable at transaxle by pulling cable out of vehicle speed sensor.
5. Remove screws and bolts securing instrument cluster to instrument panel, then pull cluster out slightly and disconnect electrical connectors.
6. Disconnect speedometer cable from instrument cluster, then remove cluster from instrument panel.
7. Reverse procedure to install.

1995

1. Disconnect battery ground cable.
2. If equipped with tilt steering column, tilt steering wheel down.
3. Remove four steering column shroud screws and lower steering column shroud.
4. Remove four bolts securing steering column to instrument panel frame, then lower steering column.
5. Disconnect speedometer cable from speedometer head by squeezing speedometer cable retainer.
6. Remove eight cap screws securing instrument panel finish panel to instrument panel.
7. Pull finish panel away from instrument panel and disconnect electrical connectors.
8. Remove I/P finish panel.
9. Remove instrument cluster retaining screws and bolts.
10. Pull instrument cluster out slightly and disconnect three electrical connectors from rear of cluster.
11. Remove instrument cluster from instrument panel.

RADIO
REPLACE

1. Disconnect battery ground cable.
2. Using radio remover No. T87P-19061-A or equivalent, pull radio out from its mounting position and disconnect antenna and electrical connectors, **Fig. 1.**
3. Remove radio from vehicle.
4. Reverse procedure to install.

WIPER MOTOR
REPLACE
FRONT

1. Disconnect battery ground cable.
2. Remove wiper arm attaching nut cover, then attaching nut and pull wiper arm from pivot shaft.
3. With hood closed, remove seven screw covers from cowl grille screws.
4. Remove seven cowl grille screws, then cowl grille.
5. Pry up four baffle retaining clips, then remove baffle trim piece.
6. Remove wiper linkage retaining clip, then disconnect wiper linkage from motor. Ensure that wiper motor is in the PARK position before disconnecting linkage.
7. Disconnect two motor electrical connectors, then remove three mounting bolts and motor.
8. Reverse procedure to install. **Torque** wiper motor mounting bolts to 61-87 inch lbs.

REAR

1. Disconnect battery ground cable.
2. Lift wiper arm attaching nut cover and remove nut, then pull wiper arm from pivot shaft.
3. Remove shaft seal from outer bushing attaching nut, then remove outer bushing attaching nut and outer bushing.
4. Remove liftgate trim panel as follows:
   a. Remove three push-in retainers and hi-mount stop lamp cover.
   b. Remove liftgate seaming welt from along trim panel, then disengage 10 retaining clips and remove trim panel.
   c. Remove cargo area lamp.
5. Disconnect wiper motor electrical connector, then remove three wiper motor mounting bolts and wiper motor.
6. Reverse procedure to install noting the following:
   a. **Torque** wiper motor mounting bolts to 61-87 inch lbs. and outer

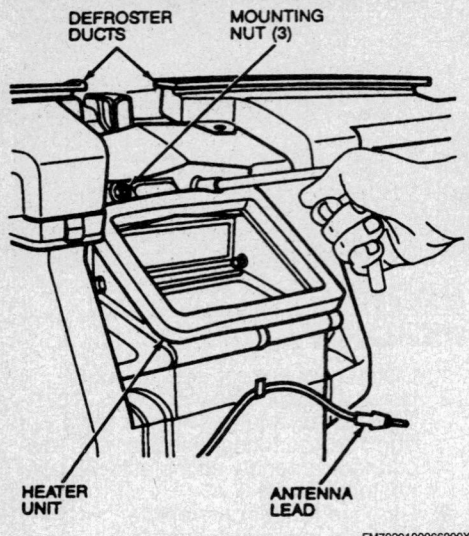

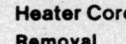

Fig. 2 Heater unit removal

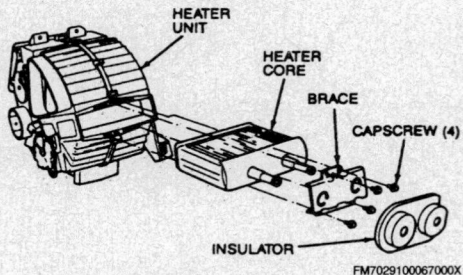

Fig. 3 Heater core removal

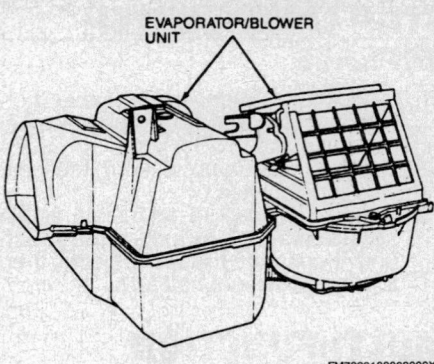

Fig. 4 Evaporator core

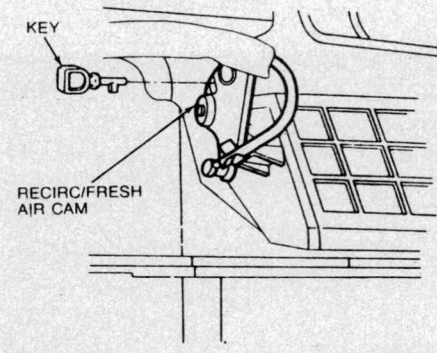

Fig. 5 Recirc/Fresh air cable adjustment

bushing attaching nut to 35-52 inch lbs.

b. Turn wiper switch to the ON position and allow pivot shaft to move through three or four cycles, then turn wiper switch off.

c. Position wiper arm on pivot shaft so tip of blade is .79-.98 inch from rear window molding.

d. **Torque** wiper arm attaching nut to 61-87 inch lbs.

WIPER SWITCH
REPLACE

The windshield wiper switch is serviced with the multi-function switch as a unit. Refer to "Multi-Function Switch, Replace" for procedure.

WIPER TRANSMISSION
REPLACE

1. Disconnect battery ground cable.
2. With hood closed, remove seven screw covers from cowl grille screws.
3. Remove seven cowl grille screws, the cowl grille.
4. Pry up four baffle retaining clips, then remove baffle trim piece.
5. Remove two retaining screws from each pivot shaft, then remove pivot shaft and wiper linkage assembly.
6. Reverse procedure to install. **Torque** pivot shaft retaining screws to 61-87 inch lbs.

BLOWER MOTOR
REPLACE

1. Disconnect battery ground cable, then remove trim panel below glove compartment.

2. Remove wiring bracket and bolt, then disconnect blower motor electrical connector.
3. Remove three blower motor attaching bolts, then blower motor.
4. Remove blower wheel retaining clip, then blower wheel from blower motor.
5. Reverse procedure to install.

HEATER CORE
REPLACE

1. Disconnect battery ground cable.
2. Disconnect heater hoses at bulkhead, then remove instrument panel.
3. Disconnect mode selector and temperature control cables from cams and retaining clips.
4. Loosen capscrew that secures heater to blower clamp, then remove three heater unit mounting nuts, **Fig. 2**.
5. Disconnect antenna lead from retaining clip, then remove heater unit.
6. Remove insulator, then four brace capscrews and brace.
7. Remove heater core from heater unit, **Fig. 3**.
8. Reverse procedure to install.

EVAPORATOR CORE
REPLACE

If a leaking evaporator core is suspected, leak test the core before removing it from the vehicle. If the core needs to be replaced, replace the evaporator/blower unit as an assembly, **Fig. 4**.

1. Disconnect battery ground cable, then discharge A/C system.
2. Using a suitable spring coupling tool, disconnect high-pressure line and accumulator/drier inlet tube from evaporator core at bulkhead and plug ports to prevent entrance of dirt or moisture.
3. Remove glove compartment, then remove trim panel below glove compartment.
4. Disconnect two electrical connectors from resistor assembly, then electrical connector from blower motor.
5. Remove right dash side panel, then right lower dash trim panel and capscrews.
6. Remove support bar and bolts, then support plate and bolts.
7. Disconnect cable from recirc/fresh air cam and retaining clip.
8. Loosen capscrew that secures evaporator to heater clamp, then remove four mounting nuts from evaporator/blower unit.
9. Remove evaporator/blower unit.
10. Reverse procedure to install, adjusting Recirc/Fresh air cable as follows:

a. Move air cable to the FRESH position on climate control assembly.
b. Remove glove compartment.
c. Insert Cable Locating Key tool No. E7GH-18C408-A or equivalent through the fresh air door cam key slot and recirc door key boss opening to secure cam in its proper position as shown in **Fig. 5**.
d. Disconnect cable from retaining clip next to Recirc/Fresh air cam, then connect cable to retaining clip.
e. Remove cable locating key, then ensure that Recirc/Fresh air lever moves its full stroke.
f. Leak test, evacuate and charge A/C system.

1.8L/4-112 Engine

NOTE: On Air Bag Equipped Models, Refer To "Air Bag System Precautions" Located In The Front Of This Manual For System Disarming & Arming Procedures.

INDEX

PRECAUTIONS

AIR BAG SYSTEMS

Refer to "Air Bag System Precautions" in the front of this manual for system disarming and arming procedures.

FUEL SYSTEM PRESSURE RELIEF

1. Start engine, then remove rear seat cushions to gain access to fuel pump electrical connections.
2. Disconnect fuel pump electrical connections and wait for engine to stall.
3. Connect fuel pump electrical connections and install rear seat cushion.

ENGINE MOUNT

REPLACE

1. Install a suitable engine removal sling onto engine lifting brackets.
2. Place an engine hoist into position and support engine.
3. Remove engine vibration dampener, then the engine mount.
4. Reverse procedure to install.

ENGINE

REPLACE

AUTOMATIC TRANSAXLE

1. Relieve fuel system pressure as described in "Precautions."
2. Disconnect battery ground cable.
3. Marking hinge locations for installation reference, remove hood.
4. Discharge A/C system, then drain cooling system.
5. Remove air duct connecting throttle body to resonance chamber.
6. Disconnect power brake vacuum supply hose from power brake, then any necessary vehicle speed control vacuum hoses from intake plenum.
7. Disconnect the following electrical connectors:

   a. Power steering pump.
   b. Water thermoswitch.
   c. Temperature sending unit.
   d. Oil pressure switch.
   e. Fuel injector wiring harness.
   f. Oxygen sensor.
   g. Throttle position sensor.
   h. Distributor.
8. Disconnect all engine ground straps, then the ignition coil high-tension lead from the distributor.
9. Disconnect accelerator and kickdown cable bracket from throttle cam.
10. Remove accelerator and kickdown cable bracket from intake plenum and set assembly aside.
11. Disconnect heater core inlet and outlet hoses at bulkhead.
12. Remove necessary fuel line clips, then disconnect fuel pressure and return lines from the fuel rail.
13. Remove upper radiator hose, then disconnect cooling fan electrical connector.
14. Disconnect radiator thermoswitch electrical connector, then remove starter motor.
15. Raise and support vehicle.
16. Remove righthand upper, righthand lower and lefthand lower splash shields.
17. Remove lower radiator hose, then disconnect two transaxle cooling lines from the radiator and plug lines.
18. Remove A/C line mounting bracket from radiator and position aside.
19. Remove halfshaft bearing support, then the inspection plate from oil pan.
20. Place a wrench on the crankshaft pulley, then rotate crankshaft and remove the torque converter nuts.
21. Remove power steering and A/C accessory drive belt.
22. Remove timing belt as described in "Timing Belt, Replace."
23. Remove crankshaft pulley mounting bolts from crankshaft pulley guide plate.
24. Remove crankshaft pulley, crankshaft pulley guide plate and timing belt out-

er and inner guide plates.
25. Remove exhaust flex-pipe and mounting assembly from exhaust manifold.
26. Remove A/C compressor, then remove power steering pump and bracket assembly leaving hoses connected. Suspend pump with wire and position out of the way.
27. Remove all accessible transaxle to engine bolts from engine block.
28. Lower vehicle, then remove radiator mounting brackets and resonance duct.
29. Remove radiator, fan and shroud assembly from vehicle.
30. Remove vacuum chamber canister, then pressure regulator and bracket assembly.
31. Remove shutter valve actuator and bracket assembly, position aside.
32. Remove water pump and alternator accessory drive belt, then remove alternator.
33. Install a suitable engine removal sling onto engine lifting brackets, then place an engine hoist into position and support engine.
34. Remove oil pan to transaxle attaching bolts and remaining transaxle to engine bolts from engine block.
35. Remove engine vibration dampener, then the front engine mount.
36. Carefully separate engine from transaxle, then remove engine from the vehicle.
37. Reverse procedure to install.

MANUAL TRANSAXLE

1. Relieve fuel system pressure as described in "Precautions."
2. Disconnect battery ground cable.
3. Marking hinge locations for installation reference, remove hood.
4. Discharge A/C system, then drain cooling system.
5. Remove resonance duct and air cleaner assembly.
6. Remove battery and battery tray.
7. Disconnect accelerator cable from

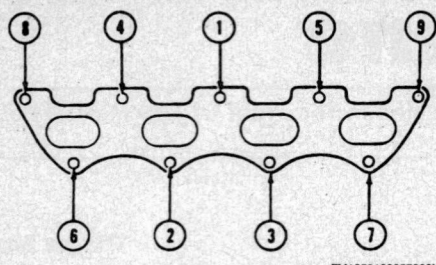

Fig. 1 Intake manifold nut tightening sequence

throttle cam, then remove cable bracket from intake plenum.

8. Remove upper radiator hose from thermostat housing and radiator.
9. Disconnect radiator thermoswitch electrical connectors, then remove radiator overflow hose from the radiator filler neck.
10. Disconnect cooling fan electrical connectors, then remove radiator mounting brackets.
11. Disconnect the following electrical connectors:
    a. Alternator and oil pressure switch.
    b. Throttle position sensor and idle speed control.
    c. Manual lever position switch and fuel injector wiring harness.
    d. Back-up lamp switch and water thermoswitch.
    e. Oxygen sensor, power steering pump and distributor.
12. Disconnect all engine ground straps, then the ignition coil high tension lead from the distributor.
13. Disconnect fuel pressure and return lines.
14. Disconnect heater core inlet and outlet hoses.
15. Disconnect power brake supply, purge control and speed control vacuum hoses.
16. Raise and support vehicle.
17. Remove righthand upper and lower splash shields.
18. Remove clutch slave cylinder pipe bracket from transaxle leaving hose connected. Position slave cylinder aside, taking care not to damage pipe or hose.
19. Disconnect shift control rod and extension bar from transaxle.
20. Remove battery duct, then disconnect lower radiator hose from radiator.
21. Disconnect transaxle cooling lines from radiator, then remove power steering and A/C accessory drive belt.
22. Remove power steering pump and bracket assembly leaving hoses connected.
23. Position power steering assembly aside and suspend it with wire.
24. Remove A/C hose routing bracket from transaxle crossmember and position A/C hose aside.
25. Remove A/C compressor leaving hoses connected, then position aside and suspend with wire.
26. Disconnect speedometer cable from transaxle.

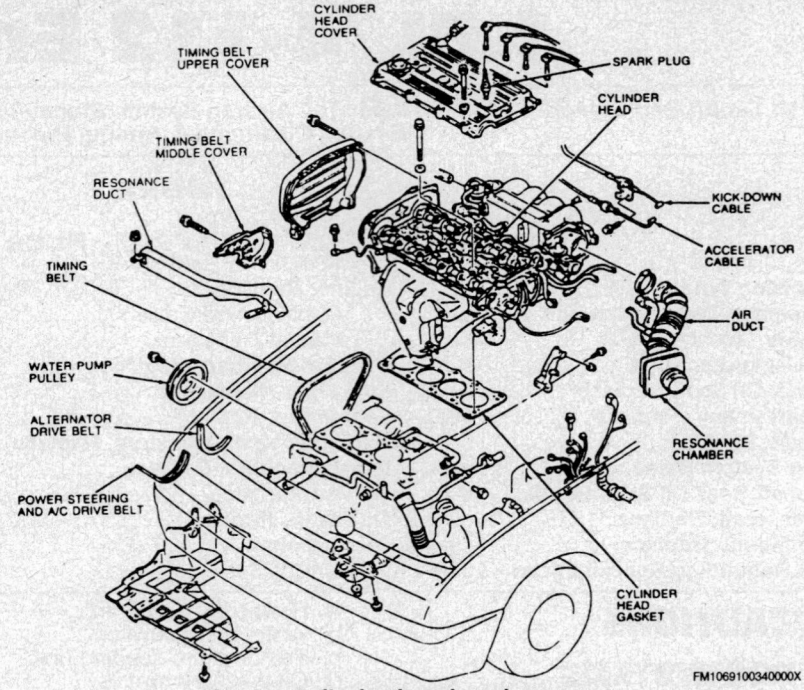

Fig. 2 Cylinder head replacement

27. Remove exhaust pipe mounting flange and support bracket from exhaust manifold.
28. Disconnect starter motor "S" terminal from starter motor solenoid.
29. Remove nut from starter solenoid "B" terminal and disconnect wire from terminal.
30. Remove stabilizer bar, then the tie rod ends from steering knuckles.
31. Remove halfshafts from transaxle.
32. Remove front and rear transaxle mount attaching nuts from crossmember.
33. Lower vehicle, then remove radiator, fan and shroud assembly.
34. Install a suitable engine removal sling onto engine lifting brackets.
35. Place an engine hoist into position and support engine.
36. Remove engine vibration dampener and engine mount.
37. Remove transaxle upper mount and support bracket.
38. Remove engine and transaxle as an assembly.
39. Remove engine intake plenum support bracket.
40. Remove starter motor from transaxle housing, then the transaxle front mount.
41. Remove oil pan to transaxle bolts and transaxle to engine attaching bolts from the engine block.
42. Separate transaxle from engine, then remove clutch assembly from engine.
43. Reverse procedure to install.

INTAKE MANIFOLD
REPLACE

1. Relieve fuel system pressure as described in "Precautions."
2. Disconnect battery ground cable.

3. Disconnect necessary vacuum hoses from intake manifold and plenum.
4. Remove vacuum chamber canister from intake plenum.
5. Disconnect idle speed control and bypass air hoses from intake plenum.
6. Disconnect accelerator and kickdown cables from throttle cam, then remove bracket from intake plenum.
7. Disconnect throttle body electrical connector, then remove fuel rail assembly from manifold.
8. Remove two bolts from transaxle vent tube and remove vent tube from intake plenum.
9. Remove intake manifold upper retaining nuts, then raise and support vehicle.
10. Remove intake plenum support bracket, then the intake manifold lower retaining nuts.
11. Lower vehicle and remove intake manifold, intake plenum and throttle body as an assembly.
12. Reverse procedure to install. Install intake manifold retaining nuts in order shown in **Fig. 1. Torque** nuts to 14-19 ft. lbs.

EXHAUST MANIFOLD
REPLACE

1. Disconnect battery ground cable.
2. Remove resonance duct, then disconnect upper radiator hose.
3. Remove cooling fan, then raise and support vehicle.
4. Remove exhaust pipe from exhaust manifold and remove gasket.
5. Remove two bolts from exhaust pipe support bracket.
6. Remove lefthand side lower splash shield, then the cooling fan lower mounting bolts.

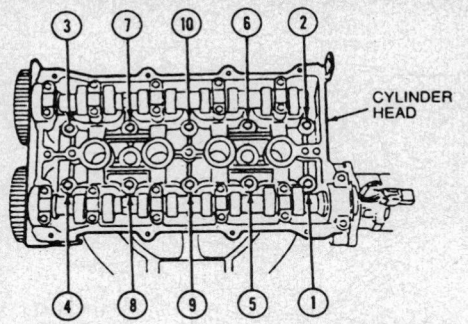

Fig. 3 Cylinder head bolt loosening sequence

FM1069100341000X

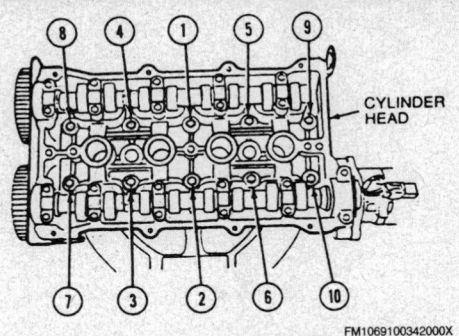

Fig. 4 Cylinder head bolt tightening sequence

FM1069100342000X

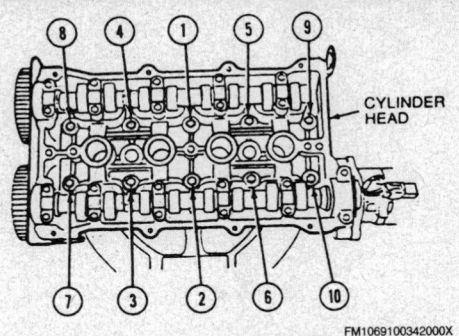

VALVE SPRING COMPRESSOR
VALVE SPRING COMPRESSOR BRACKETS
1/2 INCH DRIVE SOCKET
VALVE SPRING COMPRESSOR BAR
CYLINDER HEAD

FM1069100343000X

Fig. 5 Valve keepers, valve seats, valve springs & valve replacement

7. Lower vehicle and disconnect oxygen sensor electrical connector.
8. Remove manifold heat shield, then manifold mounting nuts and manifold assembly.
9. Remove all gasket material from cylinder head and manifold.
10. Reverse procedure to install.

CYLINDER HEAD
REPLACE

1. Relieve fuel system pressure as described in "Precautions."
2. Disconnect battery ground cable.
3. Drain cooling system, then remove timing belt upper and middles covers, **Fig. 2.**
4. Rotate crankshaft and align timing marks located on camshaft pulleys and seal plate.
5. Loosen timing belt tensioner lock bolt and temporarily secure tensioner spring in the fully extended position.
6. Remove timing belt from camshaft pulleys and position so that it is not damaged during the removal and installation of the cylinder head. **Do not allow timing belt to be contaminated by oil or grease.**
7. Disconnect vacuum hoses from cylinder head cover, then spark plug wires from spark plugs.
8. Remove cylinder head cover and gasket, then the air duct from resonance chamber to throttle body.
9. Disconnect accelerator and kickdown cables from throttle cam, then remove accelerator and kickdown cable bracket from intake plenum.
10. Disconnect all vacuum lines from intake plenum, then all necessary electrical connectors from cylinder head, exhaust manifold, intake plenum and throttle body.
11. Disconnect ground straps, then remove upper radiator hose.
12. Remove transaxle to engine block upper righthand bolt.
13. Disconnect fuel pressure and return lines and plug lines.
14. Disconnect ignition coil high tension lead from distributor, then all necessary hoses from cylinder head and intake plenum.
15. Remove two bolts from transaxle vent tube routing brackets, then raise and support vehicle.

16. Remove bolt from water pump to cylinder head hose bracket.
17. Remove exhaust mounting flange and exhaust pipe support bracket from exhaust manifold.
18. Remove intake plenum support bracket, then lower vehicle.
19. Remove cylinder head bolts in sequence shown in **Fig. 3.**
20. Remove cylinder head assembly along with intake plenum and exhaust manifold from vehicle.
21. Reverse procedure to install, noting the following:
    a. **Torque** cylinder head bolts to 56-60 ft. lbs. in sequence shown in **Fig. 4.**
    b. Perform steps 6-12 in "Installation procedure of "Timing Belt, Replace."

HYDRAULIC LASH ADJUSTERS
REPLACE

1. Remove camshafts as described in "Camshafts, Replace."
2. Mark hydraulic lash adjusters and cylinder head with alignment marks so the adjusters can be installed in their original positions.
3. Remove adjusters from cylinder head.
4. Reverse procedure to install, applying clean engine oil to adjusters before installation.

VALVE KEEPERS, VALVE SEATS, VALVE SPRINGS & VALVE
REPLACE

1. Disconnect battery ground cable.
2. Remove hydraulic lash adjusters as described in "Hydraulic Lash Adjusters, Replace."
3. Install two Valve Spring Compressor Brackets tool No. T89P-6565-A2 or equivalent, onto necessary camshaft cap bolt holes as shown in **Fig. 5.**
4. Install Valve Spring Compressor Bar tool No. T87C-6565-A or equivalent through bracket assemblies.
5. Install a 1/2 drive socket handle onto spring compressor.
6. Align spring compressor squarely

over valve spring upper seat, then compress spring and remove valve keepers with a magnet.
7. Release spring compressor and remove valve spring upper seat, valve spring, valve spring lower seat and valve.
8. Reverse procedure to install, noting the following:
    a. Lubricate valve stem prior to installation.
    b. When installing valve spring ensure compressed end of spring goes into cylinder head first.
    c. After installation tap end of valve stem lightly with a plastic hammer to ensure that keepers are fully seated.

TIMING BELT
REPLACE

REMOVAL

1. Remove upper timing belt cover and gasket, **Fig. 6.**
2. Loosen water pump pulley attaching bolts, then remove water pump and alternator accessory drive belt.
3. Remove water pump pulley, then raise and support vehicle.
4. Remove right wheel, then righthand upper and lower splash shields.
5. Remove A/C and power steering accessory drive belts.
6. Remove crankshaft pulley, crankshaft pulley guide plate and timing belt outer and inner guide plates.
7. Remove timing belt middle and lower covers along with gaskets.
8. Rotate crankshaft and align timing marks located on camshaft pulleys and seal, plate, **Fig. 7.**
9. If timing belt is to be reused, mark an arrow on timing belt to indicate its rotational direction for installation reference.
10. Loosen timing belt tensioner and remove belt.

INSTALLATION

1. Temporarily secure timing belt tensioner in far left position with spring

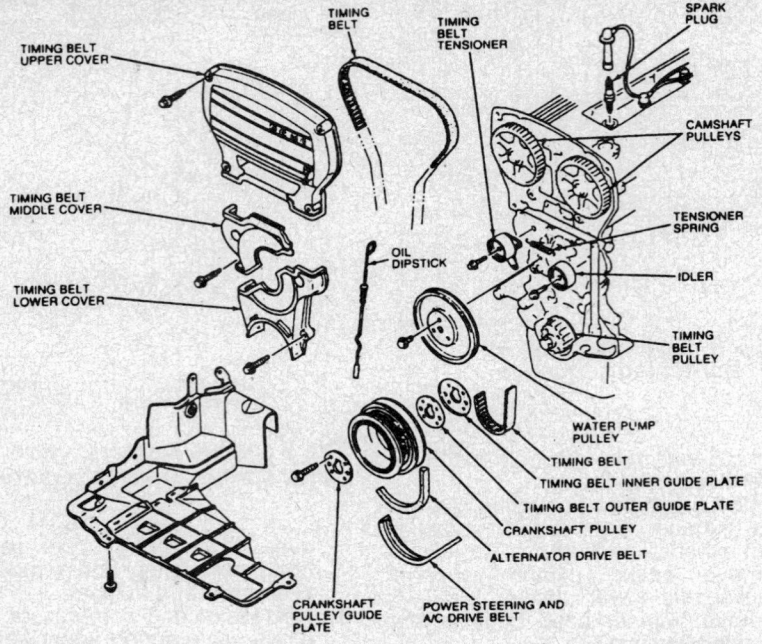

Fig. 6 Exploded view of timing belt assembly

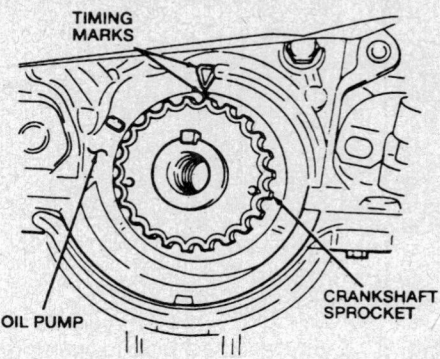

Fig. 7 Camshaft pulley timing mark alignment

fully extended, then tighten lock bolt.

2. Ensure that timing marks on timing belt pulley and engine block are aligned, **Fig. 8.**
3. Ensure timing marks on camshaft pulleys and seal plate are aligned, **Fig. 7.**
4. Install timing belt.
5. Loosen tensioner lock bolt, then using a suitable prying tool, position timing belt tensioner so that timing belt is taut, tighten lock bolt.
6. Turn crankshaft pulley two turns clockwise and align timing belt pulley mark with mark on engine block.
7. Ensure camshaft pulley marks are aligned with seal plate marks. If marks are not aligned, remove belt and repeat procedure.
8. Turn crankshaft pulley 1 and 5/6 turns clockwise and align timing belt pulley mark with tension set mark (approximately 10 o'clock position) as shown in **Fig. 9.**
9. Apply tension to timing belt tensioner and install tensioner lock bolt. Torque lock bolt to specifications.
10. Turn crankshaft 2 and 1/6 turns clockwise and check that timing marks are aligned.
11. Measure timing belt deflection by applying 22 lbs. of pressure on belt between camshaft pulleys. Deflection should be within 0.35–0.45 inch. If deflection is not within specification, loosen tensioner lock bolt and adjust tensioner as necessary.
12. Turn crankshaft two turns clockwise and ensure all timing marks are aligned. If timing marks are not aligned, repeat procedure beginning at step 4.
13. Install timing belt lower and middle covers along with gaskets.
14. Install timing belt inner and outer guide plates, crankshaft pulley and crankshaft pulley guide plate. Torque bolts to specification.
15. Install A/C and power steering accessory drive belt.
16. Install righthand upper and righthand lower splash shields.
17. Install water pump pulley, then alternator and water pump pulley accessory drive belt.
18. Install right wheel, then lower vehicle.
19. Install timing belt upper cover and gasket. Torque bolts to specification.

CAMSHAFT
REPLACE

1. Remove distributor assembly, then remove camshaft pulley as described in "Camshaft Pulley, Replace."
2. Remove seal plate, then loosen camshaft bolts in order shown in **Fig. 10.**
3. Remove camshaft caps noting their mounting locations for installation reference.
4. Remove camshaft and camshaft oil seal.
5. Reverse procedure to install, noting the following:
   a. Apply clean engine oil to camshaft journals and bearings.
   b. Ensure exhaust camshaft groove is installed into distributor drive gear.
   c. Install camshaft caps according to cap numbers and arrow marks.
   d. Install camshaft cap bolts and **torque** in sequence shown in **Fig. 11** to 8-10 ft. lbs.

CAMSHAFT PULLEY
REPLACE

1. Remove timing belt as described in "Timing Belt, Replace."

2. Disconnect vacuum hoses from cylinder head cover, then spark plug wires from spark plugs.
3. Remove cylinder head cover and gasket.
4. Holding camshaft with a wrench, remove camshaft pulley lock bolt.
5. Remove camshaft pulley.
6. Reverse procedure to install, aligning camshaft pulley timing mark with mark on seal plate.

CAMSHAFT OIL SEAL
REPLACE

1. Remove camshaft pulley as described in "Camshaft Pulley, Replace."
2. Remove seal plate mounting bolts, then the seal plate.
3. Using Locknut Pin Remover tool No. T78P-3504-N or equivalent, remove camshaft oil seal.
4. Reverse procedure to install, applying a small amount of engine oil to lip of seal prior to installation.

VALVE STEM SEAL
REPLACE

1. Remove valve keepers, valve seats, valve spring as described in "Valve Keepers, Valve Seats, Valve Springs & Valve, Replace."
2. Assemble Valve Stem Seal Remover tool No. T89P-6510-D and Slide Hammer tool No. T59L-100-B or equivalent, and remove valve seal from cylinder head.
3. Reverse procedure to install.

CRANKSHAFT REAR OIL SEAL
REPLACE

1. Remove flywheel (manual transmission) or flexplate (automatic transmission).
2. Remove rear cover mounting bolts and rear cover.
3. Using a screwdriver protected with a rag, remove crankshaft rear oil seal.

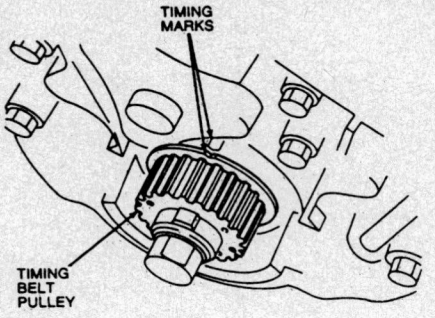

Fig. 8 Timing belt pulley timing marks alignment

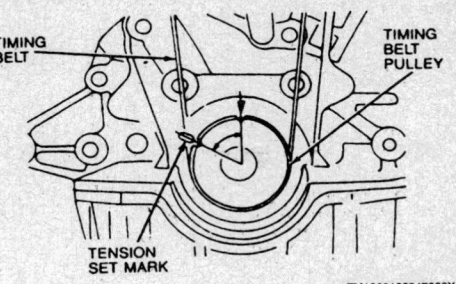

Fig. 9 Timing belt pulley to tension set mark alignment

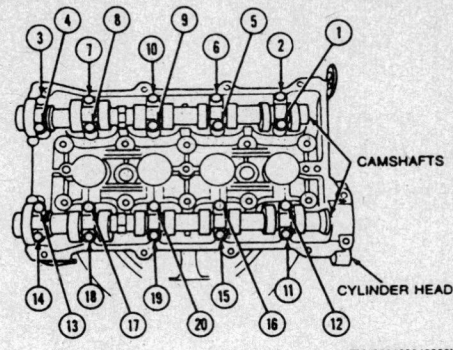

Fig. 10 Camshaft cap bolt loosening sequence

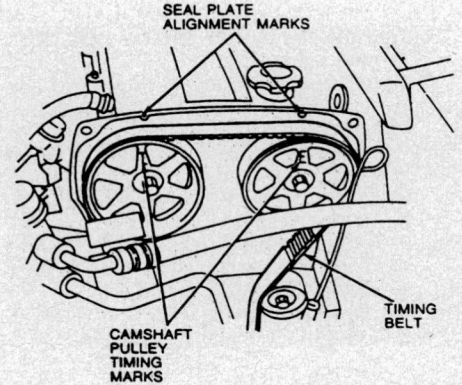

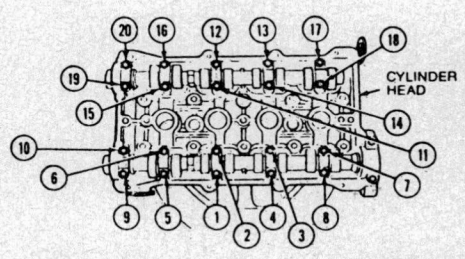

Fig. 11 Camshaft cap bolt tightening sequence

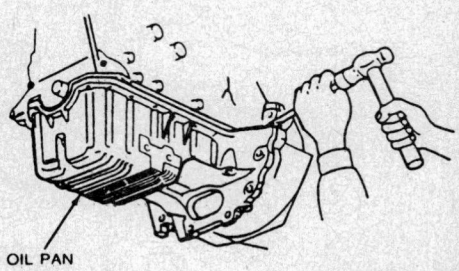

Fig. 12 Oil pan removal

4. Reverse procedure to install, applying a small amount of engine oil to lip of new oil seal.

OIL PAN
REPLACE

1. Raise and support vehicle.
2. Drain engine oil, then remove right-hand upper slash shield.
3. Remove righthand and lefthand lower splash shields.
4. Remove exhaust pipe front mounting flange and exhaust pipe support bracket from exhaust manifold.
5. Remove oil pan to transaxle mounting bolts, then support oil pan with a jack stand.
6. Remove oil pan to engine block attaching bolts. **Do not force a prying tool between engine block and oil pan when trying to remove pan. This may cause damage to oil pan contact surface.**
7. Using a suitable prying tool, carefully pry oil pan from engine block at point shown in **Fig. 12**.
8. Reverse procedure to install.

OIL PUMP
REPLACE

1. Remove timing belt as described in "Timing Belt, Replace."
2. Remove timing belt pulley lock bolt.
3. Using a steering wheel puller remove timing belt pulley, then the woodruff key.
4. Remove oil pan and oil strainer as described in "Oil Pan, Replace."
5. Remove A/C compressor mounting bolts and position compressor aside.
6. Remove A/C compressor mounting bracket, then the mounting bolt from oil dipstick tube bracket.
7. Remove alternator lower mounting bolt.
8. Remove oil pump mounting bolts and oil pump.
9. Reverse procedure to install.

BELT TENSION DATA
ALTERNATOR/WATER PUMP BELT

Adjust the tension of the belt using either Belt Tension Gauge tool No. 021-0028A or equivalent, or deflection method.

Using Belt Tension Gauge tool No. 021-0028A or equivalent, position the gauge on the longest accessible span of the belt and use the following specifications: **New Belt** (no run time), adjust tension to 85.8-103.4 lbs. Run the engine for 10 minutes, then readjust belt tension; **Used Belt** (more than 10 minutes of run time), adjust tension to 68.2-85.8 lbs.

If using the deflection method, use the following specifications: **New Belt** (no run time), belt deflection measurement should be 0.31-0.35 inch; **Used Belt** (more than 10 minutes of run time), belt deflection measurement should be 0.35-0.39 inch.

POWER STEERING & A/C COMPRESSOR BELT

Adjust the tension of the belt using either Belt Tension Gauge tool No. 021-0028A or equivalent, or deflection method.

Using Belt Tension Gauge tool No. 021-0028A or equivalent, position the gauge on the longest accessible span of the belt and use the following specifications, **New Belt** (no run time), adjust tension to 110-132 lbs. Run the engine for 10 minutes and readjust tension. **Used Belt** (more than 10 minutes of run time), adjust tension to 95-110 lbs.

If you are using the deflection method, **New Belt** (no run time) belt deflection measurement should be 0.31-0.35 inch. **Used Belt** (more than 10 minutes of run time), belt deflection measurement should be 0.35-0.39 inch.

COOLING SYSTEM BLEED

After filling cooling system, run engine for approximately 12 minutes with radiator pressure cap off, then top off radiator. Secure cap, then and with engine running, fill coolant reservoir to FULL HOT mark with coolant.

THERMOSTAT
REPLACE

1. Ensure that engine is cool, remove radiator cap and open draincock. Allow

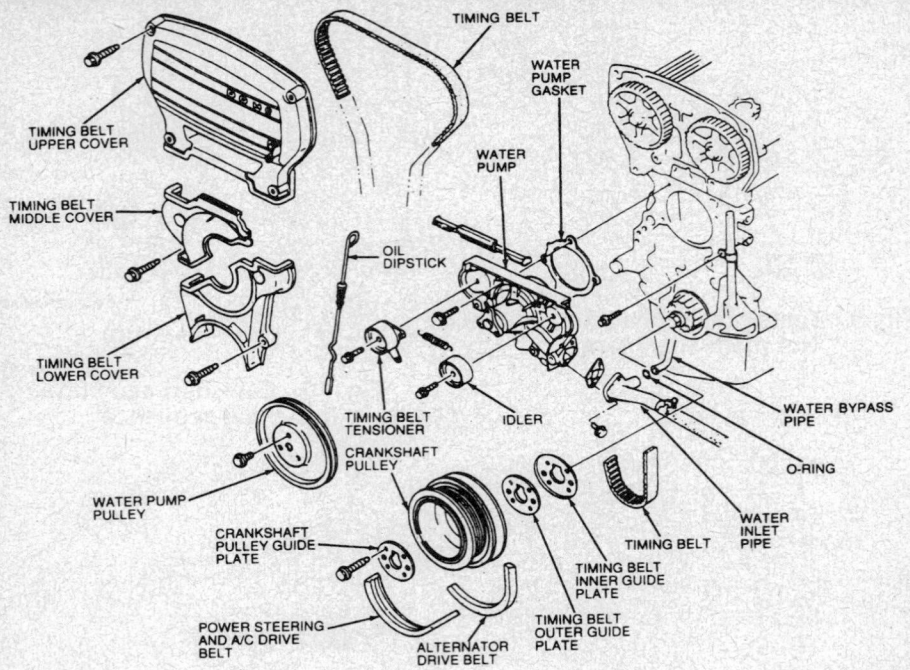

Fig. 13   Water pump removal

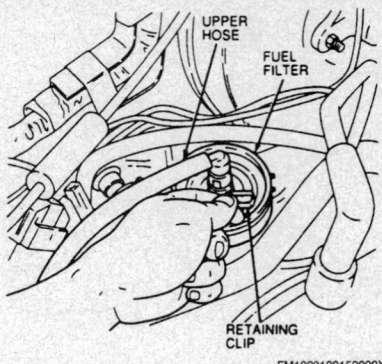

FM1029100152000X

Fig. 14   Fuel filter removal

coolant to drain below level of thermostat housing.
2. Remove air intake tube and disconnect water thermoswitch connector.
3. Disconnect engine wiring harness ground strap from connector above housing.
4. Disconnect exhaust gas oxygen sensor electrical connector, then remove upper radiator hose from housing.
5. Remove thermostat housing retaining bolt and nut, then the thermostat and gasket.
6. Clean mating surfaces of housing and cylinder head, then install thermostat in cylinder head.
7. Position gasket and thermostat housing on cylinder head and install housing bolt and nut, tighten to specification.
8. Install upper radiator hose and connect EGO sensor electrical connector.
9. Connect engine ground strap to connector above housing, then the water thermoswitch connector.
10. Install air intake tube and refill cooling system with 50/50 coolant mixture. Add coolant until radiator remains full.
11. Start engine until upper hose is warm. Check for leaks and refill if necessary.
12. Run engine for 12 minutes, then top off radiator. Securely install radiator cap with engine running.
13. Fill coolant recovery reservoir to the Full Hot mark with 50/50 mixture.

WATER PUMP
REPLACE

1. Drain cooling system, then remove timing belt as described in "Timing Belt, Replace."
2. Raise and support vehicle, then re-

move oil dipstick tube bracket bolt from water pump.
3. Remove bolts and gasket from water inlet pipe, **Fig. 13.**
4. Remove all but uppermost water pump mounting bolt, then lower vehicle.
5. Remove upper mounting bolt and water pump assembly.
6. Remove gasket material from water pump.
7. Reverse procedure to install, refer to "Timing Belt, Replace" for timing belt installation.

RADIATOR
REPLACE

1. Disconnect battery ground cable.
2. Drain cooling system.
3. Raise and support vehicle.
4. Remove right front fender splash shield and left front fender splash shield.
5. Remove lower radiator hose from radiator.
6. **On vehicles with automatic transaxle,** remove lower oil cooler inlet tube from radiator.
7. **On all models,** lower vehicle.
8. **On vehicles with automatic transaxle and A/C,** remove air deflector seal located between radiator and fan shroud.
9. **On all models,** remove upper oil cooler inlet tube from radiator.
10. Remove engine air intake resonator from radiator support upper bracket.
11. Disconnect electric cooling fan motor electrical connector.
12. Disconnect high speed fan control switch electrical connector. If necessary, remove high speed switch from radiator.

13. Remove three fan shroud bolts and the fan shroud.
14. Remove upper radiator hose.
15. Remove two radiator support upper brackets.
16. Remove oil cooler tube bracket bolts from radiator.
17. Remove radiator coolant overflow hose from radiator.
18. Remove radiator from vehicle by lifting it straight up.
19. Reverse procedure to install.
20. Fill cooling system, then start engine and check for coolant leaks.

FUEL PUMP
REPLACE

1. Relieve fuel system pressure as outlined under "Precautions."
2. Disconnect battery ground cable.
3. Remove rear seat cushion.
4. Disconnect fuel pump assembly electrical connector.
5. Remove ground strap and fuel pump cover attaching screws, then remove cover.
6. Remove fuel hose clips, then disconnect and cap fuel hoses.
7. Using suitable nut removal tool, remove fuel pump spanner nut.
8. Remove fuel pump and discard gasket.
9. Reverse procedure to install. Install new gasket.

FUEL FILTER
REPLACE

1. Relieve fuel system pressure as outlined under "Precautions."
2. Disconnect battery ground cable.
3. Place suitable container below fuel filter to collect excess fuel.
4. Remove fuel filter upper hose clip, **Fig. 14.**
5. Disconnect and cap fuel filter upper hose.
6. Loosen filter mounting clamp.
7. Raise and support vehicle.
8. Remove filter hose lower clip, then disconnect and cap lower hose.
9. Lower vehicle an remove fuel filter.
10. Reverse procedure to install.

TIGHTENING SPECIFICATIONS

Year	Component	Torque/ Ft. Lbs.
1992-95	Accelerator & Kickdown Cable Bracket	69-95 ③
	A/C Compressor Mounting Bracket	30-40
	Alternator Lower Mounting Bolt	27-38
	Camshaft Cap	100–126 ②
	Camshaft Pulley Lock Bolt	36-45
	Clutch Release Cylinder	12-17
	Connecting Rod Cap	35-37
	Crankshaft Pulley	109–152 ③
	Crankshaft Rear Cover	69-95 ③
	Cylinder Head	①
	Cylinder Head Cover	43-78 ③
	Distributor Mounting Bolts	14-19
	Exhaust Flex Pipe To Converter	51-69
	Engine Coolant Temperature Sensor	52-78 ③
	Engine Lifting Bracket	27-38
	Engine Mount	49-69
	Engine Oil Dipstick Bracket	6-8
	Engine Support Bracket	69-86
	Engine Vibration Dampener	41-59
	Exhaust Manifold Heat Shield	69-95 ③
	Exhaust Manifold Nuts	28-34
	Exhaust Mounting Flange To Exhaust Manifold	23-34
	Flexplate Bolts	71-76
	Flywheel Bolts	71-76
	Fuel Rail Mounting Bolts	14-19
	Halfshaft Bearing Support	31-46
	Idler Mounting Bolt	27-38
	Intake Plenum & Manifold Assembly To Cylinder Head Nuts	①
	Main Bearing Cap	40-43

Year	Component	Torque/ Ft. Lbs.
1992-95 —Cont'd	Oil Jet Bolt	104–156 ③
	Oil Pan Drain Plug	22-30
	Oil Pan To Engine Block	6-8
	Oil Pan To Transaxle	27-38
	Oil Pressure Switch	9-13
	Oil Pump	14-19
	Oil Pump Cover	52–78 ③
	Oil Strainer	69-95 ③
	Power Steering Pump Bracket	27-38
	Radiator Mounting Bracket	69-95 ③
	Seal Plate	69-95 ③
	Shift Control Rod To Transaxle	12-17
	Spark Plugs	11-17
	Starter Motor	27-38
	Temperature Gauge Sending Unit	56-82 ③
	Thermostat Housing Bolt & Nut	14-19
	Timing Belt Cover	6-8
	Timing Belt Pulley	80-87
	Timing Belt Tensioner	27-38
	Timing Belt Upper Cover	6-8
	Torque Converter Nuts	25-36
	Transaxle Front Mount	27-38
	Transaxle To Engine	②
	Transaxle Upper Mount Bolts	32-45
	Transaxle Upper Mount Nuts	49-69
	Water Pump Bolts	14-19
	Water Pump Inlet Fitting To Water Pump	14-19
	Water Pump Pulley	69-95 ③

① —Refer to text.
② —Automatic transaxle, 41–59; manual transaxle, 47–66.
③ —Inch lbs.

Note: On Air Bag Equipped Models, Refer To "Air Bag System Precautions" Located In The Front Of This Manual For System Disarming & Arming Procedures.

INDEX

PRECAUTIONS

AIR BAG SYSTEMS

Refer to "Air Bag System Precautions" in the front of this manual for system disarming and arming procedures.

FUEL SYSTEM PRESSURE RELIEF

Fuel pressure must be relieved prior to servicing any fuel system component.
1. Remove back seat cushion.
2. Disconnect fuel pump connector.
3. Run engine until fuel in system is consumed.
4. Reconnect fuel pump connector and install back seat cushion.

ENGINE MOUNT
REPLACE

Refer to "Engine Mount, Replace" procedure in "1.8L/4-112" section when replacing engine mounts.

ENGINE
REPLACE

AUTOMATIC TRANSAXLE

1. Relieve fuel system pressure as described in "Precautions."
2. Disconnect battery ground cable.
3. Marking hinge locations for installation reference, remove hood.
4. Discharge A/C system, then drain engine oil and cooling system.
5. Remove air duct.
6. Remove crankcase ventilation hose from the rocker arm cover and the vacuum hose from bottom side of throttle body.
7. Disconnect power brake vacuum supply hose from power brake, then any necessary vehicle speed control vacuum hoses from intake plenum.
8. Disconnect the following electrical connectors:

  a. Power steering pump.
  b. Water thermoswitch.
  c. Temperature sending unit.
  d. Oil pressure switch.
  e. Fuel injector wiring harness.
  f. Heated Oxygen sensor.
  g. Throttle position sensor.
  h. Electronic ignition coil.
  i. Radio suppressor.
  j. Alternator harness.
9. Disconnect all engine ground straps, then the ignition coil high-tension lead from the distributor.
10. Disconnect accelerator and kickdown cable bracket from throttle cam.
11. Remove accelerator and kickdown cable bracket from intake plenum and set assembly aside.
12. Disconnect heater core inlet and outlet hoses at bulkhead.
13. Remove necessary fuel line clips, then disconnect fuel pressure and return lines from the fuel rail.
14. Remove upper radiator hose, then disconnect cooling fan electrical connector.
15. Remove idle air control valve and radiator cooling fan.
16. Disconnect radiator thermoswitch electrical connector, then remove starter motor.
17. Raise and support vehicle.
18. Remove righthand upper, righthand lower and lefthand lower splash shields.
19. Remove lower radiator hose, then disconnect two transaxle cooling lines from the radiator and plug lines.
20. Remove A/C line mounting bracket from radiator and position aside.
21. Remove halfshaft bearing support, then the inspection plate from oil pan.
22. Place a wrench on the crankshaft pulley, then rotate crankshaft and remove the torque converter nuts.
23. Remove power steering and A/C accessory drive belt.
24. Remove timing belt as described in "Timing Belt, Replace."
25. Remove crankshaft pulley mounting bolts from crankshaft pulley guide plate.

26. Remove crankshaft pulley, crankshaft pulley guide plate and timing belt outer and inner guide plates.
27. Remove exhaust flex-pipe and mounting assembly from exhaust manifold.
28. Remove A/C compressor, then remove power steering pump and bracket assembly leaving hoses connected. Suspend pump with wire and position out of the way.
29. Remove all accessible transaxle to engine bolts from engine block.
30. Lower vehicle, then remove radiator mounting brackets and resonance duct.
31. Remove radiator and fan shroud assembly from vehicle.
32. Remove vacuum chamber canister, then pressure regulator and bracket assembly.
33. Remove shutter valve actuator and bracket assembly, position aside.
34. Remove water pump and alternator accessory drive belt, then remove alternator.
35. Install a suitable engine removal sling onto engine lifting brackets, then place an engine hoist into position and support engine.
36. Remove oil pan to transaxle attaching bolts and remaining transaxle to engine bolts from engine block.
37. Remove engine vibration dampener, then the front engine mount.
38. Carefully separate engine from transaxle, then remove engine from the vehicle.
39. Reverse procedure to install.

MANUAL TRANSAXLE

1. Relieve fuel system pressure as described in "Precautions."
2. Disconnect battery ground cable.
3. Marking hinge locations for installation reference, remove hood.
4. Discharge A/C system, then drain engine oil and cooling system.
5. Remove air cleaner assembly.
6. Remove battery and battery tray.
7. Remove crankcase ventilation hose from the rocker arm cover and the

vacuum hose from bottom side of throttle body.

8. Disconnect accelerator cable from throttle lever, then remove cable bracket from intake plenum.
9. Remove upper radiator hose from thermostat housing and radiator.
10. Disconnect radiator thermoswitch electrical connectors, then remove radiator overflow hose from the radiator filler neck.
11. Disconnect cooling fan electrical connectors, then remove radiator mounting brackets.
12. Disconnect the following electrical connectors:
    a. Alternator and oil pressure switch.
    b. Throttle position sensor and idle speed control.
    c. Manual lever position switch and fuel injector wiring harness.
    d. Back-up lamp switch and water thermoswitch.
    e. Oxygen sensor, power steering pump and distributor.
    f. Fuel Charging Harness.
    g. Radio Suppressor.
13. Disconnect engine ground strap from stud on LH side of cylinder head, near El coil.
14. Disconnect fuel pressure and return lines.
15. Disconnect heater core inlet and outlet hoses.
16. Disconnect power brake supply hose, purge control and speed control vacuum hoses.
17. Raise and support vehicle.
18. Remove righthand upper and lower splash shields.
19. Remove clutch slave cylinder pipe bracket from transaxle leaving hose connected. Position slave cylinder aside, taking care not to damage pipe or hose.
20. Disconnect shift control rod and extension bar from transaxle.
21. Remove battery duct, then disconnect lower radiator hose from radiator.
22. Disconnect transaxle cooling lines from radiator, then remove power steering and A/C accessory drive belt.
23. Remove power steering pump and bracket assembly leaving hoses connected.
24. Position power steering assembly aside and suspend it with wire.
25. Remove A/C hose routing bracket from transaxle crossmember and position A/C hose aside.
26. Remove A/C compressor leaving hoses connected, then position aside and suspend with wire.
27. Disconnect speedometer cable from transaxle.
28. Remove exhaust pipe mounting flange and support bracket from exhaust manifold.
29. Disconnect starter motor relay wire from starter.
30. Remove positive battery cable from starter motor.
31. Remove stabilizer bar, then the tie rod ends from steering knuckles.
32. Remove halfshafts from transaxle.
33. Remove front and rear transaxle mount attaching nuts from crossmember.
34. Lower vehicle, then remove radiator, fan and shroud assembly.
35. Install a suitable engine removal sling onto engine lifting brackets.
36. Place an engine hoist into position and support engine.
37. Remove engine vibration dampener and engine mount.
38. Remove transaxle upper mount and support bracket.
39. Remove engine and transaxle as an assembly.
40. Remove engine intake plenum support bracket.
41. Remove starter motor from transaxle housing, then the transaxle front mount.
42. Remove oil pan to transaxle bolts and transaxle to engine attaching bolts from the engine block.
43. Separate transaxle from engine, then remove clutch assembly from engine.
44. Reverse procedure to install.

INTAKE MANIFOLD
REPLACE

1. Relieve fuel system pressure as outlined under "Precautions."
2. Disconnect battery ground cable and drain coolant system.
3. Remove air intake tube.
4. Disconnect fuel injector harness from EEC-IV harness.
5. Disconnect crankshaft position sensor.
6. Disconnect fuel supply and return lines.
7. Disconnect camshaft position sensor.
8. Remove throttle and kickdown cables from throttle lever.
9. Remove throttle cable bracket.
10. Remove power brake vacuum supply and PCV hoses.
11. Remove vacuum hose from bottom of throttle body.
12. Remove nuts from intake manifold.
13. Remove intake manifold from vehicle.
14. Reverse procedure to install.

EXHAUST MANIFOLD
REPLACE

1. Relieve fuel system pressure as outlined under "Precautions," then disconnect battery ground cable.
2. Remove accessory drive belt.
3. Remove alternator and cooling fan and shroud assembly.
4. Remove exhaust manifold heat shield.
5. Raise and support vehicle.
6. Disconnect catalytic converter inlet pipe.
7. Lower vehicle.
8. Remove exhaust manifold nuts and remove the exhaust manifold.
9. Reverse procedure to install.

CYLINDER HEAD
REPLACE

1. Raise and secure hood.
2. Relive fuel pressure refer to "Precautions" procedure.
3. Disconnect battery ground cable.
4. Drain cooling system and disconnect heater hose at fitting located under intake manifold.
5. Remove air cleaner assembly.
6. Remove PCV hose from air cleaner assembly.
7. Label, then disconnect and or remove all electrical connectors, vacuum hoses, accelerator and transaxle kickdown cables and brackets from cylinder head assembly.
8. Remove upper radiator hose.
9. Remove oil level tube mounting nut from cylinder head stud.
10. Remove power steering hose and A/C line retainer bracket bolts from alternator bracket.
11. Remove accessory drive belt, then alternator and drive belt automatic tensioner.
12. Raise vehicle, then remove right side splash shield.
13. Remove crankshaft dampener, catalytic converter inlet pipe and starter motor wiring harness retaining clip below intake manifold.
14. Set engine No. 1 cylinder to TDC.
15. Lower vehicle.
16. Support engine with floor jack.
17. Remove righthand engine mount dampener, then right hand mount retaining bolts from mount bracket on engine.
18. Loosen righthand engine mount thrubolt and roll mount back out of way.
19. Remove timing belt cover.
20. Loosen belt tensioner attaching bolt, then pry tensioner as far forward as possible. Tighten attaching bolt in this position.
21. Remove timing belt.
22. Roll righthand engine mount bracket back into position, then install mounting bolts.
23. Lower floor jack, then remove heater hose support bracket retaining bolt (starter motor bolt).
24. Remove alternator bracket to cylinder head mounting bolt.
25. Remove rocker arm cover.
26. Remove and set aside cylinder head bolts and washers (used if needed for squish height check). **New bolts must be used for final assembly.**
27. Remove cylinder head with exhaust and intake manifolds attached.
28. Remove cylinder head gasket. **Do not lay cylinder head flat. Damage to the spark plugs, valves or gasket surfaces may result.**
29. Reverse procedure to install, noting the following:
    a. Before final installation of the cylinder head, check piston squish height as described in "Squish Height Check."
    b. **Torque** new cylinder head bolts in sequence shown in **Fig. 1**, first to

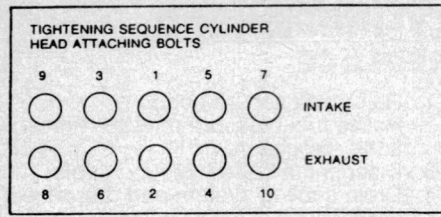

Fig. 1 Cylinder head bolt tightening sequence

44 ft. lbs. Loosen bolts approximately two turns, then torque bolts in sequence to 44 ft. lbs. Turn bolts an additional 90 degrees in sequence, then an additional 90 degrees.

c. Crankshaft must be rotated so that the No. 1 piston is 90 degrees before top dead center (BTDC). Turn crankshaft until the pulley keyway is at 9 o'clock position, then time valve train by turning camshaft until keyway is at the 6 o'clock position. **Camshaft and crankshaft must not be turned until after the installation of the timing gears and timing belt.**

30. If any parts other than cylinder head gasket (such as crankshaft, pistons and connecting rods) have been replaced or if cylinder head gasket surface has been reworked, it is necessary to inspect clearance of piston dome to cylinder head dome at piston TDC as follows:
   a. Clean all gasket material from cylinder head mating surfaces.
   b. Place a small amount of soft lead solder on piston spherical areas.
   c. Rotate crankshaft to lower piston in bore and install cylinder head gasket. If possible, install a used gasket for this inspection.
   d. Install used cylinder head bolts and **torque** to 30-44 ft. lbs. in sequence shown in **Fig. 1.**
   e. Rotate crankshaft to move piston through its TDC position.
   f. Remove cylinder head and measure thickness of compressed solder to determine piston dome to cylinder head dome clearance at TDC. Solder thickness should be .039-.070 inch.

VALVE CLEARANCE SPECIFICATIONS

Refer to "Valve Adjustment" for valve clearance specifications.

VALVE ADJUSTMENT

The 1.9L/4-116 engine is equipped with an overhead camshaft and hydraulic lash adjuster. Valve stem to rocker arm clearance is measured with tappet completely

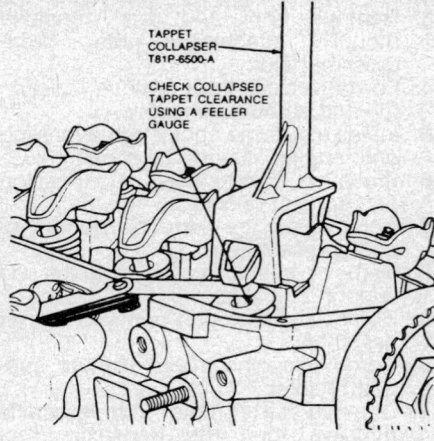

Fig. 2 Tappet clearance inspection

collapsed. Perform the following procedure when measuring valve tappet clearance:

1. Connect an auxiliary starter switch, then crank engine with ignition switch OFF until No. 1 piston is on TDC after compression stroke.
2. Position tappet collapsing tool No. T8-1P-6500-A or equivalent on rocker arm, then slowly apply pressure to bleed tappet. Continue to apply pressure until lifter plunger bottoms. Hold tappet in this position and check clearance between rocker arm and valve stem tip using a suitable feeler gauge, **Fig. 2.** Collapsed tappet clearance should be .000-.177 inch, with preferred clearance of .087 inch. If clearance is less than specified, check for worn or damaged fulcrums, tappets or camshaft lobes.
3. With No. 1 piston at TDC end of compression stroke, check the following valves as outlined: No. 1 and 2 intake and No. 1 exhaust.
4. Rotate crankshaft 180° from present position, then check the following valves: No. 3 intake & No. 3 exhaust.
5. Rotate crankshaft 180° from present position, then check the following valves: No. 4 intake & Nos. 2 and 4 exhaust.

CRANKSHAFT DAMPER
REPLACE

1. Disconnect battery ground cable.
2. Remove accessory drive belt.
3. Raise and support vehicle.
4. Remove right side splash shield.
5. Remove flywheel inspection cover.
6. Hold flywheel using a suitable tool.
7. Remove crankshaft dampener bolt and washer and dampener.
8. reverse procedure to install.

TIMING BELT
REPLACE

1. Disconnect battery ground cable.
2. Remove accessory drive belt.
3. Remove drive belt tensioner.
4. Remove timing belt cover retaining nuts.

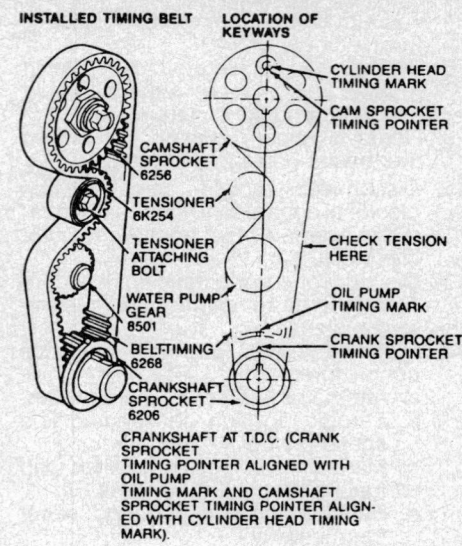

Fig. 3 Timing mark alignment

5. Remove timing belt cover.
6. Align timing mark on camshaft sprocket with timing mark on cylinder head, **Fig. 3.** Ensure crankshaft sprocket is aligned with the timing mark on the oil pump housing.
7. Loosen the timing belt tensioner bolt.
8. Pry tensioner away from timing belt and tighten bolt.
9. Remove spark plugs.
10. Raise and support vehicle.
11. Remove righthand splash shield.
12. Remove crankshaft dampener.
13. Remove timing belt from vehicle.
14. Reverse procedure to install, noting the following:
   a. Install timing belt over sprockets in a counterclockwise direction starting at crankshaft. Keep belt span between the crankshaft and camshaft tight while installing over remaining sprockets.
   b. Loosen tensioner bolt and allow tensioner to contact timing belt.
   c. Rotate engine two complete turns. Ensure timing marks align and tighten tensioner bolt.
   d. Tighten attaching bolts to specifications.

CAMSHAFT
REPLACE

1. Disconnect battery ground cable and remove air intake duct.
2. Remove rocker arm cover.
3. Remove accessory drive belt.
4. Remove timing belt as outlined under "Timing Belt & Replace."
5. Remove rocker arms and tappets as follows:
   a. Remove hex flange nut.
   b. Remove fulcrums and rocker arms.
   c. Remove tappet guide retainers and tappet guides.
   d. Remove tappets.
6. Remove EDIS coil assembly.
7. Remove camshaft sprocket and key.

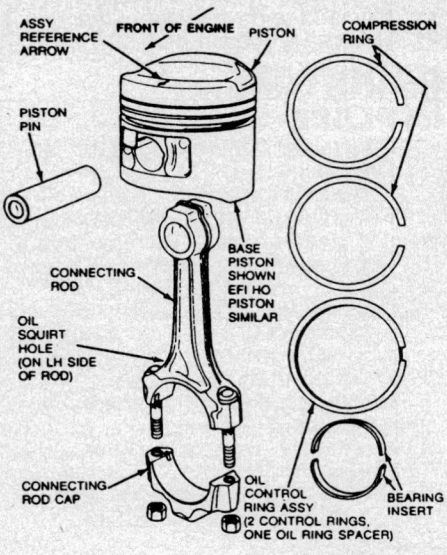

Fig. 4   Piston & rod assembly

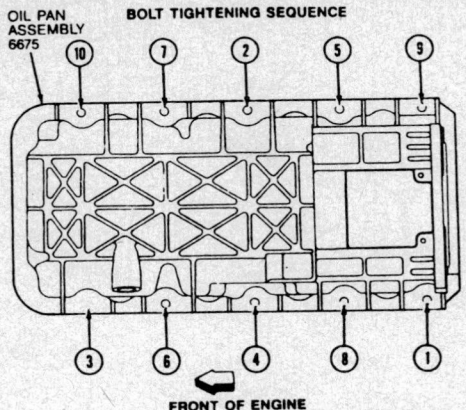

Fig. 5   Oil pan tightening sequence

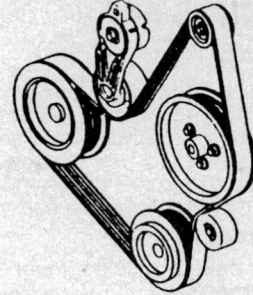

A/C, POWER STEERING, ALTERNATOR

ALTERNATOR ONLY

POWER STEERING, ALTERNATOR

Fig. 6   Serpentine belt routing

8. Remove camshaft thrust plate.
9. Remove cup plug from rear of cylinder head.
10. Remove camshaft through rear of cylinder head toward transaxle. Use care not to damage bearing surfaces.
11. Reverse procedure to install, noting the following:
   a. Coat camshaft lobes and bearing surfaces with oil prior to installation.
   b. Adjust valves as outlined under "Valves Adjust."
   c. Install cup plug using sealant part No. ESE-M46217-A, or equivalent. **Use sparingly, excess sealant can clog oil holes in camshaft.**

CAMSHAFT SEAL
REPLACE

1. Disconnect battery ground cable.
2. Remove accessory drive belt.
3. Remove timing belt as outlined under "Timing Belt, Replace."
4. Remove camshaft sprocket.
5. Using a suitable tool, remove camshaft seal.
6. Reverse procedure to install, using seal installing tool No. T81P-6292-A, or equivalent.

PISTON & ROD ASSEMBLY

Assemble piston to connecting rod with connecting rod oil squirt hole and arrow on piston in position shown in **Fig. 4.**

CRANKSHAFT SEAL
REPLACE

FRONT

1. Disconnect battery ground cable.
2. Remove accessory drive belt.
3. Raise and support vehicle.
4. Remove righthand splash shield.

5. Remove timing belt as outlined under "Timing Belt Replace."
6. Remove crankshaft sprocket and belt guide.
7. Remove front crankshaft seal from oil pump body using a suitable seal remover.
8. Reverse procedure to install, using seal installer tool No. T81P-6700-A, or equivalent.

REAR

1. Disconnect battery ground cable.
2. Remove transaxle and flywheel assembly.
3. Remove engine cover plate.
4. With a sharp awl, punch a hole in metal part of rear crankshaft seal.
5. Remove seal using jet plug remover tool No. T77L-9533-B, or equivalent.
6. Reverse procedure to install, using seal installation tool Nos. T88P-6701-B2 and T88P-6701-B1, or equivalent.

OIL PAN
REPLACE

1. Disconnect battery ground cable.
2. Raise and support vehicle.
3. Drain engine oil into a suitable container.
4. Remove catalytic converter inlet pipe.
5. Remove two oil pan to transaxle bolts.
6. Remove ten oil pan to cylinder block bolts.
7. Gently pry pan away from cylinder block and remove pan from vehicle.
8. Reverse procedure to install, noting the following:
   a. Tighten oil pan bolts in sequence shown in **Fig. 5.**
   b. Ensure oil pan is lined up flush with rear face of cylinder block.

OIL PUMP
REPLACE

1. Disconnect battery ground cable.
2. Remove accessory drive belt and tensioner.
3. Support engine with a suitable floor jack.
4. Remove right engine mount dampener.
5. Remove right engine mount bolts from mount bracket.

6. Loosen mount through bolt and roll engine mount aside.
7. Remove timing belt as outlined under "Timing Belt Replace."
8. Raise and support vehicle.
9. Remove right side splash shield.
10. Remove catalytic converter inlet pipe.
11. Drain engine oil and remove oil pan as outlined under "Oil Pan, Replace."
12. Remove crankshaft sprocket and timing belt guide.
13. Disconnect crank angle sensor.
14. Remove six oil pump to engine bolts.
15. Remove oil pump assembly from engine.
16. Reverse procedure to install, noting the following:
   a. Position pump drive gear to allow pump to pilot over crankshaft and seat firmly on cylinder block.
   b. When oil pump bolts are tighten, gasket must not be below cylinder block sealing surface.

BELT TENSION DATA

This engine uses an automatic belt tensioner that sets and maintains drive belt tension. There is no provision for adjustment.

SERPENTINE DRIVE BELT

BELT ROUTING

Refer to **Fig. 6** for serpentine belt routing.

BELT, REPLACE

Removal

1. Using a ⅜ inch drive ratchet or breaker bar inserted in automatic tensioner, pull tool toward front of vehicle.
2. While releasing belt tension, remove drive belt from tensioner pulley and slip it off remaining accessory pulleys.

Installation

1. Route belt as outlined under "Serpentine Drive Belt."
2. Using a ⅜ inch drive ratchet or breaker bar inserted in automatic tensioner, pull tool toward front of vehicle.
3. While holding tool, slip drive belt behind tensioner pulley and release tool.
4. Ensure that all V-grooves make proper contact with pulleys.

TENSIONER, REPLACE

1. Remove accessory drive belt as outlined under "Serpentine Drive Belt."
2. Remove automatic tensioner mounting bolt.
3. Remove tensioner from engine.
4. Reverse procedure to install.

COOLING SYSTEM BLEED

After filling cooling system, run engine for approximately 12 minutes with radiator pressure cap off, then top off radiator. Secure cap, then and with engine running, fill coolant reservoir to FULL HOT mark with coolant.

THERMOSTAT

REPLACE

1. Disconnect battery cable and wiring connector from thermo switch in thermostat housing, if equipped.
2. Remove radiator cap, then attach a hose to drain tube and open draincock. Drain coolant level until its below water outlet connection. Close the draincock.
3. Loosen upper hose at radiator, then remove water outlet housing retaining bolts. Lift clear of engine and remove thermostat. Do not pry housing off.
4. Clean outlet housing and cylinder head mating surfaces.
5. Position thermostat and seat so it will compress gasket. Position outlet to cylinder head, using a new gasket and install retaining bolts.

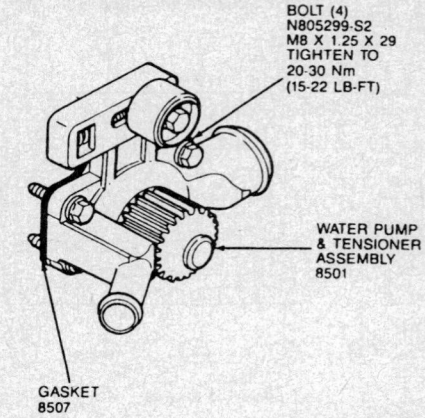

BOLT (4)
N805299-S2
M8 X 1.25 X 29
TIGHTEN TO
20-30 Nm
(15-22 LB-FT)

WATER PUMP
& TENSIONER
ASSEMBLY
8501

GASKET
8507

FM1089100067000X

Fig. 7   Water pump replacement

6. Connect top hose to radiator and tighten clamp. Ensure that draincock is closed.
7. Fill cooling system with recommended coolant as follows:
   a. Add 50 percent coolant, then add water until radiator is full. Allow coolant level to settle, then add more coolant until radiator remain full.
   b. Install radiator cap to first notch, connect battery cable and wire connector to thermo switch. Start engine and let idle until upper hose is warm, then carefully remove radiator cap and top off coolant level.
   c. Install cap securely and fill reservoir to FULL COLD mark with proper concentrate. Add water to FULL HOT mark. Check for leaks.

WATER PUMP

REPLACE

1. Disconnect battery ground cable and drain cooling system.
2. Remove accessory drive belt and tensioner.
3. Remove timing belt as outlined under "Timing Belt, Replace."
4. Raise and support vehicle.
5. Remove lower radiator hose.
6. Disconnect heater hose from water pump.
7. Lower vehicle.
8. Support engine with a suitable floor jack.
9. Remove right engine mount bolts and pivot mount aside.
10. Remove water pump bolts, raise engine and remove water pump, **Fig. 7.**
11. Reverse procedure to install.

RADIATOR

REPLACE

1. Disconnect battery ground cable.
2. Drain cooling system.
3. Raise and support vehicle.
4. Remove RH front fender splash shield and LH front fender splash shield.
5. Remove lower radiator hose from radiator.
6. **On vehicles with automatic transaxle,** remove lower oil cooler inlet tube from radiator.
7. **On all models,** lower vehicle.
8. **On vehicles with automatic transaxle and A/C,** remove air deflector seal located between radiator and fan shroud.
9. **On all models,** remove upper oil cooler inlet tube from radiator.
10. Disconnect electric cooling fan motor electrical connector.
11. Disconnect high speed fan control switch electrical connector. If necessary, remove high speed switch from radiator.
12. Remove three fan shroud bolts and the fan shroud.
13. **On models equipped with A/C,** remove upper radiator air deflector from radiator and position aside.
14. **On all models,** remove upper radiator hose.
15. Remove two radiator support upper brackets.
16. Remove oil cooler tube bracket bolts from radiator.
17. Remove radiator coolant overflow hose from radiator.
18. Remove radiator from vehicle by lifting it straight up.
19. Reverse procedure to install.
20. Fill cooling system, then start engine and check for coolant leaks.

FUEL PUMP

REPLACE

Refer to "Fuel Pump, Replace" procedure in "1.8L/4-112" section when replacing fuel pump.

FUEL FILTER

REPLACE

Refer to "Fuel Filter, Replace" procedure in "1.8L/4-112" section when replacing fuel filter.

TIGHTENING SPECIFICATIONS

Year	Component	Torque/Ft. Lbs.	Year	Component	Torque/Ft. Lbs.
1992-95	Alternator To Alternator Brace Arm	15–22	1992-95 —Cont'd	Oil Filter Adapter To Oil Pump	21–26
	Alternator Bracket To Engine Block	30–40		Oil Gallery Pipe Plugs	8–12
	Alternator Pivot Attaching Bolt	30–40		Oil Pan Drain Plug	15–22
	Camshaft Position Sensor To Head	15–22		Oil Pan To Block	15–22
	Camshaft Sprocket To Cam	70–85		Oil Pan To Transaxle	30–40
	Camshaft Thrust Plate To Head	6–9		Oil Pump To Block	8–12
	Coil Bracket To Head	6–8		Oil Separator To Block	6–8
	Coil To Bracket	36-60 ③		Pick Up & Screen To Pump	7–9
	Connecting Rod Cap To Rod	26–30		Rocker Arm Bolt	17–22
	Crankshaft Damper Attaching Bolt	81–96		Rocker Arm Cover To Head	48-108 ③
	Crankshaft Position Sensor To Oil Pump	24-30 ③		Spark Plug	8–15
	Crankshaft Rear Seal Retainer To Block	15–22		Thermostat Housing To Head	6–9
	Cylinder Head To Block	①		Timing Belt Cover Stud To Block	7–9
	EGR Valve To Intake Manifold ②	48-84 ③		Timing Belt Cover Stud To Block Stud Nut	36-60 ③
	Engine To Transaxle	27–38		Timing Tensioner Attaching Bolt	17–22
	Exhaust Manifold To Cylinder Head	16–19		Transaxle To Engine	40–59
	Flywheel To Crankshaft	54–67		Water Pump To Block	15–22
	Heat Shield To Exhaust Manifold Nut	48-60 ③			
	Heat Shield To Exhaust Manifold Stud	24-84 ③			
	Intake Manifold To Head	12–15			
	Main Bearing Cap To Block	67–80			

① —Refer to text.
② —California models.
③ —Inch lbs.

Clutch & Manual Transaxle

INDEX

ADJUSTMENTS

CLUTCH

The Escort and Tracer use a hydraulic clutch control system. This system consists of a fluid reservoir, master cylinder, pressure line and slave cylinder. The clutch master cylinder is mounted on the bulkhead near the brake master cylinder. This hydraulic system utilizes brake fluid from the brake master cylinder reservoir. This system has no provisions for adjustment.

CLUTCH PEDAL

To determine if the pedal height requires adjustment, measure the distance from the bulkhead to the upper center of pedal pad. The distance should be 7.72-8.03 inches. Use the following procedure if adjustment is required.
1. Disconnect clutch switch electrical connector.
2. Loosen clutch switch locknut.
3. Turn clutch switch until correct height is achieved.
4. **Torque** locknut to 10-13 ft. lbs.
5. Measure pedal freeplay, pedal freeplay travel should be between 0.20-0.51 inch.
6. Connect electrical connector.

CLUTCH PEDAL FREEPLAY ADJUSTMENT

To determine if the pedal freeplay requires adjustment, depress clutch pedal by hand until clutch resistance is felt. Measure the distance between upper pedal height and where the resistance is felt. Freeplay should be 0.20-0.51 inch. Use the following procedure if adjustment is necessary.
1. Loosen clutch pedal pushrod locknut.
2. Turn pushrod until pedal freeplay is within specification.
3. Check that disengagement height is correct when the pedal is fully depressed. Minimum disengagement height is 1.6 inches.
4. **Torque** pushrod locknut to 9-12 ft. lbs.

HYDRAULIC SYSTEM SERVICE

CLUTCH SLAVE CYLINDER, REPLACE

1. Disconnect pressure line from slave cylinder, then plug line to prevent leakage.
2. Remove slave cylinder retaining bolts, then cylinder.
3. Reverse procedure to install. **Torque** slave cylinder retaining bolts to 12-17 ft. lbs.

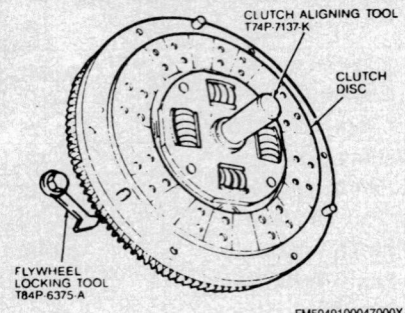

Fig. 1   Clutch disc installation

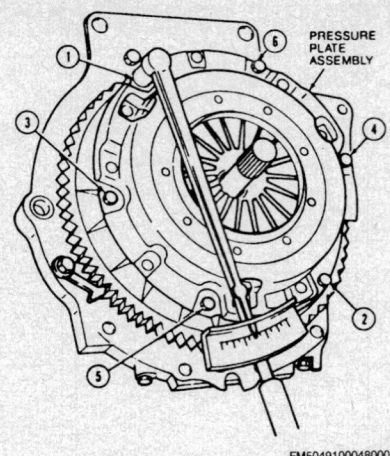

Fig. 2   Pressure plate tightening sequence

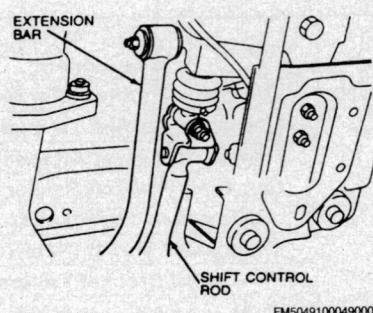

Fig. 3   Extension bar & shift control rod

HYDRAULIC CLUTCH BLEED

The clutch hydraulic system must be bled whenever the pressure line is disconnected.

The fluid in the reservoir must be maintained at the ³/₄ level or higher during air bleeding.

1. Remove bleeder cap from slave cylinder and attach vinyl hose to bleeder screw, place other end of hose in container.
2. Slowly pump clutch pedal several times.
3. With clutch pedal depressed, loosen bleeder screw to release trapped air.
4. Tighten bleeder screw.
5. Repeat steps 2 through 4 until no air bubbles appear in fluid.

CLUTCH MASTER CYLINDER, REPLACE

1. Remove battery and battery tray assembly.
2. Disconnect clutch pressure line from master cylinder.
3. Using needle nose vise grips or equivalent. clamp off brake fluid feed line to clutch master cylinder.
4. Disengage clamp, then remove brake fluid feed hose from clutch master cylinder.
5. From inside vehicle, remove master cylinder retaining nut.
6. From inside engine compartment, remove master cylinder retaining nut, then master cylinder.
7. Align clutch pedal pushrod, then install master cylinder. **Torque** retaining nuts to 14-19 ft. lbs.
8. Connect master cylinder pressure line, then **torque** pressure line retaining nut to 10-16 ft. lbs.
9. Install hose and clamp assembly, then battery and tray.
10. Bleed air from system.

CLUTCH
REPLACE

1. Remove transaxle as described under "Transaxle, Replace."

2. Install Flywheel Locking Tool No. T84P-6375-A or equivalent in a transaxle mounting hole on engine block, then engage tooth of locking tool into flywheel ring gear.
3. Loosen pressure plate cover attaching bolts evenly to avoid distorting cover. If same pressure plate and cover are to be installed, mark cover and flywheel so pressure plate can be installed in original position.
4. Remove pressure plate and clutch disc from flywheel.
5. Reverse procedure to install, noting the following:
   a. Clean splines on clutch disc and transaxle input shaft, then apply a small amount of Clutch Grease part No. C1AZ-19590-B or equivalent to clutch disc and input shaft splines. **Avoid getting grease on clutch face.**
   b. Position clutch disc plate onto flywheel as shown in **Fig. 1.**
   c. Ensure three dowel pins on flywheel are aligned with dowel pins on pressure plate.
   d. Finger tighten cover attaching bolts, then align clutch disc using tool T74P-7137-K or equivalent.
   e. Evenly **torque** bolts to 13-20 ft. lbs. in sequence shown, **Fig. 2.**
   f. Remove alignment tool, then install transaxle and perform clutch bleed procedure.

TRANSAXLE
REPLACE

1. Remove battery and battery tray assembly.
2. Remove air duct hose and resonance chamber from engine.
3. Disconnect speedometer cable at transaxle assembly.
4. Remove retaining clip from slave cylinder line, then disconnect slave cylinder line from slave cylinder and plug hose.

5. Disconnect ground strap from transaxle.
6. Remove tie wrap, then disconnect three electrical connectors located above transaxle.
7. Remove electrical connector support bracket.
8. Mount Engine Support Bar tool No. D88L-6000-A or equivalent, and attach it to engine hangers.
9. Remove three nuts from upper transaxle mounts.
10. Loosen upper mount pivot nut, then rotate mount out of way.
11. Remove three bolts, then upper transaxle mount bracket.
12. Remove two upper transaxle-to-engine bolts.
13. Raise and support vehicle.
14. Remove front wheel and tire assemblies.
15. Remove inner fender splash shields.
16. Drain transaxle fluid.
17. Remove halfshaft assemblies from transaxle, refer to "Front Suspension" section in this chapter for this procedure.
18. Install two Transaxle Plugs (Part No. T88C-7025-AH) or equivalent, between differential side gears.
19. Remove plenum support bracket.
20. Remove starter motor, refer to "Electrical Section" in this chapter for this procedure.
21. Remove extension bar from transaxle, **Fig. 3.**
22. Remove shift control rod from transaxle assembly, **Fig. 3.**
23. Remove both lower splash shields.
24. Remove two transaxle mount-to-crossmember nuts.
25. Remove lower crossmember.
26. Remove front transaxle mount.
27. Position transmission jack or equivalent, under transaxle, then secure jack to transaxle assembly.
28. Remove five lower engine-to-transaxle bolts.
29. Lower transaxle out of vehicle.
30. Reverse procedure to install. Tighten all bolts to specification.

TIGHTENING SPECIFICATIONS

Year	Component	Torque/ Ft. Lbs.
1992-95	Back-Up Lamp Switch	14–22
	Control Arm Front Bolt	69–86
	Control Arm Rear Nut	55–69
	Extension Bar Nut	12–17
	Flywheel Bolts	①
	Front Transaxle Mount Bolts	12–17
	Guide Plate Lower Bolts	16–25
	Guide Plate Upper Bolt	6-8
	Lower Engine To Transaxle Bolts	27–38
	Lower Crossmember Nuts	47–66
	Lower Crossmember Bolts	47–66
	Neutral Switch	14–22
	Pressure Plate To Flywheel	13–20
	Rear Cover Bolts	6-8

Year	Component	Torque/ Ft. Lbs.
1992-95 —Cont'd	Shaft Locknuts	94–145
	Shift Arm	9-10
	Shift Control Rod	23–34
	Speedometer Driven Gear Retaining Bolt	6-9
	Steering Knuckle To Strut bolts	69–86
	Transaxle Drain Plug	29–43
	Transaxle Mount To Crossmember Nuts	27–38
	Transaxle To Engine Bolts (Lower)	27–38
	Transaxle To Engine Bolts (Upper)	47–66
	Wheel Lug Nut	65–88

① —1.8L/4-112, 71–76 ft. lbs.; 1.9L/4-116, 54–67 ft. lbs.

Rear Suspension

INDEX

DESCRIPTION

The rear suspension uses double-acting, oil filled shock/strut assemblies with straight wound coil springs. the rear wheels and brake drums/rotors are supported by a sealed roller bearing mounted on a spindle. A staked nut is used to retain the bearing and hub in position on the spindle. The staked nut cannot be reused. **Rear lateral links base part No. 5A995** are available in a solid (left side) and adjustable (right side) type. Both types are interchangeable side-to-side. When replacement of the solid link is necessary, an adjustable link should be installed.

WHEEL BEARING
ADJUST

1. Raise and support vehicle, then remove rear wheel.
2. **On models with disc brakes,** remove brake caliper and rotor.
3. **On models with drum brakes,** remove brake drum.
4. **On all models,** position a dial indicator to wheel hub.
5. Push and pull wheel hub by hand and measure wheel bearing play.
6. If wheel bearing play exceeds .002 inch, check and adjust locknut torque or replace wheel bearing if necessary.

REAR WHEEL SPINDLE
REPLACE
DISC BRAKES

1. Raise and support vehicle, then remove rear wheel.
2. Remove cap from rear wheel hub, then remove brake caliper and rotor.
3. Remove nut securing rear wheel hub to rear wheel spindle and hub, then remove bolts securing brake dust shield.
4. Remove nuts and bolts securing rear shock/strut assembly to rear wheel spindle.
5. Remove bolt and washer securing rear trailing arm to rear wheel spindle.
6. Remove rear stabilizer bar as described under "Stabilizer Bar, Replace."
7. Remove nuts and bolts securing front and rear lateral links to rear wheel spindle, then remove spindle.
8. Reverse procedure to install. Tighten nuts and bolts to specification.

DRUM BRAKES

1. Raise and support vehicle, then remove rear wheel.
2. Remove cap from rear wheel hub, then remove rear brake drum.
3. Remove nut securing rear wheel hub to rear wheel spindle, then the hub from the spindle.

4. Remove drum brake backing plate from spindle.
5. Remove nuts and bolts securing rear shock/strut assembly to rear wheel spindle.
6. Remove bolt and washer securing rear trailing arm to rear wheel spindle.
7. Remove rear stabilizer bar as described under "Stabilizer Bar, Replace."
8. Remove nuts and bolts securing front and rear lateral links to rear wheel spindle, then remove spindle.
9. Reverse procedure to install. Tighten nuts and bolts to specification.

SHOCK ABSORBER
REPLACE

1. Raise and support vehicle, then remove rear wheel.
2. Remove clip securing flexible brake hose to rear shock/strut assembly.
3. Remove nuts and bolts securing rear shock/strut assembly to rear wheel spindle assembly.
4. **On hatchback and wagon models,** remove quarter lower trim panel.
5. **on all models,** remove mounting block nuts, then rear shock/strut assembly from vehicle.
6. Reverse procedure to install. Tighten nuts and bolts to specification.

COIL SPRING
REPLACE

1. Remove rear shock/strut assembly as described under "Shock Absorber, Replace."
2. Position rear shock/strut assembly into a vise and secure assembly at mounting block.
3. Remove cap and loosen piston rod nut one turn. Do not remove piston rod nut at this time.
4. Install an appropriate coil spring compressor onto coil spring and compress spring.
5. Remove piston rod nut, washer, retainer and mounting block and coil spring.
6. Reverse procedure to install. **Torque** piston rod nut to 41-50 ft. lbs.

STABILIZER BAR
REPLACE

1. Raise and support vehicle, then remove stabilizer nuts, washers, bushings, sleeves and bolts.
2. Remove bolts securing stabilizer bar brackets and grommets to rear suspension crossmember, then remove stabilizer bar from vehicle.
3. Reverse procedure to install noting the following:
   a. Tighten stabilizer bar bracket bolts to specification.
   b. Install stabilizer bar washers, bushings, sleeve and nut and tighten so that .64-.72 inches of thread is exposed.

LATERAL LINKS & TRAILING LINK
REPLACE

1. Raise and support vehicle, then remove rear wheel.
2. Remove rear stabilizer bar as described under "Stabilizer Bar, Replace."
3. Remove cap covering front and rear lateral link pivot bolts, then position a floor jack stand under rear suspension crossmember.
4. Remove bolts securing rear suspension crossmember to vehicle frame, then lower floor jack stand to allow rear suspension crossmember to be lowered from vehicle frame.
5. Remove front and rear lateral link pivot nut, washer and bolt from the crossmember, then remove front and rear lateral links from crossmember.
6. Remove bolt, washers and nut securing front and rear lateral links to rear wheel spindle, then remove front and rear lateral links.
7. Remove nuts securing parking brake cable and cable bracket to trailing link.
8. Remove trailing link bolts and washers from vehicle frame and rear wheel spindle, then remove rear trailing link.
9. Reverse procedure to install. Tighten nuts and bolts to specification.

TIGHTENING SPECIFICATIONS

Year	Component	Torque/ Ft. Lbs.	Year	Component	Torque/ Ft. Lbs.
1992-95	Front Trailing Arm Bolt	69-93	1992-95 —Cont'd	Stabilizer Bar Bracket Bolts	36-48
	Lateral Link Nut At Wheel Spindle	63-86		Stabilizer Bar To Suspension Crossmember	32-43
	Lateral Link To Crossmember Nut	50-70		Trailing Arm Bolt	49-69
	Shock/Strut Mounting Block Nuts	22-27		Wheel Hub Nut	130-174
	Shock/Strut Piston Rod Nut	41-50		Wheel Lug Nuts	65-88
	Shock/Strut To Wheel Spindle	69-93			

Front Suspension & Steering

INDEX

DESCRIPTION

The front suspension is a McPherson strut design with cast steering knuckles. The shock absorber strut assembly includes a mounting block, a thrust bearing, an upper spring seat, a rubber spring seat, a bound stopper and coil spring mounted to the shock strut.

The front wheels and brake rotors are supported by a sealed roller bearing mounted in the steering knuckle. A snap ring holds the bearing in the knuckle. The halfshaft is secured to the front hub assembly with a staked nut. The staked nut cannot be reused.

WHEEL BEARING
ADJUST

1. Raise and support vehicle, then remove front wheel, brake caliper and rotor.
2. Position a dial indicator to wheel hub, then push and pull wheel hub by hand and measure wheel bearing play.
3. If wheel bearing play exceeds .002 inch, check and adjust locknut torque or, if necessary, replace wheel bearing.
4. Install brake rotor, caliper and wheel, then lower vehicle.

WHEEL BEARING
REPLACE

1. Remove front hub/steering knuckle assembly as described under Hub/Steering Knuckle, Replace."

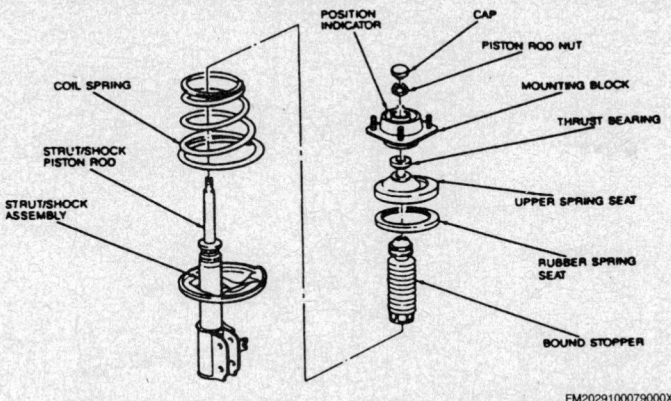

Fig. 1 Exploded view of front strut assembly

Tightening Torque:
A: 37-52 N·m (27-38 LB-FT)
B: 64-89 N·m (47-66 LB-FT)

Fig. 2 Crossmember bolt tightening sequence

2. Position front hub/steering knuckle assembly on a press and press front hub out of steering knuckle using a suitable removal tool.
3. Remove E-clip from steering knuckle, then position steering knuckle onto a press.
4. Using a suitable bearing remover, press bearing out of steering knuckle.
5. Reverse procedure to install.

WHEEL HUB & STEERING KNUCKLE
REPLACE

1. Raise and support vehicle, then remove front wheel, brake caliper and rotor.
2. Remove nut securing halfshaft to hub, then remove outer tie rod at steering knuckle.
3. Remove nuts and bolts securing shock/strut assembly to steering knuckle, then separate shock/strut assembly from steering knuckle.
4. Remove nut and bolt securing lower ball joint to steering knuckle, then separate ball joint from steering knuckle.
5. Remove front hub/steering knuckle assembly from halfshaft.
6. Reverse procedure to install. Tighten ball joint nut, shock/strut assembly bolts and front hub nut to specification.

BALL JOINT INSPECTION

The following procedure has been revised by a Technical Service Bulletin.
Secure ball joint bracket into a vise. Thread ball joint attaching nut onto ball joint stud until nut bottoms out on stud. Install a torque wrench onto nut and measure torque required to keep stud in motion. Correct turning torque should be 14-25 ft. lbs.

BALL JOINT
REPLACE

1. Remove nut and bolt securing ball joint to steering knuckle.
2. Remove nuts securing ball joint to lower control arm, then remove ball joint.
3. Reverse procedure to install.

COIL SPRING
REPLACE

1. Remove front shock/strut assembly as described under "Front Shock/Strut Assembly, Replace."
2. Remove cap from top of shock/strut assembly.
3. Secure shock/strut assembly mounting block in a vise, then turn piston rod nut one full revolution to loosen.
4. Install an appropriate spring compressor onto shock/strut spring, then compress spring.
5. Remove nut, mounting block, thrust bearing, upper spring seat, rubber spring seat, coil spring and bound stopper **Fig. 1.**
6. Reverse procedure to install.

STRUT
REPLACE

1. Raise and support vehicle, then remove front wheel.
2. Remove clip securing flexible brake hose to shock/strut assembly.
3. Remove two nuts and bolts securing shock/strut assembly to steering knuckle.
4. Remove upper mounting block nuts on strut tower, then remove shock/strut assembly.
5. Reverse procedure to install noting the following:
   a. Position shock/strut assembly into wheel housing ensuring that direction indicator on mounting block faces inboard.
   b. Tighten upper mounting block to strut tower nuts to and shock/strut assembly bolts to specification.

CONTROL ARM
REPLACE

1. Raise and support vehicle, then remove stabilizer bar nuts, washers, bushings, sleeves and bolts.
2. Remove lower control arm front bushing bolt and washer, then remove bolts securing lower control arm rear bushing retaining strap.

3. Remove nut and bolt securing lower ball joint to steering knuckle, then separate steering knuckle from lower ball joint.
4. Remove lower control arm.
5. Reverse procedure to install noting the following:
   a. Tighten lower control arm pivot bolt nut, ball joint retaining bolt and nut, lower control arm rear bushing retaining strap bolts and lower control arm front pivot bolt to specification.
   b. Install stabilizer bar bolts, sleeves, bushings, washers and nuts and tighten so that .67-.75 inches of thread is showing.

STABILIZER BAR
REPLACE

1. Support engine with three bar engine support No. D88L-6000-A or equivalent, then raise and support vehicle.
2. Remove front wheels, then remove nuts securing steering gear mounting brackets.
3. Position steering gear slightly forward, then remove stabilizer bar nuts, washers, bushings, sleeves and bolts from lower control arm.
4. Remove rear crossmember nuts from rear transaxle mount and vehicle frame.
5. Loosen front crossmember bolts and nuts from front transaxle mount and vehicle frame, then lower rear end of crossmember.
6. Remove nuts and bolts securing chassis frame to vehicle frame, then lower chassis frame. **Engine and transaxle mounts will support the chassis frame when unbolting chassis frame from vehicle frame.**
7. Unbolt stabilizer bar from chassis frame and remove stabilizer bar from vehicle.
8. Reverse procedure to install noting the following:
   a. Tighten stabilizer bar to chassis frame bolts to specification.

b. Tighten chassis frame to vehicle frame bolts to specification.

c. **Tighten** crossmember to vehicle frame and transaxle mounts as shown in **Fig. 2.**

d. Install stabilizer bar bolts, sleeves, bushings, washers and nuts and tighten so that .67–.75 inches of thread is showing.

e. Tighten steering gear bracket nuts to specification.

POWER STEERING GEAR
REPLACE

1. From inside of the vehicle, remove nuts securing set plate, then remove set plate **Fig. 3.**
2. Remove intermediate shaft to pinion shaft bolt from inside of vehicle.
3. Raise and support vehicle, then remove front wheels.
4. Remove cotter pins and nuts securing tie rod ends to steering knuckles.
5. Separate tie rod end from steering knuckle using a suitable tie rod end separator.
6. Remove two screws from power steering line retaining bracket, then remove bracket from steering gear housing.
7. Disconnect return and the high-pressure line from steering gear and plug lines.
8. **On vehicles equipped with a manual transaxle,** disconnect extension bar and shift control rod from transaxle.
9. **On all vehicles,** remove nuts from two steering gear mounting brackets, then remove splash shield from left wheelwell.
10. Remove steering gear from left side of vehicle.
11. Reverse procedure to install noting following:
    a. Tighten steering gear mounting bracket, extension bar nut and shift control rod nut to specification.
    b. **On vehicles equipped with a 1.9L/4-116 engine** install a new strap to hold power steering lines to gear housing.
    c. Tighten return line, high-pressure line flare nut, tie rod end nuts and intermediate shaft to pinion shaft bolts to specification.

POWER STEERING PUMP
REPLACE

1.8L/4-112 ENGINE

1. Loosen reservoir to pump hose clamp and pull hose from reservoir, then plug hose.
2. Remove two reservoir mounting bolts and lift reservoir from its mounting position.
3. Loosen return hose clamp and pull return hose from reservoir, then plug hose.

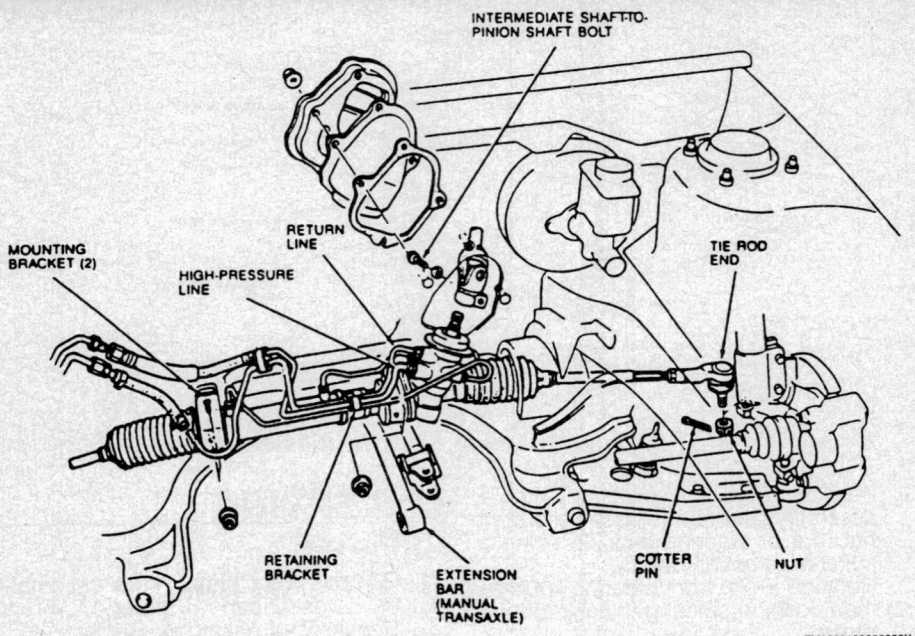

Fig. 3 Power steering system components

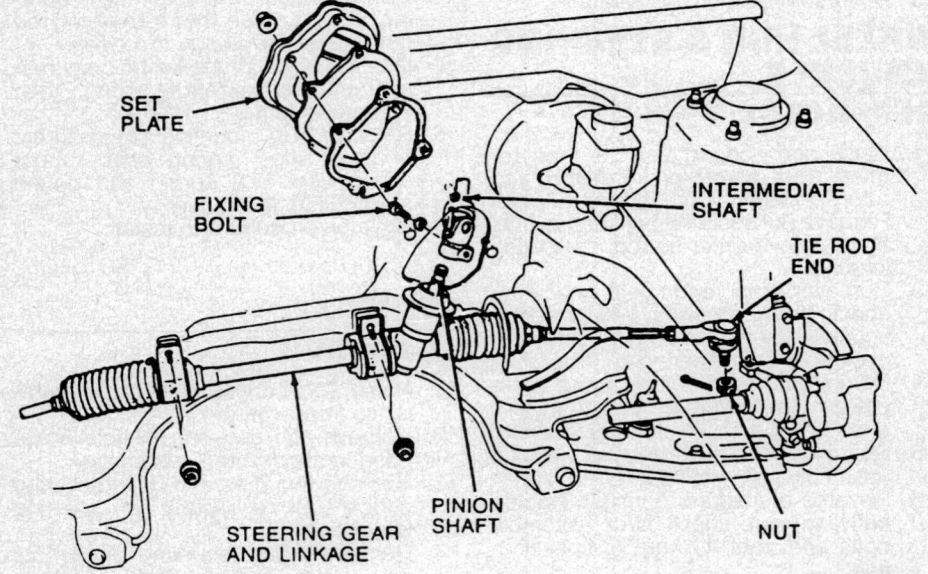

Fig. 4 Exploded view of manual steering gear

4. Remove reservoir from vehicle.
5. Disconnect electrical connector from power steering pressure switch.
6. Loosen high-pressure line flare nut and disconnect line from pump, then plug line.
7. Raise and support vehicle, then remove five front undercover bolts and remove undercover.
8. Remove belt tensioner adjustment bolt, then accessory drive belt from pulley.
9. Lower vehicle, then remove three pump mounting bracket bolts and pump and bracket.
10. Reverse procedure to install. Tighten pump mounting bolts to and high-pressure line flare nut to specification.

1.9L/4-116 ENGINE

The following procedure has been revised by a Techincal Service Bulletin.

1. Drain radiator, then loosen belt tensioner and remove drive belt from pulley.
2. Remove belt tensioner bolt, then tensioner.
3. Support engine with a floor jack, then remove engine vibration dampener nut and bolt and remove dampener.
4. Remove two front engine mount nuts, then loosen engine mount pivot bolt and position engine mount aside.
5. Raise engine to access power steering pump pulley, then hold pulley in position with a suitable tool and re-

move three pulley mounting bolts and pulley.

6. Lower engine, then position engine mount and install two nuts.
7. Raise and support vehicle, then loosen clamp and disconnect return line from pump.
8. Loosen flare nut from high-pressure line and disconnect line from pump.
9. Remove two passenger side splash shields, then remove four A/C compressor mounting bolts and position compressor aside.
10. Remove lower radiator hose, then remove three power steering pump mounting bolts and pump.
11. Reverse procedure to install noting the following:
    a. Tighten A/C compressor mounting

bolts to specification.
    b. Position power steering pump pulley, then hold in position with a suitable tool and install and tighten mounting bolts to specification.
    c. Tighten belt tensioner mounting bolt to specification.

MANUAL STEERING GEAR
REPLACE

Refer to **Fig. 4** when replacing manual steering gear.
1. From inside of vehicle, remove nuts securing set plate, remove set plate, **Fig. 4.**
2. Remove intermediate shaft to pinion shaft bolt from inside of vehicle.

3. Raise and support vehicle, then remove front wheels.
4. Remove cotter pins and nuts securing tie rod ends to steering knuckles.
5. Separate tie rod end from steering knuckle using tie rod end separator No. T85M-3395-A or equivalent.
6. **On vehicles equipped with manual transaxle,** disconnect extension bar.
7. **On all vehicles,** remove nuts securing steering gear brackets to bulkhead, then remove the brackets.
8. Remove steering gear from vehicle.
9. Reverse procedure to install noting the following:
    a. Tighten steering gear bracket nuts, extension bar nut, tie rod end nut and intermediate shaft to pinion shaft bolt to specification.

TIGHTENING SPECIFICATIONS

Year	Component	Torque/Ft. Lbs.
1992-95	A/C Compressor	30–40
	Belt Tensioner Bolt	30–41
	Chassis Frame To Vehicle Frame	69-93
	Extension Bar (Manual Trans.)	23–34
	Hub Nut	174-235
	Intermediate Shaft To Pinion Shaft	13–20
	Lower Ball Joint To Lower Control Arm	69–86
	Lower Ball Joint To Steering Knuckle	32-43
	Lower Control Arm Front Pivot Nut	69–93
	Lower Control Arm Retaining Strap	69-86
	Halfshaft Locknut	174-235
	Power Steering Gear Line Flare Nuts	22–28
	Power Steering Pump Pulley	15–22
	Power Steering Pump	27–38
	Power Steering Pump Pressure Line Flare Nuts	12–17
	Shock/Strut Assembly To Steering Knuckle	69-93
	Shock/Strut Piston Nut	58-81
	Shock/Strut Upper Mounting Block Nuts	22-30
	Stabilizer Bar To Chassis Frame	32-43
	Steering Gear Bracket Nuts	27-38
	Tie Rod End Nut	31–42
	Wheel Lug Nuts	65-88

Wheel Alignment

INDEX

PRELIMINARY INSPECTION

1. Inspect tires for proper inflation and similar tread wear.
2. Inspect hub and bearing for excessive wear, repair as required.
3. Inspect ball joints.
4. Inspect tie rod ends for excessive looseness.
5. Check wheel and tire runout.
6. Inspect vehicle ride height.
7. Inspect rack and pinion for looseness at frame.
8. Ensure proper strut operation.
9. Check suspension and steering components for damage, replace as required.

FRONT WHEEL ALIGNMENT
CAMBER

1. Raise and support front of vehicle.
2. From inside engine compartment, remove mounting block nuts located on top of strut tower.

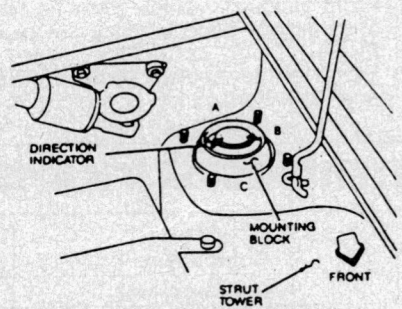

Direction Indicator	Difference from Standard Position	
	Camber Angle	Caster Angle
A	+ 14'	+ 14'
B	+ 29'	0°
C	+ 14'	- 14'

FM2049100035000X

Fig. 1   Font camber adjustment

3. Push mounting block downward and turn to desired position, **Fig. 1.**
4. Install mounting block nuts, then **torque** to 22-30 ft. lbs.

TOE

1. Loosen left and right tie rod locknuts.
2. Release clips at small ends of steering gear boots.
3. Turn tie rods equally until desired toe-in setting is reached. Left and right tie rods are both righthand threads. One turn of the tie rod (both sides) makes a toe-in change of about 0.24 inch.
4. **Torque** tie rod locknuts to 25-29 ft. lbs.

REAR WHEEL ALIGNMENT
TOE

Only the righthand link is adjustable. If the thrust angle is not within specification, install an adjustable link on the lefthand side of vehicle, then readjust rear toe.

1. Loosen lateral link locknuts.
2. Turn lateral link adjustment link to adjust. One turn of link is about 0.44 inch.
3. **Torque** locknuts to 41-47 ft. lbs.

INDEX OF SERVICE OPERATIONS

NOTE: For Service Operations Not Listed Below, Refer To The Table Of Contents In The Front Of This Manual.

Specifications

GENERAL ENGINE SPECIFICATIONS

| Year | Engine | | Fuel System | Bore x Stroke Inches | Comp. Ratio | Net HP @ RPM③ | Maximum Torque Ft. Lbs. @ RPM③ | Normal Oil Pressure psi |
	Liter/CID	VIN Code ②						
1992–95	1.3L/4-81	H	EFI①	2.78 x 3.29	9.7	63 @ 5000	73 @ 3000	50–64④

CID— Cubic Inch Displacement.
① —Aisin Kogyo port fuel injection.

② —The eighth digit of the VIN denotes engine code.

③ —Ratings are net, as installed in vehicle.
④ —At 3000 RPM w/engine hot.

TUNE UP SPECIFICATIONS

Year & Engine	Spark Plug Gap	Ignition Timing BTDC				Curb Idle Speed		Fast Idle Speed		Fuel Pump Pressure, psi
		Firing Order Fig.	Man. Trans.	Auto. Trans.	Mark Fig.	Man. Trans.	Auto. Trans.	Man. Trans.	Auto. Trans.	
1992–93										
1.3L/4-81	.041	A	10①	10①	B	700	850N	②	②	30-38③
1994-95										
1.3L/4-81	.041	A	10④	10④	D⑤	650-750	700-800	②	②	30-38⑥

BTDC— Before Top Dead Center.
N— Neutral
P—Park
①—With STI connector grounded, refer to Fig. C.
②—Controlled by ECA (Electronic Control Assembly).
③—Removing rear seat cushion, then release fuel system by starting engine & disconnecting fuel pump electrical connector. After engine has stalled, place ignition switch in the Off position. Connect a suitable fuel pressure gauge to fuel pump outlet connection. Connect a jumper wire between fuel pump test connector terminals, then place ignition switch in On position & check fuel pressure.
④—With jumper wire connected between DCL TEN & GND terminals. Refer to Fig. E.
⑤—On 1994 models, align pointer with white mark on pulley. On 1995 models, align pointer with yellow mark on pulley.
⑥—Remove fuel tank filler cap & allow fuel tank pressure to release . Start engine, then disconnect fuel pump relay electrical connector. Fuel pump relay is located under the LH side of the instrument panel. After engine has stalled, place ignition switch in Off position & connect fuel pump relay electrical connector. Connect a suitable fuel pressure test gauge to fuel hose between fuel filter & fuel rail. Connect a jumper wire between DCL F/P terminal & GND terminal, Fig. E.

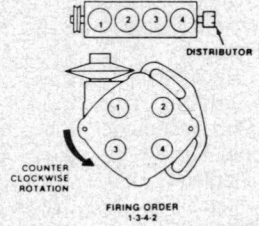

Fig. A

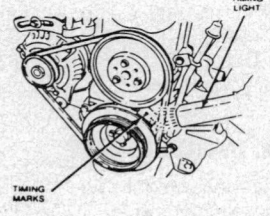

Fig. B

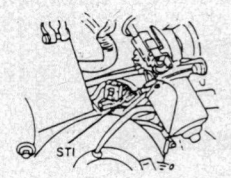

Fig. C

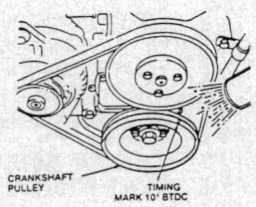

Fig. D

Fig. E

FRONT WHEEL ALIGNMENT SPECIFICATIONS

Year	Model	Caster Angle, Degrees		Camber Angle, Degrees				Toe-In, Inch	Kingpin Inclination, Degrees
		Limits	Desired	Limits		Desired			
				Left	Right	Left	Right		
1992-93	Festiva	+1/3 to +1 5/6	+1 7/12	-1/4 to +1 7/12	-1/4 to +1 7/12	+2/3	+2/3	.02 to .26	14 11/60
1994-95	Aspire	+1 5/12 to +2 5/12	+1 2/3	+1/12 to +1 7/12	+1/12 to +1 7/12	+5/6	+5/6	.2 to .26	14

REAR WHEEL ALIGNMENT SPECIFICATIONS

Year	Model	Camber		Toe-In Inch
		Limits	Desired	
1992-93	Festiva	-1 to +1/2 ①	-1/4 ①	0 to .24
1994-95	Aspire	-1 to +1/2	-1/4	0 to .24

①—Revised per Technical Service Bulletin No. 91-11B-16.

COOLING SYSTEM & CAPACITY DATA

Year	Engine	Coolant Capacity, Qts.		Radiator Cap Relief Pressure psi.	Thermo. Opening Temp.	Fuel Tank Gals.	Engine Oil Refill Qts. ①	Transaxle Oil	
		Less A/C	With A/C					Man. Trans. Pts.	Auto. Trans. Qts ②
1992–93	1.3L/4-81	5.3	5.3	13	③	10	3.4	5.2	5.6
1994–95	1.3L/4-81	5.8	6.3	13	③	10	3.6	5.2	6.6

①—Includes filter change.　　　　②—Approximate, make final check w/dipstick.　　　　③—Sub-valve, 185°; main valve, 190°.

LUBRICANT DATA

Year	Model	Lubricant Type			
		Transaxle		Power Steering	Brake System
		Manual	Automatic		
1992–95	All	Mercon	Mercon	①	DOT 3

①—Type F auto. trans. fluid. @

Electrical

NOTE: On Air Bag Equipped Models, Refer To "Air Bag System Precautions" Located In The Front Of This Manual For System Disarming & Arming Procedures.

INDEX

PRECAUTIONS
AIR BAG SYSTEMS

Refer to "Air Bag System Precautions" in the front of this manual for system disarming and arming procedures.

FUSE PANEL & FLASHER LOCATION

The fuse panel is located left side of the steering column, behind access panel. The flashers are located below instrument panel in upper left hand corner, behind ECA.

RELAY CENTER LOCATION

The relay center is located near the main fuse panel in the engine compartment, next to the battery.

STARTER
REPLACE
AUTOMATIC TRANSAXLE

1. Disconnect battery ground cable.
2. Remove two upper starter motor mounting bolts.
3. Raise and support vehicle.
4. Remove two manifold to cylinder block bracket bolts, then the bracket.
5. Remove mounting bracket to support bracket bolt.
6. Remove support bracket.
7. Remove two nuts and washers that secure mounting bracket to starter motor.
8. Disconnect the "B" and "S" terminal connectors at starter solenoid.
9. Remove lower starter motor mounting bolt.
10. Remove starter motor.

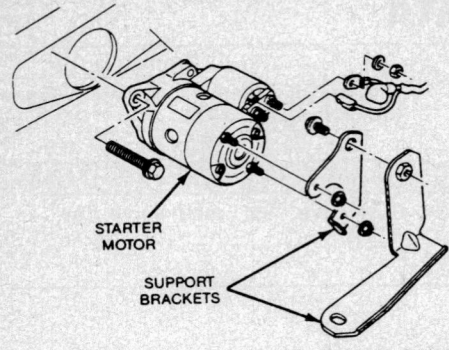

Fig. 1 Starter motor replacement

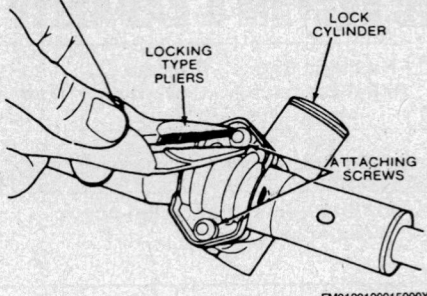

Fig. 2 Ignition lock removal

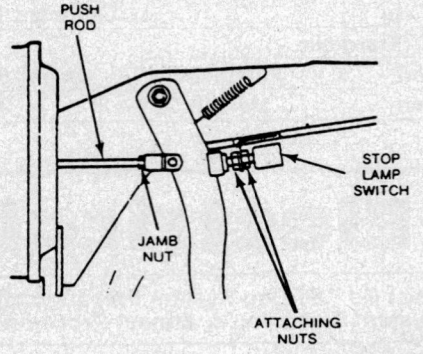

Fig. 4 Stop light switch replacement

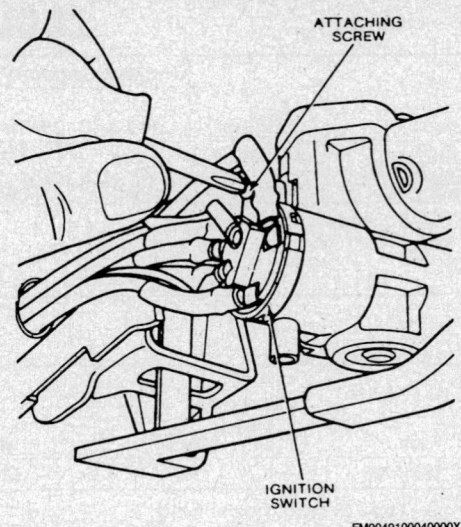

Fig. 3 Ignition switch screw location

11. Reverse procedure to install. **Torque** starter motor retaining bolts to 23-34 ft. lbs.

MANUAL TRANSAXLE

1. Disconnect battery ground cable, then raise and support front of vehicle.
2. Disconnect all electrical connections at starter, **Fig. 1.**
3. Remove starter motor support bracket to transaxle attaching bolts.
4. Remove starter motor attaching bolts and the starter motor.
5. Reverse procedure to install. **Torque** starter motor retaining bolts to 23-34 ft. lbs.

DISTRIBUTOR
REPLACE

1. Disconnect battery ground cable.
2. Disconnect coil wire from distributor.
3. Remove distributor cap attaching screws.
4. Pull off distributor cap and swing it aside.
5. Disconnect distributor electrical connector.
6. If the distributor is not being replaced, scribe a reference mark across distributor base flange and cylinder head. This reference mark will allow installation without changing timing.
7. Remove distributor unit, then O-ring at base of distributor.
8. Reverse procedure to install, noting the following:
   a. Install new O-ring.
   b. During installation of distributor, ensure offset tangs engage with camshaft slots.
   c. If distributor unit was not replaced, align scribe marks made during removal and **torque** mounting bolts to 14-18 ft. lbs.
   d. If a new distributor is being installed, the ignition timing should be checked and adjusted.

IGNITION LOCK
REPLACE

1. Disconnect battery ground cable.
2. Remove steering wheel, combination switch and ignition switch as outlined under Combination Switch, Replace.

3. Using suitable locking pliers, remove attaching screws, then the mounting cap and lock housing from steering column jacket, **Fig. 2.**
4. To install ignition lock, proceed as follows:
   a. Position lock housing on steering column jacket, then install mounting cap and new attaching screws. Tighten screws only enough to hold lock housing in position on column jacket.
   b. Turn lock mechanism with ignition key to verify correct operation of lock. If lock binds, reposition on jacket slightly until mechanism functions properly.
   c. Tighten attaching screws until heads break off, then reinstall parts removed in step 1 to complete installation.

IGNITION SWITCH
REPLACE

1. Disconnect battery ground cable.
2. Remove upper and lower steering column trim covers.
3. Disengage switch harness from retaining clip, then remove retaining screw and ignition switch from lock housing, **Fig. 3.**
4. To install switch, proceed as follows:
   a. Push ignition switch into lock housing bore until switch tang engages lock cylinder. **If necessary, turn lock cylinder with ignition key until switch tang aligns with switch slot.**
   b. Install switch retaining screw, position wire harness as necessary,

then close harness retaining clip.
   c. Reinstall upper and lower trim covers.

HEADLAMP SWITCH
REPLACE

The headlamp/turn signal switch is mounted on the steering column as part of the combination switch assembly.
1. Disconnect battery ground cable.
2. Remove combination switch as outlined previously.
3. Remove attaching screws, then separate headlamp/turn signal switch from combination switch.
4. Rotate switch handle to parking light detent.
5. Remove switch handle attaching screws and plate, then rotate handle out of switch body. **Use care to prevent loss of detent balls and springs.**
6. Reverse procedure to install.

STOP LIGHT SWITCH
REPLACE

1. Disconnect battery ground cable.
2. Disconnect wiring from switch.
3. Remove locknut, then the switch from brake pedal support, **Fig. 4.**
4. Reinstall switch and locknut, then adjust switch as follows:
   a. Connect ohmmeter across switch terminals.
   b. Rotate switch toward brake pedal until ohmmeter indicates infinite resistance.
   c. Rotate switch toward brake pedal an additional 1/2 turn, then tighten locknut and reconnect wiring.

COMBINATION SWITCH
REPLACE
FESTIVA

1. Disconnect battery ground cable.
2. Remove steering wheel as outlined under "Steering Wheel, Replace."

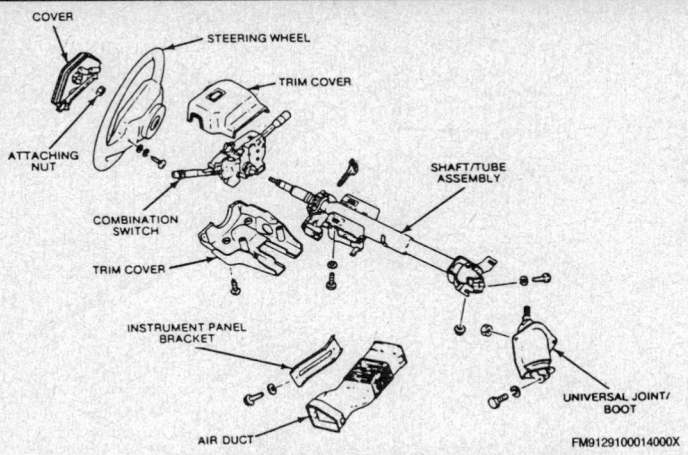

Fig. 5 Upper steering column components

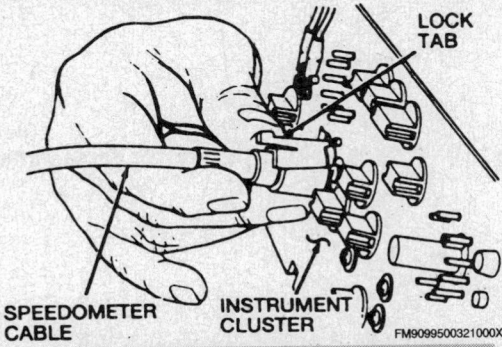

Fig. 7 Speedometer cable clip removal. Aspire

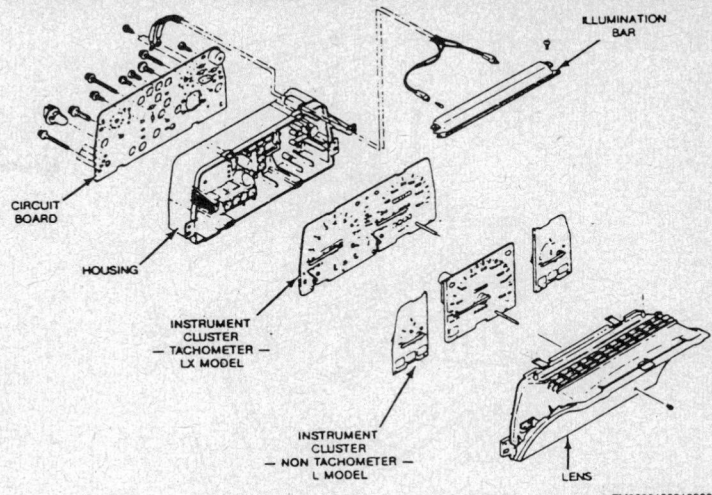

Fig. 6 Instrument cluster components. Festiva

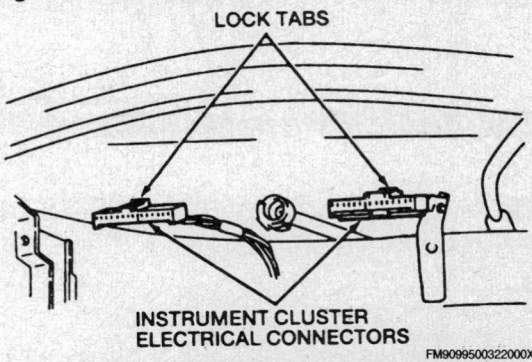

Fig. 8 Instrument cluster electrical connector clip removal. Aspire

3. Remove upper and lower steering column trim covers, **Fig. 5.**
4. Disengage wire harness retaining clip, then disconnect harness connectors from back of switch.
5. Working from below steering column, loosen band clamp securing switch hub to steering column jacket, then pull switch assembly off steering column.
6. Reverse procedure to install.

ASPIRE

1. Disconnect battery ground cable, then wait one minute for back-up power supply to be depleted.
2. Remove steering wheel as described under "Steering Wheel, Replace."
3. Remove upper and lower steering column shrouds.
4. **On models equipped with air bag,** apply two strips of tape across sliding contact to prevent accidental rotation, then proceed as follows:
   a. Remove three air bag sliding contact screws and pull sliding contact off steering column.
   b. Remove air bag sliding contact ground wire, then disconnect the air bag sliding contact electrical connector.
   c. Remove air bag sliding contact.
5. **On all models,** Remove multi-function switch screws, then disconnect the multi-function switch electrical connectors.
6. Slide multi-function switch off steering column.
7. Reverse procedure to install.

TURN SIGNAL SWITCH
REPLACE

Refer to "Headlamp Switch, Replace," for turn signal switch replacement procedure.

STEERING WHEEL
REPLACE
FESTIVA

1. Remove two screws from back of steering wheel, then disconnect horn wire.
2. Remove steering wheel cover, then steering wheel retaining nut.
3. Mark steering wheel and column shaft for assembling.
4. Remove steering wheel with steering wheel puller tool No. T67L-3600-A or equivalent.
5. Reverse procedure to install. **Torque** steering wheel retaining nut to 29-36 ft. lbs.

ASPIRE

1. Remove air bag module as outlined under "Air Bag Systems".
2. Remove two screws from back of steering wheel, then disconnect horn wire.
3. Remove steering wheel cover, then

steering wheel retaining nut.
4. Mark steering wheel and column shaft for assembling.
5. Remove steering wheel with steering wheel puller tool No. T67L-3600-A or equivalent.
6. Reverse procedure to install. **Torque** steering wheel retaining nut to 29-36 ft. lbs.

INSTRUMENT CLUSTER
REPLACE
FESTIVA

1. Disconnect battery ground cable.
2. **On models equipped with tilt steering column,** release tilt lock, then lower steering column to seat. On models equipped with conventional steering column, remove upper and lower steering column trim covers.
3. **On all models,** remove cluster bezel attaching screws and pull bezel away from cluster.
4. If applicable, disconnect electrical wiring from rear window defogger or wiper switch.
5. Remove instrument cluster attaching screws, then pull cluster outward and disconnect speedometer cable and electrical connectors from rear of cluster.
6. Remove cluster from vehicle, **Fig. 6.**
7. Reverse procedure to install.

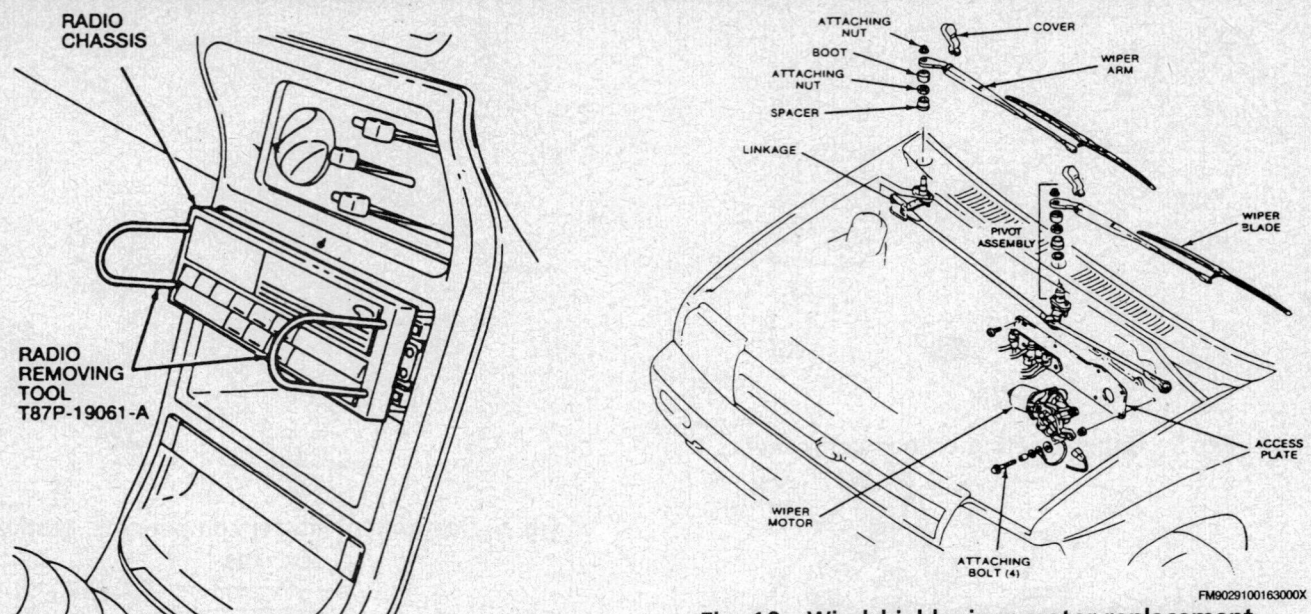

Fig. 9 Radio removal. Aspire

Fig. 10 Windshield wiper motor replacement

Fig. 11 Rear wiper motor replacement. Festiva

ASPIRE

1. Disconnect battery ground cable.
2. Remove instrument cluster bezel attaching screws and pull bezel away from instrument cluster.
3. Disconnect speedometer cable at transaxle.
4. Remove four instrument cluster screw, then pull instrument cluster away from instrument panel.
5. By pressing individual locking tabs, Figs. 7 and 8, disconnect speedometer cable and electrical connectors from back of cluster and remove cluster.
6. Reverse procedure to install.

RADIO
REPLACE
FESTIVA

1. Disconnect battery ground cable.
2. Remove radio/heater control panel bezel attaching screws, then the bezel.
3. Remove radio to instrument panel attaching screws.
4. Pull radio outward, disconnect antenna lead and all electrical connections, then remove radio from instrument panel.
5. Reverse procedure to install.

ASPIRE

1. Disconnect battery ground cable.
2. Using radio removing tool No. T87P-19061-A, or equivalent, pull radio chassis to access electrical connections and antenna, Fig. 9.
3. On models equipped with amplifier, disconnect electrical connector.
4. On all models, remove radio.
5. Reverse procedure to install

WIPER MOTOR
REPLACE
FRONT
Festiva

1. Disconnect battery ground cable.
2. Disconnect electrical connector, then remove wiper motor to dash panel attaching bolts, Fig. 10.
3. Remove mounting plate attaching screws and pull plate away from dash panel.
4. Using suitable tool, pry linkage pivot from motor output arm, then remove wiper motor from vehicle.
5. Reverse procedure to install. Ensure ground wire is securely fastened to left upper attaching bolt of motor.

Aspire

1. Disconnect battery ground cable.
2. Disconnect electrical connector, then remove wiper motor to dash panel attaching bolts, Fig. 10.

3. Remove mounting plate attaching screws and pull plate away from dash panel.
4. Remove two EGR solenoid vacuum valve bracket nuts and slide intake manifold vacuum outlet fitting and cap off access plate.
5. Using suitable tool, pry linkage pivot from motor output arm, then remove wiper motor from vehicle.
6. Reverse procedure to install. Ensure ground wire is fastened to left upper attaching bolt of motor.

REAR
Festiva

1. Disconnect battery ground cable.
2. Lift cover, then remove wiper arm attaching nut and the wiper arm, Fig. 11.
3. Pull off shaft seal and remove outer bushing attaching nut and outer bushing.
4. Using suitable tool, pry trim panel off inner portion of liftgate.
5. Peel back wire harness electrical

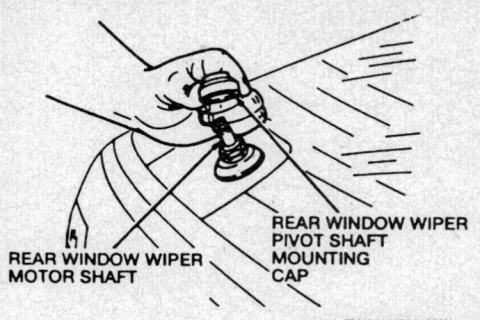

Fig. 12 Rear wiper motor pivot shaft. Aspire

tape, then disconnect wiper motor electrical connector.

6. Remove wiper motor to liftgate attaching bolts, then the wiper motor.
7. Check inner and outer bushings and shaft O-ring for damage, and replace parts as necessary.
8. Reverse procedure to install. Cycle wiper motor several times to ensure motor is in Park position before installing wiper arm. When properly installed, tip of wiper blade should be approximately 3 inches from edge of liftgate window seal.

Aspire

1. Disconnect battery ground cable.
2. Remove rear wiper pivot arm, then the rear wiper pivot shaft mounting cap from shaft, **Fig. 12.**
3. Remove two rear wiper pivot shaft cowl nuts, then the mounting spacer.
4. Remove rear wiper motor cover, then the liftgate trim panel.
5. Disconnect wiper motor electrical connectors.
6. Remove four wipers motor bolts, then the rear wiper motor.
7. Reverse procedure to install.

WIPER SWITCH
REPLACE

WINDSHIELD WIPER SWITCH/INTERVAL WIPER MODULE

The wiper switch and interval wiper module (if equipped) are mounted on the steering column as part of the combination switch assembly.
1. Disconnect battery ground cable.
2. Remove combination switch as outlined previously.
3. Remove wiper switch/interval wiper module attaching screws, then disengage switch from combination switch, **Fig. 13.**
4. Using a thin screwdriver, disengage switch handle lock tab and pull handle from switch assembly.
5. Remove plunger, spring and O-ring from handle.
6. Reverse procedure to install.

REAR WIPER

1. Disconnect battery ground cable.

2. **On models equipped with tilt steering column,** release tilt lock, then lower steering column to seat. On models equipped with conventional steering column, remove upper and lower steering column trim covers.
3. **On all models,** remove cluster bezel attaching screws and pull bezel away from cluster.
4. Depress switch lock tabs, then disconnect electrical connector and remove switch from bezel, **Fig. 11.**
5. Reverse procedure to install.

WIPER TRANSMISSION
REPLACE

1. Remove front wiper motor as outlined previously.
2. Remove wiper arms, then the pivot assembly protective boots, **Fig. 10.**
3. Remove pivot attaching nuts and spacers, then the linkage through opening in access panel.
4. Reverse procedure to install.

BLOWER MOTOR
REPLACE

FESTIVA

1. Disconnect battery ground cable.
2. Remove instrument panel spacer brace and air flow duct located below steering column.
3. Disconnect blower motor electrical wiring.
4. Remove blower motor attaching screws and the blower motor.
5. Remove blower wheel retaining nut and washer, then pull wheel off blower motor shaft.
6. Reverse procedure to install.

ASPIRE

1. Disconnect battery ground cable.
2. Remove instrument panel spacer brace and air flow duct located below steering column.
3. Remove lower LH nut and pull blower motor housing out from behind evaporator case.
4. Remove blower motor attaching screws and the blower motor.
5. Remove blower wheel circlip, then pull wheel off blower motor shaft.
6. Remove three blower motor cover retaining screws, then the cover.
7. Reverse procedure to install.

HEATER CORE
REPLACE

FESTIVA

1. Disconnect battery ground cable.
2. Remove combination switch as outlined previously.
3. Remove instrument panel hood attaching screws, then push hood rearward to gain access to switch electrical connections. Disconnect all switch wiring as necessary, then remove hood.

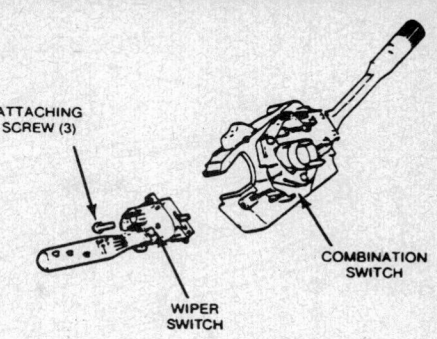

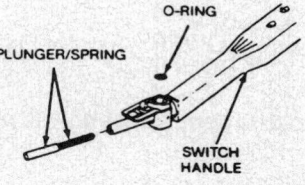

Fig. 13 Windshield wiper switch & interval wiper module replacement

4. Remove instrument cluster as outlined previously.
5. Working from underneath center of instrument panel, remove center mounting bracket bolts, then the mounting bracket.
6. Disconnect and remove lefthand and righthand heater ducts.
7. Remove glove box.
8. Remove fuse panel cover, then the fuse panel attaching screws. Push fuse panel forward, but do not remove from vehicle.
9. Remove shift lever console and radio.
10. Remove air conditioning/heater control panel, then disconnect cigar lighter electrical connector.
11. Working from underneath instrument panel, disconnect all air conditioning/heater control cables that will interfere with instrument panel removal.
12. Remove trim inserts concealing instrument panel attaching bolts.
13. Remove the seven attaching bolts and two stud nuts retaining instrument panel, **Fig. 14.**
14. Disconnect any remaining electrical wiring, then remove instrument panel from vehicle.
15. Working from engine compartment, disconnect hoses from heater core.
16. Disconnect wiring from blower motor and blower motor resistor.
17. Disengage wiring harness and antenna lead from bracket on front of plenum.
18. Loosen screw securing connector duct to plenum, then remove upper and lower plenum to cowl panel attaching nuts.
19. Disengage plenum from defroster ducts, then pull outward and remove plenum from vehicle.
20. Disconnect link connecting the two defroster doors, then remove screws and clips securing plenum halves together.

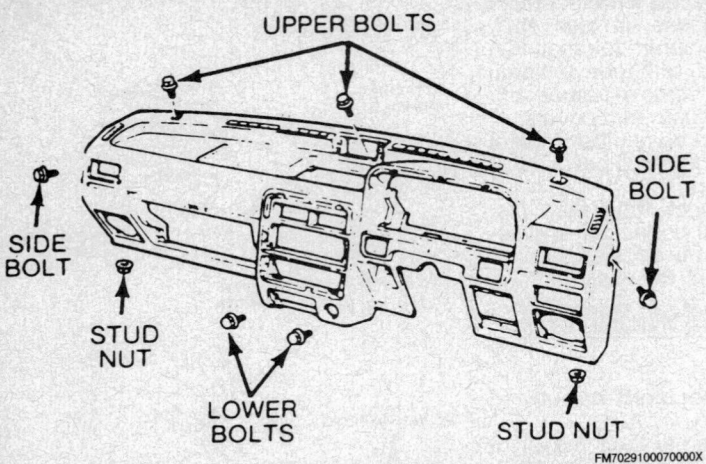

Fig. 14 Instrument panel bolt & nut location. Festiva

FM7029100070000X

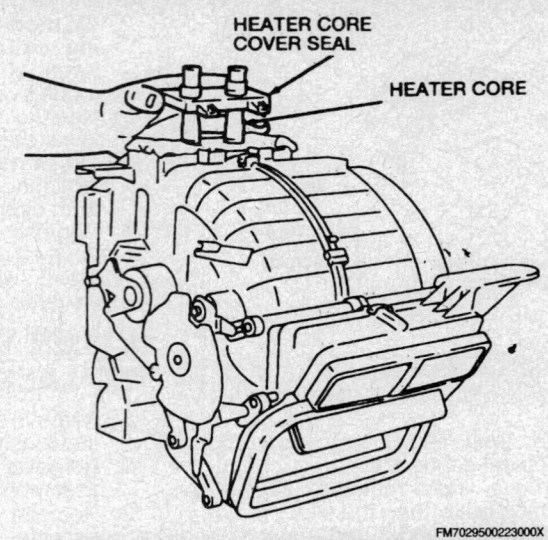

Fig. 15 Heater core replacement. Aspire

FM7029500223000X

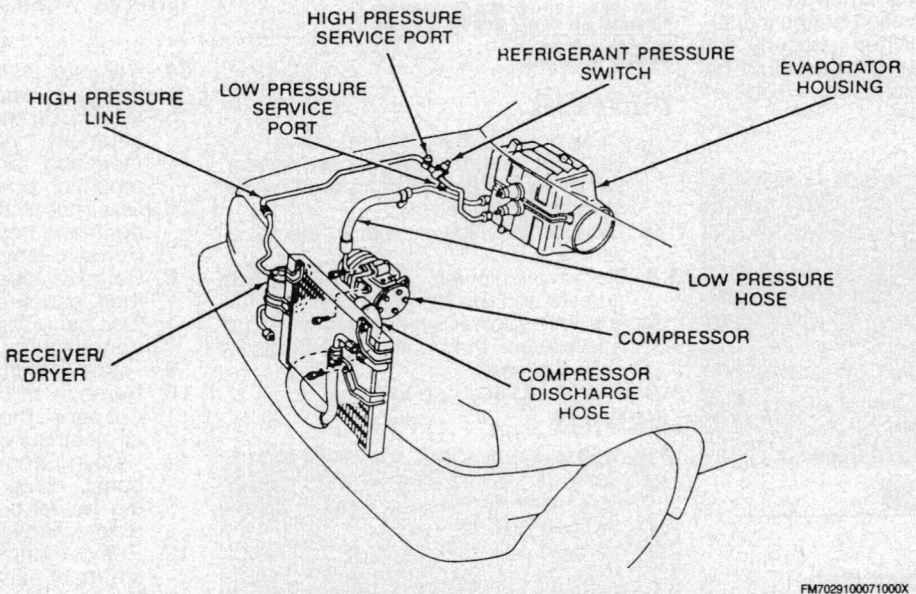

Fig. 16 Evaporator hose routing. Festive less power steering

FM7029100071000X

21. Separate plenum halves and remove heater core.
22. Remove tube insert from bottom of heater core.
23. Reverse procedure to install.

ASPIRE

1. Disconnect battery ground cable, then drain the engine coolant.
2. Disconnect inlet and outlet heater hoses in engine compartment.
3. Remove instrument panel, then disconnect wiring harness and antenna from routing bracket on front of heater core case.
4. Loosen clamp securing evaporator register duct to heater core case.
5. Remove two retaining nuts from upper and lower right side of heater core case.
6. Remove lower left side nut, then disconnect heater core case from windshield defroster nozzle connectors and remove heater core case.
7. Remove four heater core cover seal screws and seal, then the heater core, **Fig. 15.**
8. Reverse procedure to install.

EVAPORATOR CORE
REPLACE
FESTIVA

1. Disconnect battery ground cable.

2. Discharge refrigerant from A/C system.
3. Working from inside engine compartment, disconnect low and high pressure lines from evaporator outlet fitting, **Figs. 16 and 17.**
4. Remove two glove box retaining screws, then glove box assembly.
5. Disconnect two electrical connectors from thermostat, **Fig. 18.**
6. Disconnect cable from thermostat.
7. Disengage wire harness retaining clamps from top of evaporator housing.
8. Loosen clamp screw securing connector duct to evaporator housing, **Fig. 19.**
9. Disconnect drain hose from evaporator housing.

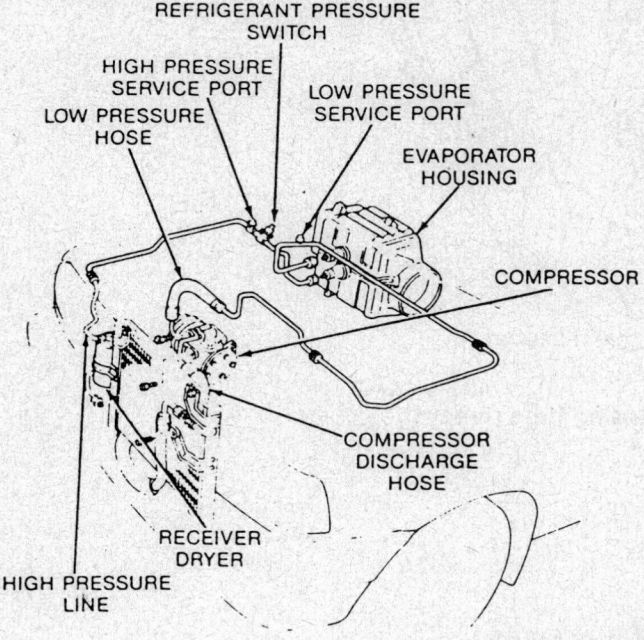

Fig. 17 Evaporator hose routing. Festiva w/power steering

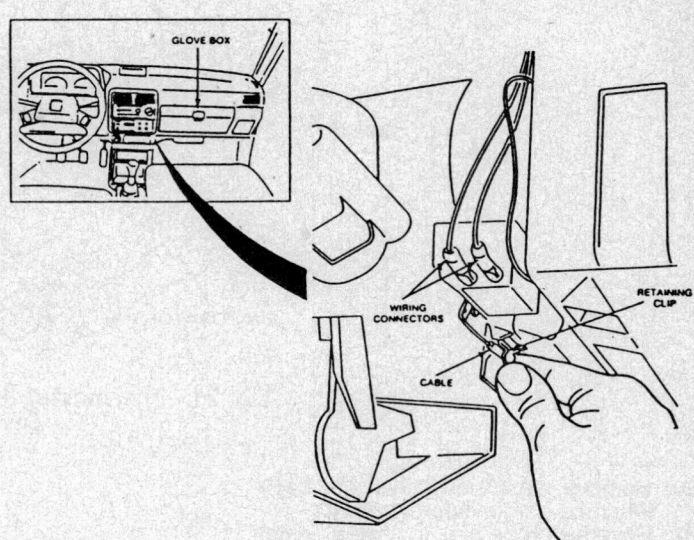

Fig. 18 Evaporator case electrical connections. Festiva

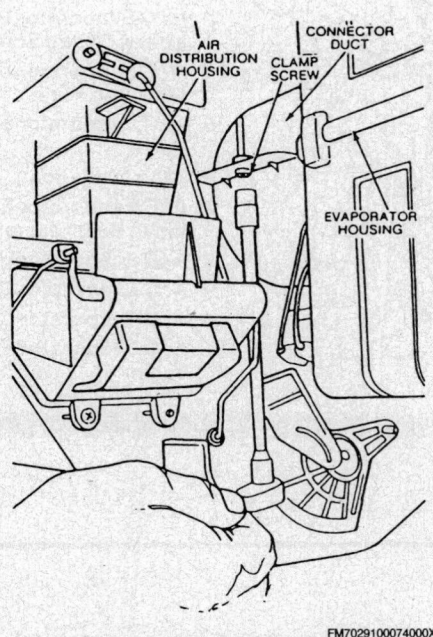

Fig. 19 Evaporator case clamp screw location. Festiva

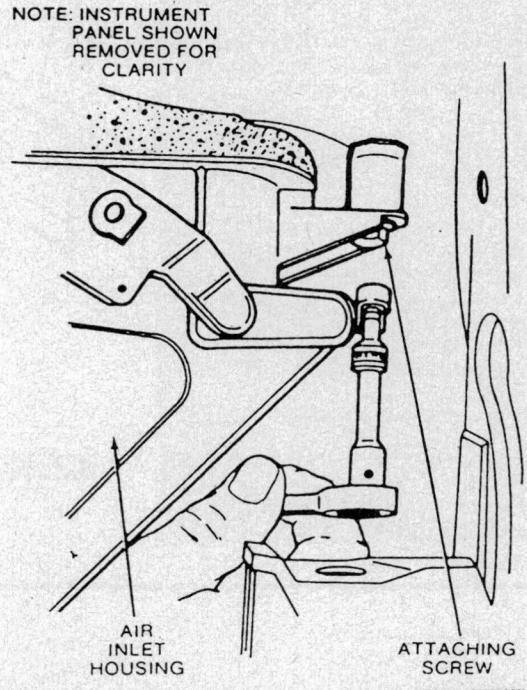

Fig. 20 Air inlet attaching bolt. Festiva

10. Remove air inlet duct attaching bolt, **Fig. 20.**
11. Remove bolt attaching base of evaporator housing to dash panel.
12. Remove nuts attaching top of evaporator housing to dash panel.
13. Remove evaporator housing.

14. Remove the ten clips securing the upper evaporator housing to lower housing.
15. Remove upper evaporator housing.
16. Remove thermostat retaining screws, then thermostat. **Fig. 21.**
17. Pull sensing tube from between evap-

orator core fins as the thermostat is removed.
18. Remove evaporator core from lower housing, then tube separation insert from between inlet and outlet tubes.
19. Remove staples securing capillary tube insulator.

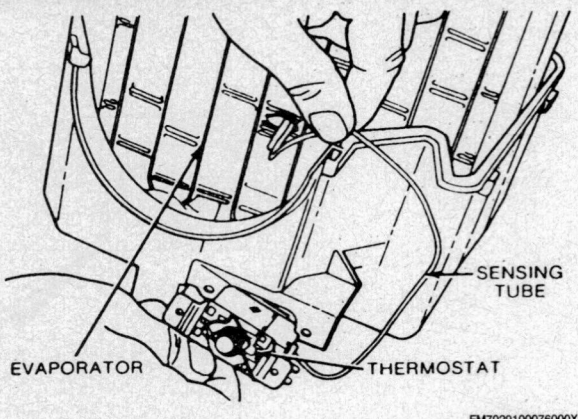

Fig. 21 Thermostat & sensing tube removal.
Festiva

FM7029100076000X

20. Remove expansion valve and capillary tube from evaporator core.
21. Reverse procedure to install. Install new O-ring seals.

ASPIRE

1. Disconnect battery ground cable.
2. Discharge refrigerant from A/C system.
3. Working from inside engine compartment, disconnect low and high pressure lines from evaporator outlet fitting.
4. Remove two glove box retaining screws, then glove box assembly.
5. Disconnect two electrical connectors from thermostat.
6. Disconnect cable from thermostat.
7. Disengage wire harness retaining clamps from top of evaporator housing.
8. Loosen clamp screw securing connector duct to evaporator housing.
9. Disconnect drain hose from evaporator housing on lower evaporator case.
10. Remove evaporator housing.
11. Remove the six clips securing the upper evaporator housing to lower housing.
12. Remove upper evaporator housing, **Fig. 22.**
13. Remove evaporator core from lower case.
14. Reverse procedure to install. Install new O-ring seals.

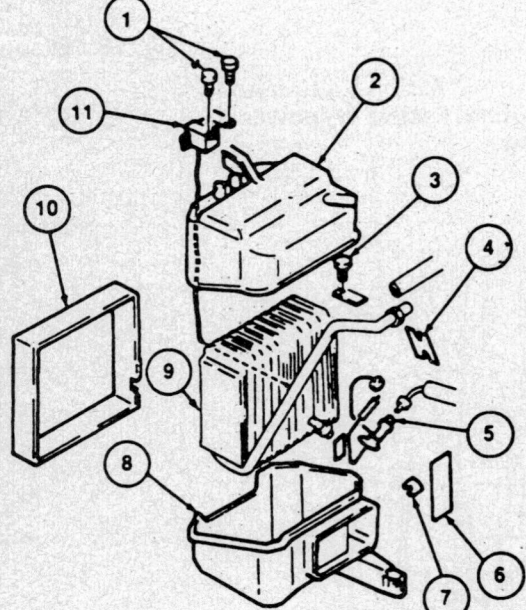

1 A/C Evaporator Temperature Control Thermostat Screws (2 Req'd)
2 A/C Evaporator Upper Case
3 A/C Evaporator Upper and Lower Cases Screw
4 A/C Evaporator Case Mounting Plate
5 A/C Evaporator Expansion Valve
6 Tube Insulation
7 A/C Evaporator Expansion Valve Bulb Clamp
8 A/C Evaporator Lower Case
9 A/C Evaporator Core
10 A/C Evaporator Core Seal
11 A/C Evaporator Expansion Valve

FM7029500224000X

Fig. 22 Exploded view of evaporator assembly. Aspire

Engine

NOTE: On Air Bag Equipped Models, Refer To "Air Bag System Precautions" Located In The Front Of This Manual For System Disarming & Arming Procedures.

INDEX

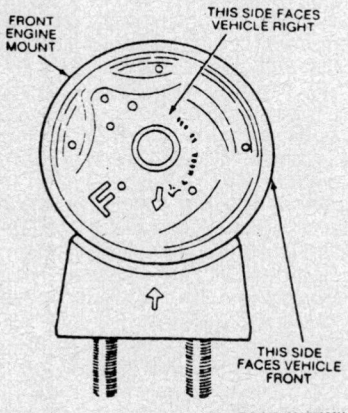

Fig. 1 Front engine mount installation. Festiva

FM1069100355000X

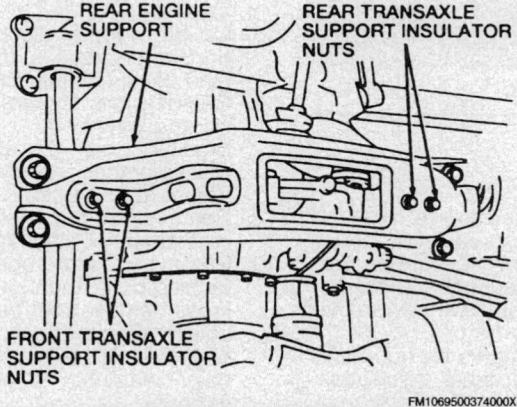

Fig. 2 Rear engine support. Aspire

FM1069500374000X

PRECAUTIONS

AIR BAG SYSTEMS

Refer to "Air Bag System Precautions" in the front of this manual for system disarming and arming procedures.

FUEL SYSTEM PRESSURE RELIEF

Festiva

1. Remove rear seat cushion.
2. Run engine, then disconnect fuel pump electrical connector and allow engine to until it stalls.
3. After engine has stalled, turn ignition switch to Off position.

Aspire

1. Remove fuel tank filler cap and allow fuel tank pressure to release.
2. Start engine, then disconnect fuel pump relay electrical connector. Fuel pump relay is located under the LH side of the instrument panel.

ENGINE MOUNT

REPLACE

FRONT MOUNT

Festiva

1. Remove mount through bolt attaching nut.
2. Support engine using suitable tool, then remove through bolt.
3. Raise and support front of vehicle.
4. Remove front mount to crossmember attaching nuts, raise engine as necessary, and remove mount from crossmember.
5. Reverse procedure to install. Position mount as shown in **Fig. 1.**

REAR MOUNT

Festiva

1. Raise and support front of vehicle.
2. Support engine using suitable tool, then remove rear mount to crossmember attaching nut.
3. Remove mount to engine bracket attaching bolts, raise engine as necessary, then remove mount from crossmember.
4. Reverse procedure to install.

Aspire

1. Disconnect battery ground cable.
2. Support engine using engine support tool No. 014-00750, or equivalent, then raise and support vehicle.
3. Remove two front transaxle support insulator nuts from rear engine mount, **Fig. 2.**
4. Remove four rear engine support mount bolts, **Fig. 3,** then the engine support.
5. Reverse procedure to install tightening bolts to specifications.

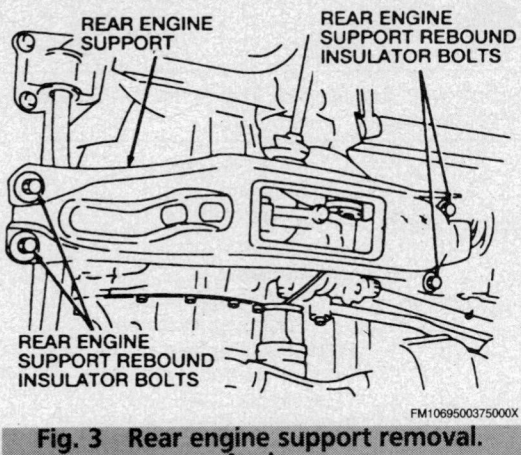

**Fig. 3   Rear engine support removal.
Aspire**

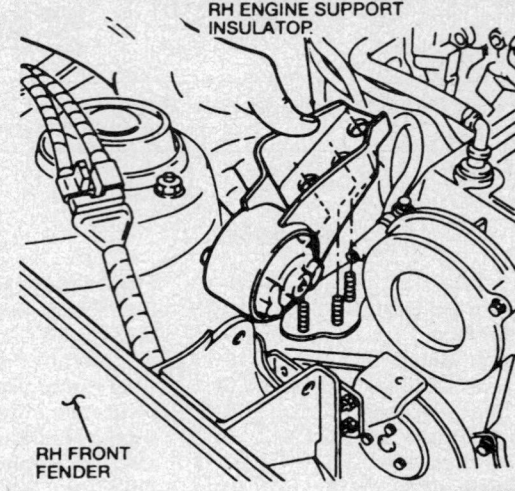

**Fig. 4   Right engine mount removal.
Aspire**

RIGHT MOUNT

Aspire

1. Remove engine air cleaner assembly, then support engine with suitable jack.
2. Remove three engine mount nuts and washers.
3. Remove engine mount through bolt, then the engine mount, **Fig. 4.**
4. Reverse procedure to install. Tighten to specifications.

ENGINE
REPLACE

FESTIVA

The engine and transaxle are removed as an assembly on these vehicles.
1. Relieve fuel system pressure as outlined under "Precautions," then disconnect battery cables, then remove battery and battery tray.
2. Scribe alignment marks on hood and hood hinges to facilitate installation, then remove hood.
3. Drain cooling system, crankcase and transaxle, then discharge air conditioning system.
4. Remove air cleaner and oil dipstick.
5. Disconnect electrical connectors and hoses, then remove cooling fan and radiator as an assembly.
6. Disconnect accelerator cable at carburetor and bracket.
7. Disconnect speedometer cable.
8. Disconnect and mark all remaining hoses, lines and electrical connections that will interfere with engine/transaxle removal.
9. Raise and support vehicle, then disconnect catalytic converter from exhaust system.
10. Remove A/C compressor, if equipped, and position aside. **Do not disconnect lines from compressor.**
11. Disconnect lower control arms from steering knuckles.
12. Separate halfshafts from transaxle and install suitable holding tool for differential side gear.
13. **On vehicles with automatic transaxles,** remove nut which connects shift lever to manual shaft assembly, then shift cable from transaxle.
14. **On vehicles with manual transaxles,** disconnect clutch control cable, then the shift control rod from transaxle.
15. **On all models,** disconnect stabilizer bar from transaxle, then support engine using suitable tool.
16. Remove rear crossmember to chassis attaching bolts.
17. Working through access hole in crossmember, remove front engine mount attaching nut.
18. Remove rear engine mount to crossmember attaching nut.
19. Remove crossmember to chassis attaching bolts, then lower and remove crossmember from vehicle.
20. Lower vehicle, attach suitable hoist to engine, then raise vehicle again to gain clearance for engine/transaxle removal.
21. Remove right engine mount through bolt, raise engine/transaxle assembly slightly, then guide assembly out through bottom of vehicle.
22. Reverse procedure to install.

ASPIRE

The engine and transaxle must be removed as an assembly.
1. Relieve fuel system pressure as outlined under "Precautions," then disconnect battery cables and remove battery and battery tray.
2. Scribe alignment marks on hood and hood hinges to facilitate installation, then remove hood.
3. Drain cooling system, crankcase and transaxle fluid, then discharge air conditioning system.
4. Remove air cleaner and oil dipstick.
5. Disconnect electrical connectors and hoses, then remove cooling fan and radiator as an assembly.
6. Disconnect accelerator cable at carburetor and bracket.
7. Disconnect speedometer cable and remove bracket.
8. Disconnect and mark all remaining hoses, lines and electrical connections that will interfere with engine/transaxle removal.
9. **On models with automatic transaxles,** disconnect Park/Neutral position switch, kickdown solenoid electrical connector and transaxle ground, then the shift cable and bracket.
10. **On models equipped with power steering,** remove two power steering bolts and separate pump from engine. Disconnect power steering lines from engine.
11. **On all models,** raise and support vehicle, then drain transaxle fluid.
12. Disconnect exhaust inlet pipe.
13. Remove A/C compressor.
14. Disconnect lower control arms from steering knuckles.
15. Separate halfshafts from transaxle and install suitable holding tool for differential side gear.
16. **On models with automatic transaxles,** remove six transaxle case to cylinder block front bracket and rear case bracket bolts, then the four flywheel to torque converter nuts.
17. **On models with manual transaxles,** remove six transaxle case to cylinder block front bracket and rear case bracket bolts, then disconnect clutch control cable, then the shift control rod from transaxle.
18. **On all models,** disconnect stabilizer bar from transaxle, then support engine using suitable tool.
19. Remove rear transaxle crossmember to chassis attaching bolts.
20. Remove two front transaxle crossmember nuts.
21. Remove rear engine mount to crossmember attaching nut.
22. Remove crossmember to chassis attaching bolts, then lower and remove crossmember from vehicle.
23. Lower vehicle, attach suitable hoist to engine, then raise vehicle again to gain clearance for engine/transaxle removal.

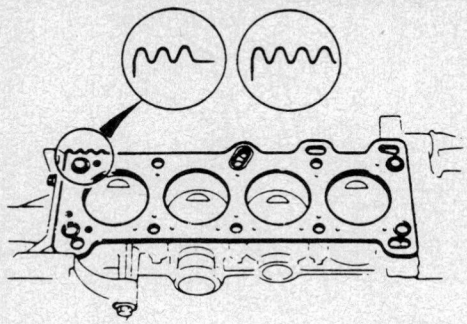

Fig. 5 Head gasket position

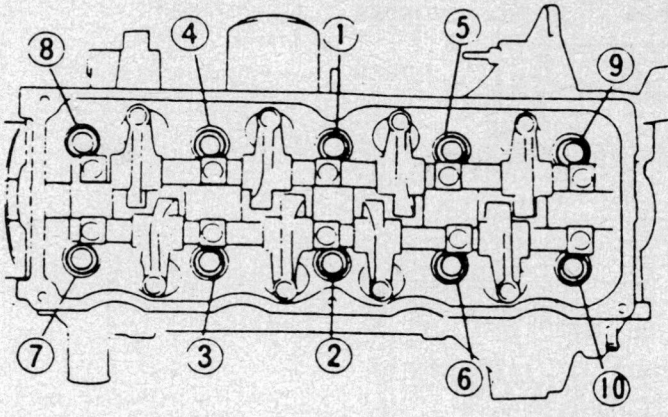

Fig. 6 Cylinder head bolt tightening sequence

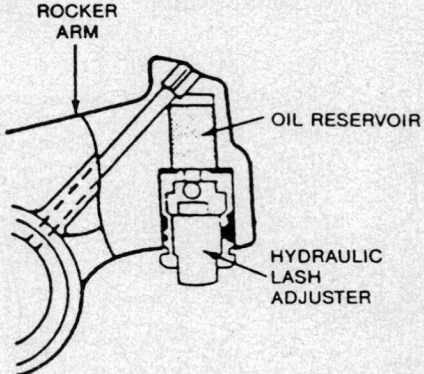

Fig. 7 Hydraulic valve lash adjuster assembly

24. Remove right engine mount through bolt, raise engine/transaxle assembly slightly, then guide assembly out through bottom of vehicle.
25. Reverse procedure to install. Tighten to specifications.

INTAKE MANIFOLD
REPLACE

1. Relieve fuel system pressure as outlined under "Precautions," then disconnect battery ground cable, then drain cooling system.
2. Remove air cleaner assembly, then disconnect accelerator cable from carburetor.
3. Disconnect and mark all hoses, lines and electrical connections that will interfere with manifold removal.
4. Remove retaining bolts, then the intake manifold.
5. Clean manifold and cylinder head mating surfaces.
6. Reverse procedure to install using a new manifold gasket. Tighten to specifications.

EXHAUST MANIFOLD
REPLACE

1. Relieve fuel system pressure as outlined under "Precautions," then raise and support vehicle.
2. Remove catalytic converter inlet pipe to manifold and pulse air tube to inlet pipe attaching nuts and washers.
3. Remove inlet pipe support bracket attaching bolts, then lower vehicle.
4. Remove air cleaner assembly, then the exhaust manifold heat shroud.
5. Remove oxygen sensor wiring from routing bracket, then disconnect sensor electrical connector.
6. Remove pulse air tube routing bracket attaching bolt and clamp, then the pulse air tube and gaskets.
7. Remove exhaust manifold to cylinder head attaching nuts, then the manifold.
8. Reverse procedure to install, using new gaskets. Tighten to specifications.

CYLINDER HEAD
REPLACE

1. Disconnect battery ground cable, then drain engine coolant.
2. Remove timing belt covers and timing belt as outlined previously.
3. Remove rocker arm cover.
4. Remove intake and exhaust manifolds.
5. Disconnect spark plug wires and remove spark plugs from cylinder head.
6. Disconnect distributor electrical connections, scribe alignment marks on distributor base flange and cylinder head, then remove distributor mounting bolts and the distributor.
7. Remove front and rear engine lifting eyes, then disconnect ground wire from cylinder head.
8. Disconnect all remaining electrical wiring that will interfere with cylinder head removal.
9. Remove upper radiator hose, then the bypass hose and bracket.
10. Remove cylinder head attaching bolts, cylinder head and gasket.
11. Reverse procedure to install, noting the following:
    a. Ensure cylinder head and block mating surfaces are clean and free of gasket material.
    b. When installing head gasket, ensure serrated edges of gasket are positioned as shown, **Fig. 5**.
    c. Install cylinder head and attaching bolts, then tighten bolts to specifications in sequence shown, **Fig. 6**.

VALVE ARRANGEMENT
FRONT TO REAR

1.3L/4-81 .... I-E-I-E-E-I-E-I

VALVE CLEARANCE SPECIFICATIONS

This engine is equipped with hydraulic valve lash adjusters, no adjustment is required.

VALVE ADJUSTMENT

These engines are equipped with hydraulic valve lash adjusters, **Fig. 7, which are not adjustable.**

ROCKER ARMS

1. Remove rocker arm cover.
2. Alternately and evenly loosen rocker shaft attaching bolts, then carefully lift rocker shaft assemblies from cylinder head. **Do not remove hydraulic valve lash adjusters from rocker arms unless necessary.**
3. Remove rocker arms and springs from rocker shaft.
4. Measure outside diameter of rocker shaft and inside diameter of rocker arm shaft bore. The maximum difference between these two measurements should not exceed .004 inch. Check hydraulic valve lash adjuster for wear and damage and replace as necessary.
5. Pour engine oil into rocker reservoir, then apply engine oil to hydraulic valve lash adjuster and install in rocker arm, if removed. Use care not to damage O-ring when installing.
6. Assemble rocker arms and springs to rocker shaft, **Fig. 8**. Rocker arms and shafts can be identified as shown in **Fig. 9**.
7. Install assembled rocker shaft assemblies, with oil holes facing down, to cylinder head and **torque** attaching bolts alternately and evenly in sequence shown in **Fig. 8** to value listed at rear of this section. When tightening rocker shaft attaching bolts, pull back on rocker arm springs.

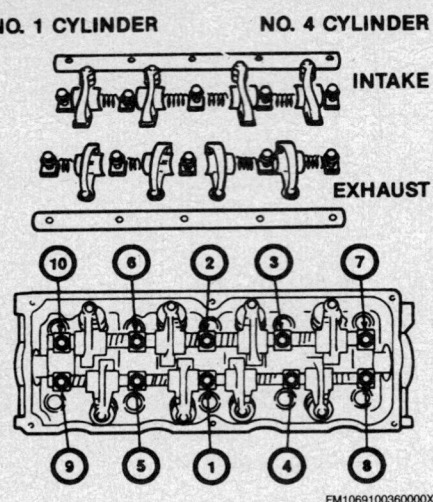

Fig. 8 Rocker arm assembly bolt tightening sequence

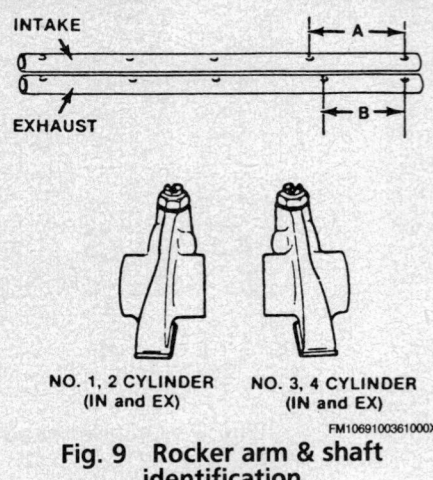

Fig. 9 Rocker arm & shaft identification

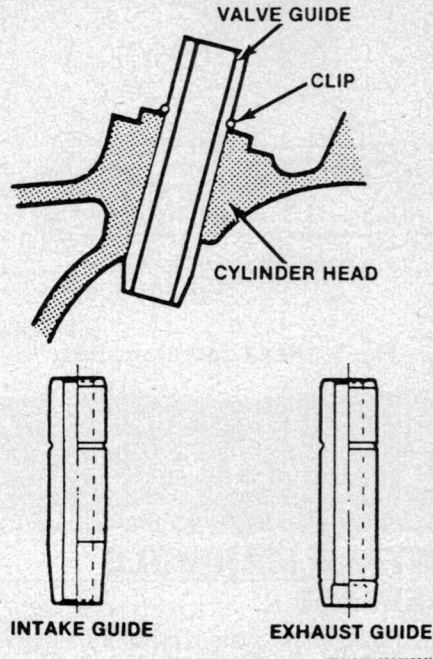

Fig. 10 Valve guide replacement

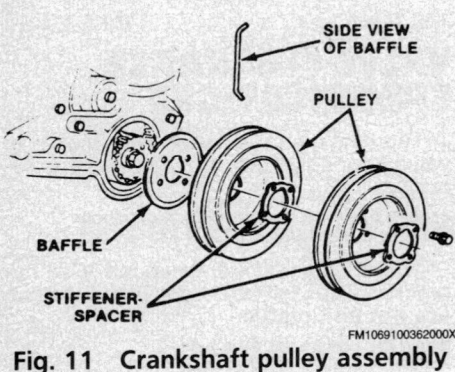

Fig. 11 Crankshaft pulley assembly

VALVE GUIDES

Valve guides can be replaced using valve guide remover tool No. T87C-6510-A. When removing valve guide, drive out toward camshaft side of cylinder head. When installing valve guide, drive in until clip just contacts cylinder head, **Fig. 10**.

HYDRAULIC LIFTERS
REPLACE

The hydraulic valve lash adjusters are located in the rocker arms, **Fig. 7**. Refer to "Rocker Arms" procedure.

FRONT COVER
REPLACE

1. Relieve fuel system pressure as outlined under "Precautions," then remove accessory drive belts.
2. Remove water pump pulley to pump hub attaching bolts, then the pulley.
3. Remove right inner fender panel to gain access to crankshaft pulley.
4. Remove outer crankshaft pulley attaching bolts, then the outer stiffener/spacer and outer pulley, **Fig. 11**.

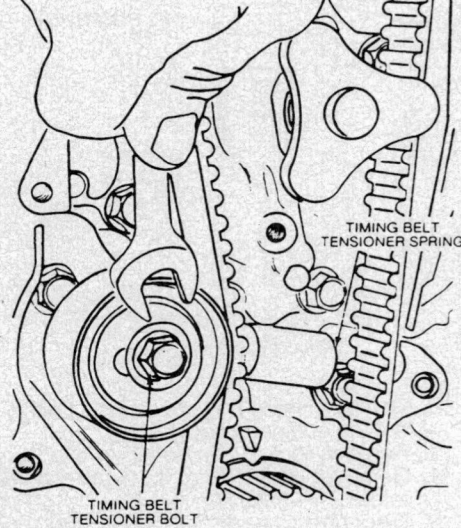

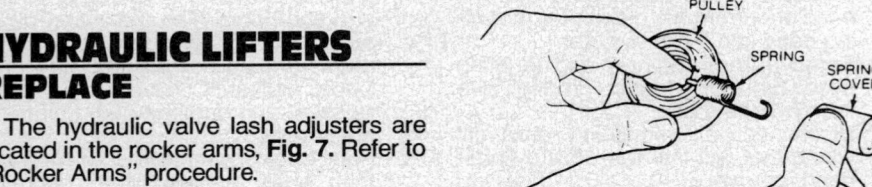

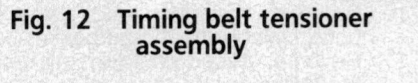

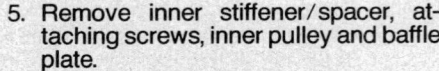

Fig. 12 Timing belt tensioner assembly

5. Remove inner stiffener/spacer, attaching screws, inner pulley and baffle plate.
6. Remove attaching bolts, then the upper and lower timing covers.
7. Reverse procedure to install. When installing crankshaft pulley, ensure curved lip on baffle plate and deep recess of inner pulley face outward.

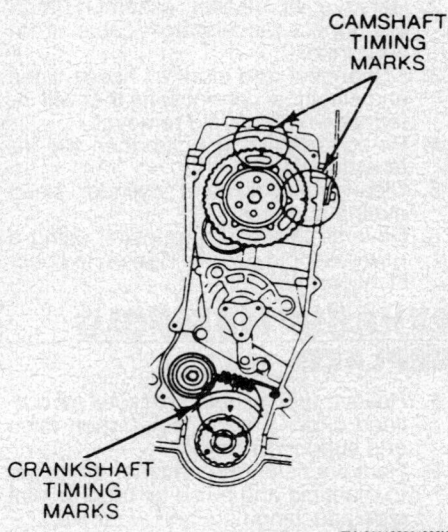

Fig. 13 Valve timing mark alignment

TIMING BELT
REPLACE

1. Remove timing belt covers as outlined previously under "Front Cover, Replace."
2. Remove timing belt tensioner pulley attaching bolt, then the tensioner pulley, spring and spring cover, **Fig. 12**.
3. If reusing old belt, mark direction of rotation on belt to aid installation.
4. Remove timing belt from crankshaft and camshaft sprockets.
5. Check crankshaft and camshaft sprockets, tensioner pulley and timing belt for wear or damage. Replace components as necessary.

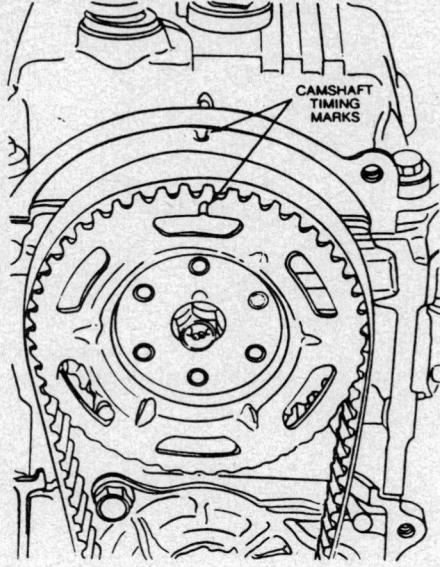

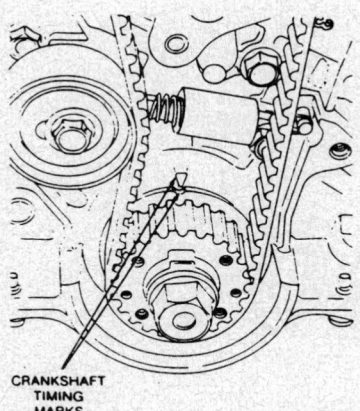

Fig. 14 Camshaft & crankshaft valve timing marks

6. Align camshaft and crankshaft sprocket timing marks with marks on cylinder head and oil pump housing, **Fig. 13.**
7. Install timing belt. If reusing old belt, ensure belt is installed so that direction of rotation mark made during removal is positioned correctly.
8. Install spring and spring cover onto tensioner pulley, **Fig. 12,** then install pulley and attaching bolt. Do not tighten bolt at this time.
9. Install tensioner spring onto anchor tightening pulley attaching bolt to specifications.
10. Reinstall timing belt covers.

CAMSHAFT TIMING

1. Align crankshaft pulley timing notch with TC mark on timing belt cover tab.
2. Remove timing belt upper cover.
3. Camshaft timing marks should be aligned, **Fig. 14.** If camshaft timing cannot be viewed, rotate crankshaft pulley one revolution, aligning notch with timing cover TC mark.
4. If camshaft timing marks are aligned,

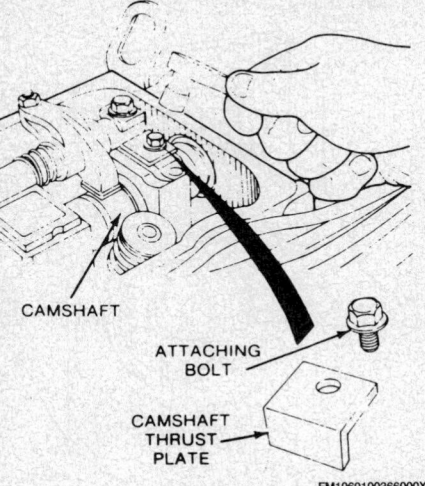

Fig. 15 Camshaft thrust plate

the camshaft is properly timed to the crankshaft. If camshaft timing marks are not properly aligned, refer to "Timing Belt, Replace" procedure.

CAMSHAFT
REPLACE

1. Remove rocker arm shaft assembly retaining bolts, then the rocker shaft assemblies.
2. Remove timing belt as outlined under "Timing Belt, Replace."
3. To prevent camshaft rotation, position suitable open end wrench on flats on front part of camshaft, then remove camshaft sprocket retaining bolt and camshaft sprocket.
4. Remove camshaft thrust plate attaching bolt, then the thrust plate, **Fig. 15.**
5. Carefully slide camshaft out of LH side of cylinder head.
6. Lubricate camshaft journals and lobes, then install camshaft and thrust plate.
7. Reverse procedure to install. Tighten to specifications.

CAMSHAFT FRONT OIL SEAL
REPLACE

1. Disconnect battery ground cable.
2. Remove engine cleaner assembly, then remove timing belt as outlined under "Timing Belt, Replace."
3. Remove rocker arm cover, then the camshaft sprocket.
4. Using a suitable tool, drive camshaft front seal into cylinder head, then cut seal with side cutters and remove seal. Use caution to prevent damaging bearing surface.
5. Lubricate front seal bore and seal lip with engine oil, then drive new seal into cylinder head using tool No. T87C-6019-A or equivalent, **Fig. 16.**

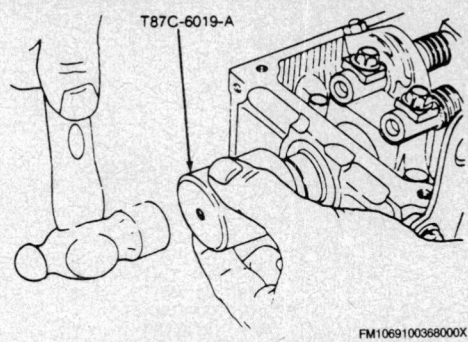

Fig. 16 Camshaft front oil seal installation

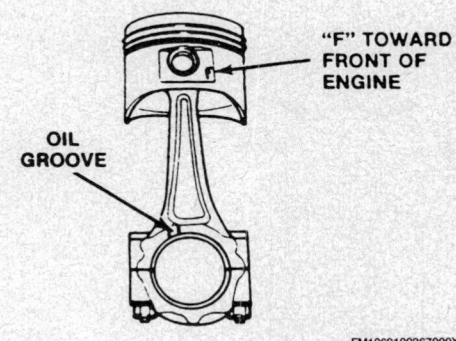

Fig. 17 Piston & rod assembly

6. Install camshaft sprocket and retaining bolt. Hold sprocket with large screwdriver, then tighten retaining bolt to specifications.
7. Reverse procedure to install. Tighten to specifications.

PISTON & ROD ASSEMBLY

Assemble piston to connecting rod so that "F" mark on piston pin bore and oil groove on connecting rod face toward front of engine, **Fig. 17.** After installing connecting rod, check side clearance with feeler gauge. Clearance should not exceed .012 inch.

CRANKSHAFT SEAL
REPLACE

1. Remove timing belt as outlined under "Timing Belt, Replace."
2. Position shift lever in 4th gear, then apply parking brake.
3. Remove crankshaft sprocket retaining bolt, then the sprocket and key.
4. Using suitable tool, pry old seal from oil pump assembly.
5. Clean seal bore, then lubricate and press in new seal using suitable tool, **Fig. 18.**
6. Reinstall key and sprocket onto crankshaft.
7. Coat sprocket retaining bolt threads with non-hardening type sealer, then install bolt.
8. Reinstall timing belt.

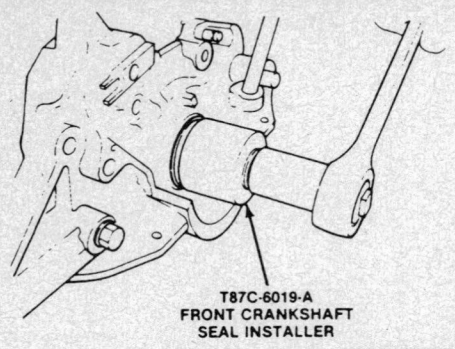

T87C-6019-A
FRONT CRANKSHAFT
SEAL INSTALLER

FM1069100369000X

Fig. 18 Crankshaft front seal installation

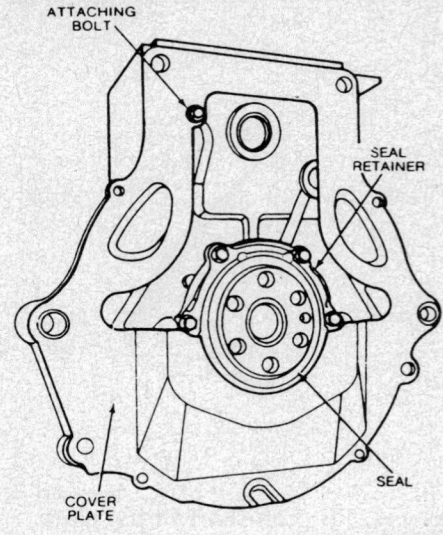

ATTACHING BOLT

SEAL RETAINER

SEAL

COVER PLATE

FM1069100370000X

Fig. 19 Rear cover assembly

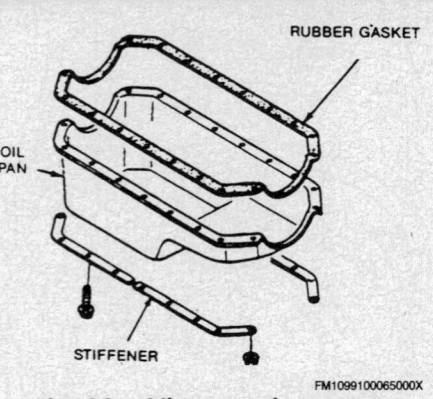

RUBBER GASKET

OIL PAN

STIFFENER

FM1099100065000X

Fig. 20 Oil pan replacement

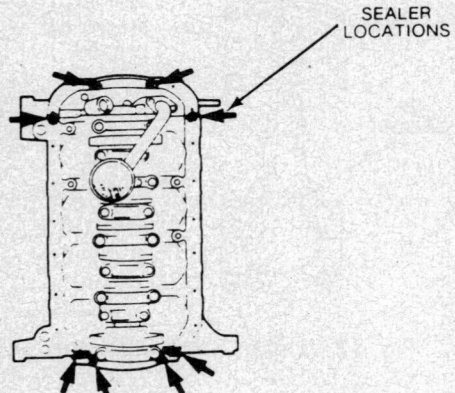

SEALER LOCATIONS

FM1099100066000X

Fig. 21 Cylinder block sealant application

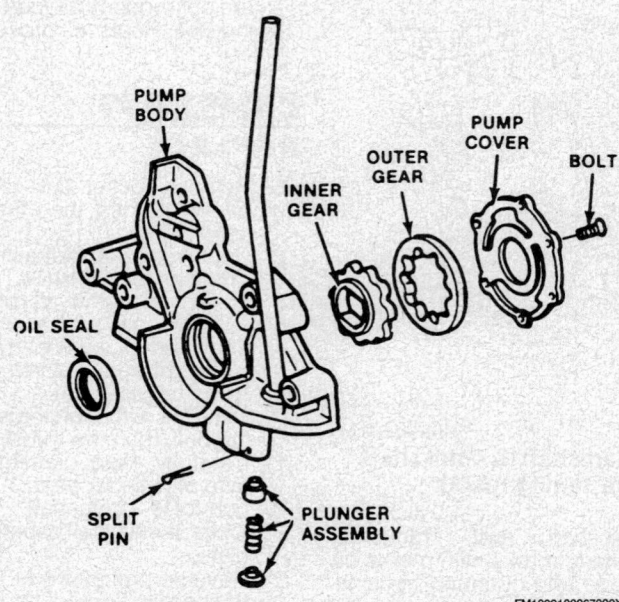

PUMP BODY

INNER GEAR

OUTER GEAR

PUMP COVER

BOLT

OIL SEAL

SPLIT PIN

PLUNGER ASSEMBLY

FM1099100067000X

Fig. 22 Exploded view of oil pump assembly

CRANKSHAFT REAR OIL SEAL
REPLACE

1. Remove transaxle as outlined in "Clutch & Manual Transaxle."
2. Remove flywheel attaching bolts and flywheel, then the engine rear cover plate, **Fig. 19.**
3. Remove seal retainer attaching bolts and seal retainer, then carefully pry out oil seal using suitable tool.
4. Reverse procedure to install, noting the following:
   a. Tighten to specifications.
   b. Lubricate, then install seal using suitable tool. **Ensure hollow side of seal faces toward engine.**
   c. Install seal retainer and tighten to specifications. Trim off excess gasket material after installation.
   d.

OIL PAN
REPLACE

1. Disconnect battery ground cable, raise and support vehicle, then drain crankcase.
2. Remove flywheel housing dust cover.
3. **On Aspire models, remove exhaust inlet pipe.**
4. **On all models, remove oil pan to cyl-**

inder block attaching bolts, nuts and stiffeners, **Fig. 20.**
5. Remove oil pan from vehicle. **If crankshaft interferes with pan removal, it may be necessary to rotate the crankshaft to provide clearance between pan and counterweights.**
6. Remove oil pan baffle.
7. Reverse procedure to install, noting the following:
   a. Before installing pan, ensure pan and cylinder block mating surfaces are free from oil and old gasket material.
   b. Apply suitable sealer across joint line of cylinder block and front and rear engine covers as shown in **Fig. 21.**

OIL PUMP
REPLACE
REMOVAL

1. Raise and support vehicle, then drain engine oil.
2. Remove crankshaft sprocket as outlined under "Crankshaft Front Seal, Replace."
3. Remove oil pan as outlined under "Oil Pan, Replace."
4. Remove oil pump to cylinder block attaching bolts, then the oil pump.

INSTALLATION

1. Ensure oil pump and cylinder block mating surfaces are clean and free from old gasket material.

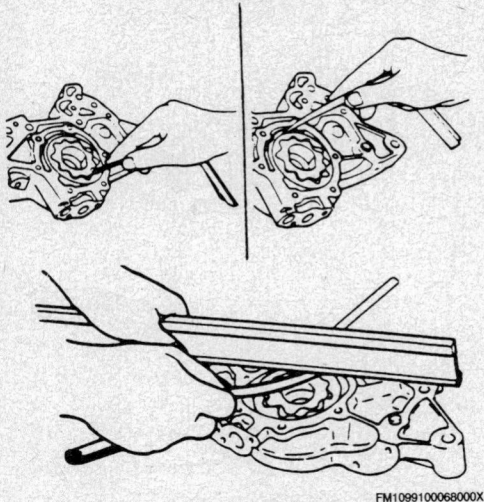

Fig. 23   Oil pump clearance inspection

2. Apply a thick film of sealer to both sides of oil pump gasket, then install gasket, oil pump and attaching bolts.
3. Install pickup tube and screen assembly using new gasket.
4. Install crankshaft sprocket and oil pan.

OIL PUMP SERVICE

DISASSEMBLE

1. Remove pickup tube and screen assembly.
2. Remove oil pump cover attaching bolts, then the cover and inner and outer gears, **Fig. 22.**
3. If necessary, pry oil seal from pump body.
4. Remove split pin, then the relief valve plunger assembly from pump body.

INSPECTION

1. Inspect pump body gear pocket and relief valve bore for excessive wear or scoring. Replace pump body, if necessary.
2. Inspect relief valve plunger assembly for scoring, burrs or excessive wear. Replace plunger assembly as necessary.
3. Reinstall inner and outer gears into pump body.
4. Measure clearance between inner gear tip and outer gear as shown in **Fig. 23.** Clearance should not exceed .0078 inch.
5. Measure outer gear to pump body clearance. Clearance should not exceed .0087 inch.
6. Using a suitable straightedge, measure gear endplay as shown in **Fig. 23.** endplay should not exceed .0055 inch.
7. If above clearances are beyond specified limits, replace gears or pump body as required.

ASSEMBLE

1. Place relief valve plunger assembly into pump body, then install split pin.

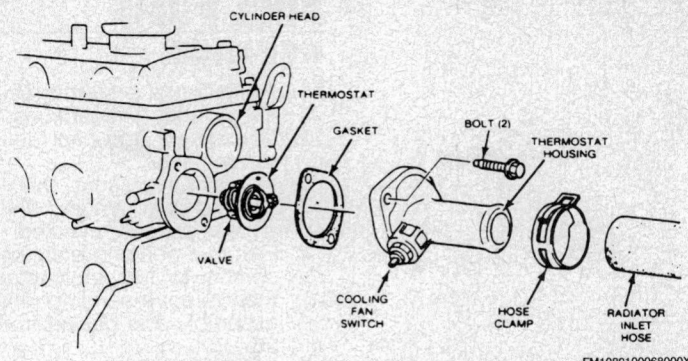

Fig. 24   Thermostat replacement

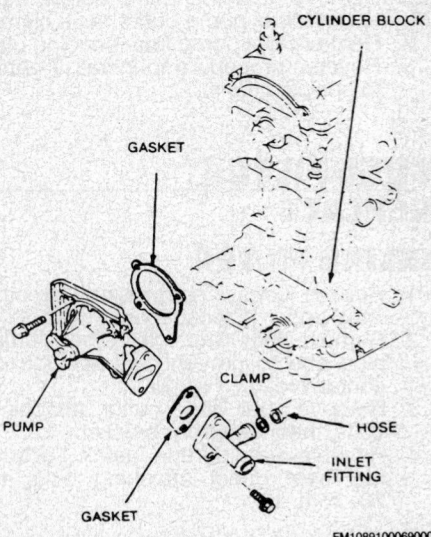

Fig. 25   Water pump replacement

2. If oil seal was removed, drive in new seal using seal installing tool No. T87C-6019-A or equivalent.
3. Lubricate, then install gears into pump body.
4. Install pump cover and attaching bolts. Coat bolt threads with Loctite or equivalent before installation.

BELT TENSION DATA

Belt	Tension, Inch Lbs.. New	Used
FESTIVA		
A/C Comp.	110–125	92–110
Alternator	110–132	95–110
ASPIRE		
A/C Comp.	110–132	95–110
Alternator	86–103	68–86

COOLING SYSTEM BLEED

This engine does not require a specified bleed procedure. After filling cooling system, run engine to operating temperature with radiator/pressure cap off. Air will then automatically be bled through cap opening.

THERMOSTAT
REPLACE

To avoid possibility of personal injury or damage to vehicle, ensure ignition switch is in Off position before disconnecting wire from cooling fan temperature switch. If wire is disconnected from temperature switch with ignition switch in On position, cooling fan will turn On.
1. Remove radiator pressure cap from radiator filler neck.
2. Drain coolant level below radiator upper hose.
3. Disconnect electrical connector from cooling fan switch on thermostat housing, **Fig. 24.**
4. Disconnect upper radiator hose at thermostat housing, then remove two thermostat housing retaining bolts from cylinder head.
5. Remove thermostat housing and gasket.
6. Remove thermostat.
7. Reverse procedure to install. Tighten to specifications.

WATER PUMP
REPLACE

1. Drain cooling system.
2. Remove timing belt as outlined previously.
3. Disconnect lower radiator and heater hoses from water pump inlet.
4. Remove water pump attaching bolts and the water pump, **Fig. 25.**
5. Ensure water pump and cylinder block mating surfaces are clean and free from old gasket material.
6. Coat both sides of water pump gasket with suitable sealer, then install gasket, water pump and attaching bolts. Tighten to specifications.
7. Connect lower radiator and heater hoses to pump inlet.
8. Install timing belt.

RADIATOR
REPLACE

1. Disconnect battery ground cable, then the cooling fan motor electrical connector.

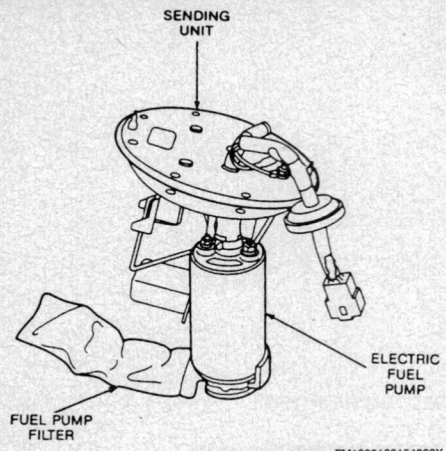

SENDING UNIT

ELECTRIC FUEL PUMP

FUEL PUMP FILTER

FM1029100154000X

Fig. 26 Fuel pump & sending unit assembly

FUEL PUMP
REPLACE

1. Relieve fuel system pressure as outlined under "Precautions."
2. Disconnect and cap fuel supply and return lines.
3. Remove rear seat, then fold carpet forward until sending unit/fuel pump access plate is revealed.
4. Remove sending unit/fuel pump assembly to fuel tank attaching bolts, then remove sending unit/fuel pump assembly and gasket from tank, **Fig. 26.**
5. Remove fuel filter from fuel pump, then disconnect fuel pump electrical leads from sending unit.
6. Remove retaining clamp screw, then remove fuel pump outlet hose clamp.
7. Remove fuel pump from sending unit.
8. Reverse procedure to install. Tighten to specifications.

FUEL FILTER
REPLACE

INLINE FILTER

1. Relieve fuel system pressure as outlined under "Precautions."
2. Remove fuel filter inlet tube clamp, plug end to prevent fuel spillage or contamination, **Fig. 27.**
3. Remove fuel filter outlet attaching bolts, then filter from bracket.
4. Reverse procedure to install. **Torque** fuel filter outlet attaching bolts to 18-25 ft. lbs.

2. Remove radiator cap, then drain engine coolant.
3. Disconnect all coolant hoses to radiator.
4. **On models with automatic transaxles,** disconnect oil cooler lines.
5. **On all models,** disconnect wiring harness from routing clamps on fan shroud.
6. Remove four radiator support upper bracket securing bolts.
7. Remove upper radiator support brackets, then the radiator and fan shroud as an assembly.
8. Reverse procedure to install.

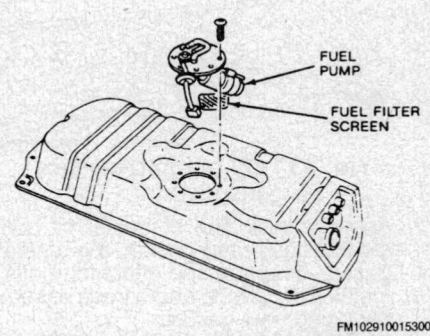

PRESSURE REGULATOR

FUEL RAIL

FUEL FILTER

TO CANISTER

INJECTOR

FUEL PUMP

FUEL FILTER SCREEN

FM1029100153000X

Fig. 27 Fuel filter locations

IN-TANK FILTER

1. Relieve fuel system pressure as outlined under "Precautions."
2. Remove fuel pump as outlined under "Fuel Pump, Replace."
3. Pull filter from fuel pickup tube end, **Fig. 27.**
4. Reverse procedure to install.

TIGHTENING SPECIFICATIONS

Torque specifications are for clean and lightly lubricated threads only. Dry or dirty threads produce increased friction which prevents accurate measurement of tightness.

Year	Component	Torque/Ft. Lbs.
1992-95	Camshaft Sprocket	36-45
	Connecting Rod Cap Bolts	①
	Cover Plate	69-95②
	Crankshaft Pulley Bolts	9-12.6
	Crankshaft Rear Seal Retainer	69-95②
	Crankshaft Sprocket	80-87
	Crossmember Bolts	47-66
	Cylinder Head Bolts	③
	Engine Mount (Front) To Crossmember Nuts	32-38
	Engine Mount (Rear) To Crossmember Nut	21-34
	Engine To Transaxle	41-59
	Exhaust Manifold To Cylinder Head	12-17
	Flywheel Cover	61-87②
	Flywheel To Crankshaft	71-76
	Gusset Plate	27-38
	Heat Shroud Bolts	12-17

Year	Component	Torque/Ft. Lbs.
1992-95 —Cont'd	Intake Manifold To Cylinder Head	14-20
	Main Bearing Cap Bolts	40-43
	Oil Pan To Engine	69-78②
	Oil Pump Attaching Bolts	14-19
	Oil Pump Inlet Tube	71-97②
	Rocker Arm Shaft	16-21
	Side Mount Nuts	28-40
	Spark Plug	15-22
	Tensioner Bolt	14-19
	Thermostat Housing Attaching Bolts	14-22
	Timing Belt Cover Attaching Bolts	69-95②
	Torque Converter To Flex Plate	26-36
	Water Pump Pulley Attaching Bolts	36-45
	Water Pump To Engine	14-19

①—Torque bolts to 11-13 ft. lbs., then to 22-25 ft. lbs.
②—Inch lbs.
③—Torque bolts in sequence to 35-40 ft. lbs., then to 56-60 ft. lbs.

Clutch & Manual Transaxle

NOTE: On Air Bag Equipped Models, Refer To "Air Bag System Precautions" Located In The Front Of This Manual For System Disarming & Arming Procedures.

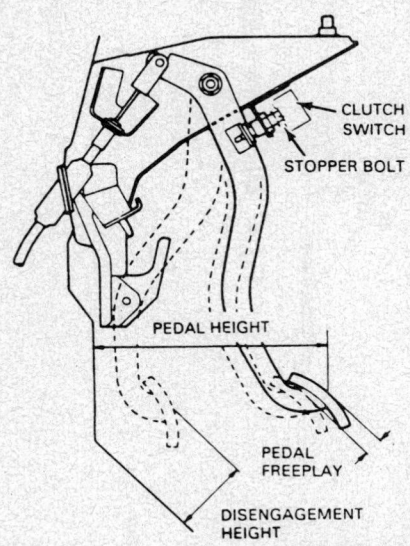

Fig. 1   Clutch pedal adjustments

FM5049100050000X

PRECAUTIONS

AIR BAG SYSTEMS

Refer to "Air Bag System Precautions" in the front of this manual for system disarming and arming procedures.

ADJUSTMENTS

CLUTCH PEDAL HEIGHT

1. Disconnect clutch cable at release lever so that cable will not interfere with measurement.
2. Move carpeting and insulation away from pedal area.
3. Measure distance from upper center of pedal to dash panel as shown in **Fig. 1**.
4. **On Festiva models,** measurement should be 8.2-8.4 inches.
5. **On Aspire models,** measurement should be 8.075 inches.
6. **On all models,** if distance is not as specified, proceed to next step.
7. Inspect clutch pedal mounting for damaged, worn or missing parts. Replace parts as necessary. If pedal mounting is satisfactory, proceed to next step.
8. Remove instrument panel bracket and air duct located underneath steering column.

9. Loosen clutch switch locknut, then turn switch in or out as required until pedal height is as specified previously. Tighten locknut.
10. Reconnect clutch cable to release lever, then adjust pedal freeplay as outlined below.
11. Recheck pedal height measurement. If height adjustment is not within specification, check clutch cable for binding or damage.
12. Reinstall air duct and instrument panel bracket.

PEDAL FREEPLAY

1. Move clutch pedal back and forth and measure freeplay, **Fig. 1**.
2. Pedal freeplay should be .350-.590 inch. If freeplay is not as specified, proceed to next step.
3. Pull back on release lever, then measure clearance between lever and cable pin, **Fig. 2**. Clearance should be .060-.100 inch.
4. If clearance is not as specified, thread adjuster in or out until specified clearance is obtained.
5. Recheck freeplay. If freeplay is still not within specified limits, inspect clutch release components for damage.

CLUTCH

REPLACE

1. Remove transaxle as described further on in this section.
2. If pressure plate will be reused, scribe alignment marks on pressure plate and flywheel to aid installation.
3. Prevent flywheel from turning using suitable tool, then loosen pressure plate attaching bolts one turn at a time until all spring tension is released.
4. Remove attaching bolts, pressure plate and clutch disc, **Fig. 3**.
5. If new clutch disc is being installed, sand friction surfaces of pressure plate and flywheel with medium grit emery cloth to break glaze on surface. After sanding is completed, remove grit with an alcohol soaked shop towel.
6. Install clutch disc with damper springs facing **away** from flywheel, then install pressure plate and attaching bolts.
7. Install suitable clutch alignment tool, then **torque** attaching bolts evenly to 17 ft. lbs. Remove tool.
8. Reinstall transaxle. Tighten to specifications.

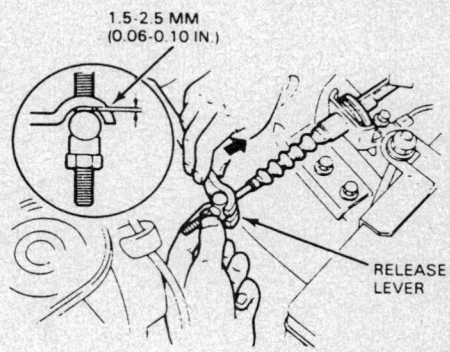

1.5-2.5 MM (0.06-0.10 IN.)

RELEASE LEVER

FM5049100051000X

Fig. 2   Clearance check between release lever & cable pin

TRANSAXLE

REPLACE

1. Disconnect battery ground cable, then raise and support vehicle.
2. Disconnect all electrical wiring and speedometer cable from transaxle.
3. Loosen clutch cable adjuster nut and disengage cable from release lever.
4. Remove starter motor, then the two bolts located at top of clutch housing, **Fig. 4**.
5. Support engine using suitable support fixture.
6. Remove shift rod to input shaft rail attaching nut and bolt.
7. Remove lower control arm to steering knuckle attaching nuts and bolts, then disengage halfshafts from transaxle. Install differential plugs T87C-7025-C or equivalent into transaxle to prevent movement of side gears.
8. Remove NVH bracket attaching bolts and bracket, then the crossmember.
9. Position suitable transmission jack under transaxle, then secure transaxle to jack with safety chain.
10. Remove remaining attaching bolts, then pull transaxle away from engine and lower out of vehicle.
11. Reverse procedure to install, noting the following:
    a. Tighten to specifications.
    b. When installing halfshafts, use new circlips.
    c. **Torque** clutch housing to engine attaching bolts to 57 ft. lbs.
12. After installation is completed, adjust clutch pedal freeplay.

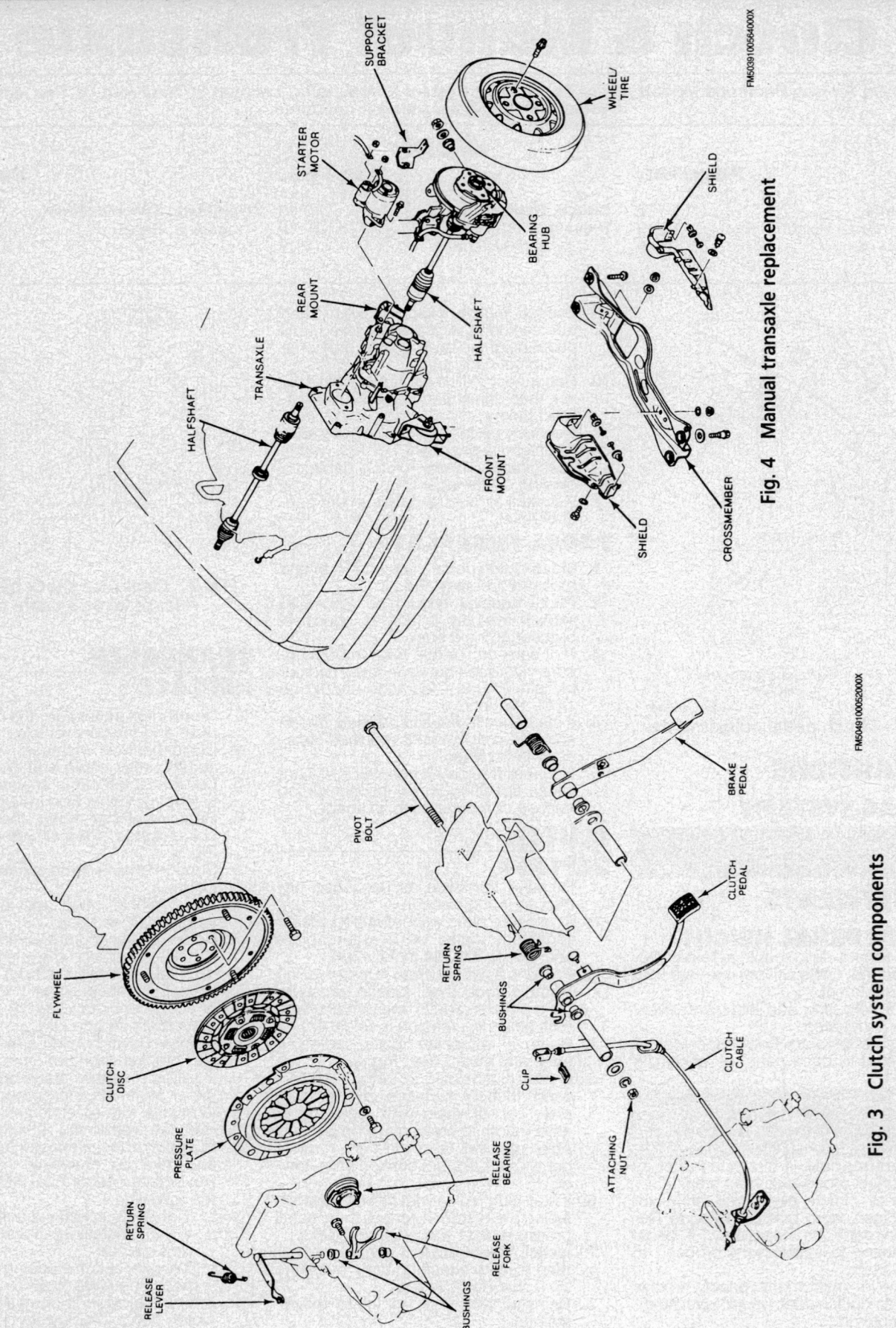

SUPPORT BRACKET

STARTER MOTOR

WHEEL/TIRE

BEARING HUB

REAR MOUNT

HALFSHAFT

SHIELD

TRANSAXLE

HALFSHAFT

SHIELD

FRONT MOUNT

CROSSMEMBER

SHIELD

FM50391005640000X

Fig. 4 Manual transaxle replacement

PIVOT BOLT

BRAKE PEDAL

RETURN SPRING

CLUTCH PEDAL

BUSHINGS

FLYWHEEL

CLIP

CLUTCH CABLE

CLUTCH DISC

ATTACHING NUT

PRESSURE PLATE

RELEASE BEARING

RETURN SPRING

RELEASE LEVER

RELEASE FORK

BUSHINGS

FM50491000520000X

Fig. 3 Clutch system components

TIGHTENING SPECIFICATIONS

Year	Component	Torque/Ft. Lbs.	Year	Component	Torque/Ft. Lbs.
1992-95	Back-Up Lamp Switch	15–22	1992-95 —Cont'd	Shift Gate Frame	6–8
	Baffle Plate	6–8		Shift Lever Housing	5–7
	Clutch Pedal Pivot Bolt	14–25		Shift Rod to Shift Lever	12–17
	Flywheel	71–76		Stabilizer Rod	23–34
	Pressure Plate	13–20		Transaxle Case	14–19
	Release Fork	26–30		Shift Rod To Transaxle	23–34
	Detent Plug	11–15		Transaxle To Engine	47–66
	Oil Guide	6–8		Transaxle Mount	14–19
	Release Bearing fork	26–30		Transaxle Stud Nut	23–34
	Reverse Detent Plate	6–8		Wheel Lug Nuts	65–87

Rear Axle & Suspension

INDEX

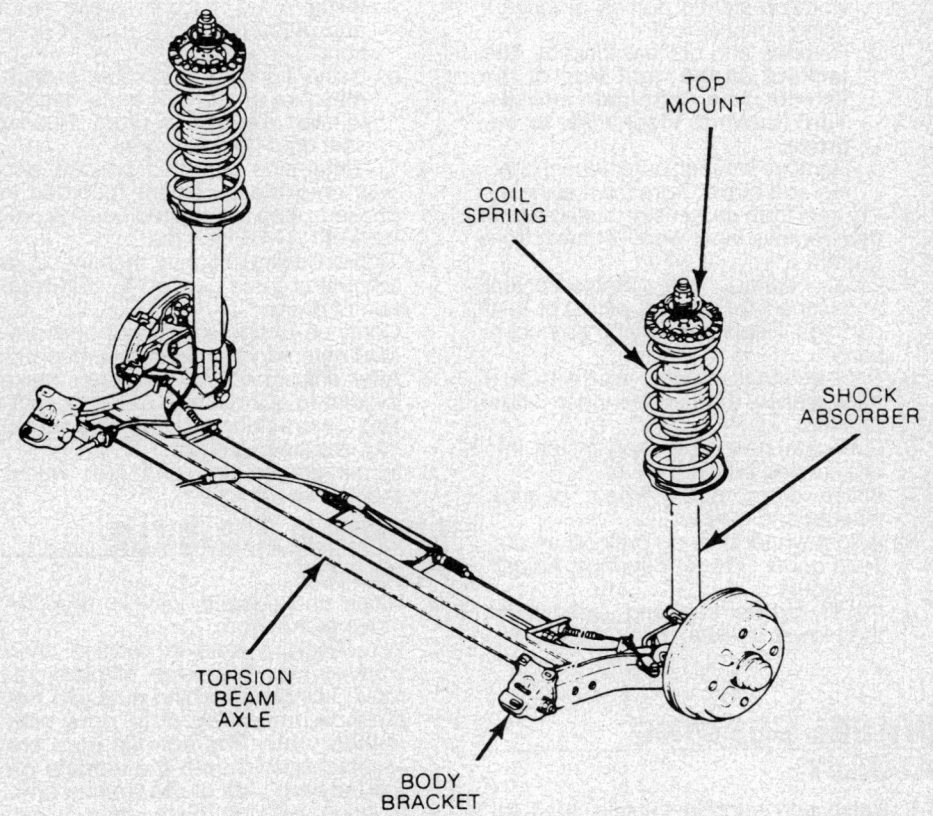

TOP MOUNT

COIL SPRING

SHOCK ABSORBER

TORSION BEAM AXLE

BODY BRACKET

FM2039100040000X

Fig. 1   Rear axle & suspension

DESCRIPTION

The rear suspension, **Fig. 1,** is of the McPherson strut design, with the strut at each wheel seated in a tower in the cargo compartment. Suspension action is carried out through the use of semi-independent trailing arms, which are integral with the torsion beam type rear axle.

The torsion beam axle provides positive control of trailing arm alignment, while doubling as a stabilizer to limit sway during hard cornering. Bushings and rubber insulators, installed at key attachment points, keep vibration and road noise to a minimum.

The brake drum and bearing hub is an integral assembly which rides on a spindle attached to the trailing arms. The assembly is supported by opposed tapered roller bearings located within the bearing hub.

REAR AXLE
REPLACE

1. Raise and support rear of vehicle so that struts are fully extended, then remove rear wheels.
2. Remove struts as outlined further on in this section.
3. Disconnect all brake lines that will interfere with axle removal.
4. Disconnect parking brake cable at backing plates, then remove equalizer and cables from axle.
5. If necessary, remove backing plates and spindles from trailing arms.
6. Remove axle assembly to body bracket pivot bolts, then lower axle assembly out of vehicle.

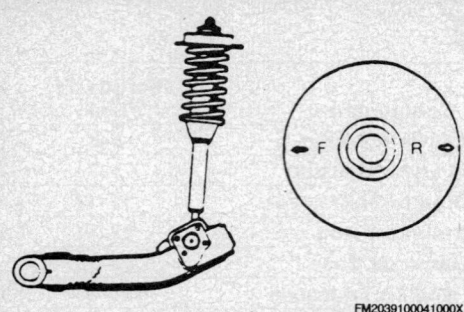

Fig. 2   Bushing on trailing arm position

7. If axle bushings require replacement, proceed as follows:
   a. Using bushing remover tool No. D80L-1002-L or equivalent, press bushings out of trailing arm from inboard side.
   b. Lubricate new bushings with soapy water, then position on outboard edges of trailing arm. Ensure marks on bushing face are aligned parallel with trailing arm axis, **Fig. 2.** Press bushings into trailing arms using tool mentioned in previous step. **To distinguish between right and left bushings, note the "F" and "R" marks molded into the bushing. When properly installed, the letters should be right side up with the "F" facing toward front of vehicle.**
8. Raise axle assembly, then align pivot bolt holes and install pivot bolts. Do not tighten bolts at this time.
9. If removed, install backing plates and spindles.
10. Install parking brake equalizer assembly on axle, then connect parking brake cables to parking brake levers at backing plates.
11. Connect brake lines at routing brackets and clip in place.
12. Install struts and rear wheels, then lower vehicle to allow suspension to reach normal ride height.
13. With vehicle on level surface, tighten pivot bolts.
14. After installation is completed, check rear suspension alignment as follows:
   a. Mark center of underbody at a position equidistant between left and right body bracket inboard mounting bolts.
   b. Measure distance from center mark obtained in previous step to centers of right and left strut lower mounting bolts.
   c. If measurement obtained on right and left sides are not within .200 inch, shift body brackets side to side to center suspension.
   d. After adjustment is completed, tighten upper body bracket bolts.

HUB & BEARING
REPLACE

1. Raise and support vehicle, then remove rear wheel.

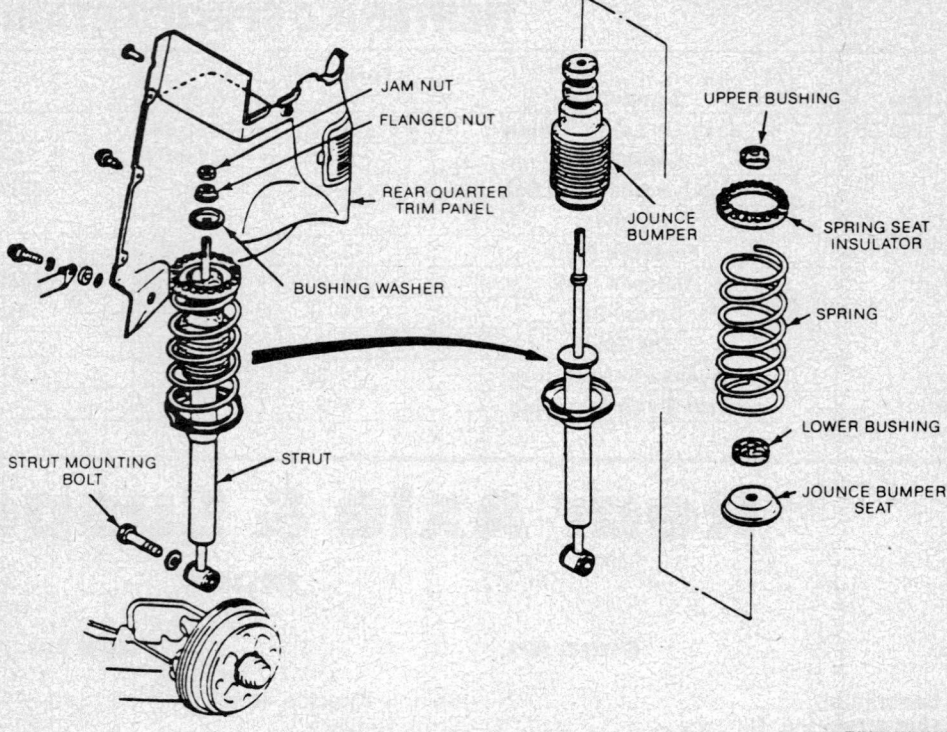

Fig. 3   Exploded view of strut assembly

2. Remove brake drum as follows:
   a. Remove grease cap, then pry upward on staked portion of locknut using suitable tool.
   b. Remove and discard locknut. **The locknut on the right side of the vehicle has lefthand threads. Turn locknut clockwise to remove.**
   c. Remove washer, outer wheel bearing and brake drum from spindle.
3. Pry seal from drum using suitable tool, then remove inner wheel bearing from drum.
4. Clean bearings with suitable solvent and inspect for scoring, pitting or heat damage. Replace bearings as necessary.
5. Pack bearings and hub area with suitable grease, then install inner wheel bearing.
6. Lubricate new seal, then install into drum using suitable driver.
7. Install drum, outer wheel bearing, washer and locknut.
8. Adjust wheel bearing preload as outlined under "Wheel Bearings, Adjust" procedure.
9. Install grease cap and rear wheel, then lower vehicle.

WHEEL BEARING
ADJUST

1. Raise and support vehicle, then remove rear wheel and grease cap.
2. While rotating brake drum, **torque** locknut to 18-22 ft. lbs.
3. Loosen locknut until it can be turned by hand, then measure seal drag as follows:
   a. Install a lug nut onto brake drum and place nut at 12 o'clock position.
   b. Using an inch lb. torque wrench, measure amount of force needed to start rotation of drum. Record seal drag measurement.
4. To determine specified preload, add seal drag measurement recorded in previous step to required bearing preload of 1.3-4.3 inch lbs.
5. Tighten locknut slightly, then measure amount of force needed to start rotation of drum.
6. Continue to tighten locknut until preload determined in step 4 is reached.
7. After adjustment is completed, stake locknut to spindle with a drift. **If splitting or cracking occurs after staking, replace locknut.**
8. Install grease cap and rear wheel, then lower vehicle.

SPINDLE KNUCKLE
REPLACE

1. Raise and support vehicle, then remove brake drum.
2. Wire backing plate in position, then working from rear side of plate, remove spindle attaching nuts. **Do not confuse mounting stud nuts with spindle nuts. The spindle nuts are located underneath the vehicle on the inboard side of the trailing arm.**
3. Position backing plate, then install spindle. Tighten spindle attaching nuts.
4. Reinstall brake drum, then lower vehicle.

STRUT
REPLACE
REMOVAL

1. Raise and support vehicle, then remove rear wheel.
2. Compress spring using suitable tool.
3. Working from cargo compartment, remove rear quarter trim panel.
4. Remove jam and flanged nuts from strut rod, then the bushing washer and upper bushing, **Fig. 3**.
5. Remove lower mounting bolt, then pull strut downward and separate it from spring and seat insulator.
6. Remove lower bushing and jounce bumper seat from strut rod, then slide jounce bumper and shield off strut.
7. Inspect all bushings, bumpers and insulators for damage or deterioration. Replace components as necessary.

INSTALLATION

1. Slide jounce bumper, shield, bumper seat and lower bushing onto strut rod.
2. If upper spring seat insulator requires replacement, install insulator onto upper end of spring so that end of coil seats firmly against step in insulator.
3. Position spring on strut, ensuring end of coil seats firmly against step in strut spring seat.
4. Compress spring, then working from wheelwell area, guide upper end of strut rod into tower mounting hole.
5. Line up lower end of strut with mounting hole in trailing arm, then install lower mounting bolt several turns to hold strut in position.
6. Install upper bushing, bushing washer and flanged nut onto upper end of strut rod. Tighten flanged nut, then lock in position with jam nut.
7. Tighten lower mounting bolt, then remove spring compressor.
8. Install wheel, then lower vehicle.

TIGHTENING SPECIFICATIONS

Year	Component	Torque/Ft. Lbs.	Year	Component	Torque/Ft. Lbs.
1992-95	Body Bracket Lower Mounting Bolt	69-86	1992-95 —Cont'd	Strut Rod Upper Nut	12-18
	Body Bracket Upper Mounting Bolt	40-50		Torsion Beam Pivot Bolt	69-86
	Brake Backing Plate	32-45		Wheel Spindle Support Nut	32-45
	Strut Lower Attaching Bolt	50-60		Wheel Lug Nuts	65-87

Front Suspension & Steering

INDEX

DESCRIPTION

The front suspension, **Fig. 1**, is of the strut design, utilizing single pivot lower control arms with integral ball joints. The front wheels ride on forged steering knuckles, which are clamped to the ball joints on the lower end, and bolted to the lower bracket of the strut assembly on the upper end. A front stabilizer bar, connected to the lower control arms, is used to limit body sway during hard cornering and doubles as a trailing arm to maintain lower control arm alignment.

HUB & BEARING
REPLACE

Refer to "Steering Knuckle, Replace," for hub and bearing replacement procedure.

STRUT
REPLACE

REMOVAL

1. Raise and support vehicle, ensuring strut is fully extended, then remove front wheel.
2. Remove brake line clip, then disengage brake line from strut assembly.
3. Remove strut to steering knuckle attaching bolts and nuts.
4. Working from engine compartment, remove nuts securing strut mounting block to shock tower.
5. Pull lower end of strut outward to disengage strut from steering knuckle, then lower strut assembly and remove from vehicle.

INSTALLATION

1. Position strut, together with spacer plate, into shock tower, ensuring white alignment mark faces outward.
2. Install mounting block attaching nuts.
3. Connect steering knuckle to lower strut bracket, then install attaching bolts and nuts. Tighten to specifications.
4. Position brake line in cutout in strut lower bracket, then install retaining clip.
5. Install front wheel, then lower vehicle.

STRUT SERVICE

DISASSEMBLE

1. Remove strut as outlined previously.
2. Compress spring using suitable spring compressor.
3. Pry out mounting block cap, then re-

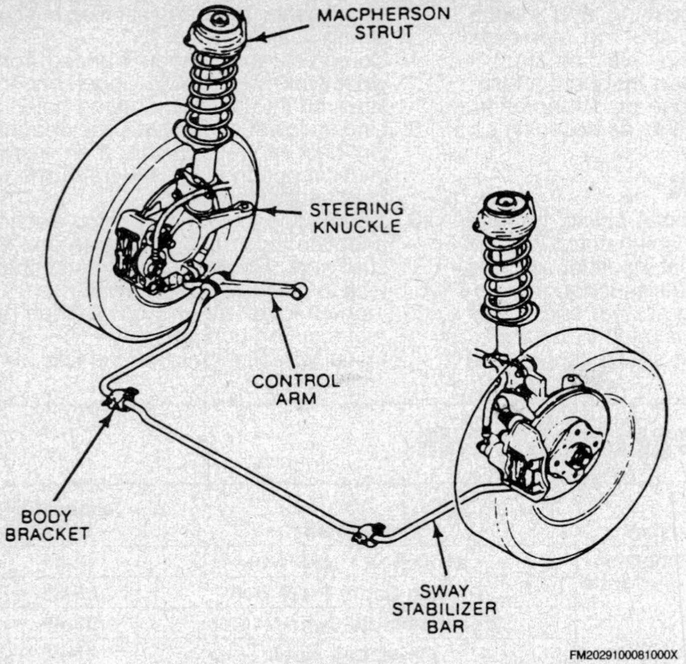

Fig. 1 Front suspension

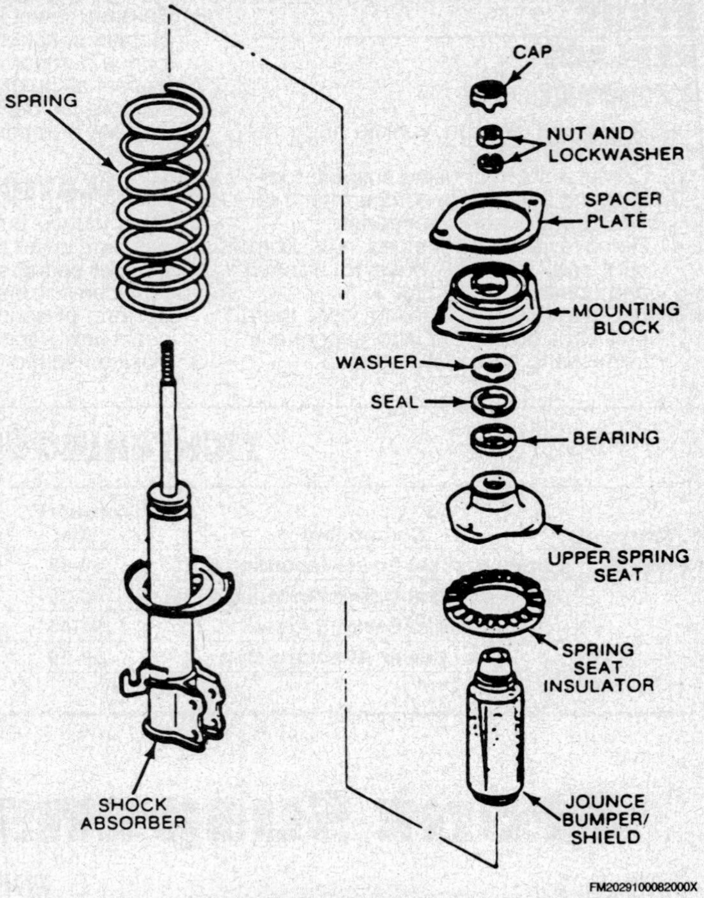

move upper attaching nut and lockwasher, **Fig. 2.**

4. Remove spacer plate, mounting block, washer, seal and bearing from strut rod.
5. Remove upper spring seat, seat insulator and spring, then the jounce bumper and shield.
6. Inspect all components for excessive wear or damage. Replace components as necessary.

ASSEMBLE

1. Slide jounce bumper and shield over strut rod and onto main body of strut assembly.
2. Compress spring using suitable spring compressor, then install spring, seat insulator and upper seat. Ensure spring ends are positioned against steps in seats.
3. Install bearing, seal and washer on strut rod.
4. Install mounting block, ensuring that white alignment mark is positioned on same side of strut as steering knuckle mounting bracket.
5. Install spacer plate, lock washer and attaching nut.
6. Remove spring compressor, then install mounting block cap.
7. Reinstall strut assembly into vehicle.

CONTROL ARM
REPLACE
REMOVAL

1. Raise and support vehicle, then remove pivot bolt at frame bracket.
2. Remove ball joint clamp bolt and nut at steering knuckle.
3. Remove stabilizer bar bushing retaining nut from rear of control arm, then

Fig. 2 Exploded view of front strut assembly

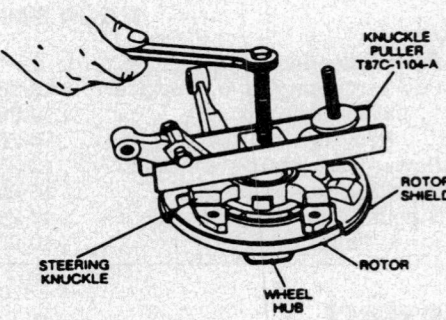

Fig. 3 Hub & rotor/steering knuckle separation

remove bushing washer and bushing.

4. Pry ball joint stud out of steering knuckle, then disengage control arm from stabilizer bar and remove from vehicle.

INSPECTION

1. Check control arm for cracks and pivot bushing for deterioration. If bushing requires replacement, remove and install bushing using suitable tools.
2. Check ball joint stud rotating torque with suitable torque wrench. Rotating torque should be 16-27 inch lbs. If rotating torque is not as specified, replace control arm.

INSTALLATION

1. Install stabilizer bar into control arm. If removed, ensure front bushing washer is positioned with dished side facing front of vehicle.
2. Raise inner part of control arm and install pivot bolt. Do not tighten bolt at this time.
3. Connect ball joint stud to steering knuckle, then install clamp bolt and nut.
4. Install rear stabilizer bar bushing and washer. Ensure rear washer is positioned with dished side facing rear of vehicle, then install attaching nut.
5. Tighten pivot bolt and ball joint clamp bolt attaching nuts to specifications.

STEERING KNUCKLE
REPLACE

1. Raise and support vehicle, then remove front wheel.
2. Unstake halfshaft attaching nut using suitable chisel, apply brakes to prevent hub assembly from turning, then remove and discard attaching nut.
3. Remove brake hose to strut bracket retaining clip.
4. Remove cotter pin and tie rod attaching nut, then separate tie rod from

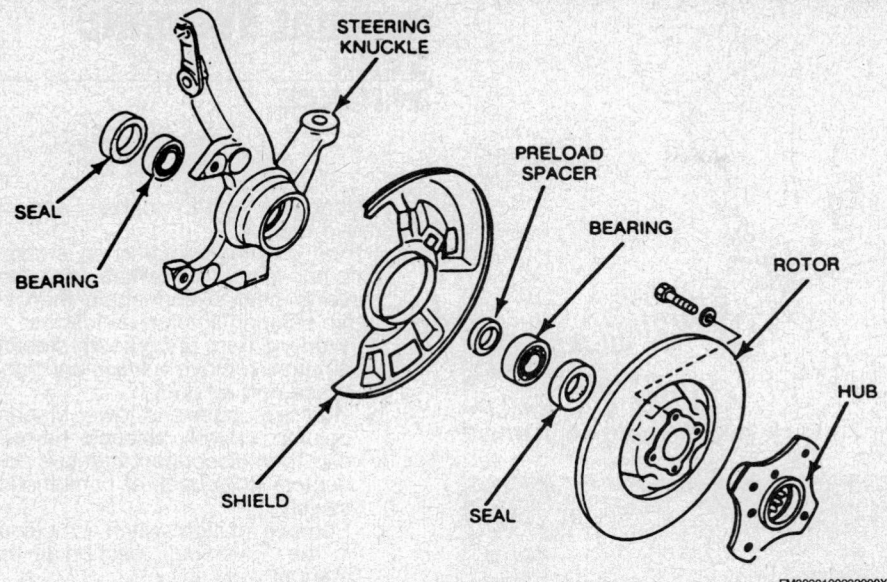

Fig. 4 Exploded view of steering knuckle & hub/rotor assembly

FM3039100232000X

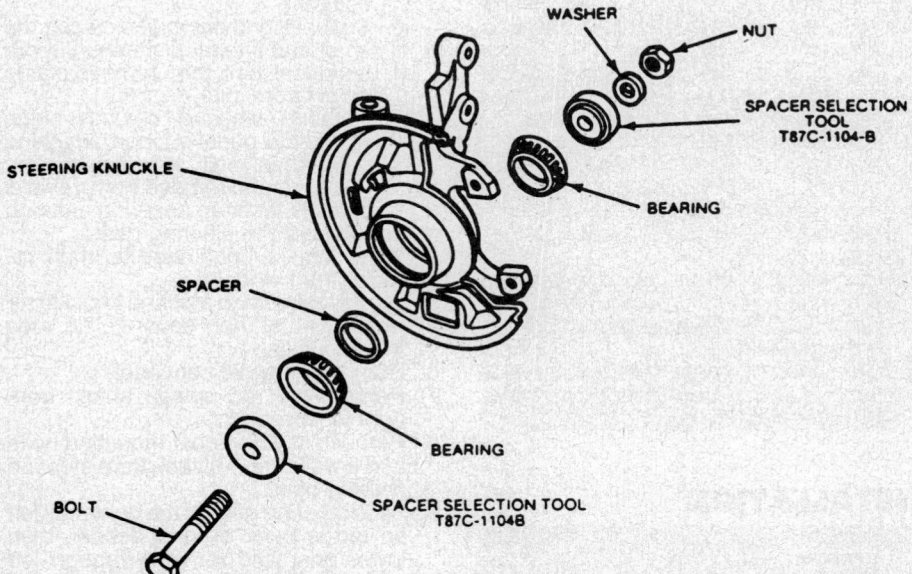

Fig. 5 Bearing preload spacer selection tool installation

FM3039100233000X

Stamped mark	Thickness
1	6.285 mm (0.2474 in)
2	6.325 mm (0.2490 in)
3	6.365 mm (0.2506 in)
4	6.405 mm (0.2522 in)
5	6.445 mm (0.2538 in)
6	6.485 mm (0.2554 in)
7	6.525 mm (0.2570 in)
8	6.565 mm (0.2586 in)
9	6.605 mm (0.2602 in)
10	6.645 mm (0.2618 in)
11	6.685 mm (0.2634 in)
12	6.725 mm (0.2650 in)
13	6.765 mm (0.2666 in)
14	6.805 mm (0.2682 in)
15	6.845 mm (0.2698 in)
16	6.885 mm (0.2714 in)
17	6.925 mm (0.2730 in)
18	6.965 mm (0.2746 in)
19	7.005 mm (0.2762 in)
20	7.045 mm (0.2778 in)
21	7.085 mm (0.2794 in)

FM3039100234000X

Fig. 6 Bearing preload spacer identification chart

13. Inspect bearings, hub, steering knuckle and dust shield for damage or excessive wear. Replace components as necessary.
14. If original bearings and steering knuckle are being used, proceed to step 15. If bearings or steering knuckle require replacement, proceed as follows to select proper bearing preload spacer:
   a. Drive new inner and outer bearing races into steering knuckle using suitable tools.
   b. Lubricate races and new bearings with engine oil, then install bearings into steering knuckle.
   c. Install spacer selection tool kit T87C-1104-B, original spacer and hardware shown in **Fig. 5** onto steering knuckle, then clamp steering knuckle in soft jaw vise.
   d. Tighten center bolt in increments. After bolt is tightened to specification, remove assembly from vise and rotate steering knuckle to seat bearings.
   e. Again clamp steering knuckle in vise, then measure the amount of torque necessary to start rotation of center bolt using an inch lb. torque wrench.
   f. If torque reading is 2.2-10.4 inch lbs., spacer is correct thickness. If torque reading is less than 2.2 inch lbs., a thinner spacer must be used. If torque reading is greater than 10.4 inch lbs., a thicker spacer must be used. Twenty one spacers of various thicknesses are available for service. Each spacer has a number stamped on it for identification purposes, **Fig. 6**. Changing

steering knuckle using suitable tool.
5. Remove brake caliper attaching bolts, then lift caliper assembly off steering knuckle. **Do not allow caliper to hang unsupported from brake hose. Wire caliper in place as required.**
6. Remove ball joint to steering knuckle clamp bolt and nut, then pry downward on control arm and disconnect joint from knuckle.
7. Remove steering knuckle to strut bracket attaching bolts and nuts, then slide hub/rotor assembly together with steering knuckle off end of halfshaft. If difficulty is encountered separating hub from halfshaft, tap end of shaft with plastic mallet to facilitate removal.

8. Separate hub/rotor assembly from steering knuckle using tool shown in **Fig. 3.**
9. Remove bearing preload spacer from hub, **Fig. 4. The spacer is pre-selected to yield correct bearing preload. Save spacer to use during assembling.**
10. Clamp hub/rotor assembly in soft jaw vise, scribe alignment marks on hub and rotor, then remove hub to rotor attaching bolts and separate rotor from hub.
11. Using suitable bearing remover, press hub shaft from outer bearing, then remove outer grease seal from hub.
12. Using suitable seal remover, pry inner grease seal from steering knuckle bore, then remove inner bearing.

the spacer by one number, either up or down, will result in a 1.7-3.5 inch lb. change in bearing preload.

15. Pack bearings and hub with suitable high temperature grease, then install inner bearing into steering knuckle.
16. Lubricate seal lip, then install new inner seal using suitable tool.
17. Place original bearing preload spacer, or spacer selected in step 14, into steering knuckle.
18. Lubricate seal lip, then install outer wheel bearing and new outer seal into knuckle.
19. Position rotor onto hub, aligning marks made during disassembling, then install attaching bolts.
20. Place hub/rotor assembly into steering knuckle bore, then press assembly fully into knuckle using suitable tools.
21. Follow steps 1 through 7 in reverse order to complete installation and note the following:
    a. Apply a thin coat of grease to half-shaft splines before installing steering knuckle and hub/rotor assembly.
    b. When installing new halfshaft attaching nut, apply brakes to prevent hub assembly from turning. Stake nut into groove on halfshaft after tightening.
    c. Tighten tie rod end to steering knuckle attaching nut, then install new cotter pin. **If holes in attaching nut do not line up with hole in ball stud, tighten nut as required until cotter pin can be installed. Never loosen nut when installing cotter pin.**

STABILIZER BAR
REPLACE

1. Raise and support vehicle.
2. Remove stabilizer bar mounting bracket attaching nuts, then the brackets and split bushings.
3. Remove stabilizer bar to control arm attaching nuts, then the rear washers and bushings.
4. Pull stabilizer bar forward and remove from vehicle. If necessary, remove front bushings and washers from bar.
5. Reverse procedure to install, noting the following:
    a. When installing bushing washers, ensure front washer is installed with dished side facing front of vehicle and rear washer is positioned with dished side facing rear of vehicle.
    b. When installing split bushings, ensure split side faces forward and that bushings are positioned next to white locating marks on bar.

POWER STEERING GEAR
REPLACE
REMOVAL

1. Disconnect battery ground cable.

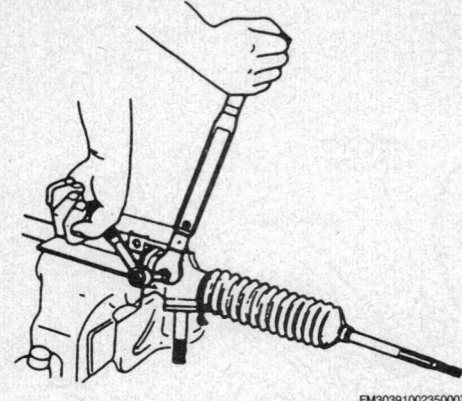

Fig. 7 Rack yoke preload adjustment

FM3039100235000X

2. Remove steering column tube boot retainer and pry up boot.
3. Remove steering column gear input shaft coupling bolt, then raise and support vehicle.
4. Remove power steering hose bracket and disconnect power steering return hose.
5. Remove front wheel and tire assemblies, then tie rod cotter pins and end nuts.
6. Separate tie rod ends from steering knuckles using appropriate tool, then remove the tie rod splash shields.
7. Remove front catalytic converter front inlet exhaust pipe and lower for easier access.
8. Place alignment marks on tie rod end, jam nut, and tie rod to ease installation.
9. Loosen jam nut and remove right tie rod end.
10. Remove four steering gear mounting bolts and washers.
11. Slide steering gear to the left and pull right tie rod through fender opening, then the steering gear.

INSTALLATION

1. Position steering gear in its mounting location.
2. Attach intermediate shaft to steering gear pinion and **torque** bolt to 13-20 ft. lbs.
3. Guide intermediate shaft into steering column hole, then lower vehicle.
4. With assistance in lifting the steering gear, align intermediate shaft with universal joint and install mounting bolt.
5. Raise and support vehicle, then install the four steering gear washer and bolts. **Torque** mounting bolts to 23-34 ft. lbs.
6. Install right tie rod end and attach tie rod ends to steering knuckles. **Torque** tie rod end nuts to 23-34 ft. lbs.
7. Install catalytic converter, tie rod splash shields and front wheel and tire assemblies.
8. Lower vehicle and attach power steering lines.
9. Add power steering fluid and bleed system following procedure outlined under "Power Steering System Bleed."

MANUAL STEERING GEAR
REPLACE

1. Disconnect battery cables and remove battery.
2. Scribe alignment marks on steering column lower universal joint and steering gear pinion shaft, then remove steering column as follows:
    a. Working from underneath steering column, remove instrument panel brace and air duct.
    b. Remove upper and lower steering column covers, release harness clip, then disconnect harness connectors from back of combination switch.
    c. Remove ignition switch as outlined in the "Electrical," section of this manual.
    d. Remove steering column upper mounting bracket to instrument panel attaching nuts, then lower column.
    e. Scribe alignment marks on column shaft and intermediate shaft upper universal joint, then remove clamp screw from joint.
    f. Remove steering column hinge bracket to pedal support attaching nuts, then pull steering column rearward and remove from vehicle.
3. Cut plastic tie strap securing steering column boot to steering gear.
4. Raise and support vehicle, then remove front wheels.
5. Remove tie rod to steering knuckle attaching nuts, then separate tie rods from knuckle.
6. Remove catalytic converter.
7. Remove tie rod splash shield from right inner fender.
8. Remove steering gear mounting bolts and lower gear until free from steering column boot.
9. Slide steering gear to the right until left tie rod is clear of inner fender, then lower gear and remove through left side of vehicle. **When sliding gear as required, guide gear carefully to prevent damage to boots.**
10. Reverse procedure to install, aligning all marks made during removal. Adjust rack yoke preload, as follows:
    a. Remove steering gear as previously described.
    b. With rack centered, measure pinion rotating torque. Pinion torque should be 8-12 inch lbs. within 90 degrees of centered position, and should not exceed 13 inch lbs. when turned beyond 90° of center.
    c. If pinion rotating torque is not as specified in previous step, loosen yoke adjusting bolt locknut and turn adjusting bolt as required until specified rotational torque is reached, **Fig. 7.**
    d. After adjustment is completed, hold adjusting bolt in position and tighten locknut.

POWER STEERING SYSTEM BLEED

1. Add specified power steering fluid to "L" mark on power steering reservoir dip stick.
2. Start engine and run until reaching normal operating temperature.
3. Turn steering wheel from lock to lock 10 times, then turn off engine with wheels in straight ahead position.
4. Check fluid level and add if necessary to between the "L" and "H" mark on power steering reservoir dip stick.

TIGHTENING SPECIFICATIONS

Year	Component	Torque/Ft. Lbs.
1992-95	Ball Joint Pinch Bolt	32-40
	Control Arm Bushing Retaining Nuts	47-57
	Control Arm Frame Bracket Pivot Bolt	32-40
	Disc Brake Caliper Attaching Bolts	29-36
	Halfshaft Nut	116-174
	Rotor Attaching Bolts	33-40
	Stabilizer Mounting Bracket Nuts	40-50
	Stabilizer Rear Bushing Nut	43-52
	Steering Gear Mounting Bolts	23-34
	Steering Knuckle Bolts	69-86
	Steering Rack Support Cover	29-43
	Strut Rod Nut	40-50
	Tie Rod Ball Joints	43-58
	Tie Rod End Nut	22-33
	Upper Mounting Block Bolts	22-27
	Wheel Lug Nuts	65-87

Wheel Alignment

INDEX

PRELIMINARY INSPECTION

1. Inspect tires for proper inflation and similar tread wear.
2. Inspect hub and bearing for excessive wear, repair as required.
3. Inspect ball joints.
4. Inspect tie rod ends for excessive looseness.
5. Check wheel and tire runout.
6. Inspect vehicle ride height.
7. Inspect rack and pinion for looseness at frame.
8. Ensure proper strut operation.
9. Check suspension and steering components for damage, replace as required.

FRONT WHEEL ALIGNMENT

CASTER

Caster is not adjustable, **Fig. 1.** If caster angles are not within specification, check for damaged or bent suspension components, deteriorated bushings, or distorted body mounting points.

CAMBER

Camber angle, **Fig. 1,** is controlled by the position of the strut mounting block in the shock tower. The mounting block can be positioned in the tower in two ways, resulting in a camber variation of approximately 1/2°. If the camber setting has not been changed previously, the white alignment mark on the mounting block will be positioned on the outboard side of the strut assembly, **Fig. 2.** Changing the position of the alignment mark 180° will increase camber angle approximately 1/2°, **Fig. 3.** If the alignment mark is already positioned inboard of the strut, changing the mounting block position can only result in camber being reduced by approximately 1/2°. To adjust camber setting, proceed as follows:

1. Raise and support vehicle and remove front wheels.
2. Remove upper strut attaching nuts.
3. Lower strut sufficiently so that mounting studs clear tower, then rotate mounting block 180° as necessary.
4. Reposition strut in tower, then install attaching nuts and **torque** to 32 to 45 ft. lbs.

TOE-IN

1. Ensure tires are properly inflated, then position vehicle on suitable alignment rack.

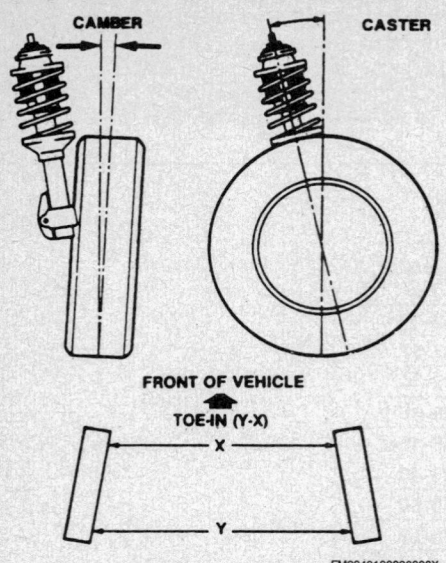

Fig. 1   Front wheel alignment settings

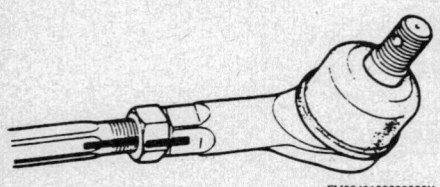

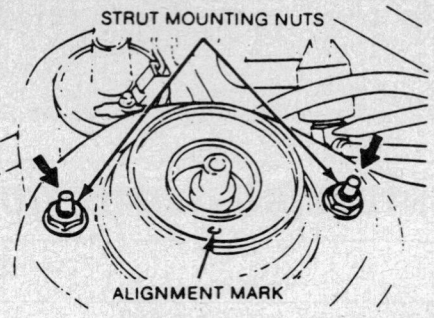

Fig. 2   Front strut camber alignment mark

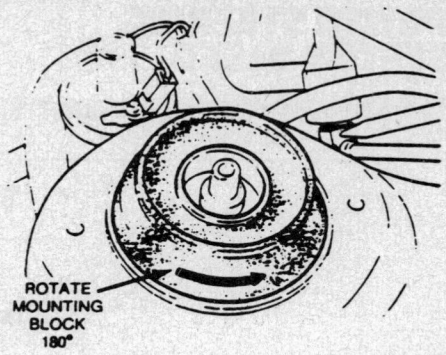

Fig. 3   Front camber adjustment

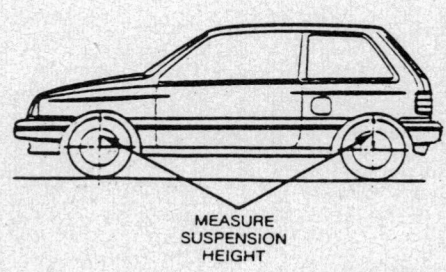

Fig. 5   Vehicle ride height measurement

in or out an equal amount until toe setting is within specification.
5. After adjustment is completed, tighten jam nuts and boot clamps.

REAR WHEEL ALIGNMENT

Rear camber and toe-in are determined by the configuration of the trailing arms on the torsion beam rear axle. No provision for adjustment is provided. The only rear suspension adjustment possible is the lateral positioning of the rear axle. This adjustment should only be performed if replacing the rear axle assembly. Refer to "Axle Assembly, Replace" procedure in "Rear Axle & Suspension" section for adjustment procedure.

VEHICLE RIDE HEIGHT

Prior to checking suspension height, remove heavy items from vehicle, such as tool boxes etc. Suspension height is measured from ground to the fender cut out

Fig. 4   Tie rod, tie rod end & jam nut position marking

2. Bounce vehicle several times to normalize ride height, then check toe setting. If toe setting is not within specification, proceed to next step.
3. Mark relationship between tie rods, tie rod ends and jam nuts, then loosen tie rod boot clamps to prevent twisting or damage to boots, **Fig. 4.**
4. Adjust toe-in by turning both tie rods

above the center of the wheel and tire assembly, **Fig. 5.** This measurement should be performed at all four wheels. Readings from side to side and front to rear should not vary by more than .4 inch. **It should be noted that uneven tire wear will increase the variance in the measurements and should be taken into consideration. If variance is more than .4 inch, check springs and suspension components for wear and damage.**

AIR CONDITIONING

TABLE OF CONTENTS

System Testing

INDEX

PRECAUTIONS

SAFETY

The refrigerant used in most air conditioning systems prior to 1994 is R12, more recent vehicles have a R134a system. **The same safety precautions should be observed for both refrigerants.**

Protective goggles should be worn when opening any refrigerant lines. R12 is readily absorbed by most types of oil. For this reason, a bottle of sterile mineral oil and a quantity of weak boric acid solution must always be kept nearby when servicing the air conditioning system. **If liquid coolant does touch the eyes, immediately use a few drops of sterile mineral oil to wash them out, then wash the eyes clean with the weak boric acid solution. Seek a doctor's aid immediately even though the irritation may have ceased.**

The freon refrigerant used in vehicle A/C systems will usually be in a vapor state when being handled in a repair shop. But if a portion of the liquid coolant should come in contact with the hands or face, note that its temperature momentarily will be at least 22° below zero.

When checking a system for leaks with a torch type leak detector, do not breathe the vapors coming from the flame. Do not recover refrigerant in the area of a live flame. A poisonous phosgene gas is produced when R12 is burned. While the small amount of this gas produced by a leak detector is not harmful unless inhaled directly at the flame.

Never allow the temperature of refrigerant drums to exceed 125°F. The resultant increase in temperature will cause a corresponding increase in pressure which may cause the safety plug to release or the drum to burst.

If it is necessary to heat a drum of refrigerant when charging a system, the drum should be placed in water that is no hotter than 125°F. Never use a blowtorch, or other open flame. If possible, a pressure release mechanism should be attached before the drum is heated.

CLEANLINESS

Air conditioning systems are extremely sensitive to moisture and dirt. The importance of clean working conditions is extremely important, as the smallest particle of foreign matter in an air conditioning system will contaminate the refrigerant, causing rust, ice or damage to the compressor. For this reason, all replacement parts are sold in vacuum sealed containers and should not be opened until they are to be installed in the system. If, for any reason, a part has been removed from its container for any length of time, the part must be completely flushed using only R12 to remove any dust or moisture that may have accumulated during storage. In cases of collision repairs where the system has been open for any length of time, the entire system must be purged completely and a new receiver-drier must be installed because the element of the existing unit will have become saturated and unable to remove any moisture from the system once the system is recharged.

When making gauge connections, purge the gauge lines first by cracking the charging valve and allowing a small amount of refrigerant to flow through the lines, then connect the lines immediately. Cleanliness is especially important when servicing compressors because of the very close tolerances used in these units. Consequently, repairs to the compressor itself should not be attempted unless all proper tools are at hand and a virtually spotless work area is provided.

GENERAL SERVICE

Use care when disconnecting or connecting refrigerant lines; always use a backup wrench and be careful not to overtighten any connection. Overtightening may result in a line or flare seat distortion and a system leak.

When making pressure checks on systems having service valves, be sure valve is in the intermediate position. If turned in too far, the hose connection will be closed, a position used for isolating the compressor. When closing the gauge port, do not overtighten the valve or damage to the seat will result.

After disconnecting gauge lines, check the valve areas to be sure service valves are correctly seated and Schraeder valves, if used, are not leaking.

DESCRIPTION
R12 SYSTEMS

R12 is non-explosive, non-flammable and non-corrosive. It has practically no odor and is heavier than air. Although it is classified as a safe refrigerant, certain precautions must be observed to protect the components involved and the person working on the system. Use only R12 such as Motorcraft YN-1A or YN-7 or equivalent.

Do not use refrigerant that was canned for pressure operated accessories (such as boat horns). This type is not pure Refrigerant and will cause a system malfunction. Liquid R12, at normal atmospheric pressures and temperatures, evaporates so quickly that it has a tendency to freeze anything it contacts.

R134a SYSTEMS

The major components of R134a air conditioning systems are similar to those used previously on R12 fixed orifice tube type systems. R12 and R134a components are similar in design and function. As a result, all diagnosis and testing procedures for R12 components can be used for R134a system components. However, it should be noted that R134a system components can only be replaced with other R134a components. R134a components cannot be replaced with components used with R12 systems. The same rule applies for R12 components, they cannot be replaced with R134a components.

To identify which type of air conditioning system a particular vehicle has, visually inspect the system for identification tags located on major components. R134a system components have yellow R134a NON-CFC tags. These systems can also be identified by a gold colored air conditioning compressor clutch and green colored O-rings used throughout the system.

EXERCISE SYSTEM

An important fact most car owners ignore is that the A/C system must be used periodically. Car manufacturers caution that when the air conditioner is not used regularly, particularly during cold months, it should be turned on for a few minutes once every two or three weeks while the engine is running. This keeps the system in good operating condition.

Checking out the system for the effects of disuse before the onset of summer is one of the most important aspects of A/C system servicing.

First clean out the condenser core,

mounted in most cases at the front of the vehicle's radiator. All obstructions, such as leaves, bugs, and dirt, must be removed, as they will reduce heat transfer and impair the efficiency of the system. Make sure the space between the condenser and the radiator also is free of foreign matter.

Ensure the evaporator water drain is open. The evaporator cools and dehumidifies the air before it enters the car.

PERFORMANCE TEST

R134a systems require the use of special service equipment designed specifically for R134a systems. R12 servicing equipment cannot be used on R134a systems.

EXCEPT ASPIRE, CAPRI, ESCORT, FESTIVA, PROBE & TRACER

Refrigerant system problems are diagnosed by checking refrigerant pressures and clutch cycle rate and times. Compare pressures and cycle time to charts shown in **Figs. 1 and 2.** Conditional requirements for refrigerant system tests must be satisfied to obtain accurate pressure readings. If findings do not fall between lines on respective charts, refer to **Fig. 3** to determine specific cause of improper readings.

After necessary repairs have been performed, take pressure readings while meeting conditional requirements to ensure problem has been corrected.

Visual inspection of the system may determine problems with the refrigerant system. By making a visual inspection, some of the following problems can be diagnosed: obstructed air passages, broken belts, disconnected or broken wires, loose or broken mounting brackets and refrigerant leaks.

A refrigerant leak will usually appear as an oily residue at the leakage point in the system.

ASPIRE

1. Connect manifold gauge set to system.
2. Start engine and turn A/C system on.
3. As soon as system is stabilized, record high and low pressures as indicated by manifold gauges.
4. Low side pressure should be 20-41 psi, and high side pressure should be 185-263 psi.
5. As low side pressure drops, high side pressure should rise. As low side pressure rises, high side pressure should drop.
6. Record center duct temperature.
7. Determine and record ambient temperature
8. Compare test readings with charts shown in **Fig. 4**

CAPRI

1. Connect manifold gauge set to system.
2. Turn A/C system on and operate blower motor at high speed with engine running at 2000 RPM.
3. Open all windows and move recirc/fresh air lever to Recirc position.
4. Position one thermometer in center

console duct and another thermometer in blower inlet under righthand side of dash.
5. Allow A/C system to stabilize for 5-10 minutes, then note high pressure gauge reading which should be 199-220 psi. If necessary, attempt to raise excessively low pressure by covering the condenser or lower high pressure by spraying water through condenser. If pressure cannot be brought within specifications, record stabilized pressure and perform necessary system diagnosis.

FESTIVA

1. Connect manifold gauge set to system.
2. Turn A/C system on and operate blower motor at high speed with engine running at 2000 RPM.
3. Open all windows and move recirc/fresh air lever to Recirc position.
4. Position one thermometer in center console duct and another thermometer in blower inlet under righthand side of dash.
5. Measure and record relative humidity at blower inlet using a psycrometer.
6. Allow A/C system to stabilize for 5-10 minutes, then note high pressure gauge reading which should be 199-220 psi. If necessary, attempt to raise excessively low pressure by covering the condenser or lower high pressure by spraying water through condenser. If pressure cannot be brought within specifications, record stabilized pressure and perform necessary system diagnosis.
7. Determine difference in temperatures at air inlet and center console duct and compare temperature difference to relative humidity on graph, **Fig. 5.** If intersection of lines on graph are within hatched lines, the A/C system is operating satisfactorily.

PROBE
1992

1. Connect manifold gauge set to system.
2. Start and run engine at 2000 RPM, then turn A/C system On.
3. Set temperature control to cool and blower motor to high.
4. If compressor clutch does not engage, jumper battery power to green/black wire at clutch connector.
5. Wait until air conditioning system stabilizes, then check readings at high and low pressure gauges.
6. Normal reading for high pressure gauge should be 199-220 psi. Normal reading for low pressure gauge should be 19-21 psi. or 28-43 psi. for 1992 models.
7. If pressure is not within specifications, record stabilized pressure and perform necessary system diagnosis.

1993-94

1. Connect manifold gauge set to system.
2. Start engine and turn on A/C system.
3. As soon as system is stabilized, record high and low pressures as

IMPORTANT — TEST REQUIREMENTS

The following test conditions must be established to obtain accurate pressure readings:

- Run engine at 1500 rpm for 10 minutes.
- Operate A/C system on max A/C (recirculating air).
- Run blower at max speed.
- Stabilize in car temperature @ 70°F to 80°F (21°C to 22°C).

TOTAL CLUTCH CYCLE TIME — SECONDS

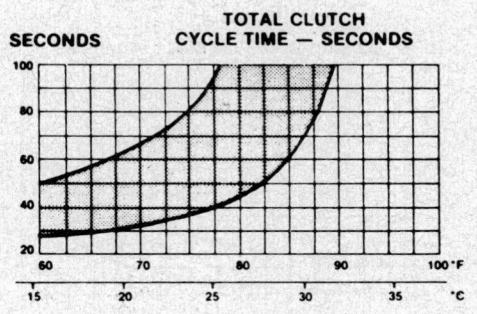

NORMAL CLUTCH CYCLE RATE PER MINUTE

CYCLES/MINUTE

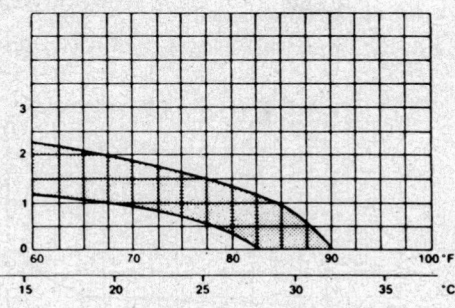

AMBIENT TEMPERATURES

NORMAL CLUTCH OFF TIME — SECONDS

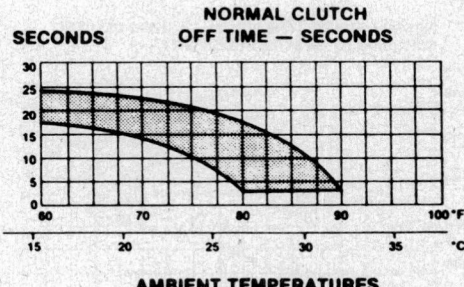

AMBIENT TEMPERATURES

NORMAL CLUTCH ON TIME — SECONDS

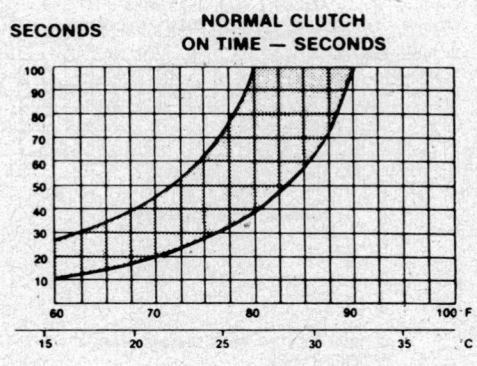

AMBIENT TEMPERATURES

NORMAL CENTER REGISTER DISCHARGE TEMPERATURES

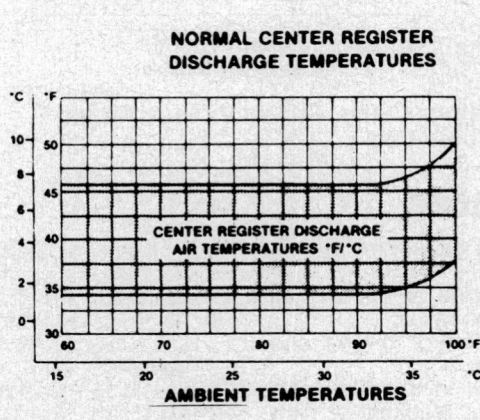

AMBIENT TEMPERATURES

NORMAL FIXED ORIFICE TUBE CYCLING CLUTCH REFRIGERANT SYSTEM PRESSURES

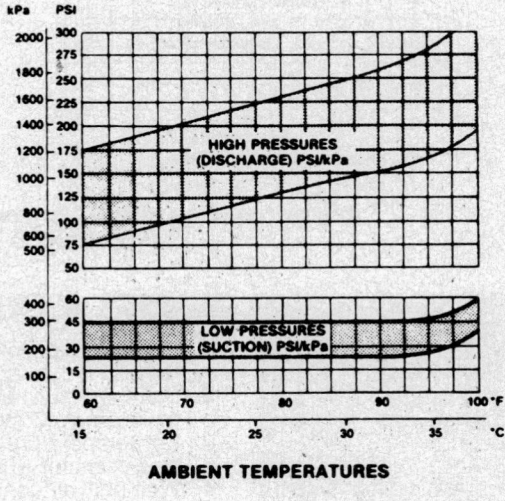

AMBIENT TEMPERATURES

FM7029100026000X

Fig. 1 Refrigerant pressure & temperature charts. Continental, Cougar, Mark VII, Mark VII, Mustang, Sable, Taurus, Tempo, Topaz, Thunderbird, 1993–94 Probe & 1994 Escort & Tracer

IMPORTANT — TEST REQUIREMENTS

The following test conditions must be established to obtain accurate clutch cycle rate and cycle time readings:

- Run engine at 1500 rpm for 10 minutes.
- Operate A/C system on max A/C (recirculating air).
- Run blower at max speed.
- Stabilize in car temperature @ 70°F to 80°F (21°C to 22°C).

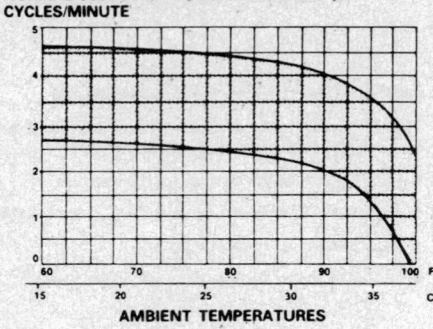

NORMAL CLUTCH CYCLE RATE PER MINUTE
CYCLES/MINUTE

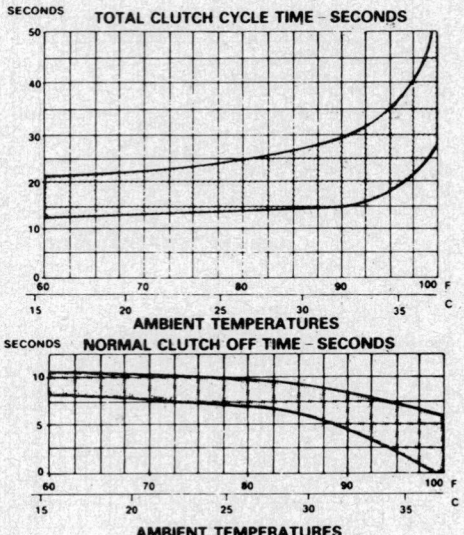

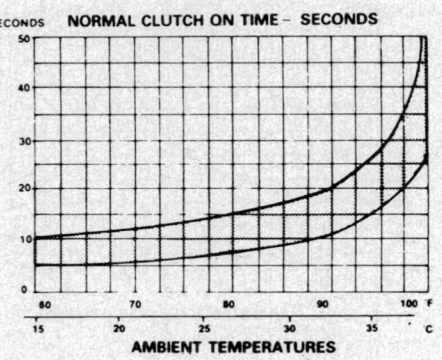

NORMAL CLUTCH ON TIME – SECONDS

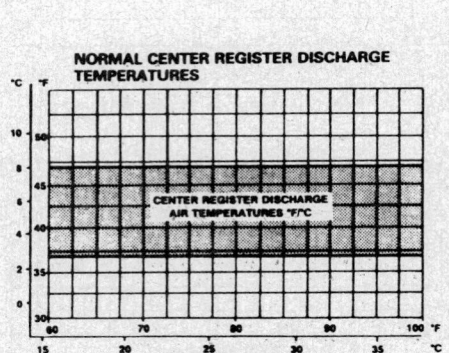

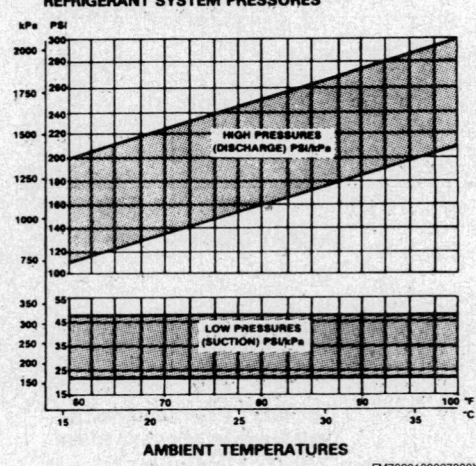

Fig. 2   Refrigerant pressure & temperature charts. Crown Victoria, Grand Marquis & Town Car

FM7029100027000X

---

shown by manifold gauges.

4. High side pressure should read 178-235 psi. As low pressure drops, high pressure should rise.
5. When clutch disengages, low side pressure should rise and high side pressure should drop.
6. Determine A/C clutch cycle rate per minute (1 cycle is A/C clutch On time plus Off time).
7. Record A/C Off time in seconds.
8. Record A/C On time in seconds.
9. Record center duct temperature.
10. Determine and record ambient temperature.
11. Compare test readings with applicable chart, **Fig. 1.**
12.

ESCORT & TRACER
1992-93

1. Connect manifold gauge set to system.
2. Start and run engine at 2000 RPM, then turn A/C system On.
3. Set temperature control to MAX and blower motor to III.
4. Wait until air conditioning system stabilizes, then check readings at high and low pressure gauges.
5. Normal reading for high pressure gauge should be 171-235 psi. Normal reading for low pressure gauge should be 21-23 psi.
6. If pressure is not within specifications, record stabilized pressure and perform necessary system diagnosis.

1994

1. Connect manifold gauge set to system.
2. Start engine and turn on A/C system.
3. As soon as system is stabilized, record high and low pressures as shown by manifold gauges.
4. Low side pressure should be 35-50 psi. High side pressure should be 178-235 psi. As low pressure drops, high pressure should rise.
5. When clutch disengages, low side pressure should rise and high side pressure should drop.
6. Determine A/C clutch cycle rate per minute (1 cycle is A/C clutch On time plus Off time).

NOTE: System test requirements must be met to obtain accurate test readings for evaluation. Refer to the normal refrigerant system pressure/temperature and the normal clutch cycle ratio and times charts.

High (Discharge) Pressure	Low (Suction) Pressure	Clutch Cycle Time			Component — Causes
		Rate	On	Off	
High	High	Continuous Run			Condenser — Inadequate Airflow
High	Normal to High				Engine Overheating
Normal to High	Normal				Air in Refrigerant Refrigerant Overcharge (a) Humidity or Ambient Temp Very High (b)
Normal	High				Fixed Orifice Tube — Missing O Rings Leaking/Missing
Normal	High	Slow	Long	Long	Clutch Cycling Switch — High Cut In
Normal	Normal	Slow or No Cycle	Long or Continuous	Normal or No Cycle	Moisture in Refrigerant System Excessive Refrigerant Oil
		Fast	Short	Short	Clutch Cycling Switch — Low Cut In or High Cut Out
Normal	Low	Slow	Long	Long	Clutch Cycling Switch — Low Cut Out
Normal to Low	High	Continuous Run			Compressor — Low Performance
Normal to Low	Normal to High				A/C Suction Line — Partially Restricted or Plugged (c)
Normal to Low	Normal	Fast	Short	Normal	Evaporator — Restricted Airflow
			Short to Very Short	Normal to Long	Condenser fixed orifice Tube or A/C Liquid Line — Partially Restricted or Plugged
			Short to Very Short	Short to Very Short	Low Refrigerant Charge
			Short to Very Short	Long	Evaporator Core — Partially Restricted or Plugged
Normal to Low	Low	Continuous Run			A/C Suction Line — Partially Restricted or Plugged (d) Clutch Cycling Switch — Sticking Closed
Low	Normal	Very Fast	Very Short	Very Short	Clutch Cycling Switch — Cycling Range Too Close
Erratic Operation or Compressor Not Running		—	—	—	Clutch Cycling Switch — Dirty Contacts or Sticking Open Poor Connection at A/C Clutch Connector or Clutch Cycling Switch Connector A/C Electrical Circuit Erratic

Additional Possible Cause Components Associated with Inadequate Compressor Operation

- Compressor Drive Belt — Loose
- Compressor Clutch — Slipping
- Clutch Coil Open — Shorted or Loose Mounting
- Control Assembly Switch — Dirty Contacts or Sticking Open
- Clutch Wiring Circuit — High Resistance Open or Blown Fuse

Additional Possible Cause Components Associated with a Damaged Compressor

- Compressor Clutch — Seized
- Clutch Cycling Switch — Sticking Closed
- Suction Accumulator Drier — Refrigerant Oil Bleed Hole Plugged
- Refrigerant Leaks

(a) Compressor may make noise on initial run. This is slugging condition caused by excessive liquid refrigerant.
(b) Compressor clutch may not cycle in ambient temperatures above 80°F depending on humidity conditions.
(c) Low pressure reading will be normal to high if pressure is taken at accumulator and if restriction is downstream of service access valve.
(d) Low pressure reading will be low if pressure is taken near the compressor and restriction is upstream of service access valve.

FM7029100028000X

Fig. 3 Refrigerant system pressure evaluation chart

7. Record A/C Off time in seconds.
8. Record A/C On time in seconds.
9. Record center duct temperature.
10. Determine and record ambient temperature.
11. Compare test readings with applicable chart, Fig. 1.

LEAK TEST

R134a systems require the use of special service equipment designed specifically for R134a systems. R12 servicing equipment cannot be used on R134a systems.

Testing the refrigerant system for leaks is one of the most important phases of troubleshooting. One or more of the methods outlined will prove useful in detecting leaks or checking connections if service work is performed. Before beginning any

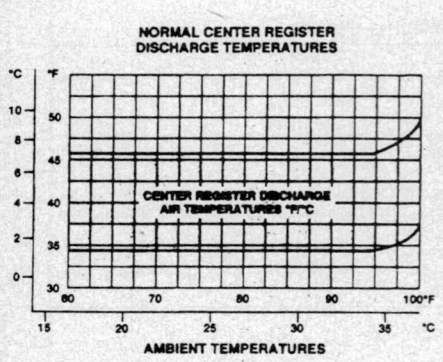

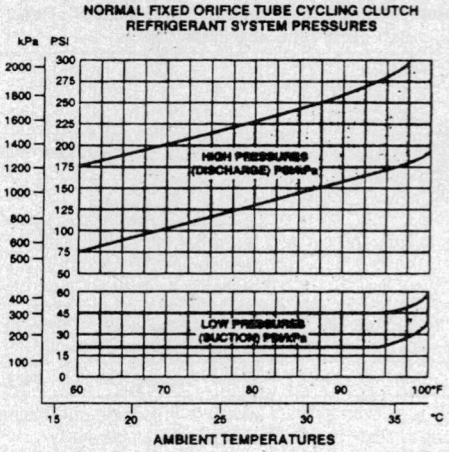

FM7029400001000X

Fig. 4   Refrigerant pressure & temperature charts. Aspire

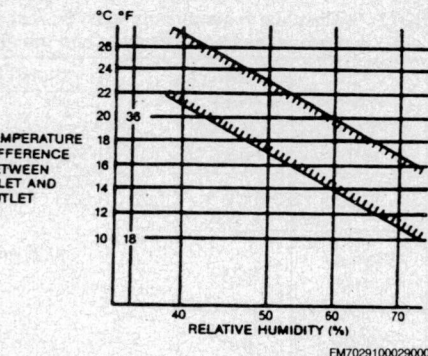

FM7029100029000X

Fig. 5   A/C system performance chart. Festiva

leak test, attach a manifold gauge set and note pressure. If little or no pressure is indicated, a partial charge must be installed. Check all connections, compressor head gasket, oil filler plug and compressor shaft seal for leaks.

ELECTRONIC DETECTORS

There are a number of electronic leak detectors available to perform leak tests. Refer to operating instructions for the unit being used and observe these general procedures:
1. Move the detector probe one inch per second in areas of suspected leaks.
2. Position the probe below the test point, as refrigerant gas is heavier than air.
3. Be sure to check service access gauge port valve fittings, particularly when valve caps are missing, as dirt accumulations can destroy the sealing area of valve core when manifold gauge set is attached. Replace missing valve caps after cleaning valve core area. **Valve caps should only be finger tightened. Using pliers to tighten valve caps may distort sealing surface of valve.**
4. Check for leaks in manifold gauge set and hoses, as well as the rest of the system.

FLAME-TYPE (HALIDE) DETECTORS

When using flame-type detectors, avoid inhaling fumes produced by burning refrigerant. Do not use this type detector where concentrations of combustible or explosive gases, dusts or vapors may exist.
1. Adjust detector flame as low as possible to obtain maximum sensitivity. Be sure copper element is cherry red and not burned away. The flame will be almost colorless.
2. Slowly move detector along areas of suspected leaks. A slight leak will cause the flame to change to a bright yellow-green color. A significant leak will be indicated by a brilliant blue flame. Position detector under areas

being tested as refrigerant gas is heavier than air. **The presence of dust in the pickup hose may cause a change in the color of the flame. If not recognized, a false diagnosis could be made. Store leak detector in a clean place and ensure hose is free of dust before leak testing.**
3. Check for leaks in the manifold gauge set and hoses, as well as the rest of the system.
4. Use a small fan to ventilate areas where the leak detector indicates refrigerant constantly. These areas are contaminated with refrigerant and must be ventilated before leak can be pinpointed.

FLUID LEAK DETECTORS

Apply leak detector solution around joints to be tested. A cluster of bubbles will form immediately if there is a leak. A white foam that forms after a short while will indicate an extremely small leak. In some confined areas such as sections of the evaporator and condenser, electronic leak detectors will be more useful.

DISCHARGING SYSTEM

R134a systems require the use of special service equipment designed specifically for R134a systems. R12 servicing equipment cannot be used on R134a systems.
R12 recovery stations cannot be used on R134a systems. A separate recovery station must be used on R134a systems. The refrigerants are not compatible and will contaminate the R12 recovery station.

The use of refrigerant recovery and recycling stations allows the recovery and reuse of refrigerant after contaminants and moisture have been removed.

When using a recovery or recycling station, follow the manufacturer's operating instructions, noting the following:
1. **Use extreme caution and observe all safety and service precautions related to use of refrigerants.**
2. Connect refrigerant recycling station hose(s) to vehicle A/C service port(s)

and recovery station inlet fitting. Hoses used should have shutoff devices or check valves within 12 inches of hose ends to minimize introduction of air into recycling station and to minimize amount of refrigerant released when hose(s) is disconnected.
3. Turn recycling station On to start recovery process. Allow recycling station to pump refrigerant from A/C system until station pressure gauge indicates vacuum.
4. After vehicle A/C system has been evacuated, close station inlet valve, if equipped.
5. Turn station Off. On some stations the pump will automatically be turned Off by a low pressure switch.
6. Allow vehicle A/C system to remain closed for approximately two minutes. Observe vacuum level indicated on gauge. If pressure does not rise, disconnect recycling station hose(s).
7. If system pressure rises, repeat steps 3 through 6 until vacuum level remains stable for two minutes.
8. Service A/C system as necessary, then evacuate and recharge A/C system.

SYSTEM EVACUATION

R134a systems require the use of special service equipment designed specifically for R134a systems. R12 servicing equipment cannot be used on R134a systems.

Vacuum pumps suitable for removing air and moisture from A/C systems are commercially available. A specification for system pump down used here is 28–29½ inches vacuum. This reading can be attained at or near sea level only. For each 1000 feet of altitude, the reading will be 1 inch of vacuum less than the standard specification given. For example, at 5000 feet elevation, only 23–24½ inches of vacuum can be obtained. **The system must be completely discharged before it can be evacuated. Damage to the vacuum pump will result if pressurized refrigerant is allowed to enter the pump assembly.**
1. Connect vacuum pump to gauge manifold. With gauges connected into system, remove cap from vacuum hose connector. Install center hose from gauge manifold to vacuum pump

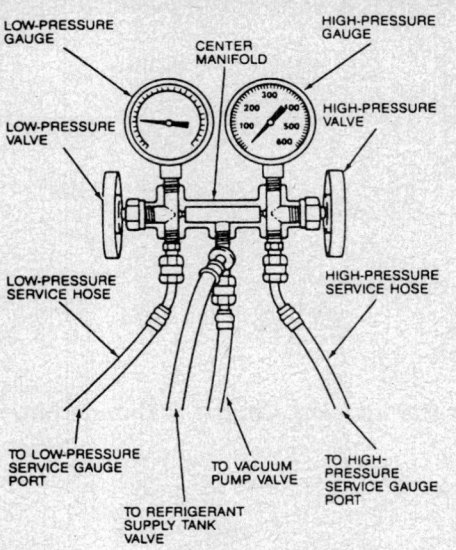

Fig. 6 Refrigerant system service connections

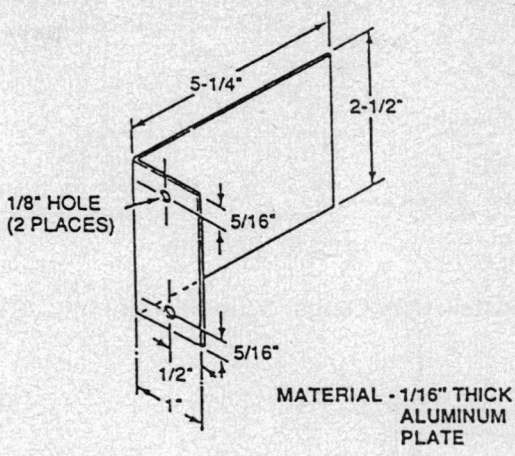

Fig. 7 Evaporator case baffle. Cougar & Thunderbird

connector. Midposition high and low side compressor service valve (if used). Open high and low side gauge manifold hand valves.

2. Operate vacuum pump a minimum of 30 minutes for air and moisture removal. Watch compound gauge to see that system pumps down into a vacuum. System will reach 28-29½ inches Hg vacuum in a maximum of 5 minutes. If system does not pump down, check all connections and leak test if necessary.

3. Close gauge manifold hand valves and shutoff vacuum pump.

4. Check ability of system to hold vacuum. Watch compound gauge to see that gauge does not rise at a faster rate than 1 inch vacuum every 4 or 5 minutes. If compound gauge rises at too rapid a rate, install partial charge and leak test. Then discharge system as outlined above.

5. If system holds vacuum, charge system with refrigerant.

CHARGING SYSTEM

R134a systems require the use of special service equipment designed specifically for R134a systems. R12 servicing equipment cannot be used on R134a systems.

A number of manufacturers are producing refrigerant products which are described as being direct replacements for refrigerant R12. The use of any unauthorized substitute refrigerant may severely damage A/C components. R12 is the only authorized refrigerant to be used in any air conditioning system for Ford vehicle.

Refer to "A/C Specifications" for refrigerant capacities.

When charging from small cans, do not open manifold gauge set high pres- sure (discharge) gauge valve, as this can cause the containers to explode.

1. Connect manifold gauge set **Fig. 6**, then set valves closed to center hose, disconnect vacuum pump from manifold gauge set.

2. Connect center hose of manifold gauge set to refrigerant supply.

3. Purge air from center hose by loosening hose at manifold gauge set and open refrigerant drum valve. When refrigerant escapes from hose, tighten center hose connection at manifold gauge set.

4. On vehicles so equipped, disconnect wire harness connector at clutch cycling pressure switch. Install jumper wire across terminals of connector.

5. On all models, open manifold gauge set low side valve and allow refrigerant to enter system. Refrigerant can must be kept upright if vehicle low pressure service gauge port is not on suction accumulator/drier or suction accumulator fitting.

6. When system stops drawing refrigerant in, start engine and set control lever to A/C position and blower switch to "HI" position to draw remaining refrigerant into system.

7. When specified weight of refrigerant is in system, close gauge set low pressure valve and refrigerant supply valve.

8. On vehicles so equipped, remove jumper wire from clutch cycling pressure switch connector and connect connector to pressure switch.

9. On all models, operate system until pressures stabilize to check operation and system pressures. During high ambient temperatures, a high volume fan may be necessary to blow air through the radiator and condenser to cool engine and prevent excessive refrigerant system pressures.

10. When charging is complete and system operating pressures are normal, disconnect manifold gauge set from vehicle and install protective caps on service gauge port valves.

TECHNICAL SERVICE BULLETINS

AIR CONDITIONING & COOLING FAN INOPERATIVE

1992 Capri

An inoperative engine cooling fan and air conditioning system may be caused by a pressure spike resulting in a blown fuse. The 20 amp cooling fan fuse should be replaced with a 25 amp fuse.

POOR OR NO A/C PERFORMANCE

1993 Mark VIII & Taurus

A/C service ports on vehicles equipped with R134a may leak, resulting in poor A/C system performance. This condition may be caused by the material used in the grommet which seals the service ports.

The corrective action for this condition is to replace both service ports with new ports which have valve pin grommets made from an improved material.

1. Discharge refrigerant at low pressure service port located on the suction line near the compressor.

2. Remove manifold gauge set or refrigerant recycling station from service port.

3. Using R134a high side A/C fitting socket tool No. D94L-19703-A or equivalent, remove high pressure service port and install replacement service port (part No. F3AZ-19E762-A).

4. Using R134a low side A/C fitting socket tool No. D94L-19703-B or equivalent, remove low pressure service port and install replacement service port (part No. F3AZ-19E762-B).

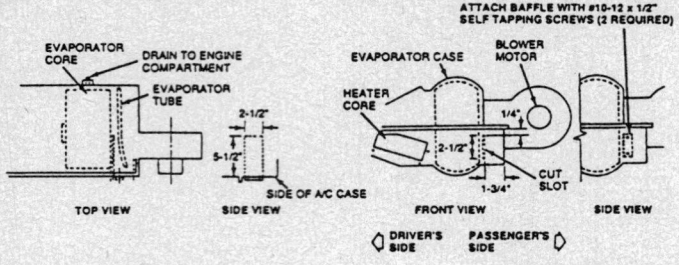

Fig. 8   Baffle installation. Cougar & Thunderbird

FM7029100032000X

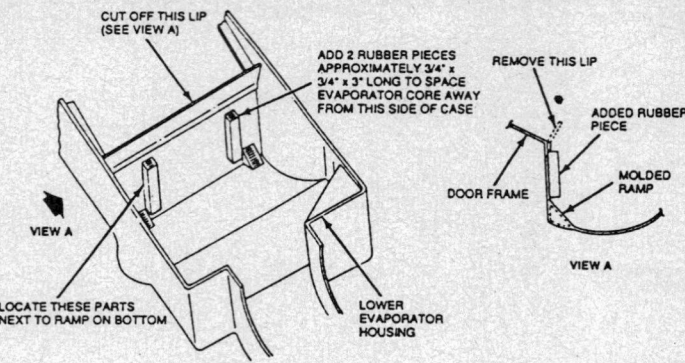

FM7029100033000X

Fig. 9   Lower evaporator housing. Cougar & Thunderbird

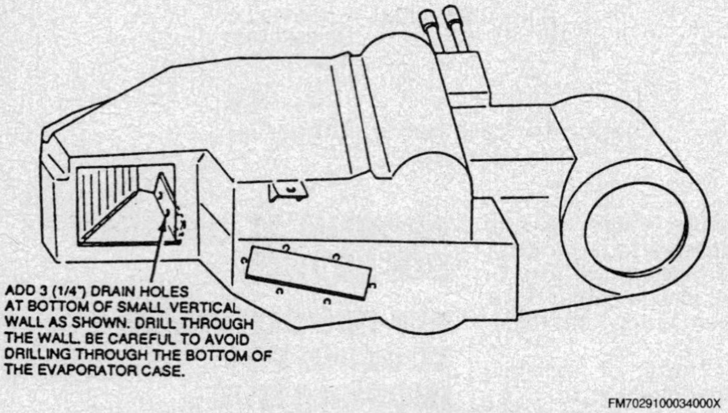

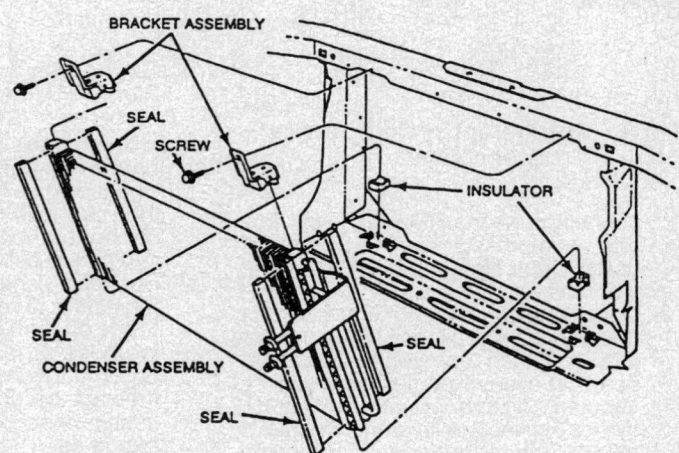

ADD 3 (1/4") DRAIN HOLES AT BOTTOM OF SMALL VERTICAL WALL AS SHOWN. DRILL THROUGH THE WALL. BE CAREFUL TO AVOID DRILLING THROUGH THE BOTTOM OF THE EVAPORATOR CASE.

FM7029100034000X

Fig. 10   Evaporator case drain holes. Cougar & Thunderbird

FM7029100035000X

Fig. 11   Condenser seal installation. 1992 Cougar & Thunderbird

CONDENSATION LEAKS INTO PASSENGER COMPARTMENT

Cougar & Thunderbird

This condition exists when sizeable water droplets formed by A/C condensation are forced into the passenger compartment by a build-up of high-velocity air in the evaporator case.

To correct this condition, a baffle must be installed in the evaporator case to prevent the build-up of high-velocity air. Install baffle into evaporator case as follows:

1. Using aluminum plate stock about 1/16 inch thick, make baffle as shown in **Fig. 7.**
2. To gain access to evaporator case, push inward on sides of glove compartment assembly to free attaching tabs at its rear corners.
3. Working through glove compartment opening, cut a 1/16 inch wide by 2½ inch long slot in the evaporator case. Fix this slot in the location shown in **Fig. 8.**
4. Slide baffle into slot. **Ensure baffle's flange faces passenger side of vehicle. If flange faces driver's side, the attaching screws could puncture evaporator core.**
5. Secure baffle to evaporator case using two No. 10-12X½ inch self-tapping screws.
6. Check for vibrational noise by operating system in all modes. If vibration is detected, remove baffle and slightly alter angle of its bend.
7. Check for air leaks that may have been created during modification of evaporator case. Seal leaks with black rope sealant (Part No. D6AZ-19560-A) or equivalent.
8. Install glove compartment and test drive vehicle. Execute several hard right and left turns to force out any condensation that may have accumulated in the evaporator case.
9. If aluminum baffle does not stop flow of airborne water droplets, proceed as follows:
   a. Inform vehicle owner that there will be a noticeable difference in the air temperature between the driver's side instrument panel register and passenger's side instrument panel register. This temperature difference could be as much as 20°.
   b. Remove evaporator case from vehicle.
   c. Remove three screws and pull air inlet duct away from evaporator case.
   d. Using a small saw, cut the top of the evaporator case between the dotted lines shown in **Fig. 8.**
   e. Remove evaporator core from case.
   f. Cut off temperature door frame as shown in **Fig. 9.**
   g. Install two pieces of 3/4 inch X 3/4 inch X 3 inches stiff foam rubber inside the case in the locations shown in **Fig. 10.** These foam pieces serve to shift the evaporator core as far as possible to the passenger side of the vehicle.
   h. Obtain cover service kit (Part No. E9SZ-19B735-A), then tightly hold cover against the case while drilling five 3/16 inch cover attaching holes.
   i. Install evaporator core in case.
   j. Using the five screws provided in the cover kit, attach the cover to the case. Seal all holes in the case with caulking cord rope sealer (Part No. D6AZ-19560-A) or equivalent.
10. Drill three 1/4 inch drain holes at the bottom edge of the small vertical wall in the evaporator case as shown in **Fig. 10.** These holes will allow accumulation to drain back into the heater core area. **Do not drill through the bottom of the evaporator case.**
11. Install evaporator case and road test vehicle, make several hard left and right hand turns to force out any remaining condensation through the floor ducts.

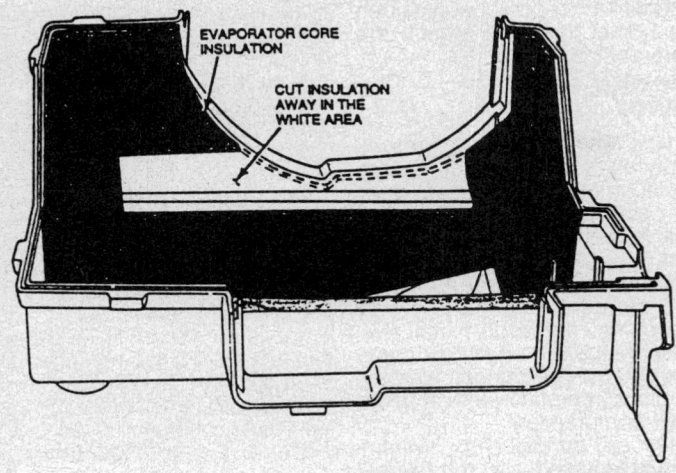

EVAPORATOR CORE
INSULATION

CUT INSULATION
AWAY IN THE
WHITE AREA

FM7029200036000X

Fig. 12 Evaporator core case installation. 1992 Probe

2. If switch fails to have continuity, install new switch (Part No. E25Y-19E61-A).
3. Using a small flat punch, apply butyl sealer (Part No. C9AZ-19554-B) to top of wiring harness connector.

POOR A/C COOLING PERFORMANCE

1992 Cougar & Thunderbird

This condition may be caused by a missing A/C condenser front seal to the radiator support, which will restrict adequate airflow through the condenser.
1. Install seals as shown in **Fig. 11.**
2. Place adhesive side of seal toward condenser ensuring seals do not contact condenser fins.
3. Ensure seals contact radiator support and are tucked behind support.

VIBRATION FROM WATER PUMP & PULLEY MISALIGNMENT

1992 Mustang

On these models, a vibration at the front of the engine may occur because the water pump pulley hub and pulley are misaligned. This is caused by an interference condition between the water pump hub and pulley inside contour.

To correct this problem, install a new water pump assembly with more clearance around the pulley hub mounting face.

INTERMITTENT LOSS OF A/C COOLING

1992 Tempo & Topaz

This condition may be caused by the lack of continuity in the A/C clutch cycling pressure switch. This condition may be caused by corrosion in the switch assembly. To correct this condition, proceed as follows.
1. Test clutch cycling pressure switch for continuity.

A/C CONDENSATION DRAINING INTO PASSENGER COMPARTMENT

1992 Probe

On these models, condensation may leak from the A/C evaporator case onto the carpet below the air discharge connector to the heater case. This occurs as a result of excessive insulation surrounding the evaporator core acting as a dam and retaining water.

If this condition occurs, remove a portion of evaporator core case insulation, **Fig. 12.**

SYSTEM SERVICE

INDEX

OIL CHARGE

R12 systems require the use of a 500 viscosity mineral based refrigerant oil known as YN-9. This type of refrigerant oil was made specifically for R12 systems and is not suitable for use in R134a systems. Never use R12 refrigerant oil YN-9 in R134a systems.

The refrigerant oil required for R134a air conditioning systems is a polyalkalylene glycol (PAG) oil. Ford specification part No. WSH-M1C231-B or equivalent. This type of refrigerant oil is designed specifically for R134a systems and is not suitable for use in R12 systems. Never use an R134a refrigerant oil in R12 systems.

EXCEPT CAPRI, FESTIVA & TRACER

Nippondenso 10P13 Compressor

A new service replacement compressor contains 7.75 ounces of a special paraffin base refrigerant oil (Part No. Motorcraft YN-9). Before installing replacement compressor, drain oil from old and new compressors. If three to five ounces of oil was drained from old compressor, install the same amount of oil drained from old compressor. If more than five ounces was drained from old compressor, install five ounces of new refrigerant oil in new compressor. If less than three ounces was removed from old compressor, install three ounces in new compressor.

When replacing the accumulator/dryer drill a 1/2 inch hole in old accumulator body and drain oil from hole. Add same amount of new oil plus two ounces to new accumulator/dryer.

When other air conditioning system components are replaced, add the following quantities of refrigerant oil: Evaporator core, 3 fluid ounces; Condenser, 1 fluid ounce.

Replacement of other components such as an orifice tube or hoses does not require the addition of any refrigerant oil.

Ford FS6 & Nippondenso 6P148 Compressors

A new service replacement compressor contains 10 fluid ounces of refrigerant oil. Before installing replacement compressor, drain 4 fluid ounces of oil from compressor in order to maintain total system oil charge within specified limits.

When other air conditioning system components are replaced, add the following quantities of 500 viscosity refrigerant oil: Accumulator, same amount drained from old accumulator plus 1 ounce (drain accumulator through pressure switch fitting); Evaporator core, 3 fluid ounces; Condenser, 1 fluid ounce.

Replacement of other components such as valves or hoses does not require the addition of any refrigerant oil.

Tecumseh HR-980 Compressors

A new service replacement 4 cylinder compressor contains 8 fluid ounces of refrigerant oil. Before installing replacement compressor, drain 4 fluid ounces of oil from compressor in order to maintain total system oil charge within specified limits.

When other air conditioning system components are replaced, add the following quantities of 500 viscosity refrigerant oil: Accumulator, same amount drained from old accumulator plus 1 ounce (drain accumulator through pressure switch fitting); Evaporator core, 3 fluid ounces; Condenser, 1 fluid ounce.

Replacement of other components such as valves or hoses does not require the addition of any refrigerant oil.

Nippondenso 10P15 Series Compressors

A new service replacement compressor contains 8 fluid ounces of refrigerant oil. Before installing replacement compressor, drain oil from compressor into a clean graduated container, then pour 5 ounces of clean refrigerant oil into compressor to maintain total system oil charge limits.

When other air conditioning system components are replaced, add the following quantities of refrigerant oil: Accumulator, same amount drained from old accumulator plus 1 ounce (drain accumulator by drilling 1/2 inch hole in accumulator body); Evaporator core, 3 fluid ounces; Condenser, 1 fluid ounce.

Replacement of other components such as valves or hoses does not require the addition of any refrigerant oil.

Nippondenso 10PA17 Compressor

A new service replacement compressor contains 8 ounces of refrigerant oil. Before installing replacement compressor, drain oil from old compressor. If three to five ounces of oil was drained from old compressor, drain new compressor and install the same amount of oil drained from old compressor. If more than five ounces was drained from old compressor, install five ounces of new refrigerant oil in new compressor. If less than three ounces was removed from old compressor, install three ounces in new compressor.

When other air conditioning system components are replaced, add the following quantities of refrigerant oil: Accumulator, same amount drained from old accumulator plus 2 ounces; Evaporator core, 3 fluid ounces; Condenser, 1 fluid ounce.

Replacement of other components such as an orifice tube or hoses does not require the addition of any refrigerant oil.

Ford FX-15 Axial 10 Cylinder Compressor

A new service replacement compressor contains 7 fluid ounces of refrigerant oil. Before installing replacement compressor, drain oil from old compressor. If three to five ounces of oil were drained from old compressor, then drain new compressor and install the same amount of oil drained from old compressor. If more than five ounces were drained from old compressor, install five ounces of new refrigerant oil in new compressor. If less then three ounces was removed from old compressor, install three ounces in new compressor.

When other air conditioning system components are replaced, add the following quantities of refrigerant oil: Accumulator, same amount drained from old accumulator plus 1 ounce; Evaporator core, 3 fluid ounces; Condenser, 1 fluid ounce.

Replacement of other components such as valves or hoses does not require the addition of any refrigerant oil.

Ford FS-10 Swash Plate 10 Cylinder Compressor

A new service replacement compressor contains 7 fluid ounces of refrigerant oil. Before installing replacement compressor, drain oil from old compressor. If three to five ounces of oil were drained from old compressor, then drain new compressor and install the same amount of oil drained from old compressor. If more than five ounces were drained from old compressor, install five ounces of new refrigerant oil in new compressor. If less then three ounces was removed from old compressor, install three ounces in new compressor.

When other air conditioning system components are replaced, add the following quantities of refrigerant oil: Accumulator, same amount drained from old accumulator plus 2 ounces; Evaporator core, 3 fluid ounces; Condenser, 1 fluid ounce.

Replacement of other components such as valves or hoses does not require the addition of any refrigerant oil.

CAPRI

When replacing system components, add the following quantities of refrigerant oil: Compressor, 2.0-3.4 ounces; Condenser, 1 ounce; Evaporator 1 ounce; Receiver-drier, .5 ounce.

ASPIRE

When replacing system components, add or drain the following quantities of refrigerant oil: Compressor, drain 1.7 ounces; Condenser, add 1.0 ounce; Receiver-drier, add amount drained from old drier plus .34 ounce.

FESTIVA

When replacing system components, add or drain the following quantities of refrigerant oil: Compressor, drain 1.2 ounces; Condenser, add 1.0 ounce; Evaporator, add 3.0 ounces; Receiver-drier, add amount drained from old drier plus 1 ounce.

TRACER

Refer to "Nippondenso 10P13 Compressor," for oil charge specifications.

OIL LEVEL CHECK

The oil level of these compressors should be checked whenever refrigerant has been lost due to leakage or through normal system servicing.

Air Conditioning Specifications

INDEX

A/C SPECIFICATIONS

Model	Engine	Refrigerant Type	Refrigerant Capacity, Lbs.	A/C Compressor Model	Refrigeration Oil		Compressor Oil Level Check, Inches	Compressor Clutch Air Gap Inch
					Viscosity	Total System Capacity, Ounces		
1992								
Capri	All	R12	1.4	—	500	10	①	.016–.028
Continental	All	R12	2.5	Ford FX-15	②	7	①	.018–.033
Cougar	All	R12	2.6	FX-15	②	7	①	.018–.033
Crown Victoria	All	R12	2.50	Ford FX-15	②	7	①	.018–.033
Escort	All	R12	2.12	Nippondenso 10P13	②	8	①	.021–.036
Festiva	All	R12	1.56	—	500	10	①	.016–.028
Grand Marquis	All	R12	2.50	Ford FX-15	②	7	①	.018–.033
Mark VII	All	R12	2.5	Nippondenso 10PA17	②	8	①	.014–.026
Mustang	2.3L/4-140	R12	2.5	Nippondenso 10P15	②	8	①	.021–.036
	5.0L/V8-302	R12	2.5	Nippondenso 6P148	②	10	①	.021–.036
Probe	2.2L/4-133	R12	2.5	Nippondenso 10P15A	500	3.3	①	.016–.028
	3.0L/V6-182	R12	2.5	Nippondenso 10P15	②	8	①	.021–.036
Sable	3.0L/V6-182	R12	2.50	Ford FX-15	②	7	①	.018–.033
	3.8L/V6-232	R12	2.5	Ford FX-15	②	7	①	.018–.033
Taurus	3.0L/V6-182	R12	2.50	Ford FX-15	②	7	①	.018–.033
	3.0L/V6-182 SHO	R12	2.50	Nippondenso 10P15F	②	8	①	.021–.036
	3.8L/V6-232	R12	2.5	Ford FX-15	②	7	①	.018–.033
Tempo	2.3L/4-140	R12	2.25	FX-15	500	10	①	.018–.033
	3.0L/V6-182	R12	2.25	Nippondenso 10P15	500	10	①	.021–.036
Thunderbird	All	R12	2.6	FX-15	②	7	①	.018–.033
Topaz	2.3L/4-140	R12	2.25	FX-15	500	10	①	.018–.033
	3.0L/V6-182	R12	2.25	Nippondenso 10P15	500	10	①	.021–.036
Town Car	All	R12	2.5	Ford FX-15	②	7	①	.018–.033
Tracer	All	R12	2.12	Nippondenso 10P13	②	8	①	.021–.036
1993								
Capri	All	R12	1.4	—	500	10	①	.016–.028
Continental	All	R12	3.2	Ford FX-15	②	7	①	.018–.033
Cougar	All	R12	2.6	FX-15	②	7	①	.018–.033
Crown Victoria	All	R12	2.50	Ford FX-15	②	7	①	.018–.033
Escort	All	R12	2.12	Nippondenso 10P13	②	8	①	.021–.036
Festiva	All	R12	1.56	—	500	10	①	.016–.028
Grand Marquis	All	R12	2.50	Ford FX-15	②	7	①	.018–.033
Mark VIII	All	R134a	3.2	Nippondenso 10PA17	③	8		.021–.036
Mustang	2.3L/4-140	R12	2.5	Nippondenso 10P15C	②	8	①	.021–.036
	5.0L/V8-302	R12	2.5	Nippondenso 6P148	②	10	①	.021–.036

A/C SPECIFICATIONS-Continued

Model	Engine	Refrigerant Type	Refrigerant Capacity, Lbs.	A/C Compressor Model	Refrigeration Oil			Compressor Clutch Air Gap Inch
					Viscosity	Total System Capacity, Ounces	Compressor Oil Level Check, Inches	
1993-Continued								
Probe	2.2L/4–133	R12	2.5	Nippondenso 10P15A	500	3.3	①	.016–.028
	3.0L/V6-182	R12	2.5	Nippondenso 10P15	②	8	①	.021–.036
Sable	3.0L/V6-182	R12	2.50	Ford FX-15	②	7	①	.018–.033
	3.8L/V6-232	R12	2.5	Ford FX-15	②	7	①	.018–.033
Taurus	3.0L/V6-182	R12	2.50	Ford FX-15	②	7	①	.018–.033
	3.0L/V6-182 SHO	R12	2.50	Nippondenso 10P15F	②	8	①	.021–.036
	3.8L/V6-232	R12	2.5	Ford FX-15	②	7	①	.018–.033
Tempo	2.3L/4-140	R12	2.25	FX-15	500	10	①	.018–.033
	3.0L/V6-182	R12	2.25	Nippondenso 10P15	500	10	①	.021–.036
Thunderbird	All	R12	2.6	FX-15	②	7	①	.018–.033
Topaz	2.3L/4-140	R12	2.25	FX-15	500	10	①	.018–.033
	3.0L/V6-182	R12	2.25	Nippondenso 10P15	500	10	①	.021–.036
Town Car	All	R12	2.5	Ford FX-15	②	7	①	.018–.033
Tracer	All	R12	2.12	Nippondenso 10P13	②	8	①	.021–.036
1994								
Aspire	All	R134a	1.55	Panasonic 19703	③	5.9	①	.016–.024
Capri	All	R134a	1.2	TRS090	③	4.2	①	.016–.024
Continental	All	R12	2.5	Ford FS-10	②	7	①	.018–.033
	All	R134a	2.5	Ford FS-10	③	7	①	.018–.033
Cougar	All	R134a	2.25	Ford FS-10	③	7	①	.018–.033
Crown Victoria	All	R134a	2.50	Ford FS-10	③	7	①	.018–.033
Escort	1.8L/4-112	R134a	1.75	Ford FS-10	③	8	①	.018–.033
	1.9L/4-116	R134a	1.75	Nippondenso 10P13	③	8	①	.021–.036
Grand Marquis	All	R134a	2.50	Ford FS-10	③	7	①	.018–.033
Mark VIII	All	R134a	2.13	Ford FS-10	③	7	①	.021–.036
Mustang	All	R134a	2.13	Ford FS-10	③	7	①	.021–.036
Probe	All	R134a	1.64	Panasonic 19703	—	6.76	①	.016–.028
Sable	3.0L/V6-182	R134a	2.50	Ford FS-10	③	7	①	.018–.033
	3.8L/V6-232	R134a	2.5	Ford FS-10	③	7	①	.018–.033
Taurus	3.0L/V6-182	R134a	2.50	Ford FS-10	③	7	①	.018–.033
	3.0L/V6-182 SHO	R134a	2.50	Nippondenso 10P15F	③	8	①	.021–.036
	3.8L/V6-232	R134a	2.50	Ford FS-10	③	7	①	.018–.033
Tempo	2.3L/4-140	R134a	2.0	Ford FS-10	③	7	①	.018–.033
	3.0L/V6-182	R134a	2.0	Nippondenso 10P15C	③	8	①	.021–.036
Thunderbird	All	R134a	2.25	Ford FS-10	③	7	①	.018–.033
Topaz	2.3L/4-140	R134a	2.0	Ford FS-10	③	7	①	.018–.033
	3.0L/V6-182	R134a	2.0	Nippondenso 10P15C	③	8	①	.021–.036
Town Car	All	R134a	2.4	Ford FS-10	③	7	①	.018–.033
Tracer	1.8L/4-112	R134a	1.75	Ford FS-10	③	8	①	.021–.036
	1.9L/4-116	R134a	1.75	Nippondenso 10P13	③	8	①	.021–.036

① —Note that "Oil Level Inches' cannot be checked.

② — oil, part No. Motorcraft YN-9.

③ —Polyalkyene glycol refrigerant oil, part No. YN-12.

CHARGING VALVE LOCATION

Model	High Pressure Fitting	Low Pressure Fitting
Aspire	High Pressure Line From Compressor	Low Pressure Line From Compressor
Capri	High Pressure Line From Compressor	Low Pressure Line From Compressor
Continental	High Pressure Line From Compressor	Accumulator
Cougar	High Pressure Line From Compressor	Low Pressure Line From Compressor
Crown Victoria	High Pressure Line From Compressor	Accumulator
Escort	High Pressure Line From Compressor	Low Pressure Line From Compressor
Festiva	High Pressure Line Next to Pressure Switch	Low Pressure Line From Compressor
Grand Marquis	High Pressure Line From Compressor	Accumulator
Mark VII	High Pressure Line From Compressor	Low Pressure Line From Compressor
Mark VIII	High Pressure Line From Compressor	Low Pressure Line From Compressor
Probe	High Pressure Line From Compressor	Low Pressure Line From Compressor
Sable	High Pressure Line From Compressor	Accumulator
Taurus	High Pressure Line From Compressor	Accumulator
Tempo	High Pressure Line From Compressor	Low Pressure Line From Compressor
Thunderbird	High Pressure Line From Compressor	Low Pressure Line From Compressor
Topaz	High Pressure Line From Compressor	Low Pressure Line From Compressor
Town Car	High Pressure Line From Compressor	Accumulator
Tracer	High Pressure Line From Compressor	Low Pressure Line From Compressor

BELT TENSION

Engine	New, Lbs.	Used, Lbs.
1992-93		
1.3L/4-81	110-125	92-110
1.6L/4-97	110-132	110-132
1.8L/4-112	110-132	95-110
1.9L/4-116	①	①
2.0L/4-121	①	①
2.2L/4-133	.24-.31 ④	.27-.35 ②
2.3L/4-140	①	①
2.5L/4-152	160-190	160-190
3.0L/V6-182	①	①
3.0L/V6-182 SHO	220-265	220-265
3.2L/V6-195 SHO	220-265	220-265
3.8L/V6-232	①	①
4.6L/V8-281	①	①
5.0L/V8-302	①	①
1994		
1.3L/4-81	50-60	43-50
1.8L/4-112	110-132	95-110
1.9L/4-116	①	①
2.0L/4-121	①	①
2.3L/4-140	①	①
2.5L/4-152	160-190	110-150
3.0L/V6-182	①	①

BELT TENSION-Continued

Engine	New, Lbs.	Used, Lbs.
1994-Continued		
3.0L/V6-182 SHO	220-265	148-192
3.2L/V6-195 SHO	①	①
3.8L/V6-232	①	①
4.6L/V8-281	①	①
5.0L/V8-302	①	①

① —Drive belt tension is not adjustable.
Drive belt tensioner automatically
adjusts tensioner.
② —Deflection in inches.

COOLING FANS

NOTE: On Air Bag Equipped Models, Refer To "Air Bag System Precautions" Located In The Front Of This Manual For System Disarming & Arming Procedures.

TABLE OF CONTENTS

Variable Speed Fans

INDEX

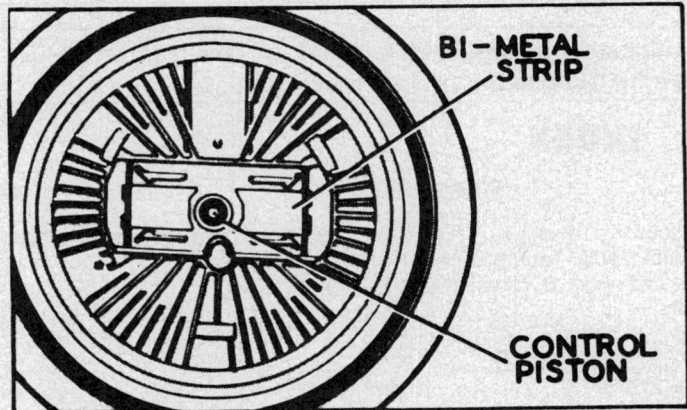

Fig. 1 Variable-speed fan w/flat bi-metal thermostatic spring

FM1089100013000X

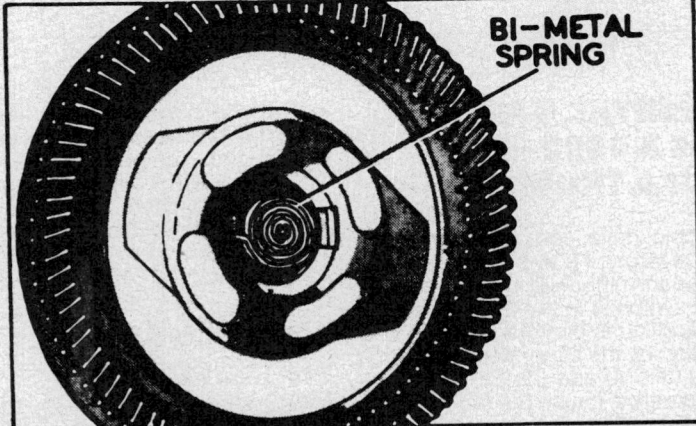

Fig. 2 Variable-speed fan w/coiled bi-metal thermostatic spring

FM1089100014000X

DESCRIPTION

The fan drive clutch is a fluid coupling containing silicone oil. Fan speed is regulated by the torque-carrying capacity of the silicone oil. The more silicone oil in the coupling, the greater the fan speed; the less silicone oil, the slower the fan speed.

Two types of fan drive clutches are in use. On one, **Fig. 1,** a bi-metallic strip and control piston on the front of the fluid coupling regulates the amount of silicone oil entering the coupling. The bi-metallic strip bows outward with an increase in surrounding temperature and allows a piston to move outward. The piston opens a valve regulating the flow of silicone oil into the coupling from a reserve chamber. The silicone oil is returned to the reserve chamber through a bleed hole when the valve is closed.

On the other type of fan drive clutch, **Fig. 2,** a heat-sensitive, bi-metal spring connected to an opening plate brings about a similar result. Both units cause the fan speed to increase with a rise in temperature and to decrease as the temperature goes down.

In some cases a Flex-Fan is used instead of a fan drive clutch. Flexible blades vary the volume of air being drawn through the radiator, automatically increasing the pitch at low engine speeds.

SYSTEM DIAGNOSIS & TESTING

FAN DRIVE CLUTCH TEST

Do not operate the engine until the fan has been first checked for possible cracks and separations.

Run the engine at a fast idle speed (1000 RPM) until normal operating temperature is reached. This process can be speeded up by blocking off the front of the radiator with cardboard. Regardless of temperatures, the unit must be operated for at least five minutes immediately before being tested.

Stop the engine and, using a glove or a cloth to protect the hand, immediately check the effort required to turn the fan. If considerable effort is required, it can be assumed that the coupling is operating satisfactorily. If very little effort is required to turn the fan, it is an indication that the coupling is not operating properly and should be replaced.

If the clutch fan is the coiled bi-metal spring type, it may be tested while the vehicle is being driven. To check, disconnect the bi-metal spring and rotate 90° counterclockwise. This disables the temperature-controlled free-wheeling feature and the clutch performs like a conventional fan. If this cures the overheating condition, replace the clutch fan.

COMPONENT SERVICE

To prevent silicone fluid from draining into fan drive bearing, do not store or place drive unit on bench with rear of shaft pointing downward.

The removal procedure for either type of fan clutch assembly is generally the same for all cars. Merely unfasten the unit from the water pump and remove the assembly from the car.

The variable speed fan with flat bi-metal thermostatic spring may be partially disassembled for inspection and cleaning. Remove screws holding the assembly together and separate the fan from the drive clutch. Next remove the metal strip on the front by pushing one end of it toward the fan clutch body so it clears the retaining bracket. Then push the strip to the side so that its opposite end will spring out of place. Now remove the small control piston underneath it.

Check the piston for free movement of the coupling device. If the piston sticks, clean it with emery cloth. If the bi-metal strip is damaged, replace the entire unit. These strips are not interchangeable.

When reassembling, install the control piston so that the projection on the end of it will contact the metal strip. Then install the metal strip. After reassembly, clean the clutch drive with a cloth soaked in solvent. Avoid dipping the clutch assembly in any type of liquid. Install the assembly in the reverse order of removal.

The coil spring type of fan clutch cannot be disassembled, serviced or repaired. If it does not function properly it must be replaced with a new unit.

Electric Cooling Fans

NOTE: On Air Bag Equipped Models, Refer To "Air Bag System Precautions" Located In The Front Of This Manual For System Disarming & Arming Procedures.

NOTE: Wire Color Code & Electrical Symbol Identification Located At The Front Of This Manual Can Be Used As An Aid When Using Wiring Circuits Found In This Section.

INDEX

DESCRIPTION
CAPRI, ESCORT & TRACER

The electric cooling fan draws air through the radiator to dissipate heat absorbed by coolant. The fan will operate when the coolant has reached a specific temperature. The coolant temperature switch matches fan operation to coolant heat load. At 212°F, the switch will open and begin fan operation. When the coolant temperature drops to 200°F, the switch will close, stopping the fans operation. The 1.9L/4-116 Escort cooling fan is controlled by the Powertrain Control Module PCM (ECA).

CONTINENTAL, SABLE, TAURUS & 1992–93 COUGAR & THUNDERBIRD

The electric drive cooling fan system consists of a fan and a two-speed electric motor. This fan motor will only run when the ignition switch is in the Run position.

The cooling fan is controlled during engine operation by the integrated relay control module (IRCM) and the EEC-IV module. These controls cause the fan to run at low speed when the engine temperature reaches approximately 215°F, or when the A/C is on and vehicle does not provide enough air flow. The fan will continue to run until engine temperature drops to approximately 210°F.

The cooling fan will run at high speed when fan has been operating at low speed, but engine temperature is still above 230°F, or during idle when engine temperature has reached approximately 236°F. The cooling fan will begin to operate at low speed when engine temperature drops to approximately 224°F. The cooling fan does not cycle with A/C.

1994 COUGAR & THUNDERBIRD

The electric drive cooling fan system consists of a fan and a two-speed electric motor. This fan motor will only run when the ignition switch is in the Run position.

The cooling fan is controlled during engine operation by the constant control relay module (CCRM) and the powertrain

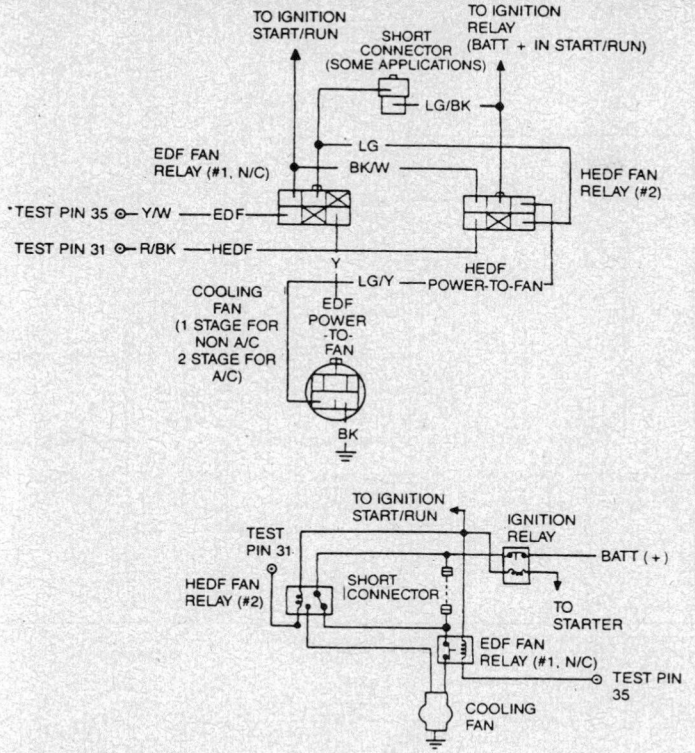

Fig. 1 Cooling fan wiring diagram. 1992–93 Continental, Cougar, Sable, Taurus & Thunderbird & Probe w/3.0L/V6-182 engine

control module (PCM). These controls cause the fan to run at low speed when the engine temperature reaches approximately 222°F, or when the A/C is on and vehicle does not provide enough air flow. The fan will continue to run until engine temperature drops to approximately 214°F.

The cooling fan will run at high speed when fan has been operating at low speed, but engine temperature is still above 228°F, and stops running when engine temperature drops to approximately 224°F. The cooling fan does not cycle with A/C.

TEMPO & TOPAZ

The electric fan system consists of a fan and electric motor. This system uses a coolant temperature switch, mounted in the thermostat housing, to sense coolant temperature. Vehicles equipped with A/C have a cooling fan controller and a cooling fan relay. Models equipped with a standard heater, the cooling fan is powered through the cooling fan relay.

The cooling fan is wired to operate only when the ignition switch is in the Run position.

On vehicles equipped with A/C, the cooling fan motor will be energized whenever the A/C cycling pressure switch closes, with the select lever in the A/C or defrost position. The A/C clutch coil will be energized once voltage is supplied to the fan motor. The A/C clutch will cycle with the A/C clutch cycling pressure switch. The fan motor will stay energized as the clutch cycles, if the cycling pressure

switch "open intervals" are less than 2-3 minutes. If the coolant temperature switch closes in the A/C mode at approximately 210°F, the fan motor will run until coolant temperature drops below approximately 193°F.

ASPIRE & FESTIVA

The cooling fan system consists of an electro-mechanical fan, a temperature switch and a temperature relay.

The temperature switch, located in the thermostat housing, senses engine coolant temperature; while the relay, located in the left front corner of the engine compartment between the battery and headlamp, provides the ground path to complete the circuit.

When coolant temperature is below approximately 194°F, the temperature switch is closed, while the relay contacts are held open by the magnetism produced in the relay coil. When temperature is above approximately 207°F, the temperature switch is opened, allowing the relay contacts to close, thereby completing the ground circuit and activating the cooling fan.

Vehicles equipped with air conditioning have an added relay in the circuit, allowing the bypassing of the engine temperature portion of the circuit, and enabling fan activation any time the air conditioning system is in use.

MUSTANG

1992–93

This system consists of a single speed fan, which operates only when the ignition switch is in the run position. The cooling fan is controlled during vehicle operation by the integrated relay control module (IRCM) and EEC-IV module. The cooling fan should operate when coolant temperature reaches 221°F, or with the air conditioning on and vehicle speed below 43 mph. The fan will continue to run until coolant temperature drops to 201°F, or vehicle speed reaches at least 48 mph.

1994

This system consists of a dual-speed fan, which operates only when the ignition switch is in the run position. The cooling fan is controlled during vehicle operation by the constant control relay module (CCRM) and powertrain control module (PCM). The cooling fan should operate when coolant temperature reaches 221°F, or with the air conditioning on and vehicle speed below 43 mph. The fan will continue to run until coolant temperature drops to 200°F, or vehicle speed reaches at least 48 mph.

PROBE
1992 w/2.2L/4-134 ENGINE
Manual Transaxle

A single normally closed relay supplies power to the fan motor. The fan motor is controlled by the coolant temperature switch. When the air conditioning is being used, the wide-open throttle-A/C cutoff relay controls the cooling fan relay to operate the fan. An electric signal is sent to the ECA to maintain idle quality.

Electronic Automatic Transaxle

A two-speed cooling fan is used on these models. The cooling fan relay (CFR) and high speed fan relay (HSFR) combine to provide both speeds. The CFR produces the low speed operation. The HSFR provides high speed operation when excessive temperature is reached, or when the A/C compressor is operating.

1992 w/3.0L/V6-182 ENGINE

Cooling fan operation is controlled entirely by the Electronic Control Assembly (ECA) and integral relay controller.

1993–94

The cooling fan incorporates a two-speed cooling electric motor which is mounted within the cooling shroud behind the radiator. The Cooling Fan Engine Coolant Temperature (ECTF) sensor measures coolant temperature and sends a signal to the PCM which will activate the cooling fan accordingly. The cooling fan motor can be activated to operate on low or high speed.

1992–93 MODELS EXCEPT CAPRI, ESCORT, FESTIVA, MUSTANG, TRACER & PROBE w/2.2L/4–134 ENGINE

The electric cooling fan system consists of a two speed fan on all 3.0L/V6-182,

3.2L/V6-195 SHO and 3.8L/V6-232 engines with automatic transaxles or a single speed fan on 3.0L/V6-182 SHO engines with a manual transaxle and 2.3L/4-140 engines. The electric cooling fan motor is mounted within a shroud behind the radiator assembly. The Constant Control Module (CCRM) (Integrated Relay Control Module IRCM) actuates the fan motor when the engine coolant reaches a specified temperature, when the engine reaches a specified speed, or when the air conditioning clutch is activated, if equipped.

The Constant Control Module ((CCRM) (Integrated Relay Control Module (IRCM)) interfaces with the PCM (EEC-IV) system to provide control for the cooling fan, air conditioning clutch and the fuel pump. The IRCM also contains the EEC power relay which provides vehicle battery power (VPWR) to the EEC-IV processor.

MARK VIII

The variable control relay module (VCRM) is used to control the engine cooling fan operation speed and A/C clutch operation in addition to other non-A/C functions. The VCRM control fan operation when required will increase and decrease fan speed as necessary depending on refrigerant system high side pressure. The VCRM also can turn the A/C clutch circuit off if the high side pressure exceeds 425 psi. The VCRM is connected electrically to the powertrain control module (PCM), with the A/C high side pressure (ACP) sensor, A/C clutch coil circuit and the fan control circuit.

Another feature of the VCRM is the ability to stop fan control operation at vehicle speeds in excess of approximately 45 mph. Fan operation will resume when vehicle speed drops approximately 42 mph. One exception is when the high side pressure is above 300 psi. The fan control will not shut off when the high side pressure is above 300 psi. In the event of an ACP sensor failure, the fan control will continue to operate.

SYSTEM DIAGNOSIS & TESTING

The cooling fan systems used on models not listed in this section are controlled by the Powertrain Control Module. **Consult the latest edition of MOTOR'S "Auto Engine Tune-Up & Electronics Manual" for Powertrain Control (EEC-IV) diagnostic procedures and testing on these models.**

Refer to wiring diagrams in **Figs. 1 through 29** when performing diagnosis and testing procedures.

Perform visual inspection prior to performing any diagnosis and testing procedures.

1. Check coolant level and condition.
2. Check condition of radiator, thermostat and hoses.
3. Check for fan blade interference.
4. Check for proper mounting of fan motor.
5. Check for proper fan blade attachment to motor.
6. Check for blown fuses.

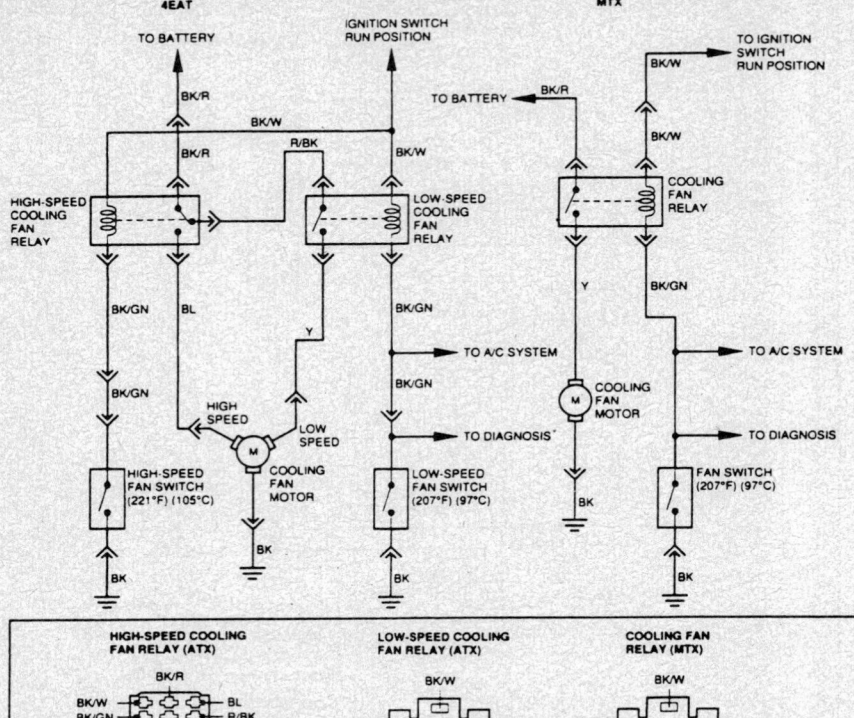

Fig. 2   Cooling fan wiring diagram. 1992–93 Escort & Tracer w/1.8L/4-122 engine

7. Check wiring harnesses for damaged wires and poor or corroded connectors.
8. Ensure battery is fully charged.

CAPRI

Refer to **Fig. 30** for symptom charts and **Fig. 31** for diagnostic test steps.

TEMPO & TOPAZ

Less A/C

Voltage readings can be obtained using Rotunda Digital Volt/Ohmmeter, tool No. 007-00001, or equivalent.

Refer to **Fig. 32** for diagnosis of the cooling fan system less A/C.

With A/C

Refer to **Fig. 33** for diagnosis of the cooling fan system with A/C.

Diagnosis of the cooling fan controller can be performed by taking voltage and continuity readings at the controller connector, with the connector plugged into the controller. The readings should be obtained at the indicated connector pins. if the indicated reading is not present, refer to system diagnosis to determine origin of problem.

Refer to **Fig. 34** for diagnosis of cooling fan controller.

ESCORT & TRACER

Refer to **Figs. 35 and 36** for symptom charts and **Figs. 37 through 42** for diagnostic test steps.

FESTIVA

Refer to **Fig. 43** for symptom chart and **Fig. 44** for diagnostic test steps.

1992–93 MUSTANG

Refer to **Figs. 45 and 46** for diagnostic test steps.

PROBE

1992
2.2L/4–133 Engine

Refer to **Fig. 47** for symptom chart and **Fig. 48** for diagnostic test steps.

1993–94
2.0L/4-122 Engine

Refer to **Fig. 49** for symptom chart and **Fig. 50** for diagnostic test steps.

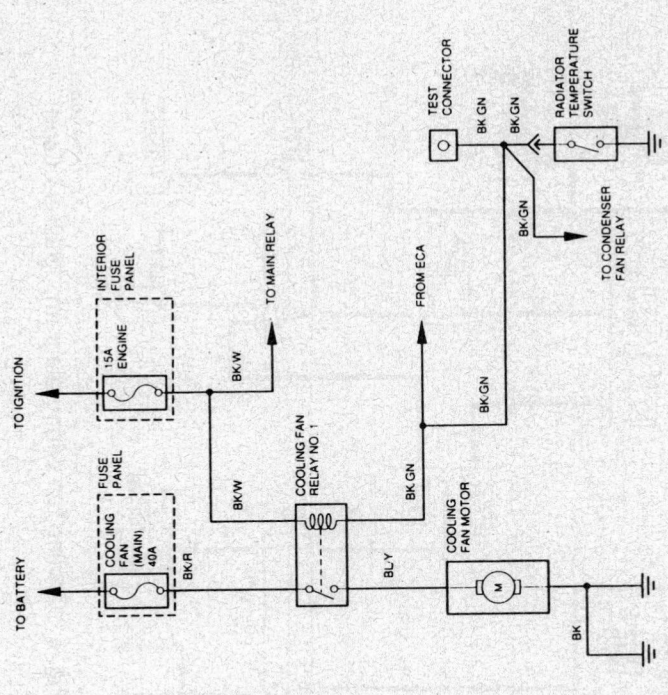

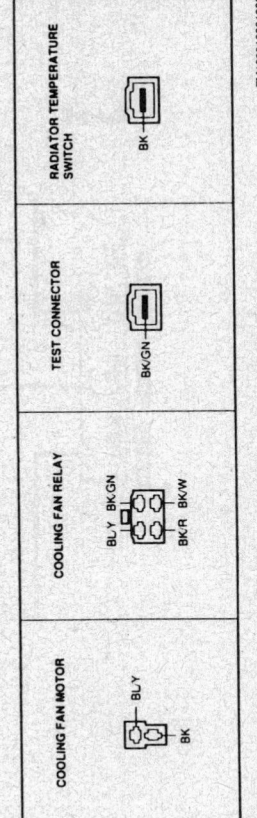

Fig. 4   Cooling fan wiring diagram. 1992 Probe w/2.2L/4-133 engine & manual transaxle

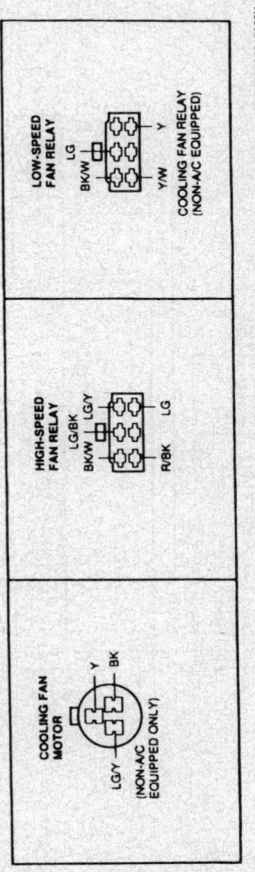

Fig. 3   Cooling fan wiring diagram. 1992-93 Escort & Tracer w/1.9L/4-116 engine

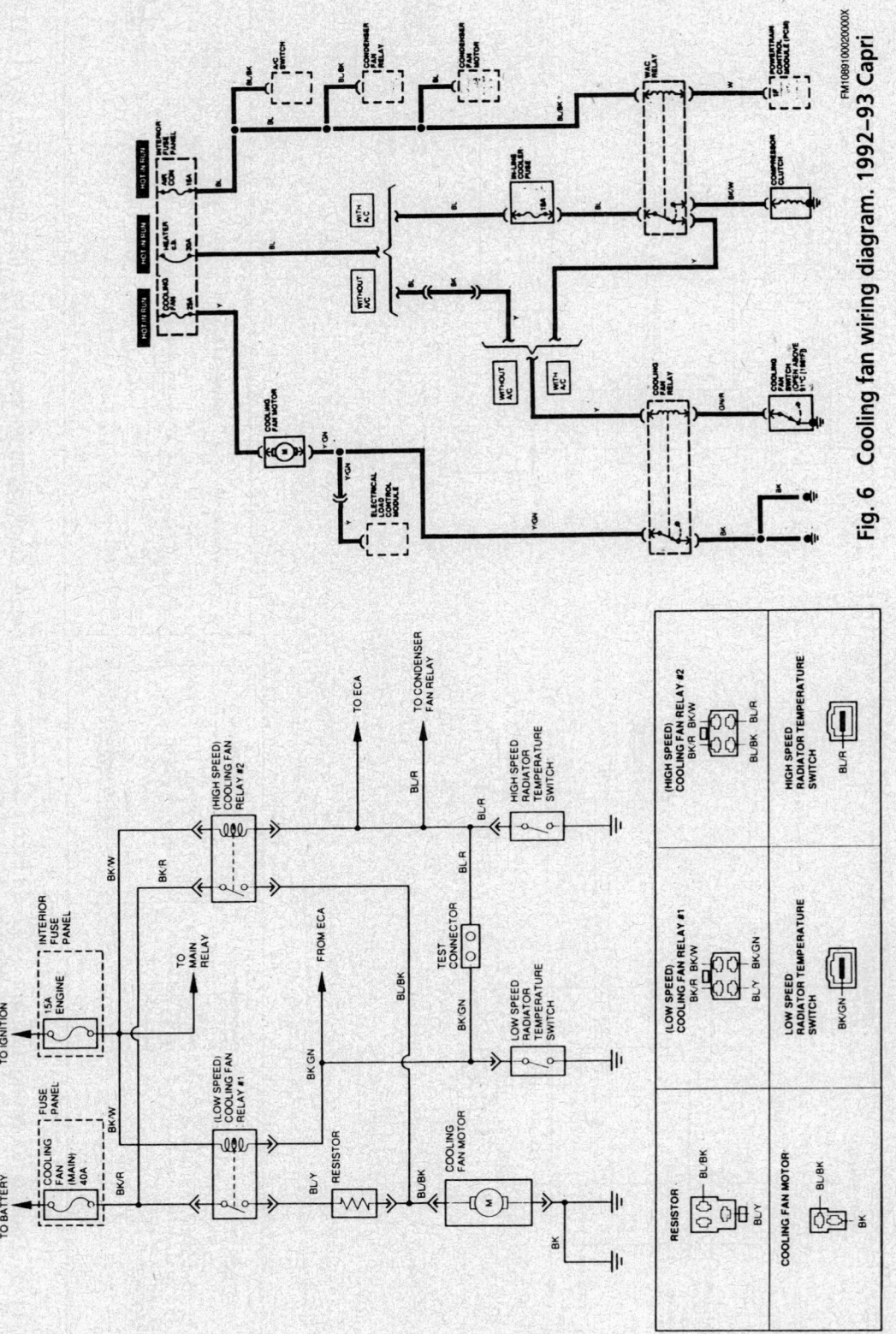

Fig. 6 Cooling fan wiring diagram. 1992–93 Capri

Fig. 5 Cooling fan wiring diagram. 1992 Probe w/2.2L/4-133 engine & automatic transaxle

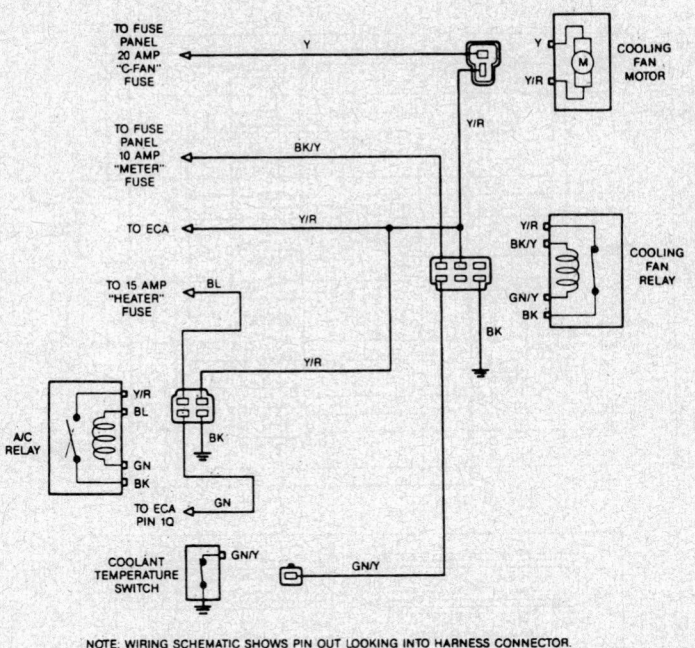

Fig. 7   Cooling fan wiring diagram. Festiva

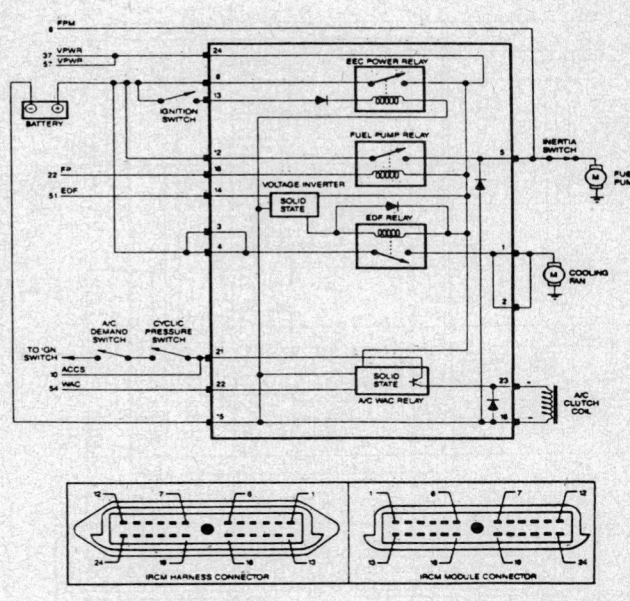

Fig. 8   Cooling fan wiring diagram. 1992–93 Mustang

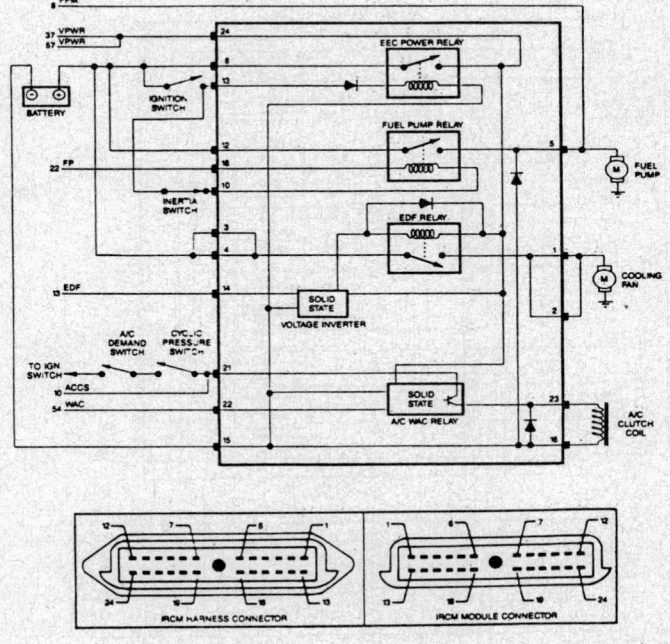

Fig. 9   Cooling fan wiring diagram. 1992–93 Tempo/Topaz w/2.3L/4–140 engine

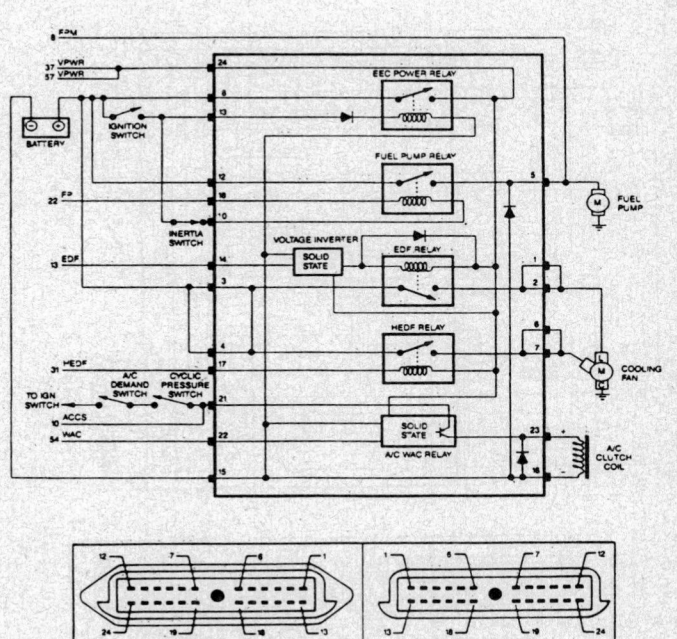

Fig. 10   Cooling fan wiring diagram. 1992–93 Tempo/Topaz w/3.0L/V6–182 engine

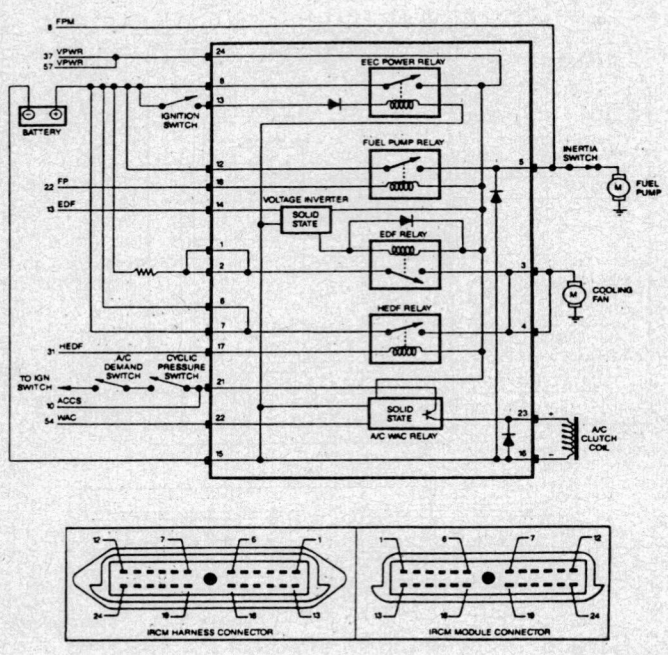

Fig. 11   Cooling fan wiring diagram. 1992–93 Sable & Taurus w/3.0L/V6-182 engine

FM1089200025000X

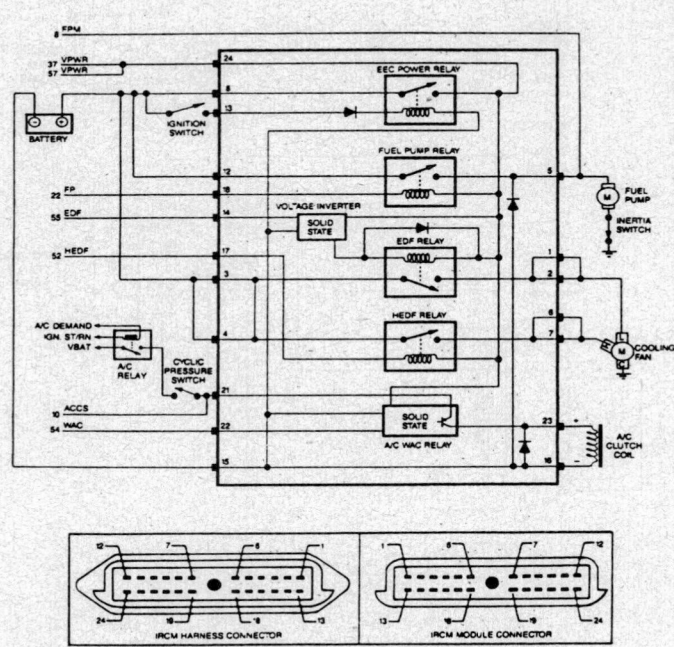

Fig. 12   Cooling fan wiring diagram. 1992 Probe w/3.0L/V6-182 engine

FM1089200026000X

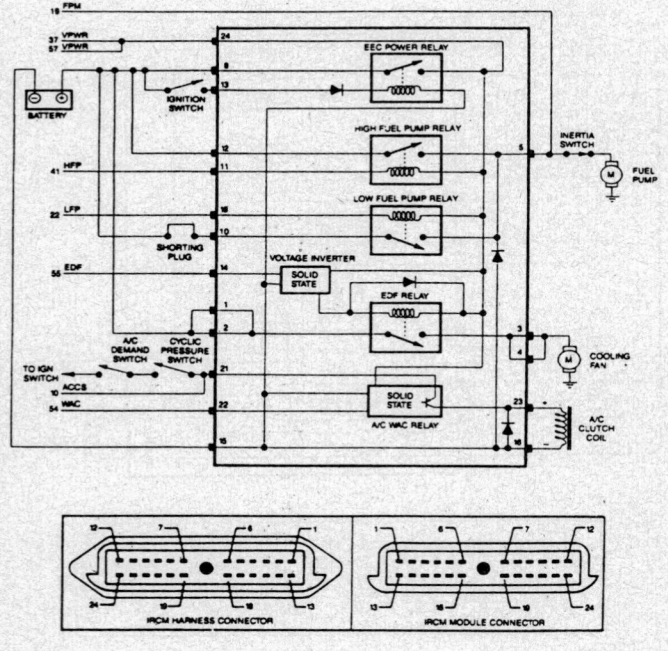

Fig. 13   Cooling fan wiring diagram. 1992–93 Taurus SHO

FM1089200027000X

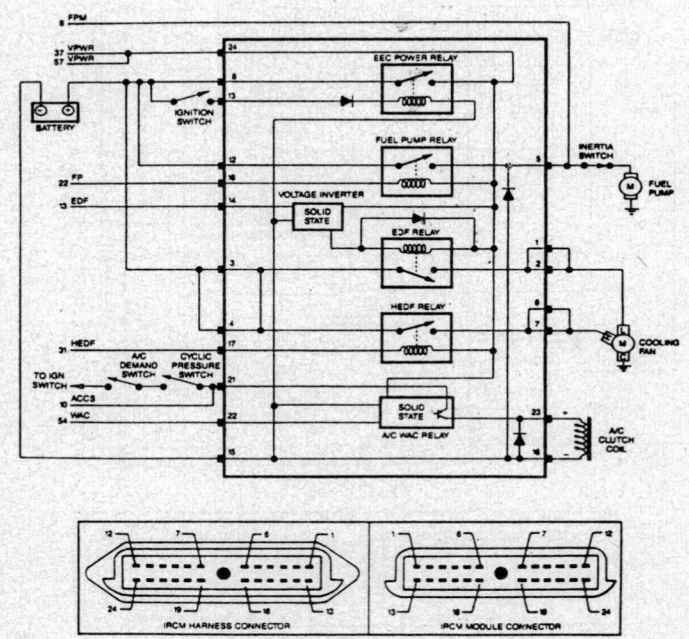

Fig. 14   Cooling fan wiring diagram. 1992–93 Continental & Sable/Taurus w/3.8L/V6-232 engine

FM1089200028000X

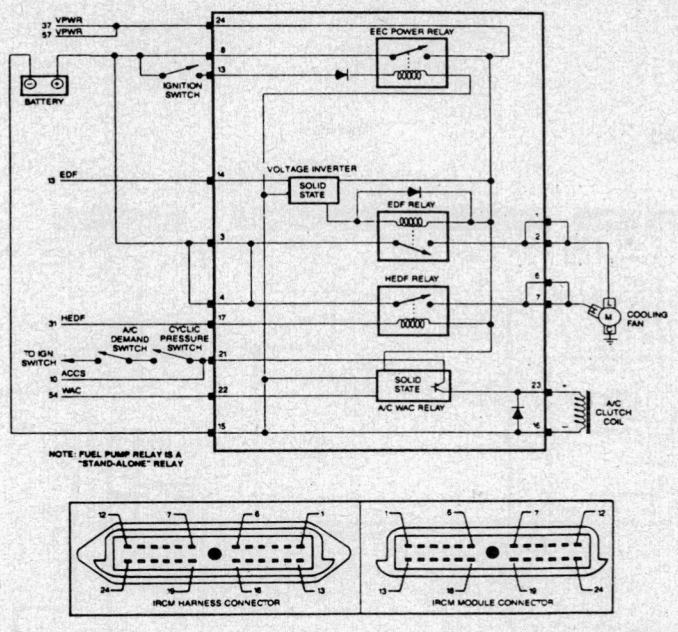

Fig. 15 Cooling fan wiring diagram. 1992–93 Thunderbird SC

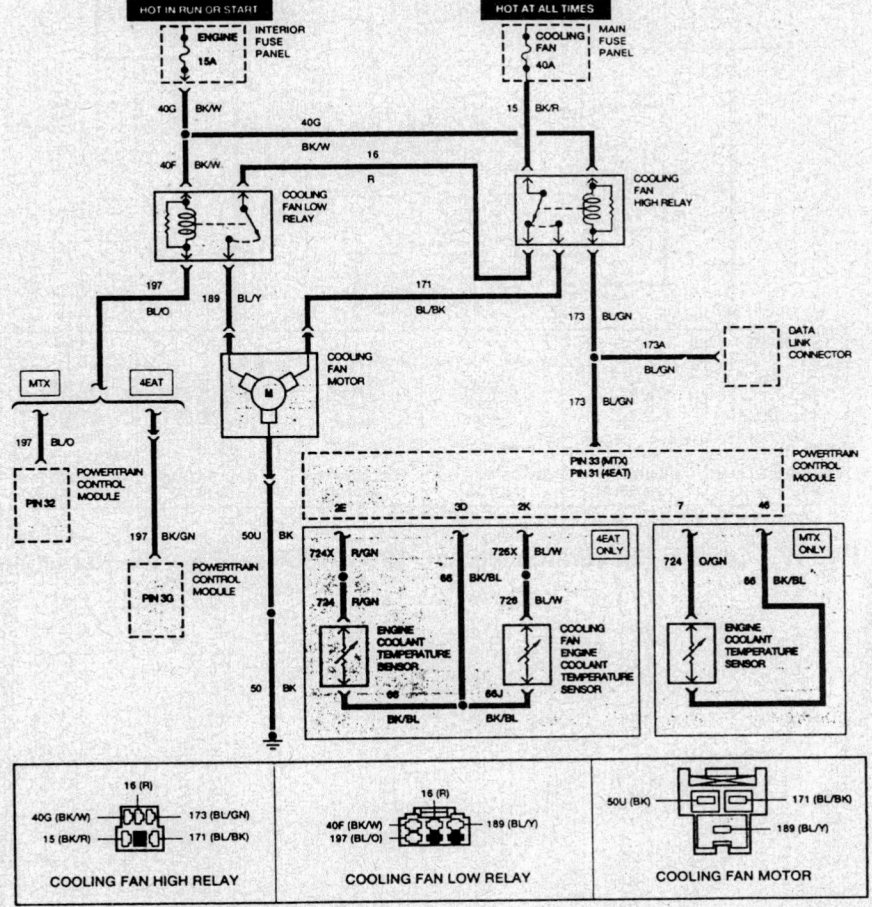

Fig. 16 Cooling fan wiring diagram. 1993 Probe w/2.0L/4–122 engine

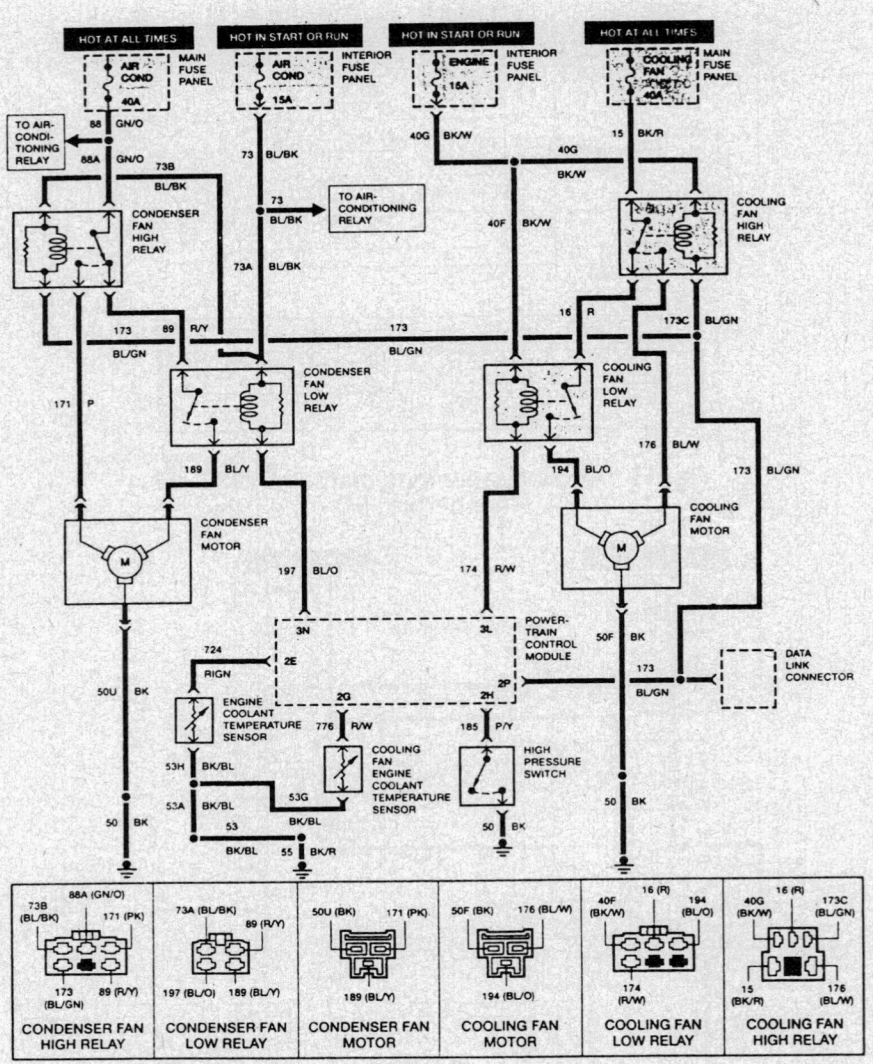

Fig. 17   Cooling fan wiring diagram. 1993 Probe w/2.5L/V6-152 engine

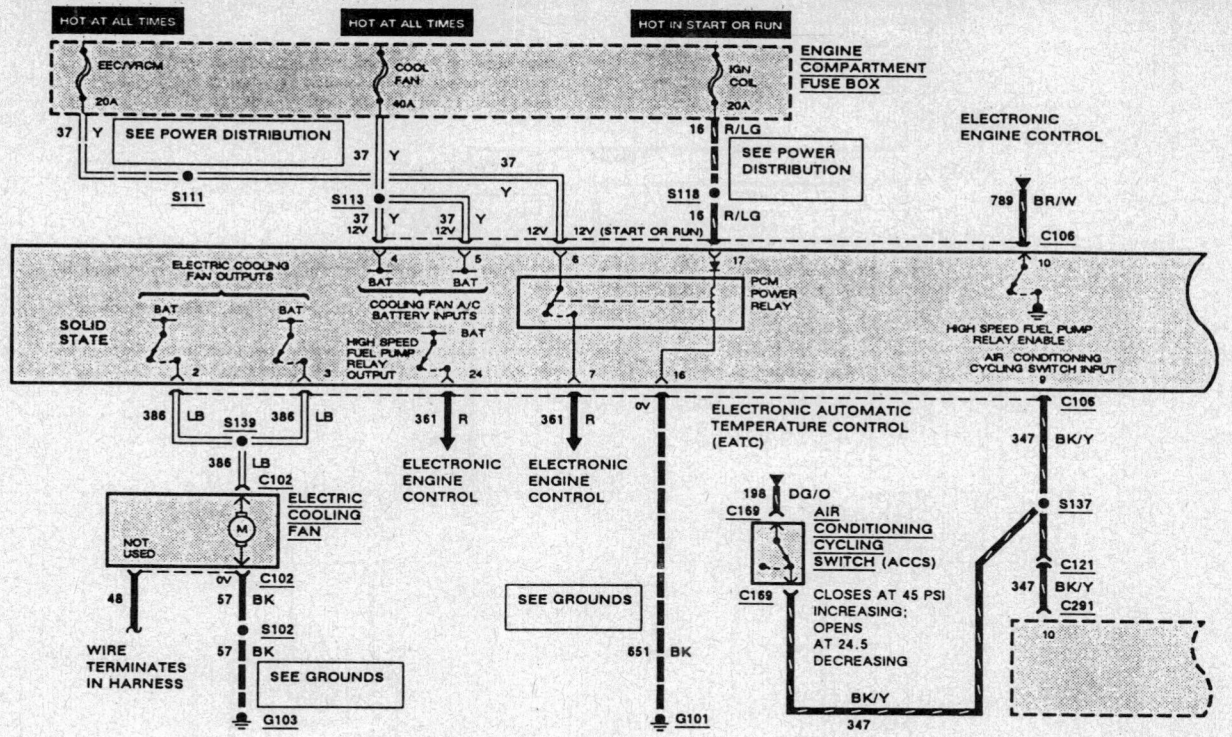

Fig. 18   Cooling fan wiring diagram (Part 1 of 2). 1993 Mark VIII

FM1089100032010X

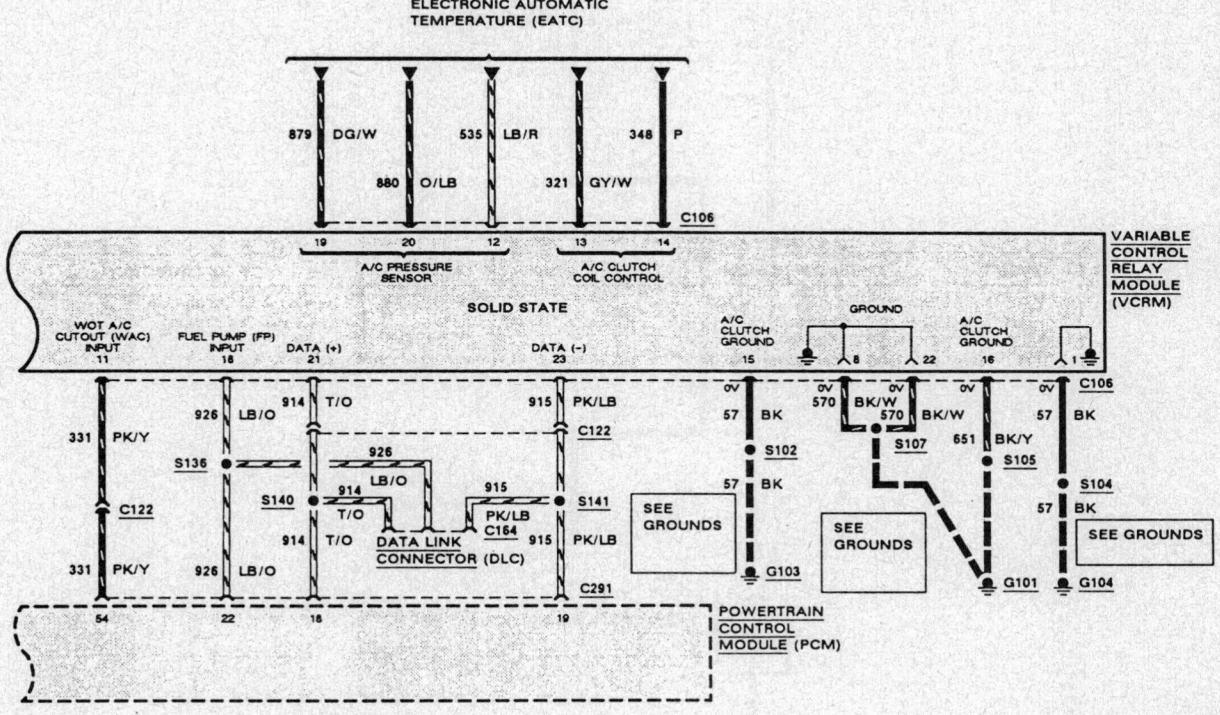

Fig. 18   Cooling fan wiring diagram (Part 2 of 2). 1993 Mark VIII

FM1089100032020X

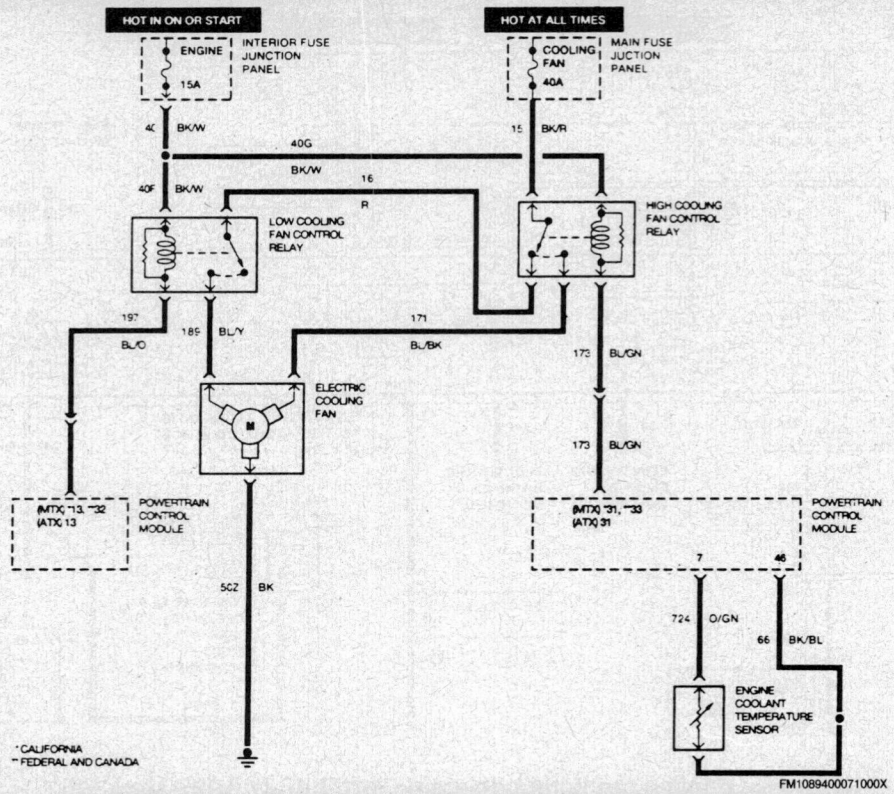

Fig. 19 Cooling fan wiring diagram. 1994 Probe w/2.0L/4-122 engine

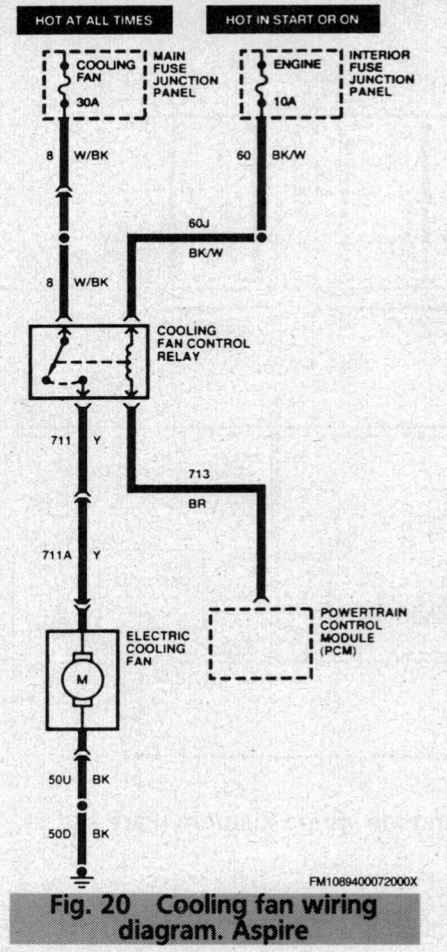

Fig. 20 Cooling fan wiring diagram. Aspire

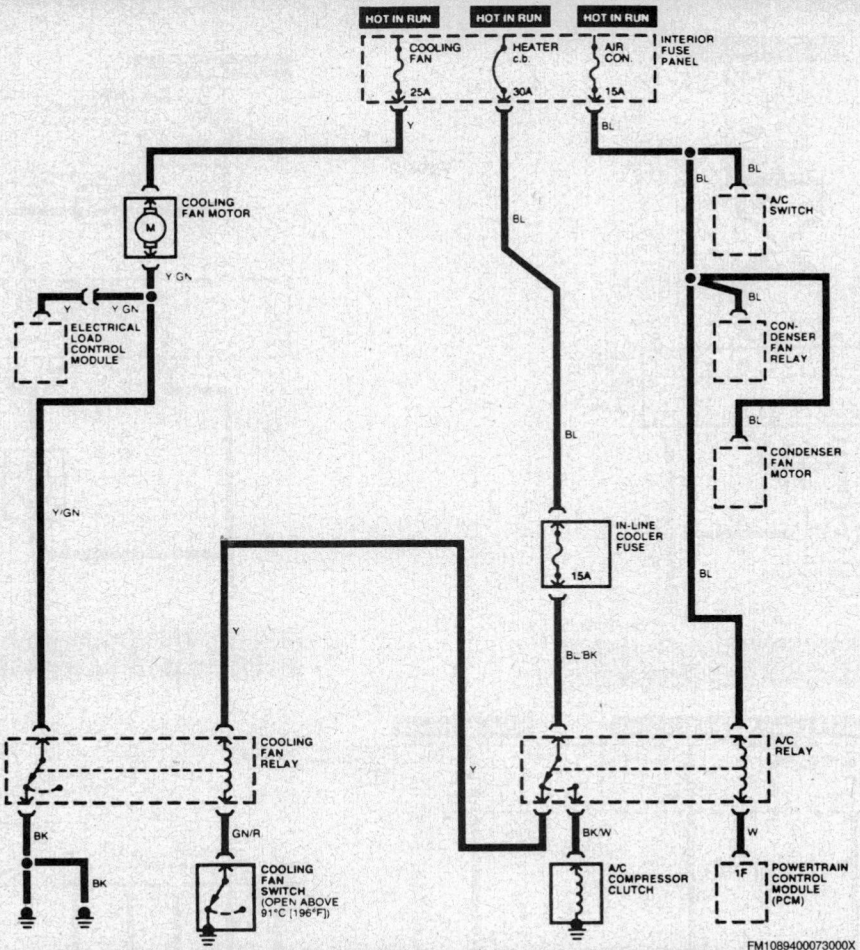

Fig. 21 Cooling fan wiring diagram. 1994 Capri

FM1089400073000X

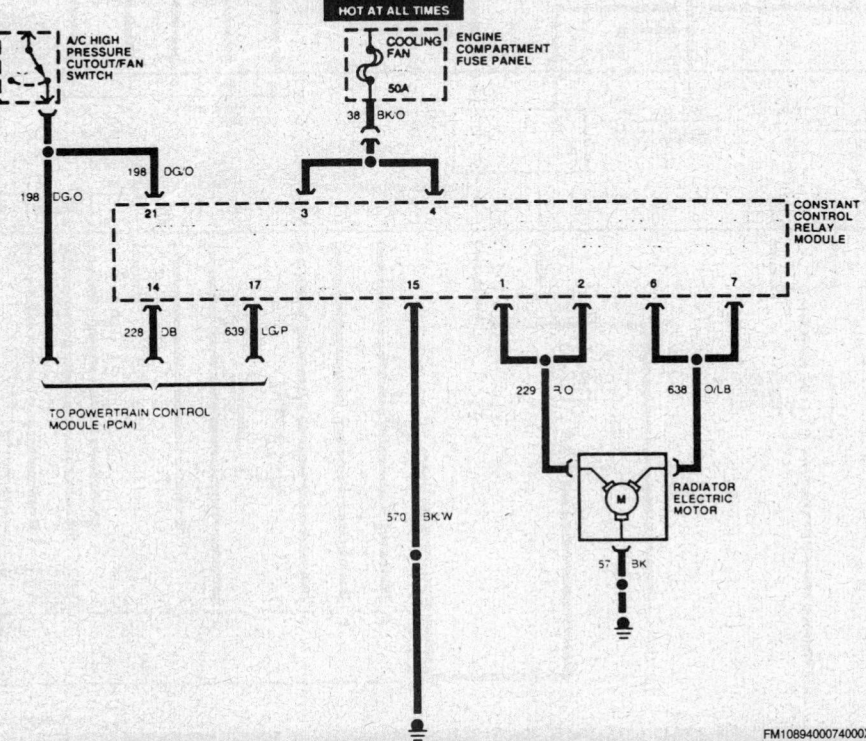

Fig. 22 Cooling fan wiring diagram. 1994 Mustang

FM1089400074000X

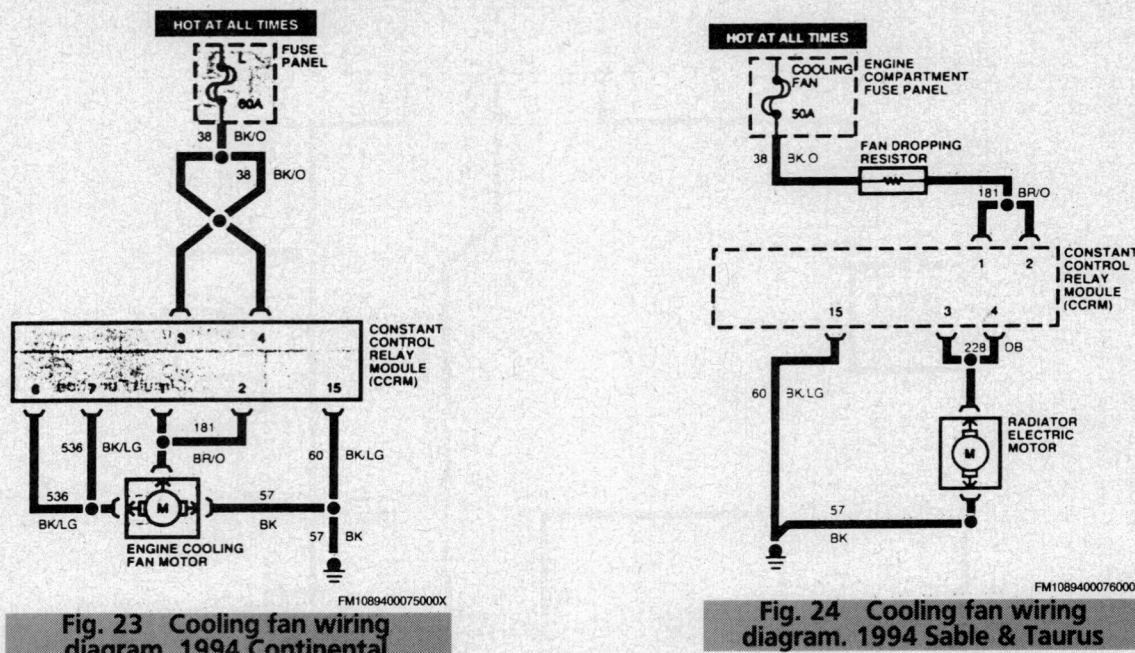

Fig. 23 Cooling fan wiring diagram. 1994 Continental

Fig. 24 Cooling fan wiring diagram. 1994 Sable & Taurus

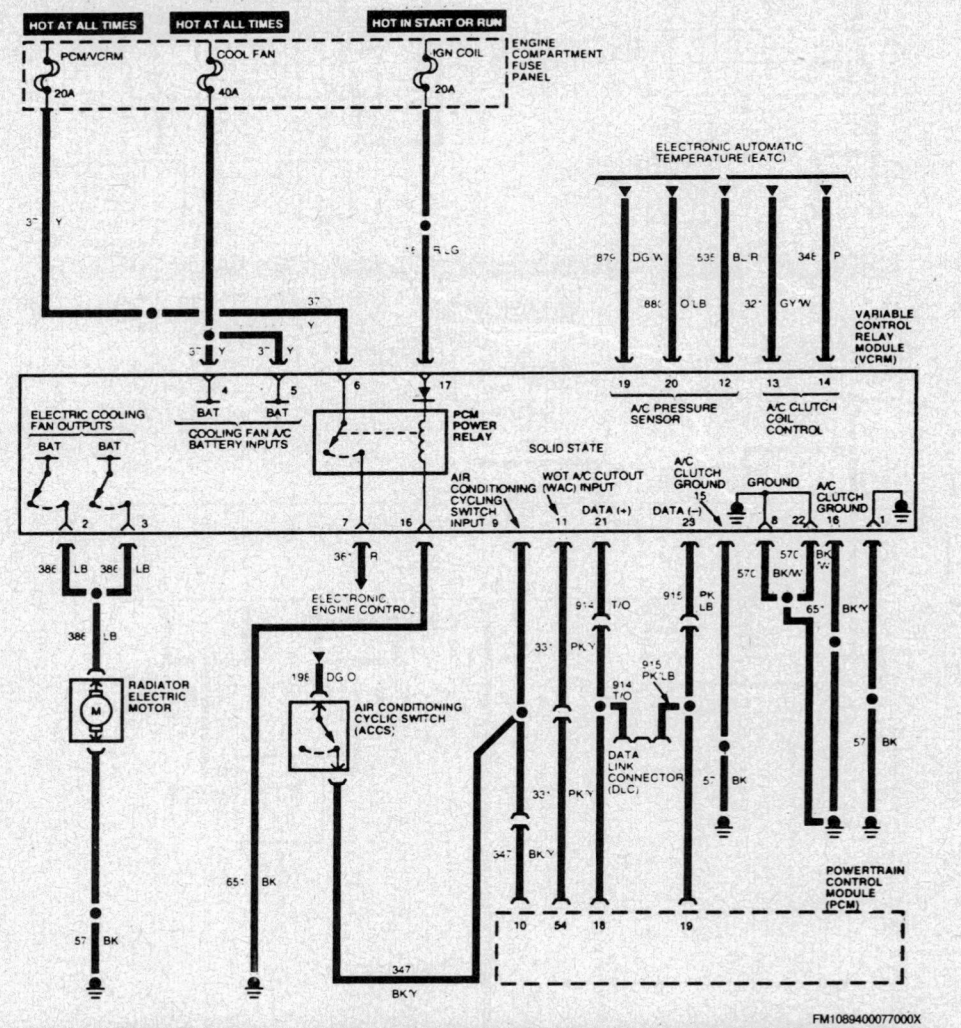

Fig. 25 Cooling fan wiring diagram. 1994 Mark VIII

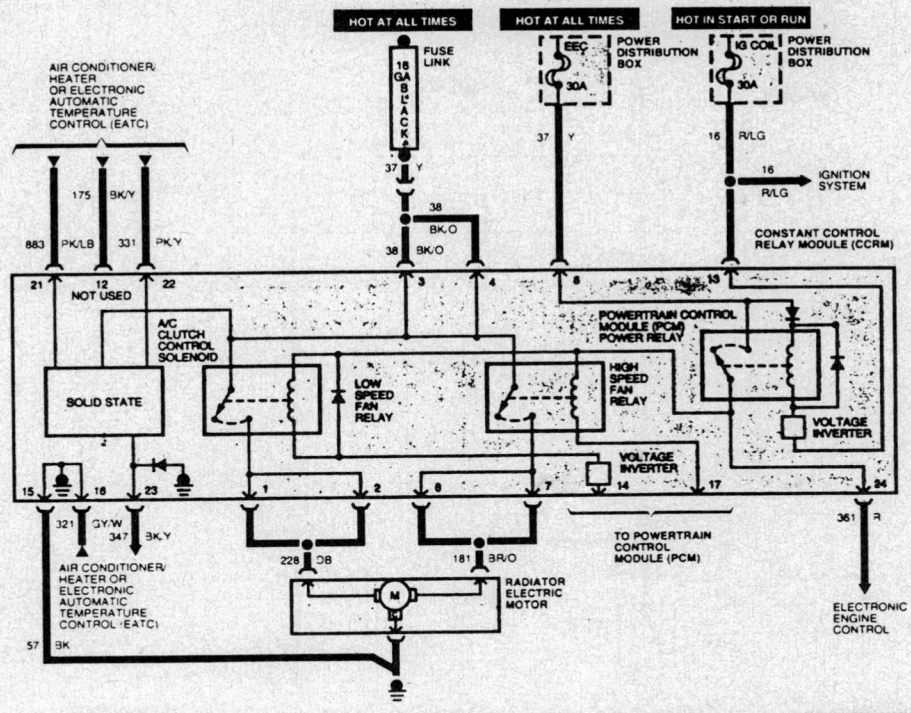

Fig. 26 Cooling fan wiring diagram. 1994 Cougar & Thunderbird

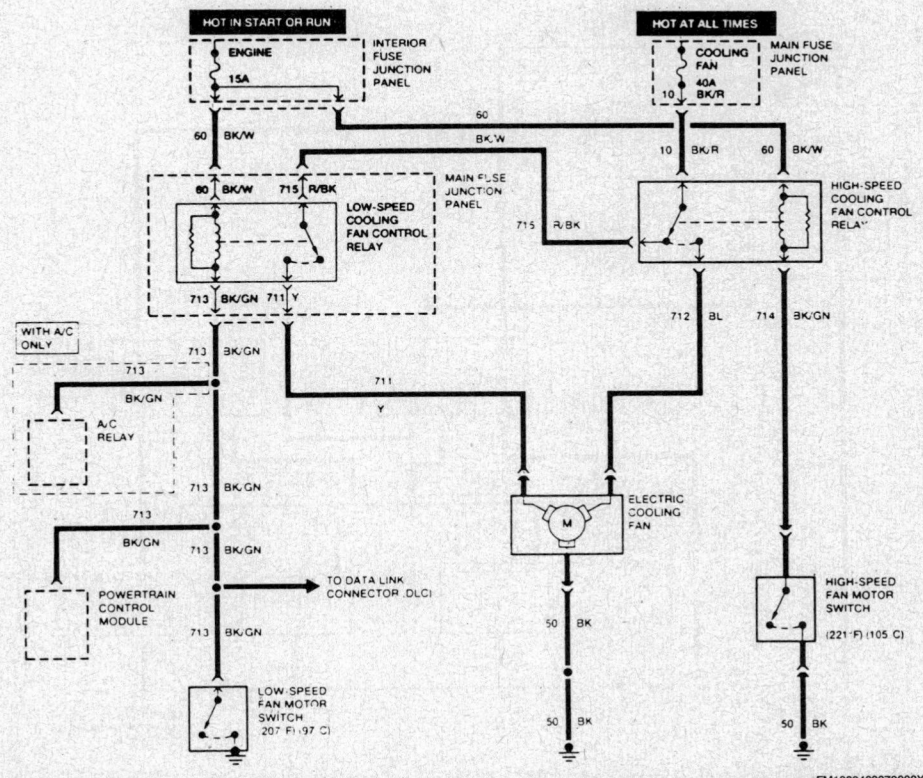

Fig. 27 Cooling fan wiring diagram. 1994 Escort & Tracer w/1.8L/4-122 engine & automatic trans.

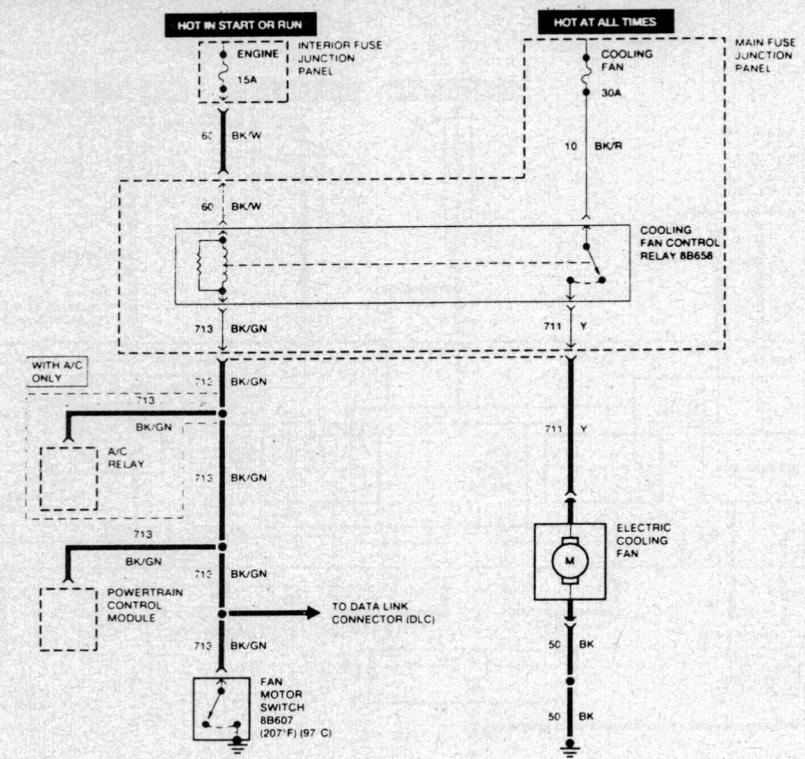

Fig. 28 Cooling fan wiring diagram. 1994 Escort & Tracer w/1.8L/4-122 engine & manual trans.

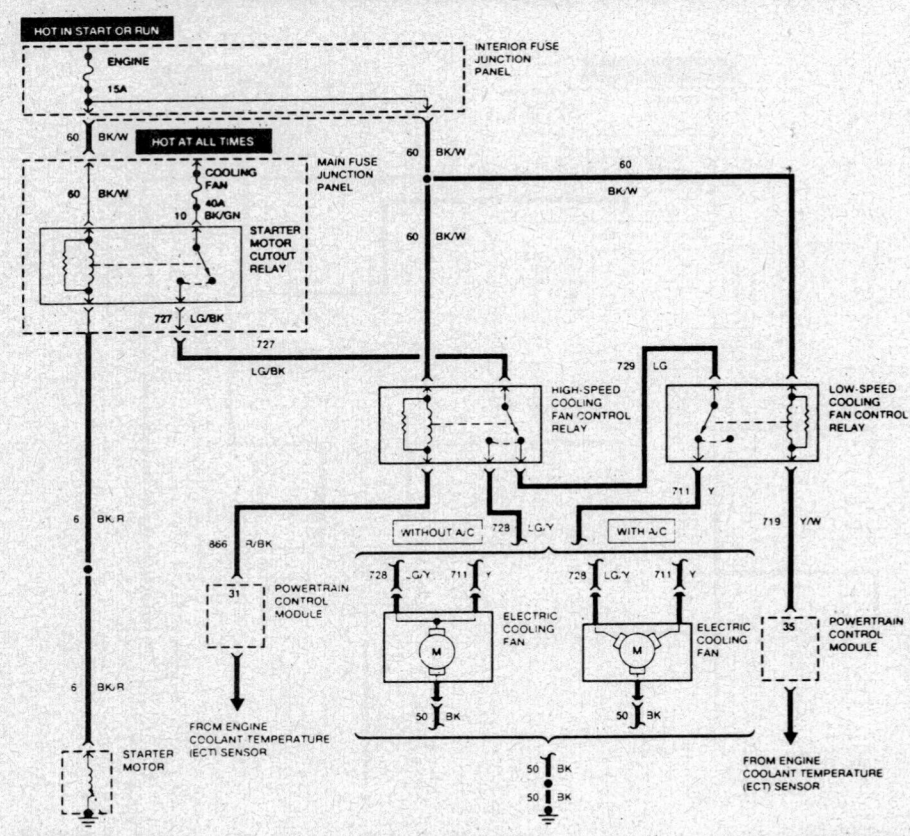

Fig. 29 Cooling fan wiring diagram. 1994 Escort & Tracer w/1.9L/4-116 engine

CONDITION	POSSIBLE SOURCE	ACTION
• Overheating	• Fuse	• Go to EC1.
	• Cooling fan switch.	• Go to EC17.
	• Cooling fan relay.	• Go to EC15.
	• Cooling fan motor.	• Go to EC12.
	• A/C relay.	• Go to EC7.
	• Circuit.	• Go to EC4.

FM1089100033010X

Fig. 30   Symptom diagnosis charts (Part 1 of 2). Capri

CONDITION	POSSIBLE SOURCE	ACTION
• Fan Runs Erratically or Intermittently	• Cooling fan switch.	• Go to EC17.
	• Cooling fan relay.	• Go to EC15.
	• Cooling fan motor.	• Go to EC12.
	• A/C relay.	• Go to EC7.
	• Circuit.	• Go to EC4.
• Fan Runs Continuously	• Cooling fan relay.	• Go to EC15.
	• Cooling fan switch.	• Go to EC17.
	• A/C relay.	• Go to EC7.
	• Circuit.	• Go to EC4.
• Fan Does Not Run When A/C is ON	• A/C relay.	• Go to EC7.
	• Cooling fan relay.	• Go to EC15.
	• Cooling fan motor.	• Go to EC12.
	• Circuit.	• Go to EC4.

FM1089100033020X

Fig. 30   Symptom diagnosis charts (Part 2 of 2). Capri

	TEST STEP	RESULT	▶	ACTION TO TAKE
EC6	CHECK THE LEAD TO A/C CONTROL AMPLIFIER (A/C ONLY)			
	• Key OFF.	Yes	▶	GO to EC7.
	• Measure the resistance of the BL wire between the A/C relay and the A/C control amplifier.	No	▶	SERVICE BL wire.
	• Is the resistance less than 5 ohms?			
EC7	CHECK A/C RELAY (A/C ONLY)			
	• Disconnect A/C Relay.	Yes	▶	GO to EC8.
	• Measure the resistance between the following terminals and verify the resistances:	No	▶	SERVICE/REPLACE A/C relay.

From	To	Resistances
BL	Y	Less than 5 ohms
BL	BK/Y	Greater than 10,000 ohms

- Apply 12 volts to the BL terminal as shown below.
- Ground the W terminal.
- Measure the resistance between the following terminals and verify the resistances:

From	To	Resistances
BL	Y	Greater than 10,000 ohms
BL	BK/Y	Less than 5 ohms

From	To	Resistances
BL	Y	Greater than 10,000 ohms
BL	BK/W	Less than 5 ohms

A/C RELAY — 1991 model

MEASURE RESISTANCE FROM THIS BL TERMINAL TO EITHER THE Y OR THE BK/Y TERMINAL AS DIRECTED ABOVE.

A/C RELAY — 1992 model

MEASURE RESISTANCE FROM THIS BL TERMINAL TO EITHER THE Y OR THE BK/W TERMINAL AS DIRECTED ABOVE.

- Are the resistances correct?
- Are resistances correct?

FM1089100034020X

Fig. 31   Diagnostic test steps (Part 2 of 5). Capri

	TEST STEP	RESULT	▶	ACTION TO TAKE
EC1	CHECK FUSES			
	• Locate interior fuse panel.	Yes	▶	GO to EC4.
	• Key OFF.	No	▶	GO to EC2.
	• Check the 15 amp air conditioning and the 20 amp cooling fuses.			
	• Are the fuses good?			
EC2	CHECK SYSTEM			
	• Replace blown fuse(s).	Yes	▶	GO to EC3.
	• Key ON.	No	▶	GO to EC4.
	• Did fuse(s) blow again?			
EC3	CHECK FOR SHORTS TO GROUND			
	• Key OFF.	Yes	▶	SERVICE wire(s) in question.
	• Disconnect the BL wire at the air conditioning fuse and the Y wire at the cooling fuse.	No	▶	GO to EC4.
	• Measure the resistance of the BL and then the Y wire to ground.			
	• Are the resistances less than 5 ohms?			
EC4	CHECK SUPPLY TO COOLING FAN MOTOR			
	• Disconnect cooling fan motor connector.	Yes	▶	GO to EC5. (A/C only) GO to EC11. (non A/C only)
	• Key ON.			
	• Measure the voltage on the Y wire at the connector.	No	▶	SERVICE Y wire.
	• Reconnect the cooling fan motor connector.			
	• Is the voltage greater than 10 volts?			
EC5	CHECK SUPPLY TO A/C RELAY (A/C ONLY)			
	• Disconnect the A/C relay connector.	Yes	▶	GO to EC6.
	• Measure the voltage on the BL wire at the relay connector.	No	▶	SERVICE BL wire.
	• Reconnect the A/C relay connector.			
	• Is the voltage greater than 10 volts?			

FM1089100034010X

Fig. 31   Diagnostic test steps (Part 1 of 5). Capri

	TEST STEP	RESULT	▶	ACTION TO TAKE
EC8	CHECK LEAD BETWEEN A/C RELAY AND COOLING FAN RELAY (A/C ONLY)			
	• Disconnect the cooling fan relay connector.	Yes	▶	GO to EC9.
	• Measure the resistance of the Y wire between the A/C relay and the cooling fan relay.	No	▶	SERVICE Y wire.
	• Reconnect the cooling fan relay connector.			
	• Is the resistance less than 5 ohms?			
EC9	CHECK LEAD BETWEEN A/C RELAY AND ECA (A/C ONLY)			
	• Disconnect the ECA connector.	Yes	▶	GO to EC10.
	• Measure the resistance of the W wire between the A/C relay and the ECA.	No	▶	SERVICE W wire.
	• Reconnect the ECA connector.			
	• Is the resistance less than 5 ohms?			
EC10	CHECK LEAD BETWEEN A/C RELAY AND COMPRESSOR CLUTCH (A/C ONLY)			
	• Disconnect the compressor clutch connector.	Yes	▶	GO to EC11.
	• Measure the resistance on the BK/Y wire between the A/C relay and the compressor clutch.	No	▶	SERVICE BK/Y wire.
	• Reconnect the compressor clutch connector.			
	• Is the resistance less than 5 ohms?			
EC11	CHECK SUPPLY TO COOLING FAN RELAY (NON-A/C ONLY)			
	• Access cooling fan relay connector.	Yes	▶	GO to EC12..
	• Key ON.	No	▶	SERVICE Y wire.
	• Measure the voltage on the Y wire at the cooling fan relay.			
	• Is the voltage greater than 10 volts?			
EC12	CHECK COOLING FAN MOTOR			
	• Locate the cooling fan motor connector.	Yes	▶	GO to EC13.
	• Ground the Y/GN wire at the connector.	No	▶	SERVICE/REPLACE cooling fan motor.
	• Does the cooling fan motor turn on?			

FM1089100035030X

Fig. 31   Diagnostic test steps (Part 3 of 5). Capri

TEST STEP		RESULT	▶	ACTION TO TAKE
EC13	CHECK LEAD BETWEEN COOLING FAN RELAY AND COOLING FAN MOTOR			
	• Key OFF	Yes	▶	GO to EC14.
	• Measure the resistance of the Y/GN wire between the cooling fan relay and the cooling fan motor.	No	▶	SERVICE Y/GN wire.
	• Is the resistance less than 5 ohms?			
EC14	CHECK COOLING FAN RELAY GROUND			
	• Measure the resistance of the BK wire between the cooling fan relay and ground.	Yes	▶	GO to EC15.
		No	▶	SERVICE BK wire.
	• Is the resistance less than 5 ohms?			
EC15	CHECK COOLING FAN RELAY			
	• Disconnect the cooling fan relay connector.	Yes	▶	GO to EC16.
	• Measure the resistance between the Y/GN terminal and the BK terminal at the relay.	No	▶	SERVICE/REPLACE cooling fan relay.
	• Is the resistance less than 5 ohms?			
	• Apply 12 volts to the Y terminal at the relay.			
	• Ground the GN/R terminal at the relay.			
	• Measure the resistance between the Y/GN terminal and the BK terminal at the relay.			
	• Reconnect the cooling fan relay.			
	• Is the resistance greater than 10,000 ohms?			
EC16	CHECK LEAD BETWEEN COOLING FAN RELAY AND COOLING FAN SWITCH			
	• Measure the resistance of the GN/R wire between the cooling fan relay and the cooling fan switch.	Yes	▶	GO to EC17.
		No	▶	SERVICE GN/R wire.
	• Is the resistance less than 5 ohms?			

FM1089100034040X

Fig. 31 Diagnostic test steps (Part 4 of 5). Capri

TEST STEP		RESULT	▶	ACTION TO TAKE
EC17	FAN SWITCH FUNCTION			
	• Disconnect the cooling fan switch connector.	Yes	▶	RETURN to condition chart.
	• Using a VOM check the continuity of the switch from terminal GN/R to ground.	Yes	▶	GO to EC18. (A/C only)
	• Start up the engine and observe the continuity of the switch on the VOM as engine warms up.	No	▶	SERVICE/REPLACE cooling fan switch.
	• If continuity is still present in the switch by the time the engine is hot, remove the fan switch from the engine.			
	• Place the switch in a 50% water and glycol mixture with a 150°C (250°F) range thermometer.			
	• Heat the water and monitor the switch continuity using VOM, and verify the opening and closing temperature as the water is heated then cooled.			
	• Does the switch operate at the approximate specified temperatures? Refer to Specifications.			
EC18	CHECK SYSTEM FOR OPERATION WHEN A/C IS TURNED ON (A/C ONLY)			
	• Turn the A/C on.	Yes	▶	RETURN to condition chart.
	• Does the cooling fan motor turn on?	No	▶	SERVICE/REPLACE cooling fan motor.

FM1089100034050X

Fig. 31 Diagnostic test steps (Part 5 of 5). Capri

ENGINE COOLING FAN DIAGNOSIS

	TEST	RESULT	▶	ACTION TO TAKE
1	• Disconnect motor lead. Jumper motor negative to ground and motor positive to B +.	Motor does not run.	▶	REPLACE motor.
		Motor runs	▶	CONNECT motor lead and GO to Test 2.
2	• Disconnect electrical connector at cooling fan temperature switch.	(OK)	▶	GO to Test 3.
	• With ignition switch in RUN position, check for voltage on Circuit 197 (T/O). Should equal battery voltage.	(⊘)	▶	CHECK for open or short circuit in Circuit 197 (T/O). SERVICE as necessary. CHECK cooling fan operation.
3	• Jumper cooling fan temperature switch connector pins together.	(OK)	▶	REPLACE cooling fan temperature switch. CHECK cooling fan operation.
	• With ignition switch in RUN position, cooling fan motor should run.	(⊘)	▶	LEAVE jumper connected. GO to Test 4.
4	• Disconnect connector at fan relay (on radiator support LH side near headlamp).	(OK)	▶	GO to Test 5.
	• Check for voltage at Terminals No. 2 (relay coil) and No. 4 (relay output to fan motor).	(⊘)	▶	SERVICE Circuit 182 and 37 at relay connector. CONNECT the temperature switch. CHECK cooling fan operation.
5	• Connect connector at fan relay.	Motor runs	▶	REPLACE relay. CHECK cooling fan operation.
	• Jumper Circuits 37 to 28 at fan relay (Terminals No. 3 and No. 4).	Motor does not run.	▶	GO to Test 6.
6	• Disconnect connector at fan motor.	(OK)	▶	GO to Test 7.
	• Check for voltage on Circuit 228 (BR/Y).	(⊘)	▶	*CHECK Circuit 228 BR/Y for open. SERVICE wiring between fan motor and temperature switch connector. CONNECT cooling fan relay connector. CHECK cooling fan operation.
	• With ignition switch in RUN position and cooling fan temperature switch connector jumpered, Circuit 228 (BR/Y) should have battery voltage.			

*Service non-cycling circuit breaker as required.

FM1089100035000X

Fig. 32 Cooling fan system diagnosis. Tempo & Topaz, less A/C

ENGINE COOLING FAN DIAGNOSIS

	TEST STEP	RESULT	▶	ACTION TO TAKE
1	• Check fuse and fuse link.	Good	▶	GO to Step 2.
		Bad	▶	REPLACE fuse and RE-TEST.
2	• Determine when fan does or does not operate. NOTE: The fan controller incorporates internal circuit protection that opens the fan circuit in case of a short in the fan relay coil.	A. Operates during A/C operation only.	▶	GO to Step 3.
		B. Does not operate during A/C operation or during high engine coolant temperatures.	▶	GO to Step 12.
		C. Operates during high engine coolant temperatures only.	▶	GO to Step 8.
3	• Turn the ignition switch to RUN, and unplug connector at coolant temperature switch. Jumper connector to ground with A/C and DEFROST off.	Fan motor runs	▶	GO to Step 4.
		Fan motor does not run	▶	GO to Step 5.
4	• Verify the coolant switch ground by checking the ground circuit (No. 182) for continuity. Verify the coolant has exceeded 210°F (84.7°C) by idling a cold engine for approximately 25 minutes. Vehicles with temperature gauge should indicate toward the high end of normal band.	Fan motor runs	▶	Cooling fan system is OK.
		Fan motor does not run	▶	REPLACE coolant temperature switch.
5	• Unplug connector from cooling fan controller and check continuity of Circuit 197 from controller to coolant temperature switch.	Continuity	▶	REPLACE cooling fan controller.
		No continuity	▶	SERVICE circuit.
6	• Check fan controller system ground at terminal 5 of the fan controller.①	Ground OK	▶	GO to Step 7.
		Ground not OK	▶	SERVICE ground.
7	• Remove connector from cooling fan controller. Check for voltage at Circuits 196 and 348.①	No voltage at one or both circuits	▶	GO to Step 8.
		Voltage OK	▶	REPLACE fan controller.

①For fan controllers with prefix E5FZ or later, see Engine Cooling Fan Diagnosis for vehicles with A/C.

FM1089100036010X

Fig. 33 Cooling fan system diagnosis (Part 1 of 3). Tempo & Topaz, w/A/C

ENGINE COOLING FAN DIAGNOSIS — Continued

	TEST STEP	RESULT	►	ACTION TO TAKE
8	• Remove connector from clutch cycling pressure switch and jumper across the connector. Check to see if the fan motor engages.*	Fan motor engages	►	GO to Step 9.
		Fan motor does not engage	►	GO to Step 10.
9	• Check A/C system for refrigerant charge 344.75 kPa (50 psi) pressure at ambient temperatures about 10°C (50°F).*	No refrigerant charge	►	LEAK TEST, SERVICE, RE-CHARGE system.
		Refrigerant pressures above 344.75 kPa (50 psi)	►	REPLACE clutch cycling pressure switch.
10	• Remove connector from A/C control assembly. Jumper Circuit 294 to Circuit 348 and check for voltage.	Voltage OK	►	REPLACE A/C push button control. GO to Step 11.
		No voltage	►	SERVICE open Circuits 348, 299. GO to Step 11.
11	• Remove connector from clutch cycling pressure switch and jumper across the connector. Check to ensure fan motor engages.	Fan motor engages	►	Fan OK
		Fan motor does not engage.	►	SERVICE fan controller. Circuits 348 and 198 between A/C pressure switch and fan controller.
12	• Unplug connector at cooling fan motor. Jumper B+ and ground to motor.	Fan motor runs	►	GO to Step 13.
		Fan motor does not run	►	REPLACE motor.
13	• Remove jumper wires and connect harness connector to fan motor. Unplug connector from cooling fan controller and turn ignition switch to RUN. Check for voltage at Circuits 37, 687, 198 and 348, and fan controller ground.	No voltage at one or both circuits	►	SERVICE circuit(s).
		Voltage and ground OK at circuits	►	GO to Step 14.
14	• Jumper Circuit 37 to Circuit 228A (terminal No. 2 of fan relay) at the cooling fan controller.	Fan motor runs	►	REPLACE fan controller.
		Fan motor does not run	►	GO to Step 15.

*Fan controllers with prefix E5EZ or later, refer to Engine Cooling Fan Diagnosis for vehicles with A/C.

FM1089100037020X

Fig. 33   Cooling fan system diagnosis (Part 2 of 3). Tempo & Topaz, w/A/C

ENGINE COOLING FAN DIAGNOSIS — Continued

	TEST STEP	RESULT	►	ACTION TO TAKE
15	• Jumper Circuit 37 to Circuit 228	Fan motor runs	►	GO to Step 17.
		Fan motor does not run	►	GO to Step 16.
16	• Unplug the 5-way connector of the engine compartment mounted fan relay. Jumper Circuit 37 to Circuit 228 (fan motor).	Fan motor runs	►	GO to Step 17.
		Fan motor does not run	►	SERVICE fan motor ground.
17	• Jumper 57 Circuit to terminal 1 of fan relay. Jumper 37 circuit to the 228A Circuit.	Fan motor runs	►	SERVICE circuits
		Fan motor does not run.	►	REPLACE fan relay.

FM1089100037030X

Fig. 33   Cooling fan system diagnosis (Part 3 of 3). Tempo & Topaz w/A/C

Cooling Fan Relay Terminal No. 3	Wide-Open Throttle Cutout Switch	Engine Coolant Temp. Switch	Clutch Cycling Pressure Switch	A/C Control Assy. (A/C or Defrost Position)	Ignition Switch	(3.)Engine Cooling Fan Motor (Terminal 3)	A/C Clutch Field Coil (Terminal 6)
	O				C		
	O		C		C		
	O			C	C		
	O	C	C	C			
	O		C	C			
E	O		C	C		E	
	O	C					
E	O	C			C	E	
E	O	C	C	C	C	E	
					C		
				C	C		
E			C	C	C	E	E①
		C			C		
E		C			C	E	
E		C	C	C	C	E	E

C — Closed
E — Energized
O — FEC Ground
①3-4 Second Time Delay Before Closing On Earlier Models
②For fan controllers with prefix E53Z or later, the fan will stay energized for 2-3 minutes after the A/C cycling pressure switch opens

FM1089100038010X

Fig. 34   Cooling fan controller diagnosis (Part 1 of 4). Tempo & Topaz

TEST 1 - IGNITION SWITCH OFF — TEMPO/TOPAZ

Connector Pin Number	Voltmeter should read
1	0-volts
2	(not used)
3	0-volts
4	(not used)
5	0-volts
6	0-volts
7	0-volts
8	0-volts
9	0-volts
10	0-volts

FM1089100038020X

Fig. 34   Cooling fan controller diagnosis, ignition switch Off (Part 2 of 4). Tempo & Topaz

TEST 2 - IGNITION SWITCH IN RUN — ENGINE AND A/C OR DEFROST OFF TEMPO/TOPAZ — 50 STATES

Connector Pin Number	Voltmeter should read
1	Battery voltage with coolant temperature switch open.
2	(not used)
3	0-volts with coolant temperature switch open — Battery voltage with coolant temperature switch closed.
4	(not used)
5	0-volts — continuity with ground
6	6-volts
7	0-volts
8	0-volts
9	Battery voltage
10	0-volts

FM1089100038030X

Fig. 34   Cooling fan controller diagnosis, ignition switch in Run with engine & A/C Off (Part 3 of 4). Tempo & Topaz

TEST 3: IGNITION SWITCH IN RUN — ENGINE RUNNING AND A/C OR DEFROST ON — TEMPO/TOPAZ

Connector Pin Number	Voltmeter should read
1 (c)	0-volts with clutch cycling pressure switch closed or coolant temperature switch closed.
2	(not used)
3 (c), (d)	Battery voltage with coolant temperature switch closed and/or clutch cycling pressure switch closed (a) — 0-volts otherwise.
4	(not used)
5	0-volts
6	6-volts during normal operation — 0-volts during wide-open throttle operation (b).
7	Battery voltage
8 (a), (d)	Battery voltage when A/C clutch cycling pressure switch is closed and throttle is normal (c) — 0-volts with cycling switch open or throttle closed.
9	Battery voltage
10	Battery voltage when A/C clutch cycling pressure switch and high pressure cut-out switch closed — 0-volts if switch is open.

(a) When Pin 6 is grounded, Pin 8 will have 0 volts.
(b) High pressure cutout switch (if used) must then be closed.
(c) On fan controllers with prefix E53Z or later the fan motor will stay energized when the WOT switch is open. The fan motor will stay energized if the A/C cycling pressure switch opens for less than 2-3 minutes.
(d) 0 volts if short/overload occurs in fan relay coil circuits.

NOTE: Indicated voltages in the 50 states and Canada procedures can vary, depending on the type of meter used.

FM1089100038040X

Fig. 34   Cooling fan controller diagnosis, engine running & A/C On (Part 4 of 4). Tempo & Topaz

CONDITION	POSSIBLE SOURCE	ACTION
• Cooling Fan Always Runs	• Relay(s). • Circuit. • ECA. • Motor. • Switch.	• GO to EC4. • GO to EC10. (1.9L)
• Cooling Fan Never Runs (Overheating)	• Relay(s). • Circuit. • ECA. • Motor. • Switch.	• GO to EC1. • GO to EC10. (1.9L)
• Cooling Fan Runs but No High Speed	• Relay(s). • Circuit. • ECA. • Motor. • Switch.	• GO to EC2. • GO to EC10. (1.9L)
• Cooling Fan Runs but No Low Speed	• Relay(s). • Circuit. • ECA. • Motor. • Switch.	• GO to EC2. • GO to EC10. (1.9L)

FM1089100039000X

Fig. 35   Symptom chart. 1992–93 Escort & Tracer

CONDITION	POSSIBLE SOURCE	ACTION
• Engine Overheats	• Water thermostat. • Engine coolant (weak or low). • Electric cooling fan system.	• GO to Pinpoint Test A1. • SEE Symptom Chart.
• Cooling Fan Runs Continuously	• Relay(s). • Circuit. • Powertrain control module. • Electric cooling fan. • Fan motor switch.	• GO to Pinpoint Test C1 for 1.8L vehicles.
• Cooling Fan Never Runs (Overheating)	• Fuse(s). • Relay(s). • Circuit. • PCM (1.9L). • Electric cooling fan. • Fan motor switches.	• 1.8L: GO to Pinpoint Test B1.
• Cooling Fan Runs, No High Speed (1.8L 4EAT, 1.9L)	• Relay(s). • Circuit. • PCM (1.9L). • Electric cooling fan. • Fan motor switches.	• 1.8L: GO to Pinpoint Test D1.
• Cooling Fan Runs, No Low Speed (1.8L 4EAT, 1.9L)	• Relay(s). • Circuit. • PCM (1.9L). • Electric cooling fan. • Fan motor switches.	• 1.8L: GO to Pinpoint Test E1.

FM1089400082000X

Fig. 36 Symptom chart. 1994 Escort & Tracer

TEST STEP	RESULT ►	ACTION TO TAKE
EC1 CHECK FUSE		
• Access the interior fuse panel. • Check the 15 amp engine fuse. • Is the fuse good? NOTE: If the fuse blows again, check for a short in the "BK/W" wire.	Yes No	► GO to [EC2]. ► REPLACE the engine fuse.

FM1089100040010X

Fig. 37 Diagnostic test step EC1 (Part 1 of 11). Escort & Tracer

TEST STEP	RESULT ►	ACTION TO TAKE
EC2 CHECK VOLTAGE TO RELAY(S)		
• Key ON. • Measure the voltage on the "BK/W" wire at low-speed cooling fan relay. • Is the voltage greater than 10 volts? If equipped with 1.8L 4EAT or 1.9L A/C: • Measure the voltage on the "BK/W" wire at high speed cooling fan relay. • Is the voltage greater than 10 volts?	Yes No	► GO to [EC3]. ► REPAIR/REPLACE the "BK/W" wire.

FM1089100040020X

Fig. 37 Diagnostic test step EC2 (Part 2 of 11). Escort & Tracer

TEST STEP	RESULT ►	ACTION TO TAKE
EC3 CHECK VOLTAGE TO RELAY(S)		
• Key ON. • Measure the voltage on the "BK/R" (1.8L) or "LG/BK" (1.9L) wire at high-speed cooling fan relay. • Is the voltage greater than 10 volts? If equipped with 1.9L A/C or 1.8L 4EAT: • Measure the resistance of the "LG" (1.9L) or "R/BK" (1.8L) wire between high-speed cooling fan relay and low-speed cooling fan relay. • Is the resistance less than 5 ohms?	Yes No	► GO to [EC4]. ► REPAIR/REPLACE the wire(s).

FM1089100040030X

Fig. 37 Diagnostic test step EC3 (Part 3 of 11). Escort & Tracer

	TEST STEP	RESULT ►	ACTION TO TAKE
EC4	CHECK COOLING FAN RELAY		

• Key ON.
• Ground the "Y/W" (1.9L) or "BK/GN" (1.8L) at cooling fan relay (1.8L MTX or 1.9L non-A/C) or low-speed cooling fan relay (1.8L 4EAT or 1.9L A/C).
• Measure the resistance between the following wire colors at the relay:

Vehicle Type	Wire Colors	Resistance
1.8L 4EAT	"R/BK", "Y"	less than 5 ohms
1.8L MTX	"BK/R", "Y"	less than 5 ohms
1.9L Non-A/C	"LG/BK", "Y"	less than 5 ohms
1.9L A/C	"LG", "Y"	less than 5 ohms

• Are the resistances less than 5 ohms?

RESULT	ACTION TO TAKE
Yes	► GO to [EC5].
No	► REPAIR/REPLACE cooling fan relay.

FM1089100040040X

Fig. 37 Diagnostic test step EC4 (Part 4 of 11). Escort & Tracer

	TEST STEP	RESULT ►	ACTION TO TAKE
EC5	CHECK COOLING FAN RELAY		

With 1.8L 4EAT or 1.9L A/C only:
• Ground the "BK/GN" (1.8L) or "R/BK" (1.9L) wire at the high-speed cooling fan relay.
• Measure the resistances between the following wires at the relay:
  1.8L — "BK/R" and "BL"
  1.9L — "LG/BK" and "LG/Y"
• Turn the ignition switch to the ON position.
• Measure the resistances between the following wires at the relay:
  1.8L — "BK/R" and "R/BK"
  1.9L — "LG/BK" and "LG"
• Are the resistances less than 5 ohms?

RESULT	ACTION TO TAKE
Yes	► GO to [EC6].
No	► REPAIR/REPLACE high speed cooling fan relay.

FM1089100040050X

Fig. 37 Diagnostic test step EC5 (Part 5 of 11). Escort & Tracer

	TEST STEP	RESULT ►	ACTION TO TAKE
EC6	CHECK CONTINUITY BETWEEN RELAYS AND MOTOR		

• Key OFF.
• Access the cooling fan relays.
• Measure the resistance of the "Y" wire between cooling fan relay (1.8L MTX or 1.9L Non-A/C) or low-speed cooling fan relay (1.8L 4EAT or 1.9 A/C) and the cooling fan motor.
If equipped with 1.8L 4EAT or 1.9L A/C only:
• Measure the resistance of the "LG/Y" (1.9L) or "BL" (1.8L) wire between high-speed cooling fan relay and the cooling fan motor.
• Are the resistances less than 5 ohms?

RESULT	ACTION TO TAKE
Yes	► GO to [EC7].
No	► REPAIR/REPLACE the wires.

FM1089100040060X

Fig. 37 Diagnostic test step EC6 (Part 6 of 11). Escort & Tracer

	TEST STEP	RESULT ►	ACTION TO TAKE
EC7	CHECK COOLING FAN MOTOR GROUND		

• Key OFF.
• Access the cooling fan motor.
• Measure the resistance of the "BK" wire to the ground.
• Is the resistance less than 5 ohms?

RESULT	ACTION TO TAKE
Yes	► GO to [EC8].
No	► REPAIR/REPLACE the "BK" wire.

FM1089100040070X

Fig. 37 Diagnostic test step EC7 (Part 7 of 11). Escort & Tracer

TEST STEP		RESULT	►	ACTION TO TAKE
EC8	CHECK COOLING FAN MOTOR			
• Key OFF. • Apply 12 volts to the "Y" wire at the motor. • Does the motor run at low speed? If equipped with 1.8L 4EAT or 1.9L A/C: • Apply 12 volts to the "BL" wire (1.8L) or the "LG/Y" (1.9L) at the motor. • Does the motor run at high speed?		Yes	►	GO to EC9 . (1.9L) GO to EC10 . (1.8L)
		No	►	REPLACE the motor.

FM1089100040080X

Fig. 37 Diagnostic test step EC8 (Part 8 of 11). Escort & Tracer

TEST STEP		RESULT	►	ACTION TO TAKE
EC9	CHECK CONTINUITY FROM RELAYS TO ECA (1.9L ONLY)			
• Key ON. • Ground the "Y/W" wire at the ECA. • Does the motor run at low speed? If equipped with A/C: • Disconnect the "Y/W" wire at the ECA. • Ground the "R/BK" wire at the ECA. • Does the motor run at high speed?		Yes	►	Engine/Emissions
		No	►	REPAIR/REPLACE the wires.

FM1089100040090X

Fig. 37 Diagnostic test step EC9 (Part 9 of 11). Escort & Tracer

TEST STEP		RESULT	►	ACTION TO TAKE
EC10	FAN MOTOR FUNCTION WITH BYPASSED FAN SWITCH (1.8L ONLY)			
• Disconnect the cooling fan switch connector (at the water outlet connection). **WARNING: TO AVOID PERSONAL INJURY AND COMPONENT DAMAGE, KEEP HANDS CLEAR OF THE FAN BLADES AT ALL TIMES.** • Ground the "BK/GN" terminal in the connector and note whether the fan motor runs. • Does the fan motor run with the "BK/GN" terminal grounded?		Yes	►	GO to EC11 .
		No	►	SERVICE the "BK/GN" wire.

COOLING FAN SWITCH (MTX)
EM-02

FM1089100040100X

Fig. 37 Diagnostic test step EC10 (Part 10 of 11). Escort & Tracer

TEST STEP		RESULT	►	ACTION TO TAKE
EC11	FAN SWITCH FUNCTION (1.8L ONLY)			
• Disconnect the cooling fan switch connector. • Start up the engine. • Using a VOM as the engine warms up, check the continuity of the switch. • If no continuity exists by the time the engine is hot, remove the switch from the engine. • Place the switch in 50% glycol and water with a 150° C (250° F), range thermometer. • Heat the water and monitor the switch continuity using a VOM. • Verify that the switch closes and opens at the specified temperature. (See the specifications.) • Does the switch show continuity when the engine becomes hot, or does it operate at specified temperatures?		Yes	►	RETURN to the symptom chart.
		No	►	REPLACE the cooling fan switch.

FM1089100040110X

Fig. 37 Diagnostic test step EC11 (Part 11 of 11). Escort & Tracer

	TEST STEP	RESULT	►	ACTION TO TAKE
A1	CHECK THERMOSTAT			
	• Check water thermostat as outlined in the Water Thermostat component test in this section. • Does the water thermostat operate correctly?	Yes No	► ►	GO to A2. REPLACE the water thermostat.
A2	CHECK ENGINE COOLANT			
	• Check engine coolant • If coolant level is low, inspect the following ares for leaks: — All hoses and hose connections. — Engine block core plugs and drain plugs. — Radiator core and draincock. — Engine oil (internal leak). — Reservoir. • Is the engine coolant OK?	Yes No (Coolant weak) No (Coolant level low)	► ► ►	GO to A3. REPLACE coolant. PRESSURE TEST the cooling system
A3	VISUALLY INSPECT SYSTEM			
	• Repeat the inspection and verification procedures as outlined in this section. • Check the following areas closely: — Radiator (for blockages). — Electric cooling fan and blades for damage. • Is system OK?	Yes No	► ►	GO to B1. SERVICE as necessary.

FM1089400083000X

Fig. 38 Test A: engine overheats. 1994 Escort & Tracer

TEST STEP	RESULT	▶	ACTION TO TAKE
B1 CHECK FUSE • Key OFF. • Locate the interior fuse junction panel. • Check the 15A ENGINE fuse. • **Is the fuse OK?** NOTE: If the fuse fails again, check for a short in the "BK/W" wire.	Yes No	▶ ▶	GO to **B2**. REPLACE the 15A ENGINE fuse.
B2 CHECK FUSE • Key OFF. • Locate the main fuse junction panel. • Check the 40A (1.8L 4EAT) or 30A (1.8L MTX) COOLING FAN fuse. • **Is the fuse OK?**	Yes No	▶ ▶	GO to **B5**. GO to **B3**.
B3 CHECK SYSTEM • Key OFF. • Replace the 40A (1.8L 4EAT) or 30A (1.8L MTX) COOLING FAN fuse. • **Does the fuse fail again?**	Yes No	▶ ▶	GO to **B4**. GO to **B5**.
B4 CHECK FOR SHORTS TO GROUND • Key OFF. • Remove the 40A (1.8L 4EAT) or 30A (1.8L MTX) COOLING FAN fuse. • Locate and disconnect the high-speed cooling fan control relay connector (1.8L 4EAT) or the cooling fan control relay (1.8L MTX). • Measure the resistance of the "BK/R" wire between the low terminal of the 40A (1.8L 4EAT) or 30A (1.8L MTX) COOLING FAN fuse socket and ground. • **Is the resistance greater than 10,000 ohms?**	Yes No	▶ ▶	GO to **B5**. SERVICE the "BK/R" wire.
B5 CHECK VOLTAGE TO RELAY(S) • Key ON. • Measure the voltage on the "BK/W" wire at low-speed cooling fan control relay (1.8L 4EAT) or at the cooling fan control relay (1.8L MTX). • Measure the voltage on the "BK/W" wire at the high-speed cooling fan control relay (1.8L 4EAT). • **Are the voltages greater than 10 volts?**	Yes No	▶ ▶	GO to **B6**. SERVICE the "BK/W" wire(s).
B6 CHECK VOLTAGE TO RELAY(S) • Key ON. • Disconnect the high-speed cooling fan control relay connector (1.8 4EAT) or the cooling fan control relay connector (1.8 MTX). • Measure the voltage on the "BK/R" wire at the high-speed cooling fan control relay connector (1.8L 4EAT) or at the cooling fan control relay connector (1.8L MTX). • **Are the voltages greater than 10 volts?**	Yes No	▶ ▶	GO to **B7**. SERVICE the "BK/R" wire.

FM1089400084010X

Fig. 39 Test B: cooling fan never runs (Part 1 of 3). 1994 Escort & Tracer

TEST STEP	RESULT	▶	ACTION TO TAKE
B7 CHECK LOW-SPEED COOLING FAN CONTROL RELAY • Disconnect the cooling fan control relay connector (1.8L MTX) or the low-speed cooling fan control relay connector (1.8L 4EAT). • Connect a jumper wire between the "BK/W" wire at the cooling fan control relay connector or the low-speed cooling fan control relay connector and the coinciding terminal on the relay. • Key ON. • Ground the "BK/GN" terminal at the cooling fan control relay connector or low-speed cooling fan control relay connector. • Measure the resistance between the following wire terminals at the relay.	Yes (1.8L 4EAT) Yes (1.8L MTX) No	▶ ▶ ▶	GO to **B8**. Go to **B9** REPLACE the cooling fan control relay in question.

Vehicle Type	Wire Colors	Resistance
1.8L 4EAT	R/BK, Y	Less than 5 ohms
1.8L MTX	BK·R, Y	Less than 5 ohms

TEST STEP	RESULT	▶	ACTION TO TAKE
• **Are the resistances (as indicated in the chart above) correct?**			
B8 CHECK HIGH-SPEED COOLING CONTROL FAN RELAY (1.8L 4EAT) • Disconnect the high-speed cooling fan control relay connector. • Connect a jumper wire between the "BK/W" wire at the high-speed cooling fan control relay connector and the corresponding terminal on the relay. • Ground the "BK/GN" terminal at the high-speed cooling fan control relay. • Key OFF. • Measure the resistance between the "BK/R" and "R/BK" wire at the fan control relay. • Key ON. • Measure the resistance between the "BK/R" and "BL" wire terminals at the fan control relay. • **Are the resistances less than 5 ohms?**	Yes No	▶ ▶	GO to **B9**. REPLACE the high-speed cooling fan control relay in question.
B9 CHECK CONTINUITY BETWEEN RELAYS AND MOTOR • Key OFF. • Disconnect the electric cooling fan connector. • Disconnect the cooling fan control relay connector or the low-speed cooling fan control relay connector. • Measure the resistance of the "Y" wire between the cooling fan control relay connector (1.8L MTX) or low-speed cooling fan control relay (1.8L 4EAT) and the electric cooling fan connector. • Disconnect the high-speed cooling fan control relay connector (1.8L 4EAT only). • Measure the resistance of the "BL" wire between the high-speed cooling fan control relay connector and the electric cooling fan connector. • **Are the resistances less than 5 ohms?**	Yes No	▶ ▶	GO to **B10**. SERVICE the wire(s) in question.
B10 CHECK ELECTRIC COOLING FAN GROUND • Key OFF. • Disconnect the electric cooling fan connector. • Measure the resistance of the "BK" wire at the electric cooling fan connector and ground. • **Is the resistance less than 5 ohms?**	Yes No	▶ ▶	GO to **B11**. SERVICE the "BK" wire.

FM1089400084020X

Fig. 39 Test B: cooling fan never runs (Part 2 of 3). 1994 Escort & Tracer

TEST STEP	RESULT	▶	ACTION TO TAKE
B11 CHECK ELECTRIC COOLING FAN • Key OFF. • Disconnect the electric cooling fan connector. • Apply 12 volts to the "Y" wire terminal at the electric cooling fan. • Ground the "BK" wire terminal at the electric cooling fan and the motor should run (at low speed for 1.8L 4EAT). • Apply 12 volts to the "BL" wire terminal at the electric cooling fan (for 1.8L 4EAT). • Ground the "BK" wire at the electric cooling fan and the motor should run (high speed for 1.8L 4EAT). • **Does the electric cooling fan operate correctly?**	Yes No	▶ ▶	GO to **B12**. REPLACE the electric cooling fan.
B12 CHECK ELECTRIC COOLING FAN FUNCTION WITH BYPASSED FAN MOTOR SWITCH • Disconnect the fan motor switch(es) connector(s) (at the water outlet connection). **WARNING: TO AVOID PERSONAL INJURY AND COMPONENT DAMAGE, KEEP HANDS CLEAR OF THE FAN BLADES AT ALL TIMES.** • Key ON. • Ground the "BK/GN" terminal in the connector(s) and note whether the electric cooling fan runs. BK/GN FAN MOTOR SWITCH Q3514-G • **Does the electric cooling fan run with the "BK/GN" terminal grounded?**	Yes No	▶ ▶	GO to **B13**. SERVICE the "BK/GN" wire.
B13 CHECK FAN MOTOR SWITCH FUNCTION • Disconnect the fan motor switch connector(s). • Start the engine. • Using a Rotunda 73 Digital Multimeter 105-00051 as the engine warms up, check the continuity of the fan motor switch. • If no continuity exists by the time the engine is hot, remove the fan motor switches from the engine. • Place the fan motor switches in 50% glycol and water with a 150°C (250°F) range thermometer. • Heat the water and monitor the fan motor switch continuity using a Rotunda 73 Digital Multimeter 105-00051. • Verify that the fan motor switches closes and opens at the specified temperature (see the specifications at the end of this section). • **Does the fan motor switch show continuity when the engine becomes hot, or does it operate at specified temperatures?**	Yes No	▶ ▶	SERVICE the "BK" wire between the high-speed fan motor switch and ground (1.8L 4EAT Only). Otherwise, RETURN to the Symptom Chart. REPLACE the fan motor switch.

FM1089400084030X

Fig. 39 Test B: cooling fan never runs (Part 3 of 3). 1994 Escort & Tracer

TEST STEP	RESULT	▶	ACTION TO TAKE
C1 CHECK COOLING FAN CONTROL RELAY CONTROL CIRCUITS NOTE: Engine temperature must be below minimum fan motor switch closing temperature. If the engine is hot, allow it to cool before performing this test. • Key ON. • Locate and disconnect the cooling fan control relay connector (1.8L MTX) or low-speed cooling fan control relay connector (1.8L 4EAT). • Locate and disconnect high-speed cooling fan control relay connector (1.8L 4EAT only). • Locate and disconnect the PCM connectors. • Locate and disconnect the A/C relay connector (A/C only). • Measure the resistance of the "BK/GN" wire between the cooling fan control relay connector (1.8L MTX) or low-speed cooling fan control relay connector (1.8L 4EAT only) and ground. • Measure the resistance of the "BK/GN" wire between the high-speed cooling fan control relay connector and ground (1.8L 4EAT only). • **Are the resistances less than 5 ohms?**	Yes No	▶ ▶	GO to **C2**. REPLACE the fan control relays in question.
C2 CHECK FAN MOTOR SWITCH • Locate and disconnect the fan motor switch connector(s). • Measure the resistance of the fan motor switch between the "BK/GN" wire terminal at the fan motor switch and ground. • Measure the resistance between the terminals of the high-speed fan motor switch (1.8L 4EAT only). • **Are the resistances greater than 10,000 ohms?**	Yes No	▶ ▶	SERVICE the "BK/GN" wire in question. REPLACE the fan motor switch.

FM1089400085000X

Fig. 40 Test C: cooling fan runs continuously. 1994 Escort & Tracer

TEST STEP	RESULT	▶	ACTION TO TAKE
D1 CHECK POWER SUPPLY TO HIGH-SPEED COOLING FAN CONTROL RELAY (1.8L 4EAT ONLY) • Locate and disconnect the high-speed cooling fan relay connector. • Key ON. • Measure the voltage on the "BK/W" at the high-speed cooling fan control relay connector. • **Is the voltage greater than 10 volts?**	Yes No	▶ ▶	GO to **D2**. SERVICE the "BK/W" wire.
D2 CHECK HIGH-SPEED COOLING FAN CONTROL RELAY • Key OFF. • Disconnect the high-speed cooling fan control relay connector. • Connect a jumper wire between the "BK/W" wire at the high-speed cooling fan control relay connector and the corresponding terminal on the relay. • Ground the "BK/GN" wire terminal at the high-speed cooling fan control relay. • Measure the resistance between the "BK/R" and "R/BK" wire terminals at the fan control relay. • Key ON. • Measure the resistance between the "BK/R" and "BL" wire terminals at the fan control relay. • **Are the resistances less than 5 ohms?**	Yes No	▶ ▶	GO to **D3**. REPLACE the fan control relay.

FM1089400086010X

Fig. 41 Test D: cooling fan runs, no high speed (Part 1 of 2). 1994 Escort & Tracer

TEST STEP	RESULT	▶	ACTION TO TAKE
D3 CHECK THE HIGH-SPEED COOLING FAN CONTROL RELAY CONTROL CIRCUIT • Locate and disconnect the high-speed fan motor switch connector. **WARNING: TO AVOID PERSONAL INJURY AND COMPONENT DAMAGE, KEEP HANDS CLEAR OF FAN BLADES AT ALL TIMES.** • Key ON. • Ground the "BK/GN" wire terminal at the high-speed fan motor switch connector (harness side). • **Does the electric cooling fan run at high speed?**	Yes No	▶ ▶	GO to D4. GO to D5.
D4 CHECK HIGH-SPEED FAN MOTOR SWITCH GROUND • Disconnect the high-speed fan motor switch connector. • Measure the resistance of the "BK" wire (harness side) between the high-speed fan motor switch connector and ground. • **Is the resistance less than 5 ohms?**	Yes No	▶ ▶	REPLACE the high-speed fan motor switch. SERVICE the "BK" wire.
D5 CHECK CONTROL CIRCUIT CONTINUITY • Disconnect the high-speed cooling fan control relay and the high-speed fan motor switch connectors. • Measure the resistance of the "BK/GN" wire between the fan control relay connector and the fan motor switch connector. • **Is the resistance less than 5 ohms?**	Yes No	▶ ▶	GO to D6. SERVICE the "BK/GN" wire.
D6 CHECK WIRE TO ELECTRIC COOLING FAN • Locate and disconnect the electric cooling fan connector. • Disconnect the high-speed cooling fan control relay connector. • Measure the resistance of the "BL" wire between the high-speed cooling fan control relay connector and the electric cooling fan connector. • **Is the resistance less than 5 ohms?**	Yes No	▶ ▶	GO to D7. SERVICE the "BL" wire.
D7 CHECK ELECTRIC COOLING FAN GROUND • Disconnect the electric cooling fan connector. • Measure the resistance of the "BK" wire between the electric cooling fan connector and ground. • **Is the resistance less than 5 ohms?**	Yes No	▶ ▶	REPLACE the electric cooling fan. SERVICE the "BK" wire.

FM1089400086020X

Fig. 41   Test D: cooling fan runs, no high speed (Part 2 of 2). 1994 Escort & Tracer

TEST STEP	RESULT	▶	ACTION TO TAKE
E1 CHECK POWER SUPPLY TO RELAYS (1.8L 4EAT ONLY) • Locate and disconnect the low-speed cooling fan control relay and the high-speed cooling fan control relay connectors. • Key ON. • Measure the voltage on the "BK/W" wire at the low-speed cooling fan control relay connector and the high-speed cooling fan control relay connector. • Measure the voltage on the "BK/R" wire at the high-speed cooling fan control relay connector. • **Are the voltages greater than 10 volts?**	Yes No	▶ ▶	GO to E2. SERVICE the wire in question.

FM1089400087010X

Fig. 42   Test E: cooling fan runs, no low speed (Part 1 of 3). 1994 Escort & Tracer

TEST STEP	RESULT	▶	ACTION TO TAKE
E2 CHECK LOW-SPEED COOLING FAN RELAY • Disconnect the low-speed cooling fan control relay connector. • Connect a jumper wire between the "BK/W" wire at the low-speed cooling fan control relay connector and the corresponding terminal on the relay. • Key ON. • Ground the "BK/GN" terminal at the low-speed cooling fan control relay. • Measure the resistance between the "R/BK" and "Y" wire terminals on the fan control relay. • **Is the resistance less than 5 ohms?**	Yes No	▶ ▶	GO to E3. REPLACE the low-speed cooling fan control relay.
E3 CHECK HIGH-SPEED COOLING FAN CONTROL RELAY • Key OFF. • Disconnect the high-speed cooling fan control relay connector. • Connect a jumper wire between the "BK/W" wire at the high-speed cooling fan control relay connector and the corresponding terminal on the high-speed cooling fan control relay. • Ground the "BK/GN" wire terminal at the high-speed cooling fan control relay. • Measure the resistance between the "BK/R" and "R/BK" wire terminals at the high-speed cooling fan control relay. • Key ON. • Measure the resistance between the "BK/R" and "BL" wire terminals at the high-speed cooling fan control relay. • **Are the resistances less than 5 ohms?**	Yes No	▶ ▶	GO to E4. REPLACE the high-speed relay.
E4 CHECK WIRE BETWEEN RELAYS • Disconnect the low-speed cooling fan control relay and high-speed cooling fan control relay connectors. • Measure the resistance of the "R/BK" wire between the low-speed control relay connector and the high-speed control relay connector. • **Is the resistance less than 5 ohms?**	Yes No	▶ ▶	GO to E5. SERVICE the "R/BK" wire.
E5 CHECK LOW-SPEED COOLING FAN CONTROL RELAY CONTROL CIRCUIT • Key OFF. • Disconnect the low-speed cooling fan control relay connector and the low-speed fan motor switch connector. • Measure the resistance of the "BK/GN" wire between the low-speed cooling fan control relay connector and the low-speed fan motor switch connector. • **Is the resistance less than 5 ohms?**	Yes No	▶ ▶	GO to E6. SERVICE the "BK/GN" wire.

FM1089400087020X

Fig. 42   Test E: cooling fan runs, no low speed (Part 2 of 3). 1994 Escort & Tracer

TEST STEP	RESULT	▶	ACTION TO TAKE
E6 CHECK LOW-SPEED COOLING FAN SWITCH FUNCTION • Disconnect the low-speed fan motor switch connector. • Start the engine. • Using a VOM as the engine warms up, check the continuity of the low speed fan motor switch. • If no continuity exists by the time the engine is hot, remove the low speed fan motor switch from the engine. • Place the low speed fan motor switch in 50 percent glycol and water with a 150°C (250°F) range thermometer. • Heat the water and monitor the low speed fan motor switch continuity using a VOM. • Verify that the low speed fan motor switch closes and opens at the specified temperature (see the specifications at the end of this section). • **Does the low speed fan motor switch show continuity when the engine becomes hot, or does it operate at specified temperatures?**	Yes No	▶ ▶	REPLACE the electric cooling fan. REPLACE the low-speed fan motor switch.

FM1089400087030X

Fig. 42   Test E: cooling fan runs, no low speed (Part 3 of 3). 1994 Escort & Tracer

SYMPTOM	POSSIBLE CAUSE	ACTION TO TAKE
Cooling fan never runs or runs improperly	• Fuse • Cooling fan relay • Coolant temperature switch • Harness • Fan motor • A/C Relay	Go to CF1
Cooling fan always runs	• Cooling fan relay • Coolant temperature switch • Harness • Fan motor • A/C Relay	Go to CG1
Cooling fan does not run with A/C on	• A/C Relay • Circuit	Go to CG4

FM1089100041000X

Fig. 43   Symptom chart. Festiva

TEST STEP	RESULT	▶	ACTION TO TAKE
CF2 CHECK VOLTAGE SUPPLY • Key on, engine off. • Measure voltage at cooling fan motor yellow terminal. • Is voltage greater than 10V?	Yes No	▶ ▶	GO to CF3 . SERVICE yellow wire from 20 amp "cooling fan" fuse to cooling fan motor.

FM1089100042020X

Fig. 44   Test Step CF2 (Part 2 of 14). Festiva

TEST STEP	RESULT	▶	ACTION TO TAKE
CF1 SYSTEM INTEGRITY CHECK • Check for fully charged battery. • Check for blown fuses, corrosion, poor electrical connections, signs of opens, shorts or damage to the wiring harness. Check the cooling fan and shroud for obstruction, loose fan blade, misalignment of fan and other damage. • Key on, engine off. • Coolant temperature switch disconnected. • Shake the wiring harness vigorously from the cooling fan motor to the cooling fan relay, the coolant temperature switch and the fuse panel; look for signs of opens or shorts. • Tap each connector, the cooling fan relay, the 20 amp cooling fan fuse and look for signs of bad connections, bad crimps or loose wires. • Does the system appear to be in good condition?	Yes No	▶ ▶	GO to CF2 . REPAIR or Replace faulty components as required. NOTE: If a blown 20 amp "cooling fan" fuse is replaced and fails immediately, there is a short to ground in the yellow wire from fuse panel to the cooling fan motor.

FM1089100042010X

Fig. 44   Test Step CF1 (Part 1 of 14). Festiva

TEST STEP		RESULT	▶	ACTION TO TAKE
CF3	GROUND COOLING FAN MOTOR			
• Key on, engine off. • Ground Y/R terminal at cooling fan motor with jumper wire. • Does cooling fan operate?		Yes No	▶ ▶	GO to CF4 . SERVICE motor side of cooling fan harness; if all OK, replace cooling fan motor.

FM1089100042030X

Fig. 44   Test Step CF3 (Part 3 of 14). Festiva

TEST STEP		RESULT	▶	ACTION TO TAKE
CF4	CHECK POWER AT RELAY			
• Key on, engine off. • Disconnect cooling fan relay. • Measure voltage at cooling fan relay Y/R wire. • Is voltage greater than 10V?		Yes No	▶ ▶	GO to CF5 . SERVICE Y/R wire from Cooling Fan Motor to cooling fan relay, A/C relay and ECA.

FM1089100042040X

Fig. 44   Test Step CF4 (Part 4 of 14). Festiva

TEST STEP		RESULT	▶	ACTION TO TAKE
CF5	CHECK VOLTAGE SUPPLY TO RELAY			
• Key on, engine off. • Cooling fan relay disconnected. • Measure voltage at cooling fan relay BK/Y terminal. • Is voltage greater than 10V?		Yes No	▶ ▶	GO to CF6 . SERVICE BK/Y wire from cooling fan relay to 10 amp "METER" fuse.

FM1089100042050X

Fig. 44   Test Step CF5 (Part 5 of 14). Festiva

TEST STEP		RESULT	▶	ACTION TO TAKE
CF6	CHECK RELAY OPERATION			
• Key off. • Remove cooling fan relay. • Apply battery power to relay "A" terminal. • Measure resistance between relay "B" and "C" terminals. • Ground relay "D" terminal with a jumper wire. • Is resistance greater than 10,000 ohms with "D" terminal grounded and less than 5 ohms with "D" terminal ungrounded?		Yes No	▶ ▶	RECONNECT relay. GO to CF7 . REPLACE cooling fan relay.

NOTE: Connector shown looking into relay.

FM1089100042060X

Fig. 44   Test Step CF6 (Part 6 of 14). Festiva

TEST STEP		RESULT	▶	ACTION TO TAKE
CF7	CHECK COOLANT TEMPERATURE SWITCH VOLTAGE			
• Key on, engine off. • Coolant temperature switch disconnected. • Measure voltage at coolant temperature switch GN/R terminal. • Is voltage greater than 10V?		Yes No	▶ ▶	GO to CF8 . SERVICE GN/R wire from cooling fan relay to coolant temperature switch.

FM1089100042070X

Fig. 44   Test Step CF7 (Part 7 of 14). Festiva

TEST STEP		RESULT	▶	ACTION TO TAKE
CF8	CHECK COOLANT TEMPERATURE SWITCH OPERATION			
• Let engine cool completely. • Remove radiator cap. • Place thermometer/pyrometer probe in radiator (under coolant surface). • Measure resistance between coolant temperature switch terminal and ground. • Start engine. Run until coolant temperature exceeds 97°C (207°F), and then shut engine off.		Yes No	▶ ▶	SERVICE cooling fan relay ground (BK wire). REPLACE cooling fan switch.

SWITCH OPERATION

COOLANT	TEMPERATURE	RESISTANCE
Below opening temp.	97°C (rising)	10,000 ohms or greater
Above	97°C	0-5 ohms
Below closing temp.	90°C (falling)	10,000 ohms or greater

• Does switch open at 97°C (207°F) and then close when coolant temperature falls below 90°C (194°F)?

FM1089100042080X

Fig. 44   Test Step CF8 (Part 8 of 14). Festiva

TEST STEP		RESULT	▶	ACTION TO TAKE
CG1	SYSTEM INTEGRITY CHECK			
• Turn key on. • Check for signs of shorted wires, worn insulation and signs of damage to the wiring harness. • Shake the wiring harness vigorously and look for signs of shorts. • Inspect the cooling fan motor, look for signs of shorting or damage to the motor. • Check "METER" fuse. • Does the system appear to be in good condition?		Yes No	▶ ▶	GO to CG2 . REPAIR or replace faulty component(s) as required.

FM1089100042090X

Fig. 44   Test Step CG1 (Part 9 of 14). Festiva

TEST STEP		RESULT	▶	ACTION TO TAKE
CG2	CHECK FOR SHORTS			
• Key off. • Disconnect cooling fan motor. • Disconnect cooling fan relay. • Disconnect A/C relay. • Disconnect ECA. • Measure resistance between cooling fan motor connector Y/R terminal and ground. • Is resistance greater than 10,000 ohms?		Yes No	▶ ▶	GO to CG3 . SERVICE shorts in Y/R from cooling fan motor to cooling fan relay, A/C relay and ECA.

FM1089100042100X

Fig. 44   Test Step CG2 (Part 10 of 14). Festiva

TEST STEP	RESULT	►	ACTION TO TAKE
CG3 CHECK FAN MOTOR			
• Key on, engine off. • Disconnect Y/R wire from cooling fan motor connector (pull wire out of connector). • Does cooling fan motor continue to operate?	Yes	►	RECONNECT Y/R wire. Replace cooling fan motor, shorted internal.
	No	►	RECONNECT Y/R wire. GO to CG4 .

FM1089100042110X

Fig. 44   Test Step CG3 (Part 11 of 14). Festiva

TEST STEP	RESULT	►	ACTION TO TAKE
CG4 CHECK POWER TO RELAY			
• Disconnect ECA. • Key on. • A/C on, blower on. • Measure voltage at the A/C relay connector.	Yes	►	GO to CG5
	No Y/R	►	SERVICE Y/R wire from cooling fan motor to A/C relay and ECA. If all OK, SERVICE GIN wire to ECA.
Vehicle / **Wire Color** 1.3L EFI / Y/R and BL			
• Are both readings greater than 10V?	No BL	►	SERVICE BL wire or 15 amp HEATER fuse as required.

FM1089100042120X

Fig. 44   Test Step CG4 (Part 12 of 14). Festiva

TEST STEP	RESULT	►	ACTION TO TAKE
CG5 CHECK RELAY OPERATION			
• Remove A/C relay. • Jump battery power to A/C relay "A" terminal. • Measure resistance between A/C relay "B" and "C" terminals. • Ground A/C relay "D" terminal with a jumper wire. • Is reading greater than 10,000 ohms with "D" terminal open and less than 5 ohms with relay terminal grounded?	Yes	►	REINSTALL relay. GO to CG6
	No	►	REPLACE A/C relay.

FM1089100042130X

Fig. 44   Test Step CG5 (Part 13 of 14). Festiva

TEST STEP	RESULT	►	ACTION TO TAKE
CG6 CHECK POWER FROM RELAY			
• Key on. • Disconnect thermostatic switch. • Disconnect ECA. • Measure resistance at A/C Relay. • A/C on, blower on.	No	►	SERVICE relay ground (BK wire), or SERVICE GN wire as required.
	Yes	►	GO to CF4 .
Terminals / **Resistance** BK—Ground / 0-5 ohms GN—Ground			
• Are resistances OK?			

FM1089100042140X

Fig. 44   Test Step CG6 (Part 14 of 14). Festiva

FAN MOTOR INOPERATIVE

TEST	RESULT	►	ACTION TO TAKE
TEST 1			
• Disconnect motor lead. Jumper negative to ground and positive to B + at motor.	Motor does not run	►	REPLACE motor.
	Motor runs	►	CONNECT motor lead and GO to Test 2.
TEST 2			
• Unplug connector at cooling fan temperature switch. Jumper from connector to ground on Circuit 45. Turn ignition switch to RUN	Motor runs	►	CHECK switch ground. If ground is OK, REPLACE coolant temperature switch.
	Motor does not run	►	GO to Test 3.
TEST 3			
• Turn ignition switch to OFF and remove jumper installed in Test 2. Check continuity of Circuit 45 from cooling fan controller (terminal 1) to cooling fan temperature switch.	Continuity ⊘	►	CHECK Circuit 45 for an open.
	Continuity OK	►	JUMPER coolant temperature switch wire to ground and GO to Test 4.
TEST 4			
• Jumper from B + to Circuit 687 at cooling fan controller (terminal 8). Do not disconnect wiring connector from controller.	Motor runs	►	CHECK ignition feed Circuit 687 for an open.
	Motor does not run	►	REMOVE jumper and GO to Test 5.
TEST 5			
• Disconnect the wiring connector at the cooling fan controller. Jumper B + to Circuit 228 (terminal 5).	Motor does not run	►	CHECK Circuit 228 for an open.
	Motor runs	►	REMOVE jumper and GO to Test 6.
TEST 6			
• Connect a jumper from Circuit 68 to 228 (terminals 2 and 5) at the cooling fan controller connector.	Motor does not run	►	CHECK Circuit 68 for an open.
	Motor runs	►	REPLACE cooling fan controller and REMOVE jumper from temperature switch wire.

FM1089100043000X

Fig. 45   Diagnostic chart, fan motor inoperative. 1992–93 Mustang

FAN MOTOR OPERATES WHEN ENGINE TEMPERATURE REACHES SWITCH SET POINT BUT DOES NOT OPERATE IN THE A/C MODE

NOTE: A/C CLUTCH CIRCUIT WILL NOT ENERGIZE WITHOUT BATTERY VOLTAGE AT PINS OF COOLING FAN CONTROLLER.

TEST	RESULT	►	ACTION TO TAKE
TEST 1			
• Place A/C function selector switch in an A/C or DEFROST position. Start engine and wait five seconds.	Fan motor does not engage	►	GO to Test 2.
	Fan motor engages and disengages repeatedly	►	GO to Test 9.
TEST 2			
• Check 20 amp fuse in fuse panel.	Blown	►	REPLACE.
	Good fuse	►	GO to Test 3.
TEST 3			
• Disconnect A/C clutch cycling pressure switch. Jump across connector.	Fan motor engages	►	GO to Test 4.
	Fan motor does not engage	►	GO to Test 6.
TEST 4			
• Check A/C system for loss of refrigerant charge.	No refrigerant charge	►	Leak test, SERVICE and CHARGE system.
	Refrigerant system has charge with low pressure above 344.75 kPa (50 psi)	►	GO to Test 5.
TEST 5			
• Check for continuity across the A/C clutch cycling pressure switch. Remove switch connector.	No continuity	►	REPLACE the A/C clutch cycling pressure switch
	Continuity	►	GO to Test 8.
TEST 6			
• Check for voltage on Circuit 348 at A/C clutch cycling pressure switch.	Voltage OK	►	GO to Test 8.
	No voltage	►	GO to Test 7.
TEST 7			
• Check for voltage on Circuits 296 and 348 at function selector switch in instrument panel.	Voltage on Circuit 296 but not on 348	►	SERVICE A/C control assembly.
	No voltage on Circuit 296	►	TRACE Circuits 296 and 297 toward ignition switch.

FM1089100044010X

Fig. 46   Diagnostic chart, fan does not operate in A/C mode (Part 1 of 2). 1992–93 Mustang

FAN MOTOR OPERATES WHEN ENGINE TEMPERATURE REACHES SWITCH SET POINT BUT DOES NOT OPERATE IN THE A/C MODE — Continued

TEST	RESULT	►	ACTION TO TAKE
TEST 8			
• Check for voltage on 883 Circuit at Pin 6 of cooling fan controller.	Voltage	►	GO to Test 9.
	No voltage	►	SERVICE open 883 BK/W Circuit to controller.
TEST 9			
• Ground 57 Circuit at Pin 4 of controller — controller must be connected	Electro-drive fan runs	►	SERVICE ground circuit.
	Electro-drive fan does not run	►	REPLACE controller.

FM1089100044020X

Fig. 46   Diagnostic chart, fan does not operate in A/C mode (Part 2 of 2). 1992–93 Mustang

SYMPTOM	POSSIBLE CAUSE	ACTION TO TAKE
• Cooling Fan never runs - May cause overheating.	• Fuses • Motor • Cooling Fan Relay • Resistor (4EAT only) • Motor ground • Coolant Temperature Switch • Resistor (2.2L 4EAT only)	• INSPECT, REPLACE. • GO to CF1.
• Cooling Fan Runs constantly.	• Coolant Temperature Switch • High Speed Fan Switch • High Speed Fan Relay • Cooling Fan Relay • Circuit • ECA	• GO to EC1.
• No High Speed Fan (2.2L 4EAT only).	• High Speed Fan Relay • High Speed Fan Switch • Resistor • Circuit	• GO to HS1.
• No Fan Operation with A/C on. NOTE: Confirm A/C System functions properly.	• WAC Relay • Circuit	JUMP WAC Relay BK/GN (MTX) or BL/R (4EAT) to ground. If fan operates, REPLACE WAC Relay. If fan does not operate, SERVICE BK/GN or BL/R wires.

FM1089100045000X

Fig. 47   Symptom chart. 1992 Probe w/2.2L/4-133 engine

	TEST STEP	RESULT	►	ACTION TO TAKE
CF1	DISCONNECT COOLANT TEMPERATURE SWITCH			
• Key on. • Engine cold. • Disconnect Coolant Temperature Switch (CTS). • Ground CTS Connector BK/GN terminal. • Does Cooling Fan run?		Yes	►	REPLACE Coolant Temperature Switch.
		No	►	GO to CF2.

FM1089100046010X

Fig. 48   Diagnostic chart CF1 (Part 1 of 18). 1992 Probe w/2.2L/4-133 engine

	TEST STEP	RESULT	►	ACTION TO TAKE
CF2	GROUND CFR			
• Key on. • Engine cold. • Ground BK/GN terminal of Cooling Fan Relay. • Does Cooling Fan run?		Yes	►	SERVICE BK/GN from Cooling Fan Relay to CTS.
		No	►	GO to CF3.

FM1089100046020X

Fig. 48   Diagnostic chart CF2 (Part 2 of 18). 1992 Probe w/2.2L/4-133 engine

	TEST STEP	RESULT	►	ACTION TO TAKE
CF3	CHECK POWER TO RELAY			
• Key on. • Measure voltage at Cooling Fan Relay BK/R and BK/W terminals. • Are both readings 10V or greater?		Yes	►	GO to CF4.
		No	►	SERVICE wire in question.

FM1089100046030X

Fig. 48   Diagnostic chart CF3 (Part 3 of 18). 1992 Probe w/2.2L/4-133 engine

	TEST STEP	RESULT	►	ACTION TO TAKE
CF4	CHECK RELAY OPERATION			
• Key on. • Measure voltage at Cooling Fan Relay BL/W terminal. • Ground Relay BK/GN terminal. • Is voltage greater than 10V with BK/GN grounded and less than 1V with BK/GN open?		Yes	►	GO to CF5.
		No	►	REPLACE Relay.

FM1089100046040X

Fig. 48   Diagnostic chart CF4 (Part 4 of 18). 1992 Probe w/2.2L/4-133 engine

	TEST STEP	RESULT	►	ACTION TO TAKE
CF5	JUMP POWER TO MOTOR			
• Key on. • Jump battery power to Engine Cooling Fan Motor Harness Connector BL/Y terminal (MTX vehicles) or BL/BK terminal (4EAT vehicles). • Does motor run?		Yes (4EAT)	►	GO to CF6.
		Yes (MTX)	►	SERVICE BL/W wire from Cooling Fan Relay to Cooling Fan Motor for opens or shorts.
		No	►	SERVICE motor ground connection (BK wire). If all OK, REPLACE Cooling Fan Motor.

FM1089100046050X

Fig. 48   Diagnostic chart CF5 (Part 5 of 18). 1992 Probe w/2.2L/4-133 engine

	TEST STEP	RESULT	►	ACTION TO TAKE
CF6	JUMP ACROSS RESISTOR			
• Key on. • Jump CTS BK/GN wire to ground. • Disconnect Resistor. • Jump Resistor Harness Connector BL/W and BL/BK together. • Does fan motor run?		Yes	►	REPLACE resistor.
		No	►	SERVICE BL/W or BL/BK wires.

FM1089100046060X

Fig. 48   Diagnostic chart CF6 (Part 6 of 18). 1992 Probe w/2.2L/4-133 engine

	TEST STEP	RESULT	►	ACTION TO TAKE
HS1	CHECK HIGH SPEED FAN SWITCH			
• Key on. • Disconnect High Speed Fan Switch (HSFS). • Ground HSFS LB/R terminal. • Does fan motor run?		Yes	►	REPLACE High Speed Fan Switch.
		No	►	GO to HS2.

FM1089100046070X

Fig. 48   Diagnostic chart HS1 (Part 7 of 18). 1992 Probe w/2.2L/4-133 engine

TEST STEP	RESULT	▶	ACTION TO TAKE
HS2 GROUND RELAY			
• Key on. • Ground LB/R terminal of High Speed Fan Relay. • Does fan motor run?	Yes No	▶ ▶	SERVICE LB/R wire. GO to HS3 .

FM1089100046080X

Fig. 48 Diagnostic chart HS2 (Part 8 of 18). 1992 Probe w/2.2L/4-133 engine

TEST STEP	RESULT	▶	ACTION TO TAKE
HS3 CHECK POWER TO RELAY			
• Key on. • Measure voltage at High Speed Fan Relay BK/W and BK/R terminals. • Are both readings 10V or greater?	Yes No	▶ ▶	GO to HS4 . SERVICE wire in question.

FM1089100046090X

Fig. 48 Diagnostic chart HS3 (Part 9 of 18). 1992 Probe w/2.2L/4-133 engine

TEST STEP	RESULT	▶	ACTION TO TAKE
HS4 CHECK RELAY OPERATION			
• Key on. • Measure voltage at High Speed Fan Relay BL/BK terminal. • Ground LB/R terminal. • Is voltage greater than 10V with LB/R grounded, and 0V with LB/R open?	Yes No	▶ ▶	GO to HS5 . REPLACE relay.

FM1089100046100X

Fig. 48 Diagnostic chart HS4 (Part 10 of 18). 1992 Probe w/2.2L/4-133 engine

TEST STEP	RESULT	▶	ACTION TO TAKE
HS5 CHECK RESISTOR			
• Key off. • Disconnect Resistor. • Measure resistance across Resistor (BL/W to BL/BK). • Is resistance between 100 and 10,000 ohms?	Yes No	▶ ▶	SERVICE BL/BK wire from High Speed Fan Relay to Fan Motor. REPLACE Resistor.

FM1089100046110X

Fig. 48 Diagnostic chart HS5 (Part 11 of 18). 1992 Probe w/2.2L/4-133 engine

TEST STEP	RESULT	▶	ACTION TO TAKE
EC1 DISCONNECT CTS			
• Key on. • Cold engine. • Disconnect Coolant Temperature Switch. • Does fan stop?	Yes No	▶ ▶	REPLACE Coolant Temperature Switch. GO to EC2 .

FM1089100046120X

Fig. 48 Diagnostic chart EC1 (Part 12 of 18). 1992 Probe w/2.2L/4-133 engine

TEST STEP	RESULT	▶	ACTION TO TAKE
EC2 DISCONNECT ECA			
• Key on. • Cold engine. • Disconnect ECA. • Does fan stop?	Yes MTX Yes 4EAT No	▶ ▶ ▶	SERVICE BK/GN wire from Cooling Fan Relay and WAC Relay to ECA. SERVICE BK/GN wire from Cooling Fan Relay to ECA - or - BL/R wire from High Speed Fan Relay and WAC Relay to ECA. GO to EC3 .

FM1089100046130X

Fig. 48 Diagnostic chart EC2 (Part 13 of 18). 1992 Probe w/2.2L/4-133 engine

TEST STEP	RESULT	▶	ACTION TO TAKE
EC3 CHECK CFR BK/BL FOR SHORTS			
• Key off. • Disconnect Cooling Fan Relay (CFR). • Disconnect ECA. • Disconnect Coolant Temperature Switch (CTS). • Measure resistance between Cooling Fan Relay (CFR) Connector BK/GN terminal and ground. • Is resistance greater than 10,000 ohms?	Yes No	▶ ▶	RECONNECT CFR. RECONNECT CTS. GO to EC4 . SERVICE BK/GN for shorts.

FM1089100046140X

Fig. 48 Diagnostic chart EC3 (Part 14 of 18). 1992 Probe w/2.2L/4-133 engine

TEST STEP	RESULT	▶	ACTION TO TAKE
EC4 CHECK RELAY OPERATION			
• Key on, cold engine. • Disconnect ECA. • Disconnect Cooling Fan Relay. • Does fan stop?	Yes No MTX No 4EAT	▶ ▶ ▶	REPLACE Cooling Fan Relay. SERVICE BL/W from Cooling Fan Relay to Fan Motor (shorted to power). If all OK, REPLACE Fan Motor. GO to EC5 .

FM1089100046150X

Fig. 48 Diagnostic chart EC4 (Part 15 of 18). 1992 Probe w/2.2L/4–133 engine

TEST STEP	RESULT	▶	ACTION TO TAKE
EC5 DISCONNECT HSFS			
• Key on, cold engine. • Disconnect High Speed Fan Switch. • Does fan stop?	Yes No	▶ ▶	REPLACE High Speed Fan Switch. GO to EC6 .

FM1089100046160X

Fig. 48 Diagnostic chart EC5 (Part 16 of 18). 1992 Probe w/2.2L/4–133 engine

TEST STEP		RESULT	▶	ACTION TO TAKE
EC6	CHECK HSF RELAY BL/R FOR SHORTS			
• Key off.		No	▶	SERVICE BL/R wire
• Disconnect ECA. • Disconnect High Speed Fan Switch • Disconnect High Speed Fan Relay • Measure resistance between HSF Relay BL/R and ground. • Is resistance greater than 10,000 ohms?		Yes	▶	GO to EC7

FM1089100046170X

Fig. 48 Diagnostic chart EC6 (Part 17 of 18). 1992 Probe w/2.2L/4-133 engine

TEST STEP		RESULT	▶	ACTION TO TAKE
EC7	CHECK HSF RELAY OPERATION			
• Key on, cold engine. • Disconnect High Speed Fan Relay. • Does fan stop?		Yes	▶	REPLACE High Speed Fan Relay.
		No	▶	SERVICE BL/BK from HSF Relay to Fan Motor (shorted to power). If all OK, REPLACE Fan Motor.

FM1089100046180X

Fig. 48 Diagnostic chart EC7 (Part 18 of 18). 1992 Probe w/2.2L/4-133 engine

SYMPTOM CHART		
CONDITION	POSSIBLE SOURCE	ACTION
• Cooling Fan Never Runs (May Cause Overheating)	• Fuses. • Circuit. • Cooling fan relays. • Cooling fan motor.	• GO to CLF1.
• Cooling Fan Runs Constantly	• Circuit. • Cooling fan relays. • Cooling fan motor. • Engine Coolant Temperature (ECT) sensor.	• GO to CLF5.
• No High Speed Cooling Fan Operation	• Circuit. • Cooling fan high relay. • Cooling fan motor.	• GO to CLF4.
• No Low Speed Cooling Fan Operation	• Circuit. • Cooling fan relays. • Cooling fan motor.	• GO to CLF4.

FM1089300047000X

Fig. 49 Symptom chart. 1993-94 Probe w/2.0L/4-122 engine

TEST STEP		RESULT	▶	ACTION TO TAKE
CLF1	CHECK FUSES			
• Key OFF. • Check the 15A ENGINE fuse located in the interior fuse panel and the 40A COOLING FAN fuse located in the main fuse panel. • Are the fuses OK?		Yes No	▶ ▶	GO to CLF4. GO to CLF2.
CLF2	CHECK SYSTEM			
• Key OFF. • Replace the blown fuse(s). • Key ON. • Do(es) the fuse(s) fail again?		Yes No	▶ ▶	GO to CLF3. GO to CLF4.
CLF3	CHECK FOR SHORT(S) TO GROUND			
• Key OFF. • Remove the 40A COOLING FAN fuse. • Locate and disconnect the 10-pin interior fuse panel connector. • Locate and disconnect the cooling fan low and high relay connectors. • Measure the resistance of the "BK/W" wire between the 10-pin interior fuse panel and ground. • Measure the resistance of the "BK/R" wire between the left terminal of the 40A COOLING FAN fuse holder in the main fuse panel and ground. • Are the resistances less than 5 ohms?		Yes No	▶ ▶	SERVICE the wire(s) in question. REPLACE the 40A COOLING FAN fuse and/or the 15A ENGINE fuse. GO to CLF4.

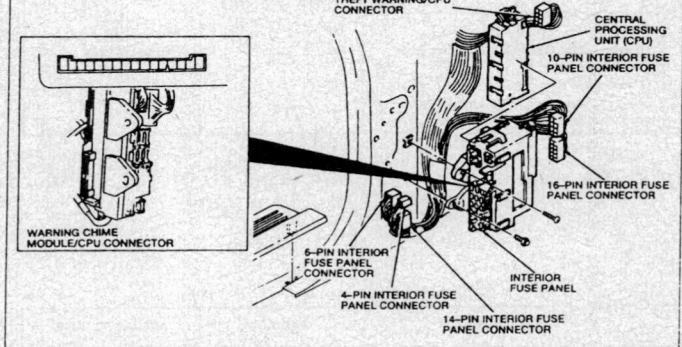

FM1089300048010X

Fig. 50 Diagnostic chart (Part 1 of 3). 1993-94 Probe w/2.0L/4-122 engine

TEST STEP		RESULT	▶	ACTION TO TAKE
CLF4	CHECK POWER SUPPLY			
• Key OFF. • Locate and disconnect the cooling fan low relay connector and the cooling fan high relay connector. • Key ON. • Measure the voltage of the "BK/W" wire at the cooling fan low and high relay connectors. • Measure the voltage on the "BK/R" wire at the cooling fan high relay connector. • Are the voltages greater than 10 volts?		Yes No	▶ ▶	GO to CLF5. SERVICE the wire(s) in question.
CLF5	CHECK COOLING FAN HIGH RELAY			
• Key OFF. • Disconnect the cooling fan high relay. • Apply 12 volts to the "BK/R" wire terminal and the "BK/W" wire terminal on the cooling fan high relay. • Measure the voltage of the "R" wire terminal on the cooling fan high relay. • Apply ground to the "BL/GN" wire terminal on the cooling fan high relay. • Measure the voltage of the "BL/BK" wire terminal on the cooling fan high relay. • Is the voltage greater than 10 volts on the "R" wire terminal with the key OFF, and greater than 10 volts on the "BL/BK" wire terminal with the key ON and the "BL/GN" wire terminal grounded?		Yes No	▶ ▶	GO to CLF6. REPLACE the cooling fan high relay.
CLF6	CHECK WIRE TO COOLING FAN MOTOR			
• Key OFF. • Disconnect the cooling fan high relay connector. • Locate and disconnect the cooling fan motor connector. • Measure the resistance of the "BL/BK" wire between the cooling fan high relay connector and the cooling fan motor connector. • Measure the resistance of the "BL/BK" wire between the cooling fan high relay connector and ground. • Is the resistance less than 5 ohms between the cooling fan high relay connector and the cooling fan motor connector, and greater than 10,000 ohms between the cooling fan high relay connector and ground?		Yes (Cooling fan never runs) Yes (No high speed cooling fan operation) Yes (No low speed cooling fan operation or cooling fan runs constantly) No	▶ ▶ ▶ ▶	GO to CLF10. REPLACE the cooling fan motor. GO to CLF7. SERVICE the wire in question.
CLF7	CHECK WIRE BETWEEN COOLING FAN HIGH AND LOW RELAY			
• Key OFF. • Disconnect the cooling fan low relay connector. • Measure the voltage of the "R" wire at the cooling fan low relay connector. • Is the voltage greater than 10 volts?		Yes No	▶ ▶	GO to CLF8. SERVICE the "R" wire.
CLF8	CHECK COOLING FAN LOW RELAY			
• Key OFF. • Disconnect the cooling fan low relay. • Apply 12 volts to the "BK/W" wire terminal and the "R" terminal on the cooling fan low relay. • Measure the voltage of the "BL/Y" wire terminal on the cooling fan low relay. • Apply ground to the "BL/O" wire terminal on the cooling fan low relay. • Measure the voltage of the "BL/Y" wire terminal on the cooling fan low relay. • Is the voltage less than 1 volt with the key OFF, and greater than 10 volts with the key ON and the relay grounded?		Yes No	▶ ▶	GO to CLF9. REPLACE the cooling fan low relay.

FM1089300048020X

Fig. 50 Diagnostic chart (Part 2 of 3). 1993-94 Probe w/2.0L/4-122 engine

TEST STEP		RESULT	▶	ACTION TO TAKE
CLF9	CHECK WIRE BETWEEN COOLING FAN LOW RELAY AND COOLING FAN MOTOR			
• Key OFF. • Disconnect the cooling fan low relay connector and the cooling fan motor connector. • Measure the resistance of the "BL/Y" wire between the cooling fan low relay connector and the cooling fan motor connector. • Measure the resistance of the "BL/Y" wire between the cooling fan low relay connector and ground. • Is the resistance less than 5 ohms between the cooling fan low relay connector and the cooling fan motor connector, and greater than 10,000 ohms between the cooling fan low relay connector and ground?		Yes No	▶ ▶	GO to CLF10. SERVICE the wire in question.
CLF10	CHECK COOLING FAN MOTOR GROUND			
• Key OFF. • Disconnect the cooling fan motor connector. • Measure the resistance of the "BK" wire (harness side) between the cooling fan motor connector and ground. • Is the resistance less than 5 ohms?		Yes No	▶ ▶	REPLACE the cooling fan motor. SERVICE the "BK" wire.

FM1089300048030X

Fig. 50 Diagnostic chart (Part 3 of 3). 1993-94 Probe w/2.0L/4-122 engine

SYMPTOM CHART

CONDITION	POSSIBLE SOURCE	ACTION
• Cooling Fan Never Runs (May Cause Overheating)	• Fuses. • Circuit. • Cooling fan relays. • Cooling fan motor.	• GO to CLF1.
• Cooling Fan Runs Constantly	• Circuit. • Cooling fan relays. • Cooling fan motor. • High pressure switch. • Engine coolant temperature sensor.	• GO to CLF5.
• No High Speed Cooling Fan Operation	• Circuit. • Cooling fan high relay. • Cooling fan motor.	• GO to CLF4.

FM1089300049010X

Fig. 51 Symptom chart (Part 1 of 2). 1993–94 Probe w/2.5L/V6-153 engine

SYMPTOM CHART

CONDITION	POSSIBLE SOURCE	ACTION
• No Low Speed Cooling Fan Operation	• Circuit. • Cooling fan relays. • Cooling fan motor.	• GO to CLF4.
• Condenser Fan Never Runs	• Fuses. • Circuit. • Condenser fan relays. • Condenser fan motor.	• GO to CDF1.
• Condenser Fan Runs Constantly	• Circuit. • Condenser fan relays. • Condenser fan motor. • High pressure switch. • Engine coolant temperature sensor.	• GO to CDF5.
• No High Speed Condenser Fan Operation	• Circuit. • Condenser fan high relay. • Condenser fan motor.	• GO to CDF4.
• No Low Speed Condenser Fan Operation	• Circuit. • Condenser fan relays. • Condenser fan motor.	• GO to CDF4.

FM1089300049020X

Fig. 51 Symptom chart (Part 2 of 2). 1993–94 Probe w/2.5L/V6-153 engine

TEST STEP	RESULT	► ACTION TO TAKE
CLF1 CHECK FUSES • Key OFF. • Check the 15A ENGINE fuse located in the interior fuse panel and the 40A COOLING FAN fuse located in the main fuse panel. • Are the fuses OK?	Yes No	► GO to CLF4. ► GO to CLF2.
CLF2 CHECK SYSTEM • Key OFF. • Replace the blown fuse(s). • Key ON. • Does the fuse(s) fail again?	Yes No	► GO to CLF3. ► GO to CLF4.

FM1089300050010X

Fig. 52 Diagnostic chart (Part 1 of 4). 1993–94 Probe w/2.5L/V6-153 engine

TEST STEP	RESULT	► ACTION TO TAKE
CLF5 CHECK COOLING FAN HIGH RELAY • Key OFF. • Disconnect the cooling fan high relay connector. • Apply 12 volts to the "BK/R" wire terminal and the "BK/W" wire terminal on the cooling fan high relay. • Measure the voltage of the "R" wire terminal on the cooling fan high relay. • Apply ground to the "BL/GN" wire terminal on the cooling fan high relay. • Measure the voltage on the "BL/W" wire terminal on the cooling fan high relay. • Is the voltage greater than 10 volts on the "R" wire terminal with ground not applied, and greater than 10 volts on the "BL/W" wire terminal with ground applied?	Yes No	► GO to CLF6. ► REPLACE the cooling fan high relay.
CLF6 CHECK WIRE TO COOLING FAN MOTOR • Key OFF. • Disconnect the cooling fan high relay connector. • Locate and disconnect the cooling fan motor connector. • Measure the resistance of the "BL/W" wire between the cooling fan high relay connector and the cooling fan motor connector. • Measure the resistance of the "BL/W" wire between the cooling fan high relay connector and ground. • Is the resistance less than 5 ohms between the cooling fan high relay connector and the cooling fan motor connector, and greater than 10,000 ohms between the cooling fan high relay connector and ground?	Yes (Cooling fan never runs) Yes (No high speed cooling fan operation) Yes (No low speed cooling fan operation or cooling fan runs constantly) No	► GO to CLF10. ► REPLACE the cooling fan motor. ► GO to CLF7. ► SERVICE the wire in question.
CLF7 CHECK WIRE BETWEEN COOLING FAN HIGH AND LOW RELAY • Key OFF. • Reconnect the cooling fan high relay. • Disconnect the cooling fan low relay connector. • Measure the voltage on the "R" wire at the cooling fan low relay connector. • Is the voltage greater than 10 volts?	Yes No	► GO to CLF8. ► SERVICE the "R" wire.
CLF8 CHECK COOLING FAN LOW RELAY • Key OFF. • Disconnect the cooling fan low relay connector. • Apply 12 volts to the "BK/W" wire terminal and the "R" wire terminal on the cooling fan low relay. • Measure the voltage of the "BL/W" wire terminal on the cooling fan low relay. • Apply ground to the "R-W" wire terminal on the cooling fan low relay. • Measure the voltage of the "BL/O" wire terminal on the cooling fan low relay. • Is the voltage less than 1 volt with ground not applied, and greater than 10 volts with ground applied?	Yes No	► GO to CLF9. ► REPLACE the cooling fan low relay.

FM1089300050030X

Fig. 52 Diagnostic chart (Part 3 of 4). 1993–94 Probe w/2.5L/V6-153 engine

TEST STEP	RESULT	► ACTION TO TAKE
CLF3 CHECK FOR SHORT(S) TO GROUND • Key OFF. • Remove the 40A COOLING FAN fuse. • Locate and disconnect the 10-pin interior fuse panel connector. • Locate and disconnect the cooling fan low and high relay connectors. • Measure the resistance of the "BK/W" wire between the 10-pin interior fuse panel and ground. • Measure the resistance of the "BK/R" wire between the left terminal of the 40A COOLING FAN fuse holder in the main fuse panel and ground. • Are the resistances less than 5 ohms?	Yes No	► SERVICE the wire(s) in question. ► REPLACE the 40A COOLING FAN fuse and/or the 15A ENGINE fuse. GO to CLF4.

THEFT WARNING/CPU CONNECTOR

CENTRAL PROCESSING UNIT (CPU) CONNECTOR

10-PIN INTERIOR FUSE PANEL CONNECTOR

16-PIN INTERIOR FUSE PANEL CONNECTOR

WARNING CHIME MODULE/CPU CONNECTOR

6-PIN INTERIOR FUSE PANEL CONNECTOR

INTERIOR FUSE PANEL

4-PIN INTERIOR FUSE PANEL CONNECTOR

14-PIN INTERIOR FUSE PANEL CONNECTOR

TEST STEP	RESULT	► ACTION TO TAKE
CLF4 CHECK POWER SUPPLY • Key OFF. • Reconnect the 10-pin interior fuse panel connector. • Locate and disconnect the cooling fan low relay connector and the cooling fan high relay connectors. • Key ON. • Measure the voltage of the "BK/W" wire at the cooling fan low connector and at the high relay connector. • Measure the voltage of the "BK/R" wire at the cooling fan high relay connector. • Are the voltages greater than 10 volts?	Yes No	► GO to CLF5. ► SERVICE the wire(s) in question.

FM1089300050020X

Fig. 52 Diagnostic chart (Part 2 of 4). 1993–94 Probe w/2.5L/V6-153 engine

TEST STEP	RESULT	► ACTION TO TAKE
CLF9 CHECK WIRE BETWEEN COOLING FAN LOW RELAY AND COOLING FAN MOTOR • Key OFF. • Disconnect the cooling fan low relay connector and the cooling fan motor connector. • Measure the resistance of the "BL/O" wire between the cooling fan low relay connector and the cooling fan motor connector. • Measure the resistance of the "BL/O" wire between the cooling fan low relay connector and ground. • Is the resistance less than 5 ohms between the cooling fan low relay connector and the cooling fan motor connector, and greater than 10,000 ohms between the cooling fan low relay connector and ground?	Yes No	► GO to CLF10. ► SERVICE the wire in question.
CLF10 CHECK COOLING FAN MOTOR GROUND • Key OFF. • Disconnect the cooling fan motor connector. • Measure the resistance of the "BK" wire (harness side) between the cooling fan motor connector and ground. • Is the resistance less than 5 ohms?	Yes No	► REPLACE the cooling fan motor. ► SERVICE the "BK" wire.

FM1089300050040X

Fig. 52 Diagnostic chart (Part 4 of 4). 1993–94 Probe w/2.5L/V6-153 engine

TEST STEP	RESULT	▶	ACTION TO TAKE
B1 CHECK FUSES			
• Key off. • Check the 10A ENGINE fuse located in the interior fuse junction panel and the 30A COOLING FAN fuse located in the main fuse junction panel. • **Are the fuses OK?**	Yes No	▶ ▶	GO to **B4**. GO to **B2**.
B2 CHECK SYSTEM			
• Key off. • Replace the blown fuse(s). • Key ON. • **Do(es) the fuse(s) fail again?**	Yes No	▶ ▶	GO to **B3**. GO to **B4**.

FM1089400089010X

Fig. 53 Test B: cooling fan never runs (Part 1 of 2). Aspire

TEST STEP	RESULT	▶	ACTION TO TAKE
C1 CHECK COOLING FAN CONTROL RELAY			
• Key off. • Disconnect the cooling fan control relay connector. • Jumper the "BK/W" wire terminal and the "W/BK" wire terminal on the cooling fan control relay to the battery positive terminal. • Measure the voltage on the "Y" wire terminal on the cooling fan control relay. • Jumper the "BR" wire terminal on the cooling fan control relay to the battery negative terminal. • Measure the voltage on the "Y" wire terminal on the cooling fan control relay. • **Is the voltage greater than 10 volts with the "BR" wire jumper to the battery positive terminal, and less than 1 volt with the "BR" wire not connected to the battery negative terminal?**	Yes No	▶ ▶	REFER to the PC/ED Manual [4], Section 6B to diagnose the cooling fan control relay circuit. REPLACE the cooling fan control relay.

FM1089400090000X

Fig. 54 Test C: cooling fan runs continuously. Aspire

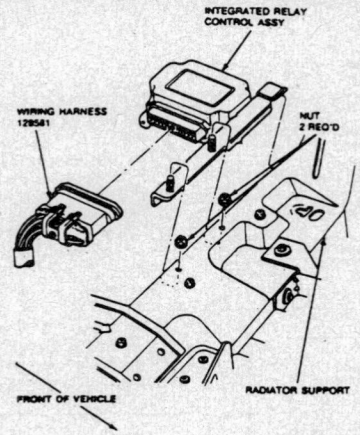

INTEGRATED RELAY CONTROL ASSY

WIRING HARNESS 12A581

NUT 2 REQ'D

FRONT OF VEHICLE

RADIATOR SUPPORT

FM1089100051000X

Fig. 55 Cooling fan module/constant control relay module (integrated relay) replacement. Continental

2.5L/4-152 Engine

Refer to **Fig. 51** for symptom chart and **Fig. 52** for diagnostic test steps.

ASPIRE

Refer to **Figs. 53 and 54** for diagnostic test procedures.

COMPONENT REPLACEMENT

COOLING FAN MODULE/CONSTANT CONTROL RELAY MODULE (INTEGRATED RELAY CONTROL ASSEMBLY)

Continental

1. Disconnect battery ground cable, then remove radiator sight shield.
2. Disconnect electrical connector, then remove integrated relay control as-

TEST STEP	RESULT	▶	ACTION TO TAKE
B3 CHECK FOR SHORT(S) TO GROUND			
• Key off. • Remove the 30A COOLING FAN fuse and/or 10A ENGINE fuse. • Disconnect the cooling fan control relay. • Measure the resistance of the "BK/W" wire between the bottom terminal of the 10A ENGINE fuse holder and ground. • Measure the resistance of the "BK/R" wire between the left terminal of the 30A COOLING FAN fuse holder and ground. • **Are the resistances less than 5 ohms?**	Yes No	▶ ▶	SERVICE the wire(s) in question. REPLACE the 10A ENGINE fuse and/or the 30A COOLING FAN fuse. GO to **B4**.
B4 CHECK ELECTRIC COOLING FAN			
• Key off. • Disconnect the electric cooling fan connector. • Jumper the "Y" wire terminal on the electric cooling fan to the battery positive terminal. • Jumper the "BK" wire terminal on the electric cooling fan to the battery negative terminal. • **Does the electric cooling fan operate?**	Yes No	▶ ▶	GO to **B5**. REPLACE the electric cooling fan.
B5 CHECK ELECTRIC COOLING FAN GROUND			
• Key off. • Disconnect the electric cooling fan connector. • Measure the resistance of the "BK" wire between the electric cooling fan connector and ground. • **Is the resistance less than 5 ohms?**	Yes No	▶ ▶	GO to **B6**. SERVICE the "BK" wire for open.
B6 CHECK COOLING FAN CONTROL RELAY			
• Key off. • Disconnect the cooling fan control relay connector. • Jumper the "BK/W" wire terminal and the "W/BK" wire terminal on the cooling fan control relay to the battery positive terminal. • Measure the voltage on the "Y" wire terminal on the cooling fan control relay. • Jumper the "BR" wire terminal on the cooling fan control relay to the battery negative terminal. • Measure the voltage on the "Y" wire terminal on the cooling fan control relay. • **Is the voltage greater than 10 volts with the "BR" wire jumper to the battery negative terminal, and less than 1 volt with the "BR" wire not connected to the battery negative terminal?**	Yes No	▶ ▶	GO to **B7**. REPLACE the cooling fan control relay.
B7 CHECK POWER SUPPLY TO COOLING FAN CONTROL RELAY			
• Key off. • Disconnect the cooling fan control relay connector. • Key ON. • Measure the voltage on the "BK/W" wire at the cooling fan control relay connector. • Measure the voltage on the "W/BK" wire at the cooling fan control relay connector. • **Are the voltages greater than 10 volts?**	Yes No	▶ ▶	GO to **B8**. SERVICE the wire(s) in question for opens.
B8 CHECK ELECTRIC COOLING FAN CIRCUIT			
• Key off. • Disconnect the cooling fan control relay connector. • Reconnect the electric cooling fan. • Jumper the "Y" wire at the cooling fan control relay connector to the battery positive terminal. • **Does the electric cooling fan operate?**	Yes No	▶ ▶	REFER to the PC/ED Manual [3], Section 6B to diagnose the cooling fan control relay circuit. SERVICE the "Y" wire.

FM1089400089020X

Fig. 53 Test B: cooling fan never runs (Part 2 of 2). Aspire

sembly from radiator support, **Fig. 55.**
3. Disconnect electrical fan connector, then separate connector located at top of fan shroud.
4. Remove male terminal connector clip from shroud mounting tab, then remove air bag crash sensor.
5. Remove fan shroud from radiator.
6. Lift cooling fan module to disengage from lower radiator clip and end tab.
7. Slide cooling fan module clear of radiator hose connector, then remove two engine wire harness clips from side of fan shroud. Lift module past radiator.
8. Reverse procedure to install. **Torque** shroud to radiator nuts and bolts to 36 inch lbs.

Cougar, Sable, Taurus & Thunderbird

1. Disconnect battery ground cable, then remove radiator sight shield.
2. Disconnect electrical connector, then remove integrated relay control assembly from radiator support.
3. Reverse procedure to install.

Mustang, Probe w/3.0L/V6-182, Tempo & Topaz

1. Disconnect battery ground cable, then IRCM electrical connector.
2. **On Tempo and Topaz**, remove bolts retaining module to lefthand strut tower.
3. **On 1992-93 Mustang**, remove bolts retaining module to righthand shock tower.

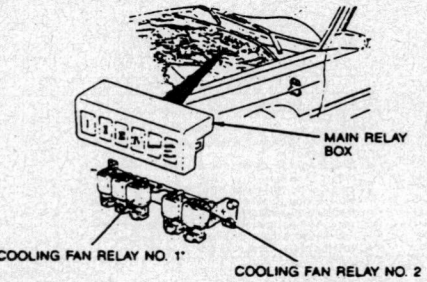

MAIN RELAY BOX

COOLING FAN RELAY NO. 1*

COOLING FAN RELAY NO. 2

*COOLING FAN RELAY NO. 1 IS ONLY FOR MODELS EQUIPPED WITH 4EAT

FM1089100052000X

Fig. 56 Cooling fan relay replacement. Probe

4. **On 1994 Mustang,** remove module bracket retainers and bracket from radiator support, then separate module from bracket.
5. **On Probe,** remove bolts retaining module to engine cowl, near brake booster assembly.
6. **On all models,** reverse procedure to install.

COOLING FAN RELAY

ASPIRE, CAPRI & FESTIVA

The cooling fan relay is located in the lefthand side of the engine compartment, near the battery.
1. Disconnect battery ground cable.
2. Remove screw from the top of the relay.
3. Remove protective boot.

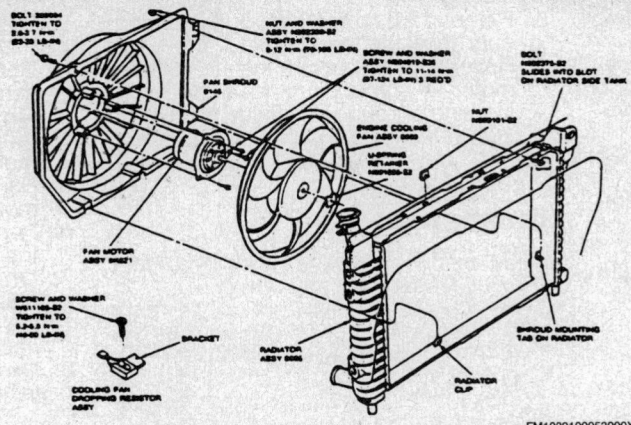

Fig. 57 Cooling fan motor replacement. Sable & Taurus w/3.0L/V6-182 engine

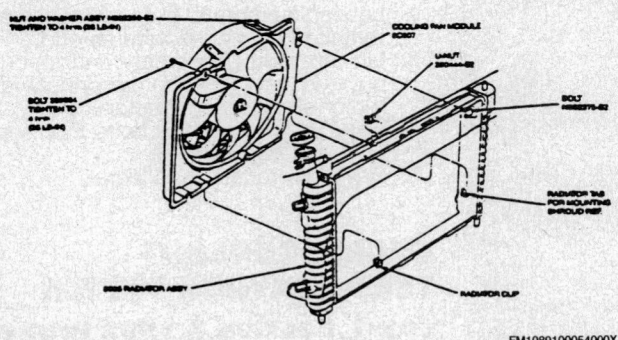

Fig. 58 Cooling fan motor replacement. Sable & Taurus w/3.0L/V6-182 & 3.8L/V6-232 engines

Item	Part Number	Description
1A	N807390-S2	Screw and Washer Assy
2B	N802350-S2	Nut and Washer Assy
3	8C607	Motor and Fan Assy
4	N623330-S2	Nut
5	N802375-S2	Bolt

Item	Part Number	Description
6	—	Radiator Tab for Mounting Shroud
7	8005	Radiator Assy
A		Tighten to 8-11.5 N-m (6-8.5 Lb-Ft)
B		Tighten to 2.5-3.5 N-m (2-2.6 Lb-Ft)

Fig. 59 Cooling fan motor replacement. Taurus SHO w/3.2L/V6-195 engine

4. Disconnect electrical connector.
5. Reverse procedure to install.

ESCORT & TRACER

The cooling fan main relays are located in the fuse block on the lefthand side of the engine compartment. The high and low speed cooling fan relays (2 and 3) are mounted on a single bracket inside the lefthand front fender apron. The air cleaner assembly must be removed to gain access to the relays. Disconnect battery ground cable prior to servicing.

PROBE

1992 w/2.2L/4-133 Engine

The cooling fan relays are located in the lefthand side of the bulkhead within the main relay box. A bracket is used to attach each relay to the bulkhead, **Fig. 56.**
1. Disconnect battery ground cable, then remove relay from bracket.
2. Disconnect electrical connector.
3. Reverse procedure to install.

1993—94

The cooling fan relays are located on the radiator cowl support.
1. Disconnect battery ground cable.
2. Pull relay from electrical connector.
3. Reverse procedure to install.

COOLING FAN MOTOR

Capri

1. Disconnect battery ground cable.

2. Remove fan wiring harness from routing clamps, then disconnect harness connector.
3. Remove four screws retaining fan shroud to radiator, then remove shroud and fan motor.
4. Remove fan retaining nut and washer, then the fan from motor shaft.
5. Remove three fan motor retaining screws and washers, then the fan motor from shroud.
6. Reverse procedure to install. **Torque** motor to shroud screws to 3-4 ft. lbs. and four fan shroud to radiator retaining screws to 23-34 ft. lbs.

Cougar & Thunderbird

1. Disconnect battery ground cable.
2. Disconnect fan motor wiring connector located at side of fan shroud.
3. Remove male terminal connector retaining clip from shroud mounting tab.
4. Remove overflow hose from shroud, then two upper shroud to radiator support retaining bolts.
5. Lift cooling fan motor past radiator.
6. Reverse procedure to install.

Tempo & Topaz

1. Disconnect battery ground cable.
2. Disconnect electrical connector at fan motor, then disconnect wire loom

from clip on shroud (push down on two lock fingers, then pull connector from motor end).
3. Remove two nuts retaining fan motor and shroud assembly, then lift from vehicle.
4. Remove retaining clip from motor shaft and remove fan. A metal burr may be present on motor shaft after retaining clip has been removed. If necessary, remove burr to facilitate in fan removal.
5. Remove three screws, then withdraw fan motor from shroud.
6. Reverse procedure to install, noting the following:
   a. **Torque** motor to shroud attaching nuts and washers to 44-66 inch lbs.
   b. **Torque** fan, motor, and shroud assembly to radiator retaining nut to 35-41 inch lbs.
   c. **Torque** fan, motor, and shroud assembly to radiator retaining screw to 31-41 inch lbs.

Escort & Tracer

1. Disconnect battery ground cable.
2. **On models with 1.8L/4-110 engines,** remove the resonance duct from the radiator iso-mounts.

3. **On all models,** disconnect cooling fan electrical connector.
4. Remove three radiator shroud attaching bolts from radiator, then lift shroud and fan motor assembly out from vehicle.
5. Remove cooling fan retainer clip, then the fan from motor.
6. Disconnect cooling fan motor electrical harness retainers, then remove harness from retainers.
7. Remove cooling fan motor attaching screws, then the motor from shroud.
8. Reverse procedure to install.

Aspire, Festiva & Probe

1. Disconnect battery ground cable, then the cooling fan wiring harness connectors from routing clamps.
2. Remove four screws attaching fan and shroud to radiator, then the fan and shroud.
3. Remove fan attaching nut and washer, then the fan from motor shaft.
4. Remove attaching screws, then separate fan motor from shroud.
5. Reverse procedure to install, noting the following for Probe models only:
   a. **Torque** fan motor to shroud bolts to 23-46 ft. lbs.
   b. **Torque** fan to fan motor attaching nut and washer to 69-95 inch lbs.
   c. **Torque** shroud to radiator bolts to 61-87 inch lbs.

Mustang

1. Disconnect battery ground cable, then remove fan wiring harness from routing clips.
2. Disconnect wiring harness from fan motor connector (pull up on single lock finger to separate connector).
3. Remove shroud retaining screws, then the fan assembly from vehicle.
4. Remove retaining clip from end of motor shaft, then the fan. A small metal burr may be present on motor after retaining clip is removed. Removal of clip may be necessary prior to fan removal.

5. Remove fan motor to shroud retaining nuts, then the fan motor.
6. Reverse procedure to install. **Torque** motor to shroud nuts to 48-62 inch lbs. and shroud to radiator screws to 70-95 inch lbs.

Continental

1. Disconnect battery ground cable, then remove radiator sight shield.
2. Disconnect electrical connector, then remove constant control relay module (CCRM) assembly from radiator support.
3. Disconnect radiator fan motor electrical connector.
4. Pull apart male/female connector at top of fan shroud, then remove male terminal connector clip from shroud mounting tab.
5. Remove air bag crash sensor.
6. Remove radiator fan/motor and shroud assembly mounting bolts.
7. Lift fan/motor and shroud assembly upward to disengage from lower radiator clip and end tab.
8. Remove radiator fan and motor assembly from radiator.
9. Remove fan blade retaining clip and fan blade from radiator electric fan motor shaft.
10. Remove radiator electric motor retaining screws and motor from fan shroud.
11. Reverse procedure to install, **torque** fan shroud mounting bolts to 36 inch lbs.

Sable & Taurus

Refer to **Fig. 57** for models with 3.0L/V6-182 engine, **Fig. 58** for models with 3.0L/V6-182 and 3.8L/V6-232 engines and **Fig. 59** for models with 3.2L/V6-195 SHO engine.
1. Disconnect battery ground cable, then remove radiator sight shield.

2. Disconnect fan motor wiring connector.
3. Remove bolts attaching fan and shroud assembly to radiator.
4. **On models with 3.0L/V6-182 engine,** rotate fan and shroud assembly, then lift past radiator.
5. Remove fan U-spring retainer from motor shaft, then the fan.
6. Remove fan motor to shroud bolts, then remove motor.
7. **On models with 3.2L/V6-195 and 3.8L/V6-232 engines,** slide cooling fan module clear of radiator hose connector, then lift past radiator.
8. **On all models,** reverse procedure to install.

Mark VIII

1. Disconnect battery ground cable.
2. Loosen fan shroud from radiator, then remove lower hose from shroud.
3. Lift fan motor assembly and shroud out from vehicle, then disconnect fan motor electrical connector.
4. Remove four retaining bolts, then separate fan from shroud.
5. Reverse procedure to install.

ENGINE COOLANT TEMPERATURE SWITCH

Capri, Festiva & 1992 Probe

The cooling fan will run if the coolant temperature switch wire is disconnected and the ignition switch is in the Run position. Ensure ignition switch is in the Off position prior to disconnecting wire.
1. Disconnect battery ground cable, then drain cooling system.
2. Disconnect switch connector.
3. Remove switch from thermostat housing.
4. Reverse procedure to install. Coat switch threads with pipe sealant containing Teflon.

DASH GAUGES

INDEX

GAUGES

Coolant Temperature & Oil Pressure Indicators

COOLANT TEMPERATURE GAUGE DESCRIPTION

Magnetic Type

The temperature indicating system is a magnetic type system, which consists only of the sending unit located in the engine block or cylinder head and a temperature gauge in the instrument cluster. The sending unit changes resistance according to the temperature of engine coolant, which varies the current flow through the gauge. The pointer position varies proportionally to the current flow. The sender resistance is high when coolant temperature is low, and low when coolant temperature is high.

The pointer of the magnetic gauge remains in position when ignition is turned to the Off position. It will move to the correct indication whenever the ignition is turned back to On position.

Bimetal Type

The temperature lamp system provides the driver with an indication of engine coolant temperature by means of a switch mounted in the intake manifold and a red engine lamp mounted on the instrument panel. The temperature switch has a temperature sensitive bimetallic arm which completes the lamp circuit through the switch to engine ground.

OIL PRESSURE GAUGE DESCRIPTION

Except Capri

The oil pressure indicating system is a magnetic type system, which consists of three primary coils, one of which is wound at a 90° angle to the other two. The coils form a magnetic field which varies in direction according to the variable resistance of the sender unit which is connected between two of them. A primary magnet, to which a shaft and pointer are attached, ro-

tates to align to this primary field, resulting in pointer position. The bobbin/coil assembly is pressed into a metal housing which as two holes for dial mounting. The is no adjustment, calibration or maintenance required for these gauges.

Capri

The oil pressure indicating system consists of a sender unit mounted on the right-hand side of the engine block and a gauge mounted in the instrument cluster.

When engine oil pressure is low, the sender resistance is high, resulting in low current flow through the gauge and little pointer movement.

The oil pressure gauge is not serviceable and must be replaced as part of the temperature/oil pressure gauge assembly.

TEMPERATURE GAUGE CALIBRATION TEST

Magnetic Type

1. Turn ignition switch to On or ACC position.
2. Connect a 10 ohm resistor between gauge lead and ground. The centerline of pointer should fall within the band around the H mark.
3. Connect a 73 ohm resistor between gauge lead and ground. The centerline of pointer should fall within the band around the C mark.
4. If gauge tests within calibration, replace sender.
5. If gauge is out of calibration, replace gauge.

Bimetal Type

The instrument voltage regulator (IVR) supplies a common regulated voltage for temperature, oil pressure and fuel gauges. The IVR is malfunctioning only if all gauges show similar problems.

Test temperature gauge with Rotunda Gauge Tester 021-00055 or equivalent or with a 10 ohm resistor for high calibration and a 75 ohm resistor for low calibration as follows:

1. Turn ignition switch to On or ACC position.
2. Connect a 10 ohm resistor between gauge lead and ground. The centerline of pointer should fall within the band around the H mark.

3. Connect a 75 ohm resistor between gauge lead and ground. The centerline of pointer should fall within the band around the C mark.
4. If gauge tests within calibration, replace sender.
5. If gauge is out of calibration, replace IVR and retest.
6. If gauge is out of calibration, replace gauge.

SYSTEM DIAGNOSIS
Grand Marquis, Crown Victoria & Town Car

Refer to **Figs. 1 through 3** for coolant temperature and oil pressure indicating system diagnosis.

Capri

Refer to **Fig. 4**, for coolant temperature indicating system diagnosis. Refer to **Fig. 5**, for oil pressure indicator system diagnosis.

Sable & Taurus

Refer to **Fig. 6**, for coolant temperature indicating system diagnosis.

Tempo & Topaz

Refer to **Fig. 7**, for coolant temperature indicating system diagnosis.

Mustang

Refer to **Figs. 8 through 10** for coolant temperature indicating system and oil pressure indicating system diagnosis.

Escort & Tracer

Refer to **Figs. 11 and 12** for coolant temperature indicating system diagnosis.

Probe

Refer to **Fig. 13 and 14**, for coolant temperature indicating system diagnosis. Refer to **Figs. 15 and 16**, for oil pressure indicator system diagnosis.

Festiva

Refer to **Fig. 17**, for coolant temperature indicating system diagnosis.

Aspire

Refer to **Fig. 18**, for coolant temperature indicating system diagnosis. Refer to **Fig. 19**, for oil pressure indicating system diagnosis.

Mark VII & Mark VIII

Refer to **Figs. 20 and 21** for oil pressure and coolant temperature indicating system diagnosis.

Charging System (Voltmeter) Indicator

DESCRIPTION

A red alternator charge indicator is located in the instrument cluster. This indicator glows when there is no alternator output.

If the system is working normally, the following conditions will be present.

1. With ignition switch Off, charge indicator is Off.
2. With ignition switch in Run (engine not running), charge indicator is On.
3. With ignition switch in Run (engine running), charge indicator is Off.

SYSTEM DIAGNOSIS
Cougar, Crown Victoria, Mustang & Thunderbird

If voltage indicator will not show voltage reading with the ignition switch in Run position and the engine not running, check the I circuit (ignition switch to regulator I terminal) for an open circuit or defective voltmeter gauge.

Aspire

Refer to **Fig. 22**, for charging indicator system diagnosis.

Mark VIII

Refer to **Fig. 23**, for charging indicator system diagnosis.

Probe

Refer to **Figs. 24 and 25**, for charging indicator system diagnosis.

Capri

Refer to **Fig. 26**, for charging indicator system diagnosis.

Turbo Boost Indicating System

DESCRIPTION

The turbo boost indicating system consists of an electrically operated gauge mounted in the instrument cluster and a sensor mounted in the engine compartment. The sensor converts a vacuum signal to electrical input for the gauge.

SYSTEM DIAGNOSIS

Refer to **Figs. 27 and 28**, for turbo boost indicating system diagnosis.

WARNING SYSTEM
Fuel Level Indicating System

DESCRIPTION
Magnetic Type

The fuel level indicating system is a magnetic type system, which consists of the sending unit located in the fuel tank, an anti-slosh module located on the back of the instrument cluster, and a fuel gauge located in the instrument cluster.

The sending unit changes resistance according to the level of fuel in the fuel tank, which varies the current flow through the gauge. The pointer position varies proportionately to the current flow. In this system, the sending unit resistance is low when the fuel level is low and high when the fuel level is high.

The pointer of the magnetic gauge remains in position when the ignition is turned to the Off position. On some models, an anti-slosh module is used to dampen out fluctuating fuel signals from the sender.

Some vehicles are equipped with a low fuel warning indicator. The anti-slosh module will also actuate the low fuel indicator when the fuel level in the tank reaches 1/16 to 1/8 full.

Bimetal Type

The fuel level indicator gauge pointer is attached to a wire wound bimetal strip, which, when heated by a signal from the fuel sender unit, produces the appropriate level indication. When the current is low there is little heating effect and the point moves a short distance. As the current increases, it produces a greater heating effect, causing the pointer to move a greater distance.

PINPOINT TEST A
TEMPERATURE/OIL GAUGE
INOPERATIVE — POINTER DOES NOT MOVE

TEST STEP	RESULT	▶	ACTION TO TAKE
A1 VERIFY CONDITION			
• Observe gauge performance. • Does gauge pointer move?	No Yes	▶ ▶	GO to A2. GO to D1 for temperature gauge. GO to E1 for oil gauge.
A2 VERIFY CLUSTER PERFORMANCE			
• With the ignition ON, observe the other gauges and warning indicators for proper operation. • Do other gauges and warning indicators operate properly?	Yes No	▶ ▶	GO to C1. GO to B1.

PINPOINT TEST B
TEMPERATURE GAUGE INOPERATIVE

TEST STEP	RESULT	▶	ACTION TO TAKE
B1 VERIFY POWER AT FUSE PANEL			
• Using Rotunda Digital Volt-Ohmmeter 007-00001 or equivalent verify system voltage at load side of warning indicator fuse. • Is system voltage present at load side of fuse?	Yes No	▶ ▶	GO to C1. GO to B2.
B2 VERIFY POWER AT FUSE PANEL			
• Using Rotunda Digital Volt-Ohmmeter 007-00001 or equivalent verify system voltage at feed side of warning indicator fuse. • Is system voltage present at feed side of fuse?	Yes No	▶ ▶	REPLACE fuse. GO to A1. SERVICE wiring to fuse panel. GO to A1.

PINPOINT TEST C
TEMPERATURE/OIL GAUGE INOPERATIVE

TEST STEP	RESULT	▶	ACTION TO TAKE
C1 VERIFY POWER AT CLUSTER			
• Partially remove cluster from IP. Using Rotunda Digital Volt-Ohmmeter 007-00001 or equivalent verify system voltage at cluster connector and/or gauge terminal. • Inspect cluster connector for damage. • Is system voltage present at cluster connector and/or gauge terminal?	Yes No	▶ ▶	GO to C2. SERVICE as required. GO to A1.
C2 VERIFY GROUND CIRCUITRY AT CLUSTER			
• Using Rotunda Digital Volt-Ohmmeter 007-00001 or equivalent check continuity of cluster and gauge ground circuitry. • Is ground circuitry OK?	Yes No	▶ ▶	GO to D1 for temperature gauge. GO to E1 for oil gauge. SERVICE as required. GO to A1.

FM9099200282010X

Fig. 1 Temperature/Oil Gauge indicating system diagnosis (Part 1 of 2). 1992–93 Cougar, Crown Victoria, Grand Marquis, Thunderbird & Town Car

CALIBRATION TEST
Magnetic Type

The required test equipment consists of a Rotunda Gauge Tester part No. 021-00055 or equivalent, a pair of 22 ohm and 145 ohm resistor or another fuel sender of known quality.

1. Perform test with resistors as follows:
   a. Disconnect wiring connector at sender unit, then connect resistor between gauge lead and a suitable ground.
   b. Turn ignition switch to On position.
   c. With 145 ohm resistor, the gauge pointer should contact the Full mark.
   d. With 22 ohm resistor, the gauge pointer should contact the Empty mark.
2. Perform test with fuel sender of known quality as follows:
   a. Turn ignition switch to Off position.
   b. Disconnect wiring connector from sender and connect it to test sender.
   c. Move float rod away from fuel filter against Full stop position. Wait approximately 30 seconds, then turn ignition switch to On position. The gauge should read on or above the Full mark.
   d. Move float rod toward fuel filter against Empty stop position. Turn ignition switch to Off position. Wait approximately 30 seconds, then turn ignition switch to On position. The gauge should read on or be-

PINPOINT TEST D
TEMPERATURE GAUGE INACCURATE

TEST STEP		RESULT	▶	ACTION TO TAKE
D1	TEST SENDER CIRCUIT AT LOW			
	• Insert Rotunda Instrument Gauge, System Tester 021-00055 or equivalent. Disconnect connector at sender and connect tester to cluster side of connector. Set to 74 ohms. • Does gauge read 'C'?	Yes No	▶ ▶	GO to D2. GO to D3.
D2	TEST SENDER CIRCUIT AT HIGH			
	• Set Gauge System Tester to 10 ohms. • Does gauge read 'H'?	Yes No	▶ ▶	REPLACE sender. GO to D3.
D3	CHECK SENDER CIRCUIT WIRING			
	• Check sender circuit wiring and cluster flex circuit for shorts or opens with Rotunda Digital Volt-Ohmmeter 007-00001 or equivalent. • Is wiring OK?	Yes No	▶ ▶	REPLACE gauge. SERVICE wiring / flex circuit. GO to A1.

PINPOINT TEST E
OIL GAUGE INACCURATE

TEST STEP		RESULT	▶	ACTION TO TAKE
E1	TEST SENDER CIRCUIT AT LOW			
	• Place ignition switch in the ON position with engine OFF. Observe gauge performance. • Does gauge read 'L' or below?	Yes No	▶ ▶	GO to E2. GO to E3.
E2	CHECK GAUGE RESPONSE			
	• Disconnect oil pressure switch and short the lead to engine ground. • Does gauge read around 'O' in NORM band?	Yes No	▶ ▶	REPLACE sender / switch. GO to E3.
E3	CHECK SENDER / SWITCH WIRING			
	• Check sender / switch wiring and cluster flex circuit for shorts or opens using Rotunda Digital Volt-Ohmmeter 007-00001 or equivalent • Is wiring / flex circuit OK?	Yes No	▶ ▶	REPLACE gauge. GO to A1. SERVICE wiring / flex circuit. GO to A1.

FM9099200282020X

Fig. 1 Temperature/Oil Gauge indicating system diagnosis (Part 2 of 2). 1992–93 Crown Victoria, Grand Marquis & Town Car

PINPOINT TEST C: COOLANT TEMPERATURE READS ERRONEOUSLY

TEST STEP		RESULT	▶	ACTION TO TAKE
C1	CHECK POWER AT CLUSTER			
	• Turn ignition switch to the OFF position. • Partially remove instrument cluster. • Turn ignition switch to RUN position. • Using a voltmeter check for voltage at cluster connector pin per chart.	Yes No	▶ ▶	GO to C2. SERVICE Circuit 640 (R / Y) for open circuit. RESTORE vehicle. RETEST system

CROWN VICTORIA

Connector Pin	Circuit	Function
J2 8	640 (R / Y)	Ignition Voltage
J1 8	359 (GY / R)	Gauge Ground
J1 6	39 (R / W)	Coolant Temp Input

GRAND MARQUIS

Connector Pin	Circuit	Function
J2 12	640 (R / Y)	Ignition Voltage
J1 8	563 (O / Y)	Gauge Ground
J1 3	39 (R / W)	Coolant Temp Input

	• Is system voltage present?			
C2	CHECK CLUSTER GROUND			
	• Using an ohmmeter connected to a known good ground, connect other end to ground circuit per chart above. • Is resistance 5 ohms or less?	Yes No	▶ ▶	GO to C3. SERVICE Circuit 359 (GY / R) or Circuit 563 (O / Y) for open circuit. RESTORE vehicle. RETEST system.
C3	CHECK SENDER UNIT CIRCUIT AT LOW			
	• Insert Rotunda Instrument Gauge, System Tester 021-00055 or equivalent. Disconnect connector at sender and connect tester to instrument cluster side of connector. Set to 74 ohms. • Turn ignition switch to RUN position. • Does gauge read cold?	Yes No	▶ ▶	GO to C4. GO to C5.
C4	CHECK SENDER UNIT CIRCUIT AT HIGH			
	• Set Gauge System Tester to 10 ohms. • Does gauge read hot?	Yes No	▶ ▶	REPLACE water temperature indicator sender unit. RESTORE vehicle. RETEST system. GO to C5.
C5	CHECK COOLANT TEMPERATURE INPUT CIRCUIT			
	• With ignition switch in the RUN position and using a test lamp connected to known good ground, connect probe to sending unit connector. • Did test lamp illuminate?	Yes No	▶ ▶	GO to C7. GO to C6.

FM9099400318010X

Fig. 2 Temperature gauge system diagnosis (Part 1 of 2). 1994 Crown Victoria & Grand Marquis

low the Empty mark.
e. If gauge performs as indicated, perform fuel sender unit tests. Refer to "System Diagnosis" for fuel

sender unit tests.
f. If gauge is out of calibration at the Empty mark, or both the Empty and Full mark, replace gauge.

Bimetal Type

The required test equipment consists of a Rotunda Gauge Tester part No. 021-00055 or equivalent, a pair of 10 ohm and 75 ohm resistors or another fuel sender of good known quality.
1. Perform test with resistors as follows:
   a. Disconnect wiring connector at sender unit, then connect resistor between gauge lead and a suitable ground.
   b. Turn ignition switch to On position.
   c. With 10 ohm resistor, the gauge pointer should contact the Full mark.
   d. With 75 ohm resistor, the gauge pointer should contact the Empty mark.
2. Perform test with fuel sender of known quality as follows:
   a. Turn ignition switch to Off position.
   b. Disconnect wiring connector from sender and connect it to test sender.
   c. Move float rod away from fuel filter against Full stop position. Wait approximately 30 seconds, then turn ignition switch to On position. The gauge should read on or above the Full mark.
   d. Move float rod toward fuel filter against Empty stop position. Turn ignition switch to Off position. Wait approximately 30 seconds, then turn ignition switch to On position. The gauge should read on or below the Empty mark.
   e. If gauge performs as indicated, perform fuel sender unit tests. Refer to "System Diagnosis" for fuel sender unit tests.
   f. If gauge is out of calibration at the Empty mark, or both the Empty and Full mark, replace gauge.

SYSTEM DIAGNOSIS
MAGNETIC TYPE

Except Escort, Mark VIII, Tracer & 1994 Mustang

Refer to **Fig. 29**, for fuel indicating system diagnosis.

Escort & Tracer

Refer to **Fig. 30**, for fuel indicating system diagnosis.

Mark VIII

Refer to **Fig. 31**, for fuel indicating system diagnosis.

1994 Mustang

Refer to **Fig. 32**, for fuel indicating system diagnosis.

BIMETAL TYPE

Refer to **Figs. 33 through 37**, for fuel indicating system diagnosis.

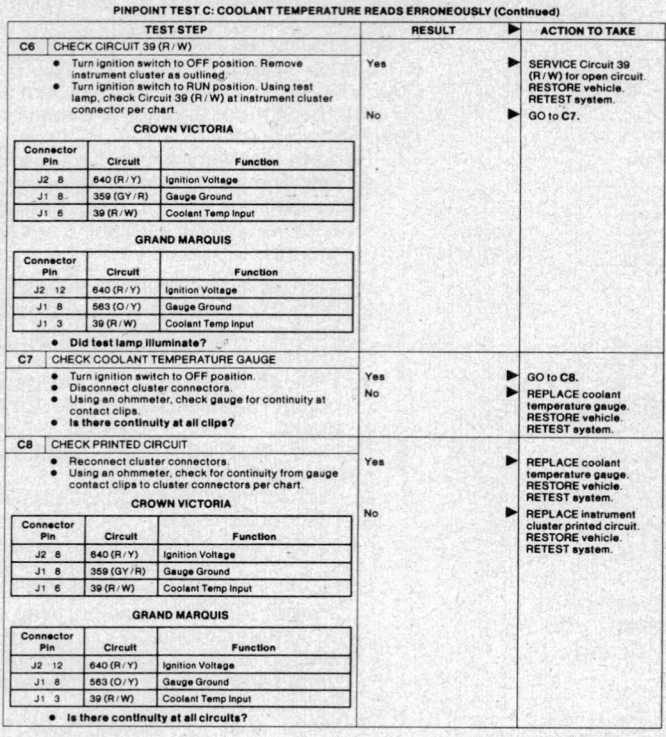

PINPOINT TEST C: COOLANT TEMPERATURE READS ERRONEOUSLY (Continued)

TEST STEP		RESULT	►	ACTION TO TAKE
C6	CHECK CIRCUIT 39 (R/W)	Yes	►	SERVICE Circuit 39 (R/W) for open circuit. RESTORE vehicle. RETEST system.
	• Turn ignition switch to OFF position. Remove instrument cluster as outlined. • Turn ignition switch to RUN position. Using test lamp, check Circuit 39 (R/W) at instrument cluster connector per chart.	No	►	GO to C7.

CROWN VICTORIA

Connector Pin	Circuit	Function
J2 8	640 (R/Y)	Ignition Voltage
J1 8	359 (GY/R)	Gauge Ground
J1 6	39 (R/W)	Coolant Temp Input

GRAND MARQUIS

Connector Pin	Circuit	Function
J2 12	640 (R/Y)	Ignition Voltage
J1 8	563 (O/Y)	Gauge Ground
J1 3	39 (R/W)	Coolant Temp Input

TEST STEP		RESULT	►	ACTION TO TAKE
	• Did test lamp illuminate?			
C7	CHECK COOLANT TEMPERATURE GAUGE	Yes	►	GO to C8.
	• Turn ignition switch to OFF position. • Disconnect cluster connectors. • Using an ohmmeter, check gauge for continuity at contact clips. • Is there continuity at all clips?	No	►	REPLACE coolant temperature gauge. RESTORE vehicle. RETEST system.
C8	CHECK PRINTED CIRCUIT	Yes	►	REPLACE coolant temperature gauge. RESTORE vehicle. RETEST system.
	• Reconnect cluster connectors. • Using an ohmmeter, check for continuity from gauge contact clips to cluster connectors per chart.	No	►	REPLACE instrument cluster printed circuit. RESTORE vehicle. RETEST system.

CROWN VICTORIA

Connector Pin	Circuit	Function
J2 8	640 (R/Y)	Ignition Voltage
J1 8	359 (GY/R)	Gauge Ground
J1 6	39 (R/W)	Coolant Temp Input

GRAND MARQUIS

Connector Pin	Circuit	Function
J2 12	640 (R/Y)	Ignition Voltage
J1 8	563 (O/Y)	Gauge Ground
J1 3	39 (R/W)	Coolant Temp Input

• Is there continuity at all circuits?

FM9099400318020X

Fig. 2 Temperature gauge system diagnosis (Part 2 of 2). 1994 Crown Victoria & Grand Marquis

PINPOINT TEST D: OIL PRESSURE READS ERRONEOUSLY

TEST STEP		RESULT	►	ACTION TO TAKE
D1	DETERMINE SYSTEM APPLICABILITY	Yes	►	GO to D2.
	• There are two systems for indicating oil pressure, thereby requiring two different test procedures. • Does vehicle have an oil pressure gauge?	No	►	GO to D8.

FM9099400319010X

Fig. 3 Oil pressure gauge system diagnosis (Part 1 of 3). 1994 Crown Victoria & Grand Marquis

PINPOINT TEST D: OIL PRESSURE READS ERRONEOUSLY (Continued)

TEST STEP		RESULT	►	ACTION TO TAKE
D2	CHECK POWER AT CLUSTER	Yes	►	GO to D3.
	• Turn ignition switch to the OFF position. • Partially remove instrument cluster. • Turn ignition switch to RUN position. • Using a voltmeter check for voltage at cluster connector pin per chart.	No	►	SERVICE Circuit 640 (R/Y) for open circuit. RESTORE vehicle. RETEST system.

CROWN VICTORIA

Connector Pin	Circuit	Function
J2 8	640 (R/Y)	Ignition Voltage
J1 3	359 (GY/R)	Gauge Ground
J1 14	31 (W/R)	Oil Pressure Input

GRAND MARQUIS

Connector Pin	Circuit	Function
J2 12	640 (R/Y)	Ignition Voltage
J2 8	31 (W/R)	Oil Pressure Input

TEST STEP		RESULT	►	ACTION TO TAKE
	• Is system voltage present?			
D3	TEST SENDER CIRCUIT AT LOW	Yes	►	GO to D4.
	• Place ignition switch in the ON position with engine OFF. Observe gauge performance. • Does gauge read "L" or below?	No	►	GO to D5.
D4	CHECK GAUGE RESPONSE	Yes	►	REPLACE oil pressure sender. RESTORE vehicle. RETEST system.
	• Disconnect oil pressure sender and short the lead to engine ground. • Does gauge indicate mid-scale or slightly above mid-scale?	No	►	GO to D5.
D5	CHECK CIRCUIT 31 (W/R)	Yes	►	GO to D6.
	• Leave oil pressure input circuit shorted to ground. • Turn ignition switch to the OFF position. Remove instrument cluster as outlined. • Using an ohmmeter connected to a known good ground, connect second lead to Connector J1, Pin 14. Measure resistance. • Is resistance 5 ohms or less?	No	►	SERVICE Circuit 31 (W/R) for open circuit. RESTORE vehicle. RETEST system.
D6	CHECK OIL PRESSURE GAUGE	Yes	►	GO to D7.
	• Disconnect instrument cluster connectors. • Using an ohmmeter check gauge for continuity at contact clips. • Is there continuity at all clips?	No	►	REPLACE oil pressure gauge. RESTORE vehicle. RETEST system.
D7	CHECK PRINTED CIRCUIT	Yes	►	REPLACE oil pressure gauge. RESTORE vehicle. RETEST system.
	• Reconnect cluster connectors. • Using an ohmmeter check for continuity from gauge contact clips to cluster connectors per chart.	No	►	REPLACE printed circuit. RESTORE vehicle. RETEST system.

CROWN VICTORIA

Connector Pin	Circuit	Function
J2 8	640 (R/Y)	Ignition Voltage
J1 3	359 (GY/R)	Gauge Ground
J1 14	31 (W/R)	Oil Pressure Input

• Is there continuity at all circuits?

FM9099400319020X

Fig. 3 Oil pressure gauge system diagnosis (Part 2 of 3). 1994 Crown Victoria & Grand Marquis

PINPOINT TEST D: OIL PRESSURE READS ERRONEOUSLY (Continued)

TEST STEP		RESULT	►	ACTION TO TAKE
D8	CHECK POWER AT CLUSTER	Yes	►	GO to D9.
	• Turn ignition switch to the OFF position. • Partially remove instrument cluster. • Turn ignition switch to RUN position. • Using a voltmeter check for voltage at cluster connector pin per chart.	No	►	SERVICE Circuit 640 (R/Y) for open circuit. RESTORE vehicle. RETEST system.

GRAND MARQUIS

Connector Pin	Circuit	Function
J2 12	640 (R/Y)	Ignition Voltage
J2 8	31 (W/R)	Oil Pressure Input

TEST STEP		RESULT	►	ACTION TO TAKE
	• Is system voltage present?			
D9	CHECK CIRCUIT 31 (W/R)	Yes	►	REPLACE oil pressure sender. RESTORE vehicle. RETEST system.
	• Disconnect oil pressure switch. Connect Circuit 31 (W/R) to known good ground. • Did indicator lamp illuminate?	No	►	GO to D10.
D10	CHECK CIRCUIT 31 (W/R) AT CLUSTER	Yes	►	SERVICE Circuit 31 (W/R) for open circuit. RESTORE vehicle. RETEST system.
	• Using a test lamp connected to a known good ground, connect probe to cluster connector J2, Pin 8. • Did test lamp illuminate?	No	►	GO to D11.
D11	CHECK OIL PRESSURE INDICATOR LAMP	Yes	►	REPLACE instrument cluster printed circuit. RESTORE vehicle. RETEST system.
	• Remove oil pressure indicator lamp as outlined. • Using an ohmmeter check bulb for continuity. • Does oil indicator bulb test OK?	No	►	REPLACE bulb. RESTORE vehicle. RETEST system.

FM9099400319030X

Fig. 3 Oil pressure gauge system diagnosis (Part 3 of 3). 1994 Crown Victoria & Grand Marquis

PINPOINT TEST C: TEMPERATURE GAUGE DIAGNOSIS

TEST STEP		RESULT	▶	ACTION TO TAKE
C1	CHECK METER FUSE			
	• Locate the interior fuse panel.	Yes	▶	GO to C4.
	• Check 10 amp METER fuse.	No	▶	GO to C2.
	• Is fuse OK?			
C2	CHECK SYSTEM			
	• Replace the 10 amp METER fuse.	Yes	▶	GO to C3.
	• Key ON.	No	▶	GO to C4.
	• Does fuse fail again?			
C3	CHECK FOR SHORTS TO GROUND			
	• Replace the 10 amp METER fuse.	Yes	▶	SERVICE BK Y wire
	• Locate and disconnect the interior fuse panel connector and instrument cluster connector.	No	▶	GO to C4.
	• Measure resistance of BK Y wire at the interior fuse panel connector to ground.			
	• Is resistance less than 5 ohms?			
C4	CHECK FOR POWER TO TEMPERATURE GAUGE			
	• Key ON.	Yes	▶	GO to C5.
	• Locate instrument cluster connector.	No	▶	SERVICE BK Y wire
	• Measure voltage on the BK/Y wire at the instrument cluster connector.			
	• Is voltage greater than 10 volts?			
C5	CHECK TEMPERATURE GAUGE			
	• Locate instrument cluster connector.	Yes	▶	GO to C6.
	• Key ON.	No	▶	REPLACE temperature gauge.
	• Place a jumper wire from the Y/W wire at instrument cluster to ground.			
	• Does temperature gauge read hot?			
C6	CHECK TEMPERATURE GAUGE WIRE CONTINUITY			
	• Key ON.	Yes	▶	GO to C7.
	• Place a jumper wire from Y/W wire at the temperature gauge sending unit to ground.	No	▶	SERVICE Y W wire between the temperature gauge sending unit and temperature gauge
	• Does the temperature gauge read hot?			
C7	CHECK TEMPERATURE GAUGE SENDING UNIT			
	• Disconnect the temperature gauge sending unit.	Yes	▶	GO to C8.
	• Does temperature gauge read cold?	No	▶	REPLACE temperature gauge sending unit.
C8	CHECK TEMPERATURE GAUGE			
	• Disconnect instrument cluster connector.	Yes	▶	REPLACE temperature gauge.
	• Does the temperature gauge still read hot?	No	▶	GO to C9.
C9	CHECK TEMPERATURE GAUGE GROUND			
	• Locate and disconnect instrument cluster connector.	Yes	▶	GO to C10.
	• Measure resistance between the BK wire at the instrument cluster connector and ground.	No	▶	SERVICE BK wire
	• Is resistance less than 5 ohms?			

FM9099100283010X

Fig. 4   Temperature indicating system diagnosis (Part 1 of 4). Capri

TEMPERATURE GAUGE — CONDITION CHART

CONDITION	POSSIBLE SOURCE	ACTION
• Temperature Gauge Always Reads Cold	• Temperature gauge wire open. • Damaged temperature gauge sending unit. • Damaged temperature gauge. • Blown 10 amp meter fuse. • Open power wire.	• Go to C1.
• Temperature Gauge Always Reads Hot	• Short to ground. • Damaged temperature gauge sending unit. • Temperature gauge.	• Go to C7.
• Temperature Gauge Inaccurate	• Open wires. • Temperature gauge sending unit.	• Go to C10.

FM9099100283020X

Fig. 4   Temperature indicating system diagnosis (Part 2 of 4). Capri

PINPOINT TEST C: TEMPERATURE GAUGE DIAGNOSIS (Continued)

TEST STEP		RESULT	▶	ACTION TO TAKE
C10	CHECK TEMPERATURE GAUGE			
	• Remove connector from temperature gauge sending unit.	Yes	▶	GO to C11.
	• Connect one lead of the Rotunda Gauge System Tester 021-00055 or equivalent to the connector and the other lead to ground.	No	▶	REPLACE temperature gauge sending unit.
	• Set gauge tester to the resistance values shown.			
	• Place ignition switch to the ON position and check to see that the needle indictor displays the correct reading.			
	• Continue each inspection for two minutes to correctly judge the condition (allowable readings are twice the width of the needle).			
	• Are readings within the allowable range?			

GAUGE SYSTEM TESTER 021-00055

18 OHMS — H
60 OHMS
223 OHMS — C

C11	CHECK TEMPERATURE GAUGE SENDING UNIT			
	• Remove temperature gauge sending unit.	Yes	▶	GO to C12.
	• Place temperature gauge sending unit in a container of water and heat to 80°C (176°F).	No	▶	REPLACE temperature gauge sending unit.
	• Measure resistance between the case and the terminal of the sending unit.			
	• Does resistance measure between 49.3 ohms and 57.7 ohms?			

FM9099100283030X

Fig. 4   Temperature indicating system diagnosis (Part 3 of 4). Capri

PINPOINT TEST C: TEMPERATURE GAUGE DIAGNOSIS (Continued)

TEST STEP		RESULT	▶	ACTION TO TAKE
C12	CHECK TEMPERATURE GAUGE SENDING UNIT			
	• Key OFF.	Yes	▶	RETURN to condition chart.
	• Measure resistance between temperature gauge sending unit casing and ground.	No	▶	REPLACE temperature gauge sending unit
	• Is resistance less than 5 ohms?			

FM9099100283040X

Fig. 4   Temperature indicating system diagnosis (Part 4 of 4). Capri

OIL PRESSURE GAUGE — CONDITION CHART

CONDITION	POSSIBLE SOURCE	ACTION
• Oil Pressure Gauge Always Reads Low	• Open signal wire. • Damaged oil pressure switch. • Damaged oil pressure gauge. • Blown fuse. • Open power wire.	• Go to B1.
• Oil Pressure Gauge Always Reads High	• Oil pressure gauge wire shorted to ground. • Damaged oil pressure switch. • Damaged oil pressure gauge.	• Go to B7.
• Oil Pressure Gauge Reads Inaccurately	• Corroded connections. • Damaged oil pressure switch.	• Go to B10.

PINPOINT TEST B: OIL PRESSURE GAUGE DIAGNOSIS

TEST STEP	RESULT	►	ACTION TO TAKE
B1 CHECK METER FUSE • Locate the interior fuse panel. • Check the 10 amp METER fuse. • Is fuse OK?	Yes No	► ►	GO to B4. GO to B2.
B2 CHECK SYSTEM • Replace the 10 amp METER fuse. • Key ON, engine running. • Does fuse fail again?	Yes No	► ►	GO to B3. GO to B4.
B3 CHECK FOR SHORTS TO GROUND • Replace the 10 amp METER fuse. • Locate and disconnect the interior fuse panel connector and instrument cluster connector. • Measure the resistance of the BK/Y wire at the interior fuse panel to ground. • Is resistance less than 5 ohms?	Yes No	► ►	SERVICE/REPLACE BK Y wire. GO to B4.
B4 CHECK FOR POWER TO THE OIL PRESSURE GAUGE • Locate the instrument cluster connector. • Key ON, engine running. • Measure voltage on the BK/Y wire at the instrument cluster connector. • Is voltage greater than 10 volts?	Yes No	► ►	GO to B5. SERVICE/REPLACE BK Y wire.

FM9099100295010X

Fig. 5 Gauge type oil pressure indicator diagnosis (Part 1 of 2). Capri

PINPOINT TEST B: OIL PRESSURE GAUGE DIAGNOSIS (Continued)

TEST STEP	RESULT	►	ACTION TO TAKE
B5 CHECK OIL PRESSURE GAUGE • Key ON. • Place a jumper wire from the Y/R wire at instrument cluster connector to ground. • Does the oil pressure gauge read high?	Yes No	► ►	GO to B6. REPLACE oil pressure gauge.
B6 CHECK OIL PRESSURE GAUGE WIRE CONTINUITY • Key ON. • Place a jumper wire from Y/R wire at the oil pressure switch connector to ground. • Does the oil pressure gauge read high?	Yes No	► ►	GO to B7. SERVICE/REPLACE Y/R wire between oil pressure switch and oil pressure gauge.
B7 CHECK OIL PRESSURE SWITCH • Disconnect the oil pressure switch. • Key ON. • Does oil pressure gauge read low?	Yes No	► ►	GO to B8. REPLACE oil pressure switch.
B8 CHECK OIL PRESSURE SWITCH • Disconnect instrument cluster connector. • Key ON. • Does oil pressure gauge still read low?	Yes No	► ►	REPLACE oil pressure switch. GO to B9.
B9 CHECK OIL PRESSURE GAUGE GROUND • Disconnect instrument cluster connector. • Measure resistance between the BK wire at the instrument cluster connector and ground. • Is the resistance less than 5 ohms?	Yes No	► ►	GO to B10 SERVICE/REPLACE BK wire.
B10 CHECK OIL PRESSURE GAUGE • Disconnect oil pressure switch. • Connect one lead of Rotunda Gauge System Tester 021-00038 or equivalent to the Y/R wire at the oil pressure connector and the other lead to ground. • Set the tester to resistance values down. • Place the ignition switch to the ON position and check to see that the needle indicator displays the correct values. • Continue each inspection for two minutes to correctly judge the condition (allowable readings are twice the width of the needle). • Are readings within the allowable range?	Yes No	► ►	REPLACE oil pressure switch. REPLACE oil pressure gauge.

FM9099100295020X

Fig. 5 Gauge type oil pressure indicator diagnosis (Part 2 of 2). Capri

**PINPOINT TEST B
TEMPERATURE/OIL GAUGE
INOPERATIVE — POINTER DOES NOT MOVE**

TEST STEP	RESULT	►	ACTION TO TAKE
B1 VERIFY CONDITION • Observe gauge performance. • Does gauge pointer move?	No Yes	► ►	GO to B2. GO to C1 for temperature gauge.
B2 VERIFY CLUSTER PERFORMANCE • With the ignition ON, observe the other gauges and warning indicators for proper operation. • Do other gauges and warning indicators operate properly?	Yes No	► ►	GO to D1. GO to C1.

**PINPOINT TEST C
TEMPERATURE/OIL GAUGE
INOPERATIVE**

TEST STEP	RESULT	►	ACTION TO TAKE
C1 VERIFY POWER AT FUSE PANEL • Using Rotunda Digital Volt-Ohmmeter 007-00001 or equivalent verify system voltage at load side of warning indicator fuse. • Is system voltage present at load side of fuse?	Yes No	► ►	GO to D1. GO to C2.
C2 VERIFY POWER AT FUSE PANEL • Using Rotunda Digital Volt-Ohmmeter 007-00001 or equivalent verify system voltage at feed side of warning indicator fuse. • Is system voltage present at feed side of fuse?	Yes No	► ►	REPLACE fuse. GO to B1. SERVICE wiring to fuse panel. GO to B1.

**PINPOINT TEST D
TEMPERATURE GAUGE
INOPERATIVE**

TEST STEP	RESULT	►	ACTION TO TAKE
D1 VERIFY POWER AT CLUSTER • Partially remove cluster from IP. Using Rotunda Digital Volt-Ohmmeter 007-00001 or equivalent verify system voltage at cluster connector and/or gauge terminal. • Inspect cluster connector for damage. • Is system voltage present at cluster connector and/or gauge terminal?	Yes No	► ►	GO to D2. SERVICE as required. GO to B1.
D2 VERIFY GROUND CIRCUITRY AT CLUSTER • Using Rotunda Digital Volt-Ohmmeter 007-00001 or equivalent check continuity of cluster and gauge ground circuitry. • Is ground circuitry OK?	Yes No	► ►	GO to E1 for temperature gauge. SERVICE as required. GO to B1.

FM9099100284010X

Fig. 6 Temperature/Oil Gauge indicating system diagnosis (Part 1 of 2). Taurus & Sable

**PINPOINT TEST E
TEMPERATURE GAUGE INACCURATE**

TEST STEP	RESULT	►	ACTION TO TAKE
E1 TEST SENDER CIRCUIT AT LOW • Insert Rotunda Instrument Gauge, System Tester 021-00055 or equivalent. Disconnect connector at sender and connect tester to cluster side of connector. Set to 74 ohms. • Does gauge read 'C'?	Yes No	► ►	GO to E2. GO to E3.
E2 TEST SENDER CIRCUIT AT HIGH • Set Gauge System Tester to 10 ohms. • Does gauge read 'H'?	Yes No	► ►	REPLACE sender. GO to E3.

**PINPOINT TEST E
TEMPERATURE GAUGE INACCURATE (Continued)**

TEST STEP	RESULT	►	ACTION TO TAKE
E3 CHECK SENDER CIRCUIT WIRING • Check sender circuit wiring and cluster flex circuit for shorts or opens with Rotunda Digital Volt-Ohmmeter 007-00001 or equivalent. • Is wiring OK?	Yes No	► ►	REPLACE gauge. SERVICE wiring/flex circuit. GO to B1.

FM9099100284020X

Fig. 6 Temperature/Oil Gauge indicating system diagnosis (Part 2 of 2). Taurus & Sable

PINPOINT TEST B: COOLANT TEMPERATURE GAUGE INOPERATIVE—POINTER DOES NOT MOVE

TEST STEP	RESULT	▶	ACTION TO TAKE
B1 VERIFY CONDITION			
• Verify condition.	Yes	▶	GO to C1.
• Does gauge pointer move?	No	▶	GO to B2.
B2 CHECK POWER TO GAUGE			
• Check power to gauge. With the ignition in RUN, check power to the instrument cluster connector, through the flex circuit, to the terminals that connect the flex circuit to the gauge. Ensure all terminals: B+, ground, and sender, are making connection to the gauge. Check all ground circuits and connections.	Yes	▶	GO to C1.
• Is voltage present at cluster and do other gauges and warning indicators operate properly?	No	▶	SERVICE power to cluster.

PINPOINT TEST C: COOLANT TEMPERATURE GAUGE INACCURATE

TEST STEP	RESULT	▶	ACTION TO TAKE
C1 TEST BOX CHECK			
• Insert Rotunda Instrument Gauge System Tester 021-00055 or equivalent in sender circuit. Disconnect connector at sender and connect tester to cluster side of connector. Set tester to LOW (74 ohms).	Yes	▶	GO to C2.
• Is pointer at 'C'?	No	▶	GO to C3.
C2 TEST BOX CHECK			
• Set tester to HIGH (10 ohms).	Yes	▶	REPLACE temperature sending unit.
• Is gauge at 'H'?	No	▶	GO to C3.
C3 CHECK SENDER WIRING			
• Check sender circuit wiring for shorts or open with ohmmeter, using Rotunda Digital Volt-Ohmmeter 007-00001 or equivalent. Verify engine and cluster ground circuits.	Yes	▶	REPLACE gauge.
• Is wiring OK?	No	▶	SERVICE wiring.

FM9099400320000X

Fig. 7 Temperature gauge system diagnosis. Tempo & Topaz

PINPOINT TEST C: COOLANT TEMPERATURE READS ERRONEOUSLY

TEST STEP	RESULT	▶	ACTION TO TAKE
C1 CHECK POWER AT CLUSTER			
• Turn ignition switch to the OFF position.	Yes	▶	GO to C2.
• Partially remove instrument cluster.	No	▶	SERVICE Circuit 640 (R/Y) for open circuit. RESTORE vehicle. RETEST system.
• Turn ignition switch to RUN position.			
• Using a voltmeter check for voltage at cluster connector pin per chart.			

Connector Pin	Circuit	Function
J1 16	640 (R/Y)	Ignition Voltage
J1 15	563 (O/Y)	Gauge Ground
J1 14	39 (R/W)	Coolant Temp Input

• Is system voltage present?

TEST STEP	RESULT	▶	ACTION TO TAKE
C2 CHECK CLUSTER GROUND			
• Using an ohmmeter connected to a known good ground, connect other end to ground circuit per chart above.	Yes	▶	GO to C3.
• Is resistance .5 ohms or less?	No	▶	SERVICE Circuit 563 (O/Y) for open circuit. RESTORE vehicle. RETEST system.
C3 CHECK SENDER UNIT CIRCUIT AT LOW			
• Insert Rotunda Instrument Gauge, System Tester 021-00055 or equivalent. Disconnect connector at water temperature indicator sender unit and connect tester to cluster side of connector. Set to 74 ohms.	Yes	▶	GO to C4.
• Turn ignition switch to RUN position.	No	▶	GO to C5.
• Does gauge read cold?			
C4 CHECK SENDER UNIT CIRCUIT AT HIGH			
• Set Gauge System Tester to 10 ohms.	Yes	▶	REPLACE water temperature indicator sender unit. RESTORE vehicle. RETEST system.
• Does gauge read hot?	No	▶	GO to C5.
C5 CHECK COOLANT TEMPERATURE INPUT CIRCUIT			
• With ignition switch in the RUN position, using a test lamp connected to known good ground, connect probe to sending unit connector.	Yes	▶	GO to C7.
• Did test lamp illuminate?	No	▶	GO to C6.
C6 CHECK CIRCUIT 39 (R/W)			
• Turn ignition switch to OFF position. Remove instrument cluster as outlined.	Yes	▶	SERVICE Circuit 39 (R/W) for open circuit. RESTORE vehicle. RETEST system.
• Turn ignition switch to RUN position. Using test lamp check Circuit 39 (R/W) at instrument cluster connector per chart.	No	▶	GO to C7.

Connector Pin	Circuit	Function
J1 16	640 (R/Y)	Ignition Voltage
J1 15	563 (O/Y)	Gauge Ground
J1 14	39 (R/W)	Coolant Temp Input

• Did test lamp illuminate?

TEST STEP	RESULT	▶	ACTION TO TAKE
C7 CHECK COOLANT TEMPERATURE GAUGE			
• Turn ignition switch to OFF position	Yes	▶	GO to C8.
• Disconnect cluster connectors.	No	▶	REPLACE instrument cluster temperature gauge. RESTORE vehicle. RETEST system.
• Using an ohmmeter, check gauge for continuity at contact clips.			
• Is there continuity at all clips?			

FM9099400321010X

Fig. 9 Temperature gauge system diagnosis (Part 1 of 2). 1994 Mustang

**PINPOINT TEST B
TEMPERATURE/OIL GAUGE
INOPERATIVE—POINTER DOES NOT MOVE**

TEST STEP	RESULT	▶	ACTION TO TAKE
B1 VERIFY CONDITION			
• Observe gauge performance.	No	▶	GO to B2.
• Does gauge pointer move?	Yes	▶	GO to C1 for temperature gauge.
B2 VERIFY CLUSTER PERFORMANCE			
• With the ignition ON, observe the other gauges and warning indicators for proper operation.	Yes	▶	GO to D1.
• Do other gauges and warning indicators operate properly?	No	▶	GO to C1.

**PINPOINT TEST C
TEMPERATURE GAUGE INACCURATE**

TEST STEP	RESULT	▶	ACTION TO TAKE
C1 TEST SENDER CIRCUIT AT LOW			
• Insert Rotunda Instrument Gauge, System Tester 021-00055 or equivalent. Disconnect connector at sender and connect tester to cluster side of connector. Set to 74 ohms.	Yes	▶	GO to C2.
• Does gauge read 'C'?	No	▶	GO to C3.
C2 TEST SENDER CIRCUIT AT HIGH			
• Set Gauge System Tester to 10 ohms.	Yes	▶	REPLACE sender.
• Does gauge read 'H'?	No	▶	GO to C3.
C3 CHECK SENDER CIRCUIT WIRING			
• Check sender circuit wiring and cluster flex circuit for shorts or opens with Rotunda Digital Volt-Ohmmeter 007-00001 or equivalent.	Yes	▶	REPLACE gauge.
• Is wiring OK?	No	▶	SERVICE wiring / flex circuit.

**PINPOINT TEST D
TEMPERATURE GAUGE
INOPERATIVE**

TEST STEP	RESULT	▶	ACTION TO TAKE
D1 VERIFY POWER AT FUSE PANEL			
• Using Rotunda Digital Volt-Ohmmeter 007-00001 or equivalent verify system voltage at load side of warning indicator fuse.	Yes	▶	GO to E1.
• Is system voltage present at load side of fuse?	No	▶	GO to D2.
D2 VERIFY POWER AT FUSE PANEL			
• Using Rotunda Digital Volt-Ohmmeter 007-00001 or equivalent verify system voltage at feed side of warning indicator fuse.	Yes	▶	REPLACE fuse. GO to C1.
• Is system voltage present at feed side of fuse?	No	▶	SERVICE wiring to fuse panel. GO to C1.

**PINPOINT TEST E
OIL GAUGE INACCURATE**

TEST STEP	RESULT	▶	ACTION TO TAKE
E1 TEST SENDER CIRCUIT AT LOW			
• Place ignition switch in the ON position with engine OFF. Observe gauge performance.	Yes	▶	GO to E2.
• Does gauge read 'L' or below?	No	▶	GO to E3.
E2 CHECK GAUGE RESPONSE			
• Disconnect oil pressure switch and short the lead to engine ground.	Yes	▶	REPLACE sender / switch.
• Does gauge rear around 'O' in NORM band?	No	▶	GO to E3.
E3 CHECK SENDER / SWITCH WIRING			
• Check sender / switch wiring and cluster flex circuit for shorts or opens using Rotunda Digital Volt-Ohmmeter 007-00001 or equivalent.	Yes	▶	REPLACE gauge.
• Is wiring / flex circuit OK?	No	▶	SERVICE wiring / flex circuit.

FM9099200286000X

Fig. 8 Temperature/Oil indicating system diagnosis. 1992–93 Mustang

PINPOINT TEST C: COOLANT TEMPERATURE READS ERRONEOUSLY (Continued)

TEST STEP	RESULT	▶	ACTION TO TAKE
C8 CHECK PRINTED CIRCUIT			
• Reconnect cluster connectors.	Yes	▶	REPLACE instrument cluster temperature gauge. RESTORE vehicle. RETEST system.
• Using an ohmmeter, check for continuity from gauge contact clips to cluster connectors per chart.	No	▶	REPLACE instrument cluster printed circuit. RESTORE vehicle. RETEST system.

Connector Pin	Circuit	Function
J1 16	640 (R/Y)	Ignition Voltage
J1 15	563 (O/Y)	Gauge Ground
J1 14	39 (R/W)	Coolant Temp Input

• Is there continuity at all circuits?

FM9099400321020X

Fig. 9 Temperature gauge system diagnosis (Part 2 of 2). 1994 Mustang

PINPOINT TEST D: OIL PRESSURE READS ERRONEOUSLY

TEST STEP		RESULT	▶	ACTION TO TAKE
D1	**CHECK POWER AT CLUSTER**			
	• Turn ignition switch to the OFF position. • Partially remove instrument cluster. • Turn ignition switch to RUN position. • Using a voltmeter check for voltage at cluster connector pin per chart.	Yes No	▶ ▶	GO to D2. SERVICE Circuit 640 (R/Y) for open circuit. RESTORE vehicle. RETEST system.

Connector Pin	Circuit	Function
J2 4	640 (R/Y)	Ignition Voltage
J2 3	875 (BK/LB)	Gauge Ground
J2 2	31 (W/R)	Oil Pressure Input

	• Is system voltage present?			
D2	**TEST SENDER CIRCUIT AT LOW**			
	• Place ignition switch in the ON position with engine OFF. Observe gauge performance. • Does gauge read "L" or below?	Yes No	▶ ▶	GO to D3. GO to D4.
D3	**CHECK GAUGE RESPONSE**			
	• Disconnect oil pressure sender and short the lead to engine ground. • Does gauge indicate mid-scale or slightly above mid-scale?	Yes No	▶ ▶	REPLACE oil pressure sender. RESTORE vehicle. RETEST system. GO to D4.
D4	**CHECK CIRCUIT 31 (W/R)**			
	• Leave oil pressure input circuit shorted to ground. • Turn ignition switch to the OFF position. Remove instrument cluster as outlined. • Using an ohmmeter connected to a known good ground, connect second lead to Connector J2, Pin 2. Measure resistance. • Is resistance .5 ohms or less?	Yes No	▶ ▶	GO to D5. SERVICE Circuit 31 (W/R) for open circuit. RESTORE vehicle. RETEST system.
D5	**CHECK OIL PRESSURE GAUGE**			
	• Disconnect instrument cluster connectors. • Using an ohmmeter check gauge for continuity at contact clips. • Is there continuity at all clips?	Yes No	▶ ▶	GO to D6. REPLACE oil pressure gauge. RESTORE vehicle. RETEST system.

FM9099400322010X

Fig. 10   Oil pressure gauge system diagnosis (Part 1 of 2). 1994 Mustang

PINPOINT TEST D: OIL PRESSURE READS ERRONEOUSLY (Continued)

TEST STEP		RESULT	▶	ACTION TO TAKE
D6	**CHECK PRINTED CIRCUIT**			
	• Reconnect cluster connectors. • Using an ohmmeter check for continuity from gauge contact clips to cluster connectors per chart.	Yes No	▶ ▶	REPLACE oil pressure gauge. RESTORE vehicle. RETEST system. REPLACE instrument cluster printed circuit. RESTORE vehicle. RETEST system.

Connector Pin	Circuit	Function
J2 4	640 (R/Y)	Ignition Voltage
J2 3	875 (BK/LB)	Gauge Ground
J2 2	31 (W/R)	Oil Pressure Input

• Is there continuity at all circuits?	

FM9099400322020X

Fig. 10   Oil pressure gauge system diagnosis (Part 2 of 2). 1994 Mustang

CONDITION	POSSIBLE SOURCE	ACTION
• Temperature Gauge and Warning Lights Not Working	• Fuse. • Circuit. • Open grounds.	• GO to A1.
• Temperature Gauge Always Reads Cold	• Temperature gauge. • Coolant temperature sender. • Open in sender circuit. • Open temperature gauge ground circuit.	• GO to D1.
• Temperature Gauge Always Reads Hot	• Temperature gauge. • Coolant temperature sender. • Circuit. • Open temperature gauge ground circuit.	• GO to D1.
• Temperature Gauge Works but is Inaccurate	• Temperature gauge. • Coolant temperature sender.	• GO to D1.

TEST STEP		RESULT	▶	ACTION TO TAKE
A1	**VERIFY COMPLAINT**			
	• Key ON, engine running. • Allow the engine to warm up. • Observe the temperature gauge performance. • Does the gauge pointer move?	Yes No	▶ ▶	GO to D1. GO to A2.
A2	**VERIFY CLUSTER PERFORMANCE**			
	• With the ignition off, observe the other gauges and warning lights for proper operation. • Do the other gauges and warning lights operate properly?	Yes No	▶ ▶	GO to C1. GO to B1.

TEST STEP		RESULT	▶	ACTION TO TAKE
B1	**VERIFY POWER AT FUSE PANEL**			
	• Key ON. • Use a voltmeter to verify system voltage at the load side of the 15 amp METER fuse. • Is the voltage greater than 10 volts?	Yes No	▶ ▶	GO to C1. GO to B2.
B2	**VERIFY POWER FEED TO FUSE PANEL**			
	• Key ON. • Use a voltmeter to verify the system voltage at the feed side of the 15 amp METER fuse. • Is the voltage greater than 10 volts?	Yes No	▶ ▶	REPLACE the 15 amp METER fuse; RETURN to A1. REPAIR the wiring to the fuse panel; RETURN to A1.

TEST STEP		RESULT	▶	ACTION TO TAKE
C1	**VERIFY POWER AT CLUSTER**			
	• Keep cluster connector(s) intact. • Partially remove the cluster from the instrument panel. • Key ON. • Measure the voltage on the "BK/Y" wire at the instrument cluster connector to ground. • Is the voltage greater than 10 volts?	Yes No	▶ ▶	GO to C2. REPAIR the "BK/Y" wire. RETURN to A1.
C2	**VERIFY GROUND CIRCUITRY AT CLUSTER**			
	• Use an ohmmeter to check the continuity of the "BK/DG" wire at the instrument cluster connector to ground. • Is the resistance less than 5 ohms?	Yes No	▶ ▶	GO to C3. REPAIR the "BK/DG" wire to ground. RETURN to A1.

FM9099200287010X

Fig. 11   Temperature indicating system diagnosis (Part 1 of 2). 1992 Escort & Tracer

TEST STEP		RESULT	▶	ACTION TO TAKE
D1	**TEST SENDER CIRCUIT AT LOW**			
	• Key OFF. • Disconnect the coolant temperature sender. • Connect one lead of the Rotunda Gauge System Tester (021-00055 or equivalent) to the "BK/O" wire at the fuel gauge sending unit connector and the other lead to ground. • Set the tester to 74 ohms. • Key ON. • Wait one minute. • Read the temperature gauge.	Gauge reads C Gauge does NOT read C Gauge Pointer does NOT move	▶ ▶ ▶	GO to D2. GO to D2. GO to D3.
D2	**TEST SENDER CIRCUIT AT HIGH**			
	• Follow the procedure from test step D1 except set the tester to 9.7 ohms. • Does the temperature gauge read H (hot)?	Yes No	▶ ▶	GO to D4. GO to D3.

TEST STEP		RESULT	▶	ACTION TO TAKE
D3	**CHECK SENDER CIRCUIT WIRING**			
	• Measure the resistance of the "BK/O" wire between the instrument cluster and the coolant temperature sender. • Is the resistance less than 5 ohms?	Yes No	▶ ▶	REPLACE the temperature gauge. REPAIR the "BK/O" wire. RETURN to A1.
D4	**CHECK TEMPERATURE SENDER (TEMPERATURE GAUGE IS INACCURATE)**			
	• Remove the temperature sender. • Place the temperature sender in a container of water and heat to 176°F (80°C). • Use an ohmmeter to measure the resistance between the case and the terminal of the temperature sender. • Does the resistance measure between 49 ohms and 58 ohms?	Yes No	▶ ▶	GO to Engine Cooling. REPLACE the coolant temperature sender.

TEST STEP		RESULT	▶	ACTION TO TAKE
E1	**VERIFY COOLANT FILL**			
	• Observe the level of the coolant in the recovery bottle while the engine is cold. • Is the coolant level at or below the full hot mark on the recovery bottle?	At the full hot mark Below the full hot mark	▶ ▶	GO to TG7. GO to E2.
E2	**VERIFY COOLANT FILL**			
	• Fill the recovery bottle with coolant to the full hot mark. • Start the vehicle and observe the CHECK COOLANT indicator light. • What is the response of the CHECK COOLANT indicator light?	Indicator light illuminates momentarily and then stays off Indicator light illuminates momentarily and then comes back on (or stays on)	▶ ▶	System is operating correctly. GO to TG7.

FM9099100287020X

Fig. 11   Temperature indicating system diagnosis (Part 2 of 2). 1992 Escort & Tracer

	TEST STEP	RESULT	►	ACTION TO TAKE
TG1	INSTRUMENTS (METER) SYSTEM CHECK (TEMPERATURE GAUGE NOT WORKING)			
	• Start engine and allow a warm-up time of 15 minutes. • Shut engine off. Turn ignition to the ON position. • Check the following items for proper operation: – Temperature gauge – Warning lights (Anti-lock, Seat Belt, Engine, Brake)	No warning lights illuminate and temperature gauge always reads cold	►	GO to TG2 .
		Warning lights illuminate and temperature gauge always reads cold	►	GO to TG3 .
		Temperature gauge always reads hot	►	GO to TG5 .
		Temperature gauge is not accurate	►	GO to TG7 .

	TEST STEP	RESULT	►	ACTION TO TAKE
PINPOINT TEST E: INSTRUMENT CLUSTER TEMPERATURE GAUGE ALWAYS READS COLD				
E1	CHECK WATER TEMPERATURE INDICATOR SENDER UNIT			
	• Perform the Water Temperature Indicator Sender Unit component test in this section. • Is the water temperature indicator sender unit OK?	Yes No	► ►	GO to E2. REPLACE the water temperature indicator sender unit.
E2	CHECK INSTRUMENT CLUSTER TEMPERATURE GAUGE			
	• Perform the Instrument Cluster Temperature Gauge component test in this section. • Is the instrument cluster temperature gauge OK?	Yes No	► ►	GO to E3. REPLACE the instrument cluster temperature gauge.

FM9099400330010X

Fig. 12 Temperature indicating system diagnosis (Part 1 of 3). 1993-94 Escort & Tracer

	TEST STEP	RESULT	►	ACTION TO TAKE
PINPOINT TEST E: INSTRUMENT CLUSTER TEMPERATURE GAUGE ALWAYS READS COLD (Continued)				
E3	CHECK WIRE BETWEEN INSTRUMENT CLUSTER AND WATER TEMPERATURE INDICATOR SENDER UNIT			
	• Key OFF. • Disconnect instrument cluster connector C (without tachometer) or A (with tachometer) and the water temperature indicator sender unit connector. • Measure the resistance of the "BK/O" wire between instrument cluster connector C (without tachometer) and A (with tachometer) and water temperature indicator sender unit connector. • Is the resistance less than 5 ohms?	Yes No	► ►	REPLACE the instrument cluster printed circuit. SERVICE the "BK/O" wire for open.

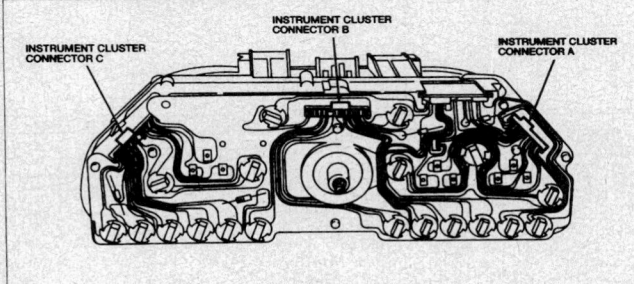

INSTRUMENT CLUSTER CONNECTOR C
INSTRUMENT CLUSTER CONNECTOR B
INSTRUMENT CLUSTER CONNECTOR A

FM9099400330020X

Fig. 12 Temperature indicating system diagnosis (Part 2 of 3). 1993-94 Escort & Tracer

	TEST STEP	RESULT	►	ACTION TO TAKE
TG2	INSTRUMENTS (METER) FUSE CHECK (TEMPERATURE GAUGE ALWAYS READS COLD/NO WARNING LIGHTS ILLUMINATE)			
	• Check instrument (METER) fuse. • Is fuse OK?	Yes No	► ►	REPAIR BK/Y wire between instrument cluster and fuse panel. REPLACE fuse. (Read note)
NOTE: If fuse blows again, check for shorts to ground in "BK/Y" wires between instruments and fuse panel. Repair "BK/Y" wire as needed.				

FM9099100288010X

Fig. 13 Temperature indicating system diagnosis (Part 1 of 5). 1992 Probe

	TEST STEP	RESULT	►	ACTION TO TAKE
TG3	TEMPERATURE GAUGE CHECK (TEMPERATURE GAUGE ALWAYS READS COLD/WARNING LIGHTS OK)			
	• Ground "Y/GN" wire at instrument connector. • Does temperature gauge still read cold?	Yes No	► ►	REPLACE temperature gauge for conventional instruments GO to TG4 .

	TEST STEP	RESULT	►	ACTION TO TAKE
TG4	TEMPERATURE GAUGE CONTINUITY CHECK (TEMPERATURE GAUGE ALWAYS READS COLD/WARNING LIGHTS OK)			
	• Ground "Y/GN" wire at water temperature sensor connector. • Does temperature gauge still read cold?	Yes No	► ►	REPAIR "Y/GN" wire between instruments (METERS) and water temperature sensor. REPLACE water temperature sensor.

	TEST STEP	RESULT	►	ACTION TO TAKE
TG5	TEMPERATURE GAUGE SHORT CHECK NO. 1 (TEMPERATURE GAUGE ALWAYS READS HOT)			
	• Remove "Y/GN" wire from water temperature sensor. • Does temperature gauge still read hot?	Yes No	► ►	GO to TG6 . REPLACE water temperature sensor.

FM9099100288020X

Fig. 13 Temperature indicating system diagnosis (Part 2 of 5). 1992 Probe

	TEST STEP	RESULT	►	ACTION TO TAKE
PINPOINT TEST F: INSTRUMENT CLUSTER TEMPERATURE GAUGE INACCURATE				
F1	CHECK WATER TEMPERATURE INDICATOR SENDER UNIT			
	• Perform the Water Temperature Indicator Sender Unit component test in this section. • Is the water temperature indicator sender unit OK?	Yes No	► ►	GO to F2. REPLACE the water temperature indicator sender unit.
F2	CHECK INSTRUMENT CLUSTER TEMPERATURE GAUGE			
	• Perform the Instrument Cluster Temperature Gauge component test in this section. • Is the instrument cluster temperature gauge OK?	Yes No	► ►	SERVICE the "BK/GN" wire between the 10-pin instrument cluster connector and ground. REPLACE the instrument cluster temperature gauge.

FM9099400330030X

Fig. 12 Temperature indicating system diagnosis (Part 3 of 3). 1993-94 Escort & Tracer

	TEST STEP	RESULT	►	ACTION TO TAKE
TG6	TEMPERATURE GAUGE SHORT CHECK NO. 2 (TEMPERATURE GAUGE ALWAYS READS HOT)			
	• Reconnect "Y/GN" wire connector at water temperature sensor. • Disconnect instrument (METER) connector. • Does temperature gauge still read hot?	Yes No	► ►	REPLACE temperature gauge. REPAIR "Y/GN" wire between water temperature sensor and instrument.

FM9099100288030X

Fig. 13 Temperature indicating system diagnosis (Part 3 of 5). 1992 Probe

TEST STEP		RESULT	▶	ACTION TO TAKE
TG7	TEMPERATURE GAUGE CHECK (TEMPERATURE GAUGE IS NOT ACCURATE)			
• Remove connector from the water temperature sensor. • Connect one lead of the Rotunda Gauge System Tester 021-00055 (or equivalent) to the "Y/GN" wire at the connector and the other lead to ground as shown. • Set the gauge tester to the resistance values shown. • Turn ignition switch to ON position and check to see that the needle indicator displays the correct values. • Continue each inspection for two minutes to correctly judge the condition (Allowable readings are twice the width of needle). • Is reading within allowable range ?		Yes No	▶ ▶	GO to ☐TG8☐. REPLACE temperature gauge for conventional instruments cluster
NOTE: Use Rotunda "Gauge System Tester" No. 021-00055 or equivalent.				

FM9099100288040X

Fig. 13   Temperature indicating system diagnosis (Part 4 of 5). 1992 Probe

TEST STEP		RESULT	▶	ACTION TO TAKE
TG8	TEMPERATURE SENSOR CHECK (TEMPERATURE GAUGE IS NOT ACCURATE)			
• Remove the water temperature sensor. • Place water temperature sensor in a container of water and heat to 80°C (176°F). • Use an ohmmeter to measure the resistance between the case and terminal of the water temperature sensor. • Does resistance read between 150 ohms and 180 ohms?		Yes No	▶ ▶	Repair Engine Cooling. REPLACE water temperature sensor.

NO. 059-00010

FM9099100288050X

Fig. 13   Temperature indicating system diagnosis (Part 5 of 5). 1992 Probe

SYMPTOM CHART

CONDITION	POSSIBLE SOURCE	ACTION
• Temperature Gauge Does Not Work	• Fuse. • Circuit. • Gauge engine coolant temperature sender. • Temperature gauge.	• GO to TG1.
• Temperature Gauge Not Reading Correctly	• Gauge engine coolant temperature sender. • Circuit. • Temperature gauge.	• GO to TG8.
• Temperature Gauge Always Reads Cold	• Fuse. • Circuit. • Gauge engine coolant temperature sender. • Temperature gauge.	• GO to TG1.
• Temperature Gauge Always Read Hot	• Gauge engine coolant temperature sender. • Circuit. • Temperature gauge.	• GO to TG8.

Pinpoint Tests — Temperature Gauge System

TEST STEP		RESULT	▶	ACTION TO TAKE
TG1	CHECK FUSE			
• Check the 15A METER fuse located in the interior fuse panel. • Is the fuse OK?		Yes No	▶ ▶	GO to TG4. GO to TG2.
TG2	CHECK SYSTEM			
• Key OFF. • Replace the 15A METER fuse. • Key ON. • Inspect the fuse. • Does the fuse fall again?		Yes No	▶ ▶	GO to TG3. GO to TG4.

FM9099300289010X

Fig. 14   Temperature indicating system diagnosis (Part 1 of 4). 1993–94 Probe

TEST STEP		RESULT	▶	ACTION TO TAKE
TG3	CHECK FOR SHORT TO GROUND			
• Key OFF. • Locate and disconnect the 14-pin interior fuse panel connector. • Remove the instrument cluster. • Locate and disconnect the 14-pin instrument cluster connector. • Measure the resistance of the "BK/Y" wire between the 14-pin interior fuse panel connector and ground. • Is the resistance less than 5 ohms?		Yes No	▶ ▶	SERVICE the "BK/Y" wire between the interior fuse panel and the instrument cluster. RECONNECT the interior fuse panel. GO to TG4.

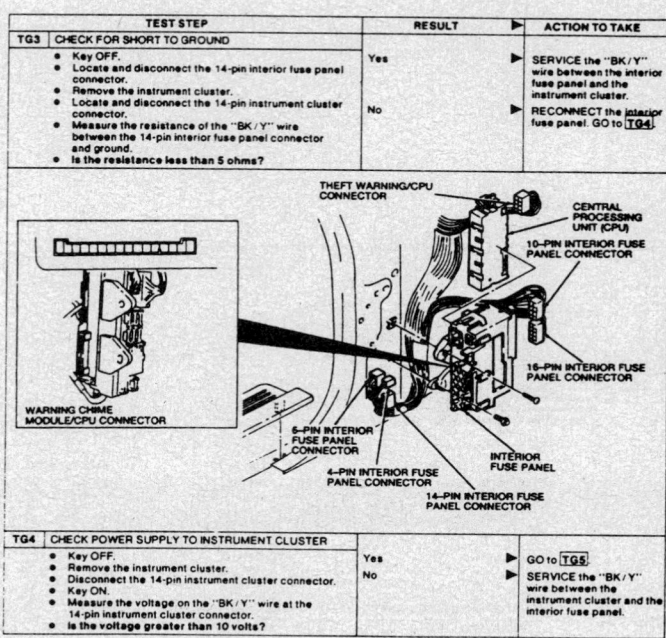

TG4	CHECK POWER SUPPLY TO INSTRUMENT CLUSTER			
• Key OFF. • Remove the instrument cluster. • Disconnect the 14-pin instrument cluster connector. • Key ON. • Measure the voltage on the "BK/Y" wire at the 14-pin instrument cluster connector. • Is the voltage greater than 10 volts?		Yes No	▶ ▶	GO to TG5. SERVICE the "BK/Y" wire between the instrument cluster and the interior fuse panel.

FM9099300289020X

Fig. 14   Temperature indicating system diagnosis (Part 2 of 4). 1993–94 Probe

TEST STEP		RESULT	▶	ACTION TO TAKE
TG5	CHECK POWER SUPPLY TO TEMPERATURE GAUGE			
• Key OFF. • Disconnect and remove the instrument cluster. • Measure the resistance of the circuit between the instrument cluster pin 1F and the temperature gauge "+" screw terminal.		Yes No	▶ ▶	GO to TG6. REPLACE the instrument cluster printed circuit board.
• Is the resistance less than 5 ohms?				
TG6	CHECK INSTRUMENT CLUSTER GROUND			
• Key OFF. • Disconnect the 14-pin instrument cluster connector. • Measure the resistance of the "BK" wire between the 14-pin instrument cluster connector and ground. • Is the resistance less than 5 ohms?		Yes No	▶ ▶	GO to TG7. SERVICE the "BK" wire.
TG7	CHECK GROUND TO TEMPERATURE GAUGE			
• Key OFF. • Disconnect and remove the instrument cluster. • Measure the resistance of the circuit between the instrument cluster pin 1I and the temperature gauge "-" screw terminal. • Is the resistance less than 5 ohms?		Yes No	▶ ▶	GO to TG8. REPLACE the instrument cluster printed circuit board.

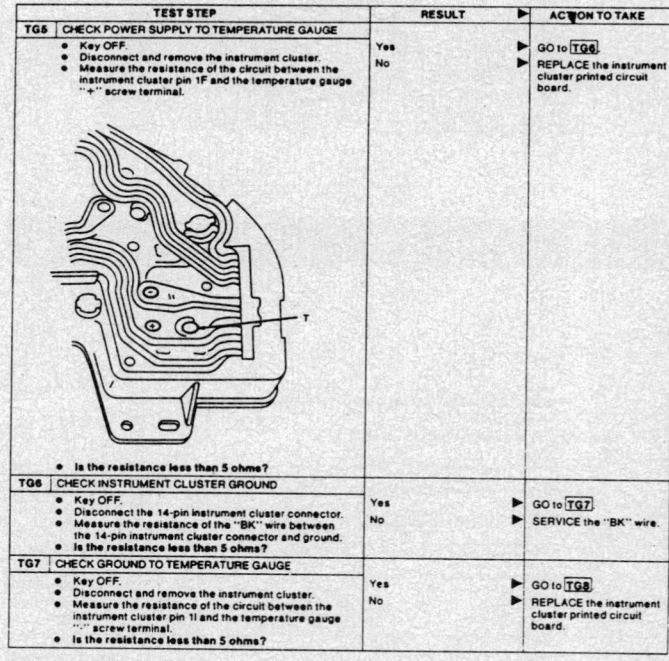

FM9099300289030X

Fig. 14   Temperature indicating system diagnosis (Part 3 of 4). 1993–94 Probe

TEST STEP	RESULT	▶	ACTION TO TAKE
TG8 CHECK SIGNAL FROM GAUGE ENGINE COOLANT TEMPERATURE SENDER • Key OFF. • Locate and disconnect the gauge engine coolant temperature sender connector. • Connect Rotunda Instrument Gauge System Tester 021-00055 or equivalent between the gauge engine coolant temperature sender connector and ground. • Key ON. • Adjust the instrument gauge system tester to the resistances shown. 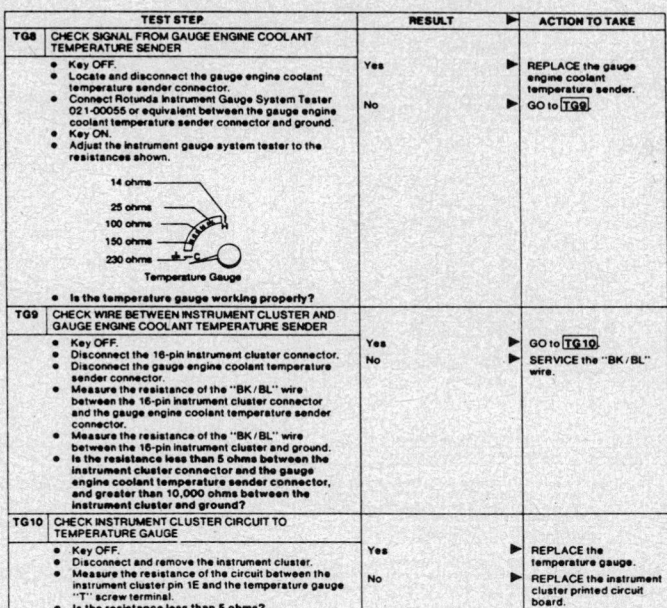 • Is the temperature gauge working properly?	Yes No	▶ ▶	REPLACE the gauge engine coolant temperature sender. GO to **TG9**
TG9 CHECK WIRE BETWEEN INSTRUMENT CLUSTER AND GAUGE ENGINE COOLANT TEMPERATURE SENDER • Key OFF. • Disconnect the 16-pin instrument cluster connector. • Disconnect the gauge engine coolant temperature sender connector. • Measure the resistance of the "BK/BL" wire between the 16-pin instrument cluster connector and the gauge engine coolant temperature sender connector. • Measure the resistance of the "BK/BL" wire between the 16-pin instrument cluster and ground. • Is the resistance less than 5 ohms between the instrument cluster connector and the gauge engine coolant temperature sender connector, and greater than 10,000 ohms between the instrument cluster and ground?	Yes No	▶ ▶	GO to **TG10** SERVICE the "BK/BL" wire.
TG10 CHECK INSTRUMENT CLUSTER CIRCUIT TO TEMPERATURE GAUGE • Key OFF. • Disconnect and remove the instrument cluster. • Measure the resistance of the circuit between the instrument cluster pin 1E and the temperature gauge "T" screw terminal. • Is the resistance less than 5 ohms?	Yes No	▶ ▶	REPLACE the temperature gauge. REPLACE the instrument cluster printed circuit board.

FM9099300289040X

Fig. 14 Temperature indicating system diagnosis (Part 4 of 4). 1993–94 Probe

TEST STEP	RESULT	▶	ACTION TO TAKE
OP4 GAUGE CONTINUITY CHECK NO. 1 (OIL PRESSURE GAUGE ALWAYS READS LOW) • Ground "Y/R" wire at oil pressure sender unit connector. • Does oil pressure gauge read high?	Yes No	▶ ▶	REPLACE oil pressure sender unit. REPAIR "Y/R" wire between instruments and oil pressure sender unit.

TEST STEP	RESULT	▶	ACTION TO TAKE
OP5 GAUGE SHORT CHECK NO. 1 (OIL PRESSURE GAUGE ALWAYS READS HIGH) • Disconnect the small instrument (METER) connector. • Does oil pressure gauge still read high?	Yes No	▶ ▶	REPLACE oil pressure gauge (part of combination gauge). GO to **OP6**.

TEST STEP	RESULT	▶	ACTION TO TAKE
OP6 GAUGE SHORT CHECK NO. 2 (OIL PRESSURE GAUGE ALWAYS READS HIGH) • Reconnect instruments (METERS) connector. • Disconnect oil pressure sender unit connector. • Does oil pressure gauge still read high?	Yes No	▶ ▶	REPAIR "Y/R" wire between instruments oil pressure sender unit and condenser. REPLACE oil pressure sender unit.

FM9099100296020X

Fig. 15 Gauge type oil pressure indicator diagnosis (Part 2 of 3). 1992 Probe

TEST STEP	RESULT	▶	ACTION TO TAKE
OP1 INSTRUMENT RELATED SYSTEM CHECK (OIL GAUGE NOT WORKING) • Turn ignition switch to ON position (engine off). • Check the following items for proper operation: – Oil pressure gauge – Warning lights – Anti-lock – Seat belt – Brake – Engine	Warning lights not working, oil pressure gauge reads low Oil pressure gauge always reads low Oil pressure gauge always reads high Oil pressure gauge not accurate	▶ ▶ ▶ ▶	GO to **OP2**. GO to **OP3**. GO to **OP5**. GO to **OP7**.

TEST STEP	RESULT	▶	ACTION TO TAKE
OP2 INSTRUMENT (METER) FUSE CHECK (WARNING LIGHTS NOT WORKING, OIL PRESSURE GAUGE READS LOW) • Check instrument (METER) fuse. • Is fuse OK?	Yes No	▶ ▶	Repair the BK/Y wire between the fuse panel and the instrument cluster. REPLACE fuse. (Read note)

NOTE: If fuse blows again, service shorts to ground in "BK/Y" wires between instruments and fuse panel.

TEST STEP	RESULT	▶	ACTION TO TAKE
OP3 GAUGE CHECK (OIL PRESSURE GAUGE ALWAYS READS LOW) • Ground "Y/R" wire at instrument (METER) connector. • Does oil pressure gauge read high?	Yes No	▶ ▶	GO to **OP4**. REPLACE oil pressure gauge.

FM9099100296010X

Fig. 15 Gauge type oil pressure indicator diagnosis (Part 1 of 3). 1992 Probe

TEST STEP	RESULT	▶	ACTION TO TAKE
OP7 OIL PRESSURE GAUGE CHECK (OIL PRESSURE GAUGE NOT ACCURATE) • Disconnect oil pressure sender unit connector. • Connect one lead of Rotunda Gauge Tester (Read note) to the "Y/R" wire of the connector and the other lead to ground. • Set tester to resistance values shown. • Turn ignition switch to ON position and check to see that needle indicator displays correct values. • Continue inspections for two minutes each to correctly judge the condition. • The allowable error is twice the width of the needle. • Are oil pressure gauge readings correct?	Yes No	▶ ▶	REPLACE oil pressure sender unit. REPLACE oil pressure gauge. NOTE: If the oil pressure gauge is still not operating correctly, the oil pressure circuit board (analog clusters only) may need to be replaced.

NOTE: Use Rotunda "Gauge System Tester" No. 021-00038 or equivalent.

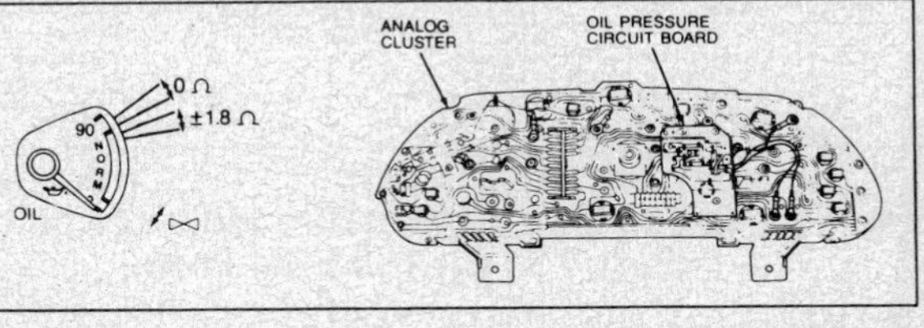

FM9099100296030X

Fig. 15 Gauge type oil pressure indicator diagnosis (Part 3 of 3). 1992 Probe

	TEST STEP	RESULT	▶	ACTION TO TAKE
OP3	CHECK FOR SHORT TO GROUND			
	• Key OFF. • Locate and disconnect the 14-pin interior fuse panel connector. • Remove the instrument cluster. • Locate and disconnect the 14-pin instrument cluster connector. • Measure the resistance of the "BK/Y" wire between the 14-pin interior fuse panel connector and ground. • Is the resistance less than 5 ohms?	Yes No	▶ ▶	SERVICE the "BK/Y" wire between the interior fuse panel and the instrument cluster. RECONNECT the interior fuse panel. GO to OP4.

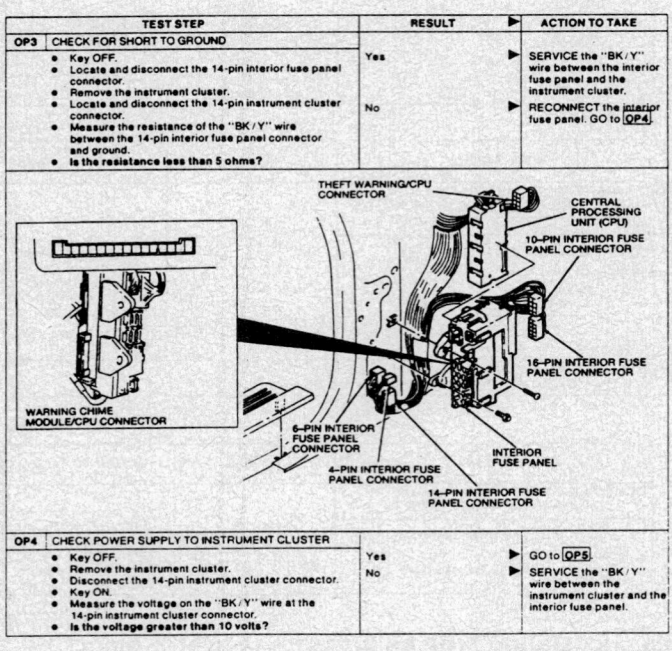

	TEST STEP	RESULT	▶	ACTION TO TAKE
OP4	CHECK POWER SUPPLY TO INSTRUMENT CLUSTER			
	• Key OFF. • Remove the instrument cluster. • Disconnect the 14-pin instrument cluster connector. • Key ON. • Measure the voltage on the "BK/Y" wire at the 14-pin instrument cluster connector. • Is the voltage greater than 10 volts?	Yes No	▶ ▶	GO to OP5. SERVICE the "BK/Y" wire between the instrument cluster and the interior fuse panel.

FM9099300297020X

Fig. 16 Gauge type oil pressure indicator diagnosis (Part 2 of 4). 1993–94 Probe

	TEST STEP	RESULT	▶	ACTION TO TAKE
OP5	CHECK POWER SUPPLY TO OIL PRESSURE GAUGE			
	• Key OFF. • Disconnect and remove the instrument cluster. • Measure the resistance of the circuit between the instrument cluster pin 1F and the oil pressure gauge "+" screw terminal.	Yes No	▶ ▶	GO to OP6. REPLACE the instrument cluster printed circuit board.

OP

	• Is the resistance less than 5 ohms?			
OP6	CHECK INSTRUMENT CLUSTER GROUND			
	• Key OFF. • Disconnect the 14-pin instrument cluster connector. • Measure the resistance of the "BK" wire between the 14-pin instrument cluster connector and ground. • Is the resistance less than 5 ohms?	Yes No	▶ ▶	GO to OP7. SERVICE the "BK" wire.
OP7	CHECK GROUND TO OIL PRESSURE GAUGE			
	• Key OFF. • Disconnect and remove the instrument cluster. • Measure the resistance of the circuit between the instrument cluster pin 1I and the oil pressure gauge "−" screw terminal. • Is the resistance less than 5 ohms?	Yes No	▶ ▶	GO to OP8. REPLACE the instrument cluster printed circuit board.
OP8	CHECK SIGNAL FROM OIL PRESSURE SENDER			
	• Key OFF. • Locate and disconnect the oil pressure sender connector. • Connect Rotunda Instrument Gauge System Tester 021-00055 or equivalent between the oil pressure sender connector and ground. • Key ON. • Adjust the instrument gauge system tester to the resistances shown.	Yes No	▶ ▶	REPLACE the oil pressure sender. GO to OP9.

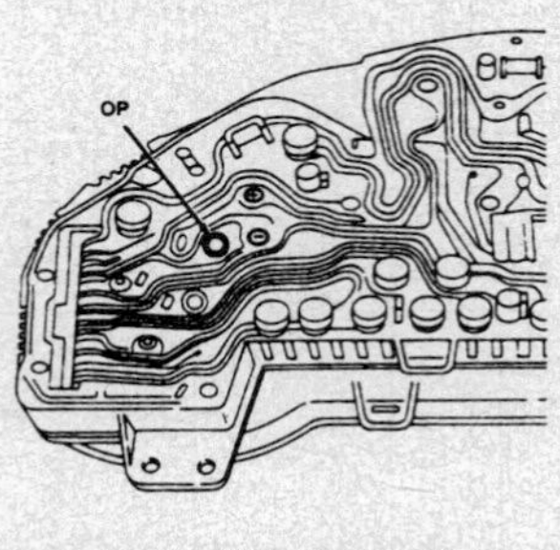

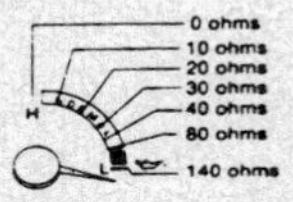

```
0 ohms
10 ohms
20 ohms
30 ohms
40 ohms
80 ohms
140 ohms
```

• Is the oil pressure gauge working properly?

FM9099300297030X

Fig. 16 Gauge type oil pressure indicator diagnosis (Part 3 of 4). 1993–94 Probe

	TEST STEP	RESULT	▶	ACTION TO TAKE
OP9	CHECK WIRE BETWEEN INSTRUMENT CLUSTER AND OIL PRESSURE SENDER			
	• Key OFF. • Remove the instrument cluster. • Disconnect the 16-pin instrument cluster connector. • Disconnect the oil pressure sender connector. • Measure the resistance of the "P/Y" wire between the 16-pin instrument cluster connector and the oil pressure sender connector. • Measure the resistance of the "P/Y" wire between the 16-pin instrument cluster connector and ground. • Is the resistance less than 5 ohms between the instrument cluster connector and the oil pressure sensor connector, and greater than 10,000 ohms between the instrument cluster and ground?	Yes No	▶ ▶	GO to OP10. SERVICE the "P/Y" wire.
OP10	CHECK INSTRUMENT CLUSTER CIRCUIT TO OIL PRESSURE GAUGE			
	• Key OFF. • Disconnect and remove the instrument cluster. • Measure the resistance of the circuit between the instrument cluster pin 2F and the oil pressure gauge "OP" screw terminal. • Is the resistance less than 5 ohms?	Yes No	▶ ▶	REPLACE the oil pressure gauge. REPLACE the instrument cluster printed circuit board.

FM9099300297040X

Fig. 16 Gauge type oil pressure indicator diagnosis (Part 4 of 4). 1993–94 Probe

CONDITION	POSSIBLE SOURCE	ACTION
• Temperature Gauge Always Reads Cold	• Fuse. • Circuit. • Temperature gauge. • Coolant temperature sending unit.	• GO to CT1.
• Temperature Gauge Always Reads Hot	• Temperature gauge. • Circuit. • Coolant temperature sending unit.	• GO to CT8.
• Temperature Gauge Works But Is Inaccurate	• Temperature gauge. • Coolant temperature sending unit.	• GO to CT9.

	TEST STEP	RESULT	▶	ACTION TO TAKE
CT1	CHECK SYSTEM INTEGRITY			
	• Visually inspect the components of the engine coolant temperature system. • Check for a blown fuse, or damage to the coolant temperature sending unit. • Check for loose or corroded connections, damage to the wiring harness and burned out warning bulbs. • Does the system appear to be in good condition?	Yes No	▶ ▶	GO to CT2. REPAIR or REPLACE the damaged component to the system.
CT2	VERIFY COMPLAINT			
	• Key ON, engine running. • Allow the engine to warm up. • Observe the gauge performance. • Does the gauge pointer move?	Yes No	▶ ▶	GO to CT10. GO to CT3.

FM9099100290010X

Fig. 17 Temperature indicating system diagnosis (Part 1 of 3). Festiva

TEST STEP	RESULT	▶	ACTION TO TAKE
CT3 VERIFY CLUSTER OPERATION			
• Key ON.	Yes	▶	GO to CT9.
• Observe the other gauges and warning lights.	No	▶	GO to CT4.
• Are the other gauges and warning lights operating properly?		◀	
CT4 CHECK METER FUSE			
• Check the 10 amp METER fuse.	Yes	▶	GO to CT6.
• Is the fuse OK?	No	▶	GO to CT5.
CT5 CHECK SYSTEM			
• Replace the 10 amp METER fuse.	Yes	▶	REPAIR the "BK/Y" wire(s) for a short to ground.
• Key ON.			
• Does the fuse fail again?	No	▶	GO to CT6.
CT6 CHECK POWER TO CLUSTER			
• Disconnect the instrument cluster connector.	Yes	▶	GO to CT7.
• Key ON.	No	▶	SERVICE the "BK/Y" wire for an open between the instrument cluster and the interior fuse panel.
• Measure the voltage on the "BK/Y" at the instrument cluster connector.			
• Is the voltage greater than 10 volts?			
CT7 CHECK GROUND AT CLUSTER			
• Disconnect the instrument cluster connector.	Yes	▶	GO to CT8.
• Measure the resistance of the "BK" wire at the instrument cluster connector to ground.	No	▶	SERVICE the "BK" wire between the instrument cluster and ground for an open.
• Is the resistance less than 5 ohms?			
CT8 CHECK COOLANT TEMPERATURE SENSOR FEED			
• Disconnect the instrument cluster connector.	Yes	▶	GO to CT9.
• Disconnect the cooling temperature sending unit connector.	No	▶	SERVICE the "Y/W" wire between the cluster and the sensor for an open.
• Measure the resistance of the "Y/W" wire between the instrument cluster connector and cooling temperature sending unit connector.			
• Is the resistance less than 5 ohms?			
CT9 CHECK SENSOR CIRCUIT (COLD)			
• Disconnect the coolant temperature sensor.	Yes	▶	GO to CT10.
• Connect one lead of Rotunda Gauge System Tester 021-00055 or equivalent to the "Y" wire at the coolant temperature sending unit and the other lead to ground.	No	▶	GO to CT11.
• Set the tester to 74 ohms.			
• Wait one minute.			
• Read the temperature gauge.			
• Does the gauge read C (cold)?			
CT10 CHECK SENSOR CIRCUIT (HOT)			
• Follow the procedure in test step CT9 except set the gauge tester to 9.7 ohms.	Yes	▶	GO to CT12.
• Does the gauge read H (hot)?	No	▶	GO to CT11.

FM9099100290020X

Fig. 17   Temperature indicating system diagnosis (Part 2 of 3). Festiva

TEST STEP	RESULT	▶	ACTION TO TAKE
CT11 CHECK FOR SHORT TO GROUND			
• Disconnect the instrument cluster.	Yes	▶	REPLACE the temperature gauge.
• Disconnect the engine coolant temperature sending unit connector.	No	▶	REPAIR the "Y/W" wire for a short to ground.
• Measure the resistance of the "Y/W" wire at the instrument cluster connector ground.			
• Is the resistance greater than 10,000 ohms?			
CT12 CHECK COOLANT TEMPERATURE SENDING UNIT			
• Remove the coolant temperature sending unit.	Yes		Visually inspect the components of the engine coolant system.
• Place the coolant temperature sending unit in a container of water and heat to 176°F.	No	▶	REPLACE the coolant temperature sensor.
• Measure the resistance between the case and the terminal of the coolant temperature sending unit.			
• Is the resistance between 49 ohms and 58 ohms?			

FM9099100290030X

Fig. 17   Temperature indicating system diagnosis (Part 3 of 3). Festiva

PINPOINT TEST F: INSTRUMENT CLUSTER TEMPERATURE GAUGE INACCURATE

TEST STEP	RESULT	▶	ACTION TO TAKE
F1 CHECK WATER TEMPERATURE INDICATOR SENDER UNIT			
• Perform the Water Temperature Indicator Sender Unit component test in this section.	Yes	▶	GO to F2.
• Is the water temperature indicator sender unit OK?	No	▶	REPLACE the water temperature indicator sender unit.

FM9099400323010X

Fig. 18   Temperature gauge system diagnosis (Part 1 of 2). Aspire

PINPOINT TEST F: INSTRUMENT CLUSTER TEMPERATURE GAUGE INACCURATE (Continued)

TEST STEP	RESULT	▶	ACTION TO TAKE
F2 CHECK INSTRUMENT CLUSTER TEMPERATURE GAUGE			
• Perform the Instrument Cluster Temperature Gauge component test	Yes	▶	SERVICE the "BK/Y" wire between the white instrument cluster connector and ground.
• Is the instrument cluster temperature gauge OK?	No	▶	REPLACE the instrument cluster temperature gauge.

PINPOINT TEST G: INSTRUMENT CLUSTER TEMPERATURE GAUGE ALWAYS READS HOT

TEST STEP	RESULT	▶	ACTION TO TAKE
G1 CHECK WATER TEMPERATURE INDICATOR SENDER UNIT			
• Perform the Water Temperature Indicator Sender Unit component test in this section.	Yes	▶	GO to G2.
• Is the water temperature indicator sender unit OK?	No	▶	REPLACE the water temperature indicator sender unit.
G2 CHECK INSTRUMENT CLUSTER TEMPERATURE GAUGE			
• Perform the Instrument Cluster Temperature Gauge component test in this section.	Yes	▶	SERVICE the "Y/BK" wire for short.
• Is the instrument cluster temperature gauge OK?	No	▶	REPLACE the instrument cluster temperature gauge.

FM9099400323020X

Fig. 18   Temperature gauge system diagnosis (Part 2 of 2). Aspire

PINPOINT TEST O: LOW OIL PRESSURE INDICATOR INOPERATIVE

TEST STEP	RESULT	▶	ACTION TO TAKE
O1 CHECK ENGINE OIL PRESSURE			
• Check the engine oil pressure.	Yes	▶	GO to O2.
• Is engine oil pressure within specification?	No	▶	service the engine.
O2 CHECK LOW OIL PRESSURE INDICATOR MINIATURE BULB			
• Key off.	Yes	▶	GO to O3.
• Remove the low oil pressure indicator miniature bulb.	No	▶	REPLACE the low oil pressure indicator miniature bulb.
• Check the continuity between the terminals of the low oil pressure indicator miniature bulb.			
• Does continuity exist?			
O3 CHECK OIL PRESSURE SENDER			
• Key off	Yes	▶	GO to O4.
• Locate and disconnect the oil pressure sender connector.	No	▶	REPLACE the oil pressure sender.
• Measure the resistance between the terminal of the oil pressure sender and ground under the following conditions:			

Engine	Resistance
Running	Greater than 10,000 ohms
Off	Less than 5 ohms

• Are the resistances correct?	

FM9099400324010X

Fig. 19   Oil pressure indicator system diagnosis (Part 1 of 2). Aspire

PINPOINT TEST O: LOW OIL PRESSURE INDICATOR INOPERATIVE (Continued)

TEST STEP	RESULT	▶	ACTION TO TAKE
O4 CHECK WIRE BETWEEN INSTRUMENT CLUSTER AND OIL PRESSURE SENDER			
• Key off.	Yes	▶	REPLACE the instrument cluster printed circuit.
• Locate and disconnect the black instrument cluster connector.	No	▶	SERVICE the "Y/R" wire.
• Disconnect the oil pressure sender connector.			
• Measure the resistance of the "Y/R" wire between the black instrument cluster connector and the oil pressure sender connector.			
• Measure the resistance of the "Y/R" wire between the black instrument cluster connector and ground.			
• Is the resistance less than 5 ohms between the instrument cluster and the oil pressure sender, and greater than 10,000 ohms between the instrument cluster and ground?			

FM9099400324020X

Fig. 19   Oil pressure indicator system diagnosis (Part 2 of 2). Aspire

ENGINE LAMP DOES NOT COME ON ENGINE OVERHEATING

TEST STEP	RESULT ▶	ACTION TO TAKE
A1 CHECK LAMP OPERATION		
• Turn ignition switch to RUN position.	(OK) ▶	GO to A2.
• Lamp should light.	(ØK) ▶	GO to A3.
A2 BYPASS TEMPERATURE		
• Disconnect BR/GR wire at oil pressure switch (top of oil filter housing).	(OK) ▶	CONNECT BR/GR wire at oil pressure switch. REPLACE temperature switch. CHECK system operation.
• Disconnect BR/P wire at temperature switch and jumper to ground.		
• With ignition switch in RUN position, lamp should light.	(ØK) ▶	SERVICE open circuit between lamp and temperature switch. CHECK system operation.
A3 BYPASS OIL PRESSURE SWITCH		
• Disconnect BR/GR wire at oil pressure switch (top of oil filter housing) and jumper wire to ground.	(OK) ▶	REPLACE oil pressure switch, CHECK system operation.
• With ignition switch in RUN position, lamp should light.	(ØK) ▶	GO to A4.
A4 CHECK FUSE		
• Check fuse 18 for continuity.	(OK) ▶	CHECK for and SERVICE open circuit between Fuse 18 and oil pressure switch, including ENGINE lamp bulb. CHECK system operation.
	(ØK) ▶	REPLACE fuse. CHECK system operation.

FM9099100291010X

Fig. 20 Temperature/oil indicating system diagnosis (Part 1 of 3). Mark VII

TEMP LAMP DOES NOT COME ON — ENGINE OVERHEATING

TEST STEP	RESULT ▶	ACTION TO TAKE
B1 CHECK LAMP OPERATION		
• Disconnect R/LB wire at starter relay on LH fender apron.	(OK) ▶	CONNECT R/LB Wire to starter relay. REPLACE TEMP switch. CHECK system operation.
• Turn ignition switch to START position.		
• Lamp should light.	(ØK) ▶	GO to B2.
B2 BYPASS TEMP SWITCH		
• Disconnect BR/P Wire at TEMP switch and jumper to ground.	(OK) ▶	SERVICE open Circuit 39 R/W between TEMP lamp and ignition switch terminal P2. CHECK lamp operation.
• Turn ignition switch to RUN position.		
• Lamp should light.	(ØK) ▶	GO to B3.
B3 CHECK FUSE		
• Check fuse 18 in fuse panel for continuity.	(OK) ▶	CHECK and SERVICE open circuit between fuse 18 and TEMP switch, including TEMP lamp bulb, as necessary. CHECK system operation.
	(ØK) ▶	REPLACE Fuse 18. CHECK system operation.

MAGNETIC TEMP/OIL GAUGE INOPERATIVE — POINTER DOES NOT MOVE

TEST STEP	RESULT ▶	ACTION TO TAKE
C1 VERIFY CONDITION		
• Verify condition.	Gauge pointer does not move ▶	GO to C2.
	Gauge pointer moves ▶	GO to D1.
C2 CHECK OTHER GAUGES		
• Check power to cluster. With ignition on, observe other gauges and warning lamps for proper operation. If necessary, use Rotunda Digital Volt/Ohm Meter 007-00001 or equivalent or test lamp to verify voltage at B+ terminal of cluster connector.	Other gauges and warning lamps operate correctly; voltage present at cluster ▶	GO to D1.
	Other gauges and warning lamps do not operate correctly; no voltage present at cluster ▶	SERVICE power to cluster.

FM9099100291020X

Fig. 20 Temperature/oil indicating system diagnosis (Part 2 of 3). Mark VII

TEMP/OIL GAUGE INACCURATE

TEST STEP	RESULT ▶	ACTION TO TAKE
D1 TEST BOX CHECK		
• Insert Instrument Gauge, System Tester, Rotunda 021-00055 or equivalent in sender circuit. Disconnect connector at sender and connect tester to cluster side of connector. Set tester to LOW (73 ohms).	Gauge reads C ▶	GO to D2.
	Pointer does not move ▶	GO to D3.
D2 TEST BOX CHECK		
• Set tester to HIGH (10 ohms).	Gauge reads H ▶	REPLACE sender.
	Gauge does not read H ▶	GO to D3.
D3 CHECK SENDER WIRING		
• Check sender circuit wiring for shorts or open with ohmmeter, using Rotunda Digital Volt-Ohmmeter 007-00001, or equivalent.	(OK) ▶	REPLACE gauge.
	(ØK) ▶	SERVICE wiring.

TEMP LAMP STAYS ON — ENGINE NOT OVERHEATING

TEST STEP	RESULT ▶	ACTION TO TAKE
E1 BYPASS SWITCH		
• Disconnect BR/P Wire at TEMP switch.	(OK) ▶	REPLACE TEMP switch. CHECK system operation.
• Turn ignition switch to RUN position.		
• TEMP lamp should be off.	(ØK) ▶	SERVICE short circuit between TEMP lamp and ignition switch, or between TEMP lamp and TEMP switch. CHECK system operation.

FM9099100291030X

Fig. 20 Temperature/oil indicating system diagnosis (Part 3 of 3). Mark VII

PINPOINT TEST B: FUEL LEVEL READS ERRONEOUSLY (Continued)

TEST STEP	RESULT	▶	ACTION TO TAKE
B3 CHECK FUEL GAUGE (CONT'D)			
• Jumper tester lead to fuel gauge 8 terminal on instrument cluster. • Set resistance to 22 ohms. • Connect instrument cluster connector. • Connect battery ground cable. • Turn ignition switch to RUN position. • Does gauge read empty?	Yes No	▶ ▶	GO to B4. REPLACE fuel gauge. RESTORE system. RETEST system.
B4 CHECK PRINTED CIRCUIT			
• Disconnect battery ground cable. • Disconnect instrument cluster connector. • Check continuity of printed circuit between the following terminals:	Yes No	▶ ▶	Go to B5. REPLACE printed circuit. RESTORE system. RETEST system.

PIN	FUEL GAUGE
3	Hot in Start/Run
8	Fuel Gauge Input
6	Fuel Gauge Ground

TEST STEP	RESULT	▶	ACTION TO TAKE
• Is there continuity for each circuit of printed circuit?			
B5 CHECK FUEL GAUGE			
• Set tester to 145 ohms. • Turn ignition switch to RUN, wait 60 seconds and read fuel gauge. • Does fuel gauge read full?	Yes No	▶ ▶	Diagnose lamp out system GO to B6.
B6 CHECK FUEL GAUGE (CONT'D)			
• Turn ignition switch to OFF position. • Disconnect battery ground cable. • Remove instrument cluster • Jumper test lead to fuel gauge 8 terminal or instrument cluster. • Connect instrument cluster connector. • Connect battery ground cable. • Turn ignition switch to RUN. • Does gauge read full?	Yes No	▶ ▶	SERVICE Circuit 205 (DB/LG) for open. RESTORE vehicle. RETEST system. REPLACE fuel gauge. RESTORE system. RETEST system.

FM9099400325010X

Fig. 21 Temperature indicating system diagnosis (Part 1 of 2). Mark VIII

PINPOINT TEST C: COOLANT TEMPERATURE READS ERRONEOUSLY (Continued)

TEST STEP	RESULT	▶	ACTION TO TAKE
C3 CHECK CIRCUIT 39 (R/W) • Turn ignition switch to OFF position. • Remove instrument cluster. • Disconnect instrument cluster connector. • Measure resistance between temperature gauge sender connector and Pin 7 at instrument cluster connector. • **Is resistance less than 5 ohms?**	Yes No	▶ ▶	GO to **C4**. SERVICE open in Circuit 39 (R/W). RESTORE system. RETEST system.
C4 CHECK PRINTED CIRCUIT • Check continuity of printed circuit between the following terminals:	Yes No	▶ ▶	REPLACE temperature gauge. RESTORE system. RETEST system. REPLACE temperature gauge. RESTORE system. RETEST system.

PIN	TEMPERATURE GAUGE
3	BAT
5	GRD
7	SIG

• **Is there continuity for each circuit of printed circuit?**

FM9099400325020X

Fig. 21   Temperature indicating system diagnosis (Part 2 of 2). Mark VIII

PINPOINT TEST N: CHARGING SYSTEM INDICATOR INOPERATIVE

TEST STEP	RESULT	▶	ACTION TO TAKE
N1 CHECK CHARGING SYSTEM INDICATOR MINIATURE BULB • Key off. • Remove the charging system indicator miniature bulb. • Check the continuity between the terminals of the charging system indicator miniature bulb. • **Does continuity exist?**	Yes No	▶ ▶	GO to **N2**. REPLACE the charging system indicator miniature bulb.

FM9099400326010X

Fig. 22   Charging system indicator diagnosis (Part 1 of 2). Aspire

PINPOINT TEST N: CHARGING SYSTEM INDICATOR INOPERATIVE (Continued)

TEST STEP	RESULT	▶	ACTION TO TAKE
N2 CHECK WIRE BETWEEN INSTRUMENT CLUSTER AND GENERATOR • Key off. • Disconnect the generator connector. • Key ON. • Ground the "BR" wire on the generator connector. • **Does the charging system indicator illuminate?**	Yes No	▶ ▶	service the generator. GO to **N3**.
N3 CHECK WIRE BETWEEN INSTRUMENT CLUSTER AND GENERATOR • Key off. • Locate and disconnect the black instrument cluster connector. • Disconnect the generator connector. • Measure the resistance of the "BR" wire between the black instrument cluster connector and the generator connector. • Measure the resistance of the "BR" wire between the black instrument cluster connector and ground. • **Is the resistance less than 5 ohms between the instrument cluster and the generator, and greater than 10,000 ohms between the instrument cluster and ground?**	Yes No	▶ ▶	REPLACE the instrument cluster printed circuit. SERVICE the "BR" wire.

FM9099400326020X

Fig. 22   Charging system indicator diagnosis (Part 2 of 2). Aspire

PINPOINT TEST D: CHARGE INDICATION READS ERRONEOUSLY

TEST STEP	RESULT	▶	ACTION TO TAKE
D1 CHECK CIRCUIT 904 (LG/R) FOR VOLTAGE • Disconnect voltage regulator connector at generator. • Turn ignition switch to the RUN position. • Using a test lamp, check for voltage at Circuit 904 (LG/R). • **Is voltage present?**	Yes No	▶ ▶	GO to **D5**. GO to **D2**.
D2 CHECK FOR VOLTAGE AT INSTRUMENT CLUSTER • Disconnect battery ground cable. • Remove the instrument cluster. • Reconnect battery ground cable. Make sure instrument cluster is properly connected. • Turn ignition switch to the RUN position. • Using a test lamp, check for voltage at Pin 11 Circuit 904 (LG/R) at cluster connector. • **Is voltage present?**	Yes No	▶ ▶	SERVICE Circuit 904 (LG/R) for open circuit. RESTORE vehicle. RETEST system. GO to **D3**.
D3 CHECK FOR VOLTAGE SUPPLY TO INSTRUMENT CLUSTER • Using test lamp, check for voltage at Pin 12 Circuit 16 (R/LG). • **Is voltage present?**	Yes No	▶ ▶	GO to **D4**. SERVICE Circuit 16 (R/LG) for open circuit. RESTORE vehicle. RETEST system.
D4 CHECK CHARGE INDICATOR LAMP • Turn ignition switch OFF. • Remove charge indicator bulb. • Using an ohmmeter, check bulb for continuity. • **Is bulb OK?**	Yes No	▶ ▶	REPLACE printed circuit board. RESTORE vehicle. RETEST system. REPLACE charge indicator lamp. RESTORE vehicle. RETEST system.
D5 CHECK CIRCUIT 904 (LG/R) • Using a jumper wire connected to a known good ground, connect other end of jumper wire to Circuit 904 (LG/R). • **Does charge indicator lamp illuminate?**	Yes No	▶ ▶	DIAGNOSE CHARGING SYSTEM. SERVICE as necessary. SERVICE Circuit 904 (LG/R) for open circuit. RETEST system.

FM9099400327000X

Fig. 23   Charging system indicator diagnosis. Mark VIII

TEST STEP	RESULT	▶	ACTION TO TAKE
VM1 INSTRUMENTS (METER) FUSE CHECK (VOLTMETER NOT WORKING) • Check instrument (METER) fuse. • Is fuse OK?	Yes No	▶ ▶	GO to **VM2**. REPLACE fuse. (Read note)

NOTE: If fuse blows again, check for shorts to ground in "BK/Y" wire at instruments. Repair "BK/Y" wire as needed.

TEST STEP	RESULT	▶	ACTION TO TAKE
VM2 INSTRUMENTS SUPPLY CHECK (VOLTMETER NOT WORKING) • Check for 12 volts (±1 volt) on "BK/Y" wire at instruments connector. • Are there 12 volts?	Yes No	▶ ▶	GO to **VM3**. REPAIR "BK/Y" wire between instrument cluster connector and fuse panel.

TEST STEP	RESULT	▶	ACTION TO TAKE
VM3 INSTRUMENTS GROUND CHECK (VOLTMETER NOT WORKING) • Check for 12 volts (±1 volt) on "BK" wire at instruments connector. • Is there 12 volts?	Yes No	▶ ▶	REPAIR "BK" wire between instruments and ground. REPLACE voltmeter.

FM9099100292000X

Fig. 24   Charging system indicator diagnosis. 1992 Probe

SYMPTOM CHART

CONDITION	POSSIBLE SOURCE	ACTION
• Charging System Gauge Does Not Work	• Fuse. • Circuit. • Instrument cluster printed circuit board. • Charging system gauge.	• GO to VG1.
• Charging System Gauge Always Reads Low	• Circuit. • Charging system gauge.	• GO to VG4.
• Charging System Gauge Always Reads High	• Charging system gauge.	• GO to VG4.
• Charging System Gauge Is Inaccurate	• Circuit. • Charging system gauge.	• GO to VG4.

Pinpoint Tests — Charging System Gauge

TEST STEP	RESULT	▶	ACTION TO TAKE
VG1 CHECK FUSE • Key OFF. • Check the 15A METER fuse located in the interior fuse panel. • **Is the fuse OK?**	Yes No	▶ ▶	GO to **VG4**. GO to **VG2**.
VG2 CHECK SYSTEM • Key OFF. • Replace the 15A METER fuse. • Key ON. • **Does the fuse fail again?**	Yes No	▶ ▶	GO to **VG3**. GO to **VG4**.

FM9099300293010X

Fig. 25   Charging system indicator diagnosis (Part 1 of 3). 1993–94 Probe

TEST STEP		RESULT	▶	ACTION TO TAKE
VG3	CHECK FOR SHORT TO GROUND			
	• Key OFF. • Locate and disconnect the 14-pin instrument cluster connector and the 14-pin interior fuse panel connector. • Measure the resistance of the "BK/Y" wire between the 14-pin interior fuse panel connector and ground. • Is the resistance less than 5 ohms?	Yes	▶	SERVICE the "BK/Y" wire.
		No	▶	REPLACE the 15A METER fuse. GO to VG4

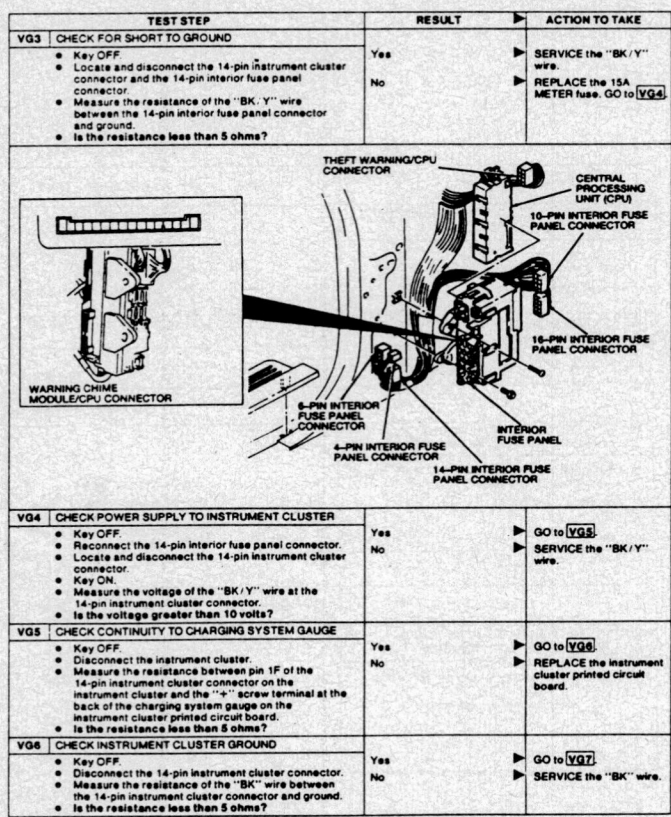

TEST STEP		RESULT	▶	ACTION TO TAKE
VG4	CHECK POWER SUPPLY TO INSTRUMENT CLUSTER			
	• Key OFF. • Reconnect the 14-pin interior fuse panel connector. • Locate and disconnect the 14-pin instrument cluster connector. • Key ON. • Measure the voltage of the "BK/Y" wire at the 14-pin instrument cluster connector. • Is the voltage greater than 10 volts?	Yes	▶	GO to VG5
		No	▶	SERVICE the "BK/Y" wire.
VG5	CHECK CONTINUITY TO CHARGING SYSTEM GAUGE			
	• Key OFF. • Disconnect the instrument cluster. • Measure the resistance between pin 1F of the 14-pin instrument cluster connector on the instrument cluster and the "+" screw terminal at the back of the charging system gauge on the instrument cluster printed circuit board. • Is the resistance less than 5 ohms?	Yes	▶	GO to VG6
		No	▶	REPLACE the instrument cluster printed circuit board.
VG6	CHECK INSTRUMENT CLUSTER GROUND			
	• Key OFF. • Disconnect the 14-pin instrument cluster connector. • Measure the resistance of the "BK" wire between the 14-pin instrument cluster connector and ground. • Is the resistance less than 5 ohms?	Yes	▶	GO to VG7
		No	▶	SERVICE the "BK" wire.

FM9099300293020X

Fig. 25   Charging system indicator diagnosis (Part 2 of 3). 1993–94 Probe

CONDITION	POSSIBLE SOURCE	ACTION
• Gauge Always Reads Low	• Open signal wire. • Open power wires. • Damaged voltage gauge. • Corroded or loose connections. • Charging system.	• Go to A1.
• Gauge Always Reads High	• Damaged voltage gauge. • Corroded or loose connections. • Charging system.	• Go to A1.
• Gauge Is Inaccurate	• Damaged voltage gauge. • Corroded or loose connections.	• Go to A1.

TEST STEP		RESULT	▶	ACTION TO TAKE
A1	CHECK METER FUSE			
	• Locate interior fuse panel. • Check 10 amp METER fuse. • Is fuse OK?	Yes	▶	GO to A4.
		No	▶	GO to A2.
A2	CHECK SYSTEM			
	• Replace the 10 amp METER fuse. • Key ON. • Does fuse fail again?	Yes	▶	GO to A3.
		No	▶	GO to A4.
A3	CHECK FOR SHORTS TO GROUND			
	• Replace the 10 amp METER fuse. • Disconnect the interior fuse panel connector and instrument cluster connector. • Measure resistance of BK/Y wire at the interior fuse panel connector to ground. • Is resistance less than 5 ohms?	Yes	▶	SERVICE BK/Y wire.
		No	▶	GO to A4.
A4	CHECK FOR POWER TO VOLTAGE GAUGE			
	• Key ON. • Locate the instrument cluster connector. • Measure the voltage on the BK/Y wire at the instrument cluster connector. • Is voltage greater than 10 volts?	Yes	▶	GO to A5.
		No	▶	SERVICE BK/Y wire between instrument cluster and interior fuse panel.
A5	CHECK VOLTAGE GAUGE GROUND			
	• Measure resistance between the BK wire at instrument cluster connector and ground. • Is resistance less than 5 ohms?	Yes	▶	REPLACE voltage gauge.
		No	▶	SERVICE BK wire.

FM9099100294000X

Fig. 26   Charging system indicator diagnosis. Capri

TEST STEP		RESULT	▶	ACTION TO TAKE
VG7	CHECK CHARGING SYSTEM GAUGE GROUND			
	• Key OFF. • Disconnect the instrument cluster. • Measure the resistance between pin 1I of the 14-pin instrument cluster connector on the instrument cluster and the "—" screw terminal at the back of the charging system gauge on the instrument cluster printed circuit board. • Is the resistance less than 5 ohms?	Yes	▶	REPLACE the charging system gauge.
		No	▶	REPLACE the instrument cluster printed circuit board.

FM9099300293030X

Fig. 25   Charging system indicator diagnosis (Part 3 of 3). 1993–94 Probe

TEST STEP		RESULT	▶	ACTION TO TAKE
BG1	CHECK BOOST SENSOR SUPPLY (BOOST GAUGE NOT WORKING)			
	• Key ON. • Check for 12 volts (±1 volt) on the "BK/Y" wire at the boost sensor connector. • Is there 12 volts?	Yes	▶	GO to BG2
		No	▶	REPAIR "BK/Y" wire between boost sensor and fuse panel.
BG2	CHECK BOOST SENSOR OUTPUT (BOOST GAUGE NOT WORKING)			
	• Key ON. • Check for 2.5 volts (±.5 volt) on the "LG/Y" wire at the boost sensor connector. • Is there 2.5 volts?	Yes	▶	GO to BG4
		No	▶	GO to BG3

FM9099100299010X

Fig. 27   Turbo boost indicating system diagnosis (Part 1 of 2). Probe

TEST STEP		RESULT	▶	ACTION TO TAKE
BG3	CHECK BOOST SENSOR GROUND (BOOST GAUGE NOT WORKING)			
	• Check for continuity between ground and the "BK" wire at the boost sensor connector. • Is there continuity?	Yes	▶	REPLACE boost sensor.
		No	▶	REPAIR "BK" wire between boost sensor and ground.
BG4	CHECK BOOST SENSOR OUTPUT (BOOST GAUGE NOT WORKING)			
	• Key ON. • Check for 2.5 volts (±.5 volt) on the "LG/Y" wire at the instruments connector. • Is there 2.5 volts?	Yes	▶	GO to BG5
		No	▶	REPAIR "LG/Y" wire between instruments and boost sensor.
BG5	CHECK BOOST GAUGE (BOOST GAUGE NOT WORKING)			
	• Disconnect the boost sensor. • Place a jumper between the "Y/BL" (pin 1H) and the "LG/Y" wires at the instrument connectors. • Key ON. • Does the boost gauge read full scale?	Yes	▶	REPLACE boost sensor.
		No	▶	REPLACE tachometer.

FM9099100299020X

Fig. 27   Turbo boost indicating system diagnosis (Part 2 of 2). Probe

TURBO BOOST GAUGE — CONDITION CHART

CONDITION	POSSIBLE SOURCE	ACTION
• Turbo Boost Gauge Always Reads Low	• Open wires. • Damaged boost sensor. • Damaged boost gauge. • Blown fuse. • Corroded or loose connections.	• Go to D1.
• Turbo Boost Gauge Always Reads High	• Damaged signal wire. • Damaged boost sensor. • Damaged boost gauge.	• Go to D4.
• Turbo Boost Gauge Is Erratic	• Corroded or loose connections. • Damaged boost sensor. • Damaged boost gauge.	• Go to D4.

PINPOINT TEST D: TURBO BOOST GAUGE DIAGNOSIS

TEST STEP		RESULT	▶	ACTION TO TAKE
D1	**CHECK METER FUSE** • Locate the interior fuse panel. • Check the 10 amp METER fuse. • **Is fuse OK?**	Yes No	▶ ▶	GO to D4. GO to D2.
D2	**CHECK SYSTEM** • Replace the 10 amp METER fuse. • Key ON. • Does fuse fail again?	Yes No	▶ ▶	GO to D3. GO to D4.
D3	**CHECK FOR SHORTS TO GROUND** • Replace the 10 amp METER fuse. • Locate and disconnect the interior fuse panel connector and instrument cluster connector. • Measure resistance of BK/Y at the interior fuse panel to ground. • Is resistance less than 5 ohms?	Yes No	▶ ▶	SERVICE the BK/Y wire. GO to D4.
D4	**CHECK FOR POWER TO THE BOOST GAUGE** • Locate the instrument cluster connector. • Key ON. • Measure voltage on the BK·Y wire at the instrument cluster connector. • Is voltage greater than 10 volts?	Yes No	▶ ▶	GO to D5. SERVICE BK/Y wire.
D5	**CHECK GROUND WIRES** • Locate and disconnect the instrument cluster 8 pin connector and the boost sensor connector. • Measure the resistance on the BK wire from each connector to ground. • Is resistance less than 5 ohms?	Yes No	▶ ▶	GO to D6. SERVICE BK wire.
D6	**CHECK VOLTAGE AT BOOST SENSOR** • Locate and disconnect boost sensor connector. • Key ON. • Measure voltage across Y/GN and BK wires at the boost sensor connector. • Is the voltage greater than 10 volts?	Yes No	▶ ▶	GO to D7. SERVICE Y/GN and BK wires as needed, going to the boost sensor.

FM9099100300010X

Fig. 28 Turbo boost indicating system diagnosis (Part 1 of 2). Capri

PINPOINT TEST D: TURBO BOOST GAUGE DIAGNOSIS (Continued)

TEST STEP		RESULT	▶	ACTION TO TAKE
D7	**CHECK BOOST GAUGE SIGNAL WIRE** • Locate and disconnect instrument cluster 8-pin connector. • Disconnect boost sensor. • Measure resistance of the W/BL wire between the instrument cluster connector and boost sensor connector. • Is resistance less than 5 ohms?	Yes No	▶ ▶	GO to D8. SERVICE W/BL wire.
D8	**CHECK TURBO BOOST GAUGE** • Locate the instrument cluster 8 pin connector. • Key ON. • Ground W/BL wire at the turbo boost gauge (instrument cluster connector). • Does the turbo boost gauge read low? • Apply 12 volts to W/BL wire at the turbo boost gauge (instrument cluster connector). • Does turbo boost gauge read high?	Yes No	▶ ▶	GO to D9. REPLACE turbo boost gauge.
D9	**CHECK BOOST SENSOR** • Disconnect boost sensor connector. • Place a jumper wire between Y/GN and W/BL wires on connector. • Key ON. • Does turbo boost gauge read high?	Yes No	▶ ▶	REPLACE boost sensor. RETURN to condition chart.

FM9099100300020X

Fig. 28 Turbo boost indicating system diagnosis (Part 2 of 2). Capri

FUEL GAUGE INOPERATIVE — POINTER DOES NOT MOVE — PINPOINT TEST A

TEST STEP		RESULT	▶	ACTION TO TAKE
A1	**VERIFY CONDITION** • Verify condition.	Gauge pointer does not move	▶	GO to A2.
		Gauge pointer moves	▶	GO to D1.
A2	**CHECK OTHER GAUGES** • Check power to cluster. With ignition ON, observe other gauges and warning indicators for proper operation. If necessary, use Rotunda Digital Volt-Ohmmeter 007-00001 or equivalent or a test lamp to verify voltage at B+ terminal of cluster connector.	Other gauges and warning indicators operate properly; voltage present at cluster	▶	GO to C1.
		Other gauges and warning indicators do not operate properly; no voltage present at cluster	▶	GO to B1.

PINPOINT TEST B: FUEL GAUGE INOPERATIVE

TEST STEP		RESULT	▶	ACTION TO TAKE
B1	**VERIFY POWER AT FUSE PANEL** • Use voltmeter to verify system voltage at load side of warning indicators fuse.	System voltage present at load side of fuse	▶	GO to C1.
		System voltage NOT present at load side of fuse	▶	GO to B2.
B2	**VERIFY POWER AT FUSE PANEL** • Use voltmeter to verify system voltage at feed side of warning indicator fuse.	System voltage present at feed side of fuse	▶	REPLACE fuse. GO to A1.
		System voltage NOT present at feed side of fuse	▶	SERVICE wiring to fuse panel. GO to A1.

FM9099200275010X

Fig. 29 Fuel indicating system diagnosis (Part 1 of 5). Models w/magnetic gauge except Escort, Mark VIII, Tracer & 1994 Mustang

PINPOINT TEST C: CLUSTER DIAGNOSIS

TEST STEP		RESULT	▶	ACTION TO TAKE
C1	**VERIFY POWER AT CLUSTER** • Cluster connectors installed. • Partially remove cluster. • Check for voltage at cluster connector and gauge terminal. • Use Rotunda Digital Volt-Ohmmeter 007-00001 or equivalent.	Voltage present at cluster connector and gauge terminal	▶	GO to C2.
		Voltage not present at cluster and/or gauge terminal	▶	SERVICE circuit. GO to A1.
C2	**VERIFY GROUND CIRCUIT AT CLUSTER** • Use Rotunda Digital Volt-Ohmmeter 007-00001 or equivalent to check continuity of cluster and gauge ground circuits.	Continuity	▶	GO to D1.
		No continuity or high resistance	▶	SERVICE circuit. GO to A1.

PINPOINT TEST D: FUEL GAUGE DIAGNOSIS

TEST STEP		RESULT	▶	ACTION TO TAKE
D1	**TEST BOX CHECK (LOW)** • Turn ignition to OFF position. • Insert Rotunda Gauge System Tester 021-00055 or equivalent in sender circuit. • Disconnect 14405 connector under instrument panel and connect tester to cluster side of connector. • Set tester to 22 ohms. • Turn ignition to RUN position, wait 60 seconds and read fuel gauge.	Fuel gauge reads empty	▶	GO to D4.
		Fuel gauge does not read empty	▶	GO to D2.
D2	**TEST BOX CHECK (RETEST)** • Turn ignition switch to OFF position. • Turn ignition switch to RUN position. • Tap lightly on instrument panel, wait 60 seconds and read fuel gauge.	Fuel gauge reads empty	▶	GO to D4.
		Fuel gauge does not read empty	▶	GO to D3.
D3	**SLOSH MODULE BYPASS TEST** • Turn ignition switch to OFF position. • Remove instrument cluster and inspect flexible circuit. • Remove anti-slosh module and connect a jumper wire from Gauge Tester directly to fuel gauge "S" terminal. • Install instrument cluster. • Turn ignition switch to RUN position and read fuel gauge.	Fuel gauge reads empty	▶	REMOVE anti-slosh module. GO to D1.
		Fuel gauge does not read empty	▶	REPLACE fuel gauge. INSTALL anti-slosh module. GO to D1.
D4	**TEST BOX CHECK (HIGH)** • Turn ignition switch to OFF position. • With Rotunda Gauge System Tester 021-00055 or equivalent connected as in Step D1, set tester to 145 ohms. • Turn ignition switch to RUN position. • Wait 60 seconds and read fuel gauge.	Fuel gauge reads full	▶	GO to D6.
		Fuel gauge does not read full	▶	GO to D5.

FM9099200275020X

Fig. 29 Fuel indicating system diagnosis (Part 2 of 5). Models w/magnetic gauge except Escort, Mark VIII, Tracer & 1994 Mustang

PINPOINT TEST D: FUEL GAUGE DIAGNOSIS (Continued)

	TEST STEP	RESULT	▶	ACTION TO TAKE
D5	ANTI-SLOSH MODULE BYPASS TEST			
	• Turn ignition switch to OFF position. • Remove instrument cluster and inspect flexible circuit. • Remove anti-slosh module. • Connect a jumper wire from tester to fuel gauge "S" terminal. • Turn ignition switch to RUN position and read fuel gauge.	Fuel gauge reads full	▶	REPLACE anti-slosh module. GO to D1.
		Fuel gauge does not read full	▶	REPLACE fuel gauge. GO to D1.
D6	INSPECT FUEL TANK			
	• Inspect fuel tank for damage or distortion.	Damaged	▶	REPLACE fuel tank.
		Not damaged	▶	GO to E1.

PINPOINT TEST E: FUEL SENDER DIAGNOSIS

	TEST STEP	RESULT	▶	ACTION TO TAKE
E1	TEST BOX CHECK—EMPTY STOP			
	• Connect one lead of Digital Volt-Ohmmeter 007-00001 or equivalent to the fuel sender signal lead and the other lead to ground. NOTE: Float rod is against empty stop (closest to filter).	Ohmmeter reads 14-18 ohms	▶	GO to E2.
		Ohmmeter reads less than 14 ohms or greater than 18 ohms	▶	REPLACE fuel sender.
E2	TEST BOX CHECK—FULL STOP			
	• Connect one lead of Digital Volt-Ohmmeter 007-00001 or equivalent to the fuel sender signal and the other lead to sender ground. NOTE: Float rod is against full stop.	Ohmmeter reads 155-165 ohms	▶	GO to E3.
		Ohmmeter reads less than 155 ohms or greater than 165 ohms	▶	REPLACE fuel sender.
E3	TEST BOX CHECK—FLOAT ROD TRAVEL			
	• Connect one lead of Digital Volt-Ohmmeter 007-00001 or equivalent to the fuel sender signal lead and the other lead to sender ground. • Slowly move float rod from full stop to empty stop.	Ohmmeter reading jumps to open condition while decreasing	▶	REPLACE fuel sender.
		Ohmmeter reading decreases slowly	▶	GO to E4.
E4	FUEL SENDER INSPECTION			
	• Inspect fuel sender. • Inspect float and float rod.	Float rod is distorted	▶	REPLACE sender.
		Float is badly distorted/damaged hitting the filter.	▶	REPLACE sender.

FM9099200275030X

Fig. 29 Fuel indicating system diagnosis (Part 3 of 5). Models w/magnetic gauge except Escort, Mark VIII, Tracer & 1994 Mustang

PINPOINT TEST G: INDICATOR STAYS OFF CONTINUALLY (Continued)

	TEST STEP	RESULT	▶	ACTION TO TAKE
G2	CHECK ELFW MODULE			
	• Turn ignition to the OFF position. • Disconnect circuit 14405 connector under instrument panel and connect a 33 ohm resistor between fuel sender feed to gauge and ground. • Turn ignition to ON position. • Wait two minutes, read gauge.	Indicator off	▶	GO to H3.
		Indicator on, gauge at 1/4 or above	▶	GO to A1.
		Indicator on, gauge at 1/8 to 1/4		Low fuel warning operating properly.
G3	CHECK INDICATOR			
	• With ignition switch in the ON-ACC position, ground indicator circuit between indicator and low fuel module.	Indicator on	▶	REPLACE ELFW/Anti-Slosh module on instrument cluster.
		Indicator off	▶	CHECK power circuit to lamp. REPLACE lamp.

FM9099200275050X

Fig. 29 Fuel indicating system diagnosis (Part 5 of 5). Models w/magnetic gauge except Escort, Mark VIII, Tracer & 1994 Mustang

PINPOINT TEST E: FUEL SENDER DIAGNOSIS (Continued)

	TEST STEP	RESULT	▶	ACTION TO TAKE
E5	HARNESS CONNECTOR CHECK—EMPTY STOP			
	• Attach all fuel indication connectors. • Move float rod to empty stop position. • Turn ignition to the RUN position. • Wait 60 seconds. • Read fuel gauge.	Gauge reads empty	▶	GO to E6.
		Gauge reads greater than empty	▶	GO to A1.
E6	HARNESS CONNECTOR CHECK—FULL STOP			
	• Attach all fuel indication connectors. • Move float rod to full stop position. • Turn ignition to the RUN position. • Wait 60 seconds. • Read fuel gauge.	Gauge reads full	▶	Fuel sender OK.
		Gauge reads less than full	▶	GO to A1.

PINPOINT TEST F: INDICATOR STAYS ON CONTINUALLY — MORE THAN 1/4 TANK OF FUEL

	TEST STEP	RESULT	▶	ACTION TO TAKE
F1	VERIFY CONDITION			
	• Verify condition.	Indicator stays on with more than 1/4 tank of fuel	▶	GO to F2.
F2	CHECK ELFW MODULE			
	• Turn ignition to the OFF position. • Disconnect Circuit 14405 connector under instrument panel and connect a 56 ohm resistor between fuel sender feed to gauge and ground. • Turn ignition to the RUN position. • Wait two minutes.	Indicator on, gauge at 1/4	▶	GO to F3.
		Indicator off	▶	REPLACE ELFW/Anti-Slosh module at instrument cluster.
F3	CHECK GAUGE AND INDICATOR			
	• Turn ignition to the OFF position. • Replace the resistor from Test F2 with a 33 ohm resistor. • Turn ignition to the RUN position. • Wait two minutes.	Indicator off	▶	GO to G3.
		Indicator on, gauge pointer indicates 1/4 tank or above	▶	GO to A1.
		Indicator on, gauge indicates 1/8 to 1/4 tank	▶	ELFW/Anti-Slosh module operating properly.

PINPOINT TEST G: INDICATOR STAYS OFF CONTINUALLY

	TEST STEP	RESULT	▶	ACTION TO TAKE
G1	VERIFY CONDITION			
	• Verify condition.	Indicator stays off	▶	GO to F2.

FM9099200275040X

Fig. 29 Fuel indicating system diagnosis (Part 4 of 5). Models w/magnetic gauge except Escort, Mark VIII, Tracer & 1994 Mustang

	TEST STEP	RESULT	▶	ACTION TO TAKE
A1	VERIFY COMPLAINT			
	• Key ON. • Observe the fuel gauge performance. • Does the gauge pointer move?	Yes	▶	GO to D1.
		No	▶	GO to A2.
A2	VERIFY CLUSTER PERFORMANCE			
	• With the ignition ON, observe the other gauges and warning lights for proper operation. • Do the other gauges and warning lights operate properly?	Yes	▶	GO to C1.
		No	▶	GO to B1.

	TEST STEP	RESULT	▶	ACTION TO TAKE
B1	VERIFY POWER AT FUSE PANEL			
	• Key ON. • Use a voltmeter to verify system voltage at the load side of the 15 amp METER fuse. • Is the voltage greater than 10 volts?	Yes	▶	GO to C1.
		No	▶	GO to B2.
B2	VERIFY POWER AT FUSE PANEL			
	• Key ON. • Use a voltmeter to verify system voltage at the feed side of the 15 amp METER fuse. • Is the voltage greater than 10 volts?	Yes	▶	REPLACE the 15 amp METER fuse; RETURN to A1.
		No	▶	REPAIR the wiring to the fuse panel; RETURN to A1.

	TEST STEP	RESULT	▶	ACTION TO TAKE
C1	VERIFY POWER AT CLUSTER			
	• Have cluster connector(s) remain intact. • Partially remove the cluster from the instrument panel. • Key ON. • Measure the voltage on the "BK/Y" wire at the instrument cluster connector to ground. • Is the voltage greater than 10 volts?	Yes	▶	GO to C2.
		No	▶	REPAIR the "BK/Y" wire; RETURN to A1.
C2	VERIFY GROUND CIRCUITRY AT CLUSTER			
	• Use an ohmmeter to check the continuity of the "BK/GN" wire at the instrument cluster connector to ground. • Is the resistance less than 5 ohms?	Yes	▶	GO to D1.
		No	▶	REPAIR the "BK/GN" wire to ground. RETURN to A1.

FM9099200276010X

Fig. 30 Fuel indicating system diagnosis (Part 1 of 6). Escort & Tracer w/magnetic gauge

TEST STEP	RESULT	▶	ACTION TO TAKE
D1 CHECK FUEL GAUGE (EMPTY)			
• Key OFF.	Yes.	▶	GO to D5.
• Disconnect the fuel gauge sending unit.	No	▶	GO to D2.
• Connect one lead of the Rotunda Gauge System Tester (021-00055 or equivalent) to the "Y" wire at the fuel gauge sending unit connector and the other lead to ground.			
• Set the tester to 22 ohms.			
• Key ON.			
• Wait one minute.			
• Read the fuel gauge.			
• Does the fuel gauge read E (empty)?			
D2 RE-CHECK FUEL GAUGE (EMPTY)			
• Place the ignition switch in the OFF position. Then return to the ON position. Tap on the instrument panel.	Yes	▶	GO to D5.
• Wait one minute.	No	▶	GO to D3.
• Read the fuel gauge.			
• Does the fuel gauge read E (empty)?			
D3 CHECK PRINTED CIRCUIT BOARD			
• Key OFF.	Yes	▶	GO to D4.
• Disconnect the instrument cluster and anti-slosh module.	No	▶	REPLACE the instrument cluster printed circuit board.
• Measure the resistance of the circuit between the S-terminal of the fuel gauge and the anti-slosh module.			
• Is the resistance less than 5 ohms?			
D4 CHECK ANTI-SLOSH MODULE (EMPTY)			
• Turn the ignition switch to the OFF position.	Yes	▶	REPLACE the anti-slosh module; RETURN to D1.
• Remove instrument cluster. Inspect the flex circuit.	No	▶	REPLACE the fuel gauge. Install the anti-slosh module and RETURN to D1.
• Remove the slosh module.			
• Connect the jumper wire from the Gauge Tester directly to the fuel gauge S-terminal.			
• Install the instrument cluster.			
• Turn the ignition switch to the ON position.			
• Read the fuel gauge.			
• Does the fuel gauge read E (empty)?			
D5 CHECK FUEL GAUGE SENDING UNIT WIRE			
• Key OFF.	Yes	▶	GO to D6.
• Disconnect the instrument cluster and the fuel gauge sending unit.	No	▶	SERVICE the "Y" wire between the instrument cluster and the fuel gauge sending unit.
• Measure the resistance of the "Y" wire between the instrument cluster and the fuel gauge sending unit.			
• Is the resistance less than 5 ohms?			
D6 CHECK FUEL SENDING UNIT GROUND			
• Key OFF.	Yes	▶	GO to D7.
• Measure the resistance of the "BK/GN" wire at the fuel gauge sending unit connector to ground.	No	▶	SERVICE the "BK/GN" wire from the fuel gauge sending unit to ground.
• Is the resistance less than 5 ohms?			

FM9099200276020X

Fig. 30 Fuel indicating system diagnosis (Part 2 of 6). Escort & Tracer w/magnetic gauge

TEST STEP	RESULT	▶	ACTION TO TAKE
F3 CHECK FLOAT ROD TRAVEL			
• Remove the fuel gauge sending unit from the fuel tank.	Ohmmeter reading jumps to open condition while decreasing	▶	REPLACE the fuel gauge sending unit.
• Connect a Digital-Voltmeter-Ohmmeter to the "Y" and "BK/GN" wires at the fuel gauge sending unit.	Ohmmeter reading decreases slowly	▶	GO to F4.
• Slowly move the float rod from the full stop position to the empty stop position.			
• What does the ohmmeter reading do?			
F4 INSPECT FUEL GAUGE SENDING UNIT			
• Inspect the fuel gauge sending unit.	Float rod is distorted.	▶	REPLACE the fuel gauge sending unit.
• Inspect the float for looseness, damage, and make sure it is not hitting the filter.	Float is badly distorted/damaged. Float is hitting the filter. Float is loose on the float rod	▶	REPLACE the fuel gauge sending unit.
• Inspect the float rod for damage or distortion.			
• What is the condition of the fuel gauge sending unit?	If not distorted/damaged	▶	GO to F5.
F5 CHECK HARNESS CONNECTOR (EMPTY STOP)			
• Attach all the fuel indication connectors.	Yes	▶	GO to F6.
• Move the float rod to the empty stop position.	No	▶	GO to A1.
• Turn the ignition switch to the ON position.			
• Wait one minute.			
• Read the fuel gauge.			
• Does the fuel gauge read empty?			
F6 CHECK HARNESS CONNECTOR (FULL STOP)			
• Attach all the fuel indication connectors.	Yes	▶	Fuel gauge sending unit checks OK.
• Move the float rod to the full stop position.	No	▶	GO to A1.
• Turn the ignition switch to the ON position.			
• Wait one minute.			
• Read the fuel gauge.			
• Does the fuel gauge read full?			

Low Fuel Warning Light Stays On Continually — More than 1/4 Tank Fuel Indication

TEST STEP	RESULT	▶	ACTION TO TAKE
G1 VERIFY CONDITION			
• Verify the condition.	Indicator lamp stays on with more than 1/4 tank fuel gauge indication	▶	GO to G2.

FM9099200276040X

Fig. 30 Fuel indicating system diagnosis (Part 4 of 6). Escort & Tracer w/magnetic gauge

TEST STEP	RESULT	▶	ACTION TO TAKE
D7 CHECK FUEL GAUGE (FULL)			
• Key OFF.	Yes	▶	GO to D9.
• Disconnect the fuel gauge sending unit.	No	▶	GO to D8.
• Connect one lead of the Rotunda Gauge System Tester (021-00055 or equivalent) to the "Y" wire at the fuel gauge sending unit connector and the other lead to ground.			
• Set the tester to 145 ohms.			
• Key ON.			
• Wait one minute.			
• Read the fuel gauge.			
• Does the fuel gauge read F (full)?			
D8 CHECK ANTI-SLOSH MODULE (FULL)			
• Turn the ignition switch to the OFF position.	Yes	▶	REPLACE the anti-slosh module; RETURN to D1.
• Remove the instrument cluster. Inspect the flex circuit.	No	▶	REPLACE the fuel gauge; RETURN to D1.
• Remove the slosh module.			
• Connect the jumper wire from the Gauge Tester directly to the fuel gauge S-terminal.			
• Install the instrument cluster.			
• Turn the ignition switch to the ON position.			
• Read the fuel gauge.			
• Does the fuel gauge read F (full)?			
D9 FUEL SENDER DIAGNOSIS			
• Inspect the fuel tank for distortion or damage.	Yes	▶	GO to F1.
• Is the fuel tank OK?	No	▶	REPLACE the fuel tank.

Fuel Gauge Not Operating Correctly

TEST STEP	RESULT	▶	ACTION TO TAKE
F1 CHECK FUEL GAUGE SENDING UNIT (EMPTY)			
• Remove the fuel gauge sending unit from the fuel tank.	Yes	▶	GO to F2.
• Connect a Digital-Voltmeter-Ohmmeter to the "Y" and "BK/GN" wires at the fuel gauge sending unit.	No	▶	REPLACE the fuel gauge sending unit.
• Adjust the float rod to the empty stop position (closest to the filter).			
• Is the resistance between 14-18 ohms?			
F2 CHECK FUEL GAUGE SENDING UNIT (FULL)			
• Remove the fuel gauge sending unit from the fuel tank.	Yes	▶	GO to F3.
• Connect a Digital-Voltmeter-Ohmmeter to the "Y" and "BK/GN" wires at the fuel gauge sending unit.	No	▶	REPLACE the fuel gauge sending unit.
• Adjust the float rod to the full stop position.			
• Is the resistance between 155-185 ohms?			

FM9099200276030X

Fig. 30 Fuel indicating system diagnosis (Part 3 of 6). Escort & Tracer w/magnetic gauge

TEST STEP	RESULT	▶	ACTION TO TAKE
G2 CHECK ANTI-SLOSH MODULE			
• Key OFF.	Indicator lamp is OFF. Gauge pointer should indicate approximately 1/4 tank	▶	GO to G3.
• Disconnect the fuel gauge sending unit.			
• Connect one lead of the Rotunda Gauge System Tester (021-00055 or equivalent) to the "Y" wire at the fuel gauge sending unit connector (leading to the instrument cluster) and the other lead to ground.	Indicator lamp is ON	▶	REPLACE the anti-slosh module at the instrument cluster.
• Set the tester to 56 ohms.			
• Key ON.			
• Wait one minute.			
• Read the fuel gauge.			
• What are the conditions?			
G3 CHECK GAUGE AND LAMP			
• Replace the resistor from test step G2 with a 30 ohm resistor and follow the procedure outlined in test step G2.	Indicator lamp is OFF	▶	GO to H3.
• What are the conditions?	Lamp is ON, gauge is at 1/4 or above	▶	GO to A1.
	Indicator lamp is ON. Gauge pointer should indicate approximately 1/8 to 1/16 tank	▶	Low fuel warning system operates properly.

Low Fuel Warning Light Stays Off Continually

TEST STEP	RESULT	▶	ACTION TO TAKE
H1 VERIFY CONDITION			
• Verify vehicle is equipped with a low fuel warning feature.	Indicator lamp stays OFF	▶	GO to H2.
• Verify the condition.			
H2 CHECK ANTI-SLOSH/LFW MODULE			
• Key OFF.	Indicator lamp is OFF	▶	GO to H3.
• Disconnect the fuel gauge sending unit.	Lamp is ON, gauge is at 1/4 tank or above	▶	GO to A1.
• Connect one lead of the Rotunda Gauge System Tester (021-00055 or equivalent) to the "Y" wire at the fuel gauge sending unit connector (leading to the instrument cluster) and the other lead to ground.	Indicator lamp is ON. Gauge pointer should indicate approximately 1/8 to 1/16 tank	▶	Low fuel warning system operates properly.
• Set the tester to 30 ohms.			
• Key ON.			
• Wait one minute.			
• Read the fuel gauge.			
• What are the conditions?			
H3 CHECK LOW FUEL WARNING LIGHT			
• Turn the ignition switch to the ON position.	Yes	▶	REPLACE the anti-slosh module on the instrument cluster.
• Ground the low fuel warning light between the light and the anti-slosh module.	No	▶	GO to H4.
• Does the low fuel warning light illuminate?			

FM9099200276050X

Fig. 30 Fuel indicating system diagnosis (Part 5 of 6). Escort & Tracer w/magnetic gauge

	TEST STEP	RESULT	▶	ACTION TO TAKE
H4	**CHECK LOW FUEL WARNING INDICATOR LIGHT POWER CIRCUIT**			
	• Disconnect the instrument cluster connector. • Key ON. • Measure the voltage on the "BK/Y" wire at the instrument cluster connector. • Is the voltage greater than 10 volts?	Yes No	▶ ▶	REPLACE the low fuel warning indicator light. REPLACE the 15 amp METER fuse and/or SERVICE the "BK/Y" wire.

FM9099200276060X

Fig. 30   Fuel indicating system diagnosis (Part 6 of 6).
Escort & Tracer w/magnetic gauge

PINPOINT TEST A
FUEL GAUGE INOPERATIVE—POINTER DOES NOT MOVE

	TEST STEP	RESULT	▶	ACTION TO TAKE
A1	**VERIFY CONDITION**			
	• Verify condition. • Does pointer move?	No Yes	▶ ▶	GO to A2. GO to D1.
A2	**CHECK OTHER GAUGES**			
	• Check power to cluster. With ignition ON, observe other gauges and warning indicators for proper operation. If necessary, use Rotunda Digital Volt-Ohmmeter 007-00001 or equivalent or a test lamp to verify voltage at B+ terminal of cluster connector. • Does gauges and warning indicators operate properly and is voltage present at cluster?	Yes No	▶ ▶	GO to A3. GO to B1.
A3	**CHECK POWER AT MESSAGE CENTER**			
	• With ignition switch in RUN, observe message center display. • Does message center display illuminate and is voltage present at message center?	Yes No	▶ ▶	GO to D1. GO to B1.

PINPOINT TEST B
FUEL GAUGE INOPERATIVE

	TEST STEP	RESULT	▶	ACTION TO TAKE
B1	**VERIFY POWER AT FUSE PANEL**			
	• Use voltmeter to verify system voltage at load side of fuse. • Is voltage present at load side of fuse?	Yes No	▶ ▶	GO to C1. GO to B2.
B2	**VERIFY POWER AT FUSE PANEL**			
	• Use voltmeter to verify system voltage at feed side of fuse. • Is voltage present at feed side of fuse?	Yes No	▶ ▶	REPLACE fuse. GO to A1. SERVICE wiring to fuse panel. GO to A1.

FM9099300277010X

Fig. 31   Fuel indicating system diagnosis (Part 1 of 5).
Mark VIII

PINPOINT TEST C
CLUSTER DIAGNOSIS

	TEST STEP	RESULT	▶	ACTION TO TAKE
C1	**VERIFY POWER AT CLUSTER**			
	• Cluster and message center connectors installed. • Partially remove cluster. • Check for voltage at cluster connector, message center connector and gauge terminal. • Use Rotunda Digital Volt-Ohmmeter 007-00001 or equivalent. • Is voltage at cluster connector, message center connector and gauge terminal?	Yes No	▶ ▶	GO to C2. SERVICE circuit. GO to A1.
C2	**VERIFY GROUND CIRCUIT AT CLUSTER**			
	• Use Rotunda Digital Volt-Ohmmeter 007-00001 or equivalent to check continuity of cluster, message center and gauge ground circuits. • Is there continuity?	Yes No	▶ ▶	GO to D1. SERVICE circuit. GO to A1.

Instrument Cluster Printed Circuit

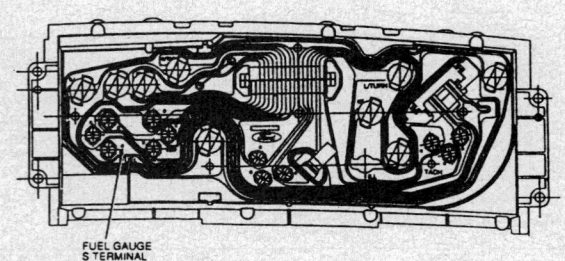

FUEL GAUGE
S TERMINAL

PINPOINT TEST D
FUEL GAUGE DIAGNOSIS

	TEST STEP	RESULT	▶	ACTION TO TAKE
D1	**TEST BOX CHECK (LOW)**			
	• Turn ignition to OFF position. • Insert Rotunda Instrument Gauge System Tester 021-00055 or equivalent in sender circuit. • Disconnect 14405 connector at RH cowl panel and connect tester to message center side of connector. • Set tester to 22 ohms. • Turn ignition to RUN position, wait 60 seconds and read fuel gauge. • Does gauge read EMPTY?	Yes No	▶ ▶	GO to D4. GO to D2.
D2	**TEST BOX CHECK (RETEST)**			
	• Turn ignition switch to OFF position. • Turn ignition switch to RUN position. • Tap lightly on instrument panel, wait 60 seconds and read fuel gauge. • Does gauge read EMPTY?	Yes No	▶ ▶	GO to D4. GO to D3.

FM9099300277020X

Fig. 31   Fuel indicating system diagnosis (Part 2 of 5).
Mark VIII

PINPOINT TEST D
FUEL GAUGE DIAGNOSIS (Continued)

	TEST STEP	RESULT	▶	ACTION TO TAKE
D3	**MESSAGE CENTER BYPASS TEST**			
	• Turn ignition switch to OFF position. • Remove message center and inspect flexible circuit. • Connect Gauge Tester directly to fuel gauge 'S' terminal. • Install instrument cluster. • Turn ignition switch to RUN position and read fuel gauge. • Does gauge read EMPTY?	Yes No	▶ ▶	GO to D6. REPLACE fuel gauge. INSTALL message center. GO to D1.
D4	**TEST BOX CHECK (HIGH)**			
	• Turn ignition switch to OFF position. • With Rotunda Gauge System Tester 021-00055 or equivalent connected as in Step D1, set tester to 145 ohms. • Turn ignition switch to RUN position. • Wait 60 seconds and read fuel gauge. • Does gauge read FULL?	Yes No	▶ ▶	GO to D8. GO to D5.
D5	**MESSAGE CENTER BYPASS TEST**			
	• Turn ignition switch to OFF position. • Remove instrument cluster and inspect flexible circuit. • Remove message center. • Connect gauge tester to fuel gauge 'S' terminal. • Turn ignition switch to RUN position and read fuel gauge. • Does gauge read FULL?	Yes No	▶ ▶	GO to D6. REPLACE fuel gauge. GO to D1.
D6	**CHECK MESSAGE CENTER CONTINUITY**			
	• Turn ignition switch to OFF. • Remove message center. • Connect jumper wire between Pin 3 and Pin 4 of message center connector. • Is there continuity between fuel tank sending unit and pump and fuel gauge?	Yes No	▶ ▶	REPLACE message center. GO to D7.
D7	**CHECK CONTINUITY BETWEEN MESSAGE CENTER AND FUEL GAUGE**			
	• Use Rotunda Digital Volt-Ohmmeter 007-00001 or equivalent to check continuity between message center and fuel gauge. • Is there continuity?	Yes No	▶ ▶	GO to D8. SERVICE open in circuit 29 (Y/W) between message center and fuel tank sending unit and pump.
D8	**INSPECT FUEL TANK**			
	• Inspect fuel tank for damage or distortion. • Is there damage?	Yes No	▶ ▶	REPLACE fuel tank. GO to E1.

PINPOINT TEST E
FUEL SENDER DIAGNOSIS

	TEST STEP	RESULT	▶	ACTION TO TAKE
E1	**TEST BOX CHECK—EMPTY STOP**			
	• Connect one lead of Digital Volt-Ohmmeter 007-00001 or equivalent, to the fuel sender signal lead and the other lead to ground. NOTE: Float rod is against empty stop (closest to filter).	Ohmmeter reads 14-18 ohm Ohmmeter reads less than 14 ohm or greater than 18 ohm	▶ ▶	GO to E2. REPLACE fuel tank sending unit and pump.

FM9099300277030X

Fig. 31   Fuel indicating system diagnosis (Part 3 of 5).
Mark VIII

PINPOINT TEST E
FUEL SENDER DIAGNOSIS (Continued)

	TEST STEP	RESULT	►	ACTION TO TAKE
E2	TEST BOX CHECK—FULL STOP			
	• Connect one lead of Digital Volt-Ohmmeter 007-00001 or equivalent, to the fuel sender signal lead and the other lead to sender ground. NOTE: Float rod is against full stop.	Ohmmeter reads 155-165 ohms	►	GO to E3.
		Ohmmeter reads less than 155 ohms or greater than 165 ohms	►	REPLACE fuel tank sending unit and pump.
E3	TEST BOX CHECK—FLOAT ROD LEVEL			
	• Connect one lead to Digital Volt-Ohmmeter 007-00001 or equivalent, to the fuel sender signal lead and the other lead to sender ground. • Slowly move float rod from full stop to empty stop.	Ohmmeter reading jumps to open condition while decreasing	►	REPLACE fuel tank sending unit and pump.
		Ohmmeter reading decreases slowly	►	GO to E4.
E4	FUEL SENDER INSPECTION			
	• Inspect fuel sender. • Inspect float and float rod.	Float rod is distorted	►	REPLACE fuel tank sending unit and pump.
		Float is badly distorted/damaged hitting the filter	►	REPLACE fuel tank sending unit and pump. GO to E5.
E5	HARNESS CONNECTOR CHECK—EMPTY STOP			
	• Attach all fuel indication connectors. • Move float rod to EMPTY STOP position. • Turn ignition to RUN position. • Wait 60 seconds. • Read fuel gauge. • Does gauge read EMPTY?	Yes	►	GO to E6.
		No	►	GO to A1.
E6	HARNESS CONNECTOR CHECK—FULL STOP			
	• Attach all fuel indication connectors. • Move float rod to FULL STOP position. • Turn ignition to RUN position. • Wait 60 seconds. • Read fuel gauge. • Does gauge read FULL?	Yes	►	Fuel sender OK.
		No	►	GO to A1.

PINPOINT TEST F
LOW FUEL LEVEL WARNING MESSAGE STAYS ON CONTINUALLY—MORE THAN 1/4 TANK OF FUEL

	TEST STEP	RESULT	►	ACTION TO TAKE
F1	VERIFY CONDITION			
	• Verify condition.	Warning message stays on with more than 1/4 tank showing on gauge	►	REFER to for Low Fuel Level Warning Diagnosis.

PINPOINT TEST G
LOW FUEL LEVEL WARNING STAYS OFF CONTINUALLY

	TEST STEP	RESULT	►	ACTION TO TAKE
G1	VERIFY CONDITION			
	• Verify condition.	Warning message stays off with less than 1/4 tank showing on gauge	►	REFER to for Low Fuel Level Warning Diagnosis.

FM9099300277040X

Fig. 31   Fuel indicating system diagnosis (Part 4 of 5). Mark VIII

Fuel Level Warning (LOW FUEL LEVEL)

	CONDITION	POSSIBLE SOURCE	ACTION
•	Higher Than Expected RANGE Readings	• Open in circuit between message center and PCM. • No fuel flow signal from PCM.	• Check continuity of circuit 305 (LB/PK). Service as required. • Verify that output from PCM Pin 34 is greater than 0 volts but less than 12 volts (about 2 volts at idle). If no voltage is present, replace PCM.
		• Improper message center grounds.	• Check continuity to ground at message center Pin 28 and Pin 35. Service as required.
		• Incorrect PCM.	• Verify that correct PCM is installed in vehicle.
		• Intermittent opens in circuit from fuel sender.	• Verify fuel sender operation.
•	Lower Than Expected RANGE Readings	• Open in circuit between message center and VSS. • Intermittent or no speed signal from VSS.	• Check continuity of circuit 150 (DG/W). Service as required. • Verify speedometer operation. If OK, verify speed signal between message center Pin 11 and Pin 28 using an A/C voltmeter. Voltage should be between 1 volt and 6 volts. If no voltage is present, service circuits 150 (DG/W) and 359 (GY/R).
		• Improper grounding.	• Check continuity to ground at message center Pin 28 and Pin 35. Service as required.
•	Continuous Display of FUEL LEVEL ERROR Message	• Open circuit between message center and fuel sender. • Open circuit between fuel sender and ground. • Worn or damaged fuel sender. • Message center inoperative.	• Check continuity of circuit 29 (Y/W). Service as required. • Check continuity of circuit 359 (GY/R). Service as required. • Verify that input on message center Pin 3 is 15-160 ohms with ignition in RUN. If FUEL LEVEL ERROR is still displayed, replace message center.

FM9099300277050X

Fig. 31   Fuel indicating system diagnosis (Part 5 of 5). Mark VIII

PINPOINT TEST B: FUEL LEVEL READS ERRONEOUSLY

	TEST STEP	RESULT	►	ACTION TO TAKE
B1	VERIFY POWER AT FUSE PANEL			
	• Use voltmeter to verify system voltage at load side of warning indicator Fuse 15 (10A). • Is voltage present at load side of fuse	Yes	►	GO to B3.
		No	►	GO to B2.
B2	VERIFY POWER AT FUSE PANEL			
	• Use voltmeter to verify system voltage at feed side of warning indicator Fuse 15 (10A). • Is voltage present at feed side of fuse?	Yes	►	REPLACE fuse. RESTORE vehicle.
		No	►	SERVICE wiring to fuse panel. RETEST system.
B3	VERIFY POWER AT CLUSTER			
	• Instrument cluster connectors installed. • Partially remove instrument cluster. • Check for voltage at instrument cluster connector and gauge terminal. • Use Rotunda Digital Volt-Ohmmeter 007-00001 or equivalent. • Is voltage at instrument cluster connector and gauge terminal?	Yes	►	GO to B4.
		No	►	SERVICE Circuit 640 (R/Y) for open circuit. RESTORE vehicle. RETEST system.
B4	VERIFY GROUND CIRCUIT AT CLUSTER			
	• Use Rotunda Digital Volt-Ohmmeter 007-00001 or equivalent to check continuity of instrument cluster and gauge ground circuits. • Is there continuity?	Yes	►	GO to B5.
		No	►	SERVICE circuit 563 (O/Y) for open circuit. RESTORE vehicle. RETEST system.

FM9099400328010X

Fig. 32   Fuel indicating system diagnosis (Part 1 of 3). 1994 Mustang

PINPOINT TEST B: FUEL LEVEL READS ERRONEOUSLY (Continued)

	TEST STEP	RESULT	►	ACTION TO TAKE
B5	CHECK TEST BOX (LOW)			
	• Turn ignition switch to OFF position. • Insert Rotunda Instrument Gauge System Tester 021-00055 or equivalent in sender circuit. • Disconnect rear lamp wiring connector under instrument panel and connect tester to cluster side of connector. • Set tester to 22 ohms. • Turn ignition switch to RUN position, wait 60 seconds and read fuel gauge. • Does fuel gauge read EMPTY?	Yes	►	GO to B8.
		No	►	GO to B6.
B6	CHECK TEST BOX (RETEST)			
	• Turn ignition switch to OFF position. • Turn ignition switch to RUN position. • Tap lightly on instrument cluster, wait 60 seconds and read fuel gauge. • Does fuel gauge read EMPTY?	Yes	►	GO to B8.
		No	►	GO to B7.
B7	ANTI-SLOSH MODULE BYPASS TEST			
	• Turn ignition switch to OFF position. • Remove instrument cluster and inspect instrument cluster printed circuit. • Remove instrument cluster gauge amplifier and connect a jumper wire from Gauge Tester directly to fuel gauge 'SIG' terminal. • Install instrument cluster. • Turn ignition switch to RUN position and read fuel gauge. • Does fuel gauge read EMPTY?	Yes	►	REPLACE instrument cluster gauge amplifier. RESTORE vehicle. RETEST system.
		No	►	REPLACE fuel gauge. INSTALL instrument cluster gauge amplifier. RESTORE vehicle. RETEST system.
B8	CHECK TEST BOX (HIGH)			
	• Turn ignition switch to OFF position. • With Rotunda Gauge System Tester 021-00055 or equivalent connected as in Step D1, set tester to 145 ohms. • Turn ignition switch to RUN position. • Wait 60 seconds and read fuel gauge. • Does fuel gauge read FULL?	Yes	►	GO to B10.
		No	►	GO to B9.
B9	ANTI-SLOSH MODULE BYPASS TEST			
	• Turn ignition switch to OFF position. • Remove instrument cluster and inspect instrument cluster printed circuit. • Remove instrument cluster gauge amplifier. • Connect a jumper wire from tester to fuel gauge 'SIG' terminal. • Turn ignition switch to RUN position and read fuel gauge. • Does fuel gauge read FULL?	Yes	►	REPLACE instrument cluster gauge amplifier. RESTORE vehicle. RETEST system.
		No	►	REPLACE fuel gauge. RESTORE vehicle. RETEST system.
B10	INSPECT FUEL TANK			
	• Inspect fuel tank for damage or distortion. • Is there damage?	Yes	►	REPLACE fuel tank. RESTORE vehicle. RETEST system.
		No	►	GO to B11.
B11	CHECK TEST BOX - EMPTY STOP			
	• Connect one lead of Digital Volt-Ohmmeter 007-00001 or equivalent to the fuel sender signal lead and the other lead to ground. NOTE: Float rod is against empty stop (closest to filter). • Does ohmmeter read between 14-18 ohms?	Yes	►	GO to B12.
		No	►	REPLACE fuel tank sending unit. RESTORE vehicle. RETEST system.

FM9099400328020X

Fig. 32   Fuel indicating system diagnosis (Part 2 of 3). 1994 Mustang

PINPOINT TEST B: FUEL LEVEL READS ERRONEOUSLY (Continued)

TEST STEP		RESULT	▶	ACTION TO TAKE
B12	CHECK TEST BOX - FULL STOP			
	• Connect one lead of Digital Volt-Ohmmeter 007-00001 or equivalent to the fuel sender signal lead and the other lead to sender ground. NOTE: Float rod is against full stop. • Does ohmmeter read between 155-165 ohms?	Yes No	▶ ▶	GO to B13. REPLACE fuel tank sending unit. RESTORE vehicle. RETEST system.
B13	CHECK FLOAT ROD LEVEL			
	• Connect one lead to Digital Volt-Ohmmeter 007-00001 or equivalent to the fuel sender signal lead and the other lead to sender ground. • Slowly move float rod from full stop to empty stop. • Does ohmmeter reading slowly decrease?	Yes No	▶ ▶	GO to B14. REPLACE fuel tank sending unit. RESTORE vehicle. RETEST system.
B14	CHECK ANTI-SLOSH/LOW FUEL WARNING			
	• Turn ignition switch to the OFF position. • Connect Rotunda Instrument Gauge System Tester 021-00055 or equivalent in sender circuit. • Disconnect Circuit rear lamp wiring connector under instrument panel and connect tester to cluster side of connector. • Set tester to 56 ohms. • Turn ignition switch to the RUN position, wait 60 seconds. • Is low fuel indicator on?	Yes No	▶ ▶	REPLACE instrument cluster gauge amplifier/low fuel warning module. RESTORE vehicle. RETEST system. GO to B15.
B15	CHECK GAUGE AND INDICATOR			
	• Turn ignition switch to the OFF position. • Reset tester to 33 ohms. • Turn ignition switch to the RUN position. • Wait 60 seconds. • Is indicator on, and gauge showing 1/8 tank?	Yes No	▶ ▶	Instrument cluster gauge amplifier operating properly. RESTORE vehicle. RETEST system. GO to B16.
B16	CHECK INDICATOR			
	• With ignition switch in the ON position, ground indicator circuit between indicator and low fuel level warning switch. • Is indicator on?	Yes No	▶ ▶	REPLACE instrument cluster gauge amplifier. RESTORE vehicle. RETEST system. GO to B17.
B17	CHECK INDICATOR BULB			
	• Turn ignition switch switch off. • Remove instrument cluster as outlined. • Remove indicator bulb using an ohmmeter check bulb continuity. • Does bulb test OK?	Yes No	▶ ▶	REPLACE instrument cluster printed circuit. RESTORE vehicle. RETEST system. REPLACE damaged indicator bulb. RESTORE vehicle. RETEST system.

FM9099400328030X

Fig. 32 Fuel indicating system diagnosis (Part 3 of 3). 1994 Mustang

TEST STEP		RESULT	▶	ACTION TO TAKE
A8	CHECK FUEL TANK SENDING UNIT GROUND			
	• Measure resistance between the BK wire at the fuel tank sending unit and ground. • Is resistance less than 5 ohms?	Yes No	▶ ▶	GO to A9. SERVICE the BK wire.
A9	CHECK FUEL GAUGE SYSTEM			
	• Key ON. • Does fuel gauge system operate correctly?	Yes No	▶ ▶	RETURN to condition chart. REPLACE fuel tank sending unit.

FM9099100278020X

Fig. 33 Fuel indicating system diagnosis (Part 2 of 2). Capri

FUEL GAUGE — CONDITION CHART

CONDITION	POSSIBLE SOURCE	ACTION
• Fuel Gauge Always Reads Empty	• Open or damaged wires. • Damaged fuel gauge. • Blown fuse. • Damaged fuel sender.	• Go to A1.
• Fuel Gauge Always Reads Full	• Yellow wire shorted to ground. • Damaged fuel gauge. • Damaged fuel sender.	• Go to A6.
• Fuel Gauge Reads Inaccurately	• Corroded connections. • Damaged fuel gauge.	• Go to A5.

TEST STEP		RESULT	▶	ACTION TO TAKE
A1	CHECK METER FUSE			
	• Locate the interior fuse panel. • Check the 10 amp METER fuse. • Is the fuse OK?	Yes No	▶ ▶	GO to A4. GO to A2.
A2	CHECK SYSTEM			
	• Replace the 10 amp METER fuse. • Key ON. • Does the fuse fail again?	Yes No	▶ ▶	GO to A3. GO to A4.
A3	CHECK FOR SHORTS TO GROUND			
	• Replace the 10 amp METER fuse. • Disconnect the interior fuse panel connector and instrument cluster connector. • Measure resistance of the BK/Y wire at the interior fuse panel connector to ground. • Is resistance less than 5 ohms?	Yes No	▶ ▶	SERVICE BK/Y wire. GO to A4.
A4	CHECK FOR POWER TO FUEL GAUGE			
	• Key ON. • Locate instrument cluster connector. • Measure voltage on the BK/Y wire at the instrument cluster connector. • Is voltage greater than 10 volts?	Yes No	▶ ▶	GO to A5. SERVICE BK/Y wire.
A5	CHECK FUEL GAUGE			
	• Key ON. • Ground Y wire at the instrument cluster connector. • Does fuel gauge read full?	Yes No	▶ ▶	GO to A6. REPLACE fuel gauge.
A6	CHECK FUEL GAUGE			
	• Apply 12 volts to Y wire at the instrument cluster connector. • Does fuel gauge read empty?	Yes No	▶ ▶	GO to A7. REPLACE fuel gauge.
A7	CHECK FUEL GAUGE WIRE CONTINUITY			
	• Remove the rear seat cushion. • Key On. • Ground Y wire at the fuel tank sending unit. • Does fuel gauge read full?	Yes No	▶ ▶	GO to A8. SERVICE Y wire between instrument cluster and fuel tank sending unit.

FM9099100278010X

Fig. 33 Fuel indicating system diagnosis (Part 1 of 2). Capri

TEST STEP		RESULT	▶	ACTION TO TAKE
FG1	INSTRUMENT RELATED SYSTEM CHECK (FUEL GAUGE NOT WORKING)			

	• Turn ignition switch to ON position (engine off).
	• Check the following items for proper operation:
	  – Fuel gauge
	  – Warning lights (Anti-Lock, Seat belt, Engine, Brake)
		Warning lights not working and fuel gauge reads empty
		
		Fuel gauge always reads empty (warning lights OK)
		
		Fuel gauge always reads full
		
		Fuel gauge not accurate
			▶
			
			▶
			
			▶
			
			▶
				GO to FG2 .
				
				GO to FG3 .
				
				GO to FG6 .
				
				GO to FG8 .

TEST STEP		RESULT	▶	ACTION TO TAKE
FG2	INSTRUMENT (METER) FUSE CHECK (WARNING LIGHTS NOT WORKING, FUEL GAUGE READS EMPTY)			
	• Check instrument (METER) fuse. • Is fuse OK?	Yes No	▶ ▶	Repair BK/Y wire from fuse panel to instrument cluster. REPLACE fuse. (Read note)

NOTE: If fuse blows again, check for shorts to ground in "BK/Y" wires between instruments and fuse panel. Repair "BK/Y" wires as needed.

FM9099100279010X

Fig. 34 Fuel indicating system diagnosis (Part 1 of 6). 1992 Probe

TEST STEP		RESULT	▶	ACTION TO TAKE
FG3	FUEL GAUGE CHECK (FUEL GAUGE ALWAYS READS EMPTY, WARNING LIGHTS OK)			
	• Ground "Y" wire at instrument (METER) connector. • Cycle the ignition switch OFF and ON. • Does fuel gauge read full?	Yes No	▶ ▶	GO to FG4 . REPLACE fuel gauge (analog cluster)

CONVENTIONAL INSTRUMENTS

FM9099100279020X

Fig. 34 Fuel indicating system diagnosis (Part 2 of 6). 1992 Probe

TEST STEP	RESULT	▶	ACTION TO TAKE
FG5 FUEL GAUGE CONTINUITY CHECK NO. 2 (FUEL GAUGE ALWAYS READS EMPTY, WARNING LIGHTS OK)			
A • Ground "BK/LG" wire at fuel tank sender unit connector. • Cycle the ignition switch OFF and ON. • Does fuel gauge read correctly?	Yes	▶	REPAIR "BK/LG" wire between fuel tank sender unit and ground.
	No	▶	GO to **B** .
B • Ground "BK/LG" wire at harness connector (at instrument cluster). • Cycle the ignition switch OFF and ON. • Does fuel gauge read correctly?	Yes	▶	REPAIR "BK/LG" wire between harness connector and instrument cluster.
	No	▶	REPLACE fuel tank sender unit. **NOTE:** Before replacing the sender unit, inspect the float arm assembly for proper attachment to the pump housing.

TEST STEP	RESULT	▶	ACTION TO TAKE
FG6 FUEL GAUGE SHORT CHECK NO. 1 (FUEL GAUGE ALWAYS READS FULL)			
• Disconnect the small instrument (METER) connector. • Cycle the ignition switch OFF and ON. • Does fuel gauge still read full?	Yes	▶	REPLACE fuel gauge (analog cluster)
	No	▶	GO to **FG7**

FM9099100279030X

Fig. 34   Fuel indicating system diagnosis (Part 3 of 6).
1992 Probe

TEST STEP	RESULT	▶	ACTION TO TAKE
FG8 FUEL GAUGE CHECK (FUEL GAUGE NOT ACCURATE)			
• Disconnect fuel tank sender unit connector. • Connect one lead of Rotunda Gauge Tester (Read note) to the "Y" wire of the connector and the other lead to ground. • Set tester to resistance values shown. • Turn ignition switch to ON position and check to see that needle indicator displays correct values. • Continue inspections for two minutes each, to correctly judge the condition. • The allowable error is twice the width of the needle. • Are fuel gauge readings correct?	Yes	▶	GO to **FG9** .
	No	▶	REPLACE fuel gauge.
NOTE: Use Rotunda "Gauge System Tester" No. 021-00055 or equivalent.			

CONVENTIONAL

7 Ω
18.5 Ω
32.5 Ω
51 Ω
95 Ω
FUEL

FM9099100279050X

Fig. 34   Fuel indicating system diagnosis (Part 5 of 6).
1992 Probe

TEST STEP	RESULT	▶	ACTION TO TAKE
FG7 FUEL GAUGE SHORT CHECK NO. 2 (FUEL GAUGE ALWAYS READS FULL)			
• Reconnect instruments (METERS) connector. • Disconnect fuel tank sender unit connector. • Cycle the ignition switch OFF and ON. • Does fuel gauge still read full?	Yes	▶	REPAIR "Y" wire between instruments and fuel tank sender unit.
	No	▶	REPLACE fuel tank sender unit. **Note:** Before replacing the sender unit, inspect the float arm assembly for proper attachment to the pump housing.

FM9099100279040X

Fig. 34   Fuel indicating system diagnosis (Part 4 of 6).
1992 Probe

TEST STEP	RESULT	▶	ACTION TO TAKE
FG9 FUEL GAUGE UNIT CHECK (FUEL GAUGE NOT ACCURATE)			

• Remove fuel tank sender unit:
  – Remove the service hole cover.
  – Disconnect the connector from the fuel tank sender unit.
  – Disconnect the main fuel hose.
  – Use a screwdriver to remove the fuel tank sender unit.
• Connect an ohmmeter to fuel tank sender unit.
• Are resistance values as listed?
	Yes	▶	CHECK for loose or dirty connections at fuel tank sender unit (connector C401).

	No	▶	REPLACE fuel tank sender unit. **NOTE:** Before replacing the sender unit, inspect the float arm assembly for proper attachment to the pump housing.

WARNING: WHEN REMOVING FUEL TANK SENDER UNIT, KEEP SPARKS, CIGARETTES, AND OPEN FLAMES AWAY FROM FUEL TANK.

FM9099100279060X

Fig. 34   Fuel indicating system diagnosis (Part 6 of 6).
1992 Probe

Symptom Chart — Fuel Gauge and Low Fuel Warning System

CONDITION	POSSIBLE SOURCE	ACTION
• Fuel Gauge Always Reads Empty	• Blown fuse. • Circuit. • Fuel sending unit. • Fuel indicator module. • Fuel gauge.	• GO to FG1.
• Fuel Gauge Not Reading Correctly	• Circuit. • Fuel sending unit. • Fuel indicator module. • Fuel gauge.	• GO to FG1.
• Fuel Gauge Always Reads Full	• Circuit. • Fuel sending unit. • Fuel indicator module. • Fuel gauge.	• GO to FG1.
• Low Fuel Warning Lamp Does Not Work	• Circuit. • Fuel indicator module. • Low fuel warning lamp bulb.	• GO to FG15.
• Low Fuel Warning Lamp Works Continuously	• Circuit. • Fuel indicator module.	• GO to FG16.

Pinpoint Tests — Fuel Gauge and Low Fuel Warning System

TEST STEP	RESULT	▶	ACTION TO TAKE
FG1 CHECK FUSE			
• Check the 15A METER fuse located in the interior fuse panel. • Is the fuse OK?	Yes	▶	GO to **FG4**
	No	▶	GO to **FG2**
FG2 CHECK SYSTEM			
• Key OFF. • Replace the 15A METER fuse. • Key ON. • Inspect the fuse. • Does the fuse fail again?	Yes	▶	GO to **FG3**
	No	▶	GO to **FG4**

FM9099300280010X

Fig. 35   Fuel indicating system diagnosis (Part 1 of 5).
1993–94 Probe

FG4	CHECK SIGNAL FROM FUEL SENDING UNIT	RESULT	▶	ACTION TO TAKE
	• Key OFF.	Yes	▶	GO to FG5
	• Locate and disconnect the fuel pump assembly connector.	No	▶	GO to FG6
	• Connect Rotunda Instrument Gauge System Tester 021-00055 or equivalent between the "R" wire on the fuel pump assembly connector and ground.			
	• Key ON.			
	• Adjust the instrument gauge system tester to the resistances shown in chart.			
	NOTE: The fuel gauge system is equipped with a fuel indicator circuit. Therefore, the instrument gauge tester must remain at the specified resistance for approximately 1 minute to allow the fuel gauge to read the proper level.			

Fuel Gauge	Resistance (ohms)
F	7.0
3 4	19.0
1 2	35.0
1 4	65.0
E	105.0
Low Fuel Warning Lamp On	90.0

	• Is the fuel gauge and low fuel warning lamp operating properly?			
FG5	CHECK FUEL SENDING UNIT GROUND			
	• Key OFF.	Yes	▶	REPLACE the fuel sending unit.
	• Disconnect the fuel pump assembly connector.	No	▶	SERVICE the "Y" or "BK" wire.
	NOTE: The "Y" wire changes to a "BK" wire at an in-line connector.			
	• Measure the resistance of the "Y" wire between the fuel pump assembly connector and ground.			
	• Is the resistance less than 5 ohms?			
FG6	CHECK POWER SUPPLY TO INSTRUMENT CLUSTER			
	• Key OFF.	Yes	▶	GO to FG7
	• Disconnect the 14-pin instrument cluster connector.	No	▶	SERVICE the "BK/Y" wire between the instrument cluster and the interior fuse panel.
	• Key ON.			
	• Measure the voltage on the "BK/Y" wire at the 14-pin instrument cluster connector.			
	• Is the voltage greater than 10 volts?			
FG7	CHECK CIRCUIT TO FUEL INDICATOR MODULE AND LOW FUEL WARNING LAMP			
	• Key OFF.	Yes	▶	GO to FG8
	• Disconnect and remove the instrument cluster.	No	▶	REPLACE the instrument cluster printed circuit board.
	• Locate the fuel indicator module on the back of the instrument cluster.			
	• Locate and disconnect the low fuel warning lamp bulb.			
	• Measure the resistance of the circuit between pin 1F of the instrument cluster and pin F of the fuel indicator module.			
	• Measure the resistance of the circuit between pin 1F of the instrument cluster and the low fuel warning lamp bulb connector.			
	• Are the resistances less than 5 ohms?			

FM9099300280030X

**Fig. 35 Fuel indicating system diagnosis (Part 3 of 5).
1993–94 Probe**

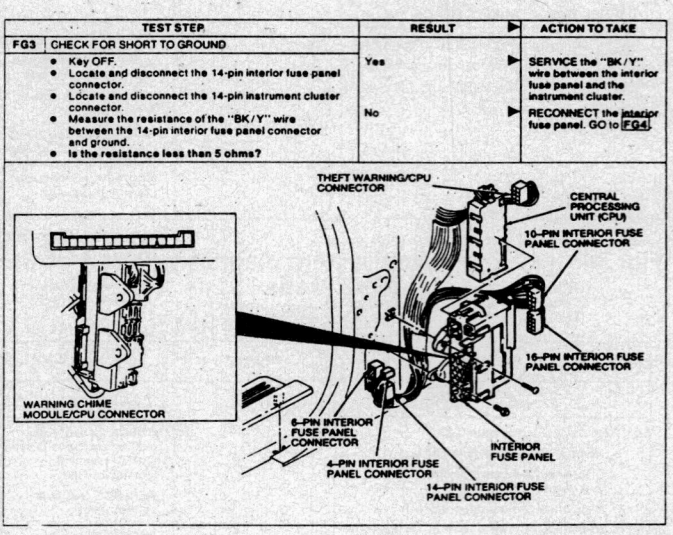

FG3	CHECK FOR SHORT TO GROUND	RESULT	▶	ACTION TO TAKE
	• Key OFF.	Yes	▶	SERVICE the "BK/Y" wire between the interior fuse panel and the instrument cluster.
	• Locate and disconnect the 14-pin interior fuse panel connector.			
	• Locate and disconnect the 14-pin instrument cluster connector.	No	▶	RECONNECT the interior fuse panel. GO to FG4.
	• Measure the resistance of the "BK/Y" wire between the 14-pin interior fuse panel connector and ground.			
	• Is the resistance less than 5 ohms?			

FM9099300280020X

**Fig. 35 Fuel indicating system diagnosis (Part 2 of 5).
1993–94 Probe**

FG8	CHECK INSTRUMENT CLUSTER GROUND	RESULT	▶	ACTION TO TAKE
	• Key OFF.	Yes	▶	GO to FG9
	• Disconnect and remove the instrument cluster.	No	▶	SERVICE the "BK" wire.
	• Measure the resistance of the "BK" wire between the instrument cluster connector pin 1I and ground.			
	• Is the resistance less than 5 ohms?			
FG9	CHECK GROUND TO FUEL INDICATOR MODULE AND FUEL GAUGE			
	• Key OFF.	Yes	▶	GO to FG10
	• Disconnect and remove the instrument cluster.	No	▶	REPLACE the instrument cluster printed circuit board.
	• Measure the resistance of the circuit between instrument cluster connector terminal pin 1I and the fuel indicator module connector pin C.			
	• Measure the resistance of the circuit between the instrument cluster connector terminal 1I and the fuel gauge "−" terminal.			
	• Are the resistances less than 5 ohms?			
FG10	CHECK WIRE BETWEEN INSTRUMENT CLUSTER AND FUEL PUMP ASSEMBLY			
	• Key OFF.	Yes	▶	GO to FG11
	• Disconnect the 14-pin instrument cluster connector.	No	▶	SERVICE the "R" and/or the "Y" wire(s) in question.
	• Disconnect the fuel pump assembly connector.			
	• Measure the resistance between the "Y" wire of the 14-pin instrument cluster connector and the "R" wire of the fuel pump assembly connector.			
	• Is the resistance less than 5 ohms?			
FG11	CHECK FOR SHORT BETWEEN INSTRUMENT CLUSTER AND FUEL PUMP ASSEMBLY			
	• Key OFF.	Yes	▶	GO to FG12
	• Disconnect the 14-pin instrument cluster connector.	No	▶	SERVICE the "Y" wire.
	• Disconnect the fuel pump assembly connector.			
	• Measure the resistance of the "Y" wire between the 14-pin instrument cluster connector and ground.			
	• Is the resistance greater than 10,000 ohms?			
FG12	CHECK FUEL SENDING UNIT INPUT TO FUEL GAUGE AND FUEL INDICATOR MODULE			
	• Key OFF.	Yes (checking fuel gauge)	▶	GO to FG13
	• Disconnect and remove the instrument cluster.			
	• Disconnect the fuel indicator module connector.	Yes (checking low fuel warning lamp)	▶	GO to FG15
	• Measure the resistance of the circuit between the instrument cluster pin 1H and the fuel indicator module connector pin A.			
	• Measure the resistance of the circuit between the instrument cluster pin 1H and the fuel gauge pin F.	No	▶	REPLACE the instrument cluster circuit board.
	• Are the resistances less than 5 ohms?			
FG13	CHECK CIRCUIT BETWEEN FUEL INDICATOR MODULE AND FUEL GAUGE			
	• Key OFF.	Yes	▶	GO to FG14
	• Disconnect and remove the instrument cluster.	No	▶	REPLACE the instrument cluster printed circuit board.
	• Disconnect the fuel indicator module connector on the back of the instrument cluster.			
	• Measure the resistance of the circuit between the fuel indicator module connector pin B and the fuel gauge "+" terminal.			
	• Is the resistance less than 5 ohms?			

FM9099300280040X

**Fig. 35 Fuel indicating system diagnosis (Part 4 of 5).
1993–94 Probe**

FG14	CHECK FUEL INDICATOR MODULE	RESULT	▶	ACTION TO TAKE
	• Key OFF.	Yes	▶	REPLACE the fuel gauge.
	• Reconnect the fuel indicator module.	No	▶	REPLACE the fuel indicator module.
	• Disconnect the 16-pin instrument cluster connector. Leave the 14-pin instrument cluster connected.			
	• Remove the "+" screw of the fuel gauge.			
	• Key ON.			
	• Measure the voltage on the "+" terminal of the fuel gauge on the instrument cluster printed circuit board.			
	• Is the voltage greater than 10 volts?			
FG15	CHECK LOW FUEL WARNING LAMP BULB			
	• Key OFF.	Yes	▶	GO to FG16
	• Remove and remove the instrument cluster.	No	▶	REPLACE the low fuel warning lamp bulb.
	• Remove the low fuel warning lamp bulb.			
	• Measure the resistance across the terminals of the low fuel warning lamp bulb.			
	• Is the resistance approximately 12.6 ohms?			
FG16	CHECK CIRCUIT BETWEEN FUEL INDICATOR MODULE AND LOW FUEL WARNING LAMP			
	• Key OFF.	Yes	▶	REPLACE the fuel indicator module.
	• Disconnect and remove the instrument cluster.	No	▶	REPLACE the instrument cluster printed circuit board.
	• Remove the low fuel warning lamp bulb.			
	• Disconnect the fuel indicator module connector on the back of the instrument cluster.			
	• Measure the resistance of the circuit between the fuel indicator module connector pin D and the low fuel warning lamp bulb connector.			
	• Is the resistance less than 5 ohms?			

FM9099300280050X

**Fig. 35 Fuel indicating system diagnosis (Part 5 of 5).
1993–94 Probe**

CONDITION	POSSIBLE SOURCE	ACTION
• Gauge Always Reads Empty	• Fuse. • Circuit. • Fuel tank sending unit. • Fuel gauge.	• GO to FG1.
• Gauge Always Reads Full	• Circuit. • Fuel tank sending unit. • Fuel gauge.	• GO to FG7.
• Gauge Inaccurate	• Wire connections. • Fuel tank sending unit. • Fuel gauge.	• GO to FG9.

TEST STEP		RESULT	▶	ACTION TO TAKE
FG1	CHECK SYSTEM INTEGRITY			
	• Visually inspect the components of the fuel gauge system. • Check for a blown fuse, damage to the fuel gauge, loose or corroded wire connections. • Does the system appear to be in good condition?	Yes No	▶ ▶	GO to FG2. SERVICE the damaged components in the system.
FG2	CHECK FUSE			
	• Check the 10 amp METER fuse. • Is the 10 amp METER fuse OK? NOTE: If the fuse fails after replacement, check for a short to ground in the "BK/Y" wire(s).	Yes No	▶ ▶	GO to FG3. REPLACE the 10 amp METER fuse.

FM9099100281010X

Fig. 36 Fuel indicating system diagnosis (Part 1 of 3). Festiva

TEST STEP		RESULT	▶	ACTION TO TAKE
FG3	CHECK INSTRUMENT CLUSTER SUPPLY			
	• Disconnect the instrument cluster connector. • Disconnect the "BK/Y" wire from the internal fuse panel. • Measure the resistance of the "BK/Y" wire between the instrument cluster connector and the interior fuse panel. • Is the resistance less than 5 ohms?	Yes No	▶ ▶	GO to FG4. SERVICE the "BK/Y" wire between the instrument cluster and internal fuse panel for an open.
FG4	CHECK FUEL GAUGE OPERATION			
	• Ground the "Y" wire at the instrument cluster connector. • Cycle the ignition key OFF and ON. • Does the fuel gauge read full?	Yes No	▶ ▶	GO to FG5. REPLACE the fuel gauge.
FG5	CHECK FUEL TANK SENDING UNIT SIGNAL			
	• Disconnect the fuel tank sending unit connector. • Ground the "Y" wire at the fuel tank sending unit connector. • Cycle the ignition key OFF and ON. • Does the fuel gauge read full?	Yes No	▶ ▶	GO to FG6. REPAIR the "Y" wire between the instrument cluster and the fuel tank sending unit.
FG6	CHECK GROUND AT FUEL TANK SENDING UNIT			
	• Disconnect the fuel tank sending unit connector. • Measure the resistance of the "BK" wire between the fuel tank sending unit connector and ground. • Is the resistance less than 5 ohms? NOTE: Before replacing the fuel tank sending unit, inspect the float arm assembly for proper attachment to the pump housing.	Yes No	▶ ▶	REPLACE the fuel tank sending unit. REFER to note. REPAIR or REPLACE the "BK" wire between the fuel tank sending unit and ground.
FG7	CHECK FOR SHORT TO FUEL GAUGE			
	• Disconnect the instrument cluster connector. • Cycle the ignition switch OFF and ON. • Does the fuel gauge still read full?	Yes No	▶ ▶	REPLACE the fuel gauge on the instrument cluster. GO to FG8.
FG8	CHECK FOR SHORT AT FUEL TANK SENDING UNIT			
	• Connect the instrument cluster. • Disconnect the fuel tank sending unit connector. • Cycle the ignition switch OFF and ON. • Does the fuel gauge still read full? NOTE: Before replacing the sending unit, inspect the float arm assembly for proper attachment to the pump housing.	Yes No	▶ ▶	REPAIR or REPLACE the "Y" wire between the instrument cluster and the fuel tank sending unit. REPLACE the fuel tank sending unit. REFER to note.

FM9099100281020X

Fig. 36 Fuel indicating system diagnosis (Part 2 of 3). Festiva

TEST STEP		RESULT	▶	ACTION TO TAKE
FG9	CHECK FUEL GAUGE FOR INACCURACY			
	• Disconnect the fuel tank sending unit connector. • Connect Rotunda Gauge System Tester 021-00055 or equivalent between the "Y" wire at the fuel tank sending unit connector and ground. • Set the tester to the resistances shown below. • Turn the key to the ON position and check to see that the needle indicator displays the correct values. • Continue the inspections for two minutes each, to correctly judge the condition. • The allowable error is twice the width of the needle. • Are the fuel gauge readings correct?	Yes No	▶ ▶	GO to FG10. REPLACE the fuel gauge.

TEST STEP		RESULT	▶	ACTION TO TAKE
FG10	CHECK RESISTANCE OF FUEL TANK SENDING UNIT			
	• Remove the service hole cover. • Disconnect the fuel tank sending unit connector. • Disconnect the main fuel hose. • Remove the fuel tank sending unit. • Measure the resistance of the fuel tank sending unit as the float arm is moved up and down. • Does the resistance vary from 1 to 105 ohms?	Yes No	▶ ▶	CHECK for loose or dirty connections at the fuel tank sending unit. REPLACE the fuel tank sending unit.

FM9099100281030X

Fig. 36 Fuel indicating system diagnosis (Part 3 of 3). Festiva

PINPOINT TEST B: FUEL GAUGE ALWAYS READS EMPTY

TEST STEP		RESULT	▶	ACTION TO TAKE
B1	CHECK FUEL TANK SENDING UNIT			
	• Perform the Fuel Tank Sending Unit component test • Is the fuel tank sending unit OK?	Yes No	▶ ▶	GO to B2. REPLACE the fuel tank sending unit.
B2	CHECK FUEL GAUGE			
	• Perform the Fuel Gauge component test • Is the fuel gauge OK?	Yes No	▶ ▶	GO to B3. REPLACE the fuel gauge.
B3	CHECK FUEL GAUGE GROUND			
	• Key off. • Disconnect the white instrument cluster connector. • Measure the resistance of the "BK/Y" wire between pin 9A of the white instrument cluster connector and ground. • Is the resistance less than 5 ohms?	Yes No	▶ ▶	GO to B4. SERVICE the "BK/Y" wire for open.
B4	CHECK FUEL TANK SENDING UNIT GROUND			
	• Key off. • Disconnect the fuel tank assembly connector. • Measure the resistance of the "BK/Y" wire between the fuel tank assembly connector and ground. • Is the resistance less than 5 ohms?	Yes No	▶ ▶	GO to B5. SERVICE the "BK/Y" wire for open.
B5	CHECK WIRE BETWEEN INSTRUMENT CLUSTER AND FUEL TANK SENDING UNIT			
	• Key off. • Disconnect the white instrument cluster connector and the fuel tank assembly connector. • Measure the resistance of the "Y/W" wire between the white instrument cluster connector and the fuel tank assembly connector. • Is the resistance less than 5 ohms?	Yes No	▶ ▶	REPLACE the instrument cluster printed circuit. SERVICE the "Y/W" wire for open.

PINPOINT TEST C: FUEL GAUGE INACCURATE

TEST STEP		RESULT	▶	ACTION TO TAKE
C1	CHECK FUEL TANK SENDING UNIT			
	• Perform the Fuel Tank Sending Unit component test • Is the fuel tank sending unit OK?	Yes No	▶ ▶	GO to C2. REPLACE the fuel tank sending unit.
C2	CHECK FUEL TANK SENDING UNIT GROUND			
	• Key off. • Disconnect the fuel tank assembly connector. • Measure the resistance of the "BK/Y" wire between the fuel tank assembly connector and ground. • Is the resistance less than 5 ohms?	Yes No	▶ ▶	GO to C3. SERVICE the "BK/Y" wire.

FM9099400329010X

Fig. 37 Fuel indicating system diagnosis (Part 1 of 2). Aspire

PINPOINT TEST C: FUEL GAUGE INACCURATE (Continued)

TEST STEP	RESULT	▶	ACTION TO TAKE
C3 CHECK FUEL GAUGE ● Perform the Fuel Gauge component test ● Is the fuel gauge OK?	Yes	▶	SERVICE the "BK/Y" wire between the white instrument cluster connector and ground.
	No	▶	REPLACE the fuel gauge.

PINPOINT TEST D: FUEL GAUGE ALWAYS READS FULL

TEST STEP	RESULT	▶	ACTION TO TAKE
D1 CHECK FUEL TANK SENDING UNIT ● Perform the Fuel Tank Sending Unit component test ● Is the fuel tank sending unit OK?	Yes	▶	GO to **D2**.
	No	▶	REPLACE the fuel tank sending unit.
D2 CHECK FUEL GAUGE ● Perform the Fuel Tank Sending Unit component test ● Is the fuel tank sending unit OK?	Yes	▶	SERVICE the "Y/W" wire for short.
	No	▶	REPLACE the fuel gauge.

FM9099400329020X

**Fig. 37   Fuel indicating system diagnosis (Part 2 of 2).
Aspire**

STARTER MOTORS
TABLE OF CONTENTS

Ford Motorcraft Starters
INDEX

APPLICATION CHART

Model	Year
Continental	1992-93
Cougar	1992-93
Crown Victoria	1992-94
Escort	1992-94
Grand Marquis	1992-94
Mark VII	1992
Mark VIII	1993-94
Mustang	1992-94
Sable	1992-94
Taurus	1992-94
Tempo	1992-94
Topaz	1992-94
Town Car	1992-94
Tracer	1992-94

GENERAL INFORMATION

SOLENOID SWITCHES

The solenoid switch on a cranking motor not only closes the circuit between the battery and the cranking motor but also shifts the drive pinion into mesh with the engine flywheel ring gear. This is done by means of a linkage between the solenoid switch plunger and the shift lever on the cranking motor.

There are two windings in the solenoid; a pull-in winding and a hold-in winding. Both windings are energized when the external control switch is closed. They produce a magnetic field which pulls the plunger in so that the drive pinion is shifted into mesh, and the main contacts in the solenoid switch are closed to connect the battery directly to the cranking motor. Closing the main switch contacts shorts out the pull-in winding since this winding is connected across the main contacts. The magnetism produced by the hold-in winding is sufficient to hold the plunger in, and shorting out the pull-in winding reduces drain on the battery. When the control switch is opened, it disconnects the hold-in winding from the battery. When the hold-in winding is disconnected from the battery, the shift lever spring withdraws the plunger from the solenoid, opening the solenoid switch contacts and at the same time withdrawing the drive pinion from mesh. Proper operation of the switch depends on maintaining a definite balance between the magnetic strength of the pull-in and hold-in windings.

This balance is established in the design by the size of the wire and the number of turns specified. An open circuit in the hold-in winding or attempts to crank with a discharged battery will cause the switch to chatter.

STARTER MOTOR SERVICE

To obtain full performance data on a starting motor or to determine the cause of abnormal operation, the starting motor should be submitted to a no-load and torque test. These tests are best performed with the starter mounted on a starter bench tester.

From a practical standpoint, however, a simple torque test may be made quickly with the starter in the car. Make sure the battery is fully charged and that the starter circuit wires and terminals are in good condition. Then operate the starter to see if the engine turns over normally. If it does not, the torque developed is below standard and the starter should be removed for further checking.

DESCRIPTION

This type of starter motor, **Fig. 1,** has the starter solenoid mounted on the starter housing. The starter relay connects battery power to the starter solenoid, causing it to energize. On models equipped with manual transmission, a clutch switch in the starter control circuit prevents operation unless the clutch pedal is depressed. On models equipped with automatic transmission, a neutral safety switch in the starter control circuit prevents operation of the starter unless the selector lever is in the "Neutral" or "Park" position.

When the starter solenoid is energized, a magnetic field is created in the solenoid windings. The plunger core is drawn to the solenoid coil and a lever connected to the drive assembly engages the drive pinion gear into the flywheel ring gear. When the plunger is all the way in, its contact disk closes the circuit between the battery and the motor feed terminals. This sends current to the motor and the drive pinion gear cranks the flywheel to start the engine. When the current flows to the engine, the solenoid pull-in coil is bypassed and the hold-in coil keeps the drive pinion gear engaged with the flywheel until the ignition switch is released from the "On" position.

FORD—Starter Motors

TROUBLESHOOTING

When trouble develops in the starting motor circuit, and the starter cranks the engine slowly or not at all, several preliminary checks can be made to determine whether the trouble lies in the battery, in the starter, in the wiring between them, or elsewhere. Many conditions besides defects in the starter itself can result in poor cranking performance.

To make a quick check of the starter system, turn on the headlights. They should burn with normal brilliance. If they do not, the battery may be run down.

If the battery is in a charged condition so that lights burn brightly, operate the starting motor. Any one of three things will happen to the lights: (1) They will go out, (2) dim considerably or (3) stay bright without any cranking action taking place.

IF LIGHTS GO OUT

If the lights go out as the starter switch is closed, it indicates that there is a poor connection between the battery and starting motor. This poor connection will most often be found at the battery terminals. Correction is made by removing the cable clamps from the terminals, cleaning the terminals and clamps, replacing the clamps and tightening them securely. A coating of corrosion inhibitor (petroleum jelly will do) may be applied to the clamps and terminals to retard the formation of corrosion.

IF LIGHTS DIM

If the lights dim considerably as the starter switch is closed and the starter operates slowly or not at all, the battery may be run down, or there may be some mechanical condition in the engine or starting motor that is throwing a heavy burden on the starting motor. This imposes a high discharge rate on the battery which causes noticeable dimming of the lights.

Check the battery state of charge. If it is charged, the trouble probably lies in either the engine or starting motor itself. In the engine, tight bearings or pistons or heavy oil place an added burden on the starting motor. Low temperatures also hamper starting motor performance since it thickens engine oil and makes the engine considerably harder to crank and start. Also, a battery is less efficient at low temperatures.

In the starting motor, a bent armature, loose pole shoe screws or worn bearings, any of which may allow the armature to drag, will reduce cranking performance and increase current draw.

In addition, more serious internal damage is sometimes found. Thrown armature windings or commutator bars, which sometimes occur on over-running clutch drive starting motors, are usually caused by excessive overrunning after starting. This is the result of such conditions as the driver keeping the starting switch closed too long after the engine has started, the driver opening the throttle too wide in starting, or improper carburetor fast idle adjustment. Any of these subject the overrunning clutch to extra strain so it tends to

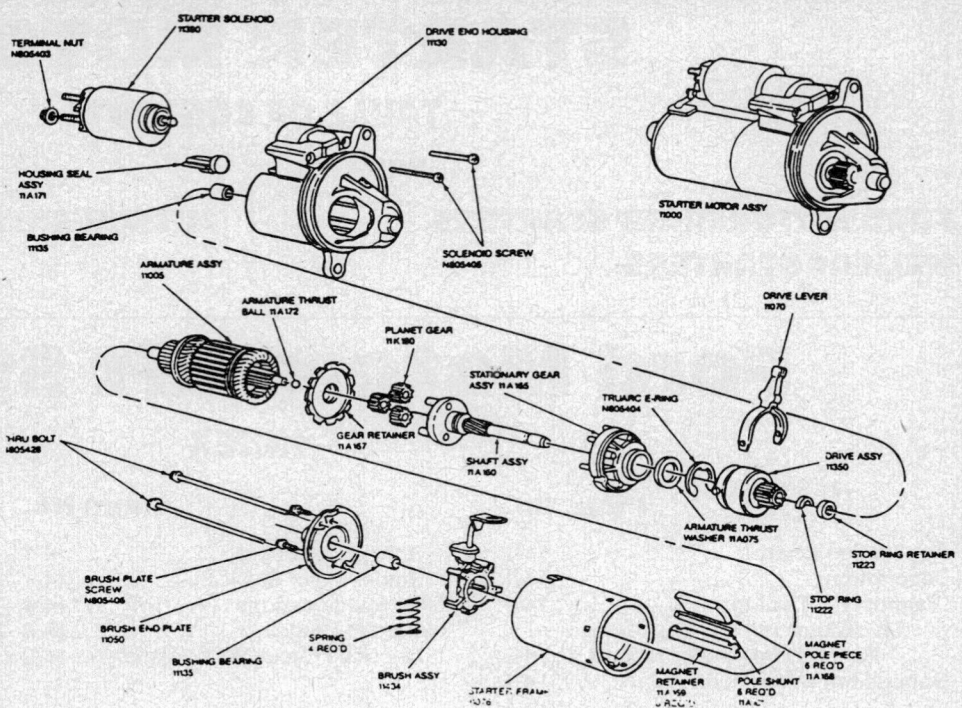

Fig. 1   Ford Motorcraft gear reduced permanent magnet starter motor

seize, spinning the armature at high speed with resulting armature damage.

Another cause may be engine backfire during cranking which may result, among other things, from ignition timing being too far advanced.

To avoid such failures, the driver should pause a few seconds after a false start to make sure the engine has come completely to rest before another start is attempted. In addition, the ignition timing should be checked if engine backfiring has caused the trouble.

LIGHTS STAY BRIGHT, NO CRANKING ACTION

This condition indicates an open circuit at some point, either in the starter itself, the starter switch or control circuit. The solenoid control circuit can be eliminated momentarily by placing a heavy jumper lead across the solenoid main terminals to see if the starter will operate. This connects the starter directly to the battery and, if it operates, it indicates that the control circuit is not functioning normally. The wiring and control units must be checked to locate the trouble.

If the starter does not operate with the jumper attached, it will probably have to be removed from the engine so it can be examined in detail.

CHECKING CIRCUIT WITH VOLTMETER

Excessive resistance in the circuit between the battery and starter will reduce cranking performance. The resistance can be checked by using a voltmeter to measure voltage drop in the circuits while the starter is operated. There are three checks to be made:

1. Voltage drop between car frame and grounded battery terminal post (not cable clamp).
2. Voltage drop between car frame and starting motor field frame.
3. Voltage drop between insulated battery terminal post and starting motor terminal stud (or the battery terminal stud of the solenoid).

Each of these should show no more than one-tenth (0.1) volt drop when the starting motor is cranking the engine. Do not use the starter for more than 30 seconds at a time to avoid overheating it.

If excessive voltage drop is found in any of these circuits, make correction by disconnecting the cables, cleaning the connections carefully, and then reconnecting the cables firmly in place. A coating of petroleum jelly on the battery cables and terminal clamps will retard corrosion.

On some models, extra long battery cables may be required due to the location of the battery and starter. This may result in somewhat higher voltage drop than the above recommended 0.1 volt. The only means of determining the normal voltage drop in such cases is to check several of these vehicles. Then when the voltage drop is well above the normal figure for all cars checked, abnormal resistance will be indicated and correction can be made as already explained.

STARTER DRIVE TROUBLE

Starter drive troubles are easy to diagnose and they usually cannot be confused with ordinary starter difficulties. If the starter does not turn over at all or if it drags, look for trouble in the starter or electrical supply system. Concentrate on the starter drive or ring gear if the starter is noisy, if it turns but does not engage the engine, or if

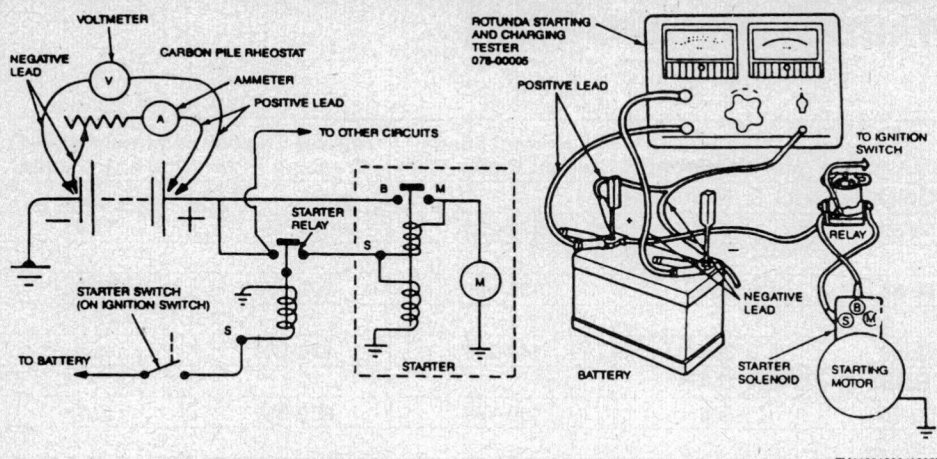

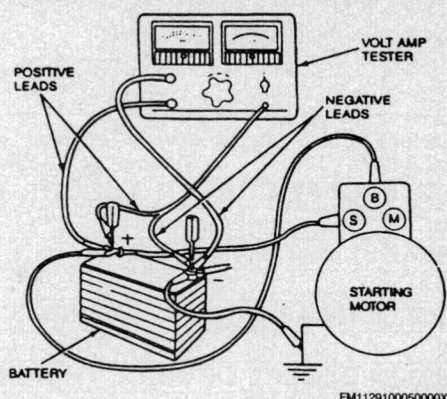

Fig. 2   Gear reduced permanent magnet starter cranking circuit test connections

Fig. 3   Starter no load test connection. Gear reduced permanent magnet starter motor

the starter won't disengage after the engine is started. After the starter is removed, the trouble can usually be located quickly.

Worn or chipped ring gear or starter pinion are the usual causes of noisy operation. Before replacing either or both of these parts try to find out what caused the damage. With the Bendix type drive, incomplete engagement of the pinion with the ring gear is a common cause of tooth damage. The wrong pinion clearance on starter drives of the over-running clutch type leads to poor meshing of the pinion and ring gear and too rapid tooth wear.

A less common cause of noise with either type of drive is a bent starter armature shaft. When this shaft is bent, the pinion gear alternately binds and then only partly meshes with the ring gear. Most manufacturers specify a maximum of .003 inch radial runout on the armature shaft.

When Clutch Drive Fails

The over-running clutch type drive seldom becomes so worn that it fails to engage since it is directly activated by a fork and lever. The only thing that is likely to happen is that, once engaged, it will not turn the engine because the clutch itself is worn out. A much more frequent difficulty and one that rapidly wears ring gear and teeth is partial engagement. Proper meshing of the pinion is controlled by the end clearance between the pinion gear and the starter housing or pinion stop, if used.

On some starters, the solenoids are completely enclosed in the starter housing and the pinion clearance is not adjustable. If the clearance is not correct, the starter must be disassembled and checked for excessive wear of solenoid linkage, shift lever mechanism, or improper assembly of parts.

Failure of the over-running clutch drive to disengage is usually caused by binding between the armature shaft and the drive.

If the drive, particularly the clutch, shows signs of overheating it indicates that it is not disengaging immediately after the engine starts. If the clutch is forced to overrun too long and dissolve and turns a bluish color. For the cause of the binding, look for rust or gum between the armature shaft and the drive, or for burred splines. Excess oil on the drive will lead to gumming, and inadequate air circulation in the flywheel housing will cause rust.

Over-running clutch drives cannot be overhauled in the field so they must be replaced. In cleaning, never soak them in a solvent because the solvent may enter the clutch and dissolve the sealed-in lubricant. Wipe them off lightly with kerosene and lubricate them sparingly with Lubriplate 777 or equivalent.

When Bendix Drive Fails

When a Bendix type drive doesn't engage the cause usually is one of three things: either the drive spring is broken, one of the drive spring bolts has sheared off, or the screw shaft threads won't allow the pinion to travel toward the flywheel. In the first two cases, remove the drive by unscrewing the setscrew under the last coil of the drive spring and replace the broken parts. Gummed or rusty screw shaft threads are fairly common causes of Bendix drive failure and are easily cleaned with a little kerosene or steel wool, depending on the trouble. Here again, as in the case of over-running clutch drives, use light oil sparingly, and be sure the flywheel housing has adequate ventilation. There is usually a breather hole in the bottom of the flywheel housing which should be open.

The failure of a Bendix drive to disengage or to mesh properly is most often caused by gummed or rusty screw shaft threads. When this is not true, look for mechanical failure within the drive itself.

DIAGNOSIS & TESTING

FORD MOTORCRAFT STARTER w/GEAR REDUCED PERMANENT MAGNET

Starter Load Test

1. Connect test equipment as shown in **Fig. 2,** ensuring no current is flowing through ammeter and heavy duty carbon pile rheostat portion of circuit.
2. Disconnect push-on "S" connector at starter relay, then connect remote control starter switch between positive battery terminal and "S" terminal.
3. Using remote starter, crank engine with ignition in the "Off" position, then determine exact reading on voltmeter.
4. Stop cranking engine, then reduce resistance of carbon pile until voltmeter indicates same reading as obtained with starter cranking the engine. Ammeter should indicate 140–200 amps.

Starter No-Load Test

1. Connect test equipment as shown in **Fig. 3.** Ensure current is not flowing through ammeter. Ensure starter is securely mounted in vise.
2. Disconnect starter from battery, then reduce resistance of rheostat until voltmeter indicates reading obtained while starter was running.
3. Ammeter should indicate starter no load current draw, refer to "Starter Specifications."
4. If current exceeds specifications, check for rubbing armature, bent starter shaft, binding starter bearings, or electrical shorts in armature or starter brush assembly.

STARTER SPECIFICATIONS

Starter Frame Dia., Inch	Brush Spring Tension, Ounces	No Load Amps	Max Load Amps	Normal Load Current Draw, Amps	Normal Engine Cranking RPM	Minimum Stall Ft. Lbs. @ 5 Volts
1992 EXCEPT COUGAR, ESCORT, THUNDERBIRD & TRACER						
3.0	64	60-80	800	130-220	140-220	11.0
1992 ESCORT & TRACER						
3.0	64	60-80	800	130-190	200-250	10.0
1992 COUGAR & THUNDERBIRD						
3.0	64	60-80	800	140-220	130-220	11.0
1993-94 EXCEPT COUGAR, THUNDERBIRD & TOWN CAR						
3.0	64	60-80	800	130-190	200-250	10.0
1993-94 COUGAR & THUNDERBIRD						
3.0	64	60-80	800	140-200	130-180	11.0
4.0	80	80	500	150-250	180-250	9.5
1993-94 TOWN CAR						
3.0	64	60-80	800	150-210	170-210	11.0

Mitsubishi Starters

INDEX

APPLICATION CHART

Model	Year
Capri	1992-94
Festiva	1992-93
Probe ①	1993-94
Aspire	1994

①—Automatic Trans.

GENERAL INFORMATION

Refer to "Ford Motorcraft Starters" for general information.

DESCRIPTION

The starter system has two electrical circuits a low current and high current. The low current is the control circuit. It includes ignition switch, starter solenoid, neutral safety switch or clutch switch. The high current connects starter to the battery positive terminal. This circuit uses heavy gauge cables because of high current flow required to operate the starter motor, **Figs. 1 and 2.**

TROUBLESHOOTING

Refer to "Ford Motorcraft Starters" for troubleshooting information.

ENGINE CRANKS SLOWLY

1. Undercharged battery.
2. Loose connections or corroded battery cables.
3. Starter motor.

ENGINE WILL NOT CRANK

1. Undercharged battery.
2. Ignition switch.
3. Clutch pedal position switch or manual lever position switch.
4. Loose or corroded cable connections.
5. Worn or damaged ignition circuit grounds.
6. Starter motor.
7. Starter solenoid.

ENGINE WILL NOT CRANK/STARTER MOTOR SPINS

1. Starter motor.
2. Flywheel ring gear.

ENGINE STARTS WITH CLUTCH ENGAGED

1. Starter clutch pedal position switch or manual lever position switch.

DIAGNOSIS & TESTING

PINION DEPTH ADJUSTMENT

Except 1993-94 Probe

1. Connect one 12 volt battery as shown, **Fig. 3.**
2. Disconnect field coil connector from "M" terminal.
3. With battery connected, solenoid should released pinion gear.
4. With pinion extended, measure gap between pinion gear and collar. Pinion clearance should be .020-.080 inch, **If test must be repeated, allow solenoid to cool.**
5. If clearance is not within limits, check for improper installation or worn parts and replace as necessary. Clearance may be adjusted by adding or removing shims between solenoid and the drive end housing as necessary.

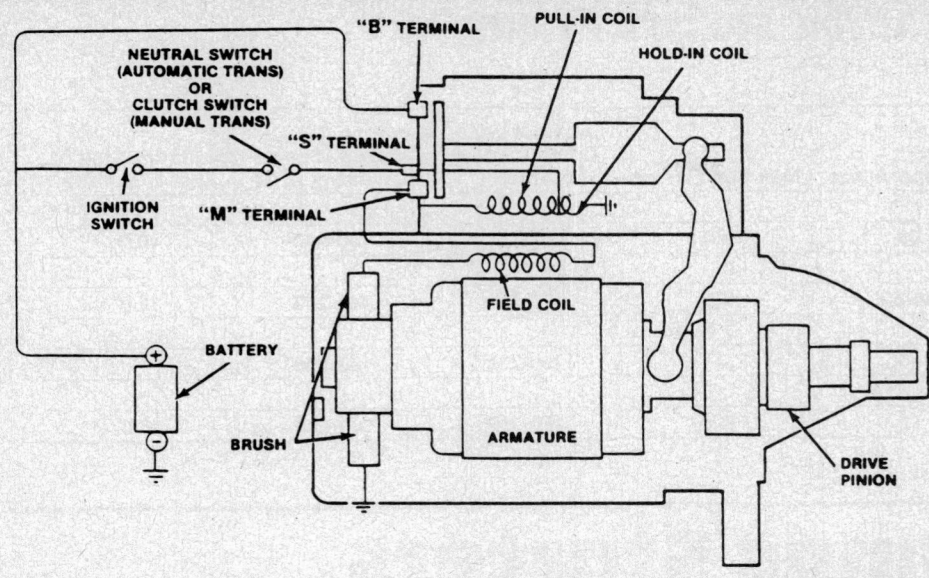

Fig. 1 Cross-sectional view of Mitsubishi starter motor

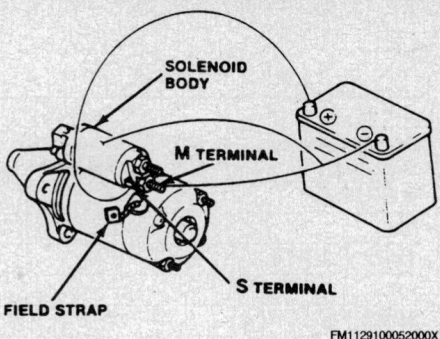

Fig. 3 Pinion depth adjustment.
Except 1993–94 Probe

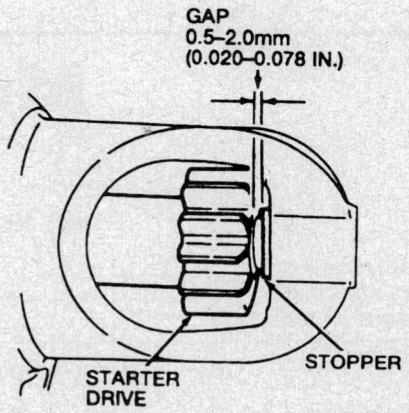

Fig. 4 Starter drive pinion gap measurement. 1993-94 Probe

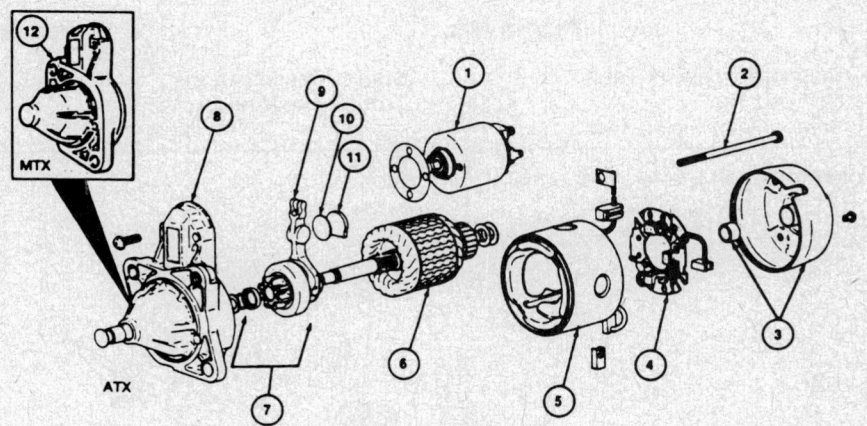

Item	Description
1	Starter Solenoid
2	Thru Bolt
3	Brush End Plate and Bushing
4	Brush Holder
5	Starter Field Coil
6	Starter Motor Armature

Item	Description
7	Starter Drive
8	Drive End Housing (ATX)
9	Drive Lever and Pin
10	Drive Lever and Pin Plate
11	Drive Lever and Pin Seal
12	Drive End Housing (MTX)

Fig. 2 Exploded view of Mitsubishi starter motor

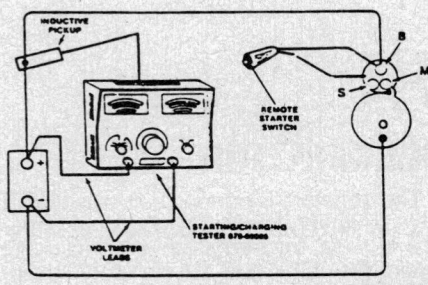

Fig. 5 Starter load test connection

1993–94 Probe

1. Disconnect "M" terminal wire.
2. Connect positive battery lead to starter solenoid S-terminal. **Do not apply battery voltage for more than 10 seconds.**
3. Connect negative battery lead to clean, rust-free portion of the starter field coil.
4. Measure clearance between starter drive and stopper, **Fig. 4.** Starter drive pinion gap should measure .020–.078 inch.
5. If starter pinion gap is not within specifications, increase or decrease number of washers between magnetic switch and starter field coil.

NO LOAD TEST

1. Connect test equipment as shown, **Fig. 5.**
2. Connect remote starter switch, ensuring starter turns smoothly.
3. **On Aspire, Capri, Festiva and Tracer models,** voltmeter should read no less than 11.5 volts and ammeter should read no morea than 60 amps.
4. **On 1992 Probe models,** voltmeter should read no less than 11 volts and ammeter should read no more than 90 amps.
5. **On 1993-94 Probe models,** voltmeter should read no less than 11 volts and ammeter should read no more than 70 amps.
6. **On all models,** if voltage is lower or amperage is higher, check battery or repair starter as necessary.

STARTER SPECIFICATIONS

Starter Frame Dia., Inch	Brush Spring Tension, Ounces	No Load Amps	Max Load Amps	Normal Load Current Draw, Amps	Normal Engine Cranking RPM	Minimum Stall Ft. Lbs. @ 5 Volts
ASPIRE						
4.0	32-69	60	800	150-250	180-250	10.0
1992 CAPRI						
3.0	64	60-80	800	130-220	140-220	11.0
1992 FESTIVA						
4.0	32-68	60	—	150-250	180-250	—
1993 FESTIVA, 1993-94 CAPRI & PROBE						
3.0	64	70	800	130-190	200-250	10.0

Melmac Starters

INDEX

Refer to "Ford Motorcraft Starters" for general information.

APPLICATION CHART

Model	Year
Probe	1992-94

DESCRIPTION

The armature is connected to the starter drive pinion shown in **Fig. 1**. As the armature moves forward from the magnetic field of the pull-in coil, the starter drive pinion is moved toward the flywheel. At the end of its travel, the starter drive pinion engages with the flywheel. Once the starter drive pinion and flywheel are fully engaged, the contact disc completes the circuit between the B and M terminals and the armature rotates. A hold-in coil is energized by the S-terminal, to supply he additional magnetic force required to keep the contact disc engaged as the starter draws current and the system voltage drops.

Item	Description	Item	Description
1	Stationary Gear	11	Seal
2	Starter Solenoid	12	Ball Bearing Spacer
3	Output Shaft	13	Solenoid Screw
4	Planetary Gears (3)	14	Drive End Housing
5	Through Bolt	15	Stop Ring
6	Brush Assembly Screw	16	Stop Ring Retainer
7	Rear Cover	17	Pinion Drive Assembly
8	Brush Assembly	18	Drive Lever
9	Armature Assembly	19	Drive Lever Disk
10	Starter End Frame	20	Drive Lever Disk Stop

FM1129100054000X

Fig. 1 Exploded view of starter motor assembly

TROUBLESHOOTING

Refer to "Ford Motorcraft Starters" for troubleshooting information.

CONDITION	POSSIBLE SOURCE	ACTION
• Starter Motor Cranks Slowly	• Loose or corroded battery cable connections. • Undercharged battery. • Loose or corroded starter motor connections. • Malfunctioning starter motor.	• GO to Pinpoint Test A1.
• Starter Motor Does Not Crank but Starter Solenoid Operates	• Loose or corroded connections at starter solenoid. • Undercharged battery. • Malfunctioning starter motor.	• GO to Pinpoint Test B1.
• Starter Motor Does Not Crank and Starter Solenoid Does Not Click	• Loose or corroded battery cable connections. • Undercharged battery. • Damaged Manual Lever Position (MLP) sensor or Starter Clutch Pedal Position (SCPP) switch. • Faulty ignition circuit grounds. • Malfunctioning starter motor. • Malfunctioning ignition switch.	• GO to Pinpoint Test C1.
• Starter Motor Spins but Does Not Crank Engine	• Malfunctioning starter motor. • Damaged flywheel.	• GO to Pinpoint Test D1.
• Starter Motor Cranks but Engine Does Not Start	• Undercharged battery. • Malfunction in the fuel system. • Malfunction in the ignition system.	• GO to Pinpoint Test F1.
• Starter Motor Remains Engaged and Runs With Engine	• Battery cable improperly positioned on the starter solenoid. • Damaged starter solenoid. • Malfunctioning starter motor.	• GO to Pinpoint Test G1.
• Unusual Starter Motor Noise During Starter Motor Overrun	• Starter motor improperly mounted. • Malfunctioning starter motor. • Improper starter drive engagement to flywheel.	• GO to Pinpoint Test E1.

FM1129400083000X

Fig. 2 Starter motor diagnostic symptom chart. 1994 Probe

TEST STEP		RESULT	▶	ACTION TO TAKE
B1	CHECK STARTER MOTOR CONNECTIONS			
	• Inspect the starter motor terminals for loose or corroded connections. • Are the starter motor terminal connections clean and tight?	Yes	▶	GO to B2.
		No	▶	CLEAN and TIGHTEN starter motor connections.
B2	CHECK BATTERY			
	• Check the battery. • Is the battery ok?	Yes	▶	PERFORM On Vehicle Testing in this section.
		No	▶	CHARGE or REPLACE the battery.

FM1129400085000X

Fig. 4 Test B: starter motor does not crank , but starter solenoid operates. 1994 Probe

TEST STEP		RESULT	▶	ACTION TO TAKE
D1	CHECK FLYWHEEL			
	• Remove the starter motor. Refer to procedure in this section. • Inspect the flywheel for damage. • Is the flywheel damaged?	Yes	▶	REPLACE the flywheel.
		No	▶	PERFORM Bench Test procedures in this section.

FM1129400087000X

Fig. 6 Test D: starter motor spins, but does not crank engine. 1994 Probe

TEST STEP		RESULT	▶	ACTION TO TAKE
E2	CHECK STARTER DRIVE ENGAGEMENT			
	• Remove the starter motor. • Inspect the starter drive and flywheel for damage. Refer to the inspection procedure in this section. • Are the starter drive and flywheel ok?	Yes	▶	PERFORM the Bench Tests procedures in the section.
		No	▶	REPLACE as necessary.

FM1129400088020X

Fig. 7 Test E: unusual starter motor noise during starter motor overrun (Part 2 of 2). 1994 Probe

TEST STEP		RESULT	▶	ACTION TO TAKE
G1	CHECK STARTER MOTOR TERMINALS			
	• Inspect the starter motor connectors for corrosion and incorrect installation. • Are the starter motor connectors clean and installed properly?	Yes	▶	PERFORM the Bench Tests procedures in this section.
		No	▶	CLEAN or ADJUST starter motor connectors.

FM1129400090000X

Fig. 9 Test G: starter motor remains engaged & runs w/engine. 1994 Probe

TEST STEP		RESULT	▶	ACTION TO TAKE
A1	CHECK BATTERY CONNECTIONS			
	• Inspect the battery terminals for loose or corroded connections. • Are the battery terminals clean and tight?	Yes	▶	GO to A2.
		No	▶	CLEAN and TIGHTEN battery cable corrections.
A2	CHECK BATTERY			
	• Check the battery. • Is the battery ok?	Yes	▶	GO to A3.
		No	▶	CHARGE or REPLACE the battery.
A3	CHECK STARTER MOTOR CONNECTIONS			
	• Inspect the starter motor terminals for loose or corroded connections. • Are the starter motor terminal connections clean and tight?	Yes	▶	PERFORM On Vehicle Testing in this section.
		No	▶	CLEAN and TIGHTEN starter motor connections.

FM1129400084000X

Fig. 3 Test A: starter motor cranks slowly. 1994 Probe

TEST STEP		RESULT	▶	ACTION TO TAKE
C1	CHECK BATTERY CONNECTIONS			
	• Inspect the battery terminals for loose or corroded connections. • Are the battery terminals clean and tight?	Yes	▶	GO to C2.
		No	▶	CLEAN and TIGHTEN battery cable connections.
C2	CHECK BATTERY			
	• Check the battery. • Is the battery ok?	Yes	▶	GO to C3.
		No	▶	CHARGE or REPLACE the battery.
C3	CHECK POWER SUPPLY TO STARTER MOTOR			
	• Key off. • Disconnect the starter motor connectors. • Key in START position. • Measure the voltage on the "BK/R" wire at the starter motor connector. • Is the voltage greater than 10 volts?	Yes	▶	GO to C4.
		No		diagnose the manual lever position sensor or starter clutch pedal position switch circuit.
C4	CHECK STARTER MOTOR GROUND CIRCUIT			
	• Perform the Starter Motor Ground Circuit test in this section. • Is the starter motor ground circuit ok?	Yes	▶	REMOVE the starter motor and PERFORM the Bench Test procedures in this section.
		No	▶	REPAIR or REPLACE the battery ground cable and/or engine ground cable as necessary.

FM1129400086000X

Fig. 5 Test C: starter motor does not crank/starter solenoid does not crank. 1994 Probe

TEST STEP		RESULT	▶	ACTION TO TAKE
E1	CHECK STARTER MOTOR MOUNTING			
	• Inspect the starter motor mounting. • Check the starter motor bolts for looseness. • Is the starter motor mounted properly?	Yes	▶	GO to E2.
		No	▶	REMOUNT or REPLACE the starter motor.

FM1129400088010X

Fig. 7 Test E: unusual starter motor noise during starter motor overrun (Part 1 of 2). 1994 Probe

TEST STEP		RESULT	▶	ACTION TO TAKE
F1	CHECK BATTERY			
	• Check the battery. • Is the battery ok?	Yes	▶	
		No		diagnose the fuel and ignition system. CHARGE or REPLACE the battery.

FM1129400089000X

Fig. 8 Test F: starter motor cranks, but engine does not start. 1994 Probe

DIAGNOSIS & TESTING

DIAGNOSTIC PINPOINT TESTS

1994 Probe

Refer to **Fig. 2** to diagnose starter motor problems by symptom, then refer to pinpoint tests, **Figs. 3 through 9**, for corrective action.

NO LOAD TEST

1. Connect a fully charged battery, then test equipment as shown in **Fig. 10**.
2. Engage remote starter switch.

3. The starter motor should eject the pinion and run smoothly. If the starter does not run smoothly, repair or replace as necessary.
4. While the starter motor is running, check the voltmeter and ammeter readings.
5. The voltage reading should be greater than 11 volts and ammeter should read no more than 90 amps.
6. If voltage or amperage is not as specified, replace the starter motor.

STARTER MOTOR PINION TEST

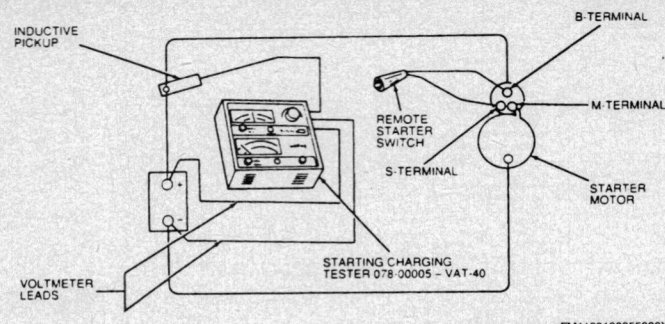

Fig. 10   Starter motor no-load test electrical connections

1. Remove starter motor from vehicle.
2. Place starter motor in bench vise and secure it.
3. Using a fully charged battery, connect the negative lead of the battery to the case of the starter motor. **Do not leave the positive lead from the battery connected to the starter for more than ten seconds.**
4. Touch the positive lead from the battery to the S-terminal, then ensure the pinion ejects.
5. If the pinion does not eject, repair or replace starter motor as necessary.
6. Remove positive lead from starter motor, pinion should return to its original position.
7. If the pinion does not return to original position, repair or replace starter motor.

STARTER SPECIFICATIONS

Year	Starter Frame Dia., Inch	Brush Spring Tension, Ounces	No Load Amps	Max Load Amps	Normal Load Current Draw, Amps	Normal Engine Cranking RPM	Minimum Stall Ft. Lbs. @ 5 Volts
1992-94	3.0	64	60-80	800	130-190	200-250	10

ALTERNATORS

TABLE OF CONTENTS

Ford Motorcraft Alternator

INDEX

APPLICATION CHART

Model	Year
Continental	1992-94
Cougar	1992-94
Crown Victoria	1992-94
Escort ①	1992-94
Grand Marquis	1992-94
Mark VII	1992
Mark VIII	1993-94
Mustang	1992-94
Sable	1992-94
Taurus	1992-94
Tempo ②	1992-94
Thunderbird ③	1992-94
Topaz ②	1992-94
Town Car	1992-94
Tracer ①	1992-94

①—1.9L/4-116 engine.
②—2.3L/4-140 engine.
③—3.8L/V6-232 & 4.6L/V8-281 engines.

PRECAUTIONS

1. Be certain that battery polarity is correct when servicing units. Reversed battery polarity will damage rectifiers and regulators.
2. If booster battery is used for starting, be sure to use correct polarity in hook up.
3. When a fast charger is used to charge a vehicle battery, the vehicle battery cables should be disconnected unless the fast charger is equipped with a special Alternator Protector, in which case the vehicle battery cables need not be disconnected. Also the fast charger should never be used to start a vehicle as damage to rectifiers will result.
4. Unless the system includes a load relay or field relay, grounding the alternator output terminal will damage the alternator and/or circuits. This is true even when the system is not in operation since no circuit breaker is used and the battery is applied to the alternator output terminal at all times. The field or load relay acts as a circuit breaker in that it is controlled by the ignition switch.
5. Before making any "on vehicle" tests of the alternator or regulator, the battery should be checked and the circuit inspected for faulty wiring or insulation, loose or corroded connections and poor ground circuits.
6. Check alternator belt tension to be sure the belt is tight enough to prevent slipping under load.
7. The ignition switch should be off and the battery ground cable disconnected before making any test connections to prevent damage to the system.
8. The vehicle battery must be fully charged or a fully charged battery may be installed for test purposes.

DESCRIPTION

The electrical charging system is a negative ground system consisting of an integral alternator/voltage regulator (IGR), charge indicator, storage battery and the necessary wiring and cables.

The "I" circuit, or ignition circuit is used to turn on the alternator regulator, **Fig. 1**. This circuit is powered up with the ignition switch in the Run position. The circuit also turns the indicator lamp on if there is a fault in the charging system.

The "A" circuit, or battery sense circuit, is used to sense battery voltage. This circuit also supplies power to the alternator stator and coil. With the system functioning normally, the alternator output current is determined by the voltage at the "A" circuit voltage (battery sense voltage). The "A" circuit voltage is compared to a set voltage inside the regulator to maintain correct alternator output. The set voltage will vary with temperature and is typically higher in the winter than in the summer, allowing for better battery recharge in the winter and reducing the chance of overcharging the battery in the summer.

The "S" circuit, or stator and coil circuit, is used to feedback a voltage signal from the alternator to the regulator. This voltage is typically one-half battery voltage and is used by the regulator to turn off the indicator.

If an ammeter is used in the charging system, **Fig. 2**, the regulator 1 terminal and the alternator stator terminal are not used. When the ignition switch is turned ON, the field relay closes and electrical current passes through the regulator A terminal and is metered to the alternator field. When the engine is started, the alternator field rotates causing the alternator to operate.

Some vehicles are equipped with electronic voltage regulators. These solid state regulators are used in conjunction with other components in the charging system such as an alternator with a high field current requirement, a warning indicator lamp shunt resistor (500 ohms) and a wiring harness with a regulator connector. Some vehicles are equipped with Integral Alternator/Regulator (IAR) charging system. This system has a solid state voltage regulator located in the rear of the alternator.

When replacing system components, note the following precautions:

1. Always use the proper alternator in the system.
2. Do not use an electro-mechanical regulator in the system since the wiring harness connector will not index properly with this type of regulator.
3. **On models with external voltage regulator,** the electronic regulators are color coded for proper installation. The black color coded unit is installed in systems equipped with a warning indicator lamp. The blue color coded regulator is installed in systems equipped with an ammeter.
4. **On all models,** the systems use a 500 ohm resistor on the rear of the instrument cluster on vehicles equipped with a warning indicator lamp.

On systems with an indicator lamp, closing the ignition switch energizes the warning lamp and turns on the regulator output stage. The alternator receives maximum field current and is ready to generate an output voltage. As the alternator rotor speed increases, the output and stator terminal voltages increase from zero to the system regulation level determined by the regulator setting. When the ignition switch is turned off, the solid state relay circuit turns the output stage off, interrupting current flow through the regulator so there is not a current drain on the battery.

On vehicles equipped with an ammeter, the operating principle is similar.

The ammeter indicates current flow into (charge) or out of (discharge) the vehicle battery.

DIAGNOSIS & TESTING

In-Vehicle Testing

The operations and on vehicle test procedures for the side terminal alternator are same as for rear terminal alternator. However, the internal wiring and bench test procedures differ.

DIAGNOSTIC PINPOINT TESTS

The charging system may be diagnosed by referring to the symptom chart, **Fig. 3,** then following the diagnostic pinpoint test procedures in **Figs. 4 and 5.**

REGULATOR TESTS

S CIRCUIT TEST— W/AMMETER

Except Alternators w/Integral Regulator

1. Connect the positive lead of the voltmeter to the S terminal of the regulator wiring plug **Fig. 6.** Turn the ignition switch to the "On." position. Do not start the engine.

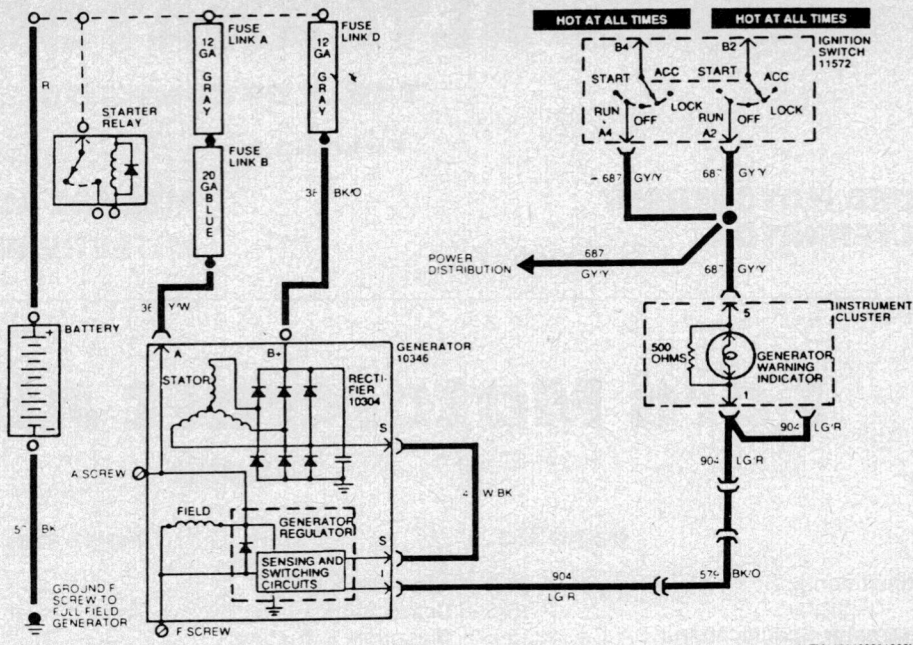

Fig. 1   Alternator electrical circuit

Fig. 2   Ammeter charging circuit. Except alternator w/integral regulator

2. The voltmeter reading should indicate battery voltage.
3. If there is no voltage reading, disconnect the positive voltmeter lead from the positive battery clamp and repair the S wire lead from the ignition switch to the regulator wiring plug.
4. Connect the positive voltmeter lead to the positive battery cable terminal and repeat the Charging System Test Procedures.

Alternators w/Integral Regulator

For test procedures, refer to "S & I Circuit Test-With Indicator Light."

S & I CIRCUIT TEST— W/INDICATOR LIGHT

Except Alternators w/Integral Regulator

1. Disconnect regulator wiring plug, then install a suitable jumper wire between connector "A" and "F" terminals, **Fig. 7.**
2. With the engine idling and negative voltmeter lead connected to battery ground, connect positive lead of voltmeter to S terminal and then to I terminal of regulator wiring plug, **Fig. 6.** Voltage of S circuit should read approximately ½ of the I circuit. If volt-

CONDITION	POSSIBLE SOURCE	ACTION
• Charge Indicator is Inoperative or Intermittent	• System wiring • Warning indicator lamp bulb • Generator regulator • Stator and field coil • Generator • Battery • Fuse • Fuse link	• Go to Pinpoint Test A.
• Generator is Inoperative	• Fuse link • Battery • System wiring • Drive belt • Generator • Generator regulator	• Go to Pinpoint Test B.

FM1129400092000X

Fig. 3   Diagnostic symptom chart

	TEST STEP	RESULT	▶	ACTION TO TAKE
A1	LAMP CHECK NO. 1 • Engine OFF. • Ignition switch in OFF position. • **Is charge indicator on?**	Yes No	▶ ▶	GO to A4. GO to A2.
A2	LAMP CHECK NO. 2 • Engine OFF. • Ignition switch in RUN position. • **Is charge Indicator on?**	Yes No	▶ ▶	GO to A3. GO to A5.
A3	LAMP CHECK NO. 3 • Ignition switch in RUN position. • Engine running. • **Is charge indicator on?**	Yes No	▶ ▶	GO to A9. Lamp test complete.
A4	IMPROPER 'I' CIRCUIT WIRING • Ignition switch in OFF position. • Check for voltage at 'I' circuit. • **Is voltage present?**	Yes No	▶ ▶	CHECK for voltage feed from always hot circuit to 'I' circuit. CHECK for damaged or improper wiring to charge indicator lamp at instrument cluster.

FM1129400093010X

Fig. 4   Test A: charge indicator is inoperative or intermittent (Part 1 of 4)

	TEST STEP	RESULT	▶	ACTION TO TAKE
A5	INOPERATIVE INDICATOR LAMP • Ignition switch in RUN position. • Engine OFF. • Disconnect generator regulator connector and ground 'I' terminal. • **Is charge indicator on?**	Yes No	▶ ▶	GO to A7. GO to A6.

A TERMINAL
S
A
I
GENERATOR REGULATOR WIRING PLUG
I TERMINAL
Motorcraft
JUMPER WIRE
NEGATIVE BATTERY CABLE CLAMP

	TEST STEP	RESULT	▶	ACTION TO TAKE
A6	RESISTANCE / BULB TEST • Check for voltage at 'I' terminal of generator regulator connector. • **Is voltage present?**	Yes No	▶ ▶	CHECK for burned out indicator lamp bulb or high resistance in lamp circuit. CHECK for an open in 'I' circuit wiring.
A7	STATOR AND FIELD COIL VOLTAGE FAULT • Reconnect generator regulator. • Engine OFF. • Check voltage 'S' terminal. • **Is voltage present?**	Yes No	▶ ▶	GO to A8. REPLACE generator regulator.

TESTER POSITIVE LEAD
TESTER GROUND LEAD
TERMINAL "S"
CLIP TO GENERATOR HOUSING

FM1129400093020X

Fig. 4   Test A: charge indicator is inoperative or intermittent (Part 2 of 4)

	TEST STEP	RESULT	▶	ACTION TO TAKE
A8	PINPOINT STATOR AND FIELD COIL VOLTAGE FAULT • Disconnect 1-pin stator connector. • Ignition switch in RUN position. • Engine OFF. • **Is charge indicator on?**	Yes No	▶ ▶	REPLACE generator. REPLACE generator regulator.

	TEST STEP	RESULT	▶	ACTION TO TAKE
A9	OPEN CIRCUIT CHECK • Check generator regulator, stator and field coil and Battery Positive Voltage (B+) output terminal connections for looseness or corrosion and service before checking voltage. • With ignition switch in RUN position, engine off, check voltage at battery positive voltage (B+) and 'A' terminal. • **Is battery voltage present?**	Yes No	▶ ▶	GO to A10. SERVICE wiring or fuse / fuse link for an open circuit between battery and generator or generator regulator.
A10	VOLTAGE DROP TEST 'A' TERMINAL • Ignition switch in RUN position. • Engine OFF. • Measure voltage between battery positive post and generator regulator 'A' terminal. • **Is voltage difference more than 0.25 volt?**	Yes No	▶ ▶	CHECK for high resistance in wiring between generator regulator 'A' terminal and battery. SERVICE as required. GO to A11.
A11	VOLTAGE DROP TEST — BATTERY POSITIVE VOLTAGE (B+) TERMINAL • Ignition switch in RUN position. • Engine running. • Blower on HIGH, headlamps ON. • Measure voltage between generator battery positive voltage (B+) output terminal and battery positive terminal. • **Is difference less than 1.5 volts?**	Yes No	▶ ▶	GO to A12. CHECK for high resistance in wiring between generator Battery Positive Voltage (B+) output terminal and battery. SERVICE as required.

FM1129400093030X

Fig. 4   Test A: charge indicator is inoperative or intermittent (Part 3 of 4)

	TEST STEP	RESULT	▶	ACTION TO TAKE
A12	'I' CIRCUIT CHECK • Ignition switch in RUN position. • Blower on HI. • Engine running. • Disconnect generator regulator connector. • **Is charge indicator on?**	Yes No	▶ ▶	SERVICE 'I' circuit for a short to ground. GO to A13.
A13	'S' CIRCUIT CHECK • Reconnect generator regulator connector. • Engine running. • Measure voltage at 'S' circuit at generator and at generator regulator. • **What is the voltage reading?**	Voltage approximately one-half 'A' circuit battery voltage at both locations Voltage approximately one-half 'A' circuit battery voltage at generator but not at generator regulator No voltage at either location	▶ ▶ ▶	GO to A14. SERVICE open in 'S' circuit wiring. GO to A15.
A14	VOLTAGE OUTPUT CHECK • Engine running at 2000 rpm. • Measure battery voltage. • **Is battery voltage above 16 volts?**	Yes No	▶ ▶	CHECK generator for generator brush holder or generator rotor short to ground. CHECK generator regulator screws for tightness, or high resistance in 'A' circuit. If no concern found, REPLACE generator regulator. REPLACE generator regulator.
A15	NO VOLTAGE CHECK • Ground 'F' screw on generator regulator. • Check for voltage at 'S' terminal. • **Is voltage approximately one-half battery voltage?**	Yes No	▶ ▶	REPLACE generator regulator. REPLACE generator regulator.

FM1129400093040X

Fig. 4   Test A: charge indicator is inoperative or intermittent (Part 4 of 4)

TEST STEP	RESULT	▶	ACTION TO TAKE
B1 PRELIMINARY CHECKS • Preliminary Checks: — Fuse link — Battery terminals and cable clamps — Wiring and ground connections to generator, generator regulator and engine — Generator drive belt tension • Are components OK?	Yes No	▶ ▶	GO to B2. SERVICE and/or REPLACE as necessary. GO to B2.
B2 BASE VOLTAGE AND NO LOAD TEST • Connect voltmeter to battery posts. Read battery voltage — this is base reading. • Start engine, run at 1500 rpm with no electrical load. Voltage should increase but not more than 3 volts. • Does voltage increase more than 3 volts?	Yes No No increase	▶ ▶ ▶	GO to B12. GO to B3. GO to B5.

FM1129400094010X

Fig. 5 Test B: generator is inoperative (Part 1 of 3)

TEST STEP	RESULT	▶	ACTION TO TAKE
B13 GENERATOR REGULATOR GROUND CHECK • Check for loose generator regulator ground screws. • Is ground OK?	Yes No	▶ ▶	GO to B14. SERVICE ground screws. GO to B2.
B14 ENGINE GROUND CHECK • Check for bad engine ground. • Is ground OK?	Yes No	▶ ▶	GO to B15. SERVICE engine ground. GO to B2.
B15 GENERATOR GROUND CHECK • Check generator ground. • Is ground OK?	Yes No	▶ ▶	GO to B16. SERVICE generator ground. GO to B2.
B16 REPEAT NO LOAD TEST • Start engine, run at 1500 rpm with no electrical load. • Voltage should increase but not more than 3 volts. • Does voltage increase more than 3 volts?	No Yes	▶ ▶	GO to B3. GO to B17.
B17 'A' AND 'F' VOLTAGE CHECKS • Turn ignition switch OFF. • Measure voltage at generator regulator 'A' and 'F' terminal screws. • Terminal voltages should be the same as battery voltage. • Is there battery voltage at both terminal screws?	Yes No	▶ ▶	REPLACE generator regulator. GO to B2. REPLACE generator assembly. GO to B2.

FM1129400094030X

Fig. 5 Test B: generator is inoperative (Part 3 of 3)

TEST STEP	RESULT	▶	ACTION TO TAKE
B3 LOAD TEST • Increase engine idle speed to 2000 rpm. • Turn heater-A/C blower on HIGH and headlamps on high beam. • Is voltage a minimum of 0.5 volt over base voltage?	Yes No	▶ ▶	GO to B4. GO to B5.
B4 BATTERY DRAIN TEST — IGNITION SWITCH OFF • Concern can still be battery drain. Turn OFF ignition switch, install test lamp in series with positive battery cable and check to isolate problem circuit. • Is there a battery drain?	Yes	▶	CHECK vehicle circuits for drain.
B5 UNDER-VOLTAGE TEST • Disconnect generator regulator. • Check resistance between generator regulator 'A' and 'F' terminals on generator regulator. • Is resistance more than 2.4 ohms?	Yes No	▶ ▶	GO to B6. CHECK generator for shorted field circuit and REPLACE generator assembly if required. If generator is OK, REPLACE generator regulator. GO to B2.
B6 'A' TERMINAL VOLTAGE CHECK • Reconnect generator regulator. • Measure 'A' terminal voltage. • Is there battery voltage?	Yes No	▶ ▶	GO to B7. SERVICE 'A' circuit wiring.
B7 'F' TERMINAL VOLTAGE CHECK — IGNITION SWITCH OFF • Generator regulator connected. • Ignition switch OFF. • Measure generator regulator 'F' terminal voltage with ignition switch OFF. • Is there battery voltage?	Yes No	▶ ▶	GO to B8. REPLACE generator assembly. GO to B2.
B8 'F' TERMINAL VOLTAGE CHECK — IGNITION SWITCH IN RUN • Turn ignition switch to RUN position (engine off). • Measure generator regulator 'F' terminal voltage. • Is voltage more than 1.5 volts?	Yes No	▶ ▶	GO to B9. GO to B10.
B9 'I' CIRCUIT TESTS • Perform 'I' circuit tests. • Is circuit OK?	Yes No	▶ ▶	REPLACE generator regulator. GO to B2. SERVICE 'I' circuit wiring. GO to B2.
B10 JUMPERED LOAD TEST • Repeat Load Test measuring voltage to generator Battery Positive Voltage (B+) output terminal from battery negative clamp. • Does voltage rise 0.5 volt or more?	Yes No	▶ ▶	SERVICE generator to starter relay wiring. GO to B2. GO to B11.
B11 LOAD TEST REPEAT — 'F' TERMINAL • Connect a jumper wire from generator rear housing to generator regulator 'F' terminal. • Repeat load test measuring voltage at Battery Positive Voltage (B+) output terminal. • Does voltage rise 0.5 volt or more?	Yes No	▶ ▶	REPLACE generator regulator. GO to B2. REPLACE generator assembly. GO to B2.
B12 OVER-VOLTAGE TEST • Turn ignition switch to RUN position (engine off). • Measure voltage at generator regulator 'A' terminal and starter solenoid. • Is voltage difference 0.5 volt or less?	Yes No	▶ ▶	GO to B13. SERVICE A circuit wiring. GO to B2.

FM1129400094020X

Fig. 5 Test B: generator is inoperative (Part 2 of 3)

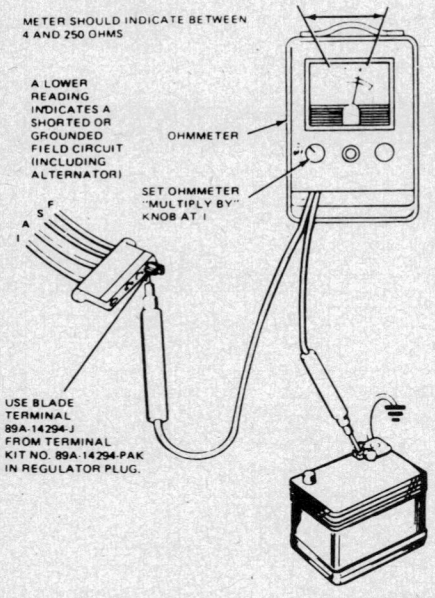

METER SHOULD INDICATE BETWEEN 4 AND 250 OHMS

A LOWER READING INDICATES A SHORTED OR GROUNDED FIELD CIRCUIT (INCLUDING ALTERNATOR)

OHMMETER

SET OHMMETER "MULTIPLY BY" KNOB AT I

USE BLADE TERMINAL 89A-14294-J FROM TERMINAL KIT NO. 89A-14294-PAK IN REGULATOR PLUG.

FM1129100066000X

Fig. 6 Regulator plug voltage test

age readings are as specified, remove jumper wire, replace regulator and connect wiring plug.

3. If no voltage is present, the wiring is at fault. Service the faulty circuit.

Alternators w/Integral Regulator

1. Disconnect electrical connector from regulator. Connect a jumper wire from the regulator A lead to connector plug A lead. Add a jumper wire from the regulator F screw to the alternator rear housing, **Fig. 8.**
2. With engine idling and voltmeter neg-

ative lead connected to alternator rear housing, connect voltmeter positive lead to S terminal and then to I terminal of regulator electrical connector. Voltage at S circuit should read approximately one-half of the I circuit. If voltage readings are normal, remove jumper wire. Replace regulator and connect electrical connector to regulator.

3. If no voltage is present, remove jumper wires and service faulty circuit or alternator.
4. Connect voltmeter positive lead to positive battery terminal.
5. Connect electrical connector to regulator and replace bulb, if equipped.

FIELD CIRCUIT DRAIN TEST

Alternators w/Integral Regulator

Connect voltmeter negative lead to the alternator rear housing for all of the following voltage readings.

1. Turn ignition switch to the "Off" position, then connect voltmeter positive lead to the regulator "F" terminal screw. Battery voltage should be present.
2. If less than battery voltage is present, disconnect regulator electrical connector and connect voltmeter positive lead to connector I terminal. No voltage should be present.

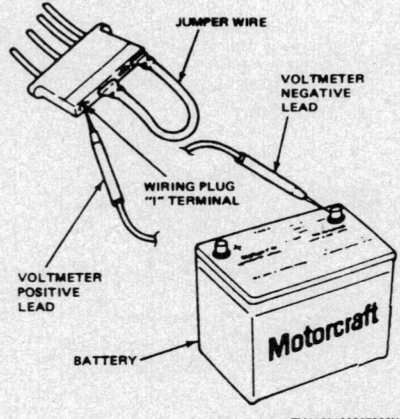

JUMPER WIRE

VOLTMETER NEGATIVE LEAD

WIRING PLUG "I" TERMINAL

VOLTMETER POSITIVE LEAD

BATTERY

Motorcraft

FM1129100067000X

Fig. 7 Testing regulator S & I circuit. External Voltage Regulator (EVR)

3. If voltage is present, repair circuit between I lead and ignition switch. If no voltage is present, proceed to following step.
4. Connect voltmeter positive lead to the connector S terminal.
5. No voltage should be present. If voltage is present, disconnect alternator electrical connector. Again, connect voltmeter positive lead to the regulator connector S terminal.
6. If voltage is still present, repair circuit between S lead and alternator connector. If no voltage is present, replace alternator rectifier assembly.

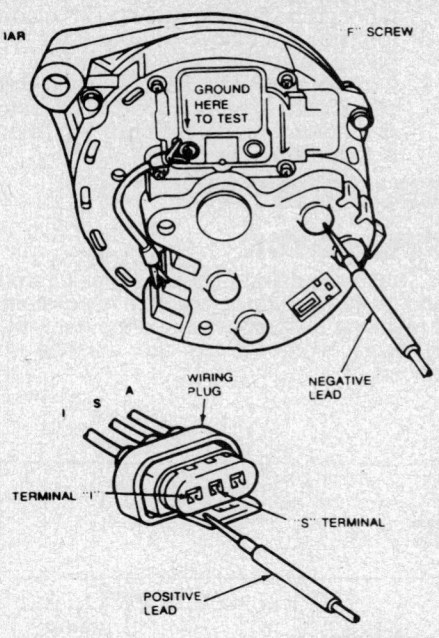

Fig. 8 Testing regulator S & I circuit. Integral Alternator Regulator (IAR)

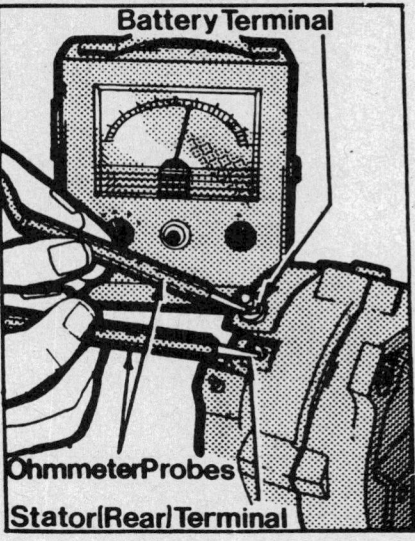

Fig. 9 Side terminal alternator rectifier short or grounded & stator grounded test

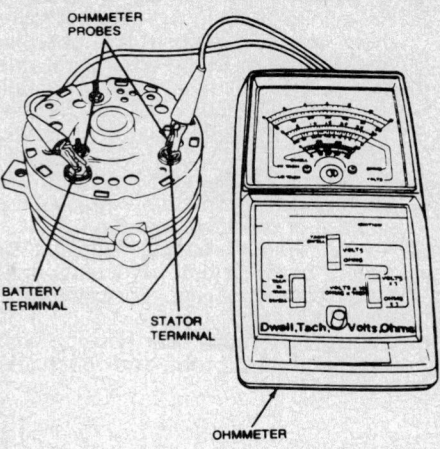

Fig. 10 Rear terminal alternator rectifier short or grounded & stator grounded test

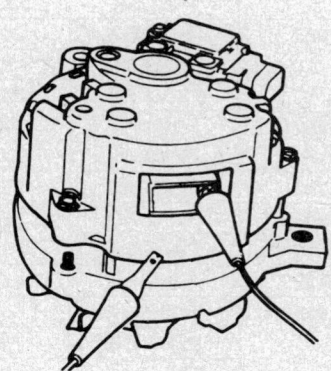

Fig. 11 Alternator w/integral regulator rectifier short or grounded & stator grounded test

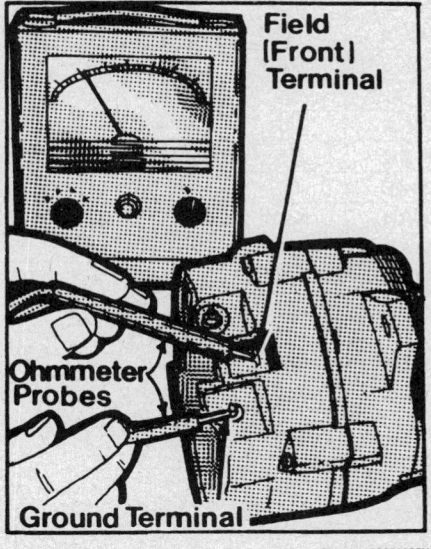

Fig. 12 Side terminal alternator field open or short circuit test

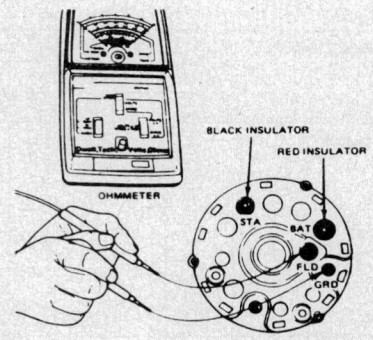

Fig. 13 Rear terminal alternator field open or short circuit test

Bench Testing

RECTIFIER SHORT OR GROUNDED & STATOR GROUNDED TEST

Using a suitable ohmmeter, connect one probe to the alternator BAT or B+ terminal, **Figs. 9 through 11,** the other probe to the STA terminal (rear blade terminal). Then, reverse the ohmmeter probes and repeat the test. A reading of about 6-6.5 ohms should be obtained in one direction and no needle movement with the probes reversed. A reading in both directions indicates a bad positive diode, a grounded positive diode plate, grounded BAT or B+ terminal or a shorted radio suppression capacitor, if equipped.

Perform the same test using the STA and GND (ground) terminals of the alternator. A reading in both directions indicates either a bad negative diode, a grounded stator winding, a grounded stator terminal, a grounded positive diode plate, or a shorted radio capacitor, if equipped.

Infinite readings (no needle movement) in all four probe positions in the proceeding tests indicates an open terminal lead connection inside the alternator.

FIELD OPEN OR SHORT CIRCUIT TEST
Except Alternators w/Integral Regulators

Using a suitable ohmmeter, connect the alternator field terminal with one probe and the ground terminal with the other probe, **Figs. 12 and 13.** Then, spin the alternator pulley. The ohmmeter reading should be 2.4 and 100 ohms, and should fluctuate while the pulley is turning. An infinite reading (no meter movement) indicates an open brush lead, worn or stuck brushes, or a bad rotor assembly. An ohmmeter reading less than 2.4 ohms indicates a grounded brush assembly, a grounded field terminal or a bad rotor.

Regulators w/Integral Regulator

1. Using a suitable ohmmeter, connect regulator A blade terminal with one probe and the regulator "F" screw head with the other probe, **Fig. 14.**
2. Spin the alternator pulley and note meter reading, then reverse probes and repeat step 1. In one probe direction ohmmeter reading should be between 2.2 and 100 ohms and may fluctuate while pulley is turning. In the other direction, reading should fluctuate between 2.2 and approximately 9 ohms.

3. An infinite reading, no meter movement, in one direction and approximately 9 ohms in the other, indicates an open brush lead, worn or stuck brushes, defective rotor or a loose regulator to brush holder attaching screw.
4. An ohmmeter reading less than 2.2 ohms in both directions indicates a shorted or defective regulator.
5. An ohmmeter reading significantly over 9 ohms in both directions indicates a defective regulator or loose "F" terminal screw.
6. Connect alternator rear housing with one ohmmeter probe and touch the

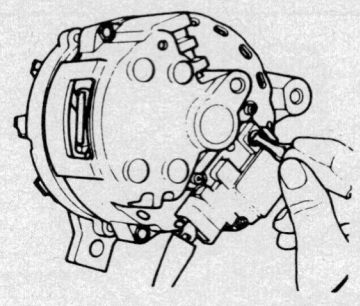

FM1129100074000X

Fig. 14 Alternator w/integral regulator field open or short circuit test

other probe first to regulator "A" blade terminal and then to the regulator "F" screw head.
7. If ohmmeter reads less than infinite at either point, a grounded brush lead, grounded rotor or defective regulator is indicated.

ADJUSTMENTS
REGULATOR

These regulators are factory calibrated and sealed and no adjustment is possible. If regulator calibration values are not within specifications, the regulator must be replaced.

ALTERNATOR SPECIFICATIONS

Model	Year	Alternator Model	Amp Rating
Continental	1992	FODZ-E	130
	1993	FODU-CA	100
	1994	—	130
Cougar	1992	E9PZ-A	75
	1993	EASF-BA	65
		E9DF-BB	75
		FODU-AB	95
		F3SU-AA	110
		F4SU-AB	130
	1994	F4SU-A	130
Crown Victoria & Grand Marquis	1992	EASF-BA	65
	1993	F1VU-B1	95
		F3AU-AC	130
	1994	F3VU	95
Escort	1992	FOCZ-C	75
	1993	FOCU-AC	75
	1994	—	75
Mark VII	1992	FOPZ-C	100
Mark VIII	1993	F3LU-BB	120
Mustang	1992	E7PZ-M	75
	1993	E7PF-PA	75
	1994	—	130
Sable	1992	FODZ-E	130
	1993	F3DU-BB	130

Model	Year	Alternator Model	Amp Rating
Sable-Cont'd	1994	F1DU-AA	130
		FODU-B	130
Taurus	1992	F1DZ-B	130
		FODZ-E	130
	1993	F3DU-DA	90
		F3DU-CB	120
		F3DU-BB	130
	1994	F1DU-A	130
		FODU-B	130
Tempo & Topaz	1992	F13U-AA	95
	1993	F2PU-ED	95
	1994	F23U-CA	95
Thunderbird	1992	E9PZ-A	75
	1993	EASF-BA	65
		E9DF-BB	75
		FODU-AB	95
		F3SU-AA	110
		F4SU-AB	130
	1994	F4SU-A	130
Town Car	1992	FIVY-B	95
	1993	FIPU-AC	95
	1994	F3VU	95
Tracer	1992	EFHD	75
	1993	FOCU-AC	75
	1994	—	75

Mitsubishi Alternator

INDEX

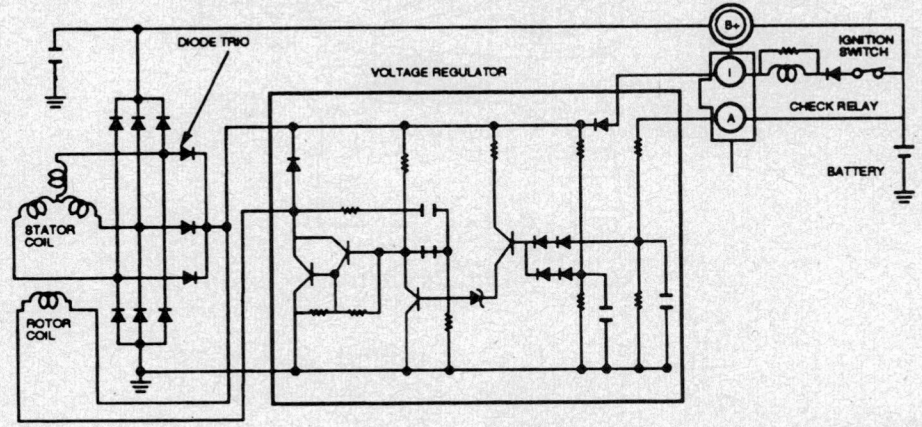

FM1129400095000X

Fig. 1   Battery sensing circuit

APPLICATION CHART

Model	Year
Aspire	1994
Capri	1992-94
Escort ③	1992-94
Festiva	1992-93
Taurus	1992-94
Tempo ①	1992-94
Thunderbird ②	1992-94
Topaz ①	1992-94
Tracer ③	1992-94

① —3.0L/V6-182 engine.
② —3.8L/V6-232 SC engine.
③ —1.8L/4-112 engine.

PRECAUTIONS

Refer to "Ford Motorcraft Alternator" section for service precautions.

DESCRIPTION

The electrical charging system is a negative ground system consisting of an integral alternator/voltage regulator (IGR), charge indicator, storage battery and the necessary wiring and cables.

With the ignition switch in the RUN position, voltage is applied through the charge indicator circuit to the voltage regulator. This turns the regulator on allowing current to flow from the battery sense circuit to the alternator field coil. When the engine is started, the alternator begins to generate alternating current (AC) which is converted to direct current (DC) by the rectifier assembly which is integrated into the alternator assembly.

This current is then supplied to the vehicles electrical system through the output stud located on the rear of the alternator assembly. Once the alternator begins generating current, a voltage signal is taken from the stator and is fed back to the regulator circuit, turning off the charge indicator.

With the system functioning normally, the alternator output current is determined by the voltage at the circuit voltage (battery sense voltage). The circuit voltage is compared to a set voltage inside the regulator to maintain correct alternator output. The set voltage will vary with temperature and is typically higher in the winter than in the summer, allowing for better battery recharge in the winter and reducing the chance of overcharging the battery in the summer.

Alternator output is supplied through battery positive voltage output connection to the battery and electrical system. This connection is the "B" terminal located on the back of the alternator.

The "I" or "L" circuit is used to turn on the alternator regulator. This circuit is powered up with the ignition switch in the On position. This circuit is also used to turn the charge indicator on if there is a fault in the charging system operation.

The "A" or "S" circuit is used to sense battery voltage. This voltage is used by the alternator regulator to determine alternator output, **Fig. 1**. This circuit is also used to supply power to the stator and coil.

This unit produces alternating current which is changed to direct current by rectifier diodes for distribution to the vehicle electrical system. The electronic voltage regulator is part of the rotor, brush and brush holder assembly. No regulated adjustments are required on this unit, **Figs. 2 and 3**.

DIAGNOSIS & TESTING

BASE VOLTAGE TEST

1. Ensure battery is fully charged.
2. With ignition switch and all electrical accessories off, connect suitable voltmeter to battery terminals.
3. Read and record battery voltage reading. This reading will be used for subsequent tests outlined below.

ALTERNATOR UNDERCHARGES

Current Output Test

1. Connect test leads of Charging System Analyzer tool No. 078-00005 or equivalent to vehicle, following tool manufacturer's instructions.
2. Turn on all electrical accessories, then start engine and allow to run between 2500-3000 RPM.
3. Read and record maximum current output. Current output should be within 10 percent of rated alternator output.
4. If current output is within specifications outlined in previous step, alternator is functioning properly. If current output is below specification, proceed to "Voltage Output Test."

Voltage Output Test

The following test must be performed with a fully charged battery.
1. With charging system analyzer connected as outlined in previous test, start engine and run at approximately 2500 RPM.
2. With all electrical accessories off, read and record current output.
3. If recorded reading is less than 5 amps, proceed to next step. If current reading is greater than 5 amps, voltage loss in charging circuit is indicated. Check battery, alternator and engine ground cable connections. Clean or repair connections as necessary.
4. Connect positive lead of voltmeter to "L" terminal of alternator connector and negative lead to alternator case, **Fig. 4**. Ensure that "L" terminal connector remains connected during test.
5. If reading obtained at "L" terminal is less than 14.4 volts, proceed to "Reg-

ulator Power Source Test." If reading obtained is 14.4-15 volts, a problem exists in alternator stator or rectifier.

Regulator Power Source Test

1. Turn ignition switch On, but do not start engine.
2. Disconnect "S" terminal connector from rear of alternator, then connect voltmeter positive lead to "S" terminal connector harness and negative lead to alternator case, **Fig. 5.** Read and record voltage.
3. If reading obtained is at base voltage obtained earlier, proceed to "Rotor Field Coil Test." If reading is less than base voltage, check for defective circuit between battery and "S" terminal.

Rotor Field Coil Test

1. Disconnect ground cable at battery and "B" terminal wire at alternator.
2. Connect suitable ohmmeter to "L" and "F" terminals of alternator as shown in **Fig. 6. The "F" terminal is mounted internally and can be accessed through hole in rear of alternator. Ensure that ohmmeter lead does not contact alternator housing during test.** Read and record reading.
3. If reading obtained in previous step is 3-6 ohms, field coil is satisfactory. Proceed to "L Terminal Voltage Test."
4. If ohms are not as indicated, a problem exists in the rotor, slip rings or brushes.

"L" Terminal Voltage Test

1. Reconnect battery ground cable and output wire to "B" terminal at rear of alternator.
2. With ignition switch "On," connect voltmeter positive lead to "L" terminal metal connector, and negative lead to alternator case. Read and record reading.
3. If reading obtained in previous step is 1-3 volts, a problem exists in the stator or rectifier. If reading obtained is above 3 volts, a problem exists in the regulator.

ALTERNATOR OVERCHARGES

Voltage Output Test

The following test must be performed with a fully charged battery.
1. Connect test leads of Charging System Analyzer tool No. 078-00005 or equivalent to vehicle, following tool manufacturer's instructions, then start engine and run at approximately 2500 RPM.
2. With all electrical accessories off, read and record current output.
3. If reading is less than 5 amps, connect positive lead of voltmeter to "L" terminal of alternator connector and negative lead to alternator case, **Fig. 4.** Ensure that "L" terminal connector remains connected during test.
4. Restart engine, run at 2500 RPM, and read and record voltage output. If

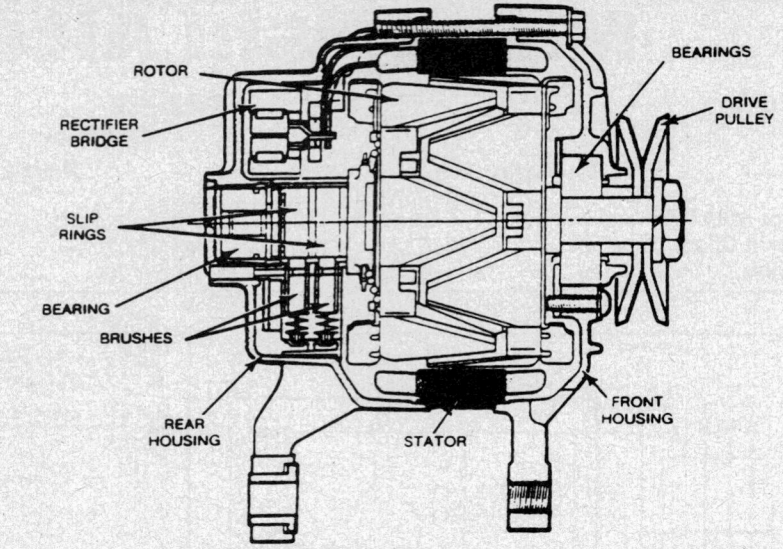

Fig. 2   Mitsubishi alternator

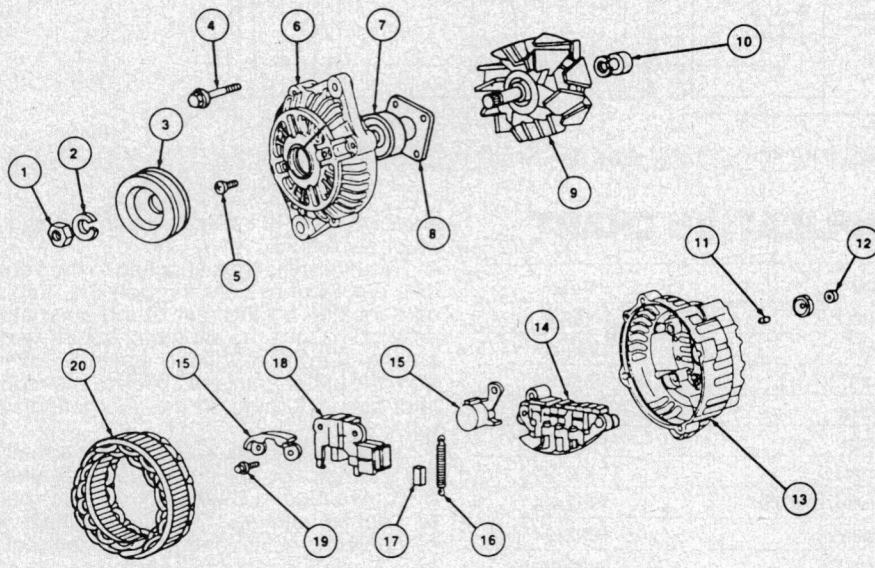

Fig. 3   Exploded view of Mitsubishi alternator

Item	Description
1	Nut
2	Washer
3	Pulley
4	Through Bolt (4 Req'd)
5	Screw (4 Req'd)
6	Front Housing
7	Front Bearing
8	Bearing Retainer
9	Rotor

Item	Description
10	Rear Bearing
11	Plug
12	Nut and Terminal Insulator
13	Rear Housing
14	Rectifier Assy
15	Shield
16	Brush Spring (2 Req'd)
17	Brush (2 Req'd)
18	Regulator
19	Screw (2 Req'd)
20	Stator

reading is 14.4-15 volts, alternator is operating properly. If reading is greater than 15 volts, proceed to "Regulator Power Source Test."

Regulator Power Source Test

1. Turn ignition switch On, but do not start engine.

2. Disconnect "S" terminal connector from rear of alternator, then connect voltmeter positive lead to "S" terminal connector harness and negative lead to alternator case, **Fig. 5.** Read and record voltage.
3. If reading obtained is at base voltage recorded earlier, proceed to "Rotor Field Coil Test." If reading is less than

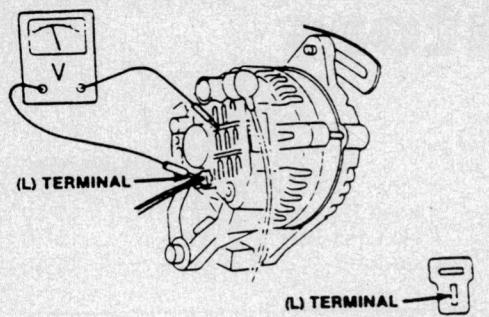

Fig. 4 Voltage output test connections

FM1129100076000X

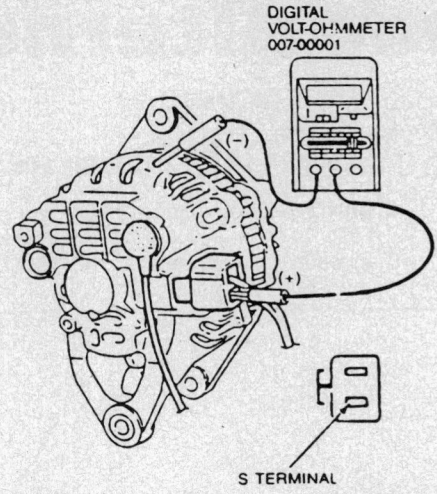

Fig. 5 Regulator power source test connections

FM1129100077000X

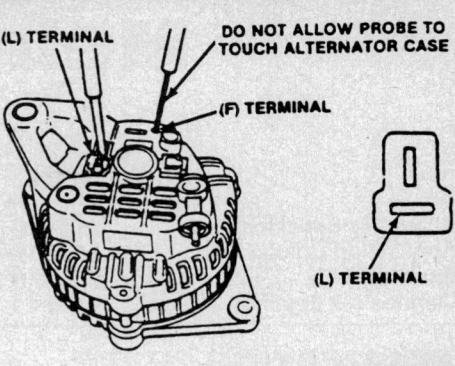

Fig. 6 Rotor field coil test connections

FM1129100078000X

base voltage, check for defective circuit between ignition switch and "S" terminal.

4. Reconnect terminal connector.

Rotor Field Coil Test

1. Disconnect ground cable at battery and "B" terminal wire at alternator.

2. Connect suitable ohmmeter to "L" and "F" terminals of alternator as shown in **Fig. 5**. The **"F" terminal is mounted internally and can be accessed through hole in rear of al-**

ternator. **Ensure that ohmmeter lead does not contact alternator housing during test.** Read and record reading.

3. If reading obtained in previous step is 3-6 ohms, a regulator problem is indicated.

4. If ohms are not as indicated, a problem exists in the rotor, slip rings or brushes.

ALTERNATOR SPECIFICATIONS

Model	Year	Alternator	
		Model	Amp Rating
Aspire	**1994**	—	**62**
Capri	1992	FOJY-A	85
	1993	FOPU-AC	85
	1994	—	**70**
Escort	1992	FOCZ-C	75
	1993	FOCU-AC	75
	1994	—	**65**
Festiva	1992	FOBZ-A	50
	1993	B113-18300-B	50
Tempo/Topaz	1992	F13U-AA	95
	1993	F2PU-ED	95
	1993-94	FO2U-AC	90
Thunderbird	1992	E9PZ-A	75
	1993	EASF-BA	65
		E9DF-BB	75
		FODU-AB	95
		F3SU-AA	110
		F4SU-AB	130
	1994	**F3SU-A**	**110**
Tracer	1992	FOCZ-C	75
	1993	FOCU-AC	75
	1994	—	**65**

Melmac Alternators

INDEX

APPLICATION CHART

Model	Year
Probe	1992-94

PRECAUTIONS

Refer to "Ford Motorcraft Alternator" section for service precautions.

DESCRIPTION

The electrical charging system is a negative ground system consisting of an alternator with an integral rectifier and regulator, Fig. 1

The "B" terminal is connected internally to the rectifier bridge output. Externally, the cable connected to the "B" terminal supplies Direct Current (DC) output to the electrical system to charge the battery and operate vehicle accessories while the engine is running.

The "L" terminal is connected internally (through a network of integrated circuits) to the field coil. When the ignition switch is turned on, the field coil is energized to "turn on" the regulator power transistor.

The "S" terminal is connected internally to the voltage regulator sensing circuit. Externally, the "S" terminal is connected to the ignition side of the ignition switch. The "S" circuit is used to tell the voltage regulator how much alternator output is required.

The Integrated Circuit (IC) electronic voltage regulator is part of the rotor, brush, and brush holder assembly. There is no voltage adjustment. The IC regulator automatically reduces regulated voltage when the ambient temperature increases, so that battery charging voltage is maintained at the correct level.

DIAGNOSIS & TESTING

NO-LOAD TEST

1. Connect Rotunda Digital Volt-Ohmmeter tool No. 105-00051-1 or equivalent to battery terminals according to manufacturers specifications.
2. Record voltage reading, this reading is called base voltage.
3. Start engine, then raise engine speed to 1500 rpm with no electrical loads.
4. Record voltage reading. Voltage reading should be between 14.1-14.7 volts.

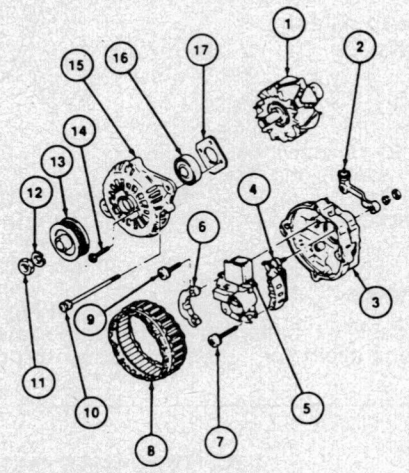

Item	Description
1	Generator Rotor
2	Generator Terminal Adapter
3	Generator Rear Housing
4	Rectifier
5	Generator Regulator
6	Plastic Shield
7	Rectifier Screw
8	Stator and Coil
9	Generator Regulator Screw (2)
10	Housing Bolt
11	Generator Pulley Nut
12	Generator Pulley Washer
13	Generator Pulley
14	Front Bearing Plate Screws (4)
15	Generator Front Housing
16	Generator Front Bearing
17	Front Bearing Plate

FM1129400097000X

Fig. 1   Exploded view of Melmac alternator

5. If voltage reading does not increase 2.5 volts over base voltage with engine operating at 1500 rpm, perform "Load Test."
6. If voltage increase is greater than 2.5 volts, repair or replace alternator as necessary.

LOAD TEST

Do not ground "B" terminal wire or possible electrical damage will result.
1. Connect Rotunda Starting/Charging

Tester tool No. 078-00005 or equivalent as follows:
  a. Carefully disconnect "B" terminal wire from alternator.
  b. Connect positive lead of tester to "B" wire.
  c. Connect negative lead of tester to "B" terminal.
2. turn on as many electrical accessories as possible, to force the alternator the charge at its maximum voltage.
3. Start engine, then raise engine speed to 2,500 to 3,000 rpm.

CONDITION	POSSIBLE SOURCE	ACTION
• System Does Not Charge	• Loose or worn drive belt. • Corroded battery connections. • Battery. • Generator.	• GO to Pinpoint Test A1.
• System Overcharges	• Generator.	
• Battery Voltage Gauge Reads High	• Generator. • Battery voltage gauge.	• GO to Pinpoint Test B1.
• Battery Voltage Gauge Reads Low	• Loose or worn drive belt. • Loose or corroded battery cables. • Battery. • Generator. • Battery voltage gauge.	• GO to Pinpoint Test C1.
• Generator Noisy	• Loose or worn drive belt. • Bent generator pulley. • Generator.	• GO to Pinpoint Test D1.
• Battery Does Not Hold a Charge	• Loose or worn drive belt. • Damaged battery cables. • Battery. • Generator.	• GO to Pinpoint Test E1.

FM1129400098000X

Fig. 2   Diagnostic symptom chart

TEST STEP	RESULT	▶	ACTION TO TAKE
A1 CHECK BATTERY CONNECTIONS • Inspect the battery cables for loose or corroded connections. • Are the battery cables clean and tight?	Yes No	▶ ▶	GO to A2 CLEAN or TIGHTEN the battery cables.
A2 CHECK DRIVE BELT TENSION • Is the drive belt adjusted properly?	Yes No	▶ ▶	GO to A3. ADJUST or REPLACE the drive belt.
A3 CHECK BATTERY • Is the battery OK?	Yes No	▶ ▶	PERFORM the Generator component tests REPLACE the battery.

FM1129400099000X

Fig. 3   Test A: system does not charge

TEST STEP	RESULT	▶	ACTION TO TAKE
B1 CHECK GENERATOR • Is the generator OK?	Yes No	▶ ▶	diagnose the battery voltage gauge. REPAIR or REPLACE the generator.

FM1129400100000X

Fig. 4   Test B: battery voltage gauge reads high

TEST STEP	RESULT	▶	ACTION TO TAKE
C1 CHECK BATTERY CONNECTIONS • Inspect the battery cables for loose or corroded connections. • Are the battery cables clean and tight?	Yes No	▶ ▶	GO to C2. CLEAN or TIGHTEN the battery cables.
C2 CHECK DRIVE BELT TENSION • Is the drive belt adjusted properly?	Yes No	▶ ▶	GO to C3. ADJUST or REPLACE the drive belt.
C3 CHECK BATTERY • Is the battery OK?	Yes No	▶ ▶	GO to C4. REPLACE the battery.
C4 CHECK GENERATOR • Is the generator OK?	Yes No	▶ ▶	diagnose the battery voltage gauge. REPAIR or REPLACE the generator.

FM1129400101000X

Fig. 5   Test C: battery voltage gauge reads low

TEST STEP	RESULT	▶	ACTION TO TAKE
D1 CHECK DRIVE BELT TENSION • Is the drive belt adjusted properly?	Yes No	▶ ▶	GO to D2. ADJUST or REPLACE the drive belt.

FM1129400102010X

Fig. 6   Test D: generator noisy (Part 1 of 2)

TEST STEP	RESULT	▶	ACTION TO TAKE
E1 CHECK BATTERY CONNECTIONS • Inspect the battery cables for loose or corroded connections. • Are the battery cables clean and tight?	Yes No	▶ ▶	GO to E2. CLEAN or TIGHTEN the battery cables.
E2 CHECK DRIVE BELT TENSION • Is the drive belt adjusted properly?	Yes No	▶ ▶	PERFORM the Battery component tests ADJUST or REPLACE the drive belt.

FM1129400103000X

Fig. 7   Test E: battery does not hold a charge

TEST STEP	RESULT	▶	ACTION TO TAKE
D2 CHECK GENERATOR PULLEY • Remove the generator drive belt. • Inspect the generator pulley for damage. • Is the generator pulley OK?	Yes No	▶ ▶	PERFORM the Generator Bench Test REPLACE the generator pulley.

FM1129400102020X

Fig. 6   Test D: generator noisy (Part 2 of 2)

4. Record the maximum alternator output. If the amperage output is within ten percent of its rated output, the alternator is functioning correctly.

CHARGING SYSTEM VOLTAGE OUTPUT TEST

1. With the ignition switch in the On position, engine Off, check voltage at the alternator wiring connector terminals are as follows:
   a. "B" terminal voltage reading should be approximately 12 volts.
   b. "L" terminal voltage reading should be approximately 1 volt.
   c. "S" terminal voltage reading should be approximately 12 volts.
2. If voltage readings are as specified, check wiring harness between battery and "B" terminal.

3. If voltage readings are below specification, check the wiring harness. If wiring harness checks good, repair or replace alternator as necessary.

DIAGNOSTIC PINPOINT TESTS

Refer to symptom chart, **Fig. 2** to verify condition, then refer to **Figs. 3 through 7** for pinpoint test procedures.

ALTERNATOR SPECIFICATIONS

| Model | Year | Alternator | |
		Model	Amp Rating
Probe	1992	FO2Z-G	70
	1993	FS111-8300-A	80
		KL111-8300-D	90
	1994	—	80
		—	90

SPEED CONTROL SYSTEMS

NOTE: On Air Bag Equipped Models, Refer To "Air Bag System Precautions" Located In The Front Of This Manual For System Disarming & Arming Procedures.

INDEX

DESCRIPTION

ESCORT, MUSTANG, TEMPO, TOPAZ & TRACER

The speed control system is controlled by the ON-OFF, SET-ACCEL, COAST and RESUME switches. The system contains vacuum hoses, servo (throttle actuator) assembly, speed sensor, amplifier, check valve assembly, and depending on model and year, a clutch switch, a manual lever position switch, stop light switch, or vacuum dump valve, an actuator (servo) and an actuator cable.

To operate the speed control system, vehicle speed must exceed 30 mph. When the ON-OFF switch is actuated, the system is ready to accept a set speed signal. When vehicle speed stabilizes (above 30 mph), and the ON switch is engaged, the operator may depress or release the SET-ACCEL button. This speed will be maintained until a new speed has been set, brake pedal has been depressed, or the system is turned off.

The vehicle speed may be reduced by applying the brake or clutch pedal and then resetting the speed using the method outlined above or by depressing the COAST switch. When the vehicle has slowed to the desired speed, the COAST switch is released and the new speed is set automatically. If the vehicle speed is reduced below 30 mph (48 km/h), the operator must manually increase the speed and reset the system.

CONTINENTAL, COUGAR & THUNDERBIRD

The speed control system consists of operator controls, servo assembly, speed sensor, stoplamp switch, vacuum dump valve, horn relay, vacuum reservoir, check valve, amplifier assembly and all necessary wires and vacuum hoses. The servo assembly is mounted in the engine compartment and is connected to the throttle linkage with an actuator cable. The servo is connected to the vacuum reservoir and manifold through the check valve. The amplifier assembly is located behind the glove compartment, under the instrument panel. The speed control sensor is located on the transmission or transaxle.

To operate the speed control system, vehicle speed must exceed 30 mph. When the ON-OFF switch is actuated, the system is ready to accept a set speed signal. When vehicle speed stabilizes (above 30 mph), and the ON switch is engaged, the operator may depress or release the SET-ACCEL button. This set speed will be maintained until a new speed has been set, the brake pedal has been depressed, or the system is turned off.

The vehicle speed may be reduced by applying the brake or clutch pedal and then resetting the speed using the method outlined above or by depressing the COAST switch. When the vehicle has slowed to the desired speed, the COAST switch is released and the new speed is set automatically. If the vehicle speed is reduced below 30 mph (48 km/h), the operator must manually increase the speed and reset the system.

The vehicle set speed may be increased manually by pressing the accelerator until the higher speed is reached, then depressing and releasing the SET/ACCEL button. Set speed can also be increased by depressing and holding the SET/ACCEL button. When set speed increases to the desired level, release the SET ACCEL button.

MARK VII

The speed control amplifier assembly function is integrated into the EEC-IV Electronic Control Assembly (ECA). The servo assembly is mounted in the engine compartment and is connected to the throttle linkage with an actuator cable. The servo is also connected to an aspirator and a manifold vacuum source through check valves. The speed control sensor is located on the transmission.

The Aspirator is connected to the thermactor air pump and is used to improve speed control performance when engine load is high. The check valves switch the servo's vacuum source from the manifold to the air pump according to which has the strongest vacuum signal available. The check valves also keep vacuum from leaking back into the source not being used.

The vacuum dump valve provides an additional safety feature in the system. Normally, when the brake pedal is depressed, an electrical signal from the stop lamps to the ECA will turn off the system. In addition, the vacuum dump valve will mechanically release the vacuum in the servo when the brake pedal is depressed. This releases the throttle independently of the ECA control.

The Integrated Vehicle Speed Control (IVSC) system for these models consists of operator controls, a servo (throttle actuator) assembly, a speed sensor (Models with non-electronic instrument cluster only), a clutch switch (Manual Trans.), stop lamp switch, vacuum dump valve, horn relay, two check valves, aspirator (except Cougar and Thunderbird), and necessary wires and vacuum hoses. On models with an electronic instrument cluster, the electronic speedometer assembly generates the speed signal and therefore does not require a speed sensor.

SABLE & TAURUS

The Integrated Vehicle Speed Control (IVSC) system for these models, **Fig. 1**, consists of operator controls, a servo (throttle actuator) assembly, a speed sensor, a clutch switch (Manual Trans.), a stop lamp switch, a vacuum dump valve, a horn relay, a vacuum reservoir, a check valve, and necessary wires and vacuum hoses.

The speed control amplifier assembly function is integrated into the EEC-IV Electronic Control Assembly (ECA). The servo assembly is mounted in the engine compartment and is connected to the throttle linkage with an actuator cable. The servo is also connected to a vacuum reservoir and to a manifold vacuum source through a check valve. The speed control sensor is located on the transaxle.

The vacuum dump valve, **Fig. 2**, provides a safety feature in the system. Normally, when the brake pedal is depressed, an electrical signal from the stop lamps to the ECA will turn off the system. In addition, the vacuum dump valve will mechanically release the vacuum in the servo when the brake pedal is depressed. This releases the throttle independently of the ECA control.

System Activation

To operate the speed control system, vehicle speed must be no less then 26 mph for all models except Sable and Taurus with 2.5L/4-153 engine, or 35 mph for Sable and Taurus models with 2.5L/4-153 engine. Activate the system by pressing the ON switch on the steering wheel, then depress and release the SET ACCEL switch. This will result in the current speed being maintained until a new speed is set by the operator, the brake or clutch pedals

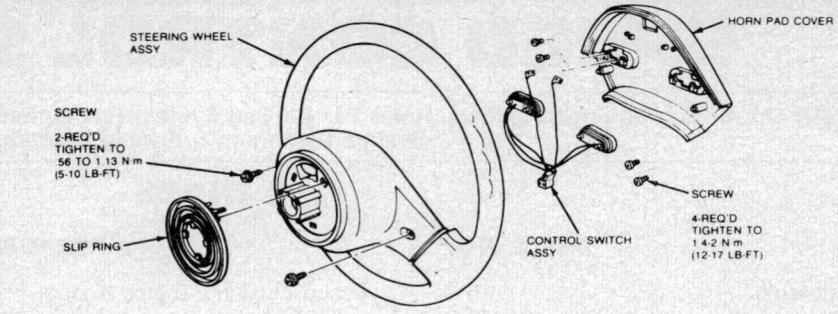

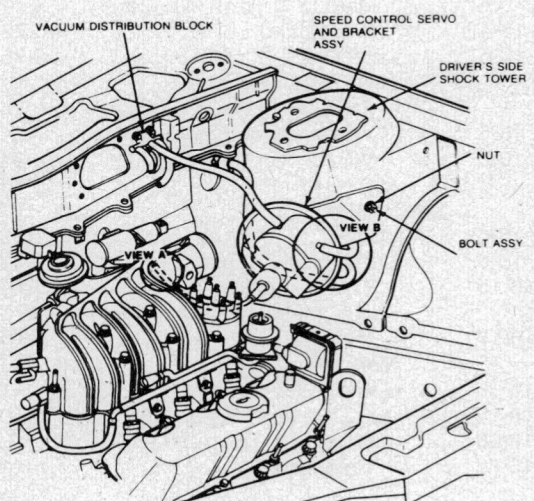

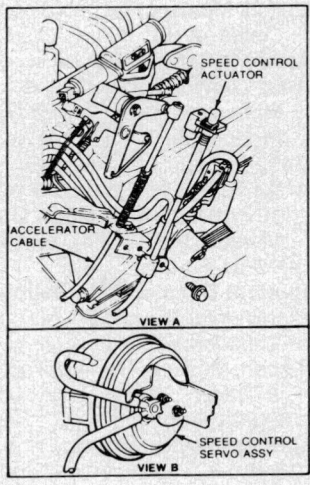

Fig. 1   Speed control components. Sable & Taurus

FM1109100122000X

are depressed, or the OFF switch is depressed.

Decreasing Set Speed

The vehicle speed may be reduced by applying the brake or clutch pedal and then resetting the speed using the forgoing method or by depressing the COAST switch. When the vehicle has slowed to the desired speed, the COAST switch is released and the new speed is set automatically. If the vehicle speed is reduced below 30 or 25 mph (as stated previously), the operator must manually increase the speed and reset the system.

Increasing Speed

The vehicle set speed may be manually increased at any time by depressing the accelerator until the higher speed is reached and stabilized, then depressing and releasing the SET ACCEL button.

Speed may also be increased by depressing the SET ACCEL switch button at speeds over 30 or 25 mph (as stated previously) and holding it in that position. The vehicle will then automatically increase speed. When the desired rate of speed is attained and the button is released, that new set speed will be maintained.

Resume

When the speed control system is deactivated by depressing the brake or clutch pedal, the set speed prior to deactivation may be re-established by holding the RE-

SUME switch for two seconds. The RESUME switch is hinged on the side closest to the SET ACCEL switch. Therefore, it should be depressed on the side farthest from the SET ACCEL switch. The resume feature will not function if the system is deactivated with the OFF switch, if the vehicle speed has been reduced to below 30 or 25 mph (as stated previously), or if the ignition switch is turned off.

1992 CROWN VICTORIA, GRAND MARQUIS & TOWN CAR (EARLY PRODUCTION)

This speed control system consists of a servo assembly, actuator cable, deactivator switch, vehicle speed sensor, stoplamp switch, horn relay and steering wheel switches. On Crown Victoria, Grand Marquis and Mark VIII models, the system operates independent of engine vacuum, therefore no vacuum lines are required.

On Town car models, a speed control amplifier is located behind the glove compartment. A vacuum reservoir mounted to the front bumper, supplies vacuum to the servo during periods of high engine load. Vacuum is fed from the reservoir by a plastic tube attached to the 14290 wire harness. A three-port check valve behind the servo connects the reservoir and manifold check lines and prevents reservoir vacuum from leaking back to the engine.

System Activation

To operate the speed control system, vehicle speed must be greater than 30 mph. At this time, the system is activated and is ready to accept a set speed signal by pressing the ON and SET ACCEL switches on the steering wheel. This will set speed at its current speed until a new speed is set by the operator, the brake pedal is depressed or the OFF switch is depressed.

Decreasing Set Speed

Vehicle speed may be reduced by applying the brake pedal and the resetting the speed using the system activation method or by depressing the COAST switch. When the vehicle is slowed to the desired speed, the COAST switch is released and the new vehicle speed is set automatically. If the vehicle speed is reduced below the minimum operating speed, the operator must manually increase the speed and reset the system.

Increasing Set Speed

Vehicle set speed may be manually increased at any time by depressing the accelerator until the higher speed is reached and stabilized, then depressing and releasing the SET ACCEL button.

Set speed can also be increased by depressing the SET ACCEL button and holding it in that position. The vehicle will then automatically increase speed. When desired speed has been obtained and the button has been released, that new speed will be maintained.

Resume

When the speed control system is deactivated by depressing the brake pedal, the set speed prior to system deactivation may be reset by momentarily depressing the RESUME button. The RESUME function of the system will not function if the system is deactivated using the OFF switch, or if vehicle speed has been reduced below the minimum speed of 30 mph.

1992 TOWN CAR (LATE PRODUCTION), 1993–94 CROWN VICTORIA, GRAND MARQUIS, MARK VIII & TOWN CAR

This speed control system consists of a servo assembly, actuator cable, deactivator switch, vehicle speed sensor, stoplamp switch, horn relay and steering wheel switches. On Crown Victoria, Grand Marquis and Mark VIII models, the system operates independent of engine vacuum, therefore no vacuum lines are required.

On Town car models, a speed control amplifier is located behind the glove compartment. A vacuum reservoir mounted to the front bumper, supplies vacuum to the servo during periods of high engine load. Vacuum is fed from the reservoir by a plastic tube attached to the 14290 wire harness. A three-port check valve behind the servo connects the reservoir and manifold check lines and prevents reservoir vacuum from leaking back to the engine.

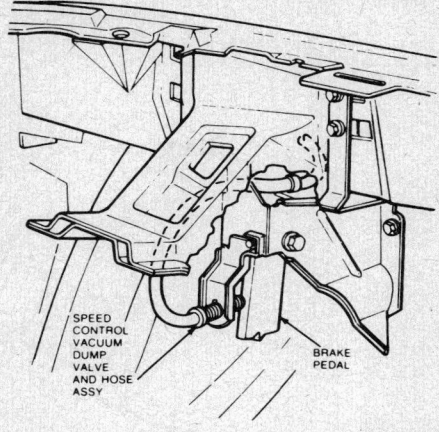

SPEED CONTROL VACUUM DUMP VALVE AND HOSE ASSY

BRAKE PEDAL

FM1109100123000X

Fig. 2 Vacuum dump valve. Sable & Taurus

System Activation

To operate the speed control system, vehicle speed must be greater than 30 mph. At this time, the system is activated and is ready to accept a set speed signal by pressing the ON and SET ACCEL switches on the steering wheel. This will set speed at its current speed until a new speed is set by the operator, the brake pedal is depressed or the OFF switch is depressed.

Decreasing Set Speed

Vehicle speed may be reduced by applying the brake pedal and the resetting the speed using the system activation method or by depressing the COAST switch. When the vehicle is slowed to the desired speed, the COAST switch is released and the new vehicle speed is set automatically. If the vehicle speed is reduced below the minimum operating speed, the operator must manually increase the speed and reset the system.

Increasing Set Speed

Vehicle set speed may be manually increased at any time by depressing the accelerator until the higher speed is reached and stabilized, then depressing and releasing the SET ACCEL button.

Set speed can also be increased by depressing the SET ACCEL button and holding it in that position. The vehicle will then automatically increase speed. When desired speed has been obtained and the button has been released, that new speed will be maintained.

Resume

When the speed control system is deactivated by depressing the brake pedal, the set speed prior to system deactivation may be reset by momentarily depressing the RESUME button. The RESUME function of the system will not function if the system is deactivated using the OFF switch, or if vehicle speed has been reduced below the minimum speed of 30 mph.

1992 PROBE

The speed control system consists of operator controls, a servo (throttle actuator) assembly, speed control amplifier, clutch switch (MTX), neutral safety switch (4EAT) and brake switch.

Due to the low vacuum generated by the turbocharged engine, an electrical motor-driven actuator is used in place of a vacuum actuator.

1993–94 PROBE

The speed control system consists of a speed control module, speed control switches, clutch pedal position switch (MTX models), brake switch, actuator, actuator cable and a vacuum dump valve.

To operate the speed control system, vehicle speed must be greater than 30 mph. At this time, the system is activated and is ready to accept a set speed signal by pressing the ON and SET ACCEL switches on the steering wheel. This will set speed at its current speed until a new speed is set by the operator, the brake pedal is depressed, the clutch pedal is depressed or the OFF switch is depressed.

Increasing Set Speed

Vehicle set speed can be increased in three ways: manually using the accelerator, pressing the SET ACCEL switch, tapping the SET ACCEL switch (Tap-Up). To manually increase set speed, depress the accelerator until the higher speed is reached and stabilized, then depress and release the SET ACCEL switch. Set speed can also be increased by depressing the SET ACCEL switch and holding it in that position, vehicle speed will then automatically increase, when desired speed has been obtained, release the switch. To increase vehicle speed using the Tap-Up method, tap the SET ACCEL switch once for each 1 mph until vehicle reaches desired speed.

Resume

When the speed control system is deactivated by depressing the brake pedal, the set speed prior to system deactivation may be reset by momentarily depressing the RESUME button. The RESUME function of the system will not function if the system is deactivated using the OFF switch, or if vehicle speed has been reduced below the minimum speed of 30 mph.

CAPRI

The speed control system consists of operator controls, an electronic throttle actuator, electronic control unit, clutch and brake switches and an electronic speed sensor.

The operator controls are mounted in the steering wheel. The electronic actuator is mounted in the engine compartment and is connected to the throttle by a cable. The clutch and brake switches are mounted to the pedal assembly. The electronic control unit is located behind the instrument panel. The electronic speed sensor is located on the speedometer cable at the upper and lower cable connection in the engine compartment.

FORD—Speed Control Systems

PRECAUTIONS

AIR BAG SYSTEMS

Refer to "Air Bag System Precautions" in the front of this manual for system disarming and arming procedures.

ADJUSTMENTS

ESCORT, MUSTANG, TEMPO, TOPAZ & TRACER

Linkage Actuator Cable (Chain Type)

1. **On all models except Mustang,** with the engine off, set throttle linkage so throttle is closed.
2. Remove locking pin.
3. Pull bead chain through adjuster.
4. Install locking pin into the hole which keeps the chain taught, but does not open throttle.
5. **On Mustang,** remove speed control actuator cable retaining clip.
6. Push actuator cable through adjuster until slight tension is felt.
7. Insert cable retaining clip and snap into place.

Linkage Actuator Cable (Cable Type)

1. Remove cable adjusting clip from cable housing.
2. Pull lightly on cable until all slack is taken out.
3. Maintaining light pressure on cable, install cable adjusting clip and snap into place.

Vacuum Dump Valve

1. Firmly depress brake pedal and hold.
2. Push dump valve in until valve collar bottoms against retaining clip.
3. Place a .05-.10 inch shim between white button on valve and pad on brake pedal, **Fig. 3.**
4. Firmly pull brake pedal rearward to its normal position, then allow dump valve to move into position in retaining clip.

Clutch Switch

1. Secure clutch pedal in the full up position.
2. Loosen switch mounting screw, then slide switch forward toward clutch pedal until switch plunger cap is .030 inch from contacting switch housing.
3. Release clutch pedal, then test drive vehicle to ensure switch is operating properly.

CONTINENTAL, COUGAR & THUNDERBIRD

LINKAGE ACTUATOR CABLE

1. Remove cable adjusting clip from cable housing, **Figs. 4 through 6.**
2. Pull lightly on cable until all slack is taken out.
3. Maintaining light pressure on cable, install cable adjusting clip and snap into place.

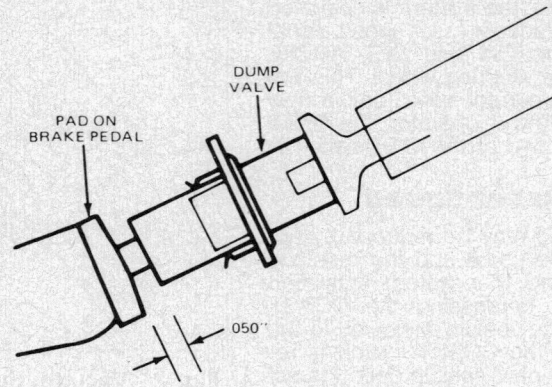

VIEW SHOWING CORRECTLY ADJUSTED DUMP VALVE

DUMP VALVE BLACK HOUSING MUST CLEAR WHITE PLASTIC PAD ON BRAKE PEDAL WITH BRAKE PEDAL PULLED TO REARMOST POSITION.

FM1109100096000X

Fig. 3   Dump valve adjustment

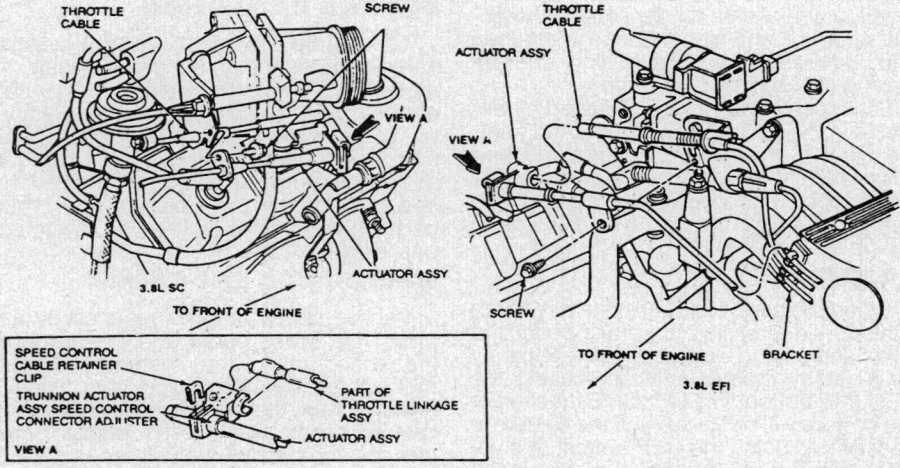

FM1109100116000X

Fig. 4   Linkage actuator cable adjustment. Cougar & Thunderbird w/3.8L/V6-231 engine

VACUUM DUMP VALVE

1. Firmly depress brake pedal and hold.
2. Push dump valve in until valve collar bottoms against retaining clip.
3. Place a .05-.10 inch shim between white button on valve and pad on brake pedal.
4. Firmly pull brake pedal rearward to its normal position, then allow dump valve to move into position in retaining clip.

CLUTCH INTERLOCK THREE FUNCTION SWITCH

Continental

1. Disconnect wiring harness from switch.
2. Using volt-ohmmeter, probe switch terminals for correct for correct switch function.
3. EFI switch (terminals 5 and 6) should be normally open, and close within

approximately 2 inches of clutch pedal travel.

4. Speed control release switch (terminals 3 and 4) should be normally closed, and open within approximately 2 inches of clutch travel.
5. Clutch interlock switch (terminals 1 and 2) should be normally open, and close when clutch pedal has been moved to approximately 1 inch from full travel.

Cougar & Thunderbird

1. Disconnect switch electrical connector, **Fig. 7.**
2. Using a volt-ohmmeter, check for continuity at the following switch terminals:
   a. EFI switch terminals 5 and 6 should be open with clutch pedal released. Terminals 5 and 6 should show continuity within two inches of clutch pedal travel.
   b. Speed control release switch terminals 3 and 4 should show conti-

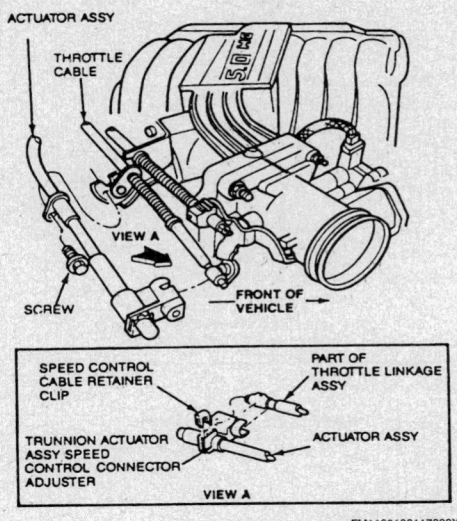

Fig. 5 Linkage actuator cable adjustment. Cougar & Thunderbird w/5.0L/V8-302 engine

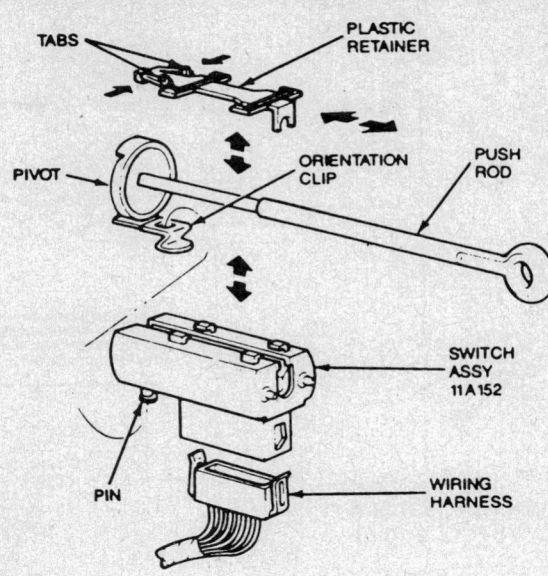

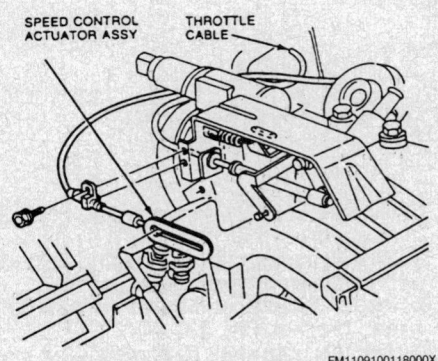

Fig. 6 Linkage actuator cable adjustment. Continental

The above N.C. or N.O. contact positions are referenced with the switch installed and the clutch pedal at the up or clutch engaged position.

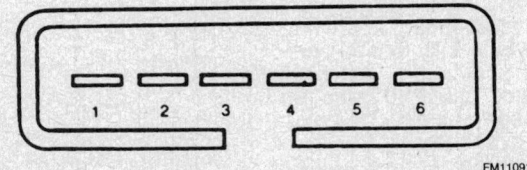

Fig. 7 Clutch interlock three function switch. Cougar & Thunderbird

nuity with clutch pedal released. Terminals 3 and 4 should open within two inches of clutch pedal travel.

c. Clutch interlock switch terminals 1 and 2 should be open with clutch pedal released. Terminals 1 and 2 should close within one inch from full clutch pedal travel.

MARK VII, SABLE & TAURUS

Actuator Cable

1. Remove speed control actuator cable retaining clip, **Figs. 8 through 10.**
2. Push actuator cable through adjuster until slight tension is felt.
3. Insert cable retaining clip and snap into place.

Bead Chain

1. Remove locking pin.
2. Pull bead chain through adjuster.
3. Insert locking pin in best hole of adjuster for tight bead chain without opening throttle plate.

Vacuum Dump Valve

The vacuum dump valve, **Figs. 2 and 11,** is adjusted in its mounting bracket. It should be adjusted closed (no vacuum leak) when the brake pedal is released, and open when the pedal is depressed. Use a hand vacuum pump to make this adjustment.

Clutch Switch

1. Prop clutch pedal, **Fig. 12,** in full up position (pawl fully released from sector).
2. Loosen switch mounting screw.
3. Slide switch forward toward clutch pedal until switch plunger cap is .30 inch from contacting switch housing, then tighten attaching screw.
4. Remove prop from clutch pedal and test drive for clutch switch cancellation of a speed control.

1992 CROWN VICTORIA, GRAND MARQUIS & TOWN CAR (EARLY PRODUCTION)

Actuator Cable

1. Remove cable retaining clip.

2. Pull actuator cable end tube to take up any slack in cable.
3. Maintaining a light tension on cable, insert cable retaining clip and snap into place.
4. Verify that throttle linkage operates freely and smoothly.

Vacuum Dump Valve

1. Holding brake pedal down, push dump valve forward through its adjustment collar, **Fig. 13.**
2. With a .05 inch (1.27mm) shim positioned on the surface of the adapter (9C962), pull brake pedal fully rearward.
3. Release brake pedal and remove shim.
4. Adapter should be in contact with white dump valve plunger and not in black dump valve housing. **If adapter comes into contact with black dump valve housing, stop lamps could activate with temperature changes.**

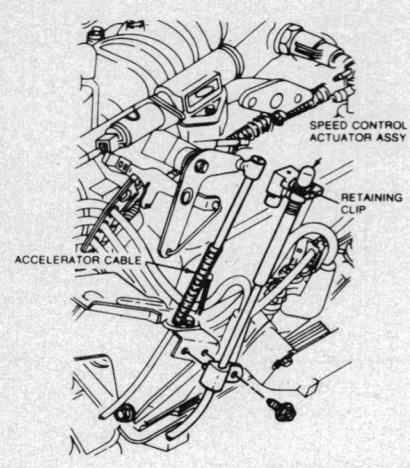

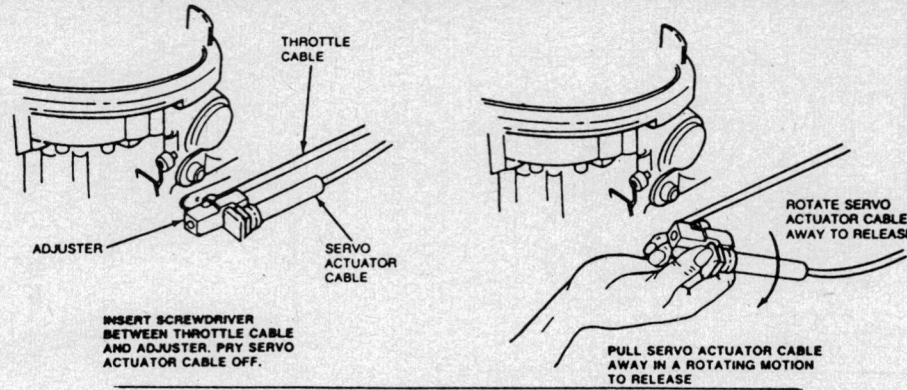

Fig. 8   Actuator cable. Sable & Taurus w/3.0L/V6-182 engine

1992 TOWN CAR (LATE PRODUCTION), 1993–94 CROWN VICTORIA, GRAND MARQUIS, MARK VIII & TOWN CAR

Actuator Cable

1. Remove retaining clip from actuator cable adjuster at throttle.
2. Ensure throttle is in fully closed position.
3. Pull on actuator cable to take up slack, then loosen at least one notch so there is approximately .118 inch (3mm) of slack in cable.
4. Insert cable clip and snap into place.
5. Ensure that throttle linkage operates freely and smoothly.

1992 PROBE

ACTUATOR CABLE

2.2L/4-133 Engine

1. **On models equipped with electric actuator,** remove plastic cover.
2. **On all models,** loosen locknut and adjusting nuts, **Fig. 14.**
3. Carefully pull on cable housing trying not to move actuator rod.
4. Position adjusting nut A until there is 0.039-0.118 inch clearance between nut A and bracket.
5. Tighten locknut B, then replace actuator plastic cover if removed.

3.0L/V6-182 Engine

1. Remove speed control actuator cable retaining clip.
2. Push actuator cable through adjuster until slight tension is felt.
3. Insert cable retaining clip, then snap into place.

1993–94 PROBE

Actuator Cable

1. Remove retaining clip from actuator cable housing.

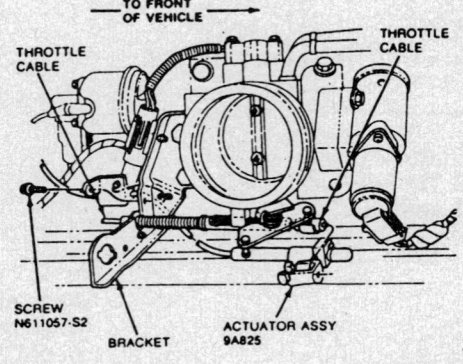

Fig. 9   Actuator cable. Mark VII, Grand Marquis & Town Car

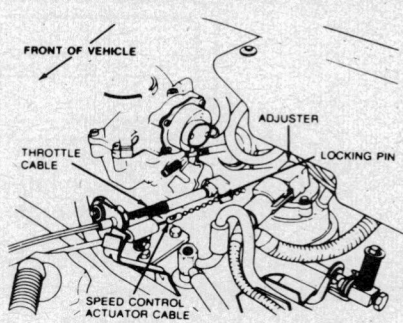

Fig. 10   Actuator cable. Sable & Taurus w/2.5L/4-153 engine

2. Pull lightly on cable until all slack is taken out.
3. Insert cable clip and snap into place.

Vacuum Dump Valve

When the brake pedal is released and in the upright position, the plunger of the vacuum dump valve should protrude 4-5 mm from the body. If plunger length is greater than specified, adjust valve position in the adjusting clip, **Fig. 15.**

CAPRI

ACTUATOR CABLE

Cable At Throttle Body

A setting tool must be fabricated as shown in **Fig. 16,** to adjust speed control cables.

1. Disconnect cable from cruise control actuator.
2. Slightly loosen cable retaining nuts at bracket on cylinder head cover.
3. Insert setting tool between nut "B" and bracket, **Fig. 17.**
4. Tighten both nuts to eliminate all cable slack.
5. Loosen nut "A" only enough to remove tool. Do not adjust nut "B."
6. Tighten nut "A" without moving nut "B."

Cable At Actuator

To be performed after throttle body end adjustment.

1. Slightly loosen cable retaining nuts at bracket.
2. Insert setting tool between bracket and nut "D," **Fig. 18.**
3. Tighten both nuts to eliminate all slack at throttle body end of cable.
4. Loosen nut "C" only enough to remove setting tool . Do not adjust nut "D."
5. Tighten nut "C" without moving nut "D."

CLUTCH PEDAL HEIGHT

Measure the distance from the center of the clutch pedal to lower dash panel (front area of footwell). Pedal height must be 8.44-8.64 inches. Adjust if necessary as follows:

1. Loosen locknut and turn clutch switch until desired pedal height is obtained.
2. Tighten locknut when clutch pedal height is achieved.

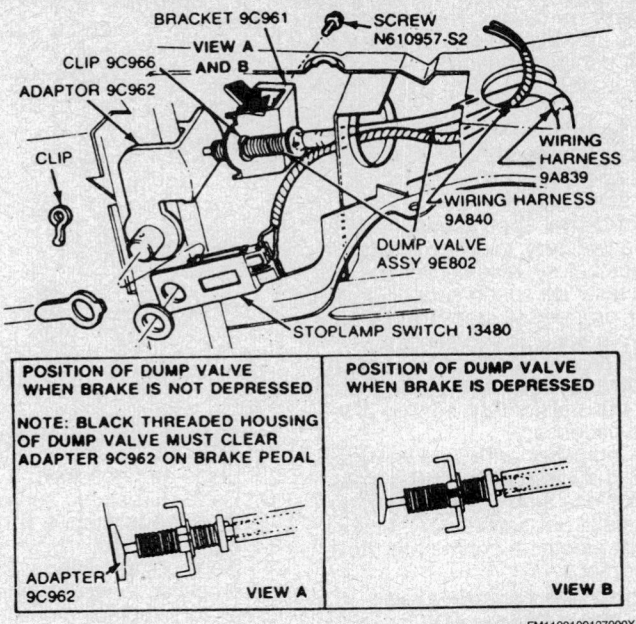

Fig. 11 Vacuum dump valve. Mark VII

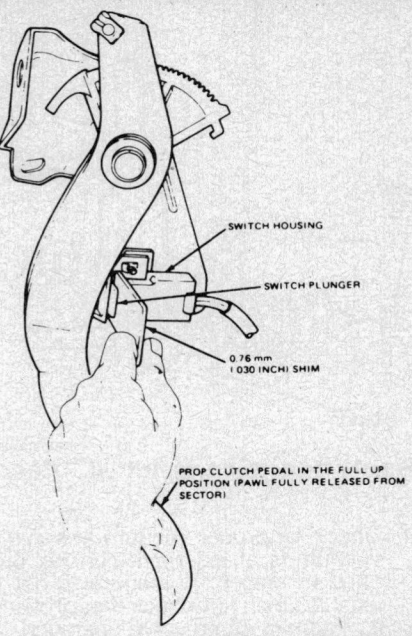

Fig. 12 Clutch switch. Sable & Taurus

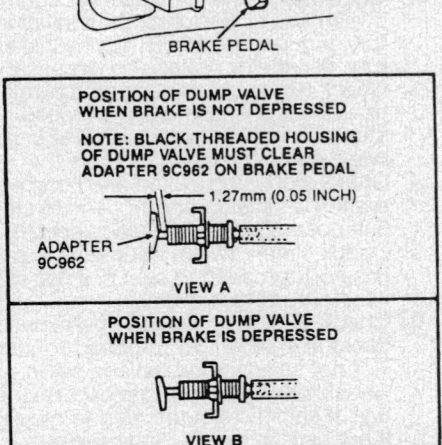

Fig. 13 Vacuum dump valve adjustment. 1992 Crown Victoria, Grand Marquis & Town Car (Early Production)

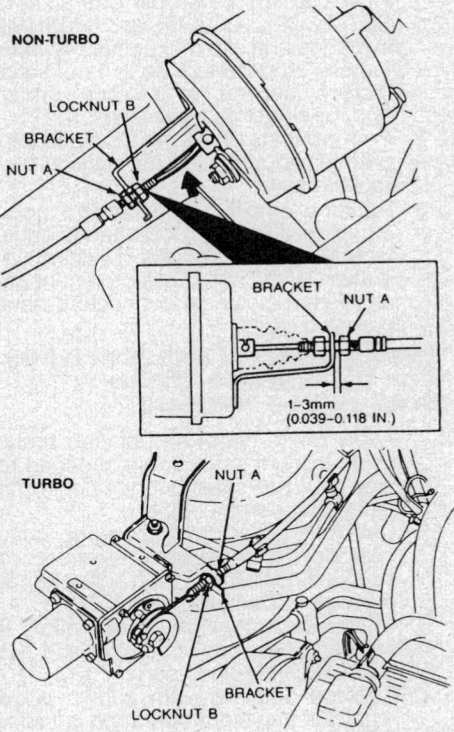

Fig. 14 Actuator cable adjustment. 1992 Probe

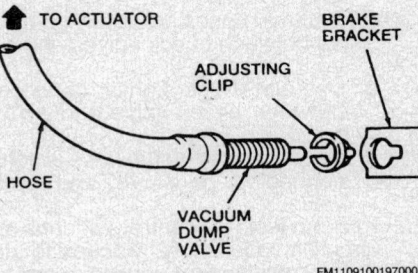

Fig. 15 Vacuum dump valve replacement. 1993–94 Probe

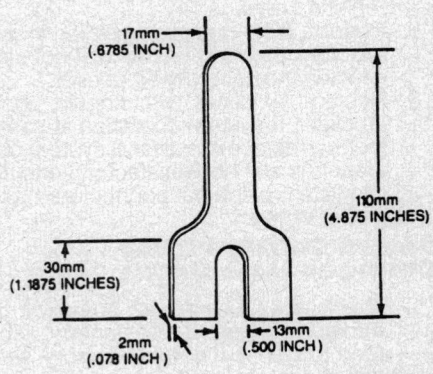

Fig. 16 Tool fabrication for cable adjustments. Capri

SYSTEM DIAGNOSIS & TESTING

ESCORT, MUSTANG, TEMPO, TOPAZ & TRACER

1992

Refer to wiring diagrams **Figs. 19, 20 and 21** and "Component Testing" when performing the following diagnostic procedures.

Speed Control Is Inoperative

1. Apply brake pedal and check if brake lights work. If brake lights work, proceed to step 2. If brake lights do not work, check stop lamp circuit and stop lamps.
2. **On models with manual transmission,** check to ensure proper opera-

tion of clutch deactivator switch. If switch operation is satisfactory, proceed to step 3. If switch operation is not satisfactory, service or replace as necessary.
3. **On all models,** check for proper operation of actuator lever and throttle linkage. If satisfactory, proceed to step 4. If not satisfactory, adjust or service as necessary.

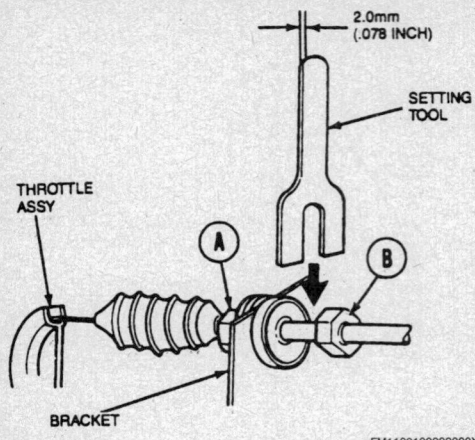

Fig. 17   Location of nut "B." Capri

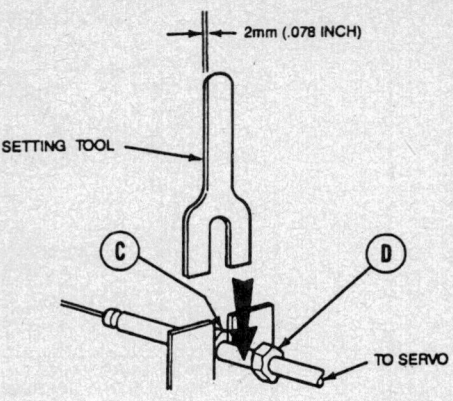

Fig. 18   Location of nut "D." Capri

4. Check for proper vacuum at servo. If vacuum is at least 2.5 inch Hg, proceed to step 5. If vacuum is not at least 2.5 inch Hg, check the following:
   a. Vacuum dump valve operation.
   b. Vacuum supply hose is tightly connected to VAC port on manifold check valve and to vacuum manifold.
   c. Vacuum hoses are tightly connected between check valves and servo.
   d. Vacuum hose tightly connected between check valve and aspirator.
   e. Vacuum dump valve hose is tightly connected to servo and dump valve.
5. Perform tests on control switches and circuit. If satisfactory, proceed to step 6. If not satisfactory, service or replace as necessary.
6. Perform tests on servo. If satisfactory, proceed to step 7. If not satisfactory, replace servo.
7. Perform tests on speed sensor. If satisfactory, proceed to step 8. If not satisfactory, replace speed sensor.
8. Replace amplifier with known good amplifier. If system operation is satisfactory, replace amplifier. If system operation is still not satisfactory, ensure all system electrical connectors have proper contact.

Speed Continuously Changes Up & Down

1. Check to ensure proper operation of actuator linkage. If satisfactory, proceed to step 2. If not satisfactory, service or replace actuator linkage.
2. **On Mustang and Tempo/Topaz models,** check continuity of circuits 147, 148 and 149. If continuity exists, proceed to steps 4 or 5. If continuity does not exist, repair or replace wiring as necessary.
3. **On Escort/Tracer models,** check continuity of servo to amplifier circuits. If continuity exists, proceed to step 4. If continuity does not exist, repair or replace wiring as necessary.
4. **On all models,** check speedometer cable for proper routing, ensure no

sharp bends or binding exists. If cable operation is satisfactory, proceed to step 5. If cable operation is not satisfactory, service or replace speedometer cable.
5. Perform tests on servo. If servo operation is satisfactory, proceed to step 6. If servo operation is not satisfactory, replace servo.
6. Check for proper speed sensor operation. If satisfactory, proceed to step 7. If not satisfactory, replace sensor.
7. Perform tests on speed sensor. If satisfactory, proceed to step 8. If not satisfactory, replace speed sensor.
8. Check for proper operation of vacuum dump valve. If satisfactory, proceed to step 9. If not satisfactory, service or replace as necessary.
9. Replace amplifier with known good amplifier. If system operation is satisfactory, replace amplifier. If system operation is still not satisfactory, ensure all system electrical connectors have proper contact.

Speed Control Operates But Does Not Resume, Accelerate Or Coast Down Properly

1. Check to ensure proper operation of SET-ACCEL, COAST, and RESUME switches and slip ring circuits. If satisfactory, proceed to step 2. If not satisfactory, service or replace switch and/or circuit as necessary.
2. Perform tests on servo. If satisfactory, proceed to step 3. If not satisfactory, replace servo.
3. Replace amplifier with known good amplifier. If system operation is satisfactory, replace amplifier. If system operation is still not satisfactory, ensure all system electrical connectors have proper contact.

Speed Control System Does Not Disengage When Brakes Are Applied

1. Apply brake pedal and ensure brake lights work. If satisfactory, proceed to step 2. If not satisfactory, check and repair stop lamp circuit.
2. Check for proper vacuum dump valve operation. If satisfactory, proceed to step 3. If not satisfactory, adjust or replace as necessary.
3. Check for proper servo operation. If satisfactory, proceed to step 4. If not satisfactory, replace servo.
4. Replace amplifier with known good amplifier. If system operation is satisfactory, replace amplifier. If system operation is still not satisfactory, ensure all system electrical connectors have proper contact.

Speed Gradually Increases Or Decreases After Speed Is Set

1. Check for proper operation of bead chain and actuator cable. If satisfactory, proceed to step 2. If not satisfactory, adjust or replace as necessary.
2. Check for proper vacuum dump valve operation. If satisfactory, proceed to step 3. If not satisfactory, adjust or re-

place as necessary.
3. Perform tests on servo. If satisfactory, proceed to step 4. If not satisfactory, replace servo.
4. Replace amplifier with known good amplifier. If system operation is satisfactory, replace amplifier. If system operation is still not satisfactory, ensure all system electrical connectors have proper contact.

Speed Will Not Set In System

1. Check for proper throttle linkage operation. If satisfactory, proceed to step 2. If not satisfactory, adjust or replace as necessary.
2. Check for proper operation of control switch and system circuits. If satisfactory, proceed to step 3. If not satisfactory, service or replace as necessary.
3. Check for proper vacuum dump valve operation. If satisfactory, proceed to step 4. If not satisfactory, service or replace as necessary.
4. Check stop lamp switch and lamp operation. If satisfactory, proceed to step 5. If not satisfactory, replace switch.
5. Check clutch switch operation. If satisfactory, proceed to step 6. If not satisfactory, replace switch.
6. Check to ensure proper operation of servo. If satisfactory, proceed to step 7. If not satisfactory, replace servo.
7. Check for proper speed sensor operation. If satisfactory, proceed to step 8. If not satisfactory, replace sensor.
8. Replace amplifier with known good amplifier. If system operation is satisfactory, replace amplifier. If system operation is still not satisfactory, ensure all system electrical connectors have proper contact.

Speed Control Does Not Disengage When Clutch Pedal Is Depressed

1. Check for proper stop light switch operation. If satisfactory, proceed to step 2. If not satisfactory, service or replace as necessary.
2. Check for proper clutch switch operation. If satisfactory, proceed to step 3. If not satisfactory, replace clutch switch.
3. Examine all connectors to ensure proper contact.

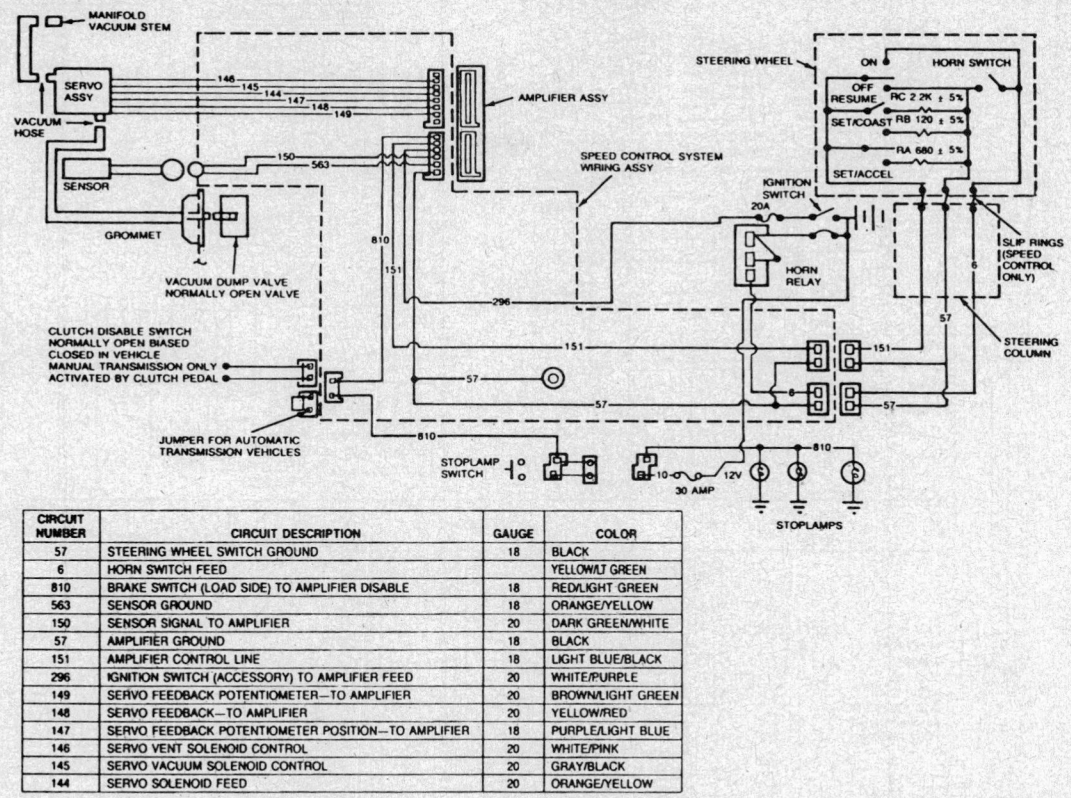

CIRCUIT NUMBER	CIRCUIT DESCRIPTION	GAUGE	COLOR
57	STEERING WHEEL SWITCH GROUND	18	BLACK
6	HORN SWITCH FEED		YELLOW/LT GREEN
810	BRAKE SWITCH (LOAD SIDE) TO AMPLIFIER DISABLE	18	RED/LIGHT GREEN
563	SENSOR GROUND	18	ORANGE/YELLOW
150	SENSOR SIGNAL TO AMPLIFIER	20	DARK GREEN/WHITE
57	AMPLIFIER GROUND	18	BLACK
151	AMPLIFIER CONTROL LINE	18	LIGHT BLUE/BLACK
296	IGNITION SWITCH (ACCESSORY) TO AMPLIFIER FEED	20	WHITE/PURPLE
149	SERVO FEEDBACK POTENTIOMETER—TO AMPLIFIER	20	BROWN/LIGHT GREEN
148	SERVO FEEDBACK—TO AMPLIFIER	20	YELLOW/RED
147	SERVO FEEDBACK POTENTIOMETER POSITION—TO AMPLIFIER	18	PURPLE/LIGHT BLUE
146	SERVO VENT SOLENOID CONTROL	20	WHITE/PINK
145	SERVO VACUUM SOLENOID CONTROL	20	GRAY/BLACK
144	SERVO SOLENOID FEED	20	ORANGE/YELLOW

FM1109100097000X

Fig. 19 Wiring circuit. 1992 Mustang

Speed Control Operation Is Intermittent

1. Check when intermittent operation occurs. If intermittent operation occurs when vehicle is at cruising speed, proceed to step 2. If intermittent operation occurs when operating control buttons or turning steering wheel, proceed to step 4.
2. Check that there is at least 2.5 inches Hg of vacuum supplied to servo. If satisfactory, proceed to step 3. If not satisfactory, service vacuum supply as needed.
3. Perform servo (throttle actuator) assembly test. If test result is satisfactory, substitute amplifier with a known good amplifier and proceed to step 4. If not satisfactory, replace servo assembly.
4. Perform control switch and circuit test. If test results are satisfactory, substitute amplifier with known good amplifier and proceed to step 5. If test results are not satisfactory, repair circuits or replace horn pad assembly as necessary. **When replacing horn pad assembly, clean or service copper brushes and steering wheel ring.**
5. If system operation is satisfactory, replace amplifier.

1993—94

Diagnostic and troubleshooting procedures consist of a series of pinpoint tests designed to locate faults to be serviced in the speed control system. The system can be diagnosed using the Rotunda Speed Control Tester 007-00013 or equivalent.

Refer to wiring diagrams **Figs. 22, 23 and 24** and "Component Testing" when performing the following diagnostic procedures. **On 1993—94 Escort and Tracer models,** refer to **Fig. 25,** for diagnostic symptom chart.

Refer to **Figs. 26 through 45,** for diagnostic pinpoint tests.

CONTINENTAL, COUGAR & THUNDERBIRD

Diagnostic and troubleshooting procedures consist of symptom diagnosis and a series of pinpoint tests designed to locate faults to be serviced in the speed control system. Refer to wiring diagram **Figs. 46 through 49** when performing the following diagnostic procedures.

SYMPTOM DIAGNOSIS
Speed Control Is Inoperative

1. Apply brake pedal and check if brake lights work. If brake lights work, proceed to step 2. If brake lights do not work, check stop lamp circuit and stop lamps.
2. **On models with manual transmission,** check to ensure proper operation of clutch deactivator switch. If switch operation is satisfactory, proceed to step 3. If switch operation is not satisfactory, service or replace as necessary.
3. **On all models,** check for proper operation of actuator lever and throttle linkage. If satisfactory, proceed to step 4. If not satisfactory, adjust or service as necessary.
4. Ensure that all system vacuum hoses are tightly connected and are free of cuts, cracks and kinks.
5. Disconnect hose between check valve and servo, at servo end. Apply 18 inches of vacuum to open end of hose. If vacuum can be pumped and held, proceed to step 6 or 7. If vacuum cannot be pumped or held, replace check valve.
6. **On Thunderbird SC models,** disconnect hose between aspirator check valves and manifold check valve at manifold check valve end. Apply 18 inches of vacuum to open end of hose. If vacuum can be pumped and held, proceed to step 7. If vacuum cannot be pumped or held, replace aspirator check valves.
7. **On all models,** check vacuum dump valve. If valve operation is satisfactory, proceed to step 8. If valve operation is not satisfactory, adjust or replace as necessary.
8. Perform tests on control switches and circuits. If satisfactory, proceed to step 9. If not satisfactory, repair or replace as necessary.
9. Perform tests on servo. If servo operation is satisfactory, proceed to step 10. If servo operation is not satisfactory, replace servo.

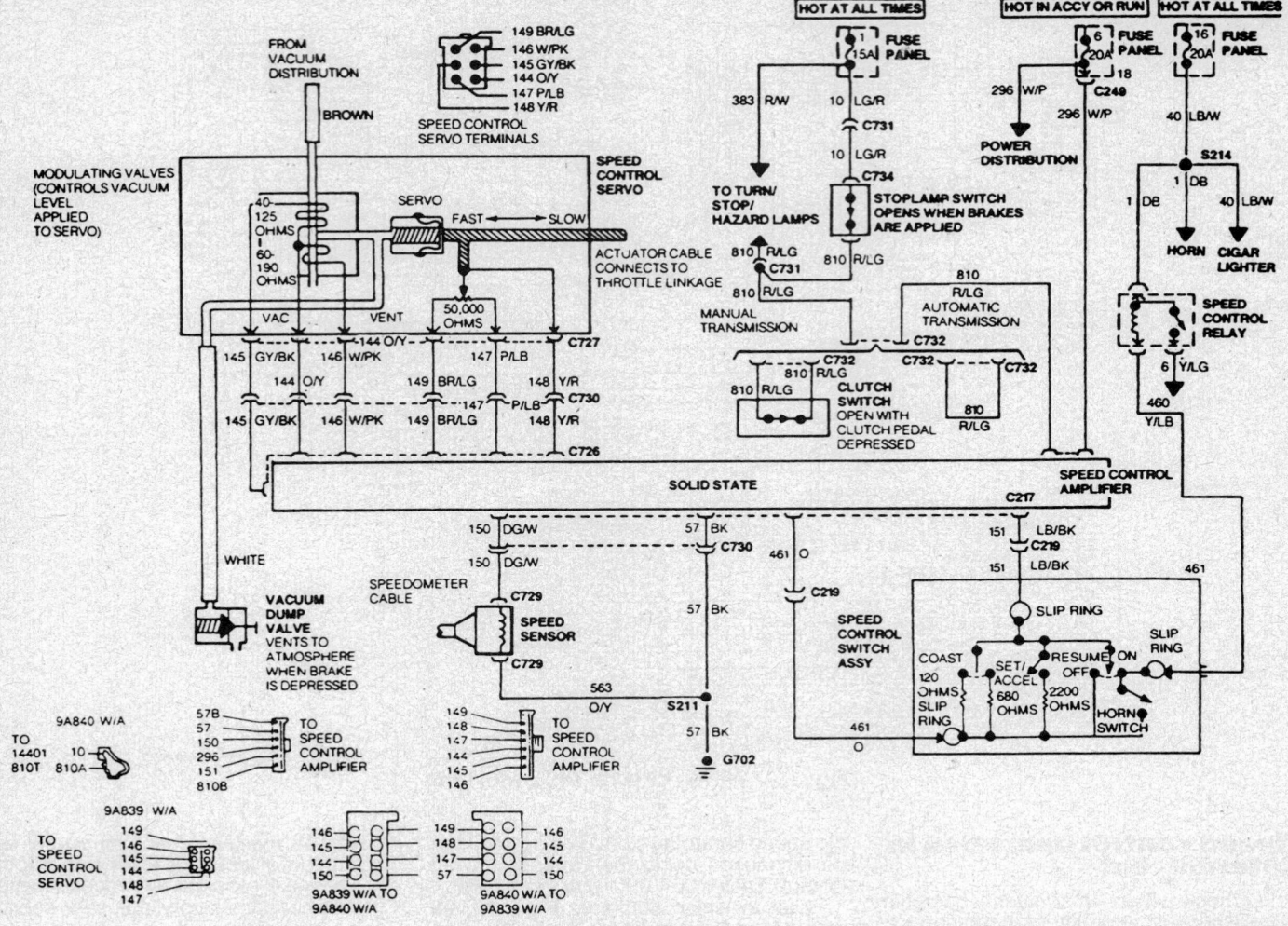

Fig. 20   Wiring circuit. 1992 Tempo & Topaz

10. Perform tests on speed sensor. If sensor operation is satisfactory, proceed to step 11. If sensor operation is not satisfactory, replace sensor.

11. Replace amplifier with known good amplifier. If system operation is satisfactory, replace amplifier. If system operation is still not satisfactory, ensure all system electrical connectors have proper contact.

Speed Continuously Changes Up & Down

1. Check actuator linkage for proper operation. If satisfactory, proceed to step 2. If not satisfactory, adjust or replace actuator linkage.

2. Check continuity of circuits 147, 148 and 149. If continuity exists, proceed to step 3. If continuity does not exist, repair or replace wiring as necessary.

3. Ensure that all system vacuum hoses are tightly connected and are free of cuts, cracks and kinks.

4. Disconnect hose between check valve and servo, at servo end. Apply 18 inches of vacuum to open end of hose. If vacuum can be pumped and held, proceed to steps 5 or 6. If vacu-

um cannot be pumped or held, replace check valve.

5. **On Thunderbird SC models,** disconnect hose between aspirator check valves and manifold check valve at manifold check valve end. Apply 18 inches of vacuum to open end of hose. If vacuum can be pumped and held, proceed to step 6. If vacuum cannot be pumped or held, replace aspirator check valves as necessary.

6. **On all models,** check speedometer cable for proper routing, ensure no sharp bends or binding exists. If cable operation is satisfactory, proceed to step 7. If cable operation is not satisfactory, service or replace speedometer cable.

7. Perform tests on servo. If servo operation is satisfactory, proceed to step 8. If servo operation is not satisfactory, replace servo.

8. Perform tests on speed sensor. If satisfactory, proceed to step 9. If not satisfactory, replace speed sensor.

9. Check for proper operation of vacuum dump valve. If satisfactory, proceed to step 10. If not satisfactory, service or replace as necessary.

10. Replace amplifier with known good amplifier. If system operation is satisfactory, replace amplifier. If system operation is still not satisfactory, ensure all system electrical connectors have proper contact.

Speed Control Operates But Does Not Resume, Accelerate Or Coast Down Properly

1. Check to ensure proper operation of SET-ACCEL, COAST, and RESUME switches and slip ring circuits. If satisfactory, proceed to step 2. If not satisfactory, service or replace switch and/or circuit as necessary.

2. Ensure that all system vacuum hoses are tightly connected and are free of cuts, cracks and kinks.

3. Disconnect hose between check valve and servo, at servo end. Apply 18 inches of vacuum to open end of hose. If vacuum can be pumped and held, proceed to steps 4 or 5. If vacuum cannot be pumped or held, replace check valve.

4. **On Thunderbird SC models,** disconnect hose between aspirator

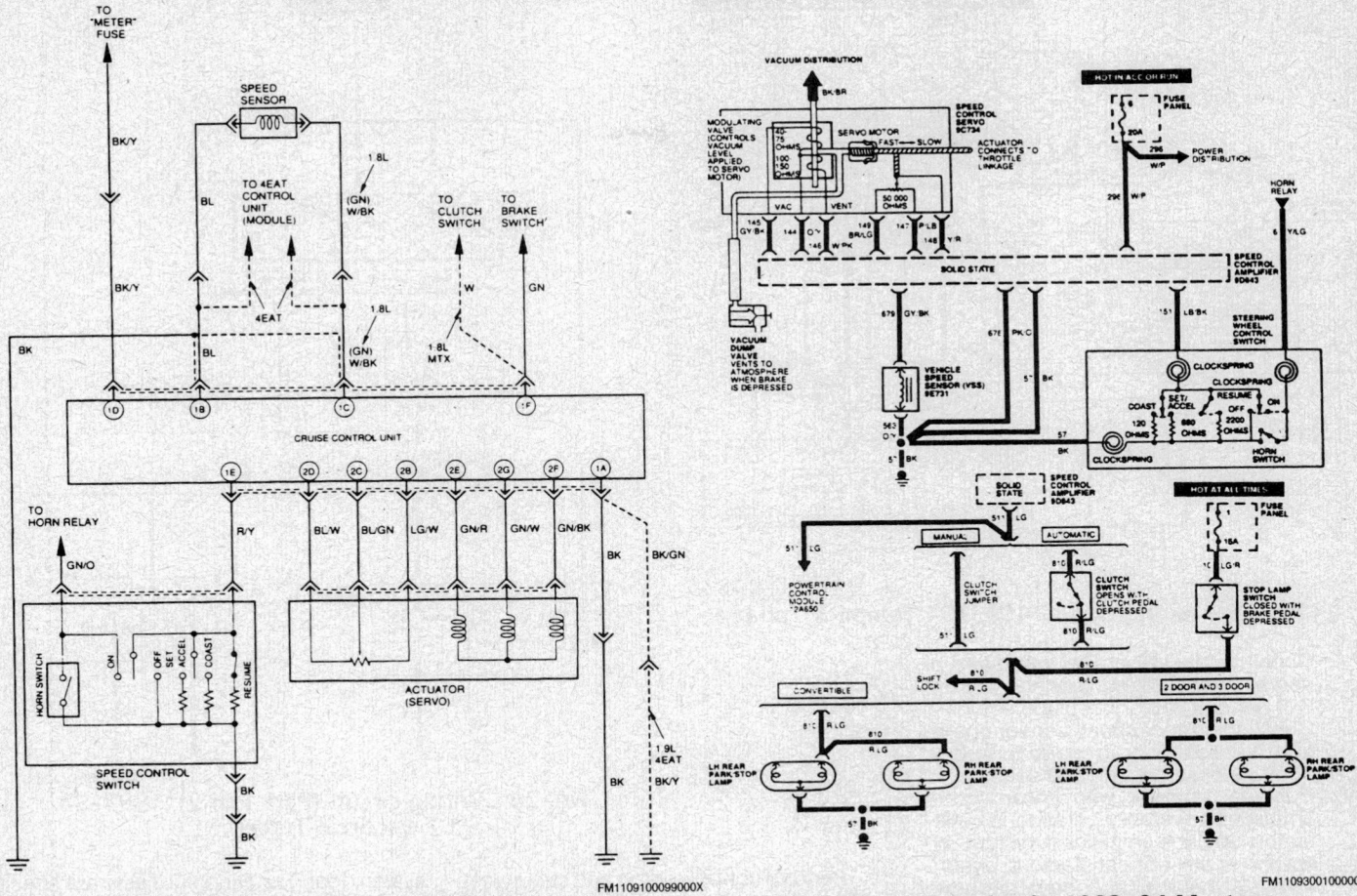

Fig. 21 Wiring circuit. 1992 Escort & Tracer

Fig. 22 Wiring circuit. 1993–94 Mustang

check valves and manifold check valve at manifold check valve end. Apply 18 inches of vacuum to open end of hose. If vacuum can be pumped and held, proceed to step 3. If vacuum cannot be pumped or held, replace aspirator check valves as necessary.

5. **On all models,** perform tests on servo. If satisfactory, proceed to step 6. If not satisfactory, replace servo.

6. Replace amplifier with known good amplifier. If system operation is satisfactory, replace amplifier. If system operation is still not satisfactory, ensure all system electrical connectors have proper contact.

Speed Control System Does Not Disengage When Brakes Are Applied

1. Apply brake pedal and ensure brake lights work. If satisfactory, proceed to step 2. If not satisfactory, check and repair stop lamp circuit.

2. Check for proper vacuum dump valve operation. If satisfactory, proceed to step 3. If not satisfactory, adjust or replace as necessary.

3. Check for proper servo operation. If satisfactory, proceed to step 4. If not satisfactory, replace servo.

4. Replace amplifier with known good

amplifier. If system operation is satisfactory, replace amplifier. If system operation is still not satisfactory, ensure all system electrical connectors have proper contact.

Speed Gradually Increases Or Decreases After Speed Is Set

1. Check for proper operation of bead chain and actuator cable. If satisfactory, proceed to step 2. If not satisfactory, adjust or replace as necessary.

2. Check for proper vacuum dump valve operation. If satisfactory, proceed to step 3. If not satisfactory, adjust or replace as necessary.

3. Ensure that all system vacuum hoses are tightly connected and are free of cuts, cracks and kinks.

4. Disconnect hose between check valve and servo, at servo end. Apply 18 inches of vacuum to open end of hose. If vacuum can be pumped and held, proceed to steps 5 or 6. If vacuum cannot be pumped or held, replace check valve.

5. **On Thunderbird SC models,** disconnect hose between aspirator check valves and manifold check valve at manifold check valve end. Apply 18 inches of vacuum to open end of hose. If vacuum can be

pumped and held, proceed to step 6. If vacuum cannot be pumped or held, replace aspirator check valves as necessary.

6. **On all models,** perform tests on servo. If satisfactory, proceed to step 7. If not satisfactory, replace servo.

7. Replace amplifier with known good amplifier. If system operation is satisfactory, replace amplifier. If system operation is still not satisfactory, ensure all system electrical connectors have proper contact.

Speed Will Not Set In System

1. Check for proper throttle linkage operation. If satisfactory, proceed to step 2. If not satisfactory, adjust or replace as necessary.

2. Check for proper operation of control switch and system circuits. If satisfactory, proceed to step 3. If not satisfactory, service or replace as necessary.

3. Check for proper vacuum dump valve operation. If satisfactory, proceed to step 4. If not satisfactory, service or replace as necessary.

4. Check stop lamp switch and lamp operation. If satisfactory, proceed to step 5. If not satisfactory, replace switch.

5. Check clutch switch operation. If satisfactory, proceed to step 6. If not satisfactory, replace switch.

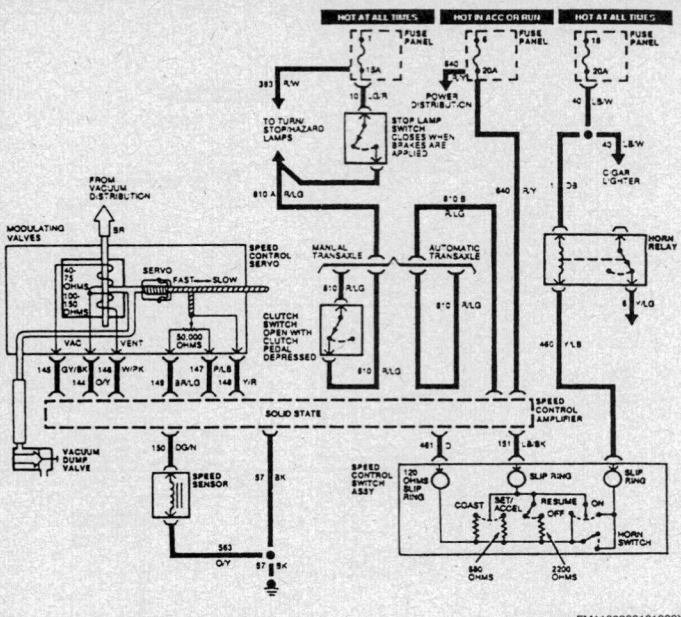

Fig. 23   Wiring circuit. 1993–94 Tempo & Topaz

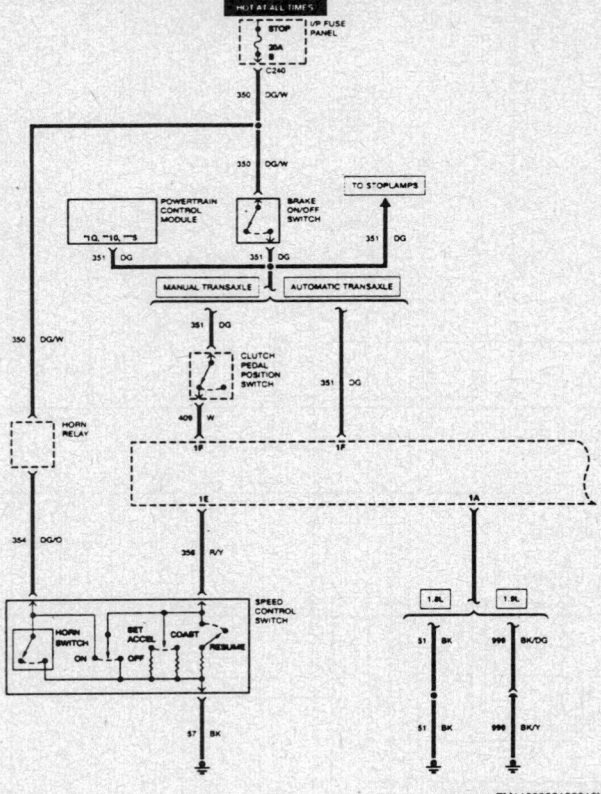

Fig. 24   Wiring circuit (Part 1 of 2). 1993–94 Escort & Tracer

6. Check to ensure proper operation of servo. If satisfactory, proceed to step 7. If not satisfactory, replace servo.
7. Check for proper speed sensor operation. If satisfactory, proceed to step 8. If not satisfactory, replace sensor.
8. Replace amplifier with known good amplifier. If system operation is satisfactory, replace amplifier. If system operation is still not satisfactory, ensure all system electrical connectors have proper contact.

Speed Control Does Not Disengage When Clutch Pedal Is Depressed

1. Check for proper stop light switch operation. If satisfactory, proceed to step 2. If not satisfactory, service or replace as necessary.
2. Check for proper clutch switch operation. If satisfactory, proceed to step 3. If not satisfactory, replace clutch switch.
3. Examine all connectors to ensure proper contact.

Speed Control Operation Is Intermittent

1. Check when intermittent operation occurs. If intermittent operation occurs when vehicle is at cruising speed, proceed to step 2. If intermittent operation occurs when operating control buttons or turning steering wheel, proceed to step 4.
2. Check that there is at least 2.5 inches Hg of vacuum supplied to servo. If satisfactory, proceed to step 3. If not satisfactory, service vacuum supply as needed.
3. Perform servo (throttle actuator) assembly test. If test result is satisfactory, substitute amplifier with a known good amplifier and proceed to step 5. If not satisfactory, replace servo assembly.

4. Perform control switch and circuit test. If test results are satisfactory, substitute amplifier with known good amplifier and proceed to step 5. If test results are not satisfactory, repair circuits or replace horn pad assembly as necessary. **When replacing horn pad assembly, clean or service copper brushes and steering wheel ring.**
5. If system operation is satisfactory, replace amplifier.

PINPOINT TESTS

Refer to **Figs. 50 through 54** for diagnostic pinpoint test procedures.

MARK VII, SABLE & TAURUS

Do not depart from the instructions provided here. Anyone who departs from the following instructions must first establish that he may compromise his personal safety and the vehicle integrity by his choice of methods, tools or parts.

The Integrated Vehicle Speed Control (IVSC) contains a self-test capability, consisting of a Key On, Engine Off (KOEO) and Key On, Engine Running (KOER) routine, which utilizes output error codes similar to EEC-IV subsystem "Quick Tests." These "Quick Tests" then refer to Pinpoint Tests for specific components diagnosis.

Testing for the IVSC is divided into two formats: the Quick Test and the Pinpoint Tests. The Quick Test is a functional IVSC

system test. The Pinpoint Tests are specific component tests.

The Quick Test checks all IVSC components except the speed sensor, which must be checked separately. To test and service the IVSC system, perform the quick test first. If the system passes, check the speed sensor. If failure codes are generated, do only the Pinpoint Test specified by that particular failure code.

After all test and services have been completed, repeat the entire Quick Test to verify that the IVSC system operates properly.

TEST EQUIPMENT

Use Super (STAR II) Tester No. 007-00041, or Inductive Dwell-Tach-Volt-Ohmmeter (VOM) 0-20 VDC No.059-00010, or equivalent to perform the IVSC Quick Test and display error codes. A Rotunda Breakout Box 014-00322 or equivalent can also be used for convenience during Pinpoint Testing.

EQUIPMENT HOOKUP

Using The STAR Tester

1. Turn ignition switch to the Off position.
2. Connect color-coded adapter cable leads to STAR tester.
3. Connect two service connectors from adapter cable to vehicles appropriate Self-Test connectors.
4. After equipment hookup, proceed to Self-Testing.

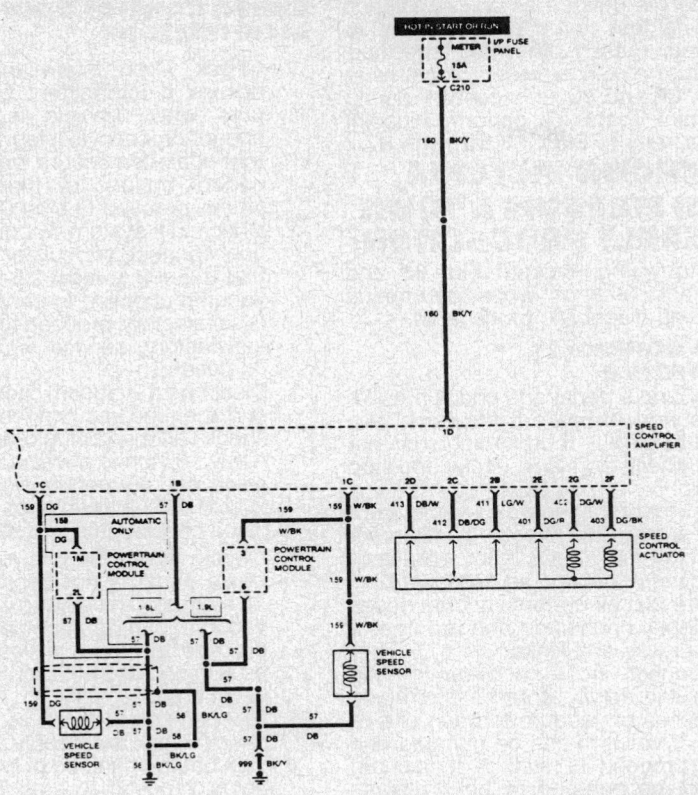

Fig. 24   Wiring circuit (Part 2 of 2). 1993–94 Escort & Tracer

FM1109300102020X

Quick Test Self-Test

Quick Test Self-Test is divided into two specialized tests: Key On, Engine Off, and Key On, Engine Running. The Self-Test is not a conclusive test by itself, but is used as a part of the functional Quick Test diagnostic procedure. The processor stores the Self-Test program in its permanent memory. When activated, it checks the IVSC system by testing its functional capability and verifies that various sensors and actuators are connected and operating properly.

The Key On, Engine Off and Engine Running tests are functional tests which only detect faults that are present at the time of the Self-Test.

Key On, Engine Off Test

At this time, a test of the IVSC system is conducted power applied and engine at rest. The fault must be present at the time of testing for errors to be detected in this test.

Key On, Engine Running Test

At this time, a test of the IVSC system is conducted with the engine running. The system is checked under actual operating conditions and at normal operating temperatures. The actuators are exercised and checked for corresponding results.

Service Codes

The EEC-IV system communicates service information by way of the Self-Test codes. These service codes are two digit numbers representing the results of the Self-Test.

The service codes are transmitted on the Self-Test output (found in the Self-Test connector) in the form of timed pulses, and read by the technician on a voltmeter or on the STAR tester, **Fig. 55.**

Reading Codes-Analog Voltmeter

When a service code is reported on the analog voltmeter for a function test, it will represent itself as a pulsing or sweeping movement of the voltmeter's needle across the dial face of the voltmeter, **Fig. 56.** Therefore, a single-digit number of three will be reported by three needle pulses (sweeps). However as previously stated, a service code is represented by a two digit number, such as 2-3. As a result, the Self-Test service code of 2-3 will appear on the voltmeter as two needle pulses (sweeps), then, after a two second pause, the needle will pulse (sweep) three times.

Reading Codes, Self-Test Automatic Readout (STAR) Rotunda 007-00004, or STAR Rotunda 007-000717, or Equivalent

After hooking up the STAR tester and turning on its power switch, the tester will run a display check and the numerals 88 will flash in the display window, **Fig. 57.** A steady 00 will then appear to signify that the STAR tester is ready to start the Self-Test and receive the tests service codes.

Using Analog Voltmeter

1. Turn ignition switch to the Off position.
2. Connect a jumper wire from Self-Test input (STI) to Pin 2, Signal Return on the Self-Test connector.
3. Set analog VOM on a DC voltage range to read from 0-15 volts DC. Connect VOM from battery (+) to Pin 4 Self-Test Output (STO) in the Self-Test connector.
4. After equipment hookup proceed to Self-Testing.

QUICK TEST PROCEDURE Description

The Quick Test is a functional test of the IVSC system consisting of basic Test Steps (described below). Otherwise, inaccurate diagnosis or the replacement of satisfactory components may result.

Quick Test Steps

1. Perform a visual check for obvious faults then properly prepare the vehicle for testing.
2. Ensure proper equipment is used for gathering test data is ready prior to testing.
3. Key On, Engine Off Self Test is a static check of IVSC inputs and outputs.
4. Key On, Engine Running Self-Test is a dynamic check of the engine in operation.

Visual Check & Vehicle Preparation

Correct test results for the Quick Test are dependent on the proper operation of related non-IVSC components systems. It may be necessary to correct faults in these areas before the IVSC will pass the Quick Test.

Before hooking up any equipment to diagnose the IVSC system, make the following checks:

1. Check all engine vacuum hoses for leaks or pinched hoses (servo to dump valve and servo to manifold vacuum).
2. Check IVSC and EEC system wiring harness electrical connections for proper connections, faulty connectors, corrosion and proper routing of harness. It may be necessary to disconnect or disassemble the connector assembly to perform some of the inspections.
3. Check EEC-IV and IVSC sensors and actuators for physical damage.
4. Perform all safety steps required to start and run operation vehicle tests.
5. Apply emergency brake. Place the shift lever in PARK (NEUTRAL for manual transmission).
6. Turn off all electrical loads.
7. Verify engine coolant is at specified level.
8. Start engine and idle until upper radiator hose is hot and pressurized and throttle is off fast idle.
9. Turn ignition key off.
10. Service items as required, then proceed to equipment hookup.

To receive the service codes, press the push button at the front of the STAR tester. The button will latch down, and a colon will appear in the display window in the front of the 00 numerals. The colon must be displayed to receive the service codes.

If for any reason the technician wishes to clear the display window during the Self-Test, he must turn off the vehicle's engine, press the tester's push button once to unlatch it (colon will disappear), then press the button again to latch down the button (colon will appear again). Every time the STAR tester is turned off, the low battery indicator (LO BAT) should show briefly at the upper left corner to the tester's display window. If the LO BAT indicator shows steadily at any other time during the operation of the STAR tester with any service code, turn its power switch to OFF and replace the 9-volt battery in the tester.

The STAR tester will display the last service code received, even after it has been disconnected from the vehicle. It will hold the service code on the display until the power is turned off or the push button is unlatched and latched.

QUICK TESTS

Refer to **Figs. 58 through 63** to perform system Quick Tests.

PINPOINT TESTS

Instructions For Using The Pinpoint Tests

1. Do not run any of the following Pinpoint Tests unless you are so instructed by the Quick Test. Each Pinpoint Test assumes that a fault has been detected in the system with direction to enter a specific service routine. Performing any Pinpoint Test without direction from the Quick Test may produce incorrect results and cause replacement of satisfactory components.
2. Do not replace any component unless the test result indicates that it should be replaced.
3. When more than one service code is received, always start service with the first code received.
4. Do not measure voltage or resistance at the ECA or connect any test lights to it, unless otherwise specified.
5. Isolate both ends of a circuit, and turn the ignition key off whenever checking it for shorts or continuity, unless otherwise specified.
6. Disconnect solenoids and switches from the harness before measuring for continuity, resistance or energizing by way of 12 volt source, unless otherwise instructed.
7. In using the Pinpoint Tests, follow each step in order, starting from the first step in the appropriate test. Follow each step until the fault is found.
8. After completing any service to the IVSC system, verify that all components are properly reconnected and repeat the Quick Test.
9. An open is defined as any resistance reading greater than 5 ohms, unless otherwise specified.

10. A short is defined as any resistance reading less than 10,000 ohms to ground, unless otherwise specified. Refer to electrical wiring diagrams in **Figs. 64 and 65** as necessary during Pinpoint Tests. To perform Pinpoint Tests, refer to **Figs. 66 through 87.**

1992 CROWN VICTORIA, GRAND MARQUIS & TOWN CAR (EARLY PRODUCTION)

Refer to wiring diagram **Fig. 88** and "Component Testing" when performing the following diagnostic procedures.

Speed Control Is Inoperative

1. Apply brake pedal and check if brake lights work. If brake lights work, proceed to step 2. If brake lights do not work, check stop lamp circuit and stop lamps.
2. Check for proper operation of actuator lever and throttle linkage. If satisfactory, proceed to step 3. If not satisfactory, adjust or service as necessary.
3. Ensure that all system vacuum hoses are tightly connected and are free of cuts, cracks and kinks.
4. Disconnect hose between check valve and servo, at servo end. Apply 18 inches of vacuum to open end of hose. If vacuum can be pumped and held, proceed to step 5. If vacuum cannot be pumped or held, replace check valve.
5. Check vacuum dump valve. If valve operation is satisfactory, proceed to step 6. If valve operation is not satisfactory, adjust or replace as necessary.
6. Disconnect reservoir vacuum line at check valve. Apply 18 inches of vacuum to open end of hose. If vacuum can be pumped and held, proceed to step 8. If vacuum cannot be pumped and held, proceed to step 7.
7. Disconnect reservoir vacuum line from reservoir port and plug open end, then supply 18 inches of vacuum to other end of line disconnected from the servo check valve. If vacuum can be pumped and held, replace reservoir and repeat step 6. If vacuum cannot be pumped and held, replace reservoir vacuum hose.
8. Perform tests on control switches and circuits. If control switches and circuits are satisfactory, proceed to step 9. If control switches or circuits are not satisfactory, repair or replace as necessary.
9. Perform tests on servo. If servo operation is satisfactory, proceed to step 10. If servo operation is not satisfactory, replace servo.
10. Perform tests on speed sensor. If sensor operation is satisfactory, proceed to step 11. If sensor operation is not satisfactory, replace sensor.
11. Replace amplifier with known good amplifier. If system operation is satisfactory, replace amplifier. If system operation is still not satisfactory, ensure all system electrical connectors have proper contact.

Speed Control Operation Is Intermittent

1. Check when intermittent operation occurs. If intermittent operation occurs when vehicle is at cruising speed, proceed to step 2. If intermittent operation occurs when operating control buttons or turning steering wheel, proceed to step 8.
2. Check all system vacuum lines for tight connections, cuts or kinks. Check that there is at least 2.5 inches Hg of vacuum supplied to servo. If vacuum is satisfactory, proceed to step 3. If not satisfactory, service vacuum supply as needed.
3. Disconnect vacuum hose at servo end, then the vacuum reservoir line at check valve and plug open valve port. Apply 18 inches of vacuum to hose at servo end. If vacuum holds, proceed to step 4. If vacuum does not hold, replace check valve and repeat step 3.
4. Check that dump is closed when brake pedal is not depressed. Apply 18 inches of vacuum to dump valve. If vacuum can be pumped and held, proceed to step 5. If vacuum cannot be pumped and held, replace or adjust valve as necessary.
5. Disconnect reservoir vacuum line at check valve, then apply 18 inches of vacuum to open end of line. If vacuum holds, proceed to step 7. If vacuum does not hold, proceed to step 6.
6. Disconnect vacuum line from reservoir port and plug open end, then apply 18 inches of vacuum to other end of line disconnected from servo check valve. If vacuum holds, replace reservoir and repeat step 4. If vacuum does not hold, replace reservoir vacuum line.
7. Perform servo tests. If tests are satisfactory, proceed to step 8. If tests are not satisfactory, replace servo.
8. Perform control switch and circuit test. If test results are satisfactory, substitute amplifier with known good amplifier and proceed to step 9. If test results are not satisfactory, repair circuits or replace horn pad assembly as necessary. **When replacing horn pad assembly, clean or service copper brushes and steering wheel ring.**
9. If system operation is satisfactory, replace amplifier.

Speed Control Operates But Does Not Resume, Accelerate Or Coast Down Properly

1. Check to ensure proper operation of SET-ACCEL, COAST, and RESUME switches and slip ring circuits. If satisfactory, proceed to step 2. If not satisfactory, service or replace switch and/or circuit as necessary.
2. Ensure that all system vacuum hoses are tightly connected and are free of cuts, cracks and kinks.
3. If vehicle symptoms involve acceleration or resume functions, proceed as follows:

a. Check all system vacuum lines for tight connections, cuts or kinks. Check that there is at least 2.5 inches Hg of vacuum supplied to servo. If vacuum is satisfactory, proceed to step b. If not satisfactory, service vacuum supply as needed.

b. Disconnect vacuum hose at servo end, then the vacuum reservoir line at check valve and plug open valve port. Apply 18 inches of vacuum to hose at servo end. If vacuum holds, proceed to step c. If vacuum does not hold, replace check valve and repeat step b.

c. Check that dump is closed when brake pedal is not depressed. Apply 18 inches of vacuum to dump valve. If vacuum can be pumped and held, proceed to step d. If vacuum cannot be pumped and held, replace or adjust valve as necessary.

d. Disconnect reservoir vacuum line at check valve, then apply 18 inches of vacuum to open end of line. If vacuum holds, proceed to step 4. If vacuum does not hold, proceed to step e.

e. Disconnect vacuum line from reservoir port and plug open end, then apply 18 inches of vacuum to other end of line disconnected from servo check valve. If vacuum holds, replace reservoir and repeat step c. If vacuum does not hold, replace reservoir vacuum line.

4. Perform servo tests. If tests are satisfactory, proceed to step 5. If tests are not satisfactory, replace servo.

5. Replace amplifier with known good amplifier. If system operation is satisfactory, replace amplifier. If system operation is still not satisfactory, ensure all system electrical connectors have proper contact.

Speed Gradually Increases Or Decreases After Speed Is Set

1. Check for proper operation of throttle linkage and actuator cable. If satisfactory, proceed to step 2. If not satisfactory, adjust or replace as necessary.

2. Check circuits 147, 148 and 149 for continuity. If there is continuity in all circuits, proceed to step 3. If there is not continuity in all circuits, repair or replace circuits as necessary.

3. Perform test on servo. If servo operation is satisfactory, proceed to step 4. If servo operation is not satisfactory, replace servo.

4. Perform speed sensor test. If sensor operation is satisfactory, proceed to step 5. If sensor operation is not satisfactory, replace sensor.

5. Check all electrical and vacuum connections. Check all vacuum lines for any leaks. If electrical and vacuum lines are satisfactory, proceed to step 6. If electrical and vacuum lines are not satisfactory, repair or replace as necessary.

6. Replace amplifier with known good amplifier. If system operation is satisfactory, replace amplifier. If system operation is still not satisfactory, ensure all system electrical connectors have proper contact.

Speed Control System Does Not Disengage When Brakes Are Applied

1. Apply brake pedal and ensure brake lights work. If satisfactory, proceed to step 2. If not satisfactory, check and repair stop lamp circuit.

2. Check for proper vacuum dump valve operation. If satisfactory, proceed to step 3. If not satisfactory, adjust or replace as necessary.

3. Check for proper servo operation. If satisfactory, proceed to step 4. If not satisfactory, replace servo.

4. Replace amplifier with known good amplifier. If system operation is satisfactory, replace amplifier. If system operation is still not satisfactory, ensure all system electrical connectors have proper contact.

"Speed Control" Display In Electronic Cluster Does Not Turn On

1. Check color of amplifier. If amplifier is brown, proceed to step 2. If amplifier is tan, replace amplifier with a brown amplifier.

2. Remove eight and six pin connectors from amplifier. Turn ignition switch to the RUN position, then connect a digital voltmeter with a DC voltage scale from orange/light blue (circuit 203) of eight pin connector to black (ground) circuit of the six pin connector. If voltmeter reads approximately five volts DC, proceed to step 4. If voltmeter does not read approximately five volts DC, proceed to step 3.

3. Check for continuity in orange/light blue (circuit 203) from eight-pin connector to cluster connector. If continuity exists, proceed to step 4. If continuity does not exist, repair open in circuit 203.

4. Turn ignition switch to the RUN position, then connect a jumper wire between orange/light blue (circuit 203) of the eight pin connector to the black (ground) in six pin connector. If speed control display comes on, replace the amplifier. If display does not come on, problem is in the instrument cluster.

"Speed Control" Display In Electronic Cluster Does Not Turn Off

1. Check color of amplifier. If amplifier is brown, proceed to step 2. If amplifier is tan, replace amplifier with a brown amplifier.

2. Substitute amplifier with a known good amplifier. If display operation is not satisfactory, proceed to step 3. If display operation is satisfactory, replace amplifier.

3. Ensure that orange/light blue (circuit 203) from eight pin amplifier connector to instrument cluster is not shorted to ground. If circuit is satisfactory, problem is in instrument cluster. If circuit is not satisfactory, repair or replace as necessary.

1992 TOWN CAR (LATE PRODUCTION), 1993–94 CROWN VICTORIA, GRAND MARQUIS, MARK VIII & TOWN CAR

Prior to beginning any system testing perform "Visual Inspection." Refer to servo connector terminal identification **Fig. 89**, and system wiring circuit **Figs. 90 through 93** when performing system diagnosis and testing. Refer to **Figs. 94 through 107** for pinpoint tests.

Visual Inspection

1. Check horn and stoplamp for operation.
2. Check all system wiring and electrical connectors.
3. Check throttle linkage and actuator cable for proper adjustment and smooth operation.

1992 PROBE

The wiring diagrams in **Figs. 108 through 110** may be used as a diagnostic aid when performing the diagnostic and testing procedures.

2.2L/4-133 Engine

Refer to **Fig. 111**, for system diagnosis and testing.

1992 w/3.0L/V6-182 Engine

Refer to **Fig. 112**, for symptom chart, then to **Fig. 113** for system diagnosis and testing.

1993–94 PROBE

Prior to beginning any system testing perform "Visual Inspection." Refer to "Component Testing," system wiring circuit, **Fig. 114** and speed control symptom chart **Fig. 115** when performing system diagnosis and testing. Refer to **Fig. 116** for pinpoint tests.

Visual Inspection

1. Check horn and stoplamp for operation.
2. Check all system wiring and electrical connectors.
3. Check throttle linkage and actuator cable for proper adjustment and smooth operation.

CAPRI

The wiring diagram in **Fig. 117.** may be used as a diagnostic aid when performing testing procedures in **Fig. 118.**

COMPONENT DIAGNOSIS & TESTING ESCORT, MUSTANG, TEMPO, TOPAZ & TRACER

VISUAL INSPECTION

A visual inspection is an important part of the system test. When performing a visual inspection, check all components for abnormal conditions such as bare, broken, or disconnected wires, damaged or disconnected vacuum reserve tanks and hoses. In order for the speed control system to function properly, it is necessary that the speedometer cables be properly routed and securely attached. The servo (throttle actuator) assembly and throttle linkage should operate freely and smoothly. The bead chain should have not more than 1/4 inch freeplay.

CONTROL SWITCH TEST

Disconnect connector at the amplifier assembly, **Figs. 19 through 24.** Perform the following checks:

1. Connect a voltmeter, part No. 014-00407 or equivalent between the light blue-black lead and ground. With ignition switch in the ON position, depress speed control ON button and check for battery voltage.
2. Turn ignition off and connect an ohmmeter between the light blue-black hash lead and ground.
3. Rotate steering wheel throughout its full range while making the following checks:
   a. Depress OFF button and check for a reading between 0 and 1 ohm.
   b. Depress SET ACCEL button and check for a reading between 714 and 646 ohms.
   c. Depress COAST button and check for a reading between 126 and 114 ohms.
   d. **On models with RESUME,** depress RESUME button and check for a reading between 2310 and 2090 ohms.
4. If resistance values are within specification but needle fluctuates, remove steering wheel and clean the brushes. Apply a light coat of lubricant ESA-M1C189A or equivalent to the slip rings. If resistance values are above the allowable limits, check switches and ground circuit.
5. Reconnect amplifier connector.

SPEED SENSOR TEST

1. Disconnect electrical connector from speed sensor, **Figs. 19 through 24,** then connect an ohmmeter between the speed sensor terminals at speed sensor end.
2. Ohmmeter should read 200-300 ohms, a reading of 0 ohms indicates a shorted coil and a maximum reading indicates an open coil.
3. Replace sensor if reading is not satisfactory.

SERVO (THROTTLE ACTUATOR) ASSEMBLY TEST

Except Escort & Tracer

1. Disconnect eight pin connector from amplifier.
2. Connect ohmmeter between orange/yellow (circuit 144) and gray/black (circuit 145) leads at eight pin connector, **Figs. 19 through 24.** Resistance should measure 40-75 ohms.

3. Connect ohmmeter between orange/yellow (circuit 144) and white/pink (circuit 146) leads at connector. Resistance should measure 100-150 ohms.
4. Connect ohmmeter between purple/light blue (circuit 147) and Yellow/Red (circuit 148) leads. Resistance should measure 20,000-30,000 ohms.
5. Connect ohmmeter between purple/light blue (circuit 147) and brown/light green (circuit 149) leads. Resistance should measure 40,000-60,000 ohms.
6. If proper resistance is not obtained check wiring and servo separately for damage, replace or service as necessary.

Escort & Tracer

1. Disconnect eight pin connector from amplifier.
2. Connect ohmmeter between DG/R and DG/BK leads, **Figs. 21 and 24.** Resistance should measure 40-70 ohms.
3. Connect ohmmeter between DG/R and DG/W leads. Resistance should measure 110-140 ohms.
4. Connect ohmmeter between DB/W and LG/W leads. Resistance should measure 40,000-60,000 ohms.
5. Connect ohmmeter between DB/DG and DB/W leads. Resistance should measure 20,000-30,000 ohms.
6. Connect ohmmeter between DB/DG and LG/W leads. Resistance should measure 20,000-30,000 ohms.
7. If proper resistance is not obtained check wiring and servo separately for damage, replace or service as necessary.

AMPLIFIER TEST

When performing this test use a voltmeter with a 5000 ohm/volt rating or higher. Using a test lamp may damage amplifier due to excess current draw.

"ON" Circuit Test

1. Turn ignition switch to the ON position.
2. Connect voltmeter between white/purple (circuit 296) and ground in the six pin connector at the amplifier. If voltmeter indicates battery voltage, proceed to step 3. If voltmeter does not indicate battery voltage, check fuse voltage, then repair circuit or replace fuse as necessary.
3. Connect a voltmeter to light blue/black (circuit 151) and ground at the six pin connector at the amplifier, then set speed control switch to the ON position. If voltmeter indicates battery voltage, proceed to step 4. If voltmeter does not indicate battery voltage, refer to "Control Switch Test."
4. With voltmeter connected as in step 4, release ON button. If voltmeter reading is zero, proceed to step 5. If voltmeter reading is approximately 7.8 volts, ON circuit is engaged.

5. Check ground at the amplifier (either black wire on amplifier six pin connector). If there is no ground on the amplifier, check system ground wiring and connections. Also check fuse number 6 or 20 amp fuse and circuit breaker, repair or replace as necessary. If ground is present at amplifier, proceed to step 6.
6. If voltmeter still reads zero, substitute, but do not install a know good amplifier, then recheck ON circuit operation.

Brake Circuit Test

1. Connect voltmeter between light green wire (circuit 511) and ground at the six pin connector.
2. Voltmeter should indicate battery voltage with brake pedal depressed and less than one volt with brake pedal released. If voltage is not satisfactory, check for any of the following:
   a. Faulty wiring.
   b. Burned out stoplamps.
   c. Burned out stoplamp fuse.
   d. Faulty clutch or stoplamp switch.

Horn Relay Test (Escort, Tempo, Tracer & Topaz)

1. Connect a voltmeter between wire of relay and ground.
2. Voltmeter should indicate battery voltage.
3. If voltmeter does not indicate battery voltage, check for voltage at supply lead.
4. If voltage is indicated at supply lead, replace the relay.
5. If no voltage is indicated at supply lead, check fuse and wiring for an open or short and repair or replace as necessary.

Off Circuit Test

1. Turn ignition switch to the RUN position.
2. Connect a voltmeter to the light blue/black wire (circuit 151), depress Off switch on steering wheel, then read voltage.
3. Voltage should drop to zero indicating ON circuit is de-energized.
4. If voltage does not drop to zero, perform "Control Switch Test."
5. If switches are checked and found to be satisfactory, substitute amplifier with a known good amplifier, then repeat test.

Set-Accelerate Circuit Test

1. Turn ignition switch to the ON position.
2. **On models except 1993-94 Escort and Tracer,** connect a voltmeter between the light blue/black wire (circuit 151) and ground at the six pin connector.
3. **On 1993-94 Escort and Tracer,** connect a voltmeter between the light red/yellow wire (circuit 151) and ground at the six pin connector.
4. Depress and hold SET ACCEL button on steering wheel. The voltmeter should read approximately 4.5 volts.
5. Rotate steering wheel and watch for voltmeter fluctuations. If voltage var-

ies more than 0.5 volts, perform "Control Switch Test."

Coast Circuit Test

1. Turn ignition switch to the ON position.
2. **On models except 1993-94 Escort and Tracer,** connect a voltmeter between the light blue/black wire (circuit 151) and ground at the six pin connector.
3. **On 1993-94 Escort and Tracer,** connect a voltmeter between the light red/yellow wire (circuit 151) and ground at the six pin connector.
4. Depress and hold COAST button on steering wheel, voltmeter should read approximately 1.5 volts.
5. Rotate steering wheel back and forth and check for voltmeter fluctuations. If voltage varies more than .05 volts, perform "Control Switch Test."

Resume Circuit Test

1. Turn ignition switch to the ON position.
2. **On models except 1993-94 Escort and Tracer,** connect a voltmeter between the light blue/black wire (circuit 151) and ground at the six pin connector.
3. **On 1993-94 Escort and Tracer,** connect a voltmeter between the light red/yellow wire (circuit 151) and ground at the six pin connector.
4. Depress and hold RESUME button on steering wheel, voltmeter should read approximately 6.5 volts.
5. Rotate steering wheel back and forth and check for voltmeter fluctuations. If voltage varies more than .05 volts, perform "Control Switch Test."
6. If all circuits are satisfactory, perform the "Servo Assembly Test," substituting a known good amplifier. **Do not substitute a known good amplifier until the servo assembly test has been successfully completed.**

Simulated Road Test

1. **On rear wheel drive models,** raise and support rear of vehicle using jack stands on each side of the axle, then block front wheels. **Never attempt to use the vehicle bumper jack when performing this test.**
2. **On front wheel drive models** place jack stands under lower control arm assemblies in order to keep halfshafts in a lateral position, then block rear wheels. **Never attempt to use the vehicle bumper jack when performing this test.**
3. **On all models except 1993-94 Escort and Tracer,** start engine, then shift transmission to D.
4. **On 1993-94 Escort and Tracer models w/automatic transaxle,** start engine, then shift transmission to overdrive.
5. **On 1993-94 Escort and Tracer models w/manual transaxle,** start engine, then shift transmission to fourth gear.
6. **On all models,** turn speed control system on. **If any time during the fol-**

lowing steps the system should appear to go out of control and overspeed, be prepared to turn speed control system off at once using the speed control system OFF button or ignition switch.

7. Accelerate and hold at 35 mph.
8. Press and release SET ACCEL button. Hold foot pressure very lightly on accelerator pedal. Speed should continue at 35 mph for a short period of time, then gradually start to surge due to lack of engine load.
9. Press OFF button, engine should decelerate to idle. Stop drive wheels with service brakes.
10. Press ON button, accelerate and hold speed at 35 mph.
11. Press and hold SET ACCEL button, then slowly remove foot from accelerator. Engine RPM should gradually increase.
12. When speed reaches 50 mph, release SET ACCEL button. Vehicle speed should stay at 50 mph for a short time before surging begins.
13. Press COAST button and hold, engine should return to idle speed. Slow drive wheels to 35 mph.
14. Release COAST button, speed should set at 35 mph and surging should soon start.
15. Press and release brake pedal. Speed control system should shutoff and engine speed should decelerate to idle.
16. Set speed at 50 mph, then using brakes, decelerate to 35 mph, maintain speed using the accelerator. Depress and release RESUME button, speed should return to 50 mph.

Brake Stop Lamp Switch & Circuit Test

Perform this test only when the brake application will not disconnect the speed control system.

1. Check stoplamp operation by applying approximately 6 lbs. of pressure to the brake pedal. If more than 6 lbs. of pressure is required, check brake pedal actuation and stop lamp switch.
2. If stop lamps do not function properly, check stop lamp switch, circuit fuse or bulbs.
3. If stop lamps function properly, check for battery voltage on wire (circuit 296) at amplifier six pin connector.
4. Depress brake pedal until stoplamps are lit.
5. Check voltage on dark/green stripe lead at amplifier 6 pin connector. The difference between this and the voltage reading in step 3, must not exceed 1.5 volts.
6. Check voltage on red/light green lead at amplifier 6 pin connector. The difference between this and the voltage reading in step 3, must not exceed 1.5 volts.
7. If voltage difference is greater than 1.5 volts, a high resistance in the circuit exists which must be found and corrected.
8. Perform "Vacuum Dump Valve Test."

Vacuum Dump Valve Test

1. Disconnect vacuum hose (white stripe) from servo that leads to dump valve.
2. Connect a hand vacuum pump tool No. 021-00037 or equivalent to hose, and draw vacuum. If a vacuum can not be obtained, either the hose or dump valve are leaking, and should be replaced.
3. Depress brake pedal, vacuum should be released. If vacuum is not released, adjust or replace dump valve.

Clutch Switch Test

This switch functions magnetically. Do not use magnetized tools near this switch.

1. If switch is open when clutch pedal is released, speed control will not operate. This must be corrected before performing any other tests. **Use only a voltmeter of 5000 ohm/volt rating or higher when performing the clutch switch test.**
2. Disconnect switch pigtail connector from speed control harness connector, then connect an ohmmeter to the two switch connector terminals.
3. With clutch pedal in the fully released position, the resistance should be less than 5 ohms. With clutch pedal fully depressed, the circuit should be open.
4. If switch does not function as described, replace switch.

CONTINENTAL, COUGAR & THUNDERBIRD

VISUAL INSPECTION

A visual inspection is an important part of the system test. When performing a visual inspection, check all components for abnormal conditions such as bare, broken, or disconnected wires, damaged or disconnected vacuum reserve tanks and hoses. In order for the speed control system to function properly, it is necessary that the speedometer cables be properly routed and securely attached. The servo (throttle actuator) assembly and throttle linkage should operate freely and smoothly. The bead chain should have not more than 1/4 inch freeplay.

CONTROL SWITCH TEST

Disconnect connector at the amplifier assembly, **Figs. 46 through 48.** Perform the following checks:

1. Connect a voltmeter, part No. 014-00407 or equivalent between the light blue-black lead and ground. With ignition switch in the ON position, depress speed control ON button and check for battery voltage.
2. Turn ignition off and connect an ohmmeter between the light blue-black hash lead and ground.
3. Rotate steering wheel throughout its full range while making the following checks:
   a. Depress OFF button and check for a reading between 0 and 1 ohm.
   b. Depress SET ACCEL button and check for a reading between 646 and 714 ohms.

c. Depress COAST button and check for a reading between 126 and 114 ohms.

d. Depress RESUME button and check for a reading between 2310 and 2090 ohms.

4. If resistance values are within specification but needle fluctuates, remove steering wheel and clean the brushes. Apply a light coat of lubricant ESA-M1C189A or equivalent to the slip rings. If resistance values are above the allowable limits, check switches and ground circuit.

5. Reconnect amplifier connector.

SPEED SENSOR TEST

1. Disconnect 6-pin electrical connector at amplifier, then connect an ohmmeter between dark green/white (circuit 150) and black (circuit 57).

2. Ohmmeter should read approximately 200 ohms. If reading is satisfactory, proceed to step 3. If reading is zero, a shorted coil or wire is indicated.

3. Disconnect electrical connector from speed sensor, then connect an ohmmeter between the speed sensor terminals at speed sensor end.

4. Ohmmeter should read approximately 200 ohms, a reading of 0 ohms indicates a shorted coil and a maximum reading indicates an open coil.

5. Replace sensor if reading is not satisfactory.

SERVO (THROTTLE ACTUATOR) ASSEMBLY TEST

1. Disconnect eight pin connector from amplifier.

2. Connect an ohmmeter between orange/yellow (circuit 144) and gray/black (circuit 145) leads at eight pin connector. Resistance should measure 40-125 ohms.

3. Connect ohmmeter between orange/yellow (circuit 144) and white/pink (circuit 146) leads at connector. Resistance should measure 60-190 ohms.

4. If resistance readings are satisfactory, proceed to step 5. If resistance readings are not satisfactory, check wiring and servo separately for damage and replace or service as necessary.

5. Start engine and check as follows:

a. Ensure servo is disconnected from amplifier.

b. Connect orange/yellow (circuit 144) to battery positive terminal.

c. Connect white/pink (circuit 146) lead of servo to ground and momentarily touch gray/black (circuit 145) lead of servo to ground.

d. Servo throttle actuator arm should pull in and engine speed should increase.

e. Remove white/pink (circuit 146) from ground, servo should release. **Do not short orange/yellow (circuit 144) to either the white/pink (circuit 146) or gray/black (circuit 145). Amplifier could be damaged.**

AMPLIFIER TEST

When performing this test use a voltmeter with a 5000 ohm/volt rating or higher. Using a test lamp may damage amplifier due to excessive current draw.

"ON" Circuit Test

1. Turn ignition switch to the ON position.

2. Connect voltmeter between white/purple (circuit 296) and ground in the six pin connector at the amplifier. If voltmeter indicates battery voltage, proceed to step 3. If voltmeter does not indicate battery voltage, check fuse voltage, then repair circuit or replace fuse as necessary.

3. Connect a voltmeter to light blue/black (circuit 151) and ground at the six pin connector at the amplifier, then set speed control switch to the ON position. If voltmeter indicates battery voltage, proceed to step 4. If voltmeter does not indicate battery voltage, refer to "Control Switch Test."

4. With voltmeter connected as in step 4, release ON button. If voltmeter reading is zero, proceed to step 5. If voltmeter reading is approximately 7.8 volts, ON circuit is engaged.

5. Check ground at the amplifier (either black wire on amplifier six pin connector). If there is no ground on the amplifier, check system ground wiring and connections. Also check 20 amp fuse and circuit breaker, repair or replace as necessary. If ground is present at amplifier, proceed to step 6.

6. If voltmeter still reads zero, substitute, but do not install a known good amplifier, then recheck ON circuit operation.

Brake Circuit Test

1. Connect ohmmeter between light green wire (circuit 511) and ground at the six pin connector.

2. Resistance should be less than 5 ohms.

3. If resistance is greater than 5 ohms, check for improper wiring, burnt out stoplamps or clutch switch malfunction.

Off Circuit Test

1. Turn ignition switch to the RUN position.

2. Connect a voltmeter to light blue/black wire (circuit 151), depress OFF switch on steering wheel, then read voltage.

3. Voltage should drop to zero indicating ON circuit is de-energized.

4. If voltage does not drop to zero, perform "Control Switch Test."

5. If switches are checked and found to be satisfactory, substitute amplifier with a known good amplifier, then repeat test.

Set-Accel Circuit Test

1. Turn ignition switch to the ON position.

2. Connect a voltmeter between the light blue/black wire (circuit 151) and ground at the six pin connector.

3. Depress and hold SET ACCEL button on steering wheel, voltmeter should read approximately 4.5 volts.

4. Rotate steering wheel and watch for voltmeter fluctuations. If voltage varies more than 0.5 volts, perform "Control Switch Test."

Coast Circuit Test

1. Turn ignition switch to the ON position.

2. Connect a voltmeter between light blue/black wire (circuit 151) and ground at six pin connector.

3. Depress and hold COAST button on steering wheel, voltmeter should read approximately 1.5 volts.

4. Rotate steering wheel back and forth and check for voltmeter fluctuations. If voltage varies more than .05 volts, perform "Control Switch Test."

Resume Circuit Test

1. Turn ignition switch to the ON position.

2. Connect a voltmeter between light blue/black wire (circuit 151) and ground at six pin connector.

3. Depress and hold RESUME button on steering wheel, voltmeter should read approximately 6.5 volts.

4. Rotate steering wheel back and forth and check for voltmeter fluctuations. If voltage varies more than .05 volts, perform "Control Switch Test."

5. If all circuits are satisfactory, perform the "Servo Assembly Test," substituting a known good amplifier. **Do not substitute a known good amplifier until the servo assembly test has been successfully completed.**

SIMULATED ROAD TEST

1. **On Cougar and Thunderbird models,** raise and support rear of vehicle using jack stands on each side of the axle, then block front wheels. **Never attempt to use vehicle bumper jack when performing this test.**

2. **On Continental models** place jack stands under lower control arm assemblies in order to keep halfshafts in a lateral position, then block rear wheels. **Never attempt to use vehicle bumper jack when performing this test.**

3. **On all models,** start engine, then shift transmission to D.

4. Turn speed control system on. **If at anytime during the following steps the system should appear to go out of control and overspeed, be prepared to turn speed control system off at once using the speed control system OFF button or ignition switch.**

5. Accelerate and hold at 35 mph.

6. Press and release SET ACCEL button. Hold foot pressure very lightly on accelerator pedal. Speed should continue at 35 mph for a short period of time, then gradually start to surge due to lack of engine load.

7. Press OFF button, engine should decelerate to idle. Stop drive wheels with service brakes.

CONDITION	POSSIBLE SOURCE	ACTION
• Speed Control Does Not Work	• Fuse(s). • Circuit. • Vehicle speed sensor. • Actuator. • Speed control amplifier. • Speed control switch. • Vacuum dump valve.	• CHECK the 15 amp METER fuse and the 20 amp STOP fuse. REPLACE if necessary. • GO to A1.

FM1109200103010X

Fig. 25   Diagnostic symptom chart (Part 1 of 2). Escort & Tracer

CONDITION	POSSIBLE SOURCE	ACTION
• Speed Control Operation Is Intermittent	• Circuit. • Actuator. • Speed control amplifier. • Speed control switch.	• GO to B1.
• Speed Control Operates But Does Not Accelerate Or Coast Down Properly	• Circuit. • Actuator. • Speed control amplifier. • Speed control switch.	• GO to C1.
• Speed Continuously Changes Up and Down	• Circuit. • Vehicle speed sensor. • Actuator. • Speed control amplifier. • Vacuum dump valve.	• GO to D1.
• Speed Control Does Not Disengage When Brakes Are Applied	• Actuator. . • Speed control amplifier. • Vacuum dump valve. • Stop lamps. • Brake on/off switch.	• GO to E1. • REFER to the brake on/off switch and circuit test in this section.
• Speed Will Not Set In System	• Circuit. • Vehicle speed sensor. • Actuator. • Speed control amplifier. • Speed control switch. • Vacuum dump valve. • Stoplamps.	• GO to F1.
• Speed Control System Does Not Disengage When Clutch Pedal Is Depressed (MTX Only)	• Clutch pedal position switch. • Actuator. • Speed control amplifier.	• GO to G1. If OK, clutch pedal position switch adjustment • REFER to Actuator Tests in this section. • REFER to Amplifier Tests in this section.
• Speed Gradually Increases Or Decreases After Speed Is Set	• Actuator. • Vacuum dump valve.	• GO to H1.
• Speed Control Operates But Does Not Resume, Accelerate, Or Coast Down Properly	• Circuit. • Actuator. • Speed control amplifier. • Speed control switch.	• GO to J1.

FM1109200103020X

Fig. 25   Diagnostic symptom chart (Part 2 of 2). Escort & Tracer

8. Press ON button, accelerate and hold speed at 35 mph.
9. Press and hold SET ACCEL button, then slowly remove foot from accelerator. Engine RPM should gradually increase.
10. When speed reaches 50 mph, release SET ACCEL button. Vehicle speed should stay at 50 mph for a short time before surging begins.
11. Press COAST button and hold, engine should return to idle speed. Slow drive wheels to 35 mph.
12. Release COAST button, speed should set at 35 mph and surging should soon start.
13. Press and release brake pedal. Speed control system should shutoff and engine speed should decelerate to idle.
14. Set speed at 50 mph, then using brakes, decelerate to 35 mph, maintain speed using the accelerator. Depress and release RESUME button, speed should return to 50 mph.

STOPLAMP SWITCH & CIRCUIT TEST

Perform this test only when the brake application will not disconnect the speed control system.
1. Check stoplamp operation by applying approximately 6 lbs. of pressure to the brake pedal. If more than 6 lbs. of

pressure is required, check brake pedal actuation and stop lamp switch.
2. If stop lamps do not function properly, check stop lamp switch, circuit fuse or bulbs.
3. If stoplamps function properly, check for battery voltage on white/purple wire (circuit 296) at amplifier six pin connector.
4. Depress brake pedal until stoplamps are lit.
5. Check voltage on light green lead (circuit 511) at amplifier 6 pin connector. The difference between this and the voltage reading in step 3, must not exceed 1.5 volts.
6. If voltage difference is greater than 1.5 volts, a high resistance in the circuit exists which must be found and corrected.
7. Perform "Vacuum Dump Valve Test."

VACUUM DUMP VALVE TEST

1. Disconnect vacuum hose (white stripe) from servo that leads to dump valve.
2. Connect a hand vacuum pump tool No. 021-00037 or equivalent to hose, and draw vacuum. If a vacuum can not be obtained, either the hose or dump valve are leaking, and should be replaced.

3. Depress brake pedal, vacuum should be released. If vacuum is not released, adjust or replace dump valve.

1993–94 PROBE
Road Test

1. Start Engine.
2. Turn speed control system on. **If any time during the following steps the system should appear to go out of control and overspeed, be prepared to turn speed control system off at once using the speed control system OFF button or ignition switch.**
3. Accelerate and hold at 35 mph.
4. Press and release SET ACCEL button. Hold foot pressure very lightly on accelerator pedal. Speed should continue at 35 mph.
5. Press OFF button, engine should decelerate.
6. Press ON button, accelerate and hold speed at 35 mph.
7. Press and hold SET ACCEL button, then slowly remove foot from accelerator. Engine RPM should gradually increase.
8. When speed reaches 50 mph, release SET ACCEL button. Vehicle speed should stay at 50 mph.
9. Press COAST button and hold, engine should return to idle speed. Slow drive wheels to 35 mph.
10. Release COAST button, speed should set at 35 mph.
11. Press and release brake pedal. Speed control system should shutoff and engine speed should decelerate to idle.
12. Set speed at 50 mph, then using brakes, decelerate to 35 mph, maintain speed using the accelerator. Depress and release RESUME button, speed should return to 50 mph.
13. Press and release OFF button.

Vacuum Dump Valve Test

The vacuum dump valve should be checked whenever brake application does not disengage the speed control.
1. Disconnect dump valve-to-actuator vacuum hose (with yellow stripe) at actuator.
2. Connect Rotunda Vacuum Tester 021-00037 or equivalent to end of hose at actuator.
3. Pump vacuum to approximately 10-15 inches.
4. Depress brake pedal. The vacuum should release.
5. If vacuum does not release, adjust or release vacuum dump valve.

Continued on page 16-66

DIAGNOSTIC CHART INDEX

Test	Description	Year	Page No.	Fig. No.
COUGAR & THUNDERBIRD				
A	Speed Control Inoperative	1992-94	16-29	50
B	Speed Control Operates But Does Not Resume, Accelerate Or Coast Down Properly	1992-94	16-30	51
C	Set Speed Fluctuates	1992-94	16-31	52
D	Speed Control Does Not Disengage When Brakes Are Applied	1992-94	16-31	53
E	Speed Control Does Not Disengage When Clutch Is Applied	1992-94	16-32	54
CROWN VICTORIA, GRAND MARQUIS, MARK VIII & 1993-94 TOWN CAR				
A	Speed Control Inoperative	1993-94	16-53	103
B	Set Speed Fluctuates	1993-94	16-54	104
C	Speed Control Does Not Disengage When Brakes Are Applied	1993-94	16-54	105
D	Speed Control Indicator Does Not Turn On	1993-94	16-55	106
E	Speed Control Indicator Does Not Turn Off	1993-94	16-55	107
ESCORT & TRACER				
A	Speed Control Inoperative	1992-93	16-22	26
A	Speed Control Inoperative	1994	16-22	27
B	Speed Control Operation Is Intermittent	1992-93	16-23	29
B	Speed Control Intermittent	1994	16-23	30
C	Speed Control Operates But Does Not Accelerate Or Coast Down Properly	1992-93	16-24	32
D	Speed Continuously Changes Up & Down	1992-93	16-24	33
D	Set Speed Fluctuates	1994	16-25	34
E	Speed Control Does Not Disenage When Brakes Are Applied	1992-93	16-25	36
E	Speed Control Does Not Disengage When Brakes Are Applied	1994	16-26	37
F	Speed Will Not Set In System	1992-93	16-26	39
F	Speed Control System Does Not Disengage When Clutch Pedal Is Depressed	1994 ①	16-27	40
G	Speed Control System Does Not Disengage When Clutch Pedal Is Depressed	1992-93	16-27	41
G	Speed Gradually Increases Or Decreases After Speed Is Set	1994	16-27	42
H	Speed Gradually Increases Or Decreases After Speed Is Set	1992-93	16-27	43
H	Speed Will Not Set In System	1994	16-27	44
J	Speed Control Operates But Does Not Resume, Accelerate Or Coast Down Properly	1992-93	16-27	45
MARK VII				
A	Speed Control Switches	1992	16-38	68
B	Brake On/Off (BOO)	1992	16-39	69
C	Servo Solenoids	1992	16-41	70
D	Speed Does Not Increase During Dynamic Test	1992	16-42	71
E	Does Not Hold Speed During Dynamic Test	1992	16-44	73
F	Speed Does Not Increase During Dynamic Test	1992	16-44	74
G	Speed Sensor	1992	16-45	75
Q	No Codes, Codes Not Listed	1992	16-47	78
MUSTANG				
A	Speed Control Inoperative	1992-93	16-22	26
A	Speed Control Inoperative	1994	16-22	28
B	Speed Control Operation Is Intermittent	1992-93	16-23	29
B	Speed Control Intermittent	1994	16-23	31
C	Speed Control Operates But Does Not Resume, Accelerate Or Coast Down Properly	1992-94	16-24	32
D	Speed Continuously Changes Up And Down	1992-93	16-24	33
D	Speed Control Does Not Disengage When Brakes Are Applied	1994	16-25	35
E	Speed Control Does Not Disengage When Brakes Are Applied	1992-93	16-25	36

Continued

DIAGNOSTIC CHART INDEX –Continued

Test	Description	Year	Page No.	Fig. No.
MUSTANG				
E	Speed Control System Does Not Disengage When Clutch Pedal Is Applied	1994	16–26	38
F	Speed Control System Does Not Disengage When Clutch Pedal Is Depressed	1992-93	16–27	40
G	Speed Gradually Increases Or Decreases After Speed Is Set	1992-93	16–27	42
PROBE				
SC	Speed Control Inoperative	1993-94	16–61	116
SABLE & TAURUS				
A	Speed Control Switches	1992–93	16–38	68
A	Does Not Hold Speed During Dynamic Test	1994	16–47	79
B	Brake On/Off (BOO)	1992-93	16–39	69
B	Speed Does Not Increase During Dynamic Test	1994	16–48	80
C	Servo Solenoids	1992-93	16–41	70
C	Speed Does Not Decrease During Dynamic Test	1994	16–48	81
D	Speed Control Switches	1994	16–48	82
E	Does Not Hold Speed During Dynamic Test	1992-93	16–43	72
E	Stoplight Switch	1994	16–48	83
F	Speed Does Not Increase During Dynamic Test	1992-93	16–44	74
F	Servo Solenoids	1994	16–49	84
G	Speed Sensor	1992-93	16–45	76
G	Speed Control Erratic	1994	16–49	85
H	Clutch Switch	1992-93	16–46	77
H	Vehicle Speed Sensor Not Operating	1994	16–49	86
J	Clutch Pedal Position Switch Not Operating Properly	1994	16–50	87
Q	No Codes, Codes Not Listed	1992-93	16–47	78
TEMPO & TOPAZ				
A	Speed Control Inoperative	1992–94	16–22	26
B	Speed Control Operation Is Intermittent	1992–94	16–23	29
C	Speed Control Operates But Does Not Resume, Accelerate Or Coast Down Properly	1992–94	16–24	32
D	Speed Continuously Changes Up And Down	1992-94	16–24	33
E	Speed Control Does Not Disengage When Brakes Are Applied	1992-94	16–25	36
F	Speed Control System Does Not Disengage When Clutch Pedal Is Depressed	1992-94	16–27	40
G	Speed Gradually Increases Or Decreases After Speed Is Set	1992-94	16–27	42
1992 TOWN CAR (LATE PRODUCTION)				
A	Speed Control Does Not Work	1992	16–52	94
B	Speed Continuously Changes	1992	16–52	95
C	Coast/Tap-Down Inoperative	1992	16–52	96
D	Coast/Tap-Up Inoperative	1992	16–53	97
E	Resume Inoperative	1992	16–53	98
F	Speed Control Does Not Disengage When Brake Is Applied	1992	16–53	99
G	Off Switch Inoperative	1992	16–53	100
H	Electronic Cluster Display Does Not Turn On	1992	16–53	101
I	Electronic Cluster Display Does Not Turn Off	1992	16–53	102

①—Manual transaxle.

TEST STEP	RESULT	▶	ACTION TO TAKE
A1 VERIFY CONDITION			GO to A2.
A2 CHECK CONNECTIONS • Check all electrical and vacuum connections. • Are all connections OK?	Yes No		GO to A3. SERVICE or REPLACE as required.
A3 CHECK STOPLAMPS • Press brake pedal. • Are stoplamps operating?	Yes No		GO to A4 if manual transmission. If automatic transmission, GO to A5. SERVICE stoplamp circuit.
A4 CHECK CLUTCH SWITCH (MANUAL TRANSMISSION) • Check clutch switch for proper operation. • Does switch operate properly?	Yes No		GO to A5. SERVICE as required.
A5 CHECK ACTUATOR CABLE CONNECTION TO THROTTLE BODY AND SERVO • Check that actuator cable is attached to the throttle body accelerator linkage. • Check that actuator cable is attached to servo linkage. • Are cables attached?	Yes No		GO to A6. ADJUST or SERVICE as required.
A6 CHECK LINKAGE OPERATION • Check the throttle linkage for proper operation. • Does linkage operate properly?	Yes No		GO to A7. SERVICE as required.
A7 CHECK VACUUM • Check vacuum at servo. • Is vacuum OK? NOTE: 8.42 kPa (2.5 in-Hg) is minimum vacuum for normal servo operation. The vacuum source hose is attached to the 7.9mm (5/16 inch), engine vacuum fitting port.	Yes No		GO to A9. GO to A8.

FM1109200104010X

Fig. 26   Test A: Speed Control Inoperative (Part 1 of 2). Tempo & Topaz & 1992–93 Escort, Mustang & Tracer

TEST STEP	RESULT	▶	ACTION TO TAKE
A8 CHECK DUMP VALVE • Check vacuum dump valve. • Is valve OK?	Yes No		GO to A11. SERVICE or ADJUST as required.
A9 PERFORM CONTROL SWITCHES AND CIRCUIT TEST • Perform control switches and circuit tests as outlined. • Are circuits and switches OK?	Yes No		GO to A10. SERVICE or REPLACE switches or circuits as required.
A10 PERFORM SERVO TESTS • Perform servo tests. • Are tests successful?	Yes No		GO to A11. REPLACE servo.
A11 PERFORM VSS TEST • Perform VSS test • Is test successful?	Yes No		GO to A12. REPLACE VSS.
A12 PERFORM AMPLIFIER TEST • Perform amplifier test • Is test successful?	Yes No		INSTALL a new amplifier. EXAMINE all connectors carefully for proper contact. SERVICE as required. REMOVE substitute amplifier.

FM1109200104020X

Fig. 26   Test A: Speed Control Inoperative (Part 2 of 2). Tempo & Topaz & 1992–93 Escort, Mustang & Tracer

TEST STEP	RESULT	▶	ACTION TO TAKE
A1 CHECK CONNECTIONS • Check all electrical and vacuum connections. • Are the connections OK?	Yes No		GO to A2. SERVICE or REPLACE as required.
A2 CHECK STOPLAMPS • Apply the brakes and observe the stoplamps. Perform the Brake On/Off (BOO) Switch and Circuit Test as described in this section. • Are the stoplamps working?	Yes No		GO to A3 if manual transaxle. If automatic transaxle, GO to A4. SERVICE the stoplamp circuit.
A3 CHECK CLUTCH PEDAL POSITION SWITCH (MTX) • Check the Clutch Pedal Position (CPP) switch for proper operation. Perform the Clutch Pedal Position Switch Test as described in this section. • Does the CPP switch operate properly?	Yes No		GO to A4. SERVICE the CPP switch as required.
A4 CHECK THROTTLE LINKAGE • Check the throttle linkage actuator cable. • Is the cable OK?	Yes No		GO to A5. ADJUST or SERVICE as required.
A5 CHECK LINKAGE OPERATION • Check the throttle linkage for proper operation and adjustment. • Does the throttle linkage operate properly?	Yes No		GO to A6. SERVICE and ADJUST as required.
A6 CHECK VACUUM • Start the engine and run until at normal operating temperature. • Check vacuum at the speed control servo. NOTE: 8.42 kPa (2.5 in.-Hg) is minimum for normal speed control servo operation. The vacuum source hose is attached to the 7.9mm (5/16-inch), engine vacuum fitting port. • Is vacuum operating at normal specifications?	Yes No		GO to A8. GO to A7.

FM1109400207010X

Fig. 27   Test A: Speed Control Inoperative (Part 1 of 2). 1994 Escort & Tracer

TEST STEP	RESULT	▶	ACTION TO TAKE
A7 CHECK SPEED CONTROL VACUUM DUMP VALVE • Perform the Speed Control Vacuum Dump Valve Test as described in this section. • Is the speed control dump valve OK?	Yes No		SERVICE or REPLACE the vacuum hose as required. SERVICE or ADJUST as required.
A8 PERFORM SPEED CONTROL ACTUATOR SWITCH ASSEMBLY TESTS • Perform the Speed Control Actuator Switch Assembly Tests as described in this section. • Are the speed control actuator switches and/or circuits OK?	Yes No		GO to A9. SERVICE or REPLACE the speed control actuator switches or circuits as required.
A9 PERFORM SPEED CONTROL SERVO TESTS • Perform the Speed Control Servo Tests as described in this section. • Is the speed control servo OK?	Yes No		GO to A10. REPLACE the speed control servo.
A10 PERFORM VEHICLE SPEED SENSOR TEST • Perform the Vehicle Speed Sensor Test as described in this section. • Is the vehicle speed sensor OK?	Yes No		REPLACE the speed control amplifier. REPLACE the vehicle speed sensor.

FM1109400207020X

Fig. 27   Test A: Speed Control Inoperative (Part 2 of 2). 1994 Escort & Tracer

TEST STEP	RESULT	▶	ACTION TO TAKE
A1 CHECK CONNECTIONS • Check all electrical and vacuum connections. • Are all connections OK?	Yes No		GO to A2. SERVICE or REPLACE as required.
A2 CHECK STOPLAMPS • Apply brake pedal. • Are stoplamps operating properly?	Yes No		GO to A3. SERVICE stoplamp circuit.
A3 CHECK SPEED CONTROL ACTUATOR CABLE CONNECTION TO THROTTLE BODY AND SPEED CONTROL SERVO • Check to see if speed control actuator cable is attached to throttle body accelerator linkage. • Check to see if speed control actuator cable is attached to speed control servo linkage. • Is speed control actuator cable attached to both?	Yes No		GO to A4. ADJUST or SERVICE as required.
A4 CHECK LINKAGE OPERATION • Check the throttle linkage for proper operation. • Does linkage operate properly?	Yes No		GO to A5. SERVICE as required.

FM1109400208010X

Fig. 28   Test A: Speed Control Inoperative (Part 1 of 4). 1994 Mustang

TEST STEP	RESULT	▶	ACTION TO TAKE
A5 CHECK VACUUM HOSES Check to see if: • Vacuum supply hose is tightly connected to VAC port on speed control vacuum valve and to vacuum outlet manifold, and free of cuts, cracks and kinks. • Vacuum hoses are tightly connected between speed control vacuum valves and speed control servo, and free of cuts, cracks and kinks. • Vacuum hose is tightly connected between speed control vacuum valve and speed control vacuum reservoir, and free of cuts, cracks and kinks. • Speed control dump valve hose is tightly connected to the speed control servo and speed control dump valve, and free of cuts, cracks and kinks. • Are all checks successful?	Yes No		GO to A6. SERVICE as required.
A6 CHECK SPEED CONTROL VACUUM VALVE AND SPEED CONTROL VACUUM RESERVOIR • Disconnect the hose between speed control vacuum valve and speed control servo, at the speed control servo end. • Apply 60.6 kPa (18 in-Hg) vacuum to open end of hose. • Can vacuum be pumped to and held at 60.6 kPa (18 in-Hg) vacuum?	Yes No		GO to A7. SERVICE as required.
A7 CHECK SPEED CONTROL DUMP VALVE • Disconnect the hose (white stripe) between speed control dump valve and speed control servo at the speed control servo end. • Apply 60.6 kPa (18 in-Hg) to open end of hose. • Can vacuum be pumped up and held at 60.6 kPa (18 in-Hg) vacuum?	Yes No		GO to A8. SERVICE or ADJUST as required.
A8 PERFORM SPEED CONTROL ACTUATOR SWITCH TEST • Perform speed control actuator switch test as outlined. • Are tests successful?	Yes No		GO to A9. SERVICE circuits or REPLACE speed control actuator switch assembly or air bag sliding contact.
A9 CHECK SPEED CONTROL SERVO • Separate speed control servo from speed control amplifier. • Connect the Circuit 144 (O/Y) lead of the speed control servo to the battery positive terminal. • Connect the Circuit 146 (W/PK) lead of the speed control servo to ground, and momentarily touch the Circuit 145 (GY/BK) lead of the speed control servo to ground. • The throttle actuator arm should pull in and the engine speed should increase. The arm should hold in that position or slowly release. • When Circuit 146 (W/PK) is removed from ground the throttle actuator arm should release. • Does speed control servo operate properly?	Yes No		GO to A10. REPLACE speed control servo.
A10 CHECK VSS • Disconnect 6-pin connector at speed control amplifier. • With an ohmmeter measure resistance between Circuit 150 (DG/W, VSS signal) and Circuit 57 (BK, ground). • Is the resistance approximately 200-300 ohms?	Yes No		GO to A11. REPLACE vehicle speed sensor.

FM1109400208020X

Fig. 28   Test A: Speed Control Inoperative (Part 2 of 4). 1994 Mustang

TEST STEP	RESULT	▶	ACTION TO TAKE
A11 CHECK SPEED CONTROL AMPLIFIER • Disconnect 8-pin connector at speed control amplifier. • Measure resistance between the following circuits of the connector and check against the normal values. Circuits / Normal Resistance: 144 (O/Y) and 145 (GY/BK) — 40-75 ohms 144 (O/Y) and 146 (W/PK) — 100-150 ohms 147 (P/LB) and 148 (Y/R) — 20k-30k ohms 147 (P/LB) and 149 (B/LG) — 40k-60k ohms • Are all resistance values within limits?	Yes No	▶ ▶	INSTALL a new speed control amplifier. EXAMINE all connectors carefully for proper contact. SERVICE as required. REMOVE substitute speed control amplifier.
A12 CHECK INTERMITTENT ACTION • Note carefully when intermittent action occurs. • Determine whether intermittent action occurs while cruising or if it occurs while using control buttons or turning steering wheel. • Does intermittent action occur while cruising?	Yes No	▶ ▶	GO to A13. GO to A15.
A13 CHECK VACUUM TO SPEED CONTROL SERVO • Check vacuum supply to speed control servo. NOTE: 8.42 kPa (2.5 in-Hg) is minimum vacuum for normal speed control servo operation. The vacuum source hose is attached to the 7.9mm (5/16 inch) engine vacuum-fitting port. • Is vacuum supply OK?	Yes No	▶ ▶	GO to A14. SERVICE vacuum supply.
A14 CHECK SPEED CONTROL SERVO • Separate speed control servo from speed control amplifier. • Connect the Circuit 144 (O/Y) lead of the speed control servo to the battery positive terminal. • Connect the Circuit 146 (W/PK) lead of the speed control servo to ground, and momentarily touch the Circuit 145 (GY/BK) lead of the speed control servo to ground. • The throttle actuator arm should pull in and the engine speed should increase. The arm should hold in that position or slowly release. • When Circuit 146 (W/PK) is removed from ground the throttle actuator arm should release. • Does speed control servo operate properly?	Yes No	▶ ▶	SUBSTITUTE known good speed control amplifier if OK — properly INSTALL speed control amplifier. REPLACE speed control servo.
A15 PERFORM SPEED CONTROL ACTUATOR SWITCH TEST • Perform speed control actuator switch test as outlined. • Are tests successful?	Yes No	▶ ▶	SUBSTITUTE known good speed control amplifier if OK — properly INSTALL speed control amplifier. SERVICE circuits. REPLACE speed control actuator switch assembly or air bag sliding contact as required.
A16 VERIFY ACCELERATOR OPERATION • Verify that engine is properly tuned. • Check accelerator action and actuator cable adjustment. • Is accelerator operation OK?	Yes No	▶ ▶	GO to A17. ADJUST or CORRECT as required.

FM1109400208030X

Fig. 28 Test A: Speed Control Inoperative (Part 3 of 4). 1994 Mustang

TEST STEP	RESULT	▶	ACTION TO TAKE
A17 CHECK SPEED CONTROL DUMP VALVE • Disconnect the hose (white stripe) between speed control dump valve and speed control servo at the speed control servo end. • Apply 60.6 kPa (18 in-Hg) to open end of hose. • Can vacuum be pumped up and held at 60.6 kPa (18 in-Hg) vacuum?	Yes No	▶ ▶	GO to A18. ADJUST or SERVICE as required.
A18 CHECK VACUUM HOSES Check to see if: • Vacuum supply hose is tightly connected to VAC port on speed control vacuum valve and to vacuum outlet manifold, and free of cuts, cracks and kinks. • Vacuum hoses are tightly connected between speed control vacuum valves and speed control servo, and free of cuts, cracks and kinks. • Vacuum hose is tightly connected between speed control vacuum valve and speed control vacuum reservoir, and free of cuts, cracks and kinks. • Dump valve hose is tightly connected to the speed control servo and speed control dump valve, and free of cuts, cracks and kinks. • Are all checks successful?	Yes No	▶ ▶	GO to A19. SERVICE as required.
A19 CHECK SPEED CONTROL VACUUM VALVE AND SPEED CONTROL VACUUM RESERVOIR • Disconnect the hose between speed control vacuum valve and speed control servo, at the speed control servo end. Apply 60.6 kPa (18 in-Hg) vacuum to open end of hose. • Can vacuum be pumped to and held at 60.6 kPa (18 in-Hg) vacuum?	Yes No	▶ ▶	GO to A20. SERVICE as required.
A20 CHECK SPEED CONTROL SERVO • Separate speed control servo from speed control amplifier. • Connect the Circuit 144 (O/Y) lead of the speed control servo to the battery positive terminal. • Connect the Circuit 146 (W/PK) lead of the speed control servo to ground, and momentarily touch the Circuit 145 (GY/BK) lead of the speed control servo to ground. • The throttle actuator arm should pull in and the engine speed should increase. The arm should hold in that position or slowly release. • When Circuit 146 (W/PK) is removed from ground the throttle actuator arm should release. • Does speed control servo operate properly?	Yes No	▶ ▶	GO to A11. REPLACE speed control servo.

FM1109400208040X

Fig. 28 Test A: Speed Control Inoperative (Part 4 of 4). 1994 Mustang

TEST STEP	RESULT	▶	ACTION TO TAKE
B1 VERIFY THE CONDITION • Note carefully when intermittent action occurs.		▶	GO to B2.
B2 INSPECT VISUALLY • Perform Visual Inspection Test.	Intermittent action occurs while cruising Intermittent action occurs while using control buttons or turning steering wheel	▶ ▶	GO to B3. GO to B5.
B3 CHECK VACUUM TO SPEED CONTROL SERVO • Check vacuum supply to speed control servo. NOTE: 8.42 kPa (2.5 in-Hg) is minimum vacuum for normal speed control servo operation. The vacuum source hose is attached to the 7.9mm (5/16 inch) engine vacuum-fitting port. • Is vacuum OK?	Yes No	▶ ▶	GO to B4. SERVICE vacuum supply.
B4 PERFORM SPEED CONTROL SERVO ASSEMBLY TEST • Perform Speed Control Servo Assembly Test. Lightly tap speed control servo body while making test. • Is test successful?	Yes No	▶ ▶	SUBSTITUTE known good speed control amplifier if OK — properly INSTALL speed control amplifier. REPLACE speed control servo assembly.
B5 PERFORM CONTROL SWITCHES AND CIRCUIT TEST • Perform control switches and circuit tests. • Are tests successful?	Yes No	▶ ▶	SUBSTITUTE known good speed control amplifier if OK — properly INSTALL speed control amplifier. SERVICE circuits. REPLACE horn pad assembly. CLEAN or SERVICE three copper brushes and steering wheel slip ring.

FM1109200105000X

Fig. 29 Test B: Speed Control Operation Is Intermittent. Tempo & Topaz & 1992–93 Escort, Mustang & Tracer

TEST STEP	RESULT	▶	ACTION TO TAKE
B1 INSPECT VISUALLY • Perform system inspection. • Note carefully when intermittent action occurs. • Does the intermittent condition occur while cruising or while operating the control buttons or turning the steering wheel?	If intermittent action occurs while cruising If intermittent action occurs while using control buttons or turning steering wheel	▶ ▶	GO to B2. GO to B4.
B2 CHECK VACUUM TO SPEED CONTROL SERVO • Start the engine and run until at normal operating temperature. • Check the vacuum supply to speed control servo. NOTE: 8.42 kPa, 2.5 inches (of Hg) is minimum vacuum for normal speed control servo operation. The vacuum source hose is attached to the 7.9 mm (5/16-inch) engine vacuum-fitting port. • Is vacuum operating at normal specifications?	Yes No	▶ ▶	GO to B3. SERVICE the vacuum supply.
B3 PERFORM SPEED CONTROL SERVO TESTS • Perform the Speed Control Servo Tests as described in this section. Lightly tap the body while making test. • Is the speed control servo OK?	Yes No	▶ ▶	SUBSTITUTE a known good speed control amplifier. If OK, properly INSTALL a speed control amplifier. REPLACE the speed control servo.

FM1109400209010X

Fig. 30 Test B: Speed Control Intermittent (Part 1 of 2). 1994 Escort & Tracer

TEST STEP	RESULT	▶	ACTION TO TAKE
B4 PERFORM SPEED CONTROL ACTUATOR SWITCH ASSEMBLY TESTS • Perform the Speed Control Actuator Switch Assembly Tests as outlined in this section. • Are the switches and/or circuits OK?	Yes No	▶ ▶	SUBSTITUTE a known good speed control amplifier. If system now functions properly, INSTALL a speed control amplifier. SERVICE the circuits, REPLACE the horn pad assembly. SERVICE or REPLACE the clock spring assembly.

FM1109400209020X

Fig. 30 Test B: Speed Control Intermittent (Part 2 of 2). 1994 Escort & Tracer

TEST STEP	RESULT	▶	ACTION TO TAKE
B1 CHECK THE FOLLOWING SWITCHES AND CIRCUITS • Check the SET ACCEL switch, RESUME switch, COAST switch and air bag sliding contact circuits. • Are all circuits and switches OK?	Yes No	▶ ▶	GO to B2. SERVICE the circuit as required.

FM1109400210010X

Fig. 31 Test B: Speed Control Intermittent (Part 1 of 2). 1994 Mustang

TEST STEP		RESULT	▶	ACTION TO TAKE
B2	CHECK VACUUM HOSES			
	Check to see if: • Vacuum supply hose is tightly connected to VAC port on speed control vacuum valve and to vacuum outlet manifold, and free of cuts, cracks and kinks. • Vacuum hoses are tightly connected between speed control vacuum valves and speed control servo, and free of cuts, cracks and kinks. • Vacuum hose is tightly connected between speed control vacuum valve and speed control vacuum reservoir, and free of cuts, cracks and kinks. • Dump valve hose is tightly connected to the speed control servo and speed control dump valve, and free of cuts, cracks and kinks. • **Are all checks successful?**	Yes No	▶ ▶	GO to B3. SERVICE as required.
B3	CHECK SPEED CONTROL VACUUM VALVE AND SPEED CONTROL VACUUM RESERVOIR			
	• Disconnect the hose between speed control vacuum valve and speed control vacuum servo, at the speed control servo end. • Apply 60.6 kPa (18 in-Hg) vacuum to open end of hose. • **Can vacuum be pumped to, and held at, 60.6 kPa (18 in-Hg) vacuum?**	Yes No	▶ ▶	GO to B4. SERVICE as required.
B4	CHECK SPEED CONTROL			
	• Separate speed control servo from speed control amplifier. • Connect the Circuit 144 (O/Y) lead of the speed control servo to the battery positive terminal. • Connect the Circuit 146 (W/PK) lead of the speed control servo to ground, and momentarily touch the Circuit 145 (GY/BK) lead of the speed control servo to ground. • The throttle actuator arm should pull in and the engine speed should increase. The arm should hold in that position or slowly release. • When Circuit 146 (W/PK) is removed from ground the throttle actuator arm should release. • **Does speed control servo operate properly?**	Yes No	▶ ▶	GO to B5. REPLACE speed control servo.
B5	CHECK SPEED CONTROL AMPLIFIER			
	• Disconnect 8-pin connector at speed control amplifier. • Measure resistance between the following circuits of the connector and check against the normal values.	Yes No	▶ ▶	REPLACE speed control amplifier. CHECK circuit connections for proper contact. SERVICE as required.

Circuits	Normal Resistance
.44 (O/Y) and 145 (GY/BK)	40-75 ohms
144 (O/Y) and 146 (W/PK)	100-150 ohms
147 (P/LB) and 148 (Y/R)	20k-30k ohms
147 (P/LB) and 149 (B/LG)	40k-60k ohms

• **Are all resistance values within limits?**

FM1109400210020X

Fig. 31   Test B: Speed Control Intermittent (Part 2 of 2). 1994 Mustang

TEST STEP		RESULT	▶	ACTION TO TAKE
C1	VERIFY THE CONDITION		▶	GO to C2.
C2	CHECK THE FOLLOWING SWITCHES AND CIRCUITS			
	• Check the SET-ACCEL switch, RESUME switch, COAST switch, slip ring circuits and brush contacts. • **Are circuits OK?**	Yes No	▶ ▶	GO to C3. SERVICE the circuit as required.
C3	TEST SPEED CONTROL SERVO			
	• Perform speed control servo test. • **Is test successful?**	Yes No	▶ ▶	GO to C4. REPLACE speed control servo.
C4	TEST SPEED CONTROL AMPLIFIER			
	• Perform speed control amplifier test • **Does test correct condition?**	Yes No	▶ ▶	REPLACE speed control amplifier. CHECK circuit connections for proper contact. SERVICE as required.

FM1109200106010X

Fig. 32   Test C: Speed Control Operates But Does Not Resume, Accelerate Or Coast Down Properly (Part 1 of 2). Mustang, Tempo & Topaz

TEST STEP		RESULT	▶	ACTION TO TAKE
C1	PERFORM VISUAL INSPECTION TEST			
	• Visually inspect the system. • **Does the visual inspection pass?**	Yes No	▶ ▶	GO to C2. SERVICE or REPLACE the affected circuit.
C2	PERFORM CONTROL SWITCHES AND CIRCUIT TESTS			
	• Perform the control switches and circuit tests • **Are the switches and/or circuits OK?**	Yes No	▶ ▶	GO to C3. SERVICE the circuits or REPLACE the horn pad assembly.
C3	PERFORM SERVO TESTS			
	• Perform the servo tests • **Is the actuator OK?**	Yes No	▶ ▶	SUBSTITUTE a known good amplifier. If OK — REPLACE the amplifier. REPLACE the actuator.

FM1109200106020X

Fig. 32   Test C: Speed Control Operates But Does Not Accelerate Or Coast Down Properly (Part 2 of 2). Escort & Tracer

TEST STEP		RESULT	▶	ACTION TO TAKE
D1	VERIFY CONDITION		▶	GO to D2.
D2	CHECK THROTTLE LINKAGE			
	• Check throttle linkage for proper operation and adjustment. • **Is operation and adjustment OK?**	Yes No	▶ ▶	GO to D3. SERVICE or ADJUST as required.
D3	CONTINUITY CHECK			
	• Check continuity of circuits 147, 148 and 149. • **Is there continuity in all circuits?**	Yes No	▶ ▶	GO to D4. SERVICE or REPLACE wiring as necessary.
D4	CHECK SPEEDOMETER CABLES			
	• Check speedometer cables for proper routing, no sharp bends or binding. • **Are cables properly routed?**	Yes No	▶ ▶	GO to D5. SERVICE as required.
D5	TEST SPEED CONTROL SERVO			
	• Perform speed control servo test as outlined. • **Is test successful?**	Yes No	▶ ▶	GO to D6. REPLACE as required.
D6	TEST VSS			
	• Perform VSS test as outlined. • **Is test successful?**	Yes No	▶ ▶	GO to D7. REPLACE VSS.
D7	CHECK SPEED CONTROL METER VALVE			
	• Check speed control metering valve. • **Is speed control metering valve OK?**	Yes No	▶ ▶	GO to D8. SERVICE or ADJUST as required.
D8	TEST SPEED CONTROL AMPLIFIER			
	• Perform speed control amplifier test as outlined. • **Is test successful?**	Yes No	▶ ▶	REPLACE speed control amplifier. CHECK circuit connections for good contacts. SERVICE as required.

FM1109200107010X

Fig. 33   Test D: Speed Continuously Changes Up & Down (Part 1 of 2). Tempo & Topaz & 1992-93 Mustang

TEST STEP		RESULT	▶	ACTION TO TAKE
D1	VERIFY THE CONDITION		▶	GO to D2.
D2	CHECK THROTTLE LINKAGE			
	• Check the throttle linkage for proper operation and adjustment. • **Does the throttle linkage operate properly?**	Yes No	▶ ▶	GO to D3. SERVICE and ADJUST as required.
D3	CHECK CONTINUITY			
	• Check the continuity of the actuator to amplifier circuits. • **Is there continuity on the wires from the actuator to the amplifier?**	Yes No	▶ ▶	GO to D4. SERVICE or REPLACE wiring as necessary.
D4	PERFORM ACTUATOR TESTS			
	• Perform the Actuator Tests as described in this section. • **Is the actuator OK?**	Yes No	▶ ▶	GO to D5. REPLACE the actuator.
D5	CHECK SPEEDOMETER CABLES			
	• Check the speedometer cables for proper routing, no sharp bends or binding. • **Are the cables OK?**	Yes No	▶ ▶	GO to D6. SERVICE as required.
D6	CHECK VEHICLE SPEED SENSOR			
	• Check the vehicle speed sensor for free operation. • **Is the vehicle speed sensor operating freely?**	Yes No	▶ ▶	GO to D7. REPLACE the vehicle speed sensor.
D7	PERFORM VEHICLE SPEED SENSOR TEST			
	• Perform the Vehicle Speed Sensor Test as described in this section. • **Is the vehicle speed sensor OK?**	Yes No	▶ ▶	GO to D8. REPLACE the vehicle speed sensor.
D8	CHECK VACUUM DUMP VALVE			
	• Perform the Vacuum Dump Valve Test as described in this section. • **Is the vacuum dump valve OK?**	Yes No	▶ ▶	GO to D9. SERVICE or ADJUST as required.
D9	PERFORM AMPLIFIER TEST			
	• Perform the Amplifier Test as described in this section. • **Is the problem corrected?**	Yes No	▶ ▶	REPLACE the amplifier. CHECK the circuit connections for good contacts. SERVICE as required.

FM1109200107020X

Fig. 33   Test D: Speed Continuously Changes Up & Down (Part 2 of 2). 1992–93 Escort & Tracer

TEST STEP	RESULT	▶	ACTION TO TAKE
D1 PERFORM SYSTEM INSPECTION			
• Visually inspect the system.	Yes	▶	GO to D2.
• **Does the visual inspection pass?**	No	▶	SERVICE or REPLACE the affected circuit.
D2 CHECK THROTTLE LINKAGE			
• Check the throttle linkage for proper operation and adjustment.	Yes	▶	GO to D3.
• **Does the throttle linkage operate properly?**	No	▶	SERVICE and ADJUST as required.
D3 CHECK CONTINUITY			
• Check the continuity of all six of the speed control servo to speed control amplifier circuits.	Yes	▶	GO to D4.
• **Is there continuity on the wires from the speed control servo to the speed control amplifier?**	No	▶	SERVICE or REPLACE wiring as necessary.
D4 PERFORM SPEED CONTROL SERVO TESTS			
• Perform the Speed Control Servo Tests as described in this section.	Yes	▶	GO to D5.
• **Is the speed control servo OK?**	No	▶	REPLACE the speed control servo.

FM1109400211010X

Fig. 34 Test D: Set Speed Fluctuates (Part 1 of 2). 1994 Escort & Tracer

TEST STEP	RESULT	▶	ACTION TO TAKE
D5 CHECK SPEEDOMETER CABLES			
• Check the speedometer cables for proper routing, no sharp bends or binding.	Yes	▶	GO to D6.
• **Are the speedometer cables OK?**	No	▶	SERVICE as required.
D6 CHECK VEHICLE SPEED SENSOR			
• Check the vehicle speed sensor for free operation.	Yes	▶	GO to D7.
• **Is the vehicle speed sensor operating freely?**	No	▶	REPLACE the vehicle speed sensor.
D7 PERFORM VEHICLE SPEED SENSOR TEST			
• Perform the Vehicle Speed Sensor Test as described in this section.	Yes	▶	GO to D8.
• **Is the vehicle speed sensor OK?**	No	▶	REPLACE the vehicle speed sensor.
D8 CHECK SPEED CONTROL DUMP VALVE			
• Perform the Speed Control Dump Valve Test as described in this section.	Yes	▶	REPLACE the speed control amplifier.
• **Is the speed control dump valve OK?**	No	▶	SERVICE or ADJUST as required.

FM1109400211020X

Fig. 34 Test D: Set Speed Fluctuates (Part 2 of 2). 1994 Escort & Tracer

TEST STEP	RESULT	▶	ACTION TO TAKE
D1 CHECK STOPLIGHT SWITCH AND CIRCUITRY			
• Make sure the stoplamps operate properly.	Yes	▶	GO to D2.
• Apply brake pedal until stoplamps are lit.	No	▶	SERVICE stoplamp circuit as required. VERIFY fuses are not open. GO to D2.
• Check for battery voltage at speed control amplifier on Circuit 296 (W/P).			
• Measure voltage at speed control amplifier on Circuit 810 (R/LG).			
• The difference between the two readings should not exceed 1.5 V.			
• **Is the difference between two voltage readings within limit?**			
D2 CHECK SPEED CONTROL DUMP VALVE			
• Disconnect the hose (white stripe) between speed control dump valve and speed control servo at the speed control servo end.	Yes	▶	GO to D3.
• Apply 60.6 kPa (18 in-Hg) to open end of hose.	No	▶	ADJUST or SERVICE as required.
• **Can vacuum be pumped up and held at 60.6 kPa (18 in-Hg) vacuum?**			
D3 CHECK SPEED CONTROL SERVO			
• Check speed control servo operation and throttle linkage.	Yes	▶	GO to D4.
• **Are speed control servo operation and linkage OK?**	No	▶	REPLACE speed control servo.
D4 CHECK SPEED CONTROL AMPLIFIER			
• Disconnect 8-pin connector at speed control amplifier.	Yes	▶	REPLACE speed control amplifier.
• Measure resistance between the following circuits of the connector and check against the normal values.	No	▶	CHECK contacts of electrical connector. SERVICE as required.

Circuits	Normal Resistance
144 (O/Y) and 145 (GY/BK)	40-75 ohms
144 (O/Y) and 146 (W/PK)	100-150 ohms
147 (P/LB) and 148 (Y/R)	20k-30k ohms
147 (P/LB) and 149 (B/LG)	40k-60k ohms

• **Are all resistance values within limits?**

FM1109400212000X

Fig. 35 Test D: Speed Control Does Not Disengage When Brakes Are Applied. 1994 Mustang

TEST STEP	RESULT	▶	ACTION TO TAKE
E1 VERIFY THE CONDITION		▶	GO to E2.
E2 CHECK STOPLAMPS			
• Apply brakes and observe stoplamps.	Yes	▶	GO to E3.
• Do stoplamps operate?	No	▶	SERVICE stoplamp circuit as required. VERIFY fuses are not open. GO to E3.
E3 CHECK SPEED CONTROL METER VALVE			
• Check speed control metering valve.	Yes	▶	GO to E4.
• Is speed control metering valve OK?	No	▶	ADJUST or SERVICE as required.
E4 CHECK SPEED CONTROL SERVO			
• Check speed control servo operation and throttle linkage.	Yes	▶	GO to E5.
• Are speed control servo operation and linkage OK?	No	▶	REPLACE speed control servo.
E5 TEST SPEED CONTROL AMPLIFIER			
• Perform Speed Control Amplifier Amplifier Test as outlined.	Yes	▶	REPLACE speed control amplifier.
• Is test successful?	No	▶	CHECK contacts of electrical connector. SERVICE as required.

FM1109200108010X

Fig. 36 Test E: Speed Control Does Not Disengage When Brakes Are Applied (Part 1 of 2). Tempo, Topaz & 1992–93 Mustang

TEST STEP	RESULT	▶	ACTION TO TAKE
E1 VERIFY THE CONDITION		▶	GO to **E2**.
E2 CHECK STOPLAMPS			
• Apply the brakes and observe the stoplamps. Perform the Brake On/Off Switch and Circuit Test as described in this section.	Yes	▶	GO to **E3**.
• **Are the stoplamps working?**	No	▶	SERVICE the lamps and circuit as required. VERIFY that the fuses are not open. GO to **E3**.
E3 CHECK VACUUM DUMP VALVE			
• Perform the Vacuum Dump Valve Test as described in this section.	Yes	▶	GO to **E4**.
• **Is the vacuum dump valve OK?**	No	▶	ADJUST or SERVICE as required.
E4 PERFORM ACTUATOR TESTS			
• Perform the Actuator Tests as described in this section.	Yes	▶	GO to **E5**.
• **Is the actuator OK?**	No	▶	REPLACE the actuator.
E5 PERFORM AMPLIFIER TEST			
• Perform the Amplifier Test as described in this section.	Yes	▶	REPLACE the amplifier.
• **Is the problem corrected?**	No	▶	CHECK the contacts of the electrical connector. SERVICE as required.

FM1109200108020X

Fig. 36 Test E: Speed Control Does Not Disengage When Brakes Are Applied (Part 2 of 2). 1992–93 Escort & Tracer

	TEST STEP	RESULT	▶	ACTION TO TAKE
E1	PERFORM SYSTEM INSPECTION ● Visually inspect the system. ● **Does the visual inspection pass?**	Yes No	▶ ▶	GO to **E2**. SERVICE or REPLACE the affected circuit.
E2	CHECK STOPLAMPS ● Perform the Brake On/Off Switch and Circuit Test as described in this section. ● **Are the stoplamps working?**	Yes No	▶ ▶	GO to **E3**. SERVICE the stoplamps and circuit as required. VERIFY that the fuses are not open. GO to **E3**.
E3	CHECK SPEED CONTROL DUMP VALVE ● Perform the Speed Control Dump Valve Test as described in this section. ● **Is the speed control dump valve OK?**	Yes No	▶ ▶	GO to **E4**. ADJUST or SERVICE as required.
E4	PERFORM SPEED CONTROL SERVO TESTS ● Perform the Speed Control Servo Tests as described in this section. ● **Is the speed control servo OK?**	Yes No	▶ ▶	REPLACE the speed control amplifier. REPLACE the speed control servo.

FM1109400213000X

Fig. 37 Test E: Speed Control Does Not Disengage When Brakes Are Applied. 1994 Escort & Tracer

	TEST STEP	RESULT	▶	ACTION TO TAKE
E1	CHECK CIRCUIT 810 (LG/R) ● Disconnect stoplight switch, and clutch pedal position switch. ● Using an ohmmeter, check resistance of Circuit 810 (LG/R) between stoplight switch connector and pedal position switch connector. ● Is resistance 5 ohms or less?	Yes No	▶ ▶	GO to E2. SERVICE Circuit 810 (LG/R) for open. RETEST system.
E2	CHECK CLUTCH PEDAL POSITION SWITCH CONTINUITY ● Gain access to the clutch pedal position switch. ● Using an ohmmeter, check clutch pedal position switch continuity, with clutch pedal released. ● Is resistance 5 ohms or less?	Yes No	▶ ▶	LEAVE ohmmeter connected. GO to E3. REPLACE clutch pedal position switch. RETEST system.
E3	CHECK CLUTCH PEDAL POSITION SWITCH OUTPUT ● Apply clutch pedal. ● Measure resistance of clutch pedal position switch. ● Does ohmmeter show open circuit?	Yes No	▶ ▶	GO to E4. REPLACE clutch pedal position switch. RETEST system.
E4	CHECK SPEED CONTROL SERVO ● Check speed control servo operation and throttle linkage. ● Are speed control servo operation and linkage OK?	Yes No	▶ ▶	GO to E5. REPLACE speed control servo.
E5	TEST SPEED CONTROL AMPLIFIER ● Perform speed control servo amplifier test as outlined. ● Is test successful?	Yes No	▶ ▶	REPLACE speed control servo. CHECK contacts of electrical connector. SERVICE as required.

FM1109400214000X

Fig. 38 Test E: Speed Control System Does Not Disengage When Clutch Pedal Is Applied. 1994 Mustang

	TEST STEP	RESULT	▶	ACTION TO TAKE
F1	VERIFY THE CONDITION		▶	GO to F2.
F2	CHECK THROTTLE LINKAGE ● Check the throttle linkage for proper operation and adjustment. ● Does the throttle linkage operate properly?	Yes No	▶ ▶	GO to F3. ADJUST or SERVICE as required.
F3	CHECK CONNECTIONS ● Check the system circuit connections. ● Are the connections OK?	Yes No	▶ ▶	GO to F4. SERVICE as required.
F4	PERFORM CONTROL SWITCH AND CIRCUIT TESTS ● Perform the Control Switch and Circuit Tests as described in this section. ● Are the switches and/or circuits OK?	Yes No	▶ ▶	GO to F5. SERVICE the switch circuit as required.
F5	CHECK VACUUM DUMP VALVE ● Perform the Vacuum Dump Valve Test as described in this section. ● Is the vacuum dump valve OK?	Yes No	▶ ▶	GO to F6 for manual transaxle, F7 for automatic transaxle. ADJUST or SERVICE as required.
F6	CHECK CLUTCH PEDAL POSITION SWITCH (MTX) ● Check the clutch pedal position switch for proper operation. Perform the Clutch Pedal Position Switch Test as described in this section. ● Does the clutch pedal position switch operate properly?	Yes No	▶ ▶	GO to F7. SERVICE the switch as required.

FM1109200110010X

Fig. 39 Test F: Speed Will Not Set In System (Part 1 of 2). 1992–93 Escort & Tracer

	TEST STEP	RESULT	▶	ACTION TO TAKE
F7	CHECK STOPLAMPS ● Apply the brakes and observe the stoplamps. Perform the Brake On/Off Switch and Circuit Test as described in this section. ● Are the stoplamps working?	Yes No	▶ ▶	GO to F8. SERVICE the lamps and circuit as required. VERIFY that the fuses are not open.
F8	PERFORM ACTUATOR TESTS ● Perform the Actuator Tests as described in this section. ● Is the actuator OK?	Yes No	▶ ▶	GO to F9. REPLACE the actuator.
F9	PERFORM VEHICLE SPEED SENSOR TEST ● Perform the Vehicle Speed Sensor Test as described in this section. ● Is the vehicle speed sensor OK?	Yes No	▶ ▶	SUBSTITUTE a known good amplifier. If OK, REPLACE the amplifier. REPLACE the vehicle speed sensor.

FM1109200110020X

Fig. 39 Test F: Speed Will Not Set In System (Part 2 of 2). 1992–93 Escort & Tracer

TEST STEP		RESULT	▶	ACTION TO TAKE
F1	VERIFY			
	• Verify system disengages when stoplamp switch is activated. • Check clutch switch operation. • Do both operate properly?	Yes	▶	SERVICE or REPLACE wire assembly 9A840 as required.
		No	▶	SERVICE or REPLACE as required.

FM1109200109000X

Fig. 40 Test F: Speed Control System Does Not Disengage When Clutch Pedal Is Depressed. Tempo & Topaz & 1992–93 Mustang & 1994 Escort & Tracer w/Manual Transaxle

TEST STEP		RESULT	▶	ACTION TO TAKE
G1	VERIFY THE CONDITION			
	• Verify that the system disengages when the brake on/off switch is activated. • Check the clutch pedal position switch operation. Perform the Clutch Pedal Position Switch Test as described in this section. • Is everything OK?	Yes	▶	SERVICE or REPLACE the wire assembly as required.
		No	▶	SERVICE or REPLACE as required.

FM1109200112000X

Fig. 41 Test G: Speed Control System Does Not Disengage When Clutch Pedal Is Depressed. 1992–93 Escort & Tracer

TEST STEP		RESULT	▶	ACTION TO TAKE
G1	VERIFY			
	• Verify that engine is properly tuned. • Check accelerator action and actuator cable adjustment. • Is accelerator operation OK?	Yes	▶	GO to G2.
		No	▶	ADJUST or CORRECT as required.
G2	CHECK SPEED CONTROL METER VALVE			
	• Check speed control metering valve. • Is speed control metering valve OK?	Yes	▶	GO to G3.
		No	▶	ADJUST or SERVICE as required.
G3	TEST SPEED CONTROL SERVO			
	• Perform speed control servo test. • Is test successful?	Yes	▶	PERFORM speed control amplifier test. REPLACE if required.
		No	▶	REPLACE speed control servo.

FM1109200111000X

Fig. 42 Test G: Speed Gradually Increases Or Decreases After Speed Is Set. Tempo & Topaz & 1992–93 Mustang & 1994 Escort & Tracer

TEST STEP		RESULT	▶	ACTION TO TAKE
H1	VERIFY THE CONDITION			
	• Verify that engine is properly tuned. • Check the accelerator action and actuator cable adjustment. • Is everything OK?	Yes	▶	GO to H2.
		No	▶	ADJUST or CORRECT as required.
H2	CHECK VACUUM DUMP VALVE			
	• Perform the Vacuum Dump Valve Test as described in this section. • Is the vacuum dump valve OK?	Yes	▶	GO to H3.
		No	▶	ADJUST or SERVICE as required.
H3	PERFORM ACTUATOR TESTS			
	• Perform the Actuator Test as described in this section. • Is the actuator OK?	Yes	▶	PERFORM the amplifier test. REPLACE if required.
		No	▶	REPLACE the actuator.

FM1109200113000X

Fig. 43 Test H: Speed Gradually Increases Or Decreases After Speed Is Set. 1992–93 Escort & Tracer

TEST STEP		RESULT	▶	ACTION TO TAKE
H1	CHECK THROTTLE LINKAGE			
	• Check the throttle linkage for proper operation and adjustment. • Does the throttle linkage operate properly?	Yes	▶	GO to H2.
		No	▶	ADJUST or SERVICE as required.
H2	CHECK CONNECTIONS			
	• Check the system circuit connections. • Are the connections OK?	Yes	▶	GO to H3.
		No	▶	SERVICE as required.
H3	PERFORM CONTROL SWITCH AND CIRCUIT TESTS			
	• Perform the Control Switch and Circuit Tests as described in this section. • Are the switches and/or circuits OK?	Yes	▶	GO to H4.
		No	▶	SERVICE the switch circuit as required.
H4	CHECK SPEED CONTROL DUMP VALVE			
	• Perform the Speed Control Dump Valve Test as described in this section. • Is the speed control dump valve OK?	Yes	▶	GO to H5 for manual transaxle, H6 for automatic transaxles.
		No	▶	ADJUST or SERVICE as required.
H5	CHECK CLUTCH PEDAL POSITION SWITCH (MTX)			
	• Check the clutch pedal position switch for proper operation. Perform the Clutch Pedal Position Switch Test as described in this section. • Does the clutch pedal position switch operate properly?	Yes	▶	GO to H6.
		No	▶	SERVICE the switch as required.
H6	CHECK STOPLAMPS			
	• Apply the brakes and observe the stoplamps. Perform the Brake On/Off Switch and Circuit Test as described in this section. • Are the stoplamps working?	Yes	▶	GO to H7.
		No	▶	SERVICE the lamps and circuit as required. VERIFY that the fuses are not open.
H7	PERFORM SPEED CONTROL ACTUATOR TESTS			
	• Perform the Speed Control Actuator Tests as described in this section. • Is the speed control amplifier OK?	Yes	▶	GO to H8.
		No	▶	REPLACE the speed control servo.

FM1109400215010X

Fig. 44 Test H: Speed Will Not Set In System (Part 1 of 2). 1994 Escort & Tracer

TEST STEP		RESULT	▶	ACTION TO TAKE
H8	PERFORM VEHICLE SPEED SENSOR TEST			
	• Perform the Vehicle Speed Sensor Test as described in this section. • Is the vehicle speed sensor OK?	Yes	▶	SUBSTITUTE a known good speed control amplifier. If OK, REPLACE the speed control amplifier.
		No	▶	REPLACE the vehicle speed sensor.

FM1109400215020X

Fig. 44 Test H: Speed Will Not Set In System (Part 2 of 2). 1994 Escort & Tracer

TEST STEP		RESULT	▶	ACTION TO TAKE
J1	VERIFY THE CONDITION			GO to J2.
J2	PERFORM CONTROL SWITCHES AND CIRCUIT TESTS			
	• Perform the Control Switches and Circuit Tests as described in this section. • Are the switches and/or circuits OK?	Yes	▶	GO to J3.
		No	▶	SERVICE the circuit as required.
J3	PERFORM ACTUATOR TESTS			
	• Perform the Actuator Tests as described in this section. • Is the actuator OK?	Yes	▶	GO to J4.
		No	▶	REPLACE the actuator.
J4	PERFORM AMPLIFIER TEST			
	• Perform the Amplifier Test as described in this section. • Is the problem corrected?	Yes	▶	REPLACE the amplifier.
		No	▶	CHECK the circuit connections for proper contact. SERVICE as required.

FM1109200114000X

Fig. 45 Test J: Speed Control Operates But Does Not Resume, Accelerate Or Coast Down Properly. 1992–93 Escort & Tracer

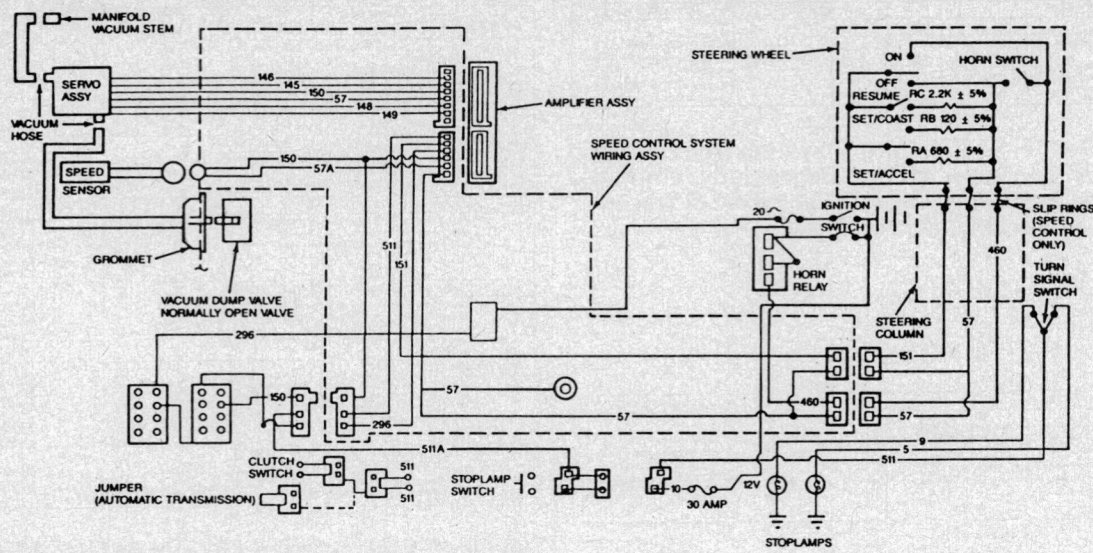

CIRCUIT NUMBER	CIRCUIT DESCRIPTION	GAUGE	COLOR	CIRCUIT NUMBER	CIRCUIT DESCRIPTION	GAUGE	COLOR
57	STEERING WHEEL SWITCH GROUND	18	BLACK	151	AMPLIFIER CONTROL LINE	18	LIGHT BLUE/BLACK
460	HORN SWITCH FEED		YELLOW	296	IGNITION SWITCH (ACCESSORY) TO AMPLIFIER FEED	20	PURPLE/ORANGE
5	RH REAR TURN SIGNAL LAMP	14	ORANGE/LIGHT BLUE	149	SERVO FEEDBACK POTENTIOMETER—TO AMPLIFIER	20	BROWN/LIGHT GREEN
9	LH REAR TURN SIGNAL LAMP	14	LIGHT GREEN/ORANGE	148	SERVO FEEDBACK—TO AMPLIFIER	20	YELLOW/RED
511	STOPLAMP SWITCH TO TURN SIGNAL SWITCH	18	LIGHT GREEN	147	SERVO FEEDBACK POTENTIOMETER POSITION—TO AMPLIFIER	18	PURPLE/LIGHT GREEN
511A	BRAKE SWITCH (LOAD SIDE) TO AMPLIFIER DISABLE	18	LIGHT GREEN	146	SERVO VENT SOLENOID CONTROL	20	WHITE/PINK
57A	SENSOR GROUND	18	BLACK	145	SERVO VACUUM SOLENOID CONTROL	20	GRAY/BLACK
150	SENSOR SIGNAL TO AMPLIFIER	20	DARK GREEN	144	SERVO SOLENOID FEED	20	ORANGE/YELLOW
57	AMPLIFIER GROUND	18	BLACK				

FM1109100119000X

Fig. 46   Wiring circuit. 1992 Continental, Cougar & Thunderbird

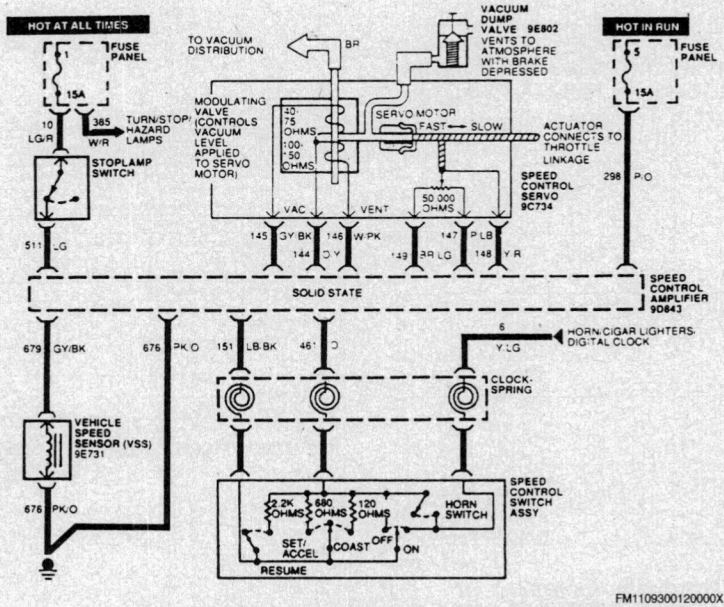

FM1109300120000X

Fig. 47   Wiring circuit. 1993–94 Continental

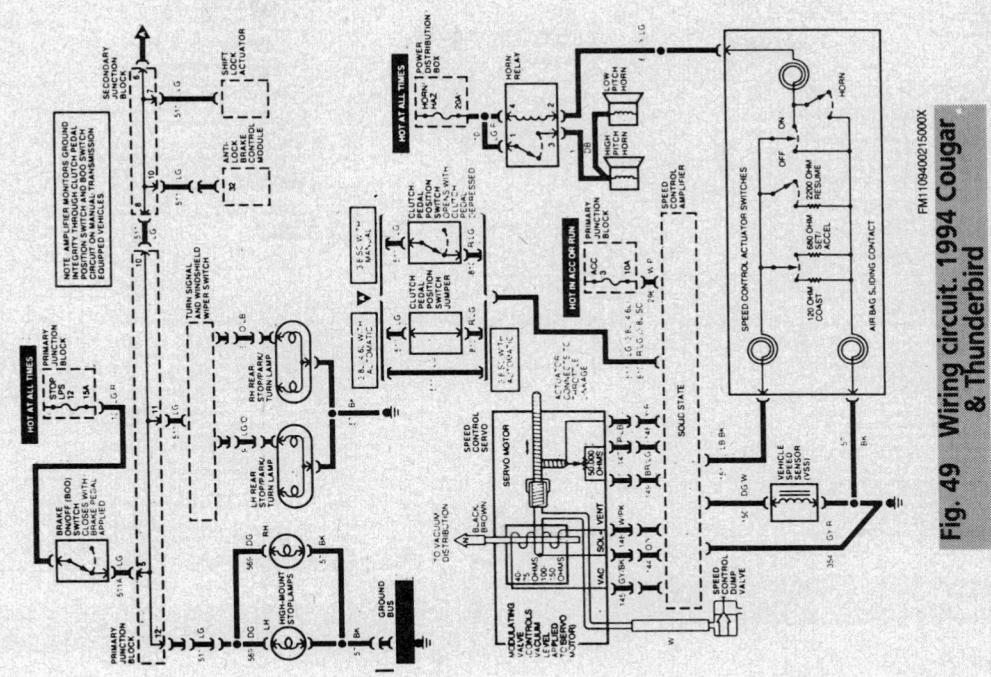

Fig. 49 Wiring circuit, 1994 Cougar & Thunderbird

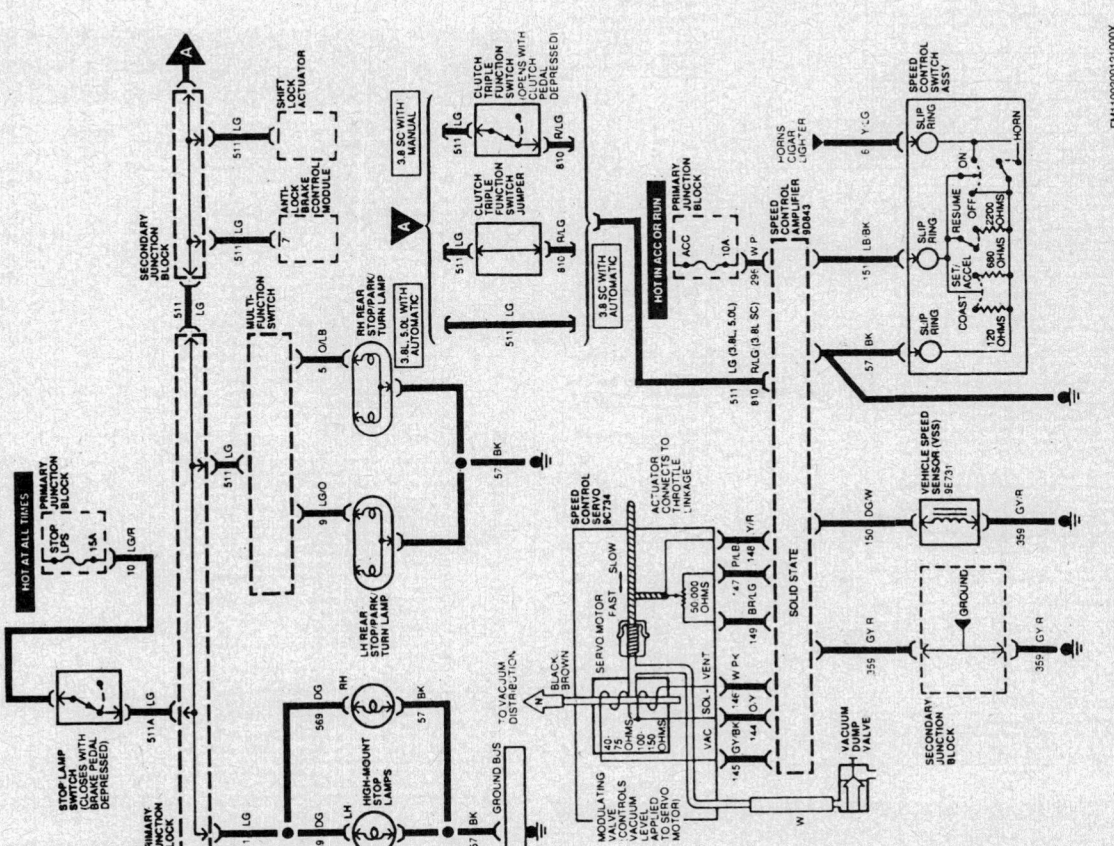

Fig. 48 Wiring circuit, 1993 Cougar & Thunderbird

TEST STEP		RESULT	▶	ACTION TO TAKE
A1	CHECK CONNECTIONS			
	• Check all electrical and vacuum connections. • Are all connections OK?	Yes No	▶ ▶	GO to A2. SERVICE or REPLACE as required.
A2	CHECK STOPLAMPS			
	• Apply brake pedal. • Are stoplamps operating?	Yes No	▶ ▶	GO to A3 if manual transmission. If automatic transmission, GO to A4. SERVICE stoplamp circuit.
A3	CHECK CLUTCH PEDAL POSITION SWITCH (MANUAL TRANSMISSION)			
	• Check clutch pedal position switch for proper operation. • Does clutch pedal position switch operate properly?	Yes No	▶ ▶	GO to A4. SERVICE as required.
A4	CHECK SPEED CONTROL ACTUATOR CABLE CONNECTION TO THROTTLE BODY AND SPEED CONTROL SERVO			
	• Check speed control actuator cable attachment to throttle body accelerator linkage. • Check speed control actuator cable attachment to servo linkage. • Is speed control actuator cable attached to both?	Yes No	▶ ▶	GO to A5. SERVICE as required.
A5	CHECK LINKAGE OPERATION			
	• Check the throttle linkage for proper operation. • Does linkage operate properly?	Yes No	▶ ▶	GO to A6. SERVICE as required.
A6	CHECK VACUUM HOSES			
	• Check to see if: ◦ Vacuum supply hose is tightly connected to VAC port on speed control vacuum valve and to vacuum manifold, and free of cuts, cracks and kinks. ◦ Vacuum hoses are tightly connected between speed control vacuum valve and speed control servo, and free of cuts, cracks and kinks. ◦ Vacuum hose is tightly connected between speed control vacuum valve and speed control vacuum aspirator, and free of cuts, cracks and kinks. ◦ Speed control dump valve hose is tightly connected to the speed control servo and speed control dump valve, and free of cuts, cracks and kinks. • Are all checks successful?	Yes No	▶ ▶	GO to A7. SERVICE as required.

FM1109400216010X

Fig. 50   Test A: Speed Control Inoperative (Part 1 of 4). Cougar & Thunderbird

TEST STEP		RESULT	▶	ACTION TO TAKE
A7	CHECK THE CHECK VALVE			
	• Disconnect the hose between speed control vacuum valve and speed control servo, at the speed control servo end. • Apply 60.6 kPa (18 in-Hg) vacuum to open end of hose. • Can vacuum be pumped to and held at 60.6 kPa (18 in-Hg) vacuum?	Yes No	▶ ▶	GO to A8. SERVICE as required.
A8	CHECK ASPIRATOR CHECK VALVE (3.8L SC only)			
	• Disconnect hose between three-way check valve and speed control vacuum aspirator at manifold vacuum valve end. • Apply 60.6 kPa (18 in-Hg) vacuum to open end of hose. • Can vacuum be pumped to and held at 60.6 kPa (18 in-Hg) vacuum?	Yes No	▶ ▶	GO to A9. SERVICE as required.
A9	CHECK DUMP VALVE			
	• Disconnect the hose (white stripe) between speed control dump valve and speed control servo at the speed control servo end. • Apply 60.6 kPa (18 in-Hg) to open end of hose. • Can vacuum be pumped up and held at 60.6 kPa (18 in-Hg) vacuum?	Yes No	▶ ▶	GO to A10. SERVICE as required.
A10	PERFORM SPEED CONTROL ACTUATOR SWITCH ASSEMBLY			
	• Perform speed control actuator switch assembly test as outlined. • Are tests successful?	Yes No	▶ ▶	GO to A11. SERVICE or REPLACE speed control actuator switch assembly, air bag sliding contact as required.
A11	CHECK SPEED CONTROL SERVO			
	• Separate speed control servo from speed control amplifier. • Connect the Circuit 144 (O/Y) lead of the speed control servo to the battery positive terminal. • Connect the Circuit 146 (W/PK) lead of the speed control servo to ground, and momentarily touch Circuit 145 (GY/BK) lead of the speed control servo to ground. • The throttle actuator arm should pull in and the engine speed should increase. The arm should hold in that position or slowly release. • When Circuit 146 (W/PK) is removed from ground, the throttle actuator arm should release. • Does speed control servo operate properly?	Yes No	▶ ▶	GO to A12. REPLACE speed control servo.
A12	CHECK VSS			
	• Disconnect 6-pin connector at speed control amplifier. • With an ohmmeter measure resistance between Circuit 150 (DG/W, VSS signal) and Circuit 57 (BK, ground). • Is the resistance approximately 200-300 ohms?	Yes No	▶ ▶	GO to A13. REPLACE vehicle speed sensor.

FM1109400216020X

Fig. 50   Test A: Speed Control Inoperative (Part 2 of 4). Cougar & Thunderbird

TEST STEP		RESULT	▶	ACTION TO TAKE
A13	PERFORM SPEED CONTROL AMPLIFIER TEST			
	• Disconnect 8-pin connector at speed control amplifier. • Measure resistance between the following circuits of the connector, and check against the normal values.	Yes No	▶ ▶	INSTALL a new speed control amplifier. EXAMINE all connectors carefully for proper contact. SERVICE as required. REMOVE substitute speed control amplifier.

Circuits	Normal Resistance
144 (O/Y) and 145 (GY/BK)	40-75 ohms
144 (O/Y) and 146 (W/PK)	100-150 ohms
147 (P/LB) and 148 (Y/R)	20 K-30 K ohms
147 (P/LB) and 149 (B/LG)	40 K-60 K ohms

TEST STEP		RESULT	▶	ACTION TO TAKE
	• Are all resistances within limit?			
A14	CHECK INTERMITTENT ACTION			
	• Note carefully when intermittent action occurs. • Determine whether intermittent action occurs while cruising or it occurs while using control buttons or turning steering wheel. • Does intermittent action occur while cruising?	Yes No	▶ ▶	GO to A15. GO to A17.
A15	CHECK VACUUM TO SPEED CONTROL SERVO			
	• Check vacuum supply to speed control servo. NOTE: 8.42 kPa (2.5 in-Hg) is minimum vacuum for normal speed control servo operation. The vacuum source hose is attached to the 7.9mm (5/16 inch) engine vacuum-fitting port. • Is vacuum supply OK?	Yes No	▶ ▶	GO to A16. SERVICE vacuum supply.
A16	CHECK SPEED CONTROL SERVO			
	• Separate speed control servo from speed control amplifier. • Connect Circuit 144 (O/Y) lead of the speed control servo to the battery positive terminal. • Connect Circuit 146 (W/PK) lead of the speed control servo to ground, and momentarily touch Circuit 145 (GY/BK) lead of the speed control servo to ground. • The throttle actuator arm should pull in and the engine speed should increase. The arm should hold in that position or slowly release. • When Circuit 146 (W/PK) is removed from ground the throttle actuator should release. • Does speed control servo operate properly?	Yes No	▶ ▶	SUBSTITUTE known good speed control amplifier if OK — properly INSTALL amplifier. REPLACE speed control servo assembly.
A17	PERFORM SPEED CONTROL ACTUATOR SWITCH ASSEMBLY TEST			
	• Perform Speed Control Switch Assembly Test as outlined. • Are tests successful?	Yes No	▶ ▶	SUBSTITUTE known good speed control amplifier if OK — properly INSTALL speed control amplifier. SERVICE circuits. REPLACE speed control actuator switch assembly or air bag sliding contact as required.
A18	CHECK ACCELERATOR OPERATION			
	• Verify that engine is properly tuned. • Check accelerator action and actuator cable adjustment. • Is accelerator operation OK?	Yes No	▶ ▶	GO to A19. ADJUST or CORRECT as required.

FM1109400216030X

Fig. 50   Test A: Speed Control Inoperative (Part 3 of 4). Cougar & Thunderbird

TEST STEP		RESULT	▶	ACTION TO TAKE
B1	CHECK THE FOLLOWING SWITCHES AND CIRCUITS			
	• Check the SET-ACCEL switch, RESUME switch, COAST switch, air bag sliding contact circuits. • Are all circuits and switches OK?	Yes No	▶ ▶	GO to B2. SERVICE as required.

FM1109400217010X

Fig. 51   Test B: Speed Control Operates But Does Not Resume, Accelerate Or Coast Down Properly (Part 1 of 2). Cougar & Thunderbird

TEST STEP		RESULT	▶	ACTION TO TAKE
A19	CHECK SPEED CONTROL DUMP VALVE			
	• Disconnect the hose (white stripe) between speed control dump valve and speed control servo at speed control servo end. • Apply 60.6 kPa (18 in-Hg) to open end of hose. • Can vacuum be pumped up and held at 60.6 (18 in-Hg) vacuum?	Yes No	▶ ▶	GO to A20. ADJUST or SERVICE as required.
A20	CHECK VACUUM HOSES			
	• Check to see if: ◦ Vacuum supply hose is tightly connected to VAC port on speed control vacuum valve and to vacuum outlet manifold, and free of cuts, cracks and kinks. ◦ Vacuum hoses are tightly connected between speed control vacuum valve and speed control servo, and free of cuts, cracks and kinks. ◦ Vacuum hose is tightly connected between speed control vacuum valve and speed control vacuum aspirator, and free of cuts, cracks and kinks. ◦ Speed control dump valve hose is tightly connected to the speed control servo and dump valve, and free of cuts, cracks and kinks. • Are all connections OK?	Yes No	▶ ▶	GO to A21. SERVICE as required.
A21	CHECK THE SPEED CONTROL VACUUM VALVE			
	• Disconnect the hose between speed control vacuum valve and speed control servo, at the speed control servo end. Apply 60.6 kPa (18 in-Hg) vacuum to open end of hose. • Can vacuum be pumped to and held at 60.6 kPa (18 in-Hg) vacuum?	Yes No	▶ ▶	GO to A22. SERVICE as required.
A22	CHECK ASPIRATOR CHECK VALVE (3.8L SC)			
	• Disconnect hose between three-way check valve and the speed control vacuum aspirator. • Apply 60.6 kPa (18 in-Hg) vacuum to open end of hose. • Can vacuum be pumped to and held at 60.6 kPa (18 in-Hg) vacuum?	Yes No	▶ ▶	GO to A23. SERVICE as required.
A23	TEST SPEED CONTROL SERVO			
	• Separate speed control servo from speed control amplifier. • Connect Circuit 144 (O/Y) lead of the speed control servo to the battery positive terminal. • Connect Circuit 146 (W/PK) lead of the speed control servo to ground, and momentarily touch Circuit 145 (GY/BK) lead of the speed control servo to ground. • The throttle actuator arm should pull in and the engine speed should increase. The arm should hold in that position or slowly release. • When Circuit 146 (W/PK) is removed from ground the throttle actuator should release. • Does speed control servo operate properly?	Yes No	▶ ▶	PERFORM Speed Control Amplifier Test. REPLACE speed control amplifier if required. REPLACE speed control servo.

FM1109400216040X

Fig. 50   Test A: Speed Control Inoperative (Part 4 of 4). Cougar & Thunderbird

TEST STEP		RESULT	▶	ACTION TO TAKE
B2	CHECK VACUUM HOSES			
	• Check to see if:	Yes	▶	GO to B3.
	• Vacuum supply hose is tightly connected to VAC port on speed control vacuum valve and to vacuum outlet manifold, and free of cuts, cracks and kinks.	No	▶	SERVICE as required.
	• Vacuum hoses are tightly connected between speed control vacuum valve and speed control servo, and free of cuts, cracks and kinks.			
	• Vacuum hose is tightly connected between speed control vacuum valve and speed control vacuum aspirator, and free of cuts, cracks and kinks.			
	• Speed control dump valve hose is tightly connected to the speed control servo and speed control dump valve, and free of cuts, cracks and kinks.			
	• Are all connections OK?			
B3	CHECK THE SPEED CONTROL VACUUM VALVE			
	• Disconnect the hose between speed control vacuum valve and speed control servo, at the speed control servo end.	Yes	▶	GO to B4.
	• Apply 60.6 kPa (18 in-Hg) vacuum to open end of hose.	No	▶	SERVICE as required.
	• Can vacuum be pumped to, and held at, 60.6 kPa (18 in-Hg) vacuum?			
B4	CHECK SPEED CONTROL VACUUM ASPIRATOR CHECK VALVE (3.8L SC only)			
	• Disconnect hose between three-way check valve and speed control vacuum aspirator.	Yes	▶	GO to B5.
	• Apply 60.6 kPa (18 in-Hg) vacuum to open end of hose.	No	▶	SERVICE as required.
	• Can vacuum be pumped to and held at 60.6 kPa (18 in-Hg) vacuum?			
B5	TEST SPEED CONTROL AMPLIFIER			
	• Disconnect 8-pin connector at speed control amplifier.	Yes	▶	REPLACE speed control amplifier.
	• Measure resistance between the following circuits of the connector, and check against the normal values.	No	▶	CHECK circuit connections for proper contact. SERVICE as required.

Circuits	Normal Resistance
144 (O/Y) and 145 (GY/BK)	40-75 ohms
144 (O/Y) and 146 (W/PK)	100-150 ohms
147 (P/LB) and 148 (Y/R)	20 K-30 K ohms
147 (P/LB) and 149 (B/LG)	40 K-60 K ohms

• Are all resistances within limit?

FM1109400217020X

Fig. 51   Test B: Speed Control Operates But Does Not Resume, Accelerate Or Coast Down Properly (Part 2 of 2). Cougar & Thunderbird

TEST STEP		RESULT	▶	ACTION TO TAKE
C1	CHECK THROTTLE LINKAGE			
	• Check throttle linkage for proper operation and adjustment.	Yes	▶	GO to C2.
	• Are operation and adjustment OK?	No	▶	SERVICE or ADJUST as required.
C2	CONTINUITY CHECK			
	• Check continuity of Circuits 147 (P/LB), 148 (Y/R) and 149 (BR/LG).	Yes	▶	GO to C3.
	• Is there continuity in all circuits?	No	▶	SERVICE or REPLACE wiring as necessary.

FM1109400218010X

Fig. 52   Test C: Set Speed Fluctuates (Part 1 of 3). Cougar & Thunderbird

TEST STEP		RESULT	▶	ACTION TO TAKE
C9	CHECK SPEED CONTROL AMPLIFIER			
	• Disconnect 8-pin connector at speed control amplifier.	Yes	▶	REPLACE speed control amplifier.
	• Measure resistance between the following circuits of the connector, and check against the normal values.	No	▶	CHECK circuit connections for good contacts. SERVICE as required.

Circuits	Normal Resistance
144 (O/Y) and 145 (GY/BK)	40-75 ohms
144 (O/Y) and 146 (W/PK)	100-150 ohms
147 (P/LB) and 148 (Y/R)	20 K-30 K ohms
147 (P/LB) and 149 (B/LG)	40 K-60 K ohms

• Are all resistances within limit?

FM1109400218030X

Fig. 52   Test C: Set Speed Fluctuates (Part 3 of 3). Cougar & Thunderbird

TEST STEP		RESULT	▶	ACTION TO TAKE
C3	CHECK VACUUM HOSES			
	• Check to see if:	Yes	▶	GO to C4.
	• Vacuum supply hose is tightly connected to VAC port on speed control vacuum valve and to vacuum outlet manifold, and free of cuts, cracks and kinks.	No	▶	SERVICE or REPLACE wiring as necessary.
	• Vacuum hoses are tightly connected between speed control vacuum valve and speed control servo, and free of cuts, cracks and kinks.			
	• Vacuum hose is tightly connected between speed control vacuum valve and speed control vacuum aspirator, and free of cuts, cracks and kinks.			
	• Speed control dump valve hose is tightly connected to the speed control servo and speed control dump valve, and free of cuts, cracks and kinks.			
	• Are all connections OK?			
C4	CHECK THE SPEED CONTROL VACUUM VALVE			
	• Disconnect the hose between speed control vacuum valve and servo, at the servo end.	Yes	▶	GO to C5.
	• Apply 60.6 kPa (18 in-Hg) vacuum to open end of hose.	No	▶	SERVICE as required.
	• Can vacuum be pumped to and held at 60.6 kPa (18 in-Hg) vacuum?			
C5	CHECK ASPIRATOR CHECK VALVE (3.8L SC ONLY)			
	• Disconnect hose between three-way check valve and speed control vacuum aspirator.	Yes	▶	GO to C6.
	• Apply 60.6 kPa (18 in-Hg) vacuum to open end of hose.	No	▶	SERVICE as required.
	• Can vacuum be pumped to and held at 60.6 kPa (18 in-Hg) vacuum?			
C6	CHECK VSS			
	• Disconnect 8-pin connector at speed control amplifier.	Yes	▶	GO to C7.
	• With an ohmmeter, measure resistance between Circuit 150 (DG/W, VSS signal) and Circuit (57, ground).	No	▶	REPLACE vehicle speed sensor.
	• Is the resistance approximately 200-300 ohms?			
C7	CHECK SPEEDOMETER CABLES			
	• Check speedometer cables for proper routing, no sharp bends or binding.	Yes	▶	GO to C8.
	• Are cables OK?	No	▶	SERVICE as required.
C8	CHECK SPEED CONTROL DUMP VALVE			
	• Disconnect the hose (white stripe) between speed control dump valve and speed control servo at the speed control servo end.	Yes	▶	GO to C9.
	• Apply 60.6 kPa (18 in-Hg) to open end of hose.	No	▶	SERVICE or ADJUST as required.
	• Can vacuum be pumped up and held at 60.6 kPa (18 in-Hg) vacuum?			

FM1109400218020X

Fig. 52   Test C: Set Speed Fluctuates (Part 2 of 3). Cougar & Thunderbird

TEST STEP		RESULT	▶	ACTION TO TAKE
D1	CHECK STOPLIGHT SWITCH AND CIRCUITRY			
	• Make sure the stoplamps operate properly.	Yes	▶	GO to D2.
	• Apply brake pedal until stoplamps are lit.	No	▶	SERVICE stoplamp circuit as required. VERIFY fuses are not open. GO to D3.
	• Check for battery voltage at speed control amplifier on Circuit 296 (W/P).			
	• Measure voltage at speed control amplifier on Circuit 810 (R/LG) or 511 (LG).			
	• The difference between the two readings should not exceed 1.5 V.			
	• Is the difference between two voltage readings within limit?			
D2	CHECK SPEED CONTROL DUMP VALVE			
	• Disconnect the hose (white stripe) between speed control dump valve and speed control servo at the speed control servo end.	Yes	▶	GO to D3.
	• Apply 60.6 kPa (18 in-Hg) to open end of hose.	No	▶	ADJUST or SERVICE as required.
	• Can vacuum be pumped up and held at 60.6 kPa (18 in-Hg) vacuum?			
D3	CHECK SPEED CONTROL SERVO			
	• Check speed control servo operation and throttle linkage.	Yes	▶	GO to D4.
	• Are speed control servo operation and linkage OK?	No	▶	REPLACE speed control servo.
D4	TEST SPEED CONTROL AMPLIFIER			
	• Disconnect 8-pin connector at speed control amplifier.	Yes	▶	REPLACE speed control amplifier.
	• Measure resistance between the following circuits of the connector, and check against the normal values.	No	▶	CHECK contacts of electrical connector. SERVICE as required.

Circuits	Normal Resistance
144 (O/Y) and 145 (GY/BK)	40-75 ohms
144 (O/Y) and 146 (W/PK)	100-150 ohms
147 (P/LB) and 148 (Y/R)	20 K-30 K ohms
147 (P/LB) and 149 (B/LG)	40 K-60 K ohms

• Are all resistances within limit?

FM1109400219000X

Fig. 53   Test D: Speed Control Does Not Disengage When Brakes Are Applied. Cougar & Thunderbird

TEST STEP	RESULT	▶	ACTION TO TAKE
E1 VERIFY STOPLAMP SWITCH OPERATION			
• Verify that speed control system disengages when brakes are applied (stoplight switch operates properly).	Yes	▶	GO to E2.
• **Does stoplight switch operate properly?**	No	▶	GO to D1.
E2 PERFORM CLUTCH PEDAL POSITION SWITCH TEST			
• Disconnect the wiring harness from the clutch pedal position switch.	Yes	▶	GO to E3.
• Using a volt-ohmmeter, probe the clutch pedal position switch terminals for correct clutch pedal position switch function.	No	▶	REPLACE clutch pedal position switch.
• PCM terminals 5 and 6 should be normally open, and should close within approximately 50mm (2 inch) of clutch pedal travel.			
• Speed control release switch (terminals 3 and 4) should be normally closed, and should open within approximately 50mm (2 inch) of clutch travel.			
• Clutch pedal position switch (terminals 1 and 2) should be normally open and close when the clutch pedal has been moved to approximately 25mm (1 inch) from full travel.			
• **Does clutch pedal position switch check OK?**			
E3 CHECK CLUTCH PEDAL POSITION OPERATION			
• Disconnect the connector at speed control amplifier.	Yes	▶	GO to E4.
• Check for battery voltage at Circuit 810 (R/LG).	No	▶	SERVICE Circuit 511 (LG) or 810 (R/LG) or clutch pedal position switch as required.
• **Is there a battery voltage?**			
E4 CHECK CLUTCH PEDAL POSITION OPERATION			
• Apply clutch pedal.	Yes	▶	REPLACE speed control amplifier.
• Check voltage at the speed control amplifier connector in Circuit 810 (R/LG).	No	▶	REPLACE clutch pedal position switch.
• **Is there a zero voltage?**			

FM1109400220000X

Fig. 54 Test E: Speed Control Does Not Disengage When Clutch Is Applied. Cougar & Thunderbird

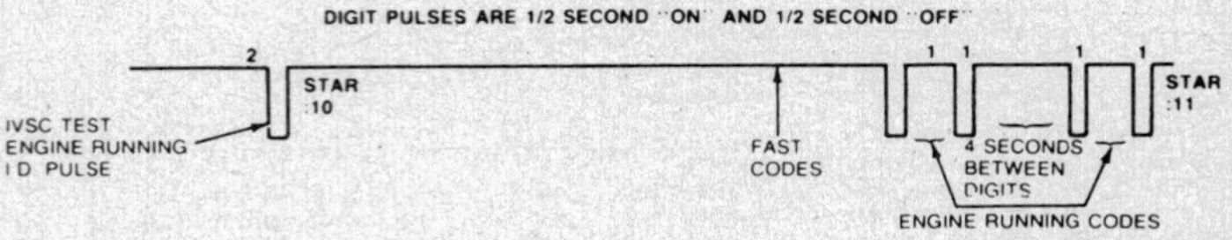

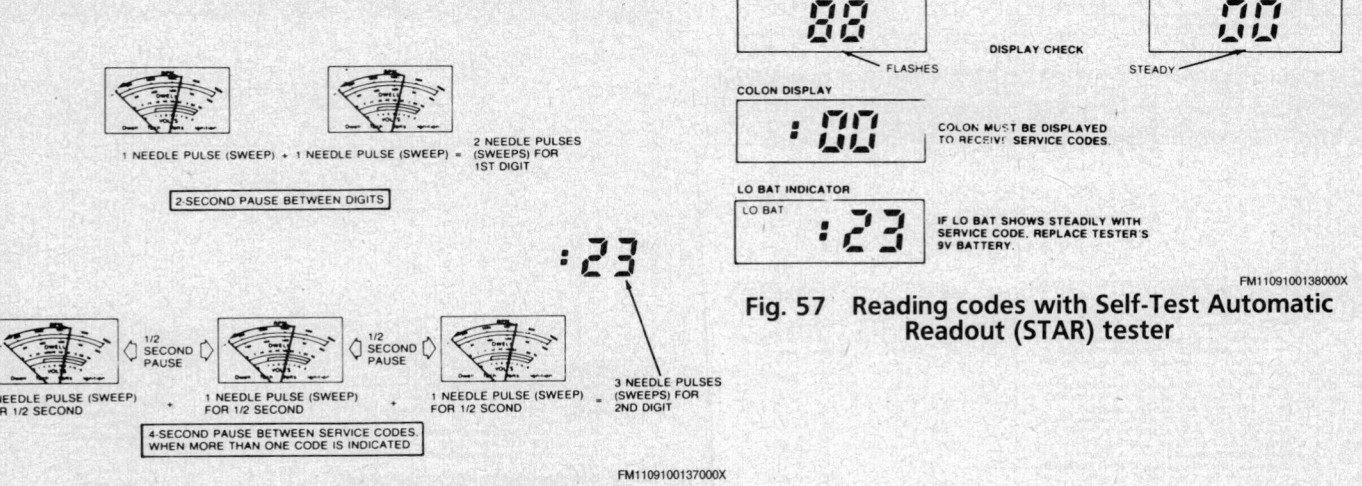

Fig. 55 Self-Test output code format

FM1109100136000X

Fig. 57 Reading codes with Self-Test Automatic Readout (STAR) tester

FM1109100138000X

Fig. 56 Reading codes with analog voltmeter

FM1109100137000X

A	CODE OUTPUT

To activate the KOEO IVSC test, do the following:
- Place transaxle shift lever in PARK (AXOD or ATX) or NEUTRAL (MTX).
- Leave single STI connector unplugged; plug in multipin self-test connector.
- Turn on STAR tester by moving slide switch to ON position.
- Press STAR pushbutton.
- Turn ignition key to RUN position.
- Press speed control ON switch.
- Observe code 10 on STAR display (indicates IVSC test in progress).
- Press speed control OFF, COAST, ACCEL, RESUME buttons; top brake pedal once; depress clutch pedal once (if so equipped).
NOTE: Do not depress throttle during KOEO self-test.
- Observe and record all Service Codes indicated. One of the following outputs will occur.

RESULTS		ACTION TO TAKE
Code Displayed		
11	▶	KEY ON ENGINE OFF TEST indicates a pass. GO To Step B.
Any other code(s)	▶	KEY ON ENGINE OFF TEST indicates a fault. Record codes and GO To Step B.
NO CODES OUTPUTTED	▶	Repeat SELF-TEST and verify that no service codes are present. GO To Pinpoint Test Step Q1.

FM1109100139010X

Fig. 58 Quick Test: Key On, Engine Off Self-Test (Part 1 of 2). Mark VII, 1992 Sable & Taurus

B	RESULTS AND ACTION TO TAKE

- Using the KEY ON ENGINE OFF service codes from Step A, follow the instructions in the ACTION TO TAKE column in this step.
- When more than one service code is received always start with the first code received.
- Whenever a service is made, REPEAT QUICK TEST.

NOTE: Before proceeding to the specified Pinpoint Test, read the instructions on how to use the Pinpoint Tests at the beginning of the Pinpoint Test section.

RESULT	ACTION TO TAKE
ON DEMAND SERVICE CODES	
23	► Check throttle position sensor. Refer to EEC-IV system diagnosis in the Auto Engine Tune Up & Electronics Manual
47	► GO to Pinpoint Test Step A1 .
48	► Go to Pinpoint Test Step A3 .
49	►
53	► GO to Pinpoint Test Step A5 .
63	► Check throttle position sensor. Refer to EEC-IV system diagnosis in the Auto Engine Tune Up & Electronics Manual
74	► Check brake On/Off Circuit. Refer to EEC-IV system diagnosis in the Auto Engine Tune Up & Electronics Manual
75	► GO to Pinpoint Test Step B1
67	► GO to Pinpoint Test Step B4
81	►
82	► Check air management system operation. Refer to EEC-IV system diagnosis in the Auto Engine Tune Up & Electronics Manual
	GO to Pinpoint Test Step C1
	GO to Pinpoint Test Step C5

NOTE: Service codes 23. 53. 63 and 67 are common with EEC-IV Diagnostics. These service codes must be diagnosed using the EEC-IV system diagnosis in the Auto Engine Tune Up & Electronics Manual.

*Can be purchased as a separate item.

FM1109100139020X

Fig. 58 Quick Test: Key On, Engine Off Self-Test (Part 2 of 2). Mark VII, 1992 Sable & Taurus

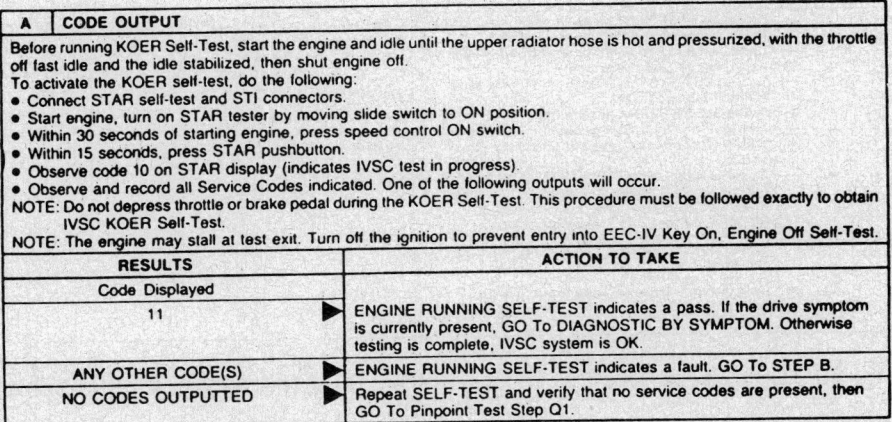

A	CODE OUTPUT

Before running KOER Self-Test, start the engine and idle until the upper radiator hose is hot and pressurized, with the throttle off fast idle and the idle stabilized, then shut engine off.

To activate the KOER self-test, do the following:

- Connect STAR self-test and STI connectors.
- Start engine, turn on STAR tester by moving slide switch to ON position.
- Within 30 seconds of starting engine, press speed control ON switch.
- Within 15 seconds, press STAR pushbutton.
- Observe code 10 on STAR display (indicates IVSC test in progress).
- Observe and record all Service Codes indicated. One of the following outputs will occur.

NOTE: Do not depress throttle or brake pedal during the KOER Self-Test. This procedure must be followed exactly to obtain IVSC KOER Self-Test.

NOTE: The engine may stall at test exit. Turn off the ignition to prevent entry into EEC-IV Key On, Engine Off Self-Test.

RESULTS	ACTION TO TAKE
Code Displayed	
11	► ENGINE RUNNING SELF-TEST indicates a pass. If the drive symptom is currently present, GO To DIAGNOSTIC BY SYMPTOM. Otherwise testing is complete, IVSC system is OK.
ANY OTHER CODE(S)	► ENGINE RUNNING SELF-TEST indicates a fault. GO To STEP B.
NO CODES OUTPUTTED	► Repeat SELF-TEST and verify that no service codes are present, then GO To Pinpoint Test Step Q1.

FM1109100140010X

Fig. 59 Quick Test: Key On, Engine Running Self-Test (Part 1 of 2). Mark VII, 1992 Sable & Taurus

B	RESULTS AND ACTION TO TAKE

- Using the ENGINE RUNNING service codes from Step A, follow the instructions in the ACTION TO TAKE column in this step.
- When more than one service code is received, always start service with the first code received.
- Whenever a service is made, REPEAT QUICK TEST.

RESULT	ACTION TO TAKE
ENGINE RUNNING SERVICE CODES	
27 ▶	Go to Pinpoint Test Step E1
28 ▶	GO to Pinpoint Test Step E3
36 ▶	Go to Pinpoint Test Step D1
37 ▶	GO to Pinpoint Test Step F1

FM1109100140020X

Fig. 59   Quick Test: Key On, Engine Running Self-Test (Part 2 of 2). Mark VII, 1992 Sable & Taurus

	TEST STEP	RESULT ▶	ACTION TO TAKE
A1	CODE OUPUT		
	• To activate the KOEO IVSC test, do the following: — Place transmission shift lever in PARK. — Leave single STI connector unplugged; plug in multi-pin self-test connector. — Turn on SUPER STAR II Tester by moving slide switch to ON position. — Press SUPER STAR II push button. — Turn ignition key to RUN position. — Within 10 seconds, press speed control ON switch. — Observe code 10 on SUPER STAR II display (indicates IVSC test in progress). — Press speed control OFF, COAST, ACCEL, RESUME buttons; tap brake pedal once. NOTE: Do not depress throttle during KOEO self-test. — Observe and record all Diagnostic Trouble Codes indicated. One of the following outputs will occur.	Code 111 displayed ▶ Any other code(s) ▶ No codes output ▶	Key On Engine Off Test indicates a pass. GO to Key On Engine Running (KOER) Self-Test. Key On Engine Off Test indicates a fault. Record codes and GO to Step B. REPEAT Self-Test and verify that no DTC's are present. GO to Pinpoint Test Step Q1.

FM1109300141010X

Fig. 60   Quick Test: Key On, Engine Off Self-Test (Part 1 of 2). 1993 Sable & Taurus

TEST STEP	RESULT ▶	ACTION TO TAKE
B1 RESULTS AND ACTION TO TAKE • Using the Key On Engine Off service codes from Step A, follow the instructions in the ACTION TO TAKE column in this step. • When more than one DTC is received always start with the first code received. • Whenever a service is made, REPEAT Quick Test. NOTE: Before proceeding to the specified Pinpoint Test, read the instructions on how to use the Pinpoint Tests at the beginning of the Pinpoint Test section.	ON DEMAND DIAGNOSTIC TROUBLE CODES Code 121 ▶ Code 457 ▶ Code 458 ▶ Code 459 ▶ Code 123 ▶ Code 122 ▶ Code 536 ▶ Code 528 ▶ Code 567 ▶ Code 568 ▶	After service, return to this section and REPEAT Quick Test. GO to Pinpoint Test Step A1. GO to Pinpoint Test Step A3. GO to Pinpoint Test Step A5. After service, return to this section and REPEAT Quick Test. After service, return to this section and REPEAT Quick Test. GO to Pinpoint Test Step B1. After service, return to this section and REPEAT Quick Test. GO to Pinpoint Test Step C1. GO to Pinpoint Test Step C5. NOTE: DTC's 121, 123, 122 and 528 are common with EEC-IV Diagnostics.

FM1109300141020X

Fig. 60 Quick Test: Key On, Engine Off Self-Test (Part 2 of 2). 1993 Sable & Taurus

TEST STEP	RESULT ▶	ACTION TO TAKE
A1 CODE OUTPUT • Before running KOER Self-Test, start the engine and idle until the upper radiator hose is hot and pressurized, with the throttle off fast idle and the idle stabilized, then shut engine off. To activate the KOER self-test, do the following: • Connect SUPER STAR II self-test and STI connectors. • Start engine, turn on SUPER STAR II Tester by moving slide switch to ON position. • Within 30 seconds of starting engine, press speed control ON switch. • Within 15 seconds, press SUPER STAR II pushbutton. • Observe code 10 on SUPER STAR II display (indicates IVSC test in progress). • Observe and record all DTC's indicated. One of the following outputs will occur. NOTE: Do not depress throttle or brake pedal during the KOER Self-Test. This procedure must be followed exactly to obtain IVSC KOER Self-Test. NOTE: The engine may stall at test exit. Turn off the ignition to prevent entry into EEC-IV Key On, Engine Off Self-Test.	Code 111 displayed ▶ Any other code(s) ▶ No codes outputted ▶	Engine Running Self-Test indicates a pass. If the drive symptom is currently present, GO to DIAGNOSTIC BY SYMPTOM. Otherwise testing is complete, IVSC system is OK. Engine Running Self-Test indicates a fault. GO to Step B. Repeat Self-Test and verify that no DTC's are present, then GO to Pinpoint Test Step G1.

FM1109300142010X

Fig. 61 Quick Test: Key On, Engine Running Self-Test (Part 1 of 2). 1993 Sable & Taurus

TEST STEP		RESULT	▶	ACTION TO TAKE
B1	RESULTS AND ACTION TO TAKE	ENGINE RUNNING DIAGNOSTIC TROUBLE CODES		
	• Using the Engine Running DTC's from Step A, follow the instructions in the ACTION TO TAKE column in this step. • When more than one DTC is received, always start service with the first code received. • Whenever a service is made, REPEAT QUICK TEST.	Code 453	▶	GO to Pinpoint Test Step E1.
		Code 454	▶	GO to Pinpoint Test Step E5.
		Code 455	▶	GO to Pinpoint Test Step D1.
		Code 456	▶	GO to Pinpoint Test Step F1.

FM1109300142020X

Fig. 61 Quick Test: Key On, Engine Running Self-Test (Part 2 of 2). 1993 Sable & Taurus

TEST STEP		RESULT	▶	ACTION TO TAKE
S1	CODE DISPLAYED	Yes	▶	Key On Engine Off Test indicates a pass. GO to Key On Engine Running (KOER) Self-Test.
	• To activate the KOEO IVSC test, do the following: — Place transmission shift lever in PARK. — Leave single STI connector unplugged; plug in multi-pin data link connector. — Turn on SUPER STAR II Tester by moving slide switch to ON position. — Press SUPER STAR II push button. — Turn ignition switch to RUN position. — Within 10 seconds, press speed control ON switch. — Observe code 10 on SUPER STAR II display (indicates IVSC test in progress). — Press speed control OFF, COAST, ACCEL, RESUME buttons, tap brake pedal once. NOTE: Do not depress throttle during KOEO self-test. — Observe and record all Diagnostic Trouble Codes indicated. • Is code 111 displayed?	No	▶	GO to S2.
S2	CHECK FOR CODE	Yes	▶	Key On Engine Off Test indicates a concern. Record DTCs and GO to S3.
	• Check the display. • Is any code displayed?	No	▶	REPEAT Self-Test and verify that no DTCs are present. GO to G1.
S3	CHECK FOR CODE 121	Yes	▶	
	• Using the Key On Engine Off DTC's from Step S1, follow the instructions in the ACTION TO TAKE column in this step. • When more than one DTC is received, always start with the first DTC received. • Whenever a service is performed, REPEAT Quick Test. NOTE: Before proceeding to the specified Pinpoint Test, read the instructions on how to use the Pinpoint Tests at the beginning of the Pinpoint Test section. • Is Code 121 displayed?	No	▶	GO to S4.
S4	CHECK FOR CODE 457	Yes	▶	GO to D1.
	• Check the display. • Is Code 457 displayed?	No	▶	GO to S5.
S5	CHECK FOR CODE 458	Yes	▶	GO to D3.
	• Check the display. • Is Code 458 displayed?	No	▶	GO to S6.
S6	CHECK FOR CODE 459	Yes	▶	GO to D5.
	• Check the display. • Is Code 459 displayed?	No	▶	GO to S7.
S7	CHECK FOR CODE 123	Yes	▶	
	• Check the display. • Is Code 123 displayed?	No	▶	GO to S8.

FM1109400221010X

Fig. 62 Quick Test: Key On, Engine Off Self-Test (Part 1 of 2). 1994 Sable & Taurus

TEST STEP		RESULT	▶	ACTION TO TAKE
S8	CHECK FOR CODE 122	Yes	▶	
	• Check the display. • Is Code 122 displayed?	No	▶	GO to S9.
S9	CHECK FOR CODE 536	Yes	▶	GO to E1.
	• Check the display. • Is Code 536 displayed?	No	▶	GO to S10.
S10	CHECK FOR CODE 528	Yes	▶	
	• Check the display. • Is Code 528 displayed?	No	▶	GO to S11.
S11	CHECK FOR CODE 567	Yes	▶	GO to F1.
	• Check the display. • Is Code 567 displayed?	No	▶	GO to S12.
S12	CHECK FOR CODE 568	Yes	▶	GO to F9.
	• Check the display. • Is Code 568 displayed?	No	▶	GO to S1.

FM1109400221020X

Fig. 62 Quick Test: Key On, Engine Off Self-Test (Part 2 of 2). 1994 Sable & Taurus

TEST STEP		RESULT	▶	ACTION TO TAKE
T1	CHECK FOR OUTPUT	Yes	▶	Engine Running Self-Test indicates a pass. If speed control system is inoperative, GO to Pinpoint Test Step J. If clutch does not disengage the speed control system, GO to Pinpoint Test J. Otherwise testing is complete, IVSC system is OK.
	• Before running KOER Self-Test, start the engine and idle until the upper radiator hose is hot and pressurized, with the throttle off fast idle and the idle stabilized, then shut engine off. To activate the KOER self-test, do the following: • Connect SUPER STAR II data link and STI connectors. • Start engine, turn on SUPER STAR II Tester by moving slide switch to ON position. • Within 30 seconds of starting engine, press speed control ON switch. • Within 15 seconds, press SUPER STAR II pushbutton. • Observe code 10 on SUPER STAR II display (indicates IVSC test in progress). • Observe and record all DTC's indicated. NOTE: Do not press throttle or brake pedal during KOER Self-Test. This procedure must be followed exactly to obtain IVSC KOER Self-Test. NOTE: The engine may stall at test exit. Turn off the ignition switch to prevent entry into EEC-IV Key On, Engine Off Self-Test. • Is Code 111 displayed?	No	▶	GO to T2.
T2	CHECK FOR CODE	Yes	▶	Engine Running Self-Test indicates a concern. GO to T3.
	• Check the display. • Is any code displayed?	No	▶	REPEAT Self-Test and verify that no DTCs are present, then GO to H1.
T3	CHECK FOR CODE 453	Yes	▶	GO to A1.
	• Using the Engine Running DTC's from Step S, follow the instructions in the ACTION TO TAKE column in this step. • When more than one DTC is received, always start service with the first code received. • Whenever a service is made, REPEAT QUICK TEST. • Is code 453 displayed?	No	▶	GO to T4.
T4	CHECK FOR CODE 454	Yes	▶	GO to A5.
	• Check the display. • Is Code 454 displayed?	No	▶	GO to T5.
T5	CHECK FOR CODE 455	Yes	▶	GO to B1.
	• Check the display. • Is Code 455 displayed?	No	▶	GO to T6.
T6	CHECK FOR CODE 456	Yes	▶	GO to C1.
	• Check the display. • Is Code 456 displayed?	No	▶	GO to T1.

FM1109400222000X

Fig. 63 Quick Test: Key On, Engine Running Self-Test. 1994 Sable & Taurus

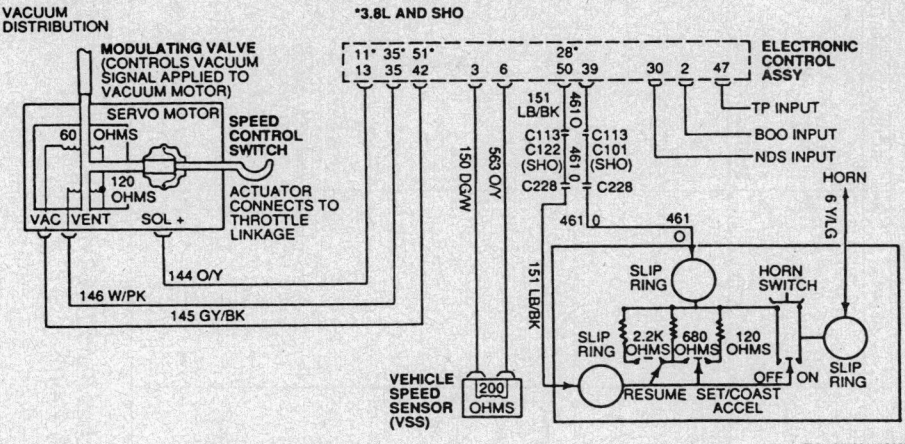

Fig. 64   Wiring circuit. 1992 Sable & Taurus

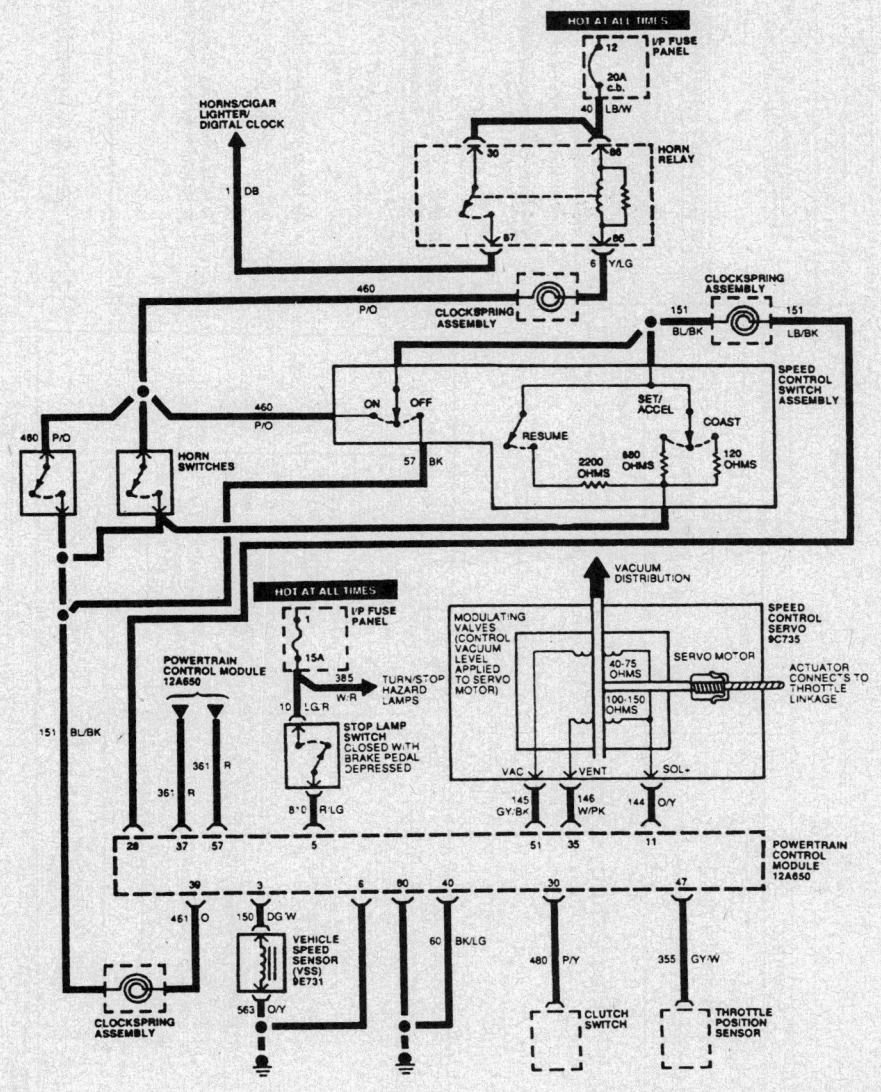

Fig. 65   Wiring circuit. 1993–94 Sable & Taurus

Fig. 66 Diagnostic by symptom chart. Mark VII

SYMPTOM	RESULT	ACTION TO TAKE
• Speed control does not work. • Code "11" displayed on QUICK TESTS.		GO to G.

FM1109100145000X

Fig. 66 Diagnostic by symptom chart. Mark VII

Fig. 67 Diagnostic by symptom chart. 1992 Sable & Taurus

SYMPTOM	RESULT	ACTION TO TAKE
• Speed control does not work. • Code "11" displayed on QUICK TESTS.		GO to G.
• Clutch does not disengage speed control on MTX vehicle.		GO to H.

FM1109100146000X

Fig. 67 Diagnostic by symptom chart. 1992 Sable & Taurus

Fig. 68 Test A: Speed Control Switches (Part 2 of 3). Mark VII & 1992–93 Sable & Taurus

	TEST STEP	RESULT	ACTION TO TAKE
A1	**SERVICE CODE 47** • Did you press the OFF, COAST, ACCEL, and RESUME buttons during the IVSC KOEO Self-Test?	Yes No	GO to A2. RERUN IVSC KOEO Self-Test.
A2	**SWITCH DOES NOT FUNCTION** • Key Off, wait 10 seconds. • Disconnect ECA 60 Pin connector. Inspect for damaged pins, corrosion, loose wires, etc. Service as necessary. • Install Breakout box, leave ECA disconnected. • Measure resistance between test Pin 50 and test Pin 39 per table below. • Rotate steering wheel through its full range while making resistance checks.		

DVOM Range	Button Pressed	Resistance Range
200 ohm	OFF	0-4 ohms
200 ohm	COAST	114-126 ohms
2000 ohm	ACCEL	646-714 ohms
5000 ohm	RESUME	2090-2310 ohms

	RESULT	ACTION TO TAKE
• Are resistances within range?	No Yes	REPLACE switches. REPLACE ECA.
• Do resistance values fluctuate within the ranges, or go above and below the ranges, as steering wheel is rotated?	No Yes	Switches OK. CLEAN brushes and slip rings, relubricate slip rings.

FM1109100147020X

Fig. 68 Test A: Speed Control Switches (Part 2 of 3). Mark VII & 1992–93 Sable & Taurus

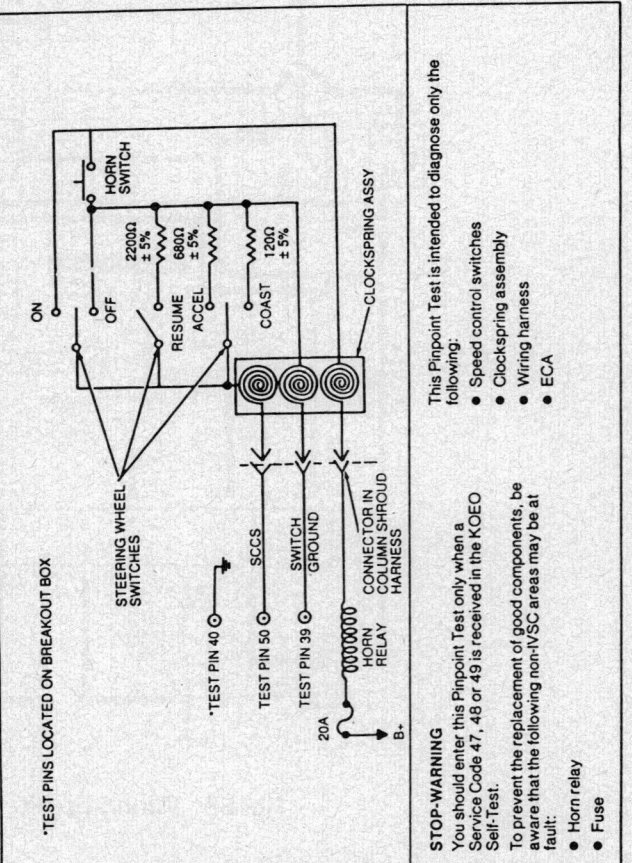

*TEST PINS LOCATED ON BREAKOUT BOX

FM1109100147010X

STOP-WARNING

You should enter this Pinpoint Test only when a Service Code 47, 48 or 49 is received in the KOEO Self-Test.

To prevent the replacement of good components, be aware that the following non-IVSC areas may be at fault:
- Horn relay
- Fuse

This Pinpoint Test is intended to diagnose only the following:
- Speed control switches
- Clockspring assembly
- Wiring harness
- ECA

Fig. 68 Test A: Speed Control Switches (Part 1 of 3). Mark VII & 1992–93 Sable & Taurus

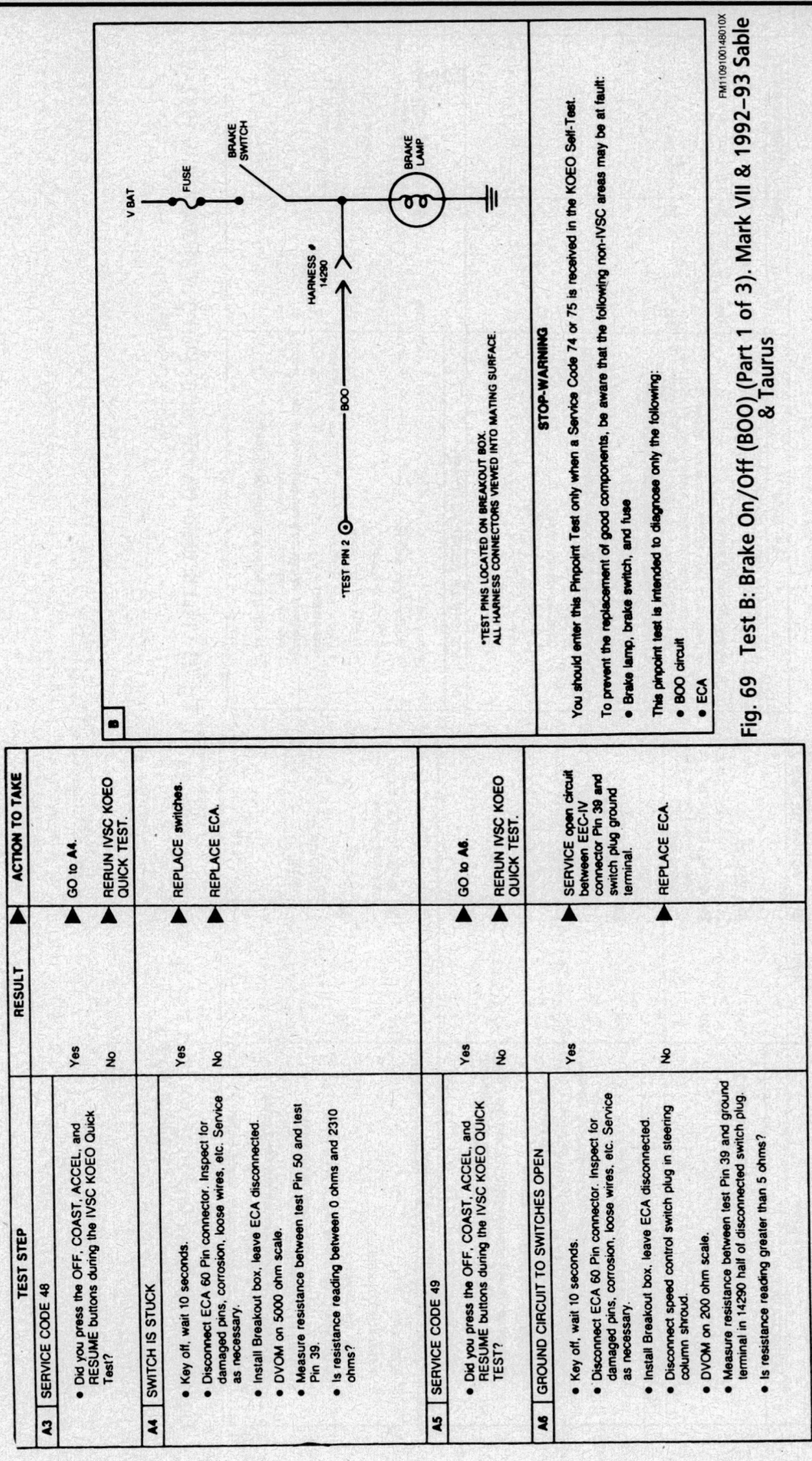

TEST STEP	RESULT		ACTION TO TAKE
A3 SERVICE CODE 48			
• Did you press the OFF, COAST, ACCEL, and RESUME buttons during the IVSC KOEO Quick Test?	Yes	▲	GO to A4.
	No	▲	RERUN IVSC KOEO QUICK TEST.
A4 SWITCH IS STUCK			
• Key off, wait 10 seconds. • Disconnect ECA 60 Pin connector. Inspect for damaged pins, corrosion, loose wires, etc. Service as necessary. • Install Breakout box, leave ECA disconnected. • DVOM on 5000 ohm scale. • Measure resistance between test Pin 50 and test Pin 39. • Is resistance reading between 0 ohms and 2310 ohms?	Yes	▲	REPLACE switches.
	No	▲	REPLACE ECA.
A5 SERVICE CODE 49			
• Did you press the OFF, COAST, ACCEL, and RESUME buttons during the IVSC KOEO QUICK TEST?	Yes	▲	GO to A6.
	No	▲	RERUN IVSC KOEO QUICK TEST.
A6 GROUND CIRCUIT TO SWITCHES OPEN			
• Key off, wait 10 seconds. • Disconnect ECA 60 Pin connector. Inspect for damaged pins, corrosion, loose wires, etc. Service as necessary. • Install Breakout box, leave ECA disconnected. • Disconnect speed control switch plug in steering column shroud. • DVOM on 200 ohm scale. • Measure resistance between test Pin 39 and ground terminal in 14290 half of disconnected switch plug. • Is resistance reading greater than 5 ohms?	Yes	▲	SERVICE open circuit between EEC-IV connector Pin 39 and switch plug ground terminal.
	No	▲	REPLACE ECA.

FM110910014703OX

Fig. 68   Test A: Speed Control Switches (Part 3 of 3). Mark VII & 1992–93 Sable & Taurus

B

V BAT — FUSE — BRAKE SWITCH

BRAKE LAMP

HARNESS # 14290

BOO

*TEST PIN 2

*TEST PINS LOCATED ON BREAKOUT BOX.
ALL HARNESS CONNECTORS VIEWED INTO MATING SURFACE.

STOP-WARNING

You should enter this Pinpoint Test only when a Service Code 74 or 75 is received in the KOEO Self-Test.

To prevent the replacement of good components, be aware that the following non-IVSC areas may be at fault:
• Brake lamp, brake switch, and fuse

This pinpoint test is intended to diagnose only the following:
• BOO circuit
• ECA

FM110910014801OX

Fig. 69   Test B: Brake On/Off (BOO) (Part 1 of 3). Mark VII & 1992–93 Sable & Taurus

	TEST STEP	RESULT ▲	ACTION TO TAKE ▲
B1	SERVICE CODE 74		
	• Did you press brake during the KOEO Self-Test?	Yes	GO to B2.
		No	RERUN KOEO Self-Test, PRESS brake once during test.
B2	BOO CIRCUIT CYCLING		
	• Key off, wait 10 seconds. • Disconnect ECA 60 Pin connector. Inspect for damaged pins, corrosion, loose wires, etc. Service as necessary. • Install Breakout box, leave ECA disconnected. • DVOM on 20V scale. • Measure voltage between test Pin 2 and test Pin 40 at the Breakout box while depressing and releasing brake. • Does the voltage cycle?	Yes	REPLACE ECA. RETEST.
		No	GO to B3.
B3	BOO CIRCUIT SHORT TO GROUND		
	• Key off. • Breakout box installed. • ECA disconnected. • DVOM on 200 Ohm scale. • Disconnect BOO circuit from 14290 harness (12 pin connector). • Measure resistance between test Pin 2 at the Breakout box and ground. • Is resistance reading greater than 5 ohms?	No	SERVICE BOO circuit short to ground.
		Yes	SERVICE stoplamp circuit.

Fig. 69 Test B: Brake On/Off (BOO) (Part 2 of 3). Mark VII & 1992–93 Sable & Taurus

FM1109100148020X

	TEST STEP	RESULT	ACTION TO TAKE ▲
B4	BOO CIRCUIT CYCLING CODE 75		
	• Key off, wait 10 seconds. • Disconnect ECA 60 Pin connector. Inspect for damaged pins, corrosion, loose wires, etc. Service as necessary. • Install Breakout box, leave ECA disconnected. • DVOM on 20V scale. • Measure voltage between test Pin 2 and test Pin 40 at the Breakout box while depressing and releasing brake. • Does the voltage cycle?	Yes	REPLACE ECA. RERUN QUICK TEST.
		No	GO to B5.
B5	BOO CIRCUIT SHORT TO POWER		
	• Key off. • Breakout box installed. • ECA disconnected. • DVOM on 20V scale. • Disconnect BOO circuit from 14290 harness (12 pin connector). • Measure voltage between test Pin 2 at the Breakout box and Engine Block Ground. • Is voltage reading greater than 10.5V?	Yes	SERVICE BOO circuit short to power.
		No	BOO circuit OK. SERVICE stoplamp circuit.

Fig. 69 Test B: Brake On/Off (BOO) (Part 3 of 3). Mark VII & 1992–93 Sable & Taurus

FM1109100148030X

Fig. 70 Test C: Servo Solenoids (Part 1 of 3). Mark VII & 1992–93 Sable & Taurus

TEST STEP	RESULT	ACTION TO TAKE
C SERVICE CODE 81 OR SERVICE CODES 81 AND 82 **STOP WARNING**: You should enter this Pinpoint Test only when a Service Code 81 and/or 82 is received in a KOEO Self-Test. This Pinpoint Test is intended to diagnose only the following: • Servo Vent Solenoid • Servo Vacuum Solenoid • SOL+, SCVNT, and SCVAC Circuits • ECA	NOTE: Correct solenoid resistance values are: ♦ VENT SOLENOID Nominal - 120 ohms Range - 100 to 150 ohms ♦ VACUUM SOLENOID Nominal - 60 ohms Range - 40-75 ohms (diagram: SOL+ TEST PIN, SCVNT TEST PIN, SCVAC TEST PIN, VENT SOLENOID, VACUUM SOLENOID, IVSC SPEED CONTROL SERVO)	
C1 VENT SOLENOID TEST • Key off. • Disconnect ECA 60 pin connector. Inspect for damaged pins, corrosion, loose wires, etc. Service as necessary. • Install Breakout Box (leave ECA disconnected). • DVOM on 200 ohm scale. • Measure resistance between the SOL+ test pin and the SCVNT test pin.	Resistance is between 100 and 150 ohms	▲ If code 82 is also present, GO to C6. Otherwise, GO to C4.
	Resistance is less than 100 ohms	▲ REPLACE servo. REPEAT QUICK TEST.
	Resistance is greater than 150 ohms	▲ GO to C2.

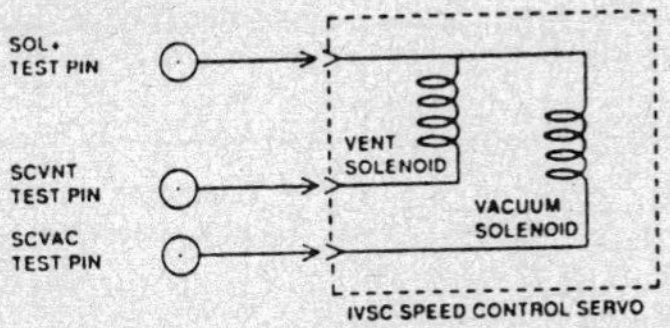

FM1109100150010X

Fig. 70 Test C: Servo Solenoids (Part 2 of 3). Mark VII & 1992–93 Sable & Taurus

TEST STEP	RESULT	ACTION TO TAKE
C2 CHECK CONTINUITY OF SOL+ CIRCUIT • Disconnect harness connector from the servo. • DVOM on 200 ohm scale. • Measure resistance of the SOL+ wire.	Resistance is greater than 5 ohms	▲ SERVICE open circuit. REPEAT QUICK TEST.
	Resistance is less than 5 ohms	▲ GO to C3.
C3 CHECK CONTINUITY OF SCVNT CIRCUIT • Disconnect harness connector from the servo. • DVOM on 200 ohm scale. • Measure resistance of the SCVNT wire.	Resistance is greater than 5 ohms	▲ SERVICE open circuit. REPEAT QUICK TEST.
	Resistance is less than 5 ohms	▲ REPLACE servo. REPEAT QUICK TEST.
C4 SOL+ CIRCUIT SHORT TO GROUND TEST • Disconnect harness connector from the servo. • DVOM on 200,000 ohm scale. • Measure resistance between the SOL+ test pin and test pin 60 (ground).	Resistance is less than 10,000 ohms	▲ SERVICE shorted circuit. REPEAT QUICK TEST. (NOTE: Short may have damaged the ECA.)
	Resistance is greater than 10,000 ohms	▲ GO to C5.
C5 SCVNT CIRCUIT SHORT TO GROUND TEST • Disconnect harness connector from the servo. • DVOM on 200,000 ohm scale. • Measure resistance between the SCVNT test pin and test pin 60 (ground).	Resistance is less than 10,000 ohms	▲ SERVICE shorted circuit. REPEAT QUICK TEST.
	Resistance is greater than 10,000 ohms	▲ REPLACE the ECA. REPEAT QUICK TEST.
SERVICE CODE 82 ONLY **C6** VACUUM SOLENOID TEST • Key off. • Disconnect ECA 60 pin connector. Inspect for damaged pins, corrosion, loose wires, etc. Service as necessary. • Install Breakout Box (leave ECA disconnected). • DVOM on 200 ohm scale. • Measure resistance between the SOL+ test pin and the SCVAC test pin.	Resistance is between 40 and 75 ohms	▲ GO to C9.
	Resistance is less than 40 ohms	▲ REPLACE servo. REPEAT QUICK TEST.
	Resistance is greater than 75 ohms	▲ GO to C7.

FM1109100150020X

D | STOP-WARNING

You should enter this Pinpoint Test only when Service Code 36 is received in the KOER Self-Test.

This Pinpoint Test is intended to diagnose only the following:
- Actuator cable
- ECA
- Vacuum hose connections
- Check valve
- Dump valve adjustment

	TEST STEP	RESULT	ACTION TO TAKE
D1	SERVICE CODE 36 • Repeat KOER Self-Test of QUICK TEST. Be sure that the speed control ON button is pressed before pressing the SUPER STAR II push button.	▲ Code 36 still present ▲ No Code 36	▲ GO to D2 ▲ Increase vehicle speed test passed SERVICE any other service code(s) as necessary
D2	CHECK ACTUATOR CABLE CONNECTION TO THROTTLE BODY • Is actuator cable attached to throttle body accelerator linkage?	▲ Yes ▲ No	▲ GO to D3 ▲ CONNECT servo cable to throttle body accelerator linkage REPEAT QUICK TEST
D3	CHECK VACUUM HOSES • Is servo vacuum supply hose tightly connected to VAC port on check valve and to the vacuum manifold, and free of cuts, cracks and kinks? • Are vacuum hoses tightly connected between check valves and servo, and free of cuts, cracks and kinks? • Is vacuum hose tightly connected between check valve and reservoir, and free of cuts, cracks and kinks? • Is the dump valve hose tightly connected to the servo and to the dump valve, and free of cuts, cracks and kinks?	▲ Yes ▲ No	▲ GO to D4 ▲ SERVICE hoses REPEAT QUICK TEST
D4	CHECK THE CHECK VALVE • Disconnect the hose between check valve and servo, at the servo end • Apply 60.6 kPa (18 in-Hg) vacuum to open end of hose • Can vacuum be pumped to, and held at, 60.6 kPa (18 in-Hg) vacuum?	▲ Yes ▲ No	▲ GO to D6 ▲ GO to D5

FM11091001510X

Fig. 71   Test D: Speed Does Not Increase During Dynamic Test (Part 1 of 2). Mark VII

	TEST STEP	RESULT	ACTION TO TAKE
C7	CHECK CONTINUITY OF SOL+ CIRCUIT • Disconnect harness connector from the servo. • DVOM on 200 ohm scale. • Measure resistance of the SOL+ wire.	▲ Resistance is greater than 5 ohms ▲ Resistance is less than 5 ohms	▲ SERVICE open circuit. REPEAT QUICK TEST. ▲ GO to C8.
C8	CHECK CONTINUITY OF SCVAC CIRCUIT • Disconnect harness connector from the servo. • DVOM on 200 ohm scale. • Measure resistance of the SCVAC wire.	▲ Resistance is greater than 5 ohms ▲ Resistance is less than 5 ohms	▲ SERVICE open circuit. REPEAT QUICK TEST. ▲ REPLACE servo REPEAT QUICK TEST.
C9	SOL+ CIRCUIT SHORT TO GROUND TEST • Disconnect harness connector from the servo. • DVOM on 200,000 ohm scale. • Measure resistance between the SOL+ test pin and test pin 60 (ground).	▲ Resistance is less than 10,000 ohms ▲ Resistance is greater than 10,000 ohms	▲ SERVICE shorted circuit. REPEAT QUICK TEST. (NOTE: Short may have damaged the ECA.) ▲ GO to C10.
C10	SCVAC CIRCUIT SHORT TO GROUND TEST • Disconnect harness connector from the servo. • DVOM on 200,000 ohm scale. • Measure resistance between the SCVAC test pin and test pin 60 (ground).	▲ Resistance is less than 10,000 ohms ▲ Resistance is greater than 10,000 ohms	▲ SERVICE shorted circuit. REPEAT QUICK TEST. ▲ REPLACE the ECA. REPEAT QUICK TEST.

FM11091001500030X

Fig. 70   Test C: Servo Solenoids (Part 3 of 3). Mark VII & 1992–93 Sable & Taurus

E

STOP-WARNING

You should enter this Pinpoint Test only when Service Codes 27 and/or 28 are received in the KOER Self-Test.

This Pinpoint Test is intended to diagnose only the following:
- Speed control servo
- Vacuum hose connections
- Vacuum reservoir
- Check valve

TEST STEP	RESULT	ACTION TO TAKE
E1 SERVICE CODE 27 • Repeat Engine Running Self-Test of QUICK TEST. Be sure that the speed control ON button is pressed before pressing the STAR push button.	Code 27 still present? No Code 27	GO to E2. Servo leaks down test passed. SERVICE any other service code(s) as necessary.
E2 CHECK VACUUM HOSES • Is vacuum supply hose tightly connected to VAC port on check valve and to vacuum manifold, and free of cuts, cracks and kinks? • Is vacuum hose tightly connected between check valve and servo, and free of cuts, cracks and kinks? • Is vacuum hose tightly connected between check valve and reservoir, and free of cuts, cracks and kinks? • Is dump valve hose tightly connected to the servo and dump valve, and free of cuts, cracks and kinks?	Yes No	GO to E3. SERVICE vacuum hoses. REPEAT QUICK TEST.
E3 CHECK VACUUM RESERVOIR • Disconnect hose between the check valve and vacuum reservoir, at check valve end. • Install vacuum pump to open end of hose to reservoir. • Apply 60.6 kPa (18 in. Hg) vacuum to the reservoir. • Does reservoir hold vacuum?	Yes No	GO to E4. REPLACE vacuum reservoir. REPEAT QUICK TEST.
E4 CHECK THE CHECK VALVE • Disconnect the hose between check valve and servo, at the servo end. • Apply 60.6 kPa (18 in. Hg) vacuum to open end of hose. • Can vacuum be pumped to, and held at, 60.6 kPa (18 in. Hg) vacuum?	Yes No	REPLACE servo. REPEAT QUICK TEST. REPLACE check valve. REPEAT QUICK TEST.
E5 SERVICE CODE 28 • REPEAT engine running SELF-TEST of QUICK TEST. Be sure that the speed control ON button is pressed before pressing the STAR push button.	Code 28 still present? No Code 27	REPLACE servo. REPEAT QUICK TEST. Servo leaks up test passed. SERVICE any other service code(s) as necessary.

FM11091001520000X

Fig. 72 Test E: Does Not Hold Speed During Dynamic Test. 1992–93 Sable & Taurus

---

TEST STEP	RESULT	ACTION TO TAKE
D5 CHECK VACUUM RESERVOIR • Disconnect hose between check valve and vacuum reservoir, at check valve end. • Install vacuum pump to open end of hose to reservoir. • Apply 60.6 kPa (18 in. Hg) vacuum to the reservoir. • Does reservoir hold vacuum?	Yes No	REPLACE check valve. REPEAT QUICK TEST. REPLACE vacuum reservoir. REPEAT QUICK TEST.
D6 CHECK DUMP VALVE ADJUSTMENT • Is the dump valve adjusted properly so that the valve is closed when the brake pedal is not depressed?	Yes No	GO to C1. ADJUST dump valve. REPEAT QUICK TEST.

FM11091001510102AX

Fig. 71 Test D: Speed Does Not Increase During Dynamic Test (Part 2 of 2). Mark VII

TEST STEP	RESULT	ACTION TO TAKE
D5 CHECK ASPIRATOR CHECK VALVE • Disconnect hose between check valves at manifold check valve end. • Apply 60.6 kPa (18 in. Hg) vacuum to open end of hose. • Can vacuum be pumped to and held at 60.6 kPa (18 in. Hg) vacuum?	Yes No	REPLACE manifold check valve. REPEAT QUICK TEST. REPLACE aspirator check valve. REPEAT QUICK TEST.
D6 CHECK DUMP VALVE ADJUSTMENT • Is the dump valve adjusted properly so that the valve is closed when the brake pedal is not depressed?	Yes No	REPLACE ECA. REPEAT QUICK TEST. ADJUST dump valve. REPEAT QUICK TEST.

FM11091001510102BX

Fig. 71 Test D: Speed Does Not Increase During Dynamic Test (Part 2 of 2). 1992–93 Sable & Taurus

F — STOP-WARNING

You should enter this Pinpoint Test only when a Service Code 37 is received in the KOER Self-Test.

This Pinpoint Test is intended to diagnose only the following:
- Actuator cable
- Throttle shaft and linkage
- Throttle position sensor
- ECA

TEST STEP	RESULT	ACTION TO TAKE
F1 SERVICE CODE 37 • Repeat KOER Self-Test of QUICK TEST. Be sure that the speed control ON button is pressed before pressing the SUPER STAR II push button.	Code 37 still present?	GO to F2.
	No Code 37	Decrease vehicle speed test passed. SERVICE any other service code(s) as necessary.
F2 CHECK FOR THROTTLE SHAFT/LINKAGE BINDING • Is the throttle shaft or throttle linkage binding, maintaining a part throttle opening?	Yes	SERVICE to eliminate binding. REPEAT QUICK TEST.
	No	GO to F3.
F3 CHECK FOR SPEED CONTROL LINKAGE BINDING • Is the actuator cable binding?	Yes	REPLACE the actuator cable. REPEAT QUICK TEST.
	No	GO to F4.
F4 CHECK FOR THROTTLE POSITION SENSOR BINDING • Is throttle position sensor binding at a part throttle opening?	Yes	REPLACE the throttle position sensor. REPEAT QUICK TEST.
	No	REPLACE the ECA. REPEAT QUICK TEST.

Fig. 74 Test F: Speed Does Not Increase During Dynamic Test. Mark VII & 1992–93 Sable & Taurus

FM1109100154000X

E — STOP-WARNING

You should enter this Pinpoint Test only when Service Codes 27 and/or 28 are received in the KOER Self-Test.

This Pinpoint Test is intended to diagnose only the following:
- Speed control servo
- Vacuum hose connections
- Vacuum reservoir
- Check valve

TEST STEP	RESULT	ACTION TO TAKE
E1 SERVICE CODE 27 • Repeat Engine Running Self-Test of QUICK TEST. Be sure that the speed control ON button is pressed before pressing the STAR push button.	Code 27 still present?	GO to E2.
	No Code 27	Servo leaks down test passed. SERVICE any other service code(s) as necessary.
E2 CHECK VACUUM HOSES • Is vacuum supply hose tightly connected to VAC port on manifold check valve and to vacuum manifold, and free of cuts, cracks and kinks? • Are vacuum hoses tightly connected between check valves and servo, and free of cuts, cracks and kinks? • Is vacuum hose tightly connected between check valve and aspirator, and free of cuts, cracks and kinks? • Is dump valve hose tightly connected to the servo and dump valve, and free of cuts, cracks and kinks?	Yes	GO to E3.
	No	SERVICE vacuum hoses. REPEAT QUICK TEST.
E3 CHECK THE CHECK VALVE • Disconnect the hose between check valve and servo, at the servo end. • Apply 60.6 kPa (18 in. Hg) vacuum to open end of hose. • Can vacuum be pumped to, and held at, 60.6 kPa (18 in. Hg) vacuum?	Yes	REPLACE servo. REPEAT QUICK TEST.
	No	REPLACE check valve. REPEAT QUICK TEST.
E4 CHECK ASPIRATOR CHECK VALVE • Disconnect hose between check valves at manifold check valve end. • Apply 60.6 kPa (18 in. Hg) vacuum to open end of hose. • Can vacuum be pumped to and held at 60.6 kPa (18 in. Hg) vacuum?	Yes	REPLACE manifold check valve. REPEAT QUICK TEST.
	No	REPLACE aspirator check valve. REPEAT QUICK TEST.
E5 SERVICE CODE 28 • REPEAT engine running SELF-TEST of QUICK TEST. Be sure that the speed control ON button is pressed before pressing the STAR push button.	Code 28 still present?	REPLACE servo. REPEAT QUICK TEST.
	No Code 27	Servo leaks up test passed. SERVICE any other service code(s) as necessary.

Fig. 73 Test E: Does Not Hold Speed During Dynamic Test. Mark VII

FM1109100153000X

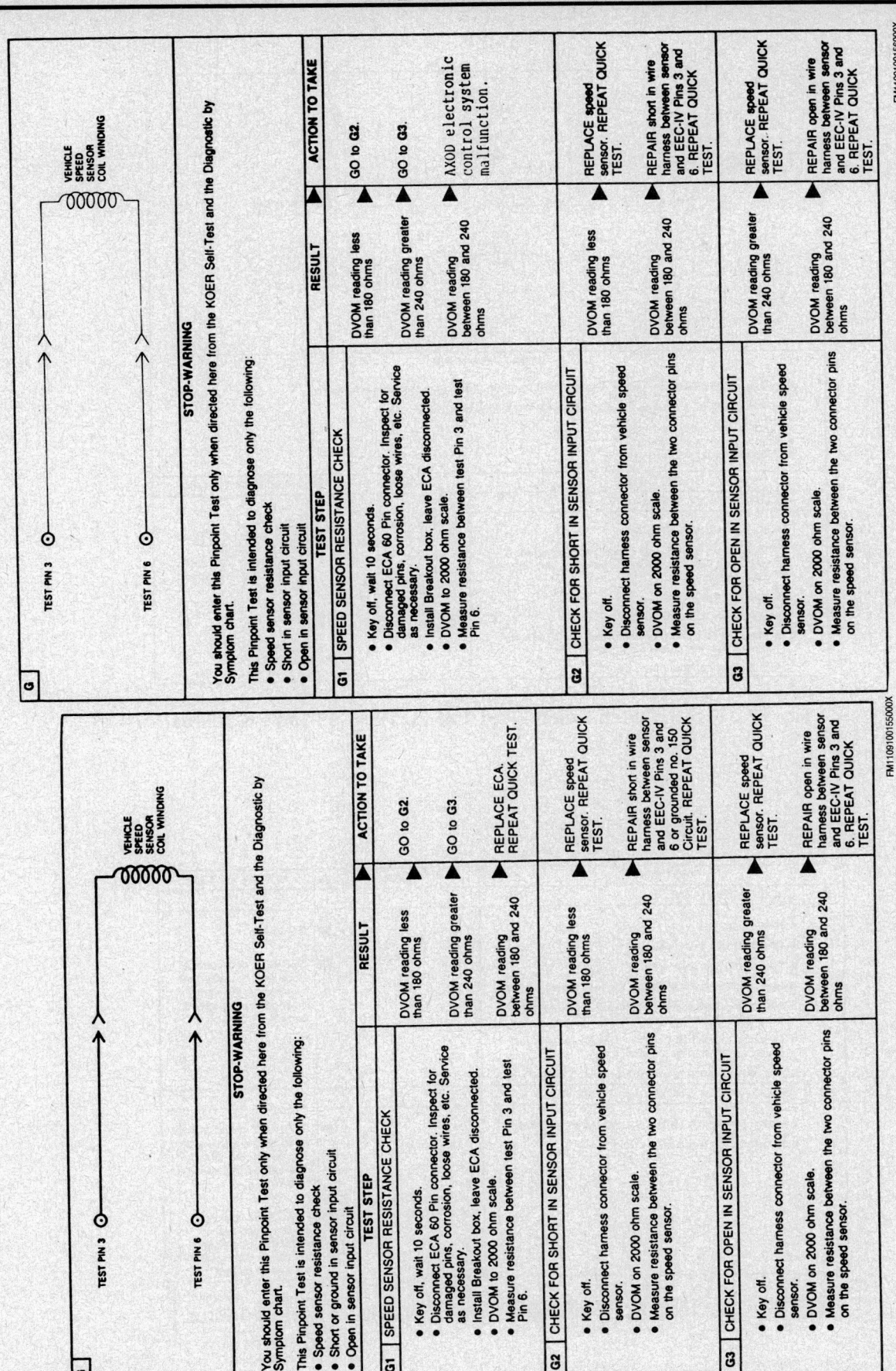

Fig. 75 Test G: Speed sensor. Mark VII

G

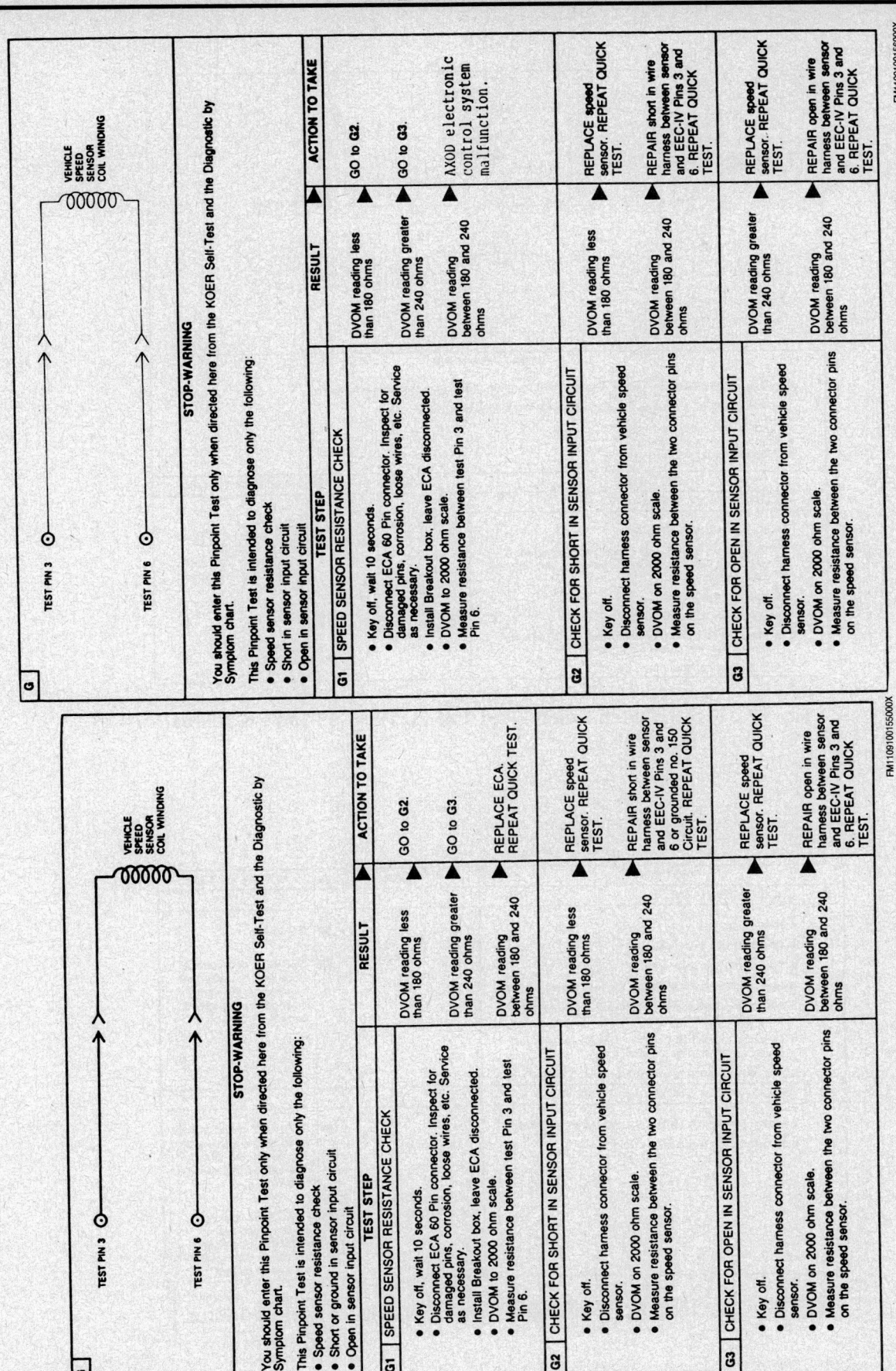

(Diagram: VEHICLE SPEED SENSOR COIL WINDING — TEST PIN 3, TEST PIN 6)

STOP-WARNING

You should enter this Pinpoint Test only when directed here from the KOER Self-Test and the Diagnostic by Symptom chart.

This Pinpoint Test is intended to diagnose only the following:
• Speed sensor resistance check
• Short or ground in sensor input circuit
• Open in sensor input circuit

TEST STEP	RESULT	►	ACTION TO TAKE
G1 SPEED SENSOR RESISTANCE CHECK			
• Key off, wait 10 seconds.	DVOM reading less than 180 ohms	►	GO to G2.
• Disconnect ECA 60 Pin connector. Inspect for damaged pins, corrosion, loose wires, etc. Service as necessary.	DVOM reading greater than 240 ohms	►	GO to G3.
• Install Breakout box, leave ECA disconnected.	DVOM reading between 180 and 240 ohms	►	REPLACE ECA. REPEAT QUICK TEST.
• DVOM to 2000 ohm scale.			
• Measure resistance between test Pin 3 and test Pin 6.			
G2 CHECK FOR SHORT IN SENSOR INPUT CIRCUIT			
• Key off.	DVOM reading less than 180 ohms	►	REPLACE speed sensor. REPEAT QUICK TEST.
• Disconnect harness connector from vehicle speed sensor.	DVOM reading between 180 and 240 ohms	►	REPAIR short in wire harness between sensor and EEC-IV Pins 3 and 6 or grounded no. 150 Circuit. REPEAT QUICK TEST.
• DVOM on 2000 ohm scale.			
• Measure resistance between the two connector pins on the speed sensor.			
G3 CHECK FOR OPEN IN SENSOR INPUT CIRCUIT			
• Key off.	DVOM reading greater than 240 ohms	►	REPLACE speed sensor. REPEAT QUICK TEST.
• Disconnect harness connector from vehicle speed sensor.	DVOM reading between 180 and 240 ohms	►	REPAIR open in wire harness between sensor and EEC-IV Pins 3 and 6. REPEAT QUICK TEST.
• DVOM on 2000 ohm scale.			
• Measure resistance between the two connector pins on the speed sensor.			

FM1109100155000X

Fig. 76 Test G: Speed Sensor. 1992–93 Sable & Taurus

G

(Diagram: VEHICLE SPEED SENSOR COIL WINDING — TEST PIN 3, TEST PIN 6)

STOP-WARNING

You should enter this Pinpoint Test only when directed here from the KOER Self-Test and the Diagnostic by Symptom chart.

This Pinpoint Test is intended to diagnose only the following:
• Speed sensor resistance check
• Short in sensor input circuit
• Open in sensor input circuit

TEST STEP	RESULT	►	ACTION TO TAKE
G1 SPEED SENSOR RESISTANCE CHECK			
• Key off, wait 10 seconds.	DVOM reading less than 180 ohms	►	GO to G2.
• Disconnect ECA 60 Pin connector. Inspect for damaged pins, corrosion, loose wires, etc. Service as necessary.	DVOM reading greater than 240 ohms	►	GO to G3.
• Install Breakout box, leave ECA disconnected.	DVOM reading between 180 and 240 ohms	►	AXOD electronic control system malfunction.
• DVOM to 2000 ohm scale.			
• Measure resistance between test Pin 3 and test Pin 6.			
G2 CHECK FOR SHORT IN SENSOR INPUT CIRCUIT			
• Key off.	DVOM reading less than 180 ohms	►	REPLACE speed sensor. REPEAT QUICK TEST.
• Disconnect harness connector from vehicle speed sensor.	DVOM reading between 180 and 240 ohms	►	REPAIR short in wire harness between sensor and EEC-IV Pins 3 and 6. REPEAT QUICK TEST.
• DVOM on 2000 ohm scale.			
• Measure resistance between the two connector pins on the speed sensor.			
G3 CHECK FOR OPEN IN SENSOR INPUT CIRCUIT			
• Key off.	DVOM reading greater than 240 ohms	►	REPLACE speed sensor. REPEAT QUICK TEST.
• Disconnect harness connector from vehicle speed sensor.	DVOM reading between 180 and 240 ohms	►	REPAIR open in wire harness between sensor and EEC-IV Pins 3 and 6. REPEAT QUICK TEST.
• DVOM on 2000 ohm scale.			
• Measure resistance between the two connector pins on the speed sensor.			

FM1109100156000X

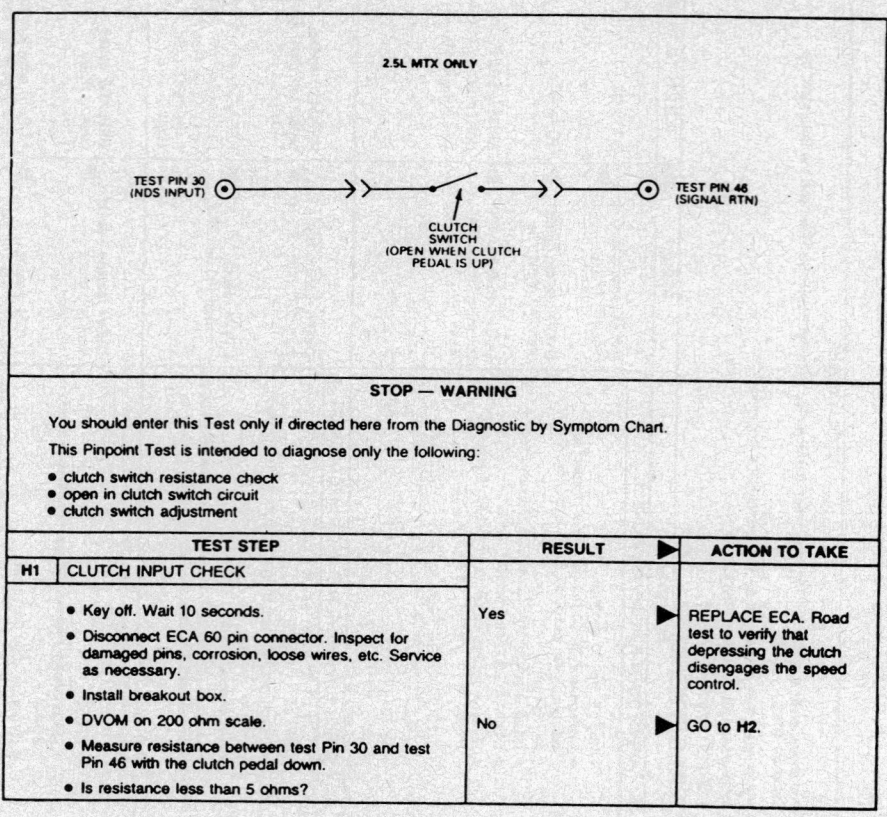

2.5L MTX ONLY

TEST PIN 30
(NDS INPUT)

TEST PIN 46
(SIGNAL RTN)

CLUTCH
SWITCH
(OPEN WHEN CLUTCH
PEDAL IS UP)

STOP — WARNING

You should enter this Test only if directed here from the Diagnostic by Symptom Chart.

This Pinpoint Test is intended to diagnose only the following:

● clutch switch resistance check
● open in clutch switch circuit
● clutch switch adjustment

TEST STEP	RESULT ▶	ACTION TO TAKE
H1 CLUTCH INPUT CHECK		
● Key off. Wait 10 seconds. ● Disconnect ECA 60 pin connector. Inspect for damaged pins, corrosion, loose wires, etc. Service as necessary. ● Install breakout box. ● DVOM on 200 ohm scale. ● Measure resistance between test Pin 30 and test Pin 46 with the clutch pedal down. ● Is resistance less than 5 ohms?	Yes No	▶ REPLACE ECA. Road test to verify that depressing the clutch disengages the speed control. ▶ GO to H2.

FM1109100157010X

Fig. 77   Test H: Clutch Switch (Part 1 of 2). 1992–93 Sable & Taurus

TEST STEP	RESULT ▶	ACTION TO TAKE
H2 CHECK WIRE HARNESS		
● Key off. ● Breakout box installed. ● DVOM on 200 ohm scale. ● Locate clutch switch (under the instrument panel). ● Measure resistance between test Pin 30 and the clutch switch harness connector. ● Measure resistance between test Pin 46 and the clutch switch harness connector. ● Are all resistance readings less than 5 ohms?	Yes No	▶ GO to H3. ▶ SERVICE open circuit. Road test to verify that depressing the clutch disengages the speed control.
H3 CHECK CLUTCH SWITCH ADJUSTMENT		
● Check that clutch switch is adjusted as outlined. ● Is clutch switch adjusted properly?	Yes No	▶ REPLACE clutch switch. Road test to verify that depressing the clutch disengages the speed control. ▶ READJUST clutch switch. Road test to verify that depressing the clutch disengages the speed control.

FM1109100157020X

Fig. 77   Test H: Clutch Switch (Part 2 of 2). 1992–93 Sable & Taurus

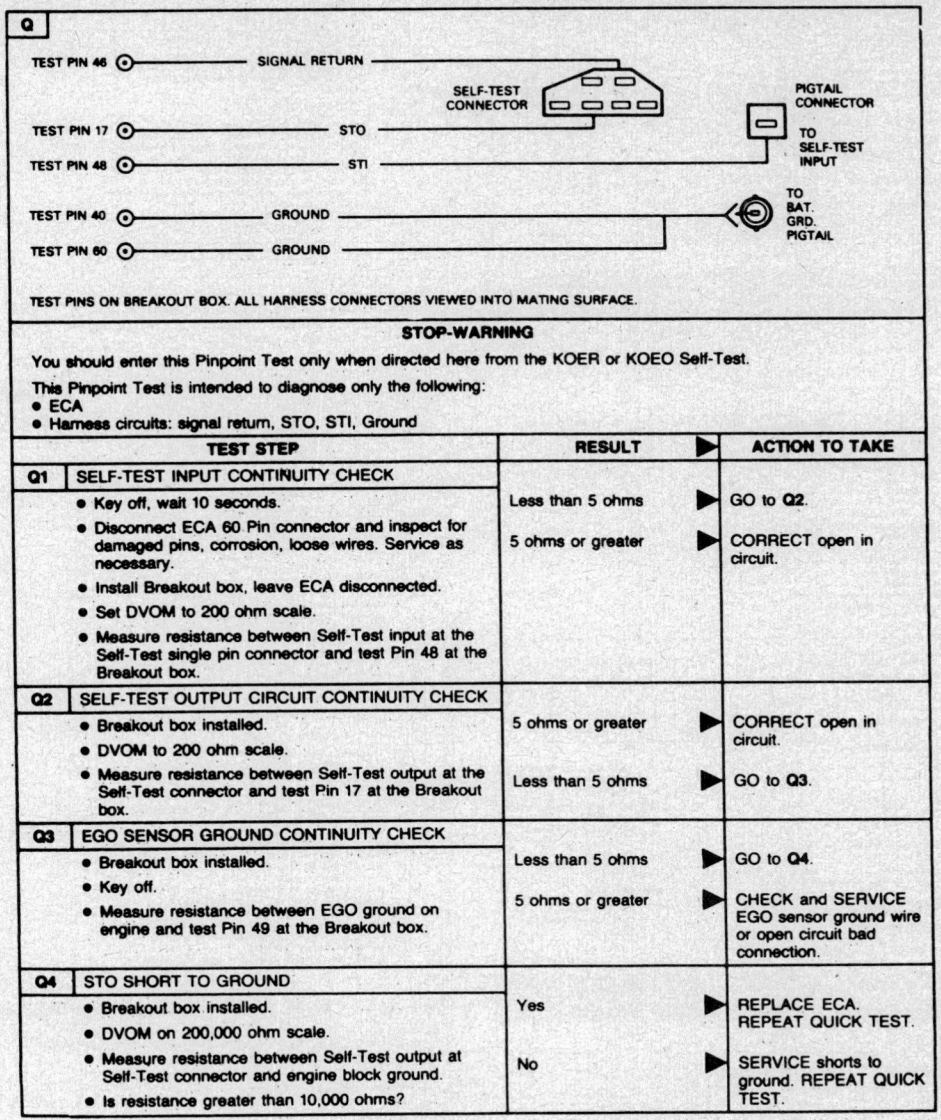

Q

TEST PIN 46	SIGNAL RETURN
TEST PIN 17	STO
TEST PIN 48	STI
TEST PIN 40	GROUND
TEST PIN 60	GROUND

SELF-TEST CONNECTOR

PIGTAIL CONNECTOR TO SELF-TEST INPUT

TO BAT. GRD. PIGTAIL

TEST PINS ON BREAKOUT BOX. ALL HARNESS CONNECTORS VIEWED INTO MATING SURFACE.

STOP-WARNING

You should enter this Pinpoint Test only when directed here from the KOER or KOEO Self-Test.

This Pinpoint Test is intended to diagnose only the following:
- ECA
- Harness circuits: signal return, STO, STI, Ground

	TEST STEP	RESULT ▶	ACTION TO TAKE
Q1	**SELF-TEST INPUT CONTINUITY CHECK** ● Key off, wait 10 seconds. ● Disconnect ECA 60 Pin connector and inspect for damaged pins, corrosion, loose wires. Service as necessary. ● Install Breakout box, leave ECA disconnected. ● Set DVOM to 200 ohm scale. ● Measure resistance between Self-Test input at the Self-Test single pin connector and test Pin 48 at the Breakout box.	Less than 5 ohms 5 ohms or greater	▶ GO to **Q2**. ▶ CORRECT open in circuit.
Q2	**SELF-TEST OUTPUT CIRCUIT CONTINUITY CHECK** ● Breakout box installed. ● DVOM to 200 ohm scale. ● Measure resistance between Self-Test output at the Self-Test connector and test Pin 17 at the Breakout box.	5 ohms or greater Less than 5 ohms	▶ CORRECT open in circuit. ▶ GO to **Q3**.
Q3	**EGO SENSOR GROUND CONTINUITY CHECK** ● Breakout box installed. ● Key off. ● Measure resistance between EGO ground on engine and test Pin 49 at the Breakout box.	Less than 5 ohms 5 ohms or greater	▶ GO to **Q4**. ▶ CHECK and SERVICE EGO sensor ground wire or open circuit bad connection.
Q4	**STO SHORT TO GROUND** ● Breakout box installed. ● DVOM on 200,000 ohm scale. ● Measure resistance between Self-Test output at Self-Test connector and engine block ground. ● Is resistance greater than 10,000 ohms?	Yes No	▶ REPLACE ECA. REPEAT QUICK TEST. ▶ SERVICE shorts to ground. REPEAT QUICK TEST.

FM1109100158000X

Fig. 78   Test Q: No Codes, Codes Not Listed. Mark VII & 1992–93 Sable & Taurus

	TEST STEP	RESULT ▶	ACTION TO TAKE
A1	**CHECK FOR DIAGNOSTIC TROUBLE CODE 453** ● Repeat Engine Running Self-Test of QUICK TEST. Be sure that the speed control ON button is pressed before pressing the SUPER STAR II push button. ● **Is diagnostic trouble code 453 present?**	Yes No	▶ GO to A2. ▶ Speed control servo leaks down test passed. SERVICE any other Diagnostic Trouble Code as necessary.
A2	**CHECK VACUUM HOSES** ● Check to see if: ● Vacuum supply hose is tightly connected to VAC port on speed control vacuum valve and to vacuum manifold, and free of cuts, cracks and kinks. ● Vacuum hose is tightly connected between speed control vacuum valve and speed control servo, and free of cuts, cracks and kinks. ● Vacuum hose is tightly connected between speed control vacuum valve and speed control vacuum reservoir, and free of cuts, cracks and kinks. ● Speed control dump hose is tightly connected to the speed control vacuum reservoir and speed control dump valve, and free of cuts, cracks and kinks. ● **Are all checks satisfactory?**	Yes No	▶ GO to A3. ▶ SERVICE vacuum hoses. REPEAT Quick Test.

FM1109400223010X

Fig. 79   Test A: Does Not Hold Speed During Dynamic Test (Part 1 of 2). 1994 Sable & Taurus

	TEST STEP	RESULT ▶	ACTION TO TAKE
A3	**CHECK SPEED CONTROL VACUUM RESERVOIR** ● Disconnect hose between the speed control vacuum valve and speed control vacuum reservoir at speed control vacuum valve end. ● Install vacuum pump to open end of hose to speed control vacuum reservoir. ● Apply 60.6 kPa (18 in-Hg) vacuum to the speed control vacuum reservoir. ● **Does speed control vacuum reservoir hold vacuum?**	Yes No	▶ GO to A4. ▶ REPLACE speed control vacuum reservoir. REPEAT Quick Test.
A4	**CHECK THE SPEED CONTROL VACUUM VALVE** ● Disconnect hose between speed control vacuum valve and speed control servo, at the speed control servo end. ● Apply 60.6 kPa (18 in-Hg) vacuum to open end of hose. ● **Can vacuum be pumped to, and held at 60 kPa (18 in-Hg) vacuum?**	Yes No	▶ REPLACE speed control servo. REPEAT Quick Test. ▶ REPLACE speed control vacuum valve. REPEAT Quick Test.
A5	**CHECK FOR DIAGNOSTIC TROUBLE CODE 454** ● REPEAT Engine Running Self-Test. Be sure that the speed control ON button is pressed before pressing the SUPER STAR II push button. ● **Is diagnostic trouble code 454 present?**	Yes No	▶ REPLACE speed control servo. REPEAT Quick Test. ▶ Speed control servo leaks up test passed. SERVICE any other Diagnostic Trouble Code as necessary.

FM1109400223020X

Fig. 79   Test A: Does Not Hold Speed During Dynamic Test (Part 2 of 2). 1994 Sable & Taurus

TEST STEP		RESULT	▶	ACTION TO TAKE
B1	CHECK FOR DIAGNOSTIC TROUBLE CODE 455			
	• Repeat KOER Self-Test of Quick Test. Be sure that the speed control ON button is pressed before pressing the SUPER STAR II push button. • Is diagnostic trouble code 455 present?	Yes No	▶ ▶	GO to **B2**. Increase vehicle speed test passed. SERVICE any other Diagnostic Trouble Code as necessary.
B2	CHECK ACTUATOR CABLE CONNECTION TO THROTTLE BODY AND SPEED CONTROL SERVO			
	• Check to see if: • Actuator cable is attached to throttle body accelerator linkage. • Actuator cable is attached to speed control servo linkage. • Are all checks satisfactory?	Yes No	▶ ▶	GO to **B3**. SERVICE as necessary.

FM1109400224010X

Fig. 80 Test B: Speed Does Not Increase During Dynamic Test (Part 1 of 2). 1994 Sable & Taurus

TEST STEP		RESULT	▶	ACTION TO TAKE
B3	CHECK VACUUM HOSES			
	• Check to see if: • Speed control servo vacuum supply hose is tightly connected to VAC port on speed control vacuum valve and to the vacuum manifold, and free of cuts, cracks and kinks. • Vacuum hoses are tightly connected between speed control vacuum valves and speed control servo, and free of cuts, cracks and kinks. • Vacuum hose is tightly connected between speed control vacuum valve and speed control vacuum reservoir, and free of cuts, cracks and kinks. • The speed control dump valve hose is tightly connected to the speed control servo and to the speed control dump valve, and free of cuts, cracks and kinks. • Are all checks satisfactory?	Yes No	▶ ▶	GO to **B4**. SERVICE hoses. REPEAT Quick Test.
B4	VACUUM LEAK DOWN CHECK			
	• Disconnect the hose between speed control vacuum valve and speed control vacuum servo, at the speed control servo end. • Apply 60.6 kPa (18 in-Hg) vacuum to open end of hose. • Can vacuum be pumped to, and held at 60.6 kPa (18in-Hg) vacuum?	Yes No	▶ ▶	GO to **B6**. GO to **B5**.
B5	CHECK SPEED CONTROL VACUUM RESERVOIR			
	• Disconnect hose between speed control vacuum valve and speed control vacuum reservoir, at speed control vacuum valve end. • Install pump to open end of hose to speed control vacuum reservoir. • Apply 60.6 kPa (18 in-Hg) vacuum to the speed control vacuum reservoir. • Does speed control vacuum reservoir hold vacuum?	Yes No	▶ ▶	REPLACE speed control vacuum valve. REPEAT Quick Test. REPLACE speed control vacuum reservoir. REPEAT Quick Test.
B6	CHECK SPEED CONTROL DUMP VALVE			
	• Check speed control dump valve. • Is the speed control dump valve adjusted properly so that the speed control dump valve is closed when the brake pedal is not applied?	Yes No	▶ ▶	GO to **F1**. ADJUST speed control dump valve. REPEAT Quick Test.

FM1109400224020X

Fig. 80 Test B: Speed Does Not Increase During Dynamic Test (Part 2 of 2). 1994 Sable & Taurus

TEST STEP		RESULT	▶	ACTION TO TAKE
C1	CHECK FOR DIAGNOSTIC TROUBLE CODE 456			
	• Repeat KOER Self-Test of Quick Test. Be sure that the speed control ON button is pressed before pressing the SUPER STAR II push button. • Is diagnostic trouble code 456 present?	Yes No	▶ ▶	GO to **C2**. Decrease vehicle speed test passed. SERVICE any other Diagnostic Trouble Code(s) as necessary.

FM1109400225010X

Fig. 81 Test C: Speed Does Not Decrease During Dynamic Test (Part 1 of 2). 1994 Sable & Taurus

TEST STEP		RESULT	▶	ACTION TO TAKE
C2	CHECK FOR THROTTLE SHAFT/LINKAGE BINDING			
	• Check for throttle/shaft linkage binding. • Is the throttle or shaft throttle linkage binding, maintaining a part throttle opening?	Yes No	▶ ▶	SERVICE to eliminate binding. REPEAT Quick Test. GO to **C3**.
C3	CHECK FOR SPEED CONTROL LINKAGE BINDING			
	• Check for speed control linkage binding. • Is the actuator cable binding?	Yes No	▶ ▶	REPLACE the actuator cable. REPEAT Quick Test. GO to **C4**.
C4	CHECK FOR TP SENSOR BINDING			
	• Check for TP sensor binding. • Is TP sensor binding at a part throttle opening?	Yes No	▶ ▶	REPLACE the throttle position sensor. REPEAT Quick Test. REPLACE the powertrain control module. REPEAT Quick Test.

FM1109400225020X

Fig. 81 Test C: Speed Does Not Decrease During Dynamic Test (Part 2 of 2). 1994 Sable & Taurus

TEST STEP		RESULT	▶	ACTION TO TAKE
D1	CHECK FOR DIAGNOSTIC TROUBLE CODE 457			
	• Diagnostic trouble code 457 displayed. • Did you press the OFF, COAST, ACCEL and RESUME buttons during the IVSC KOEO Self-Test?	Yes No	▶ ▶	GO to **D2**. REPEAT IVSC KOEO Self-Test.
D2	SWITCH DOES NOT FUNCTION			
	• Turn ignition switch OFF, wait 10 seconds. • Disconnect powertrain control module 60-pin connector. Inspect for damaged pins, corrosion, loose pins, etc. Service as necessary. • Install EEC-IV 60-Pin Breakout Box, leave powertrain control module disconnected. • Measure resistance between test Pin 28 and test Pin 39 per table below. • Rotate steering wheel through its full range while making resistance checks.	Yes No	▶ ▶	REPLACE powertrain control module. REPLACE speed control actuator switch assembly.

DVOM Range	Button Pressed	Resistance Range
200 ohm	OFF	0-4 ohms
200 ohm	COAST	114-126 ohms
2000 ohm	ACCEL	646-714 ohms
5000 ohm	RESUME	2090-2310 ohms

• Are resistances within range?				

FM1109400226010X

Fig. 82 Test D: Speed Control Switches (Part 1 of 2). 1994 Sable & Taurus

TEST STEP		RESULT	▶	ACTION TO TAKE
D3	DIAGNOSTIC TROUBLE CODE 458			
	• Diagnostic trouble code 458 displayed. • Did you press the OFF, COAST, ACCEL and RESUME buttons during the IVSC KOEO Quick Test?	Yes No	▶ ▶	GO to **D4**. REPEAT IVSC KOEO Quick Test.
D4	SWITCH IS STUCK			
	• Turn ignition switch OFF, wait 10 seconds. • Disconnect powertrain control module 60-pin connector. Inspect for damaged pins, corrosion, loose wires, etc. Service as necessary. • Install breakout box, leave powertrain control module disconnected. • Rotunda Digital Volt-Ohmmeter (DVOM) 014-00407 or equivalent, on 5000 ohm scale. • Measure resistance between test Pin 28 and test Pin 39. • Is resistance reading between 0 ohms and 2310 ohms?	Yes No	▶ ▶	REPLACE speed control actuator switch assembly. REPLACE powertrain control module.
D5	DIAGNOSTIC TROUBLE CODE 459			
	• Diagnostic trouble code 459 displayed. • Did you press the OFF, COAST, ACCEL and RESUME buttons during the IVSC KOEO QUICK TEST?	Yes No	▶ ▶	GO to **D6**. REPEAT IVSC KOEO Quick Test.
D6	GROUND CIRCUIT TO SWITCHES OPEN			
	• Turn ignition switch OFF, wait 10 seconds. • Disconnect powertrain control module 60-pin connector. Inspect for damaged pins, corrosion, loose wires, etc. Service as necessary. • Install breakout box, leave powertrain control module disconnected. • Disconnect speed control actuator switch assembly connector in steering column shroud. • Set DVOM on 200 ohm scale. • Measure resistance between test Pin 39 and ground terminal of disconnected speed control actuator switch assembly connector. • Is resistance reading greater than five ohms?	Yes No	▶ ▶	SERVICE open circuit between PCM connector Pin 39 and speed control actuator switch assembly connector ground terminal. REPLACE powertrain control module.

FM1109400226020X

Fig. 82 Test D: Speed Control Switches (Part 2 of 2). 1994 Sable & Taurus

TEST STEP		RESULT	▶	ACTION TO TAKE
E1	CHECK FOR DIAGNOSTIC TROUBLE CODE 536			
	• Diagnostic trouble code 536 displayed. • Did you apply brake pedal during the KOEO Self-Test?	Yes No	▶ ▶	GO to **E2**. REPEAT KOEO Self-Test. PRESS brake pedal once during test.

FM1109400227010X

Fig. 83 Test E: Stoplight Switch (Part 1 of 2). 1994 Sable & Taurus

TEST STEP		RESULT	▶	ACTION TO TAKE
E2	STOPLIGHT SWITCH CIRCUIT CYCLING			
	• Turn ignition switch OFF, wait 10 seconds. • Disconnect powertrain control module 60-pin connector. Inspect for damaged pins, corrosion, loose wires, etc. Service as necessary. • Install breakout box, leave powertrain control module disconnected. • Rotunda Digital Volt-Ohmmeter (DVOM) 014-00407 or equivalent, on 20 volt scale. • Measure voltage between test Pin 5 and test Pin 40 at the breakout box while pressing and releasing brake pedal. • Does the voltage cycle?	Yes No	▶ ▶	REPLACE powertrain control module. RETEST. GO to **E3**.
E3	STOPLIGHT SWITCH CIRCUIT SHORT TO GROUND			
	• Turn ignition switch OFF. • Set DVOM on 200 ohm scale. • Disconnect stoplight switch circuit from 14290 harness (12-pin connector). • Measure resistance between test Pin 5 at the breakout box and ground. • Is resistance reading greater than five ohms?	Yes No	▶ ▶	SERVICE stoplight circuit. GO to **E4**.
E4	BOO CIRCUIT SHORT TO POWER			
	• Turn ignition switch OFF. • Set DVOM on 20 volt scale. • Disconnect stoplight switch circuit from 14290 harness (12-pin connector). • Measure voltage between test Pin 5 at the breakout box and engine block ground. • Is voltage reading greater than 10.5 volts?	Yes No	▶ ▶	SERVICE stoplight circuit short to power. SERVICE stoplight circuit.

FM1109400227020X

Fig. 83 Test E: Stoplight Switch (Part 2 of 2). 1994 Sable & Taurus

TEST STEP	RESULT	▶	ACTION TO TAKE
F1 VENT SOLENOID TEST • Turn ignition switch OFF. • Disconnect powertrain control module 60 pin connector. Inspect for damaged pins, corrosion, loose wires, etc. Service as necessary. • Install Breakout box, leave powertrain control module disconnected. • Set DVOM on 200 ohm scale. • Measure resistance between test Pin 11 and test Pin 35. • **Is resistance between 100-150 ohms?**	Yes No	▶ ▶	If code 568 is also set, GO to F6, if not, GO to F11. GO to F2.
F2 CHECK RESISTANCE READING • Check resistance reading. • **Is resistance less than 100 ohms?**	Yes No	▶ ▶	REPLACE speed control servo. REPEAT Quick Test. GO to F3.
F3 VERIFY RESISTANCE READING • Check resistance reading. • **Is resistance greater than 150 ohms?**	Yes No	▶ ▶	GO to F4. GO to F1.

FM1109400228010X

Fig. 84   Test F: Servo Solenoids (Part 1 of 3). 1994 Sable & Taurus

TEST STEP	RESULT	▶	ACTION TO TAKE
G1 SELF-TEST INPUT CONTINUITY CHECK • Turn ignition switch OFF, wait 10 seconds. • Disconnect powertrain control module 60-Pin connector. Inspect for damaged pins, corrosion, loose wires, etc. Service as necessary. • Install breakout box, leave powertrain control module disconnected. • Set DVOM to 200 ohm scale. • Measure resistance between Self Test input at the Self Test single pin connector and test Pin 48 at the breakout box. • **Is resistance less than five ohms?**	Yes No	▶ ▶	GO to G2. CORRECT open in Circuit 200 (BR).
G2 SELF-TEST OUTPUT CIRCUIT CONTINUITY CHECK • Measure resistance between Self-Test output at the data-link connector (DLC) and test Pin 17 at the breakout box. • **Is resistance less than five ohms?**	Yes No	▶ ▶	GO to G3. CORRECT open in Circuit 201 (T/R).

FM1109400229010X

Fig. 85   Test G: Speed Control Erratic (Part 1 of 2). 1994 Sable & Taurus

TEST STEP	RESULT	▶	ACTION TO TAKE
F4 CHECK CONTINUITY OF SOL+ CIRCUIT • Disconnect harness connector from the speed control servo. • Set DVOM on 200 ohm scale. • Measure resistance between test Pin 11 and Circuit 144 (SOL+, O/Y) at the harness connector. • **Is resistance less than 5 ohms?**	Yes No	▶ ▶	GO to F5. SERVICE open in Circuit 144 (O/Y). REPEAT Quick Test.
F5 CHECK CONTINUITY OF SCVNT CIRCUIT • Disconnect harness connector from the speed control servo. • Set DVOM on 200 ohm scale. • Measure resistance between test Pin 35 and Circuit 146 (SCVNT, W/PK) at the harness connector. • **Is resistance less than 5 ohms?**	Yes No	▶ ▶	REPLACE speed control servo. REPEAT Quick Test. SERVICE open in Circuit 145 (W/PK). REPEAT Quick Test.
F6 VACUUM SOLENOID TEST • Turn ignition switch OFF. • Disconnect powertrain control module 60 pin connector. Inspect for damaged pins, corrosion, loose wires, etc. Service as necessary. • Install Breakout box, leave powertrain control module disconnected. • Set DVOM on 200 ohm scale. • Measure resistance between test Pin 11 and test Pin 51. • **Is resistance between 40-75 ohms?**	Yes No	▶ ▶	GO to F11. GO to F7.
F7 CHECK RESISTANCE BETWEEN TEST PIN 11 AND 51 • Check resistance reading. • **Is resistance less than 40 ohms?**	Yes No	▶ ▶	REPLACE speed control servo. REPEAT Quick Test. GO to F8.
F8 VERIFY RESISTANCE BETWEEN TEST PIN 11 AND 51 • Check resistance reading. • **Is resistance greater than 75 ohms?**	Yes No	▶ ▶	GO to F9. GO to F6.
F9 MEASURE RESISTANCE BETWEEN CIRCUIT 144 FROM PIN 11 • Disconnect harness connector from the speed control servo. • Set DVOM on 200 ohm scale. • Measure resistance between test Pin 11 and Circuit 144 (SOL+, O/Y) at the harness connector. • **Is resistance less than 5 ohms?**	Yes No	▶ ▶	GO to F10. SERVICE open in Circuit 144 (O/Y). REPEAT Quick Test.
F10 MEASURE RESISTANCE FROM PIN 51 • Disconnect harness connector from the speed control servo. • Set DVOM on 200 ohm scale. • Measure resistance between test Pin 51 and Circuit 145 (SCVAC, GY/BK) at the harness connector. • **Is resistance less than 5 ohms?**	Yes No	▶ ▶	REPLACE speed control servo. REPEAT Quick Test. SERVICE open in Circuit 145 (GY/BK). REPEAT Quick Test
F11 CHECK SOL+ SHORT TO GROUND • Disconnect the harness connector from the speed control servo. • Set DVOM on 200,000 ohm scale. • Measure resistance between test Pin 11 and test Pin 40 at Breakout Box. • **Is resistance greater than 10,000 ohms?**	Yes No	▶ ▶	GO to F12. SERVICE short in Circuit 144 (O/Y). REPEAT Quick Test (short may have damaged powertrain control module).

FM1109400228020X

Fig. 84   Test F: Servo Solenoids (Part 2 of 3). 1994 Sable & Taurus

TEST STEP	RESULT	▶	ACTION TO TAKE
G3 HEATED OXYGEN SENSOR GROUND CONTINUITY CHECK • Turn ignition switch OFF. • Measure resistance between HO2S ground on engine and test Pin 49 at the breakout box. • **Is resistance less than five ohms?**	Yes No	▶ ▶	GO to G4. CHECK and SERVICE HO2S sensor ground wire or open Circuit 89 (O) bad connection.
G4 STO SHORT TO GROUND • Set DVOM on 200,000 ohm scale. • Measure resistance between Self Test output at the DLC and engine block ground. • **Is resistance greater than 10,000 ohms?**	Yes No	▶ ▶	REPLACE powertrain control module. REPEAT Quick Test. SERVICE shorts to ground. REPEAT Quick Test.

FM1109400229020X

Fig. 85   Test G: Speed Control Erratic (Part 2 of 2). 1994 Sable & Taurus

TEST STEP	RESULT	▶	ACTION TO TAKE
H1 VSS RESISTANCE CHECK • Turn ignition switch OFF, wait 10 seconds. • Disconnect powertrain control module 60 pin connector. Inspect for damaged pins, corrosion, loose wires, etc. Service as necessary. • Install breakout box, leave powertrain control module disconnected. • Set Rotunda Digital Volt-Ohmmeter (DVOM) 014-00407 or equivalent, on 2000 ohm scale. • Measure resistance between test Pin 3 and test Pin 6. • **Is resistance between 180-240 ohms?**	Yes No	▶ ▶	CHECK for DTC 452 in PCM continuous memory. PERFORM diagnostics as required. GO to H2.
H2 CHECK RESISTANCE READING • Check resistance reading. • **Is resistance less than 180 ohms?**	Yes No	▶ ▶	GO to H4. GO to H3.
H3 VERIFY RESISTANCE READING • Check resistance reading. • **Is resistance greater than 240 ohms?**	Yes No	▶ ▶	GO to H6. GO to H1.

FM1109400230010X

Fig. 86   Test H: Vehicle Speed Sensor Not Operating (Part 1 of 2). 1994 Sable & Taurus

TEST STEP	RESULT	▶	ACTION TO TAKE
F12 CHECK SCVNT SHORT TO GROUND • Disconnect the harness connector from the speed control servo. • Set DVOM on 200,000 ohm scale. • Measure resistance between test Pin 35 and test Pin 40 at Breakout Box. • **Is resistance greater than 10,000 ohms?**	Yes No	▶ ▶	GO to F13. SERVICE short in Circuit 146 (W/PK). REPEAT Quick Test.
F13 CHECK SCVAC SHORT TO GROUND • Disconnect the harness connector from the speed control servo. • Set DVOM on 200,000 ohm scale. • Measure resistance between test Pin 51 and test Pin 40 at Breakout Box. • **Is resistance greater than 10,000 ohms?**	Yes No	▶ ▶	REPLACE powertrain control module. REPEAT Quick Test. SERVICE short in Circuit 145 (GY/BK). REPEAT Quick Test.

FM1109400228030X

Fig. 84   Test F: Servo Solenoids (Part 3 of 3). 1994 Sable & Taurus

TEST STEP	RESULT	▶	ACTION TO TAKE
H4 CHECK FOR SHORT IN VSS INPUT CIRCUIT • Turn ignition switch OFF. • Disconnect harness connector from vehicle speed sensor. • Set DVOM on 2000 ohm scale. • Measure resistance between the two connector pins on the vehicle speed sensor. • **Is resistance between 180-240 ohms?**	Yes No	▶ ▶	SERVICE short in wire harness between vehicle speed sensor and PCM Pins 3 and 6 or grounded Circuit 150 (DG/W). REPEAT Quick Test. GO to H5.
H5 CHECK RESISTANCE ON VSS • Check resistance reading. • **Is resistance less than 180 ohms?**	Yes No	▶ ▶	REPLACE vehicle speed sensor. REPEAT Quick Test. GO to H6.
H6 CHECK FOR OPEN IN VSS INPUT CIRCUIT • Turn ignition switch OFF. • Disconnect harness connector from vehicle speed sensor. • Set DVOM on 2000 ohm scale. • Measure resistance between the two connector pins on the vehicle speed sensor. • **Is resistance greater than 240 ohms?**	Yes No	▶ ▶	REPLACE vehicle speed sensor. REPEAT Quick Test. GO to H4.

FM1109400230020X

Fig. 86   Test H: Vehicle Speed Sensor Not Operating (Part 2 of 2). 1994 Sable & Taurus

TEST STEP		RESULT	▶	ACTION TO TAKE
J1	**CLUTCH PEDAL INPUT CHECK**			
	• Turn ignition switch OFF, Wait 10 seconds. • Disconnect powertrain control module (PCM) 60 pin connector. Inspect for damaged pins, corrosion, loose wires, etc. Service as necessary. • Install Breakout Box. • Set DVOM on 200 ohm scale. • Measure resistance between test Pin 30 and test Pin 46 with the clutch pedal down. • **Is resistance less than five ohms?**	Yes	▶	REPLACE powertrain control module. Road test to verify that applying the clutch pedal disengages the speed control.
		No	▶	GO to J2.
J2	**CHECK WIRE HARNESS**			
	• Turn ignition switch OFF. • Locate clutch pedal position switch (under the instrument panel). • Measure resistance between test Pin 30 and the clutch pedal position switch harness connector. • Measure resistance between test Pin 46 and the clutch pedal position switch harness connector. • **Are all resistance readings less than five ohms?**	Yes	▶	GO to J3.
		No	▶	SERVICE open Circuit 480 (P/Y) or Circuit 359 (GY/R). Road test to verify that applying the clutch pedal disengages the speed control.

FM110940023101OX

Fig. 87 Test J: Clutch Pedal Position Switch Not Operating Properly (Part 1 of 2). 1994 Sable & Taurus

TEST STEP		RESULT	▶	ACTION TO TAKE
J3	**CHECK CLUTCH PEDAL POSITION SWITCH ADJUSTMENT**			
	• Check that clutch pedal position switch is adjusted as outlined. • **Is clutch pedal position switch adjusted properly?**	Yes	▶	REPLACE clutch pedal position switch. Road test to verify that applying the clutch pedal disengages the speed control.
		No	▶	RE-ADJUST clutch pedal position switch. Road test to verify that applying the clutch pedal disengages the speed control.

FM110940023102OX

Fig. 87 Test J: Clutch Pedal Position Switch Not Operating Properly (Part 2 of 2). 1994 Sable & Taurus

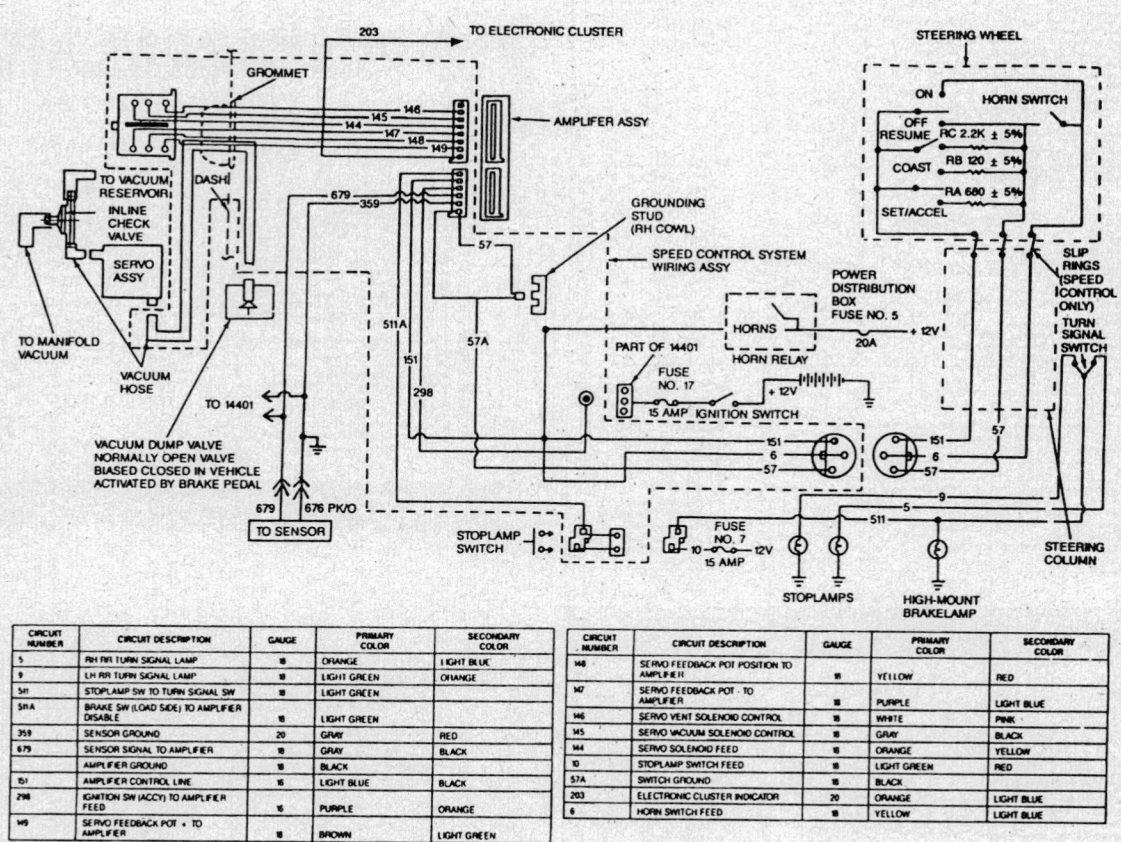

CIRCUIT NUMBER	CIRCUIT DESCRIPTION	GAUGE	PRIMARY COLOR	SECONDARY COLOR
5	RH RR TURN SIGNAL LAMP	18	ORANGE	LIGHT BLUE
9	LH RR TURN SIGNAL LAMP	18	LIGHT GREEN	ORANGE
511	STOPLAMP SW TO TURN SIGNAL SW	18	LIGHT GREEN	
511A	BRAKE SW (LOAD SIDE) TO AMPLIFIER DISABLE	18	LIGHT GREEN	
359	SENSOR GROUND	20	GRAY	RED
679	SENSOR SIGNAL TO AMPLIFIER	18	GRAY	BLACK
57	AMPLIFIER GROUND	18	BLACK	
151	AMPLIFIER CONTROL LINE	18	LIGHT BLUE	BLACK
298	IGNITION SW (ACCY) TO AMPLIFIER FEED	16	PURPLE	ORANGE
149	SERVO FEEDBACK POT + TO AMPLIFIER	18	BROWN	LIGHT GREEN

CIRCUIT NUMBER	CIRCUIT DESCRIPTION	GAUGE	PRIMARY COLOR	SECONDARY COLOR
148	SERVO FEEDBACK POT POSITION TO AMPLIFIER	18	YELLOW	RED
147	SERVO FEEDBACK POT - TO AMPLIFIER	18	PURPLE	LIGHT BLUE
146	SERVO VENT SOLENOID CONTROL	18	WHITE	PINK
145	SERVO VACUUM SOLENOID CONTROL	18	GRAY	BLACK
144	SERVO SOLENOID FEED	18	ORANGE	YELLOW
10	STOPLAMP SWITCH FEED	18	LIGHT GREEN	RED
57A	SWITCH GROUND	18	BLACK	
203	ELECTRONIC CLUSTER INDICATOR	20	ORANGE	LIGHT BLUE
6	HORN SWITCH FEED	18	YELLOW	LIGHT BLUE

FM110920015900OX

Fig. 88 Wiring circuit. 1992 Crown Victoria, Grand Marquis & Town Car (Early Production)

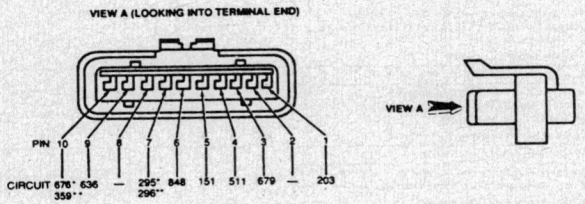

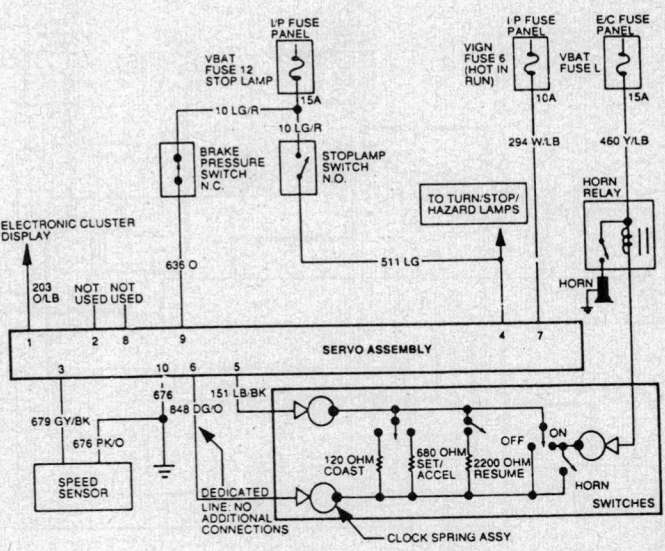

Key to Circuit Numbers and Wire Colors

Description	Pin	Circuit	Wire Harness / Wire Color
Speed Control Servo Connector			14401 Harness
Electronic Cluster Indicator	1	203	O/LB
Not Used	2		
Vehicle Speed Signal	3	679	GY/BK
Stoplamp Switch Feed	4	511	LG
Command Signal	5	151	LB/BK
Command Return	6	848	DG/O
Ignition Switch Feed	7	295* 296**	LB/PK * W/P **
Not Used	8		
Deactivator Switch	9	636	O
Ground	10	676* 359**	PK·O * GY·R **
Deactivator Switch Connector			14401 Harness
Battery Feed	·	10	LG/R
Speed Control Servo	·	636	O

* Town Car
** Crown Victoria · Grand Marquis

FM1109100163000X

Fig. 89 Servo connector terminal identification. 1992 Town Car (Late Production) & 1993–94 Crown Victoria, Grand Marquis, Mark VIII & Town Car

FM1109200164000X

Fig. 90 Wiring circuit. 1992 Town Car (Late Production)

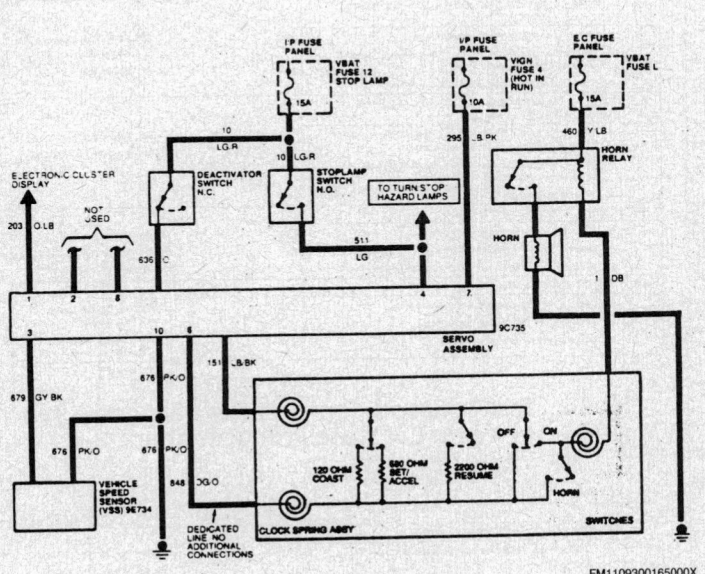

FM1109300165000X

Fig. 91 Wiring circuit. 1993–94 Town Car

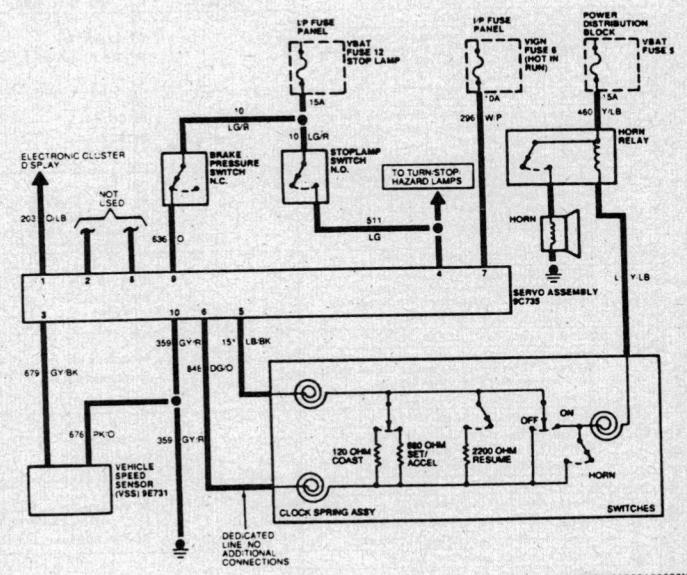

FM1109300166000X

Fig. 92 Wiring circuit. 1993–94 Crown Victoria & Grand Marquis

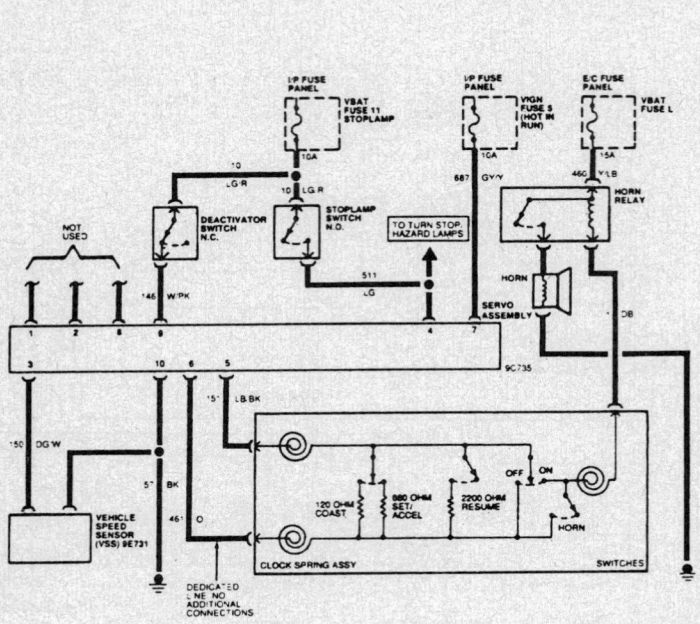

Fig. 93   Wiring circuit. Mark VIII

	TEST STEP	RESULT	►	ACTION TO TAKE
A1	VERIFY POWER TO SERVO			
	• Disconnect 14401 harness connector from servo assembly. • Use a VOM to make the specified measurements at the connector. • With ignition switch in RUN position, measure voltage between Pin 7 (B+, Circuit 294) and Pin 10 (GND, Circuit 676). • Is there battery voltage?	Yes No	► ►	GO to A4. GO to A2.
A2	CHECK IGNITION CIRCUIT			
	• With ignition switch in RUN position, measure voltage between Pin 7 (B+, Circuit 294) and a ground point on the chassis. • Is there battery voltage?	Yes No	► ►	GO to A3. SERVICE ignition fuse or circuit as required.
A3	CHECK MODULE GROUND CIRCUIT			
	• Measure resistance between Pin 10 (GND, Circuit 676) and a ground point on the chassis. • Is resistance less than 1 ohm?	No Yes	► ►	SERVICE ground circuit. REPEAT Step A1.
A4	CHECK DEACTIVATOR SWITCH CIRCUIT			
	• With no brakes applied, measure voltage between Pin 9 (DEACT, Circuit 636) and Pin 10 (GND, Circuit 676). • Is there battery voltage?	Yes NO	► ►	GO to A8. GO to A5.
A5	CHECK DEACTIVATOR SWITCH			
	• Remove 12A581 harness connector from deactivator switch. Measure resistance between two pins of switch with no brakes applied. • Is resistance less than 1 ohm?	Yes NO	► ►	GO to A6. REPLACE switch.
A6	VERIFY POWER AT DEACTIVATOR SWITCH HARNESS CONNECTOR			
	• Measure voltage between Circuit 10 of deactivator switch connector and chassis ground. • Is there battery voltage?	Yes No	► ►	GO to A7. SERVICE blown fuse or open in circuit.
A7	CHECK FOR OPEN CIRCUIT BETWEEN DEACTIVATOR SWITCH AND SERVO			
	• Measure resistance of Circuit 636 from deactivator switch connector to Pin 9 (Circuit 636) of servo connector. • Is resistance less than 1 ohm?	Yes No	► ►	REPEAT Step A4. SERVICE open circuit in harness.
A8	CHECK BRAKE SWITCH			
	• With no brakes applied, measure voltage between Pin 4 (BRK, Circuit 511) and Pin 10 (GND, Circuit 676). • Is there battery voltage?	No Yes	► ►	GO to A9. REPLACE switch.
A9	CHECK BRAKE CIRCUIT			
	• Measure resistance between Pin 4 (BRK, Circuit 511) and Pin 10 (GND, Circuit 676). • Is resistance less than 10 ohms?	Yes No	► ►	GO to A10. SERVICE brakelamp bulbs or circuit.

Fig. 94   Test A: Speed Control Does Not Work (Part 1 of 2). 1992 Town Car (Late Production)

	TEST STEP	RESULT	►	ACTION TO TAKE
A10	CHECK FOR STUCK ON SWITCH			
	• With no steering wheel switches depressed, measure voltage between Pin 5 (command, Circuit 151) and Pin 10 (GND, Circuit 676). • Is there battery voltage?	No Yes	► ►	GO to A11. REPLACE switch.
A11	CHECK ON SWITCH OPERATION			
	• With steering wheel ON switch depressed, measure voltage between Pin 5 (command, Circuit 151) and Pin 10 (GND, Circuit 676). • Is there battery voltage?	Yes No	► ►	GO to A13. GO to A12.
A12	CHECK FOR OPEN CIRCUIT IN SWITCH GROUND			
	• With horn depressed, measure voltage between Pin 6 (command RTN, Circuit 848) and chassis ground. • Is there battery voltage?	Yes No	► ►	REPLACE switch. SERVICE open, blown fuse, failed relay or open in switch return circuit.
A13	CHECK FOR STUCK COMMAND SWITCHES			
	• With no steering wheel switches depressed, measure resistance between Pin 5 (command, Circuit 151) and Pin 6 (command RTN, Circuit 848). • Is resistance greater than 3k ohms?	Yes No	► ►	GO to A14. REPLACE inoperative switch.
A14	CHECK SET/ACCEL SWITCH OPERATION			
	• With the SET/ACCEL switch depressed, measure resistance between Pin 5 (command, Circuit 151) and Pin 6 (command RTN, Circuit 848). • Is resistance between 646 and 714 ohms?	Yes No	► ►	GO to A15. REPLACE switch.
A15	CHECK VEHICLE SPEED SENSOR CIRCUIT			
	• Measure resistance between Pin 3 (VSS, Circuit 679) and Pin 10 (GND, Circuit 676). • Is resistance between 200 and 300 ohms?	Yes No	► ►	GO to A17. GO to A16.
A16	CHECK SPEED SENSOR			
	• Remove speed sensor connector. • Measure resistance across sensor terminals. • Is resistance between 200 and 300 ohms?	Yes No	► ►	CHECK for opens in wiring or short in Circuit 679. REPLACE speed sensor.
A17	CHECK FOR BROKEN OR BINDING CABLE			
	• Remove actuator cable from servo assembly. • Check for broken or binding cable by pulling on cable ball slug to ensure throttle moves freely. • Is cable OK?	Yes No	► ►	REPLACE servo assembly. REPLACE cable.

Fig. 94   Test A: Speed Control Does Not Work (Part 2 of 2). 1992 Town Car (Late Production)

	TEST STEP	RESULT	►	ACTION TO TAKE
B1	VERIFY CONDITION OCCURS ONLY WHILE USING SPEED CONTROL			
	• Verify that engine is properly tuned. • Verify that condition does not occur when driving without speed control. • Does condition occur without speed control?	Yes No	► ►	SERVICE engine as required. GO to B2.
B2	CHECK FOR BINDING IN ACTUATOR CABLE AND THROTTLE BODY LINKAGE			
	• Check for binding or sticking of actuator cable or throttle linkage and throttle plate. • Make sure accelerator cable bracket and servo bracket are not loose. • Are components OK?	Yes No	► ►	GO to B3. SERVICE as required.
B3	CHECK SPEED SENSOR			
	• Remove speed sensor connector. • Measure resistance across sensor terminals. • Is resistance between 200 and 300 ohms?	Yes No	► ►	GO to B4. SERVICE speed sensor or circuit as required.
B4	CHECK SERVO ASSEMBLY			
	• Substitute known good servo assembly. • Test vehicle for proper operation. • Does system operate properly?	Yes No	► ►	REPLACE servo assembly. CHECK MAP sensor and EVP.

Fig. 95   Test B: Speed Continuously Changes. 1992 Town Car (Late Production)

	TEST STEP	RESULT	►	ACTION TO TAKE
C1	CHECK COAST SWITCH OPERATION			
	• Disconnect 14401 harness connector from servo assembly. • With COAST switch depressed, measure resistance between Pin 5 (command RTN, Circuit 151) and Pin 6 (command RTN, Circuit 848) while rotating steering wheel through full range. • Is resistance between 114 and 126 ohms?	Yes No	► ►	GO to C2. REPLACE switch.
C2	CHECK COMMAND SWITCH RETURN CIRCUIT			
	• Measure resistance between Pin 6 (command RTN, Circuit 848) and Pin 10 (GND, Circuit 676). • Is resistance greater than 1 ohm?	Yes No	► ►	Switch circuit OK. SERVICE short in switch return circuit.

Fig. 96   Test C: Coast/Tap-Down Inoperative. 1992 Town Car (Late Production)

TEST STEP	RESULT	►	ACTION TO TAKE
D1 CHECK ACCEL/TAP-UP SWITCH OPERATION • Disconnect 14401 harness connector from servo assembly. • With ACCEL/TAP-UP switch depressed, measure resistance between Pin 5 (command, Circuit 151) and Pin 6 (command RTN, Circuit 848) while rotating steering wheel through full range. • Is resistance between 646 and 714 ohms?	Yes No	► ►	GO to D2. REPLACE switch.
D2 CHECK COMMAND SWITCH RETURN CIRCUIT • Measure resistance between Pin 6 (command RTN, Circuit 848) and Pin 10 (GND, Circuit 676). • Is resistance greater than 1 ohm?	Yes No	► ►	Switch circuit OK. SERVICE short in switch return circuit.

FM1109200172000X

Fig. 97 Test D: Coast/Tap-Up Inoperative. 1992 Town Car (Late Production)

TEST STEP	RESULT	►	ACTION TO TAKE
E1 CHECK RESUME SWITCH OPERATION • Disconnect 14401 harness connector from servo assembly. • With RESUME switch depressed, measure resistance between Pin 5 (command, Circuit 151) and Pin 6 (command RTN, Circuit 848) while rotating steering wheel through full range. • Is resistance between 2090 and 2310 ohms?	Yes No	► ►	GO to E2. REPLACE switch.
E2 CHECK COMMAND SWITCH RETURN CIRCUIT • Measure resistance between Pin 6 (command RTN, Circuit 848) and Pin 10 (GND, Circuit 676). • Is resistance greater than 1 ohm?	Yes No	► ►	Switch circuit OK. SERVICE ground in switch return circuit.

FM1109200173000X

Fig. 98 Test E: Resume Inoperative. 1992 Town Car (Late Production)

TEST STEP	RESULT	►	ACTION TO TAKE
F1 CHECK BRAKE SWITCH CIRCUIT • Disconnect 14401 harness connector at the servo. • With brakes applied, measure voltage between Pin 4 (BRK, Circuit 511) and Pin 10 (GND, Circuit 676). • Is there battery voltage?	Yes No	► ►	REPLACE servo assembly. SERVICE switch, fuse or open circuit.
F2 CHECK FOR BINDS IN ACTUATOR CABLE AND THROTTLE BODY ATTACHMENT • Remove actuator cable from servo assembly. • Check for broken or binding cable by pulling on cable ball slug to ensure throttle moves freely. • Is cable OK?	Yes No	► ►	REPLACE servo assembly SERVICE as required.

FM1109200174000X

Fig. 99 Test F: Speed Control Does Not Disengage When Brake Is Applied. 1992 Town Car (Late Production)

TEST STEP	RESULT	►	ACTION TO TAKE
G1 CHECK OFF SWITCH OPERATION • Disconnect 14401 harness connector from servo assembly. • With OFF switch depressed, measure resistance between Pin 5 (command, Circuit 151) and Pin 6 (command RTN, Circuit 848) while rotating steering wheel through full range. • Is resistance less than 4 ohms?	Yes No	► ►	REPLACE servo assembly. REPLACE switch.

FM1109200175000X

Fig. 100 Test G: Off Switch Inoperative. 1992 Town Car (Late Production)

TEST STEP	RESULT	►	ACTION TO TAKE
H1 CHECK VOLTAGE AT SERVO ASSEMBLY CONNECTOR • Disconnect 14401 harness connector from servo assembly. • With ignition switch in RUN position, measure voltage between Pin 1 (Circuit 203) and Pin 10 (GND, Circuit 676). • Is voltage approximately 5 volts?	Yes No	► ►	GO to H3. GO to H2.
H2 CHECK CIRCUIT CONTINUITY • Measure resistance of Circuit 203 from Pin 1 of servo connector to cluster connector. • Is resistance less than 1 ohm?	Yes No	► ►	GO to H3. SERVICE open in circuit.
H3 DISPLAY TURN ON TEST • With ignition switch in RUN position, connect Pin 1 (Circuit 203) to Pin 10 (GND, Circuit 676). • Does "Speed Control" display turn on?	Yes No	► ►	REPLACE servo assembly and REPEAT test. INSTRUMENT CLUSTER

FM1109200176000X

Fig. 101 Test H: Electronic Cluster Display Does Not Turn On. 1992 Town Car (Late Production)

TEST STEP	RESULT	►	ACTION TO TAKE
I1 CHECK CIRCUIT 203 • Check for short to ground in Circuit 203. • Is there a short?	Yes No	► 	SERVICE wiring and verify display OFF. INSTRUMENT CLUSTER

FM1109200177000X

Fig. 102 Test I: Electronic Cluster Display Does Not Turn Off. 1992 Town Car (Late Production)

TEST STEP	RESULT	►	ACTION TO TAKE
A1 VERIFY POWER TO SPEED CONTROL SERVO • Disconnect 14290 harness connector from speed control servo. • Turn ignition switch to RUN. • With a Rotunda Digital Multimeter 105-00050 or equivalent, measure voltage between Pin 7 (B+, Circuit 295 (LB/PK)[2] or 296 (W/P)[3]) and Pin 10 (GND, Circuit 676 (PK/O)[2] or 57 (BK)[3]. • Is there battery voltage?	Yes No	► ►	GO to A4. GO to A2.
A2 CHECK IGNITION CIRCUIT • With ignition switch in RUN, measure voltage between Pin 7 (B+, Circuit 295 (LB/PK)[2] or 296 (W/P)[3] and a ground on the chassis. • Is there battery voltage?	Yes No	► ►	GO to A3. SERVICE ignition fuse 4[2] or 6[3] in instrument panel or circuit 295 (LB/PK)[2] or 296 (W/P)[3] as required.
A3 CHECK SPEED CONTROL SERVO GROUND CIRCUIT • Measure resistance between Pin 10 (GND, Circuit 676 (PK/O)[2] or 57 (BK)[3] and a ground point on the chassis. • Is resistance less than one ohm?	Yes No	► ►	SERVICE ground circuit 676 (PK/O)[2] or 57 (BK)[3]. REPEAT Step A1.
A4 CHECK DEACTIVATOR SWITCH CIRCUIT • Leave ignition switch in RUN. • With no brakes applied, place a 12 Volt Circuit Test Light between Pin 9 (Circuit 636 (O)) and Pin 10 (GND, Circuit 57 (BK). • Is the light illuminated?	Yes No	► ►	GO to A7. GO to A5.

FM1109400232010X

Fig. 103 Test A: Speed Control Inoperative (Part 1 of 4). 1993-94 Crown Victoria, Grand Marquis, Mark VIII & Town Car

TEST STEP	RESULT	►	ACTION TO TAKE
A5 VERIFY POWER AT DEACTIVATOR SWITCH HARNESS CONNECTOR • Remove 14401 harness connector from deactivator switch. • Place 12 Volt Circuit Test Light between Circuit 10 (LG/R) of deactivator switch connector and chassis ground. • Is the light illuminated?	Yes No	► ►	GO to A6. SERVICE blown Fuse 11 or open Circuit 10 (LG/R).
A6 CHECK FOR OPEN CIRCUIT BETWEEN DEACTIVATOR SWITCH AND SPEED CONTROL SERVO • Measure resistance of Circuit 636 (O) from deactivator switch connector to Pin 9 of speed control servo connector. • Is resistance less than 1 ohm?	Yes No	► ►	REPLACE deactivator switch. SERVICE open Circuit 636 (O) in harness.
A7 CHECK STOPLIGHT SWITCH CIRCUIT • With no brakes applied, measure voltage between Pin 4 (BRK, Circuit 511 (LG)) and Pin 10 (GND, Circuit 676 (PK/O)[2] or 57 (BK)[3]). • Is there battery voltage?	Yes No	► ►	REPLACE stoplight switch. GO to A8.
A8 CHECK STOPLIGHT SWITCH CIRCUITRY • With brakes applied, measure voltage between Pin 4 (Circuit 511 (LG)) and Pin 10 (Circuit 676 (PK/O)[2] or 57 (BK)[3]). • Is there battery voltage?	Yes No	► ►	GO to A12. GO to A9.
A9 CHECK STOPLIGHT SWITCH • Remove electrical connector from stoplight switch. • Measure resistance between two terminals of stoplight switch with brakes applied. • Is resistance less than five ohms?	Yes No	► ►	GO to A10. REPLACE stoplight switch.
A10 VERIFY POWER AT STOPLIGHT SWITCH HARNESS CONNECTOR • Measure voltage between Circuit 10 (LG/R) of stoplight switch connector and chassis ground. • Is there battery voltage?	Yes No	► ►	GO to A11. SERVICE blown fuse 12[2] or 7[3] or open in Circuit 10 (LG/R).
A11 CHECK FOR OPEN CIRCUIT BETWEEN STOPLIGHT SWITCH AND SPEED CONTROL SERVO • Measure resistance of Circuit 511 (LG) from stoplight switch connector to Pin 4 of speed control servo connector. • Is resistance less than five ohms?	Yes No	► ►	REPEAT Step A7. SERVICE open in Circuit 511 (LG).
A12 CHECK FOR STUCK ON SPEED CONTROL ACTUATOR SWITCH ASSEMBLY • With no steering wheel switches pressed, measure voltage between Pin 5 (Circuit 151 (LB/BK)) and Pin 10 (GND, Circuit 676 (PK/O)[2] or 57 (BK)[3]). • Is there battery voltage?	Yes No	► ►	REPLACE speed control actuator switch assembly. GO to A13.
A13 CHECK ON SWITCH OPERATION • With steering wheel ON switch pressed, measure voltage between Pin 5 (Circuit 151 (LB/BK)) and Pin 10 (GND, Circuit 676 (PK/O)[2] or 57 (BK)[3]). • Is there battery voltage?	Yes No	► ►	GO to A17. GO to A14.

FM1109400232020X

Fig. 103 Test A: Speed Control Inoperative (Part 2 of 4). 1993-94 Crown Victoria, Grand Marquis, Mark VIII & Town Car

TEST STEP	RESULT	▶	ACTION TO TAKE
A14 VERIFY POWER AT AIR BAG SLIDING CONTACT CONNECTOR AT BASE OF STEERING COLUMN			
• Disconnect air bag sliding contact at the base of steering column. • Measure voltage between Circuit 1 (DB)[2] or 6 (Y/LG)[3] at air bag sliding contact connector and Pin 10 (Circuit 676 (PK/O)[2] or 57 (BK)[3]) of speed control servo connector. • **Is there battery voltage?**	Yes No	▶ ▶	GO to **A15**. CHECK fuse in the power distribution box, Circuit 460 (Y/LB), horn relay and bracket and Circuit 1 (DB)[2] or 6 (Y/LG)[3]. SERVICE as necessary.
A15 CHECK AIR BAG SLIDING CONTACT			
• Disconnect speed control actuator switch assembly. • Measure resistance across each of the air bag sliding contact windings between the air bag sliding contact connector at the base of steering column and speed control switches connector in the steering wheel. • **Is each resistance reading between 0.25-0.5 ohm?**	Yes No	▶ ▶	GO to **A16**. REPLACE air bag sliding contact.
A16 CHECK FOR OPEN CIRCUIT BETWEEN AIR BAG SLIDING CONTACT AND SPEED CONTROL SERVO			
• Measure resistance in Circuits 151 (LB/BK) and 848 (DG/O) between air bag sliding contact connector at base of steering column and speed control servo. • **Is each resistance reading less than five ohms?**	Yes No	▶ ▶	REPLACE speed control actuator switch assembly. SERVICE open in Circuit 151 (LB/BK) or Circuit 848 (DG/O).
A17 CHECK FOR STUCK COMMAND SWITCHES			
• With no steering wheel switches pressed, measure resistance between Pin 5 (Circuit 151 (LB/BK)) and Pin 6 (Circuit 848 (DG/O)). • **Is resistance greater than 3k ohm?**	Yes No	▶ ▶	GO to **A18**. REPLACE speed control actuator switch assembly.
A18 CHECK SET/ACCEL SWITCH OPERATION			
• With the SET/ACCEL switch pressed, measure resistance between Pin 5 (Circuit 151 (LB/BK)) and Pin 6 (Circuit 848 (DG/O)). • **Is resistance between 646 and 714 ohms?**	Yes No	▶ ▶	GO to **A19**. REPLACE speed control actuator switch assembly.
A19 CHECK VSS CIRCUIT			
• Measure resistance between Pin 3 (Circuit 679 (GY/BK) and Pin 10 (Circuit 676 (PK/O) or 57 (BK)). • **Is resistance between 200 and 300 ohms?**	Yes No	▶ ▶	GO to **A21**. GO to **A20**.
A20 CHECK VSS			
• Remove VSS connector. • Measure resistance across VSS terminals. • **Is resistance between 200 and 300 ohms?**	Yes No	▶ ▶	CHECK for opens or shorts in Circuit 679 (GY/BK) or 676 (PK/O). REPLACE vehicle speed sensor.
A21 CHECK FOR BROKEN OR BINDING CABLE			
• Remove speed control actuator from speed control servo. • Check for broken or binding cable by pulling on cable ball slug to ensure throttle moves freely. • **Is cable OK?**	Yes No	▶ ▶	REPLACE speed control servo. REPLACE speed control actuator

FM1109400232030X

Fig. 103   Test A: Speed Control Inoperative (Part 3 of 4). 1993-94 Crown Victoria, Grand Marquis, Mark VIII & Town Car

TEST STEP	RESULT	▶	ACTION TO TAKE
A22 CHECK COAST SWITCH OPERATION			
• Disconnect 14290 harness connector from speed control servo. • With COAST switch pressed, measure resistance between Pin 5 (Circuit 151 (LB/BK)) and Pin 6 (Circuit 848 (DG/O)) while rotating steering wheel through full range. • **Is resistance between 114 and 126 ohms?**	Yes No	▶ ▶	GO to **A23**. REPLACE speed control actuator switch assembly. RECONNECT speed control servo.
A23 CHECK COMMAND SWITCH RETURN CIRCUIT			
• Measure resistance between Pin 6 (Circuit 848 (DG/O)) and Pin 10 (GND, Circuit 676 (PK/O)[2], 57 (BK)[3]). • **Is resistance greater than one ohm?**	Yes No	▶ ▶	REPLACE speed control servo. SERVICE short in Circuit 848 (DG/O). RECONNECT speed control servo.
A24 CHECK SET/ACCEL SWITCH OPERATION			
• Disconnect 14290 harness connector from speed control servo. • With SET/ACCEL switch pressed, measure resistance between Pin 5 (Circuit 151 (LB/BK)) and Pin 6 (Circuit 848 (DG/O)) while rotating steering wheel through full range. • **Is resistance between 646 and 714 ohms?**	Yes No	▶ ▶	GO to **A25**. REPLACE speed control actuator switch assembly. RECONNECT speed control servo.
A25 CHECK COMMAND SWITCH RETURN CIRCUIT			
• Measure resistance between Pin 6 (Circuit 848 (DG/O)) and Pin 10 (GND Circuit 676 (PK/O)[2] or 57 (BK)[3]). • **Is resistance greater than one ohm?**	Yes No	▶ ▶	REPLACE speed control servo. SERVICE short in Circuit 848 (DG/O). RECONNECT speed control servo.
A26 CHECK RESUME SWITCH OPERATION			
• Disconnect 14290 harness connector from speed control servo assembly. • With RESUME switch pressed, measure resistance between Pin 5 (Circuit 151 (LB/BK)) and Pin 6 (Circuit 848 (DG/O)) while rotating steering wheel through full range. • **Is resistance between 2090 and 2310 ohms?**	Yes No	▶ ▶	GO to **A27**. REPLACE speed control actuator switch assembly. RECONNECT speed control servo.
A27 CHECK COMMAND SWITCH RETURN CIRCUIT			
• Measure resistance between Pin 6 (Circuit 848 (DG/O)) and Pin 10 (GND Circuit 676 (PK/O)[2] or 57 (BK)[3]). • **Is resistance greater than one ohm?**	Yes No	▶ ▶	REPLACE speed control servo. SERVICE short in Circuit 848 (DG/O). RECONNECT speed control servo.
A28 CHECK OFF SWITCH OPERATION			
• Disconnect 14290 harness connector from speed control servo. • With OFF switch pressed, measure resistance between Pin 5 (Circuit 151 (LB/BK)) and Pin 6 (Circuit 848 (DG/O)) while rotating steering wheel through full range. • **Is resistance less than four ohms?**	Yes No	▶ ▶	REPLACE speed control servo. REPLACE speed control actuator switch assembly. RECONNECT speed control servo.

FM1109400232040X

Fig. 103   Test A: Speed Control Inoperative (Part 4 of 4). 1993-94 Crown Victoria, Grand Marquis, Mark VIII & Town Car

TEST STEP	RESULT	▶	ACTION TO TAKE
B1 VERIFY CONDITION OCCURS ONLY WHILE USING SPEED CONTROL			
• Verify that engine is properly tuned. • Verify that condition does not occur when driving without speed control. • **Does condition occur without speed control?**	Yes No	▶ ▶	 GO to **B2**.
B2 CHECK FOR BINDING IN SPEED CONTROL ACTUATOR CABLE AND THROTTLE BODY LINKAGE			
• Check for binding or sticking of speed control actuator cable or throttle linkage and throttle plate. • Make sure throttle cable bracket and speed control servo bracket are not loose. • **Are components OK?**	Yes No	▶ ▶	GO to **B3**. SERVICE as required.
B3 CHECK VSS			
• Remove VSS connector. • Measure resistance across sensor terminals. • **Is resistance between 200 and 300 ohms?**	Yes No	▶ ▶	CHECK continuity across Circuit 679 (GY/BK) and 676 (PK/O). GO to **B4**. REPLACE vehicle speed sensor.
B4 CHECK SPEED CONTROL SERVO ASSEMBLY			
• Substitute known good speed control servo. • Test vehicle for proper operation. • **Does system operate properly?**	Yes No	▶ ▶	REPLACE speed control servo. CHECK MAP sensor and EGR valve position (EVP).

FM1109400233000X

Fig. 104   Test B: Set Speed Fluctuates. 1993-94 Crown Victoria, Grand Marquis, Mark VIII & Town Car

TEST STEP	RESULT	▶	ACTION TO TAKE
C1 CHECK DEACTIVATOR SWITCH CIRCUIT			
• Turn ignition switch to RUN. • Disconnect 14290 harness connector from the speed control servo. • With no brakes applied, place a 12 Volt Circuit Test Light between Pin 9 (Circuit 636 (O)) and Pin 10 (GND, Circuit 57 (BK)). • **Is the light illuminated?**	Yes No	▶ ▶	GO to **C2**. GO to **A1**.
C2 CHECK DEACTIVATOR SWITCH OPERATION			
• Leave ignition switch in RUN position. • Fully apply brakes with the 12 Volt Circuit Test Light still between Pin 9 (Circuit 636 (O)) and Pin 10 (GND, Circuit 57 (BK)). • **Does the light turn off?**	Yes No	▶ ▶	GO to **C3**. REPLACE deactivator switch.
C3 CHECK STOPLIGHT SWITCH CIRCUIT			
• With brakes applied, measure voltage between Pin 4 (Circuit 511 (LG)) and Pin 10 (GND, Circuit 57 (BK)). • **Is there battery voltage?**	Yes No	▶ ▶	GO to **C4**. SERVICE stoplight switch, Fuse 7 or open in Circuit 511 (LG) or Circuit 10 (LG/R). RECONNECT speed control servo.

FM1109400234010X

Fig. 105   Test C: Speed Control Does Not Disengage When Brakes Are Applied (Part 1 of 2). 1993-94 Crown Victoria, Grand Marquis, Mark VIII & Town Car

TEST STEP	RESULT	▶	ACTION TO TAKE
C4 CHECK FOR BINDS IN SPEED CONTROL ACTUATOR CABLE AND THROTTLE LINKAGE ATTACHMENT			
• Remove speed control actuator cable from speed control servo. • Check for broken or binding cable by pulling on cable ball slug to ensure throttle moves freely. • **Is cable OK?**	Yes No	▶ ▶	REPLACE speed control servo. SERVICE as required. RECONNECT speed control servo.

FM1109400234020X

Fig. 105   Test C: Speed Control Does Not Disengage When Brakes Are Applied (Part 2 of 2). 1993-94 Crown Victoria, Grand Marquis, Mark VIII & Town Car

	TEST STEP	RESULT	▶	ACTION TO TAKE
D1	CHECK VOLTAGE AT SPEED CONTROL SERVO ASSEMBLY CONNECTOR			
	• Disconnect 14401 harness connector from speed control servo.	Yes	▶	GO to D3.
	• With ignition switch in RUN, measure voltage between Pin 1 (Circuit 203 (O/LB) and Pin 10 (GND Circuit 676 (PK/O)⁵ or 57 (BK)⁶).	No	▶	GO to D2.
	• Is voltage approximately five volts?			
D2	CHECK CIRCUIT CONTINUITY			
	• Measure resistance of Circuit 203 (O/LB) from Pin 1 of speed control servo connector to instrument cluster connector.	Yes	▶	GO to D3.
	• Is resistance less than one ohm?	No	▶	SERVICE open in Circuit 203 (O/LB).
D3	DISPLAY TURN ON TEST			
	• With ignition switch in RUN, connect Pin 1 (Circuit 203 (O/LB)) to Pin 10 (GND Circuit 676⁵ (PK/O) or 57 (BK)⁶).	Yes	▶	REPLACE speed control servo and REPEAT test.
	• Does Speed Control display turn on?	No	▶	SERVICE instrument cluster.

FM1109400235000X

Fig. 106   Test D: Speed Control Indicator Does Not Turn On. 1993-94 Crown Victoria, Grand Marquis, Mark VIII & Town Car

	TEST STEP	RESULT	▶	ACTION TO TAKE
E1	CHECK CIRCUIT 203			
	• Check for short to ground in Circuit 203 (O/LB).	Yes	▶	SERVICE Circuit 203 (O/LB).
	• Is there a short?	No	▶	SERVICE instrument cluster.

FM1109400236000X

Fig. 107   Test E: Speed Control Indicator Does Not Turn Off. 1993-94 Crown Victoria, Grand Marquis, Mark VIII & Town Car

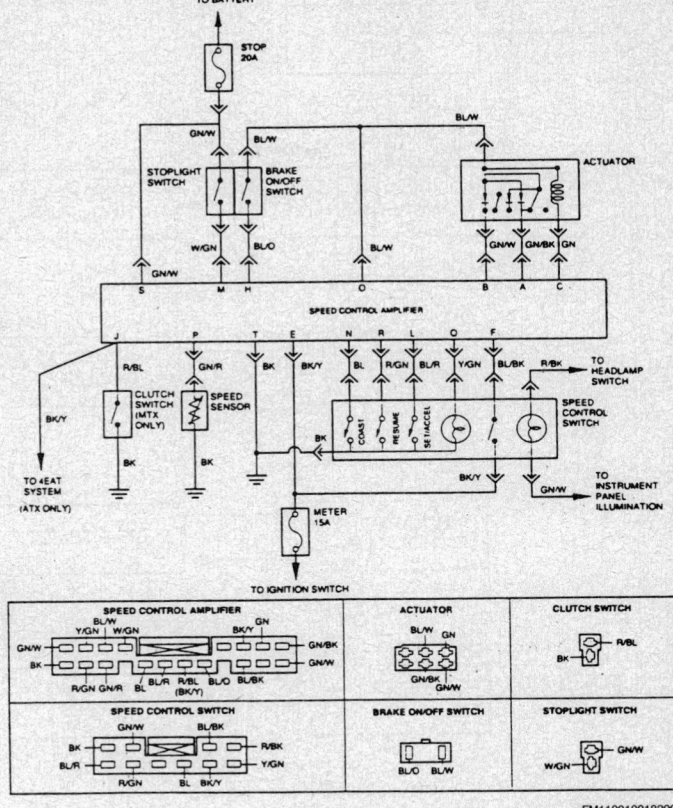

FM1109100182000X

Fig. 109   Wiring circuit. 1992 Probe w/2.2L/4-133 turbo

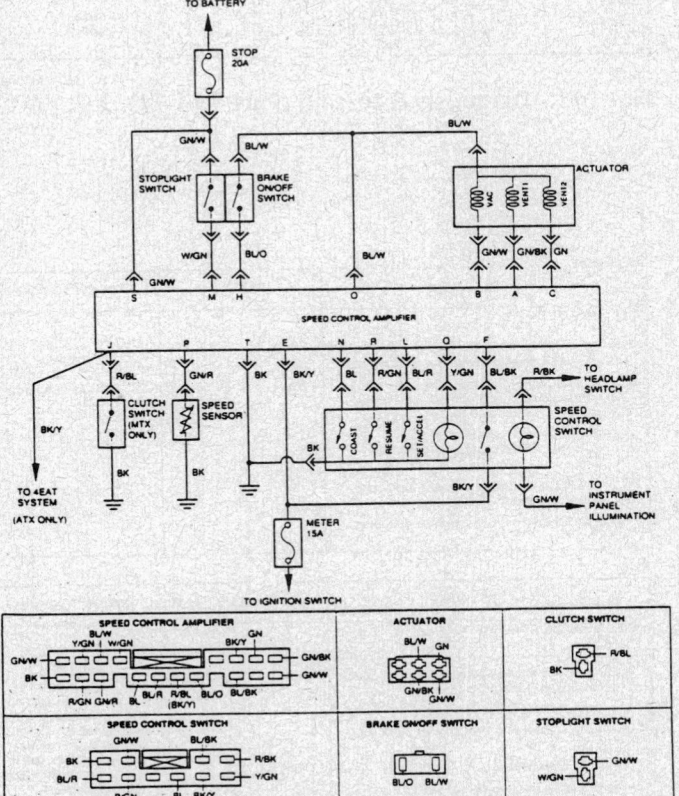

FM1109100181000X

Fig. 108   Wiring circuit. 1992 Probe w/2.2L/4-133 less turbo

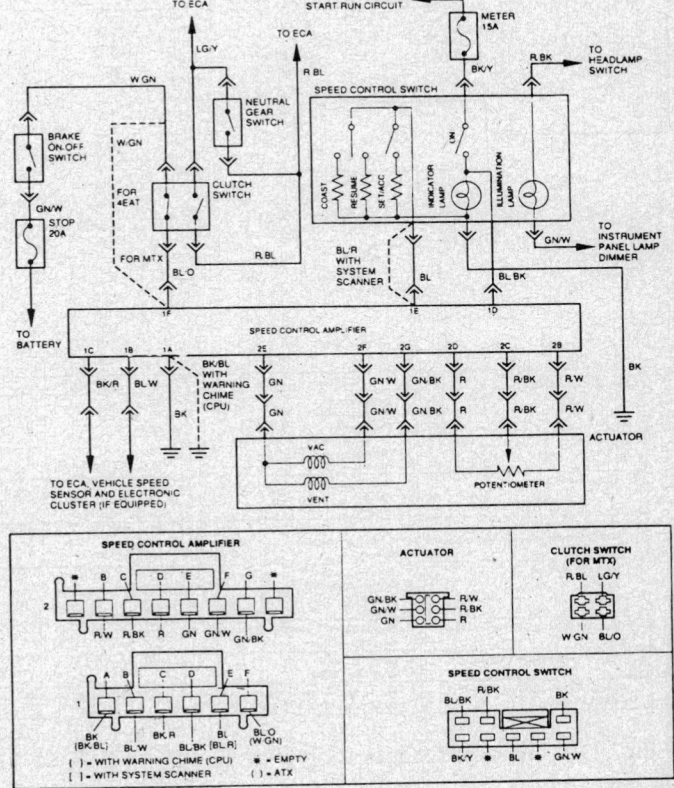

FM1109200184000X

Fig. 110   Wiring circuit. 1992 Probe w/3.0L/V6-182

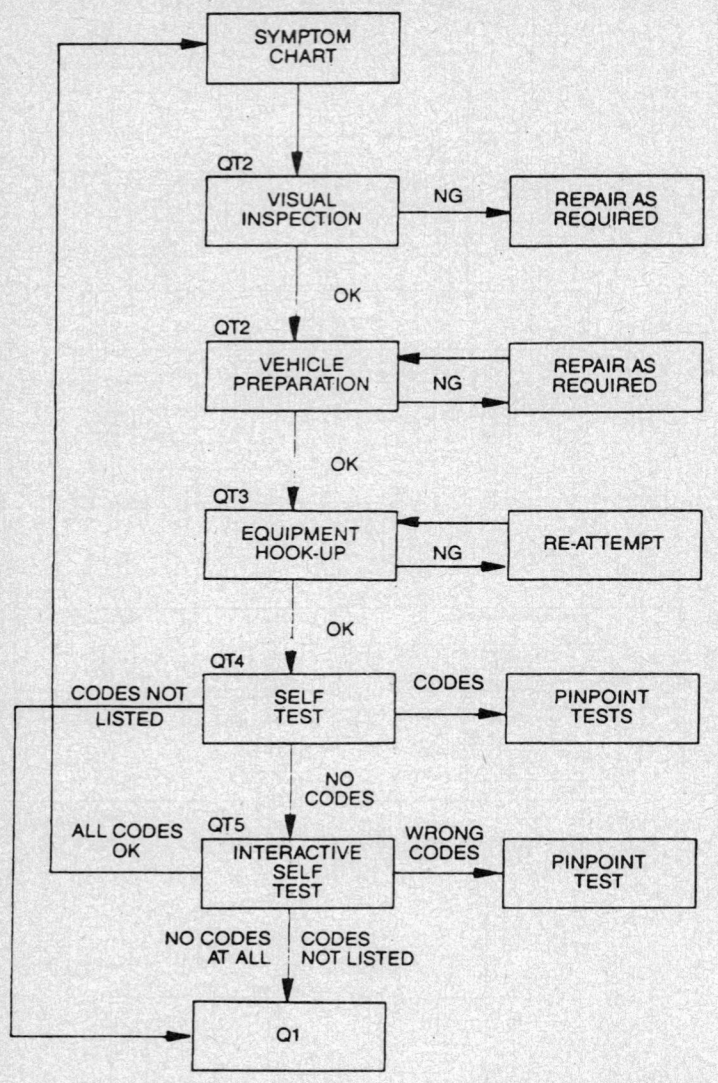

Fig. 111 Diagnosis & testing (Part 1 of 14). 2.2L/4-133

FM1109100185010X

Codes	Code Pattern	Component
Code Number		
Code 1		Actuator
Code 5		Stop Fuse
Code 7		Brake On/Off Switches
Code 11		Control Switches
Code 15		Control Amplifier
Code 21		Set Switch
Code 22		Coast Switch
Code 23		Resume Switch
Code 31		Brake On/Off Switches
Code 35		Clutch Or Manual Lever Position Switches
Code 37		Speed Sensor

FM1109100185030X

Fig. 111 Diagnosis & testing (Part 3 of 14). 2.2L/4-133

CONDITION	POSSIBLE SOURCE	ACTION
• Will Not Set	• Vacuum hose. • Actuator cable. • Switches. • Control amplifier. • Actuator. • Circuit.	• GO to T1. • GO to QT1.
• Intermittent Operation	• Control amplifier. • Actuator. • Circuit.	• GO to QT1
• RESUME, COAST and/or ACCELERATION Switches Do Not Work	• Switches. • Control amplifier. • Circuit.	• GO to QT1.
• Speed Fluctuates	• Actuator cable. • Control amplifier. • Switches. • Circuit.	• GO to T1. • GO to QT1.
• Does Not Disengage With Brakes	• Brake ON/OFF switch(es). • Control amplifier.	• GO to QT1.
• Does Not Disengage With Clutch	• Clutch switch. • Control amplifier.	• GO to QT1.
• Abnormal Operation in COAST or ACCELERATION	• Steering wheel slip rings and brush assembly lubrication.	• REFER to "Steering Columns."

FM1109100185020X

Fig. 111 Diagnosis & testing (Part 2 of 14). 2.2L/4-133

	TEST STEP	RESULT	▶	ACTION TO TAKE
QT1	VISUAL CHECK			
	• Check the following components for damage: —Speed Control System harness for proper connections, bent or broken pins, corrosion, loose wires and proper routing. —Speed Control Amplifier, Sensors, Switches, and Actuators for physical damage. —Speed Control Actuator cable for routing, corrosion, bends, and binding. • Are all Speed Control System components OK?	Yes No	▶ ▶	GO to QT2 . REPAIR as required.

	TEST STEP	RESULT	▶	ACTION TO TAKE
QT2	VEHICLE PREPARATION			
	• Perform all the following safety steps required to run Speed Control Quick Test: —Apply Parking Brake. —Place shift lever in PARK (NEUTRAL on MTX). —Block drive wheels. —Turn off all electrical loads such as Headlamps, Radios, A/C-Heater, Blower Fans, Wipers, etc. • Have all safety steps been performed and all electrical loads turned off?	Yes No	▶ ▶	GO to QT3 . Personal safety and correct diagnostic results are dependent on Test Step QT2. Do not proceed with Quick Test if vehicle preparation cannot be performed.

FM1109100185040X

Fig. 111 Diagnosis & testing (Part 4 of 14). 2.2L/4-133

TEST STEP	RESULT	►	ACTION TO TAKE
QT3 EQUIPMENT HOOKUP • Turn ignition key OFF. • Locate the Speed Control Amplifier. • Connect a test lamp between "GN/W" and the open terminal on the Speed Control Amplifier as shown (leave the amplifier connector connected). 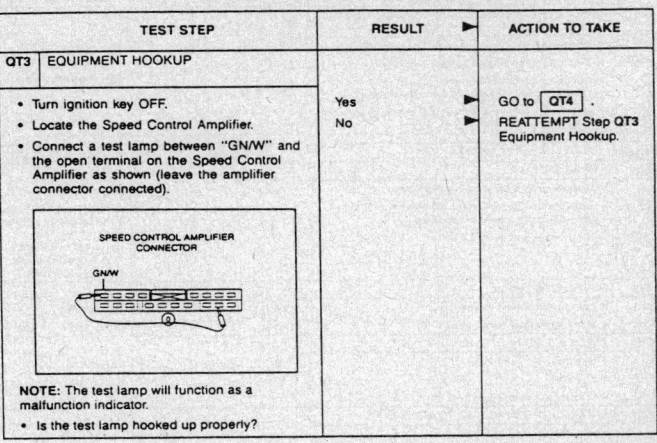 NOTE: The test lamp will function as a malfunction indicator. • Is the test lamp hooked up properly?	Yes No	► ►	GO to QT4 . REATTEMPT Step QT3 Equipment Hookup.

FM1109100185050X

Fig. 111   Diagnosis & testing (Part 5 of 14).
2.2L/4-133

TEST STEP	RESULT	►	ACTION TO TAKE
QT4 SELF TEST • Turn ignition key OFF. • Speed Control main switch OFF. • Verify that the vehicle has been properly prepared per Quick Test Steps QT2 and QT3. • Turn ignition key to the ON position. • Turn Speed Control main switch ON. • Move control lever upward to RESUME position and hold it more than 3 seconds. • Release control lever. The test lamp should illuminate for 3 seconds, and then go out for 2 seconds. • The Speed Control Unit is now in self test mode. • The test lamp will now indicate any codes that have been triggered.	Code 1 (Actuator) Code 5 (Stop Fuse) Code 7 (Brake ON/OFF Switch) Code 11 (Control Switch) Code 15 (Amplifier) No Codes Codes Not Listed	► ► ► ► ► ► ►	GO to SP1 . GO to SU1 . GO to SP2 . GO to SP6 . GO to SU1 . GO to QT5 . GO to SU1 .

FM1109100185060X

Fig. 111   Diagnosis & testing (Part 6 of 14).
2.2L/4-133

TEST STEP	RESULT	►	ACTION TO TAKE
QT5 INTERACTIVE SELF TEST • Turn ignition switch OFF. • Speed Control main switch OFF. • Verify that the vehicle has been properly prepared per Quick Test Steps QT2 and QT3. • Turn ignition switch ON. For ATX, move the shift lever to D or R position. • Move control lever to RESUME position and hold it. • Turn main control switch to ON. • Release RESUME lever. • The system is now in Interactive self test mode. • Verify the chart below:	Yes No (Code 21) No (Code 22) No (Code 31) No (Code 35, ATX) No (Code 35, MTX) No (Code 37) No (Codes Not Listed) No Codes At All	► ► ► ► ► ► ► ► ►	RETURN to Symptom Chart. GO to SP6 . GO to SP6 . GO to SP2 . GO to SP9 . GO to SP10 . GO to SP13 . GO to SU1 . GO to SU1 .

Input/Depress/Select	Code
SET/COAST BUTTON	21
COAST/ACCEL Button	22
Brake On/Off Switch	31
Shifter in "P" or "N" (ATX)	35
Clutch Switch (MTX)	35
Drive Vehicle Above 25 MPH (Speed Sensor)	37

• Does the corresponding code flash from the test lamp when each input is exercised?

FM1109100185070X

Fig. 111   Diagnosis & testing (Part 7 of 14).
2.2L/4-133

TEST STEP	RESULT	►	ACTION TO TAKE
SP1 ACTUATOR SIGNALS CHECK • Key OFF. • Disconnect Speed Control Amplifier and Actuator Connectors. • Ground the "GN/BK", "GN/W", "GN" and "BL/W" wires at the Speed Control Amplifier leading to the Actuator. • Check for continuity between ground and the "BN/BK", "GN/W", "GN" and "BL/W" wires at the Actuator. • Is there continuity?	Yes No	► ►	GO to SP2. REPAIR the wire in question between the Speed Control Amplifier and the Actuator.
SP2 BRAKE ON/OFF SIGNAL CHECK • Disconnect the Speed Control Amplifier. • Measure the resistance between the "BL/W" and "BL/O" wires at the Speed Control Amplifier. • Is the resistance less than 5 Ohms with the brake released and greater than 10,000 Ohms with the brake depressed?	Yes No	► ►	GO to SP5. GO to SP3.
SP3 BRAKE ON/OFF SIGNAL CHECK • Disconnect the Speed Control Amplifier. • Disconnect brake ON/OFF switch. • Measure the resistance of the "BL/W" wire between the Speed Control Amplifier and the "BL/W" wire on the brake ON/OFF switch. • Is the resistance less than 5 Ohms?	Yes No	► ►	GO to SP4. REPAIR "BL/W" wire between the Speed Control Amplifier and the Brake ON/OFF switch.
SP4 BRAKE ON/OFF SIGNAL CHECK • Disconnect the Speed Control Amplifier. • Disconnect the brake ON/OFF switch. • Measure the resistance between the "BL/O" wire at the Speed Control Amplifier and the "BL/O" wire at the brake ON/OFF switch. • Is the resistance less than 5 OHMs?	Yes No	► ►	REPLACE Brake ON/OFF switch. REPAIR "BL/O" wire between the Speed Control Amplifier and the brake On/Off switch.
SP5 BRAKE ON/OFF SIGNAL CHECK NOTE: Before beginning this Test Step, be sure the Brake Lamp System is operational. • Disconnect the Speed Control Amplifier connector. • Measure the voltage on the "W/GN" wire at the Speed Control Amplifier connector. • Is the voltage greater than 10.5V with the brake pedal depressed and less than 0.5V with the brake pedal released?	Yes 2.2L Non-Turbo Yes 2.2L Turbo No	► ► ►	GO to SU9. GO to SU7. REPAIR the "W/GN" wire between the brake ON/OFF switch and the Speed Control Amplifier.
SP6 SPEED CONTROL SWITCH GROUND CHECK • Disconnect the speed control switch. • Measure the resistance between the "BK" wire at the speed control switch and ground. • Is the resistance less than 5 ohms?	Yes No	► ►	GO to SP7. REPAIR "BK" wire from the Speed Control Switch and ground.

FM1109100185080X

Fig. 111   Diagnosis & testing (Part 8 of 14). 2.2L/4-133

TEST STEP	RESULT	►	ACTION TO TAKE
SP7 SPEED CONTROL SWITCH CHECK • Connect the Speed Control Amplifier and Speed Control Switch. • Check function of the Speed Control Switch by measuring the resistance of the following wire colors between the switch and ground.	Yes No	► ►	GO to SP8. REPLACE the Speed Control Switch.

Coast: "BL" wire	Depressed — Less than 5 ohms Released — Greater than 10,000 ohms
Resume: "R/GN"	Depressed — Less than 5 ohms Released — Greater than 10,000 ohms
Set/Accel: "BL/R"	Depressed — Less than 5 ohms Released — Greater than 10,000 ohms

• Are the resistances verified?

TEST STEP	RESULT	►	ACTION TO TAKE
SP8 CHECK LEAD BETWEEN SPEED CONTROL SWITCH AND SPEED CONTROL AMPLIFIER • Key OFF. • Disconnect the Speed Control Amplifier and the Speed Control Switch connectors. • Measure the resistance of the following wires between the Amplifier connector and the Switch connector. Wire "BL" "R/GN" "BL/R" • Are the resistances less than 5 ohms?	Yes No	► ►	REPLACE the Speed Control Switch. SERVICE the wire in question.

FM1109100185090X

Fig. 111   Diagnosis & testing (Part 9 of 14). 2.2L/4-133

TEST STEP	RESULT	▶	ACTION TO TAKE
SP9 — **PARK/NEUTRAL SIGNAL CHECK (ATX)**			
• Disconnect the Speed Control Amplifier connector.	Yes	▶	Check starting system electrical circuit.
• Measure the voltage on the "BK/Y" wire at the Speed Control Amplifier connector under the following conditions:	No	▶	SERVICE the "BK/Y" wire.

Shift Selector	Voltage
Park	0V
Reverse	10V
Neutral	0V
Drive	10V
Drive	10V
Low	10V

TEST STEP	RESULT	▶	ACTION TO TAKE
• Are the approximate voltages verified?			
SP10 — **CLUTCH SWITCH SIGNAL CHECK**			
• Disconnect the Speed Control Amplifier.	Yes	▶	GO to SP13.
• Measure the resistance between ground and the "R/BL" wire at the Speed Control Amplifier.	No	▶	GO to SP11.
• Is the resistance less than 5 Ohms with the clutch pedal depressed and greater than 10,000 Ohms with the clutch pedal released?			
SP11 — **CLUTCH SWITCH SIGNAL CHECK**			
• Disconnect the Speed Control Amplifier.	Yes	▶	REPAIR the "R/BL" wire between the Clutch Switch and the Speed Control Amplifier
• Measure the resistance between ground and the "R/BL" wire at the clutch switch.			
• Is the resistance less than 5 Ohms with the clutch pedal depressed and greater than 10,000 Ohms with the clutch pedal released?	No	▶	GO to SP12.
SP12 — **CLUTCH SWITCH GROUND CHECK**			
• Disconnect the clutch switch.	Yes	▶	REPLACE the Clutch Switch.
• Measure the resistance between the "BK" wire at the clutch switch and ground.	No	▶	REPAIR the "BK" wire to ground.
• Is the resistance less than 5 ohms?			

FM1109100185100X

Fig. 111   Diagnosis & testing (Part 10 of 14). 2.2L/4-133

TEST STEP	RESULT	▶	ACTION TO TAKE
SP13 — **SPEED SENSOR INPUT CHECK**			
NOTE: For vehicles equipped with conventional instrumentation, the Speed Sensor is located in the Instrument Cluster with a "GN/R" wire. For vehicles equipped with the electronic instrumentation, the Speed Sensor is located on the transaxle with a "Y/W" wire.	Yes (Conventional Cluster)	▶	GO to SP15.
	Yes (Electronic Cluster)	▶	GO to SP14.
• Disconnect the Speed Control Amplifier.	No	▶	REPAIR the "GN/R" wire between the Speed Sensor and Speed Control Amplifier.
• Disconnect the Vehicle Speed Sensor. Refer to the illustration for analog connector location.			
• Measure the resistance between the "GN/R" wire at the Speed Control Amplifier and the Vehicle Speed Sensor.			
• Is the resistance less than 5 Ohms?			

TEST STEP	RESULT	▶	ACTION TO TAKE
SP14 — **SPEED SENSOR SIGNAL CHECK (ELECTRONIC CLUSTER)**			
• Disconnect the Speed Sensor.	Yes	▶	GO to SU1.
• Measure the resistance between the terminals of the Speed Sensor.	No	▶	REPLACE the Speed Sensor. Refer to the NOTE in SP13 for Speed Sensor location.
• Is the resistance between 175 and 225 Ohms?			

FM1109100185110X

Fig. 111   Diagnosis & testing (Part 11 of 14). 2.2L/4-133

TEST STEP	RESULT	▶	ACTION TO TAKE
SP15 — **SPEED SENSOR SIGNAL CHECK (CONVENTIONAL CLUSTER)**			
• Disconnect the Speedometer Cable at the Transaxle.	Yes	▶	GO to SU1.
• Disconnect the Speed Control Amplifier.	No	▶	REPLACE the Speedometer Head.
• Check for continuity between ground and the "GN/R" wire at the Speed Control Amplifier.			
• Does continuity exist 4 times per one Speedometer Cable rotation?			

TEST STEP	RESULT	▶	ACTION TO TAKE
SU1 — **KAPWR CHECK**			
• Disconnect the Speed Control amplifier.	Yes	▶	GO to SU2.
• Measure the voltage on the "GN/W" wire at the Speed Control Amplifier connector.	No	▶	CHECK the "STOP" fuse. If the fuse is OK, REPAIR the "GN/W" wire between the Speed Control Amplifier and Battery (+) terminal
• Is the voltage above 10.5 volts?			
SU2 — **METER FUSE CHECK**			
• Locate the interior Fuse panel.	Yes	▶	GO to SU5.
• Is the 15A Meter fuse good?	No	▶	GO to SU3.
SU3 — **CHECK SYSTEM**			
• Replace the blown fuse.	Yes	▶	GO to SU4.
• Key ON.	No	▶	GO to SU5.
• Did the fuse blow again?			
SU4 — **CHECK FOR POWER START TO GROUND**			
• Key OFF.	Yes	▶	SERVICE the "BK/Y" wire.
• Disconnect the "BK/Y" wire from the interior fuse panel.	No	▶	GO to SU5.
• Measure the resistance of the "BK/Y" wire between the fuse panel and ground.			
• Is the resistance less than 5 Ohms?			
• Reinstall the "BK/Y" wire.			
SU5 — **KEYPWR CHECK**			
• Disconnect the Speed Control Amplifier.	Yes	▶	GO to SU6.
• Measure the voltage on the "BK/Y" wire at the Speed Control Amplifier Connector.	No	▶	REPAIR the "BK/Y" wire between the Speed Control Unit and the ignition switch.
• Is the voltage above 10.5V with the ignition switch on and below 1.5 volts with the ignition switch off?			
SU6 — **SPEED CONTROL POWER CHECK**			
• Key ON.	Yes	▶	GO to SU9.
• Disconnect the Speed Control Amplifier.	No	▶	GO to SU7.
• Measure the voltage on the "BL/BK" wire at the Speed Control Amplifier.			
• Is the voltage greater than 10.5 volts with the main speed control switch on and less than 1.5 volts with the switch off?			

FM1109100185120X

Fig. 111   Diagnosis & testing (Part 12 of 14). 2.2L/4-133

TEST STEP	RESULT	▶	ACTION TO TAKE
SU7 — **SPEED CONTROL POWER CHECK**			
• Key ON.	Yes	▶	REPAIR the "BL/BK" wire between the main Speed Control Switch and the Speed Control Unit.
• Measure the voltage on the "BL/BK" wire at the main speed control switch.			
• Is the voltage above 10.5 volts with the main speed control switch on and below 1.5 volts with the switch off?	No	▶	GO to SU8.
SU8 — **SPEED CONTROL POWER CHECK**			
• Key ON.	Yes	▶	REPLACE the Speed Control Switch.
• Disconnect the speed control switch.	No	▶	REPAIR the "BK/Y" wire between the Speed Control Switch and the ignition switch.
• Measure the voltage on the "BK/Y" wire at the speed control switch.			
• Is the voltage above 10.5 volts with the ignition switch on and below 1.5 volts with the ignition switch off?			
SU9 — **SPEED CONTROL GROUND CHECK**			
• Key OFF.	Yes 2.2L Turbo	▶	GO to SU11.
• Disconnect the Speed Control Amplifier.	Yes 2.2L Non-Turbo	▶	GO to SU10.
• Measure the resistance between the "BK" wire at the Speed Control Amplifier and ground.	No	▶	REPAIR the "BK" wire between the Speed Control Amplifier and ground.
• Is the resistance less than 5 ohms?			
SU10 — **CHECK ACTUATOR RESISTANCE (2.2L NON-TURBO)**			
• Key OFF.	Yes	▶	GO to SU12.
• Disconnect the Actuator connector.	No	▶	REPLACE the Speed Control Amplifier.
• Reconnect the amplifier connector.			
• Measure the resistance between the actuator terminals as shown:			

Terminals	Resistance
"BL/W" — "GN"	60-90 ohms
"BL/W" — "GN/BK"	60-90 ohms
"BL/W" — "GN/W"	60-90 ohms
"GN" — "GN/BK"	150-190 ohms
"GN" — "GN/W"	150-190 ohms
"GN/BK" — "GN/W"	150-190 ohms

TEST STEP	RESULT	▶	ACTION TO TAKE
• Are the resistances verified?			
SU11 — **CHECK ACTUATOR RESISTANCE (2.2L TURBO)**			
• Disconnect the Actuator Connector.	Yes	▶	GO to SU12.
• Measure resistance between terminals as shown:	No	▶	REPLACE the Speed Control Amplifier.

Terminals	Resistance
"GN" — "BL/W"	90-120 ohms
"GN" — "GN/BK"	90-120 ohms
"GN" — "GN/W"	90-120 ohms
"BL/W" — "GN/BK"	5-25 ohms
"BL/W" — "GN/W"	5-25 ohms
"GN/BK" — "GN/W"	5-25 ohms

• Are the resistances correct?

FM1109100185130X

Fig. 111   Diagnosis & testing (Part 13 of 14). 2.2L/4-133

TEST STEP	RESULT	▶	ACTION TO TAKE
SU12 CHECK ACTUATOR OPERATION (2.2L NON-TURBO AND 2.2L TURBO) • Reconnect all Speed Control System related connectors. • Start engine. • Drive the vehicle on road or hoist at 35 mph. • Verify the operation of the Speed Control System as shown below:	Yes No	▶ ▶	RETURN to the Symptom Chart. REPLACE the Actuator.

Action to Take	Result
Press "ON"	"ON" indicator illuminates
Press "SET"	Speed holds at 35 mph
Press "ACCEL"	Speed increases gradually
Press and hold "COAST" for 5 seconds	Speed decreases until released
Depress brake pedal	Speed decreases
Press "RESUME" (above 30 mph)	Speed increases to last set speed
Press "OFF"	"ON" indicator shuts off and speed decreases

• Are functions verified?

2.2L Non-Turbo Only

TEST STEP	RESULT	▶	ACTION TO TAKE
T1 CHECK VACUUM SUPPLY • Key ON, engine idling. • Connect vacuum gauge to actuator vacuum hose. • Increase engine speed to 2000 RPM. • Is vacuum present? NOTE: 2.5 in-Hg vacuum is minimum for normal operation.	Yes No	▶ ▶	GO to T2. SERVICE vacuum hose.
T2 CHECK CABLE ADJUSTMENT • Check cable deflection at actuator. • Does cable have 1-3 mm of deflection?	Yes No	▶ ▶	RETURN to Symptom Chart. ADJUST cable.

FM1109100185140X

Fig. 111 Diagnosis & testing (Part 14 of 14). 2.2L/4-133

CONDITION	POSSIBLE SOURCE	ACTION
• Will Not Set	• Vacuum hose. • Actuator cable. • Switches. • Control amplifier. • Actuator. • Circuit.	• GO to T1. • GO to U1.
• Intermittent Operation	• Control amplifier. • Actuator. • Circuit.	• GO to U1.
• RESUME, COAST and/or ACCELERATION Switches Do Not Work	• Switches. • Control amplifier. • Circuit.	• GO to U6.
• Speed Fluctuates	• Actuator cable. • Control amplifier. • Switches. • Circuit.	• GO to T1. • GO to U1.
• Does Not Disengage With Brakes	• BOO switch(es). • Control amplifier.	• GO to U1.
• Does Not Disengage With Clutch	• Clutch switch. • Control amplifier.	• GO to U1.
• Abnormal Operation In COAST Or ACCELERATION	• Steering wheel slip rings and brush assembly lubrication.	

FM1109200187000X

Fig. 112 Symptom chart. 1992 3.0L/V6-182

TEST STEP	RESULT	▶	ACTION TO TAKE
T1 CHECK VACUUM SUPPLY • Key ON, engine idling. • Connect a vacuum gauge to actuator vacuum hose. • Increase the engine speed to 2000 RPM. • Is the vacuum present? NOTE: 2.5 in-Hg vacuum is minimum for normal operation.	Yes No	▶ ▶	GO to T2. SERVICE vacuum hose.
T2 CHECK CABLE ADJUSTMENT • Check the cable deflection at the actuator as shown. • Does the cable have 1-3mm of deflection?	Yes No	▶ ▶	GO to T3. ADJUST cable.
T3 CHECK DUMP VALVE • Connect a vacuum pump to the dump valve hose at the actuator. • Apply 5-10 in-Hg vacuum. • Step on the brake pedal. • Is the vacuum held before stepping on the brake and released after stepping on the brake?	Yes No, vacuum always held No, vacuum never held	▶ ▶ ▶	RETURN to Symptom Chart. ADJUST or REPLACE dump valve. SERVICE hose at dump valve.

FM1109200188010X

Fig. 113 Diagnosis & testing (Part 1 of 5). 1992 3.0L/V6-182

TEST STEP	RESULT	▶	ACTION TO TAKE
U1 CHECK FUSES • Check the 20 amp STOP and 15 amp METER fuse. • Are the fuses OK? NOTE: If the fuse(s) fail after replacing and turning the key ON, service the "GN/W" wire and/or the "BK/Y" wire for a short to ground.	Yes No	▶ ▶	GO to U2. REPLACE the fuse(s) in question.
U2 CHECK BRAKE ON/OFF SWITCH • Disconnect the speed control amplifier. • Key ON. • Clutch pedal released (MTX). • Measure the voltage at the speed control amplifier 8 pin connector "W/GN" (4EAT) or "BL·O" (MTX). • Push the brake pedal. • Is the voltage above 10 volts with the brake pedal depressed and less than 1 volt with the brake pedal released?	Yes, 4EAT Yes, MTX No, 4EAT No, MTX	▶ ▶ ▶ ▶	GO to U5. GO to U4. SERVICE "W/GN" wire from speed control amplifier to brake On/Off switch. GO to U3.
U3 CHECK BRAKE ON/OFF TO CLUTCH SWITCH • Key ON. • Measure the voltage at the clutch switch "W/GN" wire. • Depress the brake pedal. • Is the voltage above 10 volts with the pedal depressed and less than 1 volt with the pedal released?	Yes No	▶ ▶	GO to U4. SERVICE "W/GN" wire from brake ON/OFF switch to clutch switch.

FM1109200188020X

Fig. 113 Diagnosis & testing (Part 2 of 5). 1992 3.0L/V6-182

TEST STEP	RESULT	▶	ACTION TO TAKE
U4 CHECK CLUTCH SWITCH • Disconnect the speed control amplifier. • Measure the voltage at the speed control amplifier 8 pin connector "BL/O" wire. • Key ON. • Depress the brake pedal. • Depress the clutch pedal. • Is the voltage greater than 10 volts with the clutch released and less than 1 volt with the clutch depressed?	Yes No	▶ ▶	GO to U5. SERVICE "BL/O" wire or clutch switch as required.
U5 CHECK POWER TO AMPLIFIER • Disconnect the speed control amplifier. • Key ON. • Measure the voltage at the speed control amplifier "BL/BK" wire (6 pin connector). • Are 10-14 volts present with the speed control ON and less than 1 volt present with the speed control OFF?	Yes No	▶ ▶	GO to U6. SERVICE "BL/BK" wire, or speed control On/Off switch.
U6 CHECK GROUND • Key OFF. • Disconnect the speed control amplifier. • Measure the resistance between the speed control amplifier "BK" wire ("BK/BL" wire if the vehicle is equipped with a warning chime) (6 pin connector) and ground (battery -). • Is the resistance less than 5 ohms?	Yes No	▶ ▶	GO to U7. SERVICE "BK" or "BK/BL" wire connection to ground
U7 CHECK CONTROL SWITCHES • Key OFF. • Disconnect the speed control amplifier. • Measure the resistance between the "BL" wire (6 pin connector) and ground (Battery -). • Actuate the switches.	Yes No	▶ ▶	GO to U8. SERVICE "BL" wire, switch ground ("BK" wire) or switch.

Switch	Resistance (ohms)
Set/Accel	646-714
Coast	114-146
Resume	2090-2310

• Are the resistances OK?

FM1109200188030X

Fig. 113 Diagnosis & testing (Part 3 of 5). 1992 3.0L/V6-182

TEST STEP	RESULT	▶	ACTION TO TAKE
U8 CHECK ACTUATOR • Key OFF. • Disconnect the speed control amplifier. • Measure the resistance between the following speed control amplifier wires: Wires / Resistance (ohms) GN-GN/W / 40-70 GN/W-GN/BK / 140-220 GN-GN/BK / 100-150 R-R/W / 40K-60K R/BK-R/W / 20K-30K • Are the resistances OK?	Yes No	▶ ▶	GO to **U9**. SERVICE wires in question, if all OK REPLACE actuator.
U9 CHECK ACTUATOR • Transmission in NEUTRAL. • Parking brake applied. • Wheels blocked. • Start the engine. • Speed control switch ON. • Jump the speed control amplifier "GN" to battery (+). • Jump the speed control amplifier "GN/BK" to battery (-). • Momentarily jump the speed control amplifier "GN/W" to battery (-). • Does the engine speed increase with the "GN/W" wire grounded and return to normal with the "GN/W" wire open?	Yes No	▶ ▶	TURN key OFF. GO to **U10**. REPLACE actuator.

FM1109200188040X

Fig. 113   Diagnosis & testing (Part 4 of 5). 1992 3.0L/V6-182

TEST STEP	RESULT	▶	ACTION TO TAKE
U10 CHECK SPEED SENSOR • Connect a voltmeter between the "BK/R" and "BL/W" wires at the speed control amplifier. • Place the voltmeter into the AC position. • Drive the vehicle at the rated speeds below and verify their corresponding voltages. Speed (mph) / Approximate Voltage (volts) 0 / 0 5 / .8 10 / 1.2 15 / 1.6 20 / 2.0 25 / 2.3 30 / 2.6 35 / 3.0 40 / 3.3 45 / 3.5 50 / 3.8 55 / 4.02 • Are the voltages correct?	Yes No	▶ ▶	REPLACE the speed control amplifier. GO to **U11**.
U11 CHECK SPEED SENSOR CONTINUITY • Key OFF. • Disconnect the speed sensor, speed control amplifier and ECA. • Measure the resistance of the "BK/R" and "BL/W" wires between the speed sensor connector, the speed control amplifier connector and the ECA connector. • Are the resistances less than 5 ohms?	Yes No	▶ ▶	REPLACE the speed sensor. SERVICE the wire in question.

FM1109200188050X

Fig. 113   Diagnosis & testing (Part 5 of 5). 1992 3.0L/V6-182

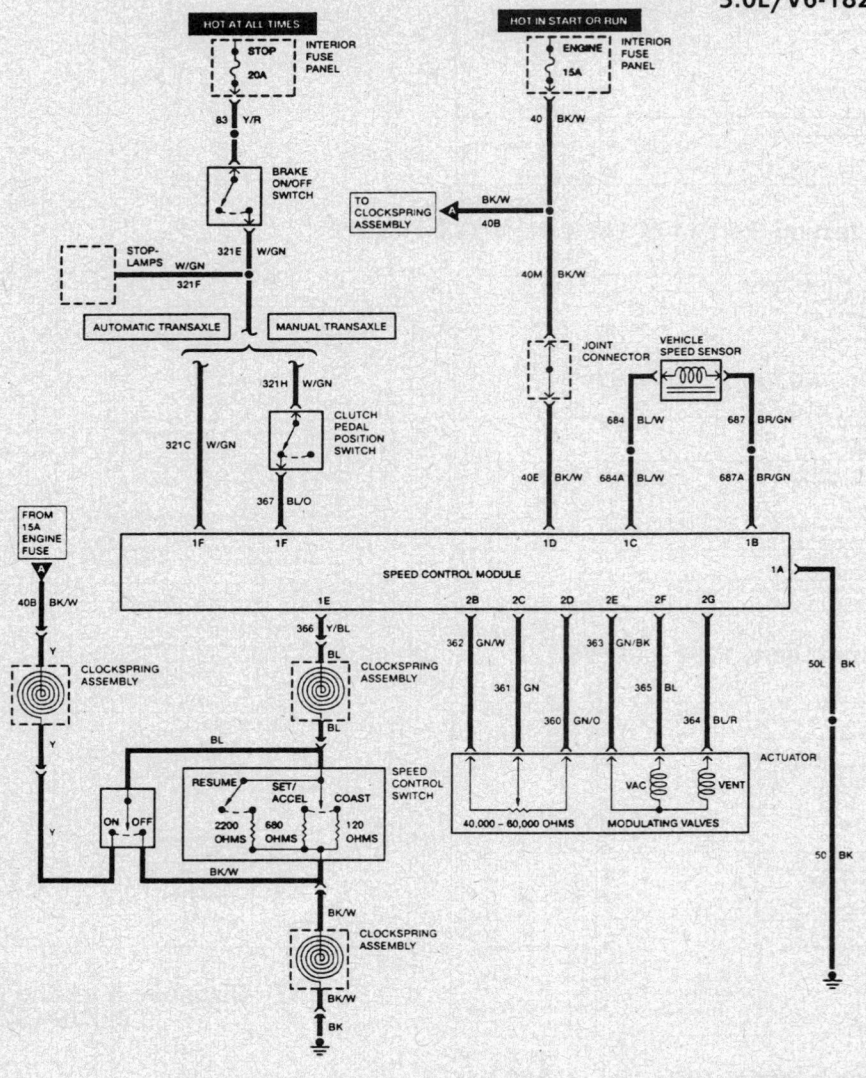

FM1109300194000X

Fig. 114   Wiring Circuit. 1993–94 Probe

CONDITION	POSSIBLE SOURCE	ACTION
• Speed Control Does Not Operate	• Fuse. • Circuit. • Vehicle speed sensor. • Actuator. • Speed control module. • Speed control switch.	• GO to SC1. • GO to SC4. • GO to SC10. • GO to SC17. • GO to SC4. • GO to SC12.
• Speed Control Will Not Set Speed	• Circuit. • Vehicle speed sensor. • Speed control module. • Speed control switch.	• GO to SC4. • GO to SC10. • GO to SC4. • GO to SC12.
• Speed Control Works Intermittently	• Circuit. • Vehicle speed sensor. • Actuator. • Speed control module.	• GO to SC4. • GO to SC10. • GO to SC17. • GO to SC4.
• Speed Control Switch(es) Do(es) Not Operate	• Circuit. • Speed control module. • Speed control switch(es).	• GO to SC4. • GO to SC4. • GO to SC12.
• Set Speed Fluctuates	• Vehicle speed sensor. • Actuator. • Speed control module.	• GO to SC10. • GO to SC17. • GO to SC4.
• Speed Control Does Not Shut Off With Brake Depressed	• Circuit. • Brake on / off switch. • Actuator. • Speed control module. • Vacuum dump valve.	• GO to SC4. • GO to SC5. • GO to SC17. • GO to SC4. • REFER to the vacuum dump valve test
• Speed Control Does Not Shut Off With Clutch Depressed	• Circuit. • Clutch pedal position switch. • Actuator. • Speed control module.	• GO to SC4. • GO to SC9. • GO to SC17. • GO to SC4.
• Speed Control Sets At A Lower Speed Than Selected	• Speed control switch. • Actuator. • Speed control module.	• GO to SC14.

FM1109300195000X

Fig. 115   Speed Control Symptom Chart. 1993–94 Probe

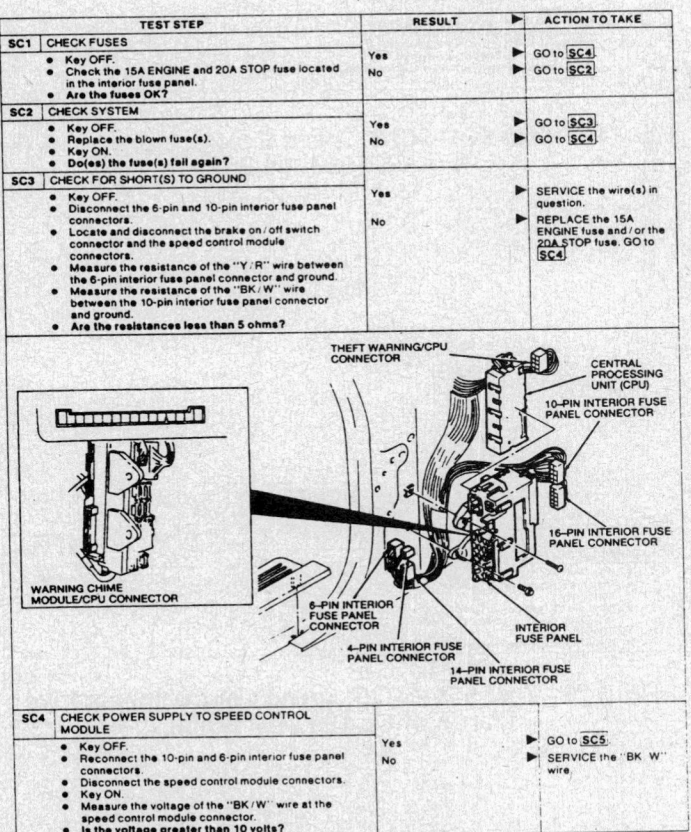

	TEST STEP	RESULT	▶	ACTION TO TAKE
SC1	CHECK FUSES • Key OFF. • Check the 15A ENGINE and 20A STOP fuse located in the interior fuse panel. • Are the fuses OK?	Yes No	▶ ▶	GO to SC4. GO to SC2.
SC2	CHECK SYSTEM • Key OFF. • Replace the blown fuse(s). • Key ON. • Do(es) the fuse(s) fail again?	Yes No	▶ ▶	GO to SC3. GO to SC4.
SC3	CHECK FOR SHORT(S) TO GROUND • Key OFF. • Disconnect the 6-pin and 10-pin interior fuse panel connectors. • Locate and disconnect the brake on / off switch connector and the speed control module connectors. • Measure the resistance of the "Y / R" wire between the 6-pin interior fuse panel connector and ground. • Measure the resistance of the "BK / W" wire between the 10-pin interior fuse panel connector and ground. • Are the resistances less than 5 ohms?	Yes No	▶ ▶	SERVICE the wire(s) in question. REPLACE the 15A ENGINE fuse and / or the 20A STOP fuse. GO to SC4.
SC4	CHECK POWER SUPPLY TO SPEED CONTROL MODULE • Key OFF. • Reconnect the 10-pin and 6-pin interior fuse panel connectors. • Disconnect the speed control module connectors. • Key ON. • Measure the voltage of the "BK / W" wire at the speed control module connector. • Is the voltage greater than 10 volts?	Yes No	▶ ▶	GO to SC5. SERVICE the "BK / W" wire.

FM1109300196010X

Fig. 116   Test SC1–SC20: Speed Control Inoperative (Part 1 of 6). 1993–94 Probe

	TEST STEP	RESULT	▶	ACTION TO TAKE
SC5	CHECK STOPLAMPS • Key OFF. • Depress the brake pedal. • Do the stoplamps illuminate?	Yes No	▶ ▶	GO to SC6.
SC6	CHECK SPEED CONTROL CUTOFF CIRCUIT • Key OFF. • Disconnect the speed control module connectors. • Clutch pedal released (MTX). • Depress the brake pedal. • Measure the voltage on the "W / GN" wire (4EAT) or the "BL / O" wire (MTX) at the speed control module connector. • Is the voltage greater than 10 volts?	Yes (4EAT) Yes (MTX) No (4EAT) No (MTX)	▶ ▶ ▶ ▶	GO to SC10. GO to SC9. SERVICE the "W / GN" wire. GO to SC7.
SC7	CHECK WIRE BETWEEN SPEED CONTROL MODULE AND CLUTCH PEDAL POSITION SWITCH • Key OFF. • Disconnect the speed control module connectors and the clutch pedal position switch connector. • Measure the resistance of the "BL / O" wire between the speed control module connector and the clutch pedal position switch connector. • Measure the resistance of the "BL / O" wire between the speed control module connector and ground. • Is the resistance less than 5 ohms between the speed control module connector and the clutch pedal position switch connector, and greater than 10,000 ohms between the speed control module connector and ground?	Yes No	▶ ▶	GO to SC8. SERVICE the "BL / O" wire.
SC8	CHECK WIRE BETWEEN BRAKE ON / OFF SWITCH AND CLUTCH PEDAL POSITION SWITCH • Key OFF. • Disconnect the brake on / off switch connector. • Disconnect the clutch pedal position switch connector. • Measure the resistance of the "W / GN" wire between the brake on / off switch connector and the clutch pedal position switch connector. • Is the resistance less than 5 ohms?	Yes No	▶ ▶	GO to SC9. SERVICE the "W / GN" wire.
SC9	CHECK CLUTCH PEDAL POSITION SWITCH • Key OFF. • Reconnect the brake on / off switch connector. • Disconnect the clutch pedal position switch connector. • Depress the clutch pedal. • Measure the resistance between the "W / GN" wire terminal and the "BL / O" wire terminal on the clutch pedal position switch. • Release the clutch pedal. • Measure the resistance between the "W / GN" wire terminal and the "BL / O" wire terminal on the clutch pedal position switch. • Is the resistance less than 5 ohms with the clutch pedal released, and greater than 10,000 ohms with the clutch pedal depressed?	Yes No	▶ ▶	GO to SC10. REPLACE the clutch pedal position switch.

FM1109300196020X

Fig. 116   Test SC1–SC20: Speed Control Inoperative (Part 2 of 6). 1993–94 Probe

TEST STEP	RESULT	►	ACTION TO TAKE
SC10 CHECK WIRES BETWEEN SPEED CONTROL MODULE AND VEHICLE SPEED SENSOR			
• Key OFF. • Reconnect the clutch pedal position switch connector. • Disconnect the speed control module connectors. • Locate and disconnect the vehicle speed sensor connector. • Measure the resistance of the "BL/W" wire and the "BR/GN" wire between the speed control module connector and the vehicle speed sensor connector. • Measure the resistance of the "BL/W" wire between the speed control module connector and ground. • Is the resistance less than 5 ohms between the speed control module connector and the vehicle speed sensor connector, and greater than 10,000 ohms between the speed control module connector and ground?	Yes No	► ►	GO to SC11. SERVICE the wire(s) in question.

TEST STEP	RESULT	►	ACTION TO TAKE
SC11 CHECK VEHICLE SPEED SENSOR			
• Reconnect the speed control module connectors and the vehicle speed sensor connector. • Connect a Rotunda Digital Volt-Ohmmeter 105-00051 or equivalent between the "BR/GN" wire and the "BL/W" wire at the speed control module connector with the speed control module connected. • Place the voltmeter in the AC volts position. • Drive the vehicle at the speeds indicated below and verify their corresponding voltages:	Yes No	► ►	GO to SC12. REPLACE the vehicle speed sensor.

Speed km/h (mph)	Approximate AC Voltage (volts)
0 (0)	0
8 (5)	1.40
16 (10)	2.10
24 (15)	2.80
32 (20)	3.40
40 (25)	3.85
48 (30)	4.25
56 (35)	4.55
64 (40)	4.80
72 (45)	5.00
80 (50)	5.20
88 (55)	5.40
96 (60)	5.50

TEST STEP	RESULT	►	ACTION TO TAKE
• Are the voltages OK?			
SC12 CHECK POWER SUPPLY TO SPEED CONTROL SWITCH			
• Key OFF. • Locate and disconnect the clockspring/speed control switch connector. • Key ON. • Measure the voltage of the "BK/W" wire at the clockspring/speed control switch connector. • Is the voltage greater than 10 volts?	Yes No	► ►	GO to SC13. SERVICE the "BK/W" wire.

FM1109300196030X

Fig. 116 Test SC1–SC20: Speed Control Inoperative (Part 3 of 6). 1993–94 Probe

TEST STEP	RESULT	►	ACTION TO TAKE
SC13 CHECK GROUND TO SPEED CONTROL SWITCH			
• Key OFF. • Disconnect the clockspring/speed control switch connector. • Measure the resistance of the "BK" wire between the clockspring/speed control switch connector (harness side) and ground. • Is the resistance less than 5 ohms?	Yes No	► ►	GO to SC14. SERVICE the "BK" wire.
SC14 CHECK SPEED CONTROL SWITCH			
• Key OFF. • Disconnect the speed control switch connector. • Measure the resistance between the "BL" wire terminal and the "BK/W" wire terminal at the speed control switch connector (switch side) while depressing the following switches:	Yes No	► ►	GO to SC15. REPLACE the speed control switch.

Switch	Resistance Measurement
ON	Greater than 10,000 ohms
OFF	Less than 5 ohms
SET-ACCEL	Approximately 680 ohms
COAST	Approximately 120 ohms
RESUME	Approximately 2200 ohms

TEST STEP	RESULT	►	ACTION TO TAKE
• Are the resistances OK?			
SC15 CHECK CLOCKSPRING			
• Key OFF. • Reconnect the speed control switch connector. • Disconnect the clockspring/speed control switch connector. • Measure the resistance between the "Y/BL" wire and the "BK" wire at the clockspring/speed control switch connector (clockspring side) while depressing the following switches:	Yes No	► ►	GO to SC16. REPLACE the clockspring assembly.

Switch	Resistance Measurement
ON	Greater than 10,000 ohms
OFF	Less than 5 ohms
SET-ACCEL	Approximately 680 ohms
COAST	Approximately 120 ohms
RESUME	Approximately 2200 ohms

TEST STEP	RESULT	►	ACTION TO TAKE
• Are the resistances OK?			
SC16 CHECK WIRE BETWEEN CLOCKSPRING AND SPEED CONTROL MODULE			
• Key OFF. • Disconnect the clockspring/speed control switch connector and the speed control module connectors. • Measure the resistance of the "Y/BL" wire between the clockspring/speed control switch connector and the speed control module connector. • Measure the resistance of the "Y/BL" wire between the clockspring/speed control switch connector and ground. • Is the resistance less than 5 ohms between the clockspring/speed control switch connector and the speed control module connector, and greater than 10,000 ohms between the clockspring/speed control switch connector and ground?	Yes No	► ►	GO to SC17. SERVICE the "Y/BL" wire.

FM1109300196040X

Fig. 116 Test SC1–SC20: Speed Control Inoperative (Part 4 of 6). 1993–94 Probe

TEST STEP	RESULT	►	ACTION TO TAKE
SC17 CHECK WIRES FROM ACTUATOR TO SPEED CONTROL MODULE			
• Key OFF. • Disconnect the speed control module 8-pin connector. • Locate and disconnect the actuator connector. • Measure the resistance of the following wires between the speed control module 8-pin connector and the actuator connector, and between the actuator connector and ground:	Yes No	► ►	GO to SC18. SERVICE the wire(s) in question.

Wire Color
BL/R
BL
GN/BK
GN/O
GN
GN/W

TEST STEP	RESULT	►	ACTION TO TAKE
• Are the resistances less than 5 ohms between the actuator connector and the speed control module 8-pin connector, and greater than 10,000 ohms between the actuator connector and ground?			
SC18 CHECK ACTUATOR			
• Key OFF. • Reconnect the actuator connector. • Disconnect the 8-pin connector from the speed control module. • Measure the resistances between the following wires at the 8-pin speed control module connector:	Yes No	► ►	GO to SC19. REPLACE the actuator.

Wire Colors	Resistance
GN/W - GN	20K-30K ohms
GN/O - GN/W	40K-60K ohms
GN/O - GN	20K-30K ohms
BL - GN/BK	40-70 ohms
BL - BL/R	150-210 ohms
GN/BK - BL/R	110-140 ohms

TEST STEP	RESULT	►	ACTION TO TAKE
• Are the resistances OK?			
SC19 CHECK ACTUATOR OPERATION			
• Key OFF. • Disconnect the 8-pin speed control module connector. • Apply 12 volts to the "GN/BK" wire at the speed control module connector. • Apply ground to the "BL/R" wire at the speed control module connector. • Key ON, engine running. **CAUTION:** Do NOT ground the "BL" wire for more than 1 second to prevent over revving of the engine or damage to the actuator. • Momentarily touch the "BL" wire with a jumper to ground. • Remove the jumper. • Did the actuator arm pull in when ground was applied to the "BL" wire and release when the "BL" wire was removed?	Yes No	► ►	GO to SC20. REPLACE the actuator.

FM1109300196050X

Fig. 116 Test SC1–SC20: Speed Control Inoperative (Part 5 of 6). 1993–94 Probe

TEST STEP	RESULT	►	ACTION TO TAKE
SC20 CHECK SPEED CONTROL MODULE GROUND			
• Key OFF. • Disconnect the speed control module 8-pin connector. • Measure the resistance of the "BK" wire between the speed control module 8-pin connector and ground. • Is the resistance less than 5 ohms?	Yes No	► ►	REPLACE the speed control module. SERVICE the "BK" wire.

FM1109300196060X

Fig. 116 Test SC1–SC20: Speed Control Inoperative (Part 6 of 6). 1993–94 Probe

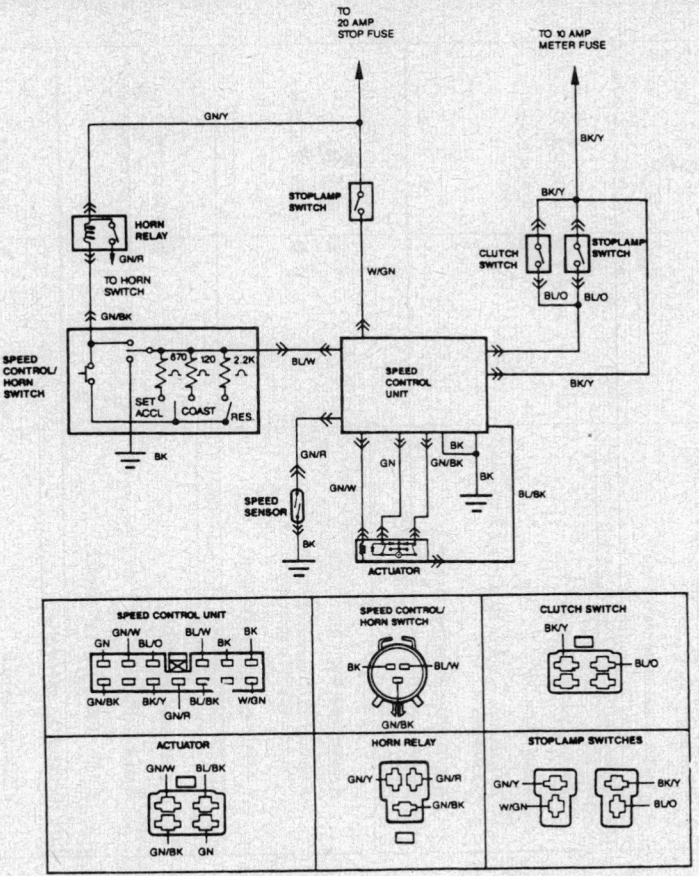

Fig. 117 Wiring circuit. Capri

CONDITION	POSSIBLE SOURCE	ACTION
• Speed Control System Does Not Operate	• Fuse.	• Go to CC1.
	• Speed / horn switch.	• Go to CC16.
	• Speed control unit.	• Go to CC24.
	• Actuator.	• Go to CC23.
	• Speed sensor.	• Go to CC21.
	• Circuit.	• Go to CC5.
• Speed Control System Will Not Set Speed	• Speed / horn switch.	• Go to CC16.
	• Speed sensor.	• Go to CC21.
	• Speed control unit.	• Go to CC24.
	• Circuit.	• Go to CC5.
• Speed Control System Works Intermittently	• Actuator.	• Go to CC23.
	• Speed control unit.	• Go to CC24.
	• Speed sensor.	• Go to CC21.
	• Circuit.	• Go to CC5.
• Speed / Horn Switch Position Do Not Operate	• Speed / horn switch.	• Go to CC16.
	• Speed control unit.	• Go to CC24.
	• Actuator.	• Go to CC23.
	• Circuit.	• Go to CC5.
• Set Speed Fluctuates	• Actuator.	• Go to CC23.
	• Speed sensor.	• Go to CC21.
	• Speed control unit.	• Go to CC24.
	• Circuit.	• Go to CC5.
• Speed Control System Does Not Shut Off With Brakes Depressed	• Stoplamp switch.	• Go to CC10.
	• Speed control unit.	• Go to CC24.
	• Actuator.	• Go to CC23.
	• Circuit.	• Go to CC5.
• Speed Control System Does Not Shut Off With Clutch Depressed	• Clutch switch.	• Go to CC7.
	• Speed control unit.	• Go to CC24.
	• Actuator.	• Go to CC23.
	• Circuit.	• Go to CC5.

FM1109100205010X

Fig. 118 Diagnosis & testing (Part 1 of 6). Capri

TEST STEP		RESULT	ACTION TO TAKE
CC6	**CHECK STOPLAMP SWITCH**		
• Key OFF.			
• Depress the brake pedal.			
• Measure the voltage on the BL/O wire at the switch connector			
• Is the voltage greater than 10 volts?		Yes	GO to CC7.
		No	REPLACE stoplamp switch.
CC7	**CHECK CLUTCH SWITCH**		
• Release the brake pedal.			
• Depress the clutch.			
• Measure the voltage on the BL/O wire at the switch connector.			
• Is the voltage greater than 10 volts?		Yes	GO to CC8.
		No	REPLACE clutch switch.
CC8	**CHECK LEAD FROM SWITCHES TO SPEED CONTROL UNIT**		
• Locate speed control unit.			
• Measure the resistance of the BL/O wire between the switches and the speed control unit.			
• Is the resistance less than 5 ohms?		Yes	GO to CC9.
		No	SERVICE BL/O wire.
CC9	**CHECK POWER SUPPLY TO STOPLAMP SWITCH**		
• Locate stoplamp switch.			
• Measure voltage on the GN/Y wire at the connector.			
• Is the voltage greater than 10 volts?		Yes	GO to CC10.
		No	SERVICE GN/Y wire.
CC10	**CHECK STOPLAMP SWITCH**		
• Depress brake pedal.			
• Measure the voltage on the W/GN wire at the connector.			
• Is the voltage greater than 10 volts?		Yes	GO to CC11.
		No	REPLACE stoplamp switch.

FM11091002050030X

Fig. 118 Diagnosis & testing (Part 3 of 6). Capri

TEST STEP		RESULT	ACTION TO TAKE
CC1	**CHECK FUSES**		
• Key OFF.			
• Access interior fuse panel.			
• Check the 20 amp stop fuse and the 10 amp meter fuse.			
• Are the fuses good?		Yes	GO to CC4.
		No	GO to CC2.
CC2	**CHECK SYSTEM**		
• Replace blown fuses.			
• Key ON.			
• Did the fuse(s) blow again?		Yes	GO to CC3.
		No	GO to CC4.
CC3	**CHECK FOR SHORTS TO GROUND**		
• Key OFF.			
• Disconnect the GN/Y wire from the stop fuse.			
• Measure the resistance of the GN/Y wire to ground.			
• Disconnect the BK/Y wire from the meter fuse.			
• Measure the resistance of the BK/Y wire to ground.			
• Are the resistances less than 5 ohms?		Yes	SERVICE wire(s) in question.
		No	GO to CC4.
CC4	**CHECK POWER SUPPLY TO SPEED CONTROL UNIT**		
• Locate speed control unit.			
• Key ON.			
• Measure the voltage on the BK/Y wire.			
• Is the voltage greater than 10 volts?		Yes	GO to CC5.
		No	SERVICE BK/Y wire.
CC5	**CHECK SUPPLY TO STOPLAMP AND CLUTCH SWITCHES**		
• Locate clutch and stop switches.			
• Measure the voltage on the BK/Y wire at each connector.			
• Are the voltages greater than 10 volts?		Yes	GO to CC6.
		No	SERVICE BK/Y wire.

FM11091002050020X

Fig. 118 Diagnosis & testing (Part 2 of 6). Capri

Fig. 118 Diagnosis & testing (Part 5 of 6). Capri

TEST STEP	RESULT	ACTION TO TAKE
CC16 CHECK SPEED/HORN SWITCH • Disconnect the BL/W wire from the connector. • Connect the positive lead of the ohmmeter to the BL/W terminal of the connector and the negative lead to ground. • Verify the resistances on the BL/W terminal of the connector while holding the speed/horn switch in the following positions: Switch Position — Resistance OFF — Greater than 10,000 ohms ON — Greater than 10,000 ohms SET — Approximately 680 ohms RESUME — Approximately 2,200 ohms COAST — Approximately 120 ohms ACC — Approximately 680 ohms • Are the resistances correct?	Yes No	GO to CC17. REPLACE speed/horn switch.
CC17 CHECK LEAD BETWEEN SPEED/HORN SWITCH AND SPEED CONTROL UNIT • Key OFF. • Locate the speed control unit. • Measure the resistance of the BL/W wire between the speed/horn switch and the speed control unit. • Is the resistance less than 5 ohms?	Yes No	GO to CC18. SERVICE BL/W wire.
CC18 CHECK SPEED CONTROL UNIT GROUND • Measure the resistance of the BK wires to ground. • Are the resistances less than 5 ohms?	Yes No	GO to CC19. SERVICE BK wire(s).
CC19 CHECK LEAD BETWEEN SPEED CONTROL UNIT AND SPEED SENSOR • Locate speed sensor. • Measure the resistance of the GN/R wire between the speed control unit and the speed sensor. • Is the resistance less than 5 ohms?	Yes No	GO to CC20. SERVICE GN/R wire.

FM1109100205050X

Fig. 118 Diagnosis & testing (Part 4 of 6). Capri

TEST STEP	RESULT	ACTION TO TAKE
CC11 CHECK LEAD TO SPEED CONTROL UNIT • Key OFF. • Locate the speed control unit. • Measure the resistance of the W/GN wire between the stoplamp switch and the speed control unit. • Is the resistance less than 5 ohms?	Yes No	GO to CC12. SERVICE W/GN wire.
CC12 CHECK POWER SUPPLY TO HORN RELAY • Locate horn relay. • Key ON. • Measure the voltage on the GN/Y wire at the horn relay. • Is the voltage greater than 10 volts?	Yes No	GO to CC13. SERVICE GN/Y wire.
CC13 CHECK CONTINUITY THROUGH HORN RELAY • Measure the voltage on the GN/BK wire at the relay connector. • Is the voltage greater than 10 volts?	Yes No	GO to CC14. REPLACE horn relay.
CC14 CHECK LEAD BETWEEN HORN RELAY AND SPEED/HORN SWITCH • Locate the speed/horn switch. • Measure the voltage on the GN/BK wire at the speed/horn switch. • Is the voltage greater than 10 volts?	Yes No	GO to CC15. SERVICE GN/BK wire.
CC15 CHECK SPEED/HORN SWITCH GROUND • Key OFF. • Measure the resistance of the BK wire between the speed/horn switch and ground. • Is the resistance less than 5 ohms?	Yes No	GO to CC16. SERVICE BK wire.

FM1109100205040X

COMPONENT REPLACEMENT

ESCORT, MUSTANG, TEMPO, TOPAZ & TRACER

SERVO (THROTTLE ACTUATOR) ASSEMBLY ACTUATOR CABLE

Except Mustang

1. Remove air cleaner assembly.
2. Remove screw or push-pin, then disconnect speed control actuator cable from accelerator cable bracket.
3. Disconnect speed control actuator cable from accelerator cable.
4. Remove two vacuum hoses and electrical connector from servo assembly.
5. Remove cable tie around actuator cable, if equipped.
6. Remove two screws/nuts from servo mounting bracket.
7. Carefully remove servo and cable assembly.
8. Remove two fasteners holding cable cover to servo.
9. Pull off cover and remove cable assembly, then remove servo mounting bracket.
10. Reverse procedure to install.

1992 Mustang

1. Disconnect speed control actuator cable from accelerator cable bracket.
2. Disconnect servo electrical connector from inside engine compartment.
3. Apply parking brake, then raise and support left front side of vehicle.
4. Remove left front wheel, then the inner fender splash shield.
5. Remove two vacuum hoses from servo.
6. Remove two servo mounting bracket-to-pillar attaching screws.
7. Remove two actuator cable cover-to-servo attaching nuts, then the cable and cover.
8. Remove servo-to-mounting bracket attaching nuts and the servo.
9. Reverse procedure to install.

1993–94 Mustang

1. Disconnect servo wiring at amplifier, and disconnect white stripe vacuum hose from dump valve in passenger compartment.
2. Disconnect speed control actuator cable from accelerator cable.
3. Remove grommet and wiring from passenger compartment.
4. Raise and support vehicle.
5. Remove front tire and LH side wheel.
6. Remove inner fender splash shield.
7. Remove brown striped vacuum hose from servo assembly.
8. Remove two screws retaining servo mounting bracket to A-pillar.
9. Remove two nuts from actuator cable cover at servo. Remove cable, cable cover and rubber boot.
10. Remove nuts retaining servo to mounting bracket.
11. If replacing servo with service stock, remove two bolt assemblies from front of servo.
12. Reverse procedure to install.

ACTUATOR CABLE

1. Remove servo assembly, then discard cable.
2. Attach new actuator cable to servo assembly.
3. Install servo assembly.

TEST STEP		RESULT		ACTION TO TAKE
CC20 CHECK SPEED SENSOR GROUND				
• Measure the resistance of the BK wire between the speed sensor and ground.		Yes	▶	GO to CC21.
• Is the resistance less than 5 ohms?		No	▶	SERVICE BK wire.
CC21 CHECK SPEED SENSOR				
• Disconnect speedometer cable at the transaxle.		Yes	▶	GO to CC22.
• Disconnect the GN/R wire from the speed control unit.		No	▶	REPLACE speed sensor.
• Check for continuity between ground and the GN/R wire at the speed sensor.				
• Does continuity exist four times per one speedometer cable rotation?				
CC22 CHECK LEADS TO ACTUATOR				
• Locate actuator connector.		Yes	▶	GO to CC23.
• Measure the resistance of the GN/W, GN, BL/BK and GN/BK wires between the speed control unit and the actuator.		No	▶	SERVICE wire in question.
• Are the resistances less than 5 ohms?				
CC23 CHECK ACTUATOR				
• Disconnect actuator connector.		Yes	▶	GO to CC24.
• Apply 12 volts and ground to the following terminals.		No	▶	REPLACE actuator.
• Check to see the actuator responds as indicated.				

GN/W	GN	GN/BK	BL/BK	Control Cable Operation
GND	GND	+ 12 volts	+ 12 volts	Pull cable
N/C	GND	N/C	+ 12 volts	Lock cable
+ 12 volts	GND	+ 12 volts	+ 12 volts	Extend cable
N/C	N/C	+ 12 volts	+ 12 volts	Release cable

+ 12 volts — Apply 12 volts
GND — Apply Ground
N/C — No connection
• Are the control cable operations verified?

TEST STEP		RESULT		ACTION TO TAKE
CC24 CHECK SPEED CONTROL UNIT				
• Start engine.		Yes	▶	RETURN to condition chart.
• Drive safely at approximately 40 mph.				
• Operate speed control system.		No	▶	REPLACE speed control unit.
• Does system operate correctly?				

FM1109100205060X

Fig. 118   Diagnosis & testing (Part 6 of 6). Capri

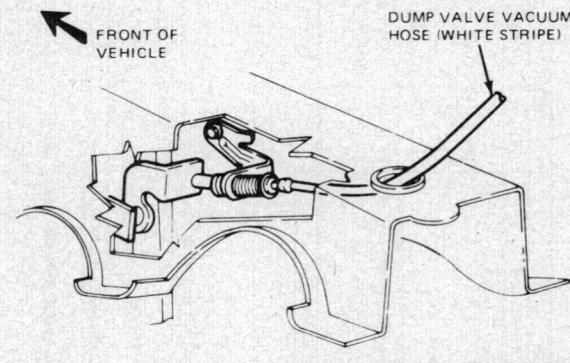

FM1109100115000X

Fig. 119   Dump valve removal

CONTROL SWITCH OR BRUSH ASSEMBLY

1. **On vehicles less air bag module,** proceed as follows:
   a. Remove two screws from rear of steering wheel to remove pad cover.

b. Remove foam insert, if equipped, then disconnect wiring connector from steering wheel.

c. Disconnect two horn wire connectors from steering wheel pad cover.

d. Remove speed control switches from steering wheel pad cover by removing two attaching screws from each side.

e. Reverse procedure to install.

2. **On vehicles equipped with air bag module,** disarm air bag system as described under "Precautions," then proceed as follows:

a. Remove pad by removing four screws from back of steering wheel. **Place air bag module on flat surface with plastic side facing upwards.**

b. Disconnect air bag module to clockspring electrical connector. **Place air bag pad on a flat surface with the trim cover facing up.**

c. Remove speed control switches from steering wheel.

d. Reverse procedure to install.

SPEED SENSOR

1. Raise and support vehicle, then loosen sensor to transmission retaining nut.

2. Remove speed sensor and driven gear from transmission, then disconnect speed sensor electrical connector.

3. Disconnect speedometer cable, by pulling it from speed sensor.

4. Remove speed sensor.

5. Reverse procedure to install.

AMPLIFIER ASSEMBLY

The amplifier is located either on, or to the left of the steering column under the instrument panel.

1. Remove screws holding amplifier assembly to the mounting bracket.

2. Disconnect amplifier electrical connectors, then remove amplifier assembly.

3. Reverse procedure to install.

VACUUM DUMP VALVE

1. Remove vacuum hose from valve, **Fig. 119.**

2. Remove valve from the bracket.

3. Reverse procedure to install.

GROUND BRUSH

1. **On models less air bag module,** proceed as follows:

a. Remove steering wheel by removing two screws from rear of steering wheel.

b. Remove foam insert, then the electrical connector from the steering wheel.

2. **On models with air bag module,** proceed as follows:

a. Remove four screws from rear of steering wheel, then the air bag module. **Place air bag module on a flat surface with the trim cover facing up.**

3. **On all models,** remove electrical connectors from steering wheel pad,

clockspring and horn.

4. Loosen steering wheel retaining screw approximately five turns.

5. Use steering wheel puller tool No. T67L-3600-A, or equivalent, to free steering wheel from shaft. **Do not use a knock-off type puller or strike retaining bolt with a hammer as damage to the steering wheel shaft bearing may occur.**

6. Remove steering column lower trim shroud, then the straps securing brush assembly wire at ignition switch and column tube.

7. Separate speed control brush wire harness from connector, then remove screw securing brush assembly to upper bearing retainer plate.

8. Remove brush assembly wire and connector assembly through opening in upper bearing retaining plate.

9. Reverse procedure to install, noting the following:

a. **Torque** ground brush retaining screws to 18-26 inch lbs.

b. **Torque** new steering wheel bolt to 23-33 ft. lbs.

CLUTCH DEACTIVATOR SWITCH

1. Remove bracket mounting screw(s).

2. Disconnect electrical connector, then remove switch and bracket assembly.

3. Remove switch from bracket.

4. Reverse procedure to install.

CONTINENTAL, COUGAR & THUNDERBIRD

SERVO ASSEMBLY

Continental

1. Remove screws, then disconnect speed control cable actuator cable from accelerator cable bracket and intake manifold support bracket.

2. Disconnect speed control actuator cable from accelerator cable.

3. Disconnect servo electrical connector.

4. Remove two servo bracket assembly to shock tower retaining nuts.

5. Remove servo bracket and cable, then the two vacuum hoses and electrical connector from servo assembly.

6. Remove two servo to mounting bracket retaining nuts.

7. Remove servo and cable assembly, then the two cable cover to servo retaining nuts.

8. Pull off cover and remove cable assembly from servo.

9. Reverse procedure to install, **torque** retaining nuts to 45-65 inch lbs.

Cougar & Thunderbird

1. Disconnect speed control actuator cable from accelerator cable.

2. Disconnect servo wiring at (14290) wiring assembly connection, located near radiator support.

3. Raise and support vehicle, then remove left front tire and wheel assembly.

4. Remove inner fender splash shield, then lower vehicle.

5. Remove two vacuum hoses from servo assembly.

6. Remove two servo mounting bracket to body support retaining screws.

7. Remove two nuts from actuator cable cover at servo.

8. Remove cover, cable and rubber boot from servo.

9. Remove two servo to mounting bracket retaining nuts.

10. Reverse procedure to install, **torque** retaining nuts to 45-61 inch lbs.

SPEED SENSOR

1. Raise and support vehicle.

2. **On Continental models,** remove speed sensor mounting clip to transaxle retaining bolt, then the sensor and driven gear from transaxle.

3. **On Cougar and Thunderbird models,** remove speed sensor mounting clip to transmission retaining bolt, then the sensor and driven gear from transmission.

4. **On all models,** disconnect speed sensor electrical connector and speedometer cable from speed sensor.

5. Remove driven gear retainer, then the driven gear from sensor.

6. Reverse procedure to install.

AMPLIFIER ASSEMBLY

The amplifier is located either on, or to the left of the steering column under the instrument panel.

1. Remove screws holding amplifier assembly to the mounting bracket.

2. Disconnect amplifier electrical connectors, then remove amplifier assembly.

3. Reverse procedure to install, **torque** retaining screws to 44-62 inch lbs.

ACTUATOR CABLE

1. Remove servo assembly, then discard cable.

2. Attach new actuator cable to servo assembly.

3. Install servo assembly.

VACUUM DUMP VALVE

1. Remove vacuum hose from valve.

2. Remove valve from the bracket.

3. Reverse procedure to install.

CONTROL SWITCHES

Continental

1. Remove air bag module retaining nuts, then the air bag module from the steering wheel.

2. Disconnect electrical connectors leading to switch assembly.

3. Remove two switch to steering wheel retaining screws and washers.

4. Remove switch and wiring assembly.

5. Reverse procedure to install, reactivate air bag and **torque** air bag module retaining screws to 36-48 inch lbs..

Cougar & Thunderbird

1. Remove steering wheel horn cover and pad assembly by pulling pad at upper middle edge.

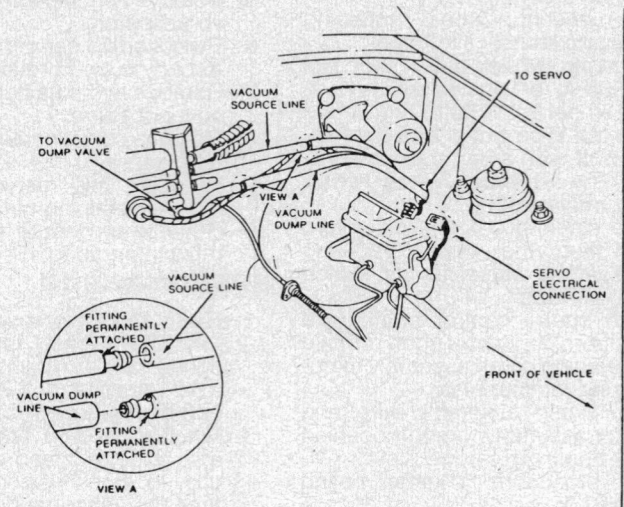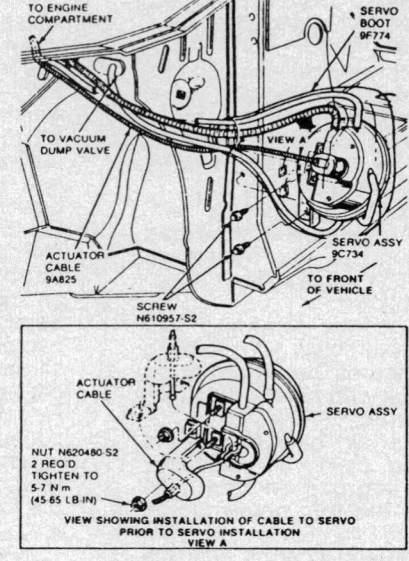

Fig. 120 Servo assembly replacement. Mark VII

2. Disconnect two horn wires from terminals on cover.
3. **On models with sport wheel,** remove four retaining screws from speed control switches, then the speed control switches and harness from steering wheel.
4. **On models less sport wheel,** using finger pressure, pry and remove speed control switches and harness assembly from steering wheel.
5. **On all models,** reverse procedure to install.

CLUTCH INTERLOCK THREE FUNCTION SWITCH

1. Disconnect wiring harness from switch.
2. Pull down orientation clip to separate it from tab on the switch.
3. Rotate switch half-turn to expose plastic retainer.
4. Push tabs together to allow retainer to slide rearward and separate from the switch.
5. Remove switch from push rod.
6. Reverse procedure to install.

SPEED CONTROL & HORN BRUSH CONTACT PLATE

Continental

1. Remove four nut and washers retaining air bag module to the steering wheel.
2. Disconnect air bag electrical connector from clockspring contact connector.
3. Remove air bag module from steering wheel. **Place air bag module on a flat surface with the trim cover facing up.**
4. Remove and discard steering wheel attaching bolt.
5. Grasp rim of steering wheel at opposing points, then pull steering wheel from shaft. **Do not use steering wheel puller.**

6. Remove tilt lever, if equipped, ignition lock cylinder, then the lower trim panel and lower steering column shroud.
7. Separate speed control brush wire harness from the connector, then remove the wire harness retainers from the steering column.
8. Remove screw securing brush assembly to upper steering column.
9. Reverse procedure to install. **Torque** the new steering wheel retaining nut to 23-33 ft. lbs.

Cougar & Thunderbird

1. Remove horn cover and pad assembly by pulling up on upper middle edge.
2. Disconnect two horn wires from terminals on cover pad, then loosen steering wheel retaining bolt four to six turns.
3. Using steering wheel puller tool No. T67L-3600-A or equivalent, pull steering wheel upward until steering wheel is loose on shaft.
4. Remove and discard steering wheel bolt.
5. Remove steering wheel.
6. With steering wheel facing down, remove three speed control and horn brush contact plate to steering wheel retaining bolts.
7. Disconnect speed control wiring harness from contact plate terminal and remove contact plate.
8. Reverse procedure to install, ensure slip rings are covered with Speed Control Slip Ring Grease No. E8AZ-19590-A or equivalent and **torque** steering wheel retaining bolt to 23-33 ft. lbs.

BRUSH ASSEMBLY

Continental

1. Set front wheels in a straight ahead position.
2. Remove four air bag module retaining

nuts, then lift air bag module from steering wheel.
3. Remove and discard steering wheel retaining bolt, then grasp rim of steering wheel and pull off.
4. Remove tilt lever, then the upper and lower steering column shroud.
5. Separate speed control brush wire harness at connector and remove harness retainers from steering column.
6. Remove brush assembly to upper steering column retaining screw.
7. Reverse procedure to install, **torque** retaining screw to 18-26 inch lbs. and new steering wheel bolt to 23-33 ft. lbs.

Cougar & Thunderbird

1. Remove steering wheel horn pad cover and steering wheel as described in "Speed Control & Horn Brush Contact Plate."
2. Remove steering column lower trim shroud.
3. Separate speed control brush wire harness at connector, then remove wire harness retainers from steering column.
4. Remove brush assembly to upper steering column retaining screw.
5. Reverse procedure to install, **torque** retaining screw to 18-26 inch lbs.

VACUUM RESERVOIR

Continental

1. Raise and support vehicle, then remove left front tire and wheel assembly.
2. Remove inner fender splash shield.
3. Remove hose connection at check valve in engine compartment.
4. Remove vacuum reservoir assembly to A-pillar retaining screw, then slide reservoir forward to release hook.
5. Remove vacuum reservoir assembly

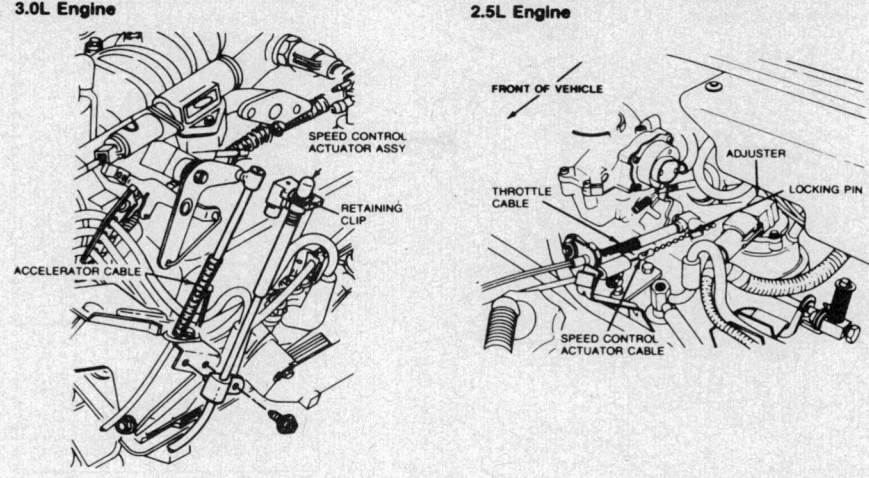

Fig. 121   Speed control actuator cable disconnect. Sable & Taurus

by pulling hose through cowl side panel.
6. Reverse procedure to install.

MARK VII, SABLE & TAURUS

SERVO ASSEMBLY

Mark VII

1. Remove air cleaner assembly, and position to front of vehicle.
2. Separate speed control actuator cable from the accelerator cable.
3. **On Mark VII models,** disconnect servo electrical connector, **Fig. 120.**
4. Apply parking brake.
5. Raise and support lefthand front of vehicle.
6. Remove left front wheel assembly.
7. Remove inner fender splash shield.
8. Remove two servo assembly vacuum hoses from servo.
9. **On Mark VII models,** remove two servo mounting bracket to A-pillar attaching screws.
10. Remove two actuator cable cover-to-servo retaining nuts, then the cover, cable, and rubber boot.
11. Remove two servo-to-mounting bracket retaining nuts.
12. Remove two bolts from front of servo.
13. Reverse procedure to install.

Sable & Taurus

1. Disconnect speed control actuator cable, **Fig. 9 or 121** from accelerator cable bracket and/or intake manifold support bracket.
2. Disconnect speed control actuator cable with adjuster from accelerator cable.
3. Remove two vacuum hoses and electrical connector from servo assembly, **Fig. 122.**
4. Remove two nuts holding servo to mounting bracket.
5. Carefully remove servo and cable assembly.
6. Remove two nuts holding cable cover to servo.

7. Pull off cover, then remove cable assembly.
8. Attach cable to servo.
9. Attach cable cover to servo with two nuts.
10. **On Crown Victoria, Town Car and Grand Marquis models,** while feeding actuator cable along the dash panel, reposition the servo assembly.
11. **On all models,** attach servo to mounting bracket.
12. **On Continental, Sable and Taurus models,** feed actuator cable under air cleaner duct.
13. **On all models,** snap actuator cable with adjuster onto accelerator cable.
14. Connect actuator cable to accelerator cable bracket and install push pin.
15. Install two vacuum hoses and electrical connector at servo.

ACTUATOR CABLE

To replace actuator assembly, remove servo assembly, attach new actuator cable assembly to servo, and install complete assembly.

SPEED SENSOR (SABLE & TAURUS w/AXOD TRANSAXLE)

Removal

1. Raise and support vehicle.
2. Remove bolt retaining speed sensor mounting clip to transaxle.
3. **On 1993-94 models,** remove Y-pipe and heated oxygen sensors from exhaust pipe, then remove exhaust heat shield.
4. **On all models,** remove sensor and driven gear from transaxle, **Fig. 123.**
5. Disconnect electrical connector and speedometer cable from speed sensor.
6. Disconnect speedometer cable by pulling it out of speed sensor. **Do not attempt to remove spring retainer clip with speedometer cable in sensor.**
7. Remove driven gear retainer, then the driven gear from sensor.

Installation

1. Position driven gear to speed sensor. Install gear retainer.
2. Connect electrical connector.
3. Ensure internal O-ring is properly seated in sensor housing. Snap speedometer cable into sensor housing.
4. Insert sensor assembly into transaxle housing. Install retaining bolt.
5. **On 1993-94 models,** install Y-pipe and heated oxygen sensors to exhaust sensors.
6. **On all models,** lower vehicle and verify proper speedometer/odometer operation.

SPEED SENSOR (SABLE & TAURUS w/MTX TRANSAXLE)

Removal

1. Raise and support vehicle.
2. Loosen sensor retaining nut.
3. Remove sensor from transaxle, **Fig. 124.**
4. Disconnect sensor electrical connector.
5. Disconnect speedometer cable by pulling it out of speed sensor. **Do not attempt to remove spring retaining clip with speedometer cable in sensor.**

Installation

1. Connect electrical connector.
2. Ensure internal O-ring is properly seated in sensor housing. Snap speedometer cable into sensor housing.
3. Insert sensor assembly into transaxle housing. Tighten retaining nut.
4. Lower vehicle.

EEC-IV ELECTRONIC CONTROL ASSEMBLY (ECA)

VACUUM DUMP VALVE

Removal

1. Remove vacuum hose from valve.
2. Remove valve from bracket.

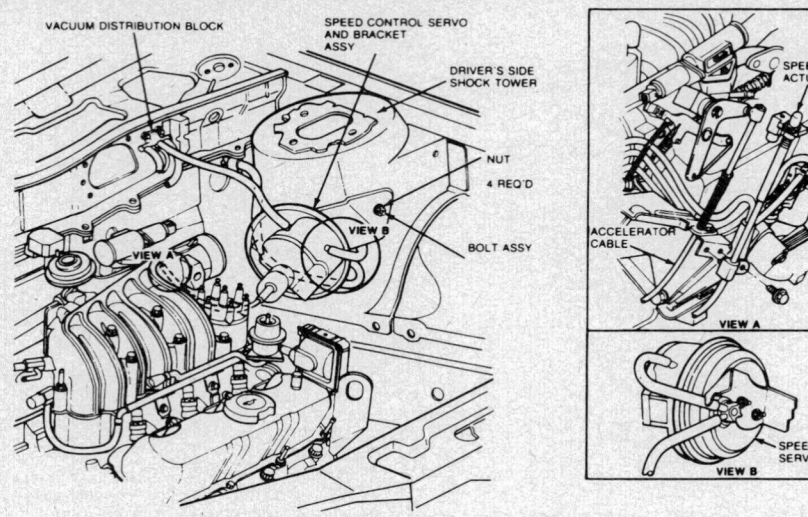

Fig. 122 Servo assembly electrical & vacuum connections. Sable & Taurus

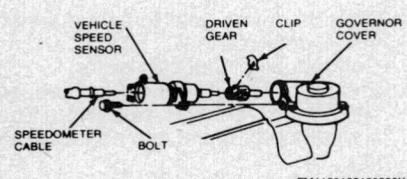

Fig. 123 Speed sensor replacement. Sable & Taurus w/AXOD transaxle

Installation

1. Install valve to bracket.
2. Connect vacuum hose.
3. Adjust valve as described under "Adjustments."

CONTROL SWITCHES

Mark VII

1. Remove four nut and washers retaining air bag module to steering wheel.
2. Disconnect air bag electrical connector from clockspring contact connector, then remove air bag module from steering wheel. **Place air bag on a flat surface with the trim cover facing up.**
3. Remove horn buttons by gently prying with a small screwdriver.
4. Disconnect horn wiring harness connector.
5. Remove Phillips head screws from speed control switch assemblies.
6. Disconnect speed control switches from wiring harness, then remove switches.
7. Reverse procedure to install.

Sable & Taurus

1. Remove four air bag module retaining nuts.
2. Remove module from steering wheel, then disconnect contact assembly from module. **Place air bag module on a flat surface, with the trim cover facing up.**

3. Disconnect electrical connectors from switch.
4. Remove two screws and washers retaining switch to steering wheel.
5. Remove switch and wiring assembly.
6. Reverse procedure to install.

GROUND BRUSH

Mark VII

1.
2. Center vehicle front wheels in the straight ahead position.
3. Remove four nut and washer assemblies retaining air bag module to steering wheel.
4. Disconnect air bag electrical connector from clockspring contact connector, then remove air bag module from steering wheel. **Place air bag module on bench with trim pad facing up.**
5. Remove steering wheel retaining bolt, then discard bolt.
6. Install Steering Wheel Puller tool No. T67L-3600-A or equivalent, then remove steering wheel.
7. Remove tilt lever, if equipped.
8. Remove ignition lock cylinder assembly.
9. If a new contact assembly is to be installed, remove ignition lock mechanism.
10. Remove lower trim panel, then lower steering column shroud.
11. Disconnect contact assembly wiring harness.
12. Apply two pieces of tape across contact assembly stator and rotor to prevent accidental rotation.
13. Remove three contact assembly retaining screw, then lift contact assembly off steering column shaft.
14. Disconnect speed control brush wiring harness at connector, then remove wiring harness retainers from steering column.
15. Remove screw retaining brush assembly to upper steering column, then

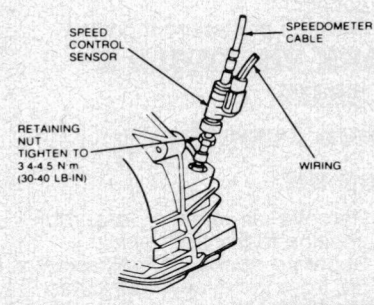

Fig. 124 Speed sensor replacement. Sable & Taurus w/MTX transaxle

brush and harness assembly.
16. Reverse procedure to install, noting the following:
   a. **Torque** contact assembly retaining screws to 18-26 inch. lbs.
   b. Ensure wiring is positioned so that no interference in encountered when installing the air bag module.

CLOCKSPRING ASSEMBLY

1. Center vehicle front wheels in the straight ahead position.
2. Remove four nut and washer assemblies retaining air bag module to steering wheel.
3. Disconnect air bag electrical connector from clockspring contact connector, then remove air bag module from steering wheel. **Place air bag module on bench with trim pad facing up.**
4. Remove steering wheel retaining bolt.
5. Install Steering Wheel Puller tool No. T67L-3600-A or equivalent, then remove steering wheel.
6. Remove tilt lever, if equipped.
7. Remove ignition lock cylinder assembly.
8. If a new contact assembly is to be installed, remove ignition lock mechanism.

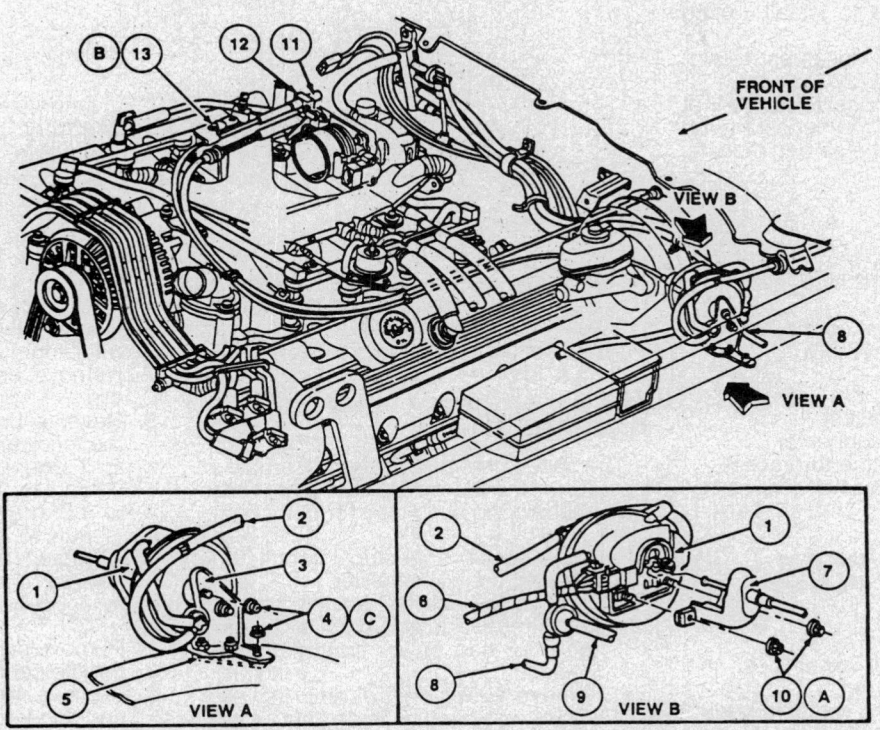

Fig. 125   Speed control system components. 1992 Crown Victoria, Grand Marquis & Town Car (Early Production)

Item	Description
1	Servo and Hose Assy
2	Hose Assy (To Dump Valve)
3	Servo Bracket
4C	Nut
5	Plate Assy
6	Electrical Connection
7	Actuator (Cable) Assy
8	To Vacuum Reservoir
9	To Manifold Vacuum
10A	Nut
11	Dust Tube
12	Adjuster Fitting
13B	Screw
A	Tighten to 4-6 N·m (36-53 Lb-In)
B	Tighten to 3-4 N·m (27-35 Lb-In)
C	Tighten to 5-7 N·m (45-61 Lb-In)

FM1109200161000X

9. Remove lower trim panel, then lower steering column shroud.
10. Disconnect contact assembly wiring harness.
11. Apply two pieces of tape across contact assembly stator and rotor to prevent accidental rotation.
12. Remove three contact assembly retaining screw, then lift contact assembly off steering column shaft.
13. Reverse procedure to install, noting the following:
    a. **Torque** contact assembly retaining screws to 18-26 inch. lbs.
    b. Ensure wiring is positioned so that no interference in encountered when installing the air bag module.

CLUTCH SWITCH

Removal

1. Remove screw attaching switch to bracket.
2. Disconnect electrical connector.
3. Remove switch assembly.

Installation

1. Install switch on bracket.
2. Connect electrical connector.
3. Install attaching switch to bracket.
4. Adjust clutch switch as described under "Adjustments."

SPEED CONTROL/HORN BRUSH CONTACT PLATE

Mark VII

1. Place vehicle front wheels in the straight ahead position.
2. Remove four nut and washers retaining air bag module to the steering wheel.
3. Disconnect air bag electrical connector from clockspring contact connector.
4. Remove air bag module from steering wheel. **Place air bag module on a flat surface with the trim cover facing up.**
5. Disconnect speed control and horn switches from contact assembly.
6. Remove steering wheel retaining bolt, install steering wheel puller, part No. T67L-3600-A, or equivalent, then remove steering wheel. **Route contact assembly wiring harness through steering wheel as wheel is lifted off.**
7. Remove tilt lever, if equipped, then the lower trim panel and lower steering column shroud.
8. Disconnect contact assembly wiring harness, then apply two pieces of tape across contact assembly stator and rotor, to prevent accidental rotation.
9. Remove three contact assembly retaining screws, then lift contact assembly from steering column shaft.
10. Disconnect speed control brush wiring harness from connector, then remove wiring harness retainers from steering column.
11. Remove screw, retaining brush assembly to upper steering column, then remove brush and harness assembly.

12. Reverse procedure to install. **Torque** brush retaining screw and contact assembly screws to 18-26 inch lbs., then the steering wheel retaining nut to 23-33 ft. lbs.

SPEED CONTROL AMPLIFIER ASSEMBLY

The speed control amplifier assembly is located on the LH side of the instrument panel behind the lamp dimmer potentiometer.

1. Disconnect two electrical connectors at speed control amplifier.
2. Remove two screws attaching speed control amplifier and bracket assembly to air bag power supply module bracket.
3. Remove speed control amplifier and bracket assembly from instrument panel.
4. Remove two bolts and nuts attaching speed control amplifier assembly to mounting bracket.
5. Reverse procedure to install.

VACUUM RESERVOIR

1. Raise and support vehicle, then remove lefthand front wheel.
2. Remove inner fender splash shield.
3. Remove hose from check valve.
4. Remove screw retaining vacuum reservoir assembly to A-pillar. Slide reservoir forward to release hook.
5. Remove vacuum reservoir assembly by pulling hose through cowl side panel.
6. Reverse procedure to install.

1992 CROWN VICTORIA, GRAND MARQUIS & TOWN CAR (EARLY PRODUCTION)

Refer to **Fig. 125** when replacing system components.

SERVO ASSEMBLY

1. Remove actuator cable retaining clip from adjuster fitting.
2. Push actuator dust tube out of adjuster fitting attached to throttle cable.
3. Remove two vacuum hoses and electrical connector from servo assembly.
4. Remove two servo to mounting bracket retaining nuts.

5. Remove servo and cable assembly from bracket.
6. Remove two cable housing to servo retaining nuts.
7. Remove cable ball end from servo clip.
8. Reverse procedure to install, noting the following:
    a. **Torque** cable housing retaining nuts to 36-53 inch lbs.
    b. **Torque** servo to mounting bracket nuts to 45-61 inch lbs.
    c. Adjust actuator cable as necessary.

ACTUATOR CABLE

1. Remove screw attaching resonator to throttle cable bracket.
2. Remove two hoses from resonator and loosen clamp at throttle body, then pull resonator from throttle body and position out of the way.
3. Remove screw attaching actuator cable to throttle cable bracket.
4. Disconnect actuator cable from throttle cable, then remove two servo to mounting bracket retaining nuts.
5. Remove servo and cable assembly from bracket.
6. Remove two cable housing to servo retaining nuts, then pull housing from servo.
7. Remove cable ball end from servo clip.
8. Remove cable from retaining clips, then pull out from under fuel lines.
9. Reverse procedure to install, noting the following:
    a. **Torque** cable housing retaining nuts to 36-53 inch lbs.
    b. **Torque** servo to mounting bracket nuts to 45-61 inch lbs.
    c. Adjust actuator cable as necessary.
    d. Ensure cable is routed underneath fuel lines and placed back into retaining clips.

SPEED SENSOR

1. Raise and support vehicle.
2. Remove speed sensor mounting clip to transmission attaching bolt.
3. Remove sensor and driven gear from transmission, then disconnect electrical connector.

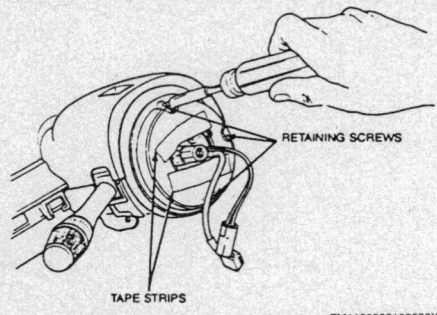

Fig. 126 Contact assembly removal. 1992 Crown Victoria, Grand Marquis & Town Car (Early Production)

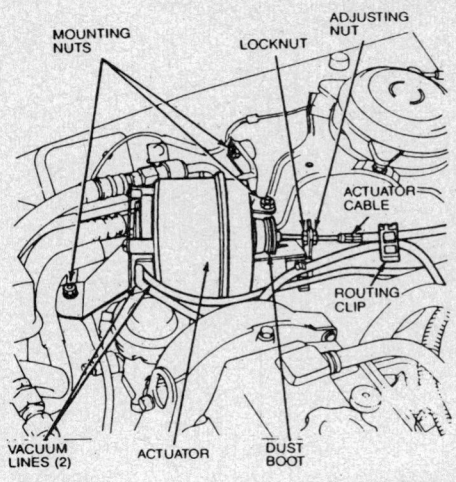

Fig. 127 Actuator replace. Vacuum

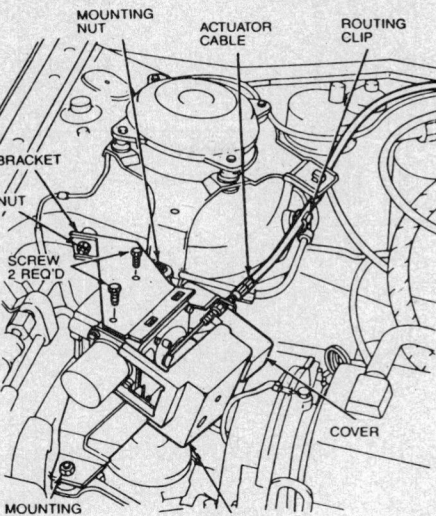

Fig. 128 Actuator replace. Electric

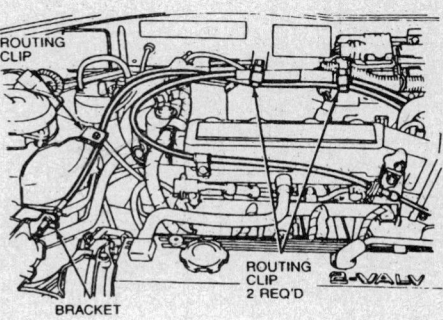

Fig. 129 Actuator cable replace (Part 1 of 2)

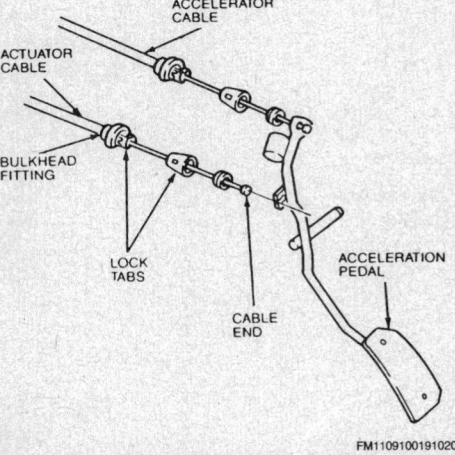

Fig. 129 Actuator cable replace (Part 2 of 2)

4. Remove driven gear retainer and driven gear from sensor.
5. Reverse procedure to install.

AMPLIFIER ASSEMBLY

Town Car

The amplifier is located behind the glove box.
1. Remove two amplifier to bracket retaining screws.
2. Pull amplifier out and disconnect two electrical connectors.
3. Reverse procedure to install. **Ensure correct amplifier is installed, brown colored amplifier for models with electronic cluster and tan colored amplifier for models with analog cluster.**

Crown Victoria & Grand Marquis

The amplifier is mounted to the same bracket as the warning chime module and wiper module. This bracket is located in the lower area of the instrument panel between the steering column and transmission tunnel.
1. Remove warning chime module from bracket.
2. Remove three bracket to instrument panel retaining screws, then lower bracket.
3. Remove two amplifier to bracket retaining screws.
4. Pull amplifier out and disconnect wiring harness connector.
5. Reverse procedure to install. **Ensure correct amplifier is installed, brown colored amplifier for models with electronic cluster and tan colored amplifier for models with analog cluster.**

VACUUM DUMP VALVE

1. Remove vacuum hose from valve.
2. Remove valve from brake pedal support.
3. Reverse procedure to install, adjust valve as described in "Adjustments."

VACUUM RESERVOIR

1. Raise and support vehicle.

2. Remove upper lefthand nut that holds reservoir assembly to bumper isolator. **Do not loosen any other nut.**
3. Slide reservoir assembly off bumper stud.
4. Disconnect vacuum line from reservoir assembly, then remove reservoir.
5. Reverse procedure to install, **torque** nut to 23-39 ft. lbs.

CONTROL SWITCHES

1. Remove four air bag module to steering wheel retaining nuts.
2. Disconnect air bag electrical connector from clockspring contact connector.
3. Remove air bag module from steering wheel. **Place air bag module on a bench with trim cover facing upward.**
4. Pry speed control switch bezels off of steering wheel.
5. Remove four speed control switch assembly retaining screws.
6. Disconnect speed control and horn

switch connectors, then remove control switch and wire assemblies.
7. Reverse procedure to install, noting the following:
   a. **When reconnecting control and horn switch wiring connectors, ensure that the wires are positioned so that there is no interference when air bag module is installed.**
   b. Position air bag module on steering wheel so that clockspring contact connector can be connected to the module.
   c. **Torque** air bag module retaining nuts to 36-53 inch lbs.

CLOCKSPRING ASSEMBLY

1. Position front wheels in a straight ahead position.
2. Remove four air bag module to steering wheel retaining nuts.
3. Disconnect air bag electrical connector from clockspring contact connector.
4. Remove air bag module from steering wheel. **Place air bag module on a bench with trim cover facing upward.**
5. Disconnect speed control switches and horn switch from clockspring contact assembly.
6. Remove steering wheel retaining bolt.
7. Using steering wheel puller tool No. T67L-3600-A or equivalent, remove steering wheel.
8. Remove tilt lever, then the lower trim panel and lower steering column shroud.
9. Disconnect contact assembly wiring harness.
10. Apply two pieces of tape across contact assembly stator and rotor to prevent accidental rotation, **Fig. 126.**
11. Remove three contact assembly retaining screws, then lift contact assembly off steering column shaft.
12. Reverse procedure to install, noting the following:
   a. **Torque** contact spring retaining screws to 18-26 inch lbs.
   b. **Torque** steering wheel retaining bolt to 23-33 ft. lbs.
   c. **When reconnecting control and horn switch wiring connectors, ensure that the wires are posi-**

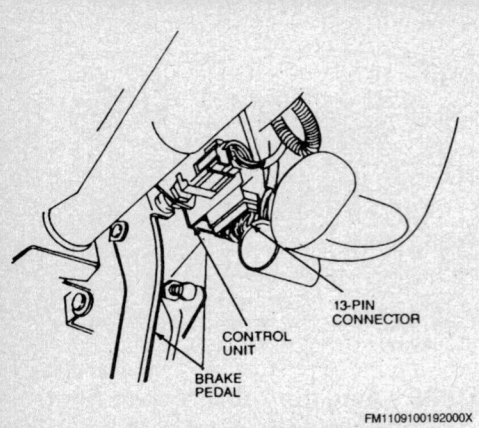

Fig. 130 Control unit replace

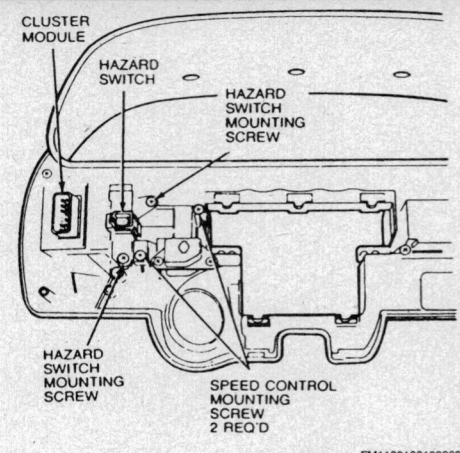

Fig. 131 Main control switch replace

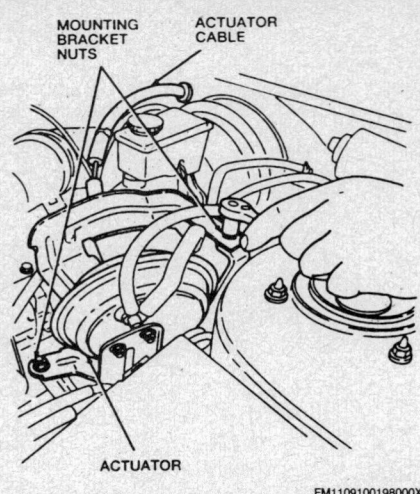

Fig. 132 Actuator Replacement

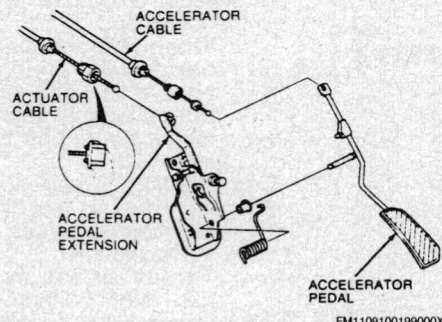
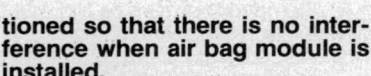

Fig. 133 Accelerator Cable Replacement

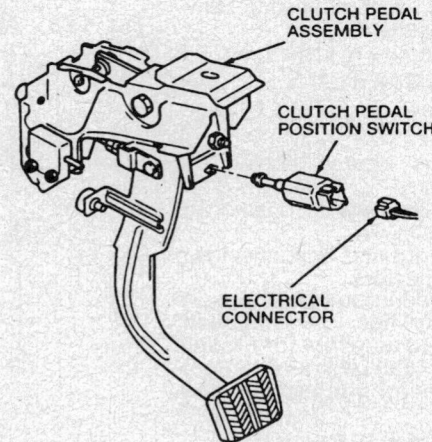

Fig. 134 Clutch Pedal Position Switch Replacement

tioned so that there is no interference when air bag module is installed.

d. Position air bag module on steering wheel so that clockspring contact connector can be connected to the module.

e. **Torque** air bag module retaining nuts to 36-53 inch lbs.

1992 TOWN CAR (LATE PRODUCTION), 1993—94 CROWN VICTORIA, GRAND MARQUIS, MARK VIII & TOWN CAR

Servo

1. Remove retaining clip from actuator cable adjuster fitting.
2. Push actuator tube out of adjuster fitting attached to throttle cable.
3. Disconnect harness connector at servo, then remove two servo assembly to vehicle attaching nuts.
4. Remove actuator cable cap from servo by depressing cap locking arm and rotating cap counterclockwise.
5. Remove cable ball slug from servo pulley by pushing slug from out of pulley slot.
6. Reverse procedure to install, **torque** assembly attaching nuts to 45-61 inch lbs.

Actuator Cable

1. Remove screw attaching resonator to throttle cable bracket.
2. Remove two hoses from resonator, then loosen clamp at throttle body.
3. Pull resonator from throttle body and position out of the way.
4. Disconnect actuator cable from accelerator cable, then remove actuator cable cap from servo by depressing cap locking arm and rotating cap counterclockwise.
5. Remove cable ball slug from servo pulley by pushing slug from out of pulley slot.
6. Reverse procedure to install, adjust cable as described in "Adjustments."

Speed Sensor

1. Raise and support vehicle.
2. Remove speed sensor mounting clip to transmission retaining bolt.
3. Disconnect electrical connector from sensor.
4. Remove driven gear retainer, then the driven gear from the sensor.
5. Reverse procedure to install.

Control Switches

1. Remove four air bag module to steering wheel retaining nuts.
2. Disconnect air bag electrical connector from clockspring contact connector.
3. Remove air bag module from steering wheel. **Place air bag module on a bench with trim cover facing upward.**
4. Pry speed control switch bezels off of steering wheel.
5. Remove four speed control switch assembly retaining screws.
6. Disconnect speed control and horn switch connectors, then remove control switch and wire assemblies.
7. Reverse procedure to install, noting the following:
   a. **When reconnecting control and horn switch wiring connectors, ensure that the wires are positioned so that there is no interference when air bag module is installed.**

b. Position air bag module on steering wheel so that clockspring contact connector can be connected to the module.

c. **Torque** air bag module retaining nuts to 36–53 inch lbs.

Clockspring Assembly

1. Position front wheels in a straight ahead position.
2. Remove four air bag module to steering wheel retaining nuts.
3. Disconnect air bag electrical connector from clockspring contact connector.
4. Remove air bag module from steering wheel. **Place air bag module on a bench with trim cover facing upward.**
5. Disconnect speed control switches and horn switch from clockspring contact assembly.
6. Remove steering wheel retaining bolt.
7. Using steering wheel puller tool No. T67L-3600-A or equivalent, remove steering wheel.
8. Remove tilt lever, then the lower trim panel and lower steering column shroud.
9. Disconnect contact assembly wiring harness.
10. Apply two pieces of tape across contact assembly stator and rotor to prevent accidental rotation.
11. Remove three contact assembly retaining screws, then lift contact assembly off steering column shaft.
12. Reverse procedure to install, noting the following:
    a. **Torque** contact spring retaining screws to 18–26 inch lbs.
    b. **Torque** steering wheel retaining bolt to 23–33 ft. lbs.
    c. **When reconnecting control and horn switch wiring connectors, ensure that the wires are positioned so that there is no interference when air bag module is installed.**
    d. Position air bag module on steering wheel so that clockspring contact connector can be connected to the module.
    e. **Torque** air bag module retaining nuts to 36–53 inch lbs.

Deactivator Switch

1. Disconnect electrical connector from switch.
2. Unscrew switch from brake proportioning valve.
3. Reverse procedure to install, **torque** switch to 12–14 ft. lbs., then bleed brake system.

1992 PROBE

Vacuum Actuator

1. Disconnect battery negative cable.
2. Disconnect actuator electrical connector.
3. Remove actuator cable routing clip, then two actuator vacuum lines, **Fig. 127.**
4. Loosen adjusting nut and locknut then pull dust boot back to gain access to

actuator rod.
5. Remove actuator cable from actuator rod and bracket.
6. Remove three actuator mounting nuts, then the actuator.
7. Reverse procedure to install.

Electric Actuator

1. Disconnect battery ground cable, then remove wiring routing clip from actuator cable.
2. Disconnect actuator electrical connector, then remove actuator bracket, **Fig. 128.**
3. Remove actuator cover, then loosen adjusting nut and locknut.
4. Remove actuator cable, two actuator mounting nuts, then the actuator.
5. Reverse procedure to install.

Actuator Cable

1. **On models equipped with electric actuator,** remove plastic cover.
2. **On models equipped with vacuum actuator,** remove dust boot from actuator.
3. **On all models,** loosen adjusting nut and locknut, **Fig. 129.**
4. Remove actuator cable from cable bracket.
5. Remove actuator cable from cable routing clips, then squeeze lock tabs and remove cable end from pedal assembly.
6. Squeeze lock tabs securing cable housing to bulkhead, **Fig. 129,** then remove cable through engine compartment.
7. Reverse procedure to install.

Clutch/Brake Switch

1. Disconnect battery ground cable.
2. Disconnect brake switch electrical connector.
3. Remove switch locknut, then the switch.
4. Install adjuster nut onto switch, then switch into bracket.
5. Install locknut onto switch.
6. Adjust switch so that pedal height is 8.42 inches (214 mm).
7. Tighten locknut.

Control Unit

1. Remove instrument panel lower panel, lap duct and defrost duct.
2. Remove control unit 13 pin electrical connector, **Fig. 130.**
3. Remove control unit retaining bolt, then the control unit.
4. Reverse procedure to install.

Main Control Switches

1. Remove cluster module, if necessary, **Fig. 131.**
2. Remove two hazard switch-to-cluster module retaining screws, then the hazard switch.
3. Remove screws securing speed control switch to cluster.
4. Reverse procedure to install.

1993–94 PROBE

Actuator

1. Disconnect battery ground cable.

2. Remove two mounting bracket nuts, **Fig. 132.**
3. Disconnect actuator electrical connector.
4. Remove three vacuum hoses.
5. Remove cable adjusting clip from cable housing.
6. Remove two mounting nuts and bracket from cable side of actuator.
7. Slide cable and housing away from actuator.
8. Disconnect cable and remove actuator.
9. Reverse procedure to install.

Actuator Cable

1. Disconnect actuator cable from accelerator pedal extension, **Fig. 133.**
2. Remove actuator as previously outlined.
3. Detach actuator cable sealing grommet from bulkhead.
4. Remove actuator cable from vehicle.
5. Reverse procedure to install. Adjust cable after installation.

Brake On/Off Switch

The brake on/off switch is located to the right of the steering column base, above the accelerator pedal bracket.
1. Disconnect battery ground cable.
2. Disconnect electrical connector from back of switch.
3. Rotate switch 90 degrees in either direction and remove it from mounting bracket.
4. Reverse procedure to install.

Clutch Pedal Position (CPP) Switch

1. Disconnect battery ground cable.
2. Disconnect electrical connector from back of switch, **Fig. 134.**
3. Rotate switch 90 degrees in either direction and remove it from mounting bracket.
4. Reverse procedure to install.

Vacuum Dump Valve

1. Remove vacuum hose from valve.
2. Remove valve from mounting bracket.
3. Reverse procedure to install.

Speed Control Module

1. Disconnect battery ground cable.
2. Remove two control module mounting nuts.
3. Disconnect two speed control module electrical connectors, then remove control module.
4. Reverse procedure to install.

Speed Control Switches

1. Remove four air bag bolts from back of steering wheel.
2. Disconnect air bag/horn electrical connector from air bag module.
3. Disconnect speed control switches from electrical connector.
4. Remove air bag module from steering wheel.
5. Remove speed control switch attaching screws.
6. Remove speed control switch assembly.

7. Reverse procedure to install. **Torque air bag module bolts to 36-49 inch lbs.**

CAPRI

Control Switches

1. Remove air bag module. **Place air bag module on bench with trim cover facing up.**
2. Disconnect speed control harness connector.
3. Using a small flat blade screwdriver, pry out horn switches and disconnect horn wires.
4. Remove speed control switches retaining screws.

5. Remove speed control switches and harness assembly.
6. Reverse procedure to install.

Control Module

The control module is mounted under the front of the floor console. The ashtray can be removed to gain access to the module for testing.

1. Disconnect battery ground cable.
2. Remove front console side covers, then front console.
3. Remove control unit retaining screws, then disconnect electrical connector.
4. Remove control unit.

5. Reverse procedure to install.

Cable/Actuator Assembly

1. Remove two bolts from cable actuator.
2. Release cable from accelerator pedal, then pull cable into engine compartment.
3. Loosen locknut, then remove cable from actuator.
4. Loosen locknut, then remove cable from bracket and throttle linkage.
5. Remove cable/actuator assembly.
6. Reverse procedure to install. **Torque cable/actuator assembly retaining bolts to 6-8 ft. lbs.**

WIPER SYSTEMS
TABLE OF CONTENTS

Front Wiper System
INDEX

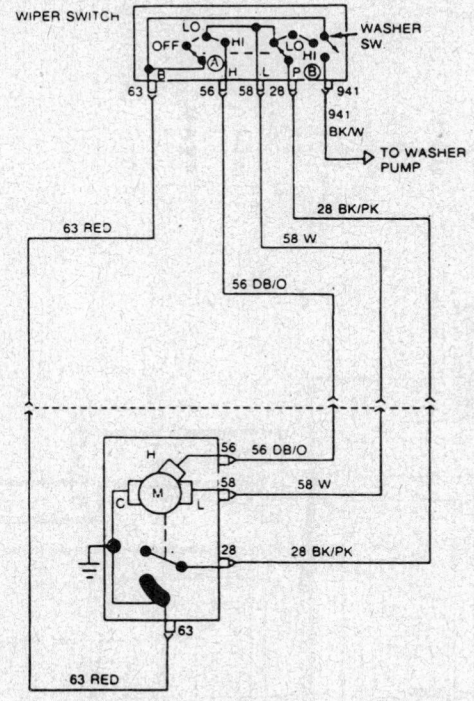

Fig. 1   Standard wiper system wiring
schematic. 1992–93 Tempo & Topaz

FM9029100085000X

SYSTEM DIAGNOSIS & TESTING

WIRING DIAGRAMS & DIAGNOSTIC PROCEDURES

Tempo & Topaz

Refer to **Figs. 1 through 4** for wiper system wiring schematics, and **Fig. 5** for diagnostic procedures.

Crown Victoria, Grand Marquis & Town Car

Refer to **Figs. 6 and 7** for wiper system wiring schematics, and **Fig. 8** for diagnostic procedures.

Continental, Cougar, Mark VII, Mark VIII, Mustang, Sable, Taurus & Thunderbird

Refer to **Figs. 9 through 18** for wiper system wiring schematics, and **Figs. 19 through 24** for diagnostic procedures.

Aspire, Capri, Festiva & Probe

Refer to **Figs. 25 through 28** for wiper system wiring schematic, and **Figs. 29 through 33** for diagnostic and testing procedures.

Escort & Tracer

Refer to **Figs. 34 and 35** for wiper system wiring schematic, and **Figs. 36 and 37** for diagnostic and testing procedures.

PINPOINT TESTS

On **1993-94 models**, pinpoint tests are used to locate specific system faults to be serviced. Refer to the "Diagnostic Chart Index," and system wiring schematics when performing diagnosis.

1993–94 Continental

Refer to **Figs. 38 through 45** for pinpoint test procedures.

1993–94 Cougar, Mustang, Tempo, Thunderbird & Topaz

Refer to **Figs. 46 through 53** for 1993 pinpoint test procedures. Refer to **Figs. 54 through 72** for 1994 pinpoint test procedures.

1993–94 Crown Victoria, Grand Marquis & Town Car

Refer to **Figs. 74 through 79** for pinpoint test procedures.

1993–94 Mark VIII, Sable & Taurus

Refer to **Figs. 80 through 85** for pinpoint test procedures.

Escort & Tracer

Refer to **Fig. 86** for diagnostic test procedures.

Aspire & 1993–94 Probe

Refer to **Figs. 87 through 96** for pinpoint test procedures.

Continued on page 17-52

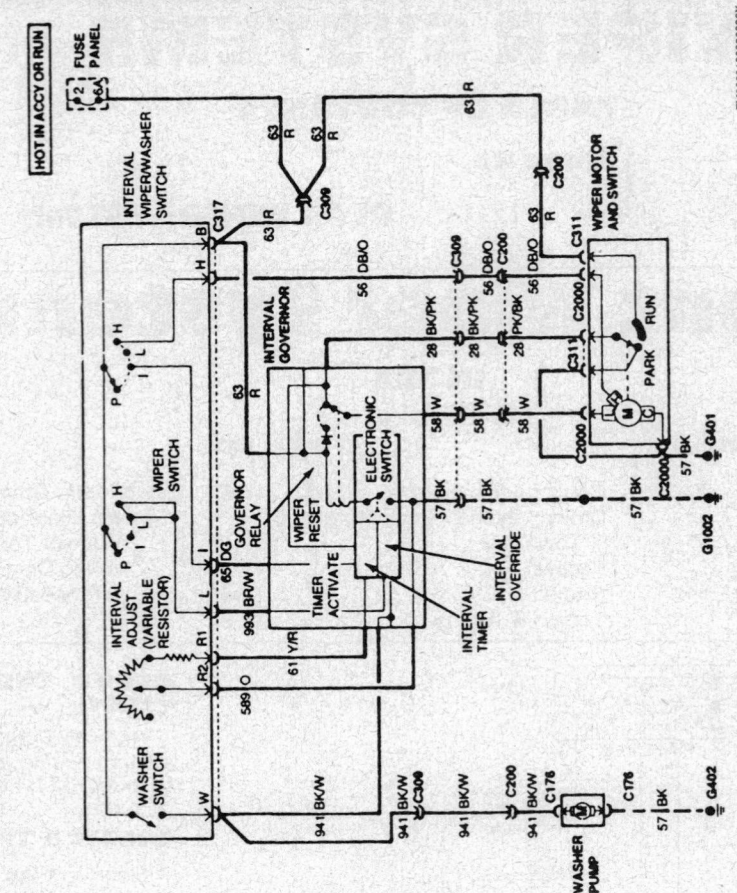

Fig. 3 Intermittent wiper system wiring schematic. Tempo & Topaz

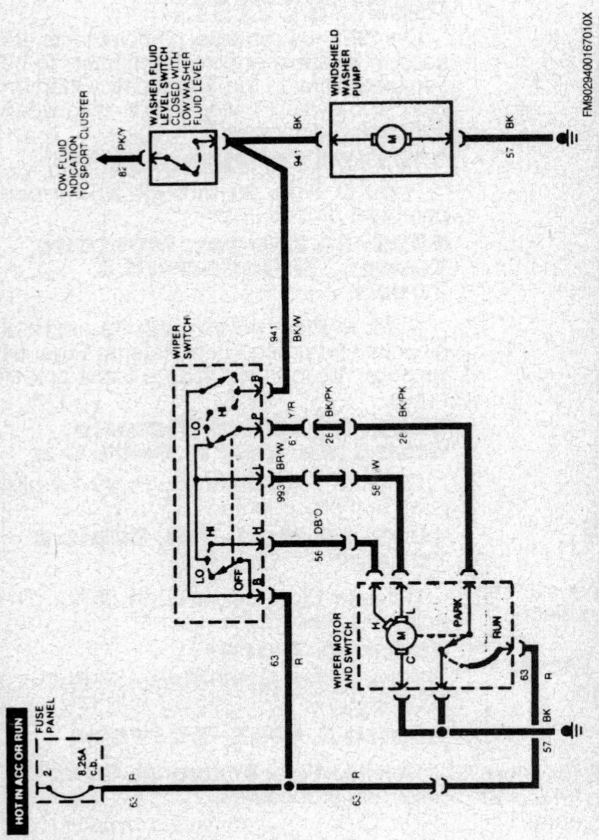

Fig. 2 Two-speed wiper system wiring schematic (Part 1 of 2). 1994 Tempo & Topaz

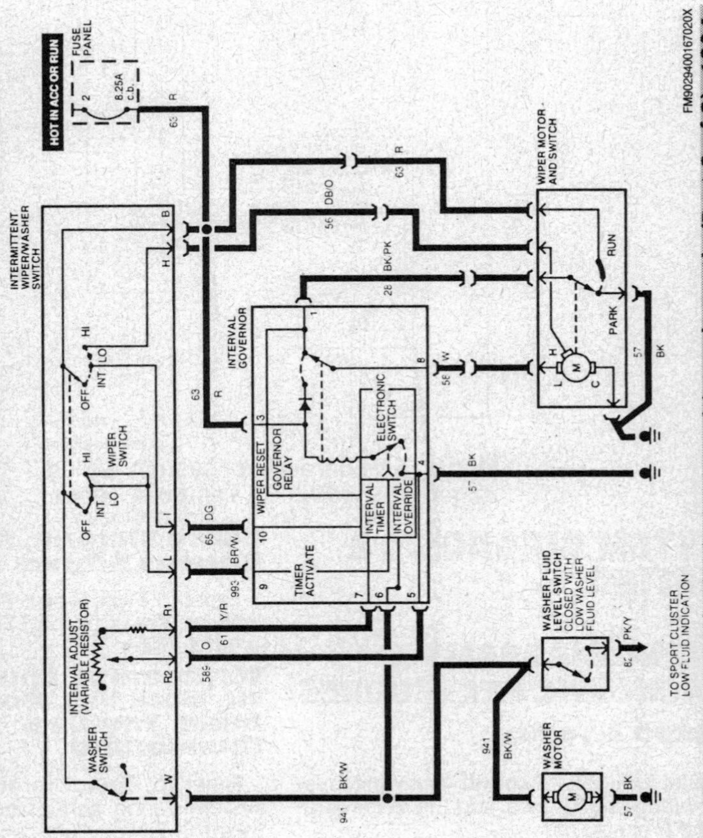

Fig. 2 Two-speed wiper system wiring schematic (Part 2 of 2). 1994 Tempo & Topaz

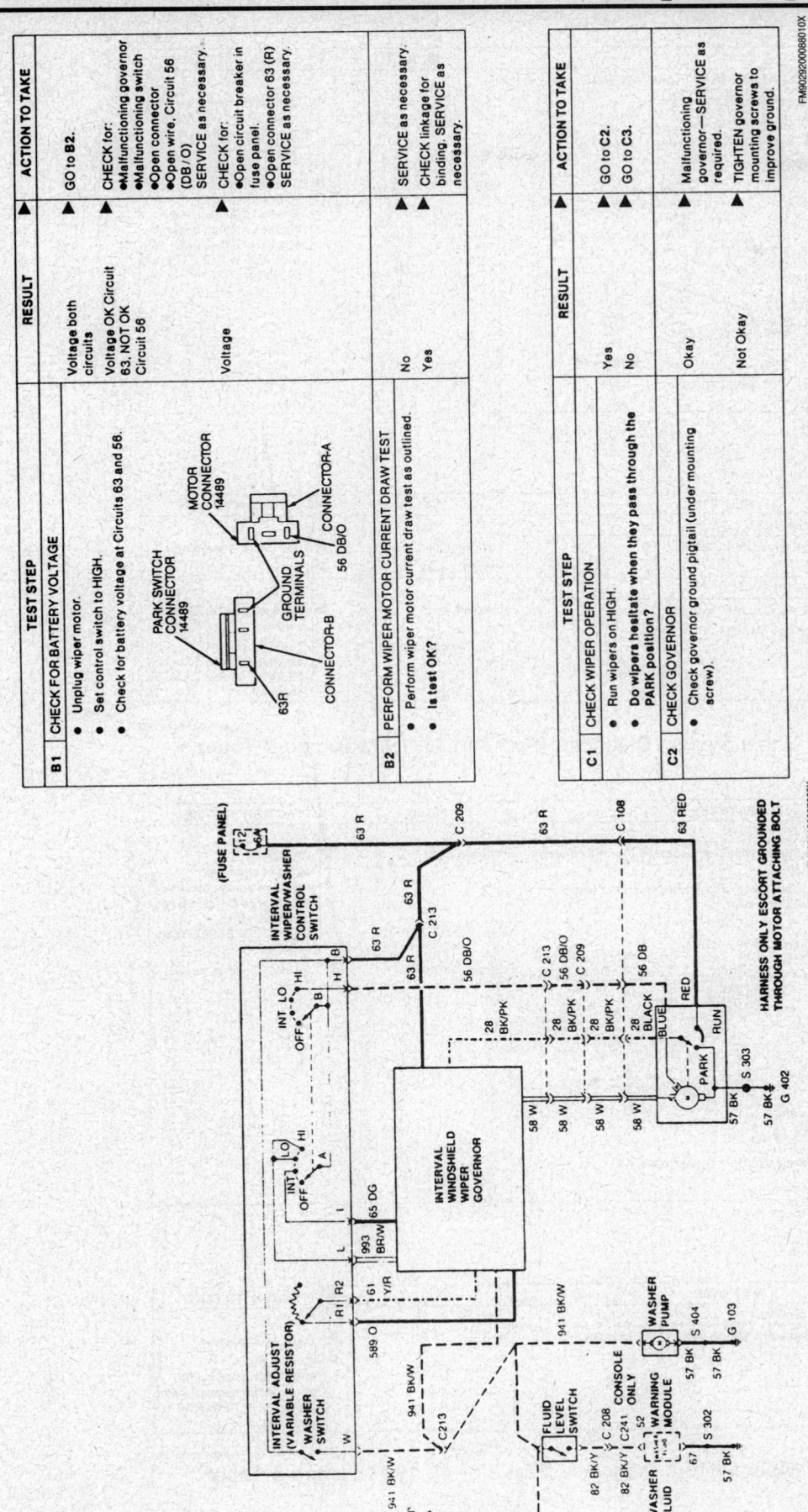

TEST STEP	RESULT	ACTION TO TAKE
B1 CHECK FOR BATTERY VOLTAGE • Unplug wiper motor. • Set control switch to HIGH. • Check for battery voltage at Circuits 63 and 56.	Voltage both circuits	GO to **B2**.
	Voltage OK Circuit 63, NOT OK Circuit 56	CHECK for: • Malfunctioning governor • Malfunctioning switch • Open connector • Open wire, Circuit 56 (DB/O) SERVICE as necessary.
	Voltage	CHECK for: • Open circuit breaker in fuse panel. • Open connector 63 (R) SERVICE as necessary.
B2 PERFORM WIPER MOTOR CURRENT DRAW TEST • Perform wiper motor current draw test as outlined. • Is test OK?	No	SERVICE as necessary.
	Yes	CHECK linkage for binding. SERVICE as necessary.
C1 CHECK WIPER OPERATION • Run wipers on HIGH. • Do wipers hesitate when they pass through the PARK position?	Yes	GO to **C2**.
	No	GO to **C3**.
C2 CHECK GOVERNOR • Check governor ground pigtail (under mounting screw).	Okay	Malfunctioning governor—SERVICE as required.
	Not Okay	TIGHTEN governor mounting screws to improve ground.

Fig. 5 Wiper System Diagnosis (Part 1 of 4). 1992 Tempo & Topaz

Fig. 4 Interval control circuit schematic. Tempo & Topaz

TEST STEP		RESULT	►	ACTION TO TAKE
C3	CHECK CIRCUIT 58 FOR BATTERY VOLTAGE			
	• Unplug wiper motor.	Yes	►	CHECK for malfunctioning wiper motor. PERFORM low speed current draw test. GO to **E1**. SERVICE as required.
	• Set wiper switch on LOW.			
	• Check Circuit 58 for battery voltage.			
	• **Is voltage good?**	No	►	CHECK for: • Open connector • Malfunctioning switch • Malfunctioning governor • Open wire Circuit 58 (W) SERVICE or REPLACE as necessary.

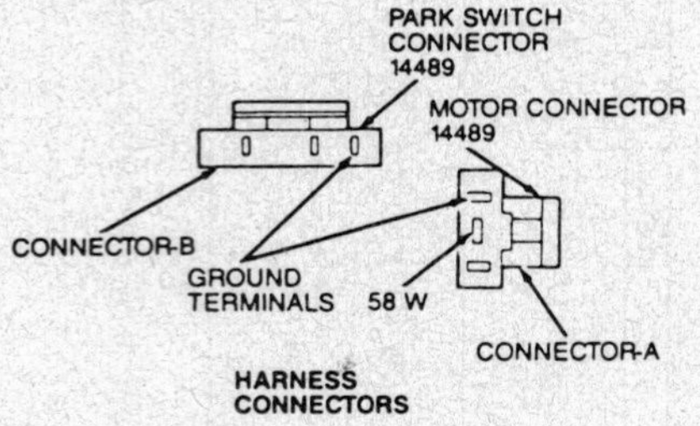

TEST STEP		RESULT	►	ACTION TO TAKE
D1	WIPER PARK TEST			
	• Perform Wiper Park Test E 1.	Wipers fail to park	►	REPLACE wiper motor
		Wipers park	►	GO to **D2**.
D2	CHECK WIPER SWITCH			
	• Unplug wiper control switch.	Wipers stop	►	REPLACE wiper control switch.
	• Turn ignition switch to RUN.	Wipers continue to run	►	CHECK for: • Malfunctioning governor SERVICE or REPLACE as required.

FM9029200088020X

Fig. 5   Wiper System Diagnosis (Part 2 of 4). 1992 Tempo & Topaz

TEST STEP		RESULT	►	ACTION TO TAKE
E1	CHECK WIPER MOTOR			
	• Stop wipers with ignition switch so that they are not in PARK position.	Wipers park	►	CHECK for: • Open connection • Malfunctioning governor • Open wire Circuit 58 (W) or 28 (BK / PK) SERVICE or REPLACE as required.
	• Unplug wiper motor and connect jumpers to motor connector as shown.	Wipers do not park	►	REPLACE wiper motor.

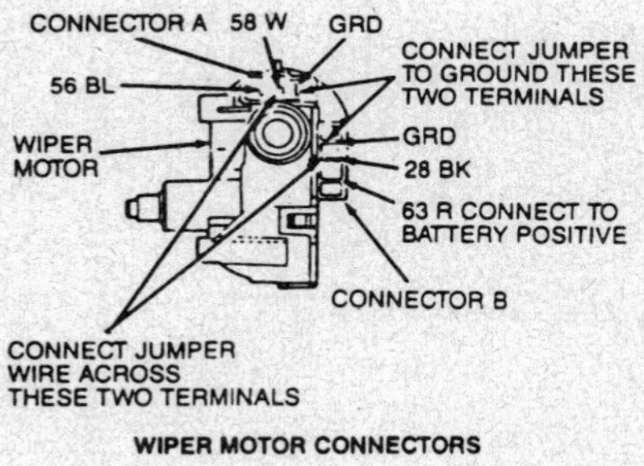

TEST STEP		RESULT	►	ACTION TO TAKE
F1	CHECK OPERATION			
	• **Do wipers work OK on INT, LOW and HIGH?**	Yes	►	REPLACE governor.
		No	►	CHECK for: • Malfunctioning switch • Malfunctioning governor SERVICE or REPLACE as required.

FM9029200088030X

Fig. 5   Wiper System Diagnosis (Part 3 of 4). 1992 Tempo & Topaz

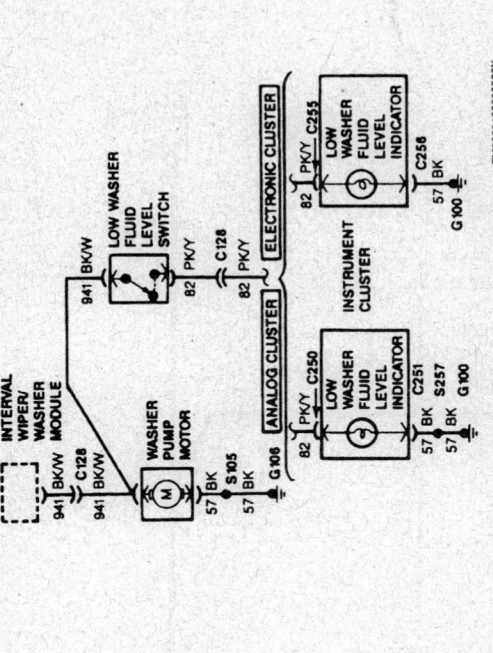

Fig. 7   Washer circuit schematic. Crown Victoria, Grand Marquis & Town Car

CONDITION	POSSIBLE SOURCE	ACTION
• Windshield wipers do not operate	• Open circuit breaker.	• Replace CB. If it goes again, check for short circuit.
	• Poor ground at wiper motor.	• Jumper motor case to car body. If motor operates, service ground.
	• Switch.	• Perform switch test. Service as required.
	• Bent or damaged linkage.	• Service or replace.
• Wipers will not park in off or will not pause in interval mode •	• Worn or damaged motor, switch, wiring or interval governor assembly.	• Perform Parking Test.
	• Circuit 941 open.	• Service as required.
• In interval mode no wipe(s) after wash	• Interval governor assembly inoperative.	• Replace governor.
	• Motor.	• Perform motor test. Service as required.
	• Open in wiring.	• Service as required.
• Poor ground to interval governor assembly	• Inoperative governor on intermittent wiper system.	• Replace governor.

Fig. 8   Wiper system diagnosis. Crown Victoria, Grand Marquis & Town Car

TEST STEP	RESULT	▲	ACTION TO TAKE
G1	**CHECK WIPER OPERATION**		
• Check operation of wipers.			
• Do wipers work OK?			
	Yes	▲	**CHECK for:** • Low washer fluid • Split, loose, pinched or kinked washer hose • Malfunctioning washer pump motor • Malfunctioning switch • Open Circuit 941 (BK/W) • Open connector SERVICE or REPLACE as necessary.
	No	▲	**CHECK for:** • Open circuit breaker in fuse panel • Open wire, Circuit 63 (R) SERVICE or REPLACE as necessary.

Fig. 5   Wiper System Diagnosis (Part 4 of 4). 1992 Tempo & Topaz

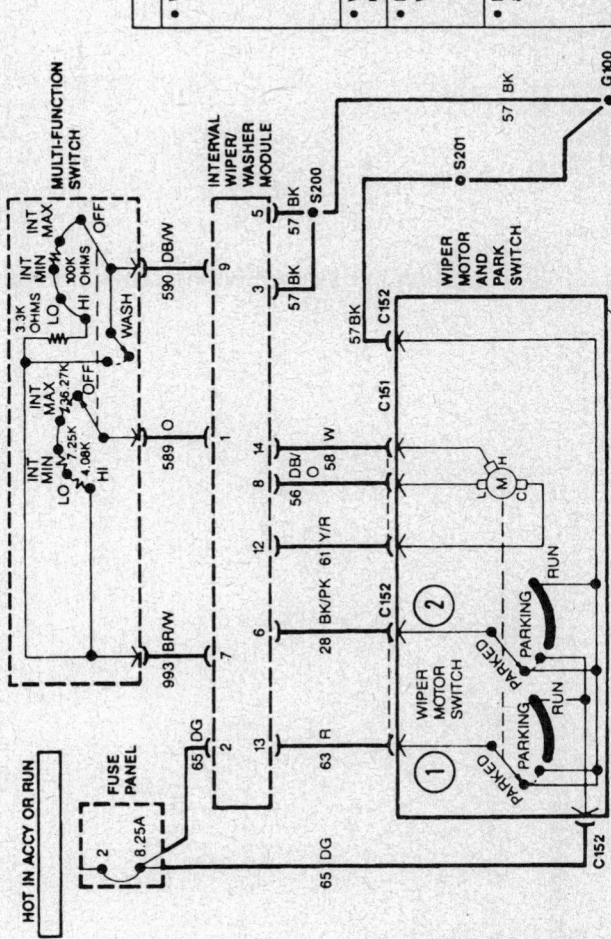

Fig. 6   Wiper circuit schematic. Crown Victoria, Grand Marquis & Town Car

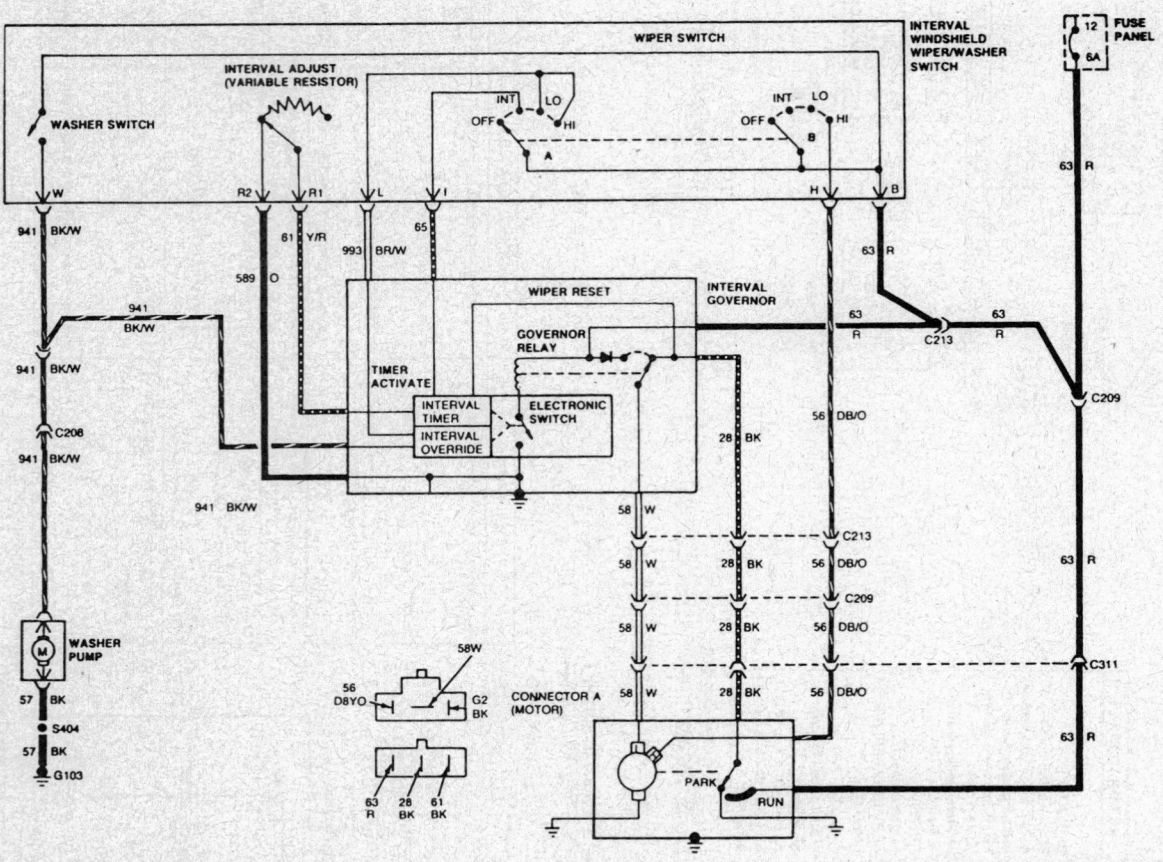

Fig. 9 Wiper system wiring schematic (Intermittent). 1992–93 Mustang

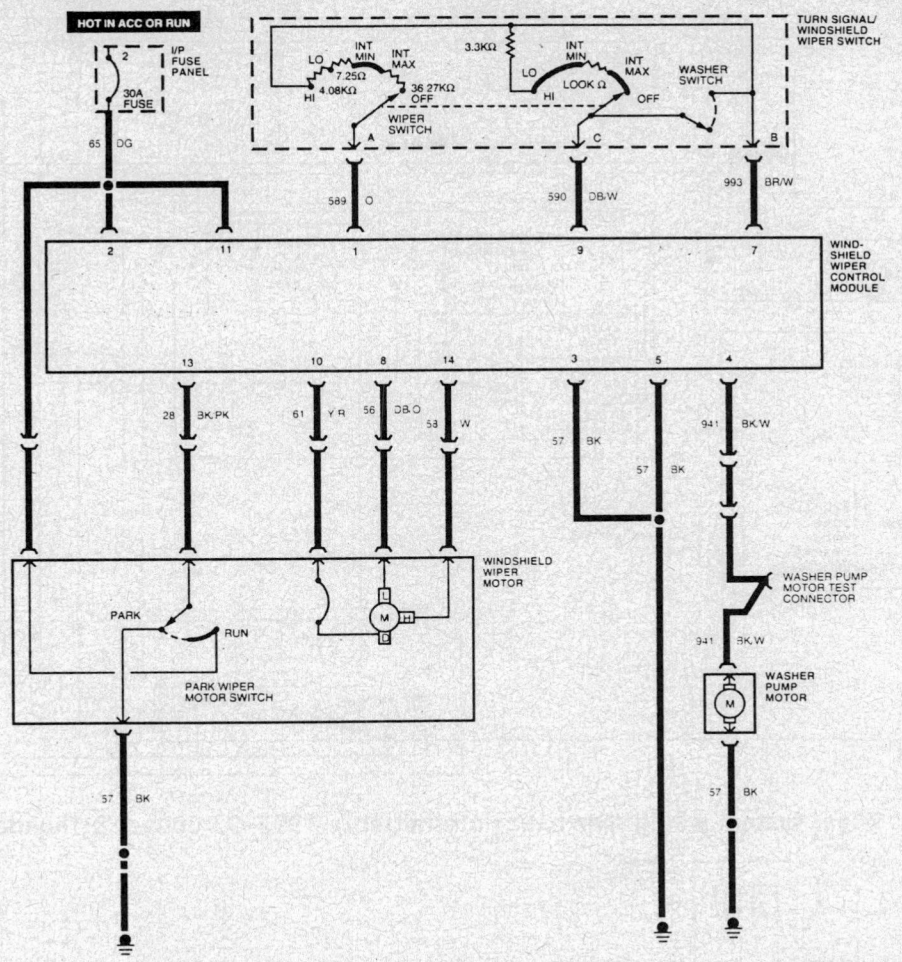

Fig. 10 Wiper system wiring schematic. 1994 Mustang

FM9029400175000X

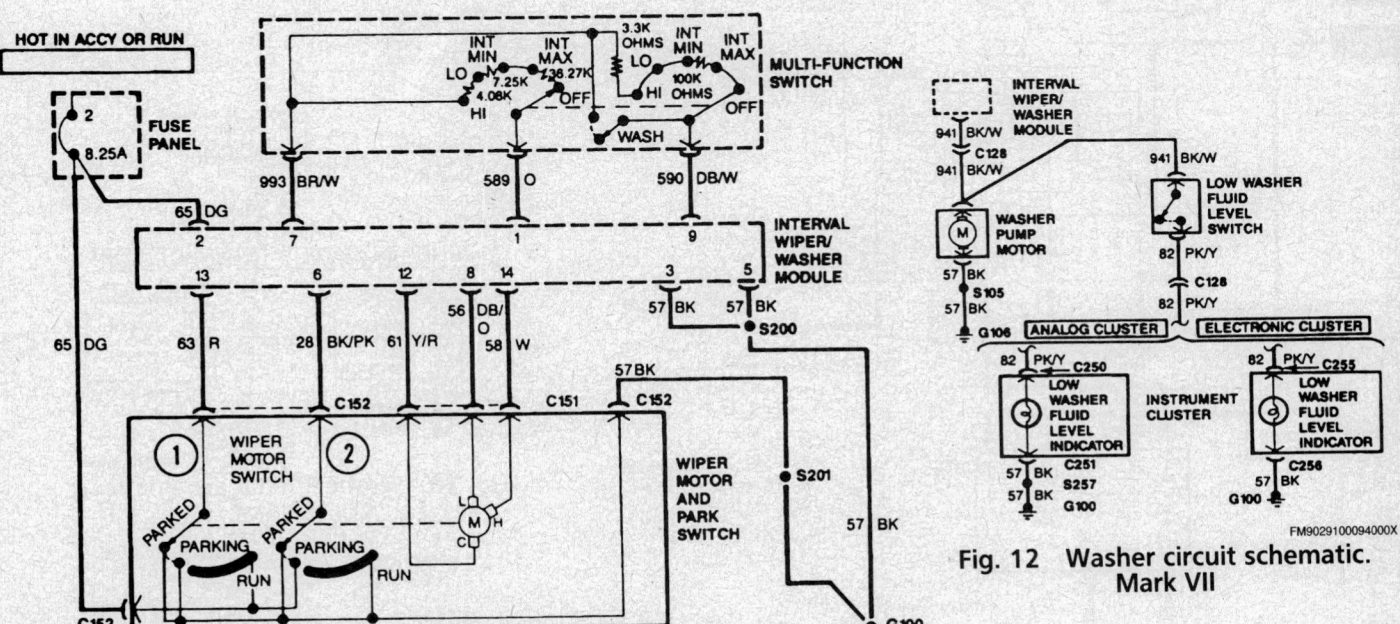

Fig. 11 Wiper circuit schematic. Mark VII

FM9029100093000X

Fig. 12 Washer circuit schematic. Mark VII

FM9029100094000X

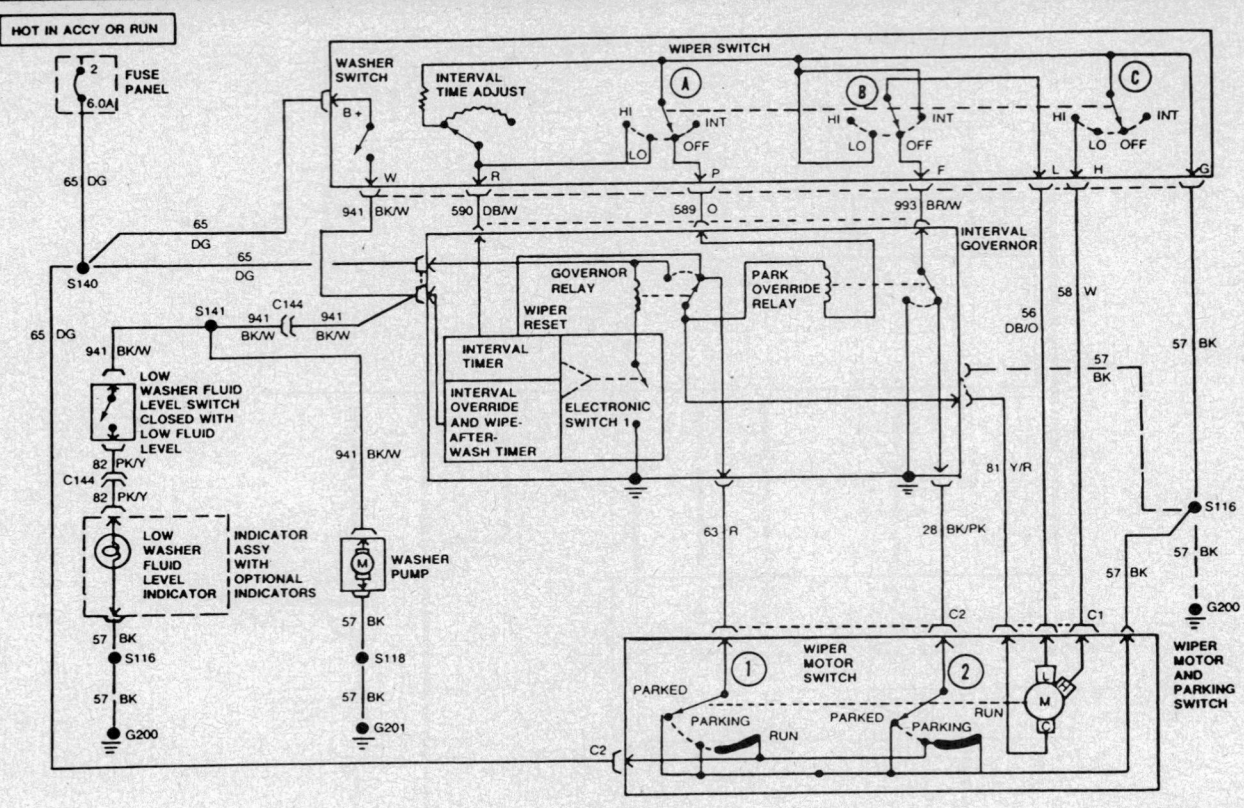

Fig. 13 Wiper system wiring schematic (Intermittent). 1992–93 Cougar & Thunderbird

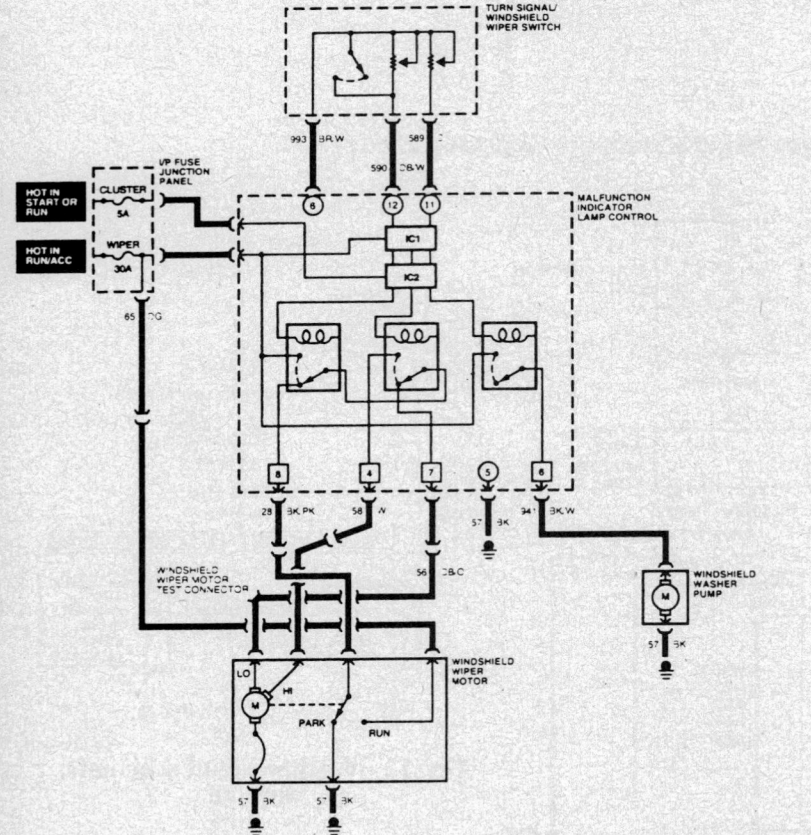

Fig. 14 Wiper & turn signal wiring schematic. 1994 Cougar & Thunderbird

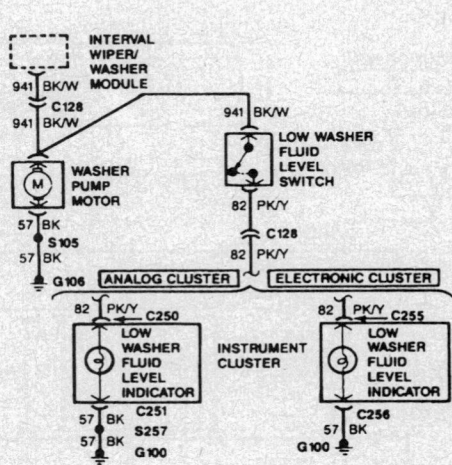

Fig. 16 Washer circuit schematic. Continental

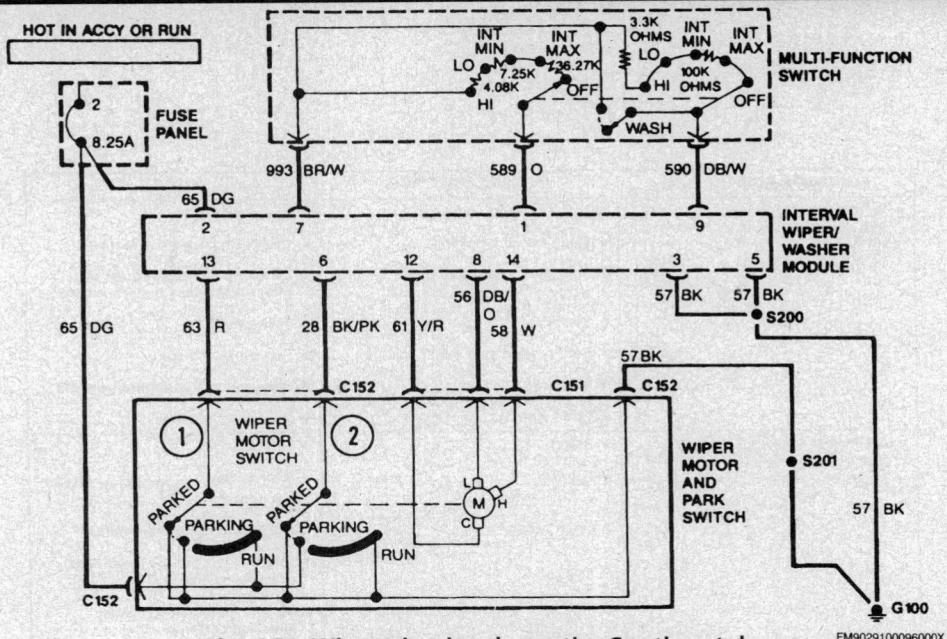

Fig. 15   Wiper circuit schematic. Continental

FM9029100096000X

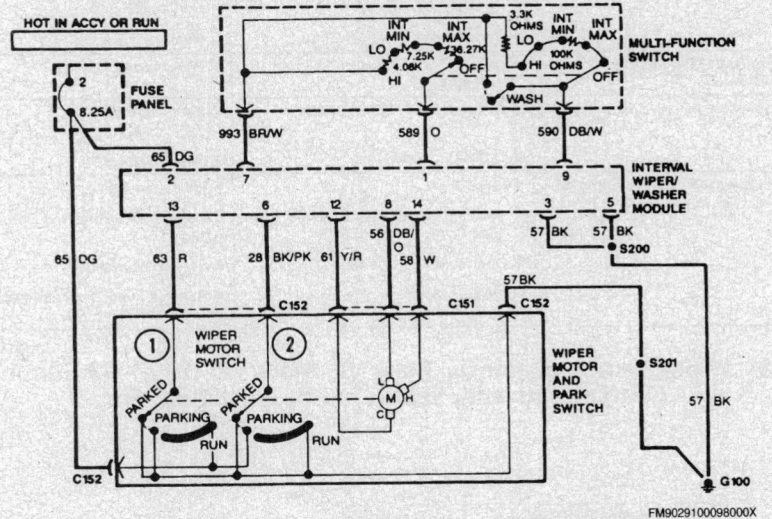

Fig. 17   Wiper circuit schematic. Sable & Taurus

FM9029100098000X

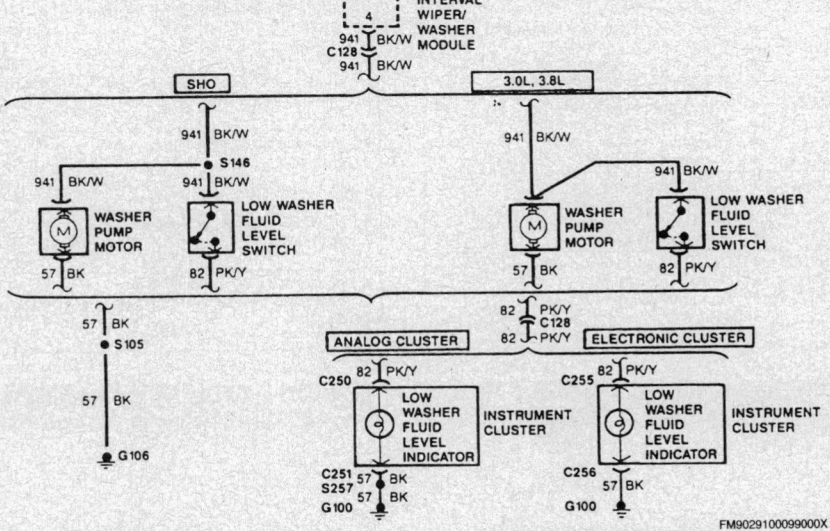

Fig. 18   Washer circuit schematic. Mark VIII, Sable & Taurus

FM9029100099000X

CONDITION (IGNITION ON)	POSSIBLE SOURCE	ACTION
• Windshield wipers inoperative in ALL switch positions.	NOTE: Check in sequence. • Open circuit breaker. • Poor ground at wiper motor. • Switch. • Bent or damaged motor linkage. • Motor. • Open wire or connector.	• Check and replace if required. • Jumper motor case to car body. If motor now works service ground. • Test switch. • Service as required. • Perform motor current draw test. • Service as required.
• Windshield wipers inoperative or erratic in LOW or INTERVAL (HIGH ok).	• Switch. • Motor. • Open wiring. • Poor interval governor ground. • Inoperative interval governor.	• Test switch. • Perform motor current draw test for low speed. • Check circuit No. 58 (White). • Check circuit No. 61 (yellow-red) Continental only. • Service as required (tighten attaching screws). • Check circuit No. 57 (BL) Continental only. • Replace governor.
• Wipers won't stop in OFF or INTERVAL	• Motor, switch, wiring or governor assembly.	• Perform parking test.
• Interval systems only: No wipe(s) after wash.	• Circuit No. 941 (BK/W) open. • Governor inoperative.	• Service as required. • Replace governor.
Windshield washer does not operate.	• Low fluid level. • Split, loose, pinched or kinked hose. • Open in wiring or switch. • Washer Motor.	• Fill as required. • Inspect, service as required. • Service as required. • Replace motor, seal and impeller assembly.

FM9029100100000X

Fig. 19 Wiper system diagnosis. Mark VII, Mark VIII, 1992–93 Continental, Cougar, Mustang, Sable, Taurus & Thunderbird

CONDITION	POSSIBLE SOURCE
• Windshield Washer Does Not Operate	• Low fluid level. • Split, loose, pinched or kinked washer hose. • Open in wiring or turn signal and windshield wiper switch. • Windshield washer pump. • Windshield wiper governor.
• Windshield Wipers Inoperative At High Speed	• Windshield wiper motor. • Windshield wiper governor. • Windshield wiper switch. • Damaged circuitry.
• Windshield Wipers Inoperative At Low Speed	• Windshield wiper motor. • Windshield upper governor. • Windshield wiper switch. • Damaged circuitry.
• Windshield Wipers Continue to Run When Switch is Turned Off.	• Damaged windshield wiper motor. • Damaged circuitry. • Damaged windshield wiper governor. • Damaged switch.

FM9029400177010X

Fig. 20   Wiper system diagnosis (Part 1 of 2). 1994 Crown Victoria, Grand Marquis & Town Car

CONDITION	POSSIBLE SOURCE
• Windshield Wipers Inoperative—All Control Switch Positions	• Open circuit breaker. • Poor ground at windshield wiper motor. • Turn signal and windshield wiper switch. • Bent or damaged windshield wiper mounting arm and pivot shaft. • Windshield wiper governor.
• Wipers Will Not Park in Proper Position	• Worn or damaged windshield wiper motor , turn signal and windshield wiper switch wiring or windshield wiper governor.
• In INTERVAL Mode No Wipe(s) After Wash	• Circuit 941 open. • Windshield wiper governor inoperative.
• Inoperative Windshield Wiper Governor on Intermittent Wiper System	• Windshield wiper motor . • Open in wiring. • Poor ground to windshield wiper governor assembly.

FM9029400177020X

Fig. 20   Wiper system diagnosis (Part 2 of 2). 1994 Crown Victoria, Grand Marquis & Town Car

CONDITION	POSSIBLE SOURCE
• Windshield Wipers Inoperative in ALL Switch Positions	**NOTE:** Check in sequence. • Open circuit breaker. • Poor ground at wiper motor. • Wiper switch. • Bent or damaged motor linkage. • Motor. • Open wire or connector. • Windshield wiper governor.
• Windshield Wipers Inoperative or Erratic in LO or INT (HI OK)	• Wiper switch. • Motor. • Open wiring. • Inoperative windshield wiper governor.
• Wipers Will Not Park in OFF or Will Not Pause in INT Mode	• Motor, wiper switch, wiring or governor assembly.
• No Wipe(s) After Wash (Washer OK)	• Open circuit breaker. • Poor ground at wiper motor. • Bent or damaged motor linkage. • Motor. • Open wire or connector. • Windshield wiper governor.
• Windshield Washer Does Not Operate	• Low fluid level. • Split, loose, pinched or kinked hose. • Open in wiring or wiper switch. • Washer motor. • Windshield wiper governor.
• Low Washer Fluid Indicator Always ON or OFF	• Circuit short to ground. • Open ground. • Binding float. • Damaged switch.

FM9029400178000X

Fig. 21   Wiper system diagnosis. 1994 Continental

CONDITION	POSSIBLE SOURCE
• Windshield Wipers Will Not Park at Proper Position	• Turn signal and windshield wiper switch.
• Windshield Wipers Will Not Stop in OFF or INTERVAL	• Windshield wiper motor switch, wiring or windshield wiper governor assembly.
• Internal Systems Only: No Wipe(s) After Wash	• Circuit 941 (BK/W) open. • Windshield wiper governor inoperative.
• Windshield Washer Does Not Operate	• Low fluid level. • Split, loose, pinched or kinked window washer hose. • Open in wiring or turn signal and windshield wiper switch. • Windshield washer pump. • Replace windshield washer pump. • Windshield wiper governor.
• Rear Windshield Wiper Does Not Operate	• Rear windshield wiper motor. • Rear windshield wiper/washer switch. • Blown fuse. • Circuit.
• Rear Windshield Wiper Operates Constantly	• Rear windshield wiper/washer switch. • Circuit.

FM9029400179020X

Fig. 22   Wiper system diagnosis (Part 2 of 2). 1994 Sable & Taurus

CONDITION	POSSIBLE SOURCE
• Windshield Wipers Inoperative in ALL Turn Signal and Windshield Wiper Switch Positions	**NOTE:** Check in sequence. • Blown fuse. • Poor ground at Windshield wiper motor. • Turn signal and windshield wiper switch. • Bent or damaged windshield wiper motor linkage. • Windshield wiper motor. • Open wire or connector. • Windshield wiper governor.
• Windshield Wipers Inoperative or Erratic in LO	• Turn signal and windshield wiper switch. • Windshield wiper motor. • Open wiring. • Inoperative windshield wiper governor.
• Windshield Wipers Inoperative in INTERVAL	• Turn signal and windshield wiper switch • Windshield wiper motor. • Open wiring.

FM9029400179010X

Fig. 22   Wiper system diagnosis (Part 1 of 2). 1994 Sable & Taurus

CONDITION	POSSIBLE SOURCE
• Windshield Washer System Does Not Operate	• Low fluid level. • Split, loose, pinched or kinked windshield washer hose. • Circuitry open/shorted. • Damaged turn signal and windshield wiper switch. • Damaged windshield wiper control module. • Damaged windshield washer pump.
• No Wipe After Wash	• Damaged wiper control module. • Damaged turn signal and windshield wiper switch. • Damaged circuitry.
• Windshield Wipers Inoperative in All Control Switch Positions	• Open fuse. • Poor ground at windshield wiper motor. • Damaged turn signal and windshield wiper switch. • Open circuitry or connector. • Damaged windshield wiper control module. • Damaged windshield wiper motor linkage.
• Windshield Wipers Inoperative at High Speed	• Damaged windshield wiper motor. • Damaged turn signal and windshield wiper switch • Damaged circuitry.
• Windshield Wipers Inoperative at Low Speed	• Damaged turn signal and windshield wiper switch. • Damaged windshield wiper motor. • Open circuitry. • Damaged windshield wiper control module.
• Windshield Wipers Inoperative at Interval Setting	• Damaged turn signal and windshield wiper switch. • Open circuitry. • Damaged windshield wiper control module.
• Windshield Wipers Will Not Park at Proper Position	• Damaged windshield wiper motor. • Damaged windshield wiper control module. • Damaged turn signal and windshield wiper switch
• Windshield Wipers Continue to Run When Turn Signal and Windshield Wiper Switch Are Turned OFF	• Damaged turn signal and windshield wiper switch. • Damaged windshield wiper motor. • Damaged windshield wiper control module.

FM9029400180000X

Fig. 23   Wiper system diagnosis. 1994 Mustang

CONDITION	POSSIBLE SOURCE
• Windshield Wipers Inoperative in ALL Control Switch Positions	NOTE: Check in sequence. • Turn signal and windshield wiper switch. • Bent or damaged windshield wiper mounting arm and pivot shaft. • Windshield wiper motor. • Open wire or connector.
• Windshield Wipers Inoperative at Low Speed	• Turn signal and windshield wiper switch. • Windshield wiper motor. • Open wiring. • Poor malfunction indicator lamp control ground. • Inoperative windshield wiper governor.
• Windshield Wipers Inoperative at Interval Setting	• Windshield wiper motor. • turn signal and windshield wiper switch. • Wiring. • Malfunction indicator lamp control.
• Windshield Washer Does Not Operate	• Low fluid level. • Split, loose, pinched, or kinked window washer hose. • Open in wiring or turn signal and windshield wiper switch. • Windshield washer pump.
• Windshield Wipers Inoperative at High Speed	• Windshield wiper motor. • Windshield wiper switch. • Damaged circuitry.
• Windshield Wipers Continue to Run When Switch is Turned OFF	• Damaged windshield wiper motor. • Damaged circuitry. • Damaged switch. • Damaged malfunction indicator lamp control.
• Windshield Wipers Will Not Park at Proper Position	• Damaged windshield wiper motor. • Damaged circuitry. • Damaged malfunction indicator lamp control. • Damaged windshield wiper switch.

FM9029400181000X

Fig. 24 Wiper system diagnosis. 1994 Cougar & Thunderbird

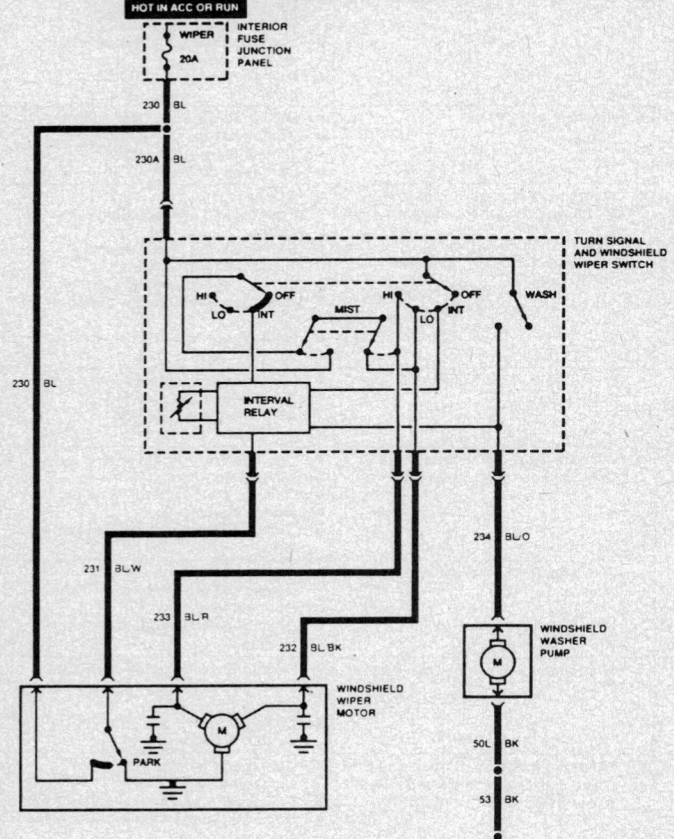

FM9029400183010X

Fig. 25 Wiper circuit schematic (Part 1 of 2). Aspire w/interval function

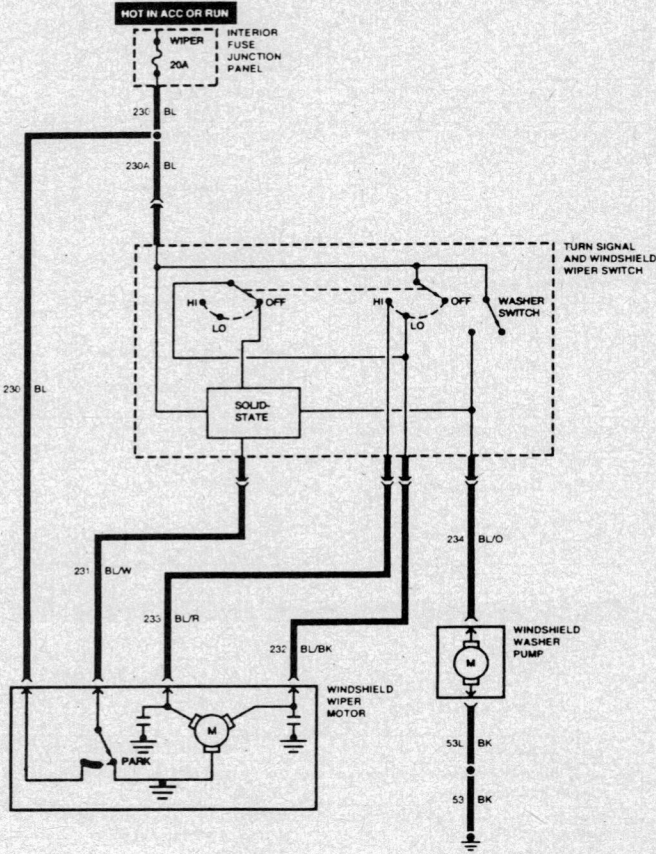

FM9029400183020X

Fig. 25 Wiper circuit schematic (Part 2 of 2). Aspire less interval function

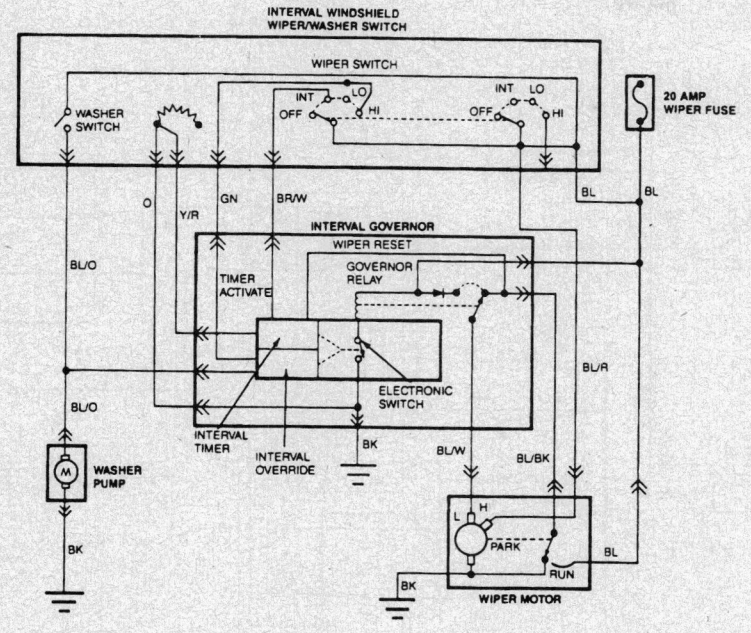

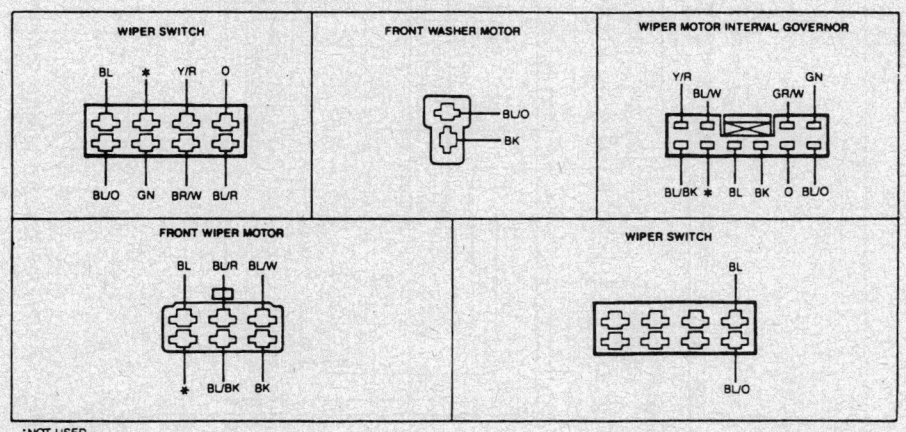

FM9029100108000X

Fig. 26 Wiper system wiring schematic. Capri

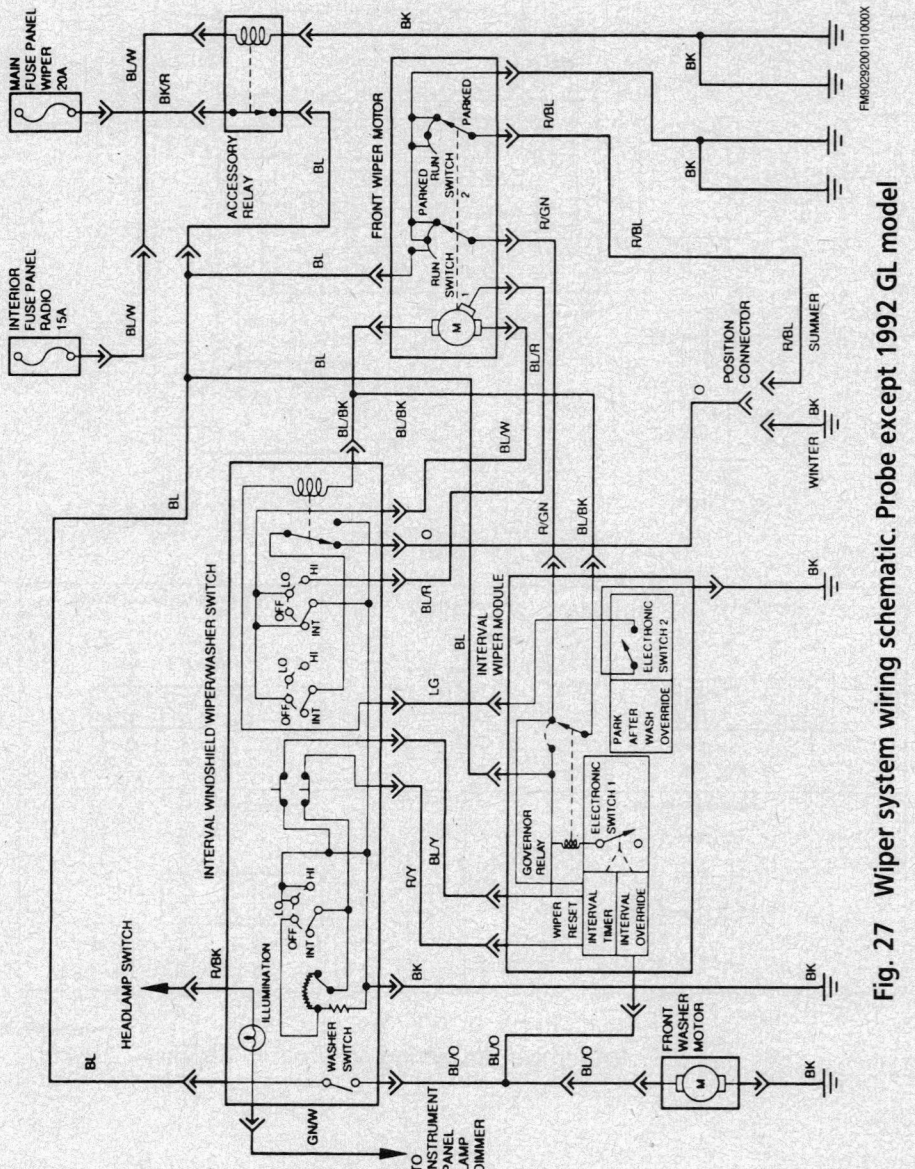

Fig. 27 Wiper system wiring schematic. Probe except 1992 GL model

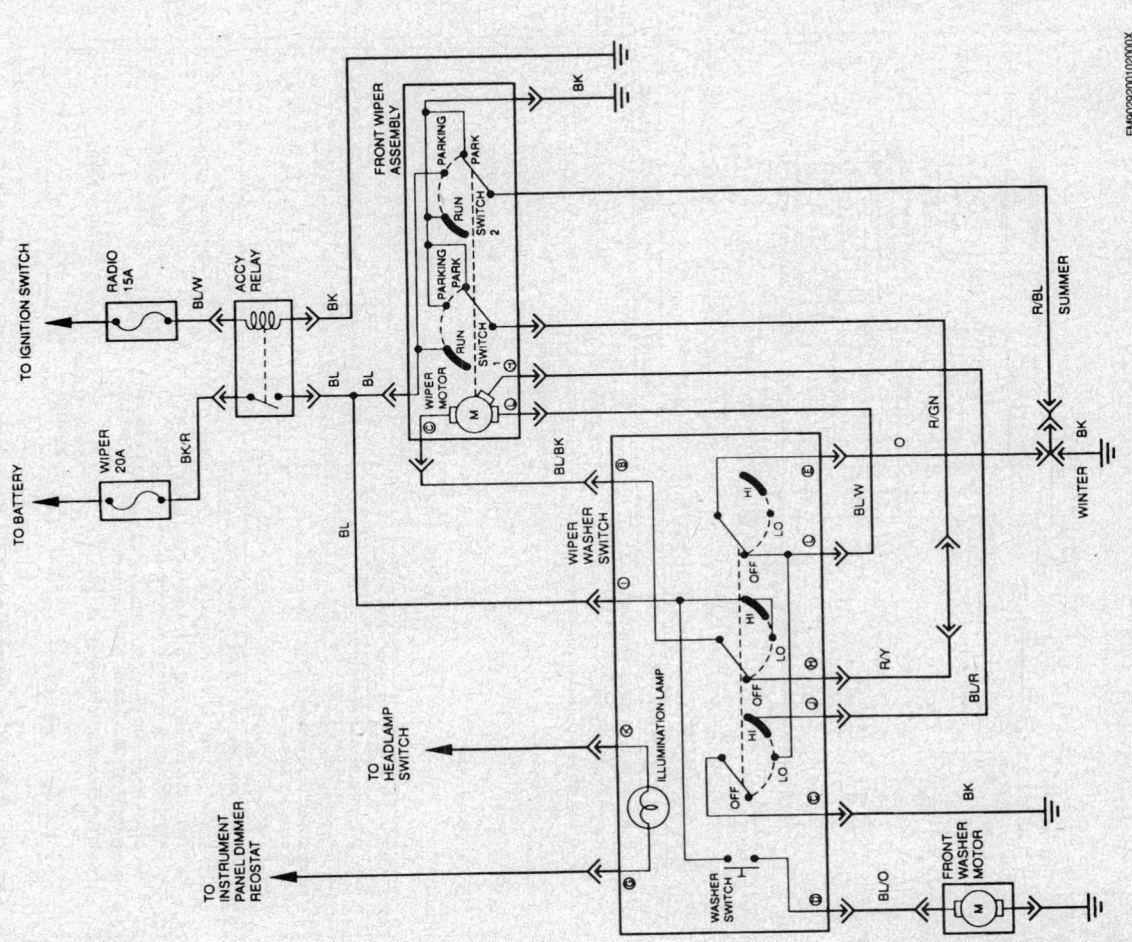

CONDITION	POSSIBLE SOURCE
Windshield Washers Inoperative	• Fuse. • Circuit. • Windshield wiper/washer switch. • Windshield washer pump.
Rear Window Washer Inoperative	• Fuse. • Circuit. • Rear window wiper washer switch. • Rear window washer pump.
Windshield Wipers Inoperative — All Windshield Wiper Switch Positions	• Fuse. • Circuit. • Windshield wiper motor. • Windshield wiper/washer switch.
Windshield Wipers Inoperative At High Speed	• Circuit. • Windshield wiper/washer switch. • Windshield wiper motor.
Windshield Wipers Inoperative At Low Speed	• Circuit. • Windshield wiper/washer switch. • Windshield wiper motor.
Windshield Wipers Inoperative At Interval Setting	• Circuit. • Windshield wiper/washer switch.
Windshield Wipers Will Not Park Below Windshield	• Windshield wiper motor. • Windshield wiper motor ground.
Windshield Wipers Will Not Turn Off	• Circuit. • Windshield wiper/washer switch.
Rear Window Wiper Inoperative	• Fuse. • Circuit. • Rear window wiper washer switch. • Rear window wiper motor.
Rear Window Wiper Will Not Turn Off	• Circuit. • Rear window wiper/washer switch. • Rear window wiper motor.
Rear Window Wiper Will Not Park	• Rear window wiper motor. • Rear window wiper motor ground.

Fig. 29 Wiper system diagnosis. Aspire

Fig. 28 Wiper system wiring schematic. 1992 Probe GL

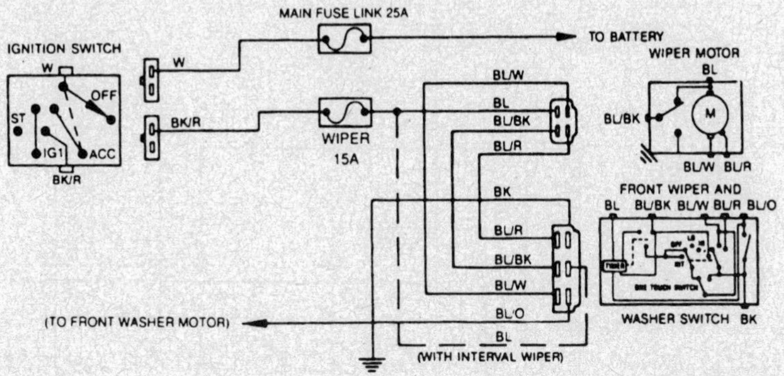

TEST STEP	RESULT	ACTION TO TAKE
WW4 CHECK WINDSHIELD WIPER/WASHER SWITCH GROUND • Disconnect the W.W. switch connector. • Check for continuity to ground on the "BK" wire at the W.W. switch. • Is there continuity?	Yes No	GO to WW5 SERVICE the "BK" wire to ground.
WW5 CHECK WINDSHIELD WIPER/WASHER SWITCH OPERATION • Disconnect the W.W. switch connector. • Check for continuity to the "BK" terminal. W.W. Switch | Terminal Low | "BL/W" High | "BL/R" • Is there continuity between the terminals?	Yes No	SERVICE the "BL/W" wire and the "BL/R" wire from the W.W. switch to the W.W. motor. REPLACE the W.W. switch.
WW6 CHECK POWER TO WIPER FUSE • Remove the wiper fuse at the interior fuse panel. • Check for 12 volts at the wiper fuse (ignition switch side). • Are there 12 volts?	Yes No	SERVICE the fuse and/or the "BL" wire to the W.W. motor. SERVICE the "BK/R" wire to the ignition switch.
WW7 CHECK WINDSHIELD WIPER SWITCH • Disconnect the wiper switch connector. • Does the wiper motor stop? NOTE: If the wiper is running at high speed, repair the "BL/R" wire. If the wiper is running at low speed, repair the "BL/W" wire.	Yes No	REPLACE the wiper switch. REPAIR the shorted wire between the wiper switch and the wiper motor (see note).

WW8 CHECK WINDSHIELD WIPER MOTOR CONTINUITY
• Place the wipers out of the park position.
• Be sure the wiper switch is OFF.
• Remove the wiper fuse.
• Disconnect the wiper motor connector.
• Check for continuity to ground at the following places:
  Motor case.
  Motor "BL/BK" terminal.
• Is there continuity?
	Yes
	No
	(Motor case)
	
	No
	("BL/BK" terminal)
		GO to WW10
		REPAIR the ground of the wiper motor.
		
		REPLACE the wiper motor.

WW9 CHECK WINDSHIELD WIPER SWITCH SUPPLY • Disconnect the wiper switch connector. • Key ON. • Check for 12 volts at the "BL" wire of the wiper switch connector. • Are there 12 volts?	Yes No	GO to WW10 REPAIR the "BL" wire between the wiper fuse and the wiper switch.

Fig. 30   Wiper system diagnosis & testing (Part 2 of 3). 1992 Festiva

TEST STEP	RESULT	ACTION TO TAKE

WW1 CHECK WINDSHIELD WIPER FUNCTION
• Turn the ignition switch ON.
• Check all the wiper switch positions in the order shown.
  Low speed
  High speed
  Park
  Interval
  One-touch
	Wiper not working
	Low not working
	High not working
	Park not working
	Wiper won't stop
	Interval not working
	One-touch not working
		GO to WW2
		GO to WW3
		GO to WW3
		GO to WW8
		GO to WW7
		GO to WW9
		REPLACE the windshield wiper switch.

WW2 CHECK WINDSHIELD WIPER MOTOR SUPPLY • Disconnect the wiper motor connector. • Key ON. • Check for 12 volts on the "BL" wire at the wiper motor connector. • Are there 12 volts?	Yes No	GO to WW3 GO to WW6
WW3 CHECK WINDSHIELD WIPER MOTOR GROUND • Disconnect the W.W. motor connector. • Check for continuity to ground on the "BL/W" wire at the W.W. motor with the W.W. switch on low. • Check for continuity to ground on the "BL/R" wire at the W.W. motor with the W.W. switch on high. • Is there continuity for both high and low?	Yes No (wiper not working) No (low or high not working)	REPLACE the wiper motor. GO to WW4 GO to WW5

Fig. 30   Wiper system diagnosis & testing (Part 1 of 3). 1992 Festiva

Fig. 31 Wiper system diagnosis & testing (Part 2 of 5). Capri

TEST STEP	RESULT	ACTION TO TAKE
FW1 FRONT WIPER FUSE CHECK • Check 20 amp wiper fuse. • Is fuse OK?	Yes No	GO to FW4. GO to FW2.
FW2 WIPER SWITCH, GOVERNOR AND WIPER MOTOR PARK SWITCH SUPPLY CHECK • Replace fuse. • Turn key ON. • Check wiper fuse. • Is fuse OK?	Yes No	GO to FW4. GO to FW3.

FW3 WIPER SWITCH, GOVERNOR AND WIPER MOTOR PARK SWITCH SUPPLY SHORT CHECK
• Key OFF.
• Disconnect BL wire connectors from wiper switch, governor, and wiper motor.
• Measure resistance of BL wire between each component connector and ground.
  • Wiper switch
  • Governor
  • Wiper motor
• Is resistance greater than 10,000 ohms?
	Yes
	No
		GO to FW4.
		SERVICE each affected BL wire between the component connector and the fuse.

FW4 CHECK SUPPLY AT WIPER SWITCH, WIPER GOVERNOR AND WIPER MOTOR • Access the wiper switch, wiper governor and the wiper motor connectors. • Key ON. • Measure the voltage on the BL wire at the wiper motor connectors. • Is the voltage greater than 10 volts?	Yes No	GO to FW5. SERVICE BL wire in question.

Fig. 30 Wiper system diagnosis & testing (Part 3 of 3). 1992 Festiva

TEST STEP	RESULT	ACTION TO TAKE
WW10 CHECK POWER TO WIPER SWITCH • Place the wipers in the park position. • Disconnect the wiper switch connector. • Key ON. • Check for 12 volts on the "BL/BK" wire at the wiper switch connector. • Are there 12 volts?	Yes No	REPLACE the wiper switch. GO to WW11
WW11 CHECK WIPER MOTOR PARK RANGE • Place the wiper motor in the park position. • Disconnect the wiper motor connector. • Check the continuity between the wiper motor terminals "BL/BK" and "BL". • Is there continuity?	Yes No	REPAIR the "BL/BK" wire between the wiper switch and the wiper motor. REPLACE the wiper motor.

Fig. 31 Wiper system diagnosis & testing (Part 1 of 5). Capri

CONDITION	POSSIBLE SOURCE	ACTION
Wiper Not Working	• Wiper fuse. • Governor ground. • Wiper motor ground. • Circuit.	• Go to FW1. • Go to FW9. • Go to FW10. • Go to FW4.
Low Wiper Speed Not Working	• Wiper switch. • Wiper governor. • Wiper motor. • Circuit.	• Go to FW5. • Go to FW8. • Go to FW12. • Go to FW4.
High Wiper Speed Not Working	• Wiper switch • Wiper motor. • Circuit.	• Go to FW5. • Go to FW12. • Go to FW4.
Intermittent Wiper Speed Not Working	• Wiper switch. • Wiper governor. • Wiper motor. • Circuit.	• Go to FW14. • Go to FW15. • Go to FW12. • Go to FW4.
Wiper Not Working With Washer Working	• Wiper motor. • Wiper governor. • Circuit.	• Go to FW12. • Go to FW8. • Go to FW4.
Park Not Working	• Wiper switch. • Wiper governor. • Wiper motor. • Circuit.	• Go to FW5. • Go to FW8. • Go to FW13. • Go to FW4.

Part 4 of 5

TEST STEP			RESULT	ACTION TO TAKE
FW8	**CHECK WIPER GOVERNOR**			
• Key ON.				
• Check the wiper governor operation by measuring the voltage on the following terminals at the wiper governor connector in the stated wiper switch position.			Yes	GO to FW9.
			No	SERVICE wiper governor.
Switch Position	Terminal Color	Voltage		
OFF	BL/W, BL/BK	Less than 1 volt		
LOW	BL/W, BL/BK	Greater than 10 volts less than 1 volt		
HIGH	BL/W, BL/BK, BL/R	Greater than 10 volts less than 1 volt		
INT	BL/W, BL/BK	Greater than 10 volts less than 1 volt during each cycle		
• Are the voltages correct?				
FW9	**CHECK HI-SPEED LEAD BETWEEN WIPER SWITCH AND WIPER MOTOR**			
• Disconnect the wiper motor connector.			Yes	GO to FW10.
• Measure the voltage on the BL/R wire at the harness connector.			No	SERVICE BL/R wire.
• Is the voltage greater than 10 volts?				
FW10	**CHECK LEADS BETWEEN WIPER GOVERNOR AND WIPER MOTOR**			
• Key OFF.			Yes	GO to FW11.
• Measure the resistance of the BL/W and BL/BK wires between the wiper governor and the wiper motor.			No	SERVICE wire in question.
• Are the resistances less than 5 ohms?				
FW11	**CHECK WIPER MOTOR GROUND**			
• Measure the resistance on the BK wire between the wiper motor and ground.			Yes	GO to FW12.
• Is the resistance less than 5 ohms?			No	SERVICE BK wire.

FM9029100109040X

Fig. 31   Wiper system diagnosis & testing (Part 4 of 5). Capri

Part 3 of 5

TEST STEP			RESULT	ACTION TO TAKE
FW5	**WIPER SWITCH CHECK**			
• Key OFF.			Yes	GO to FW6.
• Disconnect wiper switch connector.			No	REPLACE wiper switch.
• Measure resistance between the BL terminal and the following terminals at the switch:				
Switch Position	Terminal	Resistance		
OFF	All wires	Greater than 10,000 ohms		
INT	BR/W	Less than 5 ohms		
	All others	Greater than 10,000 ohms		
LOW	GN	Less than 5 ohms		
	All others	Greater than 10,000 ohms		
HI	GN and BL/R	Less than 5 ohms		
	All others	Greater than 10,000 ohms		
• Are the resistances correct?				
FW6	**CHECK LEADS BETWEEN WIPER SWITCH AND WIPER GOVERNOR**			
• Access the wiper governor.			Yes	GO to FW7.
• Measure the resistance of the following wires between the wiper switch and the wiper governor:			No	SERVICE wires in question.
• O				
• Y/R				
• GN				
• BR/W				
• Are the resistances less than 5 ohms?				
FW7	**CHECK WIPER GOVERNOR GROUND**			
• Measure the resistance of the BK wire between the governor and ground.			Yes	GO to FW8.
• Is the resistance less than 5 ohms?			No	SERVICE BK wire.

FM9029100109030X

Fig. 31   Wiper system diagnosis & testing (Part 3 of 5). Capri

Fig. 32 (1992 Probe)

TEST STEP	RESULT	ACTION TO TAKE

WW1 WINDSHIELD WIPER SYSTEM CHECK
• Turn ignition key to "ON" position.
• Check the following wiper system operations:
  – Low speed
  – High speed
  – Intermittent
  – Mist
  – Park
	Wipers not working	GO to WW2

	Low not working	GO to WW9
	High not working	GO to WW14
	Intermittent not working	GO to WW16
	Mist not working	GO to WW18
	Park not working	GO to WW20
WW2 WIPER FUSE CHECK (WIPERS NOT WORKING) • Check WIPER fuse. • Is fuse OK?	Yes	GO to WW3
	No	REPLACE fuse. (Read note)

NOTE: If fuse blows again check for shorts to ground in "BL" wires at wiper/washer switch (connector C271), intermittent unit (connector C237), and front wiper motor (connector C900). Repair "BL" wires as needed.

TEST STEP	RESULT	ACTION TO TAKE
WW3 INTERMITTENT SUPPLY CHECK (WIPERS NOT WORKING) • Check for 12 volts (±1 volt) on "BL" wire at intermittent unit (connector C237). • Is there 12 volts?	Yes	GO to WW4
	No	REPAIR "BL" wire between fuse panel and intermittent unit.

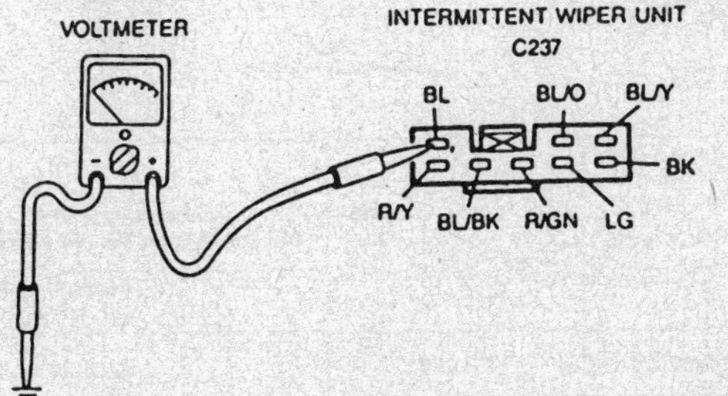

INTERMITTENT WIPER UNIT C237

BK, BL/Y, BL/O, LG, RGN, BL/BK, BL, R/Y

VOLTMETER

FM90291001003010X

Fig. 32 Wiper system diagnosis & testing (Part 1 of 18). 1992 Probe

Fig. 31 (Capri)

TEST STEP	RESULT	ACTION TO TAKE
FW12 CHECK WIPER MOTOR • Key ON. • Put the wiper switch in the low position. • Do the wipers operate?	Yes	GO to FW13.
	No	SERVICE/REPLACE wiper motor.
• Put the wiper switch in the high position. • Do the wipers operate faster?		
FW13 CHECK WIPER MOTOR PARK SYSTEM • Key ON. • Turn the wiper switch to low. • Turn wiper switch off while wiper is not in the park position. • Measure the voltage on the BL/W wire until the wiper reaches the park position. • Is the voltage greater than 10 volts while not in park position?	Yes	GO to FW14.
	No	SERVICE/REPLACE wiper motor.
FW14 CHECK THE INTERVAL WIPER SWITCH • Turn the interval switch to the following positions: • Measure the resistance of the Y/R terminal to the O terminal at the wiper switch for each position listed in the table. • Are readings similar to these given in the following table?	Yes	GO to FW15.
	No	SERVICE/REPLACE the wiper switch.
FW15 CHECK WIPER GOVERNOR • Key ON. • Move the wiper switch to the INT position. • Move the interval switch to the first position. • Do the wipers operate intermittently? • Turn the interval switch to increase the time interval. • Does length of time between wipe cycles increase?	Yes	RETURN to condition chart.
	No	SERVICE/REPLACE wiper governor.

Resistance Table

Slow	1.5K ohms (± 10-15%)
1	9.3K ohms (± 10-15%)
2	7.6K ohms (± 10-15%)
3	5.8K ohms (± 10-15%)
4	4.2 ohms (± 10-15%)
5	2.4K ohms (± 10-15%)
Fast	750 ohms

FM90291001009050X

Fig. 31 Wiper system diagnosis & testing (Part 5 of 5). Capri

TEST STEP	RESULT ►	ACTION TO TAKE
WW4 WIPER MOTOR SUPPLY CHECK (WIPERS NOT WORKING)		
• Check for 12 volts (±1 volt) on "BL/BK" wire at intermittent unit (connector C237). See illustration in TEST STEP WW3 • Is there 12 volts?	Yes ► No ►	GO to WW8 . GO to WW5 .

TEST STEP	RESULT ►	ACTION TO TAKE
WW5 INTERMITTENT UNIT GROUND CHECK (WIPERS NOT WORKING)		
• Check for continuity between ground and "BK" wire at intermittent unit (connector C237). See illustration in TEST STEP WW3 • Is there continuity?	Yes ► No ►	GO to WW6 . REPAIR "BK" wire between intermittent unit and ground.

TEST STEP	RESULT ►	ACTION TO TAKE
WW6 SIGNAL GROUND CHECK (WIPERS NOT WORKING)		
• Check for continuity between ground and "LG" wire at intermittent unit (connector C237). See illustration in TEST STEP WW3 • Is there continuity?	Yes ► No ►	GO to WW7 REPLACE intermittent unit.

TEST STEP	RESULT ►	ACTION TO TAKE
WW7 SIGNAL GROUND CHECK (WIPERS NOT WORKING)		
• Disconnect wiper/washer switch (connector C271). • Check for continuity between ground and "LG" wire at intermittent unit (connector C237). See illustration in TEST STEP WW3 • **Is there continuity?**	Yes ► No ►	REPAIR "LG" wire between wiper/washer switch and intermittent unit. REPLACE wiper/washer switch.

FM9029100103020X

Fig. 32 Wiper system diagnosis & testing (Part 2 of 18). 1992 Probe

TEST STEP	RESULT ►	ACTION TO TAKE
WW8 WIPER MOTOR SUPPLY CHECK (WIPERS NOT WORKING)		
• Check for 12 volts (± volt) on "BL/BK" wire at wiper motor (connector C900). • Is there 12 volts?	Yes ► No ►	REPLACE wiper motor. REPAIR "BL/BK" wire between intermittent unit and wiper motor.

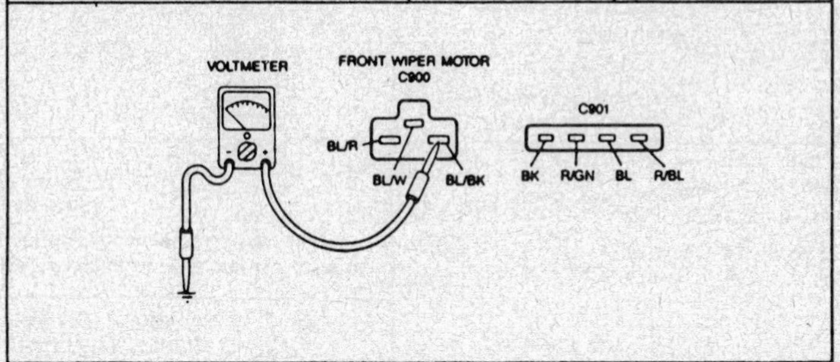

FM9029100103030X

Fig. 32 Wiper system diagnosis & testing (Part 3 of 18). 1992 Probe

TEST STEP	RESULT ►	ACTION TO TAKE
WW9 WIPER MOTOR CHECK (LOW NOT WORKING)		
• Turn ignition key to "OFF" position. • Disconnect wiper motor connectors C900 and C901. • Apply 12 volts (±1 volt) and ground to wiper motor as shown. • Does wiper motor work?	Yes ► No ►	GO to WW10 . REPLACE wiper motor.

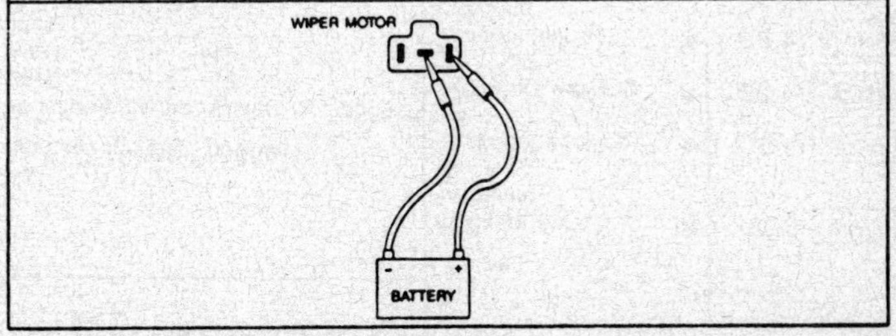

FM9029100103040X

Fig. 32 Wiper system diagnosis & testing (Part 4 of 18). 1992 Probe

TEST STEP	RESULT ►	ACTION TO TAKE
WW10 LOW SIGNAL CHECK (LOW NOT WORKING)		
• Place wiper switch in "LO" position. • Check for continuity between ground and "BL/W" wire at wiper/washer switch (connector C271). • Is there continuity?	Yes ► No ►	GO to **WW11** . REPLACE wiper/washer switch.

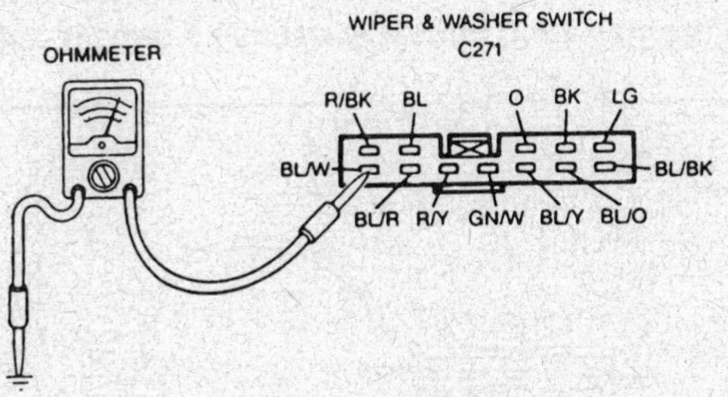

FM9029100103050X

Fig. 32 Wiper system diagnosis & testing (Part 5 of 18). 1992 Probe

TEST STEP	RESULT ►	ACTION TO TAKE
WW11 LOW SIGNAL CHECK (LOW NOT WORKING)		
• Check for continuity between ground and "BL/W" wire at wiper motor (connector C900). • Is there continuity?	Yes ► No ►	GO to **WW12** . REPAIR "BL/W" wire between wiper/washer switch and wiper motor.

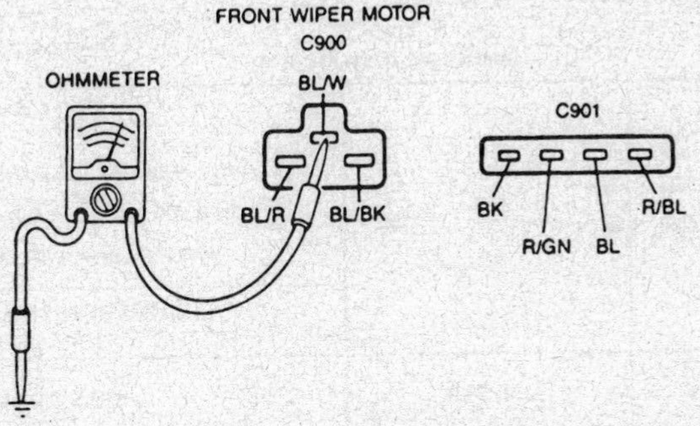

FM9029100103060X

Fig. 32 Wiper system diagnosis & testing (Part 6 of 18). 1992 Probe

TEST STEP	RESULT ►	ACTION TO TAKE
WW12 INTERMITTENT SIGNAL CHECK (LOW NOT WORKING)		
• Check for continuity between ground and "R/Y" wire at wiper/washer switch (connector C271). See illustration in TEST STEP WW10 • Is there continuity?	Yes ► No ►	GO to **WW13** . REPLACE wiper/washer switch.

FM9029100103070X

Fig. 32 Wiper system diagnosis & testing (Part 7 of 18). 1992 Probe

WW14 — Top Left

TEST STEP	RESULT		ACTION TO TAKE
WW14 WIPER MOTOR CHECK (HIGH NOT WORKING)			
• Turn ignition key to "OFF" position. • Disconnect wiper motor connectors C900 and C901. • Apply 12 volts (±1 volt) and ground to wiper motor as shown. • Does wiper motor work?	Yes	▲	GO to WW15 .
	No	▲	REPLACE wiper motor.

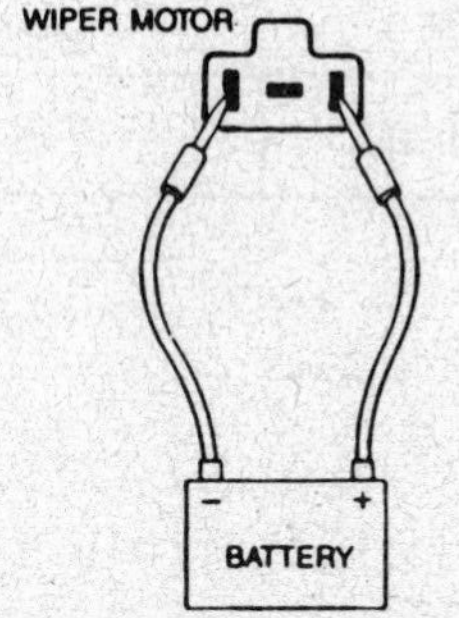

WIPER MOTOR

BATTERY + −

FM90291001030090X

Fig. 32   Wiper system diagnosis & testing (Part 9 of 18). 1992 Probe

WW16 — Top Right

TEST STEP	RESULT		ACTION TO TAKE
WW16 INTERMITTENT SIGNAL CHECK (INTERMITTENT NOT WORKING)			
• Turn ignition key to "OFF" position. • Place wiper switch in "INT" position. • Ground "R/Y" wire at intermittent unit (connector C237). • Does wiper motor work?	Yes	▲	GO to WW17 .
	No	▲	REPLACE intermittent unit.

INTERMITTENT WIPER UNIT C237

BK
BL/O BL/Y
LG
R/GN
BL/BK
BL
R/Y

FM90291001031100X

Fig. 32   Wiper system diagnosis & testing (Part 11 of 18). 1992 Probe

WW13 — Bottom Left

TEST STEP	RESULT		ACTION TO TAKE
WW13 INTERMITTENT SIGNAL CHECK (LOW NOT WORKING)			
• Check for continuity between ground and "R/Y" wire at intermittent unit (connector C237). • Is there continuity?	Yes	▲	REPLACE intermittent unit.
	No	▲	REPAIR "R/Y" wire between wiper/washer switch and intermittent unit.

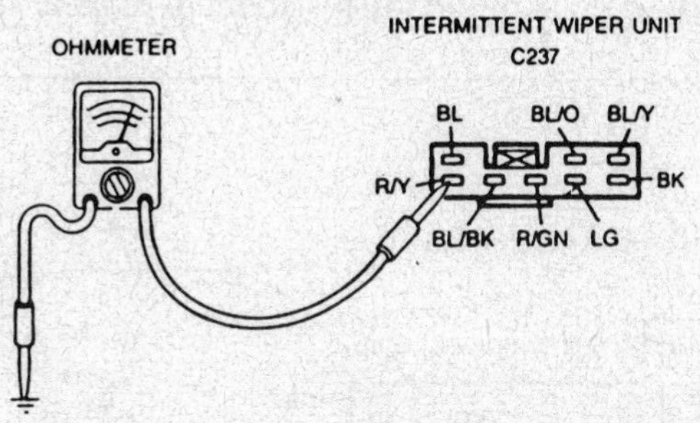

OHMMETER

INTERMITTENT WIPER UNIT C237

BK
BL/O BL/Y
LG
BL R/GN
BL/BK
R/Y

FM90291001030080X

Fig. 32   Wiper system diagnosis & testing (Part 8 of 18). 1992 Probe

WW15 — Bottom Right

TEST STEP	RESULT		ACTION TO TAKE
WW15 HIGH SIGNAL CHECK (HIGH NOT WORKING)			
• Place wiper switch in "HI" position. • Check for continuity between ground and "BL/R" wire at wiper/washer switch (connector C271). • Is there continuity?	Yes	▲	REPAIR "BL/R" wire between wiper/washer switch and wiper motor.
	No	▲	REPLACE wiper/washer switch.

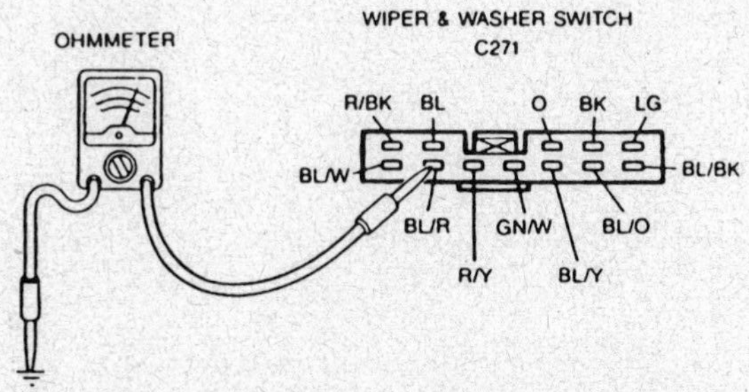

OHMMETER

WIPER & WASHER SWITCH C271

LG BL/BK
O BK BL/O
BL BL/Y
GN/W
R/BK BL/R
BL R/Y
BL/W

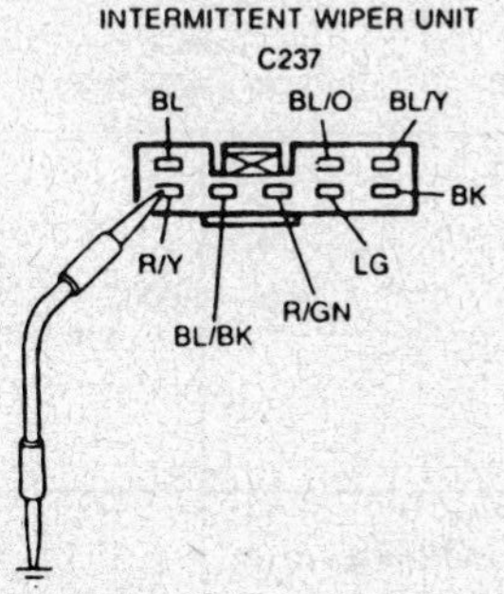

FM90291001031000X

Fig. 32   Wiper system diagnosis & testing (Part 10 of 18). 1992 Probe

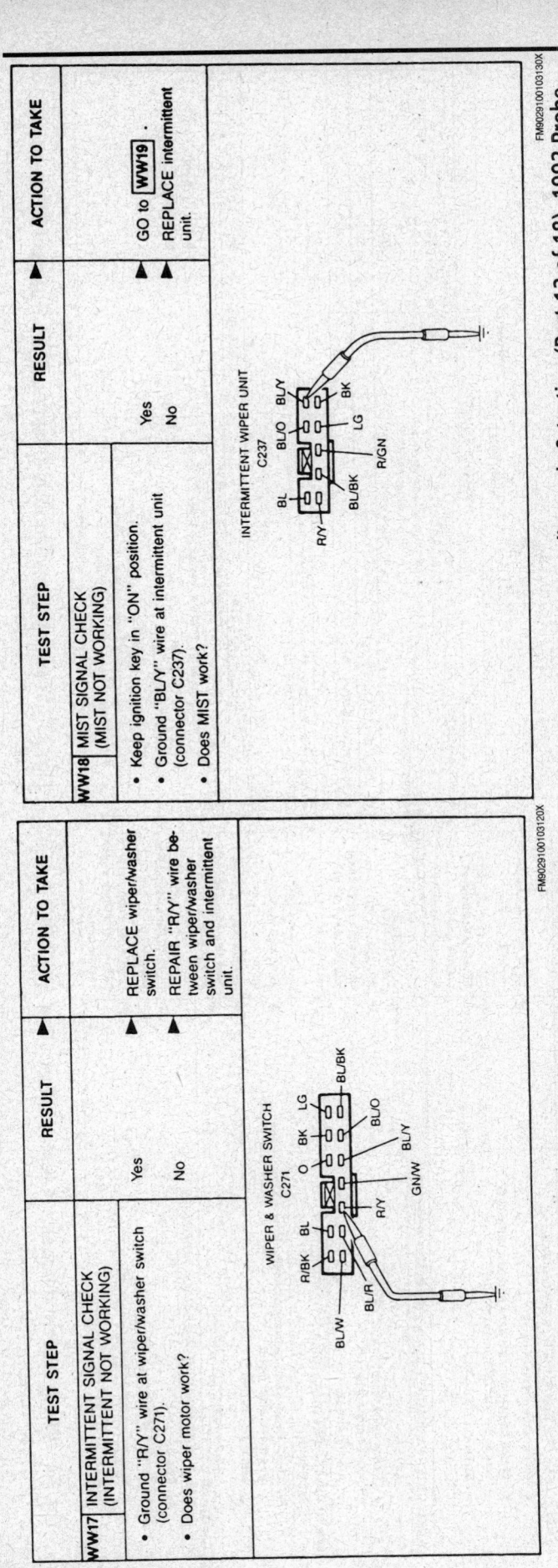

Top-left table (Part 13):

TEST STEP	RESULT	ACTION TO TAKE
WW18 MIST SIGNAL CHECK (MIST NOT WORKING) • Keep ignition key in "ON" position. • Ground "BL/Y" wire at intermittent unit (connector C237). • Does MIST work?	Yes	GO to **WW19**.
	No	REPLACE intermittent unit.

INTERMITTENT WIPER UNIT C237

Fig. 32 Wiper system diagnosis & testing (Part 13 of 18). 1992 Probe

FM9029100103130X

Top-right table (Part 15):

TEST STEP	RESULT	ACTION TO TAKE
WW20 PARK SWITCH CHECK (PARK NOT WORKING) • Turn ignition switch to "OFF" position. • Disconnect the larger of the wiper motor connectors C901. • Apply 12 volts (±1 volt) to the "R/GN" wire. • Does wiper park?	Yes	GO to **WW24**.
	No	GO to **WW21**.

C901 / BATTERY / FRONT WIPER MOTOR C900

Fig. 32 Wiper system diagnosis & testing (Part 15 of 18). 1992 Probe

FM9029100103150X

Bottom-left table (Part 12):

TEST STEP	RESULT	ACTION TO TAKE
WW17 INTERMITTENT SIGNAL CHECK (INTERMITTENT NOT WORKING) • Ground "R/Y" wire at wiper/washer switch (connector C271). • Does wiper motor work?	Yes	REPLACE wiper/washer switch.
	No	REPAIR "R/Y" wire between wiper/washer switch and intermittent unit.

WIPER & WASHER SWITCH C271

Fig. 32 Wiper system diagnosis & testing (Part 12 of 18). 1992 Probe

FM9029100103120X

Bottom-right table (Part 14):

TEST STEP	RESULT	ACTION TO TAKE
WW19 MIST SIGNAL CHECK (MIST NOT WORKING) • Ground "BL/Y" wire at wiper/washer switch (connector C271). • Does MIST work?	Yes	REPLACE wiper/washer switch.
	No	REPAIR "BL/Y" wire between wiper/washer switch and intermittent unit.

WIPER & WASHER SWITCH C271

Fig. 32 Wiper system diagnosis & testing (Part 14 of 18). 1992 Probe

FM9029100103140X

TEST STEP		RESULT ▶	ACTION TO TAKE
WW21	PARK SIGNAL CHECK (PARK NOT WORKING)		
	• Apply 12 volts (±1 volt) to "R/GN" wire at intermittent unit (connector C237). • Does wiper park?	Yes ▶ No ▶	REPAIR "R/GN" wire between intermittent unit and wiper motor. GO to WW22.

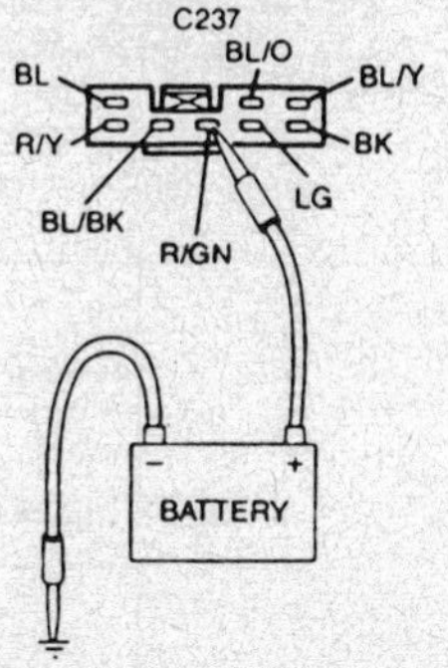

FM9029100103160X

Fig. 32 Wiper system diagnosis & testing (Part 16 of 18). 1992 Probe

TEST STEP		RESULT ▶	ACTION TO TAKE
WW22	OFF SIGNAL CHECK (PARK NOT WORKING)		
	• Check for continuity between ground and "LG" wire at wiper/washer switch (connector C271). • Is there continuity?	Yes ▶ No ▶	GO to WW23. REPLACE wiper/washer switch.

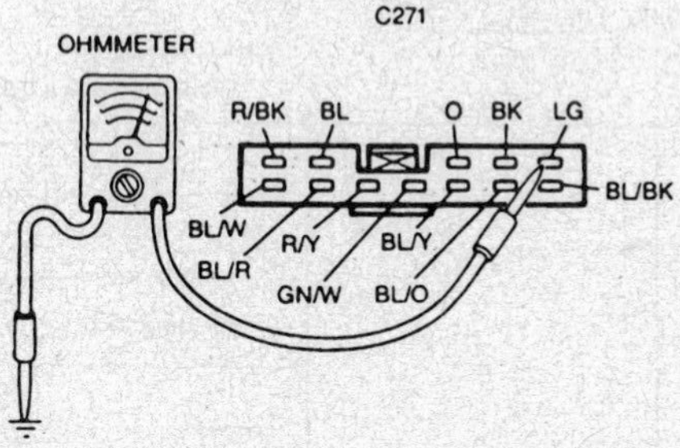

FM9029100103170X

Fig. 32 Wiper system diagnosis & testing (Part 17 of 18). 1992 Probe

TEST STEP		RESULT ▶	ACTION TO TAKE
WW23	CHECK OFF SIGNAL (PARK NOT WORKING)		
	• Remove the interval module. • Check for continuity between ground and the "LG" wire at the interval module terminal. • Is there continuity?	Yes ▶ No ▶	REPLACE the interval module. REPAIR the "LG" wire between the interval module and the wiper / washer switch.
WW24	CHECK PARK SWITCH SUPPLY (PARK NOT WORKING)		
	• Key ON. • Check for 12 volts (±1 volt) on the "BL" wire at the wiper motor connector. • Are there 12 volts?	Yes ▶ No ▶	GO to WW25. REPAIR the "BL" wire between the fuse panel and the wiper motor.
WW25	CHECK PARK SWITCH GROUND (PARK NOT WORKING)		
	• Check for continuity between ground and the "BK" wire at the wiper motor. • Is there continuity?	Yes ▶ No ▶	REPLACE the wiper motor. REPAIR the "BK" wire between the wiper motor and ground.
WW26	CHECK WIPER SWITCH (WIPERS WON'T STOP)		
	• Key ON. • Turn the wiper switch ON. • Disconnect the windshield wiper switch. • Does the wiper motor stop?	Yes ▶ No ▶	REPLACE the windshield wiper switch. CHECK for a shorted wire between the wiper switch and the motor.

FM9029100103180X

Fig. 32 Wiper system diagnosis & testing (Part 18 of 18). 1992 Probe

SYMPTOM CHART

CONDITION	POSSIBLE SOURCE	ACTION
• Wipers Do Not Work	• Fuses. • ACCY relay. • Wiper / washer switch. • Front wiper assembly. • Wiper motor.	• GO to SW1. • GO to SW4. • GO to SW7. • GO to SW7. • GO to SW7.
• Low Wipers Do Not Work	• Circuit.	• GO to SW9.
• High wipers Do Not Work	• Circuit.	• GO to SW12.
• Park Does Not Work	• Circuit.	• GO to SW15.
• Wipers Do Not Stop	• Circuit.	• GO to SW18.

TEST STEP		RESULT ▶	ACTION TO TAKE
SW1	CHECK FUSES		
	• Check the 20 amp WIPER fuse and 15 amp RADIO fuse. • Are the fuses OK? NOTE: If the fuse(s) fail after replacement and turning the ignition key to ON, service the "BL / W" wire and / or the "BK / R" wire for a short to ground.	Yes ▶ No ▶	GO to SW2. REPLACE the fuse(s) in question.

FM9029200104010X

Fig. 33 Wiper system diagnosis & testing (Part 1 of 4). 1992 Probe GL

Fig. 33 Wiper system diagnosis & testing (Part 3 of 4). 1992 Probe GL

TEST STEP	RESULT	ACTION TO TAKE
SW9 CHECK WIPER MOTOR (LOW NOT WORKING) • Disconnect the front wiper assembly. • Apply 12 volts to the "BL/BK" terminal and ground to the "BL/W" terminal at the front wiper assembly. • Does the wiper motor run?	Yes ▲ No ▲	GO to SW10 REPLACE the front wiper assembly.
SW10 CHECK LOW SIGNAL SUPPLY (LOW NOT WORKING) • Disconnect the front wiper assembly and wiper/washer switch. • Measure the resistance of the following wires between the front wiper assembly connector and wiper/washer switch connector. — "BL/BK" wire — "BL/W" wire • Are the resistances less than 5 ohms?	Yes ▲ No ▲	GO to SW11 SERVICE the wire(s) in question.
SW11 CHECK WIPER/WASHER SWITCH GROUND (LOW NOT WORKING) • Disconnect the wiper/washer switch. • Measure the resistance of the "BK" wire between the wiper/washer switch connector and ground. • Is the resistance less than 5 ohms?	Yes ▲ No ▲	REPLACE the wiper/washer switch. SERVICE the "BK" wire.
SW12 CHECK WIPER MOTOR (HIGH NOT WORKING) • Disconnect the front wiper assembly. • Apply 12 volts to the "BL/BK" terminal and ground to the "BL/R" terminal of the front wiper assembly. • Does the wiper motor run?	Yes ▲ No ▲	GO to SW13 REPLACE the front wiper assembly.
SW13 CHECK HIGH SIGNAL SUPPLY (HIGH NOT WORKING) • Disconnect the wiper/washer switch and front wiper assembly. • Measure the resistance of the following wires between the front wiper assembly connector and wiper/washer switch connector. — "BL/BK" wire — "BL/R" wire • Are the resistances less than 5 ohms?	Yes ▲ No ▲	GO to SW14 SERVICE the wire(s) in question.
SW14 CHECK WIPER/WASHER SWITCH GROUND (HIGH NOT WORKING) • Disconnect the wiper/washer switch. • Measure the resistance of the "BK" wire between the wiper/washer switch connector and ground. • Is the resistance less than 5 ohms?	Yes ▲ No ▲	REPLACE the wiper/washer switch. SERVICE the "BK" wire.

FM90292001040 30X

Fig. 33 Wiper system diagnosis & testing (Part 3 of 4). 1992 Probe GL

Fig. 33 Wiper system diagnosis & testing (Part 2 of 4). 1992 Probe GL

TEST STEP	RESULT	ACTION TO TAKE
SW2 CHECK POWER TO ACCY RELAY • Disconnect the ACCY relay. • Key ON. • Measure the voltage on the "BL/W" and "BK/R" wires at the ACCY relay connector. • Are the voltages greater than 10 volts?	Yes ▲ No ▲	GO to SW3. SERVICE the wire in question.
SW3 CHECK ACCY RELAY GROUND • Disconnect the ACCY relay. • Measure the resistance of the "BK" wire between the ACCY relay connector and ground. • Is the resistance less than 5 ohms?	Yes ▲ No ▲	GO to SW4. SERVICE the "BK" wire.
SW4 CHECK ACCY RELAY • Key ON. • Measure the voltage on the "BL" wire at the ACCY relay connector. • Is the voltage greater than 10 volts?	Yes ▲ No ▲	GO to SW5. REPLACE the ACCY relay.
SW5 CHECK POWER TO WIPER SWITCH AND ASSEMBLY • Key ON. • Measure the voltage on the "BL" wires at the wiper/washer switch connector and the front wiper assembly connector. • Are the voltages greater than 10 volts?	Yes ▲ No ▲	GO to SW6. SERVICE the "BL" wire(s) in question.
SW6 CHECK WIPER/WASHER SWITCH AND FRONT WIPER ASSEMBLY GROUND • Disconnect the wiper/washer switch and front wiper assembly. • Measure the resistance between the: — "BK" wire at the wiper/washer switch connector and ground. — "BK" wire at the front wiper assembly connector and ground. • Are the resistances less than 5 ohms?	Yes ▲ No ▲	GO to SW7. SERVICE the "BK" wire(s) in question.
SW7 CHECK WIPER MOTOR • Disconnect the front wiper assembly. • Apply 12 volts to the "BL/BK" terminal on the front wiper assembly, and ground the "BL/W" terminal on the wiper assembly. • Does the wiper motor run?	Yes ▲ No ▲	GO to SW8. REPLACE the front wiper assembly.
SW8 CHECK WIPER MOTOR SUPPLY • Disconnect the front wiper assembly and wiper/washer switch. • Measure the resistance of the following wires between the front wiper assembly connector and wiper/washer switch connector. — "BL/BK" wire — "BL/R" wire — "BL/W" wire — "R/GN" wire • Are the resistances less than 5 ohms?	Yes ▲ No ▲	REPLACE the wiper/washer switch. REPLACE the wire(s) in question.

FM90292001040 20X

Fig. 33 Wiper system diagnosis & testing (Part 2 of 4). 1992 Probe GL

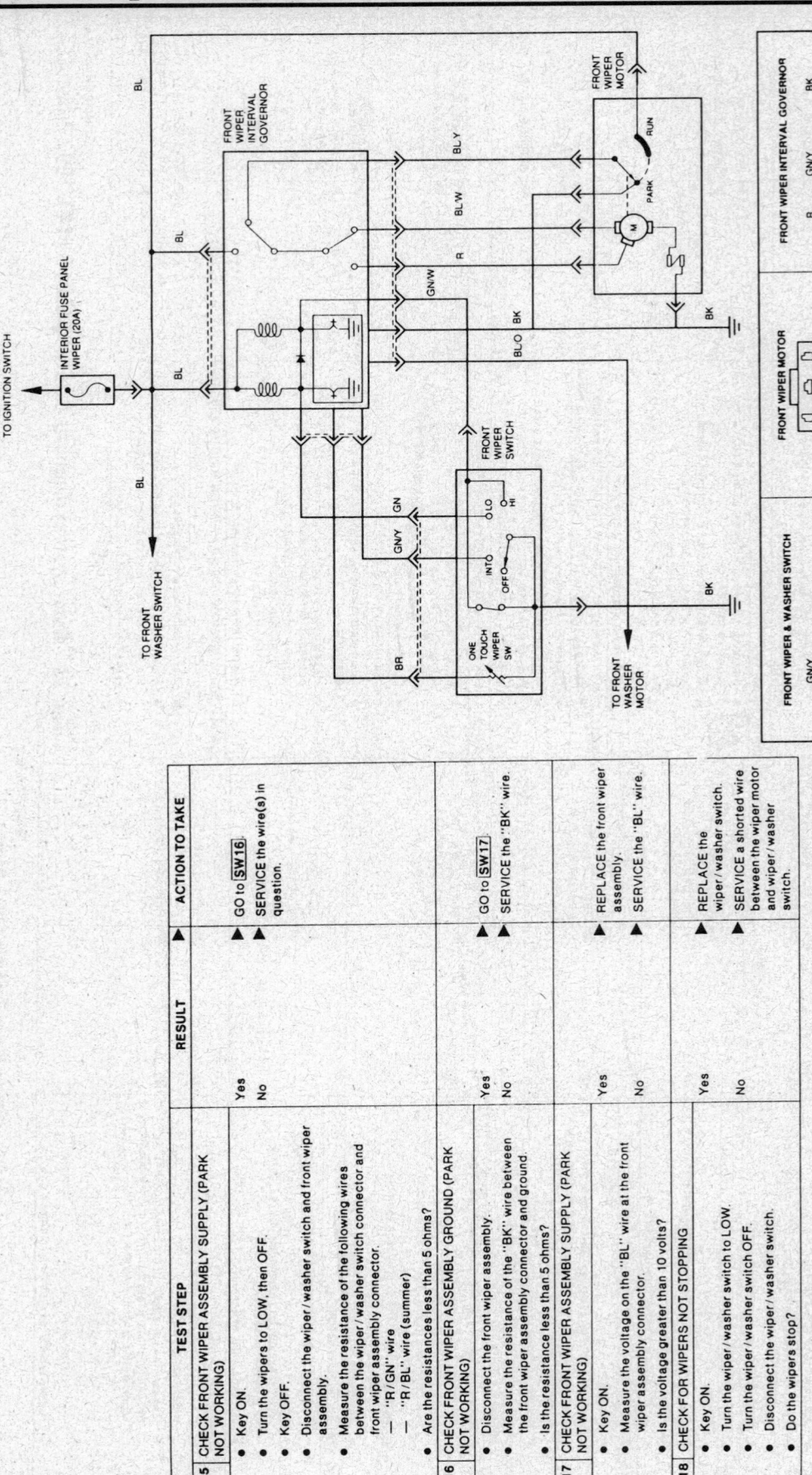

Fig. 34 Wiper system wiring schematic. 1992 Escort & Tracer

Fig. 33 Wiper system diagnosis & testing (Part 4 of 4). 1992 Probe GL

TEST STEP		RESULT	ACTION TO TAKE
SW15 CHECK FRONT WIPER ASSEMBLY SUPPLY (PARK NOT WORKING) • Key ON. • Turn the wipers to LOW, then OFF. • Key OFF. • Disconnect the wiper/washer switch and front wiper assembly. • Measure the resistance of the following wires between the wiper/washer switch connector and front wiper assembly connector. — "R/GN" wire — "R/BL" wire (summer) • Are the resistances less than 5 ohms?		Yes No	▲ GO to **SW16**. ▲ SERVICE the wire(s) in question.
SW16 CHECK FRONT WIPER ASSEMBLY GROUND (PARK NOT WORKING) • Disconnect the front wiper assembly. • Measure the resistance of the "BK" wire between the front wiper assembly connector and ground. • Is the resistance less than 5 ohms?		Yes No	▲ GO to **SW17**. ▲ SERVICE the "BK" wire.
SW17 CHECK FRONT WIPER ASSEMBLY SUPPLY (PARK NOT WORKING) • Key ON. • Measure the voltage on the "BL" wire at the front wiper assembly connector. • Is the voltage greater than 10 volts?		Yes No	▲ REPLACE the front wiper assembly. ▲ SERVICE the "BL" wire.
SW18 CHECK FOR WIPERS NOT STOPPING • Key ON. • Turn the wiper/washer switch to LOW. • Turn the wiper/washer switch OFF. • Disconnect the wiper/washer switch. • Do the wipers stop?		Yes No	▲ REPLACE the wiper/washer switch. ▲ SERVICE a shorted wire between the wiper motor and wiper/washer switch.

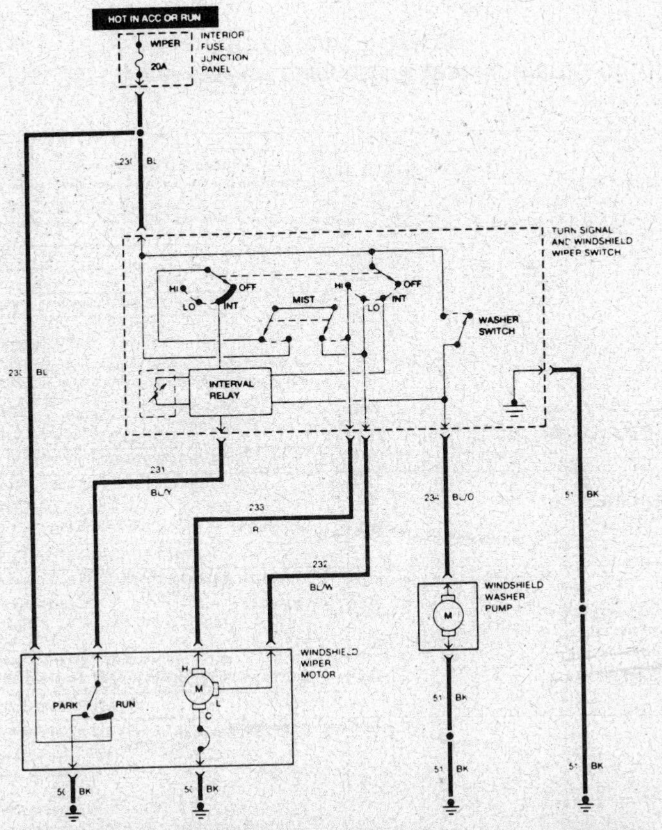

Fig. 36 — Wiper system diagnosis & testing (Part 2 of 5)

TEST STEP	RESULT	ACTION TO TAKE
WW2 CHECK SYSTEM • Replace the fuse. • Key ON. • Check the 20 amp WIPER fuse. • Is the fuse OK?	Yes No	GO to WW4 GO to WW3
WW3 CHECK INTERVAL GOVERNOR AND WIPER MOTOR POWER SUPPLY FOR SHORT • Key OFF. • Disconnect "BL" wire from interior fuse panel. • Disconnect the interval governor and wiper motor connectors. • Check the following wires for shorts to ground by touching one terminal of ohmmeter to one end of the wire and touching the other ohmmeter terminal to ground and read the resistance. Wire / From / To "BL" / Fuse Panel / Interval Governor "BL" / Fuse Panel / Interval Governor "BL" / Fuse Panel / Wiper Motor • Is the resistance greater than 10,000 ohms?	Yes No	REPLACE the interval governor. REPAIR/REPLACE the affected wire.
WW4 CHECK WIPER MOTOR SUPPLY • Key ON. • Place the wiper switch in the LOW and then in the HIGH position. • Check the 20 amp WIPER fuse. • Is the fuse OK?	Yes No	Wiper system OK. GO to WW5.
WW5 CHECK WIPER MOTOR POWER SUPPLY • Key OFF. • Disconnect the interval governor and wiper motor connectors. • Check the following wires for shorts to ground by touching one terminal of an ohmmeter to one end of the wire and touching the other ohmmeter terminal to ground and read resistance. Wire / From / To "R" / Interval Governor / Wiper Motor "BL/W" / Interval Governor / Wiper Motor • Is the resistance greater than 10,000 ohms?	Yes No	REPLACE the wiper motor. REPAIR/REPLACE the affected wire.
WW6 CHECK INTERVAL GOVERNOR SUPPLY VOLTAGE • Interval governor connector disconnected. • Key ON. • Measure the voltage on "BL" wires at the interval governor. • Is the voltage greater than 10 volts?	Yes No	GO to WW7 REPAIR/REPLACE the "BL" wires as necessary.

FM90292001107020X

Fig. 36 Wiper system diagnosis & testing (Part 2 of 5). 1992 Escort & Tracer

Fig. 35 Washer/Wiper system wiring schematic. 1993-94 Escort & Tracer

FM90294001185000X

Fig. 36 — Wiper system diagnosis & testing (Part 1 of 5)

TEST STEP	RESULT	ACTION TO TAKE
WW1 CHECK WIPER FUSE • Locate the interior fuse panel. • Check the 20 amp WIPER fuse. • Is the fuse OK?	Yes No	GO to WW6 GO to WW2

FM90292001107010X

Fig. 36 Wiper system diagnosis & testing (Part 1 of 5). 1992 Escort & Tracer

Part 4 of 5 (upper table)

TEST STEP	RESULT	ACTION TO TAKE
WW13 CHECK WIPER SWITCH FEED • Key OFF. • Disconnect the interval governor and wiper switch. • Measure the resistance of the following wires from the interval governor to the wiper switch: "GN/W" "GN" "GN/Y" "BR" • Is the resistance of each wire less than 5 ohms?	Yes ▶ No ▶	GO to WW14. REPAIR/REPLACE the affected wire.
WW14 CHECK WIPER SWITCH OPERATION • Wiper switch connector disconnected. • Connect one terminal of an ohmmeter to wiper switch ground. Connect the terminal of the ohmmeter to the following wiper switch terminals with the wiper switch in the indicated positions:<table><tr><th>Switch Terminal</th><th>Switch Position</th></tr><tr><td>"GN/W"</td><td>HIGH</td></tr><tr><td>"GN"</td><td>LOW</td></tr><tr><td>"GN/Y"</td><td>INT</td></tr></table>• Is the resistance of the "GN/W", "GN" and "GN/Y" terminals less than 5 ohms?	Yes ▶ No ▶	Wiper System checks out OK - RETURN to symptom chart. REPLACE the wiper switch.
WW15 CHECK WIPER SWITCH SUPPLY INTEGRITY SWITCH • Key OFF. • Interval governor connector disconnected. • Wiper switch connector disconnected. • Check the following wires for shorts to ground by connecting one terminal to ground and touching the end of the indicated wire and read resistance.<table><tr><th>Wire</th><th>From</th><th>To</th></tr><tr><td>"GN/W"</td><td>Interval Governor</td><td>Wiper Switch</td></tr><tr><td>"GN"</td><td>Interval Governor</td><td>Wiper Switch</td></tr><tr><td>"GN/Y"</td><td>Interval Governor</td><td>Wiper Switch</td></tr><tr><td>"BR"</td><td>Interval Governor</td><td>Wiper Switch</td></tr></table>• Is the resistance measured at each wire greater than 10,000 ohms?	Yes ▶ No ▶	REPLACE the wiper switch. REPAIR/REPLACE the affected wire.
WW16 CHECK WIPER MOTOR PARK SUPPLY • Key ON (will not operate in ACC) • Measure the voltage on the "BL" wire at the wiper motor. • Is the voltage greater than 10 volts?	Yes ▶ No ▶	GO to WW17. REPAIR/REPLACE the "BL" wire.

Fig. 36   Wiper system diagnosis & testing (Part 4 of 5). 1992 Escort & Tracer

FM90292001070400X

Part 3 of 5 (lower table)

TEST STEP	RESULT	ACTION TO TAKE
WW7 CHECK WIPER SWITCH GROUND • Key OFF. • Measure the resistance of the "BK" wire at the front wiper switch to ground. • Is the resistance less than 5 ohms?	Yes ▶ No ▶	GO to WW8. REPAIR/REPLACE the "BK" wire.
WW8 CHECK WIPER MOTOR GROUND • Measure the resistance of the wiper motor body to ground. • Is the resistance less than 5 ohms?	Yes ▶ No ▶	GO to WW9. REPAIR the ground circuit between the wiper motor body and ground.
WW9 CHECK WIPER MOTOR OPERATION • Key OFF. • Wiper motor connector disconnected. • Connect the "BK" wire terminal of the wiper motor to ground. • Connect the negative terminal of a 12-volt power source to ground. • With a jumper wire, apply 12 volts to the following wiper motor terminals: HIGH ("R" wire) LOW ("BL/W" wire) • Do the wipers operate at HIGH and LOW-speeds?	Yes ▶ No ▶	GO to WW10. REPLACE the motor.
WW10 CHECK WIPER MOTOR FEED • Measure the resistance of the following wires from the interval governor to the wiper motor. "R" wire "BL/W" wire • Is the resistance less than 5 ohms?	Yes ▶ No ▶	GO to WW11. REPAIR/REPLACE the affected wire.
WW11 CHECK INTERVAL GOVERNOR GROUND • Measure the resistance of the "BK" wire from the interval governor to ground. • Is the resistance less than 5 ohms?	Yes ▶ No ▶	GO to WW12. REPAIR/REPLACE the wire.
WW12 CHECK INTERVAL GOVERNOR OPERATION • Interval governor connected. • Key ON. • With a jumper wire, individually ground each of the following interval governor terminals and note the wiper operation.<table><tr><th>Relay Terminal</th><th>Wiper Function</th></tr><tr><td>"GN/W"</td><td>HIGH</td></tr><tr><td>"GN"</td><td>LOW</td></tr><tr><td>"GN/Y"</td><td>INT</td></tr></table>• Do the wipers function correctly in each mode as the terminals of the governor are grounded?	Yes ▶ No ▶	GO to WW13. REPAIR/REPLACE the interval governor.

Fig. 36   Wiper system diagnosis & testing (Part 3 of 5). 1992 Escort & Tracer

FM90292001070300X

CONDITION	POSSIBLE SOURCE
Windshield Washer Inoperative	• Blown fuse. • Windshield washer pump. • Turn signal and windshield wiper switch. • Circuit.
Rear Window Washer Inoperative	• Blown fuse. • Rear window washer pump. • Rear window wiper washer switch. • Circuit.
Windshield Wipers Inoperative - All Control Switch Positions	• Blown fuse. • Turn signal and windshield wiper switch. • Windshield wiper motor. • Circuit.
Windshield Wipers Inoperative at High Speed	• Turn signal and windshield wiper switch. • Windshield wiper motor. • Circuit.
Windshield Wipers Inoperative at Low Speed	• Turn signal and windshield wiper switch. • Windshield wiper motor. • Circuit.
Windshield Wiper Inoperative at Interval Setting	• Turn signal and windshield wiper switch. • Circuit.
Windshield Wipers Will Not Turn Off	• Turn signal and windshield wiper switch. • Circuit.
Rear Window Wiper Inoperative	• Rear window wiper motor. • Rear window wiper washer switch. • Circuit.
Rear Window Wiper Will Not Turn Off	• Rear window wiper washer switch. • Circuit.
Windshield Wipers Will Not Park Below Windshield Glass	• Windshield wiper motor.
Rear Window Wiper Will Not Park	• Rear window wiper motor.

Fig. 37 Wiper system diagnosis. 1993-94 Escort & Tracer

FM90294001860000X

TEST STEP		RESULT	ACTION TO TAKE
WW17 CHECK PARK GROUND FEED			
• Key OFF. • Disconnect the interval governor and wiper motor. • Measure the resistance of the "BL/Y" wire between the interval governor and wiper motor. • Is the resistance less than 5 ohms?		Yes No	GO to **WW18**. REPAIR/REPLACE the "BL/Y" wire.
WW18 CHECK INTERVAL GOVERNOR PARK CIRCUIT			
• Disconnect the interval governor connector. • Measure the resistance between the "BL/Y" terminal and the "BL/W" terminal at the interval governor connector. • Is the resistance less than 5 ohms?		Yes No	REPLACE the wiper motor. REPLACE the interval governor.

FM90292001070050X

Fig. 36 Wiper system diagnosis & testing (Part 5 of 5). 1992 Escort & Tracer

DIAGNOSTIC CHART INDEX

Test	Description	Year	Page No.	Fig. No.
ASPIRE				
A	Windshield Washer Inoperative	1994	17-50	87
B	Rear Washer Inoperative	1994	17-50	88
C	Wipers Inoperative	1994	17-50	89
D	Wipers Inoperative At High Speeds	1994	17-50	90
E	Wipers Inoperative At Low Speed	1994	17-50	91
F	Wipers Will Not Park Below Windshield	1994	17-50	92
G	Wipers Will Not Turn Off	1994	17-51	93
H	Rear Wiper Inoperative	1994	17-51	94
I	Rear Wiper Will Not Turn Off	1994	17-51	95
CONTINENTAL				
A	Washer Inoperative	1993	17-31	38
B	Wipers Inoperative At High Speeds	1993	17-32	39
C	Wipers Inoperative At Low Speed Interval	1993	17-33	40
D	Wipers Inoperative At Low Speed	1993	17-33	41
A	Windshield Washer Does Not Operate	1994	17-34	42
B	Wipers Inoperative At All Switch Positions	1994	17-34	43
C	Wipers Inoperative At Interval	1994	17-34	44
D	Wipers Inoperative At Low Speed	1994	17-35	45
CROWN VICTORIA, GRAND MARQUIS & TOWN CAR				
A	Washer Does Not Operate	1993-94	17-43	74
B	Wipers Inoperative At High Speed	1993-94	17-44	75
C	Wipers Inoperative At Low Speed	1993-94	17-44	76
D	Wipers Inoperative At Low Speed Interval	1993-94	17-45	77
E	Wipers Will Not Park Below Windshield	1993-94	17-45	78
F	Wipers Will Not Turn Off	1993-94	17-45	79
ESCORT & TRACER				
WW	Front Wiper System Diagnostic Tests	1993-94	17-49	86
MARK VIII, SABLE & TAURUS				
A	Washer Inoperative	1993-94	17-46	80
B	Wipers Inoperative At High Speed	1993-94	17-46	81
C	Wipers Inoperative At Low Speed	1993-94	17-47	82
D	Wipers Inoperative At Slow Speed Interval	1993-94	17-47	83
E	Wipers Will Not Park Below Windshield	1993-94	17-48	84
F	Wipers Will Not Turn Off	1993-94	17-48	85
PROBE				
FWS	Front Washer System	1993-94	17-51	96
1993 COUGAR, MUSTANG, TEMPO, THUNDERBIRD & TOPAZ				
A	Wipers Will Not Park	1993	17-35	46
B	Washer Does Not Operate	1993	17-35	47
C	Wipers Inoperative	1993	17-36	48
D	Wipers Inoperative Or Erratic On Low/High Speed Works	1993	17-36	49
E	Wipers Continue To Run When Switch Is Turned Off	1993	17-36	50
F	Wipers Do Not Wipe After Wash Switch Is Pulled	1993	17-37	51
G	Washers Inoperative	1993	17-37	52
H	Wipers Inoperative On Interval/Low Or High Speed Works	1993	17-37	53

Continued

DIAGNOSTIC CHART INDEX –Continued

Test	Description	Year	Page No.	Fig. No.
1994 COUGAR & THUNDERBIRD				
A	Washer Does Not Operate	1994	17-39	61
B	Wipers Inoperative In All Switch Positions	1994	17-39	62
C	Wipers Inoperative At High Speeds	1994	17-39	63
D	Wipers Inoperative At Low Speed	1994	17-40	64
E	Wipers Inoperative At Interval Setting	1994	17-40	65
F	Wipers Will Not Park At Proper Position	1994	17-40	66
G	Wipers Continue To Run When Switch Is Turned Off	1994	17-41	67
1994 MUSTANG				
A	Washer Inoperative	1994	17-41	68
B	Wipers Inoperative In All Switch Positions	1994	17-41	69
C	Wipers Inoperative At Low Speeds	1994	17-41	70
D	Wipers Inoperative At Interval Setting	1994	17-42	71
E	Wipers Will Not Park At Proper Position	1994	17-42	72
F	Wipers Continue To Run When Switch Is Turned Off	1994	17-42	73
1994 TEMPO & TOPAZ				
A	Windshield Washer Inoperative	1994	17-38	54
B	Wipers Inoperative In All Switch Positions	1994	17-38	55
C	Windshield Wipers Inoperative Or Erratic On Low, High Speed Works	1994	17-38	56
D	Wipers Continue To Run When Wiper Switch Is Turned Off	1994	17-38	57
E	No Wipe After Wash, Interval & Low Speed OK	1994	17-38	58
F	Windshield Wipers Inoperative In INT, Low & High Speed OK	1994	17-38	59
G	Wipers Do Not Park	1994	17-39	60

TEST STEP	RESULT	►	ACTION TO TAKE
A1 CHECK FLUID LEVEL • Check fluid level in reservoir. • Is fluid level good?	Yes No	► ►	GO to A2. Fill Reservoir.
A2 CHECK WASHER OPERATION • Activate washer switch. • Check pump for operation.	Motor inoperative Motor operates, but will not squirt fluid Pump squirts fluid but wipers do not wipe	► ► ►	GO to A3. GO to A8. GO to A10.
A3 CHECK WCM OUTPUT • Turn ignition on. • Depress washer switch. • Check for battery voltage at circuit 941 (BK/W) at washer pump. • Is battery voltage present?	Yes No	► ►	GO to A7. GO to A4.
A4 CHECK FOR POWER TO WCM • Check for battery voltage at circuit 65 (DG) of the WCM Pin J1-2. • Is battery voltage present?	Yes No	► ►	GO to A5. CHECK for • Open circuit breaker. • Open connector. • Open wire circuit 65 (DG). SERVICE as required.

FM9029300110010X

Fig. 38   Test A: Washer Inoperative (Part 1 of 2). 1993 Continental

	TEST STEP	RESULT	ACTION TO TAKE
B1	CHECK FOR VOLTAGE AT WIPER MOTOR • Turn ignition on. • Turn wiper switch to HI. • Unplug wiper motor. • Check for battery voltage at circuits 65 (DG) and 56 (DB/O).	Voltage at both circuits OK.	GO to B4.
		Voltage at circuit 65 (DG) is OK. Voltage at circuit 56 (DB/O) is not OK.	GO to B2.
		Voltage at both circuits not OK.	CHECK for: • Open circuit breaker in fuse panel. • Open connector. • Open wire circuit 65 (DG). SERVICE as required.
B2	CHECK WIRING AND SWITCH • Disconnect connector from wiper control module (WCM). • Measure resistance between circuits 993 (BR/W) and 589 (O). • Is there continuity?	Yes	GO to B3.
		No	CHECK for: • Open wire between wiper switch and WCM. • Damaged wiper switch. SERVICE as required.
B3	CHECK WCM OUTPUT VOLTAGE • Plug WCM connector into WCM. • Check for battery voltage at circuit 56 (DB/O) of the WCM connector. • Is battery voltage present?	Yes	CHECK for open wire between WCM and wiper motor. SERVICE as required.
		No	REPLACE WCM.
B4	PERFORM WIPER GROUND WIRE TEST • Ground wiper motor case to body ground. • Does motor run?	Yes	SERVICE motor ground. GO to B5.
		No	GO to B5.
B5	PERFORM WIPER MOTOR CURRENT DRAW TEST • Perform wiper motor current draw test. • Is current draw OK?	Yes	CHECK linkage. SERVICE as required.
		No	SERVICE as required.

FM90293001110000X

Fig. 39 Test B: Wipers Inoperative At High Speeds. 1993 Continental

	TEST STEP	RESULT	ACTION TO TAKE
A5	CHECK CONTINUITY OF SWITCH • Disconnect connector from WCM. • Depress washer switch. • Measure resistance between circuit 993 (BR/W) and circuit 590 (DB/W). • Is there continuity?	Yes	GO to A6.
		No	CHECK for: • Open wire between wiper switch and WCM. • Damaged wiper/washer switch. SERVICE or REPLACE as required.
A6	CHECK FOR VOLTAGE TO MOTOR • Reconnect connector to WCM. • Turn ignition switch to run position. • Depress washer switch. • Measure voltage at circuit 58 (W) at WCM connector. • Is battery voltage present?	Yes	CHECK for: • Open circuit 58 (W) between WCM and wiper motor.
		No	REPLACE damaged WCM.
A7	CHECK GROUND AT WASHER PUMP • Using an ohmmeter, check ground at the pump. • Is the ground functional?	Yes	REPLACE washer pump.
		No	SERVICE ground.
A8	INSPECT HOSE AND NOZZLE • visually inspect washer hose and nozzle for blockage or hose kinks. • Is hose blocked or kinked?	Yes	CLEAN, REPLACE, or SERVICE nozzle or hose.
		No	GO to A9.
A9	CHECK FOR BLOCKAGE AT WASHER PUMP OUTLET • Disconnect hose at reservoir and check for blockage at washer pump outlet. • Is hose blocked at washer pump outlet?	Yes	REMOVE washer pump from reservoir and clean.
		No	REPLACE washer pump.
A10	TEST FOR POWER TO WIPER MOTOR • Disconnect connector from wiper motor. • Turn ignition to run position. • Depress and release washer switch. • Check for battery voltage between circuit 58 (W) and 61 (Y/R). • Is battery voltage present?	Yes	PERFORM wiper motor current draw test. SERVICE as required.
		No	GO to A11.
A11	TEST FOR BATTERY VOLTAGE AT WCM OUTPUT PIN • Turn ignition to RUN position. • Depress and release washer switch. • Check for battery voltage between circuits 58 (W) and 61 (Y/R) at WCM connector. • Is battery voltage present?	Yes	CHECK for: • Unseated connector. • Open circuit 58 (W) between WCM and wiper motor.
		No	REPLACE WCM.

FM90293001100020X

Fig. 38 Test A: Washer Inoperative (Part 2 of 2). 1993 Continental

Test C

TEST STEP	RESULT	ACTION TO TAKE
C1 CHECK FOR BATTERY VOLTAGE AT WIPER MOTOR • Turn ignition on. • Turn wiper switch to interval. • Unplug wiper motor. • Check for battery voltage at circuits 65 (DG) and 58 (W).	Voltage at circuit 65 (DG) is battery voltage, Voltage at circuit 58 (W) switches from ground to battery voltage.	▲ GO to C5.
	Voltage at circuit 65 (DG) is OK. Voltage at circuit 58 (W) is not OK (does not switch between battery voltage and ground).	▲ GO to C2.
	Voltage at circuit 65 (DG) is not OK.	▲ CHECK for: • Open circuit breaker in fuse panel. • Open connector. • Open wire circuit 65 (DG). SERVICE as required.
C2 CHECK WIRING BETWEEN SWITCH AND WCM SIGNAL • Disconnect connector from wiper control module (WCM). • Measure resistance between circuits 993 (BR/W) and 598 (O). • Is resistance 11.3k ohms?	Yes	▲ GO to C3.
	No	▲ CHECK for: • Open wire between wiper switch and WCM. • Damaged wiper switch. SERVICE as required.
C3 CHECK INTERVAL DWELL RESISTANCE SIGNAL • Disconnect connector from switch. • Measure resistance between circuits 590 (DB/W) and 993 (BR/W). • Is resistance 100k ohms or less?	Yes	▲ GO to C4.
	No	▲ CHECK for: • Open wire between wiper switch and WCM. • Damaged wiper switch. SERVICE as required.
C4 CHECK WCM OUTPUT VOLTAGE • Plug WCM connector into WCM. • Check for battery voltage at circuit 58 (W) of the WCM connector. • Is there battery voltage?	Yes	▲ CHECK for: • Open wire between WCM and wiper motor. SERVICE as required.
	No	▲ REPLACE WCM.
C5 PERFORM WIPER GROUND WIRE TEST • Ground wiper motor case to body ground. • Does motor run?	Yes	▲ SERVICE Motor Ground. GO to C6.
	No	▲ GO to C6.
C6 PERFORM WIPER MOTOR CURRENT DRAW TEST • Perform wiper motor current draw test. • Is current draw OK?	Yes	▲ CHECK linkage. SERVICE as required.
	No	▲ SERVICE as required.

FM90293001112000X

Fig. 40 Test C: Wipers Inoperative At Low Speed Interval. 1993 Continental

Test D

TEST STEP	RESULT	ACTION TO TAKE
D1 CHECK FOR VOLTAGE AT WIPER MOTOR • Turn ignition on. • Turn wiper switch to interval. • Unplug wiper motor. • Check for battery voltage at circuits 65 (DG) and 58 (W).	Voltage at circuit 65 (DG) is battery voltage. Voltage at circuit 58 (W) switches from ground to battery voltage.	▲ GO to D5.
	Voltage at circuit 65 (DG) is OK. Voltage at circuit 58 (W) is not OK (Does not switch between battery voltage and ground).	▲ GO to D2.
	Voltage at circuits 65 (DG) is not OK.	▲ CHECK for: • Open circuit breaker in fuse panel. • Open connector. • Open wire circuit 65 (DG). SERVICE as required.
D2 CHECK MODE SELECT SIGNAL • Disconnect connector from wiper control module (WCM). • Measure resistance between circuits 993 (BR/W) and 589 (DB/W). • Is resistance 4.08 ohms?	Yes	▲ GO to D3.
	No	▲ CHECK for: • Open wire between wiper switch and WCM. • Damaged wiper switch. SERVICE as required.
D3 CHECK WCM OUTPUT VOLTAGE • Plug WCM connector into WCM. • Check for battery voltage at circuit 58 (W) of the WCM connector. • Is battery voltage present?	Yes	▲ CHECK for: • Open wire between WCM and wiper motor. SERVICE as required.
	No	▲ REPLACE WCM.
D4 PERFORM WIPER GROUND WIRE TEST • Ground wiper motor case to body ground. • Does motor run?	Yes	▲ GO to D6.
	No	▲ SERVICE motor ground. GO to D6.
D5 PERFORM WIPER MOTOR CURRENT DRAW TEST • Perform wiper motor current draw test. • Is current draw OK?	Yes	▲ CHECK linkage and SERVICE as required.
	No	▲ SERVICE as required.

FM90293001113000X

Fig. 41 Test D: Wipers Inoperative At Low Speed. 1993 Continental

TEST STEP	RESULT	▶	ACTION TO TAKE
A1 CHECK FLUID LEVEL • Check fluid level in windshield washer reservoir. • **Is fluid level good?**	Yes No	▶ ▶	GO to A2. Fill Windshield Washer Reservoir.
A2 CHECK WASHER OPERATION • Activate washer switch. • **Do windshield washers operate?**	Yes No	▶ ▶	GO to A10. GO to A3.
A3 CHECK WASHER OPERATION (Continued) • Activate washer switch. • **Does windshield washer pump motor operate?**	Yes No	▶ ▶	GO to A8. GO to A4.
A4 CHECK WINDSHIELD WIPER GOVERNOR OUTPUT • Turn ignition switch to RUN. • Press washer switch knob. • Check for battery voltage at circuit 941 (BK/W) at windshield washer pump. • **Is battery voltage present?**	Yes No	▶ ▶	GO to A8. GO to A5.
A5 CHECK FOR POWER TO WINDSHIELD WIPER GOVERNOR • Check for battery voltage at circuit 65 (DG) of the windshield wiper governor Pin J1-2. • **Is battery voltage present?**	Yes No	▶ ▶	GO to A6. CHECK for: • Open circuit breaker. • Open connector. • Open wire circuit 65 (DG). SERVICE as required.
A6 CHECK CONTINUITY OF SWITCH • Disconnect connector from windshield wiper governor. • Press washer switch knob. • Measure resistance between circuit 993 (BR/W) and circuit 590 (DB/W). • **Is there continuity?**	Yes No	▶ ▶	GO to A7. CHECK for: • Open wire between wiper switch and windshield wiper governor. • Damaged turn signal and windshield wiper switch. SERVICE or REPLACE as required. REFER to Section 11-05.
A7 CHECK FOR VOLTAGE TO WINDSHIELD WASHER PUMP MOTOR • Reconnect connector to windshield wiper governor. • Turn ignition switch to RUN position. • Press washer switch knob. • Measure voltage at circuit 56 (DB/O) at windshield wiper governor connector. • **Is battery voltage present?**	Yes No	▶ ▶	CHECK for: • Open circuit 56 (DB/O) between windshield wiper governor and wiper motor. REPLACE damaged windshield wiper governor.
A8 CHECK GROUND AT WINDSHIELD WASHER PUMP • Using an ohmmeter, check ground at the windshield washer pump. • **Is the ground functional?**	Yes No	▶ ▶	REPLACE washer pump. SERVICE ground.

FM9029400187010X

Fig. 42   Test A: Windshield Washer Does Not Operate (Part 1 of 2). 1994 Continental

TEST STEP	RESULT	▶	ACTION TO TAKE
A9 INSPECT HOSE AND NOZZLE JETS • Visually inspect washer hose and nozzle jets for blockage or hose kinks. • **Is hose blocked or kinked?**	Yes No	▶ ▶	CLEAN, REPLACE, or SERVICE nozzle jets or hoses. GO to A10.
A10 CHECK FOR BLOCKAGE AT WINDSHIELD WASHER PUMP OUTLET • Disconnect hose at windshield washer reservoir and check for blockage at washer pump outlet. • **Is hose blocked at washer pump outlet?**	Yes No	▶ ▶	REMOVE windshield washer pump from windshield washer reservoir and clean. REPLACE windshield washer pump.
A11 TEST FOR POWER TO WINDSHIELD WIPER MOTOR • Disconnect connector from windshield wiper motor. • Turn ignition switch to RUN position. • Press and release washer switch knob. • Check for battery voltage between circuit 56 (DB/O) and 61 (Y/R). • **Is battery voltage present?**	Yes No	▶ ▶	PERFORM Wiper Motor Current Draw Test as outlined. SERVICE as required. GO to A12.
A12 TEST FOR BATTERY VOLTAGE AT WINDSHIELD WIPER GOVERNOR OUTPUT PIN • Turn ignition switch to RUN position. • Press and release washer switch knob. • Check for battery voltage between circuits 56 (DB/O) and 61 (Y/R) at windshield wiper governor connector. • **Is battery voltage present?**	Yes No	▶ ▶	CHECK for: • Unseated connector. • Open circuit 56 (DB/O) between windshield wiper governor and windshield wiper motor. REPLACE windshield wiper governor.

FM9029400187020X

Fig. 42   Test A: Windshield Washer Does Not Operate (Part 2 of 2). 1994 Continental

TEST STEP	RESULT	▶	ACTION TO TAKE
B1 CHECK FOR SUPPLY VOLTAGE AT MOTOR • Turn ignition switch to RUN. • Turn wiper switch to HI. • Unplug wiper motor. • Check for battery voltage at circuit 65 (DG). • **Is battery voltage present?**	Yes No	▶ ▶	GO to B2. CHECK for: • Open circuit breaker in fuse panel. • Open connector. • Open wire circuit 65 (DG). • Poor ground connection. SERVICE as required.
B2 CHECK FOR BATTERY VOLTAGE AT THE WINDSHIELD WIPER GOVERNOR • Check for battery voltage at circuit 65 (DG) pin 2 of connector. • **Is battery voltage present?**	Yes No	▶ ▶	GO to B3. SERVICE open in power feed to windshield wiper governor. CHECK for: • Open wire in circuit 65 (DG). • Open unseated connector.

FM9029400188010X

Fig. 43   Test B: Wipers Inoperative At All Switch Positions (Part 1 of 2). 1994 Continental

TEST STEP	RESULT	▶	ACTION TO TAKE
B3 CHECK FOR BATTERY VOLTAGE TO MOTOR WINDINGS • Turn ignition switch to RUN. • Turn wiper switch to HI. • Disconnect connector from wiper motor. • Check for battery voltage between circuits 61 (Y/R) and 58 (W). • **Is battery voltage present?**	Yes No	▶ ▶	GO to B6. GO to B4.
B4 CHECK FOR BATTERY VOLTAGE AT WINDSHIELD WIPER GOVERNOR CONNECTOR • Check for battery voltage between pins 12 and 14 (circuits 61 (Y/R) and 58 (W)) of windshield wiper governor connector. • **Is battery voltage present?**	Yes No	▶ ▶	CHECK for: • Open wire circuits 58 (W) or 61 (Y/R). • Open connector. • Unseated connector. GO to B5.
B5 CHECK WIRING BETWEEN WINDSHIELD WIPER GOVERNOR AND SWITCH • Disconnect connector from windshield wiper governor. • Measure resistance between circuits 993 (BR/W) and 589 (O). • **Is resistance less than one ohm?**	Yes No	▶ ▶	REPLACE windshield wiper governor. CHECK for: • Open wire between wiper switch and windshield wiper governor. • Damaged wiper switch. SERVICE as required.
B6 CHECK WIPER SWITCH CONTINUITY • Disconnect harness from the wiper switch. • Check continuity between terminals for circuits 993 (BR/W) and 589 (O). • **Is resistance less than one ohm?**	Yes No	▶ ▶	CHECK for open wire between switch and windshield wiper governor. SERVICE as required. CHECK for damaged switch. SERVICE as required.
B7 PERFORM WIPER MOTOR CURRENT DRAW TEST • **Is current draw OK?**	Yes No	▶ ▶	CHECK linkage. SERVICE as required. SERVICE wiper motor as required.

FM9029400188020X

Fig. 43   Test B: Wipers Inoperative At All Switch Positions (Part 2 of 2). 1994 Continental

TEST STEP	RESULT	▶	ACTION TO TAKE
C1 CHECK MODE SELECT INPUT SIGNAL • Disconnect connector from windshield wiper governor. • Measure resistance between circuits 993 (BR/W) and 589 (O). • **Is resistance between 10.5K and 12.0K ohms?**	Yes No	▶ ▶	GO to C3. GO to C2.
C2 CHECK MODE SELECT SIGNAL AT WIPER SWITCH • Disconnect harness from the wiper switch. • Measure resistance between terminals for circuits 993 (BR/W) and 589 (O). • **Is resistance between 10.5K and 12.0K ohms?**	Yes No	▶ ▶	CHECK for open wire between switch and windshield wiper governor. SERVICE as required. CHECK for damaged switch. SERVICE as required.

FM9029400189010X

Fig. 44   Test C: Wipers Inoperative At Interval (Part 1 of 2). 1994 Continental

TEST STEP	RESULT	▶	ACTION TO TAKE
C3 CHECK INTERVAL SELECT INPUT SIGNAL • Rotate interval control on the wiper switch from MIN to MAX. • Measure resistance between circuits 590 (DB/W) and 993 (BR/W). • **Is resistance less than 104k ohms?**	Yes No	▶ ▶	REPLACE windshield wiper governor. GO to C4.
C4 CHECK INTERVAL SELECT INPUT SIGNAL AT WIPER SWITCH • Disconnect harness from wiper switch. • Rotate interval control on the wiper switch from MIN to MAX. • Measure resistance between terminals of wiper switch for circuits 590 (DB/W) and 993 (BR/W). • **Is resistance less than 104K ohms?**	Yes No	▶ ▶	CHECK for open wires between the wiper switch and the windshield wiper governor. CHECK for damaged wiper switch. SERVICE as required.

FM9029400189020X

Fig. 44   Test C: Wipers Inoperative At Interval (Part 2 of 2). 1994 Continental

TEST STEP		RESULT	▶	ACTION TO TAKE
D1	**CHECK FOR BATTERY VOLTAGE TO MOTOR WINDINGS** • Turn ignition switch to RUN. • Turn wiper switch to LO. • Disconnect connector from wiper motor. • Check for battery voltage between circuits 61 (Y/R) and 56 (DB/O). • **Is voltage present?**	Yes No	▶ ▶	GO to **D5**. GO to **D2**.
D2	**CHECK FOR BATTERY VOLTAGE AT WINDSHIELD WIPER GOVERNOR CONNECTOR** • Check for battery voltage between pins 12 and 8 (circuits 61 (Y/R) and 56 (DB/O)) of windshield wiper governor connector. • **Is voltage present?**	Yes No	▶ ▶	CHECK for: • Open wire circuits 56 (DB/O) or 61 (Y/R). • Open connector. • Unseated connector. GO to **D3**.
D3	**CHECK WIRING BETWEEN WINDSHIELD WIPER GOVERNOR AND SWITCH** • Disconnect connector from windshield wiper governor. • Measure resistance between circuit 993 (BR/W) and 589 (O). • **Is resistance between 3.5K and 4.5K ohms?**	Yes No	▶ ▶	REPLACE windshield wiper governor. CHECK for: • Open wire between wiper switch and windshield wiper governor. • Damaged wiper switch. SERVICE as required.
D4	**CHECK CONTROL LINE SIGNAL AT WIPER SWITCH** • Disconnect harness from the wiper switch. • Check continuity between terminals for circuits 993 (BR/W) and 589 (O). • **Is resistance between 3.5K and 4.5K ohms?**	Yes No	▶ ▶	SERVICE open wire between switch and windshield wiper governor. SERVICE damaged switch.
D5	**WIPER MOTOR CURRENT DRAW TEST** • Perform wiper motor current draw test as outlined. • **Is current draw OK?**	Yes No	▶ ▶	CHECK linkage. SERVICE wiper motor as required. SERVICE as required.

FM9029400190000X

Fig. 45 Test D: Wipers Inoperative At Low Speed. 1994 Continental

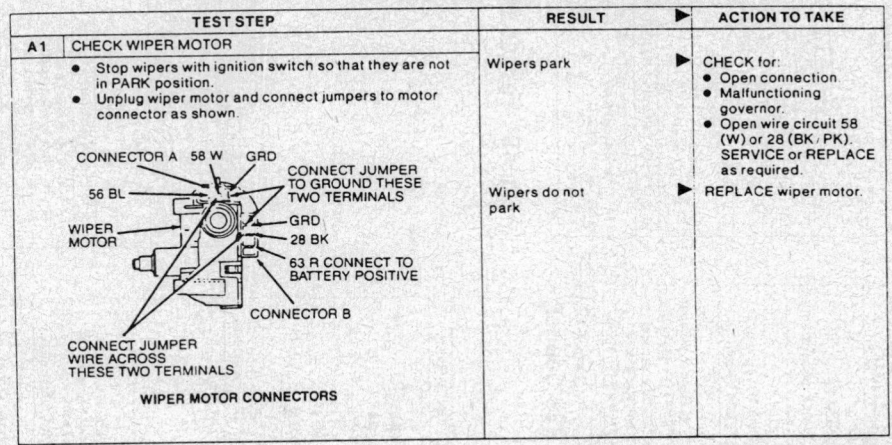

TEST STEP		RESULT	▶	ACTION TO TAKE
A1	**CHECK WIPER MOTOR** • Stop wipers with ignition switch so that they are not in PARK position. • Unplug wiper motor and connect jumpers to motor connector as shown.	Wipers park Wipers do not park	▶ ▶	CHECK for: • Open connection. • Malfunctioning governor. • Open wire circuit 58 (W) or 28 (BK/PK). SERVICE or REPLACE as required. REPLACE wiper motor.

FM9029300114000X

Fig. 46 Test A: Wipers Will Not Park. 1993 Cougar, Mustang, Tempo, Thunderbird & Topaz

TEST STEP		RESULT	▶	ACTION TO TAKE
B1	**CHECK FLUID LEVEL** • Check level of fluid in reservoir. • **Is fluid level good?**	Yes No	▶ ▶	GO to **B2**. FILL reservoir.
B2	**ACTIVATE WASHER SWITCH** • Activate washer switch. • Check motor for operation.	Motor inoperative Motor operates, but will not squirt fluid	▶ ▶	GO to **B5**. GO to **B3**.
B3	**INSPECT HOSE AND NOZZLE** • Visually inspect washer hose and nozzle for blockage or hose kinks. • **Is hose blocked or kinked?**	Yes No	▶ ▶	CLEAN, REPLACE or SERVICE nozzle or hoses. GO to **B4**.
B4	**CHECK FOR BLOCKAGE AT WASHER PUMP OUTLET** • Disconnect hose at reservoir and check for blockage at washer pump outlet. • **Is hose blocked at washer pump outlet?**	Yes No	▶ ▶	REMOVE washer pump from reservoir and CLEAN. REPLACE washer pump.
B5	**CHECK VOLTAGE AT WASHER PUMP** • Using a voltmeter or test lamp, check for voltage at washer pump by activating washer switch. • **Is there voltage?**	Yes No	▶ ▶	GO to **B6**. GO to **B7**.
B6	**CHECK GROUND AT PUMP** • Using an ohmmeter, check ground at washer pump. • **Is ground functional?**	No Yes	▶ ▶	SERVICE ground. REPLACE pump.

FM9029300115010X

Fig. 47 Test B: Washer Does Not Operate (Part 1 of 2). 1993 Cougar, Mustang, Tempo, Thunderbird & Topaz

Fig. 47 Test B: Washer Does Not Operate (Part 2 of 2). 1993 Cougar, Mustang, Tempo, Thunderbird & Topaz

	TEST STEP	RESULT	ACTION TO TAKE
B7	CHECK FOR POWER AT SWITCH • Check for power at wiper switch by operating wipers. • Do wipers operate?	Yes No	GO to B8. GO to B9.
B8	CHECK FOR POWER OUT OF WASHER SWITCH • Using a voltmeter or test lamp, check for power out of washer switch or washer circuit. • Is there power?	Yes No	GO to B10. GO to B11.
B9	CHECK HEATER BLOWER • Activate heater blower. • Is blower operational?	Yes No	GO to B10. SERVICE open circuit in power feed wiring.
B10	CHECK WIPER/WASH CIRCUIT BREAKER • Check wiper/wash circuit breaker, refer to Section 18-01 for location. • Is circuit breaker operational?	Yes No	GO to B11. REPLACE circuit breaker.
B11	CHECK SWITCH CIRCUITS • Check switch circuits. • Are switch circuits functional?	Yes No	GO to B12. REPLACE switch.
B12	CHECK FOR POWER TO SWITCH • Using a voltmeter or test lamp, check for power to washer switch or washer circuit. • Is there power?	Yes No	SERVICE wiper/washer wiring and connectors. CHECK for electrical system fault before wiper/washer switch.

FM90293001150020X

Fig. 48 Test C: Wipers Inoperative. 1993 Cougar, Mustang, Tempo, Thunderbird & Topaz

	TEST STEP	RESULT	ACTION TO TAKE
C1	CHECK FOR BATTERY VOLTAGE • Unplug wiper motor. • Set control switch to HIGH. • Check for battery voltage at Circuits 63 and 56.	Voltage both circuits Voltage OK Circuit 63, NOT OK Circuit 56 Voltage	GO to C2. CHECK for: ●Malfunctioning wiper switch ●Open connector ●Open wire, Circuit 56 (DB/O) SERVICE as necessary. CHECK for: ●Open circuit breaker in fuse panel. ●Open connector 63 (R) SERVICE as necessary.
C2	PERFORM WIPER MOTOR CURRENT DRAW TEST • Perform wiper motor current draw test as outlined. • Is test OK?	No Yes	SERVICE as necessary. CHECK linkage for binding. SERVICE as necessary.

MOTOR CONNECTOR 14489 — PARK SWITCH CONNECTOR 14489 — GROUND TERMINALS — CONNECTOR-A — CONNECTOR-B — 56 DB/O — 63R

FM90293001160000X

Fig. 49 Test D: Wipers Inoperative Or Erratic On Low/High Speed Works. 1993 Cougar, Mustang, Tempo, Thunderbird & Topaz

	TEST STEP	RESULT	ACTION TO TAKE
D1	CHECK WIPER OPERATION • Run wipers on HI. • Do wipers hesitate when they pass through the park position?	Yes No	GO to D2. GO to D4.
D2	CHECK GOVERNOR • Set wiper switch in LO. • Check voltage at governor circuits 993 (BR/W) and 58(W).	Both circuits OK. No voltage at circuit 58 (W) Voltage at circuit 993 (BR/W) but no voltage at circuit 58 (W) (measured at module connector).	GO to D4. GO to D3. REPLACE IWW module.
D3	CHECK WIRING • Check voltage at circuit 993 (BR/W) at wiper switch. • Is voltage present?	Yes No	SERVICE wire open between wiper switch and governor. SERVICE wiper switch.
D4	CHECK CIRCUIT 58 (W) FOR BATTERY VOLTAGE • Unplug wiper motor. • Set wiper switch on LO. • Check circuit 58 (W) for battery voltage. • Is voltage good?	Yes No	CHECK for malfunctioning wiper motor. PERFORM low speed current draw test. GO to E1. SERVICE as required. CHECK for: ● Unseated connector. ● Open wire circuit 58 (W) between IWW and motor. SERVICE as required.

FM90293001170000X

Fig. 50 Test E: Wipers Continue To Run When Switch Is Turned Off. 1993 Cougar, Mustang, Tempo, Thunderbird & Topaz

	TEST STEP	RESULT	ACTION TO TAKE
E1	WIPER PARK TEST • Perform wiper motor park test A1. • Do wipers park?	Yes No	GO to E2. REPLACE wiper motor.
E2	CHECK WIPER SWITCH • Unplug wiper switch. • Turn ignition to RUN. • Do wipers stop?	Yes No	GO to E4. GO to E3.
E3	CHECK INTERVAL WIPER GOVERNOR • Plug in wiper switch. • Turn ignition to RUN. • Check for voltage at circuit 58 (W) at module connector. • Is battery voltage present?	Yes No	GO to E4. CHECK for short in wiring circuits 56 (DB/O) or 58 (W).
E4	CHECK FOR VOLTAGE AT SWITCH • Check for voltage at circuit 993 (BR/W) or 941 (BK/W) or 65 (DG) at the wiper/washer switch output. • Is battery voltage present?	Yes No	REPLACE malfunctioning wiper/washer switch. REPLACE malfunctioning IWW module.

FM90293001180000X

Test G: Washers Inoperative

	TEST STEP	RESULT	ACTION TO TAKE
G1	**CHECK WIPER OPERATION** • Check operation of wipers. • **Do wipers work OK?**	Yes	CHECK for: •Low washer fluid •Split, loose, pinched or kinked washer hose •Malfunctioning washer pump motor •Open Circuit 941 (BK/W) •Open connector. SERVICE or REPLACE as necessary.
		No	Check for: •Open circuit breaker in fuse panel •Open wire, Circuit 63 (R). SERVICE or REPLACE as necessary.

FM02930012000X

Fig. 52   Test G: Washers Inoperative. 1993 Cougar, Mustang, Tempo, Thunderbird & Topaz

Test F: Wipers Do Not Wipe After Wash Switch Is Pulled

	TEST STEP	RESULT	ACTION TO TAKE
F1	**CHECK OPERATION** • **Do wipers function normally on INT, LO, and HI?**	Yes No	GO to F2. GO to D1.
F2	**CHECK FOR VOLTAGE FROM WASHER SWITCH** • Activate the washer switch. • Check for voltage at circuit 941 (BK/W) input to the IWW module. • **Is battery voltage present?**	Yes No	GO to F3. GO to F4.
F3	**CHECK IWW MODULE OPERATION** • Activate the washer switch. • Measure voltage at circuit 58 (W) at the IWW module connector. • **Is battery voltage present?**	Yes	CHECK for: • Unseated connector. • Open circuit between IWW module and wiper motor. SERVICE as required.
		No	GO to F6.
F4	**CHECK FOR BATTERY VOLTAGE AT THE WIPER/WASHER SWITCH OUTPUT** • Activate the washer switch. • Measure the voltage at circuit 941 (BK/W) at the wiper/washer switch. • **Is battery voltage present?**	Yes	CHECK for open circuit between wiper/washer switch and IWW module. SERVICE as required.
		No	GO to F5.
F5	**CHECK FOR BATTERY VOLTAGE AT WIPER SWITCH INPUT** • Unplug wire harness connector from wiper/washer switch. • Measure voltage at circuit 63 (R) input to wiper/washer switch. • **Is battery voltage present?**	Yes	CHECK for: • Unseated connector. • Damaged wiper switch. SERVICE as required.
		No	SERVICE open circuit between fuse panel and wiper switch.
F6	**CHECK FOR BATTERY VOLTAGE AT INPUT TO IWW MODULE** • Check for battery voltage at circuit 63 (R) input to IWW module. • **Is battery voltage present?**	Yes No	REPLACE IWW module. SERVICE open circuit between fuse panel and IWW module.

FM02930011900X

Fig. 51   Test F: Wipers Do Not Wipe After Wash Switch Is Pulled. 1993 Cougar, Mustang, Tempo, Thunderbird & Topaz

Test H: Wipers Inoperative On Interval/Low Or High Speed Works

	TEST STEP	RESULT	ACTION TO TAKE
H1	**CHECK FOR BATTERY VOLTAGE AT CIRCUIT 65 (DG)** • Turn wiper switch to interval position. • Check for battery voltage at circuit 65 (DG) input to the IWW module. • **Is battery voltage present?**	Yes No	GO to H2. GO to H3.
H2	**CHECK INTERVAL ADJUST FEATURE OF WIPER SWITCH** • Disconnect connector from wiper switch. • Measure resistance between terminals R1 and R2 of the wiper switch as the wiper switch is rotated through the interval range.	Resistance varies uniformly Short or open	REPLACE IWW module. REPLACE wiper/washer switch.
H3	**CHECK FOR BATTERY VOLTAGE AT CIRCUIT 65 (DG) AT WIPER SWITCH** • Turn wiper switch to interval position. • Measure voltage output of wiper switch at I terminal. • **Is battery voltage present?**	Yes	SERVICE open circuit between wiper/washer switch and IWW module.
		No	SERVICE or REPLACE wiper switch.

FM02930012100X

Fig. 53   Test H: Wipers Inoperative On Interval/Low Or High Speed Works. 1993 Cougar, Mustang, Tempo, Thunderbird & Topaz

TEST STEP		RESULT	▶	ACTION TO TAKE
A1	CHECK FLUID LEVEL			
	• Check level of fluid in reservoir. • **Is fluid level OK?**	Yes	▶	GO to B2.
		No	▶	FILL reservoir.
A2	ACTIVATE WASHER SWITCH			
	• Activate washer switch. • **Does washer pump run?**	Yes	▶	GO to A3.
		No	▶	GO to A5.
A3	INSPECT HOSE AND NOZZLE			
	• Visually inspect washer hose filter and nozzle for blockage or hose kinks. • **Are blockages or kinks present?**	Yes	▶	CLEAN, REPLACE or SERVICE as necessary.
		No	▶	GO to A4.
A4	CHECK FOR BLOCKAGE AT WASHER PUMP OUTLET			
	• Disconnect hose at reservoir and check for blockage at washer pump outlet. • **Is pump outlet blocked?**	Yes	▶	REMOVE washer pump from reservoir and CLEAN or REPLACE pump.
		No	▶	GO to A5.
A5	CHECK VOLTAGE AT WASHER PUMP			
	• Using a voltmeter, check for B+ at washer pump by activating washer switch. • **Is B+ present?**	Yes	▶	GO to A6.
		No	▶	GO to A7.
A6	CHECK GROUND AT PUMP			
	• Using an ohmmeter, check ground at washer pump. • **Is ground OK?**	Yes	▶	REPLACE pump.
		No	▶	SERVICE ground.
A7	CHECK WIPER OPERATION			
	• Turn on windshield wiper. • **Do wipers operate?**	Yes	▶	GO to A8.
		No	▶	GO to B1.

FM9029400168010X

Fig. 54   Test A: Windshield Washer Inoperative (Part 1 of 2). 1994 Tempo & Topaz

TEST STEP		RESULT	▶	ACTION TO TAKE
A8	CHECK FOR VOLTAGE AT WIPER SWITCH			
	• Activate washer switch. • Check for voltage at terminal W (circuit 941) of the wiper switch. • **Is voltage present?**	Yes	▶	SERVICE for open circuit between washer switch and washer pump.
		No	▶	SERVICE wiper switch.

FM9029400168020X

Fig. 54   Test A: Windshield Washer Inoperative (Part 2 of 2). 1994 Tempo & Topaz

TEST STEP		RESULT	▶	ACTION TO TAKE
B1	CHECK FOR BATTERY VOLTAGE			
	• Unplug wiper motor. • Set control switch to HIGH. Ignition switch to ACC position. • Check for battery voltage at Circuits 63 (R) and 56 (DB/O).	Voltage both circuits	▶	GO to B2.
		Voltage OK Circuit 63, NOT OK Circuit 56	▶	CHECK for: • Battery voltage at Circuits 63 and 56 of the wiper switch • Unseated connector • Open wire, Circuit 56 (DB/O) SERVICE as necessary.
		No Voltage	▶	CHECK for: • Open circuit breaker in fuse panel. • Open circuit 63 (R) SERVICE as necessary.
B2	CHECK MOTOR GROUNDS			
	• Check wiper motor ground circuits at connector A and B. • **Are grounds OK?**	Yes	▶	GO to B3.
		No	▶	SERVICE as required.
B3	PERFORM WIPER MOTOR CURRENT DRAW TEST			
	• Perform wiper motor current draw test as outlined.	Current draw OK	▶	CHECK linkage for binding. SERVICE as necessary.
		Current draw not OK	▶	SERVICE motor.

FM9029400169000X

Fig. 55   Test B: Wipers Inoperative In All Switch Positions. 1994 Tempo & Topaz

TEST STEP		RESULT	▶	ACTION TO TAKE
C1	CHECK WIPER OPERATION			
	• Run wipers on HI. • **Do wipers hesitate when they pass through the park position?**	Yes	▶	GO to C2.
		No	▶	GO to C4.
C2	CHECK WIPER MOTOR GROUND			
	• Check motor ground circuits at connectors A and B. • **Are grounds OK?**	Yes	▶	GO to C3.
		No	▶	SERVICE wiring at motor connector or tighten mounting screws to improve ground.
C3	CHECK WIPER MOTOR			
	• Perform wiper motor current draw test in high speed. • **Is current draw OK?**	Yes	▶	GO to C4.
		No	▶	SERVICE motor as required.

FM9029400170010X

Fig. 56   Test C: Windshield Wipers Inoperative Or Erratic On Low, High Speed Works (Part 1 of 2). 1994 Tempo & Topaz

TEST STEP		RESULT	▶	ACTION TO TAKE
C4	CHECK GOVERNOR			
	• Set wiper switch in LOW. • Unplug governor connector. Check for battery voltage at circuit 993 (BR/W) and ground at circuit 57 (BK)	Both circuits OK	▶	GO to C6.
		No voltage at circuit 993 (BR/W).	▶	GO to C5.
		No ground	▶	SERVICE ground circuit 57 (BK).
C5	CHECK WIPER SWITCH			
	• Check circuit 993 (BR/W) voltage at wiper switch. • **Is voltage present?**	Yes	▶	SERVICE for open circuit 993 (BR/W) between governor and wiper switch.
		No	▶	SERVICE wiper switch.
C6	CHECK CIRCUIT 58 (W)			
	• Reconnect governor to harness. • Unplug wiper motor connector. • With wiper switch at LOW, check circuit 58 (W) for battery voltage at the motor.	Yes	▶	CHECK for malfunctioning wiper motor. PERFORM low speed current draw test. SERVICE motor as required.
		No	▶	GO to C7.
C7	CHECK FOR OPEN CIRCUIT			
	• Check for open in circuit 58 (W) between governor and wiper motor.	Circuit OK	▶	REPLACE IWW.
		Circuit OPEN	▶	SERVICE as required.

FM9029400170020X

Fig. 56   Test C: Windshield Wipers Inoperative Or Erratic On Low, High Speed Works (Part 2 of 2). 1994 Tempo & Topaz

TEST STEP		RESULT	▶	ACTION TO TAKE
D1	CHECK WIPER SWITCH			
	• Unplug wiper switch; turn ignition to RUN. • **Do wipers stop?**	Yes	▶	SERVICE wiper switch.
		No	▶	GO to D2.
D2	CHECK WIRING AT WIPER MOTOR			
	• With the wiper switch still disconnected, check for voltage at circuit 58 (DB/O) of the wiper motor. • **Is voltage present?**	Yes	▶	SERVICE for short circuit.
		No	▶	GO to D3.
D3	CHECK WIRING AT GOVERNOR			
	• Reconnect wiper switch. Disconnect governor and put ignition in RUN and switch at OFF. • Check for voltage at circuits 58 (W), 65 (DG), 993 (BR/W) and 941 (BK/W). • **Is voltage present?**	Yes	▶	SERVICE for short circuit(s).
		No	▶	GO to D4.
D4	CHECK GOVERNOR			
	• Reconnect governor. • With ignition in RUN probe terminal of circuit 58 (W) at the wire harness side of the governor connector. • **Is voltage present?**	Yes	▶	REPLACE governor.
		No	▶	REPLACE wiper motor.

FM9029400171000X

Fig. 57   Test D: Wipers Continue To Run When Wiper Switch Is Turned Off. 1994 Tempo & Topaz

TEST STEP		RESULT	▶	ACTION TO TAKE
E1	CHECK FOR VOLTAGE FROM WIPER SWITCH			
	• With the governor connected, activate the washer switch. • Check for voltage at circuit 941 (BK/W) and 58 (W) at the harness side of the governor connector. • **Is battery voltage present?**	Yes	▶	REPLACE governor.
		No	▶	GO to E2.

FM9029400172010X

Fig. 58   Test E: No Wipe After Wash, Interval & Low Speed OK (Part 1 of 2). 1994 Tempo & Topaz

TEST STEP		RESULT	▶	ACTION TO TAKE
E2	CHECK VOLTAGE AT WIPER SWITCH			
	• Unplug the wiper switch connector. • Activate the washer switch. Check for voltage at terminal W of the switch (circuit 941). • **Is battery voltage present?**	Yes	▶	SERVICE for open circuit between governor and wiper switch.
		No	▶	SERVICE wiper switch.

FM9029400172020X

Fig. 58   Test E: No Wipe After Wash, Interval & Low Speed OK (Part 2 of 2). 1994 Tempo & Topaz

TEST STEP		RESULT	▶	ACTION TO TAKE
F1	CHECK FOR VOLTAGE AT CIRCUIT 65			
	• Disconnect the governor from the harness. • Turn the wiper switch to INT and check for battery voltage at circuit 65 (DG) of the governor connector. • **Is battery voltage present?**	Yes	▶	GO to F2.
		No	▶	GO to F3.
F2	CHECK INTERVAL RESISTANCE CIRCUITS			
	• Measure resistance between circuits 61 (Y/R) and 589 (O) at the governor connector as the wiper switch is rotated thru the interval range. • **Does the resistance vary uniformly?**	Yes	▶	REPLACE governor.
		No	▶	GO to F4.
F3	CHECK FOR VOLTAGE AT THE WIPER SWITCH			
	• Turn wiper switch to INT. • Check for battery voltage at terminal 1 of the wiper switch (circuit 65). • **Is battery voltage present?**	Yes	▶	CHECK for open in circuit 65 (DG) between wiper switch and governor.
		No	▶	SERVICE wiper switch.
F4	CHECK RESISTANCE AT WIPER SWITCH			
	• Measure resistance between terminals R1 and R2 of the wiper switch as it is rotated through the interval range. • **Does resistance vary uniformly?**	Yes	▶	CHECK for open in circuit 589 (O) or 61 (Y/R) between wiper switch and governor.
		No	▶	SERVICE wiper switch.

FM9029400173000X

Fig. 59   Test F: Windshield Wipers Inoperative In INT, Low & High Speed OK. 1994 Tempo & Topaz

Fig. 60 Test G: Wipers Do Not Park. 1994 Tempo & Topaz

TEST STEP		RESULT	▶	ACTION TO TAKE
G1	CHECK WIPER MOTOR	Yes	▶	GO to G2.
	• Stop wipers with ignition switch so that they are not in the PARK position. • Unplug motor connectors and connect jumpers to terminals 58 / 28 and 57 / 57 of the motor. • Connect motor ground terminals to a suitable ground point and terminal 63 to battery positive. • **Do wipers PARK with jumpers in place?**	No	▶	REPLACE wiper motor.
G2	CHECK MOTOR GROUND	Yes	▶	GO to G3.
	• Check continuity of circuit 57 to ground at motor connectors. • **Is ground OK?**	No	▶	SERVICE ground circuit as required.
G3	CHECK CIRCUITS TO INTERVAL GOVERNOR MODULE	Yes	▶	GO to G4.
	• Check continuity of circuits 58 and 28 between the motor and interval governor (IWW). • **Is continuity present?**	No	▶	SERVICE circuit(s) as required.
G4	CHECK FOR BATTERY VOLTAGE AT THE MOTOR	Yes	▶	REPLACE Interval Governor Module.
	• Check for battery voltage at circuit 63 of the motor connector. • **Is voltage present?**	No	▶	SERVICE circuit as required.

FM9029400174000X

Fig. 62 Test B: Wipers Inoperative In All Switch Positions. 1994 Cougar & Thunderbird

TEST STEP		RESULT	▶	ACTION TO TAKE
B1	CHECK FOR BATTERY VOLTAGE	Yes	▶	GO to B2.
	• Unplug windshield wiper motor. • Set control turn signal and windshield wiper switch to HIGH. • Check for battery voltage at Circuits 65 and 56. • **Is battery voltage present?**	No	▶	CHECK for: • Malfunctioning turn signal and windshield wiper switch. • Open connector. • Open wire, Circuit 56 or 65 (DB / O). SERVICE as necessary.
B2	PERFORM WIPER MOTOR CURRENT DRAW TEST	Yes	▶	CHECK linkage for binding. SERVICE as necessary.
	• Perform wiper motor current draw test as outlined. • **Is test OK?**	No	▶	SERVICE as necessary.

FM9029400197000X

Fig. 61 Test A: Washer Does Not Operate (Part 1 of 2). 1994 Cougar & Thunderbird

TEST STEP		RESULT	▶	ACTION TO TAKE
A1	CHECK FLUID LEVEL	Yes	▶	GO to A2.
	• Check level of fluid in windshield washer reservoir. • **Is fluid level good?**	No	▶	FILL reservoir.
A2	CHECK WASHER SYSTEM OPERATION	Yes	▶	GO to A11.
	• Activate turn signal and windshield wiper switch. • Check washer pump operation. • **Does washer pump squirt fluid?**	No	▶	GO to A3.
A3	CHECK PUMP OPERATION	Yes	▶	GO to A9.
	• Activate turn signal and windshield wiper switch. • Check washer operation. • **Does pump run but not squirt fluid?**	No	▶	GO to A4.
A4	INSPECT HOSE AND NOZZLE	Yes	▶	CLEAN, REPLACE or SERVICE windshield washer nozzle jet and bracket or window washer hoses.
	• Visually inspect window washer hose and windshield washer nozzle jet and bracket for blockage or hose kinks. • **Is window washer hose blocked or kinked?**	No	▶	GO to A5.
A5	CHECK FOR BLOCKAGE AT WASHER PUMP OUTLET	Yes	▶	REMOVE windshield washer hose from windshield washer reservoir and CLEAN.
	• Disconnect window washer hose at windshield washer reservoir and check for blockage at windshield washer pump outlet. • **Is window washer hose blocked at windshield washer pump outlet?**	No	▶	REPLACE windshield washer pump.
A6	CHECK VOLTAGE AT WASHER PUMP	Yes	▶	GO to A7.
	• Using a voltmeter or test lamp, check for voltage at windshield washer pump by activating turn signal and windshield wiper switch. • **Is there voltage?**	No	▶	GO to A8.
A7	CHECK GROUND AT PUMP	No	▶	SERVICE ground.
	• Using an ohmmeter, check ground at windshield washer pump. • **Is ground functional?**	Yes	▶	REPLACE windshield washer pump.
A8	CHECK FOR POWER AT SWITCH	Yes	▶	GO to A9.
	• Check for power at turn signal and windshield wiper switch by operating windshield wiper motors. • **Do windshield wiper motors operate?**	No	▶	GO to A10.
A9	CHECK FOR POWER OUT OF WASHER SWITCH	Yes	▶	GO to A11.
	• Using a voltmeter or test lamp, check for power out of Circuit 941 (BK / W) while activating switch. • **Is there power?**	No	▶	GO to A12.
A10	CHECK HEATER BLOWER	Yes	▶	GO to A11.
	• Activate heater blower. • **Is blower operational?**	No	▶	SERVICE open circuit in power feed wiring.
A11	CHECK WIPER / WASH CIRCUIT FUSE	Yes	▶	GO to A12.
	• Check wiper / wash fuse. Refer to Section 18-01 for location. • **Is circuit breaker operational?**	No	▶	REPLACE fuse.
A12	CHECK SWITCH CIRCUITS	Yes	▶	GO to A13.
	• Check turn signal and windshield wiper switch circuits. • **Are turn signal and windshield wiper switch circuits functional?**	No	▶	REPLACE turn signal and windshield wiper switch.

FM9029400191010X

Fig. 61 Test A: Washer Does Not Operate (Part 2 of 2). 1994 Cougar & Thunderbird

TEST STEP		RESULT	▶	ACTION TO TAKE
A13	CHECK FOR POWER TO SWITCH	Yes	▶	SERVICE wiper / washer wiring and connectors.
	• Using an ohmmeter test switch as outlined. • **Does switch test OK?**	No	▶	SERVICE switch.

FM9029400191020X

Fig. 63 Test C: Wipers Inoperative At High Speeds (Part 1 of 2). 1994 Cougar & Thunderbird

TEST STEP		RESULT	▶	ACTION TO TAKE
C1	CHECK OPERATION	Yes	▶	GO to C4.
	• Turn turn signal and windshield wiper switch to LOW. • **Does low speed work?**	No	▶	GO to C2.
C2	CHECK FOR SUPPLY VOLTAGE AT MOTOR	Yes	▶	GO to C3.
	• Turn ignition switch on. • Turn turn signal and windshield wiper switch to HI. • Unplug windshield wiper motor. • Check for battery voltage at Circuit 65 (DG). • **Is battery voltage present?**	No	▶	CHECK for: • Open circuit breaker in fuse junction panel. • Open connector. • Open wire Circuit 65 (DG). • Poor ground connection. SERVICE as required.
C3	CHECK FOR BATTERY VOLTAGE AT THE MALFUNCTION INDICATOR LAMP CONTROL	Yes	▶	GO to C4.
	• Check for battery voltage at Circuit 65 (DG) Pin 5 of connector at fuse junction panel. • **Is battery voltage present?**	No	▶	SERVICE open in power feed to malfunction indicator lamp control. CHECK for: • Open wire in Circuit 65 (DG). • Open unseated connector.
C4	CHECK FOR BATTERY VOLTAGE TO MOTOR WINDINGS	Yes	▶	GO to C7.
	• Turn ignition switch to RUN. • Turn turn signal and windshield wiper switch to HI. • Disconnect connector from windshield wiper motor. • Check for battery voltage between Circuits 61 (Y / R) and 58 (W). • **Is battery voltage present?**	No	▶	GO to C5.

FM9029400192010X

Fig. 63 Test C: Wipers Inoperative At High Speeds (Part 2 of 2). 1994 Cougar & Thunderbird

TEST STEP		RESULT	▶	ACTION TO TAKE
C5	CHECK FOR BATTERY VOLTAGE AT MALFUNCTION INDICATOR CONTROL CONNECTOR	Yes	▶	CHECK for: • Open wire. • Open connector. • Unseated connector.
	• Check for battery voltage between malfunction indicator lamp control and Pin 2 of fuse junction panel. • **Is battery voltage present?**	No	▶	GO to C6.
C6	CHECK WIRING BETWEEN MALFUNCTION INDICATOR LAMPS CONTROL AND SWITCH	Yes	▶	REPLACE malfunction indicator lamp control.
	• Disconnect connector from malfunction indicator lamp control. • Measure resistance between Circuits 993 (BR / W) and 589 (O). • **Is resistance less than 1.0 ohm?**	No	▶	CHECK for: • Open wire between turn signal and windshield wiper switch and malfunction indicator lamp control. • Damaged turn signal and windshield wiper switch. SERVICE as required.
C7	CHECK WIPER SWITCH CONTINUITY	Yes	▶	GO to C8.
	• Disconnect harness from the turn signal and windshield wiper switch. • Check continuity between terminals for Circuits 993 (BR / W) and 589 (O). • **Is resistance less than 1.0 ohm?**	No	▶	CHECK for damaged turn signal and windshield wiper switch. SERVICE as required.
C8	PERFORM WIPER MOTOR CURRENT DRAW TEST	Yes	▶	CHECK linkage. SERVICE as required.
	• Perform windshield wiper current draw test as outlined. • **Is current draw OK?**	No	▶	SERVICE windshield wiper motor as required.

FM9029400192020X

TEST STEP		RESULT	▶	ACTION TO TAKE
D1	CHECK OPERATION • Turn turn signal and windshield wiper switch to HIGH. • **Does high speed work?**	Yes No	▶ ▶	GO to D4. GO to D2.
D2	CHECK FOR SUPPLY VOLTAGE • Turn ignition switch to RUN. • Turn turn signal and windshield wiper switch to HI. • Unplug windshield wiper motor. • Check for battery voltage at Circuit 65 (DG) • **Is voltage present?**	Yes No	▶ ▶	GO to D3. CHECK for: • Open circuit breaker in fuse junction panel. • Open connector. • Open wire Circuit 65 (DG). • Poor ground connection. SERVICE as required.
D3	CHECK FOR BATTERY VOLTAGE AT THE MALFUNCTION INDICATOR LAMP CONTROL • Check for battery voltage at Circuit 65 (DG) Pin 5 of connector on fuse junction panel. • **Is voltage present?**	Yes No	▶ ▶	GO to D4. SERVICE open in power feed to malfunction indicator lamp control. CHECK for: • Open wire in Circuit 65 (DG) • Open unseated connector.

FM9029400193010X

Fig. 64 Test D: Wipers Inoperative At Low Speed (Part 1 of 2). 1994 Cougar & Thunderbird

TEST STEP		RESULT	▶	ACTION TO TAKE
E3	CHECK MODE SELECT SIGNAL AT WIPER SWITCH • Disconnect harness from the turn signal and windshield wiper switch. • Measure resistance between terminals for Circuits 993 (BR/W) and 589 (O). • **Is resistance between 10.5k ohms and 12.0k ohms?**	Yes No	▶ ▶	CHECK for open wire between turn signal and windshield wiper switch and windshield wiper governor. SERVICE as required. CHECK for damaged turn signal and windshield wiper switch. SERVICE as required.
E4	CHECK INTERVAL SELECT INPUT SIGNAL • Rotate interval control on the turn signal and windshield wiper switch from "S" to "F". • Measure resistance between Circuits 590 (DB/W) and 993 (BR/W). • **Is resistance 3.3k-103.3k ohms?**	Yes No	▶ ▶	REPLACE windshield wiper governor. GO to E5.
E5	CHECK INTERVAL SELECT INPUT SIGNAL AT WIPER SWITCH • Disconnect harness from turn signal and windshield wiper switch. • Rotate interval control on the turn signal and windshield wiper switch from "S" to "F". • Measure resistance between terminals of turn signal and windshield wiper switch for Circuits 590 (DB/W) and 993 (BR/W). • **Is resistance 3.3k-103.3k ohms?**	Yes No	▶ ▶	CHECK for open wires between the turn signal and windshield wiper switch and the windshield wiper governor. SERVICE as required. CHECK for damaged turn signal and windshield wiper switch. SERVICE as required.

FM9029400194020X

Fig. 65 Test E: Wipers Inoperative At Interval Setting (Part 2 of 2). 1994 Cougar & Thunderbird

TEST STEP		RESULT	▶	ACTION TO TAKE
D4	CHECK FOR BATTERY VOLTAGE TO MOTOR WINDINGS • Turn ignition switch to RUN. • Turn turn signal and windshield wiper switch to LO. • Disconnect connector from windshield wiper motor. • Check for battery voltage between Circuits 58 and 56 (DB/O). • **Is voltage present?**	Yes No	▶ ▶	GO to D7. GO to D5.
D5	CHECK FOR BATTERY VOLTAGE AT MALFUNCTION INDICATOR LAMP CONTROL • Check for battery voltage between Circuits 58 (W) and 56 (DB/O)) of connector. • **Is voltage present?**	Yes No	▶ ▶	CHECK for: • Open wire Circuits 56 (DB/O) or 58 (W). • Open connector. • Unseated connector. GO to D6.
D6	CHECK WIRING BETWEEN WIPER CONTROL MODULE AND SWITCH • Disconnect connector from malfunction indicator lamp control. • Measure resistance between Circuit 993 (BR/W) and 589 (O). • **Is resistance between 3.5 and 4.5 ohms?**	Yes No	▶ ▶	REPLACE malfunction indicator lamp control. CHECK for: • Open wire between turn signal and windshield wiper switch and malfunction indicator lamp control. • Damaged turn signal and windshield wiper switch. SERVICE as required.
D7	CHECK CONTROL LINE SIGNAL AT WIPER SWITCH • Disconnect harness from the turn signal and windshield wiper switch. • Check continuity between terminals for Circuits 993 (BR/W) and 589 (O). • **Is resistance between 3.5 and 4.5 ohms?**	Yes No	▶ ▶	GO to D8. SERVICE damaged turn signal and windshield wiper switch.
D8	PERFORM WIPER MOTOR CURRENT DRAW TEST • Perform windshield wiper current draw test as outlined. • **Is current draw OK?**	Yes No	▶ ▶	CHECK linkage. SERVICE windshield wiper motor as required. SERVICE as required.

FM9029400193020X

Fig. 64 Test D: Wipers Inoperative At Low Speed (Part 2 of 2). 1994 Cougar & Thunderbird

PINPOINT TEST F: WINDSHIELD WIPERS WILL NOT PARK AT PROPER POSITION

TEST STEP		RESULT	▶	ACTION TO TAKE
F1	CHECK FOR WIRE CONTINUITY • Turn turn signal and windshield wiper switch to OFF position. • Turn ignition switch to OFF position. • Disconnect connector from windshield wiper motor. • Check for continuity between Circuits 28 (BK/PK) and 56 (DB/O). • **Is there continuity?**	Yes No	▶ ▶	GO to F4. GO to F2.
F2	CHECK FOR MALFUNCTION INDICATOR LAMP CONTROL CONTINUITY • Gain access to malfunction indicator lamp control at fuse junction panel. • Disconnect malfunction indicator lamp control connector. • Measure continuity between Pins 7 and 8 of malfunction indicator lamp control. • **Is there continuity?**	Yes No	▶ ▶	CHECK for: • Unseated connectors. • Open circuit between malfunction indicator lamp control and windshield wiper motor. SERVICE as required. GO to F3.

FM9029400195010X

Fig. 66 Test F: Wipers Will Not Park At Proper Position (Part 1 of 2). 1994 Cougar & Thunderbird

TEST STEP		RESULT	▶	ACTION TO TAKE
F3	CHECK WIPER SWITCH FUNCTIONALITY • Measure resistance between Circuits 589 (O) and 993 (BR/W). • **Is resistance between 45k ohms and 50k ohms?**	Yes No	▶ ▶	REPLACE malfunction indicator lamp control. CHECK for: • Unseated turn signal and windshield wiper switch connector. • Open Circuit (589 (O) or 993 (BR/W)). • Damaged turn signal and windshield wiper switch. SERVICE as required.
F4	CHECK CIRCUIT 65 (DG) • Turn ignition switch to RUN position. • Disconnect windshield wiper motor. • Using a voltmeter, connect one lead to a known good ground. • Connect the other lead to Circuit 65 (DG). • Read voltage. • **Is battery voltage present?**	Yes No	▶ ▶	GO to F5. SERVICE Circuit 65 (DG). RESTORE vehicle. RETEST system.
F5	CHECK CIRCUIT 57 (BK) • Connect one lead of voltmeter to Circuit 65 (DG) at windshield wiper motor connector. • Connect second lead of voltmeter to Circuit 57 (BK) at windshield wiper motor connector. • Read voltage. • **Is battery voltage present?**	Yes No	▶ ▶	GO to F6. SERVICE Circuit 57 (BK). RESTORE vehicle. RETEST system.
F6	CHECK CIRCUIT 28 (BK/PK) TO GROUND • Reconnect windshield wiper motor. • Connect one lead of ohmmeter to Circuit 28 (BK/PK) at windshield wiper motor connector. • Connect second lead to ground terminal of windshield wiper motor. • Read ohmmeter. • **Is continuity present?**	Yes No	▶ ▶	GO to F7. REPLACE windshield wiper motor. RESTORE vehicle. RETEST system.
F7	CHECK WINDSHIELD WIPER MOUNTING ARM AND PIVOT SHAFT • Inspect windshield wiper mounting arm and pivot shaft. • **Is windshield wiper mounting arm bent or cracked?**	Yes No	▶ ▶	SERVICE as required. RESTORE vehicle. RETEST system. GO to F8.
F8	TURN SIGNAL AND WINDSHIELD WIPER SWITCH CONTINUITY TEST • Perform turn signal and windshield wiper switch continuity test as outlined. • **Did turn signal and windshield wiper switch test OK?**	Yes No	▶ ▶	REPLACE malfunction indicator lamp control. RESTORE vehicle. RETEST system. REPLACE turn signal and windshield wiper switch. RESTORE vehicle. RETEST system.

FM9029400195020X

Fig. 66 Test F: Wipers Will Not Park At Proper Position (Part 2 of 2). 1994 Cougar & Thunderbird

TEST STEP		RESULT	▶	ACTION TO TAKE
E1	CHECK OPERATION • Set wipers to interval. • **Does slow(s) speed work?**	Yes No	▶ ▶	GO to E2. GO to D1.
E2	CHECK MODE SELECT INPUT SIGNAL • Disconnect connector from malfunction indicator lamp control. • Measure resistance between Circuits 993 (BR/W) and 589 (O). • **Is resistance between 10.5k ohms and 12.0k ohms?**	Yes No	▶ ▶	GO to E4. GO to E3.

FM9029400194010X

Fig. 65 Test E: Wipers Inoperative At Interval Setting (Part 1 of 2). 1994 Cougar & Thunderbird

TEST STEP	RESULT	►	ACTION TO TAKE
G1 CHECK FOR SHORTED MALFUNCTION INDICATOR LAMP CONTROL • Disconnect connector from windshield wiper motor. • Disconnect wires at malfunction indicator lamp control. • Measure continuity between Circuits 28 (BK/PK). • **Is there continuity?**	Yes No	► ►	GO to **G2**. CHECK for: • Unseated component. • Damaged windshield wiper motor. SERVICE as required.
G2 CHECK WIRING BETWEEN MALFUNCTION INDICATOR LAMP CONTROL AND MOTOR • Measure continuity of Circuits 28 (BK/PK) and 56 (DB/O) at malfunction indicator lamp control connector? • **Is there continuity?**	Yes No	► ►	SERVICE open circuit between malfunction indicator lamp control and windshield wiper motor. GO to **G3**.
G3 CHECK WIPER SWITCH • Measure resistance between Circuits 589 (O) and 993 (BR/W). • **Is resistance between 45k ohms and 50k ohms?**	Yes No	► ►	REPLACE malfunction indicator lamp control. CHECK for: • Open Circuit (993 (BR/W) or 589 (O)) between turn signal and windshield wiper switch and malfunction indicator lamp control. • Damaged turn signal and windshield wiper switch. SERVICE as required.

FM9029400196000X

Fig. 67   Test G: Wipers Continue To Run When Switch Is Turned Off. 1994 Cougar & Thunderbird

TEST STEP	RESULT	►	ACTION TO TAKE
A1 WINDSHIELD WASHERS INOPERATIVE • Check fluid level of windshield washer reservoir. • **Is windshield washer reservoir empty?**	Yes No	► ►	FILL windshield washer reservoir. GO to **A2**.

FM9029400198010X

Fig. 68   Test A: Washer Inoperative (Part 1 of 2). 1994 Mustang

TEST STEP	RESULT	►	ACTION TO TAKE
A2 TURN ON WASHER SWITCH • Check operation or windshield washer pump. • **Does windshield washer pump run?**	Yes No	► ►	GO to **A3**. GO to **A6**.
A3 INSPECT NOZZLE FOR BLOCKAGE • Inspect windshield washer nozzle jet and bracket for blockage. • **Are windshield washer nozzle jet and bracket blocked?**	Yes No	► ►	CLEAN or REPLACE windshield washer nozzle jet and bracket. GO to **A4**.
A4 INSPECT HOSE, FILTER, CHECK VALVE FOR BLOCKAGE OR KINKS • Inspect hose for blockage or kinks. • **Are any blockages or kinks present?**	Yes No	► ►	CLEAN, SERVICE or REPLACE as necessary. GO to **A5**.
A5 INSPECT PUMP OUTLET FOR BLOCKAGE • Inspect pump outlet for blockage. • **Is windshield washer pump outlet blocked or obstructed?**	Yes No	► ►	REMOVE washer pump from reservoir and clean. RETEST system. REPLACE washer pump. RETEST system.
A6 CHECK FOR VOLTAGE AT WASHER PUMP • Using a voltmeter, actuate the turn signal and windshield wiper switch and check for voltage at windshield washer pump. • **Is battery voltage present?**	Yes No	► ►	GO to **A7**. GO to **A8**.
A7 CHECK PUMP GROUND • Check ground at pump connector. • **Is connector properly grounded?**	Yes No	► ►	REPLACE windshield washer pump. SERVICE ground.
A8 TURN ON WINDSHIELD WIPERS • Check operation of windshield wipers. • **Do wipers operate?**	Yes No	► ►	GO to **A9**. GO to Pinpoint Test B.
A9 CHECK WIPER SWITCH RESISTANCE AT WIPER CONTROL MODULE • Unplug connector from wiper control module. • Depress windshield washer switch on end of turn signal and windshield wiper switch. • Check continuity between Circuits 993 (BR/W) and 590 (DB/W). • **Is there continuity?**	Yes No	► ►	GO to **A11**. GO to **A10**.
A10 CHECK WIPER SWITCH • Unplug wiper switch connector. • Depress turn signal and windshield wiper switch. • Check for continuity between terminals B and W. • **Is there continuity?**	Yes No	► ►	SERVICE for open circuit between turn signal and windshield wiper switch and wiper control module. SERVICE turn signal and windshield wiper switch.
A11 CHECK WASHER PUMP CIRCUIT • Check continuity of Circuit 941 (BK/W) from wiper control module to windshield washer pump. • **Is there continuity?**	Yes No	► ►	REPLACE wiper control module. SERVICE for open circuit.

FM9029400198020X

Fig. 68   Test A: Washer Inoperative (Part 2 of 2). 1994 Mustang

TEST STEP	RESULT	►	ACTION TO TAKE
B1 CHECK FOR SUPPLY VOLTAGE AT MOTOR • Turn ignition switch to RUN. • Turn turn signal and windshield wiper switch to HI. • Unplug windshield wiper motor. • Check for battery voltage at Circuit 65 (DG). • **Is battery voltage present?**	Yes No	► ►	GO to **B2**. GO to **B3**.
B2 CHECK FOR BATTERY VOLTAGE AT THE WINDSHIELD WIPER CONTROL MODULE • Check for battery voltage at Circuit 65 (DG) Pin 2 of connector. • **Is battery voltage present?**	Yes No	► ►	GO to **B4**. SERVICE Circuit 65 (DG) for open circuit. RESTORE vehicle. RETEST system.
B3 CHECK CIRCUIT 65 (DB) SUPPLY • Using test lamp check for voltage at fuse 2 (30A). • **Is voltage present at both sides of circuit breaker?**	Yes No	► ►	SERVICE Circuit 65 (DG) for open circuit. RESTORE vehicle. RETEST system. REPLACE fuse.
B4 CHECK FOR BATTERY VOLTAGE TO MOTOR WINDINGS • Turn ignition switch to RUN. • Turn turn signal and windshield wiper switch to HI. • Disconnect connector from windshield wiper motor. • Check for battery voltage between Circuits 61 (Y/R) and 58 (W). • **Is battery voltage present?**	Yes No	► ►	GO to **B8**. GO to **B5**.
B5 CHECK FOR BATTERY VOLTAGE AT WINDSHIELD WIPER CONTROL MODULE CONNECTOR • Check for battery voltage between Pins 10 and 14 (Circuits 61 (Y/R) and 58(W) of windshield wiper control module connector with turn signal and windshield wiper switch in HI position. • **Is battery voltage present?**	Yes No	► ►	SERVICE Circuit 61 (Y/R) or Circuit 58 (W) for open circuit. RESTORE vehicle. RETEST system. GO to **B6**.
B6 CHECK WIRING BETWEEN WINDSHIELD WIPER CONTROL MODULE AND TURN SIGNAL AND WINDSHIELD WIPER SWITCH • Disconnect connector from windshield wiper control module. • Measure resistance between Circuits 993 (BR/W) and 589 (O) with turn signal and windshield wiper switch in HI position. • **Is resistance less than one ohm?**	Yes No	► ►	REPLACE windshield wiper control module. RESTORE vehicle. RETEST system. GO to **B7**.
B7 CHECK TURN SIGNAL AND WINDSHIELD WIPER SWITCH CONTINUITY • Disconnect harness from the turn signal and windshield wiper switch. • Check continuity between terminals for Circuits 993 (BR/W) and 589 (O) with turn signal and windshield wiper switch in the HI position. • **Is resistance less than one ohm?**	Yes No	► ►	SERVICE Circuit 993 (BR/W) or Circuit 589 (O) for open circuit. RESTORE vehicle. RETEST system. REPLACE turn signal and windshield wiper switch. RESTORE vehicle. RETEST system.

FM9029400199010X

Fig. 69   Test B: Wipers Inoperative In All Switch Positions (Part 1 of 2). 1994 Mustang

TEST STEP	RESULT	►	ACTION TO TAKE
B8 WINDSHIELD WIPER MOTOR CURRENT DRAW TEST • Perform windshield wiper motor current draw test as outlined. • **Is current draw OK?**	Yes No	► ►	CHECK linkage as outlined. RESTORE vehicle. RETEST system. REPLACE windshield wiper motor. RESTORE vehicle. RETEST system.

FM9029400199020X

Fig. 69   Test B: Wipers Inoperative In All Switch Positions (Part 2 of 2). 1994 Mustang

TEST STEP	RESULT	►	ACTION TO TAKE
C1 CHECK FOR BATTERY VOLTAGE TO MOTOR WINDINGS • Turn ignition switch to RUN. • Turn turn signal and windshield wiper switch to LO. • Disconnect connector from windshield wiper motor. • Check for battery voltage between Circuits 61 (Y/R) and 56 (DB/O). • **Is voltage present?**	Yes No	► ►	GO to **C5**. GO to **C2**.
C2 CHECK FOR BATTERY VOLTAGE AT WINDSHIELD WIPER CONTROL MODULE CONNECTOR • Check for battery voltage between Pins 10 and 8 (Circuits 61 (Y/R) and 56 (DB/O)) of windshield wiper control module connector. • **Is voltage present?**	Yes No	► ►	SERVICE Circuit 56 (DB/O) or Circuit 61 (Y/R) for open circuit. RESTORE vehicle. RETEST system. GO to **C3**.
C3 CHECK WIRING BETWEEN WINDSHIELD WIPER CONTROL MODULE AND TURN SIGNAL AND WINDSHIELD WIPER SWITCH • Disconnect connector from with windshield wiper control module. • Measure resistance 4 between Circuit 993 (BR/W) and 589 (O) with turn signal and windshield wiper switch in LO position. • **Is resistance between 3.5K and 4.5K ohms?**	Yes No	► ►	REPLACE windshield wiper control module. RESTORE vehicle. RETEST system. GO to **C4**.
C4 CHECK CONTROL LINE SIGNAL AT TURN SIGNAL AND WINDSHIELD WIPER SWITCH • Disconnect harness from the turn signal and windshield wiper switch. • Check continuity between terminals for Circuits 993 (BR/W) and 589 (O) with turn signal and windshield wiper switch in LO position. • **Is resistance between 3.5K and 4.5K ohms?**	Yes No	► ►	SERVICE Circuit 993 (BR/W) or Circuit 589(O) for open circuit. RESTORE vehicle. RETEST system. REPLACE damaged turn signal and windshield wiper switch. RESTORE vehicle. RETEST system.
C5 WINDSHIELD WIPER MOTOR CURRENT DRAW TEST • Perform windshield wiper motor current draw test as outlined. • **Is current draw OK?**	Yes No	► ►	CHECK linkage as outlined. RESTORE vehicle. RETEST system. REPLACE windshield wiper motor. RESTORE vehicle. RETEST system.

FM9029400200000X

Fig. 70   Test C: Wipers Inoperative At Low Speeds. 1994 Mustang

	TEST STEP	RESULT	▶	ACTION TO TAKE
D1	CHECK MODE SELECT INPUT SIGNAL			
	• Disconnect connector from windshield wiper control module. • Measure resistance between Circuits 993 (BR/W) and 589 (O) with turn signal and windshield wiper switch at interval setting. • Is resistance between 10.5K and 12.0K ohms?	Yes No	▶ ▶	GO to D3. GO to D2.
D2	CHECK MODE SELECT SIGNAL AT TURN SIGNAL AND WINDSHIELD WIPER SWITCH			
	• Disconnect harness from the turn signal and windshield wiper switch. • Measure resistance between terminals for Circuits 993 (BR/W) and 589 (O) with turn signal and windshield wiper switch at interval setting. • Is resistance between 10.5K and 12.0K ohms?	Yes No	▶ ▶	SERVICE Circuit 993 (BR/W) or Circuit 589 (O) for open circuit. RESTORE vehicle. RETEST system. REPLACE damaged turn signal and windshield wiper switch. RESTORE vehicle. RETEST system
D3	CHECK INTERVAL SELECT INPUT SIGNAL			
	• Rotate interval control on the turn signal and windshield wiper switch from MIN to MAX. • Measure resistance between Circuits 590 (DB/W) and 993 (BR/W). • Is resistance less than 104k ohms?	Yes No	▶ ▶	REPLACE windshield wiper control module. RESTORE vehicle. RETEST system. GO to D4.
D4	CHECK INTERVAL SELECT INPUT SIGNAL AT TURN SIGNAL AND WINDSHIELD WIPER SWITCH			
	• Disconnect harness from turn signal and windshield wiper switch. • Rotate interval control on the turn signal and windshield wiper switch from MIN to MAX. • Measure resistance between terminals of wiper switch for Circuits 590 (DB/W) and 993 (BR/W). • Is resistance less than 104K ohms?	Yes No	▶ ▶	SERVICE Circuit 590 (DB/W) or Circuit 993 (BR/W) for open circuit. RESTORE vehicle. RETEST system. REPLACE damaged turn signal and windshield wiper switch. RESTORE vehicle. RETEST system

FM9029400201000X

Fig. 71   Test D: Wipers Inoperative At Interval Setting. 1994 Mustang

	TEST STEP	RESULT	▶	ACTION TO TAKE
E1	CHECK WIPER MOTOR GROUND			
	• Unplug wiper motor connector. Check for ground at Circuit 57 (BK). • Is ground OK?	Yes No	▶ ▶	GO to E2. SERVICE open circuit.
E2	CHECK FOR POWER AT WIPER MOTOR			
	• Place ignition in RUN and turn signal/wiper switch at OFF. • Check for battery voltage between Circuit 65 (DG) and Circuit 57 (BK) at the motor connector. • Is battery voltage present?	Yes No	▶ ▶	GO to E3. SERVICE open circuits.
E3	CHECK MOTOR CIRCUIT CONTINUITY THROUGH WIPER CONTROL MODULE			
	• With wiper switch at OFF, check continuity of Circuit 28 (BK/PK) to 56 (DB/O) and Circuit 61 (Y/R) to 57 (BK). • Is continuity OK?	Yes No	▶ ▶	GO to E5. GO to E4.
E4	CHECK CIRCUITS TO WIPER CONTROL MODULE			
	• Check continuity of Circuits 28, 56, 61, and 57 from wiper motor to wiper control module. • Is continuity OK?	Yes No	▶ ▶	REPLACE wiper control module. SERVICE open circuits.

FM9029400202010X

Fig. 72   Test E: Wipers Will Not Park At Proper Position (Part 1 of 2). 1994 Mustang

	TEST STEP	RESULT	▶	ACTION TO TAKE
E5	CHECK WIPER LINKAGE			
	• Check that wiper linkage is not bent, cracked or mispositioned from motor shaft. • Is linkage OK?	Yes No	▶ ▶	REPLACE wiper motor. SERVICE linkage.

FM9029400202020X

Fig. 72   Test E: Wipers Will Not Park At Proper Position (Part 2 of 2). 1994 Mustang

	TEST STEP	RESULT	▶	ACTION TO TAKE
F1	CHECK CONNECTIONS			
	• Check that wiper motor and wiper control module connectors are fully seated. • Are connections OK?	Yes No	▶ ▶	GO to F2. SERVICE as required. RECHECK system.
F2	CHECK CIRCUIT CONTINUITY THROUGH WIPER CONTROL MODULE			
	• Disconnect windshield wiper motor. • With wiper switch at OFF, check continuity of Circuit 28 (BK/PK) to 56 (DB/O) and Circuit 61 (Y/R) to 57 (BK) at motor connector. • Is there continuity?	Yes No	▶ ▶	REPLACE wiper motor. GO to F3.
F3	CHECK CIRCUITS TO WIPER CONTROL MODULE			
	• Check continuity of Circuits 28, 56, 61 and 57 from wiper motor to wiper control module. • Is continuity OK?	Yes No	▶ ▶	GO to F4. SERVICE circuits as required.
F4	CHECK CIRCUITS TO WINDSHIELD WIPER SWITCH			
	• With wiper switch at OFF, measure resistance between Circuits 589 (O) and 933 (BR/W) at wiper module. • Is resistance 45k ohms to 50k ohms?	Yes No	▶ ▶	REPLACE wiper control module. GO to F5.
F5	CHECK CIRCUIT CONTINUITY			
	• Check continuity of Circuits 589 (O) and 993 (BR/W) between wiper switch and wiper control module. • Is continuity OK?	Yes No	▶ ▶	REPLACE wiper switch. SERVICE open circuits.

FM9029400203000X

Fig. 73   Test F: Wipers Continue To Run When Switch Is Turned Off. 1994 Mustang

TEST STEP	RESULT	▶	ACTION TO TAKE
A1 CHECK FLUID LEVEL			
• Check fluid level in reservoir. • **Is fluid level good?**	Yes No	▶ ▶	GO to A2. Fill Reservoir.
A2 CHECK WASHER OPERATION			
• Activate washer switch. • Check pump for operation.	Motor inoperative Motor operates, but will not squirt fluid Pump squirts fluid but wipers do not wipe	▶ ▶ ▶	GO to A3. GO to A8. GO to A10.
A3 CHECK WCM OUTPUT			
• Turn ignition on. • Depress washer switch. • Check for battery voltage at circuit 941 (BK/W) at washer pump. • **Is battery voltage present?**	Yes No	▶ ▶	GO to A7. GO to A4.
A4 CHECK FOR POWER TO WCM			
• Check for battery voltage at circuit 65 (DG) of the WCM Pin J1-2. • **Is battery voltage present?**	Yes No	▶ ▶	GO to A5. CHECK for • Open circuit breaker. • Open connector. • Open wire circuit 65 (DG). SERVICE as required.

FM9029300122010X

Fig. 74 Test A: Washer Does Not Operate (Part 1 of 2). 1993–94 Crown Victoria, Grand Marquis & Town Car

TEST STEP	RESULT	▶	ACTION TO TAKE
A5 CHECK CONTINUITY OF SWITCH			
• Disconnect connector from WCM. • Depress washer switch. • Measure resistance between circuit 993 (BR/W) and circuit 590 (DB/W). • **Is there continuity?**	Yes No	▶ ▶	GO to A6. CHECK for: • Open wire between wiper switch and WCM. • Damaged wiper/washer switch. SERVICE or REPLACE as required.
A6 CHECK FOR VOLTAGE TO MOTOR			
• Reconnect connector to WCM. • Turn ignition switch to run position. • Depress washer switch. • Measure voltage at circuit 58 (W) at WCM connector. • **Is battery voltage present?**	Yes No	▶ ▶	CHECK for: • Open circuit 58 (W) between WCM and wiper motor. REPLACE damaged WCM.
A7 CHECK GROUND AT WASHER PUMP			
• Using an ohmmeter, check ground at the pump. • **Is the ground functional?**	Yes No	▶ ▶	REPLACE washer pump. SERVICE ground.
A8 INSPECT HOSE AND NOZZLE			
• visually inspect washer hose and nozzle for blockage or hose kinks. • **Is hose blocked or kinked?**	Yes No	▶ ▶	CLEAN, REPLACE, or SERVICE nozzle or hoses. GO to A9.
A9 CHECK FOR BLOCKAGE AT WASHER PUMP OUTLET			
• Disconnect hose at reservoir and check for blockage at washer pump outlet. • **Is hose blocked at washer pump outlet?**	Yes No	▶ ▶	REMOVE washer pump from reservoir and clean. REPLACE washer pump.
A10 TEST FOR POWER TO WIPER MOTOR			
• Disconnect connector from wiper motor. • Turn ignition to run position. • Depress and release washer switch. • Check for battery voltage between circuit 58 (W) and 61 (Y/R). • **Is battery voltage present?**	Yes No	▶ ▶	PERFORM wiper motor current draw test. SERVICE as required. GO to A11.
A11 TEST FOR BATTERY VOLTAGE AT WCM OUTPUT PIN			
• Turn ignition to RUN position. • Depress and release washer switch. • Check for battery voltage between circuits 58 (W) and 61 (Y/R) at WCM connector. • **Is battery voltage present?**	Yes No	▶ ▶	CHECK for: • Unseated connector. • Open circuit 58 (W) between WCM and wiper motor. REPLACE WCM.

FM9029300122020X

Fig. 74 Test A: Washer Does Not Operate (Part 2 of 2). 1993–94 Crown Victoria, Grand Marquis & Town Car

Fig. 75 Test B: Wipers Inoperative At High Speed (Part 1 of 2). 1993–94 Crown Victoria, Grand Marquis & Town Car

TEST STEP	RESULT	ACTION TO TAKE
B1 CHECK OPERATION • Does low speed work?	Yes No	GO to B4. GO to B2.

Fig. 75 Test B: Wipers Inoperative At High Speed (Part 1 of 2). 1993–94 Crown Victoria, Grand Marquis & Town Car

Fig. 75 Test B (Part 2 of 2)

TEST STEP	RESULT	ACTION TO TAKE
B2 CHECK FOR SUPPLY VOLTAGE AT MOTOR • Turn ignition on. • Turn wiper switch to HI. • Unplug wiper motor. • Check for battery voltage at circuit 65 (DG). • Is battery voltage present?	Yes No	GO to B3. CHECK for: • Open circuit breaker in fuse panel. • Open connector. • Open wire circuit 65 (DG). • Poor ground connection. SERVICE as required.
B3 CHECK FOR BATTERY VOLTAGE AT THE WCM • Check for battery voltage at circuit 65 (DG) pin 2 of connector. • Is battery voltage present?	Yes No	GO to B4. SERVICE open in power feed to module. CHECK for: • Open wire in circuit 65 (DG). • Open unseated connector.
B4 CHECK FOR BATTERY VOLTAGE TO MOTOR WINDINGS • Turn ignition switch to RUN. • Turn wiper switch to HI. • Disconnect connector from wiper motor. • Check for battery voltage between circuits 61 (Y/R) and 56 (DB/O). • Is battery voltage present?	Yes No	GO to B7. GO to B5.
B5 CHECK FOR BATTERY VOLTAGE AT WCM CONNECTOR • Check for battery voltage between pins 12 and 14 (circuits 61 (Y/R) and 56 (DB/O)) of WCM connector. • Is battery voltage present?	Yes No	CHECK for: • Open wire circuits 56 (DB/O) or 61 (Y/R). • Open connector. • Unseated connector. GO to B6.
B6 CHECK WIRING BETWEEN (WCM) AND SWITCH • Disconnect connector from wiper control module (WCM). • Measure resistance between circuits 993 (BR/W) and 589 (O). • Is there continuity?	Yes No	REPLACE WCM. CHECK for: • Open wire between wiper switch and WCM. • Damaged wiper switch. SERVICE as required.
B7 CHECK WIPER SWITCH CONTINUITY • Disconnect harness from the wiper switch. • Check continuity between terminals for circuits 993 (BR/W) and 589 (O). • Is there continuity?	Yes No	CHECK for open wire between switch and WCM. SERVICE as required. CHECK for damaged switch. SERVICE as required.
B8 PERFORM WIPER MOTOR CURRENT DRAW TEST • Is current draw OK?	Yes No	CHECK linkage. SERVICE as required. SERVICE wiper motor as required.

Fig. 75 Test B: Wipers Inoperative At High Speed (Part 2 of 2). 1993–94 Crown Victoria, Grand Marquis & Town Car

Fig. 76 Test C: Wipers Inoperative At Low Speed. 1993–94 Crown Victoria, Grand Marquis & Town Car

TEST STEP	RESULT	ACTION TO TAKE
C1 CHECK OPERATION • Does high speed work?	Yes No	GO to C4. GO to C2.
C2 CHECK FOR SUPPLY VOLTAGE • Turn ignition on. • Turn wiper switch to HI. • Unplug wiper motor. • Check for battery voltage at circuit 65 (DG). • Is voltage present?	Yes No	GO to C3. CHECK for: • Open circuit breaker in fuse panel. • Open connector. • Open wire circuit 65 (DG). • Poor ground connection. SERVICE as required.
C3 CHECK FOR BATTERY VOLTAGE AT THE WCM • Check for battery voltage at circuit 65 (DG) pin 2 of connector. • Is voltage present?	Yes No	GO to C4. SERVICE open in power feed to module. CHECK for: • Open wire in circuit 65 (DG). • Open unseated connector.
C4 CHECK FOR BATTERY VOLTAGE TO MOTOR WINDINGS • Turn ignition switch to RUN. • Turn wiper switch to LO. • Disconnect connector from wiper motor. • Check for battery voltage between circuits 61 (Y/R) and 58 (W). • Is voltage present?	Yes No	GO to C7. GO to C5.
C5 CHECK FOR BATTERY VOLTAGE AT WCM CONNECTOR • Check for battery voltage between pins 12 and 8 (circuits 61 (Y/R) and 58 (W)) of WCM connector. • Is voltage present?	Yes No	CHECK for: • Open wire circuits 58 (W) or 61 (Y/R). • Open connector. • Unseated connector. GO to C6.
C6 CHECK WIRING BETWEEN (WCM) AND SWITCH • Disconnect connector from wiper control module (WCM). • Measure resistance between circuit 993 (BR/W) and 589 (O). • Is resistance 4.08k ohms?	Yes No	REPLACE WCM. CHECK for: • Open wire between wiper switch and WCM. • Damaged wiper switch. SERVICE as required.
C7 CHECK CONTROL LINE SIGNAL AT WIPER SWITCH • Disconnect harness from the wiper switch. • Check continuity between terminals for circuits 993 (BR/W) and 589 (O). • Is resistance 4.08k ohms?	Yes No	SERVICE open wire between switch and WCM. SERVICE damaged switch.
C8 PERFORM WIPER MOTOR CURRENT DRAW TEST • Is current draw OK?	Yes No	CHECK linkage. SERVICE wiper motor as required. SERVICE as required.

Fig. 76 Test C: Wipers Inoperative At Low Speed. 1993–94 Crown Victoria, Grand Marquis & Town Car

Test E: Wipers Will Not Park Below Windshield. 1993–94 Crown Victoria, Grand Marquis & Town Car

	TEST STEP	RESULT	ACTION TO TAKE
E1	CHECK FOR WIRE CONTINUITY • Turn wiper switch to OFF position. • Disconnect connector from wiper motor. • Check for continuity between circuits 28 (BK/PK) and 58 (W). • Is there continuity?	Yes No	PERFORM motor parking test. GO to E2.
E2	CHECK FOR WCM CONTINUITY • Turn ignition to OFF. • Disconnect connector from wiper control module. • Measure continuity between pins J1-6 and J1-8 of WCM. • Is there continuity?	Yes No	CHECK for: • Unseated connectors. • Open circuit between WCM and wiper motor. SERVICE as required. GO to E3.
E3	CHECK WIPER SWITCH FUNCTIONALITY • Turn wiper switch to OFF position. • Measure resistance between circuits 589 (O) and 993 (BR/W). • Is resistance approximately 47.6k ohms?	Yes No	REPLACE WCM. CHECK for: • Unseated wiper switch connector. • Open circuit (589 (O) or 993 (BR/W)). • Damaged wiper switch. SERVICE as required.

Fig. 78 Test E: Wipers Will Not Park Below Windshield. 1993–94 Crown Victoria, Grand Marquis & Town Car

FM9029300126000X

Test F: Wipers Will Not Turn Off. 1993–94 Crown Victoria, Grand Marquis & Town Car

	TEST STEP	RESULT	ACTION TO TAKE
F1	CHECK FOR SHORTED WCM • Disconnect connector from wiper motor. • Turn ignition to RUN position. • Turn wiper switch to OFF position. • Measure continuity between circuits 28 (BK/PK) and between circuits 61 (Y/R) and 63 (R). • Is there continuity?	Yes No	CHECK for: • Unseated component. • Damaged wiper motor. SERVICE as required. GO to F2.
F2	CHECK WIRING BETWEEN WCM AND MOTOR • Measure continuity of circuits 28 (BK/PK) and 58 (W) and between circuits 61 (Y/R) and 63 (R) at WCM connector? • Is there continuity?	Yes No	SERVICE open circuit between WCM and wiper motor. GO to F3.
F3	CHECK WIPER SWITCH • Measure resistance between circuits 589 (O) and 993 (BR/W). • Is resistance approximately 47.6k ohms?	Yes No	REPLACE WCM. CHECK for: • Open circuit (993 (BR/W) or 589 (O)) between wiper switch and WCM. • Damaged wiper switch. SERVICE as required.

Fig. 79 Test F: Wipers Will Not Turn Off. 1993–94 Crown Victoria, Grand Marquis & Town Car

FM9029300127000X

Test D: Wipers Inoperative At Low Speed Interval. 1993–94 Crown Victoria, Grand Marquis & Town Car

	TEST STEP	RESULT	ACTION TO TAKE
D1	CHECK OPERATION • Does low speed work?	Yes No	GO to D2. GO to C1.
D2	CHECK MODE SELECT INPUT SIGNAL • Disconnect connector from wiper control module (WCM). • Measure resistance between circuits 993 (BR/W) and 589 (O). • Is resistance 11.3k ohms?	Yes No	GO to D4. GO to D3.
D3	CHECK MODE SELECT SIGNAL AT WIPER SWITCH • Disconnect harness from the wiper switch. • Resistance between terminals for circuits 993 (BR/W) and 589 (O). • Is resistance 11.3k ohms?	Yes No	CHECK for open wire between switch and WCM. SERVICE as required. CHECK for damaged switch. SERVICE as required.
D4	CHECK INTERVAL SELECT INPUT SIGNAL • Rotate interval control on the wiper switch from min to max. • Measure resistance between circuits 590 (DB/W) and 993 (BR/W). • Is resistance 3.3k-100k ohms?	Yes No	REPLACE WCM. GO to D5.
D5	CHECK INTERVAL SELECT INPUT SIGNAL AT WIPER SWITCH • Disconnect harness from wiper switch. • Rotate interval control on the wiper switch from min to max. • Measure resistance between terminals of wiper switch for circuits 590 (DB/W) and 993 (BR/W). • Is resistance 3.3k-100k ohms?	Yes No	CHECK for open wires between the wiper switch and the WCM. SERVICE as required. CHECK for damaged wiper switch. SERVICE as required.

Fig. 77 Test D: Wipers Inoperative At Low Speed Interval. 1993–94 Crown Victoria, Grand Marquis & Town Car

FM9029300125000X

Fig. 80 Test A: Washer Inoperative (Part 2 of 2). 1993–94 Mark VIII, Sable & Taurus

TEST STEP	RESULT	ACTION TO TAKE
A10 TEST FOR POWER TO WIPER MOTOR • Disconnect connector from wiper motor. • Turn ignition to run position. • Depress and release washer switch. • Check for battery voltage between circuit 56 (DB/O) and 61 (Y/R). • Is battery voltage present?	Yes No	PERFORM wiper motor current draw test. SERVICE as required. GO to A11.
A11 TEST FOR BATTERY VOLTAGE AT WIPER CONTROL MODULE OUTPUT PIN • Turn ignition to RUN position. • Depress and release washer switch. • Check for battery voltage between circuits 56 (DB/O) and 61 (Y/R) at wiper control module connector. • Is battery voltage present?	Yes No	CHECK for: • Unseated connector. • Open circuit 56 (DB/O) between wiper control module and wiper motor. REPLACE wiper control module.

FM90293001280020X

Fig. 81 Test B: Wipers Inoperative At High Speed (Part 1 of 2). 1993–94 Mark VIII, Sable & Taurus

TEST STEP	RESULT	ACTION TO TAKE
B1 CHECK OPERATION • Does low speed work?	Yes No	GO to B4. GO to B2.
B2 CHECK FOR SUPPLY VOLTAGE AT MOTOR • Turn ignition on. • Turn wiper switch to HI. • Unplug wiper motor. • Check for battery voltage at circuit 65 (DG). • Is battery voltage present?	Yes No	GO to B3. CHECK for: • Open circuit breaker in fuse panel. • Open connector. • Open wire circuit 65 (DG). • Poor ground connection. SERVICE connection as required.
B3 CHECK FOR BATTERY VOLTAGE AT THE WIPER CONTROL MODULE • Check for battery voltage at circuit 65 (DG) pin 2 of connector. • Is battery voltage present?	Yes No	GO to B4. SERVICE open in power feed to module. CHECK for: • Open wire in circuit 65 (DG). • Open unseated connector.
B4 CHECK FOR BATTERY VOLTAGE TO MOTOR WINDINGS • Turn ignition switch to RUN. • Turn wiper switch to HI. • Disconnect connector from wiper motor. • Check for battery voltage between circuits 61 (Y/R) and 58 (W). • Is battery voltage present?	Yes No	GO to B7. GO to B5.
B5 CHECK FOR BATTERY VOLTAGE AT WIPER CONTROL MODULE CONNECTOR • Check for battery voltage between pins 12 and 14 (circuits 61 (Y/R) and 58 (W)) of wiper control module connector. • Is battery voltage present?	Yes No	CHECK for: • Open wire circuits 56 (DB/O) or 61 (Y/R). • Open connector. • Unseated connector. GO to B6.

FM90293001290010X

Fig. 80 Test A: Washer Inoperative (Part 1 of 2). 1993–94 Mark VIII, Sable & Taurus

TEST STEP	RESULT	ACTION TO TAKE
A1 CHECK FLUID LEVEL • Check fluid level in reservoir. • Is fluid level good?	Yes No	GO to A2. Fill reservoir.
A2 CHECK WASHER OPERATION • Activate washer switch. • Check pump for operation.	Motor inoperative Motor operates, but will not squirt fluid Pump squirts fluid but wipers do not wipe	GO to A3. GO to A8. GO to A10.
A3 CHECK WIPER CONTROL MODULE OUTPUT • Turn ignition on. • Depress washer switch. • Check for battery voltage at circuit 941 (BK/W) at washer pump. • Is battery voltage present?	Yes No	GO to A7. GO to A4.
A4 CHECK FOR POWER TO WIPER CONTROL MODULE • Check for battery voltage at circuit 65 (DG) of the wiper control module. • Is battery voltage present?	Yes No	GO to A5. CHECK for: • Open circuit breaker. • Open connector. • Open wire circuit 65 (DG). SERVICE as required.
A5 CHECK CONTINUITY OF SWITCH • Disconnect connector from wiper control module. • Depress washer switch. • Measure resistance between circuit 993 (BR/W) and circuit 590 (DB/W). • Is there continuity?	Yes No	GO to A6. CHECK for: • Open wire between wiper switch and wiper control module. • Damaged wiper/washer switch. SERVICE or REPLACE as required.
A6 CHECK FOR VOLTAGE TO MOTOR • Reconnect connector to wiper control module. • Turn ignition switch to run position. • Depress washer switch. • Measure voltage at circuit 56 (DB/O) at wiper control module connector. • Is battery voltage present?	Yes No	CHECK for: • Open circuit 56 (DB/O) between wiper control module and wiper motor. REPLACE damaged wiper control module.
A7 CHECK GROUND AT WASHER PUMP • Using an ohmmeter, check ground at the pump. • Is the ground functional?	Yes No	REPLACE washer pump. SERVICE ground.
A8 INSPECT HOSE AND NOZZLE • Visually inspect washer hose and nozzle for blockage or hose kinks. • Is hose blocked or kinked?	Yes No	CLEAN, REPLACE, or SERVICE nozzle or hoses. GO to A9.
A9 CHECK FOR BLOCKAGE AT WASHER PUMP OUTLET • Disconnect hose at reservoir and check for blockage at washer pump outlet. • Is hose blocked at washer pump outlet?	Yes No	REMOVE washer pump from reservoir and clean. REPLACE washer pump.

FM90293001280010X

Test C: Wipers Inoperative At Low Speed (Part 1 of 2)

TEST STEP	RESULT	ACTION TO TAKE
C1 CHECK OPERATION • Does high speed work?	Yes No	GO to C4. GO to C2.
C2 CHECK FOR SUPPLY VOLTAGE • Turn ignition on. • Turn wiper switch to HI. • Unplug wiper motor. • Check for battery voltage at circuit 65 (DG). • Is voltage present?	Yes No	GO to C3. CHECK for: • Open circuit breaker in fuse panel. • Open connector. • Open wire circuit 65 (DG). • Poor ground connection. SERVICE as required.
C3 CHECK FOR BATTERY VOLTAGE AT THE WIPER CONTROL MODULE • Check for battery voltage at circuit 65 (DG) pin 2 of connector. • Is voltage present?	Yes No	GO to C4. SERVICE open in power feed to module. CHECK for: • Open wire in circuit 65 (DG). • Open unseated connector.
C4 CHECK FOR BATTERY VOLTAGE TO MOTOR WINDINGS • Turn ignition switch to RUN. • Turn wiper switch to LO. • Disconnect connector from wiper motor. • Check for battery voltage between circuits 61 (Y/R) and 56 (DB/O). • Is voltage present?	Yes No	GO to C7. GO to C5.

FM90293001300010X

Fig. 82 Test C: Wipers Inoperative At Low Speed (Part 1 of 2). 1993–94 Mark VIII, Sable & Taurus

Test D: Wipers Inoperative At Slow Speed Interval (Part 1 of 2)

TEST STEP	RESULT	ACTION TO TAKE
D1 CHECK OPERATION • Does slow speed work?	Yes No	GO to D2. GO to C1.
D2 CHECK MODE SELECT INPUT SIGNAL • Disconnect connector from wiper control module. • Measure resistance between circuits 993 (BR/W) and 589 (O). • Is resistance between 10.5k ohms and 12.0k ohms?	Yes No	GO to D4. GO to D3.
D3 CHECK MODE SELECT SIGNAL AT WIPER SWITCH • Disconnect harness from the wiper switch. • Resistance between terminals for circuits 993 (BR/W) and 589 (O). • Is resistance between 10.5k ohms and 12.0k ohms?	Yes	CHECK for open wire between switch and wiper control module. SERVICE as required.
D4 CHECK INTERVAL SELECT INPUT SIGNAL • Rotate interval control on the wiper switch from "S" to "F". • Measure resistance between circuits 590 (DB/W) and 993 (BR/W). • Is resistance 3.3k–103.3k ohms?	No Yes No	CHECK for damaged switch. SERVICE as required. REPLACE wiper control module. GO to D5.

FM90293001310010X

Fig. 83 Test D: Wipers Inoperative At Slow Speed Interval (Part 1 of 2). 1993–94 Mark VIII, Sable & Taurus

Test B: Wipers Inoperative At High Speed (Part 2 of 2)

TEST STEP	RESULT	ACTION TO TAKE
B6 CHECK WIRING BETWEEN WIPER CONTROL MODULE AND SWITCH • Disconnect connector from wiper motor. • Measure resistance between circuits 993 (BR/W) and 589 (O). • Is resistance less than 1.0 ohm?	Yes No	REPLACE wiper control module. CHECK for: • Open wire between wiper switch and wiper control module. SERVICE as required. • Damaged wiper switch. SERVICE as required.
B7 CHECK WIPER SWITCH CONTINUITY • Disconnect harness from the wiper switch. • Check continuity between terminals for circuits 993 (BR/W) and 589 (O). • Is resistance less than 1.0 ohm?	Yes No	CHECK for open wire between switch and wiper control module. SERVICE as required. CHECK for damaged switch. SERVICE as required.
B8 PERFORM WIPER MOTOR CURRENT DRAW TEST • Is current draw OK?	Yes No	CHECK linkage. SERVICE as required. SERVICE wiper motor as required.

FM90293001290020X

Fig. 81 Test B: Wipers Inoperative At High Speed (Part 2 of 2). 1993–94 Mark VIII, Sable & Taurus

Test C: Wipers Inoperative At Low Speed (Part 2 of 2)

TEST STEP	RESULT	ACTION TO TAKE
C5 CHECK FOR BATTERY VOLTAGE AT WIPER CONTROL MODULE CONNECTOR • Check for battery voltage between pins 12 and 8 (circuits 61 (Y/R) and 56 (DB/O)) of wiper control module connector. • Is voltage present?	Yes No	CHECK for: • Open wire circuits 56 (DB/O) or 61 (Y/R). • Open connector. • Unseated connector. GO to C6.
C6 CHECK WIRING BETWEEN WIPER CONTROL MODULE AND SWITCH • Disconnect connector from wiper control module. • Measure resistance between circuit 993 (BR/W) and 589 (O). • Is resistance between 3.5 and 4.5 ohms?	Yes No	REPLACE wiper control module. CHECK for: • Open wire between wiper switch and wiper control module. SERVICE as required. • Damaged wiper switch. SERVICE as required.
C7 CHECK CONTROL LINE SIGNAL AT WIPER SWITCH • Disconnect harness from the wiper switch. • Check continuity between terminals for circuits 993 (BR/W) and 589 (O). • Is resistance between 3.5 and 4.5 ohms?	Yes No	SERVICE open wire between switch and wiper control module. SERVICE damaged switch.
C8 PERFORM WIPER MOTOR CURRENT DRAW TEST • Is current draw OK?	Yes No	CHECK linkage. SERVICE wiper motor as required. SERVICE wiper motor as required.

FM90293001300020X

Fig. 82 Test C: Wipers Inoperative At Low Speed (Part 2 of 2). 1993–94 Mark VIII, Sable & Taurus

	TEST STEP	RESULT	▶	ACTION TO TAKE
D5	CHECK INTERVAL SELECT INPUT SIGNAL AT WIPER SWITCH			
	• Disconnect harness from wiper switch. • Rotate interval control on the wiper switch from "S" to "F". • Measure resistance between terminals of wiper switch for circuits 590 (DB/W) and 993 (BR/W). • **Is resistance 3.3k-103.3k ohms?**	Yes	▶	CHECK for open wires between the wiper switch and the wiper control module. SERVICE as required.
		No	▶	CHECK for damaged wiper switch. SERVICE as required.

FM9029300131020X

Fig. 83   Test D: Wipers Inoperative At Slow Speed Interval (Part 2 of 2). 1993–94 Mark VIII, Sable & Taurus

	TEST STEP	RESULT	▶	ACTION TO TAKE
E1	CHECK FOR WIRE CONTINUITY			
	• Turn wiper switch to OFF position. • Disconnect connector from wiper motor. • Check for continuity between circuits 28 (BK/PK) and 56 (DB/O). • **Is there continuity?**	Yes	▶	PERFORM motor parking test.
		No	▶	GO to E2.
E2	CHECK FOR WIPER CONTROL MODULE CONTINUITY			
	• Turn ignition to OFF. • Disconnect connector from wiper control module. • Measure continuity between Pins 6 and 8 of wiper control module. • **Is there continuity?**	Yes	▶	CHECK for: • Unseated connectors. • Open circuit between wiper control module and wiper motor. SERVICE as required.
		No	▶	GO to E3.
E3	CHECK WIPER SWITCH FUNCTIONALITY			
	• Turn wiper switch to OFF position. • Measure resistance between circuits 589 (O) and 993 (BR/W). • **Is resistance between 45k ohms and 50k ohms?**	Yes	▶	REPLACE wiper control module.
		No	▶	CHECK for: • Unseated wiper switch connector. • Open circuit (589 (O) or 993 (BR/W)). • Damaged wiper switch. SERVICE as required.

FM9029300132000X

Fig. 84   Test E: Wipers Will Not Park Below Windshield. 1993–94 Mark VIII, Sable & Taurus

	TEST STEP	RESULT	▶	ACTION TO TAKE
F1	CHECK FOR SHORTED WIPER CONTROL MODULE			
	• Disconnect connector from wiper motor. • Turn ignition to RUN position. • Turn wiper switch to OFF position. • Measure continuity between circuits 28 (BK/PK) and between circuits 61 (Y/R) and 63 (R). • **Is there continuity?**	Yes	▶	CHECK for: • Unseated component. • Damaged wiper motor. SERVICE as required.
		No	▶	GO to F2.
F2	CHECK WIRING BETWEEN WIPER CONTROL MODULE AND MOTOR			
	• Measure continuity of circuits 28 (BK/PK) and 56 (DB/O) and between circuits 61 (Y/R) and 63 (R) at wiper control module connector? • **Is there continuity?**	Yes	▶	SERVICE open circuit between wiper control module and wiper motor.
		No	▶	GO to F3.

FM9029300133010X

Fig. 85   Test F: Wipers Will Not Turn Off (Part 1 of 2). 1993–94 Mark VIII, Sable & Taurus

	TEST STEP	RESULT	▶	ACTION TO TAKE
F3	CHECK WIPER SWITCH			
	• Measure resistance between circuits 589 (O) and 993 (BR/W). • **Is resistance between 45k ohms and 50k ohms?**	Yes	▶	REPLACE wiper control module.
		No	▶	CHECK for: • Open circuit (993 (BR/W) or 589 (O)) between wiper switch and wiper control module. • Damaged wiper switch. SERVICE as required.

FM9029300133020X

Fig. 85   Test F: Wipers Will Not Turn Off (Part 2 of 2). 1993–94 Mark VIII, Sable & Taurus

Fig. 86 Test WW: Front Wiper System Diagnostic Tests (Part 1 of 4). 1993-94 Escort & Tracer

TEST STEP	RESULT	▶	ACTION TO TAKE
WW1 CHECK FUSE • Locate the interior fuse panel. • Check the 20 amp WIPER fuse. • Is the fuse OK?	Yes No	▶ ▶	GO to **WW6**. GO to **WW2**.
WW2 CHECK SYSTEM • Replace the fuse. • Key ON. • Check the 20 amp WIPER fuse. • Is the fuse OK?	Yes No	▶ ▶	GO to **WW4**. GO to **WW3**.

FM9029300219010X

Fig. 86 Test WW: Front Wiper System Diagnostic Tests (Part 1 of 4). 1993-94 Escort & Tracer

Fig. 86 Test WW: Front Wiper System Diagnostic Tests (Part 2 of 4)

TEST STEP	RESULT	▶	ACTION TO TAKE
WW3 CHECK FOR POWER SHORT TO GROUND • Key OFF. • Locate and disconnect the interior fuse panel connector. NOTE: The front wiper switch is part of the interval wiper/washer switch. • Locate and disconnect the interval governor, front wiper switch and wiper motor connectors. • Measure the resistance between the "DB" wire at the interior fuse panel connector and ground. • Is the resistance less than 5 ohms?	Yes No	▶	REPAIR/REPLACE the "DB" wire in question. GO to **WW6**.
WW4 CHECK SYSTEM OPERATION • Key ON. • Place the wiper switch in the LOW and then in the HIGH position. • Check the 20 amp WIPER fuse. • Is the fuse OK?	Yes No	▶	Wiper system OK. GO to **WW5**.
WW5 CHECK SYSTEM FOR SHORT(S) TO GROUND • Key OFF. • Replace the 20 amp WIPER fuse. • Disconnect the interval governor and wiper motor connectors. • Check the following wires for shorts to ground by touching one terminal of an ohmmeter to one end of the wire and touching the other ohmmeter terminal to ground and reading the resistance. Wire | From | To "R" | Interval Governor | Wiper Motor "DB/W" | Interval Governor | Wiper Motor • Is the resistance less than 5 ohms?	Yes No	▶ ▶	REPAIR/REPLACE the wire in question. REPLACE the wiper motor.
WW6 CHECK INTERVAL GOVERNOR POWER SUPPLY • Disconnect the interval governor connector. • Key ON. • Measure the voltage on the "DB" wires at the interval governor connector. • Is the voltage greater than 10 volts?	Yes No	▶ ▶	GO to **WW7**. REPAIR/REPLACE the "DB" wire(s) in question.
WW7 CHECK FRONT WIPER SWITCH GROUND • Key OFF. • Measure the resistance between the "BK" wire at the front wiper switch and ground. • Is the resistance less than 5 ohms?	Yes No	▶ ▶	GO to **WW8**. REPAIR/REPLACE the "BK" wire.
WW8 CHECK FRONT WIPER MOTOR GROUND • Measure the resistance between the "BK" wire at the front wiper motor and ground. • Is the resistance less than 5 ohms?	Yes No	▶ ▶	GO to **WW9**. REPAIR/REPLACE the "BK" wire.

FM9029300219020X

Fig. 86 Test WW: Front Wiper System Diagnostic Tests (Part 2 of 4). 1993-94 Escort & Tracer

Fig. 86 Test WW: Front Wiper System Diagnostic Tests (Part 3 of 4)

TEST STEP	RESULT	▶	ACTION TO TAKE

WW9 CHECK WIPER MOTOR OPERATION
• Key OFF.
• Disconnect the wiper motor connector.
• Connect the "BK" wire terminal of the wiper motor to ground.
• Connect the negative terminal of a 12 volt power source to ground.
• With jumper wire, apply 12 volts to the following wiper motor terminals:
  HIGH ("R" wire)
  LOW ("DB/W" wire)
• Do the wipers operate at HIGH and LOW-speeds?
	Yes
	No
		▶
		▶
			GO to **WW10**.
			REPLACE the front wiper motor.

WW10 CHECK WIPER MOTOR FEED • Measure the resistance of the following "R" and "DB/W" wires from the interval governor to the wiper motor. • Is the resistance less than 5 ohms?	Yes No	▶ ▶	GO to **WW11**. REPAIR/REPLACE the wire in question.
WW11 CHECK INTERVAL GOVERNOR GROUND • Measure the resistance of the "BK" wire from the interval governor to ground. • Is the resistance less than 5 ohms?	Yes No	▶ ▶	GO to **WW12**. REPAIR/REPLACE the "BK" wire.
WW12 CHECK INTERVAL GOVERNOR OPERATION • Interval governor connected. • Key ON. • With a jumper wire, individually ground each of the following interval governor terminals and note the wiper operation. Terminal | Wiper Function "DG/W" | HIGH "DG" | LOW "DG/Y" | INT • Do the wipers function correctly in each mode as the terminals of the interval governor are grounded?	Yes No	▶ ▶	GO to **WW13**. REPAIR/REPLACE the interval governor.

WW13 CHECK FRONT WIPER SWITCH FEED
• Key OFF.
• Disconnect the interval governor and front wiper switch.
• Measure the resistance of the following wires from the interval governor to the front wiper switch:
  "DG/W"
  "DG"
  "DG/Y"
  "BR"
• Is the resistance of each wire less than 5 ohms?
	Yes
	No
		▶
		▶
			GO to **WW14**.
			REPAIR/REPLACE the wire in question.

FM9029300219030X

Fig. 86 Test WW: Front Wiper System Diagnostic Tests (Part 3 of 4). 1993-94 Escort & Tracer

TEST STEP	RESULT	▶	ACTION TO TAKE
WW14 CHECK FRONT WIPER SWITCH OPERATION • Disconnect the front wiper switch connector. • Connect one lead of an ohmmeter to the terminal of the wiper switch "BK" wire (ground). Connect the other lead of the ohmmeter to the following wiper switch terminals with the wiper switch in the indicated positions and measure the resistances. Switch Terminal | Switch Position "DG/W" | HIGH "DG" | LOW "DG/Y" | INT • Is the resistance of the "DG/W", "DG" and "DG/Y" terminals less than 5 ohms?	Yes No	▶ ▶	Wiper System checks out OK - RETURN to symptom chart. REPLACE the front wiper switch.
WW15 CHECK SYSTEM FOR SHORT(S) TO GROUND • Key OFF. • Disconnect the interval governor connector. • Disconnect the wiper switch connector. • Check the following wires for shorts to ground by connecting one lead of an ohmmeter to ground and touching the other lead of the ohmmeter to the indicated wire and measure the resistance. Wire | From | To "DG/W" | Interval Governor | Wiper Switch "DG" | Interval Governor | Wiper Switch "DG/Y" | Interval Governor | Wiper Switch "BR" | Interval Governor | Wiper Switch • Is the resistance measured at each wire less than 5 ohms?	Yes No	▶ ▶	REPAIR/REPLACE the wire in question. REPLACE the wiper switch.
WW16 CHECK FRONT WIPER MOTOR POWER SUPPLY • Key ON (will not operate in ACC). • Measure the voltage on the "DB" wire at the front wiper motor. • Is the voltage greater than 10 volts?	Yes No	▶ ▶	GO to **WW17**. REPAIR/REPLACE the "DB" wire.
WW17 CHECK PARK GROUND FEED • Key OFF. • Disconnect the interval governor and front wiper motor. • Measure the resistance of the "DB/Y" wire between the interval governor and wiper motor. • Is the resistance less than 5 ohms?	Yes No	▶ ▶	GO to **WW18**. REPAIR/REPLACE the "DB/Y" wire.
WW18 CHECK INTERVAL GOVERNOR PARK CIRCUIT • Disconnect the interval governor connector. • Measure the resistance between the "DB/Y" terminal and the "DB/W" terminal at the interval governor. • Is the resistance less than 5 ohms?	Yes No	▶ ▶	REPLACE the front wiper motor. REPLACE the interval governor.

FM9029300219040X

Fig. 86 Test WW: Front Wiper System Diagnostic Tests (Part 4 of 4). 1993-94 Escort & Tracer

TEST STEP	RESULT	▶	ACTION TO TAKE
A1 CHECK WINDSHIELD WASHER PUMP • Key off. • Locate and disconnect the windshield washer pump connector. • Apply 12 volts to the "BL/O" wire terminal on the windshield washer pump. • Apply ground to the "BK" wire terminal on the windshield washer pump. • Does the windshield washer pump operate?	Yes No	▶ ▶	GO to A2. REPLACE the windshield washer pump.
A2 CHECK WINDSHIELD WASHER PUMP GROUND • Key off. • Disconnect the windshield washer pump connector. • Measure the resistance of the "BK" wire between the windshield washer pump connector and ground. • Is the resistance less than 5 ohms?	Yes No	▶ ▶	GO to A3. SERVICE the "BK" wire.

FM9029400204010X

Fig. 87 Test A: Windshield Washer Inoperative (Part 1 of 2). 1994 Aspire

TEST STEP	RESULT	▶	ACTION TO TAKE
A3 CHECK WINDSHIELD WIPER/WASHER SWITCH • Perform the Windshield Wiper/Washer Switch component test in this section. • Is the windshield wiper/washer switch OK?	Yes No	▶ ▶	SERVICE the "BL/O" wire. REPLACE the turn signal and windshield wiper switch.

FM9029400204020X

Fig. 87 Test A: Windshield Washer Inoperative (Part 2 of 2). 1994 Aspire

TEST STEP	RESULT	▶	ACTION TO TAKE
B1 CHECK REAR WINDOW WASHER PUMP • Key off. • Locate and disconnect the rear window washer pump connector. • Apply 12 volts to the "BL/GN" wire terminal on the rear window washer pump. • Apply ground to the "BL/Y" wire terminal on the rear window washer pump. • Does the rear window washer pump operate?	Yes No	▶ ▶	GO to B2. REPLACE the rear window washer pump.
B2 CHECK POWER TO REAR WINDOW WASHER PUMP • Key off. • Disconnect the rear window washer pump connector. • Key ON. • Measure the voltage on the "BL/GN" wire at the rear window washer pump connector. • Is the voltage greater than 10 volts?	Yes No	▶ ▶	GO to B3. SERVICE the "BL/GN" wire.
B3 CHECK REAR WINDOW WASHER SWITCH • Key off. • Locate and disconnect the turn signal and windshield wiper switch connector. • Measure the resistance between the "BL/Y" and "BK" wire terminals on the turn signal and windshield wiper switch under the following conditions: Rear Window Washer Switch / Resistance On / Less than 5 ohms Off / Greater than 10,000 ohms • Are the resistances OK?	Yes No	▶ ▶	GO to B4. REPLACE the turn signal and windshield wiper switch.
B4 CHECK REAR WINDOW WASHER SWITCH GROUND • Key off. • Disconnect the turn signal and windshield wiper switch connector. • Measure the resistance of the "BK" wire between the turn signal and windshield wiper switch connector and ground. • Is the resistance less than 5 ohms?	Yes No	▶ ▶	SERVICE the "BL/Y" wire between the rear window washer pump and the turn signal and windshield wiper switch. SERVICE the "BK" wire.

FM9029400205000X

Fig. 88 Test B: Rear Washer Inoperative. 1994 Aspire

TEST STEP	RESULT	▶	ACTION TO TAKE
C1 CHECK FUSE • Key off. • Check the 20A WIPER fuse located in the interior fuse junction panel. • Is the fuse OK?	Yes No	▶ ▶	GO to C4. GO to C2.
C2 CHECK SYSTEM • Key off. • Replace the 20A WIPER fuse. • Key ON. • Does the fuse fail again?	Yes No	▶ ▶	GO to C3. GO to C4.

FM9029400206010X

Fig. 89 Test C: Wipers Inoperative (Part 1 of 2). 1994 Aspire

TEST STEP	RESULT	▶	ACTION TO TAKE
C3 CHECK FOR SHORT TO GROUND • Key off. • Remove the 20A WIPER fuse. • Disconnect the windshield wiper motor connector and the turn signal and windshield wiper switch connector. • Measure the resistance of the "BL" wire between the bottom terminal of the 20A WIPER fuse holder and ground. • Is the resistance less than 5 ohms?	Yes No	▶ ▶	SERVICE the "BL" wire. REPLACE the 20A WIPER fuse. GO to C4.
C4 CHECK POWER SUPPLY TO WINDSHIELD WIPER MOTOR AND WINDSHIELD WIPER SWITCH • Key off. • Disconnect the windshield wiper motor connector and the turn signal and windshield wiper switch connector. • Key ON. • Measure the voltage on the "BL" wire at the windshield wiper motor connector and the turn signal and windshield wiper switch connector. • Is the voltage greater than 10 volts?	Yes No	▶ ▶	GO to C5. SERVICE the "BL" wire.
C5 CHECK WINDSHIELD WIPER MOTOR • Perform the Windshield Wiper Motor component test in this section. • Is the windshield wiper motor OK?	Yes No	▶ ▶	GO to C6. REPLACE the windshield wiper motor.
C6 CHECK WINDSHIELD WIPER/WASHER SWITCH • Perform the Windshield Wiper/Washer Switch component test in this section. • Is the windshield wiper/washer switch OK?	Yes No	▶ ▶	SERVICE the "BL/W", "BL/R", and/or "BL/BK" wires between the turn signal and windshield wiper switch and the windshield wiper motor. REPLACE the turn signal and windshield wiper switch.

FM9029400206020X

Fig. 89 Test C: Wipers Inoperative (Part 2 of 2). 1994 Aspire

TEST STEP	RESULT	▶	ACTION TO TAKE
D1 CHECK WINDSHIELD WIPER MOTOR • Perform the Windshield Wiper Motor component test in this section. • Is the windshield wiper motor OK?	Yes No	▶ ▶	GO to D2. REPLACE the windshield wiper motor.
D2 CHECK WINDSHIELD WIPER/WASHER SWITCH • Perform the Windshield Wiper/Washer Switch component test in this section. • Is the windshield wiper/washer switch OK?	Yes No	▶ ▶	SERVICE the "BL/R" wire between the turn signal and windshield wiper switch and the windshield wiper motor. REPLACE the turn signal and windshield wiper switch.

FM9029400207000X

Fig. 90 Test D: Wipers Inoperative At High Speeds. 1994 Aspire

TEST STEP	RESULT	▶	ACTION TO TAKE
E1 CHECK WINDSHIELD WIPER MOTOR • Perform the Windshield Wiper Motor component test in this section. • Is the windshield wiper motor OK?	Yes No	▶ ▶	GO to E2. REPLACE the windshield wiper motor.

FM9029400208010X

Fig. 91 Test E: Wipers Inoperative At Low Speeds (Part 1 of 2). 1994 Aspire

TEST STEP	RESULT	▶	ACTION TO TAKE
E2 CHECK WINDSHIELD WIPER/WASHER SWITCH • Perform the Windshield Wiper/Washer Switch component test in this section. • Is the windshield wiper/washer switch OK?	Yes No	▶ ▶	SERVICE the "BL/BK" wire between the turn signal and windshield wiper switch and the windshield wiper motor. REPLACE the turn signal and windshield wiper switch.

FM9029400208020X

Fig. 91 Test E: Wipers Inoperative At Low Speeds (Part 2 of 2). 1994 Aspire

TEST STEP	RESULT	▶	ACTION TO TAKE
F1 CHECK WINDSHIELD WIPER MOTOR • Perform the Windshield Wiper Motor component test in this section. • Is the windshield wiper motor OK?	Yes No	▶ ▶	GO to F2. REPLACE the windshield wiper motor.
F2 CHECK WIRE BETWEEN WINDSHIELD WIPER SWITCH AND WINDSHIELD WIPER MOTOR • Key off. • Locate and disconnect the turn signal and windshield wiper switch connector. • Disconnect the windshield wiper motor connector. • Measure the resistance of the "BL/W" wire between the turn signal and windshield wiper switch connector and the windshield wiper motor connector. • Is the resistance less than 5 ohms?	Yes No	▶ ▶	REPLACE the turn signal and windshield wiper switch. SERVICE the "BL/W" wire.

FM9029400209000X

Fig. 92 Test F: Wipers Will Not Park Below Windshield. 1994 Aspire

TEST STEP	RESULT	▶	ACTION TO TAKE
G1 CHECK WINDSHIELD WIPER/WASHER SWITCH • Perform the Windshield Wiper/Washer Switch component test in this section. • Is the windshield wiper/washer switch OK?	Yes No	▶ ▶	REPLACE the windshield wiper motor. REPLACE the turn signal and windshield wiper switch.

FM9029400210000X

Fig. 93   Test G: Wipers Will Not Turn Off. 1994 Aspire

TEST STEP	RESULT	▶	ACTION TO TAKE
H1 CHECK FUSE • Key off. • Check the 15A R.WIPER fuse located in the interior fuse junction panel. • Is the fuse OK?	Yes No	▶ ▶	GO to H4. GO to H2.
H2 CHECK SYSTEM • Key off. • Replace the 15A R.WIPER fuse. • Key ON. • Does the fuse fail again?	Yes No	▶ ▶	GO to H3. GO to H4.
H3 CHECK FOR SHORT TO GROUND • Key off. • Disconnect the rear window wiper motor connector and the rear window washer motor connector. • Remove the 15A R.WIPER fuse. • Measure the resistance of the "BL/GN" wire between the bottom terminal of the 15A R.WIPER fuse holder and ground. • Is the resistance less than 5 ohms?	Yes No	▶ ▶	SERVICE the "BL/GN" wire. REPLACE the 15A R.WIPER fuse. GO to H4.

FM9029400211010X

Fig. 94   Test H: Rear Wiper Inoperative (Part 1 of 2). 1994 Aspire

TEST STEP	RESULT	▶	ACTION TO TAKE
H4 CHECK POWER SUPPLY TO REAR WINDOW WIPER MOTOR • Key off. • Disconnect the rear window wiper motor connector. • Key ON. • Measure the voltage of the "BL/GN" wire at the rear window wiper motor connector. • Is the voltage greater than 10 volts?	Yes No	▶ ▶	GO to H5. SERVICE the "BL/GN" wire.
H5 CHECK REAR WINDOW WIPER MOTOR • Key off. • Disconnect the rear window wiper motor connector. • Apply 12 volts to the "BL/GN" wire terminal on the rear window wiper motor. • Apply ground to the "BK/BL" wire terminal on the rear window wiper motor. • Does the rear window wiper motor operate?	Yes No	▶ ▶	GO to H6. REPLACE the rear window wiper motor.
H6 CHECK REAR WINDOW WIPER SWITCH • Key off. • Locate and disconnect the turn signal and windshield wiper switch connector. • Measure the resistance between the "BK/BL" and "BK" wire terminals on the turn signal and windshield wiper switch under the following conditions: 	Rear Wiper Switch	Resistance
---	---
On	Less than 5 ohms
Off	Greater than 10,000 ohms | • Are the resistances OK?	Yes No	▶ ▶	GO to H7. REPLACE the turn signal and windshield wiper switch.
H7 CHECK REAR WINDOW WIPER SWITCH GROUND • Key off. • Disconnect the turn signal and windshield wiper switch connector. • Measure the resistance of the "BK" wire between Pin 13 of the turn signal and windshield wiper switch connector and ground. • Is the resistance less than 5 ohms?	Yes No	▶ ▶	SERVICE the "BK/BL" wire between the rear window wiper motor and the turn signal and windshield wiper switch. SERVICE the "BK" wire.

FM9029400211020X

Fig. 94   Test H: Rear Wiper Inoperative (Part 2 of 2). 1994 Aspire

TEST STEP	RESULT	▶	ACTION TO TAKE
I1 CHECK REAR WINDOW WIPER SWITCH • Key off. • Locate and disconnect the turn signal and windshield wiper switch connector. • Measure the resistance between the "BK/BL" and "BK" wire terminals on the turn signal and windshield wiper switch under the following conditions: 	Rear Wiper Switch	Resistance
---	---
On	Less than 5 ohms
Off	Greater than 10,000 ohms | • Are the resistances OK?	Yes No	▶ ▶	SERVICE the "BK/BL" wire between the rear window wiper motor and the turn signal and windshield wiper switch. REPLACE the turn signal and windshield wiper switch.

FM9029400212000X

Fig. 95   Test I: Rear Wiper Will NOt Turn Off. 1994 Aspire

TEST STEP	RESULT	▶	ACTION TO TAKE
FWS1 CHECK FUSE • Key OFF. • Check the 20A WIPER fuse located in the interior fuse panel. • Is the fuse OK?	Yes No	▶ ▶	GO to **FWS4**. GO to **FWS2**.
FWS2 CHECK SYSTEM • Key OFF. • Replace the 20A WIPER fuse. • Key ON. • Does the fuse fail again?	Yes No	▶ ▶	GO to **FWS3**. GO to **FWS4**.

FM9029300134010X

Fig. 96   Test FWS: Front Washer System (Part 1 of 3). 1993–94 Probe

COMPONENT DIAGNOSIS & TESTING

TEMPO & TOPAZ

WIPER MOTOR

Refer to wiring schematics **Figs. 1 through 4** when performing the following test procedures.

High Speed Test

1. Turn ignition switch to ON.
2. Turn wiper switch to HI.
3. Check voltage at motor connector terminal 56. If voltage is present proceed to step 5.
4. If voltage is not present proceed as follows:
   a. Check voltage at wiper switch terminal 63. If voltage is present, replace wiper switch.
   b. If voltage is not present at terminal 63, check circuit back to source.
5. If voltage is present at terminal 56 and motor will not run, proceed as follows:
   a. Ground motor to body.
   b. If motor runs, repair ground.
   c. If motor does not run, replace motor.

Low Speed Test

1. Turn ignition switch to ON.
2. Turn wiper switch to LO.
3. Check voltage at motor connector (white wire) terminal 58. If voltage is present proceed to step 5.
4. If voltage is not present proceed as follows:
   a. Check voltage at (red wire) terminal 63. If voltage is present, replace wiper switch.
   b. If voltage is not present at terminal 63, check circuit back to source.
5. If voltage is present at terminal 58 and motor will not run, proceed as follows:
   a. Ground motor to body.
   b. If motor runs, repair ground.
   c. If motor does not run, replace motor.

Park Operation Test

1. Turn ignition switch to ON.
2. Turn wiper switch to OFF.
3. Check voltage at motor and park switch connector terminals 28 (black/pink), 58 (white) and 63 (red). If voltage is not present at all three terminals, proceed as directed in steps 5 through 7.
4. If voltage is present at all three terminals and wipers are not parked, proceed as follows:
   a. Ground motor to body.
   b. If motor parks, repair ground.
   c. If motor does not park, replace motor.
5. If voltage is present only at terminal 63, replace wiper motor.
6. If voltage is present only at terminals 28 and 63, replace wiper switch.
7. If voltage still is not present at terminal

58, check terminals 28 and 58 back to wiper switch.

Current Draw Test

1. Disconnect wiper motor linkage.
2. Disconnect wiper motor electrical connector.
3. Make test connections as shown in **Fig. 97**. Alternately connect red test lead to wiper motor low and high speed connectors.
4. Current draw at either terminal should not exceed 3 amps.

WIPER SWITCH

Continuity Test

When testing a non-intermittent wiper

	TEST STEP	RESULT	►	ACTION TO TAKE
FWS3	CHECK FOR SHORT TO GROUND			
	• Key OFF. • Locate and disconnect the 14-pin combination switch connector, the front wiper motor connector, and the 10-pin interior fuse panel connector. • Measure the resistance of the "BL" wire between the 10-pin interior fuse panel connector and ground. • Is the resistance less than 5 ohms?	Yes No	► ►	SERVICE the "BL" wire. REPLACE the 20A WIPER fuse. GO to FWS4.

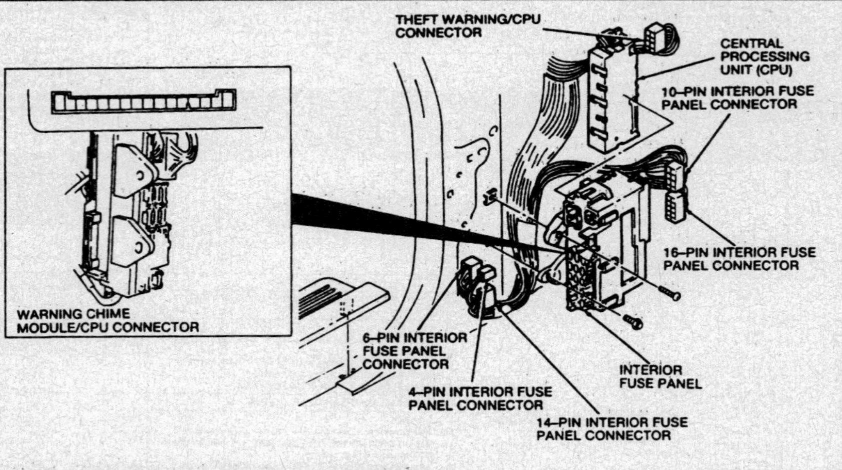

	TEST STEP	RESULT	►	ACTION TO TAKE
FWS4	CHECK POWER SUPPLY TO FRONT WASHER SWITCH			
	• Key OFF. • Reconnect the front wiper motor connector and the 10-pin interior fuse panel connector. • Locate and disconnect the 14-pin combination switch connector (harness side). • Key ON. • Measure the voltage of the "BL" wire at the 14-pin combination switch connector. • Is the voltage greater than 10 volts?	Yes No	► ►	GO to FWS5. SERVICE the "BL" wire.
FWS5	CHECK FRONT WASHER SWITCH			
	• Key OFF. • Reconnect the 14-pin combination switch connector. • Key ON. • Depress the front washer switch. • Measure the voltage of the "BL/O" wire at the 14-pin combination switch connector. • Release the front washer switch. • Measure the voltage of the "BL/O" wire at the 14-pin combination switch connector. • Is the voltage greater than 10 volts with the front washer switch depressed, and less than 1 volt with the front washer switch released?	Yes No	► ►	GO to FWS6. REPLACE the combination switch.

FM9029300134020X

Fig. 96   Test FWS: Front Washer System (Part 2 of 3). 1993–94 Probe

	TEST STEP	RESULT	►	ACTION TO TAKE
FWS6	CHECK WIRE BETWEEN FRONT WASHER SWITCH AND FRONT WASHER MOTOR			
	• Key OFF. • Disconnect the 14-pin combination switch connector and the front washer motor connector. • Measure the resistance of the "BL/O" wire between the 14-pin combination switch connector and the front washer motor connector. • Measure the resistance of the "BL/O" wire between the 14-pin combination switch connector and ground. • Is the resistance less than 5 ohms between 14-pin combination switch connector and the front washer motor connector, and greater than 10,000 ohms between the 14-pin combination switch connector and ground?	Yes No	► ►	GO to FWS7. SERVICE the "BL/O" wire.
FWS7	CHECK FRONT WASHER MOTOR GROUND			
	• Key OFF. • Disconnect the front washer motor connector. • Measure the resistance of the "BK" wire between the front washer motor connector and ground. • Is the resistance less than 5 ohms?	Yes No	► ►	REPLACE the front washer motor. SERVICE the "BK" wire.

FM9029300134030X

Fig. 96   Test FWS: Front Washer System (Part 3 of 3). 1993–94 Probe

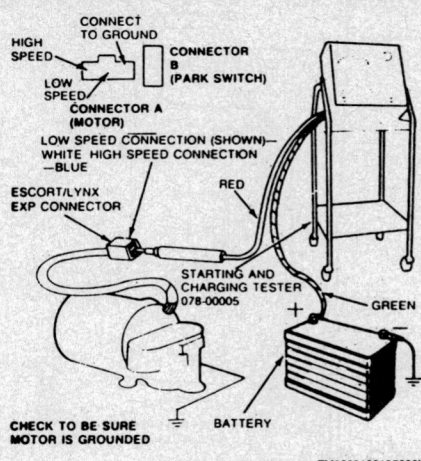

Fig. 97 Wiper motor current draw test. Tempo & Topaz

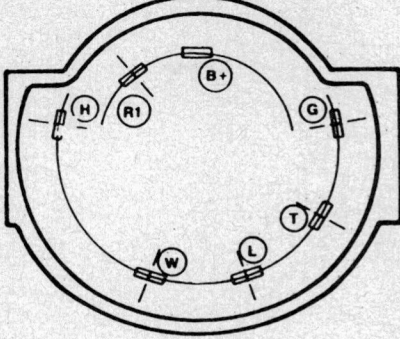

STANDARD WIPER SWITCH

SWITCH POSITION	CONTINUITY BETWEEN TERMINALS
OFF	R1 AND L
LOW	B+ AND L
HIGH	B+ AND H
WASH	B+ AND W

NOTE: T-TERMINAL IS SWITCH ILLUMINATION

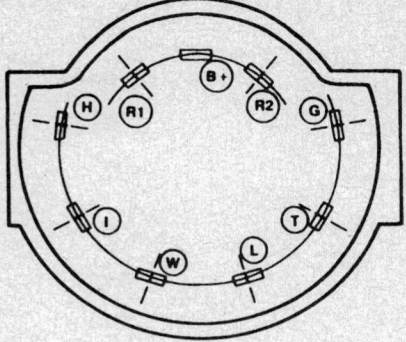

INTERVAL WIPER SWITCH

SWITCH POSITION	CONTINUITY BETWEEN TERMINALS
OFF	NO CONTINUITY
INTERVAL	B+ AND I
LOW	B+ AND L
HIGH	B+ AND H AND L
WASH	B+ AND W

NOTE: THERE SHOULD BE CONTINUITY BETWEEN TERMINALS R1 AND R2 THROUGHOUT VARIABLE RESISTANCE RANGE (MINIMUM 420 TO 880 OHMS, MAXIMUM 7,000 TO 13,000 OHMS) T-TERMINAL IS SWITCH ILLUMINATION

Fig. 98 Wiper switch continuity test. Tempo & Topaz

switch, a self-powered test lamp or an ohmmeter can be used to check continuity. When testing an intermittent wiper switch, use only an ohmmeter to check continuity.

When taking test readings move the switch lever to detect marginal switch operation.

Refer to **Fig. 98** for switch terminal identification and continuity readings.

CIRCUIT BREAKER

1. Remove circuit breaker from fuse panel.
2. Using a multimeter, adjust current draw to equal the circuit breaker rating.
3. Connect circuit breaker to tester for 10 minutes. If circuit breaker opens within the time specified, replace it.
4. Readjust current draw to equal twice the circuit breaker rating.
5. Connect circuit breaker to tester. The ammeter current reading should drop to zero within 30 seconds. If circuit breaker does not open within the time specified, replace it.

CROWN VICTORIA, GRAND MARQUIS & TOWN CAR

WIPER MOTOR

Current Draw Test

Motor terminals may be too small to make necessary test connections. If necessary use jumper wires with suitable connector sleeves between motor and test equipment.
1. Disconnect wiper linkage from output arm and electrical connectors from motor.
2. Make test connections as shown, **Fig. 99**. Alternately connect the battery negative jumper wire to high and low speed wiper terminals.
3. Current draw at either terminal should not exceed 3.5 amps.
4. If current draw is excessive, check output arm and wind latch assembly. If output arm assembly is satisfactory, repair or replace motor.

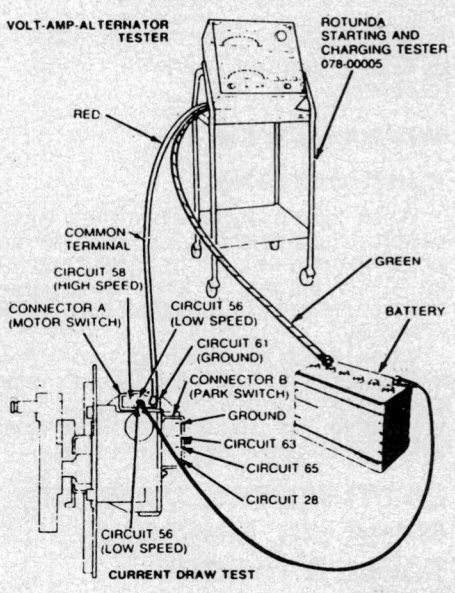

Fig. 99 Wiper motor current draw test. Crown Victoria, Grand Marquis & Town Car

Park Operation Test

Refer to wiring schematics, **Fig. 6**, when performing the following test procedures.
1. Turn ignition switch to ON.
2. Turn wiper switch to LO. Ensure wiper operation is proper.
3. With wipers in a vertical position turn wiper switch to OFF. Ensure wipers cycle once then park below the windshield.
4. If wipers do not function as described, proceed to test steps 5 through 10 according to wiper malfunction.

5. If wipers stop without cycling and parking proceed as follows:
   a. Disconnect wiper motor park switch electrical connector.
   b. With ignition switch ON, check for battery voltage at park switch electrical connector (dark green wire) terminal 65. If battery voltage is not present repair the circuit.
   c. If battery voltage is present at terminal 65, check motor housing ground. Repair as needed.
   d. If motor housing ground is good, turn ignition switch to OFF, then disconnect both wiper motor electrical connectors.
   e. Using an ohmmeter, check for continuity between wiring harness terminals 28 and 56. If no continuity is present, repair the open circuit.
   f. If continuity is present between terminals 28 and 56, check for ground at wiper motor terminal 28. If ground is open, replace the motor.
   g. If ground is good at wiper motor terminal 28, check for continuity between wiring harness circuits 61 and 63. If continuity exists, proceed to step J.
   h. If continuity does not exist between wiring harness terminals 61 and 63, repair the open circuit. If open circuit is traced to interval governor, check for continuity between wiper switch terminals P and G. If open exists between terminals P and G, replace the wiper switch.
   i. If open does not exist between wiper switch terminals P and G, replace the interval governor.
   j. Check for continuity between wiper motor terminals 63 and 65. If no continuity is present, replace motor.

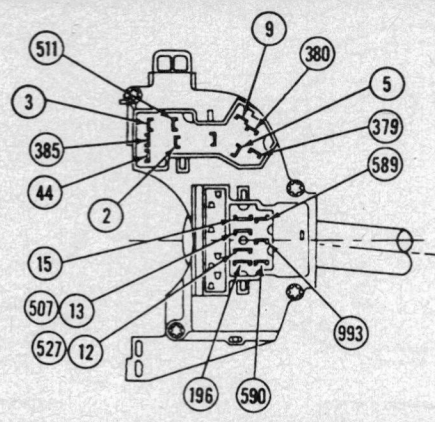

SWITCH ACTUATOR POSITION	CONTINUITY BY CIRCUIT NUMBER
Wiper/Washer Switching	
● Wash OFF and Wiper OFF	Resistance No. 993 to 590, 103.3K ohms ± 10%. No. 993 to 589, 47.6K ohms ± 10%.
● Wash ON and Wiper OFF	Open No. 993 to 590; Resistance No. 993 to 589, 47.6K ohms ± 10%.
● Wiper OFF and Wash OFF	Resistance No. 993 to 590, 103.3K ohms ± 10%. No. 993 to 589, 47.6K ohms ± 10%.
● Wiper LO or Low Speed and Wash OFF	Resistance No. 993 to 590, 3.3K ohms ± 10%. No. 993 to 589, 4.08K ohms ± 10%.
● Wiper HI or High Speed and Wash OFF	Resistance No. 993 to 590, 3.3K ohms ± 10%. Open No. 993 to 589.
● Wiper Interval and Wash OFF	Resistance No. 993 to 589, 11.33 K ohms ± 10%. No. 993 to 590, Gradually decreasing from 103.3 K ohms to 3.3 K ohms from Maximum Delay to Minimum Delay.

Fig. 100 Wiper switch continuity test. Crown Victoria, Mark VII, Grand Marquis & Town Car

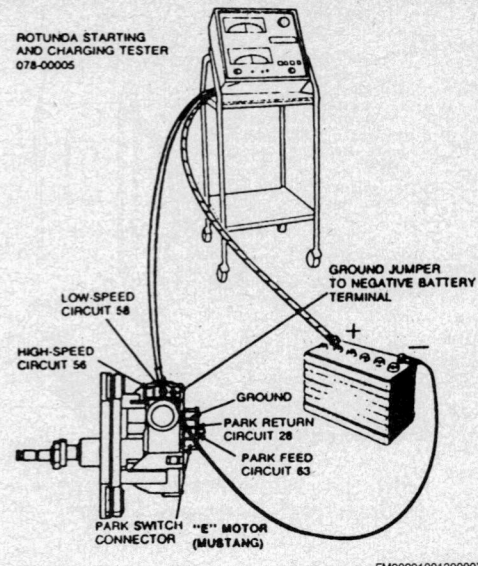

Fig. 101 Wiper motor current draw test. Mustang

Figs. 102 and 103. Alternately ground the high and low speed wiper motor terminals.

b. Current draw at either terminal should not exceed 3.5 amps.

Park Operation Test, Mustang

1. Turn ignition switch to ON.
2. Turn wiper switch to ON.
3. When wipers are in a non-parked position, turn ignition switch to OFF.
4. Make test connections as shown, **Fig. 104.** Wiper motor should run one full cycle then park.
5. If wiper motor does not run to park, or will not park, replace it.
6. If wiper motor stops, check for continuity at wiper switch and wiper system wiring. Replace or repair as needed.
7. If continuity and the wiper switch test good, and wiper motor will not stop in OFF or INT position, replace the governor.

Park Operation Test, Continental, Cougar, Mark VII, Sable, Taurus

Refer to wiring schematics **Figs. 11 through 18** when performing the following test procedures.

1. Turn ignition switch to ON.
2. Turn wiper switch to LO. Ensure wiper operation is proper.
3. With wipers in a vertical position turn wiper switch to OFF. Ensure wipers cycle once then park below the windshield.
4. If wipers do not function as described, perform test steps 5 through 10 according to wiper malfunction.
5. If wipers stop without cycling and parking, proceed as follows:
   a. Disconnect wiper motor park switch electrical connector.

6. If wipers park below the windshield and the motor stays running, replace the wiper motor.
7. If wipers jam or stall when parking below the windshield and the motor runs in reverse, proceed as follows:
   a. Check wiper linkage. Repair as needed.
   b. If wiper linkage is satisfactory, check wiper motor arm and windlatch assembly. If bent or cracked parts are found, replace wiper motor.
8. If wipers travel into the next cycle and then parks on the windshield, runs constantly in OFF or INT positions or stops at bottom of windshield without depress parking, proceed as follows:
   a. Perform wiper switch continuity test as described under "Wiper Switch" for these models.
   b. **On non-intermittent systems,** if wiper switch continuity test is good, service wiper motor park switch.
   c. **On intermittent systems,** if wiper switch continuity test is good, check for voltage at washer terminal 941. If voltage is present repair as needed.
   d. If voltage is not present at washer terminal 941, disconnect wiper motor electrical connectors and proceed to next step.
   e. Check for continuity between terminals 61 and 63. If open exists, replace governor.
   f. If continuity is present between terminals 61 and 63, replace wiper motor.

WIPER SWITCH

Continuity Test

When testing a non-intermittent wiper switch, a self-powered test lamp or an ohmmeter can be used to check continuity. When testing an intermittent wiper switch, use only an ohmmeter to check continuity.

When taking test readings move the switch lever to detect marginal switch operation.

Refer to **Fig. 100** for switch terminal identification and continuity readings.

CONTINENTAL, MARK VII, MARK VIII, MUSTANG, SABLE & TAURUS

WIPER MOTOR

Current Draw Test

1. Disconnect battery.
2. Disconnect wiper linkage from motor.
3. **On Mustang models** proceed as follows:
   a. Disconnect electrical connector from motor.
   b. Make test connections as shown, **Fig. 101.** Alternately connect the red jumper wire to high and low speed wiper motor terminals. Current draw at either terminal should not exceed three amps.
4. **On Continental, Cougar, Mark VII and Sable & Taurus models** proceed as follows:
   a. Make test connections as shown

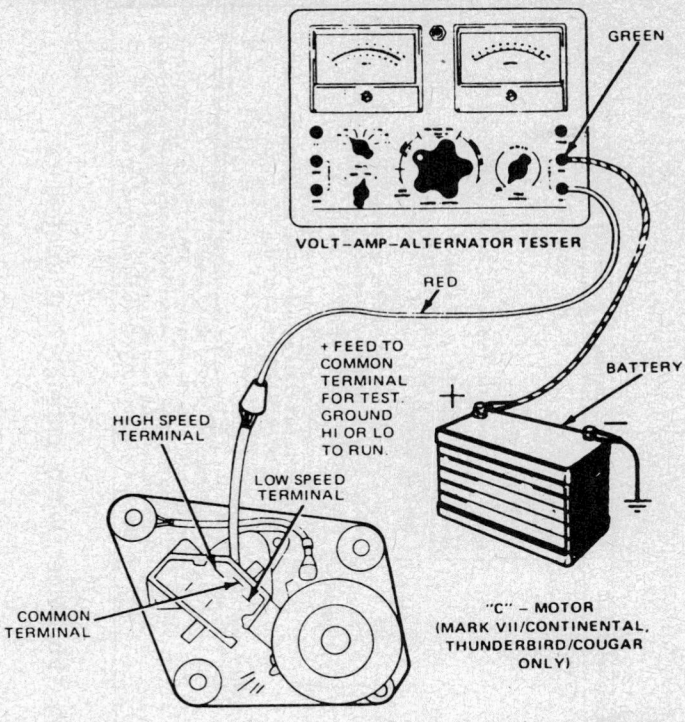

FM9029100140000X

Fig. 102 Wiper motor current draw test. Mark VII

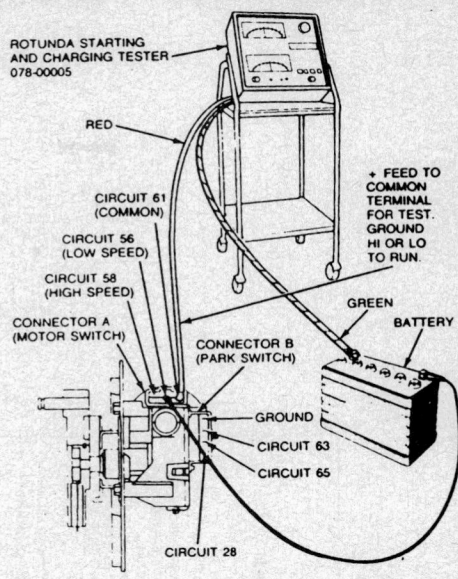

FM9029100141000X

Fig. 103 Wiper motor current draw test. Continental, Sable & Taurus

b. With ignition switch ON, check for battery voltage at park switch electrical connector (dark green wire) terminal 65. If battery voltage is not present repair the circuit.

c. If battery voltage is present at terminal 65, check motor housing ground. Repair as needed.

d. If motor housing ground is good, turn ignition switch to OFF, then disconnect wiper motor electrical connectors.

e. Using an ohmmeter, check for continuity between wiring harness terminals 28 and 56. If no continuity is present, repair open circuit.

f. If continuity does exist between terminals 28 and 56, check for ground at wiper motor terminal 28. If ground is open, replace wiper motor.

g. If ground is good at wiper motor terminal 28, check for continuity between wiring harness circuits 61 and 63. If continuity exist proceed to step J.

h. If continuity does not exist between wiring harness terminals 61 and 63, repair the open circuit. If open circuit is traced to interval governor, check for continuity between wiper switch terminals P and G. If open exists between terminals P and G, replace the wiper switch.

i. If open does not exist between wiper switch terminals P and G, replace the interval governor.

j. Check for continuity between wiper motor terminals 63 and 65, if no continuity is present, replace wiper motor.

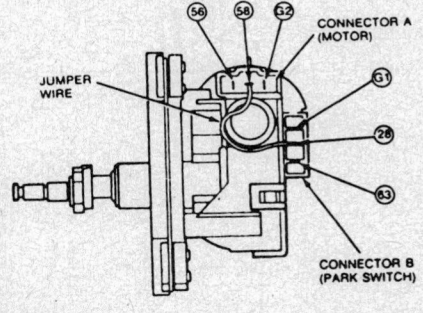

CIRCUIT NO.	DESCRIPTION	COLOR
56	WIPER SWITCH TO MOTOR (HIGH)	DB/O
58	WIPER SWITCH TO MOTOR (LOW)	W
28	WIPER SWITCH TO MOTOR (PARK RETURN)	BLK
63	WIPER SWITCH TO MOTOR (PARK AND RETURN)	R
G1	GROUND	BLK
G2	GROUND	BLK

FM9029100142000X

Fig. 104 Wiper motor park operation test (Non-Depressed). Mustang

6. If wipers park below the windshield and the motor stays running, replace wiper motor.

7. If wipers jam or stall when parking below the windshield and the motor runs in reverse, proceed as follows:
   a. Check wiper linkage. Repair as needed.
   b. If wiper linkage is satisfactory, service windlatch assembly and wiper motor arm.

8. If wipers travel into the next cycle and then park on the windshield, run constantly in OFF or INT positions or stop at bottom of windshield without depress parking, proceed as follows:

a. Perform wiper switch continuity test as described under "Wiper Switch."

b. **On non-intermittent systems,** if wiper switch continuity test is good, replace wiper motor.

c. **On intermittent systems,** if wiper switch continuity test is good, check for voltage at washer terminal 941. If voltage is present repair as needed.

d. If voltage is not present at washer terminal 941, disconnect wiper motor electrical connectors and proceed to next step.

e. Check for continuity between terminals 61 and 63. If open exist replace governor.

f. If continuity exist between terminals 61 and 63, replace wiper motor.

WIPER SWITCH

Continuity Test

When testing a non-intermittent wiper switch, a self-powered test lamp or an ohmmeter can be used to check continuity. When testing an intermittent wiper switch, use only an ohmmeter to check continuity.

When taking test readings move the switch lever to detect marginal switch operation.

Refer to **Figs. 105 through 107** for switch terminal identification and continuity readings.

CIRCUIT BREAKER

Continental, Sable & Taurus

1. Remove circuit breaker from fuse panel.

2. Using a multimeter, adjust current draw to equal the circuit breaker rating.

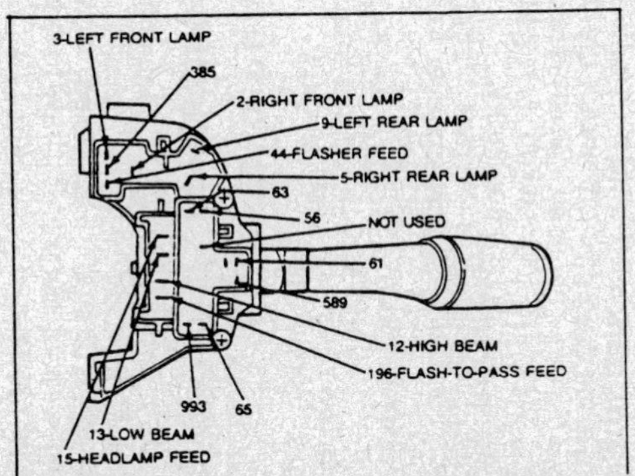

NO 385 HAZARD FEED
NO 3 LEFT FRONT LAMP
HAZARD KNOB
NO 511 STOPLAMP FEED
NO 2 RIGHT FRONT TURN SIGNAL
NO 9 LEFT REAR 7
NO 380 LEFT CORNERING LAMP
NO 5 RIGHT REAR TURN SIGNAL
NO 379 RIGHT CORNERING LAMP
NO 50(L) LOW
NO 58 (H) HIGH
NO 993 INTERVAL SW.
NO 28 AUTO DIM
NO 57 (G) GROUND
NO 65
NO 941 WASH
NO 589 INTERVAL SW (P)
NO 63 AUTO DIM
NO 590 INTERVAL SW (R)
NO 65 AUTO DIM
NO 196 FLASH-TO-PASS FEED
NO 527 AUTO DIM
NO 12 HIGH BEAM
NO 507 AUTO DIM
NO 13 LOW BEAM
NO 15 HEADLAMP FEED
NO 44 TURN SIGNAL FEED

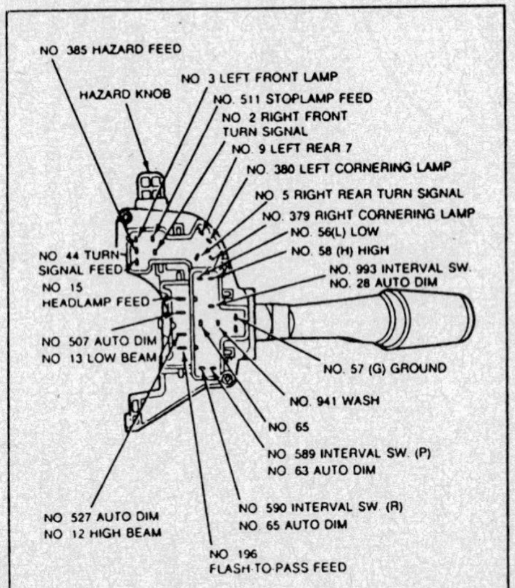

SWITCH ACTUATOR POSITION

Interval Wiper/Washer Switching;
* Wash OFF.
* Wash ON.
* Wiper ON or OFF. Wash OFF.
* Wiper LO or low speed. Wash OFF.
* Wiper HI or high speed.
* Wiper Interval at maximum knob travel or maximum time between wipe cycles. Wash OFF.

CONTINUITY BY CIRCUIT NUMBER

Open No. 65 to 941.
Closed No. 65 to 941.
Closed No. 56 to 993 (i.e. Terminal No. 993/28); No. 57 to 589 (i.e. Terminal No. 589/63).
Open No. 57 to 56 and 58; No. 65 to 941.
Resistance No. 57 to 590 (Terminal No. 590/65) greater than 420 ohms but less than 880 ohms
Closed No. 57 to 56 and 590 (Terminal No. 590/65).
Open No. 57 to 58 and 589 (i.e. Terminal No. 589/63); No. 56 to 993 (i.e. Terminal No. 993/28); No. 65 to 941.
Closed No. 57 to 58 and 590 (Terminal No. 590/65).
Open No. 57 to 56 and 589 (i.e. Terminal No. 589/63); No. 56 to 993 (i.e. Terminal No. 993/28); No. 65 to 941.
Closed No. 57 to 56.
Open No. 57 to 58 and 589 i.e. Terminal No. 589/63); No. 65 to 941. Resistance No. 57 to 590 (Terminal No. 590/65) greater than 7000 ohms but less than 13,000 ohms. **Note:** If knob is then rotated toward the OFF or minimum time between wipe cycles, then the resistance should decrease to less than 880 ohms but greater than 420 ohms.

Fig. 106 Wiper switch continuity test. Continental

FM90291001144000X

3-LEFT FRONT LAMP
385
2-RIGHT FRONT LAMP
9-LEFT REAR LAMP
44-FLASHER FEED
5-RIGHT REAR LAMP
NOT USED
61
56
589
63
12-HIGH BEAM
196-FLASH-TO-PASS FEED
65
993
13-LOW BEAM
15-HEADLAMP FEED

Interval Wiper/Washer Switching;
* Wash OFF.
* Wash ON.
* Wiper O or OFF. Wash OFF.
* Wiper LO or low speed. Wash OFF.
* Wiper HI or high speed. Wash OFF.
* Wiper Interval at maximum knob travel or maximum time between wipe cycles. Wash OFF.

Open 63 to 941.
Closed 63 to 941.
Open 63 to 56, 993, 65
Resistance 61 to 589 greater than 420 ohms but less than 880 ohms.
Closed 63 to 993.
Open 63 to 56 and 65
Resistance 61 to 589 greater than 420 ohms but less than 880 ohms.
Closed 63 to 56 and 993
Open 63 to 65
Resistance 61 to 589 greater than 420 ohms but less than 880 ohms.
Closed 63 to 65.
Open 63 to 56 and 993.
Resistance 61 to 589 greater than 7000 ohms but less than 13,000 ohms. **NOTE:** If knob is then rotated toward the OFF or minimum time between wipe cycles, then the resistance should decrease to less than 880 ohms but greater than 420 ohms.

FM90291001143000X

Fig. 105 Wiper switch continuity test. Mustang

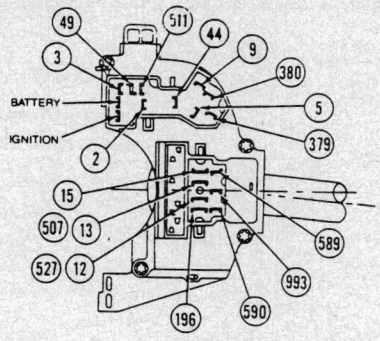

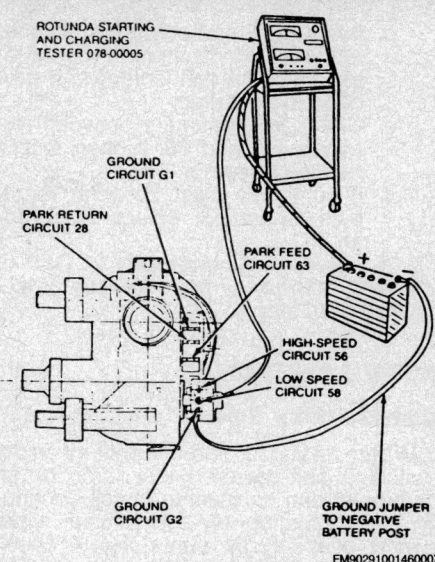

SWITCH ACTUATOR POSITION	CONTINUITY BY CIRCUIT NUMBER
Wiper/Washer Switching	
● Wash OFF and Wiper OFF	Resistance No. 993 to 590, 103.3K ohms ± 10%. No. 993 to 589, 47.6K ohms ± 10%.
● Wash ON and Wiper OFF	Open No. 993 to 590; Resistance No. 993 to 589, 47.6K ohms ± 10%.
● Wiper OFF and Wash OFF	Resistance No. 993 to 590, 103.3K ohms ± 10%. No. 993 to 589, 47.6K ohms ± 10%.
● Wiper LO or Low Speed and Wash OFF	Resistance No. 993 to 590, 3.3K ohms ± 10%. No. 993 to 589, 4.08K ohms ± 10%.
● Wiper HI or High Speed and Wash OFF	Resistance No. 993 to 590, 3.3K ohms ± 10%. Open No. 993 to 589.
● Wiper Interval and Wash OFF	Resistance No. 993 to 589, 11.33 ohms ± 10%. No. 993 to 590, Gradually decreasing from 103.3 K ohms to 3.3 K ohms from Maximum Delay to Minimum Delay.

Fig. 107   Wiper switch continuity test. Mark VII, Sable & Taurus

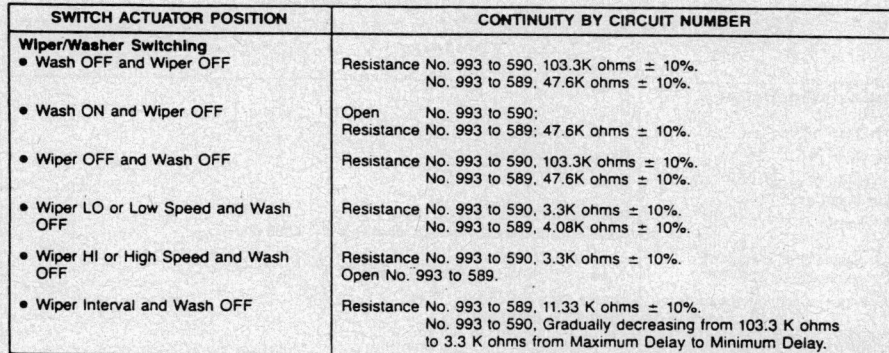

Fig. 108   Wiper motor current draw test. Cougar & Thunderbird

3. Connect circuit breaker to tester for 10 minutes. If circuit breaker opens within the time specified, replace it.
4. Readjust current draw to equal twice the circuit breaker rating.
5. Connect circuit breaker to tester. The ammeter current reading should drop to zero within 30 seconds. If circuit breaker does not open within the time specified, replace it.

GOVERNOR

Continental, Sable & Taurus

1. Ensure wiper motor current draw, and wiper switch continuity are within specifications.
2. Ensure wiper system continuity is good.
3. If steps 1 and 2 are proper, replace the electronic governor.

COUGAR & THUNDERBIRD

WIPER MOTOR

Current Draw Test

1. Ensure wipers are in park position.
2. Disconnect battery.
3. Remove wiper arm and blade assemblies.
4. Remove wiper module vacuum manifolds.
5. Disconnect wiper module electrical connectors.
6. Remove one nut and five screws retaining the wiper module. Remove module from vehicle.
7. Remove linkage drive arm-to-motor crankpin retaining clip. Separate drive arm from crankpin.

8. Remove three wiper motor retaining screws. Remove motor.
9. Make test connections as shown, **Fig. 108.** Alternately connect red jumper wire to high and low speed wiper motor terminals.
10. Current draw at either terminal should not exceed 3.5 amps. Replace or repair as needed.
11. Install wiper motor. Ensure wiper motor is in the park position.
12. Install linkage drive arm to motor crankpin. Install retaining clip.
13. Install wiper module.
14. Connect wiper module electrical connectors.
15. Install wiper module vacuum manifolds.
16. Install wiper arm and blade assemblies.
17. Reconnect battery.

Park Operation Test

Refer to wiring schematics, **Fig. 13,** when performing the following test procedures.
1. Turn ignition switch to ON.
2. Turn wiper switch to LO. Ensure wiper operation is proper.
3. With wipers in a vertical position turn wiper switch to OFF. Ensure wipers cycle once then park below the windshield.
4. If wipers do not function as described, perform test steps 5 through 10 according to wiper malfunction.
5. If wipers stop without cycling and parking proceed as follows:
   a. Disconnect wiper motor park switch electrical connector.

b. With ignition switch ON, check for battery voltage at park switch electrical connector (red wire) terminal 63. If battery voltage is not present repair the circuit.
c. If battery voltage is present at terminal 63, check motor housing ground. Repair as needed.
d. If motor housing ground is good, turn ignition switch to OFF, then disconnect wiper motor electrical connectors.
e. Using an ohmmeter, check for continuity between wiring harness terminals 28 and 58. If continuity does not exist, repair the open circuit.
f. If continuity does exist between terminals 28 and 56, check for ground at wiper motor terminal 28. If ground is open, replace wiper motor.
g. If ground is good at wiper motor terminal 28, check for continuity between wiring harness circuits G2 and 63. If continuity does not exist, repair the open circuit. If open circuit is traced to interval governor, check for continuity between wiper switch terminals P and G. If open exists between terminals P and G, replace the wiper switch.
h. If open does not exist between wiper switch terminals P and G, replace the interval governor.
6. If wipers travel into the next cycle, then park on the windshield, proceed as follows:
   a. Perform wiper switch continuity test as described under "Wiper Switch" for these models.
   b. **On non-intermittent systems,** if wiper switch continuity test is good, replace wiper motor.
   c. **On intermittent systems,** if wiper switch continuity test is good, check for voltage at washer terminal 941. If voltage is present repair as needed.

d. If voltage is not present at washer terminal 941, disconnect wiper motor electrical connectors and proceed to next step.

e. Check for continuity between terminals G2 and 63. If open exists, replace governor.

f. If continuity exist between terminals G2 and 63, replace wiper motor.

7. **If wipers run constantly in OFF or INT positions,** perform test procedures in step 6.

WIPER SWITCH

Continuity Test

When testing a non-intermittent wiper switch, a self-powered test lamp or an ohmmeter can be used to check continuity. When testing an intermittent wiper switch, use only an ohmmeter to check continuity.

When taking test readings move the switch lever to detect marginal switch operation.

Refer to **Fig. 109** for switch terminal identification and continuity readings.

PROBE

Refer to **Figs. 27 and 28** for wiper system wiring schematic, and **Figs. 32 and 33** for diagnostic and testing procedures.

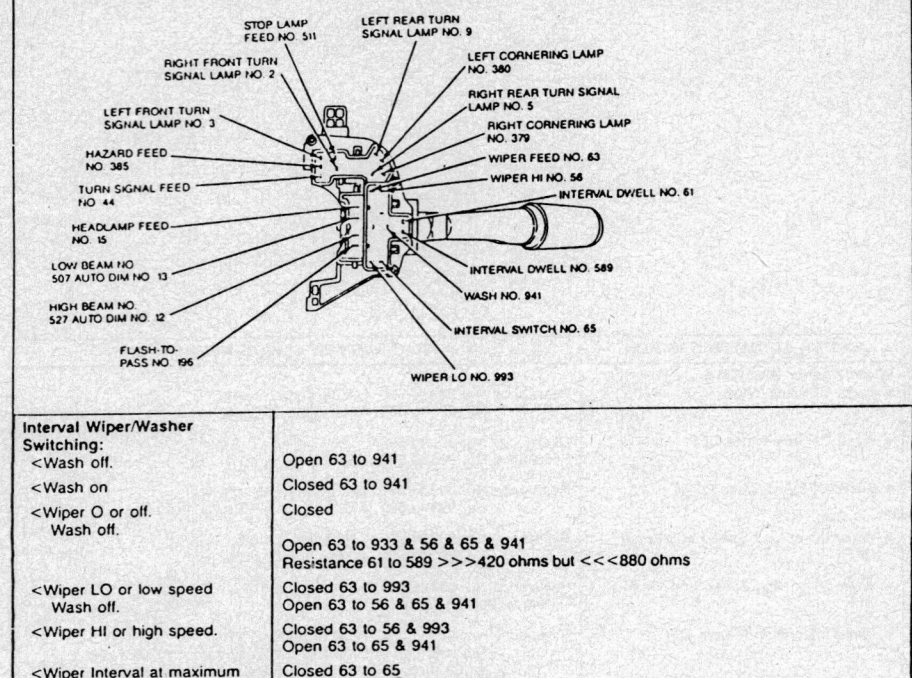

Interval Wiper/Washer Switching:	
<Wash off.	Open 63 to 941
<Wash on	Closed 63 to 941
<Wiper O or off. Wash off.	Closed
	Open 63 to 933 & 56 & 65 & 941 Resistance 61 to 589 >>>420 ohms but <<<880 ohms
<Wiper LO or low speed. Wash off.	Closed 63 to 993 Open 63 to 56 & 65 & 941
<Wiper HI or high speed.	Closed 63 to 56 & 993 Open 63 to 65 & 941
<Wiper Interval at maximum knob travel or maximum time between wipe cycles. <Wash off.	Closed 63 to 65 Open 63 to 993 & 56 & 941
	Resistance 61 to 589 >7K ohms but <13K ohms. Note: If knob is then rotated towards the "off" or minimum time between wiper cycles, then the resistance should decrease to >420 ohms but <880 ohms

Remove wire harness and connectors from switch. Testing for electrical malfunction is accomplished with a continuity tester and an ohm meter.

FM9029100147000X

Fig. 109 Wiper switch continuity test. Cougar & Thunderbird

FESTIVA

Refer to **Fig. 30** for diagnostic and testing procedures.

ASPIRE

Refer to **Fig. 29** for diagnostic and testing procedures.

CAPRI

Refer to **Fig. 31** for diagnostic and testing procedures.

Rear Wiper System

INDEX

SYSTEM DIAGNOSIS & TESTING

SABLE & TAURUS

WIPER SWITCH

Continuity Test

Refer to **Fig. 1** for rear wiper system wiring schematic. Refer to **Figs. 4 through 3** for switch terminal identification and test readings.

When testing a non-intermittent wiper switch, a self-powered test lamp or an ohmmeter can be used to check continuity. When testing an intermittent wiper switch, use only an ohmmeter to check continuity.

When taking test readings move the switch lever to detect marginal switch operation.

ASPIRE & FESTIVA

Refer to **Figs. 6 and 7 for wiper system wiring circuits.** Refer to **Figs. 8 and 9** for Festiva diagnostic and testing procedures. Refer to "Front Wiper System" under "System Diagnosis & Testing" for Aspire rear wiper system diagnosis and diagnostic tests.

PROBE

Refer to **Fig. 10** for rear wiper system wiring schematic, and **Figs. 11 and 12** for diagnostic and testing procedures.

TRACER & ESCORT

Refer to **Fig. 13** for rear wiper system wiring schematic, and **Figs. 14 through 16** for diagnostic and testing procedures.

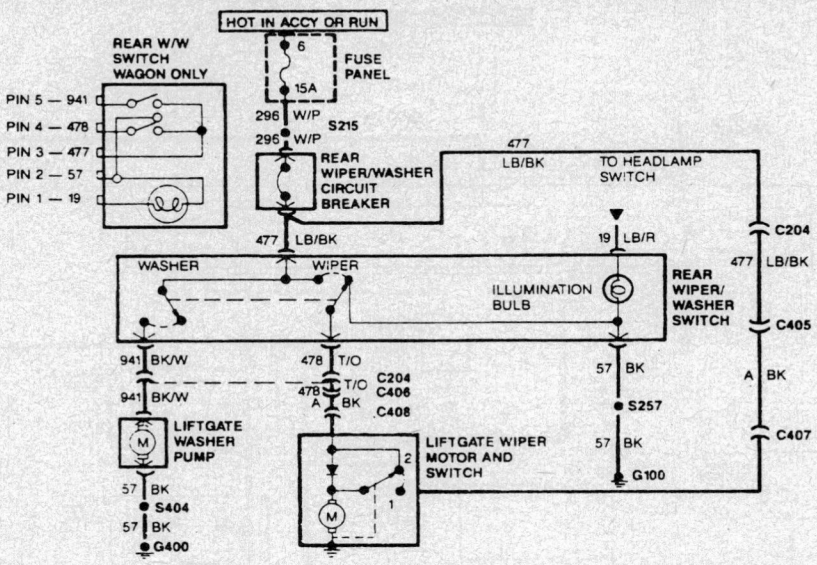

Fig. 1 Wiper system wiring schematic. 1992–93 Sable & Taurus

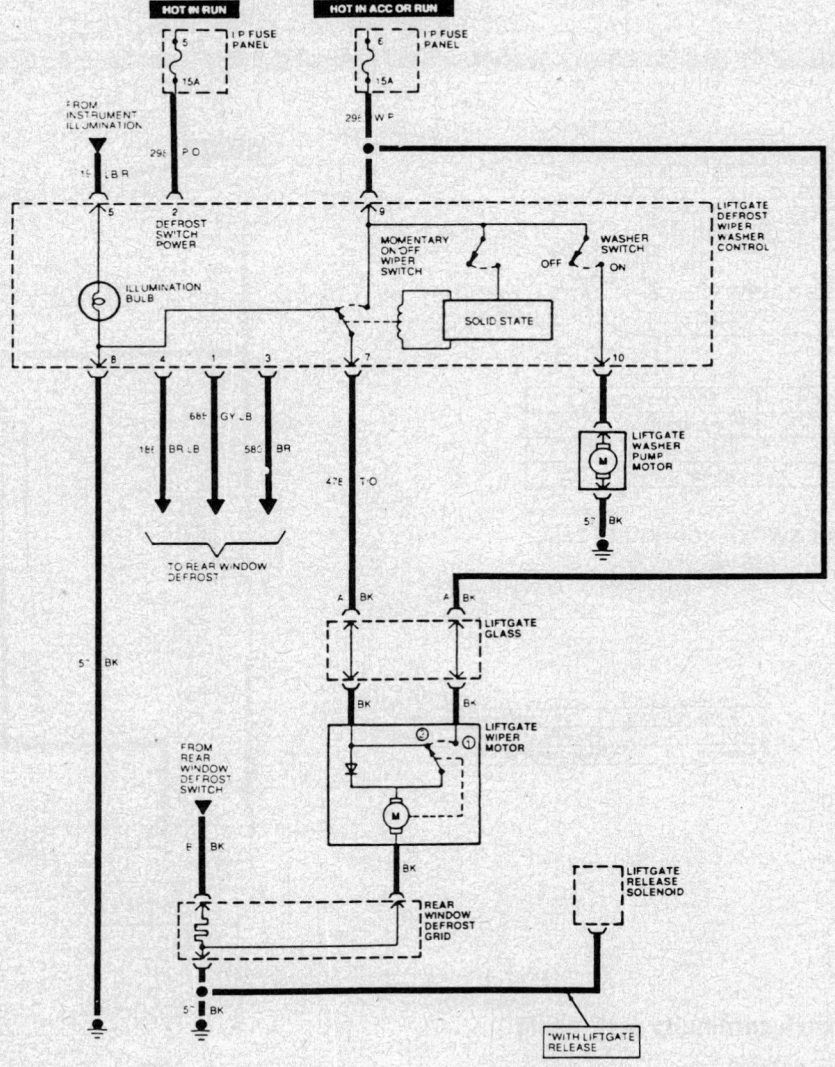

Fig. 2 Wiper system wiring diagram. 1994 Sable

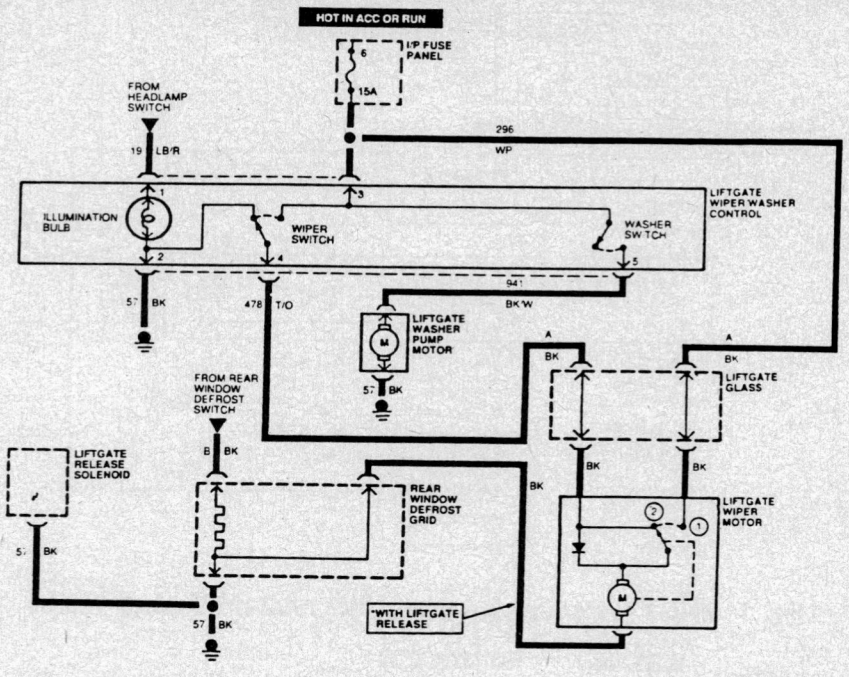

Fig. 3   Wiper system wiring diagram. 1994 Taurus

FM9029400215000X

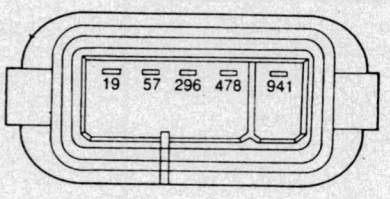

SWITCH POSITION	SWITCH TERMINALS
OFF	57 AND 478
ON	296 AND 478
WASH(ON)	296, 478 AND 941

Fig. 4   Wiper switch continuity test. Taurus

FM9029200149000X

SWITCH POSITIONS	SWITCH TERMINALS
OFF	57 AND 478
WASH (ON)	296, 478 AND 941

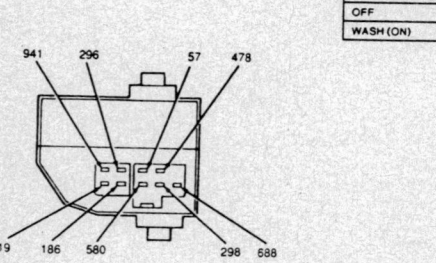

Fig. 5   Wiper switch continuity test. Sable

FM9029200150000X

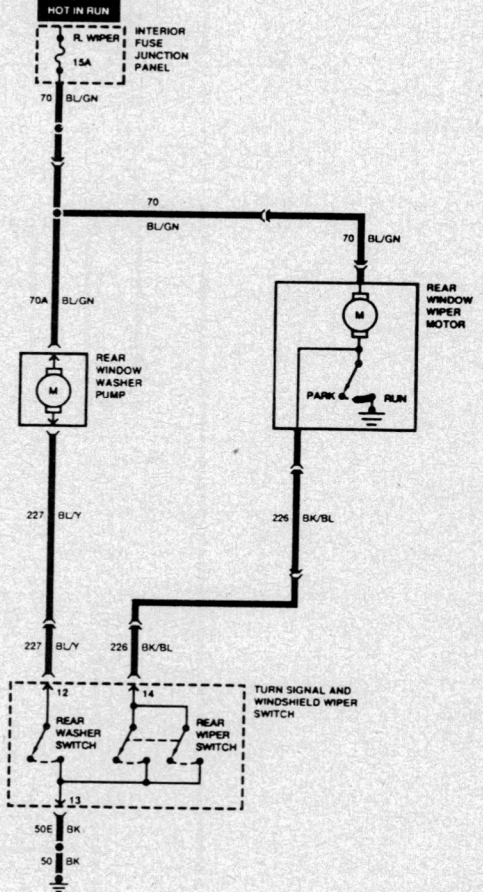

Fig. 6   Wiper circuit schematic. Aspire

FM9029400184000X

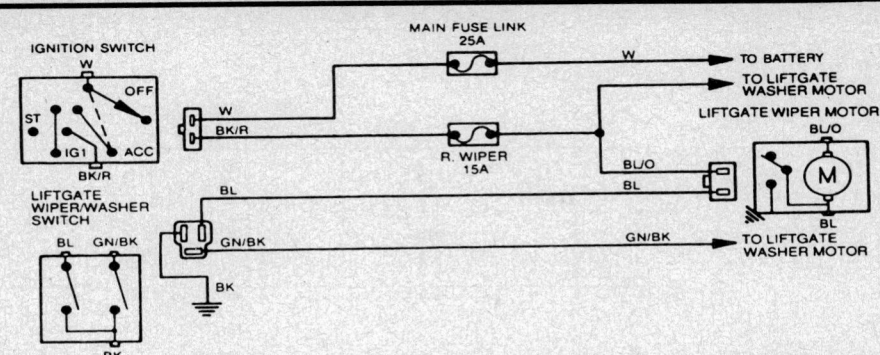

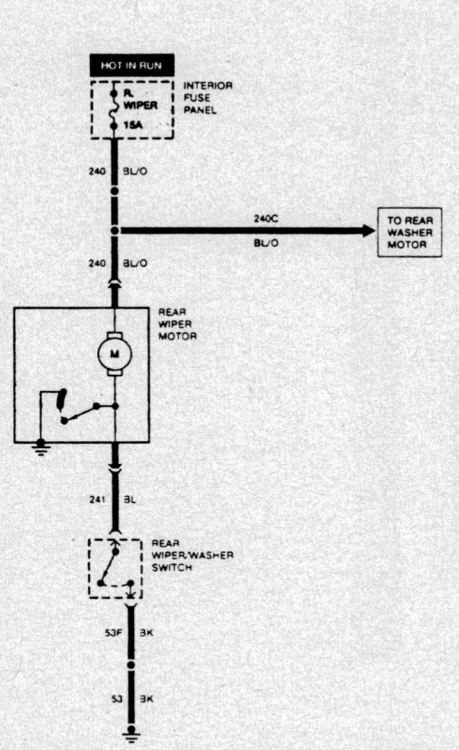

Fig. 7 Wiper circuit schematic. Festiva

TEST STEP		RESULT	▶	ACTION TO TAKE
LW1	SELECT SYMPTOM FROM DIAGNOSTIC MENU			
	● Turn the ignition switch to the ON position.	Wiper not working	▶	GO to **LW2**.
	● Turn the rear wiper switch to the ON position.	Park not working	▶	GO to **LW8**.
		Wiper runs continuously	▶	GO to **LW7**.
LW2	CHECK FUSE			
	● Check the 15 amp R. WIPER fuse.	Yes	▶	GO to **LW3**.
	● Is the fuse OK?	No	▶	REPLACE the 15 amp R. WIPER fuse.
	NOTE: If the fuse fails again, check the "BL/O" wire(s) for a short to ground.			
LW3	CHECK LIFTGATE WIPER SUPPLY			
	● Disconnect the liftgate wiper motor connector.	Yes	▶	GO to **LW4**.
	● Turn the key ON.	No	▶	SERVICE the "BL/O" wire between the liftgate wiper motor and the interior fuse panel for an open.
	● Measure the voltage on the "BL/O" wire at the liftgate wiper motor connector.			
	● Is the voltage greater than 10 volts?			
LW4	CHECK LIFTGATE WIPER MOTOR GROUND			
	● Disconnect the liftgate wiper motor.	Yes	▶	REPLACE the liftgate wiper motor.
	● Turn the liftgate wiper/washer switch to the ON position.	No	▶	GO to **LW5**.
	● Measure the resistance of the "BL" wire at the liftgate wiper motor to ground.			
	● Is the resistance less than 5 ohms?			
LW5	CHECK LIFTGATE WIPER MOTOR CONTINUITY			
	● Disconnect the liftgate wiper motor.	Yes	▶	GO to **LW6**.
	● Disconnect the liftgate wiper/washer switch.	No	▶	SERVICE the "BL" wire for an open.
	● Measure the resistance of the "BL" wire between the liftgate wiper motor connector and liftgate wiper/washer switch connector.			
	● Is the resistance less than 5 ohms?			

FM9029200151010X

Fig. 8 Wiper system diagnosis & testing (Part 1 of 2). 1992 Festiva

TEST STEP		RESULT	▶	ACTION TO TAKE
LW6	CHECK LIFTGATE WIPER/WASHER SWITCH GROUND			
	● Disconnect the wiper/washer switch connector.	Yes	▶	REPLACE the wiper/washer switch.
	● Measure the resistance of the "BK" wire at the wiper/washer switch connector to ground.	No	▶	REPAIR the "BK" wire between the liftgate wiper/washer switch and ground.
	● Is the resistance less than 5 ohms?			
LW7	CHECK FOR SHORT TO GROUND			
	● Disconnect the liftgate wiper motor.	Yes	▶	SERVICE the "BL" wire for a short to ground.
	● Disconnect the liftgate wiper/washer switch.	No	▶	GO to **LW8**.
	● Measure the resistance of the "BL" wire at the liftgate wiper motor connector to ground.			
	● Is the resistance less than 5 ohms?			
LW8	CHECK LIFTGATE WIPER/WASHER MOTOR CONTINUITY			
	● Place the liftgate wiper out of the park position by turning the ignition switch to the OFF position when the wiper is in the center of travel.	Yes	▶	REPLACE the liftgate wiper/washer switch.
	● Disconnect the wiper motor connector.	No Wiper motor case	▶	REPAIR the case ground of the liftgate wiper motor.
	● Measure the resistance at the following places: — between the liftgate wiper motor case and ground. — between the liftgate wiper motor "BL" terminal and ground.	No Wiper motor "BL" terminal	▶	REPLACE the liftgate wiper motor.
	● Are the resistances less than 5 ohms?			

FM9029200151020X

Fig. 8 Wiper system diagnosis & testing (Part 2 of 2). 1992 Festiva

Fig. 9 Wiper system diagnosis & testing (Part 1 of 3). 1993 Festiva

CONDITION	POSSIBLE SOURCE	ACTION
• Rear Wiper Does Not Operate	• Fuse. • Circuit. • Rear wiper / washer switch. • Rear wiper motor.	• GO to RW1.
• Rear Wiper Does Not Park	• Rear wiper motor. • Rear wiper motor ground.	• GO to RW8.
• Rear Wiper Operates Constantly	• Circuit. • Rear wiper / washer switch. • Rear wiper motor.	• GO to RW6.

FM9029300217010X

Fig. 9 Wiper system diagnosis & testing (Part 2 of 3). 1993 Festiva

	TEST STEP	RESULT	ACTION TO TAKE
RW1	CHECK FUSE • Key OFF. • Check the 15A R.WIPER fuse located in the interior fuse panel. • Is the fuse OK?	Yes No	▲ GO to RW4. ▲ GO to RW2.
RW2	CHECK SYSTEM • Key OFF. • Replace the 15A R.WIPER fuse. • Key ON. • Does the fuse fall again?	Yes No	▲ GO to RW3. ▲ GO to RW4.
RW3	CHECK FOR SHORT TO GROUND • Disconnect the rear wiper motor connector. • Remove the 15A R.WIPER fuse. • Measure the resistance of the "BL / O" wire between the bottom terminal of the 15A R.WIPER fuse holder and ground. • Is the resistance less than 5 ohms?	Yes No	▲ SERVICE the "BL / O" wire between the interior fuse panel and the rear wiper motor. ▲ REPLACE the 15A R.WIPER fuse. GO to RW4.
RW4	CHECK POWER SUPPLY TO REAR WIPER MOTOR • Key OFF. • Disconnect the rear wiper motor connector. • Key ON. • Measure the voltage of the "BL / O" wire at the rear wiper motor connector. • Is the voltage greater than 10 volts?	Yes No	▲ GO to RW5. ▲ SERVICE the "BL / O" wire between the interior fuse panel and the rear wiper motor.

FM9029300217020X

Fig. 9 Wiper system diagnosis & testing (Part 3 of 3). 1993 Festiva

	TEST STEP	RESULT	ACTION TO TAKE
RW5	CHECK REAR WIPER MOTOR GROUND CIRCUIT • Key OFF. • Disconnect the rear wiper motor connector. • Turn the rear wiper switch off. • Measure the resistance of the "BL" wire between the rear wiper motor connector and ground. • Turn the rear wiper switch on. • Measure the resistance of the "BL" wire between the rear wiper motor connector and ground. • Is the resistance less than 5 ohms with the rear wiper switch on, and greater than 10,000 ohms with the rear wiper switch off?	Yes No	▲ REPLACE the wiper motor. ▲ GO to RW6.
RW6	CHECK WIRE BETWEEN REAR WIPER MOTOR AND REAR WIPER / WASHER SWITCH • Key OFF. • Disconnect the rear wiper motor connector and the rear wiper / washer switch connector. • Measure the resistance of the "BL" wire between the rear wiper motor connector and the rear wiper / washer switch connector. • Measure the resistance of the "BL" wire between the rear wiper motor connector and ground. • Is the resistance less than 5 ohms between the rear wiper motor connector and the rear wiper / washer switch connector, and greater than 10,000 ohms between the rear wiper motor connector and ground?	Yes No	▲ GO to RW7. ▲ SERVICE the "BL" wire.
RW7	CHECK REAR WIPER / WASHER SWITCH GROUND • Key OFF. • Disconnect the rear wiper / washer switch connector. • Measure the resistance of the "BK" wire between the rear wiper / washer switch connector and ground. • Is the resistance less than 5 ohms?	Yes No	▲ REPLACE the rear wiper / washer switch. ▲ SERVICE the "BK" wire.
RW8	CHECK REAR WIPER PARK POSITION • Key ON. • Operate the rear wiper. • When the rear wiper is out of the park position turn the key OFF. • Disconnect the rear wiper motor connector. • Measure the resistance between the "BL" wire terminal on the rear wiper motor and ground. • Key OFF. • When the rear wiper is in the park position turn the key OFF. • Disconnect the rear wiper motor connector. • Measure the resistance between the "BL" wire terminal on the rear wiper motor and ground. • Is the resistance less than 5 ohms with the rear wiper in a position other than park, and greater than 10,000 ohms with the rear wiper in the park position?	Yes No	▲ REPLACE the rear wiper motor. ▲ REPAIR the rear wiper motor case ground.

FM9029300217030X

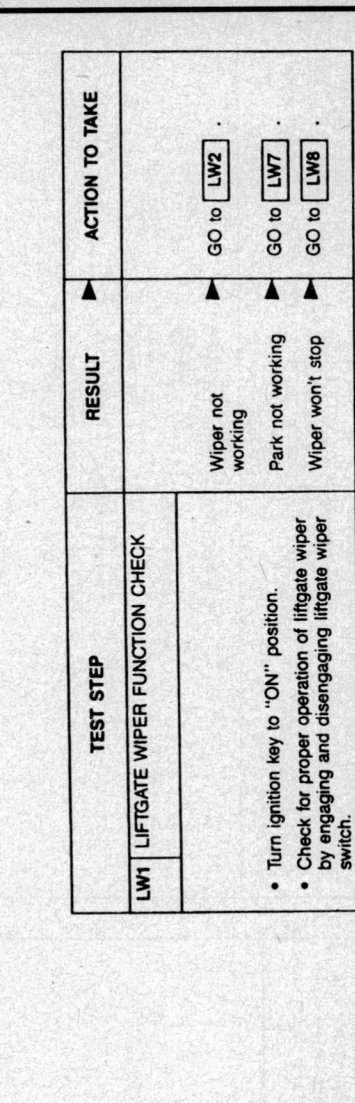

TEST STEP		RESULT	ACTION TO TAKE
LW1	**LIFTGATE WIPER FUNCTION CHECK**	▲	▲
	• Turn ignition key to "ON" position. • Check for proper operation of liftgate wiper by engaging and disengaging liftgate wiper switch.	Wiper not working	GO to LW2 .
		Park not working	GO to LW7 .
		Wiper won't stop	GO to LW8 .

FM9029100153010X

Fig. 11 Wiper system diagnosis & testing (Part 1 of 8). 1992 Probe

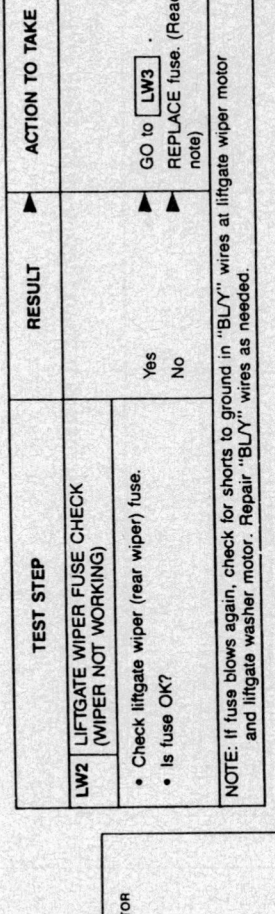

TEST STEP		RESULT	ACTION TO TAKE
LW2	**LIFTGATE WIPER FUSE CHECK (WIPER NOT WORKING)**	▲	▲
	• Check liftgate wiper (rear wiper) fuse. • Is fuse OK?	Yes	GO to LW3 .
		No	REPLACE fuse. (Read note)
NOTE: If fuse blows again, check for shorts to ground in "BL/Y" wires at liftgate wiper motor and liftgate washer motor. Repair "BL/Y" wires as needed.			

FM9029100153020X

Fig. 11 Wiper system diagnosis & testing (Part 2 of 8). 1992 Probe

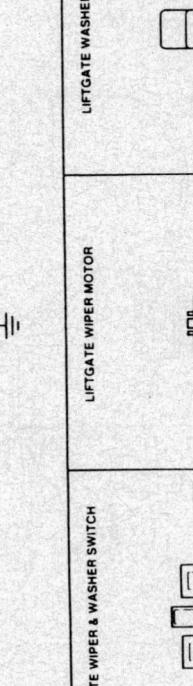

Fig. 10 Wiper system wiring schematic. Probe

TEST STEP	RESULT ►	ACTION TO TAKE
LW3 LIFTGATE WIPER MOTOR CHECK (WIPER NOT WORKING)		
• Disconnect liftgate wiper motor. • Apply 12 volts (±1 volt) and ground directly to motor as shown. • Does motor operate properly?	Yes ► No ►	GO to LW4 . REPLACE liftgate wiper motor.

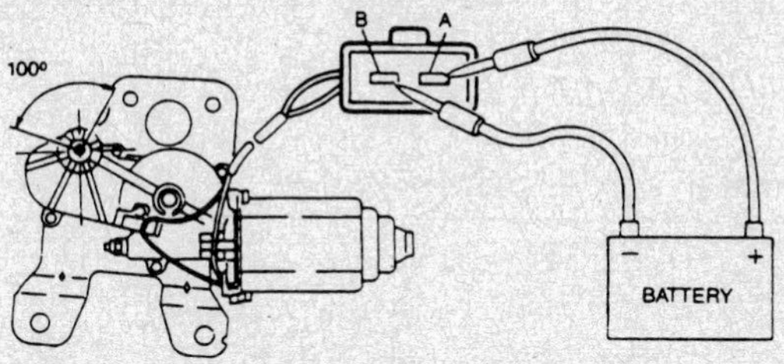

REAR WIPER MOTOR
B
A
100°
BATTERY
−
+

FM9029100153030X

Fig. 11 Wiper system diagnosis & testing (Part 3 of 8). 1992 Probe

TEST STEP	RESULT ►	ACTION TO TAKE
LW4 LIFTGATE WASHER CHECK (WIPER NOT WORKING)		
• Turn on liftgate washer. • Does washer operate properly?	Yes ► No ►	GO to LW5 . REPAIR "BK" wire between liftgate wiper/washer switch and ground.

FM9029100153040X

Fig. 11 Wiper system diagnosis & testing (Part 4 of 8). 1992 Probe

TEST STEP	RESULT ►	ACTION TO TAKE
LW5 LIFTGATE WIPER SUPPLY CHECK (WIPER NOT WORKING)		
• Check for 12 volts (±1 volt) on "BL/Y" wire at liftgate wiper motor connector. • Is there 12 volts?	Yes ► No ►	GO to LW6 . REPAIR "BL/Y" wire between liftgate wiper motor and liftgate wiper fuse.

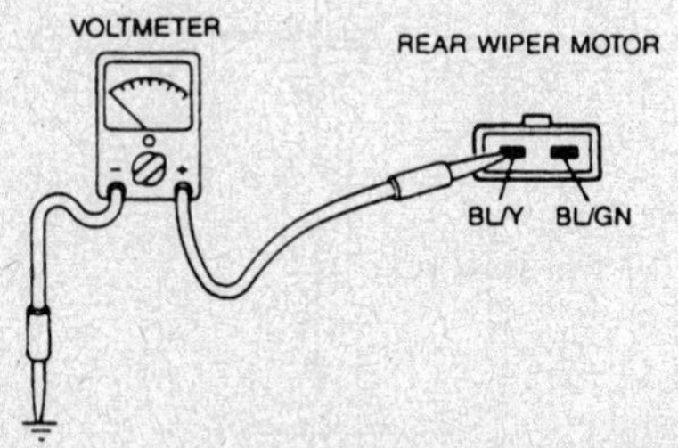

VOLTMETER
REAR WIPER MOTOR
BL/Y
BL/GN

SHOWN LOOKING INTO BACK OF CONNECTOR

FM9029100153050X

Fig. 11 Wiper system diagnosis & testing (Part 5 of 8). 1992 Probe

TEST STEP	RESULT ►	ACTION TO TAKE
LW6 LIFTGATE SWITCH CONTINUITY CHECK (WIPER NOT WORKING)		
• Remove rear wiper fuse. • Push liftgate wiper switch to "ON" position. • Check continuity between ground and liftgate wiper/washer switch "BL/GN" wire connector. • Is there continuity?	Yes ► No ►	REPAIR "BL/GN" wire between liftgate wiper/washer switch and liftgate wiper motor. REPLACE liftgate wiper/washer switch.

REAR WIPER SWITCH
OHMMETER
GN/W
R/BK
BL/BK
BL/GN
BK

SHOWN LOOKING INTO BACK OF CONNECTOR

FM9029100153060X

Fig. 11 Wiper system diagnosis & testing (Part 6 of 8). 1992 Probe

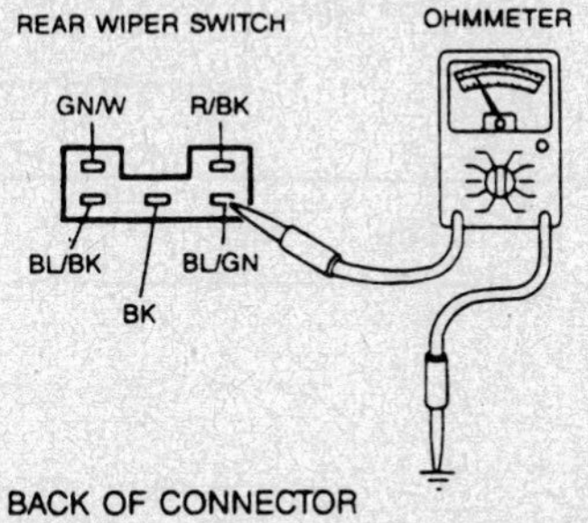

TEST STEP		RESULT		ACTION TO TAKE
LW8	LIFTGATE WIPER/WASHER SWITCH CHECK (WIPER WILL NOT STOP) • Engage liftgate wiper. • Disconnect liftgate wiper/washer switch connector. • Does wiper motor stop?	▲		▲
			Yes	▲ REPLACE liftgate wiper/washer switch.
			No	▲ REPAIR "BL/GN" wire between liftgate wiper motor and liftgate wiper/washer switch.

FM902910015308OX

Fig. 11 Wiper system diagnosis & testing (Part 8 of 8). 1992 Probe

TEST STEP		RESULT		ACTION TO TAKE
RWS1	CHECK FUSE • Key OFF. • Check the 15A REAR WIPER fuse located in the interior fuse panel. • Is the fuse OK?	▲		▲
		Yes	▲	GO to RWS4
		No	▲	GO to RWS2
RWS2	CHECK SYSTEM • Key OFF. • Replace the 15A WIPER fuse. • Key ON. • Does the fuse fail again?			
		Yes	▲	GO to RWS3
		No	▲	GO to RWS4

FM9029300154010X

Fig. 12 Test RWS: Rear Washer System (Part 1 of 3). 1993–94 Probe

TEST STEP		RESULT		ACTION TO TAKE

LW7	LIFTGATE SWITCH CONTINUITY CHECK (PARK NOT WORKING)
	• Place liftgate wiper out of park position by turning ignition key to "OFF" position when wiper is in the center of travel.
	• Remove wiper fuse.
	• Turn the liftgate wiper/washer switch to "OFF" position.
	• Check for continuity to ground at the following places:
	  – Wiper motor case
	  – Wiper motor "BL/Y" wire connector
		▲		▲

		No continuity at: – Wiper motor case	▲	REPAIR case ground of liftgate wiper motor.
		– Wiper motor "BL/Y" wire	▲	REPLACE liftgate wiper motor.

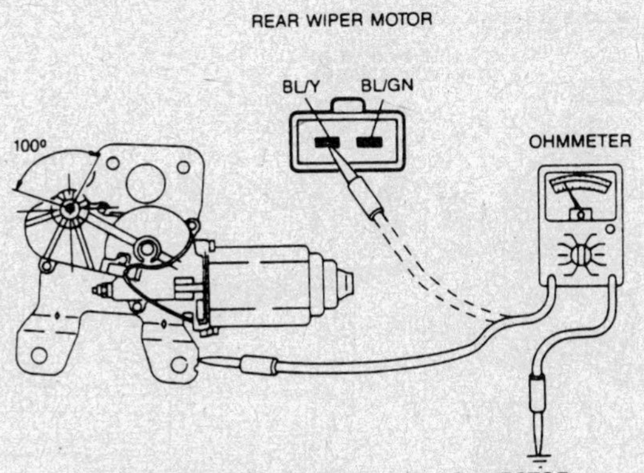

REAR WIPER MOTOR

BL/Y BL/GN

OHMMETER

SHOWN LOOKING INTO BACK OF CONNECTOR

FM902910015307OX

Fig. 11 Wiper system diagnosis & testing (Part 7 of 8). 1992 Probe

TEST STEP		RESULT	ACTION TO TAKE
RWS6	**CHECK WIRE BETWEEN REAR WASHER SWITCH AND REAR WASHER MOTOR**		
	• Key OFF. • Disconnect the rear washer motor connector and the rear washer switch connector. • Measure the resistance of the "BL/Y" wire between the rear washer motor connector and the rear washer switch connector. • Measure the resistance of the "BL/Y" wire between the rear washer motor connector and ground. • Is the resistance less than 5 ohms between the rear washer motor connector and the rear washer switch connector, and greater than 10,000 ohms between the rear washer motor connector and ground?	Yes No	▲ GO to RWS7. ▲ SERVICE the "BL/Y" wire.
RWS7	**CHECK REAR WASHER SWITCH**		
	• Key OFF. • Disconnect the rear washer switch connector. • Depress the rear washer switch. • Measure the resistance between the "BK" wire terminal and the "BL/Y" wire terminal on the rear washer switch. • Release the rear washer switch. • Measure the resistance between the "BK" wire terminal and the "BL/Y" wire terminal on the rear washer switch. • Is the resistance less than 5 ohms with the rear washer switch depressed, and greater than 10,000 ohms with the rear washer switch released?	Yes No	▲ SERVICE the "BK" wire. ▲ REPLACE the rear washer switch.

FM902930015403GX

Fig. 12 Test RWS: Rear Washer System (Part 3 of 3). 1993–94 Probe

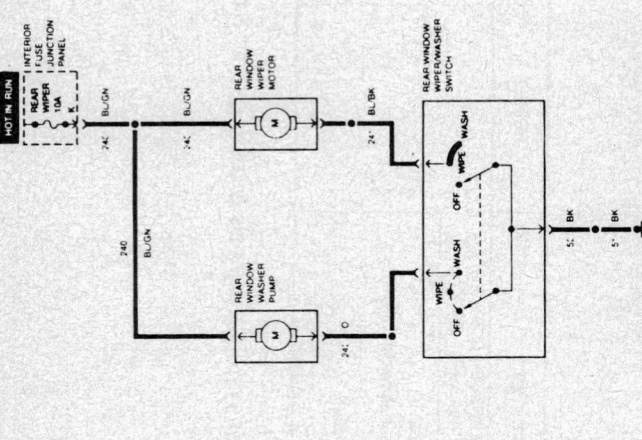

FM902940021300GX

Fig. 13 Washer/Wiper system wiring schematic. 1993-94 Escort & Tracer

---

TEST STEP		RESULT	ACTION TO TAKE
RWS3	**CHECK FOR SHORT TO GROUND**		
	• Key OFF. • Locate and disconnect the 14-pin interior fuse panel connector, the rear washer motor connector and the rear wiper motor connector. • Measure the resistance of the "BL/GN" wire between the 14-pin interior fuse panel connector and ground. • Is the resistance less than 5 ohms?	Yes No	▲ SERVICE the "BL/GN" wire. ▲ REPLACE the 15A REAR WIPER fuse. GO to RWS4.
RWS4	**CHECK POWER SUPPLY TO REAR WASHER MOTOR**		
	• Key OFF. • Reconnect the 14-pin interior fuse panel connector and the rear wiper motor connector. • Locate and disconnect the rear washer motor connector at the rear washer motor. • Key ON. • Measure the voltage on the "BL/GN" wire at the rear washer motor connector. • Is the voltage greater than 10 volts?	Yes No	▲ GO to RWS5. ▲ SERVICE the "BL/GN" wire.
RWS5	**CHECK REAR WASHER MOTOR GROUND CIRCUIT**		
	• Key OFF. • Disconnect the rear washer switch. • Depress the rear washer switch. • Measure the resistance of the "BL/Y" wire between the rear washer motor connector and ground. • Release the rear washer switch. • Measure the resistance of the "BL/Y" wire between the rear washer motor connector and ground. • Is the resistance less than 5 ohms with the rear washer switch depressed, and greater than 10,000 ohms with the rear washer switch released?	Yes No	▲ REPLACE the rear washer motor. ▲ GO to RWS6.

CENTRAL PROCESSING UNIT (CPU)
10-PIN INTERIOR FUSE PANEL CONNECTOR
16-PIN INTERIOR FUSE PANEL CONNECTOR
INTERIOR FUSE PANEL
14-PIN INTERIOR FUSE PANEL CONNECTOR
THEFT WARNING/CPU CONNECTOR
6-PIN INTERIOR FUSE PANEL CONNECTOR
4-PIN INTERIOR FUSE PANEL CONNECTOR
WARNING CHIME MODULE/CPU CONNECTOR

FM902930015402GX

Fig. 12 Test RWS: Rear Washer System (Part 2 of 3). 1993–94 Probe

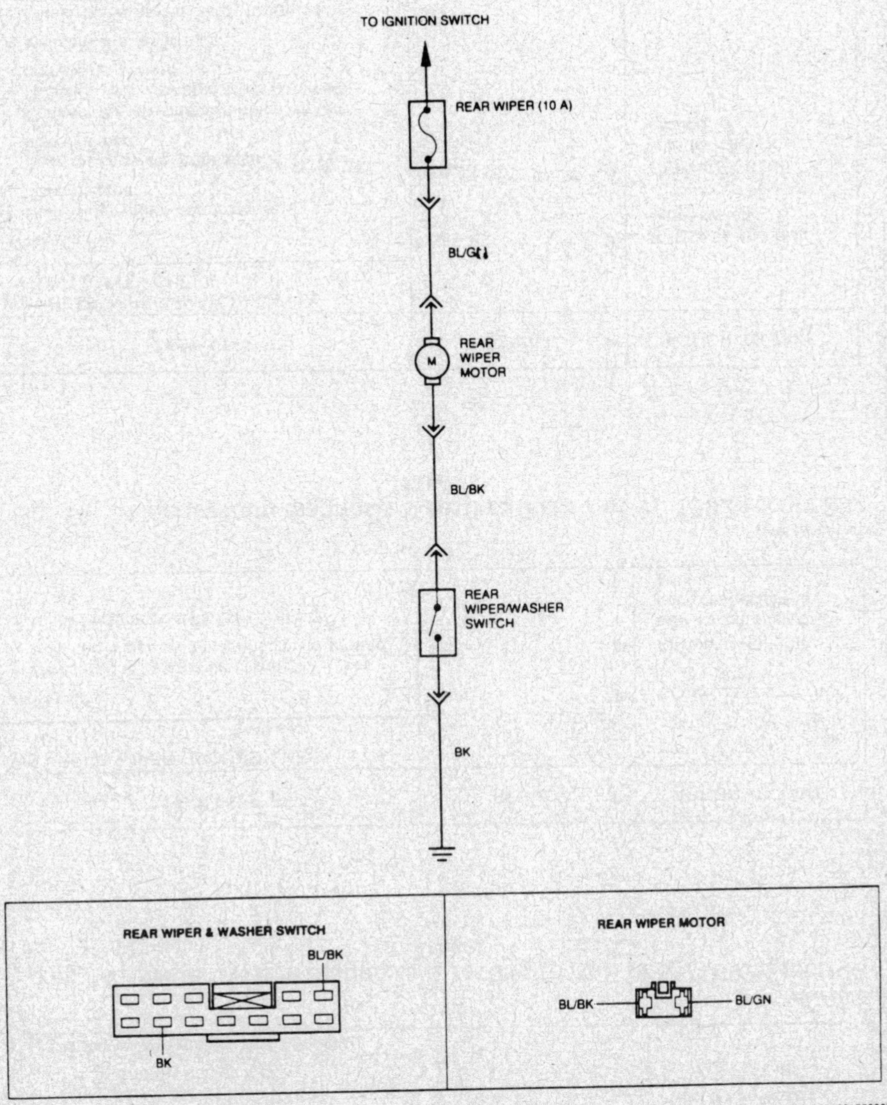

SYMPTOM	POSSIBLE CAUSE	ACTION
Wiper Does Not Operate	• Wiper motor. • Wiper switch. • Blown fuse. • Wiper circuit.	• GO to LW1.
Wiper Operates Constantly	• Wiper switch. • Wiper circuit.	GO to LW8.

FM9029100156010X

Fig. 14 Wiper system diagnosis & testing (Part 1 of 9). 1992 Escort & Tracer

TEST STEP	RESULT	▲ ACTION TO TAKE
LW1 REAR WIPER FUSE CHECK • Access the fuse panel. • Check the rear wiper 10 amp fuse. • Is the fuse OK?	Yes ▲	GO to LW4 .
	No ▲	GO to LW2 .

FM9029100156020X

Fig. 14 Wiper system diagnosis & testing (Part 2 of 9). 1992 Escort & Tracer

TEST STEP	RESULT	▲ ACTION TO TAKE
LW2 REAR WIPER MOTOR SUPPLY INTEGRITY CHECK • Replace the rear wiper fuse. • Key ON. • Check the rear wiper fuse. • Is the fuse OK?	Yes ▲	GO to LW3 .
	No ▲	SERVICE the "BL/GN" wire for short to ground.

FM9029100156030X

Fig. 14 Wiper system diagnosis & testing (Part 3 of 9). 1992 Escort & Tracer

TEST STEP	RESULT	▲ ACTION TO TAKE
LW3 REAR WIPER SYSTEM CHECK • Key ON. • Rear wipers ON. • Check the rear wiper fuse. • Is the fuse OK?	Yes ▲	System OK.
	No ▲	REPLACE the wiper motor.

FM9029100156040X

Fig. 14 Wiper system diagnosis & testing (Part 4 of 9). 1992 Escort & Tracer

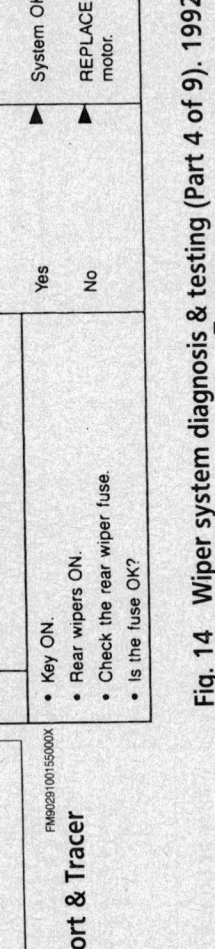

FM9029100156000X

Fig. 13 Wiper system wiring schematic. 1992 Escort & Tracer

TEST STEP	RESULT	ACTION TO TAKE
LW4 REAR WIPER MOTOR VOLTAGE CHECK • Key ON. • Rear wiper motor connector is disconnected. • Measure voltage on the "BL/GN" wire at the wire motor connector. • Is the voltage greater than 10 volts?		
	Yes	GO to LW5 .
	No	SERVICE the "BL/GN" wire for an open.

Fig. 14   Wiper system diagnosis & testing (Part 5 of 9). 1992 Escort & Tracer

FM902910015605OX

TEST STEP	RESULT	ACTION TO TAKE
LW5 REAR WIPER SWITCH VOLTAGE CHECK • Key ON. • Reconnect the rear wiper motor connector. • Disconnect the rear wiper switch connector. • Measure the voltage on the "BL/BK" wire at the wiper switch connector. • Is the voltage greater than 10 volts?		
	Yes	GO to LW6 .
	No	SERVICE the "BL/BK" wire for an open.

Fig. 14   Wiper system diagnosis & testing (Part 6 of 9). 1992 Escort & Tracer

FM902910015606OX

TEST STEP	RESULT	ACTION TO TAKE
LW6 REAR WIPER GROUND CHECK • Key OFF. • Measure the resistance of the "BK" wire from the wiper switch connector to ground. • Is the resistance less than 5 ohms?		
	Yes	GO to LW7 .
	No	SERVICE the "BK" wire for an open or poor connection to ground.

Fig. 14   Wiper system diagnosis & testing (Part 7 of 9). 1992 Escort & Tracer

FM902910015607OX

TEST STEP	RESULT	ACTION TO TAKE
LW7 REAR WIPER SWITCH CHECK • Rear wiper switch connector is disconnected. • Jumper "BL/BK" wire at wiper switch connector to ground. • Key ON. • Do the rear wipers operate?		
	Yes	REPLACE the rear wiper switch.
	No	REPLACE the rear wiper motor.

Fig. 14   Wiper system diagnosis & testing (Part 8 of 9). 1992 Escort & Tracer

FM902910015608OX

TEST STEP	RESULT	ACTION TO TAKE
LW8 REAR WIPER SWITCH SUPPLY INTEGRITY CHECK • Key OFF. • Rear wiper motor connector is disconnected. • Rear wiper switch connector is disconnected. • Connect the ohmmeter terminal to the "BL/BK" wire. Connect other ohmmeter terminal to ground. • Measure the resistance. • Is resistance greater than 10,000 ohms?		
	Yes	REPLACE the rear wiper switch.
	No	SERVICE "BL/BK" wire for short to ground.

Fig. 14   Wiper system diagnosis & testing (Part 9 of 9). 1992 Escort & Tracer

FM902910015609OX

	TEST STEP	RESULT	▶	ACTION TO TAKE
RW1	**CHECK FUSE** • Locate the interior fuse panel. • Check the 10 amp REAR WIPER fuse. • Is the fuse OK? NOTE: If the fuse fails when the ignition is turned ON, check the "DB/DG" wire for a short to ground. Repair/replace as necessary.	Yes No	▶ ▶	GO to **RW2**. REPLACE the fuse.
RW2	**CHECK REAR WASHER MOTOR POWER SUPPLY** • Key ON. • Measure the voltage on the "DB/DG" wire at the rear washer motor connector. • Is the voltage greater than 10 volts?	Yes No	▶ ▶	GO to **RW3**. REPAIR/REPLACE the "DB/DG" wire.
RW3	**CHECK REAR WIPER/WASHER SWITCH VOLTAGE FEED** • Measure the voltage on the "O" wire at the rear wiper switch. • In the voltage greater than 10 volts?	Yes No	▶ ▶	GO to **RW4**. REPAIR/REPLACE the "O" wire.
RW4	**CHECK REAR WASHER SWITCH GROUND** • Measure the resistance between the "BK" wire at the rear wiper/washer switch and ground. • Is the resistance less than 5 ohms?	Yes No	▶ ▶	GO to **RW5**. REPAIR/REPLACE the "BK" wire.
RW5	**CHECK REAR WASHER MOTOR** • Key OFF. • Place a jumper wire from the "O" wire at the rear washer motor connector to ground. • Key ON. • Does the rear washer motor operate?	Yes No	▶ ▶	REPLACE the rear wiper/washer switch. REPLACE the washer motor.

FM9029300157000X

Fig. 15   Wiper system diagnosis & testing. 1993 Escort & Tracer

	TEST STEP	RESULT	▶	ACTION TO TAKE
H1	**CHECK FUSE** • Key OFF. • Locate the interior fuse junction panel. • Check the 10A REAR WIPER fuse. • Is the fuse OK?	Yes No	▶ ▶	GO to H4. GO to H2.
H2	**CHECK SYSTEM** • Key OFF. • Replace the fuse. • Key ON. • Check the 10A REAR WIPER fuse. • Is the fuse OK?	Yes No	▶ ▶	GO to H4. GO to H3.
H3	**CHECK FOR SHORT TO GROUND** • Key OFF. • Disconnect the 15-pin interior fuse junction panel connector. • Disconnect the rear window washer pump and rear window wiper motor connectors. • Measure the resistance of the "BL/GN" wire between the interior fuse junction panel connector and ground. • Is the resistance greater than 10,000 ohms?	Yes No	▶ ▶	RECONNECT the 15-pin interior fuse junction panel connector. GO to H4. SERVICE the "BL/GN" wire.
H4	**CHECK REAR WINDOW WIPER SWITCH** • Perform the Rear Window Wiper/Washer Switch component test in this section. • Does the switch test OK?	Yes No	▶ ▶	GO to H5. REPLACE the rear window wiper/washer switch.
H5	**CHECK REAR WINDOW WIPER MOTOR** • Perform the Rear Window Wiper Motor component test in this section. • Does the motor test OK?	Yes No	▶ ▶	GO to H6. REPLACE the rear window wiper motor.
H6	**CHECK POWER SUPPLY TO REAR WINDOW WIPER MOTOR** • Key OFF. • Disconnect the rear window wiper motor connector. • Key ON. • Measure the voltage on the "BL/GN" wire at the rear window wiper motor connector. BL/BK — [ ] — BL/GN REAR WINDOW WIPER MOTOR • Is the voltage greater than 10 volts?	Yes No	▶ ▶	GO to H7. SERVICE the "BL/GN" wire.

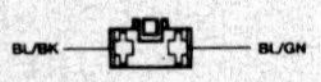

FM9029400218010X

Fig. 16   Wiper system diagnosis & testing (Part 1 of 2). 1994 Escort & Tracer

TEST STEP	RESULT	▶	ACTION TO TAKE
H7 CHECK REAR WINDOW WIPER SWITCH GROUND			
• Key OFF.	Yes	▶	SERVICE the "BL/BK" wire between the rear window wiper motor and the rear window wiper/washer switch.
• Disconnect the rear window wiper/washer switch.			
• Measure the resistance of the "BK" wire between the rear window wiper/washer switch connector and ground.			
• **Is the resistance less than 5 ohms?**	No	▶	SERVICE the "BK" wire.

PINPOINT TEST I: REAR WINDOW WIPER WILL NOT SHUT OFF

TEST STEP	RESULT	▶	ACTION TO TAKE
I1 CHECK REAR WINDOW WIPER SWITCH			
• Perform the Rear Window Wiper/Washer Switch component test in this section.	Yes	▶	SERVICE the "BL/BK" wire between the rear window wiper motor and the rear window wiper/washer switch.
• **Does the switch test OK?.**	No	▶	REPLACE the rear window wiper/washer switch.

FM9029400218020X

Fig. 16 Wiper system diagnosis & testing (Part 2 of 2). 1994 Escort & Tracer

PASSIVE RESTRAINT SYSTEMS

AIR BAG SYSTEM 18-1

AUTOMATIC SEAT BELTS 18-19

Air Bag System

INDEX

AIR BAG SYSTEM DISARMING & ARMING

On models with passenger's side air bag, both air bag modules must be disconnected to properly disarm system.

CAPRI

1992

Disarming

1. Disconnect battery ground cable and battery backup power supply.
2. Remove four nut and washer assemblies securing air bag to steering wheel.
3. Carefully disconnect air bag connector from clock spring.
4. **On models with passenger's side air bag,** open glove compartment and rotate completely down past stops. Carefully disconnect passenger air bag connector.
5. **On all models,** attach a jumper wire to the air bag terminals on driver air bag clock spring, **Fig. 1.**
6. **On models with passenger's side air bag,** install a jumper wire between the air bag terminals on wiring harness side of passenger's air bag connector, **Fig. 1.**
7. **On all models,** connect battery ground cable and backup power supply.

Arming

1. Disconnect battery ground cable and backup power supply.
2. Remove jumper wire from air bag terminals on clock spring assembly.
3. Connect driver's side air bag connector.
4. Position air bag on steering wheel and secure with four nut and washer assemblies. Tighten to specifications.
5. **On models with passenger air bag,** remove jumper wire from air bag ter-

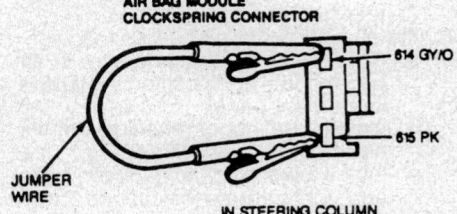

AIR BAG MODULE CLOCKSPRING CONNECTOR

614 GY/O

615 PK

JUMPER WIRE

IN STEERING COLUMN

FM8019200899000X

Fig. 1 Air bag jumper wire connections

minals on passenger air bag wiring connector in harness, then connect passenger air bag connector and close glove compartment door.
6. **On all models,** connect backup power supply and battery ground cable.
7. Place ignition switch from in the Run position and note air bag warning lamp operation. Indicator lamp should illuminate for approximately 6 seconds, and then turn off. If warning lamp does not illuminate or remains illuminated continuously or flashes, refer to "Diagnosis & Testing."

1993 (EARLY PRODUCTION)

Disarming

1. Disconnect positive battery cable and back-up power supply.
2. Remove four nut and washer assemblies retaining air bag module to steering wheel.
3. Disconnect air bag connector.
4. Connect Rotunda Air Bag Simulator tool No. 105-00008 or equivalent to clock spring connector in base of steering wheel.
5. Connect positive battery cable and back-up power supply.

Arming

1. Disconnect positive battery cable and

backup power supply.
2. Remove air bag Simulator from clock spring connector at base of steering wheel.
3. Connect air bag connector.
4. Position air bag on steering wheel and secure with four nut and washer assemblies. Tighten to specifications.
5. Connect positive battery cable and back-up power supply.
6. Place ignition switch from in the Run position and note air bag warning lamp operation. Indicator lamp should illuminate for approximately 6 seconds, and then turn off. If warning lamp does not illuminate or remains illuminated continuously or flashes, refer to "Diagnosis & Testing."

1993 (LATE PRODUCTION)

Disarming

1. Disconnect battery ground cable.
2. Wait one minute for back-up power supply to deplete stored energy.
3. Remove four bolts retaining air bag module to steering wheel.
4. Disconnect air bag connector.
5. Connect Rotunda Air Bag Simulator tool No. 105-00008 or equivalent to vehicle harness at top of steering column.
6. Connect battery ground cable.

Arming

1. Disconnect battery ground cable.
2. Wait one minute for backup power supply to deplete stored energy.
3. Remove air bag Simulator from vehicle harness at top of steering column.
4. Connect air bag connector.
5. Position air bag on steering wheel and secure with four bolts. Tighten to specifications.
6. Connect battery ground cable.
7. Place ignition switch from in the Run position and note air bag warning lamp operation. Indicator lamp should

illuminate for approximately 6 seconds, and then turn off. If warning lamp does not illuminate or remains illuminated continuously or flashes, refer to "Diagnosis & Testing."

1994

Refer to "Escort & Tracer" in this section for air bag disarming and arming procedures.

MARK VII

Disarming

1. Disconnect battery positive cable.
2. Remove four nut and washer assemblies retaining driver air bag module to steering wheel.
3. Carefully disconnect air bag module connector.
4. Attach Rotunda Air Bag Simulator tool No. 105-00008 or equivalent, on clock spring to simulate air bag.
5. Connect battery positive cable.

Arming

1. Disconnect battery positive cable.
2. Remove air bag simulator from air bag terminals on clock spring assembly.
3. Connect air bag module connector.
4. Position air bag assembly on steering wheel and secure with four nut and washer assemblies. Tighten to specifications.
5. Connect battery positive cable.
6. Place ignition switch from in the Run position and note air bag warning lamp operation. Indicator lamp should illuminate for approximately 6 seconds, and then turn off. If warning lamp does not illuminate or remains illuminated continuously or flashes, refer to "Diagnosis & Testing."

MARK VIII

Disarming

1. **On 1993 models,** disconnect battery positive cable.
2. **On 1994 models,** disconnect battery ground cable, then the battery positive cable.
3. **On all models,** wait one minute for backup power supply to discharge.
4. Remove two screw and washer assemblies retaining driver air bag module to the steering wheel.
5. Disconnect driver air bag module connector.
6. Connect Rotunda Air Bag Simulator tool No. 105-00010 or equivalent to vehicle harness at top of steering column.
7. Remove passenger air bag as follows:
   a. Remove righthand and lefthand finish panel.
   b. Open glove compartment, press sides inward and lower glove compartment to floor.
   c. Working through glove compartment opening, remove two lower air bag module retaining bolts.
   d. Remove three remaining air bag module retaining screws from side of air bag cover.
   e. Disconnect electrical connector at-

tached to lefthand side of air bag while removing air bag module.
8. Install Rotunda Air Bag Simulator tool No. 105-00010 or equivalent on vehicle air bag harness connector in place of air bag.
9. **On 1993 models,** connect battery positive cable.
10. **On 1994 models,** connect battery positive cable, then the battery ground cable.

Arming

1. **On 1993 models,** disconnect battery positive cable.
2. **On 1994 models,** disconnect battery ground cable, then the battery positive cable.
3. **On all models,** wait one minute for backup power supply to deplete stored energy.
4. Remove air bag Simulator from clock spring connector at top of steering column.
5. Connect driver air bag connector.
6. Position driver air bag on steering wheel and secure with two screw and washer assemblies. Tighten to specifications.
7. Remove air bag Simulator from passenger harness connector.
8. Install passenger air bag as follows:
   a. Connect electrical connector to air bag module and position module in instrument panel.
   b. Install three upper retaining screws and tighten to specifications.
   c. Install lower module retaining bolts and tighten to specifications.
   d. Return glove compartment to correct position, then install instrument panel finish panel.
9. **On 1993 models,** connect battery positive cable.
10. **On 1994 models,** connect battery positive cable, then the battery ground cable.
11. **On all models,** place ignition switch from in the Run position and note air bag warning lamp operation. Indicator lamp should illuminate for approximately 6 seconds, and then turn off. If warning lamp does not illuminate or remains illuminated continuously or flashes, refer to "Diagnosis & Testing."

CONTINENTAL

Disarming

1. Disconnect battery positive cable
2. Wait one minute for backup power supply to deplete.
3. Remove four nut and washer assemblies retaining driver air bag module to the steering wheel.
4. Disconnect driver air bag module connector.
5. Open glove compartment and rotate completely past stops. Disconnect passenger's side air bag connector.
6. On 1992 models, attach Rotunda Air Bag Simulator tool No. 105-00008 or equivalent to air bag terminals on clock spring assembly to simulate air bag.
7. On 1993-94 models, attach Rotunda

Air Bag Simulator tool No. 105-00010 or equivalent to air bag terminals on clock spring assembly to simulate air bag.
8. **On 1992 models,** attach Rotunda Air Bag Simulator tool No. 105-00008 or equivalent to air bag terminals on wiring harness side of passenger air bag module connector.
9. **On 1993-94 models,** attach Rotunda Air Bag Simulator tool No. 105-00010 or equivalent to air bag terminals on wiring harness side of passenger air bag module connector.
10. **On all models,** connect positive battery cable.

Arming

1. Disconnect battery positive cable.
2. Wait one minute for backup power supply to discharge.
3. Remove air bag simulator from vehicle harness connector at top of steering column.
4. Connect driver air bag connector.
5. Position air bag assembly on steering wheel and secure with four nut and washer assemblies. Tighten to specifications.
6. Remove air bag simulator from vehicle harness connector at passenger air bag.
7. Connect passenger air bag connector.
8. Connect battery positive cable.
9. Place ignition switch from in the Run position and note air bag warning lamp operation. Indicator lamp should illuminate for approximately 6 seconds, and then turn off. If warning lamp does not illuminate or remains illuminated continuously or flashes, refer to "Diagnosis & Testing."

COUGAR & THUNDERBIRD

Disarming

1. Disconnect battery ground cable, then the battery positive cable.
2. Wait approximately one minute for backup power supply to discharge.
3. Remove two bolt and washer assemblies retaining driver side air bag assembly to steering wheel.
4. Disconnect driver side air bag connector, then remove air bag from steering wheel. Position air bag module on work bench with trim cover facing upward.
5. Connect Rotunda air bag simulator tool No. 105-00010 or equivalent to vehicle air bag wiring harness at top of steering column.
6. Remove passenger side air bag module as follows:
   a. Using a small screwdriver, detach dampening rod from righthand side of glove compartment.
   b. Pull lefthand side of glove compartment inward and allow glove compartment to drop downward.
   c. Remove air duct attaching screws, then the air duct.
   d. Remove two vertically positioned bolts from each side of air bag module.
   e. Remove the two remaining air bag

module attaching bolts.

f. Push air bag module outward from instrument panel. Do not handle air bag module by deployment doors.

g. Disconnect electrical connector, then remove air bag module. Position air bag module on work brench with trim cover facing upward.

7. Connect Rotunda air bag simulator tool No. 105-00010 or equivalent to vehicle air bag wiring harness in place of the passenger side air bag module.

8. Reconnect battery positive cable, then the ground cable.

Arming

1. Disconnect battery ground cable, then the battery positive cable.

2. Wait approximately one minute for backup power supply to discharge.

3. Disconnect Rotunda air bag simulator tool No. 105-00010 or equivalent from vehicle air bag wiring harness at top of steering column.

4. Connect driver side air bag electrcial connector to air bag module.

5. Position dirver side air bag module to steering wheel, then install attaching bolts and washers. **Torque** attaching screws to 90 to 122 inch lbs.

6. Disconnect Rotunda air bag simulator tool No. 105-00010 or equivalent from vehicle passenger side harness.

7. Connect electrcial connector to passenger side air bag module.

8. Install passenger side air bag module as described under "Component Service."

9. Connect battery positive cable, then the negative cable.

10. Place ignition switch in the Run position and note air bag warning lamp operation. Indicator lamp should illuminate for approximately 6 seconds, and then turn off. If warning lamp does not illuminate or remains illuminated continuously or flashes, refer to "Diagnosis & Testing."

CROWN VICTORIA & GRAND MARQUIS
Disarming

1. **On 1992-93 models,** disconnect battery positive cable.

2. **On 1994 models, disconnect battery ground cable, then the battery positive cable.**

3. **On all models,** wait one minute for backup power supply to discharge.

4. Remove four nut and washer assemblies retaining driver air bag module to the steering wheel.

5. Disconnect driver air bag module connector.

6. **On 1992 models,** connect Rotunda Air Bag simulator tool No. 105-00008 or equivalent to vehicle harness at top of steering column.

7. **On 1993-94 models,** connect Rotunda Air Bag simulator tool No. 105-00010 or equivalent to vehicle harness at top of steering column.

8. **On models with passenger's side air bag,** remove passenger air bag as follows:

a. Remove righthand instrument panel lower molding.

b. **On Crown Victoria,** remove righthand instrument cluster finish panel retaining screws, then the panel.

c. **On Grand Marquis,** remove righthand register applique retaining screws, then the applique.

d. Remove cluster finish panel retaining screws, then the panel.

e. **On both models,** open glove compartment, press sides inward and lower glove compartment to floor.

f. Working through glove compartment opening, remove two front air bag module retaining screws.

g. Remove two rear air bag module retaining screws, then disconnect electrical connector and remove air bag module.

9. **On 1992 models,** install Rotunda Air Bag Simulator tool No. 105-00008 or equivalent, on vehicle air bag harness connector.

10. **On 1993-94 models,** install Rotunda Air Bag Simulator tool No. 105-00010 or equivalent, on vehicle air bag harness connector.

11. **On 1992-93 models,** connect battery positive cable.

12. **On 1994 models, connect battery positive cable, then the battery ground cable.**

Arming

1. **On 1992-93 models,** disconnect battery positive cable.

2. **On 1994 models, disconnect battery ground cable, then the battery positive cable.**

3. **On all models,** wait one minute for backup power supply to deplete stored energy.

4. Remove air bag simulator from vehicle harness at top of steering column.

5. Connect driver air bag connector.

6. Position driver air bag on steering wheel and secure with four nut and washer assemblies. Tighten to specifications.

7. **On models with passenger's side air bag,** remove air bag Simulator from vehicle harness connector.

8. Install passenger air bag as follows:

a. Connect electrical connector to air bag module and position module in instrument panel.

b. Install two rear retaining screws and tighten to specifications.

c. Install two front retaining screws and tighten to specifications.

d. Return glove compartment to correct position, then install instrument cluster finish panel.

e. **On Grand Marquis,** install righthand register applique and **torque** retaining screws to 17-27 inch lbs.

f. **On all models,** Install instrument panel lower molding.

9. **On 1992-93 models,** connect battery positive cable.

10. **On 1994 models, connect battery positive cable, then the battery ground cable.**

11. **On all models,** place ignition switch

from in the Run position and note air bag warning lamp operation. Indicator lamp should illuminate for approximately 6 seconds, and then turn off. If warning lamp does not illuminate or remains illuminated continuously or flashes, refer to "Diagnosis & Testing.

MUSTANG, TEMPO & TOPAZ

1. **On 1992-93 models,** disconnect battery positive cable.

2. **On 1994 models, disconnect battery ground cable, then the battery positive cable.**

3. **On all models,** wait one minute for back-up power supply to deplete stored energy.

4. Remove four nut and washer assemblies retaining driver air bag module to steering wheel.

5. Disconnect air bag module connector.

6. **On 1992 models,** attach Rotunda Air Bag simulator tool No. 105-00008 or equivalent to vehicle harness at top of steering wheel.

7. **On 1993-94 models,** attach Rotunda Air Bag simulator tool No. 105-00010 or equivalent, to vehicle harness at top of steering wheel.

8. **On 1992-93 models,** connect battery positive cable.

9. **On 1994 models, connect battery positive cable, then the battery ground cable.**

Arming

1. **On 1992-93 models,** disconnect battery positive cable.

2. **On 1994 models, disconnect battery ground cable, then the battery positive cable.**

3. **On all models,** wait one minute for backup power supply to deplete stored energy.

4. Remove air bag simulator from vehicle harness connector at top of steering column.

5. Connect driver air bag connector.

6. Position driver air bag on steering wheel and secure with four nut and washer assemblies. Tighten to specifications.

7. **On 1992-93 models,** connect battery positive cable.

8. **On 1994 models, connect battery positive cable, then the battery ground cable.**

9. **On all models,** place ignition switch from in the Run position and note air bag warning lamp operation. Indicator lamp should illuminate for approximately 6 seconds, and then turn off. If warning lamp does not illuminate or remains illuminated continuously or flashes, refer to "Diagnosis & Testing.

SABLE & TAURUS
Disarming

1. **On 1992-93 models,** disconnect battery positive cable.

2. **On 1994 models, disconnect battery ground cable, then the battery positive cable.**

3. **On all models,** wait one minute for

backup power supply to discharge.

4. Remove four nut and washer assemblies retaining driver air bag module to the steering wheel.

5. Disconnect driver air bag module connector.

6. Connect Rotunda Air Bag Simulator tool No. 105-00010 or equivalent to clockspring to simulate air bag.

7. **On models with passenger's side air bag,** remove passenger air bag as follows:
   a. Remove righthand and lefthand finish panel.
   b. Remove instrument panel finish panel retaining spear clips.
   c. open glove compartment, press sides inward and lower glove compartment to floor.
   d. Working through glove compartment opening, remove two lower air bag module retaining bolts.
   e. Remove four remaining air bag module retaining screws from side of air bag cover, then disconnect electrical connector attached to lefthand side of air bag and remove air bag module.

8. Connect Rotunda Air Bag Simulator tool No. 105-00010 or equivalent to wiring harness.

9. **On 1992-93 models,** connect battery positive cable.

10. **On 1994 models, connect battery positive cable, then the battery ground cable.**

Arming

1. **On 1992-93 models,** disconnect battery positive cable.

2. **On 1994 models, disconnect battery ground cable, then the battery positive cable.**

3. **On all models,** wait one minute for backup power supply to deplete stored energy.

4. Remove air bag Simulator from clock spring connector.

5. Connect driver air bag connector.

6. Position driver air bag on steering wheel and secure with four nut and washer assemblies. Tighten to specifications.

7. **On models with passenger's side air bag,** remove air bag simulator tool from vehicle harness connector.

8. Install passenger air bag as follows:
   a. Connect electrical connector to air bag module and position module in instrument panel.
   b. Install four upper retaining screws and tighten to specifications.
   c. Install lower module retaining bolts and tighten to specifications.
   d. Return glove compartment to correct position.
   e. Install instrument panel finish panel locator pin into air bag bushing locator, then align spear clips and press finish panel into place.

9. **On 1992-93 models,** connect battery positive cable.

10. **On 1994 models, connect battery positive cable, then the battery ground cable.**

11. **On all models,** place ignition switch from in the Run position and note air bag warning lamp operation. Indicator lamp should illuminate for approximately 6 seconds, and then turn off. If warning lamp does not illuminate or remains illuminated continuously or flashes, refer to "Diagnosis & Testing."

TOWN CAR
Disarming

1. **On 1992-93 models,** disconnect battery positive cable.

2. **On 1994 models, disconnect battery ground cable, then the battery positive cable.**

3. **On all models,** wait one minute for backup power supply to discharge.

4. Remove four nut and washer assemblies retaining driver air bag module to the steering wheel.

5. Disconnect driver air bag module connector.

6. **On 1992 models,** attach Rotunda Air Bag Simulator tool No. 105-00008 or equivalent to vehicle harness at top of steering column.

7. **On 1993-94 models,** attach Rotunda Air Bag Simulator tool No. 105-00010 or equivalent to vehicle harness at top of steering column.

8. **On all models,** remove instrument panel moldings, instrument panel finish panel retaining screws, then the panel.

9. Open glove compartment, press sides inward and lower glove compartment to floor.

10. Working through glove compartment opening, remove two lower air bag module retaining bolts.

11. Remove four remaining air bag module retaining screws, then disconnect electrical connector and remove air bag module.

12. **On 1992 models,** install Rotunda Air Bag Simulator tool No. 105-00008 or equivalent on vehicle passenger's side air bag harness connector.

13. **On 1993-94 models,** install Rotunda Air Bag simulator tool No. 105-00010 or equivalent on vehicle passenger's side air bag harness connector.

14. **On 1992-93 models,** connect battery positive cable.

15. **On 1994 models, connect battery positive cable, then the battery ground cable.**

Arming

1. **On 1992-93 models,** disconnect battery positive cable.

2. **On 1994 models, disconnect battery ground cable, then the battery positive cable.**

3. **On all models,** wait one minute for backup power supply to deplete stored energy.

4. Remove air bag Simulator from vehicle harness at top of steering column.

5. Connect driver air bag connector.

6. Position driver air bag on steering wheel and secure with four nut and washer assemblies. Tighten to specifications.

7. Remove air bag Simulator from passenger harness connector.

8. Install passenger air bag as follows:
   a. Connect electrical connector to air bag module and position module in instrument panel.
   b. Install four upper retaining screws and tighten to specifications.
   c. Install lower module retaining bolts and tighten to specifications.
   d. Return glove compartment to correct position, then install instrument panel finish panel.
   e. Install instrument panel moldings.

9. **On 1992-93 models,** connect battery positive cable.

10. **On 1994 models, connect battery positive cable, then the battery ground cable.**

11. **On all models,** place ignition switch from in the Run position and note air bag warning lamp operation. Indicator lamp should illuminate for approximately 6 seconds, and then turn off. If warning lamp does not illuminate or remains illuminated continuously or flashes, refer to "Diagnosis & Testing."

PROBE

Disarming

1. Disconnect battery ground cable.

2. Wait one minute for back-up power supply to deplete stored energy.

3. Remove four bolts retaining air bag module to steering wheel.

4. Disconnect air bag connector.

5. Connect Rotunda Air Bag simulator tool No. 105-00009 or equivalent to vehicle harness at top of steering column.

6. Connect battery ground cable.

Arming

1. Disconnect battery ground cable.

2. Wait one minute for backup power supply to deplete stored energy.

3. Remove air bag simulator from vehicle harness at top of steering column.

4. Connect air bag connector.

5. Position air bag on steering wheel and secure with four bolts. Tighten to specifications.

6. Connect battery ground cable.

7. Place ignition switch from in the Run position and note air bag warning lamp operation. Indicator lamp should illuminate for approximately 6 seconds, and then turn off. If warning lamp does not illuminate or remains illuminated continuously or flashes, refer to "Diagnosis & Testing." Verify system operation.

ASPIRE
Disarming

1. Disconnect battery ground cable.

2. Wait one minute for back-up power supply to deplete stored energy.

3. Remove four bolts retaining air bag module to steering wheel.

4. Disconnect driver's side air bag connector.

5. Connect air bag simulator to vehicle harness above glove compartment.

6. Remove passenger's side air bag module.
7. Connect Rotunda Air Bag Simulator tool No. 105-00009 or equivalent to passenger's side air bag vehicle harness.
8. Connect battery ground cable.

Arming

1. Disconnect battery ground cable.
2. Wait one minute for backup power supply to deplete stored energy.
3. Remove air bag simulator from vehicle harness at top of steering column.
4. Connect driver's side air bag connector.
5. Position driver's side air bag on steering wheel and secure with four bolts. Tighten to specifications.
6. Remove air bag simulator from vehicle harness above glove compartment.
7. Install passenger's side air bag module.
8. Connect battery ground cable.
9. Place ignition switch from in the Run position and note air bag warning lamp operation. Indicator lamp should illuminate for approximately 6 seconds, and then turn off. If warning lamp does not illuminate or remains illuminated continuously or flashes, refer to "Diagnosis & Testing." Verify system operation.

ESCORT & TRACER

1994

Disarming

1. Disconnect battery positive cable.
2. Wait one minute for back-up power supply to deplete stored energy.
3. Remove bolts retaining air bag module to steering wheel.
4. Disconnect air bag connector.
5. Connect Rotunda Air Bag Simulator tool No. 105-00010 or equivalent to vehicle harness at top of steering column.
6. Connect battery positive cable.

Arming

1. Disconnect battery positive cable.
2. Wait one minute for backup power supply to deplete stored energy.
3. Remove air bag Simulator from vehicle harness at top of steering column.
4. Connect air bag connector.
5. Position air bag on steering wheel and secure with two bolts. Tighten to specifications.
6. Connect battery positive cable.
7. Place ignition switch from in the Run position and note air bag warning lamp operation. Indicator lamp should illuminate for approximately 6 seconds, and then turn off. If warning lamp does not illuminate or remains illuminated continuously or flashes, refer to "Diagnosis & Testing."

PRECAUTIONS

GENERAL SAFETY PRECAUTIONS

Always wear safety glasses when servicing an air bag vehicle and when handling an air bag module.

Because of the critical operating requirements of the system, do not attempt to repair sensor assemblies, the slip ring/clock spring assembly, the monitor assembly or the air bag module. Corrections are made by replacement only.

Never probe the connectors on the air bag module. Doing so may result in air bag deployment which could result in personal injury.

All component replacements and wiring repairs must be made with the air bag system disarmed. Refer to "Precautions" at the beginning of this section.

The instruction Disconnect always refers to a connector. Never detach a part from vehicle when instructed to Disconnect.

If a vehicle equipped with an air bag system is involved in a crash where the fenders or grille area have been damaged, the sensors in the area of damage must be replaced whether or not the air bag deployed.

HANDLING & STORAGE OF LIVE AIR BAG MODULE

When carrying a live air bag module, ensure bag and trim cover are pointed away from body. In the unlikely event of an accidental deployment, the bag will then deploy with minimal chance of injury. In addition, when placing a live air bag module on a bench or other surface, always place bag and trim cover face up, away from the surface. This will reduce the motion of the module if it is accidentally deployed.

HANDLING OF DEPLOYED AIR BAG MODULE

After deployment, the air bag surface may contain deposits of sodium hydroxide, a product of the gas generating combustion that is irritating to the skin. Always wear gloves and safety glasses when handling a deployed air bag module.

COLLISION INSPECTION

All system components should be inspected for dents, cracks, exposure to excessive heat and other damage. The air bag sliding contact, steering wheel and steering column should also be inspected. All air bag system wiring should be checked for chaffing and interference with other vehicle components. If a vehicle has any degree of frontal body damage, the dash sensors should be inspected for dents, cracks, deformation and other damage and replaced with a new unit as necessary. Dash sensors should also be checked for secure mounting. If deployment has take place the air bag modules must be replaced. When repairing the vehicle, the system should be disarmed as described under "Air Bag System Disarm-

ing & Arming." When performing service procedures, do not expose sensors or wiring or other air bag system components to heat guns, welding or spray guns. If deployment has take place, the air bag module(s) and clock spring should be replaced. When handling a deployed air bag module, wear gloves and safety glasses. Deployed air bag modules may contain deposits of sodium hydroxide.

DIAGNOSIS & TESTING

Refer to MOTOR's Air Bag Manual for system diagnosis and testing procedures.

COMPONENT SERVICE

The electrical circuit necessary for system deployment is powered directly from battery and back-up power supply. To avoid accidental deployment and possible personal injury, the air bag system must be disarmed prior to repairing or replacing any system components.

Fasteners used on air bag components must be replaced after removal. The fasteners are coated with an epoxy adhesive, making them non-reusable.

DRIVER AIR BAG MODULE, REPLACE

1. Disarm air bag system as described under "Air Bag System Disarming & Arming."
2. On 1994 Capri, Continental, Crown Victoria, Grand Marquis, Tempo, Topaz, Town Car and 1992-93 models except Probe, remove four nut and washer assemblies retaining air bag module to steering wheel.
3. On Mark VIII and 1994 Cougar, Escort, Mustang, Sable, Taurus, Thunderbird and Tracer, remove covers, then remove two screws retaining air bag module to steering wheel.
4. On Aspire and Probe, remove four bolts retaining air bag module to steering wheel.
5. On all models, disconnect air bag electrical connector from slip ring/clock spring connectors and remove air bag assembly, **Fig. 2.**
6. Reverse procedure to install, noting the following:
   a. Tighten mounting nut and washer assemblies to specifications.
   b. Arm air bag system as described under "Air Bag System Disarming & Arming."

PASSENGER AIR BAG MODULE, REPLACE

Aspire

1. Disarm air bag system as described under "Air Bag System Disarming & Arming."
2. Open glove compartment door, then remove two glove compartment retaining screws.
3. Remove glove compartment.
4. Remove four air bag module retaining bolts.

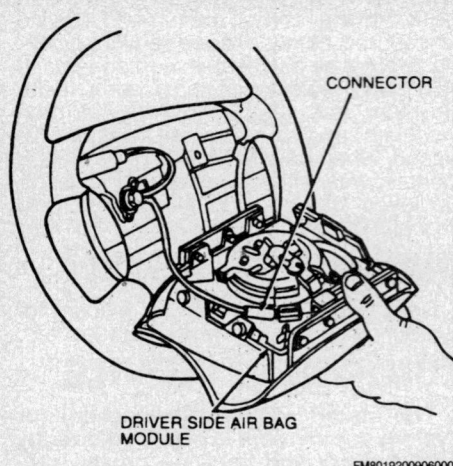

Fig. 2 Driver's side air bag module electrical connector disengagement

5. Push air bag module outward from inside instrument panel. **Do not handle air bag module by deployment doors.**
6. Disconnect electrical connector, then remove air bag module, **Fig. 3.**
7. Reverse procedure to install, noting the following:
   a. Tighten passenger air bag module bolts to specifications.
   b. Arm air bag system as described under "Air Bag System Disarming & Arming."

Capri

1. Disarm air bag system as described under "Air Bag System Disarming & Arming."
2. Remove three glove compartment retaining screws.
3. Remove glove compartment.
4. Remove by-pass air flow to heater ducts.
5. Remove attaching screw and smaller vent tube.
6. Remove four air bag module retaining bolts.
7. Disconnect electrical connector, then remove air bag module, **Fig. 4.**
8. Reverse procedure to install, noting the following:
   a. Tighten passenger air bag module bolts to specifications.
   b. Arm air bag system as described under "Air Bag System Disarming & Arming."

Continental

1. Disarm air bag system as described under "Air Bag System Disarming & Arming."
2. Open glove compartment and rotate down completely, past stops.
3. Disconnect passenger air bag electrical connector.
4. Remove two bolts securing lower passenger air bag mounting bracket to instrument panel.
5. Remove instrument panel shelf molding.
6. Remove two screws securing front of air bag to instrument panel.

7. Carefully remove passenger air bag by pushing on air bag assembly from inside panel. **Do not handle air bag by grabbing edges of deployment doors.**
8. Reverse procedure to install, noting the following:
   a. Tighten lower passenger air bag mounting bracket bolts and attaching screws to specifications.
   b. Arm air bag system as described under "Air Bag System Disarming & Arming."

Cougar & Thunderbird

1. Disarm air bag system as described under "Air Bag System Disarming & Arming."
2. Using a small screwdriver, detach dampening rod from righthand side of glove compartment.
3. Pull lefthand side of glove compartment inward and allow glove compartment to drop downward.
4. Remove air duct attaching screws, then the air duct.
5. Remove the two vertically positioned bolts from each side of the air module.
6. Remove the two remaining air bag module attaching bolts.
7. Push air bag module outward from inside instrument panel. **Do not handle air bag module by deployment doors.**
8. Disconnect electrical connector, then remove air bag module.
9. Reverse procedure to install, noting the following:
   a. Tighten passenger air bag module bolts to specifications.
   b. Arm air bag system as described under "Air Bag System Disarming & Arming."

Crown Victoria & Grand Marquis

1. Disarm air bag system as described under "Air Bag System Disarming & Arming."
2. Remove righthand instrument panel lower molding.
3. **On Crown Victoria,** remove righthand instrument cluster finish panel retaining screws and remove panel.
4. **On Grand Marquis,** remove righthand register applique retaining screws and remove applique.
5. Remove cluster finish panel retaining screws and remove panel.
6. **On all models,** open glove compartment, press sides inward and lower glove compartment to floor.
7. Through glove compartment opening, remove two front air bag module retaining bolts.
8. Remove two rear air bag module retaining screws. Disconnect electrical connector and remove module, **Fig. 5.**
9. Reverse procedure to install, noting the following:
   a. Tighten screws to specifications.
   b. Arm air bag system as described under "Air Bag System Disarming & Arming."

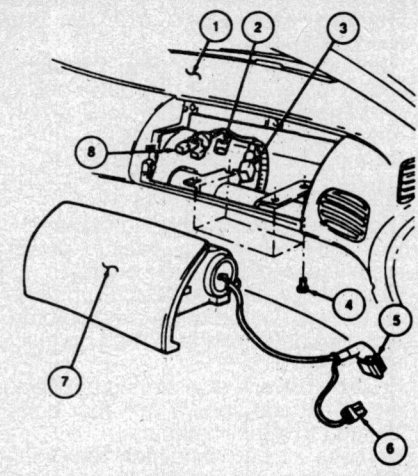

Fig. 3 Passenger's side air bag module replacement. Aspire

Mark VIII

1. Disarm air bag system as described under "Air Bag System Disarming & Arming."
2. Remove righthand end finish panel, then the lefthand end finish panel.
3. Remove instrument panel lower trim cover.
4. Remove lower steering column shroud.
5. Place ignition switch in the Rum position, then depress ignition key warning switch retainer pin through access hole. Remove the ignition key warning switch.
6. Remove upper steering column shroud, then remove two screws and upper steering column cover.
7. Remove lefthand finish panel to instrument panel attaching screws, then pull finish panel rearward and disconnect the two electrical connectors.
8. Detach righthand side of instrument cluster from the eight snap in retainers.
9. Open glove compartment, then detach glove compartment door cable and pin.
10. Press side of glove compartment inward and lower glove compartment to floor.
11. Remove two side defroster duct retaining screws.
12. Through glove compartment opening, remove two lower air bag module retaining screws.
13. From side of air bag cover remove the three remaining air module retaining screws.
14. Disconnect electrical connector from lefthand side of air bag, then remove air bag module, **Fig. 6.**
15. Reverse procedure to install, noting the following:
   a. Tighten screws to specifications.
   b. Arm air bag system as described under "Air Bag System Disarming & Arming."

Mustang

1. Disarm air bag system as described under "Air Bag System Disarming &

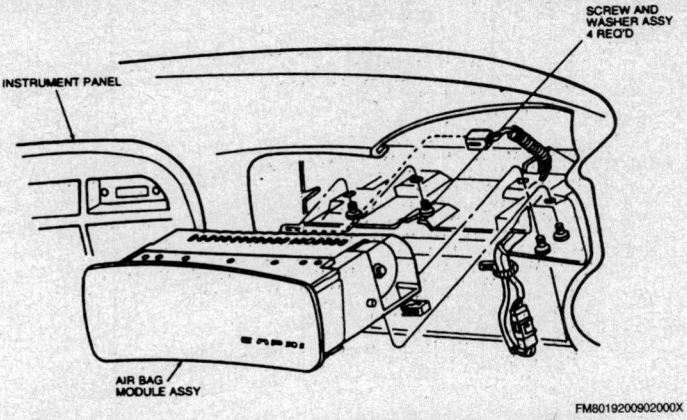

Fig. 4 Passenger's side air bag module replacement. Capri

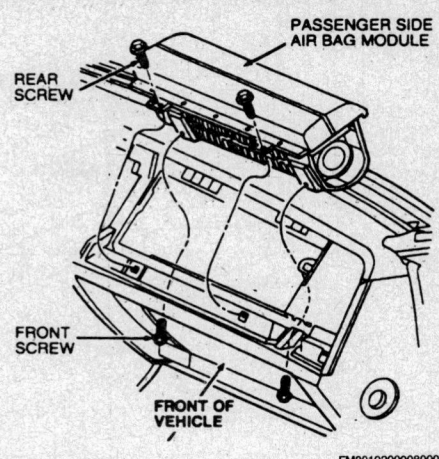

Fig. 5 Passenger's side air bag module replacement. Crown Victoria & Grand Marquis

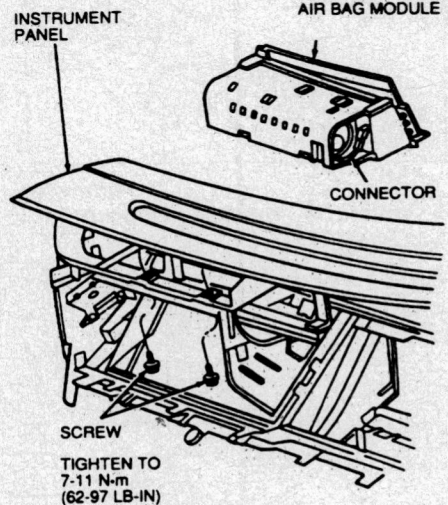

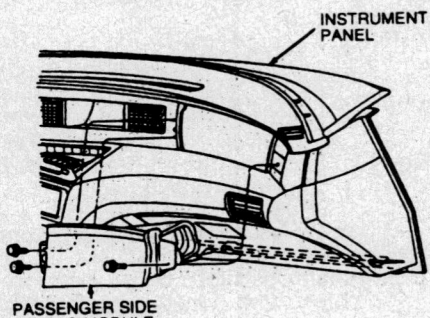

Fig. 6 Passenger's side air bag module replacement. Mark VIII, Sable & Taurus

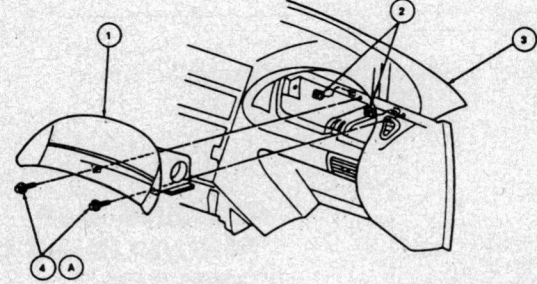

Fig. 7 Passenger's side air bag module replacement. Mustang

Arming.''
2. Open glove compartment door, then push inward on side of glove compartment. Lower glove compartment assembly to floor.
3. Remove two attaching screws, then the right hand A/C duct.
4. Remove the two air bag module to instrument panel reinforcement attaching bolts.
5. Disconnect air bag electrical connector.

6. Detach air bag electrical connector to instrument panel reinforcement retainer.
7. Pull each corner of air bag module to disengage from instrument panel.
8. Push air bag module outward from inside instrument panel. **Do not handle air bag module by deployment doors.**
9. Remove air bag module, **Fig. 7.**
10. Reverse procedure to install, noting the following:
    a. Tighten passenger air bag module bolts to specifications.
    b. Arm air bag system as described under ''Air Bag System Disarming & Arming.''

Probe

1. Disarm air bag system as described under ''Air Bag System Disarming & Arming.''
2. From under lefthand side of instrument panel pad, disconnect two air bag module electrical connectors.
3. Remove glove compartment.
4. Remove glove compartment upper cover attaching screws and the cover.
5. Disconnect air bag module electrical connectors.
6. Remove four air bag module to instrument panel attaching bolts.
7. Push air bag module outward from inside instrument panel. **Do not handle**

air bag module by deployment doors.
8. Remove air bag module, **Fig. 8.**
9. Reverse procedure to install, noting the following:
    a. Tighten passenger air bag module bolts to specifications.
    b. Arm air bag system as described under ''Air Bag System Disarming & Arming.''

Sable & Taurus

1. Disarm air bag system as described under ''Air Bag System Disarming & Arming.''
2. Remove right and left finish panels.
3. Remove instrument panel finish panel retaining spear clips.
4. Open glove compartment, press sides inward and lower to floor.
5. Through glove compartment opening, remove two lower air bag module retaining bolts.
6. Remove four remaining air bag module retaining screws from side of air bag cover.
7. Disconnect electrical connector attached to left side air bag and carefully remove module, **Fig. 6.**
8. Reverse procedure to install, noting the following:
    a. Tighten screws to specifications.
    b. Arm air bag system as described under ''Air Bag System Disarming

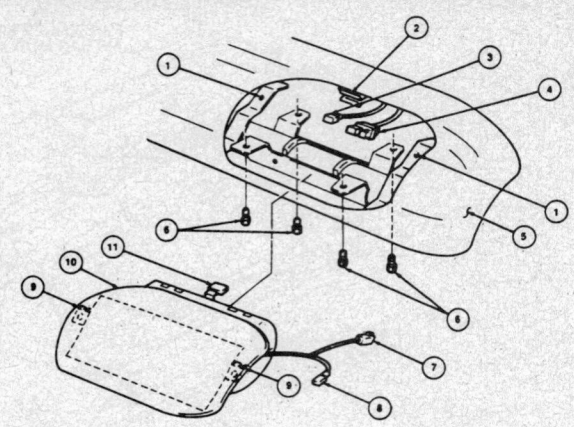

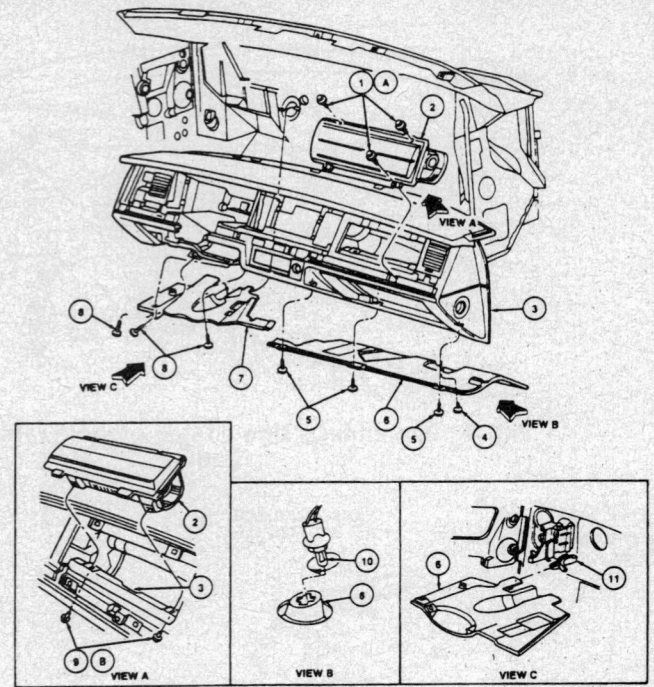

Item	Part Number	Description
1	—	Passenger Side Air Bag Module Guide Pin Holes
2	—	Clip
3	—	Electrical Connector (BLUE)
4	—	Electrical Connector (ORANGE)
5	04262	Instrument Panel Pad
6	—	Passenger Side Air Bag Module Bolts
7	—	Electrical Connector (ORANGE)
8	—	Electrical Connector (BLUE)
9	—	Passenger Side Air Bag Module Guide Pins
10	044A74	Passenger Side Air Bag Module
11	—	Tab

FM8019200898000X

Fig. 8　Passenger's side air bag module replacement. Probe

FM8019200907000X

Fig. 9　Passenger's side air bag module replacement. Town Car

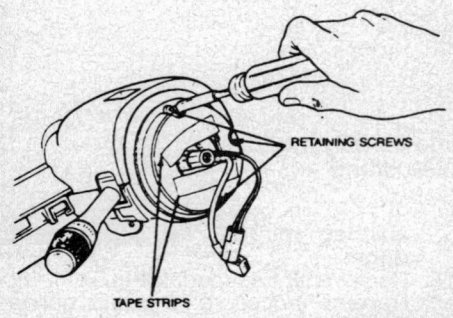

FM8019200905000X

Fig. 10　Slip ring/sliding contact taped in position

Town Car

& Arming."

1. Disarm air bag system as described under "Air Bag System Disarming & Arming."
2. Remove instrument panel moldings.
3. Remove instrument panel finish panel retaining screws and remove panel.
4. Open glove compartment, press sides inward and lower glove compartment to floor.
5. Through glove compartment opening, remove two lower air bag module retaining bolts.
6. Remove four remaining air bag module retaining screws, disconnect electrical connector and remove module, **Fig. 9.**
7. Reverse procedure to install, noting the following:
   a. Tighten screws to specifications.
   b. Arm air bag system as described under "Air Bag System Disarming & Arming."

AIR BAG SLIP RING/SLIDING CONTACT, REPLACE

Removal

1. Place front wheels in the straight ahead position.
2. Disarm air bag system as described under "Air Bag System Disarming & Arming."
3. Remove driver's side air bag module as described under "Driver Air Bag Module, Replace."
4. Remove steering wheel attaching bolt or nut.
5. Remove steering wheel from upper shaft using steering wheel remover tool No. T67L-3600-A or equivalent.
6. Remove upper and lower shrouds, if necessary.
7. Disconnect air bag slip ring connector from column harness. **Before removing air bag clock spring type slip ring from steering shaft, clock spring must be taped, Fig. 10, to prevent clock spring rotor from being turned accidentally and damaging clock spring.**
8. Remove two retaining screws and the slip ring/sliding contact.

Installation

1222222Service replacement slip ring/sliding contact will contain a locking insert to prevent rotation. This insert should not be removed until slip ring is installed.

1. **On Aspire,** if sliding contact has been accidentally rotated, proceed as follows:
   a. Rotate sliding contact in the clock-

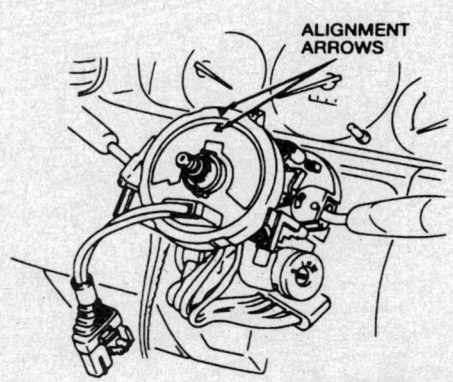

FM8019400901000X

Fig. 11　Sliding contact arrow mark alignment. Aspire

wise direction until the stop is contacted.
   b. Rotate sliding contact approximately $2\frac{3}{4}$ turns counterclockwise.
   c. Align arrow marks on sliding contact and sliding contact housing, **Fig. 11.**
2. **On all models,** place air bag slip ring/sliding contact onto steering shaft and install two retaining screws that attach slip ring to retainer plate, ensuring ground wire pigtail is secured with lower retaining screw.
3. If a new slip ring/sliding contact is being installed, remove locking insert.
4. Connect slip ring/slip ring wire to column harness.
5. Install upper and lower shrouds.
6. Position steering wheel on end of steering wheel shaft, aligning mark on steering wheel with mark on shaft to

ensure straight ahead steering wheel position corresponds to straight ahead position of front wheels.

7. Install steering wheel attaching nut.
8. Install driver's side air bag module as described under "Driver Air Bag Module, Replace."
9. Arm air bag system as described under "Air Bag System Disarming & Arming."

SENSOR, REPLACE

ASPIRE

Front Sensor

1. Disarm air bag system as described under "Air Bag System Disarming & Arming."
2. Raise and support vehicle, then remove wheel and tire assembly.
3. Remove front fender splash shield.
4. Disconnect front sensor electrical connector.
5. Remove front sensor attaching bolts and front sensor.
6. Reverse procedure to install, noting the following:
   a. Position sensor with arrow on top toward front of vehicle.
   b. Tighten screws to specifications.
   c. Arm air bag system as described under "Air Bag System Disarming & Arming."

Center Sensor

1. Disarm air bag system as described under "Air Bag System Disarming & Arming."
2. Remove center sensor attaching bolts.
3. Disconnect center sensor electrical connectors, then remove center sensor.
4. Reverse procedure to install, noting the following:
   a. Tighten screws to specifications.
   b. Arm air bag system as described under "Air Bag System Disarming & Arming."

Safing Sensor

1. Disarm air bag system as described under "Air Bag System Disarming & Arming."
2. Remove driver's side air bag as described under "Air Bag, Replace."
3. Remove steering wheel attaching nut, then the steering wheel.
4. Remove turn signal and windshield washer switch.
5. Remove lower steering column shaft bolt.
6. Remove two lower steering column mounting bracket nuts.
7. Remove two upper steering column mounting bolts.
8. Place alignment marks on lower steering column shaft and steering gear input shaft for use during installation.
9. Remove steering column.
10. Remove two instrument cluster finish panel attaching screws, then the finish panel.
11. Disconnect speedometer cable at transaxle.

12. Remove four instrument cluster attaching screws.
13. Pull instrument cluster away from instrument panel, then disconnect electrical connectors and speedometer cable.
14. Remove the instrument cluster.
15. Remove fuse panel to instrument panel attaching screws, then remove instrument panel lower finish panel.
16. Remove parking brake console panel.
17. Remove air bag diagnostic monitor as described under "Diagnostic Monitor, Replace."
18. Remove screws attaching the climate control panel, then disconnect cables and remove climate control panel.
19. Remove glove compartment.
20. Remove passenger's side air bag as described under "Passenger Air Bag, Replace."
21. Remove instrument panel screw access covers.
22. Remove instrument panel to mounting bracket lower attaching bolts.
23. Remove instrument panel side mounting bolts.
24. Loosen hood release cable lock nut, then detach cable.
25. Move instrument panel forward, then disconnect electrical connectors and cables.
26. Remove instrument panel.
27. Remove three defroster duct attaching screws, then the defroster duct.
28. Disconnect safing sensor electrical connector.
29. Remove three safing sensor attaching nuts, then the safing sensor.
30. Reverse procedure to install, noting the following:
   a. Tighten screws to specifications.
   b. Arm air bag system as described under "Air Bag System Disarming & Arming."

CAPRI

Front Sensor

1. Disarm air bag system as described under "Air Bag System Disarming & Arming."
2. For righthand side, remove headlamp bezel and splash shield.
3. Disconnect sensor electrical connector.
4. Remove sensor attaching bolts, then the sensor.
5. Reverse procedure to install, noting the following:
   a. Position sensor with arrow on top toward front of vehicle.
   b. Tighten screws to specifications.
   c. Arm air bag system as described under "Air Bag System Disarming & Arming."

Center Sensor

1. Disarm air bag system as described under "Air Bag System Disarming & Arming."
2. Remove front bumper assembly from vehicle.
3. Disconnect sensor electrical connector.
4. Remove sensor attaching bolts, then

the sensor.
5. Reverse procedure to install, noting the following:
   a. Position sensor with arrow on top toward front of vehicle.
   b. Tighten screws to specifications.
   c. Arm air bag system as described under "Air Bag System Disarming & Arming."

CONTINENTAL

Right Front Sensor

1. Disarm air bag system as described under "Air Bag System Disarming & Arming."
2. Remove heated windshield relay, if equipped.
3. Disconnect right front sensor electrical connector.
4. Remove screws attaching sensor to righthand fender apron, then remove sensor.
5. Reverse procedure to install, noting the following:
   a. Position sensor with arrow toward front of vehicle.
   b. Tighten attaching screws to specifications.
   c. Arm air bag system as described under "Air Bag System Disarming & Arming."

Left Front Sensor

1. Disarm air bag system as described under "Air Bag System Disarming & Arming."
2. Disconnect left front sensor electrical connector.
3. Remove screws attaching sensor to lefthand fender apron, then remove sensor.
4. Reverse procedure to install, noting the following:
   a. Tighten retaining screws to specifications.
   b. Arm air bag system as described under "Air Bag System Disarming & Arming."

Rear Sensor

1. Disarm air bag system as described under "Air bag System Disarming."
2. Remove two bolts attaching rear sensor to dash panel in engine compartment.
3. Disconnect sensor electrical connector and remove sensor.
4. Reverse procedure to install, noting the following:
   a. Tighten retaining screws and attaching nuts to specifications.
   b. Arm air bag system as described under "Air Bag System Disarming & Arming."

COUGAR & THUNDERBIRD

Right Front Sensor

1. Disarm air bag system as described under "Air Bag System Disarming & Arming."
2. Remove upper radiator sight shield.
3. Disconnect right front sensor electrical connector.
4. Remove screws attaching sensor, then remove sensor.

5. Reverse procedure to install, noting the following:
   a. Position sensor with arrow toward front of vehicle.
   b. Tighten attaching screws to specifications.
   c. Arm air bag system as described under "Air Bag System Disarming & Arming."

Left Front Sensor

1. Disarm air bag system as described under "Air Bag System Disarming & Arming."
2. Remove radiator upper sight shield.
3. Remove windshield washer reservoir.
4. Disconnect left front sensor electrical connector.
5. Remove sensor retaining screws, then remove sensor.
6. Reverse procedure to install, noting the following:
   a. Tighten retaining screws to specifications.
   b. Arm air bag system as described under "Air Bag System Disarming & Arming."

CROWN VICTORIA, GRAND MARQUIS & TOWN CAR

Right Front Sensor

1. Disarm air bag system as described under "Air Bag System Disarming & Arming."
2. Remove battery, if necessary.
3. Disconnect right front sensor electrical connector.
4. Remove screws attaching sensor to righthand fender apron, then remove sensor.
5. Reverse procedure to install, noting the following:
   a. Position sensor with arrow toward front of vehicle.
   b. Tighten attaching screws to specifications.
   c. Arm air bag system as described under "Air Bag System Disarming & Arming."

Left Front Sensor

1. Disarm air bag system as described under "Air Bag System Disarming & Arming."
2. Remove washer fluid reservoir, if necessary.
3. Disconnect left front sensor electrical connector.
4. Remove screws attaching sensor to lefthand fender apron, then remove sensor.
5. Reverse procedure to install, noting the following:
   a. Tighten retaining screws to specifications.
   b. Arm air bag system as described under "Air Bag System Disarming & Arming."

Rear Sensor

1. Disarm air bag system as described under "Air Bag System Disarming & Arming."
2. Remove lefthand kick panel.
3. Remove connector bracket.

4. Disconnect rear sensor wiring connector from wiring assembly connector.
5. Remove two screws retaining rear sensor to lefthand kick panel, then remove sensor.
6. Reverse procedure to install, noting the following:
   a. Tighten retaining screws to specifications.
   b. Arm air bag system as described under "Air Bag System Disarming & Arming."

ESCORT & TRACER

Right Front Sensor

1. Disarm air bag system as described under "Air Bag System Disarming & Arming."
2. Remove upper radiator deflector.
3. Remove radiator grille.
4. Remove righthand parking lamp.
5. Remove righthand headlamp.
6. Remove two righthand sensor bracket retaining bolts.
7. Remove two righthand sensor bracket nuts, then remove mounting bracket.
8. Remove four radiator bracket bolts, then position radiator rearward.
9. Disconnect sensor electrical connector.
10. Remove three righthand sensor and bracket bolts, then remove sensor.
11. Reverse procedure to install, noting the following:
    a. Tighten retaining screws to specifications.
    b. Arm air bag system as described under "Air Bag System Disarming & Arming."

Left Front Sensor

1. Disarm air bag system as described under "Air Bag System Disarming & Arming."
2. **On models equipped with 1.9L/4-116 engine and A/C,** remove upper radiator deflector.
3. **On all models,** remove radiator grille.
4. Remove lefthand parking lamp.
5. Remove lefthand headlamp.
6. Remove two lefthand sensor bracket retaining bolts, then disconnect electrical connector.
7. Remove two engine compartment fuse junction panel nuts, then position junction panel aside.
8. **On models equipped with 1.8L/4-112 engine,** remove two ignition coil nuts and position ignition coil aside. Remove ignition coil mounting bracket.
9. **On models with 1.9L/4-116 engine,** remove three ignition control module bracket nuts, then position ignition control module and bracket aside.
10. **On all models,** remove A/C line bracket nut, then position A/C line aside.
11. Remove four radiator bracket bolts, then position radiator rearward.
12. Remove three lefthand sensor and bracket bolts, then remove lefthand sensor. Note wiring harness routing

for use during installation.
13. Reverse procedure to install, noting the following:
    a. Tighten retaining screws to specifications.
    b. Arm air bag system as described under "Air Bag System Disarming & Arming."

Safing Sensor

1. Disarm air bag system as described under "Air Bag System Disarming & Arming."
2. Loosen lefthand front door scuff plate attaching screws.
3. Remove two quarter trim panel grommets.
4. Detach retainer, then remove cowl side trim panel.
5. Remove fuse panel retaining nut, then detach fuse panel from upper retainer and position aside.
6. Disconnect safing sensor electrical connector.
7. Remove safing sensor retaining bolts, then the safing sensor
8. Reverse procedure to install, noting the following:
   a. Tighten retaining screws to specifications.
   b. Arm air bag system as described under "Air Bag System Disarming & Arming."

MARK VII

Right Front Sensor

1. Disarm air bag system as described under "Air Bag System Disarming & Arming."
2. Remove or loosen righthand radiator clamp.
3. Remove air filter assembly.
4. Disconnect sensor electrical connector and wiring locator.
5. Remove screws retaining sensor to bracket, then remove sensor.
6. Reverse procedure to install, noting the following:
   a. Position sensor with arrow pointing toward front of vehicle.
   b. Tighten retaining screws to specifications.
   c. Arm air bag system as described under "Air Bag System Disarming & Arming."

Left Front Sensor

1. Disarm air bag system as described under "Air Bag System Disarming & Arming."
2. Remove battery and battery tray.
3. Disconnect left front sensor electrical connector.
4. Remove sensor retaining screws, then remove sensor from lefthand radiator support.
5. Remove screws attaching sensor to lefthand fender apron, then remove sensor.
6. Reverse procedure to install, noting the following:
   a. Tighten retaining screws to specifications.
   b. Arm air bag system as described under "Air Bag System Disarming & Arming."

Front Center Sensor

1. Disarm air bag system as described under "Air Bag System Disarming & Arming."
2. Remove or loosen righthand radiator clamp.
3. Remove air filter assembly.
4. Disconnect sensor electrical connector and wiring locator.
5. Remove screws retaining sensor to bracket, then remove sensor.
6. Reverse procedure to install, noting the following:
   a. Position sensor with arrow pointing toward front of vehicle.
   b. Tighten retaining screws to specifications.
   c. Arm air bag system as described under "Air Bag System Disarming & Arming."

Rear Sensor

1. Disarm air bag system as described under "Air Bag System Disarming & Arming."
2. Remove hood release handle and parking brake assembly.
3. Remove lefthand kick panel.
4. Disconnect rear sensor wiring connector from wiring assembly connector.
5. Remove two screws retaining rear sensor to lefthand kick panel, then remove sensor.
6. Reverse procedure to install, noting the following:
   a. Tighten retaining screws to specifications.
   b. Arm air bag system as described under "Air Bag System Disarming & Arming."

MARK VIII

Front Sensor

1. Disarm air bag system as described under "Air Bag System Disarming & Arming."
2. Remove radiator upper sight shield.
3. Disconnect sensor electrical connector and wiring locator.
4. Remove screws retaining sensor to bracket, then remove sensor.
5. Reverse procedure to install, noting the following:
   a. Position sensor with arrow pointing toward front of vehicle.
   b. Tighten retaining screws to specifications.
   c. Arm air bag system as described under "Air Bag System Disarming & Arming."

Safing Sensor

1. Disarm air bag system as described under "Air Bag System Disarming & Arming."
2. Remove lefthand kick panel.
3. Disconnect rear sensor wiring connector from wiring assembly connector.
4. Remove two screws retaining rear sensor to lefthand kick panel, then remove sensor.
5. Reverse procedure to install, noting the following:

a. Tighten retaining screws to specifications.
b. Arm air bag system as described under "Air Bag System Disarming & Arming."

MUSTANG

Right Front Sensor

1. Disarm air bag system as described under "Air Bag System Disarming & Arming."
2. Remove air cleaner assembly.
3. Disconnect right front sensor electrical connector.
4. Remove screws attaching sensor, then remove sensor.
5. Reverse procedure to install, noting the following:
   a. Position sensor with arrow toward front of vehicle.
   b. Tighten attaching screws to specifications.
   c. Arm air bag system as described under "Air Bag System Disarming & Arming."

Left Front Sensor

1. Disarm air bag system as described under "Air Bag System Disarming & Arming."
2. Remove battery, then plastic wiring shield.
3. Disconnect left front sensor electrical connector.
4. Remove lefthand sensor support bracket.
5. Remove sensor retaining screws, then remove sensor.
6. Reverse procedure to install, noting the following:
   a. Tighten retaining screws to specifications.
   b. Arm air bag system as described under "Air Bag System Disarming & Arming."

Front Center Sensor (1992–93)

1. Disarm air bag system as described under "Air Bag System Disarming & Arming."
2. Loosen fascia, radiator and A/C condenser.
3. Remove air filter assembly.
4. Disconnect sensor electrical connector and wiring locator.
5. Remove screws retaining sensor to bracket, then remove sensor.
6. Reverse procedure to install, noting the following:
   a. Position sensor with arrow pointing toward front of vehicle.
   b. Tighten retaining screws to specifications.
   c. Arm air bag system as described under "Air Bag System Disarming & Arming."

Rear Sensor (1992–93)

1. Disarm air bag system as described under "Air Bag System Disarming & Arming."
2. Remove rear seat cushion and quarter trim panel, then remove two screws retaining rear sensor to B-pillar.

3. Disconnect sensor electrical connector and remove sensor.
4. Reverse procedure to install, noting the following:
   a. Tighten retaining screws and attaching nuts to specifications.
   b. Arm air bag system as described under "Air Bag System Disarming & Arming."

PROBE

Left & Right Front Sensors

1. Disarm air bag system as described under "Air Bag System Disarming & Arming."
2. Remove front bumper cover.
3. Raise and support front of vehicle, then remove and tire assembly.
4. Remove front fender splash shield.
5. Disconnect sensor electrical connector.
6. Remove sensor attaching bolts, then the sensor.
7. Reverse procedure to install, noting the following:
   a. Position sensor with arrow toward front of vehicle.
   b. Tighten attaching screws to specifications.
   c. Arm air bag system as described under "Air Bag System Disarming & Arming."

Center Front Sensor

1. Disarm air bag system as described under "Air Bag System Disarming & Arming."
2. Remove radiator upper air deflector.
3. Remove sensor attaching bolts, then disconnect electrical connectors and remove sensor.
4. Reverse procedure to install, noting the following:
   a. Position sensor with arrow toward front of vehicle.
   b. Tighten attaching screws to specifications.
   c. Arm air bag system as described under "Air Bag System Disarming & Arming."

Safing Sensor

1. Disarm air bag system as described under "Air Bag System Disarming & Arming."
2. Remove console front finish panels.
3. Disconnect sensor electrical connector.
4. Remove sensor attaching bolts, then the sensor.
5. Reverse procedure to install, noting the following:
   a. Position sensor with arrow toward front of vehicle.
   b. Tighten attaching screws to specifications.
   c. Arm air bag system as described under "Air Bag System Disarming & Arming."

SABLE & TAURUS

Right Front Sensor

1. Disarm air bag system as described under "Air Bag System Disarming & Arming."

2. Remove front bumper assembly.
3. Disconnect right front sensor electrical connector.
4. Remove one wiring retainer on rail, and two screws attaching sensor to righthand lower outer radiator support.
5. Remove screws attaching sensor to righthand fender apron, then remove sensor.
6. Reverse procedure to install, noting the following:
   a. Position sensor with arrow toward front of vehicle.
   b. Tighten attaching screws to specifications.
   c. Arm air bag system as described under "Air Bag System Disarming & Arming."

Left Front Sensor

1. Disarm air bag system as described under "Air Bag System Disarming & Arming."
2. Remove front bumper, then the inner fender splash shield.
3. Disconnect left front sensor electrical connector.
4. Remove screws attaching sensor to lefthand fender apron, then remove sensor.
5. Reverse procedure to install, noting the following:
   a. Tighten retaining screws to specifications.
   b. Arm air bag system as described under "Air Bag System Disarming & Arming."

Center Front Sensor

1. Disarm air bag system as described under "Air bag System Disarming."
2. Remove radiator sight shield.
3. Disconnect center front sensor electrical connector.
4. Remove screws retaining center front sensor to radiator support, then remove sensor.
5. Reverse procedure to install, noting the following.
   a. Position sensor with arrow on top pointing toward front of vehicle.
   b. Tighten screws to specifications.
   c. Rearm air bag system as described under "Air bag System Disarming."
   d. Verify air bag indicator lamp.

Rear Sensor Center Cowl

1. Disarm air bag system as described under "Air Bag System Disarming & Arming."
2. Remove two bolts attaching rear sensor to dash panel in engine compartment.
3. Disconnect sensor electrical connector and remove sensor.
4. Reverse procedure to install, noting the following:
   a. Tighten retaining screws and attaching nuts to specifications.
   b. Arm air bag system as described under "Air Bag System Disarming & Arming."

Rear Lefthand Kick Panel Sensor

1. Disarm air bag system as described under "Air Bag System Disarming & Arming."
2. Remove lefthand kick panel.
3. Remove connector bracket.
4. Disconnect rear sensor wiring connector from wiring assembly connector.
5. Remove two screws retaining rear sensor to lefthand kick panel, then remove sensor.
6. Reverse procedure to install, noting the following:
   a. Tighten retaining screws to specifications.
   b. Arm air bag system as described under "Air Bag System Disarming & Arming."

TEMPO & TOPAZ

Right Front Sensor

1. Disarm air bag system as described under "Air Bag System Disarming & Arming."
2. Remove inner fender splash shield.
3. Disconnect right front sensor electrical connector.
4. Remove screws attaching sensor to righthand fender apron, then remove sensor.
5. Reverse procedure to install, noting the following:
   a. Position sensor with arrow toward front of vehicle.
   b. Tighten attaching screws to specifications.
   c. Arm air bag system as described under "Air Bag System Disarming & Arming."

Left Front Sensor

1. Disarm air bag system as described under "Air Bag System Disarming & Arming."
2. Remove inner fender splash shield.
3. Disconnect left front sensor electrical connector.
4. Remove screws attaching sensor to lefthand fender apron, then remove sensor.
5. Reverse procedure to install, noting the following:
   a. Tighten retaining screws to specifications.
   b. Arm air bag system as described under "Air Bag System Disarming & Arming."

Front Center Sensor

1. Disarm air bag system as described under "Air Bag System Disarming & Arming."
2. Remove air induction resonator.
3. Remove air filter assembly.
4. Disconnect sensor electrical connector and wiring locator.
5. Remove screws retaining sensor to bracket, then remove sensor.
6. Reverse procedure to install, noting the following:
   a. Position sensor with arrow pointing toward front of vehicle.
   b. Tighten retaining screws to specifi-

cations.
   c. Arm air bag system as described under "Air Bag System Disarming & Arming."

Rear Sensor

1. Disarm air bag system as described under "Air Bag System Disarming & Arming."
2. Remove two nuts attaching rear sensor to dash panel in engine compartment.
3. Disconnect sensor electrical connector and remove sensor.
4. Reverse procedure to install, noting the following:
   a. Tighten retaining screws and attaching nuts to specifications.
   b. Arm air bag system as described under "Air Bag System Disarming & Arming."

DIAGNOSTIC MONITOR, REPLACE

Aspire

1. Disarm air bag system as described under "Air Bag System Disarming & Arming."
2. Locate diagnostic monitor assembly (blue box) mounted behind radio and shift control console.
3. Remove shift control console panel.
4. Disconnect electrical connectors.
5. Remove diagnostic monitor attaching nuts, then the monitor.
6. Reverse procedure to install, noting the following:
   a. Tighten attaching screws to specifications.
   b. Arm air bag system as described under "Air Bag System Disarming & Arming."

Capri

1. Disarm air bag system as described under "Air bag System Disarming."
2. Locate diagnostic monitor assembly (blue box) mounted behind fuse panel.
3. Depress two tabs and disengage monitor.
4. Disconnect electrical connectors and remove monitor.
5. Reverse procedure to install, noting the following:
   a. Tighten attaching screws to specifications.
   b. Arm air bag system as described under "Air Bag System Disarming & Arming."

Continental, Tempo & Topaz

1. Disarm air bag system as described under "Air Bag System Disarming & Arming."
2. Remove screws attaching steering

column opening cover to instrument panel, then remove the cover.

3. Remove four bolster attaching bolts, then remove the bolster.
4. Disconnect diagnostic monitor electrical wiring connectors.
5. Remove screws attaching diagnostic monitor and bracket assembly to instrument panel brace, then remove assembly.
6. **On Continental,** remove two screws attaching monitor to bracket.
7. **On Tempo & Topaz,** depress tabs and remove monitor from bracket.
8. **On all models,** reverse procedure to install, noting the following:
   a. Tighten attaching screws to specifications.
   b. Arm air bag system as described under "Air Bag System Disarming & Arming."

Crown Victoria, Grand Marquis & Town Car

1. Disarm air bag system as described under "Air Bag System Disarming & Arming."
2. Open glove compartment door and depress sides to release retaining tabs. Allow door to drop down.
3. Depress mounting tabs on diagnostic monitor. Slide monitor off of bracket.
4. Disconnect diagnostic monitor electrical wiring connectors and remove monitor.
5. Reverse procedure to install, noting the following:
   a. Rearm air bag system as described under "Air bag System Disarming."
   b. Verify air bag indicator lamp.

Escort & Tracer

1. Disarm air bag system as described under "Air Bag System Disarming & Arming."
2. Locate diagnostic monitor assembly mounted behind shift control console.
3. Remove shift control console panel.
4. slide diagnostic monitor from mounting bracket.
5. Disconnect electrical connectors.
6. Reverse procedure to install. Arm air bag system as described under "Air Bag System Disarming & Arming."

Mark VII, Mark VIII, Sable & Taurus

1. Disarm air bag system as described under "Air Bag System Disarming & Arming."
2. Lower glove compartment past stops.
3. **On Mark VII,** remove heater duct above glove compartment.
4. **On all models,** disconnect two electrical connectors, then remove monitor.
5. Reverse procedure to install, noting the following:

a. Rearm air bag system as described under "Air bag System Disarming."
b. Verify air bag indicator lamp.

Mustang

1. Disarm air bag system as described under "Air bag System Disarming."
2. Remove radio, then disconnect diagnostic monitor (blue box with two connectors mounted below climate control head).
3. Remove screws attaching diagnostic monitor and bracket on instrument panel brace and remove assembly.
4. Reverse procedure to install, noting the following:
   a. Tighten attaching screws to specifications.
   b. Arm air bag system as described under "Air Bag System Disarming & Arming."

Probe

1. Disarm air bag system as described under "Air Bag System Disarming & Arming."
2. Locate diagnostic monitor (blue box) located under instrument panel near speed control amplifier.
3. Disconnect electrical connectors, then slide diagnostic monitor from bracket.
4. Reverse procedure to install. Arm air bag system as described under "Air Bag System Disarming & Arming."

BACKUP POWER SUPPLY, REPLACE

Except 1992 Capri & 1993 (Early Production) Capri

The backup power supply is combined with the diagnostic monitor. Refer to "Diagnostic Monitor, Replace" for replacement procedure.

1992 Capri & 1993 (Early Production) Capri

1. Disarm air bag system as described under "Air Bag System Disarming & Arming."
2. Open glove box past stops, press in sides.
3. Remove power supply (blue box, one connector) retaining screws.
4. Disconnect connector from power supply unit.
5. Reverse procedure to install. Arm air bag system as described under "Air Bag System Disarming & Arming."

AIR BAG DISPOSAL

Proper air bag disposal procedures must be observed when scrapping a vehi-

cle containing a deployed air bag, scrapping a vehicle with a live air bag, disposing of a live but electrically inoperative air bag module or scrapping a deployed air bag.

AIR BAG DEPLOYMENT

Remote deployment is to be performed outdoors with all personnel a minimum of 20 feet away to ensure safety.

1. Remove driver and passenger air bag modules from vehicle.
2. Cut the two module connector wires and strip 1 inch of insulation from the ends. Obtain two wires a minimum of 20 feet long. Connect one end of each wire to each of the air bag module wires.
3. Place the module with the trim cover facing upward on a flat surface in a remote area such as a parking lot or field. **Do not place the module with the trim cover facing down, as the forces of the deploying air bag may cause the module to ricochet and cause personal injury.**
4. Remaining at least 20 feet away from the module, deploy the air bag by touching the other ends of the two wires to the terminals of a 12 volt vehicle battery.
5. If successful, a loud report will be heard and the air bag material will be visible coming from the top of the module. Allow at least 10 minutes before handling the air bag components to allow for cooling.

TECHNICAL SERVICE BULLETINS

SERVICE CODE 34 DISPLAYED

PROBE

1993 (Built Through 9/30/93)

A damaged or bent insertion bar in the combination switch to air bag module electrical connector may be the cause of this trouble code. Inspect harness connector insertion bar. Replace combination switch as necessary.

INTERMITTENT CODES 6 OR 32

CONTINENTAL, CROWN VICTORIA, GRAND MARQUIS, MARK VII, MUSTANG, SABLE, TAURUS, TEMPO, TOPAZ & TOWN CAR

1992

This intermittent trouble code may be cause by high resistance or an open circuit in the sliding contact assembly. Replace sliding contact as necessary.

TIGHTENING SPECIFICATIONS

Year	Component	Torque/Inch Lbs.
ASPIRE		
1994	Driver Side Air Bag Module	80–115
	Lefthand & Righthand Crash Sensors	80–115
	Passenger Side Air Bag Module	80–91
	Safing Sensor	80–115
	Sliding Contact Screws	18–26
	Steering Wheel	29–36 ①
CAPRI		
1992-94	Driver Side Air Bag Module	17–26
	Center Crash Sensor	84–108
	Passenger Side Air Bag Module	62–97
	Rear Crash Sensor Bolt	17–23 ①
	Rear Crash Sensor Screw	27–35
	Righthand & Lefthand Crash Sensors	15–18 ①
	Steering Wheel	23–33 ①
CONTINENTAL		
1992	Driver Side Air Bag Module To Steering Wheel	36–49
	Front Sensor To Fender Apron Screws	91–122
	Passenger Side Air Bag Module Assembly Screw	24–32
	Passenger Side Air Bag Mounting Bracket	68–92
	Rear Sensor Retaining Screws	23–32
	Rear Sensor Support Screws	91–122
	Rear Sensor To Dash Panel Nuts	29–40
	Steering Wheel	23–33 ①
1993-94	Driver Side Air Bag Module To Steering Wheel	35–50
	Instrument Panel Bolster Bolts	5–8 ①
	Righthand & Lefthand Front Sensor To Radiator & GOP Bracket Screws	91–122
	Passenger Side Air Bag Module Assembly Screw	24–33
	Passenger Side Air Bag Mounting Bracket	68–92
	Safing Sensor Retaining Screws	24–33

Year	Component	Torque/Inch Lbs.
CONTINENTAL-Continued		
1993-94 —Cont'd	Safing Sensor Support Screws	90–122
	Safing Sensor To Dash Panel Nuts	90–122
	Steering Wheel	23–33 ①
COUGAR & THUNDERBIRD		
1994	Driver Side Air Bag Module To Steering Wheel	8–10 ①
	Righthand & Lefthand Front Sensor Screws	8–10 ①
	Passenger Side Air Bag Module Lower Bolts	62–97
	Lefthand Kick Panel Safing Sensor	8–10 ①
	Steering Wheel	23–33 ①
CROWN VICTORIA & GRAND MARQUIS		
1992	Driver Side Air Bag Module To Steering Wheel Nuts	24–33
	Center Sensor Retaining Screws	7–9 ①
	Diagnostic Bracket Screws	39–53
	Front Sensor Screws	5–7
	Front Sensor To Radiator Support Screws	91–122
	Instrument Cluster Finish Panel Screws	17–27
	Instrument Panel Screws	7–10 ①
	Insulator Screws	13–27
	Lower Retaining Screws	17–35
	Passenger Side Air Bag Module Retaining Nuts (Front)	68–92
	Passenger Side Air Bag Module Retaining Nuts (Rear)	24–32
	Rear Sensor Retaining Screws	36–53
	Rear Sensor To Cowl Panel Screws	61–81
	Steering Wheel	23–33 ①
	Upper Retaining Screws	4–8
1993	Front Sensor Screws	8–10 ①
	Instrument Cluster Finish Panel Screws	17–27

Continued

TIGHTENING SPECIFICATIONS-Continued

Year	Component	Torque/Inch Lbs.
CROWN VICTORIA & GRAND MARQUIS-Continued		
1993 —Cont'd	Instrument Panel Register Applique Screws	17–27
	Passenger Side Air Bag Module Retaining Screws, Front	67–92
	Passenger Side Air Bag Module Retaining Screws, Rear	24–33
	Rear Sensor To Cowl Side Panel Screws	61–81
	Righthand & Lefthand Front Sensor To Radiator Support Screws	91–122
	Steering Wheel	23–33 ①
1994	Driver Side Air Bag Module To Steering Wheel Nuts	24–33
	Diagnostic Module Bracket Screws	39–53
	Instrument Cluster Finish Panel Screws	18–26
	Instrument Panel Register Applique Screws	18–26
	Passenger Side Air Bag Module Retaining Screws, Front	67–92
	Passenger Side Air Bag Module Retaining Screws, Rear	24–33
	Safing Sensor Screws	40–53
	Righthand & Lefthand Front Sensor Screws	7–10
	Steering Wheel	23–33 ①
ESCORT & TRACER		
1992-94	Driver Side Air Bag Module	35–53
	Steering Wheel	34–46 ①
MARK VII		
1992	Air Bag Module To Steering Wheel Nuts	36–49
	Air Bag Retaining Nuts	22–32
	Air Bag Sensor Nut	80–111
	Front Center Sensor To Radiator Support Screws	91–122
	Front Sensors To Fender Apron Screws	91–122
	Radiator Sensor Screw (Right)	38–53
	Rear Sensor To Dash Panel Screws	91–122
	Sensor Bracket Screw	40–53
	Steering Wheel	23–33 ①
MARK VIII		
1993	Driver Side Air Bag Module Nuts	91–122
	Diagnostic Monitor Bracket Screws	39–53
	Lefthand Kick Panel Safing Sensor To Cowl Side Panel Screws	91–122
	Passenger Air Bag Module Retaining Bolts, Front	9–18
	Passenger Air Bag Module Retaining Screws, Rear	62–97

Year	Component	Torque/Inch Lbs.
MARK VIII-Continued		
1993 —Cont'd	Righthand & Lefthand Front Sensor To Grille Opening Reinforcement Bracket Screws	91–122
	Steering Wheel	23–33 ①
1994	Driver Side Air Bag Module Bolts	8–10 ①
	Lefthand Kick Panel Safing Sensor To Cowl Side Panel Screws	8–10 ①
	Passenger Air Bag Module Retaining Bolts, Upper	9–18
	Passenger Air Bag Module Retaining Screws, Lower	62–97
	Righthand & Lefthand Front Sensor To Grille Opening Reinforcement Bracket Screws	8–10
	Steering Wheel	23–33 ①
MUSTANG		
1992	Air Bag Module To Steering Wheel	24–32
	Center Sensor Screw	10–12 ①
	Front Center Sensor To Radiator Support Screws	79–107
	Front Sensors To Bracket Screws	80–107
	Front Sensors To Fender Apron Screws	80–107
	Lefthand B-Pillar Sensor Screws	61–81
	Sensor Assembly Bracket Screw	19–25
	Steering Wheel	25–34 ①
1993	Driver Side Air Bag Module To Steering Wheel	24–32
	Center Sensor Screw	80–106
	Front Center Sensor To Radiator Support Screws	80–106
	Lefthand B-Pillar Sensor Screws	90–122
	Righthand & Lefthand Front Sensor To Bracket Screws	80–106
	Righthand & Lefthand Front Sensor To Fender Apron Screws	80–106
	Sensor Assembly Bracket Screw	19–25
	Steering Wheel	25–34 ①
1994	Driver Side Air Bag Module To Steering Wheel	8–10 ①
	Righthand & Lefthand Front Sensor Screws	8–10 ①
	Diagnostic Monitor Bracket Screw	8–10 ①
	Steering Wheel	25–34 ①
PROBE		
1992-94	Center Radiator Crash Sensor Bolts	79–112
	clock spring Screws	18–26
	Driver Side Air Bag Module Bolts	61–86
	Lefthand Crash Sensor Bolts	79–112
	Passenger Side Air Bag Module	22–33
	Righthand Crash Sensor Bolts	79–112

Continued

TIGHTENING SPECIFICATIONS-Continued

Year	Component	Torque/Inch Lbs.
PROBE -Continued		
1992-94 —Cont'd	**Safing Sensor Bolts**	61–86
	Steering Wheel	29–36 ①
SABLE & TAURUS		
1992	**Air Bag Module To Steering Wheel Nuts**	36–49
	Front Sensor Screws	61–81
	Front Sensor To Radiator Support Screws	61–81
	Instrument Cluster Finish Panel Screws	17–27
	Instrument Panel Screws	7–10
	Insulator Screw	13–27
	Lower Retaining Screws	17–35
	Passenger Air Bag Module Retaining Bolts (Lower)	68–92
	Passenger Air Bag Module Retaining Screws (Front & Rear)	11–15
	Rear Sensor To Dash Panel Screws	91–122
	Steering Wheel	22–33 ①
	Upper Retaining Screws	4–8
1993	**Driver Side Air Bag Module To Steering Wheel Nuts, Except SHO**	36–49
	Driver Side Air Bag Module To Steering Wheel Nuts, SHO	8–10 ①
	Front Sensor Screws	61–81
	Instrument Cluster Finish Panel Screws	17–27
	Instrument Panel Screws	7–10
	Insulator Screw	13–27
	Lower Retaining Screws	17–35
	Passenger Side Air Bag Module Retaining Screws, Front & Rear	11–15
	Passenger Side Air Bag Module Retaining Bolts, Lower	68–92
	Rear Sensor To Dash Panel Screws	91–122
	Righthand & Lefthand Front Sensor To Radiator Support Screws	61–81
	Steering Wheel	22–33 ①
	Upper Retaining Screws	4–8
1994	**Driver Side Air Bag Module To Steering Wheel Nuts, Except SHO**	35–50

Year	Component	Torque/Inch Lbs.
SABLE & TAURUS-Continued		
1994	**Driver Side Air Bag Module To Steering Wheel Nuts, SHO**	8–10 ①
	Center Radiator Sensor Screws	60–81
	Instrument Cluster Finish Panel Screws	17–27
	Instrument Panel Screws	7–10
	Insulator Screw	13–27
	Lower Retaining Screws	17–35
	Passenger Side Air Bag Module Retaining Screws, Front	11–16
	Passenger Side Air Bag Module Retaining Screws, Rear	62–97
	Lefthand Kick Panel Safing Screws	60–81
	Steering Wheel	22–33 ①
	Upper Retaining Screws	4–8
TEMPO & TOPAZ		
1992	**Air Bag Diagnostic Monitor Screws**	39–53
	Air Bag Module To Steering Wheel Nut	36–49
	Diagnostic Bracket Screws	31–35
	Diagnostic Monitor Screw	39–53
	Front Center Sensor To Radiator Support Screws	91–122
	Front Sensors To Fender Apron	61–81
	Knee Bolster Bolts	62–97
	Rear Sensor To Dash Panel Nuts	31–44
	Sensor Self–Tapping Screw	24–32
	Steering Wheel	27–34 ①
1993	**Air Bag Module To Steering Wheel Nut**	36–49
	Air Bag Monitor Screws	39–53
	Diagnostic Bracket Screws	31–35
	Diagnostic Monitor Screw	39–53
	Front Center Sensor To Radiator Support Screws	91–122
	Knee Bolster Bolts	62–97
	Rear Sensor To Dash Panel Nuts	31–44
	Righthand & Lefthand Front Sensor To Radiator Support Screws	61–81
	Sensor Self–Tapping Screw	24–32
	Steering Wheel	27–34 ①
1994	**Air Bag Module To Steering Wheel Nut**	35–50

Continued

TIGHTENING SPECIFICATIONS-Continued

Year	Component	Torque/Inch Lbs.
TEMPO & TOPAZ -Continued		
1994	**Air Bag Monitor Screws**	39–53
	Diagnostic Bracket Screws	31–35
	Diagnostic Monitor Screw	39–53
	Front Center Sensor To Radiator Support Screws	90–122
	Knee Bolster Bolts	62–97
	Rear Sensor To Dash Panel Nuts	31–44
	Righthand & Lefthand Front Sensor To Radiator Support Screws	60–81
	Sensor Self–Tapping Screw	24–33
	Steering Wheel	27–34 ①
TOWN CAR		
1992	**Air Bag Module To Steering Wheel Nuts**	35–50
	Center Sensor Retaining Screws	7–9 ①
	Diagnostic Bracket Screws	39–53
	Front Sensor Screws	5–7
	Front Sensor To Radiator Support Screws	91–122
	Instrument Cluster Finish Panel Screws	17–27
	Instrument Panel Screws	7–10 ①
	Insulator Screws	13–27
	Lower Retaining Screws	17–35
	Passenger Air Bag Module Retaining Nuts (Front)	68–92
	Passenger Air Bag Module Retaining Nuts (Rear)	24–32
	Rear Sensor Retaining Screws	36–53
	Rear Sensor To Cowl Panel Screws	40–55
	Steering Wheel	22–33
	Upper Retaining Screws	4–8
1993	**Driver Side Air Bag Module To Steering Wheel Nuts**	35–55
	Diagnostic Bracket Screws	39–53
	Front Sensor Screws	5–7
	Instrument Cluster Finish Panel Screws	17–27
	Instrument Panel Screws	7–10 ①
	Insulator Screws	13–27
	Lower Retaining Screws	17–35
	Passenger Air Bag Module Retaining Bolts, Front	62–97
	Passenger Air Bag Module Retaining Screws, Rear	4–8
	Rear Sensor To Cowl Panel Screws	35–41
	Rear Sensor To Cowl Side Panel Screws	40–55

Continued

TIGHTENING SPECIFICATIONS-Continued

Year	Component	Torque/Inch Lbs.
TOWN CAR-Continued		
1993 —Cont'd	Righthand & Lefthand Front Sensor To Radiator Support Screws	91–122
	Steering Wheel	22–33
	Upper Retaining Screws	4–8
1994	Driver Side Air Bag Module To Steering Wheel Nuts	35–50
	Diagnostic Bracket Screws	39–53
	Front Sensor Screws	7–10 ①
	Instrument Cluster Finish Panel Screws	17–27
	Instrument Panel Screws	7–10 ①
	Insulator Screws	13–27
	Lower Retaining Screws	17–35
	Passenger Side Air Bag Module Retaining Bolts	5–8 ①
	Passenger Side Air Bag Module Retaining Screws	24–35
	Rear Sensor To Cowl Side Panel Screws	40–53
	Righthand & Lefthand Front Sensor To Radiator Support Screws	7–10 ①
	Steering Wheel	22–33
	Upper Retaining Screws	4–8

①—Ft. Lbs.

Automatic Seat Belts

NOTE: On Air Bag Equipped Models, Refer To "Air Bag System" In This Chapter For System Disarming & Arming Procedures.

INDEX

CONDITION	POSSIBLE SOURCE	ACTION
• Belt Appears to Run Fine But Motor Stalls at A-pillar, Motor Could Get Warm	• "A" limit switch wire shorted to ground. "A" limit switch not opening.	• Check for pinched wire along A-pillar, or behind LH or RH side cowl panel. Check that carrier reaches "A" limit switch.
• Fasten Belt Indicator (IP) Remains Lit After 7-10 Seconds of Running to B-pillar, Belt Appears to Run Fine But Motor Stalls at B-pillar, Motor Could Get Warm	• "B" limit switch wire is shorted to ground. • Obstruction.	• Check for pinched wire under guide attachment screws. • Check for trim screw, obstruction in track or track seal that prevents the carrier from reaching the "B" limit switch.
• Belt Will Not Run, Module May Be Burned	• Motor wire shorted to ground.	• Check for short to ground on the motor circuit breaker terminals.
• Belt Will Not Run	• Inertia switch tripped. • Motor wire not connected.	• Reset (depress) fuel pump inertia switch button. • Check for unconnected connectors on the motor, or behind LH and RH side cowl panels.
• Belt Runs to A-pillar Only, Belt Will Not Run Back to B-pillar	• Door switch wire shorted to ground. • "B" limit switch wire not connected. • "B" limit switch plunger stuck in depressed position.	• Check for pinched wire behind door trim panel. • Check for unconnected connectors near motor, behind LH and RH side cowl panel, or on "B" limit switch. • Correct jammed switch or replace "B" limit switch.
• Belt Runs to B-pillar Only, Belt Will Not Run Forward to A-pillar.	• Door switch wire not connected. • "A" limit switch wire not connected. • Obstruction.	• Check for unconnected connectors on door latch switch, or behind LH and RH side cowl panel. • Check for unconnected connectors behind LH and RH side cowl panel, or on "A" limit switch. • Check for a trim screw, track seal or jammed track locking pawl that prevents the carrier from reaching the "A" limit switch.
• Opening/Closing Door Causes Both Belts to Move	• Damaged Door Ajar lamp assembly.	• Replace Door Ajar lamp assembly.
• Turning Ignition Off Causes Belt to Move to A-pillar	• Damaged Door Ajar lamp assembly.	• Replace Door Ajar lamp assembly.
• Fasten Belt Indicator Remains On, Chime Sounds for Four to Eight Seconds	• Connector to shoulder emergency release retractor switches not connected.	• Check for unconnected connectors in console near shoulder strap connector.
• Excessive Noise While Motor is Running	• Motor adjustment knob on top of motor hits body.	• Loosen motor, slide motor downward, then tighten motor.

FM8019100342000X

Fig. 1   Troubleshooting chart

PRECAUTIONS

AIR BAG SYSTEMS

Refer to "Air Bag System" in this chapter for system disarming and arming procedures.

DESCRIPTION

The motorized seat belt, which operates electrically, restrains the driver and front seat passenger in the vehicle through the use of an automatic shoulder belt.

After entering the vehicle, closing the door and turning the ignition switch to its On position, a motor will cause the shoulder belt to slide along a drive belt track, starting at the front body A-pillar and ending at the center B-pillar. The shoulder belt will automatically adjust itself and will lock tight only on extremely hard braking or impacts of 5 mph or more. When the ignition is in any position and the door is opened or ajar, the shoulder belt will move forward to the A-pillar.

If the shoulder belt should stall before it reaches the B-pillar, the indicator lamp will begin to flash after nine seconds and will continue flashing until the shoulder belt is in its locked position. If indicator lamp continues to flash, refer to "Manual System Override."

On Cougar and Thunderbird, ensure the shoulder belt is latched to the emergency release buckle at the A-pillar.

EMERGENCY RELEASE

1. **On Tempo and Topaz,** emergency release levers are located in the center console above the emergency brake lever.
2. **On Cougar and Thunderbird,** emergency release buttons are located on the shoulder belt upper anchor.

MANUAL SYSTEM OVERRIDE

If shoulder belt does not move or stops before reaching the B-pillar position, perform the following steps before driving vehicle.

1. With ignition switch in Off position, open and fully close doors, then place ignition switch in Run position.
2. Using a screwdriver, remove access cover at lower end of B-pillar interior trim panel and turn override knob clockwise to move shoulder belt manually until it stops at B-pillar position.
3. If shoulder belt still does not move to B-pillar, drive belt may be broken, or motor drive gear stripped. Grasp belt and pull toward B-pillar while turning override knob clockwise.

TROUBLESHOOTING

Refer to **Fig. 1** for troubleshooting procedures.

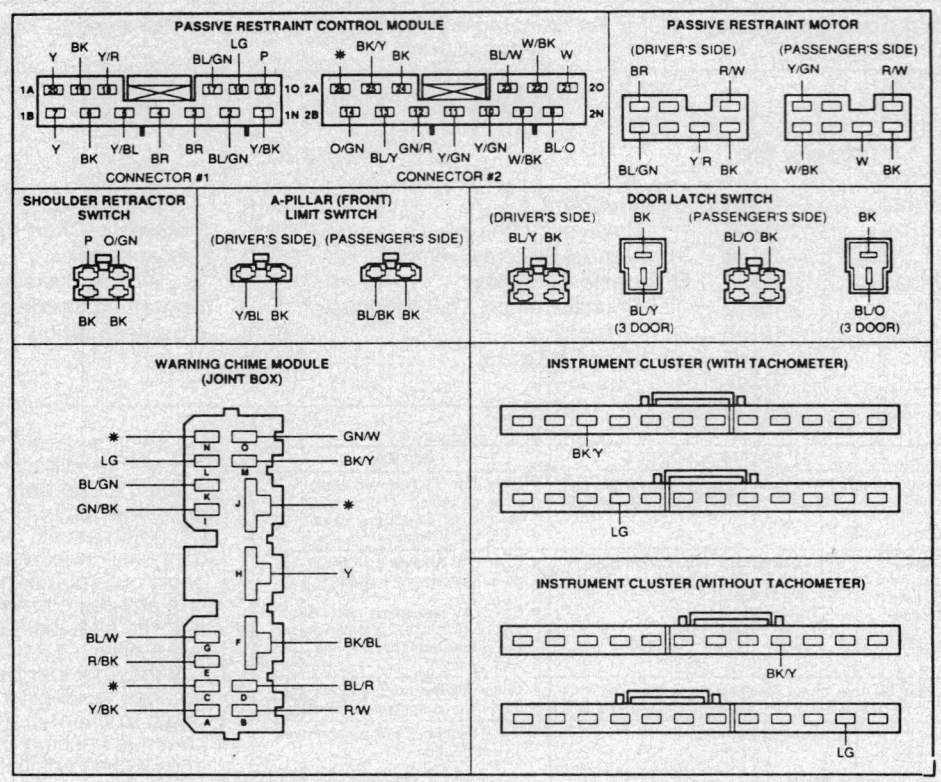

Fig. 2   Restraint system wiring circuit & pin identification (Part 1 of 2).
1992–93 Escort & Tracer

DIAGNOSIS & TESTING

Refer to **Figs. 2 through 15** for seat belt system wiring circuits and connector pin identification.

ESCORT & TRACER

1992–93

Refer to **Fig. 16** for system diagnostic procedures.

1994

Refer to pinpoint test reference chart, **Fig. 17,** and pinpoint tests, **Figs. 18 through 22,** for system diagnostic procedures.

COUGAR, TEMPO, THUNDERBIRD & TOPAZ

Refer to "Driver and Passenger Operational Logic Chart," "Function Table" and "System Diagnostic Chart," **Figs. 23 through 27,** along with the related pinpoint charts, **Figs. 28 through 42,** for system diagnostic procedures.

FESTIVA

Refer to **Fig. 43** for system diagnostic procedures.

PROBE

Refer to **Fig. 44** for system diagnostic procedures.

Continued on page 18-46

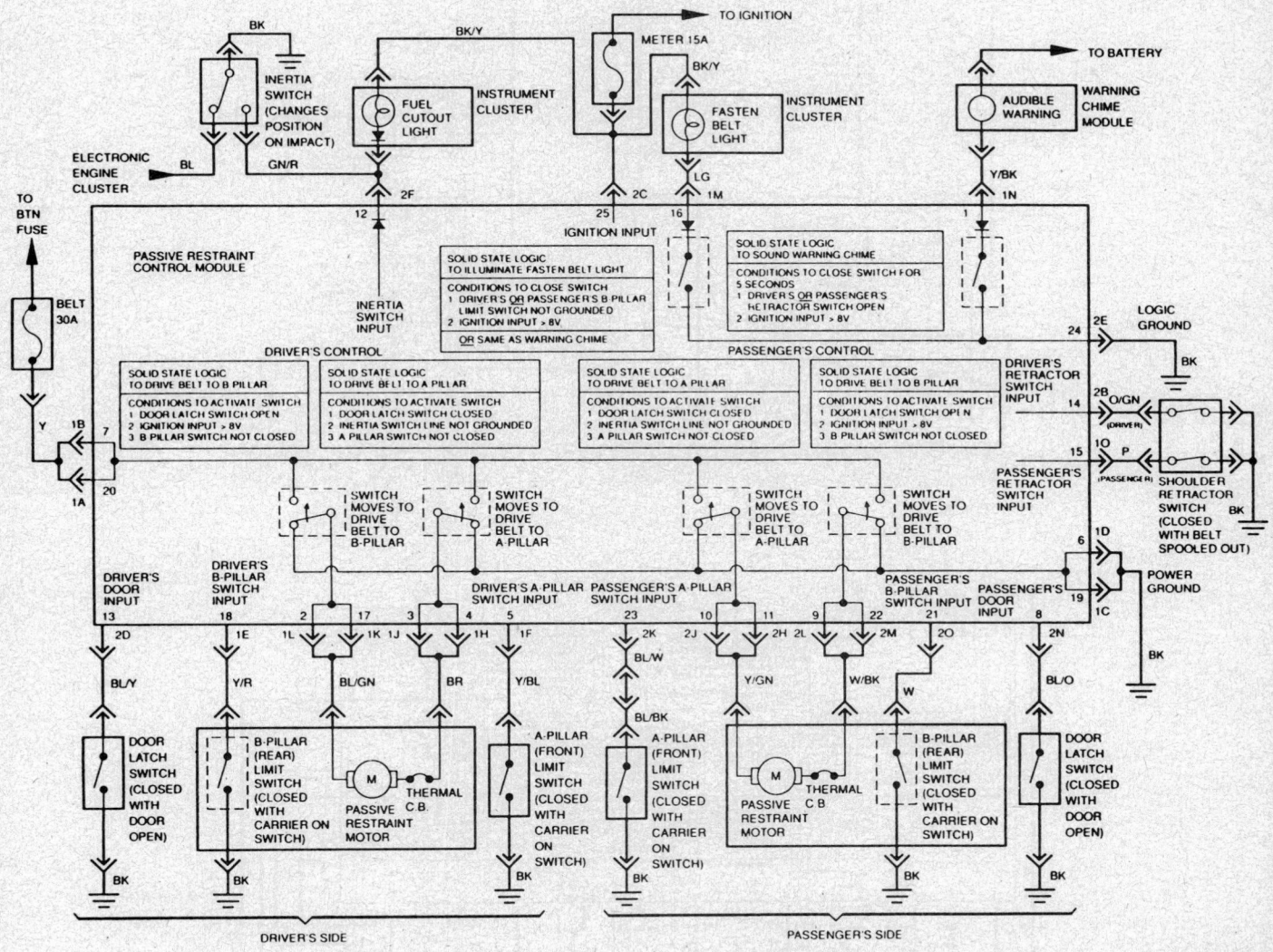

Fig. 2 Restraint system wiring circuit & pin identification (Part 2 of 2). 1992–93 Escort & Tracer

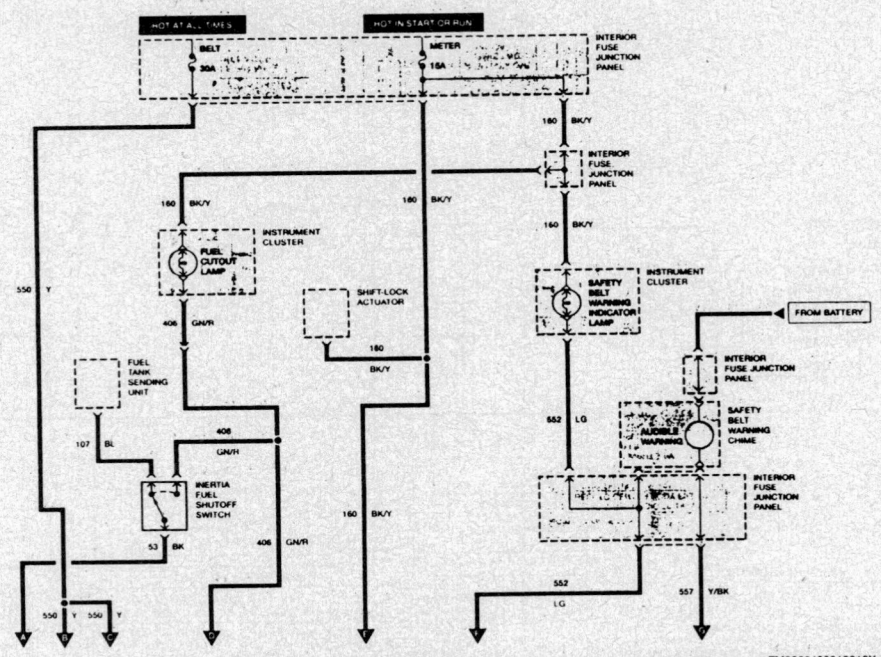

Fig. 3 Restraint system wiring circuit (Part 1 of 2). 1994 Escort & Tracer

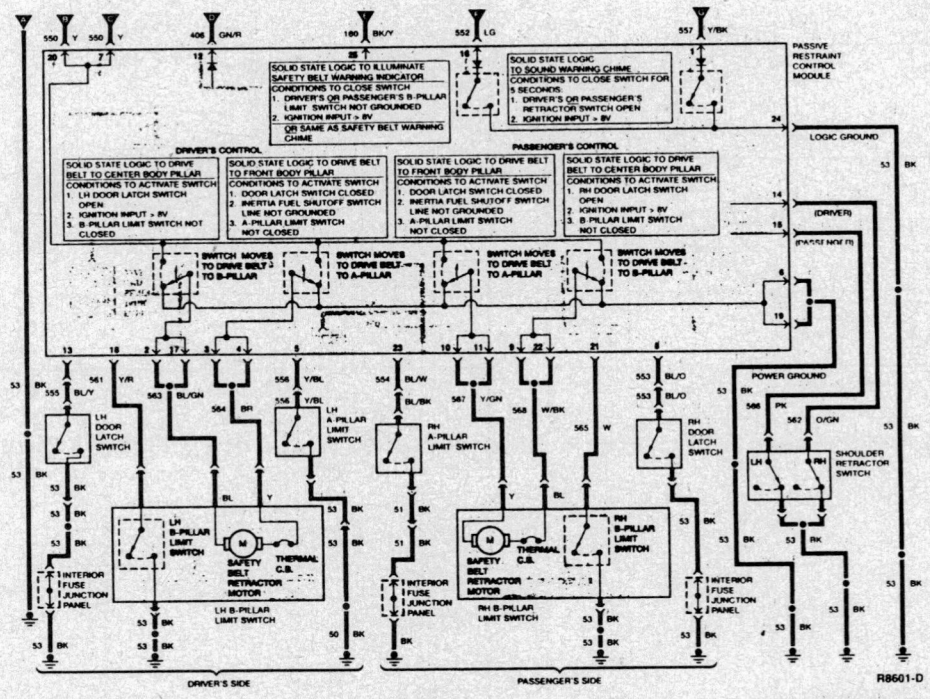

Fig. 3 Restraint system wiring circuit (Part 2 of 2). 1994 Escort & Tracer

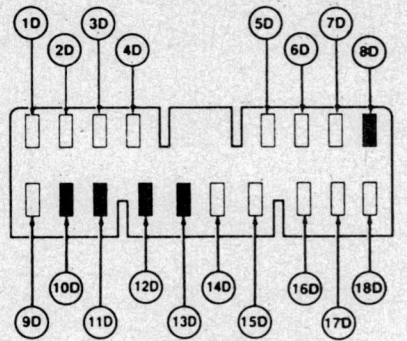

INTERIOR FUSE JUNCTION PANEL

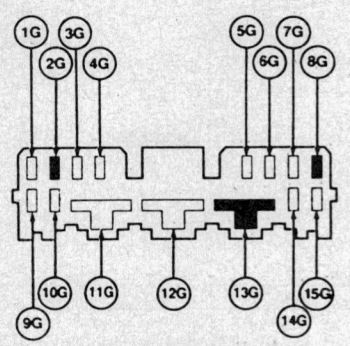

INTERIOR FUSE JUNCTION PANEL

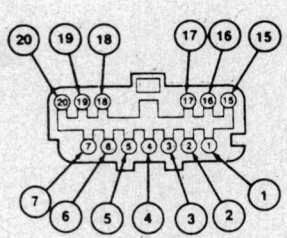

PASSIVE RESTRAINT CONTROL
MODULE (CONNECTOR #1)

Pin	Circuit	Circuit Function
1D	330 (BL/R)	Battery Power
2D	330 (BL/R)	Battery Power
3D	301 (R/BK)	Right Front Park Lamp
4D	160 (BK/Y)	START/ON Power
5D	160 (BK/Y)	START/ON Power
6D	363 (GN/W)	Right Turn Input
7D	661 (BK/BL)	Powertrain Control Module
8D	—	NOT USED
9D	301 (R/BK)	Left Front Park Lamp
10D	—	NOT USED
11D	—	NOT USED
12D	—	NOT USED
13D	—	NOT USED
14D	160 (BK/Y)	START/ON Power
15D	160 (BK/W)	START/ON Power
16D	364 (GN/BK)	Left Turn Input
17D	240 (BL/GN)	ON Power
18D	360 (BK/R)	Battery Power

FM8029400014000X

Fig. 4   Interior fuse junction panel 18–pin connector terminal identification. 1994 Escort & Tracer

Pin	Circuit	Circuit Function
1G	557 (Y/BK)	Passive Restraint Control Module
2G	—	NOT USED
3G	301 (R/BK)	Rear Park Lamps
4G	574 (BL/W)	Driver's Seat Belt Buckle Switch
5G	364 (GN/BK)	Left Rear Turn/Hazard Lamp
6G	240 (BL/GN)	ON Power
7G	552 (LG)	Passive Restraint Control Module
8G	—	NOT USED
9G	331 (R/W)	Lamp Switch
10G	330 (BL/R)	Battery Power
11G	661 (BK/BL)	Heated Back Window Grid
12G	550 (Y)	Battery Power
13G	—	NOT USED
14G	160 (BK/Y)	START/ON Power
15G	363 (GN/W)	Right Rear Turn/Hazard Lamp

FM8029400015000X

Fig. 5   Interior fuse junction panel 15-pin connector terminal identification. 1994 Escort & Tracer

Pin	Circuit	Circuit Function
20	550 (Y)	Battery Power
19	53 (BK)	Ground
18	561 (Y/R)	Left B-Pillar Limit Switch
17	563 (BL/GN)	Left Safety Belt Retractor Motor
16	552 (LG)	Fasten Belts Indicator Output
15	566 (PK)	Right Shoulder Retractor Switch
7	550 (Y)	Battery Power
6	53 (BK)	Ground
5	556 (Y/BL)	Left A-Pillar Limit Switch
4	564 (BR)	Left Safety Belt Retractor Motor
3	564 (BR)	Left Safety Belt Retractor Motor
2	563 (BL/GN)	Left Safety Belt Retractor Motor
1	557 (Y/BK)	Sound Chime Output

FM8029400016000X

Fig. 6   Passive restraint control module connector No. 1 terminal identification. 1994 Escort & Tracer

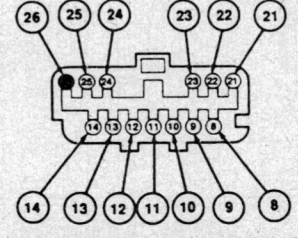

PASSIVE RESTRAINT CONTROL MODULE
(CONNECTOR #2)

Pin	Circuit	Circuit Function
26	—	NOT USED
25	160 (BK/Y)	Switched Power
24	53 (BK)	Ground
23	554 (BL/W)	Right A-Pillar Limit Switch
22	568 (W/BK)	Right Safety Belt Retractor Motor
21	565 (W)	Right B-Pillar Limit Switch
14	562 (O/GN)	Left Shoulder Retractor Switch
13	555 (BL/Y)	Left Front Door Latch Switch
12	406 (GN/R)	Inertial Fuel Shutoff Switch
11	567 (Y/GN)	Right Safety Belt Retractor Motor
10	567 (Y/GN)	Right Safety Belt Retractor Motor
9	568 (W/BK)	Right Safety Belt Retractor Motor
8	553 (BL/O)	Right Front Door Latch Switch

FM8029400017000X

Fig. 7   Passive restraint control module connector No. 2 terminal identification. 1994 Escort & Tracer

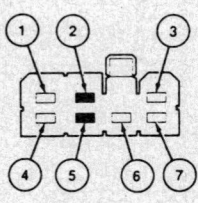

LH B-PILLAR LIMIT SWITCH

Pin	Circuit	Circuit Function
1	564 (BR)	Passive Restraint Control Module Motor Input
2	—	NOT USED
3	331 (R/W)	Lamp Switch Input
4	563 (BL/GN)	Passive Restraint Control Module Motor Input
5	—	NOT USED
6	561 (Y/R)	Passive Restraint Control Module B-Pillar Limit Switch Input
7	53 (BK)	Ground

FM8029400018000X

Fig. 8   Lefthand B-pillar limit switch terminal identification. 1994 Escort & Tracer

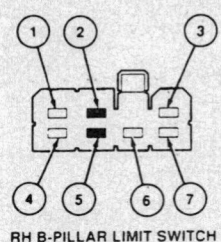

RH B-PILLAR LIMIT SWITCH

Pin	Circuit	Circuit Function
1	567 (Y/GN)	Passive Restraint Control Module Motor Input
2	—	NOT USED
3	331 (R/W)	Lamp Switch Input
4	568 (W/BK)	Passive Restraint Control Module Motor Input
5	—	NOT USED
6	565 (W)	Passive Restraint Control Module B-Pillar Limit Switch Input
7	53 (BK)	Ground

FM8029400019000X

Fig. 9   Righthand B-pillar limit switch terminal identification. 1994 Escort & Tracer

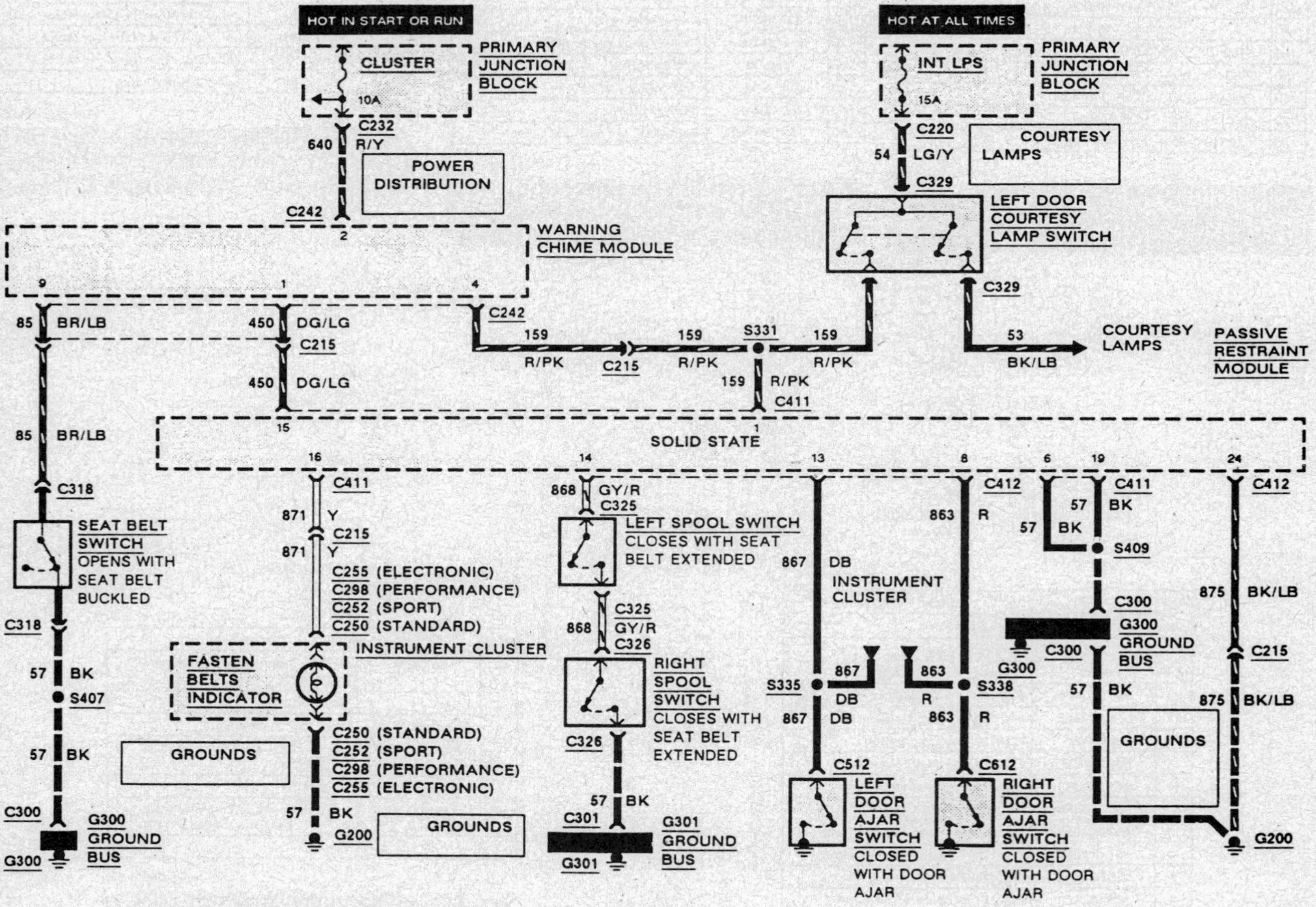

FM8019100344010X

Fig. 10   Restraint system wiring circuit & pin identification (Part 1 of 3). Cougar & Thunderbird

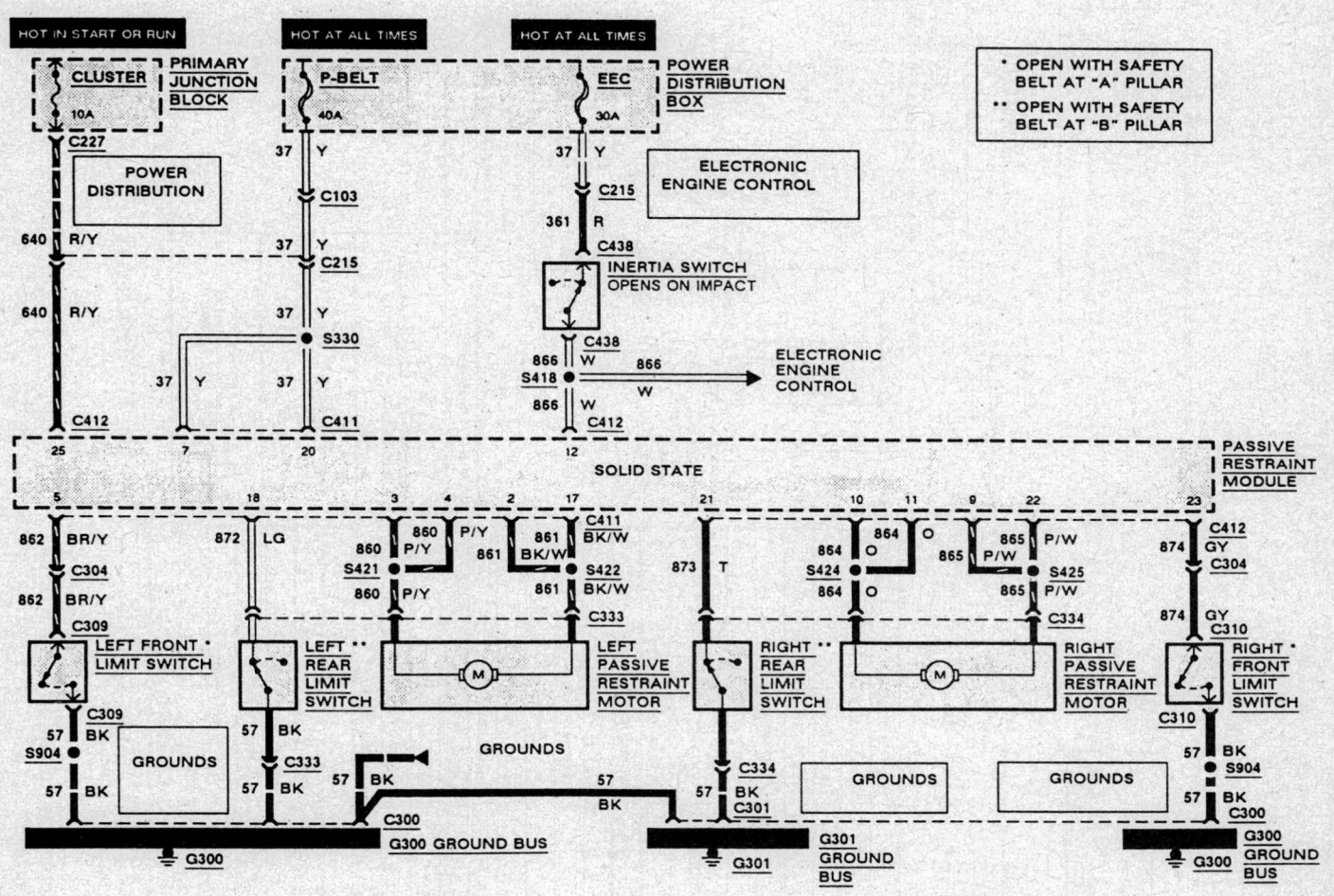

Fig. 10 Restraint system wiring circuit & pin identification (Part 2 of 3). Cougar & Thunderbird

FM8019100344020X

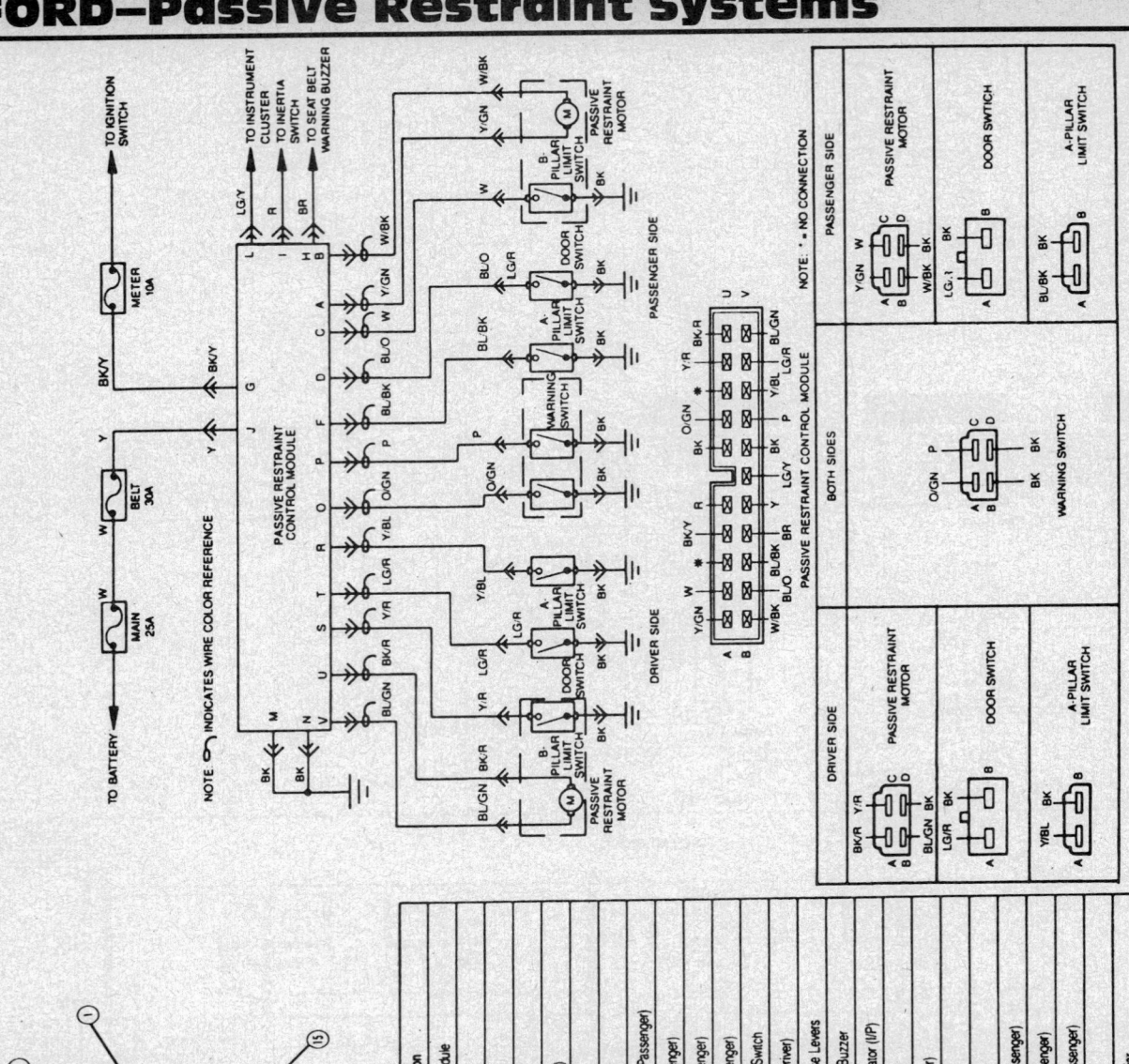

Fig. 11 Restraint system wiring circuit & pin identification. Festiva

Pin Number	Circuit Number	Circuit Color	Circuit Identification
1	159	Red/Pink	Warning Chime Module
2	861	Black/White	Left Motor (Driver)
3	860	Purple/Yellow	Left Motor (Driver)
4	860	Purple/Yellow	Left Motor (Driver)
5	862	Brown/Yellow	Left Limit A (Driver)
6	57	Black	Ground
7	38	Black/Orange	Battery
8	863	Red	Right Door Open (Passenger)
9	865	Purple/White	Right Motor (Passenger)
10	864	Orange	Right Motor (Passenger)
11	864	Orange	Right Motor (Passenger)
12	866	White	Fuel Pump Inertia Switch
13	867	Dark Blue	Left Door Open (Driver)
14	868	Gray/Red	Emergency Release Levers
15	450	Dark Green/Light Green	Safety Belt Timer Buzzer
16	871	Yellow	Fasten Belts Indicator (I/P)
17	861	Black/White	Left Motor (Driver)
18	872	Light Green	Left Limit B (Driver)
19	57	Black	Ground
20	38	Black/Orange	Battery
21	873	Tan	Right Limit B (Passenger)
22	865	Purple/White	Right Motor (Passenger)
23	874	Gray	Right Limit A (Passenger)
24	875	Black/Lt. Blue	Ground
25	640	Red/Yellow	Run/Start/Door Ajar
26	No Connection	—	—

NOTE: To handle the electrical load, the control module uses two pins (7 and 20) for power, and two pins (6 and 19) for ground.

Fig. 10 Restraint system wiring circuit & pin identification (Part 3 of 3). Cougar & Thunderbird

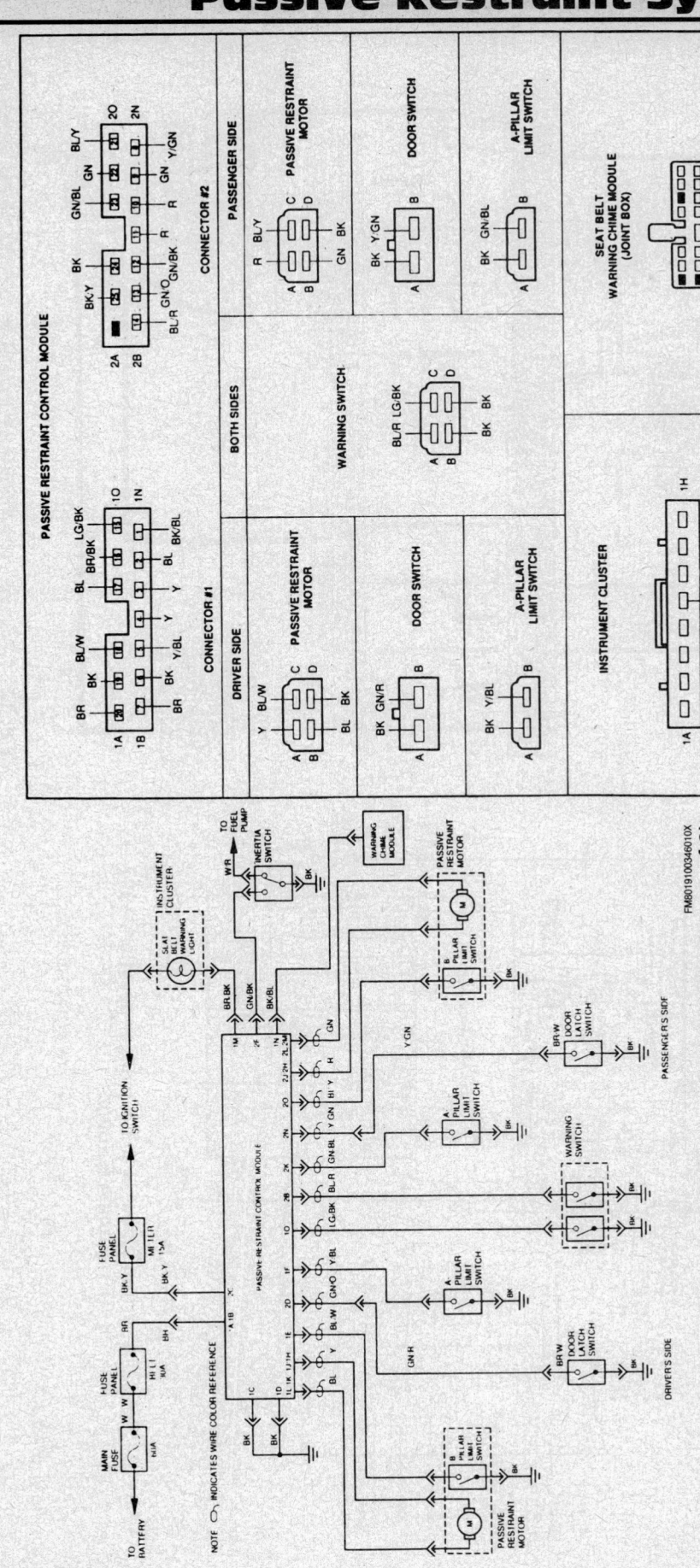

Fig. 12 Restraint system wiring circuit & pin identification (Part 2 of 2).
Probe

Fig. 12 Restraint system wiring circuit & pin identification (Part 1 of 2).
Probe

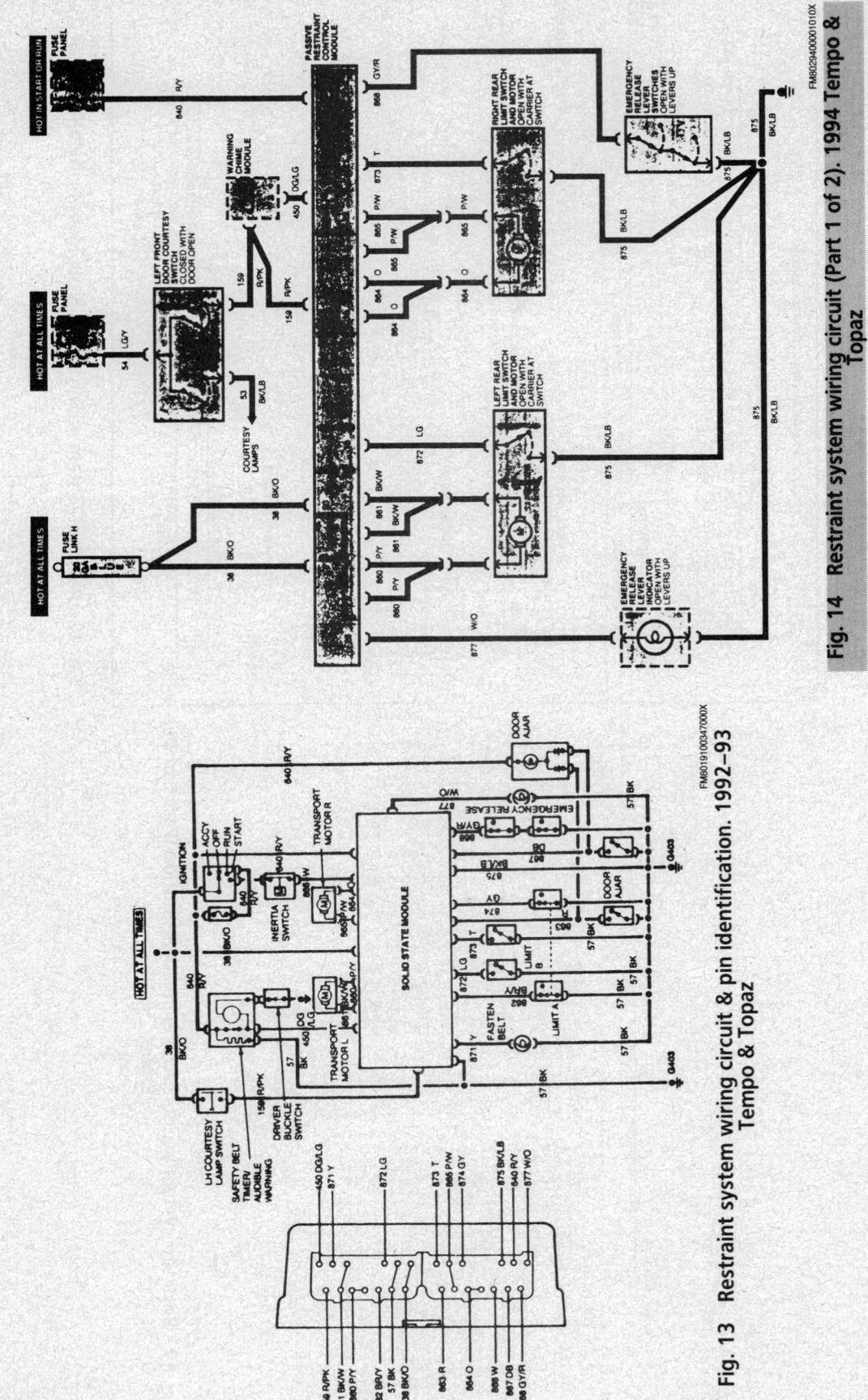

Fig. 14 Restraint system wiring circuit (Part 1 of 2). 1994 Tempo & Topaz

Fig. 13 Restraint system wiring circuit & pin identification. 1992–93 Tempo & Topaz

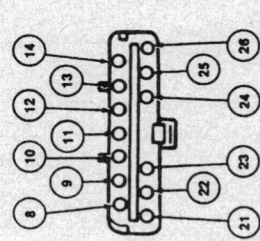

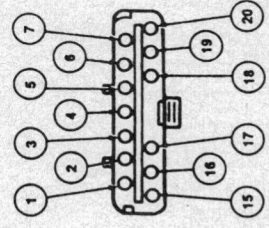

FM8029400002000X

Pin No.	Circuit	Circuit Function
15	450 (DG/LG)	Safety Belt Buzzer Timer
16	871 (Y)	Fasten Belt Indicator
17	861 (BK/W)	LH Rear Motor
18	872 (LG)	LH B-Pillar Limit Switch
19	57 (BK)	Ground
20	38 (BK/O)	Battery
21	873 (T)	RH B-Pillar Limit Switch
22	865 (P/W)	RH Rear Motor
23	874 (GY)	RH A-Pillar Limit Switch
24	875 (BK/LB)	Ground
25	640 (W/Y)	Run/Start/Door Ajar
26	877 (W/O)	Release Lever Warning Indicator

Pin No.	Circuit	Circuit Function
1	159 (R/PK)	Lamps On/Key Warning Buzzer
2	861 (BK/W)	LH Rear Motor
3	860 (P/Y)	LH Rear Motor
4	860 (P/Y)	LH Rear Motor
5	862 (BR/Y)	LH A-Pillar Limit Switch
6	57 (BK)	Ground
7	38 (BK/O)	Battery
8	863 (R)	RH Door Open
9	865 (P/W)	RH Rear Motor
10	864 (O)	RH Rear Motor
11	864 (O)	RH Rear Motor
12	866 (W)	Inertia Fuel Shutoff Switch
13	867 (DB)	LH Door Open
14	868 (GY/R)	Emergency Release Levers

(Continued)

Fig. 15 Passive restraint module connector terminal identification. 1994 Tempo & Topaz

FM8029400001020X

Fig. 14 Restraint system wiring circuit (Part 2 of 2). 1994 Tempo & Topaz

SYMPTOM CHART

CONDITION	POSSIBLE SOURCE	ACTION
• Neither Belt Will Leave the B-Pillar	• Battery feed to module. • Inertia switch input grounded by inertia switch or faulty fuel cutout light circuit.	• GO to PR1. • GO to PR6.
• Neither Belt Will Leave the A-Pillar	• Power to module. • Ignition line input.	• GO to PR1. • GO to PR4.
• One Belt Will Not Leave the B-Pillar	• Door switch input open. • A-pillar limit switch input grounded. • Motor / motor wiring.	• GO to PR7. • GO to PR8. • GO to PR10.
• One Belt Will Not Leave the A-Pillar	• Door switch input grounded. • B-pillar limit switch input grounded. • Motor / motor wiring.	• GO to PR7. • GO to PR9. • GO to PR10.
• Belt Carrier (Transport) Jumps or Clicks at B-Pillar While Ignition is ON	• B-pillar limit switch input open. • Wiring and connectors between B-pillar limit switch and passive restraint module.	• GO to PR9. • GO to PR9.
• Belt Carrier (Transport) Jumps or Clicks at A-Pillar While Door is Open	• A-pillar limit switch input is open. • Wiring and connectors between A-pillar limit switch and passive restraint module.	• GO to PR8. • GO to PR8.
• Fasten Belt Indicator and / or Warning Chime Turn ON Intermittently or Remain ON	• B-pillar limit switch open. • Wiring / connectors between retractor / B-pillar limit switch and module. • Retractor switch input open.	• GO to PR9. • GO to PR9. • GO to PR11.
• Fasten Belt Indicator and / or Warning Chime Do Not Turn ON When Intended	• B-pillar limit switch input. • Retractor switch input. • Fasten belt indicator. • Warning chime module.	• GO to PR9. • GO to PR11. • GO to PR12. • GO to PR13.

TEST STEP		RESULT	▶	ACTION TO TAKE
PR1	**CHECK FUSES**			
	• Locate the interior fuse panel. • Check the 30 amp BELT and 10 amp METER fuses. • Are the fuses OK?	Yes No	▶ ▶	GO to PR4. GO to PR2.
PR2	**CHECK SYSTEM**			
	• Replace the blown fuse(s). • Key ON. • Did the fuse(s) fail again?	Yes No	▶ ▶	GO to PR3. GO to PR4.

FM8019200348010X

Fig. 16   System diagnosis (Part 1 of 11). 1992–93 Escort & Tracer

TEST STEP		RESULT	▶	ACTION TO TAKE
PR3	**CHECK FOR SHORT TO GROUND**			
	• Key OFF. • Locate and disconnect the interior fuse panel connectors. • Measure the resistance between the "Y" wire and / or the "BK / Y" wire at the interior fuse panel connector(s) and ground. • Are the resistance(s) less than 5 ohms?	Yes No	▶ ▶	REPAIR / REPLACE the wire(s) in question. GO to PR4.
PR4	**CHECK PASSIVE RESTRAINT CONTROL MODULE BATTERY / IGNITION SUPPLY**			
	• Key OFF. • Disconnect the passive restraint control module connectors. • Measure the voltage on the "Y" wire at connector #1. • Key ON. • Measure the voltage on the "BK / Y" wire at connector #2. • Are the voltages greater than 10 volts?	Yes No	▶ ▶	GO to PR5. REPAIR / REPLACE the wire(s) in question.
PR5	**CHECK PASSIVE RESTRAINT CONTROL MODULE GROUNDS**			
	• Key OFF. • Disconnect the passive restraint control module connectors. • Measure the resistance between each "BK" wire at the passive restraint control module connectors and ground. • Are the resistances less than 5 ohms?	Yes No	▶ ▶	GO to PR6. REPAIR / REPLACE the "BK" wire in question.
PR6	**CHECK INERTIA SWITCH INPUT**			
	• Key OFF. • Disconnect the passive restraint control module connector (#2). • Measure the resistance between the "GN / R" wire at the passive restraint control module connector (#2) and ground ("BK" wire) with the inertia switch in the following positions. (To trip the inertia switch strike it firmly.)	Yes No	▶ ▶	GO to PR7. GO to PR6-1.

Switch Position	Resistance
Open (tripped, popped out)	Less than 5 ohms
Closed (set, pushed in)	Greater than 10,000 ohms

	• Are the resistances OK?			

FM8019200348020X

Fig. 16   System diagnosis (Part 2 of 11). 1992–93 Escort & Tracer

TEST STEP		RESULT	▶	ACTION TO TAKE
PR6-1	**CHECK INERTIA SWITCH GROUND**			
	• Locate and disconnect the fuel pump inertia switch. • Measure the resistance between the "BK" wire at the inertia switch connector and ground. • Is the resistance less than 5 ohms?	Yes No	▶ ▶	GO to PR6-2. REPAIR / REPLACE the "BK" wire. REPEAT PR6 to verify correction.
PR6-2	**CHECK INERTIA SWITCH**			
	• Disconnect and remove the fuel pump inertia switch. • Measure the resistance between the "GN / R" and "BK" terminals of the inertia switch under the following conditions:	Yes No	▶ ▶	GO to PR6-3. REPLACE the fuel pump inertia switch. REPEAT PR6 to verify correction.

Switch Position	Resistance
Open (tripped, popped out)	Less than 5 ohms
Closed (set, pushed in)	Greater than 10,000 ohms

	• Are the resistances OK? NOTE: Depress the button to close (set) the inertia switch. Sharply shake to open (trip) the inertia switch. If the button does not trip, replace the inertia switch.			
PR6-3	**CHECK INERTIA SWITCH LEAD**			
	• Measure the resistance of the "GN / R" wire between the passive restraint control module and the fuel pump inertia switch. • Is the resistance less than 5 ohms?	Yes No	▶ ▶	GO to PR6-4. REPAIR / REPLACE the "GN / R" wire. REPEAT PR6 to verify correction.
PR6-4	**CHECK FUEL CUT OUT LIGHT CIRCUIT**			
	• Key OFF. • Connect the passive restraint control module connectors. • Measure the voltage on the "GN / R" wire at the passive restraint control module (connector #2). • Is the voltage greater than 7 volts?	Yes No	▶ ▶	REPEAT PR6 to verify correction. REPLACE the fuel cut out indicator light in the instrument panel. REPEAT PR6 to verify correction.

FM8019200348030X

Fig. 16   System diagnosis (Part 3 of 11). 1992–93 Escort & Tracer

TEST STEP		RESULT	▶	ACTION TO TAKE
PR7	**CHECK DOOR SWITCH INPUTS**			
	• Key OFF. • Disconnect the passive restraint control module connectors. • Measure the resistance between the following wires at the passive restraint control module connectors under the following conditions:	Yes No	▶ ▶	GO to PR8. GO to PR7-1.

Door Position	Driver's side (BL / Y and BK)	Passenger's side (BL / O and BK)
Door Open	Less than 5 ohms	Less than 5 ohms
Door Closed	Greater than 10,000 ohms	Greater than 10,000 ohms

	• Are the resistances OK?			

TEST STEP		RESULT	▶	ACTION TO TAKE
PR7-1	**CHECK DOOR SWITCH GROUNDS**			
	• Locate and disconnect the driver's and passenger's door switch connectors (inside the door). • Measure the resistance between the "BK" wire at the door switch connectors and ground. • Are the resistances less than 5 ohms?	Yes No	▶ ▶	GO to PR7-2. REPAIR / REPLACE the "BK" wire in question. REPEAT PR7 to verify correction.
PR7-2	**CHECK DOOR SWITCH**			
	• Measure the resistance between the following wires at the door switch connectors under the following conditions:	Yes No	▶ ▶	GO to PR7-3. REPLACE the door latch assembly in question. REPEAT PR7 to verify correction.

Door Position	Driver's side (BL / Y and BK)	Passenger's side (BL / O and BK)
Door Open	Less than 5 ohms	Less than 5 ohms
Door Closed	Greater than 10,000 ohms	Greater than 10,000 ohms

	• Are the resistances OK?			

FM8019200348040X

Fig. 16   System diagnosis (Part 4 of 11). 1992–93 Escort & Tracer

TEST STEP	RESULT	▶	ACTION TO TAKE
PR7-3 CHECK DOOR SWITCH LEAD	Yes	▶	REPEAT PR7.
• Disconnect the door switches and passive restraint control module connectors.	No	▶	REPAIR / REPLACE the wire in question. REPEAT PR7 to verify correction.
• Measure the resistance of the following wires:			

	From the Module	To the Door Latch Switch
Driver's Side	BL / Y	BL / Y
Passenger's Side	BL / O	BL / O

• Are the resistances OK?

TEST STEP	RESULT	▶	ACTION TO TAKE
PR8 CHECK A-PILLAR (FRONT) LIMIT SWITCH INPUTS	Yes	▶	GO to PR9.
• Position the carriers at the A-pillars.	No	▶	GO to PR8-1.
• Key OFF.			
• Disconnect the passive restraint control module connectors.			
• Measure the resistance between the following wires at the passive restraint control module connectors under the following conditions:			

Carrier Position	Driver's side (Y BL and BK)	Passenger's side (BL / BK and BK)
Carrier at A-pillar	Less than 5 ohms	Less than 5 ohms
Carrier not at A-pillar	Greater than 10,000 ohms	Greater than 10,000 ohms

• Are the resistances OK?

TEST STEP	RESULT	▶	ACTION TO TAKE
PR8-1 CHECK A-PILLAR (FRONT) LIMIT SWITCH GROUND	Yes	▶	GO to PR8-2.
• Locate and disconnect the A-pillar (front) limit switch connectors.	No	▶	REPAIR / REPLACE the "BK" wire(s) in question. REPEAT PR8 to verify correction.
• Measure the resistance between the "BK" wires at the limit switch connectors and ground.			
• Are the resistances less than 5 ohms?			

FM8019200348050X

Fig. 16   System diagnosis (Part 5 of 11). 1992–93 Escort & Tracer

TEST STEP	RESULT	▶	ACTION TO TAKE
PR8-2 CHECK A-PILLAR (FRONT) LIMIT SWITCH	Yes	▶	GO to PR8-3.
• Disconnect the A-pillar (front) limit switch connectors.	No	▶	REPLACE the A-pillar (front) limit switch(es). REPEAT PR8 to verify correction.
• Measure the resistance between the following wires at the limit switches under the following conditions:			

Carrier Position	Driver's side (Y / BL and BK)	Passenger's side (BL / BK and BK)
Carrier at A-pillar	Less than 5 ohms	Less than 5 ohms
Carrier not at A-pillar	Greater than 10,000 ohms	Greater than 10,000 ohms

• Are the resistances OK?

TEST STEP	RESULT	▶	ACTION TO TAKE
PR8-3 CHECK A-PILLAR (FRONT) LIMIT SWITCH LEAD	Yes	▶	REPEAT PR8.
• Key OFF.	No	▶	REPAIR / REPLACE the wire in question. REPEAT PR8 to verify correction.
• Disconnect the A-pillar (front) limit switches and the passive restraint control module connectors.			
• Measure the resistances of the "Y / BL" wire (driver's side) and the "BL / BK" to "BL / W" wire (passenger's side) between the module and limit switch.			
• Are the resistances less than 5 ohms?			

TEST STEP	RESULT	▶	ACTION TO TAKE
PR9 CHECK B-PILLAR (REAR) LIMIT SWITCH INPUTS	Yes	▶	GO to PR10.
• Key OFF.	No	▶	GO to PR9-1.
• Disconnect the passive restraint control module connectors.			
• Measure the resistance between the following wires at the passive restraint control module connectors under the following conditions:			

Carrier Position	Driver's side (Y / R and BK)	Passenger's side (W and BK)
Carrier at B-pillar	Less than 5 ohms	Less than 5 ohms
Carrier not at B-pillar	Greater than 10,000 ohms	Greater than 10,000 ohms

• Are the resistances OK?

FM8019200348060X

Fig. 16   System diagnosis (Part 6 of 11). 1992–93 Escort & Tracer

TEST STEP	RESULT	▶	ACTION TO TAKE
PR9-1 CHECK B-PILLAR (REAR) LIMIT SWITCH GROUND	Yes	▶	GO to PR9-2.
• Locate and disconnect the B-pillar (rear) limit switch connectors.	No	▶	REPAIR / REPLACE the "BK" wire(s) in question. REPEAT PR9 to verify correction.
• Measure the resistance between the "BK" wire at the limit switch connectors and ground.			
• Are the resistances less than 5 ohms?			
PR9-2 CHECK B-PILLAR (REAR) LIMIT SWITCH	Yes	▶	GO to PR9-3.
• Disconnect the B-pillar (rear) limit switch connectors.	No	▶	REPLACE the passive restraint track and motor assembly in question. REPEAT PR9 to verify correction.
• Measure the resistance between the following wires at the limit switches under the following conditions:			

Carrier Position	Driver's side (Y / R and BK)	Passenger's side (W and BK)
Carrier at B-pillar	Less than 5 ohm	Less than 5 ohm
Carrier not at B-pillar	Greater than 10,000 ohms	Greater than 10,000 ohms

• Are the resistances OK?

TEST STEP	RESULT	▶	ACTION TO TAKE
PR9-3 CHECK B-PILLAR (REAR) LIMIT SWITCH LEAD	Yes	▶	REPEAT PR9.
• Key OFF.	No	▶	REPAIR / REPLACE the wire in question. REPEAT PR9 to verify correction.
• Disconnect the B-pillar (rear) limit switches and the passive restraint control module connectors.			
• Measure the resistances of the "Y / R" wire (driver's side) and the "W" wire (passenger's side) between the module and limit switch.			
• Are the resistances less than 5 ohms?			

FM8019200348070X

Fig. 16   System diagnosis (Part 7 of 11). 1992–93 Escort & Tracer

TEST STEP	RESULT	▶	ACTION TO TAKE
PR10 CHECK PASSIVE RESTRAINT MOTOR INPUTS	Yes	▶	GO to PR11.
• Key OFF.	No	▶	GO to PR10-1.
• Disconnect the passive restraint control module connectors.			
• Make the following connections at the passive restraint control module connectors to move the carrier from the A-pillar to the B-pillar.			

	FROM A TO B	
Reference	Driver's Side	Passenger's Side
Ground	BR (Pin 1J or 1H)	Y / GN (Pin 2J or 2H)
12 V	BL - GN (Pin 1L or 1K)	W - BK (Pin 2L or 2M)

• Does the carrier move from the A-pillar to the B-pillar?
• Reverse the power and ground leads.
• Does the carrier move from the B-pillar to the A-pillar?

TEST STEP	RESULT	▶	ACTION TO TAKE
PR10-1 CHECK PASSIVE RESTRAINT MOTOR	Yes	▶	GO to PR10-2.
• Key OFF.	No	▶	REPLACE the passive restraint track and motor assembly. REPEAT PR10 to verify correction.
• Disconnect the passive restraint motor connectors.			
• Make the following connections at the passive restraint motors to move the carrier from the A-pillar to the B-pillar.			

	FROM A TO B	
Reference	Driver's Side	Passenger's Side
Ground	BL	Y
12 V	Y	BL

• Does the carrier move from the A-pillar to the B-pillar?
• Reverse the power and ground leads.
• Does the carrier move from the B-pillar to the A-pillar?

FM8019200348080X

Fig. 16   System diagnosis (Part 8 of 11). 1992–93 Escort & Tracer

TEST STEP		RESULT	▶	ACTION TO TAKE
PR10-2 CHECK PASSIVE RESTRAINT MOTOR LEADS				
• Key OFF.		Yes	▶	REPEAT **PR10**.
• Disconnect the passive restraint module connectors and passive restraint motors.		No	▶	REPAIR / REPLACE the wire(s) in question. REPEAT **PR10** to verify correction.
• Measure the resistance of the following wires between the module and the motor.				
— "BL / GN" (driver's side) - pins 1L and 1K				
— "BR" (driver's side) - pins 1J and 1H				
— "W / BK" (passenger's side) - pins 2L and 2M				
— "Y / GN" (passenger's side) - pins 2J and 2H				
• Are the resistances less than 5 ohms?				

TEST STEP		RESULT	▶	ACTION TO TAKE
PR11 CHECK RETRACTOR SWITCH INPUTS				
• Disconnect the passive restraint control module connectors.		Yes	▶	GO to **PR12**.
• Measure the resistance between the following wires at the passive restraint control module connectors under the following conditions:		No	▶	GO to **PR11-1**.

Shoulder Belt Position	Driver's side (O / GN and BK)	Passenger's side (P and BK)
Shoulder Belt Buckled	Less than 5 ohms	Less than 5 ohms
Shoulder Belt Spooled In	Greater than 10,000 ohms	Greater than 10,000 ohms

• Are the resistances OK?

TEST STEP		RESULT	▶	ACTION TO TAKE
PR11-1 CHECK RETRACTOR SWITCH GROUNDS				
• Locate and disconnect the retractor switch connector (in the center console).		Yes	▶	GO to **PR11-2**.
• Measure the resistance between the "BK" wires at the retractor switch connector and ground.		No	▶	REPAIR / REPLACE the "BK" wire(s) in question. REPEAT **PR11** to verify correction.
• Are the resistances less than 5 ohms?				

FM8019200348090X

Fig. 16 System diagnosis (Part 9 of 11). 1992–93 Escort & Tracer

TEST STEP		RESULT	▶	ACTION TO TAKE
PR12-2 CHECK FASTEN BELT WARNING LIGHT				
• Key OFF.		Yes	▶	GO to **PR12-3**.
• Locate the instrument cluster connectors.		No	▶	REPLACE the bulb. REPEAT **PR12** to verify correction.
• Apply 12 volts to the "BK / Y" wire at the instrument cluster connector.				
• Ground the "LG" wire at the instrument cluster connector.				
• Does the fasten belt indicator light illuminate?				
NOTE: If the fasten belt indicator light doesn't illuminate after replacing the bulb, then service the instrument cluster.				

TEST STEP		RESULT	▶	ACTION TO TAKE
PR12-3 CHECK FASTEN BELT WARNING LIGHT LEAD				
• Measure the resistance of the "LG" wire between the passive restraint control module and instrument cluster.		Yes	▶	REPEAT **PR12**.
		No	▶	REPAIR / REPLACE the "LG" wire. REPEAT **PR12** to verify correction.
• Is the resistance less than 5 ohms?				

TEST STEP		RESULT	▶	ACTION TO TAKE
PR13 CHECK WARNING CHIME OUTPUT				
• Disconnect the passive restraint control module connector (# 1).		Yes	▶	REPLACE the passive restraint control module. REPEAT the test.
• Ground the "Y / BK" wire at the passive restraint control module connector (# 1).				
• Does the warning chime sound?		No	▶	GO to **PR13-1**.

TEST STEP		RESULT	▶	ACTION TO TAKE
PR13-1 CHECK WARNING CHIME MODULE				
• Locate the warning chime module connector.		Yes	▶	GO to **PR13-2**.
• Key in the ignition switch.		No	▶	DIAGNOSE / SERVICE the warning chime module.
• Doors closed (or door switches depressed).				
• Ground the "Y / BK" wire (pin A) at the warning chime module connector.				
• Does the warning chime module sound?				
PR13-2 CHECK WARNING CHIME MODULE LEAD				
• Key OFF.		Yes	▶	REPEAT **PR13**.
• Disconnect the passive restraint control module connector (# 1).		No	▶	REPAIR / REPLACE the "Y / BK" wire. REPEAT **PR13** to verify correction.
• Locate and disconnect the warning chime module connector.				
• Measure the resistance of the "Y / BK" wire between the warning chime module connector and the passive restraint module connector (# 1).				
• Is the resistance less than 5 ohm?				

FM8019200348110X

Fig. 16 System diagnosis (Part 11 of 11). 1992–93 Escort & Tracer

TEST STEP		RESULT	▶	ACTION TO TAKE
PR11-2 CHECK RETRACTOR SWITCH				
• Disconnect the retractor switch connector.		Yes	▶	GO to **PR11-3**.
• Measure the resistance between the following wires at the retractor switch under the following conditions:		No	▶	REPLACE the center console spool and belt assembly. REPEAT **PR11** to verify correction.

Shoulder Belt Position	Driver's side (O / GN and BK)	Passenger's side (P and BK)
Shoulder Belt Buckled	Less than 5 ohms	Less than 5 ohms
Shoulder Belt Spooled In	Greater than 10,000 ohms	Greater than 10,000 ohms

• Are the resistances OK?

NOTE: The retractor switch is part of the center console spool and belt assembly.

TEST STEP		RESULT	▶	ACTION TO TAKE
PR11-3 CHECK RETRACTOR SWITCH LEADS				
• Disconnect the passive restraint control module connectors and retractor switch.		Yes	▶	REPEAT **PR11**.
• Measure the resistance of the following wires between the retractor switch and module.		No	▶	REPAIR / REPLACE the wire in question. REPEAT **PR11** to verify correction.
— "O / GN" (driver's side)				
— "P" (passenger's side)				
• Are the resistances less than 5 ohms?				

TEST STEP		RESULT	▶	ACTION TO TAKE
PR12 CHECK FASTEN BELT WARNING LIGHT OUTPUT				
• Disconnect the passive restraint control module connector (# 1).		Yes	▶	GO to **PR13**.
• Key ON.		No	▶	GO to **PR12-1**.
• Ground the "LG" wire at the passive restraint control module connector (# 1).				
• Does the fasten belt indicator light illuminate?				

TEST STEP		RESULT	▶	ACTION TO TAKE
PR12-1 CHECK FASTEN BELT WARNING LIGHT POWER SUPPLY				
• Locate the instrument cluster connector.		Yes	▶	GO to **PR12-2**.
• Key ON.		No	▶	REPAIR / REPLACE the "BK / Y" wire. REPEAT **PR12** to verify correction.
• Measure the voltage on the "BK / Y" wire at the instrument cluster connector.				
• Is the voltage greater than 10 volts?				

FM8019200348100X

Fig. 16 System diagnosis (Part 10 of 11). 1992–93 Escort & Tracer

CONDITION	POSSIBLE SOURCE	ACTION
• Neither Belt Will Leave the Center Body Pillar or Front Body Pillar	• Power to passive restraint control module. • Circuit. • Passive restraint control module.	• GO to Pinpoint Test A1.
• One Belt Will Not Leave the Center Body Pillar	• Door latch switch input open. • A-pillar limit switch input grounded. • Motor / motor wiring. • Passive restraint control module.	• GO to Pinpoint Test B1.
• One Belt Will Not Leave the Front Body Pillar	• Door latch switch input grounded. • B-pillar limit switch input grounded. • Safety belt retractor motor wiring. • Passive restraint control module.	• GO to Pinpoint Test C1.
• Belt Carrier (Transport) Jumps or Clicks at Center Body Pillar While Ignition Is ON	• B-pillar limit switch input open. • Wiring and connectors between B-pillar limit switch and passive restraint control module.	• GO to Pinpoint Test D1.
• Belt Carrier (Transport) Jumps or Clicks at Front Body Pillar While Door Is Open	• A-pillar limit switch input is open. • Wiring and connectors between A-pillar limit switch and passive restraint control module.	• GO to Pinpoint Test E1.

FM8029400007000X

Fig. 17 Pinpoint test reference chart. 1994 Escort & Tracer

DIAGNOSTIC CHART INDEX

Test	Description	Year	Page No.	Fig. No.
COUGAR & THUNDERBIRD				
A	Track "A" Limit Switch	1992-94	18-38	28
B	Track "B" Limit Switch	1992-94	18-38	29
C	Door Ajar Switch	1992-94	18-38	30
D	Shoulder Belt Retractor Switch	1992-93	18-39	31
E	Grounds	1992-94	18-39	34
F	Voltage Check	1992-94	18-40	35
G	Motor	1992-93	18-40	36
H	Warnings	1992-93	18-40	38
J	Restraint Module	1992-94	18-41	41
K	Passive Restraint Quick Test	1992-93	18-41	42
ESCORT & TRACER				
A	Neither Belt Will Leave The Center Body Pillar Or Front Body Pillar	1994	18-34	18
B	One Belt Will Not Leave The Front Body Pillar	1994	18-34	19
C	One Belt Will Not Leave The Center Body Pillar	1994	18-34	20
D	Belt Carrier Jumps Or Clicks At Center Body Pillar While Ignition Is On	1994	18-35	21
E	Belt Carrier Jumps Or Clicks At Front Body Pillar While Door Is Open	1994	18-35	22
FESTIVA				
PR	System Diagnosis	1992-93	18-42	43
PROBE				
PR	System Diagnosis	1992-94	18-43	44
TEMPO & TOPAZ				
A	Track "A" Limit Switch	1992-94	18-38	28
B	Track "B" Limit Switch	1992-94	18-38	29
C	Door Ajar Switch	1992-94	18-38	30
D	Spool Release Switch	1992-93	18-39	32
D	Emergency Release Lever Switches Diagnosis	1994	18-39	33
E	Grounds	1992-94	18-39	34
F	Voltage Check	1992-94	18-40	35
G	Motor	1992-94	18-40	37
H	Warnings	1992-93	18-40	39
H	Warning Indicators Diagnosis	1994	18-40	40
J	Restraint Module	1992-94	18-41	41

TEST STEP	RESULT	►	ACTION TO TAKE
B1 CHECK DOOR LATCH SWITCH • Perform the Door Latch Switch component test in this section. • Does the door latch switch test OK?	Yes No	► ►	Go to B2. REPLACE the door latch switch.
B2 CHECK THE B-PILLAR LIMIT SWITCH • Perform the B-Pillar Limit Switch component test in this section on the inoperative side of the vehicle. • Does the B-pillar limit switch test OK?	Yes No	► ►	Go to B3. REPLACE the front seat shoulder strap track.
B3 CHECK THE SAFETY BELT RETRACTOR MOTOR • Perform the Safety Belt Retractor Motor component test in this section on the inoperative safety belt retractor motor. • Does the safety belt retractor motor test OK?	Yes No	► ►	Go to B4. REPLACE the front seat shoulder strap track.
B4 CHECK WIRE BETWEEN PASSIVE RESTRAINT CONTROL MODULE AND DOOR LATCH SWITCH • Key OFF. • Locate and disconnect the passive restraint control module connector #2. • Disconnect the door latch switch connector. • Measure the resistance of the "BL/Y" wire (driver's side inoperative) or "BL/O" switch (passenger's side inoperative) between the passive restraint control module connector and ground. • Is the resistance greater than 10,000 ohms?	Yes No	► ►	Go to B5. SERVICE the wire in question.

FM8029400009010X

Fig. 19   Test B: One Belt Will Not Leave The Front Body Pillar (Part 1 of 2). 1994 Escort & Tracer

TEST STEP	RESULT	►	ACTION TO TAKE
A1 CHECK FUSES. • Locate the fuse junction panel. • Check the 30 A BELT and 15 A METER fuses. • Are the fuses OK?	Yes No	► ►	GO to A4. GO to A2.
A2 CHECK SYSTEM • Replace the blown fuse(s). • Key ON. • Did the fuse(s) fail again?	Yes No	► ►	GO to A3. GO to A4.

FM8029400008010X

Fig. 18   Test A: Neither Belt Will Leave The Center Body Pillar Or Front Body Pillar (Part 1 of 2). 1994 Escort & Tracer

TEST STEP	RESULT	►	ACTION TO TAKE
B5 CHECK WIRE BETWEEN PASSIVE RESTRAINT CONTROL MODULE AND B-PILLAR LIMIT SWITCH • Key OFF. • Disconnect the passive restraint control module connector #1 (driver's side inoperative) or #2 (passenger's side inoperative). • Disconnect the B-pillar limit switch connector on the inoperative side of the vehicle. • Measure the resistance of the "Y/R" wire (driver's side inoperative) or "W" wire (passenger's side inoperative) between the passive restraint control module connector and ground. • Is the resistance greater than 10,000 ohms?	Yes No	► ►	Go to B6. SERVICE the wire in question.
B6 CHECK WIRES TO SAFETY BELT RETRACTOR MOTOR • Key OFF. • Disconnect the passive restraint control module connector #1 (driver's side inoperative) or #2 (passenger's side inoperative). • Disconnect the B-pillar limit switch connector on the inoperative side of the vehicle. • Measure the resistances of the "BL/GN" and "BR" wires (driver's side inoperative) or "Y/GN" and "W/BK" wires (passenger's side inoperative) between the passive restraint control module connector and the B-pillar limit switch connector. • Are the resistances less than 5 ohms?	Yes No	► ►	REPLACE the passive restraint control module. SERVICE the wire(s) in question.

FM8029400009020X

Fig. 19   Test B: One Belt Will Not Leave The Front Body Pillar (Part 2 of 2). 1994 Escort & Tracer

TEST STEP	RESULT	►	ACTION TO TAKE
A3 CHECK FOR SHORT TO GROUND • Key OFF. • Locate and disconnect the passive restraint control module connectors, instrument cluster connectors, and shift lock actuator connector. • Locate and disconnect the 18-pin and 15-pin interior fuse junction panel connectors. • Measure the resistance between the "Y" wire and/or the "BK/Y" wire between the interior fuse junction panel connector(s) and ground. • Are the resistance(s) less than 5 ohms?	Yes No	► ►	SERVICE the wire(s) in question. GO to A4.
A4 CHECK PASSIVE RESTRAINT CONTROL MODULE BATTERY/IGNITION SUPPLY • Key OFF. • Disconnect the passive restraint control module connectors. • Measure the voltage on the "Y" wires at passive restraint control module connector #1. • Key ON. • Measure the voltage on the "BK/Y" wire at passive restraint control module connector #2. • Are the voltages greater than 10 volts?	Yes No	► ►	GO to A5. SERVICE the wire(s) in question.
A5 CHECK PASSIVE RESTRAINT CONTROL MODULE GROUNDS • Key OFF. • Disconnect the passive restraint control module connectors. • Measure the resistance between each "BK" wire at the passive restraint control module connectors and ground. • Are the resistances less than 5 ohms?	Yes No	► ►	REPLACE the passive restraint control module. SERVICE the "BK" wire in question.

FM8029400008020X

Fig. 18   Test A: Neither Belt Will Leave The Center Body Pillar Or Front Body Pillar (Part 2 of 2). 1994 Escort & Tracer

TEST STEP	RESULT	►	ACTION TO TAKE
C1 CHECK DOOR LATCH SWITCH • Perform the Door Latch Switch component test in this section on the inoperative side of the vehicle. • Does the door latch switch test OK?	Yes No	► ►	Go to C2. REPLACE the door latch switch
C2 CHECK A-PILLAR LIMIT SWITCH • Perform the A-Pillar Limit Switch component test in this section on the inoperative side of the vehicle. • Does the A-pillar limit switch test OK?	Yes No Yes	► ►	Go to C3. REPLACE the front seat shoulder strap track.
C3 CHECK SAFETY BELT RETRACTOR MOTOR • Perform the Safety Belt Retractor Motor component test in ... on the inoperative belt retractor motor. • Does the safety belt retractor motor test OK?	Yes No	► ►	Go to C4. REPLACE the front seat shoulder strap track.
C4 CHECK WIRE BETWEEN PASSIVE RESTRAINT CONTROL MODULE AND COURTESY LAMP SWITCH • Key OFF. • Locate and disconnect the passive restraint control module connector #2. • Disconnect the door latch switch connector on the inoperative side of the vehicle. • Measure the resistance of the "BL/Y" wire (driver's side inoperative) or "BL/O" wire (passenger's side inoperative) between the passive restraint control module connector #2 and the door latch switch connector. • Is the resistance less than 5 ohms?	Yes No	► ►	Go to C5. SERVICE the wire in question.
C5 CHECK DOOR LATCH SWITCH GROUND • Disconnect the door latch switch connector on the inoperative side of the vehicle. • Measure the resistance of the "BK" wire between the door latch switch connector and ground. • Is the resistance less than 5 ohms?	Yes No	► ►	Go to C6. SERVICE the "BK" wire.

FM8029400010010X

Fig. 20   Test C: One Belt Will Not Leave The Center Body Pillar (Part 1 of 2). 1994 Escort & Tracer

TEST STEP	RESULT	▶ ACTION TO TAKE
C6 CHECK WIRE BETWEEN PASSIVE RESTRAINT CONTROL MODULE AND A-PILLAR LIMIT SWITCH • Key OFF. • Disconnect the passive restraint control module connector #1 (driver's side inoperative) or #2 (passenger's side inoperative). • Disconnect the A-pillar limit switch connector on the inoperative side of the vehicle. • Measure the resistance of the "Y BL" wire (driver's side inoperative) or "BL W" wire (passenger's side inoperative) between the passive restraint control module connector and ground. • **Is the resistance greater than 10,000 ohms?**	Yes No	▶ Go to C7. ▶ SERVICE the wire in question.
C7 CHECK WIRES TO SAFETY BELT RETRACTOR MOTOR • Key OFF. • Disconnect the passive restraint control module connectors #1 (driver's side inoperative) or #2 (passenger's side inoperative). • Disconnect the B-pillar limit switch connector on the inoperative side of the vehicle. • Measure the resistances of the "BL GN" and "BR" wires (driver's side inoperative) or "Y GN" and "W BK" wires (passenger's side inoperative) between the passive restraint control module connector and the B-pillar limit switch connector. • **Are the resistances less than 5 ohms?**	Yes No	▶ REPLACE the passive restraint control module. ▶ SERVICE the wire(s) in question.

FM8029400010020X

Fig. 20 Test C: One Belt Will Not Leave The Center Body Pillar (Part 2 of 2). 1994 Escort & Tracer

TEST STEP	RESULT	▶ ACTION TO TAKE
D1 CHECK B-PILLAR LIMIT SWITCH • Perform the B-Pillar Limit Switch component test in this section on the inoperative side(s) of the vehicle. • **Does the B-pillar limit switch test OK?**	Yes No	▶ Go to D2. ▶ REPLACE the front seat shoulder strap track.
D2 CHECK WIRES TO B-PILLAR LIMIT SWITCH • Key OFF. • Locate and disconnect the passive restraint control module connector #1 (driver's side inoperative) or #2 (passenger's side inoperative). • Disconnect the B-pillar limit switch connector on the inoperative side(s) of the vehicle. • Measure the resistance of the "Y R" wire (driver's side inoperative) or "W" wire (passenger's side inoperative) between the passive restraint control module connector and the B-pillar limit switch connector. • Is the resistance less than 5 ohms?	Yes No	▶ Go to D3. ▶ SERVICE the wire in question.
D3 CHECK B-PILLAR LIMIT SWITCH • Disconnect the B-pillar limit switch connector on the inoperative side(s) of the vehicle. • Measure the resistance of the "BK" wire between the B-pillar limit switch connector and ground. • **Is the resistance less than 5 ohms?**	Yes No	▶ REPLACE the passive restraint control module. ▶ SERVICE the "BK" wire.

FM8029400011000X

Fig. 21 Test D: Belt Carrier Jumps Or Clicks At Center Body Pillar While Ignition Is On. 1994 Escort & Tracer

TEST STEP	RESULT	▶ ACTION TO TAKE
E1 CHECK A-PILLAR LIMIT SWITCH • Perform the A-Pillar Limit Switch component test in this section on the inoperative side(s) of the vehicle. • **Does the a-pillar limit switch test OK?**	Yes No	▶ GO to E2. ▶ REPLACE the front seat shoulder strap track.

FM8029400012010X

Fig. 22 Test E: Belt Carrier Jumps Or Clicks At Front Body Pillar While Door Is Open (Part 1 of 2). 1994 Escort & Tracer

TEST STEP	RESULT	▶ ACTION TO TAKE
E2 CHECK WIRE TO A-PILLAR LIMIT SWITCH • Key OFF. • Locate and disconnect the passive restraint control module connector #1 (driver's side inoperative) or #2 (passenger's side inoperative). • Disconnect the A-pillar limit switch connector on the inoperative side(s) of the vehicle. • Measure the resistance of the "Y BL" wire (driver's side inoperative) or "BL W" wire (passenger's side inoperative) between the passive restraint control module connector and the A-pillar limit switch connector. • Is the resistance less than 5 ohms?	Yes No	▶ GO to E3. ▶ SERVICE the wire(s) in question.
E3 CHECK A-PILLAR LIMIT SWITCH GROUND • Disconnect the A-pillar limit switch connector on the inoperative side(s) of the vehicle. • Measure the resistance of the "BK" wire between the A-pillar limit switch connector and ground. • Is the resistance less than 5 ohms?	Yes No	▶ REPLACE the passive restraint control module. ▶ SERVICE the "BK" wire.

FM8029400012020X

Fig. 22 Test E: Belt Carrier Jumps Or Clicks At Front Body Pillar While Door Is Open (Part 2 of 2). 1994 Escort & Tracer

Vehicle Condition	EFI Fuel Switch (Inertia)		Door Ajar Switch		A Pillar Limit Switch		B Pillar Limit Switch	
	Closed	Open	Closed	Open	Closed	Open	Closed	Open
Ignition ON (after entry)								
• Door Closed Before Belt starts to move from A to B-Pillar	X		X			X	X	
• Door Closed Belt moving from A to B-Pillar	X		X		X		X	
• Door Closed Before belt stopped at B-Pillar	X		X		X			X
• Open Door Before belt starts to move from B to A-Pillar	X			X	X			X
• Door Opened Belt moving from B to A-Pillar	X			X	X		X	
• Door Opened Belt stopped at A-Pillar	X			X	X		X	
Ignition OFF (before exit)								
• Parked — Door Closed Belt at B-Pillar	X		X		X			X
• Parked — Open Door Before belt starts to move from B to A-Pillar	X			X	X			X
• Parked — Door Opened Belt moving from B to A-Pillar	X			X	X		X	
• Parked — Door Opened Belt stopped at A-Pillar	X			X	X		X	
• Parked — Close Door Belt stays at A-Pillar	X		X		X		X	
Impact — Ignition On/Off								
• Ign. On — Door Opened (upon impact) Belt stays at B-Pillar		X		X	X			X
• Ign. Off — Door Open (after impact) Belt moves from B to A-Pillar (Belt at A-Pillar)		X		X	X		X	

FM80192003490000X

Fig. 23 Driver & passenger operational logic chart. Cougar, Thunderbird & 1992–93 Tempo & Topaz

Vehicle Condition	MFI Inertia Fuel Shutoff Switch		Door Ajar Switch		A Pillar Limit Switch		B Pillar Limit Switch	
	Closed	Open	Closed	Open	Closed	Open	Closed	Open
Ignition ON (after entry)								
●Door Closed Before Belt Starts to Move from A to B-Pillar	X		X		X		X	
●Door Closed, Belt Moving from A to B-Pillar	X			X	X		X	
●Door Closed Before Belt Stopped at B-Pillar	X			X	X			X
●Open Door Before Belt Starts to Move from B to A-Pillar	X		X		X			X

(Continued)

FM8029400003010X

Fig. 24   Driver & passenger operational logic chart (Part 1 of 2). 1994 Tempo & Topaz

Vehicle Condition	MFI Inertia Fuel Shutoff Switch		Door Ajar Switch		A Pillar Limit Switch		B Pillar Limit Switch	
	Closed	Open	Closed	Open	Closed	Open	Closed	Open
●Door Opened, Belt Moving From B to A-Pillar	X		X		X		X	
Door Opened, Belt Stopped at A-Pillar	X		X			X	X	
Ignition OFF (before exit)								
●Parked—Door Closed, Belt at B-Pillar	X			X	X			X
●Parked—Open Door Before Belt Starts to Move from B to A-Pillar	X		X		X			X
●Parked—Door Opened, Belt Moving from B to A-Pillar	X		X		X		X	
●Parked—Door Opened, Belt Stopped at A-Pillar	X		X			X	X	
●Parked—Close Door, Belt Stays at A-Pillar	X			X	X		X	
Impact—Ignition On/Off								
●Ignition On—Door Opened (Upon Impact), Belt Stays at B-Pillar		X	X		X			X
●Ignition Off—Door Open (After Impact), Belt Moves from B to A-Pillar (Belt at A-Pillar)		X	X			X	X	

FM8029400003020X

Fig. 24   Driver & passenger operational logic chart (Part 2 of 2). 1994 Tempo & Topaz

Action	Result
Belt doesn't properly reach B-pillar; after approximately 7.5 seconds	Fasten belt indicator (IP) flashes
Release lever in UP position, Ignition ON	1. Fasten belt indicator (IP) flashes 2. Release lever warning indicator flashes 3. Chime sounds continuously

FM8019200350000X

Fig. 25   Function table. Cougar, Tempo, Thunderbird & Topaz

CONDITION	POSSIBLE SOURCE	ACTION
• Belt Transport Motor Will Not Operate	• Battery. • Inertia switch. • Wiring. • Door Ajar switch. • Function control module. • Motor.	• Test battery, replace if necessary. • Reset switch. If system is still not operating, Go to Pinpoint Test F. • Go to Pinpoint Test E. • Go to Pinpoint Test C. • Go to Pinpoint Test J. • Go to Pinpoint Test G.
• Belt Transport Motor Only Moves Belt to A-pillar, Warning Chime and Warning Indicator Do Not Function, Inertia Switch Not Activated	• Wiring. • Function control module. • B-pillar limit switch.	• Go to Pinpoint Test F. • Go to Pinpoint Test J. • Go to Pinpoint Test B.
• Belt Transport Motors Not Operating, Warning Chime and Indicator Do Not Function	• Battery. • Inertia switch. • Limit switches. • Function control module. • Wiring.	• Test battery, replace if necessary. • Reset switch. If system is still not operating, Go to Pinpoint Test F. • Go to Pinpoint Tests A and B. • Go to Pinpoint Test J. • Go to Pinpoint Test E.
• Driver Belt Transport Always Remains at B-pillar, Once Positioned at B-pillar, Driver Must Release Shoulder Belt Emergency Buckle	• Wiring. • Driver front "A" limit switch. • Door Ajar switch.	• Go to Pinpoint Test E. • Go to Pinpoint Test A. • Go to Pinpoint Test C.
• Driver Belt Transport Motor Continues to Run After Reaching A-pillar Position. Motor Will Shut Off By Module After Six Seconds of Operation	• Driver front "A" limit switch. • Door Ajar switch.	• Go to Pinpoint Test A. • Go to Pinpoint Test C.
• Driver Belt Transport Always Remains at A-pillar	• Driver rear "B" limit switch. • Door Ajar switch.	• Go to Pinpoint Test B. • Go to Pinpoint Test C.
• Passenger Belt Transport Always Remains at B-pillar Once it Has Been Positioned at B-pillar, Passenger Will Have to Activate Emergency Release Buckle to Release Belt	• Passenger front "A" limit switch. • Wiring.	• Go to Pinpoint Test A. • Go to Pinpoint Test C.
• Passenger Belt Transport Always Remains at A-pillar, When Door Switch and Ignition Logic Try to Send Belt Transport to B-pillar, the Fasten Belt Indicator Will Remain On, Indicating Belt is Not Properly Positioned at B-pillar	• Passenger rear "B" limit switch. • Wiring.	• Go to Pinpoint Test B. • Go to Pinpoint Test F.
• Safety Belt Indicator and Chime Will Not Turn Off Even Though Belt(s) are at B-pillar	• Driver/Passenger rear "B" limit switch. • Wiring.	• Go to Pinpoint Test B. • Go to Pinpoint Test F.
• Belts Will Never Move With Ignition ON. Belts Will Move to A-pillar Only With Ignition OFF	• Wiring. • Inertia switch always open.	• Go to Pinpoint Test E. • Go to Pinpoint Test F.
• Belt Transport Motors Will Be Activated By Door Switch and Ignition Signals Even Though Inertia Switch is Tripped	• Wiring. • Inertia switch always shorted.	• Go to Pinpoint Test E. • Go to Pinpoint Test F.
• Fasten Belts Indicator Does Not Turn ON	• Wiring. • Bulb burnt.	• Go to Pinpoint Test H. • Check bulb. Replace if necessary.
• Fasten Belts Indicator Stays ON	• Wiring. • Retractor switch. • Bulb shorted to battery positive.	• Go to Pinpoint Test H. • Go to Pinpoint Test D. • Check bulb. Replace if necessary.

FM8019200351010X

Fig. 26   System diagnostic chart (Part 1 of 5). Cougar, Thunderbird & 1992–93 Tempo & Topaz

CONDITION	POSSIBLE SOURCE	ACTION
• Webbing Cannot Be Extracted	• Retractor blocked internally. • Foreign material in retractor. • Excessive spring load.	• Check, replace retractor unit if necessary. • Check, replace if necessary if necessary. • Check, replace retractor unit if necessary.
• Shoulder Belt Webbing Does Not Retract	• Insufficient spring load. • Retractor blocked internally. • Foreign material in retractor. • Bezel not located properly.	• Check, replace retractor unit if necessary. • Check, replace unit if necessary. • Clean, replace if necessary. • Locate properly.
• Shoulder Belt Webbing Twisted on Occupant	• Belt installed improperly.	• Check, correct orientation.
• Shoulder Belt Webbing Frayed	• Excessive wear, or sharp object cutting belt.	• Check retractor unit, replace if necessary.
• Lap Belt System Will Not Release	• Internal component failure. • Foreign material in buckle. • Buckle cannot be felt or seen. • Buckle falls down between seat and console.	• Check, and replace if necessary. • Clean and replace if necessary. • Locate or install buckle assembly. • Install grommet.
• Lap Belt Retractor Locks Prior to Tongue Engaging Into Buckle	• Customer does not use continuous motion to connect tongue into buckle.	• Refer to Owner Guide.
• Lap Belt Tongue Does Not Reach Buckle	• Webbing too short for occupant.	• Obtain belt service extender.
• Lap Belt Does Not Go Around Child Seat	• Webbing too short for child seat design.	• Obtain belt service extender.
• Excessive Pressure on Occupant During Normal Wearing	• Excessive retraction efforts. • Webbing too short to accommodate occupant.	• Check, replace retractor unit if necessary. • Obtain belt service extender.

FM8019200351030X

Fig. 26 System diagnostic chart (Part 3 of 5). Cougar, Thunderbird & 1992–93 Tempo & Topaz

CONDITION	POSSIBLE SOURCE	ACTION
• Belt Appears to Run Fine But Motor Stalls at A-pillar, Motor Could Get Warm	• "A" limit switch wire shorted to ground. "A" limit switch not opening.	• Check for pinched wire along A-pillar, or behind LH or RH side cowl panel. Check that carrier reaches "A" limit switch.
• Fasten Belt Indicator (IP) Remains Lit After 7-10 Seconds of Running to B-pillar and chime sounds. Belt Appears to Run Fine But Motor Stalls at B-pillar, Motor Could Get Warm	• "B" limit switch wire is shorted to ground. • Obstruction.	• Check for pinched wire under guide attachment screws. • Check for trim screw, obstruction in track or track seal that prevents the carrier from reaching the "B" limit switch.
• Belt Will Not Run, Module May Be Burned	• Motor wire shorted to ground.	• Check for short to ground on the motor circuit breaker terminals.
• Belt Will Not Run	• Inertia switch tripped. • Motor wire not connected.	• Reset (depress) fule pump inertia switch button. • Check for unconnected connectors on the motor, or behind LH and RH side cowl panels.

FM8019200351050X

Fig. 26 System diagnostic chart (Part 5 of 5). Cougar, Thunderbird & 1992–93 Tempo & Topaz

CONDITION	POSSIBLE SOURCE	ACTION
• Driver Belt Remains at B-Pillar, Does Not Move to A-Pillar	• Wiring. • Driver front "A" limit switch open. • Driver Door Ajar switch always open circuit.	• Go to Pinpoint Test A. • Go to Pinpoint Test A. • Go to Pinpoint Test C.
• Driver Belt Remains at A-Pillar, Does Not Move to B-Pillar	• Wiring. • Driver rear "B" limit switch open. • Driver Door Ajar switch always shorted to ground.	• Go to Pinpoint Test B. • Go to Pinpoint Test B. • Go to Pinpoint Test C.
• Passenger Belt Remains at B-Pillar, Does Not Move to A-Pillar	• Wiring. • Passenger front "A" limit switch open. • Passenger Door Ajar switch always open circuit.	• Go to Pinpoint Test A. • Go to Pinpoint Test A. • Go to Pinpoint Test C.
• Passenger Belt Remains at A-Pillar, Does Not Move to B-Pillar	• Wiring. • Passenger rear "B" limit switch open. • Passenger Door Ajar switch always shorted to ground.	• Go to Pinpoint Test A. • Go to Pinpoint Test B. • Go to Pinpoint Test C.
• Excessive Pressure on Occupant During Normal Wear	• Retractor spring wound too tightly.	• Replace.
• Tranaport System Does Not Move Belt Forward	• Anchor tab trim binds with track and/or vertical trim. • Electrical failure, "A" limit switch open.	• Adjust. • Go to Pinpoint Test A.
• Transport System Does Not Move Rearward	• Anchor tab trim binds with track and/or vertical trim. • Electrical failure, "B" limit switch open.	• Adjust. • Go to Pinpoint Test B.
• Transport System Moves Too Slowly	• Anchor tab cover binds with track and/or trim. • Low battery voltage. • Transport motor. • Tape distorted. • Gear stripped.	• Adjust. • Lubricate track. • Check, replace if necessary. • Go to Pinpoint Test G. • Check, replace if necessary. • Check, replace if necessary.
• Excessive Slack in Webbing	• Broken rewind spring. • Webbing interfering with retractor boot.	• Check, replace retractor unit if necessary. • Adjust boot or retractor on support assembly not installed properly.
• Shoulder Belt Will Not Move Rearward Past Top of B-pillar or Forward	• Insufficient strength. NOTE: System might be distorted through occupant use of belt as assist handle. • Foreign material or object in track assembly. • Shoulder belt retractor locked up. • Drive tape broken. • Dust seal ragged.	• Install new track. • Clean track and lubricate with Emralon 329 ESB-M99C71-A or equivalent. • Refer to Manual Override System. • Check, replace if necessary. • Check, replace if necessary.
• Lap Belt Retractor Webbing Protrudes Into Door Opening	• Retractor assembly blocked. • Foreign material in retractor. • Insufficient strength from rewind spring.	• Check, replace if necessary. • Check, replace if necessary. • Check, replace if necessary.

FM8019200351020X

Fig. 26 System diagnostic chart (Part 2 of 5). Cougar, Thunderbird & 1992–93 Tempo & Topaz

CONDITION	POSSIBLE SOURCE	ACTION
• Belt Runs to A-pillar Only, Belt Will Not Run Back to B-pillar	• Door switch wire shorted to ground. • "B" limit switch wire not connected. • "B" limit switch plunger stuck in depressed position.	• Check for pinched wire behind door trim panel. • Check for unconnected connectors near motor, behind LH and RH side cowl panel, or on "B" limit switch. • Correct jammed switch or replace "B" limit switch.
• Belt Runs to B-pillar Only, Belt Will Not Run Forward to A-pillar.	• Door switch wire not connected. • "A" limit switch wire not connected. • Obstruction.	• Check for unconnected connectors on door latch switch, or behind LH and RH side cowl panel. • Check for unconnected connectors behind LH and RH side cowl panel, or on "A" limit switch. • Check for trim screw, track seal or jammed track locking pawl that prevents the carrier from reaching the "A" limit switch.
• Opening/Closing Door Causes Both Belts to Move	• Damaged Door Ajar indicator assembly.	• Replace Door Ajar indicator assembly
• Turning Ignition Off Causes Belt to Move to A-pillar	• Damaged Door Ajar indicator assembly	• Replace Door Ajar indicator assembly
• Fasten Belt Indicator Remains On, Chime Sounds for Four to Eight Seconds Once Belts Reach B-pillar	• Connector to shoulder emergency release retractor switches not connected.	• Check for unconnected connectors in console near shoulder strap connector
• Excessive Noise While Motor is Running	• Motor Adjustment knob on top of motor hits body.	• Loosen motor, slide motor downward, then tighten motor.

FM8019200351040X

Fig. 26 System diagnostic chart (Part 4 of 5). Cougar, Thunderbird & 1992–93 Tempo & Topaz

CONDITION	POSSIBLE SOURCE	ACTION
• Safety Belt Retractor Motor Will Not Operate	• Safety belt retractor motor. • Battery. • Grounds. • Passive restraint module.	• Go to Pinpoint Test G. • Go to Pinpoint Test F • Go to Pinpoint Test E. • Go to Pinpoint Test J.
• Safety Belt Warning Indicator Lamp and Safety Belt Warning Chime Will Not Operate	• Safety belt warning indicator lamp. • Safety belt warning chime. • Battery. • Grounds. • Passive restraint module.	• Go to Pinpoint Test H. • Go to Pinpoint Test F. • Go to Pinpoint Test E. • Go to Pinpoint Test J.
• Shoulder Belt Remains at A-Pillar, Will Not Move to B-Pillar	• Safety belt retractor motor. • Battery. • Grounds. • B-Pillar limit switch. • Door ajar switch. • Passive restraint module.	• Go to Pinpoint Test G. • Go to Pinpoint Test F. • Go to Pinpoint Test E. • Go to Pinpoint Test B. • Go to Pinpoint Test C. • Go to Pinpoint Test J.
• Shoulder Belt Remains at B-Pillar, Will Not Move to A-Pillar	• Safety belt retractor motor. • Battery. • Grounds. • A-Pillar limit switch. • Door ajar switch. • Passive restraint module.	• Go to Pinpoint Test G. • Go to Pinpoint Test F. • Go to Pinpoint Test E. • Go to Pinpoint Test A. • Go to Pinpoint Test C. • Go to Pinpoint Test J.
• Safety Belt Warning Indicator Lamp and Safety Belt Warning Chime Will Not Turn Off Even Though Shoulder Belts Are at B-Pillar	• B-Pillar limit switch. • Passive restraint module.	• Go to Pinpoint Test B. • Go to Pinpoint Test J.
• Safety Belt Retractor Motor Continues to Run After Shoulder Belt Carrier Reaches A-Pillar	• A-Pillar limit switch. • Door ajar switch. • Passive restraint module.	• Go to Pinpoint Test A. • Go to Pinpoint Test C. • Go to Pinpoint Test J.
• Safety Belt Retractor Motor Continues to Run After Shoulder Belt Carrier Reaches B-Pillar	• B-Pillar limit switch. • Door ajar switch. • Passive restraint module.	• Go to Pinpoint Test B. • Go to Pinpoint Test C. • Go to Pinpoint Test J.

FM8029400004010X

Fig. 27 System diagnostic chart (Part 1 of 2). 1994 Tempo & Topaz

CONDITION	POSSIBLE SOURCE	ACTION
• Excessive Pressure on Occupant During Normal Wear. Webbing Cannot Be Extracted	• Shoulder belt retractor.	• Check, replace if necessary.
• Excessive Slack in Webbing	• Shoulder belt retractor.	• Check, replace if necessary.
• Webbing Does Not Retract	• Twisted webbing. • Shoulder belt retractor.	• Correct orientation. • Check, replace if necessary.
• Shoulder Belt Carrier Will Not Move	• Front seat shoulder strap track. • Front seat shoulder strap drive belt. • Front seat shoulder strap track inner seal. • Front seat shoulder strap track outer seal.	• Adjust, replace if necessary. • Replace. • Replace • Replace
• Lap Belt Retractor Locks Prior to Tongue Engaging into Buckle	• Discontinuous extracting motion.	• Refer to Owner Guide.

FM8029400004020X

Fig. 27 System diagnostic chart (Part 2 of 2). 1994 Tempo & Topaz

	TEST STEP	RESULT	▶	ACTION TO TAKE
A1	CHECK HARNESS AND "A" LIMIT SWITCH CLOSED POSITION			
	• Remove access cover over the motor of the side to be checked. • Rotate the motor by hand so that the transport is somewhere in between both ends of track but at least 3 inches from either end of track. • Remove passive restraint module to gain access to mating connector. • Set Digital Volt-Ohmmeter on 200 ohm scale, use Rotunda Digital Volt-Ohmmeter 007-00001 or equivalent. • Measure resistance between pins of mating connector for the passive restraint module: Driver side between Pins 5 and 24. Passenger side between Pins 23 and 24. • Is resistance greater than 10 ohms?	No Yes	▶ ▶	GO to A2. GO to A3.

FM8019200352010X

Fig. 28 Test A: Track "A" Limit Switch (Part 1 of 2). Cougar, Tempo, Thunderbird & Topaz

	TEST STEP	RESULT	▶	ACTION TO TAKE
A2	CHECK HARNESS AND "A" LIMIT SWITCH OPEN POSITION			
	• Rotate the motor by hand so that the transport is at the A-pillar. • Measure resistance between pins of mating connector for the passive restraint module. Driver side between Pins 5 and 24. Passenger side between Pins 23 and 24. • Is resistance greater than 500k ohms?	No Yes	▶ ▶	GO to A4. Switch and wiring OK.
A3	CHECK "A" LIMIT SWITCH CLOSED POSITION			
	• Remove the trim over the track and the "A" limit switch. • Disconnect the connector from the limit switch. • Measure resistance between pins of the limit switch. • Is resistance greater than 10 ohms?	No Yes	▶ ▶	GO to A5. REPLACE switch. INSTALL original passive restraint module.
A4	CHECK "A" LIMIT SWITCH OPEN POSITION			
	• Remove the trim over the track and the "A" limit switch. • Make sure carrier fully depresses plunger of limit switch. • Disconnect the connector from the limit switch. • Measure resistance between pins of the limit switch. • Is resistance greater than 500k ohms?	No Yes	▶ ▶	REPLACE switch. INSTALL original passive restraint module. GO to A5.
A5	CHECK HARNESS FROM MODULE MATING CONNECTOR TO LIMIT SWITCH			
	• Measure resistance between pins of the limit switch harness to pins of the Passive Restraint Module mating connector: Driver side—one limit switch pin to Pin 24 (ground), other limit switch pin to Pin 5. Passenger side—one limit switch pin to Pin 24 (ground), other limit switch pin to Pin 23. • Is continuity present?	Yes No	▶ ▶	Wiring OK. CORRECT wiring. INSTALL original passive restraint module.

FM8019200352020X

Fig. 28 Test A: Track "A" Limit Switch (Part 2 of 2). Cougar, Tempo, Thunderbird & Topaz

	TEST STEP	RESULT	▶	ACTION TO TAKE
B1	CHECK HARNESS AND "B" LIMIT SWITCH CLOSED POSITION			
	• Remove access cover over the motor of the side to be checked. • Rotate the motor by hand so that the transport is somewhere in between both ends of track but at least 3 inches from either end of track. • Remove passive restraint module to gain access to mating connector. • Set Digital Volt-Ohmmeter on 200 ohm scale, use Rotunda Digital Volt-Ohmmeter 007-00001 or equivalent. • Measure resistance between pins of mating connector for passive restraint module: Driver side between Pins 18 and 24. Passenger side between Pins 21 and 24. • Is resistance greater than 10 ohms?	No Yes	▶ ▶	GO to B2. GO to B3.
B2	CHECK HARNESS AND "B" LIMIT SWITCH OPEN POSITION			
	• Rotate the motor by hand so that the transport is at the B-pillar. • Measure resistance between pins of mating connector for the passive restraint module: Driver side between Pins 18 and 24. Passenger side between Pins 21 and 24. • Is resistance greater than 500k ohms?	No Yes	▶ ▶	GO to B4. Switch and wiring OK.
B3	CHECK "B" LIMIT SWITCH CLOSED POSITION			
	• Remove the trim over the track and the "B" limit switch. • Disconnect the connector from the limit switch. • Measure resistance between pins of the limit switch. • Is resistance greater than 10 ohms?	No Yes	▶ ▶	GO to B5. REPLACE switch. INSTALL original passive restraint module.
B4	CHECK "B" LIMIT SWITCH OPEN POSITION			
	• Remove the trim over the track and the "B" limit switch. • Make sure carrier fully depresses plunger of limit switch. • Disconnect the connector from the limit switch. • Measure resistance between pins of the limit switch. • Is resistance greater than 500k ohms?	No Yes	▶ ▶	REPLACE switch. INSTALL original passive restraint module. GO to B5.

FM8019200353010X

Fig. 29 Test B: Track "B" Limit Switch (Part 1 of 2). Cougar, Tempo, Thunderbird & Topaz

	TEST STEP	RESULT	▶	ACTION TO TAKE
B5	CHECK HARNESS FROM MODULE MATING CONNECTOR TO LIMIT SWITCH			
	• Measure resistance between pins of the limit switch harness to pins of the Passive Restraint Module mating connector: Driver side—one limit switch pin to Pin 24 (ground), other limit switch pin to Pin 18. Passenger side—one limit switch pin to Pin 24 (ground), other limit switch pin to Pin 21. • Is continuity present?	Yes No	▶ ▶	Wiring OK. CORRECT wiring. INSTALL original passive restraint module.

FM8019200353020X

Fig. 29 Test B: Track "B" Limit Switch (Part 2 of 2). Cougar, Tempo, Thunderbird & Topaz

	TEST STEP	RESULT	▶	ACTION TO TAKE
C1	CHECK HARNESS AND DOOR LATCH SWITCH			
	• Turn ignition to OFF (position 0). • Remove passive restraint module to gain access to mating connector. • Set Digital Volt-Ohmmeter on 20K ohm scale, use Rotunda Digital Volt-Ohmmeter 007-00001 or equivalent. • Measure resistance between pins of mating connector for passive restraint module: Driver side between Pins 13 and 24. Passenger side between Pins 8 and 24. • Fully close door. • Is resistance greater than 500k ohms?	No Yes	▶ ▶	GO to C3. GO to C2.
C2	CHECK HARNESS AND DOOR LATCH SWITCH (CONTINUED)			
	• With door open measure resistance. • Is resistance greater than 10 ohms?	No Yes	▶ ▶	Switch and wiring OK. GO to C3.
C3	CHECK DOOR AJAR (LATCH) SWITCH			
	• Remove door trim panel. • Disconnect wiring harness from door latch switch. • Measure resistance between switch terminal and ground (latch). • Fully close door. • Is resistance greater than 500k ohms?	No Yes	▶ ▶	REPLACE switch. INSTALL original passive restraint module. GO to C4.
C4	CHECK DOOR AJAR (LATCH) SWITCH (CONTINUED)			
	• With door open measure resistance. • Is resistance greater than 10 ohms?	No Yes	▶ ▶	GO to C5. REPLACE switch. INSTALL original passive restraint module.

FM8019200354010X

Fig. 30 Test C: Door Ajar Switch (Part 1 of 2). Cougar, Tempo, Thunderbird & Topaz

TEST STEP		RESULT	▶	ACTION TO TAKE
C5	CHECK HARNESS DOOR AJAR (LATCH) SWITCH			
	• Measure resistance between pins of the door latch switch harness to pins of the passive restraint module mating connector: Driver side—door switch harness pin to Pin 13. Passenger side—door switch harness pin to Pin 8. • Is continuity present?	Yes	▶	Switch and wiring OK.
		No	▶	CORRECT wiring concern. INSTALL original passive restraint module.

FM8019200354020X

Fig. 30 Test C: Door Ajar Switch (Part 2 of 2). Cougar, Tempo, Thunderbird & Topaz

TEST STEP		RESULT	▶	ACTION TO TAKE
D1	CHECK SHOULDER BELT RETRACTOR SWITCH (BUCKLE ENGAGED)			
	• Disconnect switch at connector attached to bracket on inboard side of seat track. • Set Digital Volt-ohmmeter 007-00001 or equivalent on 200 ohm scale. • Probe across switch connector terminals with shoulder belt tongue and buckle engaged	Switch Closed (less than 10 ohms)	▶	GO to D2.
		Switch Open (more than 10 ohms)	▶	Malfunctioning switch. REPLACE retractor assembly.
D2	CHECK SHOULDER BELT RETRACTOR SWITCH (BUCKLE DISENGAGED)			
	• Repeat procedure described in Step D1, except with shoulder belt tongue and buckle DISENGAGED and shoulder belt retracted in excess of 305mm (12 inches) from engaged position.	Switch Closed (less than 100K)	▶	Malfunctioning switch. REPLACE retractor assembly.
		Switch Open (more than 100K)	▶	Switch OK. CONNECT harness to switch.

FM8019200355000X

Fig. 31 Test D: Shoulder Belt Retractor Switch. Cougar & Thunderbird

TEST STEP		RESULT	▶	ACTION TO TAKE
D1	CHECK SPOOL RELEASE SWITCH			
	• Disconnect both switches connected in series, located at retractor release mechanism. • Set Digital Volt Ohmmeter on 200 ohm scale, use Rotunda Digital Volt Ohmmeter 007-00001 or an equivalent. • Measure resistance across switch terminals. • Is resistance less than 10 ohms?	Yes	▶	GO to D2.
		No	▶	REPLACE switch.
D2	CHECK RELEASE MECHANISM			
	• When one or both release mechanism levers are in UP position, switch should be open. • Is resistance less than 10 ohms?	Yes	▶	REPLACE switch.
		No	▶	Switch is OK. Connect harness to switch.

FM8019200356000X

Fig. 32 Test D: Spool Release Switch. 1992–93 Tempo & Topaz

TEST STEP		RESULT	▶	ACTION TO TAKE
D1	CHECK EMERGENCY RELEASE LEVER SWITCHES HARNESS			
	• Remove passive restraint control module to gain access to mating connector. • With Rotunda Digital Multimeter 105-00050, or equivalent, measure resistance between Pin 14 (Circuit 868, GY·R) and Pin 24 (Circuit 875, BK. LB) of mating connector for passive restraint control module. • Is continuity present?	Yes	▶	GO to D2.
		No	▶	SERVICE respective wiring.
D2	CHECK EMERGENCY RELEASE SWITCH			
	• Disconnect both switches connected in series, located at retractor release mechanism. • With Rotunda Digital Multimeter 105-00050 or equivalent, measure resistance across switch terminals. • Is resistance less than 10 ohms?	Yes	▶	GO to D3.
		No	▶	REPLACE switch.
D3	CHECK RELEASE MECHANISM			
	• When one or both release mechanism levers are in UP position, switch should be open. • Is resistance less than 10 ohms?	Yes	▶	REPLACE switch. REPEAT
		No	▶	Switch OK. Connect harness to switch.

FM8029400005000X

Fig. 33 Test D: Emergency Release Lever Switches Diagnosis. 1994 Tempo & Topaz

TEST STEP		RESULT	▶	ACTION TO TAKE
E1	CHECK LOGIC GROUND			
	• Remove passive restraint module to gain access to mating connector. • Set Digital Volt-Ohmmeter on 200 ohm scale, use Rotunda Digital Volt-Ohmmeter 007-00001 or equivalent. • Measure resistance between Pin 24 of mating connector for passive restraint module to chassis ground. • Is continuity present?	Yes	▶	GO to E2.
		No	▶	CORRECT wiring concern. INSTALL original passive restraint module.
E2	CHECK MOTOR POWER GROUND			
	• Measure resistance between Pin 6 of mating connector for passive restraint module to chassis ground. • Is continuity present?	Yes	▶	GO to E3.
		No	▶	CORRECT wiring. INSTALL original passive restraint module.

FM8019200357010X

Fig. 34 Test E: Grounds (Part 1 of 2). Cougar, Tempo, Thunderbird & Topaz

TEST STEP		RESULT	▶	ACTION TO TAKE
E3	CHECK SECOND MOTOR POWER GROUND			
	• Measure resistance between Pin 19 of mating connector for passive restraint module to chassis ground. • Is continuity present?	Yes	▶	Grounds OK.
		No	▶	CORRECT wiring. INSTALL original passive retraint module.

FM8019200357020X

Fig. 34 Test E: Grounds (Part 2 of 2). Cougar, Tempo, Thunderbird & Topaz

TEST STEP		RESULT	▶	ACTION TO TAKE
F1	CHECK B + CONNECTION			
	• Remove passive restraint module to gain access to mating connector. • Set Digital Volt-Ohmmeter on 20V scale, measure voltage on passive restraint mating connector between Pin 7 and Pin 24. • Is battery voltage present?	Yes No	▶ ▶	GO to F2. CHECK fuse. CHECK ground. CORRECT wiring. INSTALL original passive restraint module.
F2	CHECK B + CONNECTION			
	• Measure voltage on passive restraint mating connector between Pin 20 and Pin 24. • Is battery voltage present?	Yes No	▶ ▶	GO to F3. CHECK fuse. CHECK ground. CORRECT wiring. INSTALL original passive restraint module.
F3	CHECK RUN / START CONNECTION—IGNITION OFF			
	• Measure voltage on passive restraint mating connector between Pin 25 and Pin 24 with ignition switch in OFF position. • Is battery voltage present?	Yes No	▶ ▶	CORRECT wiring. INSTALL original passive restraint module. GO to F4.
F4	CHECK RUN / START CONNECTION—IGNITION ON			
	• Measure voltage on passive restraint mating connector between Pin 25 and Pin 24 with ignition switch in RUN position. • Is battery voltage present?	Yes No	▶ ▶	GO to F5. CHECK fuse. CHECK ground. CORRECT wiring. INSTALL original passive restraint module.
F5	CHECK INERTIA SWITCH			
	• Measure voltage on passive restraint mating connector between Pin 12 and Pin 24 with ignition switch in RUN position. • Is battery voltage present?	Yes No	▶ ▶	CORRECT wiring. INSTALL original passive restraint module. GO to F6.
F6	MEASURE VOLTAGE			
	• Using Rotunda Digital Volt Ohmmeter 007-00001 or an equivalent measure voltage between Pin 12 and Pin 24 with ignition switch in RUN position. • Is battery voltage present?	Yes No	▶ ▶	System OK. RESET fuel pump inertia switch and RECHECK. CHECK fuse. CHECK ground. CORRECT wiring. INSTALL original passive restraint module.

FM8019200358000X

Fig. 35   Test F: Voltage Check. Cougar, Tempo, Thunderbird & Topaz

TEST STEP		RESULT	▶	ACTION TO TAKE
G1	BELT TO A-PILLAR			
	• Remove module to gain access to passive restraint module mating connector. • Install jumpers in passive restraint module mating connector. Motors will run while jumpers are connected. Driver—Pin 2 to Pin 6 or Pin 17 to Pin 19 Pin 3 to Pin 7 or Pin 4 to Pin 20 Passenger—Pin 9 to Pin 6 or Pin 22 to Pin 19 Pin 10 to Pin 7 or Pin 11 to Pin 20	Motor directs drive belt toward A-pillar Motor does not run	▶ ▶	GO to G2. CHECK fuse. CHECK motor circuit breaker. CHECK wiring to motor. INSTALL original passive restraint module.
G2	BELT TO B-PILLAR			
	• Install jumpers in mating connector. Motors will run while jumpers are connected. Driver—Pin 3 to Pin 6 or Pin 4 to Pin 19 Pin 2 to Pin 7 or Pin 17 to Pin 20 Passenger—Pin 10 to Pin 6 or Pin 11 to Pin 19 Pin 9 to Pin 7 or Pin 22 to Pin 20	Motor runs toward B-pillar Motor does not run	▶ ▶	System OK. CHECK fuse. CHECK motor circuit breaker. CHECK wiring to motor. INSTALL original passive restraint module.

FM8019200359000X

Fig. 36   Test G: Motor. Cougar & Thunderbird

TEST STEP		RESULT	▶	ACTION TO TAKE
G1	BELT TO A-PILLAR			
	• Remove module to gain access to passive restraint module mating connector. • Install jumpers in passive restraint module mating connector Driver—Pin 2 to Pin 6 and Pin 17 to Pin 19. Passenger—Pin 9 to Pin 6 and Pin 22 to Pin 19 • Install temporary jumpers (motor will run while jumpers are connected). Driver—Pin 3 to Pin 7 or Pin 4 to Pin 20 Passenger—Pin 10 to Pin 7 or Pin 11 to Pin 20	Motor directs drive belt toward A-pillar Motor does not run	▶ ▶	GO to G2. CHECK fuse. CHECK motor circuit breaker. CHECK wiring to motor. INSTALL original passive restraint module.
G2	BELT TO B-PILLAR			
	• Install jumpers in mating connector. Driver—Pin 3 to Pin 6 and Pin 4 to Pin 19. Passenger—Pin 10 to Pin 6 and Pin 11 to Pin 19 • Install temporary jumpers (motor runs while jumpers are connected). Driver—Pin 2 to Pin 7 or Pin 17 to Pin 20 Passenger—Pin 9 to Pin 7 or Pin 22 to Pin 20	Motor runs toward B-pillar Motor does not run	▶ ▶	System OK. CHECK fuse. CHECK motor circuit breaker. CHECK wiring to motor. INSTALL original passive restraint module. GO to G3.
G3	MOTOR RESISTANCE CHECK			
	• Using Rotunda Digital Volt Ohmmeter 007-00001 or equivalent, measure resistance between transport motor pins. Resistance should be 0.9 to 1.5 ohms. Driver side—Pins 2 and 3. Passenger—Pins 9 and 10. • Is resistance within specification?	Yes No	▶ ▶	Motor OK. REPLACE motor.

FM8019200360000X

Fig. 37   Test G: Motor. Tempo & Topaz

TEST STEP		RESULT	▶	ACTION TO TAKE
H1	CHECK FASTEN BELT INDICATOR			
	• Remove module to gain access to mating connector. • Install jumper in mating connector to connect Pin 16 to Pin 7. • Does fasten belt indicator light?	Yes No	▶ ▶	System OK. CHECK fuse. CHECK bulb. INSTALL original passive restraint module.
H2	CHECK CHIME WARNING			
	• Place ignition key in ignition. • Install jumper in mating connector to connect Pin 1 to Pin 7.	Chime sounds from 4 to 8 seconds Chime does not sound	▶ ▶	System OK. CHECK fuse. CHECK chime module. INSTALL original passive restraint module.

FM8019200361000X

Fig. 38   Test H: Warnings. Cougar & Thunderbird

TEST STEP		RESULT	▶	ACTION TO TAKE
H1	CHECK FASTEN BELT INDICATOR			
	• Remove module to gain access to mating connector to connect. • Install jumper in mating connector to connect Pin 16 to Pin 7. • Does FASTEN BELT indicator in instrument panel light?	Yes No	▶ ▶	System OK. CHECK fuse. CHECK bulb. INSTALL original passive restraint module.
H2	CHECK CHIME WARNING			
	• Place ignition key in ignition. • Install jumper in mating connector to connect Pin 1 to Pin 7. • Does chime sound?	Yes No	▶ ▶	System OK. CHECK fuse. CHECK chime module. INSTALL original passive restraint module.
H3	CHECK "PUSH LEVER DOWN" INDICATOR			
	• Install jumper in mating connector to connect Pin 26 to Pin 7. • Does "push lever down" indicator light?	Yes No	▶ ▶	System OK. CHECK fuse. CHECK bulb. INSTALL original passive restraint module.

FM8019200362000X

Fig. 39   Test H: Warnings. 1992–93 Tempo & Topaz

TEST STEP		RESULT	▶	ACTION TO TAKE
H1	CHECK FASTEN BELT INDICATOR			
	• Install jumper in mating connector to connect Pin 16 (Circuit 871, Y) to Pin 7 (Circuit 38, BK/O). • Does FASTEN BELT indicator in instrument panel light?	Yes No	▶ ▶	Fasten belt indicator OK. GO to H3. GO to H2.
H2	CONTINUITY CHECK			
	• With Rotunda Digital Multimeter 105-00050 or equivalent, measure resistance across Circuit 871, Y (Pin 16) of mating connector. • Is continuity present?	Yes No	▶ ▶	CHECK fuse. CHECK bulb. SERVICE if necessary. GO to H3. SERVICE Circuit 871, Y. GO to H3.
H3	CHECK CHIME WARNING			
	• Place ignition key in ignition. • Install jumper in mating connector to connect Pin 1 (Circuit 159 R/PK) to Pin 7 (Circuit 38 BK O). • Does chime sound?	Yes No	▶ ▶	Chime OK. GO to H4.
H4	CONTINUITY CHECK			
	• With Rotunda Digital Multimeter 105-00050 or equivalent, measure resistance across Circuit 159, R/PK (Pin 1) and across Circuit 450, DG/LG (Pin 15) of mating connector. • Is continuity present?	Yes No	▶ ▶	CHECK fuse. CHECK chime module. SERVICE if necessary. GO to H5. SERVICE respective circuit. GO to H5.

FM8029400006010X

Fig. 40   Test H: Warning Indicators Diagnosis (Part 1 of 2). 1994 Tempo & Topaz

TEST STEP		RESULT	▶	ACTION TO TAKE
H5	CHECK "PUSH LEVER DOWN" INDICATOR			
	• Install jumper in mating connector to connect Pin 26 (Circuit 877, W/O) to Pin 7 (Circuit 38, BK/O). • Does "push lever down" indicator light?	Yes No	▶ ▶	System OK. GO to H6.
H6	CONTINUITY CHECK			
	• With Rotunda Digital Multimeter 105-00050 or equivalent, measure resistance across Circuit 877, O (Pin 26) of mating connector. • Is continuity present?	Yes No	▶ ▶	CHECK fuse. CHECK bulb. SERVICE if necessary. INSTALL original passive restraint control module. SERVICE Circuit 877 (O). REPEAT Step H6.

FM8029400006020X

Fig. 40   Test H: Warning Indicators Diagnosis (Part 2 of 2). 1994 Tempo & Topaz

TEST STEP	RESULT	▶	ACTION TO TAKE
J1 CHECK SYSTEM			
• All system switches, grounds, voltages and wiring must be correct prior to checking module.	Yes	▶	GO to J2.
• Is system functional?	No	▶	CORRECT condition. GO to J2.
J2 CHECK BELT FUNCTION			
• Operate system per driver and Passenger Operational Logic Chart.	Yes	▶	GO to J3.
• Does belt function agree with chart?	No	▶	REPLACE module.

FM8019200363010X

Fig. 41   Test J: Restraint Module (Part 1 of 2). Cougar, Tempo, Thunderbird & Topaz

TEST STEP	RESULT	▶	ACTION TO TAKE
J3 CHECK WARNING FUNCTION			
• Operate warnings per the Function Table — Warnings	Yes	▶	System OK.
• Does warning functions agree with chart?	No	▶	REPLACE module.

FM8019200363020X

Fig. 41   Test J: Restraint Module (Part 2 of 2). Cougar, Tempo, Thunderbird & Topaz

PASSIVE RESTRAINT FAULT/TEST REFERENCE GUIDE

FAULT/TEST	PERFORM TEST
Battery Feed	K-1
Ground Feed	K-2
Inertia Switch	K-3
Warning Chime Module-Audible Warning Function	K-4
Warning Chime Module-Visual Warning Function	K-5
Ignition Feed	K-6
Fasten Belt Indicator Warning Lamp	K-7
Shoulder Belt Spool Switch	K-8
Motor Wiring Shorts	K-9
Motor Forward Movement	K-10
Motor Reverse Movement	k-11
Limit Switch A	K-12
Limit Switch B	K-13
Door Switch	K-14

PINPOINT TEST K: PASSIVE RESTRAINT QUICK TEST

TEST STEP	RESULT	▶	ACTION TO TAKE
K1 CHECK BATTERY FEED			
• Examine battery A and battery B lamps.	Yes	▶	Battery feed OK.
• Are both lamps on?	No	▶	CHECK fuse link. CHECK wiring and connections between fuse link and belt module connector. SERVICE as required.
K2 CHECK GROUND FEED			
• Examine motor ground A, motor ground B, and logic ground lamps.	Yes	▶	Ground feed OK.
• Are all lamps on?	No	▶	CHECK wiring and connections between ground inertia switch and belt module connector. SERVICE as required.
K3 CHECK INERTIA SWITCH			
• Turn ignition to RUN and watch fuel pump lamp.	Yes	▶	Inertia switch OK.
• Is fuel pump lamp on?	No	▶	RESET inertia switch. CHECK wiring between inertia switch and belt. SERVICE as required.

FM8019200364010X

Fig. 42   Test K: Passive Restraint Quick Test (Part 1 of 4). Cougar & Thunderbird

TEST STEP	RESULT	▶	ACTION TO TAKE
K4 CHECK WARNING CHIME MODULE AUDIBLE WARNING FUNCTION			
• Insert key in ignition.	Yes	▶	Warning chime module OK.
• Toggle warning chime switch and listen for sound.	No	▶	CHECK wiring and connections between chime and belt module connector. SERVICE as required.
• Does chime sound when switch is toggled?			
K5 CHECK WARNING CHIME MODULE—VISUAL WARNING FUNCTION			
• Turn ignition to OFF then to RUN and watch safety belt chime lamp.	Safety belt chime lamp lights for 4-8 seconds	▶	Safety belt chime OK.
	Safety belt chime lamp stays lit or does not light	▶	CHECK warning chime module. CHECK wiring and connections between warning chime module and belt module connector. SERVICE as required.
K6 CHECK IGNITION FEED			
• Turn ignition to OFF then to RUN and watch run start lamp.	Yes	▶	Ignition feed OK.
• Does run/start lamp light?	No	▶	CHECK fuse. CHECK wiring and connections between fuse and belt module connector. SERVICE as required.
K7 CHECK FASTEN BELT INDICATOR WARNING LAMP			
• Toggle fasten belt indicator switch and watch fasten belt warning indicator lamp on instrument panel.	Yes	▶	Fasten belt indicator OK.
• Does warning indicator lamp light when switch is toggled?	No	▶	CHECK bulb. CHECK wiring and connections between lamp and belt module connector. SERVICE as required.
K8 CHECK SHOULDER BELT SPOOL SWITCH			
• Pull out shoulder belt and watch safety belt warning indicator lamp.	Lamp off when belt is extended: more than 800mm (31.5 inches) Lamp on when belt is retracted.	▶	Shoulder belt spool switch OK.
	Lamp on when belt is extended; more than 800mm (31.5 inches) Lamp off when belt is retracted.	▶	CHECK if switch wire is shorted to ground. ENSURE switch functions properly. CHECK wiring and connections between spool switch and belt module connector. SERVICE as required.

FM8019200364020X

Fig. 42   Test K: Passive Restraint Quick Test (Part 2 of 4). Cougar & Thunderbird

TEST STEP	RESULT	▶	ACTION TO TAKE
K9 CHECK MOTOR WIRING FOR SHORTS			
• Examine four lamps below motor switch.	All lamps on 1/2 bright	▶	Motor wiring OK.
	One to four lamps off	▶	CHECK wiring for open. SERVICE as required.
	Two ground short lamps on	▶	CHECK for motor wire shorted to ground between motor and belt module connector.
	Two power short lamps off	▶	SERVICE as required.
K10 CHECK MOTOR FORWARD MOVEMENT			
• Position motor switch to FWD, watch belt carrier and four lamps below motor switch.	Carrier moves forward, two FWD lamps stay on when switch is in FWD position	▶	Forward movement OK.
• Release switch when carrier reaches limit A.	Belt does not move	▶	CHECK for obstructions in track. CHECK circuit breaker on motor. CHECK wiring and connections to motor. SERVICE as required.
K11 CHECK MOTOR REVERSE MOVEMENT			
• Position motor switch REV, watch belt carrier and four lamps below motor switch.	Carrier moves forward, two REV lamps stay on when switch is in REV position	▶	Rearward movement OK.
• Release switch when carrier reaches limit B.	Belt does not move	▶	CHECK for obstructions in track. CHECK circuit breaker on motor. CHECK wiring and connections to motor. SERVICE as required.
K12 CHECK LIMIT SWITCH A			
• Move carrier forward to limit A, and watch limit A lamp.	Lamp on when not at limit and off when at limit	▶	Limit switch A OK.
	Lamp off when not at limit and on at limit	▶	CHECK to ENSURE limit switch connector is properly connected and switch plunger is not stuck. SERVICE as required. ENSURE carrier fully reaches limit A, and that limit A wire is not shorted to ground. SERVICE as required. CHECK if switch works (remove switch from track and toggle, lamp should blink).

FM8019200364030X

Fig. 42   Test K: Passive Restraint Quick Test (Part 3 of 4). Cougar & Thunderbird

TEST STEP		RESULT	▶	ACTION TO TAKE
K13	CHECK LIMIT SWITCH B			
	• Move carrier rearward to limit B, and watch limit B lamp	Lamp on when not at limit and off when at limit	▶	Limit switch B OK.
		Lamp off when not at limit and on at limit	▶	CHECK to ENSURE limit switch connector is properly connected and switch plunger is not stuck. SERVICE as required. ENSURE carrier fully reaches limit B, and that limit B wire is not shorted to ground. SERVICE as required. CHECK if switch works (remove switch from track and toggle, lamp should blink).
K14	CHECK DOOR SWITCH			
	• Open and close door and watch door switch lamp.	Lamp is on when door is open and off when door is closed	▶	Door switch OK.
		Lamp is off when door is open and on when door is closed	▶	CHECK door ajar switch connections and ground and door latch ground. SERVICE as required. CHECK to ENSURE door latch operates properly and that door switch wire is not shorted to ground. SERVICE as required.

FM8019200364040X

Fig. 42 Test K: Passive Restraint Quick Test (Part 4 of 4). Cougar & Thunderbird

CONDITION	POSSIBLE SOURCE	ACTION
• Passive Restraint System Does Not Operate	• Blown fuse(s). • Passive restraint module. • Circuit open/shorted. • Inertia switch.	• GO to PR1. • RESET the inertia switch. If open (tripped-switch not depressed), GO to PR7.
• Passive Restraint System Operates on One Side Only	• Passive restraint motor. • Limit switches. • Door switches. • Circuit open/shorted.	• GO to PR9.
• Passive Restraint Motor Stays On All the Time	• Passive restraint motor. • Limit Switches. • Circuit open/shorted. • Track assembly.	• GO to PR4. • CHECK track assembly.
• Seat Belt Warning Indicator Light Does Not Illuminate	• Seat belt warning switch. • Fuses. • Passive restraint module. • Circuit open/shorted. • Warning chime module. • Bulb.	
• Seat Belt Warning Buzzer Does Not Sound For Warning Purposes	• Seat belt warning switch. • Passive restraint module. • Circuit open/shorted. • Ignition key reminder switch. • Warning chime module.	• GO to PR18.

TEST STEP		RESULT	▶	ACTION TO TAKE
PR1	CHECK FUSE(S) • Check inertia switch/tripped. • Locate the interior fuse panel. • Check the 30A BELT and 10A METER fuses. • Are the fuses good?	Yes No	▶ ▶	GO to PR4. GO to PR2.
PR2	CHECK SYSTEM • Replace the blown fuse(s). • Key ON. • Did the fuse(s) blow again?	Yes No	▶ ▶	GO to PR3. GO to PR4.
PR3	CHECK FOR SHORT TO GROUND • Key OFF. • Disconnect the "Y" and "BK/Y" wires from the interior fuse panel. • Measure the resistance of the wire in question to ground. • Are the resistance(s) less than 5 ohms?	Yes No	▶ ▶	SERVICE the wire(s) in question. GO to PR4.
PR4	CHECK POWER SUPPLY TO THE PASSIVE RESTRAINT MODULE • Key OFF. • Disconnect the passive restraint module connector. • Measure the voltage on the "Y" wire at the connector. • Is the voltage greater than 10 volts?	Yes No	▶ ▶	GO to PR5. SERVICE the "Y" wire.

FM8019100365010X

Fig. 43 System diagnosis (Part 1 of 6). Festiva

TEST STEP		RESULT	▶	ACTION TO TAKE
PR5	CHECK POWER SUPPLY TO PASSIVE RESTRAINT MODULE • Measure the voltage on the "BK/Y" wire at the connector.	Yes No	▶ ▶	GO to PR6. SERVICE the "BK/Y" wire.

CONDITION	VOLTAGE
Key OFF	0V
Key ON	Above 10V

• Are the voltages within specifications?

PR6	CHECK PASSIVE RESTRAINT MODULE GROUNDS • Key OFF. • Disconnect the passive restraint module connector. • Measure the resistance of the "BK" wires at pin M, N of the connector to ground. • Is the resistance less than 5 ohms?	Yes No	▶ ▶	GO to PR7. SERVICE the "BK" wire.
PR7	CHECK INERTIA SWITCH • Locate the inertia switch. • Measure the resistance of the "GN/W" wire at the inertia switch connector to ground in the following conditions:	Yes No	▶ ▶	GO to PR8. REPLACE the inertia switch.

CONDITION	RESISTANCE
Open (tripped — switch not depressed)	Greater than 10,000 ohms
Closed (set — switch depressed)	Less than 5 ohms

• Are the resistances within specifications?

PR8	CHECK THE LEAD BETWEEN THE INERTIA SWITCH TO THE PASSIVE RESTRAINT MODULE • Disconnect the passive restraint module connector. • Measure the resistance of the "R" wire between the passive restraint module and inertia switch. • Is the resistance less than 5 ohms?	Yes No	▶ ▶	GO to PR9. SERVICE the "R" wire.
PR9	CHECK DOOR SWITCH GROUND • Locate the driver's and passenger's door switch connectors. • Measure the resistance of the "BK" wire at the connector in the respective door to ground. • Are the resistances less than 5 ohms?	Yes No	▶ ▶	GO to PR10. SERVICE the "BK" wire in question.

FM8019100365020X

Fig. 43 System diagnosis (Part 2 of 6). Festiva

TEST STEP		RESULT	▶	ACTION TO TAKE
PR10	CHECK DOOR SWITCHES • Measure the resistance on the "LG/R" (driver's side door) and the "LG/R" (passenger's side door) at the connector to ground.	Yes No	▶ ▶	GO to PR11. REPLACE the door latch assembly.

CONDITION	RESISTANCE
Door open	Less than 5 ohms
Door closed	Greater than 10,000 ohms

• Are the resistances within specifications?

PR11	CHECK THE LEAD BETWEEN THE DOOR SWITCH AND THE PASSIVE RESTRAINT MODULE • Disconnect the passive restraint module connectors and both door switch connectors. • Measure the resistance of the following wires between the door switch and the module.	Yes No	▶ ▶	GO to PR12. SERVICE the wire in question.

CONDITION	RESISTANCE
LH door switch "LG/R" and module "LG/R"	less than 5 ohms
RH door switch "LG/R" and module "BL/O"	less than 5 ohms

• Are the resistances within specifications?

PR12	CHECK THE A-PILLAR LIMIT SWITCH GROUND • Locate the A-pillar limit switches (driver and passenger side). • Measure the resistance of the "BK" wires to ground. • Are the resistances less than 5 ohms?	Yes No	▶ ▶	GO to PR13. SERVICE the "BK" wire in question.
PR13	CHECK THE A-PILLAR LIMIT SWITCHES • Open door. • Measure the voltage on the "Y/BL" (driver's side) and the "BL/BK" (passenger's side) at the limit switch connector.	Yes No	▶ ▶	GO to PR14. REPLACE the A-pillar limit switch in question.

POSITION	VOLTAGE
Belt in motion toward A-pillar	Above 10V
Everywhere else	0V

• Are the voltages within specifications?

PR14	CHECK THE B-PILLAR LIMIT SWITCH GROUND • Locate the B-pillar limit switches (driver's and passenger's side). • Measure the resistance of the "BK" wires to ground. • Are the resistances less than 5 ohms?	Yes No	▶ ▶	GO to PR15. SERVICE the "BK" wire in question.

FM8019100365030X

Fig. 43 System diagnosis (Part 3 of 6). Festiva

PR15 / PR16 / PR17 / PR18 (Part 4)

TEST STEP	RESULT	▶	ACTION TO TAKE
PR15 CHECK THE B-PILLAR LIMIT SWITCHES			
• Door open, belt in A-pillar position.	Yes	▶	GO to **PR16**.
• Key ON, close door.	No	▶	REPLACE the track and motor assembly in question.
• Measure the voltage on the "Y/R" (driver's side) and the "W" (passenger's side) at the limit switch connector.			

POSITION	VOLTAGE
Belt in B-pillar position	0V
Everywhere else	Above 4.5V

• Are the voltages within specifications?			
PR16 CHECK PASSIVE RESTRAINT MOTOR			
• Key ON, door open.	Yes	▶	GO to **PR17**.
• Disconnect the passive restraint motor connector.	No	▶	REPLACE the track and motor assembly.
• Ground the "BK/R" (U) (driver's side) or the "Y/GN" (A) (passenger's side) wire at the motor connector.			
• Apply 12 volts to either the "BL/GN" (V) (driver's side) or the "W/BK" (B) (passenger's side) wire at the connector.			
• Does the belt move from pillar A to pillar B?			
• Reverse the power and ground leads.			
• Does the belt move from pillar B to pillar A?			
PR17 CHECK LEADS BETWEEN THE PASSIVE RESTRAINT MODULE AND THE MOTOR			
• Key OFF.	Yes	▶	REPLACE the passive restraint module.
• Disconnect the passive restraint module connectors.	No	▶	SERVICE the wire(s) in question.
• Measure the resistance of the following wires between the module and the motor.			

Driver Side Connector	Passenger Side Connector
"BL/GN" (V)	"Y/GN" (A)
"BK/R" (U)	"W/BK" (B)

• Are the resistances less than 5 ohms?			
PR18 CHECK WARNING SWITCH GROUND			
• Disconnect the warning switch connector located in center console between seat belt retractors.	Yes	▶	GO to **PR19**.
• Measure the resistance of both "BK" wires to ground.	No	▶	SERVICE the "BK" wire(s).
• Are the resistances less than 5 ohms?			

FM8019100365040X

Fig. 43 System diagnosis (Part 4 of 6). Festiva

PR22 (Part 6)

TEST STEP	RESULT	▶	ACTION TO TAKE
PR22 CHECK LEADS BETWEEN MODULE AND WARNING LAMP/BUZZER			
• Key OFF.			
• Measure the resistance of the "LG/Y" wire between the passive restraint module and the instrument cluster.	No	▶	SERVICE the "LG/Y" wire and/or the "BR" wire.
• Measure the resistance of the "BR" wire between the module and the warning chime (CPU).			
• Are the resistances less than 5 ohms?			

FM8019100365060X

Fig. 43 System diagnosis (Part 6 of 6). Festiva

PR19 / PR20 / PR21 (Part 5)

TEST STEP	RESULT	▶	ACTION TO TAKE
PR19 CHECK WARNING SWITCH OPERATION			
• Reconnect the warning switch.	Yes	▶	GO to **PR20**.
• Measure the resistance of the "P" (passenger's side) and "O/GN" (driver's side) between the switch and ground.	No	▶	REPLACE the center console spool and belt assembly.

Condition	Resistance
Shoulder belt latched	Less than 5 ohms
Shoulder belt unlatched (and belt allowed to retract in the console)	Greater than 10,000 ohms

• Are the resistances within specifications?			
PR20 CHECK LEADS BETWEEN WARNING SWITCH AND PASSIVE RESTRAINT MODULE			
• Disconnect the warning switch connector and both module connectors.	Yes	▶	GO to **PR21**.
• Measure the resistance of the following wires between the warning switch and the module.	No	▶	SERVICE the wire in question.

	Wire Color	Resistance
Driver Side	"O/GN"	Less than 5 ohms
Passenger Side	"P"	Less than 5 ohms

• Are the resistances within specifications?			
PR21 CHECK THE PASSIVE RESTRAINT MODULES SEAT BELT WARNING OUTPUT			
• Reconnect the connectors.	Yes	▶	GO to **PR22**.
• Measure voltage on the "LG/Y" and "BR" wires at the module under the following conditions.	No	▶	REPLACE the passive restraint module.
• Turn key off and then on for each measurement.			

Condition	"LG/Y"	"BR"
Both shoulder belts latched	<2V for 4-8 sec then 10V	<2V for 4-8 sec then 10V
Either shoulder belt unlatched	<2V	<2V for 4-8 sec then 10V

• Are the voltages within specifications?			

FM8019100365050X

Fig. 43 System diagnosis (Part 5 of 6). Festiva

Condition / Possible Source / Action

CONDITION	POSSIBLE SOURCE	ACTION
• Neither Belt Will Leave The B-pillar	• Battery feed to module. • Inertia switch input grounded.	• GO to PR1. • GO to PR7.
• Neither Belt Will Leave The A-pillar	• Power to module. • Ignition line input.	• GO to PR1. • GO to PR5.
• One Belt Will Not Leave The B-pillar	• Door switch input open. • A-pillar limit switch input grounded. • Motor/motor wiring.	• GO to PR8. • GO to PR9. • GO to PR11.
• One Belt Will Not Leave The A-pillar	• Door switch input grounded. • B-pillar limit switch input grounded. • Motor/motor wiring.	• GO to PR8. • GO to PR10. • GO to PR11.
• Belt Carrier (Transport) Jumps or Clicks at B-pillar While Ignition is ON	• B-pillar limit switch input open. • Wiring and connectors between B-pillar switch and Passive Restraint Module.	• GO to PR10. • GO to PR10.
• Belt Carrier (Transport) Jumps or Clicks at A-pillar While Door is Open	• A-pillar limit switch input is open. • Wiring and connectors between A-pillar switch and Passive Restraint Module.	• GO to PR9. • GO to PR9.
• Seat Belt Warning Light and/or Warning Chime Turn ON Intermittently or Remain ON	• B-pillar limit switch open. • Wiring connectors between Retractor/B-pillar limit switch and module. • Retractor switch input open.	• GO to PR10. • GO to PR10. • GO to PR12.
• Seat Belt Warning Light and/or Warning Chime Do Not Turn ON When Intended	• B-pillar limit switch input. • Retractor switch input. • Seat belt warning light. • Warning chime module.	• GO to PR10. • GO to PR12. • GO to PR13. • GO to PR14.

PR1 / PR2 / PR3 (Probe Part 1)

TEST STEP	RESULT	▶	ACTION TO TAKE
PR1 CHECK FUSES			
• Locate the interior fuse panel.	Yes	▶	GO to **PR4**.
• Check the 30 amp BELT fuse and 15 amp METER fuse.	No	▶	GO to **PR2**.
• Are the fuses OK?			
PR2 CHECK SYSTEM			
• Replace the blown fuse(s).	Yes	▶	GO to **PR3**.
• Key ON.	No	▶	GO to **PR4**.
• Does the fuse(s) fail again?			
PR3 CHECK FOR SHORT(S) TO GROUND			
• Key OFF.	Yes	▶	SERVICE the wire(s) in question.
• Disconnect the "BR" and "BK/Y" wires from the interior fuse panel.	No	▶	GO to **PR4**.
• Measure the resistance of the wire in question between the interior fuse panel connector and ground.			
• Are the resistances less than 5 ohms?			

FM8019200366010X

Fig. 44 System diagnosis (Part 1 of 10). Probe

TEST STEP	RESULT	▶	ACTION TO TAKE
PR4 CHECK SUPPLY TO PASSIVE RESTRAINT • Key OFF. • Disconnect the passive restraint module connector #1. • Key ON. • Measure the voltage on the "BR" wires at the passive restraint module connector #1. • Are the voltages greater than 10 volts?	Yes No	▶ ▶	GO to PR5. SERVICE the "BR" wires.
PR5 CHECK SUPPLY TO PASSIVE RESTRAINT MODULE • Key OFF. • Disconnect the passive restraint module connector #2. • Key ON. • Measure the voltage on the "BK/Y" wire at the passive restraint module connector #2. • Is the voltage greater than 10 volts?	Yes No	▶ ▶	GO to PR6. SERVICE the "BK/Y" wire.
PR6 CHECK PASSIVE RESTRAINT MODULE GROUND • Key OFF. • Disconnect the passive restraint module connectors #1 and #2. • Measure the resistances of the "BK" wires between the passive restraint module connectors #1 and #2 and ground. • Are the resistances less than 5 ohms?	Yes No	▶ ▶	GO to PR7. SERVICE the "BK" wire(s) in question.
PR7 CHECK INPUT TO INERTIA SWITCH • Key OFF. • Disconnect the passive restraint module connector #2. • Measure the resistance of the "GN/BK" wire at the passive restraint module connector #2 to ground. • Is the resistance greater than 10,000 ohms?	Yes No	▶ ▶	GO to PR8. GO to PR7-1.

TEST STEP	RESULT	▶	ACTION TO TAKE
PR7-1 CHECK INERTIA SWITCH GROUND • Locate and disconnect the fuel pump inertia switch. • Measure the resistance of the "BK" wire between the fuel pump inertia switch connector and ground. • Is the resistance less than 5 ohms?	Yes No	▶ ▶	GO to PR7-2. SERVICE the "BK" wire. REPEAT PR7 to verify condition.

Fig. 44   System diagnosis (Part 2 of 10). Probe

FM8019200366020X

TEST STEP	RESULT	▶	ACTION TO TAKE
PR7-2 CHECK INERTIA SWITCH • Disconnect and remove the fuel pump inertia switch. • Measure the resistance between the "GN/BK" and "BK" terminals of the fuel pump inertia switch under the following conditions:	Yes No	▶ ▶	GO to PR7-3. REPLACE the fuel pump inertia switch. REPEAT PR7 to verify condition.

Switch Position	Resistance
Open (tripped) poped out	Less than 5 ohms
Closed (set) pushed in	Greater than 10,000 ohms

• Are the resistances OK?

NOTE: Shake the inertia switch sharply to open (trip). Press the switch in to close (set) the fuel pump inertia switch circuit. If the inertia switch does not open and close replace it.

TEST STEP	RESULT	▶	ACTION TO TAKE
PR7-3 CHECK FOR OPENS AND SHORTS • Key OFF. • Disconnect the fuel pump inertia switch and the passive restraint module connectors #1 and #2. • Measure the resistance of the: — "GN/BK" wire between the fuel pump inertia switch connector and the passive restraint module connector. — "GN/BK" wire between the passive restraint module connector and ground. • Is the resistance less than 5 ohms for the "GN/BK" wire between the fuel pump inertia switch and passive restraint module; and greater than 10,000 ohms between the passive restraint module connector and ground?	Yes No	▶ ▶	REPEAT PR7. SERVICE the "GN/BK" wire. REPEAT PR7 to verify condition.
PR8 CHECK DOOR SWITCH INPUTS • Key OFF. • Disconnect the passive restraint module connectors #1 and #2. • Measure the resistances at the passive restraint module connectors under the following conditions: — "GN/O" wire and ground (driver's side) — "Y/GN" wire and ground (passenger's side)	Yes No	▶ ▶	GO to PR9. GO to PR8-1.

Door Position	Driver's Side "GN/O" and Ground	Passenger's Side "Y/GN" and Ground
Door Open	Less than 5 ohms	Less than 5 ohms
Door Closed	Greater than 10,000 ohms	Greater than 10,000 ohms

• Are the resistances OK?

FM8019200366030X

Fig. 44   System diagnosis (Part 3 of 10). Probe

TEST STEP	RESULT	▶	ACTION TO TAKE
PR8-1 CHECK DOOR SWITCH GROUNDS • Locate and disconnect the driver's and passenger's door switches (inside the door). • Measure the resistance of the "BK" wires between the door switch connectors and ground. • Are the resistances less than 5 ohms?	Yes No	▶ ▶	GO to PR8-2. SERVICE the "BK" wire(s) in question. REPEAT PR8 to verify condition.
PR8-2 CHECK DOOR SWITCHES • Key OFF. • Disconnect the door switches. • Measure the resistance between the "BR/W" wire and the "BK" wire at the door switch connectors under the following conditions:	Yes No	▶ ▶	GO to PR8-3. REPLACE the door latch assembly in question. REPEAT PR8 to verify condition.

Door Position	Driver's and Passenger's Side ("BR/W" and "BK")
Door Open	Less than 5 ohms
Door Closed	Greater than 10,000 ohms

• Are the resistances OK?

TEST STEP	RESULT	▶	ACTION TO TAKE
PR8-3 CHECK DOOR SWITCH SUPPLIES • Disconnect the door switches and the passive restraint module connectors #1 and #2. • Measure the resistances of the wires between the passive restraint module connectors and the door switch connectors:	Yes No	▶ ▶	REPEAT PR8. SERVICE the wire(s) in question. REPEAT PR8 to verify condition.

Door Position	From The Passive Restraint Module Connector	To The Door Switch Connector
Driver's Side	"GN/O"	"BR/W"
Passenger's Side	"Y/GN"	"BR/W"

• Are the resistances less than 5 ohms?

FM8019200366040X

Fig. 44   System diagnosis (Part 4 of 10). Probe

TEST STEP	RESULT	▶	ACTION TO TAKE
PR9 CHECK A-PILLAR LIMIT SWITCH INPUTS • Position the carriers at the A-pillars. • Key OFF. • Disconnect the passive restraint module connectors #1 and #2. • Measure the resistances at the passive restraint module connectors under the following conditions: — "Y/BL" wire and ground (driver's side) — "GN/BL" wire and ground (passenger's side)	Yes No	▶ ▶	GO to PR10. GO to PR9-1.

Carrier Position	Driver's Side ("Y/BL" and ground)	Passenger's Side ("GN/BL" and ground)
Carrier at A-pillar	Less than 5 ohms	Less than 5 ohms
Carrier not at A-pillar	Greater than 10,000 ohms	Greater than 10,000 ohms

• Are the resistances OK?

TEST STEP	RESULT	▶	ACTION TO TAKE
PR9-1 CHECK A-PILLAR LIMIT SWITCH GROUNDS • Locate and disconnect the A-pillar limit switches (driver and passenger side). • Measure the resistances between the "BK" wires at the A-pillar limit switch connectors and ground. • Are the resistances less than 5 ohms?	Yes No	▶ ▶	GO to PR9-2. SERVICE the "BK" wire(s) in question. REPEAT PR9 to verify condition.
PR9-2 CHECK A-PILLAR LIMIT SWITCHES • Disconnect the A-pillar limit switches. • Measure the resistances at the A-pillar limit switches, between the wires under the following conditions: — "Y/BL" wire and "BK" wire (driver's side) — "GN/BL" wire and "BK" wire (passenger's side)	Yes No	▶ ▶	GO to PR9-3. REPLACE the A-pillar limit switch in question. REPEAT PR9 to verify condition.

Carrier Position	Driver's Side "Y/BL" and "BK"	Passenger's Side "GN/BL" and "BK"
Carrier at A-pillar	Less than 5 ohms	Less than 5 ohms
Carrier not at A-pillar	Greater than 10,000 ohms	Greater than 10,000 ohms

• Are the resistances OK?

FM8019200366050X

Fig. 44   System diagnosis (Part 5 of 10). Probe

PR9-3 CHECK A-PILLAR LIMIT SWITCH SUPPLIES

TEST STEP	RESULT	▶	ACTION TO TAKE
• Key OFF. • Disconnect the A-pillar limit switches and the passive restraint module connectors #1 and #2. • Measure the resistance of the "Y/BL" wire (driver's side) and the "GN/BL" wire (passenger's side) between the A-pillar limit switch connector and the passive restraint module connector. • Are the resistances less than 5 ohms?	Yes No	▶ ▶	REPEAT **PR9**. SERVICE the wire(s) in question. REPEAT **PR9** to verify condition.

PR10 CHECK B-PILLAR LIMIT SWITCH INPUTS

TEST STEP	RESULT	▶	ACTION TO TAKE
• Key OFF. • Disconnect the passive restraint module connectors #1 and #2. • Measure the resistance at the passive restraint module connectors under the following conditions: — between the "BL/W" wire and ground (driver's side) — between the "BL/Y" wire and ground (passenger's side)	Yes No	▶ ▶	GO to **PR11**. GO to **PR10-1**.

Carrier Position	Driver's Side "BL/W" and ground	Passenger's Side "BL/Y" and ground
Carrier at B-pillar	Less than 5 ohms	Less than 5 ohms
Carrier not at B-pillar	Greater than 10,000 ohms	Greater than 10,000 ohms

• Are the resistances OK?

PR10-1 CHECK B-PILLAR LIMIT SWITCH GROUNDS

TEST STEP	RESULT	▶	ACTION TO TAKE
• Locate and disconnect the B-pillar limit switches. • Measure the resistance of the "BK" wires between the B-pillar limit switch connectors and ground. • Are the resistances less than 5 ohms?	Yes No	▶ ▶	GO to **PR10-2**. SERVICE the "BK" wire(s) in question. REPEAT **PR10** to verify condition.

FM8019200366060X

Fig. 44 System diagnosis (Part 6 of 10). Probe

PR10-2 CHECK B-PILLAR LIMIT SWITCH

TEST STEP	RESULT	▶	ACTION TO TAKE
• Disconnect the B-pillar limit switches. • Measure the resistance at the B-pillar limit switch under the following conditions: — between the "BL/W" wire and ground (driver's side) — between the "BL/Y" wire and ground (passenger's side)	Yes No	▶ ▶	GO to **PR10-3**. REPLACE the passive restraint track and motor assembly in question. REPEAT **PR10** to verify condition.

Carrier Position	Driver's Side ("BL/W" and "BK")	Passenger's Side ("BL/Y" and "BK")
Carrier at B-pillar	Less than 5 ohms	Less than 5 ohms
Carrier not at B-pillar	Greater than 10,000 ohms	Greater than 10,000 ohms

• Are the resistances OK?

PR10-3 CHECK B-PILLAR LIMIT SWITCH SUPPLIES

TEST STEP	RESULT	▶	ACTION TO TAKE
• Key OFF. • Disconnect the B-pillar limit switches and passive restraint module connectors #1 and #2. • Measure the resistance of the "BL/W" wire (driver's side) and the "BL/Y" wire (passenger's side) between the B-pillar limit switch and the passive restraint module connector. • Are the resistances less than 5 ohms?	Yes No	▶ ▶	REPEAT **PR10**. SERVICE the wire(s) in question. REPEAT **PR10** to verify condition.

PR11 CHECK PASSIVE RESTRAINT MOTOR INPUTS

TEST STEP	RESULT	▶	ACTION TO TAKE
• Key OFF. • Disconnect the passive restraint module connectors #1 and #2. • Make the following connections at the passive restraint module connectors to move the carrier from the A-pillar to the B-pillar.	Yes No	▶ ▶	GO to **PR12**. GO to **PR11-1**.

Reference	Driver's Side	Passenger's Side
Ground	"Y" (pin 1J or 1H)	"R" (pin 2J or 2H)
12 volts	"BL" (pin 1L or 1K)	"GN" (pin 2L or 2M)

• Reverse the power and ground connections to move the carrier from the B-pillar to the A-pillar.
• Does the carrier move from the A-pillar to the B-pillar and back to the A-pillar?

FM8019200366070X

Fig. 44 System diagnosis (Part 7 of 10). Probe

PR11-1 CHECK PASSIVE RESTRAINT MOTORS

TEST STEP	RESULT	▶	ACTION TO TAKE
• Key OFF. • Disconnect the passive restraint module connectors #1 and #2. • Disconnect the passive restraint motors. • Make the following connections at the passive restraint motors to move the carrier from the A-pillar to the B-pillar.	Yes No	▶ ▶	GO to **PR11-2**. REPLACE the passive restraint motor(s) in question. REPEAT **PR11** to verify condition.

Reference	Driver's Side	Passenger's Side
Ground	"Y"	"R"
12 volts	"BL"	"GN"

• Reverse the power and ground leads to move the carrier from the B-pillar to the A-pillar.
• Does the carrier move from the A-pillar to the B-pillar and back to the A-pillar?

PR11-2 CHECK PASSIVE RESTRAINT MOTOR SUPPLIES

TEST STEP	RESULT	▶	ACTION TO TAKE
• Key OFF. • Disconnect the passive restraint module connectors #1 and #2 and passive restraint motors. • Measure the resistance of the following wires between the passive restraint module connector and passive restraint motor connector. — "BL" (driver's side) pins 1L and 1K — "Y" (driver's side) pins 1J and 1H — "GN" (passenger's side) pins 2L and 2M — "R" (passenger's side) pins 2J and 2H • Are the resistances less than 5 ohms?	Yes No	▶ ▶	REPEAT **PR11**. SERVICE the wire(s) in question. REPEAT **PR11** to verify condition.

PR12 CHECK RETRACTOR SWITCH INPUTS

TEST STEP	RESULT	▶	ACTION TO TAKE
• Key OFF. • Disconnect the passive restraint module connectors #1 and #2. • Measure the resistance at the passive restraint module connectors under the following conditions: — between the "BL/R" wire and ground (driver's side) — between the "LG/BK" wire and ground (passenger's side)	Yes No	▶ ▶	GO to **PR13**. GO to **PR12-1**.

Shoulder Belt Position	Driver's Side "BL/R" and ground	Passenger's side "LG/BK" and ground
Shoulder belt buckled	Less than 5 ohms	Less than 5 ohms
Shoulder belt spooled in	Greater than 10,000 ohms	Greater than 10,000 ohms

• Are the resistances OK?

FM8019200366080X

Fig. 44 System diagnosis (Part 8 of 10). Probe

PR12-1 CHECK RETRACTOR SWITCH GROUNDS

TEST STEP	RESULT	▶	ACTION TO TAKE
• Key OFF. • Disconnect the retractor switches located in the center console. • Measure the resistance of the "BK" wires between the retractor switch connectors and ground. • Are the resistances less than 5 ohms?	Yes No	▶ ▶	GO to **PR12-2**. SERVICE the "BK" wire(s) in question. REPEAT **PR12** to verify condition.

PR12-2 CHECK RETRACTOR SWITCHES

TEST STEP	RESULT	▶	ACTION TO TAKE
• Key OFF. • Disconnect the retractor switches. • Measure the resistance at the retractor switch under the following conditions: — between the "BL/R" wire and the "BK" wire (driver's side) — between the "LG/BK" wire and the "BK" wire (passenger's side)	Yes No	▶ ▶	GO to **PR12-3**. REPLACE the retractor switch(es) in question. REPEAT **PR12** to verify condition.

Shoulder Belt Position	Driver's Side "BL/R" and "BK"	Passenger's Side "LG/BK" and "BK"
Shoulder belt buckled	Less than 5 ohms	Less than 5 ohms
Shoulder belt spooled in	Greater than 10,000 ohms	Greater than 10,000 ohms

• Are the resistances OK?

PR12-3 CHECK RETRACTOR SWITCH SUPPLIES

TEST STEP	RESULT	▶	ACTION TO TAKE
• Key OFF. • Disconnect the retractor switches and the passive restraint module connectors #1 and #2. • Measure the resistance of the "BL/R" wire (driver's side) and the "LG/BK" wire (passenger's side) between the retractor switch connectors and the passive restraint module connectors. • Are the resistances less than 5 ohms?	Yes No	▶ ▶	REPEAT **PR12**. SERVICE the wire(s) in question. REPEAT **PR12** to verify condition.

PR13 CHECK SEAT BELT WARNING LIGHT INPUT

TEST STEP	RESULT	▶	ACTION TO TAKE
• Key OFF. • Disconnect the passive restraint module connectors #1 and #2. • Key ON. • Connect the "BR/BK" wire at the passive restraint module connector to ground. • Does the seat belt warning light illuminate?	Yes No	▶ ▶	GO to **PR14**. GO to **PR13-1**.

FM8019200366090X

Fig. 44 System diagnosis (Part 9 of 10). Probe

TEST STEP	RESULT	▶	ACTION TO TAKE
PR13-1 CHECK SUPPLY TO SEAT BELT WARNING LIGHT			
• Key ON.	Yes	▶	GO to **PR13-2**.
• Measure the voltage on the "BK/Y" wire at the instrument cluster connector.	No	▶	SERVICE the "BK/Y" wire. REPEAT **PR13** to verify condition.
• Is the voltage greater than 10 volts?			
PR13-2 CHECK SEAT BELT WARNING LIGHT			
• Key ON.	Yes	▶	GO to **PR13-3**.
• Connect pin 1E of the instrument cluster to ground.	No	▶	REPLACE the seat belt warning light. REPEAT **PR13** to verify condition.
• Does the seat belt warning light illuminate?			
PR13-3 CHECK FOR CONTINUITY BETWEEN INSTRUMENT CLUSTER AND PASSIVE RESTRAINT MODULE			
• Key OFF.	Yes	▶	REPEAT **PR13**.
• Disconnect the passive restraint module connectors #1 and #2 and the instrument cluster.	No	▶	SERVICE the "BR/BK" wire. REPEAT **PR13** to verify condition.
• Measure the resistance of the "BR/BK" wire between the passive restraint module connector and instrument cluster connector.			
• Is the resistance less than 5 ohms?			

TEST STEP	RESULT	▶	ACTION TO TAKE
PR14 CHECK WARNING CHIME OUTPUT			
• Key OFF.	Yes	▶	REPLACE the passive restraint module. REPEAT the test.
• Disconnect the passive restraint module connectors #1 and #2.			
• Key ON.			
• Connect the "BK/BL" wire at the passive restraint module connector to ground.	No	▶	GO to **PR14-1**.
• Does the warning chime sound?			

TEST STEP	RESULT	▶	ACTION TO TAKE
PR14-1 CHECK SUPPLY TO WARNING CHIME			
• Disconnect the warning chime module from the joint box.	Yes	▶	GO to **PR14-2**.
• Key ON.	No	▶	SERVICE the supply wire to the ROOM fuse. REPEAT **PR14** to verify condition.
• Measure the voltages on pins 1B, 1J, and 1K at the joint box CPU connector.			
• Are the voltages greater than 10 volts?			
PR14-2 CHECK WARNING CHIME			
• Key ON.	Yes	▶	SERVICE the "BK/BL" wire between the warning chime module and the passive restraint module. REPEAT **PR14** to verify condition.
• Connect pin 1H of the CPU joint box connector to ground.			
• Does the warning chime sound?			
	No	▶	REPLACE the warning chime module. REPEAT **PR14** to verify condition.

FM8019200366100X

Fig. 44   System diagnosis (Part 10 of 10). Probe

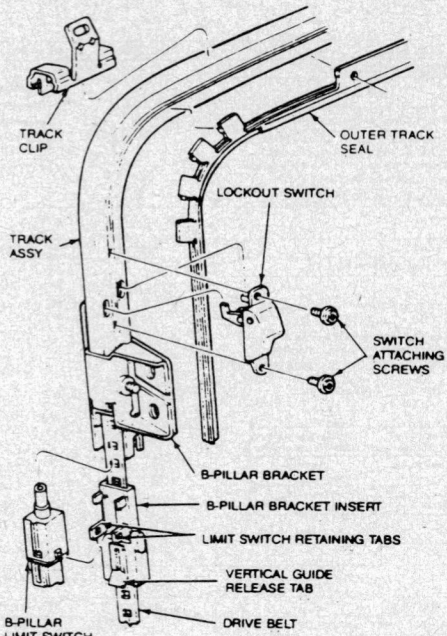

FM8019100367000X

Fig. 45   Vertical drive belt disengagement. Cougar & Thunderbird

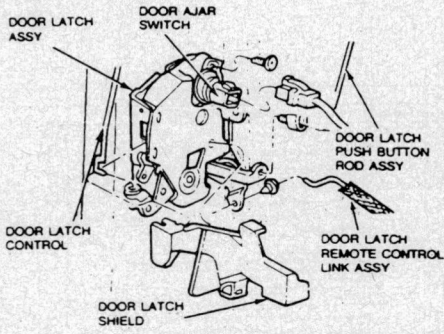

FM8019100369000X

Fig. 47   Door ajar switch removal. Cougar & Thunderbird

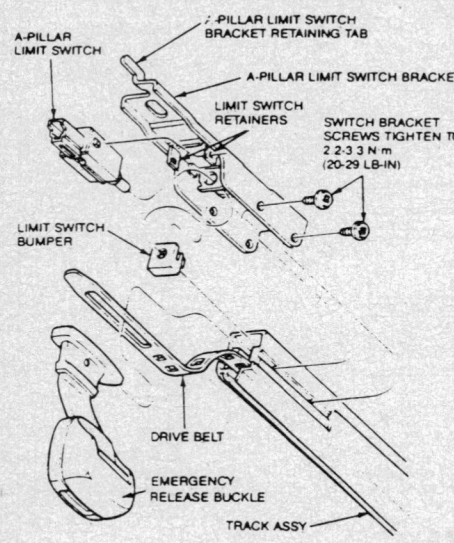

FM8019100368000X

Fig. 46   A-pillar track assembly. Cougar & Thunderbird

COMPONENT REPLACEMENT

DRIVE BELT

COUGAR & THUNDERBIRD

Removal

1. Cycle shoulder belt to full forward position. Disengage shoulder belt from mini buckle.
2. Remove rear seat back and cushion.
3. Remove A-pillar and quarter panel trim.
4. Disconnect electrical connectors from A- and B-pillars limit switches.
5. Remove upper bolt used to retain vertical belt guide to inner quarter panel.
6. Using release tab, disengage vertical belt guide from B-pillar bracket **Fig. 45.**
7. Remove two bolts retaining track assembly to B-pillar.
8. Remove A-pillar limit switch bracket attaching screws.
9. While holding track assembly securely, remove two bolts retaining track assembly to roof rail.
10. Rotate track assembly downward at rear to disengage A-pillar limit switch bracket from A-pillar.
11. While holding track assembly, rotate thumb wheel on motor counterclockwise to allow tape to disengaged from motors drive gear.
12. Remove track assembly from vehicle, then remove A-pillar limit switch bracket from track assembly.
13. Gently slide buckle assembly forward out of track assembly, **Fig. 46.**
14. Remove buckle assembly from drive belt.

Installation

Prior to installation, lubricate track using suitable grease.

1. Insert drive belt at front of track assembly, then install buckle assembly into large slot at front end of drive belt **Fig. 47.**
2. Slide drive belt and buckle assembly into track assembly far enough to allow installation of A-pillar limit switch and bracket assembly, then secure switch and bracket.
3. Install drive belt into vertical guide.
4. Rotate thumb wheel on motor clockwise to feed drive belt through motor guide and into lower guide.
5. Rotate track assembly downward at rear and position retaining tab on A-pillar limit switch bracket into forward hole in A-pillar. Then rotate track assembly upward.
6. Engage vertical guide retaining tab into B-pillar bracket. Install but do not tighten screw and bolts used to secure track assembly to roof rail and A-pillar.
7. Secure B-pillar bracket to B-pillar.

Tempo/Topaz—4-Door

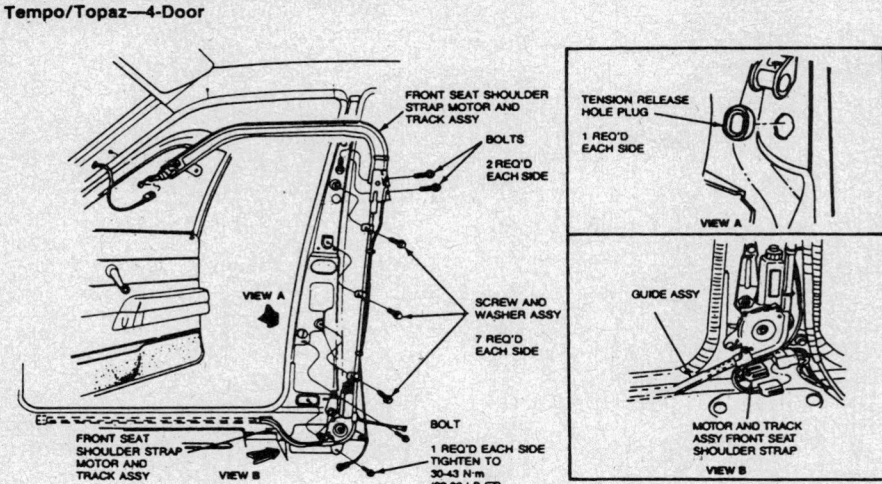

Tempo/Topaz—2-Door

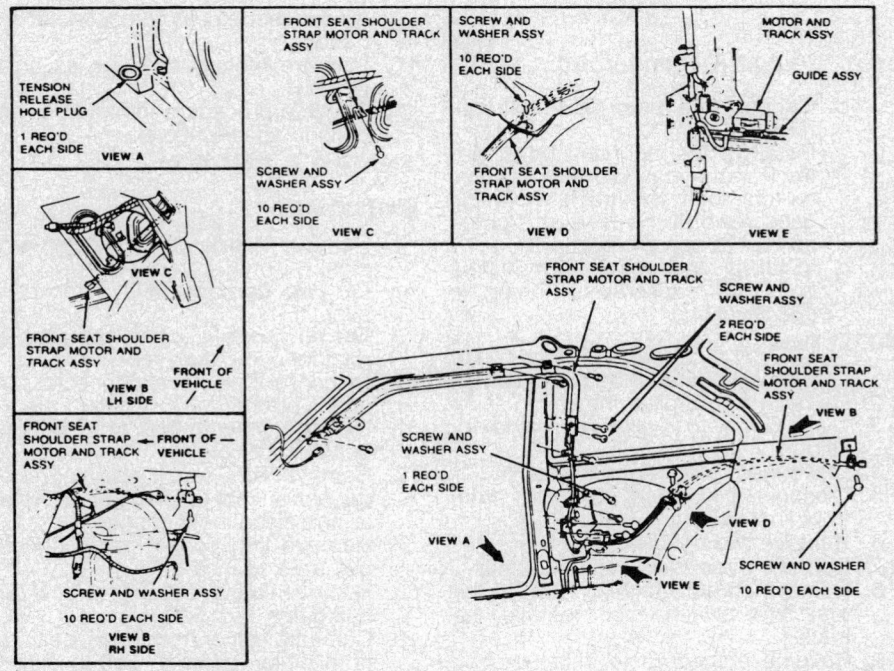

Fig. 48   Motorized seat belt system. Tempo & Topaz

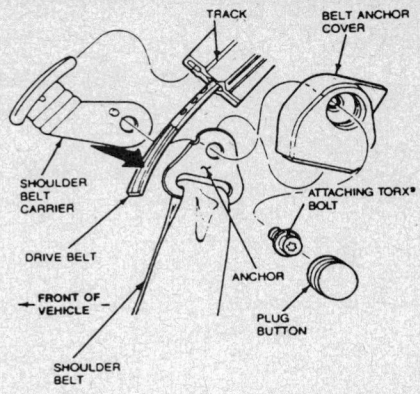

Fig. 49   Shoulder belt upper anchor assembly. Tempo & Topaz

3. Install retainer into large slot at front end of tape.
4. Slide drive belt at rear of track until end is approximately 1/2 inch in the upper track slot.
5. Install limit switch and track assembly, noting the following:
   a. Apply Threadlock and Sealer No. E0AZ-19554-AA or equivalent to limit switch retaining screws.
   b. Tighten A-pillar limit switch retaining screws to specifications.

TRACK ASSEMBLY

COUGAR & THUNDERBIRD

Removal

1. Cycle shoulder belt to the full forward position, then disengage shoulder belt from mini buckle.
2. Remove rear seat back and cushion.
3. Remove A-pillar and quarter panel trim.
4. Disconnect electrical connectors from A-pillar limit switch and motor assembly.
5. Remove two bolts used to retain vertical belt guide to inner quarter panel.
6. Remove three bolts retaining lower belt guide to quarter inner panel.
7. Remove two bolts retaining motor assembly to quarter panel inner panel.
8. Disengage vertical belt guide at B-pillar bracket.
9. Remove bolts retaining track assembly to B-pillar.
10. Remove screw holding A-pillar limit switch bracket to A-pillar, **Fig. 46.**
11. While holding track assembly securely, remove bolts holding track assembly to roof rail, **Fig. 50.**
12. Rotate track assembly downward at rear to disengage A-pillar limit switch bracket from A-pillar.
13. Remove track and motor assembly from vehicle.

Installation

1. Position retaining tab on A-pillar limit switch bracket into forward hole in A-pillar, then rotate track assembly upward, **Fig. 46.**
2. Loosely install screws and bolts used to secure track assembly to roof rail and A-pillar.

Tighten bolts to specifications.
8. Tighten A-pillar limit switch attachment bolt to specifications.
9. Install retaining vertical guide to inner quarter panel sheet metal bolt.
10. Reconnect electrical connectors at A and B-pillars limit switches.
11. Install quarter trim panel and A-pillar moldings.
12. Cycle mini buckle to B-pillar position.
13. Insert tongue of shoulder belt into mini buckle. Ensure belt is not twisted.

TEMPO & TOPAZ

Removal

Refer to **Fig. 48** for the following procedure.
1. Remove track assembly as described under "Track Assembly" in this section.
2. Remove two screws retaining front A-pillar switch bracket to track assembly.
3. Carefully slide shoulder belt retainer forward off track, **Fig. 49.** Drive belt should slide out of track with shoulder belt retainer.
4. Remove shoulder belt retainer from drive belt.

Installation

1. Lubricate track assembly with Lithium/Teflon Grease No. E7FZ-19590-A or equivalent.
2. Insert drive belt at front of track A-pillar.

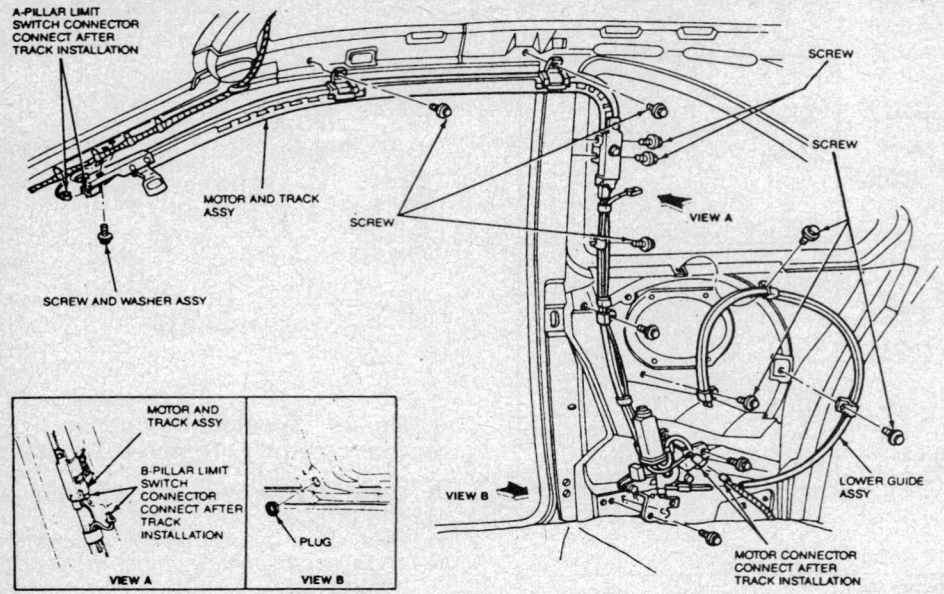

Fig. 50   Motorized seat belt system. Cougar & Thunderbird

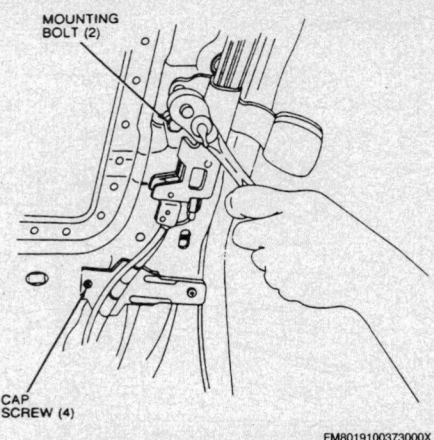

Fig. 51   Side track replacement. Probe

3. Secure B-pillar bracket to B-pillar. Tighten bolts to specifications.
4. Tighten A-pillar limit switch attaching bolts to specifications.
5. Tighten two bolts holding track assembly to roof rail to specifications.
6. Engage locating tab on motor bracket into slot in quarter panel inner sheet metal, then install two motor attaching bolts. Tighten bolts to specifications.
7. Engage vertical guide retaining tab into B-pillar bracket, then secure guide to quarter panel inner sheet metal. Tighten attaching bolts to specifications.
8. Secure lower belt guide to quarter inner panel. Tighten attaching bolts to specifications.
9. Connect electrical connectors at A-pillar limit switch and motor.
10. Install quarter trim panel and A-pillar moldings.
11. Cycle mini buckle to B-pillar position, then insert tongue of shoulder belt into mini buckle.
12. Cycle system to ensure proper operation.

ESCORT & TRACER

1. Disconnect battery ground cable.
2. Disconnect shoulder belt from carrier, then cycle carrier to the B-pillar (On position).
3. Remove A to B pillar trim panel, then the B-pillar trim panel.
4. Disconnect front limit switch electrical connector.
5. Disconnect two motor electrical connectors.
6. Remove all track and motor assembly mounting bolts and capscrews.
7. Remove track and motor assembly.
8. Reverse procedure to install, noting the following:
   a. Position track and motor assembly into position and install one track mounting bolt to hold in position.

b. Connect two motor electrical connectors.
c. Install motor mounting bolts, two track mounting bolts at rear limit switch, then the track mounting capscrews at the B-pillar. Tighten screws to specifications.
d. Install all remaining track mounting bolts and capscrews. Tighten to specifications.

FESTIVA

1. Disconnect shoulder belt from carrier.
2. Remove A to B pillar trim.
3. Cycle carrier to B-pillar (retracted position).
4. Disconnect battery ground cable.
5. Disconnect electrical connector from front limit switch.
6. Remove two headliner clips.
7. Remove three track mounting bolts.
8. Remove screw attaching track to the rear limit switch, then remove the track.
9. Reverse procedure to install, noting the following:
   a. Pull off A-pillar molding near instrument panel to ease A to B-pillar trim installation.
   b. Tighten track mounting bolts to specifications.

PROBE

1. Disconnect shoulder belt from carrier.
2. Cycle carrier to B-pillar (retracted position).
3. Disconnect battery ground cable.
4. Remove A-B pillar trim panel and quarter trim panel.
5. Disconnect electrical connector from front limit switch.
6. Remove upper track mounting screw and bolts.
7. Remove two side track mounting bolts. Fig. 51.
8. Remove four cable retaining cap screws and three motor mounting bolts.

9. Disconnect electrical connector from motor.
10. Remove motor and track as an assembly.
11. Reverse procedure to install. Tighten bolts to specifications.

TEMPO & TOPAZ

Removal

1. Remove A-pillar and B-pillar moldings.
2. On two door models, remove rear seat.
3. On all models, cycle shoulder belt retainer completely forward.
4. Disconnect electrical connectors at A and B-pillars.
5. Remove plug button from shoulder belt anchor cover.
6. Remove Torx screw retaining shoulder belt anchor to shoulder belt retainer and disconnect anchor.
7. Remove two screws retaining drive belt track to motor.
8. Remove screw retaining vertical drive belt guide, Fig. 52.
9. Carefully disconnect drive belt track from motor, allowing belt to pass by gear teeth without engagement.
10. Remove screw from A-pillar bracket to A-pillar.
11. Remove two bolts securing track assembly to B-pillar.
12. Remove two screws retaining track assembly to inner roof rail.
13. Remove screws from overhead track retaining clips.
14. Disengage vertical guide release tab at B-pillar bracket.
15. Rotate track inboard to remove track limit switch retaining tab from slot in A-pillar.
16. Carefully slide drive belt out of vertical guide.

Installation

1. Insert drive belt in vertical track.
2. Insert retaining tab on limit switch bracket into slot in A-pillar.
3. Engage vertical guide retaining tab into B-pillar.

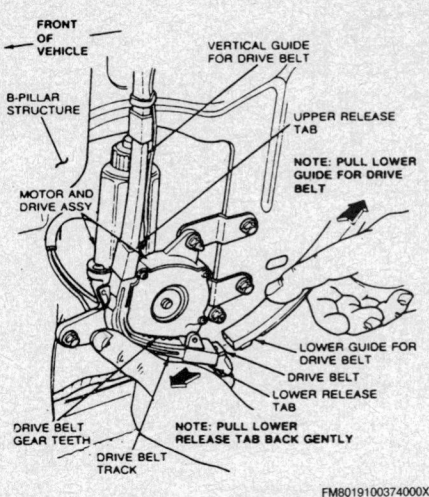

Fig. 52 Drive belt replacement. Tempo & Topaz

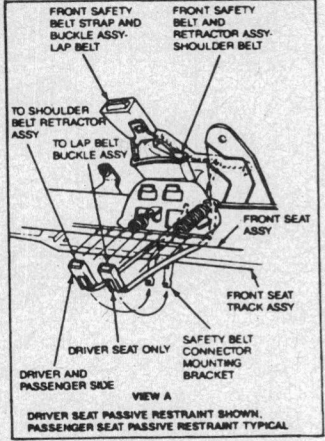

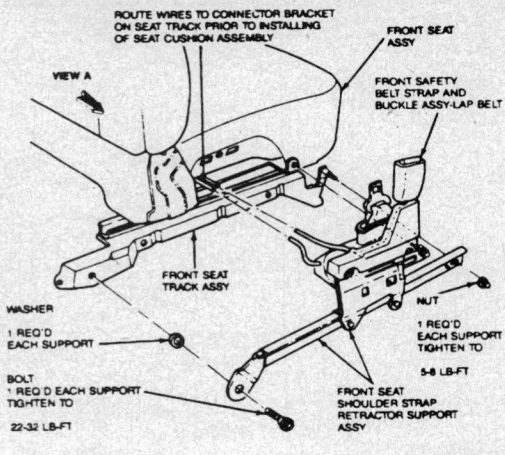

Fig. 53 Retractor assembly replacement. Cougar & Thunderbird

4. Install two retaining bolts at B-pillar. Tighten bolts to specifications.
5. Install screws in overhead track retaining clips, then install screw retaining A-pillar switch bracket to A-pillar.
6. Position drive belt guide at motor.
7. Align drive belt and guides. Ensure belt does not bind, then install two screws.
8. Install shoulder belt bolt and tighten to specifications.
9. Install plug button and connect electrical connectors.
10. Ensure proper operation of restraint system, then install garnish moldings.
11. Install front seat shoulder belt track to track assembly as follows:
    a. Return shoulder belt track carrier to retracted position (B-pillar).
    b. Pull belt from retractor on the console. Allow belt to lay flat across seat back without twisting.
    c. Install shoulder belt to track assembly by inserting anti-rotation pin in strap carrier and aligning it with notch in belt anchor.
    d. Install Torx head retaining bolt and tighten to specifications.
12. Ensure system operates correctly.
13. Install quarter trim panel.

RETRACTOR ASSEMBLY
COUGAR & THUNDERBIRD
Removal

1. Cycle shoulder straps to A-pillar position.
2. Disconnect shoulder belt from emergency release buckle of motor and track carrier assembly, allowing safety straps to retract into retractor.
3. Disconnect seat wiring at floor, then remove front seat and seat track assembly.
4. Remove support assembly with belt/retractor assembly and lap belt buckle/strap assembly still attached, **Fig. 53.**
5. Remove front retaining nut and bolt.

6. Remove rear Torx head bolt retaining support assembly to seat track.
7. Remove support assembly.
8. Remove Torx head bolt retaining lap belt buckle assembly to support assembly. Remove buckle assembly.
9. Remove nut and washer retaining shoulder strap retractor assembly to shoulder strap support.
10. Rotate retractor up and away from support assembly until hooks disengage.
11. Remove retractor from support assembly by pulling stud out of hole.

Installation

1. Insert retractor mounting stud into hole in support assembly.
2. With retractor pivoted up approximately 45°, loosely install retaining nut and washer.
3. Rotate retractor down toward support assembly. Ensure both retractor housing locking hooks engage into support assembly and retractor attachment bracket is on opposite side of support assembly.
4. Position lap belt buckle and strap assembly to indexing tabs on belt and retractor assembly mounting strap.
5. Ensure mounting holes are aligned and install Torx head bolt to support assembly.
6. Position support assembly with belt/retractor assembly and lap belt buckle strap assembly attached, to seat and track assembly.
7. Ensure safety belt wire and connectors are properly routed between seat frame and seat track.
8. Install retaining nut and bolts. **Rubber washer must be installed between the support assembly and seat track at rear attachment.** Refer to **Fig. 53.**
9. Secure safety belt wiring connectors to metal connector mounting bracket on seat track.
10. Install front seat and seat track assembly. Connect wiring to floor harness.
11. Connect shoulder safety strap to emergency release buckle.

12. Ensure proper operation of restraint system.

ESCORT & TRACER

1. Disconnect battery ground cable.
2. Remove parking brake console mounting screws, then lift console and remove shoulder belts.
3. Remove parking brake console.
4. Disconnect electrical connector from retractor, then slide seat forward and remove retractor.
5. Reverse procedure to install. Tighten retractor mounting bolts to specifications.

FESTIVA

1. Disconnect shoulder belt from carrier and remove retractor cover.
2. Disconnect electrical connector and remove retractor mounting bolt.
3. Remove retractor assembly.
4. Reverse procedure to install. Tighten bolt to specifications.

PROBE

1. Disconnect both shoulder belts from carriers.
2. Remove floor console.
3. Remove two retractor assembly mounting bolts.
4. Disconnect electrical connector and remove retractor assembly.
5. Reverse procedure to install.

TEMPO & TOPAZ

1. Remove plug at shoulder belt retainer anchor cover, then disconnect belt anchor at retainer.
2. Remove console attaching screws, then armrest, if equipped.
3. Disengage shoulder harness opening bezel from console, **Fig. 54.**
4. Remove shoulder belt retractor.
5. Reverse procedure to install, noting the following:
    a. Cycle shoulder belts to B-pillar prior to reinstalling belt anchor to belt retainer.
    b. Tighten shoulder belt retaining bolts to specifications.
    c. Tighten retractor to floor brace retaining bolts to specifications.

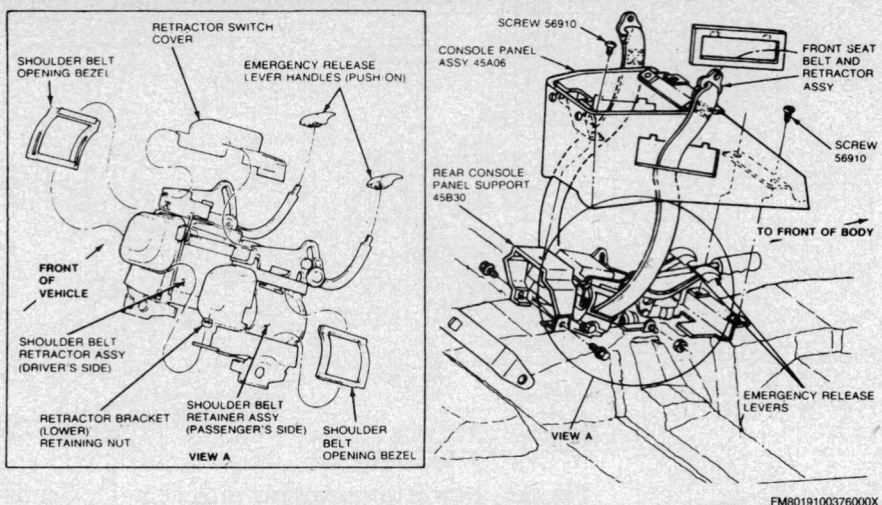

Fig. 54   Shoulder harness disengagement. Tempo & Topaz

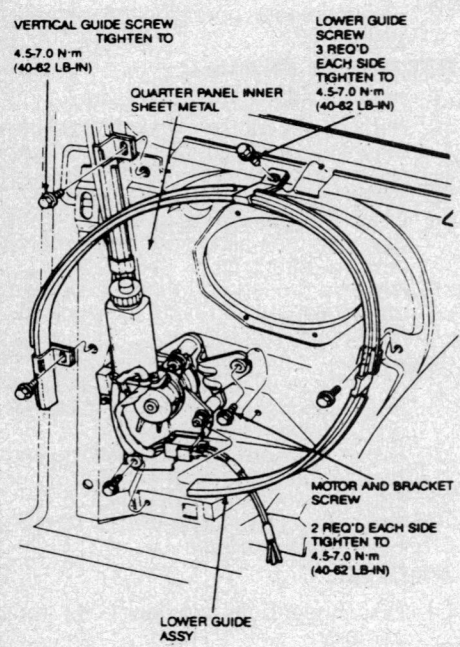

Fig. 55   Motor & bracket assembly replacement. Cougar & Thunderbird

MOTOR

Cougar & Thunderbird

1. Remove rear seat back and cushion.
2. Remove A-pillar and quarter panel trim.
3. Remove lower bolt holding vertical guide to quarter panel inner sheet metal, **Fig. 55.**
4. Disengage lower guide from motor guide.
5. Disconnect electrical connector at motor.
6. Remove two bolts holding motor to quarter panel inner sheet metal.
7. Disengage vertical guide from motor guide, **Fig. 56.**
8. Rotate thumb wheel on motor counterclockwise to disengage drive belt from motor drive gear.

9. Remove motor and bracket assembly from vehicle.
10. Reverse procedure to install. Tighten bolts to specifications.

Festiva

1. Unbuckle shoulder belt from carrier.
2. Cycle carrier to retracted position (B-pillar).
3. Disconnect battery ground cable.
4. Remove A to B-pillar trim, then fold rear seat forward.
5. Loosen side shelf screws to access rear quarter trim panel.
6. Remove rear quarter trim panel.
7. Remove two limit switch bolts and two capscrews retaining drive belt tube.
8. Remove screw securing track to rear limit switch.
9. Remove three motor mounting bolts, then pull motor out and disconnect electrical connector.
10. Reverse procedure to install.
11. Tighten motor mounting bolts, drive belt tube capscrews, and rear limit switch bolts to specifications.

Escort, Probe & Tracer

The motor is serviced with the track as an assembly. Refer to "Track Assembly" in this section for replacement procedures.

Tempo & Topaz

1. **On two-door models,** remove quarter trim panel.
2. **On four-door models,** remove B-pillar trim.
3. **On all models,** remove drive belt track retaining screws from motor.
4. Remove screw from vertical drive belt guide adjacent to motor. Slide drive belt track down and out of the way for motor removal.
5. Disconnect electrical connectors.
6. Remove hex nuts from motor mounting bracket studs.
7. Reverse procedure to install.

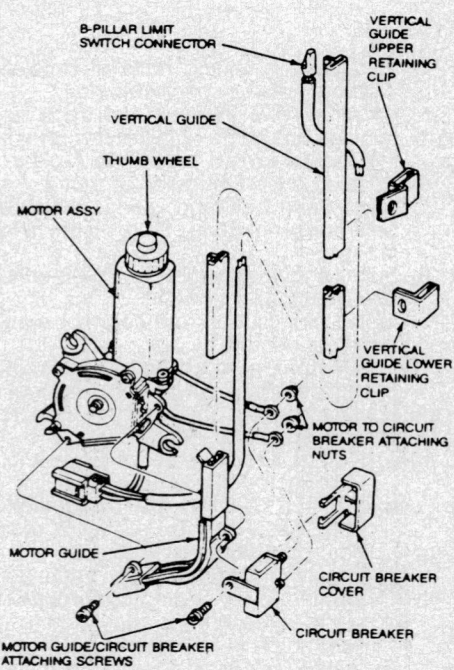

Fig. 56   Vertical guide disengagement. Cougar & Thunderbird

PASSIVE RESTRAINT MODULE

Cougar & Thunderbird

1. Remove lefthand luggage compartment trim panel.
2. Disengage two cover retaining push pins and remove cover **Fig. 57.**
3. Remove processor assembly from bracket, processor snaps on bracket.
4. Disconnect electrical connectors and remove processor.
5. Reverse procedure to install.

Escort, Festiva & Tracer

1. Disconnect battery ground cable.

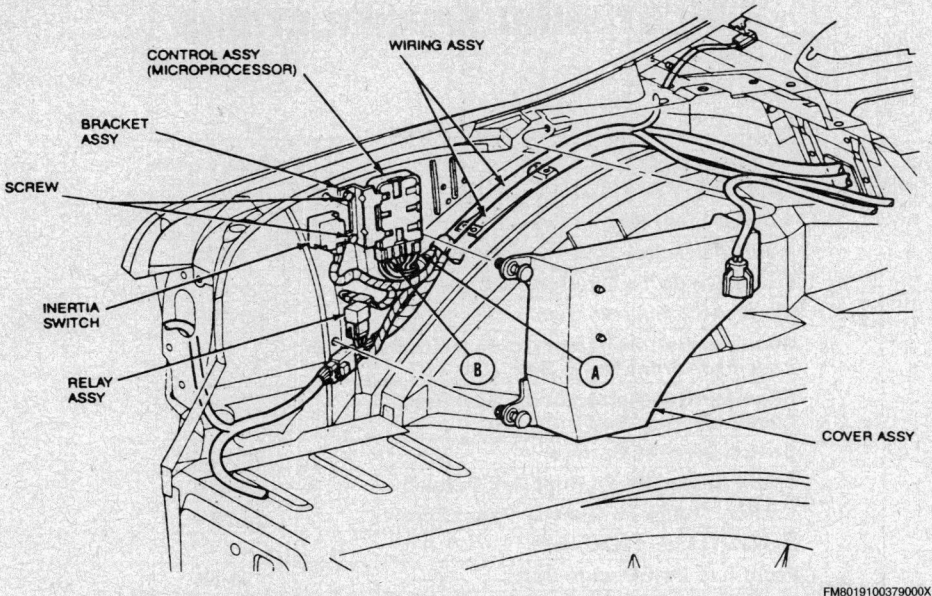

CONTROL ASSY (MICROPROCESSOR)

WIRING ASSY

BRACKET ASSY

SCREW

INERTIA SWITCH

RELAY ASSY

COVER ASSY

FM8019100379000X

Fig. 57 Passive restraint module replacement. Cougar & Thunderbird

2. Remove two mounting bolts, then disconnect electrical connectors.
3. Remove module from below driver's seat.
4. Reverse procedure to install. Check passive restraint system for proper operation.

Probe

1. Disconnect battery ground cable.
2. Remove quarter trim panel.
3. Remove three module mounting plate bolts.
4. Disconnect two electrical connectors from module.
5. Remove module from mounting plate.
6. Reverse procedure to install. Ensure proper operation of restraint system.

Tempo & Topaz

1. Open glove compartment door.

2. Remove two module mounting bracket screws.
3. Disconnect module connectors and slide module off bracket.
4. Reverse procedure to install.

TRACK LIMIT SWITCH

Tempo & Topaz

1. Disconnect switch from wiring harness.
2. Using ohmmeter, probe across connector terminals. Switch must open when plunger is depressed.
3. Remove Torx bolt and move spacer downward.
4. Reverse procedure to install.

Escort & Tracer

The limit switch is serviced with the track and motor as an assembly. Refer to

"Track Assembly, Removal" for replacement procedure.

Cougar & Thunderbird

1. Disconnect switch from wiring harness.
2. Remove Torx bolt and move spacer downward, **Figs. 45 and 46.**
3. Remove limit switches.
4. Reverse procedure to install.

RETRACTOR SWITCH
Cougar & Thunderbird

1. Disconnect switch at connector attached to bracket on inboard side of driver's side seat track.
2. Remove attaching bolts on retractor support assembly, then remove support assembly.
3. Separate retractor switch from support assembly, by removing two screws.
4. Reverse procedure to install.

TIGHTENING SPECIFICATIONS

Component	Torque/Ft. Lbs.
COUGAR & THUNDERBIRD	
A-Pillar Limit Switch Bracket Screws	40-62 ①
B-Pillar Bracket To B-Pillar Bolts	17-24
Lower Guide To Quarter Panel Screws	66-88 ①
Motor Attaching Screws	66-88 ①
Shoulder Belt Retractor To Seat Track Assembly Front Nut & Bolt	5-8
Shoulder Belt Retractor To Seat Track Assembly Torx Bolt	23-29
Switch Bracket Screws	20-29 ①
Track Assembly To Roof Rail Screws	66-88 ①
Vertical Guide To Quarter Panel Screws	66-88 ①
ESCORT & TRACER	
Front Lap Belt Buckle Bolt	28-58
Front Lap Belt Retractor Mounting Bolts	28-58
Front Retractor Mounting Bolts	28-58
Motor Mounting Bolts (3-Door Hatchback)	28-58
Motor Mounting Bolts (Except 3-Door Hatchback)	69-104 ①
Rear Shoulder Belt Anchor Bolt	28-58
Rear Shoulder Belt Retractor Mounting Bolts	28-58
Track Mounting Bolts & Capscrews	69-104 ①
Track Mounting Bolts (At Rear Limit Switch)	13-19
Track Mounting Capscrews (At B-Pillar)	17-33 ①
FESTIVA	
Anchor Bracket Bolts	28-58
Drive Belt Tube Capscrews	3-4
Limit Switch Bolts	6-8
Passive Restraint Motor Retaining Bolts	6-8
Retractor Mounting Bolt	23-34
Seat Belt Guide Belt	28-58
Track Mounting Bolts	6-8
PROBE	
Motor Mounting Bolts	28-58
Rear Seat Buckle Retaining Belt	28-39
Side Track Mounting Bolts	28-58
Upper Track Mounting Bolts	28-58
TEMPO & TOPAZ	
A-Pillar Limit Switch Retaining Screws	5-8
Drive Belt Track Retaining Screws	5-8
Drive Belt Track To B-Pillar Retaining Bolts	17-24
Retractor Retaining Bolts	23-29
Shoulder Belt Retaining Bolt	8-12

① —Inch Lbs.

DASH PANEL SERVICE

NOTE: On Air Bag Equipped Models, Refer To Air Bag System Precautions Located In The Front Of This Manual For System Disarming And Arming Procedures.

INDEX

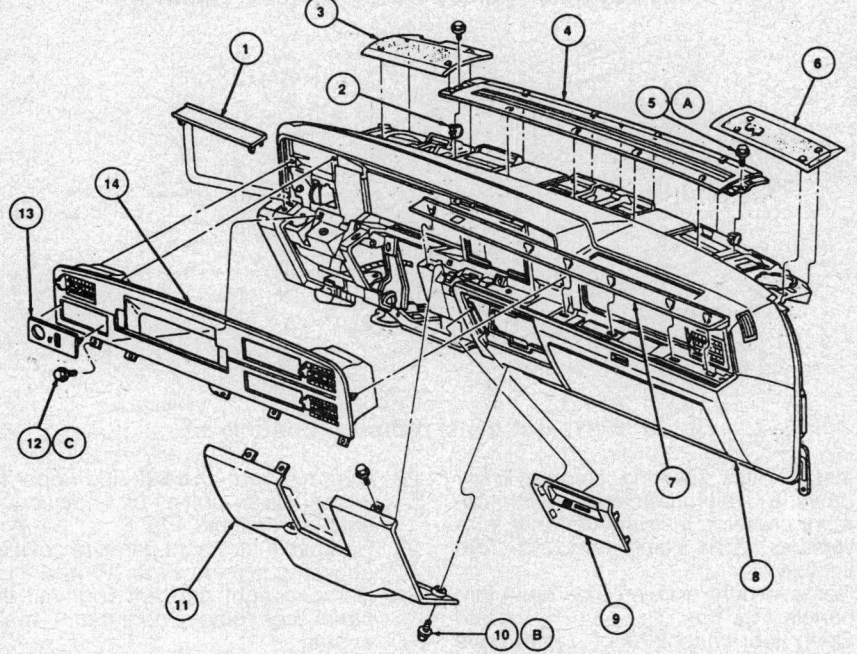

Item	Part Number	Description
1	04269	LH Moulding Assy
2	N803685-S32	Push In Nut (2 Req'd)
3	045G67	LH Exterior Defroster Grille Assy
4	046B62	Defroster Opening Grille Assy
5A	N804251-S36B	Screw and Washer (2 Req'd)
6	045G66	RH Exterior Defroster Grille Assy
7	04268	RH Moulding Assy
8	04304	Instrument Panel Assy
9	04608	Finish Lower Center Panel Assy

Item	Part Number	Description
10B	N800312-S2	Self Tapping Screw (5 Req'd)
11	046A72	Steering Column Opening Cover and Pad Assy
12C	N56922-S368	Self Tapping Screw and Washer (5 Req'd)
13	046B12	Control Name Plate Assy
14	044D70	Cluster Opening Finish Panel Assy
A		Tighten to 2-2.9 N·m (18-25 Lb-In)
B		Tighten to 3.5-5.2 N·m (31-46 Lb-In)
C		Tighten to 1.7-2.3 N·m (16-20 Lb-In)

FM9149100018000X

Fig. 1   Trim & accessory panel removal. Continental

PRECAUTIONS

AIR BAG SYSTEMS

Refer to "Air Bag System Precautions" in the front of this manual for system disarming and arming procedures.

DASH PANEL
REPLACE
CONTINENTAL

1. Disconnect battery ground cable.
2. Remove four nut and washer assem-

blies attaching driver air bag module to steering wheel, then verify air bag lamp after reactivating system.
3. Disconnect driver air bag module electrical connector and remove air bag from vehicle. **Place air bag on bench with trim cover facing up.**
4. Remove right side finish moulding by pulling upward to unsnap five clips and disconnect wiring, **Fig. 1.**
5. Open glove compartment door and depress side inward and lower glove box assembly toward floor.
6. Remove four screws attaching passenger air bag module to instrument panel.
7. Disconnect passenger air bag module electrical connector and remove air bag from vehicle. **Place air bag on bench with trim cover facing up.**
8. Remove left side finish moulding by pulling upward to unsnap two clips.
9. Remove four screws retaining lower steering column cover and remove cover.
10. Remove four screws attaching lower instrument panel steering column reinforcement and remove reinforcement.
11. Remove three screws retaining upper steering column shroud and remove shroud.
12. Remove one tilt/wheel lever retaining screw and remove lever.
13. Remove lock cylinder by pushing a small Allen wrench into groove located beneath lock cylinder. Place key into ignition and gently wiggle to work cylinder free.
14. Remove lower steering column shroud by pulling out.
15. Remove bolt retaining steering wheel and remove wheel.
16. Remove bolt attaching PRNDL cable to steering column.
17. Disconnect all steering column electrical connectors, **Fig. 2.**
18. Disconnect hood and brake release cables.
19. Remove two lower shaft universal joint retention nuts. Pull lower shaft away from steering column.
20. Remove four push pins holding left and right close-out panels in place.

Remove close-out panels, **Fig. 3.**
21. Remove four nuts retaining steering column, then lower column.
22. Remove two screws at steering column opening, retaining instrument panel to brake pedal support.
23. Remove two screws under ash receptacle, which holds instrument panel to A/C plenum case.
24. Remove headlamp switch knob.
25. Remove five screws from cluster opening finish panel and remove panel, **Fig. 1.**
26. Remove four screws retaining A/C control. Disconnect electrical connectors and one vacuum connector.
27. Remove four screws retaining cluster, then disconnect electrical connectors.
28. Remove three screws to remove glove box assembly.
29. Remove three screws located above left side of glove compartment, **Fig. 4.**
30. Remove both speaker grilles by snapping out to release. Disconnect electrical connector at right side grille.
31. Remove two screws seated in plastic push clips and remove center defrost grille.
32. Open engine compartment hood, disconnect all electrical connectors of main wire loom.
33. Disengage rubber grommet from dash panel and feed wiring and connectors through hole into instrument panel area.
34. Remove three screws at both left and right side cowl trim panels, then remove panels.
35. Remove lower two screws at instrument panel, one at each end, **Fig. 4.**
36. Remove three upper instrument panel retaining screws and carefully lower instrument panel. Disconnect all electrical and vacuum connections. Remove instrument panel from the vehicle.
37. Reverse procedure to install.

COUGAR & THUNDERBIRD

1992–93

1. Disconnect battery ground cable.
2. Disconnect all underhood wiring connectors from main wiring harness. Remove rubber grommet seal from dash panel and push wiring harness and connectors into passenger compartment.
3. Remove steering column lower trim cover.
4. Remove six steering column lower opening reinforcement retaining screws.
5. Remove steering column upper and lower shrouds.
6. Disconnect steering column wiring connectors, **Fig. 5.**
7. Remove shift interlock switch.
8. Disconnect steering column lower universal joint.
9. Support steering column and remove four nuts retaining column to support. Remove column from vehicle.
10. Remove one screw retaining left side of instrument panel to parking brake bracket.

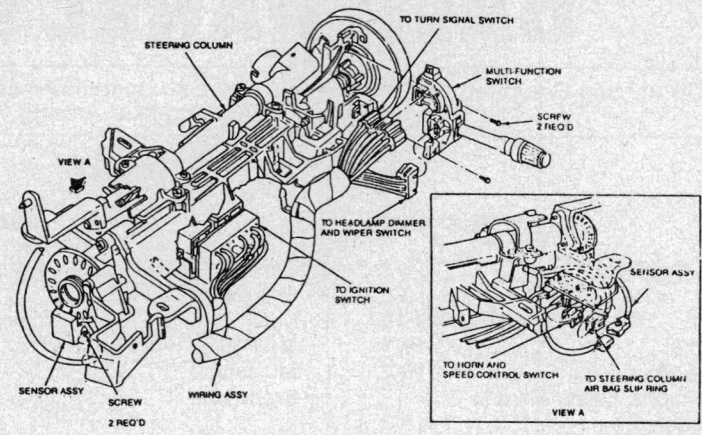

Fig. 2   Steering column electrical connectors. Continental

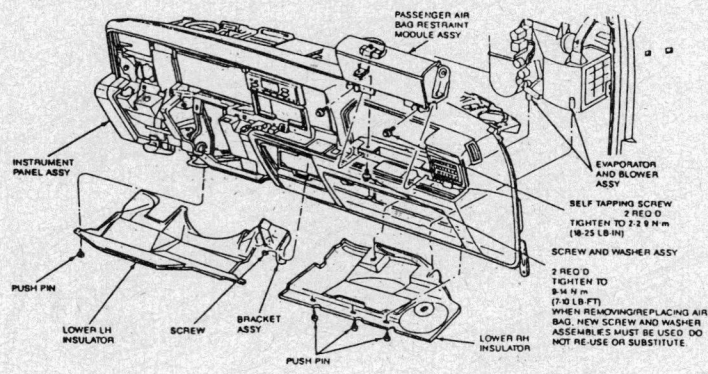

Fig. 3   Close out panel removal. Continental

11. Install lower steering column lower opening reinforcement. Reinforcement prevents instrument panel from twisting when being removed from vehicle.
12. Remove right and left side cowl trim panels, **Fig. 6.**
13. Open floor console door and remove container and mat to gain access to two console to floor pan retaining screws. Remove screws, **Fig. 7.**
14. **On models with 5 speed manual transmission,** remove gear shift knob.
15. **On all models,** remove two rear finish panel retaining screws.
16. Tilt finish panel forward and disconnect electrical connectors, then remove finish panel.
17. Remove two front console to instrument panel retaining screws and remove console.
18. Remove two nuts retaining center of instrument panel to floor.
19. Open glove compartment, squeeze sides of bin and lower to full open position.
20. From underneath instrument panel and through glove compartment opening, disconnect wiring, and heater-A/C vacuum lines and control cables.
21. Remove two retaining screws from both the left and right sides of the instrument panel, **Fig. 8.**

22. Remove right and left side upper finish panels by pulling up to disengage snap-in retainers, **Fig. 9.**
23. Remove instrument panel to cowl top attaching screws, **Figs. 10 and 11.**
24. Remove right and left roof rail trim panel, then remove door frame weather strip.
25. Carefully pull instrument panel away from cowl and disconnect any remaining wiring or controls.
26. Remove instrument panel from the vehicle.
27. Reverse procedure to install.

1994

1. Disconnect battery ground cable.
2. Loosen main wiring connector bolt, located in lefthand rear of engine compartment, then separate connectors.
3. Remove radio antenna stanchion and disconnect radio antenna lead in cable from lead base of radio antenna stanchion.
4. Remove LH and RH windshield side garnish mouldings.
5. Remove LH and RH door scuff plate retaining screws, then lift scuff plates to allow removal of weatherstrips from body flanges.
6. Remove LH and RH cowl side trim panels.
7. Remove steering column covers, then the ignition lock cylinder as described in "Electrical" section.

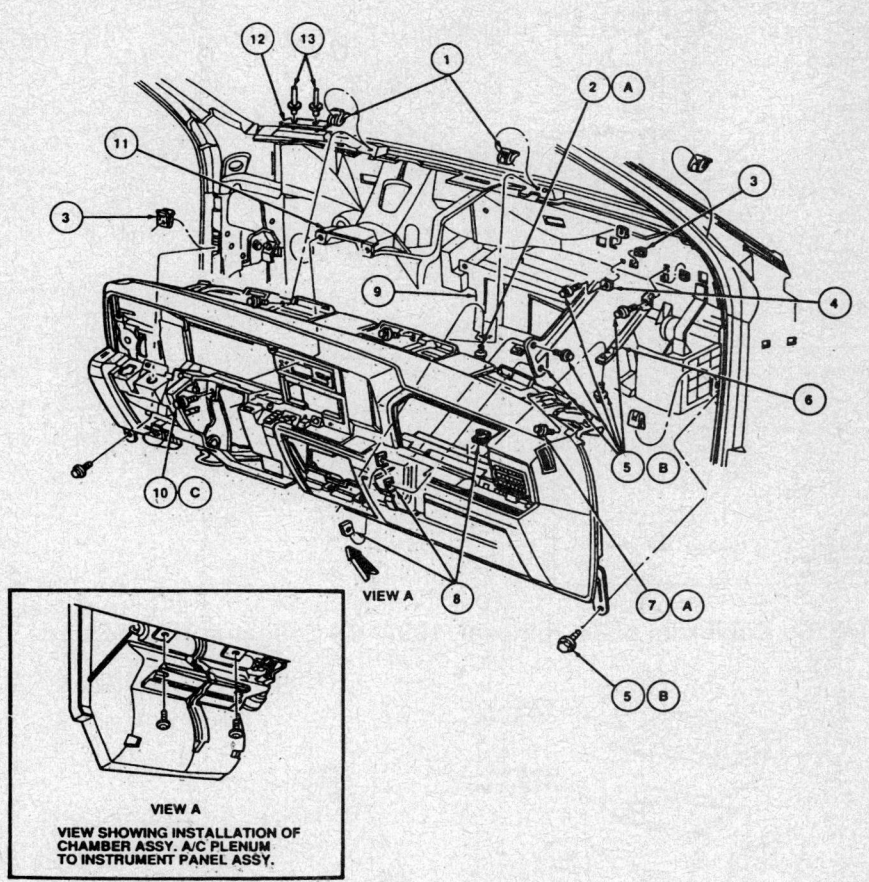

Fig. 4 Instrument panel removal. Continental

Item	Part Number	Description
1	N801911-S100	Nut (3 Req'd)
2A	N803876-S36B	Self Tapping Screw (2 Req'd)
3	N800854-S2	U-Nut (2 Req'd)

Item	Part Number	Description
4	042C64	Instrument Panel-to-Cowl Top Brace
5B	N802408-S2	Screw and Washer (7 Req'd)
6	045A78	Passenger Air Bag Support Bracket

FM9149100021000X

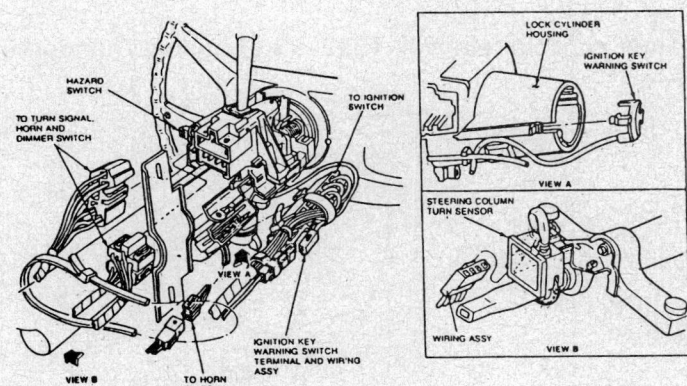

Fig. 5 Steering column wiring connectors. 1992–93 Cougar & Thunderbird

FM9149100022000X

8. Remove steering column shrouds.
9. Install ignition lock cylinder to prevent steering wheel from turning.
10. Disconnect turn signal and windshield wiper switch electrical connectors.
11. Remove A/C evaporator register duct from under steering column tube.
12. Remove pinch bolt attaching steering column tube to steering column lower yoke and slightly spread the joint with screwdriver.
13. While supporting steering column tube, remove four steering column tube retaining nuts.
14. Remove interlock cable retaining screws and shift actuator cable fitting.
15. Carefully remove steering column tube from vehicle.
16. Loosen main wiring connector bolt at LH side of steering column opening and separate connectors.
17. Pull back floor carpet and disconnect window regulator safety relay switch wiring and the powertrain control module from main wiring.
18. Open glove compartment and unsnap hydraulic lift from RH side of glove compartment.
19. Remove three retaining screws at bottom of glove compartment door hinge, then pull glove compartment from instrument panel
20. Reach through glove compartment opening and disconnect wiring and vacuum hoses and connectors from evaporator housing.
21. Disconnect wiring connector from speed control amplifier and bracket assembly.
22. Remove floor console panel.
23. Using putty knife or suitable tool, insert under LH or RH corner of instrument panel upper finish panel and pry up to release one snap clip.
24. Unsnap remaining four clips by pulling up by hand.
25. Remove two nuts retaining LH side of instrument panel to cowl side.
26. Remove two nuts and one bolt retaining instrument panel to instrument panel console bracket.
27. Remove nut attaching RH side of instrument panel to cowl side, **Fig. 12.**
28. Remove six bolts retaining top of instrument panel to dash panel.
29. Carefully pull instrument panel away from windshield glass while checking for and disconnecting any remaining wiring connectors. Disengage antenna wire grommet from sheet metal and pull radio antenna lead in cable through.
30. Reverse procedure to install.

CROWN VICTORIA, GRAND MARQUIS & TOWN CAR

1. Position front wheels straight ahead.
2. Disconnect battery ground cable.
3. Remove instrument panel righthand and lefthand moldings, **Fig. 13.**
4. Remove headlamp control knobs.
5. Remove finish panel to instrument panel attaching screws.
6. Pull finish panel from instrument panel, then disconnect electrical connectors.

7. Remove finish panel.
8. Remove right and left lower insulation panels, then remove bulb and socket assembly, **Fig. 14.**
9. Remove lower instrument panel steering column cover attaching screws.
10. Remove lower steering column reinforcement attaching bolts.
11. Remove ignition lock cylinder.
12. Remove tilt lever.
13. Remove upper and lower steering column shrouds.
14. Disconnect steering column electrical connectors, then disconnect PRNDL cable from column, **Fig. 15. Do not rotate steering column shaft.**
15. Remove steering column to instrument panel attaching nuts, then lower steering column.
16. Install lock cylinder, ensuring steering column does not turn.
17. Open glove compartment door, then depress sides inward and lower assembly towards floor.
18. Remove instrument panel to dash panel attaching bolts through glove compartment opening, **Fig. 16.**
19. Remove right and left side cowl trim panels.
20. Disconnect all underhood wiring connectors from main wiring loom. Remove rubber grommet from dash panel and push wiring harness and connectors into passenger compartment.
21. Disconnect instrument panel electrical connectors at right and left side cowl panels.
22. Remove right and left side instrument panel attaching screws.
23. Remove upper finish panel.
24. Disconnect electrical connectors, vacuum hoses, demister hose, heater A/C vacuum lines and radio antenna.
25. Close glove box, then support instrument panel and remove instrument panel to cowl top attaching screws, then disconnect any electrical connectors.
26. Remove instrument panel.
27. Reverse procedure to install.

ESCORT & TRACER

1. Disconnect battery ground cable.
2. If equipped with a standard column, remove four column retaining bolts and lower steering column.
3. Remove instrument cluster bezel retaining screws, **Fig. 17,** then the bezel.
4. Disconnect speedometer cable at the transaxle by pulling cable out of vehicle speed sensor.
5. Remove instrument cluster retaining screws, **Fig. 18,** then pull the cluster out slightly and disconnect electrical connectors.
6. Disconnect speedometer cable from back of cluster, then remove the cluster.
7. Disconnect hood release cable from LH lower dash trim panel.
8. Remove dash side panels by prying each panel away from I/P.
9. Remove four retaining screws and the

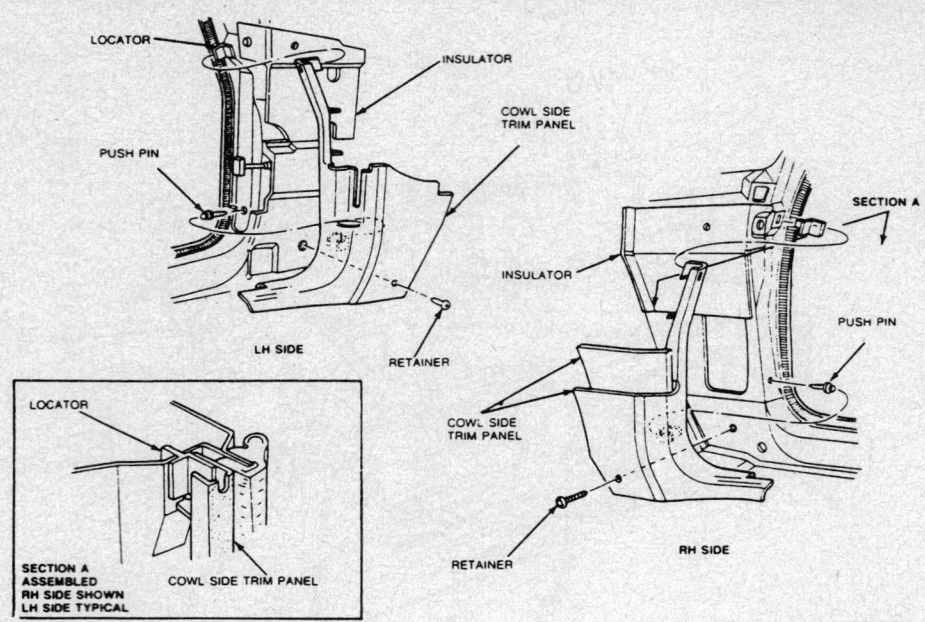

Fig. 6 Cowl trim panel removal. 1992–93 Cougar & Thunderbird

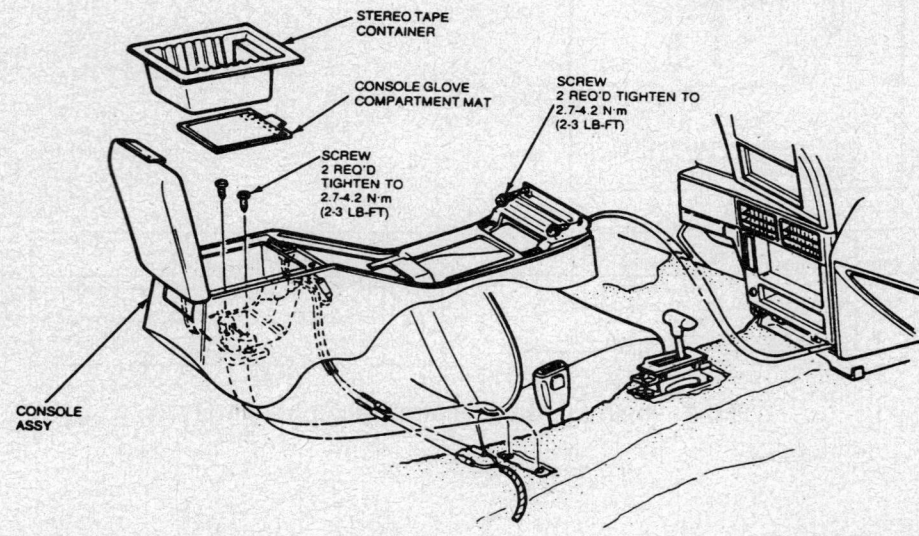

Fig. 7 Floor console removal. 1992–93 Cougar & Thunderbird

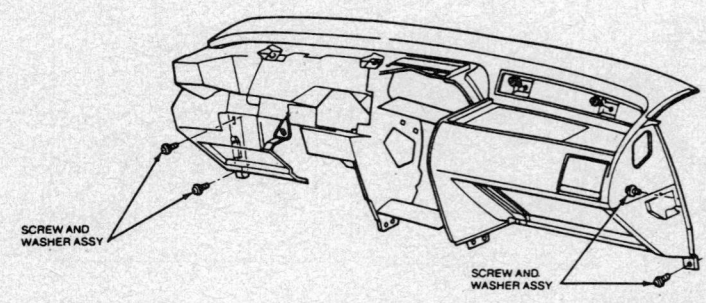

Fig. 8 I/P retaining screws removal. 1992–93 Cougar & Thunderbird

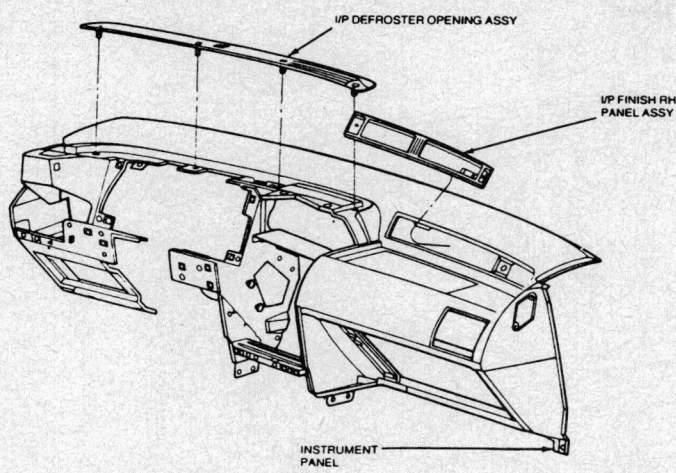

Fig. 9 Upper finish panel removal. 1992–93 Cougar & Thunderbird

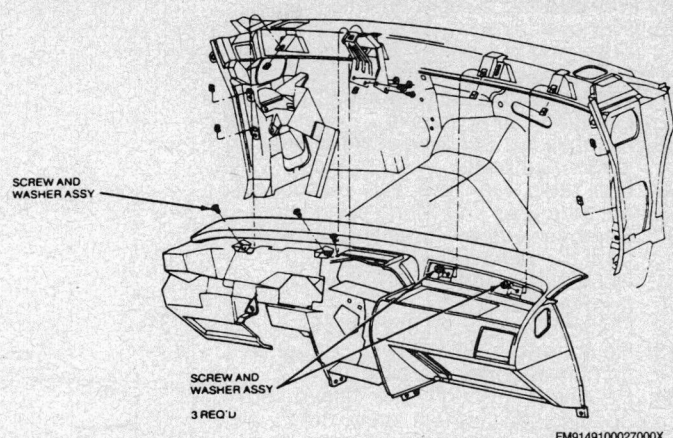

Fig. 10 I/P from cowl removal. 1992–93 Cougar & Thunderbird

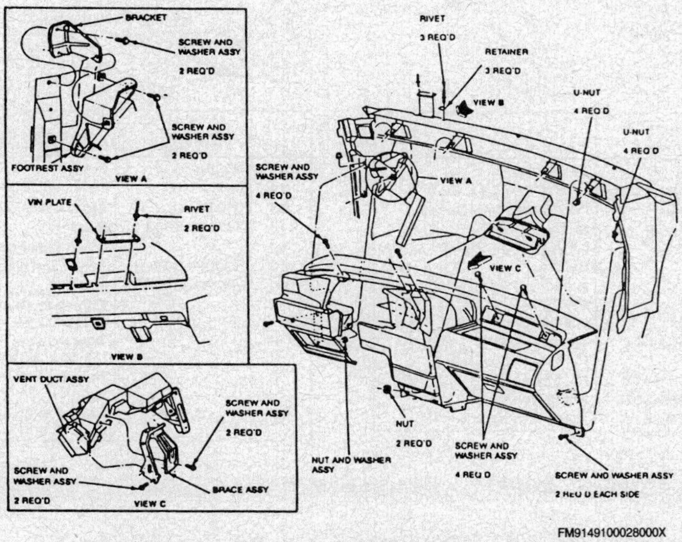

Fig. 11 I/P from cowl removal. 1992–93 Cougar & Thunderbird

left lower trim panel, then disconnect all necessary electrical connectors.
10. Remove two glove compartment hinge screws, then the compartment door.
11. Remove the climate control assembly, ashtray and seven accessory console retaining screws.
12. Disconnect the antenna, radio wire connector and cigar lighter.
13. Remove the RH lower dash trim panel retaining screws.
14. Support the steering column, then remove four retaining bolts and lower column away from I/P.
15. Disconnect amplifier wire connectors, then remove four I/P frame bolts to floor pan.
16. Remove the bolt from both lower I/P panel mounts and two bolts from both upper I/P mounts, **Fig. 19.**
17. Remove the defroster duct bezel retaining screws, then the bezel.
18. Remove three upper I/P to cowl retaining bolts, then the I/P from the vehicle.
19. Reverse procedures to install.

FESTIVA

1. Disconnect battery ground cable.
2. Pry out trim insert in the center of the steering wheel cover.
3. Remove steering wheel attaching nut, then the attaching screws located to the left and right of the steering column stud.
4. Remove two screws from the back of the steering wheel spokes, freeing steering wheel cover assembly, with cover bracket and horn buttons. Disconnect horn wire and remove cover assembly.
5. Mark steering wheel and steering column shaft for assembly reference and remove wheel with steering wheel puller tool No. T67L-3600-A or equiv-

alent.
6. Remove five screws from lower steering column cover, and remove upper and lower steering column covers.
7. Release wiring harness clip and unplug four harness connectors from the back of the combination switch.
8. From below the steering column, loosen band clamp securing switch hub to steering column jacket.
9. Pull combination switch assembly off the steering column.
10. Remove screws securing instrument cluster bezel and move bezel rearward, **Fig. 20.**
11. Disconnect switch electrical connectors from switches on instrument cluster bezel, then remove instrument cluster bezel.
12. **On models equipped with tachometer,** disconnect tachometer at rear of instrument panel.
13. **On models without tachometer,** disconnect speedometer cable at transaxle.
14. **On all models,** remove instrument cluster attaching screws.
15. Move cluster rearward and disconnect cluster electrical wiring.
16. **On models with tachometer,** disconnect speedometer cable from the instrument cluster.
17. **On all models,** remove instrument cluster from vehicle.
18. Remove steering column inner shield attaching nuts, **Fig. 21,** then remove shield.
19. Remove two shield bracket attaching bolts, then remove bracket.
20. Remove left and right heater ducts, **Fig. 22.**
21. Remove screws securing glove box hinges to the glove box, then the glove box.
22. Remove cover from fuse panel, then the screws securing fuse panel.
23. Push the fuse panel forward, but do not remove fuse panel.
24. Remove shift lever knob, then the console attaching screws, **Fig. 23.** **Remove only the three screws shown in the figure. The remaining screw secures the console stiffener bracket.**

25. Remove the center console.
26. Remove support bracket attaching bolts and nut below ashtray assembly, then remove bracket.
27. Remove radio and heater-A/C control bezel attaching screws.
28. Remove two screws securing radio to instrument panel.
29. Pull radio rearward and disconnect antenna lead and wiring connectors.
30. Remove rubber mounting insulator from the radio ground stud.
31. Remove nut and radio ground wire from ground stud.
32. Remove radio from the vehicle.
33. Remove four heater-A/C control assembly attaching screws.
34. Reaching through the glove box opening, disconnect recirc/fresh air door cable at the door operating lever, **Fig. 24.**
35. Disconnect mode selector cable at function control lever, **Fig. 25.**
36. Disconnect temperature control cable from control lever, **Fig. 26.**
37. Pull control assembly away from instrument panel, then disconnect blower motor, illumination lamp and lighter wiring connectors.
38. Remove snap in trim inserts concealing the instrument panel attaching bolts, **Fig. 27.**
39. Remove seven instrument panel attaching bolts and two attaching nuts, **Fig. 28.**
40. Disconnect any remaining electrical connectors, and remove instrument panel.
41. Reverse procedure to install.

ASPIRE

1. Disconnect battery ground cable.
2. Remove driver's side air bag module.
3. Remove steering wheel as described in "Electrical" section.
4. Remove instrument cluster as described in "Electrical" section.
5. Remove instrument panel finish panel and retaining screws. Push interior fuse junction panel forward but do not remove.
6. Remove parking brake console panel.
7. Remove shift console panel.
8. Remove air bag diagnostic monitor.
9. Remove climate control assembly retaining screws.
10. Disconnect control cables and remove climate control assembly.
11. Open glove compartment and remove glove compartment retaining screws.
12. Remove glove compartment.
13. Remove passenger side air bag module.
14. Remove instrument panel access hole cover and tapping screw located in center of instrument panel.
15. Remove instrument panel lower mounting bolts.
16. Remove side instrument panel access hole covers and instrument panel side bolts.
17. Loosen hood release locknut and remove the cable.
18. Pull instrument panel back, disconnect any electrical connectors and climate control assembly cables, then remove instrument panel.

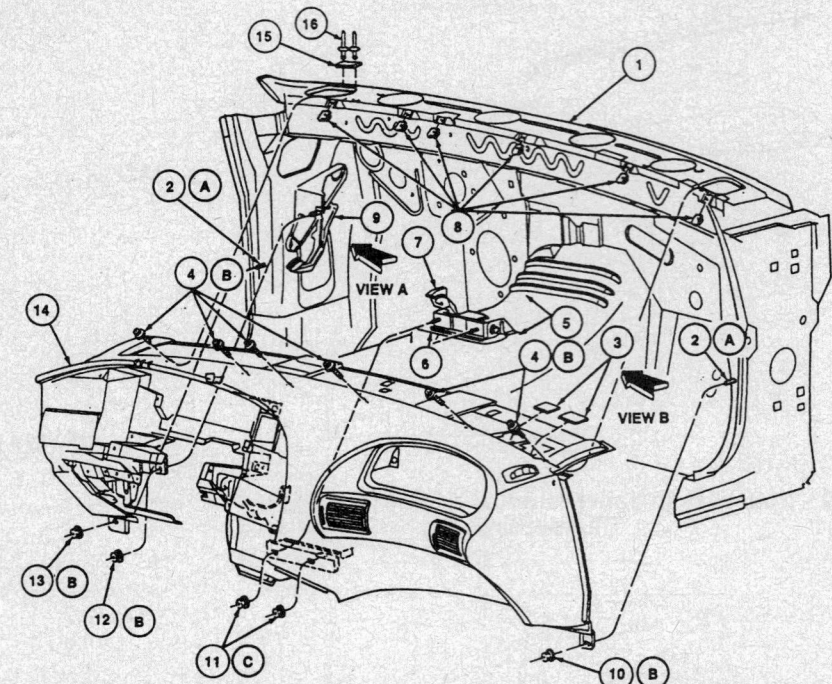

Item	Part Number	Description
1	01610	Dash Panel
2A	N806966-S36B	Stud (1 Req'd Ea. Side)
3	046B90	Instrument Panel Gasket
4B	N806486-S36B	Bolt
5	—	Instrument Panel to Floor Bracket
6	04444	Instrument Panel Center Support
7	042C51	Instrument Panel Brackets
8	N800854-S32	U-Nut (6 Req'd)
9	2780	Parking Brake Control
10B	N80803-S411	Nut (1 Req'd)
11C	N621905-S32B	Nut (2 Req'd)
12B	N80836-S411	Nut (1 Req'd)

Item	Part Number	Description
13B	N8083-S411	Nut (1 Req'd)
14	04320	Instrument Panel
15	01631	Vehicle Identification Plate
16	383554-S36B	Rivet
17	—	Driver Side Foot Rest
18C	N800394-S36B	Screw and Washer
19D	W611633-S411	Bolt
A		Tighten to 40.2-54.7 N·m (30-40 Lb-Ft)
B		Tighten to 53.1-71.9 N·m (39-53 Lb-Ft)
C		Tighten to 10-14 N·m (84-120 Lb-In)
D		Tighten to 25.5-34.5 N·m (19-25 Lb-Ft)

FM9149400072000X

Fig. 12   Instrument panel removal. 1994 Cougar & Thunderbird

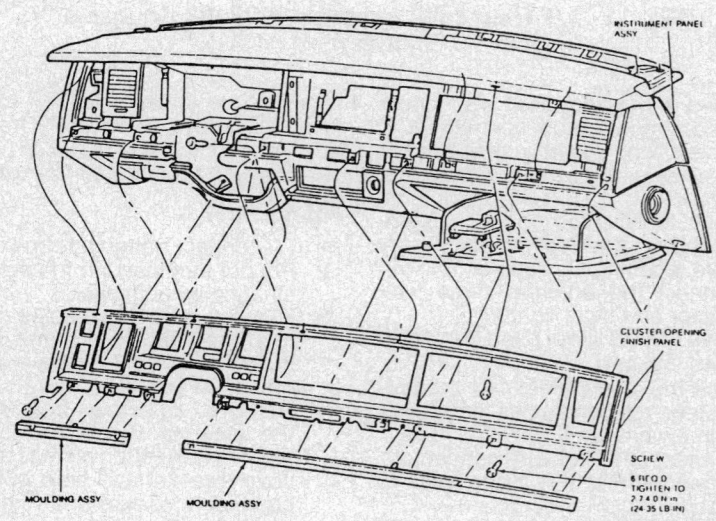

FM9149100029000X

Fig. 13   I/P moulding removal. Crown Victoria, Grand Marquis & Town Car

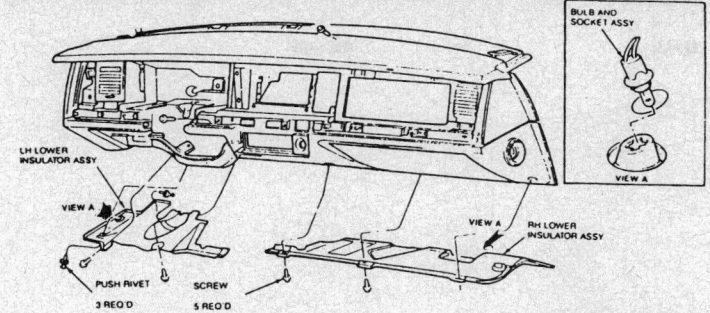

Fig. 14 I/P insulator panel removal. Crown Victoria, Grand Marquis & Town Car

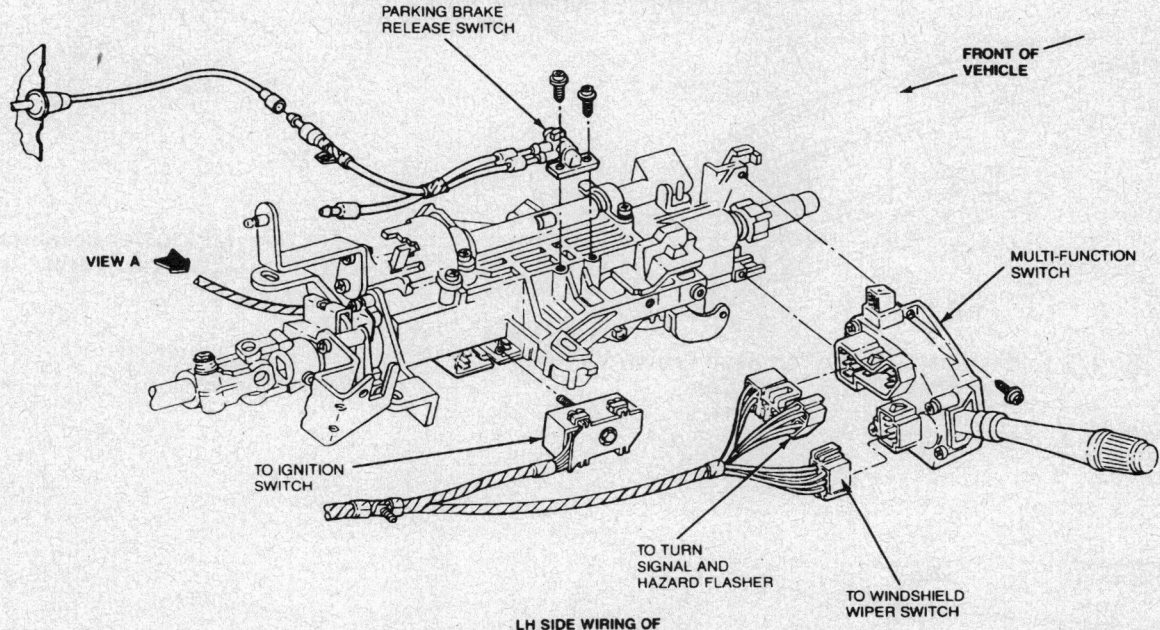

Fig. 15 Steering column electrical connectors. Crown Victoria, Grand Marquis & Town Car

19. Reverse procedure to install, noting the following:
   a. Install instrument panel side bolts, **torque** to 14—18 ft. lbs.
   b. **Torque** tapping screw to 71—97 ft. lbs., then install tapping screw access hole cover.
   c. Install instrument panel lower bolts, **torque** to 14—18 ft. lbs.

MARK VII
1. Disconnect battery ground cable.
2. Disconnect all underhood wiring connectors from main wiring harness, **Fig. 29.** Remove rubber grommet seal from dash panel and push wiring harness and connectors into passenger compartment.
3. Remove left and right side sound insulators, then remove bulb and socket assemblies from insulators, **Fig. 30.**
4. Remove steering column opening trim cover, then cover steel reinforcement, **Fig. 30.**
5. Remove two hood release to cowl panel attaching screws, then right and left side cowl trim panels, **Fig. 31.**
6. Remove five steering column trim shroud attaching screws, remove shroud.
7. Disconnect all steering column electrical connectors, **Fig. 32.**
8. Remove four steering column to support attaching nuts, then lower steering column, **Fig. 33.**
9. Remove defroster opening grill panel.
10. Remove screws attaching floor console to instrument panel and floor, and move console rearward.
11. Remove instrument panel to floor attaching screws. Remove instrument panel to cowl attaching screws.
12. Remove instrument panel to parking brake support brake attaching bolt, **Fig. 34.**
13. Disconnect main wiring harness in the following areas:
   a. Behind the instrument panel.
   b. Right side of steering column support.
   c. At blower motor.
   d. Right and left side cowl panels.
14. Disconnect radio antenna lead from the radio, then any vacuum hoses attached to the instrument panel.
15. Remove right and left side A-pillar garnish moldings, **Fig. 35.**
16. Remove three screws attaching instrument panel to dash panel.
17. Remove instrument panel from the vehicle.

18. Reverse procedure to install.

MARK VIII
1. Disconnect positive battery cable, then ground positive battery cable for one minute to de-energize back-up power supply.
2. Loosen main wiring harness connector bolt in engine compartment at LH side of dash panel. Remove three screws retaining left and right door scuff plates. Lift scuff plates and remove door weatherstrip from body flanges.
3. Remove left and right roof inner side mouldings.
4. Remove instrument panel defroster grille by lifting rear edge upward to unsnap eight retainers and two retainers at each front corner.
5. Disconnect automatic lamp wire harness at electrical connector, then remove grille.
6. Remove left and right side sound insulators from under instrument panel.
7. Remove left and right cowl side trim panels.
8. Remove floor console, heater and A/C duct from instrument panel to console.

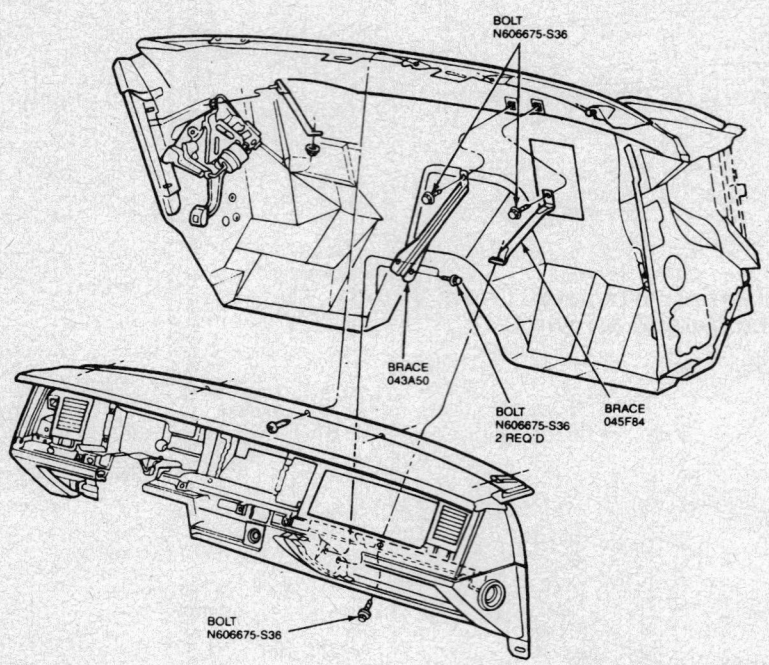

Fig. 16 I/P to dash panel brace removal. Crown Victoria, Grand Marquis & Town Car

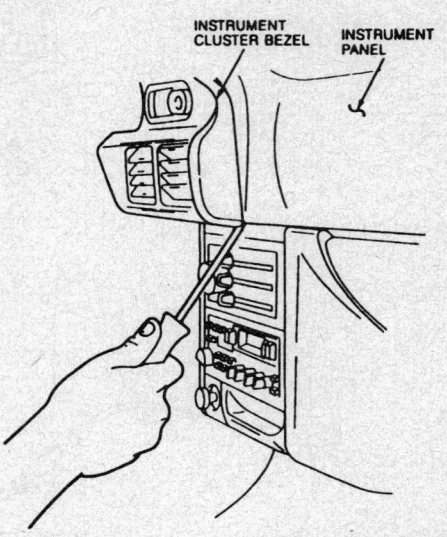

Fig. 17 I/P cluster bezel removal. Escort & Tracer

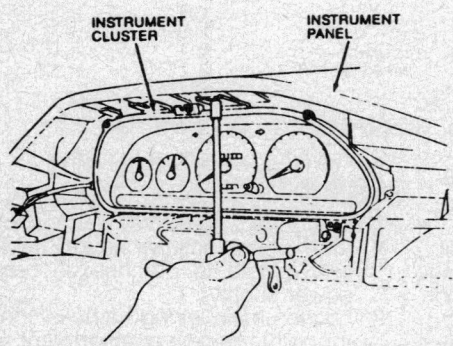

Fig. 18 I/P cluster removal. Escort & Tracer

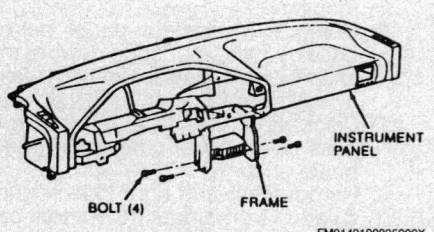

Fig. 19 I/P lower mounts removal. Escort & Tracer

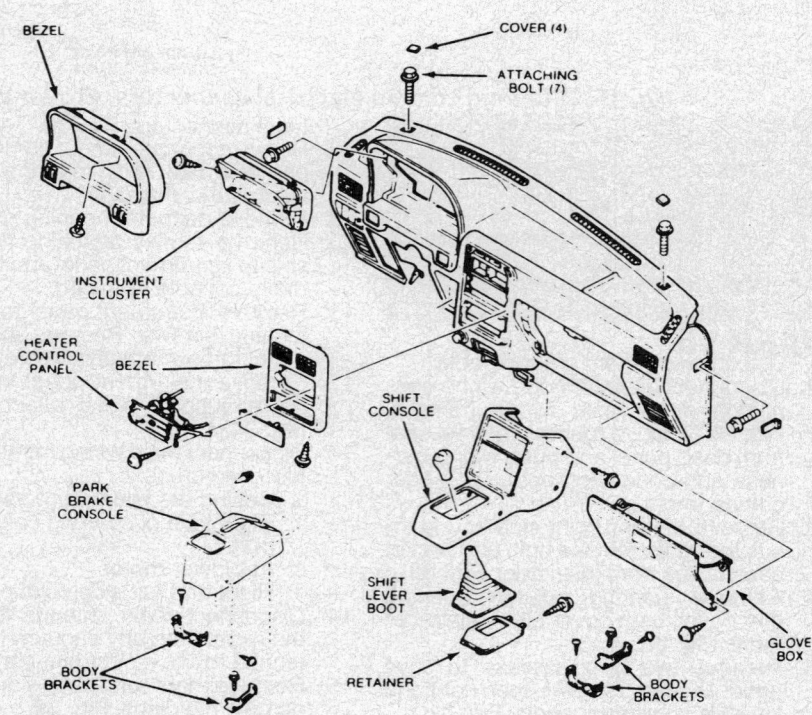

Fig. 20 Exploded view of I/P. Festiva

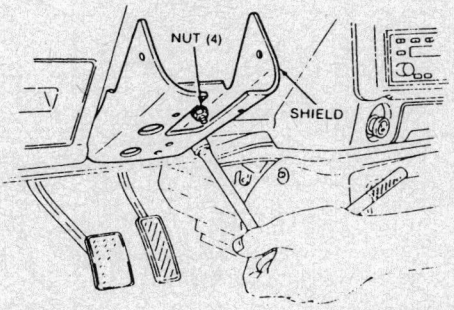

Fig. 21 Steering column lower shield removal. Festiva

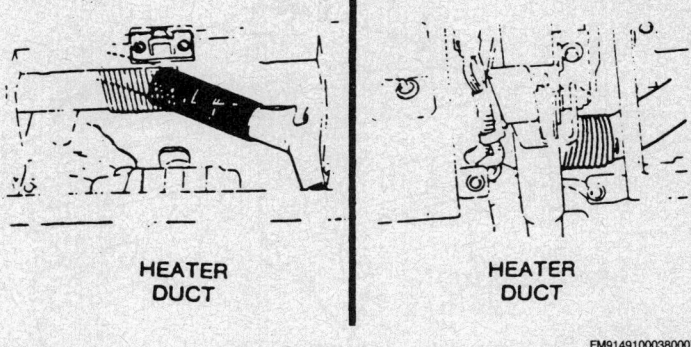

Fig. 22 Heater ducts removal. Festiva

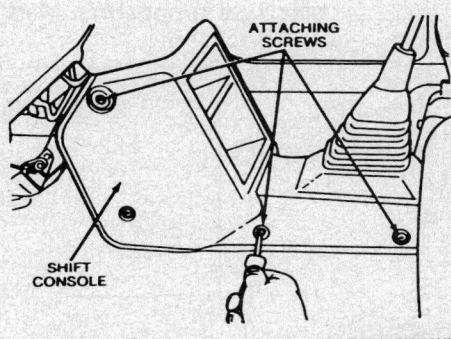

Fig. 23 Console housing removal. Festiva

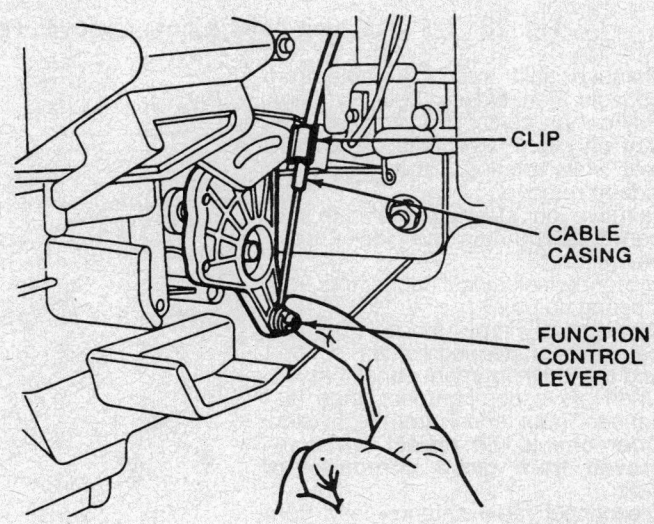

Fig. 25 Mode selector cable disconnection. Festiva

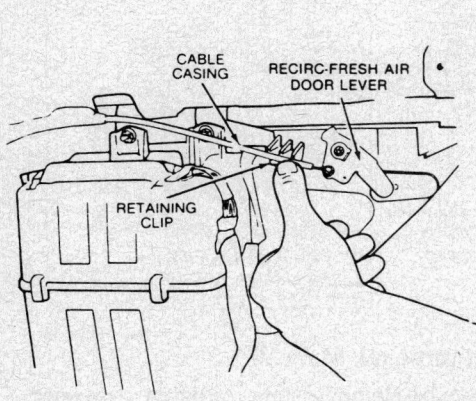

Fig. 24 Recirc/fresh air door cable disconnection. Festiva

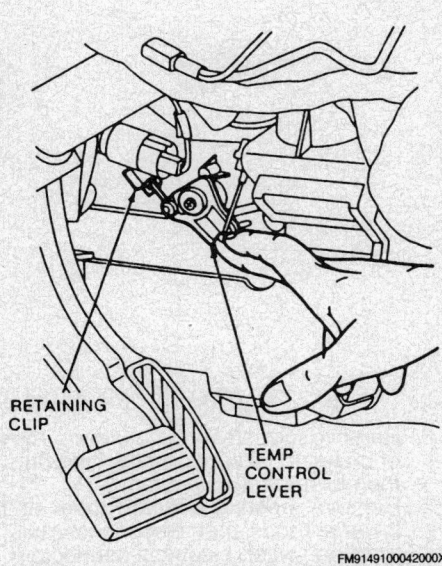

Fig. 26 Temperature control cable disconnection. Festiva

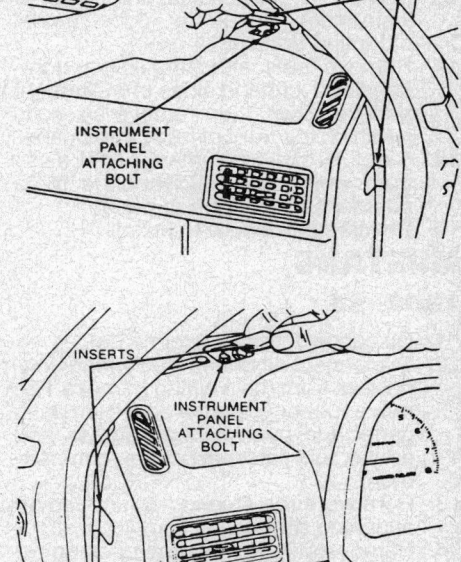

Fig. 27 Trim inserts removal. Festiva

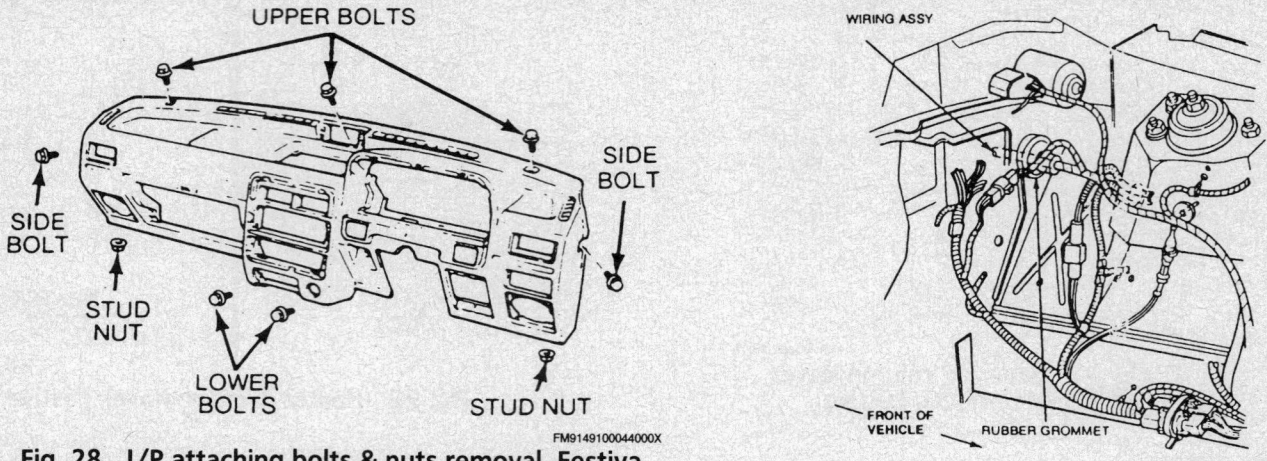

UPPER BOLTS

SIDE BOLT

SIDE BOLT

STUD NUT

LOWER BOLTS

STUD NUT

FM9149100044000X

Fig. 28 I/P attaching bolts & nuts removal. Festiva

9. Remove shift interlock cable from console, then release cable from pawl. Pull out on center tab to release detent on clip. Push cable clip toward rear while rotating clip to passenger side to remove.
10. Remove four steering column to support attaching nuts, then lower steering column.
11. Disconnect electrical connectors from steering column.
12. Disconnect wiring harness from lefthand side of steering column support and behind instrument panel, **Fig. 36.**
13. Open glove compartment, then disconnect door check from right side. **Door check will retract when removed from glove compartment side.**
14. Disconnect radio antenna lead from radio and vacuum hoses attached to instrument panel.
15. Disconnect sniffer tube and wiring harness from instrument panel evaporator case assembly.
16. Remove two bolts attaching center of instrument panel to floor tunnel mounting bracket.
17. Remove nuts attaching lower righthand and lefthand sides of instrument panel to cowl, then remove six bolts retaining top front of instrument panel.
18. Carefully pull instrument panel away from windshield to disengage three retainers at top edge of panel.
19. Reverse procedure to install.

MUSTANG

1992–93

1. Disconnect battery ground cable.
2. Disconnect all underhood wiring connectors from main wiring harness. Remove rubber grommet seal from dash panel and push wiring harness and connectors into passenger compartment.
3. Remove three steering column cover attaching screws.
4. Remove steering column opening reinforcement attaching bolts, then remove lower reinforcement attaching bolts and reinforcement.
5. Remove two hood release mechanism attaching nuts.

WIRING ASSY

FRONT OF VEHICLE

RUBBER GROMMET

FM9149100045000X

Fig. 29 Engine compartment electrical connectors. Mark VII

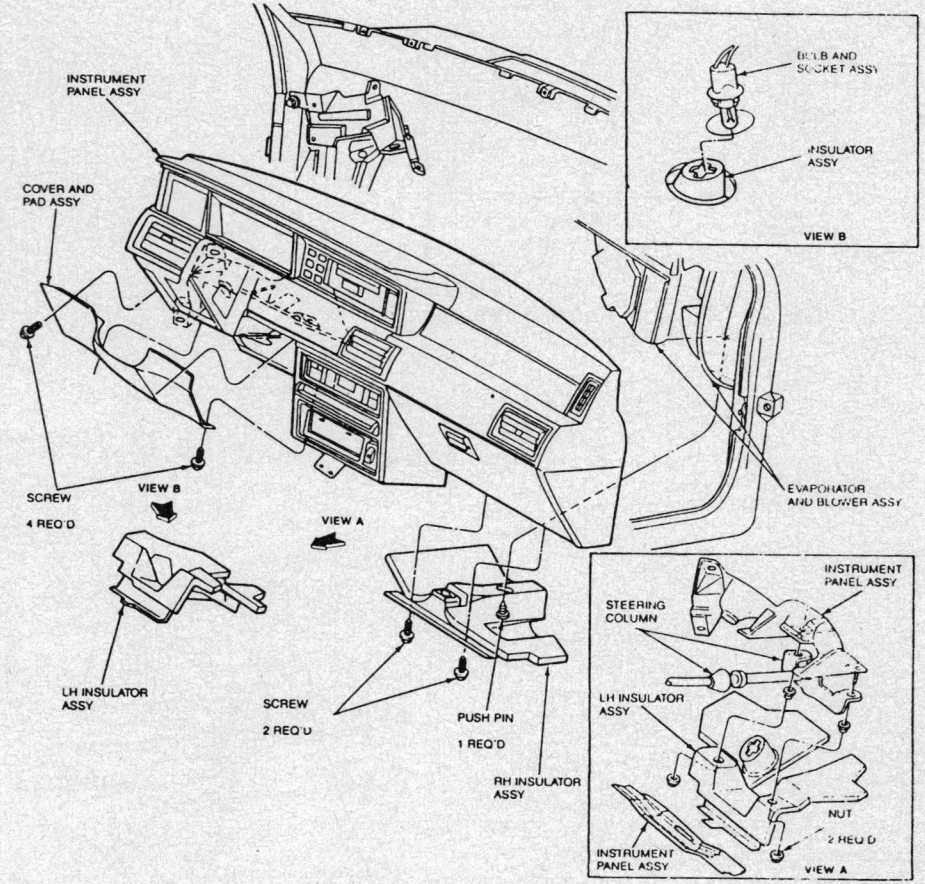

INSTRUMENT PANEL ASSY

COVER AND PAD ASSY

SCREW 4 REQ'D

VIEW B

VIEW A

LH INSULATOR ASSY

SCREW 2 REQ'D

PUSH PIN 1 REQ'D

RH INSULATOR ASSY

BULB AND SOCKET ASSY

INSULATOR ASSY

VIEW B

EVAPORATOR AND BLOWER ASSY

INSTRUMENT PANEL ASSY

STEERING COLUMN

LH INSULATOR ASSY

INSTRUMENT PANEL ASSY

NUT 2 REQ'D

VIEW A

FM9149100046000X

Fig. 30 Insulator panel removal. Mark VII

6. Remove four steering column to lower brake pedal support attaching nuts, then lower steering column.
7. Remove steering column upper and lower shrouds, then disconnect multifunction switch electrical connectors.
8. Remove console assembly as follows:
   a. Remove two access covers at rear of console to gain access to armrest retaining bolts.
   b. Remove four armrest to floor bracket retaining bolts and remove armrest assembly, **Fig. 37.**
   c. **On models with automatic transmission,** remove shift lever opening finish panel.
   d. **On models with manual transmission,** remove shift knob and slide boot and finish panel up shift lever to remove.
   e. **On all models,** position emergen-

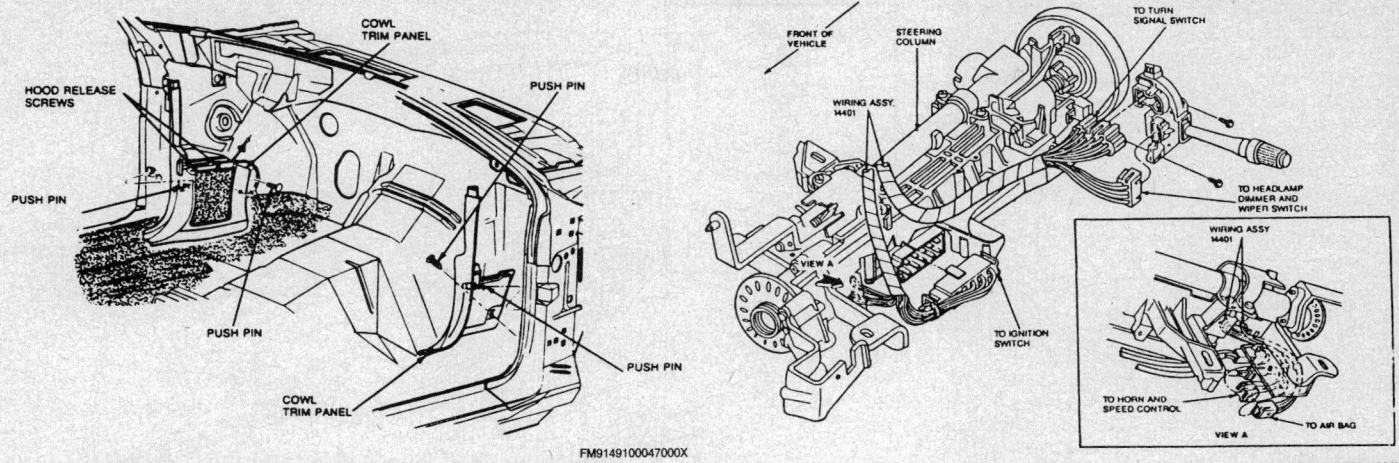

Fig. 31 Hood release cable removal. Mark VII

Fig. 32 Steering column electrical connectors. Mark VII

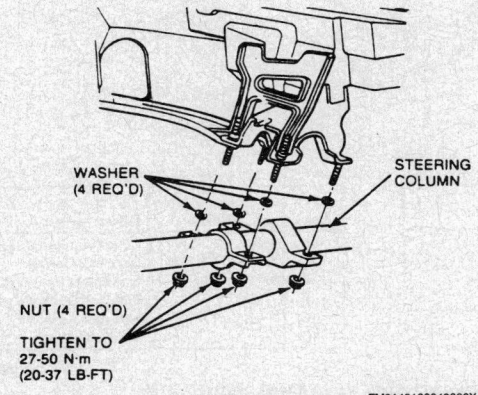

Fig. 33 Steering column support removal. Mark VII

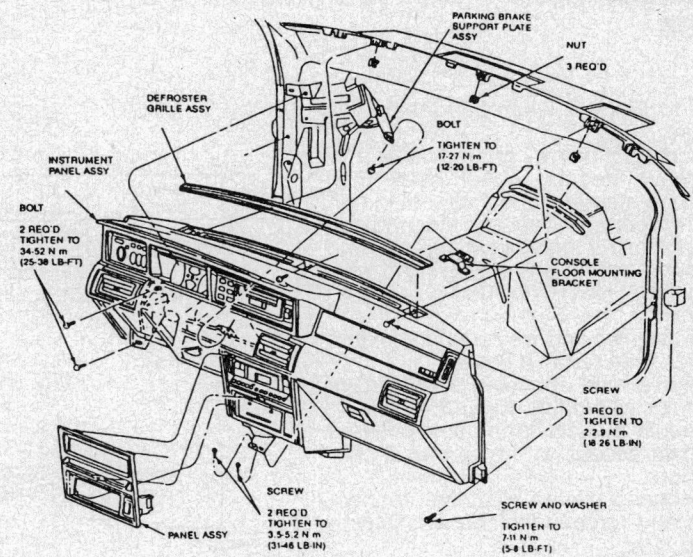

Fig. 34 I/P to cowl attaching screws removal. Mark VII

cy brake lever in the up position.
f. Remove four top finish panel retaining screws, then disconnect necessary electrical connectors and remove panel, **Fig. 38.**
g. Remove two console to rear floor bracket attaching screws.
h. Insert a small screwdriver into two notches at bottom of front upper finish panel and snap out, **Fig. 39.**
i. Remove radio, then using a small screwdriver pry radio finish cover from front of console.
j. Open glove compartment door and drop glove compartment assembly down. If equipped with remote control fuel filler door, switch must be removed. Remove two instrument panel to console retaining screws.
k. Remove four console to bracket retaining screws.
l. Remove console from the vehicle.
9. Remove brake pedal support attaching nut.
10. Snap out defroster grille, then remove screws from speaker covers and snap out.
11. Remove front screws attaching right and left scuff plates at cowl trim panel.
12. Remove right and left side cowl panels.
13. Disconnect right and left side cowl panel electrical connectors, then re-

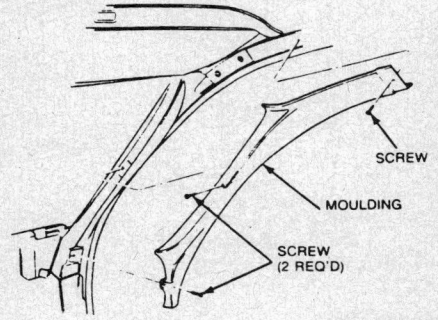

Fig. 35 A-pillar molding removal. Mark VII

rnove cowl side retaining bolts from each side of panel assembly, **Fig. 40.**
14. Remove cowl top attaching screws.
15. Gently pull instrument panel away from cowl, then disconnect air conditioning controls and wire connectors.
16. Remove instrument panel form vehicle.
17. Reverse procedure to install.

1994

1. Disconnect battery ground cable.
2. Disconnect all underhood wiring connectors from main wiring harness.
3. Disengage rubber grommet seal from dash panel and push main wiring and connectors into passenger compartment.
4. Remove two screws retaining steering column opening cover and instrument panel reinforcement. Remove steering column opening cover.
5. Remove instrument panel reinforcement by removing two bolts.
6. Remove console panel.
7. Remove four nuts retaining steering column to lower instrument panel support. Lower steering column tube to floor.
8. Remove upper and lower steering column shroud and disconnect wiring from turn signal, windshield wiper switch, ignition switch and shift solenoid.
9. Remove LH and RH cowl side trim panel.

10. Disconnect wiring at LH and RH cowl sides.
11. Remove instrument panel cowl side retaining bolts and nut.
12. Remove instrument panel upper finish panel.
13. Remove three cowl top screw attachments, **Fig. 41**.
14. Gently pull instrument panel away from cowl, then disconnect air conditioner control, speedometer cable and wire connectors.
15. Reverse procedure to install, noting the following.
    a. **Torque** instrument panel retaining screws to 68—91 inch lbs.
    b. **Torque** instrument panel nut to 30—41 ft. lbs.
    c. **Torque** steering column opening cover and reinforcement 68-91 inch lbs.
    d. **Torque** ignition switch connector to 15-19 inch lbs.

PROBE

1992

Refer to **Fig. 42**, when performing this procedure.
1. Disconnect battery ground cable.
2. Remove steering wheel insert, then remove steering wheel attaching nut.
3. Mark steering wheel and steering column shaft for assembly reference and remove wheel with steering wheel puller tool No. T67L-3600-A or equivalent.
4. Remove two screws securing column cover, then remove cover.
5. Remove nine attaching screws from the cluster module, **Fig. 43**.
6. Carefully pull cluster module outward to gain access to the electrical connectors.
7. Disconnect seven electrical connectors and remove ignition illumination bulb.
8. Remove cluster module, then loosen two cover hinge screws, **Fig. 44**.
9. Remove six screws from the instrument cluster cover, then remove the cover.
10. Remove lower cluster cover panel, then the four attaching screws from the cluster.
11. Disconnect electrical connectors from the back of the cluster, and remove cluster.
12. **On models with automatic transmission,** remove floor console as follows:
    a. Remove two screws securing selector knob to selector lever.
    b. Remove selector trim piece.
    c. Remove four screws securing selector bezel, then lift bezel to gain access to the selector illumination bulb and the shift control switch.
    d. Disconnect illumination bulb and shift control switch electrical harness, then remove bezel.
    e. Remove front ash receptacle and cigar lighter.
    f. Remove four front mounting screws, then position front seat to gain access to the console rear access hole covers.
    g. Remove access hole covers from each side of the console, **Fig. 45**.
    h. Remove rear retaining bolts, then position front seats all the way to the rear.
    i. Lift console from the rear and disconnect electrical connectors for the mirror and ride control switches.
    j. Apply parking brake and remove console.
13. **On models with manual transmission,** remove floor console as follows:
    a. Slide shifter boot down and remove shift knob.
    b. Remove trim panel and boot.
    c. Remove front ash receptacle and cigar lighter.

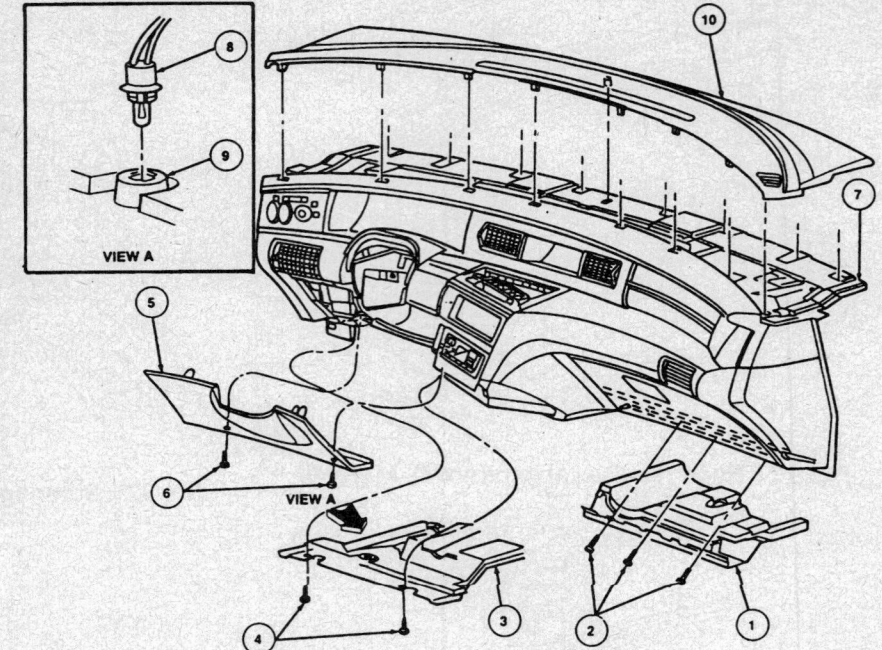

VIEW A

Item	Part Number	Description
1	—	RH Insulator Assy
2	N803876-S36B	Screw (3 Req'd)
3	—	LH Insulator Assy
4	N803876-S36B	Screw (2 Req'd)

Item	Part Number	Description
5	—	Cover and Pad Assy
6	N800507-S36B	Screw (2 Req'd)
7	—	Instrument Panel Assy
8	—	Bulb and Socket Assy
9	—	Insulator Assy
10	—	Defroster Grille

FM9149100052000X

Fig. 36   Trim panels removal. Mark VIII

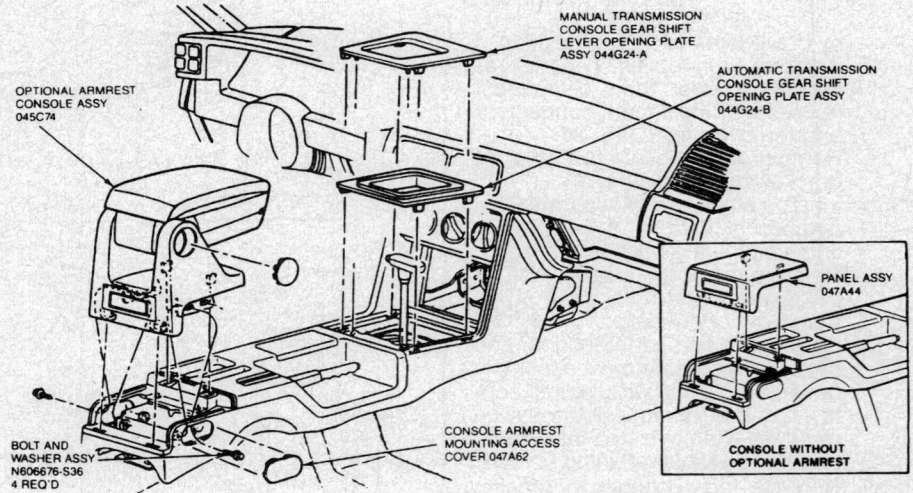

MANUAL TRANSMISSION CONSOLE GEAR SHIFT LEVER OPENING PLATE ASSY 044G24-A

AUTOMATIC TRANSMISSION CONSOLE GEAR SHIFT OPENING PLATE ASSY 044G24-B

OPTIONAL ARMREST CONSOLE ASSY 045C74

PANEL ASSY 047A44

BOLT AND WASHER ASSY N606676-S36 4 REQ'D

CONSOLE ARMREST MOUNTING ACCESS COVER 047A62

CONSOLE WITHOUT OPTIONAL ARMREST

FM9149100053000X

Fig. 37   Console trim plates & armrest. 1992–93 Mustang

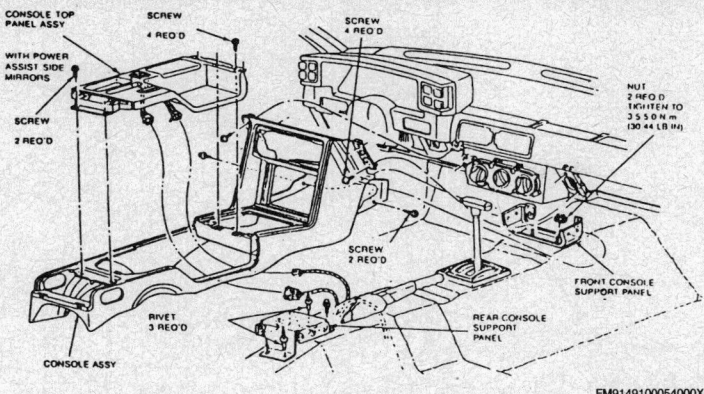

Fig. 38   Center console removal. 1992–93 Mustang

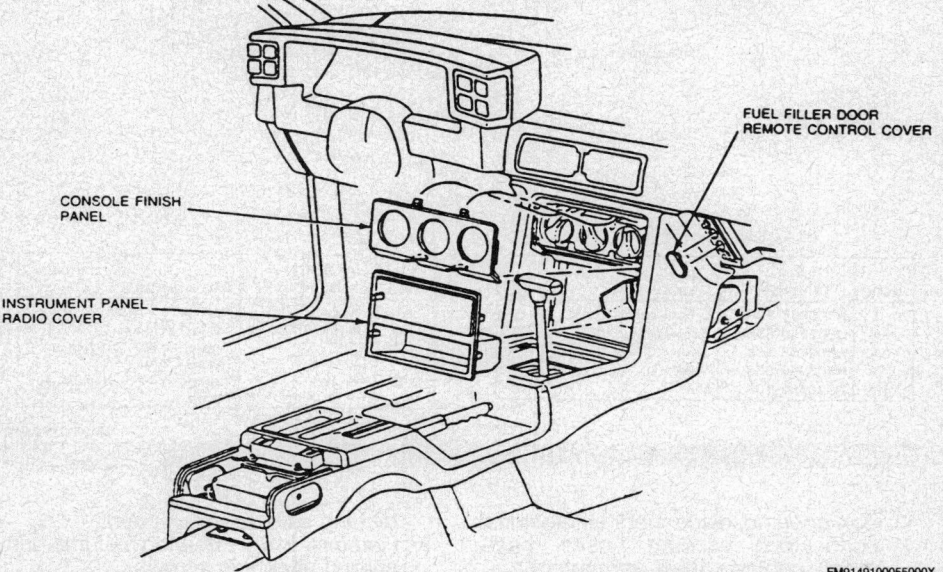

Fig. 39   Radio cover & upper finish panel removal. 1992–93 Mustang

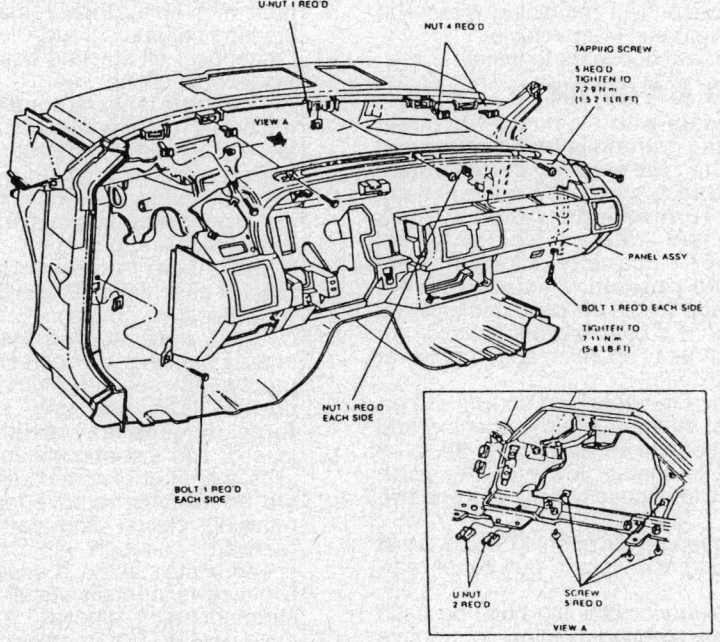

Fig. 40   I/P mounting bolts & nuts removal. 1992–93 Mustang

d. Remove four front console mounting screws, then position front seats to gain access to console rear access hole covers.

e. Remove four rear retaining bolts, then position front seats all the way to the rear.

f. Lift console from the rear and disconnect electrical connectors for the mirror and ride control switches.

g. Apply parking brake and remove console.

14. Remove hood release handle from cable.

15. Remove right and left side console kick panels.

16. Remove left and right instrument panel dash side covers.

17. Remove bezel cover from heater-A/C control assembly face.

18. Remove four attaching screws from control assembly housing.

19. Remove left and right sound deadening panels from instrument panel.

20. Remove REC/FRESH control cable from REC/FRESH selector door assembly.

21. Disconnect blower switch and control assembly illumination electrical connectors.

22. Remove temperature control cable from the temperature blend door assembly at the right side of heater case.

23. Remove function selector cable from function control doors assembly at the let side of heater case.

24. Noting position of cables for assembly reference, remove control assembly and cables as an assembly.

25. Remove two radio retaining screws, disconnect antenna and electrical connectors.

26. Remove radio and/or tape player from the vehicle.

27. Remove trip computer display cover bezel from the instrument panel, if equipped.

28. Remove two attaching screws from trip computer display housing and pull housing straight out of the dash.

29. Disconnect electrical connector from rear of trip computer display.

30. Remove dash panel access cover to gain access to center instrument panel mounting nut, then remove nut, **Fig. 46.**

31. Remove remaining instrument panel mounting bolts, then lift instrument panel toward rear of vehicle, then disconnect remaining electrical connectors.

32. Remove instrument panel from vehicle.

33. Reverse procedure to install.

1993–94

1. Disconnect battery ground cable.

2. Loosen hood release cable nut, then remove hood release cable from lower instrument panel cover.

3. Remove lower instrument panel cover attaching screw.

4. Remove courtesy lamp from lower in-

strument panel cover, then the lower instrument panel cover.

5. Remove four lower steering column panel attaching screws, then separate upper and lower steering column panels.
6. Remove ignition switch illumination bulb from lower steering column panel.
7. Remove upper and lower steering column panels.
8. Remove two upper steering column bolts and lower steering column, **Fig. 47.**
9. Remove instrument cluster and glove compartment.
10. Remove two hush panel attaching screws, then courtesy lamp bulb from hush panel.
11. Remove hush panel and floor console.
12. Remove climate control assembly.
13. Remove two side instrument panel covers and four side instrument panel bolts.
14. Remove upper and four lower instrument panel bolts, **Fig. 48.**
15. Remove A-pillar trim, then move instrument panel forward and disconnect electrical connectors.
16. Remove instrument panel.
17. Reverse procedure to install.

SABLE & TAURUS

1. Position front wheels straight ahead.
2. Disconnect battery ground cable, then back-up power supply, **Fig. 49,** behind glove compartment. Open glove box past its stops.
3. Remove four finish panel retaining screws on cluster, **Fig. 50,** then the instrument cluster.
4. Remove tilt lever, if equipped, then two bolts and reinforcement from under steering column.
5. Remove four nuts and cover plate from under steering column. Do not rotate steering column shaft, **Fig. 51.**
6. Disconnect parking brake release cable and wiring connector.
7. Remove four steering column retaining nuts to instrument panel, then lower column to the seat. Install lock cylinder to ensure the steering column from turning.
8. Remove screw at steering column opening attaching instrument panel to brace, **Fig. 51.**
9. Remove instrument panel retaining screw from brace, **Fig. 52,** behind the radio.
10. Remove RH sound insulator from under glove box, then three glove box door retaining screws.
11. Remove air cleaner, battery and battery tray, then disconnect main wiring loom in engine compartment. Disengage rubber grommet from dash panel and feed wiring into passenger compartment.
12. Remove LH and RH cowl side trim panels, then disconnect wires from instrument panel at each side.
13. Remove one instrument panel retaining screw from both sides of panel.
14. Using the steering column and glove

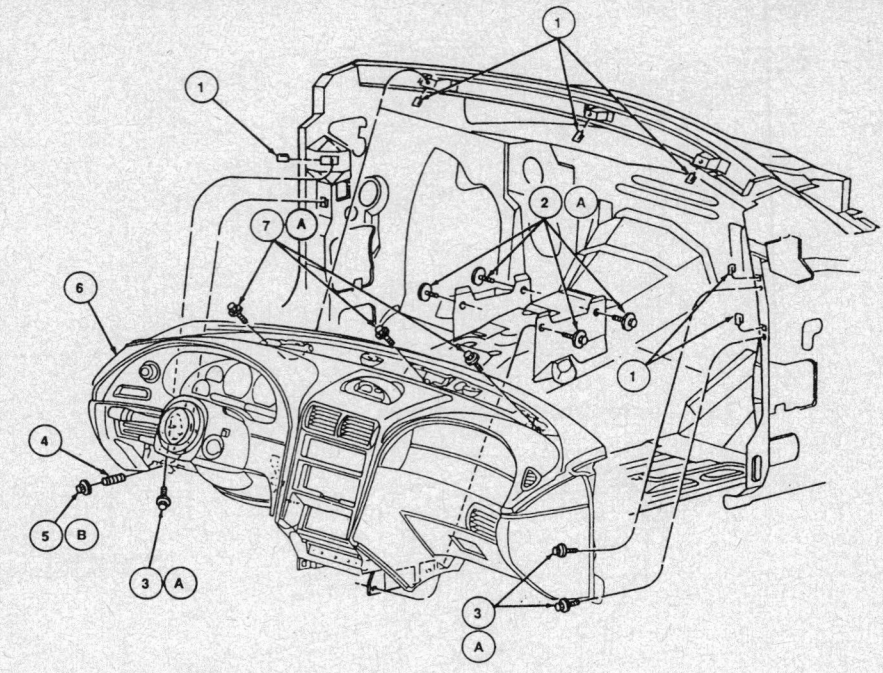

Item	Part Number	Description
1	N800854-S36	U-Lock Nut (6 Req'd)
2A	N802850-S36M	Screw (4 Req'd)
3A	N802408-S36	Screw (3 Req'd)
4	N806966-S36	Stud
5B	N620482-S36	Nut

Item	Part Number	Description
6	04320	Instrument Panel
7A	N606678-S36	Screw (3 Req'd)
A		Tighten to 7.6-10.4 N·m (68-91 Lb-In)
B		Tighten to 40-56 N·m (30-41 Lb-Ft)

FM9149400074000X

Fig. 41   Instrument panel removal. 1994 Mustang

box opening, disconnect all electrical connectors, vacuum hoses, heater/AC control cables and antenna.
15. Support panel, then remove three instrument retaining screws from cowl top. Disconnect remaining wires and remove panel from vehicle.
16. Reverse procedures to install.

TEMPO & TOPAZ

On models with air bags, whenever the steering column is being separated from the I/P, the steering column must be locked to prevent the column from rotating. Turn ignition switch to lock position and rotate steering wheel about 16° counterclockwise until locked into position. This will prevent any damage to the air bag clockspring.
1. Disconnect battery ground cable.
2. Disconnect speedometer cable at transaxle.
3. Remove two retaining screws at bottom of steering column opening and snap column cover out, **Fig. 53.**
4. Remove snap-in lower cluster finish panels to expose two screws and two bolts.
5. Remove cluster opening finish panel retaining screws and pull panel rearward.
6. Remove two retaining bolts on each side of steering column to remove column opening reinforcement.
7. Remove speed control module at-

taching screws, if equipped.
8. Remove lower steering column trim shroud attaching screws.
9. Loosen, but do not remove, attaching steering column to support bracket nuts and bolts, then remove upper steering column shroud.
10. Disconnect all steering column electrical connections.
11. **On console shift automatic transmission,** remove interlock cable attaching screw, then disconnect cable from steering column.
12. Loosen steering column to intermediate shaft clamp connection, then remove attaching bolt.
13. Remove steering column to support bracket attaching nuts and bolts to remove steering column.
14. Carefully open steering column shaft in area of clamp on each side of bolt groove with steering column in locked position. **Do not use excessive force, damage may result.**
15. Inspect two steering column bracket clips, if bent or distorted, replace.
16. **On all models,** remove four screws retaining cluster and carefully pull rearward enough to disengage speedometer cable. Loosely install two screws to retain cluster during instrument panel removal.
17. Open glove compartment and depress sides of bin, allowing stops to move beyond instrument panel walls.

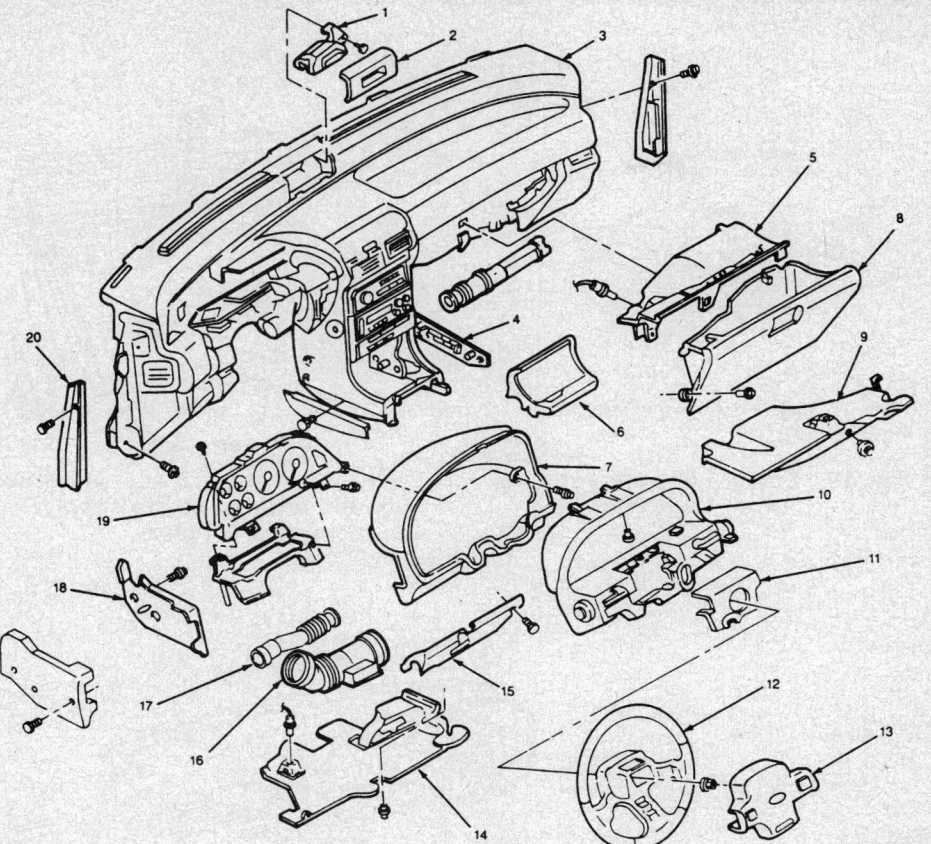

Fig. 42   Exploded view of I/P. 1992 Probe

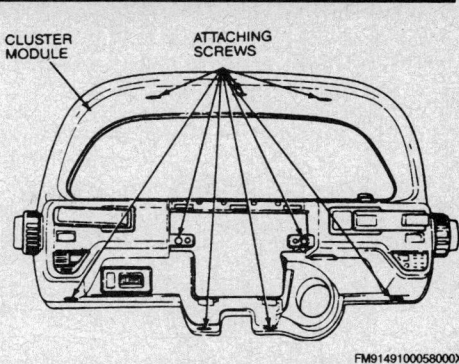

Fig. 43   Cluster module removal. 1992 Probe

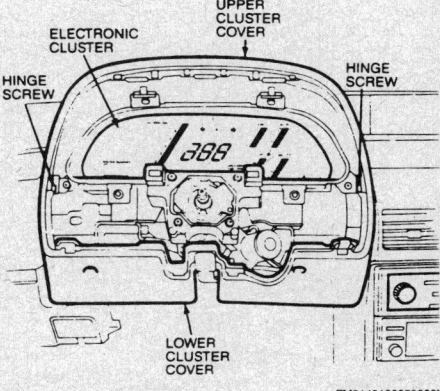

Fig. 44   Hinge screws from cluster removal. 1992 Probe

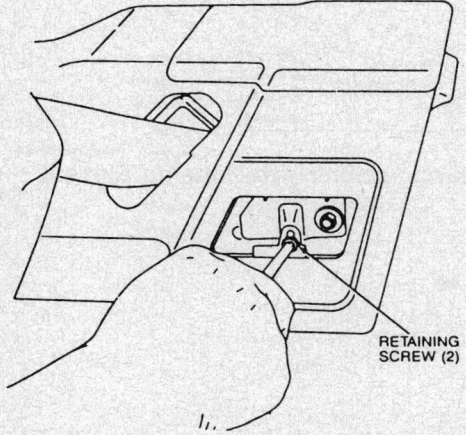

Fig. 45   Console retaining bolt removal. 1992 Probe

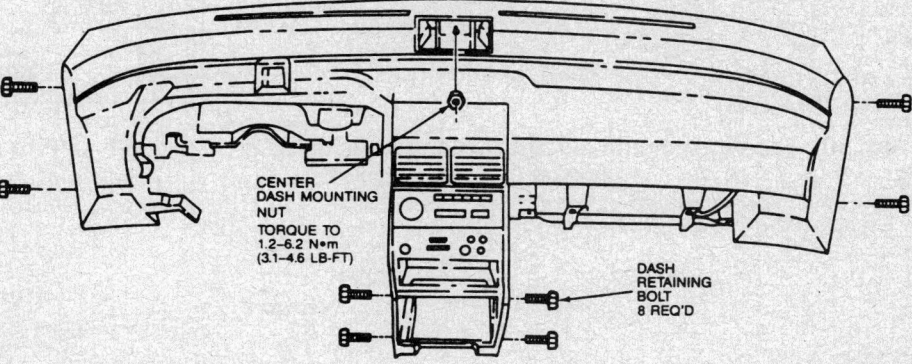

Fig. 46   I/P attaching bolts & nuts removal. 1992 Probe

18. Using steering column, cluster and glove compartment openings, and by reaching under instrument panel, disconnect all electrical connections, vacuum hoses, heater-A/C control cables and radio antenna.
19. Disconnect all underhood electrical connectors of main wire loom. Disengage rubber grommet from dash panel and feed wire and connectors into instrument panel area.
20. Remove one instrument panel to steering column support bracket retaining nut, accessible through steering column opening.
21. Remove two lower instrument panel to cowl side retaining screws, **Fig. 54.**
22. Remove two instrument panel vertical brace retaining screws.
23. Remove four instrument panel cowl top retaining screws.
24. Remove instrument panel from the vehicle.
25. Reverse procedure to install.

CAPRI

1. Disconnect battery ground cable.
2. Remove both lower cowl trim panels by pulling back door opening weatherstrip and removing push pin and screw.
3. Remove front and rear floor consoles as follows:
   a. Slide front seat completely rearward and remove screws retaining rear console to front console.
   b. Raise parking lever maximum distance.
   c. Raise rear console and pull backwards to remove.
   d. **On models equipped with auto-**

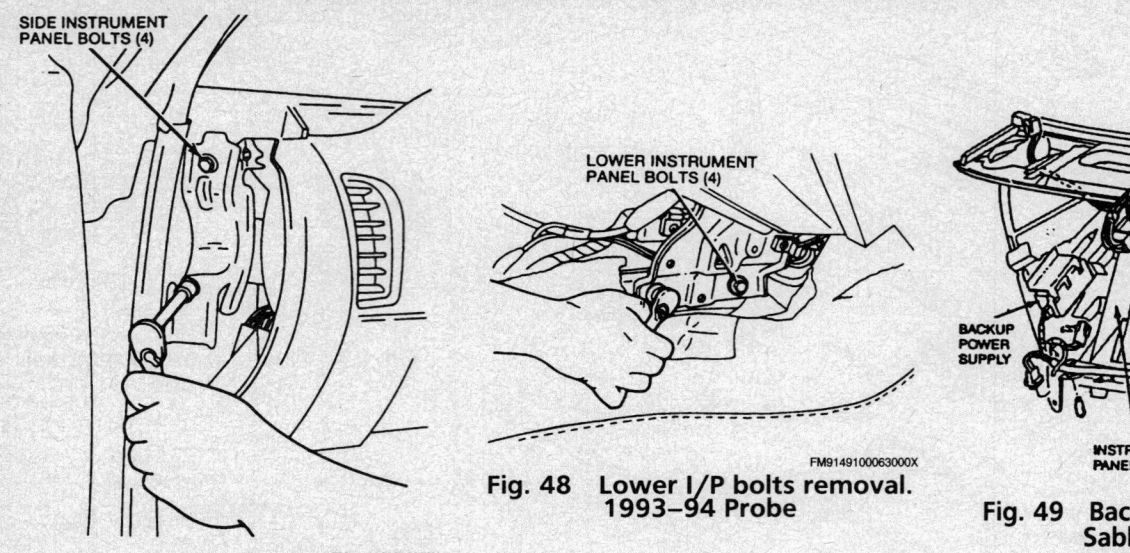

Fig. 47 Upper I/P bolts removal. 1993—94 Probe

Fig. 48 Lower I/P bolts removal. 1993—94 Probe

Fig. 49 Back-up power supply. Sable & Taurus

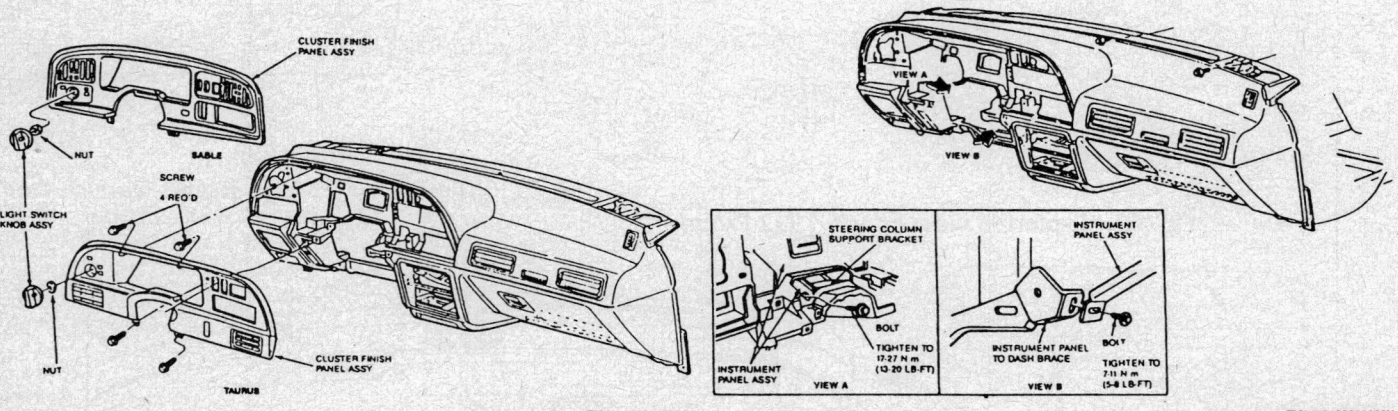

Fig. 50 Steering column electrical connectors. Sable & Taurus

Fig. 51 I/P to steering column attachments. Sable & Taurus

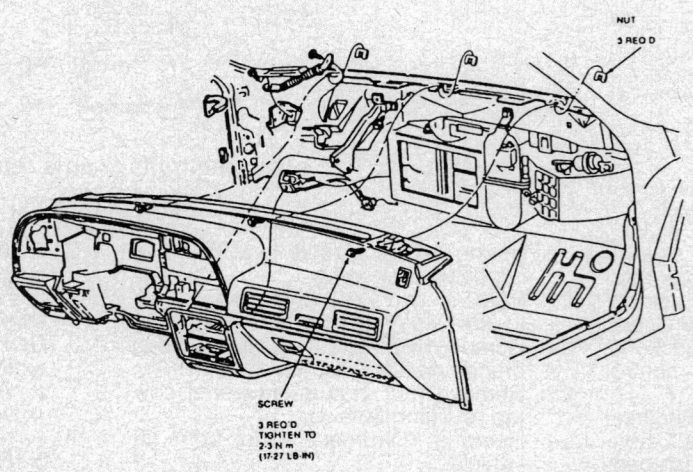

Fig. 52 I/P to dash brace removal. Sable & Taurus

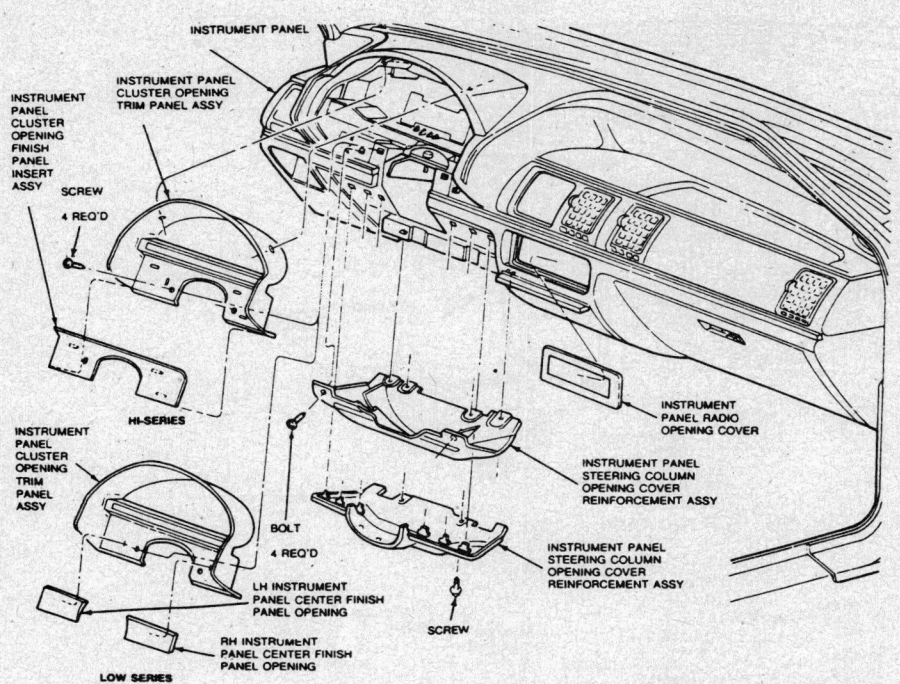

Fig. 53 Finish panels removal. Tempo & Topaz

FM9149100068000X

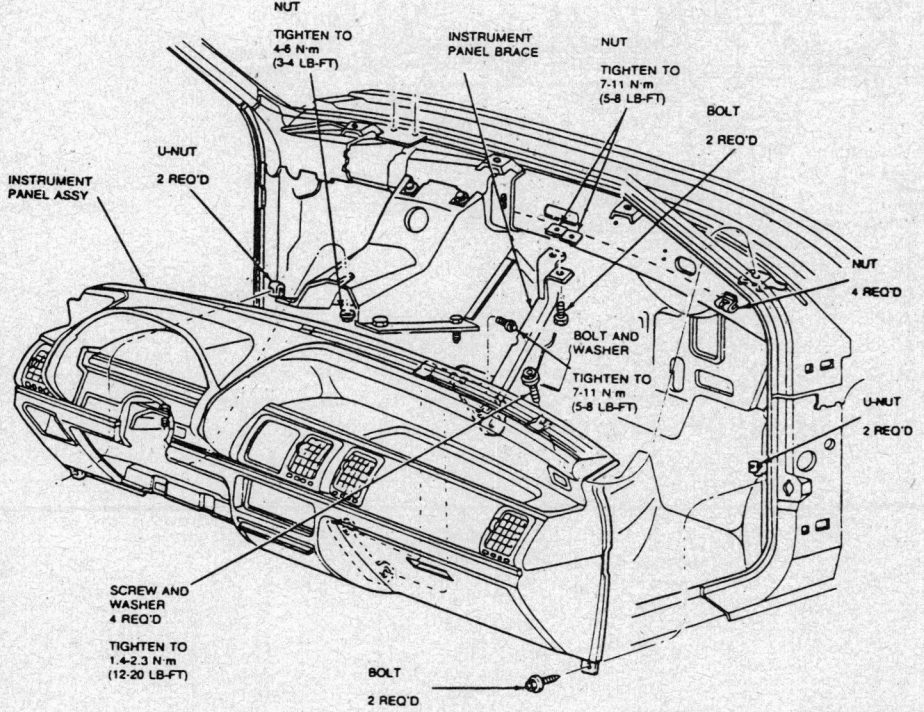

Fig. 54 I/P panel removal. Tempo & Topaz

FM9149100069000X

matic transaxles, remove shift handle.

e. **On all models,** raise ash tray and disconnect wiring on bottom, then remove center carpet panels and brackets if necessary.

f. **On manual transaxle,** remove screws retaining manual shift lever boot to bottom of front console.

g. Remove screws and front console leaving shift knob and boot on shift lever.

h. Unscrew shift knob with boot and remove from shift lever if necessary.

i. **On automatic transaxle,** remove screws and shift quadrant, then disconnect quadrant lamp connector.

4. Remove storage compartment, then four heater/radio bezel retaining screws, **Fig. 55.**

5. Disconnect speedometer cable at transaxle, then remove four instrument cluster retaining screws and slide cluster outward.

6. Press lock tab to release speedometer cable at back of cluster and remove connectors from the rear of cluster.

7. Disconnect electrical connectors from clock and switches in bezel.

8. Remove trim cover located on LH and RH Side of steering column, then remove steering column as follows:

a. Remove access panel and trim cover, then the defroster duct connecting hose and lower shroud.

b. Loosen column lower retaining nuts, then remove upper retaining bolts.

c. With column resting on I/P brace, remove ignition lock shield and ignition switch retaining screw.

d. Disconnect electrical connectors from turn signal and hazard switch.

e. Remove steering shaft universal joint pinch bolts and carefully pull column out of I/P.

9. Loosen nut retaining hood release cable and remove radio.

10. Remove control panel, then tag and remove all wiring harness retainers and connectors from I/P.

11. Remove three screws and washers located near base of windshield.

12. Remove two bolts and washers from each side of I/P, an access panel is provided for upper bolts.

13. Remove two screws and washers retaining I/P to center floor bracket, then two screws retaining I/P to column support.

14. Carefully slide I/P outward and disconnect ducts and wiring, **Fig. 56.**

15. Remove lamps, screws and upper glove compartment support bracket.

16. Remove screws, radio support bracket and defroster grilles.

17. Remove two screws above instrument cluster, three screws above glove compartment and two screws from underside of I/P.

18. Remove I/P panel pad and passenger side register from pad.

19. Reverse procedure to install.

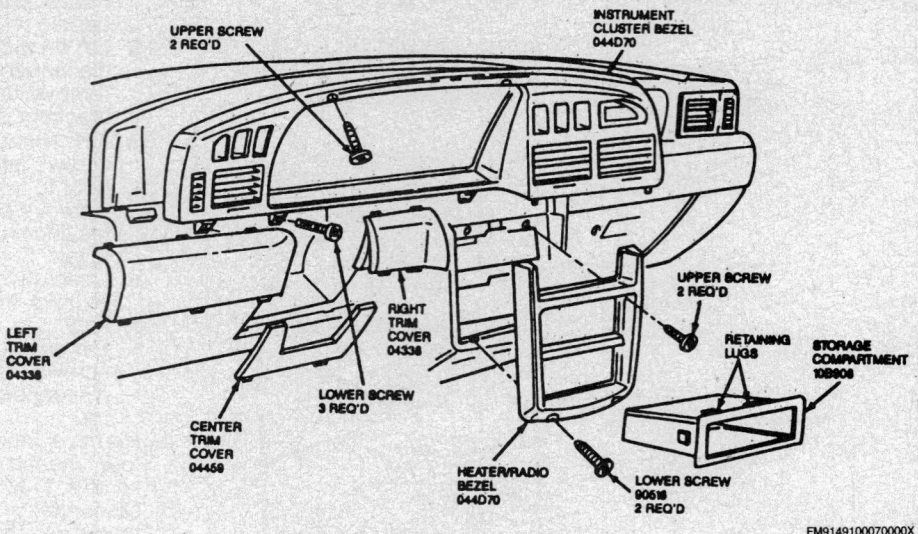

Fig. 55   I/P removal. Capri

FM9149100070000X

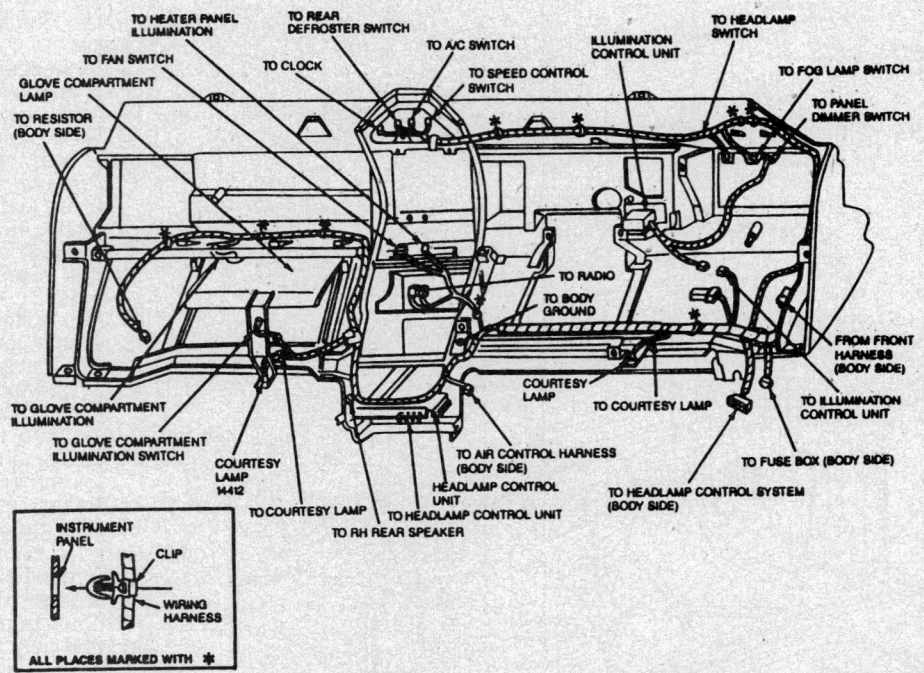

Fig. 56   I/P wiring. Capri

FM9149100071000X

STEERING COLUMNS

NOTE: On Air Bag Equipped Models, Refer To Air Bag System Precautions Located In The Front Of This Manual For System Disarming & Arming Procedures.

NOTE: Models Equipped With "Automatic Ride Control System" Utilize A Steering Sensor Located On The Steering Column Assembly. For Replacement Of Sensor, Refer To "Automatic Ride Control System" In The "Active Suspension" Section.

TABLE OF CONTENTS

Vehicles Less Air Bag System

INDEX

STEERING COLUMN
REPLACE

When servicing steering columns, care should be exercised since they are extremely susceptible to damage. Dropping or leaning on column or striking sharp blows on end of steering shaft or shift levers could loosen or shear plastic fasteners which maintain column rigidity. It is important that only the specified screws, bolts and nuts be used during the mandatory assembly sequence and they be tightened to specifications to ensure proper breakaway action of the column under impact. Avoid using excessively long bolts, as they may prevent a portion of the steering column from collapsing under impact. When removing or installing, steering wheel, ignition switch or lock, turn signal switch, adjusting transmission linkage, or installing and adjusting neutral-start or back-up light switch, refer to appropriate car chapter. If a shift tube shows a sheared plastic injection, a new shift tube must be installed. If a steering shaft shows a sheared plastic, or if the steering column has been collapsed, a complete new column must be installed. On some models, the attaching brackets will shear under impact and must also be replaced.

COUGAR & THUNDERBIRD

Refer to **Figs. 1 and 2** for steering column component identification.

1. Disconnect battery ground cable.
2. Remove bolts retaining lower lefthand finish panel. Carefully pull finish panel to disengage retaining clips.
3. Remove bolts retaining lower lefthand reinforcement panel, then the panel.
4. Remove screws retaining lower and upper steering column shrouds, then the shrouds.
5. Disconnect ignition key courtesy light, cruise control, ignition switch, multifunction switch and steering shock absorber sensor electrical connectors.
6. Remove pinch bolt from steering shaft U-joint.
7. Remove nuts retaining steering column.
8. Disconnect hazard warning electrical connector.
9. Remove screw retaining starter interlock switch, then the switch.
10. Remove steering column from vehicle.
11. Reverse procedure to install, noting the following:
    a. **Torque** U-joint pinch bolt to 30–42 ft. lbs.
    b. **Torque** new steering wheel attaching bolt to 23–33 ft. lbs.

PROBE

Refer to **Fig. 3**, for steering column component identification.

1. Disconnect battery ground cable, then remove steering wheel as described in "Electrical" section of "Ford Probe" chapter.

2. Remove two steering column cover screws, then the cover.
3. Remove nine instrument cover screws, then carefully pull instrument cover outward and remove ignition illumination bulb. Disconnect electrical connectors and remove cover.
4. Loosen two instrument cluster cover hinge screws.
5. Remove six instrument cluster cover attaching screws, then the cover.
6. Remove lower panel.
7. Remove lap and defroster ducts.
8. Disconnect four electrical connectors from turn signal switch assembly.
9. Remove U-joint cinch bolt from lower end of steering shaft.
10. Remove hinge bracket mounting nuts.
11. Remove four cluster support nuts.
12. Remove four nuts and two bolts from upper steering column bracket, then the steering shaft assembly.
13. Raise dust boot covering intermediate shaft U-joint at steering rack, then remove cinch bolt from U-joint.
14. Remove four intermediate shaft dust cover assembly attaching nuts, then the intermediate shaft assembly.
15. Guide lower U-joint onto steering rack pinion while an assistant holds intermediate shaft and dust cover assembly. Install and **torque** cinch bolt to 13–20 ft. lbs.
16. Install dust cover assembly with retaining nuts.
17. Guide steering column into upper intermediate U-joint while an assistant holds the column. Do not install cinch bolt at this time.

18. Install hinge bracket nuts. Do not tighten at this time.
19. Install four upper column bracket bolts.
20. **Torque** hinge bracket nuts to 12-17 ft. lbs and upper bracket bolts to 12-17 ft. lbs.
21. Install and **torque** support nuts and cluster support nuts to 6.5-10 ft. lbs.
22. Connect ignition switch electrical connectors.
23. Install instrument cluster cover. Tighten attaching screws and two hinge screws.
24. Connect seven instrument cluster electrical connectors.
25. Install ignition illumination bulb.
26. Install instrument cover with nine attaching screws.
27. Install lap and defroster ducts and lower panel.
28. Install steering column cover.
29. Install steering wheel as described in "Electrical" section of "Ford Probe" chapter.
30. Reconnect battery negative cable.

TEMPO & TOPAZ

Refer to **Figs. 4 and 5** for steering column component identification.
1. Disconnect battery ground cable.
2. Remove steering column cover from lower portion of instrument panel, then the speed control module, if equipped.
3. Remove lower steering column shroud.
4. Loosen, but do not remove two nuts and bolts attaching steering column to support bracket. Remove upper shroud.
5. Disconnect all column electrical connectors. On console shift (automatic transaxle) remove interlock cable retaining screw, then disconnect cable from steering column.
6. Loosen steering column to intermediate shaft clamp and remove nut or bolt.
7. Remove two nuts and bolts attaching column to support bracket and lower column to floor. With steering column locked, pry open steering column shaft clamp to disengage shafts. **Do not use excessive force, since damage to components may result.**
8. Remove column and inspect bracket clips for damage. Replace clips if bent or excessively distorted.
9. Engage lower steering shaft to intermediate shaft. Loosely install nut and bolt.
10. Place steering column under instrument panel, align bolts of support bracket with outer tube and loosely install two nuts. Check for presence of two clips on outer bracket. **These clips must be present to ensure adequate performance of system.**
11. Loosely install bolts through outer tube upper bracket and clips and into support bracket.
12. Connect all electrical connectors. On console shift automatic transaxles, in-

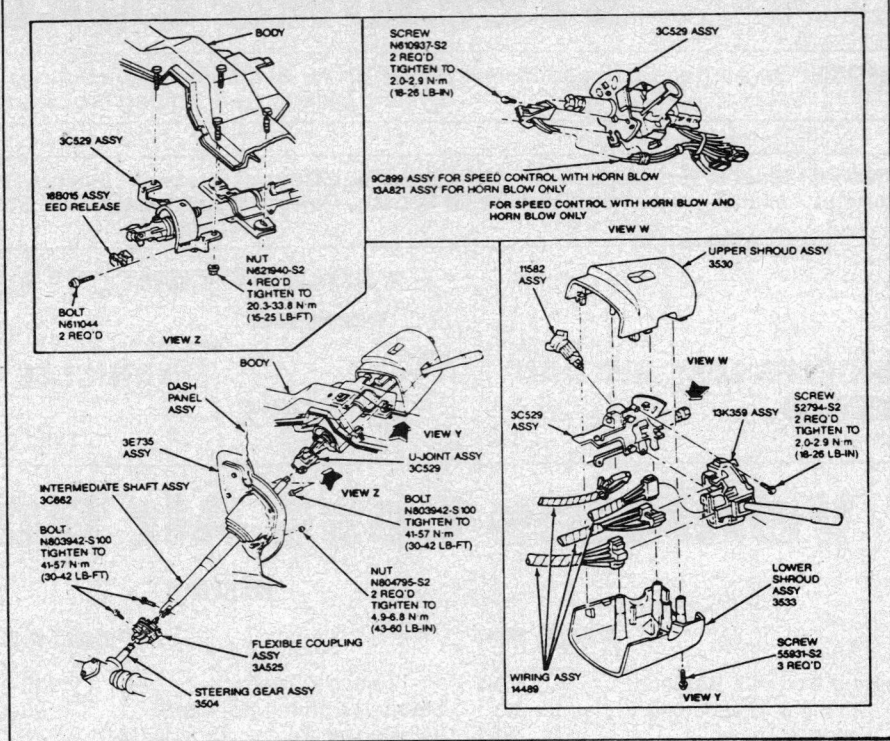

Fig. 1   Steering column installation. Cougar & Thunderbird

stall interlock cable and retaining screw. **Torque** retaining screw to 30-38 inch lbs.
13. Install upper shroud, **torque** mounting nut and bolt to 17-25 ft. lbs.
14. Turn steering column left and right one complete turn to align intermediate shaft. **Torque** steering shaft clamp nut to 20-30 ft. lbs.
15. Install lower trim shroud and instrument panel reinforcement section.
16. Install steering column cover on instrument panel.
17. Connect battery ground cable and check steering column for proper operation.

ESCORT & TRACER

Refer to **Fig. 6** for steering column component identification.
1. Remove steering wheel and multi-function switch as described in "Electrical" section of "Ford Escort & Mercury Tracer" chapter.
2. Disconnect ignition switch electrical connector, then remove shift-lock cable mounting bracket bolt, place bracket and cable aside.
3. Remove four steering column upper mounting bracket bolts, then lower column.
4. Remove five set plate mounting nuts, then the set plate.
5. Remove intermediate shaft to pinion shaft bolt, two steering column lower mounting bracket nuts, then the column.

6. Reverse procedure to install, noting the following:
   a. **Torque** intermediate shaft to pinion shaft bolt to 30-36 ft. lbs.
   b. **Torque** column upper mounting bracket bolts to 80-123 inch lbs.
   c. **Torque** shift lock cable mounting bracket bolt to 37-55 inch lbs.

FESTIVA

Refer to **Fig. 7** for steering column component identification.
1. Remove steering wheel, combination switch and ignition switch as described in "Electrical" section of "Ford Festiva" chapter.
2. Remove four shield nuts, then the column shield.
3. Remove two upper steering column to instrument panel mounting nuts, then lower upper end of column to gain access to intermediate shaft universal joint.
4. Make an index mark at juncture of steering shaft and intermediate shaft upper universal joint for proper alignment during installation. Remove universal joint clamp screw.
5. Loosen two steering column hinge bracket to clutch/brake support nuts, then pull steering column towards the rear and disengage it from the universal joint.
6. If steering gear needs to be removed, index mark and remove the upper universal joint. Mark universal joint, so that ends are installed correctly.
7. If upper universal joint was removed, align index marks made during re-

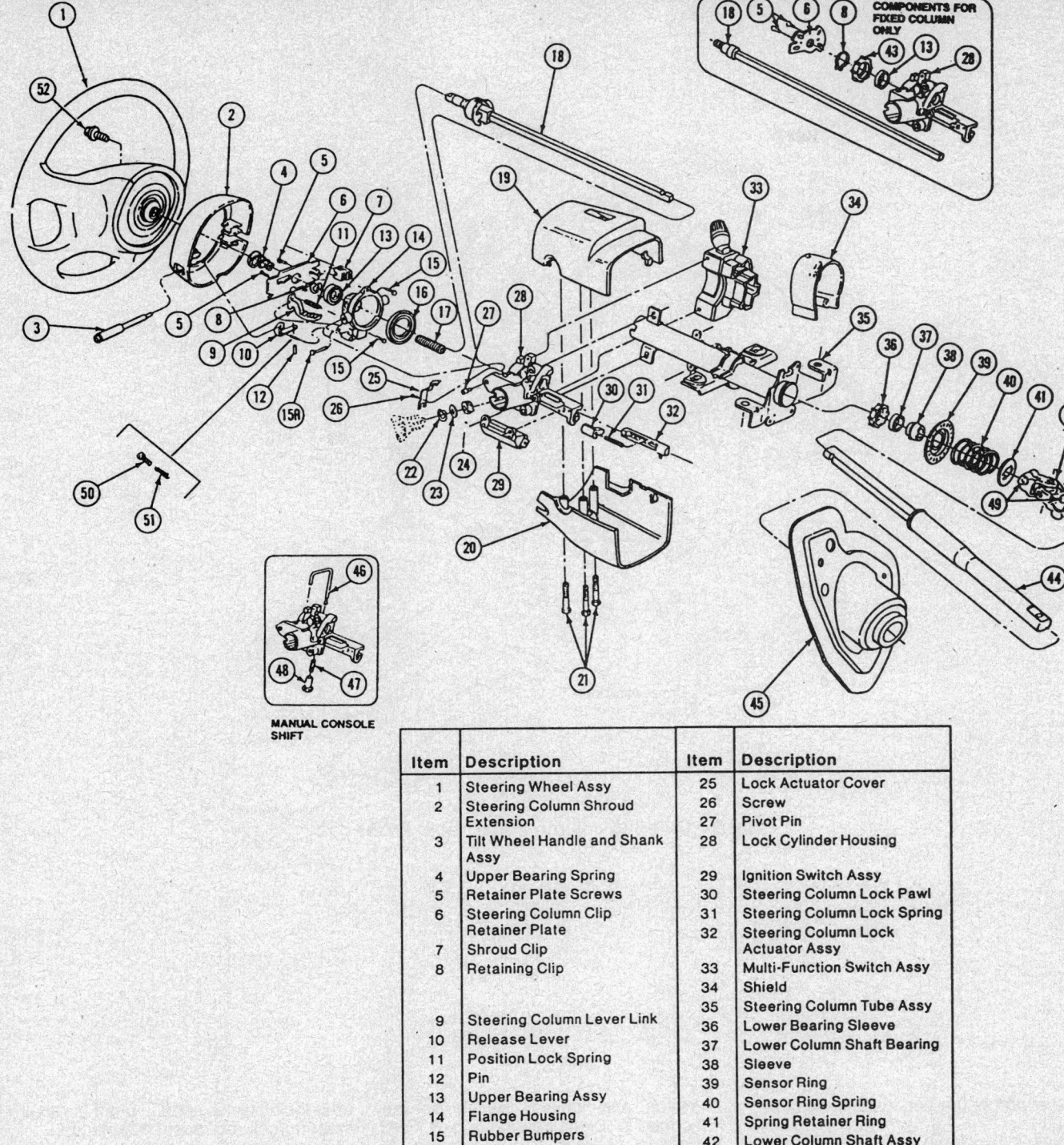

COMPONENTS FOR FIXED COLUMN ONLY

MANUAL CONSOLE SHIFT

Item	Description	Item	Description
1	Steering Wheel Assy	25	Lock Actuator Cover
2	Steering Column Shroud Extension	26	Screw
3	Tilt Wheel Handle and Shank Assy	27	Pivot Pin
4	Upper Bearing Spring	28	Lock Cylinder Housing
5	Retainer Plate Screws	29	Ignition Switch Assy
6	Steering Column Clip Retainer Plate	30	Steering Column Lock Pawl
7	Shroud Clip	31	Steering Column Lock Spring
8	Retaining Clip	32	Steering Column Lock Actuator Assy
9	Steering Column Lever Link	33	Multi-Function Switch Assy
10	Release Lever	34	Shield
11	Position Lock Spring	35	Steering Column Tube Assy
12	Pin	36	Lower Bearing Sleeve
13	Upper Bearing Assy	37	Lower Column Shaft Bearing
14	Flange Housing	38	Sleeve
15	Rubber Bumpers	39	Sensor Ring
15A	Pin	40	Sensor Ring Spring
16	Bearing Assy	41	Spring Retainer Ring
17	Position Spring	42	Lower Column Shaft Assy
18	Shaft Assy	43	Upper Bearing
19	Upper Shroud	44	Intermediate Shaft
20	Lower Shroud	45	Lower Column Boot Assy
21	Screws	46	Lock Actuator Lever (Manual Trans. Only)
22	Retainer	47	Lock Actuator Spring
23	Bearing	48	Lock Actuator Knob
24	Lock Gear	49	Bolt
		50	Cap
		51	Spring
		52	Steering Wheel Attaching Bolt

FM6049100043000X

Fig. 2 Exploded view of steering column. Cougar & Thunderbird

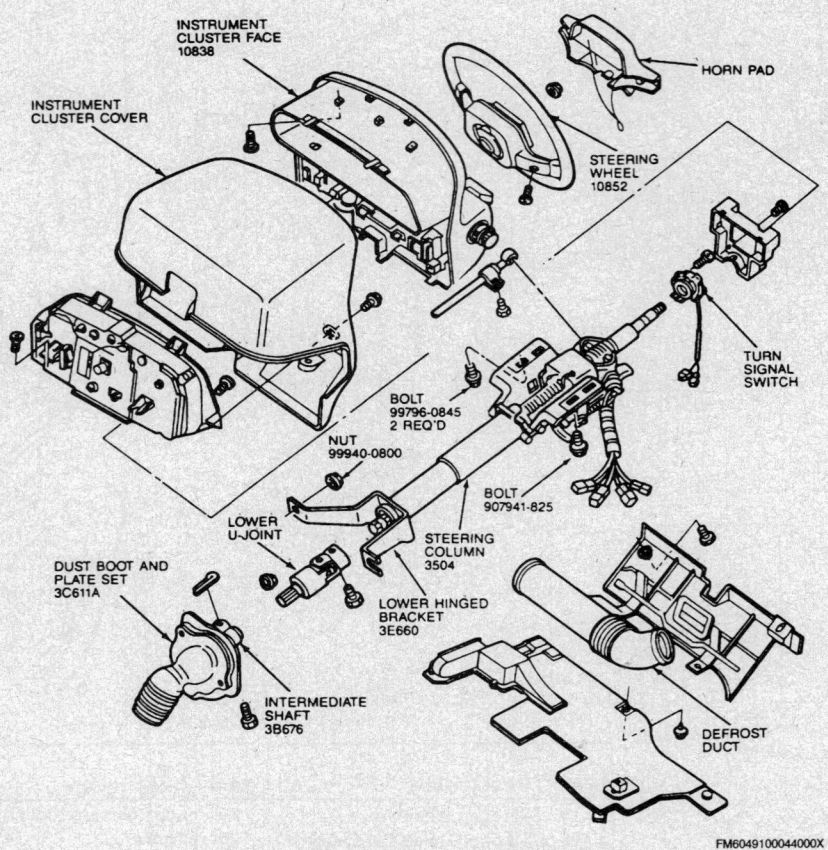

INSTRUMENT
CLUSTER FACE
10838

INSTRUMENT
CLUSTER COVER

HORN PAD

STEERING
WHEEL
10852

TURN
SIGNAL
SWITCH

BOLT
99796-0845
2 REQ'D

NUT
99940-0800

BOLT
907941-825

STEERING
COLUMN
3504

LOWER U-JOINT

DUST BOOT AND
PLATE SET
3C611A

LOWER HINGED
BRACKET
3E660

INTERMEDIATE
SHAFT
3B676

DEFROST
DUCT

FM6049100044000X

Fig. 3   Steering column installation. Probe

moval procedure and install joint onto shaft.

8. Install joint clamp bolt, but do not tighten, then install steering column aligning index marks on column shaft and universal joint.

9. Install column hinge bracket with pedal support studs. Do not tighten universal joint.

10. Tighten hinge bracket nuts, then raise the upper end of column to seat under instrument panel, position shim clips on column upper bracket flanges.

11. Install two upper steering column retaining nuts, then the steering column shield and nuts.

12. Install steering wheel, combination switch and ignition switch as described in "Electrical" section of "Ford Festiva" chapter.

STEERING COLUMN SERVICE
COUGAR, TEMPO, THUNDERBIRD & TOPAZ

Refer to **Figs. 2, 4 and 5** for component locations when repairing the steering column assembly.

ESCORT & TRACER

The steering column is serviced as a unit. If service other than the steering col-

umn lock or intermediate shaft is required, steering column must be replaced.

FESTIVA

The steering column is serviced as a unit. If service other than the combination switch or ignition switch assembly is required, steering column must be replaced.

PROBE

The steering column is serviced as a unit. If service other than the steering wheel, combination switch, steering angle sensor or ignition switch assembly is required, steering column must be replaced.

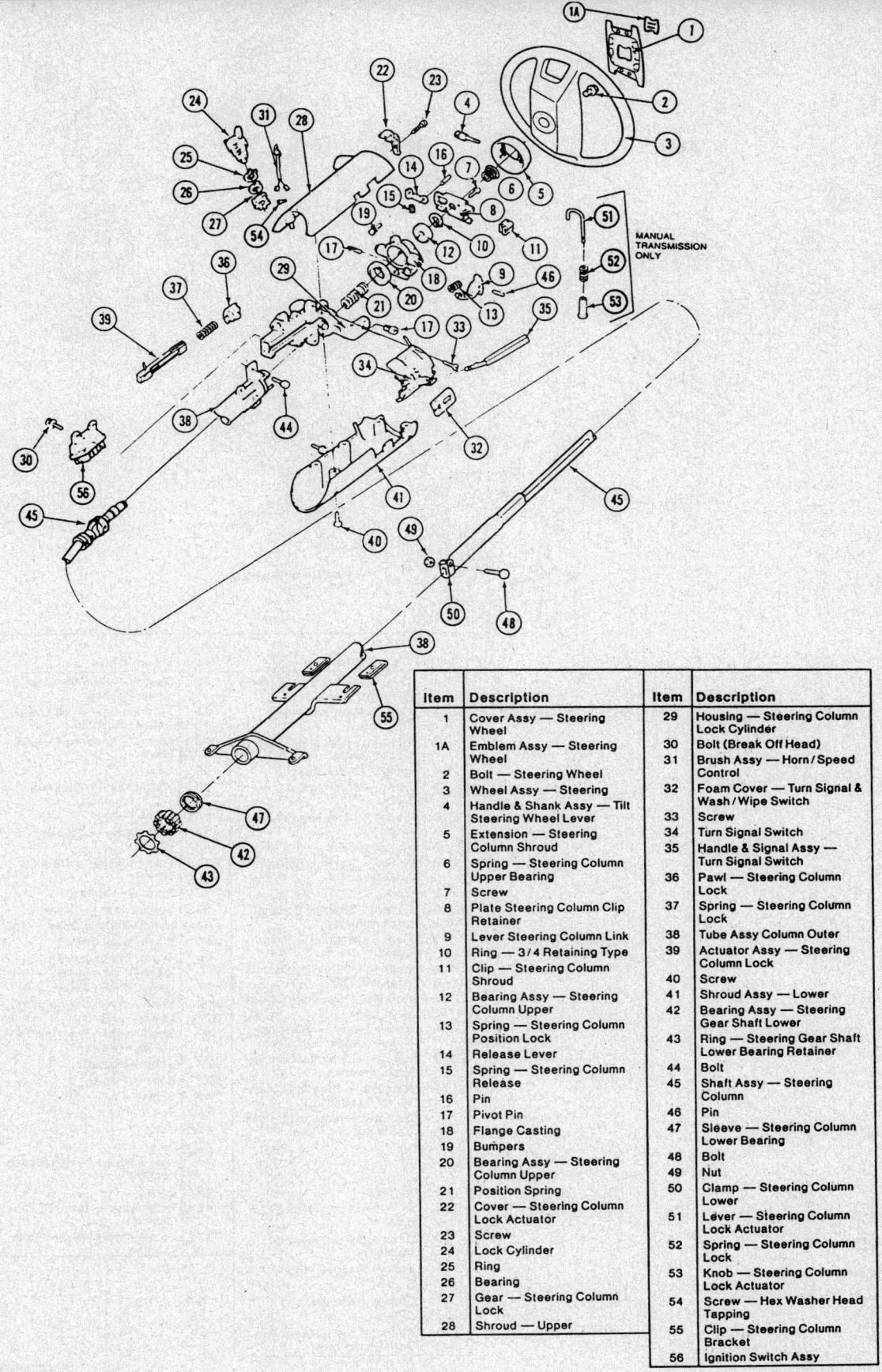

Item	Description	Item	Description
1	Cover Assy — Steering Wheel	29	Housing — Steering Column Lock Cylinder
1A	Emblem Assy — Steering Wheel	30	Bolt (Break Off Head)
2	Bolt — Steering Wheel	31	Brush Assy — Horn/Speed Control
3	Wheel Assy — Steering	32	Foam Cover — Turn Signal & Wash/Wipe Switch
4	Handle & Shank Assy — Tilt Steering Wheel Lever	33	Screw
5	Extension — Steering Column Shroud	34	Turn Signal Switch
6	Spring — Steering Column Upper Bearing	35	Handle & Signal Assy — Turn Signal Switch
7	Screw	36	Pawl — Steering Column Lock
8	Plate Steering Column Clip Retainer	37	Spring — Steering Column Lock
9	Lever Steering Column Link	38	Tube Assy Column Outer
10	Ring — 3/4 Retaining Type	39	Actuator Assy — Steering Column Lock
11	Clip — Steering Column Shroud	40	Screw
12	Bearing Assy — Steering Column Upper	41	Shroud Assy — Lower
13	Spring — Steering Column Position Lock	42	Bearing Assy — Steering Gear Shaft Lower
14	Release Lever	43	Ring — Steering Gear Shaft Lower Bearing Retainer
15	Spring — Steering Column Release	44	Bolt
16	Pin	45	Shaft Assy — Steering Column
17	Pivot Pin	46	Pin
18	Flange Casting	47	Sleeve — Steering Column Lower Bearing
19	Bumpers	48	Bolt
20	Bearing Assy — Steering Column Upper	49	Nut
21	Position Spring	50	Clamp — Steering Column Lower
22	Cover — Steering Column Lock Actuator	51	Lever — Steering Column Lock Actuator
23	Screw	52	Spring — Steering Column Lock
24	Lock Cylinder	53	Knob — Steering Column Lock Actuator
25	Ring	54	Screw — Hex Washer Head Tapping
26	Bearing	55	Clip — Steering Column Bracket
27	Gear — Steering Column Lock	56	Ignition Switch Assy
28	Shroud — Upper		

FM6049100045000X

Fig. 4 Exploded view of tilt steering column. Tempo & Topaz

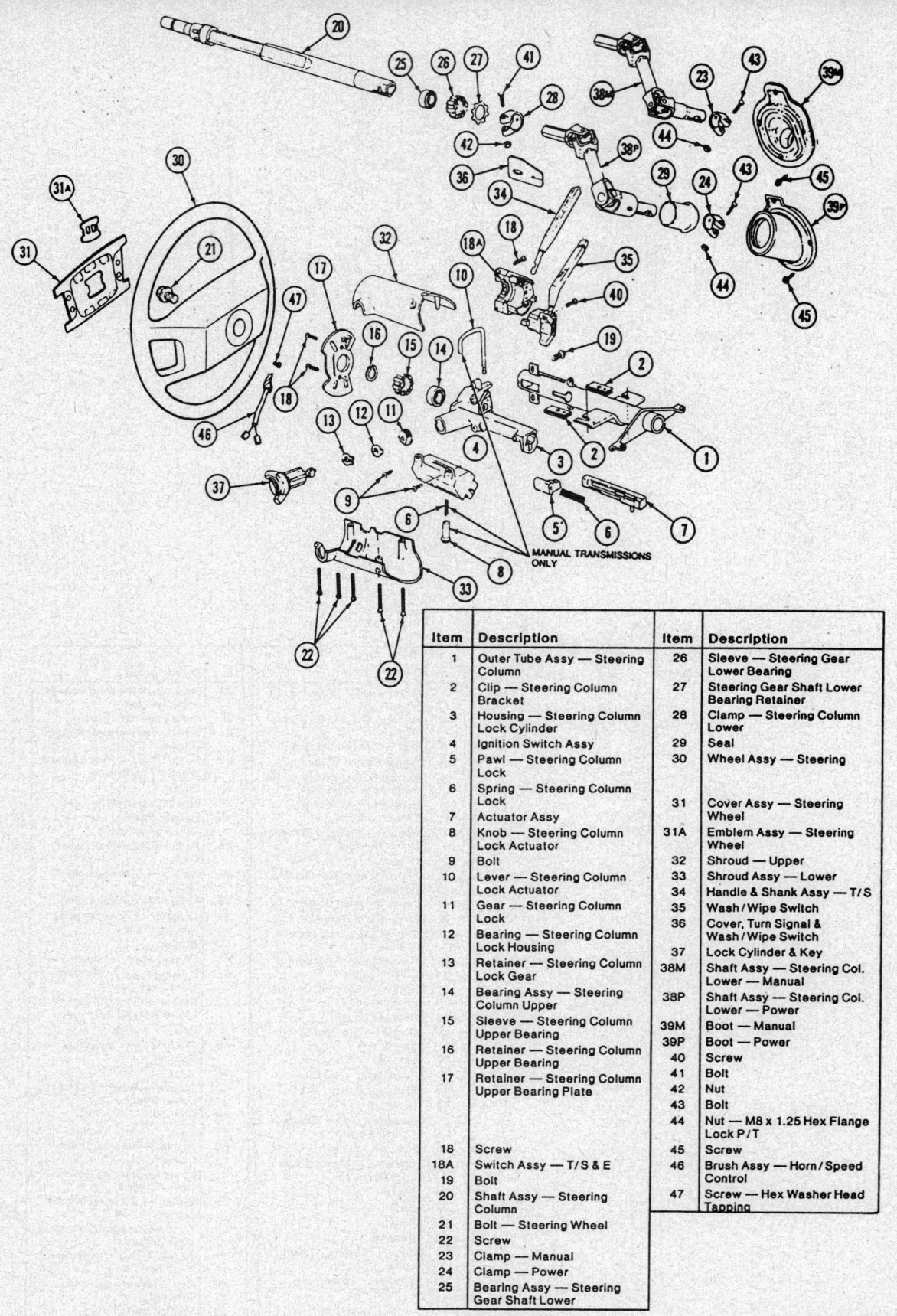

MANUAL TRANSMISSIONS
ONLY

Item	Description	Item	Description
1	Outer Tube Assy — Steering Column	26	Sleeve — Steering Gear Lower Bearing
2	Clip — Steering Column Bracket	27	Steering Gear Shaft Lower Bearing Retainer
3	Housing — Steering Column Lock Cylinder	28	Clamp — Steering Column Lower
4	Ignition Switch Assy	29	Seal
5	Pawl — Steering Column Lock	30	Wheel Assy — Steering
6	Spring — Steering Column Lock	31	Cover Assy — Steering Wheel
7	Actuator Assy	31A	Emblem Assy — Steering Wheel
8	Knob — Steering Column Lock Actuator	32	Shroud — Upper
9	Bolt	33	Shroud Assy — Lower
10	Lever — Steering Column Lock Actuator	34	Handle & Shank Assy — T/S
11	Gear — Steering Column Lock	35	Wash/Wipe Switch
12	Bearing — Steering Column Lock Housing	36	Cover, Turn Signal & Wash/Wipe Switch
13	Retainer — Steering Column Lock Gear	37	Lock Cylinder & Key
14	Bearing Assy — Steering Column Upper	38M	Shaft Assy — Steering Col. Lower — Manual
15	Sleeve — Steering Column Upper Bearing	38P	Shaft Assy — Steering Col. Lower — Power
16	Retainer — Steering Column Upper Bearing	39M	Boot — Manual
17	Retainer — Steering Column Upper Bearing Plate	39P	Boot — Power
		40	Screw
		41	Bolt
		42	Nut
		43	Bolt
		44	Nut — M8 x 1.25 Hex Flange Lock P/T
18	Screw	45	Screw
18A	Switch Assy — T/S & E	46	Brush Assy — Horn/Speed Control
19	Bolt	47	Screw — Hex Washer Head Tapping
20	Shaft Assy — Steering Column		
21	Bolt — Steering Wheel		
22	Screw		
23	Clamp — Manual		
24	Clamp — Power		
25	Bearing Assy — Steering Gear Shaft Lower		

FM6049100046000X

Fig. 5 Exploded view of fixed steering column. Tempo & Topaz

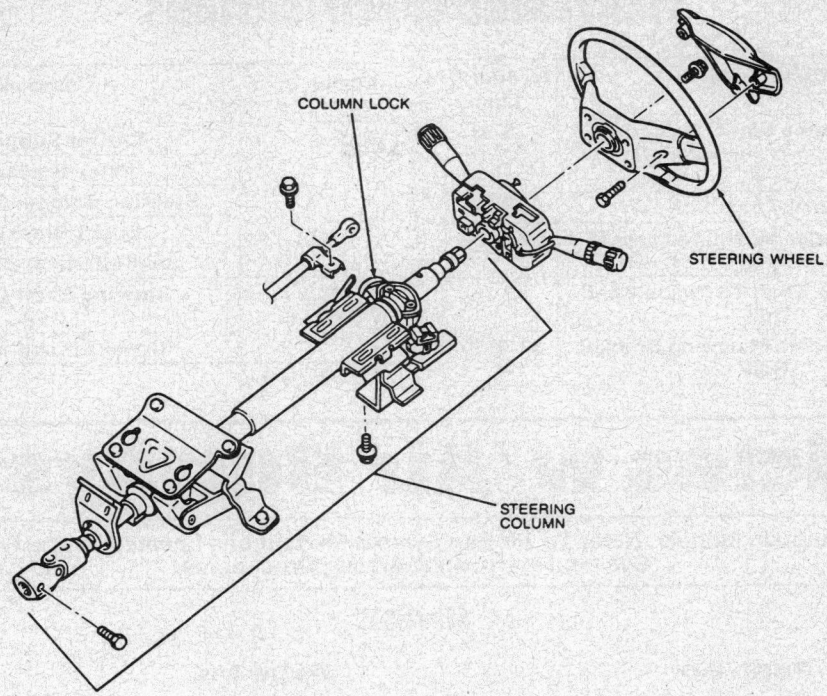

COLUMN LOCK

STEERING WHEEL

STEERING COLUMN

FM6049100047000X

Fig. 6 Steering column component locations. Escort & Tracer

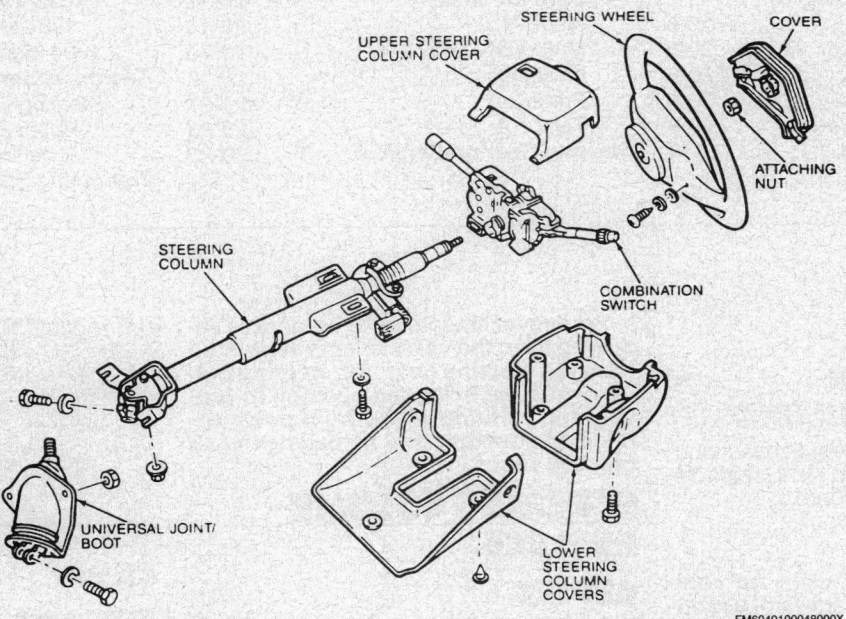

UPPER STEERING COLUMN COVER

STEERING WHEEL

COVER

ATTACHING NUT

STEERING COLUMN

COMBINATION SWITCH

UNIVERSAL JOINT/ BOOT

LOWER STEERING COLUMN COVERS

FM6049100048000X

Fig. 7 Steering column component locations. Festiva

TIGHTENING SPECIFICATIONS

Model	Component	Torque/Ft. Lbs.	Model	Component	Torque/Ft. Lbs.
Cougar/ Thunderbird	Steering Wheel Bolt	23-33	Probe	Cluster Support Nuts	7-10
				Hinge Bracket Nuts	12-17
	U-Joint Pinch Bolt	30-42		Steering Column Support Nuts	7-10
Escort/ Tracer	Column Upper Mounting Bracket Bolts	80-123 ①		Upper Bracket Bolts	12-17
				Shift Interlock Cable Screw	30-38
	Intermediate Shaft To Pinion Shaft Bolt	30-36	Tempo/ Topaz	Steering Shaft Clamp Nut	20-30
	Shift Lock Cable Mounting Bracket Bolt	37-55 ①		Upper Shroud Nut & Bolt	17-25

① —Inch lbs.

Vehicles w/Air Bag System

NOTE: On Air Bag Equipped Models, Refer To Air Bag System Precautions Located In The Front Of This Manual For System Disarming & Arming Procedures.

INDEX

PRECAUTIONS

AIR BAG SYSTEM DISARMING & ARMING

Refer to "Air Bag System Precautions" in the front of this manual for system disarming and arming procedures.

DESCRIPTION

The steering column used on vehicles equipped with air bags is of a modular construction and features easy to service electrical switches. The washer/wiper switch and the combination turn signal/hazard/horn/flash to pass/dimmer switch are attached with self-tapping screws.

The vehicle is equipped with either a brush type slip ring or a clockspring type slip ring. Removal and installation procedures for the two types are the same except where noted.

Fasteners used on steering column components must be replaced after removal. The fasteners are coated with an epoxy adhesive, making them non-reusable.

Whenever the steering column is removed from the vehicle, or is separated from the steering gear, the steering column must be in locked position to prevent the steering wheel from being rotated accidentally and damaging the air bag slip ring.

STEERING COLUMN
REPLACE

ASPIRE

Refer to **Fig. 1** for repacement.
1. Remove steering wheel, then the turn signal and windshield wiper switch and ignition switch as described in "Electrical" section.
2. Remove lower steering column shaft lower bolt.
3. Remove two lower, then the two upper steering column mounting bracket bolts.
4. Once free, lower upper end of steering column as necessary to access steering column gear input shaft coupling at lower end.
5. Mark juncture of steering column gear input shaft coupling and lower steer-
ing column shaft to assure correct alignment during assembly
6. Remove steering column.
7. Reverse procedure to install, noting the following:
   a. Ensure steering column gear input shaft coupling is not upside-down.
   b. Align index marks between lower steering column shaft and steering column gear input shaft coupling.

CAPRI
Removal

1. Ensure wheels are in straight ahead position.
2. Remove ignition key and rotate steering wheel slightly until it locks.
3. Remove steering column access panel and trim cover, then the defroster duct connecting hose.
4. Remove steering column lower shroud, then loosen column lower retaining nuts.
5. Remove column upper retaining bolts, then, with column resting on instrument panel brace, remove ignition lock shield, brake-shift interlock mechanism and ignition switch retain-

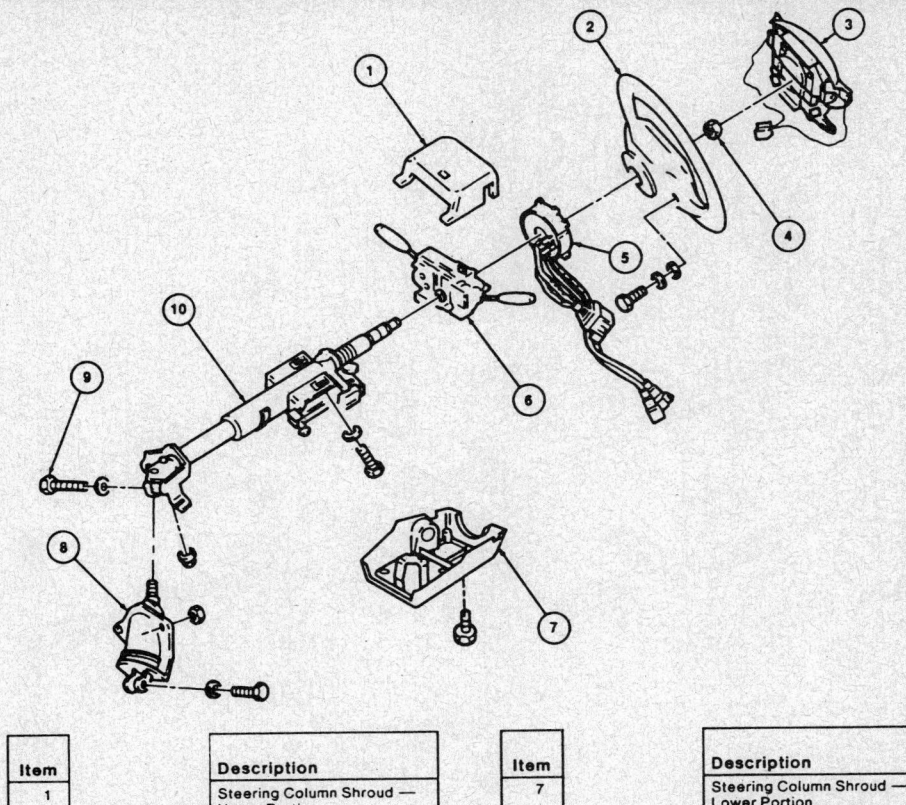

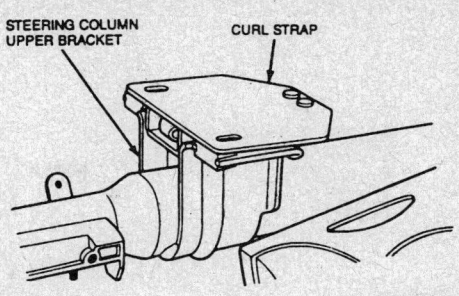

Fig. 2 Correct installation of curl strap. Capri

Item	Description
1	Steering Column Shroud — Upper Portion
2	Steering Wheel
3	Driver Side Air Bag Module
4	Steering Wheel Nut
5	Air Bag Sliding Contact
6	Turn Signal and Windshield Wiper Switch

Item	Description
7	Steering Column Shroud — Lower Portion
8	Steering Column Tube Boot / Steering Column Gear Input Shaft Coupling
9	Lower Steering Column Shaft Bolt
10	Steering Column

FM6049400065000X

Fig. 1 Exploded view of steering column. Aspire

ing screw. **Ignition switch will come out with shield.**

6. Disconnect electrical connectors from turn signal and hazard switch, then the harness connectors from key warning, windshield wiper switch and slip ring assembly.

7. Tape clockspring inner and outer halves to prevent rotation. **Do not remove wire connectors from clockspring attaching point. Wires are to be disconnected from harness at two connectors remotely mounted on steering column.**

8. Remove steering shaft universal pinch bolt, then carefully pull column out of instrument panel and remove from vehicle.

Installation

1. Carefully guide column assembly into instrument panel, ensuring curl strap is installed correctly and retaining clips are tight, **Fig. 2.**

2. Connect harness connectors for key warning, wiper switch and slip ring assembly, then the connectors to turn signal switch and hazard switch.

3. Install ignition switch and lock shield, then **torque** retaining bolts and nut to 11-14 ft. lbs.

4. Install brake-shift interlock mechanism, then connect steering shaft uni-

versal joint and install pinch bolt. Do not tighten pinch bolt.

5. Ensure curl strap is in place with retaining clips and install upper column retaining bolts. **Do not tighten bolts.**

6. **Torque** lower column retaining nuts to 14-19 ft. lbs., upper bolts to 17-22 ft. lbs. and universal pinch bolt to 14-19 ft. lbs.

7. Install defroster duct connecting hose, then the lower column shroud.

8. Install access panel and trim cover.

9. Check column components for proper operation.

CONTINENTAL, SABLE & TAURUS

Refer to **Figs. 3 through 6** for steering column component identification.

1. Disconnect battery ground cable, then center front wheels to straight ahead position.

2. Remove four air bag module retaining nuts, then lift module off steering wheel.

3. Disconnect air bag wiring harness connector from air bag module, then remove air bag module from vehicle. **Place air bag module face up with retaining studs facing downward, touching bench.**

4. Disconnect speed control wire har-

ness from steering wheel, then remove steering wheel retaining bolt. **Discard bolt.**

5. Install steering wheel puller tool No. T67L-3600-A, or equivalent, then remove steering wheel from column. **Ensure contact assembly wiring harness does not get caught on wheel assembly when lifting off shaft.**

6. Remove righthand and lefthand lower moldings from instrument panel by pulling up and snapping out of retainers.

7. Remove instrument panel lower trim cover.

8. Remove air bag clockspring contact assembly as follows:
   a. Apply two strips of tape across contact assembly stator and rotor to prevent accidental rotation.
   b. Remove three contact assembly retaining screws, then pull contact assembly off steering column shaft.

9. Remove tilt lever by unscrewing it from column.

10. Rotate ignition lock cylinder to Run position, then, using a 1/8 inch pin punch, depress lock cylinder retaining pin through access hole and remove lock cylinder.

11. Remove four screws retaining upper and lower column shrouds, then remove shrouds from steering column.

12. Remove instrument panel reinforcement brace.

13. **On models equipped with column shift,** disconnect PRND21 cable from actuator housing by removing one screw, then disconnect cable loop from shift tube hook.

14. **On all models,** remove two multifunction switch retaining screws and set multi-function switch aside.

15. Remove wiring connector from ignition switch.

16. Remove column skid plate, then pinch bolt from steering shaft flex coupling.

17. While supporting steering column assembly, remove four column assembly retaining nuts.

18. Lower steering column, then disconnect vacuum hoses at parking brake release switch.

19. Disconnect shift cable from selector lever pivot, then remove shift cable and bracket from lower column mounting.

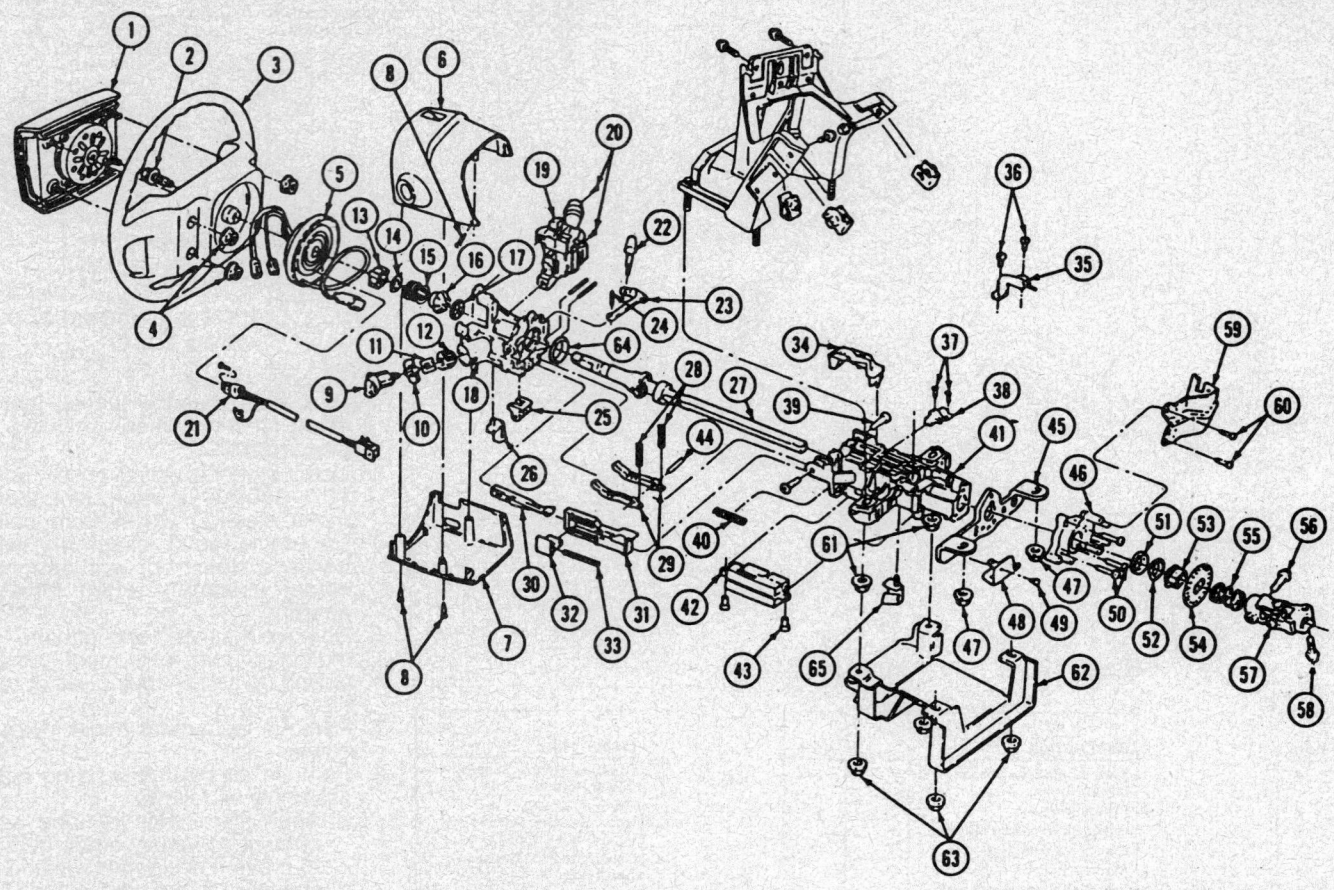

Fig. 3   Exploded view of steering column. 1992 Sable & Taurus w/console shift

FM6049100051000X

Item	Description
1	Air Bag Module
2	Steering Wheel Bolt
3	Steering Wheel
4	Air Bag Module Retaining Nuts
5	Air Bag Clockspring Contact Assy
6	Upper Column Shroud
7	Lower Column Shroud
8	Shroud Retaining Screws
9	Ignition Lock Cylinder Assy
10	Retainer
11	Bearing
12	Gear — Steering Lock
13	Turn Signal Cancelling Cam
14	Snap Ring
15	Spring — Upper Bearing
16	Tolerance Ring
17	Bearing — Upper (Small)
18	Lock Cylinder Housing
19	Multi-Function Switch
20	Screws
21	Horn Brush Assy
22	Tilt Release Lever
23	Tilt Actuator Lever

Item	Description
24	Tilt Actuator Lever Pin
25	Cam Steering Column Lock
26	Clip Wiring — Upper
27	Steering Shaft Assy
28	Spring Lock Lever
29	Lever Steering Column Lock
30	Lock Actuator Assy — Upper
31	Lock Actuator Assy — Lower
32	Pawl — Steering Column Lock (Shaft)
33	Spring — Steering Column Lock (Shaft)
34	Shield
35	Trans Control Selector Position Insert
36	Screws
37	Screws
38	Parking Brake Vacuum Release Switch
39	Tilt Pivot Screws
40	Spring — Steering Column Position Lock
41	Actuator Housing
42	Ignition Switch
43	Screws
44	Pin — Pivot Lever
45	Lower Column Bracket
46	Lower Bearing Housing Retainer

Item	Description
47	Lower Column Mounting Nuts
48	Bracket
49	Screw
50	Lower Bearing Housing Retaining Screws
51	Lower Column Bearing Sleeve
52	Lower Column Bearing
53	Tolerance Ring — Lower
54	Sensor Ring
55	Spring
56	Bolt — Flange Yoke
57	Steering Shaft U — Joint Assy
58	Bolt
59	Shift Cable Bracket
60	Shift Cable Bracket Mounting Screws
61	Upper Column Mounting Nuts
62	Absorber — Steering Column Impact
63	Nuts
64	Bearing — Upper (Large)
65	Clip Wiring — Lower

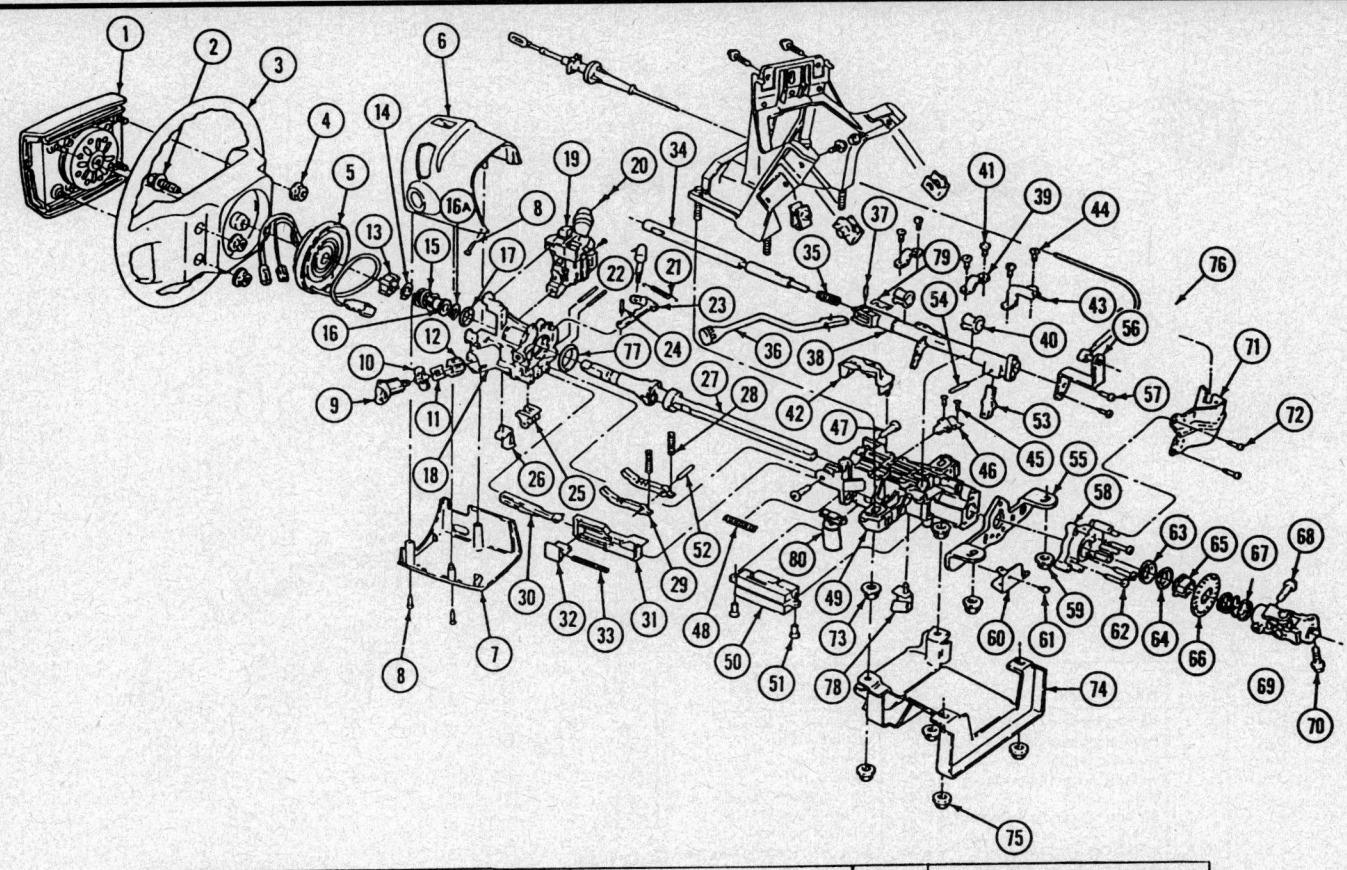

Fig. 4 Exploded view of steering column. 1992 Continental & Sable & Taurus w/Column Shift

Item	Description				
1	Air Bag Module	28	Spring Lock Lever	53	Pawl Steering Column Lock Shifter
2	Steering Wheel Bolt	29	Lever Steering Column Lock	54	Pin — Steering Column Lock Shifter
3	Steering Wheel	30	Lock Actuator Assy — Upper	55	Lower Column Bracket
4	Air Bag Module Retaining Nuts	31	Lock Actuator Assy — Lower	56	Trans Control Selector Lower Lever
5	Air Bag Clockspring Contact Assy	32	Pawl — Steering Column Lock (Shaft)	57	Screws
6	Upper Column Shroud	33	Spring — Steering Column Lock (Shaft)	58	Lower Bearing Housing Retainer
7	Lower Column Shroud	34	Plunger Trans Control Select	59	Lower Column Mounting Nuts
8	Shroud Retaining Screws	35	Spring — Trans Control Selector Return	60	Bracket
9	Ignition Lock Cylinder Assy	36	Shift Lever	61	Screw
10	Retainer	37	Shift Lever Pin	62	Lower Bearing Housing Retaining Screws
11	Bearing	38	Trans Selector Control Tube	63	Lower Column Bearing Sleeve
12	Gear — Steering Lock	39	Trans Gear Shift Tube Clamps	64	Lower Column Bearing
13	Turn Signal Cancelling Cam	40	Bushings	65	Tolerance Ring — Lower
14	Snap Ring	41	Screws	66	Sensor Ring
15	Spring — Upper Bearing	42	Shield	67	Spring
16	Sleeve	43	Trans Control Selector Position Insert	68	Bolt — Flange Yoke
16A	Ring	44	Screws	69	Steering Shaft U — Joint Assy
17	Bearing — Upper (Small)	45	Screws	70	Bolt
18	Lock Cylinder Housing	46	Parking Brake Vacuum Release Switch	71	Shift Cable Bracket
19	Multi — Function Switch	47	Tilt Pivot Screws	72	Shift Cable Bracket Mounting Screws
20	Screws	48	Spring — Steering Column Position Lock	73	Upper Column Mounting Nuts
21	Spring	49	Actuator Housing	74	Absorber — Steering Column Impact
22	Tilt Release Lever	50	Ignition Switch	75	Nuts
23	Tilt Actuator Lever	51	Screws	76	Shift Cable Assembly
24	Tilt Actuator Lever Pin	52	Pin — Pivot Lever	77	Bearing — Upper (Large)
25	Cam Steering Column Lock			78	Clip Wiring — Lower
26	Clip Wiring — Upper			79	Clip
27	Steering Shaft Assy			80	Solenoid and Bracket

FM6049200052000X

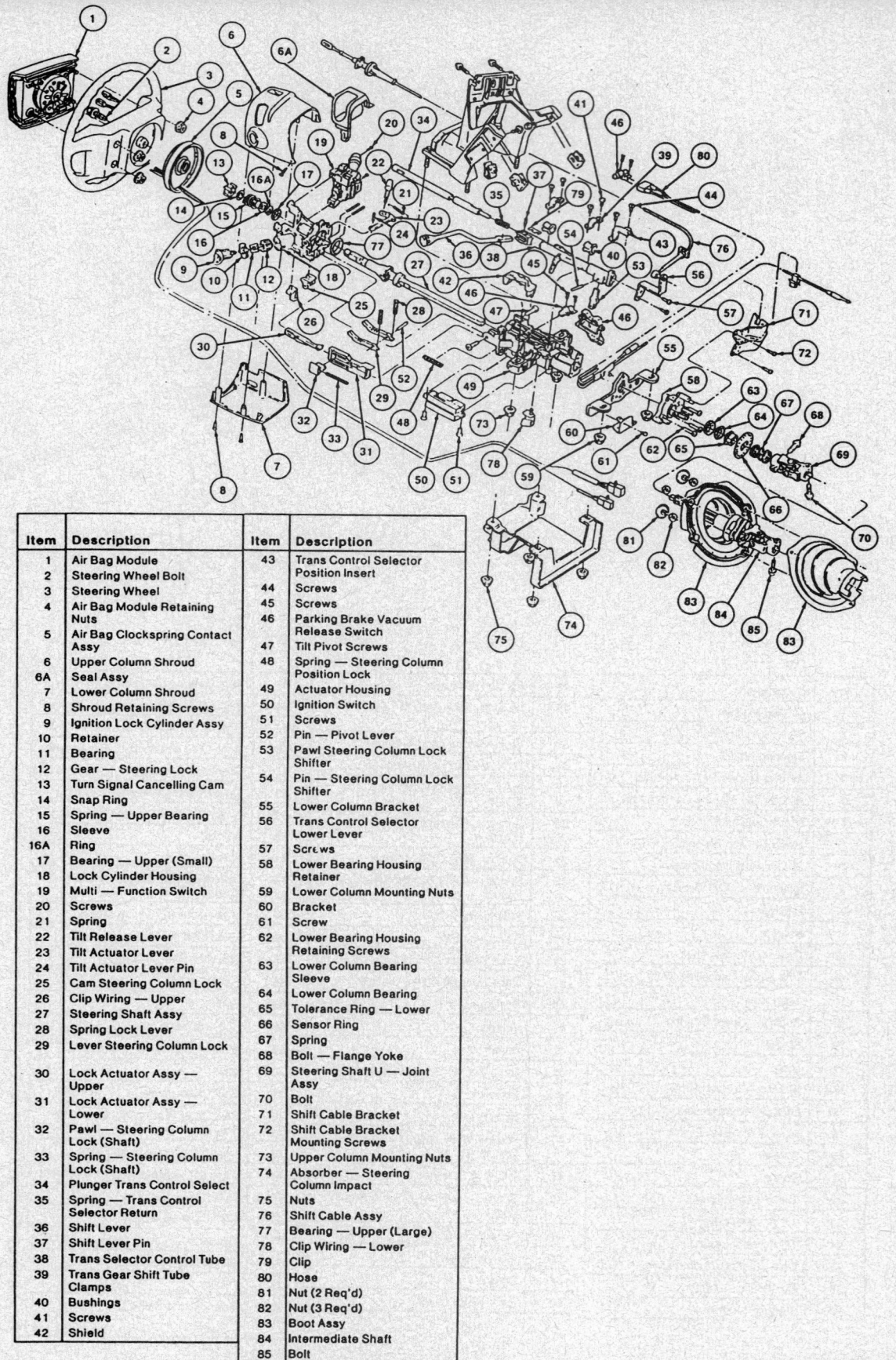

Item	Description	Item	Description
1	Air Bag Module	43	Trans Control Selector Position Insert
2	Steering Wheel Bolt	44	Screws
3	Steering Wheel	45	Screws
4	Air Bag Module Retaining Nuts	46	Parking Brake Vacuum Release Switch
5	Air Bag Clockspring Contact Assy	47	Tilt Pivot Screws
6	Upper Column Shroud	48	Spring — Steering Column Position Lock
6A	Seal Assy	49	Actuator Housing
7	Lower Column Shroud	50	Ignition Switch
8	Shroud Retaining Screws	51	Screws
9	Ignition Lock Cylinder Assy	52	Pin — Pivot Lever
10	Retainer	53	Pawl Steering Column Lock Shifter
11	Bearing	54	Pin — Steering Column Lock Shifter
12	Gear — Steering Lock	55	Lower Column Bracket
13	Turn Signal Cancelling Cam	56	Trans Control Selector Lower Lever
14	Snap Ring	57	Screws
15	Spring — Upper Bearing	58	Lower Bearing Housing Retainer
16	Sleeve	59	Lower Column Mounting Nuts
16A	Ring	60	Bracket
17	Bearing — Upper (Small)	61	Screw
18	Lock Cylinder Housing	62	Lower Bearing Housing Retaining Screws
19	Multi — Function Switch	63	Lower Column Bearing Sleeve
20	Screws	64	Lower Column Bearing
21	Spring	65	Tolerance Ring — Lower
22	Tilt Release Lever	66	Sensor Ring
23	Tilt Actuator Lever	67	Spring
24	Tilt Actuator Lever Pin	68	Bolt — Flange Yoke
25	Cam Steering Column Lock	69	Steering Shaft U — Joint Assy
26	Clip Wiring — Upper	70	Bolt
27	Steering Shaft Assy	71	Shift Cable Bracket
28	Spring Lock Lever	72	Shift Cable Bracket Mounting Screws
29	Lever Steering Column Lock	73	Upper Column Mounting Nuts
30	Lock Actuator Assy — Upper	74	Absorber — Steering Column Impact
31	Lock Actuator Assy — Lower	75	Nuts
32	Pawl — Steering Column Lock (Shaft)	76	Shift Cable Assy
33	Spring — Steering Column Lock (Shaft)	77	Bearing — Upper (Large)
34	Plunger Trans Control Select	78	Clip Wiring — Lower
35	Spring — Trans Control Selector Return	79	Clip
36	Shift Lever	80	Hose
37	Shift Lever Pin	81	Nut (2 Req'd)
38	Trans Selector Control Tube	82	Nut (3 Req'd)
39	Trans Gear Shift Tube Clamps	83	Boot Assy
40	Bushings	84	Intermediate Shaft
41	Screws	85	Bolt
42	Shield		

FM6049300053000X

Fig. 5 Exploded view of steering column. 1993 Continental & Sable & Taurus w/Column Shift

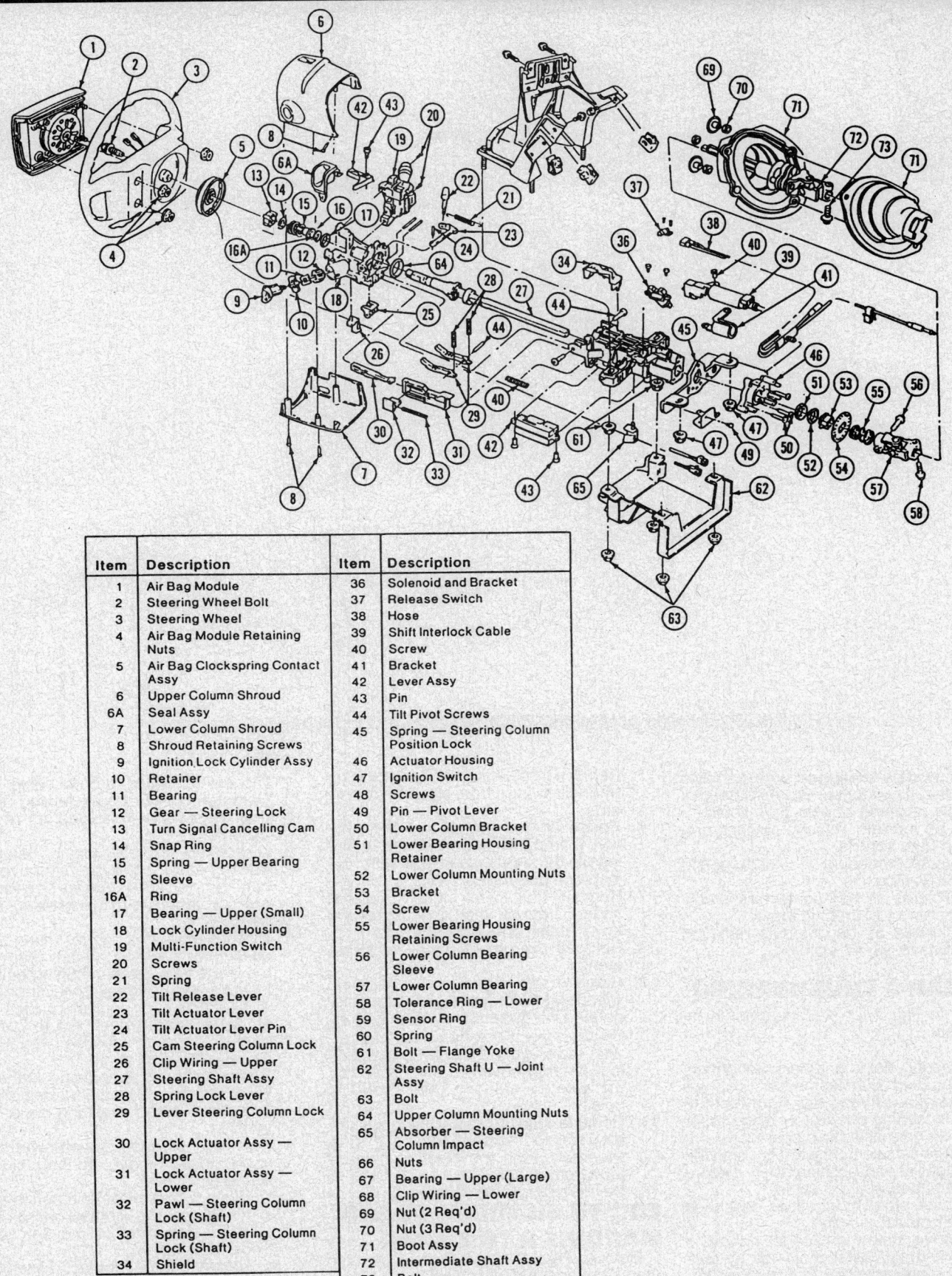

Item	Description	Item	Description
1	Air Bag Module	36	Solenoid and Bracket
2	Steering Wheel Bolt	37	Release Switch
3	Steering Wheel	38	Hose
4	Air Bag Module Retaining Nuts	39	Shift Interlock Cable
5	Air Bag Clockspring Contact Assy	40	Screw
		41	Bracket
6	Upper Column Shroud	42	Lever Assy
6A	Seal Assy	43	Pin
7	Lower Column Shroud	44	Tilt Pivot Screws
8	Shroud Retaining Screws	45	Spring — Steering Column Position Lock
9	Ignition Lock Cylinder Assy	46	Actuator Housing
10	Retainer	47	Ignition Switch
11	Bearing	48	Screws
12	Gear — Steering Lock	49	Pin — Pivot Lever
13	Turn Signal Cancelling Cam	50	Lower Column Bracket
14	Snap Ring	51	Lower Bearing Housing Retainer
15	Spring — Upper Bearing	52	Lower Column Mounting Nuts
16	Sleeve	53	Bracket
16A	Ring	54	Screw
17	Bearing — Upper (Small)	55	Lower Bearing Housing Retaining Screws
18	Lock Cylinder Housing	56	Lower Column Bearing Sleeve
19	Multi-Function Switch	57	Lower Column Bearing
20	Screws	58	Tolerance Ring — Lower
21	Spring	59	Sensor Ring
22	Tilt Release Lever	60	Spring
23	Tilt Actuator Lever	61	Bolt — Flange Yoke
24	Tilt Actuator Lever Pin	62	Steering Shaft U — Joint Assy
25	Cam Steering Column Lock		
26	Clip Wiring — Upper	63	Bolt
27	Steering Shaft Assy	64	Upper Column Mounting Nuts
28	Spring Lock Lever	65	Absorber — Steering Column Impact
29	Lever Steering Column Lock		
30	Lock Actuator Assy — Upper	66	Nuts
		67	Bearing — Upper (Large)
31	Lock Actuator Assy — Lower	68	Clip Wiring — Lower
32	Pawl — Steering Column Lock (Shaft)	69	Nut (2 Req'd)
		70	Nut (3 Req'd)
33	Spring — Steering Column Lock (Shaft)	71	Boot Assy
		72	Intermediate Shaft Assy
34	Shield	73	Bolt

FM60493000054000X

Fig. 6 Exploded view of steering column. 1993 Sable & Taurus w/console shift

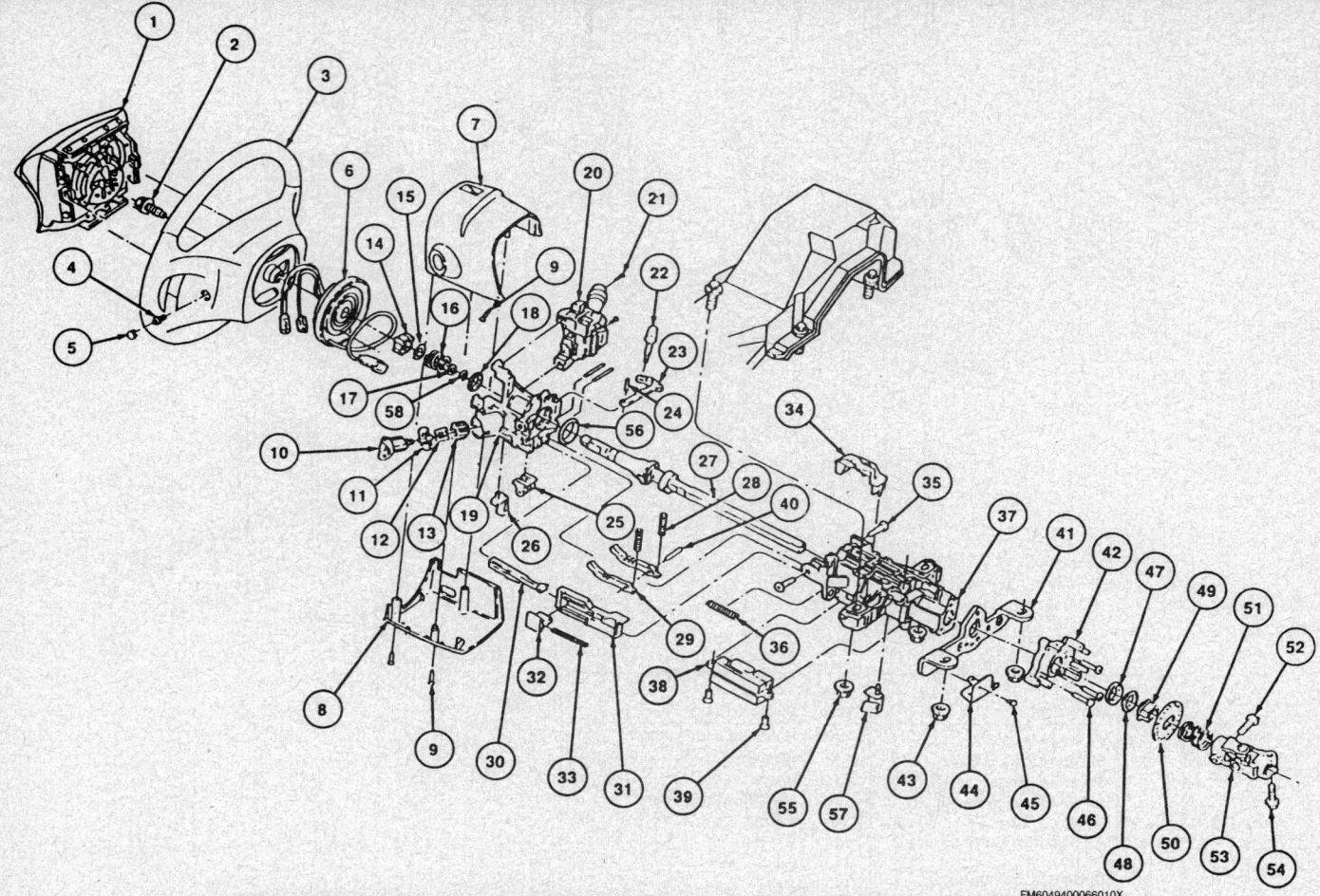

Fig. 7 Exploded view of steering column (Part 1 of 2). Cougar & Thunderbird

FM6049400066010X

20. **On models equipped with console shift,** remove four brake shift interlock cable retaining screws, then cable.
21. **On all models,** remove steering column from vehicle.
22. Reverse procedure to install, noting the following:
   a. **Torque** air bag contact assembly screws to 18–26 ft. lbs.
   b. **Torque** air bag module retaining nuts to 36–47 inch lbs.

COUGAR & THUNDERBIRD

Refer to **Fig. 7** for steering column replacement.

All steering column tube components are assembled with fasteners. They are designed with a thread locking system to prevent loosening due to vibrations associated with normal vehicle operation.
1. Ensure vehicle front wheels are in the straight-ahead position, then disconnect battery ground cable.
2. Remove steering wheel as described in "Electrical" section .
3. Remove instrument panel righthand and lefthand lower moldings by pulling up and snapping out of retainers.
4. Remove instrument panel lower trim cover, then the air bag sliding contact.

5. Remove tilt steering column lock lever by unscrewing it from steering column tube.
6. Rotate ignition switch to RUN position, then press ignition switch retaining pin through access hole with 1/8—inch drift and remove switch.
7. Remove four lower steering column shroud screws, then the upper and lower steering column shrouds.
8. Remove instrument panel reinforcement.
9. Remove turn signal and windshield wiper switch screws, then the turn signal and windshield and wiper switch.
10. Remove pinch bolt from steering column lower yoke, then, while supporting steering column tube assembly, the steering column tube assembly nuts.
11. Remove ignition/shifter interlock cable retaining screws and cable end assembly, then the steering column tube from vehicle.
12. Reverse procedure to install.

CROWN VICTORIA, GRAND MARQUIS & TOWN CAR

Refer to **Figs. 8 and 9** for steering column component.identification.

Ensure front wheels are in the straight ahead position.

1. Disconnect battery ground cable.
2. Remove four air bag retaining nuts, then lift module from steering wheel assembly.
3. Disconnect air bag wiring harness from air bag module, then remove air bag from vehicle. **Place air bag module on bench with pad facing upward.**
4. Disconnect speed control wiring harness from steering wheel, then remove steering wheel retaining bolt.
5. Install steering wheel puller tool No. T67 L-3600-A, or equivalent, then remove steering wheel. Route wiring harness through steering wheel as wheel is lifted off shaft.
6. Remove the righthand and lefthand lower moldings from instrument panel by pulling up and snapping out of retainers.
7. Remove instrument panel lower trim cover, then remove air bag clockspring as follows:
   a. Place two strips of tape horizontally across the contact assembly stator and rotor to prevent accidental rotation.
   b. Remove three contact assembly retaining screws, then pull contact assembly off steering column shaft.

Item	Description	Item	Description
1	Driver Side Air Bag Module	30	Steering Column Lock Actuator Assy — Upper
2	Steering Wheel Bolt	31	Steering Column Lock Lever Actuator
3	Steering Wheel	32	Steering Column Lock Pawl (Shaft)
4	Air Bag Module Retaining Screws (2 Req'd)	33	Steering Column Lock Spring (Shaft)
5	Trim Plug (2 Req'd)	34	Wiring Shield
6	Air Bag Sliding Contact	35	Tilt Pivot Screws
7	Upper Steering Column Shroud	36	Steering Column Position Spring
8	Lower Steering Column Shroud	37	Steering Actuator Housing
9	Shroud Retaining Screws	38	Ignition Switch
10	Ignition Switch Lock Cylinder Assy	39	Screws
11	Steering Column Upper Bearing Retainer	40	Steering Column Lock Actuator Lever Pin
12	Steering Column Lock Housing Bearing	41	Steering Column Instrument Panel Clamp
13	Steering Column Lock Gear	42	Steering Column Lower Bearing Retainer
14	Turn Indicator Cancel Cam	43	Lower Column Mounting Nuts
15	Snap Ring	44	Wire Connector Bracket
16	Steering Column Upper Bearing Spring	45	Screw
17	Steering Column Tube Bearing Sleeve (Upper)	46	Lower Bearing Housing Retaining Screws
18	Steering Column Tube Bearing (Lower)	47	Steering Column Tube Bearing Sleeve (Lower)
19	Lock Cylinder Housing	48	Steering Column Tube Bearing (Lower)
20	Turn Signal and Windshield Wiper Switch	49	Tolerance Ring — Lower
21	Screws	50	Suspension Height Sensor Control Ring
22	Tilt Steering Column Lock Lever	51	Steering Shaft Lower Bearing Spring
23	Steering Column Release Lever	52	Bolt — Flange Yoke
24	Steering Column Lock Actuator Lever Pin	53	Steering Column Lower Yoke
25	Steering Column Lock Cam	54	Bolt
26	Wiring Harness Retainer	55	Upper Column Mounting Nuts
27	Steering Gear Input Worm Gear and Rack	56	Steering Column Tube Bearing Upper (Large)
28	Steering Column Locking Lever Spring	57	Wiring Harness Retainer Lower
29	Steering Column Locking Lever Steering Column Lock Left Hand Lever	58	Steering Column Lower Bearing Tolerance Ring

FM6049400066020X

Fig. 7   Exploded view of steering column (Part 2 of 2). Cougar & Thunderbird

8. Remove tilt lever by unscrewing it from the column.
9. Rotate ignition lock cylinder to the Run position, then, using 1/8 inch pin punch, depress lock cylinder retaining pin through access hole and remove lock cylinder.
10. Remove four lower shroud retaining screws, then the column shrouds.
11. Remove two instrument panel reinforcement brace retaining bolts, then the reinforcement.
12. Remove steering column to parking brake control shake brace.
13. Disconnect gear position indicator cable from actuator housing.
14. Remove two multi-function switch retaining screws, then position switch aside.
15. Remove pinch bolt from steering column to extension shaft, then compress extension shaft toward engine and separate from column shaft U-joint.
16. Disconnect shift cable from selector lever pivot.
17. Remove shift cable and bracket from lower column mounting.
18. Support steering column assembly, then remove four column retaining nuts. Lower column, then disconnect vacuum hoses.
19. Remove steering column from vehicle.
20. Reverse procedure to install, noting the following:
   a. **Torque** air bag clockspring assembly retaining screws to 18-26 inch lbs.
   b. **Torque** U-joint pinch bolt to 26-41 ft. lbs.
   c. **Torque** air bag module retaining nuts to 3-4 ft. lbs.

ESCORT & TRACER

Refer to **Fig. 10** for replacement.
1. Remove steering wheel, then the turn signal and windshield wiper switch as described in "Electrical" section.
2. Disconnect ignition switch electrical connector.
3. Remove ignition/shifter interlock cable mounting bracket bolt, then position aside.
4. Remove four steering column upper mounting bracket bolts, then lower steering column.
5. Remove five floor opening cover nuts, then remove floor opening cover plate and steering column tube boot.

6. Remove intermediate shaft to pinion shaft bolt.
7. Remove two steering column support bracket nuts, then the steering column.
8. Reverse procedure to install. Ensure steering column upper mounting bracket bolts are tightened to specifications.

MARK VII

Refer to **Fig. 11** for steering column component identification.
1. Disconnect battery ground cable.
2. Center front wheels to the straight ahead position.
3. Remove four air bag module retaining nuts, then lift module off steering wheel.
4. Disconnect the air bag wiring harness connector from air bag module, then remove air bag module from vehicle. **Place air bag module face up with retaining studs downward touching bench.**
5. Disconnect speed control wire harness from steering wheel, then remove steering wheel retaining bolt. **Discard bolt.**

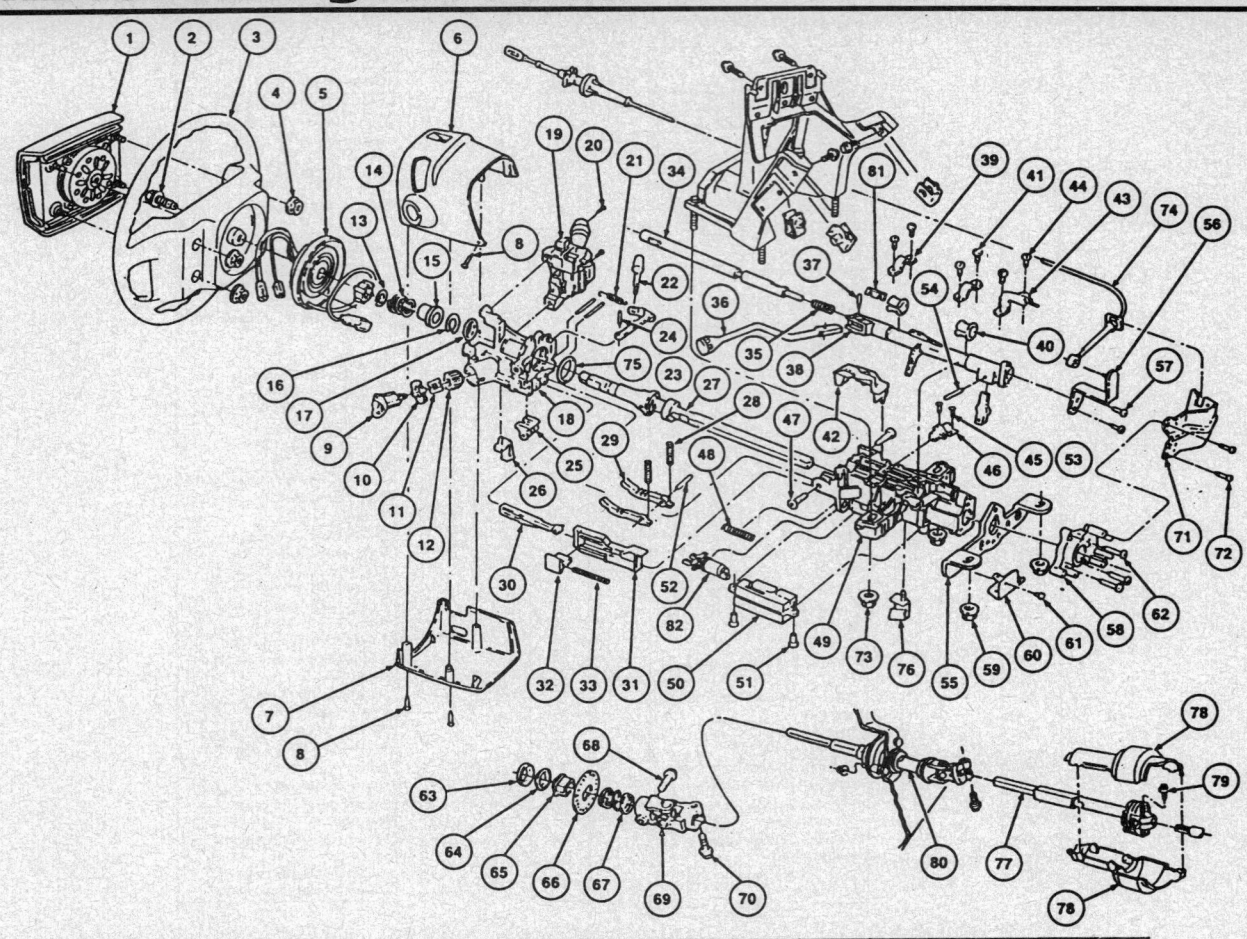

Item	Description				
1	Air Bag Module	28	Spring Lock Lever	56	Trans Control Selector Lower Lever
2	Steering Wheel Bolt	29	Lever Steering Column Lock	57	Screws
3	Steering Wheel	30	Lock Actuator Assy — Upper	58	Lower Bearing Housing Retainer
4	Air Bag Module Retaining Nuts	31	Lock Actuator Assy — Lower	59	Lower Column Mounting Nuts
5	Air Gag Clockspring Contact Assy	32	Pawl — Steering Column Lock (Shaft)	60	Bracket
6	Upper Column Shroud	33	Spring — Steering Column Lock (Shaft)	61	Screw
7	Lower Column Shroud	34	Plunger Trans Control Select	62	Lower Bearing Housing Retaining Screws
8	Shroud Retaining Screws	35	Spring — Trans Control Selector Return	63	Lower Column Bearing Sleeve
9	Ignition Lock Cylinder Assy	36	Shift Lever	64	Lower Column Bearing
10	Retainer	37	Shift Lever Pin	65	Tolerance Ring — Lower
11	Bearing	38	Trans Selector Control Tube	66	Sensor Ring
12	Gear — Steering Lock	39	Trans Gear Shift Tube Clamps	67	Spring
13	Turn Signal Cancelling Cam	40	Bushings	68	Screw — Flange Yoke
14	Snap Ring	41	Screws	69	Steering Shaft U — Joint Assy
15	Spring — Upper Bearing	42	Shield	70	Bolt
16	Ring	43	Trans Control Selector Position Insert	71	Shift Cable Bracket
16A	Sleeve	44	Screws	72	Shift Cable Bracket Mounting Screws
17	Bearing — Upper (Small)	45	Screws	73	Upper Column Mounting Nuts
18	Lock Cylinder Housing	46	Parking Brake Vacuum Release Switch	74	Shift Cable Assembly
19	Multi — Function Switch	47	Tilt Pivot Screws	75	Bearing Upper (Large)
20	Screws	48	Spring — Steering Column Position Lock	76	Clip Wiring Lower
21	Spring	49	Actuator Housing	77	Intermediate Shaft
22	Tilt Release Lever	50	Ignition Switch	78	Shield Assembly
23	Tilt Actuator Lever	51	Screws	79	Flange Bolt
24	Tilt Actuator Lever Pin	52	Pin — Pivot Lever	80	Upper Extension Shaft Assy.
25	Cam Steering Column Lock	53	Pawl Strg Col Lock Shifter	81	Clip
26	Clip Wiring — Upper			82	Solenoid and Bracket
27	Steering Shaft Assy				

FM60492000055000X

Fig. 8 Exploded view of steering column. 1992 Crown Victoria, Grand Marquis, & Town Car

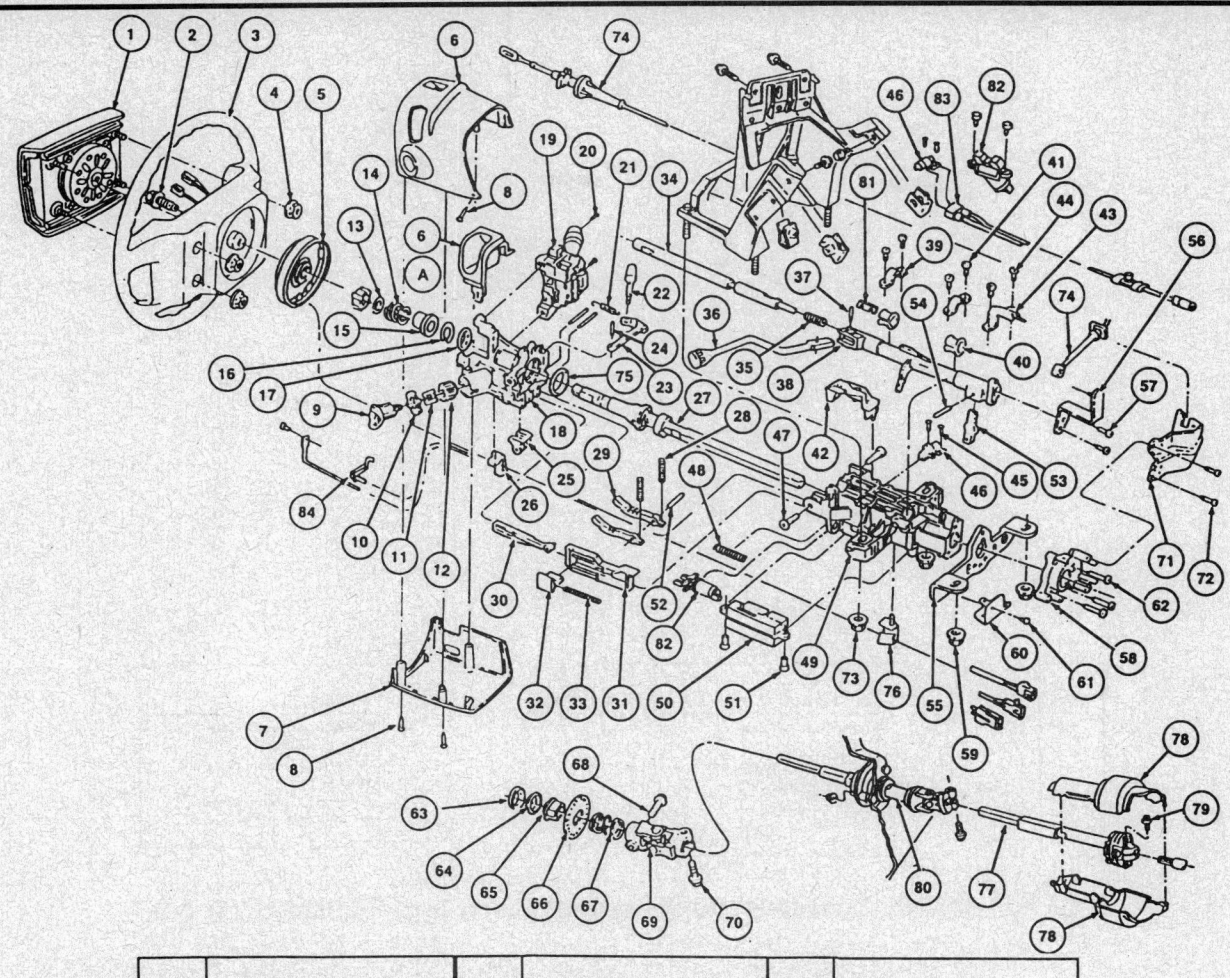

Item	Description	Item	Description	Item	Description
1	Air Bag Module	30	Lock Actuator Assy — Upper	56	Trans Control Selector Lower Lever
2	Steering Wheel Bolt	31	Lock Actuator Assy — Lower	57	Screws
3	Steering Wheel	32	Pawl — Steering Column Lock (Shaft)	58	Lower Bearing Housing Retainer
4	Air Bag Module Retaining Nuts	33	Spring — Steering Column Lock (Shaft)	59	Lower Column Mounting Nuts
5	Air Bag Clockspring Contact Assy	34	Plunger Trans Control Select	60	Bracket
6	Upper Column Shroud	35	Spring — Trans Control Selector Return	61	Screw
6A	Seal Assy	36	Shift Lever	62	Lower Bearing Housing Retaining Screws
7	Lower Column Shroud	37	Shift Lever Pin	63	Lower Column Bearing Sleeve
8	Shroud Retaining Screws	38	Trans Selector Control Tube	64	Lower Column Bearing
9	Ignition Lock Cylinder Assy	39	Trans Gear Shift Tube Clamps	65	Tolerance Ring — Lower
10	Retainer	40	Bushings	66	Sensor Ring
11	Bearing	41	Screws	67	Spring
12	Gear — Steering Lock	42	Shield	68	Screw — Flange Yoke
13	Turn Signal Cancelling Cam	43	Trans Control Selector Position Insert	69	Steering Shaft U — Joint Assy
14	Snap Ring	44	Screws	70	Bolt
15	Spring — Upper Bearing	45	Screws	71	Shift Cable Bracket
16	Ring	46	Parking Brake Vacuum Release Switch	72	Shift Cable Bracket Mounting Screws
16A	Sleeve	47	Tilt Pivot Screws	73	Upper Column Mounting Nuts
17	Bearing — Upper (Small)	48	Spring —Steering Column Position Lock	74	Shift Cable Assy
18	Lock Cylinder Housing	49	Actuator Housing	75	Bearing Upper (Large)
19	Multi-Function Switch	50	Ignition Switch	76	Clip Wiring — Lower
20	Screws	51	Screws	77	Intermediate Shaft
21	Spring	52	Pin — Pivot Lever	78	Shield Assy
22	Tilt Release Lever	53	Pawl Strg Col Lock Shifter	79	Flange Bolt
23	Tilt Actuator Lever	54	Pin — Steering Column Lock Shifter	80	Upper Extension Shaft Assy
24	Tilt Actuator Lever Pin	55	Lower Column Bracket	81	Clip
25	Cam Steering Column Lock			82	Solenoid and Bracket
26	Clip Wiring — Upper			83	Hose
27	Steering Shaft Assy			84	Anti-Theft Assy
28	Spring Lock Lever				
29	Lever Steering Column Lock				

FM6049300056000X

Fig. 9 Exploded view of steering column. 1993 Crown Victoria, Grand Marquis, & Town Car

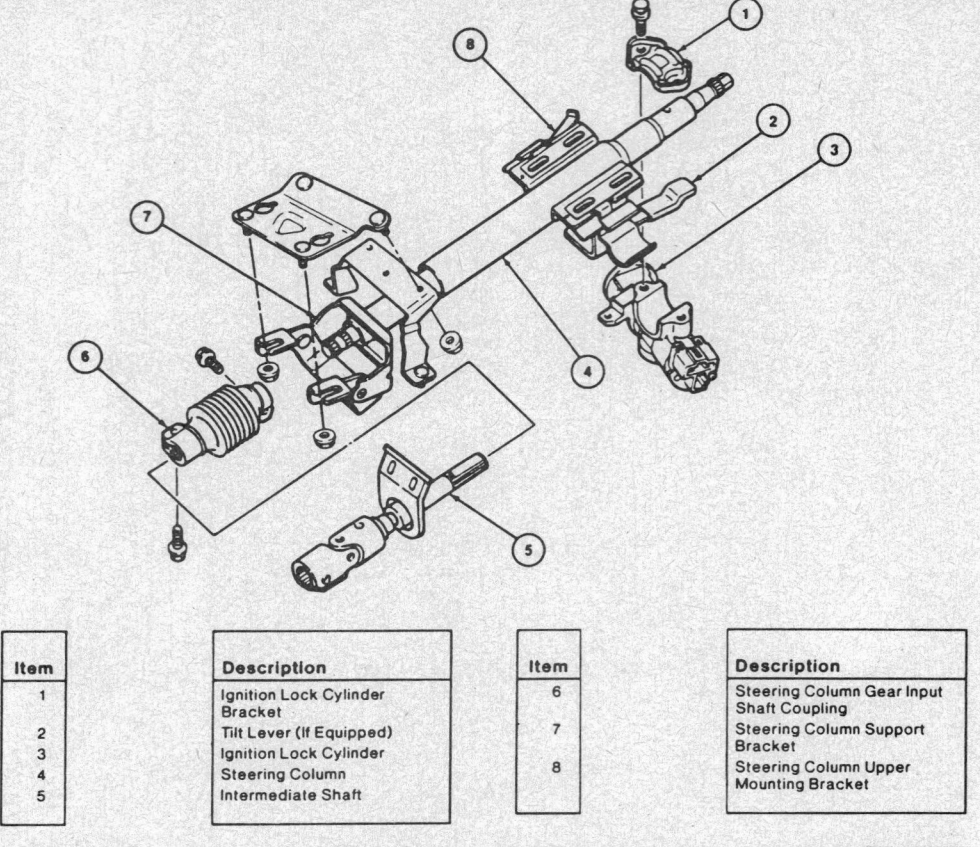

Item	Description	Item	Description
1	Ignition Lock Cylinder Bracket	6	Steering Column Gear Input Shaft Coupling
2	Tilt Lever (If Equipped)	7	Steering Column Support Bracket
3	Ignition Lock Cylinder	8	Steering Column Upper Mounting Bracket
4	Steering Column		
5	Intermediate Shaft		

FM6049400067000X

Fig. 10   Exploded view of steering column. Escort & Tracer

6. Install steering wheel puller tool No. T67L-3600-A, or equivalent, then remove steering wheel from column. **Ensure contact assembly wiring harness does not get caught on wheel assembly when lifting off shaft.**
7. Remove righthand and lefthand lower moldings from instrument panel by pulling up and snapping out of retainers.
8. Remove instrument panel lower trim cover.
9. Remove air bag clockspring contact assembly as follows:
   a. Apply two strips of tape across contact assembly stator and rotor to prevent accidental rotation.
   b. Remove three contact assembly retaining screws, then pull contact assembly off steering column shaft.
10. Remove tilt lever by unscrewing it from column.
11. Rotate ignition lock cylinder to Run position, then using a 1/8 inch pin punch, depress lock cylinder retaining pin through access hole and remove lock cylinder.
12. Remove four screws retaining the upper and lower column shrouds, then remove shrouds from steering column.

13. Remove instrument panel reinforcement.
14. Remove two interlock cable retaining screws, then cable from column.
15. Remove two multi-function switch retaining screws, then set multi-function switch aside.
16. Remove parking brake vacuum release assembly or disconnect vacuum hose at switch.
17. Remove pinch bolt from steering shaft flex coupling.
18. Remove interlock cable retaining screws, then cable end assembly.
19. While supporting column assembly, remove four column assembly retaining nuts.
20. Remove steering column from vehicle.
21. Reverse procedure to install, noting the following:
   a. **Torque** air bag clockspring assembly to 18–26 inch lbs.
   b. **Torque** New steering wheel retaining bolt to 23–33 ft. lbs.
   c. **Torque** air bag module retaining nuts to 36–47 inch lbs.

MARK VIII

Refer to **Fig. 12** for steering column component identification.

Removal

1. Ensure front wheels are in straight ahead position.
2. Remove steering wheel as described in "Electrical" section of "Lincoln" chapter.
3. Remove righthand and lefthand lower moldings from instrument panel by pulling up and snapping out of retainers.
4. Remove instrument panel lower trim cover.
5. Ensure steering column shaft alignment mark is at 12 o'clock position, then remove lower steering column shroud.
6. Disconnect clockspring assembly wire harness, then apply two strips of tape across clockspring assembly stator and rotor to prevent accidental rotation.
7. Remove clockspring assembly retaining screws and pull clockspring assembly off steering column shaft.
8. Remove tilt lever, then rotate ignition lock cylinder to RUN position. Depress retaining pin through access hole using 1/8 inch drift and remove lock cylinder.
9. Remove upper column shroud, then the instrument panel reinforcement.
10. Remove multi-function switch and set

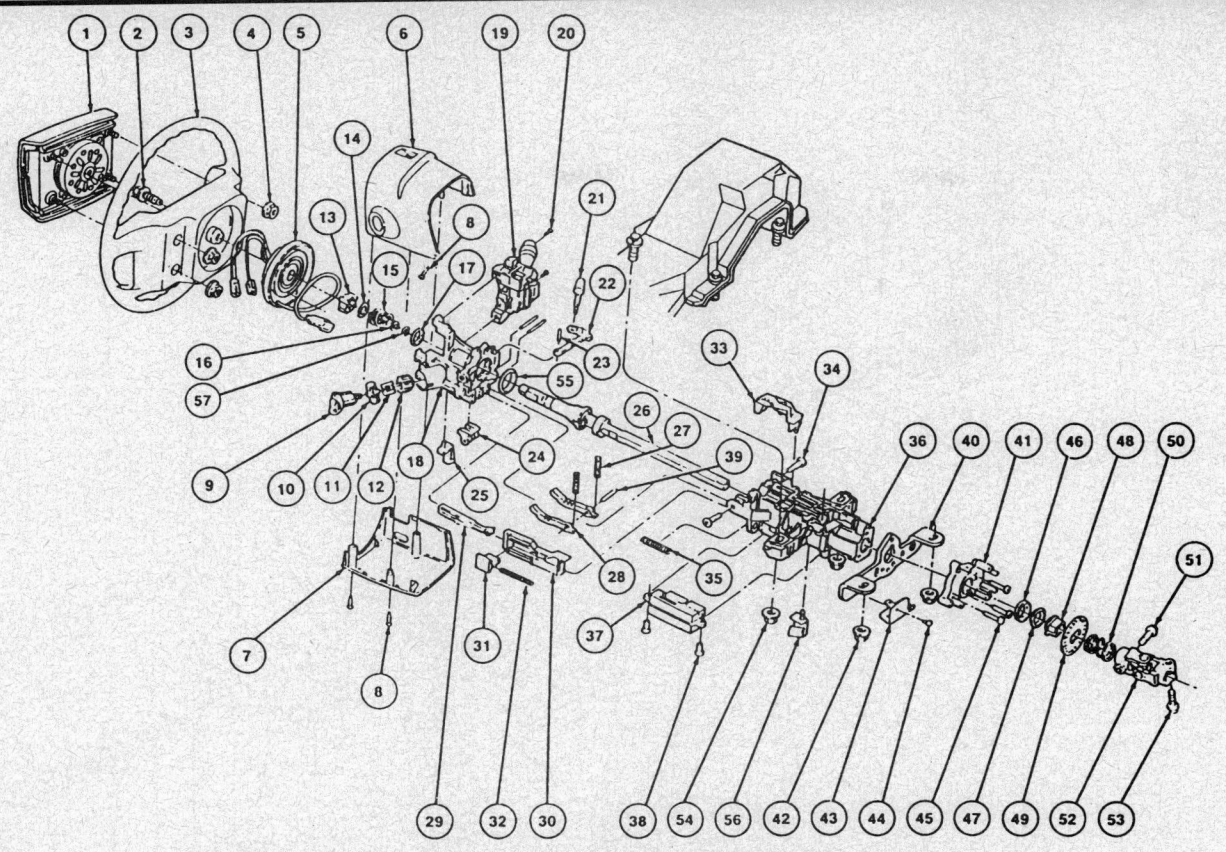

Item	Description	Item	Description
1	Air Bag Module	31	Pawl — Steering Column Lock (Shaft)
2	Steering Wheel Bolt	32	Spring — Steering Column Lock (Shaft)
3	Steering Wheel		
4	Air Bag Module Retaining Nuts	33	Shield
5	Air Bag Clockspring Contact Assy	34	Tilt Pivot Screws
6	Upper Column Shroud	35	Spring — Steering Column Position Lock
7	Lower Column Shroud		
8	Shroud Retaining Screws	36	Actuator Housing
9	Ignition Lock Cylinder Assy	37	Ignition Switch
10	Retainer	38	Screws
11	Bearing	39	Pin — Pivot Lever
12	Gear — Steering Lock	40	Lower Column Bracket
13	Turn Signal Cancelling Cam	41	Lower Bearing Housing Retainer
14	Snap Ring	42	Lower Column Mounting Nuts
15	Spring — Upper Bearing	43	Bracket
16	Sleeve	44	Screw
17	Bearing — Upper (Small)	45	Lower Bearing Housing Retaining Screws
18	Lock Cylinder Housing	46	Lower Column Bearing Sleeve
19	Multi-Function Switch	47	Lower Column Bearing
20	Screws	48	Tolerance Ring — Lower
21	Tilt Release Lever	49	Sensor Ring
22	Tilt Actuator Lever	50	Spring
23	Tilt Actuator Lever Pin	51	Bolt — Flange Yoke
24	Cam Steering Column Lock	52	Steering Shaft U — Joint Assy
25	Clip Wiring — Upper	53	Bolt
26	Steering Shaft Assy	54	Upper Column Mounting Nuts
27	Spring Lock Lever	55	Bearing — Upper (Large)
28	Lever Steering Column Lock	56	Clip Wiring — Lower
29	Lock Actuator Assy — Upper	57	Tolerance Ring
30	Lock Actuator Assy — Lower		

FM60492000057000X

Fig. 11   Exploded view of steering column. 1992 Mark VII

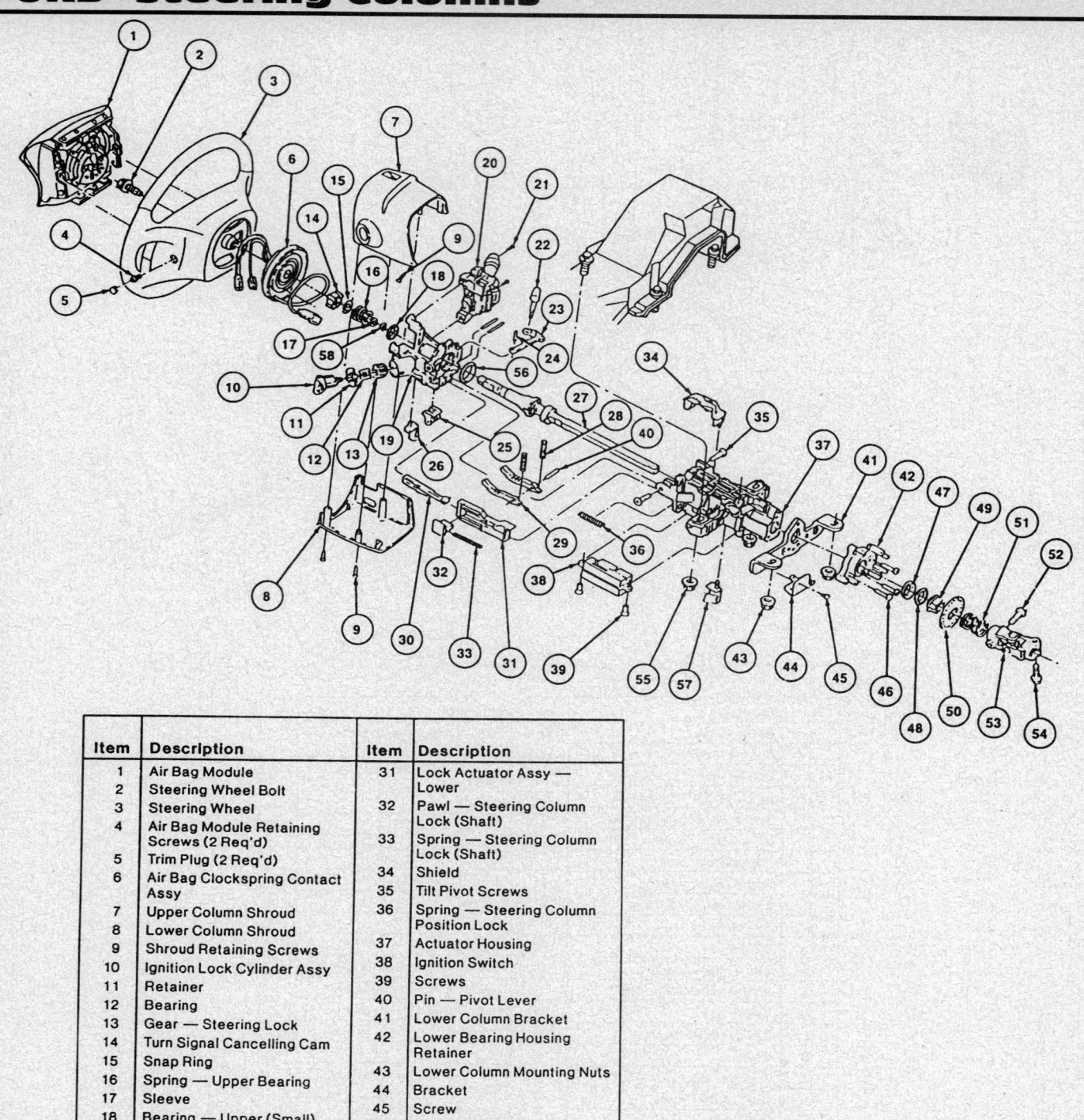

Item	Description	Item	Description
1	Air Bag Module	31	Lock Actuator Assy — Lower
2	Steering Wheel Bolt	32	Pawl — Steering Column Lock (Shaft)
3	Steering Wheel	33	Spring — Steering Column Lock (Shaft)
4	Air Bag Module Retaining Screws (2 Req'd)	34	Shield
5	Trim Plug (2 Req'd)	35	Tilt Pivot Screws
6	Air Bag Clockspring Contact Assy	36	Spring — Steering Column Position Lock
7	Upper Column Shroud	37	Actuator Housing
8	Lower Column Shroud	38	Ignition Switch
9	Shroud Retaining Screws	39	Screws
10	Ignition Lock Cylinder Assy	40	Pin — Pivot Lever
11	Retainer	41	Lower Column Bracket
12	Bearing	42	Lower Bearing Housing Retainer
13	Gear — Steering Lock	43	Lower Column Mounting Nuts
14	Turn Signal Cancelling Cam	44	Bracket
15	Snap Ring	45	Screw
16	Spring — Upper Bearing	46	Lower Bearing Housing Retaining Screws
17	Sleeve	47	Lower Column Bearing Sleeve
18	Bearing — Upper (Small)	48	Lower Column Bearing
19	Lock Cylinder Housing	49	Tolerance Ring — Lower
20	Multi-Function Switch	50	Sensor Ring
21	Screws	51	Spring
22	Tilt Release Lever	52	Bolt — Flange Yoke
23	Tilt Actuator Lever	53	Steering Shaft U-Joint Assy
24	Tilt Actuator Lever Pin	54	Bolt
25	Cam Steering Column Lock	55	Upper Column Mounting Nuts
26	Clip Wiring — Upper	56	Bearing — Upper (Large)
27	Steering Shaft Assy	57	Clip Wiring — Lower
28	Spring Lock Lever	58	Tolerance Ring
29	Lever Steering Column Lock		
30	Lock Actuator Assy — Upper		

Fig. 12 Exploded view of steering column. Mark VIII

FM6049100058000X

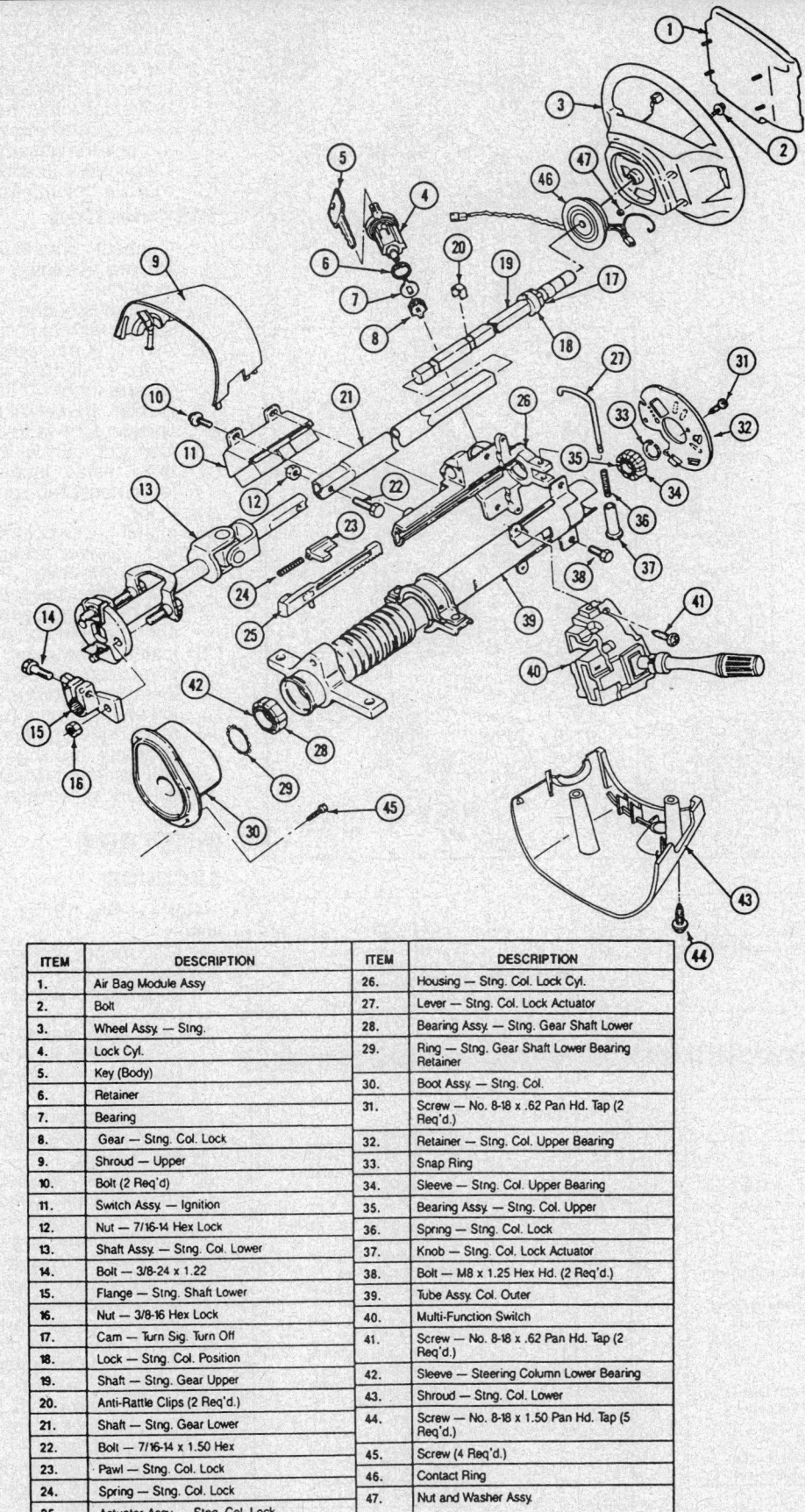

ITEM	DESCRIPTION	ITEM	DESCRIPTION
1.	Air Bag Module Assy.	26.	Housing — Stng. Col. Lock Cyl.
2.	Bolt	27.	Lever — Stng. Col. Lock Actuator
3.	Wheel Assy. — Stng.	28.	Bearing Assy. — Stng. Gear Shaft Lower
4.	Lock Cyl.	29.	Ring — Stng. Gear Shaft Lower Bearing Retainer
5.	Key (Body)	30.	Boot Assy. — Stng. Col.
6.	Retainer	31.	Screw — No. 8-18 x .62 Pan Hd. Tap (2 Req'd.)
7.	Bearing		
8.	Gear — Stng. Col. Lock	32.	Retainer — Stng. Col. Upper Bearing
9.	Shroud — Upper	33.	Snap Ring
10.	Bolt (2 Req'd)	34.	Sleeve — Stng. Col. Upper Bearing
11.	Switch Assy. — Ignition	35.	Bearing Assy. — Stng. Col. Upper
12.	Nut — 7/16-14 Hex Lock	36.	Spring — Stng. Col. Lock
13.	Shaft Assy. — Stng. Col. Lower	37.	Knob — Stng. Col. Lock Actuator
14.	Bolt — 3/8-24 x 1.22	38.	Bolt — M8 x 1.25 Hex Hd. (2 Req'd)
15.	Flange — Stng. Shaft Lower	39.	Tube Assy. Col. Outer
16.	Nut — 3/8-16 Hex Lock	40.	Multi-Function Switch
17.	Cam — Turn Sig. Turn Off	41.	Screw — No. 8-18 x .62 Pan Hd. Tap (2 Req'd.)
18.	Lock — Stng. Col. Position		
19.	Shaft — Stng. Gear Upper	42.	Sleeve — Steering Column Lower Bearing
20.	Anti-Rattle Clips (2 Req'd.)	43.	Shroud — Stng. Col. Lower
21.	Shaft — Stng. Gear Lower	44.	Screw — No. 8-18 x 1.50 Pan Hd. Tap (5 Req'd.)
22.	Bolt — 7/16-14 x 1.50 Hex		
23.	Pawl — Stng. Col. Lock	45.	Screw (4 Req'd.)
24.	Spring — Stng. Col. Lock	46.	Contact Ring
25.	Actuator Assy. — Stng. Col. Lock	47.	Nut and Washer Assy.

FM6049100059000X

Fig. 13 Exploded view of steering column. 1992—93 Mustang

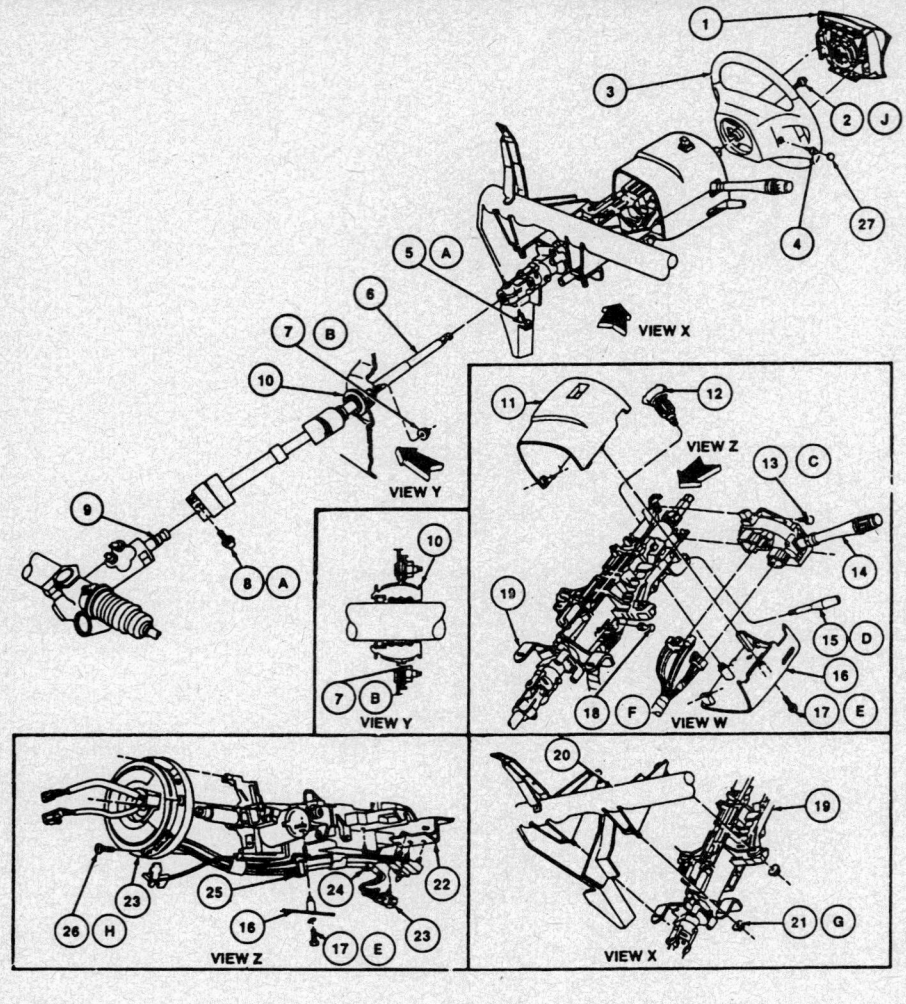

Item	Description	Item	Description
1	Driver Side Air Bag Module	5A	Bolt
2J	Bolt	6	Steering Column Gear Input Shaft Coupling
3	Steering Wheel		
4	Screw	7B	Nut

FM6049400068010X

Fig. 14 Exploded view of steering column (Part 1 of 2). 1994 Mustang

Item	Description	Item	Description
8A	Bolt	24	Wiring Harness Retainer
9	Steering Gear	25	Wiring Harness Retainer
10	Steering Column Tube Boot	26H	Bolt (3 Req'd)
11	Upper Steering Column Shroud	27	Plug
12	Lock Cylinder	A	Tighten to 40.3-54.7 N·m (29.7-40.3 Lb-Ft)
13C	Bolt (2 Req'd)	B	Tighten to 7.6-10.4 N·m (67.3-92.1 Lb-In)
14	Turn Signal and Windshield Wiper Switch	C	Tighten to 2.1-2.9 N·m (18.6-25.7 Lb-In)
15D	Tilt Wheel Handle and Shank	D	Tighten to 3.4-4.8 N·m (30.1-42.5 Lb-In)
16	Lower Steering Column Shroud	E	Tighten to 0.6-1.0 N·m (5.3-8.9 Lb-In)
17E	Bolt (4 Req'd)	F	Tighten to 0.9-1.3 N·m (8.0-11.5 Lb-In)
18F	Bolt	G	Tighten to 12.7-17.3 N·m (112.4-153.1 Lb-In)
19	Steering Column Tube		
20	Brake Pedal Support Bracket	H	Tighten to 2.1-2.9 N·m (18.6-25.7 Lb-In)
21G	Nut (4 Req'd)		
22	Wire Connector Bracket	J	Tighten to 34-46 N·m (25.0-34.0 Lb-Ft)
23	Air Bag Sliding Contact		

FM6049400068020X

Fig. 14 Exploded view of steering column (Part 2 of 2). 1994 Mustang

aside, then the parking brake vacuum release assembly or disconnect vacuum hoses at switch.

11. Remove pinch bolt from steering shaft universal joint, then the column assembly retaining nuts while supporting column assembly.
12. Disconnect interlock assembly, then remove column from vehicle.

Installation

1. Connect interlock assembly and **torque** retaining screws to 12-17 inch lbs.
2. Position steering column in place and secure with four nuts.
3. Align column lower universal joint to lower shaft, then install one bolt and **torque** to 29-41 ft. lbs.
4. Install multi-function switch and **torque** screws to 18-26 inch lbs.
5. Connect all electrical connectors, then install instrument panel reinforcement brace and **torque** to 25-38 ft. lbs.
6. Install upper column shroud, then the lock cylinder assembly.
7. Install tilt lever, then align air bag clockspring assembly to column shaft and mounting bosses and slide clockspring assembly onto shaft.
8. Install clockspring retaining screws and **torque** screws to 35-44 inch lbs.
9. Install lower column shroud, then the lower instrument panel cover.
10. Snap righthand and lefthand lower instrument moldings into place, then install steering wheel as described in "Electrical" section of "Lincoln" chapter.

MUSTANG

1992-93

Refer to **Fig. 13,** for component identification.

1. Disconnect battery ground cable.
2. Remove two nuts retaining flexible coupling to flange on steering input haft.
3. Disengage safety strap and bolt assembly from flexible coupling.
4. Remove steering column trim shrouds.
5. Remove steering column cover and hood release mechanism directly under column.
6. Disconnect all electrical connectors from column switches (turn signal, wash/wipe, ignition and key warning buzzer connecting wire).
7. Remove four screws retaining dust boot to dash panel.
8. Remove four nuts retaining column to brake pedal support.
9. Lower column to clear four mounting bolts, then pull column out, so U-joint assembly passes through clearance hole in dash panel.
10. Reverse procedure to install, noting the following:
    a. Engage safety strap and bolt assembly to flange on steering gear input shaft.
    b. Install two nuts retaining steering column lower shaft and U-joint assembly to flange on steering gear

input shaft. **Torque** nuts to 20-37 ft. lbs.

c. **Safety strap must be properly positioned to prevent metal to metal contact after tightening nuts.**

d. **Flexible coupling must not be distorted when nuts are tightened.**

e. Pry steering shaft up or down with suitable pry bar to achieve plus or minus 1/8 inch coupling insulator flatness.

1994

Refer to **Fig. 14** for relacement.

Do not remove steering wheel and driver side air bag module as an assembly unless the column is locked or the steering column gear input shaft coupling is secured to keep it from turning. This will avoid damage to the air bag sliding contact assembly.

1. Disconnect battery ground cable, then remove steering column gear input shaft coupling to steering column bolt.
2. Remove upper and lower steering column shrouds.
3. Remove hood release mechanism directly under steering column tube assembly, then disconnect all electrical connectors from steering column.
4. Loosen steering column tube boot to dash panel nuts.
5. Remove four steering column tube assembly to cross bar beam nuts, then lower steering column tube assembly enough to clear mounting bolts.
6. **On models equipped with automatic transmission,** remove ignition/shifter interlock cable.
7. **On all models,** pull steering column out.

PROBE

1. Ensure wheels are in straight ahead position.
2. Remove steering wheel as described in "Electrical" section of "Ford Probe" chapter.
3. Apply two strips of tape across clockspring and housing to prevent accidental rotation, **Fig. 15.**
4. Remove three clockspring assembly screws and pull clockspring assembly off steering column shaft.
5. Remove clockspring ground wire screw, then disconnect clockspring electrical connector and remove clockspring assembly.
6. Remove combination switch as described in "Electrical" section of "Ford Probe" chapter.
7. Loosen hood release cable nut, then remove hood release cable from lower instrument panel cover.
8. Remove lower instrument panel screw, then disconnect courtesy lamp electrical connector.
9. Remove lower instrument panel.
10. Disconnect all necessary electrical connectors.
11. **On models equipped with automatic transaxle,** disconnect shiftlock cable.

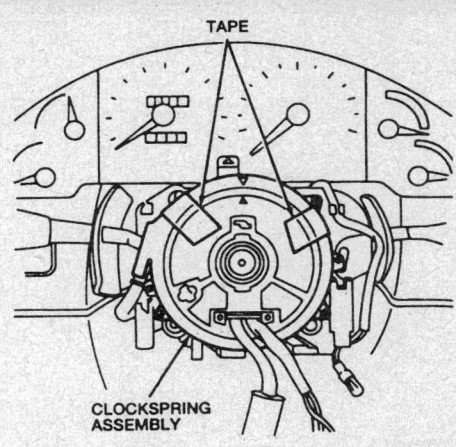

Fig. 15 Air bag clockspring securing. Probe

12. **On all models,** remove intermediate shaft bolt, two lower column bracket nuts, then the two upper column bracket bolts.
13. Remove steering column from vehicle.
14. Reverse procedure to install, noting the following:
    a. **Torque** intermediate shaft bolt to 13-20 ft. lbs.
    b. **Torque** lower column bracket nut and upper column bracket bolts to 12-17 ft. lbs.
    c. **Torque** clockspring screws to 18-26 inch lbs.

TEMPO & TOPAZ

Refer to **Fig. 16** for steering column component identification.

1. Disconnect battery ground cable.
2. Park vehicle with wheels in straight ahead position, then turn ignition switch to Lock position and rotate steering wheel approximately 16° counterclockwise until locked into position.
3. Remove steering column cover on lower portion of instrument panel to expose instrument panel reinforcement section.
4. Remove lower steering column shroud.
5. Loosen, but do not remove, two nuts and two bolts retaining steering column to support bracket, then remove upper shroud.
6. Disconnect all steering column electrical connections.
7. Loosen steering column to intermediate shaft clamp connection and remove bolt or nut.
8. Remove two nuts and two bolts attaching steering column to support bracket.
9. Pry steering column shaft open in area of clamp on each side of bolt groove, with steering column locked. Open enough to be able to disengage shafts with minimal effort. **Do not use excessive force.**
10. Inspect two steering column bracket clips for damage. If clips have been bent or excessively distorted, they must be replaced.

11. Engage lower steering shaft to intermediate shaft and hand start clamp and bolt nut.
12. Align two bolts on steering column support bracket assembly with outer tube mounting holes and hand start two nuts.
13. Check for presence of two clips on outer bracket. The clips must be present to ensure adequate performance of vital parts and systems.
14. Hand start two bolts through outer tube upper bracket and clip into support bracket nuts.
15. Connect all electrical connectors at steering column.
16. Install upper shroud.
17. **Torque** steering column mounting nut and bolts to 15-25 ft. lbs.
18. Unlock steering column and cycle steering wheel one turn left and one turn right to align intermediate shaft into column shaft. **Engine must be running on vehicles equipped with power steering.**
19. **Torque** steering shaft clamp nut to 20-30 Ft. lbs.
20. Install lower trim shroud with five attaching screws.
21. Install steering column cover on instrument panel.
22. Connect battery ground cable and check steering column for proper operation.

STEERING COLUMN SERVICE

EXCEPT ASPIRE, CAPRI, PROBE & 1994 MUSTANG

Refer to **Figs. 3 through 13 and 16** for steering column service.

CAPRI

Disassemble

1. Remove steering column as previously described, then place column in a soft-jawed vise.
2. Remove steering wheel as described in "Electrical" section of "Mercury Capri" chapter.

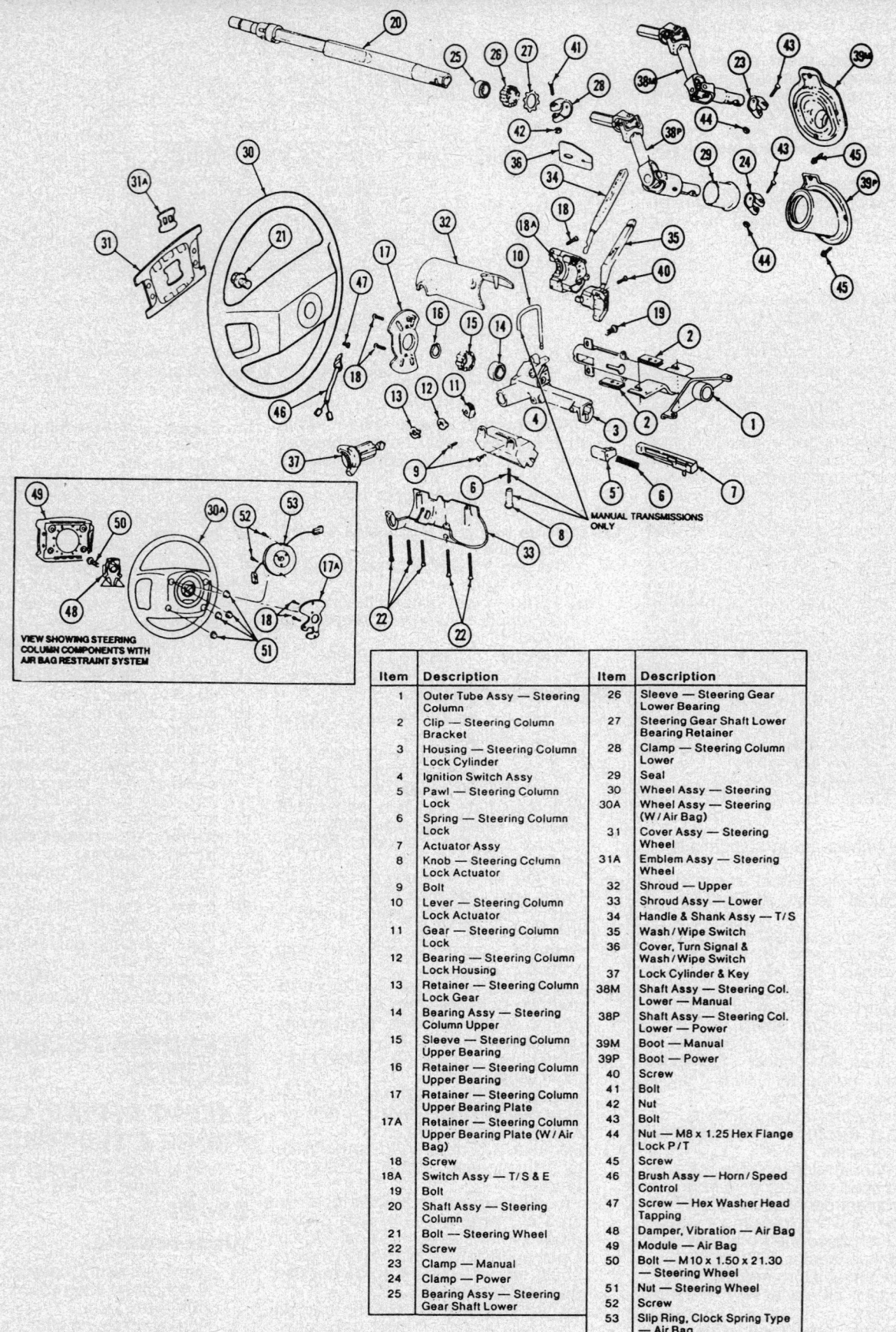

Fig. 16 Exploded view of steering column. Tempo & Topaz

FM60491000061000X

Item	Description	Item	Description
1	Outer Tube Assy — Steering Column	26	Sleeve — Steering Gear Lower Bearing
2	Clip — Steering Column Bracket	27	Steering Gear Shaft Lower Bearing Retainer
3	Housing — Steering Column Lock Cylinder	28	Clamp — Steering Column Lower
4	Ignition Switch Assy	29	Seal
5	Pawl — Steering Column Lock	30	Wheel Assy — Steering
6	Spring — Steering Column Lock	30A	Wheel Assy — Steering (W / Air Bag)
7	Actuator Assy	31	Cover Assy — Steering Wheel
8	Knob — Steering Column Lock Actuator	31A	Emblem Assy — Steering Wheel
9	Bolt	32	Shroud — Upper
10	Lever — Steering Column Lock Actuator	33	Shroud Assy — Lower
11	Gear — Steering Column Lock	34	Handle & Shank Assy — T/S
12	Bearing — Steering Column Lock Housing	35	Wash / Wipe Switch
13	Retainer — Steering Column Lock Gear	36	Cover, Turn Signal & Wash / Wipe Switch
14	Bearing Assy — Steering Column Upper	37	Lock Cylinder & Key
15	Sleeve — Steering Column Upper Bearing	38M	Shaft Assy — Steering Col. Lower — Manual
16	Retainer — Steering Column Upper Bearing	38P	Shaft Assy — Steering Col. Lower — Power
17	Retainer — Steering Column Upper Bearing Plate	39M	Boot — Manual
17A	Retainer — Steering Column Upper Bearing Plate (W / Air Bag)	39P	Boot — Power
		40	Screw
		41	Bolt
18	Screw	42	Nut
18A	Switch Assy — T/S & E	43	Bolt
19	Bolt	44	Nut — M8 x 1.25 Hex Flange Lock P/T
20	Shaft Assy — Steering Column	45	Screw
21	Bolt — Steering Wheel	46	Brush Assy — Horn / Speed Control
22	Screw	47	Screw — Hex Washer Head Tapping
23	Clamp — Manual	48	Damper, Vibration — Air Bag
24	Clamp — Power	49	Module — Air Bag
25	Bearing Assy — Steering Gear Shaft Lower	50	Bolt — M10 x 1.50 x 21.30 — Steering Wheel
		51	Nut — Steering Wheel
		52	Screw
		53	Slip Ring, Clock Spring Type — Air Bag

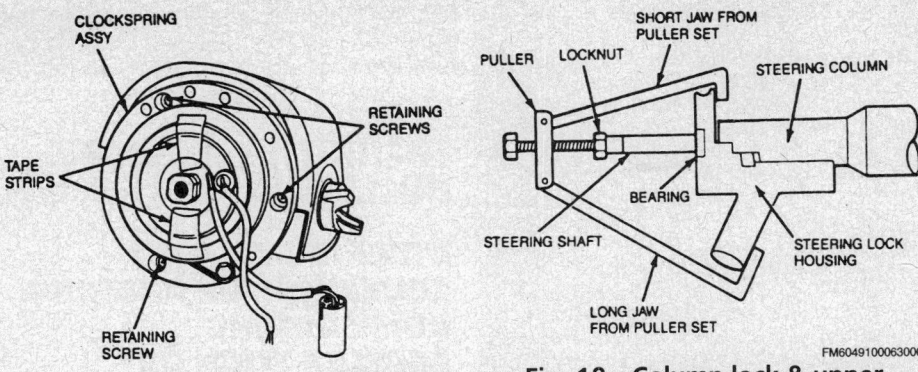

Fig. 17 Air bag clockspring securing. Capri

Fig. 18 Column lock & upper bearing assembly removal. Capri

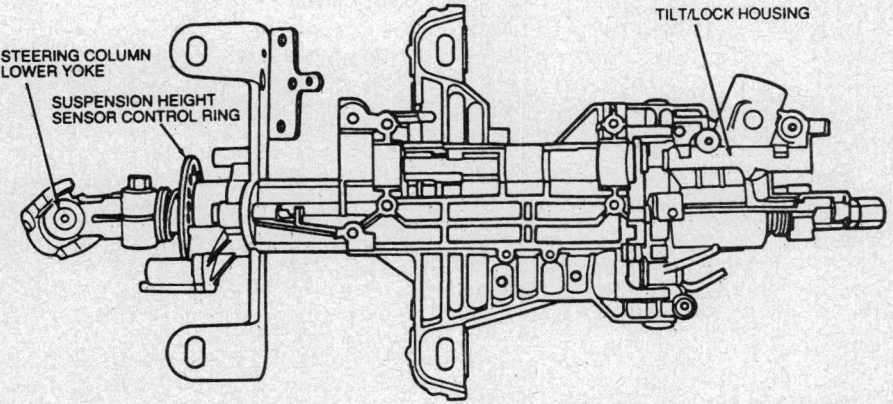

Fig. 19 Steering column components. 1994 Mustang

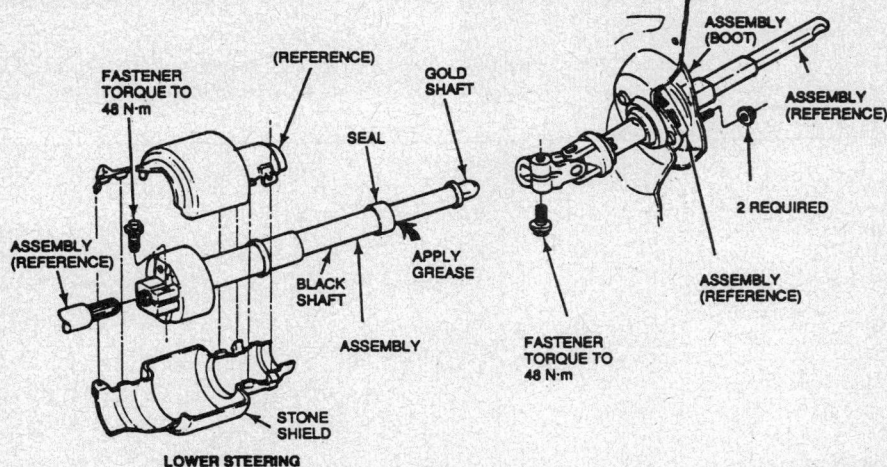

Fig. 20 Steering shaft & seal lubrication. 1992–93 Grand Marquis & Town Car

3. Place two pieces of tape on clockspring as shown in **Fig. 17**, to prevent rotation or damage to clockspring.
4. Remove clockspring, then with ignition key installed, rotate tumbler assembly to Run position while pushing tumbler release pin using a 1/8 inch drift and remove tumbler assembly.
5. Remove upper column shroud, then the key warning sensor.
6. Remove bearing retaining plate, then the snap ring and discard.

7. Remove multi-function switch, then the column lock and upper bearing assembly using a puller as shown in **Fig. 18**. If steering shaft shear pins break during housing and bearing removal, entire shaft and column must be replaced. To determine if pins have sheared, measure steering shaft from top end of shaft to center of U-joint bearing. Measurement should be 24.80-24.88 inches. If less than specified, pins have

sheared.

Assemble

1. Install steering column lock and upper bearing assembly and **torque** bolts to 12-2- ft. lbs.
2. Prick punch steering column upper shaft serration diameter enough to ensure an interference fit between bearing inner race and steering column upper shaft.
3. Position bearing and insulator on steering column upper shaft, then work bearing and insulator as far down steering column upper shaft as possible.
4. Place a 1½ inch piece of pipe with a ¾ inch inside diameter over end of steering column upper shaft and install steering wheel retaining bolt with a flat washer. Tighten steering wheel bolt until bearing is seated, then remove bolt and washer.
5. Install new snap ring, then the multi-function switch.
6. Install bearing retaining plate, then the key warning sensor.
7. Install upper column shroud, then the tumbler assembly by turning tumbler and pressing retaining pin. Ensure tumbler operates properly.
8. Install clockspring assembly, then remove tape strips.
9. Install steering wheel as described in "Electrical" section of "Mercury Capri" chapter.
10. Ensure curl strap is secured by retaining clips, then install steering column as previously described.

ASPIRE & PROBE

The steering column is serviced as a unit. If service other than the air bag clockspring, combination switch or ignition switch assembly is required, Steering column must be replaced.

1994 MUSTANG

Disassemble

1. Remove steering column tube as described under "Steering Column, Replace."
2. Remove steering column lower yoke, steering column upper bearing spring, suspension height sensor control ring and steering column upper bearing tolerance ring, **Fig. 19.**
3. Remove turn indicator cancel cam, pushing up with flat-bladed screwdriver. Note direction of flush surface.
4. Remove ignition switch, then the steering column bearing retainer and spring.
5. Remove steel steering column upper bearing tolerance ring and steering column tube bearing sleeve, then the plastic steering column upper bearing retainer from ignition switch bore.
6. Remove metal steering column lock housing bearing from ignition switch bore, then the steering column lock gear.
7. Remove two pivot bolts, then the lock cylinder housing. **Use caution. Steering column position spring will release when bolts are removed.**

8. Remove steering gear input worm gear and rack from steering column tube assembly

9. Remove steering column lock lever actuator and steering actuator housing.

10. Remove lower steering column tube bearing and steering column lower bearing retainer.

11. Use drift to remove tilt position lever, then remove steering column lock left hand lever and steering column locking lever springs.

12.

Assemble

1. Install steering gear input worm gear and rack into steering actuator housing.

2. Install lower steering column tube bearing and steering column instrument panel clamp. Tighten to specifications.

3. Install suspension height sensor control ring, steering column upper bearing tolerance ring, steering column upper bearing spring and steering column lower yoke to steering gear input worm gear and rack. Tighten to specifications.

4. Position steering column lock lever actuator, steering actuator housing in lock cylinder housing, then spray actuators with multi-purpose grease part No. D7AZ-19584-AA or equivalent.

5. Position actuator cam in lock cylinder housing and install cam pivot pin with small hammer. Tap pin in until flush with lock cylinder housing.

6. Install one steering column locking lever spring and righthand steering column locking lever with steering column lock actuator lever pin.

7. Tap steering column lock actuator lever pin into place while driving out drift.

8. Support steering actuator housing in vise and drive steering column lock actuator lever pin flush with steering actuator housing.

9. Place two nuts or spacers to hold steering column lock lefthand lever/righthand steering column locking lever away from steering actuator housing.

10. Lube pivot bolts with multi-purpose grease part No. DOAZ-19584-AA or equivalent, then position steering column position spring on lock cylinder housing and install lock cylinder housing and pivot bolts. Tighten pivot bolts to specifications.

11. Install steel steering column upper bearing tolerance ring and steering column tube bearing sleeve over steering column.

12. Install steering column upper bearing spring and new steering column upper bearing retainer on top side of steering column upper bearing spring using 3/4—inch by 2/3—inch PVC pipe.

13. Install turn indicator cancel cam, flush surface facing up.

14. Install ignition switch, then align pin from ignition switch with slot in lock/column assembly and position slot in lock/column assembly with index mark on casting. Tighten screws to specifications.

15. Install steering column lock gear, then coat lock gear with multi-purpose grease part No. DOAZ-19584-AA or equivalent.

16. Install metal steering column lock housing bearing, then coat lock gear with multi-purpose grease part No. DOAZ-19584-AA or equivalent.

17. Install steering column upper bearing retainer.

18. Install steering column tube as described under "Steering Column, Replace."

TECHNICAL SERVICE BULLETINS

STEERING COLUMN SQUEAKING OR RUBBING NOISE DURING ACCELERATION OR BRAKING

1992—93 Grand Marquis & Town Car

A squeaking or rubbing noise in the steering column during acceleration or braking may be caused by the steering shaft rubbing on the shaft seal. Lubricate shaft and seal assembly as follows:

1. Lock steering column in straight ahead position, then remove plastic stone shield, **Fig. 20**.

2. Remove lower steering column shaft from vehicle, as described under "Steering Column, Replace," then pull back rubber seal cap located on black tube, **Fig. 20**.

3. Using multipurpose grease spray, insert spray nozzle extension between gold shaft and black tube, then apply grease.

4. Pull rubber seal back into original position and stroke gold shaft until it slides freely.

5. Install shaft into vehicle as described under "Steering Column, Replace."

6. Install stone shield.

TIGHTENING SPECIFICATIONS

Model	Component	Torque/Ft. Lbs.
Aspire	Air Bag Sliding Contact Screws	18-26 ①
	Lower Steering Column Mounting Bracket Nuts	13-20
	Lower Steering Column Shaft Lower Bolt	13-20
	Lower Steering Column Shaft Upper Bolt	13-20
	Steering Column Gear Input Shaft Bolt	13-20
	Steering Gear Bolts	27-38
	Upper Steering Column Mounting Bracket Bolts	12-17
Capri	Ignition Switch & Lock Shield Bolts & Nut	11-14
	Lower Column Nuts	14-19
	Universal Pinch Bolts	14-19
	Upper Bolts	17-22
Continental, Sable & Taurus	Air Bag Contact Assembly Screws	18-26
	Air Bag Module Nuts	36-47
Cougar & Thunderbird	Clockspring Assembly Screw	18-26 ①
	Column Lower Mounting Bracket Bolt	5-8
	Ignition Switch Screw	5-8
	Interlock Cable Screws	12-17 ①
	Intermediate Shaft To Flex Coupling Bolt	30-42
	Intermediate Shaft To U-Joint Bolt	30-42
	Lock Housing Pivot Bolt	14-20
	Lower Column Bearing Bolt	5-8
	Shift Control Tube Screw	5-8
	Steering Column Boot	43-60
	Steering Column Mounting Nut	9-14
	Steering Shaft Yoke Coupling Screw	31-41
	Tilt Lever	28-44 ①
Crown Victoria, Grand Marquis & Town Car	Air Back Clockspring Assembly Screws	18-26 ①
	Air Bag Module Nuts	3-4
	U-Joint Pinch Bolt	26-41

TIGHTENING SPECIFICATIONS—Continued

Model	Component	Torque/Ft. Lbs.
Escort & Tracer	Ignition/Shifter Interlock Cable Mounting Bracket Bolt	35-53 ①
	Intermediate Shaft To Pinion Shaft Bolt	30-37
	Steering Column Gear Input Shaft Coupling To Intermediate Shaft Bolt	13-20
	Steering Column Shaft To Steering Column Gear Input Shaft Coupling Bolt	30-37
	Steering Column Upper Mounting Bracket Bolts	80-124 ①
Mark VII	Air Bag Clockspring Assembly	18-26 ①
	Air Bag Module Nuts	36-47
	Steering Wheel Bolt (New)	23-33
Mark VIII	Interlock Assembly Screws	12-17 ①
	Column Lower Universal Joint To Lower Shaft Bolt	29-41
	Multi-Function Switch Screws	18-26 ①
	Instrument Panel Reinforcement Brace	25-38
	Clockspring Screws	35-44
Mustang	Cross Bar Beam To Column Collar Nuts ③	22-30
	Ignition/Shifter Interlock Cable Screws ③	10-13 ①
	Ignition Switch Screws ③	5-8
	Lock Cylinder Housing Pivot Bolts ③	14-20
	Lower Steering Column Tube Bearing & Steering Column Instrument Panel Clamp Screws ③	5-8
	Steering Column Gear Input Shaft Coupling To Steering Column Bolt ③	30-40
	Steering Column Lower Shaft & U-Joint Assembly To Steering Gear Input Shaft Flange ②	20-37
	Steering Column Lower Yoke Bolt ③	31-42
Probe	Clockspring Screws	18-26
	Intermediate Shaft Bolt	13-20
	Lower Column Bracket Nut	12-17
	Upper Column Bracket Bolts	12-17
Tempo & Topaz	Steering Column Mounting Nuts & Bolts	15-25
	Steering Shaft Clamp Nut	20-30

①—Inch lbs.
② 1992—93.
③ 1994.

MANUAL STEERING GEARS

TABLE OF CONTENTS

Aspire & Festiva Rack & Pinion

INDEX

TROUBLESHOOTING

STEERING FEELS HEAVY W/VEHICLE RAISED

1. Poor lubrication, foreign material in mechanism, damaged or binding ball joint.
2. Improper steering gear preload.
3. Faulty steering gear.
4. Faulty steering shaft joint.
5. Worn or cracked steering gear bushings.
6. Faulty suspension component.

STEERING WHEEL PULLS

1. Faulty steering linkage.
2. Faulty wheel or tire.
3. Faulty in brake system.
4. Faulty suspension component.
5. Uneven tire wear.
6. Tire inflation incorrect.
7. Fatigued front coil springs.

INSTABILITY WHEN DRIVING

1. Worn or damaged steering joints.
2. Improper steering gear preload.
3. Damaged steering linkage.
4. Damaged wheel or tire.
5. Faulty suspension component.

UNSTABLE STEERING

1. Faulty steering gear.
2. Faulty steering joints.
3. Faulty steering linkage.

EXCESSIVE STEERING WHEEL PLAY

1. Worn steering gear.
2. Worn or damaged steering joints.
3. Loose steering gear mounting bolts.

POOR STEERING WHEEL RETURN

1. Damaged or binding steering joints.
2. Improper steering gear preload.
3. Faulty wheel or tire.
4. Faulty suspension component.

STEERING WHEEL VIBRATES

1. Damaged steering linkage.
2. Loose steering gear mounting bolts.
3. Damaged or binding steering joints.
4. Worn or faulty front wheel bearing.
5. Faulty wheel or tire.
6. Faulty suspension component.

ABNORMAL NOISE

1. Loose steering gear mounting bolt.
2. Faulty steering gear.
3. Obstruction near steering column.
4. Loose steering linkage.
5. Worn steering joints.

EXCESSIVE STEERING EFFORT

1. Tire under inflation.
2. Excessive uneven tire wear.
3. Insufficient lubrication or steering gear housing bellows damage, allowing entry of foreign matter.
4. Abnormal wear, damage or seizure of front wheel spindle connecting rod or end.
5. Steering gear damage.
6. Steering column gear input shaft coupling binding.
7. Front suspension lower arm ball joint friction excessive.
8. Steering gear preload incorrect.
9. Steering gear insulator worn or damaged.
10. No lubricant in steering gear housing.

ADJUSTMENTS

RACK PRELOAD/SUPPORT YOKE

Festiva

1. Loosen locknut.
2. Install Yoke Adjustment tool No. T90P-3504-JH or equivalent, **torque** yoke plug to 8.7 inch lbs., then loosen bolt 10–40°.
3. Using Pinion Shaft tool No. T86P-3504-K or equivalent, measure pinion torque, 9–11.5 inch lbs. should be indicated at neutral position ±90°, 14.7 inch lbs. or less should be indicated in any other position.
4. If pinion torque is not as specified, turn adjusting bolt to correct, then tighten adjusting bolt locknut.

Aspire

1. Remove steering gear.
2. Loosen yoke plug, then **torque** yoke plug to 22–30 inch lbs.
3. Use spring scale tool No. T74P-3504-Y or equivalent, to measure force needed to turn steering wheel input worm gear 180° from steering gear rack center position, **Fig. 1**.
4. Adjust steering gear input worm gear to position where most turning force was needed.
5. **Torque** yoke plug to 48 inch lbs., then back it off 5–35°.
6. Install yoke locking nut, **Fig. 2**, and **torque** to 29–36 ft. lbs.
7. Install steering gear.

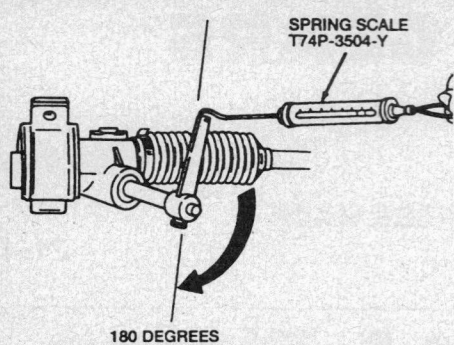

Fig. 1 Rack preload/support yoke adjustment. Aspire

FM6039400028000X

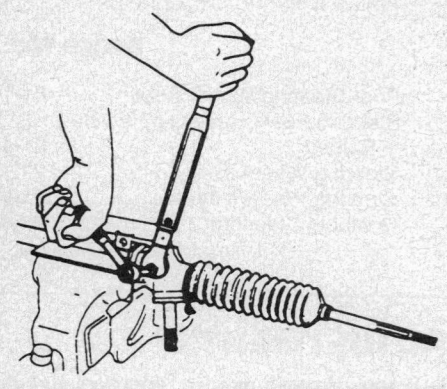

Fig. 2 Yoke locknut installation. Aspire

FM6039400029000X

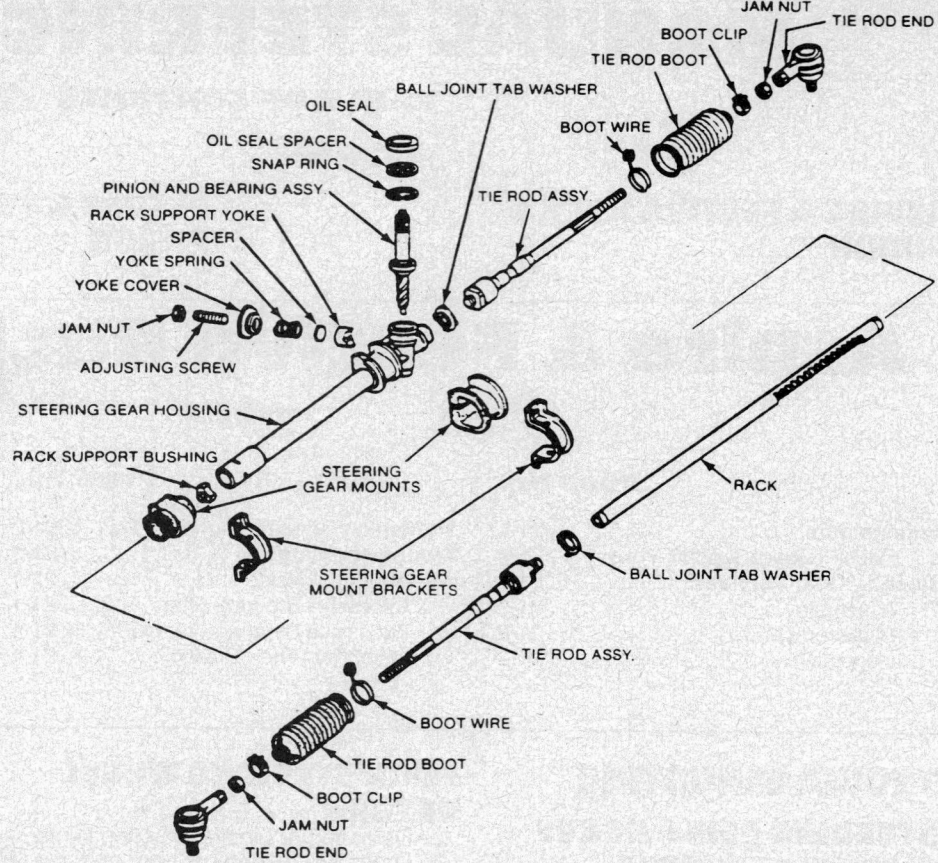

Fig. 3 Exploded view of steering gear assembly

FM6039100016000X

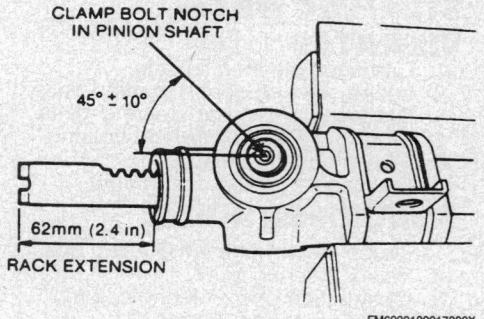

Fig. 4 Rack & pinion/bearing assembly installation

FM6039100017000X

STEERING GEAR SERVICE

DISASSEMBLE

1. Remove mount brackets and rubber mounts, then position steering gear in suitable soft jaw vise.
2. Mark position of tie rod ends in relation to tie rods, then remove tie rod ends and boots.
3. Disengage tab washers from ball joints using suitable tool, extend rack from either side of housing, then remove tie rods from rack.
4. Remove rack preload adjusting screw and jam nut from yoke cover, **Fig. 3.**
5. Remove cover and yoke spring from housing, then the spacer and yoke.
6. Carefully pry pinion oil seal from housing, then remove seal spacer, snap ring and pinion and bearing assembly.
7. Remove rack from pinion side of housing. **If rack is removed through right side (bushing end) of housing, damage to bushing may result.**
8. If pinion lower bearing is to be replaced, remove it at this time using suitable slide hammer type puller.
9. Press the three rack support bushing lock tabs inward, then remove bushing from right side of housing using puller mentioned in previous step.

INSPECTION

1. Inspect rack and pinion gear teeth for abnormal wear, and steering gear housing for cracks or damage. Replace components as necessary.
2. Position rack in V blocks, then check runout in center portion of rack using suitable dial indicator. If runout exceeds .012 inch for Festiva or .0039 inch for Aspire, replace rack and pinion gear.
3. Rotate pinion bearings and check for looseness or rough operation. If upper bearing requires replacement, replace bearing and pinion gear as an assembly.
4. Check fit of rack support bushing on rack for looseness or abnormal wear. Replace bushing as necessary.
5. Check tie rod ball joints and tie rod ends for free flexing without excessive looseness. Replace joints and tie rod ends as required.
6. Check tie rods for bending and boots for cuts, nicks or abrasions. Replace parts as necessary.

ASSEMBLE

1. Lubricate rack and pinion teeth, pinion bearings, housing, pinion oil seal lips, rack support yoke and bushing and rack using lithium-based greased. **Ensure rack vent holes remain open and are not clogged with grease after lubrication.**
2. Install rack support bushing into right end of housing, engaging lock tabs with housing slots.
3. If lower pinion bearing requires replacement, install it at this time into housing using suitable bushing installer.
4. Install rack through left side of housing, ensuring rack teeth face pinion bore. When properly positioned, left side of rack should extend approximately 2.4 inches from end of housing, **Fig. 4.**
5. Install pinion and upper bearing assembly into housing. When bearing is fully seated, pinion notch for steering column universal joint clamp bolt should face forward 35°-55° as seen from top end of pinion shaft when rack is centered, **Fig. 4.**
6. Install pinion bearing snap ring with

beveled side facing upward, then the seal spacer tabbed side down. Ensure tab is positioned in snap ring gap.

7. Wrap pinion shaft teeth with suitable tape to prevent damage to oil seal lip, then drive seal into housing using suitable tool.

8. Place new ball joint tab washers on rack ends, then install tie rods onto rack and tighten to specifications.

9. Using a suitable punch, stake tab washer lips into notches on rack, then bend washer tabs against flats on ball joints.

10. Install boots and tie rod ends.

11. Install rack support yoke, spacer and yoke spring into housing. Ensure spacer is positioned with raised center facing outward.

12. Apply sealant to yoke cover threads, then install cover and tighten to specifications.

13. Check and adjust rack yoke preload adjustment as outlined under "Adjustments, Rack Preload Support Yoke."

TIGHTENING SPECIFICATIONS

Year	Component	Torque/ Ft. Lbs.
ASPIRE		
1994	Ball Joints	8-9
	Front Wheel Spindle Connecting Rod	25-36
	Front Wheel Spindle Connecting Rod End Nut	31-42
	Steering Column Gear Input Shaft Coupling Bolt	13-20
	Steering Gear Bolts	27-38
	Wheel Hub Bolts	65-87
	Yoke Locking Nut	29-36
FESTIVA		
1992-93	Ball Joints	43-58
	Steering Gear	23-34
	Steering Rack Support Cover	29-43
	Steering Rack Support Cover Adjusting Screw	8.8 ①
	Support Yoke Locknut	29-36
	Tie Rod Jam Nut	7.4-11
	Tie Rod End Stud Nut	26-30

①—Inch lbs.

Escort & Tracer Rack & Pinion

INDEX

DESCRIPTION

The manual rack and pinion steering gear is sealed against entry of water and dirt by boots at each end of the steering gear housing and at the pinion shaft. The steering gear is lubricated at assembly and must be removed and disassembled if lubrication is needed. The rack is positioned and guided in the housing by a bushing at the right end, and a support yoke holding it in engagement with the pinion at the left end. The support yoke is spring loaded against the rack and a yoke plug adjusting bolt and locknut keep the rack fully engaged with the pinion under load. Rubber mounts at each end of the steering gear housing cushion the steering gear mount to minimize vibration.

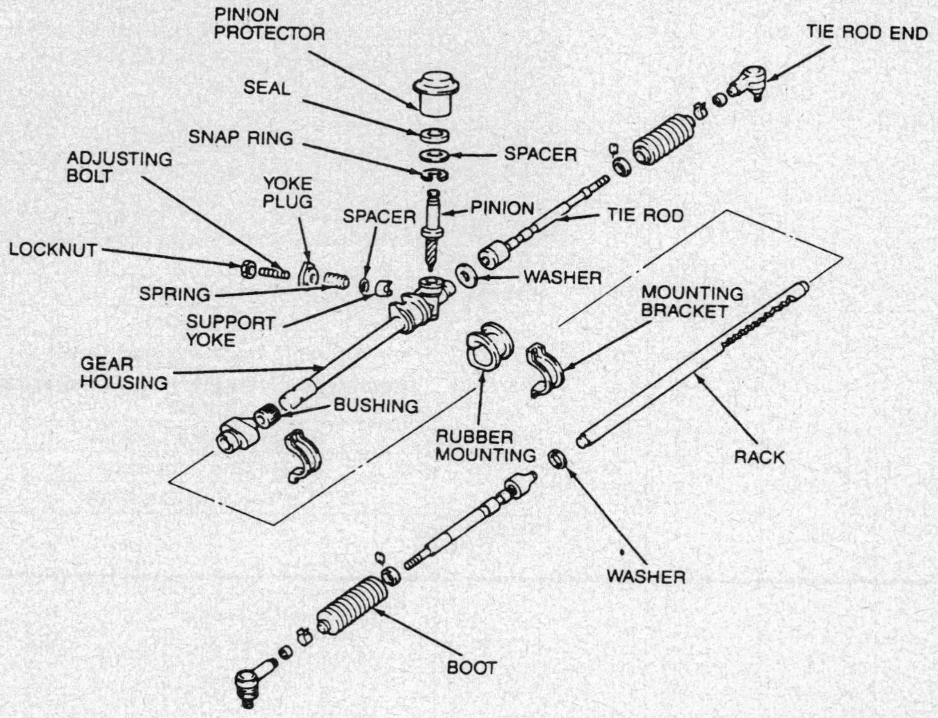

Fig. 1 Exploded view of manual rack & pinion

FM6039100018000X

TROUBLESHOOTING

STEERING FEELS HEAVY w/VEHICLE RAISED

1. Poor lubrication, foreign material in mechanism, damaged or binding ball joint.
2. Improper steering gear preload.
3. Faulty steering gear.
4. Faulty steering shaft joint.
5. Worn or cracked steering gear bushings.
6. Faulty suspension component.

STEERING WHEEL PULLS

1. Faulty steering linkage.
2. Faulty wheel or tire.
3. Faulty in brake system.
4. Faulty suspension component.

INSTABILITY WHEN DRIVING

1. Worn or damaged steering joints.
2. Improper steering gear preload.
3. Damaged steering linkage.
4. Damaged wheel or tire.
5. Faulty suspension component.

UNSTABLE STEERING

1. Faulty steering gear.
2. Faulty steering joints.
3. Faulty steering linkage.

EXCESSIVE STEERING WHEEL PLAY

1. Worn steering gear.
2. Worn or damaged steering joints.
3. Loose steering gear mounting bolts.

POOR STEERING WHEEL RETURN

1. Damaged or binding steering joints.
2. Improper steering gear preload.
3. Faulty wheel or tire.
4. Faulty suspension component.

STEERING WHEEL VIBRATES

1. Damaged steering linkage.
2. Loose steering gear mounting bolts.
3. Damaged or binding steering joints.

4. Worn or faulty front wheel bearing.
5. Faulty wheel or tire.
6. Faulty suspension component.

ABNORMAL NOISE

1. Loose steering gear mounting bolt.
2. Faulty steering gear.
3. Obstruction near steering column.
4. Loose steering linkage.
5. Worn steering joints.

ADJUSTMENTS

RACK PRELOAD/SUPPORT YOKE

1. Loosen locknut.
2. Install Yoke Adjustment tool No. T90P-3504-JH or equivalent, **torque**

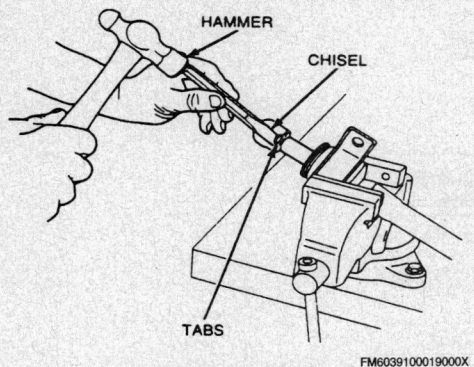

Fig. 2   Tie rod removal

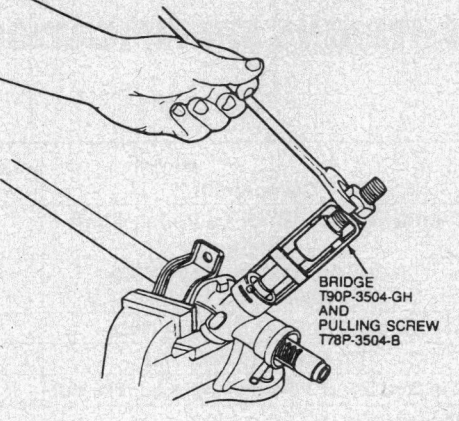

Fig. 3   Pinion & bearing removal

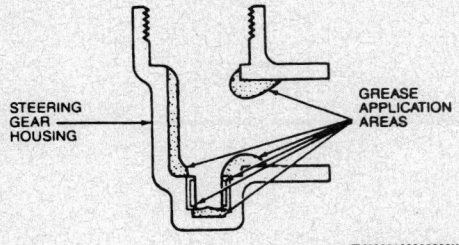

Fig. 5   Steering gear housing lubricant points

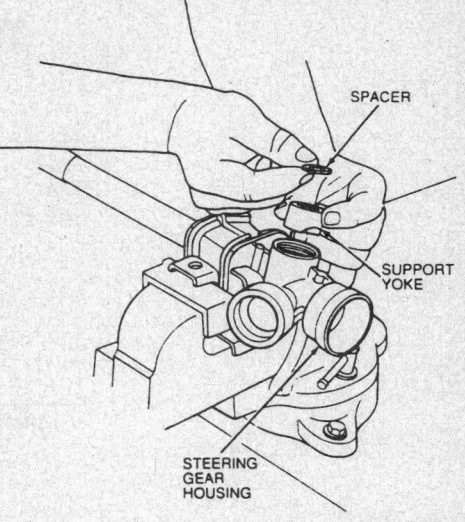

Fig. 4   Spacer & support yoke removal

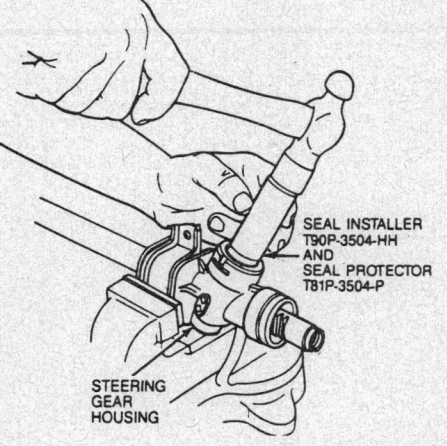

Fig. 6   Pinion oil seal installation

yoke plug to 8.7 inch lbs., then loosen bolt 10–40°.
3. Using Pinion Shaft tool No. T86P-3504-K or equivalent, measure pinion torque, 9–12 inch lbs. should be indicated at neutral position ±90°, 14.7 inch lbs. or less should be indicated in any other position.
4. If pinion torque is not as specified, turn adjusting bolt to correct, then tighten adjusting bolt locknut.

STEERING GEAR SERVICE

DISASSEMBLE

1. Place alignment marks on tie rod and tie rod end, then remove end.
2. Remove tie rod boot small clips **Fig. 1**, then remove boot wire at steering gear housing.
3. Slide boot off tie rods.
4. Using suitable hammer and cold chisel, **Fig. 2**, straighten tie rod to rack tabs.
5. Unscrew tie rod from rack, then remove rods and washers.
6. Remove rack mount brackets and bushings as required.
7. Remove pinion protector, then using suitable screwdriver or seal remover, remove pinion oil seal from shaft. **Do not score pinion shaft.**
8. Remove pinion oil seal spacer, then pinion bearing snap ring.
9. Using Bridge tool No. T90P-3504-GH and Pulling Screw tool No. T78P-

3504-B or equivalents, **Fig. 3**, remove pinion and bearing assembly from housing.
10. Remove locknut, adjusting bolt, yoke plug and spring.
11. Remove spacer and yoke support, **Fig. 4.**
12. Pull rack out left side of housing to remove. **If rack is remove through rack bushing at right side of housing, bushing damage may result.**
13. At steering gear housing, depress bushing locking tabs.
14. Remove rack support bushing from right side of steering gear.
15. Lower pinion bearing is not serviceable, if damaged, replace rack housing.

ASSEMBLE

1. Lubricate rack teeth, pinion bearing and housing, **Fig. 5,** with appropriate grease.
2. Lubricate pinion oil seal lips, rack support yoke and rack. **Do not plug rack vent holes.**

3. Using suitable grease, lubricate rack support bushing, then install bushing to right side of housing engaging bushing tabs to housing slots.
4. If replacing pinion bearing, install new bearing with suitable tool, bearing may be started with a pinion as alignment tool but cannot be seated with pinion. **Do not strike pinion with hammer.**
5. Install rack through LH side of housing, with teeth facing pinion bore.
6. Install pinion and bearing to housing.
7. Install pinion bearing snap ring with beveled side up (toward oil seal), then oil seal tab spacer tab side down, locating tab in snap ring.
8. Using Seal Installer tool No. T90P-3504-HH and tool No. T81P-3504-P or equivalents, **Fig. 6**, install oil seal.
9. Install washers and tie rod to rack, then bend tabs downward.
10. Install boots and tie rod ends.
11. Center rack ensuring tie rods are equally extended.
12. Lubricate rack support yoke, then install to housing.
13. Install spacer and yoke spring.
14. Apply sealant to yoke plug threads, then install plug, adjusting nut and locknut to housing.
15. Adjust rack preload as outlined in "Adjustments, Rack Preload/Support Yoke."

TIGHTENING SPECIFICATIONS

Year	Component	Torque/Ft. Lbs.
1992–94	Intermediate Shaft To Pinion Shaft Bolts	13–20
	Rack Preload/Support Yoke Adjustment Bolt	8.7 ①
	Steering Gear Bracket Nuts	27–38
	Tie Rod End Jam Nut	25–29
	Tie Rod Stud To Steering Knuckle Nut	31–42

① —Inch lbs.

POWER STEERING

NOTE: On Air Bag Equipped Models, Refer To Air Bag System Precautions Located In The Front Of This Manual For System Disarming & Arming Procedures.

TABLE OF CONTENTS

Power Steering Pressure Specifications

Year	Vehicle	Engine	Minimum Flow ① ②	Minimum Relief Pressure, psi	Maximum Relief Pressure, psi	Pump Model ③	Maximum Free Flow @ 1500 RPM ①
1992	Continental	3.8L	1.5	1300	1480	HBC-KH	2.95
	Cougar/Thunderbird	3.8L ④	1.25	1200	1380	HBC-JW	2.6
		3.8L ⑤	1.4	1200	1380	HBC-JV	3.0 ⑥
		5.0L ④	1.3	1200	1380	HBC-KF	2.6
		5.0L ⑩	1.4	1200	1380	HBC-KG	3.1 ⑥
	Crown Victoria	4.6L	1.5	1200	1380	HBD-AA	3.4 ⑥
	Escort/Tracer	1.8L	—	1067	—	—	—
	Escort	1.9L	.85	1100	1200	—	2.2
	Festiva	1.3L	—	—	—	—	—
	Grand Marquis	4.6L	1.5	1200	1380	HBD-AA	3.4 ⑥
	Mark VII	5.0L ⑨	1.6	1300	1480	HBC-KH	2.95
	Mustang	2.3L	2.2	950	1130	HBC-KA	2.6
		5.0L	2.2	1050	1230	HBC-KC	2.6
	Probe	All	—	1066	1138	—	—
	Sable/Taurus	3.0L	.9	1400	1530	HBC-KC	2.6
		3.8L	.9	1400	1530	HBC-KC	2.6
	Taurus SHO	3.0L	.9	1400	1530	—	2.6
	Tempo/Topaz	2.3L	.85	1200	1380	—	2.2
		3.0L	.66	1280	1380	—	2.4
	Town Car	4.6L	1.5	1200	1380	HBD-AA	3.4 ⑥
1993	Continental	3.8L	1.5	1300	1480	HBC-KH	2.95
	Cougar/Thunderbir	3.8L ④	1.25	1200	1380	HBC-JW	2.6
		3.8L ⑤	1.4	1200	1380	HBC-JV	3.0 ⑥
		5.0L ④	1.3	1200	1380	HBC-KF	2.6
		5.0L ⑩	1.4	1200	1380	HBC-KG	3.1 ⑥
	Crown Victoria	4.6L	1.5	1200	1380	HBD-AA	3.4 ⑥

POWER STEERING PRESSURE SPECIFICATIONS –Continued

Year	Vehicle	Engine	Minimum Flow ① ②	Minimum Relief Pressure, psi	Maximum Relief Pressure, psi	Pump Model ③	Maximum Free Flow @ 1500 RPM ①
1993 —Cont'd	Escort/Tracer	1.8L	—	—	—	—	—
		1.9L	—	—	—	—	—
	Festiva	1.3L	—	—	—	—	—
	Grand Marquis	4.6L	1.5	1200	1380	HBD-AA	3.4 ⑥
	Mark VIII	4.6L	1.4	1200	1380	HBD-AN	2.7
	Mustang	2.3L	2.2	950	1130	HBC-KA	2.6
		5.0L	2.2	1050	1230	HBC-KC	2.6
	Probe	2.0L	—	—	—	—	—
		2.5L	—	—	—	—	—
	Sable/Taurus	3.0L	.9	1400	1530	HBC-KE	2.6
		3.8L	.9	1400	1530	HBC-KE	2.6
	Taurus SHO	3.0L	.9	1400	1530	—	2.6
	Tempo/Topaz	2.3L	.85	1200	1380	—	2.2
		3.0L	.66	1280	1380	—	2.4
	Town Car	4.6L	1.5	1200	1380	HBD-AA	3.4 ⑥
1994	Aspire	1.3L	—	—	—	—	—
	Continental	3.8L	1.5	1300	1380	HBC-HM	3.0
	Cougar/Thunderbird	3.8L ④	1.25	1200	1380	HBC-JB	2.6
		5.0L ④	1.3	1200	1380	HBC-KF	2.6
		3.8L ⑤ ⑩	1.4	1200	1380	HBC-JA	3.0 ⑨
		5.0L ⑩	1.4	1200	1380	HBC-KG	3.1 ⑨
	Crown Victoria	4.6L	1.5	1200	1380	HBD-AA	3.4 ⑨
	Escort/Tracer	1.8L	—	—	—	—	—
		1.9L	1.1	850	1030	HBC-GL & HBC-GM	2.2
	Grand Marquis	4.6L	1.5	1200	1380	HBD-AA	3.4 ⑥
	Mark VIII	4.6L	1.6	1200	1480	HBC-JG	2.6
	Mustang	3.8L	1.3	850	1130	HBC-HX & HBC-GW	2.6
		5.0L ①	1.4	950	1230	HBU-JD	2.6
		5.0L ⑦	1.35	950	1230	HBC-HX	2.6
		5.0L ⑧	1.4	950	1230	HBC-GU	2.6
	Probe	2.0L	—	—	—	—	—
		2.5L	—	—	—	—	—
	Sable/Taurus	3.0L	.9	1200	1480	HBC-GF	2.6
		3.8L	.9	1300	1530	HBC-GF	2.6
	Taurus SHO	3.0L	.9	1400	1530	HBC-GF	2.6
	Tempo/Topaz	2.3L	.85	1200	1380	HBC-GL	2.2
		3.0L	.66	1280	1380	HBC-GL	2.4
	Town Car	4.6L	1.5	1200	1380	HBC-FU	3.4

① —Gallons per minute.
② —Flow is dependent on pump model, engine RPM and pulley ratio. Engine idle speed must be within specifications when checking minimum flow.
③ —Power steering pump identification tag is located on the reservoir body.
④ —Base model.
⑤ —Super coupe or XR7.
⑥ —Measured w/vehicle not moving.
⑦ —Automatic transaxle.
⑧ —Manual transaxle.
⑨ —With handling package.
⑩ —EVO variable assist.

Power Steering Pumps

TABLE OF CONTENTS

Application Chart

Year	Model	Type	Page No.
1992	Capri	1	22-4
	Continental	2	22-6
	Cougar	2	22-6
	Crown Victoria	6	22-10
	Escort	2	22-6
	Escort GT	3	22-8
	Festiva	4	22-9
	Grand Marquis	6	22-10
	Mark VII	2	22-6
	Mustang	2	22-6
	Probe	3	22-8
	Sable	2	22-6
	Taurus	2	22-6
	Taurus SHO	5	22-10
	Tempo w/2.3L	6	22-10
	Tempo w/3.0L	5	22-10
	Thunderbird	2	22-6
	Topaz w/2.3L	6	22-10
	Topaz w/3.0L	5	22-10
	Town Car	6	22-10
	Tracer	2	22-6
	Tracer LTS	3	22-8
1993	Capri	1	22-4
	Continental	2	22-6
	Cougar	2	22-6
	Crown Victoria	6	22-10
	Escort	2	22-6
	Escort GT	3	22-8
	Festiva	4	22-4
	Grand Marquis	6	22-10
	Mark VIII	6	22-10
	Mustang	2	22-6
	Probe	3	22-8
	Sable	2	22-6

Year	Model	Type	Page No.
1993 —Cont'd	Taurus	2	22-6
	Taurus SHO	5	22-10
	Tempo w/2.3L	6	22-10
	Tempo w/3.0L	5	22-10
	Thunderbird	2	22-6
	Topaz w/2.3L	6	22-10
	Topaz w/3.0L	5	22-10
	Town Car	6	22-10
	Tracer	2	22-6
	Tracer LTS	3	22-8
1994	Aspire	4	22-9
	Capri	1	22-4
	Continental	2	22-6
	Cougar	2	22-6
	Crown Victoria	6	22-10
	Escort	2	22-6
	Escort GT	3	22-8
	Grand Marquis	6	22-10
	Mark VIII	6	22-10
	Mustang	2	22-6
	Probe	3	22-8
	Sable	2	22-6
	Taurus	2	22-6
	Taurus SHO	5	22-10
	Tempo w/2.3L	6	22-10
	Tempo w/3.0L	5	22-10
	Thunderbird	2	22-6
	Topaz w/2.3L	6	22-10
	Topaz w/3.0L	5	22-10
	Town Car	6	22-10
	Tracer	2	22-6
	Tracer LTS	3	22-8

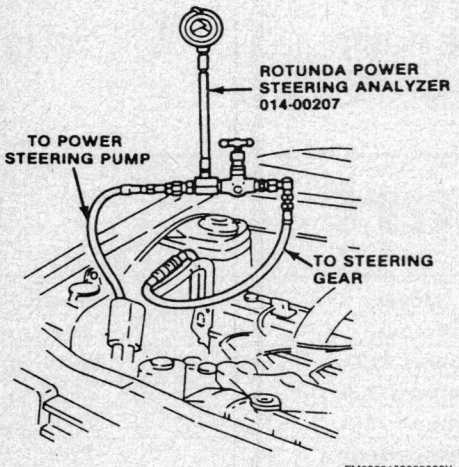

Fig. 1   Pressure test analyzer

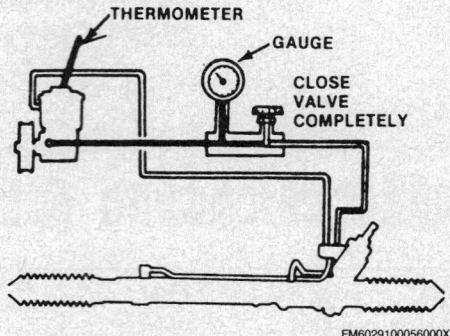

Fig. 2   Power steering pump pressure test

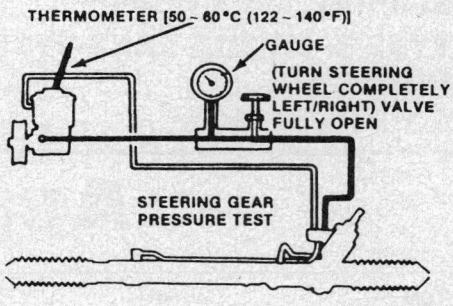

Fig. 3   Steering gear pressure test

TROUBLESHOOTING

HEAVY STEERING WHEEL MOVEMENT

1. Loose or damaged belt.
2. Low fluid level or air in fluid.
3. Twisted or crimped hose or pipe.
4. Fluid leakage.
5. Low hydraulic pressure.
6. Insufficient tire pressure.
7. Improperly adjusted wheel alignment.
8. Faulty ball joint linkage.
9. Binding steering shaft.

IMPROPER STEERING WHEEL RETURN

1. Incorrect tire pressure.
2. Improperly adjusted wheel alignment.
3. Faulty ball joint linkage.
4. Restricted, over tightened or bent steering shaft.

UNEVEN STEERING EFFORT

1. Loose belt.
2. Loose steering shaft bolt(s).
3. Rough steering linkage operation.
4. Faulty steering gear.

STEERING WHEEL PULLS

1. Incorrect tire pressure.
2. Improper preload adjustment.
3. Faulty wheel bearing.
4. Improperly adjusted wheel alignment.
5. Faulty steering gear.

FLUID LEAKAGE

1. Hose coupling.
2. Damaged or clogged hose.
3. Faulty reservoir tank.
4. Faulty steering pump.
5. Faulty steering gear.

ABNORMAL NOISE

1. Loose power steering pump.
2. Loose steering gear.
3. Loose pump bracket.
4. Loose pump pulley nut.
5. Improperly adjusted belt.
6. Faulty steering gear.
7. Faulty steering pump.
8. Obstruction near steering column or pressure hose.
9. Loose steering linkage.

DIAGNOSIS & TESTING

POWER STEERING PRESSURE TEST

During the following procedure, power steering pressure may exceed 1200 psi. Ensure proper tool fit prior to performing test. Exercise extreme caution or damage or personal injury may result.

1. Disconnect power steering pump pressure hose where it connects to tubing, Install Power Steering System Analyzer tool No. 014-00207 and Adapter tool No. 014-00454 or equivalents, torque fitting to 29-36 ft. lbs., Fig. 1.
2. Position thermometer in power steering pump reservoir. Ensure gauge valve is set open to allow normal system function. Do not hold steering wheel against a stop for more than 10 seconds at a time.
3. Start engine, then slowly turn steering wheel from lock to lock ten times to bleed system.
4. If required, turn steering wheel fully left and right several times to raise fluid temperature to 122-140°F (50-60°C). Gauge valve must be briefly closed to read operating pressures. Do not leave valve closed for more than 15 seconds.
5. To measure pump output pressure, close gauge set valve, Fig. 2, then increase engine speed to 1000-1500 RPM, read pressure, then open valve. Operating pressure should be 924 psi, if pressure is low, service or replace pump.
6. To measure pressure at gear, open valve, then increase engine speed to 1000-1500 RPM, turn steering wheel fully left and right, read pressure, Fig. 3. Operating pressure should be 924 psi, if pressure is low, service or replace steering gear.
7. Remove gauge set and adapter, connect high pressure hose and tighten.
8. Start engine, then slowly turn steering wheel lock to lock ten times to bleed system.

POWER STEERING SYSTEM FLUSH

If the power steering pump has been serviced, flush the power steering gear and lines prior to installation.

1. Remove and flush power steering pressure hose, then reinstall.
2. Place gear fluid return line in suitable container, then plug reservoir return line at reservoir.

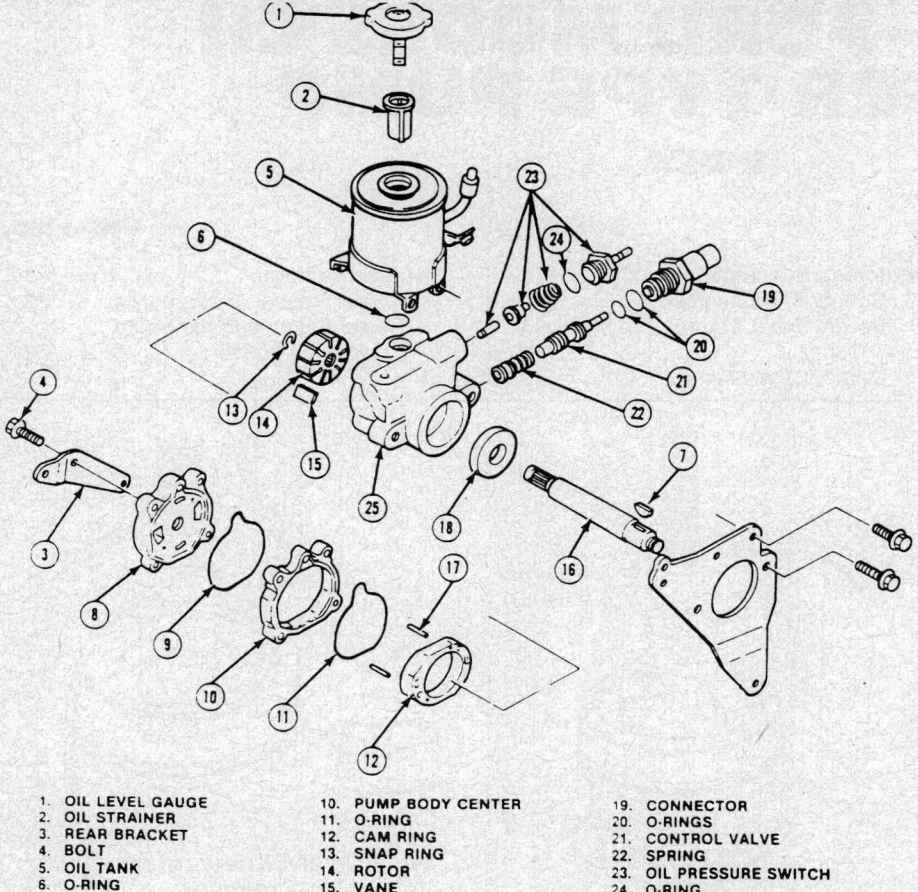

4. Remove rear bracket, then front bracket.
5. Remove oil reservoir, then reservoir O-ring.
6. Remove rear cover and O-ring.
7. Remove pump center body and O-ring.
8. Remove cam ring, then shaft rear snap ring.
9. Remove vanes from rotor.
10. Remove rotor from shaft. Note position of rotor for reference during assembly.
11. Remove pump shaft from front of pump.
12. **On Capri models,** remove front bracket attaching bolts and bracket.
13. **On all models,** remove dowel pins from pump body if necessary.
14. Remove shaft oil seal.
15. Remove pressure regulator valve if necessary.
16. Remove pressure switch if necessary.

Inspection

1. Inspect vanes and rotor faces for scored or chipped faces, wear or burring, replace as required.
2. Measure clearance between vane and rotor groove, .0004–.0024 inch should be indicated.
3. Inspect rotor thrust faces, bushing diameter and shaft seal diameter for excessive wear or scoring.
4. If bushing is scored or excessively worn or O-ring grooves are damaged, replace housing. Measure clearance between bushing and shafts .001–.004 inch should be indicated.

Assemble

Wash all parts except seals in chlorinated solvent, and dry with compressed air or allow to drip dry. Do not use cloth to dry.
1. Install pressure switch, if removed.
2. Install pressure regulator valve, if removed.
3. Install new shaft oil seal using a suitable socket. Coat seal lip with suitable lithium base grease.
4. Install dowel pins in pump body, if removed.
5. Install pump shaft, then rotor in position noted during disassembly.
6. Install rotor to shaft snap ring. Ensure snap ring is fully seated in groove.
7. Install vanes in rotor with rounded edges facing out.
8. Install cam ring onto dowel pins.
9. Install pump body center and front O-ring.
10. Install pump body rear and O-ring.
11. Install reservoir and O-ring.
12. Install short bolt into tank bracket and tighten.
13. Install rear mounting bracket and attaching bolts.
14. Install front mounting bracket and attaching bolts.
15. Install pulley key in shaft slot.
16. Install pulley as described under "Drive Pulley, Replace."
17. Rotate pulley and ensure smooth operation, if pulley does not operate smoothly, disassemble pump and check cause.

1. OIL LEVEL GAUGE	10. PUMP BODY CENTER	19. CONNECTOR
2. OIL STRAINER	11. O-RING	20. O-RINGS
3. REAR BRACKET	12. CAM RING	21. CONTROL VALVE
4. BOLT	13. SNAP RING	22. SPRING
5. OIL TANK	14. ROTOR	23. OIL PRESSURE SWITCH
6. O-RING	15. VANE	24. O-RING
7. KEY	16. SHAFT	25. PUMP BODY
8. PUMP BODY REAR	17. DOWEL PIN	
9. O-RING	18. OIL SEAL	

FM6029100058000X

Fig. 4 Exploded view of power steering pump

3. Fill reservoir using Motorcraft DEXRON II part No. ESW-M2C-138-CJ or equivalent.
4. Disconnect coil wire, then raise and support front wheels.
5. Add about two quarts of fluid while cranking engine with starter and turning steering wheel right to left.
6. When all the fluid is added, stop cranking engine.
7. Remove reservoir return line plug, then connect line to reservoir.
8. Fill reservoir to specified level.
9. Crank engine with starter and add fluid until level remains constant.
10. While cranking engine, rotate steering wheel from stop to stop. **Front wheels must be off the ground during steering wheel stop to stop rotation.**
11. Check fluid level, add as required.
12. Start engine, allow to run for several minutes.
13. Rotate steering wheel from far left to right several times.
14. Turn off engine, check fluid level add as required.

COMPONENT SERVICE

DRIVE PULLEY, REPLACE

1. Remove drive belt.

2. Disconnect ground wire from front of cylinder head.
3. Disconnect pressure switch electrical connector from steering pump.
4. Remove pump adjusting bolts, block and nut.
5. Remove pump pivot bolt.
6. Remove pump and position on upper radiator support.
7. Hold pump pulley from rotating by installing a screwdriver through pulley holes.
8. Loosen pulley retaining nut until it becomes flush with end of pump shaft.
9. Hold pulley and tap on shaft until pulley loosens.
10. Remove nut and pulley.
11. Check pulley, belt and key for excessive wear or damage.
12. Reverse procedure to install.

PUMP SERVICE

Refer to **Fig. 4,** for reference, when servicing steering pump.

Disassemble

1. Remove pump pulley as described under "Drive Pulley, Replace."
2. Remove pulley key.
3. Remove reservoir cap and strainer, then drain fluid from pump.

TYPE 2–FORD MODEL CII SLIPPER-TYPE PUMP

INDEX

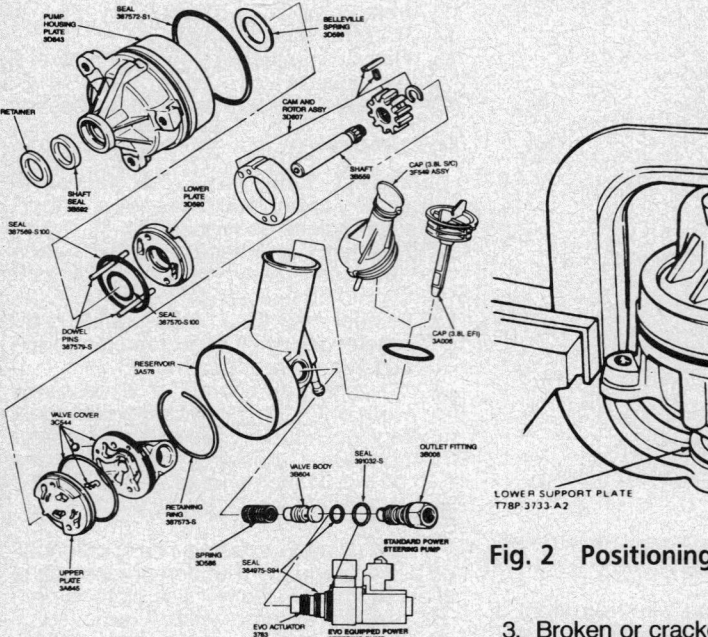

Fig. 1 Exploded view of Ford Model CII power steering pump

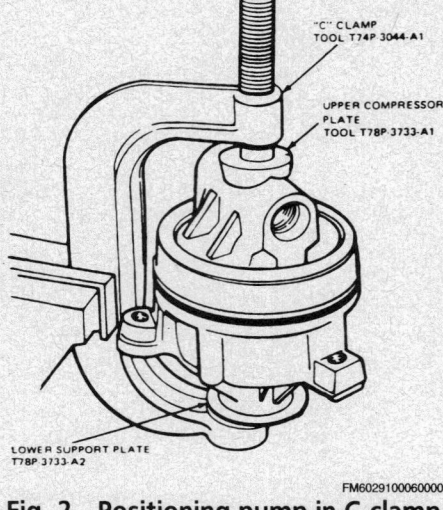

Fig. 2 Positioning pump in C-clamp

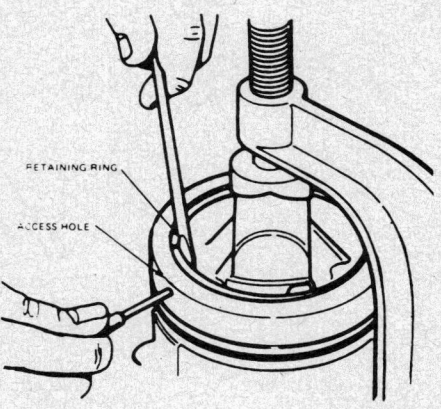

Fig. 3 Valve cover retaining ring removal

DESCRIPTION

The Ford model CII power steering pump is a belt driven 10-slipper type pump incorporating a fiberglass filled nylon reservoir. The reservoir is attached to the rear side of the aluminum pump housing assembly. The pump body is encased within the housing and reservoir assembly. The pump design incorporates a pump pressure fitting which allows the pump pressure line to swivel. A pressure sensitive identification tag is attached to the reservoir body. This tag indicates the basic model number and the suffix.

TROUBLESHOOTING

POWER STEERING PUMP LEAKS

1. Excessive fluid fill.
2. Dipstick missing, loose, damaged or missing O-ring.
3. Broken or cracked fluid reservoir.
4. Loose or damaged hose fittings.
5. Shaft seal not pressed flush with housing surface.
6. Shaft seal damage.
7. Rotor shaft damage, helical grooving or OD has an axial scratch.
8. Shaft bushing worn.
9. Plugged drainback hole.
10. Damaged or missing reservoir O-ring.
11. Damaged or missing outlet fitting O-rings.
12. Excessive pump assembly bracket vibration.
13. Plate and bushing reservoir seal groove damage, metal chips or foreign material in seal groove.
14. Faulty outlet fitting.

POWER STEERING PUMP NOISE, MOAN OR WHINE

1. Fluid aeration.
2. Low fluid.
3. Hose grounded.
4. Steering column grounded.
5. Valve cover O-ring or baffle missing or damaged.
6. Interference between components in pumping elements.
7. Loose or poor bracket alignment.
8. Cam contour damaged.

COMPONENT SERVICE

DISASSEMBLE

1. Remove pulley from pump, **Fig. 1**.
2. Remove outlet fitting, flow control valve and flow control valve spring from pump, then remove reservoir.
3. Place a suitable C-clamp in a vise.
4. Position Lower Support Plate tool No. T78P-3733-A2, or equivalent, over pump rotor shaft.
5. Install Upper Compressor Plate tool No. T78P-3733-A1, or equivalent, into upper portion of C-clamp.
6. While holding Compressor tool, place pump assembly into C-clamp with rotor shaft facing downward, **Fig. 2**.
7. Tighten C-clamp until a slight bottoming of valve cover is observed.
8. Through small hole located on side of pump housing, insert a suitable drift and push inward on valve cover snap ring. While pushing inward on snap ring, place a screwdriver under snap ring edge and remove ring from housing, **Fig. 3**.
9. Loosen C-clamp and remove Lower Support Plate tool No. T78P-3733-A2, or equivalent, then remove pump assembly.
10. Remove pump valve cover and O-ring.
11. Remove rotor shaft, upper plate, cam and rotor assembly and two dowel pins.

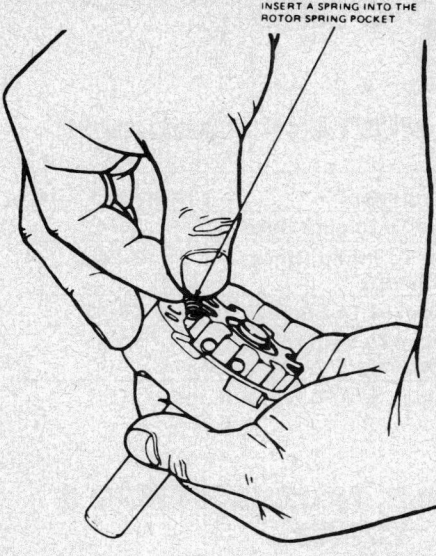

Fig. 4 Slipper springs installation

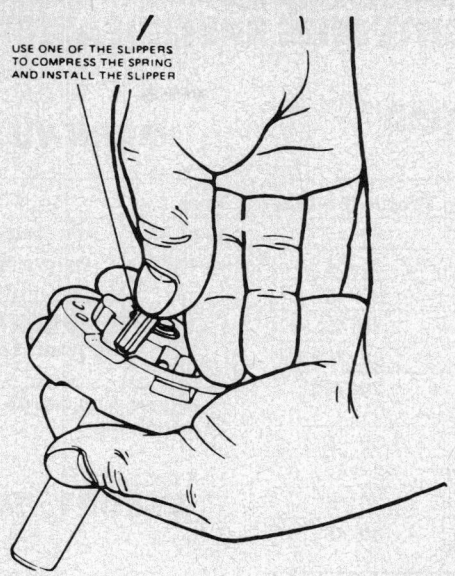

Fig. 5 Slipper installation

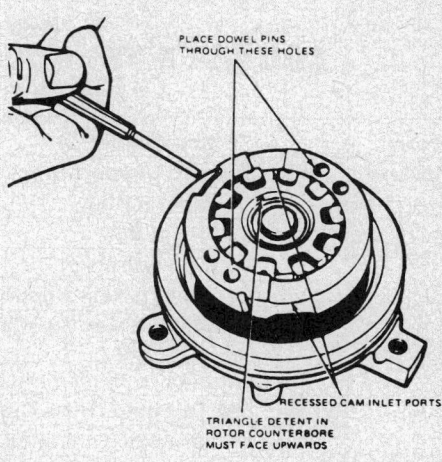

Fig. 6 Assembling cam, slippers & rotor

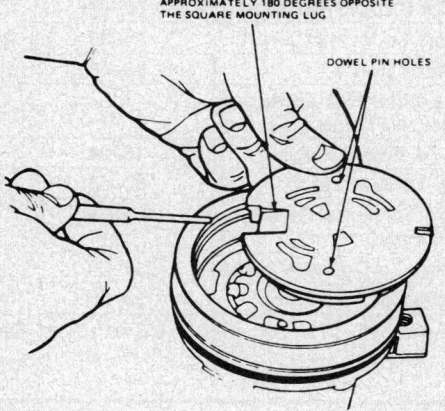

Fig. 7 Upper pressure plate installation

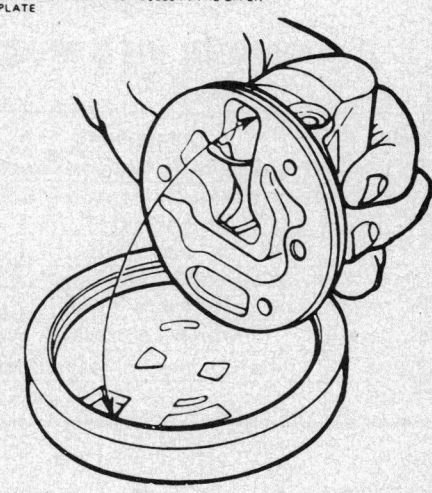

Fig. 8 Valve cover installation

and slippers remain in position.

8. Apply Loctite No. 242 or 271 adhesive or equivalent to outside diameter of seal and Locquic NF or T primer or equivalent to seal bore in housing. Install rotor shaft seal using Seal Driver tool No. T78P-3733-A3, or equivalent. Using a plastic mallet, drive seal into bore until properly seated.

9. Position pump plate on flat surface with pulley side facing downward.

10. Install two dowel pins and spring into housing. **Spring must be inserted with dished surface facing upward.**

11. Lubricate inner and outer O-ring seals with power steering fluid, then install seals on lower pressure plate.

12. Install lower pressure plate into housing and over dowel pin with O-ring seals facing toward front of pump. Position assembly on C-clamp. Place Seal Driver tool No. T78P-3733-A3, or equivalent, into rotor shaft hole and press on lower plate lightly until it bottoms in pump housing. This will seat the outer O-ring seal.

13. Install cam, rotor and slippers and rotor shaft assembly into pump housing over dowel pins. When installing assembly into pump housing, stepped holes must be used for dowel pins and notch in cam insert must be toward reservoir and approximately 180° opposite square mounting lug on housing, **Fig. 6.**

14. Position upper pressure plate over dowel pins with recess directly over recessed notch on cam insert and approximately 180° opposite square mounting lug, **Fig. 7.**

15. Lubricate O-ring seal with power steering fluid, then position O-ring on valve cover. Ensure plastic baffle is securely in position on valve cover. A coat of petroleum jelly may be used to hold baffle in position.

16. Insert valve cover over dowel pins. Ensure outlet fitting hole in valve cover is aligned with square mounting lug

12. Remove lower plate and spring, by tapping housing on a flat surface.

13. Using a suitable screwdriver, remove rotor shaft seal.

ASSEMBLE

1. Position rotor on rotor shaft splines with triangle detent on rotor counterbore facing upward, **Fig. 1.**

2. Install snap ring into groove on end of rotor shaft.

3. Position insert cam over rotor. Ensure recessed notch on insert cam is facing upward.

4. With rotor extended upward approximately half out of cam, insert spring into rotor pocket, **Fig. 4.**

5. Use a slipper to compress spring, then install slipper with groove facing cam, **Fig. 5.**

6. Perform steps 4 and 5 on slipper cavity beneath opposite inlet recess.

7. While holding cam stationary, index rotor left or right one space and install another spring and slipper until all ten rotor cavities have been filled. Use care when turning rotor that springs

on housing, **Fig. 8.**

17. Place assembly in C-clamp and compress valve cover into pump housing until snap ring groove on housing is exposed.

18. Install valve cover snap ring in pump housing. Ensure snap ring ends are near access hole in pump housing.

19. Remove pump assembly from C-clamp.

20. Lubricate O-ring seal with power steering fluid, then place seal on pump housing.

21. Install reservoir on pump housing.

22. Install flow control valve and spring into valve cover.

23. Lubricate O-ring seals with power steering fluid, then place seals on outlet fitting.

24. Install outlet fitting on valve cover. Tighten outlet fitting to specifications. Use care not to cock flow control valve when installing. Do not force valve forward otherwise damage to housing may result.

TIGHTENING SPECIFICATIONS

COUGAR & THUNDERBIRD

Year	Component	Torque/Ft. Lbs.
1992–94	Front Bolts To Support Bracket	30–45
	Outlet Fitting	25–34
	Pivot Bolt	30–45
	Pump To Bracket	30–45
	Pump Bracket To Rear Support	18–24
	Quick Connect Power Steering Fitting	20–25
	Rear Support To Engine Head	30–45
	Return Hose To Pump (Hose Clamp)	12–24 ①
	Support Bracket To Engine	30–45
	Support Bracket To Water Pump Housing	30–45

①—Inch lbs.

MARK VII & MUSTANG

Year	Component	Torque/Ft. Lbs.
1992–94	Front Bolts To Support Bracket	30–45
	Outlet Fitting To Reservoir & Valve Cover	25–34
	Pivot Bolt	30–45
	Pressure Hose Tube Nut To Pump Pressure Fitting	10–25
	Pump To Bracket	30–45
	Pump Bracket To Rear Support	①

MARK VII & MUSTANG -Continued

Year	Component	Torque/Ft. Lbs.
1992–94 —Cont'd	Rear Support To Engine Head	30–45
	Return Hose To Pump (Hose Clamp)	12–24 ②
	Support Bracket To Engine	30–45
	Support Bracket To Water Pump Housing	30–45

①—Less A/C, 30–45 ft. lbs., w/A/C, 18–24 ft. lbs.
②—Inch lbs.

ESCORT, SABLE, TAURUS, TEMPO & TOPAZ

Year	Component	Torque/Ft. Lbs.
1992–94	Front Bolts To Support Bracket	30–45
	Outlet Fitting To Valve Cover	25–39
	Pivot Bolt	30–45
	Pressure Hose Tube Nut To Pump Pressure Fitting	①
	Pulley To Pulley Hub	15–24
	Pump To Bracket	30–45
	Return Hose To Pump (Hose Clamp)	8–24 ②
	Support Bracket To Cylinder Head	15–24
	Support Bracket To Engine	30–45

①—Except Sable & Taurus, 10–15 ft. lbs., Sable & Taurus, 31–39 ft. lbs.
②—Inch lbs.

TYPE 3–MAZDA VANE-TYPE PUMP

NOTE: These Pumps Are Not Serviceable. If Service Is Necessary, Pump Must Be Replaced.

TYPE 4–ASPIRE & FESTIVA VANE-TYPE PUMP

INDEX

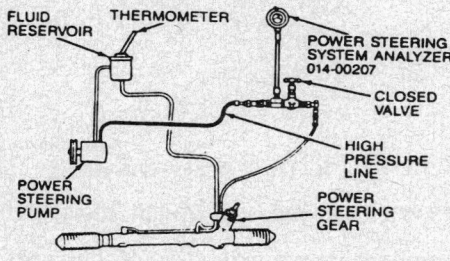

Fig. 1 Pressure test connections

TROUBLESHOOTING

HEAVY STEERING WHEEL MOVEMENT

1. Loose or damaged belt.
2. Low fluid level or air in fluid.
3. Twisted or crimped hose or pipe.
4. Fluid leakage.
5. Low hydraulic pressure.
6. Insufficient tire pressure.
7. Improperly adjusted wheel alignment.
8. Faulty ball joint linkage.
9. Binding steering shaft.

POOR STEERING WHEEL RETURN

1. Incorrect tire pressure.
2. Improperly adjusted wheel alignment.
3. Faulty ball joint linkage.
4. Restricted, over tightened or bent steering shaft.

UNEVEN STEERING EFFORT

1. Loose belt.
2. Loose steering shaft bolt(s).
3. Rough steering linkage operation.
4. Faulty steering gear.

STEERING WHEEL PULLS

1. Incorrect tire pressure.
2. Improper preload adjustment.
3. Faulty wheel bearing.
4. Improperly adjusted wheel alignment.
5. Faulty steering gear.

FLUID LEAKAGE

1. Hose coupling.
2. Damaged or clogged hose.
3. Faulty reservoir tank.
4. Faulty steering pump.
5. Faulty steering gear.

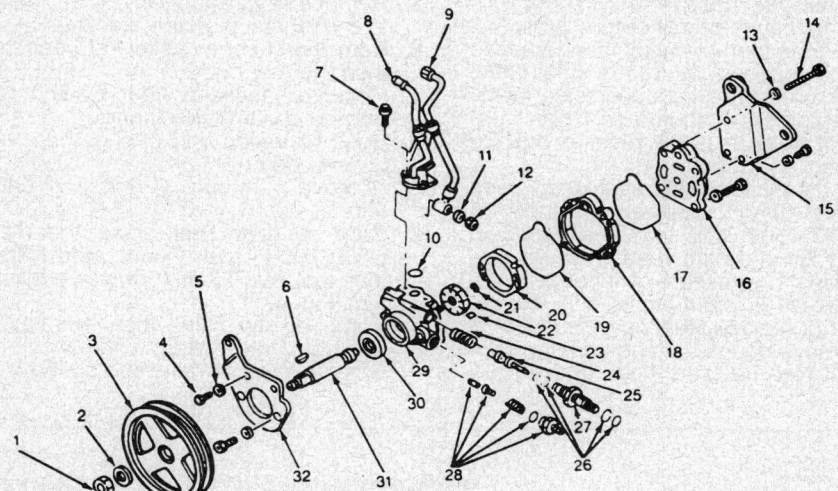

1. NUT	9. HIGH PRESSURE LINE	17. O-RING	25. CONTROL VALVE
2. WASHER	10. O-RING	18. CENTER BODY	26. O-RING
3. PULLEY	11. WASHER	19. O-RING	27. VALVE FITTING
4. BOLT	12. NUT	20. CAM RING	28. PRESSURE SWITCH ASSEMBLY
5. WASHER	13. WASHER	21. RETAINING RING	29. FRONT BODY
6. KEY	14. BOLT	22. ROTOR	30. SEAL
7. BOLT	15. REAR BRACKET	23. VANE	31. SHAFT
8. RETURN LINE	16. REAR BODY	24. SPRING	32. FRONT BRACKET

Fig. 2 Exploded view of power steering pump

ABNORMAL NOISE

1. Loose power steering pump.
2. Loose steering gear.
3. Loose pump bracket.
4. Loose pump pulley nut.
5. Improperly adjusted belt.
6. Faulty steering gear.
7. Faulty steering pump.
8. Obstruction near steering column or pressure hose.
9. Fluid aeration.
10. Loose steering linkage.

DIAGNOSIS & TESTING

POWER STEERING PRESSURE TEST

During the following procedure, power steering pressure may exceed 1200 psi. Ensure proper tool alignment prior to performing test. Exercise extreme caution or damage and/or personal injury may result.

1. Disconnect power steering pump pressure hose where it connects to tubing, Install Power Steering System Analyzer tool No. 014-00207 and Adapter tool No. 014-00454 or equivalents, **torque** fitting to 29-36 ft. lbs., **Fig. 1.**
2. Position thermometer in power steering pump reservoir. **Ensure gauge valve is open to allow normal system function. Do not hold steering wheel against a stop for more than 10 seconds at a time.**
3. Start engine, then slowly turn steering wheel from lock to lock ten times to bleed system.
4. If required, turn steering wheel fully left and right several times to raise fluid temperature to 122-140°F

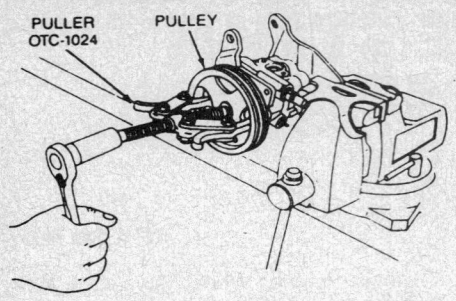

Fig. 3 Pump pulley removal

(50-60°C). **Gauge valve must be briefly closed to read operating pressures. Do not leave valve closed for more than 15 seconds.**

5. To measure pump output pressure, close gauge set valve, then increase engine speed to 1000-1500 RPM, read pressure, then open valve. Operating pressure should be 1031-1138 psi, if pressure is low, repair or replace pump.
6. To measure pressure at gear, open valve, then increase engine speed to 1000-1500 RPM, turn steering wheel fully left and right, read pressure. Operating pressure should be 1031-1138 psi, if pressure is low, repair or replace steering gear.
7. Remove gauge set and adapter, connect high pressure hose and **torque**

fitting to 29-36 ft. lbs.
8. Remove thermometer, then start engine, slowly turn steering wheel lock to lock ten times to bleed system.

COMPONENT SERVICE
OVERHAUL

1. Secure power steering pump in a soft-jawed vise.
2. Remove both pressure and return lines from pump, **Fig. 2.**
3. Remove pulley nut, washer and O-ring.
4. Remove pump pulley and keyway using tool No. OCT-1024 or equivalent, **Fig. 3.**
5. Remove front and rear bracket bolts and washers, then the brackets.
6. Remove rear body bolts and washers, then the rear body.
7. Remove shaft and rotor by first removing shaft retaining ring.
8. Remove vanes and O-ring, then the center body.
9. Remove cam ring O-ring and cam ring.
10. Remove dust seal using tool No. D80L-100-Q and Impact Slide Hammer tool No. T50T-100-A or equivalent, **Fig. 4.**
11. Remove valve fitting, then remove O-ring from valve fitting.
12. Remove control valve and spring.

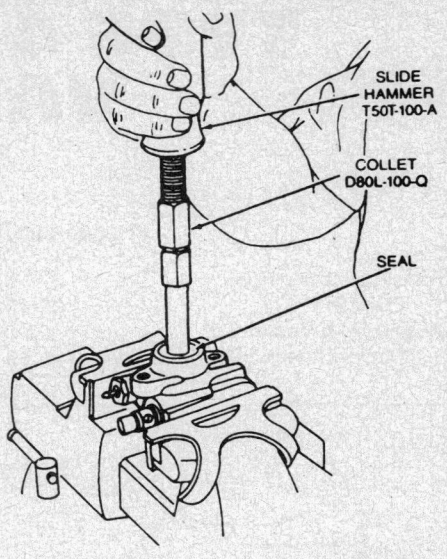

Fig. 4 Dust seal removal

13. Remove pressure switch fitting and spring.
14. Remove pressure switch spring seat and plunger.
15. Reverse procedure to assemble, noting the following:
    a. When installing vanes, rounded edge of vanes should face toward center of rotor.

TIGHTENING SPECIFICATIONS

Year	Component	Torque/Ft. Lbs.
1992–94	Fluid Reservoir Bolts	60–84 ①
	High Pressure Hose Nut	29–36
	Pump Attaching Bolt	27–40
	Pump Attaching Locknut	27–38

①—Inch lbs.

TYPE 5—ATSUGI VANE-TYPE PUMP

NOTE: These Pumps Are Not Serviceable. If Service Is Necessary, Pump Must Be Replaced.

TYPE 6—FORD CIII SLIPPER-TYPE PUMP

NOTE: These Pumps Are Not Serviceable. If Service Is Necessary, Pump Must Be Replaced.

Power Steering Gears

TABLE OF CONTENTS

APPLICATION CHART

Year	Model	Type	Page No.
1992	Capri	1	22-12
	Continental	2①	22-15
	Cougar	2	22-15
	Cougar LS & XR7	2①	22-15
	Crown Victoria	3①	22-29
	Escort	2	22-15
	Escort GT	4	22-32
	Festiva	5	22-35
	Grand Marquis	3①	22-29
	Mark VII	2	22-15
	Mustang	2	22-15
	Probe GL & LX	6	22-37
	Probe GT	7①	22-39
	Sable	2	22-15
	Sable w/3.8L	2①	22-15
	Taurus	2	22-15
	Taurus w/3.8L	2①	22-15
	Thunderbird	2	22-15
	Thunderbird LX & SC	2①	22-15
	Tempo	2	22-15
	Topaz	2	22-15
	Town Car	3①	22-29
	Tracer	2	22-15
	Tracer LTS	4	22-32
1993	Capri	1	22-12
	Continental	2①	22-15
	Cougar	2①	22-15
	Crown Victoria	3①	22-29
	Escort	2	22-15

Year	Model	Type	Page No.
1993 —Cont'd	Festiva	5	22-25
	Grand Marquis	3①	22-29
	Mark VIII	2①	22-15
	Mustang	2	22-15
	Probe	8	22-42
	Sable	2①	22-15
	Taurus	2①	22-15
	Thunderbird	2①	22-15
	Tempo	2	22-15
	Topaz	2	22-15
	Town Car	3①	22-29
	Tracer	2	22-15
1994	Aspire	5	22-35
	Capri	1	22-12
	Continental	2①	22-15
	Cougar	2①	22-15
	Crown Victoria	3①	22-29
	Escort	2	22-15
	Grand Marquis	3①	22-29
	Mark VIII	2①	22-15
	Mustang	2	22-15
	Probe	8	22-42
	Sable	2①	22-15
	Taurus	2①	22-15
	Thunderbird	2①	22-15
	Tempo	2	22-15
	Topaz	2	22-15
	Town Car	3①	22-29
	Tracer	2	22-15

① —Refer to "Power Steering Assist Systems."

TYPE 1–CAPRI RACK & PINION STEERING GEAR

NOTE: On Air Bag Equipped Models, Refer To "Air Bag System Precautions" Located In The Front Of This Manual For System Disarming & Arming Procedures.

INDEX

PRECAUTIONS

AIR BAG SYSTEMS

Refer to "Air Bag System Precautions" in the front of this manual for system disarming and arming procedures.

TROUBLESHOOTING

Refer to "Capri Steering Pump" for troubleshooting power steering system.

DIAGNOSIS & TESTING

POWER STEERING PRESSURE TEST

Refer to "Capri Steering Pump" for power steering system pressure test.

POWER STEERING SYSTEM SERVICE

Power Steering System Bleed

Refer to "Capri Steering Pump" for power steering bleed procedure.

Adjustments

RACK YOKE PRELOAD

1. Remove steering gear, the position in suitable soft-jawed vise.
2. Measure pinion torque using a suitable inch lb. wrench and Adapter tool No. T87C-3504-C or equivalent, **torque** should be 5.3–13.3 inch lbs.
3. If not as indicated, readjust pinion torque by tightening or loosening adjusting plug.

Component Service

STEERING GEAR SERVICE

Disassemble

1. Position steering gear in a soft jawed vise.
2. Disconnect valve body to steering gear hydraulic tubes, Fig. 1.
3. Remove steering gear mounting brackets and bushings.

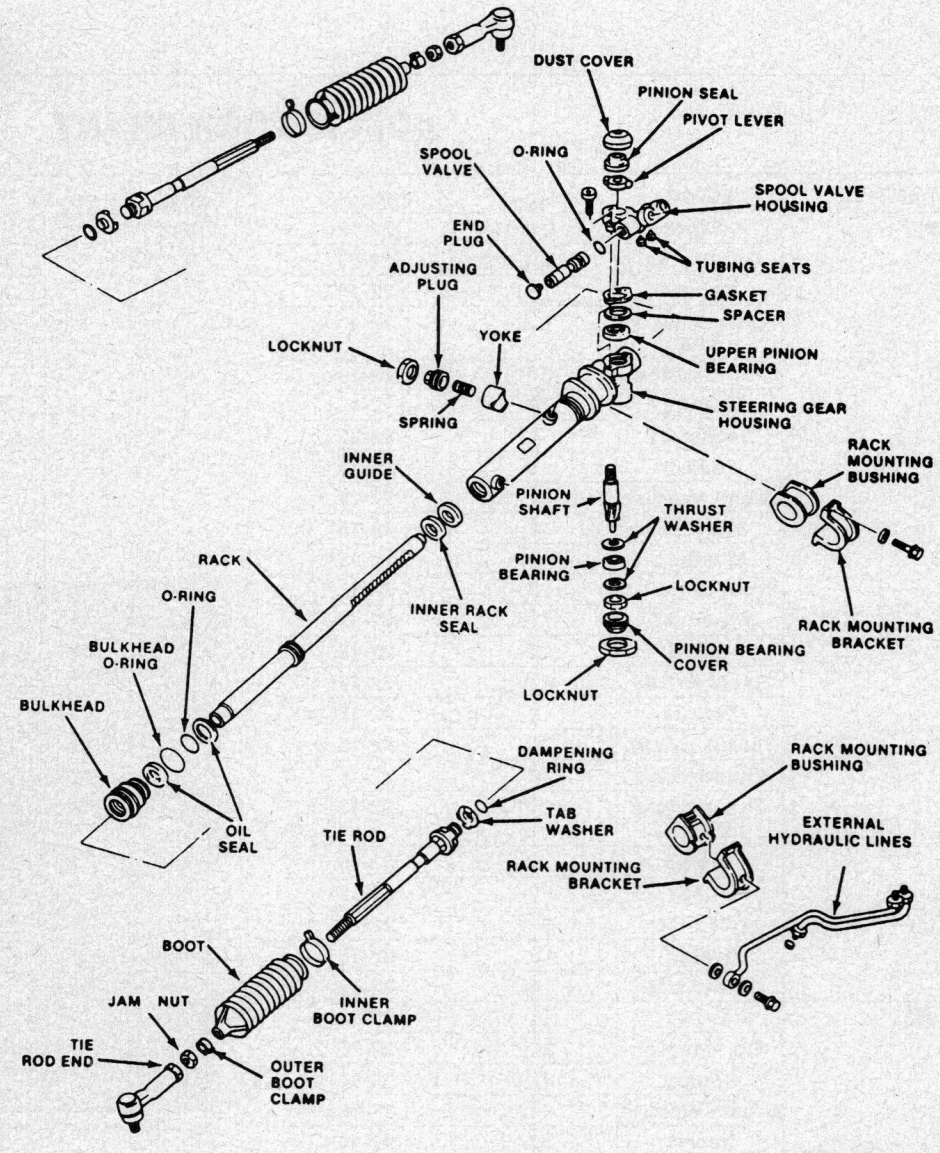

Fig. 1   Exploded view of rack & pinion steering gear

FM60291000072000X

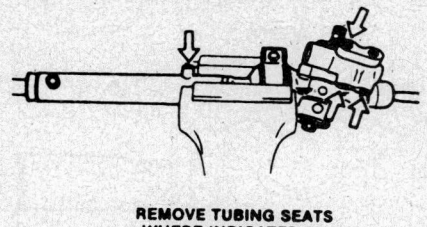

REMOVE TUBING SEATS WHERE INDICATED BY ARROWS

FM6029100073000X

Fig. 2   Tubing seat locations

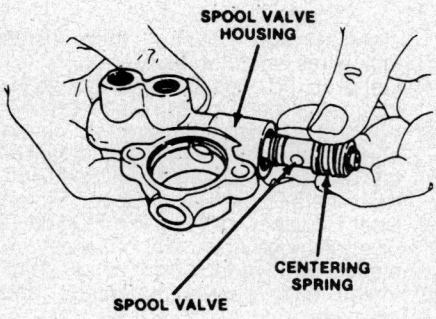

SPOOL VALVE HOUSING

CENTERING SPRING

SPOOL VALVE

FM6029100076000X

Fig. 5   Spool valve installation

4. Using two screwdrivers and a self tapping screw, remove brass tubing seats from steering gear housing, **Fig. 2**.
5. Using a suitable cold chisel, remove pinion shaft dust boot.
6. Using a No. 40 Torx bit, remove valve body attaching bolts and valve body.
7. Wrap cloth around valve body, then position valve body in vise.
8. Remove valve body end plug, then remove pivot lever collar, **Fig. 3**.
9. Using a suitable punch in pivot lever hole, slide spool valve part way out of valve body.
10. Carefully remove spool valve from valve body, then remove spool valve O-ring.
11. Place alignment marks on tie rods, jam nuts and tie rod ends so they can be installed in the same position.
12. Remove tie rod ends and jam nuts from tie rods.
13. Remove tie rod boots from steering gear housing.
14. Using a suitable cold chisel, uncrimp tie rod washer tabs.
15. Position rack in a soft jawed vise, then using a suitable wrench, remove tie rods from rack.
16. Loosen locknut, then remove adjusting plug, spring and yoke from steering gear.
17. Protect outer bulkhead with a cloth, then remove outer bulkhead using a pipe wrench.
18. Remove O-ring from outer bulkhead and discard.
19. Pull pinion shaft assembly out through lower bearing side of steering gear housing.
20. Using a wooden dowel, drive upper pinion bearing out of housing.
21. Remove rack from steering gear

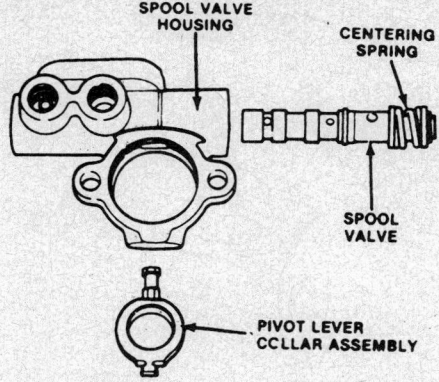

SPOOL VALVE HOUSING

CENTERING SPRING

SPOOL VALVE

PIVOT LEVER COLLAR ASSEMBLY

FM6029100074000X

Fig. 3   Exploded view of valve body

housing in direction indicated in **Fig. 4**.
22. Using Rack Inner Seal Remover tool No. T87C-3504-A or equivalent, remove rack inner guide and seal.

Inspection

Check rack and pinion teeth for wear and damage. Position rack in V-blocks and check runout using a suitable dial indicator. Rack runout should not exceed .012 inch. Check pinion bearing for looseness and wear. If rack, pinion or pinion bearings are found to be unsatisfactory, the rack and pinion must be replaced as a set.

Check steering gear housing for wear and damage. Check tie rod ball units for looseness and smoothness of operation. Check for bent tie rods or tie rod ends. Check tie rod boots for damage. If any components are found to be unsatisfactory, they should be replaced.

Check rack bushing located inside steering gear housing for wear. The bushing and steering gear housing must be replaced as an assembly. Check yoke sliding surface for wear and replace as necessary. Check outer bulkhead bushing for wear and replace as necessary.

Check pivot lever collar for wear and damage and replace as necessary. Also check spool valve for wear and damage and polish with crocus cloth as necessary.

Assemble

1. Install replacement O-rings on spool valve. Apply molybdenum disulfide grease to spool valve pivot lever hole. Lubricate remainder of spool valve with automatic transmission fluid.
2. Position spool valve into valve body, **Fig. 5**.
3. Apply molybdenum disulfide grease to pivot lever hose in valve body and to ends of pivot lever collar and bushing, install pivot lever into valve housing, ensuring spherical ends are properly seated.
4. Install valve body end plug, **Fig. 1**.
5. Lubricate inner rack guide and seal with automatic transmission fluid, then install guide and seal using Rack Inner Seal Removal tool No. T87C-3504-A or equivalent. Push guide and seal into housing until fully seated.
6. Apply grease to rack teeth, then position Rack Seal Protector tool No.

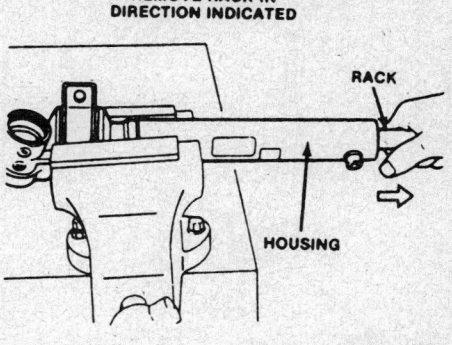

REMOVE RACK IN DIRECTION INDICATED

RACK

HOUSING

FM6029100075000X

Fig. 4   Rack from steering gear housing removal

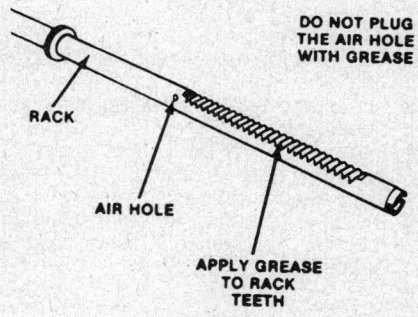

DO NOT PLUG THE AIR HOLE WITH GREASE

RACK

AIR HOLE

APPLY GREASE TO RACK TEETH

FM6029100077000X

Fig. 6   Applying grease to rack

D83P-3504-K or equivalent over rack teeth. When applying grease teeth, do not cover rack air hole, **Fig. 6**.
7. Apply ATF to rack piston seal, then install seal on the rack, using Piston Seal Replacer tool No. T81P-3504-L with Pusher tool No. T75L-3517-A2 and Sizer tool No. T81P-3504-K or equivalents.
8. Lubricate rack piston and housing cylinder bore with automatic transmission fluid, then slide rack into housing until fully seated. Remove rack seal protector from rack teeth.
9. Using Pinion Cover Centering tool No. T81P-3504-Y or equivalent, install replacement bushing into outer bulkhead. Also install replacement sealing ring, O-rings and oil seal on outer bulkhead. Prior to installation, lubricate bushing and seals with automatic transmission fluid.
10. Position outer bulkhead to steering gear housing, then wrap bulkhead with a cloth for protection and tighten with a pipe wrench, **Fig. 7**.
11. Stake outer bulkhead to rack housing using a suitable punch, **Fig. 8**.
12. Position lower pinion bearing onto pinion shaft, then tighten and stake nut to pinion shaft. Prior to staking, tighten to specifications.
13. Install pinion shaft assembly, with rack and pinion positioned as shown in **Fig. 9**.
14. Apply grease to upper pinion bearing, then install bearing using Upper Pinion Seal Replacer tool No. T78P-3504-D or equivalent.

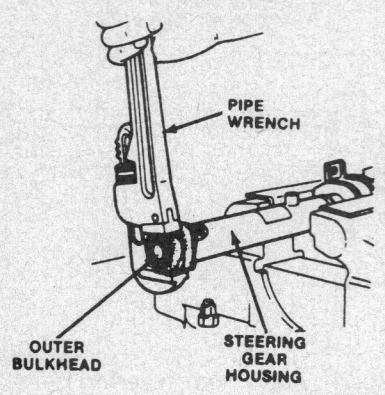

Fig. 7 Tightening outer bulkhead

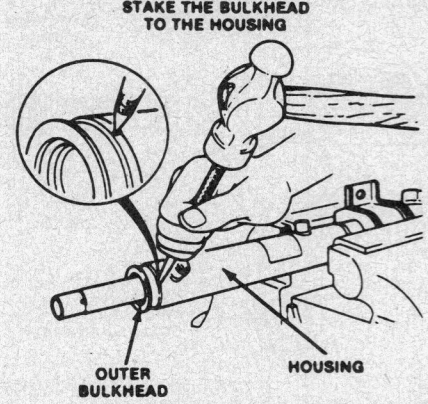

Fig. 8 Staking outer bulkhead to housing

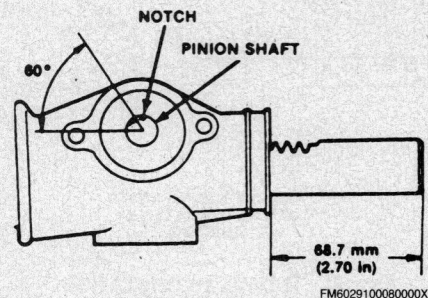

Fig. 9 Positioning rack & pinion

15. Tighten pinion bearing cover to specifications.
16. Install and tighten housing locknut to specifications.
17. Position valve body and gasket to steering gear housing, then install Torx attaching bolts.
18. Install yoke, spring, adjusting plug and locknut. Tighten adjusting plug to specifications.

19. Adjust preload as outlined under "Rack Yoke Preload."
20. After completing adjustment, tighten adjuster plug locknut to specifications.
21. Position rack in soft jawed vise, then install tie rod and tighten to specifications.
22. Stake tie rod tab washer at two locations.
23. Install tie rod boots over tie rod and

steering gear housing, then install lock wires and clamps.
24. Install tie rod ends and jam nuts, aligning marks made during disassembly.
25. Wrap electrical tape around pinion shaft, then apply grease to shaft. Apply grease to pinion shaft seal lips, then install seal using Upper Pinion Seal Replacer tool No. T78P-3504-D or equivalent. After seal has been installed, remove tape from pinion shaft.
26. Install rack support bushings and brackets.
27. Install replacement tubing seats, then connect hydraulic tubing to steering gear and valve body.

TIGHTENING SPECIFICATIONS

Year	Component	Torque/Ft. lbs.
1992–94	Pinion Bearing Cover	39.1–47.1 ①
	Pinion Bearing Housing Locknut	28.9–36.2
	Pinion Cover	28.9–36.2
	Pinion Shaft Nut	28.9–36.2
	Tie Rod End	26–29
	Tie Rod To Rack	43.4–57.9
	Wheel Lug Nuts	67–88

①—Inch lbs.

TYPE 2—FORD INTEGRAL RACK & PINION STEERING GEAR

NOTE: Also Refer To "Type 1-Ford Variable Assist Power Steering (VAPS) System" For Continental, Sable And Taurus Models Equipped w/VAPS System, Or "Type 2-Ford Variable Assist Electronic Variable Orifice (EVO) System" For Cougar, Mark VIII And Thunderbird Models Equipped w/EVO System.

NOTE: On Air Bag Equipped Models, Refer To "Air Bag System Precautions" Located In The Front Of This Manual For System Disarming & Arming Procedures.

INDEX

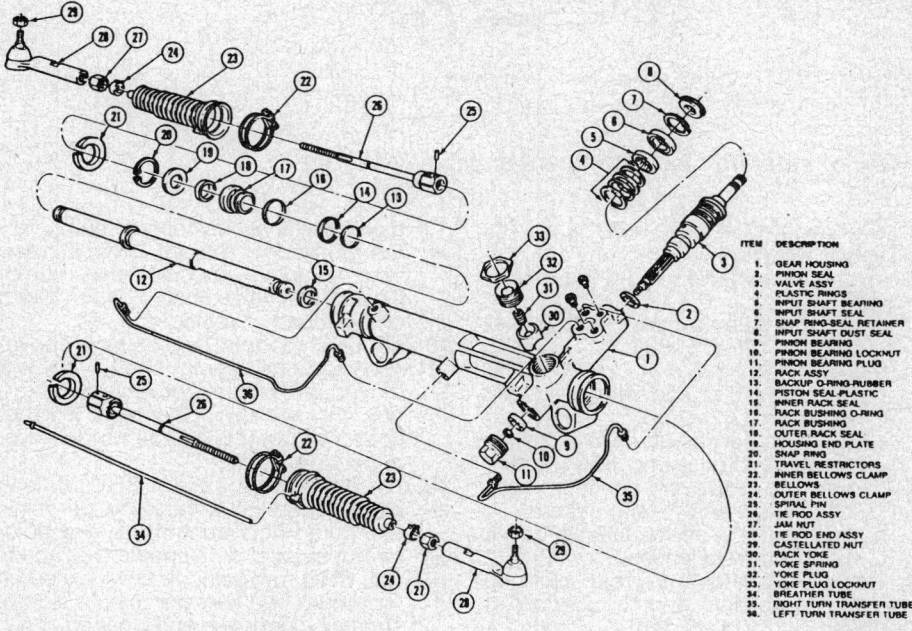

ITEM	DESCRIPTION
1.	GEAR HOUSING
2.	PINION SEAL
3.	VALVE ASSY
4.	PLASTIC RINGS
5.	INPUT SHAFT BEARING
6.	INPUT SHAFT SEAL
7.	SNAP RING-SEAL RETAINER
8.	INPUT SHAFT DUST SEAL
9.	PINION BEARING
10.	PINION BEARING LOCKNUT
11.	PINION BEARING PLUG
12.	RACK ASSY
13.	BACKUP O-RING-RUBBER
14.	PISTON SEAL-PLASTIC
15.	INNER RACK SEAL
16.	RACK BUSHING O-RING
17.	RACK BUSHING
18.	OUTER RACK SEAL
19.	HOUSING END PLATE
20.	SNAP RING
21.	TRAVEL RESTRICTORS
22.	INNER BELLOWS CLAMP
23.	BELLOWS
24.	OUTER BELLOWS CLAMP
25.	SPIRAL PIN
26.	TIE ROD ASSY
27.	JAM NUT
28.	TIE ROD END ASSY
29.	CASTELLATED NUT
30.	RACK YOKE
31.	YOKE SPRING
32.	YOKE PLUG
33.	YOKE PLUG LOCKNUT
34.	BREATHER TUBE
35.	RIGHT TURN TRANSFER TUBE
36.	LEFT TURN TRANSFER TUBE

FM6029100082000X

Fig. 1 Exploded view of steering gear. Cougar, Mark VII, Mark VIII, Mustang & Thunderbird

PRECAUTIONS

AIR BAG SYSTEMS

Refer to "Air Bag System Precautions" in the front of this manual for system disarming and arming procedures.

DESCRIPTION

These power rack and pinion steering gears, **Figs. 1 through 5**, are hydraulic-mechanical units, using an integral piston and rack to provide power assisted steering control. Internal valve controls pump flow and pressure as required during operation. The unit consists of a rotary hydraulic control valve connected to the input shaft and a boost cylinder integral with the rack.

OPERATION

The rotary control valve utilizes the relative rotational position of the input shaft and valve sleeve to control fluid flow. As the steering wheel is turned, the resistance of the wheels and weight of the vehicle cause a torsion bar to deflect, **Figs. 1 through 5**. This torsion bar deflection changes position of rotary valve and sleeve ports, thereby directing fluid under pressure to the proper end of the power cylinder. The pressure differential acting on the piston attached to the rack, provides the power assist.

The control valve is forced back to a centered position by the torsion bar when steering effort is removed. Pressure is then equalized on each side of the piston and the front wheels tend to return to a straight ahead position.

TROUBLESHOOTING

Refer to **Fig. 6**, for troubleshooting procedure.

DIAGNOSIS & TESTING

POWER STEERING PRESSURE TEST

During the following procedure, power steering system pressure may exceed 1200 psi. Ensure proper tool fit prior to performing test. Exercise extreme caution or damage or personal injury may result.

1. Prior to performing pump flow and pressure tests, ensure following conditions exist:
   a. Proper pump reservoir fluid level.
   b. Correct tire air pressure.
   c. Proper pump belt tension.
   d. Correct model and vehicle pump application.
   e. Correct size pulleys on pump and engine.
   f. Ensure system is not damaged or leaking, repair as required.
2. The following test equipment is required:
   a. Engine tachometer.
   b. Thermometer: 0–300°F (17.8–148.9°C).

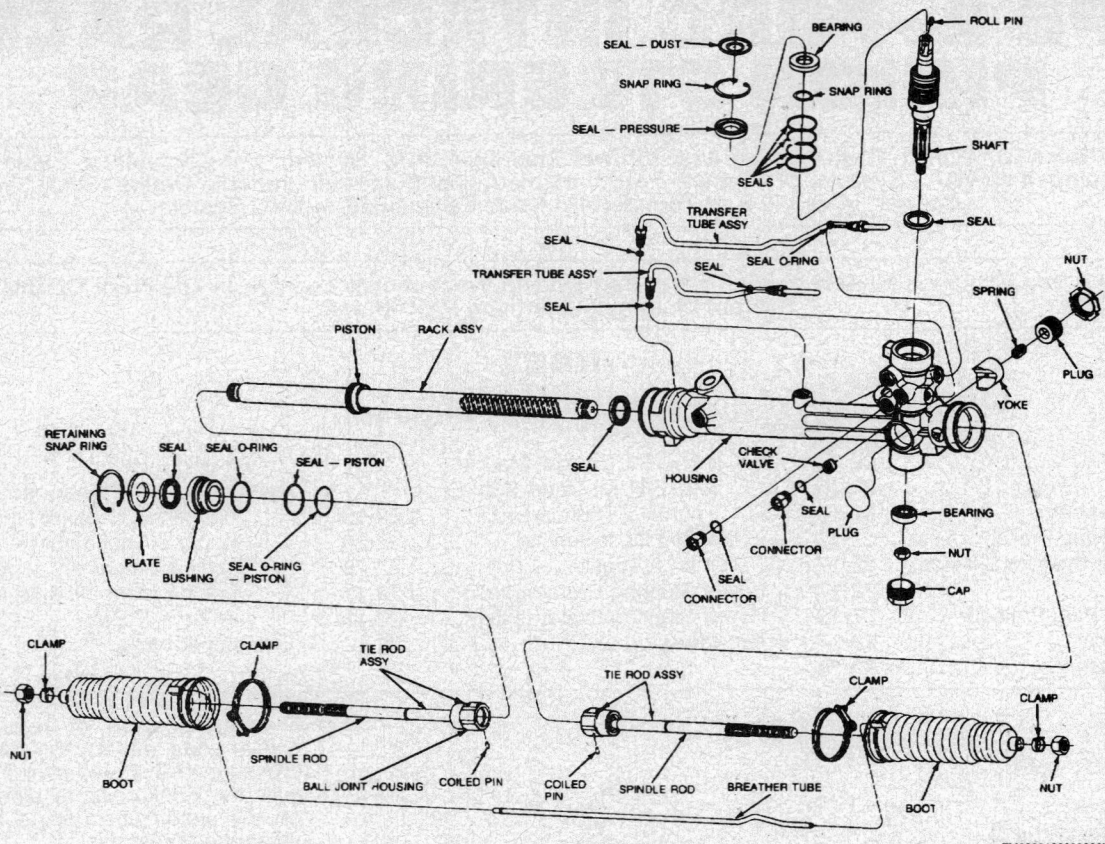

Fig. 2 Exploded view of steering gear. Continental, Sable & Taurus

c. **On all models except SHO,** Power Steering System Analyzer tool No. 014-00207 or equivalent.

d. **On SHO models,** Power Steering System Analyzer tool No. 014-00208 or equivalent.

e. **On all models,** set of adapter fittings.

3. The test procedure used in conjunction with the power steering system analyzer can be used to determine:
   a. System backpressure.
   b. Pump flow.
   c. Steering gear internal leakage.
   d. Pump relief pressure.

4. The readouts from step 3 can be used to determine which of the following conditions or components may be faulty:
   a. Hose or fitting restriction.
   b. Sticking gear valve.
   c. Insufficient pump capacity.
   d. Sticking relief valve.
   e. Suspension system binding.

5. Disconnect pump high pressure line, then connect suitable analyzer hose adapter, **Figs. 7 through 10.**

6. **On all models except SHO,** thread other analyzer adapter to pump.

7. **On SHO models,** thread adapter into steering gear.

8. **On all models,** connect analyzer hose to adapters, tighten both connections to 15 ft. lbs. maximum.

9. If required, add power steering fluid, start engine and allow to run about two minutes. Ensure idle is set to specifications.

10. With engine at idle, record the following:
    a. Flow, gallons per minute at 167-177°F (76-80°C).
    b. Pressure, psi at 167-177°F (76-80°C), at idle with gate fully open.
    c. If gallon per minute flow is below specifications, pump may require service, however continue test, check flow and relief pressure.
    d. If pressure is above 150 psi check hoses for restrictions.

11. Partially close gate valve to build up 740 psi, observe and record flow at 167-177°F (76-80°C):
    a. **On all models except SHO,** if flow drops lower than .9 gallons per minute, disassemble pump and replace cam pack, if pressure plates are cracked or worn, replace.
    b. **On SHO models,** if flow drops lower than .9 gallons per minute, replace pump.

12. **On all models,** completely close and partially open gate valve three times. **Do not allow valve to remain closed for more then five seconds.** Observe and record pressure.

13. **On all models except SHO,** if pressure is lower than specifications, replace pump flow control valve.

14. **On SHO models,** if pressure is lower than specifications, replace pump.

15. **On all models except SHO,** if pressure is above specifications, pump flow control valve should be removed and cleaned or replaced.

16. **On SHO models,** if pressure is above specifications, pump should be removed and cleaned or replaced.

17. **On all models,** increase engine speed to about 1500 RPM, observe and record flow.

18. **On all models except SHO,** if flow exceeds maximum free flow per minute, pump flow control valve should be removed and cleaned or replaced.

19. **On SHO models,** if flow exceeds maximum free flow per minute, pump should be removed and cleaned or replaced.

20. **On all models,** check idle speed, with engine at idle, turn steering wheel to left and right stops, record pressure and flow at stops.

21. Pressure at both stops should be about the same as maximum pump output pressure, flow should drop below 0.5 gallons per minute.

22. If pressure is not within specification, excessive internal leakage is indicated, remove and disassemble steering gear, replace worn or damaged parts and inspect rack piston and valve seals for damage.

23. While watching pressure gauge, turn steering wheel slightly in both directions and quickly release wheel,

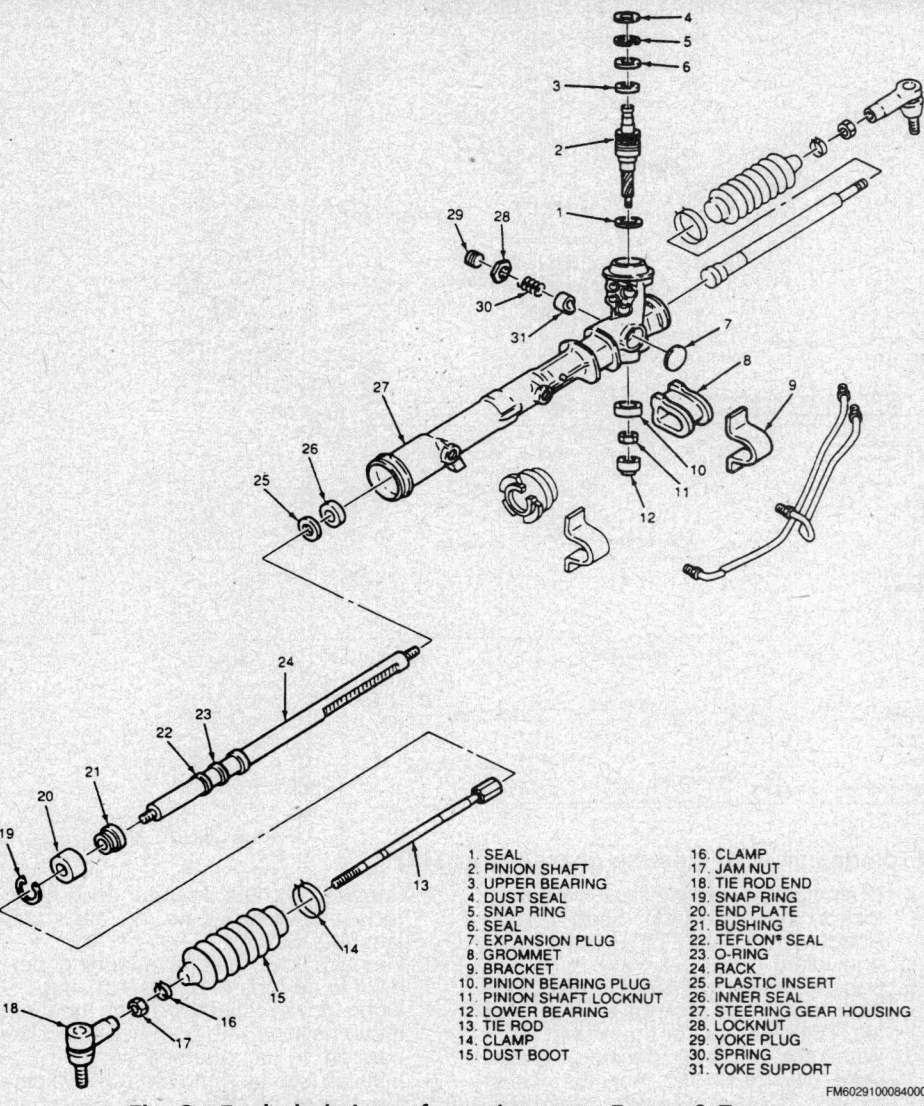

1. SEAL
2. PINION SHAFT
3. UPPER BEARING
4. DUST SEAL
5. SNAP RING
6. SEAL
7. EXPANSION PLUG
8. GROMMET
9. BRACKET
10. PINION BEARING PLUG
11. PINION SHAFT LOCKNUT
12. LOWER BEARING
13. TIE ROD
14. CLAMP
15. DUST BOOT
16. CLAMP
17. JAM NUT
18. TIE ROD END
19. SNAP RING
20. END PLATE
21. BUSHING
22. TEFLON® SEAL
23. O-RING
24. RACK
25. PLASTIC INSERT
26. INNER SEAL
27. STEERING GEAR HOUSING
28. LOCKNUT
29. YOKE PLUG
30. SPRING
31. YOKE SUPPORT

FM60291000840000X

Fig. 3   Exploded view of steering gear. Escort & Tracer

gauge needle should move from normal backpressure and snap back as the wheel is released. If needle returns slowly or sticks, the steering gear rotary valve is sticking.
24. Remove and disassemble steering as described under "Disassemble," then flush power steering hoses and pump before gear installation.
25. If problem still exists, check ball joint and linkage.
26. Disconnect and remove analyzer, then connect lines.

POWER STEERING SYSTEM SERVICE

Power Steering System Bleed

1. Air trapped in power steering system may be remove with power steering pump air evacuator assembly vacuum tester 021-00014 or equivalent.
2. **Do not use engine vacuum to purge power steering system.**
3. Remove reservoir cap.
4. Check and fill reservoir to cold fill mark with suitable fluid.
5. Disconnect ignition coil wire, then raise and support front wheels.
6. Crank engine with starter motor, then check fluid level. **Do not turn steering wheel.**
7. If fluid level has dropped, fill reservoir to cold fill mark, crank engine with starter motor while turning steering wheel lock to lock, then check fluid level.
8. Install air evacuator rubber stopper tightly to pump reservoir, then connect coil wire.
9. With engine at idle, apply 15 inch Hg maximum vacuum to pump reservoir for a minimum of three minutes, as air purges from system, vacuum will decrease, maintain adequate vacuum.
10. Release vacuum, then remove vacuum source, if fluid level has dropped, fill to cold fill mark.
11. With engine at idle, apply 15 inch Hg maximum vacuum to pump reservoir,

turn steering wheel from lock to lock ever 30 seconds for about five minutes. **Do not hold steering wheel on stops when turning.** Maintain adequate vacuum.
12. Release vacuum, then remove vacuum equipment add power steering fluid id required, install cap.
13. Start engine, turn steering wheel, check connections for oil leaks.
14. If severe aeration is indicated, repeat steps 7 through 13.

Power Steering System Flush

1. Disconnect power steering return hose.
2. Place return line in suitable container, then plug reservoir return line at reservoir.
3. Fill reservoir using Motorcraft DEXRON II part No. ESW-M2C33-F or equivalent.
4. Disconnect coil wire, then raise and support front wheels.
5. While adding about two quarts of fluid, turn ignition to start position (using ignition key), then crank engine with starter and turn steering wheel right to left.
6. When all the fluid is added, turn ignition off, and connect coil wire.
7. Remove reservoir return line plug, then connect line to reservoir.
8. Fill reservoir to specified level.
9. Lower vehicle, then start engine, slowly turn steering wheel several times lock to lock, then recheck fluid level, add as required.

Adjustments

STEERING GEAR

Continental, Cougar, Mark VII, Mark VIII, Mustang, Sable, Taurus & Thunderbird

Rack yoke bearing preload is the only service adjustment required. This adjustment is performed with the steering gear removed from the vehicle. Refer to the individual car chapters for steering gear removal.
1. Clean exterior of steering gear, then install two long bolts and washers through bushings and attach to Bench Fixture tool No. T57L-500-B or equivalent.
2. Do not remove external pressure lines unless damaged or leaking. Drain power steering fluid by rotating input shaft from lock to lock two times using Pinion Shaft Torque Adapter tool No. T74P-3504-R, or equivalent. Cover ports on valve housing with a clean shop cloth while draining gear.
3. Position an inch lb. torque wrench and Pinion Shaft Adapter tool No. T74P-3504-R, or equivalent, on input shaft splines.
4. Loosen yoke plug locknut using Pinion Housing Yoke Locknut Wrench tool No. T78P-3504-H, or equivalent,

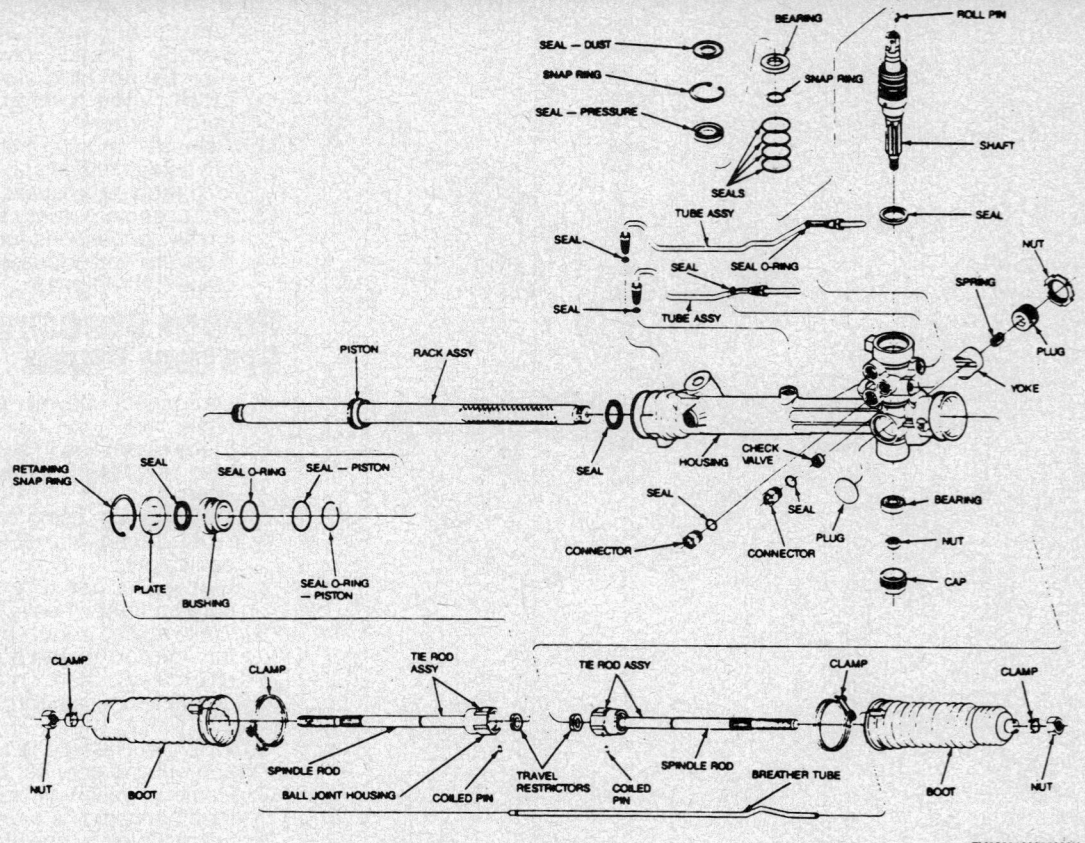

Fig. 4 Exploded view of steering gear. Taurus SHO

FM6029100085000X

then loosen yoke plug using a ³/₄ inch socket wrench, **Fig. 11.**

5. Clean yoke plug threads, then with rack at center of travel, **torque** yoke plug to 40-50 inch lbs.

6. Back off yoke plug approximately ¹/₈ turn until **torque** required to rotate input shaft is 7 to 18 inch lbs.

7. While holding yoke plug in position, tighten locknut to specifications. Using Pinion Housing Yoke Locknut Wrench tool No. T78P-3504-H, or equivalent. Recheck input shaft rotating torque after tightening locknut.

8. If the external pressure lines were removed in step two, they must be replaced with new pressure lines. Remove the copper seals from the pressure ports previous to installation of new lines.

9. Remove steering gear from holding fixture, then install external pressure lines. Tighten pump to gear and return line fittings and valve and power cylinder (gear housing) fittings to specifications.

RACK YOKE PLUG PRELOAD

Tempo & Topaz

1. Clean exterior of steering gear thoroughly.
2. Mount gear in Holding Fixture tool No. D87P-3504-B or equivalent. **Do not hold gear in vise.**
3. Do not remove external pressure lines unless they are leaking.

4. Drain gear by rotating input shaft from lock to lock with Input Shaft Torque Adapter tool No. T81P-3504-R or equivalent.

5. Loosen yoke plug locknut and yoke plug with Yoke locknut Wrench tool No. T81P-3504-G or equivalent.

6. With rack in center position, **torque** yoke plug to 44-50 inch lbs. Clean threads of yoke plug prior to tightening, **Fig. 12.**

7. Install Yoke Plug Adapter tool No. T78P-3504-G or equivalent. Mark location of 0° on housing. Back off adjuster so 48° mark lines up with 0° mark.

8. While holding yoke plug, tighten yoke plug locknut to specifications.

9. Check input shaft torque after tightening locknut.

Component Service

CONTINENTAL, COUGAR, MARK VII, MARK VIII, MUSTANG, SABLE, TAURUS & THUNDERBIRD

TIE ROD ENDS, BELLOWS & BALL JOINT SOCKETS

Disassemble

1. Install two long bolts and washers through bushings and attach gear to Holding Fixture tool No. T57L-500-B, or equivalent.

2. Loosen jam nuts on outer ends of tie rods, then remove tie rod ends and jam nuts.

3. Remove four clamps attaching bellows to tie rods and gear housing.

4. Drain power steering fluid, then remove bellows with breather tube. Use care not to damage bellows.

5. If pinion is to be removed, remove pinion before proceeding as described under Input Shaft & Valve Assembly.

6. Thread point of Roll Pin Remover tool No. T78P-3504-N or equivalent into roll pin on ball socket and tighten tool finger tight, then remove roll pins, **Fig. 13.**

7. If pinion was not removed, remove gear housing from holding fixture and place on bench to prevent damage to gear teeth.

8. Position rack so that several teeth are exposed. Hold rack using an adjustable wrench on end teeth while loosening ball sockets with Nut Wrench tool No. T74P-3504-U, or equivalent, **Fig. 14.**

Assemble

1. Install tie rod and ball socket assemblies onto rack. Hold one ball socket with 1⁵/₁₆ inch wrench while tightening other ball socket to specifications, using Nut Wrench tool No. T74P-3504-U, or equivalent. Both ball socket assemblies will be torqued simultaneously using this method. **If pinion was not removed from housing,**

ITEM	DESCRIPTION	ITEM	DESCRIPTION
1.	GEAR HOUSING	19.	END PLATE
2.	PINION SEAL	20.	SNAP RING
3.	VALVE ASSY	21.	INNER BELLOWS CLAMP*
4.	PLASTIC RINGS	22.	BELLOWS
5.	INPUT SHAFT BEARING	23.	OUTER BELLOWS CLAMP*
6.	INPUT SHAFT SEAL	24.	DRIVE RIVET
7.	SNAP RING—SEAL RETAINER	25.	INNER TIE ROD ASSY
8.	INPUT SHAFT DUST SEAL	26.	JAM NUT
9.	PINION BEARING	27.	OUTER TIE ROD END ASSY
10.	PINION BEARING LOCKNUT	28.	EXPANSION PLUG
11.	HOUSING CAP	29.	RACK YOKE
12.	RACK ASSY	30.	YOKE SPRING
13.	BACKUP O-RING (RUBBER)	31.	YOKE PLUG
14.	PISTON SEAL (PLASTIC)	32.	YOKE PLUG LOCK NUT
15.	INNER RACK SEAL	33.	BREATHER TUBE
16.	RACK BUSHING O-RING	34.	RIGHT TURN TRANSFER TUBE
17.	RACK BUSHING	35.	LEFT TURN TRANSFER TUBE
18.	OUTER RACK SEAL	36.	PLASTIC SEAL 4 REQ'D

*SCREW TYPE CLAMPS FOR SERVICE INSTALLATION ONLY

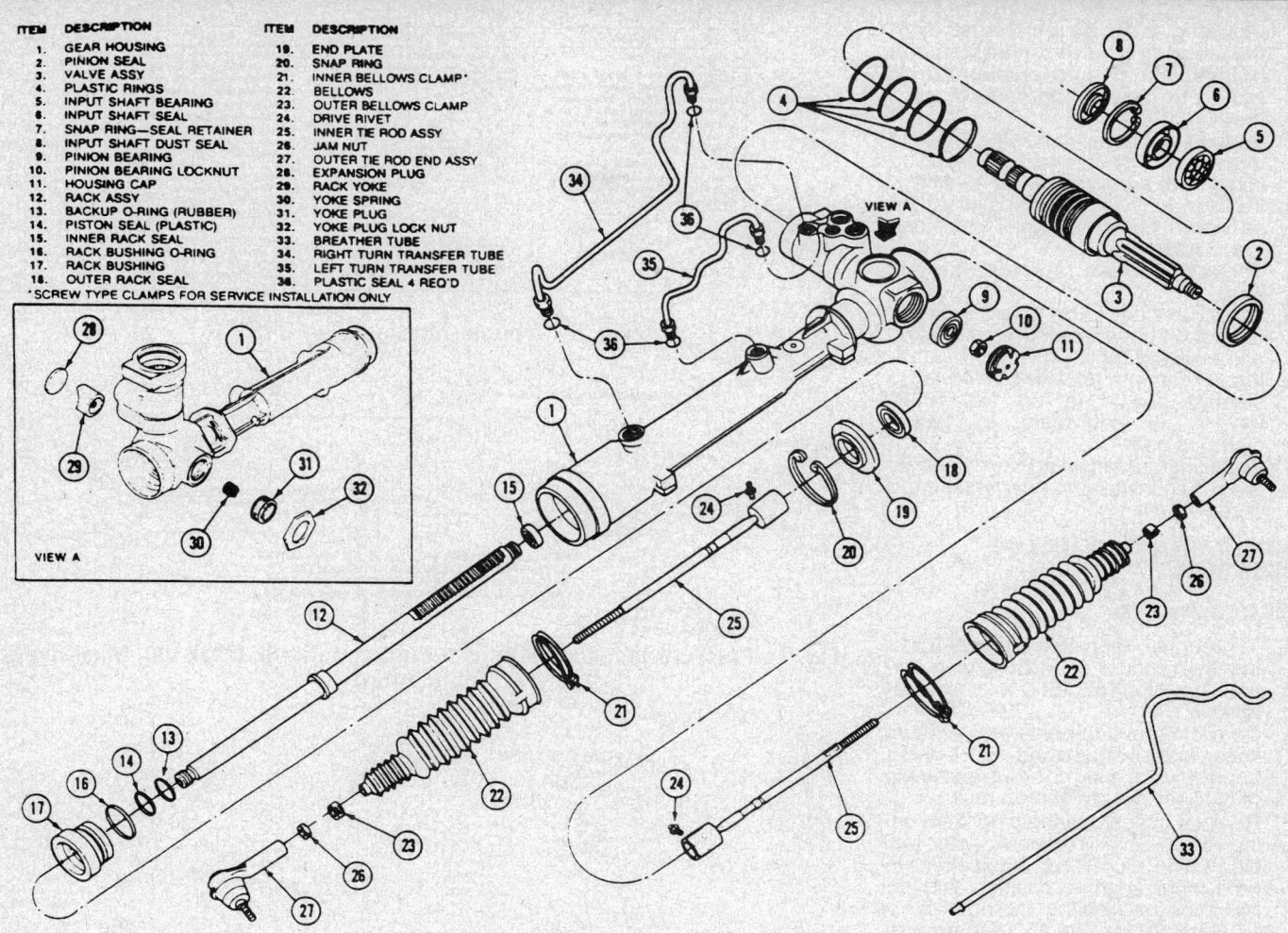

Fig. 5 Exploded view of steering gear. Tempo & Topaz

FM6029100086000X

CONDITION	POSSIBLE SOURCE	ACTION
• Wander — Vehicle wander is a condition where the vehicle wanders side to side on the roadway when it is driven straight ahead while the steering wheel is held in a firm position. Evaluation should be conducted on a level road (little road crown).	• Improper wheel alignment.	• Set alignment to specification.
	• Loose outer tie rod ends.	• Replace outer tie rod end assemblies.
	• Inner tie rod ball housing loose or worn.	• Replace inner tie rod assemblies.
	• Gear assembly mounting loose.	• Tighten mounting bolts to specification.
	• Loose suspension struts or ball joints.	• Adjust or replace as required.
	• Column intermediate shaft connecting bolts loose.	• Tighten bolts to specification.
	• Loose wheel bearings.	• Service as required.
	• Column intermediate shaft joints loose or worn.	• Replace intermediate shaft.
• Feedback — (Rattle, chuckle, knocking noises in the steering gear). Feedback is a condition where roughness is felt in the steering wheel by the driver when the vehicle is driven over rough pavement.	• Column U-joints loose.	• Replace if bad.
	• Loose outer tie rod ends.	• Replace outer tie rod end assemblies.
	• Loose/worn inner tie rod ball.	• Replace inner tie rod assemblies.
	• Gear assembly mounting loose.	• Tighten mounting bolts to specification.
	• Loose pinion bearing cap.	• Tighten cap to specification.
	• Loose pinion bearing locknut.	• Tighten locknut to specification.
	• Piston disengaged or loose on rack.	• Replace rack assembly.
	• Steering gear yoke worn.	• Replace yoke assembly.
	• Column intermediate shaft connecting bolts loose.	• Tighten bolts to specification.
	• Loose suspension struts on ball joints.	• Adjust or replace as necessary.

FM6029100087010X

Fig. 6 Troubleshooting (Part 1 of 3)

CONDITION	POSSIBLE SOURCE	ACTION
• Poor Returnability — Sticky Feel — Poor returnability is noticed when the steering fails to return to center following a turn without manual effort from the driver. In addition, when the driver returns the steering to center, it may have a sticky or catchy feel.	• Misaligned steering column or column flange rubbing steering wheel and/or flange.	• Align column.
	• Check rotational torque of intermediate shaft joints.	• If binding, replace intermediate shaft.
	• Improper wheel alignment.	• Set to specification.
	• Tight inner tie rod ball joints.	• Replace inner tie rod as required.
	• Binding in valve assembly.	• Replace input shaft valve assembly.
	• Bent or damaged rack.	• Replace rack assembly.
	• Bent or damaged sub-frame.	• Replace as necessary.
	• Column bearing binding.	• Replace bearing.
	• Tight suspension struts or lower control arm ball joints.	• Adjust or replace as required.
	• Contamination in system.	• Flush power steering system.
	• Deformed engine mounts.	• Replace as required.
• Heavy Steering Efforts (Poor or loss of assist) — A heavy effort and poor assist condition is recognized by the driver while turning corners and especially while parking. A road test will verify this condition	• Leakage/loss of fluid.	• external leakage service.
	• Low pump fluid.	• Fill as necessary.
	• Pump external leakage.	• Service.
	• Improper drive belt tension.	• Readjust belt tension.
	• Hose or cooler external leakage.	• Replace as necessary.
	• Improper engine idle speed.	• Readjust idle.
	• Pulley loose or warped.	• Replace pulley.
	• Pump/flow pressure not to specification.	
	• Hose/cooler line restrictions.	• Clear or replace as required.
	• Valve plastic ring cut or twisted.	• Replace ring.
	• Damaged/worn plastic piston ring.	• Replace ring.
	• Loose/missing rubber backup piston O-ring.	• Replace/install O-ring.
	• Loose rack piston.	• Replace rack assembly.
	• Gear assembly oil passages restricted.	• Clear/service as required.
	• Bent/damaged rack assembly.	• Replace rack assembly.

Fig. 6 Troubleshooting (Part 2 of 3)

FM6029100087020X

this step must be performed with the steering gear removed from the holding fixture and positioned on bench to prevent damage to gear teeth.

2. Support ball housing using a wooden block, then install roll pins by tapping lightly with a plastic mallet.
3. If pinion was removed, install pinion as described under Input Shaft and Valve Assembly.
4. Thoroughly clean rack and housing bore.
5. Apply lubricant to bellows clamp under cut on tie rod, then install bellows and breather tube.
6. Install clamps retaining bellows to steering gear. Use tool No. T63P-9171-A, or equivalent, to secure clamp to gear.
7. Install clamps retaining bellows to tie rods, then install jam nuts and tie rod end.

INPUT SHAFT & VALVE ASSEMBLY

Disassemble

1. Thoroughly clean steering gear housing, then mount gear in Holding Fixture tool No. T57L-500-B or equivalent.
2. Do not remove the external pressure lines unless damaged or leaking. Loosen yoke plug locknut and yoke plug to relieve preload on rack.
3. Remove pinion bearing plug, then using Pinion Shaft Torque Adapter tool No. T74P-3504-R, or equivalent, to hold input shaft in position and remove pinion bearing locknut with a $^{11}/_{16}$ inch socket, **Fig. 15. Discard pinion bearing locknut and use a new nut at assembly.**
4. Using a suitable tool, pry input shaft dust seal out of valve housing. Use care not to damage valve housing.
5. Remove snap ring from valve housing.
6. Attach Valve Body Puller tool No. T78P-3504-B, or equivalent, to input shaft and remove input shaft seal and bearing and valve body, **Fig. 16.**. On Continental, Sable & Taurus, attach Valve Body Puller (Bridge) tool No. T86P-3504-B and Valve Body Puller (Screw) tool No. T78P-3504-B or equivalent, and remove input shaft seal, input shaft and valve body.
7. Using Lower Pinion Seal Remover tool No. T78P-3504-E, or equivalent, and a suitable slide hammer, remove lower pinion shaft seal.
8. Remove pinion bearing from gear housing using Puller Attachment tool No. T58L-101-A, or equivalent, and a suitable slide hammer.
9. If necessary, remove O-rings from input shaft and valve assembly. Remove O-rings by pushing rings to one side and inserting a small pointed knife to cut ring off.

Assemble

1. Support valve housing with a wooden block, then using Lower Pinion Bear-

CONDITION	POSSIBLE SOURCE	ACTION
• Hissing Sound There is some noise in all power steering systems. One of the most common is a hissing sound most evident at standstill parking. There is no relationship between this noise and the performance of the steering gear. CAUTION: Do not hold steering wheel at full lock more than five seconds, as damage to power steering pump may result.	• Hiss may be expected when the steering wheel is at the end of travel or when turning at standstill.	• Hiss is a normal characteristic of rotary steering gears and in no way affects steering. Do not replace the rack assembly unless the hiss is extremely objectionable. A replacement rack will also exhibit a slight noise and is not always a cure for the condition. Investigate for a grounded column or a loose boot at the dash panel. Any metal-to-metal contact will transmit valve hiss into the passenger compartment through the steering column. Verify clearance between flexible coupling components. Ensure steering column shaft and gear are aligned so flexible coupling rotates in a flat plane and is not distorted as shaft rotates.

FM6029100087030X

Fig. 6 Troubleshooting (Part 3 of 3)

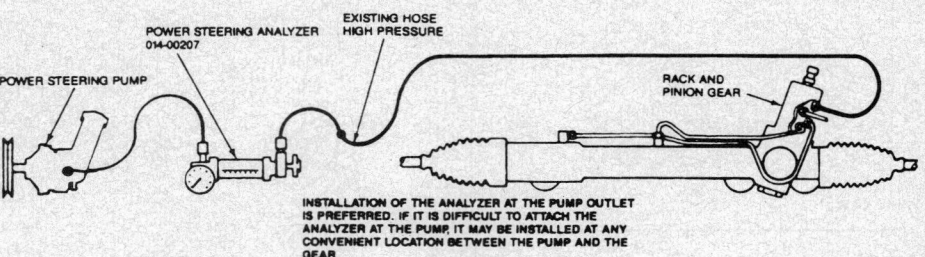

FM6029100088000X

Fig. 7 Pressure test connections. Cougar, Mark VII, Mark VIII, Mustang & Thunderbird

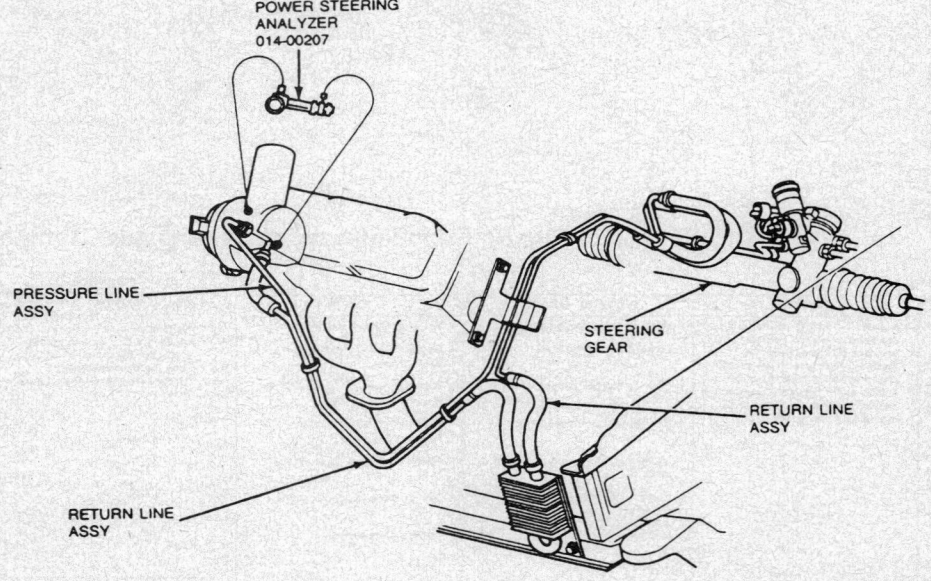

FM6029100089000X

Fig. 8 Pressure test connections. Continental

ing Replacer tool No. T78P-3504-G, or equivalent, install pinion bearing in gear bore. Seat bearing against shoulder in bore.
2. Apply grease to pinion oil seal, then position seal on Lower Pinion Seal Replacer tool No. T78P-3504-F, or equivalent, (tool No. T86P-3504-G on Continental, Sable & Taurus) with seal lip facing towards tool. Install seal in valve bore, seating seal against shoulder.
3. Position pinion end of valve assembly in a soft jawed vise.

4. Install Mandrel tool No. T75L-3517-A1, or equivalent, over sleeve, then slide one valve sleeve ring over mandrel.
5. Using Slide Pusher tool No. T75L-3517-A2, or equivalent, over mandrel, then rapidly push down on tool to force ring down into fourth groove of valve sleeve. Add one Spacer tool No. T75L-3517-A3, or equivalent, under mandrel, to align groove on the valve sleeve. Repeat procedure until all sleeve rings have been installed.

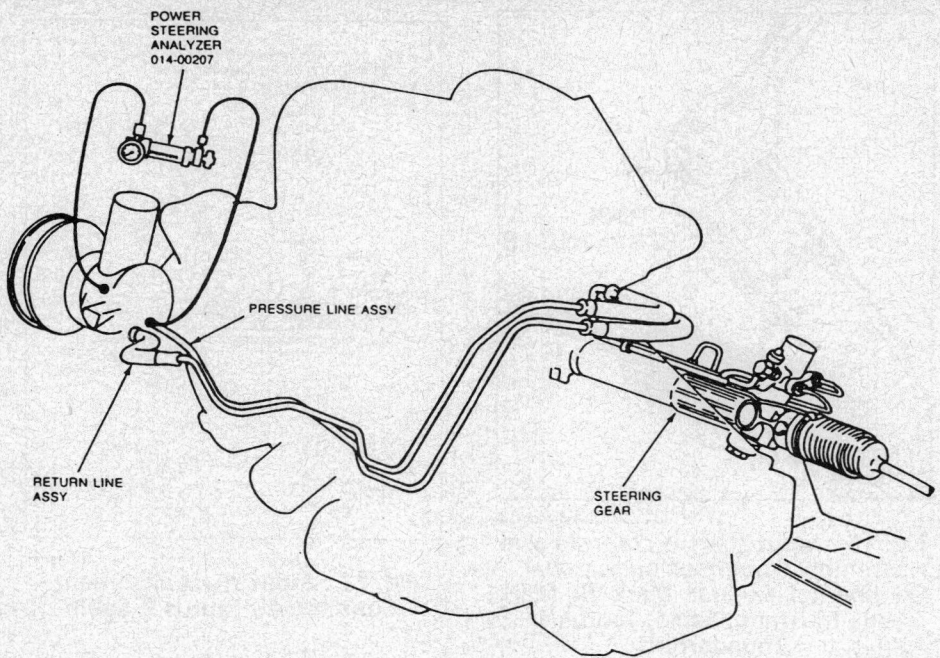

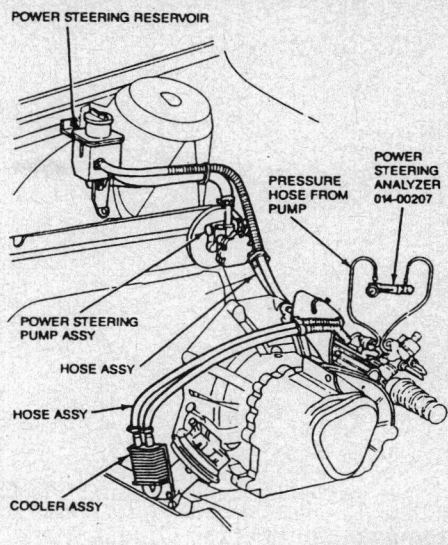

Fig. 10   Pressure test connections. Taurus SHO

Fig. 9   Pressure test connections. Sable & Taurus, except SHO

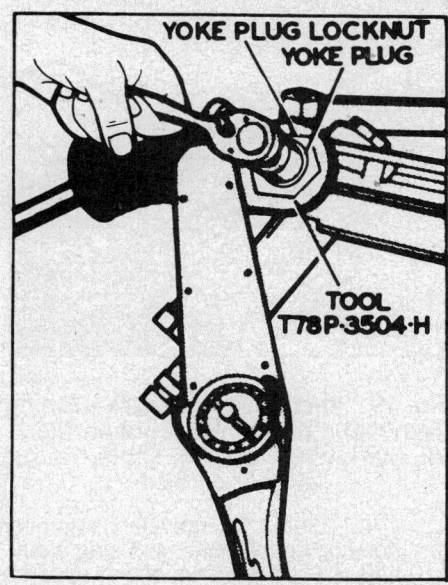

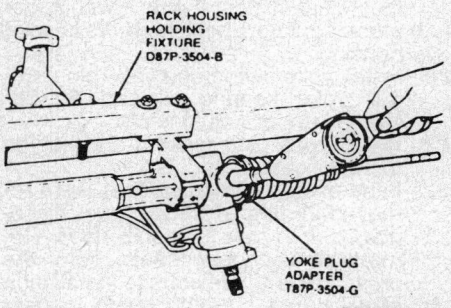

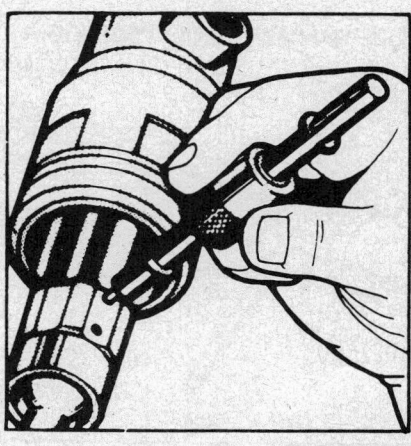

Fig. 12   Rack yoke plug preload adjustment. Tempo & Topaz

Fig. 13   Roll pin from ball socket removal. Continental, Cougar, Mark VII, Mark VIII, Mustang, Sable, Taurus & Thunderbird

Fig. 11   Loosening yoke plug locknut. Continental, Cougar, Mark VII, Mark VIII, Mustang, Sable, Taurus & Thunderbird

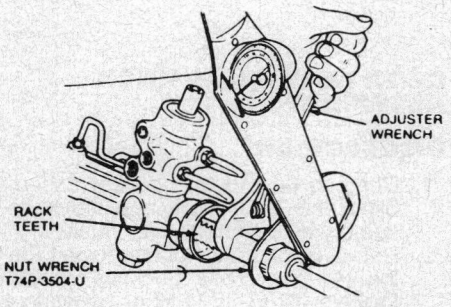

Fig. 14   Tie rod & ball socket removal. Continental, Cougar, Mark VII, Mark VIII, Mustang, Sable, Taurus & Thunderbird

6. Apply a light coat of power steering fluid to sleeve and sleeve rings.
7. Install one spacer over input shaft, then slowly install Sizing Tube tool No. T75L-3517-A4, or equivalent, over sleeve valve end of input shaft onto valve sleeve rings.
8. Remove Sizing Tube tool No. T75L-3517-A4, or equivalent, and check condition of sleeve rings. Ensure that rings turn freely in grooves.
9. If rack is removed, position rack so that mark made during disassembly is centered in valve bore. If rack was not removed, position rack in housing so that three teeth protrude from lefthand end of housing.
10. **On all models except Continental, Sable and Taurus,** align blocked tooth of input shaft with center of yoke plug hole and insert valve assembly into bore. The blocked tooth must face straight up when gear is installed in vehicle with gear in straight ahead position. Rotate input shaft assembly from side to side if necessary to mesh with rack teeth. Push valve assembly in by hand until fully seated.
11. **On Continental, Sable and Taurus models,** align input shaft flats as shown in **Fig. 17.**
12. **On all models,** using Pinion Shaft Torque Adapter tool No. T74P-3504-R, or equivalent, (tool No. T86P-3504-K for Continental, Sable & Taurus), to turn input shaft, count number of turns from center to each stop which should be approximately 1½ turns. If number of turns is unequal, pull valve assembly out of housing far enough to free pinion teeth. Rotate input shaft 60°, one tooth, in direction which required less fewer turns from center to stop. Reinstall valve assembly and check if gear is centered.

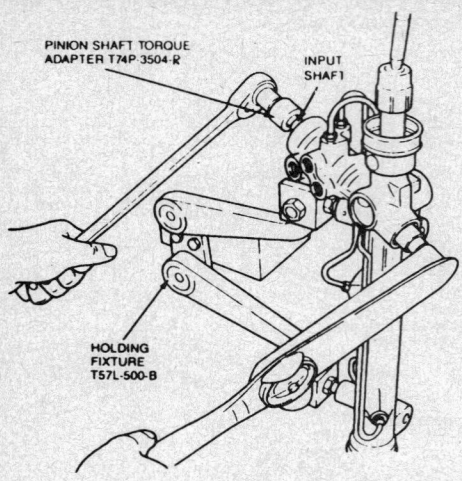

Fig. 15 Pinion bearing locknut removal. Continental, Cougar, Mark VII, Mark VIII, Mustang, Sable, Taurus & Thunderbird

Fig. 16 Input shaft & control valve assembly from housing removal. Continental, Cougar, Mark VII, Mark VIII, Mustang, Sable, Taurus & Thunderbird

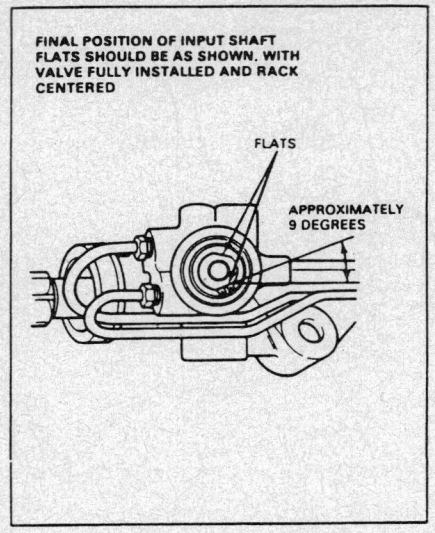

Fig. 17 Input shaft alignment. Continental, Taurus & Sable

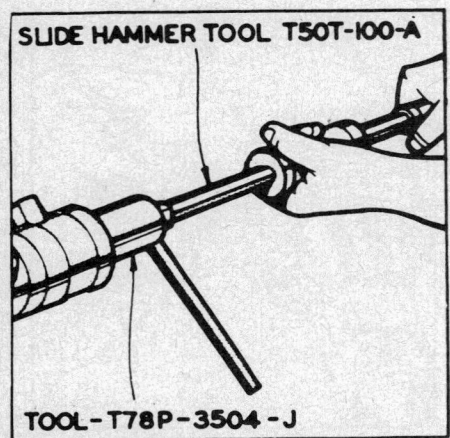

Fig. 18 Rack seal from gear housing removal. Continental, Cougar, Mark VII, Mark VIII, Mustang, Sable, Taurus & Thunderbird

19. Fill yoke housing with 2 ounces of lubricant, then install yoke. The yoke must seat against the rack with finger pressure, if not check for burrs in yoke housing.
20. Install yoke spring and yoke plug. Adjust yoke bearing preload as described under Adjustments.
21. Install yoke plug locknut and tighten to specifications.
22. If the external pressure lines were removed in step two, they must be replaced with new pressure lines. Remove the copper seals from the pressure ports previous to installation of new lines. Tighten pump to gear pressure line fitting and return line fitting and pressure line fittings at valve and power cylinder to specifications.

GEAR HOUSING & RACK ASSEMBLY

Disassemble

1. Remove tie rod and socket assemblies and input shaft and valve assembly as described previously.
2. Remove yoke plug locknut using Pinion Housing Yoke Locknut Wrench tool No. T78P-3504-H, or equivalent, then remove yoke plug using a ³/₄ inch socket.
3. Remove yoke spring and yoke bearing from gear housing.
4. Working from righthand side of gear, push rack in until it bottoms.
5. Remove snap ring from right end housing, then carefully pull rack out of housing until rack piston contacts rack bushings. Pull on rack until bushing is withdrawn from housing, then remove rack.
6. To remove rack high pressure oil seal, insert Rack Oil Seal Remover tool No.

Fig. 19 Rack seat from rack bushing removal. Continental, Cougar, Mark VII, Mark VIII, Mustang, Sable, Taurus & Thunderbird

T78P-3504-J, or equivalent, into gear housing until it bottoms. Using a suitable wrench tighten tool until expander is fully tightened, then attach a suitable slide hammer to tool and remove seal, **Fig. 18.**
7. Using O-ring tool No. T71P-19703-C, or equivalent, remove O-rings from rack piston.
8. Position rack bushing, seal end first into Rack Bushing Holding tool No. T78P-3504-L, or equivalent, then place tool and bushing in a vise. With Rack Oil Seal Remover tool No. T78P-3504-J, or equivalent, and a suitable slide hammer, remove seal, **Fig. 19.**
9. Remove O-rings from bushing with O-ring tool No. T71P-19703-C, or equivalent.

Assemble

1. Apply grease to rack high pressure oil

13. While holding input shaft with Pinion Shaft Torque Adapter tool No. T74P-3504-R, or equivalent, install a new pinion bearing locknut on pinion end of valve assembly. Tighten pinion bearing locknut to specifications. The rack must be away from stops when installing locknut.
14. Lubricate input shaft bearing, then install bearing into valve bore and seat with Upper Pinion Bearing Seal Replacer tool No. T78P-3504-D, or equivalent.
15. Lubricate input shaft seal, then install seal with seal lip facing valve assembly.
16. Install snap ring into valve bore.
17. Coat input shaft in area of dust seal with lubriplate or equivalent, then install dust seal and seat seal with Upper Pinion Bearing Seal Replacer tool No. T78P-3504-D, or equivalent.
18. Install steering gear housing cap.

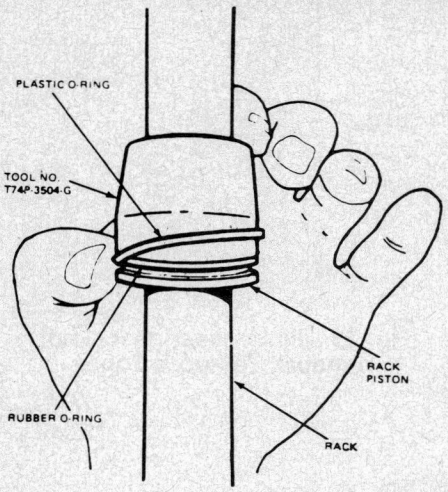

Fig. 20 Plastic O-ring on rack piston installation. Continental, Cougar, Mark VII, Mark VIII, Mustang, Sable, Taurus & Thunderbird

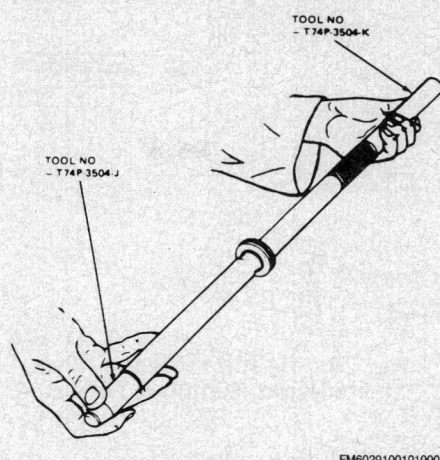

Fig. 21 Positioning sleeve protector on rack. Continental, Cougar, Mark VII, Mark VIII, Mustang, Sable, Taurus & Thunderbird

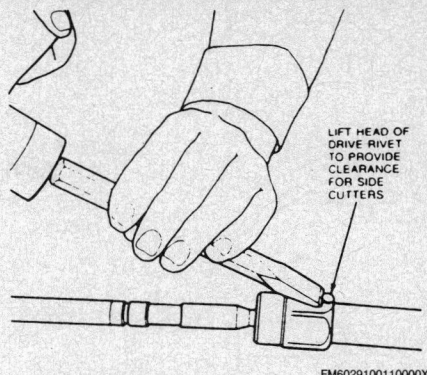

Fig. 22 Loosening tie rod retaining rivet. Tempo & Topaz

seal, position seal on tool No. T78P-3504-K, or equivalent, with lip spring facing inside. Place gear housing in vertical position, then place tool into right side of housing. Tap on tool handle until seal is seated. **Use care not to cock handle of tool when installing seal.**

2. Mark center tooth of rack so that it will be visible through valve bore.
3. Install rubber O-ring into groove on rack piston.
4. Position plastic O-ring on Teflon Ring Replacer tool No. T74P-3504-G, or equivalent, then slide tool and O-ring onto rack until they are adjacent to the rack piston. Slide plastic O-ring off tool and into piston groove over rubber O-ring, **Fig. 20.**
5. Apply lubricant ESB-M1C119-A, or equivalent, to rack teeth. Also apply a light coating of lubricant opposite rack teeth in yoke bearing contact area.
6. Install Protective Sleeve tool No. T74P-3504-K, or equivalent, over rack gear teeth to prevent damage to integral oil seal in gear housing. Also thread Rack Seal Protector Sleeve tool No. T74P-3504-J, or equivalent, over rack threads, **Fig. 21.**
7. Lubricate plastic O-ring and protective sleeves with power steering fluid.
8. Position small diameter end of Teflon Ring Sizing tool No. T78P-3504-M, or equivalent, into righthand side opening of gear housing.
9. Place rack toothed end first, into Teflon Ring Sizing tool No. T78P-3504-M, or equivalent, then carefully push rack into housing until leading end engages internal oil seal. Position tool No. Teflon Ring Sizing tool T78P-3504-M, or equivalent, so that it compresses plastic O-ring. Push rack into housing until protective sleeve protrudes from lefthand side of gear housing. Remove Teflon Ring Sizing tool No. T78P-3504-M, or equivalent,

and long protective sleeve from end of rack. Install tie rod and ball socket assembly on left end of rack to prevent rack teeth from damaging internal oil seal.
10. Install two O-rings on rack bushing.
11. Lubricate outer rack oil seal with gear lube, then using Outer Rack Seal Replacer tool No. T74P-3504-F, or equivalent, install oil seal in rack bushing with lip spring facing inside of bushing.
12. Lubricate short protective sleeve on rack end and rack bushing O-rings with gear lube.
13. Start bushing with seal end first onto rack. Position bushing and seal over protective sleeve and into housing bore. Using Teflon Ring Sizing tool No. T78P-3504-M, or equivalent, apply hand pressure to end plate and rack bushing until bushing is seated in housing bore. If bushing will not seat using hand pressure, tap bushing in using a 1 1/8 inch socket and a plastic mallet. Install snap ring and remove protective sleeve.
14. Install tie rod assemblies as described under "Tie Rod Ends, Bellows and Ball Joint Sockets."
15. Install input shaft and valve assembly as described under "Input Shaft and Valve Assembly."
16. Fill yoke plug hole with 2 ounces of lubricant. Install yoke, spring, plug and locknut. Adjust yoke bearing preload as described under Adjustments.
17. If the external pressure lines were removed, they must be replaced with new pressure lines. Remove the copper seals from the pressure ports previous to installation of new lines. Tighten pump to gear pressure line and return line fittings and pressure line fittings at valve and power cylinder to specifications.
18. Apply lubricant under cuts in tie rod, then install bellows, equalizer tube,

clamps, jam nuts and tie rod ends.

TEMPO & TOPAZ
INNER TIE ROD & BELLOWS
Disassemble

1. Mount steering gear in Holding Fixture tool No. D87P-3504-B or equivalent.
2. Remove outer tie rod ends and locknuts.
3. Remove clamps retaining bellows to gear housing, then remove bellows and breather tube.
4. With a sharp chisel, gently tap around rivet head so it lifts away from ball joint, **Fig. 22.**
5. Use side cutters to pry out drive pin, **Fig. 23.**
6. Position rack so several teeth are exposed. Hold hack with an adjustable wrench on end teeth only, while loosening ball joints nuts with Yoke Locknut Tool No. T81P-3504-G or equivalent.

Assemble

1. With several rack teeth exposed, hold rack with an adjustable wrench and tighten each tie rod ball joint assembly to specifications using Yoke Locknut Tool No. T81P-3504-G or equivalent.
2. Install a new rivet in tie rod ball housing until pin is flush with rivet head, **Fig. 24.**
3. Install bellows and breather tube.
4. Install tie rod outer ends.

INPUT SHAFT & VALVE ASSEMBLY
Disassemble

The only serviceable component of the input shaft and valve assembly are the four plastic O-rings.

1. Clean exterior of steering gear thoroughly.
2. Mount gear in Holding Fixture tool No. D87P-3504-B or equivalent. **Do not hold gear in vise.**
3. Do not remove external pressure lines unless they are leaking.
4. Loosen yoke plug locknut to relieve preload on rack.
5. Remove pinion bearing plug using Pinion Plug Spanner tool No. T83P-

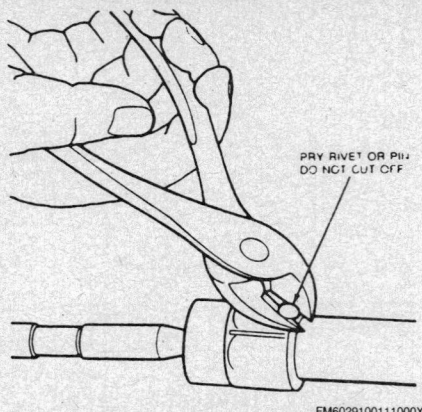

Fig. 23 Tie rod retaining rivet removal. Tempo & Topaz

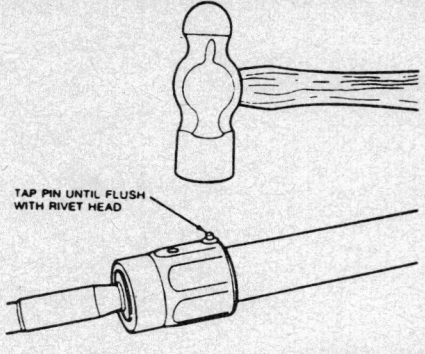

Fig. 24 Tie rod retaining rivet installation. Tempo & Topaz

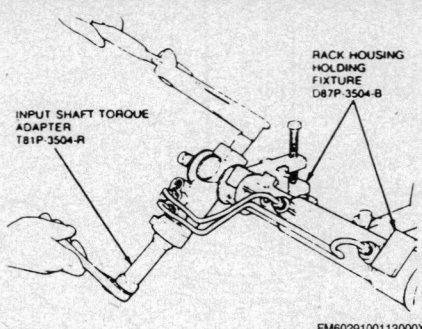

Fig. 25 Pinion bearing locknut removal. Tempo & Topaz

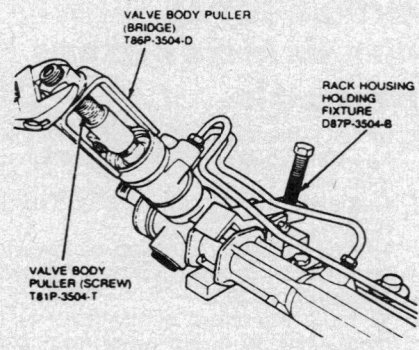

Fig. 26 Valve body puller tool. Tempo & Topaz

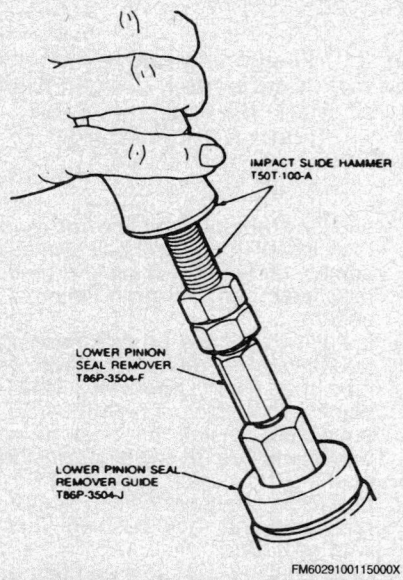

Fig. 27 Lower pinion seal removal tool. Tempo & Topaz

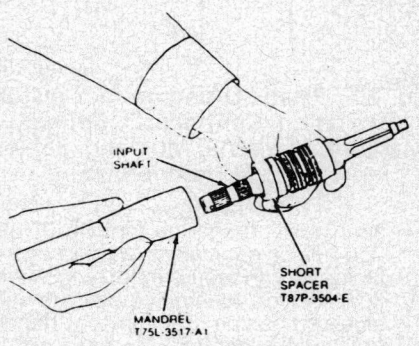

Fig. 28 Plastic valve rings installation. Tempo & Topaz

3504-AH or equivalent.

6. While holding input shaft, remove and discard pinion bearing locknut, **Fig. 25.**
7. Pry out input shaft dust seal using an appropriate tool.
8. Remove snap ring, located under dust seal, from housing.
9. Attach Valve Body Puller tool No. T86P-3504-D and Valve Body Puller tool No. T81P-3504-T or equivalent to input shaft, **Fig. 26.**
10. Turn nut to remove valve. Input shaft seal and bearing will come out with valve body.
11. Remove lower pinion shaft seal using Seal Removal Tools No. T86P-3504-F, T86P-3504-J and T50T-100-A or equivalents, **Fig. 27.**
12. Remove pinion bearing from gear housing using Puller Attachment tool No. T58L-101-B or equivalent.
13. Remove O-rings by pushing rings to one side, then inserting small pointed tool under each ring, and cutting ring off.

Assemble

1. Install steering gear pinion bearing in gear housing using Lower Pinion Bearing Replacer tool No. T81P-3504-H or equivalent. Seat bearing against shoulder in boar. **Support valve housing when seating pinion bearing.**
2. Apply Steering gear grease No. C3AZ-

19578-A or equivalent to pinion seal and place it on Lower Pinion Seal Replacer tool No. T87P-3504-C or equivalent with seal lip toward tool.

3. Install short spacer over input shaft of valve assembly, **Fig. 28.** Install mandrel part of Valve Seal Installer tool No. T75L-3517-A or equivalent over shaft and spacer. Mandrel will line up with second groove from input shaft.
4. Lubricate mandrel with power steering fluid. Place one valve sleeve over mandrel. Rapidly push ring down with pusher tool. Ring will drop into proper groove.
5. Install long spacer over input shaft. Mandrel will line up with first groove on input shaft. Repeat step 4.
6. Repeat steps 3 through 5 sliding mandrel over the pinion end of valve.
7. After four valve sleeves are installed, apply a light coat of steering gear grease to sleeve and rings.
8. Slowly install Teflon Seal Sizing tool No. T87P-3504-F or equivalent over valve sleeve rings, **Fig. 29. Ensure that rings are not being bent over or out of grooves as tube is slid over them.**

9. Continue sliding sizing tool over rings until it has passed over rings and comes off other end. Ensure rings turn freely in the grooves.
10. Position rack in housing so four complete tooth spaces protrude from left-hand end of housing, then move rack slightly, as necessary, to center tooth visible in valve bore, **Fig. 30.**
11. Position Teflon seal sizing tool in valve housing bore.
12. Position D-flat on input shaft at the 3 o'clock position and insert valve assembly into bore. **The D-flat surface must be at the 3 o'clock position in the vehicle with the gear on center position. Rotate input shaft slightly, if necessary, to mesh the pinion with the rack teeth.**
13. Push valve assembly in by hand until seated properly, then remove sizing tool.
14. Using Input Shaft Torque Adjuster tool No. T81P-3504-R or equivalent count total turns, stop to stop. From one stop, back off half the total of turns. D-flat should be ad shown in **Fig. 31.** If not, repeat steps 11 through 13.
15. Install bearing assembly in valve bore and seat with input shaft and Seal Installer tool No. T78P-3504-D or equivalent.
16. Install Input Shaft Protector tool No. T81P-3504-P or equivalent over input shaft and install input shaft seal with lip spring toward valve.
17. Remove seal protector and seat seal.

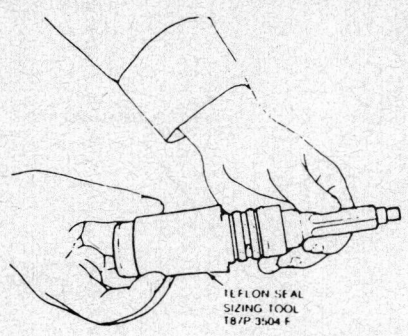

Fig. 29 Seal sizing tool installation. Tempo & Topaz

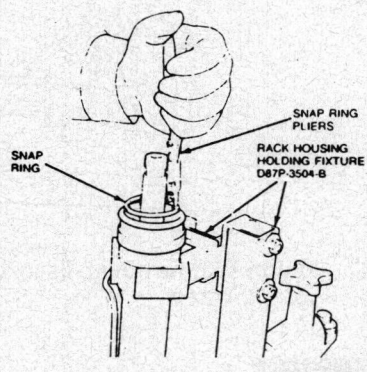

Fig. 32 Snap ring removal. Tempo & Topaz

18. Install retaining snap ring in valve bore.
19. Apply a generous amount of grease over top of input shaft pressure seal around input shaft.
20. Install dust seal and seat with Seal Installer tool No. T78P-3504-D or equivalent.
21. Install nut on pinion end of valve assembly. Holding input shaft tighten nut to specifications. **Rack must be in center position when tightening.**
22. Install steering gear pinion bearing cap, then tighten to specifications.
23. Set rack preload as outlined under "Adjustments, Rack Yoke Plug Preload."

GEAR HOUSING, RACK YOKE PLUG, RACK ASSEMBLY, RACK BUSHING & OIL SEAL

Disassemble

1. Remove tie rods and socket assemblies from both ends of rack, also remove input shaft and valve assembly from gear housing as described previously.
2. Remove yoke plug and spring. **Yoke cannot be removed at this time.**
3. Working from righthand side of gear, push rack in just far enough to enable removal of snap ring, **Fig. 32.**
4. Slowly pull rack out of righthand side of housing until rack position contacts aluminum rack bushing. Apply pulling effort and remove rack from housing.

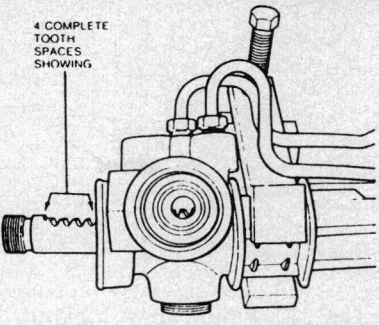

Fig. 30 Positioning rack in housing. Tempo & Topaz

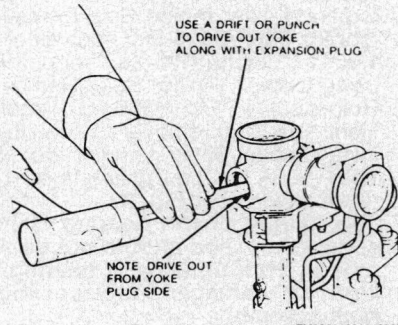

Fig. 33 Yoke & expansion plug removal. Tempo & Topaz

Do not hammer on rack until bushing is withdrawn from housing.
5. Using Rack Oil Seal Remover tool No. T87P-3504-A or equivalent, remove internal high pressure oil seal.
6. Remove plastic O-ring and rubber O-ring from rack piston.
7. Insert rack bushing into Rack Bushing Holder tool No. T78P-3504-L or equivalent, seal end first. Place tool and bushing into vice.
8. Using Rack Oil Seal Remover tool No. T87P-3504-A, remove seal.
9. Remove rubber O-ring from rack bushing.
10. Use a drift or punch to knock out yoke, along with expansion plug, **Fig. 33.**

Assemble

1. Coat new yoke with steering gear grease. Install through expansion plug opening, rack bearing surface up.
2. Slide Teflon Ring Installation tool No. T81P-3504-L or equivalent over plain end of rack up to piston.
3. Remove plastic insert from rack seal and save.
4. Install seal protector over rack teeth.
5. Lubricate rack seal protector and rack with power steering fluid.
6. Install seal with lip toward piston.
7. Install plastic insert in rack seal. Remove seal protector.
8. Apply steering gear lubricant to rack teeth and power steering fluid to the piston seal and rack seal outside diameter.
9. Install Teflon Seal Sizing tool No. T87P-3504-F or equivalent into end of gear housing.
10. Ensure yoke in positioned correctly

Fig. 31 Proper input shaft position. Tempo & Topaz

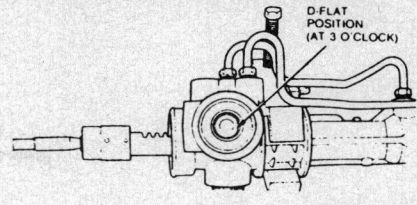

Fig. 31 Proper input shaft position. Tempo & Topaz

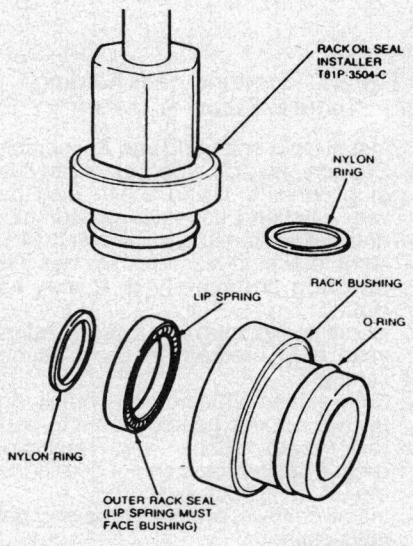

Fig. 34 Rack bushing & seal. Tempo & Topaz

then install rack, ensuring not to scratch housing piston bore.
11. Carefully push piston through sizing tool. Continue pushing on rack until it bottoms. Remove sizing tool.
12. Seat rack seal with rack by driving end of rack with a drift and plastic mallet.
13. Install lefthand tie rod hand tight to prevent potential inner seal damage due to excessive rack travel.
14. Center rack in housing.
15. Install rubber O-ring on aluminum rack bushing.
16. Apply power steering fluid to outer rack seal and install seal in rack bushing. Seal lip spring must face inside of bushing, **Fig. 34.**
17. Install Rack Seal Protector tool No. T81P-3504-N or equivalent over threads on righthand side of rack. apply power steering fluid to protective sleeve.
18. Start bushing, seal side out, on rack. Position bushing into housing. Place end plate against rack bushing. Apply hand pressure to end plate and rack bushing until bushing seats in gear housing. If rack bushing will not seat with hand pressure, a 1 1/8 inch deep socket and a plastic mallet may be used to tap bushing in place.
19. Install retaining ring and remove protective sleeve.
20. Install tie rod assemblies as previously described.

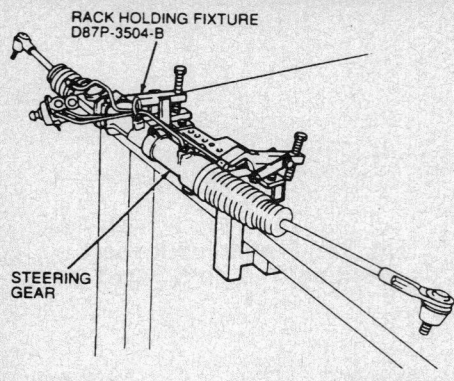

Fig. 35 Steering gear holding fixture. Escort & Tracer

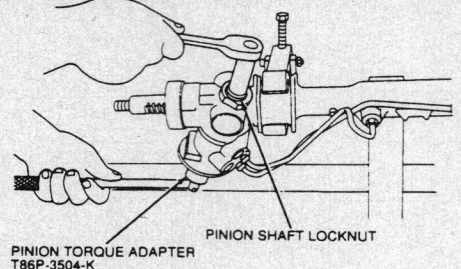

Fig. 36 Pinion shaft locknut removal. Escort & Tracer

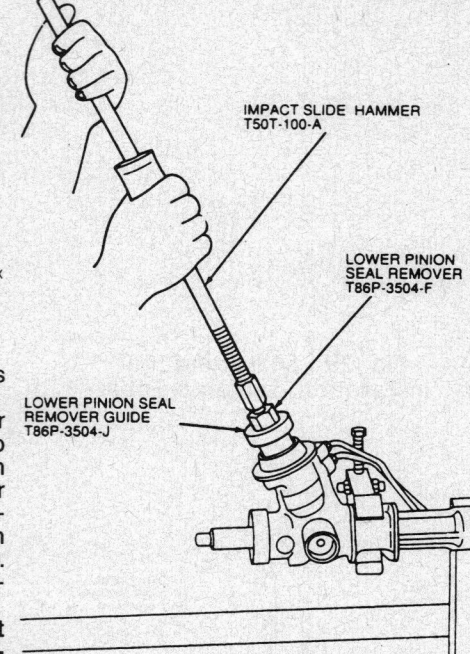

Fig. 37 Pinion seal removal. Escort & Tracer

21. Install input shaft and valve assembly.
22. Support gear on wood block at yoke plug opening. Using a 1¼ inch bar with a flat end, flatten expansion plug until flat portion is approximately ½ to ¾ of total plug diameter. **Do not flatten plug completely or it may fall out.**
23. Install spring, plug and locknut. Adjust yoke plug preload as previous described.
24. Fully extend lefthand end of rack. Apply two ounces gear lubricant to pack rack teeth. Place any remaining grease into lefthand end of gear housing.
25. Install bellows, breather tube and bellows clamps.
26. Install jam nuts and tie rod ends on tie rods.

STEERING GEAR SERVICE
ESCORT & TRACER
Disassemble

1. Install steering gear to Rack Holding Fixture tool No. D87P-3504-B or equivalent, **Fig. 35.**
2. Place installation alignment marks on tie rod end, jam nut and tie rod.
3. Remove tire rod ends and jam nuts, **Fig. 3.**
4. Remove boot clamps, the remove boots.
5. Remove tie rods, then pinion shaft dust seal.
6. Remove pinion shaft snap ring, then using Yoke Locknut Wrench tool No. T81P-3504-G or equivalent, remove yoke plug locknut.
7. Using Yoke Plug Adapter tool No. T87P-3504-G or equivalent, remove yoke plug.
8. Remove spring, then using Pinion Plug Spanner Wrench tool No. T90P-3504-AH or equivalent, remove lower pinion bearing plug.
9. Using Pinion Torque Adapter tool No. T86P-3504-K or equivalent, to hold pinion shaft, remove pinion shaft locknut, **Fig. 36.**
10. Using Valve Body Puller Bridge tool No. T86P-3504-D and Spool Valve Puller tool No. T81P-3504-T or equivalents, remove pinion shaft seal, bearing and shaft from housing.

11. Remove four valve Teflon O-rings and discard.
12. Expand Lower Pinion Seal Remover tool No. T86P-3504-F or equivalent to 1.08–1.13 inch (27.4–28.7 mm), then using Lower Pinion Seal Remover Guide tool No. T86P-3504-J or equivalent, seat seal remover to seal, then install Impact Slide Hammer tool No. T50T-100A or equivalent, then remove pinion seal, **Fig. 37.**
13. **The middle pinion bearing is not serviceable, and should not be removed from housing. If bearing is worn or damaged, replace short rack assembly.**
14. Remove rack snap ring, rack end plate, busing and rack from housing.
15. Using Piston Pin Remover tool No. T68P-6135-A7 or equivalent, remove lower pinion bearing.
16. Using Impact Slide Hammer tool No. T50T-100-A and Rack Oil Seal Remover tool No. T87P-3504-A or equivalent, remove and discard inner seal.
17. If plastic insert is removed and seal is left in housing, repeat step 17 for seal removal.
18. Using Rack Bushing tool No. T87P-3504-L, Rack Oil Seal Remover tool No. T87P-3504-A and Impact Slide Hammer tool No. T50T-100-A or equivalents, remove rack bushing seal, **Fig. 38.**
19. Remove rack bushing O-ring and discard.
20. Remove rack piston Teflon seal and discard.
21. Remove rack piston O-ring and discard.
22. If yoke support requires replacement, using suitable drift, punch out expansion plug, then remove yoke support and discard support and expansion plug.

Inspection

1. Inspect pinion shaft bearing for fit on shaft.
2. Check fluid passages for obstruction or leakage.
3. Inspect housing for cracks and stripped threads.
4. Check mating surfaces for burrs.
5. Inspect valve and piston bores for scoring.
6. Ensure pinion shaft rotates freely.
7. Inspect piston rack and pinion shaft teeth for nicks and burrs.

Assemble

1. If required, install yoke support and expansion plug.
2. Using Piston Seal Replacer tool No. T81P-3504-L or equivalent, install rack piston O-ring, then Teflon seal, **Fig. 39.**
3. Separate steering gear inner seal plastic insert and save for later installation.
4. Install Rack Oil Seal Protector tool No. T87P-3504-H or equivalent, over rack, then install plastic insert and inner seal to piston, then remove seal protector.
5. Snap plastic insert into inner seal.
6. Using suitable steering gear lubricant, pack steering rack teeth, then apply light lubricant to rack yoke contact area.
7. Using suitable power steering fluid, lubricate piston seal and gear inner seal outer edge.
8. Install Rack Piston Seal Sizer tool No. T81P-3504-K or equivalent, to end of steering gear housing, then install rack.
9. Using suitable punch and plastic hammer, drive end of rack to seat inner seal.
10. Install rack bushing O-ring, then using Rack Oil Seal Replacer tool No. T81P-3504-C or equivalent, install rack bushing seal.
11. Using Rack Oil Seal Protector tool No. T87P-3504-H or equivalent, over rack, install rack bushing and end plate, **Fig. 40.**
12. Install rack attaching snap ring to housing.
13. Using Pinion Bearing Replacer tool

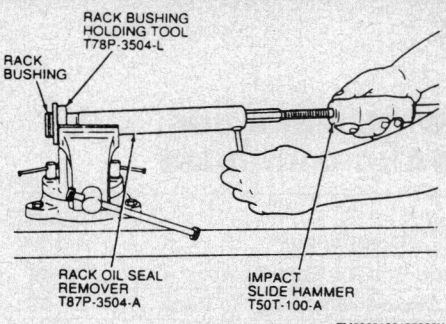

Fig. 38 Rack bushing seal removal. Escort & Tracer

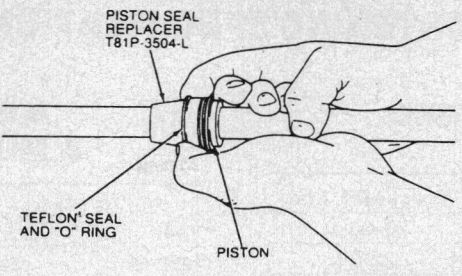

Fig. 39 Rack piston O-ring & seal installation. Escort & Tracer

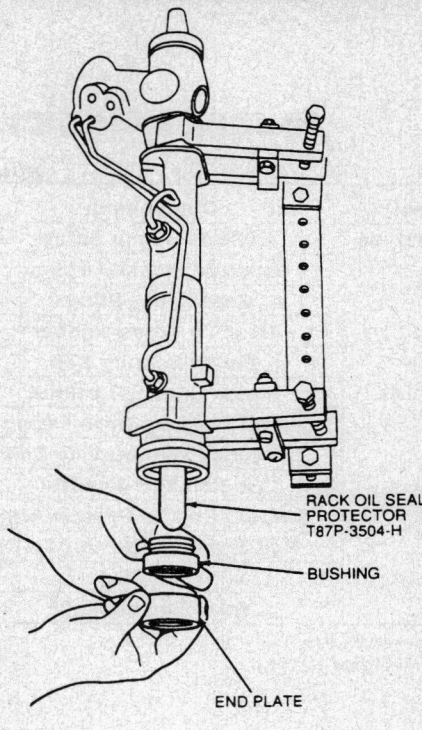

Fig. 40 Rack bushing & end plate installation. Escort & Tracer

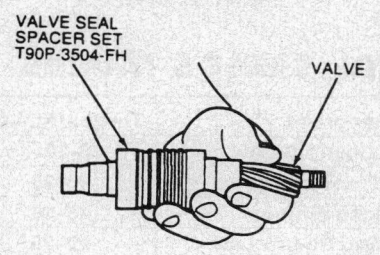

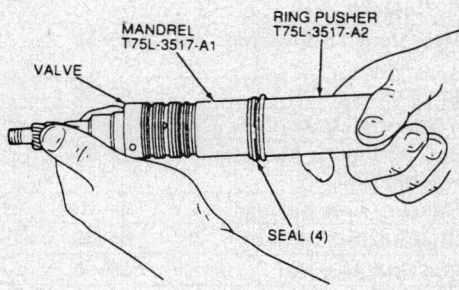

Fig. 41 Valve seal installation. Escort & Tracer

No. T90P-3504-BH and driver handle tool No. T80T-4000-W or equivalents, install lower pinion bearing.

14. Using Lower Pinion Seal Replacer tool No. T87P-3504-C and Handle tool No. T87P-3504-D or equivalents, install pinion seal.
15. Install Valve Seal Spacer Set tool No. T90P-3504-FH or equivalent, then using Mandrel tool No. T75L-3517-A1 and Ring Pusher tool No. T75L-3517-A2 or equivalents, install valve Teflon seal, **Fig. 41.**
16. Size valve Teflon seals with Teflon Ring Sizer tool No. T87P-3504-F or equivalent.
17. Center rack in housing.
18. Install Teflon Ring Sizer tool No. T87P-3504-F or equivalent, in valve housing bore. **Center of pinion shaft V-flat surface must be in 9 o'clock position.**
19. Install pinion shaft until teeth mesh with rack teeth, center of pinion shaft V-flat will be in 9 o'clock position, push shaft by hand until fully seated.
20. Using Pinion Torque Adapter tool No. T86P-3504-K or equivalent, turn pinion shaft, count number of turns from center to each stop, ensure pinion shaft is centered, is number of turn is not equal, remove shaft and reinstall.
21. Using Pinion Torque Adapter tool No. T86P-3504-K or equivalent, hold pinion shaft, then tighten shaft locknut to specifications.
22. Using Pinion Plug Spanner Wrench tool No. T90P-3504-AH or equivalent, install lower pinion bearing plug, tighten to specifications.
23. Using Upper Pinion Bearing/Seal Replacer tool No. T78P-3504-D and Bearing Spacer Ring tool No. T90P-3504-CH or equivalents, install pinion shaft bearing.
24. Install Input Shaft Seal Protector tool No. T81P-3504-P or equivalent, over pinion shaft.
25. Using Upper Pinion Bearing/Seal Replacer tool No. T78P-3504-D and Seal Spacer Ring tool No. T90P-3504-DH or equivalents, install pinion shaft.
26. Install snap ring to housing.
27. Using Pinion Dust Seal Replacer tool No. T85T-3504-CH1 or equivalent, install pinion shaft dust seal.
28. Install yoke plug bore spring, then using Yoke Plug Adapter tool No. T87P-3504-G or equivalent, install yoke plug then tighten to specifications.
29. Using Yoke Locknut Wrench tool No. T81P-3504-G or equivalent, tighten yoke plug locknut to specifications.
30. Apply ESE-MAG203-A2 to tie rods, then install to rack and tighten to specifications.
31. Install and clamp boots.
32. Install jam nuts, then tie rod ends and tighten to specifications.

TIGHTENING SPECIFICATIONS

COUGAR & THUNDERBIRD

Year	Component	Torque/Ft. Lbs.
1992–94	Bellows Clamp Screw	20–30①
	External Transfer Tubes	22–28
	Gear Hose Fittings	20–25
	Gear To Crossmember	100–144
	Pinion Bearing Cap	40–50
	Pinion Bearing Locknut	30–40
	Pump Pressure Hose Fitting	10–15
	Steering Flex Coupling Bolt	20–30
	Tie Rod End Jam Nut	35–50
	Tie Rod End To Spindle Arm	39–54
	Tie Rod Socket Assembly To Rack	55–65
	Yoke Plug	②
	Yoke Plug Locknut	44–66

①—Inch lbs.
②—Refer to text.

ESCORT & TRACER

Year	Component	Torque/Ft. Lbs.
1992–93	A/C Compressor	30–40
	High Pressure Line To Housing Flare Nut	21–25
	Lower Pinion Bearing Plug	22–28
	Pinion Shaft Locknut	20–35
	Return Line To Housing Flare Nut	21–25
	Tie Rod End Jam Nuts	25–37
	Tie Rod To Rack	40–50
	Valve Outlet Fittings	25–40
	Yoke Plug	①
	Yoke Plug Locknut	40–50

①—Tighten to 42–44 inch lbs., then loosen 44-52°, then tighten.

MARK VII, MARK VIII & MUSTANG

Year	Component	Torque/Ft. Lbs.
1992-94	Bellows Clamp Screw	20–30①
	External Transfer Tubes	15–25
	Gear Hose Fittings	20–25
	Gear To Crossmember	30–40
	Pinion Bearing Cap	40–50
	Pinion Bearing Locknut	30–40
	Pump Pressure Hose Fitting	10–15
	Steering Flex Coupling Bolt	20–30
	Tie Rod End Jam Nut	35–50

MARK VII, MARK VIII & MUSTANG-Continued

Year	Component	Torque/Ft. Lbs.
1992–94 —Cont'd	Tie Rod End To Spindle Arm	35–47
	Tie Rod Socket Assembly To Rack	55–65
	Yoke Plug	②
	Yoke Plug Locknut	44–66

①—Inch lbs.
②—Refer to text.

CONTINENTAL, SABLE & TAURUS

Year	Component	Torque/Ft. Lbs.
1992–94	Bellows Clamp Screw	20–30①
	External Transfer Tubes	10–20
	Gear Hose Fittings	15–25
	Gear Housing Return Line	20–25
	Gear To Crossmember	85–100
	Intermediate Shaft To Steering Column	15–25
	Intermediate Shaft To Steering Gear	30–38
	Pinion Bearing Cap	40–50
	Pinion Bearing Locknut	30–40
	Pressure Line Fitting To Actuator Banjo Bolt	22–28
	Pump Pressure Line Fitting	10—15
	Tie Rod Ball Socket To Rack	55–65
	Tie Rod End Jam Nut	35–50
	Tie Rod End To Spindle Arm	35–47
	VAPS Actuator	20–25
	Yoke Plug	②
	Yoke Plug Locknut	40–50

①—Inch lbs.
②—Refer to text.

TEMPO & TOPAZ

Year	Component	Torque/Ft. Lbs.
1992–94	Flex Coupling To Gear Input Shaft Clamp Bolt	20–30
	Steering Gear	40–55
	Pinion Cap	35–45
	Pinion Locknut	20–35
	Pressure & Return Lines	20–25
	Tie Rod Ball Housing	40–50
	Tie Rod End Jam Nut	42–50
	Tie Rod End To Spindle Arm	27–32①
	Transfer Lines	15–20
	Yoke Plug Locknut	40–50

①—Tighten to specifications, then tighten to nearest cotter pin slot.

TYPE 3—FORD TORSION BAR POWER STEERING GEAR

NOTE: Also Refer To "Type 2-Ford Variable Assist Electronic Variable Orifice (EVO) System."

NOTE: On Air Bag Equipped Models, Refer To "Air Bag System Precautions" Located In The Front Of This Manual For System Disarming & Arming Procedures.

INDEX

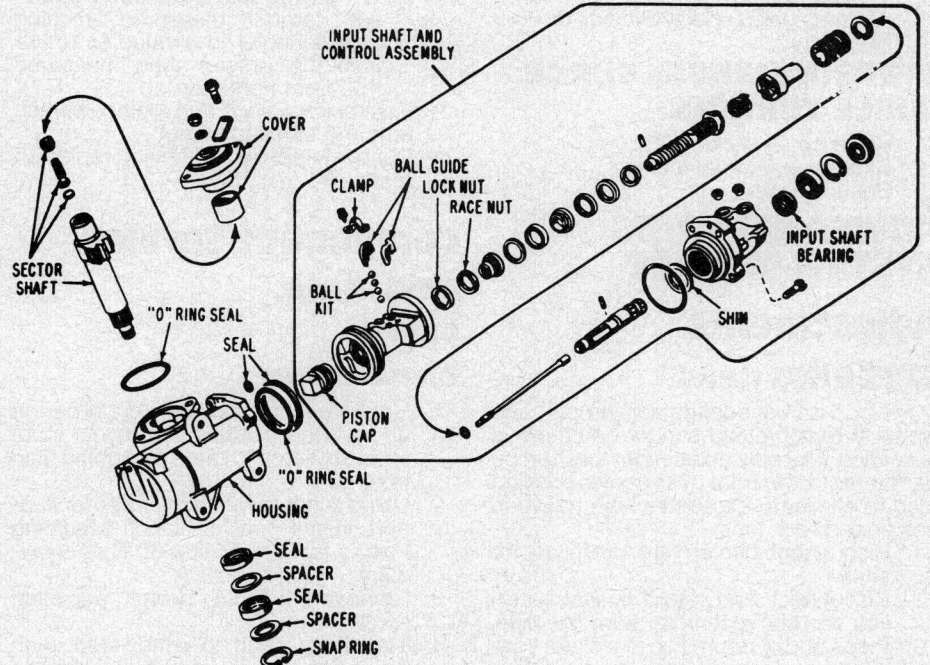

Fig. 1   Exploded view of Ford power steering gear

FM6029100124000X

PRECAUTIONS

AIR BAG SYSTEMS

Refer to "Air Bag System Precautions" in the front of this manual for system disarming and arming procedures.

DESCRIPTION

The power steering unit, **Fig. 1,** is a torsion bar type of hydraulic-assisted system. This system furnishes power to reduce the amount of turning effort required at the steering wheel. It also reduces road shock and vibrations.

The unit includes a worm and one piece rack-piston which is meshed to the gear teeth on the steering sector shaft. The unit also includes a hydraulic valve, valve actuator, input shaft and torsion bar assembly which are mounted on the end of the worm shaft and operated by a twisting action of the torsion bar.

The gear unit is designed with the one piece rack-piston, worm and sector shaft in the one housing and the valve spool in an attaching housing. This makes possible internal fluid passages between valve and cylinder, thus eliminating all external lines and hoses except the pressure and return hoses between pump and gear.

The power cylinder is an integral part of the gear housing. The piston is double acting in that fluid pressure may be applied to either side of the piston.

OPERATION

The operation of the hydraulic control valve spool is governed by the twisting of a torsion bar. All effort applied to the steering wheel is transmitted directly through the input shaft and torsion bar to the worm and piston. Any resistance to the turning of the front wheels results in twisting of the bar. The twisting of the bar increases as the front wheel turning effort increases. The control valve spool, actuated by the twisting of the torsion bar, directs fluid to the side of the piston where hydraulic assistance is required.

As the torsion bar twists, its radial motion is transferred into axial motion by three helical threads. Thus, the valve is moved off center, and fluid is directed to one side of the piston or the other.

TROUBLESHOOTING

HARD STEERING

1. Low or uneven tire pressure.
2. Improper gear adjustment.
3. Improper wheel alignment.
4. Low fluid level.
5. Twisted or bent suspension parts, frame and linkage components.
6. Tight wheel bearings.
7. Steering spindle bent.
8. Pump belt out of adjustment.
9. Pump output low.
10. Air in system.
11. Valve spool out of adjustment.

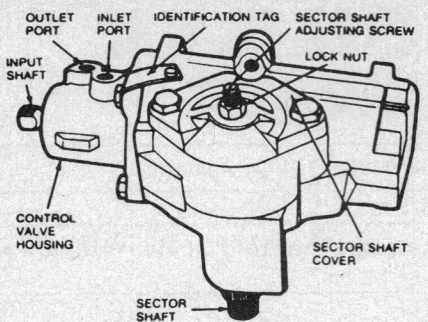

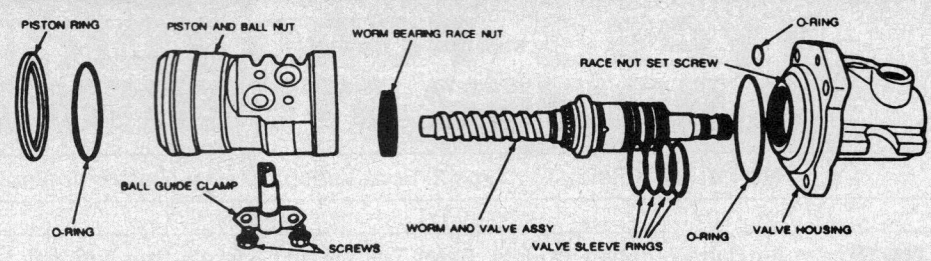

Fig. 2 Mesh load adjustment

Fig. 3 Ball nut & valve housing disassembled

12. Valve spool sticking.
13. Steering linkage binding.

HARD STEERING STRAIGHT AHEAD

1. Steering adjustment too tight.
2. Steering gear shaft binding.

HARD STEERING WHILE TURNING OR PARKING

1. Oil level low.
2. Pump pressure low.
3. Pressure loss in steering gear due to leakage past O-rings.
4. Pressure loss between valve spool and sleeve.
5. Pressure loss past piston ring or scored housing bore.

LOOSE STEERING

1. Loose wheel bearings.
2. Loose tie rod ends or linkage.
3. Worn ball joints.
4. Worn suspension parts.
5. Insufficient mesh load.
6. Insufficient worm bearing preload.
7. Valve spool out of adjustment.

ERRATIC STEERING

1. Oil or brake fluid on brake lining.
2. Out of round brake drums.
3. Improperly adjusted brakes.
4. Under-inflated tires.
5. Broken spring or other details in suspension system.
6. Improper caster adjustment.
7. Fluid level low.

BINDING OR POOR RECOVERY

1. Steering gear shaft binding.
2. Steering gear out of adjustment.
3. Steering linkage binding.
4. Valve spool binding due to dirt or burred edges.
5. Valve spool out of adjustment.
6. Interference at sector shaft and ball stud.

LOSS OF POWER ASSIST

1. Pump inoperative.
2. Hydraulic lines damaged.
3. Power cylinder damaged.
4. Valve spool out of adjustment.

LOSS OF POWER ASSIST IN ONE DIRECTION

1. Valve spool out of adjustment.

NOISY PUMP

1. Air being drawn into pump.
2. Lines touching other parts of car.
3. Oil level low.
4. Excessive backpressure caused by obstructions in lines.
5. Excessive wear of internal parts.

POOR RETURN TO CENTER

1. Valve spool sticking.
2. Valve spool out of adjustment.
3. All items given under "Binding or Poor Recovery."

STEERING WHEEL SURGE WHILE TURNING

1. Valve spool sticking.
2. Excessive internal leakage.
3. Belt slippage.

POWER STEERING SYSTEM SERVICE

Adjustments

STEERING GEAR

Preload (thrust bearing adjustment) and worm-to-rack preload cannot be changed in service. The only adjustment that can be performed is the total over-center position load to eliminate excessive lash between sector and rack teeth.

1. Disconnect pitman arm from sector shaft.
2. Disconnect fluid return line at reservoir and cap reservoir return line pipe.
3. Place end of return line in a clean container and cycle steering wheel in both directions as required to discharge fluid from gear.
4. Remove ornamental cover from wheel hub and turn steering wheel 45° from left stop.
5. Using an inch lb. torque wrench on steering wheel nut, determine torque required to rotate shaft slowly through an approximately 1/4 turn from the 45° position.
6. Turn steering gear back to center, then determine torque required to rotate shaft back and forth across center position.
7. Loosen adjuster nut and turn adjusting screw, **Fig. 2,** until reading is as follows:

a. **On models with 0-5000 miles,** reset if total meshload over mechanical center if not 15-24 inch lbs.
b. **On models with 0-5000 miles,** set torque rocking across center to a values 11-15 inch lbs. greater than that measured 45° from right stop.
c. **On all models with more than 5000 miles,** reset if meshload measured while rocking input shaft over center is less then 10 inch lbs. greater then the torque 45° from right stop.
d. **On all models over 5000 miles,** set torque measured rocking across center to a value of 10-14 inch lbs. greater than measured 45° from right stop.

8. Recheck readings and replace pitman arm and steering wheel.
9. Connect fluid return line and replenish reservoir.

Component Service

OVERHAUL

GEAR

Disassemble

1. Hold steering gear over drain pan in an inverted position and cycle input shaft six times to drain remaining fluid from gear.
2. Using suitable mounting pads for support, install gear in Bench Mounting Fixture tool No. T57L-500-B or equivalent.
3. Remove locknut from adjusting screw.
4. Turn input shaft to either stop, then turn it back approximately 1 5/8 turns to center the gear. **Input shaft spline indexing flat should be facing downward.**
5. Remove two sector shaft cover bolts.
6. Tap lower end of sector shaft with a soft-faced hammer to loosen it, then lift cover and shaft from housing as a unit. Discard O-ring.
7. Turn sector shaft cover counterclockwise off adjuster screw.
8. Remove valve housing attaching bolts. Lift valve housing from gear housing while holding piston to prevent it from rotating off worm shaft. Remove valve housing and lube passage O-rings and discard.
9. Remove valve housing attaching

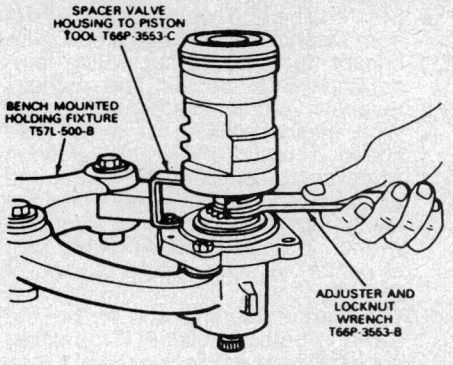

Fig. 4 Input shaft removal

Fig. 5 Assembling piston on worm shaft

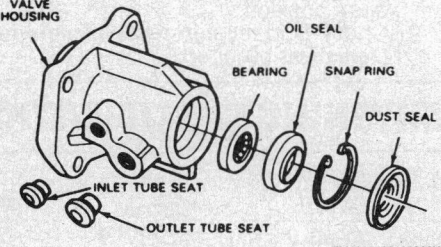

Fig. 7 Valve housing disassembled

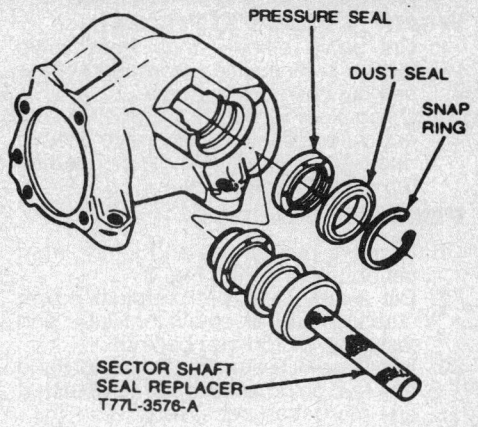

Fig. 6 Steering gear housing disassembled

bolts and ID tag, while holding piston separate valve housing from housing, remove and discard O-rings.

10. With piston held, remove ball clamp screws and guide clamp, **Fig. 3.**
11. With finger over ball guide opening, turn piston so ball guide faces downward over clean container, then allow guide tubes to drop to container.
12. Rotate input shaft from stop to stop, until all balls fall from piston, then remove valve assembly from piston. **Ensure all balls have been remove. Worm may no longer be removed from piston.**
13. Install valve body to Bench Mounting Fixture tool No. T57L-500-B or equivalent, then loosen valve housing race nut lockscrew. Using Adjuster Locknut Wrench tool No. T66P-3553-B and Spacer Valve Housing tool No. T66P-3553-C or equivalents, remove worm bearing race.
14. Slide input shaft, worm and valve assembly from valve housing, **Fig. 4.**

Assemble

1. Install worm and valve in housing.
2. Install retaining nut in housing, then torque nut using Adjuster and Locknut Wrench tool No. T66P-3553 or equivalent. Because length of tool required to torque nut will affect torque wrench reading, the following formula must be used to determine torque. Torque (using tool T66P-3553-B, or equivalent) equals (length of torque wrench x 72 ft. lbs.)/(length of torque wrench + 5.5 inches).
3. Install race nut screw and tighten to specifications.
4. Place piston on bench with ball guide holes facing up. Insert worm shaft into piston so that first groove is in alignment with hole nearest to center of piston, **Fig. 5.**
5. Place ball guide into piston. Place balls in guide (27 minimum), turning worm clockwise (viewed from input end of shaft). If all balls have not been fed into guide upon reaching right stop, rotate input shaft in one direction and then in the other while installing balls. After balls have been installed, do not rotate input shaft or piston more than 3½ turns off the right stop to prevent balls from falling out of circuit.

6. Securing guides to ball nut with clamp and tighten to specifications.
7. Apply petroleum jelly to piston seal.
8. Place a new O-ring on valve housing.
9. Slide piston and valve into gear housing, being careful not to damage seal.
10. Align lube passage in valve housing with one in gear housing, place O-ring in gear housing oil passage hole, then identification tag and install but do not tighten attaching bolts at this time.
11. Rotate ball nut so that teeth are in same plane as sector teeth. Tighten valve housing attaching bolts.
12. Position sector shaft cover O-ring in gear housing. Turn input shaft as required to center piston.
13. Apply petroleum jelly to sector shaft journal, then position sector shaft and cover into gear housing. Install air conditioner line mounting bracket, if equipped, and two sector shaft cover bolts, then tighten to specifications.
14. Attach an inch lb. torque wrench to input shaft and adjust mesh load as outlined previously.

GEAR HOUSING

1. Remove lower end housing snap ring, **Fig. 6.**
2. Using Puller Attachment tool No. T58L-101-B or equivalent, remove and discard dust and pressure seals. **Bearing is not a serviceable and must be replaced as an assembly.**
3. Using suitable multi purpose grease, lubricate new pressure, dust seal and sector shaft seal bore.
4. Install dust seal on sector shaft, using Seal Replacer tool No. T77L-3576-A or equivalent, with seal raised lip toward tool, then install pressure seal with lip away from tool, pressure seal flat side should be against flat side of dust deal.
5. Install tool to sector shaft bore, then drive tool until seals clear snap ring grooves. **Do not bottom seal against**

bearing or seals will not function properly.
6. Install snap ring in housing groove.

REPLACEMENT

Valve Housing

1. Using Puller Attachment tool No. T58L-101-B or equivalent, remove and discard dust seal, **Fig. 7.**
2. Remove snap ring from valve housing, then turn fixture so valve housing is upside down.
3. Install Bearing Remover tool No. T65P-3524-A2 and Installer tool No. T65P-3524-A3 or equivalents to valve body opposite the oil seal, then gently tap bearing and seal from housing, discard seal. **Exercise care when inserting and removing tool to prevent damage to valve bore in housing.**
4. Remove oil inlet and outlet tube seats with Rack Bushing Holding Tool No. T74P-3504-L, or equivalent, if damaged.
5. Coat tube seats with petroleum jelly and position them in housing. Install and tighten tube nuts to press seats to proper location, using Brass Tube Seat Replacer tool No. T74P-3504-M or equivalent.
6. Coat bearing and seal surface in housing with a film of petroleum jelly.
7. Install bearing with metal side that covers rollers facing downward, then using Bearing Installer tool No. T65P-3524-A or equivalent, seat bearing, ensuring smooth bearing operation.
8. Dip new oil seal in premium power steering fluid or equivalent, then place it in housing with metal side of seal facing outward. Drive seal into housing until outer edge of seal does not quite clear snap ring.
9. Place snap ring in housing, then drive on ring until snap ring seats in its groove to locate seal properly.
10. Apply coating of suitable multipurpose grease between seals.
11. Place dust seal in housing with dished side (rubber side) facing outward. Drive dust seal in place so that it is located behind undercut in input shaft when it is installed.

Worm & Valve Sleeves

1. Cut valve sleeve rings from valve sleeve, then position worm end of assembly in soft jawed vice.
2. Using Tool Kit No. T75L-3517-A1, or equivalent, install four valve sleeve rings. After installing rings ensure they turn freely in grooves.

Piston & Ball Nut

1. Remove plastic ring and O-ring from piston and ball nut, **Fig. 3.**
2. Dip a new O-ring in premium power steering fluid or equivalent lube and install on piston and ball nut.
3. Install new Teflon ring on piston and ball nut, being careful not to stretch it any more than necessary.

INSPECTION

Valve Spool Centering Check

The "out of car" procedure for valve centering check is the same as for the "in car" except the torque and simultaneous pressure reading must be made at the right and left stops instead of either side of center.

1. Install a 2000 psi pressure gauge in pressure line between pump outlet port and steering gear inlet port. Make sure that valve on gauge in is fully open position.
2. Check fluid level in reservoir and replenish as required.
3. Start engine and cycle steering wheel from stop-to-stop to bring steering lubricant up to normal operating temperature. Stop engine and recheck reservoir. Add fluid as necessary.
4. With engine running at a fast idle speed (1000 RPM) and steering wheel centered, attach an inch-pound torque wrench to steering wheel retaining nut. Apply sufficient torque to wrench in each direction (either side of center) to get a gauge reading of 250 psi.
5. The torque reading should be the same in both directions. If the difference between readings exceed 4 inch lbs., the shaft and control assemblies must be replaced.

TIGHTENING SPECIFICATIONS

Year	Component	Torque/Ft. Lbs.
1992–94	Ball Return Guide Clamp Screw	42–70 ①
	Flex Coupling To Gear Input Shaft Bolt	20–30
	Gear To Side Rail Bolts	50–65
	Hose Clamps	1–2
	Meshload Adjusting Screw Locknut	35–45
	Piston End Cap	70–110
	Pitman Arm To Sector Shaft Nut	200–250

Year	Component	Torque/Ft. Lbs.
1992–94 —Cont'd	Pressure Hose To Gear	16–25
	Race Nut Setscrew	15–25 ①
	Return Hose To Gear	25–34
	Sector Shaft Cover Bolts	55–70
	Valve Housing To Gear Housing	30–45

①—Inch lbs.

TYPE 4–NIPPON RACK & PINION STEERING GEAR

NOTE: On Air Bag Equipped Models, Refer To "Air Bag System Precautions" Located In The Front Of This Manual For System Disarming & Arming Procedures.

INDEX

PRECAUTIONS

AIR BAG SYSTEMS

Refer to "Air Bag System Precautions" in the front of this manual for system disarming and arming procedures.

DESCRIPTION

The power steering system consists of a rack and pinion steering gear, a power steering pump, a fluid reservoir and interconnecting hydraulic lines. The power steering system uses hydraulic pressure generated by the power steering pump to reduce the effort required to turn the steering wheel.

The rack and pinion gear is held in place by two mounting brackets and moulded rubber grommets. The gear is a hydraulic mechanical unit that uses and integral piston and rack design to provide power assisted steering control.

On models equipped with 1.9L engine, the middle bearing is not serviceable and should not be removed from the steering gear housing. If the bearing is worn or damaged, replace short rack assembly.

TROUBLESHOOTING

STEERING FEELS HEAVY

1. Poor lubrication.
2. Foreign material in mechanism.
3. Faulty ball joint.
4. Improper steering gear preload.
5. Faulty steering gear.
6. Faulty steering shaft joint.
7. Power steering fluid leakage.
8. Low fluid level or air in system.
9. Faulty power steering oil pump or drive belt.
10. Clogged lines.
11. Faulty wheel or tire.
12. Faulty suspension component.

STEERING WHEEL PULLS

1. Faulty steering linkage.
2. Faulty wheel or tire.

3. Fault in brake system.
4. Faulty suspension component.

GENERAL INSTABILITY

1. Faulty steering ball joint.
2. Improper steering pinion preload.
3. Faulty steering linkage.
4. Faulty wheel or tire.
5. Faulty suspension component.

STEERING FEELS UNSTABLE

1. Faulty power steering drive belt.
2. Faulty steering gear.
3. Faulty ball joint.
4. Faulty steering linkage.

EXCESSIVE STEERING WHEEL PLAY

1. Faulty steering gear.
2. Faulty ball joint.
3. Loose steering gear mounting bolts.

IMPROPER STEERING WHEEL RETURN

1. Faulty ball joint.
2. Improper steering pinion preload.
3. Faulty wheel or tire.
4. Faulty suspension component.

STEERING WHEEL VIBRATES

1. Faulty steering linkage.
2. Loose steering gear mounting bolts.
3. Faulty ball joint.
4. Faulty front wheel bearing.
5. Faulty wheel or tire.
6. Faulty suspension component.

STEERING SYSTEM NOISE

1. Loose steering gear mounting bolts.
2. Faulty steering gear.
3. Steering column obstruction.
4. Faulty steering linkage.
5. Faulty ball joint.
6. Faulty power steering pump drive belt.
7. Loose power steering pump bracket.
8. Air in power steering system.
9. Faulty power steering pump.

DIAGNOSIS & TESTING

POWER STEERING PRESSURE TEST

During the following procedure, power steering system pressure may exceed 1200 psi. Ensure proper tool fit prior to performing test. Exercise extreme caution or damage or personal injury may result.

1. Disconnect high pressure line, install Power Steering System Analyzer tool No. 014-00207 or equivalent, using appropriate adapters, **Fig. 1**. Torque adapters to 12-17 ft. lbs.
2. Install thermometer to power steering fluid reservoir.
3. **Ensure analyzer valve is open to allow system to function properly.**
4. **Do not hold steering wheel against a stop of more the 10 seconds at a time.**
5. Start engine, then bleed system by

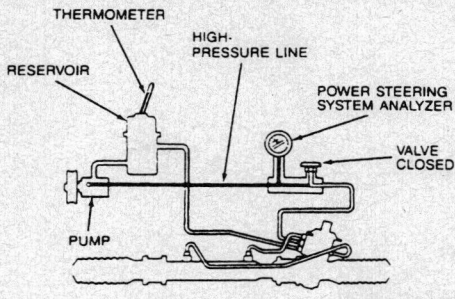

Fig. 1 Power steering pressure test connections

turning steering wheel lock to lock 10 times.
6. Check power steering fluid temperature, if fluid id not 122-140°F, turn steering wheel lock to lock until temperature is reached.
7. **The valve on the analyzer must be closed briefly to read operating pressure. Do not leave valve closed for more than 15 seconds.**
8. Measure power steering pump output pressure by closing analyzer valve and increasing engine speed to 1000-1500 RPM, 1067 psi should be indicated, if so, proceed to step 9, if pressure is low, replace power steering pump.
9. With analyzer valve open, increase engine speed to 1000-1500 RPM.
10. Turn steering wheel fully to left or right, then read measured pressure, 1067 psi should be indicated, if pressure is low, replace steering gear.
11. Remove analyzer and adapters.
12. Reconnect high pressure line, then **torque** fitting to 12-17 ft. lbs.
13. Remove thermometer, then bleed system by starting engine and slowly turning steering wheel from lock to lock 10 times.

POWER STEERING SYSTEM SERVICE

DISASSEMBLE

1. Place installation alignment marks on tie rod end, jam nut and tie rod.
2. Remove tie rod ends and jam nuts, **Fig. 2**.
3. Remove each dust boot clamp, then boot wire and discard, then remove boots.
4. Position steering gear in suitable soft jawed vise.
5. Using suitable chisel, uncrimp tie rod tabs, then remove tie rods and discard tabs.
6. Remove pinion shaft cover.
7. Using Pinion Torque Adapter tool No. T90P-3504-KH or equivalent, remove pinion shaft plug.
8. Using Pinion Seal Replacer tool No. T86P-3504-G or equivalent, remove plug bearing and seal, **Fig. 3**.
9. Remove pinion shaft locknut cover.
10. Using Pinion Torque Adapter tool No. T86-3504-K or equivalent, hold pinion shaft, then remove shaft locknut.

11. Using Torque Gauge tool No. T90P-3504-LH or equivalent, remove yoke adjustment plug locknut, then remove adjusting plug.
12. Remove spring, support yoke, pinion shaft and control valve from gear housing.
13. Using suitable seal remover, remove control valve seal ring.
14. Press bearing from pinion shaft.
15. Using Outer Box Torque Adapter tool No. T90P-3504-MH or equivalent, remove steering gear bushing.
16. Remove rack from RH side of housing, then remove rack piston seal ring and discard.
17. Using rack inner seal remover tool No. T87P-3504-A or equivalent, remove inner steering gear seal and discard, then remove guide from housing.
18. Using Lower Pinion Seal Remover tool No. T86P-3504-F, Remover tool No. T86P-3504-J and Slide Hammer tool No. T50T-100-A or equivalents, **Fig. 4**, remove pinion shaft inner seal.
19. Using Puller Attachment tool No. T58L-101-B and Slide Hammer tool No. T50T-100-A or equivalents, remove pinion bearing from housing.
20. Remove steering gear attaching brackets and grommets.

INSPECTION

1. Inspect pinion shaft teeth and bearing for damage.
2. Inspect control valve seal for damage or abnormal wear.
3. Inspect steering rack for cracks or damaged teeth.
4. Inspect steering rack piston seal ring for abnormal wear or damage.

ASSEMBLE

1. Install grommets and mounting brackets.
2. Using Pinion Bearing Installer tool No. T90P-3504-OH and Handle tool No. T80T-4000-W or equivalents, install pinion bearing to housing.
3. Using Pinion Seal Installer tool No. T90P-3504-PH and Handle tool No. T87P-3504-D or equivalents, install pinion shaft inner seal.
4. Lubricate new seal ring using Teflon Ring Expander tool No. T90P-3504-QH or equivalent, then install to steering rack piston. Ensure seal ring is properly seated. Size seal ring using Teflon Seal Sizer tool No. T90P-3504-RH.
5. Lubricate inner guide, then slide onto rack.
6. Lubricate inner seal, then using Rack Seal Protector tool No. T87P-3504-H or equivalent, slide seal on rack, then remove protector.
7. Position Teflon Seal Sizer tool No. T90P-3504-RH or equivalent, on rack, then slide steering rack onto housing until inner seal is fully seated, **Fig. 5**.
8. Install steering gear busing using Outer Box Torque Adapter tool No. T90P-3504-MH or equivalent.
9. Using suitable vacuum pump, apply 400 mm-Hg to steering gear housing, ensuring vacuum is maintained for 30

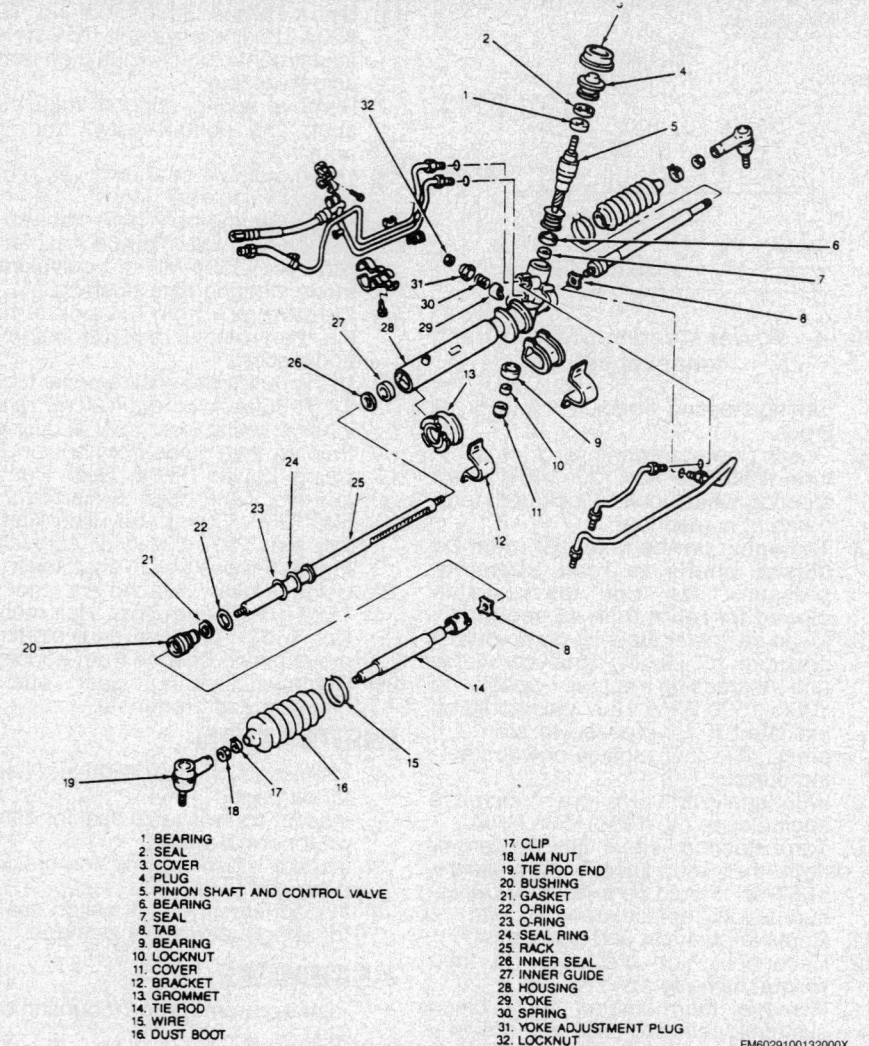

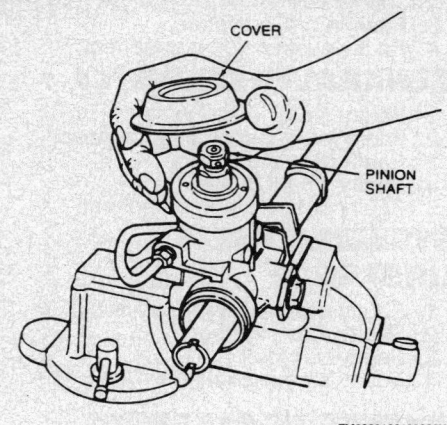

Fig. 3 Lower bearing & seal removal

Fig. 2 Exploded view of steering gear

1. BEARING		17. CLIP	
2. SEAL		18. JAM NUT	
3. COVER		19. TIE ROD END	
4. PLUG		20. BUSHING	
5. PINION SHAFT AND CONTROL VALVE		21. GASKET	
6. BEARING		22. O-RING	
7. SEAL		23. O-RING	
8. TAB		24. SEAL RING	
9. BEARING		25. RACK	
10. LOCKNUT		26. INNER SEAL	
11. COVER		27. INNER GUIDE	
12. BRACKET		28. HOUSING	
13. GROMMET		29. YOKE	
14. TIE ROD		30. SPRING	
15. WIRE		31. YOKE ADJUSTMENT PLUG	
16. DUST BOOT		32. LOCKNUT	

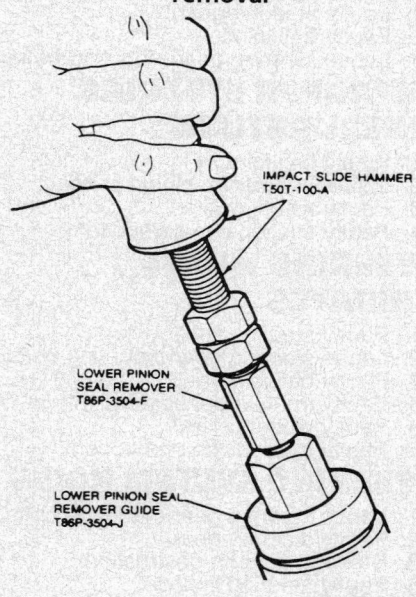

Fig. 4 Pinion shaft inner seal removal

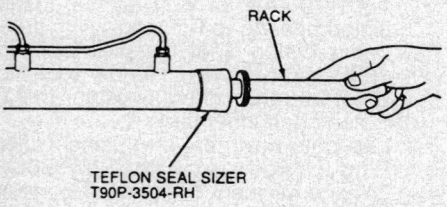

Fig. 5 Steering rack replacement

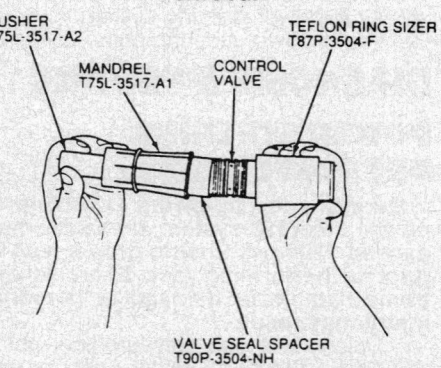

Fig. 6 Control valve seal replacement

seconds, if vacuum is not maintained, replace inner seal.

10. Using Mandrel tool No. T75L-3517-A1, Pusher tool No. T75L-3517-A2, Teflon Ring Sizer tool No. T87P-3504-F and Valve Seal Spacer tool No. T90P-3504-NH or equivalents, install control valve seal ring, **Fig. 6.**

11. Center rack in housing, then using Teflon Ring Sizer tool No. T87P-3504-F or equivalent, install pinion shaft and control valve to housing.

12. Using Pinion Torque Adapter tool No. T86P-3504-K or equivalent, hold pinion shaft, then install pinion shaft locknut and tighten to specifications.

13. Install pinion shaft locknut cover, then tighten to specifications.

14. Apply suitable sealant to pinion shaft locknut cover, then using Gear Bushing Adapter tool No. T80L-77209-A or equivalent, install pinion shaft plug seal.

15. Install bearing to pinion shaft plug, then apply suitable grease to plug seal, then using Pinion Cover Torque Adapter tool No. T90P-3504-KH or equivalent, install plug.

16. Install pinion shaft cover, support yoke and spring.

17. Apply sealant to yoke adjustment locknut, install adjustment plug and tighten to specifications.

18. Using Torque Gauge tool No. T90P-3504-H or equivalent, install yoke adjustment locknut, then tighten to specifications.

19. Using Pinion Torque Adapter tool No. T86K-3504-K or equivalent, measure pinion torque, 8.7-10 inch lbs. within a pinion rotation angle of ± 90° from rack center position should be indicated, if not as specified, repeat steps 17 and 18.

20. Install tie rods, then using suitable chisel install tie rod tabs.

21. Install dust boots with wire and clips, then tie rod end jam nut.

22. Install tie rod ends, aligning installation marks, then tighten tie rod end jam nuts to specifications.

TIGHTENING SPECIFICATIONS

Year	Component	Torque/Ft. Lbs.
1992	Intermediate Shaft To Pinion Shaft Bolt	13–20
	Pinion Shaft Locknut	29–36
	Pinion Shaft Locknut Cover	29–36
	Pressure Line Flare Nut At Gear	22–28
	Pressure Line Flare Nut At Pump	12–17
	Pump High Pressure line Fitting	12–17
	Pump Mounting Bolts	27–38
	Pump Bracket Bolt	27–40
	Return Line Flare Nut At Gear	22–28

Year	Component	Torque/Ft. Lbs.
1992 —Cont'd	Steering Gear Bracket Nuts	27–38
	Tensioner To Pump Bracket Nut & Bolt	23–34
	Tensioner To Pump Nut & Bolt	14–19
	Tie Rod End Attaching Nuts	31–42
	Tie Rod End Jam Nuts	26–86 ①
	Yoke Adjustment Nut	②
	Yoke Plug Locknut	29–36

①—Inch lbs.
②—Tighten to 43 inch lbs., then loosen ⅛ turn (45°).

TYPE 5–TSCL RACK & PINION STEERING GEAR

NOTE: On Air Bag Equipped Models, Refer To "Air Bag System Precautions" Located In The Front Of This Manual For System Disarming & Arming Procedures.

INDEX

PRECAUTIONS

AIR BAG SYSTEMS

Refer to "Air Bag System Precautions" in the front of this manual for system disarming and arming procedures.

TROUBLESHOOTING

Refer to "Festiva Steering Pump" for troubleshooting procedures.

DIAGNOSIS & TESTING

POWER STEERING PRESSURE TEST

Refer to "Festiva Steering Pump" for power steering pressure test procedure.

POWER STEERING SYSTEM SERVICE

Adjustments

VALVE HOUSING

Perform this adjustment if the valve housing, steering gear housing or pinion control valve assembly have been replaced.
1. Measure valve housing, lower bearing and spacer and steering gear housing as shown in **Fig. 1**.
2. To determine proper thickness of

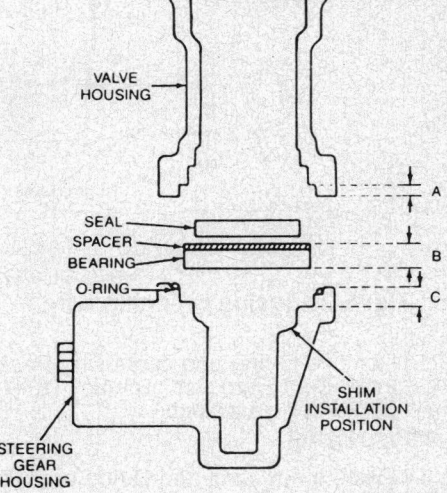

Fig. 1   Selecting proper valve housing shims

shim needed, use this formula, $T = A + C - B$. Where T is shim thickness needed.
3. Shims are available in .0020 inch only. Determine number of shims using this formula, $N = T / .0020$ inch. Where N is number of shims needed. Round up or down to the closest full number.

Component Service

STEERING GEAR

Disassemble

Refer to **Fig. 2** when performing the following procedure:
1. Secure steering gear on a soft jawed vise.
2. Remove fluid lines.
3. Place alignment marks on lefthand tie rod to ease installation.
4. Loosen jam nut and remove left tie rod end.
5. Remove boot clamps then the boot.
6. Using Lockpin Tool No. T78P-3504-N or equivalent, remove tie rod lockpins.
7. Remove tie rods from rack assembly.
8. Using Yoke Plug Locknut Remover tool No. T90C-3504-BH or equivalent, remove yoke plug locknut.
9. Remove yoke plug, spring and support yoke.
10. Remove pinion and control valve assembly retaining snap ring.
11. Remove seal using Locknut Pin Remover tool No. T78P-3504-N or equivalent, **Fig. 3**.
12. Remove valve housing attaching bolts, then valve housing, pinion and control valve assembly.
13. If present, remove shim(s) from steering gear housing, **Fig. 4**.
14. Remove steering gear O-ring.
15. Remove pinion and control valve as-

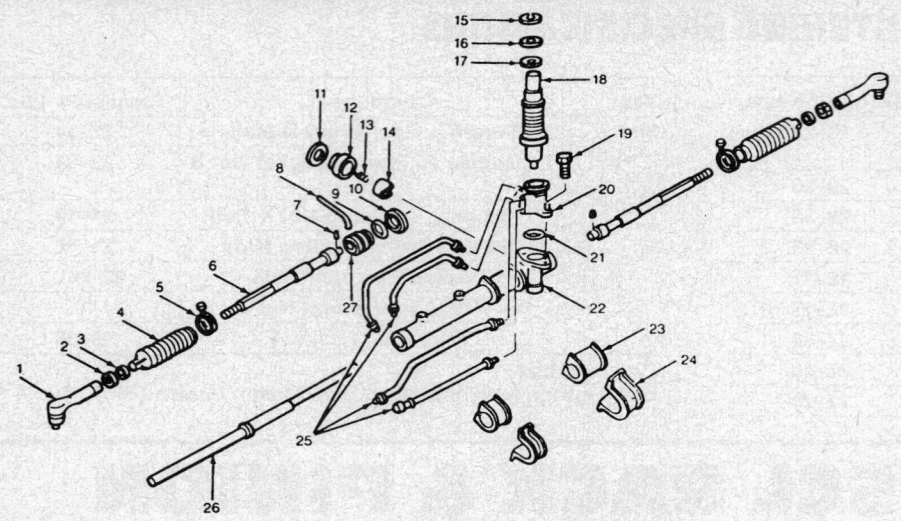

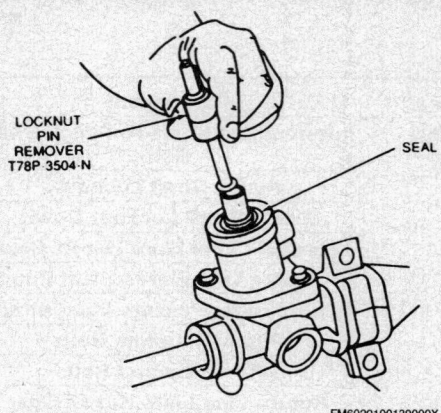

Fig. 3 . Removing control valve assembly O-ring

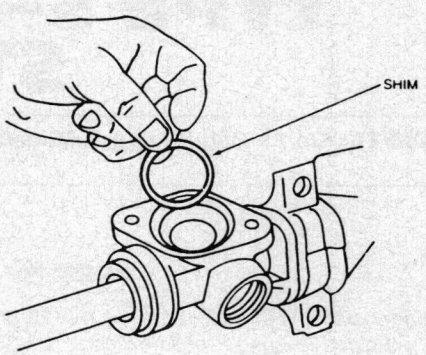

Fig. 4 Removing control valve assembly shims

Fig. 2 Steering rack exploded view

1. TIE ROD END	15. SNAP RING
2. JAM NUT	16. SEAL
3. BOOT CLIP	17. BEARING
4. BOOT	18. PINION AND CONTROL VALVE ASSEMBLY
5. BOOT WIRE	19. BOLT
6. TIE ROD	20. VALVE HOUSING
7. LOCK PIN	21. O-RING
8. RETAINING WIRE	22. STEERING GEAR HOUSING
9. O-RING	23. GROMMET
10. SEAL	24. MOUNTING BRACKET
11. LOCKNUT	25. FLUID LINES
12. YOKE PLUG	26. RACK
13. SPRING	27. RACK BUSHING
14. SUPPORT YOKE	

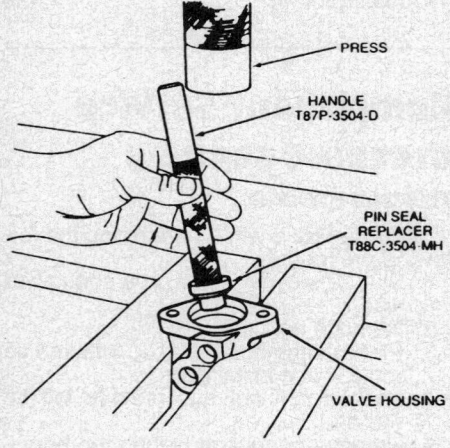

Fig. 5 Valve housing bearing removal

sembly from valve housing by lightly tapping with a rubber mallet.

16. Press bearing out of valve housing using Pinion Seal Replacer tool No. T88P-3504-MH and Handle tool No. Y87P-3504-D or equivalent, **Fig. 5.**
17. Using Outer Box Torque Adapter tool No. T88C-3504-CH or equivalent, rotate rack bushing until hooked end of retaining wire is aligned with slot in steering gear housing, **Fig. 6.**
18. Pry retaining wire from bushing hole.
19. Rotate bushing and remove retaining wire, **Fig. 7.**
20. Remove rack from right side of steering gear.

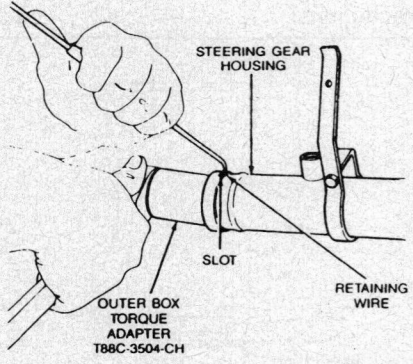

Fig. 6 Aligning retaining wire.

21. Remove O-ring and seal using Rack Inner Seal Remover tool No. T87C-3504-A or equivalent.

Assemble

1. Install a new seal and O-ring using a suitable seal and Teflon ring expander installer.
2. Install rack into steering gear.
3. Insert retaining wire through slot and into bushing hole, **Fig. 8.**
4. Install retaining wire using Outer Box Torque Adapter tool No. T88C-3504-CH or equivalent.
5. If valve housing, steering gear housing or pinion and control valve assembly has been replaced, perform valve housing adjustment procedure as outlined under "Adjustments" in this section.

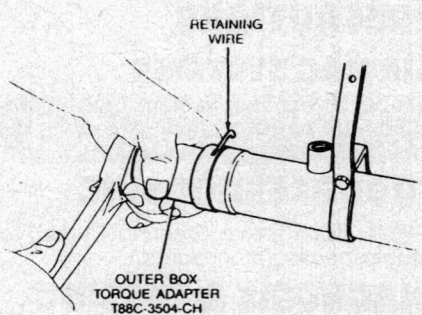

Fig. 7 Removing retaining wire

6. Insert pinion and control valve assembly into valve housing, ensuring that it seats properly.
7. Install a new O-ring.
8. Install valve housing, pinion and control valve assembly into steering gear and tighten to specifications.
9. Install bearing using Pinion Seal/Torque Adapter tool No. T88C-3504-BH or equivalent.
10. Install seal using same tool, **Fig. 9.**
11. Install snap ring, support yoke, spring and yoke plug.
12. **Torque** yoke plug to 7.2 ft. lbs. then loosen it.
13. **Torque** yoke plug to 38–38 inch lbs., then loosen it 45°.
14. Apply sealant to exposed threads of yoke plug.

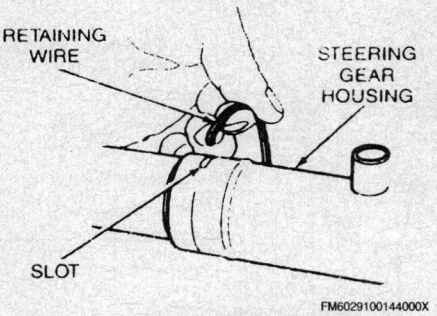

Fig. 8 Installing retainer wire

15. Install yoke plug locknut and tighten to specifications.
16. Install tie rods using a suitable pin punch on lockpins.
17. Install boots, boot wires and clips.
18. Install left tie rod end and jam nut.
19. Install fluid lines.

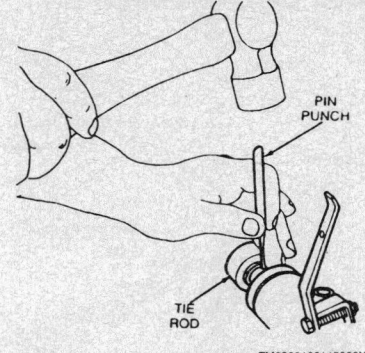

Fig. 9 Installing pinion seal

TIGHTENING SPECIFICATIONS

Year	Component	Torque/Ft. Lbs.
1992-94	Control Valve Assembly	15–19
	Fluid Reservoir Bolts	60–84 ①
	High Pressure Hose Nut	29–36
	Intermediate Shaft Clamp Bolt	13–20
	Steering Gear Attaching Bolts	23–34
	Yoke Plug	②
	Yoke Plug Locknut	36–43

①—Inch lbs.
②—Refer to text.

TYPE 6–TOKAI TRW RACK & PINION STEERING GEAR

NOTE: On Air Bag Equipped Models, Refer To "Air Bag System Precautions" Located In The Front Of This Manual For System Disarming & Arming Procedures.

INDEX

PRECAUTIONS

AIR BAG SYSTEMS

Refer to "Air Bag System Precautions" in the front of this manual for system disarming and arming procedures.

DESCRIPTION

This power rack and pinion steering gear has an integral valving and power assist system, **Fig. 1.**

The valve body is an integral part of the steering gear housing. A pressure line and return line attach the pump to the gear, while a rotary valve directs high pressure hydraulic fluid through external oil lines to the correct side of the rack piston.

TROUBLESHOOTING

Refer to "Rack & Pinion Steering Gear, Probe w/Variable Assist" for troubleshooting procedure.

POWER STEERING SYSTEM SERVICE

Adjustments

RACK PRELOAD

1. Remove rack from vehicle and mount in Holding Fixture tool No. T57L-500-B, or equivalent.
2. Measure pinion torque using an inch lb. torque wrench and Pinion Adapter tool No. T88C-3504-BH or equivalent.

Torque should be 88.5–123.9 inch lbs.
3. If pinion torque is not within specifications, loosen pinion locknut.
4. Using Torque Gauge tool No. T88C-3504-AH or equivalent, **torque** adjust cover to 7.2 ft. lbs. then loosen it.
5. **Torque** adjust cover again to 3.6 ft. lbs. then loosen the adjusting cover 45°.
6. Using Yoke Locknut Wrench tool No. T88C-3504-KH or equivalent, then tighten to specifications.

Component Service

STEERING GEAR

Disassemble

1. Mount steering gear in Holding Fix-

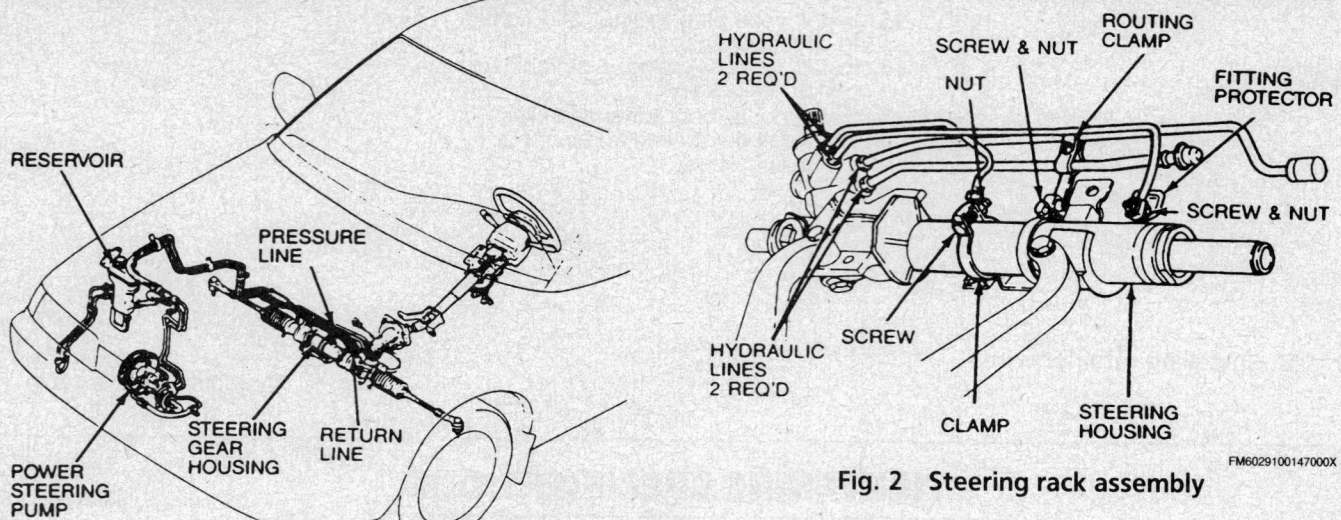

Fig. 1 Power steering system

Fig. 2 Steering rack assembly

FM6029100146000X

FM6029100147000X

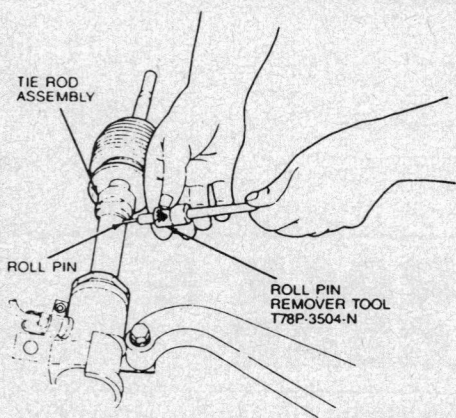

Fig. 3 Roll pin removaL

FM6029100148000X

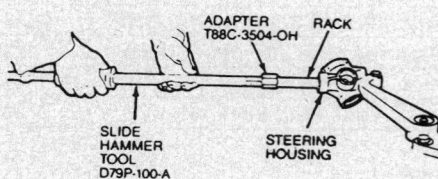

Fig. 4 Rack from housing removal

FM6029100150000X

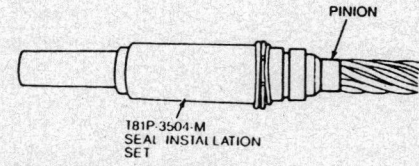

NOTE: TO REPLACE TEFLON RINGS, REMOVE SNAP RING ON PINION BEFORE INSTALLATION.

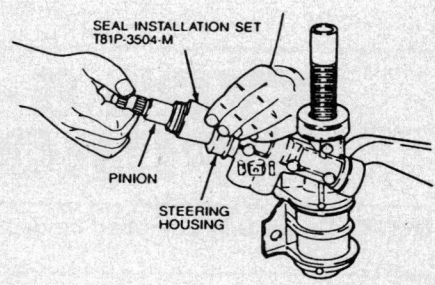

Fig. 5 Seals & pinion into housing installation

FM6029100151000X

ture tool No. T57L-500-B or equivalent.

2. Remove screw and nut from clamp, then the clamp from steering housing.

3. Note position of hydraulic lines for reference during assembly, then remove screw and nut from routing clamp and spread clamp, **Fig. 2.**

4. Remove two hydraulic lines and routing clamp from steering gear housing.

5. Remove screw and nut from fitting protector, then spread protector and remove, **Fig. 2.**

6. Remove two remaining hydraulic lines.

7. Using Roll Pin Remover tool No. T78P-3504-N or equivalent, remove roll pin, **Fig. 3.**

8. Using a 30mm crowfoot wrench, remove tie rod assembly from rack.

9. Using Torque Gauge tool No. T88C-3504-AH and Yoke Locknut Wrench tool No. T88C-3504-KH or equivalents, remove adjuster cover, locknut, spring and pressure pad.

10. Drill out the staked area, then remove the housing cover.

11. Remove snap ring from upper pinion bearing.

12. Using Pinion Torque Adapter tool No. T88C-3504-BH or equivalent, hold pinion and remove pinion locknut.

13. Using Puller Bridge tool No. T86P-3504-D, Puller tool No. T78P-3504-B and Spacer tool No. T78P-3733-A2 or equivalents, remove pinion and upper bearing from steering gear housing.

14. Remove lower bearing from steering housing.

15. Using Adapter tool No. T88C-3504-CH or equivalent, remove rack bushing assembly.

16. Using Slide Hammer tool No. D79P-100-A and Adapter tool No. T88C-3504-OH or equivalents, remove the rack from the pinion side of the steering housing, **Fig. 4.**

17. Using Seal Remover tool No. T78P-3504-J and Slide Hammer tool No. D79P-100-A or equivalent, remove inner rack seal and washer from the tube side of the steering housing, **Fig. 4.**

18. Using Seal Remover tool No. T78P-3504-J and Slide Hammer tool No. D79P-100-A or equivalents, remove inner rack seal and washer from tube side of steering housing.

Assemble

1. Using Seal Installer tool No. T88C-3504-DH or equivalent, install inner rack seal and washer.

2. Using Seal Installer tool No. T88C-3504-EH or equivalent, Install teflon seal ring and O-ring onto rack.

3. Install Protective Sleeve tool No. T85L-3504-B or equivalent onto the rack, then position Ring Sizer tool No. T88C-3504-FH or equivalent on steering housing and install rack into steering housing. Leave protective sleeve in place.

4. With protective sleeve still in place, slide outer box seal into steering housing.

5. Using Outer Box Torque Adapter tool No. T88C-3504-CH or equivalent install outer box assembly. Tighten outer box assembly to specifications, then stake box assembly in place.

6. Using Installer tool No. T88C-3504-HH or equivalent, install intermediate bearing.

7. Using Installer tool No. T87M-3504-E or equivalent, install lower pinion bearing.

8. Using Seal Installer tool No. T88C-3504-MH or equivalent, install inner pinion seal.

9. Using Seal Installation Set tool No.

T81P-3504-M or equivalent, install three teflon seals onto the pinion, **Fig. 5.**

10. Using Seal Installation Set tool No. T81P-3504-M or equivalent, install pinion into steering housing.
11. Install upper pinion bearing.
12. Install Input Shaft Seal Protector tool No. T81P-3504-P or equivalent, then install upper pinion seal into steering housing.
13. Remove screw from Torque Adapter tool No. T88C-3504-BH or equivalent, then use tool to seat upper seal, **Fig. 6.**
14. Install pinion snap ring. Ensure snap ring is fully seated in groove.
15. Using tool No. T88C-3504-BH or equivalent to hold pinion, install pinion locknut and tighten to specifications.
16. Apply suitable thread sealer to housing cover, then install housing cover and tighten to specifications.

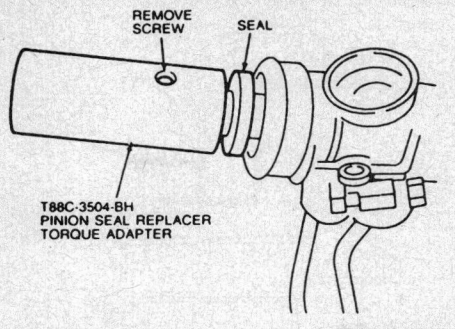

FM6029100152000X

Fig. 6 Upper seal installation

17. Using a suitable center punch, stake housing cover in place.
18. Install pressure pad, spring and adjust cover.
19. Using Yoke Torque Gauge tool No. T88C-3504-AH or equivalent, **torque** adjust cover to 7.2 ft. lbs., then loosen

adjust cover and **torque** to 3.6 ft. lbs., loosen adjust cover 45°.
20. Using Pinion Torque Adapter tool No. T88C-3504-BH, or equivalent, and a suitable inch lb. torque wrench, measure pinion torque. Pinion **torque** should measure 88.5-123.9 inch lbs., if torque is not within specifications repeat step 19 as necessary.
21. Install adjust cover locknut.
22. Using Yoke Locknut Wrench tool No. T88C-3504-KH or equivalent, tighten locknut to specifications.
23. Using a 30mm crowfoot wrench, install tie rod assembly into steering rack and tighten to specifications.
24. Install roll pin.
25. Install two hydraulic lines and routing clamp, then install clamp screw and tighten securely.
26. Install two remaining hydraulic lines, fitting protector and remaining clamp on steering housing.

TIGHTENING SPECIFICATIONS

Year	Component	Torque/Ft. Lbs.
1992	Adjust Cover	①
	Adjust Cover Locknut	36–43
	Clamp Bolt	13–20
	Differential Bearing Nut	36–43
	Housing Cover	30–40
	Hydraulic Lines (Large)	25–33
	Hydraulic Lines (Small)	18–22

Year	Component	Torque/Ft. Lbs.
1992 –Cont'd	Outer Box Assembly	65–72
	Pinion Locknut	29–36
	Pump Bolts	15–22
	Steering Gear Bolts	27–40
	Tie Rod	91–105
	Tie Rod End Locknut	51–72

①—Refer to text.

TYPE 7–NIHON RACK & PINION STEERING GEAR

NOTE: Also Refer To "Type 1-Ford Variable Assist Power Steering (VAPS) System."

NOTE: On Air Bag Equipped Models, Refer To "Air Bag System Precautions" Located In The Front Of This Manual For System Disarming & Arming Procedures.

INDEX

PRECAUTIONS

AIR BAG SYSTEMS

Refer to "Air Bag System Precautions" in the front of this manual for system disarming and arming procedures.

DESCRIPTION

This power rack and pinion steering gear is a hydraulic assisted system.

TROUBLESHOOTING

EXCESSIVE STEERING EFFORT

1. Insufficient tire pressure.
2. Loose or damaged belt.
3. Low fluid level or fluid aeration.
4. Crimped or twisted hoses or pipes.
5. Low hydraulic pressure.

6. Improperly adjusted wheel alignment.
7. Rough ball joint linkage operation.
8. Binding or bent steering shaft.

POOR STEERING WHEEL RETURN

1. Incorrect tire pressure.
2. Improperly adjusted wheel alignment.
3. Faulty ball joint linkage.
4. Restricted, over tightened or bent steering shaft.

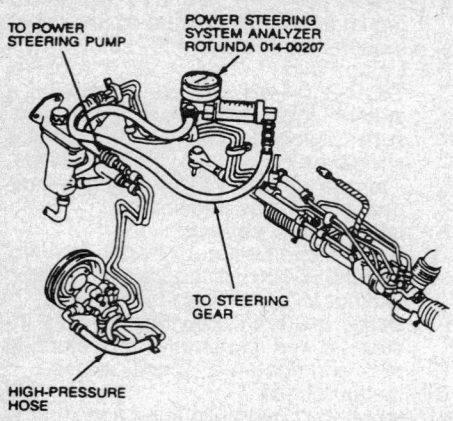

Fig. 1   Pressure test equipment connection

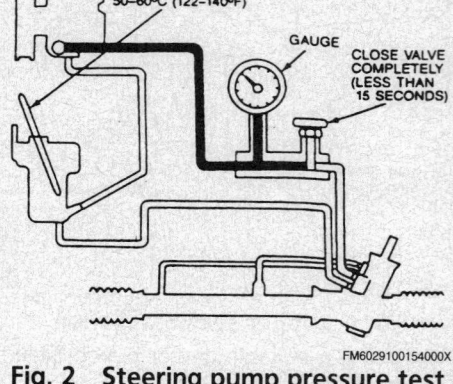

Fig. 2   Steering pump pressure test

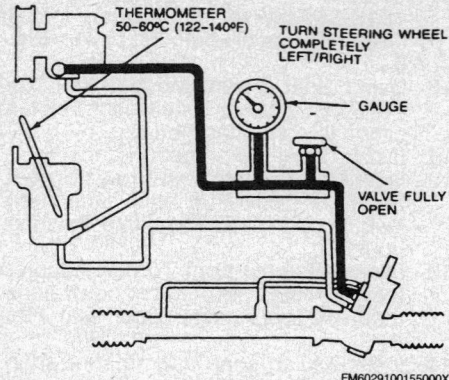

Fig. 3   Steering gear pressure test

UNEVEN STEERING EFFORT

1. Loose belt.
2. Loose steering shaft bolt(s).
3. Rough steering linkage operation.
4. Faulty steering gear.

STEERING WHEEL PULLS

1. Incorrect tire pressure.
2. Improper preload adjustment.
3. Faulty wheel bearing.
4. Improperly adjusted wheel alignment.
5. Faulty steering gear.

FLUID LEAKAGE

1. Hose coupling.
2. Damaged or clogged hose.
3. Faulty reservoir tank.
4. Faulty steering pump.
5. Faulty steering gear.

ABNORMAL NOISE

1. Loose power steering pump.
2. Loose steering gear.
3. Loose pump bracket.
4. Loose pump pulley nut.
5. Improperly adjusted belt.
6. Faulty steering gear.
7. Faulty steering pump.
8. Obstruction near steering column or pressure hose.
9. Loose steering linkage.

DIAGNOSIS & TESTING

POWER STEERING PRESSURE TEST

During the following procedure, power steering pressure may exceed 1200 psi. Ensure proper tool fit prior to performing test. Exercise extreme caution or damage or personal injury may result.

1. Disconnect power steering pump pressure hose where it connects to tubing, Install power steering system analyzer tool No. 014-00207 and adapter tool No. 014-00454 or equivalents, **torque** fitting to 29-36 ft. lbs., **Fig. 1.**
2. Position thermometer in power steering pump reservoir. **Ensure gauge**

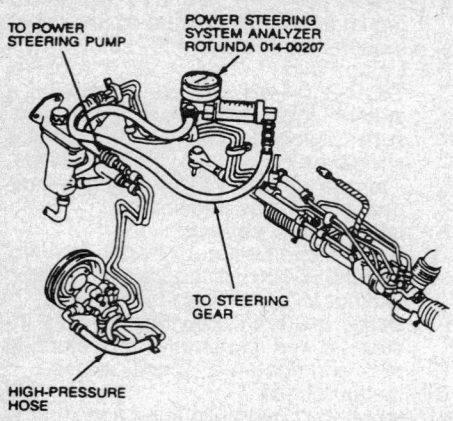

Fig. 4   Yoke locknut adjustment

valve is set open to allow normal system function. Do not hold steering wheel against a stop for more than 10 seconds at a time.

3. Start engine, then slowly turn steering wheel from lock to lock ten times to bleed system.
4. If required, turn steering wheel fully left and right several times to raise fluid temperature to 122-140°F (50-60°C). **Gauge valve must be briefly closed to read operating pressures. Do not leave valve closed for more than 15 seconds.**
5. To measure pump output pressure, close gauge set valve, **Fig. 2,** then increase engine speed to 1000-1500 RPM, read pressure, then open valve. Operating pressure should be 1066-1138 psi, if pressure is low, repair or replace pump.
6. To measure pressure at gear, open valve, then increase engine speed to 1000-1500 RPM, turn steering wheel fully left and right, read pressure, **Fig. 3.** Operating pressure should be 1066-1138 psi, if pressure is low, repair or replace steering gear.
7. Remove gauge set and adapter, connect high pressure hose and tighten.
8. Start engine, then slowly turn steering wheel lock to lock ten times to bleed system.

POWER STEERING SYSTEM SERVICE

Adjustments

RACK YOKE PRELOAD

1. With rack out of vehicle, measure pinion torque using an inch lb. torque wrench and Pinion Adapter tool No. T88C-3504-BH or equivalent. **Torque** should be 88.5-123.9 inch lbs.
2. If pinion torque is not within specification, loosen pinion locknut.
3. Using Torque Gauge tool No. T88C-3504-AH or equivalent, **torque** adjusting cover to 39-48 inch lbs. then loosen it 35°, **Fig. 4.**
4. Using Yoke Locknut Wrench tool No. T88C-3504-KH or equivalent, **torque** locknut to 29-36 ft. lbs.

Component Service

STEERING GEAR

Disassemble

1. Mount steering gear in a suitable vise equipped with soft jaws.
2. Remove external hydraulic lines connecting valve body to steering gear housing.
3. Remove solenoid valve from left mounting bracket.
4. Remove mounting brackets and rubber bushings from steering gear.
5. Scribe alignment marks on tie rods and tie rod ends, then remove tie rod ends.
6. Using a suitable chisel, uncrimp tie rod assembly lockwasher.
7. Using a 30mm crowfoot wrench, remove tie rod from steering gear.
8. Remove adjust cover locknut, **Fig. 5.**
9. Using Yoke Torque Gauge tool No. T88C-3504-AH or equivalent, remove adjust cover, spring and pressure pad.
10. Using Outer Torque Box Adapter tool No. T88C-3504-CH or equivalent, remove outer box assembly.
11. Using a screwdriver, remove pinion shaft oil seal.

Inspection

1. Check bearings for looseness, abnor-

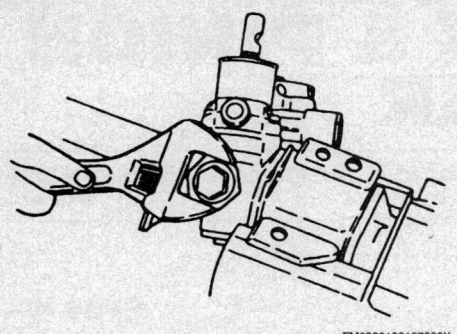

Fig. 5 Adjust cover locknut removal

mal noise or poor operation. **If pinion bearing requires replacement, replace entire steering gear assembly.**

2. Check for looseness or lack of smoothness in tie rod ball housings.
3. Check for bent tie rods or tie rod ends.
4. Check outer bulkhead bushing for wear.
5. Check tie rod boot for cracking, damage or deterioration.

Assemble

1. Lubricate outer box assembly with automatic transmission fluid.
2. Using outer torque adapter tool No. T88C-3504-CH or equivalent, install outer box assembly.
3. Stake the outer box assembly to the rack housing using a punch, **Fig. 6.**
4. Apply a thin coat of grease to lips of pinion seal, then install pinion seal using seal installer tool No. T88C-3504-BH or equivalent.
5. Install pressure pad and spring into gear housing, **Fig .**
6. Apply thread sealer to adjust cover.
7. Using torque gauge tool No. T88C-3504-AH or equivalent, install adjust cover and **torque** to 29-36 inch lbs.
8. Loosen adjust cover 35°.

9. Using pinion adapter tool No. T88C-3504-BH or equivalent, measure pinion torque, **torque** should be 88.5-123.9 inch lbs.
10. Install adjust cover locknut and **torque** to 28.9-36.2 ft. lbs.
11. Install washer and tie rod. **Torque** tie rod to 43.4-57.9 ft. lbs.
12. Bend washer tang to lock tie rod in place.
13. Slide tie rod boot over tie rod and position it on steering gear.
14. Wrap a new piece of mechanics wire around the boot twice, then around a Phillips screwdriver. Twist the wire four or five times with the screwdriver. **Ensure boot is not dented or twisted.**
15. Install outer boot clamp.
16. Install tie rod ends, ensuring index marks are aligned.
17. Install rubber mounting bushings and mounting brackets.
18. Install solenoid valve on mounting bracket.
19. Install external hydraulic lines connecting valve body to gear. Use new copper washers at each banjo fitting.

POWER STEERING SYSTEM FLUSH

If the power steering pump has been serviced, flush the power steering gear and lines prior to installation.

1. Remove and flush power steering pressure hose, then reinstall.
2. Place gear fluid return line in suitable container, then plug reservoir return line at reservoir.
3. Fill reservoir using Motorcraft DEXRON II part No. ESW-M2C-138-CJ or equivalent.
4. Disconnect coil wire, then raise and support front wheels.
5. Add about two quarts of fluid while

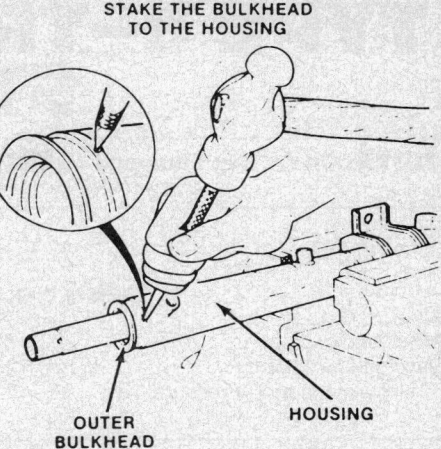

Fig. 6 Staking the bulkhead

cranking engine with starter and turning steering wheel right to left.
6. When all the fluid is added, stop cranking engine.
7. Remove reservoir return line plug, then connect line to reservoir.
8. Fill reservoir to specified level.
9. Crank engine with starter and add fluid until level remains constant.
10. While cranking engine, rotate steering wheel from stop to stop. **Front wheels must be off the ground during steering wheel stop to stop rotation.**
11. Check fluid level, add as required.
12. Start engine, allow to run for several minutes.
13. Rotate steering wheel from far left to right several times.
14. Turn off engine, check fluid level add as required.
15. Disconnect battery ground cable.
16. Depress brake pedal for at least five seconds.
17. Connect battery ground cable.

TYPE 8–TRW SSD RACK & PINION STEERING GEAR

NOTE: On Air Bag Equipped Models, Refer To "Air Bag System Precautions" Located In The Front Of This Manual For System Disarming & Arming Procedures.

INDEX

CONDITION	POSSIBLE SOURCE	ACTION
Excessive Steering Effort	Insufficient tire pressure.	ADJUST tire pressure.
	Loose or damaged belt.	ADJUST or REPLACE belt.
	Low fluid level or air in fluid.	ADD fluid or BLEED air.
	Crimped or twisted hose.	REPLACE hose.
	Crimped pipe.	REPLACE pipe.
	Leakage of fluid.	REPAIR leak.
	Insufficient power steering oil pump pressure.	REPLACE power steering pump.
	Improperly adjusted wheel alignment.	ADJUST wheel alignment.
	Linkage ball joint does not operate smoothly.	REPAIR linkage ball joint.
	Steering shaft is bent or binding.	REPLACE or REPAIR steering shaft.
Steering Wheel Pulls to One Side	Incorrect tire pressure.	ADJUST tire pressure.
	Improper preload adjustment or wear of wheel bearing.	ADJUST or REPLACE wheel bearing.
	Improperly adjusted wheel alignment.	ADJUST wheel alignment.
	Malfunction of steering gear.	INSPECT or REPLACE steering gear.
	Unevenly worn tires.	INSPECT tires for unusual wear. REPLACE as necessary.
	Dragging brake.	REPAIR brakes.
	Loose lower control arm.	TIGHTEN or REPLACE lower control arm.
Poor Steering Wheel Return	Incorrect tire pressure.	ADJUST tire pressure.
	Improperly adjusted wheel alignment.	ADJUST wheel alignment.
	Steering shaft is over-tight, restricted or bent.	REPLACE steering shaft.
	Improperly adjusted steering pinion preload.	REPAIR or REPLACE steering pinion.
	Damaged or stuck steering joints.	REPLACE steering joints.
	Ball joint sticking.	REPAIR or REPLACE ball joint.
General Instability While Driving	Incorrect tire pressure.	ADJUST tire pressure.
	Damaged or unbalanced wheel.	BALANCE or REPLACE wheel.
	Worn or damaged steering joints.	REPLACE steering joints.
	Improper steering pinion preload.	REPAIR or REPLACE steering pinion.
	Weak front coil spring.	INSPECT. REPLACE coil spring.
	Improperly adjusted wheel alignment.	ADJUST wheel alignment.
	Worn or damaged stabilizer and / or lower control arm bushing.	REPLACE stabilizer and / or lower control arm bushing.
	Damaged strut.	REPLACE strut.
Fluid Leakage	Problem at hose coupling.	REPAIR hose coupling.
	Damaged or clogged hose.	REPLACE hose.
	Damaged reserve tank.	REPLACE reserve tank.
	Overflow.	BLEED air or ADJUST fluid level.
	Malfunction of power steering pump.	REPLACE power steering pump.
	Malfunction of steering gear.	REPAIR REPLACE steering gear.
Excessive Steering Wheel Play	Worn steering gear.	REPLACE steering gear.
	Worn or damaged steering joints.	REPLACE steering joints.
	Worn or damaged lower control arm bushing.	REPLACE lower control arm bushing.
	Loose steering gear mounting bolts.	TIGHTEN bolts.
	Worn linkage or tie rod ball joint.	REPLACE linkage or tie rod ball joint.

FM6029100160010X

Fig. 1   Troubleshooting chart (Part 1 Of 2)

CONDITION	POSSIBLE SOURCE	ACTION
Abnormal Noise	Loose power steering pump.	TIGHTEN power steering pump.
	Loose steering gear.	TIGHTEN steering gear.
	Loose power steering pump bracket.	TIGHTEN power steering pump bracket.
	Loose power steering pump pulley nut.	TIGHTEN nut.
	Loose or too tight belt.	ADJUST belt.
	Air in system.	BLEED air.
	Malfunction of steering gear.	REPAIR or REPLACE steering gear.
	Malfunction of power steering pump.	REPLACE power steering pump.
	Obstruction near steering column or pressure hose.	REPAIR or REPLACE hose.
	Play or looseness in steering linkage.	TIGHTEN, ADJUST or REPLACE steering linkage.
	Worn steering joints.	REPLACE steering joints.

FM6029100160020X

Fig. 1   Troubleshooting chart (Part 2 Of 2)

FM6029100161000X

Fig. 2   Connecting Rotunda power steering system analyzer

PRECAUTIONS
AIR BAG SYSTEMS

Refer to "Air Bag System Precautions" in the front of this manual for system disarming and arming procedures.

DESCRIPTION

This power rack and pinion steering gear is a hydraulic assisted unit.

TROUBLESHOOTING

Refer to **Fig. 1**, for troubleshooting procedures.

DIAGNOSIS & TESTING
POWER STEERING
PRESSURE TEST

1. Raise and support vehicle, then remove transverse member.
2. Disconnect power steering pressure line between pump and gear, allowing fluid in line to drain.
3. Attach Rotunda power steering system analyzer 014-00207 with adapter 014-00456 between pressure hose connection as shown in **Fig. 2**. **Torque** fittings to 29-36 ft. lbs.
4. Place a thermometer in pump reservoir. Ensure valve on analyzer is OPEN to allow system to function normally. Do not hold steering wheel against stops for more than fifteen seconds at a time.
5. Bleed system as follows:
   a. Check fluid level in reservoir, and add fluid if necessary.
   b. Turn ignition switch to On position, engine not running, then turn steering wheel fully left and right ten times.
   c. Recheck fluid level, adding fluid if necessary.
   d. Repeat steps b and c until fluid level stabilizes, then start engine and

8. If pressure is too low, repair or replace pump. If pressure is too high, check for a crimped pipe and repair or replace as necessary, or replace pump.
9. Open valve on analyzer and increase engine speed to 1000-1500 RPM, then turn steering wheel all way to left or right and read pressure generated at steering gear. Pressure should be 1210-1270 psi.
10. If pressure is not within specifications, repair or replace steering gear.
11. Turn ignition to Off position, then remove analyzer and adapter.
12. Reconnect high pressure hose and **torque** connection to 17-26 ft. lbs., then bleed system as described in step 5.

POWER STEERING SYSTEM SERVICE
Adjustments

PINION PRELOAD

1. Remove steering gear from vehicle, then secure gear in a soft-jawed vise.
2. Measure pinion preload using pinion torque adapter T92C-35504-AH or equivalent. Torque at neutral position ± 90 degrees, should be 9-12 inch lbs. At any other position, torque should be 15 inch lbs.
3. If preload is not within specifications, loosen adjusting cover locknut, apply thread locking compound to exposed threads of adjusting cover, **torque** adjusting cover to 87 inch lbs. using yoke plug adapter T81P-3504-U or equivalent, then loosen it. **Torque** cover again to 39-48 inch lbs., then loosen 45 degrees.
4. Install adjusting cover locknut and **torque** to 36-43 ft. lbs. using yoke locknut wrench T88C-3504-KH or equivalent, while holding adjusting cover. **Do not allow adjusting cover to turn.**

Component Service

STEERING GEAR
Disassemble

Refer to **Fig. 3,** during disassembly procedures.

1. Remove steering gear from vehicle, then secure gear in a soft-jawed vise.
2. Remove four fluid lines and fluid line clamp, then the mounting brackets and bushings. **Before removing fluid lines, mark locations for proper assembly.**
3. Mark tie rod ends with alignment marks for reassembly, then remove tie rod ends and jam nuts.
4. Remove dust boots, then the inner tie rods.
5. Remove adjusting cover locknut using yoke locknut wrench T88C-3504-KH or equivalent, then the adjusting cover using yoke plug adapter T81P-3504-U or equivalent.
6. Remove spring and pressure pad, then the pinion snap ring.

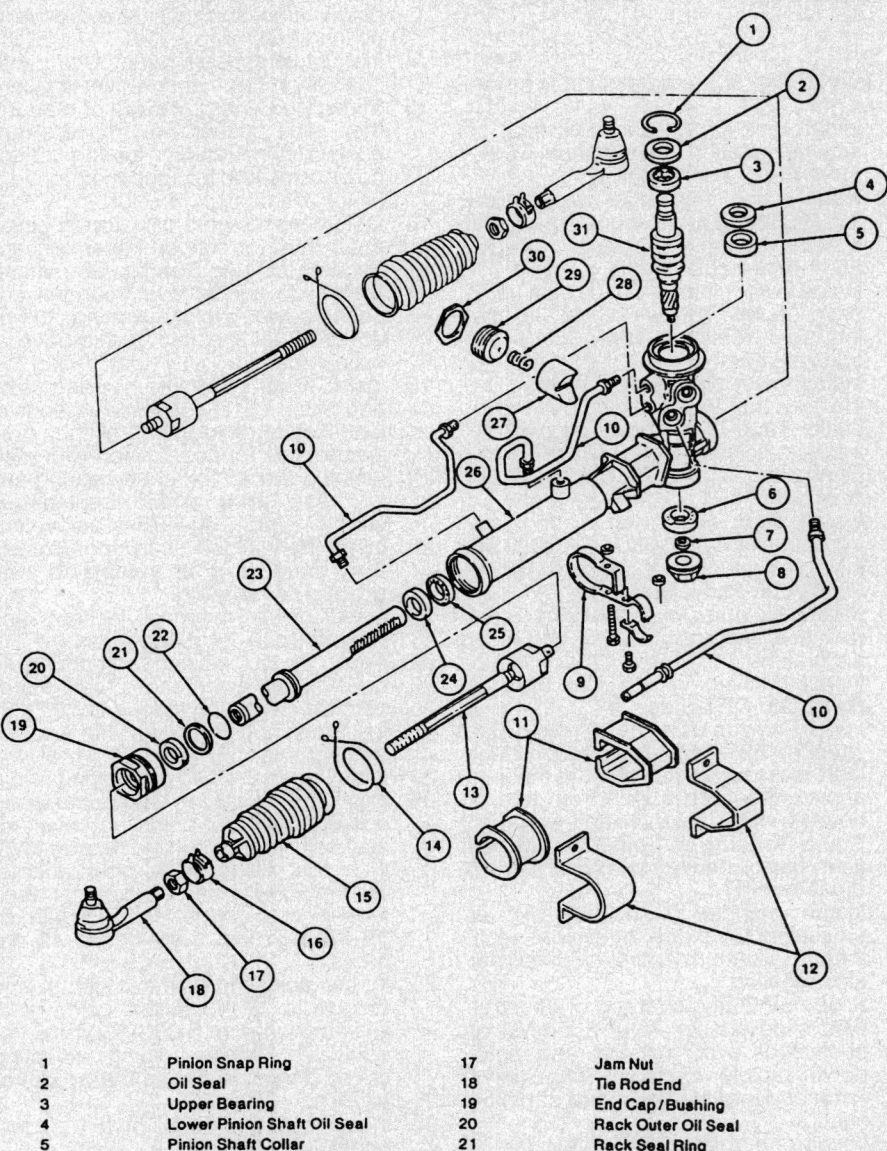

1	Pinion Snap Ring	17	Jam Nut
2	Oil Seal	18	Tie Rod End
3	Upper Bearing	19	End Cap / Bushing
4	Lower Pinion Shaft Oil Seal	20	Rack Outer Oil Seal
5	Pinion Shaft Collar	21	Rack Seal Ring
6	Lower Pinion Shaft Bearing	22	Rack O-Ring
7	Lower Bearing Locknut	23	Rack (Not Serviceable)
8	Housing Cover	24	Rack Internal Oil Seal (Not Serviceable)
9	Fluid Line Clamp	25	Spacer
10	Fluid Line	26	Housing
11	Mounting Bracket Bushings	27	Pressure Pad
12	Mounting Brackets	28	Spring
13	Inner Tie Rod	29	Adjusting Cover
14	Inner Boot Wire	30	Adjusting Cover Locknut
15	Dust Boot	31	Pinion Shaft (Not Serviceable)
16	Outer Boot Clamp		

FM6029100162000X

Fig. 3 Exploded view of steering gear

allow to idle.
e. Turn steering wheel fully left and right ten times, then verify that fluid is not foamy.
f. If air is still present in system, repeat steps b through e. **If foam is still present after repeating steps, check system for air leaks.**
g. If fluid level has decreased, add fluid and repeat step e until fluid level stabilizes.

6. Leave engine running, then if necessary, turn steering wheel fully left and right several times to raise fluid temperature to 122-140°F.
7. Close valve on analyzer briefly and increase engine speed to 1000-1500 RPM, then read pump output pressure. Pressure should be 1210-1270 psi. **Valve on analyzer must be briefly closed to read operating pressures. Do not leave valve closed for longer than 15 seconds.**

7. Drill away staked areas of housing cover, then remove housing cover.
8. Remove lower bearing locknut, then the pinion shaft, oil seal and upper bearing using valve body puller bridge T86P-3504-D or equivalent and valve body puller T78P-3504-B or equivalent.
9. Remove four O-rings from pinion shaft, then drill away staked areas of end cap using stake remover fixture T92C-3504-CH or equivalent.
10. Remove end cap using outer box torque wrench T88C-3504-NH or equivalent, secure end cap in a vise, then remove end cap bushing using blind hole puller set D80L-100-A or equivalent.
11. Remove rack and rack outer oil seal from right side of housing using impact slide hammer T50T-100-A , rack puller adapter T88C-3504-OH and adjustable rack seal protector D83P-3504-A or equivalents.
12. Remove rack internal oil seal using rack oil seal remover T78P-3504-J and impact slide hammer T50T-100-A or equivalents.
13. Remove spacer, then the lower pinion shaft bearing using pulley attachment T58P-101-B or equivalent.
14. Remove lower pinion shaft and pinion shaft collar using handle T87P-3504-D and pinion oil seal and spacer remover/replacer T92C-3504-BH. or equivalents
15. Remove rack O-ring and rack seal using O-ring tool T71P-19703-C or equivalent.

Inspection

1. Pinion shaft is not serviceable. Inspect pinion shaft for cracking, damage, and wear. If any of these conditions exist, steering gear must be replaced.
2. Inspect end cap and replace if threads are damaged.
3. Rack is not serviceable. Inspect rack for cracking, damage, or wear. If any of these conditions exist, steering gear must be replaced.
4. Rack internal oil seal is not serviceable. If evidence of leaking is found, steering gear must be replaced.

Assemble

Refer to **Fig. 3**, during assembly procedures.

1. Install rack O-ring and rack seal on rack using teflon ring expander T88C-3504-EH or equivalent.
2. Install pinion shaft collar using handle T87P-3504-D and pinion oil seal and spacer remover/replacer T92C-3504-BH or equivalents.
3. Install lower pinion shaft oil seal using drive handle T80T-4000-W and pinion seal replacer T84P-3504-F or equivalents.
4. Install lower pinion shaft bearing using drive handle and pinion bearing installer T90P-3504-OH or equivalent.
5. Install rack internal oil seal and spacer using seal installer T88C-3504-DH or equivalent.
6. Install rack using teflon ring sizing/installer T88C-3504-FH and adjustable rack oil seal protector D83P-3504-A or equivalents.
7. Seat rack outer oil seal using outer rack seal replacer T88C-3504-GH or equivalent.
8. Install bushing in end cap using a press and flat plates.
9. Install end cap using outer box torque wrench T88C-3504-NH or equivalent, then stake rack housing at two points approximately 0.06 inch from end of housing with a punch and hammer. **Stake housing at point 90 degrees from part cut away with drill during disassembly.**
10. Install mandrel T81P-3504-M1 or equivalent over top of pinion shaft, then lubricate mandrel with power steering fluid.
11. Slide one O-ring over top of mandrel, then slide pusher T81P-3504-M2 or equivalent over mandrel and push down rapidly forcing O-ring down ramp and into fourth groove of pinion shaft.
12. Install one spacer T81P-3504-M4 or equivalent over top of pinion shaft, then the mandrel over spacer.
13. Slide one O-ring over top of mandrel, then slide pusher over mandrel and push down rapidly forcing O-ring down ramp and into third groove of pinion shaft.
14. Install two spacers over top of pinion shaft, then the mandrel over spacer.
15. Slide one O-ring over top of mandrel, then slide pusher over mandrel and push down rapidly forcing O-ring down ramp and into second groove of pinion shaft.
16. Install two spacers over top of pinion shaft, then the mandrel over spacer.
17. Slide one O-ring over top of mandrel, then slide pusher over mandrel and push down rapidly forcing O-ring down ramp and into first groove of pinion shaft.
18. Install pinion shaft into housing using ring sizer T81P-3504-M3 or equivalent. Rotate pinion shaft slightly from side to side to mesh pinion with rack.
19. Install upper pinion shaft bearing and oil seal using pinion seal/torque adapter T88C-3504-BH or equivalent.
20. Install new pinion snap ring. **Ensure that snap ring is seated in ring groove of housing.**
21. Install lower bearing locknut and **torque** to 29-36 ft. lbs.
22. Apply thread locking compound to housing cover threads, then install housing cover and **torque** to 18-25 ft. lbs. Stake housing cover with a punch and hammer.
23. Install pressure pad and spring.
24. Apply thread locking compound to exposed threads of adjusting cover, install adjusting cover and **torque** to 87 inch lbs. using yoke plug adapter T81P-3504-U or equivalent, then loosen it. **Torque** cover again to 39-48 inch lbs., then loosen 45 degrees.
25. Install adjusting cover locknut and **torque** to 36-43 ft. lbs. using yoke locknut wrench T88C-3504-KH or equivalent while holding adjusting cover. **Do not allow adjusting cover to turn.**
26. Install inner tie rods, then the dust boots.
27. Install tie rod ends and jam nuts, then the mounting brackets and bushings.
28. Install fluid lines and fluid line clamp, then the steering gear in vehicle.

Power Steering Assist Systems

TABLE OF CONTENTS

Application Chart

Year	Model	Type	Page No.
1992	Continental	1	22-45
	Cougar LS & XR7	2	22-61
	Crown Victoria	2	22-61
	Grand Marquis	2	22-61
	Probe GT	1	22-45
	Sable w/3.8L	1	22-45
	Taurus w/3.8L	1	22-45
	Thunderbird LX & SC	2	22-61
	Town Car	2	22-61
1993	Continental	1	22-45
	Cougar	2	22-61
	Crown Victoria	2	22-61
	Grand Marquis	2	22-61

Year	Model	Type	Page No.
1993 —Cont'd	Mark VIII	2	22-61
	Sable	1	22-45
	Taurus	1	22-45
	Thunderbird	2	22-61
	Town Car	2	22-61
1994	Continental	1	22-45
	Cougar	2	22-61
	Crown Victoria	2	22-61
	Grand Marquis	2	22-61
	Mark VIII	2	22-61
	Sable	1	22-45
	Taurus	1	22-45
	Thunderbird	2	22-61
	Town Car	2	22-61

TYPE 1—FORD VARIABLE ASSIST POWER STEERING (VAPS) SYSTEM

NOTE: On Air Bag Equipped Models, Refer To "Air Bag System Precautions" Located In The Front Of This Manual For System Disarming & Arming Procedures.

INDEX

PRECAUTIONS

AIR BAG SYSTEMS

Refer to "Air Bag System Precautions" in the front of this manual for system disarming and arming procedures.

DESCRIPTION

The variable assist power steering (VAPS) system consists of a microprocessor-based control module, a power rack and pinion gear, an actuator valve assembly, interconnecting hose assemblies and a high efficiency power steering pump, **Fig. 1.**

The VAPS system incorporates a modified rotary valve in the gear with two independent hydraulic circuits called the primary and secondary circuits. During parking and low vehicle speed operation,

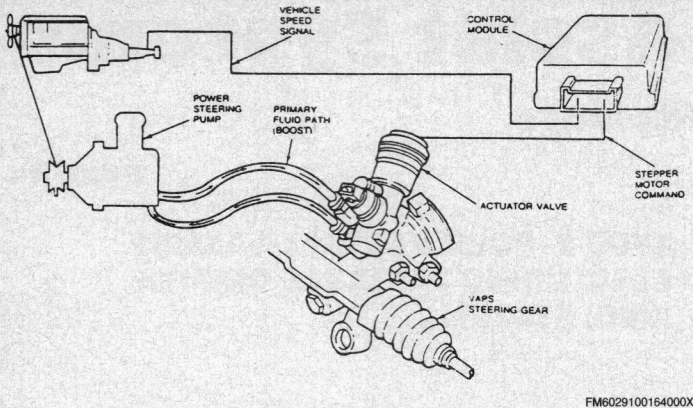

Fig. 1   VAPS system

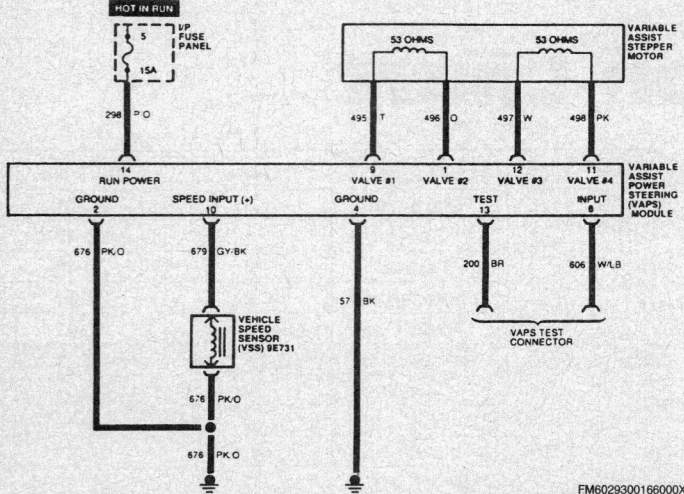

Fig. 3   VAPS system wiring diagram. 1993–94 Continental

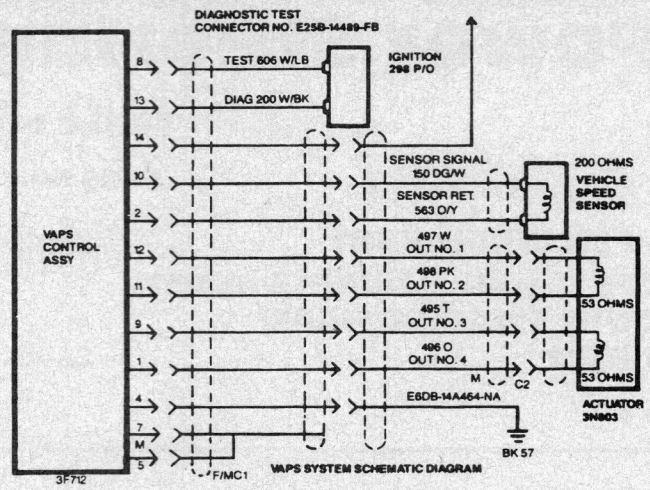

Fig. 2   VAPS system wiring diagram. 1992 Continental, Sable & Taurus

1992 PROBE

Quick Test

Prior to performing the following tests, a suitable analog volt/ohmmeter should be installed on the vehicle as shown in **Fig. 7.**

The quick test procedure should only be used when diagnosing variable assist power steering symptoms.

Quick test is divided into two specialized tests; "Key On Engine Running" and "Continuous Test."

Refer to **Figs. 8 through 13,** for quick test procedures.

POWER STEERING SYSTEM SERVICE

Component Service

STEERING GEAR ACTUATOR, REPLACE

1. Remove air inlet duct for access to actuator.
2. Disconnect VAPS electrical connector from actuator.
3. Remove pressure switch.
4. Remove two actuator to steering gear attaching bolts.
5. Lift actuator from steering gear assembly.
6. Reverse procedure to install.

VAPS MODULE, REPLACE

The VAPS module is located below the instrument panel on the righthand side of the steering column.

1. Remove four instrument panel cover attaching screws, then the cover.
2. Remove three sound package insulation push pins, then the sound package.
3. Disconnect VAPS electrical connectors.
4. Remove VAPS module.
5. Reverse procedure to install.

---

fluid flow from the pump is routed to the primary circuit by an electrically controlled actuator valve assembly. As vehicle speed increases, the actuator valve gradually opens, diverting the increased fluid volume to the secondary circuit.

The actuator valve assembly is a pressure balanced variable orifice valve, controlled by a stepper motor driven linear spool. The VAPS module receives inputs from the vehicle speed sensor and transmits signals to the stepper motor driven spool to adjust orifice opening of the actuator valve.

The VAPS module is programmed to perform a self-diagnostic check every 16 milliseconds. If a malfunction is detected, the module microprocessor deactivates its outputs allowing control assist power steering operation.

The VAPS module is programmed to perform a service diagnostic procedure when activated by a service technician.

The rotary design control valve directs fluid flow using relative rotational motion of the input shaft and valve sleeve. When the steering wheel is turned, resistance of the wheels and the weight of the vehicle will cause a torsion bar to deflect. The deflection action changes the position of the valve spool and sleeve ports, directing pressurized fluid to the appropriate end of the power cylinder. The pressure differen-

tial acts on the piston and helps move the rack to assist in the turning effort. The piston is attached directly to the rack and the housing functions as the power cylinder. The fluid in the opposite end of the power cylinder is forced to the control valve and back into the pump reservoir. When no steering effort is applied, the valve is forced back to a centered position by the torsion bar. When this occurs, pressure is equalized on both sides of the piston and the front wheels return to a straight-ahead position.

DIAGNOSIS & TESTING CONTINENTAL, SABLE & TAURUS

This portion of the power steering diagnosis procedure, applies only to the electrical components of the VAPS system. The VAPS control module, speed sensor, actuator valve, wiring harness and electrical connectors will be tested, **Figs. 2 through 4.**

The diagnostic connector to activate the diagnostic procedure is located within the engine compartment near the brake fluid reservoir and brake booster assembly, **Fig. 5.**

Refer to **Fig. 6,** for variable assist power steering electrical component diagnostic procedures.

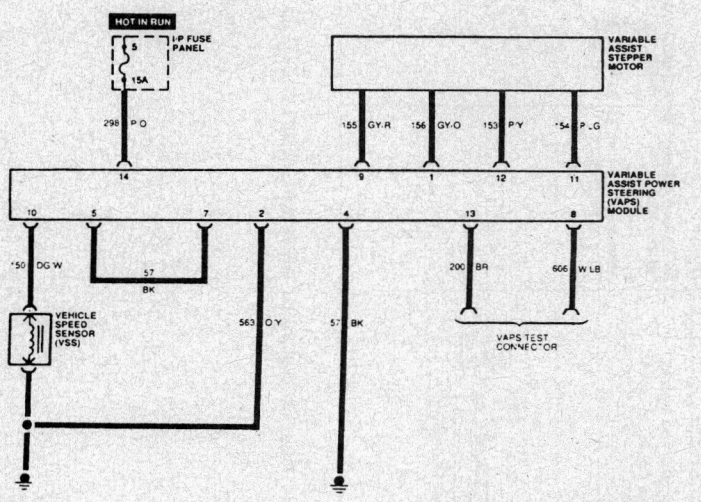

Fig. 4   VAPS system wiring diagram. 1993—94 Sable & Taurus

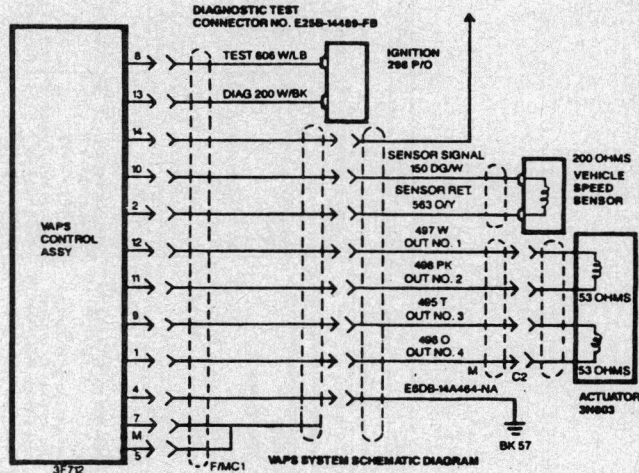

Fig. 5   Diagnostic connector location

TEST STEP	RESULT	▶	ACTION TO TAKE
A1 MODULE CHECK			
• Turn ignition switch to OFF. • Locate test connector 14489 in engine compartment near brake booster. • Connect DVOM positive lead (red) to Circuit No. 606 and negative lead (black) to vehicle ground.	Voltage reads 11V–14V	▶	GO to A2.
	Voltage reads zero	▶	GO to A3.
	Voltage reads above 14V	▶	CORRECT over-voltage condition then GO to A2.
• Position DVOM where it can be observed. • Start engine. • Observe voltage reading on DVOM.			
A2 MODULE CHECK			
• Turn ignition switch to OFF. • Connect an analog voltmeter as in Step A1. • Use jumper wire and ground Circuit No. 200.	Efforts Change? / Number of Sweeps		
	Yes 4	▶	GO to A4.
	No 4	▶	GO to A7.
	Yes 2	▶	GO to A19.
	No 2	▶	GO to A19.
	Yes 6	▶	GO to A20.
	No 6	▶	GO to A12.
• Start engine. • Rotate steering wheel for approximately 90 seconds noting any changes in steering effort. The effort required to turn the steering wheel should vary between light and heavy in both directions. • After approximately 90 seconds, voltmeter will show a sweep pattern four times between battery voltage and zero if module proveout is OK. Six or zero sweeps if a system component is malfunctioning. After a five second pause, the sweep pattern will be repeated. • Remove Circuit 200 ground before proceding to next test.	Yes 0	▶	GO to A20.
	No 0	▶	GO to A12.
A3 FUSE CHECK			
• Inspect fuse located in fuse panel on LH side below instrument panel.	Fuse good	▶	GO to A16.
	Fuse blown	▶	REPLACE fuse GO to A1.

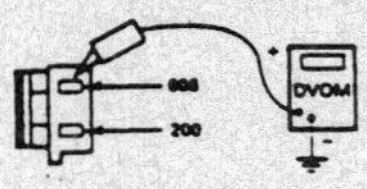

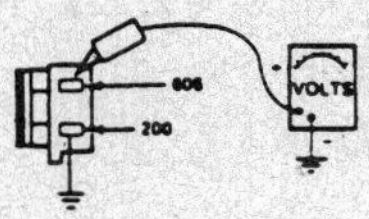

FM6029100169010X

Fig. 6   Electrical component diagnosis (Part 1 of 10). Continental

	TEST STEP	RESULT	ACTION TO TAKE
A4	TEST DRIVE VEHICLE		
	• Ensure VAPS system is connected. • Drive vehicle up to 55 mph and set speed control. • Do steering efforts change and is effort balanced (left vs. right turn direction). • While driving vehicle, note operation of speedometer.	Change in steering effort	Diagnostics complete system is OK.
		Assist only at high speed	GO to A11.
		No change in steering effort	GO to A5.
		Efforts unbalanced left to right	REPLACE steering gear assembly. REPEAT A4.
A5	SPEEDOMETER CHECK		
	• Note operation of speedometer and speed control (from Step A4). The VAPS system requires a speed signal from the vehicle speed sensor. If the speedometer or speed control does not work, these systems should be serviced using the appropriate diagnostic and service procedures.	Speedometer and speed control is operating properly	GO to A6.
		Speedometer or speed control does not operate properly	REPAIR as required. GO to A4.
A6	SPEED SENSOR CIRCUIT CHECK		
	• Disconnect VAPS connector from module. • Connect DVOM across Circuits No. 150 and No. 563. • Measure resistance.	Resistance is between 150-225 ohms	REPLACE VAPS module. GO to A4.
		Resistance is less than 150 or greater than 225 ohms	SERVICE harness. GO to A4.

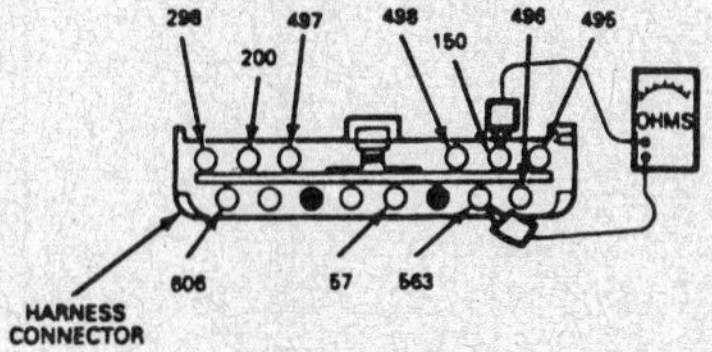

FM60291001690030X

Fig. 6 Electrical component diagnosis (Part 3 of 10)

	TEST STEP	RESULT		ACTION TO TAKE
A1	MODULE CHECK			
	• Turn ignition switch to OFF. • Locate test connector 14489 in engine compartment near brake booster. • Connect DVOM positive lead (red) to Circuit No. 606 and negative lead (black) to vehicle ground. • Position DVOM where it can be observed. • Start engine. • Observe voltage reading on DVOM.	Voltage reads 11V-14V		GO to A2.
		Voltage reads zero		GO to A3.
		Voltage reads above 14V		CORRECT over-voltage condition, then GO to A2.
A2	MODULE CHECK	Efforts Change?	Number of Sweeps	
	• Turn ignition switch to OFF. • Connect an analog voltmeter as in Step A1. • Use jumper wire and ground Circuit No. 200. • Start engine. • Rotate steering wheel for approximately 90 seconds noting any changes in steering effort. The effort required to turn the steering wheel should vary between light and heavy in both directions. • After approximately 90 seconds, voltmeter will show a sweep pattern four times between battery voltage and zero if module provesout is OK. Six or zero sweeps if a system component is malfunctioning. After a five second pause, the sweep pattern will be repeated. • Remove Circuit 200 ground before proceeding to next test.	Yes	2	GO to A4.
		No	2	GO to A7.
		Yes	4	GO to A19.
		No	4	GO to A19.
		Yes	6	GO to A20.
		No	6	GO to A12.
		Yes	0	GO to A20.
		No	0	GO to A12.
A3	FUSE CHECK			
	• Inspect fuse located in fuse panel on LH side below instrument panel.	Fuse good		GO to A16.
		Fuse blown		REPLACE fuse. GO to A1.

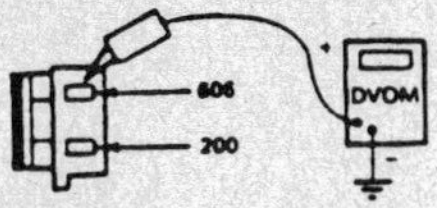

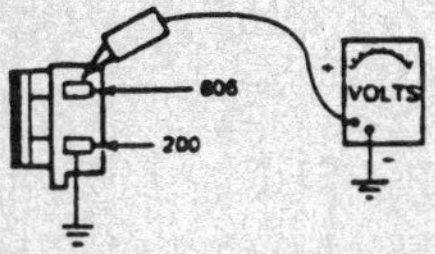

FM60291001690020X

Fig. 6 Electrical component diagnosis (Part 2 of 10). Sable & Taurus

Fig. 6 Electrical component diagnosis (Part 5 of 10)

TEST STEP	RESULT	ACTION TO TAKE
A9 ACTUATOR (MECHANICAL) CHECK • Turn ignition switch to OFF. • Remove actuator. Refer to removal procedure in this section. • Reconnect actuator connector to VAPS harness connector. • Attach DVOM to diagnostic connector (near brake booster) as shown. • Turn ignition switch to ON. • The module will go through a diagnostic check, consisting initially of the 90 second efforts change sequence. • If the actuator is mechanically operable, the actuator valve will move between its two limits of travel. This movement can be detected by watching the valve spring expand and relax between the travel limits.	Spring moves Spring does not move	▲ REPLACE steering gear assembly. GO to **A2**. ▲ REPLACE actuator. GO to **A2**.
A10 ACTUATOR (ELECTRICAL) CHECK • Turn ignition switch to OFF. • Disconnect actuator connector from harness connector. • Connect DVOM to Circuits No. 495 and No. 496. • Measure resistance. • Connect DVOM to Circuits No. 497 and No. 498. • Measure resistance.	Resistance between 43 and 70 ohms Resistance less than 43 or greater than 70 ohms	▲ GO to **A11**. ▲ REPLACE actuator. GO to **A2**.

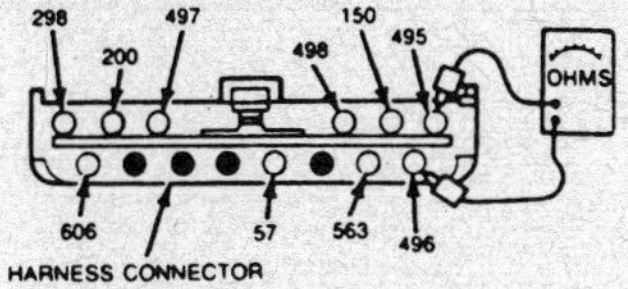

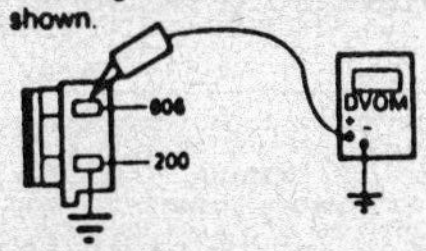

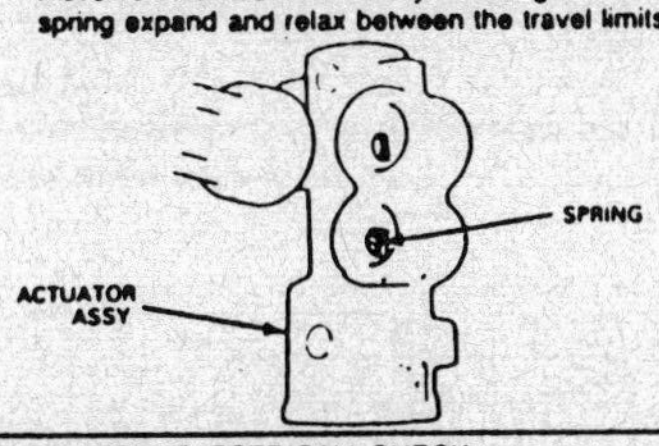

FM6029100169050X

Fig. 6 Electrical component diagnosis (Part 4 of 10)

TEST STEP	RESULT	ACTION TO TAKE
A7 ACTUATOR (ELECTRICAL) CHECK • Turn ignition switch to OFF. • Disconnect VAPS harness connector from module. • Connect DVOM to Circuits No. 495 and No. 496. • Measure resistance. • Connect DVOM to Circuits No. 497 and 498. • Measure resistance.	Resistance between 43 and 70 ohms Resistance less than 43 or greater than 70 ohms	▲ GO to **A8**. ▲ GO to **A10**.
A8 HARNESS VOLTAGE AT ACTUATOR CONNECTOR • Turn ignition switch to OFF. • Verify that VAPS connector is connected to VAPS module. • Disconnect actuator connector from VAPS harness connector. • Turn ignition switch to RUN. • Wait five seconds. • Measure DC voltage between Circuit No. 495 and ground. Then measure voltage between Circuit No. 496 and ground. • One of these two circuits should be greater than 10 volts and the other less than 2 volts. • Repeat the two steps above for Circuit No. 497 and 498.	Voltage check OK. One or more voltage readings not as specified.	▲ GO to **A9**. ▲ REPLACE VAPS module. GO to **A2**.

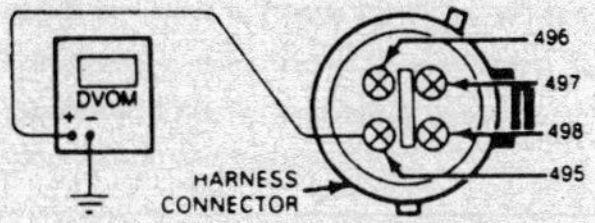

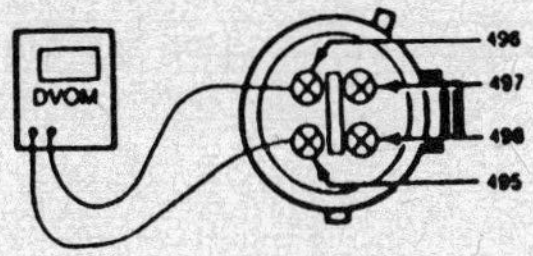

FM6029100169040X

Part 7 of 10

	TEST STEP	RESULT	ACTION TO TAKE
A13	**VAPS HARNESS AND CONNECTORS CHECK** • Disconnect VAPS connector from module. • Connect DVOM as shown.	▲ Voltage readings near given values.	▲ GO to A14.
		▲ One or more voltage values not near given values.	▲ SERVICE harness. REPEAT A13.

• Turn ignition switch to ON.
• Measure voltage at each circuit. (Circuit No. 57 to ground).

Row	Circuit No.	Function	Volts (DC)
Top	298	Power	Battery
Top	200	Diagnostic	<.1
Top	497	Actuator	<.1
Top	498	Actuator	<.1
Top	150	Speed Sensor	<.1
Top	495	Actuator	—
Bottom	606	Diagnostic	<.1
Bottom	57	Ground	<.1
Bottom	563	Speed Sensor	—
Bottom	496	Actuator	<.1
Bottom	—	VIP	<.1

Fig. 6 Electrical component diagnosis (Part 7 of 10)

FM60291001690070X

Part 6 of 10

	TEST STEP	RESULT	ACTION TO TAKE
A11	**CONTINUITY CHECK** • Turn ignition switch to OFF. • Disconnect module connector from module. • Disconnect actuator connector from actuator. • Check continuity of Circuit 495 from module connector to actuator connector. • Repeat for Circuits 496, 497 and 498.	▲ All circuits check OK.	▲ GO to A9.
		▲ Circuit fails continuity check.	▲ SERVICE harness. GO to A2.
A12	**VAPS HARNESS AND CONNECTORS CHECK** • Turn ignition switch to OFF. • Disconnect VAPS connector from module. • Connect positive lead of DVOM to Circuit No. 57 and negative lead to ground. • Measure resistance.	▲ Resistance between 0 and 15 ohms.	▲ GO to A13.
		▲ Resistance greater than 15 ohms.	▲ SERVICE harness. REPEAT A12.
		NOTE: All doors and hood must be closed for proper resistance readings	

Fig. 6 Electrical component diagnosis (Part 6 of 10)

FM60291001690060X

TEST STEP	RESULT	▶	ACTION TO TAKE
A14 VAPS HARNESS AND CONNECTORS CHECK			
• Turn ignition switch to OFF. • Measure resistance between Circuit No. 57 ground and all other indicated circuits. • Connect DVOM as shown.	Resistance values near given value	▶	GO to A15.
	One or more resistance values not near given values	▶	SERVICE harness. GO to A2.

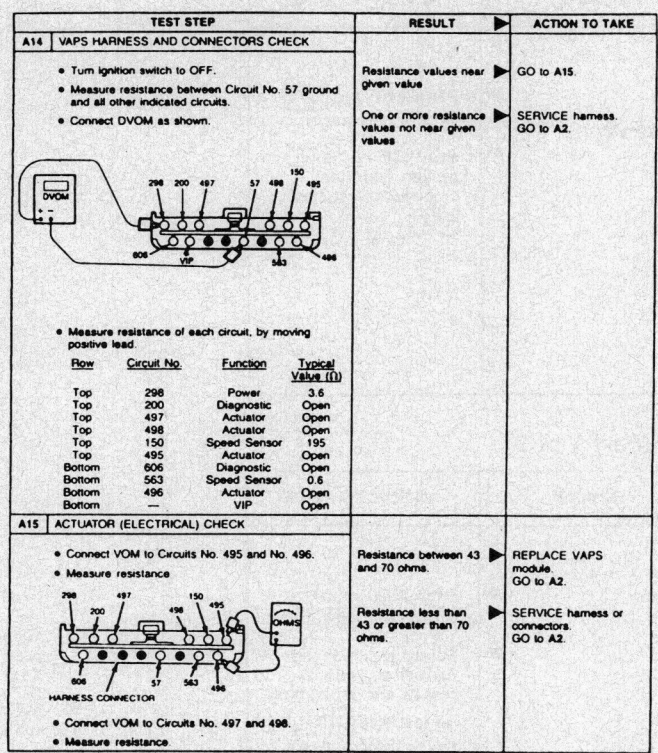

• Measure resistance of each circuit, by moving positive lead.			

Row	Circuit No.	Function	Typical Value (Ω)
Top	298	Power	3.6
Top	200	Diagnostic	Open
Top	497	Actuator	Open
Top	498	Actuator	Open
Top	150	Speed Sensor	195
Top	495	Actuator	Open
Bottom	606	Diagnostic	Open
Bottom	563	Speed Sensor	0.6
Bottom	496	Actuator	Open
Bottom	—	VIP	Open

TEST STEP	RESULT	▶	ACTION TO TAKE
A15 ACTUATOR (ELECTRICAL) CHECK			
• Connect VOM to Circuits No. 495 and No. 496. • Measure resistance	Resistance between 43 and 70 ohms.	▶	REPLACE VAPS module. GO to A2.
	Resistance less than 43 or greater than 70 ohms.	▶	SERVICE harness or connectors. GO to A2.
• Connect VOM to Circuits No. 497 and 498. • Measure resistance			

FM6029100169080X

Fig. 6   Electrical component diagnosis (Part 8 of 10)

TEST STEP	RESULT	▶	ACTION TO TAKE
A16 VAPS HARNESS AND CONNECTORS CHECK			
• Turn ignition switch to OFF. • Disconnect VAPS connector from module. • Connect positive lead of DVOM to Circuit No. 57 and negative lead to ground. • Measure resistance.	Resistance between 0 and 15 ohms	▶	GO to A17.
	Resistance greater than 15 ohms	▶	SERVICE harness. GO to A1.
	NOTE: All doors and hood must be closed for proper resistance readings.		

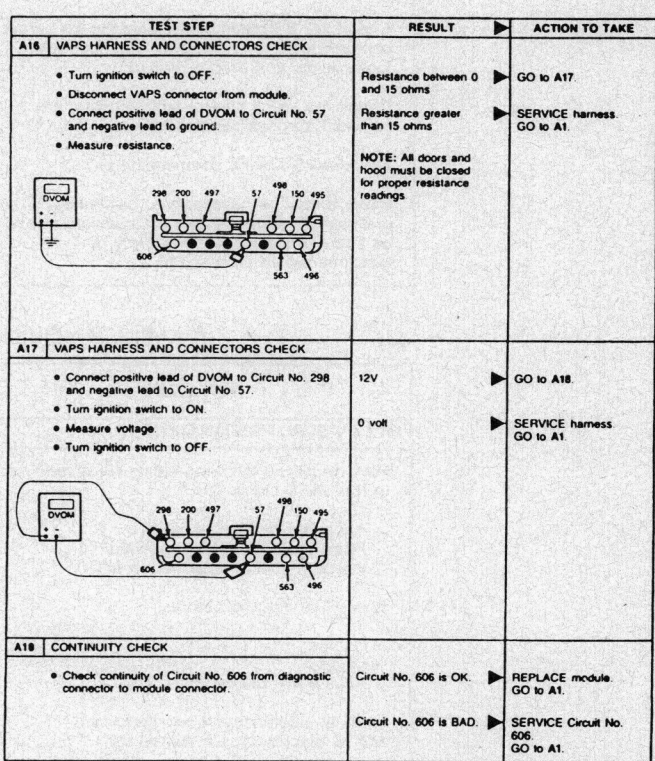

TEST STEP	RESULT	▶	ACTION TO TAKE
A17 VAPS HARNESS AND CONNECTORS CHECK			
• Connect positive lead of DVOM to Circuit No. 298 and negative lead to Circuit No. 57. • Turn ignition switch to ON. • Measure voltage. • Turn ignition switch to OFF.	12V	▶	GO to A18.
	0 volt	▶	SERVICE harness. GO to A1.

TEST STEP	RESULT	▶	ACTION TO TAKE
A18 CONTINUITY CHECK			
• Check continuity of Circuit No. 606 from diagnostic connector to module connector.	Circuit No. 606 is OK.	▶	REPLACE module. GO to A1.
	Circuit No. 606 is BAD.	▶	SERVICE Circuit No. 606. GO to A1.

FM6029100169090X

Fig. 6   Electrical component diagnosis (Part 9 of 10)

TEST STEP	RESULT	▶	ACTION TO TAKE
A19 VAPS HARNESS AND CONNECTORS CHECK (VIP PIN)			
• Turn ignition switch to OFF. • Doors and hood must be closed for proper reading. • Connect DVOM as shown. • Measure resistance between Circuit No. 57 (ground) and VIP Pin 7. Typical resistance is infinite. • Measure voltage between Circuit No. 57 (ground) and VIP. Typical voltage is less than 0.1.	Resistance and voltage values near given values	▶	GO to A4.
	One or more resistance or voltage values not near given values	▶	SERVICE harness. GO to A2
A20 VAPS HARNESS AND CONNECTORS CHECK (DIAGNOSTIC CONNECTOR)			
• Turn ignition switch to OFF. • Doors and hood must be closed for proper readings. • Disconnect VAPS harness connector from module. • Connect DVOM as shown. • Measure resistance between Circuit 606 of VAPS harness connector and Circuit 606 of diagnostic connector. Typical resistance is 2.0 ohms or less. • Measure voltage between Circuit 606 of VAPS harness connector and Circuit 606 of diagnostic connector. Typical voltage is less than 0.1. • Move leads to 200 Circuit. Measure resistance between Circuit 200 of VAPS harness connector and Circuit 200 of diagnostic connectors. Typical resistance is 2.0 ohms or less. • Measure voltage between Circuit 200 of VAPS harness connector and Circuit 200 of diagnostic connector. Typical voltage is less than 0.1.	Resistance and voltage values near given values	▶	GO to A2.
	One or more resistance or voltage values not near given value	▶	SERVICE harness. GO to A2.

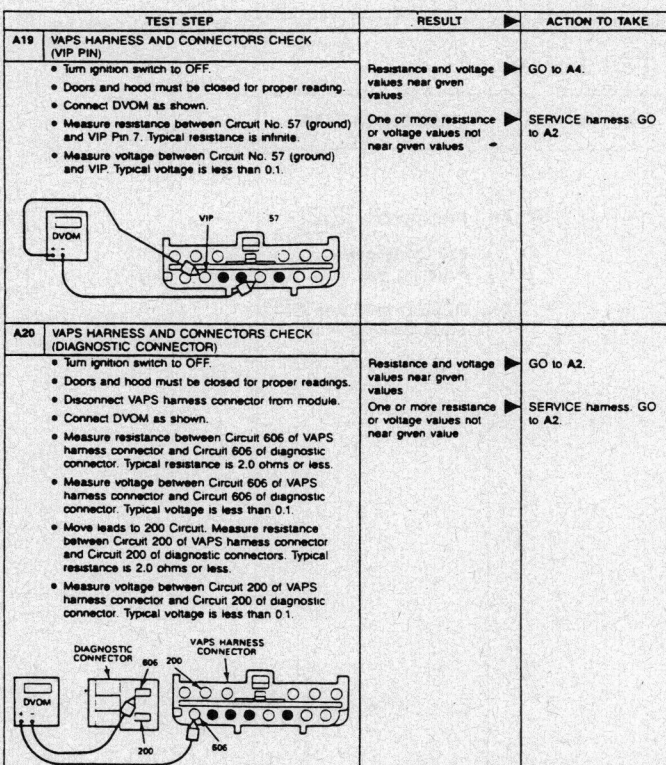

FM6029100169100X

Fig. 6   Electrical component diagnosis (Part 10 of 10)

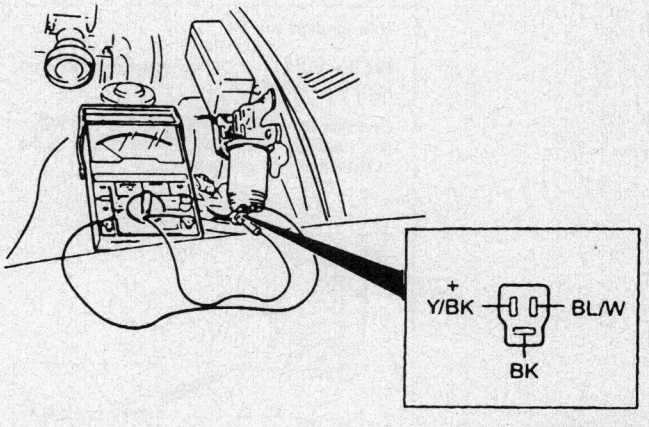

FM6029100170000X

Fig. 7   Volt/ohmmeter installation

TEST STEP	RESULT	ACTION TO TAKE
QT1 | VISUAL CHECK Check steering gear and linkage for damage, leaks, cracks, and proper mounting. Check VAPS system wiring harness for proper connections, bent or broken pins, corrosion, loose wires, and proper routing. Check the VAPS control unit, sensors, and solenoid for physical damage. Are a VAPS system components ok? **Note:** It may be necessary to disconnect or disassemble harness connector assemblies to do some of the inspections. Note pin locations before disassembly.	Yes No	▶ PROCEEED to **QT2** vehicle preparation. ▶ SERVICE fault(s) in system and then proceed to test step **QT2** .

FM6029100171010X

Fig. 8   Quick test (Part 1 of 9)

TEST STEP	RESULT	ACTION TO TAKE
QT2 | VISUAL PREPARATION Perform all the following safety steps required to run VAPS Quick Test. Apply the parking brake. Place the shift lever firmly into the park position (neutral on MTX). Turn off all electrical loads. Radios Lights A/C-Heater Blower Fans, etc... Have all safety steps been performed and all electrical loads turned off?	Yes No	▶ PROCEED to **QT3** equipment hookup. ▶ Personal safety and correct diagnostic results are dependant on test step **QT2** . Do not proceed with quick test if vehicle preparation cannot be performed.

FM6029100171020X

Fig. 8   Quick test (Part 2 of 9)

TEST STEP	RESULT	ACTION TO TAKE
QT3 | EQUIPMENT HOOKUP Turn ignition key off. Set the VOM on a DC voltage range to read from 0 to 15 volts. Connect the VOM positive lead to the Y/BK and negative lead to the BK terminals of the suspension test connector. **Note:** For correct reading of service codes use only an analog VOM. Is analog VOM hooked up properly?	Yes No	▶ PROCEED to **QT4** . Key On Engine Running Test. ▶ RE-ATTEMPT step **QT3** Equipment hookup.

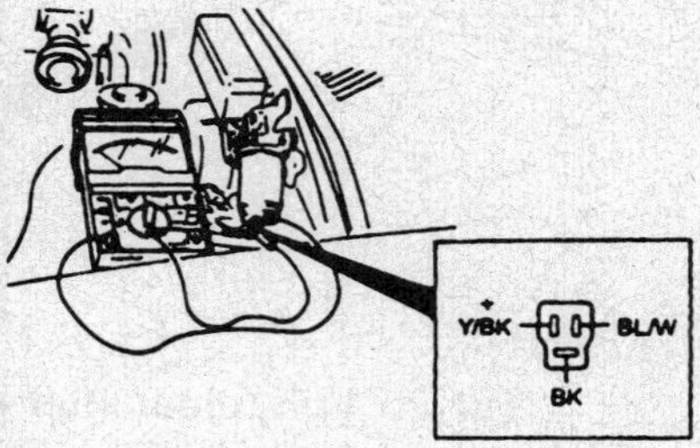

FM6029100171030X

Fig. 8   Quick test (Part 3 of 9)

TEST STEP	RESULT	ACTION TO TAKE
QT5 KEY ON ENGINE RUNNING TEST		
Turn ignition key off to reset processor.	CODE 1	PERFORM Pinpoint Test C.
Set steering wheel in the straight ahead position.	CODE 2	Indicates a pass code. PROCEED to QT6.
Key on, Engine running at idle.	CODE 3	PERFORM Pinpoint Test B.
Turn VOM on.	CODE 5	PERFORM Pinpoint Test A.
Turn the steering wheel 45 degrees left and right from center.	NO CODES	PERFORM Pinpoint Test Q.
Record any service codes.	CODE UNLISTED	PERFORM Pinpoint Test Q.

FM6029100171050X

Fig. 8   Quick test (Part 5 of 9)

TEST STEP	RESULT	ACTION TO TAKE
QT7 CONTINUOUS TEST		
Verify that a pass code was indicated in all steps of the Key On Engine Running Test.	CODE 1	Indicates a pass code. PROCEED to QT8.
Verify that the vehicle has been properly prepared per Quick Test steps QT2 and QT3.	CODE 2	PERFORM Pinpoint Test C.
Key on, Engine running at idle.	CODE 3	PERFORM Pinpoint Test B.
Activate self-test by turning analog VOM on.	CODE 5	PERFORM Pinpoint Test A.
While steering wheel is in the straight ahead position, tap, move and wiggle VAPS components and harness while observing for any service code indentification on the VOM.	NO CODES	PERFORM Pinpoint Test Q.
Record any service codes.	CODE UNLISTED	PERFORM Pinpoint Test Q.

FM6029100171070X

Fig. 8   Quick test (Part 7 of 9)

TEST STEP	RESULT	ACTION TO TAKE
QT4 KEY ON ENGINE RUNNING		
Turn ignition key off.	CODE 1	Indicates a pass code. PROCEED to QT5.
Verify that the vehicle has been properly prepared per Quick Test steps QT2 and QT3.	CODE 2	PERFORM Pinpoint Test C.
Key on, Engine running at idle.	CODE 3	PERFORM Pinpoint Test B.
Set steering wheel in the straight ahead position.	CODE 5	PERFRROM Pinpoint Test A.
Activate self-test by turning analog VOM on.	NO CODES	PERFORM Pinpoint Test Q.
Record any service codes.	CODE UNLISTED	PERFORM Pinpoint Test Q.
Note: When a service code is reported on the analog VOM, it will represent itself as a pulsing or sweeping movement of the voltmeter's needle across the dial face. Code 1 will be represented by one pulse and code 2 by two pulses and so on.		

FM6029100171040X

Fig. 8   Quick test (Part 4 of 9)

TEST STEP	RESULT	ACTION TO TAKE
QT6 KEY ON ENGINE RUNNING TEST		
Turn ignition key to reset processor.	CODE 1	PERFORM Pinpoint Test D.
Set steering wheel in the straight ahead position.	CODE 2	PERFORM Pinpoint Test C.
Key on, Engine running at idle.	CODE 3	PERFORM Pinpoint Test B.
Turn VOM on.	CODE 5	PERFORM Pinpoint Test A.
Hoist vehicle and rotate front wheels at above 10km/h (6.2 MPH).	CONSTANT 4.4 VOLTS	Pass Code. PERFORM Pinpoint Test C to verify steering angle sensor VREF and SIGRTN circuits are ok. For intermittent symptoms PROCEED to QT7.
Record any service codes.	NO CODES	PERFORM Pinpoint Test Q.
	CODE UNLISTED	PERFORM Pinpoint Test Q.

FM6029100171060X

Fig. 8   Quick test (Part 6 of 9)

TYPE 1-FORD VARIABLE ASSIST POWER STEERING (VAPS) SYSTEM

TEST STEP		RESULT	ACTION TO TAKE
QT9	**CONTINUOUS TEST**		
Turn ignition key off to reset processor.		CODE 1	PERFORM Pinpoint Test D.
Set steering wheel in the straight ahead position.		CODE 2	PEFORM Pinpoint Test C.
Key on, Engine running at idle.		CODE 3	PERFORM Pinpoint Test B.
Turn VOM on.		CODE 5	PERFORM Pinpoint Test A.
Hoist vehicle.		CONSTANT 4.4 VOLTS	Indicates a pass code. PERFORM Pinpoint Test Q to verify that the VAPS control module and circuitry are OK.
While rotating front wheels at above 10km/h (6.2MPH), tap, move and wiggle VAPS components and harness while observing for any service code indication on the VOM.		NO CODES	PERFORM Pinpoint Test Q.
Record any service codes.		CODE UNLISTED	PERFORM Pinpoint Test Q.

FM60291001710900X

Fig. 8 Quick test (Part 9 of 9)

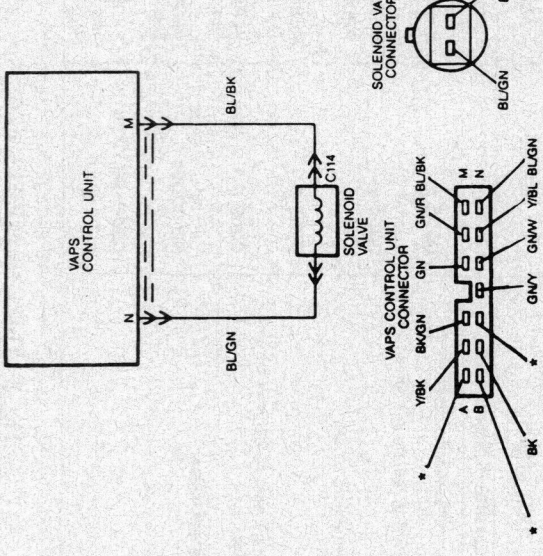

FM60291001720100X

Fig. 9 Pinpoint test A (Part 1 of 4)

TEST STEP		RESULT	ACTION TO TAKE
QT8	**CONTINUOUS TEST**		
Turn ignition key off to reset processor.		CODE 1	PERFORM Pinpoint Test C.
Set steering wheel in the straight ahead position.		CODE 2	Indicates a pass code. PROCEED to QT9.
Key on, Engine running at idle.		CODE 3	PERFORM Pinpoint Test B.
Turn VOM on.		CODE 5	PERFORM Pinpoint Test A.
While turning the steering wheel 45 degrees left and right from center, tap, move and wiggle VAPS components and harness while observing for any service code indication on the VOM.		NO CODES	PERFORM Pinpoint Test Q.
Record any Service Codes.		CODE UNLISTED	PERFORM Pinpoint Test Q.

FM60291001710800X

Fig. 8 Quick test (Part 8 of 9)

TEST STEP		RESULT	ACTION TO TAKE
A3	SOLENOID RESISTANCE CHECK		
	• VOM on 200 ohm scale. • Measure resistance between solenoid terminals. • Is resistance between 3.4 and 6.9 ohms?	Yes	GO to A4 .
		No	REPLACE solenoid.

Fig. 9   Pinpoint test A (Part 3 of 4)

TEST STEP		RESULT	ACTION TO TAKE
A4	SOLENOID CIRCUIT RESISTANCE CHECK		
	• Disconnect VAPS control unit connector and solenoid connector. • Key off. • VOM on 200 ohm scale. • Measure resistance between the following terminals. 　1 Between VAPS Control Unit connector terminal M ("BL/BK") and solenoid valve connector "BL/BK" wire. 　2 Between VAPS Control Unit connector terminal N ("BL/GN") and solenoid valve connector "BL/GN" wire. • Are resistances less than 5 ohms?	Yes	GO to A5 .
		No	REPAIR wire in question for opens.

FM60291001720030X

TEST STEP		RESULT	ACTION TO TAKE
A1	SYSTEM INTEGRITY CHECK		
	• Visually inspect all wiring, wiring harness, connectors and components for evidence of overheating, insulation damage, looseness, shorting or other damage. • Is there any cause for concern?	Yes	SERVICE as required.
		No	GO to A2

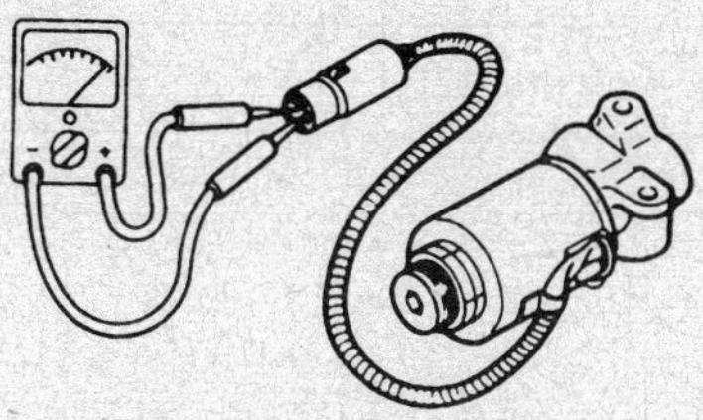

TEST STEP		RESULT	ACTION TO TAKE
A2	SOLENOID FUNCTION CHECK		
	• Disconnect solenoid valve connector. • Apply 12 volts and ground to terminals as shown and listen for actuation sound. • Is clicking sound heard when applying 12 volts?	Yes	GO to A3 .
		No	REPLACE solenoid.

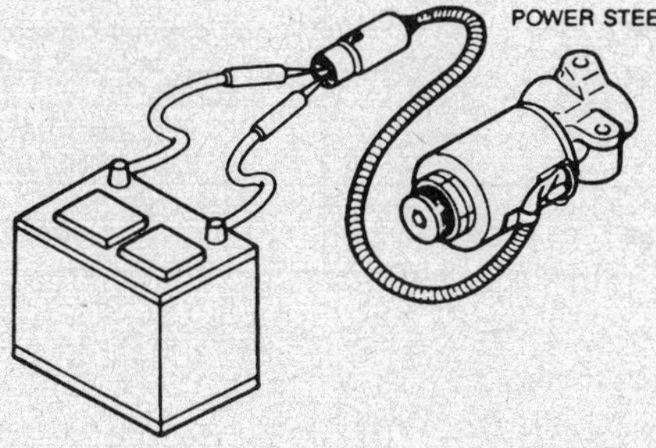

POWER STEERING SOLENOID VALVE

FM60291001720020X

Fig. 9   Pinpoint test A (Part 2 of 4)

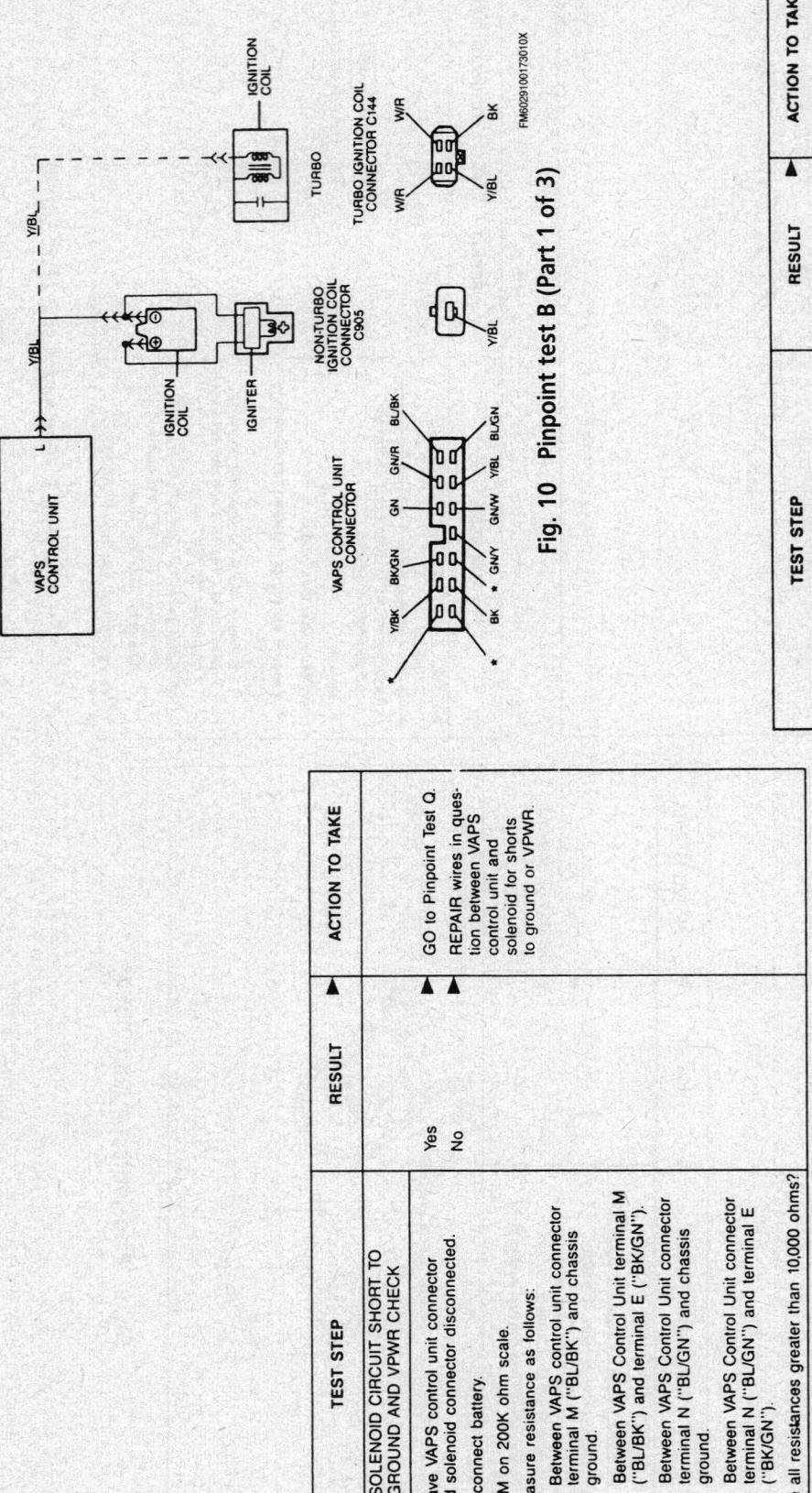

Fig. 10 Pinpoint test B (Part 1 of 3)

	TEST STEP	RESULT	ACTION TO TAKE
B1	**SYSTEM INTEGRITY CHECK** • Visually inspect all wiring, wiring harness, connectors and components for evidence of overheating, insulation damage, looseness, shorting or other damage. • Is there any cause for concern?	Yes No	SERVICE as required. GO to B2 .

Fig. 10 Pinpoint test B (Part 2 of 3)

	TEST STEP	RESULT	ACTION TO TAKE
A5	**SOLENOID CIRCUIT SHORT TO GROUND AND VPWR CHECK** • Leave VAPS control unit connector and solenoid connector disconnected. • Disconnect battery. • VOM on 200K ohm scale. • Measure resistance as follows: 1 Between VAPS control unit connector terminal M ("BL/BK") and chassis ground. 2 Between VAPS Control Unit terminal M ("BL/BK") and terminal E ("BK/GN"). 3 Between VAPS Control Unit connector terminal N ("BL/GN") and chassis ground. 4 Between VAPS Control Unit connector terminal N ("BL/GN") and terminal E ("BK/GN"). • Are all resistances greater than 10,000 ohms?	Yes No	GO to Pinpoint Test Q. REPAIR wires in question between VAPS control unit and solenoid for shorts to ground or VPWR.

Fig. 9 Pinpoint test A (Part 4 of 4)

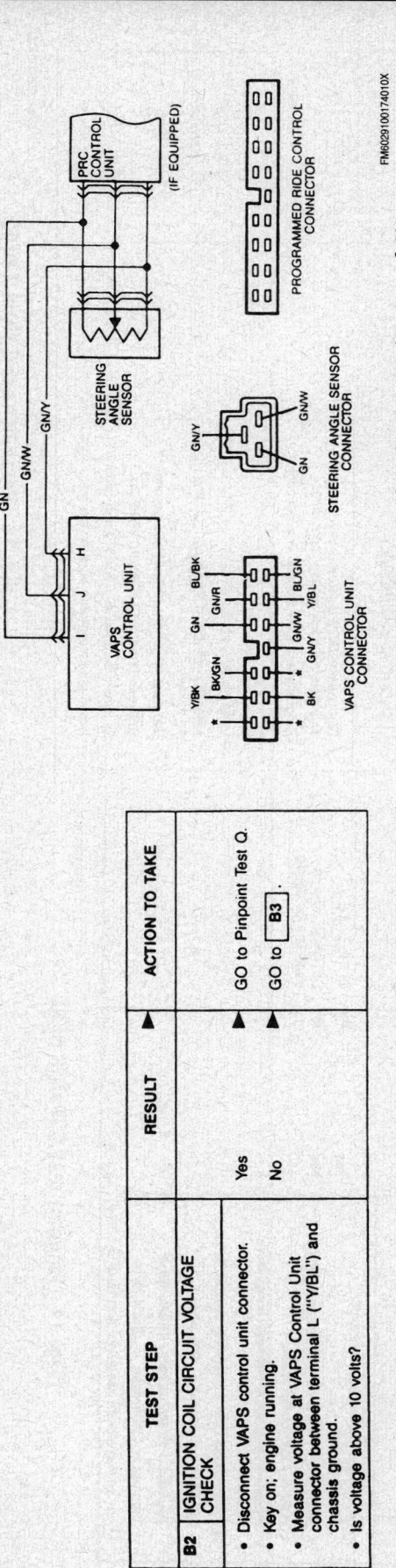

Fig. 11 Pinpoint test C (Part 1 of 8)

TEST STEP	RESULT	ACTION TO TAKE
C1 SYSTEM INTEGRITY CHECK		
• Visually inspect all wiring, wiring harness, connectors and components for evidence of overheating, insulation damage, looseness, shorting or other damage.		
• Is there any cause for concern?	Yes	SERVICE as required.
	No	GO to C2 .

FM6029100174020X

Fig. 11 Pinpoint test C (Part 2 of 8)

TEST STEP	RESULT	ACTION TO TAKE
C2 STEERING ANGLE SENSOR RESISTANCE CHECK		
• Key off.		
• Remove steering column cover and disconnect steering angle sensor connector.		GO to C3 .
• Set the steering wheel so wheels are in a straight ahead position.		REPLACE steering angle sensor.
• Measure the resistance between the following steering angle sensor terminals with the VOM meter set on the 200K scale:		
Terminal Resistance 1. ("GN") – ("GN/W") 0–15K ohms 2. ("GN") – ("GN/Y") 40–60K ohms 3. ("GN/Y") – ("GN/W") 30–50K ohms		
• Are all resistances within specification?	Yes	
	No	

Fig. 11 Pinpoint Test C (Part 3 of 8)

FM6029100174030X

FM6029100173030X

TEST STEP	RESULT	ACTION TO TAKE
B2 IGNITION COIL CIRCUIT VOLTAGE CHECK		
• Disconnect VAPS control unit connector.		
• Key on; engine running.		
• Measure voltage at VAPS Control Unit connector between terminal L ("Y/BL") and chassis ground.		
• Is voltage above 10 volts?	Yes	GO to Pinpoint Test Q.
	No	GO to B3 .

TEST STEP	RESULT	ACTION TO TAKE
B3 CIRCUIT CONTINUITY CHECK		
• Leave VAPS control unit connector disconnected.		
• Disconnect ignition coil connector.		
• VOM on 200 ohm scale.		GO to B4 .
• Measure resistance between ignition coil ("Y/BL") wire and VAPS Control Unit connector terminal L ("Y/BL").		SERVICE ("Y/BL") wire between ignition coil and VAPS control unit for opens.
• Is resistance less than 5 ohms?	Yes	
	No	

TEST STEP	RESULT	ACTION TO TAKE
B4 CIRCUIT SHORT TO GROUND AND VPWR CHECK		
• Leave VAPS control unit connector disconnected.		
• Disconnect battery.		
• VOM on 200K ohm scale.		GO to Pinpoint Test Q.
• Measure resistance between VAPS Control Unit connector terminal L ("Y/BL") and chassis ground and between terminal L ("Y/BL") and terminal E ("BK/GN").		REPAIR ("Y/BL") wire between ignition coil and VAPS control unit for short to ground or VPWR.
• Are resistances greater than 10,000 ohms?	Yes	
	No	

Fig. 10 Pinpoint test B (Part 3 of 3)

C4 — STEERING ANGLE SENSOR CHECK

TEST STEP	RESULT	ACTION TO TAKE
C4 STEERING ANGLE SENSOR CHECK • Steering angle sensor connector disconnected. • Set the steering wheel in a straight ahead position. • VOM on 200K ohms scale. • Measure the resistance as decribed in the table below. • At the straight ahead position, observe the ohmmeter reading. This is your base reading. As you turn the wheel to your left, the reading will decrease to 0 ohms. The reading will then change to 45K ohms and continue to decrease from that value. • Are all resistances within specification?	Yes No	GO to C5 . REPLACE steering angle sensor.

Terminal	Steering Wheel Position	Resistance Value
GN-GN/W	Turn the wheel a little at a time from the straight ahead position 180 degrees to the left.	Decreases approximately 20K ohms from the straight ahead value.
GN-GN/W	Straight ahead position.	0-15K ohms.

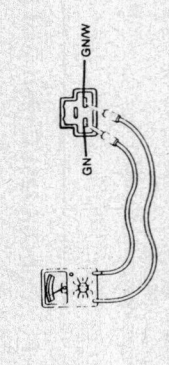

Fig. 11 Pinpoint Test C (Part 5 of 8)

C3 — STEERING ANGLE SENSOR CHECK

TEST STEP	RESULT	ACTION TO TAKE
C3 STEERING ANGLE SENSOR CHECK • Steering angle sensor connector disconnected. • Set the steering wheel in the straight ahead position. • VOM on 200K ohms scale. • Measure the resistance as decribed in the table below. • Are all resistances within specification?	Yes No	GO to C4 . REPLACE steering angle sensor.

Terminal	Steering Wheel Position	Resistance Value
GN-GN/W	Turn the wheel a little at a time from the straight ahead position 180 degrees to the right.	Increases approximately 20K ohms from the straight ahead value.
GN-GN/W	Straight ahead position.	0-15K ohms.

Fig. 11 Pinpoint Test C (Part 4 of 8)

C6 — SHORT TO VPWR CHECK

TEST STEP	RESULT	ACTION TO TAKE
C6 SHORT TO VPWR CHECK • Disconnect VAPS control unit connector and steering angle sensor connector. • Programmed Ride Control unit connector disconnected (if equipped). • Key on; engine off. • VOM on 20 volt scale. • Measure voltage at VAPS control unit as follows: Between terminal I ("GN") and ground. Between terminal J ("GN/W") and ground. Between terminal H ("GN/Y") and ground. • Do all measurements read 0 volts?	Yes No	GO to C7 SERVICE wire in question for shorts to VPWR.

Fig. 11 Pinpoint Test C (Part 7 of 8)

C5 — CIRCUIT CONTINUITY CHECK

TEST STEP	RESULT	ACTION TO TAKE
C5 CIRCUIT CONTINUITY CHECK • Steering angle sensor connector disconnected. • Disconnect VAPS control unit connector. • VOM on 200 ohms scale. • Measure resistance between connectors as follows: **VAPS Control Unit Steering Angle Sensor** Terminal I GN Wire — GN Wire Terminal J GN/W Wire — GN/W Wire Terminal H GN/Y Wire — GN/Y Wire • Are all resistance readings less than 5 ohms?	Yes No	GO to C6 . SERVICE wire in question for opens.

Fig. 11 Pinpoint test C (Part 6 of 8)

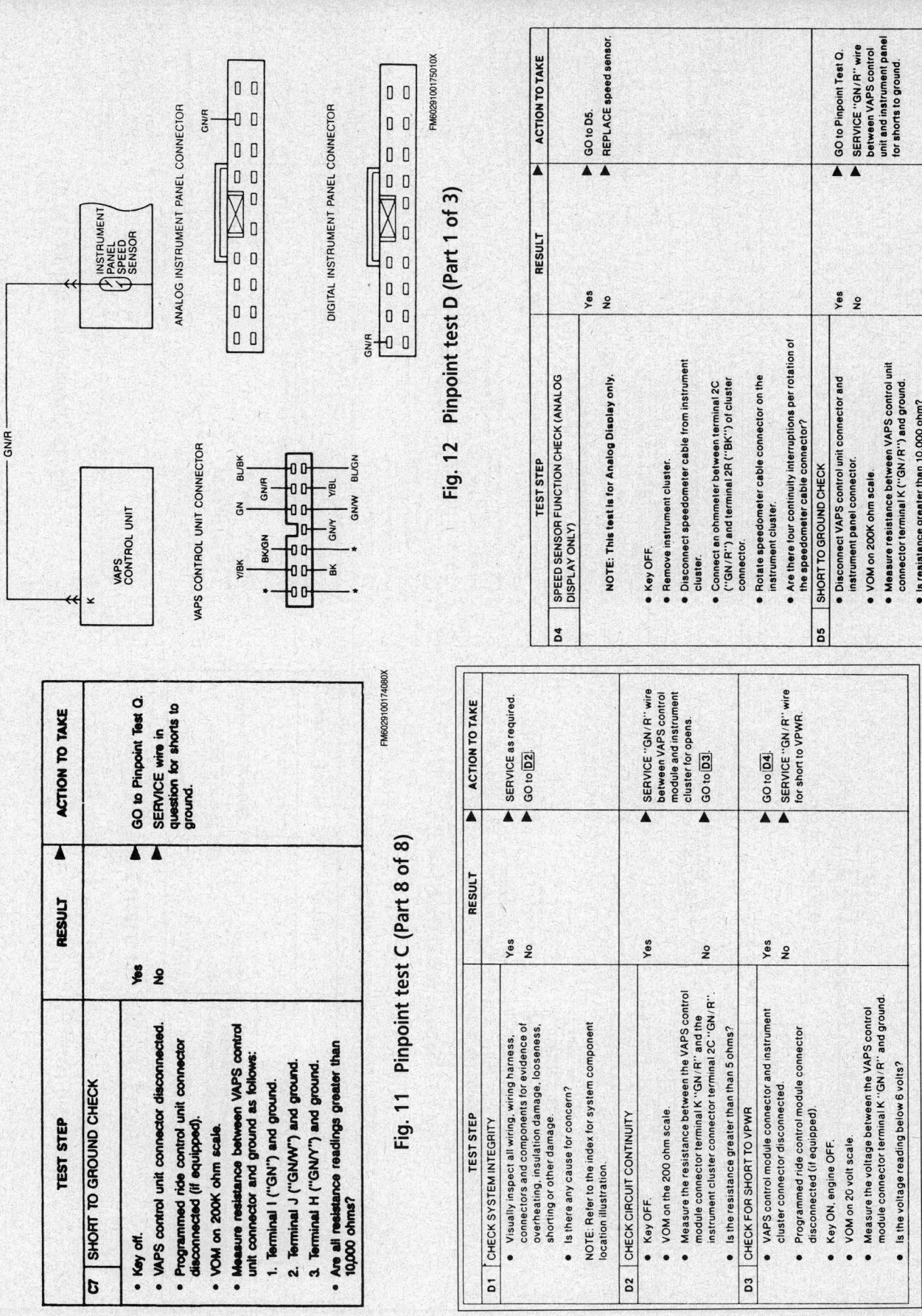

INSTRUMENT PANEL SPEED SENSOR

GN/R

VAPS CONTROL UNIT

K

ANALOG INSTRUMENT PANEL CONNECTOR

FM6029100174010X

DIGITAL INSTRUMENT PANEL CONNECTOR

GN/R

FM6029100175010X

VAPS CONTROL UNIT CONNECTOR

BU/BK
GN   GN/R
Y/BL
GN/Y   Y/BL
BK/GN   GN/W   BU/GN
Y/BK
BK   GN/Y

Fig. 12 Pinpoint test D (Part 1 of 3)

	TEST STEP	RESULT	ACTION TO TAKE
D4	SPEED SENSOR FUNCTION CHECK (ANALOG DISPLAY ONLY) NOTE: This test is for Analog Display only. • Key OFF. • Remove instrument cluster. • Disconnect speedometer cable from instrument cluster. • Connect an ohmmeter between terminal 2C ("GN/R") and terminal 2R ("BK") of cluster connector. • Rotate speedometer cable connector on the instrument cluster. • Are there four continuity interruptions per rotation of the speedometer cable connector?	Yes No	GO to D5. REPLACE speed sensor.
D5	SHORT TO GROUND CHECK • Disconnect VAPS control unit connector and instrument panel connector. • VOM on 200K ohm scale. • Measure resistance between VAPS control unit connector terminal K ("GN/R") and ground. • Is resistance greater than 10,000 ohm?	Yes No	GO to Pinpoint Test Q. SERVICE "GN/R" wire between VAPS control unit and instrument panel for shorts to ground.

FM6029100175030X

Fig. 12 Pinpoint test D (Part 3 of 3)

	TEST STEP	RESULT	ACTION TO TAKE
C7	SHORT TO GROUND CHECK • Key off. • VAPS control unit connector disconnected. • Programmed ride control unit connector disconnected (if equipped). • VOM on 200K ohm scale. • Measure resistance between VAPS control unit connector and ground as follows: 1. Terminal I ("GN") and ground. 2. Terminal J ("GN/W") and ground. 3. Terminal H ("GN/Y") and ground. • Are all resistance readings greater than 10,000 ohms?	Yes No	GO to Pinpoint Test Q. SERVICE wire in question for shorts to ground.

Fig. 11 Pinpoint test C (Part 8 of 8)

	TEST STEP	RESULT	ACTION TO TAKE
D1	CHECK SYSTEM INTEGRITY • Visually inspect all wiring, harness, connectors and components for evidence of overheating, insulation damage, looseness, shorting or other damage. • Is there any cause for concern? NOTE: Refer to the index for system component location illustration.	Yes No	SERVICE as required. GO to D2.
D2	CHECK CIRCUIT CONTINUITY • Key OFF. • VOM on the 200 ohm scale. • Measure the resistance between the VAPS control module connector terminal K ("GN/R" and the instrument cluster connector terminal 2C "GN/R". • Is the resistance greater than than 5 ohms?	Yes No	SERVICE "GN/R" wire between VAPS control module and instrument cluster for opens. GO to D3.
D3	CHECK FOR SHORT TO VPWR • VAPS control module connector and instrument cluster connector disconnected. • Programmed ride control module connector disconnected (if equipped). • Key ON, engine OFF. • VOM on 20 volt scale. • Measure the voltage between the VAPS control module connector terminal K "GN/R" and ground. • Is the voltage reading below 6 volts?	Yes No	GO to D4. SERVICE "GN/R" wire for short to VPWR.

FM6029100175020X

Fig. 12 Pinpoint test D (Part 2 of 3)

Fig. 13 Pinpoint test Q (Part 3 of 3)

TEST STEP		RESULT	ACTION TO TAKE
Q2	CHECK POWER TO VAPS CONTROL UNIT • Disconnect VAPS control unit connector. • Key ON; engine OFF. • VOM on 20 volt scale. • Measure voltage between terminal E ("BK/GN") and ground. • Is voltage above 10 volts?	Yes No	GO to Q3. REPLACE 10A fuse or REPAIR "BK/GN" wire between VAPS control unit and fuse box.
Q3	CHECK VAPS CONTROL UNIT GROUND • Leave VAPS control unit connector disconnected. • VOM on 200 ohm scale. • Measure resistance between D ("BK") and ground. • Is resistance less than 5 ohms?	Yes No	GO to Q4. REPAIR "BK" wire between VAPS control unit and chassis ground for opens.
Q4	CHECK TEST CONNECTOR GROUND • Disconnect test connector from mounting. • VOM on 200 ohm scale. • Measure resistance between "BK" wire and ground. • Is resistance reading less than 5 ohms?	Yes No	GO to Q5. REPAIR "BK" wire between test connector and chassis ground.
Q5	CHECK CONTINUITY BETWEEN VAPS CONTROL UNIT AND TEST CONNECTOR • Disconnect VAPS control unit connector. • VOM on 200 ohm scale. • Measure resistance between VAPS control unit connector terminal C ("Y/BK") and test connector terminal C "Y/BK" wire. • Is resistance less than 5 ohms?	Yes No	GO to Q6. REPAIR "Y/BK" wire between VAPS control unit and test connector for opens.
Q6	CHECK TEST CONNECTOR CIRCUIT FOR SHORT TO VPWR • Leave VAPS control unit connector disconnected. • Key ON; engine OFF. • VOM on 20 volt scale. • Measure voltage between Test connector "Y/BK" wire and ground. • Is voltage reading 0 volts?	Yes No	GO to Q7. REPAIR "Y/BK" wire between VAPS control unit and test connector for shorts to VPWR.
Q7	CHECK TEST CONNECTOR FOR SHORT TO GROUND • Leave VAPS control unit connector disconnected. • Key OFF. • VOM on 200K ohm scale. • Measure resistance between Test connector "Y/BK" wire and ground. • Is resistance greater than 10,000 ohms?	Yes No	REPLACE VAPS control unit. NOTE: If directed here from Quick Test Step Q9 "PASS Code" do not replace VAPS control unit. Re-attempt to recreate intermittent fault. REPAIR "Y/BK" wire between VAPS control unit and test connector for short to ground.

FM6029100176030X

Fig. 13 Pinpoint test Q (Part 1 of 3)

FM6029100176010X

TEST STEP		RESULT	ACTION TO TAKE
Q1	SYSTEM INTEGRITY CHECK • Visually inspect all wiring, wiring harness, connectors and components for evidence of overheating, insulation damage, looseness, shorting or other damage. • Is there any cause for concern?	Yes No	SERVICE as required. GO to Q2 .

FM6029100176020X

Fig. 13 Pinpoint test Q (Part 2 of 3)

TYPE 2–FORD VARIABLE ASSIST ELECTRONIC VARIABLE ORIFICE (EVO) SYSTEM

NOTE: On Air Bag Equipped Models, Refer To "Air Bag System Precautions" Located In The Front Of This Manual For System Disarming & Arming Procedures.

INDEX

PRECAUTIONS

AIR BAG SYSTEMS

Refer to "Air Bag System Precautions" in the front of this manual for system disarming and arming procedures.

DESCRIPTION

The electronic variable orifice system, **Fig. 1 and 2**, is designed to vary the flow from the power steering pump based on vehicle speed and the rate of steering wheel rotation. The system provides full assist at low speed for light parking effort and minimum assist at high speed for good road feel and directional stability. In the event of system failure, full assist is provided.

DIAGNOSIS & TESTING

LESS AIR SUSPENSION

Diagnosis and testing of system will require the fabrication of a service diagnostic test lamp, **Fig. 3**.

Refer to **Figs. 4 and 5**, for diagnosis and testing of the system.

1992–94 CROWN VICTORIA, GRAND MARQUIS & TOWN CAR W/AIR SUSPENSION

Diagnosis and testing requires the use of a Super Star II hand held diagnostic tester, Rotunda model No. 007-0041A or equivalent.

Refer to **Figs. 6 through 9**, for diagnosis and testing of the system.

MARK VIII

Diagnosis and testing requires the use of a Super Star II hand held diagnostic tester, Rotunda model No. 007-0041A or equivalent.

Refer to **Figs. 10 and 11**, for diagnosis and testing of the system.

POWER STEERING SYSTEM SERVICE

Component Service

CONTROL MODULE, REPLACE

COUGAR & THUNDERBIRD

With Anti-Lock Brakes

1. Turn ignition switch Off.
2. Locate module tray in luggage compartment, behind LH rear seat.
3. Disengage push-pin on LH side of tray, then swing tray down.
4. Release locking tabs retaining control module to tray, then remove control module.
5. Disconnect electrical connector from module.
6. Reverse procedure to install.

Less Anti-Lock Brakes

1. Turn ignition switch Off.
2. Locate module tray in luggage compartment, behind LH rear seat under package tray.
3. Disconnect electrical connector from module.
4. Unscrew two plastic rivets on sides of module, then pull down rivet and head assembly from module.
5. Remove control module from mounting bracket.
6. Reverse procedure to install.

CROWN VICTORIA, GRAND MARQUIS & TOWN CAR

The EVO control module and air suspension modules are one unit. Turn air suspension switch off, then proceed as follows:

1. Remove righthand luggage compartment trim panel.
2. Remove module retaining nuts.

3. Pull module out to gain access to connectors.
4. Disconnect each connector by pushing connector release button and pulling connector from module.
5. Reverse procedure to install. **Torque** attaching nuts to 5-7 ft. lbs.

ACTUATOR, REPLACE

Except Mark VIII & 1992–94 Crown Victoria, Grand Marquis & Town Car

1. Remove windshield washer reservoir.
2. Disconnect electrical connector from actuator.
3. Disconnect return hose from power steering pump, then the pressure hose from the actuator.
4. Remove threaded actuator from power steering pump, **Fig. 12. Flow control valve and spring may fall out.**
5. Reverse procedure to install. **Torque** actuator to 25-34 ft. lbs.

Mark VIII & 1992–94 Crown Victoria, Grand Marquis & Town Car

1. Disconnect EVO wiring harness connector from EVO actuator.
2. Disconnect return hose, then pressure hose from the power steering pump. Plug all openings.
3. Disconnect belt from pulley, then remove pump and pulley assembly.
4. Place power steering pump in a vise and remove EVO actuator assembly from power steering pump using a 6mm Allen hex from the back side of the actuator.
5. Install actuator assembly to pump housing, then **torque** to 10-15 ft. lbs.
6. Install pump and pulley assembly to engine. **Torque** four pump retaining bolts to 15-22 ft. lbs.
7. Remove plugs and connect return and pressure hoses to power steering pump.
8. Connect EVO wiring harness to EVO actuator assembly.
9. Purge power steering system of air.

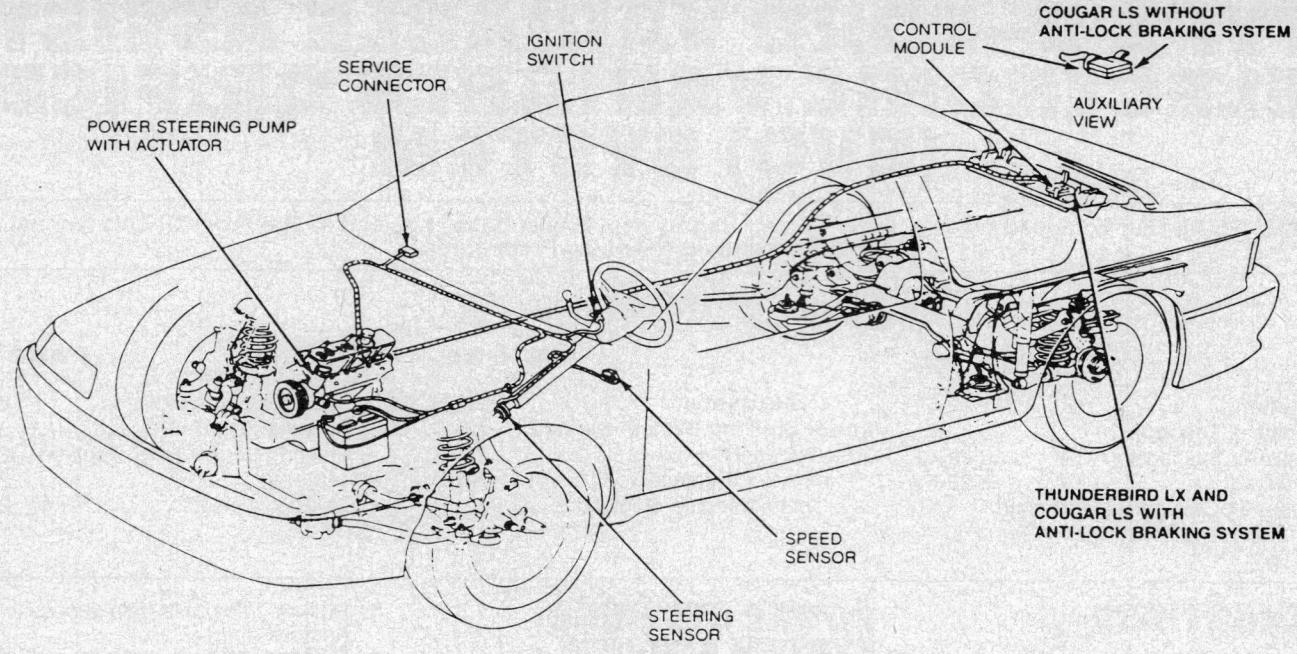

Fig. 1 Electronic variable orifice system. Cougar & Thunderbird

FM6029100178000X

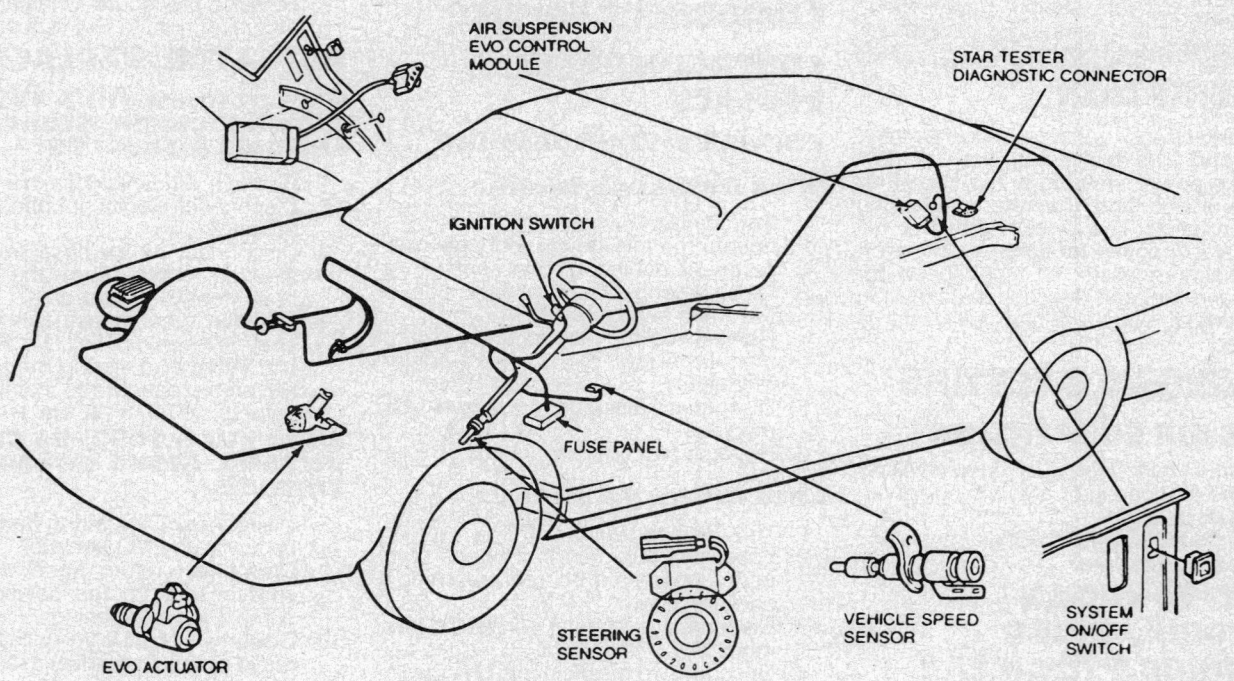

Fig. 2 Electronic variable orifice system. Except Cougar & Thunderbird

FM6029100179000X

STEERING SENSOR, REPLACE

1. Disconnect sensor electrical connector.
2. Remove sensor electrical connector from bracket under instrument panel.
3. Remove two sensor retaining screws, then the sensor, **Fig. 13**.
4. Reverse procedure to install.

STEERING SENSOR RING, REPLACE

1. Remove steering column as outlined under "Steering Column, Replace" in the "Steering Column" section.
2. Remove steering shaft from steering column, then the sensor ring.
3. Reverse procedure to install.

SPEED SENSOR, REPLACE

1. Raise and support vehicle.

2. Remove speed sensor mounting clip retaining bolt.
3. Remove speed sensor and driven gear from transmission.
4. Disconnect electrical connector from speed sensor.
5. Remove driven gear retainer, then the driven gear.
6. Reverse procedure to install. Ensure that internal O-ring is seated in sensor housing.

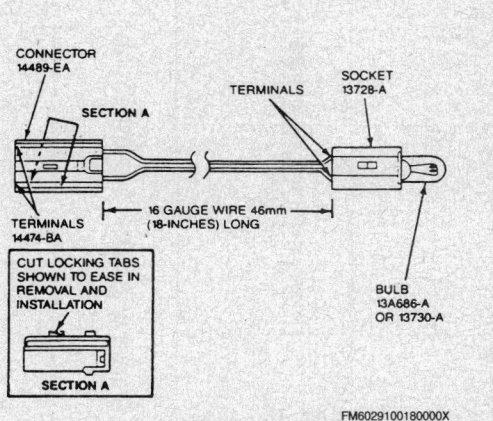

Fig. 3 Service diagnostic test lamp fabrication. Cougar & Thunderbird

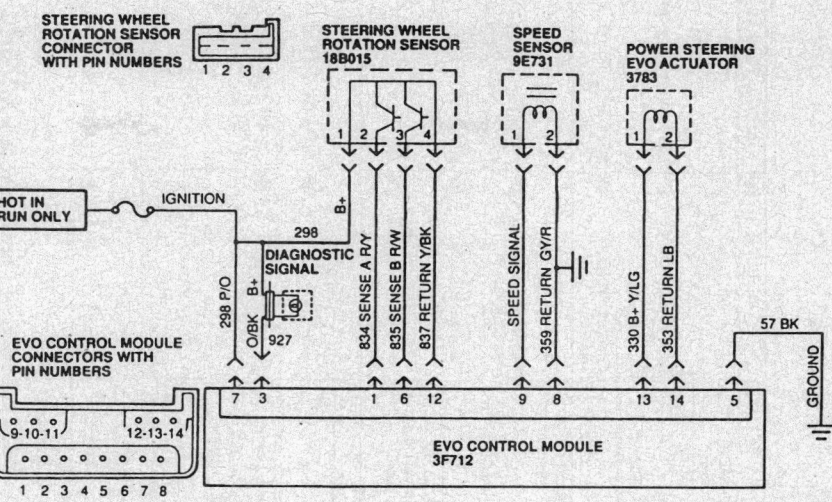

Fig. 4 Electronic variable orifice system wiring circuit

TEST STEP	RESULT ►	ACTION TO TAKE
A0 CHECK CONNECTIONS		
• Verify harness connector at EVO actuator valve on power steering pump is seated. • Verify harness connector on EVO control module is seated (located in luggage compartment). 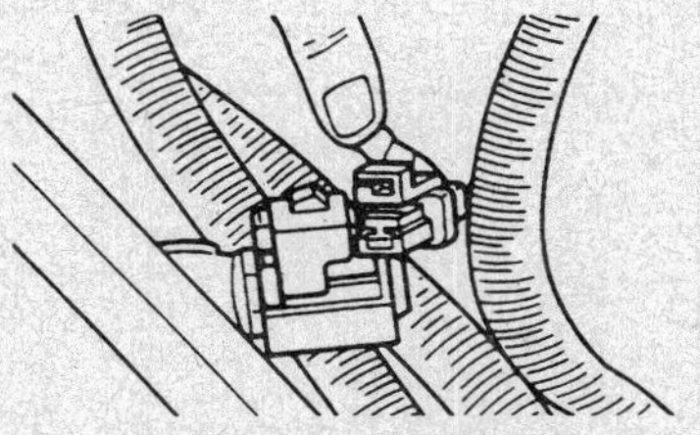 **EVO ACTUATOR VALVE CONNECTOR**	Connector was not properly seated ► Connector properly seated ►	MAKE proper connection. GO to **A1**. GO to **A1**.
A1 CONTROL MODULE CHECK		
• Turn ignition switch to OFF position. • Locate service diagnostic connector in the upper glove compartment. • Connect the EVO service diagnostic lamp to the connector in the upper glove compartment. • Start engine. When engine starts, the controller will turn on the diagnostic lamp for one second to indicate: a) control module is functional b) bulb is functional	Lamp is turned on for one second ► Lamp does NOT turn on ► Lamp flickers ►	GO to **A2**. GO to **E1**. GO to **E1**.
A2 ACTUATOR OUTPUT CIRCUIT CHECK		
• After the one second control module check, the controller will perform the Actuator Output Test. If there is a short to ground or an open circuit, after two seconds delay, the diagnostic lamp will flash a "code 6" (on for 0.5 seconds and off for 0.5 seconds, 6 times) then delay two seconds and repeat continuously until the power is turned off. During this "failure mode" the controller output will be off and both speed and steering wheel rotation inputs will be disabled. Once this "failure mode" has occured, the controller will be inoperable until power is removed and reapplied.	Lamp flashes a "code 6" (on for 0.5 seconds and off for 0.5 seconds, 6 times) then delays two seconds and repeats ► After the two second delay lamp does not flash a "code 6" (Actuator output circuit is OK) ►	GO to **B1**. GO to **A3**.

FM6029100182010X

Fig. 5 System testing (Part 1 of 8). Less air suspension

TYPE 2-FORD VARIABLE ASSIST ELECTRONIC VARIABLE ORIFICE (EVO) SYSTEM

FM60291001820030X

	TEST STEP	RESULT	ACTION TO TAKE
B1	CODE "6" ACTIVATED: EVO ACTUATOR VALVE CHECK (short to ground or an open circuit) • Turn ignition switch to OFF position. • Verify harness connection on the EVO actuator valve on power steering pump is properly seated.	Connector not properly seated Connector properly seated	Make proper connection. GO to A1. GO to B2.
B2	CHECK RESISTANCE ACROSS ACTUATOR VALVE • Ignition switch in OFF position. • Locate the control module in luggage compartment. (Refer to Removal.) • Using an ohmmeter, measure resistance across Pin No. 13 and Pin No. 14 of harness connector. Resistance should be 7-18 ohms. If the resistance is greater than 1000 ohms, the circuit is open.	Resistance is over 1000 ohms Resistance is over 18 ohms Resistance is less than 18 ohms	GO to B3. GO to B4. GO to B3.
B3	CHECK CONTINUITY OF WIRING • Ignition switch in OFF position. • Disconnect EVO harness connector from EVO actuator valve located on power steering pump. • Test continuity of circuits No. 330 and No. 353 from the actuator connector to the 14 pin EVO control module connector. • Refer to Component Location Schematic and System Schematic.	Continuity No continuity	GO to B4 SERVICE wires as necessary. GO to A0
B4	CHECK EVO ACTUATOR VALVE RESISTANCE • Disconnect EVO harness connector from EVO actuator valve located on power steering pump. • Using an ohmmeter, measure resistance across the two actuator valve connector pins.	Resistance greater than 20 ohms or less than 5 ohms Resistance is 5-20 ohms	REPLACE EVO valve. GO to B5.
B5	CHECK WIRE HARNESS FOR SHORT TO GROUND • Ignition switch in OFF position. • EVO harness disconnected from EVO actuator valve. • Disconnect EVO control module from the 14 pin connector in luggage compartment. (Refer to removal.)	Module disconnected	GO to B5.1

Fig. 5 System testing (Part 3 of 8). Less air suspension

FM60291001820020X

	TEST STEP	RESULT	ACTION TO TAKE
A3	STEERING WHEEL SENSOR CHECK • Ignition switch in RUN position. • Vehicle speed 0 km/h (MPH). • Turn steering wheel from lock to lock. The steering wheel must be rotated in one direction at least 220 degrees	Diagnostic lamp turns on for three seconds after the wheel has been sufficiently rotated Diagnostic lamp does not turn on	GO to A4 GO to C1
A4	VEHICLE SPEED SENSOR CHECK • Ignition switch in RUN position. • Steering wheel rate: 0 rpm • Operate vehicle on road and apply vehicle speed of greater than 24 km/h (15 mph)	Diagnostic lamp turns on for all speeds greater than 24 km/h (15 mph) Diagnostic lamp does not turn on	GO to A4.1 GO to D1.
A4.1	VEHICLE SPEED SENSOR SWITCH CHECK (cont'd) • Reduce vehicle speed to below 16 km/h (10 mph)	Diagnostic lamp turns off when vehicle speed drops below 16 km/h (10 mph) Diagnostic lamp does not turn off	Electrical portion of system is functioning GO to A5 GO to D1.
A5	SERVICE POWER STEERING • Perform PUMP FLOW and Pressure Tests, and REPLACE AS REQUIRED		

Fig. 5 System testing (Part 2 of 8). Less air suspension

TYPE 2-FORD VARIABLE ASSIST ELECTRONIC VARIABLE ORIFICE (EVO) SYSTEM

Fig. 5 System testing (Part 5 of 8). Less air suspension

	TEST STEP	RESULT	ACTION TO TAKE
C1	CHECK STEERING WHEEL SENSOR CONNECTION • Verify harness connection on steering wheel rotation sensor (located on lower portion of steering column) is properly seated.	Connector is properly seated	GO to **C2**.
		Connector is not properly seated	MAKE proper connection, GO to **A0**.

C2	STEERING WHEEL ROTATION SENSOR CHECK
	• Ignition switch in OFF position.
	• Disconnect EVO control module from 14 pin connector — located in luggage compartment.
	• Examine wiring harness, verify that there is no damage and
	  • Circuit No. 834 is in Pin No. 1.
	  • Circuit No. 835 is in Pin No. 6.
	  • Circuit No. 837 is in Pin No. 12.
		Damaged or crossed wires	SERVICE wires as necessary, GO to **A0**.

		No damage found	GO to **C3**.

C3	TEST STEERING WHEEL ROTATION SENSOR SIGNALS
	• Using a jumper, connect Pin No. 12 to Pin No. 5 (connector disconnected) of the 14 pin connector.
	• Start engine.
	• While rotating the steering wheel slowly, and using an analog ohmmeter set to the 1K scale, measure the resistance from
	  • Pin No. 1 to Pin No. 5
	  • Pin No. 6 to Pin No. 5
	NOTE: The resistance values will vary between meters, but the needle on all meters should swing from a low to a higher resistance and back approximately every nine degrees of steering wheel rotation.
	(After this check remove jumper.)
		Meter needle swings for both circuits (steering wheel sensor is functioning).	SHUT off engine. REPLACE EVO Control Module.

		Meter needle does not swing for both circuits	GO to **C4**.
C4	STEERING WHEEL ROTATION SENSOR WIRE CHECK • Ignition switch in the OFF position. • Unplug steering sensor (located on lower steering column) • Check wires at steering sensor connector for damage and or incorrect location. • Test continuity of circuits No. 834, No. 835 and No. 837 from steering sensor to 14 pin EVO control module connector. (Refer to System Schematic.)	DAMAGED or crossed wires	SERVICE wires as necessary.
		No Continuity	SERVICE wires as necessary, GO to **A0**.
		No problems found	GO to **C5**.

FM60291001820050X

Fig. 5 System testing (Part 4 of 8). Less air suspension

	TEST STEP	RESULT	ACTION TO TAKE
B5.1	CHECK WIRE HARNESS FOR SHORT TO GROUND (Cont'd.) • Using an ohmmeter, measure resistance between Pin No. 5 (ground) and Pin No. 13 of harness connector.	Resistance is over 1000 ohms	GO to **B5.2**.
		Resistance is less than 10 ohms	SERVICE Harness. GO to **B5.2**.
B5.2	CHECK WIRE HARNESS FOR SHORT TO GROUND (Cont'd.) • Using an ohmmeter, measure resistance between Pin No. 5 (ground) and Pin No. 14 of harness connector.	Resistance is less than 10 ohms	SERVICE Harness.
		Resistance is over 1000 ohms	GO to **B6**.
B6	CHECK HARNESS FOR SHORT TO B+ • Ignition switch in RUN position. • EVO harness disconnected from EVO actuator valve on power steering pump. • Using a voltmeter, measure the voltage across Pin No. 13 and Pin No. 5 Pin No. 14 and Pin No. 5.	Voltage is over 5 volts (short)	SERVICE wires. GO to **A0**.
		Voltage is less than 5 volts	GO to **B7**.
B7	CHECK FOR SHORT ACROSS CIRCUITS NO. 330 AND NO. 353 • Ignition switch in OFF position. • EVO harness disconnected from EVO actuator valve on power steering pump • EVO control module disconnected from 14 pin harness connector • Using an ohmmeter, measure resistance across Pin No. 13 and Pin No. 14 on harness connector.	Resistance is less than 10 ohms (short)	SERVICE wires. GO to **A0**.
		Resistance is over 1000 ohms	REPLACE EVO Control Module.

FM60291001820040X

TEST STEP	RESULT	ACTION TO TAKE

C5 CHECK FOR SHORT ACROSS CIRCUITS 834 AND 835
• Turn ignition switch to OFF position.
• Steering Sensor disconnected.
• Disconnect 14 pin connector. Measure resistance between
  Pin No. 1 and Pin No. 6
  Pin No. 1 and Pin No. 12
  Pin No. 6 and Pin No. 12
  of the 14 pin connector (in luggage compartment).
	Resistance is over 1000 ohms
	
	Resistance is less than 10 ohms (short)
		▲ GO to C6.
		
		▲ SERVICE wires as necessary. GO to A0.

C6 TEST STEERING SENSOR POWER • Using a jumper, connect Pin No. 12 to Pin No. 5 of the 14 pin connector. (Connector disconnected.) • Turn ignition switch to RUN position. • Using a voltmeter, measure the voltage between Circuits No. 298 and No. 837 at the steering sensor connector.	12 volts 0 volts (short or open circuit)	▲ GO to C7. ▲ SERVICE circuit 298. GO to A0.
C7 TEST STEERING SENSOR POWER CIRCUIT • Remove jumper from Pin 12 to Pin 5 and connect 14 pin connector. • Using a voltmeter, measure voltage between circuits No. 298 and No. 837 at the steering sensor connector.	12 volts 0 volts	▲ REPLACE steering sensor. ▲ REPLACE control module.

FM60291001820060X

Fig. 5 System testing (Part 6 of 8). Less air suspension

TEST STEP	RESULT	ACTION TO TAKE
D1 CHECK SPEED SENSOR CONNECTION • Ensure harness connection on speed sensor, (located on the transmission) is properly seated.	Connector is properly seated Connector is not properly seated	▲ GO to D2. ▲ MAKE proper connection. GO to A0.

D2 SPEED SENSOR CHECK
• Turn ignition switch to the OFF position.
• Disconnect the 14-pin electrical connector from the EVO module (located in luggage compartment).
• Ensure there is no damage to harness and that:
  • Circuit No. 150 is in Pin No. 9
  • Circuit No. 359 is in Pin No. 8
	Damaged or crossed wires
	
	No damage found
		▲ SERVICE wires. GO to A0.
		
		▲ GO to D3.

D3 TEST SPEED SENSOR GROUND CIRCUIT • Test continuity of speed sensor ground circuit No. 359 from Pin No. 8 to Pin No. 5 of 14-pin connector.	Continuity Open Circuit	▲ GO to D4. ▲ SERVICE wire or ground eyelet as necessary. GO to A0.
D4 TEST SPEED SENSOR • Turn ignition switch to RUN position. • Perform "speedometer reads 0 mph at all speeds".	Problem(s) found No Problem(s) found	▲ SERVICE. GO to A0. ▲ REPLACE EVO control module.

FM60291001820070X

Fig. 5 System testing (Part 7 of 8). Less air suspension

Fig. 5 System testing (Part 8 of 8). Less air suspension

TEST STEP	RESULT	ACTION TO TAKE
E1 DIAGNOSTIC LAMP CHECK • Check bulb in EVO Service Diagnostic Lamp. • Check connection of bulb in tool.	Bad bulb	REPLACE bulb. GO to A1.
	Good bulb (Lamp never turned on during step A1)	GO to F1.
	Good bulb (Lamp flickered during step A1)	GO to E2.
E2 RE-TEST CONTROL MODULE • Turn ignition switch to off position. • Connect EVO service diagnostic lamp to connector in upper glove compartment. • Start Engine.	Lamp is ON for one second	GO to A2.
	Lamp does not turn on	GO to F1.
	Lamp flickers	REPLACE EVO Module.
F1 EVO CONTROL MODULE CHECK • Turn ignition switch to OFF position. • Ensure 14 pin connector is properly connected to module. (Located in luggage compartment.)	Properly Connected	GO to F2.
	Connection is not properly secured	SECURE connection. GO to A1.
F2 CHECK POWER FEED • Turn ignition switch to the OFF position. • Disconnect EVO control module 14 pin connector. (Located in luggage compartment.) • Turn ignition switch to RUN position. • Using a DVOM, measure voltage from Pin No. 7 (ignition-run only) to Pin No. 5 (ground) at 14 pin connector.	12 volts	REPLACE EVO Control Module.
	0 volts	SERVICE short to ground or open in circuit No. 298 as necessary. GO to A0.

Fig. 6 Error code flow chart. 1992–94 Crown Victoria, Grand Marquis & Town Car w/air suspension

SERVICE BAY DIAGNOSTIC PROCEDURE FLOW CHART

- IGNITION OFF
- CONNECT STAR TESTER W/BUTTON RELEASED
- TURN IGNITION ON
- TURN AIR SUSPENSION ON/OFF SWITCH OFF AND THEN ON (IF EQUIPPED)
- WAIT MINIMUM OF 2 SECONDS
- DEPRESS STAR TESTER BUTTON
- CODE 10 DISPLAYED TEST IN PROGRESS (MAY TAKE UP TO TWO AND-A-HALF MINUTES)
- CODE 12 OR 13 DISPLAYED END OF AUTO TEST
- PERFORM MANUAL TESTS
  - OPEN AND CLOSE ALL FOUR DOORS (IF EQUIPPED W/REAR AIR SUSPENSION)
  - TURN STEERING WHEEL
- RELEASE STAR TEST BUTTON WAIT MINIMUM OF 2 SECONDS DEPRESS STAR TESTER BUTTON
- STAR TESTER WILL DISPLAY:
  - CODE 11 IF SYSTEM OK
  - ERROR CODES
- EXIT BY IGNITION OFF

AIR SUSPENSION/EVO STAR TESTER ERROR CODES

Code	Description
10	Diagnostic Entered, Auto Test in Progress
11	Vehicle Passed
12	Auto Test Passed
13	Automatic Test Failure
15	No Drive Cycle Errors Detected
16	EVO Short Circuit
17	EVO Open Circuit
18	Bad Valve
23	*Suspension Code, refer to Suspension Portion
26	*Suspension Code, refer to Suspension Portion
31	*Suspension Code, refer to Suspension Portion
32	*Suspension Code, refer to Suspension Portion
33	*Suspension Code, refer to Suspension Portion
39	*Suspension Code, refer to Suspension Portion
42	*Suspension Code, refer to Suspension Portion
43	*Suspension Code, refer to Suspension Portion
44	*Suspension Code, refer to Suspension Portion
45	*Suspension Code, refer to Suspension Portion
51	*Suspension Code, refer to Suspension Portion
54	*Suspension Code, refer to Suspension Portion
66	*Suspension Code, refer to Suspension Portion
70	Replace RAS/EVO Module
71	*Suspension Code, refer to Suspension Portion
72	*Suspension Code, refer to Suspension Portion
74	*Steering Wheel Rotation not Detected
80	*Insufficient Battery Voltage to Run Diagnostics

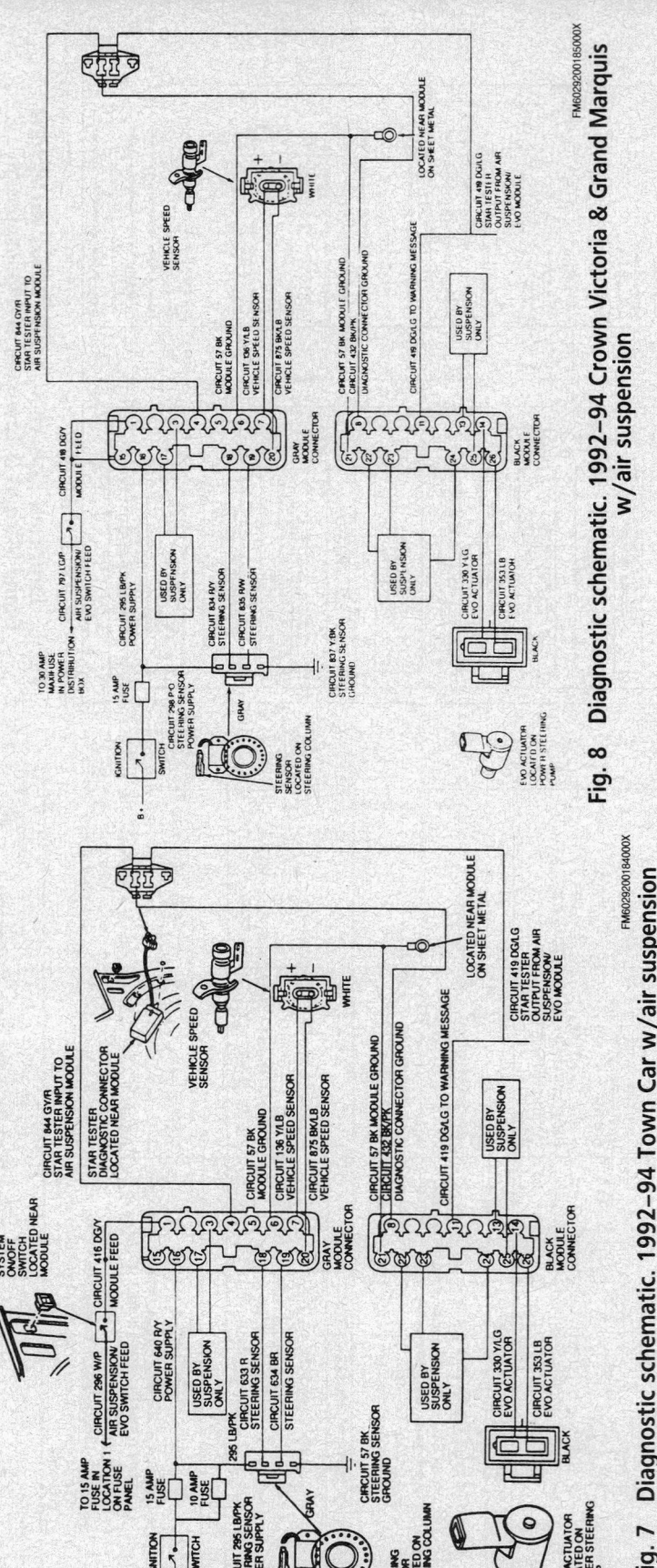

Fig. 8 Diagnostic schematic. 1992–94 Crown Victoria & Grand Marquis w/air suspension

Fig. 7 Diagnostic schematic. 1992–94 Town Car w/air suspension

TYPE 2-FORD VARIABLE ASSIST ELECTRONIC VARIABLE ORIFICE (EVO) SYSTEM

Fig. 9 System testing (Part 1 of 6). 1992–94 Crown Victoria, Grand Marquis & Town Car w/air suspension

	TEST STEP	RESULT	ACTION TO TAKE
G1	PERFORM SERVICE BAY DIAGNOSTICS	Record all codes	GO to G2.
G2	DETERMINE REQUIRED TEST STEP • Read displayed code(s). • Each code must be addressed individually. If more than one error code is detected, perform the test step required for each code. NOTE: Code 55 is only generated in drive cycle test.	Codes 16, 17 or 18 are displayed Code 74 displayed Code 55 displayed Code 11 displayed If any other codes are displayed, or if Test cannot be started with SUPER STAR Tester II.	GO to H1. GO to I1. GO to J1. GO to G3. REFER to air suspension Service
G3	SERVICE POWER STEERING • Perform Pump Flow and Pressure Tests.	None	REPLACE as required.

Fig. 9 System testing (Part 2 of 6). 1992–94 Crown Victoria, Grand Marquis & Town Car w/air suspension

	TEST STEP	RESULT	ACTION TO TAKE
H1	CODE ACTIVATED: EVO ACTUATOR VALVE CHECK (SHORT TO GROUND OR AN OPEN CIRCUIT) • Turn ignition switch to OFF position. • Verify harness connection on the EVO actuator valve on power steering pump is properly seated. • Read all codes.	Connector not properly seated Connector properly seated Code 16 displayed Code 17 displayed Code 18 displayed	MAKE proper connection. GO to G1. GO to H2. GO to H4. GO to H2. GO to H3.
H2	CHECK RESISTANCE ACROSS ACTUATOR VALVE • Ignition switch in OFF position. • Locate the control module in luggage compartment. Harness connectors can be disconnected from module without removing module. • Using an ohmmeter, measure resistance across Pin 14 and Pin 26 of harness connector. Resistance should be 7-18 ohms. If the resistance is greater than 1000 ohms, the circuit is open.	Resistance is over 1000 ohms Resistance is over 18 ohms Resistance is less than 18 ohms	GO to H3. GO to H4. GO to H3.

Fig. 9 System testing (Part 2 of 6). 1992–94 Crown Victoria, Grand Marquis & Town Car w/air suspension

	TEST STEP	RESULT	ACTION TO TAKE
H3	CHECK CONTINUITY OF WIRING • Ignition switch in OFF position. • Disconnect EVO harness connector from EVO actuator valve located on power steering pump. • Test continuity of Circuits 330 and 353 from the actuator connector to the 26-pin EVO control module connector. • Is there continuity?	Yes No	GO to H4. SERVICE wires as necessary. GO to G1.
H4	CHECK EVO ACTUATOR VALVE RESISTANCE • Disconnect EVO harness connector from EVO actuator valve located on power steering pump. • Using an ohmmeter, measure resistance across the two actuator valve connector pins.	Resistance greater than 20 ohms or less than 5 ohms Resistance is 5-20 ohms	REPLACE EVO valve. GO to H5.
H5	CHECK WIRE HARNESS FOR SHORT TO GROUND • Ignition switch in OFF position. • EVO harness disconnected from EVO actuator valve. • Disconnect EVO control module from the 26-pin connectors in luggage compartment. • Is module disconnected?	Yes	GO to H6.
H6	CHECK WIRE HARNESS FOR SHORT TO GROUND (Cont'd) • Using an ohmmeter, measure resistance between Pin No. 21 (ground) and Pin 14 of harness connector.	Resistance is over 1000 ohms Resistance is less than 10 ohms	GO to H7. SERVICE harness. GO to H7.
H7	CHECK WIRE HARNESS FOR SHORT TO GROUND (Cont'd) • Using an ohmmeter measure resistance between Pin No. 21 (ground) and Pin 26 of harness connector.	Resistance is less than 10 ohms Resistance is over 1000 ohms	SERVICE harness. GO to H8.
H8	CHECK HARNESS FOR SHORT TO B+ • Ignition switch in RUN position. • EVO harness disconnected from EVO actuator valve on power steering pump. • Using a voltmeter, measure the voltage across Pin No. 14 and Pin 21, Pin No. 26 and Pin 21 • Is voltage greater than 5 volts?	Yes No	SERVICE wires. GO to G1. GO to H9.
H9	CHECK FOR SHORT ACROSS CIRCUITS 975 AND 353 • Ignition switch in OFF position. • EVO harness disconnected from EVO actuator valve on power steering pump. • Using an ohmmeter, measure resistance across Pin 14 and Pin 26 on harness connector.	Resistance is less than 10 ohms (short) Resistance is over 1000 ohms	SERVICE wires. GO to G1. REPLACE EVO control module.

TEST STEP	RESULT	▶	ACTION TO TAKE
I1 CHECK STEERING WHEEL SENSOR CONNECTION			
• Verify harness connection on steering wheel rotation sensor (located on lower portion of steering column) is properly seated. • **Is connector properly seated?**	Yes No	▶ ▶	GO to I2. MAKE proper connection. GO to G1.
I2 STEERING WHEEL ROTATION SENSOR CHECK			
• Ignition switch in OFF position. • Disconnect EVO control module and leave connectors mated. Refer to Section 04-05. • Examine wiring harness, verify that there is no damage and • **Crown Victoria / Grand Marquis** — Circuit 834 is in Pin 18 — Circuit 835 is in Pin 19 — Circuit 837 is connected to Circuit 57. — Circuit 57 is in Pin 6 (ground) • **Lincoln Town Car** — Circuit 633 is in Pin 18 — Circuit 634 is in Pin 19 — Circuit 57 is in Pin 6 (ground) • **Are wires damaged or crossed?**	Yes No	▶ ▶	SERVICE wires as necessary. GO to G1. GO to I3.
I3 TEST STEERING WHEEL ROTATION SENSOR SIGNALS			
• Start engine. • While rotating the steering wheel slowly, and using an analog ohmmeter such as, Inductive Dwell-Tach-Volt Ohmmeter 059-00010 or equivalent, set to the 1K scale, measure the resistance from: — Pin 18 to Pin 6 — Pin 19 to Pin 6 NOTE: The resistance values will vary between meters, but the needle on all meters should swing from a low to a higher resistance and back approximately every nine degrees of steering wheel rotation.	Meter needle swings for both circuits (steering wheel sensor is functioning) Meter needle does not swing for both circuits	▶ ▶	SHUT OFF engine. REPLACE EVO control module. GO to I4.
I4 STEERING WHEEL ROTATION SENSOR WIRE CHECK			
• Disconnect EVO control module from 26-pin connectors located in luggage compartment. • Ignition switch in the OFF position. • Unplug steering sensor (located on lower steering column). • Check wires at steering sensor connector for damage and / or incorrect location. • Test continuity of Circuits 834 and 835 (Crown Victoria / Grand Marquis), 633, 634 and 57 (Lincoln Town Car) from steering sensor to EVO control module connector. (Refer to Diagnostic Schematic). • Test continuity from Circuit 837 to 57 (Crown Victoria / Grand Marquis.	Damaged or crossed wires No continuity No concerns found	▶ ▶ ▶	SERVICE wires as necessary. SERVICE wires as necessary. GO to G1. GO to I5.

FM6029200186030X

Fig. 9   System testing (Part 3 of 6). 1992–94 Crown Victoria, Grand Marquis & Town Car w/air suspension

TEST STEP	RESULT	▶	ACTION TO TAKE
I5 CHECK FOR SHORT ACROSS CIRCUITS 834 AND 835			
• Turn ignition switch to OFF position. • Steering sensor disconnected. • Disconnect pin connectors. Measure resistance between — Pin 18 and Pin 19 — Pin 18 and Pin 6 — Pin 19 and Pin 6 of the pin connectors (in luggage compartment).	Resistance is over 1000 ohms Resistance is less than 10 ohms (short)	▶ ▶	GO to I6. SERVICE wires as necessary. GO to G1.
I6 TEST STEERING SENSOR POWER CIRCUIT			
• Turn ignition switch to RUN position. • Using a voltmeter, measure the voltage between Circuits 295 and 57 (Lincoln Town Car) and 298 and 837 (Crown Victoria / Grand Marquis) at the steering sensor connector.	12V Zero volts (short or open circuit)	▶ ▶	REPLACE Steering Sensor. SERVICE Circuit 295 (Lincoln Town Car), Circuit 298 (Crown Victoria / Grand Marquis). CHECK / REPLACE fuse. GO to G1.

FM6029200186040X

Fig. 9   System testing (Part 4 of 6). 1992–94 Crown Victoria, Grand Marquis & Town Car w/air suspension

TEST STEP		RESULT	▶	ACTION TO TAKE
J1	CHECK SPEED SENSOR CONNECTION			
	• Ensure harness connection on speed sensor, (located on the transmission) is properly seated.	Connector is properly seated	▶	GO to J2.
		Connector is not properly seated	▶	MAKE proper connection. GO to G1.
J2	SPEED SENSOR CHECK			
	• Turn ignition switch to the OFF position.	Damaged or crossed wires	▶	SERVICE wires. GO to G1.
	• Disconnect electrical connectors from the EVO module (located in luggage compartment).	No damage found	▶	GO to J3.
	• Ensure there is no damage to harness and that: — Circuit 136 is in Pin 7 — Circuit 875 is in Pin 20			
J3	TEST SPEED SENSOR GROUND CIRCUIT			
	• Test continuity of speed sensor ground Circuit 875, from Pin 20 to Pin 6 of 26-pin connectors.	Continuity	▶	GO to J4.
		Open circuit	▶	SERVICE wire or ground eyelet as necessary. GO to G1.
J4	TEST SPEED SENSOR			
	• Turn ignition switch to RUN position.	Concern(s) found	▶	SERVICE as outlined GO to G1.
		No Concern(s) found	▶	REPLACE EVO control module.

FM6029200186050X

Fig. 9   System testing (Part 5 of 6). 1992–94 Crown Victoria, Grand Marquis & Town Car w/air suspension

TEST STEP		RESULT	▶	ACTION TO TAKE
K1	EVO CONTROL MODULE CHECK			
	• Turn ignition switch to OFF position.	Properly connected	▶	GO to K2.
	• Ensure pin connectors are properly connected to module (located in luggage compartment).	Connection is not properly secured	▶	SECURE connection. GO to G1.
	• Check air suspension switch connection.	Air suspension switch in luggage compartment is off	▶	TURN air suspension switch on. GO to G1.
	• Check if the air suspension switch is turned on.			
K2	CHECK POWER FEED			
	• Turn ignition switch to the OFF position.	Both 12 volts	▶	REPLACE EVO control module.
	• Disconnect EVO control module 26-pin connectors (located in luggage compartment).	Zero volts from Circuit 295 or 418	▶	SERVICE short to ground or open in circuit 418 or 295 as necessary. GO to G1.
	• Turn ignition switch to RUN position.			
	• Using DVOM, measure voltage from Pin 16 (ignition-run only) to Pin 6 (ground) at pin connectors.			
	• Measure voltage from Pin 1 to Pin6.			

FM6029200186060X

Fig. 9   System testing (Part 6 of 6). 1992–94 Crown Victoria, Grand Marquis & Town Car w/air suspension

TEST STEP		RESULT	▶	ACTION TO TAKE
C1	ELIMINATE EVO ACTUATOR			
	• Disconnect EVO actuator harness connector.	Yes	▶	REPLACE EVO actuator. REPEAT Auto Test.
	• Connect ohmmeter across EVO actuator terminals; note meter reading.	No	▶	GO to C2.
	• Does meter indicate less than 8 ohms or more than 16 ohms?			

FM6029100187010X

Fig. 10   Pinpoint Test C (Part 1 of 4). Mark VIII

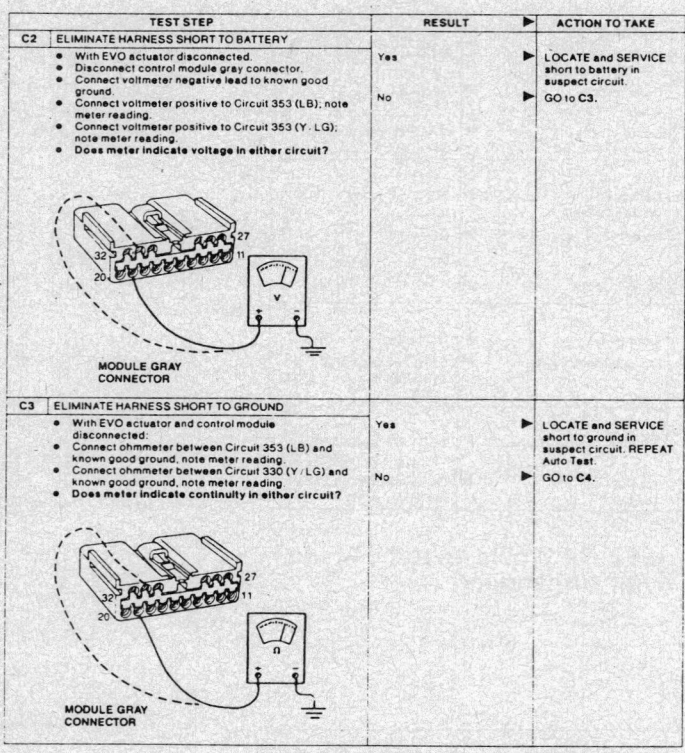

TEST STEP		RESULT	▶	ACTION TO TAKE
C2	**ELIMINATE HARNESS SHORT TO BATTERY**			
	• With EVO actuator disconnected. • Disconnect control module gray connector. • Connect voltmeter negative lead to known good ground. • Connect voltmeter positive to Circuit 353 (LB); note meter reading. • Connect voltmeter positive to Circuit 353 (Y-LG); note meter reading. • Does meter indicate voltage in either circuit?	Yes No	▶ ▶	LOCATE and SERVICE short to battery in suspect circuit. GO to C3.
C3	**ELIMINATE HARNESS SHORT TO GROUND**			
	• With EVO actuator and control module disconnected: • Connect ohmmeter between Circuit 353 (LB) and known good ground, note reading. • Connect ohmmeter between Circuit 330 (Y / LG) and known good ground, note meter reading. • Does meter indicate continuity in either circuit?	Yes No	▶ ▶	LOCATE and SERVICE short to ground in suspect circuit. REPEAT Auto Test. GO to C4.

FM6029100187020X

Fig. 10   Pinpoint Test C (Part 2 of 4). Mark VIII

TEST STEP		RESULT	▶	ACTION TO TAKE
C4	**ELIMINATE SHORT BETWEEN CIRCUITS 353 (LB) AND 330 (Y/LG)**			
	• EVO actuator and control module disconnected. • Connect ohmmeter between Circuit 353 (LB) and Circuit 330 (Y / LG); note meter reading. • Does meter indicate continuity?	Yes No	▶ ▶	LOCATE and SERVICE short between circuits. REPEAT Auto Test GO to C5.

FM6029100187030X

Fig. 10   Pinpoint Test C (Part 3 of 4). Mark VIII

TEST STEP		RESULT	▶	ACTION TO TAKE
C5	**ELIMINATE OPEN IN CIRCUIT 353 (LB) AND CIRCUIT 330 (Y/LG)**			
	• EVO actuator and control module disconnected. • Connect ohmmeter between Circuit 353 (LB) at gray control module connector and EVO connector; note meter reading. • Connect ohmmeter between Circuit 330 (Y / LG) at gray control module connector and EVO connector; note meter reading. • Does meter indicate continuity in both circuits?	Yes No	▶ ▶	REPLACE control module. REPEAT Auto Test. LOCATE and SERVICE open in suspect circuit(s). REPEAT Auto Test.

FM6029100187040X

Fig. 10   Pinpoint Test C (Part 4 of 4). Mark VIII

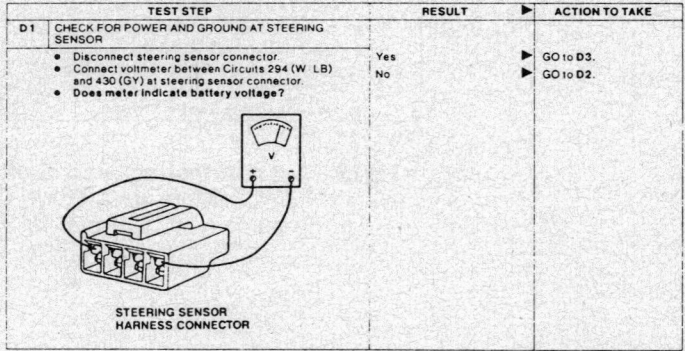

TEST STEP		RESULT	▶	ACTION TO TAKE
D1	**CHECK FOR POWER AND GROUND AT STEERING SENSOR**			
	• Disconnect steering sensor connector. • Connect voltmeter between Circuits 294 (W LB) and 430 (GY) at steering sensor connector. • Does meter indicate battery voltage?	Yes No	▶ ▶	GO to D3. GO to D2.

FM6029100188010X

Fig. 11   Pinpoint Test D (Part 1 of 4). Mark VIII

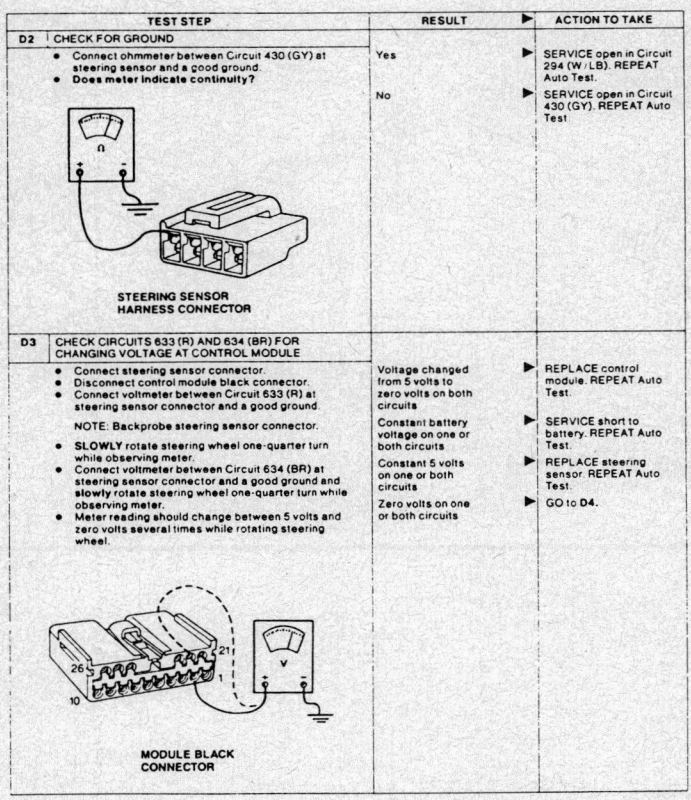

Part 2 of 4 table:

TEST STEP	RESULT	▶	ACTION TO TAKE
D2 CHECK FOR GROUND • Connect ohmmeter between Circuit 430 (GY) at steering sensor and a good ground. • **Does meter indicate continuity?**	Yes	▶	SERVICE open in Circuit 294 (W/LB). REPEAT Auto Test.
	No	▶	SERVICE open in Circuit 430 (GY). REPEAT Auto Test.
D3 CHECK CIRCUITS 633 (R) AND 634 (BR) FOR CHANGING VOLTAGE AT CONTROL MODULE • Connect steering sensor connector. • Disconnect control module black connector. • Connect voltmeter between Circuit 633 (R) at steering sensor connector and a good ground. NOTE: Backprobe steering sensor connector. • SLOWLY rotate steering wheel one-quarter turn while observing meter. • Connect voltmeter between Circuit 634 (BR) at steering sensor connector and a good ground and slowly rotate steering wheel one-quarter turn while observing meter. • Meter reading should change between 5 volts and zero volts several times while rotating steering wheel.	Voltage changed from 5 volts to zero volts on both circuits	▶	REPLACE control module. REPEAT Auto Test.
	Constant battery voltage on one or both circuits	▶	SERVICE short to battery. REPEAT Auto Test.
	Constant 5 volts on one or both circuits	▶	REPLACE steering sensor. REPEAT Auto Test.
	Zero volts on one or both circuits	▶	GO to D4.

FM6029100188020X

Fig. 11   Pinpoint Test D (Part 2 of 4). Mark VIII

Part 3 of 4 table:

TEST STEP	RESULT	▶	ACTION TO TAKE
D4 CHECK STEERING SENSOR • Connect control module black connector. • Disconnect steering sensor. • Alternately connect voltmeter between Circuits 633 (R) and 634 (BR) and a good ground. • Meter should indicate 5 volts.	5 volts at both circuits	▶	REPLACE steering sensor. REPEAT Auto Test.
	Zero volts at one or both circuits	▶	GO to D5.
D5 ISOLATE TO WIRING OR MODULE • Disconnect control module black connector. • Alternately connect ohmmeter between Circuits 633 (R) and 634 (BR) at control module and a good ground. • Meter should indicate no continuity.	No continuity in both circuits	▶	GO to D6.
	Continuity in one or both circuits	▶	SERVICE short to ground. REPEAT Auto Test.

FM6029100188030X

Fig. 11   Pinpoint Test D (Part 3 of 4). Mark VIII

Part 4 of 4 table:

TEST STEP	RESULT	▶	ACTION TO TAKE
D6 CHECK FOR OPEN • Connect ohmmeter between Circuit 633 (R) at control module black connector and steering sensor connector. • Connect ohmmeter between Circuit 634 (BR) at control module black connector and steering sensor connector.	Continuity in both circuits	▶	REPLACE control module. REPEAT Auto Test.
	No continuity in one or both circuits	▶	SERVICE open circuit(s). REPEAT Auto Test.

FM6029100188040X

Fig. 11   Pinpoint Test D (Part 4 of 4). Mark VIII

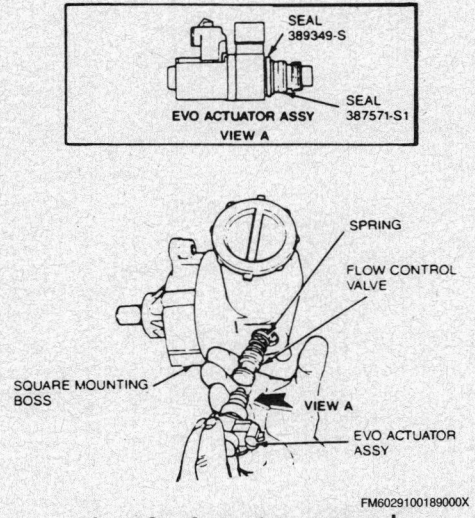

FM6029100189000X

Fig. 12   Actuator removal

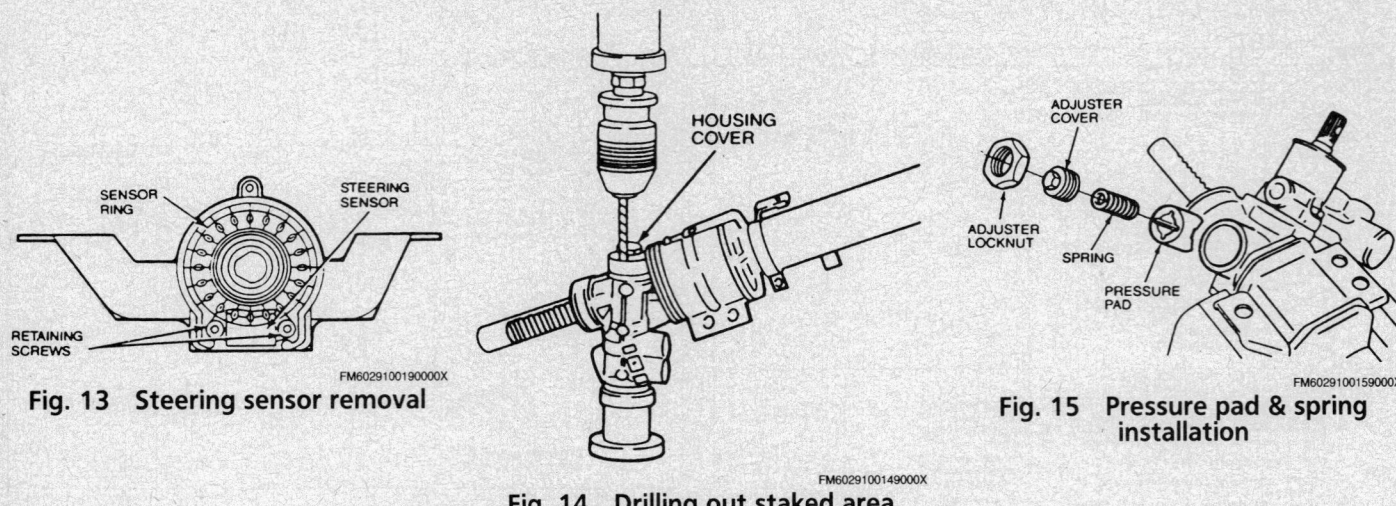

Fig. 13 Steering sensor removal

Fig. 14 Drilling out staked area

Fig. 15 Pressure pad & spring installation

DISC BRAKES
TABLE OF CONTENTS

Front Disc Brakes
INDEX

PRECAUTIONS

1. **On models equipped with anti-lock brakes,** prior to disconnecting any hydraulic lines or fittings, hydraulic system must be depressurized by pumping the brake pedal a minimum of 25 times with ignition switch in OFF position.
2. **On all models,** grease or any other foreign material must be kept off caliper, disc surfaces and external hub surfaces during service procedures. Handling brake disc and caliper should be done in a way to avoid deforming disc and nicking or scratching brake linings.
3. If inspection reveals rubber piston seals are worn or damaged, they should be replaced immediately.
4. During wheel replacement, exercise care to avoid interfering with or damaging caliper splash shield, or bleeder screw.
5. Front wheel bearings should be adjusted to specifications.
6. Ensure vehicle is centered on hoist before servicing any of front end components to avoid bending or damaging disc splash shield on full right or left wheel turns.
7. Before vehicle is moved after any brake service work, be sure to obtain firm brake pedal.
8. Caliper housing bolts should not be disturbed unless caliper requires service.
9. If front disc brake caliper piston is removed for any reason, replace piston seal. Protect disc brake caliper piston from contact with any metal or sharp objects to avoid damage.
10. Front disc brake calipers must be installed with bleeder screws in upward position to properly bleed air from system.
11. Do not attempt to clean or restore oil soaked brake shoes and linings. When contaminated linings are found, brake shoes and linings must be replaced in complete set and front disc brake rotor braking surfaces wiped clean.

DESCRIPTION

The caliper assembly consists of a pin sliding caliper housing, inner and outer shoe and lining assemblies and a single piston, **Figs. 1 through 3.** The caliper slides on two pins which also act as attaching bolts between caliper and the combination anchor plate and spindle. The outer brake shoe and lining assembly is longer than the inner brake shoe and lining assembly. Inner and outer shoe and lining assemblies are attached to the caliper by spring clips riveted to the shoe surfaces. The inner shoe is attached to the caliper by installing the spring clip to the inside of the caliper piston. The outer shoe clips directly to the caliper housing. A wear indicator is incorporated, which emits a noise when the lining is worn to a point for necessary replacement. Left and righthand inner and outer shoes are not interchangeable.

The inner shoe and lining on Mustang modes equipped with the 5.0L/V8-302 engine has a replaceable single finger anti-rattle clip and an insulator held in position by the clip. The shoe is slotted to accept the snap-on clip which loads the assembly against the caliper bridge. The inner shoe on Mustang models equipped with the 2300cc engine has a single finger anti-rattle clip, holding the shoe down against the spindle ledge. The clip does not lock into the piston. The insulator is also riveted to the shoe and is not replaceable.

TROUBLESHOOTING

BRAKE ROUGHNESS

The most common cause of brake chatter on disc brakes is a variation in thickness of the disc. If roughness or vibration is encountered during highway operation or if pedal pumping is experienced at low speeds, the disc may have excessive thickness variation. To check for this condition, measure the disc at 12 points with a micrometer at a radius approximately one inch from edge of disc. If thickness measurements vary by more than .0005 inch, the disc should be replaced with a new one.

Excessive lateral runout of braking disc may cause a "knocking back" of the pistons, possibly creating increased pedal travel and vibration when brakes are applied.

Before checking the runout, wheel bearings should be adjusted. The readjustment is very important and will be required at the completion of the test to prevent bearing failure. Be sure to make the adjustment as outlined in "Front Suspension" section.

BRAKE SYSTEM BLEED

Pressure bleeding is recommended for all hydraulic disc brake systems.

The disc brake hydraulic system can be bled manually or with pressure bleeding equipment. The brake pedal will require more pumping and frequent checking of fluid level in master cylinder during bleeding operation.

Do not use brake fluid drained from the hydraulic system when bleeding the brakes. Be sure the disc brake pistons are returned to their normal positions and the shoe and lining assemblies are properly seated. Before driving the vehicle, check brake operation to be sure a firm pedal has been obtained.

Pressure bleeding is recommended for all hydraulic brake systems.

The bleeding operation itself is fairly well standardized. The first step in all cases is to thoroughly clean the dirt from the filler cap before removing it from the master cylinder.

Pressure bleeding is fastest bleeding method because the master cylinder doesn't have to be refilled several times, and the job can be done by one person. To prevent air from the pressure tank getting into the lines, do not shake the tank while air is being added to the tank or after it has been pressurized. Set the tank in the required location, then bring the air hose to the tank. Do not move the tank during the bleeding operation. The tank should be kept at least one-third full.

On vehicles equipped with disc brakes and master cylinders without proportioners or pressure control valves located in the master cylinder outlet port, the brake metering valve or combination valve must be held in position using a suitable tool.

If air does get into the fluid, releasing the pressure will cause the bubbles to increase in size, rise to the top of the fluid, and escape. Pressure should not be greater than about 35 psi.

On vehicles equipped with plastic reservoirs, do not exceed 25 psi bleeding pressure.

When bleeding without pressure, open the bleed valve three-quarters of a turn, depress the pedal a full stroke, then allow the pedal to return slowly to its released position. After the pedal has been depressed to the end of its stroke, you should close the bleeder valve before the start of the return stroke. On models equipped with power brakes, first reduce the vacuum in the power unit to zero by pumping the brake pedal several times with the engine off before starting to bleed the system.

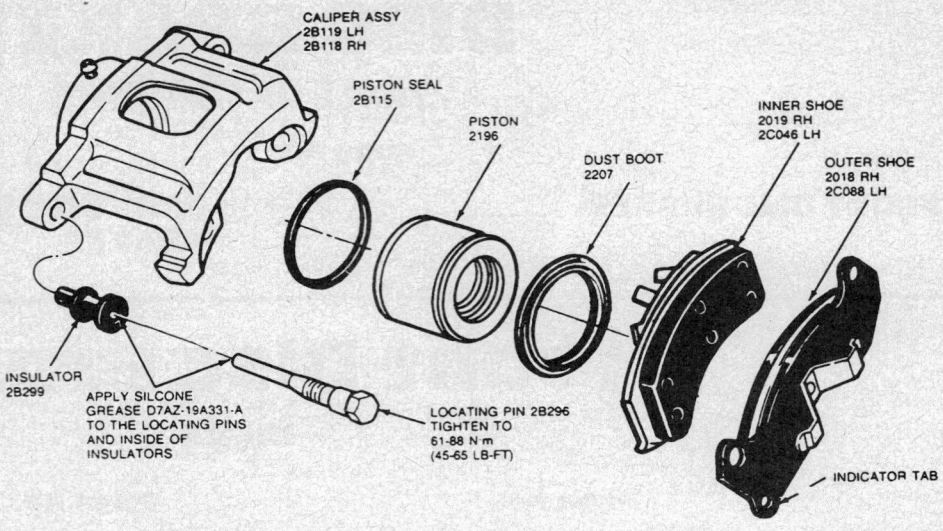

Fig. 1 Exploded view of front pin sliding disc brake caliper. Cougar, Crown Victoria, Grand Marquis, Mark VII, Mustang, Thunderbird & Town Car

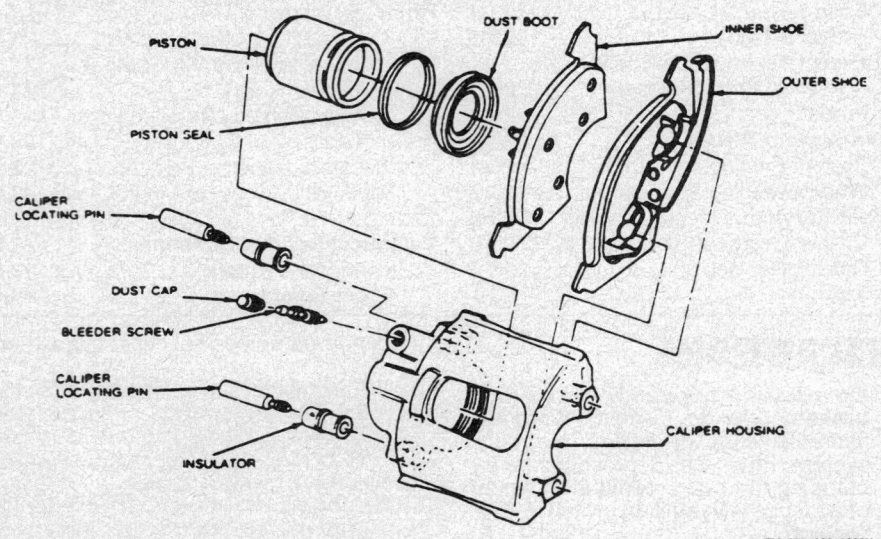

Fig. 2 Exploded view of front pin sliding disc brake caliper. Escort, Continental, Sable, Taurus, Tempo, Topaz & Tracer

Pressure bleeding eliminates the need for pedal pumping.

Discard drained or bled brake fluid. Care should be taken not to spill brake fluid, since this can damage the vehicle's finish.

Flushing is essential if there is water, mineral oil or other contaminants in the lines, and whenever new parts are installed in the hydraulic system. Fluid contamination is usually indicated by swollen and deteriorated cups and other rubber parts.

Wheel cylinders on disc brakes are equipped with bleeder valves and are bled in the same manner as wheel cylinders for drum brakes.

Bleeding is necessary on all four wheels if air has entered the system because of low fluid level or the line or lines have been disconnected. If a line is disconnected at any one wheel cylinder, the cylinder only need be bled. On brake reline jobs, bleeding is advisable to remove any air or contaminants.

Master cylinders equipped with bleeder valves should be bled first before the wheel cylinders are bled. In all cases where a master cylinder has been overhauled, it must be bled. Where there is no bleeder valve, this can be done by leaving the lines loose, actuating the brake pedal to expel the air and then tightening the lines.

After overhauling a dual master cylinder used in conjunction with disc brakes, air may be trapped between the master cylinder pistons because there is only one residual pressure valve (check valve) used in these units. Bleed the cylinder before installing it on the vehicle.

SYSTEM PRIMING

When a new master cylinder is installed or the brake system partially or completely emptied, fluid may not flow from the

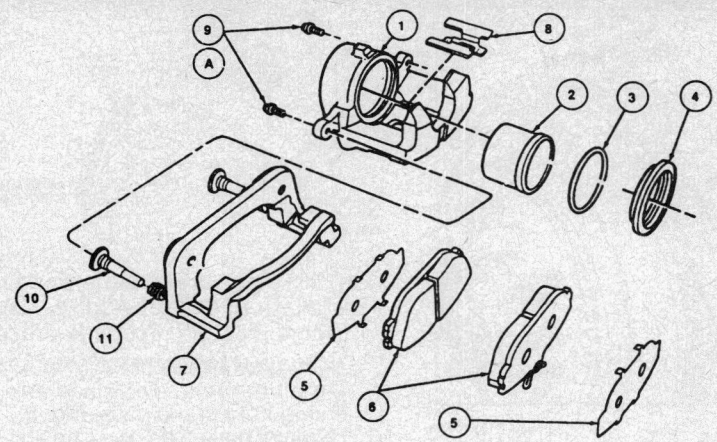

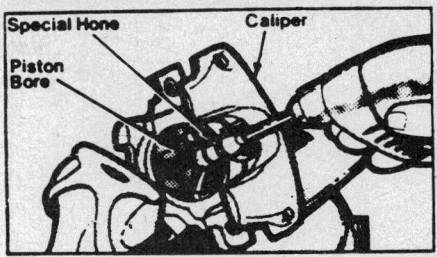

Fig. 4   Caliper piston bore honing

Item	Part Number	Description
1	2B302 RH 2B294 LH	Brake Caliper Housing Assy
2	2196	Brake Cylinder Piston
3	2B115	Brake Piston Seal
4	2207	Brake Cylinder Boot
5	2B321	Insulator (2 Req'd)
6	2018	Shoe and Lining Assy (2 Req'd)

Item	Part Number	Description
7	2B134 RH 2B135 LH	Caliper Anchor Bracket
8	2B164	Anti-Rattle Clip
9A	2N386	Brake Caliper Pinch Bolts (2 Req'd)
10	2B296	Caliper Slide Pin (2 Req'd)
11	2A492	Brake Slide Pin Boot (2 Req'd)
A		Tighten to 22-32 N-m (16-24 Lb-Ft)

Fig. 3   Exploded view of front pin sliding disk brake caliper. Mark VIII

bleeder screws during normal bleeding. It may be necessary to prime the system using the following procedure:

1. Using tubing wrench, remove brake lines from master cylinder.
2. Install short brake lines in master cylinder and position them back into the reservoir. Ensure short brake line ends are submerged in reservoir brake fluid.
3. Fill reservoir with recommended brake fluid, then cover master cylinder fluid reservoir with shop towel.
4. Pump brakes until clear, bubble-free fluid comes out of both brake lines. **If any brake fluid spills on paint, wash it off immediately with water.**
5. Remove short brake lines, then reinstall original brake lines.
6. Bleed each brake line at master cylinder using the following procedure:
   a. Have assistant pump brake pedal 10 times, then hold firm pressure on pedal.
   b. Open rearmost brake line fittings with tubing wrench until stream of brake fluid comes out. Have assistant maintain pressure on brake pedal until brake line fitting is tightened again.
   c. Repeat this operation until clear, bubble-free fluid comes out from around tube fitting.
   d. Repeat bleeding operation at front brake line fitting.
7. If any of brake lines or calipers have been removed, it may be helpful to prime system by gravity bleeding. Gravity bleed system after master cylinder is primed and bled. To prime system using gravity method, proceed as follows:
   a. Fill master cylinder with manufacturer recommended brake fluid or

equivalent.
   b. Loosen both rear bleeder screws and leave open until clear brake fluid flows out. **Check reservoir fluid level frequently. Do not allow fluid level to drop below half way.**
   c. Tighten rear bleeder screws.
   d. Loosen bleeder screw on front caliper and leave open until clear fluid flows out. **Bleed front calipers one side at a time.**
8. After master cylinder has been primed, lines bled at master cylinder and brake system primed, resume normal brake system bleeding at each wheel.

WHEEL BLEEDING SEQUENCE

Rear Wheel Drive .... RR-LR-RF-LF
Front Wheel Drive .... RR-LF-LR-RF

INSPECTION

Remove wheels and inspect brake disc, caliper and linings. The wheel bearings should be inspected at this time and repacked if necessary. Do not get any grease on the linings.

If the caliper is cracked or fluid leakage through the casting is evident, it must be replaced as a unit.

Should it become necessary to remove the caliper when installing new parts, clean all parts in alcohol, then wipe dry using lint-free cloths. Using an air hose, blow out drilled passages and bores. Check dust boots for punctures or tears. If punctures or tears are evident, install new boots during assembly.

Inspect piston bores in both housings for scoring or pitting. Bores showing light scratches or corrosion can usually be

cleaned with crocus cloth. However, bores with deep scratches or scoring may be honed, provided the diameter of the bore is not increased more than .002 inch. If the bore does not clean up within this specification, a new caliper housing should be installed (black stains on the bore walls are caused by piston seals and will do no harm).

When using a hone, **Fig. 4,** be sure to install the hone baffle before honing the bore. The baffle is used to protect the hone stones from damage. Use extreme care in cleaning the caliper after honing. Remove all dust and grit by flushing the caliper with alcohol. Wipe the caliper dry with a clean lint-free cloth, then repeat cleaning procedure.

BRAKE DISC SERVICE

Disc brake service is extremely critical due to the close tolerances required in machining the brake disc to ensure proper brake operation.

Maintaining close control of the shape of the rubbing surfaces is necessary to prevent brake roughness. In addition, the surface finish must be non-directional and maintained at a micro-inch finish. This is necessary to avoid pulls and erratic performance and promote long lining life and equal lining wear of both the left and right brakes.

Do not attempt to refinish the rubbing surfaces unless precision equipment, capable of measuring in micro inches (millionths of an inch) is available.

To check the disc lateral runout, mount a dial indicator on a convenient part (steering knuckle, tie rod, disc brake caliper housing) so the plunger of the dial indicator contacts the disc 1 inch from the outer edge, **Fig. 5.** If the total indicated runout exceeds specifications, install a new disc.

To check parallelism (thickness variation), mount dial indicators, **Fig. 6,** so the plunger contacts the rotor approximately 1 inch from the outer edge. If parallelism exceeds specifications, replace the rotor.

BRAKE PAD SERVICE

The hydraulic system must be depressurized before disconnecting any hydraulic lines or fittings. Depressurize the system by pumping the brake pedal a minimum of 25 times with the ignition switch in the OFF position.

Fig. 5   Rotor lateral runout check

Fig. 6   Rotor parallelism (thickness variation) check

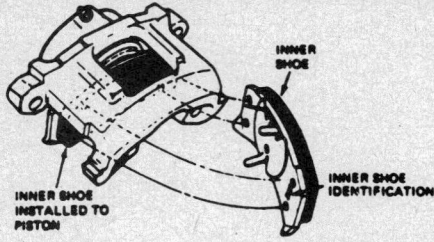

Fig. 7   Inner brake shoe to caliper installation. Except Aspire, Capri, Escort, Festiva, Probe & Tracer front disc brake rotor.

EXCEPT ASPIRE, CAPRI, ESCORT, FESTIVA, PROBE & TRACER

Removal

1. Remove brake fluid until reservoir is half full.
2. **On 1994 Continental, Sable and Taurus models,** turn air suspension service switch off.
3. **On all models,** raise and support front of vehicle, then remove wheel and tire assembly.
4. Remove caliper locating pins.
5. Lift caliper assembly from adapter plate, then remove outer shoe from caliper assembly. If necessary, slip shoe down caliper leg until clip is disengaged.
6. Remove inner shoe and lining assembly. If necessary, pull shoe straight out of piston. This should require a force as high as 20-30 lbs.
7. Suspend caliper from inner fender housing with wire to avoid damaging brake hose.
8. Remove and discard locating pin insulators and plastic sleeves.

Installation

1. Using four-inch C-clamp and block of wood 2³/₄ x 1 inch and approximately ³/₄ inch thick, seat caliper piston in bore, then remove C-clamp and wooden block. Some models have pistons made of phenolic material. Do not seat these pistons in bore by applying C-clamp directly to piston. Use extra care during this procedure to prevent damage to the piston. Metal or sharp objects cannot come into direct contact with the piston or damage may result.
2. Install locating pin insulators and plastic sleeves on caliper housing. Ensure insulators and sleeves are properly positioned.
3. Install inner shoe and lining assembly on caliper piston, **Fig. 7. Some inner brake shoes are marked LH (left-hand) and RH (righthand) and must be installed on the proper caliper. Use care to not bend spring clips too far during installation in piston, otherwise distortion and rattles**

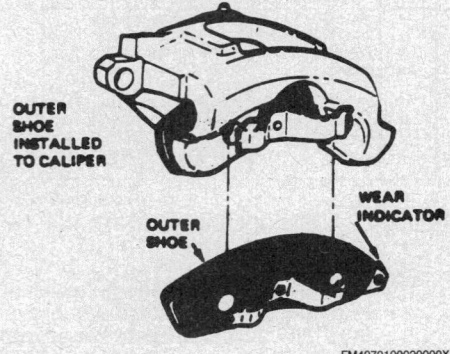

Fig. 8   Outer brake shoe to caliper installation. Except Aspire, Capri, Escort, Festiva, Probe & Tracer may result.

4. Install outer brake shoe and lining assembly, **Fig. 8.** Ensure shoes are installed on proper caliper and clip and buttons on shoe are properly seated. **Outer shoe can be identified as left-hand and righthand by wear indicator. Wear indicators must be installed toward front of vehicle.**
5. Install locating pins. **Tighten locating pins to specification.**
6. Install wheel and tire assembly, then lower vehicle.
7. **On 1994 Continental, Sable and Taurus models,** turn air suspension service switch on.
8. **On all models** refill master cylinder, then pump brake pedal several times to position brake linings before moving vehicle.

ASPIRE & FESTIVA

Removal

1. Drain approximately ¹/₃ of brake fluid from master cylinder.
2. Raise and support front of vehicle, then remove tire and wheel.
3. **On Festiva models,** remove brake pad pin retainer.
4. **On Aspire models,** place C-clamp on caliper and tighten clamp to move caliper piston approximately .118 inch in cylinder bore, then remove clamp. **Do not use screwdriver or similar tool to pry caliper piston away from**

front disc brake rotor.
5. **On all models,** disengage anti-rattle spring from brake pads, **Fig. 9.**
6. Remove brake pad pins and anti-rattle spring, then pull brake pads and shims out of caliper. **Do not discard shims found behind inner brake pad.**

Installation

1. Push piston fully back into caliper bore.
2. Apply suitable brake grease to both sides of inner shim and to back of inner brake pad.
3. Install brake pads and shims, ensuring shims are positioned correctly.
4. Install brake pad pins, anti-rattle spring and pin retainer.
5. Install wheel and lower vehicle, then check and adjust master cylinder fluid level as required.

CAPRI

Removal

1. Remove approximately ²/₃ of brake fluid from master cylinder.
2. Raise and support vehicle.
3. Remove wheel and tire assembly.
4. Using needle nose pliers, remove pad retainer spring locking in disc pad retainer pins.
5. Using a hammer and pin punch, remove disc pad retainer pins, **Fig. 10.**
6. Using screwdriver, pry caliper outward to compress caliper piston inward, then remove outboard brake pad and shim.
7. Mark shims with permanent marker so they can be installed in their original position.
8. Push caliper inward with one hand, then remove inboard brake pad with other hand.
9. Remove anchor plate clips from caliper anchor plate. Label anchor plate clips "top" and "bottom" as they are removed.

Installation

1. Install anchor plate clips. **If clips are not placed in original positions, locating tabs may contact brake rotor.**
2. Push caliper assembly inward and install inboard brake pad and shims.
3. Pry caliper outward and install outboard pad and shim. **Ensure spring tabs on back of brake are properly aligned and fully seated in caliper piston.**

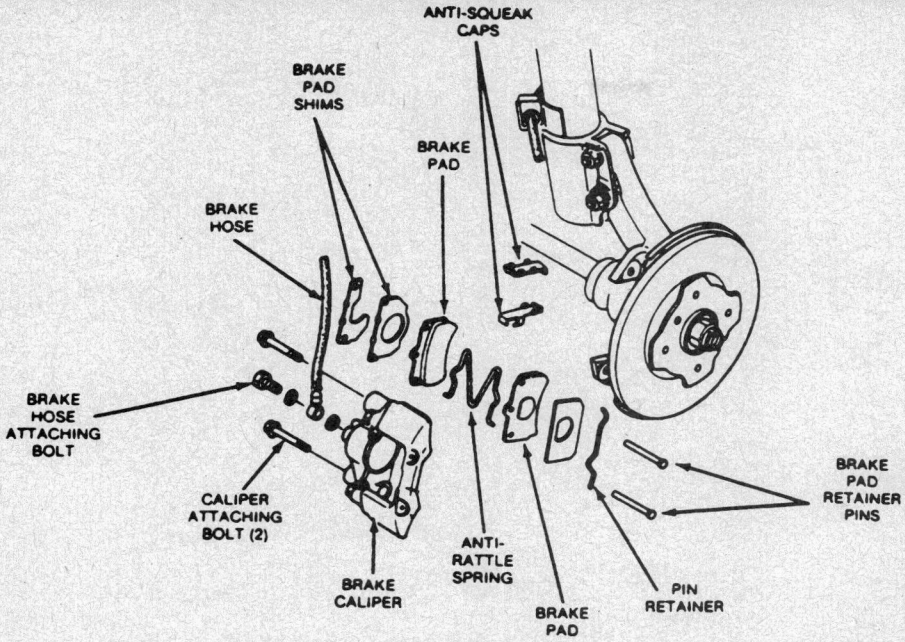

Fig. 9   Front disc brake assembly. Aspire & Festiva

FM4079100015000X

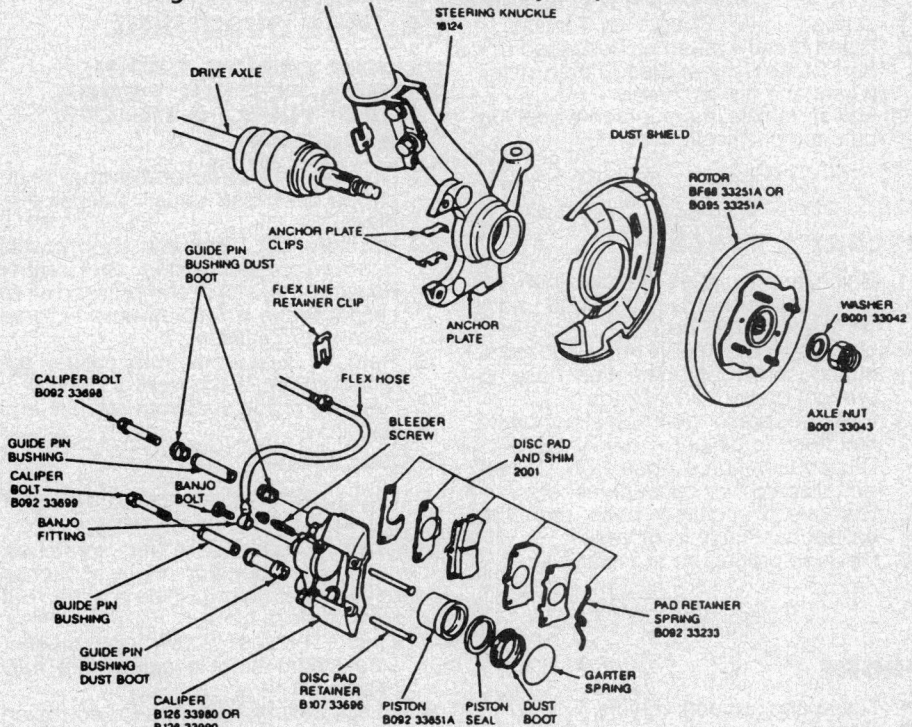

Fig. 10   Front disc brake assembly. Capri

FM4079100017000X

4. Install brake pad retaining pins, then the pin retaining spring.
5. Install wheel and tire assembly. Tighten wheel lug nuts to specification.
6. Correct brake fluid level in master cylinder as necessary.

ESCORT & TRACER
Removal

1. Raise and support vehicle, then remove wheel and tire assembly.
2. Remove two brake pad retaining pins

from caliper assembly.
3. **On 1992—93 models,** remove "M" spring, then the "W" spring, **Fig. 12.**
5. **On 1994 models,** remove "W" spring and brake pad retaining pins, then the "M" spring, **Fig. 11.**
5. **On all models,** remove brake pads and shims from caliper assembly.

Installation
1. Push piston fully into caliper bore.
2. Apply grease between shims and brake pad guide plates, then position

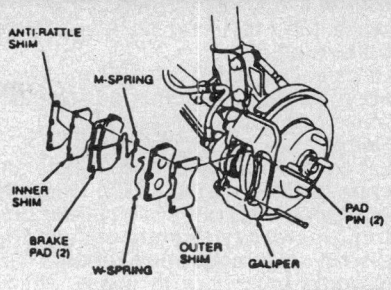

FM4079100016000X

Fig. 11   Front disc brake component locations. Escort & Tracer

brake pads and shims into caliper.
3. **On 1992—93 models,** install "W" spring, then the "M" spring.
4. **On 1994 models,** install "M" spring, then the "W" spring.
5. **On all models,** install two brake pad retaining pins, then the wheel and tire assembly.

PROBE

1. Remove approximately ²/₃ of brake fluid from master cylinder.
2. Raise and support vehicle.
3. Remove wheel and tire assembly.
4. Using screwdriver, pry caliper outboard. **Position front disc brake hose away from front disc brake caliper casting to avoid cracking front brake hose.**
5. Remove caliper mounting bolt, **Fig. 12,** then slide caliper upward.
6. Slide caliper off guide pin, then tag anti-rattle shims so shims can be reinstalled in original positions.
7. Remove brake pads from caliper anchor.
8. Remove retaining clips from brake pads.
9. Reverse procedure to install, noting the following:
   a. Ensure wear indicators are located on inboard side of caliper anchor.
   b. Correct brake fluid level in master cylinder as necessary.
   c. Road test vehicle for proper operation.

CALIPER SERVICE

CALIPER, REPLACE

The hydraulic system must be depressurized before disconnecting any hydraulic lines or fittings. Depressurize the system by pumping the brake pedal a minimum of 25 times with the ignition switch in the OFF position.

EXCEPT ASPIRE, CAPRI, ESCORT, FESTIVA, PROBE & TRACER

Before removing calipers, mark lefthand and righthand calipers so they can be installed in the same position.
1. **On 1994 Continental, Sable and Taurus models,** turn air suspension service switch off.
2. **On all models,** raise and support front of vehicle, then remove wheel and tire assembly.
3. Loosen brake tube fitting connecting

brake tube to fitting on frame. Plug brake tube.

4. Remove retaining clip from brake hose and bracket, then disconnect brake hose from caliper.
5. Remove caliper locating pins.
6. Lift caliper from rotor and spindle anchor plate assembly. **On models equipped with phenolic caliper piston, do not pry directly against the piston or damage may result.**
7. Reverse procedure to install, noting the following:
   a. Install caliper assembly over rotor with outer shoe against rotor braking surface during installation on spindle and anchor plate to prevent pinching piston boot between inner brake shoe and piston. **Ensure calipers are installed in correct position.**
   b. Bleed brake system as described under "Brake System Bleed."
   c. Pump brake pedal several times to position brake shoes before moving vehicle.

ASPIRE & FESTIVA

1. Raise and support vehicle, then remove wheel and tire.
2. Remove brake pads as described under "Brake Pad Service."
3. Remove brake hose attaching bolt, then disconnect hose from caliper. Discard seal washers located between brake hose connection and caliper.
4. Remove caliper attaching bolts, then the caliper.
5. **On Aspire models,** remove anti-squeak caps.
6. **On all models,** reverse procedure to install. Bleed brakes as described under "Brake System Bleed."

CAPRI

Removal

1. Raise and support vehicle, then remove wheel and tire assembly.
2. Remove brake pads as described under "Brake Pad Service."
3. Remove banjo bolt attaching brake flex hose to caliper.
4. Remove two copper washers sealing flex hose banjo fitting to caliper, then discard washers.
5. Remove two caliper bolts, then lift caliper off rotor.

Installation

1. Remove caliper guide pin bushing dust boots, then push out caliper guide pin bushings.
2. Lubricate guide pin bushings with disc brake caliper slide grease part No. D7AZ-19590-A or equivalent, then install bushings and dust boots.
3. Position caliper over rotor, then install caliper bolts.
4. Tighten caliper bolts to specification.
5. Install two new copper washers and banjo bolt on brake flex hose, then position flex hose on caliper assembly.
6. Tighten banjo bolt to specification.
7. Install brake pads and shims as de-

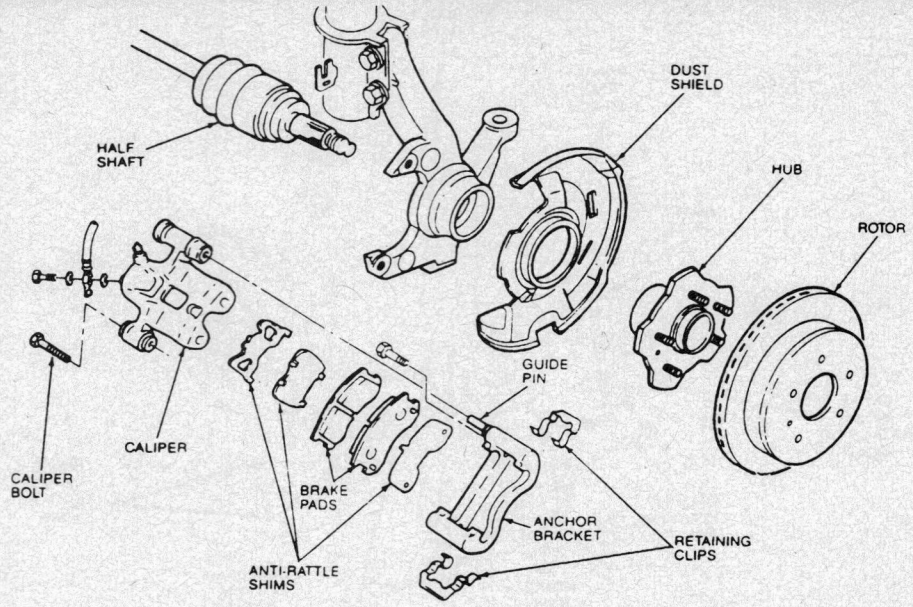

Fig. 12 Front disc brake assembly. Probe

scribed under "Brake Pad Service."
8. Bleed brake system as described under "Brake System Bleed," then install wheel and tire assembly.
9. Lower vehicle, then tighten wheel lug nuts to specification.

ESCORT & TRACER

1. Raise and support vehicle, then remove brake pads as described under "Brake Pad Service."
2. Using suitable needle nose vise grips, clamp center of brake flex hose to prevent brake fluid leakage.
3. Remove banjo bolt retaining brake flex hose to caliper.
4. Disconnect brake hose from caliper and discard two copper washers.
5. Remove two caliper bolts, then the caliper assembly from vehicle.
6. Reverse procedure to install.

PROBE

1. Raise and support vehicle.
2. Remove wheel and tire assembly.
3. Remove brake hose to caliper bolt.
4. Remove two copper washers and discard.
5. Remove caliper bolts.
6. Pivot caliper off brake pads and slide caliper off guide pin.
7. Remove guide pin bushing dust boots and push out caliper guide pin bushing.
8. Using high temperature grease D7AZ-19590-A or equivalent, lubricate guide pin bushings.
9. Reverse procedure to install. Bleed front brakes as described under "Brake System Bleed."

CALIPER OVERHAUL

EXCEPT ASPIRE, CAPRI, ESCORT, FESTIVA, PROBE, TEMPO, TOPAZ & TRACER
Disassemble

1. Remove caliper assembly from vehicle as described under "Caliper, Replace."
2. Position fiber block and shop towels between caliper piston and caliper housing, then apply compressed air to caliper brake line fitting bore to force piston from caliper.
3. Remove dust boot from caliper assembly, **Figs. 1 through 3.**
4. Remove piston seal from cylinder and discard.

Inspection

1. Check piston for scratches, scoring or damage. Replace if necessary.
2. Check caliper bore for scratches, scoring or corrosion. Light scratches or slight corrosion can be polished out using crocus cloth.
3. Ensure bleeder screw and bleeder screw bore hole in caliper are fully open.
4. Check caliper bushings for corrosion and dust boot retaining ring for damage or tension loss. Replace parts as necessary.

Assemble

1. Lubricate piston seal with clean brake fluid, then install seal in caliper bore. **Ensure seal is firmly seated in groove.**
2. Install new dust boot in outer groove of caliper bore, **Figs. 1 through 3.**
3. Coat piston with clean brake fluid and install piston in caliper bore.
4. Spread dust boot over piston as it is installed, then seat dust boot in piston groove.

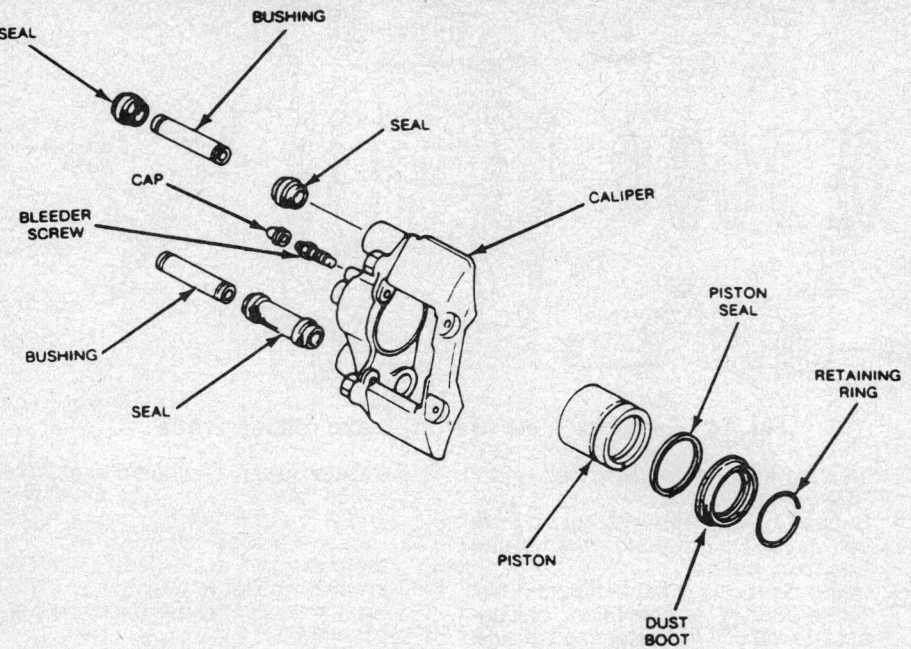

Fig. 13 Exploded view of brake caliper. Aspire & Festiva

5. Install caliper assembly as described under "Caliper, Replace."
6. **On 1994 Continental, Sable and Taurus models,** turn air suspension service switch on.

ASPIRE & FESTIVA

Disassemble

1. Remove brake pads as described under "Brake Pad Service," then the caliper as described under "Caliper, Replace."
2. Remove bleeder screw and drain remaining fluid from caliper. Install screw.
3. Remove dust boot retaining ring, **Fig. 13.**
4. Position block of wood between piston and caliper, then apply compressed air to fluid inlet port and blow piston from caliper bore. **Apply only enough pressure to ease piston out of bore.**
5. Remove dust boot from piston, then use suitable wooden pick to carefully pry piston seal from caliper bore.
6. Remove bleeder screw, then the caliper bushings and bushing seals.
7. Wash all parts in denatured alcohol and dry with compressed air.

Inspection

1. Check piston for scratches, scoring or damage. Replace if necessary.
2. Check caliper bore for scratches, scoring or corrosion. Light scratches or slight corrosion can be polished out using crocus cloth.
3. Ensure bleeder screw and bleeder screw bore hole in caliper are fully open.
4. Check caliper bushings for corrosion and dust boot retaining ring for damage or tension loss. Replace parts as necessary.

Assemble

1. Lubricate piston seal with suitable brake grease or clean brake fluid, then install into caliper bore.
2. Lubricate piston, then partially install into caliper bore. Ensure dust boot groove on piston remains above caliper bore.
3. Lubricate dust boot with suitable brake grease, then install onto piston.
4. Press piston fully inward until it bottoms in bore, then install dust boot retaining ring.
5. Install bleeder screw.
6. Install caliper bushings and new bushing seals. Lubricate inner surface of bushing seal and outer surface of bushings with suitable brake grease before installation. **Do not allow grease to enter the piston bore.**

CAPRI
Disassemble

1. Open caliper bleed screw and drain caliper. Close bleed screw.
2. Remove caliper as described under "Caliper, Replace."
3. Remove caliper guide bushing and dust boots.
4. Remove snap ring from caliper piston dust boot.
5. Position wooden block or shop towels between caliper and piston, then apply air pressure to brake hose fitting to remove piston from caliper. Use only enough air pressure to ease piston from caliper bore. **Keep hands and fingers away from piston, as personal injury may result.**
6. Remove dust boot from caliper, then use wooden or plastic pick to remove piston seal from caliper bore.

Inspection

1. Check piston for scratches, scoring or

damage. Replace if necessary.
2. Check caliper bore for scratches, scoring or corrosion. Light scratches or slight corrosion can be polished out using crocus cloth.
3. Ensure bleeder screw and bleeder screw bore hole in caliper are fully open.
4. Check caliper bushings for corrosion and dust boot retaining ring for damage or tension loss. Replace parts as necessary.

Assemble

1. Lubricate piston seal with brake fluid, then position seal in caliper bore groove.
2. Lubricate piston and caliper bore with brake fluid.
3. Install dust boot on piston, then install piston into caliper bore. Use gentle rocking motion to bottom piston in caliper bore.
4. Slide dust boot over caliper bore boss and install retaining ring.
5. Install caliper assembly as described under "Caliper, Replace."
6. Bleed brake system as described under "Brake System Bleed," then cycle brake pedal several times to seat brake pads and ensure system is functioning properly.

ESCORT & TRACER

Disassemble

1. Remove front caliper as described under "Caliper, Replace."
2. Remove front caliper sleeves and dust boots.
3. Remove caliper bleed screw cap and screw.
4. Remove snap ring from caliper piston dust seal, then the seal.
5. Position wood block or shop towels between caliper and piston, then apply air pressure to brake hose fitting to remove piston from caliper. Use only enough air pressure to ease piston from caliper bore. **Keep hands and fingers away from piston, as personal injury may result.**

Inspection

1. Check piston for scratches, scoring or damage. Replace if necessary.
2. Check caliper bore for scratches, scoring or corrosion. Light scratches or slight corrosion can be polished out using crocus cloth.
3. Ensure bleeder screw and bleeder screw bore hole in caliper are fully open.
4. Check caliper bushings for corrosion and dust boot retaining ring for damage or tension loss. Replace parts as necessary.

Assemble

1. Lubricate piston seal with brake fluid, then position seal in caliper bore groove.
2. Lubricate piston and caliper bore with brake fluid.
3. Install caliper assembly as described under "Caliper, Replace."

PROBE
Disassemble

1. Open caliper bleed screw and drain caliper. Close bleed screw.
2. Remove caliper as described under "Caliper, Replace."
3. Remove caliper guide bushing and dust boots, **Fig. 14.**
4. Remove snap ring from caliper piston dust boot.
5. Position block of wood between piston and caliper.
6. Apply air pressure to brake hose fitting. **Do not use excessive air pressure to remove piston.**
7. Remove dust boot and discard.
8. Remove piston seal from caliper and discard.

Inspection

1. Check piston for scratches, scoring or damage. Replace if necessary.
2. Check caliper bore for scratches, scoring or corrosion. Light scratches or slight corrosion can be polished out using crocus cloth.
3. Ensure bleeder screw and bleeder screw bore hole in caliper are fully open.
4. Check caliper bushings for corrosion and dust boot retaining ring for damage or tension loss. Replace parts as necessary.

Assemble

1. Lubricate new piston seal with brake fluid and install seal in caliper groove. **Ensure seal does not become twisted in caliper bore.**
2. Lubricate caliper bore and piston with brake fluid.
3. Install dust boot on piston and slide dust boot into groove.
4. Install piston in caliper bore and push down into bottom of bore.
5. Slide dust boot over boss on caliper bore and install snap ring.
6. Install caliper guide bushing, dust boot and guide pin.
7. Install caliper bolt and tighten to specification.
8. Bleed front brakes as described under "Brake System Bleed," then pump brake pedal several times to seat brake pads.
9. Check fluid level and add if necessary.
10. With vehicle in Neutral, spin each rotor to ensure brakes are not dragging.
11. Install wheel and tire assemblies.

TEMPO & TOPAZ

Tempo and Topaz disc brake calipers are not serviceable.

ROTOR
REPLACE
CAPRI

Removal

1. Raise and support vehicle, then remove wheel and tire assembly.
2. Using chisel, unstake and remove halfshaft nut and washer. **Discard nut and washer.**
3. Remove brake pads and caliper from

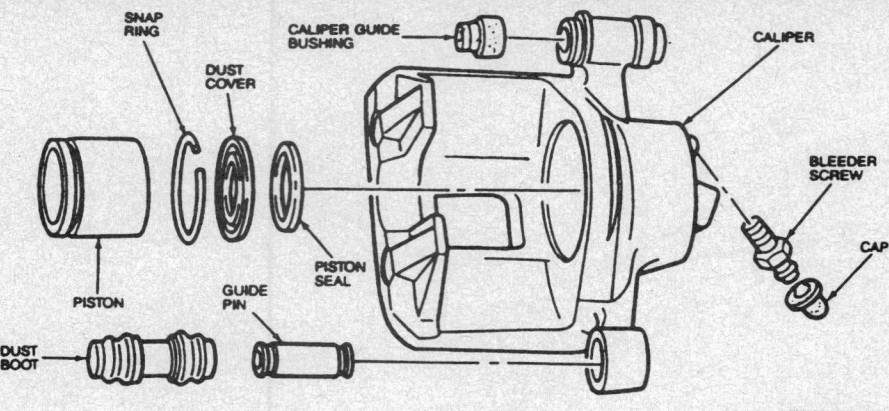

Fig. 14   Exploded view of front brake caliper. Probe

FM4079100022000X

steering knuckle as described under "Brake Pad Service."
4. Support caliper with wire strung from coil spring. **Do not disconnect brake line from caliper.**
5. Using tie rod end separator tool No. T85M-3395-A, or equivalent, disconnect tie rod end from steering knuckle.
6. Remove ball joint pinch bolt, then separate control arm from steering knuckle.
7. Remove steering knuckle to strut assembly bolts.
8. Using knuckle puller tool No. T87C-1104-A and step plate tool No. D80L-630-3, or equivalents, remove rotor and hub assembly from steering knuckle. **Dust shield is pressed onto steering knuckle. If bearings are not being serviced, leave dust shield attached to knuckle.**

Installation

1. Install rotor to hub. Tighten bolts to specification.
2. Press hub and rotor assembly into steering knuckle.
3. Position steering knuckle on strut, then install retaining bolts. Tighten bolts to specification.
4. Raise lower control arm and position lower ball joint stud in steering knuckle, then install ball joint pinch bolt.
5. Tighten pinch bolt to specification.
6. Install brake pads as described under "Brake Pad Service."
7. Install caliper as described under "Caliper, Replace."
8. Install new halfshaft retaining nut, then tighten nut to specification.
9. Install wheel and tire assembly, then tighten wheel lug nuts to specification.

MARK VII
Removal

1. Raise and support vehicle, then remove wheel and tire assembly. Use care to avoid damaging bleeder screw fitting and caliper splash shield.
2. Remove caliper assembly as described under "Caliper Service." If caliper does ot require service, do not disconnect brake hose or remove caliper from vehicle. Position caliper aside and support with wire to avoid damaging caliper or stretching hose.

Position clean cardboard spacer between linings to prevent inner shoe and lining from coming out of caliper.
3. Remove grease cap from hub, then the cotter pin, nut lock, adjusting nut and flat washer from spindle.
4. Remove outer bearing cone and roller assembly.
5. Remove hub and rotor assembly from spindle.

Installation

1. If installing new rotor, proceed as follows:
   a. Remove protective coating with suitable solvent.
   b. Pack new bearings with suitable grease, then install inner bearing cone and roller assembly in inner cup.
   c. Pack grease lightly between lips of new grease seal and install the seal.
2. If using old rotor, ensure grease in hub is clean and adequate, inner bearing and grease seal are lubricated and in good condition and rotor braking surfaces are clean.
3. On all rotors, install hub and rotor assembly on spindle, then lubricate and install outer wheel bearing. Install washer and adjusting nut finger tight.
4. Adjust wheel bearings as described in the appropriate chassis section of this manual.
5. Install nut lock, cotter pin and grease cap, then install the caliper as described under "Caliper Service."
6. Install wheel and tire assembly, then lower vehicle.
7. Pump brake pedal before moving vehicle to position brake linings, then road test vehicle.

CONTINENTAL, MARK VIII, SABLE & TAURUS
Removal

1. **On 1994 models,** turn air suspension service switch off.
2. **On all models,** raise and support vehicle, then remove wheel and tire assembly from rotor mounting face. **Use care to avoid damage or interference with front disc brake caliper bleeder screw fitting and front disc brake rotor shield.**

3. Remove caliper anchor bracket bolts. Position caliper aside and support with suitable wire to avoid damaging front disc brake caliper and hose. **Use care to prevent deformation of rotor and nicking, scratching or contaminating brake lining and rotor surfaces.**
4. Remove front disc brake rotor from hub assembly by pulling it off hub studs, noting the following:
   a. If excessive force is necessary to remove rotor, check rotor for lateral runout prior to installation.
   b. If additional force is required to remove front disc brake rotor, apply suitable rust penetrant and inhibitor on front and rear rotor/hub mating surfaces.
   c. Strike rotor between studs with plastic hammer. If rotor still will not come off, install three-jaw puller tool No. D80L-1013-A, or equivalent, and remove rotor.

Installation

Failure to clean rust and foreign material from rotor and hub mounting surfaces when installing new or old rotors will result in high rotor lateral runout, which will speed up the development of brake roughness, shudder or vibration.
1. If front disc brake rotor is being replaced, remove protective coating from new rotor with suitable carburetor cleaner.
2. If original rotor is being installed, ensure rotor braking and mounting surfaces are clean.
3. Apply suitable lubricant to pilot diameter of front disc brake rotor, then install rotor on wheel hub assembly.
4. Install caliper and caliper anchor bracket bolts on rotor. Tighten caliper anchor bracket bolts to specifications.
5. Install wheel and tire assembly to rotor mounting face, then tighten wheel hub bolt nuts to specification. **Failure to tighten wheel hub bolt nuts with torque wrench in star pattern may result in high rotor runout, which will speed development of brake roughness, shudder and vibration.**
6. Lower vehicle, then pump brake pedal to position brake linings prior to moving vehicle.
7. **On 1994 models,** turn air suspension service switch on.
8. **On all models,** road test vehicle.

COUGAR, TEMPO, THUNDERBIRD & TOPAZ
Removal

If caliper does not require servicing, do not disconnect brake hose or remove caliper from vehicle. Position caliper aside with wire to avoid damaging caliper and hose.

If excessive force must be used to remove the rotor, then the rotor should be checked for lateral runout as described under "Brake Disc Service," before installation.
1. Raise and support vehicle, then remove wheel and tire assembly.

2. Remove rotor from hub by pulling off hub studs. If additional force is necessary, proceed as follows:
   a. Apply suitable rust penetrant and inhibitor on front of rotor and hub mating surfaces.
   b. Attach three-jaw puller tool No. D80-C-1013-A, or equivalent, and remove rotor.

Installation

1. **If replacing rotor,** remove protective coating with suitable carburetor cleaner.
2. **If using original rotor,** ensure braking and mounting surfaces are clean. Remove rust if necessary.
3. Install rotor on hub assembly, then the caliper as described under "Caliper Service."
4. Install wheel and tire assembly. Tighten wheel lug nuts to specifications.
5. Pump brake pedal to position brake linings prior to moving vehicle, then road test vehicle.

ESCORT & TRACER
Removal

1. Raise and support vehicle, then remove wheel and tire assembly.
2. Remove two brake caliper bolts, then secure caliper aside with suitable wire.
3. Pull rotor away from wheel hub.

Installation

1. Press rotor to wheel hub, then position caliper.
2. Install two brake caliper bolts. Tighten caliper bolts to specifications.
3. Install tire and wheel assembly. Tighten wheel hub bolt nuts to specifications.

TECHNICAL SERVICE BULLETINS
COMPOSITE ROTORS
Continental, Sable & Taurus

The disc rotor is a hat section-type composite rotor of steel and cast iron. A Rotunda Rotor Mounting Adapter tool No. 054-00032, or equivalent, is required for use on the brake lathe for refinishing. **Failure to use the adapter will result in gouging the brake disc, making it unfit for use.**

A new design full-cast front disc brake rotor is now available for service use. If service is required, install the new full cast front disc rotors part No. F10Y-1125-B **in pairs only. Never install a full cast rotor on one side of the vehicle with a composite rotor on the other side.**

FRONT ROTOR WEAR
1992 Continental

Semi-metallic brake lining material can lead to accelerated front brake rotor wear. This can cause brake roughness, characterized by brake pedal, steering column, or vehicle body vibration during brake application.

Once it is determined they are the

source of vibration and premature brake rotor wear, the front brake pads and rotors should be replaced.

Refer to "Composite Rotors" for rotor replacement tips before attempting to replace rotors.

If the vibration originates from the front of the vehicle, replace the front brake pads and rotors. Refer to "Brake Pad Service" and "Rotor, Replace" in this section.

GROANING/GRINDING NOISE DURING MODERATE TO HEAVY BRAKING
1992 Probe

Front brake groaning or grinding noise may be heard on moderate-to-heavy braking. The concern occurs most often at ambient temperatures above 65°F. This condition may be caused by the brake pad material.

Replace front brake pads with improved brake pads part No. F42Z-2001-A and attachment kit part No. E92Z-2B321-B to eliminate the noise. Refer to "Brake Pad Service" for replacement procedure.

ROUGHNESS FROM FRONT BRAKE ROTOR WEAR/VIBRATION OF BRAKE PEDAL, STEERING COLUMN OR BODY DURING BRAKE APPLICATION
1992—93 Crown Victoria, Grand Marquis & Town Car

Premature front brake rotor wear may be caused by the use of semi-metallic and organic brake lining material. This may cause brake roughness which may result in vibration in brake pedal, steering column or vehicle body in general during brake application. Roughness can also be caused by lining material transfer from nonmetallic, non-asbestos pads under certain conditions, or from rust and corrosion build-up.

Determine the origin of the vibration and, if necessary, replace the front brake linings as described under "Brake Pad Service," and rotors as described under "Rotor, Replace." If the condition persists, replace the rear brake linings and rotors as described under "Rear Disc Brakes & Parking Brakes." Refer to the following procedure for service details. Be sure brake booster application is not present on ABS equipped vehicles.
1. Road test vehicle to determine if vibrations are coming from front of vehicle during brake application.
2. If front of vehicle is source of vibration, replace the following components:
   a. Front brake linings as described under "Brake Pad Service."
   b. **On 1992 Town Car and 1992—93 Crown Victoria and Grand Marquis,** rotors as described under "Rotor, Replace." **Ensure hub face is free from rust.**

c. **On all models,** if roughness is still present, replace rear brake linings as described under "Rear Disc Brakes & Parking Brakes."
3. Check vehicle for brake roughness.

ROUGHNESS, PULSATION OR STEERING WHEEL SHAKE

1992 COUGAR & THUNDERBIRD

Brake roughness, pulsation and steering wheel shake may occur because of uneven rotor wear. Two major causes of uneven rotor wear are abrasive brake pads (semi-metallic material) and hub or rotor high and low spots improperly oriented during assembly.

Usually these vehicles appear to be corrected by just installing new pads and rotors. However, they can repeat the condition after some time in service unless proper attention is given to the front brake pads, hub/rotor "stacked" runout and tire wear and balance.

Check front brake pads, hub/rotor "stacked" runout and tire wear/balance. Refer to the following procedures for service details.

Front Brake Pads

1. Replace front brake pads with ONLY new asbestos pads (part No. F1SZ-2001-A). **Using metallic front brake pads (part No. F0SZ-2001-A) will cause uneven rotor wear.**
2. Refer to "Brake Pad Service" for brake pad replacement procedure.

Hub/Rotor "Stacked" Runout Check

If the assembled system with a new rotor installed on the hub indicates more than .002 inch total runout (TIR), it will cause excessive thickness variation in the rotor as mileage accumulates by wearing the high spots off the rotor. Excessive thickness variation in the rotor causes brake pulsation and steering wheel shake.

High TIR is also caused by rust or other contamination trapped between the hub and rotor mounting surface or the rotor or hub high and low spots not being properly oriented during assembly.

New brake rotors should not be machined. New OEM replacement rotors are well within runout and thickness variation specifications.

To check hub/rotor "stacked" runout, proceed as follows:
1. Clean hub area where new rotor will contact. Remove rust and debris.
2. Install new rotor (part No. F1SZ-1125-A) on hub as outlined under "Rotor, Replace," noting the following:
   a. Secure rotor with at least four lug nuts.
   b. **Torque** nuts to 9 ft. lbs.
3. Using suitable dial indicator, determine total runout of system, Fig. 15. Total system (rotor and hub) runout must not exceed .002 inch. If runout exceeds specification, proceed as follows:

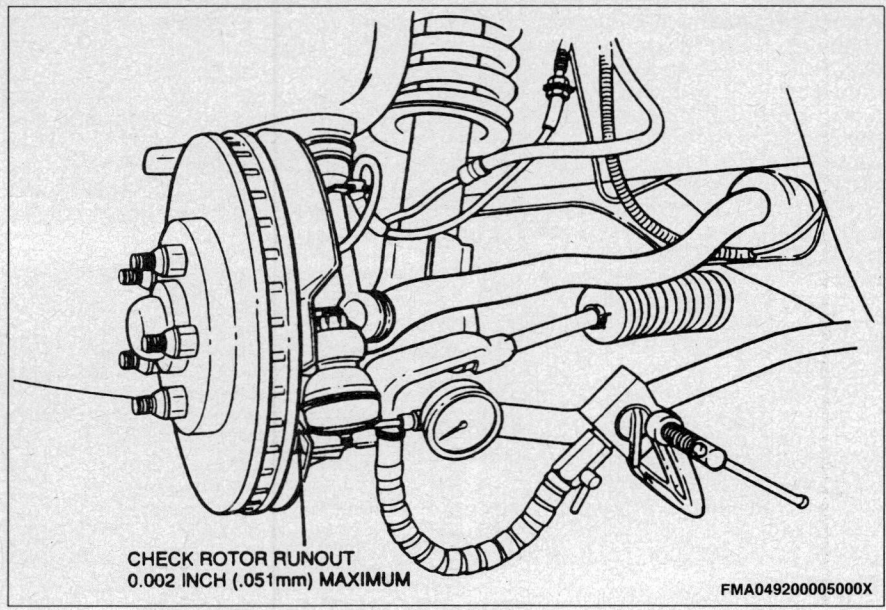

CHECK ROTOR RUNOUT
0.002 INCH (.051mm) MAXIMUM

FMA049200005000X

Fig. 15 Rotor runout check. Continental, Mark VIII, Sable & Taurus

a. Remove rotor and rotate clockwise until next hole lines up with stud.
b. Secure rotor in new position with four lug nuts. **Torque** nuts to 9 ft. lbs.
c. Repeat checking and rotation process until system measures .002 inch or less total runout.
4. If .002 inch or less runout cannot be reached, replace hub.
5. After installing new hub, repeat this check.

Tire Wear & Balance

Tire wear and balance can cause or add to a brake roughness concern. After the brake system is serviced, the tire wear and/or balance could cause enough input to be perceived as a brake roughness condition.
1. Place best tires on front of vehicle.
2. High-speed balance all tires.

SQUEAL OR GROAN DURING BRAKE APPLICATION OR RELEASE

1992 Tempo & Topaz

Semi-metallic front brake linings may squeal during brake application or groan during brake release from a stopped position. Determine the source of the noise and replace the front brake lining assemblies, noting the following:
1. Determine if squeal or groan is coming from front of vehicle.
2. If front of vehicle is source of noise, replace front brake shoe and lining assemblies as described under "Brake Pad Service." If rear of vehicle is source of noise, refer to "Rear Disc Brakes & Parking Brakes."

3. Check again for squeal or groan.
4. If noise is still present, replace rear brake lining assemblies as described under "Rear Disc Brakes & Parking Brakes."

VIBRATION DURING BRAKE APPLICATION

1992—93 Sable & Taurus Except SHO & Police Models

Brake roughness, pulsation and steering wheel shudder may occur during brake application. This may be due to disc brake rotor thickness variation or to lining material transfer — the non-uniform transfer of lining material to the rotor, producing a slip/stick condition.

Use on-vehicle brake lathes to service vehicles with brake roughness. This is more effective than servicing with off-vehicle brake lathes because it allows the steering knuckle to serve as a pilot for the rotor, resulting in improved runout. If on-vehicle brake turning equipment is not available, replace front brake rotors as described under "Rotor, Replace." Finally, replace front brake lining with a new, less aggressive lining kit as described under "Brake Pad Service."

If the customer's driving habits or the local terrain call for frequent brake application, such as frequent descents of hills/mountains while braking, the new style of linings are not recommended.

After replacing the rotors and linings, it is very important the customer limits braking to medium-to-light stops for the first 200 miles. This will greatly reduce the chance of lining transfer.

DISC BRAKE SPECIFICATIONS

Refer to "Rear Disc Brakes and Parking Brakes" for specification charts.

TIGHTENING SPECIFICATIONS

Component	Torque/Ft. Lbs.
Brake Hose Bolts	①
Caliper Bolts	②
Locating Pins ③	18–25
Locating Pins ④	45–65
Locating Pins ⑤	40–60
Wheel Lug Nuts ⑥	65–88
Wheel Lug Nuts ⑦	65–104

①—Escort, Probe & Tracer; 16 ft. lbs.
②—Aspire, Escort, Festiva & Taurus;
　　18–25 ft. lbs., Probe; 23–30 ft. lbs.
③—Continental, Escort, Sable, Taurus,
　　Tempo, Topaz & Tracer.
④—Cougar, Mustang & Thunderbird.
⑤—Crown Victoria, Grand Marquis &
　　Town Car.
⑥—Except Sable & Taurus.
⑦—Sable & Taurus.

Rear Disc Brakes & Parking Brakes

INDEX

DESCRIPTION

CONTINENTAL, COUGAR, MARK VII, MARK VIII, MUSTANG & THUNDERBIRD

Sliding caliper rear disc brakes are used on Continental, Mark VII, Mark VIII, Mustang and Thunderbird, **Figs. 1 through 3.** The caliper is basically the same as the larger front wheel caliper; however, a parking brake mechanism and a larger inner brake shoe anti-rattle spring have been added.

The parking brake lever, located at the rear of the caliper, is actuated by a cable system similar to rear drum brake applications. When the parking brake is applied, the cable rotates the lever and operating shaft, driving the caliper piston and brake shoe assembly against the rotor. An automatic adjuster in the assembly compensates for lining wear and maintains proper clearance in the parking brake mechanism.

The cast iron rotors are ventilated by curved fins located between the braking surfaces and are designed to cause the rotor to act as an air pump when the vehicle is traveling forward. The rotors are not interchangeable and are identified by a Right or Left marking cast inside the hat section of the rotor. The rotor is secured to the axle flange in the same manner as a rear brake drum. A splash shield is bolted to a forged axle adapter to protect the inboard rotor surface.

CAPRI & PROBE

Rear braking is provided by self-adjusting, single piston, floating caliper disc brakes. The caliper slides on two hol-

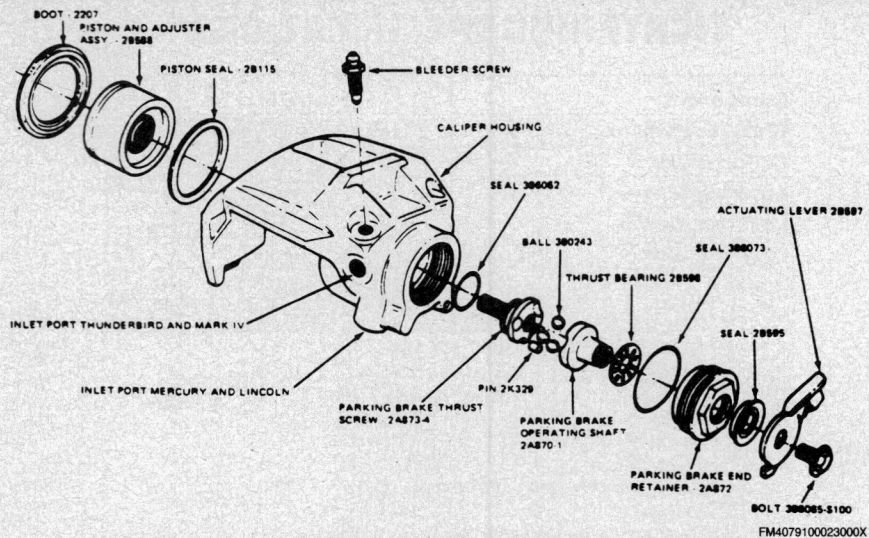

BOOT · 2207
PISTON AND ADJUSTER ASSY · 2B588
PISTON SEAL · 2B115
BLEEDER SCREW
CALIPER HOUSING
SEAL 386062
ACTUATING LEVER 2B687
BALL 386243
THRUST BEARING 2B588
SEAL 386073
SEAL 2B595
INLET PORT THUNDERBIRD AND MARK IV
PIN 2K329
INLET PORT MERCURY AND LINCOLN
PARKING BRAKE THRUST SCREW · 2A873-4
PARKING BRAKE OPERATING SHAFT 2A870-1
PARKING BRAKE END RETAINER · 2A872
BOLT 386085-S100

FM4079100023000X

Fig. 1   Rear disc brake caliper assembly. Mark VII

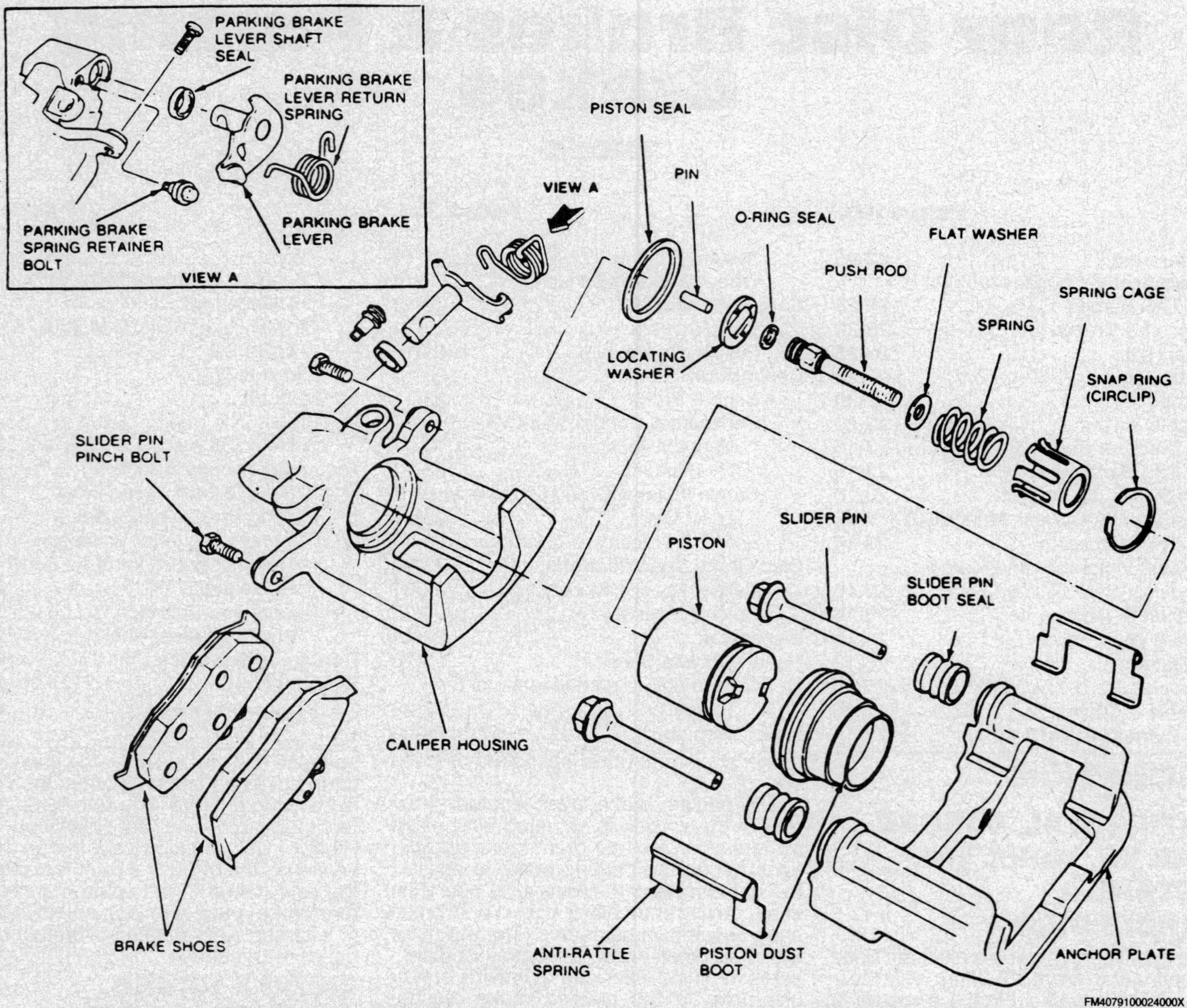

PARKING BRAKE LEVER SHAFT SEAL
PARKING BRAKE LEVER RETURN SPRING
PARKING BRAKE SPRING RETAINER BOLT
PARKING BRAKE LEVER
VIEW A

VIEW A

PISTON SEAL
PIN
O-RING SEAL
PUSH ROD
FLAT WASHER
SPRING
SPRING CAGE
SNAP RING (CIRCLIP)
LOCATING WASHER

SLIDER PIN PINCH BOLT

SLIDER PIN
SLIDER PIN BOOT SEAL

CALIPER HOUSING

PISTON

BRAKE SHOES

ANTI-RATTLE SPRING
PISTON DUST BOOT
ANCHOR PLATE

FM4079100024000X

Fig. 2   Rear disc brake caliper assembly. Continental, Cougar, Mark VIII & Thunderbird

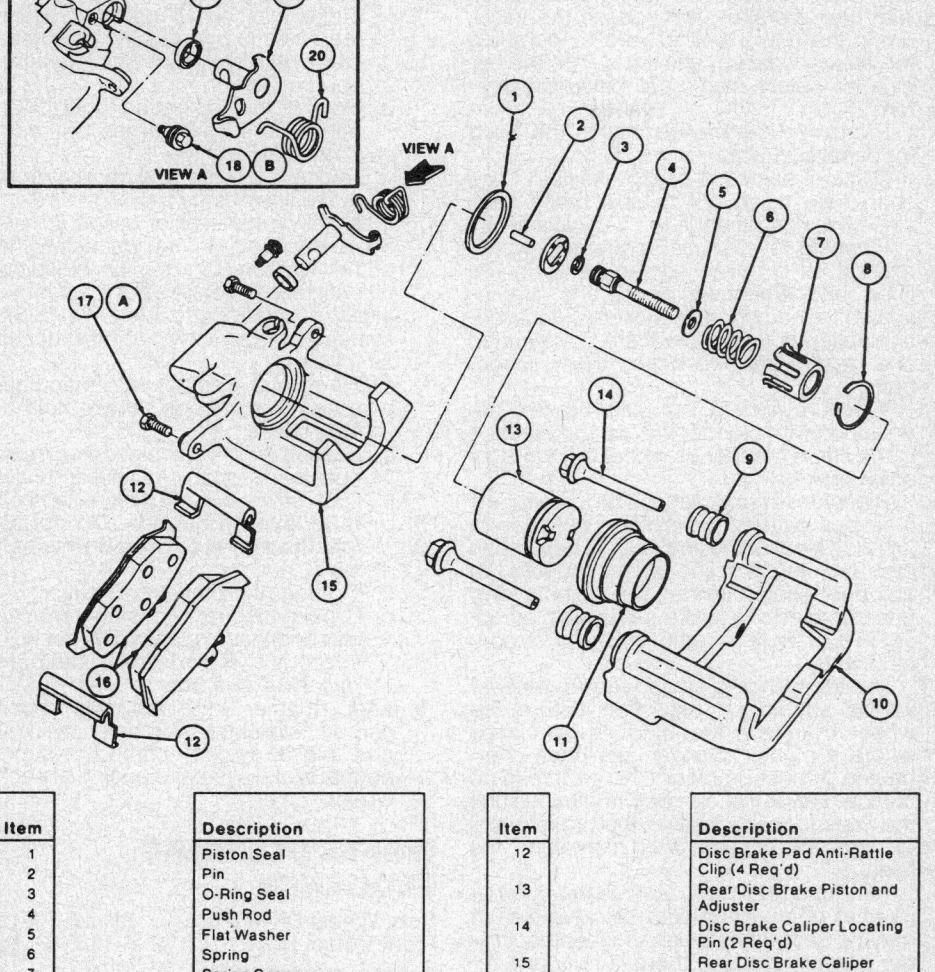

Item	Description
1	Piston Seal
2	Pin
3	O-Ring Seal
4	Push Rod
5	Flat Washer
6	Spring
7	Spring Cage
8	Snap Ring (Circlip)
9	Slider Pin Boot Seal (2 Req'd)
10	Rear Disc Support Bracket
11	Piston Dust Boot

Item	Description
12	Disc Brake Pad Anti-Rattle Clip (4 Req'd)
13	Rear Disc Brake Piston and Adjuster
14	Disc Brake Caliper Locating Pin (2 Req'd)
15	Rear Disc Brake Caliper
16	Rear Brake Shoe and Lining
17A	Rear Brake Pin Retainer (2 Req'd)
18B	Limiting Bolt
19	Parking Brake Lever Shaft Seal

FM4079400055010X

Fig. 3   Exploded view of rear disc brake caliper assembly (Part 1 of 2). Mustang

Item	Description
20	Parking Brake Lever Return Spring
21	Rear Parking Brake Cable

Item	Description
A	Tighten to 40-47 N·m (30-35 Lb-Ft)
B	Tighten to 6-9 N·m (4.5-7 Lb-Ft)

FM4079400055020X

Fig. 3   Exploded view of rear disc brake caliper assembly (Part 2 of 2). Mustang

low, stainless steel guide pins in bushings.

One guide pin is secured to the anchor bracket by a bolt. The other guide pin is held in position by the caliper retaining bolt.

The disc pads are held in the anchor bracket by two retaining clips and a "V" spring. The caliper must be removed to replace the disc pads.

During normal operation, hydraulic pressure from the master cylinder pushes the piston forward and applies pressure on the inboard brake pad. This pressure also causes the caliper to slide inward on the guide pins. As the brakes are applied, the square cut piston seal distorts. When the brake pedal is released, the square cut seal returns the piston to its normal position. If the piston moves no further than the square cut deformation limit, no self-adjustment takes place. If piston movement is greater than the deformation limit of the square cut seal, the piston and sleeve nut will travel on the threads of the spindle. This is because the loosened adjuster spring allows the sleeve nut to rotate. When the brake pedal is released, the piston returns the amount the square cut seal was deformed but it does not return to its original position. This is because the tightened adjuster spring does not allow the sleeve nut to rotate and travel on the thread. The piston can adjust outward from the caliper housing but it cannot move inward.

When the parking brake is applied inside the vehicle, the parking brake cable moves the caliper-mounted parking brake lever. This causes force to be applied to the connecting link, which pushes the piston against the inboard pad. The pressure of the piston against the inboard pad causes the caliper to slide on the guide pins, applying pressure to the outboard pad. As the piston moves outward in the caliper housing, it causes the square cut piston seal to distort. When the parking brake is released inside the vehicle, the square cut seal returns the piston to its normal position and releases the brakes.

ESCORT & TRACER

The rear disc brake system consists of a solid disc rotor and a single piston caliper. The brake pads are held in position between the caliper and the rotor by two guides, two shims and an "M" spring. It is not necessary to remove the caliper completely to replace the brake pads; the pads can be removed simply by pivoting the caliper on its mounting bracket.

The parking brake cable is attached to the caliper at the operating lever. When the parking brake is applied, the operating lever pushes the connecting link against the piston which forces application of the brake pads. When the parking brake is released, pressure against the piston is released and the brake pads return to their normal position.

CROWN VICTORIA, GRAND MARQUIS & TOWN CAR

The rear disc brake system uses a pin slider-type caliper assembly and a 11.4 inch cast iron rotor bolted to the rear axle shaft flange. The caliper has a phenolic piston with a seal and a press in type dust boot.

The inner pads are interchangeable left to right and use a three-finger clip fit inside the caliper piston. The outer pads are interchangeable left to right and use a dual-purpose clip which holds the brake pads on the caliper housing and also prevents caliper rattle.

The flanges on both inner and outer pads slide on a machined surfaces of the brake adapter.

TROUBLESHOOTING

BRAKE ROUGHNESS

The most common cause of brake chatter on disc brakes is a variation in thickness of the disc. If roughness or vibration is encountered during highway operation or if pedal pumping is experienced at low speeds, the disc may have excessive thickness variation. To check for this condition, measure the disc at 12 points with a micrometer at a radius approximately one inch from the edge of the disc. If thickness measurements vary by more than .0005 inch, the disc should be replaced with a new one.

Excessive lateral runout of braking disc may cause a "knocking back" of the pistons, possibly creating increased pedal travel and vibration when brakes are applied.

Before checking the runout, wheel bearings should be adjusted. The readjustment is very important and will be required at the completion of the test to prevent bearing failure. Be sure to make the adjustment as outlined in "Front Suspension" section.

BRAKE SYSTEM BLEED

Pressure bleeding is recommended for all hydraulic disc brake systems.

The disc brake hydraulic system can be bled manually or with pressure bleeding equipment. The brake pedal will require more pumping and frequent checking of fluid level in master cylinder during bleeding operation.

Do not use brake fluid drained from the hydraulic system when bleeding the brakes. Be sure the disc brake pistons are returned to their normal positions and the shoe and lining assemblies are properly seated. Before driving the vehicle, check brake operation to be sure a firm pedal has been obtained.

Pressure bleeding is recommended for all hydraulic brake systems.

The bleeding operation itself is fairly well standardized. The first step in all cases is to thoroughly clean the dirt from the filler cap before removing it from the master cylinder.

Pressure bleeding is fastest bleeding method because the master cylinder doesn't have to be refilled several times, and the job can be done by one person. To prevent air from the pressure tank getting into the lines, do not shake the tank while air is being added to the tank or after it has been pressurized. Set the tank in the required location, then bring the air hose to the tank. Do not move the tank during the bleeding operation. The tank should be kept at least one-third full.

On vehicles equipped with disc brakes and master cylinders without proportioners or pressure control valves located in the master cylinder outlet port, the brake metering valve or combination valve must be held in position using a suitable tool.

If air does get into the fluid, releasing the pressure will cause the bubbles to increase in size, rise to the top of the fluid, and escape. Pressure should not be greater than about 35 psi.

On vehicles equipped with plastic reservoirs, do not exceed 25 psi bleeding pressure.

When bleeding without pressure, open the bleed valve three-quarters of a turn, depress the pedal a full stroke, then allow the pedal to return slowly to its released position. After the pedal has been depressed to the end of its stroke, you should close the bleeder valve before the start of the return stroke. On models equipped with power brakes, first reduce the vacuum in the power unit to zero by pumping the brake pedal several times with the engine off before starting to bleed the system.

Pressure bleeding eliminates the need for pedal pumping.

Discard drained or bled brake fluid. Care should be taken not to spill brake fluid, since this can damage the vehicle's finish.

Flushing is essential if there is water, mineral oil or other contaminants in the lines, and whenever new parts are installed in the hydraulic system. Fluid contamination is usually indicated by swollen and deteriorated cups and other rubber parts.

Wheel cylinders on disc brakes are equipped with bleeder valves and are bled in the same manner as wheel cylinders for drum brakes.

Bleeding is necessary on all four wheels if air has entered the system because of low fluid level or the line or lines have been disconnected. If a line is disconnected at any one wheel cylinder, the cylinder only need be bled. On brake reline jobs, bleeding is advisable to remove any air or contaminants.

Master cylinders equipped with bleeder valves should be bled first before the wheel cylinders are bled. In all cases where a master cylinder has been overhauled, it must be bled. Where there is no bleeder valve, this can be done by leaving the lines loose, actuating the brake pedal to expel the air and then tightening the lines.

After overhauling a dual master cylinder used in conjunction with disc brakes, air may be trapped between the master cylinder pistons because there is only one residual pressure valve (check valve) used in these units. Bleed the cylinder before installing it on the vehicle.

SYSTEM PRIMING

When a new master cylinder is installed or the brake system partially or completely emptied, fluid may not flow from the bleeder screws during normal bleeding. It may be necessary to prime the system using the following procedure:

1. Using tubing wrench, remove brake lines from master cylinder.
2. Install short brake lines in master cylinder and position them back into the reservoir. Ensure short brake line ends are submerged in reservoir brake fluid.
3. Fill reservoir with recommended brake fluid, then cover master cylinder fluid reservoir with shop towel.
4. Pump brakes until clear, bubble-free fluid comes out of both brake lines. **If any brake fluid spills on paint, wash it off immediately with water.**
5. Remove short brake lines, then reinstall original brake lines.
6. Bleed each brake line at master cylinder using the following procedure:
   a. Have assistant pump brake pedal 10 times, then hold firm pressure on pedal.
   b. Open rearmost brake line fittings with tubing wrench until stream of brake fluid comes out. Have assistant maintain pressure on brake pedal until brake line fitting is tightened again.
   c. Repeat this operation until clear, bubble-free fluid comes out from around tube fitting.
   d. Repeat bleeding operation at front brake line fitting.
7. If any of brake lines or calipers have been removed, it may be helpful to prime system by gravity bleeding. Gravity bleed system after master cylinder is primed and bled. To prime system using gravity method, proceed as follows:
   a. Fill master cylinder with manufacturer recommended brake fluid or equivalent.
   b. Loosen both rear bleeder screws and leave open until clear brake fluid flows out. **Check reservoir fluid level frequently. Do not allow fluid level to drop below half way.**
   c. Tighten rear bleeder screws.
   d. Loosen bleeder screw on front caliper and leave open until clear fluid flows out. **Bleed front calipers one side at a time.**
8. After master cylinder has been primed, lines bled at master cylinder and brake system primed, resume normal brake system bleeding at each wheel.

WHEEL BLEEDING SEQUENCE

Rear Wheel Drive .... RR-LR-RF-LF
Front Wheel Drive .... RR-LF-LR-RF

INSPECTION

Remove wheels and inspect brake disc, caliper and linings. The wheel bearings should be inspected at this time and repacked if necessary. Do not get any grease on the linings.

If the caliper is cracked or fluid leakage through the casting is evident, it must be replaced as a unit.

Should it become necessary to remove the caliper when installing new parts, clean all parts in alcohol, then wipe dry using lint-free cloths. Using an air hose, blow out drilled passages and bores. Check dust boots for punctures or tears. If punctures or tears are evident, install new boots during assembly.

Inspect piston bores in both housings for scoring or pitting. Bores showing light scratches or corrosion can usually be cleaned with crocus cloth. However, bores with deep scratches or scoring may be honed, provided the diameter of the bore is not increased more than .002 inch. If the bore does not clean up within this specification, a new caliper housing should be installed (black stains on the bore walls are caused by piston seals and will do no harm).

When using a hone, be sure to install the hone baffle before honing the bore. The

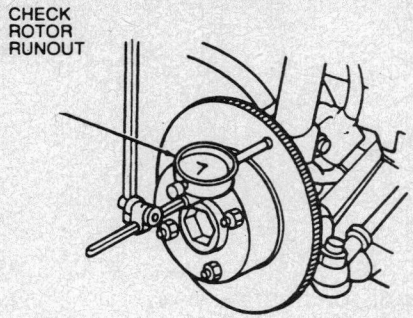

CHECK ROTOR RUNOUT

FM4079200056000X

Fig. 4   Rotor lateral runout check

baffle is used to protect the hone stones from damage. Use extreme care in cleaning the caliper after honing. Remove all dust and grit by flushing the caliper with alcohol. Wipe the caliper dry with a clean lint-free cloth, then repeat cleaning procedure.

BRAKE DISC SERVICE

Disc brake service is extremely critical due to the close tolerances required in machining the brake disc to ensure proper brake operation.

Maintaining close control of the shape of the rubbing surfaces is necessary to prevent brake roughness. In addition, the surface finish must be non-directional and maintained at a micro-inch finish. This is necessary to avoid pulls and erratic performance and promote long lining life and equal lining wear of both the left and right brakes.

Do not attempt to refinish the rubbing surfaces unless precision equipment, capable of measuring in micro inches (millionths of an inch) is available.

To check the disc lateral runout, mount a dial indicator on a convenient part (steering knuckle, tie rod, disc brake caliper housing) so the plunger of the dial indicator contacts the disc 1 inch from the outer edge, **Fig. 4.** If the total indicated runout exceeds specifications, install a new disc.

To check parallelism (thickness variation), mount dial indicators so the plunger contacts the rotor approximately 1 inch from the outer edge. If parallelism exceeds specifications, replace the rotor.

BRAKE PAD SERVICE

The hydraulic system must be depressurized before disconnecting any hydraulic lines or fittings. Depressurize the system by pumping the brake pedal a minimum of 25 times with the ignition switch in the OFF position.

After performing any service work, obtain a firm brake pedal before moving vehicle.

MARK VII
Replacement

To remove shoe and lining assemblies, remove caliper as described under "Caliper Service." It is not necessary to disconnect the brake hose. After removing the caliper, support it with a length of wire to avoid damaging the brake hose. To replace the shoe and lining assemblies, refer to "Caliper Service." Ensure proper parking brake adjustment as described under "Adjustments."

CONTINENTAL, COUGAR, MARK VIII & THUNDERBIRD
Removal

1. Raise and support rear of vehicle, then remove wheel and tire assembly.
2. Remove brake hose bracket to shock unit bracket screw.
3. Remove retaining clip, then disconnect parking brake cable from lever.
4. Using open end wrench to hold slider pin in position, remove upper pinch bolt, **Fig. 5.** Loosen, but do not lower slider pin pinch bolt.
5. Carefully rotate caliper away from rotor, then remover inner and outer brake pads and anti-rattle springs from anchor plate.

Installation

1. Using rear caliper piston adjuster tool No. T87P-2588-A, or equivalent, rotate caliper piston clockwise until fully seated, **Fig. 6.** Position one of two piston slots so it will engage nib on rear of brake pad, **Fig. 7.**
2. Position inner and outer brake pads on anchor plate, then install anti-rattle springs.
3. Carefully rotate caliper assembly over brake rotor. Ensure brake pads and anti-rattle springs are properly positioned, **Fig. 8.**
4. Apply suitable thread sealer and locking compound to pinch bolt threads. Install and tighten pinch bolts to specification, while holding slider pin in position with suitable open end wrench.
5. Position parking brake cable to lever, then install retaining clip.
6. Position brake hose and bracket to shock unit bracket and install attaching bolt.
7. Install wheel and tire assembly, then lower vehicle.
8. Cycle brake pedal several times to position brake pads and caliper piston.

PROBE
Removal

1. Remove approximately two-thirds of brake fluid from master cylinder.
2. Raise and support vehicle, then remove wheel and tire assembly.
3. Loosen parking brake cable housing adjusting nut, then remove cable housing from bracket and parking lever.

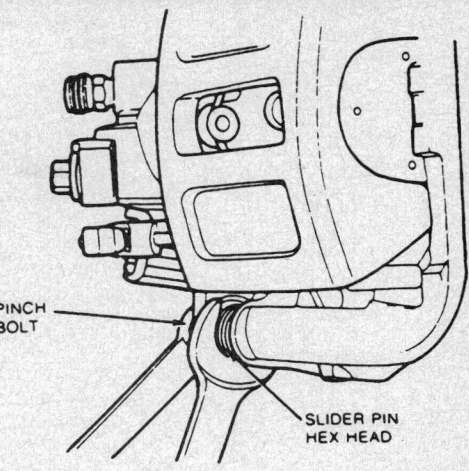

PINCH BOLT

SLIDER PIN HEX HEAD

FM4079100033000X

Fig. 5   Slider pin removal. Continental, Cougar, Mark VIII & Thunderbird

4. **On 1993-94 models,** turn brake adjuster screw counterclockwise with suitable Allen wrench to pull caliper piston inward. Turn brake adjuster screw until it stops.
5. **On all models,** remove lower caliper retaining bolt, then pivot caliper to clear brake pads. If necessary, pry caliper outward.
6. Remove caliper, then support caliper with wire from strut assembly.
7. Remove V-springs from disc pads, then the disc pads, anti-rattle shims and retaining clips. If disc pads and anti-rattle shims are to be reused, they must be installed in their original positions, **Fig. 9.**
8. If necessary, remove and resurface rotor at this time. **Rotor must be machined while it is bolted to hub. Rotor and hub are mounted as an assembly on rotor lathe to decrease possibility of rotor runout.**

Installation

1. Install disc pad retaining clips, then position anti-rattle shims on disc pads.
2. Position disc pads into caliper anchor bracket.
3. Install V-springs into disc pads.
4. Lubricate guide pin bushings with High Temperature Grease part No. D7AZ-19590-A or equivalent.
5. Install caliper on guide pin, then pivot caliper over brake disc pads.
6. Install caliper retaining bolt, then tighten to specifications.
7. Bleed brake system.
8. Position parking brake cable into parking brake lever and bracket.
9. Adjust parking brake cable so there is no clearance between cable end and parking brake lever.
10. Tighten parking brake cable locknut to 14-21 ft. lbs.
11. Install wheel and tire assembly.

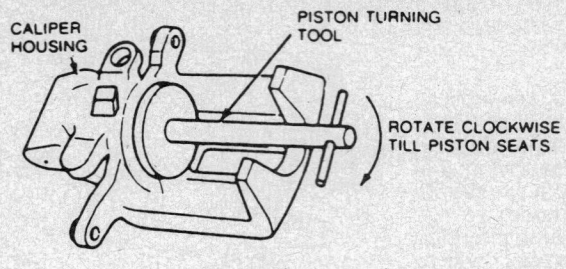

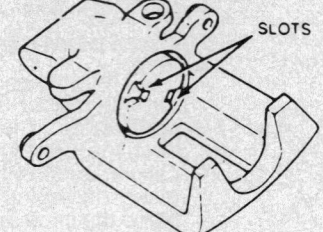

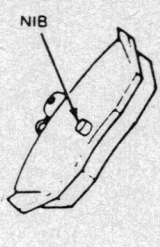

FM4079100036000X

Fig. 7   Caliper piston to brake pad nib positioning. Continental, Cougar, Mark VIII & Thunderbird

FM4079100035000X

Fig. 6   Caliper pin seating. Continental, Cougar, Mark VIII & Thunderbird

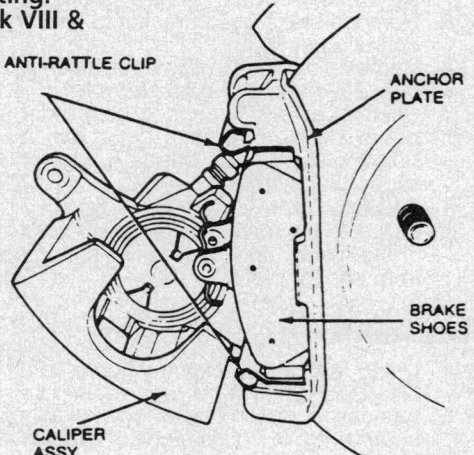

FM4079100034000X

Fig. 8   Anti-rattle clip positioning. Continental, Cougar, Mark VIII & Thunderbird

CAPRI
Replacement

1. Remove approximately 2/3 of brake fluid from master cylinder.
2. Raise and support vehicle.
3. Remove wheel and tire assembly.
4. Using needle nose pliers, remove parking brake return springs at back of caliper, **Fig. 10.**
5. Loosen parking brake cable housing adjusting nut, then remove cable housing from bracket on rear lower control arm.
6. Loosen attaching bolt connecting parking brake cable bracket to rear caliper.
7. Remove parking brake cable from rear caliper, then loosen lower caliper bolt.
8. Pivot caliper upward on upper caliper guide pin.
9. Remove disc pad retaining spring, then the disc pad and shims.
10. Remove anchor plate clips from caliper anchor plate.
11. Remove and resurface rotor if necessary.
12. Reverse procedure to install.

ESCORT & TRACER
Replacement

1. Raise and support vehicle, then remove rear wheel assembly.
2. If necessary, remove screw plug, then turn adjustment gear counterclockwise with Allen wrench to pull the piston fully inward, **Fig. 11.**
3. Remove caliper lower lock bolt.
4. Using screwdriver, pivot caliper on its mounting bracket to access brake pads, **Fig. 12. If upper lock bolt requires lubrication or service, remove and suspend caliper using wire or equivalent.**
5. Reverse procedure to install, noting the following:
   a. Lubricate caliper lock bolt, then tighten to specifications.
   b. If necessary, turn adjustment gear

clockwise with Allen wrench until brake pads just touch rotor, then loosen gear 1/3 turn.
   c. Install screw plug, then tighten to specifications.

SABLE & TAURUS
Removal

1. Raise and support vehicle, then remove wheel and tire assembly.
2. Remove brake hose bracket to shock absorber bracket screw.
3. Remove retaining clip from parking brake cable at caliper, then the cable end from parking brake lever.
4. Hold slider pin hex heads with open end wrench, then remove upper caliper pinch bolt.
5. Rotate caliper away from rotor, then remove inner and outer brake pads.

Installation

1. Using brake piston turning tool No. T87P-2588-A, or equivalent, rotate piston clockwise until fully seated. **Ensure one of two slots in piston face is positioned so it will engage nub on brake pad.**
2. Install inner and outer brake pads in anchor plate.

3. Rotate caliper assembly over rotor into position on anchor plate. **Ensure brake pads are installed properly.**
4. Remove residue from upper pinch bolt threads, then apply one drop of Threadlock and Sealer part No. EOAZ-19554-BA or equivalent.
5. Install and tighten pinch bolts to specifications while holding slider pins with open end wrench.
6. Attach cable end to parking brake lever, then install cable clip on caliper assembly.
7. Position brake flex hose and bracket assembly to shock absorber bracket, then install bolt. Tighten bolt to specifications.
8. Install wheel and tire assembly. Tighten wheel lug nuts to specifications.

CROWN VICTORIA, GRAND MARQUIS & TOWN CAR
Replacement

1. Remove master cylinder cap and check fluid level in reservoir. Remove brake fluid until reservoir is half full. Discard removed fluid.
2. Raise and support vehicle, then remove wheel and tire assembly.
3. Remove caliper as previously described.
4. Remove inner and outer brake linings.
5. Inspect both rotor braking surfaces. Minor scoring or buildup of lining material does not require machining or replacement of the rotor assembly. Hand sand glaze from both rotor braking surfaces using garnet paper 100-A (medium grit) or aluminum oxide 150-J (medium).
6. Suspend caliper inside fender housing with wire. Use care not to damage caliper or stretch brake hose.
7. **Use care to prevent damaging plastic piston. Metal or sharp objects cannot come in direct contact with piston surface or damage will result.** Using a four-inch C-clamp and wood block approximately 2 3/4 inch x 1 inch and at least 3/4 inch thick, seat caliper piston in piston bore. **This procedure must be done to provide clearance for caliper assembly to fit over rotor.**
8. Remove all rust buildup from inside of caliper legs (outer shoe contact area).
9. Install inner shoe and lining assembly in caliper piston(s). Do not bend shoe

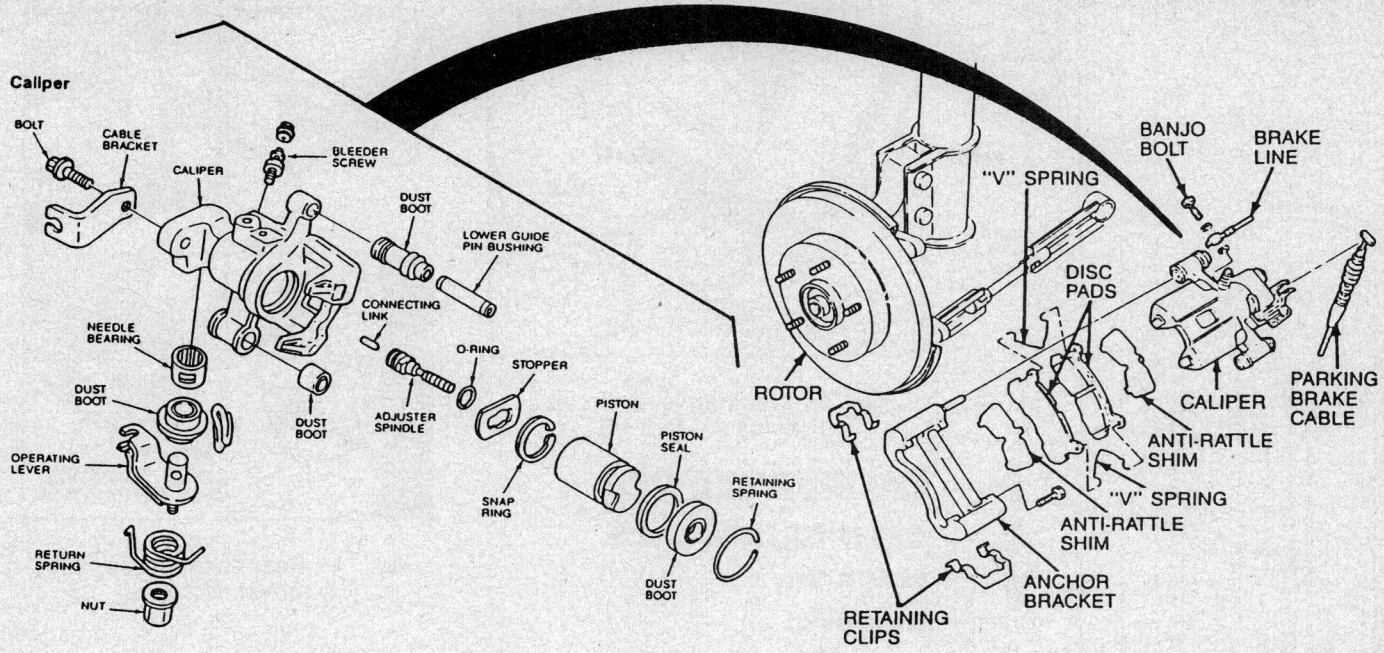

Fig. 9   Exploded view of caliper assembly. Probe

FM4079100037000X

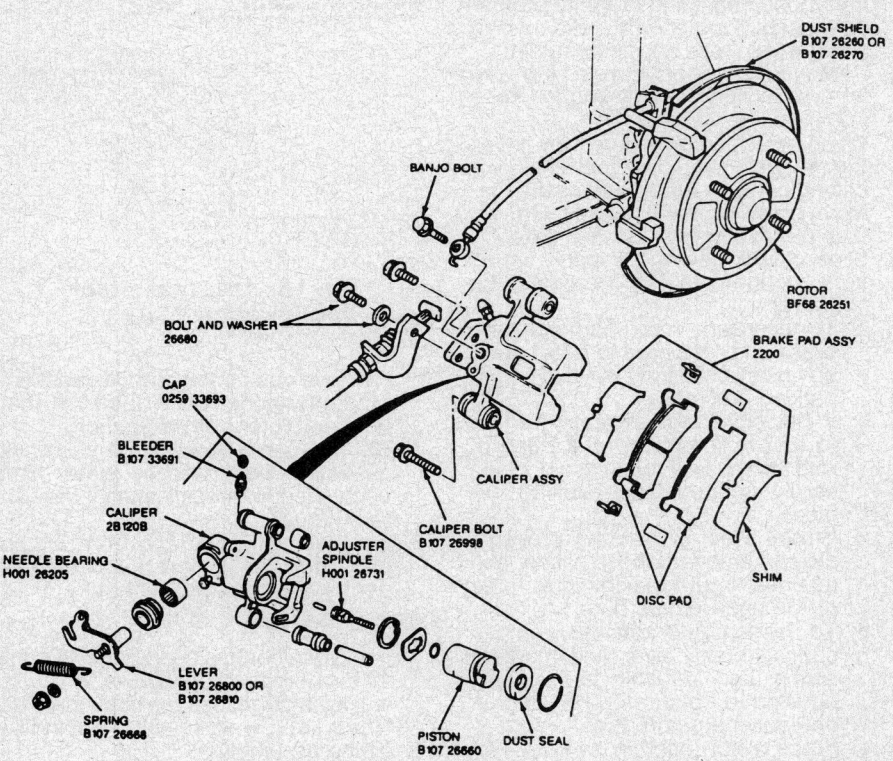

Fig. 10   Exploded view of rear disc brake assembly. Capri

FM4079100038000X

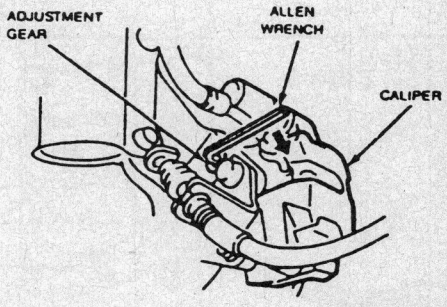

FM4079100042000X

Fig. 11   Rear disc brake adjustment gear location. Escort & Tracer

2. Remove brake hose bracket to shock absorber bracket screw.
3. Remove parking brake rear cable and conduit clip at rear disc brake caliper, then the parking brake rear cable and conduit end from rear parking brake cable.
4. Hold disc brake caliper locating pin hex-heads with open-end wrench, then remove upper rear brake pin retainer.
5. Rotate brake caliper away from rotor.
6. Remove inner and outer rear brake shoe and lining and anti-rattle clip from rear disc support bracket.

Installation

1. Ensure one of two slots in rear disc brake piston face is positioned so it will engage nib on rear brake shoe and lining.
2. Using rear caliper piston adjuster tool No. T87P-2588-A, or equivalent, rotate rear disc brake piston and adjuster clockwise until it is fully seated.
3. Insert anti-rattle clips, then install in-

clips during installation in piston or distortion and rattles can occur.
10. Install outer pad in caliper assembly. Ensure clips are correctly seated.
11. Install caliper assembly as previously outlined.

MUSTANG
Removal

1. Raise and support vehicle, then remove wheel and tire assembly.

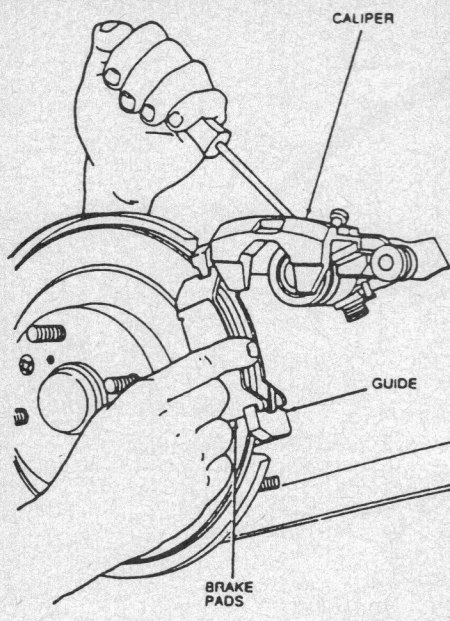

Fig. 12 Rear disc brake pad removal. Escort & Tracer

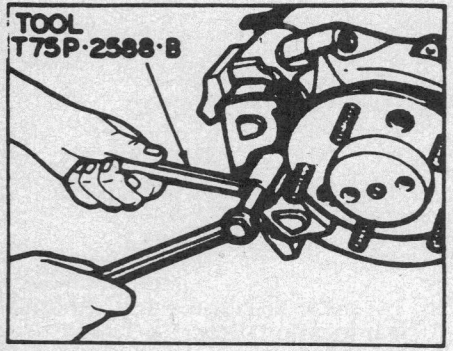

Fig. 15 Piston depth adjustment for lining installation

ner and outer rear brake shoes and linings on rear disc support bracket.

4. Rotate brake caliper assembly over rotor into position on rear disc brake support bracket. Ensure brake shoes and linings and anti-rattle clips are installed correctly.
5. Apply suitable sealer to upper brake pin retainer threads, then install rear brake pin retainer. Tighten brake pin retainer to specifications while holding caliper locating pins with open-end wrench.
6. Attach parking brake rear cable and conduit end to rear parking brake cable, then install cable clip on caliper assembly. Tighten screw to specifications.
7. Install wheel and tire assembly. Tighten wheel hub bolt nuts to specification.

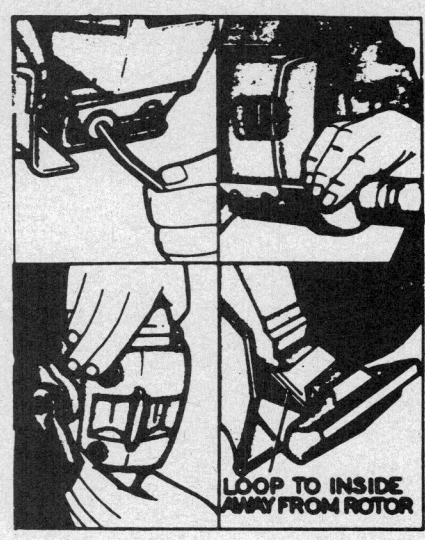

Fig. 13 Parking lever & cable removal. Mark VII

CALIPER SERVICE

CALIPER, REPLACE

MARK VII

Removal

1. Raise and support vehicle, then remove tire and wheel assemblies.
2. Disconnect fitting on rear brake tube from hose end fitting at frame mounted bracket. Plug end of brake tube to prevent fluid loss and entry of dirt.
3. Remove horse shoe retaining clip from hose fitting and disengage hose from bracket.
4. Disconnect parking cable from lever, **Fig. 13**, using care to avoid kinking or cutting cable or return spring, then remove screw from caliper key, **Fig. 14**, then remove caliper locating pins.
5. Slide caliper key and support spring from anchor plate, **Fig. 14**, noting the following:
   a. If necessary, use hammer and brass drift. Use care to avoid damaging key on sliding ways or hitting parking brake lever.
   b. If caliper cannot be removed due to rust build-up on outer edge of rotor, scrape off loose scale, being careful not to damage braking surfaces.
   c. If rotor wear or scoring prevents caliper removal, loosen caliper end retainer 1/2 turn maximum to force piston back into its bore.
   d. To loosen end retainer, remove parking brake lever and mark or scribe end retainer and caliper housing to be sure end retainer is not loosened more than 1/2 turn.
   e. Force piston back in its bore, Fig. 15, and move caliper back and forth to center rotor and remove caliper. **If retainer must be loosened more than 1/2 turn, use caution, as seal between thrust screw and housing may break, allowing brake fluid to enter parking brake mechanism chamber. In this case, end retainer must be removed and internal parts cleaned and lubricated.**

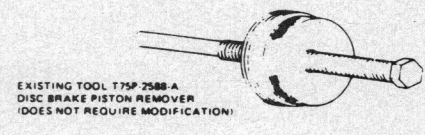

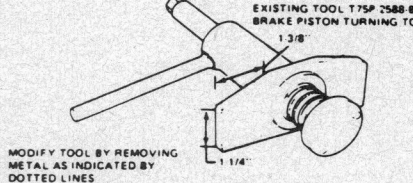

Fig. 14 Rear caliper assembly removal. Mark VII

EXISTING TOOL T75P-2588-A
DISC BRAKE PISTON REMOVER
(DOES NOT REQUIRE MODIFICATION)

EXISTING TOOL T75P-2588-B
BRAKE PISTON TURNING TOOL
1 3/8

MODIFY TOOL BY REMOVING METAL AS INDICATED BY DOTTED LINES

Fig. 16 Disc brake tool modification. Mark VII

6. Remove outer shoe and lining assembly from anchor plate, then the rotor nuts and rotor from axle shaft.
7. Remove inner brake shoe and lining assembly from anchor plate. Mark each shoe for identification if they are to be reused.
8. Remove anti-rattle clip from anchor plate, then the flexible hose from caliper by removing hollow bolt.

Installation

1. If end retainer has been loosened only 1/2 turn, proceed as follows:
   a. Reinstall caliper in anchor plate using key. Do not install shoe and lining assembly.
   b. Tighten end retainer to specification, then install parking brake actuating lever on its keyed spline. Lever arm must point down and rearward so parking brake cable will pass freely under axle.
   c. Tighten screw to specification. **Parking brake lever must rotate freely after tightening retainer screw.**
2. Remove caliper from anchor plate. If new shoe and lining assemblies are to

be installed, piston must be bottomed in caliper bore using tool No. T75P-2588-B, or equivalent, to provide clearance.

3. Remove rotor and install caliper, without lining and shoe assemblies, in anchor plate using key only.
4. Install tool and, while holding shaft, rotate tool handle counterclockwise until tool seats firmly against piston, **Fig. 15.**
5. Loosen handle about 1/4 turn and, while holding handle, rotate tool shaft clockwise until piston is fully bottomed in bore (piston will continue to turn even after it is bottomed). Turn tool handle until there is no further inward movement of piston and there is firm seating force.
6. Remove caliper from mounting plate and reinstall rotor. For use on some vehicles, tool No. T75P-2588-B, or equivalent, must be slightly modified, Fig. 16.
7. Ensure brake shoe anti-rattle clip is in place in lower inner brake shoe support on anchor plate with loop of clip toward inside of anchor plate, **Fig. 14.**
8. Position inner brake shoe and lining assembly on anchor plate, then install rotor and two nuts.
9. Install outer brake shoe with lower flange ends against caliper abutments and brake shoe upper flanges over shoulders on caliper legs. Shoe upper flanges should fit tightly against machined shoulder surfaces. **If old brake shoe and lining assemblies are reused, ensure shoes are installed in their original positions, as marked during removal.**
10. Lubricate caliper and anchor sliding ways with D7AE-019590 grease, using care to prevent lubricant from getting on braking surfaces.
11. Position caliper housing lower V-groove on anchor plate lower abutment surfaces.
12. Rotate caliper until it is completely over rotor, being careful not to damage piston dust boot, then pull caliper outboard until inner shoe and lining is firmly seated against rotor.
13. Measure clearance between outer lining and rotor. Clearance must be between 1/32 and 3/32 inch. If it is greater, remove caliper and move piston outward to narrow gap. Follow procedure in steps 2 through 6 and note that 1/4 turn of shaft counterclockwise moves piston about 1/16 inch. **A clearance greater than specified limit may allow adjuster to be pulled out of piston when service brake is applied, causing parking brake to fail to adjust. This would require replacement of piston/adjuster assembly.**
14. While holding caliper against anchor plate upper abutment surfaces, center caliper over lower anchor plate abutment, then position caliper support spring and key in slot and slide them into opening between lower end of caliper and lower anchor plate abutment until key semi-circular slot is centered over retaining screw

threaded hole in anchor plate.
15. Install key retaining screw and tighten to specification, then reinstall brake hose on caliper.
16. Place new gasket on each side of the fitting outlet, then install bolt through washers and fitting. Tighten to specification.
17. Lubricate pins and inside of insulator with D7AZ-19A331-A or equivalent silicone grease and add one drop of Loctite EOAC-19554-A or equivalent to locating pin threads.
18. Install locating pins through caliper insulators and into anchor plate. Tighten to specification.
19. Connect parking brake lever to lever on caliper.
20. Bleed brake system as described under "Brake System Bleed."
21. With engine running, pump brake pedal lightly about 40 times, allowing one second between pedal applications. Alternatively, with engine off, pump brake pedal lightly about 10 times to discharge accumulator, then pump brake pedal firmly about 30 times.
22. Check parking brake for excessive travel or very light effort. If found, repeat pumping brake pedal and, if necessary, check parking brake cable tension.
23. Install wheel and tighten nuts to specification. **Before moving vehicle, make certain a firm brake pedal has been obtained.**

CONTINENTAL, COUGAR, MARK VIII & THUNDERBIRD

Removal

1. Raise and support rear of vehicle, then remove wheel and tire assembly.
2. Disconnect brake hose from caliper assembly.
3. Remove retaining clip, then disconnect parking brake cable from lever arm.
4. Using open end wrench to hold slider pin in position, remove pinch bolts, **Fig. 5.**
5. Lift caliper assembly from anchor plate, then remove slider pins and boots.

Installation

1. Apply suitable silicone dielectric compound to slider pins and inside of boots.
2. Place slider pins and boots on anchor plate, then position caliper assembly on anchor plate. Check to be sure brake pads and anti-rattle springs are properly positioned, **Fig. 8.**
3. Apply suitable sealer and thread locking compound to pinch bolt threads, then install pinch bolts.
4. Using open end wrench to hold slider pin in position, tighten pinch bolts to specification.
5. Attach parking brake cable to lever arm, then install retaining clip.
6. Using replacement washers, connect brake hose to caliper. Tighten retaining bolt to specifications.
7. Bleed brake system as described un-

der "Brake System Bleed," then install wheel and tire assembly.
8. Cycle brake pedal several times to position brake pads and caliper piston.

PROBE

Removal

1. Raise and support vehicle, then remove wheel and tire assembly.
2. Loosen parking brake cable housing adjustment nut, then remove cable housing from bracket and parking brake lever.
3. Remove banjo bolt attaching brake flex hose to caliper.
4. Remove two copper washers from banjo fitting, then discard washers.
5. Remove lower caliper retaining bolt.
6. Pivot caliper off disc pads, then slide caliper off guide pin.

Installation

1. Lubricate guide pin bushings with High Temperature Grease part No. D7AZ-19590-A or equivalent.
2. Install caliper onto guide pin, then pivot caliper over disc pads.
3. Install lower caliper retaining bolt, then tighten bolt to specifications.
4. Install two new copper washers and banjo bolt on brake flex hose banjo fitting.
5. Position flex hose on caliper. Tighten banjo bolt to specifications.
6. Position parking brake cable into parking brake lever and bracket.
7. Adjust parking brake cable so there is no clearance between cable end and parking brake lever.
8. Tighten parking brake cable locknut to specifications.
9. Install wheel and tire assembly.

CAPRI

1. Raise and support vehicle, then remove wheel and tire assembly.
2. Remove brake pads as described under "Brake Pad Service."
3. Remove clip brake flex hose to strut assembly clip.
4. Remove brake flex hose to caliper assembly banjo bolt.
5. Remove two copper washers sealing flex hose banjo fitting, then discard washers.
6. Remove lower caliper retaining bolt.
7. Using cold chisel, remove upper caliper guide pin dust cap. This will allow access to Allen head on guide pin.
8. Using Allen wrench, loosen and remove upper caliper guide pin.
9. Lift caliper off rotor.
10. Remove guide pin and guide pin bushing dust boots from caliper assembly.
11. Lubricate guide pin and guide pin bushing with Disc Brake Caliper Slide Grease part No. D7AZ-19590-A or equivalent.
12. Install guide pin and guide pin bushing dust boots.
13. Install brake pads and shims as described under
14. Position caliper over rotor. **To provide necessary clearance, it may**

be necessary to rotate caliper piston.

15. Tighten upper guide pin, then install dust cap with plastic hammer.
16. Install lower caliper retaining bolt through lower caliper guide pin bushing. Tighten lower bolt to specifications.
17. Install flex hose banjo bolt with two new copper washers onto brake flex hose.
18. Position flex hose on caliper. Tighten banjo bolt to specifications.
19. Bleed braking system as described under "Brake System Bleed," then install wheel and tire assembly.

ESCORT & TRACER

Removal

1. Remove wheel and tire assembly, then the brake pads as described under "Brake Pad Service."
2. Remove brake flex hose clip from strut assembly bracket.
3. Remove brake flex hose to caliper banjo bolt, **Fig. 17.**
4. Remove two copper washers sealing flex hose banjo fitting, then discard washers.
5. Remove lower caliper bolt.
6. Using cold chisel, remove upper caliper guide pin dust cap. This will give access to Allen head guide pin.
7. Using Allen wrench, loosen and remove upper caliper guide pin.
8. Lift caliper off rotor.

Installation

Before installation, remove upper and lower guide pin bushings and lubricate with high temperature grease D7AZ-19590-A or equivalent.

1. Install brake pads and shims as described under "Brake Pad Service."
2. Position caliper over rotor, then install caliper retaining bolts and tighten to specification.
3. Install two new copper washers and banjo bolt on flex hose banjo fitting.
4. Position flex hose on caliper and install banjo bolt. Tighten bolt to specification.
5. Bleed brake system as described under "Brake System Bleed," then install wheel and tire assembly.

SABLE & TAURUS

Removal

Handle caliper assembly and rotor with care to avoid nicking, scratching or contaminating the brake pads or deforming the rotor.

After any service, pump the brake pedal to obtain a firm brake pedal before moving the vehicle. Riding the brake pedal (common with left foot application) must be avoided while driving.

1. Raise and support vehicle, then remove wheel and tire assembly.
2. Remove brake flex hose from caliper assembly.
3. Remove retaining clip from parking brake at caliper, then disengage parking brake cable end from lever arm, **Fig. 18.**

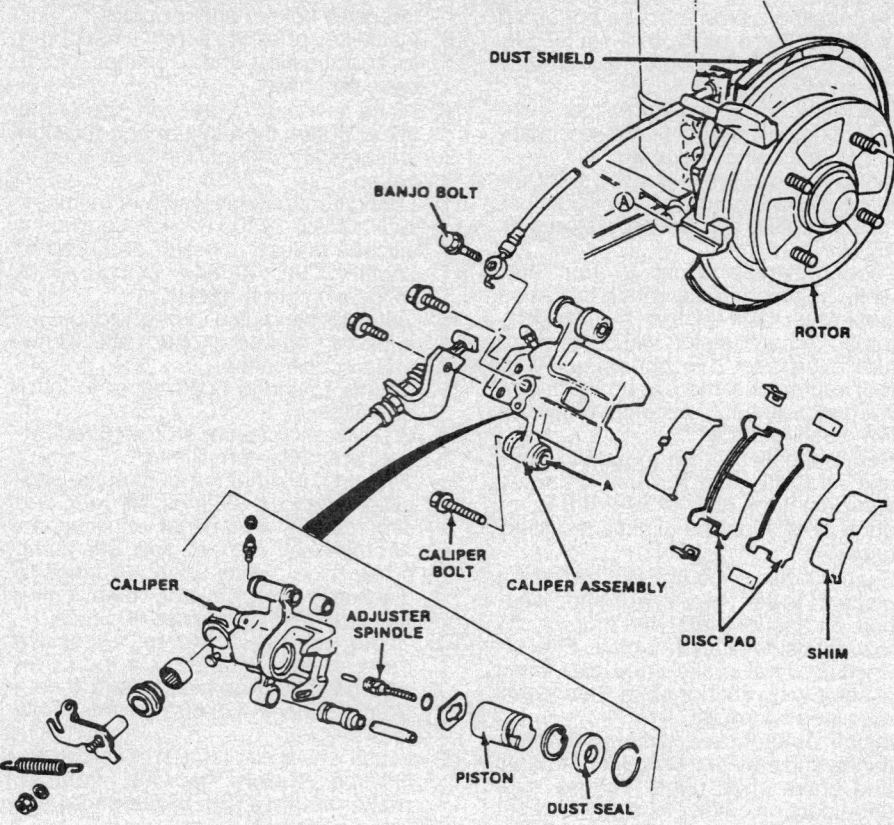

4. Hold slider pin hex-heads with open end wrench, then remove pinch bolts.
5. Lift caliper assembly away from anchor plate.
6. Remove slider pins and boots from anchor plate.

Installation

1. Apply Silicone Dielectric Compound part No. D7AZ-19A331-A or equivalent to inside of slider pin boots and to slider pins.
2. Position slider pins and boots in anchor plate.
3. Position caliper assembly on anchor plate. **Ensure brake pads are installed properly.**
4. Remove residue from pinch bolt threads, then apply one drop of Threadlock and Sealer part No. EOAZ-19554-BA or equivalent.
5. Install pinch bolts, then tighten bolts to specifications, while holding slider pins with open end wrench.
6. Attach cable end to parking brake lever, then install cable retaining clip on caliper assembly.
7. Using new copper washers, connect brake flex hose to caliper. Tighten banjo bolt to specifications.
8. Bleed brake system as described under "Brake System Bleed," then install wheel and tire assembly.
9. Tighten wheel lug nuts to specifications.

CROWN VICTORIA, GRAND MARQUIS & TOWN CAR

Visually check caliper. If the caliper housing is leaking, it should be replaced. If a seal is leaking, the caliper must be disassembled and new seals and dust boot installed. If a piston is seized in the bore, replace caliper. Care must be taken when removing plastic piston.

Removal

1. Raise and support vehicle, then remove wheel and tire assembly.
2. Remove flexible brake hose retaining bolt from caliper, then plug hose and caliper fitting.
3. Using Torx drive bit tool No. D79P-2100-T40, or equivalent, remove caliper locating pins.
4. Lift caliper off rotor and anchor plate using rotating motion. **Do not pry directly against plastic piston or damage to piston will result.**

Installation

1. Retract piston fully into piston bore and position caliper assembly above rotor with anti-rattle spring located on lower adapter support arm.
2. Install caliper over rotor with rotating motion. Ensure inner shoe is correctly positioned.
3. Install caliper locating pins. **Caliper locating pins must be inserted and started by hand.**
4. Tighten locating pins to specifications.
5. Remove plugs from caliper fittings,

Fig. 17 Exploded view of caliper assembly. Escort & Tracer

FM40791000044000X

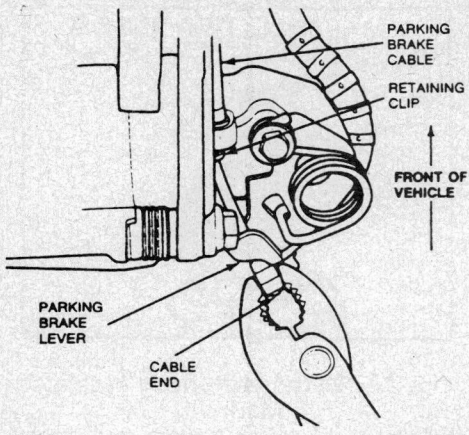

Fig. 18 Parking brake retaining clip location. Sable & Taurus

then install flexible brake hose on caliper with new gasket on each side of fitting outlet.

6. Insert retaining bolt through washers and fittings. Tighten bolt to specifications.
7. Bleed brake system as described under "Brake System Bleed."
8. Pump brake pedal to position brake linings prior to moving vehicle.

MUSTANG

Removal

1. Raise and support vehicle, then remove wheel and tire assembly.
2. Remove rear wheel brake hose from rear disc brake caliper assembly.
3. Remove retaining clip from parking brake rear cable and conduit at rear disc brake caliper.
4. Disengage parking brake rear cable and conduit end from rear parking brake cable.
5. Hold disc brake caliper locating pin hex-heads with open end wrench and remove rear brake pin retainers.
6. Lift rear disc brake caliper assembly away from rear disc support bracket. Do not pinch or damage boot material.
7. Remove disc brake caliper locating pins and boots from rear disc support bracket.

Installation

1. Apply suitable silicone dielectric compound to inside of locating pin boots and to disc brake caliper locating pins.
2. Position disc brake caliper locating pins and boots in rear disc support bracket. Position rear disc brake caliper assembly and rear disc support bracket. Ensure rear brake shoes and linings and disc brake pad anti-rattle clips are installed correctly.
3. Apply a drop of Threadlock and Sealer part No. E01Z-19554-AA or equivalent, to rear brake pin retainer threads.
4. Install pinch bolts. Tighten to specifications while holding disc brake caliper locating pins with open-end wrench.
5. Attach parking brake rear cable and conduit end to rear parking brake ca-

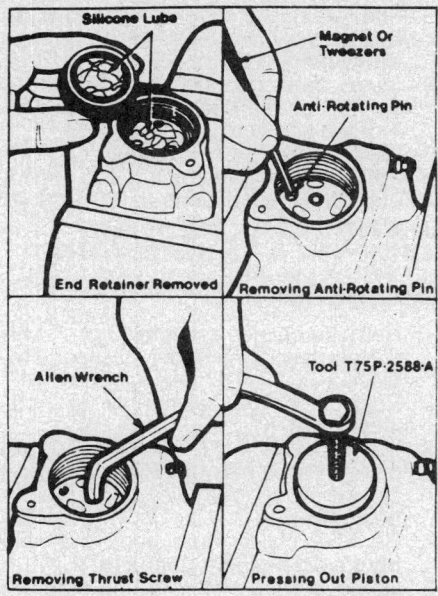

Fig. 19 Rear disc brake caliper disassembly. Mark VII

ble.
6. Install cable retaining clip on rear disc brake caliper assembly. Tighten screw to specification.
7. Using new washers, connect rear wheel brake hose to rear disc brake caliper. Tighten bolt to specification.
8. Bleed brake system as described under "Brake System Bleed."
9. Install wheel and tire assembly. Tighten wheel hub bolt nuts to specifications.

CALIPER OVERHAUL

MARK VII

Disassemble

1. Remove caliper assembly as described previously.
2. Remove caliper end retainer, operating shaft, thrust bearing and balls, Fig. 1.
3. Remove thrust screw anti-rotation pin with magnet or tweezers. If pin cannot be removed with magnet or tweezers, proceed with the following procedure:
   a. With tool No. T75P-2588B, or equivalent, force piston approximately one inch from caliper bore.
   b. Push piston back into caliper housing with tool, then with tool in position, hold tool shaft in place and rotate handle counterclockwise until thrust screw clears anti-rotation pin. Remove thrust screw and anti-rotation pin.
4. Remove thrust screw by rotating with 1/4 inch Allen wrench.
5. Install tool No. T75P-2588-A, or equivalent, through back of caliper housing and remove piston assembly, Fig. 19. Use care not to damage polished surface in thrust screw bore and do not attempt to remove or press adjuster can, as it is press fit in piston.

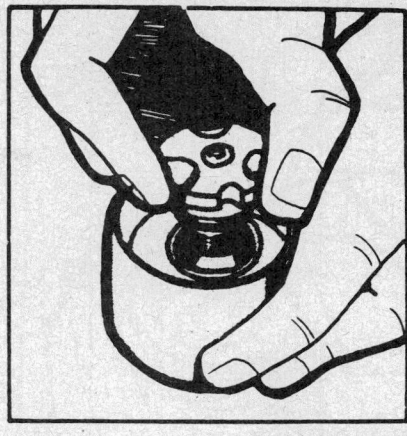

Fig. 20 Parking brake adjuster operation check. Mark VII

6. Remove and discard piston seal, boot, thrust O-ring seal, end retainer, O-ring and end retainer lip seal.

Cleaning & Inspection

1. Clean all metal parts with alcohol, then, using clean, dry compressed air, blow out and dry all grooves and passages making sure caliper bore and component parts are free of any foreign material.
2. Inspect caliper bore for damage or excessive wear. Thrust screw must be smooth and free of pits. If piston is pitted, scored or chrome plating is worn, replace piston and adjuster assembly.
3. Adjuster can must be bottomed in piston to be properly seated and provide consistent brake operation. If adjuster can is loose, appears high in piston, is damaged, or if brake adjustment is usually too tight, too loose or not functioning, replace piston/adjuster assembly. Check adjuster operation by assembling thrust screw into piston/adjuster assembly, then pull two parts apart about 1/4 inch and release them, Fig. 20. When pulling on two parts, brass drive ring must remain stationary, causing nut to rotate. When releasing two parts, nut must remain stationary and drive ring must rotate. If action does not follow this pattern, replace piston/adjuster assembly.
4. Inspect ball pockets, threads, grooves, bearing surfaces of thrust screw, operating shaft, balls and anti-rotation pin for wear, brinnelling or pitting. Replace operating shaft, balls, thrust screw and anti-rotation pin if any of these parts are worn or damaged. Polished appearance on ball paths is acceptable if there is no sign of wear into surface.
5. Inspect thrust bearing for corrosion, pitting or wear and replace as necessary.
6. Inspect end plug bearing surface for wear or brinelling and replace as necessary. A polished appearance on bearing surface is acceptable if there is no sign of wear into surface.

Fig. 21 Piston/adjuster assembly filling. Mark VII

7. Inspect operating lever for damage and replace as necessary.

Assemble

1. Coat new caliper piston seal with clean brake fluid and install it in caliper making certain seal is not twisted and is fully seated in groove.
2. Install new dust boot by seating flange squarely in outer groove of caliper bore, then coat piston/adjuster assembly with clean brake fluid and install it in caliper bore. Spread dust boot over piston as it is installed and seat dust boot in piston groove.
3. Install caliper in vise, **Fig. 21**, and fill piston/adjuster assembly with clean brake fluid.
4. Coat new thrust screw O-ring with clean brake fluid and install it in thrust screw groove.
5. Install thrust screw into piston adjuster assembly until top surface of thrust screw is flush with bottom of threaded bore, being careful to avoid cutting O-ring seal. Index notches on thrust screw and caliper housing and install anti-rotation pin. **Thrust screw and operating shafts are not interchangeable from side to side since ramp direction in ball pockets are different. The pocket surfaces of operating shaft and thrust screws are stamped "R" (Right) and "L" (Left).**
6. Place ball in each of three pockets of thrust screw and apply liberal amount of silicone grease M1C-169-A on parking brake components, then install operating shaft on balls.
7. Coat thrust bearing with silicone grease and install it on operating shaft, then install a new lip seal and O-ring on end retainer.
8. Lightly coat O-ring seal and lip seal with silicone grease and install end retainer in caliper. Firmly hold operating shaft against internal mechanism while installing end retainer to prevent misalignment of balls. If lip seal moves out of position, reseat seal. Tighten

end retainer to specification. **Parking brake lever must rotate freely after tightening.**

9. Install parking brake lever on keyed spline facing down and rearward. Tighten screw to specification.
10. Bottom piston using tool No. T75P-2588-B, or equivalent, **Fig. 22**, and install caliper as described previously.

CONTINENTAL, COUGAR, MARK VIII & THUNDERBIRD

Disassemble

1. Remove caliper assembly from vehicle as described under "Caliper, Replace."
2. Position caliper assembly in soft-jawed vise.
3. Using tool No. T75P-2588-B, or equivalent, rotate caliper piston counterclockwise to remove from caliper bore, **Fig. 6**.
4. Remove piston dust boot and seal from caliper piston bore, **Fig. 2**.
5. Remove snap ring retaining pushrod to caliper. Use care when removing, as snap ring and spring cover are under spring load.
6. Remove spring cover, spring, washer, key plate and pushrod and strut pin from caliper.
7. Remove O-ring from pushrod.
8. Remove parking brake lever return spring, then the brake lever stop bolt and pull lever from caliper.

Cleaning & Inspection

1. Clean all metal components with isopropyl alcohol.
2. Use compressed air to clean out passages and grooves.
3. Inspect caliper bore for damage and excessive wear.
4. Inspect caliper piston for pitting, scoring or worn plating and replace as necessary.

Assemble

1. Apply light coating of silicone dielectric compound to parking brake lever bore and parking brake lever seal, then position seal into caliper bore, **Fig. 2**.
2. Apply silicone dielectric compound to parking brake lever shaft, then insert shaft into caliper housing bore.
3. Install O-ring into groove on pushrod, then apply silicone dielectric compound to recesses in pushrod.
4. Place strut pin into caliper housing and into recess of parking brake lever shaft.
5. Position pushrod into caliper housing bore, ensuring strut pin is properly located between shaft recesses and recess at end of pushrod.
6. Position key plate over pushrod, so washer nib is located in hole in caliper housing.
7. Install flat washer, spring and spring cage into caliper bore.
8. Install snap ring using rear caliper spring compressor set tool No. T87P-2588-P, or equivalent. Ensure snap ring is properly seated in recess.

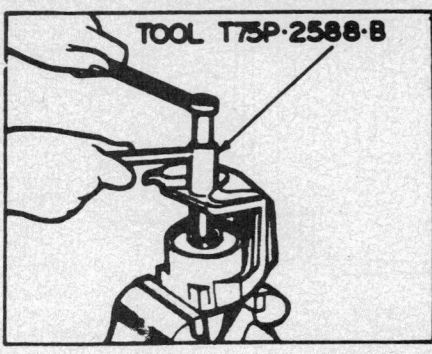

TOOL T75P·2588·B

Fig. 22 Piston bottoming in caliper. Mark VII

9. Lubricate replacement piston seal with clean brake fluid, then install seal into caliper bore groove.
10. Lubricate piston and dust boot with clean brake fluid, then install dust boot into caliper bore.
11. Position piston into dust boot, seating dust boot in piston groove.
12. Using tool No. rear caliper spring compressor set tool No. T75P-2588-B, or equivalent, turn piston in clockwise direction until piston is fully seated in caliper bore, **Fig. 6**.
13. Position one of two slots on piston so it will engage nib on rear of disc pad when caliper is installed, **Fig. 7**.
14. Install caliper assembly as described under "Caliper, Replace."

PROBE
Disassemble

1. Remove caliper as previously described under "Caliper, Replace."
2. Open bleeder screw and drain brake fluid from caliper through brake flex hose fitting. After draining fluid, close bleeder screw.
3. Remove caliper guide bushing and dust boots, **Fig. 9**.
4. Pry retaining spring off dust boot with screwdriver, then remove piston.
5. remove dust boot and discard boot.
6. Remove piston seal from caliper and discard. **Use plastic or wooden pick to remove seal. Metal tool can scratch or nick seal groove resulting in possible seal leak.**
7. Remove stopper snap ring.
8. Remove adjusting spindle, stopper and connecting link. Separate adjuster spindle and stopper.
9. Remove O-ring from adjuster spindle, then discard O-ring.
10. Remove parking brake return spring, then operating lever nut and lockwasher.
11. Mark relationship between operating lever and shaft, then remove operating lever from shaft.
12. Remove seal from caliper housing.
13. Remove the shaft from caliper housing, then the needle bearings.

Inspection

1. Inspect caliper bore, piston seal groove and piston for cuts, deep scratches and pitting whenever cali-

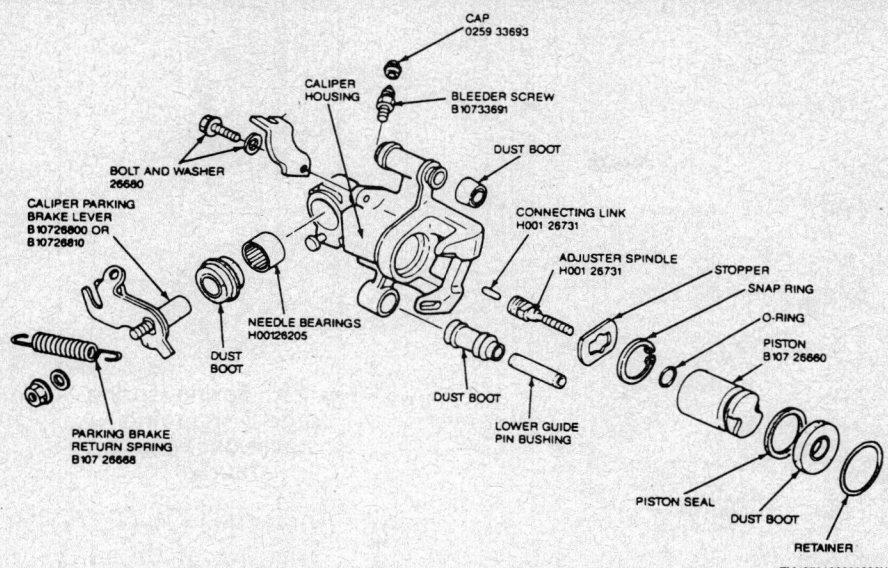

Fig. 23   Exploded view of rear caliper assembly. Capri

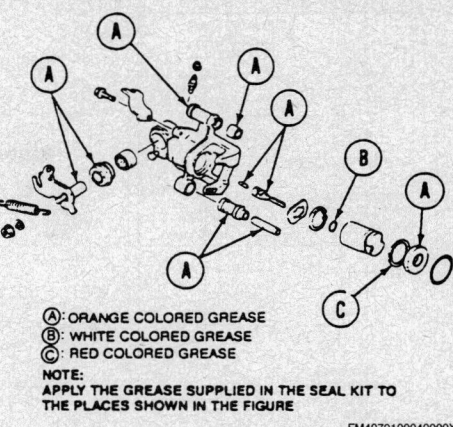

(A): ORANGE COLORED GREASE
(B): WHITE COLORED GREASE
(C): RED COLORED GREASE

NOTE:
APPLY THE GREASE SUPPLIED IN THE SEAL KIT TO
THE PLACES SHOWN IN THE FIGURE

FM4079100040000X

Fig. 24   Lubrication points of rear caliper assembly. Capri

per is rebuilt. Piston and piston bore may be lightly polished with crocus cloth. If deep scratches cannot be removed, replace component.
2. Caliper seal groove must be free of deep scratches which would prevent seal from operating properly.
3. Inspect upper guide pin and lower guide pin bushing for wear.
4. Inspect bushing dust boots for damage or poor sealing.

Assemble

1. Lubricate needle bearings with orange grease included in caliper rebuilding kit part No. FOJY-2221-A.
2. Align opening in bearing with bore in caliper housing, then install needle bearing.
3. Install operating shaft into caliper housing.
4. Install operating lever. Align marks made during removal.
5. Install lockwasher nut.
6. Install connecting link into operating shaft.
7. Install O-ring onto adjuster spindle, then position stopper onto adjuster spindle so pin will align with caliper housing.
8. Install adjuster spindle in caliper by aligning adjuster spindle pins with caliper holes.
9. Install parking brake return spring.
10. Lubricate new piston seal with brake fluid and install in caliper groove, then lubricate caliper bore and caliper piston with brake fluid.
11. Install dust boot in caliper bore.
12. Install piston in caliper bore by rotating piston until seated.
13. Install upper guide pin dust boot, then the lower guide pin bushing dust boot.
14. Install caliper upper guide pin, then the lower guide pin bushing.
15. Install caliper as described under "Caliper, Replace."

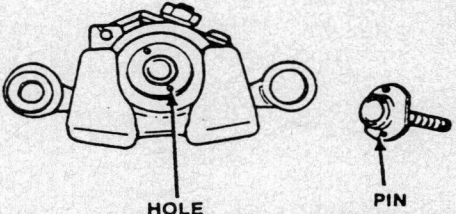

HOLE   PIN

FM4079100041000X

Fig. 25   Adjuster spindle pin adjustment. Capri

CAPRI

Disassemble

1. Remove caliper as described under "Caliper, Replace."
2. Open bleeder screw and drain brake fluid from caliper through brake flex hose fitting. After draining fluid, close the bleeder screw.
3. Remove caliper guide bushing and dust boots, **Fig. 23.**
4. Pry retaining spring off dust boot with screwdriver, then remove piston.
5. Remove dust boot and discard boot.
6. Remove piston seal from caliper and discard. **Use plastic or wooden pick to remove seal. Metal tool can scratch or nick seal groove resulting in possible seal leak.**
7. Remove parking brake mechanism from caliper housing.

Inspection

1. Inspect caliper bore, piston seal groove and piston for cuts, deep scratches and pitting whenever caliper is rebuilt. Piston and piston bore may be lightly polished with crocus cloth. If deep scratches cannot be removed, replace caliper.
2. Seal groove in caliper must be free of deep scratches which would prevent seal from operating properly.

3. Inspect upper guide pin and lower guide pin bushing for wear.
4. Inspect bushing dust boots for damage or poor sealing.

Assemble

1. Lubricate needle bearings with special grease included in caliper rebuilding kit part No. FOJY-2221-A, **Fig. 24.**
2. Install adjuster spindle in caliper by aligning pins of adjuster spindle with holes of caliper, **Fig. 25.**
3. Lubricate new piston seal with brake fluid and install in caliper groove.
4. Lubricate caliper bore and caliper piston with brake fluid.
5. Install dust boot in caliper bore, then the wire retainer spring.
6. Install piston in caliper bore by rotating piston until seated.
7. Install upper guide pin dust boot, then the lower guide pin bushing dust boot.
8. Install caliper upper guide pin, then the lower guide pin bushing.
9. Install brake pads as described under "Brake Pad Service."
10. Tighten upper guide pin with Allen wrench, then install dust cap with plastic hammer.
11. Install lower caliper bolt, then tighten bolt to specifications.
12. Bleed brake system as described under "Brake System Bleed," then pump brake pedal several times to seat pads.
13. Check fluid level in master cylinder, then spin each rotor to ensure brakes are not dragging.
14. Install wheel and tire assembly. Tighten wheel lug nuts to specifications.

ESCORT & TRACER

Disassemble

1. Remove disc pads as described under "Brake Pad Service," then disconnect brake hose from caliper.
2. Open bleeder screw and drain brake fluid from caliper.
3. Remove caliper guide bushing and dust boots, **Fig. 17.**
4. Pry retaining spring off dust boot, then remove piston.
5. Remove dust boot and discard, then

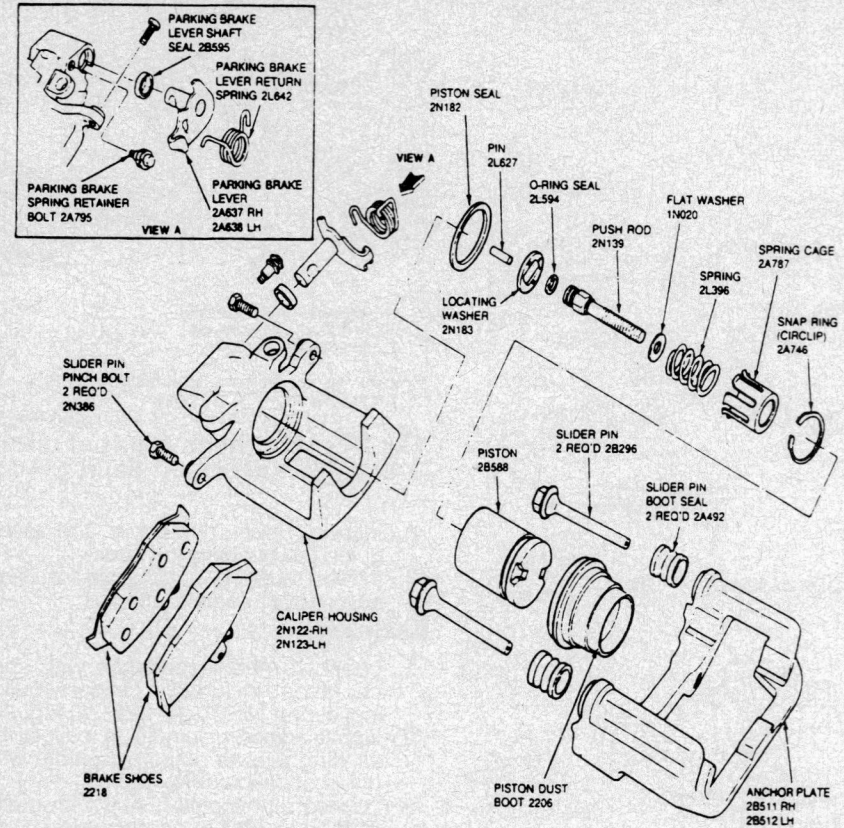

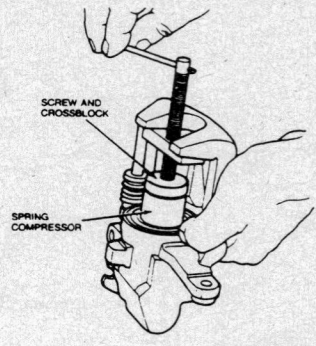

Fig. 29 Spring, spring cage & snap ring installation. Sable & Taurus

Fig. 26 Exploded view of rear caliper assembly. Sable & Taurus

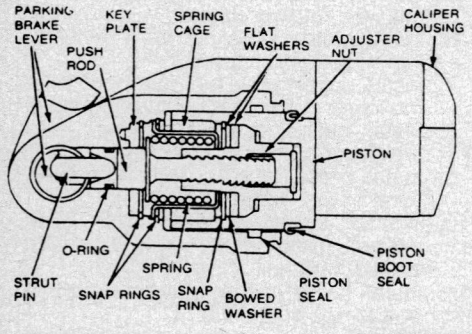

Fig. 27 Cross-sectional view of rear caliper component locations. Sable & Taurus

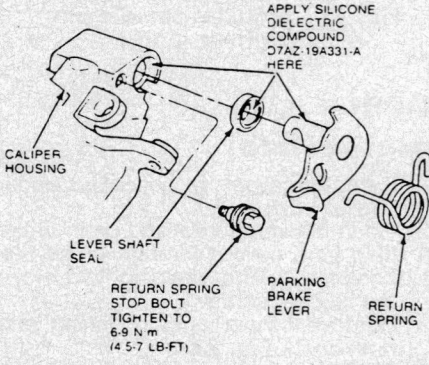

Fig. 28 Parking brake lever lubrication points. Sable & Taurus

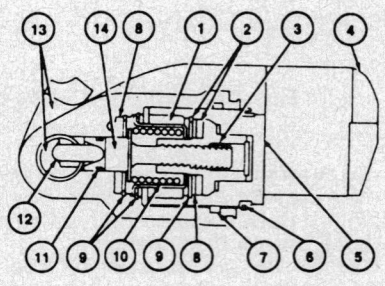

Item	Description
1	Parking Brake Spring Retainer
2	Flat Washer
3	Adjuster Nut
4	Rear Disc Brake Caliper
5	Rear Disc Brake Piston and Adjuster
6	Piston Dust Boot
7	Piston Seal
8	Locating Washer

Fig. 30 Cross-sectional view of rear disc brake caliper (Part 1 of 2). Mustang

remove piston seal from caliper and discard.
6. Remove parking brake mechanism from caliper housing.

Assemble

Clean caliper, anchor plate and rotor assembly and inspect for signs of brake fluid leakage, excessive wear or damage. The caliper must be inspected for leakage both in piston boot area and operating shaft seal area. Lightly sand or wire brush any rust or corrosion from caliper and anchor plate sliding surfaces and inner brake shoe abutment surfaces in anchor plate. Inspect brake shoes for wear. Linings must not be worn to less than 1/8 inch of shoe surface.

Lubricate all new seals with brake fluid before installation.
1. Install needle bearings, dust boot and parking brake lever, **Fig. 17.**
2. Install adapter spindle in caliper.
3. Install dust boot into caliper bore, then the retaining spring.
4. Install caliper piston.
5. Install upper and lower guide pin dust boots.
6. Install anchor plate clips, brake pads, shims and spring retainer.
7. Install caliper on anchor plate, then tighten upper guide pin and install dust cap.
8. Install lower guide pin and tighten to specification.

9. Bleed brake system as described under "Brake System Bleed," then pump brake pedal several times to seat brake pads.
10. Check brake fluid level, adding fluid as necessary, then install wheel and tire assembly.

SABLE & TAURUS

Disassemble

Refer to **Figs. 26 and 27,** during disassembly and assembly.
1. Remove caliper assembly as described under "Caliper, Replace."
2. Mount caliper assembly in soft-jawed vise, or use vise jaw protectors.
3. Using brake piston turning tool No. T87P-2588-A, or equivalent, turn piston counterclockwise to remove piston from caliper piston bore.
4. Remove and discard piston dust boot seal and piston seal from caliper bore.

5. Using snap ring (circlip) pliers, remove snap ring retaining pushrod assembly from caliper. **Snap ring and spring cover are under spring load. Care should be taken when removing snap ring.**
6. Remove spring cover, spring, washer, key plate from cylinder bore, then pull out pushrod and strut pin.
7. Remove and discard O-ring seal from pushrod.
8. Remove parking brake lever return spring, then unscrew parking brake lever stop bolt. Pull parking brake lever out of caliper housing, **Fig. 28.**

Inspection

1. Clean all metal parts with Isopropyl Alcohol. Use clean, dry compressed air to clean out and dry grooves and passages. Ensure caliper bore and component parts are completely free of any foreign material.
2. Inspect caliper bores for damage or excessive wear. If piston is pitted, scored or plating is worn off, replace piston assembly.

Assemble

Refer to **Figs. 26 and 27** during disassembly and assembly.
1. Lightly grease parking brake lever bore and lever shaft seal with Silicone Dielectric Compound part No. D7AZ-19A331-A. Press parking brake lever shaft seal into caliper bore.
2. Grease parking brake shaft recess and slightly grease parking brake lever shaft, **Fig. 28.** Insert shaft into bore in caliper housing.
3. Screw lever stop bolt into caliper housing. Tighten stop bolt to specifications.
4. Attach parking brake lever return spring to stop bolt, then insert free end into parking brake lever slot.
5. Install new O-ring seal in groove of pushrod. Grease recess at pushrod end with Silicone Dielectric Compound.
6. Position strut pin into caliper housing and in recess of parking brake lever shaft. Insert pushrod into pushrod bore of caliper housing. Ensure pin is positioned correctly between shaft recess and recess at end of rod.
7. Place key plate over pushrod so locating nib fits into drilled locating hole in caliper housing. Install flat washer, pushrod, spring and spring cover.
8. Insert outer spacer into piston bore.
9. Insert inner spacer into piston bore, then install snap ring inside of inner spacer.
10. Position spring compressor tool No. T87P-2588-B, or equivalent, **Fig. 29.** Lightly screw tool clockwise to compress spring. Install snap ring. **Snap ring should click into place. Do not over compress spring.**
11. Lubricate piston seal with brake fluid, then install new piston seal in groove in caliper housing.
12. Coat piston and piston dust boot with clean brake fluid, then install dust boot into piston bore of caliper.

13. Spread dust boot over piston, then seat dust boot in piston groove.
14. Using brake piston turning tool No. T87P-2588-A, or equivalent, rotate piston clockwise until piston is fully seated. **Ensure one slot in piston face is positioned so it will engage with nib on brake pad.**
15. Install caliper as described under "Caliper, Replace."

CROWN VICTORIA, GRAND MARQUIS & TOWN CAR

Visually check caliper. If the caliper housing is leaking, it should be replaced. If a seal is leaking, the caliper must be disassembled and new seals and dust boot installed. If a piston is seized in the bore, replace caliper. Care must be taken when removing plastic piston.

Disassemble

1. Remove caliper from caliper mounting bracket as described under "Caliper, Replace."
2. Remove outer pad by slipping down caliper leg until clip is disengaged, then inner pad by pulling it straight out of piston.
3. Place shop towels between the caliper piston and caliper bridge. Do not place fingers between these areas. Two methods can be used to remove the piston from the caliper bore, one method is using low volume air pressure and other is hydraulic pressure. If air pressure is not available, slowly apply brake pedal until pedal drops to floor. This method can only be done one caliper at a time. If air pressure is to be used, proceed as follows:
   a. Disconnect flexible hose from caliper assembly, then remove caliper from vehicle.
   b. Using air nozzle, lightly apply air pressure to brake hose inlet until piston is free from caliper. **Do not use shop pressure if it cannot be adjusted down to safe level (15-30 psi) or personal injury and/or damage to components could result.**
4. Remove seal and dust boot from caliper assembly.

Cleaning & Inspection

Clean all metal parts with Isopropyl alcohol. Then clean out and dry grooves and passage ways with compressed air. Ensure caliper bore and component parts are cleaned thoroughly. Check cylinder bore and piston for damage or excessive wear.

Examine piston for surface irregularities or small chips and cracks. Minor surface imperfections are allowable, provided they do not enter the dust boot groove area. Replace piston if damaged.

Assemble

1. Coat new seal with clean brake fluid, then install in caliper assembly.
2. Coat dust boot with clean brake fluid, then install in caliper assembly.
3. Coat piston with clean brake fluid, then place piston in caliper assembly and push firmly into caliper bore.

4. With piston seated, completely seat piston using a 4 inch C-clamp and a block of wood approximately 2 3/4 inch x 1 inch x 3/4 inch thick.
5. Ensure dust boot is tight in boot groove on piston and in caliper.
6. Install brake pads as described under "Brake Pad Service," then the caliper as described under "Caliper, Replace."

MUSTANG

Disassemble

Refer to **Fig. 30** when disassembling the rear disc brake caliper.
1. Remove rear disc brake caliper as described under "Caliper, Replace."
2. Mount rear disc brake caliper vise, using vise jaw protectors.
3. Using rear caliper piston adjuster tool No. T87P-2588-A, or equivalent, turn rear disc brake piston and adjuster counterclockwise and remove rear disc brake piston and adjuster from caliper piston bore.
4. Remove and discard piston dust boot seal and piston seal from caliper bore.
5. Use suitable snap ring pliers to remove snap ring (circlip) retaining push rod assembly to rear disc brake caliper.
6. From caliper bore, remove spring cover, spring, washer, key plate and pull out push rod and strut pin.
7. Remove and discard O-ring seal from push rod.
8. Remove parking brake return spring, then unscrew limiting bolt and pull rear parking rake cable out of rear disc brake caliper.

Assemble

Refer to **Fig. 30** when assembling the rear disc brake caliper.
1. Lightly grease parking brake lever bore and lever shaft seal with suitable lubricant, then press parking brake lever shaft seal into caliper bore.
2. Grease parking brake shaft recess and slightly grease rear parking brake cable. Insert rear parking brake cable into bore in caliper housing.
3. Screw limiting bolt into caliper housing. Tighten to specifications.
4. Attach parking brake return spring to limiting bolt and insert free end into rear parking brake cable slot.
5. Install new O-ring seal in groove of push rod, then grease recess at push rod end with suitable lubricant.
6. Position strut pin into rear disc brake caliper and in recess of rear parking brake cable, then insert push rod into push rod bore of caliper. Ensure rod is properly positioned between shaft recess at recess at end of push rod.
7. Place key plate over push rod so locating nib fits into drilled locating hole in rear disc brake caliper.
8. Install flat washer push rod spring and spring cover in order.
9. Insert outer, then the inner spacer into piston bore.
10. Install snap ring inside of inner spacer.

Item	Description
9	Parking Brake Lever Pin Retainer Clip
10	Brake Shoe Hold Down Spring
11	Parking Brake Lever Shaft Seal
12	Strut Pin
13	Rear Parking Brake Cable
14	Push Rod

FM4079400057020X

Fig. 30 Cross-sectional view of disc brake caliper (Part 2 of 2). Mustang

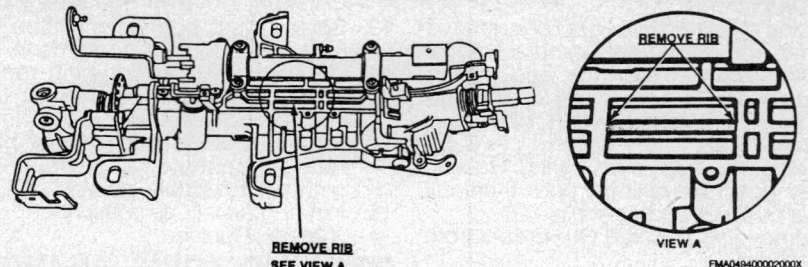

REMOVE RIB
SEE VIEW A

VIEW A

FMA049400002000X

Fig. 32 Vacuum hose rib location. 1992 Crown Victoria, Grand Marquis & Town Car

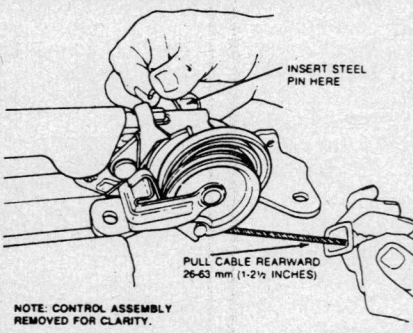

INSERT STEEL PIN HERE

PULL CABLE REARWARD
26-63 mm (1-2½ INCHES)

NOTE: CONTROL ASSEMBLY REMOVED FOR CLARITY.

FM4079400058000X

Fig. 31 Self-adjuster reel rotation. Mustang

11. Position spring compressor and screw and cross-block on push rod and lightly screw caliper spring compressor tool No. T87P-2588-B, or equivalent, clockwise to compress spring. Install snap ring (circlip).
12. Install new piston seal in groove in rear disc brake caliper after lubricating seal with suitable brake fluid.
13. Ensure one slot in piston face is positioned so it will engage with nib on rear brake shoe and lining.
14. Coat rear disc brake piston and adjuster and piston boot with suitable clean brake fluid.
15. Install dust boot into piston bore of rear disc brake caliper, then spread dust boot over rear disc brake piston and adjuster and seat dust boot in piston groove.
16. Rotate rear disc brake piston and adjuster seat dust boot and adjuster clockwise, using rear caliper piston adjuster tool No. T87P-2588-A, or equivalent, until piston is fully seated.
17. Install rear disc brake caliper assembly as described under "Caliper, Replace."

ROTOR
REPLACE
MARK VII
Removal

1. Remove caliper assembly as described under "Caliper Service." If caliper does not require service, do not disconnect flexible hose. Support caliper with wire hook so hose is not stretched or twisted.
2. Remove anchor plate.
3. remove rotor nuts, then the rotor from axle shaft.

Installation

1. If installing new rotor, remove protective coating from rotor using suirable solvent.
2. On all rotors, lubricate hub pilot diameter wirh wuitable lubricant to ease future service.
3. Mount rotor on hub, then install nuts.
4. Install anchor plate, then the inner and outer shoe and lining assemblies with anti-rattle springs.
5. Install caliper as described under "Caliper Service."

CONTINENTAL, COUGAR, MARK VIII & THUNDERBIRD
Removal

1. Remove rear disc brake caliper assembly as described under "Caliper Service." If caliper assembly does not need service, do not disconnect flexible hose from rear disc brake caliper. Support caliper with suitable wire so flexible hose is not stretched or twisted.
2. Remove rear disc support bracket to rear wheel knuckle bolts, then the rear disc support bracket and brake shoes and linings.
3. Remove two nuts, then the rotor from rear hub.

Installation

1. If installing new rotor, remove protective coating from rotor with suitable carburetor cleaner.
2. Lubricate rear hub pilot diameter with suitable grease to ease future removal.
3. Install rotors on axle shaft flange, then the two nuts.
4. Install inner and outer brake shoes and linings in rear disc support bracket.
5. Install rear disc support bracket as follows:
   a. Clean rear disc support bracket and bolt threads, then add one drop of suitable sealer to each bolt.
   b. Install caliper/rear support bracket assembly to rear wheel knuckle.
   c. Install bolts, then tighten to specifications.
6. Install inner and outer brake shoes and linings as described under "Brake Pad Service."
7. Install rear disc brake caliper as described under "Caliper Service."

PROBE
1992
Removal

1. Raise and support vehicle, then remove wheel and tire assembly.
2. Remove two anchor bracket bolts, then the caliper and anchor bracket assembly. Support caliper with suitable wire strung from coil spring. Do not disconnect brake line from caliper.
3. Remove grease cap.
4. Using cape chisel, unstake and remove wheel bearing nut and washer. Discard nut.
5. Remove rotor.
6. **On models equipped with anti-lock brakes,** remove ABS signal ring from rotor.

Installation

1. **On models equipped with anti-lock brakes, install** ABS signal ring to rotor.
2. **On all models,** install rotor on spindle, then the washer and new wheel bearing nut. Tighten wheel bearing nut to specifications.
3. Stake wheel bearing nut using cold chisel with rounded cutting edge. **If nut splits or cracks after staking, it must be replaced with new nut.**
4. Install grease cap, then the caliper and anchor bracket assembly. Tighten anchor bracket bolts to specifications.
5. Install wheel and tire assembly. Tighten wheel lug nuts to specifications.

1993–94
Removal

1. Raise and support vehicle, the remove wheel and tire assembly.
2. Using cape chisel, unstake, remove and discard rear axle wheel hub retainer.
3. Remove two anchor plate bolts, then the caliper and caliper anchor plate assembly. Support caliper with suitable wire strung from rear shock absorber. Do not disconnect brake hose from caliper.
4. Remove rotor.

Installation

1. Install rotor on wheel hub.
2. Install caliper and anchor plate assembly. Tighten anchor plate bolts to specifications.
3. Install new rear axle wheel hub retainer. Tighten retainer to specifications.
4. Stake new rear axle wheel hub retainer using cold chisel with rounded cutting edge. **If rear axle wheel hub re-**

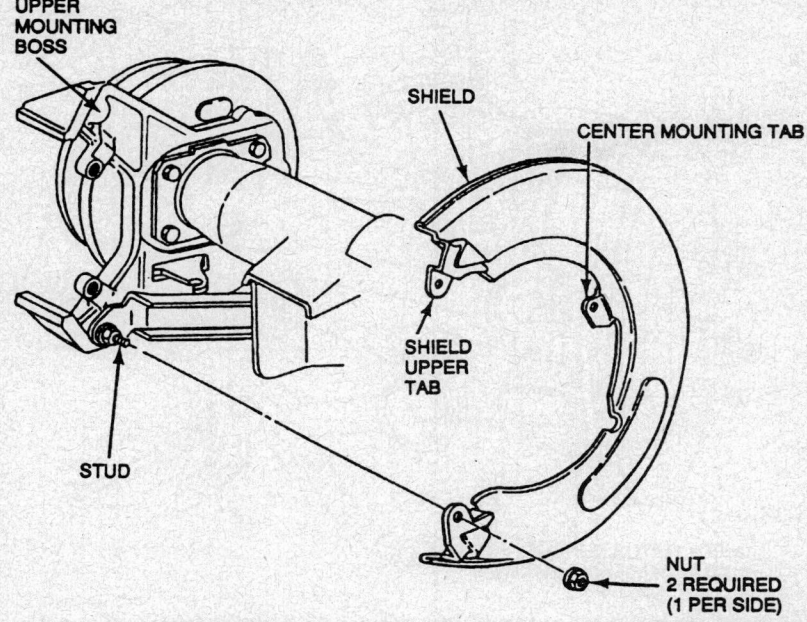

Fig. 33 Brake adapter brace removal. 1992–93 Crown Victoria, Grand Marquis & Town Car

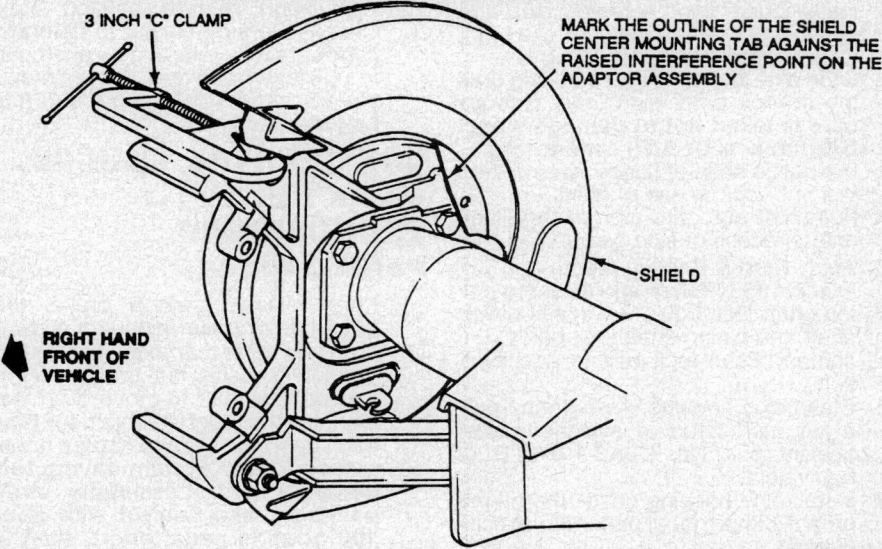

Fig. 34 Brake lining shield positioning. 1992–93 Crown Victoria, Grand Marquis & Town Car

tainer splits or cracks after staking, it must be replaced with new rear axle wheel hub retainer.

5. Install hub grease cap, then the wheel and tire assembly. Tighten wheel hub bolt nuts to specifications.

CAPRI
Removal

1. Raise and support vehicle, then remove wheel and tire assembly.
2. Using cape chisel, unstake and remove halfshaft nut and washer. Discard nut if it cannot be reused.
3. Remove disc brake pads as described under "Brake Pad Service," then the caliper as described under

"Caliper Service." Support caliper by suitable wire strung from coil spring. Do not disconnect brake line from caliper.

4. Remove grease cap, then carefully raise staked portion of locknut using small cape chisel.
5. Remove and discard locknut. Locknuts are threaded left and right. Lefthand threaded locknut is located on the righthand side of the vehicle. Turn this locknut clockwise to loosen. Righthand threaded locknut is turned counterclockwise to loosen.
6. Remove washer and outer bearing from bearing hub, then the brake rotor/bearing hub assembly.

Installation

1. Ensure bearings and hub area contain adequate lubricant, then position brake rotor/bearing hub assembly on spindle.
2. Install outer bearing, washer and new locknut. **Keep hub centered on spindle to prevent damage to grease seal and spindle threads.**
3. Adjust bearing preload, then install grease cap.
4. Install caliper as described under "Caliper Service," then the brake pads as described under "Brake Pad Service."
5. Install wheel and tire assembly, then tighten wheel lug nuts to specifications.

ESCORT & TRACER

1. Raise and support vehicle, then remove wheel and tire assembly.
2. Remove rear brake shoe and lining as described under "Brake Pad Service."
3. Remove two rear disc brake rotor screws.
4. Using screwdriver, pivot rear disc brake caliper on rear disc support bracket and remove rotor.
5. Reverse procedure to install.

SABLE & TAURUS
Removal

1. Remove rear disc brake caliper assembly as described under "Caliper Service." If caliper does not require service, do not disconnect flexible hose. Support rear disc brake caliper with suitable wire so brake hose is not stretched or twisted.
2. Remove upper and lower rear disc support bracket to rear disc brake adapter bolts, then the bracket.
3. Remove two nuts, then the rotor from hub.

Installation

1. Clean all foreign material and locking compound residue from bolts and mating surface of rear disc brake adapter and rear disc support bracket.
2. Position support bracket, then add one drop of suitable sealant to each bolt and mounting surface. Tighten bolts to specifications.
3. Install rear disc brake caliper assembly as described under "Caliper Service."

CROWN VICTORIA, GRAND MARQUIS & TOWN CAR
Removal

1. Raise and support vehicle, then remove wheel and tire assembly.
2. Remove rear disc brake caliper assembly as described under "Caliper Service." If caliper does not require service, do not disconnect brake hose or remove caliper. Position caliper aside and support with suitable wire to avoid damaging caliper.
3. Remove rotor push nuts, then the disc brake rotor. If additional force is re-

quired, proceed as follows:
  a. Apply rust penetrant and inhibitor part No. D7AZ-19A501-AA or equivalent to rotor/flange mating surface.
  b. Install three-jaw puller tool No. D80L-1013-A, or equivalent, then remove rear disc brake rotor. **If excessive force is necessary to remove rotor, rear disc brake rotor should be checked for lateral runout prior to installation.**

Installation

1. If installing new rotor, remove protective coating with suitable carburetor cleaner. If installing original rotor, ensure rotor braking and mounting surfaces are clean.
2. Install rotor and peasants.
3. Install caliper as described under "Caliper Service."
4. Install wheel and tire assembly, then lower vehicle and tighten wheel hub bolt nuts to specifications.
5. Pump brake pedal to position brake shoes and linings prior to moving vehicle, then road test vehicle.

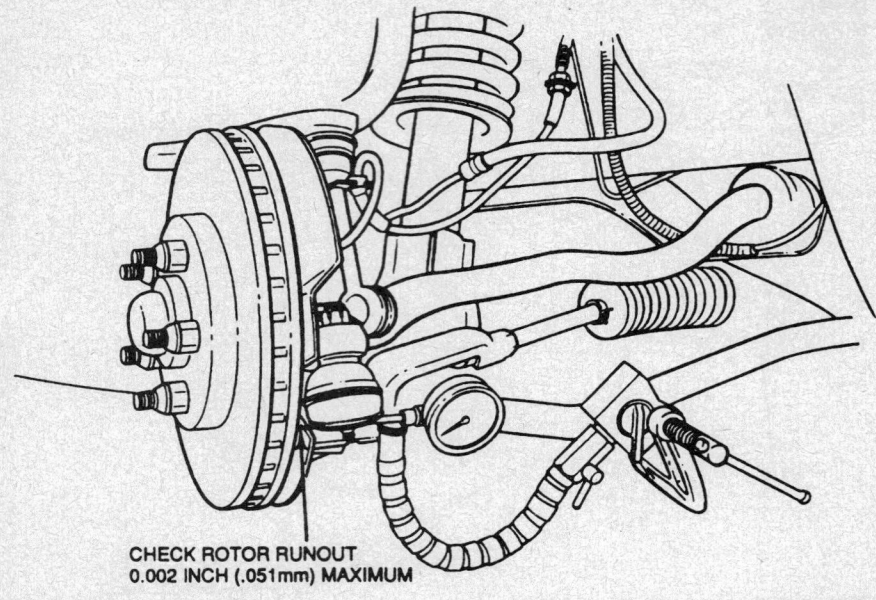

CHECK ROTOR RUNOUT
0.002 INCH (.051mm) MAXIMUM

FMA049200005000X

Fig. 35 Total system runout measurement. 1992 Cougar & Thunderbird

PARKING BRAKE SERVICE

CROWN VICTORIA, GRAND MARQUIS & TOWN CAR

Parking Brake Linings, Replace

The parking brake system is a drum type design mounted in the hubs of the rear brake rotors.

1. Raise and support vehicle, then remove wheel and tire assembly.
2. Remove caliper as previously outlined, then the rotor assembly.
3. Drain differential fluid from axle by removing cover.
4. Remove lock bolt from differential pinion shaft, then the pinion shaft from differential.
5. Push axle shaft inward to gain access to axle shaft C-lock, then remove C-lock.
6. Remove ABS speed sensor, then the axle shaft from axle housing.
7. Disconnect brake cable from lever, then the brake shoe retaining pins and springs.
8. Set adjuster assembly to shortest length.
9. Slightly pull shoe assemblies away from backing plate, then spread to remove adjuster.
10. Lift shoe assemblies over support, then remove shoes and actuating lever as an assembly.
11. Install lower return springs and actuating lever to brake shoe assemblies.
12. Ensure actuator boot is correctly positioned through backing plate.
13. Install shoe assemblies by first inserting lever through boot and lowering shoes into position.
14. Install upper return (adjuster) spring, then the adjuster assembly.

15. Install brake shoe retaining pins and springs.
16. Connect brake cable to lever.
17. Slide axle shaft into axle housing until the splines enter side gear. **Ensure care is taken not to damage wheel bearing seal or ABS sensor ring.**
18. Push axle shaft at flange inward, then install C-lock at end of shaft.
19. Pull shaft outboard until each C-lock enters recess of side gears.
20. Apply Stud & Bearing Mount part No. EOAZ-19554-BA or equivalent to pinion shaft lock bolt, then install pinion shaft and pinion shaft lock bolt.
21. tighten pinion lock bolt to specifications.
22. Clean axle housing cover, then apply a $3/16$ inch bead of silicone rubber sealant part No. D6AZ-19562-B or equivalent.
23. Install axle housing cover, then tighten bolts in diagonal pattern to specifications.
24. Fill axle with lubricant until fluid level is $1/4$ inch below bottom of fill hole.
25. Center brake shoes on backing plate, then, using an eight-inch micrometer, adjust brake shoes until a measurement of 7.065-7.072 inch is obtained.
26. Install rotor and caliper as previously described.

ADJUSTMENTS

MARK VII

Parking Brake

1. Fully release parking brake, then place transmission in neutral and support vehicle at rear axle.
2. Tighten adjuster nut until levers on calipers just begin to move, then loosen adjuster nut until levers just return to stop position.

3. Apply and release parking brake. Check levers on caliper to determine if they are fully returned by attempting to pull lever rearward. If lever moves, the adjustment is too tight and must be readjusted.

CONTINENTAL, COUGAR, MARK VIII & THUNDERBIRD

Parking Brake

1. Fully release parking brake, then place transmission in neutral and support vehicle at rear axle.
2. Tighten adjuster nut until levers on calipers just start to move, then loosen nut just enough to obtain full travel to off position. **If brake cables are replaced in any system having foot-actuated control assembly, stroke parking brake control with about 100 pounds pedal effort, then repeat adjustment.**
3. The lever is in off position when $1/4$ inch diameter pin can be freely inserted past side of lever into $1/4$ inch diameter holes in cast iron housing.
4. Apply and release parking brake, then apply and release service brake pedal with moderate force. Check parking brake levers on calipers to determine if they are fully returned to off position. **If $1/4$ inch pin cannot be freely inserted, adjustment is too tight. Repeat adjustment procedure. Also, if levers do not return to off position, parking and service brake function will be affected as vehicle is driven.**

PROBE

Parking Brake

Normal parking brake adjustment is

made at hand lever between seats.
1. Remove six screws in center console, then the console.
2. Tighten parking brake adjusting nut on left side of parking brake lever. This shortens equalizer cable. Tighten adjusting nut until it takes seven to 10 notches to fully set parking brake.

ESCORT & TRACER

Parking Brake

1. Start engine and shift gearshift lever into reverse position.
2. With vehicle moving in reverse, depress brake pedal several times.
3. Shift gearshift lever into park position, then stop engine.
4. Remove parking brake console.
5. Turn adjusting nut until parking brake lever stroke is five to seven notches when pulled with force of 22 lbs.
6. Install parking brake console.

SABLE & TAURUS

Parking Brake

The parking brake is self-adjusting. No initial adjustment is necessary.

MUSTANG

Parking Brake

if any component in the parking brake system requires service or if the rear axle housing is removed, the cable tension must be released as follows:
1. Place parking brake control in released position.
2. Remove console top panel as follows:
   a. Disconnect battery ground cable.
   b. Remove console finish panel by carefully prying up from retaining clips, then disconnect electrical connectors.
3. With assistant inside vehicle, raise and support vehicle.
4. Have another assistant pull parking brake cable and equalizer rearward approximately 1 to 2 1/2 inches, **Fig. 31**, to rotate self-adjuster reel backward.
5. Insert steel lockpin through holes in lever and parking brake control assembly to lock ratchet wheel in cable-released position. **Do not remove steel lockpin until parking brake rear cable and conduit are connected to parking brake cable and equalizer. Pin removal releases the tension in the ratchet wheel, causing spring to unwind and release tension. If pin is removed without parking brake rear cable and conduit attached, entire assembly must be removed to reset spring tension.**

TECHNICAL SERVICE BULLETINS

PARKING BRAKE CANNOT SET IMMEDIATELY AFTER SHIFTING TRANSMISSION CONTROL TO PARK OR NEUTRAL

1992 Crown Victoria, Grand Marquis & Town Car

Customers may complain the parking brake cannot be set immediately after shifting the transmission control to park or neutral positions. Customers may also complain the pedal will follow their foot upward after the downward stroke, and they must reapply the parking brake two or three times before it will set. This is caused by a low rate of the automatic parking brake release vacuum switch mounted on the steering column.

Install a new vacuum switch and two new vacuum hose assemblies with improved vacuum flow rate. Use the following procedure.
1. Lower steering column.
2. Grind off one rib which interferes with new vacuum hose connector, **Fig. 32.**
3. Install new hose.

EXCESSIVE REAR LINING WEAR

1992—93 Crown Victoria, Grand Marquis & Town Car

Excessive rear brake lining wear may be caused by some ambient dust getting by the current brake lining shields. Replace worn or contaminated linings with new linings.

Install improved 1993-level rear brake shields to reduce contamination. Brake shield replacement can be accomplished without removing axle shafts or rear disc brake adapters. Refer to the following procedure and instruction sheet included in Rear Shoe and Lining Service Kit for details.
1. **On models equipped with ABS,** remove both rear wheel speed sensors from adapters. Cover sensors with cloth to protect from metal particles. Sensors are magnetized and may not operate properly if contaminated.
2. Remove disc brake calipers and support with suitable wire. **Do NOT let calipers hang from hose.**
3. Remove disc rotors, then cover interior of brake adapters with cloth or other cover sufficient to prevent metal particles from entering parking brake system.
4. Remove bolt holding brace from bottom of brake adapter and install stud from kit **Fig. 33.** Tighten stud to specifications.
5. Install shield over nut, then snug nut against shield.
6. Move shield upper tab into position

with upper mounting boss on brake adapter and carefully hold in position with 3-inch C-clamp. Anvil portion of clamp should be centered over shield tab hole, **Fig. 34.**
7. Ensure shield tab is located squarely on adapter mounting boss, then tighten clamp with threaded portion against upper adapter leg.
8. Mark outline of shield center mounting tab against raised interference point on back of adapter assembly. This must be ground flat to allow shield to fit properly at final installation.
9. Remove clamp, then loosen bottom nut two or three turns and allow shield to hang from stud or remove shield from adapter.
10. Center punch middle of circle previously marked around C-clamp and drill 7/32 inch hole through adapter leg as follows:
    a. Grind raised portion of casting (on back side of adapter) flat with surface.
    b. Remove stock beyond mark to allow sufficient clearance for center tab to fit flat against adapter.
11. Place shield upper mounting tab over hole, then proceed as follows:
    a. Start self-tapping mounting screw to permit proper location, then carefully inspect area previously ground to assure flat mounting of center tab to back of adapter.
    b. Grind additional material as required to provide flat, non-interfering fit.
12. **Torque** nut to 17 ft. lbs., then the self-tapping upper screw to 11 ft. lbs.
13. On lefthand side, remove jounce bumper from axle assembly. This is not necessary on righthand side.
14. Center punch drill location through center tab hole, then drill center mounting hole in three steps to prevent damage to inside of adapter plate as follows:
    a. Begin with 1/16 inch drill.
    b. Follow with 1/8 inch drill.
    c. Finish with 7/32 inch drill. Install self-tapping screw and **torque** to 11 ft. lbs.
15. Using brake cleaning solvent spray, remove all metal chips.
16. **On models equipped with ABS,** wipe off wheel speed sensor and inspect for metal shavings and clean if further required.
17. Install sensor and **torque** mounting screw to 3—5 ft. lbs.
18. **On models without ABS,** ensure center tab does not interfere with sensor hole plug, preventing proper flat attachment.
19. **On all models,** install rotor.
20. Remove caliper pins and wipe pins and bushing interiors clean of any debris. Apply coating of suitable silicone dielectric compound to pin surface.
21. Insert pins and install caliper. **Torque** pins to 24 ft. lbs.
22. Repeat procedure for opposite side of vehicle.
23. Install left jounce bumper.

ROUGHNESS, PULSATION OR STEERING WHEEL SHAKE

1992 COUGAR & THUNDERBIRD

Brake roughness, pulsation and steering wheel shake may occur because of uneven rotor wear. Two major causes of uneven rotor wear are abrasive brake pads (semi-metallic material) and hub or rotor high and low spots improperly oriented during assembly.

Usually these vehicles appear to be corrected by just installing new pads and rotors. However, they can repeat the condition after some time in service unless proper attention is given to front brake pads, hub/rotor "stacked" runout and tire wear and balance.

Check front brake pads, hub/rotor "stacked" runout and tire wear/balance. Refer to the following procedures for service details.

Front Brake Pads

1. Replace front brake pads with ONLY new asbestos pads (part No. F1SZ-2001-A). Using metallic front brake pads (part No. F0SZ-2001-A) will cause uneven rotor wear.
2. Refer to "Brake Pad Service" for brake pad replacement procedure.

Hub/Rotor "Stacked" Runout Check

If the assembled system with new rotor installed on hub indicates more than .002 inch total runout (TIR), it will cause excessive thickness variation in the rotor as mileage accumulates by wearing the high spots off the rotor. Excessive thickness variation in the rotor causes brake pulsation and steering wheel shake.

High TIR is also caused by rust or other contamination trapped between the hub and rotor mounting surface or the rotor or hub high and low spots not being properly oriented during assembly.

New brake rotors should not be machined. New OEM replacement rotors are well within runout and thickness variation specifications.

To check hub/rotor "stacked" runout, proceed as follows:

1. Clean hub area where new rotor will contact. Remove rust and debris.
2. Install new rotor, part No. F1SZ-1125-A, on hub, noting the following:
   a. Secure rotor with at least four lug nuts.
   b. **Torque** nuts to 9 ft. lbs.
3. Using suitable dial indicator, determine total runout of system, Fig. 35. Total system (rotor and hub) runout must not exceed .002 inch. If runout exceeds specification, proceed as follows:
   a. Remove rotor and rotate clockwise until next hole lines up with stud.
   b. Secure rotor in new position with four lug nuts. **Torque** nuts to 9 ft. lbs.
   c. Repeat checking and rotation process until system measures .002 inch or less total runout.
4. If .002 inch or less runout cannot be reached, replace hub.
5. After installing new hub, repeat this check.

Tire Wear & Balance

Tire wear and balance can cause or add to a brake roughness concern. After the brake system is serviced, the tire wear and/or balance could cause enough input to be perceived as a brake roughness condition.

1. Place best tires on front of vehicle.
2. High-speed balance all tires.

DISC BRAKE SPECIFICATIONS
ROTOR SPECIFICATIONS

Model	Year	Nominal Thickness Inch	Minimum Refinish Thickness Inch	Thickness Variation (Parallelism) Inch	Lateral Runout (T.I.R.) Inch	Finish (Micro-Inch)
Aspire	1994	.500	.043	.0006	.003	10-80
Capri	1992-94 ③	.710	0.630	.0004	.004	—
	1992-94 ④	.390	0.350	.0040	.004	—
Continental	1992 ③	1.020	.970	.0004	.002	10-80
	1992 ④	1.020	.974	.0005	.002	10-80
	1993 ③	1.020	.974	.0003	.003	10-80
	1994 ③	1.020	.974	.0003	.003	15-125
	1993-94 ④	.550	.500	.0004	.001	16-25
Cougar & Thunderbird	1992 ③	1.024	.935	.0005	.003	10-80
	1992 ④	.945	.900	.0005	.004	16-25
	1993 ③	1.024	.974	.0005	.003	10-80
	1994 ③	1.024	.974	.0004	.003	10-80
	1993-94 ④	.709	.657	.0004	.002	16-25
Crown Victoria & Grand Marquis	1992 ③	1.030	.972	.0005	.003	10-80
	1992-94 ④	.500	.440	.0005	.003	10-80
	1993-94 ③	1.030	.974	.0004	.003	10-80
Escort	1992-94 ③	.870	.790	—	.004	—
	1992-94 ④	.350	.280	—	.004	—
Festiva	1992-93	—	.460	—	—	—
Mark VII	1992 ③	1.030	.972	.0005	.003	15-125
	1992 ④	.945	.895	.0005	.004	16-125
Mark VIII	1993-94 ③	1.024	.974	.0004	.003	10-80
	1993-94 ④	.709	.657	.0004	.002	16-25
Mustang	1992-93 ①	.870	.810	②	.003	10-81

Continued

DISC BRAKE SPECIFICATIONS–Continued
ROTOR SPECIFICATIONS-Continued

Model	Year	Nominal Thickness Inch	Minimum Refinish Thickness Inch	Thickness Variation (Parallelism) Inch	Lateral Runout (T.I.R.) Inch	Finish (Micro-Inch)
Mustang—Cont'd	1992-93 ⑦	1.030	.972	.0005	.003	15-125
	1994 ③ ⑤	1.030	.970	.0004	.001	10-80
	1994 ③ ⑥	1.100	1.040	.0040	.001	10-80
	1994 ④	.550	.500	.0004	.002	16-25
Probe	1992 ③	.940	.860	.0040	.003	—
	1992 ④	.390	.350	—	.003	—
	1993 ③	.940	.860	.0010	.004	—
	1993 ④	.390	.350	.0010	.004	—
	1994 ③	—	.860	.0010	.004	—
	1994 ④	—	.315	—	—	—
Sable & Taurus	1992-93 ③	1.024	.974	.0005	.003	10-80
	1992 ④	.094	.900	.0005	.002	16-25
	1994 ③	1.020	.974	.0004	.002	15-125
	1993-94 ④	.094	.500	.0004	.002	16-25
Tempo & Topaz	1992-94	.945	.882	.0005	.003	10-80
Town Car	1992 ③	1.030	.972	.0005	.003	10-80
	1993-94 ③	1.030	.974	.0004	.003	10-80
	1992-94 ④	.500	.440	.0005	.003	10-80
Tracer	1992-94 ③	0.870	.790	—	.004	—
	1992-94 ④	0.350	.280	—	.004	—

① —Except 5.0L/V8-302 engine.
② —Models w/steel wheels, .0005 inch; models w/aluminum wheels, .0003 inch.
③ —Front brakes.
④ —Rear brakes.
⑤ —Except Cobra Mustang.
⑥ —Cobra Mustang.
⑦ —5.0L/V8-302 engine. @

CALIPER SPECIFICATIONS

Model	Year	Caliper Bore Diameter Inch
Aspire	1994	—
Capri	1992-94 ③	2.000
	1992-94 ④	1.190
Continental	1992 ③	2.598
	1992 ④	1.790
	1993-94 ③	2.598
	1993-94 ④	1.690
Cougar & Thunderbird	1992-94 ③	1.598
	1992-94 ④	1.790
Crown Victoria & Grand Marquis	1992-94 ③	2.880
	1992-94 ④	1.890
Escort	1992-94 ③	2.120
	1992-94 ④	1.190
Festiva	1992-93	2.120
Mark VII	1992 ③	2.870
	1992 ④	2.100
Mark VIII	1993-94 ③	2.598
	1994-94 ④	1.790

Model	Year	Caliper Bore Diameter Inch
Mustang	1992-93 ①	2.360
	1992-93 ②	2.870
	1994 ③	⑤
	1994 ④	1.500
Probe	1992-93 ③	2.120
	1992-93 ④	1.190
	1994	—
Sable & Taurus	1992 ③	2.598
	1992 ④	1.790
	1993-94 ③	2.850
	1993-94 ④	1.690
Tempo & Topaz	1992-94	2.362
Town Car	1992-94 ③	2.850
	1992-94 ④	1.890
Tracer	1992-94 ③	2.120
	1992-94 ④	1.190

① —Except Mustang w/5.0L/V8-302 engine.
② —Mustang w/5.0L/V8-302 engine.
③ —Front brakes.
④ —Rear brakes.
⑤ —Except Cobra Mustang, 2.60 inches; Cobra Mustang, 1.5 inches.

TIGHTENING SPECIFICATIONS

Component	Torque/Ft. Lbs.
Brake Hose To Caliper Bolt ④	16-22
Brake Hose To Caliper Bolt ⑤	18-24
Caliper Bolts ④	29-36
Key Screw	12-16
Locating Pins ③	29-37
Parking Brake Stop Bolt	8-9
Wheel Cylinder Bolts	7-9
Wheel Lug Nuts ①	65-88
Wheel Lug Nuts ②	65-104

①—Except Sable & Taurus.
②—Sable & Taurus.
③—Except Escort, Probe & Tracer.
④—Escort, Probe & Tracer.
⑤—1994 Mustang.

DRUM BRAKES

NOTE: Refer to "Application Chart" to determine which type brakes are used on vehicle being serviced.

TABLE OF CONTENTS

Application Chart

Model	Year	Type
Aspire	1994	4
Cougar	1992-94	6
Escort	1992-94	7
Festiva	1992-93	4
Mustang	1992-93	1
Probe	1992	5
Probe	1993-94	8
Sable	1992-94	3
Taurus	1992-94	3
Tempo	1992-94	2
Thunderbird	1992-94	6
Topaz	1992-94	2
Tracer	1992-94	7

Type 1

INDEX

PRECAUTIONS

When working on or around brake assemblies, care must be taken to prevent breathing asbestos dust, as many manufacturers incorporate asbestos fibers in the production of brake linings. During routine service operations the amount of asbestos dust from brake lining wear is at a low level, due to a chemical break down during use and a few precautions will minimize exposure. **Do not sand or grind brake linings unless suitable local exhaust ventilation equipment is used to prevent excessive asbestos exposure.**

The brake shoe and lining assemblies should be replaced if the lining is worn to within 1/32 inch of rivet heads (riveted linings) or brake shoe (bonded linings). It is recommended that both front and/or rear wheel sets be replaced whenever a respective shoe and lining assembly is replaced.

If a visual inspection does not adequately determine the condition of the linings, the brake shoe and lining assemblies should be removed and inspected. If shoes do not require replacement, reinstall them in their original positions. Brake shoes and linings should also be replaced if cracked or damaged.

1. Wear suitable respirator approved for asbestos dust use during all repair procedures.
2. When cleaning brake dust from brake

parts, use vacuum cleaner with highly efficient filter system. If suitable vacuum cleaner is not available, use water soaked rag. **Do not use compressed air or dry brush to clean brake parts.**

3. Keep work area clean, using same equipment as for cleaning brake parts.
4. Properly dispose of rags and vacuum cleaner bags by placing them in plastic bags.
5. Do not smoke or eat while working on brake systems. **Never use gasoline, kerosene, alcohol, motor oil, transmission fluid, or any fluid containing mineral oil to clean brake system components. These fluids will damage rubber caps and seals. If system contamination is suspected, check brake fluid in reservoir for dirt, discoloration, or separation (break down) of brake fluid into distinct layers. Drain and flush hydraulic system with clean brake fluid if contamination is suspected.**

INSPECTION

1. Inspect components for damage and unusual wear. Replace as necessary.
2. Inspect wheel cylinders. Boots which are torn, cut, or heat damaged indicate need for wheel cylinder replacement. Fluid spilling from boot center hole, or wetness around wheel cylinder ends indicates cup leakage and need for wheel cylinder replacement. **A small amount of fluid is always present and is considered normal, acting as lubricant for cylinder pistons.**
3. Inspect backing plate for evidence of seal leakage. If leakage exists, refer to individual chassis chapters for axle seal replacement procedure.
4. Inspect backing plate bolts and ensure they are tight.
5. Check adjuster screw operation. If satisfactory, lightly lubricate adjusting screw and washer with suitable brake lube. If operation is unsatisfactory, replace.
6. Using fine emery cloth or other suitable abrasive, clean rust and dirt from shoe contact surfaces on backing plate.

BRAKE SERVICE

REMOVAL

1. Raise and support rear of vehicle, then remove tire and wheel assembly.
2. Remove brake drum. If brake lining is dragging on brake drum, back off brake adjustment by rotating adjustment screw. Refer to individual chassis chapter for procedure. **If brake drum is rusted or corroded to axle flange and cannot be removed, lightly tap axle flange to drum mounting surface with suitable hammer.**
3. Install suitable wheel cylinder clamp over ends of wheel cylinder to retain pistons in bore.

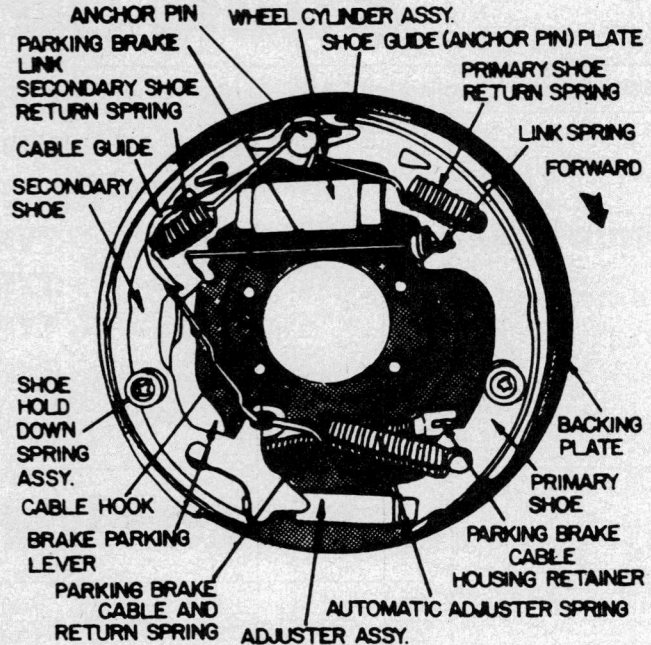

Fig. 1 Drum brake assembly

FM4079100050000X

4. Remove adjuster lever spring, primary and secondary shoe return springs using suitable pair of brake spring pliers, **Fig. 1.**
5. Remove shoe guide plate and adjuster cable and guide plate.
6. Using suitable tool, compress hold-down springs, then remove spring retainers, hold-down springs and pins.
7. Separate springs and remove from backing plate.
8. Disengage parking brake lever from secondary shoe.
9. Remove parking brake lever from cable.
10. Separate all components from brake shoes.
11. Clean dirt from brake drum, backing plate and all other components. **Do not use compressed air or dry brush to clean brake parts. Many brake parts contain asbestos fibers which, if inhaled, can cause serious injury. Clean brake parts with water soaked rag or suitable vacuum cleaner to minimize airborne dust.**

INSTALLATION

1. Lightly lubricate backing plate shoe contact surfaces with suitable brake lube.
2. Engage parking brake lever tang with secondary shoe.
3. Position brake shoes on backing plate, primary (short lining) shoe facing front of vehicle and secondary (long lining) facing rear. Secure brake shoes with hold-down springs, pins and retainers.
4. Install parking brake link and spring between shoes.

5. Loosen parking brake adjustment nut, then install parking brake cable on parking brake lever.
6. Install shoe guide plate and adjuster cable eyelet on anchor. Ensure adjuster cable crimp faces out.
7. Ensure parking brake link is properly positioned between brake shoes and wheel cylinder links are engaged in shoe web.
8. Using suitable brake spring pliers, install primary return spring from brake shoe to anchor, then the secondary return spring from brake shoe to anchor.
9. Remove wheel cylinder clamp installed during removal of brake shoes.
10. Tighten adjuster screw assembly to thread limit and back off 1/2 turn.
11. Install adjuster screw assembly between shoes. Ensure toothed wheel is on secondary shoe side. **Adjuster screw assemblies are stamped R (right) and L (left). To ensure proper adjuster operation, they must be installed on their respective sides.**
12. Hook adjuster cable hook into adjuster lever hole, then position adjuster spring hook in large hole in primary shoe web. Using suitable brake spring pliers, install adjuster spring in adjuster lever hole.
13. Ensure adjuster cable is properly seated in cable guide, then pull adjuster lever, cable and adjuster spring down and toward rear, engaging lever pivot hook in large hole of secondary shoe web.
14. After installation, check adjuster operation by pulling adjuster cable between cable guide and adjuster lever toward secondary shoe sufficiently to

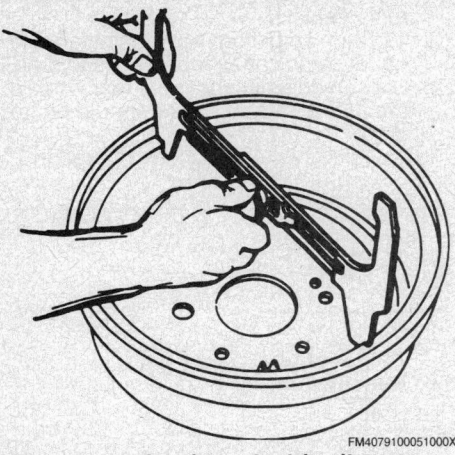

Fig. 2   Brake drum inside diameter measurement

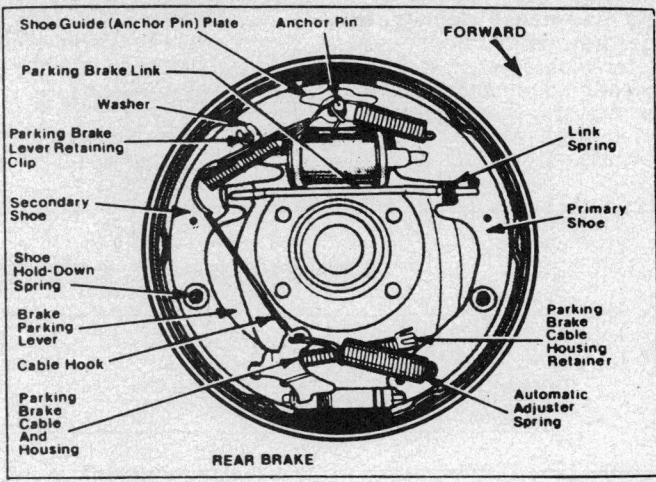

Fig. 4   Rear drum type brakes

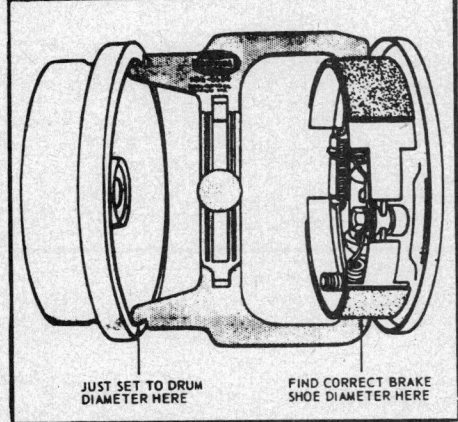

Fig. 3   Brake adjustment gauge

lift adjuster lever past one tooth on adjuster screw assembly. Adjuster lever should snap into position behind next tooth, then, upon release of adjuster cable, rotate toothed wheel one notch. If operation is not satisfactory, recheck installation.

15. Ensure brake shoe upper ends are seated against anchor pin and shoe assemblies are centered on backing plate. If not, back off parking brake adjustment.
16. Using suitable brake drum to shoe gauge, **Fig. 2,** measure brake drum inside diameter. Adjust brake shoes to dimension obtained on outside portion of gauge using adjuster screw.
17. Install brake drum, then the wheel and tire assembly.
18. If any hydraulic brake connections have been opened, bleed brake system as described in "Hydraulic Brake Systems" chapter.
19. Adjust parking brake. Refer to individual chassis chapter for procedures.
20. Inspect all hydraulic lines and connections for leakage and repair as necessary.
21. Check master cylinder fluid level and replenish as necessary.
22. Check brake pedal for proper feel and return.

23. Lower vehicle and road test. **Do not severely apply brakes immediately after installation of new brake linings or permanent damage may occur to linings, and/or brake drums may become scored. Brakes must be used moderately during first several hundred miles of operation to ensure proper burnishing of linings.**

ADJUSTMENTS

SERVICE BRAKES

1. Use brake shoe adjustment gauge, **Fig. 3,** to obtain drum inside diameter. Tighten adjusting knob on gauge to hold this setting.
2. Place opposite side of gauge over brake shoes and adjust shoes by turning adjuster screw until gauge just slides over linings. Rotate gauge around lining surface to assure proper lining diameter adjustment and clearance.
3. Install brake drum and wheel. Final adjustment is accomplished by making several firm reverse stops, using brake pedal.

Self-Adjusting Brakes

The self adjusting brakes, **Fig. 4,** have self-adjusting shoe mechanisms, assuring correct lining to drum clearances at all times. The automatic adjusters operate only when the brakes are applied as the vehicle is moving rearward.

Although the brakes are self-adjusting, an initial adjustment is necessary after the brake shoes have been relined or replaced, or when the length of the star wheel adjuster has been changed during some other service operation.

Frequent usage of an automatic transmission forward range to halt vehicle motion may prevent the automatic adjusters from functioning, thereby inducing low pedal heights. Should low pedal heights be encountered, it is recommended that numerous forward and reverse stops be performed with a firm pedal effort until satisfactory pedal height is obtained.

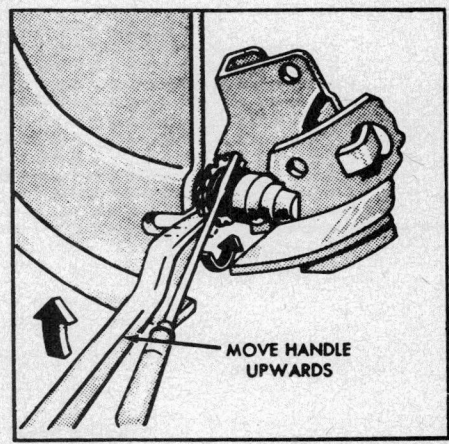

Fig. 5   Brake adjustment backing off by disengaging adjusting lever

If a low pedal height condition cannot be corrected by making numerous reverse stops (provided the hydraulic system is free of air), it indicates the self-adjusting mechanism is not functioning. It will be necessary to remove brake drums, then clean, free up and lubricate the adjusting mechanism. Then Adjust the brakes, being sure the parking brake is fully released.

Initial Adjustment

1. Remove adjusting hole cover from brake backing plate and, from backing plate side, turn adjusting screw upward with screwdriver or other suitable tool to expand shoes until slight drag is felt when drums are rotated.
2. Remove drum.
3. While holding adjusting hole out of engagement with adjusting screw, **Fig. 5,** back off adjusting screw about one full turn with fingers. **If finger movement will not turn screw, free it up. If this is not done, adjusting lever will not turn screw during vehicle operation. Lubricate screw with oil and coat with wheel bearing grease. Any other adjustment**

procedure may cause damage to adjusting screw with consequent self-adjuster problems.

4. Install wheel and drum and adjusting hole cover. Adjust brakes on remaining wheels in same manner.
5. If pedal height is not satisfactory, drive vehicle and make sufficient reverse stops with firm pedal effort until proper pedal height is obtained.

PARKING BRAKE

1. Make sure parking brake is released.
2. Place transmission in neutral and raise vehicle.
3. Tighten adjusting nut against cable equalizer to cause rear brakes to drag.
4. Loosen adjusting nut until rear wheels are fully released. There should be no drag.
5. Lower vehicle and check operation.

DRUM BRAKE SPECIFICATIONS

| Year | Model | Brake Drum | | |
		Inside Dia., Inch	Bore Limit (Max.), Inch	Max. Runout, Inch
1992-93	Mustang	9.00	9.06	.007

TIGHTENING SPECIFICATIONS

Year	Component	Torque/Ft. Lbs.
1992-93	Parking Brake Stop Bolt	8-9
	Wheel Cylinder Attaching Bolts	7-9
	Wheel Lug Nuts	65-88

Type 2

INDEX

PRECAUTIONS

When working on or around brake assemblies, care must be taken to prevent breathing asbestos dust, as many manufacturers incorporate asbestos fibers in the production of brake linings. During routine service operations the amount of asbestos dust from brake lining wear is at a low level, due to a chemical break down during use and a few precautions will minimize exposure. **Do not sand or grind brake linings unless suitable local exhaust ventilation equipment is used to prevent excessive asbestos exposure.**

The brake shoe and lining assemblies should be replaced if the lining is worn to within 1/32 inch of rivet heads (riveted linings) or brake shoe (bonded linings). It is recommended that both front and/or rear wheel sets be replaced whenever a respective shoe and lining assembly is replaced.

If a visual inspection does not adequately determine the condition of the linings, the brake shoe and lining assemblies should be removed and inspected. If shoes do not require replacement, reinstall them in their original positions. Brake shoes and linings should also be replaced if cracked or damaged.

1. Wear suitable respirator approved for asbestos dust use during all repair procedures.
2. When cleaning brake dust from brake parts, use vacuum cleaner with highly efficient filter system. If suitable vacuum cleaner is not available, use water soaked rag. **Do not use compressed air or dry brush to clean brake parts.**
3. Keep work area clean, using same equipment as for cleaning brake parts.
4. Properly dispose of rags and vacuum cleaner bags by placing them in plastic bags.
5. Do not smoke or eat while working on brake systems. **Never use gasoline, kerosene, alcohol, motor oil, transmission fluid, or any fluid containing mineral oil to clean brake system components. These fluids will** damage rubber caps and seals. If **system contamination is suspected, check brake fluid in reservoir for dirt, discoloration, or separation (break down) of brake fluid into distinct layers. Drain and flush hydraulic system with clean brake fluid if contamination is suspected.**

INSPECTION

1. Inspect components for damage and unusual wear. Replace as necessary.
2. Inspect wheel cylinders. Boots which are torn, cut, or heat damaged indicate need for wheel cylinder replacement. Fluid spilling from boot center hole, or wetness around wheel cylinder ends indicates cup leakage and need for wheel cylinder replacement. **A small amount of fluid is always present and is considered normal, acting as lubricant for cylinder pistons.**
3. Inspect backing plate for evidence of seal leakage. If leakage exists, refer to individual chassis chapters for axle seal replacement procedure.

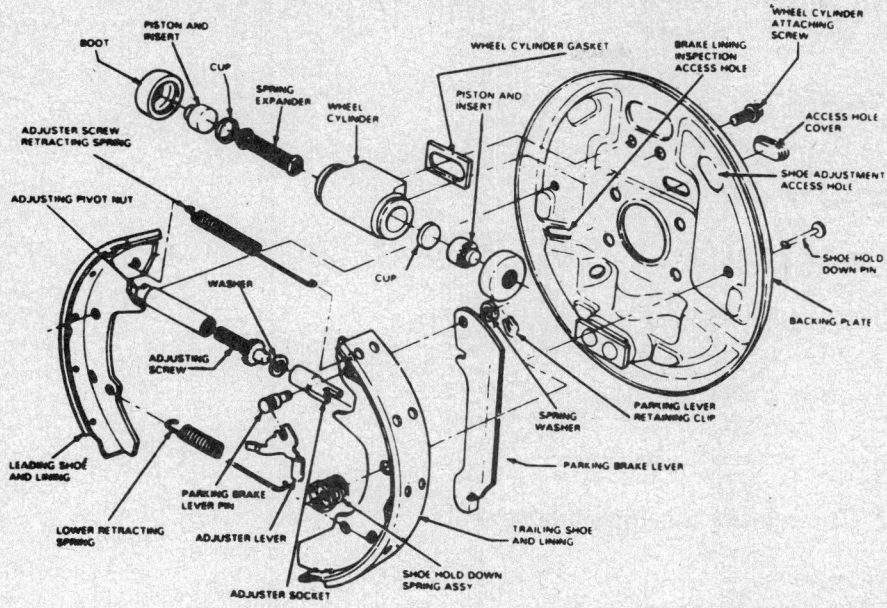

Fig. 1 Drum brake assembly

FM4089100007000X

BRAKE SERVICE

REMOVAL

4. Inspect backing plate bolts and ensure they are tight.
5. Check adjuster screw operation. If satisfactory, lightly lubricate adjusting screw and washer with suitable brake lube. If operation is unsatisfactory, replace.
6. Using fine emery cloth or other suitable abrasive, clean rust and dirt from shoe contact surfaces on backing plate.

BRAKE SERVICE

REMOVAL

1. Raise and support rear of vehicle, then remove tire and wheel assembly.
2. Remove brake drum. If brake lining is dragging on brake drum, back off brake adjustment. Refer to individual chassis chapters for procedure.
3. Using suitable tool, remove hold-down retainers, springs and pins, **Fig. 1.**
4. Remove brake shoes and adjuster assemblies from backing plate by lifting up and away from wheel cylinder assembly. **When removing brake shoe and adjuster assemblies, use care not to bend adjusting lever.**
5. Remove parking brake cable from parking brake lever.
6. Remove lower retracting spring, adjuster screw retracting spring and adjuster lever.
7. Separate brake shoes, then remove parking brake lever retaining clip and spring washer and slide lever off parking brake lever pin on trailing shoe.
8. Clean dirt from brake drum, backing plate and all other components. **Do not use compressed air or dry brush to clean brake parts. Many brake parts contain asbestos fibers which, if inhaled, can cause serious injury. Clean brake parts with water soaked rag or suitable vacuum cleaner to minimize airborne dust.**

INSTALLATION

1. Lightly lubricate backing plate shoe contact surfaces with suitable brake lubrication.
2. Remove brake drum hub grease seal and bearings, then clean and repack bearings and reinstall. Install new grease seal.
3. Assemble parking brake lever to trailing shoe, then install spring washer and retaining clip. Using suitable pliers, crimp retaining clip until securely fastened.
4. Attach parking brake cable to parking brake lever.
5. Assemble lower retracting spring to leading and trailing shoe assemblies, then spread lower part of shoes and install on backing plate.
6. Using suitable tool, install hold-down springs.
7. Tighten adjuster assembly, then back off 1/2 turn. Install adjuster assembly between leading shoe slot and trailing shoe/parking brake lever slot. Adjuster socket end slot must fit into trailing shoe/parking brake lever. **Adjuster assemblies are stamped R (right) and L (left). To ensure proper adjuster operation, they must be installed on their respective sides. Letter must be installed in upright position, facing wheel cylinder to ensure deeper of two slots in adjuster socket fits in parking brake lever.**
8. Install adjuster lever in parking brake lever groove and into adjuster socket slot.
9. Using suitable brake spring pliers, install adjusting screw retracting spring from leading shoe slot to adjuster lever notch.

10. Install brake drum. Refer to individual chassis chapters for wheel bearing adjustment procedure.
11. Install tire and wheel assembly.
12. If any hydraulic connections have been opened, bleed brake system.
13. Adjust parking brake. Refer to individual chassis chapters for procedure.
14. Inspect all hydraulic lines and connection for leakage, and repair as necessary.
15. Check master cylinder fluid level and replenish as necessary.
16. Check brake pedal for proper feel and return.
17. Lower vehicle and road test. **Do not severely apply brakes immediately after installation of new brake linings or permanent damage may occur to linings, and/or brake drums may become scored. Brakes must be used moderately during first several hundred miles of operation to ensure proper burnishing of linings.**

ADJUSTMENTS

SERVICE BRAKES

Although the brakes are self-adjusting, **Fig. 2,** an initial adjustment will be necessary after a brake repair. The initial adjustment can be obtained as follows:
1. Determine inside diameter of drum brake surface using brake shoe gauge tool No. D81L-1103-A, or equivalent. Adjust brake shoe diameter to fit gauge. Hold automatic adjusting lever out of engagement while rotating adjusting screw and ensure screw turns freely.
2. Install drum and wheel assembly, then adjust wheel bearings as shown in **Fig. 3.**
3. Complete adjustment by applying brakes several times, then check brake operation by making several stops from varying speeds. **If brake drum cannot be removed for brake servicing, remove rubber plug from backing plate inspection hole.**
4. Remove brake line to axle retention bracket. This will allow sufficient room for insertion of suitable tool to disengage adjusting lever and back off adjusting screw.

PARKING BRAKE

1. Pump brake pedal three times before making adjustment.
2. Place transmission in neutral, then raise and support vehicle.
3. Position parking brake control assembly in 12th notch position (two notches from full application).
4. Tighten adjusting nut until rear wheel brakes drag slightly with control assembly fully released. Repeat procedure as necessary to ensure proper adjustment.
5. Position control assembly in 12th notch, then loosen adjusting nut enough to eliminate rear brake drag with control assembly fully released.
6. Lower vehicle and check operation of parking brake.

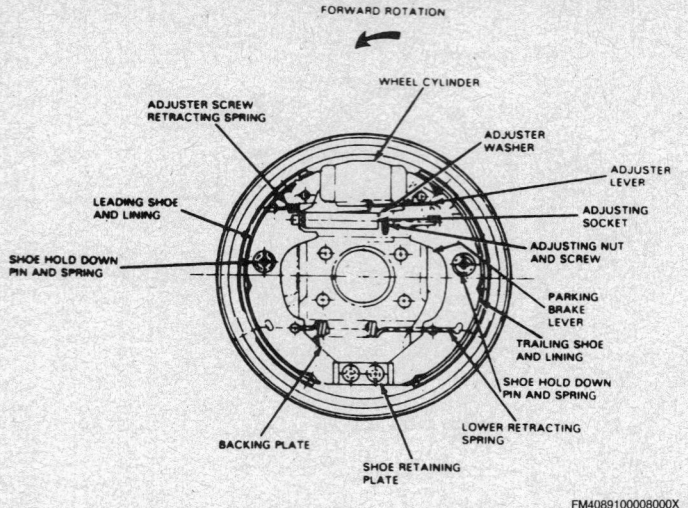

Fig. 2 Drum brake assembly adjustments

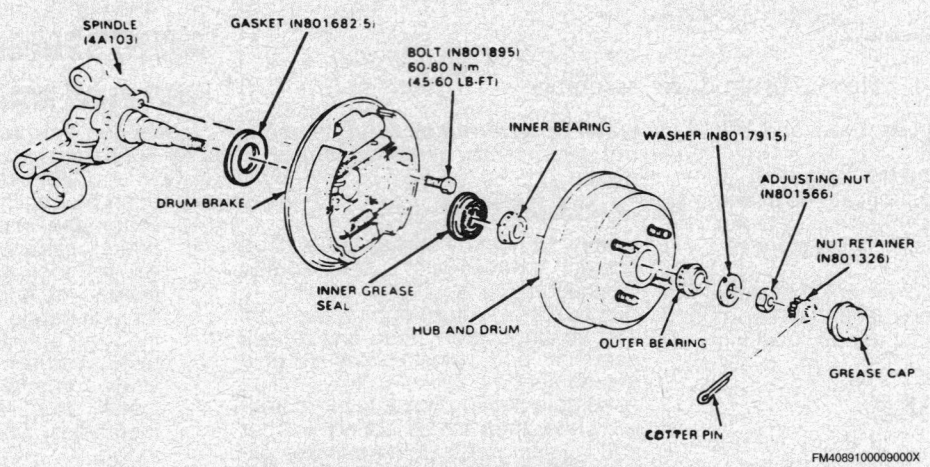

Fig. 3 Rear wheel bearing assembly

DRUM BRAKE SPECIFICATIONS

		Brake Drum		
Year	Model	Inside Dia. Inch	Bore Limit (Max.) Inch	Max. Runout Inch
1992-94	Tempo/ Topaz	8.06	8.12	.005

TIGHTENING SPECIFICATIONS

Year	Component	Torque/Ft. Lbs.
1992-94	Parking Brake Stop Bolt	8-9
	Wheel Cylinder Bolts	7-9
	Wheel Lug Nuts	65-88

Type 3

INDEX

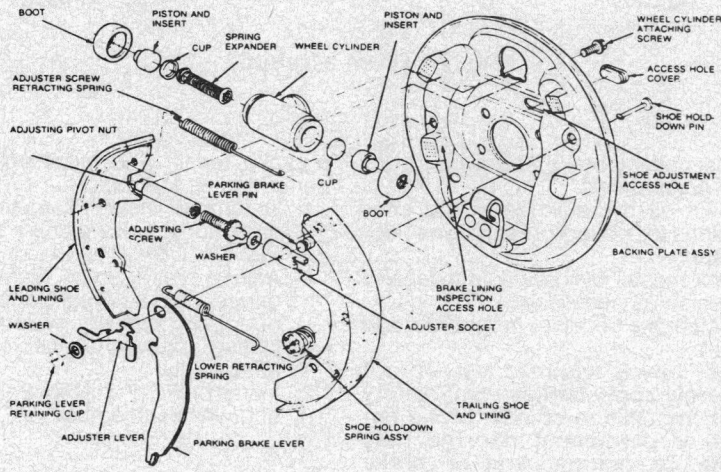

FM4089100010000X

Fig. 1   Drum brake assembly

PRECAUTIONS

When working on or around brake assemblies, care must be taken to prevent breathing asbestos dust, as many manufacturers incorporate asbestos fibers in the production of brake linings. During routine service operations the amount of asbestos dust from brake lining wear is at a low level, due to a chemical break down during use and a few precautions will minimize exposure. **Do not sand or grind brake linings unless suitable local exhaust ventilation equipment is used to prevent excessive asbestos exposure.**

The brake shoe and lining assemblies should be replaced if the lining is worn to within 1/32 inch of rivet heads (riveted linings) or brake shoe (bonded linings). It is recommended that both front and/or rear wheel sets be replaced whenever a respective shoe and lining assembly is replaced.

If a visual inspection does not adequately determine the condition of the linings, the brake shoe and lining assemblies should be removed and inspected. If shoes do not require replacement, reinstall them in their original positions. Brake shoes and linings should also be replaced if cracked or damaged.
1. Wear suitable respirator approved for asbestos dust use during all repair procedures.
2. When cleaning brake dust from brake parts, use vacuum cleaner with highly efficient filter system. If suitable vacuum cleaner is not available, use water soaked rag. **Do not use compressed air or dry brush to clean brake parts.**
3. Keep work area clean, using same equipment as for cleaning brake parts.
4. Properly dispose of rags and vacuum cleaner bags by placing them in plastic bags.
5. Do not smoke or eat while working on brake systems. **Never use gasoline, kerosene, alcohol, motor oil, transmission fluid, or any fluid containing mineral oil to clean brake system components. These fluids will damage rubber caps and seals. If system contamination is suspected, check brake fluid in reservoir for dirt, discoloration, or separation (break down) of brake fluid into distinct layers. Drain and flush hydraulic system with clean brake fluid if contamination is suspected.**

INSPECTION

1. Inspect components for damage and unusual wear. Replace as necessary.
2. Inspect wheel cylinders. Boots which are torn, cut, or heat damaged indicate need for wheel cylinder replacement. Fluid spilling from boot center hole, or wetness around wheel cylinder ends indicates cup leakage and need for wheel cylinder replacement. **A small amount of fluid is always present and is considered normal, acting as lubricant for cylinder pistons.**

3. Inspect backing plate for evidence of seal leakage. If leakage exists, refer to individual chassis chapters for axle seal replacement procedure.
4. Inspect backing plate bolts and ensure they are tight.
5. Check adjuster screw operation. If satisfactory, lightly lubricate adjusting screw and washer with suitable brake lube. If operation is unsatisfactory, replace.
6. Using fine emery cloth or other suitable abrasive, clean rust and dirt from shoe contact surfaces on backing plate.

BRAKE SERVICE

REMOVAL

1. Raise and support rear of vehicle, then remove tire and wheel assembly.
2. Remove brake drum. If brake lining is dragging on brake drum, back off brake adjustment. Refer to individual chassis chapters for procedures.
3. Using suitable tool, remove shoe hold-down springs and pins, **Fig. 1.**
4. Lift brake shoes, springs and adjuster assembly off backing plate and wheel cylinder assembly, being careful not to bend adjusting lever.
5. Remove parking brake cable from parking brake lever.
6. Remove retracting springs from lower brake shoe attachments and upper shoe to adjusting lever attachment points, then separate shoes and disengage adjuster mechanism.
7. Clean dirt from brake drum, backing plate and all other components. **Do not use compressed air or dry brush to clean brake parts. Many brake parts contain asbestos fibers which, if inhaled, can cause serious industry. Clean brake parts with water soaked rag or suitable vacuum cleaner to minimize airborne dust.**

INSTALLATION

1. Lightly lubricate backing plate shoe contact surfaces with suitable brake lubrication.
2. Apply thin uniform coat of suitable brake lube to adjuster screw threads and socket end of adjusting screw.
3. Install stainless steel washer over socket end of adjusting screw and install socket, then turn adjusting screw fully into adjusting pivot nut and back off 1/2 turn.

4. Assemble parking brake lever to trailing shoe and lining assembly by installing spring washer and a new horseshoe retaining clip. Crimp clip until it retains lever to shoe securely.
5. Attach parking brake cable to parking brake lever.
6. Attach lower shoe retracting spring to leading and trailing shoe assemblies and install on backing plate. It will be necessary to stretch retracting spring as shoes are installed downward over anchor plate to inside of shoe retaining plate.
7. Install adjuster screw assembly between leading shoe slot and the slot in trailing shoe and parking brake lever. Adjuster socket end slot must fit into the trailing shoe and parking brake lever. **Adjuster socket blade is marked "R" or "L" for right and left side brake assemblies. The R or L adjuster blade must be installed with letter R or L in upright position (facing wheel cylinder) on correct side to ensure deeper of two slots in adjuster sockets fits into parking brake lever.**
8. Assemble adjuster lever in groove located in parking brake lever pin and into slot of adjuster socket that fits into trailing shoe web.
9. Attach upper retracting spring to leading shoe slot and, using suitable tool, stretch other end of spring into notch on adjuster lever. **If adjuster lever does not contact star wheel after installing spring, adjuster socket may be improperly installed.**
10. Install brake drum. Refer to individual chassis chapters for wheel bearing adjustment procedure.
11. Install tire and wheel assembly.
12. If any hydraulic connections have been opened, bleed brake system as described in "Hydraulic Brake System section."

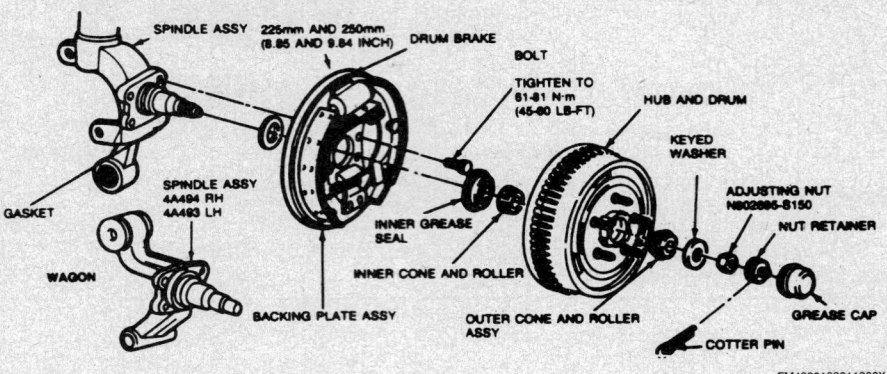

Fig. 2 Drum assembly

13. Adjust parking brake as described under "Adjustments."
14. Inspect all hydraulic lines and connections for leakage, repairing as necessary.
15. Check master cylinder fluid level and replenish as necessary.
16. Check brake pedal for proper feel and return.
17. Lower vehicle and road test. **Do not severely apply brakes immediately after installation of new brake linings or permanent damage may occur to linings, and/or brake drums may become scored. Brakes must be used moderately during first several hundred miles of operation to ensure proper burnishing of linings.**

ADJUSTMENTS
SERVICE BRAKES

Although the brakes are self-adjusting, an initial adjustment will be required after a brake repair. The initial adjustment is performed as follows:

1. Determine inside diameter of brake drum surface using brake shoe gauge tool No. D81L-1103-A, or equivalent. Adjust brake shoe diameter to fit gauge. Hold automatic adjusting lever out of engagement while rotating adjusting screw and ensure screw rotates freely.
2. Install brake drum, **Fig. 2,** then the tire and wheel assembly.

PARKING BRAKE

1. Ensure parking brake is released.
2. With transmission in neutral, raise and support vehicle.
3. Tighten parking brake nut against brake equalizer until rear brakes drag, then loosen nut until rear brakes are fully released.
4. Lower vehicle, then check parking brake operation.

DRUM BRAKE SPECIFICATIONS

| | | Brake Drum | | |
Year	Model	Inside Dia., Inch	Bore Limit (Max.), Inch	Max. Runout, Inch
SABLE & TAURUS				
1992-94	Except Sta. Wagon	8.86	8.92	.005
	Sta. Wagon	9.84	9.90	.005

TIGHTENING SPECIFICATIONS

Year	Component	Torque/Ft. Lbs.
1992-94	Parking Brake Stop Bolt	8-9
	Wheel Cylinder Attaching Bolts	7-9
	Wheel Lug Nuts	65-104

Type 4

INDEX

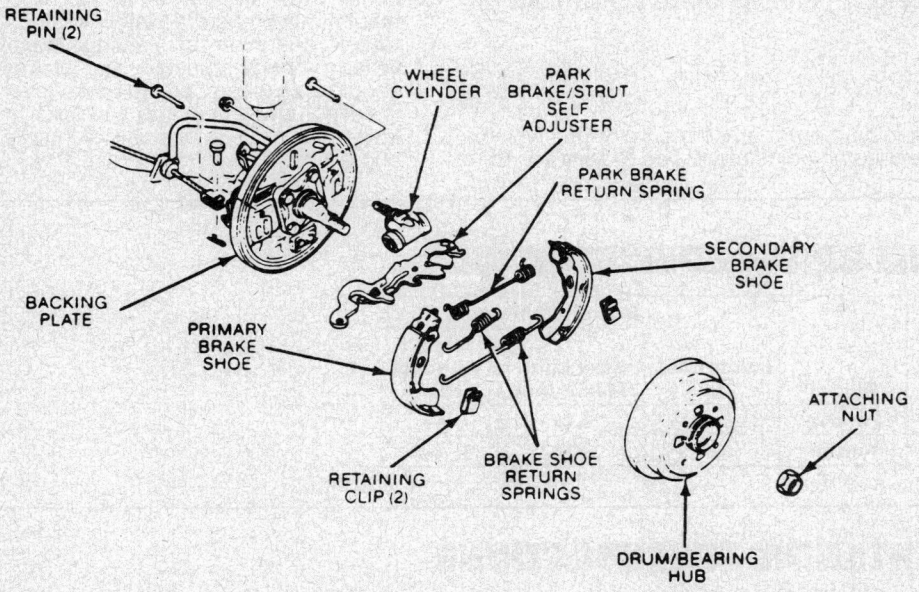

Fig. 1 Disassembled view of drum brake assembly

INSPECTION

1. Inspect components for damage and unusual wear. Replace as necessary.
2. Inspect wheel cylinders. Boots which are torn, cut, or heat damaged indicate need for wheel cylinder replacement. Fluid spilling from boot center hole, or wetness around wheel cylinder ends indicates cup leakage and need for wheel cylinder replacement. **A small amount of fluid is always present and is considered normal, acting as lubricant for cylinder pistons.**
3. Inspect backing plate for evidence of seal leakage. If leakage exists, refer to individual chassis chapters for axle seal replacement procedure.
4. Inspect backing plate bolts and ensure they are tight.
5. Check adjuster screw operation. If satisfactory, lightly lubricate adjusting screw and washer with suitable brake lube. If operation is unsatisfactory, replace.
6. Using fine emery cloth or other suitable abrasive, clean rust and dirt from shoe contact surfaces on backing plate.

PRECAUTIONS

When working on or around brake assemblies, care must be taken to prevent breathing asbestos dust, as many manufacturers incorporate asbestos fibers in the production of brake linings. During routine service operations the amount of asbestos dust from brake lining wear is at a low level, due to a chemical break down during use and a few precautions will minimize exposure. **Do not sand or grind brake linings unless suitable local exhaust ventilation equipment is used to prevent excessive asbestos exposure.**

The brake shoe and lining assemblies should be replaced if the lining is worn to within 1/32 inch of rivet heads (riveted linings) or brake shoe (bonded linings). It is recommended that both front and/or rear wheel sets be replaced whenever a respective shoe and lining assembly is replaced.

If a visual inspection does not adequately determine the condition of the linings, the brake shoe and lining assemblies should be removed and inspected. If shoes do not require replacement, reinstall them in their original positions. Brake shoes and linings should also be replaced if cracked or damaged.

1. Wear suitable respirator approved for asbestos dust use during all repair procedures.
2. When cleaning brake dust from brake parts, use vacuum cleaner with highly efficient filter system. If suitable vacuum cleaner is not available, use water soaked rag. **Do not use compressed air or dry brush to clean brake parts.**
3. Keep work area clean, using same equipment as for cleaning brake parts.
4. Properly dispose of rags and vacuum cleaner bags by placing them in plastic bags.
5. Do not smoke or eat while working on brake systems. **Never use gasoline, kerosene, alcohol, motor oil, transmission fluid, or any fluid containing mineral oil to clean brake system components. These fluids will damage rubber caps and seals. If system contamination is suspected, check brake fluid in reservoir for dirt, discoloration, or separation (break down) of brake fluid into distinct layers. Drain and flush hydraulic system with clean brake fluid if contamination is suspected.**

BRAKE SERVICE

REMOVAL

1. Raise and support vehicle, then remove rear wheel.
2. Remove locknut and brake drum. **Locknut on right side of vehicle has lefthand threads. Turn locknut clockwise to remove.**
3. Remove hold-down clips and retaining pins, **Fig. 1.**
4. Remove all return springs, then the primary and secondary brake shoes.
5. Remove cotter pin, then the clevis pin from parking brake strut/self adjuster. Disengage parking cable from self adjuster.

INSTALLATION

1. Clean backing plate with factory approved vacuum cleaner.
2. Lubricate backing plate shoe pads with suitable high temperature brake grease.
3. Install and position parking brake strut/self adjuster onto backing plate.
4. Install upper return spring to primary brake shoe, then position shoe on backing plate and install retaining pin and hold-down clip, **Fig. 1.**

5. Connect upper return spring to secondary brake shoe, then position secondary shoe on backing plate and install retaining pin and hold-down clip.
6. Install parking brake return spring.
7. Install lower return spring onto primary and secondary shoes.
8. Connect parking cable onto self adjuster, then install clevis and cotter pins.
9. Push on adjuster cam with screwdriver to position self adjuster in fully released position.
10. Install brake drum and locknut.
11. Push brake pedal down several times to set self adjuster, then install rear wheel.
12. Adjust parking brake as required.

ADJUSTMENTS

SERVICE BRAKES

These models are equipped with self-

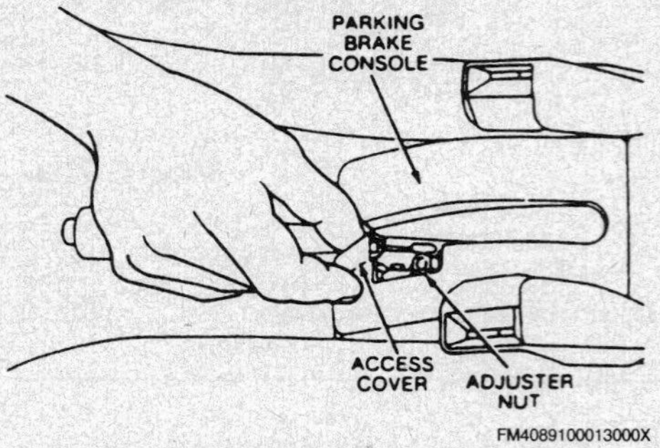

Fig. 2 Parking brake adjustment

adjusting drum brake mechanisms, which require no adjustment. The brakes are ad-

PARKING BRAKE

justed as necessary, whenever the service brakes are applied.
1. Ensure parking lever is in fully released position.
2. Remove adjuster nut access cover from parking brake console, **Fig. 2.**
3. Remove adjuster nut locking clip, then raise and support rear of vehicle.
4. Tighten adjuster nut until slight drag is felt when rear wheels are rotated.
5. Loosen adjuster nut in small increments until brake drag is eliminated.
6. Check operation of parking brake. When properly adjusted, rear brakes should lock when parking brake lever is pulled upward eight to 11 clicks.
7. Lower vehicle, then install locking clip and access cover.

DRUM BRAKE SPECIFICATIONS

| Year | Model | Brake Drum | | |
		Inside Dia., Inch	Bore Limit (Max.), Inch	Max. Runout, Inch
1992–93	Festiva	6.69	6.75	—
1994	Aspire	6.69	6.75	—

TIGHTENING SPECIFICATIONS

Year	Component	Torque/Ft. Lbs.
1992–94	**Parking Brake Stop Bolt**	8-9
	Wheel Cylinder Bolts	7-9
	Wheel Lug Nuts	65-88

Type 5

INDEX

PRECAUTIONS

When working on or around brake assemblies, care must be taken to prevent breathing asbestos dust, as many manufacturers incorporate asbestos fibers in the production of brake linings. During routine service operations the amount of asbestos dust from brake lining wear is at a low level, due to a chemical break down during use and a few precautions will minimize exposure. **Do not sand or grind brake linings unless suitable local exhaust ventilation equipment is used to prevent excessive asbestos exposure.**

The brake shoe and lining assemblies should be replaced if the lining is worn to within $1/32$ inch of rivet heads (riveted linings) or brake shoe (bonded linings). It is recommended that both front and/or rear wheel sets be replaced whenever a respective shoe and lining assembly is replaced.

If a visual inspection does not adequately determine the condition of the linings, the brake shoe and lining assemblies should be removed and inspected. If

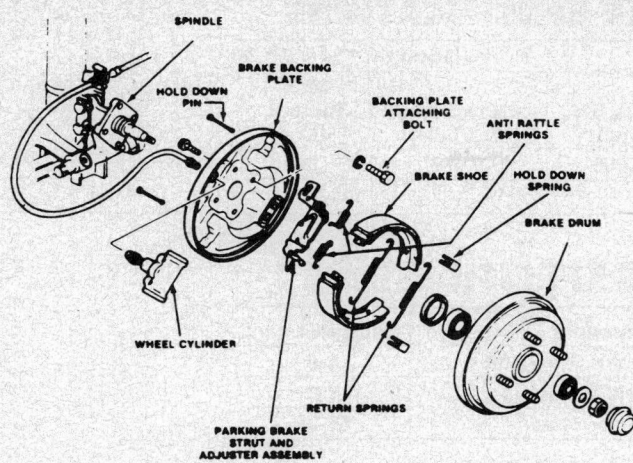

Fig. 1 Exploded view of rear drum brake

shoes do not require replacement, reinstall them in their original positions. Brake shoes and linings should also be replaced if cracked or damaged.

1. Wear suitable respirator approved for asbestos dust use during all repair procedures.
2. When cleaning brake dust from brake parts, use vacuum cleaner with highly efficient filter system. If suitable vacuum cleaner is not available, use water soaked rag. **Do not use compressed air or dry brush to clean brake parts.**
3. Keep work area clean, using same equipment as for cleaning brake parts.
4. Properly dispose of rags and vacuum cleaner bags by placing them in plastic bags.
5. Do not smoke or eat while working on brake systems. **Never use gasoline, kerosene, alcohol, motor oil, transmission fluid, or any fluid containing mineral oil to clean brake system components. These fluids will damage rubber caps and seals. If system contamination is suspected, check brake fluid in reservoir for dirt, discoloration, or separation (break down) of brake fluid into distinct layers. Drain and flush hydraulic system with clean brake fluid if contamination is suspected.**

INSPECTION

1. Inspect components for damage and unusual wear. Replace as necessary.
2. Inspect wheel cylinders. Boots which are torn, cut, or heat damaged indicate need for wheel cylinder replacement. Fluid spilling from boot center hole, or wetness around wheel cylinder ends indicates cup leakage and need for wheel cylinder replacement. **A small amount of fluid is always present and is considered normal, acting as lubricant for cylinder pistons.**
3. Inspect backing plate for evidence of seal leakage. If leakage exists, refer to individual chassis chapters for axle seal replacement procedure.
4. Inspect backing plate bolts and ensure they are tight.
5. Check adjuster screw operation. If satisfactory, lightly lubricate adjusting screw and washer with suitable brake lube. If operation is unsatisfactory, replace.
6. Using fine emery cloth or other suitable abrasive, clean rust and dirt from shoe contact surfaces on backing plate.

BRAKE SERVICE
REMOVAL

1. Raise and support rear of vehicle.
2. Remove wheel and tire assembly, then the grease cap.
3. Using suitable chisel, raise staked portion of wheel bearing locknut.
4. Remove rear bearing locknut. To do so, turn locknut at lefthand rear wheel bearing counterclockwise and locknut at righthand rear wheel bearing clockwise.
5. Remove outer wheel bearing, then remove brake drum and bearing hub assembly.
6. Remove brake shoe hold-down springs, then pull front shoe away from backing plate. Disconnect return springs and remove front shoe, **Fig. 1.**
7. Remove return springs from rear shoe, then disconnect anti-rattle spring attaching rear shoe to parking brake strut and remove rear shoe.
8. If necessary, remove adjuster assembly.

INSTALLATION

1. Lubricate six shoe contact pads with high temperature grease D7AZ-19590-A or equivalent, then the adjuster mechanism toothed quadrant and anchor plate.
2. Position rear brake shoe in parking brake strut and install rear hold-down pin and spring.
3. Hook brake shoe return springs in position on rear brake shoe.
4. Connect brake shoe return springs to front shoe and push into place against backing plate.
5. Install front brake shoe hold-down pin and spring.
6. Insert screwdriver between knurled quadrant and parking brake strut, then twist screwdriver until quadrant touches backing plate.
7. Install drum, then firmly apply brakes two or three times to adjust rear brakes.

ADJUSTMENTS
BRAKE PEDAL HEIGHT

1. Check distance from center of pedal pad to floor.
2. Distance should be 8.74-8.94 inches.
3. If adjustment is required, loosen stop lamp switch locknut.
4. Rotate switch until pedal height is 8.74-8.94 inches.
5. After adjustment, tighten switch locknut.

BRAKE PEDAL FREEPLAY

1. If equipped with power brakes, depress pedal a few times in order eliminate vacuum in power booster.
2. Depress brake pedal by hand, then check brake pedal freeplay (until valve plunger contacts stopper plate, then resistance is felt). Freeplay should be .16-.28 inch.
3. If adjustment is required, loosen clevis locknut on brake pedal pushrod.
4. Turn clevis to obtain .16-.28 inch freeplay.
5. After adjustment, tighten clevis locknut.

PARKING BRAKE

1. Normal parking brake adjustment is made at hand lever between seats. Remove six screws in center console, then the console.
2. Tighten parking brake adjusting nut on left side of parking brake lever. This shortens equalizer cable. Tighten adjusting nut until it takes seven to 10 notches to fully set parking brake.

DRUM BRAKE SPECIFICATIONS

| Year | Model | Brake Drum | | |
		Inside Dia., Inch	Bore Limit (Max.), Inch	Max. Runout, Inch
1992	Probe	9.055	9.078	.005

TIGHTENING SPECIFICATIONS

Year	Component	Torque/Ft. Lbs.
1992	Parking Brake Stop Bolt	8-9
	Wheel Cylinder Bolts	7-9
	Wheel Lug Nuts	65-88

Type 6
INDEX

PRECAUTIONS

When working on or around brake assemblies, care must be taken to prevent breathing asbestos dust, as many manufacturers incorporate asbestos fibers in the production of brake linings. During routine service operations the amount of asbestos dust from brake lining wear is at a low level, due to a chemical break down during use and a few precautions will minimize exposure. **Do not sand or grind brake linings unless suitable local exhaust ventilation equipment is used to prevent excessive asbestos exposure.**

The brake shoe and lining assemblies should be replaced if the lining is worn to within 1/32 inch of rivet heads (riveted linings) or brake shoe (bonded linings). It is recommended that both front and/or rear wheel sets be replaced whenever a respective shoe and lining assembly is replaced.

If a visual inspection does not adequately determine the condition of the linings, the brake shoe and lining assemblies should be removed and inspected. If shoes do not require replacement, reinstall them in their original positions. Brake shoes and linings should also be replaced if cracked or damaged.

1. Wear suitable respirator approved for asbestos dust use during all repair procedures.

2. When cleaning brake dust from brake parts, use vacuum cleaner with highly efficient filter system. If suitable vacuum cleaner is not available, use water soaked rag. **Do not use compressed air or dry brush to clean brake parts.**
3. Keep work area clean, using same equipment as for cleaning brake parts.
4. Properly dispose of rags and vacuum cleaner bags by placing them in plastic bags.
5. Do not smoke or eat while working on brake systems. **Never use gasoline, kerosene, alcohol, motor oil, transmission fluid, or any fluid containing mineral oil to clean brake system components. These fluids will damage rubber caps and seals. If system contamination is suspected, check brake fluid in reservoir for dirt, discoloration, or separation (break down) of brake fluid into distinct layers. Drain and flush hydraulic system with clean brake fluid if contamination is suspected.**

INSPECTION

1. Inspect components for damage and unusual wear. Replace as necessary.
2. Inspect wheel cylinders. Boots which are torn, cut, or heat damaged indicate need for wheel cylinder replacement.

Fluid spilling from boot center hole, or wetness around wheel cylinder ends indicates cup leakage and need for wheel cylinder replacement. **A small amount of fluid is always present and is considered normal, acting as lubricant for cylinder pistons.**
3. Inspect backing plate for evidence of seal leakage. If leakage exists, refer to individual chassis chapters for axle seal replacement procedure.
4. Inspect backing plate bolts and ensure they are tight.
5. Check adjuster screw operation. If satisfactory, lightly lubricate adjusting screw and washer with suitable brake lube. If operation is unsatisfactory, replace.
6. Using fine emery cloth or other suitable abrasive, clean rust and dirt from shoe contact surfaces on backing plate.

BRAKE SERVICE

REMOVAL

1. Raise and support rear of vehicle, then remove tire and wheel assembly.
2. Remove brake drum.
3. Install suitable wheel cylinder clamp over ends of wheel cylinder to retain pistons in bore.
4. Disconnect parking brake cable from parking brake lever.

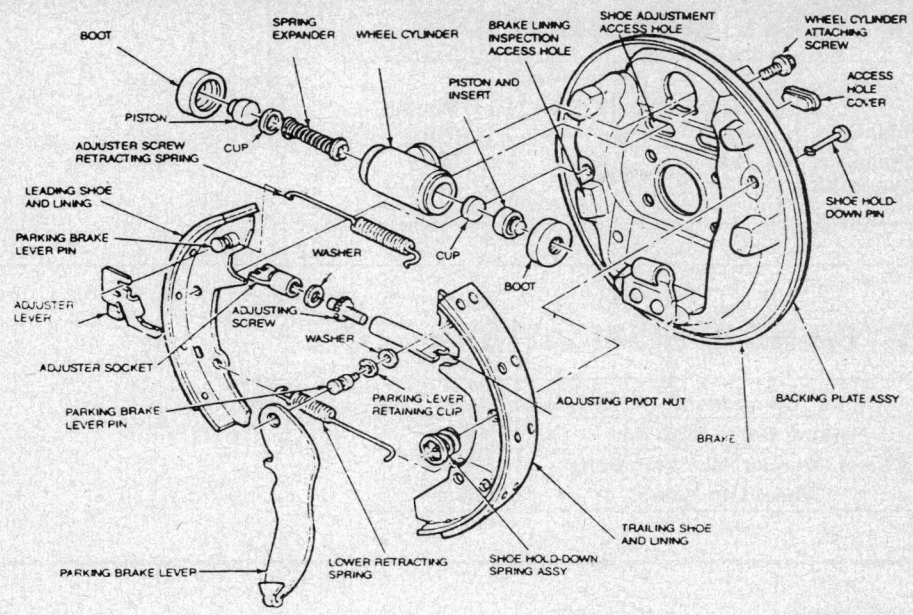

Fig. 1   Exploded view of brake drum assembly

FM4089100015000X

5. Remove two brake shoe hold-down retainers, springs and pins, **Fig. 1.**
6. Spread brake shoes over piston shoe guide slots, then lift brake shoes, springs and adjuster off backing plate as an assembly.
7. Remove adjuster spring.
8. Remove retracting springs to separate shoes.
9. Remove parking brake lever retaining clip, spring and washer.
10. Remove lever from pin.

INSTALLATION

1. Lightly lubricate backing plate shoe contact surfaces with suitable brake lube.
2. Install parking brake lever to trailing shoe with spring washer and new retaining clip, **Fig. 1.**
3. Position trailing shoe or backing plate and attach hand brake cable.
4. Install adjuster assembly to slots in brake shoes. Socket end must fit into slot in leading shoe (wider slot). Slot in adjuster nut must fit into slots in trailing shoe and parking brake lever.
5. Install adjuster lever on pin on leading shoe and to slot in adjuster socket.
6. Install upper retracting spring in slot on trailing shoe and slot in adjuster lever. Adjuster lever should contact star and adjuster assembly.
7. Assemble parking brake cable to trailing shoe and parking brake lever.
8. Install lower retracting spring to leading-trailing shoe.
9. Install assembly to backing plate fitting shoes into wheel cylinder piston slots.
10. Install adjuster socket to leading shoe and lining assembly.
11. Install brake shoe anchor pins, springs and retainers.
12. Remove brake cylinder clamp and install brake drum.

ADJUSTMENTS

BRAKE PEDAL HEIGHT

1. Run engine at normal operating condition.
2. Measure distance to top center of brake pedal pad.
3. Free height should be approximately 7.35 inches.
4. If brake pedal is not within specification, check brake pedal, booster or master cylinder to ensure correct parts are installed. Replace worn or damaged parts.

BRAKE PEDAL TRAVEL

1. With engine running in neutral or park position, block drive wheels, then release parking brake.
2. Install brake pedal effort gauge No. 021-00001, or equivalent, and check pedal travel, with 25 lbs. of pressure applied to brake pedal, travel should not exceed 3.0 inches.
3. If pedal travel exceeds specification, make several reverse stops with forward stop before each.

4. If travel still exceeds specification, remove brake drums and check brake adjusters, system may require bleeding.

PARKING BRAKE

1. Apply and release parking brake several times, then place transmission in neutral position.
2. Raise and support vehicle.
3. Release tensioner by rotating locking lever away from threaded rod. Tensioner spring will take up slack and preload cables. **Do not pull down on locking lever, as it will pull cables down and cause improper tension.**

TECHNICAL SERVICE BULLETINS

BRAKE PEDAL PULSATION FROM DRUM ROUGHNESS

1992–93 Cougar & Thunderbird

Rear brake drum roughness may occur because of the rear drum's manufacturing tolerances.

Install new rear brake drums in axle sets which are manufactured to revised tolerances to minimize rear brake roughness. Refer to "Brake Service" for service details.

ROUGHNESS, PULSATION OR STEERING WHEEL SHAKE

1992 Cougar & Thunderbird

Brake roughness, pulsation and steering wheel shake may occur because of uneven rotor wear due to abrasive brake pads or hub or rotor high and low spots (improper orientation during assembly). Usually these vehicles appear to be corrected by just installing new pads and rotors. However, they can repeat the condition after some time in service unless proper attention is given to rear brake drums.

Rear brake drums can contribute to the complaint. Brakes may feel as if the front brake concern was not fully corrected. In some cases, vibration is found in rear drums from an out of specification condition.

1. Use parking brake moderately instead of service brakes from 55 mph to 45 mph to determine if rear brakes are contributing to concern.
2. If roughness is present, service rear drums as necessary. Refer to "Brake Service" for service details.

DRUM BRAKE SPECIFICATIONS

| Year | Model | Brake Drum | | |
		Inside Dia., Inch	Bore Limit (Max.), Inch	Max. Runout, Inch
1992-94	Cougar & Thunderbird	9.80	9.90	.007

TIGHTENING SPECIFICATIONS

Year	Component	Torque/Ft. Lbs.
1992-94	Parking Brake Stop Bolt	8-9
	Wheel Cylinder Attaching Bolts	7-9
	Wheel Lug Nuts	65-88

Type 7

INDEX

PRECAUTIONS

When working on or around brake assemblies, care must be taken to prevent breathing asbestos dust. Many manufacturers incorporate asbestos fibers in the production of brake linings. During routine service operations, the amount of asbestos dust from brake lining wear is at a low level due to a chemical break down during use. **Do not sand or grind brake linings unless suitable local exhaust ventilation equipment is used to prevent excessive asbestos exposure.**

The brake shoe and lining assemblies should be replaced if the lining is worn to within 1/32 inch of rivet heads (riveted linings) or brake shoe (bonded linings). It is recommended that both front and/or rear wheel sets be replaced whenever a respective shoe and lining assembly is replaced.

If a visual inspection does not adequately determine the condition of the linings, the brake shoe and lining assemblies should be removed and inspected. If shoes do not require replacement, reinstall them in their original positions. Brake shoes and linings should also be replaced if cracked or damaged.

1. Wear suitable respirator approved for asbestos dust use during all repair procedures.
2. When cleaning brake dust from brake parts, use vacuum cleaner with highly efficient filter system. If suitable vacuum cleaner is not available, use water soaked rag. **Do not use compressed air or dry brush to clean brake parts.**
3. Keep work area clean, using same equipment as for cleaning brake parts.
4. Properly dispose of rags and vacuum cleaner bags by placing them in plastic bags.
5. Do not smoke or eat while working on brake systems. **Never use gasoline, kerosene, alcohol, motor oil, transmission fluid, or any fluid containing mineral oil to clean brake system components. These fluids will damage rubber caps and seals. If system contamination is suspected, check brake fluid in reservoir for dirt, discoloration, or separation (break down) of brake fluid into distinct layers. Drain and flush hydraulic system with clean brake fluid if contamination is suspected.**

INSPECTION

1. Inspect components for damage and unusual wear. Replace as necessary.
2. Inspect wheel cylinders. Boots which are torn, cut, or heat damaged indicate need for wheel cylinder replacement. Fluid spilling from boot center hole, or wetness around wheel cylinder ends indicates cup leakage and need for wheel cylinder replacement. **A small amount of fluid is always present and is considered normal, acting as lubricant for cylinder pistons.**
3. Inspect backing plate for evidence of seal leakage. If leakage exists, refer to individual chassis chapters for axle seal replacement procedure.
4. Inspect backing plate bolts and ensure tightness.
5. Check adjuster screw operation. If satisfactory, lightly lubricate adjusting screw and washer with suitable brake lube. If operation is unsatisfactory, replace.
6. Using fine emery cloth or other suitable abrasive, clean rust and dirt from shoe contact surfaces on backing plate.

BRAKE SERVICE

REMOVAL

1. Raise and support vehicle, then remove wheel and tire assembly.
2. Remove brake drum screws, then the brake drum.
3. Remove wheel hub as described in specific chassis chapter.
4. Remove brake shoe retracting springs, **Fig. 1**, using screwdriver to push in and twist spring to disengage it from pin.
5. Remove righthand anti-rattle spring.
6. Push and turn brake shoe hold down springs and remove.

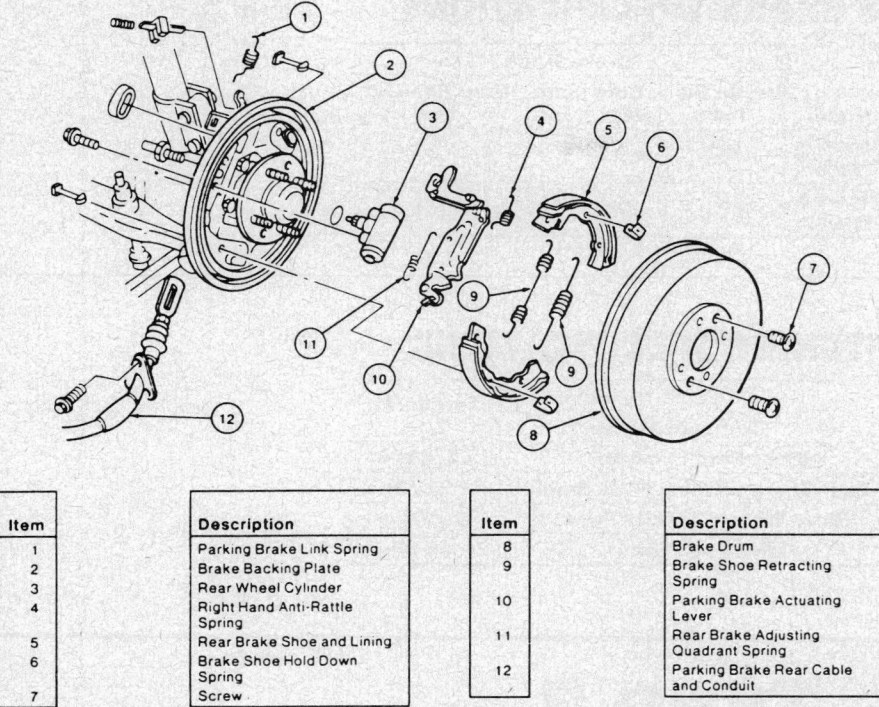

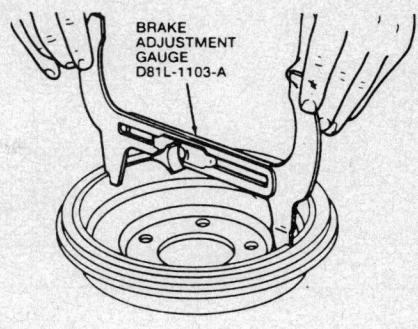

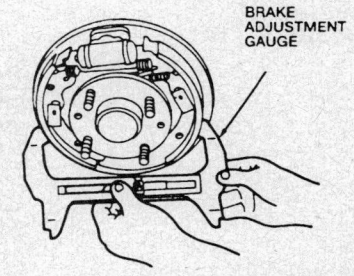

Item	Description	Item	Description
1	Parking Brake Link Spring	8	Brake Drum
2	Brake Backing Plate	9	Brake Shoe Retracting Spring
3	Rear Wheel Cylinder	10	Parking Brake Actuating Lever
4	Right Hand Anti-Rattle Spring	11	Rear Brake Adjusting Quadrant Spring
5	Rear Brake Shoe and Lining	12	Parking Brake Rear Cable and Conduit
6	Brake Shoe Hold Down Spring		
7	Screw		

FM4089400016000X

Fig. 1   Exploded view of drum brake

FM4089400017000X

Fig. 2   Drum brake & shoe lining measurements

7. Remove primary rear brake shoe and lining from brake backing plate, then the secondary rear brake shoe and lining.

INSTALLATION

1. If rear brake shoes and linings are to be reused, inspect rear brake shoes and linings to ensure they meet specifications.
2. Clean brake backing plate with suitable brake vacuum, then lubricate brake shoe and lining contact points and area where rear brake shoes and linings ride with suitable lubricant.
3. Tighten wheel cylinder bolts to specifications.
4. If new rear brake shoes and linings are being installed, resurface brake drums to remove glazing and ensure an equal friction surface from side to side. Resurfacing will also correct out-of-round and bell conditions.
5. Position secondary rear brake shoe and lining on brake backing plate, then install one brake shoe hold down spring.
6. Position primary rear brake shoe and lining on brake backing plate, then install other brake shoe hold down spring.
7. Install righthand anti-rattle spring, then the upper and lower brake shoe

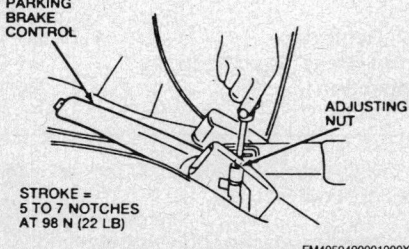

STROKE = 5 TO 7 NOTCHES AT 98 N (22 LB)

FM4059400001000X

Fig. 3   Parking brake adjustment

retracting springs.
8. Measure brake drum and rear brake shoes and linings with brake adjustment gauge tool No. D81L-1103-A, or equivalent, **Fig. 2**.
9. Inset screwdriver into knurled quadrant of rear quad operating lever stopper, **Fig. 1**, then adjust rear brake shoes and linings to same measurement of brake drum.
10. Install wheel hub as described in specific chassis section.
11. Install brake drum, then the brake drum screws. Tighten brake drum screws to specifications.
12. Install wheel and tire assembly.

ADJUSTMENTS

PARKING BRAKE

1. Start engine and move shift control selector lever into reverse position.
2. With vehicle moving in reverse, press and release brake pedal several times.
3. Move shift control selector lever into park position, then stop engine.
4. Remove parking brake console as follows:
   a. Position both front seats to rearmost position, then remove front parking brake console screws.
   b. Recline both front seats, then remove rear parking brake console screws.
   c. Unbuckle safety belts, then, with parking brake control engaged, remove parking brake console.
5. Turn adjusting nut, **Fig. 3**, until parking brake control stroke is five to seven notches when pulled with 22 lbs. of force.
6. Install parking brake console as follows:
   a. Feed safety belt ends through proper holes in parking brake console, then install parking brake console over parking brake control.
   b. Install parking brake console screws, then return both seats to original positions.

DRUM BRAKE SPECIFICATIONS

| Year | Model | Brake Drum | | |
		Inside Dia., Inch	Bore Limit (Max.), Inch	Max. Run-Out, Inch
1992	Escort & Tracer	9.00	9.04	.005
1993-94	Escort & Tracer	7.87	7.91	.005

TIGHTENING SPECIFICATIONS

Year	Component	Torque/Ft. Lbs.
1992-94	Brake Drum Screws	89-123 ①
	Rear Brake Backing Plate Bolts	33-43
	Rear Wheel Cylinder Bolts	84-108 ①
	Wheel Lug Nuts	65-87

① —Inch lbs.

Type 8

INDEX

PRECAUTIONS

When working on or around brake assemblies, care must be taken to prevent breathing asbestos dust. Many manufacturers incorporate asbestos fibers in the production of brake linings. During routine service operations the amount of asbestos dust from brake lining wear is at a low level, due to a chemical break down during use. **Do not sand or grind brake linings unless suitable local exhaust ventilation equipment is used to prevent excessive asbestos exposure.**

The brake shoe and lining assemblies should be replaced if the lining is worn to within 1/32 inch of rivet heads (riveted linings) or brake shoe (bonded linings). It is recommended that both front and/or rear wheel sets be replaced whenever a respective shoe and lining assembly is replaced.

If a visual inspection does not adequately determine the condition of the linings, the brake shoe and lining assemblies should be removed and inspected. If shoes do not require replacement, reinstall them in their original positions. Brake shoes and linings should also be replaced if cracked or damaged.

1. Wear suitable respirator approved for asbestos dust use during all repair procedures.
2. When cleaning brake dust from brake parts, use vacuum cleaner with highly efficient filter system. If suitable vacuum cleaner is not available, use water soaked rag. **Do not use compressed air or dry brush to clean brake parts.**
3. Keep work area clean, using same equipment as for cleaning brake parts.
4. Properly dispose of rags and vacuum cleaner bags by placing them in plastic bags.
5. Do not smoke or eat while working on brake systems. **Never use gasoline, kerosene, alcohol, motor oil, transmission fluid, or any fluid containing mineral oil to clean brake system components. These fluids will damage rubber caps and seals. If system contamination is suspected, check brake fluid in reservoir for dirt, discoloration, or separation (break down) of brake fluid into distinct layers. Drain and flush hydraulic system with clean brake fluid if contamination is suspected.**

INSPECTION

1. Inspect components for damage and unusual wear. Replace as necessary.
2. Inspect wheel cylinders. Boots which are torn, cut, or heat damaged indicate need for wheel cylinder replacement. Fluid spilling from boot center hole, or wetness around wheel cylinder ends indicates cup leakage and need for wheel cylinder replacement. **A small amount of fluid is always present and is considered normal, acting as lubricant for cylinder pistons.**
3. Inspect backing plate for evidence of seal leakage. If leakage exists, refer to individual chassis chapters for axle seal replacement procedure.
4. Inspect backing plate bolts and ensure they are tight.
5. Check adjuster screw operation. If satisfactory, lightly lubricate adjusting screw and washer with suitable brake lube. If operation is unsatisfactory, replace.
6. Using fine emery cloth or other suitable abrasive, clean rust and dirt from shoe contact surfaces on backing plate.

BRAKE SERVICE

REMOVAL

1. Raise and support vehicle, then re-

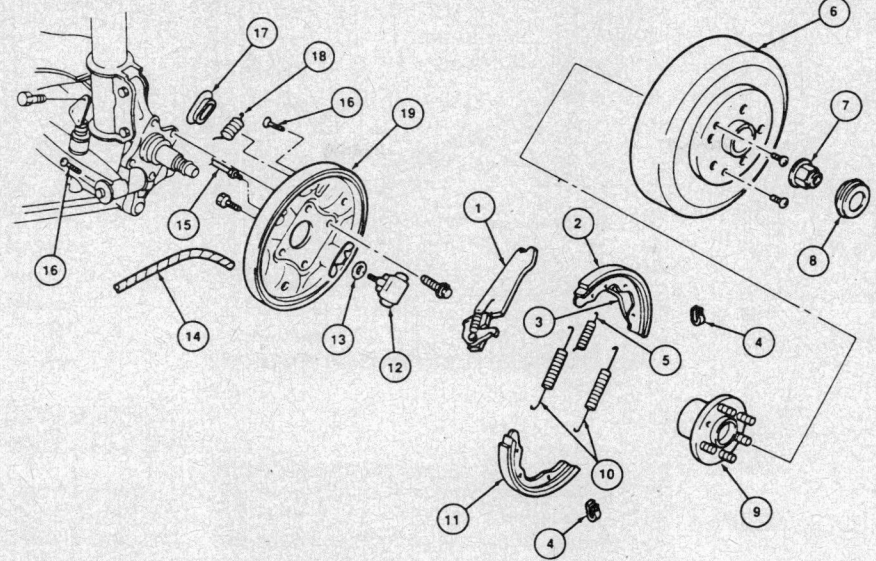

Item	Description
1	Rear Brake Strut and Quadrant
2	Trailing Brake Shoe and Lining
3	Parking Brake Cable Anchor Plates
4	Brake Shoe Hold Down Spring
5	Rear Brake Adjusting Quadrant Spring
6	Brake Drum
7	Rear Axle Wheel Hub Retainer
8	Hub Grease Cap
9	Wheel Hub

Item	Description
10	Upper Brake Shoe Retracting Spring and Lower Brake Shoe Retracting Spring
11	Leading Brake Shoe and Lining
12	Rear Wheel Cylinder
13	Wheel Cylinder Gasket
14	Parking Brake Rear Cable and Conduit
15	Brake Line
16	Brake Shoe Hold Down Spring Pin
17	Brake Adjusting Hole Cover
18	Return Spring
19	Rear Brake Backing Plate

FM4089400018000X

Fig. 1   Exploded view of rear drum brake

move wheel and tire assembly.
2. Remove grease hub cap.
3. Remove brake drum screws, then the drum, **Fig. 1.**
4. Remove wheel hub as described in specific chassis section.
5. Remove brake shoe hold down springs, **Fig. 2,** using screwdriver to push in and twist spring to disengage it from pin.
6. Remove parking brake rear cable and conduit from parking brake cable anchor plate. Remove brake shoe retracting spring.
7. Remove trailing brake shoe and lining from rear brake strut and quadrant, then the leading brake shoe and lining.

INSTALLATION

1. If brake shoes and linings are being reused, inspect shoes and linings and measure thickness. Ensure thickness meets specifications.
2. Clean rear brake backing plate with suitable vacuum, then lubricate six brake shoe and lining contact points with high temperature lubricant. Also lubricate rear brake backing plate where brake shoes and linings ride.
3. Ensure rear wheel cylinder bolts are

tightened to specifications.
4. If new brake shoes and linings are being installed, brake drums should be resurfaced to remove glazing, ensuring an equal friction surface from side-to-side and correcting out-of-round and bell conditions.
5. Position trailing brake shoe and lining in rear brake strut and quadrant and install brake shoe hold down spring pin.
6. Position leading brake shoe and lining against rear brake strut and quadrant and install brake shoe hold down spring pin.
7. Install upper and lower brake shoe retracting springs.
8. Measure brake drum with brake adjustment gauge tool No. D81L-1103-A, or equivalent, **Fig. 3.**
9. Adjust brake shoes and linings to same measurement of brake drum by inserting screwdriver into knurled quadrant of rear brake strut and quadrant.
10. Install wheel hub as described in specific chassis section.
11. Install brake drum, then the brake drum screws. Tighten screws to specifications.
12. Install grease cap, then the wheel and tire assembly.

ADJUSTMENTS
PARKING BRAKE

1. Start engine and press brake pedal several times while vehicle is moving in reverse.
2. Stop engine, then remove console panel as follows:
   a. Disconnect battery ground cable, then remove armrest base to armrest compartment screws.
   b. Remove armrest base, then the armrest compartment to ash receptacle bracket screws.
   c. Remove armrest compartment, then unsnap coin tray from console finish panel.
   d. Remove console panel nuts from console panel ash receptacle bracket.
   e. **On models equipped with manual transaxle,** unscrew shift control selector lever knob.
   f. **On models equipped with automatic transaxle,** remove console top panel.
   g. **On all models,** engage parking brake, then gently pull up on console finish panel to separate it from console panel.
   h. Remove instrument panel ash re-

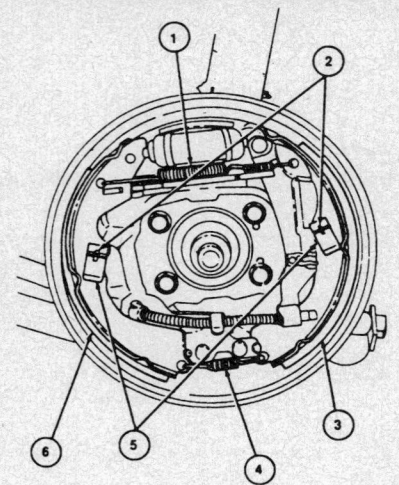

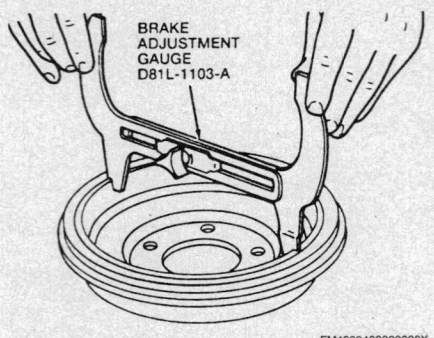

Fig. 3   Brake drum measurement

FM4089400020000X

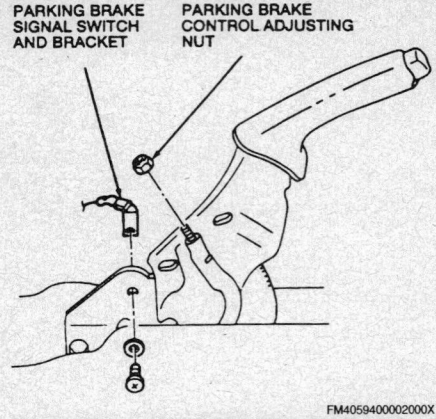

FM4059400002000X

Fig. 4   Parking brake control adjustment

Item	Description
1	Upper Brake Shoe Retracting Spring
2	Brake Shoe Hold Down Spring Pin
3	Trailing Brake Shoe and Lining
4	Lower Brake Shoe Retracting Spring
5	Brake Shoe Hold Down Spring
6	Front Brake Shoe and Lining

FM4089400019000X

Fig. 2   Brake shoe hold down pin removal

ceptacle illumination miniature bulb and socket from console finish panel.
  i. Disconnect cigar lighter knob and element electrical connectors, then remove console front finish panel screws.
  j. Remove console panel screws, then the panel from vehicle.
3. Remove three parking brake lever boot screws, then the parking brake lever boot.
4. Turn parking brake control adjusting nut at front of parking brake control, **Fig. 4**, to shorten front parking brake control cable and conduit. Tighten adjusting nut until it takes five to seven notches to fully set parking brake.
5. Turn ignition switch on, then pull parking brake control one notch to ensure parking brake warning lamp illuminates.
6. Ensure rear brakes do not drag.
7. To install console panel, reverse removal procedure.

DRUM BRAKE SPECIFICATIONS

Year	Model	Brake Drum		
		Inside Dia., Inch	Bore Limit (Max.), Inch	Max. Run-Out, Inch
1993-94	Probe	9.055	9.078	.005

TIGHTENING SPECIFICATIONS

Year	Component	Torque/Ft. Lbs.
1993-94	Brake Backing Plate Bolts	31–47
	Brake Drum Screws	89–123 ①
	Rear Axle Wheel Hub Retainer	73–131
	Rear Wheel Cylinder Bolts	7–9
	Wheel Lug Nuts	65–87

①—Inch lbs.

HYDRAULIC BRAKE SYSTEMS

INDEX

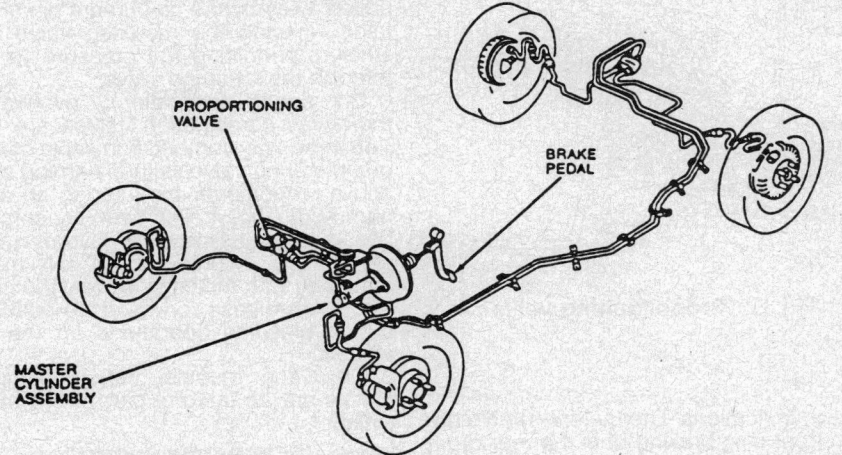

Fig. 1   Front & rear split brake system. Typical

FM4099100002000X

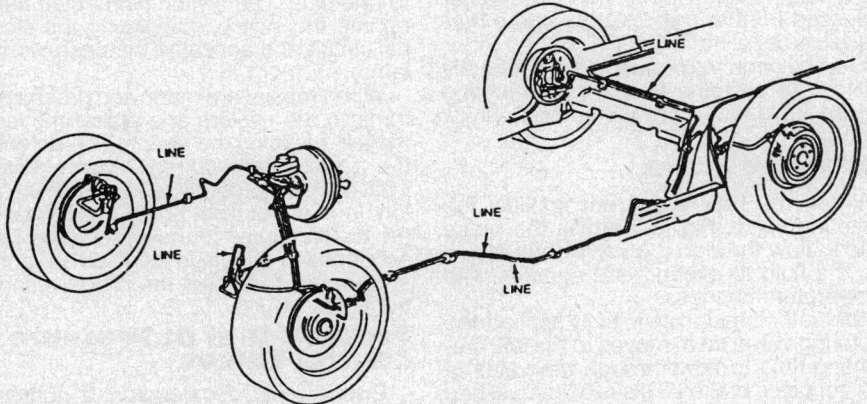

Fig. 2   Diagonally split brake system. Typical

FM4099100003000X

DESCRIPTION
FRONT & REAR SPLIT SYSTEMS

When the brake pedal is depressed, both the primary (front brake) and the secondary (rear brake) master cylinder pistons are moved simultaneously to exert hydraulic fluid pressure on their respective independent hydraulic systems. The fluid displacement of the master cylinder is proportioned to fulfill the requirements of each of the two independent hydraulic brake systems, **Fig. 1.**

If a failure of a rear (secondary) brake system should occur, initial brake pedal movement causes the unrestricted secondary piston to bottom in the master cylinder bore. Primary piston movement displaces hydraulic fluid in the primary section of the dual master cylinder to actuate the front brake system.

Should the front (primary) brake system fail, initial brake pedal movement causes the unrestricted primary piston to bottom out against the secondary piston. Continued downward movement of the brake pedal moves the secondary piston to displace hydraulic fluid in the rear brake system to actuate the rear brakes.

The increased pedal travel and the increased pedal effort required to compensate for the loss of the failed portion of the brake system provides a warning that a partial brake system failure has occurred. When the ignition switch is turned on, a brake warning light on the instrument panel provides a visual indication that one of the dual brake systems has become inoperative.

Should a failure of either the front or rear brake hydraulic system occur, the hydraulic fluid pressure differential resulting from pressure loss of the failed brake system forces the valve toward the low pressure area to light the brake warning lamp.

DIAGONALLY SPLIT SYSTEMS

This system operates on the same principles as conventional front and rear split systems using primary and secondary master cylinders moving simultaneously to exert hydraulic pressure on their respective systems, **Fig. 2.**

The hydraulic brake lines on this system, however, have been diagonally split front to rear (left front to right rear and right front to left rear) in place of separate lines to the front and rear wheels.

In the event of a system failure this would cause the remaining good system to do all the braking on one front wheel and the opposite rear wheel, thus maintaining 50% of the total braking force. The hydraulic pressure loss would result in a pressure differential in the system and cause a warning light on the dashboard to glow as in front and rear split systems.

BRAKE WARNING LIGHT SWITCHES

When a pressure differential occurs between the front and rear brake systems, the valves will shuttle toward the side with the low pressure. Movement of the differential valve forces the switch plunger upward over the tapered shoulder of the

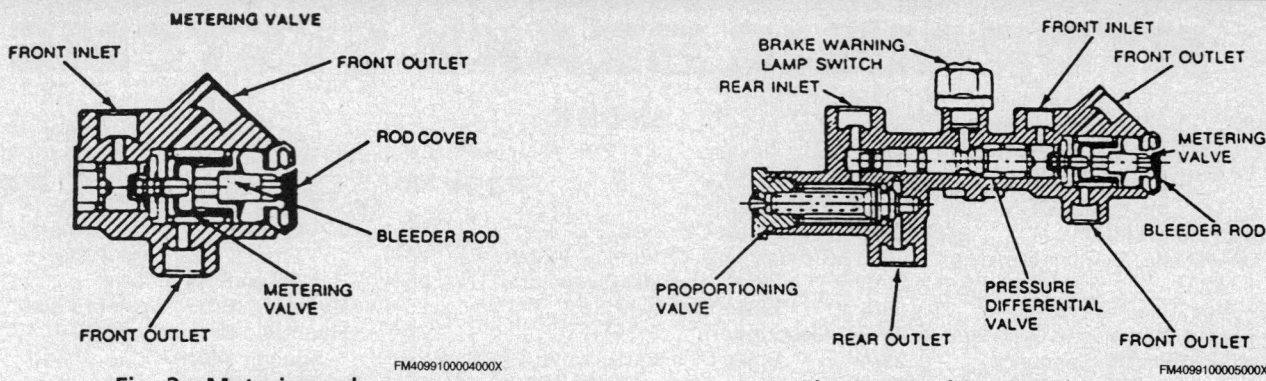

Fig. 3   Metering valve
FM4099100004000X

Fig. 4   Combination valve
FM4099100005000X

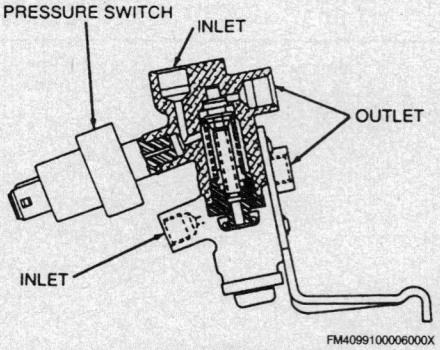

Fig. 5   Proportioning valve
FM4099100006000X

valve to close the switch contacts and light the dual brake warning lamp, signaling a brake system failure.

The valve assembly consists of two valves in a common bore that are spring loaded toward the centered position. The spring-loaded switch contact plunger rests on top of the valves in the centered position. When a pressure differential occurs between the front and rear brake systems, the valves will shuttle toward the side with the low pressure. The spring-loaded switch plunger is triggered and the ground circuit for the warning light is completed, lighting the lamp.

As pressure falls in one system, the other system's normal pressure forces the piston to the inoperative side, contacting the switch terminal, causing the warning light on the instrument panel to glow.

On front wheel drive models, a fluid level indicator replaces the pressure differential valve used in previous brake systems. It is contained inside the body of the master cylinder plastic reservoir and activates the brake warning light when fluid level is low.

Testing Warning Light System

If the parking brake light is connected into the service brake warning light system, the brake warning light will flash only when the parking brake is applied with the ignition turned ON. The same light will also glow should one of the two service brake systems fail when the brake pedal is applied.

To test the system, turn the ignition on and apply the parking brake. If the lamp fails to light, inspect for a burned out bulb, disconnected socket, a broken or disconnected wire at the switch.

To test the brake warning system, raise the car and open a wheel bleeder valve while a helper depresses the brake pedal and observes the warning light on the instrument panel. If the bulb fails to light, inspect for a burned out bulb, disconnected socket, or a broken or disconnected wire at the switch. If the bulb is not burned out, and wire continuity is proven, replace the brake warning switch.

COMBINATION VALVE

The combination valve is a metering valve, failure warning switch, and a proportioner in one assembly and is used on disc brake applications. The metering valve delays front disc braking until the rear drum brake shoes contact the drum. The failure warning switch is actuated in event of front or rear brake system failure, in turn activating a dash warning lamp. The proportioner balances front to rear braking action during rapid deceleration.

Combination valves used on diagonally split brake systems do not use metering valves instead two proportioning valves are used.

Metering Valve

When the brakes are not applied, the metering valve, **Fig. 3.** permits the brake fluid to flow through the valve, thus allowing the fluid to expand and contract with temperature changes.

When the brakes are initially applied, the metering valve, stem moves to the left, preventing fluid to flow through the valve to the front disc brakes. This is accomplished by the smooth end of the metering valve stem contacting the metering valve seal lip at 4-30 psi. The metering valve spring holds the retainer against the seal until a predetermined pressure is produced at the valve inlet port which overcomes the spring pressure and permits hydraulic pressure to actuate the front disc brakes. The increased pressure into the valve is metered through the valve seal, to the front disc brakes, producing an increased force on the diaphragm. The diaphragm then pulls the pin, in turn pulling the retainer and reduces the spring pressure on the metering valve seal. Eventually, the pressure reaches a point at which the spring is

pulled away by the diaphragm pin and retainer, leaving the metering valve unrestricted, permitting full pressure to pass through the metering valve.

On some applications, two-way or three-way combination valves are used. The three-way combination valve consists of a metering valve, failure warning switch and a proportioner mounted in an aluminum body, **Fig. 4.** The two-way combination valve consists of a failure warning switch and a proportioner. On models equipped with metering valves, the metering valve release rod must be pushed in during bleeding operations on the front wheels.

On Capri models, the proportioning valves are an integral part of the master cylinder.

Failure Warning Switch

If the rear brake system fails, the front system pressure forces the switch piston to one side. The switch pin is then forced up into the switch, completing the electrical circuit and activates the dash warning lamp.

When repairs are made and pressure returns to the system, the piston moves to the left, resetting the switch. The detent on the piston requires approximately 100-450 psi to permit full reset of the piston. In event of front brake system failure, the piston moves to the left and the same sequence of events is followed as for rear system failure except the piston resets to the right.

Proportioner Or Pressure Control Valves

During rapid deceleration, a portion of vehicle weight is transferred to the front wheels. This resultant loss of weight at rear wheels must be compensated for to avoid early rear wheel skid. The proportioner or pressure control valve, **Fig. 5.** reduces rear brake system pressure, delaying rear wheel skid. When the proportioner or pressure control valve is incorporated in the combination valve assembly, pressure developed within the valve acts against the large end of the piston, overcoming spring pressure, moving the piston. The piston then contacts the stem seat and restricts line pressure through the valve.

During normal braking operation, the proportioner or pressure control valve is

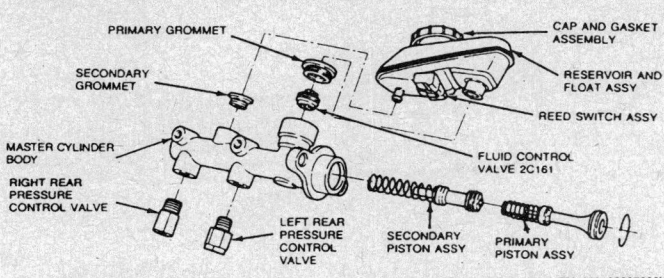

Fig. 6   Disassembled view of master cylinder

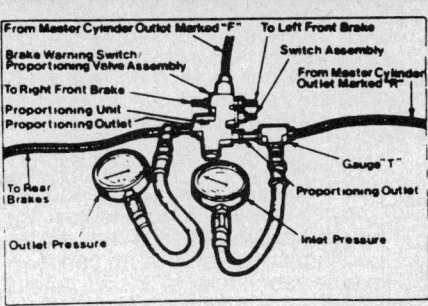

Fig. 7   Proportioning valve test gauge connection

not functional. Brake fluid flows into the proportioner or pressure control valve between the piston center hole and the valve stem, through the stop plate and to the rear brakes. Spring pressure loads the piston during normal braking, causing it to rest against the stop plate.

On diagonally split brake systems, two proportioners or pressure control valves are used. One controls the left rear brake, the other the right rear brake. On front wheel drive models less power brakes, the proportioners or pressure control valves are located in the combination valve. On front wheel drive models with power brakes, the proportioners or pressure control valves are installed in the master cylinder rear brake outlet ports, **Fig. 6.**

BRAKE DISTRIBUTION VALVE & SWITCH

This switch assembly which is used on some diagonally split brake systems, is connected to the outlet ports of the master cylinder and also to the brake warning light that warns the driver if either the primary or secondary brake system has failed.

When hydraulic pressure is equal in both primary and secondary brake systems, the switch remains centered. If pressure fails in one of the systems, hydraulic pressure moves the piston toward the inoperative side. The shoulder of the piston contacts the switch terminal, providing a ground and lighting the warning lamp.

PROPORTIONING VALVE

Description

The proportioning valve (when used), **Fig. 7,** provides balanced braking action between front and rear brakes under a wide range of braking conditions. The valve regulates the hydraulic pressure applied to the rear wheel cylinders, thus limiting rear braking action when high pressures are required at the front brakes. In this manner, premature rear wheel skid is prevented.

Testing

When a premature rear wheel slide is obtained on a brake application, it usually is an indication that the fluid pressure to the rear wheels is above the 50% reduction ratio for the rear line pressure and that malfunction has occurred within the proportioning valve.

To test the valve, install gauge set shown in **Fig. 7** in brake line between master cylinder and proportioning valve, and at output end of proportioning valve and brake line as shown. Be sure all joints are fluid tight.

Have a helper exert pressure on brake pedal (holding pressure). Obtain a reading on master cylinder output of approximately 700 psi. While pressure is being held as above, reading on valve outlet should be 550-610 psi. If the pressure readings do not meet these specifications, the valve should be removed and a new valve installed.

COMPONENT REPLACEMENT

MASTER CYLINDER

Except Capri, Escort, Sable, Taurus & Tracer

1. **On models equipped with ABS,** depress brake pedal several times to exhaust all vacuum in the system.
2. **On all models,** disconnect brake lines from master cylinder, then all necessary electrical connectors.
3. **On models equipped with ABS,** disconnect hydraulic control unit supply hose at master cylinder. Secure hose in a position to prevent brake fluid loss.
4. **On all models,** remove nuts retaining master cylinder to brake booster.
5. Remove master cylinder.
6. Reverse procedure to install. After installation is complete, fill master cylinder with manufacturer recommended brake fluid and bleed brakes.

Sable & Taurus

1. Remove brake tubes form primary and secondary fluid outlet ports. On wagon models, remove brake tubes from pressure control valves. **Sedan models do not use master cylinder mounted pressure control valves. Instead, a floor pan mounted brake differential control valve is used. This valve utilizes a mechanical linkage to the lower control arm to vary rear brake hydraulic pressure according to vehicle load.**
2. Disconnect brake warning light connector.
3. Remove brake booster-to-master cylinder attaching bolts, then slide master cylinder upward from vehicle.

4. Reverse procedure to install. After installation is complete, fill master cylinder with manufacturer recommended brake fluid and bleed brakes.

Capri

Pump brake pedal several times to exhaust any vacuum in booster.
1. Disconnect brake lines from master cylinder, then cap brake lines and master cylinder ports to prevent contamination from entering system.
2. Remove vacuum valve from booster, then disconnect pressure warning switch connector.
3. Remove two nut and washer assemblies retaining master cylinder to brake booster.
4. Remove master cylinder from brake booster. **It may be necessary to insert a small pry bar between the booster and the master cylinder to free the master cylinder.**
5. Reverse Procedure to install, noting the following:
   a. **Torque** master cylinder retaining nuts to 7-12 ft. lbs.
   b. Check and if necessary, adjust stop lamp switch.

Escort & Tracer

1. Remove the battery from vehicle.
2. Disconnect the low fluid level sensor electrical connector.
3. Loosen the brake line flare nuts, then disconnect the brake lines from the master cylinder assembly.
4. **On models with manual transaxles,** remove clamp, then pull the clutch hose from the brake/clutch fluid reservoir.
5. **On all models,** cap the lines and master cylinder ports.
6. Remove the two master cylinder retaining nuts, then master cylinder.
7. Adjust master cylinder piston to pushrod clearance as follows:
   a. Position Master Cylinder Gauge tool No. T87C-2500-A or equivalent on the end of the master cylinder, loosen the setscrew on end of master cylinder. Push the gauge plunger against the bottom of the primary piston.
   b. While holding the gauge in position, tighten the setscrew.
   c. Apply 19.7 inches Hg vacuum to the power brake with a vacuum pump.

d. Invert the gauge and place it over the power brake pushrod.

e. Ensure that there is no space between the end of the adjustment gauge and the power brake pushrod.

f. If there is space between the end of the adjustment gauge and the power brake pushrod, loosen the pushrod locknut and adjust the pushrod until there is no space.

8. Reverse procedure to install master cylinder. After master cylinder installation, the piston to pushrod clearance will be as follows:

a. With no vacuum applied, 0.016-0.024 inch.

b. With 19.7 inches Hg applied, 0.004-0.01 inch.

WHEEL CYLINDERS

Removal

1. Remove wheel, drum and brake shoes.

2. Disconnect hydraulic line at wheel cylinder. Do not pull metal line away from cylinder as the cylinder connection will bend metal line and make installation difficult. Line will separate from cylinder when cylinder is moved away from brake backing plate.

3. Remove screws holding cylinder to brake plate and remove cylinder.

Installation

1. Wipe end of hydraulic line to remove any foreign matter.

2. Place hydraulic cylinder in position. Enter tubing into cylinder and start connecting fitting.

3. Secure cylinder to backing plate and then complete tightening of tubing fitting.

4. Install brake shoes, drum and wheel.

5. Bleed system as outlined previously, and adjust brakes.

COMPONENT SERVICE

MASTER CYLINDER OVERHAUL

Disassemble

1. Clean outside of master cylinder thoroughly. Drain brake fluid from master cylinder.

2. Remove stop bolt and pressure control valves, if equipped.

3. Using a screwdriver, carefully pry up on reservoir and remove it from master cylinder body.

4. Remove fluid control valve, if equipped.

5. Depress primary piston and remove snap ring from retaining groove at open end of bore.

6. Remove primary and secondary piston assemblies from master cylinder. If secondary piston does not come out, apply air pressure to secondary outlet port to remove.

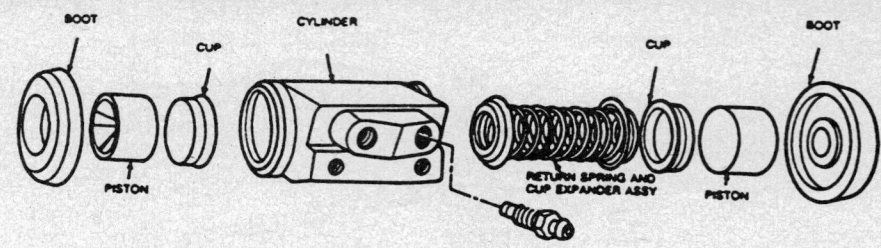

Fig. 8   Exploded view of typical wheel cylinder

FM40991000008000X

Inspection

When disassembled, wash all parts in clean brake fluid only. Use an air hose to blow out all passages, orifices and valve holes. Air dry and place parts on clean paper or lint-free cloth. Inspect master cylinder bore for scoring, rust, pitting or etching. Any of these conditions will require replacement of the housing. Inspect master cylinder pistons for scoring, pitting or distortion. Replace piston if any of these conditions exist.

If either master cylinder housing or piston is replaced, clean new parts with clean brake fluid and blow out all passages with air hose.

Examine reservoirs for foreign matter and check all passages for restrictions. If there is any suspicion of contamination or evidence of corrosion, completely flush hydraulic system as outlined below.

When overhauling a master cylinder, use all parts contained in repair kit. Before starting reassembly, dip all cups, seals, pistons, springs, check valves and retainers in clean brake fluid and place in a clean pan or on clean paper. Wash hands with soap and water only to prevent contamination of rubber parts from oil, kerosene or gasoline. During assembly, dip all parts in clean brake fluid.

Inspect through side outlet of dual master cylinder housing to make certain cup lips do not hang up on edge of hole or turn back, which would result in faulty operation. A piece of ³/₁₆ inch rod with an end rounded off will be helpful in guiding cups past hole.

When overhauling aluminum master cylinders, carefully inspect master cylinder bore for corrosion. If corroded, replace master cylinder. Do not hone or use abrasives on the bore of these cylinders.

Assemble

1. Coat replacement piston assemblies in clean heavy duty DOT 3 brake fluid before assembly.

2. Install secondary piston assembly into bore, spring end first.

3. Install primary piston assembly, spring end first.

4. Depress primary piston and install snap ring.

5. Install fluid control valve and **torque** to 8-9.6 ft. lbs.

6. Install stop bolt and pressure control valves, if equipped.

7. Lubricate new reservoir grommets with brake fluid and install in master cylinder body.

8. Install reservoir into new grommets.

9. Fill and bench bleed master cylinder.

WHEEL CYLINDERS

Overhaul

1. Referring to **Fig. 8** as a guide, remove boots, pistons, springs and cups from cylinder.

2. Place all parts, except cylinder casting in clean brake fluid. Wipe cylinder walls with clean brake fluid.

3. Examine cylinder bore. A scored bore may be honed providing the diameter is not increased more than .005 inch. Replace worn or damaged parts from the repair kit.

4. Before assembling, wash hands with soap and water only, as oil, kerosene or gasoline will contaminate rubber parts.

5. Lubricate cylinder wall and rubber cups with brake fluid.

6. Install springs, cups, pistons and boots in housing.

BRAKE SYSTEM BLEED

Pressure bleeding is recommended for all hydraulic brake systems.

The bleeding operation itself is fairly well standardized. First step in all cases is cleaning the dirt from the filler cap before removing it from the master cylinder. This should be done thoroughly.

Pressure bleeding is fastest because the master cylinder doesn't have to be refilled several times, and the job can be done by one man. To prevent air from the pressure tank getting into the lines, do not shake the tank while air is being added to the tank or after it has been pressurized. Set the tank in the required location, bring the air hose to the tank, and do not move it during the bleeding operation. The tank should be kept at least one-third full.

On vehicles equipped with disc brakes and master cylinders without proportioners or pressure control valves located in the master cylinder outlet port, the brake metering valve or combination valve must be held in position using a suitable tool.

If air does get into the fluid, releasing the pressure will cause the bubbles to increase in size, rise to the top of the fluid, and escape. Pressure should not be greater than about 35 psi.

On vehicles equipped with plastic reservoirs, do not exceed 25 psi bleeding pressure.

When bleeding without pressure, open

the bleed valve three-quarters of a turn, depress the pedal a full stroke, then allow the pedal to return slowly to its released position. It is suggested that after the pedal has been depressed to the end of its stroke, the bleeder valve should be closed before the start of the return stroke. On models with power brakes, first reduce the vacuum in the power unit to zero by pumping the brake pedal several times with the engine off before starting to bleed the system.

Pressure bleeding, of course, eliminates the need for pedal pumping.

Discard drained or bled brake fluid. Care should be taken not to spill brake fluid, since this can damage the finish of the car.

Flushing is essential if there is water, mineral oil or other contaminants in the lines, and whenever new parts are installed in the hydraulic system. Fluid contamination is usually indicated by swollen and deteriorated cups and other rubber parts.

Wheel cylinders on disc brakes are equipped with bleeder valves, and are bled in the same manner as wheel cylinders for drum brakes.

Bleeding is necessary on all four wheels if air has entered the system because of low fluid level, or the line or lines have been disconnected. If a line is disconnected at any one wheel cylinder, that cylinder only need be bled. Of course, on brake reline jobs, bleeding is advisable to remove any air or contaminants.

Master cylinders equipped with bleeder valves should be bled first before the wheel cylinders are bled. In all cases where a master cylinder has been overhauled, it must be bled. Where there is no bleeder valve, this can be done by leaving the lines loose, actuating the brake pedal to expel the air and then tightening the lines.

After overhauling a dual master cylinder used in conjunction with disc brakes, it is advisable to bleed the cylinder before installing it on the car. The reason for this recommendation is that air may be trapped between the master cylinder pistons because there is only one residual pressure valve (check valve) used in these units.

SYSTEM PRIMING

When a new master cylinder has been installed or the brake system emptied or partially emptied, fluid may not flow from the bleeder screws during normal bleeding. It may be necessary to prime the system using the following procedure:

1. Using a tubing wrench, remove the brake lines from the master cylinder.
2. Install short brake lines in the master cylinder and position them back into the reservoir, ensure that the short brake line ends are submerged in the reservoir brake fluid.
3. Fill the reservoir with recommended brake fluid, then cover master cylinder fluid reservoir with shop towel.
4. Pump the brakes until clear, bubble free fluid comes out of both brake lines. **If any brake fluid spills on paint, wash it off immediately with**

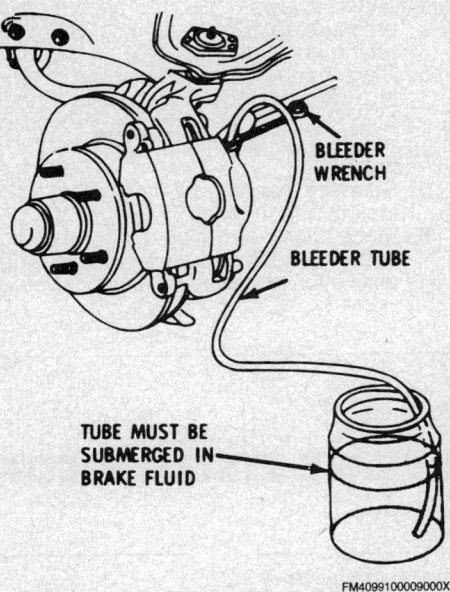

BLEEDER WRENCH

BLEEDER TUBE

TUBE MUST BE SUBMERGED IN BRAKE FLUID

FM4099100009000X

Fig. 9 Bleeding caliper

water.
5. Remove the short brake lines, then reinstall original brake lines.
6. Bleed each brake line at the master cylinder using the following procedure:
   a. Have assistant pump brake pedal 10 times, then hold firm pressure on the pedal.
   b. Open the rearmost brake line fittings with a tubing wrench until a stream of brake fluid comes out. Have assistant maintain pressure on the brake pedal until the brake line fitting is tightened again.
   c. Repeat this operation until clear, bubble free fluid comes out from around tube fitting.
   d. Repeat this bleeding operation at the front brake line fitting.
7. If any of the brake lines or calipers have been removed, it may be helpful to prime the system by gravity bleeding. this should be done after the master cylinder is primed and bled. To prime the system using the gravity method, proceed as follows:
   a. Fill the master cylinder with manufacturer recommended brake fluid or equivalent.
   b. Loosen both rear bleeder screws and leave them open until clear brake fluid flows out. **Check reservoir fluid level frequently, do not allow fluid level to drop below half full.**
   c. Tighten rear bleeder screws.
   d. Loosen bleeder screw on front caliper, leave open until clear fluid flows out. **Bleed front calipers one side at a time.**
8. After the master cylinder has been primed, the lines bled at the master cylinder and the brake system primed, normal brake system bleeding can be resumed at each wheel.

TESTING DUAL MASTER CYLINDERS

Ensure that the master cylinder compensates in both parts. This can be done by applying the brake pedal lightly (engine running with power brakes) and observing for brake fluid squirting up in the reservoirs. This may only occur in the front chamber. To determine if the rear compensating port is open, pump up the brakes rapidly and hold the pedal down. Have an observer watch the fluid in the rear reservoir while the pedal is raised. A disturbance in the fluid indicates that the compensating port is open.

WHEEL BLEEDING SEQUENCE

Rear Wheel Drive .... RR-LR-RF-LF
Front Wheel Drive .... RR-LF-LR-RF

DUAL MASTER CYLINDER BLEEDING NOTES

The following information applies to master cylinders without proportioners or pressure control valves located in the master cylinder outlet ports.

All vehicles use a self-centering valve. After any bleeding operation, turn ignition switch to ACC or ON position and depress brake pedal. Valve will center itself.

HYDRAULIC BRAKE SYSTEM FLUSH

Whenever new brake components are installed in the hydraulic system, it is recommended that the entire hydraulic system be thoroughly flushed with clean brake fluid.

It may sometime become necessary to flush out the system due to the presence of mineral oil, kerosene, gasoline, etc., which will cause swelling of rubber piston cups and valves so they become inoperative. The procedure is as follows:

Flushing is performed at each wheel in the same manner as the bleeding operation except that the bleeder valve is opened 1½ turns and the fluid is forced through the lines and bleeder valve until it emerges clear in color, **Fig. 9.** Approximately one quart of clean brake fluid is required to flush the hydraulic system. After completing the flushing operation at all bleeder valves, check to ensure the master cylinder is filled to the proper level.

HYDRAULIC TUBING

Never use copper tubing as a replacement for steel tubing. Copper tubing is subject to fatigue cracking and corrosion which could result in brake system failure.

Steel tubing is used to conduct hydraulic pressure to the brakes. All fittings, tubing and hose should be inspected for rusted, damaged or defective flared seats. The tubing is equipped with a double flare/inverted seat or I.S.O. flare to insure more positive seating in the fitting. To repair or reflare tubing, proceed as follows:

DOUBLE FLARE/INVERTED SEAT

1. Cut off the damaged seat or damaged tubing.
2. Ream out any burrs or rough edges showing on inside edges of tubing. This will make the ends of the tubing square and insure better seating on the flared end. Before flaring tubing, place a compression nut on tubing.
3. Open handles of flaring tool and rotate jaws of tool until mating jaws of tubing size are centered in the area between vertical posts.
4. Slowly close handles with tubing inserted in jaws but do not apply heavy pressure to handle as this will lock tubing in place.
5. Place gauge on edge over end of tubing and push tubing through jaws until end of tubing contacts recessed notch of gauge matching size of tubing.
6. Squeeze handles of flaring tool and lock tubing in place.
7. Place proper size plug of gauge down in end of tubing. Swing compression disc over gauge and center tapered flaring screw in recess in disc.
8. Lubricate taper of flaring or screw and screw in until plug gauge has seated in jaws of flaring tool. This action has started to invert the extended end of tubing.
9. Remove gauge and apply lubricant to tapered end of flaring screw and continue to screw down until tool is firmly seated in tubing.
10. Remove tubing from flaring tool and inspect the seat. If seat is cracked, cut off cracked end and repeat flaring operation.

HYDRAULIC BRAKE SYSTEM SPECIFICATIONS

Year	Model	Master Cylinder Bore Dia. Inch
1992	Capri	.811
	Continental	③
	Cougar & Thunderbird	.938
	Crown Victoria & Grand Marquis	1.00
	Escort & Tracer	.875
	Festiva	.750
	Mark VII	1.125
	Mustang	1.125
	Probe	.875
	Sable & Taurus	①
	Tempo & Topaz	②
	Town Car	1.000
1993	Capri	.811
	Continental	③
	Cougar & Thunderbird	.872
	Crown Victoria & Grand Marquis	1.00
	Escort &Tracer	.875
	Festiva	.750
	Mark VIII	1.125
	Mustang	.872
	Probe	.875

Year	Model	Master Cylinder Bore Dia. Inch
1993 —Cont'd	Sable & Taurus	①
	Tempo & Topaz	②
	Town Car	1.000
	Tracer	.875
1994	Aspire	④
	Capri	.811
	Continental	③
	Cougar & Thunderbird	.872
	Crown Victoria & Grand Marquis	1.00
	Escort & Tracer	.875
	Mark VIII	1.125
	Mustang	.872
	Probe	.875
	Sable & Taurus	①
	Tempo & Topaz	②
	Town Car	1.000

①—With disc & drum, stepped bore, .875 & 1.25; w/four wheel disc, 1.00 inch.
②—Stepped bore, front .776; rear 1.12 inch.
③—Stepped bore, .940 & 1.22 inch.
④—Models w/ABS .870; less ABS, .810 inch.

POWER BRAKE UNITS

NOTE: On Vehicles Equipped With Anti-Lock Brakes Refer To "Anti-Lock Brake" Section.

INDEX

Application Chart

Model	Year	Power Brake Booster Type
Aspire	1994	Single Diaphragm
Capri	1992-94	Single Diaphragm
Cougar & Thunderbird	1992-94	⑤
Crown Victoria & Grand Marquis	1992	Bendix Single Diaphragm
	1993-94	Bendix Tandem Diaphragm
Escort	1992-94	Single Diaphragm
Festiva	1992-93	Single Diaphragm
Mark VIII	1993-94	Bendix Tandem Diaphragm
Mustang	1992-93	①
	1994	Bendix Tandem Diaphragm
Probe	1992-94	Single Diaphragm
Sable & Taurus	1992-94	Bendix Single Diaphragm
Tempo & Topaz	1992-94	Single Diaphragm ②
Town Car	1992	Bendix Single Diaphragm
	1993-94	Bendix Tandem Diaphragm
Tracer	1992-94	Single Diaphragm ② ③ ④

① —2.3L engine, except convertible, Bendix Single Diaphragm; convertible, Tandem Diaphragm; 5.0L engine, Tandem Diaphragm.

② —Bendix Single Diaphragm, or Teves Single Diaphragm.

③ —The only service that may be performed on Bendix type brake booster is replacement of the grommet, check valve and pushrod adjustment. If any other malfunction is apparent, booster should be and check valve. If any other malfunction is apparent, booster should be replaced.

⑤ —Except models w/3.8 SC engine, Bendix Single Diaphragm; models w/3.8L SC engine, Bendix Tandem Diaphragm. replaced.

④ —The only service that may be performed on Teves type brake booster is replacement of grommet

DESCRIPTION

VACUUM ASSIST DIAPHRAGM TYPE

The vacuum assist diaphragm assembly multiplies the force exerted on the master cylinder piston in order to increase the hydraulic pressure delivered to the wheel cylinders while decreasing the effort necessary to obtain acceptable stopping performance.

Vacuum assist units get their energy by opposing engine vacuum to atmospheric pressure. A piston, cylinder and flexible diaphragm utilize this energy to provide brake assistance. The diaphragm is balanced with engine vacuum until the brake pedal is depressed, allowing atmospheric pressure to unbalance the unit and apply force to the brake system.

Brakes will operate even if the power unit fails. This means the conventional brake system and the power assist system are completely separate. Troubleshooting conventional and power assist systems are exactly the same until the power unit is reached. As with conventional hydraulic brakes, a spongy pedal still means air is trapped in the hydraulic system. Power brakes give higher line pressure, making leaks more critical.

BENDIX DIAPHRAGM TYPES

These units are of the vacuum suspended type. Some units are of the single diaphragm type, while others are of the tandem diaphragm type. Both single piston and double piston or split system type master cylinders are used.

The vacuum suspended diaphragm type units utilize engine manifold vacuum and atmospheric pressure for its power. It consists of three basic elements combined into a single power unit. The three basic elements of the single diaphragm type are:

1. A vacuum power section which includes a front and rear shell, a power diaphragm, a return spring and a pushrod.
2. A control valve, built integral with the power diaphragm and connected through a valve rod to the brake pedal, controls the degree of brake application or release in accordance with the pressure applied to the brake pedal.
3. A hydraulic master cylinder, attached to the vacuum power section which contains all the elements of the conventional brake master cylinder except for the pushrod, supplies fluid under pressure to the wheel brakes in proportion to the pressure applied to the brake pedal.

Operation

Upon application of the brakes, the valve rod and plunger move to the left in the power diaphragm to close the vacuum port and open the atmospheric port to admit air through the air cleaner and valve at the rear diaphragm chamber. With vacuum present in the rear chamber, a force is developed to move the power diaphragm, hydraulic pushrod and hydraulic piston or pistons to close the compensating port or ports and force fluid under pressure through the residual check valve or valves and lines into the front and rear wheel cylinders to actuate the brakes.

As pressure is developed within the master cylinder a counter force acting through the hydraulic pushrod and reaction disc against the vacuum power diaphragm and valve plunger sets up a reaction force opposing the force applied to the valve rod and plunger. This reaction force tends to close the atmospheric port and reopen the vacuum port. Since this force is in opposition to the force applied to the brake pedal by the driver it gives the driver a "feel" of the amount of brake applied. The proportion of reactive force applied to the valve plunger through the reaction disc is designed into the Master-Vac to assure maximum power consistent with maintaining pedal feel. The reaction force is in direct proportion to the hydraulic pressure developed within the brake system.

TROUBLESHOOTING

Complaints about power brake operation should be handled as if two separate systems exist. Check for faults in the hydraulic system first. If it is satisfactory, start inspecting the power brake circuit. For a quick check of proper power unit operation, press the brake pedal firmly and then start the engine. The pedal should fall away slightly and less pressure should be needed to maintain the pedal in any position.

Another check begins with installation

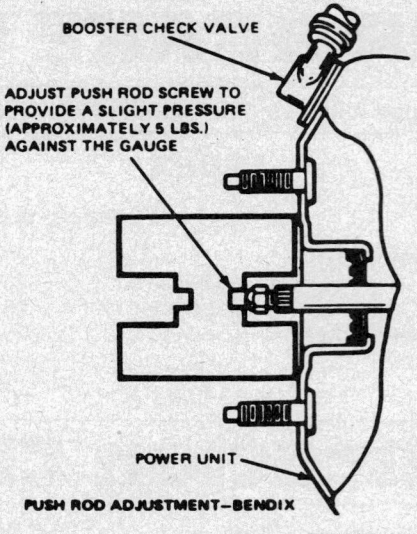

BOOSTER CHECK VALVE

ADJUST PUSH ROD SCREW TO PROVIDE A SLIGHT PRESSURE (APPROXIMATELY 5 LBS.) AGAINST THE GAUGE

POWER UNIT

PUSH ROD ADJUSTMENT—BENDIX

FM4099100010000X

Fig. 1   Master cylinder pushrod adjustment. Bendix type vacuum booster

of a suitable pressure gauge in the brake hydraulic system. Take a reading with the engine off and the power unit not operating. Maintaining the same pedal height, start the engine and take another reading. There should be a substantial pressure increase in the second reading.

Pedal free travel and total travel are critical on cars equipped with power brakes. Pedal travel should be kept strictly to specifications.

Take a manifold vacuum reading or check operation of the external vacuum pump if the power unit isn't giving enough assistance. Remember, though, currently produced emission controlled engines, manifold vacuum readings may be less than 15 inches Hg at idle. If manifold vacuum is abnormally low, tune the engine and then try the power brakes again. Naturally, loose vacuum lines and clogged air intake filters will cut down brake efficiency. Most units have a check valve that retains some vacuum in the system when the engine is off. A vacuum gauge check of this valve will tell you when it is restricted or stuck open or closed.

Failure of the brakes to release in most instances is caused by a tight or misaligned connection between the power unit and the brake linkage. If this connection is free, look for a broken piston, diaphragm or bellows and return spring.

A simple check of the hydraulic system should be made before proceeding. Loosen the connection between the master cylinder and the brake booster. If the brakes release, the trouble is in the power unit; if the brakes still will not release, look for a restricted brake line or similar difficulties in the regular hydraulic circuit.

A residual pressure check valve is usually included immediately under the brake line connection on hydraulic assist power brakes. This valve maintains a slight hydraulic pressure within the brake lines and wheel cylinders to give better pedal re-

sponse. If it is sticking, the brakes may not release.

Power brakes that have a hard pedal are usually suffering from a milder form of the same ills that cause complete power unit failure. Collapsed or leaking vacuum lines or insufficient manifold vacuum, as well as punctured diaphragms or bellows and leaky piston seals, all lead to weak power unit operation. A steady hiss when the brake is held down means a vacuum leak that will cause poor power unit operation.

Do not immediately condemn the power unit if the brakes grab. First look for all the usual causes, such as greasy linings, scored rotors or drums. Then investigate the power unit. When the trouble has been traced to the power unit, check for a damaged reaction control. The reaction control is usually made up of a diaphragm, spring and valves that tends to resist pedal action. It is put in the system to give the pedal "feel."

BENDIX DIAPHRAGM TYPES

Hard Pedal Or No Assist

1. Air cleaner element clogged.
2. Control valve faulty.
3. Defective diaphragm.
4. Worn or distorted reaction plate or levers.
5. Cracked or broken power piston or levers.
6. Internal or external leaks.

Brakes Grab

1. Control valve defective or sticking.
2. Bind in linkage.
3. Reaction diaphragm leaking.
4. Worn or distorted levers or plate.

No Or Slow Release

1. pushrod adjustment incorrect.
2. Linkage binding.
3. Return spring defective.

ADJUSTMENTS

PUSHROD

Proper adjustment of the master cylinder pushrod is necessary to ensure proper operation of the power brake system. A pushrod that is too long will prevent the master cylinder piston from completely releasing hydraulic pressure, eventually, causing the brakes to drag. A pushrod that is too short will cause excessive brake pedal travel and cause groaning noises to come from the booster when the brakes are applied. A properly adjusted pushrod that remains assembled to the booster with which is was matched during production should not require service adjustment. However, if the booster, master cylinder or pushrod are serviced, the pushrod may require adjustment.

If the power unit pushrod requires an adjustment the Power Unit Repair Kit for the unit being serviced includes a gauge. The gauge measures from the end of the pushrod to the power unit shell.

On Capri models, pushrod length is not adjustable. To ensure the master cylinder is free to return to its rest position with no residual pressure, verify stop lamp switch adjustment.

On Escort and Tracer models, refer to "Master Cylinder, Replace" in "Hydraulic Brakes" section for adjustment procedure.

Bendix Type

1. Disconnect master cylinder from booster leaving brake lines connected, and secure cylinder to prevent lines from being damaged.
2. Start engine and operate engine at idle speed.
3. With engine running, position gauge over pushrod. Gauge should bottom against booster housing with a force of approximately 5 lbs. applied to pushrod, **Fig. 1.**
4. If force required to seat gauge exceeds 5 lb., shorten length of pushrod. If force required to seat gauge is less than 5 lbs., lengthen pushrod. **Ensure that pushrod is properly seated in booster when performing gauge check.**
5. Install master cylinder, then remove reservoir cover.
6. With engine running, observe fluid surface in reservoir when brakes are applied and released rapidly. If no movement is observed on fluid surface, pushrod is adjusted too long.

Single Diaphragm Booster

1. Remove master cylinder as previously outlined.
2. Position master cylinder gauge T87C-2500-A or equivalent on end of master cylinder.
3. Loosen setscrew and push gauge plunger against bottom of primary piston.
4. While holding gauge in position, tighten setscrew.
5. Invert gauge and place over brake booster pushrod, reading should be 0.
6. If clearance is not 0, loosen pushrod locknut and adjust pushrod.
7. Reverse procedure to install.

POWER BRAKE UNIT SERVICE

POWER BOOSTER, REPLACE

CROWN VICTORIA, GRAND MARQUIS, TEMPO & TOPAZ

1. Disconnect battery ground cable.
2. Disconnect master cylinder from booster and position aside. **It is not necessary to disconnect brake lines, but care should be taken to avoid twisting or kinking lines.**
3. Disconnect manifold vacuum hose from booster check valve.
4. Working under instrument panel, disconnect stop lamp switch electrical connector under instrument panel.
5. Remove stop lamp switch retaining pin. Slide switch off brake pedal pin enough so outer plate of switch clears

the pin, then remove switch from pin.
6. Remove booster-to-dash panel attaching screws.
7. Slide booster pushrod, nylon washers and bushing off brake pedal pin.
8. Move booster forward until booster studs clear dash panel, then remove booster.
9. Reverse procedure to install, noting the following:
   a. **On Crown Victoria and Grand Marquis, torque** booster to dash panel retaining nuts and master cylinder to booster locking nuts to 14-24 ft. lbs.
   b. **On Tempo & Topaz, torque** booster to dash panel retaining nuts and master cylinder to booster locking nuts to 13-25 ft. lbs.

COUGAR, MARK VIII & THUNDERBIRD

1. Disconnect battery ground cable and remove air cleaner.
2. Disconnect manifold vacuum hose from booster check valve.
3. Disconnect brake lines from primary and secondary outlet ports of master cylinder.
4. Remove master cylinder-to-booster attaching nuts and the master cylinder.
5. Working under instrument panel, disconnect electrical connector from stop lamp switch.
6. Remove hairpin type retainer. Slide stop lamp switch off brake pedal pin just far enough for the switch outer hole to clear the pin, then lower switch away from pin.
7. Remove booster-to-dash panel attaching nuts.
8. **On models equipped with speed control**, unfasten control amplifier from lower outboard booster stud and position aside.
9. **On all models**, slide booster pushrod, bushing and inner nylon washer off brake pedal pin.
10. Move booster forward in engine compartment until booster studs clear dash panel, then rotate front of booster toward engine and remove booster.
11. Reverse procedure to install, noting the following:
    a. Bleed brake system.
    b. **Torque** booster to dash panel retaining nuts to 14-25 ft. lbs.
    c. **Torque** master cylinder to booster locking nuts to 14-25 ft. lbs.

TOWN CAR

1. Disconnect battery ground cable.
2. Remove master cylinder from booster. Position side without disconnecting the hydraulic lines. **It is not necessary to disconnect hydraulic lines, but care should be taken so brake lines are not kinked. Kinking of brake lines can lead to tube damage.**
3. Disconnect manifold vacuum hose from booster check valve.
4. Disconnect stop lamp switch connector.
5. Remove stop lamp switch retaining

pin, then slide stop lamp switch off from brake pedal pin just far enough for outer plate of stop lamp switch to clear pin, then remove stop lamp switch.
6. Remove booster to dash panel retaining nuts, then slide booster pushrod, nylon washers and bushing off brake pedal pin.
7. Remove booster assembly from dash panel by sliding pushrod out from engine side of dash panel.
8. Reverse procedure to install, noting the following:
   a. **Torque** booster to dash panel retaining nuts to 13-25 ft. lbs.
   b. **Torque** master cylinder to booster locking nuts to 13-25 ft. lbs.

MUSTANG

3.8L/V6—232 & 5.0L/V8-302 Engines

1. Disconnect battery ground cable and remove air cleaner assembly.
2. Disconnect manifold vacuum hose from power booster check valve.
3. Disconnect hydraulic lines from master cylinder and cap open lines and ports.
4. Remove master cylinder retaining nuts and master cylinder.
5. Disconnect accelerator cable at dash panel and accelerator pedal and shaft, then reposition to gain maneuvering room for brake booster.
6. Working under instrument panel, disconnect electrical connector from stop lamp switch.
7. Remove hairpin type retainer. Slide stop lamp switch off brake pedal pin just far enough for the switch outer hole to clear the pin, then lower switch away from pin.
8. Slide brake master cylinder push rod bushing off of brake pedal pin.
9. Remove booster-to-dash panel attaching nuts.
10. **On models equipped with speed control**, unfasten control amplifier from lower outboard booster stud and position aside.
11. **On all models**, work from engine compartment and move booster forward until booster studs clear the dash panel, then raise front of unit and remove from vehicle.
12. Reverse procedure to install, noting the following:
    a. Bleed brake system.
    b. **Torque** booster to dash panel retaining nuts to 15-23 ft. lbs.
    c. **Torque** master cylinder to booster locking nuts to 15-23 ft. lbs.

2.3L/4-140 Engine

1. Disconnect battery ground cable, then remove air cleaner.
2. Disconnect accelerator cable from throttle body.
3. Remove screw that secures accelerator cable to shaft bracket, then remove cable from bracket.
4. Remove two screws that secure accelerator shaft bracket to manifold, and rotate bracket toward engine.

5. Remove RPO horn, if equipped.
6. Release fuel system pressure, then disconnect the two manifold injector connectors located near oil dipstick retaining bracket. Disconnect two fuel lines to fuel supply manifold assembly.
7. Remove engine oil dipstick tube and bracket.
8. Remove windshield wiper motor.
9. Disconnect vacuum lines located over brake booster at dash panel vacuum tee.
10. Remove bolt securing clutch cable stand, then move bracket to side rail at fender inner panel.
11. **On models equipped with speed control,** move speed control cable to one side to clear booster.
12. **On all models,** disconnect manifold booster line from booster check valve.
13. Disconnect brake lines from master cylinder, remove master cylinder attaching nuts, then master cylinder.
14. Working under instrument panel, disconnect electrical connector from stop lamp switch.
15. Remove hairpin type retainer and outer nylon washer from brake pedal pin, then slide stop lamp switch off brake pedal pin just enough for outer arm to clear pin.
16. **On models equipped with speed control,** unfasten control amplifier from lower outboard booster stud and position aside. Slide booster pushrod, bushing, and inner nylon washer off brake pedal pin.
17. **On all models,** move booster forward in engine compartment until booster studs clear dash panel, then rotate front of booster toward engine and remove booster.
18. Reverse procedure to install, noting the following:
    a. Bleed brake system.
    b. **Torque** booster to dash panel retaining nuts to 14-24 ft. lbs.
    c. **Torque** master cylinder to booster locking nuts to 14-24 ft. lbs.

SABLE & TAURUS

1. Disconnect battery ground cable.
2. Remove tubes from primary and secondary ports of master cylinder.
3. Disconnect manifold vacuum hose from booster check valve, then disconnect warning indicator.
4. Remove master cylinder retaining nuts and master cylinder.
5. Working under instrument panel, disconnect electrical connector from stop lamp switch.
6. Remove stop lamp switch retaining pin and white nylon washer. Slide switch off brake pedal pin enough so outer plate of switch clears the pin, then remove switch from pin.
7. Remove brake booster-to-dash panel attaching nuts, then slide booster pushrod and pushrod bushing off brake pedal pin.
8. Remove vacuum tee attaching bolts, then position tee aside.

9. Position wiring harness aside.
10. Remove transmission shift cable and bracket.
11. Move booster assembly forwards until it clears dash panel, then remove booster.
12. Reverse procedure to install, noting the following:
    a. Bleed brake system.
    b. **Torque** booster to dash panel retaining nuts to 12-22 ft. lbs.
    c. **Torque** master cylinder to booster locking nuts to 14-25 ft. lbs.

CAPRI, ESCORT, PROBE & TRACER

Pump brake pedal several times to exhaust any vacuum in the booster.
1. **On Capri models,** disconnect battery cables, then remove battery from vehicle.
2. **On all models,** remove master cylinder as outlined under "Master Cylinder, Replace."
3. Disconnect rubber hose connecting intake manifold to power brake unit.
4. Remove spring clip in brake pedal clevis pin.
5. Remove brake pedal clevis pin, then brake pedal pushrod from brake pedal.
6. Remove power brake unit attaching nuts, then power brake unit from vehicle.
7. Reverse procedure to install, noting the following:
    a. **Torque** booster to dash panel retaining nuts to 14-19 ft. lbs.

ASPIRE & FESTIVA

1. Remove master cylinder as described under "Master Cylinder, Replace."
2. Disconnect vacuum hose from power brake unit.
3. From under instrument panel, remove brake pedal clevis pin, then detach pushrod from brake pedal.
4. Remove power brake unit attaching nuts, then remove power brake unit.
5. Reverse procedure to install noting the following:
    a. Bleed brakes.
    b. **On Festiva models, torque** brake booster mounting nuts to 12-17 ft. lbs.
    c. **On Aspire models, torque** brake booster mounting nuts to 14-19 ft. lbs.

OVERHAUL
BENDIX, TEVES & TANDEM DIAPHRAGM BOOSTER

On Bendix, Teves and Double Diaphragm Booster type power brake units, overhaul is not required. If it has been determined that the brake booster is defective, replace power brake unit as an assembly. In some instances, the only service required is replacement of the check valve and grommet and pushrod adjustment.

SINGLE DIAPHRAGM BOOSTER
Disassembly

1. Remove brake booster from vehicle.

2. Place front shell of booster in a vise.
3. Remove clevis from valve rod and plunger assembly.
4. Remove dust boot from rear shell, then place alignment marks on front and rear shells for proper alignment during assembly.
5. Rotate rear shell counterclockwise until shell unlocks. **Rear shell is spring loaded, use caution when removing it.**
6. Remove rear shell, then remove front shell return spring and pushrod.
7. Remove front shell retainer and dust boot.
8. Remove rear shell from power piston assembly.
9. Remove rear shell bearing retainer, seal and bearing.
10. Remove retainer holding air filters and air silencer from the valve rod and plunger assembly.
11. Remove diaphragm and plate.
12. Slightly push down on valve rod and remove retainer key and stopper.
13. Remove valve rod and plunger assembly from the power piston assembly.
14. Remove air filters and air silencer from the power piston.
15. Remove reaction disc.

Assembly

Prior to assembly coat the following with silicone grease; reaction disc surface, dust seal lip, pushrod, diaphragm-to-shell contact surfaces, power piston and valve plunger oil seal.
1. Install valve rod and plunger assembly into the power piston.
2. Push down on valve rod, then align groove of the valve plunger with the slot of power piston.
3. Install the valve rod retainer key and stopper.
4. Install two air filters and air silencer into power piston.
5. Place diaphragm and plate onto power piston, ensure the diaphragm is fully seated in the groove of the power piston.
6. Install bearing, bearing seal and bearing retainer into rear shell.
7. Slide rear shell onto power piston while carefully guiding power piston through bearing seal.
8. Using the pushrod, install reaction disc into the power piston.
9. Install dust seal, front retainer and pushrod into front shell.
10. Place front shell in a vise, then install front shell return spring.
11. Place rear shell onto front shell noting alignment marks.
12. Rotate rear shell clockwise until rear shell locks into place with front shell.
13. Install dust boot onto rear shell then install clevis onto valve rod and plunger assembly.
14. Install master cylinder.

ANTI-LOCK BRAKES

TABLE OF CONTENTS

1990-92 Cougar, Mark VII & Thunderbird

NOTE: Wire Color Code & Electrical Symbol Identification Located At The Front Of This Manual Can Be Used As An Aid When Using Wiring Circuits Found In This Section.

INDEX

PRECAUTIONS

Refer to "1993-94 Cougar, Mark VIII & Thunderbird" section for precautions.

DESCRIPTION

These models are equipped with a four wheel anti-lock brake system (ABS), **Fig. 1.** The system prevents lockup by automatically modulating brake system pressure during an emergency stop situation.

By controlling wheel lockup, the vehicle's operator can maintain steering control and stop the vehicle in the shortest possible distance, under most driving conditions.

The ABS system controls the front brakes separately and the rear brakes as a pair, whenever wheel lockup begins. The brake pedal application force required to engage the system function may vary with road surface conditions. A dry surface will require a higher force, while a slippery surface will require a much less force.

During system operation, the vehicle's operator will sense a slight pulsation in the brake pedal, accompanied by a rise in brake pedal height and a clicking sound.

SYSTEM COMPONENTS
HYDRAULIC ACTUATION UNIT

The hydraulic actuation unit, **Figs. 2 and 3,** consists of two sections, the master cylinder and brake booster, which are arranged in the conventional fore and aft sequence. The booster contains a control valve, located in a parallel bore above the master cylinder.

ELECTRIC PUMP ASSEMBLY

This system uses high pressure brake fluid stored in a hydraulic accumulator, **Fig. 4,** for power assist as well as for rear wheel braking. The accumulator is a gas filled pressure chamber that stores brake fluid up to 2600 psi. The fluid is pressurized by an electric motor driven pump. The pump is switched on and off automatically by a pressure sensing switch through a relay circuit.

SOLENOID VALVE BLOCK ASSEMBLY

The solenoid valve block assembly, **Fig. 5,** contains three pairs of solenoid valves, one pair for each front wheel and the third

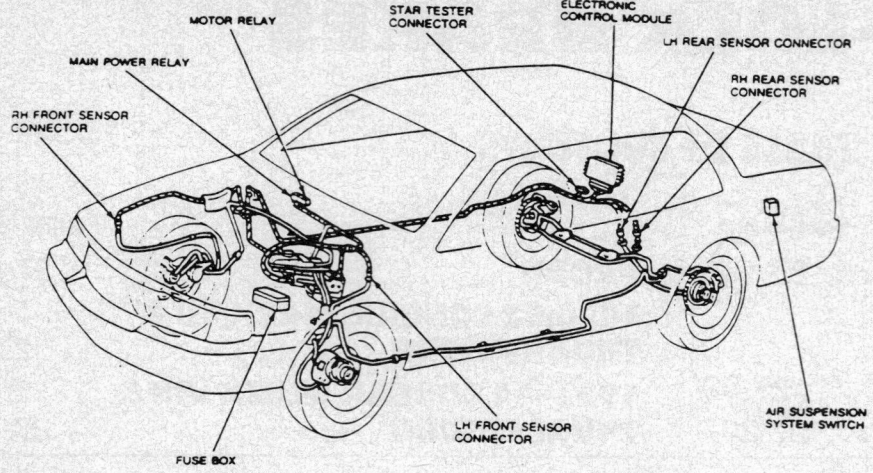

Fig. 1   Anti-lock brake system. 1990–92

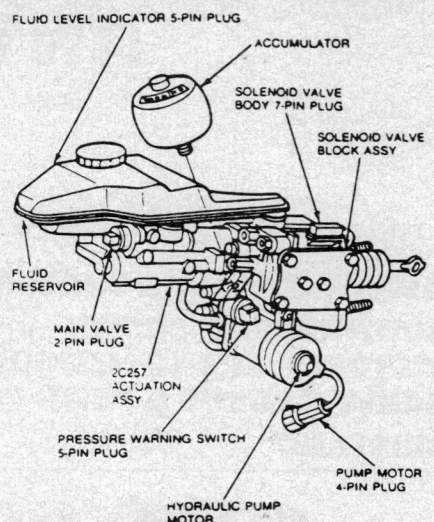

Fig. 2   Hydraulic actuation unit. 1990–92 Cougar/Thunderbird

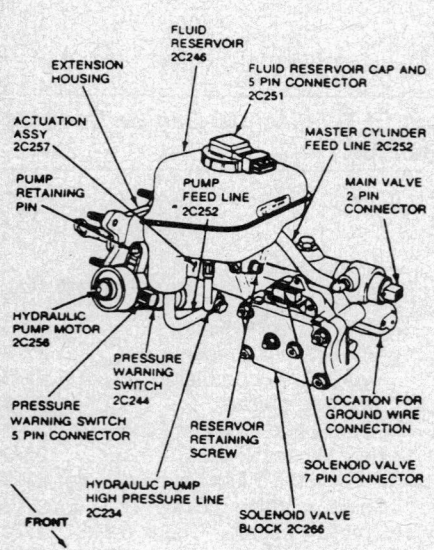

Fig. 3   Hydraulic actuation unit. Mark VII

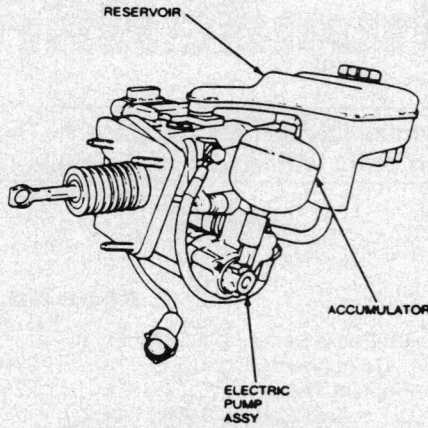

Fig. 4   Electric pump assembly. 1990–92

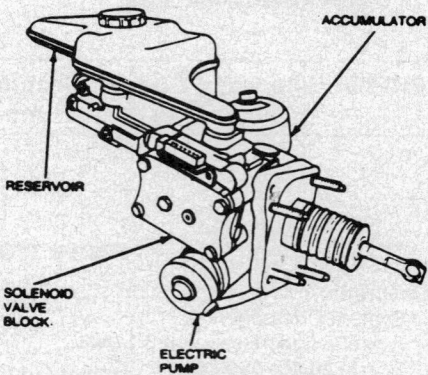

Fig. 5   Solenoid valve block assembly. 1990–92

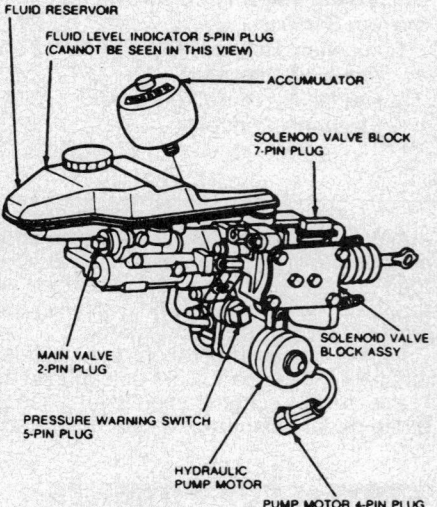

Fig. 6   Brake fluid reservoir & level indicator assembly. 1990–92

pair for both rear wheels. The paired solenoid valves are inlet and outlet valves, with the inlet valve normally open and the outlet valve normally closed. During ABS operation, the inlet and outlet valves are alternately opened and closed approximately 10 times per second to provide pressure modulation to wheel of impending lockup. The solenoid valve block is bolted to the hydraulic actuation unit, behind the lefthand shock tower.

BRAKE FLUID RESERVOIR & LEVEL INDICATOR ASSEMBLY

The brake fluid reservoir and level indicator assembly, **Fig. 6**, is a translucent, plastic container that is mounted on the top of the hydraulic actuation unit. The reservoir is connected to the pump inlet port by a low pressure hose, and to the master cylinder by a sealed feed port.

WHEEL SENSORS

This system, **Figs. 7 and 8**, uses four sets of variable reluctance sensors and toothed speed indicator rings to determine the rotational speed of each wheel. The sensors operate on magnetic induction principle. For example, as the teeth on the speed indicator ring rotate past the stationary sensor, a signal proportional to the speed of the rotation is generated and transmitted to the electronic control unit (ECU) through a coaxial cable.

The front sensors are attached to the suspension knuckles and the speed indicator rings are pressed onto the outer constant velocity joints. The rear sensors are attached to the rear caliper anchor plate and the speed indicator rings are pressed onto the rear wheel hub assemblies. The sensors and the speed indicator rings are serviced individually.

ELECTRONIC CONTROLLER

The electronic controller is located in the luggage compartment of the vehicle, behind the righthand side of the rear seat. It is an on-board self test non-repairable unit, consisting of two microprocessors and the necessary circuitry for their operation. These microprocessors are programmed identically and operate on the principle of two channel redundant data processing and plausibility criteria monitoring.

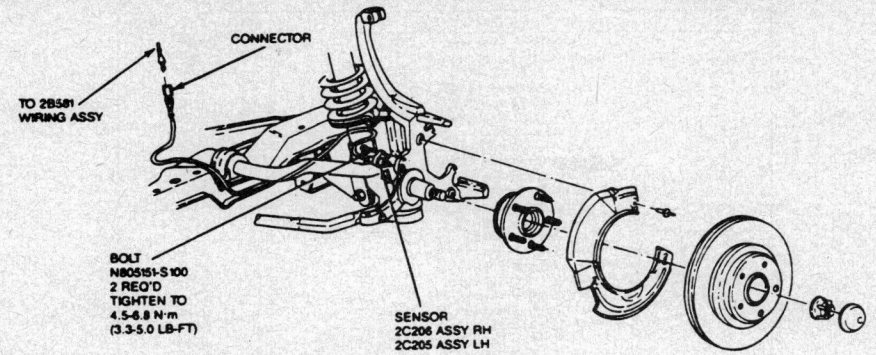

Fig. 7 Wheel sensor assembly. 1990—92 Cougar/Thunderbird

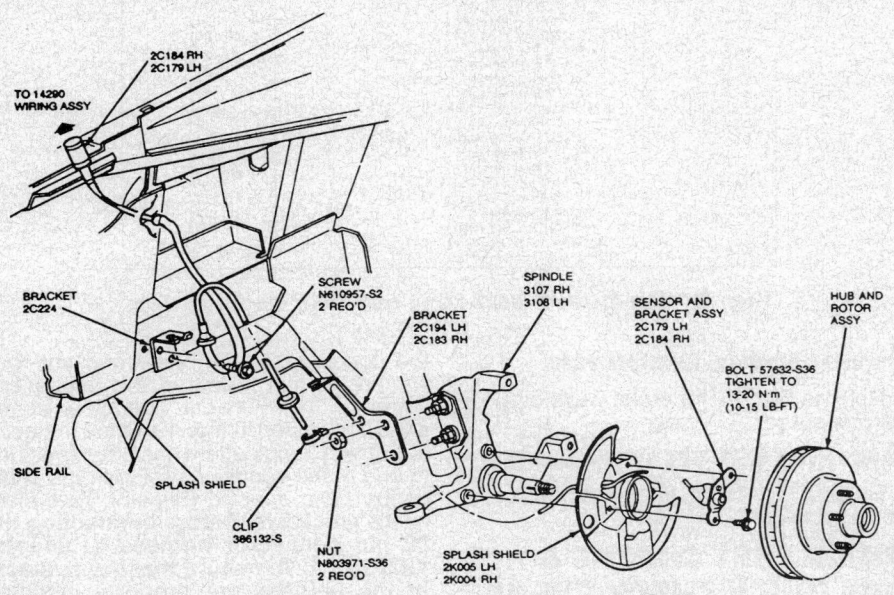

Fig. 8 Wheel sensor assembly. Mark VII

SYSTEM OPERATION

The hydraulic pump maintains system pressure between approximately 2030-2610 psi, within the accumulator and is connected by a high pressure hose to the booster chamber portion of the hydraulic actuation assembly and a control valve. When the brakes are applied, a scissor lever mechanism activates the control valve and a pressure, proportional to brake pedal travel, enters the booster chamber portion of the hydraulic actuation assembly. This pressure is transmitted through the normally open solenoid valve through the proportioning valve to the rear brakes. The same pressure moves the booster piston against the master cylinder piston, shutting off the central valves in the master cylinder. This applies pressure to the front wheels through the two front normally open solenoid valves.

The electronic controller monitors the electro-mechanical components of the system. Malfunction of the ABS system will cause the electronic controller to shutoff or inhibit the ABS function, while retaining normal power assisted braking. Malfunctions are indicated by one or two warning lamps inside the vehicle.

Loss of hydraulic fluid or power boost pressure will disable the ABS system.

The four wheel ABS system is self monitoring. When the ignition switch is turned to the RUN position, the electronic controller will perform a preliminary self check on the ABS electrical system indicated by a three or four second illumination of the amber "Check Anti-Lock Brakes" lamp in the instrument cluster. During vehicle operation, including normal and anti-lock braking, the electronic controller monitors all electrical anti-lock functions and some hydraulic system operation.

For most malfunctions of the ABS system, the amber "Check Anti-Lock Brakes" and/or the red "Brake" lamp will be illuminated. The sequence of illumination of these warning lamps, combined with the problem symptoms, can determine the appropriate diagnostic test to perform. Most malfunctions are recorded as a coded number in the controller memory, pinpointing the exact component requiring service.

DIAGNOSIS & TESTING

Ensure the following diagnosis procedures are used in the sequence and step-by-step order indicated. Following the wrong sequence or bypassing steps will only lead to unnecessary replacement of system components and/or incorrect resolution of the problem. The diagnostic procedure consists of five sub-tests: Pre-test Checks, On-Board Self-Tests, Manual Quick Tests, Warning Lamp Symptom Chart and the Diagnostic Tests. As stated previously, do not attempt to bypass any procedure steps or tests.

PRE-TEST CHECKS

1. Verify that the parking brake is completely released. If the parking brake is applied, the "Brake" lamp will be illuminated.
2. Check brake fluid. **As the fluid level drops, the red "Brake" lamp will illuminate. If fluid level continues to fall, the amber "Check Anti-Lock Brake" lamp will illuminate and the anti-lock function will be inhibited.**
3. Verify that all of the following connectors are properly connected and in good operating condition:
   a. 7 pin connector of the solenoid valve block assembly.
   b. 2 pin connector of the main valve.
   c. 5 pin connector of the fluid level indicator.
   d. 5 pin connector of the pressure warning switch.
   e. 2 pin connector on all four sensors.
   f. 4 pin connector on the pump motor.
   g. 32 pin connector of the electronic controller.
   h. 5 pin connector of the main relay.
   i. 5 pin connector of the pump motor relay.
4. Check that the fuses and diode are not damaged.
5. Ensure all battery connections are clean and tight.
6. Check ground connections on front end of hydraulic unit in luggage compartment.

ON-BOARD SELF-TEST & MAIN COMPONENT DIAGNOSIS

The ABS electronic control module is capable of performing a self-test using Star tester 007-00017 or Super Star tester 007-00019 or equivalents. If the Star tester is not available, the ABS Quick Check sheet can be used as described further on.

The ABS control module monitors system operation and stores up to seven different service codes in its memory. However, it cannot store two services codes with the same first digit. For example: the module cannot store a code 25 and a code 26 at the same time (it can store a code 25 and a code 35). The code 25 is stored first. It must be serviced, the memory must be cleared and the vehicle operated before the code 26 can be stored.

A valve service code will override any stored service code during Self-Test. The condition must be serviced before any other codes can be displayed. After the valve has been serviced, the Self-Test can be run and any stored codes will be displayed. If no codes are displayed, the system has passed the Self-Test. If any codes are displayed during the Self-Test, refer to the Self-Test Code Indexes, **Fig. 9**. These indexes will direct you to a specific pinpoint test to be run. After the pinpoint tests have been completed, the components should be serviced. After servicing these codes, repeat the Self-Test.

After all codes have been displayed and serviced, the memory will be erased by driving the vehicle above approximately 25 mph. If the Self-Test has not been completed and all codes displayed, the memory cannot be erased.

Star Tester Connection & Battery Check

1. Turn ignition switch to Off position.
2. Lower righthand module panel in luggage compartment.
3. Connect Star tester electrical connector to vehicle connector located near the electronic controller assembly.
4. Turn power switch on righthand side of Star tester to On. A steady 00 or a blank screen will appear signifying that the tester is ready to start the Self-Test and receive service codes. If the message LO BAT appears in the upper lefthand corner of the read-out display and stays On, replace the Star tester's 9 volt battery before continuing with the Self-Test. The message LO BAT will appear momentarily when the power switch is turned to the Off position.
5. With the ignition switch in the Off position, push the Self-Test button in the center of the Star tester. Push the button again. This deactivates the Self-Test sequence.
6. If the Star tester passes the Self-Test (a 00 or blank screen with button in TEST position), proceed with the On-Board Self-Test. If any service codes appear during the Self-Test, refer to the On-Board Self-Test Service Code Index, **Fig. 9**.

On-Board Self-Test Diagnosis

Refer to **Figs. 10**, for On-Board Self-Test diagnosis procedure.

Electronic Controller Diagnosis

Refer to **Fig. 11**, for electronic controller diagnosis procedure.

Main Valve Diagnosis

Refer to **Fig. 12**, for main valve diagnosis procedure.

Solenoid Valve Diagnosis

Refer to **Fig. 13**, for solenoid valve diagnosis procedure.

Wheel Sensor Diagnosis

Refer to **Fig. 14**, for wheel sensor diagnosis procedure.

SERVICE CODE (COMPONENT)	PINPOINT TEST STEP
11 (Electronic Controller)	AA1
12 (Electronic Controller-Replacer)	AA2
'21 (Main Valve)	BB1
'22 (LH Front Inlet Valve)	CC1
'23 (LH Front Outlet Valve)	CC2
'24 (RH Front Inlet Valve)	CC3
'25 (RH Front Outlet Valve)	CC4
'26 (Rear Inlet Valve)	CC5
'27 (Rear Outlet Valve and Ground)	CC6
31 (LH Front Sensor)	DD1
32 (RH Front Sensor)	DD8
33 (RH Front Sensor)	DD15
34 (LH Rear Sensor)	DD22
35 (LH Front Sensor)	DD1
36 (RH Front Sensor)	DD8
37 (RH Front Sensor)	DD15
38 (LH Rear Sensor)	DD22
41 (LH Front Sensor)	DD1
42 (RH Front Sensor)	DD8
43 (RH Rear Sensor)	DD15
44 (LH Rear Sensor)	DD22
45 (LH Front Sensor)	DD29
46 (RH Front Sensor)	DD32
47 (RH and LH Rear Sensors)	DD33
48 (Any 3 Sensors missing)	DD34
51 (LH Front Outlet Valve)	EE1
52 (RH Front Outlet Valve)	EE4
53 (Rear Outlet Valve)	EE7
54 (Rear Outlet Valve)	EE10
55 (LH Front Sensor)	DD1
56 (RH Front Sensor)	DD8
57 (RH Rear Sensor)	DD15
58 (LH Rear Sensor)	DD22
61 (FLI and PWS Circuit)	FF1
71 (LH Front Sensor)	EE1
72 (RH Front Sensor)	EE4
73 (RH Rear Sensor)	EE7
74 (LH Rear Sensor)	EE10
75 (LH Front Sensor)	DD1
76 (RH Front Sensor)	DD8
77 (RH Rear Sensor)	DD15
78 (LH Rear Sensor)	DD22
88 (Electronic Controller)	AA1
99 (Electronic Controller)	AA1

Fig. 9   On-board self-test service code index

Outlet Valve Diagnosis

Refer to **Fig. 15**, for outlet valve diagnosis procedure.

Warning Circuit Diagnosis

Refer to **Fig. 16**, for warning circuit diagnosis procedure.

QUICK TEST CHECKS & ABS QUICK CHECK SHEET

To properly conduct the Quick Test Checks an EEC-IV breakout box No. T83L-50-EEC-IV, anti-lock harness adapter No. T87P-50-ALA and a digital volt/ohmmeter (No. 007-00001), or equivalents must be used. All quick tests are performed in the vehicle's luggage compartment using the EEC-IV breakout box and the harness adapter. These group of tests will lead to specific diagnostic Pinpoint Test that will, in most cases, identify the fault/malfunction. If the fault/malfunction is not determined by the Quick Test procedure, use the following Diagnostic Lamp Symptom Chart to identify the proper diagnostic procedure to be conducted.

Refer to ABS quick check sheet **Figs. 17 and 18**, for item to be tested, ignition switch mode position, measurement taken between terminal pin numbers, tester scale/range, volt/ohm specifications and the specific pinpoint test to correct this group of malfunctions.

DIAGNOSTIC LAMP SYMPTOM CHART

If the quick test checks and ABS quick check sheet procedure does not isolate the symptom, it will be necessary to check the operation of the brake and anti-lock warning lamps. Observe the lamps and compare their On/Off operation to the conditions listed in **Fig. 19**. Once the actual warning lamp pattern has been matched to one of the conditions listed in the chart, perform the specific Pinpoint Test diagnostic procedure. **Before connecting the 32 pin connector harness to adapter T87P-50-ALA, ensure that the contacts of the harness are properly installed and are not damaged.**

PINPOINT TESTS

To properly conduct the Pinpoint Test diagnostic procedure an anti-lock harness adapter No. T87P-50-ALA, EEC-IV breakout box T83 L-50-EEC-IV, anti-lock pressure gauge No. D88M-20215-A, digital volt/ohmmeter No. 007-00001 and Super Star tester 007-00019 or equivalents.

Refer to the wiring diagram, Figs. 20, 21 and 22, when performing the Pinpoint Tests to locate wire circuits indicated in the test procedure. Each test is completely independent of the other test and within each test are sequences that can identify a problem without requiring completion of the entire diagnostic test procedure.

Refer to **Figs. 23 through 40**, for Pinpoint Test diagnostic procedures.

CLEARING CODE MEMORY

Original error codes stored in the computer memory will erase automatically if the system is operating properly and the vehicle is driven above 25 mph.

All error codes must be output, all faults corrected and vehicle driven above 25 mph before the memory will clear.

TEST STEP	RESULT	ACTION TO TAKE
1 CONNECT STAR TESTER • Turn ignition switch to OFF. • Connect Rotunda SUPER STAR II Tester 007-00028, 007-00041 or equivalent to anti-lock self-test connector. • Turn tester ON. NOTE: Do not move vehicle or turn steering wheel during test. • Depress SUPER STAR II Tester push button to test position. Display should show: COLON DISPLAY `: 00` COLON MUST BE DISPLAYED TO RECEIVE SERVICE CODES • Turn ignition switch to RUN position. • Observe tester display.	Pass code ( ) displayed and warning indicators OFF. Pass code ( ) displayed and warning indicators turn ON. Service code displayed.	▶ Vehicle OK. RETURN vehicle to customer. ▶ PERFORM Anti-Lock Quick Test. ▶ GO to 2.
2 CHECK SERVICE CODES • Record service code. NOTE: If first displayed code indicates a valve failure (first digit is 2), and no other codes appear, service that valve. Then, repeat Step 1. • Observe tester display. • Leave push button in test position. All stored codes will appear.	Service code displayed. Pass code ( ) displayed.	▶ RECORD each service code as it is displayed. ▶ SERVICE indicated fault(s). GO to 3 or GO to Quick Check.
3 CHECK FOR OTHER FAULT CODES • Repeat Step 1 to see if any other new service codes are stored in memory. • Are any service codes displayed?	No Yes	▶ GO to 4. ▶ GO to 2.
4 CHECK SYSTEM OPERATION • Turn ignition to OFF position. • Disconnect SUPER STAR II Tester. • Turn ignition to RUN position and check warning lamp sequence. • Test drive vehicle.	CHECK ANTI-LOCK and BRAKE warning lamps Off CHECK ANTI-LOCK and/or BRAKE lamp On	▶ RETURN vehicle to customer. ▶ REPEAT Step 1, or if there is no power brake, GO to Step D1.

Fig. 10 On-board self-test

QUICK TEST INDEX

Test	Description	Page No.	Fig. No.
AA	Electronic Controller	18-5	11
BB	Main Valve	18-5	12
CC	Solenoid Valve	18-5	13
DD	Wheel Sensor	18-6	14
EE	Outlet Valve	18-9	15
FF	Warning Circuit	18-10	16

TEST STEP	RESULT	▶	ACTION TO TAKE
AA1 SERVICE CODE 11 AND/OR 88 or 89 ELECTRICAL DISTURBANCE • Read all service codes. • Allow a minimum of 45 seconds to pass after each code is displayed. • Write down on paper all service codes. • After all service codes are read and written down, drive vehicle above 40 km/h (25mph) to clear memory. • Read again all service codes.	Service code 11 and/or 88 or 89 repeated. Memory erased or other service codes present except code 11 and/or 88 or 89.	▶ ▶	REPLACE electronic controller. PERFORM test step associated with service code or codes. REFER to On-Board Self Test Service Code Index.
AA2 SERVICE CODE 12: REPLACE ELECTRONIC CONTROLLER • No test step to be performed.		▶	REPLACE electronic controller.

Fig. 11 Test AA, electronic controller diagnosis

TEST STEP	RESULT	▶	ACTION TO TAKE
BB1 SERVICE CODE 21: CHECK MAIN VALVE • Disconnect main valve 2-pin plug. • Measure resistance between the main valve electrical Pins 1 and 2.	2 to 5.5 ohms Any other reading	▶ ▶	REPLACE or SERVICE cable harness (Circuit 430E or 493). REPLACE actuation assembly

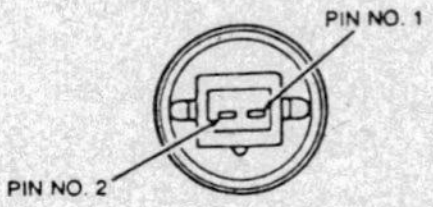

PIN NO. 1
PIN NO. 2

Fig. 12 Test BB, main valve diagnosis

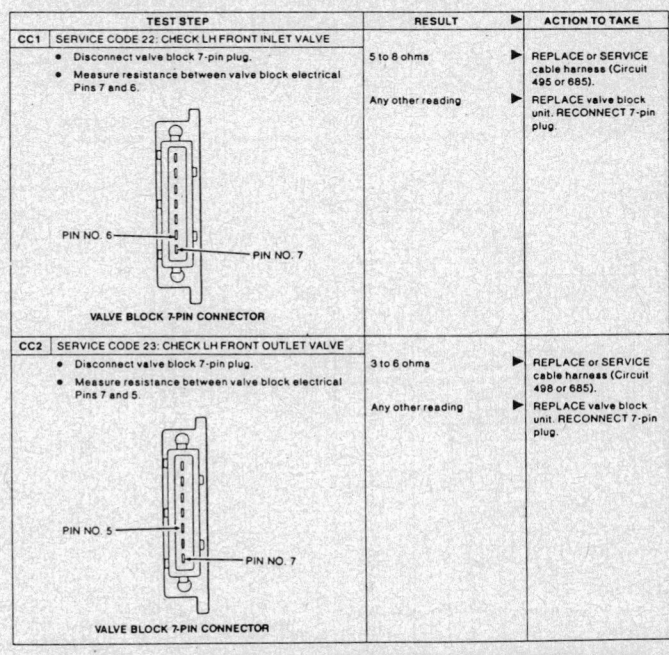

TEST STEP	RESULT	▶	ACTION TO TAKE
CC1 SERVICE CODE 22: CHECK LH FRONT INLET VALVE • Disconnect valve block 7-pin plug. • Measure resistance between valve block electrical Pins 7 and 6.	5 to 8 ohms Any other reading	▶ ▶	REPLACE or SERVICE cable harness (Circuit 495 or 685). REPLACE valve block unit. RECONNECT 7-pin plug.

PIN NO. 6 ——— PIN NO. 7

VALVE BLOCK 7-PIN CONNECTOR

TEST STEP	RESULT	▶	ACTION TO TAKE
CC2 SERVICE CODE 23: CHECK LH FRONT OUTLET VALVE • Disconnect valve block 7-pin plug. • Measure resistance between valve block electrical Pins 7 and 5.	3 to 6 ohms Any other reading	▶ ▶	REPLACE or SERVICE cable harness (Circuit 498 or 685). REPLACE valve block unit. RECONNECT 7-pin plug.

PIN NO. 5 ——— PIN NO. 7

VALVE BLOCK 7-PIN CONNECTOR

Fig. 13 Test CC, solenoid valve diagnosis (Part 1 of 5)

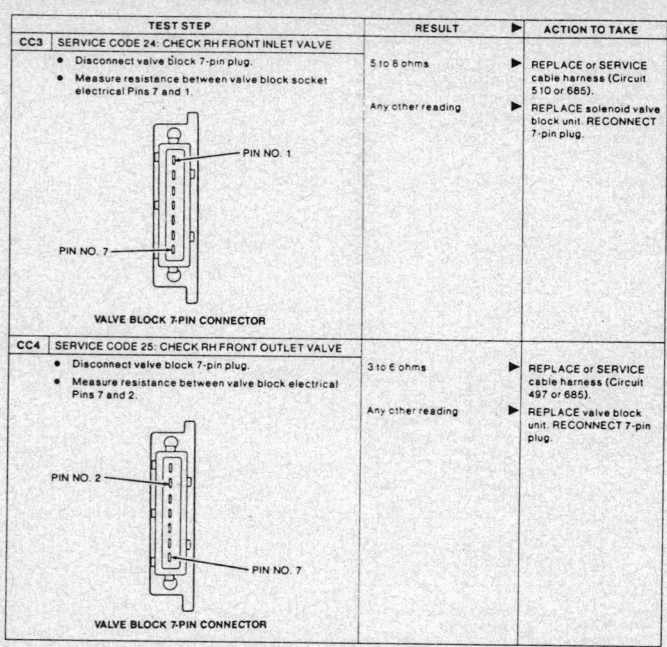

TEST STEP	RESULT	▶	ACTION TO TAKE
CC3 SERVICE CODE 24: CHECK RH FRONT INLET VALVE • Disconnect valve block 7-pin plug. • Measure resistance between valve block socket electrical Pins 7 and 1.	5 to 8 ohms Any other reading	▶ ▶	REPLACE or SERVICE cable harness (Circuit 510 or 685). REPLACE solenoid valve block unit. RECONNECT 7-pin plug.
CC4 SERVICE CODE 25: CHECK RH FRONT OUTLET VALVE • Disconnect valve block 7-pin plug. • Measure resistance between valve block electrical Pins 7 and 2.	3 to 6 ohms Any other reading	▶ ▶	REPLACE or SERVICE cable harness (Circuit 497 or 685). REPLACE valve block unit. RECONNECT 7-pin plug.

Fig. 13 Test CC, solenoid valve diagnosis (Part 2 of 5)

TEST STEP	RESULT	▶	ACTION TO TAKE
CC5 SERVICE CODE 26: CHECK REAR INLET VALVE • Disconnect valve block 7-pin plug. • Measure resistance between valve block electrical Pins 7 and 3.	5 to 8 ohms Any other reading	▶ ▶	REPLACE or SERVICE cable harness (Circuit 496 or 685). REPLACE valve block unit. RECONNECT 7-pin plug.

Fig. 13 Test CC, solenoid valve diagnosis (Part 3 of 5)

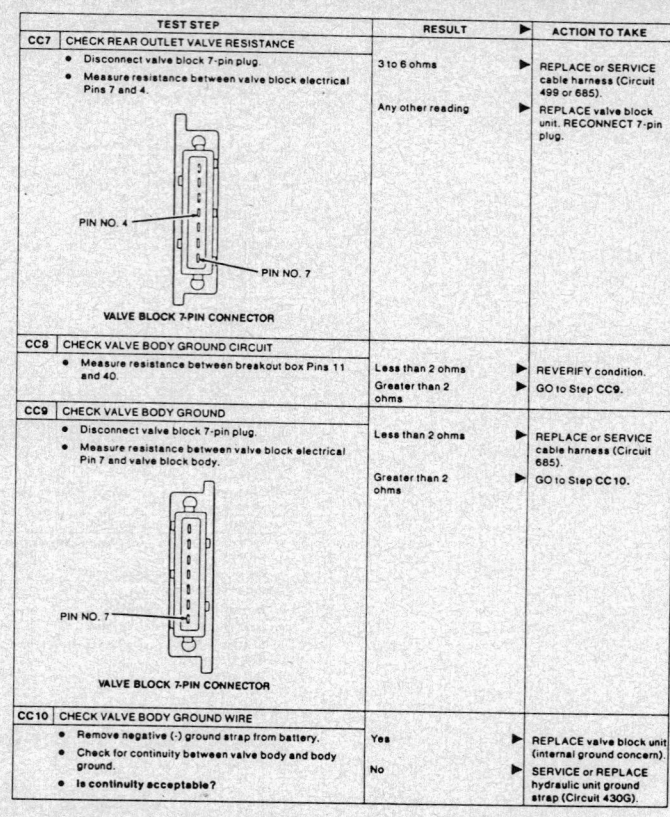

TEST STEP	RESULT	▶	ACTION TO TAKE
CC7 CHECK REAR OUTLET VALVE RESISTANCE • Disconnect valve block 7-pin plug. • Measure resistance between valve block electrical Pins 7 and 4.	3 to 6 ohms Any other reading	▶ ▶	REPLACE or SERVICE cable harness (Circuit 499 or 685). REPLACE valve block unit. RECONNECT 7-pin plug.
CC8 CHECK VALVE BODY GROUND CIRCUIT • Measure resistance between breakout box Pins 11 and 40.	Less than 2 ohms Greater than 2 ohms	▶ ▶	REVERIFY condition. GO to Step CC9.
CC9 CHECK VALVE BODY GROUND • Disconnect valve block 7-pin plug. • Measure resistance between valve block electrical Pin 7 and valve block body.	Less than 2 ohms Greater than 2 ohms	▶ ▶	REPLACE or SERVICE cable harness (Circuit 685). GO to Step CC10.
CC10 CHECK VALVE BODY GROUND WIRE • Remove negative (-) ground strap from battery. • Check for continuity between valve body and body ground. • Is continuity acceptable?	Yes No	▶ ▶	REPLACE valve block unit (internal ground concern). SERVICE or REPLACE hydraulic unit ground strap (Circuit 430G).

Fig. 13 Test CC, solenoid valve diagnosis (Part 5 of 5)

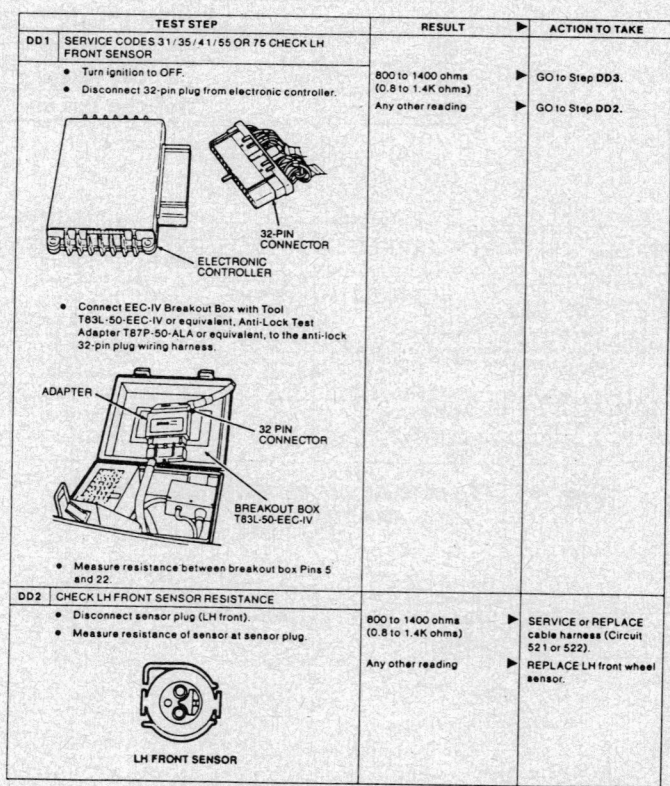

TEST STEP	RESULT	▶	ACTION TO TAKE
DD1 SERVICE CODES 31/35/41/55 OR 75 CHECK LH FRONT SENSOR • Turn ignition to OFF. • Disconnect 32-pin plug from electronic controller.	800 to 1400 ohms (0.8 to 1.4K ohms) Any other reading	▶ ▶	GO to Step DD3. GO to Step DD2.
• Connect EEC-IV Breakout Box with Tool T83L-50-EEC-IV or equivalent, Anti-Lock Test Adapter T87P-50-ALA or equivalent, to the anti-lock 32-pin plug wiring harness. • Measure resistance between breakout box Pins 5 and 22.			
DD2 CHECK LH FRONT SENSOR RESISTANCE • Disconnect sensor plug (LH front). • Measure resistance of sensor at sensor plug.	800 to 1400 ohms (0.8 to 1.4K ohms) Any other reading	▶ ▶	SERVICE or REPLACE cable harness (Circuit 521 or 522). REPLACE LH front wheel sensor.

Fig. 13 Test CC, solenoid valve diagnosis (Part 4 of 5)

Fig. 14 Test DD, wheel sensor diagnosis (Part 1 of 11)

TEST STEP		RESULT	▶	ACTION TO TAKE
DD3	**CHECK LH FRONT SENSOR VOLTAGE**			
	• Turn ignition switch OFF.	Between 0.05 and 0.70 volt AC	▶	GO to Step DD4.
	• Place vehicle on hoist and raise wheels clear of ground. Refer to Pre-Delivery Manual, Section 00-02A.	Less than 0.05 or more than 0.70 volt AC	▶	CHECK sensor mounting, air gap, or toothed wheel mounting. CORRECT as required.
	• Set multi-meter on voltage range (2V-AC).			
	• Measure voltage between Breakout box Pins 5 and 22 while spinning LH front wheel at approximately 1 revolution per second.			
DD4	**CHECK LH FRONT SENSOR CIRCUIT CONTINUITY**			
	• Check continuity between Breakout box Pins 40 and 5.	No	▶	GO to Step DD6.
	• Is continuity present?	Yes	▶	GO to Step DD5.
DD5	**CHECK LH FRONT SENSOR CIRCUITRY**			
	• Disconnect wheel sensor plug (LH front).	Yes	▶	REPLACE sensor (LH front).
	• Check for continuity between each sensor plug pin (sensor side) and vehicle ground.	No	▶	SERVICE or REPLACE cable harness (Circuit 521 or 522). RECONNECT sensor plug.
	• Is continuity present?			
DD6	**CHECK ELECTRONIC CONTROLLER TO GROUND WIRE**			
	• Check continuity between Breakout box Pin 40 and body ground.	Yes	▶	GO to Step DD7.
	• Is continuity present?	No	▶	SERVICE or REPLACE cable harness (Circuit 530A).
DD7	**CHECK LH FRONT WHEEL BEARING**			
	• Check front wheel bearing end play.	Yes	▶	ADJUST bearings or REPLACE damaged or worn parts.
	• Inspect toothed sensor ring visually for damaged teeth.	No	▶	REVERIFY condition.
	• Were loose or damaged parts found?			

Fig. 14   Test DD, wheel sensor diagnosis (Part 2 of 11)

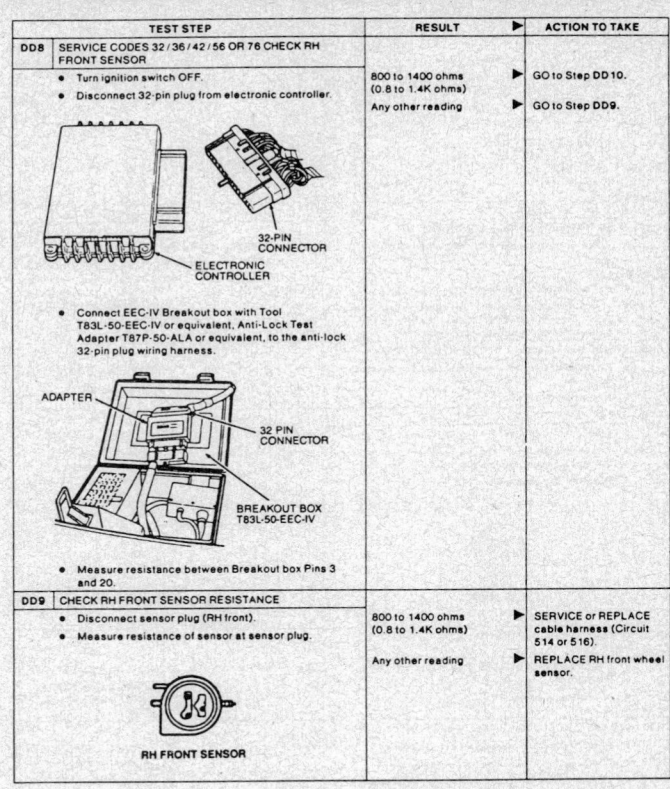

TEST STEP		RESULT	▶	ACTION TO TAKE
DD8	**SERVICE CODES 32/36/42/56 OR 76 CHECK RH FRONT SENSOR**			
	• Turn ignition switch OFF.	800 to 1400 ohms (0.8 to 1.4K ohms)	▶	GO to Step DD10.
	• Disconnect 32-pin plug from electronic controller.	Any other reading	▶	GO to Step DD9.
	• Connect EEC-IV Breakout box with Tool T83L-50-EEC-IV or equivalent, Anti-Lock Test Adapter T87P-50-ALA or equivalent, to the anti-lock 32-pin plug wiring harness.			
	• Measure resistance between Breakout box Pins 3 and 20.			
DD9	**CHECK RH FRONT SENSOR RESISTANCE**			
	• Disconnect sensor plug (RH front).	800 to 1400 ohms (0.8 to 1.4K ohms)	▶	SERVICE or REPLACE cable harness (Circuit 514 or 516).
	• Measure resistance of sensor at sensor plug.	Any other reading	▶	REPLACE RH front wheel sensor.

Fig. 14   Test DD, wheel sensor diagnosis (Part 3 of 11)

TEST STEP		RESULT	▶	ACTION TO TAKE
DD10	**CHECK RH FRONT SENSOR VOLTAGE**			
	• Place vehicle on hoist and raise wheels clear of ground.	Between 0.05 and 0.70 volts AC	▶	GO to Step DD11.
	• Set multi-meter on voltage range (2V-AC).	Less than 0.05 or more than 0.70 volts AC	▶	CHECK wheel sensor mounting, air gap, or toothed wheel mounting. CORRECT as required.
	• Measure voltage between Breakout box Pins 3 and 20 while spinning the RH front wheel at approximately 1 revolution per second.			
DD11	**CHECK RH FRONT SENSOR CIRCUIT CONTINUITY**			
	• Check continuity between Breakout box Pins 40 and 3.	Yes	▶	GO to Step DD12.
	• Is continuity present?	No	▶	GO to Step DD13.
DD12	**CHECK RH FRONT SENSOR CONTINUITY**			
	• Disconnect wheel sensor plug (RH front).	Yes	▶	REPLACE RH front sensor.
	• Check for continuity between each sensor plug (sensor side) and vehicle ground.	No	▶	SERVICE or REPLACE cable harness. RECONNECT sensor plug.
	• Is continuity present?			
DD13	**CHECK ELECTRONIC CONTROLLER TO GROUND WIRE**			
	• Check continuity between Breakout box Pin 40 and body ground.	Yes	▶	GO to Step DD14.
	• Is continuity present?	No	▶	SERVICE or REPLACE cable harness (Circuit 503A).
DD14	**CHECK RH FRONT WHEEL BEARING**			
	• Check front wheel bearing end play.	Yes	▶	ADJUST bearings or REPLACE damaged parts.
	• Inspect toothed sensor ring visually for damaged teeth.	No	▶	REVERIFY condition.
	• Were loose or damaged parts found?			

Fig. 14   Test DD, wheel sensor diagnosis (Part 4 of 11)

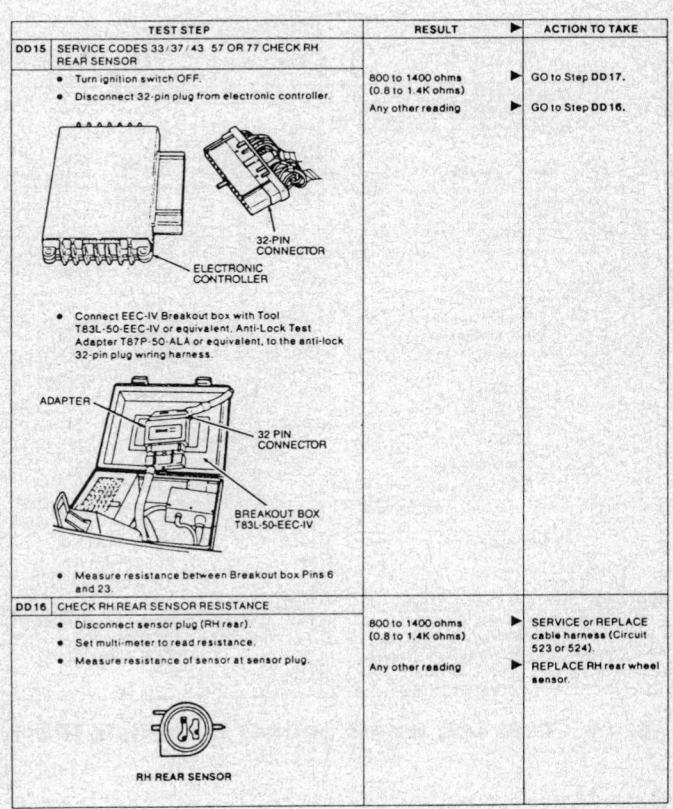

TEST STEP		RESULT	▶	ACTION TO TAKE
DD15	**SERVICE CODES 33/37/43 57 OR 77 CHECK RH REAR SENSOR**			
	• Turn ignition switch OFF.	800 to 1400 ohms (0.8 to 1.4K ohms)	▶	GO to Step DD17.
	• Disconnect 32-pin plug from electronic controller.	Any other reading	▶	GO to Step DD16.
	• Connect EEC-IV Breakout box with Tool T83L-50-EEC-IV or equivalent, Anti-Lock Test Adapter T87P-50-ALA or equivalent, to the anti-lock 32-pin plug wiring harness.			
	• Measure resistance between Breakout box Pins 6 and 23.			
DD16	**CHECK RH REAR SENSOR RESISTANCE**			
	• Disconnect sensor plug (RH rear).	800 to 1400 ohms (0.8 to 1.4K ohms)	▶	SERVICE or REPLACE cable harness (Circuit 523 or 524).
	• Set multi-meter to read resistance.	Any other reading	▶	REPLACE RH rear wheel sensor.
	• Measure resistance of sensor at sensor plug.			

Fig. 14   Test DD, wheel sensor diagnosis (Part 5 of 11)

TEST STEP		RESULT	▶	ACTION TO TAKE
DD17	CHECK RH REAR SENSOR VOLTAGE			
	• Place vehicle on hoist and raise wheels clear of ground.	Between 0.05 and 0.70 volts AC	▶	GO to Step DD18.
	• Set multi-meter on voltage range (2V-AC). • Measure voltage between Breakout box Pins 6 and 23 while spinning the RH rear wheel at approximately 1 revolution per second.	Less than 0.05 or more than 0.70 volts AC	▶	CHECK sensor mounting, air gap, or toothed wheel mounting. CORRECT as required.
DD18	CHECK RH REAR SENSOR CIRCUIT CONTINUITY			
	• Check continuity between Breakout box Pins 40 and 6.	No	▶	GO to Step DD20.
	• Is continuity present?	Yes	▶	GO to Step DD19.
DD19	CHECK RH REAR SENSOR CONTINUITY			
	• Disconnect wheel sensor plug (RH rear).	Yes	▶	REPLACE sensor (RH rear).
	• Check for continuity between each sensor plug pin (sensor side) and vehicle ground. • Is continuity present?	No	▶	SERVICE or REPLACE cable harness (Circuit 523 or 524). CONNECT sensor plug.
DD20	CHECK ELECTRONIC CONTROLLER TO GROUND WIRE			
	• Check continuity between Breakout box Pin 40 and body ground.	Yes	▶	GO to Step DD21.
	• Is continuity present?	No	▶	SERVICE or REPLACE cable harness (Circuit 530A).
DD21	CHECK FOR EXCESSIVE AXLE VIBRATION			
	• Check differential housing for excessive play. • Check rear axle bearings for excessive play.	Yes	▶	SERVICE or REPLACE damaged parts.
	• Inspect toothed sensor ring visually for damaged teeth. • Were loose or damaged parts found?	No	▶	REVERIFY condition.

Fig. 14 Test DD, wheel sensor diagnosis (Part 6 of 11)

TEST STEP		RESULT	▶	ACTION TO TAKE
DD22	SERVICE CODES 34 / 38 / 44 / 58 OR 78 CHECK LH REAR SENSOR			
	• Turn ignition switch OFF.	800 to 1400 ohms (0.8 to 1.4K ohms)	▶	GO to Step DD24.
	• Disconnect 32-pin plug from electronic controller.	Any other reading	▶	GO to Step DD23.

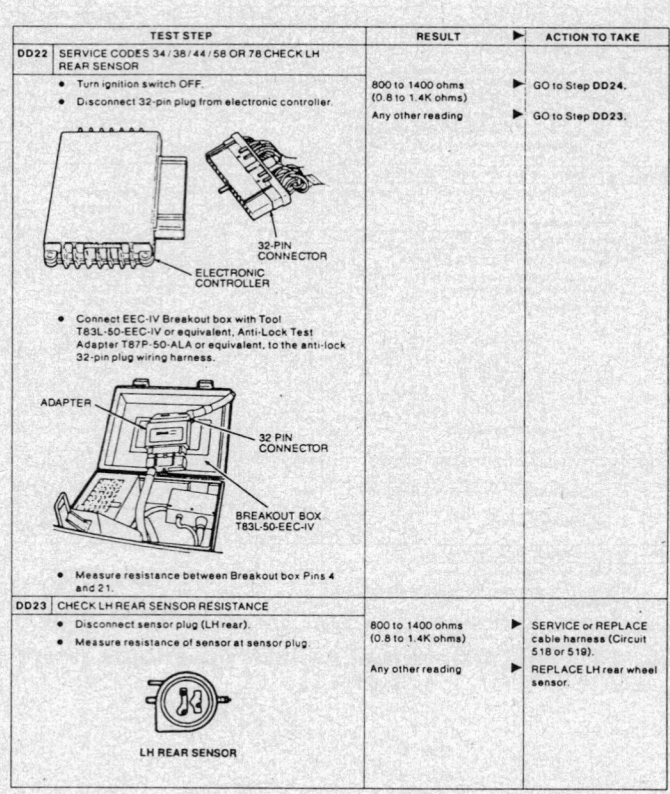

• Connect EEC-IV Breakout box with Tool T83L-50-EEC-IV or equivalent, Anti-Lock Test Adapter T87P-50-ALA or equivalent, to the anti-lock 32-pin plug wiring harness.

• Measure resistance between Breakout box Pins 4 and 21.

TEST STEP		RESULT	▶	ACTION TO TAKE
DD23	CHECK LH REAR SENSOR RESISTANCE			
	• Disconnect sensor plug (LH rear).	800 to 1400 ohms (0.8 to 1.4K ohms)	▶	SERVICE or REPLACE cable harness (Circuit 518 or 519).
	• Measure resistance of sensor at sensor plug.	Any other reading	▶	REPLACE LH rear wheel sensor.

LH REAR SENSOR

Fig. 14 Test DD, wheel sensor diagnosis (Part 7 of 11)

TEST STEP		RESULT	▶	ACTION TO TAKE
DD24	CHECK LH REAR SENSOR VOLTAGE			
	• Place vehicle on hoist and raise wheels clear of ground.	Between 0.05 and 0.70 volts AC	▶	GO to Step DD25.
	• Set multi-meter on voltage range (2V-AC). • Measure voltage between Breakout box Pins 4 and 21 while spinning the LH rear wheel at approximately 1 revolution per second.	Less than 0.05 or more than 0.70 volts AC	▶	CHECK sensor mounting, air gap, or toothed wheel mounting. CORRECT as required.
DD25	CHECK LH REAR SENSOR CIRCUIT CONTINUITY			
	• Check continuity between Breakout box Pins 40 and 4.	No	▶	GO to Step DD27.
	• Is continuity present?	Yes	▶	GO to Step DD26.
DD26	CHECK LH REAR SENSOR CONTINUITY			
	• Disconnect wheel sensor plug (LH front).	Yes	▶	REPLACE sensor (LH rear).
	• Check for continuity between each sensor. • Is continuity present?	No	▶	SERVICE or REPLACE cable harness. RECONNECT sensor plug.
DD27	CHECK ELECTRONIC CONTROLLER TO GROUND WIRE			
	• Check continuity between Breakout box Pin 40 and body ground.	Yes	▶	GO to Step DD28.
	• Is continuity present?	No	▶	SERVICE or REPLACE cable harness (Circuit 530A).
DD28	CHECK FOR EXCESSIVE AXLE VIBRATION			
	• Check differential housing for excessive play. • Check rear axle bearings for excessive play.	Yes	▶	SERVICE or REPLACE damaged parts.
	• Inspect toothed sensor ring visually for damaged teeth. • Were loose or damaged parts found?	No	▶	REVERIFY condition.

Fig. 14 Test DD, wheel sensor diagnosis (Part 8 of 11)

TEST STEP		RESULT	▶	ACTION TO TAKE
DD29	SERVICE CODE 45: CHECK FOR TWO MISSING SENSOR SIGNALS ONE BEING THE LH FRONT			
	• Turn ignition switch to OFF.	Voltage between 0.05 and 0.70V AC	▶	GO to Step DD30.
	• Disconnect 32-pin plug from Electronic Controller. • Connect EEC-IV Breakout Box T83L-50-EEC-IV with Anti-Lock Test Adapter T87P-50-ALA or equivalent to 32-pin plug wiring harness. • Place vehicle on hoist and raise until wheels are clear of ground.	Less than 0.05 or greater than 0.70 V AC	▶	CHECK out-of-range wheel for proper sensor mounting, air gap and speed indicator ring mounting. CORRECT as required.
	• Set multi-meter on 2V AC voltage range. • Measure voltage between Breakout box Pins 5 and 22 while spinning LH front wheel at approximately 1 revolution per second. • Repeat wheel sensor voltage check described in previous step for the other wheels by:			

Spinning	Measuring A/C volts between Pins
RH Front	3 and 20
RH Rear	6 and 23
LH Rear	4 and 21

TEST STEP		RESULT	▶	ACTION TO TAKE
DD30	ELECTRONIC CONTROLLER TO GROUND			
	• Check continuity between breakout box Pin 40 and body ground.	Yes	▶	GO to Step DD31.
	• Is continuity present?	No	▶	SERVICE or REPLACE cable harness (530).
DD31	CHECK WHEEL BEARINGS			
	• Check wheel bearing end play on all wheels. • Inspect toothed sensor ring visually for damaged teeth.	Yes	▶	ADJUST bearings or REPLACE damaged parts.
	• Were loose or damaged parts found?	No	▶	REVERIFY condition.

Fig. 14 Test DD, wheel sensor diagnosis (Part 9 of 11)

TEST STEP	RESULT	▶	ACTION TO TAKE
DD32 SERVICE CODE 46: CHECK FOR 2 MISSING SENSOR SIGNALS ONE BEING RH FRONT • Turn ignition switch to OFF. • Disconnect 32-pin plug from Electronic Controller. • Connect EEC-IV Breakout Box T83L-50-EEC-IV with Anti-Lock Test Adapter T87P-50-ALA or equivalent to 32-pin plug wiring harness. • Place vehicle on hoist and raise until wheels are clear of ground. • Set multi-meter on 2V AC voltage range. • Measure voltage between Breakout box Pins 3 and 20 while spinning RH front wheel at approximately 1 revolution per second. • Repeat wheel sensor voltage check described in previous step for the other wheels by:	Voltage between 0.05 and 0.70V AC	▶	GO to Step DD30.
	Less than 0.05 or greater than 0.70V AC	▶	CHECK out-of-range wheel for proper sensor mounting, air gap and speed indication ring mounting. CORRECT as required.

Spinning	Measuring A/C volts between Pins
RH Rear	6 and 23
LH Rear	4 and 21

| **DD33** SERVICE CODE 47: CHECK FOR BOTH REAR WHEEL SENSOR SIGNALS MISSING
• Turn ignition switch to OFF.
• Disconnect 32-pin plug from Electronic Controller.
• Connect EEC-IV Breakout Box T83L-50-EEC-IV with Anti-Lock Test Adapter T87P-50-ALA or equivalent to 32-pin plug wiring harness.
• Place vehicle on hoist and raise until wheels are clear of ground.
• Set multi-meter on 2V AC voltage range.
• Measure voltage between Breakout box Pins 6 and 23 while spinning RH front wheel at approximately 1 revolution per second.
• Measure voltage between Breakout box Pins 4 and 21 while spinning LH front wheel at approximately 1 revolution per second. | Voltage between 0.05 and 0.70V AC | ▶ | GO to Step DD30. |
| | Less than 0.05 or greater than 0.70V AC | ▶ | CHECK out-of-range wheel for proper sensor mounting, air gap and speed indication ring mounting. CORRECT as required. |

Fig. 14   Test DD, wheel sensor diagnosis (Part 10 of 11)

TEST STEP	RESULT	▶	ACTION TO TAKE
EE1 SERVICE CODE 51 AND/OR 71 CHECK LH FRONT SENSOR CIRCUIT CONTINUITY • Turn ignition switch OFF. • Disconnect 32-pin plug from electronic controller.	Yes	▶	GO to Step EE2.
	No	▶	GO to Step EE3.

ELECTRONIC CONTROLLER
32-PIN CONNECTOR

• Correct EEC-IV Breakout Box with Tool T83L-50-EEC-IV or equivalent, Anti-Lock Test Adapter T87P-50-ALA or equivalent, to the anti-lock 32-Pin plug wiring harness.

ADAPTER
32 PIN CONNECTOR
BREAKOUT BOX T83L-50-EEC-IV

• Check for continuity between Breakout Box Pins 40 and 5. • Is continuity present?			
EE2 CHECK LH FRONT SENSOR CONTINUITY • Disconnect wheel sensor plug (LH front). • Check for continuity between each sensor plug pin (sensor side) and vehicle ground. • Is continuity present?	Yes	▶	REPLACE SENSOR (LH front).
	No	▶	SERVICE or REPLACE cable harness. RECONNECT sensor plug.

LH FRONT SENSOR

Fig. 15   Test EE, outlet valve diagnosis (Part 1 of 6)

TEST STEP	RESULT	▶	ACTION TO TAKE
DD34 SERVICE CODE 48: ANY 3 OF 4 WHEEL SPEED SENSOR SIGNALS MISSING • Turn ignition switch to OFF. • Disconnect 32-pin plug from Electronic Controller. • Connect EEC-IV Breakout Box T83L-50-EEC-IV with Anti-Lock Test Adapter T87P-50-ALA or equivalent to 32-pin plug wiring harness. • Place vehicle on hoist and raise until wheels are clear of ground. • Set multi-meter on 2V AC voltage range. • Measure voltage between Breakout Box pins indicated below while spinning appropriate wheel at approximately 1 revolution per second.	Voltage between 0.05 and 0.70V AC	▶	GO to Step DD30.
	Less than 0.05 or greater than 0.70V AC	▶	CHECK out-of-range sensor mounting, air gap and speed indication ring mounting. CORRECT as required.

Spinning	Measuring A/C volts between Pins
LH Front	5 and 22
RH Front	3 and 20
RH Rear	6 and 23
LH Rear	4 and 21

Fig. 14   Test DD, wheel sensor diagnosis (Part 11 of 11)

TEST STEP	RESULT	▶	ACTION TO TAKE
EE3 CHECK ANTI-LOCK OPERATION LH FRONT WHEEL • Lift vehicle and rotate wheels to ensure they turn freely. • Short Pins 18, 14 and 31 to each other at breakout box. • Apply moderate brake pedal effort and check that LH front wheel will not turn. • Check to see that LH front wheel turns freely with ignition switch ON. CAUTION: Do not leave ignition on for more than 1 minute maximum, or solenoid valve damage may result.	If wheel turns freely	▶	REVERIFY condition.
	If wheel does not turn freely or pedal drops	▶	REPLACE solenoid valve block.
EE4 SERVICE CODE 52 AND/OR 72 CHECK RH FRONT SENSOR CIRCUIT CONTINUITY • Turn ignition switch OFF. • Disconnect 32-pin plug from electronic controller.	Yes	▶	GO to Step EE5.
	No	▶	GO to Step EE6.

ELECTRONIC CONTROLLER
32-PIN CONNECTOR

• Connect EEC-IV Breakout Box with Tool T83L-50-EEC-IV or equivalent, Anti-Lock Test Adapter T87P-50-ALA or equivalent, to the anti-lock 32-pin plug wiring harness.

ADAPTER
32 PIN CONNECTOR
BREAKOUT BOX T83L-50-EEC-IV

• Check for continuity between Breakout Box Pins 40 and 3.
• Is continuity present?

Fig. 15   Test EE, outlet valve diagnosis (Part 2 of 6)

TEST STEP	RESULT	▶	ACTION TO TAKE
EE5 CHECK RH FRONT SENSOR CONTINUITY • Disconnect wheel sensor plug (RH front). • Check for continuity between each sensor plug pin (sensor side) and vehicle ground. • Is continuity present?	Yes	▶	REPLACE RH front sensor.
	No	▶	SERVICE or REPLACE cable harness. RECONNECT sensor plug.

RH FRONT SENSOR

| **EE6** CHECK ANTI-LOCK OPERATION RH FRONT WHEEL
• Lift vehicle and rotate wheels to ensure they turn freely.
• Short Pins 18, 32 and 13 to each other at Breakout box.
• Apply moderate brake effort. Check that RH front wheel does not turn.
• Check to see that RH front wheel turns freely with ignition switch ON.
CAUTION: Do not leave ignition on for more than 1 minute maximum, or solenoid valve damage may result. | If wheel turns freely | ▶ | REVERIFY condition. |
| | If wheel does not turn freely or pedal drops | ▶ | REPLACE solenoid valve block. |

Fig. 15   Test EE, outlet valve diagnosis (Part 3 of 6)

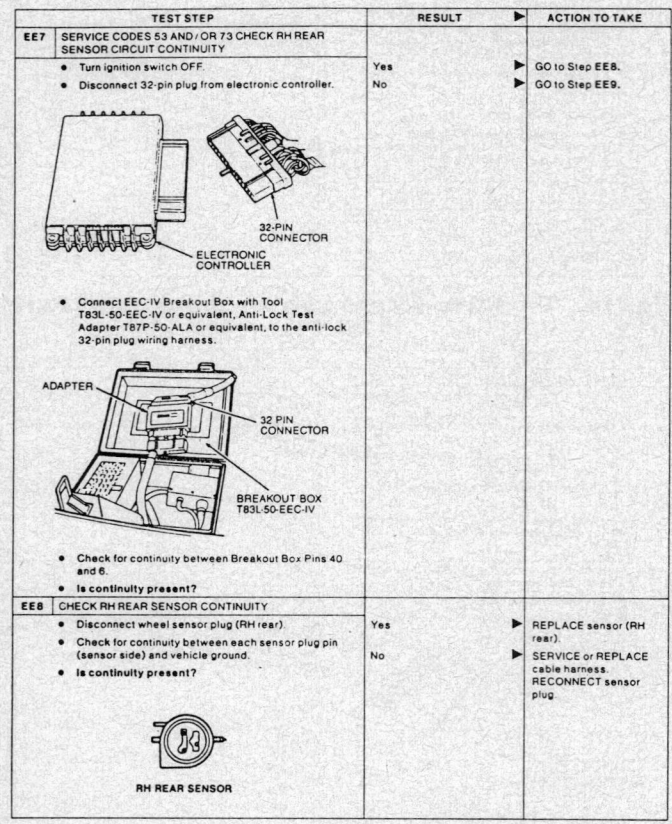

TEST STEP	RESULT	▶	ACTION TO TAKE
EE7 SERVICE CODES 53 AND / OR 73 CHECK RH REAR SENSOR CIRCUIT CONTINUITY			
• Turn ignition switch OFF.	Yes	▶	GO to Step EE8.
• Disconnect 32-pin plug from electronic controller.	No	▶	GO to Step EE9.
• Connect EEC-IV Breakout Box with Tool T83L-50-EEC-IV or equivalent, Anti-lock Test Adapter T87P-50-ALA or equivalent, to the anti-lock 32-pin plug wiring harness.			
• Check for continuity between Breakout Box Pins 40 and 6.			
• Is continuity present?			
EE8 CHECK RH REAR SENSOR CONTINUITY			
• Disconnect wheel sensor plug (RH rear).	Yes	▶	REPLACE sensor (RH rear).
• Check for continuity between each sensor plug pin (sensor side) and vehicle ground.	No	▶	SERVICE or REPLACE cable harness. RECONNECT sensor plug.
• Is continuity present?			

Fig. 15   Test EE, outlet valve diagnosis (Part 4 of 6)

TEST STEP	RESULT	▶	ACTION TO TAKE
EE9 CHECK ANTI-LOCK OPERATION: REAR WHEELS			
• Lift vehicle and rotate wheels to ensure they turn freely.	If wheel turns freely	▶	REVERIFY condition.
• Short Pins 18, 30 and 12 to each other at Breakout Box.	If wheel does not turn freely or pedal drops	▶	REPLACE solenoid valve block.
• Apply moderate brake pedal pressure. Check that rear wheels will not turn.			
• Check that rear wheels turn freely with ignition switch ON.			
CAUTION: Do not leave ignition on for more than 1 minute maximum or solenoid valve damage may result.			
EE10 SERVICE CODES 54 AND / OR 74 CHECK LH REAR SENSOR CIRCUIT CONTINUITY			
• Turn ignition switch OFF.	Yes	▶	GO to Step EE11.
• Disconnect 32-pin plug from electronic controller.	No	▶	GO to Step EE12.
• Connect EEC-IV Breakout Box with Tool T83L-50-EEC-IV or equivalent, Anti-Lock Test Adapter T87P-50-ALA or equivalent, to the anti-lock 32-pin plug wiring harness.			
• Check for continuity between Breakout Box Pins 40 and 4.			
• Is continuity present?			

Fig. 15   Test EE, outlet valve diagnosis (Part 5 of 6)

TEST STEP	RESULT	▶	ACTION TO TAKE
EE11 CHECK LH REAR SENSOR CONTINUITY			
• Disconnect wheel sensor plug (LH rear).	Yes	▶	REPLACE sensor (LH rear).
• Check for continuity between each sensor plug pin (sensor side) and vehicle ground.	No	▶	SERVICE or REPLACE cable harness. RECONNECT sensor plug.
• Is continuity present?			
EE12 CHECK ANTI-LOCK OPERATION: REAR WHEELS			
• Lift vehicle and rotate wheels to ensure they turn freely.	If wheel turns freely	▶	VERIFY condition.
• Short Pins 18, 30 and 12 to each other at Breakout box.	If wheel does not turn freely or pedal drops	▶	REPLACE solenoid valve block.
• Apply moderate brake pedal pressure. Check that rear wheels will not turn.			
• Check that rear wheels turn freely with ignition switch ON.			
CAUTION: Do not leave ignition on for more than 1 minute maximum or solenoid valve damage may result.			

Fig. 15   Test EE, outlet valve diagnosis (Part 6 of 6)

TEST STEP	RESULT	▶	ACTION TO TAKE
FF1 SERVICE CODE 61: CHECK FLI AND PWS CIRCUIT			
• Turn ignition switch OFF.	Yes	▶	GO to Step FF7.
• Disconnect 32-pin plug from electronic controller.	No	▶	GO to Step FF2.
• Connect EEC-IV Breakout Box with Tool T83L-50-EEC-IV, Anti-Lock Test Adapter T87P-50-ALA or equivalent, to the anti-lock 32-pin plug wiring harness.			
• Measure the resistance between Breakout Box Pins 25 and 27.			
NOTE: System must be pressurized for this test.			
• Is reading less than 5 ohms?			

Fig. 16   Test FF, warning circuit diagnosis (Part 1 of 5)

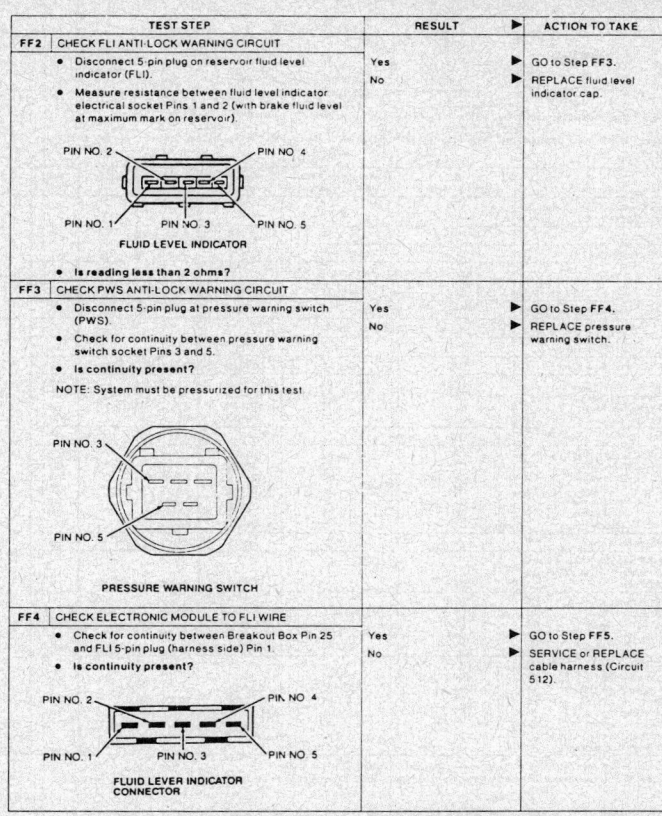

TEST STEP		RESULT	▶	ACTION TO TAKE
FF2	CHECK FLI ANTI-LOCK WARNING CIRCUIT			
	• Disconnect 5-pin plug on reservoir fluid level indicator (FLI).	Yes	▶	GO to Step FF3.
	• Measure resistance between fluid level indicator electrical socket Pins 1 and 2 (with brake fluid level at maximum mark on reservoir).	No	▶	REPLACE fluid level indicator cap.
	• Is reading less than 2 ohms?			
FF3	CHECK PWS ANTI-LOCK WARNING CIRCUIT			
	• Disconnect 5-pin plug at pressure warning switch (PWS).	Yes	▶	GO to Step FF4.
	• Check for continuity between pressure warning switch socket Pins 3 and 5.	No	▶	REPLACE pressure warning switch.
	• Is continuity present?			
	NOTE: System must be pressurized for this test.			
FF4	CHECK ELECTRONIC MODULE TO FLI WIRE			
	• Check for continuity between Breakout Box Pin 25 and FLI 5-pin plug (harness side) Pin 1	Yes	▶	GO to Step FF5.
	• Is continuity present?	No	▶	SERVICE or REPLACE cable harness (Circuit 512).

Fig. 16 Test FF, warning circuit diagnosis (Part 2 of 5)

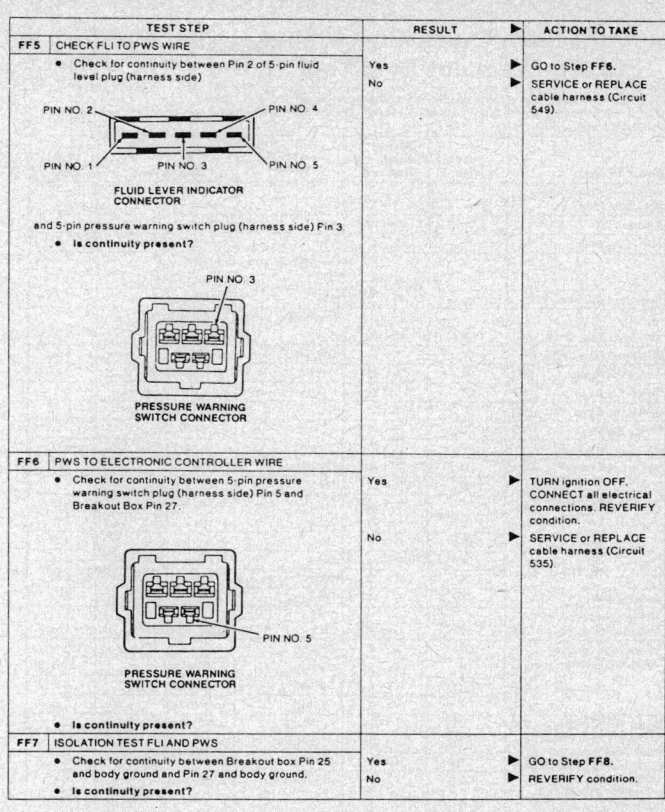

TEST STEP		RESULT	▶	ACTION TO TAKE
FF5	CHECK FLI TO PWS WIRE			
	• Check for continuity between Pin 2 of 5-pin fluid level plug (harness side)	Yes	▶	GO to Step FF6.
		No	▶	SERVICE or REPLACE cable harness (Circuit 549).
	and 5-pin pressure warning switch plug (harness side) Pin 3.			
	• Is continuity present?			
FF6	PWS TO ELECTRONIC CONTROLLER WIRE			
	• Check for continuity between 5-pin pressure warning switch plug (harness side) Pin 5 and Breakout Box Pin 27.	Yes	▶	TURN ignition OFF. CONNECT all electrical connections. REVERIFY condition.
		No	▶	SERVICE or REPLACE cable harness (Circuit 535).
	• Is continuity present?			
FF7	ISOLATION TEST FLI AND PWS			
	• Check for continuity between Breakout box Pin 25 and body ground and Pin 27 and body ground.	Yes	▶	GO to Step FF8.
	• Is continuity present?	No	▶	REVERIFY condition.

Fig. 16 Test FF, warning circuit diagnosis (Part 3 of 5)

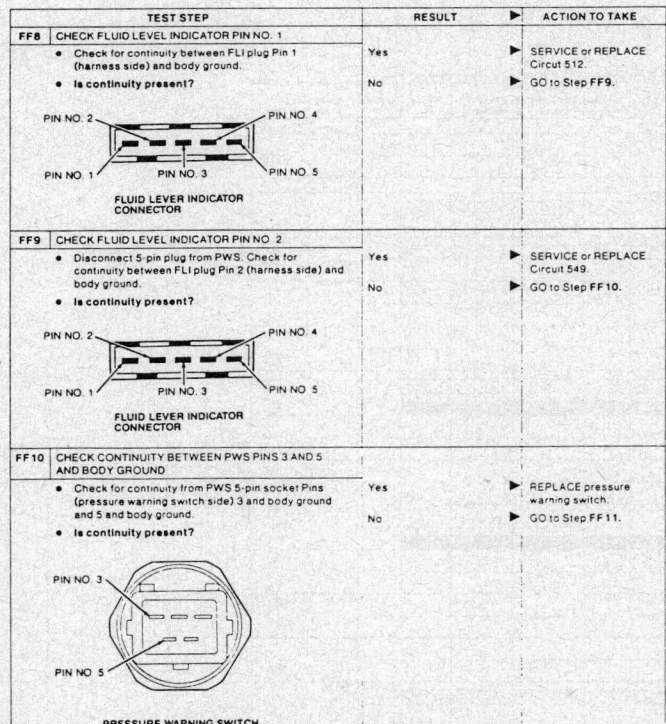

TEST STEP		RESULT	▶	ACTION TO TAKE
FF8	CHECK FLUID LEVEL INDICATOR PIN NO. 1			
	• Check for continuity between FLI plug Pin 1 (harness side) and body ground.	Yes	▶	SERVICE or REPLACE Circuit 512.
	• Is continuity present?	No	▶	GO to Step FF9.
FF9	CHECK FLUID LEVEL INDICATOR PIN NO. 2			
	• Disconnect 5-pin plug from PWS. Check for continuity between FLI plug Pin 2 (harness side) and body ground.	Yes	▶	SERVICE or REPLACE Circuit 549.
	• Is continuity present?	No	▶	GO to Step FF10.
FF10	CHECK CONTINUITY BETWEEN PWS PINS 3 AND 5 AND BODY GROUND			
	• Check for continuity from PWS 5-pin socket Pins (pressure warning switch side) 3 and body ground and 5 and body ground.	Yes	▶	REPLACE pressure warning switch.
	• Is continuity present?	No	▶	GO to Step FF11.

Fig. 16 Test FF, warning circuit diagnosis (Part 4 of 5)

TEST STEP		RESULT	▶	ACTION TO TAKE
FF11	CHECK PWS CONNECTOR PIN 5 AND GROUND			
	• Check for continuity between 5-pin PWS plug, Pin 5 (harness side) and body ground.	Yes	▶	SERVICE or REPLACE Circuit 535.
	• Is continuity present?	No	▶	CONNECT all plugs and REVERIFY condition.

Fig. 16 Test FF, warning circuit diagnosis (Part 5 of 5)

Anti-Lock Quick Check Sheet Using 60-Pin EEC-IV Breakout Box, Tool T83L-50-EEC-IV ①

NOTE: Before performing tests below, the Pre-Test Checks must be performed as outlined.
NOTE: If fault is intermittent the tests listed below will NOT find the fault. Use controller service code or call Hot-Line if this situation occurs.

Item to be Tested		Ignition Mode	Measure Between Pin Numbers	Tester Scale/Range	Specification	Test Step
No Boost/No Power Brakes (Hard Brake Pedal)		—	—	—	—	D-1
Battery Check		On	40 + 18	Volts	10 minimum	A-1
Main Power Relay		Off	40 + 9	Ohms	45 Ohms — 105 Ohms	A-6
			Place a jumper between pins 9 and 18			
		On	40 + 16	Volts	10 minimum	A-7
Power from Main Power Relay		On	40 + 15	Volts	10 minimum	A-3
			Remove jumper from pins 9 and 18			
Main Power Relay Circuit		Off	40 + 16	Continuity	Continuity	A-2
Main Power Relay Circuit		Off	15 + 40	Continuity	Continuity	A-3a
Sensor Resistance	(RR)	Off	6 + 23	K Ohms	800 to 1400 Ohms	A-8
Sensor Resistance	(LF)	Off	5 + 22	K Ohms	800 to 1400 Ohms	A-9
Sensor Resistance	(LR)	Off	4 + 21	K Ohms	800 to 1400 Ohms	A-10
Sensor Resistance	(RF)	Off	3 + 20	K Ohms	800 to 1400 Ohms	A-11
Main Valve Resistance		Off	11 + 29	Ohms	2 Ohms to 5.5 Ohms	A-12
Inlet & Outlet Valves		Off	11 + 40	Continuity	Continuity	A-13
		Off	11 + 32	Ohms	5 Ohms to 8 Ohms	A-14
		Off	11 + 30	Ohms	5 Ohms to 8 Ohms	A-15
		Off	11 + 31	Ohms	5 Ohms to 8 Ohms	A-16
		Off	11 + 12	Ohms	3 Ohms to 6 Ohms	A-17
		Off	11 + 14	Ohms	3 Ohms to 6 Ohms	A-18
		Off	11 + 13	Ohms	3 Ohms to 6 Ohms	A-19
Reservoir Warning		On	25 + 27	Ohms	Less than 5 Ohms	A-4a
Lift Fluid Level Indicator from Reservoir (Float at bottom position)		Off	25 + 27	Ohms	Infinite (Open Circuit)	4-5a
Sensor Cable Continuity Shielding to Ground	(RR)	Off	40 + 6	Continuity	No Continuity	B-1a
	(LF)	Off	40 + 5	Continuity	No Continuity	B-2a
	(LR)	Off	40 + 4	Continuity	No Continuity	B-3a
	(RF)	Off	40 + 3	Continuity	No Continuity	B-4a
Sensor Voltage (Rotate wheels at 1 revolution per second minimum) (Shut off air suspension switch in luggage compartment with vehicle on hoist if so equipped.)	(RR)	Off②	6 + 23	AC Millivolts	50-700 Millivolts	C-5
	(LF)	Off③	5 + 22	AC Millivolts	50-700 Millivolts	C-6
	(LR)	Off③	4 + 21	AC Millivolts	50-700 Millivolts	C-7
	(RF)	Off②	3 + 20	AC Millivolts	50-700 Millivolts	C-8

① If Quick Test does not isolate symptom, refer to Diagnostic Lamp Symptom Chart.
② The most accurate measurements are taken with the breakout box in back seat and an assistant is driving the vehicle 4.5-5.0 mph.

Fig. 17 ABS quick check sheet. 1991

ANTI-LOCK QUICK CHECK SHEET USING 60-PIN EEC-IV BREAKOUT BOX, TOOL T83L-50-EEC-IV ①

NOTE: Before performing tests below, the Pre-Test Checks must be performed as outlined.

NOTE: If fault is intermittent the tests listed below will NOT find the fault. Use controller service code or call Hot-Line if this situation occurs.

Item to be Tested		Ignition Mode	Measure Between Pin Numbers	Tester Scale/Range	Specification	Test Step
No Boost/No Power Brakes (Hard Brake Pedal)		—	—	—	—	D1
Battery Check		ON	40 + 18	VOLTS	10 Minimum	A1
Main Power Relay		OFF	40 + 9	OHMS	45 to 105 ohms	A22
			Place jumper between pins 9 and 18			
		ON	40 + 16	VOLTS	10 minimum	A26
Power from Main Power Relay		ON	40 + 15	VOLTS	10 minimum	A8
			Remove jumper from pins 9 and 18			
Main Power Relay Circuit		OFF	40 + 16	CONTINUITY	continuity	A4
Main Power Relay Circuit		OFF	15 + 40	CONTINUITY	continuity	A8
Sensor Resistance (RR)		OFF	6 + 23	K OHMS	0.8-1.4K ohms	A29
Sensor Resistance (LF)		OFF	5 + 22	K OHMS	0.8-1.4K ohms	A31
Sensor Resistance (LR)		OFF	4 + 21	K OHMS	0.8-1.4K ohms	A33
Sensor Resistance (RF)		OFF	3 + 20	K OHMS	0.8-1.4K ohms	A35
Main Valve Resistance		OFF	11 + 29	OHMS	2-5.5 ohms	A37
Inlet & Outlet Valves		OFF	11 + 40	CONTINUITY	continuity	A39
Inlet & Outlet Valves		OFF	11 + 32	OHMS	5-8 ohms	A42
Inlet & Outlet Valves		OFF	11 + 30	OHMS	5-8 ohms	A44
Inlet & Outlet Valves		OFF	11 + 31	OHMS	5-8 ohms	A46
Inlet & Outlet Valves		OFF	11 + 12	OHMS	3-6 ohms	A48
Inlet & Outlet Valves		OFF	11 + 14	OHMS	3-6 ohms	A50
Inlet & Outlet Valves		OFF	11 + 13	OHMS	3-6 ohms	A52
Reservoir Warning		ON	25 + 27	OHMS	less than 5 ohms	A10
Lift Fluid Indicator from Reservoir (Float at bottom position)		OFF	25 + 27	OHMS	infinite (open circuit)	A10
Sensor Cable Continuity Shielding to Ground (RR)		OFF	40 + 6	CONTINUITY	no continuity	B1
(LF)		OFF	40 + 5	CONTINUITY	no continuity	B3
(LR)		OFF	40 + 4	CONTINUITY	no continuity	B5
(RF)		OFF	40 + 3	CONTINUITY	no continuity	B7
Sensor Voltage: (Rotate wheels @ 1 revolution per second minimum) (Shut off air suspension switch in luggage compartment with vehicle on hoist if so equipped) (RR)		OFF ②	6 + 23	AC MVOLTS	50-700 mvolts	C9
(LF)		OFF ②	5 + 22	AC MVOLTS	50-700 mvolts	C10
(LR)		OFF ②	4 + 21	AC MVOLTS	50-700 mvolts	C11
(RF)		OFF ②	3 + 20	AC MVOLTS	50-700 mvolts	C12

① If Quick Test does not isolate symptom, refer to Diagnostic Indicator Symptom Chart.
② The most accurate measurements are taken with the breakout box in back seat and an assistant is driving the vehicle 4.5-5.0 mph.

Fig. 18 ABS quick check sheet. 1992

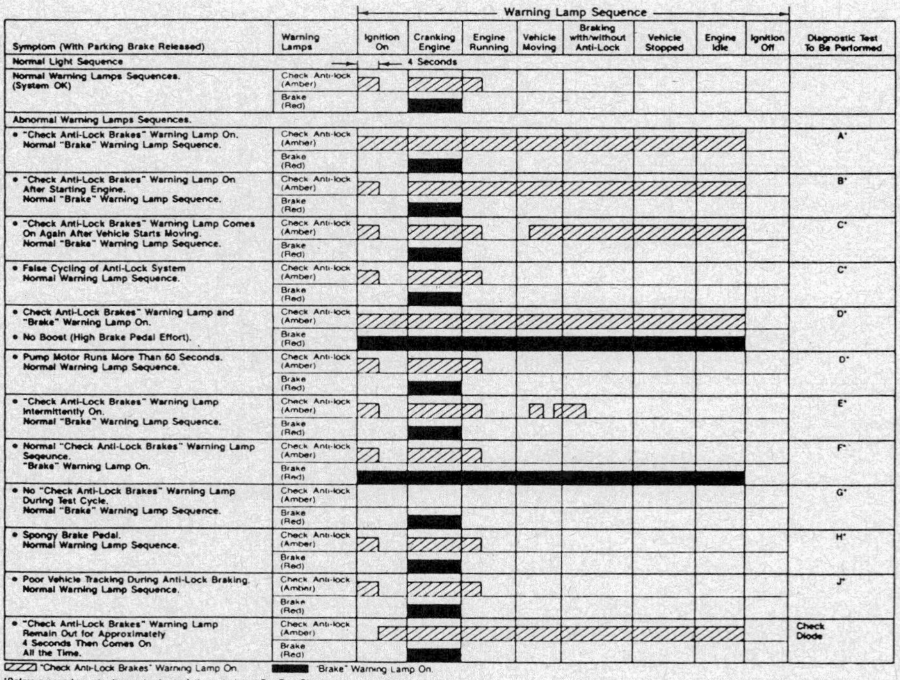

Fig. 19 Diagnostic lamp symptom chart

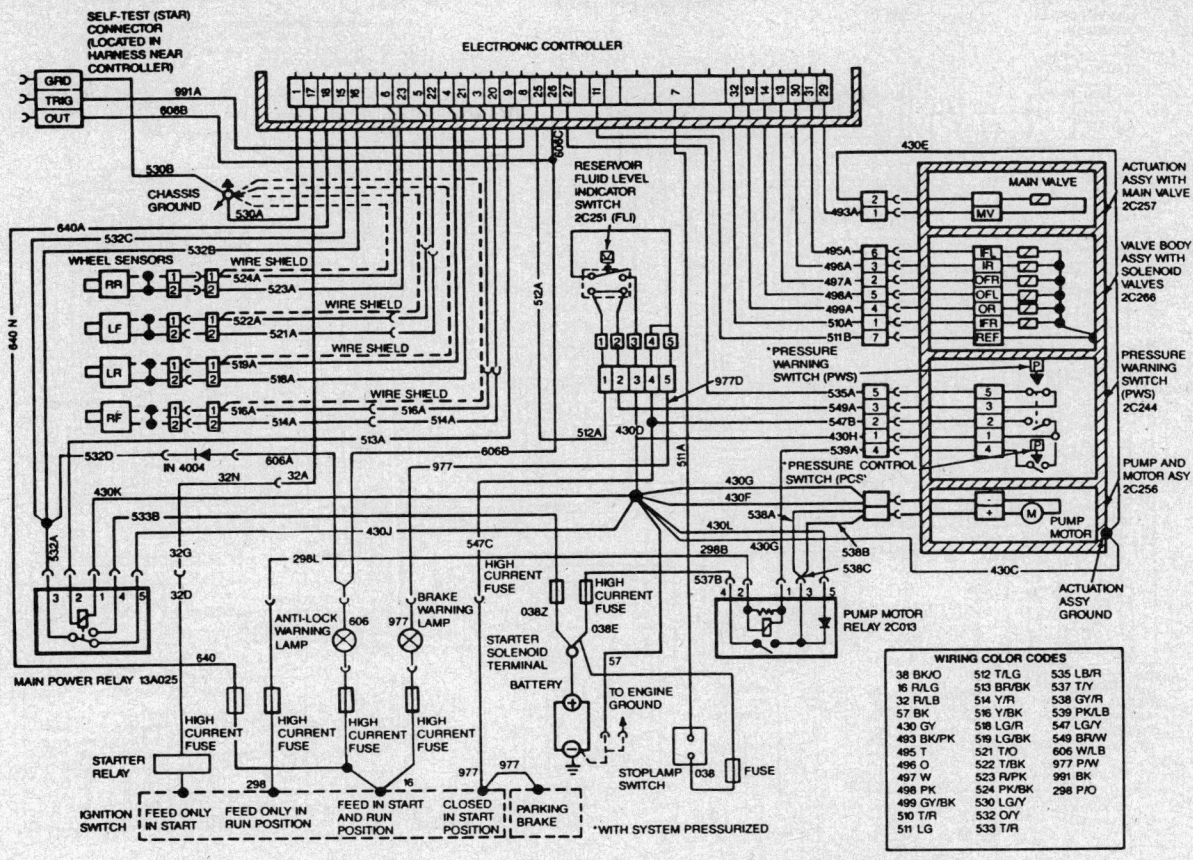

Fig. 20   ABS wiring circuit. 1990–91 Cougar/Thunderbird

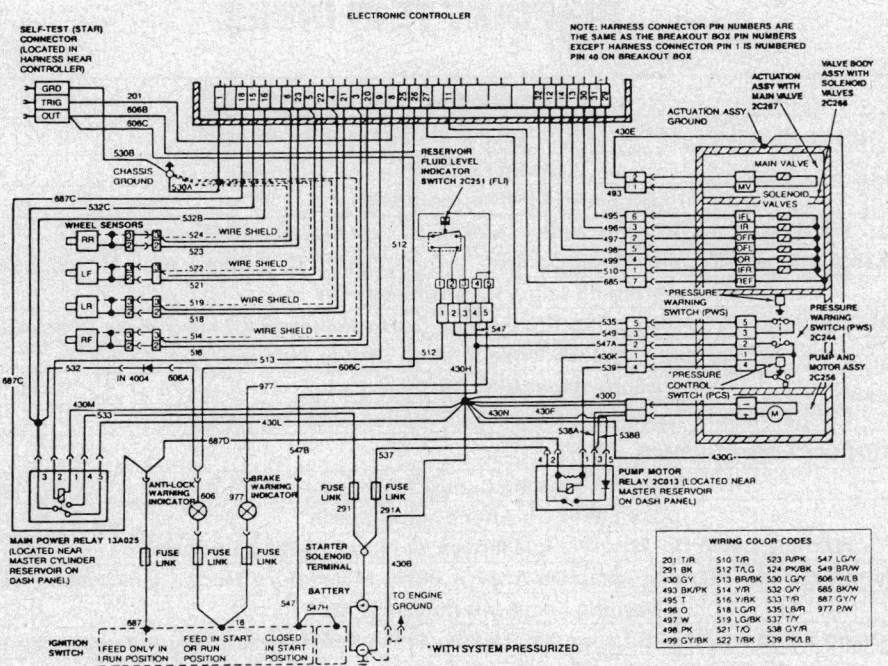

Fig. 21   ABS wiring circuit. 1992 Cougar/Thunderbird

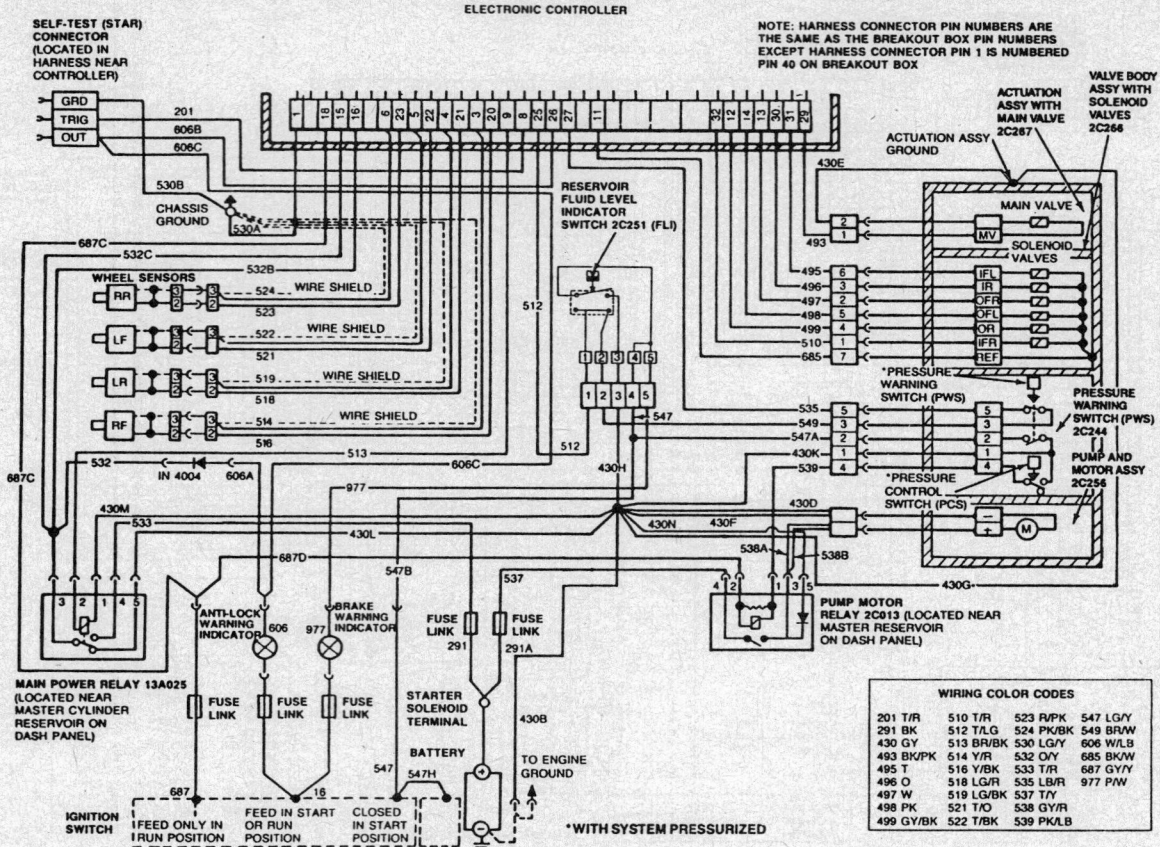

Fig. 22   ABS wiring circuit. Mark VII

PINPOINT TEST INDEX

Test	Description	Page No.	Fig. No.
1990–91 Cougar/Thunderbird			
A	Warning Lamp On	18-15	23
B	ABS Lamp On After Engine Starts	18-21	24
C	Warning Lamp On After Vehicle Moves/Or False Cycling Of System	18-21	25
D	Warning Lamp & Brake Warning Lamp On And/Or Pump Motor Runs More Than 60 Seconds	18-23	26
E	Warning Lamp Intermittently On	18-25	27
F	Brake Warning Lamp On w/ABS Lamp Off, Parking Brake Released & Lining Wear Checked	18-26	28
G	No Warning Lamp On When Ignition Switch Turned On	18-27	29
H	Spongy Pedal & No Warning Lamp	18-27	30
J	Poor Vehicle Tracking During ABS Function, Warning Lamp Off	18-27	31
Mark VII & 1992 Cougar/Thunderbird			
A	Warning Lamp On	18-28	32
B	ABS Lamp On After Engine Starts	18-32	33
C	Warning Lamp On After Vehicle Moves, Or False Cycling Of System	18-33	34
D	Warning Lamp & Brake Warning Lamp On And/Or Pump Motor Runs More Than 60 Seconds	18-33	35
E	Warning Lamp Intermittently On	18-35	36
F	Brake Warning Lamp On w/ABS Lamp Off, Parking Brake Released & Lining Wear Checked	18-36	37
G	No Warning Lamp On When Ignition Switch Turned On	18-36	38
H	Spongy Pedal & No Warning Lamp	18-37	39
J	Poor Vehicle Tracking During ABS Function, Warning Lamp Off	18-37	40

Anti-Lock Warning Lamp On (With Brake Warning Lamp Off) — Test A

Warning Lamps	Ignition On	Cranking Engine	Engine Running	Vehicle Moving	Braking with/without Anti-Lock	Vehicle Stopped	Engine Idle	Ignition Off
WARNING LIGHTS SEQUENCE								
Check Anti-Lock (Amber)	////	////////	////////	////////	////////	////////	////////	
Brake (Red)		■■■						

TEST STEP	RESULT ▶	ACTION TO TAKE
A1 32 PIN PLUG TESTING		
• Turn ignition switch OFF. • Disconnect 32-pin Plug from electronic controller.	Over 10V (OK)▶ Under 10V (OK)▶	GO to Step A2. GO to Step A1a.
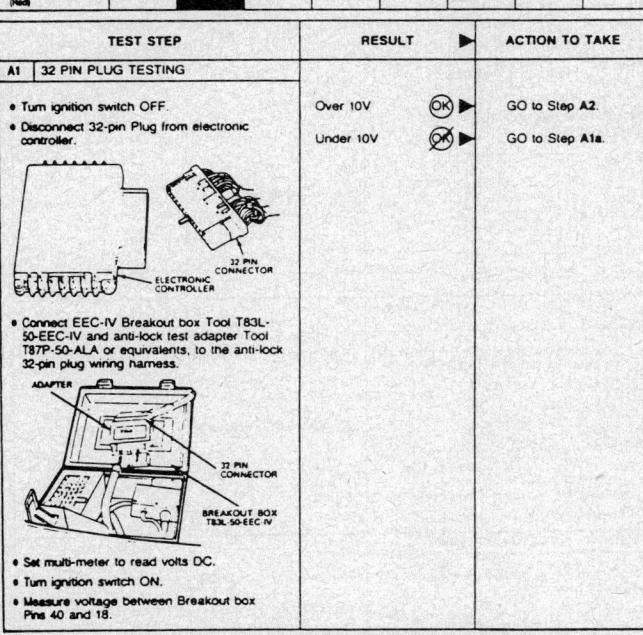		
• Connect EEC-IV Breakout box Tool T83L-50-EEC-IV and anti-lock test adapter Tool T87P-50-ALA or equivalents, to the anti-lock 32-pin plug wiring harness.		
• Set multi-meter to read volts DC. • Turn ignition switch ON. • Measure voltage between Breakout box Pins 40 and 18.		

Fig. 23   Test A, warning lamp On (Part 1 of 24). 1990–91 Cougar/Thunderbird

Anti-Lock Warning Lamp On (With Brake Warning Lamp Off) — Test A

TEST STEP	RESULT ▶	ACTION TO TAKE
A1a CHECK ELECTRONIC CONTROLLER TO GROUND WIRE		
• Check — fuse link to anti-lock warning lamp. — battery. • Remove positive battery cable. • Check continuity between Breakout box pin 40 and body ground.	Continuity ▶ No continuity ▶	GO to Step A1b. SERVICE or REPLACE cable harness (Circuit 530A).
A1b CHECK IGNITION TO ELECTRONIC CONTROLLER WIRE		
• Check continuity between Breakout box Pin 18 and ignition switch wire 640N.	Continuity ▶ No continuity ▶	RECONNECT positive battery cable. CHECK for power at ignition switch pin with switch ON. If okay, connect electronic controller and reverify symptom. SERVICE or REPLACE cable harness (Circuit 640N.)
A2 CHECK MAIN POWER RELAY SECONDARY CIRCUIT (NORMAL)		
• Turn ignition switch OFF. • Check for continuity between Breakout box Pins 40 and 16.	Continuity ▶ No continuity ▶	GO to A3 GO to A2a.

Fig. 23   Test A, warning lamp On (Part 2 of 24). 1990–91 Cougar/Thunderbird

Anti-Lock Warning Lamp On (With Brake Warning Lamp Off) — Test A

TEST STEP	RESULT ▶	ACTION TO TAKE
A2a CHECK MAIN POWER RELAY SECONDARY CIRCUIT (NORMAL)		
• Disconnect main relay from socket. • Check for continuity between main power relay socket Pins 3 and 5.	Continuity ▶ No continuity ▶	GO to Step A2b. REPLACE main power relay.
A2b CHECK MAIN POWER RELAY SECONDARY CIRCUIT WIRING HARNESS		
• Disconnect positive battery cable. • Check for continuity between main power relay socket Pin 3 and Breakout box Pin 16.	Continuity ▶ No continuity ▶	GO to Step A2c. SERVICE or REPLACE cable harness (Circuit 532A, 532B or 532D).
A2c CHECK MAIN POWER RELAY SECONDARY CIRCUIT WIRING HARNESS		
• Check for continuity between main power relay socket Pin 5 and body ground.	Continuity ▶ No continuity ▶	RECONNECT main power relay, electronic controller and battery cable and reverify symptom. SERVICE or REPLACE cable harness (Circuit 430J).

Fig. 23   Test A, warning lamp On (Part 3 of 24). 1990–91 Cougar/Thunderbird

With Anti-Lock Warning Lamp On (With Brake Warning Lamp Off) — Test A

TEST STEP	RESULT ▶	ACTION TO TAKE
A3 CHECK MAIN POWER RELAY SECONDARY CIRCUIT (NORMAL)		
• Check for continuity between Breakout box Pins 40 and 15.	Continuity ▶ No continuity ▶	GO to Step A4. GO to Step A3a.
A3a CHECK MAIN POWER RELAY SECONDARY CIRCUIT WIRING HARNESS		
• Remove main power relay. • Check for continuity between main power relay socket Pin 3 and Breakout box Pin 15.	Continuity ▶ No continuity ▶	CONNECT main power relay and electronic controller and reverify symptom. SERVICE or REPLACE cable harness (Circuit 532A, 532C or 532D).
A4 CHECK FLI AND PWS CIRCUIT		
• Turn ignition switch ON. • Set multi-meter to read resistance. • Measure the resistance between Breakout box Pins 25 and 27.	Less than 5 ohms ▶ Greater than 5 ohms ▶	GO to Step A5. GO to Step A4a.
A4a CHECK FLI ANTI-LOCK WARNING CIRCUIT		
• Disconnect 5-Pin plug on reservoir Fluid Level Indicator (FLI). • Measure resistance between fluid level indicator electrical socket Pins 1 and 2 (with brake fluid level at maximum mark on reservoir).	Less than 2 ohms ▶ Greater than 2 ohms ▶	GO to Step A4b. REPLACE fluid level indicator.

Fig. 23   Test A, warning lamp On (Part 4 of 24). 1990–91 Cougar/Thunderbird

| Anti-Lock Warning Lamp On (With Brake Warning Lamp Off) | Test A |

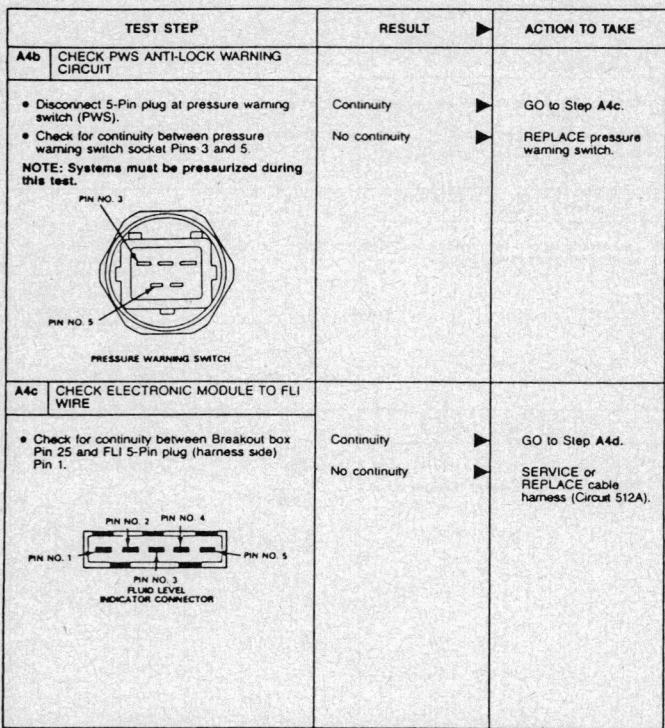

TEST STEP	RESULT	▶	ACTION TO TAKE
A4b CHECK PWS ANTI-LOCK WARNING CIRCUIT			
• Disconnect 5-Pin plug at pressure warning switch (PWS).	Continuity	▶	GO to Step A4c.
• Check for continuity between pressure warning switch socket Pins 3 and 5.	No continuity	▶	REPLACE pressure warning switch.
NOTE: Systems must be pressurized during this test.			
A4c CHECK ELECTRONIC MODULE TO FLI WIRE			
• Check for continuity between Breakout box Pin 25 and FLI 5-Pin plug (harness side) Pin 1.	Continuity	▶	GO to Step A4d.
	No continuity	▶	SERVICE or REPLACE cable harness (Circuit 512A).

Fig. 23 Test A, warning lamp On (Part 5 of 24). 1990–91 Cougar/Thunderbird

Anti-Lock Warning Lamp On (With Brake Warning Lamp Off) | Test A

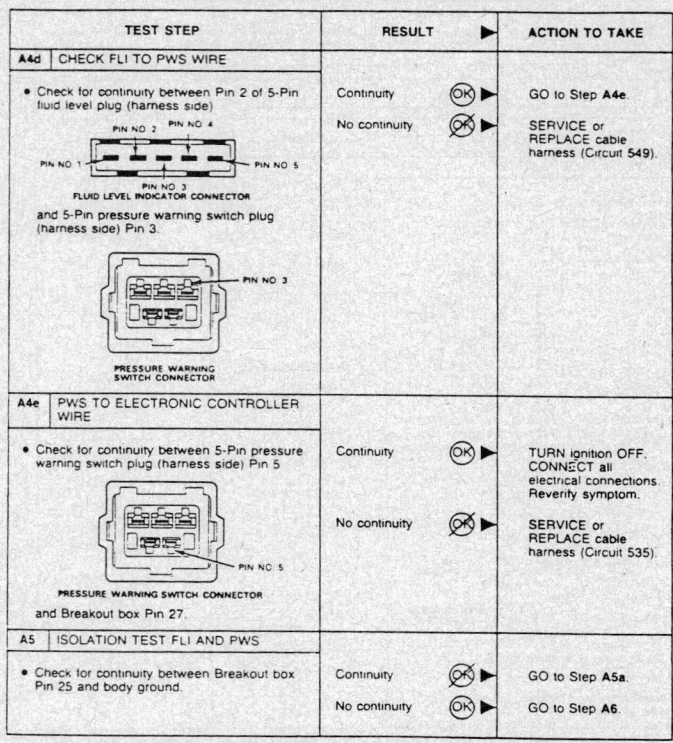

TEST STEP	RESULT	▶	ACTION TO TAKE
A4d CHECK FLI TO PWS WIRE			
• Check for continuity between Pin 2 of 5-Pin fluid level plug (harness side)	Continuity	OK ▶	GO to Step A4e.
and 5-Pin pressure warning switch plug (harness side) Pin 3.	No continuity	OK ▶	SERVICE or REPLACE cable harness (Circuit 549).
A4e PWS TO ELECTRONIC CONTROLLER WIRE			
• Check for continuity between 5-Pin pressure warning switch plug (harness side) Pin 5	Continuity	OK ▶	TURN ignition OFF. CONNECT all electrical connections. Reverify symptom.
and Breakout box Pin 27.	No continuity	OK ▶	SERVICE or REPLACE cable harness (Circuit 535).
A5 ISOLATION TEST FLI AND PWS			
• Check for continuity between Breakout box Pin 25 and body ground.	Continuity	OK ▶	GO to Step A5a.
	No continuity	OK ▶	GO to Step A6.

Fig. 23 Test A, warning lamp On (Part 6 of 24). 1990–91 Cougar/Thunderbird

Anti-Lock Warning Lamp On (With Brake Warning Lamp Off) | Test A

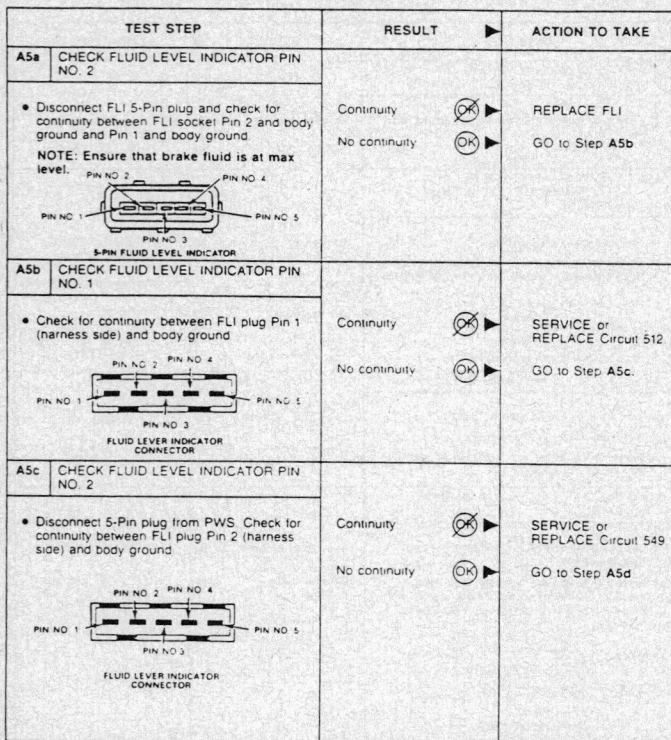

TEST STEP	RESULT	▶	ACTION TO TAKE
A5a CHECK FLUID LEVEL INDICATOR PIN NO. 2			
• Disconnect FLI 5-Pin plug and check for continuity between FLI socket Pin 2 and body ground and Pin 1 and body ground.	Continuity	OK ▶	REPLACE FLI
NOTE: Ensure that brake fluid is at max level.	No continuity	OK ▶	GO to Step A5b
A5b CHECK FLUID LEVEL INDICATOR PIN NO. 1			
• Check for continuity between FLI plug Pin 1 (harness side) and body ground.	Continuity	OK ▶	SERVICE or REPLACE Circuit 512
	No continuity	OK ▶	GO to Step A5c.
A5c CHECK FLUID LEVEL INDICATOR PIN NO. 2			
• Disconnect 5-Pin plug from PWS. Check for continuity between FLI plug Pin 2 (harness side) and body ground.	Continuity	OK ▶	SERVICE or REPLACE Circuit 549
	No continuity	OK ▶	GO to Step A5d.

Fig. 23 Test A, warning lamp On (Part 7 of 24). 1990–91 Cougar/Thunderbird

Anti-Lock Warning Lamp On (With Brake Warning Lamp Off) | Test A

TEST STEP	RESULT	▶	ACTION TO TAKE
A5d CHECK CONTINUITY BETWEEN PWS PINS 3 AND 5 AND BODY GROUND			
• Check for continuity from PWS 5-Pin socket Pins (pressure warning switch side) 3 and body ground and 5 and body ground.	Continuity	▶	REPLACE pressure warning switch.
NOTE: System should be depressurized for this test.	No continuity	▶	GO to Step A5e.
A5e CHECK PWS CONNECTOR PIN 5 AND GROUND			
• Check for continuity between 5-Pin PWS plug. Pin 5 (harness side) and body ground.	Continuity	▶	SERVICE or REPLACE Circuit 535A.
	No continuity	▶	CONNECT all plugs and reverify symptom.
A6 CHECK MAIN RELAY PRIMARY CIRCUIT RESISTANCE			
• Turn ignition switch OFF.	Resistance between 45 and 105 ohms	▶	GO to Step A7.
• Set multi-meter to read resistance.			
• Measure resistance between Breakout box Pins 40 and 9.	Any other reading	▶	GO to Step A6a.

Fig. 23 Test A, warning lamp On (Part 8 of 24). 1990–91 Cougar/Thunderbird

Anti-Lock Warning Lamp On (With Brake Warning Lamp Off) — Test A

TEST STEP	RESULT ▶	ACTION TO TAKE
A6a CHECK MAIN POWER RELAY PRIMARY COIL RESISTANCE		
• Disconnect main power relay from socket. • Set multi-meter on resistance. • Measure resistance between main power relay Pins 1 and 2.	Resistance between 45 and 105 ohms ▶	GO to Step A6b.
	Any other reading ▶	REPLACE main power relay.
A6b CHECK MAIN POWER RELAY PRIMARY TO ELECTRONIC CONTROLLER WIRE		
• Check continuity between main power relay socket Pin 2 (harness side) and Breakout box Pin 9.	Continuity ▶	GO to Step A6c.
	No continuity ▶	SERVICE or REPLACE cable harness (Circuit 513A).

Fig. 23   Test A, warning lamp On (Part 9 of 24). 1990–91 Cougar/Thunderbird

Anti-Lock Warning Lamp On (With Brake Warning Lamp Off) — Test A

TEST STEP	RESULT ▶	ACTION TO TAKE
A6c CHECK MAIN POWER RELAY PRIMARY TO GROUND WIRE		
• Check continuity between main power relay socket Pin 1 and ground.	Continuity ▶	RECONNECT all electrical connections and reverify symptom.
	No continuity ▶	SERVICE or REPLACE cable harness (Circuit 430K).
A7 CHECK MAIN POWER RELAY SECONDARY (ACTIVATED)		
• Place a jumper wire between Breakout box Pins 18 and 9. • Set multi-meter to read volts DC. • Turn ignition switch ON. • Measure voltage between Breakout box Pins 40 and 16.	Over 10V DC ▶	GO to Step A8.
	Under 10V DC ▶	CHECK high current fuse. REMOVE jumper wire and GO to Step A7a.
A7a CHECK MAIN POWER RELAY SECONDARY CIRCUIT (ACTIVE)		
• Turn ignition switch OFF. • Disconnect main power relay from socket. • Apply power (battery positive and ground) to main relay Pins 1 and 2. • Check for continuity between main power relay Pins 3 and 4.	Continuity ▶	GO to Step A7b.
	No continuity ▶	REPLACE main power relay

Fig. 23   Test A, warning lamp On (Part 10 of 24). 1990–91 Cougar/Thunderbird

Anti-Lock Warning Lamp On (With Brake Warning Lamp Off) — Test A

TEST STEP	RESULT ▶	ACTION TO TAKE
A7b CHECK MAIN POWER RELAY SECONDARY CIRCUIT POWER WIRE		
• Check continuity between main power relay socket Pin 4 (harness side) and positive battery terminal.	Continuity ▶	RECONNECT main power relay and reverify symptom.
	No continuity ▶	SERVICE or REPLACE cable harness (Circuit 533C) or high current fuse (Circuit 038Z).
A8 MEASURE RH REAR SENSOR CIRCUIT RESISTANCE		
• Turn ignition switch OFF. • Set multi-meter to read resistance. • Measure resistance between Breakout box Pin 6 and 23.	800 to 1400 ohms (0.8 to 1.4K ohms) ▶	GO to Step A9.
	Any other reading ▶	GO to Step A8a.
A8a MEASURE RH REAR SENSOR RESISTANCE		
• Disconnect sensor plug (right rear). • Set multi-meter to read resistance. • Measure resistance of sensor at sensor plug.	800 to 1400 ohms (0.8 to 1.4K ohms) ▶	SERVICE or REPLACE cable harness (Circuit 523 or 524).
	Any other reading ▶	REPLACE right rear wheel sensor.
A9 MEASURE LH FRONT SENSOR CIRCUIT RESISTANCE		
• Measure resistance between Breakout box Pins 5 and 22.	800 to 1400 ohms (0.8 to 1.4K ohms) ▶	GO to Step A10.
	Any other reading ▶	GO to Step A9a.

Fig. 23   Test A, warning lamp On (Part 11 of 24). 1990–91 Cougar/Thunderbird

Anti-Lock Warning Lamp On (With Brake Warning Lamp Off) — Test A

TEST STEP	RESULT ▶	ACTION TO TAKE
A9a MEASURE LH FRONT SENSOR RESISTANCE		
• Disconnect sensor plug (left front). • Measure resistance of sensor at sensor plug.	800 to 1400 ohms (0.8 to 1.4K ohms) ▶	SERVICE or REPLACE cable harness (Circuit 521 or 522).
	Any other reading ▶	REPLACE left front wheel sensor.
A10 MEASURE LH REAR SENSOR CIRCUIT RESISTANCE		
• Measure resistance between Breakout box Pins 4 and 21.	800 to 1400 ohms (0.8 to 1.4K ohms) ▶	GO to Step A11.
	Any other reading ▶	GO to Step A10a.
A10a MEASURE LH REAR SENSOR RESISTANCE		
• Disconnect sensor plug (left rear). • Measure resistance of sensor at left rear sensor plug.	800 to 1400 ohms (0.8 to 1.4K ohms) ▶	SERVICE or REPLACE cable harness (Circuit 518 or 519).
	Any other reading ▶	REPLACE left rear wheel sensor.
A11 MEASURE RH FRONT SENSOR CIRCUIT RESISTANCE		
• Measure resistance between Breakout box Pins 3 and 20.	800 to 1400 ohms (0.8 to 1.4K ohms) ▶	GO to Step A12.
	Any other reading ▶	GO to Step A11a.

Fig. 23   Test A, warning lamp On (Part 12 of 24). 1990–91 Cougar/Thunderbird

Anti-Lock Warning Lamp On (With Brake Warning Lamp Off) — Test A

TEST STEP	RESULT ▶	ACTION TO TAKE
A11a MEASURE RH FRONT SENSOR RESISTANCE		
• Disconnect sensor plug (RH front). • Measure resistance of sensor at sensor plug.	800 to 1400 ohms (0.8 to 1.4K ohms) ▶	SERVICE or REPLACE cable harness (Circuit 514 or 516).
RH FRONT SENSOR	Any other reading ▶	REPLACE RH front wheel sensor.
A12 MEASURE MAIN VALVE CIRCUIT RESISTANCE		
• Turn ignition switch OFF. • Set multi-meter to read resistance. • Measure the resistance between Breakout box Pins 11 and 29.	2 to 5 ohms ▶	GO to Step A13.
	Any other reading ▶	GO to Step A12a.
A12a MEASURE MAIN VALVE RESISTANCE		
• Disconnect main valve 2-Pin plug. • Measure resistance between the main valve electrical Pins 1 and 2.	2 to 5.5 ohms ▶	REPLACE or SERVICE cable harness (Circuit 430E or 493A).
PIN NO. 2 PIN NO. 1	Any other reading ▶	REPLACE actuation assembly.
A13 CHECK VALVE BLOCK GROUND CIRCUIT		
• Measure resistance between Breakout box Pins 11 and 40.	Less than 2 ohms ▶	GO to Step A14.
	Greater than 2 ohms ▶	GO to Step A13a.

Fig. 23   Test A, warning lamp On (Part 13 of 24). 1990–91 Cougar/Thunderbird

Anti-Lock Warning Lamp On (With Brake Warning Lamp Off) — Test A

TEST STEP	RESULT ▶	ACTION TO TAKE
A13a TEST VALVE PLUG PIN NO. 7		
• Disconnect valve block 7-Pin plug. • Measure resistance between valve block electrical Pin 7 and valve block body.	Less than 2 ohms ▶	SERVICE or REPLACE cable harness (Circuit 511B).
	Greater than 2 ohms ▶	GO to Step A13b.
PIN NO. 7 VALVE BLOCK 7-PIN CONNECTOR		
A13b CHECK ACTUATION ASSEMBLY GROUND WIRE		
• Remove negative (–) ground strap from battery. • Check for continuity between actuation assembly and body ground.	Continuity ▶	Go to Step A14.
	No or Poor continuity ▶	SERVICE or REPLACE actuation assembly ground strap (Circuit 430C).
A14 MEASURE RH FRONT INLET VALVE CIRCUIT RESISTANCE		
• Measure resistance between Breakout box Pins 11 and 32.	5 to 8 ohms ▶	GO to Step A15.
	Any other reading ▶	GO to Step A14a.

Fig. 23   Test A, warning lamp On (Part 14 of 24). 1990–91 Cougar/Thunderbird

Anti-Lock Warning Lamp On (With Brake Warning Lamp Off) — Test A

TEST STEP	RESULT ▶	ACTION TO TAKE
A14a MEASURE RH FRONT INLET VALVE RESISTANCE		
• Disconnect valve block 7-Pin plug. • Measure resistance between valve block electrical Pin 7 and 1.	5 to 8 ohms ▶	SERVICE or REPLACE cable harness (Circuit 510A).
	Any other reading ▶	REPLACE solenoid valve block unit. CONNECT 7-Pin plug.
PIN NO. 1 PIN NO. 7 VALVE BLOCK 7-PIN CONNECTOR		
A15 MEASURE REAR INLET VALVE CIRCUIT RESISTANCE		
• Measure resistance between Breakout box Pins 11 and 30.	5 to 8 ohms ▶	GO to Step A16.
	Any other reading ▶	GO to Step A15a.

Fig. 23   Test A, warning lamp On (Part 15 of 24). 1990–91 Cougar/Thunderbird

Anti-Lock Warning Lamp On (With Brake Warning Lamp Off) — Test A

TEST STEP	RESULT ▶	ACTION TO TAKE
A15a MEASURE REAR INLET VALVE RESISTANCE		
• Disconnect valve block 7-Pin plug. • Measure resistance between valve block electrical Pins 7 and 3.	5 to 8 ohms ▶	SERVICE or REPLACE cable harness (Circuit 496A).
	Any other reading ▶	REPLACE valve block unit. CONNECT 7-Pin plug.
PIN NO. 3 PIN NO. 7 VALVE BLOCK 7-PIN CONNECTOR		
A16 MEASURE LH FRONT INLET VALVE CIRCUIT RESISTANCE		
• Measure resistance between Breakout box Pins 11 and 31.	5 to 8 ohms ▶	GO to Step A17.
	Any other reading ▶	GO to Step A16a.

Fig. 23   Test A, warning lamp On (Part 16 of 24). 1990–91 Cougar/Thunderbird

Anti-Lock Warning Lamp On (With Brake Warning Lamp Off)	Test A

TEST STEP	RESULT ▶	ACTION TO TAKE
A16a MEASURE LH FRONT INLET VALVE RESISTANCE • Disconnect valve block 7-Pin plug. • Measure resistance between valve block electrical Pins 7 and 6.	5 to 8 ohms ▶ Any other reading ▶	SERVICE or REPLACE cable harness (Circuit 495A). REPLACE valve block unit. CONNECT 7-Pin plug.
A17 MEASURE REAR OUTLET VALVE CIRCUIT RESISTANCE • Measure resistance between Breakout box Pins 11 and 12.	3 to 6 ohms ▶ Any other reading ▶	GO to Step A18. GO to Step A17a.

PIN NO. 6
PIN NO. 7
VALVE BLOCK 7-PIN CONNECTOR

Fig. 23   Test A, warning lamp On (Part 17 of 24). 1990–91 Cougar/Thunderbird

Anti-Lock Warning Lamp On (With Brake Warning Lamp Off)	Test A

TEST STEP	RESULT ▶	ACTION TO TAKE
A17a MEASURE REAR OUTLET VALVE RESISTANCE • Disconnect valve block 7-Pin plug. • Measure resistance between valve block electrical Pins 7 and 4.	3 to 6 ohms ▶ Any other reading ▶	SERVICE or REPLACE cable harness (Circuit 499A). REPLACE valve block unit. CONNECT 7-Pin plug.
A18 MEASURE LH FRONT OUTLET VALVE CIRCUIT RESISTANCE • Measure resistance between Breakout box Pins 11 and 14.	3 to 6 ohms ▶ Any other reading ▶	GO to Step A19. GO to Step A18a.

PIN NO. 4
PIN NO. 7
VALVE BLOCK 7-PIN CONNECTOR

Fig. 23   Test A, warning lamp On (Part 18 of 24). 1990–91 Cougar/Thunderbird

Anti-Lock Warning Lamp On (With Brake Warning Lamp Off)	Test A

TEST STEP	RESULT ▶	ACTION TO TAKE
A18a MEASURE LH FRONT OUTLET VALVE RESISTANCE • Disconnect valve block 7-Pin plug. • Measure resistance between valve block electrical Pin 7 and 5.	3 to 6 ohms ▶ Any other reading ▶	SERVICE or REPLACE cable harness (Circuit 498A). REPLACE valve block unit. CONNECT 7-Pin plug.
A19 MEASURE RH FRONT OUTLET VALVE CIRCUIT RESISTANCE • Measure resistance between Breakout box Pins 11 and 13.	3 to 6 ohms ▶ Any other reading ▶	GO to Step A20. GO to Step A19a.

PIN NO. 5
PIN NO. 7
VALVE BLOCK 7-PIN CONNECTOR

Fig. 23   Test A, warning lamp On (Part 19 of 24). 1990–91 Cougar/Thunderbird

Anti-Lock Warning Lamp On (With Brake Warning Lamp Off)	Test A

TEST STEP	RESULT ▶	ACTION TO TAKE
A19a MEASURE RH FRONT OUTLET VALVE RESISTANCE • Disconnect valve block 7-Pin plug. • Measure resistance between valve block electrical Pin 7 and 2.	3 to 6 ohms ▶ Any other reading ▶	SERVICE or REPLACE cable harness (Circuit 497A). REPLACE valve block unit. CONNECT 7-Pin plug.

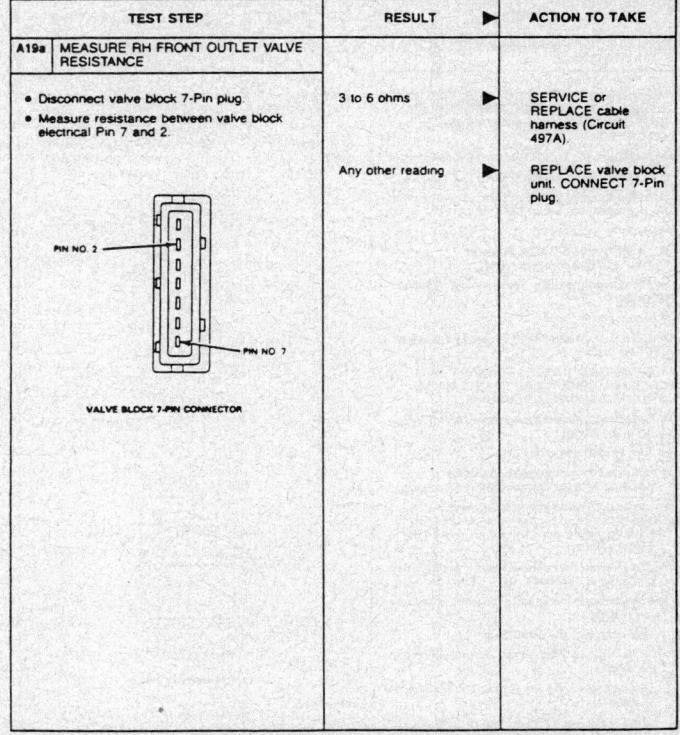

PIN NO. 2
PIN NO. 7
VALVE BLOCK 7-PIN CONNECTOR

Fig. 23   Test A, warning lamp On (Part 20 of 24). 1990–91 Cougar/Thunderbird

Anti-Lock Warning Lamp On (With Brake Warning Lamp Off) — Test A

TEST STEP	RESULT ▶	ACTION TO TAKE
A20 CHECK PWS BRAKELAMP CIRCUIT (WITH SYSTEM PRESSURE) • Vehicle must be cooled to room temperature. • Discharge the brake system as follows: a. Turn ignition switch to OFF. b. Pump brake pedal at least 20 times until you feel the pedal become hard. • Disconnect pressure warning switch 5-pin plug • Check continuity between pressure warning switch electrical Pins 1 and 2.	Continuity ⓄⓀ ▶ No continuity ⓄⓀ ▶	GO to Step A21. REPLACE pressure warning switch and pump motor relay.

PIN NO. 1 / PIN NO. 2 / PRESSURE WARNING SWITCH

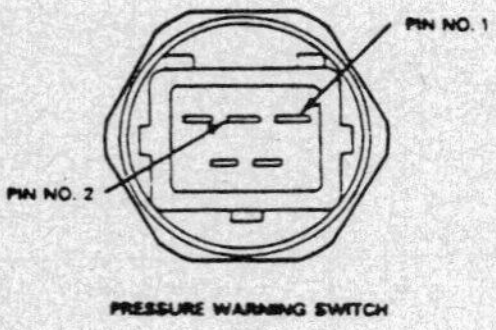

Fig. 23 Test A, warning lamp On (Part 21 of 24). 1990–91 Cougar/Thunderbird

Anti-Lock Warning Lamp On (With Brake Warning Lamp Off) — Test A

TEST STEP	RESULT ▶	ACTION TO TAKE
A21 CHECK PWS BRAKELAMP CIRCUIT (WITH SYSTEM PRESSURE) • Reconnect pressure warning switch 5-pin plug. • Turn ignition switch to ON. When pump motor stops, turn ignition switch to OFF. • Disconnect pressure warning switch 5-pin plug again. • Check for continuity between pressure warning switch electrical Pins 1 and 2.	Continuity ⓄⓀ ▶ No continuity ⓄⓀ ▶	REPLACE pressure warning switch and pump motor relay. GO to Step A22.

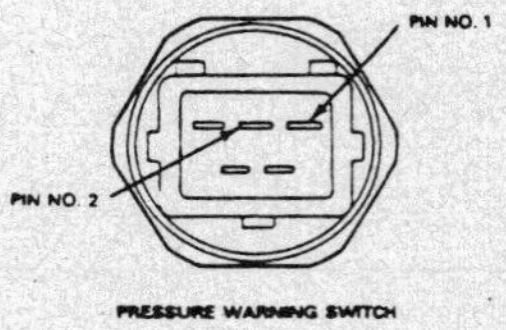

PIN NO. 1 / PIN NO. 2 / PRESSURE WARNING SWITCH

Fig. 23 Test A, warning lamp On (Part 22 of 24). 1990–91 Cougar/Thunderbird

Anti-Lock Warning Lamp On (With Brake Warning Lamp Off) — Test A

TEST STEP	RESULT ▶	ACTION TO TAKE
A22 CHECK PWS BRAKE LAMP CIRCUIT THRESHOLD **WARNING: BEFORE DISCONNECTING ANY HYDRAULIC LINES, YOU MUST ENSURE THAT THE PRESSURE SYSTEM IS DISCHARGED.** • Discharge the brake system as follows: a. Turn ignition switch OFF. b. Pump brake pedal at least 20 times until you feel the pedal become hard. • Remove accumulator. • Install Pressure Gauge Adapter T88P-20215-AH or equivalent. NOTE: Be sure sealing washers are installed correctly. • Install accumulator. • Connect Anti-Lock High Pressure Gauge to gauge nipple. **WARNING: DO NOT DISCONNECT ANTI-LOCK HIGH PRESSURE GAUGE WHILE SYSTEM IS UNDER PRESSURE.** • Reconnect pressure warning switch (PWS) 5-Pin connector. • Turn ignition switch to ON. • When pump motor stops, disconnect pressure warning switch (PWS) 5-pin plug. • Lower hydraulic accumulator pressure by slowly pumping the brake pedal until you have continuity between pressure warning switch electrical Pins 1 and 2. • Observe the hydraulic pressure gauge when continuity is reached. • If you missed the reading or want to reverify the reading: — Reconnect the 5-pin plug. — Turn the ignition switch on until the pump stops. — Disconnect the 5-pin plug and reverify the readings.	100-110 Bar (1,450-1,595 psi) ▶ Any other reading ▶	GO to Step A23. REPLACE pressure warning switch and pump motor relay.

PIN NO. 1 / PIN NO. 2 / PRESSURE WARNING SWITCH

Fig. 23 Test A, warning lamp On (Part 23 of 24). 1990–91 Cougar/Thunderbird

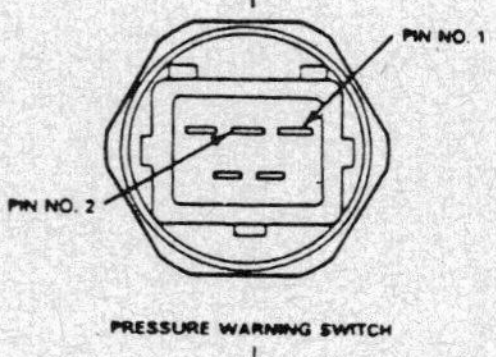

Anti-Lock Warning Lamp On (With Brake Warning Lamp Off) — Test A

TEST STEP	RESULT ▶	ACTION TO TAKE
A23 CHECK PWS HARNESS GROUND • Check for continuity between pressure warning switch 5-pin plug Pin 1 and body ground (harness side).	Continuity ▶ No continuity ▶	GO to Step A24. SERVICE or REPLACE cable harness (Circuit 430H).

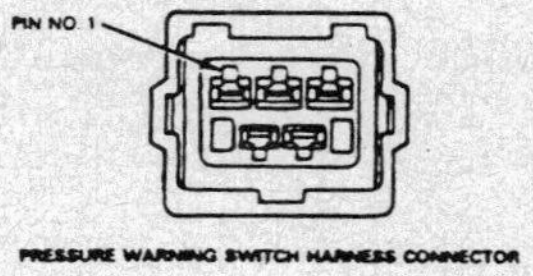

PIN NO. 1 / PRESSURE WARNING SWITCH HARNESS CONNECTOR

TEST STEP	RESULT ▶	ACTION TO TAKE
A24 REVERIFY SYSTEM SYMPTOM • Reconnect all electrical connections. • Remove Pressure Gauge Adaptor. • Install accumulator. **WARNING: Before disconnecting any hydraulic lines, you must ensure that the brake hydraulic pressure system is discharged.** • Discharge the brake system as follows: a. Turn ignition switch to OFF. b. Pump brake pedal at least 20 times until you feel the pedal become hard. • Reverify symptom.	Symptom not present ▶ Symptom still present ▶	FAULT may have been a loose electrical connection. REPLACE electronic control module.

Fig. 23 Test A, warning lamp On (Part 24 of 24). 1990–91 Cougar/Thunderbird

Anti-Lock Lamp On After Engine Starts (Brake Warning Lamp Off) — Test B

Warning Lamps	Ignition On	Cranking Engine	Engine Running	Vehicle Moving	Braking with/without Anti-Lock	Vehicle Stopped	Engine Idle	Ignition Off
WARNING LIGHTS SEQUENCE								
Check Anti-Lock (Amber)								
Brake (Red)								

TEST STEP	RESULT	►	ACTION TO TAKE
B1 CHECK CONTINUITY OF CIRCUIT 523 AND 524 • Ignition switch Off. • Disconnect 32-pin plug from controller. • Connect EEC-IV Breakout box T83L-50-EEC-IV with Anti-Lock Test Adapter T87P-50-ALA to the Anti-Lock 32-pin plug wiring harness. • Check continuity between Breakout box Pins 40 and 6.	Continuity No continuity	► ►	GO to Step B1a. GO to Step B2.
B1a CHECK CONTINUITY OF RH REAR SENSOR • Disconnect wheel sensor plug (RH rear). • Check for continuity between each sensor plug pin (sensor side) and vehicle ground.	Continuity No continuity	► ►	REPLACE sensor (RH rear). REPLACE or SERVICE cable harness (523 or 524). RECONNECT sensor plug.
B2 CHECK CONTINUITY OF CIRCUIT 521 AND 522 • Check for continuity between Breakout box Pins 40 and 5.	Continuity No continuity	► ►	GO to Step B2a. GO to Step B3.

Fig. 23 Test B, ABS lamp On after engine starts (Part 1 of 3). 1990–91 Cougar/Thunderbird

Anti-Lock Lamp On After Engine Starts (Brake Warning Lamp Off) — Test B

TEST STEP	RESULT	►	ACTION TO TAKE
B4 CHECK CONTINUITY OF CIRCUIT 514 AND 516 • Check for continuity between Breakout box Pins 40 and 3.	Continuity No continuity	► ►	GO to Step B4a. Test complete. If Anti-Lock lamp pattern remains, REPEAT Test B.
B4a CHECK CONTINUITY OF RH FRONT SENSOR • Disconnect wheel sensor plug (RH front). • Check for continuity between each sensor plug pin (sensor side) and vehicle ground.	Continuity No Continuity	► ►	REPLACE RH front sensor. REPLACE or SERVICE cable harness (514 or 516). CONNECT sensor plug

Fig. 24 Test B, ABS lamp On after engine starts (Part 3 of 3). 1990–91 Cougar/Thunderbird

Anti-Lock Lamp On After Engine Starts (Brake Warning Lamp Off) — Test B

TEST STEP	RESULT	►	ACTION TO TAKE
B2a CHECK CONTINUITY OF LH FRONT SENSOR • Disconnect wheel sensor plug (LH front). • Check for continuity between each sensor plug pin (sensor side) and vehicle ground.	Continuity No continuity	► ►	REPLACE sensor (LH front). REPLACE or SERVICE cable harness. (521 or 522) CONNECT sensor plug.
B3 CHECK CONTINUITY OF CIRCUIT 518 AND 519 • Check for continuity between Breakout box Pins 40 and 4.	Continuity No continuity	► ►	GO to Step B3a. GO to Step B4.
B3a CHECK CONTINUITY OF LH REAR SENSOR • Disconnect sensor plug (LH rear). • Check for continuity between each sensor plug pin (sensor side) and vehicle ground.	Continuity No continuity	► ►	REPLACE sensor (LH rear). REPLACE or SERVICE cable harness. (518 or 519) CONNECT sensor plug.

Fig. 24 Test B, ABS lamp On after engine starts (Part 2 of 3). 1990–91 Cougar/Thunderbird

Anti-Lock Warning Lamp On After Vehicle Starts To Move Or False Cycling Of Anti-Lock System — Test C

Warning Lamps	Ignition On	Cranking Engine	Engine Running	Vehicle Moving	Braking with/without Anti-Lock	Vehicle Stopped	Engine Idle	Ignition Off
WARNING LIGHTS SEQUENCE								
Check Anti-Lock (Amber)								
Brake (Red)								
WARNING LIGHTS SEQUENCE								
Check Anti-Lock (Amber)								
Brake (Red)								

TEST STEP	RESULT	►	ACTION TO TAKE
C1 MEASURE RH REAR SENSOR CIRCUIT RESISTANCE • Turn ignition switch OFF. • Disconnect 32-Pin plug from electronic controller. • Connect EEC-IV Breakout Box Tool T83L-50-EEC-IV and Anti-Lock Test Adapter Tool T87P-50-ALA or equivalent to anti-lock 32-Pin connector. • Set multi-meter to read resistance. • Measure resistance between Breakout box Pins 6 and 23.	800 to 1400 ohms (0.8 to 1.4K ohms) Any other reading	► ►	GO to Step C2. GO to Step C1a.
C1a MEASURE RH REAR SENSOR RESISTANCE • Disconnect sensor plug (RH rear). • Set multi-meter to read resistance. • Measure resistance of sensor at sensor plug.	800 to 1400 ohms (0.8 to 1.4K ohms) Any other reading	► ►	SERVICE or REPLACE cable harness (Circuit 523 or 524). REPLACE RH rear wheel sensor.

Fig. 25 Test C, warning lamp On after vehicle moves/or false cycling of system (Part 1 of 5). 1990–91 Cougar/Thunderbird

FORD—Anti-Lock Brakes

TEST STEP	RESULT ▶	ACTION TO TAKE
C2 MEASURE LH FRONT SENSOR CIRCUIT RESISTANCE • Measure resistance between Breakout box Pins 5 and 22.	800 to 1400 ohms (0.8 to 1.4K ohms) (OK)	GO to Step C3.
	Any other reading (OK̸)	GO to Step C2a.
C2a MEASURE LH FRONT SENSOR RESISTANCE • Disconnect wheel sensor plug (LH rear). • Measure resistance of sensor at sensor plug.	800 to 1400 ohms (0.8 to 1.4K ohms) (OK)	SERVICE or REPLACE cable harness (Circuit 521 or 522).
	Any other reading (OK̸)	REPLACE LH front wheel sensor.
C3 MEASURE LH REAR SENSOR CIRCUIT RESISTANCE • Measure resistance between Breakout box Pins 4 and 21.	800 to 1400 ohms (0.8 to 1.4K ohms) (OK)	GO to Step C4.
	Any other reading (OK̸)	GO to Step C3a.

Fig. 25 Test C, warning lamp On after vehicle moves/or false cycling of system (Part 2 of 5). 1990–91 Cougar/Thunderbird

TEST STEP	RESULT ▶	ACTION TO TAKE
C3a MEASURE LH REAR SENSOR RESISTANCE • Disconnect sensor plug (LH rear). • Measure resistance of sensor at left rear sensor plug.	800 to 1400 ohms (0.8 to 1.4K ohms) ▶	SERVICE or REPLACE cable harness (Circuit 518 or 519).
	Any other reading	REPLACE LH rear wheel sensor.
C4 MEASURE RH FRONT SENSOR CIRCUIT RESISTANCE • Measure resistance between Breakout box Pins 3 and 20.	800 to 1400 ohms (0.8 to 1.4K ohms) ▶	GO to Step C5.
	Any other reading	GO to Step C4a.
C4a MEASURE RH FRONT SENSOR RESISTANCE • Disconnect sensor plug (RH front). • Measure resistance of sensor at sensor plug.	800 to 1400 ohms (0.8 to 1.4K ohms) ▶	SERVICE or REPLACE cable harness (Circuit 514 or 516).
	Any other reading	REPLACE RH front wheel sensor.

Fig. 25 Test C, warning lamp On after vehicle moves/or false cycling of system (Part 3 of 5). 1990–91 Cougar/Thunderbird

TEST STEP	RESULT ▶	ACTION TO TAKE
C5 CHECK RH REAR SENSOR • Turn ignition switch OFF. • Turn air suspension switch in luggage compartment OFF, if so equipped. • Place vehicle on hoist and raise wheels clear of ground. • Set multi-meter on voltage range (2V-AC). • Measure voltage between Breakout box Pins 6 and 23 while spinning RH rear wheel at approximately 1 revolution per second.	Between 0.05 and 0.70 Vac (OK)	GO to Step C6.
	Less than 0.05 or more than 0.70 Vac (OK̸)	CHECK sensor mounting, air gap, or toothed wheel mounting. CORRECT as required.
C6 CHECK LH FRONT SENSOR • Measure voltage between Breakout box Pins 5 and 22 while spinning LH front wheel at approximately 1 revolution per second.	Between 0.05 and 0.70 Vac	GO to Step C7.
	Less than 0.05 or more than 0.70 Vac	CHECK sensor mounting, air gap, or toothed wheel mounting. CORRECT as required.
C7 CHECK LH REAR SENSOR • Measure voltage between Breakout box Pins 4 and 21 while spinning LH rear wheel at approximately 1 revolution per second.	Between 0.05 and 0.70 Vac	GO to Step C8.
	Less than 0.05 or more than 0.07 Vac	CHECK wheel sensor mounting, air gap, or toothed wheel mounting. CORRECT as required.

Fig. 25 Test C, warning lamp On after vehicle moves/or false cycling of system (Part 4 of 5). 1990–91 Cougar/Thunderbird

TEST STEP	RESULT ▶	ACTION TO TAKE
C8 CHECK RH FRONT SENSOR • Measure voltage between Breakout box Pins 3 and 20 while spinning RH front wheel at approximately 1 revolution per second.	Between 0.05 and 0.70 Vac	GO to Step C9.
	Less than 0.05 or more than 0.70 Vac	CHECK wheel sensor mounting, air gap, or toothed wheel mounting. CORRECT as required.
C9 CHECK FRONT WHEEL BEARINGS • Check front wheel bearing end play. • Inspect each toothed sensor ring visually for damaged teeth. NOTE: Turn air suspension switch ON when vehicle is off hoist.	Loose or damaged parts	ADJUST bearings or REPLACE faulty parts.
	Not loose or damaged ▶	REVERIFY symptom.

Fig. 25 Test C, warning lamp On after vehicle moves/or false cycling of system (Part 5 of 5). 1990–91 Cougar/Thunderbird

Anti-Lock Warning Lamp And Brake Warning Lamp On And/Or Pump Motor Runs More Than 60 Seconds	Test D

WARNING LIGHTS SEQUENCE

Warning Lamps	Ignition On	Cranking Engine	Engine Running	Vehicle Moving	Braking with/without Anti-Lock	Vehicle Stopped	Engine Idle	Ignition Off
Check Anti-Lock (Amber)								
Brake (Red)								

WARNING LIGHTS SEQUENCE

Warning Lamps	Ignition On	Cranking Engine	Engine Running	Vehicle Moving	Braking with without Anti-Lock	Vehicle Stopped	Engine Idle	Ignition Off
Check Anti-Lock (Amber)								
Brake (Red)								

TEST STEP	RESULT ▶	ACTION TO TAKE
D1 CHECK PUMP MOTOR OPERATION • Turn ignition OFF. • Pump brake pedal at least 20 times until it becomes hard. • Turn ignition switch ON. • Pump motor should run. NOTE: If pump motor is allowed to run continuously for approximately 20 minutes, a thermal safety switch (inside motor) will shut off motor. A 2-to-10 minute cool-down period is typical before normal operation can resume.	(OK) ▶ (Ⓧ) ▶	GO to D2. GO to D1a.

Fig. 26   Test D, warning lamp & brake warning lamp On and/or pump motor runs more than 60 seconds (Part 1 of 10). 1990–91 Cougar/Thunderbird

---

Anti-Lock Warning Lamp And Brake Warning Lamp On And/Or Pump Motor Runs More Than 60 Seconds	Test D

TEST STEP	RESULT ▶	ACTION TO TAKE
D1a PUMP MOTOR UNIT • Disconnect 4-pin plug on pump motor unit. • Turn ignition switch ON. • Set multi-meter on 20 Volt DC. • Connect meter to the 4-pin plug on the harness side. (Use one negative and one positive pin). • Observe voltmeter.	More than 10V DC ▶ Less than 10V DC ▶	GO to D2. GO to D1b.
D1b CHECK CONTINUITY CIRCUITS 538A, 538B AND 538C • Disconnect pump motor relay. • Check for continuity between motor relay socket Pin 3 (harness side) and each positive pin of the 4-pin motor connector (harness side).	(OK) ▶ (Ⓧ) ▶	GO to D1c. SERVICE Circuits 538A, 538B and 538C.

Fig. 26   Test D, warning lamp & brake warning lamp On and/or pump motor runs more than 60 seconds (Part 2 of 10). 1990–91 Cougar/Thunderbird

---

Anti-Lock Warning Lamp And Brake Warning Lamp On And/Or Pump Motor Runs More Than 60 Seconds	Test D

TEST STEP	RESULT ▶	ACTION TO TAKE
D1c CHECK CONTINUITY CIRCUITS 430G AND 430F • Check for continuity between ground and each negative pin of 4-Pin motor connector (harness side).	Continuity ▶ No continuity ▶	GO to D1d. SERVICE or REPLACE Circuit 430G or 430F.
D1d CHECK CONTINUITY CIRCUIT 537B • Turn ignition switch OFF. • Remove positive battery cable from battery. • Disconnect pump motor relay. PUMP MOTOR RELAY (LOCATED ON DASH PANEL IN ENGINE COMPARTMENT RH SIDE). • Check continuity between battery positive cable and motor relay socket Pin 4 (harness side).	Continuity ▶ No continuity	RECONNECT battery positive cable and GO to Step D1e. SERVICE or REPLACE Circuits 537B or 038E or high current fuse.

Fig. 26   Test D, warning lamp & brake warning lamp On and/or pump motor runs more than 60 seconds (Part 3 of 10). 1990–91 Cougar/Thunderbird

---

Anti-Lock Warning Lamp And Brake Warning Lamp On And/Or Pump Motor Runs More Than 60 Seconds	Test D

TEST STEP	RESULT ▶	ACTION TO TAKE
D1e CHECK CONTINUITY CIRCUIT 298 • Connect multi-meter to motor relay socket Pin 2 (harness side) and ignition switch lock pin (On). • Check continuity.	Continuity ▶ No continuity ▶	GO to Step D1f. REPLACE or SERVICE Circuit 298 and or fuse link.
D1f CHECK CONTINUITY CIRCUIT 430H • Disconnect 5-Pin plug of PWS. • Check for continuity between pressure warning switch 5-Pin plug Pin 1 (harness side) and ground.	Continuity ▶ No continuity ▶	GO to Step D1g. REPLACE or SERVICE Circuit 430H.
D1g CHECK CONTINUITY CIRCUIT 539A • Connect meter to 5-Pin plug Pin 4 (harness side) and motor relay socket Pin 1 (harness side). • Check for continuity.	Continuity ▶ No continuity ▶	GO to Step D1h. REPLACE or SERVICE Circuit 539A.

Fig. 26   Test D, warning lamp & brake warning lamp On and/or pump motor runs more than 60 seconds (Part 4 of 10). 1990–91 Cougar/Thunderbird

Anti-Lock Warning Lamp And Brake Warning Lamp On And/Or Pump Motor Runs More Than 60 Seconds			Test D

TEST STEP	RESULT	▶	ACTION TO TAKE
D1h PRESSURE WARNING SWITCH			
• Check for continuity between pressure warning switch Pins 1 and 4. NOTE: System must be depressurized.	Continuity	▶	GO to Step D1j.
	No continuity	▶	REPLACE pressure warning switch and pump motor relay.
D1j CHECK PUMP MOTOR RELAY			
• Set multi-meter on 200 ohm scale. • Connect meter to motor relay Pins 1 and 2.	45 to 105 Ohms	▶	GO to Step D1k.
	Other	▶	REPLACE pump motor relay.

Fig. 26   test D, warning lamp & brake warning lamp On and/or pump motor runs more than 60 seconds (Part 5 of 10). 1990–91 Cougar/Thunderbird

Anti-Lock Warning Lamp And Brake Warning Lamp On And/Or Pump Motor Runs More Than 60 Seconds			Test D

TEST STEP	RESULT	▶	ACTION TO TAKE
D1k CHECK PUMP MOTOR RELAY (CONTINUED)			
• Connect meter and check continuity between motor relay Pins 3 and 4.	No continuity	▶	GO to Step D1m.
	Continuity	▶	REPLACE pump motor relay.
D1m CHECK PUMP MOTOR RELAY (CONTINUED)			
• Connect battery to motor relay terminals 1 and 2. • Check continuity between relay Pins 3 and 4 with multi-meter.	Continuity	▶	GO to Step D1n.
	No continuity	▶	REPLACE pump motor relay.
D1n CHECK MOTOR RELAY DIODE			
• Set multi-meter to check a diode (approx. 2000 Ohm scale). Check between relay Pins 3 and 5 in both directions by reversing leads.	Diode blocks (high resistance) in one direction and conducts (low resistance) in other direction.	▶	GO to Step D1p.
	Diode blocks in both directions. Diode conducts in both directions.	▶	REPLACE pump motor relay.

Fig. 26   Test D, warning lamp & brake warning lamp On and/or pump motor runs more than 60 seconds (Part 6 of 10). 1990–91 Cougar/Thunderbird

Anti-Lock Warning Lamp And Brake Warning Lamp On And/Or Pump Motor Runs More Than 60 Seconds			Test D

TEST STEP	RESULT	▶	ACTION TO TAKE
D1p CHECK PUMP MOTOR			
• Apply 12 volts to 4-pin plug of motor (use one negative and one positive pin). • Pump motor should run.	Pump runs	▶	End of test. CONNECT all electrical plugs and relay. REVERIFY symptom.
	Pump does not operate	▶	REPLACE pump/motor assembly.
D2 CHECK PUMP MOTOR UNIT			
• Turn ignition switch OFF. • Pump brake pedal 20 times to discharge system. • Connect ammeter between battery positive cable and battery positive terminal. • Turn Off any electrical components. • Connect 4-pin motor plug. • Turn ignition switch ON. • Measure pump motor current.	Current more than 25 amps	▶	REPLACE pump motor unit.
	Current less than 25 amps	▶	GO to Step D2a.
D2a CHECK PUMP MOTOR			
• Turn ignition switch OFF. • Pump brake pedal at least 20 times, until brake pedal becomes hard. • Turn ignition switch ON. • Measure time pump takes to shut OFF.	Under 60 seconds	▶	GO to Step D2b.
	Over 60 seconds (or motor never turns on)	▶	CHECK for corroded connections at: • Motor 4-pin plug. • Body ground (Circuit 430F and D). • Motor relay Pin 4 socket (Circuit 537). • Battery to Pin 4. GO to Step D2b.

Fig. 26   Test D, warning lamp & brake warning lamp On and/or pump motor runs more than 60 seconds (Part 7 of 10). 1990–91 Cougar/Thunderbird

Anti-Lock Warning Lamp And Brake Warning Lamp On And/Or Pump Motor Runs More Than 60 Seconds			Test D

TEST STEP	RESULT	▶	ACTION TO TAKE
D2b CHECK LOW PRESSURE FLOW			
• Turn ignition switch OFF. • Disconnect low pressure hose from pump and allow fluid to flow into a suitable container. NOTE: Discard fluid after test.	Free fluid flow	▶	CONNECT low pressure hose. FILL reservoir to MAX. GO to D2c.
	Restricted flow	▶	SERVICE or REPLACE reservoir and or low pressure hose as required.
D2c CHECK VOLTAGE TO PUMP MOTOR			
• Turn ignition switch OFF. • Pump brake pedal to discharge pressure system. • Set meter to 20 Volts DC range. • Connect voltmeter in parallel at 4-Pin motor plug. • Turn ignition switch ON.	With pump running: Voltage over 8 Volts DC	▶	GO to Step D3.
	Voltage under 8 Volts DC	▶	CHECK Circuits 430G, 430F, 538A, 538B, Pin 4 to battery and relay Pins 3 and 4 for voltage drop. SERVICE or REPLACE as necessary.

Fig. 26   Test D, warning lamp & brake warning lamp On and/or pump motor runs more than 60 seconds (Part 8 of 10). 1990–91 Cougar/Thunderbird

Anti-Lock Warning Lamp And Brake Warning Lamp On And/Or Pump Motor Runs More Than 60 Seconds	Test D

TEST STEP	RESULT	▶	ACTION TO TAKE
D3 ACCUMULATOR: PRE-CHARGE	4137-9135 kPa (600-1325 psi)	▶	GO to Step D4.
• Vehicle must be cooled to room temperature. **WARNING: BEFORE DISCONNECTING ANY HYDRAULIC LINES, YOU MUST ENSURE THAT THE PRESSURE SYSTEM IS DISCHARGED.**	Under 4137 kPa (600 psi)	▶	REPLACE accumulator. Note: Measure nipple length to determine correct service replacement accumulator.
• To discharge hydraulic accumulator pressure, turn ignition OFF, pump brake pedal at least 20 times until you feel it become hard. • Remove accumulator. • Install Pressure Gauge Adaptor T88P-20215-AH or equivalent. • Install accumulator. • Install Anti-Lock Pressure Gauge Tool T85P-20215-A or equivalent. • Turn ignition switch on and read accumulator precharge pressure. (Gauge needle will spring to this point). Note: Gauge needle reading should spring to 40-90 bar (600-1325 psi) and climb to 16,203-19,306 kPa bar (2350-2800 psi). • If reading was missed, discharge accumulator as described and repeat ignition ON sequence.	Over 9135 kPa (1325 psi)	▶	REPLACE accumulator. Note: Measure nipple length to determine correct service replacement accumulator.
D4 CHECK HYDRAULIC ACTUATION UNIT	Pressure loss less than 10 bar (140 psi) on gauge	▶	GO to Step D5.
• Turn ignition switch ON; wait until pump motor stops. Wait 3 more minutes to stabilize gauge pressure. • Read pressure gauge. • Wait 5 minutes and read pressure gauge again to determine the pressure loss over those 5 minutes.	More than 10 bar (140 psi)	▶	CHECK for external leakage at actuation assembly and SERVICE. If no external leakage is found, GO to Step D4a.

Fig. 26 Test D, warning lamp & brake warning lamp On and/or pump motor runs more than 60 seconds (Part 9 of 10). 1990–91 Cougar/Thunderbird

Anti-Lock Warning Lamp And Brake Warning Lamp On And/Or Pump Motor Runs More Than 60 Seconds	Test D

TEST STEP	RESULT	▶	ACTION TO TAKE
D4a CHECK FOR HYDRAULIC LEAKS	No leakage found (OK)	▶	GO to D5.
• Check for brake fluid leaks in the following areas: a. Brake lines and calipers. b. High and low pressure hoses on actuation assembly. c. Reservoir seals and seams. d. Accumulator. NOTE: A small amount of leakage from pressure warning switch is allowable. If any leakage is found below switch, wipe off excess fluid and check for excessive leakage.	Leakage found (⊘)	▶	SERVICE or REPLACE components. CHECK system operation.
D5 CHECK PUMP PRESSURE	13100-15169 kPa (1900-2200 psi) when pump starts (OK)	▶	GO to Step D6.
• With the pressure gauge still attached and ignition switch still ON, pump brake pedal to decrease pressure until pump motor restarts.	Less than or more than 13100-15169 kPa (1900-2200 psi) (⊘)	▶	REPLACE pressure warning switch.
D6 CHECK PRESSURE WARNING SWITCH	16203 kPa (2350-2800 psi) when pump motor stops (OK)	▶	If pump motor takes longer than 60 seconds to reach 16203 kPa (2350-2800 psi), REPLACE pump/motor assembly. REVERIFY symptom.
• With the ignition switch still ON and the pressure gauge connected, observe the pressure when the pump motor stops running.	Less than 16203 kPa (2350 psi) or over 19306 kPa (2800 psi) (⊘)	▶	REPLACE pressure warning switch.

Fig. 26 Test D, warning lamp & brake warning lamp On and/or pump motor runs more than 60 seconds (Part 10 of 10). 1990–91 Cougar/Thunderbird

Anti-Lock Warning Lamp Intermittently On	Test E

Warning Lamps	Ignition On	Cranking Engine	Engine Running	Vehicle Moving	Braking with/without Anti-Lock	Vehicle Stopped	Engine Idle	Ignition Off
Check Anti-Lock (Amber)	▨	▨		▨	▨			
Brake (Red)		■						

WARNING LIGHTS SEQUENCE

TEST STEP	RESULT	▶	ACTION TO TAKE
E1 CHECK FLI AND PWS CIRCUIT	Less than 5 ohms (OK)	▶	GO to Step E2
• Disconnect 32-Pin plug from electronic controller. • Connect EEC-IV Breakout box, T83L-50-EEC-IV with Anti-Lock Test Adapter T87P-50-ALA or equivalent to the Anti-Lock 32-Pin plug wiring harness. • Turn ignition switch ON. • Set multi-meter to read resistance. • Measure the resistance between Breakout box Pins 25 and 27.	Greater than 5 ohms (⊘)	▶	GO to Step E1a
E1a CHECK FLI ANTI-LOCK WARNING CIRCUIT	Less than 2 ohms (OK)	▶	GO to Step E1b
• Disconnect 5-Pin plug on reservoir fluid level indicator (FLI). • Measure resistance between fluid level indicator electrical Pins 1 and 2 (with brake fluid at maximum fluid level).	Greater than 2 ohms (⊘)	▶	REPLACE fluid reservoir.

FLUID LEVEL INDICATOR ON RESERVOIR CONNECTOR

Fig. 27 Test E, warning lamp intermittently On (Part 1 of 5). 1990–91 Cougar/Thunderbird

Anti-Lock Warning Lamp Intermittently On	Test E

TEST STEP	RESULT	▶	ACTION TO TAKE
E1b CHECK PWS ANTI-LOCK WARNING CIRCUIT (NO SYSTEM PRESSURE)	No Continuity	▶	GO to Step E1c.
• Turn ignition switch OFF. • Pump brake pedal to discharge pressure system. • Disconnect 5-Pin plug at pressure warning switch (PWS). • Check for continuity between pressure warning switch Pins 3 and 5.	Continuity	▶	REPLACE pressure warning switch.
E1c CHECK ELECTRONIC MODULE TO FLI WIRE	Continuity	▶	GO to Step E1d.
• Check for continuity between Breakout box Pin 25 and FLI 5-Pin plug Pin 1 (harness side).	No continuity	▶	REPLACE or SERVICE cable harness (Circuit 512A).

PRESSURE WARNING SWITCH

FLUID LEVEL INDICATOR CONNECTOR

Fig. 27 Test E, warning lamp intermittently On (Part 2 of 5). 1990–91 Cougar/Thunderbird

Anti-Lock Warning Lamp Intermittently On	Test E

TEST STEP	RESULT ▶	ACTION TO TAKE
E1d CHECK FLI TO PWS WIRE • Check for continuity between 5-Pin fluid level plug Pin 2 (harness side) 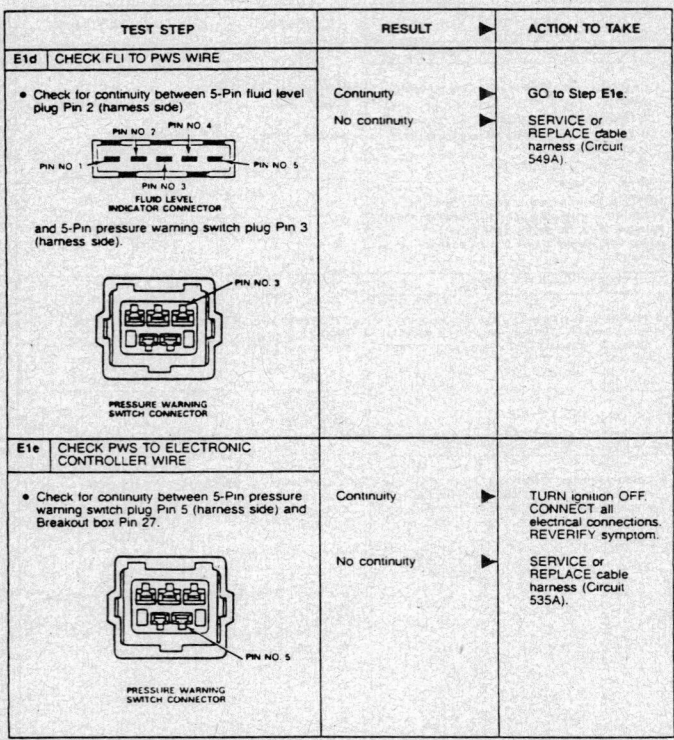 and 5-Pin pressure warning switch plug Pin 3 (harness side).	Continuity ▶ No continuity ▶	GO to Step E1e. SERVICE or REPLACE cable harness (Circuit 549A).
E1e CHECK PWS TO ELECTRONIC CONTROLLER WIRE • Check for continuity between 5-Pin pressure warning switch plug Pin 5 (harness side) and Breakout box Pin 27.	Continuity ▶ No continuity ▶	TURN ignition OFF. CONNECT all electrical connections. REVERIFY symptom. SERVICE or REPLACE cable harness (Circuit 535A).

Fig. 27 Test E, warning lamp intermittently On (Part 3 of 5). 1990–91 Cougar/Thunderbird

Anti-Lock Warning Lamp Intermittently On	Test E

TEST STEP	RESULT ▶	ACTION TO TAKE
E2 CHECK ISOLATION TEST FLI AND PWS • Check for continuity between Breakout box Pin 25 and body ground.	Continuity ▶ No continuity ▶	GO to Step E2a. REVERIFY symptom.
E2a CHECK CONTINUITY OF FLI SWITCH • Disconnect FLI plug and check for continuity between socket Pin 1 and Pins 3, 4, and 5 and Pin 2 and Pins 3, 4, and 5.	Continuity ▶ No continuity ▶	REPLACE FLI. GO to Step E2b.
E2b CHECK CONTINUITY CIRCUIT 512A • Check for continuity between FLI plug Pin 1 (harness side) and body ground.	Continuity ▶ No continuity ▶	SERVICE or REPLACE Circuit 512A. GO to Step E2c.
E2c CHECK CONTINUITY CIRCUIT 549A • Disconnect 5-Pin plug from PWS. Check for continuity between FLI plug Pin 2 (harness side) and body ground.	Continuity ▶ No continuity ▶	SERVICE or REPLACE Circuit 549A. GO to Step E2d.

Fig. 27 Test E, warning lamp intermittently On (Part 4 of 5). 1990–91 Cougar/Thunderbird

Anti-Lock Warning Lamp Intermittently On	Test E

TEST STEP	RESULT ▶	ACTION TO TAKE
E2d CHECK CONTINUITY OF PWS • Check for continuity from PWS 5-Pin socket Pin 3 to body ground, and from Pin 5 to body ground.	Continuity ▶ No continuity ▶	REPLACE pressure warning switch. GO to Step E2e.
E2e CHECK CONTINUITY CIRCUIT 535A • Check for continuity between 5-Pin PWS plug (harness side) Pin 5 and body ground.	Continuity ▶ No continuity ▶	SERVICE or REPLACE Circuit 535A. CONNECT all plugs and REVERIFY symptom.

Fig. 27 Test E, warning lamp intermittently On (Part 5 of 5). 1990–91 Cougar/Thunderbird

Brake Warning Lamp On (With Anti-Lock Lamp Off, Parking Brake Released And Brake Lining Wear Checked)	Test F

WARNING LIGHTS SEQUENCE

Warning Lamps	Ignition On	Cranking Engine	Engine Running	Vehicle Moving	Braking with/without Anti-Lock	Vehicle Stopped	Engine Idle	Ignition Off
Check Anti-Lock (Amber)	▨	▨▨▨						
Brake (Red)	██	██	██	██	██	██	██	

TEST STEP	RESULT ▶	ACTION TO TAKE
F1 CHECK BRAKE FLUID LEVEL • Turn ignition switch ON. • Pump brake pedal until pump motor starts. • When pump motor stops check brake fluid level.	Low (OK) ▶ Normal (⊗) ▶	CHECK system for external leaks. SERVICE as required. GO to Step F2.
F2 CHECK CONTINUITY FLI SWITCH • Disconnect 5-Pin plug on fluid reservoir. • Set multi-meter to measure continuity. Connect to reservoir Pins 3 and 4.	No continuity (OK) ▶ Continuity (⊗) ▶	GO to Step F3. REPLACE fluid reservoir.

Fig. 28 Test F, brake warning lamp On w/ABS lamp Off, parking brake released & lining wear checked (Part 1 of 2). 1990–91 Cougar/Thunderbird

Brake Warning Lamp On (With Anti-Lock Lamp Off, Parking Brake Released And Brake Lining Wear Checked)	Test F

TEST STEP	RESULT ▶	ACTION TO TAKE
F3 CHECK CONTINUITY PWS SWITCH (CONTINUED)		
• Turn ignition switch ON, wait until motor stops running.	Continuity ▶	REPLACE pressure warning switch.
• Disconnect Pressure Warning Switch 5-Pin plug and connect multi-meter to Pins 1 and 2 (switch side).	No continuity ▶	GO to Step F4.
• Check for continuity.		

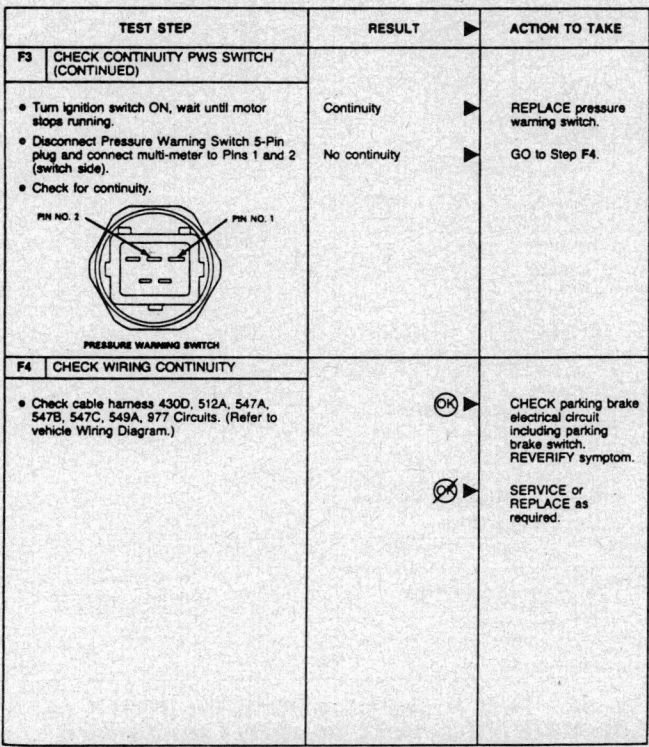

PIN NO. 2   PIN NO. 1

PRESSURE WARNING SWITCH

TEST STEP	RESULT ▶	ACTION TO TAKE
F4 CHECK WIRING CONTINUITY		
• Check cable harness 430D, 512A, 547A, 547B, 547C, 549A, 977 Circuits. (Refer to vehicle Wiring Diagram.)	⊘ ▶	CHECK parking brake electrical circuit including parking brake switch. REVERIFY symptom.
	⊘ ▶	SERVICE or REPLACE as required.

Fig. 28   Test F, brake warning lamp On w/ABS lamp Off, parking brake released & lining wear checked (Part 2 of 2). 1990–91 Cougar/Thunderbird

No Anti-Lock Warning Lamp On When Ignition Switch Turned On	Test G

Warning Lamps	Ignition On	Cranking Engine	Engine Running	Vehicle Moving	Braking with/without Anti-Lock	Vehicle Stopped	Engine Idle	Ignition Off
Check Anti-Lock (Amber)								
Brake (Red)		▨						

TEST STEP	RESULT ▶	ACTION TO TAKE
G1 CHECK FUSE AND FUSE LINKS		
• Check in-line fuse links with ignition turned ON.	Fuse Links OK ▶	GO to Step G2.
	Fuse Links ⊘ ▶	SERVICE or REPLACE as required.
G2 CHECK WARNING LAMP BULB		
• Check warning lamp bulb.	OK ▶	GO to Step G3.
	⊘ ▶	REPLACE bulb.
G3 CHECK WARNING LAMP OPERATION		
• Turn ignition switch ON.	Anti-Lock lamp goes ON ▶	SERVICE or REPLACE Circuit 606B.
• Disconnect 32-Pin connector from control module.	Anti-Lock lamp is not ON ▶	SERVICE or REPLACE connector to 14401 wire harness.

Fig. 29   Test G, no warning lamp On when ignition switch turned On. 1990–91 Cougar/Thunderbird

Spongy Brake Pedal With/Without Anti-Lock Function (No Warning Lamp)	Test H

Warning Lamps	Ignition On	Cranking Engine	Engine Running	Vehicle Moving	Braking with-without Anti-Lock	Vehicle Stopped	Engine Idle	Ignition Off
Check Anti-Lock (Amber)	▨	▨						
Brake (Red)		▨						

TEST STEP	RESULT ▶	ACTION TO TAKE
H1 CHECK COMPONENT MOUNTING		
• Check for proper brake pedal and hydraulic unit attachment.	Pedal still spongy ⊘ ▶	GO to Step H2.
• Bleed brakes as outlined.	Pedal feels normal OK ▶	Condition corrected.
H2 BLEED BRAKE SYSTEM		
• Turn off air suspension switch in luggage compartment if so equipped.	Pedal still spongy ⊘ ▶	REPLACE actuation assembly.
• Rebleed brake system.	Pedal feels normal OK ▶	Condition corrected.
• Turn on air suspension switch when vehicle is off hoist if so equipped.		

Fig. 30   Test H, spongy pedal & no warning lamp. 1990–91 Cougar/Thunderbird

Poor Vehicle Tracking During Anti-Lock Function (Warning Lamp Off)	Test J

Warning Lamps	Ignition On	Cranking Engine	Engine Running	Vehicle Moving	Braking with/without Anti-Lock	Vehicle Stopped	Engine Idle	Ignition Off
Check Anti-Lock (Amber)	▨	▨						
Brake (Red)		▨						

TEST STEP	RESULT ▶	ACTION TO TAKE
J1 VERIFY CONDITION		
• Verify condition exists as reported.	Vehicle tracks properly ▶	Condition corrected.
• Turn air suspension off if so equipped.		
• Bleed brake system per shop manual for Anti-Lock brake system.	Vehicle still tracks poorly ▶	GO to J2.
• Turn air suspension on when vehicle is off hoist.		
J2 CHECK ANTI-LOCK OPERATION — LH FRONT WHEEL		
• Turn air suspension off if so equipped.	If wheel turns freely ▶	TURN ignition switch Off. DISCONNECT wire leads. Go to Step J3.
• Lift vehicle and rotate wheels to assure they turn freely.		
• Turn ignition switch OFF.		
• Disconnect 32-Pin plug from electronic controller.	If wheel does not turn freely or pedal drops ▶	REPLACE solenoid valve block.
• Connect EEC-IV Breakout box, Tool T83L-50-EEC-IV with Anti-Lock test adapter, Tool T87P-50-ALA to the Anti-Lock 32-Pin plug wiring harness.		
• Short Pins 18, 14 and 31 to each other at Breakout box.		
• Apply moderate brake pedal effort and check that LH front wheel will not turn.		
• Check to see that LH front wheel turns freely with ignition switch ON.		
• Turn air suspension on when vehicle is off hoist if so equipped.		
CAUTION: DO NOT LEAVE IGNITION ON FOR MORE THAN 1 MINUTE MAXIMUM, OR SOLENOID VALVE DAMAGE MAY RESULT.		

Fig. 31   Test J, poor vehicle tracking during ABS function, warning lamp Off (Part 1 of 2). 1990–91 Cougar/Thunderbird

Poor Vehicle Tracking During Anti-Lock Function (Warning Lamp Off)	Test J

TEST STEP	RESULT ▶	ACTION TO TAKE
J3 CHECK ANTI-LOCK OPERATION — RH FRONT WHEEL		
• Turn air suspension off. • Short Pins 18, 32 and 13 to each other at Breakout box. • Apply moderate brake effort. Check that RH front wheel does not turn. • Check that RH front wheel turns freely with ignition switch ON. **CAUTION: DO NOT LEAVE IGNITION ON MORE THAN 1 MINUTE MAXIMUM OR SOLENOID VALVE DAMAGE MAY RESULT.**	Wheel turns freely ▶ Wheel does not turn freely or brake pedal drops ▶	TURN ignition switch OFF. DISCONNECT wire leads. GO to Step J4. REPLACE solenoid valve block.
J4 CHECK ANTI-LOCK OPERATION — REAR WHEELS		
• Turn air suspension off if so equipped. • Short Pins 18, 30 and 12 to each other at Breakout box. • Apply moderate brake pedal pressure. Check that rear wheels will not turn. • Check that rear wheels turn freely with ignition switch ON. • Turn air suspension on when vehicle is off hoist if so equipped. **CAUTION: DO NOT LEAVE IGNITION ON MORE THAN 1 MINUTE MAXIMUM OR SOLENOID VALVE DAMAGE MAY RESULT.**	Wheels turn freely ▶ Wheels do not turn freely or brake pedal drops ▶	TURN ignition switch OFF. DISCONNECT wire lead and Breakout box. LOWER vehicle. REVERIFY symptom. REPLACE solenoid valve block.

Fig. 31   Test J, poor vehicle tracking during ABS function, warning lamp Off (Part 2 of 2). 1990–91 Cougar/Thunderbird

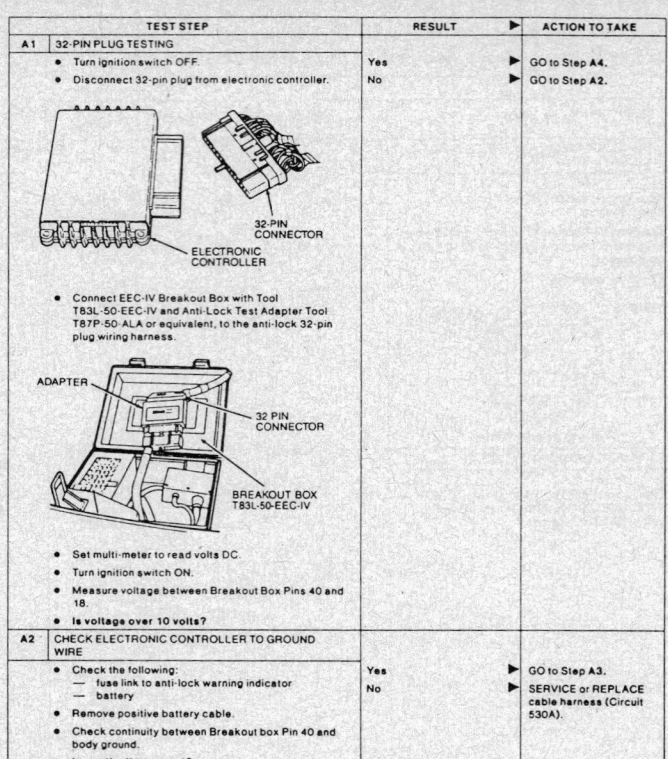

TEST STEP	RESULT	▶	ACTION TO TAKE
A1 32-PIN PLUG TESTING			
• Turn ignition switch OFF. • Disconnect 32-pin plug from electronic controller.	Yes No	▶ ▶	GO to Step A4. GO to Step A2.
• Connect EEC-IV Breakout Box with Tool T83L-50-EEC-IV and Anti-Lock Test Adapter Tool T87P-50-ALA or equivalent, to the anti-lock 32-pin plug wiring harness.			
• Set multi-meter to read volts DC. • Turn ignition switch ON. • Measure voltage between Breakout Box Pins 40 and 18. • Is voltage over 10 volts?			
A2 CHECK ELECTRONIC CONTROLLER TO GROUND WIRE			
• Check the following: — fuse link to anti-lock warning indicator — battery • Remove positive battery cable. • Check continuity between Breakout box Pin 40 and body ground. • Is continuity present?	Yes No	▶ ▶	GO to Step A3. SERVICE or REPLACE cable harness (Circuit 530A).

Fig. 32   Test A, warning lamp On (Part 1 of 18). Mark VII & 1992 Cougar/Thunderbird

TEST STEP	RESULT	▶	ACTION TO TAKE
A3 CHECK IGNITION TO ELECTRONIC CONTROLLER WIRE			
• Check continuity between Breakout Box Pin 18 and ignition switch wire 687C. • Is continuity present?	Yes No	▶ ▶	RECONNECT positive battery cable. CHECK for power at ignition switch pin with switch ON. If okay, connect electronic controller and REVERIFY condition. SERVICE or REPLACE cable harness (Circuit 687C).
A4 CHECK MAIN POWER RELAY SECONDARY CIRCUIT (NORMAL)			
• Turn ignition switch OFF. • Check for continuity between Breakout Box Pins 40 and 15. • Is continuity present?	Yes No	▶ ▶	GO to Step A8. GO to Step A5.
A5 CHECK MAIN POWER RELAY SECONDARY CIRCUIT (NORMAL)			
• Disconnect main relay from socket. • Check for continuity between main power relay socket Pins 3 and 5. • Is continuity present?	Yes No	▶ ▶	GO to Step A6. REPLACE main power relay.
A6 CHECK MAIN POWER RELAY SECONDARY CIRCUIT WIRING HARNESS			
• Disconnect positive battery cable. • Check for continuity between main power relay socket Pin 3 and Breakout box Pin 16. • Is continuity present?	Yes No	▶ ▶	GO to Step A7. SERVICE or REPLACE cable harness (Circuits 532, 532B, 532C).

Fig. 32   Test A, warning lamp On (Part 2 of 18). Mark VII & 1992 Cougar/Thunderbird

TEST STEP	RESULT	▶	ACTION TO TAKE
A7 CHECK MAIN POWER RELAY SECONDARY CIRCUIT WIRING HARNESS			
• Check for continuity between main power relay socket Pin 5 and body ground. • Is continuity present?	Yes No	▶ ▶	RECONNECT main power relay, electronic controller and battery cable and REVERIFY condition. SERVICE or REPLACE cable harness (Circuit 430L).
A8 CHECK MAIN POWER RELAY SECONDARY CIRCUIT (NORMAL)			
• Check for continuity between Breakout Box Pins 40 and 15. • Is continuity present?	Yes No	▶ ▶	GO to Step A10. GO to Step A9.
A9 CHECK MAIN POWER RELAY SECONDARY CIRCUIT WIRING HARNESS			
• Remove main power relay. • Check for continuity between main power relay socket Pin 3 and Breakout Box Pin 15. • Is continuity present?	Yes No	▶ ▶	CONNECT main power relay and electronic controller and REVERIFY condition. SERVICE or REPLACE cable harness (Circuits 532, 532B or 532C).
A10 CHECK FLI AND PWS CIRCUIT			
• Turn ignition switch ON. • Set multi-meter to read resistance. • Measure the resistance between Breakout Box Pins 25 and 27. • Is resistance less than 5 ohms?	Yes No	▶ ▶	GO to Step A16. GO to Step A11.

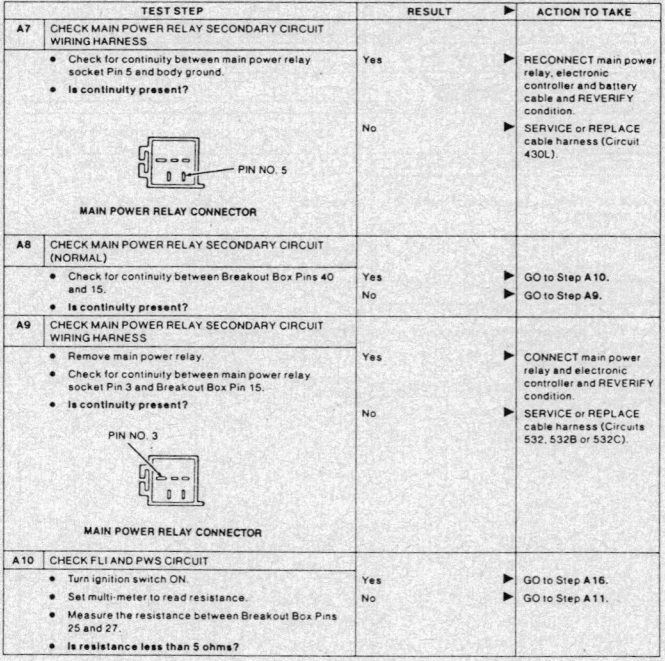

Fig. 32   Test A, warning lamp On (Part 3 of 18). Mark VII & 1992 Cougar/Thunderbird

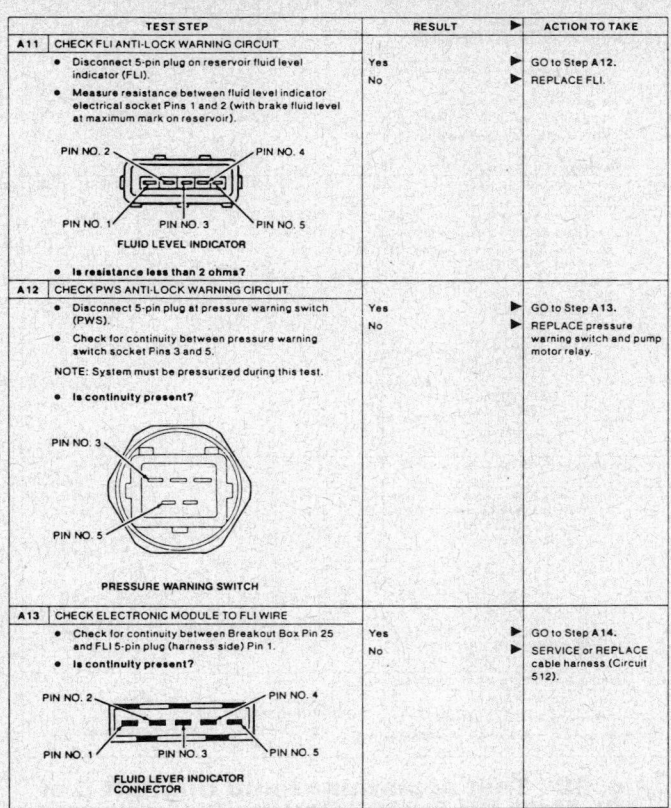

TEST STEP	RESULT	►	ACTION TO TAKE
A11 CHECK FLI ANTI-LOCK WARNING CIRCUIT			
• Disconnect 5-pin plug on reservoir fluid level indicator (FLI).	Yes	►	GO to Step A12.
• Measure resistance between fluid level indicator electrical socket Pins 1 and 2 (with brake fluid level at maximum mark on reservoir).	No	►	REPLACE FLI.
• Is resistance less than 2 ohms?			
A12 CHECK PWS ANTI-LOCK WARNING CIRCUIT			
• Disconnect 5-pin plug at pressure warning switch (PWS).	Yes	►	GO to Step A13.
• Check for continuity between pressure warning switch socket Pins 3 and 5.	No	►	REPLACE pressure warning switch and pump motor relay.
NOTE: System must be pressurized during this test.			
• Is continuity present?			
A13 CHECK ELECTRONIC MODULE TO FLI WIRE			
• Check for continuity between Breakout Box Pin 25 and FLI 5-pin plug (harness side) Pin 1.	Yes	►	GO to Step A14.
• Is continuity present?	No	►	SERVICE or REPLACE cable harness (Circuit 512).

Fig. 32   Test A, warning lamp On (Part 4 of 18). Mark VII & 1992 Cougar/Thunderbird

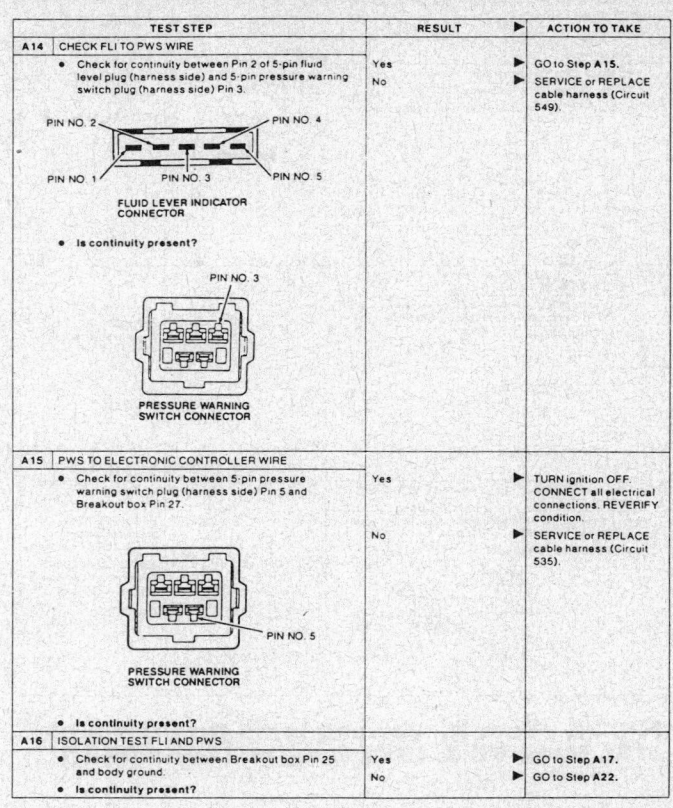

TEST STEP	RESULT	►	ACTION TO TAKE
A14 CHECK FLI TO PWS WIRE			
• Check for continuity between Pin 2 of 5-pin fluid level plug (harness side) and 5-pin pressure warning switch plug (harness side) Pin 3.	Yes	►	GO to Step A15.
• Is continuity present?	No	►	SERVICE or REPLACE cable harness (Circuit 549).
A15 PWS TO ELECTRONIC CONTROLLER WIRE			
• Check for continuity between 5-pin pressure warning switch plug (harness side) Pin 5 and Breakout box Pin 27.	Yes	►	TURN ignition OFF. CONNECT all electrical connections. REVERIFY condition.
	No	►	SERVICE or REPLACE cable harness (Circuit 535).
• Is continuity present?			
A16 ISOLATION TEST FLI AND PWS			
• Check for continuity between Breakout box Pin 25 and body ground.	Yes	►	GO to Step A17.
• Is continuity present?	No	►	GO to Step A22.

Fig. 32   Test A, warning lamp On (Part 5 of 18). Mark VII & 1992 Cougar/Thunderbird

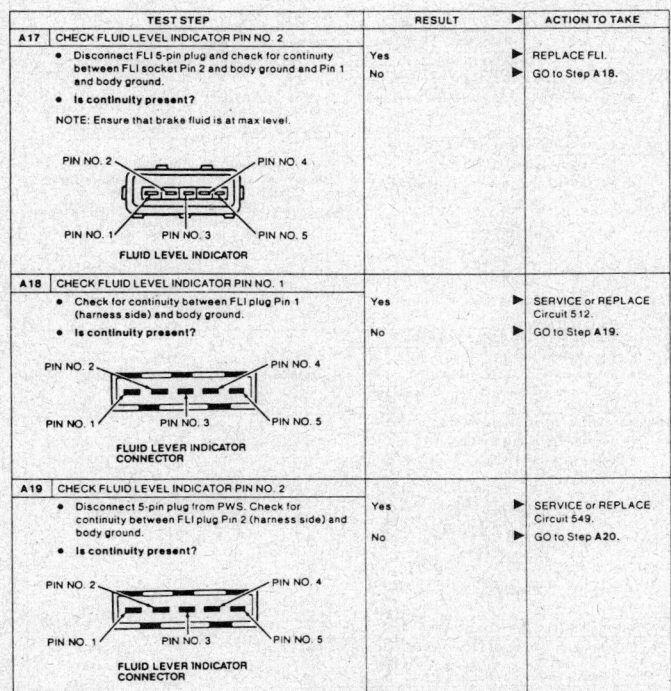

TEST STEP	RESULT	►	ACTION TO TAKE
A17 CHECK FLUID LEVEL INDICATOR PIN NO. 2			
• Disconnect FLI 5-pin plug and check for continuity between FLI socket Pin 2 and body ground and Pin 1 and body ground.	Yes	►	REPLACE FLI.
	No	►	GO to Step A18.
• Is continuity present?			
NOTE: Ensure that brake fluid is at max level.			
A18 CHECK FLUID LEVEL INDICATOR PIN NO. 1			
• Check for continuity between FLI plug Pin 1 (harness side) and body ground.	Yes	►	SERVICE or REPLACE Circuit 512.
• Is continuity present?	No	►	GO to Step A19.
A19 CHECK FLUID LEVEL INDICATOR PIN NO. 2			
• Disconnect 5-pin plug from PWS. Check for continuity between FLI plug Pin 2 (harness side) and body ground.	Yes	►	SERVICE or REPLACE Circuit 549.
• Is continuity present?	No	►	GO to Step A20.

Fig. 32   Test A, warning lamp On (Part 6 of 18). Mark VII & 1992 Cougar/Thunderbird

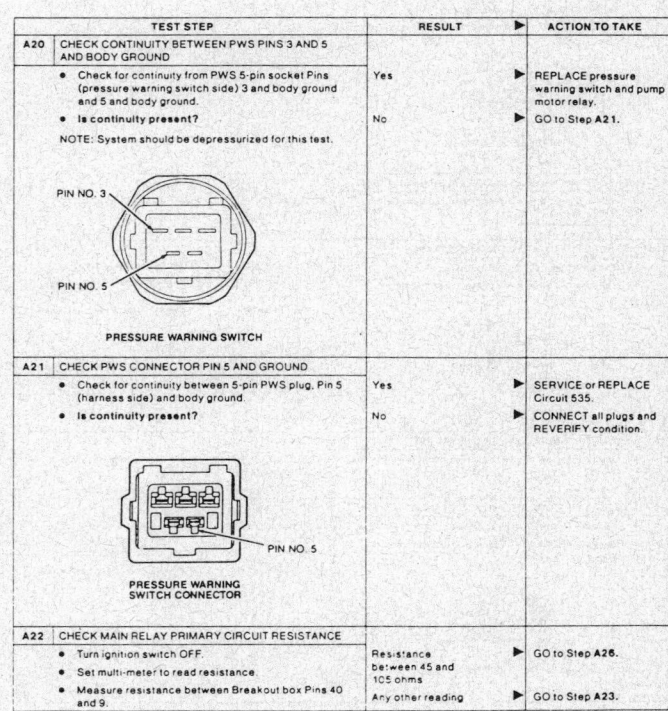

TEST STEP	RESULT	►	ACTION TO TAKE
A20 CHECK CONTINUITY BETWEEN PWS PINS 3 AND 5 AND BODY GROUND			
• Check for continuity from PWS 5-pin socket Pins (pressure warning switch side) 3 and body ground and 5 and body ground.	Yes	►	REPLACE pressure warning switch and pump motor relay.
• Is continuity present?	No	►	GO to Step A21.
NOTE: System should be depressurized for this test.			
A21 CHECK PWS CONNECTOR PIN 5 AND GROUND			
• Check for continuity between 5-pin PWS plug, Pin 5 (harness side) and body ground.	Yes	►	SERVICE or REPLACE Circuit 535.
• Is continuity present?	No	►	CONNECT all plugs and REVERIFY condition.
A22 CHECK MAIN RELAY PRIMARY CIRCUIT RESISTANCE			
• Turn ignition switch OFF.	Resistance between 45 and 105 ohms	►	GO to Step A26.
• Set multi-meter to read resistance.			
• Measure resistance between Breakout box Pins 40 and 9.	Any other reading	►	GO to Step A23.

Fig. 32   Test A, warning lamp On (Part 7 of 18). Mark VII & 1992 Cougar/Thunderbird

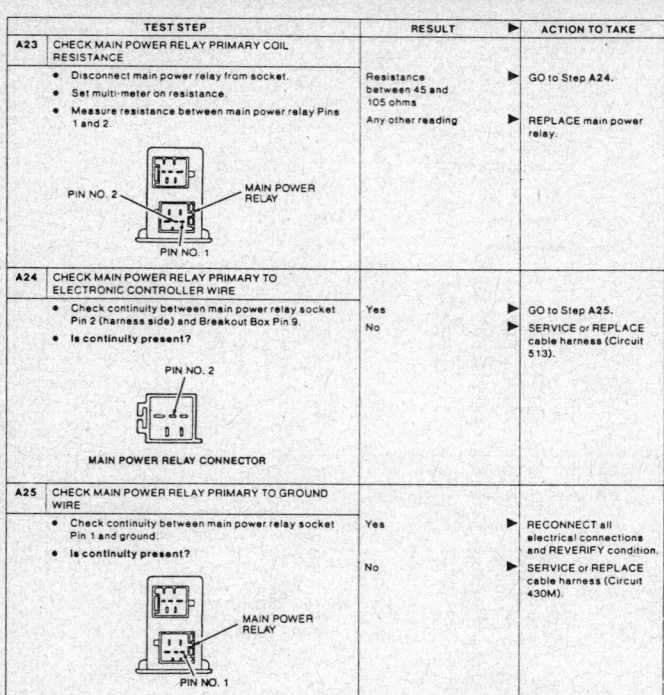

TEST STEP	RESULT	▶	ACTION TO TAKE
A23 CHECK MAIN POWER RELAY PRIMARY COIL RESISTANCE • Disconnect main power relay from socket. • Set multi-meter on resistance. • Measure resistance between main power relay Pins 1 and 2.	Resistance between 45 and 105 ohms Any other reading	▶ ▶	GO to Step A24. REPLACE main power relay.
A24 CHECK MAIN POWER RELAY PRIMARY TO ELECTRONIC CONTROLLER WIRE • Check continuity between main power relay socket Pin 2 (harness side) and Breakout Box Pin 9. • Is continuity present?	Yes No	▶ ▶	GO to Step A25. SERVICE or REPLACE cable harness (Circuit 513).
A25 CHECK MAIN POWER RELAY PRIMARY TO GROUND WIRE • Check continuity between main power relay socket Pin 1 and ground. • Is continuity present?	Yes No	▶ ▶	RECONNECT all electrical connections and REVERIFY condition. SERVICE or REPLACE cable harness (Circuit 430M).

Fig. 32   Test A, warning lamp On (Part 8 of 18). Mark VII & 1992 Cougar/Thunderbird

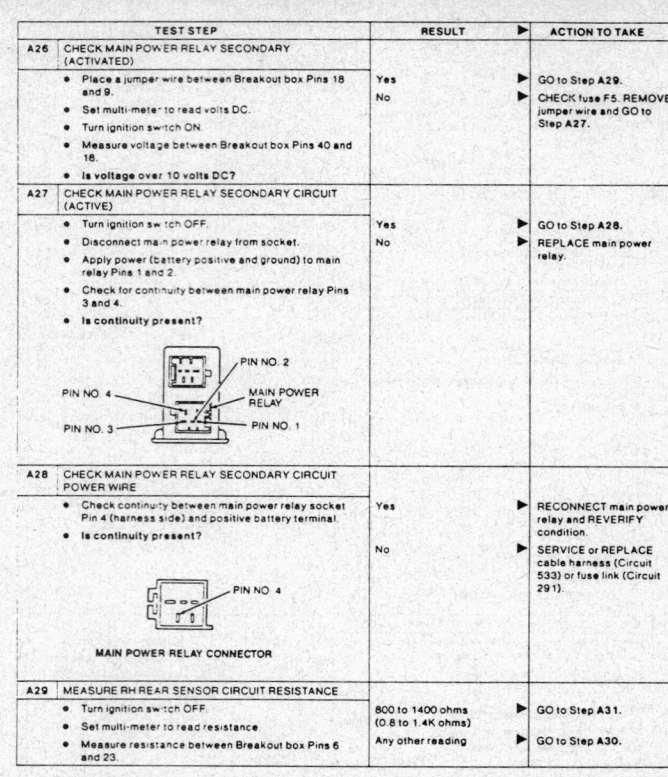

TEST STEP	RESULT	▶	ACTION TO TAKE
A26 CHECK MAIN POWER RELAY SECONDARY (ACTIVATED) • Place a jumper wire between Breakout box Pins 18 and 9. • Set multi-meter to read volts DC. • Turn ignition switch ON. • Measure voltage between Breakout box Pins 40 and 18. • Is voltage over 10 volts DC?	Yes No	▶ ▶	GO to Step A29. CHECK fuse F5. REMOVE jumper wire and GO to Step A27.
A27 CHECK MAIN POWER RELAY SECONDARY CIRCUIT (ACTIVE) • Turn ignition switch OFF. • Disconnect main power relay from socket. • Apply power (battery positive and ground) to main relay Pins 1 and 2. • Check for continuity between main power relay Pins 3 and 4. • Is continuity present?	Yes No	▶ ▶	GO to Step A28. REPLACE main power relay.
A28 CHECK MAIN POWER RELAY SECONDARY CIRCUIT POWER WIRE • Check continuity between main power relay socket Pin 4 (harness side) and positive battery terminal. • Is continuity present?	Yes No	▶ ▶	RECONNECT main power relay and REVERIFY condition. SERVICE or REPLACE cable harness (Circuit 533) or fuse link (Circuit 291).
A29 MEASURE RH REAR SENSOR CIRCUIT RESISTANCE • Turn ignition switch OFF. • Set multi-meter to read resistance. • Measure resistance between Breakout box Pins 6 and 23.	800 to 1400 ohms (0.8 to 1.4K ohms) Any other reading	▶ ▶	GO to Step A31. GO to Step A30.

Fig. 32   Test A, warning lamp On (Part 9 of 18). Mark VII & 1992 Cougar/Thunderbird

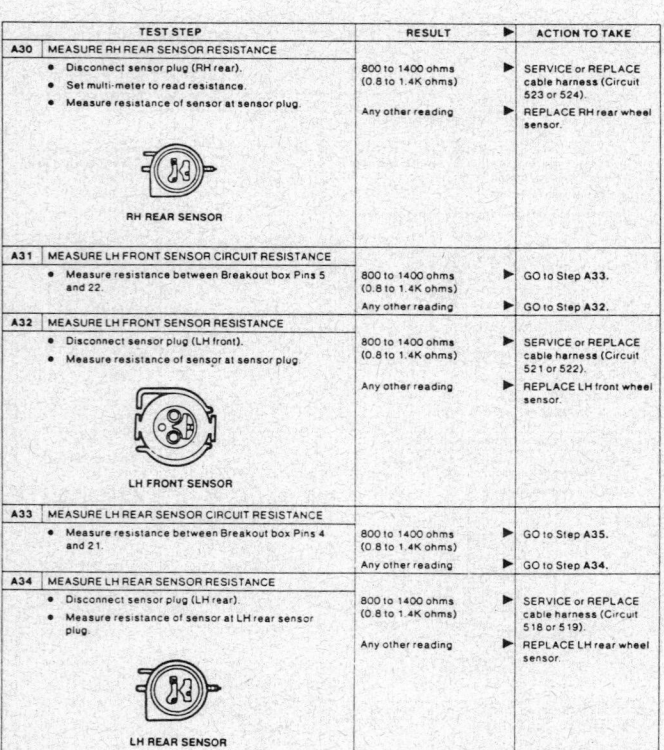

TEST STEP	RESULT	▶	ACTION TO TAKE
A30 MEASURE RH REAR SENSOR RESISTANCE • Disconnect sensor plug (RH rear). • Set multi-meter to read resistance. • Measure resistance of sensor at sensor plug.	800 to 1400 ohms (0.8 to 1.4K ohms) Any other reading	▶ ▶	SERVICE or REPLACE cable harness (Circuit 523 or 524). REPLACE RH rear wheel sensor.
A31 MEASURE LH FRONT SENSOR CIRCUIT RESISTANCE • Measure resistance between Breakout box Pins 5 and 22.	800 to 1400 ohms (0.8 to 1.4K ohms) Any other reading	▶ ▶	GO to Step A33. GO to Step A32.
A32 MEASURE LH FRONT SENSOR RESISTANCE • Disconnect sensor plug (LH front). • Measure resistance of sensor at sensor plug.	800 to 1400 ohms (0.8 to 1.4K ohms) Any other reading	▶ ▶	SERVICE or REPLACE cable harness (Circuit 521 or 522). REPLACE LH front wheel sensor.
A33 MEASURE LH REAR SENSOR CIRCUIT RESISTANCE • Measure resistance between Breakout box Pins 4 and 21.	800 to 1400 ohms (0.8 to 1.4K ohms) Any other reading	▶ ▶	GO to Step A35. GO to Step A34.
A34 MEASURE LH REAR SENSOR RESISTANCE • Disconnect sensor plug (LH rear). • Measure resistance of sensor at LH rear sensor plug.	800 to 1400 ohms (0.8 to 1.4K ohms) Any other reading	▶ ▶	SERVICE or REPLACE cable harness (Circuit 518 or 519). REPLACE LH rear wheel sensor.

Fig. 32   Test A, warning lamp On (Part 10 of 18). Mark VII & 1992 Cougar/Thunderbird

TEST STEP	RESULT	▶	ACTION TO TAKE
A35 MEASURE RH FRONT SENSOR CIRCUIT RESISTANCE • Measure resistance between Breakout box Pins 3 and 20.	800 to 1400 ohms (0.8 to 1.4K ohms) Any other reading	▶ ▶	GO to Step A37. GO to Step A36.
A36 MEASURE RH FRONT SENSOR RESISTANCE • Disconnect sensor plug (RH front). • Measure resistance of sensor at sensor plug.	800 to 1400 ohms (0.8 to 1.4K ohms) Any other reading	▶ ▶	SERVICE or REPLACE cable harness (Circuit 514 or 516). REPLACE RH front wheel sensor.
A37 MEASURE MAIN VALVE CIRCUIT RESISTANCE • Turn ignition switch OFF. • Set multi-meter to read resistance. • Measure the resistance between Breakout box Pins 11 and 29.	2 to 5 ohms Any other reading	▶ ▶	GO to Step A39. GO to Step A38.
A38 MEASURE MAIN VALVE RESISTANCE • Disconnect main valve 2-pin plug. • Measure resistance between the main valve electrical Pins 1 and 2.	2 to 5.5 ohms Any other reading	▶ ▶	REPLACE or SERVICE cable harness (Circuit 430E or 493). REPLACE actuation assembly.
A39 CHECK VALVE BLOCK GROUND CIRCUIT • Measure resistance between breakout box Pins 11 and 40. • Is resistance less than 2 ohms?	Yes No	▶ ▶	GO to Step A42. GO to Step A40.

Fig. 32   Test A, warning lamp On (Part 11 of 18). Mark VII & 1992 Cougar/Thunderbird

TEST STEP	RESULT	▶	ACTION TO TAKE
A40 TEST VALVE PLUG PIN NO. 7			
• Disconnect valve block 7-pin plug. • Measure resistance between valve block electrical Pin 7 and valve block body.	Less than 2 ohms	▶	SERVICE or REPLACE cable harness (Circuit 685).
	Greater than 2 ohms	▶	GO to Step A41.
A41 CHECK VALVE BLOCK GROUND WIRE			
• Remove negative (-) ground strap from battery. • Check for continuity between valve block and body ground. • Is good continuity present?	Yes	▶	REPLACE valve block unit (internal ground concern).
	No	▶	SERVICE or REPLACE actuation assembly ground strap (Circuit 430G).
A42 MEASURE RH FRONT INLET VALVE CIRCUIT RESISTANCE			
• Measure resistance between breakout box Pins 11 and 32.	5 to 8 ohms	▶	GO to Step A44.
	Any other reading	▶	GO to Step A40.
A43 MEASURE RH FRONT INLET VALVE RESISTANCE			
• Disconnect valve block 7-pin plug. • Measure resistance between valve block electrical Pin 7 and 1.	5 to 8 ohms	▶	SERVICE or REPLACE cable harness (Circuit 510).
	Any other reading	▶	REPLACE solenoid valve block unit. CONNECT 7-pin plug.

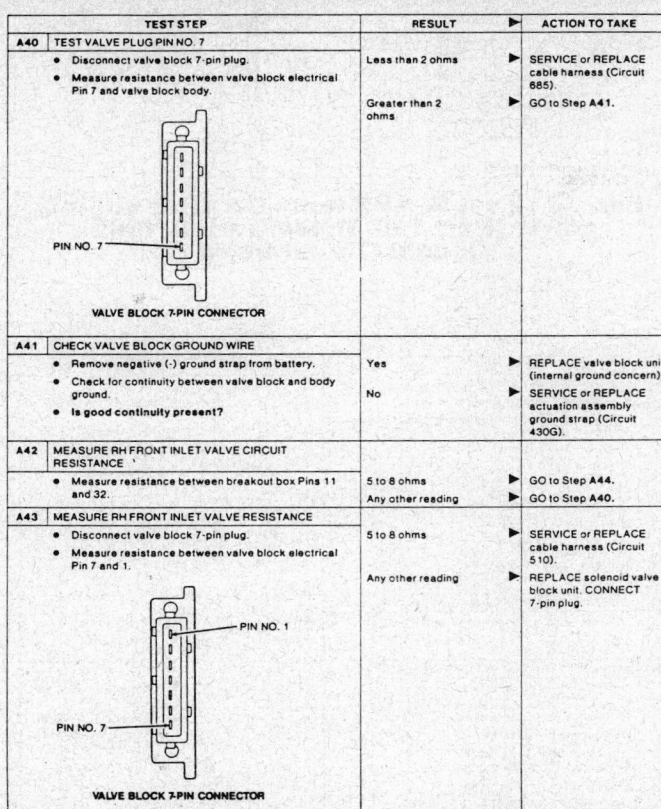

Fig. 32   Test A, warning lamp On (Part 12 of 18). Mark VII & 1992 Cougar/Thunderbird

TEST STEP	RESULT	▶	ACTION TO TAKE
A44 MEASURE REAR INLET VALVE CIRCUIT RESISTANCE			
• Measure resistance between Breakout box Pins 11 and 30.	5 to 8 ohms	▶	GO to Step A46.
	Any other reading	▶	GO to Step A45.
A45 MEASURE REAR INLET VALVE RESISTANCE			
• Disconnect valve block 7-pin plug. • Measure resistance between valve block electrical Pins 7 and 3.	5 to 8 ohms	▶	SERVICE or REPLACE cable harness (Circuit 496).
	Any other reading	▶	REPLACE valve block unit. CONNECT 7-pin plug.
A46 MEASURE LH FRONT INLET VALVE CIRCUIT RESISTANCE			
• Measure resistance between Breakout box Pins 11 and 31.	5 to 8 ohms	▶	GO to Step A48.
	Any other reading	▶	GO to Step A47.
A47 MEASURE LH FRONT INLET VALVE RESISTANCE			
• Disconnect valve block 7-pin plug. • Measure resistance between valve block electrical Pins 7 and 6.	5 to 8 ohms	▶	SERVICE or REPLACE cable harness (Circuit 495).
	Any other reading	▶	REPLACE valve block unit. CONNECT 7-pin plug.
A48 MEASURE REAR OUTLET VALVE CIRCUIT RESISTANCE			
• Measure resistance between Breakout box Pins 11 and 12.	3 to 6 ohms	▶	GO to Step A50.
	Any other reading	▶	GO to Step A49.

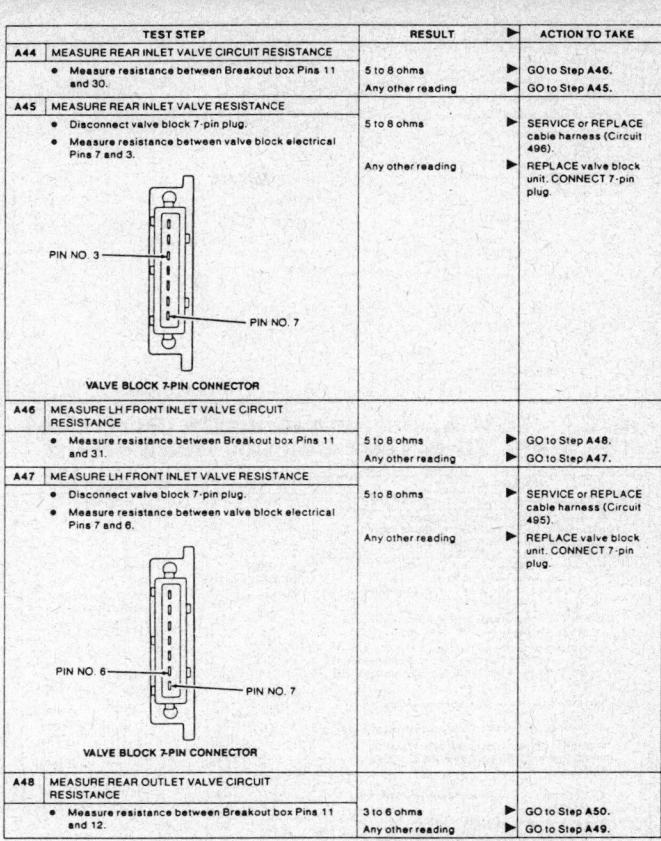

Fig. 32   Test A, warning lamp On (Part 13 of 18). Mark VII & 1992 Cougar/Thunderbird

TEST STEP	RESULT	▶	ACTION TO TAKE
A49 MEASURE REAR OUTLET VALVE RESISTANCE			
• Disconnect valve block 7-pin plug. • Measure resistance between valve block electrical Pins 7 and 4.	3 to 6 ohms	▶	SERVICE or REPLACE cable harness (Circuit 499).
	Any other reading	▶	REPLACE valve block unit. CONNECT 7-pin plug.
A50 MEASURE LH FRONT OUTLET VALVE CIRCUIT RESISTANCE			
• Measure resistance between Breakout box Pins 11 and 14.	3 to 6 ohms	▶	GO to Step A52.
	Any other reading	▶	GO to Step A51.
A51 MEASURE LH FRONT OUTLET VALVE RESISTANCE			
• Disconnect valve block 7-pin plug. • Measure resistance between valve block electrical Pins 7 and 5.	3 to 6 ohms	▶	SERVICE or REPLACE cable harness (Circuit 498).
	Any other reading	▶	REPLACE valve block unit. CONNECT 7-pin plug.
A52 MEASURE RH FRONT OUTLET VALVE CIRCUIT RESISTANCE			
• Measure resistance between Breakout box Pins 11 and 13.	3 to 6 ohms	▶	GO to Step A54.
	Any other reading	▶	GO to Step A53.

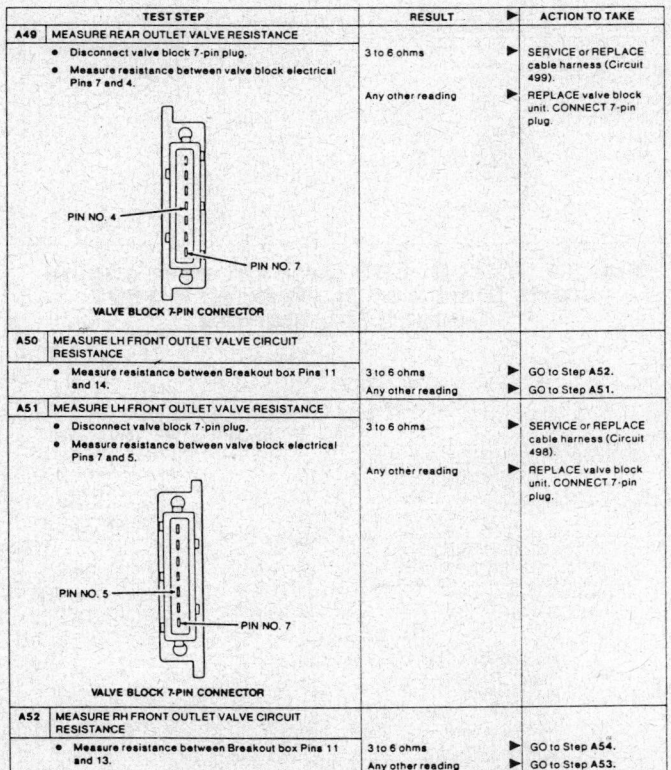

Fig. 32   Test A, warning lamp On (Part 14 of 18). Mark VII & 1992 Cougar/Thunderbird

TEST STEP	RESULT	▶	ACTION TO TAKE
A53 MEASURE RH FRONT OUTLET VALVE RESISTANCE			
• Disconnect valve block 7-pin plug. • Measure resistance between valve block electrical Pins 7 and 2.	3 to 6 ohms	▶	SERVICE or REPLACE cable harness (Circuit 497).
	Any other reading	▶	REPLACE valve block unit. CONNECT 7-pin plug.
A54 CHECK PWS BRAKELAMP CIRCUIT (NO SYSTEM PRESSURE)			
• Vehicle must be cooled to room temperature. • Discharge the brake system as follows: — Turn ignition switch OFF. — Pump brake pedal at least 20 times until you feel the pedal become hard. • Disconnect pressure warning switch 5-pin plug. • Check continuity between pressure warning switch electrical Pins 1 and 2. • Is continuity present?	Yes	▶	GO to Step A55.
	No	▶	REPLACE pressure warning switch and pump motor relay.

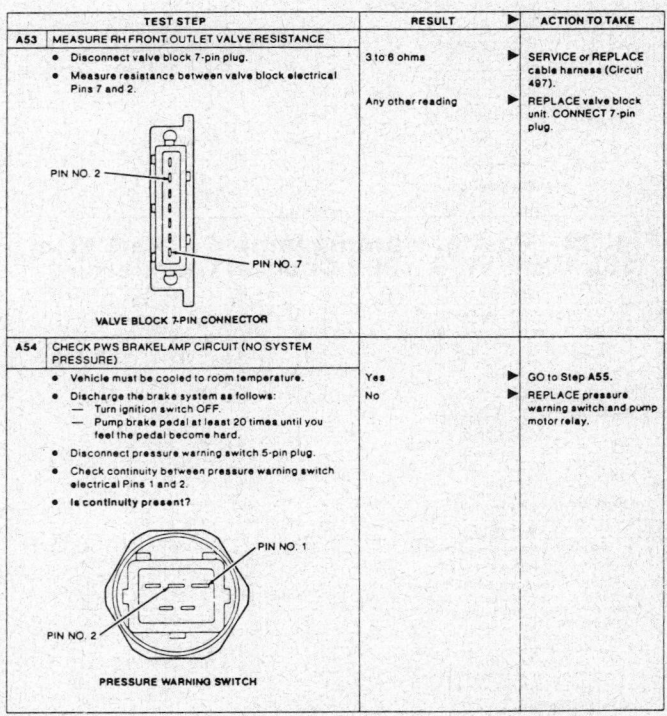

Fig. 32   Test A, warning lamp On (Part 15 of 18). Mark VII & 1992 Cougar/Thunderbird

TEST STEP	RESULT	▶	ACTION TO TAKE
A55 CHECK PWS BRAKELAMP CIRCUIT (WITH SYSTEM PRESSURE)			
• Reconnect pressure warning switch 5-pin plug. • Turn ignition switch ON. • When pump motor stops, turn ignition switch OFF. • Disconnect pressure warning switch 5-pin plug again. • Check for continuity between pressure warning switch electrical Pins 1 and 2. • Is continuity present?	Yes No	▶ ▶	REPLACE pressure warning switch and pump motor relay. GO to Step A56.

PIN NO. 1

PIN NO. 2

PRESSURE WARNING SWITCH

Fig. 32   Test A, warning lamp On (Part 16 of 18). Mark VII & 1992 Cougar/Thunderbird

TEST STEP	RESULT	▶	ACTION TO TAKE
A56 CHECK PWS BRAKELAMP CIRCUIT THRESHOLD			
WARNING: BEFORE DISCONNECTING ANY HYDRAULIC LINES, YOU MUST ENSURE THAT THE PRESSURE SYSTEM IS DISCHARGED. • Discharge the brake system as follows: — Turn ignition switch OFF. — Pump brake pedal at least 20 times until you feel it become hard. • Remove high pressure banjo bolt below brake fluid reservoir on brake booster. • Disconnect quick-connect nipple from Anti-Lock Pressure Gauge (Tool T85P-20215-A, or equivalent) and install nipple in place of the high pressure banjo bolt. NOTE: Be sure O-rings are installed correctly. • Connect Anti-Lock Pressure Gauge to gauge nipple. **WARNING: DO NOT DISCONNECT ANTI-LOCK PRESSURE GAUGE WHILE SYSTEM IS UNDER PRESSURE.** • Reconnect pressure warning switch (PWS) 5-pin connector. • Turn ignition switch ON. • When pump motor stops, disconnect pressure warning switch (PWS) 5-pin plug. • Lower hydraulic accumulator pressure by slowly pumping the brake pedal until you have continuity between pressure warning switch electrical Pins 1 and 2. • Observe the hydraulic pressure gauge when continuity is reached. • If you missed the reading or want to reverify the reading: — Reconnect the 5-pin plug. — Turn the ignition switch ON until the pump stops. — Disconnect the 5-pin plug and reverify the readings.	100-110 Bar (1,450-1,595 psi) Any other reading	▶ ▶	GO to Step A57. REPLACE pressure warning switch and pump motor relay.

PIN NO. 1

PIN NO. 2

PRESSURE WARNING SWITCH

Fig. 32   Test A, warning lamp On (Part 17 of 18). Mark VII & 1992 Cougar/Thunderbird

TEST STEP	RESULT	▶	ACTION TO TAKE
A57 CHECK PWS HARNESS GROUND			
• Check for continuity between pressure warning switch 5-pin plug Pin 1 and body ground (harness side). • Is continuity present?	Yes No	▶ ▶	GO to Step A58. SERVICE or REPLACE cable harness (Circuit 430K).

PIN NO. 1

PRESSURE WARNING SWITCH CONNECTOR

TEST STEP	RESULT	▶	ACTION TO TAKE
A58 REVERIFY SYSTEM CONDITION			
• Reconnect all electrical connections. • Re-install high pressure banjo bolt. **WARNING: BEFORE DISCONNECTING ANY HYDRAULIC LINES, YOU MUST ENSURE THAT THE BRAKE HYDRAULIC PRESSURE SYSTEM IS DISCHARGED.** • Discharge the brake system as follows: — Turn ignition switch OFF. — Pump brake pedal at least 20 times until you feel the pedal become hard. • Reverify condition. • Are conditions still present?	No Yes	▶ ▶	FAULT may have been a loose electrical connection. REPLACE electronic control module.

Fig. 32   Test A, warning lamp On (Part 18 of 18). Mark VII & 1992 Cougar/Thunderbird

TEST STEP	RESULT	▶	ACTION TO TAKE
B1 CHECK CONTINUITY OF CIRCUIT 523 AND 524			
• Turn ignition switch OFF. • Disconnect 32-pin plug from controller. • Connect EEC-IV Breakout Box T83L-50-EEC-IV with Anti-Lock Test Adapter T87P-50-ALA to the Anti-Lock 32-pin plug wiring harness. • Check continuity between Breakout box Pins 40 and 6. • Is continuity present?	Yes No	▶ ▶	GO to Step B2. GO to Step B3.

Fig. 33   Test B, ABS lamp On after engine starts (Part 1 of 3). Mark VII & 1992 Cougar/Thunderbird

TEST STEP	RESULT	▶	ACTION TO TAKE
B2 CHECK CONTINUITY OF RH REAR SENSOR			
• Disconnect wheel sensor plug (RH rear). • Check for continuity between each sensor plug pin (sensor side) and vehicle ground. • Is continuity present?	Yes No	▶ ▶	REPLACE sensor (RH rear). REPLACE or SERVICE cable harness (523 or 524). RECONNECT sensor plug.

RH REAR SENSOR

TEST STEP	RESULT	▶	ACTION TO TAKE
B3 CHECK CONTINUITY OF CIRCUITS 521 AND 522			
• Check for continuity between Breakout box Pins 40 and 5. • Is continuity present?	Yes No	▶ ▶	GO to Step B4. GO to Step B5.
B4 CHECK CONTINUITY OF LH FRONT SENSOR			
• Disconnect wheel sensor plug (LH front). • Check for continuity between each sensor plug pin (sensor side) and vehicle ground. • Is continuity present?	Yes No	▶ ▶	REPLACE sensor (LH front). REPLACE or SERVICE cable harness (521 or 522). CONNECT sensor plug.

LH FRONT SENSOR

TEST STEP	RESULT	▶	ACTION TO TAKE
B5 CHECK CONTINUITY OF CIRCUITS 518 AND 519			
• Check for continuity between Breakout box Pins 40 and 4. • Is continuity present?	Yes No	▶ ▶	GO to Step B6. GO to Step B7.
B6 CHECK CONTINUITY OF LH REAR SENSOR			
• Disconnect sensor plug (LH rear). • Check for continuity between each sensor plug pin (sensor side) and vehicle ground. • Is continuity present?	Yes No	▶ ▶	REPLACE sensor (LH rear). REPLACE or SERVICE cable harness (518 or 519). CONNECT sensor plug.

LH REAR SENSOR

Fig. 33   Test B, ABS lamp On after engine starts (Part 2 of 3). Mark VII & 1992 Cougar/Thunderbird

TEST STEP	RESULT	▶	ACTION TO TAKE
B7 CHECK CONTINUITY OF CIRCUITS 514 AND 516			
• Check for continuity between Breakout Box Pins 40 and 3. • Is continuity present?	Yes No	▶ ▶	GO to Step B8. Test COMPLETE. If Anti-Lock lamp pattern REMAINS, REPEAT Test B.
B8 CHECK CONTINUITY OF RH FRONT SENSOR			
• Disconnect wheel sensor plug (RH front). • Check for continuity between each sensor plug pin (sensor side) and vehicle ground. • Is continuity present?	Yes No	▶ ▶	REPLACE RH front sensor. REPLACE or SERVICE cable harness (514 or 516). CONNECT sensor plug.

RH FRONT SENSOR

Fig. 33   Test B, ABS lamp On after engine starts (Part 3 of 3). Mark VII & 1992 Cougar/Thunderbird

TEST STEP		RESULT	▶	ACTION TO TAKE
C1	MEASURE RH REAR SENSOR CIRCUIT RESISTANCE			
	• Turn ignition switch OFF.	800 to 1400 ohms	▶	GO to Step C3.
	• Disconnect 32-pin plug from electronic controller.	Any other reading	▶	GO to Step C2.
	• Connect EEC-IV Breakout Box T83L-50-EEC-IV with Anti-Lock Test Adapter T87P-50-ALA or equivalent to the Anti-Lock 32-pin plug wiring harness.			
	• Set multi-meter to read resistance.			
	• Measure resistance between Breakout box Pins 6 and 23.			
C2	MEASURE RH REAR SENSOR RESISTANCE			
	• Disconnect sensor plug (RH rear).	800 to 1400 ohms	▶	SERVICE or REPLACE cable harness (Circuit 523 or 524).
	• Set multi-meter to read resistance.			
	• Measure resistance of sensor at sensor plug.	Any other reading	▶	REPLACE RH rear wheel sensor.

RH REAR SENSOR

Fig. 34 Test C, warning lamp On after vehicle moves/or false cycling of system (Part 1 of 3). Mark VII & 1992 Cougar/Thunderbird

TEST STEP		RESULT	▶	ACTION TO TAKE
C9	CHECK RH REAR SENSOR			
	• Turn ignition switch OFF.	Between 0.05 and 0.70 volts AC	▶	GO to Step C10.
	• Place vehicle on hoist and raise wheels clear of ground.	Less than 0.05 or more than 0.70 volts AC	▶	CHECK sensor mounting, air gap, or toothed wheel mounting. CORRECT as required.
	• Set multi-meter on voltage range (2V-AC).			
	• Measure voltage between Breakout Box Pins 6 and 23 while spinning RH rear wheel at approximately 1 revolution per second.			
C10	CHECK LH FRONT SENSOR			
	• Measure voltage between Breakout Box Pins 5 and 22 while spinning LH front wheel at approximately 1 revolution per second.	Between 0.05 and 0.70 volts AC	▶	GO to Step C11.
		Less than 0.05 or more than 0.70 volts AC	▶	CHECK sensor mounting, air gap, or toothed wheel mounting. CORRECT as required.
C11	CHECK LH REAR SENSOR			
	• Measure voltage between Breakout Box Pins 4 and 21 while spinning LH rear wheel at approximately 1 revolution per second.	Between 0.05 and 0.70 volts AC	▶	GO to Step C12.
		Less than 0.05 or more than 0.07 volts AC	▶	CHECK wheel sensor mounting, air gap, or toothed wheel mounting. CORRECT as required.
C12	CHECK RH FRONT SENSOR			
	• Measure voltage between Breakout box Pins 3 and 20 while spinning RH front wheel at approximately 1 revolution per second.	Between 0.05 and 0.70 volts AC	▶	GO to Step C13.
		Less than 0.05 or more than 0.70 volts AC	▶	CHECK wheel sensor mounting, air gap, or toothed wheel mounting. CORRECT as required.
C13	CHECK FRONT WHEEL BEARINGS			
	• Check front wheel bearing end play.	Yes	▶	ADJUST bearings or REPLACE damaged parts.
	• Inspect each toothed sensor ring visually for damaged teeth.			
	• Were loose or damaged parts found?	No	▶	REVERIFY condition.

Fig. 34 Test C, warning lamp On after vehicle moves/or false cycling of system (Part 3 of 3). Mark VII & 1992 Cougar/Thunderbird

TEST STEP		RESULT	▶	ACTION TO TAKE
D1	CHECK PUMP MOTOR OPERATION			
	• Turn ignition OFF.	Yes	▶	GO to D15.
	• Pump brake pedal at least 20 times until it becomes hard.	No	▶	GO to D2.
	• Turn ignition switch ON.			
	• Pump motor should run.			
	• Does pump operate?			
	NOTE: If pump motor is allowed to run continuously for approximately 20 minutes, a thermal safety switch (inside motor) will shut off motor. A 2-to-10 minute cool-down period is typical before normal operation can resume.			
D2	PUMP MOTOR UNIT			
	• Disconnect 4-pin plug on pump motor unit.	Yes	▶	GO to D15.
	• Turn ignition switch ON.	No	▶	GO to D3.
	• Set multi-meter on 20 volt DC.			
	• Connect meter to the 4-pin plug on the harness side. (Use one negative and one positive pin).			
	• Observe voltmeter.			
	• Is voltage more than 10 volts DC?			

4-PIN MOTOR CONNECTOR

Fig. 35 Test D, warning lamp & brake warning lamp On and/or pump motor runs more than 60 seconds (Part 1 of 9). Mark VII & 1992 Cougar/Thunderbird

TEST STEP		RESULT	▶	ACTION TO TAKE
C3	MEASURE LH FRONT SENSOR CIRCUIT RESISTANCE			
	• Measure resistance between Breakout Box Pins 5 and 22	800 to 1400 ohms	▶	GO to Step C5.
		Any other reading	▶	GO to Step C4.
C4	MEASURE LH FRONT SENSOR RESISTANCE			
	• Disconnect wheel sensor plug (LH front).	800 to 1400 ohms	▶	SERVICE or REPLACE cable harness (Circuit 521 or 522).
	• Measure resistance of sensor at sensor plug.	Any other reading	▶	REPLACE LH front wheel sensor.

LH FRONT SENSOR

TEST STEP		RESULT	▶	ACTION TO TAKE
C5	MEASURE LH REAR SENSOR CIRCUIT RESISTANCE			
	• Measure resistance between Breakout Box Pins 4 and 21.	800 to 1400 ohms	▶	GO to Step C7.
		Any other reading	▶	GO to Step C6.
C6	MEASURE LH REAR SENSOR RESISTANCE			
	• Disconnect sensor plug (LH rear).	800 to 1400 ohms	▶	SERVICE or REPLACE cable harness (Circuit 518 or 519).
	• Measure resistance of sensor at left rear sensor plug.	Any other reading	▶	REPLACE LH rear wheel sensor.

LH REAR SENSOR

TEST STEP		RESULT	▶	ACTION TO TAKE
C7	MEASURE RH FRONT SENSOR CIRCUIT RESISTANCE			
	• Measure resistance between Breakout box Pin 3 and 20.	800 to 1400 ohms	▶	GO to Step C9.
		Any other reading	▶	GO to Step C8.
C8	MEASURE RH FRONT SENSOR RESISTANCE			
	• Disconnect sensor plug (RH front).	800 to 1400 ohms	▶	SERVICE or REPLACE cable harness (Circuit 514 or 516).
	• Measure resistance of sensor at sensor plug.	Any other reading	▶	REPLACE RH front wheel sensor.

RH FRONT SENSOR

Fig. 34 Test C, warning lamp On after vehicle moves/or false cycling of system (Part 2 of 3). Mark VII & 1992 Cougar/Thunderbird

TEST STEP		RESULT	▶	ACTION TO TAKE
D3	CHECK CONTINUITY CIRCUITS 538A AND 538B			
	• Disconnect pump motor relay.	Yes	▶	GO to D4.
	• Check for continuity between motor relay socket Pin 3 (harness side) and each positive pin of the 4-pin motor connector (harness side).	No	▶	SERVICE Circuits 538A, 538B and 538C.
	• Is continuity present?			

PIN NO. 3

MOTOR RELAY CONNECTOR

POSITIVE PIN
POSITIVE PIN

4-PIN MOTOR CONNECTOR

TEST STEP		RESULT	▶	ACTION TO TAKE
D4	CHECK CONTINUITY CIRCUITS 430D AND 430F			
	• Check for continuity between ground and each negative pin of 4-pin motor connector (harness side).	Yes	▶	GO to D5.
		No	▶	SERVICE or REPLACE Circuit 430D or 430F.
	• Is continuity present?			

NEGATIVE PIN
NEGATIVE PIN

4-PIN MOTOR CONNECTOR

Fig. 35 Test D, warning lamp & brake warning lamp On and/or pump motor runs more than 60 seconds (Part 2 of 9). Mark VII & 1992 Cougar/Thunderbird

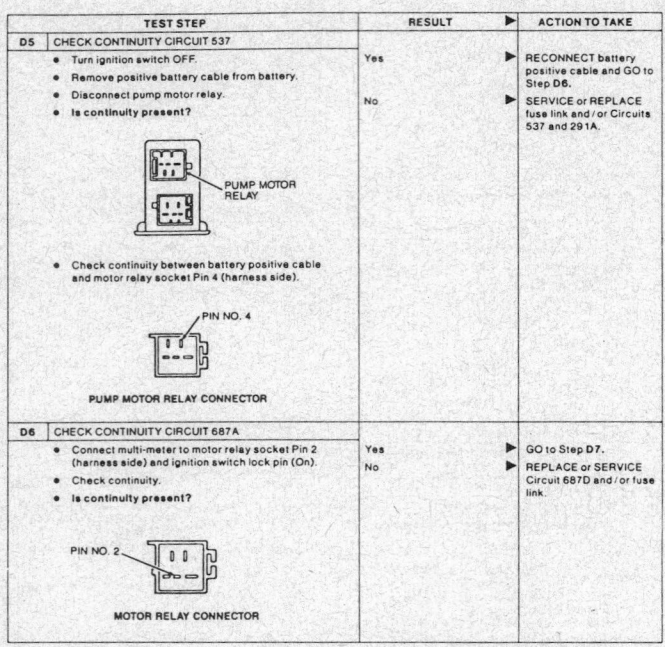

TEST STEP	RESULT	▶	ACTION TO TAKE
D5 CHECK CONTINUITY CIRCUIT 537			
• Turn ignition switch OFF. • Remove positive battery cable from battery. • Disconnect pump motor relay. • Is continuity present?	Yes No	▶ ▶	RECONNECT battery positive cable and GO to Step **D6**. SERVICE or REPLACE fuse link and / or Circuits 537 and 291A.
• Check continuity between battery positive cable and motor relay socket Pin 4 (harness side).			
D6 CHECK CONTINUITY CIRCUIT 687A			
• Connect multi-meter to motor relay socket Pin 2 (harness side) and ignition switch lock pin (On). • Check continuity. • Is continuity present?	Yes No	▶ ▶	GO to Step **D7**. REPLACE or SERVICE Circuit 687D and / or fuse link.

Fig. 35 Test D, warning lamp & brake warning lamp On and/or pump motor runs more than 60 seconds (Part 3 of 9). Mark VII & 1992 Cougar/Thunderbird

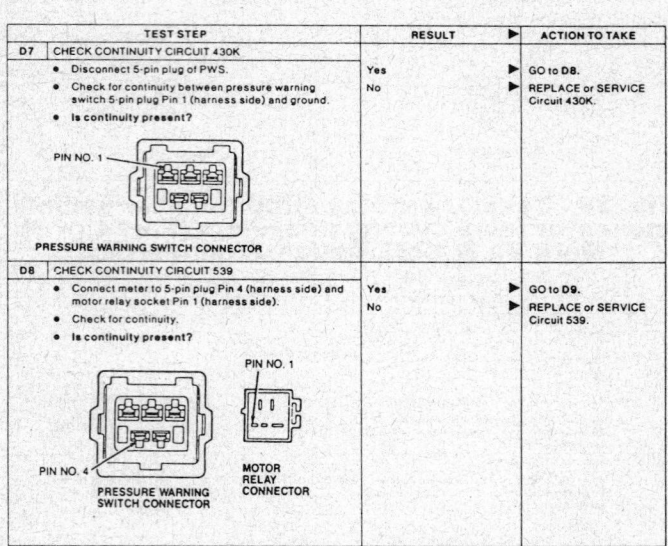

TEST STEP	RESULT	▶	ACTION TO TAKE
D7 CHECK CONTINUITY CIRCUIT 430K			
• Disconnect 5-pin plug of PWS. • Check for continuity between pressure warning switch 5-pin plug Pin 1 (harness side) and ground. • Is continuity present?	Yes No	▶ ▶	GO to **D8**. REPLACE or SERVICE Circuit 430K.
D8 CHECK CONTINUITY CIRCUIT 539			
• Connect meter to 5-pin plug Pin 4 (harness side) and motor relay socket Pin 1 (harness side). • Check for continuity. • Is continuity present?	Yes No	▶ ▶	GO to **D9**. REPLACE or SERVICE Circuit 539.

Fig. 35 Test D, warning lamp & brake warning lamp On and/or pump motor runs more than 60 seconds (Part 4 of 9). Mark VII & 1992 Cougar/Thunderbird

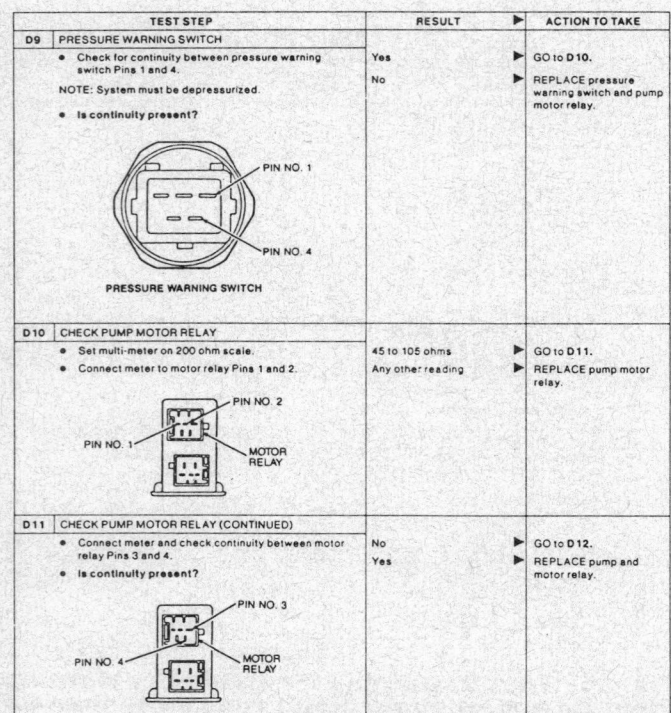

TEST STEP	RESULT	▶	ACTION TO TAKE
D9 PRESSURE WARNING SWITCH			
• Check for continuity between pressure warning switch Pins 1 and 4. NOTE: System must be depressurized. • Is continuity present?	Yes No	▶ ▶	GO to **D10**. REPLACE pressure warning switch and pump motor relay.
D10 CHECK PUMP MOTOR RELAY			
• Set multi-meter on 200 ohm scale. • Connect meter to motor relay Pins 1 and 2.	45 to 105 ohms Any other reading	▶ ▶	GO to **D11**. REPLACE pump motor relay.
D11 CHECK PUMP MOTOR RELAY (CONTINUED)			
• Connect meter and check continuity between motor relay Pins 3 and 4. • Is continuity present?	No Yes	▶ ▶	GO to **D12**. REPLACE pump and motor relay.

Fig. 35 Test D, warning lamp & brake warning lamp On and/or pump motor runs more than 60 seconds (Part 5 of 9). Mark VII & 1992 Cougar/Thunderbird

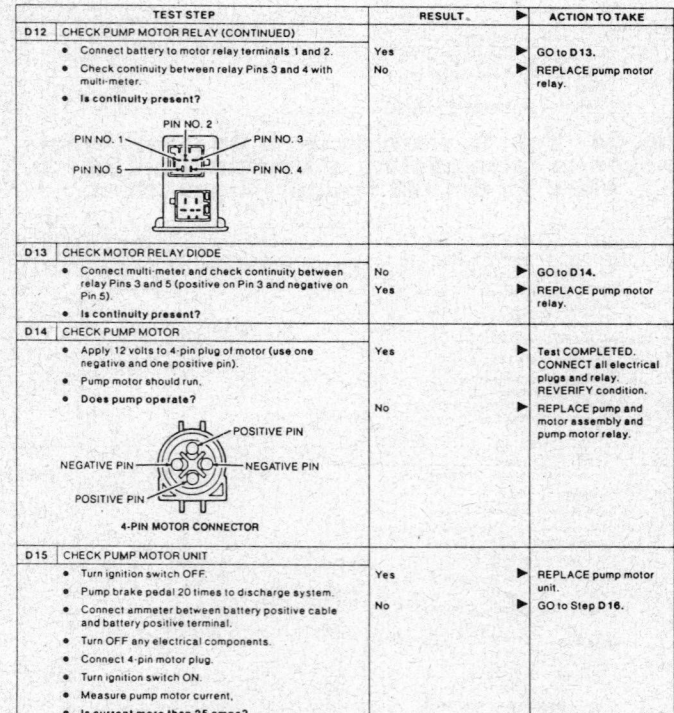

TEST STEP	RESULT	▶	ACTION TO TAKE
D12 CHECK PUMP MOTOR RELAY (CONTINUED)			
• Connect battery to motor relay terminals 1 and 2. • Check continuity between relay Pins 3 and 4 with multi-meter. • Is continuity present?	Yes No	▶ ▶	GO to **D13**. REPLACE pump motor relay.
D13 CHECK MOTOR RELAY DIODE			
• Connect multi-meter and check continuity between relay Pins 3 and 5 (positive on Pin 3 and negative on Pin 5). • Is continuity present?	No Yes	▶ ▶	GO to **D14**. REPLACE pump motor relay.
D14 CHECK PUMP MOTOR			
• Apply 12 volts to 4-pin plug of motor (use one negative and one positive pin). • Pump motor should run. • Does pump operate?	Yes No	▶ ▶	Test COMPLETED. CONNECT all electrical plugs and relay. REVERIFY condition. REPLACE pump and motor assembly and pump motor relay.
D15 CHECK PUMP MOTOR UNIT			
• Turn ignition switch OFF. • Pump brake pedal 20 times to discharge system. • Connect ammeter between battery positive cable and battery positive terminal. • Turn OFF any electrical components. • Connect 4-pin motor plug. • Turn ignition switch ON. • Measure pump motor current. • Is current more than 25 amps?	Yes No	▶ ▶	REPLACE pump motor unit. GO to Step **D16**.

Fig. 35 Test D, warning lamp & brake warning lamp On and/or pump motor runs more than 60 seconds (Part 6 of 9). Mark VII & 1992 Cougar/Thunderbird

TEST STEP	RESULT	▶	ACTION TO TAKE
D16 CHECK PUMP MOTOR • Turn ignition switch OFF. • Pump brake pedal at least 20 times, until brake pedal becomes hard. • Turn ignition switch ON. • Measure time pump takes to shut OFF.	Under 60 seconds	▶	GO to Step D17.
	Over 60 seconds (or motor never turns on)	▶	CHECK for corroded connections at: —Motor 4-pin plug. —Body ground (Circuit 430F and D). —Motor relay Pin 4 socket (Circuit 537). —Battery to Pin 4. GO to D17.
D17 CHECK LOW PRESSURE FLOW • Turn ignition switch OFF. • Disconnect low pressure hose from pump and allow fluid to flow into a suitable container. • Is flow restricted? NOTE: Discard fluid after test.	No	▶	CONNECT low pressure hose. FILL reservoir to MAX. GO to D18.
	Yes	▶	SERVICE or REPLACE reservoir and/or low pressure hose as required.
D18 CHECK VOLTAGE TO PUMP MOTOR • Turn ignition switch OFF. • Pump brake pedal to discharge pressure system. • Set meter to 20 Volts DC range. • Connect voltmeter in parallel at 4-pin motor plug. • Turn ignition switch ON. • With pump running, is voltage over 8 volts DC?	Yes	▶	GO to D19.
	No	▶	CHECK Circuits 430D, 430F, 538A, 538B, Pin 4 to battery and relay Pins 3 and 4 for voltage drop. SERVICE or REPLACE as necessary.

POSITIVE PIN — NEGATIVE PIN — NEGATIVE PIN — POSITIVE PIN

4-PIN MOTOR CONNECTOR

Fig. 35 Test D, warning lamp & brake warning lamp On and/or pump motor runs more than 60 seconds (Part 7 of 9). Mark VII & 1992 Cougar/Thunderbird

TEST STEP	RESULT	▶	ACTION TO TAKE
D19 ACCUMULATOR PRE-CHARGE • Vehicle must be cooled to room temperature. WARNING: BEFORE DISCONNECTING ANY HYDRAULIC LINES, YOU MUST ENSURE THAT THE PRESSURE SYSTEM IS DISCHARGED. • To discharge hydraulic accumulator pressure, turn ignition OFF, pump brake pedal at least 20 times until you feel it become hard. • Remove high pressure banjo bolt below brake fluid reservoir on brake booster. • Install Anti-Lock Pressure Gauge Tool T85P-20215-A or equivalent. • Turn ignition switch ON and read accumulator precharge pressure. (Gauge needle will spring to this point.) NOTE: Gauge needle reading should spring to 40-90 bar (600-1325 psi) and climb to 16,203-19306 kPa bar (2350-2800 psi). • If reading was missed, discharge accumulator as described and repeat ignition ON sequence.	4137-9135 kPa (600-1325 psi)	▶	GO to D20.
	Under 4137 kPa (600 psi)	▶	REPLACE accumulator. NOTE: Measure nipple length to determine correct service replacement accumulator.
	Over 9135 kPa (1325 psi)	▶	REPLACE accumulator. NOTE: Measure nipple length to determine correct service replacement accumulator.
D20 CHECK HYDRAULIC ACTUATION UNIT • Turn ignition switch ON; wait until pump motor stops. Wait 3 more minutes to stabilize gauge pressure. • Read pressure gauge. • Wait 5 minutes and read pressure gauge again to determine the pressure loss over those 5 minutes.	Pressure loss less than 10 bar (140 psi) on gauge	▶	GO to Step D22.
	More than 10 bar (140 psi)	▶	CHECK for external leakage at actuation assembly and SERVICE. If no external leakage is found, GO to Step D21.
D21 CHECK FOR HYDRAULIC LEAKS • Check for brake fluid leaks in the following areas: — Brake lines and calipers. — High and low pressure hoses on actuation assembly. — Reservoir seals and seams. — Accumulator. • Were any leaks found? NOTE: A small amount of leakage from pressure warning switch is allowable. If any leakage is found below switch, wipe off excess fluid and check for excessive leakage.	No	▶	GO to D22.
	Yes	▶	SERVICE or REPLACE components. CHECK system operation.
D22 CHECK PUMP PRESSURE • With the pressure gauge still attached and ignition switch still ON, pump brake pedal to decrease pressure until pump motor restarts.	13100-15169 kPa (1900-2200 psi) when pump starts	▶	GO to Step D23.
	Less than or more than 13100-15169 kPa (1900-2200 psi)	▶	REPLACE pressure warning switch and pump motor relay.

Fig. 35 Test D, warning lamp & brake warning lamp On and/or pump motor runs more than 60 seconds (Part 8 of 9). Mark VII & 1992 Cougar/Thunderbird

TEST STEP	RESULT	▶	ACTION TO TAKE
D23 CHECK PRESSURE WARNING SWITCH • With the ignition switch still ON and the pressure gauge connected, observe the pressure when the pump motor stops running.	16203 kPa (2350-2800 psi) when pump motor stops	▶	If pump motor takes longer than 60 seconds to reach 16203 kPa (2350-2800 psi), REPLACE pump motor assembly. REVERIFY condition.
	Less than 16203 kPa (2350 psi) or over 19306 kPa (2800 psi)	▶	REPLACE pressure warning switch and pump motor relay.

Fig. 35 Test D, warning lamp & brake warning lamp On and/or pump motor runs more than 60 seconds (Part 9 of 9). Mark VII & 1992 Cougar/Thunderbird

TEST STEP	RESULT	▶	ACTION TO TAKE
E1 CHECK FLI AND PWS CIRCUIT • Disconnect 32-pin plug from electronic controller. • Connect EEC-IV Breakout box T83L-50-EEC-IV with Anti-Lock Test Adapter T87P-50-ALA or equivalent to the Anti-Lock 32-pin plug wiring harness. • Turn ignition switch ON. • Set multi-meter to read resistance. • Measure the resistance between Breakout box Pins 25 and 27. • Is resistance less than 5 ohms?	Yes	▶	GO to Step E2.
	No	▶	GO to Step E2.
E2 CHECK FLI ANTI-LOCK WARNING CIRCUIT • Disconnect 5-pin plug on reservoir fluid level indicator (FLI). • Measure resistance between fluid level indicator electrical Pins 1 and 2 (with brake fluid at maximum fluid level). • Is resistance less than 2 ohms?	Yes	▶	GO to Step E3.
	No	▶	REPLACE fluid level indicator.

PIN NO. 2 — PIN NO. 4
PIN NO. 1 — PIN NO. 3 — PIN NO. 5

FLUID LEVER INDICATOR CONNECTOR

Fig. 36 Test E, warning lamp intermittently On (Part 1 of 5). Mark VII & 1992 Cougar/Thunderbird

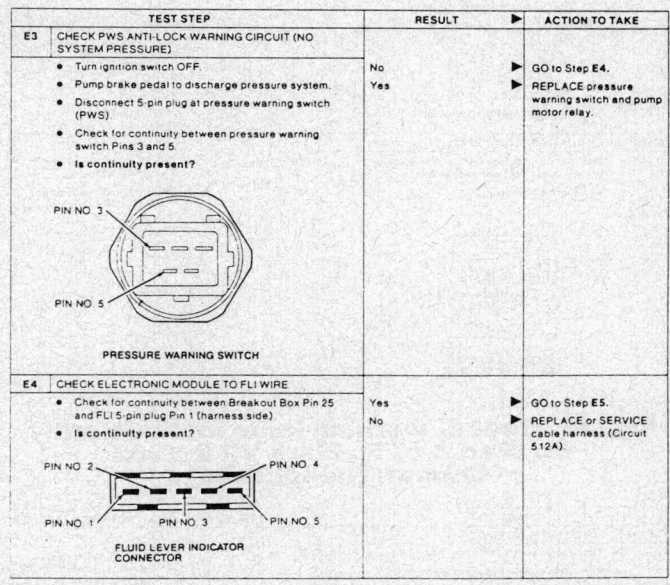

TEST STEP	RESULT	▶	ACTION TO TAKE
E3 CHECK PWS ANTI-LOCK WARNING CIRCUIT (NO SYSTEM PRESSURE) • Turn ignition switch OFF. • Pump brake pedal to discharge pressure system. • Disconnect 5-pin plug at pressure warning switch (PWS). • Check for continuity between pressure warning switch Pins 3 and 5. • Is continuity present?	No	▶	GO to Step E4.
	Yes	▶	REPLACE pressure warning switch and pump motor relay.

PIN NO. 3
PIN NO. 5

PRESSURE WARNING SWITCH

TEST STEP	RESULT	▶	ACTION TO TAKE
E4 CHECK ELECTRONIC MODULE TO FLI WIRE • Check for continuity between Breakout Box Pin 25 and FLI 5-pin plug Pin 1 (harness side). • Is continuity present?	Yes	▶	GO to Step E5.
	No	▶	REPLACE or SERVICE cable harness (Circuit 512A).

PIN NO. 2 — PIN NO. 4
PIN NO. 1 — PIN NO. 3 — PIN NO. 5

FLUID LEVER INDICATOR CONNECTOR

Fig. 36 Test E, warning lamp intermittently On (Part 2 of 5). Mark VII & 1992 Cougar/Thunderbird

TEST STEP	RESULT	▶	ACTION TO TAKE
E5 CHECK FLI TO PWS WIRE			
• Check for continuity between 5-pin fluid level plug Pin 2 (harness side) and 5-Pin pressure warning switch plug Pin 3 (harness side).	Yes	▶	GO to Step E6.
	No	▶	SERVICE or REPLACE cable harness (Circuit 549A).
• Is continuity present?			
E6 CHECK PWS TO ELECTRONIC CONTROLLER WIRE			
• Check for continuity between 5-pin pressure warning switch plug Pin 5 (harness side) and Breakout Box Pin 27.	Yes	▶	TURN ignition OFF. CONNECT all electrical connections. REVERIFY condition.
• Is continuity present?	No	▶	SERVICE or REPLACE cable harness (Circuit 535A).
E7 CHECK ISOLATION TEST FLI AND PWS			
• Check for continuity between Breakout Box Pin 25 and body ground.	Yes	▶	GO to Step E8.
• Is continuity present?	No	▶	REVERIFY condition.

Fig. 36   Test E, warning lamp intermittently On (Part 3 of 5). Mark VII & 1992 Cougar/Thunderbird

TEST STEP	RESULT	▶	ACTION TO TAKE
E11 CHECK CONTINUITY OF PWS			
• Check for continuity from PWS 5-pin socket Pin 3 to body ground, and from Pin 5 to body ground.	Yes	▶	REPLACE pressure warning switch and pump motor relay.
• Is continuity present?	No	▶	GO to Step E12.
E12 CHECK CONTINUITY CIRCUIT 535			
• Check for continuity between 5-pin PWS plug (harness side) Pin 5 and body ground.	Yes	▶	SERVICE or REPLACE Circuit 535A.
• Is continuity present?	No	▶	CONNECT all plugs and REVERIFY condition.

Fig. 36   Test E, warning lamp intermittently On (Part 5 of 5). Mark VII & 1992 Cougar/Thunderbird

TEST STEP	RESULT	▶	ACTION TO TAKE
F1 CHECK BRAKE FLUID LEVEL			
• Turn ignition switch ON.	No	▶	CHECK system for external leaks. SERVICE as required.
• Pump brake pedal until pump motor starts.			
• When pump motor stops, check brake fluid level.	Yes	▶	GO to Step F2.
• Is fluid level normal?			

Fig. 37   Test F, brake warning lamp On w/ABS lamp Off, parking brake released & lining wear checked (Part 1 of 2). Mark VII & 1992 Cougar/Thunderbird

TEST STEP	RESULT	▶	ACTION TO TAKE
E8 CHECK CONTINUITY OF FLI SWITCH			
• Disconnect FLI plug and check for continuity between socket Pin 1 and Pins 3, 4, and 5 and Pin 2 and Pins 3, 4, and 5.	Yes	▶	REPLACE FLI.
	No	▶	GO to Step E9.
• Is continuity present?			
E9 CHECK CONTINUITY CIRCUIT 512			
• Check for continuity between FLI plug Pin 1 (harness side) and body ground.	Yes	▶	SERVICE or REPLACE Circuit 512A.
• Is continuity present?	No	▶	GO to Step E10.
E10 CHECK CONTINUITY CIRCUIT 549			
• Disconnect 5-pin plug from PWS. Check for continuity between FLI plug Pin 2 (harness side) and body ground.	Yes	▶	SERVICE or REPLACE Circuit 549A.
• Is continuity present?	No	▶	GO to Step E11.

Fig. 36   Test E, warning lamp intermittently On (Part 4 of 5). Mark VII & 1992 Cougar/Thunderbird

TEST STEP	RESULT	▶	ACTION TO TAKE
F2 CHECK CONTINUITY FLI SWITCH			
• Disconnect 5-pin plug on fluid reservoir cap.	Yes	▶	GO to Step F3.
• Set multi-meter on 200 ohm range. Connect to reservoir warning cap Pins 3 and 4.	No	▶	REPLACE 5-pin fluid level indicator cap.
• Is reading above 10 ohms?			
F3 CHECK CONTINUITY PWS SWITCH (CONTINUED)			
• Turn ignition switch ON, wait until motor stops running.	Yes	▶	REPLACE pressure warning switch and pump motor relay.
• Disconnect pressure warning switch 5-pin plug and connect multi-meter to Pins 1 and 2 (switch side).	No	▶	GO to Step F4.
• Check for continuity.			
• Is continuity present?			
F4 CHECK WIRING CONTINUITY			
• Check cable harness 430H, 512, 547, 547B, 547A, 549, 977 circuits. (Refer to Vehicle Wiring Diagram).	Yes	▶	CHECK parking brake electrical circuit including parking brake switch. REVERIFY condition.
• Are circuits and connectors good?	No	▶	SERVICE or REPLACE as required.

Fig. 37   Test F, brake warning lamp On w/ABS lamp Off, parking brake released & lining wear checked (Part 2 of 2). Mark VII & 1992 Cougar/Thunderbird

TEST STEP	RESULT	▶	ACTION TO TAKE
G1 CHECK FUSE AND FUSE LINKS			
• Check in-line fuse links with ignition turned ON.	Yes	▶	GO to Step G2.
• Are fuse links OK?	No	▶	SERVICE or REPLACE as required.
G2 CHECK WARNING LAMP BULB			
• Check warning lamp bulb.	Yes	▶	GO to Step G3.
• Is bulb OK?	No	▶	REPLACE bulb.
G3 CHECK WARNING LAMP OPERATION			
• Turn ignition switch ON.	Yes	▶	SERVICE or REPLACE Circuit 606B.
• Disconnect 32-pin connector from control module.	No	▶	SERVICE or REPLACE connector to 14401 wire harness.
• Is anti-lock lamp on?			

Fig. 38   Test G, no warning lamp On when ignition switch turned On. Mark VII & 1992 Cougar/Thunderbird

TEST STEP		RESULT	►	ACTION TO TAKE
H1	CHECK COMPONENT MOUNTING			
	● Check for proper brake pedal and hydraulic unit attachment.	Pedal still spongy	►	GO to Step H2.
	● Bleed brakes as outlined.	Pedal feels normal	►	Condition corrected.
	● Does pedal feel normal?			
H2	BLEED BRAKE SYSTEM			
	● Rebleed brake system.	Pedal still spongy	►	REPLACE actuation assembly.
		Pedal feels normal	►	Condition corrected.

Fig. 39   Test H, spongy pedal & no warning lamp. Mark VII & 1992 Cougar/Thunderbird

TEST STEP		RESULT	►	ACTION TO TAKE
J1	VERIFY CONDITION			
	● Verify condition exists as reported.	Yes	►	Condition CORRECTED.
	● Bleed brake system as outlined.	No	►	GO to J2.
	● Does vehicle track properly?			

Fig. 40   Test J, poor vehicle tracking during ABS function, warning lamp Off (Part 1 of 2). Mark VII & 1992 Cougar/Thunderbird

TEST STEP		RESULT	►	ACTION TO TAKE
J2	CHECK ANTI-LOCK OPERATION—LH FRONT WHEEL			
	● Lift vehicle and rotate wheels to ensure they turn freely.	If wheel turn freely	►	TURN ignition switch OFF. DISCONNECT wire leads. GO to Step J3.
	● Turn ignition switch OFF.	If wheel does not turn freely or pedal drops	►	REPLACE solenoid valve block.
	● Disconnect 32-pin plug from electronic controller.			
	● Connect EEC-IV Breakout Box T83L-50-EEC-IV with Anti-Lock Test Adapter T87P-50-ALA to the Anti-Lock 32-pin plug wiring harness.			
	● Short Pins 18, 14, and 31 to each other at Breakout box.			
	● Apply moderate brake pedal effort and check that LH front wheel will not turn.			
	● Check to see that LH front wheel turns freely with ignition switch ON.			
	CAUTION: Do not leave ignition on for more than 1 minute maximum, or solenoid valve damage may result.			
J3	CHECK ANTI-LOCK OPERATION—RH FRONT WHEEL			
	● Short Pins 18, 32, and 13 to each other at Breakout box.	Wheel turns freely	►	TURN ignition switch OFF. DISCONNECT wire leads. GO to Step J4.
	● Apply moderate brake effort. Check that RH front wheel does not turn.	Wheel does not turn freely or brake pedal drops	►	REPLACE solenoid valve block.
	● Check that RH front wheel turns freely with ignition switch ON.			
	CAUTION: Do not leave ignition on more than 1 minute maximum or solenoid valve damage may result.			
J4	CHECK ANTI-LOCK OPERATION—REAR WHEELS			
	● Short Pins 18, 30 and 12 to each other at Breakout box.	Wheels turn freely	►	TURN ignition switch OFF. DISCONNECT wire lead and Breakout box. LOWER vehicle. REVERIFY condition.
	● Apply moderate brake pedal pressure. Check that rear wheels will not turn.	Wheels do not turn freely or brake pedal drops	►	REPLACE solenoid valve block.
	● Check that rear wheels turn freely with ignition switch ON.			
	CAUTION: Do not leave ignition on more than 1 minute maximum or solenoid valve damage may result.			

Fig. 40   Test J, poor vehicle tracking during ABS function, warning lamp Off (Part 2 of 2). Mark VII & 1992 Cougar/Thunderbird

SYSTEM SERVICE

SYSTEM DISCHARGE

Before servicing any system component which contains high pressure, it is mandatory that the hydraulic pressure in the system be completely discharged. To discharge the system, turn ignition switch to Off position, then pump brake pedal a minimum of 20 times, until an increase in pedal force is clearly felt.

SYSTEM BLEEDING

FRONT BRAKES

The front brakes can be bled in the conventional manner or with brake bleeder tool No. 104-00064 or equivalent, with or without the accumulator being charged.

Brake Bleeding Less Pressure Bleeder

1. Remove dust cap from the righthand caliper bleeder fitting. Attach a rubber drain tube to fitting. Ensure that end of tube fits snugly around fitting.
2. Submerge free end of tube in a suitable container, partially filled with clean brake fluid.
3. Loosen bleeder fitting approximately three-quarter turn, then push brake pedal down slowly through full travel and hold at that position.
4. Close bleeder fitting, then return pedal to full release position. Wait five seconds, then repeat operation until air bubbles cease to appear at submerged end of bleeder tube.
5. Repeat operation at lefthand caliper.

Brake Bleeding w/Pressure Bleeder

1. Clean all dirt from reservoir filler cap area, then attach pressure bleeder to reservoir cap opening.
2. Maintain approximately 35 psi pressure on system.
3. Remove dust cap from righthand front caliper bleeder fitting.
4. Attach a rubber drain tube to fitting. Ensure that end of tube fits snugly around fitting.

5. With ignition switch in the OFF position and brake pedal in the fully released position, open righthand front caliper bleeder fitting for 10 seconds at a time until an air free stream of brake fluid is observed from submerged end of hose.
6. Repeat procedure at lefthand caliper.

REAR BRAKES

The rear brakes can be pressure bled using brake bleeder 104-00064, or equivalent, or through the use of a fully charged accumulator.

Brake Bleeding w/Pressure Bleeder

1. Clean all dirt from reservoir filler cap area. Attach pressure bleeder to reservoir cap opening.
2. Maintain approximately 35 psi on the system.
3. Remove dust cap from righthand caliper bleeder fitting. Attach a rubber drain tube to the fitting. Ensure that end of tube fits snugly around fitting.
4. With ignition switch in the Off position, and brake pedal at rest, open righthand caliper bleeder fitting for 10 seconds at a time, until an air free stream of brake fluid flow is observed.
5. Repeat procedure at lefthand caliper.
6. Place ignition switch in the RUN position, then pump brake pedal several times to complete bleeding procedure and completely charge accumulator.
7. Siphon off excess fluid in reservoir to adjust level to the MAX mark with a fully charged accumulator.

Bleeding System Using A Fully Charged Accumulator

1. Remove dust cap from righthand caliper bleeder fitting. Attach a rubber

drain tube to fitting. Ensure that end of tube fits snugly around fitting.
2. Turn ignition switch to the RUN position. This will activate the electric pump to charge the accumulator as required.

Before proceeding with next step, ensure care is used when opening bleeder screws due to high pressures available from a completely charged accumulator.

3. Hold brake pedal in the applied position, then open righthand caliper bleeder fitting for 10 seconds at a time until an air free stream of brake fluid is observed.
4. Repeat procedure at lefthand caliper.
5. Pump brake pedal several times to complete bleeding procedure and charge accumulator.
6. Adjust brake fluid level in reservoir to MAX mark with a completely charged accumulator. **If the pump motor is allowed to operate continuously for approximately 20 minutes, a thermal safety switch inside the motor may shut the motor off, to prevent it from overheating. If an overheat condition occurs, a 2-10 minute cool down period is required before normal operation can resume.**

HYDRAULIC RESERVOIR, CHECK & FILL

Refer to **Fig. 6**, during the following procedure.

1. With ignition switch in the On position, pump brake pedal until the hydraulic pump motor begins to operate.
2. Wait until hydraulic pump motor is operating, then check brake fluid level. If fluid level drops below the MAX fill level, add enough fluid to bring level to

MAX mark.

3. Do not fill reservoir above MAX mark. Overfilling the reservoir may cause brake fluid to overflow when accumulator discharges during normal operation. **It is possible, depending on the state of the charge of the accumulator, that the fluid level could show above the MAX mark when first viewed, If so, repeat steps 1 and 2.**

COMPONENT REPLACEMENT
ACTUATION ASSEMBLY

Refer to **Figs. 2 and 3**, during the following procedure.
1. With hydraulic system discharged, disconnect battery ground cable.
2. Remove air cleaner housing and duct assembly, if necessary.
3. Label, then disconnect electrical connectors from fluid level indicator, main valve, solenoid valve block, pressure warning switch, hydraulic pump motor and ground connector from master cylinder portion of actuation assembly.
4. Disconnect and plug brake tube fittings. **Do not allow brake fluid to come in contact with any electrical connectors.**
5. Remove trim panel under steering column, then disconnect actuation assembly pushrod from brake pedal. Slide switch, pushrod and plastic bushings off pedal pin.
6. Remove four retaining nuts, securing actuation assembly to brake pedal support bracket.
7. Remove actuation assembly from engine compartment.
8. Reverse procedure to install, **torque** four hydraulic unit to pedal support nuts to 13-25 ft. lbs. and brake tube nuts to 10-18 ft. lbs.

HYDRAULIC ACCUMULATOR

1. With hydraulic system discharged, disconnect battery ground cable and electrical connector at hydraulic pump motor.
2. Using a 8 mm hex wrench, loosen and completely unscrew accumulator. **Ensure contaminants do not fall into open port.**
3. Remove O-ring.
4. Reverse procedure to install, noting the following:
   a. **Torque** accumulator to 30-34 ft. lbs.
   b. Turn ignition switch to On position and check that the red "Brake" warning lamp and the amber "Anti-Lock" warning lamp both go out after approximately 1 minute.
   c. Top off brake fluid reservoir as necessary.

ELECTRIC HYDRAULIC PUMP MOTOR

Refer to **Fig. 4**, during the following procedure.
1. Discharge hydraulic system, then dis-

connect battery ground cable.
2. Drain as much brake fluid as possible from reservoir.
3. Disconnect suction line between reservoir and pump.
4. Remove accumulator and banjo bolt attaching high pressure line to pump housing.
5. Disconnect low pressure line between fluid reservoir and pump suction port.
6. Raise and support vehicle, then disconnect electrical connector from pump motor and pressure switch. It may be necessary to disconnect left-hand tie-rod from steering knuckle to gain access to pressure warning switch electrical connector.
7. Remove bolt and spacer attaching pump and motor assembly to hydraulic actuation unit. Slide pump and motor assembly toward driver's side to clear attaching pin. Remove pump and motor assembly.
8. Reverse procedure to install. **Torque** Allen head bolt to 5-7 ft. lbs. There must be a gap of .06-.13 inch between washer on Allen head bolt and isolator bushing retainer cap. **Torque** banjo bolt to 12-15 ft. lbs.

RESERVOIR & FLUID LEVEL INDICATOR

Refer to **Fig. 6**, during the following procedure.
1. With hydraulic system discharged, disconnect battery ground cable.
2. Disconnect electrical connector from fluid level indicator.
3. Empty reservoir of as mush brake fluid as possible.
4. Remove suction line between pump and reservoir, from reservoir by rotating and pulling hose from fitting.
5. Remove reservoir by placing a flat blade screwdriver between push-in outlet and push-in stud/grommet, then prying up gently. Ensure short sleeve and O-ring are removed from booster grommet hole.
6. Reverse procedure to install.

SOLENOID VALVE BLOCK
Cougar/Thunderbird

1. Discharge system and disconnect battery ground cable.
2. Remove LH cowl vent screen and disconnect electrical connector from valve block.
3. Disconnect and plug brake lines at solenoid valve block.
4. Remove solenoid valve block.
5. Reverse procedure to install. Use new O-rings and **torque** solenoid valve block mounting bolts to 15-21 ft. lbs.

Mark VII

1. Discharge system and disconnect battery ground cable.
2. Disconnect electrical connectors from fluid reservoir cap, main valve, solenoid valve block, pressure warning switch, hydraulic pump motor and ground connector from actuation assembly.
3. Disconnect brake tubes from solenoid

valve block one at a time. Immediately plug each threaded tube opening in valve body to prevent fluid loss. **Do not allow brake fluid to contact any electrical connectors.**
4. Using an 8mm hex wrench, loosen and completely remove accumulator.
5. Working inside passenger compartment, disconnect actuation assembly pushrod from brake pedal as follows:
   a. Disconnect stoplamp switch wires at connector on brake pedal.
   b. Remove hairpin connector at stoplamp switch, then slide switch off of pedal pin far enough for switch outer hole to clear pin.
   c. Remove switch using a twisting motion, using caution not to damage switch.
   d. Remove four retaining nuts at dash panel.
6. Inside engine compartment, remove actuation assembly from dash panel.
7. Gently clamp off reservoir to actuation assembly brake fluid supply hose to prevent loss of reservoir fluid.
8. Using a 13mm hex socket, remove three nuts holding valve block to actuation assembly.
9. Slide valve block away from actuation assembly until it clears three mounting studs and remove from actuation assembly.
10. Reverse procedure to install, noting the following:
   a. Use new O-rings, lubricated with brake fluid, in four ports of valve block mounting face.
   b. **Torque** valve block mounting nuts to 15-21 ft. lbs.
   c. **Torque** four actuation assembly locknuts to 13-25 ft. lbs.
   d. Following installation, turn ignition to Run position. Wait until Brake and ABS indicators go out, the apply brake pedal with medium force and hold for 15-30 seconds and release. Repeat three times.
   e. Check for leaks at valve block tube seats and mating surface.

ELECTRONIC CONTROLLER

1. Disconnect battery ground cable.
2. Remove trim panel in luggage compartment (located behind back seat), to expose the electronic control module.
3. Disconnect the 32 pin electrical connector from the electronic controller.
4. Remove attaching bolts, then the electronic controller.
5. Reverse procedure to install. **Torque** retaining bolt to 28-48 inch lbs.

PRESSURE SWITCH

Before removing pressure warning switch, ensure hydraulic system pressure is completely discharged. Whenever the pressure warning switch assembly is replaced, the pump motor relay assembly should also be replaced.
1. Disconnect battery ground cable.
2. Raise and support vehicle.
3. Disconnect electrical connector from pressure warning switch. **It may be**

necessary to remove the lefthand front tie-rod at the steering knuckle to gain access to the switch.

4. Using socket tool T85P-20215-B, or equivalent, 1/2 to 3/8 inch adapter and a 3/8 inch ratchet, remove pressure warning switch.
5. Reverse procedure to install. **Torque** pressure warning switch to 15-25 ft. lbs.

FRONT WHEEL SENSOR
Mark VII

1. Disconnect battery ground cable.
2. Disconnect sensor electrical connector.
3. Raise and support vehicle, disengage wire grommet from shock tower, then pull sensor cable connector through hole. Use care not to damage connector.
4. Remove sensor wire from bracket on shock strut and side rail.
5. Loosen 5 mm setscrew retaining sensor to sensor bracket post. Remove sensor through hole in disc brake splash shield.
6. Reverse procedure to install, noting the following:
   a. If sensor is to be reused or adjusted, ensure sensor face is clean and free of foreign material. Carefully scrape pole face with a dull knife. Glue a new front paper spacer on pole face (spacer is marked with a "F" and is .051 inch thick). Steel sleeve around post bolt must be rotated to provide a new surface for setscrew to indent and lock into.
   b. Install sensor through brake shield onto sensor bracket post. Ensure paper spacer remains in place throughout installation.
   c. Push sensor toward toothed sensor ring, until new paper spacer contacts the ring. Holding sensor against ring, **torque** 5 mm setscrew to 21-26 inch lbs.

Cougar/Thunderbird

1. Disconnect battery ground cable.
2. Disconnect sensor electrical connector, located near radiator support.
3. Remove routing clips along wiring harness.
4. Remove Torx head screw securing sensor to spindle.

5. Reverse procedure to install. **Torque** Torx head screw to 40-60 inch lbs.

REAR WHEEL SENSOR

1. Disconnect battery ground cable.
2. Disconnect wheel sensor electrical connector, located behind wheelwell, under carpeting, inside luggage compartment.
3. Push sensor wire grommet through hole in luggage compartment floor.
4. Raise and support vehicle, then remove sensor wire from routing clips.
5. **On Cougar and Thunderbird models,** remove sensor retaining bolt with a 1/2 inch socket.
6. **On Mark VII models,** proceed as follows:
   a. Remove wheel and tire assembly, then caliper and rotor assemblies.
   b. Remove Torx head retaining bolt, then slip grommet out of rear brake splash shield and pull sensor out through the hole.
7. **On all models,** reverse procedure to install, noting the following:
   a. **On Cougar and Thunderbird models,** align sensor locating tab and bolt hole to axle, then push into position.
   b. **Torque** retaining bolt to 14-20 ft. lbs.
   c. **On Mark VII models,** loosen 5 mm setscrew on sensor and ensure sensor slides freely on sensor bracket post.
   d. If sensor is to be reused or adjusted, ensure sensor face is clean and free of foreign material. Carefully scrape pole face with a dull knife. Glue a new front paper spacer on pole face (spacer is marked with a "R" and is .043 inch thick). Steel sleeve around post bolt must be rotated to provide a new surface for setscrew to indent and lock into.
   e. **Torque** Torx head screw to 40-60 inch lbs.
   f. Push sensor toward toothed ring, until new paper sensor contacts sensor ring. Hold sensor, then **torque** 5 mm setscrew to 21-26 inch lbs.

FRONT SPEED INDICATOR RING
Cougar/Thunderbird

1. Remove wheel and tire assembly.
2. Remove caliper, rotor and hub assemblies.

3. Remove indicator ring from hub, using a three-jawed puller.
4. Support center of hub so wheel studs do not rest on work surface.
5. Position sensor ring on hub, place a flat plate on top of ring, then press until flush with top of hub.
6. Install hub, rotor and caliper assemblies, then tire and wheel assembly.

Mark VII

1. Remove wheel and tire assembly.
2. Remove caliper and assembly.
3. Position rotor assembly on an arbor press with studs facing up. Press each stud individually and carefully, only until they contact surface of sensor ring.
4. Position anti-lock sensing ring remover T85P-20202-A, or equivalent, on top of studs, then press all four studs and sensor ring out of rotor assembly together.
5. Install studs into rotor one at a time.
6. Position sensor ring on rotor, then press sensor ring onto rotor, using anti-lock sensing ring replacer T87P-20202-A, or equivalent, until sensor ring is seated. Ensure ring is pressed on straight.
7. Install rotor and caliper assemblies, then wheel and tire assembly.

REAR SPEED INDICATOR RING
Mark VII

1. Remove rear axle shaft, as described elsewhere in this manual.
2. Install pinion bearing cone remover T71P-4621-B, or equivalent, between axle shaft flange and sensor ring.
3. Position axle in arbor press, then press axle from sensor ring.
4. To install, position sensor ring with recessed side facing inboard on axle, then install piston bearing cone remover T71P-4621-B, or equivalent, on axle shaft.
5. Place bar stock on top of axle flange, then press sensor ring onto axle shaft, until a gap of 2.48-2.55 inches remains between face of sensor ring and face of flange.
6. Install axle shaft.

1993–94 Cougar, Mark VIII & Thunderbird

NOTE: Wire Color Code & Electrical Symbol Identification Located At The Front Of This Manual Can Be Used As An Aid When Using Wiring Circuits Found In This Section.

INDEX

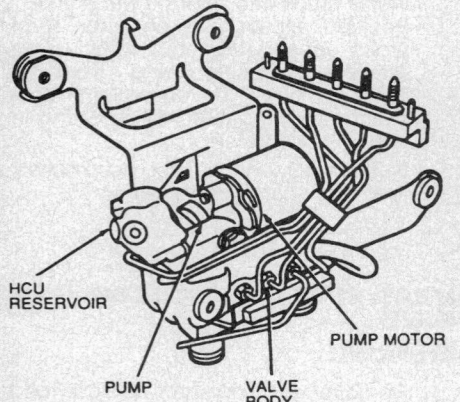

Fig. 1 Hydraulic control unit. Cougar, Mark VIII & Thunderbird

PRECAUTIONS
HYDRAULIC BRAKE FLUID COLOR

Hydraulic brake fluid must conform with the requirements of Federal Motor Vehicle Safety Standard 116. Under this standard, brake fluids are visually different from other automotive fluids such as transmission, power steering and engine.

Fluid color in a normal brake system may vary from its original color for many reasons. A brake master cylinder may show significantly different shades fluid color between the two brake master cylinder reservoirs. Color may also appear to vary between cast steel and die cast aluminum reservoirs. Some reasons for discoloration include the following:

1. Heat and/or aging.
2. Different operation temperatures or different rates of normal oxidation between two reservoir compartments.
3. Different brands and/or shades of fluid are used when topping off during normal service.
4. Dissolution of color dye used on mas-

ter cylinder internal springs during assembly.

Brake fluid contaminated with hydrocarbon/mineral based fluid (power steering or transmission fluid) can be detected by an obvious swelling of the master cylinder cap gasket. If the master cylinder cap gasket is swollen, all brake system rubber parts must be replaced. All brake tubes and hoses must be thoroughly flushed with Ford Heavy Duty Brake Fluid C6Az-19542-AA or –BA or DOT-3 equivalent before the vehicle returns to service.

DESCRIPTION
SYSTEM

These models are equipped with a four wheel anti-lock brake system (ABS), The system prevents lockup by automatically modulating brake system pressure during an emergency stop situation.

By controlling wheel lockup, the vehicle's operator can maintain steering control and stop the vehicle in the shortest possible distance, under most driving conditions.

The ABS system controls the front brakes separately and the rear brakes as a pair whenever wheel lockup begins. The brake pedal application force required to engage the system function may vary with road surface conditions. A dry surface will require a higher force, while a slippery surface will require a much lower force.

During system operation, the vehicle's operator will sense a slight pulsation in the brake pedal, accompanied by a rise in brake pedal height and a clicking sound.

TRACTION ASSIST
Mark VIII

Traction assist is designed to control wheel spin when accelerating on slippery or loose surfaces. During acceleration, if one or both rear wheels lose traction and begin to spin, the TA system will rapidly

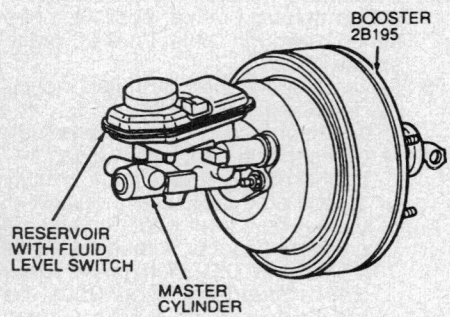

Fig. 2 Master cylinder reservoir & brake booster. Cougar, Mark VIII & Thunderbird

apply and release the appropriate rear brake(s) to reduce wheel spin and aid traction. An isolation valve will also close and the ABS pump will run, allowing brake operation only in the rear brake circuit by closing off pressure to the front brake.

SYSTEM COMPONENTS
Hydraulic Control Unit

The hydraulic control unit, **Fig. 1,** consists of a valve body assembly, pump and motor assembly, and a brake fluid reservoir with fluid level indicator assembly.

ABS Module

The ABS module is located on the hydraulic control unit mounting bracket, outside of the engine compartment attached to the outside frame rail. It is an on-board diagnostic, non-repairable unit, consisting of two microprocessors and operational circuitry for operation. The ABS module monitors system operation during normal driving as well as during anti-lock braking.

Master Cylinder Reservoir & Fluid Level Switch

The master cylinder reservoir, **Fig. 2,** is a clear translucent, plastic container with three main chambers. An integral fluid le-

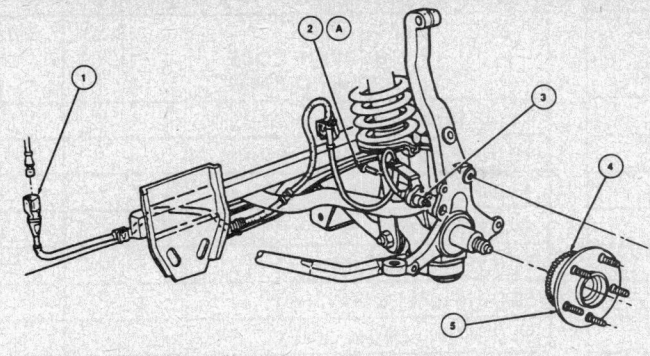

Item	Part Number	Description
1	N805151-S100	Connector
2A		Bolt (2 Req'd)
3	2C204 (RH) 2C205 (LH)	Sensor Assy

Item	Part Number	Description
4	2B663	Speed Indicator Ring
5		Hub Assy
A		Tighten to 4.5-6.8 N·m (40-60 Lb-In)

FM4029300166000X

Fig. 3 Front wheel sensor assembly. Cougar & Thunderbird

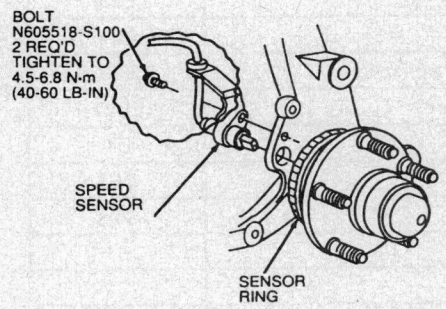

Fig. 5 Front wheel sensor assembly. Mark VIII

FM4029100168000X

vel switch with a three-pin electrical connector is part of the reservoir assembly. A low pressure hose is attached to the reservoir. This hose feeds brake fluid to the hydraulic control unit reservoir. The reservoir and cap are serviced separately.

Pedal Travel Switch

The pedal travel switch monitors brake pedal travel and sends this information to the ABS module through the wire harness. The switch adjustment is critical to brake pedal feel during ABS cycling.

The switch is located in the vacuum booster and can be serviced separately.

The switch is normally closed. When brake pedal travel exceeds the switch setting during an anti-lock stop, the ABS module senses the switch is open and grounds the pump motor relay coil. This energizes the relay and turns the pump motor on. When the pump motor is running, the master cylinder is filled with high pressure brake fluid. The brake pedal will be pushed up until the switch closes. The pump then turns off and the pedal will drop some with each ABS control cycle until the travel switch opens again and the pump is turned on again. This minimizes pedal feedback during ABS cycling.

Wheel Sensors

This system, **Figs. 3 through 6,** uses four sets of variable reluctance sensors and toothed speed indicator rings to deter-

mine the rotational speed of each wheel. The sensors operate on magnetic induction principle. For example, as the teeth on the speed indicator ring rotate past the stationary sensor, a signal proportional to the speed of the rotation is generated and transmitted to the ABS module (Electronic Control Unit (ECU)) through a coaxial cable.

The front sensors are attached to the suspension knuckles and the speed indicator rings are pressed onto the outer constant velocity joints. The rear sensors are attached to the rear caliper anchor plate and the speed indicator rings are pressed onto the rear wheel hub assemblies. The sensors and the speed indicator rings are serviced individually.

SYSTEM OPERATION

When the brakes are applied, fluid is forced from the master cylinder outlet ports to the Hydraulic Control Unit (HCU) inlet ports. This pressure is transmitted through four normally open solenoid valves inside the HCU, then through the HCU outlet ports to each wheel. The primary (rear) circuit of the master cylinder feeds the right front and left rear brakes. The secondary (front) circuit of the master cylinder feeds the left front and right rear brakes. If the ABS module senses a wheel is about to lock, based on wheel speed sensor data, it closes the circuit's solenoid valve. This prevents any more fluid from entering the circuit. Once the affected wheel comes back up to speed, the ABS module returns the valves to their normal operating condition allowing fluid to flow to the affected brake.

The ABS module monitors the electromechanical components of the system. Malfunction of the anti-lock brake system will cause the ABS module to shut off or inhibit system function, while retaining normal power assisted braking. Malfunctions are indicated by one or two warning lamps inside the vehicle.

Loss of hydraulic fluid in the HCU reservoir will disable the ABS system.

The four wheel ABS system is self monitoring. When the ignition switch is turned to the RUN position, the ABS module will

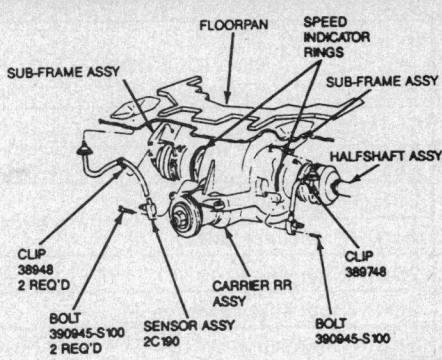

Fig. 4 Rear wheel sensor assembly. Cougar & Thunderbird

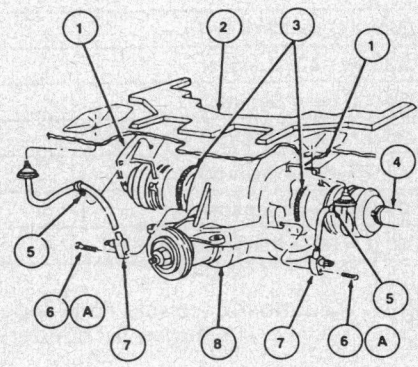

Item	Part Number	Description
1	—	Subframe
2	—	Floorpan
3	2C189	Sensor Ring
4	—	Halfshaft Assy
5	389748-S	Clip (2 Req'd)
6A	390945-S100	Bolt (2 Req'd)
7	2C190	Speed Sensor
8	—	Rear Axle Assy
A		Tighten to 18-27 N·m (14-19 Lb-Ft)

FM4029100169000X

Fig. 6 Rear wheel sensor assembly. Mark VIII

perform a preliminary self check on the ABS electrical system indicated by a three or four second illumination of the amber "Check Anti-Lock Brakes" lamp in the instrument cluster. During vehicle operation, including normal and anti-lock braking, the ABS module monitors all electrical anti-lock functions and some hydraulic system operation.

Each time the vehicle is driven, the ABS module performs a self-check. As soon as vehicle speed reaches about 19 mph, the module turns on the pump motor for about one-half second. At this time a mechanical noise may be heard. This is a normal function of the self-check by the ABS module.

For most malfunctions of the ABS system, the amber "Check Anti-Lock Brakes" and/or the red "Brake" lamps will be illuminated. The sequence of illumination of these warning lamps, combined with the problem symptoms, can determine the appropriate diagnostic test to perform. Most

SERVICE CODE (COMPONENT)	PINPOINT TEST STEP
11 (ABS Module)	AA1
22 (LH Front Inlet Valve) or reference voltage	BB1
23 (LH Front Outlet Valve)	BB4
24 (RH Front Inlet Valve)	BB6
25 (RH Front Outlet Valve)	BB8
26 (RH Rear Inlet Valve)	BB10
27 (RH Rear Outlet Valve)	BB12
28 (LH Rear Inlet Valve)	BB14
29 (LH Rear Outlet Valve)	BB16
31 (LH Front Sensor)	CC1
32 (RH Front Sensor)	CC8
33 (RH Rear Sensor)	CC15
34 (LH Rear Sensor)	CC22
35 (LH Front Sensor)	CC1
36 (RH Front Sensor)	CC8
37 (RH Rear Sensor)	CC15
38 (LH Rear Sensor)	CC22

FM4029300170010X

Fig. 7 Diagnostic trouble code index (Part 1 of 2). 1993 Cougar & Thunderbird

malfunctions are recorded as a coded number in the ABS module memory, pinpointing the exact component requiring service.

TROUBLESHOOTING

PRE-TEST CHECKS

Mark VIII

1. Ensure parking brake is fully released, otherwise "Brake" warning lamp will be illuminated.
2. Check brake fluid levels in master cylinder reservoir and hydraulic control unit reservoir. If either is low, a warning lamp will be illuminated.
3. Ensure the following connectors are connected and terminals are secure in connectors:
   a. 55-Pin connector of ABS module.
   b. 19-Pin connector of HCU valve body.
   c. 4-Pin connector of solid state pump motor relay.
   d. 4-Pin connector of pump motor.
   e. 3-Pin connector of master cylinder reservoir.
   f. 2-Pin connector of HCU reservoir.
   g. 5-Pin connector of main power relay.
   h. 2-Pin connector of each wheel speed sensor.
   i. 2-Pin connector of pedal travel switch.
   j. 2-Pin connector of stoplamp switch.

SERVICE CODE (COMPONENT)	PINPOINT TEST STEP
41 (LH Front Sensor)	CC1
42 (RH Front Sensor)	CC8
43 (RH Rear Sensor)	CC15
44 (LH Rear Sensor)	CC22
51 (LH Front Outlet Valve)	DD1
52 (RH Front Outlet Valve)	DD5
53 (RH Rear Outlet Valve)	DD9
54 (LH Rear Outlet Valve)	DD13
55 (LH Front Sensor)	CC1
56 (RH Front Sensor)	CC8
57 (RH Rear Sensor)	CC15
58 (LH Rear Sensor)	CC22
61 (FLS Circuits)	EE1
62 (Travel Switch)	EE1
63 (Pump Motor Speed Sensor)	EE7
64 (Pump Motor Pressure)	EE22
67 (Pump Motor Relay)	E1
71 (LH Front Sensor)	CC1
72 (RH Front Sensor)	CC8
73 (RH Rear Sensor)	CC15
74 (LH Rear Sensor)	CC22
75 (LH Front Sensor)	CC1
76 (RH Front Sensor)	CC8
77 (RH Rear Sensor)	CC15
78 (LH Rear Sensor)	CC22

FM4029300170020X

Fig. 7 Diagnostic trouble code index (Part 2 of 2). 1993 Cougar & Thunderbird

DIAGNOSTIC TROUBLE CODE (COMPONENT)	PINPOINT TEST STEP
11 (ABS Module)	AA1
17 (Reference Voltage)	BB1
18 (Isolation Valve No. 1)	BB18
19 (Isolation Valve No. 2)	BB20

FM4029100171010X

Fig. 8 Diagnostic trouble code index (Part 1 of 2). 1993 Mark VIII

DIAGNOSIS & TESTING

WARNING LAMP DIAGNOSIS

The anti-lock brake system uses two warning indicators to alert the driver of malfunctions in the system.

The red "Brake" warning lamp will come on for only two reasons:
1. If brake fluid level in master cylinder reservoir falls below level determined by set point of fluid level switch.
2. If parking brake is applied.

The amber "Check Anti-Lock Brake" lamp will come on for numerous reasons. It warns the driver the ABS has been turned off due to a symptom existing in the system. Normal power braking remains but the wheels may lock during a panic stop while the warning lamp is on.

DIAGNOSTIC PROCEDURE

The diagnostic procedure consists of four sections:
1. On-Board Diagnostics.
2. Quick Tests.

DIAGNOSTIC TROUBLE CODE (COMPONENT)	PINPOINT TEST STEP
22 (LH Front Inlet Valve)	BB2
23 (LH Front Outlet Valve)	BB4
24 (RH Front Inlet Valve)	BB6
25 (RH Front Outlet Valve)	BB8
26 (RH Rear Inlet Valve)	BB10
27 (RH Rear Outlet Valve)	BB12
28 (LH Rear Inlet Valve)	BB14
29 (LH Rear Outlet Valve)	BB16
31 (LH Front Sensor)	CC1
32 (RH Front Sensor)	CC8
33 (RH Rear Sensor)	CC15
34 (LH Rear Sensor)	CC22
35 (LH Front Sensor)	CC1
36 (RH Front Sensor)	CC8
37 (RH Rear Sensor)	CC15
38 (LH Rear Sensor)	CC22
41 (LH Front Sensor)	CC1
42 (RH Front Sensor)	CC8
43 (RH Rear Sensor)	CC15
44 (LH Rear Sensor)	CC22
51 (LH Front Outlet Valve)	DD1
52 (RH Front Outlet Valve)	DD5
53 (RH Rear Outlet Valve)	DD9
54 (LH Rear Outlet Valve)	DD13
55 (LH Front Sensor)	CC1
56 (RH Front Sensor)	CC8
57 (RH Rear Sensor)	CC15
58 (LH Rear Sensor)	CC22
61 (FLS Circuits)	EE1
62 (Travel Switch)	EE1
63 (Pump Motor Speed Sensor)	EE7
64 (Pump Motor Pressure)	EE22
67 (Pump Motor Relay)	E1
75 (LH Front Sensor)	CC1
76 (RH Front Sensor)	CC8
77 (RH Rear Sensor)	CC15
78 (LH Rear Sensor)	CC22

FM4029100171020X

Fig. 8 Diagnostic trouble code index (Part 2 of 2). 1993 Mark VIII

DTC	SOURCE	ACTION
11	Disturbed or defective redundancy channel. Replace anti-lock brake control module if DTC repeats.	Go to Pinpoint Test Step AA1
17	Reference voltage failure, caused by high/low battery voltage, main power relay, main fuse, wire harness, or damaged anti-lock brake control module.	Go to Pinpoint Test Step BB1
18	Open or short circuit—isolation valve #1 or wire harness.	Go to Pinpoint Test Step BB26.
19	Open or short circuit—isolation valve #2 or wire harness.	Go to Pinpoint Test Step BB29.
22	Open or short circuit—LH front inlet valve or wire harness.	Go to Pinpoint Test Step BB2.
23	Open or short circuit—LH front outlet valve or wire harness.	Go to Pinpoint Test Step BB5.
24	Open or short circuit—RH front inlet valve or wire harness.	Go to Pinpoint Test Step BB8.

FM4029400423010X

Fig. 9 Diagnostic trouble code index (Part 1 of 4) 1994

4. Codes will appear at approximately 15 second intervals. Leave button latched until all codes are output.

If the first code received is in the 20's and no other code is received, service the indicated component. No other codes can be output if a 20's code exists. After servicing the indicated 20's code, repeat the procedure for retrieving error codes.

If a code 61 is received with any other code, ignore the 61 code and service the other indicated components. If, after correcting all other malfunctions, the "Check Anti-Lock Brake" lamp is still on, service the fluid level switch circuit.

If no code, or only a code 10 is received, refer to "Quick Tests."

QUICK TESTS

To properly conduct the Quick Tests, a digital volt/ohmmeter must be used. These tests will lead to specific diagnostic pinpoint tests that will, in most cases, identify the fault.

Refer to **Figs. 10 and 11** for Quick Tests.

PINPOINT TESTS

Refer to the wiring diagrams, **Figs. 12 through 14**, when performing the Pinpoint Tests to locate wire circuits indicated in the test procedure. Each test is completely independent of the other test and within each test are sequences that can identify a problem without requiring completion of the entire diagnostic test procedure.

Refer to **Figs. 15 through 36** for test diagnostic procedures.

CLEARING DIAGNOSTIC TROUBLE CODES

Original error codes in the ABS module will erase if the system is operating properly and the vehicle is driven above 25 mph.

All error codes must be output and all faults corrected before the memory will clear. *Continued on page 27-68*

3. Warning Indicator Symptom Chart.
4. Diagnostic Pinpoint Tests.

ON-BOARD DIAGNOSTICS

The ABS module is capable of performing an on-board diagnosis using the Rotunda Super Star II Tester tool No. 007-0041B, or equivalent. The module monitors system operation and can store all defined diagnostic trouble codes in its memory. The error codes, **Figs. 7 through 9**, can be retrieved from the ABS module as follows:

1. Connect Super Star II Tester to connector located in engine compartment.
2. Turn on Super Star II Tester and latch button down in TEST position.
3. Turn ignition switch to RUN position.

Fig. 9 Diagnostic trouble code index (Part 4 of 4) 1994

DTC	SOURCE	ACTION
84	Pump unable to build pressure during an ABS stop.	Go to Pinpoint Test Step DD22
87	Pump motor running not triggered by anti-lock brake control module.	Go to Pinpoint Test Step E1.
75	Intermittent missing LH front sensor signal at speeds below 40 km/h (25mph).	Go to Pinpoint Test Step CC1
76	Intermittent missing RH front sensor signal at speeds below 40 km/h (25mph).	Go to Pinpoint Test Step CC8.
77	Intermittent missing RH rear sensor signal at speeds below 40 km/h (25mph).	Go to Pinpoint Test Step CC15.
78	Intermittent missing LH rear sensor signal at speeds below 40 km/h (25mph).	Go to Pinpoint Test Step CC22.

FM40294004230040X

Fig. 10 Quick Test. Cougar & Thunderbird

Item to be Tested	Ignition Mode	Measure Between Pin Numbers	Tester Scale/Range	Specification	Test Step
Battery Check	ON	60 + 53	VOLTS	10 Minimum	A1
Main Relay Coil	OFF	53 + 34	OHMS	45 to 90 ohms	A6
Jumper Pins 60 and 34					A5
Power from Main Relay	ON	19 + 33	VOLTS	10 minimum	A5
Remove jumper from pins 60 and 34					
Main Relay Circuit	OFF	60 + 33	CONTINUITY	continuity	A12
Sensor Resistance (RR)	OFF	27 + 45	K OHMS	0.8-1.4K ohms	C5
Sensor Resistance (LF)	OFF	30 + 48	K OHMS	0.8-1.4K ohms	C1
Sensor Resistance (LR)	OFF	28 + 46	K OHMS	0.8-1.4K ohms	C7
Sensor Resistance (RF)	OFF	29 + 47	K OHMS	0.8-1.4K ohms	C3
Valve Resistance (IFL)	OFF	3 + 20	OHMS	5-8 ohms	BB2
Valve Resistance (IFR)	OFF	3 + 38	OHMS	5-8 ohms	BB6
Valve Resistance (IRL)	OFF	3 + 54	OHMS	5-8 ohms	BB14
Valve Resistance (IRR)	OFF	3 + 55	OHMS	5-8 ohms	BB10
Valve Resistance (OFL)	OFF	3 + 2	OHMS	3-6 ohms	BB4
Valve Resistance (OFR)	OFF	3 + 21	OHMS	3-6 ohms	BB8
Valve Resistance (ORR)	OFF	3 + 18	OHMS	3-6 ohms	BB12
Valve Resistance (ORL)	OFF	3 + 36	OHMS	3-6 ohms	BB16
Reservoir Warning (FLS #2)	OFF	8 + 26	OHMS	LESS THAN 5 OHMS	A14
Pedal Travel Switch					
Pedal NOT Applied:	OFF	5 + 26	CONTINUITY	continuity	D1
With Minimum 3 Inch Apply:	OFF	5 + 26	CONTINUITY	no continuity	D2
Sensor Cable Continuity Wiring to Ground (RR)	OFF	27 + 60	CONTINUITY	no continuity	B3
(LF)	OFF	30 + 60	CONTINUITY	no continuity	B7
(LR)	OFF	28 + 60	CONTINUITY	no continuity	B1
(RF)	OFF	29 + 60	CONTINUITY	no continuity	B5
Sensor Voltage: Rotate wheels @ 1 revolution per second. (RR)	OFF	27 + 45	AC MVOLTS	100-1400 mvolts	C19
(LF)	OFF	30 + 48	AC MVOLTS	100-1400 mvolts	C17
(LR)	OFF	28 + 46	AC MVOLTS	100-1400 mvolts	C20
(RF)	OFF	29 + 47	AC MVOLTS	100-1400 mvolts	C8
Pump Motor Speed Sensor Resistance	OFF	31 + 49	OHMS	5-100 ohms	EE11

FM40293001720000X

Fig. 9 Diagnostic trouble code index (Part 3 of 4) 1994

DTC	SOURCE	ACTION
41	Missing sensor signal LH front sensor (missing front brake anti-lock sensor indicator).	Go to Pinpoint Test Step CC1.
42	Missing sensor signal RH front sensor (missing front brake anti-lock sensor indicator).	Go to Pinpoint Test Step CC8.
43	Missing sensor signal RH rear sensor (missing front brake anti-lock sensor indicator).	Go to Pinpoint Test Step CC15.
44	Missing sensor signal LH rear sensor (missing front brake anti-lock sensor indicator).	Go to Pinpoint Test Step CC22.
55	Missing sensor signal LH front sensor (long term failure).	Go to Pinpoint Test Step CC1.
56	Missing sensor signal RH front sensor (long term failure).	Go to Pinpoint Test Step CC8.
57	Missing sensor signal RH rear sensor (long term failure).	Go to Pinpoint Test Step CC15.
58	Missing sensor signal LH rear sensor (long term failure).	Go to Pinpoint Test Step CC22.
61	Short circuit to ground. FLS #2 or wire harness.	Go to Pinpoint Test Step DD1.
62	Short circuit to ground. Anti-lock brake pedal sensor switch or wire harness.	Go to Pinpoint Test Step DD1.
63	No pump motor speed sensor signal during initial check at 3.1 km/h (1.9mph), wire harness or damaged anti-lock brake control module.	Go to Pinpoint Test Step DD7.

FM40294004230030X

Fig. 9 Diagnostic trouble code index (Part 2 of 4) 1994

DTC	SOURCE	ACTION
25	Open or short circuit—RH front outlet valve or wire harness.	Go to Pinpoint Test Step BB11.
26	Open or short circuit—RH rear inlet valve or wire harness.	Go to Pinpoint Test Step BB14.
27	Open or short circuit—RH rear outlet valve or wire harness.	Go to Pinpoint Test Step BB17.
28	Open or short circuit—LH rear inlet valve or wire harness.	Go to Pinpoint Test Step BB20.
29	Open or short circuit—LH rear outlet valve or wire harness.	Go to Pinpoint Test Step BB23.
31	Open circuit—LH front sensor, wire harness, or damage anti-lock sensor indicator, sensor air gap too small/large, damaged anti-lock brake control module.	Go to Pinpoint Test Step CC1.
32	Open circuit—RH front sensor, wire harness or damaged anti-lock brake control module.	Go to Pinpoint Test Step CC8.
33	Open circuit—RH rear sensor, wire harness or damaged anti-lock brake control module.	Go to Pinpoint Test Step CC15.
34	Open circuit—LH rear sensor, wire harness or damaged anti-lock brake control module.	Go to Pinpoint Test Step CC22.
35	Open or short circuit LH front sensor, wire harness, damaged teeth on front brake anti-lock sensor indicator, sensor air gap too small/large, damaged anti-lock brake control module.	Go to Pinpoint Test Step CC1.
36	Open or short circuit RH front sensor, wire harness, damaged teeth on front brake anti-lock sensor indicator, sensor air gap too small/large, damaged anti-lock brake control module.	Go to Pinpoint Test Step CC8.
37	Open or short circuit RH rear sensor, wire harness, damaged teeth on front brake anti-lock sensor indicator, sensor air gap too small/large, damaged anti-lock brake control module.	Go to Pinpoint Test Step CC15.
38	Open or short circuit LH rear sensor, wire harness, damaged teeth on front brake anti-lock sensor indicator, sensor air gap too small/large, damaged anti-lock brake control module.	Go to Pinpoint Test Step CC22.

FM40294004230020X

Fig. 11   Quick Test (Part 2 of 2). 1994 Mark VIII

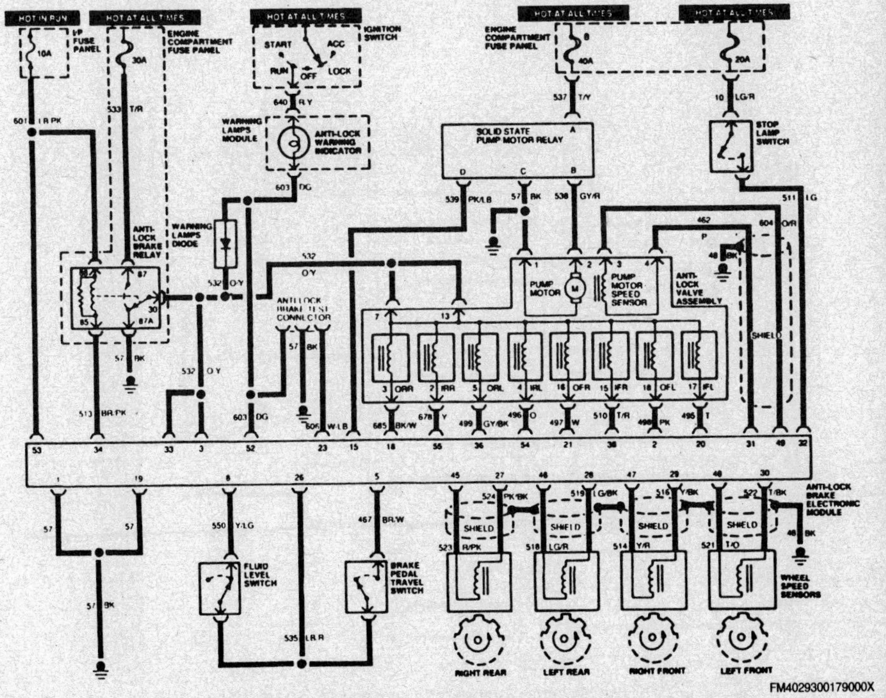

Item to be Tested	Ignition Mode	Measure Between Pin Numbers	Tester Scale Range	Specification	Test Step
Sensor Resistance (RR)	OFF	27 + 45	K OHMS	0.8-1.4K ohms	C5
Sensor Resistance (LF)	OFF	30 + 48	K OHMS	0.8-1.4K ohms	C1
Sensor Resistance (LR)	OFF	28 + 46	K OHMS	0.8-1.4K ohms	C7
Sensor Resistance (RF)	OFF	29 + 47	K OHMS	0.8-1.4K ohms	C3
Valve Resistance (IFL)	OFF	3 + 20	OHMS	5-8 ohms	BB2
Valve Resistance (IFR)	OFF	3 + 38	OHMS	5-8 ohms	BB8
Valve Resistance (IRL)	OFF	3 + 54	OHMS	5-8 ohms	BB20
Valve Resistance (IRR)	OFF	3 + 55	OHMS	5-8 ohms	BB11
Valve Resistance (OFL)	OFF	3 + 2	OHMS	3-6 ohms	BB5
Valve Resistance (OFR)	OFF	3 + 21	OHMS	3-6 ohms	BB17
Valve Resistance (ORR)	OFF	3 + 18	OHMS	3-6 ohms	BB23
Valve Resistance (ORL)	OFF	3 + 36	OHMS	3-6 ohms	
Reservoir Warning (FLS #2)	OFF	8 + 26	OHMS	LESS THAN 5 OHMS	A14
Anti-Lock Brake Pedal Sensor Switch: Pedal NOT Applied	OFF	5 + 26	CONTINUITY	Continuity	D1
With Minimum 3 Inch Apply	OFF	5 + 26	CONTINUITY	No Continuity	D2
Sensor Cable Continuity Wiring to Ground					
(RR)	OFF	27 + 60	CONTINUITY	No Continuity	B3
(LF)	OFF	30 + 60	CONTINUITY	No Continuity	B7
(LR)	OFF	28 + 60	CONTINUITY	No Continuity	B1
(RF)	OFF	29 + 60	CONTINUITY	No Continuity	B5
Sensor Voltage: Rotate Wheels @ 1 Revolution per Second					
(RR)	OFF	27 + 45	AC MVOLTS	100-1400 mvolts	C19
(LF)	OFF	30 + 48	AC MVOLTS	100-1400 mvolts	C17
(LR)	OFF	28 + 46	AC MVOLTS	100-1400 mvolts	C20
(RF)	OFF	29 + 47	AC MVOLTS	100-1400 mvolts	C18
Pump Motor Speed Sensor Resistance	OFF	31 + 49	OHMS	5-100 ohms	DD7
Valve Resistance (SV1)[3]	OFF	3 + 37	OHMS	5-8 ohms	BB26
Valve Resistance (SV2)[3]	OFF	3 + 40	OHMS	5-8 ohms	BB29

FM40294001173028X

Fig. 12   Wiring diagram. 1993 Cougar & Thunderbird

FM40293001179000X

Fig. 11   Quick Test (Part 1 of 2). Mark VIII

Item to be Tested	Ignition Mode	Measure Between Pin Numbers	Tester Scale/Range	Specification	Test Step
Battery Check	ON	60 + 53	VOLTS	10 Minimum	A1
Main Relay Coil	OFF	53 + 34	OHMS	45 to 90 ohms	A6
Jumper Pins 60 and 34					
Power from Main Relay	ON	19 + 33	VOLTS	10 Minimum	A5
Remove Jumper from Pins 60 + 34					
Main Relay Circuit	OFF	60 + 33	CONTINUITY	Continuity	A12

FM40293001173010X

Fig. 11   Quick Test (Part 2 of 2). 1993 Mark VIII

Item to be Tested	Ignition Mode	Measure Between Pin Numbers	Tester Scale/Range	Specification	Test Step
Sensor Resistance (RR)	OFF	27 + 45	K OHMS	0.8-1.4K ohms	C5
Sensor Resistance (LF)	OFF	30 + 48	K OHMS	0.8-1.4K ohms	C1
Sensor Resistance (LR)	OFF	28 + 46	K OHMS	0.8-1.4K ohms	C7
Sensor Resistance (RF)	OFF	29 + 47	K OHMS	0.8-1.4K ohms	C3
Valve Resistance (IFL)	OFF	3 + 20	OHMS	5-8 ohms	BB2
Valve Resistance (IFR)	OFF	3 + 38	OHMS	5-8 ohms	BB6
Valve Resistance (IRL)	OFF	3 + 54	OHMS	5-8 ohms	BB14
Valve Resistance (IRR)	OFF	3 + 55	OHMS	5-8 ohms	BB10
Valve Resistance (OFL)	OFF	3 + 2	OHMS	3-6 ohms	BB4
Valve Resistance (OFR)	OFF	3 + 21	OHMS	3-6 ohms	BB8
Valve Resistance (ORR)	OFF	3 + 18	OHMS	3-6 ohms	BB12
Valve Resistance (ORL)	OFF	3 + 36	OHMS	3-6 ohms	BB16
Reservoir Warning (FLS #2)	OFF	8 + 26	OHMS	LESS THAN 5 OHMS	A14
Pedal Travel Switch: Pedal NOT Applied	OFF	5 + 26	CONTINUITY	Continuity	D1
With Minimum 3 Inch Apply	OFF	5 + 26	CONTINUITY	No Continuity	D2
Sensor Cable Continuity Wiring to Ground					
(RR)	OFF	27 + 60	CONTINUITY	No Continuity	B3
(LF)	OFF	30 + 60	CONTINUITY	No Continuity	B7
(LR)	OFF	28 + 60	CONTINUITY	No Continuity	B1
(RF)	OFF	29 + 60	CONTINUITY	No Continuity	B5
Sensor Voltage: Rotate Wheels @ 1 Revolution per Second					
(RR)	OFF	27 + 45	AC MVOLTS	100-1400 mvolts	C19
(LF)	OFF	30 + 48	AC MVOLTS	100-1400 mvolts	C17
(LR)	OFF	28 + 46	AC MVOLTS	100-1400 mvolts	C20
(RF)	OFF	29 + 47	AC MVOLTS	100-1400 mvolts	C18
Pump Motor Speed Sensor Resistance	OFF	31 + 49	OHMS	5-100 ohms	EE7
Valve Resistance (SV1)[3]	OFF	3 + 37	OHMS	5-8 ohms	BB18
Valve Resistance (SV2)[3]	OFF	3 + 40	OHMS	5-8 ohms	BB20

FM40293001173028X

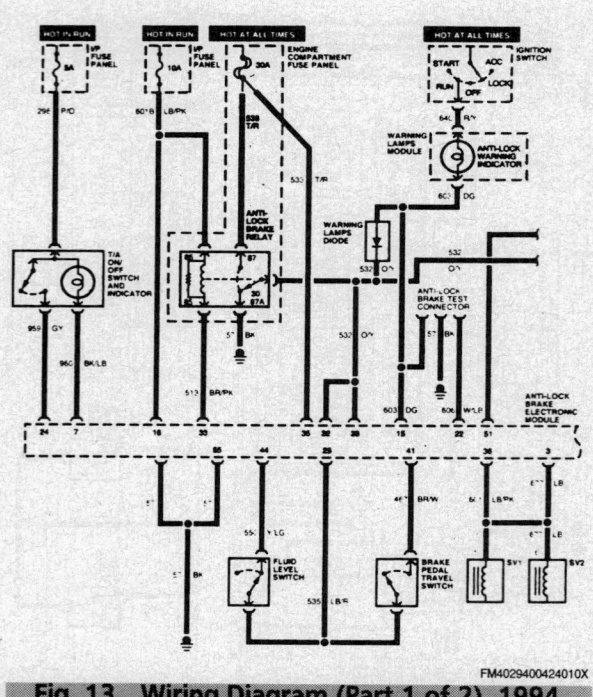

Fig. 13 Wiring Diagram (Part 1 of 2). 1994 Cougar & Thunderbird

FM4029400424010X

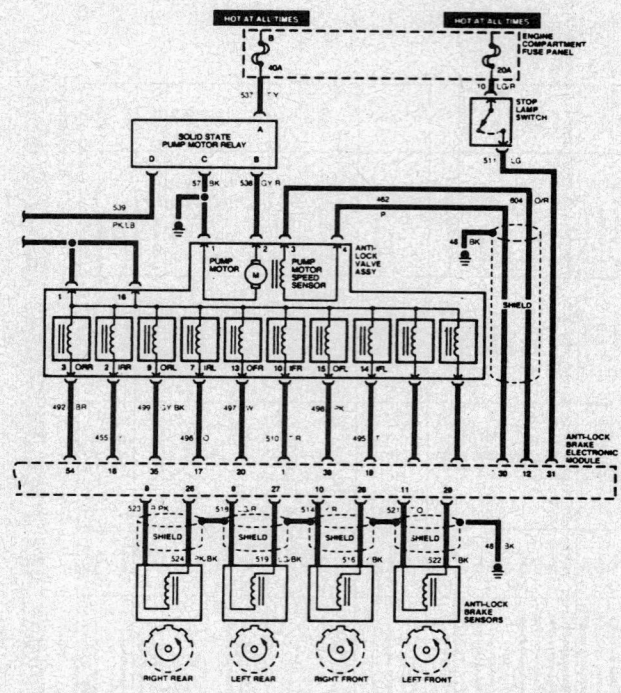

Fig. 13 Wiring Diagram (Part 2 of 2). 1994 Cougar & Thunderbird

FM4029400424020X

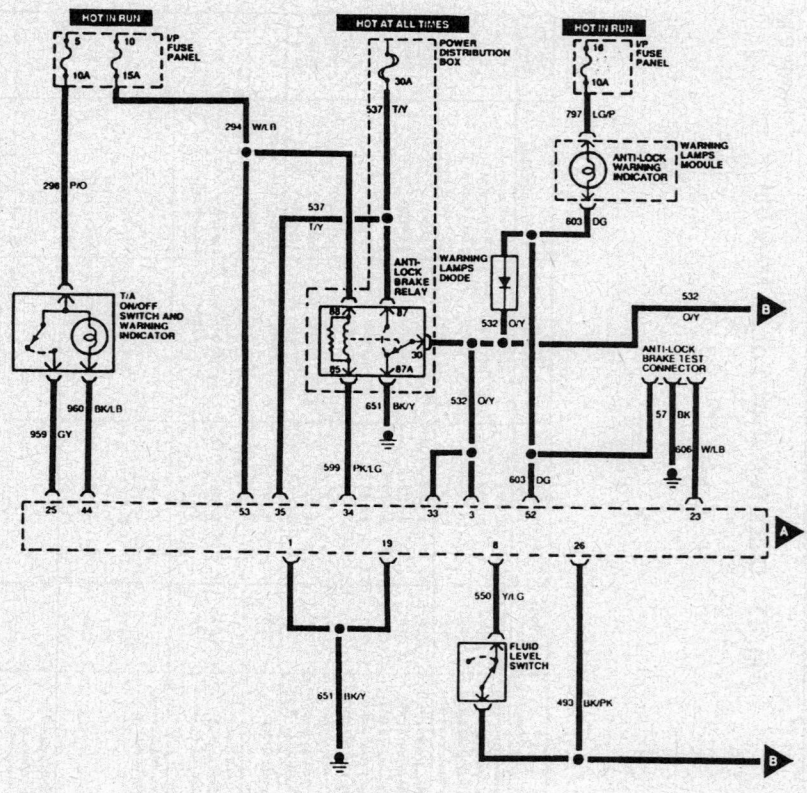

FM4029100180010X

Fig. 14 Wiring diagram (Part 1 of 2). Mark VIII

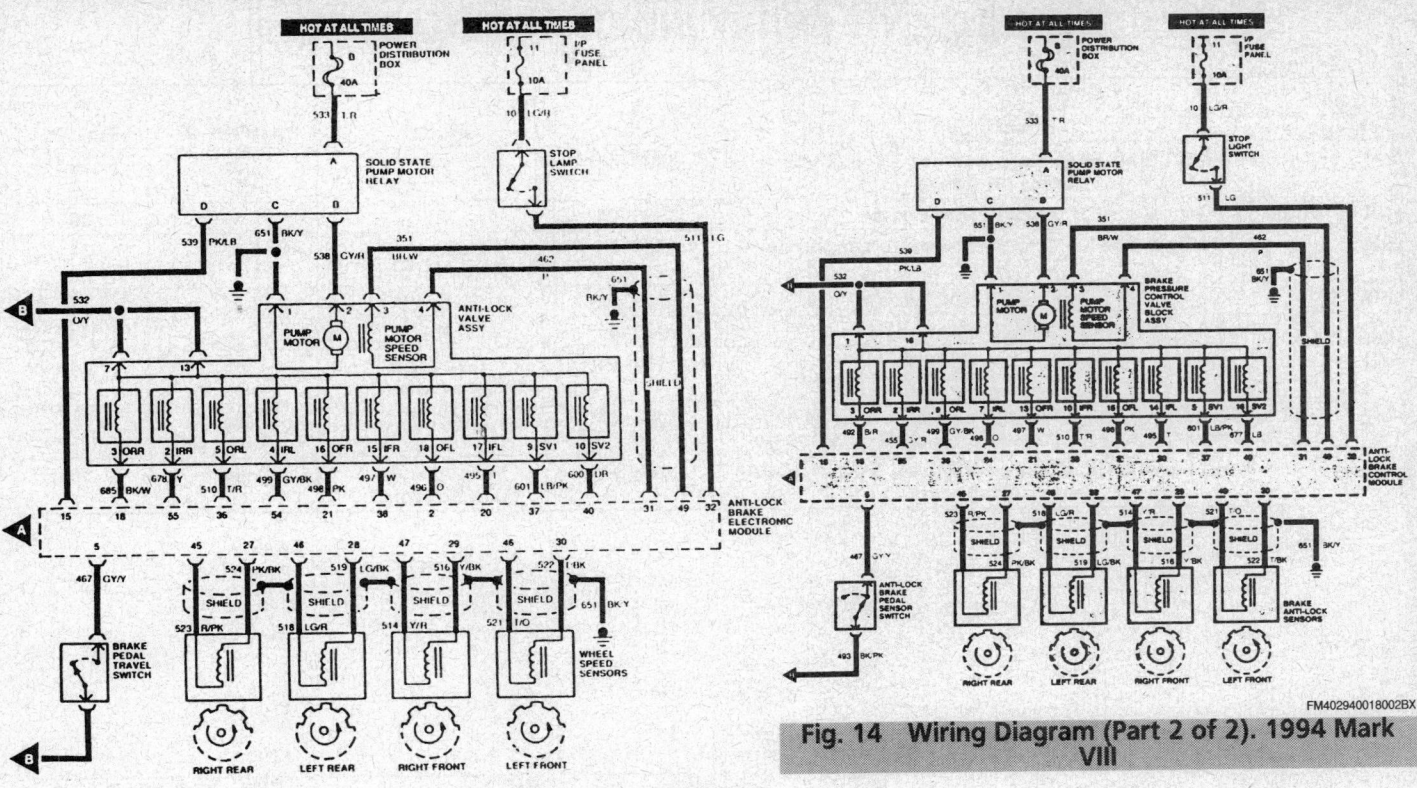

Fig. 14   Wiring diagram (Part 2 of 2). 1993 Mark VIII

Fig. 14   Wiring Diagram (Part 2 of 2). 1994 Mark VIII

DIAGNOSTIC CHART INDEX

Pinpoint Test	Description	Year	Model	Page No. 27-	Fig. No.
A	ABS Warning Lamp On w/Brake Warning Lamp Off	1992–94	Cougar & Thunderbird	48	15
A	ABS Warning Indicator On w/Brake Warning Lamp Off	1993–94	Mark VIII	49	16
B	ABS Lamp On After Engine Starts	1993–94	All	50	17
C	Warning Lamp On After Vehicle Moves/Or False Cycling Of System	1993–94	Cougar & Thunderbird	50	18
C	Anti-Lock Brake Warning Indicator On After Vehicle Starts To Move Or False Cycling Of Anti-Lock System	1993–94	Mark VIII	52	19
D	Brake Pedal Rises Or Drops Excessively During ABS Cycling	1993–94	Cougar & Thunderbird	54	20
D	Anti-Lock Brake Warning Sequence Normal - Brake Pedal Rises Or Drops Excessively During ABS Cycling	1993–94	Mark VIII	54	21
E	ABS Motor Runs Continuously	1993–94	All	55	22
F	Brake Warning Lamp On w/ABS Lamp Off, Parking Brake Released & Lining Wear Checked	1993–94	All	55	23
G	No Warning Lamp On When Ignition Switch Turned On	1993–94	Cougar & Thunderbird	55	24
G	No Anti-Lock Brake Indicator On When Ignition Turned On	1993–94	Mark VIII	55	25
H	Spongy Pedal & No Warning Lamp	1993–94	All	56	26
J	Poor Vehicle Tracking During ABS Function, Warning Lamp Off	1993–94	All	56	27
K	Warning Lamp Sequence Normal, Traction Assist Inoperative	1993–94	All	56	28

Continued

DIAGNOSTIC CHART INDEX —Continued

Pinpoint Test	Description	Year	Model	Page No. 27-	Fig. No.
L	Warning Lamp Sequence Normal, False Cycling Of Traction Assist	1993–94	All	56	29
AA	ABS Module Diagnosis	1993–94	All	56	30
BB	Solenoid Valve & Isolation Valve Diagnosis	1993–94	Cougar & Thunderbird	57	31
BB	Solenoid Valve Diagnosis	1993–94	Mark VIII	58	32
CC	Wheel Sensor Diagnosis	1993–94	All	60	33
DD	Wheel Sensor Diagnosis	1993–94	Cougar & Thunderbird	63	34
DD	Fluid Level Indicator/Anti-Lock Brake Sensor travel Switch/Pump Motor & Relay Diagnosis	1993–94	Mark VIII	65	35
EE	Fluid Level Indicator/Pedal Travel Switch/Motor Pump Diagnosis	1993	Cougar & Thunderbird	66	36

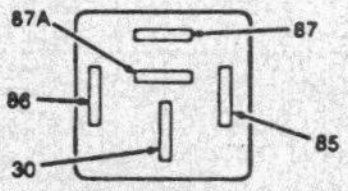

FM4029100181010X

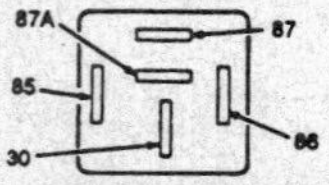

Fig. 15   Test A: ABS Warning Lamp On w/Brake Warning Lamp Off (Part 1 of 3). Cougar & Thunderbird

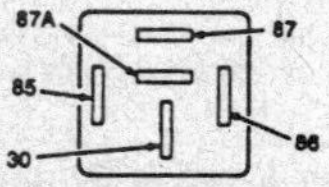

FM4029100181020X

Fig. 15   Test A: ABS Warning Lamp On w/Brake Warning Lamp Off (Part 2 of 3). Cougar & Thunderbird

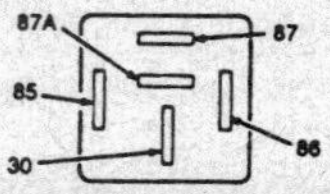

TEST STEP	RESULT	►	ACTION TO TAKE
A11 CHECK RELAY OPERATION • Apply B+ to Pin 86 and B- to Pin 85 on relay. • Check continuity between relay Pins 30 and 87. • Is continuity present?	Yes No	► ►	REVERIFY reading at Step A5. REPLACE main power relay.

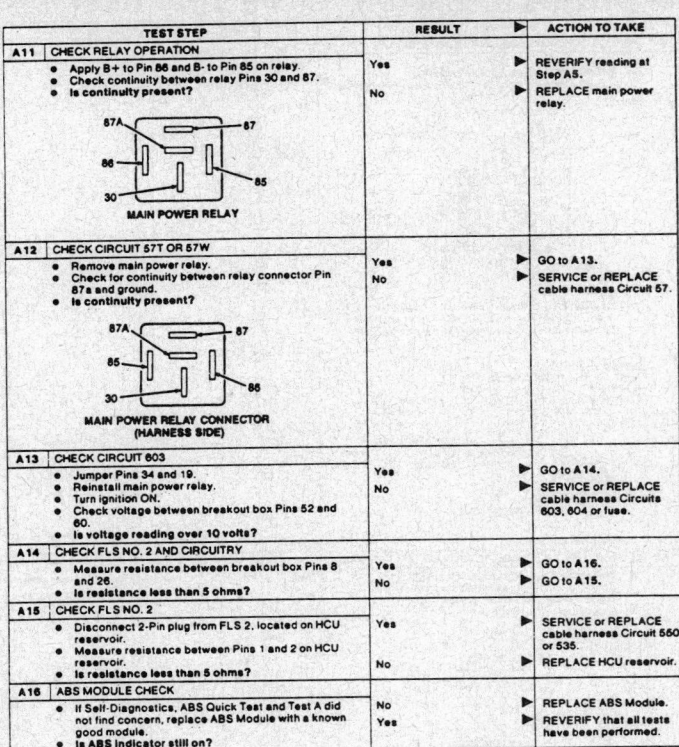

MAIN POWER RELAY

TEST STEP	RESULT	►	ACTION TO TAKE
A12 CHECK CIRCUIT 57T OR 57W • Remove main power relay. • Check for continuity between relay connector Pin 87A and ground. • Is continuity present?	Yes No	► ►	GO to A13. SERVICE or REPLACE cable harness Circuit 57.

MAIN POWER RELAY CONNECTOR (HARNESS SIDE)

TEST STEP	RESULT	►	ACTION TO TAKE
A13 CHECK CIRCUIT 603 • Jumper Pins 34 and 19. • Reinstall main power relay. • Turn ignition ON. • Check voltage between breakout box Pins 52 and 60. • Is voltage reading over 10 volts?	Yes No	► ►	GO to A14. SERVICE or REPLACE cable harness Circuits 603, 604 or fuse.
A14 CHECK FLS NO. 2 AND CIRCUITRY • Measure resistance between breakout box Pins 8 and 26. • Is resistance less than 5 ohms?	Yes No	► ►	GO to A16. GO to A15.
A15 CHECK FLS NO. 2 • Disconnect 2-Pin plug from FLS 2, located on HCU reservoir. • Measure resistance between Pins 1 and 2 on HCU reservoir. • Is resistance less than 5 ohms?	Yes No	► ►	SERVICE or REPLACE cable harness Circuit 550 or 535. REPLACE HCU reservoir.
A16 ABS MODULE CHECK • If Self-Diagnostics, ABS Quick Test and Test A did not find concern, replace ABS Module with a known good module. • Is ABS indicator still on?	No Yes	► ►	REPLACE ABS Module. REVERIFY that all tests have been performed.

FM4029100181030X

Fig. 15   Test A: ABS Warning Lamp On w/Anti-Lock Brake Warning Lamp Off (Part 3 of 3). 1993–94 Cougar & Thunderbird

TEST STEP	RESULT	►	ACTION TO TAKE
A1 CHECK POWER TO ANTI-LOCK BRAKE CONTROL MODULE • Disconnect anti-lock brake wiring from anti-lock brake control module. • Connect Rotunda EEC-IV Breakout Box 014-00322 with Anti-Lock Test Adapter T90P-50-ALA or equivalent to the anti-lock brake wiring harness. • Set multi-meter to read volts DC. • Turn ignition switch to RUN. • Measure voltage between breakout box Pins 53 and 60. • Is voltage reading over 10 volts?	Yes No	► ►	GO to A4. GO to A2.

FM4029400425010X

Fig. 16   Test A: ABS Warning Indicator On w/Brake Warning Lamp Off (Part 1 of 4). 1993–94 Mark VIII

TEST STEP	RESULT	►	ACTION TO TAKE
A2 CHECK ANTI-LOCK BRAKE CONTROL MODULE TO GROUND WIRE • Check continuity between breakout box Pin 60 and body ground. • Is continuity present?	Yes No	► ►	GO to A3. SERVICE or REPLACE cable harness Circuit 651
A3 CHECK IGNITION TO ANTI-LOCK BRAKE CONTROL MODULE WIRE • Check for continuity between breakout box Pin 53 and ignition switch wire Circuit 687. • Is continuity present?	Yes No	► ►	REVERIFY reading at Test Step A1. SERVICE or REPLACE cable harness Circuit 687, 294 or fuse 10.
A4 CHECK GROUND • Check for continuity between breakout box Pins 19 and 60. • Is continuity present?	Yes No	► ►	GO to A5. SERVICE or REPLACE cable harness Circuit 651
A5 CHECK MAIN RELAY OPERATION • Jumper Pins 34 and 60 at breakout box. • Turn ignition switch to RUN position. • Measure voltage between breakout box Pins 33 and 19. • Is voltage reading over 10 volts?	Yes No	► ►	GO to A12. GO to A6.
A6 CHECK MAIN RELAY COIL • Turn ignition switch to OFF. • Remove jumper from breakout box Pins 34 and 60. • Measure resistance between breakout box Pins 53 and 34. • Is resistance between 45 and 90 ohms?	Yes No	► ►	GO to A8. GO to A7.
A7 CHECK MAIN RELAY COIL (Continued) • Remove main power relay. MAIN POWER RELAY • Measure resistance between main relay Pins 85 and 86. • Is resistance between 45 and 90 ohms?	Yes No	► ►	SERVICE or REPLACE cable harness Circuit 599 or 294. REPLACE main relay.

FM4029400425020X

Fig. 16   Test A: ABS Warning Indicator On w/Brake Warning Lamp Off (Part 2 of 4). 1993–94 Mark VIII

TEST STEP	RESULT	►	ACTION TO TAKE
A8 CHECK POWER TO MAIN RELAY COIL • Remove main power relay. • Turn ignition switch to RUN position. MAIN POWER RELAY CONNECTOR (HARNESS SIDE) • Measure voltage between main relay connector Pin 86 and ground. • Is voltage reading over 10 volts?	Yes No	► ►	GO to A9. SERVICE cable harness Circuit 294.
A9 CHECK POWER TO RELAY • Turn ignition switch to RUN position. MAIN POWER RELAY CONNECTOR (HARNESS SIDE) • Measure voltage between main relay connector Pin 87 and ground. • Is voltage reading over 10 volts?	Yes No	► ►	GO to A10. SERVICE cable harness Circuit 537 or 30 amp fuse.
A10 CHECK CIRCUIT 532 • Turn ignition switch OFF MAIN POWER RELAY CONNECTOR (HARNESS SIDE) • Check for continuity between main relay connector Pin 30 and breakout box Pin 33. • Is continuity present?	Yes No	► ►	GO to A11. SERVICE or REPLACE cable harness Circuit 532.

FM4029400425030X

Fig. 16   Test A: ABS Warning Indicator On w/Brake Warning Lamp Off (Part 3 of 4). 1993–94 Mark VIII

TEST STEP	RESULT	▶	ACTION TO TAKE
A11 CHECK RELAY OPERATION • Apply B+ to Pin 86 and B- to Pin 85 on relay • Check continuity between relay Pins 30 and 87 • Is continuity present?	Yes No	▶ ▶	REVERIFY reading at Step A5. REPLACE main power relay
 MAIN POWER RELAY			
A12 CHECK CIRCUIT 651 • Remove main power relay • Check for continuity between relay connector Pin 87a and ground • Is continuity present?	Yes No	▶ ▶	GO to A13. SERVICE or REPLACE cable harness Circuit 651
 MAIN POWER RELAY CONNECTOR (HARNESS SIDE)			
A13 CHECK CIRCUIT 603 • Jumper Pins 34 and 19. • Reinstall main power relay. • Turn ignition switch to RUN. • Check voltage between breakout box Pins 52 and 60. • Is voltage reading over 10 volts?	Yes No	▶ ▶	GO to A14. SERVICE or REPLACE cable harness Circuits 603, 797, 38 or fuse 16.
A14 CHECK FLS NO. 2 AND CIRCUITRY • Measure resistance between breakout box Pins 8 and 26. • Is resistance less than 5 ohms?	Yes No	▶ ▶	GO to A16. GO to A15.
A15 CHECK FLS NO. 2 • Disconnect 2-pin plug from FLS 2, located on hydraulic control unit reservoir. • Measure resistance between Pins 1 and 2 on hydraulic control unit reservoir. • Is resistance less than 5 ohms?	Yes No	▶ ▶	SERVICE or REPLACE cable harness Circuit 550 or 493 REPLACE hydraulic control unit reservoir.
A16 ANTI-LOCK BRAKE CONTROL MODULE CHECK • If Diagnostic Test Mode, ABS Quick Test and Test A did not find concern, replace anti-lock brake control module with a known good anti-lock brake control module. • Is ABS indicator still on?	Yes No	▶ ▶	REVERIFY that all tests have been performed. REPLACE anti-lock brake control module.

FM4029400425040X

Fig. 16   Test A: ABS Warning Indicator On w/Brake Warning Lamp Off (Part 4 of 4). 1993–94 Mark VIII

TEST STEP	RESULT	▶	ACTION TO TAKE
B1 CHECK CONTINUITY OF CIRCUITS 518 AND 519 • Turn ignition switch OFF. • Disconnect 55-pin plug from controller. • Check continuity between Breakout Box Pins 28 and 60.	Yes No	▶ ▶	GO to B2. GO to B3.
 • Connect EEC-IV Breakout Box 014-00322 with Anti-Lock Test Adapter T90P-50-ALA or equivalent to the Anti-Lock 55-pin plug on the wiring harness. • Is continuity present?			
B2 CHECK LH REAR SENSOR TO GROUND • Disconnect LH rear wheel sensor plug. • Check for continuity between each sensor pin (sensor side) and vehicle ground. • Is continuity present?	Yes No	▶ ▶	REPLACE LH rear sensor. REPLACE or SERVICE cable harness Circuit 518 or 519.
 LH REAR SENSOR			
B3 CHECK CONTINUITY OF CIRCUITS 523 AND 524 • Check for continuity between breakout box Pins 27 and 60. • Is continuity present?	Yes No	▶ ▶	GO to B4. GO to B5.

FM4029100182010X

Fig. 17   Test B: ABS Lamp On After Engine Starts (Part 1 of 2). 1993–94

TEST STEP	RESULT	▶	ACTION TO TAKE
B4 CHECK RH REAR SENSOR TO GROUND • Disconnect RH rear wheel sensor plug. • Check for continuity between each sensor pin (sensor side) and vehicle ground. • Is continuity present?	Yes No	▶ ▶	REPLACE RH rear sensor. REPLACE or SERVICE cable harness Circuit 523 or 524.
 RH REAR SENSOR			
B5 CHECK CONTINUITY OF CIRCUITS 514 AND 516 • Check for continuity between breakout box Pin 29 and 60. • Is continuity present?	Yes No	▶ ▶	GO to B6. GO to B7.
B6 CHECK RH FRONT SENSOR TO GROUND • Disconnect RH front wheel sensor plug. • Check for continuity between each sensor pin (sensor side) and vehicle ground. • Is continuity present?	Yes No	▶ ▶	REPLACE RH front sensor. REPLACE or SERVICE cable harness Circuit 514 or 516.
 RH FRONT SENSOR			
B7 CHECK CONTINUITY OF CIRCUITS 521 AND 522 • Check for continuity between breakout box Pins 30 and 60. • Is continuity present?	Yes No	▶ ▶	GO to B8. Test Complete. If Anti-Lock indicator pattern remains, REPEAT Test B.
B8 CHECK LH FRONT SENSOR TO GROUND • Disconnect LH front wheel sensor plug. • Check for continuity between each sensor pin (sensor side) and vehicle ground. • Is continuity present?	Yes No	▶ ▶	REPLACE LH front sensor. REPLACE or SERVICE cable harness Circuit 521 or 522.
 LH FRONT SENSOR			

FM4029100182020X

Fig. 17   Test B: ABS Lamp On After Engine Starts (Part 2 of 2). 1993–94

TEST STEP	RESULT	▶	ACTION TO TAKE
C1 MEASURE LH FRONT SENSOR CIRCUIT RESISTANCE • Turn ignition switch to OFF position. • Disconnect 55-pin connector from ABS module.	Yes No	▶ ▶	GO to C3. GO to C2.
 • Connect EEC-IV Breakout Box 014-00322 with Anti-Lock Test Adapter T90P-50-ALA or equivalent to the 55-pin connector on wiring harness. • Set multi-meter to read resistance. • Measure resistance between Pins 30 and 48. • Is resistance between 800 and 1400 ohms?			
C2 CHECK LH FRONT SENSOR RESISTANCE • Disconnect LH front sensor plug. • Measure resistance of sensor at sensor plug. • Is resistance between 800 and 1400 ohms?	Yes No	▶ ▶	SERVICE or REPLACE cable harness Circuit 521 or 522. REPLACE LH front sensor.
 LH FRONT SENSOR			
C3 MEASURE RH FRONT SENSOR CIRCUIT RESISTANCE • Measure resistance between breakout box Pins 29 and 47. • Is resistance between 800 and 1400 ohms?	Yes No	▶ ▶	GO to C5. GO to C4.

FM4029100183010X

Fig. 18   Test C: Warning Lamp On After Vehicle Moves/Or False Cycling Of System (Part 1 of 7). 1993–94 Cougar & Thunderbird

TEST STEP	RESULT	▶	ACTION TO TAKE
C4 CHECK RH FRONT SENSOR RESISTANCE • Disconnect RH front sensor plug. • Measure resistance of sensor at sensor plug. • Is resistance between 800 and 1400 ohms?	Yes No	▶ ▶	SERVICE or REPLACE cable harness Circuit 514 or 516. REPLACE RH front sensor.

RH FRONT SENSOR

TEST STEP	RESULT	▶	ACTION TO TAKE
C5 MEASURE RH REAR SENSOR CIRCUIT RESISTANCE • Measure resistance between breakout box Pins 27 and 45. • Is resistance between 800 and 1400 ohms?	Yes No	▶ ▶	GO to C7. GO to C6.
C6 CHECK RH REAR SENSOR RESISTANCE • Disconnect RH rear sensor plug. • Measure resistance of sensor at sensor plug. • Is resistance between 800 and 1400 ohms?	Yes No	▶ ▶	SERVICE or REPLACE cable harness Circuit 523 or 524. REPLACE RH rear sensor.

RH REAR SENSOR

TEST STEP	RESULT	▶	ACTION TO TAKE
C7 MEASURE LH REAR SENSOR CIRCUIT RESISTANCE • Measure resistance between breakout box Pins 28 and 46. • Is resistance between 800 and 1400 ohms?	Yes No	▶ ▶	GO to C9. GO to C8.
C8 CHECK LH REAR SENSOR RESISTANCE • Disconnect LH rear sensor plug. • Measure resistance of sensor at sensor plug. • Is resistance between 800 and 1400 ohms?	Yes No	▶ ▶	SERVICE or REPLACE cable harness Circuit 518 or 519. REPLACE LH rear sensor

LH REAR SENSOR

TEST STEP	RESULT	▶	ACTION TO TAKE
C9 CHECK LH FRONT SENSOR AND CIRCUITRY TO GROUND • Check for continuity between breakout box Pins 30 and 60. • Is continuity present?	Yes No	▶ ▶	GO to C10. GO to C11.

FM4029100183020X

Fig. 18 Test C: Warning Lamp On After Vehicle Moves/Or False Cycling Of System (Part 2 of 7). 1993–94 Cougar & Thunderbird

TEST STEP	RESULT	▶	ACTION TO TAKE
C10 CHECK LH FRONT SENSOR TO GROUND • Disconnect LH front sensor plug. • Check for continuity between each sensor pin and body ground. • Is continuity present?	Yes No	▶ ▶	REPLACE LH front sensor. SERVICE or REPLACE cable harness Circuit 521 or 522.
C11 CHECK RH FRONT SENSOR AND CIRCUITRY TO GROUND • Check for continuity between breakout box Pins 29 and 60. • Is continuity present?	Yes No	▶ ▶	GO to C12. GO to C13.
C12 CHECK RH FRONT SENSOR TO GROUND • Disconnect RH front sensor plug. • Check for continuity between each sensor pin and body ground. • Is continuity present?	Yes No	▶ ▶	REPLACE RH front sensor. SERVICE or REPLACE cable harness Circuit 514 or 516.
C13 CHECK RH REAR SENSOR AND CIRCUITRY TO GROUND • Check for continuity between breakout box Pins 27 and 60. • Is continuity present?	Yes No	▶ ▶	GO to C14. GO to C15.
C14 CHECK RH REAR SENSOR TO GROUND • Disconnect RH rear sensor plug. • Check for continuity between each sensor pin and body ground. • Is continuity present?	Yes No	▶ ▶	REPLACE RH rear sensor. SERVICE or REPLACE cable harness Circuit 523 or 524.
C15 CHECK LH REAR SENSOR AND CIRCUITRY TO GROUND • Check for continuity between breakout box Pins 28 and 60. • Is continuity present?	Yes No	▶ ▶	GO to C16. GO to C17.
C16 CHECK LH REAR SENSOR TO GROUND • Disconnect LH rear sensor plug. • Check for continuity between each sensor pin and body ground. • Is continuity present?	Yes No	▶ ▶	REPLACE LH rear sensor. SERVICE or REPLACE cable harness Circuit 518 or 519.
C17 CHECK LH FRONT SENSOR VOLTAGE OUTPUT • Measure voltage between breakout box Pins 30 and 48 while spinning LH front wheel at approximately 1 revolution per second.	Between 0.10 and 1.40 volts AC Less than 0.10 or more than 1.40 volts AC	▶ ▶	GO to C18. CHECK wheel sensor mounting, air gap or toothed wheel. CORRECT as required.
C18 CHECK RH FRONT SENSOR VOLTAGE OUTPUT • Measure voltage between breakout box Pins 29 and 47 while spinning RH front wheel at approximately 1 revolution per second.	Between 0.10 and 1.40 volts AC Less than 0.10 or more than 1.40 volts AC	▶ ▶	GO to C19. CHECK wheel sensor mounting, air gap or toothed wheel. CORRECT as required.

FM4029100183030X

Fig. 18 Test C: Warning Lamp On After Vehicle Moves/Or False Cycling Of System (Part 3 of 7). 1993–94 Cougar & Thunderbird

TEST STEP	RESULT	▶	ACTION TO TAKE
C19 CHECK RH REAR SENSOR VOLTAGE OUTPUT • Measure voltage between breakout box Pins 27 and 45 while spinning RH rear wheel at approximately 1 revolution per second.	Between 0.10 and 1.40 volts AC Less than 0.10 or more than 1.40 volts AC	▶ ▶	GO to C20. CHECK wheel sensor mounting, air gap or toothed wheel. CORRECT as required.
C20 CHECK LH REAR SENSOR VOLTAGE OUTPUT • Measure voltage between breakout box Pins 28 and 46 while spinning LH rear wheel at approximately 1 revolution per second.	Between 0.10 and 1.40 volts AC Less than 0.10 or more than 1.40 volts AC	▶ ▶	GO to C21. CHECK wheel sensor mounting, air gap or toothed wheel. CORRECT as required.
C21 CHECK MOTOR SPEED SENSOR AND CIRCUITRY • Measure resistance between breakout box Pins 31 and 49. • Is resistance between 5 and 100 ohms?	Yes No	▶ ▶	GO to C27. GO to C22.
C22 CHECK PUMP MOTOR SPEED SENSOR • Disconnect 4-pin plug on pump motor. • Measure resistance between Pins S0 and S1 on pump motor. • Is resistance between 5 and 100 ohms?	Yes No	▶ ▶	SERVICE or REPLACE cable harness Circuit 462 or 604. REPLACE pump and motor.

NEGATIVE PIN
S1
S0
POSITIVE PIN

TEST STEP	RESULT	▶	ACTION TO TAKE
C23 CHECK MOTOR SPEED SENSOR SHORT TO BATTERY + • Turn ignition switch to ON. • Measure voltage between breakout box Pins 31 and 60.	No voltage 12 volts	▶ ▶	GO to C26. GO to C24.
C24 CHECK CIRCUIT 462 • Disconnect pump motor relay 4-pin plug connector. • Turn ignition switch to ON. • Measure voltage between breakout box Pins 31 and 60.	No voltage 12 volts	▶ ▶	GO to C25. SERVICE or REPLACE cable harness circuit 462.
C25 CHECK CIRCUIT 604 • Turn ignition switch to ON. • Measure voltage between breakout box Pins 49 and 60.	No voltage 12 volts	▶ ▶	REPLACE pump and motor assembly. SERVICE or REPLACE cable harness Circuit 604.
C26 CHECK MOTOR SPEED SENSOR SHORT TO GROUND • Check for continuity between breakout box Pins 31 and 60. • Is continuity present?	No Yes	▶ ▶	GO to C29. GO to C27.

FM4029100183040X

Fig. 18 Test C: Warning Lamp On After Vehicle Moves/Or False Cycling Of System (Part 4 of 7). 1993–94 Cougar & Thunderbird

TEST STEP	RESULT	▶	ACTION TO TAKE
C27 CHECK CIRCUIT 462 • Disconnect pump to motor relay 4-pin plug connector. • Check for continuity between breakout box Pins 31 and 60. • Is continuity present?	Yes No	▶ ▶	SERVICE or REPLACE cable harness circuit 462. GO to C28.
C28 CHECK CIRCUIT 604 • Check for continuity between breakout box Pins 49 and 60. • Is continuity present?	Yes No	▶ ▶	SERVICE or REPLACE cable harness Circuit 604. REPLACE pump and motor assembly.
C29 CHECK PUMP MOTOR OPERATION • Reconnect pump motor relay to pump and wire harness. • Jumper Pins 15 and 60 at breakout box. • Does pump motor run?	Yes No	▶ ▶	REPLACE controller. GO to C30.
C30 CHECK CIRCUIT 539 • Check for continuity between wire harness to pump motor relay connector Pin D and breakout box pin 15. • Is continuity present?	Yes No	▶ ▶	GO to C31. SERVICE or REPLACE cable harness circuit 539.

PUMP MOTOR RELAY CONNECTOR HARNESS SIDE
A B C D

TEST STEP	RESULT	▶	ACTION TO TAKE
C31 CHECK POWER TO RELAY • Disconnect wire harness from pump motor relay. • Check voltage between wire harness to pump motor relay connector Pin A and ground. • Is voltage reading over 10 volts?	Yes No	▶ ▶	GO to C32. SERVICE or REPLACE battery, 40 amp fuse, circuit 537, 38 or 37.

PUMP MOTOR RELAY CONNECTOR HARNESS SIDE
A B C D

FM4029100183050X

Fig. 18 Test C: Warning Lamp On After Vehicle Moves/Or False Cycling Of System (Part 5 of 7). 1993–94 Cougar & Thunderbird

TEST STEP	RESULT	▶	ACTION TO TAKE
C32 CHECK CIRCUIT 57			
• Check for continuity between wire harness to pump motor relay connector Pin C and ground. • Is continuity present?	Yes No	▶ ▶	GO to C33. SERVICE or REPLACE cable harness Circuit 57.
C33 CHECK PUMP MOTOR			
• Jumper Pins A and B on wire harness to pump motor relay connector. • Does motor run?	Yes No	▶ ▶	REPLACE pump motor relay. GO to C34.

FM4029100183060X

Fig. 18   Test C: Warning Lamp On After Vehicle Moves/Or False Cycling Of System (Part 6 of 7). 1993–94 Cougar & Thunderbird

TEST STEP	RESULT	▶	ACTION TO TAKE
C34 CHECK CIRCUIT 538			
• Check for continuity between wire harness to pump motor relay connector Pin B and switched B+ Pin on 4 Pin pump motor connector harness side.	Yes No	▶ ▶	GO to C35. SERVICE or REPLACE cable harness circuit 538.
• Is continuity present?			
C35 CHECK PUMP MOTOR GROUND			
• Check for continuity between B- pin on 4 pin pump motor connector harness side and chassis ground.	Yes No	▶ ▶	REPLACE pump motor assembly. SERVICE or REPLACE cable harness circuit 57.
• Is continuity present?			

FM4029100183070X

Fig. 18   Test C: Warning Lamp On After Vehicle Moves/Or False Cycling Of System (Part 7 of 7). 1993–94 Cougar & Thunderbird

TEST STEP	RESULT	▶	ACTION TO TAKE
C1 MEASURE LH FRONT SENSOR CIRCUIT RESISTANCE			
• Turn ignition switch to OFF position • Disconnect anti-lock brake wiring from anti-lock brake control module	Yes No	▶ ▶	GO to C3. GO to C2.

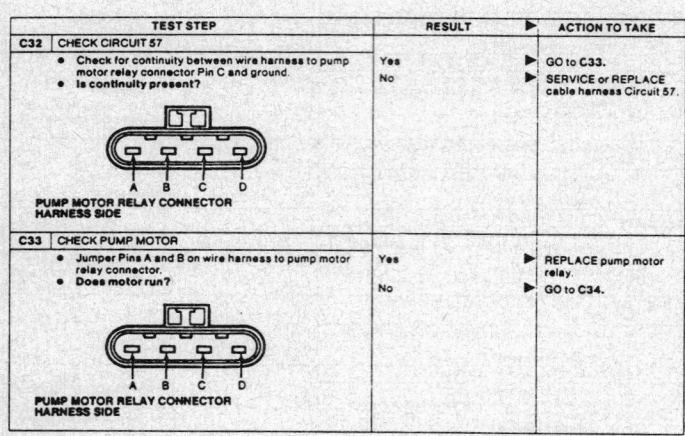

• Connect EEC-IV Breakout Box 014-00322 with Anti-Lock Test Adapter T90P-50-ALA to the 55-pin connector on anti-lock brake wiring harness

• Set multi-meter to read resistance
• Measure resistance between Pins 30 and 48
• Is resistance between 800 and 1400 ohms?

TEST STEP	RESULT	▶	ACTION TO TAKE
C2 CHECK LH FRONT BRAKE ANTI-LOCK SENSOR RESISTANCE			
• Disconnect LH front brake anti-lock sensor plug. • Measure resistance of front brake anti-lock sensor at sensor plug. • Is resistance between 800 and 1400 ohms?	Yes No	▶ ▶	SERVICE or REPLACE cable harness Circuit 521 or 522 REPLACE LH front brake anti-lock sensor

FM4029400426010Y

Fig. 19   Test C: Anti-Lock Brake Warning Indicator On After Vehicle Starts To Move Or False Cycling Of Anti-Lock System (Part 1 of 7). 1993–94 Mark VIII

TEST STEP	RESULT	▶	ACTION TO TAKE
C3 MEASURE RH FRONT BRAKE ANTI-LOCK SENSOR CIRCUIT RESISTANCE			
• Measure resistance between breakout box Pins 29 and 47 • Is resistance between 800 and 1400 ohms?	Yes No	▶ ▶	GO to C5. GO to C4.
C4 CHECK RH FRONT BRAKE ANTI-LOCK SENSOR RESISTANCE			
• Disconnect RH front brake anti-lock sensor plug. • Measure resistance of front brake anti-lock sensor at sensor plug. • Is resistance between 800 and 1400 ohms?	Yes No	▶ ▶	SERVICE or REPLACE cable harness Circuit 514 or 516. REPLACE RH front brake anti-lock sensor
C5 MEASURE RH REAR BRAKE ANTI-LOCK SENSOR CIRCUIT RESISTANCE			
• Measure resistance between breakout box Pins 27 and 45. • Is resistance between 800 and 1400 ohms?	Yes No	▶ ▶	GO to C7. GO to C6.
C6 CHECK RH REAR BRAKE ANTI-LOCK SENSOR RESISTANCE			
• Disconnect RH rear brake anti-lock sensor plug. • Measure resistance of rear brake anti-lock sensor at sensor plug. • Is resistance between 800 and 1400 ohms?	Yes No	▶ ▶	SERVICE or REPLACE cable harness Circuit 523 or 524. REPLACE RH rear brake anti-lock sensor
C7 MEASURE LH REAR BRAKE ANTI-LOCK SENSOR CIRCUIT RESISTANCE			
• Measure resistance between breakout box Pins 28 and 46. • Is resistance between 800 and 1400 ohms?	Yes No	▶ ▶	GO to C9. GO to C8.

FM4029400426020X

Fig. 19   Test C: Anti-Lock Brake Warning Indicator On After Vehicle Starts To Move Or False Cycling Of Anti-Lock System (Part 2 of 7). 1993–94 Mark VIII

TEST STEP	RESULT	▶	ACTION TO TAKE
C8 CHECK LH REAR BRAKE ANTI-LOCK SENSOR RESISTANCE • Disconnect LH rear brake anti-lock sensor plug • Measure resistance of rear brake anti-lock sensor at sensor plug • Is resistance between 800 and 1400 ohms?	Yes No	▶ ▶	SERVICE or REPLACE cable harness Circuit 518 or 519 REPLACE LH rear brake anti-lock sensor
 LH REAR BRAKE ANTI-LOCK SENSOR			
C9 CHECK LH FRONT BRAKE ANTI-LOCK SENSOR AND CIRCUITRY TO GROUND • Check for continuity between breakout box Pins 30 and 60. • Is continuity present?	Yes No	▶ ▶	GO to C10. GO to C11.
C10 CHECK LH FRONT BRAKE ANTI-LOCK SENSOR TO GROUND • Disconnect LH front brake anti-lock sensor plug • Check for continuity between each sensor pin and body ground • Is continuity present?	Yes No	▶ ▶	REPLACE LH front brake anti-lock sensor SERVICE or REPLACE cable harness Circuit 521 or 522
C11 CHECK RH FRONT BRAKE ANTI-LOCK SENSOR AND CIRCUITRY TO GROUND • Check for continuity between breakout box Pins 29 and 60. • Is continuity present?	Yes No	▶ ▶	GO to C12. GO to C13.
C12 CHECK RH FRONT BRAKE ANTI-LOCK SENSOR TO GROUND • Disconnect RH front brake anti-lock sensor plug • Check for continuity between each front brake anti-lock sensor pin and body ground. • Is continuity present?	Yes No	▶ ▶	REPLACE RH front brake anti-lock sensor SERVICE or REPLACE cable harness Circuit 514 or 516
C13 CHECK RH REAR BRAKE ANTI-LOCK SENSOR AND CIRCUITRY TO GROUND • Check for continuity between breakout box Pins 27 and 60. • Is continuity present?	Yes No	▶ ▶	GO to C14. GO to C15.
C14 CHECK RH REAR BRAKE ANTI-LOCK SENSOR TO GROUND • Disconnect RH rear brake anti-lock sensor plug. • Check for continuity between each rear brake anti-lock sensor pin and body ground. • Is continuity present?	Yes No	▶ ▶	REPLACE RH rear brake anti-lock sensor SERVICE or REPLACE cable harness Circuit 523 or 524
C15 CHECK LH REAR BRAKE ANTI-LOCK SENSOR AND CIRCUITRY TO GROUND • Check for continuity between breakout box Pins 28 and 60. • Is continuity present?	Yes No	▶ ▶	GO to C16. GO to C17.

FM4029400426030X

Fig. 19 Test C: Anti-Lock Brake Warning Indicator On After Vehicle Starts To Move Or False Cycling Of Anti-Lock System (Part 3 of 7). 1993–94 Mark VIII

TEST STEP	RESULT	▶	ACTION TO TAKE
C16 CHECK LH REAR BRAKE ANTI-LOCK SENSOR TO GROUND • Disconnect LH rear brake anti-lock sensor plug. • Check for continuity between each rear brake anti-lock sensor pin and body ground. • Is continuity present?	Yes No	▶ ▶	REPLACE LH rear brake anti-lock sensor SERVICE or REPLACE cable harness Circuit 518 or 519
C17 CHECK LH FRONT BRAKE ANTI-LOCK SENSOR VOLTAGE OUTPUT • Measure voltage between breakout box Pins 30 and 48 while spinning LH front wheel at approximately 1 revolution per second • Is voltage between 0.10 and 1.40 volts AC?	Yes No	▶ ▶	GO to C18. CHECK front brake anti-lock sensor mounting, air gap or front brake anti-lock sensor indicator. CORRECT as required.
C18 CHECK RH FRONT BRAKE ANTI-LOCK SENSOR VOLTAGE OUTPUT • Measure voltage between breakout box Pins 29 and 47 while spinning RH front wheel at approximately 1 revolution per second • Is voltage between 0.10 and 1.40 volts AC?	Yes No	▶ ▶	GO to C19. CHECK front brake anti-lock sensor mounting, air gap or front brake anti-lock sensor indicator. CORRECT as required
C19 CHECK RH REAR BRAKE ANTI-LOCK SENSOR VOLTAGE OUTPUT • Measure voltage between breakout box Pins 27 and 45 while spinning RH rear wheel at approximately 1 revolution per second • Is voltage between 0.10 and 1.40 volts AC?	Yes No	▶ ▶	GO to C20. CHECK rear brake anti-lock sensor mounting, air gap or front brake anti-lock sensor indicator. CORRECT as required
C20 CHECK LH REAR BRAKE ANTI-LOCK SENSOR VOLTAGE OUTPUT • Measure voltage between breakout box Pins 28 and 46 while spinning LH rear wheel at approximately 1 revolution per second • Is voltage between 0.10 and 1.40 volts AC?	Yes No	▶ ▶	GO to C21. CHECK rear brake anti-lock sensor mounting, air gap or rear brake anti-lock sensor indicator. CORRECT as required
C21 CHECK PUMP MOTOR SPEED SENSOR AND CIRCUITRY • Measure resistance between breakout box Pins 31 and 49 • Is resistance between 5 and 100 ohms?	Yes No	▶ ▶	GO to C23. GO to C22.

FM4029400426040X

Fig. 19 Test C: Anti-Lock Brake Warning Indicator On After Vehicle Starts To Move Or False Cycling Of Anti-Lock System (Part 4 of 7). 1993–94 Mark VIII

TEST STEP	RESULT	▶	ACTION TO TAKE
C22 CHECK PUMP MOTOR SPEED SENSOR • Disconnect 4-pin plug on pump motor. • Measure resistance between Pins S0 and S1 on pump motor • Is resistance between 5 and 100 ohms?	Yes No	▶ ▶	SERVICE or REPLACE cable harness Circuit 462 or 351 REPLACE pump motor.
 PUMP MOTOR CONNECTOR PUMP SIDE — NEGATIVE PIN / POSITIVE PIN — S1 — S0			
C23 CHECK PUMP MOTOR SPEED SENSOR SHORT TO BATTERY + • Turn ignition switch to RUN • Measure voltage between breakout box Pins 31 and 60. • Is B+ present?	Yes No	▶ ▶	GO to C24. GO to C26.
C24 CHECK CIRCUIT 462 • Disconnect pump motor relay 4-pin plug connector • Turn ignition switch to RUN • Measure voltage between breakout box Pins 31 and 60. • Is B+ present?	Yes No	▶ ▶	SERVICE or REPLACE cable harness Circuit 462. GO to C25.
C25 CHECK CIRCUIT 351 • Turn ignition switch to RUN • Measure voltage between breakout box Pins 49 and 60 • Is B+ present?	Yes No	▶ ▶	SERVICE or REPLACE cable harness Circuit 351 REPLACE pump motor.
C26 CHECK PUMP MOTOR SPEED SENSOR SHORT TO GROUND • Check for continuity between breakout box Pins 31 and 60. • Is continuity present?	Yes No	▶ ▶	GO to C27. GO to C29.
C27 CHECK CIRCUIT 462 • Disconnect pump motor relay 4-pin plug connector • Check for continuity between breakout box Pins 31 and 60. • Is continuity present?	Yes No	▶ ▶	SERVICE or REPLACE cable harness Circuit 462. GO to C28.
C28 CHECK CIRCUIT 351 • Check for continuity between breakout box Pins 49 and 60. • Is continuity present?	Yes No	▶ ▶	SERVICE or REPLACE cable harness Circuit 351. REPLACE pump and pump motor assembly
C29 CHECK PUMP MOTOR OPERATION • Reconnect pump motor relay to pump and wire harness. • Jumper Pins 15 and 60 at breakout box • Does pump motor run?	Yes No	▶ ▶	REPLACE anti-lock brake control module. GO to C30.

FM4029400426050X

Fig. 19 Test C: Anti-Lock Brake Warning Indicator On After Vehicle Starts To Move Or False Cycling Of Anti-Lock System (Part 5 of 7). 1993–94 Mark VIII

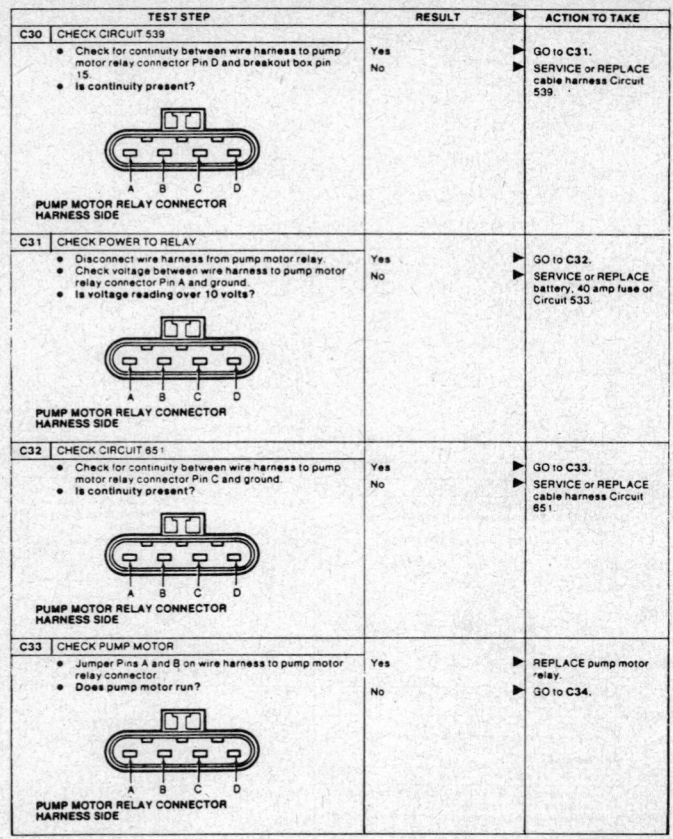

TEST STEP		RESULT	▶	ACTION TO TAKE
C30	**CHECK CIRCUIT 539**			
	• Check for continuity between wire harness to pump motor relay connector Pin D and breakout box pin 15. • Is continuity present?	Yes No	▶ ▶	GO to C31. SERVICE or REPLACE cable harness Circuit 539.
	PUMP MOTOR RELAY CONNECTOR HARNESS SIDE			
C31	**CHECK POWER TO RELAY**			
	• Disconnect wire harness from pump motor relay. • Check voltage between wire harness to pump motor relay connector Pin A and ground. • Is voltage reading over 10 volts?	Yes No	▶ ▶	GO to C32. SERVICE or REPLACE battery, 40 amp fuse or Circuit 533.
	PUMP MOTOR RELAY CONNECTOR HARNESS SIDE			
C32	**CHECK CIRCUIT 651**			
	• Check for continuity between wire harness to pump motor relay connector Pin C and ground. • Is continuity present?	Yes No	▶ ▶	GO to C33. SERVICE or REPLACE cable harness Circuit 651.
	PUMP MOTOR RELAY CONNECTOR HARNESS SIDE			
C33	**CHECK PUMP MOTOR**			
	• Jumper Pins A and B on wire harness to pump motor relay connector. • Does pump motor run?	Yes No	▶ ▶	REPLACE pump motor relay. GO to C34.
	PUMP MOTOR RELAY CONNECTOR HARNESS SIDE			

FM4029400426060X

Fig. 19   Test C: Anti-Lock Brake Warning Indicator On After Vehicle Starts To Move Or False Cycling Of Anti-Lock System (Part 6 of 7). 1993–94 Mark VIII

TEST STEP		RESULT	▶	ACTION TO TAKE
C34	**CHECK CIRCUIT 538**			
	• Check for continuity between wire harness to pump motor relay connector Pin B and switched B+ Pin on 4-pin pump motor connector harness side.	Yes No	▶ ▶	GO to C35. SERVICE or REPLACE cable harness Circuit 538
	PUMP MOTOR RELAY CONNECTOR HARNESS SIDE B- CIRCUIT 651 CIRCUIT 351 CIRCUIT 462 SWITCHED B+ CIRCUIT 538 **4 PIN PUMP MOTOR CONNECTOR HARNESS SIDE** • Is continuity present?			
C35	**CHECK PUMP MOTOR GROUND**			
	• Check for continuity between B- pin on 4-pin pump motor connector harness side and chassis ground.	Yes No	▶ ▶	REPLACE pump motor assembly. SERVICE or REPLACE cable harness Circuit 651.
	B- CIRCUIT 651 CIRCUIT 351 CIRCUIT 462 SWITCHED B+ CIRCUIT 538 **4 PIN PUMP MOTOR CONNECTOR HARNESS SIDE** • Is continuity present?			

FM4029400426070X

Fig. 19   Test C: Anti-Lock Brake Warning Indicator On After Vehicle Starts To Move Or False Cycling Of Anti-Lock System (Part 7 of 7). 1993–94 Mark VIII

TEST STEP		RESULT	▶	ACTION TO TAKE
D1	**CHECK PEDAL SWITCH—NORMAL POSITION**			
	• Disconnect pedal travel switch 2-pin plug. • Check for continuity between Pins 1 and 2. • Is continuity present?	Yes No	▶ ▶	GO to D2. REPLACE pedal travel switch.
D2	**CHECK PEDAL SWITCH—SWITCHED POSITION**			
	• Push brake pedal down at least 3 inches and hold down. • Check for continuity between pedal travel switch Pins 1 and 2. • Is continuity present? NOTE: If new pedal switch is installed and test D2 results in pedal switch not functioning again. Booster assembly must be replaced.	Yes No	▶ ▶	REPLACE pedal travel switch. GO to D3.
D3	**CHECK CIRCUITS 467 AND 535**			
	• Reconnect pedal travel switch 2-pin plug. • Connect EEC-IV breakout box 014-00322 with Anti-Lock Test Adapter T90P-50-ALA to the anti-lock 55-pin plug on the wiring harness. ANTI-LOCK TEST ADAPTER 55 PIN CONNECTOR EEC-IV BREAKOUT BOX • Check for continuity between breakout box pins 5 and 26. • Is continuity present?	Yes No	▶ ▶	GO to D4. SERVICE or REPLACE cable harness Circuit 467 or 535.
D4	**CHECK PUMP PRESSURE**			
	• Jumper Pins 15 and 60 at breakout box. (Pump should run.) • Apply brake pedal. • Does brake pedal rise?	Yes No	▶ ▶	REVERIFY that brake pedal rises or drops excessively during ABS cycling. REPLACE pump and motor.

FM4029100184000X

Fig. 20   Test D: Brake Pedal Rises Or Drops Excessively During ABS Cycling. 1993–94 Cougar & Thunderbird

TEST STEP		RESULT	▶	ACTION TO TAKE
D1	**CHECK ANTI-LOCK BRAKE PEDAL SENSOR SWITCH—NORMAL POSITION**			
	• Disconnect anti-lock brake pedal sensor switch 2-pin plug. • Check for continuity between Pins 1 and 2 • Is continuity present?	Yes No	▶ ▶	GO to D2. REPLACE anti-lock brake pedal sensor switch

FM4029400427010X

Fig. 21   Test D: Anti-Lock Brake Warning Sequence Normal - Brake Pedal Rises Or Drops Excessively During ABS Cycling (Part 1 of 2). 1993–94 Mark VIII

TEST STEP	RESULT	▶	ACTION TO TAKE
D2 CHECK ANTI-LOCK BRAKE PEDAL SENSOR SWITCH—SWITCHED POSITION			
• Push brake pedal down at least 3 inches and hold down. • Check for continuity between anti-lock brake pedal sensor switch Pins 1 and 2. • Is continuity present?	Yes	▶	REPLACE anti-lock brake pedal sensor switch.
	No	▶	GO to D3.
NOTE: If new anti-lock brake pedal sensor switch is installed and test D2 results in anti-lock brake pedal sensor switch not functioning again, power brake booster assembly must be replaced.			
D3 CHECK CIRCUITS 467 AND 535			
• Reconnect anti-lock brake pedal sensor switch 2-pin plug. • Connect EEC-IV Breakout Box 014-00322 with Anti-Lock Test Adapter T90P-50-ALA to the anti-lock 55-pin plug on the anti-lock brake wiring harness.	Yes	▶	GO to D4.
	No	▶	SERVICE or REPLACE cable harness Circuit 467 or 493.
• Check for continuity between breakout box pins 5 and 26. • Is continuity present?			
D4 CHECK PUMP PRESSURE			
• Jumper Pins 15 and 60 at breakout box. (Pump motor should run) • Apply brake pedal. • Does brake pedal rise?	Yes	▶	REVERIFY that brake pedal rises or drops excessively during ABS cycling.
	No	▶	REPLACE pump motor.

FM4029400427020X

Fig. 21 Test D: Anti-Lock Brake Warning Sequence Normal - Brake Pedal Rises Or Drops Excessively During ABS Cycling (Part 2 of 2). 1993–94 Mark VIII

TEST STEP	RESULT	▶	ACTION TO TAKE
E1 VERIFY PUMP MOTOR CONDITION			
• With vehicle standing still: • Check if pump motor runs with ignition switch in ON or OFF position. • Disconnect ABS module from wiring harness.	Pump still runs	▶	GO to E2
	Pump stops running	▶	REPLACE ABS module.

FM4029100185010X

Fig. 22 Test E: ABS Motor Runs Continuously (Part 1 of 2). 1993–94

TEST STEP	RESULT	▶	ACTION TO TAKE
E2 CHECK CIRCUIT 539			
• Disconnect pump motor relay from 4-pin plug. • Connect EEC-IV Breakout Box 014-00322 with Anti-Lock Test Adapter T90P-50-ALA to the anti-lock 55-pin plug wiring harness. • Check for continuity between breakout box Pins 15 and 60. • Is continuity present?	Yes	▶	SERVICE or REPLACE cable harness Circuit 539.
	No	▶	REPLACE pump motor relay.

FM4029100185020X

Fig. 22 Test E: ABS Motor Runs Continuously (Part 2 of 2). 1993–94

TEST STEP	RESULT	▶	ACTION TO TAKE
F1 CHECK BRAKE FLUID LEVEL			
• Check that brake fluid is no more than 4mm (0.16 inch) below MAX line located on side of master cylinder reservoir.	Low	▶	CHECK system for external leaks. SERVICE as required.
	Normal	▶	GO to F2.
F2 CHECK FLUID LEVEL SWITCH			
• Disconnect 3-pin plug on master cylinder fluid reservoir connector. • Check for continuity between Pins 1 and 3 on connector. • Is continuity present?	Yes	▶	REPLACE master cylinder reservoir fluid.
	No	▶	GO to F3.
F3 CHECK FOR GROUND CONCERN			
• Check for grounded wire harness, Circuit 977. • Is wire harness grounded?	Yes	▶	SERVICE or REPLACE cable harness Circuit 977.
	No	▶	REVERIFY BRAKE warning indicator on.

FM4029100186000X

Fig. 23 Test F: Brake Warning Lamp On w/ABS Lamp Off, Parking Brake Released & Lining Wear Checked. 1993–94

TEST STEP	RESULT	▶	ACTION TO TAKE
G1 CHECK IGNITION FEED AND FUSE			
• Check for 12 volts to lamp socket with ignition ON.	12 volts	▶	GO to G2.
	No voltage	▶	SERVICE or REPLACE cable harness Circuit 640 or Fuse
G2 CHECK WARNING INDICATOR BULB			
• Check warning indicator bulb. • Is bulb good?	Yes	▶	GO to G3.
	No	▶	REPLACE bulb.
G3 CHECK CIRCUIT 603			
• Check continuity between lamp socket and breakout box Pin 52. • Is continuity present?	No	▶	SERVICE or REPLACE cable harness Circuit 603.
	Yes	▶	GO to G4.
G4 CHECK DIODE			
• Inspect diode for damage or loose or bad connection. • Check if diode is installed backwards.	Diode good	▶	REVERIFY symptom.
	Diode damaged or installed backwards	▶	REPLACE diode.

FM4029100187000X

Fig. 24 Test G: No Warning Lamp On When Ignition Switch Turned On. 1993–94 Cougar & Thunderbird

TEST STEP	RESULT	▶	ACTION TO TAKE
G1 CHECK IGNITION FEED AND FUSE			
• Check for 12 volts to lamp socket with ignition switch in RUN. • Is B+ present?	Yes	▶	GO to G2.
	No	▶	SERVICE or REPLACE cable harness Circuit 38, 797 or Fuse 16.
G2 CHECK WARNING INDICATOR BULB			
• Check warning indicator bulb. • Is bulb good?	Yes	▶	GO to G3.
	No	▶	REPLACE bulb.
G3 CHECK CIRCUIT 603			
• Check continuity between lamp socket and breakout box Pin 52. • Is continuity present?	Yes	▶	GO to G4.
	No	▶	SERVICE or REPLACE cable harness Circuit 603.
G4 CHECK DIODE			
• Inspect diode for damage or loose or bad connection. • Check if diode is installed backwards. • Is diode good and installed correctly?	Yes	▶	REVERIFY symptom.
	No	▶	REPLACE diode.

FM4029400428000X

Fig. 25 Test G: No Anti-Lock Brake Indicator On When Ignition Turned On. 1993–94 Mark VIII

FORD—Anti-Lock Brakes

TEST STEP		RESULT		ACTION TO TAKE
H1	CHECK COMPONENT MOUNTING			
	• Check for proper brake pedal and booster/master cylinder attachment. • Bleed brake system as outlined. • Is pedal spongy?	Yes	▶	GO to H2.
		No	▶	Condition corrected.
H2	BLEED BRAKE SYSTEM			
	• Rebleed brake system. • Is pedal spongy?	Yes	▶	REPLACE master cylinder.
		No	▶	Condition corrected.

FM4029100188000X

Fig. 26 Test H: Spongy Pedal & No Warning Lamp. 1993–94

PINPOINT TEST J:
POOR VEHICLE TRACKING DURING ANTI-LOCK FUNCTION
(WARNING INDICATOR OFF)

TEST STEP		RESULT		ACTION TO TAKE
J1	VERIFY CONDITION			
	• Verify condition exists as reported. • Does vehicle track poorly?	No	▶	Condition corrected.
		Yes	▶	GO to J2.

FM4029100189010X

Fig. 27 Test J: Poor Vehicle Tracking During ABS Function, Warning Lamp Off (Part 1 of 3). 1993–94

TEST STEP		RESULT		ACTION TO TAKE
J4	CHECK ANTI-LOCK OPERATION RH REAR WHEEL			
	• Jump Pins 19 and 34 at breakout box. • Short Pins 55, 18 and 60 to each other at breakout box. • Apply moderate brake pedal effort. Check that RH rear wheel will not turn with ignition OFF. • Check that RH rear wheel turns freely with ignition ON. CAUTION: Do not leave ignition on for more than 1 minute or valve damage may result.	Wheel turns freely	▶	TURN ignition switch OFF. DISCONNECT wire leads. GO to J5.
		Wheel does not turn freely or pedal drops	▶	VERIFY correct wiring between 55-pin connector and 19-pin connector on valve block per wiring diagram.
			▶	If wiring is correct, REPLACE solenoid valve block.
J5	CHECK ANTI-LOCK OPERATION LH REAR WHEEL			
	• Jump Pins 19 and 34 at breakout box. • Short Pins 36, 54 and 60 to each other at breakout box. • Apply moderate brake pedal effort. Check that LH rear wheel turns freely with ignition ON. CAUTION: Do not leave ignition on for more than 1 minute or valve damage may result.	Wheel turns freely	▶	TURN ignition switch OFF. DISCONNECT wire leads and breakout box. LOWER vehicle. REVERIFY symptom.
		Wheel does not turn freely or pedal drops	▶	VERIFY correct wiring between 55-pin connector and 19-pin connector on valve block per wiring diagram.
			▶	If wiring is correct, REPLACE solenoid valve block.

FM4029100189030X

Fig. 27 Test J: Poor Vehicle Tracking During ABS Function, Warning Lamp Off (Part 3 of 3). 1993–94

TEST STEP		RESULT		ACTION TO TAKE
J2	CHECK ANTI-LOCK VALVE OPERATION			
	• Turn ignition switch OFF. • Disconnect 55-pin plug from electronic controller.	Wheel turns freely	▶	TURN ignition switch OFF. DISCONNECT wire leads. GO to J3.
		Wheel does not turn freely or pedal drops	▶	VERIFY correct wiring between 55-pin connector and 19-pin connector on valve block per wiring diagram.

ABS MODULE

55 PIN CONNECTOR

• Connect EEC-IV Breakout Box 014-00322 with Anti-Lock Test Adapter T90P-50-ALA to the anti-lock 55-pin connector on wire harness.

ANTI-LOCK TEST ADAPTER

55 PIN CONNECTOR

EEC-IV BREAKOUT BOX

				▶	If wiring is correct, REPLACE solenoid valve block.

• Lift vehicle and rotate wheels to ensure they turn freely.
• Jump Pins 19 and 34 at breakout box.
• Short Pins 20, 2 and 60 to each other at breakout box.
• Apply moderate brake pedal effort and check that LH front wheel will not turn.
• Check to see that LH front wheel turns freely when ignition switch is ON.

CAUTION: Do not leave ignition on for more than 1 minute, or valve damage may result.

J3	CHECK ANTI-LOCK OPERATION RH FRONT WHEEL			
	• Jump Pins 19 and 34 at breakout box. • Short Pins 38, 21 and 60 to each other at breakout box. • Apply moderate brake pedal effort. Check that RH front wheel will not turn with ignition OFF. • Check that RH front wheel turns freely with ignition ON. CAUTION: Do not leave ignition on for more than 1 minute or valve damage may result.	Wheel turns freely	▶	TURN ignition switch OFF. DISCONNECT wire leads. GO to J4.
		Wheel does not turn freely or pedal drops	▶	VERIFY correct wiring between 55-pin connector and 19-pin connector on valve block per wiring diagram.
			▶	If wiring is correct, REPLACE solenoid valve block.

FM4029100189020X

Fig. 27 Test J: Poor Vehicle Tracking During ABS Function, Warning Lamp Off (Part 2 of 3). 1993–94

TEST STEP		RESULT		ACTION TO TAKE
K2	CHECK STOPLAMP SWITCH			
	• Connect Rotunda EEC-IV Breakout Box 014-00322 with Anti-Lock Test Adapter T90P-50-ALA or equivalent to the Anti-Lock 55-Pin connector on the wire harness. • Turn ignition switch to ON position. • Measure voltage between breakout box Pins 32 and 60. NOTE: DO NOT apply brake pedal while performing this test.	No voltage	▶	GO to K3.
		12 volts	▶	REPLACE stoplamp switch or SERVICE cable harness Circuit 511.
K3	CHECK ABS FUNCTION			
	• Make an Anti-Lock stop on a slippery surface. • Notice if brake pedal rises when pump comes on or if the pedal continues downward when pump comes on.	Brake pedal rises	▶	REPLACE valve body.
		Brake pedal falls	▶	REPLACE pump and motor.

FM4029100190000X

Fig. 28 Test K: Warning Lamp Sequence Normal, Traction Assist Inoperative. 1993–94

TEST STEP		RESULT		ACTION TO TAKE
L1	RUN ON-BOARD DIAGNOSTIC			
	• Run On-Board Diagnostic.	Rear sensor code received	▶	REPLACE sensor for code received.
		No codes in ABS module	▶	VERIFY that traction assist system is false cycling.

FM4029100191000X

Fig. 29 Test L: Warning Lamp Sequence Normal, False Cycling Of Traction Assist. 1993–94

TEST STEP		RESULT		ACTION TO TAKE
AA1	DTC(s) 11: ELECTRICAL DISTURBANCE			
	• Read all DTC(s) and record. • After all DTC(s) are read and written down, drive vehicle above 40 km/h (25 mph) to clear memory. • Read all DTC(s) again.	DTC(s) 11 repeated	▶	REPLACE ABS Module.
		Memory erased or other DTC(s) present except code 11	▶	PERFORM test step associated with DTC(s). REFER to On-Board Diagnostic Trouble Code index, and SERVICE next code.

FM4029100174000X

Fig. 30 Test AA: ABS Module Diagnosis. 1993–94

27-56

1993-94 COUGAR, MARK VIII & THUNDERBIRD

Part 1 (BB1–BB2)

TEST STEP	RESULT	▶	ACTION TO TAKE
BB1 DTC(s) 22: NO REFERENCE VOLTAGE OR LH FRONT INLET VALVE • Disconnect 55-pin plug from electronic controller.	10 volts minimum Less than 10 volts	▶ ▶	GO to BB2. REPLACE or SERVICE cable harness Circuit 532, 603 or 640. NOTE: If test for code 22 continually leads to REVERIFY code 22, GO to Anti-Lock Quick Check Test.

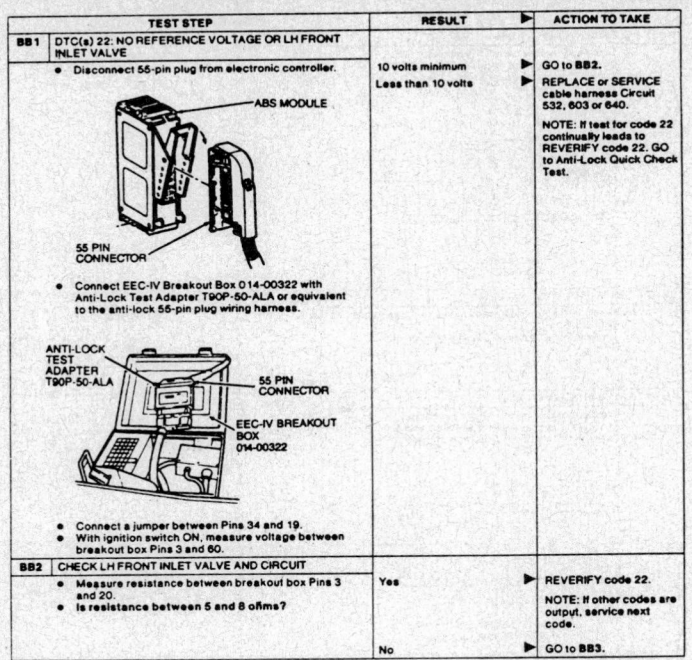

• Connect EEC-IV Breakout Box 014-00322 with Anti-Lock Test Adapter T90P-50-ALA or equivalent to the anti-lock 55-pin plug wiring harness.			
• Connect a jumper between Pins 34 and 19. • With ignition switch ON, measure voltage between breakout box Pins 3 and 60.			
BB2 CHECK LH FRONT INLET VALVE AND CIRCUIT • Measure resistance between breakout box Pins 3 and 20. • Is resistance between 5 and 8 ohms?	Yes No	▶ ▶	REVERIFY code 22. NOTE: If other codes are output, service next code. GO to BB3.

FM4029100175010X

Fig. 31 Test BB: Solenoid Valve & Isolation Valve Diagnosis (Part 1 of 6). 1993–94 Cougar & Thunderbird

Part 2 (BB3–BB6)

TEST STEP	RESULT	▶	ACTION TO TAKE
BB3 CHECK LH FRONT INLET VALVE • Disconnect valve body 19-pin connector. • Measure resistance between Pins 17 and 7. • Is resistance between 5 and 8 ohms?	Yes No	▶ ▶	REPLACE or SERVICE cable harness Circuit 495. REPLACE valve body.

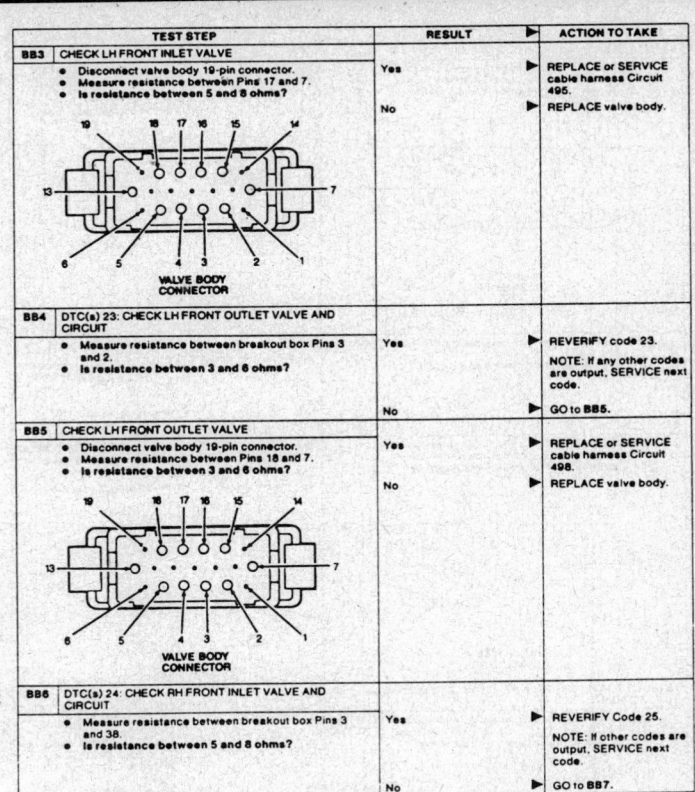

BB4 DTC(s) 23: CHECK LH FRONT OUTLET VALVE AND CIRCUIT • Measure resistance between breakout box Pins 3 and 2. • Is resistance between 3 and 6 ohms?	Yes No	▶ ▶	REVERIFY code 23. NOTE: If any other codes are output, SERVICE next code. GO to BB5.
BB5 CHECK LH FRONT OUTLET VALVE • Disconnect valve body 19-pin connector. • Measure resistance between Pins 18 and 7. • Is resistance between 3 and 6 ohms?	Yes No	▶ ▶	REPLACE or SERVICE cable harness Circuit 498. REPLACE valve body.
BB6 DTC(s) 24: CHECK RH FRONT INLET VALVE AND CIRCUIT • Measure resistance between breakout box Pins 3 and 38. • Is resistance between 5 and 8 ohms?	Yes No	▶ ▶	REVERIFY Code 25. NOTE: If other codes are output, SERVICE next code. GO to BB7.

FM4029100175020X

Fig. 31 Test BB: Solenoid Valve & Isolation Valve Diagnosis (Part 2 of 6). 1993–94 Cougar & Thunderbird

Part 3 (BB7–BB9)

TEST STEP	RESULT	▶	ACTION TO TAKE
BB7 CHECK RH FRONT INLET VALVE • Disconnect valve body 19-pin connector. • Measure resistance between Pins 15 and 7. • Is resistance between 5 and 8 ohms?	Yes No	▶ ▶	REPLACE or SERVICE cable harness Circuit 510. REPLACE valve body.

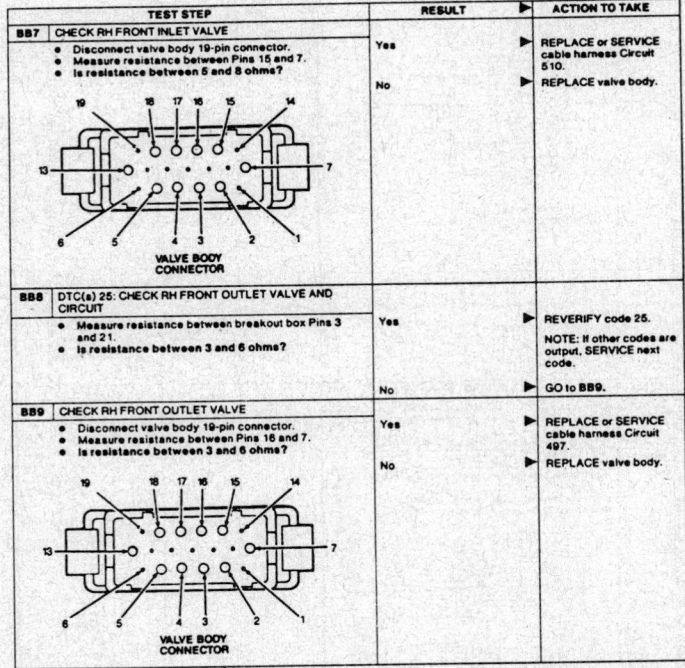

BB8 DTC(s) 25: CHECK RH FRONT OUTLET VALVE AND CIRCUIT • Measure resistance between breakout box Pins 3 and 21. • Is resistance between 3 and 6 ohms?	Yes No	▶ ▶	REVERIFY code 25. NOTE: If other codes are output, SERVICE next code. GO to BB9.
BB9 CHECK RH FRONT OUTLET VALVE • Disconnect valve body 19-pin connector. • Measure resistance between Pins 16 and 7. • Is resistance between 3 and 6 ohms?	Yes No	▶ ▶	REPLACE or SERVICE cable harness Circuit 497. REPLACE valve body.

FM4029100175030X

Fig. 31 Test BB: Solenoid Valve & Isolation Valve Diagnosis (Part 3 of 6). 1993–94 Cougar & Thunderbird

Part 4 (BB10–BB12)

TEST STEP	RESULT	▶	ACTION TO TAKE
BB10 DTC(s) 26: CHECK RH REAR INLET VALVE AND CIRCUIT • Measure resistance between breakout box Pins 3 and 55. • Is resistance between 5 and 8 ohms?	Yes No	▶ ▶	REVERIFY code 26. NOTE: If other codes are output, SERVICE next code. GO to BB11.

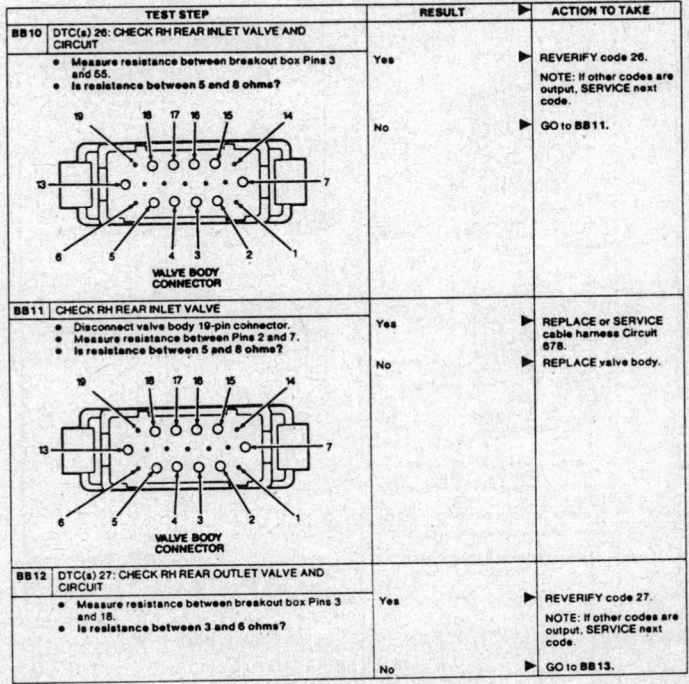

BB11 CHECK RH REAR INLET VALVE • Disconnect valve body 19-pin connector. • Measure resistance between Pins 2 and 7. • Is resistance between 5 and 8 ohms?	Yes No	▶ ▶	REPLACE or SERVICE cable harness Circuit 678. REPLACE valve body.
BB12 DTC(s) 27: CHECK RH REAR OUTLET VALVE AND CIRCUIT • Measure resistance between breakout box Pins 3 and 18. • Is resistance between 3 and 6 ohms?	Yes No	▶ ▶	REVERIFY code 27. NOTE: If other codes are output, SERVICE next code. GO to BB13.

FM4029100175040X

Fig. 31 Test BB: Solenoid Valve & Isolation Valve Diagnosis (Part 4 of 6). 1993–94 Cougar & Thunderbird

TEST STEP	RESULT	►	ACTION TO TAKE
BB13 CHECK RH REAR OUTLET VALVE			
• Disconnect valve body 19-pin connector. • Measure resistance between Pins 3 and 7. • Is resistance between 3 and 6 ohms?	Yes	►	REPLACE or SERVICE cable harness Circuit 685.
	No	►	REPLACE valve body.
BB14 DTC(s) 28: CHECK LH REAR INLET VALVE AND CIRCUIT			
• Measure resistance between breakout box Pins 3 and 54. • Is resistance between 5 and 8 ohms?	Yes	►	REVERIFY code 28. NOTE: If other codes are output, SERVICE next code.
	No	►	GO to BB15.
BB15 CHECK LH REAR INLET VALVE			
• Disconnect valve body 19-pin connector. • Measure resistance between Pins 4 and 7. • Is resistance between 5 and 8 ohms?	Yes	►	REPLACE or SERVICE cable harness Circuit 496.
	No	►	REPLACE valve body.
BB16 DTC(s) 29: CHECK LH REAR OUTLET VALVE AND CIRCUIT			
• Measure resistance between breakout box Pins 3 and 36. • Is resistance between 3 and 6 ohms?	Yes	►	REVERIFY code 29. NOTE: If other codes are output, SERVICE next code.
	No	►	GO to BB17.

FM4029100175050X

Fig. 31 Test BB: Solenoid Valve & Isolation Valve Diagnosis (Part 5 of 6). 1993–94 Cougar & Thunderbird

TEST STEP	RESULT	►	ACTION TO TAKE
BB17 CHECK LH REAR OUTLET VALVE			
• Disconnect valve body 19-pin connector. • Measure resistance between Pins 5 and 7. • Is resistance between 3 and 6 ohms?	Yes	►	REPLACE or SERVICE cable harness.
	No	►	REPLACE valve body.
BB18 DTC 18: ISOLATION VALVE 1			
• Measure resistance between breakout box Pins 3 and 37. • Is resistance between 5 and 8 ohms?	Yes	►	REVERIFY DTC 18. NOTE: If other DTC's are output, SERVICE next DTC.
	No	►	GO to BB19.
BB19 CHECK ISOLATION VALVE 1			
• Disconnect valve body 19-pin connector. • Measure resistance between Pins 7 and 9. • Is resistance between 5 and 8 ohms?	Yes	►	SERVICE or REPLACE cable harness.
	No	►	REPLACE valve body.
BB20 DTC 19: ISOLATION VALVE 2			
• Measure resistance between breakout box Pins 3 and 40. • Is resistance between 5 and 8 ohms?	Yes	►	REVERIFY DTC 19. NOTE: If other DTC's are output, SERVICE next DTC.
	No	►	GO to BB21.

FM4029100175060X

Fig. 31 Test BB: Solenoid Valve & Isolation Valve Diagnosis (Part 6 of 6). 1993–94 Cougar & Thunderbird

TEST STEP	RESULT	►	ACTION TO TAKE
BB1 DTC 17: NO REFERENCE VOLTAGE			
• Disconnect anti-lock brake wiring from anti-lock brake control module.	Yes	►	If other DTCs are output, SERVICE next DTC. If no other DTCs are output, GO to Anti-Lock Quick Check Test
	No	►	REPLACE or SERVICE cable harness Circuit 532, 537, 603, 30 amp fuse (anti-lock brake control module) or main power relay.
• Connect EEC-IV Breakout Box 014-00322 with Anti-Lock Test Adapter T90P-50-AIA to the anti-lock brake wiring harness.			
• Connect a jumper between Pins 34 and 19. • With ignition switch in RUN, measure voltage between Breakout Box Pins 3 and 60. • Is there a minimum of 10 volts?			
BB2 DTC 22: CHECK LH FRONT INLET VALVE AND CIRCUIT			
• Measure resistance between breakout box Pins 3 and 20. • Is resistance between 5 and 8 ohms?	Yes	►	GO to BB4. NOTE: If other DTCs are output, service next DTC.
	No	►	GO to BB3.

FM4029400429010X

Fig. 32 Test BB: Solenoid Valve Diagnosis (Part 1 of 8). 1993–94 Mark VIII

TEST STEP	RESULT	►	ACTION TO TAKE
BB3 CHECK LH FRONT INLET VALVE			
• Disconnect brake pressure control valve block 16-pin connector. • Measure resistance between Pins 14 and 8. • Is resistance between 5 and 8 ohms?	Yes	►	REPLACE or SERVICE cable harness Circuit 495 (T)
	No	►	REPLACE brake pressure control valve block
BB4 CHECK CIRCUIT 495			
• Disconnect valve block connector from wire harness. • Check for continuity between breakout box Pins 20 and 60. • Is continuity present?	Yes	►	REPLACE or SERVICE cable harness Circuit 495 (T)
	No	►	REVERIFY DTC 22. NOTE: If other DTCs are output, service next code.
BB5 DTC 23: CHECK LH FRONT OUTLET VALVE AND CIRCUIT			
• Measure resistance between breakout box Pins 3 and 2. • Is resistance between three and six ohms?	Yes	►	GO to BB7.
	No	►	GO to BB6.
BB6 CHECK LH FRONT OUTLET VALVE			
• Disconnect brake pressure control valve block 16-pin connector. • Measure resistance between Pins 15 and 1. • Is resistance between 3 and 6 ohms?	Yes	►	REPLACE or SERVICE cable harness Circuit 498 (PK).
	No	►	REPLACE brake pressure control valve block

FM4029400429020X

Fig. 32 Test BB: Solenoid Valve Diagnosis (Part 2 of 8). 1993–94 Mark VIII

TEST STEP	RESULT	▶	ACTION TO TAKE
BB7 CHECK CIRCUIT 498 • Disconnect valve block connector from wire harness. • Check for continuity between breakout box Pins 2 and 60. • Is continuity present?	Yes No	▶ ▶	REPLACE or SERVICE cable harness Circuit 498 (PK). REVERIFY DTC 23. NOTE: If other DTCs are output, service next code.
BB8 DTC 24: CHECK RH FRONT INLET VALVE AND CIRCUIT • Measure resistance between breakout box Pins 3 and 38. • Is resistance between 5 and 8 ohms?	Yes No	▶ ▶	GO to BB10. GO to BB9.
BB9 CHECK RH FRONT INLET VALVE • Disconnect brake pressure control valve block 16-pin connector. • Measure resistance between Pins 10 and 1. • Is resistance between 5 and 8 ohms?	Yes No	▶ ▶	REPLACE or SERVICE cable harness Circuit 510 (T·R). REPLACE brake pressure control valve block.
BB10 CHECK CIRCUIT 510 • Disconnect valve block connector from wire harness. • Check for continuity between breakout box Pins 38 and 60. • Is continuity present?	Yes No	▶ ▶	REPLACE or SERVICE cable harness Circuit 510 (T·R). REVERIFY DTC 24. NOTE: If other DTCs are output, service next code.
BB11 DTC 25: CHECK RH FRONT OUTLET VALVE AND CIRCUIT • Measure resistance between breakout box Pins 3 and 21. • Is resistance between 3 and 6 ohms?	Yes No	▶ ▶	GO to BB13. GO to BB12.

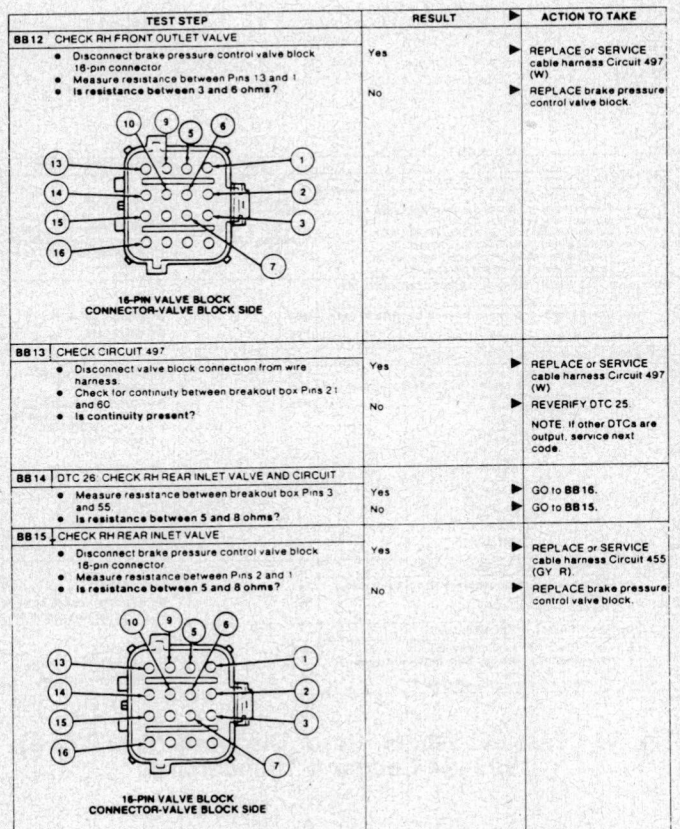

FM4029400429030X

Fig. 32   Test BB: Solenoid Valve Diagnosis (Part 3 of 8). 1993–94 Mark VIII

TEST STEP	RESULT	▶	ACTION TO TAKE
BB16 CHECK CIRCUIT 455 • Disconnect valve block connector from wire harness. • Check for continuity between breakout box Pins 55 and 60. • Is continuity present?	Yes No	▶ ▶	REPLACE or SERVICE cable harness Circuit 455 (GY·R). REVERIFY DTC 26. NOTE: If other DTCs are output, service next code.
BB17 DTC 27: CHECK RH REAR OUTLET VALVE AND CIRCUIT • Measure resistance between breakout box Pins 3 and 18. • Is resistance between 3 and 6 ohms?	Yes No	▶ ▶	GO to BB19. GO to BB18.
BB18 CHECK RH REAR OUTLET VALVE • Disconnect brake pressure control valve block 16-pin connector. • Measure resistance between Pins 3 and 1. • Is resistance between 3 and 6 ohms?	Yes No	▶ ▶	REPLACE or SERVICE cable harness Circuit 492 (BR). REPLACE brake pressure control valve block.
BB19 CHECK CIRCUIT 492 • Disconnect valve block connector from wire harness. • Check for continuity between breakout box Pins 18 and 60. • Is continuity present?	Yes No	▶ ▶	REPLACE or SERVICE cable harness Circuit 492 (BR). REVERIFY DTC 27. NOTE: If other DTCs are output, service next code.
BB20 DTC 28: CHECK LH REAR INLET VALVE AND CIRCUIT • Measure resistance between breakout box Pins 3 and 54. • Is resistance between 5 and 8 ohms?	Yes No	▶ ▶	GO to BB22. GO to BB21.

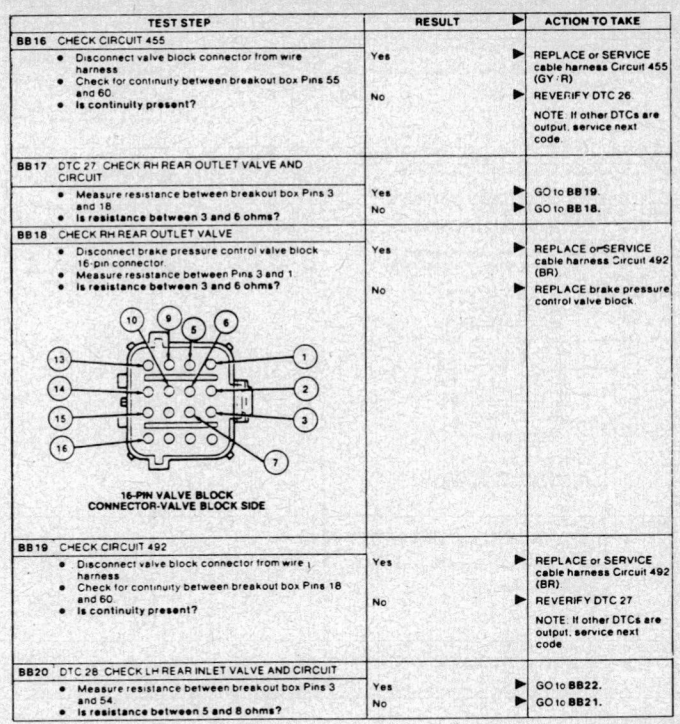

FM4029400429050X

Fig. 32   Test BB: Solenoid Valve Diagnosis (Part 5 of 8). 1993–94 Mark VIII

TEST STEP	RESULT	▶	ACTION TO TAKE
BB12 CHECK RH FRONT OUTLET VALVE • Disconnect brake pressure control valve block 16-pin connector. • Measure resistance between Pins 13 and 1. • Is resistance between 3 and 6 ohms?	Yes No	▶ ▶	REPLACE or SERVICE cable harness Circuit 497 (W). REPLACE brake pressure control valve block.

16-PIN VALVE BLOCK CONNECTOR-VALVE BLOCK SIDE

TEST STEP	RESULT	▶	ACTION TO TAKE
BB13 CHECK CIRCUIT 497 • Disconnect valve block connection from wire harness. • Check for continuity between breakout box Pins 21 and 60. • Is continuity present?	Yes No	▶ ▶	REPLACE or SERVICE cable harness Circuit 497 (W). REVERIFY DTC 25. NOTE: If other DTCs are output, service next code.
BB14 DTC 26: CHECK RH REAR INLET VALVE AND CIRCUIT • Measure resistance between breakout box Pins 3 and 55. • Is resistance between 5 and 8 ohms?	Yes No	▶ ▶	GO to BB16. GO to BB15.
BB15 CHECK RH REAR INLET VALVE • Disconnect brake pressure control valve block 16-pin connector. • Measure resistance between Pins 2 and 1. • Is resistance between 5 and 8 ohms?	Yes No	▶ ▶	REPLACE or SERVICE cable harness Circuit 455 (GY·R). REPLACE brake pressure control valve block.

FM4029400429040X

Fig. 32   Test BB: Solenoid Valve Diagnosis (Part 4 of 8). 1993–94 Mark VIII

TEST STEP	RESULT	▶	ACTION TO TAKE
BB21 CHECK LH REAR INLET VALVE • Disconnect brake pressure control valve block 16-pin connector. • Measure resistance between Pins 7 and 1. • Is resistance between five and eight ohms?	Yes No	▶ ▶	REPLACE or SERVICE cable harness Circuit 496 (O). REPLACE brake pressure control valve block.

16-PIN VALVE BLOCK CONNECTOR-VALVE BLOCK SIDE

TEST STEP	RESULT	▶	ACTION TO TAKE
BB22 CHECK CIRCUIT 496 • Disconnect valve block connector from wire harness. • Check for continuity between breakout box Pins 54 and 60. • Is continuity present?	Yes No	▶ ▶	REPLACE or SERVICE cable harness Circuit 496 (O). REVERIFY DTC 28. NOTE: If other DTCs are output, service next code.
BB23 DTC 29: CHECK LH REAR OUTLET VALVE AND CIRCUIT • Measure resistance between breakout box Pins 3 and 36. • Is resistance between three and six ohms?	Yes No	▶ ▶	GO to BB25. GO to BB24.
BB24 CHECK LH REAR OUTLET VALVE • Disconnect brake pressure control valve block 16-pin connector. • Measure resistance between Pins 9 and 1. • Is resistance between three and six ohms?	Yes No	▶ ▶	REPLACE or SERVICE cable harness Circuit 499 (GY·BK). REPLACE brake pressure control valve block.

16-PIN VALVE BLOCK CONNECTOR-VALVE BLOCK SIDE

FM4029400429060X

Fig. 32   Test BB: Solenoid Valve Diagnosis (Part 6 of 8). 1993–94 Mark VIII

TEST STEP	RESULT	▶	ACTION TO TAKE
BB25 CHECK CIRCUIT 499 • Disconnect valve block connector from wire harness. • Check for continuity between breakout box Pins 36 and 60. • Is continuity present?	Yes No	▶ ▶	REPLACE or SERVICE cable harness Circuit 499 (GY/BK). REVERIFY DTC 29. NOTE: If other DTCs are output, service next code.
BB26 DTC 18: CHECK ISOLATION VALVE # 1 AND CIRCUIT • Measure resistance between Breakout Box 3 and 37. • Is resistance between five and eight ohms?	Yes No	▶ ▶	GO to BB28. GO to BB27.
BB27 CHECK ISOLATION VALVE # 1 • Disconnect brake pressure control valve block 16-pin connector. • Measure resistance between Pins 5 and 1. • Is resistance between five and eight ohms?	Yes No	▶ ▶	REPLACE or SERVICE cable harness Circuit 601 (LB/PK). REPLACE brake pressure control valve block.
BB28 CHECK CIRCUIT 601 • Disconnect valve block connector from wire harness. • Check for continuity between breakout box Pins 37 and 60. • Is continuity present?.	Yes No	▶ ▶	REPLACE or SERVICE cable harness Circuit 601 (LB/PK). REVERIFY DTC 18. NOTE: If other DTCs are output, service next code.
BB29 DTC 19: CHECK ISOLATION VALVE # 2 AND CIRCUIT • Measure resistance between breakout box Pins 3 and 40. • Is resistance between three and six ohms?	Yes No	▶ ▶	GO to BB31. GO to BB30.

16-PIN VALVE BLOCK CONNECTOR-VALVE BLOCK SIDE

FM4029400429070X

Fig. 32 Test BB: Solenoid Valve Diagnosis (Part 7 of 8). 1993–94 Mark VIII

TEST STEP	RESULT	▶	ACTION TO TAKE
BB30 CHECK ISOLATION VALVE #2 • Disconnect brake pressure control valve block 16-pin connector. • Measure resistance between Pins 6 and 1. • Is resistance between three and six ohms?	Yes No	▶ ▶	REPLACE or SERVICE cable harness Circuit 677 (LB). REPLACE brake pressure control valve block.
BB31 CHECK CIRCUIT 677 • Disconnect valve block connector from wire harness. • Check for continuity between breakout box Pins 40 and 60. • Is continuity present?	Yes No	▶ ▶	REPLACE or SERVICE cable harness Circuit 677 (LB). REVERIFY DTC 19. NOTE: If other DTCs are output, service next code.

16-PIN VALVE BLOCK CONNECTOR-VALVE BLOCK SIDE

FM4029400429080X

Fig. 32 Test BB: Solenoid Valve Diagnosis (Part 8 of 8). 1993–94 Mark VIII

TEST STEP	RESULT	▶	ACTION TO TAKE
CC1 DTCs 31, 35, 41, 55, 71 OR 75: CHECK LH FRONT SENSOR • Turn ignition switch OFF. • Disconnect 55-pin connector from ABS Module.	Yes No	▶ ▶	GO to CC3. GO to CC2.

• Connect EEC-IV breakout box 014-00322 with Anti-Lock Test Adapter T90P-50-ALA or equivalent to the 55-pin connector on wiring harness.

TEST STEP	RESULT	▶	ACTION TO TAKE
• Measure resistance between Pins 30 and 48. • Is resistance between 800 and 1400 ohms?			
CC2 CHECK LH FRONT SENSOR RESISTANCE • Disconnect LH front wheel sensor plug. • Measure resistance of sensor at sensor plug. • Is resistance between 800 and 1400 ohms?	Yes No	▶ ▶	SERVICE or REPLACE cable harness Circuit 521 or 522. REPLACE LH front sensor.

LH FRONT SENSOR

FM4029100176010X

Fig. 33 Test CC: Wheel Sensor Diagnosis (Part 1 of 8). 1993–94

TEST STEP	RESULT	▶	ACTION TO TAKE
CC3 CHECK LH FRONT SENSOR VOLTAGE • Turn ignition switch OFF. • Place vehicle on hoist and raise wheels clear of ground. Refer to Section 00-02. • Set multi-meter to voltage range (2 volts AC). • Measure voltage between Pins 30 and 48 at breakout box while spinning LH front wheel at approximately 1 revolution per second.	Between 0.10 and 1.40 volts AC Less than 0.10 or more than 1.40 volts AC	▶ ▶	GO to CC4. CHECK sensor mounting, air gap or toothed wheel mounting. CORRECT as required.
CC4 CHECK LH FRONT SENSOR CIRCUIT CONTINUITY TO GROUND • Check continuity between breakout box Pins 30 and 60. • Is continuity present?	No Yes	▶ ▶	GO to CC6. GO to CC5.
CC5 CHECK LH FRONT SENSOR TO GROUND • Disconnect LH front wheel sensor plug. • Check for continuity between each sensor plug pin (sensor side) and vehicle ground. • Is continuity present?	Yes No	▶ ▶	REPLACE LH front sensor. SERVICE or REPLACE cable harness Circuit 521 or 522. RECONNECT sensor plug.

LH FRONT SENSOR

TEST STEP	RESULT	▶	ACTION TO TAKE
CC6 CHECK ABS MODULE TO GROUND WIRE • Check continuity between breakout box Pin 60 and body ground. • Was continuity present?	Yes No	▶ ▶	GO to CC7. SERVICE or REPLACE cable harness Circuit 57.
CC7 CHECK LH FRONT WHEEL BEARING • Check front wheel bearing end play. • Inspect toothed sensor ring visually for damaged teeth. • Were loose or damaged parts found?	Yes No	▶ ▶	REPLACE damaged/worn parts. REVERIFY symptom.

FM402910017602AX

Fig. 33 Test CC: Wheel Sensor Diagnosis (Part 2 of 8). 1993–94 Cougar & Thunderbird

TEST STEP	RESULT	▶	ACTION TO TAKE
CC3	CHECK LH FRONT BRAKE ANTI-LOCK SENSOR VOLTAGE			
• Turn ignition switch OFF. • Turn air suspension switch OFF. • Place vehicle on hoist and raise wheels clear of ground. Refer to Section 00-02. • Set multi-meter to voltage range (2 volts AC) • Measure voltage between Pins 30 and 48 at Breakout Box while spinning LH front wheel at approximately 1 revolution per second. • Is voltage between 0.10 and 1.40 volts AC?	Yes No	▶ ▶	GO to CC4. CHECK front brake anti-lock sensor mounting, air gap or front brake anti-lock sensor indicator mounting. CORRECT as required.
CC4	CHECK LH FRONT BRAKE ANTI-LOCK SENSOR CIRCUIT CONTINUITY TO GROUND			
• Check continuity between breakout box Pins 30 and 60. • Is continuity present?	Yes No	▶ ▶	GO to CC5. GO to CC6.
CC5	CHECK LH FRONT BRAKE ANTI-LOCK SENSOR TO GROUND			
• Disconnect LH front brake anti-lock sensor plug. • Check for continuity between each sensor plug pin (sensor side) and vehicle ground. • Is continuity present?	Yes No	▶ ▶	REPLACE LH front brake anti-lock sensor. SERVICE or REPLACE cable harness Circuit 521 or 522. RECONNECT sensor plug.
CC6	CHECK ANTI-LOCK BRAKE CONTROL MODULE TO GROUND WIRE			
• Check continuity between breakout box Pin 60 and body ground. • Was continuity present?	Yes No	▶ ▶	GO to CC7. SERVICE or REPLACE cable harness Circuit 651.
CC7	CHECK LH FRONT WHEEL BEARING			
• Check front wheel bearing end play. • Inspect rear brake anti-lock sensor indicator ring visually for damaged teeth. • Were loose or damaged parts found? NOTE: Turn air suspension switch ON when vehicle is off hoist.	Yes No	▶ ▶	REPLACE damaged / worn parts. REVERIFY symptom.

FM402940017602BX

Fig. 33 Test CC: Wheel Sensor Diagnosis (Part 2 of 8). 1993–94 Mark VIII

TEST STEP	RESULT	▶	ACTION TO TAKE
CC8	DTCs 32, 36, 42, 56, 72 OR 76: CHECK RH FRONT SENSOR			
• Turn ignition switch OFF. • Disconnect 55-pin connector from ABS Module.	Yes No	▶ ▶	GO to CC10. GO to CC9.

• Connect EEC-IV breakout box 014-00322 with Anti-Lock Test Adapter T90P-50-ALA or equivalent to the 55-Pin connector on wiring harness.

• Measure resistance between Pins 29 and 47. • Is resistance between 800 and 1400 ohms?			
CC9	CHECK RH FRONT SENSOR RESISTANCE			
• Disconnect RH front sensor plug. • Measure resistance of sensor at sensor plug. • Is resistance between 800 and 1400 ohms?	Yes No	▶ ▶	SERVICE or REPLACE cable harness Circuit 514 or 516. REPLACE RH front sensor.

FM402910017603OX

Fig. 33 Test CC: Wheel Sensor Diagnosis (Part 3 of 8). 1993–94

TEST STEP	RESULT	▶	ACTION TO TAKE
CC10	CHECK RH FRONT SENSOR VOLTAGE			
• Turn ignition switch OFF. • Place vehicle on hoist and raise wheels clear of ground. • Set multi-meter to voltage range (2 volts AC) • Measure voltage between Pins 29 and 47 at breakout box while spinning RH front wheel at approximately 1 revolution per second.	Between 0.10 and 1.40 volts AC Less than 0.10 or more than 1.40 volts AC	▶ ▶	GO to CC11. CHECK sensor mounting, air gap or toothed wheel mounting. CORRECT as required.
CC11	CHECK RH FRONT SENSOR CIRCUIT CONTINUITY TO GROUND			
• Check continuity between breakout box Pins 29 and 60. • Is continuity present?	No Yes	▶ ▶	GO to CC13. GO to CC12.
CC12	CHECK RH FRONT SENSOR TO GROUND			
• Disconnect RH front wheel sensor plug. • Check for continuity between each sensor plug pin (sensor side) and vehicle ground. • Is continuity present?	Yes No	▶ ▶	REPLACE RH front sensor. SERVICE or REPLACE cable harness Circuit 514 or 516. RECONNECT sensor plug.
CC13	CHECK ABS MODULE TO GROUND WIRE			
• Check continuity between breakout box Pin 60 and body ground. • Is continuity present?	Yes No Continuity	▶ ▶	GO to CC14. SERVICE or REPLACE cable harness Circuit 57.
CC14	CHECK RH FRONT WHEEL BEARING			
• Check front wheel bearing end play. • Inspect toothed sensor ring visually for damaged teeth. • Were any parts loose or damaged?	Yes No	▶ ▶	REPLACE damaged / worn parts. REVERIFY symptom.

FM402910017604AX

Fig. 33 Test CC: Wheel Sensor Diagnosis (Part 4 of 8). 1993–94 Cougar & Thunderbird

TEST STEP	RESULT	▶	ACTION TO TAKE
CC10	CHECK RH FRONT BRAKE ANTI-LOCK SENSOR VOLTAGE			
• Turn ignition switch OFF • Turn air suspension switch OFF. • Place vehicle on hoist and raise wheels clear of ground • Set multi-meter to voltage range (2 volts AC) • Measure voltage between Pins 29 and 47 at Breakout Box while spinning RH front wheel at approximately 1 revolution per second. • Is voltage between 0.10 and 1.40 volts AC?	Yes No	▶ ▶	GO to CC11. CHECK front brake anti-lock sensor mounting, air gap or front brake anti-lock sensor indicator mounting. CORRECT as required.
CC11	CHECK RH FRONT BRAKE ANTI-LOCK SENSOR CIRCUIT CONTINUITY TO GROUND			
• Check continuity between breakout box Pins 29 and 60. • Is continuity present?	Yes No	▶ ▶	GO to CC12. GO to CC13.
CC12	CHECK RH FRONT BRAKE ANTI-LOCK SENSOR TO GROUND			
• Disconnect RH front wheel front brake anti-lock sensor plug. • Check for continuity between each front brake anti-lock sensor plug pin (sensor side) and vehicle ground. • Is continuity present?	Yes No	▶ ▶	REPLACE RH front brake anti-lock sensor. SERVICE or REPLACE cable harness Circuit 514 or 516. RECONNECT sensor plug.
CC13	CHECK ANTI-LOCK BRAKE CONTROL MODULE TO GROUND WIRE			
• Check continuity between breakout box Pin 60 and body ground. • Is continuity present?	Yes No	▶ ▶	GO to CC14. SERVICE or REPLACE cable harness Circuit 651.
CC14	CHECK RH FRONT WHEEL BEARING			
• Check front wheel bearing end play. • Inspect front brake anti-lock sensor indicator visually for damaged teeth. • Were any parts loose or damaged? NOTE: Turn air suspension switch ON when vehicle is off hoist.	Yes No	▶ ▶	REPLACE damaged / worn parts. REVERIFY symptom.

FM402940017604BX

Fig. 33 Test CC: Wheel Sensor Diagnosis (Part 4 of 8). 1993–94 Mark VIII

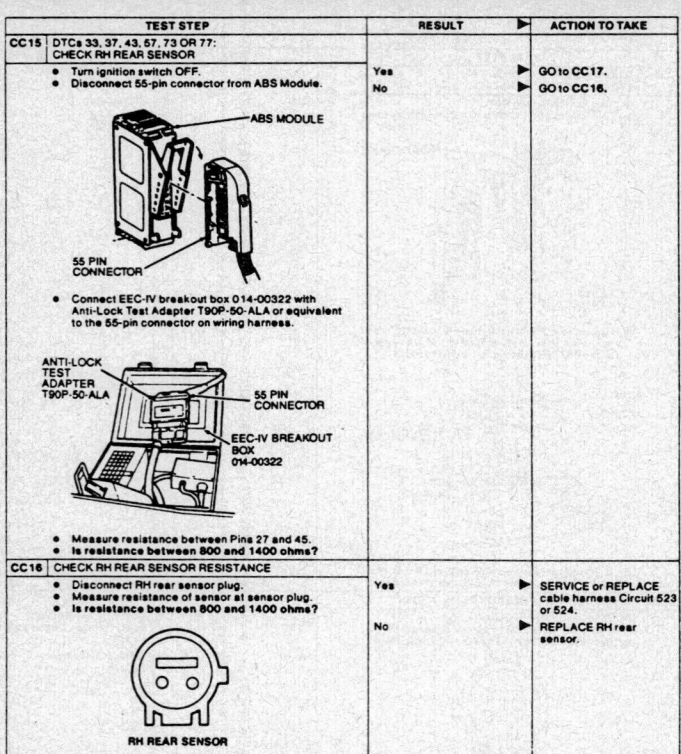

TEST STEP	RESULT	▶	ACTION TO TAKE
CC15 DTCs 33, 37, 43, 57, 73 OR 77: CHECK RH REAR SENSOR			
• Turn ignition switch OFF.	Yes	▶	GO to CC17.
• Disconnect 55-pin connector from ABS Module.	No	▶	GO to CC16.
• Connect EEC-IV breakout box 014-00322 with Anti-Lock Test Adapter T90P-50-ALA or equivalent to the 55-pin connector on wiring harness.			
• Measure resistance between Pins 27 and 45. • Is resistance between 800 and 1400 ohms?			
CC16 CHECK RH REAR SENSOR RESISTANCE			
• Disconnect RH rear sensor plug. • Measure resistance of sensor at sensor plug. • Is resistance between 800 and 1400 ohms?	Yes	▶	SERVICE or REPLACE cable harness Circuit 523 or 524.
	No	▶	REPLACE RH rear sensor.

FM4029100176050X

Fig. 33   Test CC: Wheel Sensor Diagnosis (Part 5 of 8). 1993–94

TEST STEP	RESULT	▶	ACTION TO TAKE
CC17 CHECK RH REAR SENSOR VOLTAGE			
• Turn ignition switch OFF. • Place vehicle on hoist and raise wheels clear of ground. • Set multi-meter to voltage range (2 volts AC). • Measure voltage between Pins 27 and 45 at breakout box while spinning RH rear wheel at approximately 1 revolution per second.	Between 0.10 and 1.40 volts AC	▶	GO to CC18.
	Less than 0.10 or more than 1.40 volts AC	▶	CHECK sensor mounting, air gap or toothed wheel mounting. CORRECT as required.
CC18 CHECK RH REAR SENSOR CIRCUIT CONTINUITY TO GROUND			
• Check continuity between breakout box Pins 27 and 60. • Is continuity present?	No	▶	GO to CC20.
	Yes	▶	GO to CC19.
CC19 CHECK RH REAR SENSOR TO GROUND			
• Disconnect RH rear wheel sensor plug. • Check for continuity between each sensor plug pin (sensor side) and vehicle ground. • Is continuity present?	Yes	▶	REPLACE RH rear sensor.
	No	▶	SERVICE or REPLACE cable harness Circuit 523 or 524. RECONNECT sensor plug.
CC20 CHECK ABS MODULE TO GROUND WIRE			
• Check continuity between breakout box Pin 60 and body ground. • Is continuity present?	Yes	▶	GO to CC21.
	No	▶	SERVICE or REPLACE cable harness Circuit 57.
CC21 CHECK FOR EXCESSIVE AXLE VIBRATION			
• Check differential housing for excessive play. • Check rear axle bearings for excessive play. • Inspect toothed sensor ring for damaged teeth. • Were any parts loose or damaged?	Yes	▶	SERVICE or REPLACE damaged parts.
	No	▶	REVERIFY symptom.

FM402910017606AX

Fig. 33   Test CC: Wheel Sensor Diagnosis (Part 6 of 8). 1993–94 Cougar & Thunderbird

TEST STEP	RESULT	▶	ACTION TO TAKE
CC17 CHECK RH REAR BRAKE ANTI-LOCK SENSOR VOLTAGE			
• Turn ignition switch OFF. • Turn air suspension switch OFF. • Place vehicle on hoist and raise wheels clear of ground. • Set multi-meter to voltage range (2 volts AC). • Measure voltage between Pins 27 and 45 at Breakout Box while spinning RH rear wheel at approximately 1 revolution per second. • Is voltage between 0.10 and 1.40 volts AC?	Yes	▶	GO to CC18.
	No	▶	CHECK rear brake anti-lock sensor mounting, air gap or rear brake anti-lock sensor indicator mounting. CORRECT as required.
CC18 CHECK RH REAR BRAKE ANTI-LOCK SENSOR CIRCUIT CONTINUITY TO GROUND			
• Check continuity between breakout box Pins 27 and 60. • Is continuity present?	Yes	▶	GO to CC19.
	No	▶	GO to CC20.
CC19 CHECK RH REAR BRAKE ANTI-LOCK SENSOR TO GROUND			
• Disconnect RH rear brake anti-lock sensor plug. • Check for continuity between each sensor plug pin (rear brake anti-lock sensor side) and vehicle ground. • Is continuity present?	Yes	▶	REPLACE RH rear brake anti-lock sensor.
	No	▶	SERVICE or REPLACE cable harness Circuit 523 or 524. RECONNECT sensor plug.
CC20 CHECK ANTI-LOCK BRAKE CONTROL MODULE TO GROUND WIRE			
• Check continuity between breakout box Pin 60 and body ground. • Is continuity present?	Yes	▶	GO to CC21.
	No	▶	SERVICE or REPLACE cable harness Circuit 651.
CC21 CHECK FOR EXCESSIVE AXLE VIBRATION			
• Check rear axle housing for excessive play. • Check rear axle bearings for excessive play. • Inspect rear brake anti-lock sensor indicator for damaged teeth. • Were any parts loose or damaged?	Yes	▶	SERVICE or REPLACE damaged parts.
	No	▶	REVERIFY symptom.
NOTE: Turn air suspension switch ON when vehicle is off hoist.			

FM402940017606BX

Fig. 33   Test CC: Wheel Sensor Diagnosis (Part 6 of 8). 1993–94 Mark VIII

TEST STEP	RESULT	▶	ACTION TO TAKE
CC22 DTCs 34, 38, 44, 58, 74 OR 78: CHECK LH REAR SENSOR			
• Turn ignition switch OFF. • Disconnect 55-pin connector from ABS Module. • Measure resistance between Pins 28 and 46.	Yes	▶	GO to CC24.
	No	▶	GO to CC23.
• Connect EEC-IV breakout box 014-00322 with Anti-Lock Test Adapter T90P-50-ALA or equivalent to the 55-pin connector on wiring harness.			
• Is resistance between 800 and 1400 ohms?			
CC23 CHECK LH REAR SENSOR RESISTANCE			
• Disconnect LH rear sensor plug. • Measure resistance of sensor at sensor plug. • Is resistance between 800 and 1400 ohms?	Yes	▶	SERVICE or REPLACE cable harness Circuit 518 or 519.
	No	▶	REPLACE LH rear sensor.

FM4029100176070X

Fig. 33   Test CC: Wheel Sensor Diagnosis (Part 7 of 8). 1993–94

TEST STEP	RESULT	▶	ACTION TO TAKE
CC24 CHECK LH REAR SENSOR VOLTAGE • Turn ignition switch OFF. • Place vehicle on hoist and raise wheels clear of ground. • Set multi-meter to voltage range (2 volts AC) • Measure voltage between Pins 28 and 46 at breakout box while spinning LH rear wheel at approximately 1 revolution per second.	Between 0.10 and 1.40 volts AC Less than 0.10 or more than 1.40 volts AC	▶ ▶	GO to **CC25**. CHECK sensor mounting, air gap or toothed wheel mounting. CORRECT as required.
CC25 CHECK LH REAR SENSOR CIRCUIT CONTINUITY TO GROUND • Check continuity between breakout box Pins 28 and 60. • Is continuity present?	No Yes	▶ ▶	GO to **CC27**. GO to **CC26**.
CC26 CHECK LH REAR SENSOR TO GROUND • Disconnect LH rear wheel sensor plug. • Check for continuity between each sensor plug pin (sensor side) and vehicle ground.	Yes No	▶ ▶	REPLACE LH rear sensor. SERVICE or REPLACE cable harness Circuit 518 or 519. RECONNECT sensor plug.
CC27 CHECK ABS MODULE TO GROUND WIRE • Check continuity between breakout box Pin 60 and body ground. • Is continuity present?	Yes No	▶ ▶	GO to **CC28**. SERVICE or REPLACE cable harness Circuit 57.
CC28 CHECK FOR EXCESSIVE AXLE VIBRATION • Check differential housing for excessive play. • Check rear axle bearings for excessive play. • Inspect toothed sensor ring for damaged teeth. • Were any parts loose or damaged?	Yes No	▶ ▶	SERVICE or REPLACE damaged parts. REVERIFY symptom.

FM402910017608AX

Fig. 33   Test CC: Wheel Sensor Diagnosis (Part 8 of 8). 1993–94 Cougar & Thunderbird

TEST STEP	RESULT	▶	ACTION TO TAKE
CC24 CHECK LH REAR BRAKE ANTI-LOCK SENSOR VOLTAGE • Turn ignition switch OFF. • Turn air suspension switch OFF. • Place vehicle on hoist and raise wheels clear of ground. • Set multi-meter to voltage range (2 volts AC) • Measure voltage between Pins 28 and 46 at Breakout Box while spinning LH rear wheel at approximately 1 revolution per second. • Is voltage between 0.10 and 1.40 volts AC?	Yes No	▶ ▶	GO to **CC25**. CHECK rear brake anti-lock sensor mounting, air gap or rear brake anti-lock sensor indicator mounting. CORRECT as required.
CC25 CHECK LH REAR BRAKE ANTI-LOCK SENSOR CIRCUIT CONTINUITY TO GROUND • Check continuity between breakout box Pins 28 and 60. • Is continuity present?	No Yes	▶ ▶	GO to **CC27**. GO to **CC26**.
CC26 CHECK LH REAR BRAKE ANTI-LOCK SENSOR TO GROUND • Disconnect LH rear brake anti-lock sensor plug • Check for continuity between each sensor plug pin (sensor side) and vehicle ground. • Is continuity present?	Yes No	▶ ▶	REPLACE LH rear brake anti-lock sensor. SERVICE or REPLACE cable harness Circuit 518 or 519. RECONNECT sensor plug
CC27 CHECK ANTI-LOCK BRAKE CONTROL MODULE TO GROUND WIRE • Check continuity between breakout box Pin 60 and body ground • Is continuity present?	Yes No	▶ ▶	GO to **CC28**. SERVICE or REPLACE cable harness Circuit 651
CC28 CHECK FOR EXCESSIVE AXLE VIBRATION • Check rear axle housing for excessive play. • Check rear axle bearings for excessive play. • Inspect rear brake anti-lock sensor indicator for damaged teeth. • Were any parts loose or damaged? NOTE: Turn air suspension switch ON when vehicle is off hoist.	Yes No	▶ ▶	SERVICE or REPLACE damaged parts. REVERIFY symptom.

FM402940017608BX

Fig. 33   Pinpoint CC: Wheel Sensor Diagnosis (Part 8 of 8). 1993–94 Mark VIII

TEST STEP	RESULT	▶	ACTION TO TAKE
DD1 DTC 51 AND / OR 71: CHECK LH FRONT SENSOR CIRCUIT CONTINUITY • Turn ignition switch OFF. • Disconnect 55-pin plug from ABS Module. • Check for continuity between breakout box Pins 60 and 30.	Yes No	▶ ▶	GO to **DD2**. GO to **DD3**.
• Connect EEC-IV Breakout Box, 014-00322 with Anti-Lock Test Adapter, T90P-50-ALA or equivalent to the anti-lock 55-pin plug harness. • Is continuity present?			
DD2 CHECK LH FRONT SENSOR CONTINUITY • Disconnect LH front wheel sensor plug. • Check for continuity between each sensor plug pin (sensor side) and vehicle ground. • Is continuity present?	Yes No	▶ ▶	REPLACE LH front sensor. SERVICE or REPLACE cable harness Circuit 521 or 522. RECONNECT sensor plug.
DD3 CHECK ABS MODULE TO GROUND WIRE • Check continuity between breakout box Pin 60 and body ground. • Is continuity present?	Yes No	▶ ▶	GO to **DD4**. SERVICE or REPLACE cable harness Circuit 57.

FM402910017010X

Fig. 34   Test DD: Wheel Sensor Diagnosis (Part 1 of 6). 1993–94 Cougar & Thunderbird

TEST STEP	RESULT	▶	ACTION TO TAKE
DD4 CHECK ANTI-LOCK OPERATION LH FRONT WHEEL • Lift vehicle and rotate wheels to ensure they turn freely. • Apply moderate brake pedal effort and check that LH front wheel will not turn. • Jump Pins 34 and 19. • Short Pins 2, 20 and 60 to each other at breakout box. • Check that LH front wheel turns freely with ignition switch ON. CAUTION: Do not leave ignition on for more than 1 minute, or valve damage may result.	Wheel turns freely Wheel does not turn freely or pedal drops	▶ ▶	REVERIFY symptom. REPLACE solenoid valve body.
DD5 DTC(s) 52 AND / OR 72: CHECK RH FRONT SENSOR CIRCUIT CONTINUITY • Turn ignition switch OFF. • Disconnect 55-pin plug from ABS Module. • Check for continuity between breakout box Pins 60 and 29.	Yes No	▶ ▶	GO to **DD6**. GO to **DD7**.
• Connect EEC-IV breakout box 014-00322 with Anti-Lock Test Adapter T90P-50-ALA to the anti-lock 55-pin plug wiring harness. • Is continuity present?			

FM402910017020X

Fig. 34   Test DD: Wheel Sensor Diagnosis (Part 2 of 6). 1993–94 Cougar & Thunderbird

TEST STEP	RESULT	▶	ACTION TO TAKE
DD6 CHECK RH FRONT SENSOR CONTINUITY • Disconnect RH front wheel sensor. • Check for continuity between each sensor plug pin (sensor side) and vehicle ground. • Is continuity present?	Yes No	▶ ▶	REPLACE RH front sensor. SERVICE or REPLACE cable harness Circuit 514 or 519. RECONNECT sensor plug.
DD7 CHECK ABS MODULE TO GROUND WIRE • Check continuity between breakout box Pin 60 and body ground. • Is continuity present?	Yes No	▶ ▶	GO to DD8. SERVICE or REPLACE cable harness Circuit 57.
DD8 CHECK ANTI-LOCK OPERATION RH FRONT WHEEL • Lift vehicle and rotate wheels to ensure they turn freely. • Apply moderate brake pedal effort and check that RH front wheel will not turn. • Jump Pins 34 and 19. • Short Pins 21, 38 and 60 to each other at breakout box. • Check that RH front wheel turns freely with ignition switch ON.	Wheel turns freely Wheel does not turn freely or pedal drops	▶ ▶	REVERIFY symptom. REPLACE solenoid valve body.

FM4029100177030X

Fig. 34   Test DD: Wheel Sensor Diagnosis (Part 3 of 6). 1993–94 Cougar & Thunderbird

TEST STEP	RESULT	▶	ACTION TO TAKE
DD9 DTC(s) 53 AND/OR 73: CHECK RH REAR SENSOR CIRCUIT CONTINUITY • Turn ignition switch OFF. • Disconnect 55-pin plug from ABS Module. • Check for continuity between breakout box Pins 60 and 27.	Yes No	▶ ▶	GO to DD10. GO to DD11.
• Connect EEC-IV Breakout Box 014-00322 with Anti-Lock Test Adapter T90P-50-ALA or equivalent to the anti-lock 55-pin plug wiring harness. • Is continuity present?			
DD10 CHECK RH REAR SENSOR CONTINUITY • Disconnect RH rear wheel sensor plug. • Check for continuity between each sensor plug pin (sensor side) and vehicle ground. • Is continuity present?	Yes No	▶ ▶	REPLACE RH rear sensor. SERVICE or REPLACE cable harness Circuit 523 or 524. RECONNECT sensor plug.
DD11 CHECK ABS MODULE TO GROUND WIRE • Check continuity between breakout box Pin 60 and body ground. • Is continuity present?	Yes No	▶ ▶	GO to DD12. SERVICE or REPLACE cable harness Circuit 57.

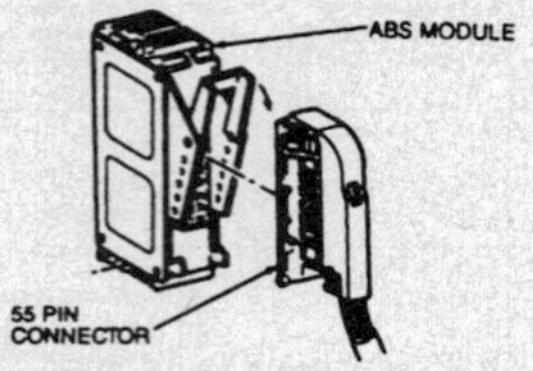

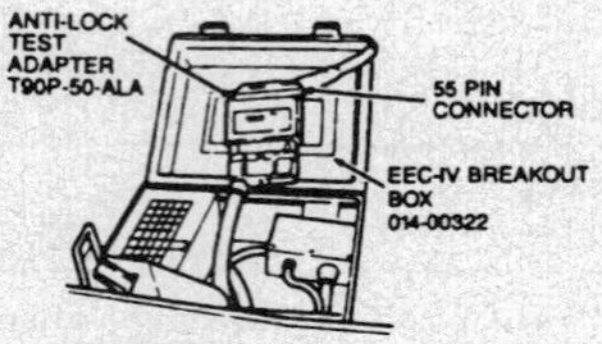

FM4029100177040X

Fig. 34   Test DD: Wheel Sensor Diagnosis (Part 4 of 6). 1993–94 Cougar & Thunderbird

TEST STEP	RESULT	▶	ACTION TO TAKE
DD12 CHECK ANTI-LOCK OPERATION RH REAR WHEEL • Lift vehicle and rotate wheels to ensure they turn freely. • Apply moderate brake pedal effort and check that RH rear wheel will not turn. • Jump Pins 34 and 19. • Short Pins 18, 55 and 60 to each other at breakout box. • Check that RH rear wheel turns freely with ignition switch ON.	Wheel turns freely Wheel does not turn freely or pedal drops	▶ ▶	REVERIFY symptom. REPLACE solenoid valve body.
DD13 DTC(s) 54 AND/OR 74: CHECK LH REAR SENSOR CIRCUIT CONTINUITY • Turn ignition switch OFF. • Disconnect 55-pin plug from ABS Module. • Check for continuity between breakout box Pins 60 and 28.	Yes No	▶ ▶	GO to DD14. GO to DD15.
• Connect EEC-IV Breakout Box 014-00322 with Anti-Lock Test Adapter T90P-50-ALA or equivalent to the anti-lock 55-pin plug wiring harness. • Is continuity present?			

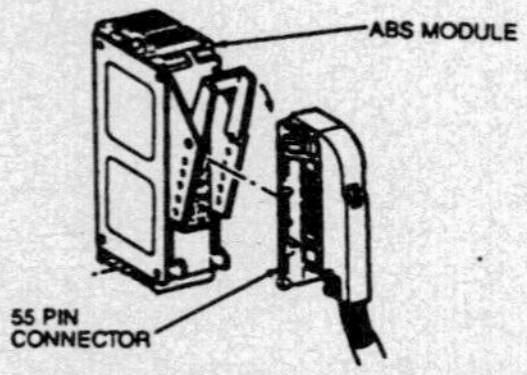

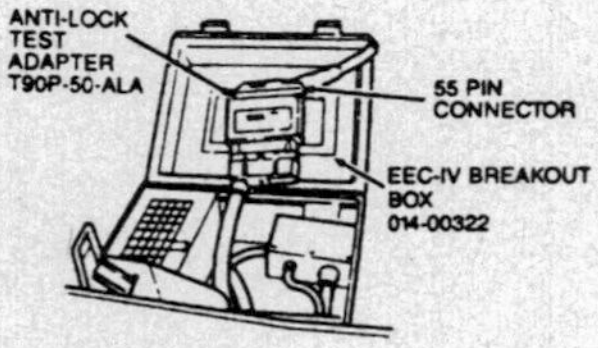

FM4029100177050X

Fig. 34   Test DD: Wheel Sensor Diagnosis (Part 5 of 6). 1993–94 Cougar & Thunderbird

TEST STEP	RESULT	▶	ACTION TO TAKE
DD14 CHECK LH REAR SENSOR CONTINUITY • Disconnect LH Rear wheel sensor plug. • Check for continuity between each sensor plug pin (sensor side) and vehicle ground. • Is continuity present?	Yes No	▶ ▶	REPLACE LH rear sensor. SERVICE or REPLACE cable harness Circuit 518 or 519. RECONNECT sensor plug.
DD15 CHECK ABS MODULE TO GROUND WIRE • Check continuity between breakout box Pin 60 and body ground. • Is continuity present?	Yes No	▶ ▶	GO to DD16. SERVICE or REPLACE cable harness Circuit 57.
DD16 CHECK ANTI-LOCK OPERATION LH REAR WHEEL • Lift vehicle and rotate wheels to ensure they turn freely. • Apply moderate brake pedal effort and check that LH rear wheel will not turn. • Jump Pins 34 and 19. • Short Pins 36, 54 and 60 to each other at breakout box. • Check that LH rear wheel turns freely with ignition switch ON. **CAUTION:** Do not leave ignition on for more than 1 minute or valve damage may result.	Wheel turns freely Wheel does not turn freely or pedal drops	▶ ▶	REVERIFY symptom. REPLACE solenoid valve body.

FM4029100177060X

Fig. 34   Test DD: Wheel Sensor Diagnosis (Part 6 of 6). 1993–94 Cougar & Thunderbird

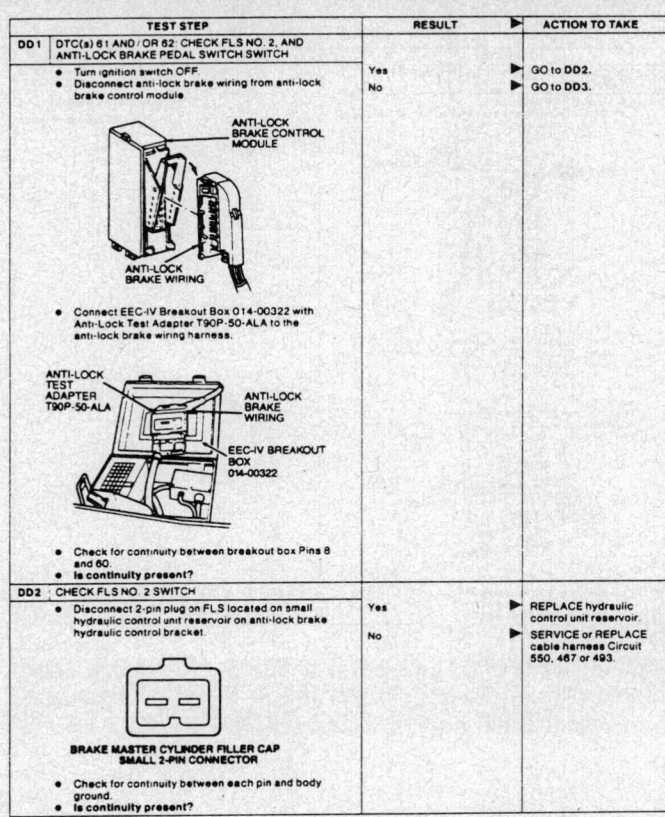

TEST STEP	RESULT	▶	ACTION TO TAKE
DD1 DTC(s) 61 AND/OR 62: CHECK FLS NO. 2, AND ANTI-LOCK BRAKE PEDAL SWITCH SWITCH • Turn ignition switch OFF. • Disconnect anti-lock brake wiring from anti-lock brake control module.	Yes No	▶ ▶	GO to DD2. GO to DD3.
• Connect EEC-IV Breakout Box 014-00322 with Anti-Lock Test Adapter T90P-50-ALA to the anti-lock brake wiring harness. • Check for continuity between breakout box Pins 8 and 60. • Is continuity present?			
DD2 CHECK FLS NO. 2 SWITCH • Disconnect 2-pin plug on FLS located on small hydraulic control unit reservoir on anti-lock brake hydraulic control bracket.	Yes No	▶ ▶	REPLACE hydraulic control unit reservoir. SERVICE or REPLACE cable harness Circuit 550, 467 or 493.
• Check for continuity between each pin and body ground. • Is continuity present?			

FM4029400430010X

Fig. 35 Test DD: Fluid Level Indicator/Anti-Lock Brake Sensor travel Switch/Pump Motor & Relay Diagnosis (Part 1 of 7). 1993–94 Mark VIII

TEST STEP	RESULT	▶	ACTION TO TAKE
DD3 CHECK FOR VOLTAGE ON FLS NO. 2 SWITCH AND CIRCUITRY • Turn ignition switch to RUN position. • Measure voltage between breakout box Pins 8 and 60. • Is B+ present?	Yes No	▶ ▶	SERVICE or REPLACE cable harness Circuit 550, 467 or 493. GO to DD4.
DD4 CHECK ANTI-LOCK BRAKE PEDAL SENSOR SWITCH AND CIRCUITRY • Check for continuity between breakout box Pins 5 and 60. • Is continuity present?	Yes No	▶ ▶	GO to DD5. GO to DD6.
DD5 CHECK ANTI-LOCK BRAKE PEDAL SENSOR SWITCH • Disconnect 2-pin plug on anti-lock brake pedal sensor switch.	Yes No	▶ ▶	REPLACE anti-lock brake pedal sensor switch. SERVICE or REPLACE cable harness Circuit 550, 467 or 493.
• Check for continuity between each pin and body ground. • Is continuity present?			
DD6 CHECK FOR VOLTAGE ON ANTI-LOCK BRAKE PEDAL SENSOR SWITCH AND CIRCUITRY • Turn ignition switch to RUN position. • Measure voltage between breakout box Pins 5 and 60. • Is B+ present?	Yes No	▶ ▶	SERVICE or REPLACE cable harness Circuit 550, 467 or 493. REVERIFY DTC 61 and/or 62.

FM4029400430020X

Fig. 35 Test DD: Fluid Level Indicator/Anti-Lock Brake Sensor travel Switch/Pump Motor & Relay Diagnosis (Part 2 of 7). 1993–94 Mark VIII

TEST STEP	RESULT	▶	ACTION TO TAKE
DD7 DTC(s) 63: CHECK PUMP MOTOR SPEED SENSOR AND CIRCUIT NOTE: The anti-lock brake control module will check the pump motor speed sensor by running the pump motor for approximately one-half second each time the ignition switch is turned to RUN and the vehicle speed reaches 30 km/h (19 mph). • Turn ignition switch OFF • Disconnect anti-lock brake wiring from anti-lock brake control module.	Yes No	▶ ▶	GO to DD9. GO to DD8.
• Connect EEC-IV Breakout Box 014-00322 with Anti-Lock Test Adapter T90P-50-ALA to the anti-lock brake wiring harness. • Check resistance between breakout box Pins 31 and 49. • Is resistance between 5 and 100 ohms?			

FM4029400430030X

Fig. 35 Test DD: Fluid Level Indicator/Anti-Lock Brake Sensor travel Switch/Pump Motor & Relay Diagnosis (Part 3 of 7). 1993–94 Mark VIII

TEST STEP	RESULT	▶	ACTION TO TAKE
DD8 CHECK PUMP MOTOR SPEED SENSOR • Disconnect 4-pin plug on pump motor. • Measure resistance between Pins S0 and S1 on pump motor. • Is resistance between 5 and 100 ohms?	Yes No	▶ ▶	SERVICE or REPLACE cable harness Circuit 462 or 351. REPLACE pump motor.
DD9 CHECK PUMP MOTOR SPEED ANTI-LOCK SENSOR SHORT TO BATTERY + • Turn ignition switch to ON. • Measure voltage between breakout box Pins 31 and 60. • Is B+ present?	Yes No	▶ ▶	GO to DD 10. GO to DD 12.
DD10 CHECK CIRCUIT 462 • Disconnect pump motor to relay 4-pin plug connector. • Turn ignition switch to ON. • Measure voltage between breakout box Pins 31 and 60.	Yes No	▶ ▶	SERVICE or REPLACE cable harness Circuit 462 GO to DD 11.
DD11 CHECK CIRCUIT 351 • Turn ignition switch to ON. • Measure voltage between breakout box Pins 49 and 60	Yes No	▶ ▶	SERVICE or REPLACE cable harness Circuit 351 REPLACE pump motor assembly relay.
DD12 CHECK PUMP MOTOR SPEED SENSOR SHORT TO GROUND • Check for continuity between breakout box Pins 31 and 60. • Is continuity present?	Yes No	▶ ▶	GO to DD 13. GO to DD 15.
DD13 CHECK CIRCUIT 462 • Disconnect pump motor to relay 4-pin plug connector. • Check for continuity between breakout box Pins 31 and 60. • Is continuity present?	Yes No	▶ ▶	SERVICE or REPLACE cable harness Circuit 462 GO to DD 14.
DD14 CHECK CIRCUIT 351 • Check for continuity between breakout box Pins 49 and 60. • Is continuity present?	Yes No	▶ ▶	SERVICE or REPLACE cable harness Circuit 351 REPLACE pump and pump motor assembly.
DD15 CHECK PUMP MOTOR OPERATION • Reconnect pump motor relay to pump and wire harness. • Jumper Pins 15 and 60 at breakout box. • Does pump motor run?	Yes No	▶ ▶	REPLACE anti-lock brake control module. GO to DD 16.

FM4029400430040X

Fig. 35 Test DD: Fluid Level Indicator/Anti-Lock Brake Sensor travel Switch/Pump Motor & Relay Diagnosis (Part 4 of 7). 1993–94 Mark VIII

TEST STEP	RESULT	▶	ACTION TO TAKE
DD16 CHECK CIRCUIT 539 • Check for continuity between wire harness to pump motor relay connector Pin D and breakout box pin 15. • Is continuity present?	Yes No	▶ ▶	GO to DD17. SERVICE or REPLACE cable harness Circuit 539
DD17 CHECK POWER TO RELAY • Disconnect wire harness from pump motor relay. • Check voltage between wire harness to pump motor relay connector pin A and ground. • Is there a minimum of 10 volts?	Yes No	▶ ▶	GO to DD18. SERVICE or REPLACE battery, 40 amp fuse or Circuit 533.
DD18 CHECK CIRCUIT 651 • Check for continuity between wire harness to pump motor relay connector pin C and ground. • Is continuity present?	Yes No	▶ ▶	GO to DD19. SERVICE or REPLACE cable harness Circuit 651

PUMP MOTOR RELAY CONNECTOR HARNESS SIDE

FM4029400430050X

Fig. 35   Test DD: Fluid Level Indicator/Anti-Lock Brake Sensor travel Switch/Pump Motor & Relay Diagnosis (Part 5 of 7). 1993–94 Mark VIII

TEST STEP	RESULT	▶	ACTION TO TAKE
DD22 DTC 64: CHECK PUMP MOTOR PRESSURE CAPABILITY • Turn ignition switch OFF. • Disconnect anti-lock brake wiring from anti-lock brake control module.	Yes No	▶ ▶	REVERIFY Code 64. REPLACE pump motor.

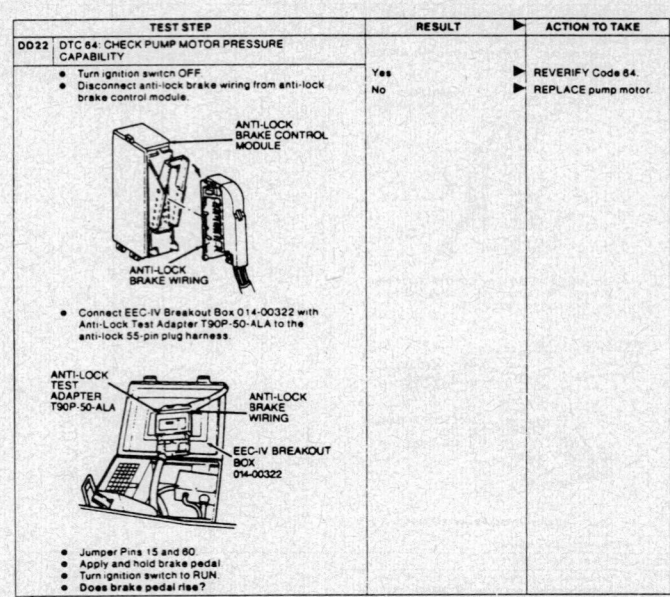

• Connect EEC-IV Breakout Box 014-00322 with Anti-Lock Test Adapter T90P-50-ALA to the anti-lock 55-pin plug harness.

• Jumper Pins 15 and 60.
• Apply and hold brake pedal.
• Turn ignition switch to RUN.
• Does brake pedal rise?

FM4029400430070X

Fig. 35   Test DD: Fluid Level Indicator/Anti-Lock Brake Sensor travel Switch/Pump Motor & Relay Diagnosis (Part 7 of 7). 1993–94 Mark VIII

TEST STEP	RESULT	▶	ACTION TO TAKE
DD19 CHECK PUMP MOTOR • Jumper Pins A and B on wire harness to pump motor relay connector. • Does motor run?	Yes No	▶ ▶	REPLACE pump motor relay. GO to DD20.
DD20 CHECK CIRCUIT 538 • Check for continuity between wire harness to pump motor relay connector pin B and switched B+ Pin on 4 pin pump motor connector harness side. • Is continuity present?	Yes No	▶ ▶	GO to DD21. SERVICE or REPLACE cable harness Circuit 538.
DD21 CHECK PUMP MOTOR GROUND • Check for continuity between B- pin on 4 Pin pump motor connector harness side and chassis ground. • Is continuity present?	Yes No	▶ ▶	REPLACE pump motor assembly. SERVICE or REPLACE cable harness Circuit 651.

PUMP MOTOR RELAY CONNECTOR HARNESS SIDE

B- CIRCUIT 651
CIRCUIT 351
CIRCUIT 462
SWITCHED B+ CIRCUIT 538
4 PIN PUMP MOTOR CONNECTOR HARNESS SIDE

FM4029400430060X

Fig. 35   Test DD: Fluid Level Indicator/Anti-Lock Brake Sensor travel Switch/Pump Motor & Relay Diagnosis (Part 6 of 7). 1993–94 Mark VIII

TEST STEP	RESULT	▶	ACTION TO TAKE
EE1 DTC(s) 61 AND 62: CHECK FLS NO. 2, AND PEDAL TRAVEL SWITCH • Turn ignition switch OFF. • Disconnect 55-pin plug from ABS Module.	No Yes	▶ ▶	GO to EE3. GO to EE2.

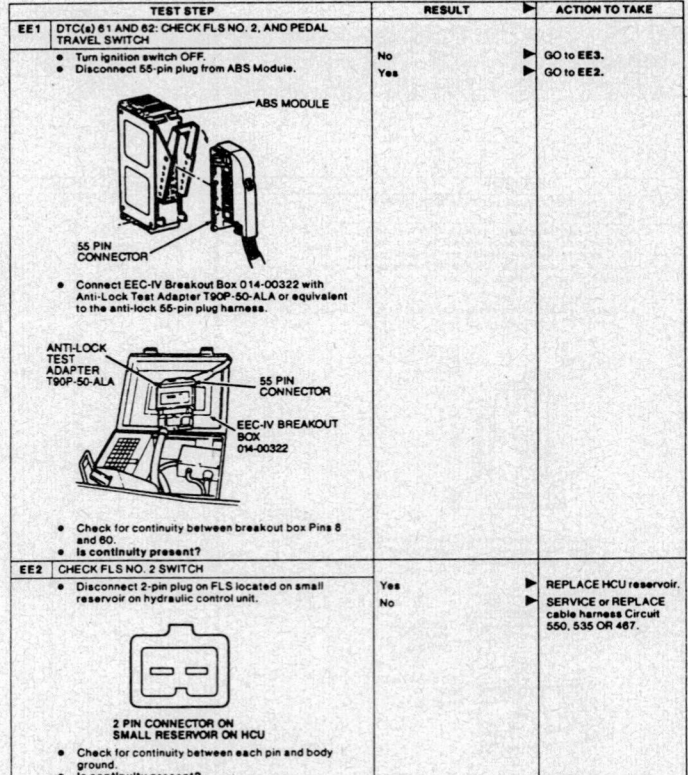

• Connect EEC-IV Breakout Box 014-00322 with Anti-Lock Test Adapter T90P-50-ALA or equivalent to the anti-lock 55-pin plug harness.

• Check for continuity between breakout box Pins 8 and 60. • Is continuity present?			
EE2 CHECK FLS NO. 2 SWITCH • Disconnect 2-pin plug on FLS located on small reservoir on hydraulic control unit.	Yes No	▶ ▶	REPLACE HCU reservoir. SERVICE or REPLACE cable harness Circuit 550, 535 OR 467.

2 PIN CONNECTOR ON SMALL RESERVOIR ON HCU

• Check for continuity between each pin and body ground.
• Is continuity present?

FM4029100178010X

Fig. 36   Test EE: Fluid Level Indicator/Pedal Travel Switch/Motor Pump Diagnosis (Part 1 of 7). 1993 Cougar & Thunderbird

TEST STEP	RESULT	▶	ACTION TO TAKE
EE3 CHECK FOR VOLTAGE ON FLS NO. 2 SWITCH AND CIRCUITRY			
• Turn ignition switch to ON position. • Measure voltage between breakout box Pins 8 and 60.	No voltage	▶	GO to EE4.
	12 volts	▶	SERVICE or REPLACE cable harness circuit 550, 467 OR 535.
EE4 CHECK PEDAL TRAVEL SWITCH AND CIRCUITRY			
• Check for continuity between breakout box Pins 5 and 60. • Is continuity present?	No	▶	GO to EE6.
	Yes	▶	GO to EE5.
EE5 CHECK PEDAL TRAVEL SWITCH			
• Disconnect 2-pin plug on pedal travel switch.	Yes	▶	REPLACE pedal travel switch.
	No	▶	SERVICE or REPLACE cable harness Circuit 550, 535 or 467.
(2 PIN BRAKE PEDAL POSITION SWITCH diagram)			
• Check for continuity between each pin and body ground. • Is continuity present?			
EE6 CHECK FOR VOLTAGE ON PEDAL TRAVEL SWITCH AND CIRCUITRY			
• Turn ignition switch to ON position. • Measure voltage between breakout box Pins 5 and 60.	No voltage	▶	REVERIFY code 61 and or 62.
	12 volts	▶	SERVICE or REPLACE cable harness circuit 550, 535 or 467.

FM4029100178020X

Fig. 36   Test EE: Fluid Level Indicator/Pedal Travel Switch/Motor Pump Diagnosis (Part 2 of 7). 1993 Cougar & Thunderbird

TEST STEP	RESULT	▶	ACTION TO TAKE
EE7 DTC(s) 63: CHECK PUMP MOTOR SPEED SENSOR AND CIRCUIT	Yes	▶	GO to EE9.
NOTE: The ABS module will check the pump motor speed sensor by running the pump motor for approximately one-half second each time the ignition is switched ON and the vehicle speed reaches 30 km/h (19 mph).	No	▶	GO to EE8.
• Turn ignition switch OFF. • Disconnect 55-pin plug from ABS Module.			
(ABS MODULE / 55 PIN CONNECTOR diagram)			
• Connect EEC-IV Breakout Box 014-00322 with Anti-Lock Test Adapter T90P-50-ALA or equivalent to the anti-lock 55-pin plug harness.			
(ANTI-LOCK TEST ADAPTER T90P-50-ALA / 55 PIN CONNECTOR / EEC-IV BREAKOUT BOX 014-00322 diagram)			
• Check resistance between breakout box Pins 31 and 49. • Is resistance between 5 and 100 ohms?			
EE8 CHECK PUMP MOTOR SPEED SENSOR	Yes	▶	SERVICE or REPLACE cable harness circuit 462 or 604.
• Disconnect 4-pin plug on pump motor. • Measure resistance between Pins S0 and S1 on pump motor. • Is resistance between 5 and 100 ohms?	No	▶	REPLACE pump and motor.
(NEGATIVE PIN / S1 / S0 / POSITIVE PIN connector diagram)			

FM4029100178030X

Fig. 36   Test EE: Fluid Level Indicator/Pedal Travel Switch/Motor Pump Diagnosis (Part 3 of 7). 1993 Cougar & Thunderbird

TEST STEP	RESULT	▶	ACTION TO TAKE
EE9 CHECK MOTOR SPEED SENSOR SHORT TO BATTERY +	No voltage	▶	GO to EE12.
• Turn ignition switch to ON. • Measure voltage between breakout box Pins 31 and 60.	12 volts	▶	GO to EE10.
EE10 CHECK CIRCUIT 462	No voltage	▶	GO to EE11.
• Disconnect pump motor to relay 4-pin plug connector. • Turn ignition switch to ON. • Measure voltage between breakout box Pins 31 and 60.	12 volts	▶	SERVICE or REPLACE cable harness Circuit 462.
EE11 CHECK CIRCUIT 604	No voltage	▶	REPLACE pump and motor assembly relay.
• Turn ignition switch to ON. • Measure voltage between breakout box Pins 49 and 60.	12 volts	▶	SERVICE or REPLACE cable harness Circuit 604.
EE12 CHECK MOTOR SPEED SENSOR SHORT TO GROUND	No	▶	GO to EE15.
• Check for continuity between breakout box Pins 31 and 60. • Is continuity present?	Yes	▶	GO to EE13.
EE13 CHECK CIRCUIT 462	Yes	▶	SERVICE or REPLACE cable harness Circuit 462.
• Disconnect pump motor to relay 4-pin plug connector. • Check for continuity between breakout box Pins 31 and 60. • Is continuity present?	No	▶	GO to EE14.
EE14 CHECK CIRCUIT 604	Yes	▶	SERVICE or REPLACE cable harness Circuit 604.
• Check for continuity between breakout box Pins 49 and 60. • Is continuity present?	No	▶	REPLACE pump and motor assembly.
EE15 CHECK PUMP MOTOR OPERATION	Yes	▶	REPLACE controller.
• Reconnect pump motor relay to pump and wire harness. • Jumper Pins 15 and 60 at breakout box. • Does pump motor run?	No	▶	GO to EE16.
EE16 CHECK CIRCUIT 539	Yes	▶	GO to EE17.
• Check for continuity between wire harness to pump motor relay connector Pin D and breakout box pin 15. • Is continuity present?	No	▶	SERVICE or REPLACE cable harness circuit 539.
(PUMP MOTOR RELAY CONNECTOR HARNESS SIDE — A B C D diagram)			

FM4029100178040X

Fig. 36   Test EE: Fluid Level Indicator/Pedal Travel Switch/Motor Pump Diagnosis (Part 4 of 7). 1993 Cougar & Thunderbird

TEST STEP	RESULT	▶	ACTION TO TAKE
EE17 CHECK POWER TO RELAY	Over 10 volts	▶	GO to EE18.
• Disconnect wire harness from pump motor relay. • Check voltage between wire harness to pump motor relay connector pin A and ground.	Less than 10 volts	▶	SERVICE or REPLACE battery, 40 amp fuse, circuit 537, 38 or 37.
(PUMP MOTOR RELAY CONNECTOR HARNESS SIDE — A B C D diagram)			
EE18 CHECK CIRCUIT 57	Yes	▶	GO to EE19.
• Check for continuity between wire harness to pump motor relay connector pin C and ground. • Is continuity present?	No	▶	SERVICE or REPLACE cable harness Circuit 57.
(PUMP MOTOR RELAY CONNECTOR HARNESS SIDE — A B C D diagram)			
EE19 CHECK PUMP MOTOR	Yes	▶	REPLACE pump motor relay.
• Jumper Pins A and B on wire harness to pump motor relay connector. • Does motor run?	No	▶	GO to EE20.
(PUMP MOTOR RELAY CONNECTOR HARNESS SIDE — A B C D diagram)			

FM4029100178050X

Fig. 36   Test EE: Fluid Level Indicator/Pedal Travel Switch/Motor Pump Diagnosis (Part 5 of 7). 1993 Cougar & Thunderbird

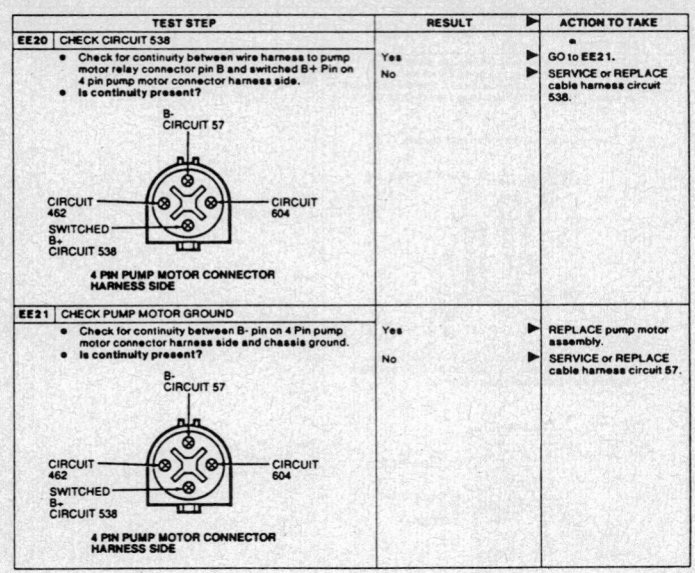

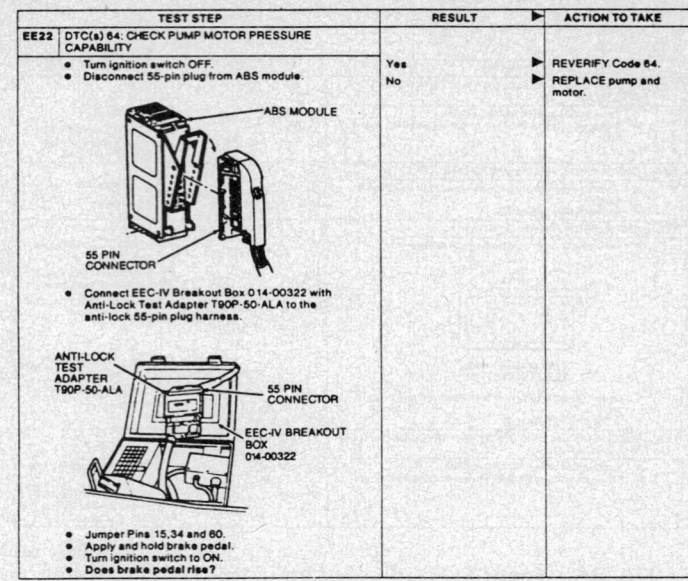

Fig. 36   Test EE: Fluid Level Indicator/Pedal Travel Switch/Motor Pump Diagnosis (Part 6 of 7). 1993 Cougar & Thunderbird

Fig. 36   Test EE: Fluid Level Indicator/Pedal Travel Switch/Motor Pump Diagnosis (Part 7 of 7). 1993 Cougar & Thunderbird

SYSTEM SERVICE

MASTER CYLINDER RESERVOIR

Brake fluid level in the master cylinder reservoir should be between 0.16 inch below the MAX line and the MAX line on the reservoir. If brake fluid is low, the red "Brake" lamp will illuminate. Fill reservoir with brake fluid C6AZ-19542-AA (ESA-M6C25-A) or DOT-3 equivalent.

Brake System Bleed

The master cylinder and hydraulic control unit must be bled using ABS test adapter tool No. T90P-50-ALA, or equivalent. If this procedure is not followed, air will be trapped in the hydraulic control unit which will eventually lead to a spongy brake pedal.

To bleed the master cylinder and HCU, disconnect the 55-pin plug from the ABS module and install the ABS test adapter to the wire harness 55-pin plug.

1. Place bleed/harness switch in bleed position.
2. Turn ignition to ON position. At this point, red OFF indicator should turn on.
3. Push motor button on adapter down to start pump motor. Red OFF indicator should turn off and green ON indicator should turn on.
4. Pump motor will run for 60 seconds once motor button is pushed. If pump motor must be stopped before 60 seconds, press abort button to turn motor off.
5. After 20 seconds of pump motor operation, push and hold valve button down for 20 seconds, then release.

Brake lines may be bled in the conventional manner. Ensure lines are bled in the following sequence:

1. RH Rear.
2. LH Front.
3. LH Rear.
4. RH Front.

Component Replace

HYDRAULIC CONTROL UNIT

Removal

1. Remove battery and battery tray.
2. Disconnect 19-pin valve body to wire harness connector.
3. Raise and support vehicle, then remove LH front tire and wheel assembly.
4. Remove inner fender splash shield.
5. **On Mark VIII models,** turn air suspension service switch off.
6. **On all models,** disconnect 2-pin fluid level switch, 4-pin pump motor, 4-pin pump motor relay and 55-pin ABS module connectors. **Do not allow brake fluid to come in contact with wiring or paint. If this occurs, rinse immediately with water.**
7. Remove low pressure feed hose from HCU reservoir.
8. Disconnect LH front brake tube from hose at hose mounting bracket.
9. Remove two lower ABS assembly mounting bracket attaching screws.
10. Lower vehicle and disconnect five brake tube connections at junction block. Remove two junction block retaining screws. **Do not allow the two upper bushings to turn in the bracket while loosening upper mounting bolts. Hold bushings with vise grips if necessary.**
11. Remove two upper ABS assembly mounting bracket bolts.
12. Remove HCU with ABS assembly.

Installation

1. Position ABS assembly and place mounting bracket hook through slot in outer frame rail.
2. Lower vehicle and install two upper mounting bolts. **Torque** bolts to 8.5-11.5 ft. lbs.
3. Raise vehicle and **torque** two lower mounting screws to 8.5-11.5 ft. lbs.
4. Install low pressure feed hose to HCU reservoir.
5. Connect LH front brake tube to hose at mounting bracket.
6. Connect two-pin fluid level switch, four-pin pump motor, four-pin pump motor relay and 55-pin ABS module connectors.
7. Lower vehicle and install two junction block retaining nuts. **Torque** to 1.7-2.4 ft. lbs.
8. Attach five tube connectors at junction block. **Torque** to 10-18 ft. lbs.
9. Install battery and battery tray.
10. Bleed brake system as described under "System Bleeding."
11. Install inner fender splash shield.
12. Install tire and wheel assembly. **Torque** lug nuts to 85-105 ft. lbs.
13. **On Mark VIII models,** turn air suspension service switch on.

ABS MODULE

1. Raise and support vehicle
2. Remove inner fender splash shield.
3. Remove pump motor relay.
4. Disconnect 55-pin connector.
5. Remove three screws attaching ABS module to mounting bracket.
6. Reverse procedure to install. Ensure three mounting holes in ABS module align with holes in mounting bracket.

WHEEL SENSOR
Front Sensor

1. Raise and support vehicle.

2. Disconnect sensor electrical connector.
3. Remove routing clips along wiring harness.
4. Remove bolt securing sensor to front spindle.
5. Remove front wheel sensor.
6. Reverse procedure to install.

Rear Sensor
1. Locate wheel sensor electrical connector inside luggage compartment, rearward of wheel well behind carpeting. Disconnect sensor connector
2. Lift luggage compartment carpet and push sensor wire grommet through hole in luggage compartment floor.
3. Remove plastic clip holding sensor wire to axle carrier housing.
4. Remove wheel sensor retaining bolt and sensor.
5. Reverse procedure to install. **Torque** sensor retaining bolt to 14-20 ft. lbs.

PEDAL TRAVEL SWITCH
1. Remove switch retaining ring with small screwdriver.
2. Pull travel switch and O-ring from booster.
3. Install pedal travel switch by pushing into booster until retaining ring snaps into position.

FRONT BRAKE SENSOR INDICATOR

1. **On Mark VIII models,** turn off air suspension service switch.
2. **On all models,** raise and support vehicle, then remove wheel and tire assembly. **Note rotor to hub position indicated by paint marks on one of the studs and rotor. Reassemble with paint marks aligned to ensure lowest mounted total indicated runout of rotor.**
3. Remove rear disc brake caliper, rear disc brake rotor and wheel hub assemblies.
4. Using suitable three-jaw puller, remove front brake anti-lock sensor indicator from wheel hub.
5. Reverse procedure to install, noting the following:
   a. Ensure front brake anti-lock sensor indicator is pressed on straight.
   b. Ensure paint mark on rotor aligns with paint mark on wheel stud to ensure lowest mounted total indicated runout of rear disc brake rotor.

REAR BRAKE SENSOR INDICATOR

Rear brake anti-lock sensor indicators must not be reused. Discard rear brake anti-lock sensor indicator after removal and replace it with a new part.
1. Remove halfshaft as described in "Drive Axles" section.
2. Position two-jaw puller tool No. D80L-1002-L, or equivalent, on inboard CV joint stub shaft pilot bearing housing, with puller jaws under sensor indicator.
3. Turn wrench clockwise until sensor indicator is removed.
4. Position bearing cone replacer tool No. T89P-20202-A, or equivalent, on press bed with pilot up, then place sensor indicator on installation tool.
5. Insert CV joint stub shaft through sensor indicator and allow it to rest on sensor indicator.
6. Allow press ram to bottom out in inboard CV joint stub shaft pilot bearing housing and press until ring contacts CV joint step.
7. Install halfshaft as described in "Drive Axles" section.

Probe

NOTE: Wire Color Code & Electrical Symbol Identification Located At The Front Of This Manual Can Be Used As An Aid When Using Wiring Circuits Found In This Section.

INDEX

PRECAUTIONS

HYDRAULIC BRAKE FLUID COLOR

Hydraulic brake fluid must conform with the requirements of Federal Motor Vehicle Safety Standard 116. Under this standard, brake fluids are visually different from other automotive fluids such as transmission, power steering and engine.

Fluid color in a normal brake system may vary from its original color for many reasons. A brake master cylinder may show significantly different shades fluid color between the two brake master cylinder reservoirs. Color may also appear to vary between cast steel and die cast aluminum reservoirs. Some reasons for discoloration include the following:
1. Heat and/or aging.
2. Different operation temperatures or different rates of normal oxidation between two reservoir compartments.
3. Different brands and/or shades of fluid are used when topping off during normal service.
4. Dissolution of color dye used on master cylinder internal springs during assembly.

Brake fluid contaminated with hydrocarbon/mineral based fluid (power steering or transmission fluid) can be detected by an obvious swelling of the master cylinder cap gasket. If the master cylinder cap gasket is swollen, all brake system rubber parts must be replaced. All brake tubes and hoses must be thoroughly flushed with Ford Heavy Duty Brake Fluid C6Az-19542-AA or —BA or DOT-3 equivalent before the vehicle returns to service.

DESCRIPTION

The Anti-Lock Brake System (ABS), **Figs. 1 through 3,** functions by releasing and applying fluid pressure to the brake calipers during certain braking conditions. During normal driving conditions the system does not function and has no effect on front-to-rear brake proportioning. When one or more wheels approaches a slip condition. The ABS automatically senses the slip and activates the pressure control function.

Through pre-programming, the control unit decides which wheel or wheel's brakes pressures need modulation. The control unit sends appropriate signals to solenoid valves located in the actuation assembly. The control valves then modulate fluid pressure which results in a pressure reduction at wheel cylinder to prevent further lock up.

The ABS electrical system consists of a control module (mounted under the driver's seat, on 1992 models, and under the lefthand kick panel on 1993–94 models), hydraulic actuation assembly and relay. These components work together along with the wheel speed sensors, sensor rotors and other brake system components to control braking.

This three-channel system has independent front wheel control and select low resistance rear wheel control. The hydraulic actuation assembly, **Fig. 4.** contains four solenoid valves, flow control valves and the pump motor.

Two solenoids for the front wheels receive independent braking signals dependent on wheel speed. The control module selects the rear wheel with the lowest resistance and sends both rear solenoids the same braking signal.

The control module continuously calculates wheel speed and activates the ABS system only when wheel lockup is sensed under severe braking conditions. When the module senses a lockup, it sends a pressure reduction signal through the relay to the actuation assembly. Hydraulic fluid flow into a buffer chamber in the actuation assembly is controlled by the solenoid.

When the wheel is no longer in danger of locking up, the module sends pressure increase signals through the relay to the actuation assembly. One signal directs the solenoid to allow fluid pressure to increase while the other activates the pump motor to further increase pressure by returning fluid from the buffer chamber. This operation continues to all wheels until no wheel is in danger of locking up.

A fail-safe function in the control module reverts the system to normal braking operation if a malfunction is detected. The control module stores malfunction codes in its internal memory to aid in diagnosis. If a failure is present, the ABS warning lamp will illuminate.

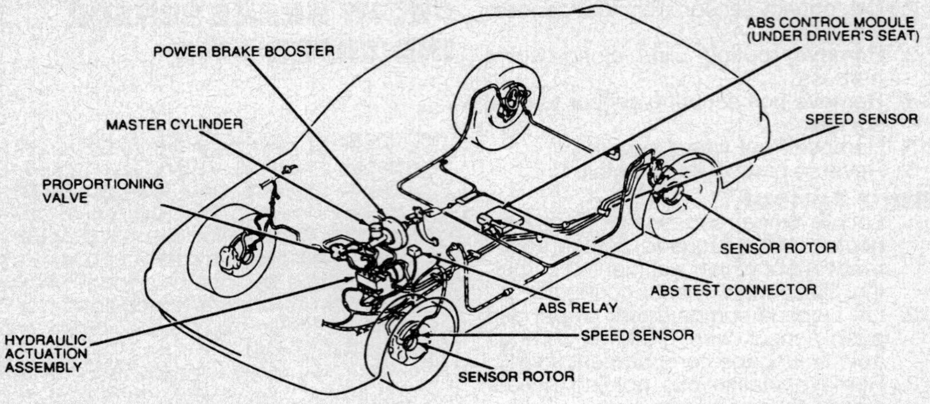

TROUBLESHOOTING

VISUAL INSPECTION

Refer to **Fig. 5.** for ABS visual component inspection.

The hydraulic actuation assembly is non-serviceable and cannot be pressure checked. If any of its components fail, it must be replaced as a complete unit. Problems in other areas that may effect ABS system include suspension and steering components, tire wear and air pressure,

Fig. 1   Anti-Lock Brake System (ABS). 1992

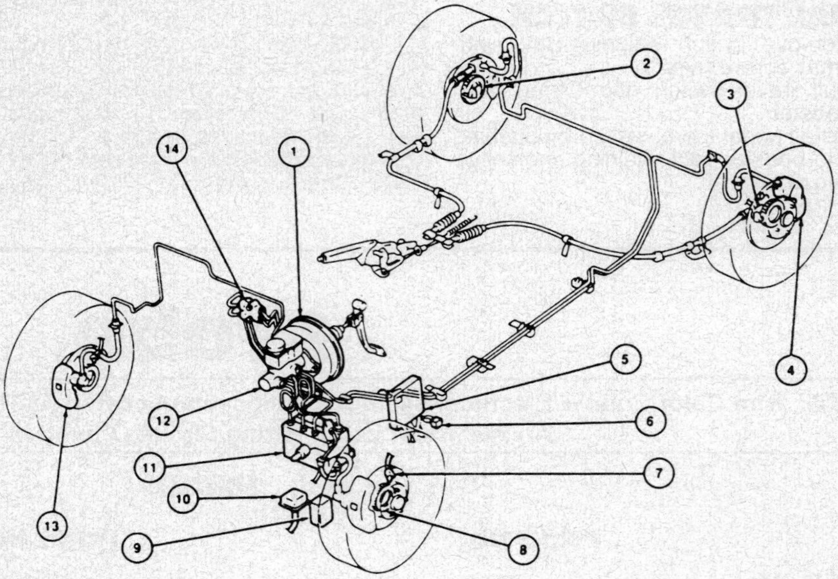

FM4029100192000X

Item	Description	Item	Description
1	Power Brake Booster	8	Front Brake Anti-Lock Sensor Indicator
2	Rear Brake Anti-Lock Sensor Indicator	9	Anti-Lock Relay
3	Rear Brake Anti-Lock Sensor	10	Data Link Connector (DLC)
4	Rear Disc Brake Caliper	11	Hydraulic Anti-Lock Actuator Assembly
5	Anti-Lock Brake Control Module	12	Brake Master Cylinder
6	ABS Test Connector	13	Front Disc Brake Caliper
7	Front Brake Anti-Lock Sensor	14	Brake Pressure Control Valve

FM4029300401000X

Fig. 2   Anti-Lock Brake System (ABS). 1993–94

wheel bearings and brake components. If inspection is satisfactory, refer to the symptom chart, **Fig. 6.**

DIAGNOSIS & TESTING

QUICK TEST

The Quick Test consists of two subtests: Key On Engine Running Test and Continuous Test. Before performing either test, an inspection of the ABS warning light is required to verify a fault has been detected by the ABS control unit, or if system is operating normally. When ABS system is operating normally, the ABS warning light will illuminate during Key On Engine Off and go off after the engine has started.

If the ABS warning light stays on after the engine starts, this indicates a present failure. Any time the ABS warning light flashes, it indicates either a present or past (intermittent) failure. All failures are stored in the ABS control unit. ABS service codes are retrieved by identifying voltage fluctua-

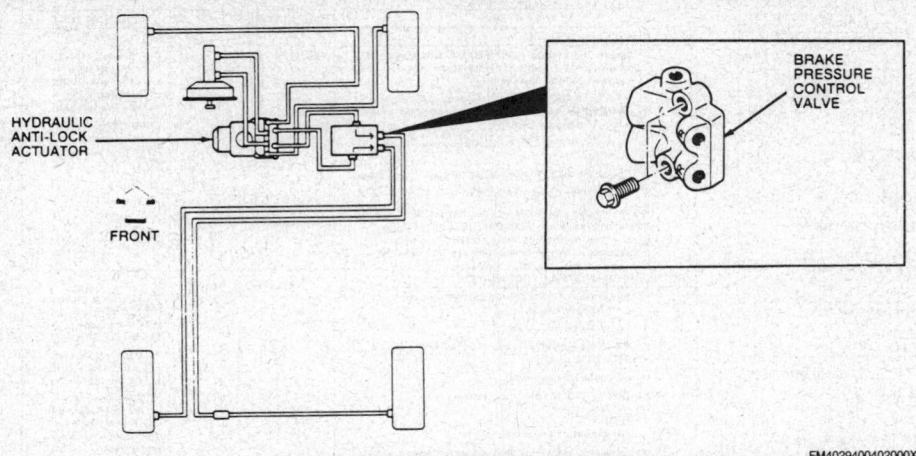

Fig. 3   ABS hydraulics. 1994

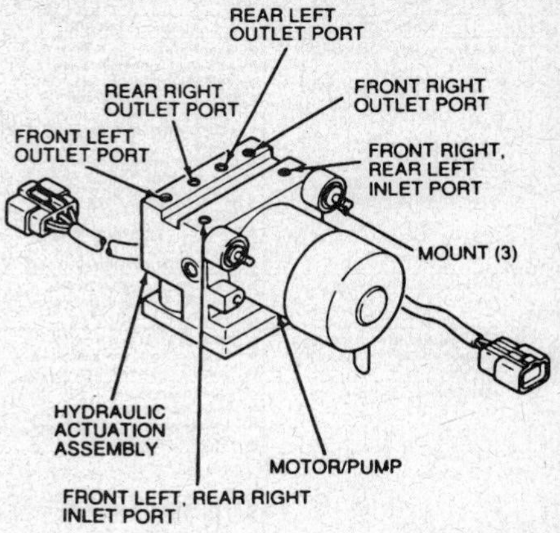

FM4029400402000X

Fig. 4   Hydraulic actuation assembly

FM4029100193000X

ELECTRICAL	MECHANICAL
• Blown fuses (10 (TURN), 15 (METER), 20 (STOP), 60 (PUMP), AND 80 (MAIN) amp)	• Insufficient ABS hydraulic fluid
• Blown ABS warning bulb	• Damaged wheel speed sensor rotors
• Shorted wires	• Damaged hydraulic actuation assembly
• Poor connections	• Damaged hydraulic system piping
• Poor connections	
• Corroded connectors	
• Poor insulation	
• Damaged wheel speed sensors	
• Damaged ABS relay(s)	
• Damaged hydraulic actuation assembly solenoids or motor	
• Damaged stoplamp switch	
• Damaged ABS control module	

FM4029100194000X

Fig. 5   Visual inspection chart

CONDITION	POSSIBLE SOURCE	ACTION
• ABS Inoperative	• Blown fuse(s). • Insufficient ABS hydraulic fluid. • ABS electrical circuit failure. • Inoperative ABS relay(s). • Hydraulic actuation assembly malfunction. • Damaged wheel speed sensor(s). • ABS control module failure.	• GO to ABS Quick Test.
• All Other Symptoms	• All other symptoms are common to all brake systems.	

FM4029100195010X

Fig. 6   Symptom chart (Part 1 of 2)

tions of a voltmeter connected to the ABS test connector.

Service codes may indicate different failures. Parting from the Quick Test may result in code identification error. The Quick Test procedure should be followed completely. ABS warning light mode inspection and ABS service code retrieval are covered in the Quick Test.

Key On Engine Running Test

When activated, this test checks the ABS control unit and system circuitry by testing its integrity and processing capability. It also verifies the various sensors and actuators are connected and operating properly. Code patterns will be indicated through the ABS test connector. The ABS warning light will indicate the type of failure.

Continuous Test

This test aids in diagnosing intermittent failures in the ABS system. It is identical to Key On Engine Running Test but also allows the technician to enter this mode of test and attempt to recreate the intermittent failure by tapping, moving and wiggling the harness and/or suspected sensor. If the voltmeter indicates a fault, the corresponding code pattern will be indicated. Remember to observe the voltmeter/ohmmeter and ABS warning light for any change which will indicate an intermittent condition has been located. Any time a repair is made, erase the ABS control unit memory and repeat the Quick Test to

ensure the repair was effective. If all phases of the Quick Test result in a pass, it is likely the problem is non-electronic. For Quick Test, refer to **Figs. 7 and 8.** Refer to **Fig. 9** for ABS warning light code identification and **Figs. 10 and 11** for service code control module logic specifications.

CLEARING MEMORY CODES

1992

To clear memory codes, refer to **Fig. 12.**

1993—94

While performing the memory cancel, the indicator should light. When the memory cancel operation has been completed, the indicator should illuminate for two or three seconds, then go off. After memory cancel, the anti-lock brake control module performs a self-diagnosis. Memory is not cancelled by disconnecting the battery. Memory codes cannot be cancelled if intervals for depressing the brake pedal exceed one second or stoplamp bulb or Brake On/Off (BOO) switch has malfunctioned. If using the analog VOM, be sure to remove the jumper wire form the Data Link Connector (DLC) after all checks and repairs are made.

Using Analog VOM

1. Connect pins TBS and GND at DLC with jumper wire, then turn key on position.

2. Output diagnostic trouble codes using analog VOM.
3. After first code is repeated, press brake pedal 10 times at intervals of less than one second.
4. Turn key off, then disconnect jumper wire at DLC.

Using Super STAR II

1. Connect Super STAR II tester, or equivalent, to DLC with super MECS adapter tool No. 007-00052, or equivalent.
2. Turn key on, then output diagnostic trouble codes using Super STAR II tester.
3. After first code is repeated, press brake pedal 10 times at intervals of less than one second.
4. Turn key off, then disconnect tester at DLC.

PINPOINT TEST

Do not perform any of the following pinpoint tests unless instructed to so by the Quick Test. Each pinpoint test assumes that a fault (malfunction) has been detected in the system with direction to enter a specific repair routine. Conducting any pinpoint test without direction from the quick test procedures may produce incorrect results and replacement of satisfactory components. Correct test results for quick test depend on the proper operation of the related components and/or systems.

Refer to wiring circuits, **Figs. 13 and 14,** when performing the Pinpoint Tests to locate wire circuits indicated in the test procedure. For Pinpoint Tests on 1992 models, refer to **Figs. 15 through 22.** For Pinpoint Tests on 1993 models, refer to

CONDITION	POSSIBLE SOURCE	ACTION
• ABS Warning Light Always ON	• Blown fuse (10 amp TURN). • ABS electrical circuit failure. • ABS warning light circuit shorted. • ABS wheel sensor failure. • ABS relay(s) failure. • Hydraulic actuation assembly failure. • ABS control module failure. • Low alternator voltage output.	• GO to ABS Quick Test.
• ABS Warning Light Flashes	• Intermittent ABS electrical circuit failure. • ABS test connector shorted to ground. • ABS control module malfunction.	• GO to ABS Quick Test.
• Noisy Hydraulic Actuation Assembly	• ABS electrical circuit failure. • Hydraulic actuation assembly failure.	• GO to ABS Quick Test.
• ABS Warning Light ON for 1.5 Seconds and OFF before Engine Started	• ABS electrical circuit failure. • ABS warning light circuit failure. • Low alternator voltage output.	• GO to ABS Quick Test.
• ABS Warning Light Always OFF	• Blown fuse (15 amp). • Blown warning light bulb. • ABS warning light circuit failure. • ABS control module failure.	• GO to ABS Quick Test.

FM4029100195020X

Fig. 6   Symptom chart (Part 2 of 2)

TEST STEP	RESULT	▶	ACTION TO TAKE
QT4 CHECK ABS WARNING LIGHT INDICATION WITH ENGINE RUNNING • Start the engine. • Drive the vehicle if necessary. (Read note.) NOTE: Certain ABS faults require that the vehicle be driven in order for the warning light to come on. Other faults will cause the light to turn on each time the engine is started. • Observe the ABS warning light.	Not illuminated	▶	Normal operation. If ABS symptom exists, there may be an intermittent problem. PROCEED to Test Step QT5. If no ABS symptoms exist and light was illuminated in Test Step QT3, ABS system is operating normally.
	Illuminated	▶	Indicates a present failure. PROCEED to Quick Test Step QT5.

FM4029100196020X

Fig. 7   Quick Test (Part 2 of 4). 1992–93

TEST STEP	RESULT	▶	ACTION TO TAKE
QT1 PERFORM VISUAL CHECK • Check for sufficient ABS hydraulic fluid, damaged wheel speed sensors or rotors, leaks, and damaged hydraulic actuation assembly. • Check the ABS system wiring harness for proper connections, bent or broken pins, corrosion, loose wires, and proper routing. • Check all of the fuses for proper connection or damage. • Check the ABS control module for physical damage. • Are all of the components OK? NOTE: It may be necessary to disconnect or disassemble harness connector assemblies to do some of the inspections. Note pin locations before disassembly. Disconnect assemblies with key OFF.	Yes No	▶ ▶	DRIVE vehicle to verify Anti-Lock Brakes symptom and PROCEED to Test Step QT2, Vehicle Preparation. SERVICE fault(s) in system and then PROCEED to Test Step QT2.

QT2   PERFORM VEHICLE PREPARATION
• Perform all of the following safety steps required to run ABS Quick Test.
• Apply the parking brake.
• Place the shift lever firmly into the PARK position (NEUTRAL on MTX).
• Block the drive wheels.
• Turn off all of the electrical loads.
  - Radios
  - Lights
  - A/C-heater blower fans, etc...
• Have all the safety steps been performed and all of the electrical loads turned OFF?
	Yes
	
	No
		▶
		
		▶
			PROCEED to Test Step QT3, ABS Warning Light Indication (Key ON-Engine OFF).
			
			Personal safety and correct diagnostic results are dependent on Test Step QT2. Do not PROCEED with Quick Test if vehicle preparation cannot be performed.

QT3 CHECK ABS WARNING LIGHT INDICATION (KEY ON-ENGINE OFF) • Turn the ignition key ON without starting the engine. • Observe the ABS warning light.	Illuminated	▶	Normal operation. PROCEED to Quick Test Step QT4.
	Not illuminated	▶	CHECK ABS warning light circuit 15 AMP fuse and bulb. GO to Pinpoint Test WL.
	Flashing	▶	Verify that test connector is not jumped or shorted to ground between "GN / BK" and "BK" wires.
	Illuminates for 1.5 Seconds and goes out before engine started	▶	GO to Pinpoint Test A.

FM4029100196010X

Fig. 7   Quick Test (Part 1 of 4). 1992–93

TEST STEP	RESULT	▶	ACTION TO TAKE

QT5   PERFORM EQUIPMENT HOOKUP
• Verify that a failure has been detected in the ABS system. (An illuminated ABS warning light in the Key ON-Engine Running mode indicates a present failure. If the ABS warning light is not illuminated in Key ON-Engine Running mode but symptom exists, it may indicate a past or intermittent problem.)
• Turn the ignition key OFF.
• If necessary, remove the driver's seat to access the ABS control module.
• Using an analog VOM:
  — Connect a jumper wire at the test connector from the "GN / BK" to the "BK" terminals (see illustration).
  — Connect an analog VOM between the "GN / R" terminal and engine ground (see illustration).
  — Set the VOM on a DC voltage range to read from 0 to 20 Volts.
  — Is the jumper wire and VOM hooked up properly as shown in illustration?
• Using Super Star II:
  — Connect a Super Star tester the to ABS Test Connector using the Probe ABS adapter 007-00099.
  — Tester in the MECS position.
  — Latch the Super Star II Tester to the "Test" position.
  — Is the Super Star II hooked up properly?
	Yes
	
	No
		▶
		
		▶
			PROCEED to QT6, ABS Service Code Retrieval.
			
			RE-ATTEMPT Step QT5, Equipment Hookup. SERVICE any faults if necessary.

TEST STEP	RESULT	▶	ACTION TO TAKE
QT6 PERFORM ABS SERVICE CODE RETRIEVAL • Verify that the ABS warning light illuminated (prior to equipment hookup) in the Key ON-Engine OFF test before continuing. • Key ON. If using a Super Star II tester, turn the key ON, wait two (2) seconds, then turn the tester ON. • Observe the ABS warning light. NOTE: When a service code is reported on the analog VOM, it will represent itself as a pulsing or sweeping movement of the Voltmeter's needle across the dial face. Codes will be repeated after all memory codes have been displayed once.	Flashes briefly, then goes out	▶	ABS System OK.
	Illuminated constantly	▶	RECORD VOM or Super Star II service codes. ERASE fault codes from memory as explained in Clearing Memory Codes. RE-ATTEMPT service code retrieval. RECORD all recreated service codes and REFER to Code Identification Chart. SERVICE recreated codes as necessary. If the problem still exists or if no codes were recreated, PROCEED to QT7. (Codes that were not recreated indicate past or intermittent faults.)
	Flashes	▶	Indicates past or intermittent fault(s). Be sure to RECORD the service codes before erasing faults. ERASE fault codes from the memory as explained in Clearing Memory Codes this section, then PROCEED to QT7.
QT7 PERFORM CONTINUOUS TEST • Hookup the VOM and jumper wire, or the Super Star II, as in Test Step QT5. • Key ON. NOTE: Use the audible warning function on the Super Star II tester by turning the "SPKR" switch ON. You will be alerted of a continuous test fault without having to visually check the tester. • Tap, move and wiggle the suspected sensor and / or harness working with short sections from the sensor to dash panel and to ABS control module. Drive vehicle, if necessary. • Keep your eyes on the ABS warning light and VOM or Super Star II for any indication. NOTE: With key ON, any fault recreated during continuous test will illuminate warning light constantly. If key is turned OFF, then back ON without clearing codes from memory, warning light will flash along with VOM or Super Star II indicating a past or intermittent fault.	Warning light illuminated constantly; audible warning from Super Star II	▶	RECORD VOM or Super Star II Service Codes and REFER to Code Identification Chart. SERVICE only the codes recreated in this test step.
	No illumination; no audible warning	▶	Normal operation. If intermittent fault cannot be recreated, turn key OFF. DISCONNECT suspect sensor and control unit from harness very carefully. Visually INSPECT all terminals for corrosion, bad crimps, improperly seated terminals, etc. RECONNECT harness connectors and RE-ATTEMPT continuous test.

FM4029100196040X

Fig. 7   Quick Test (Part 4 of 4). 1992–93

FM4029100196030X

Fig. 7   Quick Test (Part 3 of 4). 1992–93

TEST STEP	RESULT	▶ ACTION TO TAKE
QT3 CHECK ANTI-LOCK BRAKE INDICATOR		
• Turn the ignition key ON without starting the engine • Does the anti-lock brake indicator illuminate continuously?	Yes (Indicator illuminated continuously)	▶ Normal operation. PROCEED to Quick Test Step QT4
	No (Indicator not illuminated)	▶ CHECK anti-lock brake indicator circuit, 15A METER fuse and bulb. GO to Pinpoint Test G1
	No (Indicator flashing)	▶ VERIFY that Data Link Connector (DLC) is not jumped (or shorted to ground) between pins "TBS" and "GND"
	No (Indicator illuminates for 1.5 seconds and goes out before engine is started)	▶ Low generator output. GO to Pinpoint Test F1.
QT4 CHECK ANTI-LOCK BRAKE INDICATOR WITH ENGINE RUNNING		
• Start the engine • Drive the vehicle if necessary. (Read note.) NOTE: Certain ABS faults require that the vehicle be driven in order for the indicator to come on. Other faults will cause the indicator to turn on each time the engine is started. • Does the anti-lock brake indicator illuminate?	Yes (Retrieve codes using Super STAR II Tester)	▶ Indicates a present failure. PROCEED to Quick Test Step QT5
	Yes (Retrieve codes using VOM)	▶ Indicates a present failure. PROCEED to Quick Test Step QT6
	No (Indicator not illuminated)	▶ Normal operation. If ABS symptom exists, GO to Pinpoint Test H1.
QT5 PERFORM SUPER STAR II HOOKUP		
• Verify that a failure has been detected in the ABS. (An illuminated anti-lock brake indicator in the Key ON. Engine Running mode indicates a present failure. If the anti-lock brake indicator is not illuminated in Key ON. Engine Running mode but the symptom exists, it may indicate a past or intermittent problem.) • Turn the ignition key off. • Access the DLC located in the engine compartment. • Connect a Super STAR II tester to the DLC using Super MECS Adapter 007-00052 • Place the adapter in the "ABS" position • Place the tester in the "MECS" position • Latch the Super STAR II tester to the "Test" position. • Is the Super STAR II hooked up properly?	Yes No	▶ PROCEED to QT7. ABS Diagnostic Trouble Code Retrieval. ▶ RE-ATTEMPT Step QT5. Super STAR II Hookup. SERVICE any faults if necessary.

FM4029400403020X

Fig. 8   Quick Test (Part 2 of 4). 1994

TEST STEP	RESULT	▶ ACTION TO TAKE
QT1 PERFORM VISUAL CHECK		
• Check for sufficient brake fluid, damaged brake anti-lock sensors, leaks, and damaged hydraulic anti-lock actuator assembly. • Check the ABS wiring harness for proper connections, bent or broken pins, corrosion, loose wires, and proper routing. • Check all of the fuses for proper connection or damage. • Check the anti-lock brake control module for physical damage. • Are all of the components OK? NOTE: It may be necessary to disconnect or disassemble harness connector assemblies to do some of the inspections. Note pin locations before disassembly. Disconnect assemblies with key off.	Yes No	▶ DRIVE vehicle to verify Anti-Lock Brakes symptom and PROCEED to Test Step QT2. ▶ SERVICE fault(s) in system and then PROCEED to Test Step QT2.
QT2 PERFORM VEHICLE PREPARATION		
• Perform all of the following safety steps required to run ABS Quick Test. • Apply the parking brake. • Place the shift control selector lever firmly into the PARK position (NEUTRAL on MTX). • Block the drive wheels. • Turn off all of the electrical loads. — Radios — Lamps — A.C.-heater blower fans, etc. • Have all of the safety steps been performed and all of the electrical loads turned OFF?	Yes No	▶ PROCEED to Test Step QT3. ▶ Personal safety and correct diagnostic results are dependent on Test Step QT2. Do not PROCEED with Quick Test if vehicle preparation cannot be performed.

FM4029400403010X

Fig. 8   Quick Test (Part 1 of 4). 1994

Fig. 16 and **Figs. 23 through 29.** For Pinpoint Tests on 1994 models, refer to **Figs. 30 through 37.**

Observe the following when performing quick tests:

1. Do not replace any component unless test result indicates replacement.
2. When more than one service code is received always start service with first code received.
3. Do not measure voltage or resistance at processor or connect any lights to it, unless specifically instructed to do so.
4. Unless otherwise specified, isolate both ends of a circuit and turn ignition key off whenever checking for continuity or shorts.
5. Disconnect switches and solenoids from harness before measuring resistance or continuity or energizing with a 12-volt power source.
6. When repairs to the ABS system are complete, verify the proper connection of all components, then repeat the functional Quick Test.

TEST STEP	RESULT	▶ ACTION TO TAKE
QT6 PERFORM VOM HOOKUP		
• Verify that a failure has been detected in the ABS. (An illuminated anti-lock brake indicator in the Key ON. Engine Running mode indicates a present failure. If the anti-lock brake indicator is not illuminated in Key ON. Engine Running mode but the symptom exists, it may indicate a past or intermittent problem.) • Turn the ignition key off. • Access the DLC located in the engine compartment. • Connect a jumper wire at DLC from "TBS" (Test Brake System) to "GND" terminals (see illustration) • Connect an analog VOM between "FBS" (Failure Brake System) terminal and engine ground (see illustration) • Set the VOM on a DC voltage range to read from 0 to 20 volts. • Is the jumper wire and VOM hooked up properly as shown in illustration?	Yes No	▶ PROCEED to QT7. ABS Diagnostic Trouble Code Retrieval. ▶ RE-ATTEMPT Step QT6. VOM Hookup. SERVICE any faults if necessary.

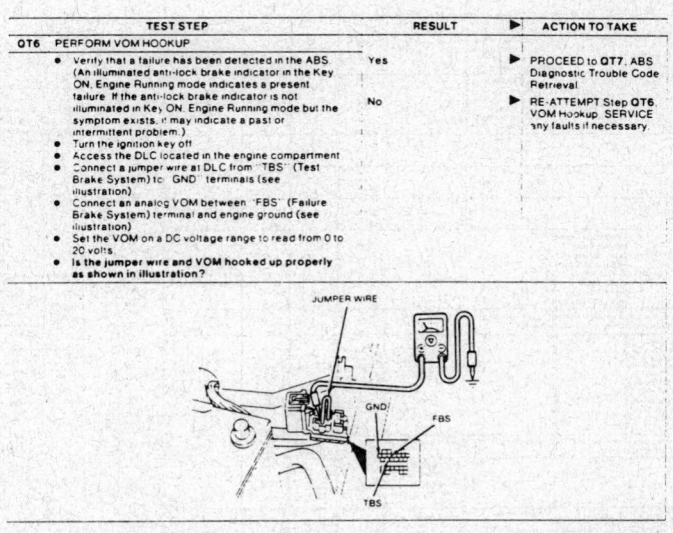

JUMPER WIRE

GND / FBS

TBS

FM4029400403030X

Fig. 8   Quick Test (Part 3 of 4). 1994

Continued on page 27-88

TEST STEP	RESULT	▶ ACTION TO TAKE
QT7 PERFORM ABS DIAGNOSTIC TROUBLE CODE RETRIEVAL • Verify that the anti-lock brake indicator illuminated (prior to equipment hookup) in the Key ON. Engine Off test before continuing. • Key ON. If using a Super STAR II tester, turn the key ON, wait two seconds, then turn the tester ON. • **Does the anti-lock brake indicator flash briefly then go out?** NOTE: When a diagnostic trouble code is reported on the analog VOM, it will represent itself as a pulsing or sweeping movement of the voltmeter's needle across the dial face. Codes will be repeated after all memory codes have been displayed once.	Yes No (Indicator illuminated constantly) No (Indicator flashes service codes)	▶ ABS system OK ▶ RECORD VOM or Super STAR II diagnostic trouble codes. ERASE diagnostic trouble codes from memory. RE-ATTEMPT diagnostic trouble code retrieval. RECORD all re-created diagnostic trouble codes and REFER to Code Identification Chart. SERVICE re-created codes as necessary. If the problem still exists or if no codes were re-created, PROCEED to QT8. (Codes that were not re-created indicate past or intermittent faults.) ▶ Indicates past or intermittent fault(s). Be sure to RECORD the diagnostic trouble codes before erasing faults. ERASE diagnostic trouble codes from the memory. then PROCEED to QT8
QT8 PERFORM CONTINUOUS TEST • Hookup the VOM and jumper wire, or the Super STAR II, as in Test Step QT5 or QT6. • Key ON. NOTE: Use the audible warning function on the Super STAR II tester by turning the "SPKR" switch ON. You will be alerted of a continuous test fault without having to visually check the tester. • Tap, move and wiggle the suspected sensor and/or harness working with short sections from the sensor to instrument panel and to anti-lock brake control module. Drive the vehicle, if necessary. • **Does the indicator illuminate continuously or is an audible warning heard from Super STAR II Tester?** NOTE: With key ON, any coded fault re-created during continuous test will illuminate indicator constantly. If the key is turned off, then back ON without clearing codes from memory, indicator will flash codes along with the VOM or Super STAR II, indicating a past or intermittent fault.	Yes No	▶ RECORD VOM or Super STAR II Diagnostic Trouble Codes and REFER to Code Identification Chart. SERVICE only the codes re-created in this test step. Normal operation. If intermittent fault cannot be re-created, turn key off. DISCONNECT suspect sensor and anti-lock brake control module from harness very carefully. Visually INSPECT all terminals for corrosion, bad crimps, improperly seated terminals, etc. RECONNECT harness connectors and RE-ATTEMPT continuous test.

FM4029400403040X

Fig. 8   Quick Test (Part 4 of 4). 1994

ABS WARNING LAMP	DIAGNOSIS INDICATION VOM	SERVICE CODE	POSSIBLE FAILURE LOCATION	ACTION TO TAKE
• Illuminated Constantly for Present Failure • Flashes According to VOM Indication for Past or Intermittent Failure	(pulse pattern)	11	RF Speed Sensor RF Sensor Rotor	GO to Pinpoint Test WSS
	(pulse pattern)	12	LF Speed Sensor LF Sensor Rotor	
	(pulse pattern)	13	RR Speed Sensor RR Sensor Rotor	
	(pulse pattern)	14	LR Speed Sensor LR Sensor Rotor	
	(pulse pattern)	15	Speed Sensor	GO to Pinpoint Test WSO
	(pulse pattern)	22	Solenoid Valve	GO to Pinpoint Test SV
	(pulse pattern)	51	Fail-Safe Relay	GO to Pinpoint Test FSR
	(pulse pattern)	53	Motor Relay Motor	GO to Pinpoint Test MMR
	(pulse pattern)	61	ABS Control Module	REPLACE ABS Control Module.
• Illuminated Constantly	No Indication	No Code	Alternator ABS Warning Light	GO to Pinpoint Test A.

FM4029100197000X

Fig. 9   Service code identification chart

Service Code	Possible Failure Location	ABS Initialized (KOEO)	Starting Up or Slowing Down	Normal Driving	Driving with ABS Operating	Warning Light	Open	Short	Other
11	Right Front Speed Sensor and Rotor	—	No pulse from Speed Sensor when actual vehicle speed reaches 7 mph.	—		ON	o	o	
			No pulse from Speed Sensor but ABS Control Module receives signal from other Speed Sensor for 20 sec.			ON	o	o	
12	Left Front Speed Sensor and Rotor	—		Incorrect pulse or no pulse from Speed Sensor when actual vehicle speed is above 6.25 mph without braking	—	ON	o	o	Incorrect voltage from Speed Sensor (Excessive gap between Sensor Rotor and Pickup Coil)
				Incorrect pulse or no pulse from Speed Sensor when actual vehicle speed is above 18.75 mph with braking		ON	o	o	
13	Right Rear Speed Sensor and Rotor			No pulse from Speed Sensor without braking		ON	o	o	
14	Left Rear Speed Sensor and Rotor			No pulse from Speed Sensor with braking		ON	o	o	
				Incorrect pulse from Speed Sensor		ON			Broken Sensor Rotor Tooth
11 / 12	Right Front Speed Sensor / Left Front Speed Sensor		Front Speed Sensor sends anti-lock brake recurrement signal to ABS Control Module before actual vehicle speed reaches 9.3 mph without braking			ON			Incorrect Speed Sensor output, Broken Front Sensor Rotor Tooth
15	Speed Sensor	Current does not flow when output from ABS Control Module to Speed Sensor — ABS Control Module detects open circuit in Speed Sensor				ON	o	—	
22	Solenoid	Power transistor circuit failure in ABS Control Module				ON	o	o	
		All solenoids are OFF and Fail Safe Relay is OFF even though ABS Control Module sends ON signal to all solenoids				ON		o	
		Solenoid is not OFF even though ABS Control Module sends OFF Signal to solenoid after Fail-Safe Relay is ON				ON	o	o	
					Solenoid is not ON even though ABS Control Module sends ON signal to solenoid	ON	o	o	
	Hydraulic Actuation Assembly				Vehicle needs more than 2 sec. for pressure reduction periods when slippage is more than 50% and/or coeff. of friction is 4 or more than 2 sec of pressure reduction control	ON after ABS operation			Hydraulic Actuation Assembly cannot reduce pressure

FM4029100198010X

Fig. 10   Service code control module logic specifications (Part 1 of 2). 1992–93

Service Code	Possible Failure Location	ABS Initialized (KOEO)	Starting Up or Slowing Down	Normal Driving	Driving with ABS Operating	Warning Light	Open	Short	Other
51	Fail-Safe Relay	IK terminal voltage does not stay 0 volts for 48 msec. after key ON			—	ON	—	o	Fail-Safe Relay stays ON
		IK terminal voltage does not stay 12 volts for 48 msec after ABS Control Module sends ON signal to Fail-Safe Relay			—	ON	o	o	Fail-Safe Relay stays OFF
53	Motor Relay	—	IK terminal voltage is 0 volts for 0.2 to 2 seconds			ON	o	o	
			IL terminal voltage is 0 volts even though 2H terminal voltage is 0 volts			ON	o	o	
			IL terminal voltage is battery voltage even though 2H terminal voltage is battery voltage			ON	—	—	Motor Relay stays ON
	Motor	No self-generated voltage from motor after motor turned OFF			—	ON	—	—	Motor Locked
61	ABS Control Module	Failure of IC (Integrated Circuit) in ABS Control Module			—	ON	o		
—		Failure of ROM, RAM, or timer in ABS Control Module				ON	o		

FM4029100198020X

Fig. 10   Service code control module logic specifications (Part 2 of 2). 1992–93

Fig. 11 Service code control module logic specifications (Part 1 of 3). 1994

Diagnostic Trouble Code	Possible Failure Location	ABS Initialized (KOEO)	Starting Up or Slowing Down	Normal Driving	Driving with ABS Operating	Anti-Lock Brake Indicator	Open	Short	Other
11	RH Front Anti-Lock Sensor and Front Brake Anti-Lock Sensor Indicator	—	No pulse from Anti-Lock Sensor when actual vehicle speed reaches 7 mph	—	—	ON	X	X	
		—	No pulse from Anti-Lock Sensor but Anti-Lock Brake Control Module receives signal from other Anti-Lock Sensor for 20 sec.	—	—	ON	X	X	Incorrect voltage from Anti-Lock Sensor (Excessive gap between Brake Anti-Lock Sensor Indicator and Pickup Coil)
12	LH Front Anti-Lock Sensor and Anti-lock Sensor Indicator	—	—	Incorrect pulse or no pulse from Anti-Lock Sensor when vehicle speed is above 6.25 mph without braking	—	ON	X	X	
		—	—	Incorrect pulse or no pulse from Anti-Lock Sensor when vehicle speed is above 18.75 mph without braking	—	ON	X	X	
13	RH Rear Brake Anti-Lock Sensor and Rear Brake Anti-Lock Sensor Indicator	—	No pulse from Anti-Lock Sensor without braking	—	—	ON	X	X	
		—	No pulse from Anti-Lock Sensor without braking	—	—	ON	X	X	
14	LH Rear Brake Anti-Lock Sensor and Rear Brake Anti-Lock Sensor Indicator Tooth	—	—	Incorrect pulse from Anti-Lock Sensor	—	ON	—	—	Broken Brake Anti-Lock Sensor Indicator Tooth

FM4029400404010X

Fig. 11 Service code control module logic specifications (Part 2 of 3). 1994

Diagnostic Trouble Code	Possible Failure Location	ABS Initialized (KOEO)	Starting Up or Slowing Down	Normal Driving	Driving with ABS Operating	Anti-Lock Brake Indicator	Open	Short	Other
11	RH Front Anti-Lock Sensor	—	Front Anti-Lock Sensor sends anti-lock brake requirement signal to Anti-Lock Brake Control Module before vehicle speed reaches 9.3 mph without braking	—	—	ON	—	—	Incorrect Anti-Lock Sensor output, Broken Front Brake Anti-Lock Sensor Indicator Tooth
12	LH Front Anti-Lock Sensor								
15	Anti-Lock Sensor	Current does not flow when output from Anti-Lock Brake Control Module to Anti-Lock Sensor — Anti-Lock Brake Control Module detects open circuit in Anti-Lock Sensor				ON	X	—	—
22	Solenoid	Power Transistor failure in Anti-Lock Brake Control Module				ON	X	X	—
		All solenoids are OFF and Fail-Safe Relay is OFF even though Anti-Lock Brake Control Module sends ON signal to all solenoids				ON	X	X	—
		Solenoid is not OFF even though Anti-Lock Brake Control Module sends OFF Signal to solenoid after Fail-Safe Relay is ON				ON	X	X	—
					Solenoid is not ON even though Anti-Lock Brake Control Module sends ON signal to solenoid	ON	X	X	—
	Hydraulic Anti-Lock Actuator Assembly				Vehicle needs more than 2 sec. for pressure reduction periods when slippage is more than 50% and/or coeff. of friction is 0.4 or more after 2 sec. of pressure reduction control	ON after ABS operation	—	—	Hydraulic Anti-Lock Actuator Assembly cannot reduce pressure

FM4029400404020X

Fig. 11 Service code control module logic specifications (Part 3 of 3). 1994

Diagnostic Trouble Code	Possible Failure Location	ABS Initialized (KOEO)	Starting Up or Slowing Down	Normal Driving	Driving with ABS Operating	Anti-Lock Brake Indicator	Open	Short	Other
51	Fail-Safe Relay	1K terminal voltage does not stay 0 volts for 48 msec. after key ON	—			ON	—	X	Fail-Safe Relay stays ON
		1K terminal voltage does not stay 12 volts for 48 msec. after Anti-Lock Brake Control Module sends ON signal to Fail-Safe Relay				ON	X	X	Fail-Safe Relay stays OFF
		—	1K terminal voltage is 0 volts for 0.2 to 2 seconds			ON	X	X	—
53	Motor Relay	—	1L terminal voltage is 0 volts even though 2H terminal voltage is 0 volts			ON	X	X	—
		1L terminal voltage is battery voltage even though 2H terminal voltage is battery voltage				ON	—	—	Motor Relay stays ON
	Motor	No self-generated voltage from motor after motor turned OFF				ON	—	—	Motor Locked
61	Anti-Lock Brake Control Module	Failure of IC (Integrated Circuit) in Anti-Lock Brake Control Module				ON	—	—	—
—		Failure of ROM, RAM, or timer to Anti-Lock Brake Control Module				ON	—	—	—

FM4029400404030X

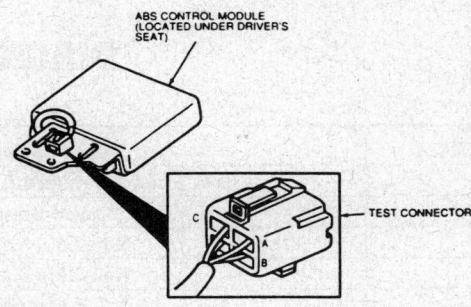

ABS CONTROL MODULE (LOCATED UNDER DRIVER'S SEAT)

TEST CONNECTOR

HOW TO CLEAR CODES IN MEMORY

Using Analog VOM:
1. Connect B ("GN/BK") and C ("BK") at Test Connector with jumper wire.
2. Key ON.
3. Output service codes using the analog VOM.
4. After first code is repeated, depress brake pedal 10 times at intervals of less than one (1) second.
5. Key OFF.
6. Disconnect the jumper wire between B and C at Test Connector.

Using Super Star II:
1. Connect Super Star II to Test Connector with Adapter 007-00099.
2. Key ON.
3. Output service codes using Super Star II.
4. After first code is repeated, depress brake pedal 10 times at intervals of less than one (1) second.
5. Key OFF.
6. Disconnect Super Star II from Test Connector.

NOTE:
1. Warning light illuminates while performing memory cancel.
2. After memory cancel, ABS Control Module performs self-diagnosis.
3. Memory is not canceled by disconnecting the battery.
4. Memory codes cannot be canceled if the following occur:
   • Intervals for depressing the brake pedal exceed one (1) second.
   • Stoplamp bulb or switch has malfunctioned.
5. Be sure to remove jumper wire from Test Connector after all checks and repairs are made.

FM4029100199000X

Fig. 12 Clearing memory codes. 1992

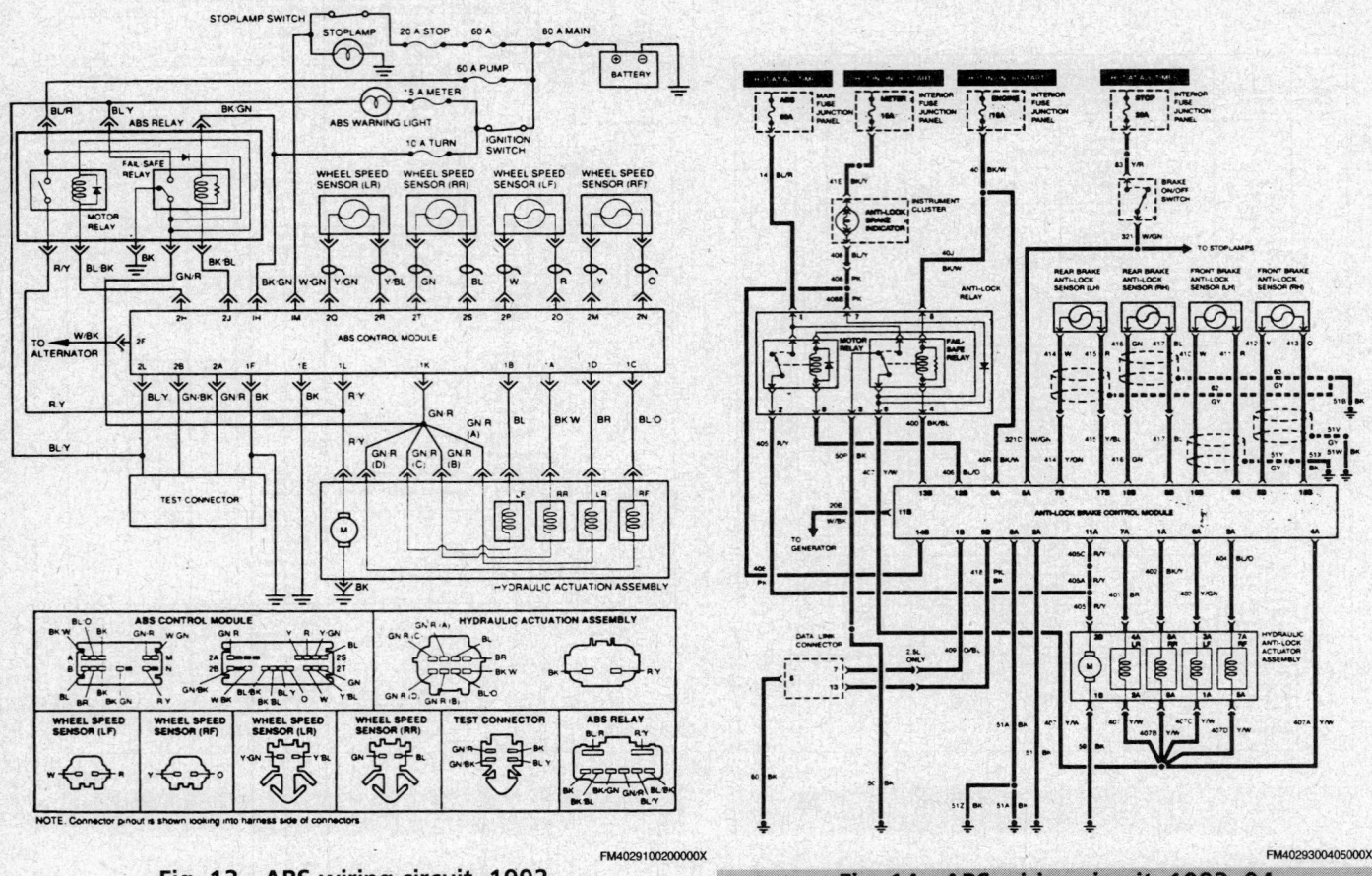

Fig. 13   ABS wiring circuit. 1992

FM4029100200000X

Fig. 14   ABS wiring circuit. 1993–94

FM4029300405000X

DIAGNOSTIC CHART INDEX

Pinpoint Test	Description	Year	Page No. 27-	Fig. No.
WSS	Wheel Speed Sensors & Sensor Rotors	1992	77	15
WSO	Wheel Speed Sensor Open	1992–93	78	16
V	Solenoid Valve	1992	78	17
FSR	Fail-Safe Relay	1992	78	18
MMR	Motor & Motor Relay	1992	80	19
HSI	Hydraulic System Inspection	1992	81	20
A	Alternator	1992	81	21
WL	Warning Light	1992	82	22
WSS	Wheel Speed Sensors & Sensor Rotors	1993	82	23
SV	Solenoid Valve	1993	83	24
FSR	Fail-Safe Relay	1993	83	25
MMR	Motor & Motor Relay	1993	84	26
HSI	Hydraulic System Inspection	1993	85	27
G	Generator	1993	85	28
WL	Warning Lamp	1993	85	29
A	Brake Anti-Lock Sensors & Sensor Indicators	1994	85	30
B	Anti-Lock Sensor Open Circuit	1994	86	31

Continued

DIAGNOSTIC CHART INDEX—Continued

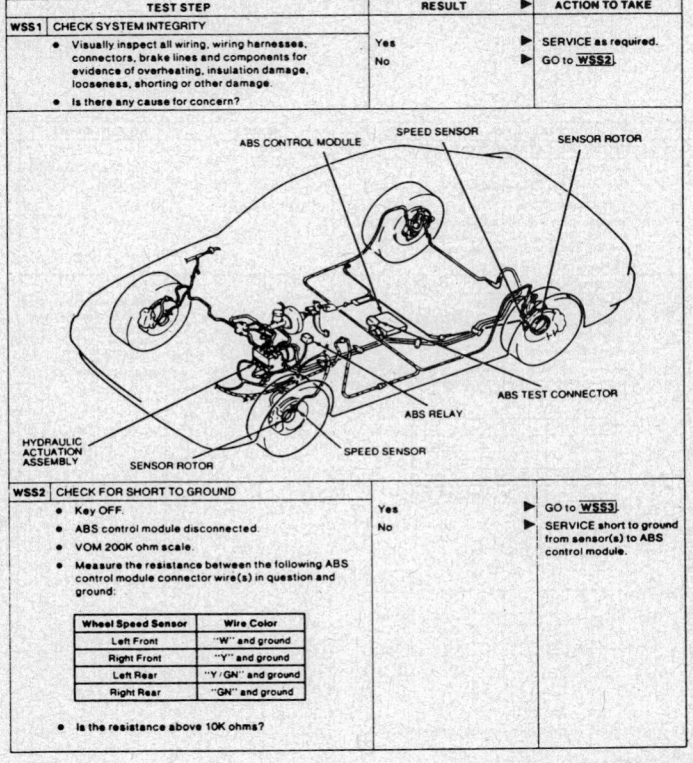

TEST STEP		RESULT	▶	ACTION TO TAKE
WSS1 CHECK SYSTEM INTEGRITY				
• Visually inspect all wiring, wiring harnesses, connectors, brake lines and components for evidence of overheating, insulation damage, looseness, shorting or other damage.		Yes	▶	SERVICE as required.
		No	▶	GO to WSS2.
• Is there any cause for concern?				

TEST STEP		RESULT	▶	ACTION TO TAKE
WSS2 CHECK FOR SHORT TO GROUND				
• Key OFF.		Yes	▶	GO to WSS3
• ABS control module disconnected.		No	▶	SERVICE short to ground from sensor(s) to ABS control module.
• VOM 200K ohm scale.				
• Measure the resistance between the following ABS control module connector wire(s) in question and ground:				

Wheel Speed Sensor	Wire Color
Left Front	"W" and ground
Right Front	"Y" and ground
Left Rear	"Y/GN" and ground
Right Rear	"GN" and ground

• Is the resistance above 10K ohms?

FM4029100201010X

Fig. 15   Test WSS: Wheel Speed Sensors & Sensor Rotors (Part 1 of 5). 1992

TEST STEP		RESULT	▶	ACTION TO TAKE
WSS3 CHECK RESISTANCE AT ABS CONTROL MODULE CONNECTOR				
• Key OFF.		Yes	▶	GO to WSS5
• ABS control module disconnected.		No	▶	GO to WSS4
• VOM 2000 ohm scale.				
• Measure the resistance between the following wire(s) in question at the ABS control module connector leading to the wheel speed sensor(s):				

Wheel Speed Sensor	Wires
Left Front	"W" and "R"
Right Front	"Y" and "O"
Left Rear	"Y/GN" and "Y·BL"
Right Rear	"GN" and "BL"

• Is the resistance reading 800-1200 ohms?

FM4029100201020X

Fig. 15   Test WSS: Wheel Speed Sensors & Sensor Rotors (Part 2 of 5). 1992

TEST STEP		RESULT	▶	ACTION TO TAKE
WSS4 CHECK RESISTANCE AT SENSOR(S)				
• Disconnect the wheel speed sensor(s) in question.		Yes	▶	REPAIR wire(s) from sensor(s) to ABS control module.
• VOM 2000 ohm scale.		No	▶	REPLACE wheel speed sensor(s).
• Measure the resistance between the following sensor pins at the connector(s) leading to the wheel speed sensor(s) in question:				

Wheel Speed Sensor	Sensor Pins
Left Front	"W" and "R"
Right Front	"Y" and "O"
Left Rear	"Y/GN" and "Y·BL"
Right Rear	"GN" and "BL"

• Is the resistance reading 800-1200 ohms?

FM4029100201030X

Fig. 15   Test WSS: Wheel Speed Sensors & Sensor Rotors (Part 3 of 5). 1992

TEST STEP	RESULT	►	ACTION TO TAKE
WSS5 CHECK SIGNAL AT ABS CONTROL MODULE CONNECTOR			
• Key OFF. • ABS control module disconnected. • VOM 5 volts AC scale. • Measure the voltage between the following wires at the ABS control module connector leading to the wheel speed sensor(s) in question while rotating wheel 60 rpm:	Yes No	► ►	GO to **WSS7**. GO to **WSS6**.

Wheel Speed Sensor	Wires
Left Front	"W" and "R"
Right Front	"Y" and "O"
Left Rear	"Y / GN" and "Y / BL"
Right Rear	"GN" and "BL"

• Is the voltage reading between 0.25 and 1.1 volts AC?

TEST STEP	RESULT	►	ACTION TO TAKE
WSS6 CHECK SENSOR AND ROTOR INSPECTION			
• Remove the wheel and tire assembly for the sensor(s) or rotor(s) in question. • Check for damage to the sensor(s) or rotor(s). • Check for objects sticking to the sensor(s) or rotor(s). • Check the sensor installation tightening torque: 16-23 N·m (12-17 lb-ft). • Check the clearance between sensor(s) and rotor(s): 0.3-1.1mm (0.012-0.043 inch). • Are the conditions OK?	Yes No	► ►	REPLACE wheel speed sensor(s). SERVICE as required.

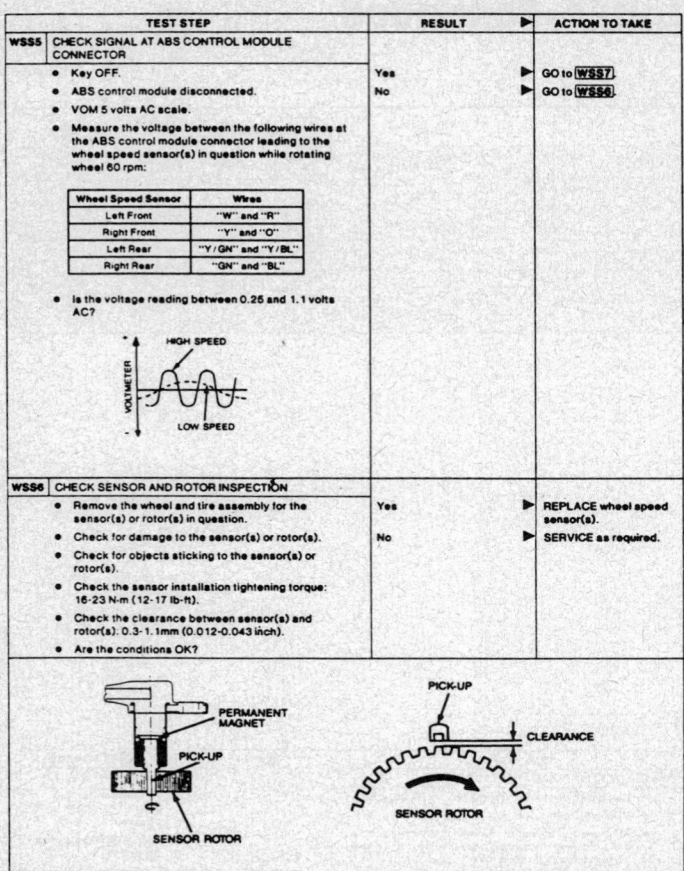

FM4029100201040X

Fig. 15 Test WSS: Wheel Speed Sensors & Sensor Rotors (Part 4 of 5). 1992

TEST STEP	RESULT	►	ACTION TO TAKE
WSS7 CHECK STOPLAMP CIRCUIT			
• Depress the brake pedal. • Check to see that the stoplamps illuminate. • Do the stoplamps operate properly?	Yes No	► ►	GO to **WSS8**. SERVICE as required.
WSS8 CHECK STOPLAMP SWITCH VOLTAGE			
• Key OFF. • Disconnect the ABS control module. • Key ON. • Measure the voltage at the ABS control module connector on the "W GN" wire for the following conditions:	Yes No	► ►	GO to Pinpoint Test **HSI**. SERVICE the "W / GN" wire between stoplamp switch and ABS control module.

Brake Pedal Position	Voltage
Depressed	Above 10 volts
Released	0-2 volts

• Are the voltage readings OK?

FM4029100201050X

Fig. 15 Test WSS: Wheel Speed Sensors & Sensor Rotors (Part 5 of 5). 1992

TEST STEP	RESULT	►	ACTION TO TAKE
WSO1 CHECK OPEN CIRCUIT			
• Drive the vehicle at 10 Km/h (6 mph). • Recheck the malfunction codes. Refer to the Quick Test in this section. • Is a Code 11, 12, 13, or 14 obtained?	Yes No	► ►	GO to Pinpoint Test **WSS**. Intermittent fault. REFER to Continuous Test.

FM4029100202000X

Fig. 16 Test WSO: Wheel Speed Sensor Open. 1992–93

TEST STEP	RESULT	►	ACTION TO TAKE
SV1 CHECK SYSTEM INTEGRITY			
• Visually inspect all wiring, wiring harness, connectors, brake lines, and components for evidence of overheating, insulation damage, looseness, shorting or other damage. • Is there any cause for concern?	Yes No	► ►	SERVICE as required. GO to **SV2**.
SV2 CHECK SOLENOID SIGNAL			
• Key ON. • VOM 20 volt scale. • Measure the voltage at 1 K ("GN / R") terminal of the ABS control module. (ABS control module must be connected.) • Does the voltage reading momentarily read above 10 volts?	Yes No	► ►	GO to **SV3**. SERVICE "GN / R" wire between ABS relay and ABS control module.

FM4029100203010X

Fig. 17 Test SV: Solenoid Valve (Part 1 of 2). 1992

TEST STEP	RESULT	►	ACTION TO TAKE
SV3 CHECK SOLENOID AT ABS MODULE			
• Key OFF. • Disconnect the ABS control module. • VOM 200 ohm scale. • Measure the resistance between the "GN/R" wire and the "BK/W", "BL", "BL/O", and "BR" wires at the ABS control module connector. • Are the resistances about 3 ohms?	Yes No	► ►	GO to Pinpoint Test **HSI**. GO to **SV4**.
SV4 CHECK SOLENOID AT HYDRAULIC ACTUATOR			
• Key OFF. • Disconnect the hydraulic actuation assembly 8-pin connector. • VOM 200 ohm scale. • Measure the resistance between the following wires at the connector leading to the hydraulic actuation assembly:	Yes No	► ►	SERVICE wire(s) between ABS control module and hydraulic actuator assembly. REPLACE hydraulic actuator assembly.

Solenoid	Wires
Left Front	"GN R" (C) and "BL"
Right Front	"GN R" (D) and "BL / O"
Left Rear	"GN R" (A) and "BR"
Right Rear	"GN R" (B) and "BK / W"

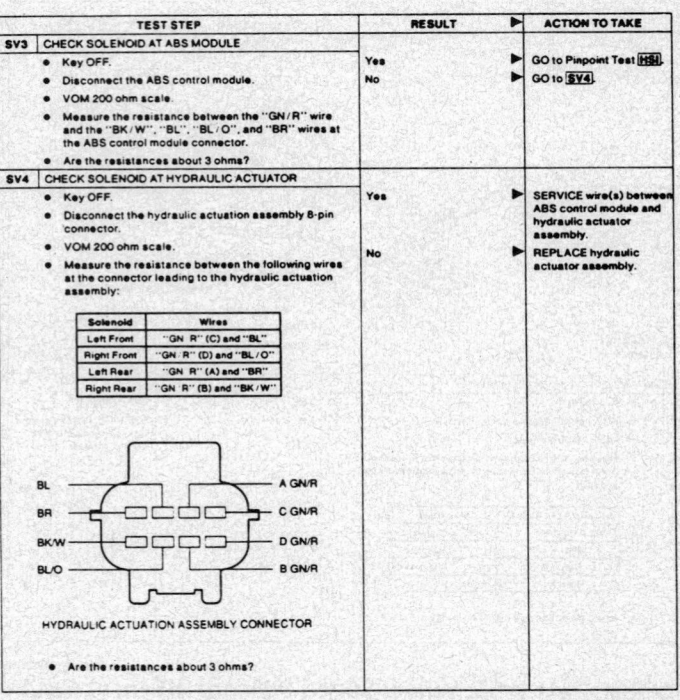

HYDRAULIC ACTUATION ASSEMBLY CONNECTOR

• Are the resistances about 3 ohms?

FM4029100203020X

Fig. 17 Test SV: Solenoid Valve (Part 2 of 2). 1992

TEST STEP	RESULT	►	ACTION TO TAKE
FSR1 CHECK SYSTEM INTEGRITY			
• Visually inspect all wiring, wiring harness, connectors, brake lines, and components for evidence of overheating, insulation damage, looseness, shorting or other damage. • Is there any cause for concern?	Yes No	► ►	SERVICE as required. GO to **FSR2**.

FM4029100204010X

Fig. 18 Test FSR: Fail-Safe Relay (Part 1 of 6). 1992

TEST STEP		RESULT	▶	ACTION TO TAKE
FSR2	**CHECK FUSE**			
• Check the 60 Amp ABS PUMP fuse and 10 Amp TURN fuse. • Are the fuses OK?		Yes No	▶ ▶	GO to **FSR3**. REPLACE fuse(s).

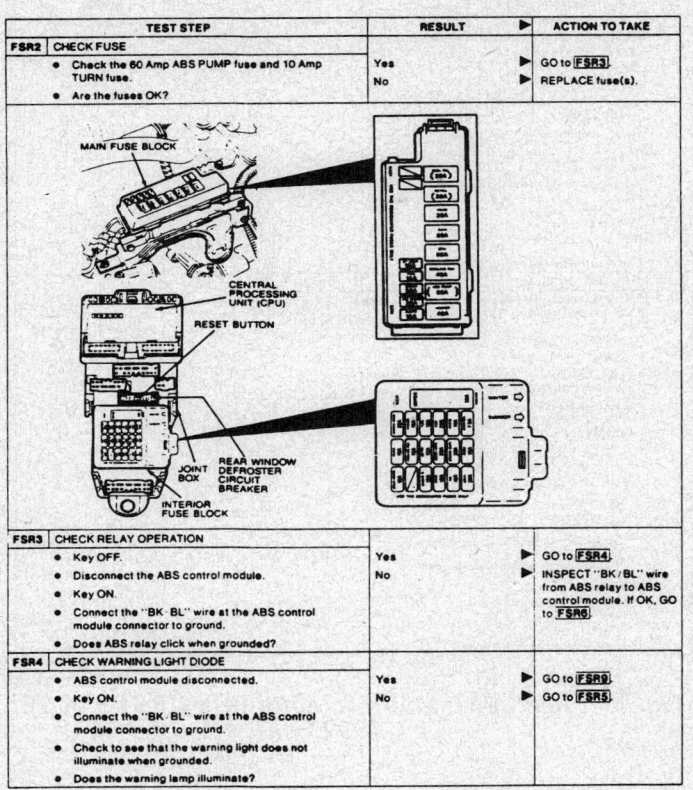

TEST STEP		RESULT	▶	ACTION TO TAKE
FSR3	**CHECK RELAY OPERATION**			
• Key OFF. • Disconnect the ABS control module. • Key ON. • Connect the "BK-BL" wire at the ABS control module connector to ground. • Does ABS relay click when grounded?		Yes No	▶ ▶	GO to **FSR4**. INSPECT "BK/BL" wire from ABS relay to ABS control module. If OK, GO to **FSR6**.
FSR4	**CHECK WARNING LIGHT DIODE**			
• ABS control module disconnected. • Key ON. • Connect the "BK-BL" wire at the ABS control module connector to ground. • Check to see that the warning light does not illuminate when grounded. • Does the warning lamp illuminate?		Yes No	▶ ▶	GO to **FSR9**. GO to **FSR5**.

FM4029100204020X

Fig. 18   Test FSR: Fail-Safe Relay (Part 2 of 6). 1992

TEST STEP		RESULT	▶	ACTION TO TAKE
FSR5	**CHECK VOLTAGE FROM RELAY**			
• ABS control module disconnected. • Key ON. • Connect the "BK/BL" wire at the ABS control module connector to ground. • VOM 20 volt scale. • Measure the voltage at the "GN/R" wire at the ABS control module connector. • Is the voltage reading above 10 volts?		Yes Yes, if directed to this Pinpoint Test from Step MMR 1 No	▶ ▶ ▶	GO to Pinpoint Test **WL**. GO to **MMR2**. GO to **FSR6**.
FSR6	**CHECK RESISTANCE**			
• Key OFF. • Disconnect the ABS relay. • VOM 200 ohm scale. • Measure the resistance between terminals e ("BK/BN") and d ("BK/BL") at the ABS relay. ABS RELAY • Is the resistance 80-100 ohms?		Yes No	▶ ▶	GO to **FSR7**. REPLACE ABS relay.

FM4029100204030X

Fig. 18   Test FSR: Fail-Safe Relay (Part 3 of 6). 1992

TEST STEP		RESULT	▶	ACTION TO TAKE
FSR7	**CHECK CONTINUITY**			
• ABS relay disconnected. • VOM 200 ohm scale. • Measure the resistance between the following terminals at the ABS relay:		Yes No	▶ ▶	GO to **FSR8**. REPLACE ABS relay.

Terminals	Resistance
B ("BK") and C ("BL/R")	Above 10,000 ohms
B ("BK") and F ("GN/R")	Below 5 ohms

ABS RELAY

• Are the resistances as specified?

FM4029100204040X

Fig. 18   Test FSR: Fail-Safe Relay (Part 4 of 6). 1992

TEST STEP		RESULT	▶	ACTION TO TAKE
FSR8	**CHECK FAIL-SAFE**			
• ABS relay disconnected. • Apply 12 volts between the terminals e ("BK/GN") and d ("BK/BL") at the ABS relay. • VOM 200 ohm scale. • Measure the resistance between the following terminals at the ABS relay:		Yes No	▶ ▶	SERVICE "GN/R" between ABS relay and ABS control module. REPLACE ABS relay.

Terminals	Resistance
C ("BL/R") and F ("GN/R")	Below 5 ohms
B ("BK") and F ("GN/R")	Above 10,000 ohms

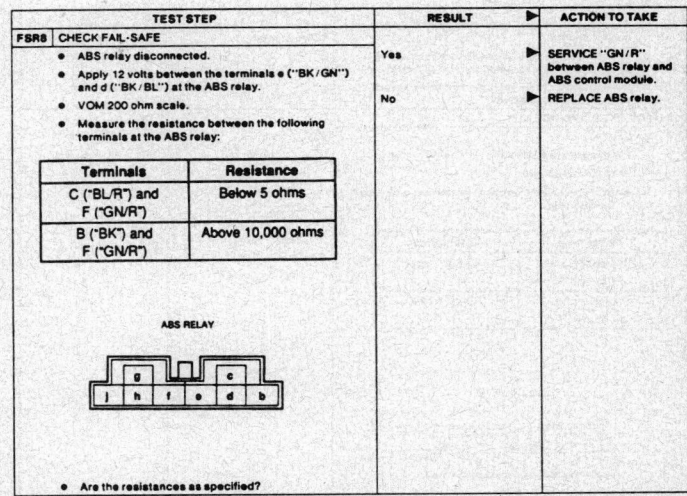

ABS RELAY

• Are the resistances as specified?

FM4029100204050X

Fig. 18   Test FSR: Fail-Safe Relay (Part 5 of 6). 1992

TEST STEP	RESULT	▶	ACTION TO TAKE
FSR9 CHECK DIODE CONTINUITY			
• Key OFF.	Yes	▶	GO to Pinpoint Test **WL**.
• Disconnect the ABS relay.	No	▶	REPLACE ABS relay.
• Using an analog VOM, measure the resistance between the following terminals at the ABS relay:			
NOTE: Reverse the analog VOM leads between the resistance checks as indicated below:			

Terminals	Resistance
J ("BL/BK") (+) to H ("BL/Y") (−)	Below 5 ohms
J ("BL/BK") (−) to H ("BL/Y") (+)	Above 10,000 ohms

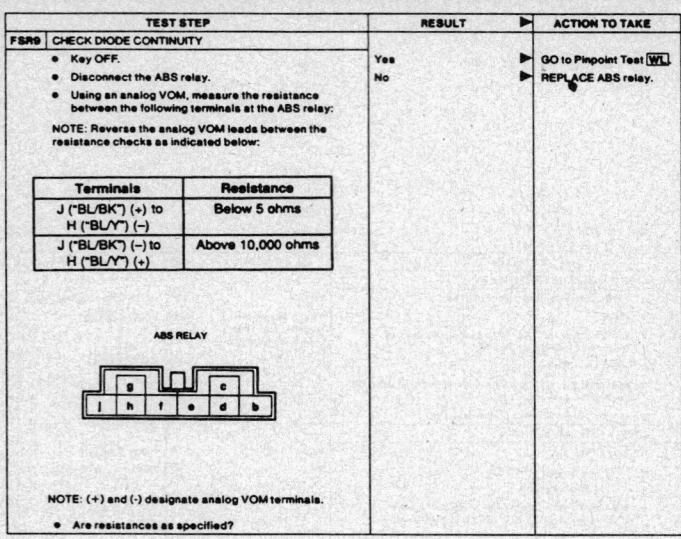

NOTE: (+) and (−) designate analog VOM terminals.

• Are resistances as specified?

Fig. 18   Test FSR: Fail-Safe Relay (Part 6 of 6). 1992

FM4029100204060X

TEST STEP	RESULT	▶	ACTION TO TAKE
MMR1 CHECK FAIL-SAFE RELAY			
• Go to the Pinpoint Test FSR and check the operation of the fail-safe relay.	Yes	▶	GO to **MMR2**.
• Does the fail-safe relay operate properly?	No	▶	REPLACE ABS relay.
MMR2 CHECK SYSTEM INTEGRITY			
• Visually inspect all wiring, wiring harness, connectors, brake lines and components for evidence of overheating, insulation damage, looseness, shorting or other damage.	Yes	▶	SERVICE as required.
	No	▶	GO to **MMR3**.
• Is there any cause for concern?			

FM4029100205010X

Fig. 19   Test MMR: Motor & Motor Relay (Part 1 of 5). 1992

TEST STEP	RESULT	▶	ACTION TO TAKE
MMR3 CHECK MOTOR RELAY OPERATION			
CAUTION: While performing this test step, do not allow motor to operate for more than two seconds.	Yes	▶	GO to **MMR10**.
	No		
• Key OFF.	Motor relay clicks but motor does not operate	▶	GO to **MMR7**.
• Disconnect the ABS control module.			
• Key ON.	Motor relay does not click and motor does not operate	▶	GO to **MMR4**.
• Connect the "BK/BL" wire to ground at the ABS control module.			
• Connect the "BL/BK" wire to ground at the ABS control module for no more than two seconds.			
• Does the motor relay click and the motor operate when wires are grounded?			
MMR4 CHECK RESISTANCE			
• Key OFF.	Yes	▶	GO to **MMR5**.
• Disconnect the ABS relay.	No	▶	REPLACE ABS relay.
• VOM 200 ohm scale.			
• Measure resistance between the following terminals on the ABS relay:			

Terminals	Resistance
F ("GN/R") and J ("BL/BK")	50-90 ohms
B ("BK") and J ("BL/BK")	50-90 ohms

• Are the resistances as specified?

FM4029100205020X

Fig. 19   Test MMR: Motor & Motor Relay (Part 2 of 5). 1992

TEST STEP	RESULT	▶	ACTION TO TAKE
MMR5 CHECK CONTINUITY			
• ABS relay disconnected.	Yes	▶	GO to **MMR6**.
• VOM 200 ohm scale.	No	▶	REPLACE ABS relay.
• Measure the resistance between the terminals c ("BL/R") and g ("R/Y").			

• Is the resistance above 10,000 ohms?

TEST STEP	RESULT	▶	ACTION TO TAKE
MMR6 CHECK MOTOR RELAY			
CAUTION: When applying voltage, connect positive (+) to terminal h ("BL/Y") at ABS relay.	Yes	▶	SERVICE "BK/BL" and/or "BL/BK" wire between ABS relay and ABS control module.
• ABS relay disconnected.	No	▶	REPLACE ABS relay.
• VOM 200 ohm scale.			
• Apply 12 volts from terminal h ("BL/Y") (+) to the j terminal "BL/BK") (−) at the ABS relay.			
• Measure the resistance between terminals c ("BL/R") and g ("R/Y") while voltage is being applied.			

• Is the resistance below 5 ohms?

FM4029100205030X

Fig. 19   Test MMR: Motor & Motor Relay (Part 3 of 5). 1992

TEST STEP	RESULT	▶	ACTION TO TAKE
MMR7 CHECK MOTOR RESISTANCE			
• Key OFF.	Yes	▶	GO to **MMR8**.
• Disconnect the hydraulic actuation assembly 2-pin connector.	No	▶	REPLACE hydraulic actuation assembly.
• VOM 200 ohm scale.			
• Measure the resistance between the "R·Y" and "BK" terminals of the motor.			

• Is the resistance less than 1 ohm?

TEST STEP	RESULT	▶	ACTION TO TAKE
MMR8 CHECK MOTOR OPERATION			
CAUTION: While performing this test step, do not allow motor to operate for more than two seconds.	Yes	▶	GO to **MMR9**.
	No	▶	REPLACE hydraulic actuation assembly.
• Hydraulic actuation assembly disconnected.			
• Apply 12 volts to the motor from the "R·Y" to the "BK" at the hydraulic actuation assembly 2-pin connector.			

• Does the motor operate when voltage is applied?

FM4029100205040X

Fig. 19   Test MMR: Motor & Motor Relay (Part 4 of 5). 1992

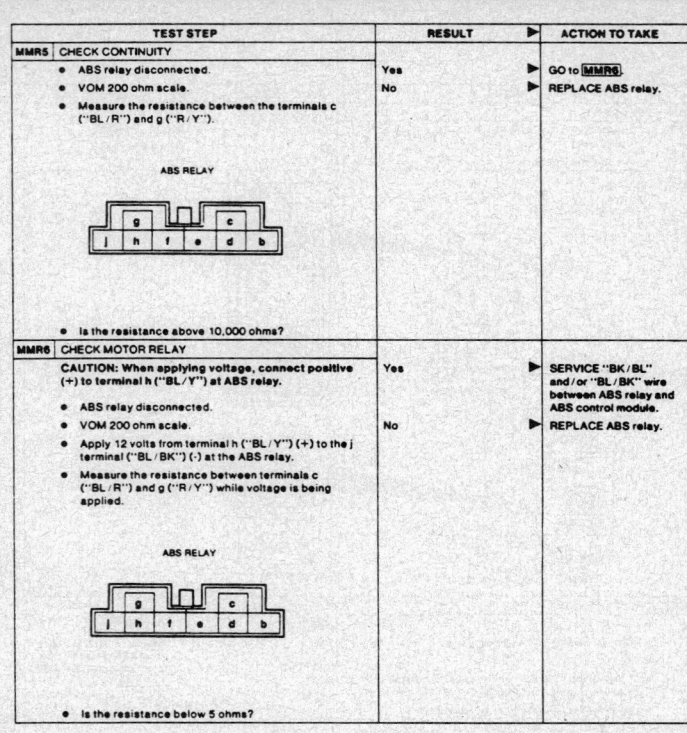

TEST STEP		RESULT	▶	ACTION TO TAKE
MMR9	**CHECK GROUND**			
	● Hydraulic actuation assembly disconnected. ● Measure the resistance between the "BK" wire at the hydraulic actuation assembly (harness side) and ground.	Yes No	▶ ▶	SERVICE "R/Y" wire between ABS relay and hydraulic actuation assembly. SERVICE "BK" wire to ground.
	● Is the resistance less than 5 ohms?			
MMR10	**CHECK RESISTANCE AT ABS CONTROL MODULE**	Yes No	▶ ▶	GO to Pinpoint Test **WL**. SERVICE "R/Y" wire between ABS control module and hydraulic actuation assembly.
	● Key OFF. ● Hydraulic actuation assembly connected. ● ABS control module disconnected. ● VOM 200 ohm scale. ● Measure the resistance between the "R/Y" wire at the ABS control module and ground. ● Is the resistance less than 1 ohm?			

FM4029100205050X

Fig. 19   Test MMR: Motor & Motor Relay (Part 5 of 5). 1992

TEST STEP		RESULT	▶	ACTION TO TAKE
HSI1	**CHECK SYSTEM INTEGRITY**	Yes No	▶ ▶	SERVICE as required. GO to **HSI2**.
	● Visually inspect all wiring, wiring harnesses, connectors, brake lines and components for evidence of overheating, insulation damage, looseness, shorting or other damage. ● Is there any cause for concern?			

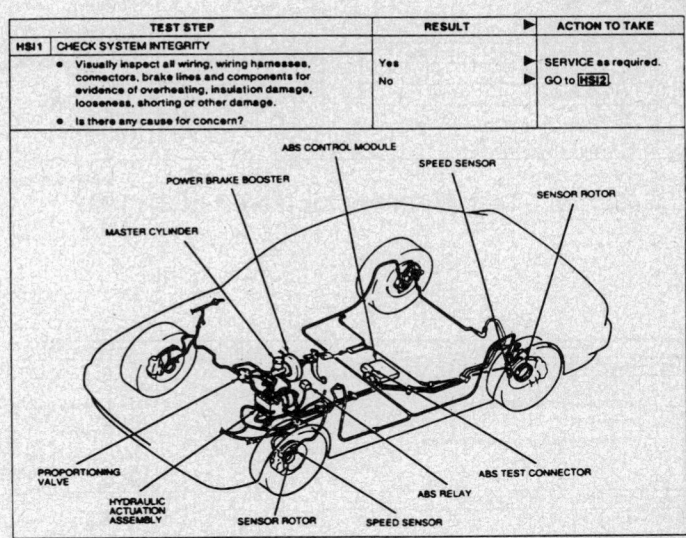

FM4029100206010X

Fig. 20   Test HSI: Hydraulic System Inspection (Part 1 of 2). 1992

TEST STEP		RESULT	▶	ACTION TO TAKE
HSI2	**CHECK HYDRAULIC PRESSURE**	Yes If directed to this Pinpoint Test from Step WSS8 If directed to this Pinpoint Test from Step SV3 No	▶ ▶	Intermittent Fault. GO to Continuous Test GO to Pinpoint Test **WL** INSPECT hydraulic system piping and wiring. If OK, REPLACE hydraulic actuator assembly.
	● Jack up the vehicle so that all the wheels are clear off the ground and the vehicle is properly supported. ● Release the parking brake. ● Check to see that there is no brake drag while rotating the wheels by hand. ● Using a jumper wire, connect the "GN/BK" and "BK" wires at the ABS test connector. ● Depress the brake pedal and have an assistant verify that the wheels will not rotate. ● With the brake pedal still depressed, turn the key ON and verify that the brake pressure is released momentarily and that each wheel rotates when pressure reduction operates as shown:			
	● Does the pressure reduction operate properly?			

FM4029100206020X

Fig. 20   Test HSI: Hydraulic System Inspection (Part 2 of 2). 1992

TEST STEP		RESULT	▶	ACTION TO TAKE
A1	**CHECK BATTERY VOLTAGE**	Yes No	▶ ▶	GO to **A2**. CHARGE or REPLACE the battery as necessary.
	● VOM 20 volt scale. ● Measure the voltage at the battery. ● Is the voltage reading as specified?			
A2	**CHECK BATTERY VOLTAGE AT ABS MODULE**	Yes No	▶ ▶	GO to **A3**. SERVICE wiring between ABS control module and battery.
	● VOM 20 volt scale. ● Measure the voltage at the ABS control module 1H ("BK/GN") terminal under the following conditions:			
	Ignition Switch / Voltage: OFF — 0 V ON — Above 10 V			
	● Is the voltage reading as specified?			
A3	**CHECK VOLTAGE AT ALTERNATOR**	Yes No	▶ ▶	GO to **A4**. SERVICE or REPLACE alternator.
	● VOM 20 volt scale. ● Measure the voltage at the B ("BK"), L ("W/BK"), and S ("BR") terminals at the alternator with the engine idling.			
	● Are the voltage readings as specified?			

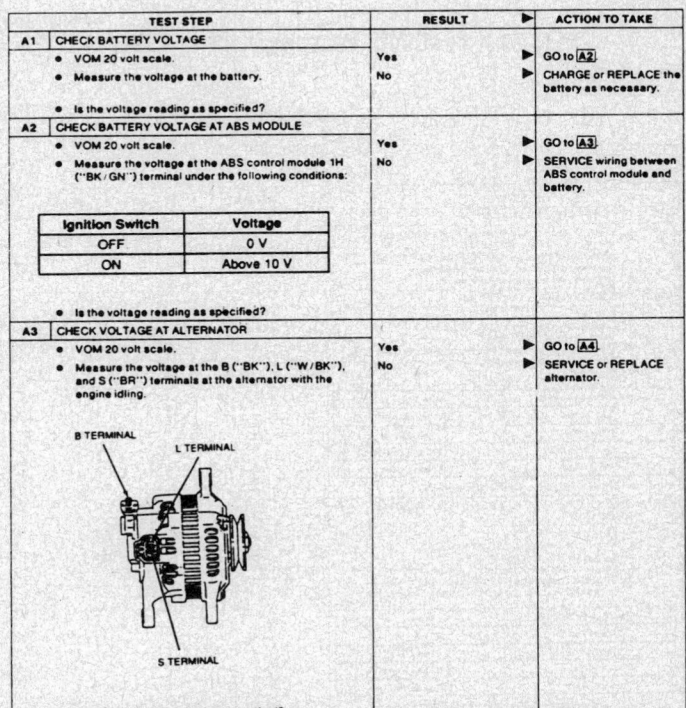

FM4029200207010X

Fig. 21   Test A: Alternator (Part 1 of 2). 1992 Probe. 1992

TEST STEP	RESULT	▶	ACTION TO TAKE
A4 CHECK ALTERNATOR VOLTAGE AT ABS MODULE • VOM 20 volt scale. • Measure the voltage at the 2F ("W/BK") terminal of the ABS control module under the following conditions:	Yes No	▶ ▶	GO to Pinpoint Test **WL**. SERVICE "W/BK" wire from ABS control module to alternator.

Condition	Voltage
Key ON Engine OFF	.8-3 V
Engine idling	Above 10 V

• Are the voltages as specified?

Fig. 21   Test A: Alternator (Part 2 of 2). 1992

FM4029200207020X

TEST STEP	RESULT	▶	ACTION TO TAKE
WL1 CHECK WARNING LIGHT OPERATION • Key OFF. • Disconnect the ABS control module. • Key ON. • Does the ABS warning light illuminate?	Yes No	▶ ▶	GO to **WL2**. REPLACE warning light 15A METER fuse and/or bulb if burned out. If OK, SERVICE "BL/Y" wire from instrument cluster to ABS relay.
WL2 CHECK FOR SHORT TO GROUND • Key ON. • ABS control module disconnected. • Disconnect the ABS relay. • Does the ABS warning light go OFF?	Yes No	▶ ▶	GO to **WL3**. SERVICE the "BL/Y" wire between the instrument cluster and ABS relay for short to ground.
WL3 CHECK SIGNAL • Key ON. • ABS control module disconnected. • ABS relay disconnected. • Connect the "BL/Y" wire at the ABS control module and the "BL/Y" wire at the ABS relay to ground. • Does the warning light illuminate when both wires are connected to ground?	Yes No Does not illuminate at all Illuminates only when grounded at ABS control module Illuminates only when grounded at ABS relay	▶ ▶ ▶ ▶	REPLACE ABS control module. REPLACE warning light 15A METER fuse and/or bulb if burned out. If OK, SERVICE "BL/Y" wire from instrument cluster to ABS relay and/or ABS control module. SERVICE "BL/Y" wire to ABS relay. SERVICE "BL/Y" wire to ABS control module.

Fig. 22   Test WL: Warning Light. 1992

FM4029100209000X

TEST STEP	RESULT	▶	ACTION TO TAKE
WSS1 CHECK SYSTEM INTEGRITY • Visually inspect all wiring, wiring harnesses, connectors, brake lines and components for evidence of overheating, insulation damage, looseness, shorting or other damage. • Is there any cause for concern?	Yes No	▶ ▶	SERVICE as required. GO to **WSS2**.
WSS2 CHECK FOR SHORT TO GROUND • Key OFF. • Locate and disconnect the ABS control module. • VOM on 200K ohm scale. • Measure the resistance between the following ABS control module connector wire(s) in question and ground:	Yes No	▶ ▶	GO to **WSS3**. SERVICE short to ground from sensor(s) to ABS control module.

Wheel Speed Sensor	Wire Color
Left Front	"W" and ground
Right Front	"Y" and ground
Left Rear	"Y/GN" and ground
Right Rear	"GN" and ground

• Is the resistance above 10K ohms?

TEST STEP	RESULT	▶	ACTION TO TAKE
WSS3 CHECK RESISTANCE AT ABS CONTROL MODULE CONNECTOR • Key OFF. • ABS control module disconnected. • VOM on 2000 ohm scale. • Measure the resistance between the following wire(s) in question at the ABS control module connector leading to the wheel speed sensor(s):	Yes No	▶ ▶	GO to **WSS5**. GO to **WSS4**.

Wheel Speed Sensor	Wires
Left Front	"W" and "R"
Right Front	"Y" and "O"
Left Rear	"Y/GN" and "Y/BL"
Right Rear	"GN" and "BL"

• Is the resistance reading 1600-2000 ohms?

FM4029300406010X

TEST STEP	RESULT	▶	ACTION TO TAKE
WSS4 CHECK RESISTANCE AT SENSOR(S) • Locate and disconnect the wheel speed sensor(s) in question. • VOM on 2000 ohm scale. • Measure the resistance between the following sensor pins at the connector(s) leading to the wheel speed sensor(s) in question.	Yes No	▶ ▶	SERVICE wire(s) from sensor(s) to ABS control module. REPLACE wheel speed sensor(s).

Wheel Speed Sensor	Sensor Pins
Left Front	"W" and "R"
Right Front	"Y" and "O"
Left Rear	"W" and "R"
Right Rear	"GN" and "BL"

• Is the resistance reading 1600-2000 ohms?

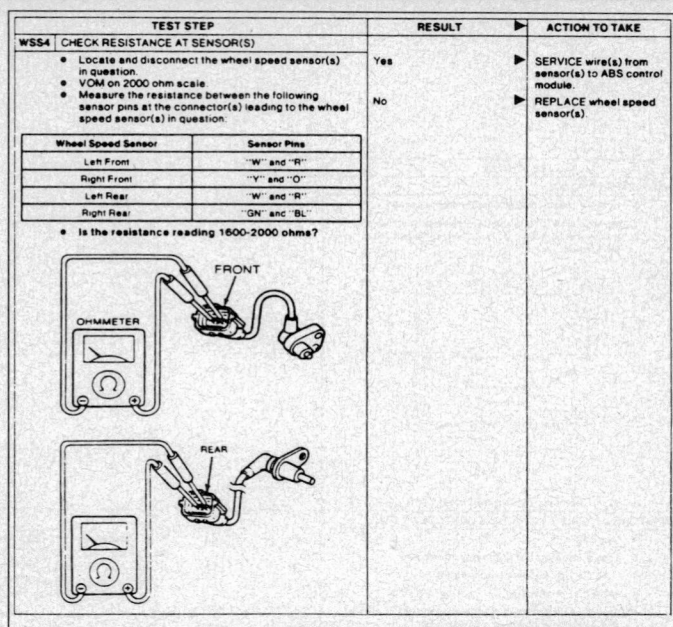

FM4029300406020X

Fig. 23   Test WSS: Wheel Speed Sensors & Sensor Rotors (Part 2 of 4). 1993

TEST STEP	RESULT	▶	ACTION TO TAKE
WSS5 CHECK SIGNAL AT ABS CONTROL MODULE CONNECTOR • Key OFF. • ABS control module disconnected. • VOM on 5 volts AC scale. • Measure the voltage between the following wires at the ABS control module connector leading to the wheel speed sensor(s) in question while rotating wheel approximately 60 rpm (approximately one wheel turn per second).	Yes No	▶ ▶	GO to **WSS7**. GO to **WSS6**.

Wheel Speed Sensor	Wires
Left Front	"W" and "R"
Right Front	"Y" and "O"
Left Rear	"Y/GN" and "Y/BL"
Right Rear	"GN" and "BL"

• Is the voltage reading between 0.25 and 3.0 volts AC?

TEST STEP	RESULT	▶	ACTION TO TAKE
WSS6 INSPECT SENSOR(S) AND ROTOR(S) • Remove the wheel and tire assembly for the sensor(s) or rotor(s) in question. • Check for damage to the sensor(s) or rotor(s). • Check for objects sticking to the sensor(s) or rotor(s). • Check the sensor installation tightening torque: 16-23 N·m (12-17 lb-ft). • Check the clearance between sensor(s) and rotor(s): 0.3-1.1mm (0.012-0.043 inch). • Are the conditions OK?	Yes No	▶ ▶	REPLACE wheel speed sensor(s). REPLACE wheel speed sensor(s) or sensor rotor(s).

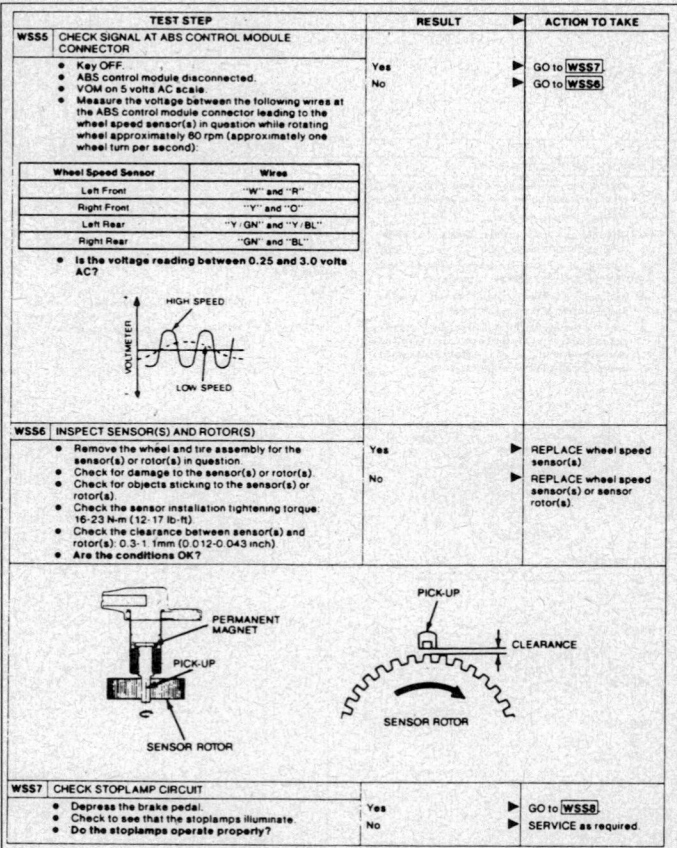

TEST STEP	RESULT	▶	ACTION TO TAKE
WSS7 CHECK STOPLAMP CIRCUIT • Depress the brake pedal. • Check to see that the stoplamps illuminate. • Do the stoplamps operate properly?	Yes No	▶ ▶	GO to **WSS8**. SERVICE as required.

FM4029300406030X

Fig. 23   Test WSS: Wheel Speed Sensors & Sensor Rotors (Part 3 of 4). 1993

TEST STEP	RESULT	▶	ACTION TO TAKE
WSS8 CHECK BRAKE ON / OFF SWITCH VOLTAGE • Key OFF. • Disconnect the ABS control module. • Key ON. • Measure the voltage on the "W / GN" wire at the ABS control module connector for the following conditions: <table><tr><td>Brake Pedal Position</td><td>Voltage</td></tr><tr><td>Depressed</td><td>Above 10 volts</td></tr><tr><td>Released</td><td>0-2 volts</td></tr></table> • Are the voltage readings OK?	Yes No	▶ ▶	GO to Pinpoint Test HSI. SERVICE the "W / GN" wire between brake on / off switch and ABS control module.

FM4029300406040X

Fig. 23   Test WSS: Wheel Speed Sensors & Sensor Rotors (Part 4 of 4). 1993

TEST STEP	RESULT	▶	ACTION TO TAKE
SV1 CHECK SYSTEM INTEGRITY • Visually inspect all wiring, wiring harness, connectors, brake lines, and components for evidence of overheating, insulation damage, looseness, shorting or other damage. • Is there any cause for concern?	Yes No	▶ ▶	SERVICE as required. GO to SV2.
SV2 CHECK SOLENOID SIGNAL • Key ON. • VOM on 20 volt scale. • Measure the voltage at 1K ("Y / W") terminal of the ABS control module. (ABS control module must be connected.) • Does the voltage reading momentarily read above 10 volts?	Yes No	▶ ▶	GO to SV3. SERVICE "Y / W" wire between ABS relay and ABS control module.

FM4029300407010X

Fig. 24   Test SV: Solenoid Valve (Part 1 of 2). 1993

TEST STEP	RESULT	▶	ACTION TO TAKE
SV3 CHECK SOLENOID AT ABS CONTROL MODULE • Key OFF. • Locate and disconnect the ABS control module. • VOM on 200 ohm scale. • Measure the resistance between the following wires at the ABS control module connector. <table><tr><td>Solenoid</td><td>Wires</td></tr><tr><td>Left Front</td><td>"Y / W" and "Y / GN"</td></tr><tr><td>Right Front</td><td>"Y / W" and "BL / O"</td></tr><tr><td>Left Rear</td><td>"Y / W" and "BR"</td></tr><tr><td>Right Rear</td><td>"Y / W" and "BK / GN"</td></tr></table> • Are the resistances about 3 ohms?	Yes No	▶ ▶	GO to Pinpoint Test HSI. GO to SV4.
SV4 CHECK SOLENOID AT HYDRAULIC ACTUATOR • Key OFF. • Locate and disconnect the hydraulic actuation assembly 8-pin connector. • VOM on 200 ohm scale. • Measure the resistance between the following wires at the connector leading to the hydraulic actuation assembly. <table><tr><td>Solenoid</td><td>Wires</td></tr><tr><td>Left Front</td><td>"Y / W" (C) and "Y / GN"</td></tr><tr><td>Right Front</td><td>"Y / W" (D) and "BL / O"</td></tr><tr><td>Left Rear</td><td>"Y / W" (A) and "BR"</td></tr><tr><td>Right Rear</td><td>"Y / W" (B) and "BK / GN"</td></tr></table> Y/GN ▢—▢ A Y/W BR ▢—▢ C Y/W BK/GN ▢—▢ D Y/W BL/O ▢—▢ B Y/W HYDRAULIC ACTUATION ASSEMBLY CONNECTOR • Are the resistances about 3 ohms?	Yes No	▶ ▶	SERVICE wire(s) between ABS control module and hydraulic actuator assembly. REPLACE hydraulic actuator assembly.

FM4029300407020X

Fig. 24   Test SV: Solenoid Valve (Part 2 of 2). 1993

TEST STEP	RESULT	▶	ACTION TO TAKE
FSR1 CHECK SYSTEM INTEGRITY • Visually inspect all wiring, wiring harness, connectors, brake lines, and components for evidence of overheating, insulation damage, looseness, shorting or other damage. • Is there any cause for concern?	Yes No	▶ ▶	SERVICE as required. GO to FSR2.

FM4029300408010X

Fig. 25   Test FSR: Fail-Safe Relay (Part 1 of 4). 1993

TEST STEP	RESULT	▶	ACTION TO TAKE
FSR2 CHECK FUSES • Check the 60A ABS fuse in the main fuse panel and the 15A METER fuse in the interior fuse panel. • Are the fuses OK?	Yes No	▶ ▶	GO to FSR3. REPLACE fuse(s).
FSR3 CHECK RELAY OPERATION • Key OFF. • Locate and disconnect the ABS control module. • Key ON. • Connect the "BK / BL" wire at the ABS module connector to ground. • Does the ABS relay click when wire is grounded?	Yes No	▶ ▶	GO to FSR4. INSPECT "BK / BL" wire from ABS relay to ABS control module. If OK, GO to FSR6.
FSR4 CHECK WARNING LAMP DIODE • ABS control module disconnected. • Key ON. • Connect the "BK / BL" wire at the ABS module connector to ground. • Check to see that the warning lamp does not illuminate when grounded. • Does the warning lamp illuminate?	Yes No	▶ ▶	GO to FSR9. GO to FSR5.
FSR5 CHECK VOLTAGE FROM RELAY • ABS control module disconnected. • Key ON. • Connect the "BK / BL" wire at the ABS module connector to ground. • VOM on 20 volt scale. • Measure the voltage at the "Y / W" wire at the ABS control module connector. • Is the voltage reading greater than 10 volts?	Yes Yes, if directed to this Pinpoint Test from Step MMR1 No	▶ ▶ ▶	GO to Pinpoint Test WL. GO to MMR2. GO to FSR6.
FSR6 CHECK RESISTANCE • Key OFF. • Locate and disconnect the ABS relay. • VOM on 200 ohm scale. • Measure the resistance between terminals e ("BK / W") and d ("BK / BL") at the ABS relay. ABS RELAY • Is the resistance 60-100 ohms?	Yes No	▶ ▶	GO to FSR7. REPLACE ABS relay.

FM4029300408020X

Fig. 25   Test FSR: Fail-Safe Relay (Part 2 of 4). 1993

TEST STEP	RESULT	▶	ACTION TO TAKE
FSR7 CHECK CONTINUITY • ABS relay disconnected. • VOM on 200 ohm scale. • Measure the resistance between the following terminals at the ABS relay. <table><tr><td>Terminals</td><td>Resistance</td></tr><tr><td>b ("BK") and c ("BL / R")</td><td>Above 10,000 ohms</td></tr><tr><td>b ("BK") and f ("Y / W")</td><td>Below 5 ohms</td></tr></table> ABS RELAY • Are the resistances as specified?	Yes No	▶ ▶	GO to FSR8. REPLACE ABS relay.
FSR8 CHECK FAIL-SAFE RELAY • ABS relay disconnected. • Apply battery voltage to terminal e ("BK / GN") and ground terminal d ("BK / BL") at the ABS relay. • VOM on 200 ohm scale. • Measure the resistance between the following terminals at the ABS relay. <table><tr><td>Terminals</td><td>Resistance</td></tr><tr><td>c ("BL / R") and f ("Y / W")</td><td>Below 5 ohms</td></tr><tr><td>b ("BK") and f ("Y / W")</td><td>Above 10,000 ohms</td></tr></table> ABS RELAY • Are the resistances as specified?	Yes No	▶ ▶	SERVICE "Y / W" wire between ABS relay and ABS control module. REPLACE ABS relay.

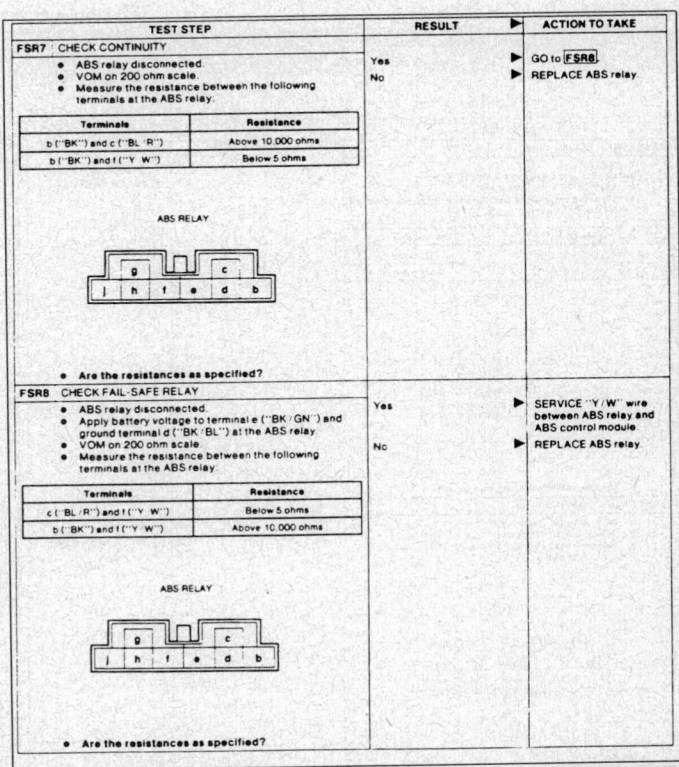

FM4029300408030X

Fig. 25   Test FSR: Fail-Safe Relay (Part 3 of 4). 1993

Fig. 25 — Test FSR: Fail-Safe Relay (Part 4 of 4)

TEST STEP	RESULT	▶	ACTION TO TAKE
FSR9 CHECK DIODE CONTINUITY • Key OFF. • Disconnect the ABS relay. • Using an analog VOM, measure the resistance between the following terminals at the ABS relay: NOTE: Reverse the analog VOM leads between the resistance checks as indicated below:	Yes No	▶ ▶	GO to Pinpoint Test **WL**. REPLACE ABS relay.

Terminals	Resistance
f ("Y/W") (+) to h ("V") (-)	Below 5 ohms
f ("Y/W") (-) to h ("V") (+)	Above 10,000 ohms

ABS RELAY

NOTE: (+) and (-) designate analog VOM terminals.
• Are resistances as specified?

FM4029300408040X

Fig. 25   Test FSR: Fail-Safe Relay (Part 4 of 4). 1993

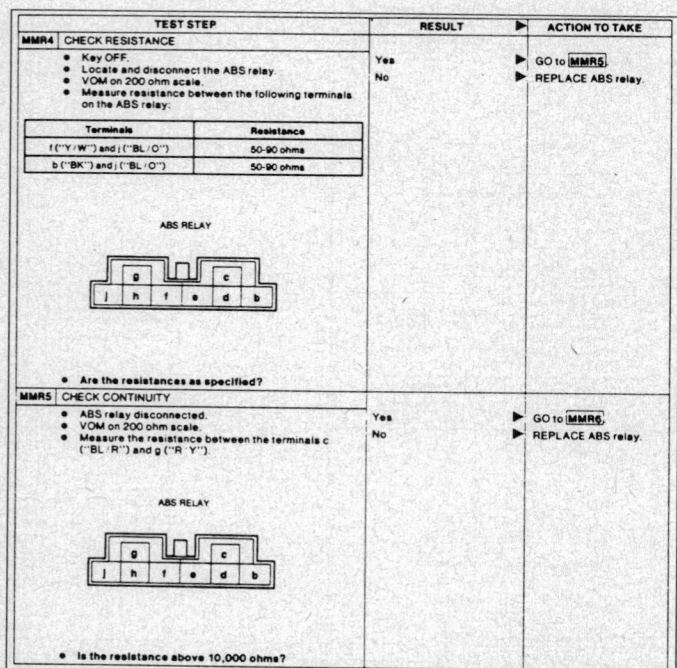

Fig. 26 — Test MMR: Motor & Motor Relay (Part 1 of 4)

TEST STEP	RESULT	▶	ACTION TO TAKE
MMR1 CHECK FAIL-SAFE RELAY • Go to the Pinpoint Test FSR and check the operation of the fail-safe relay. • Does the fail-safe relay operate properly?	Yes No	▶ ▶	GO to **MMR2**. REPLACE ABS relay
MMR2 CHECK SYSTEM INTEGRITY • Visually inspect all wiring, wiring harness, connectors, brake lines and components for evidence of overheating, insulation damage, looseness, shorting or other damage. • Is there any cause for concern?	Yes No	▶ ▶	SERVICE as required GO to **MMR3**.
MMR3 CHECK MOTOR RELAY OPERATION CAUTION: While performing this test step, do not allow motor to operate for more than two seconds. • Key OFF. • Locate and disconnect the ABS control module. • Key ON. • Connect the "BK/BL" wire to ground at the ABS control module harness connector. • Connect the "BL/O" wire to ground at the ABS control module harness connector for no more than two seconds. • Does the motor relay click and the motor operate when wires are grounded?	Yes No (Motor relay clicks but motor does not operate) No (Motor relay does not click and motor does not operate)	▶ ▶ ▶	GO to **MMR10**. GO to **MMR7**. GO to **MMR4**.

FM4029300409010X

Fig. 26   Test MMR: Motor & Motor Relay (Part 1 of 4). 1993

Fig. 26 — Test MMR: Motor & Motor Relay (Part 2 of 4)

TEST STEP	RESULT	▶	ACTION TO TAKE
MMR4 CHECK RESISTANCE • Key OFF. • Locate and disconnect the ABS relay. • VOM on 200 ohm scale. • Measure resistance between the following terminals on the ABS relay:	Yes No	▶ ▶	GO to **MMR5**. REPLACE ABS relay.

Terminals	Resistance
f ("Y/W") and j ("BL/O")	50-90 ohms
b ("BK") and j ("BL/O")	50-90 ohms

ABS RELAY

• Are the resistances as specified?

TEST STEP	RESULT	▶	ACTION TO TAKE
MMR5 CHECK CONTINUITY • ABS relay disconnected. • VOM on 200 ohm scale. • Measure the resistance between the terminals c ("BL/R") and g ("R/Y").	Yes No	▶ ▶	GO to **MMR6**. REPLACE ABS relay.

ABS RELAY

• Is the resistance above 10,000 ohms?

FM4029300409020X

Fig. 26   Test MMR: Motor & Motor Relay (Part 2 of 4). 1993

Fig. 26 — Test MMR: Motor & Motor Relay (Part 3 of 4)

TEST STEP	RESULT	▶	ACTION TO TAKE
MMR6 CHECK MOTOR RELAY CAUTION: When applying voltage, connect positive (+) to terminal h ("PK") at ABS relay. • ABS relay disconnected. • VOM on 200 ohm scale. • Apply battery voltage to the ABS relay terminal h ("PK") and ground ABS relay terminal j. • Measure the resistance between terminals c ("BL/R") and g ("R/Y") while voltage is being applied.	Yes No	▶ ▶	SERVICE "BK/BL" and/or "BL/O" wire between ABS relay and ABS control module. REPLACE ABS relay.

ABS RELAY

• Is the resistance below 5 ohms?

TEST STEP	RESULT	▶	ACTION TO TAKE
MMR7 CHECK MOTOR RESISTANCE • Key OFF. • Locate and disconnect the hydraulic actuation assembly 2-pin motor connector. • VOM on 200 ohm scale. • Measure the resistance between the "R/Y" and "BK" terminals of the motor.	Yes No	▶ ▶	GO to **MMR8**. REPLACE hydraulic actuation assembly.

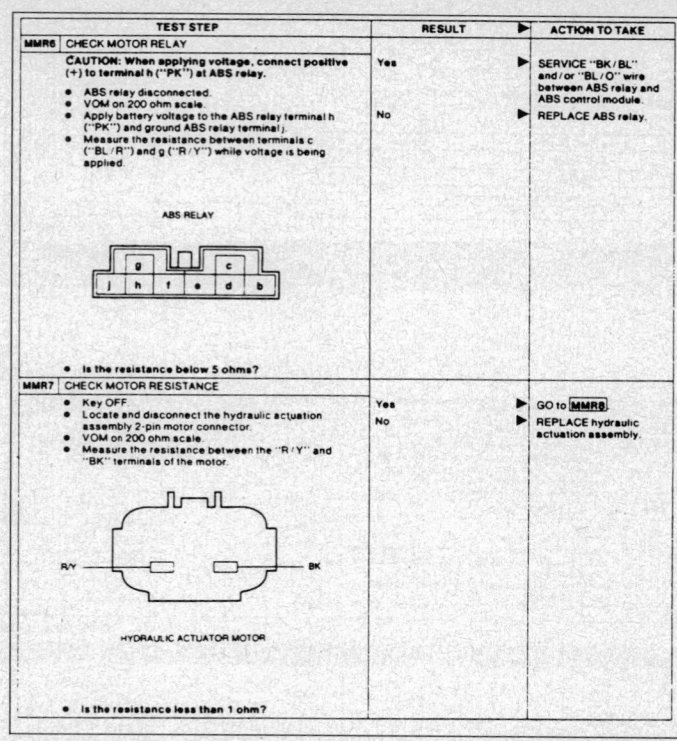

HYDRAULIC ACTUATOR MOTOR

• Is the resistance less than 1 ohm?

FM4029300409030X

Fig. 26   Test MMR: Motor & Motor Relay (Part 3 of 4). 1993

Fig. 26 — Test MMR: Motor & Motor Relay (Part 4 of 4)

TEST STEP	RESULT	▶	ACTION TO TAKE
MMR8 CHECK MOTOR OPERATION CAUTION: While performing this test step, do not allow motor to operate for more than two seconds. • Hydraulic actuation assembly 2-pin motor connector disconnected. • Apply battery voltage to the "R/Y" terminal and ground the "BK" terminal at the hydraulic actuation assembly 2-pin motor connector.	Yes No	▶ ▶	GO to **MMR9**. REPLACE hydraulic actuation assembly.

HYDRAULIC ACTUATOR MOTOR

• Does the motor operate when voltage is applied?

TEST STEP	RESULT	▶	ACTION TO TAKE
MMR9 CHECK MOTOR GROUND • Hydraulic actuation assembly 2-pin motor connector disconnected. • Measure the resistance between the "BK" wire at the hydraulic actuation assembly 2-pin motor connector (harness side) and ground.	Yes No	▶ ▶	SERVICE "R/Y" wire between ABS relay and hydraulic actuation assembly. SERVICE "BK" wire to ground

HYDRAULIC ACTUATOR MOTOR

• Is the resistance less than 5 ohms?

TEST STEP	RESULT	▶	ACTION TO TAKE
MMR10 CHECK RESISTANCE AT ABS CONTROL MODULE • Key OFF. • Hydraulic actuation assembly connected. • ABS control module disconnected. • VOM on 200 ohm scale. • Measure the resistance between the "R/Y" wire at the ABS control module and ground. • Is the resistance less than 1 ohm?	Yes No	▶ ▶	GO to Pinpoint Test **WL**. SERVICE "R/Y" wire between ABS control module and hydraulic actuation assembly.

FM4029300409040X

Fig. 26   Test MMR: Motor & Motor Relay (Part 4 of 4). 1993

TEST STEP	RESULT	▶	ACTION TO TAKE
HSI1 CHECK SYSTEM INTEGRITY			
• Visually inspect all wiring, wiring harnesses, connectors, brake lines and components for evidence of overheating, insulation damage, looseness, shorting or other damage. • Is there any cause for concern?	Yes No	▶ ▶	SERVICE as required. GO to **HSI2**.
HSI2 CHECK HYDRAULIC PRESSURE			
NOTE: This test requires an assistant. The pressure reduction operation occurs within a 2 second period. • Jack up the vehicle so that all the wheels are clear off the ground and the vehicle is properly supported. • Shift the transaxle to neutral. • Release the parking brake. • Check to see that there is no brake drag while rotating the wheels by hand. • Use a jumper wire to connect the "GN/R" and "BK" wires together at the ABS test connector, or connect the "TBS" and "GND" terminals at the data link connector. • Depress the brake pedal and have an assistant verify that the wheels will not rotate. • With the brake pedal still depressed, turn the key ON and verify that the brake pressure is released momentarily (approximately 0.5 seconds) and that each wheel rotates when pressure reduction operates as shown:	Yes (If directed to this Pinpoint Test from Quick Test Step QT4) Yes (If directed to this Pinpoint Test from Step WSS8) Yes (If directed to this Pinpoint Test from Step SV3) No	▶ ▶ ▶ ▶	ABS system functioning properly. Intermittent Fault. GO to Continuous Test in this section. GO to Pinpoint Test **WL**. INSPECT hydraulic system piping and wiring. If OK, REPLACE hydraulic actuator assembly.

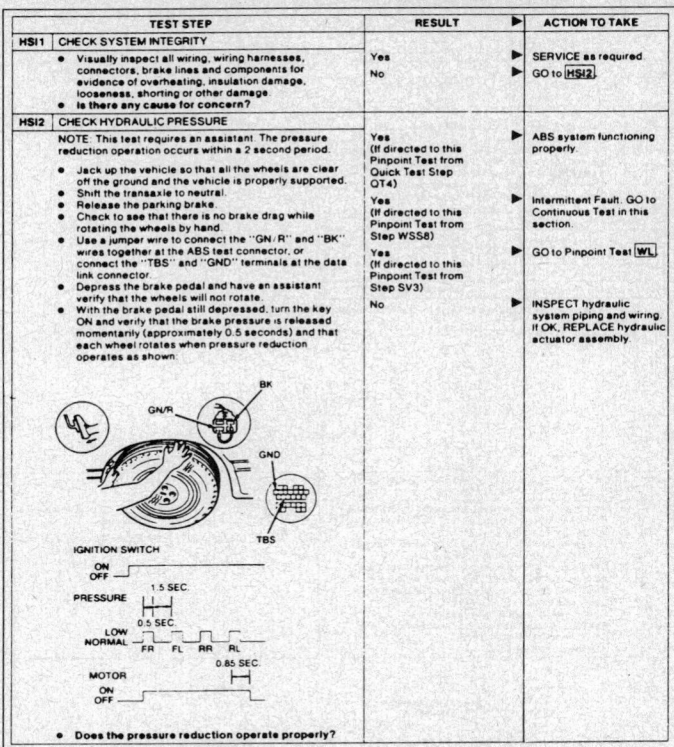

• Does the pressure reduction operate properly?

FM4029300410000X

Fig. 27   Test HSI: Hydraulic System Inspection. 1993

DTC	Caused By	Pinpoint Test Step
11	Generated by a disturbed or damaged redundancy channel. Replace control module if code repeats.	AA1
17	Generated by reference voltage failure caused by high/low battery voltage, main power relay, main fuse, wire harness, faulty electronic controller.	BB1
22	Generated by open or short circuit LH front inlet valve, wire harness.	BB2
23	Generated by open or short circuit LH front outlet valve, wire harness or faulty electronic controller.	BB5
24	Generated by open or short circuit RH front inlet valve, wire harness or faulty electronic controller.	BB8
25	Generated by open or short circuit RH front outlet valve, wire harness or faulty electronic controller.	BB11
26	Generated by open or short circuit RH rear inlet valve, wire harness or faulty electronic controller.	BB14
27	Generated by open or short circuit RH rear outlet valve, wire harness or faulty electronic controller.	BB17
28	Generated by open or short circuit LH rear inlet valve, wire harness or faulty electronic controller.	BB20
29	Generated by open or short circuit LH rear outlet valve, wire harness or faulty electronic controller.	BB23
31	Generated by open or short circuit LH front sensor, wire harness or faulty electronic controller.	CC1
32	Generated by open or short circuit RH front sensor, wire harness or faulty electronic controller.	CC8
33	Generated by open or short circuit RH rear sensor, wire harness or faulty electronic controller.	CC15
34	Generated by open or short circuit LH rear sensor, wire harness or faulty electronic controller.	CC22
35	Generated by open or short circuit LH front sensor, wire harness, damaged teeth on indicator ring, sensor air gap too small/large, faulty electronic controller at speeds greater than 40 km/h (25 mph).	CC1
36	Generated by open or short circuit RH front sensor, wire harness, damaged teeth on indicator ring, sensor air gap too small/large, or faulty electronic controller at speeds greater than 40 km/h (25 mph).	CC8
37	Generated by open or short circuit RH rear sensor, wire harness, damaged teeth on indicator ring, sensor air gap too small/large, faulty electronic controller at speeds greater than 40 km/h (25 mph).	CC15
38	Generated by open or short circuit LH rear sensor, wire harness, damaged teeth on indicator ring, sensor air gap too small/large or faulty electronic controller.	CC22
41	Generated by missing sensor signal LH front sensor (missing indicator ring).	CC1
42	Generated by missing sensor signal RH front sensor (missing indicator ring).	CC8
43	Generated by missing sensor signal RH rear sensor (missing indicator ring).	CC15
44	Generated by missing sensor signal LH rear sensor (missing indicator ring).	CC22
55	Generated by missing sensor signal LH front sensor (long term failure).	CC1
56	Generated by missing sensor signal RH front sensor (long term failure).	CC8
57	Generated by missing sensor signal RH rear sensor (long term failure).	CC15
58	Generated by missing sensor signal LH rear sensor (long term failure).	CC22
61	Generated by short circuit to ground (FLS #2).	DD1
62	Generated by short circuit to ground (pedal travel switch).	DD1
63	Generated by no pump motor speed sensor signal during initial check at 31 km/h (19 mph), wire harness or faulty electronic controller.	DD5
64	Generated by pump unable to build pressure.	DD27
75	Generated by intermittent missing sensor signal LH front sensor at speeds less than 40 km/h (25 mph).	CC1

FM4029400411010X

Fig. 29   Test WL: Warning Lamp (Part 1 of 2). 1993

TEST STEP	RESULT	▶	ACTION TO TAKE
G1 CHECK BATTERY VOLTAGE			
• VOM on 20 volt scale. • Measure the voltage at the battery. • Is the voltage reading as specified?	Yes No	▶ ▶	GO to **G2**. CHARGE or REPLACE the battery as necessary.
G2 CHECK BATTERY VOLTAGE AT ABS CONTROL MODULE			
• VOM on 20 volt scale. • Measure the voltage at the ABS control module 1H ("BK/W") terminal under the following conditions:	Yes No	▶ ▶	GO to **G3**. SERVICE wiring between ABS control module and battery.

Ignition Switch	Voltage
OFF	0 Volts
ON	Above 10 Volts

TEST STEP	RESULT	▶	ACTION TO TAKE
• Are the voltage readings as specified?			
G3 CHECK VOLTAGE AT GENERATOR			
• VOM on 20 volt scale. • Measure the voltage at the B ("BK"), L ("W/BK"), and S ("W/GN") terminals at the generator with the engine idling. • Are the voltage readings as specified?	Yes No	▶ ▶	GO to **G4**. SERVICE or REPLACE generator.
G4 CHECK GENERATOR VOLTAGE AT ABS CONTROL MODULE			
• VOM on 20 volt scale. • Measure the voltage at the 2F ("W/BK") terminal of the ABS control module under the following conditions:	Yes No	▶ ▶	GO to Pinpoint Test **WL**. SERVICE "W/BK" wire from ABS control module to generator.

Condition	Voltage
Key ON Engine Off	.8-3 Volts
Engine Idling	Above 10 Volts

• Are the voltages as specified?

FM4029300208000X

Fig. 28   Test G: Generator. 1993

DTC	Caused By	Pinpoint Test Step
76	Generated by intermittent sensor signal RH front sensor at speeds less than 40 km/h (25 mph).	CC8
77	Generated by intermittent missing sensor signal RH rear sensor at speeds less than 40 km/h (25 mph).	CC15
78	Generated by intermittent sensor signal LH rear sensor at speeds less than 40 km/h (25 mph).	CC22

FM4029400411020X

Fig. 29   Test WL: Warning Lamp (Part 2 of 2). 1993

TEST STEP	RESULT	▶	ACTION TO TAKE
A1 CHECK SYSTEM INTEGRITY			
• Visually inspect all wiring, wiring harnesses, connectors, brake lines and components for evidence of overheating, insulation damage, looseness, shorting, or other damage. • Is there any cause for concern?	Yes No	▶ ▶	SERVICE as required. GO to A2.
A2 CHECK FOR SHORT TO GROUND			
• Key off. • Locate and disconnect the anti-lock brake control module connector. • Measure the resistance between the following anti-lock brake control module connector wire(s) in question and ground:	Yes No	▶ ▶	GO to A3. SERVICE short to ground from sensor(s) to anti-lock brake control module.

Brake Anti-Lock Sensor	Wire Color
LH Front Anti-Lock Sensor	"W" and ground
RH Front Anti-Lock Sensor	"Y" and ground
LH Rear Brake Anti-Lock Sensor	"Y GN" and ground
RH Rear Brake Anti-Lock Sensor	"GN" and ground

TEST STEP	RESULT	▶	ACTION TO TAKE
• Is the resistance greater than 10K ohms?			
A3 CHECK RESISTANCE AT ANTI-LOCK BRAKE CONTROL MODULE CONNECTOR			
• Key off. • Anti-lock brake control module disconnected. • Measure the resistance between the following wire(s) in question at the anti-lock brake control module connector leading to the brake anti-lock sensor(s):	Yes No	▶ ▶	GO to A5. GO to A4.

Brake Anti-Lock Sensor	Wires
LH Front Anti-Lock Sensor	"W" and "R"
RH Front Anti-Lock Sensor	"Y" and "O"
LH Rear Brake Anti-Lock Sensor	"GN" and "Y BL"
RH Rear Brake Anti-Lock Sensor	"GN" and "BL"

• Is the resistance reading 1600-2000 ohms?

FM4029400413010X

Fig. 30   Test A: Brake Anti-Lock Sensors & Sensor Indicators (Part 1 of 4). 1994

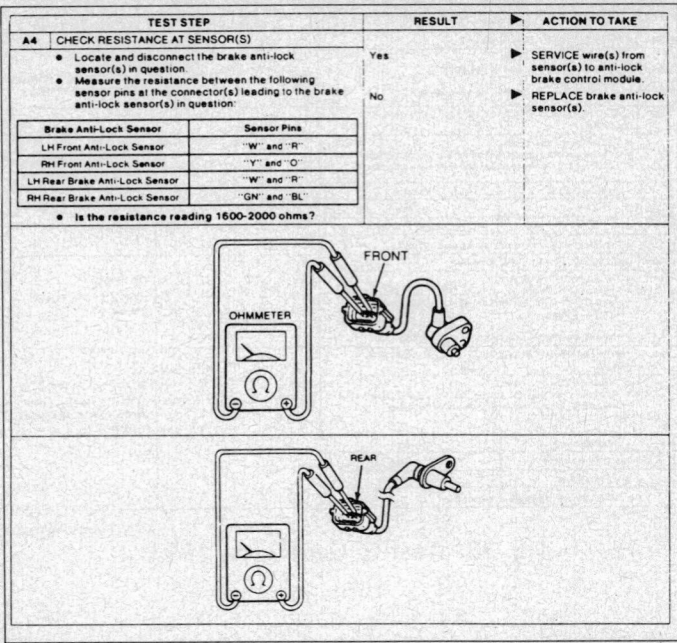

TEST STEP	RESULT	▶	ACTION TO TAKE
A4 CHECK RESISTANCE AT SENSOR(S)			
• Locate and disconnect the brake anti-lock sensor(s) in question. • Measure the resistance between the following sensor pins at the connector(s) leading to the brake anti-lock sensor(s) in question:	Yes	▶	SERVICE wire(s) from sensor(s) to anti-lock brake control module.
	No	▶	REPLACE brake anti-lock sensor(s).

Brake Anti-Lock Sensor	Sensor Pins
LH Front Anti-Lock Sensor	"W" and "R"
RH Front Anti-Lock Sensor	"Y" and "O"
LH Rear Brake Anti-Lock Sensor	"W" and "R"
RH Rear Brake Anti-Lock Sensor	"GN" and "BL"

• Is the resistance reading 1600-2000 ohms?

FM4029400413020X

Fig. 30   Test A: Brake Anti-Lock Sensors & Sensor Indicators (Part 2 of 4). 1994

TEST STEP	RESULT	▶	ACTION TO TAKE
A7 CHECK STOPLAMP CIRCUIT			
• Depress the brake pedal. • Check to see that the stoplamps illuminate. • Do the stoplamps operate properly?	Yes	▶	GO to A8.
	No	▶	SERVICE as required.
A8 CHECK BRAKE ON-OFF SWITCH VOLTAGE			
• Key off. • Disconnect the anti-lock brake control module. • Key ON. • Measure the voltage on the "W/GN" wire at the anti-lock brake control module connector for the following conditions:	Yes	▶	GO to Pinpoint Test H1.
	No	▶	SERVICE the "W/GN" wire between Brake On-Off (BOO) switch and anti-lock brake control module.

Brake Pedal Position	Voltage
Depressed	Above 10 volts
Released	0-2 volts

• Are the voltage readings OK?

FM4029400413040X

Fig. 30   Test A: Brake Anti-Lock Sensors & Sensor Indicators (Part 4 of 4). 1994

TEST STEP	RESULT	▶	ACTION TO TAKE
B1 CHECK OPEN CIRCUIT			
• Drive the vehicle at 10 km/h (6 mph). • Recheck the malfunction codes. Refer to the Quick Test in this section. • Is a Code 11, 12, 13, or 14 obtained?	Yes	▶	GO to Pinpoint Test A1.
	No (No codes)	▶	Intermittent fault. REFER to Continuous Test.
	No (Code 15 reappears)	▶	SUBSTITUTE a known good anti-lock brake control module. PERFORM Test Step B1 again.

FM4029400414000X

Fig. 31   Test B: Anti-Lock Sensor Open Circuit. 1994

TEST STEP	RESULT	▶	ACTION TO TAKE
C1 CHECK SYSTEM INTEGRITY			
• Visually inspect all wiring, wiring harness, connectors, brake lines, and components for evidence of overheating, insulation damage, looseness, shorting, or other damage. • Is there any cause for concern?	Yes	▶	SERVICE as required.
	No	▶	GO to C2.
C2 CHECK SOLENOID SIGNAL			
• Key ON. • Measure the voltage at 4A ("Y·W") terminal of the anti-lock brake control module (anti-lock brake control module must be connected). • Does the voltage reading momentarily read above 10 volts?	Yes	▶	GO to C3.
	No	▶	SERVICE "Y·W" wire between anti-lock relay and anti-lock brake control module.

FM4029400415010X

Fig. 32   Test C: Solenoid Valve (Part 1 of 2). 1994

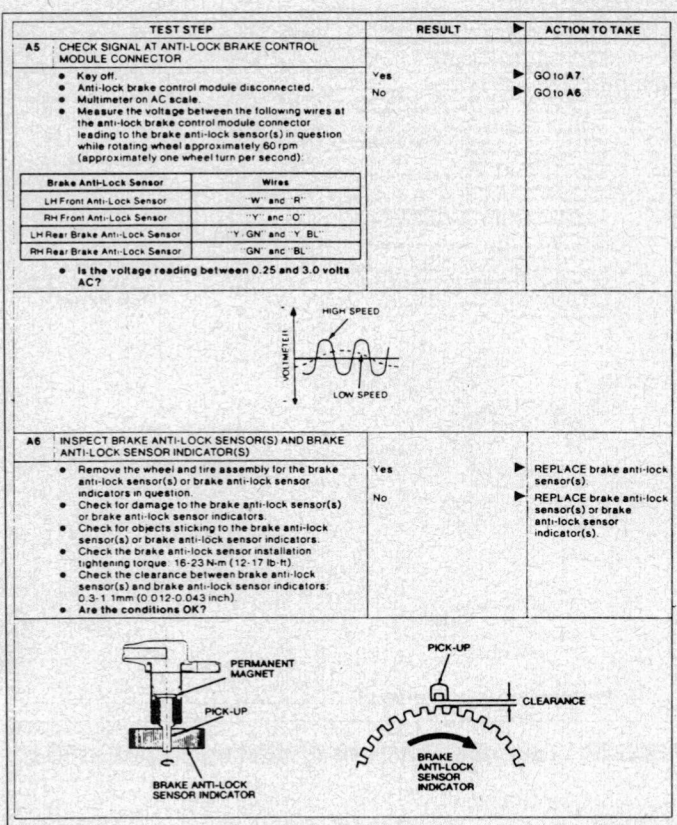

TEST STEP	RESULT	▶	ACTION TO TAKE
A5 CHECK SIGNAL AT ANTI-LOCK BRAKE CONTROL MODULE CONNECTOR			
• Key off. • Anti-lock brake control module disconnected. • Multimeter on AC scale. • Measure the voltage between the following wires at the anti-lock brake control module connector leading to the brake anti-lock sensor(s) in question while rotating wheel approximately 60 rpm (approximately one wheel turn per second):	Yes	▶	GO to A7.
	No	▶	GO to A6.

Brake Anti-Lock Sensor	Wires
LH Front Anti-Lock Sensor	"W" and "R"
RH Front Anti-Lock Sensor	"Y" and "O"
LH Rear Brake Anti-Lock Sensor	"Y·GN" and "Y·BL"
RH Rear Brake Anti-Lock Sensor	"GN" and "BL"

• Is the voltage reading between 0.25 and 3.0 volts AC?

TEST STEP	RESULT	▶	ACTION TO TAKE
A6 INSPECT BRAKE ANTI-LOCK SENSOR(S) AND BRAKE ANTI-LOCK SENSOR INDICATOR(S)			
• Remove the wheel and tire assembly for the brake anti-lock sensor(s) or brake anti-lock sensor indicators in question. • Check for damage to the brake anti-lock sensor(s) or brake anti-lock sensor indicators. • Check for objects sticking to the brake anti-lock sensor(s) or brake anti-lock sensor indicators. • Check the brake anti-lock sensor installation tightening torque. 16-23 N·m (12-17 lb-ft). • Check the clearance between brake anti-lock sensor(s) and brake anti-lock sensor indicators: 0.3-1.1mm (0.012-0.043 inch). • Are the conditions OK?	Yes	▶	REPLACE brake anti-lock sensor(s).
	No	▶	REPLACE brake anti-lock sensor(s) or brake anti-lock sensor indicator(s).

FM4029400413030X

Fig. 30   Test A: Brake Anti-Lock Sensors & Sensor Indicators (Part 3 of 4). 1994

TEST STEP	RESULT	▶	ACTION TO TAKE
C3 CHECK SOLENOID AT ANTI-LOCK BRAKE CONTROL MODULE			
• Key off. • Locate and disconnect the anti-lock brake control module. • Measure the resistance between the following wires at the anti-lock brake control module connector.	Yes	▶	GO to Pinpoint Test H1.
	No	▶	GO to C4.

Solenoid	Wires
Left Front	"Y·W" and "Y·GN"
Right Front	"Y·W" and "BL/O"
Left Rear	"Y·W" and "BR"
Right Rear	"Y·W" and "BK·Y"

• Are the resistances about 3 ohms?

TEST STEP	RESULT	▶	ACTION TO TAKE
C4 CHECK SOLENOID AT HYDRAULIC ANTI-LOCK ACTUATOR ASSEMBLY			
• Perform the Hydraulic Anti-lock Actuator Assembly component test in this section. • Is the hydraulic anti-lock actuator assembly OK?	Yes	▶	SERVICE wire(s) between anti-lock brake control module and hydraulic anti-lock actuator assembly.
	No	▶	REPLACE hydraulic anti-lock actuator assembly.

FM4029400415020X

Fig. 32   Test C: Solenoid Valve (Part 2 of 2). 1994

TEST STEP		RESULT	▶	ACTION TO TAKE
D1	CHECK SYSTEM INTEGRITY			
• Visually inspect all wiring, wiring harness, connectors, brake lines, and components for evidence of overheating, insulation damage, looseness, shorting, or other damage. • Is there any cause for concern?		Yes No	▶ ▶	SERVICE as required. GO to D2.
D2	CHECK FUSES			
• Check the 60A ABS fuse in the main fuse junction panel and the 15A METER fuse in the interior fuse junction panel. • Are the fuses OK?		Yes No	▶ ▶	GO to D3. REPLACE fuse(s).
D3	CHECK ANTI-LOCK RELAY OPERATION			
• Key off. • Locate and disconnect the anti-lock brake control module. • Key ON. • Connect the "BK/BL" wire at the anti-lock control module connector to ground. • Does the anti-lock relay click when the wire is grounded?		Yes No	▶ ▶	GO to D4. INSPECT "BK/BL" wire from anti-lock relay to anti-lock brake control module. If OK, GO to D6.
D4	CHECK ANTI-LOCK BRAKE INDICATOR DIODE			
• Anti-lock brake control module disconnected. • Key ON. • Connect the "BK/BL" wire at the anti-lock brake control module connector to ground. • Check to see that the anti-lock brake indicator does not illuminate when grounded. • Does the anti-lock brake indicator illuminate?		Yes No	▶ ▶	GO to D6. GO to D5.

FM4029400416010X

Fig. 33   Test D: Fail-Safe Relay (Part 1 of 2). 1994

TEST STEP		RESULT	▶	ACTION TO TAKE
D5	CHECK VOLTAGE FROM ANTI-LOCK RELAY			
• Anti-lock brake control module disconnected. • Key ON. • Connect the "BK/BL" wire at the anti-lock brake control module connector to ground. • Measure the voltage at the "Y/W" wire at the anti-lock brake control module connector. • Is the voltage reading greater than 10 volts?		Yes Yes, if directed to this Pinpoint Test from Step F1 No	▶ ▶ ▶	GO to Pinpoint Test G1 GO to E2 GO to D6.
D6	CHECK ANTI-LOCK RELAY			
• Perform the Anti-lock Relay component test. • Is the anti-lock relay OK?		Yes No	▶ ▶	SERVICE the "Y/W" wire between the anti-lock relay and the anti-lock brake control module. REPLACE the anti-lock relay.

FM4029400416020X

Fig. 33   Test D: Fail-Safe Relay (Part 2 of 2). 1994

TEST STEP		RESULT	▶	ACTION TO TAKE
E1	CHECK FAIL-SAFE RELAY			
• Go to the Pinpoint Test D1 and check the operation of the fail-safe relay. • Does the fail-safe relay operate properly?		Yes No	▶ ▶	GO to E2. REPLACE the anti-lock relay.
E2	CHECK SYSTEM INTEGRITY			
• Visually inspect all wiring, wiring harness, connectors, brake lines and components for evidence of overheating, insulation damage, looseness, shorting, or other damage. • Is there any cause for concern?		Yes No	▶ ▶	SERVICE as required. GO to E3.
E3	CHECK MOTOR RELAY OPERATION			
CAUTION: While performing this test step, do not allow motor to operate for more than two seconds. • Key off. • Locate and disconnect the anti-lock brake control module. • Key ON. • Connect the "BK/BL" wire to ground at the anti-lock brake control module harness connector. • Connect the "BL/O" wire to ground at the anti-lock brake control module harness connector for no more than two seconds. • Does the motor relay click and the motor operate when wires are grounded?		Yes No (Motor relay clicks but motor does not operate) No (Motor relay does not click and motor does not operate)	▶ ▶ ▶	GO to E8. GO to E5. GO to E4.
E4	CHECK ANTI-LOCK RELAY			
• Perform the Anti-Lock Relay component test in this section. • Is the anti-lock relay OK?		Yes No	▶ ▶	GO to E5. REPLACE the anti-lock relay.

FM4029400417010X

Fig. 34   Test E: Motor & Motor Relay (Part 1 of 2). 1994

TEST STEP		RESULT	▶	ACTION TO TAKE
E5	CHECK MOTOR RESISTANCE			
• Key off. • Locate and disconnect the hydraulic anti-lock actuator assembly 2-pin motor connector. • Measure the resistance between the "R/Y" and "BK" terminals of the motor.		Yes No	▶ ▶	GO to E6. REPLACE the hydraulic anti-lock actuator assembly.

HYDRAULIC ACTUATOR MOTOR

• Is the resistance less than 1 ohm?				
E6	CHECK MOTOR OPERATION			
CAUTION: While performing this test step, do not allow motor to operate for more than two seconds. • Hydraulic anti-lock actuator assembly 2-pin motor connector disconnected. • Apply battery voltage to the "R/Y" terminal and ground the "BK" terminal at the hydraulic anti-lock actuator assembly 2-pin motor connector. • Does the motor operate when voltage is applied?		Yes No	▶ ▶	GO to E7. REPLACE hydraulic anti-lock actuator assembly.
E7	CHECK MOTOR GROUND			
• Hydraulic anti-lock actuator assembly 2-pin motor connector disconnected. • Measure the resistance between the "BK" wire at the hydraulic anti-lock actuator assembly 2-pin motor connector (harness side) and ground. • Is the resistance less than 5 ohms?		Yes No	▶ ▶	SERVICE "R/Y" wire between anti-lock relay and hydraulic anti-lock actuator assembly. SERVICE "BK" wire to ground.
E8	CHECK RESISTANCE AT ANTI-LOCK BRAKE CONTROL MODULE			
• Key off. • Hydraulic anti-lock actuator assembly connected. • Anti-lock brake control module disconnected. • Measure the resistance between the "R/Y" wire at the anti-lock brake control module and ground. • Is the resistance less than 1 ohm?		Yes No	▶ ▶	GO to Pinpoint Test G1. SERVICE "R/Y" wire between anti-lock brake control module and hydraulic anti-lock actuator assembly.

FM4029400417020X

Fig. 34   Test E: Motor & Motor Relay (Part 2 of 2). 1994

TEST STEP		RESULT	▶	ACTION TO TAKE
F1	CHECK BATTERY VOLTAGE			
• Measure the voltage at the battery. • Is the voltage reading as specified?		Yes No	▶ ▶	GO to F2 CHARGE or REPLACE the battery as necessary.

FM4029400418010X

Fig. 35   Test F: Generator (Part 1 of 2). 1994

TEST STEP		RESULT	▶	ACTION TO TAKE
F2	CHECK BATTERY VOLTAGE AT ANTI-LOCK BRAKE CONTROL MODULE			
• Disconnect the anti-lock brake control module connectors. • Measure the voltage at the anti-lock brake control module 9A ("BK/W") terminal under the following conditions:		Yes No	▶ ▶	GO to F3 SERVICE wiring between anti-lock brake control module and battery.

Ignition Switch	Voltage
Off	0 Volts
ON	Above 10 Volts

• Are the voltage readings as specified?				
F3	CHECK VOLTAGE AT GENERATOR			
• Measure the voltage at the B ("BK"), L ("W/BK"), and S ("W/GN") terminals at the generator with the engine idling. Refer to Section 14-00 for testing procedures and voltage specifications. • Are the voltage readings as specified?		Yes No	▶ ▶	GO to F4 SERVICE or REPLACE generator.
F4	CHECK GENERATOR VOLTAGE AT ANTI-LOCK BRAKE CONTROL MODULE			
• Measure the voltage at the 11B ("W/BK") terminal of the anti-lock brake control module under the following conditions:		Yes No	▶ ▶	GO to Pinpoint Test G1 SERVICE "W/BK" wire from anti-lock brake control module to generator

Condition	Voltage
Key ON Engine Off	0.8-3.0 Volts
Engine Idling	Above 10 Volts

• Are the voltages as specified?

FM4029400418020X

Fig. 35   Test F: Generator (Part 2 of 2). 1994

TEST STEP		RESULT	▶	ACTION TO TAKE
G3	**CHECK ANTI-LOCK BRAKE INDICATOR SIGNAL**			
• Key ON. • Anti-lock brake control module disconnected. • ABS relay disconnected. • Connect the "PK" wire at the anti-lock brake control module and the "PK" wire at the anti-lock relay to ground. • Does the anti-lock brake indicator illuminate when both wires are connected to ground?		Yes	▶	GO to G4.
		No (Does not illuminate at all)	▶	REPLACE the 15A METER fuse and/or indicator bulb if burned out. If OK, SERVICE "PK" wire from instrument cluster to anti-lock relay and/or anti-lock brake control module.
		No (Illuminates only when grounded at anti-lock brake control module)	▶	SERVICE "PK" wire to anti-lock relay.
		No (Illuminates only when grounded at anti-lock relay)	▶	SERVICE "PK" wire to anti-lock brake control module.
G4	**CHECK GROUNDS AT ABS CONTROL MODULE**			
• Key off. • Anti-lock brake control module disconnected. • Measure the resistance between the 3A ("BK") terminal and ground and the 8A ("BK") terminal and ground at the anti-lock brake control module connector. • Are the resistances less than 5 ohms?		Yes	▶	REPLACE anti-lock brake control module.
		No	▶	SERVICE the "BK" wire(s) to ground.

FM4029400419020X

Fig. 36   Test G: Anti-Lock Brake Indicator (Part 2 of 2). 1994

TEST STEP		RESULT	▶	ACTION TO TAKE
G1	**CHECK ANTI-LOCK BRAKE INDICATOR OPERATION**			
• Key off. • Locate and disconnect the anti-lock brake control module. • Key ON. • Does the anti-lock brake indicator illuminate?		Yes	▶	GO to G2.
		No	▶	REPLACE the 15A METER fuse and/or indicator bulb if burned out. If OK, SERVICE "PK" wire or "BL-Y" wire from instrument cluster to anti-lock relay.
G2	**CHECK FOR SHORT TO GROUND**			
• Key ON. • Anti-lock brake control module disconnected. • Locate and disconnect the anti-lock relay. • Does the anti-lock brake indicator go off?		Yes	▶	GO to G3.
		No	▶	SERVICE the "PK" wire or "BL-Y" wire between the instrument cluster and anti-lock relay for short to ground

FM4029400419010X

Fig. 36   Test G: Anti-Lock Brake Indicator (Part 1 of 2). 1994

TEST STEP		RESULT	▶	ACTION TO TAKE
H1	**CHECK SYSTEM INTEGRITY**			
• Visually inspect all wiring, wiring harnesses, connectors, brake lines and components for evidence of overheating, insulation damage, looseness, shorting, or other damage. • Is there any cause for concern?		Yes	▶	SERVICE as required
		No	▶	GO to H2

FM4029400420010X

Fig. 37   Test H: Hydraulic System (Part 1 of 2). 1994

SYSTEM SERVICE
Brake System Bleed

Pressure bleeding is recommended for all hydraulic brake systems.

The bleeding operation itself is fairly well standardized. The first step in all cases is cleaning the dirt from the filler cap before removing it from the master cylinder. This should be done thoroughly.

Pressure bleeding is fastest because the master cylinder doesn't have to be refilled several times, and the job can be done by one person. To prevent air from the pressure tank getting into the lines, do not shake the tank while air is being added to the tank or after it has been pressurized. Set the tank in the required location, bring the air hose to the tank, and do not move it during the bleeding operation. The tank should be kept at least one-third full.

On vehicles equipped with disc brakes and master cylinders without proportioners or pressure control valves located in the master cylinder outlet port, the brake metering valve or combination valve must be held in position using a suitable tool.

If air does get into the fluid, releasing the pressure will cause the bubbles to increase in size, rise to the top of the fluid, and escape. Pressure should not be greater than about 35 psi.

On vehicles equipped with plastic reservoirs, do not exceed 25 psi bleeding pressure.

When bleeding without pressure, open the bleed valve 3/4 of a turn. Depress the pedal a full stroke, then allow the pedal to return slowly to its released position. After the pedal has been depressed to the end of its stroke, the bleeder valve should be closed before the start of the return stroke. Reduce the vacuum in the power unit to zero by pumping the brake pedal several times with the engine off before starting to bleed the system.

TEST STEP		RESULT	▶	ACTION TO TAKE
H2	**CHECK HYDRAULIC PRESSURE**			
NOTE: This test requires an assistant. The pressure reduction operation occurs within a two second period. • Jack up the vehicle so that all the wheels are clear of the ground and the vehicle is properly supported. • Shift the transaxle to NEUTRAL. • Release the parking brake. • Check to see that there is no brake drag while rotating the wheels by hand. • Use a jumper wire to connect the "TBS" and "GND" terminals at the data link connector. • Depress the brake pedal and have an assistant verify that the wheels will not rotate. • With the brake pedal still depressed, turn the key ON and verify that the brake pressure is released momentarily (approximately 0.5 seconds) and that each wheel rotates when pressure reduction operates as shown:		Yes (If directed to this Pinpoint Test from Quick Test Step QT4)	▶	ABS functioning properly.
		Yes (If directed to this Pinpoint Test from Step A8)	▶	Intermittent Fault. GO to Continuous Test in this section.
		Yes (If directed to this Pinpoint Test from Step C3)	▶	GO to Pinpoint Test G1.
		No	▶	INSPECT hydraulic system piping and wiring. If OK, REPLACE hydraulic anti-lock actuator assembly.
• Does the pressure reduction operate properly?				

FM4029400420020X

Fig. 37   Test H: Hydraulic System (Part 2 of 2). 1994

Pressure bleeding, of course, eliminates the need for pedal pumping.

Discard drained or bled brake fluid. Care should be taken not to spill brake fluid, since this can damage the finish of the car.

Flushing is essential if there is water, mineral oil or other contaminants in the lines, and whenever new parts are installed in the hydraulic system. Fluid con-

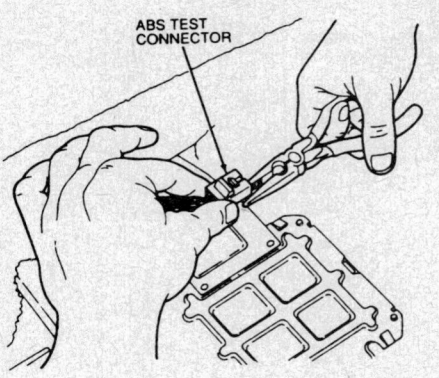

Fig. 38 ABS control module replacement. 1992

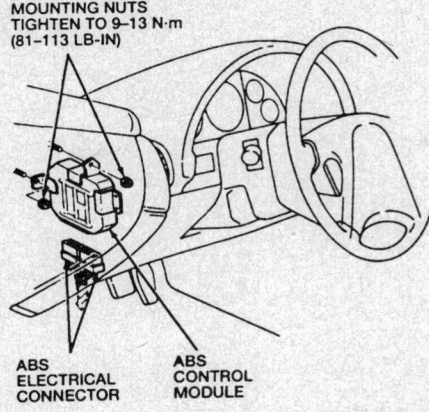

Fig. 39 ABS control module replacement. 1993-94

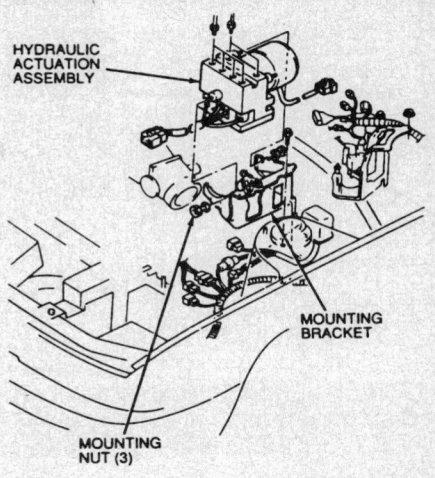

Fig. 40 Hydraulic actuation unit replacement. 1992

tamination is usually indicated by swollen and deteriorated cups and other rubber parts.

Wheel cylinders on disc brakes are equipped with bleeder valves, and are bled in the same manner as wheel cylinders for drum brakes.

Bleeding is necessary on all four wheels if air has entered the system because of low fluid level, or the line or lines have been disconnected. If a line is disconnected at any one wheel cylinder, that cylinder only needs to be bled. On brake reline jobs, bleeding is advisable to remove any air or contaminants.

Master cylinders equipped with bleeder valves should be bled first before the wheel cylinders are bled. In all cases where a master cylinder has been overhauled, it must be bled. Where there is no bleeder valve, this can be done by leaving the lines loose, actuating the brake pedal to expel the air and then tightening the lines.

After overhauling a dual master cylinder used in conjunction with disc brakes, it is advisable to bleed the cylinder before installing it on the car. The reason for this recommendation is that air may be trapped between the master cylinder pistons because there is only one residual pressure valve (check valve) used in these units.

SYSTEM PRIMING

When a new master cylinder has been installed or the brake system emptied or partially emptied, fluid may not flow from the bleeder screws during normal bleeding. It may be necessary to prime the system using the following procedure:

1. Using tubing wrench, remove brake lines from master cylinder.
2. Install short brake lines in master cylinder and position them back into reservoir. Ensure short brake line ends are submerged in reservoir brake fluid.
3. Fill reservoir with recommended brake fluid, then cover master cylinder fluid reservoir with shop towel.
4. Pump brakes until clear, bubble-free fluid comes out of both brake lines. If

any brake fluid spills on paint, wash it off immediately with water.
5. Remove short brake lines, then reinstall original brake lines.
6. Bleed each brake line at master cylinder using the following procedure:
   a. Have assistant pump brake pedal 10 times, then hold firm pressure on pedal.
   b. Open rearmost brake line fittings with tubing wrench until stream of brake fluid comes out. Have assistant maintain pressure on brake pedal until brake line fitting is tightened again.
   c. Repeat this operation until clear, bubble-free fluid comes out from around tube fitting.
   d. Repeat this bleeding operation at front brake line fitting.
7. If any of brake lines or calipers have been removed, it may be helpful to prime system by gravity bleeding. This should be done after master cylinder is primed and bled. To prime system using gravity method, proceed as follows:
   a. Fill master cylinder with manufacturer recommended brake fluid or equivalent.
   b. Loosen both rear bleeder screws and leave them open until clear brake fluid flows out. **Check reservoir fluid level frequently. Do not allow fluid level to drop below half full.**
   c. Tighten rear bleeder screws.
   d. Loosen bleeder screw on front caliper. Leave open until clear fluid flows out. **Bleed front calipers one side at a time.**
8. After master cylinder has been primed, lines bled at master cylinder and the brake system primed, normal brake system bleeding can be resumed at each wheel.

Component Replacement
ABS CONTROL MODULE
1992

1. Remove driver's seat.

2. Disconnect ABS test connector, **Fig. 38.**
3. Remove three module bolts, then disconnect electrical connectors and remove module from vehicle.
4. Reverse procedure to install.

1993-94

The ABS control module is located behind the driver's side kick panel.
1. Disconnect battery ground cable.
2. Remove driver's side kick panel, **Fig. 39.**
3. Disconnect ABS electrical connector.
4. Remove module nuts, then the control module.
5. Reverse procedure to install.

HYDRAULIC ACTUATION UNIT
1992

1. Remove air cleaner assembly.
2. Remove ignition coil and module bracket assembly.
3. Unfasten fuel filter bracket, then position filter and bracket aside.
4. Disconnect two hydraulic actuation unit electrical connectors.
5. Disconnect brake lines from hydraulic actuation unit, then remove lines necessary for unit removal. **Note routing of brake lines for installation reference.**
6. Remove nuts and washers, then carefully lift hydraulic actuation assembly from vehicle, **Fig. 40.**
7. Reverse procedure to install, noting the following:
   a. **Torque** actuation assembly nuts to 14-19 ft. lbs.
   b. **Torque** brake lines to 10-16 ft. lbs.
   c. Bleed brake system as described under "System Service."

1993-94

1. Disconnect battery ground cable, then slide fuel vapor canister out of its bracket and position aside.
2. Remove speed control servo from

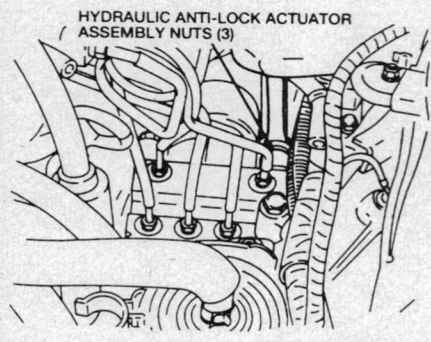

Fig. 41 Hydraulic anti-lock actuator assembly nut loosening. 1993–94.

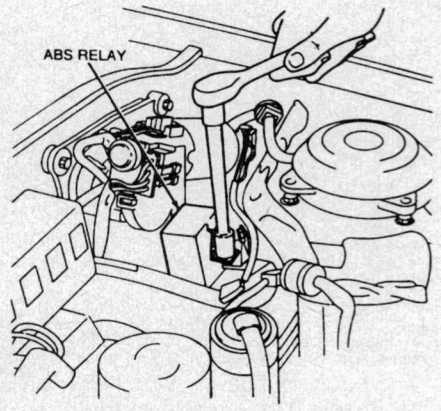

Fig. 42 ABS relay replacement. 1992

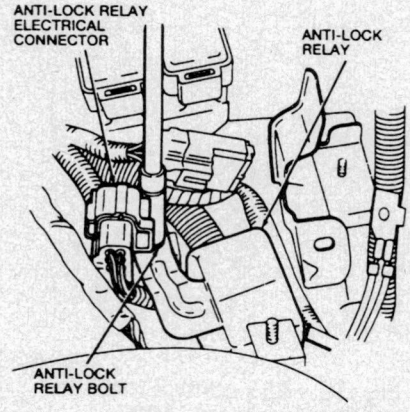

Fig. 43 ABS relay replacement. 1993–94

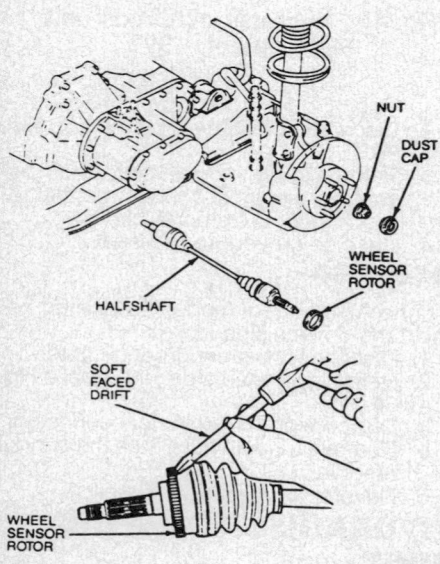

Fig. 44 Front wheel sensor rotor replacement

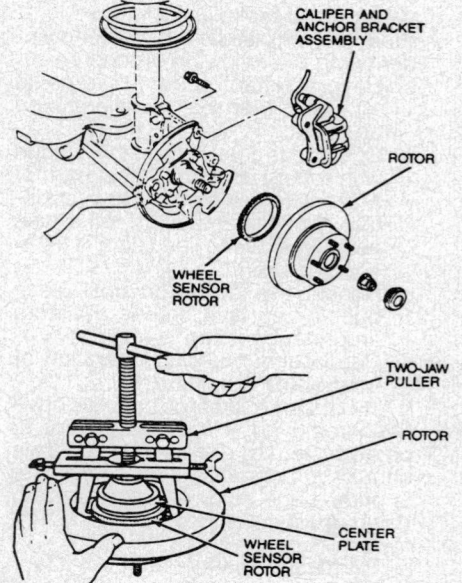

Fig. 45 Rear wheel sensor rotor replacement. 1992

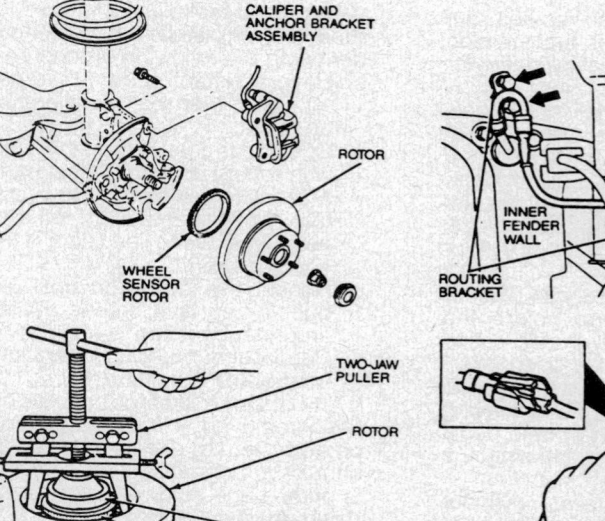

Fig. 46 Front speed sensor replacement. 1993–94

bracket as described in "Speed Controls" chapter.
3. Disconnect hydraulic anti-lock actuator assembly electrical connectors, then loosen three nuts, **Fig. 41.**
4. Remove front left brake line bolt, then use tubing wrench to remove brake line fittings from actuator assembly. **Note brake line routings to ensure proper installation.**
5. Remove actuator assembly nuts and washers, then the actuator assembly.
6. Reverse procedure to install, noting the following:
   a. **Torque** brake lines to 10–16 ft. lbs.
   b. Bleed brakes as described under "System Service."

ABS RELAY

The ABS relay is located under the main fuse block.
1. **On 1992 models,** remove ABS relay attaching nut, **Fig. 42.**
2. **On 1993-94 models,** remove ABS relay bolt, **Fig. 43.**
3. **On all models,** disconnect relay elec-

trical connector, then remove relay.
4. Reverse procedure to install.

FRONT WHEEL SENSOR ROTOR

1. Remove wheel and tire assembly.
2. Remove halfshaft.
3. Using soft faced drift, tap sensor rotor from outboard CV joint, **Fig. 44.**
4. Reverse procedure to install.

REAR WHEEL SENSOR ROTOR

1992

1. Remove wheel and tire assembly.
2. Remove caliper, anchor bracket and rotor

3. Using two-jawed puller and center plate, remove sensor rotor, **Fig. 45.**
4. Reverse procedure to install.

FRONT SPEED SENSOR

1993–94

1. Remove wheel and tire assembly.
2. Remove two bolts, then the speed sensor from knuckle.
3. Remove routing bracket from strut assembly, **Fig. 46.**
4. Disconnect wiring harness, then remove speed sensor.
5. Reverse procedure to install, noting the following:
   a. **Left and right speed sensors are not interchangeable.**
   b. **Torque** routing bracket and speed sensor to 12–17 ft. lbs.

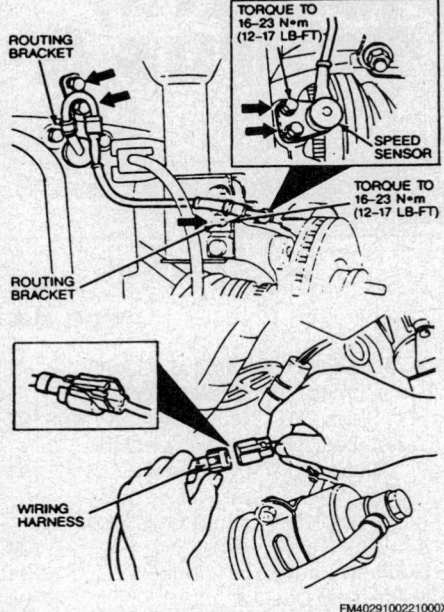

Fig. 47 Rear speed sensor replacement. 1993–94

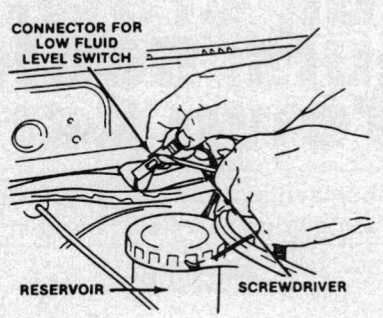

Fig. 48 Master cylinder removal. 1992

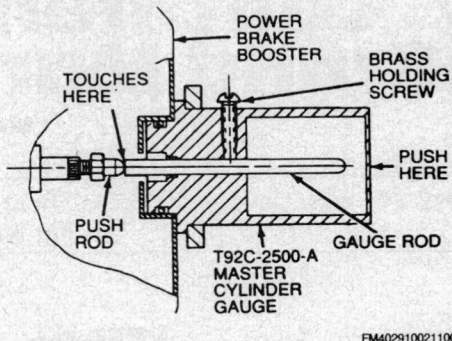

Fig. 49 Master cylinder pushrod gauge assembly. 1992

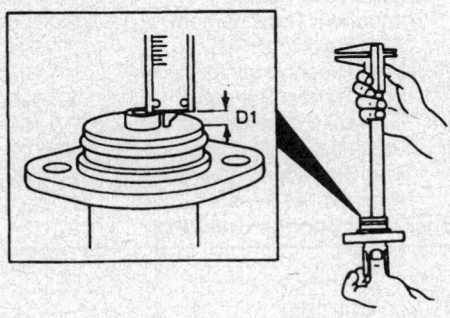

Fig. 50 Master cylinder pushrod gauge measurements. 1992

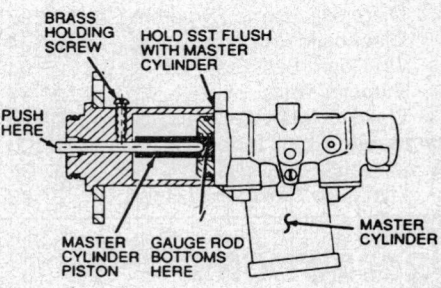

Fig. 51 Master cylinder pushrod gauge installation. 1992

REAR SPEED SENSOR

1993–94

1. Remove wheel and tire assembly.
2. Remove retaining bolt and speed sensor from knuckle.
3. Remove routing bracket from strut assembly, **Fig. 47.**
4. Remove routing bracket from inner fenders, then the interior panels as necessary to gain access to wiring harness
5. Disconnect wiring harness, then remove speed sensor.
6. Reverse procedure to install, noting the following:
   a. **Left and right speed sensors are not interchangeable.**
   b. **Torque** routing bracket nut and speed sensor bolt to 12-17 ft. lbs.

Adjustments

MASTER CYLINDER PUSHROD CLEARANCE

1992

1. Disconnect electrical connector from low fluid level sensor, **Fig. 48.**
2. Disconnect brake lines from master cylinder. **Brake fluid is caustic and must not come into contact with plastic or painted surfaces. Use extreme caution when handling this fluid which contains polyglycols and polyglycol ethers.**
3. Disconnect and cap hydraulic lines at master cylinder ports, then remove master cylinder attaching nuts and master cylinder.
4. Loosen brass holding screw on master cylinder gauge tool No. T92C-2500-A, or equivalent, and retract gauge rod, **Fig. 49.**
5. Attach gauge to power brake booster and **torque** nuts to 87-140 inch lbs.
6. Start engine and run at idle for approximately 15 seconds.
7. Gently push end of gauge rod until rod just touches power brake pushrod.
8. Tighten brass screw to secure gauge rod in place.
9. Carefully remove master cylinder gauge from power brake unit, then turn engine off.
10. Measure and record master cylinder gauge rod height, **Fig. 50.**
11. Loosen brass holding screw, then position gauge on master cylinder, **Fig. 51.**
12. Gently push end of gauge rod until end of rod just bottoms in master cylinder piston, then tighten brass screw.
13. Carefully remove gauge from master cylinder.
14. Measure and record gauge rod height.
15. Subtract first measurement from second measurement, then adjust power brake pushrod nut to shorten or lengthen pushrod an amount equal to difference between two dimensions:
    a. If first measurement is larger than second measurement, lengthen pushrod.
    b. If second measurement is larger than first measurement, shorten pushrod.

Continental, Crown Victoria, Grand Marquis, Sable, Taurus & Town Car

NOTE: Wire Color Code & Electrical Symbol Identification Located At The Front Of This Manual Can Be Used As An Aid When Using Wiring Circuits Found In This Section.

INDEX

PRECAUTIONS

HYDRAULIC BRAKE FLUID COLOR

Hydraulic brake fluid must conform with the requirements of Federal Motor Vehicle Safety Standard 116. Under this standard, brake fluids are visually different from other automotive fluids such as transmission, power steering and engine.

Fluid color in a normal brake system may vary from its original color for many reasons. A brake master cylinder may show significantly different shades fluid color between the two brake master cylinder reservoirs. Color may also appear to vary between cast steel and die cast aluminum reservoirs. Some reasons for discoloration include the following:

1. Heat and/or aging.
2. Different operation temperatures or different rates of normal oxidation between two reservoir compartments.
3. Different brands and/or shades of fluid are used when topping off during normal service.
4. Dissolution of color dye used on master cylinder internal springs during assembly.

Brake fluid contaminated with hydrocarbon/mineral based fluid (power steering or transmission fluid) can be detected by an obvious swelling of the master cylinder cap gasket. If the master cylinder cap gasket is swollen, all brake system rubber parts must be replaced. All brake tubes and hoses must be thoroughly flushed with Ford Heavy Duty Brake Fluid C6AZ-19542-AA or —BA or DOT-3 equivalent before the vehicle returns to service.

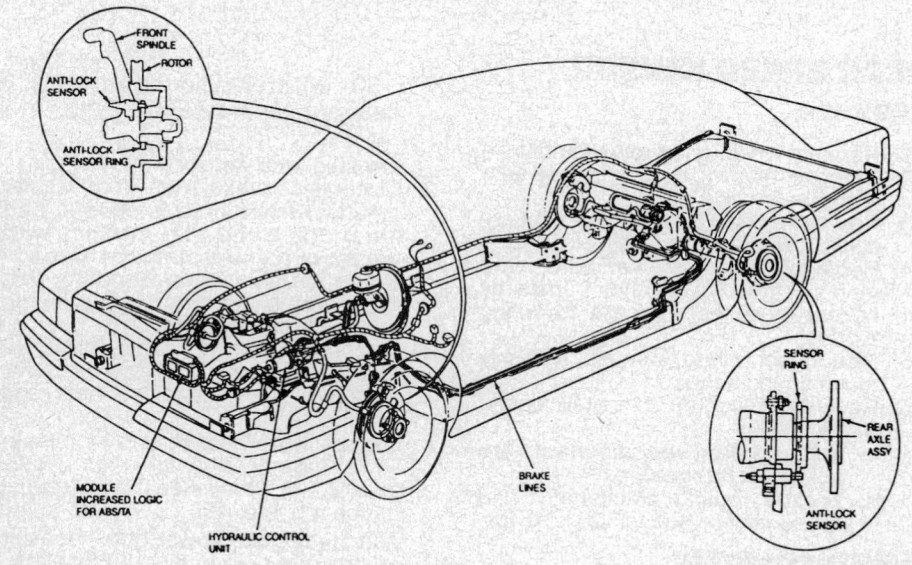

Fig. 1 Anti-lock brake system

FM4029100222000X

DESCRIPTION

The anti-lock system (ABS), **Fig. 1**, controls each brake separately. The brake pedal force required to engage the system may vary with road surface conditions. A dry surface will require a high force, while a slippery surface will require a much less force. During system operation, the driver will sense a slight brake pedal pulsation accompanied by a rise in brake pedal height and a clicking sound. The pedal effort and pedal feel during normal braking are similar to a conventional power brake system.

SYSTEM COMPONENTS

Vacuum Booster

The diaphragm type brake booster is self-contained and is mounted on the left side of engine compartment. The vacuum brake booster uses engine intake manifold vacuum and atmospheric pressure for power.

Master Cylinder

This unit is a tandem master cylinder, **Fig. 2**. The primary (rear) circuit feeds right front and left rear brakes. The secondary

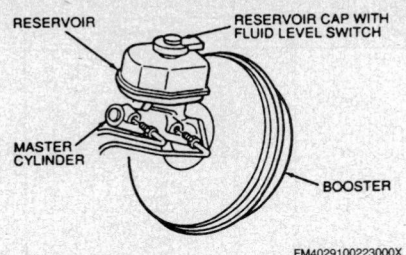

Fig. 2 Master cylinder

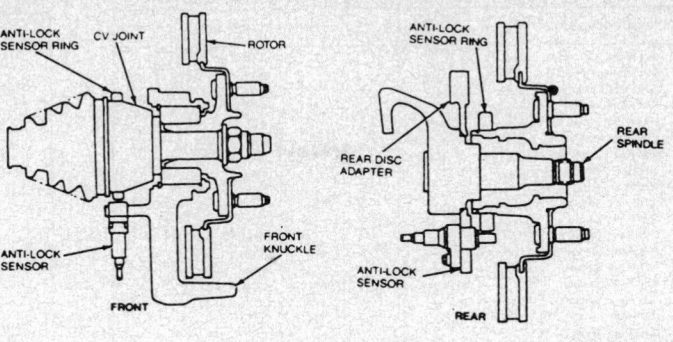

Fig. 3 Wheel sensor assembly

circuit (front) feeds left front and right rear brakes. The reservoir is a clear translucent plastic container. An integral fluid level switch is part of reservoir cap assembly, with one electrical connector pointing rearward for wire harness connection.

Hydraulic Control Unit

The Hydraulic Control Unit (HCU) is located on the front lefthand side of the engine compartment. It consists of a valve body assembly, pump, motor assembly and brake fluid reservoir with fluid lever indicator assembly. During normal braking, fluid from master cylinder enters the HCU through two inlet ports at the rear of the HCU. The fluid passes through four normally open inlet valves, one to each wheel. When the ABS module (Electronic Control Unit (ECU)) senses wheel lock conditions, the ABS module (ECU) produces a pulse to the appropriate inlet valve, which then closes the valve. This prevents any more fluid from entering the affected brake. The ABS module (ECU) senses the wheel again. If the wheel is still decelerating, the ABS module (ECU) then pulses open the normally closed valve, which decreases the pressure trapped inline.

ABS Module (Electronic Control Unit)

The ABS module (ECU) is located in the engine compartment. This unit is a self-test non-repairable unit consisting of two micro-processors which are programmed identically. The ABS module (ECU) monitors system operation during normal driving as well as during anti-lock braking. Under normal driving conditions, the micro-processors transmit short test pulses to the solenoid valves to check the electrical system. Under wheel lock conditions, the ABS module (ECU) produces signals to open and close the appropriate solenoid valves. This results in moderate pulsations in brake pedal. During anti-lock braking, moderate pulsation in the brake pedal is accompanied by a change in pedal height. This rise in pedal height will continue until the pedal travel switch closes and the pump shuts off. During normal braking, the brake pedal feel will be identical to a standard brake system.

Wheel Sensors

This system uses four sets of variable resistance sensors and toothed speed indicator rings to determine each wheel's rotational speed, **Fig. 3.** The sensors operate on a magnetic induction principle. For example, as the teeth on the speed indicator ring rotate past a stationary sensor, a signal, proportional to the speed sensor rotation, is generated and transmitted to the ABS module (ECU) through a coaxial cable.

The front wheel sensors are attached to the suspension knuckles and the front speed indicators are pressed onto the outer constant velocity joints. The rear wheel sensors are attached to the rear caliper adapter plates, and the rear speed indicator rings are pressed onto the rear hub assemblies.

Pedal Travel Switch

This system uses a pedal travel switch which monitors brake pedal travel and sends information to the ABS module (ECU) through the wiring harness. Switch adjustment is critical to pedal feel during ABS cycling. The switch is mounted on the right side of the brake pedal support, near the dump valve adapter bracket.

The switch is normally closed. When brake pedal travel exceeds the switch setting during an anti-lock stop, the electronic controller senses the switch is open and grounds the pump motor relay coil. This energizes the relay and turns the pump motor on. When the pump motor is running, the master cylinder fills with high pressure brake fluid, pushing the brake pedal up until the switch closes. When the switch closes, the pump turns off and the pedal drops with each ABS control cycle until the travel switch re-opens and the pump is turned back on. This minimizes pedal feedback during ABS cycling.

If the pedal travel switch is not adjusted properly or is not electrically connected, it will cause an incorrect pedal feel during ABS stops. Some problems with the switch or its installation will result in the pump running during an entire ABS stop. The pedal will become very firm, pushing the driver's foot up to an very high position.

OPERATION

Anti-Lock Brakes

When brakes are applied, fluid is forced from the master cylinder outlet ports to the Hydraulic Control Unit (HCU) inlet ports. This pressure is transmitted through four normally open solenoid valves contained inside the HCU, then through outlet ports of the HCU to each wheel. The primary (rear) circuit of the master cylinder feeds the right front and left rear brakes. The secondary (front) circuit feeds the left front and right rear brakes.

When the ABS module (ECU) senses wheel lock conditions based on wheel speed sensor data, it pulses against the normally open solenoid valve, closing the circuit. This prevents any more fluid from entering the circuit. The ABS module (ECU) senses the wheel again. If the wheel is still decelerating, the module pulses the normally closed valve open, decreasing the pressure trapped inline.

The ABS module (ECU) monitors the electro-mechanical components of the system. An anti-lock brake system malfunction will cause the module to shut off or inhibit the anti-lock function, while retaining the normal power assisted braking. Malfunctions are indicated by one or two warning lamps inside the vehicle.

Loss of hydraulic fluid in the HCU reservoir will disable the anti-lock brake system.

The four wheel anti-lock brake system is self-monitoring. When the ignition switch is turned to the RUN position, the ABS module (ECU) will perform a preliminary self-check on the anti-lock electrical system, indicated by a three or four second illumination of the amber "Check Anti-Lock Brakes" lamp on the instrument cluster. During vehicle operation, including normal and anti-lock braking, the ABS module (ECU) monitors all electrical anti-lock functions and some hydraulic system operation.

For most malfunctions of the anti-lock brake system, the amber "Check Anti-Lock Brakes" and/or the red "Brake" lamp will be illuminated. The sequence of illumination of these warning lamps, combined with the problem symptoms, can determine the appropriate diagnostic test to perform. Most malfunctions are recorded as a coded number in the controller memory, pinpointing the exact component requiring service.

TRACTION ASSIST

1993 Crown Victoria, Grand Marquis & Town Car

Traction Assist (TA) is designed to control wheel spin when accelerating on loose or slippery surfaces. During acceleration, if one or both rear wheels lose traction and

SERVICE CODE (COMPONENT)	PINPOINT TEST STEP
11 (Electronic Controller)	AA1
22 (Ref. Voltage of IFL)	BB1
23 (LH Front Outlet Valve)	BB3
24 (RH Front Inlet Valve)	BB4
25 (RH Front Outlet Valve)	BB5
26 (RH Rear Inlet Valve)	BB6
27 (RH Rear Outlet Valve)	BB7
28 (LH Rear Inlet Valve)	BB8
29 (LH Rear Outlet Valve)	BB9
31 (LH Front Sensor)	CC1
32 (RH Front Sensor)	CC6
33 (RH Rear Sensor)	CC11
34 (LH Rear Sensor)	CC16
35 (LH Front Sensor)	CC1
36 (RH Front Sensor)	CC6
37 (RH Rear Sensor)	CC11
38 (LH Rear Sensor)	CC16
41 (LH Front Sensor)	CC1
42 (RH Front Sensor)	CC6
43 (RH Rear Sensor)	CC11
44 (LH Rear Sensor)	CC16
51 (LH Front Outlet Valve)	DD1
52 (RH Front Outlet Valve)	DD3
53 (LH Rear Outlet Valve)	DD5
54 (LH Rear Outlet Valve)	DD7
55 (LH Front Sensor)	CC1
56 (LH Rear Sensor)	CC6
57 (RH Rear Sensor)	CC11
58 (LH Rear Sensor)	CC16
61 (FLI Circuits)	EE1
62 (Travel Switch)	EE3
63 (Pump Motor Speed Sensor)	EE5
64 (Pump Motor Pressure)	EE8
71 (LH Front Sensor)	CC1
72 (RH Front Sensor)	CC6
73 (LH Rear Sensor)	CC11
74 (LH Rear Sensor)	CC16
75 (LH Front Sensor)	CC1
76 (RH Front Sensor)	CC6
77 (LH Rear Sensor)	CC11
78 (LH Rear Sensor)	CC16

FM4029100236000X

Fig. 4   On-board self-test service code index. 1992 Continental, Sable & Taurus

SERVICE CODE (COMPONENT)	PINPOINT TEST STEP
11 (Electronic Controller)	AA1
17 (Reference Voltage)	BB1
18 (Isolation Valve No. 1)*	BB11
19 (Isolation Valve No. 2)*	BB12
22 (Ref. Voltage of IFL)	BB1
23 (LH Front Outlet Valve)	BB3
24 (RH Front Inlet Valve)	BB4
25 (RH Front Outlet Valve)	BB5
26 (RH Rear Inlet Valve)	BB6
27 (RH Rear Outlet Valve)	BB7
28 (LH Rear Inlet Valve)	BB8
29 (LH Rear Outlet Valve)	BB9
31 (LH Front Sensor)	CC1
32 (RH Front Sensor)	CC6
33 (RH Rear Sensor)	CC11
34 (LH Rear Sensor)	CC16
35 (LH Front Sensor)	CC1
36 (RH Front Sensor)	CC6
37 (RH Rear Sensor)	CC11
38 (LH Rear Sensor)	CC16
41 (LH Front Sensor)	CC1
42 (RH Front Sensor)	CC6
43 (RH Rear Sensor)	CC11
44 (LH Rear Sensor)	CC16
51 (LH Front Outlet Valve)	DD1
52 (RH Front Outlet Valve)	DD3
53 (LH Rear Outlet Valve)	DD5
54 (LH Rear Outlet Valve)	DD7
55 (LH Front Sensor)	CC1
56 (LH Rear Sensor)	CC6
57 (RH Rear Sensor)	CC11
58 (LH Rear Sensor)	CC16
61 (FLI Circuits)	EE1
62 (Travel Switch)	EE3
63 (Pump Motor Speed Sensor)	EE7
64 (Pump Motor Pressure)	EE8
66 (Pressure Switch)	EE1
67 (Pump Motor Relay)*	
71 (LH Front Sensor)	CC1
72 (RH Front Sensor)	CC6
73 (LH Rear Sensor)	CC11
74 (LH Rear Sensor)	CC16
75 (LH Front Sensor)	CC1
76 (RH Front Sensor)	CC6
77 (LH Rear Sensor)	CC11
78 (LH Rear Sensor)	CC16

*Traction Assist Codes

FM4029100237000X

Fig. 5   On-board self-test service code index. 1992 Crown Victoria, Grand Marquis & Town Car

begin to spin, the TA system will rapidly apply and release the appropriate rear brake to reduce wheel spin and aid traction. The accompanying isolation valve will also close and the ABS pump will run. The isolation valve permits brake operation only to the rear brake of the circuit by closing off pressure to the front brake.

If brakes are applied during TA operation, the ABS module receives a signal from the stoplamp switch or the pressure switch and automatically stops TA cycling.

TROUBLESHOOTING

PRE-TEST CHECKS

1. Verify parking brake is completely released. If parking brake is applied, "Brake" lamp will be illuminated.
2. Check brake fluid. **As fluid level drops, red "Brake" lamp will illuminate. If fluid level continues to fall, amber "Check Anti-Lock Brake" lamp will illuminate and anti-lock function will be inhibited.**
3. Verify all of the following connectors are properly connected and in good operating condition:
   a. 55 pin connector of the computer module.
   b. 19 pin connector of HCU valve body.
   c. 4 and 7 pin connectors of pump motor relay.
   d. 3 pin connector of master cylinder reservoir.
   e. 2 pin connector of HCU reservoir.
   f. 5 pin connector of main power relay.
   g. 2 pin connector of each wheel sensor.
   h. 2 pin connector of pedal travel switch.
   i. 2 pin connector of stoplamp switch.
4. Check fuses and diode for damage.
5. Ensure all battery connections are clean and tight.
6. Check ground connections for anti-lock system located near computer module and pump motor relay.

DIAGNOSIS & TESTING

DIAGNOSTIC PROCEDURE

Ensure the following diagnosis procedures are used in the sequence and step-by-step order indicated. Following the wrong sequence or bypassing steps will only lead to unnecessary replacement of system components and/or incorrect resolution of the problem. The diagnostic procedure consists of five sub-tests: Pre-test Checks, On-Board Self-Tests, Manual Quick Tests, Warning Lamp Symptom Chart and the Diagnostic Tests.

ON-BOARD SELF-TEST

The anti-lock brake electronic control module is capable of performing a self-test using Rotunda Super Star II tester 007-00041 or equivalent. If the Super Star tester is not available, the anti-lock Quick Check sheet can be used as described.

The anti-lock control module monitors system operation and stores all defined service codes in its memory. It is important to understand the control module cannot recognize some failures. Therefore, if a problem exists and no service codes are stored by the control module, other diagnostic steps must be followed. The module cannot store a service code if there is no power to the module. This fault code can be found by using Quick-Check Tests.

A 20 series code will override any other stored code and will not allow other codes to be output if failure exists while the Self-Test is being run. If failure is intermittent or if code was left in the computer due to improper erasing procedures, the code will be output during the Self-Test but the next code will also be output.

Star Tester Connection & Battery Check

1. Turn ignition switch to OFF position.
2. Locate Star tester connector on engine compartment right shock tower.
3. Connect Super Star tester electrical connector to vehicle connector. **One multi-pin connector is used.**
4. Turn power switch on righthand side of Super Star tester to On position. A steady 00 or blank screen will appear, signifying tester is ready to start Self-Test and receive service codes. **If message LO BAT appears in upper lefthand corner of the read-out display and stays On, replace Super Star tester's 9-volt battery before continuing with Self-Test. Message LO BAT will appear momentarily when power switch is turned to Off position.**
5. With ignition switch in Off position, push Self-Test button in center of Super Star II tester. Push button again.

DIAGNOSTIC TROUBLE CODE (COMPONENT)	PINPOINT TEST STEP
11 (ABS Module)	AA1
22 (Ref. Voltage or IFI)	BB1
23 (LH Front Outlet Valve)	BB4
24 (RH Rear Inlet Valve)	BB6
25 (RH Rear Outlet Valve)	BB8
26 (RH Front Inlet Valve)	BB10
27 (RH Front Outlet Valve)	BB12
28 (LH Rear Inlet Valve)	BB14
29 (LH Rear Outlet Valve)	BB16
31 (LH Front Sensor)	CC1
32 (RH Front Sensor)	CC8
33 (RH Rear Sensor)	CC15
34 (LH Rear Sensor)	CC22
35 (LH Front Sensor)	CC1
36 (RH Front Sensor)	CC8
37 (RH Rear Sensor)	CC15
38 (LH Rear Sensor)	CC22
41 (LH Front Sensor)	CC1
42 (RH Front Sensor)	CC8
43 (RH Rear Sensor)	CC15
44 (LH Rear Sensor)	CC22
51 (LH Front Outlet Valve)	DD1
52 (RH Front Outlet Valve)	DD5
53 (RH Rear Outlet Valve)	DD9
54 (LH Rear Outlet Valve)	DD13
55 (LH Front Sensor)	CC1
56 (RH Front Sensor)	CC8
57 (RH Rear Sensor)	CC15
58 (LH Rear Sensor)	CC22
61 (FLI Circuits)	EE1
62 (Travel Switch)	EE1
63 (Pump Motor Speed Sensor)	EE8

FM4029300239010X

Fig. 6   On-board self-test service code index (Part 1 of 2). 1993 Continental

DIAGNOSTIC TROUBLE CODE (COMPONENT)	PINPOINT TEST STEP
64 (Pump Motor Pressure)	EE30
71 (LH Front Sensor)	CC1
72 (RH Front Sensor)	CC8
73 (RH Rear Sensor)	CC15
74 (LH Rear Sensor)	CC22
75 (LH Front Sensor)	CC1
76 (RH Front Sensor)	CC8
77 (RH Rear Sensor)	CC15
78 (LH Rear Sensor)	CC22

FM4029300239020X

Fig. 6   On-board self-test service code index (Part 2 of 2). 1993 Continental

SERVICE CODE (COMPONENT)	PINPOINT TEST STEP
11 (ABS Module)	AA1
17 (Reference Voltage) [1]	BB1
18 (Isolation Valve No. 1) [1]	BB18
19 (Isolation Valve No. 2) [1]	BB20
22 (LH Front Inlet Valve) or reference voltage (ABS only)	BB1
23 (LH Front Outlet Valve)	BB4
24 (RH Front Inlet Valve)	BB6
25 (RH Front Outlet Valve)	BB8
26 (RH Rear Inlet Valve)	BB10
27 (RH Rear Outlet Valve)	BB12
28 (LH Rear Inlet Valve)	BB14
29 (LH Rear Outlet Valve)	BB16
31 (LH Front Sensor)	CC1
32 (RH Front Sensor)	CC8
33 (RH Rear Sensor)	CC15
34 (LH Rear Sensor)	CC22
35 (LH Front Sensor)	CC1
36 (RH Front Sensor)	CC8
37 (RH Rear Sensor)	CC15

FM4029300238010X

Fig. 7   On-board self-test service code index (Part 1 of 2). 1993 Crown Victoria, Grand Marquis & Town Car

SERVICE CODE (COMPONENT)	PINPOINT TEST STEP
38 (LH Rear Sensor)	CC22
41 (LH Front Sensor)	CC1
42 (RH Front Sensor)	CC8
43 (RH Rear Sensor)	CC15
44 (LH Rear Sensor)	CC22
51 (LH Front Outlet Valve)	DD1
52 (RH Front Outlet Valve)	DD5
53 (RH Rear Outlet Valve)	DD9
54 (LH Rear Outlet Valve)	DD13
55 (LH Front Sensor)	CC1
56 (RH Front Sensor)	CC8
57 (RH Rear Sensor)	CC15
58 (LH Rear Sensor)	CC22
61 (FLS Circuits)	EE1
62 (Travel Switch)	EE1
63 (Pump Motor Speed Sensor)	EE11
64 (Pump Motor Pressure)	EE32
66 (Pressure Switch) [1]	EE1
67 (Pump Motor Relay) [1]	E1
71 (LH Front Sensor)	CC1
72 (RH Front Sensor)	CC8
73 (RH Rear Sensor)	CC15
74 (LH Rear Sensor)	CC22
75 (LH Front Sensor)	CC1
76 (RH Front Sensor)	CC8
77 (RH Rear Sensor)	CC15
78 (LH Rear Sensor)	CC22

FM4029300238020X

Fig. 7   On-board self-test service code index (Part 2 of 2). 1993 Crown Victoria, Grand Marquis & Town Car

This will deactivate Self-Test sequence.

6. If Super Star tester passes Self-Test (00 or blank screen with button in TEST position), proceed with On-Board Self-Test. If any service codes appear during Self-Test, refer to On-Board Self-Test Service Code Index, **Figs. 4 through 11.**

On Board Self-Test Procedure

The anti-lock brake system is capable of self-diagnosis. However, the module as received from manufacturing is equipped with a stored diagnostic trouble code 61. This will affect service procedure.

The diagnostic trouble codes can be retrieved from the computer as follows:

1. Connect Super Star II tester to connector located in engine compartment.
2. Turn on Super Star II tester and latch button down in Test position.
3. Turn ignition switch to Run position.
4. Read first diagnostic trouble code output. After approximately 15 seconds, next code will be output. Leave button latched until all codes are output. **Ensure all codes are written down.**

If check Anti-Lock Brake warning lamp is on or intermittently comes on, refer to "Warning Lamp Diagnosis." The diagnostic procedure is as follows:

DIAGNOSTIC TROUBLE (COMPONENT)	PINPOINT TEST STEP
11 (ABS Module)	AA 1
22 (LH Front Inlet Valve)	BB 1
23 (LH Front Outlet Valve)	BB 4
24 (RH Front Inlet Valve)	BB 6
25 (RH Front Outlet Valve)	BB 8
26 (RH Rear Inlet Valve)	BB 10
27 (RH Rear Outlet Valve)	BB 12
28 (LH Rear Inlet Valve)	BB 14
29 (LH Rear Outlet Valve)	BB 16
31 (LH Front Sensor)	CC 1
32 (RH Front Sensor)	CC 8
33 (RH Rear Sensor)	CC 15
34 (LH Rear Sensor)	CC 22
35 (LH Front Sensor)	CC 1
36 (RH Front Sensor)	CC 8
37 (RH Rear Sensor)	CC 15
38 (LH Rear Sensor)	CC 22
41 (LH Front Sensor)	CC 1
42 (RH Front Sensor)	CC 8
43 (RH Rear Sensor)	CC 15
44 (LH Rear Sensor)	CC 22

FM4029300240010X

Fig. 8   On-board self-test service code index (Part 1 of 2). 1993 Sable & Taurus

DIAGNOSTIC TROUBLE (COMPONENT)	PINPOINT TEST STEP
51 (LH Front Outlet Valve)	DD 1
52 (RH Front Outlet Valve)	DD 5
53 (RH Rear Outlet Valve)	DD 9
54 (LH Rear Outlet Valve)	DD 13
55 (LH Front Sensor)	CC 1
56 (RH Front Sensor)	CC 8
57 (RH Rear Sensor)	CC 15
58 (LH Rear Sensor)	CC 22
61 (FLS Circuits)	EE 1
62 (Travel Switch)	EE 1
63 (Pump Motor Speed Sensor)	EE 7
64 (Pump Motor Pressure)	EE 29
67 (Pump Motor Relay)	E 1
71 (LH Front Sensor)	CC 1
72 (RH Front Sensor)	CC 8
73 (RH Rear Sensor)	CC 15
74 (LH Rear Sensor)	CC 22
75 (LH Front Sensor)	CC 1
76 (RH Front Sensor)	CC 8
77 (RH Rear Sensor)	CC 15
78 (LH Rear Sensor)	CC 22

FM4029300240020X

Fig. 8   On-board self-test service code index (Part 2 of 2). 1993 Sable & Taurus

DTC	Caused By	Pinpoint Test Step
11	Generated by a disturbed or damaged redundancy channel. Replace control module if code repeats.	AA 1
17	Generated by reference voltage failure caused by high / low battery voltage, main power relay, main fuse, wire harness, faulty electronic controller.	BB 1
22	Generated by open or short circuit LH front inlet valve, wire harness.	BB 2
23	Generated by open or short circuit LH front outlet valve, wire harness or faulty electronic controller.	BB 5
24	Generated by open or short circuit RH front inlet valve, wire harness or faulty electronic controller.	BB 6
25	Generated by open or short circuit RH front outlet valve, wire harness or faulty electronic controller.	BB 11
26	Generated by open or short circuit RH rear inlet valve, wire harness or faulty electronic controller.	BB 14
27	Generated by open or short circuit RH rear outlet valve, wire harness or faulty electronic controller.	BB 17
28	Generated by open or short circuit LH rear inlet valve, wire harness or faulty electronic controller.	BB 20
29	Generated by open or short circuit LH rear outlet valve, wire harness or faulty electronic controller.	BB 23
31	Generated by open or short circuit LH front sensor, wire harness or faulty electronic controller.	CC 1
32	Generated by open or short circuit RH front sensor, wire harness or faulty electronic controller.	CC 8
33	Generated by open or short circuit RH rear sensor, wire harness or faulty electronic controller.	CC 15
34	Generated by open or short circuit LH rear sensor, wire harness or faulty electronic controller.	CC 22
35	Generated by open or short circuit LH front sensor, wire harness, damaged teeth on indicator ring, sensor air gap too small / large, faulty electronic controller at speeds greater than 40 km / h (25 mph).	CC 1
36	Generated by open or short circuit RH front sensor, wire harness, damaged teeth on indicator ring, sensor air gap too small / large, or faulty electronic controller at speeds greater than 40 km / h (25 mph).	CC 8
37	Generated by open or short circuit RH rear sensor, wire harness, damaged teeth on indicator ring, sensor air gap too small / large, faulty electronic controller at speeds greater than 40 km / h (25 mph).	CC 15
38	Generated by open or short circuit LH rear sensor, wire harness, damaged teeth on indicator ring, sensor air gap too small / large or faulty electronic controller.	CC 22
41	Generated by missing sensor signal LH front sensor (missing indicator ring).	CC 1
42	Generated by missing sensor signal RH front sensor (missing indicator ring).	CC 8
43	Generated by missing sensor signal RH rear sensor (missing indicator ring).	CC 15
44	Generated by missing sensor signal LH rear sensor (missing indicator ring).	CC 22
55	Generated by missing sensor signal LH front sensor (long term failure).	CC 1
56	Generated by missing sensor signal RH front sensor (long term failure).	CC 8
57	Generated by missing sensor signal RH rear sensor (long term failure).	CC 15
58	Generated by missing sensor signal LH rear sensor (long term failure).	CC 22
61	Generated by short circuit to ground (FLS #2).	DD 1
62	Generated by short circuit to ground (pedal travel switch).	DD 1
63	Generated by no pump motor speed sensor signal during initial check at 31 km/h (19 mph), wire harness or faulty electronic controller.	DD 5
64	Generated by pump unable to build pressure.	DD 27
75	Generated by intermittent missing sensor signal LH front sensor at speeds less than 40 km / h (25 mph).	CC 1

Fig. 9   On-board self-test service code index (Part 1 of 2). 1994 Continental

DTC	Caused By	Pinpoint Test Step
76	Generated by intermittent missing sensor signal RH front sensor at speeds less than 40 km / h (25 mph).	CC 8
77	Generated by intermittent missing sensor signal RH rear sensor at speeds less than 40 km / h (25 mph).	CC 15
78	Generated by intermittent missing sensor signal LH rear sensor at speeds less than 40 km / h (25 mph).	CC 22

Fig. 9   On-board self-test service code index (Part 2 of 2). 1994 Continental

DTC	SOURCE	ACTION
11	Disturbed or defective redundancy channel. Replace control module if code repeats.	Go to Pinpoint Test step AA 1.
17	Reference voltage failure, caused by high / low battery voltage, main power relay, main fuse, wire harness, or damaged anti-lock brake control module.	Go to Pinpoint Test step BB 1.
18	Open or short circuit—isolation valve # 1, wire harness or damaged anti-lock brake control module.	Go to Pinpoint Test step BB 26.
19	Open or short circuit—isolation valve # 2, wire harness or damaged anti-lock brake control module.	Go to Pinpoint Test step BB 29.
22	Open or short circuit—LH front inlet valve, wire harness or damaged anti-lock brake control module.	Go to Pinpoint Test step BB 2.
23	Open or short circuit—LH front outlet valve, wire harness or damaged anti-lock brake control module.	Go to Pinpoint Test step BB 5.

FM4029400432010X

Fig. 10   On-board self-test service code index (Part 1 of 4). 1994 Crown Victoria, Grand Marquis & Town Car

DTC	SOURCE	ACTION
24	Open or short circuit—RH front inlet valve, wire harness or damaged anti-lock brake control module.	Go to Pinpoint Test step BB8.
25	Open or short circuit—RH front outlet valve, wire harness or damaged anti-lock brake control module.	Go to Pinpoint Test step BB11.
26	Open or short circuit—RH rear inlet valve, wire harness or damaged anti-lock brake control module.	Go to Pinpoint Test step BB14
27	Open or short circuit—RH rear outlet valve, wire harness or damaged anti-lock brake control module.	Go to Pinpoint Test step BB17.
28	Open or short circuit—LH rear inlet valve, wire harness or damaged anti-lock brake control module.	Go to Pinpoint Test step BB20.
29	Open or short circuit—LH rear outlet valve, wire harness or damaged anti-lock brake control module.	Go to Pinpoint Test BB23.
31	Open or short circuit—LH front brake anti-lock sensor, wire harness or damaged anti-lock brake control module.	Go to Pinpoint Test step CC1.
32	Open or short circuit—RH front brake anti-lock sensor, wire harness or damaged anti-lock brake control module.	Go to Pinpoint Test step CC8.
33	Open or short circuit—RH rear brake anti-lock sensor, wire harness or damaged anti-lock brake control module.	Go to Pinpoint Test step CC15.
34	Open or short circuit—LH rear brake anti-lock sensor, wire harness or damaged anti-lock brake control module.	Go to Pinpoint Test step CC22.

FM4029400432020X

Fig. 10 On-board self-test service code index (Part 2 of 4). 1994 Crown Victoria, Grand Marquis & Town Car

DTC	SOURCE	ACTION
35	Open or short circuit LH front brake anti-lock sensor, wire harness, damaged teeth on front brake anti-lock sensor indicator, sensor air gap too small/large, anti-lock brake control module fails at speeds greater than 40 km/h (25 mph).	Go to Pinpoint Test step CC1.
36	Open or short circuit RH front brake anti-lock sensor, wire harness, damaged teeth on front brake anti-lock sensor indicator, sensor air gap too small/large, anti-lock brake control module fails at speeds greater than 40 km/h (25 mph).	Go to Pinpoint Test step CC8.
37	Open or short circuit RH rear brake anti-lock sensor, wire harness, damaged teeth on rear brake anti-lock sensor indicator, sensor air gap too small/large, anti-lock brake control module fails at speeds greater than 40 km/h (25 mph).	Go to Pinpoint Test step CC15.
38	Open or short circuit LH front brake anti-lock sensor, wire harness, damaged teeth on front brake anti-lock sensor indicator, sensor air gap too small/large, anti-lock brake control module fails at speeds greater than 40 km/h (25 mph).	Go to Pinpoint Test step CC22.
41	Missing sensor signal LH front brake anti-lock sensor (missing front brake anti-lock sensor indicator).	Go to Pinpoint Test step CC1.
42	Missing sensor signal RH front brake anti-lock sensor (missing front brake anti-lock sensor indicator).	Go to Pinpoint Test step CC8.
43	Missing sensor signal RH rear brake anti-lock sensor (missing rear brake anti-lock sensor indicator).	Go to Pinpoint Test Step CC15.
44	Missing sensor signal LH rear brake anti-lock sensor (missing rear brake anti-lock sensor indicator).	Go to Pinpoint Test step CC22.

FM4029400432030X

Fig. 10 On-board self-test service code index (Part 3 of 4). 1994 Crown Victoria, Grand Marquis & Town Car

DTC	SOURCE	ACTION
55	Missing sensor signal LH front brake anti-lock sensor (long term failure).	Go to Pinpoint Test step CC1.
56	Missing sensor signal RH front brake anti-lock sensor (long term failure).	Go to Pinpoint Test step CC8.
57	Missing sensor signal RH rear brake anti-lock sensor (long term failure).	Go to Pinpoint Test step CC15.
58	Missing sensor signal RH rear brake anti-lock sensor (long term failure).	Go to Pinpoint Test step CC22.
61	Short circuit to ground—FLS #2 or wire harness.	Go to Pinpoint Test step DD1.
62	Short circuit to ground—anti-lock brake pedal sensor switch or wire harness.	Go to Pinpoint Test step DD1.
63	No pump motor speed sensor signal during initial check at 31 km/h (19 mph), wire harness or damaged anti-lock brake control module.	Go to Pinpoint Test step DD7.
64	Pump unable to build pressure during an ABS stop.	Go to Pinpoint Test step DD28.
67	Pump motor relay.	Go to Pinpoint Test step E1.
75	Intermittent missing LH front sensor signal at speeds below 40 km/h (25 mph).	Go to Pinpoint Test step CC1.
76	Intermittent missing RH front sensor signal at speeds below 40 km/h (25 mph).	Go to Pinpoint Test step CC8.
77	Intermittent missing RH rear sensor signal at speeds below 40 km/h (25 mph).	Go to Pinpoint Test step CC15.
78	Intermittent missing LH rear sensor signal at speeds below 40 km/h (25 mph).	Go to Pinpoint Test step CC22.

FM4029400432040X

Fig. 10 On-board self-test service code index (Part 4 of 4). 1994 Crown Victoria, Grand Marquis & Town Car

1. If first code received is in the 20's and no other code is received, service indicated fault. No other codes can be output if a 20's code exists. After servicing indicated 20's code, repeat procedure for retrieving diagnostic trouble codes.
2. If there are more codes stored in computer's memory, no codes will erase until all codes have been output by Super Star Tester II, all faults have been serviced and vehicle is driven about 25 mph. This means if a 20's code originally existed and was serviced, it can be ignored when running Self-Test for second time.
3. If Code 61 is received with any other code, ignore code 61 and service other indicated faults. If, after correcting all other indicated codes, Check Anti-Lock Brake lamp is still on, service indicated Code 61 fault.
4. If no code, or only a Code 10 is received, use Anti-Lock Quick Tests Checks since some faults are not recognized and retained in computer memory.

Memory Erasing

The original error codes in the computer from the assembly plant will erase automatically if everything is in working order and vehicle is driven about (25 mph). All error codes must be output, all fault corrected (anti-lock lamp off), and vehicle driven (25 mph) before memory will clear.

QUICK CHECKS

To properly conduct Quick Checks, an EEC-IV breakout box tool No. T83L-50-EEC-IV, anti-lock harness adapter tool No. T90P-50-ALA and digital volt/ohmmeter tool No. 007-00001, or equivalents, must be used. This group of tests will lead to specific diagnostic Pinpoint Tests that will, in most cases, identify the fault/malfunction. If fault/malfunction is not determined by the Quick Check procedure, use the following Diagnostic Lamp Symptom Chart to identify the proper diagnostic procedure to use.

Refer to Quick Check, **Figs. 12 through 16**, for items to be tested, ignition switch mode position, measurement taken between terminal pin numbers, tester scale/range, volt/ohm specifications and the specific pinpoint test to correct the malfunction.

DIAGNOSTIC LAMP SYMPTOM CHART

If Quick Checks do not isolate the symptom, it will be necessary to check operation of the brake and anti-lock warning lamps. Observe lamps and compare their On/Off operation to conditions listed in **Figs. 17 and 18**. Once the actual warning lamp pattern has been matched to one of the conditions listed in the chart, perform the specific Test diagnostic procedure.

PINPOINT TESTS

To properly conduct the Test diagnostic procedures, anti-lock harness adapter tool No. T90P-50-ALA, EEC-IV breakout box tool No. T83L-50-EEC-IV, digital volt/ohmmeter tool No. 007-00001 and Super Star Tester II tool No. 007-00028, or equivalents, must be used.

Continued on page 27-190

CONDITION	POSSIBLE SOURCE	ACTION
• DTC 11	• Disturbed or defective redundancy channel.	• Replace anti-lock brake control module if DTC repeats. Go to Pinpoint Test Step AA1.
• DTC 17	• Reference voltage failure, caused by high/low battery voltage, main power relay, main fuse, wire harness or damaged anti-lock brake control module.	• Go to Pinpoint Test Step BB1.
• DTC 22	• Open or short circuit—LH front inlet valve, wire harness or damaged anti-lock brake control module.	• Go to Pinpoint Test Step BB2.
• DTC 23	• Open or short circuit—LH front outlet valve, wire harness or damaged anti-lock brake control module.	• Go to Pinpoint Test Step BB5.
• DTC 24	• Open or short circuit—RH front inlet valve, wire harness or damaged anti-lock brake control module.	• Go to Pinpoint Test Step BB8.
• DTC 25	• Open or short circuit—RH front outlet valve, wire harness or damaged anti-lock brake control module.	• Go to Pinpoint Test Step BB11.
• DTC 26	• Open or short circuit—RH rear inlet valve, wire harness or damaged anti-lock brake control module.	• Go to Pinpoint Test Step BB14.
• DTC 27	• Open or short circuit—RH rear outlet valve, wire harness or damaged anti-lock brake control module.	• Go to Pinpoint Test Step BB17.
• DTC 28	• Open or short circuit—LH rear inlet valve, wire harness or damaged anti-lock brake control module.	• Go to Pinpoint Test Step BB20.

Fig. 11 On-board self-test service code index (Part 1 of 3). 1994 Sable & Taurus

CONDITION	POSSIBLE SOURCE	ACTION
• DTC 29	• Open or short circuit—LH rear outlet valve, wire harness or damaged anti-lock brake control module.	• Go to Pinpoint Test Step BB23.
• DTC 31	• Open or short circuit—LH front sensor, wire harness or damaged anti-lock brake control module.	• Go to Pinpoint Test Step CC1.
• DTC 32	• Open or short circuit—RH front sensor, wire harness or damaged anti-lock brake control module.	• Go to Pinpoint Test Step CC8.
• DTC 33	• Open or short circuit—RH rear sensor, wire harness or damaged anti-lock brake control module.	• Go to Pinpoint Test Step CC15.
• DTC 34	• Open or short circuit—LH rear sensor, wire harness or damaged anti-lock brake control module.	• Go to Pinpoint Test Step CC22.
• DTC 35	• Open or short circuit—LH front sensor, wire harness, damaged teeth on front brake anti-lock sensor indicator, sensor air gap too small/large, anti-lock brake control module fails at speed greater than 40 km/h (25 mph).	• Go to Pinpoint Test Step CC1.
• DTC 36	• Open or short circuit—RH front sensor, wire harness, damaged teeth on front brake anti-lock sensor indicator, sensor air gap too small/large, anti-lock brake control module fails at speeds greater than 40 km/h (25 mph).	• Go to Pinpoint Test Step CC8.
• DTC 37	• Open or short circuit—RH rear sensor, wire harness, damaged teeth on rear brake anti-lock sensor indicator, sensor air gap too small/large, anti-lock brake control module fails at speeds greater than 40 km/h (25 mph).	• Go to Pinpoint Test Step CC15.
• DTC 38	• Open or short circuit—LH rear sensor, wire harness, damaged teeth on rear brake anti-lock sensor indicator, sensor air gap too small/large, anti-lock brake control module fails at speeds greater than 40 km/h (25 mph).	• Go to Pinpoint Test Step CC22.
• DTC 41	• Missing sensor signal—LH front sensor (missing front brake anti-lock sensor indicator).	• Go to Pinpoint Test Step CC1.
• DTC 42	• Missing sensor signal—RH front sensor (missing front brake anti-lock sensor indicator).	• Go to Pinpoint Test Step CC8.
• DTC 43	• Missing sensor signal—RH rear sensor (missing rear brake anti-lock sensor indicator).	• Go to Pinpoint Test Step CC15.
• DTC 44	• Missing sensor signal—LH rear sensor (missing rear brake anti-lock sensor indicator).	• Go to Pinpoint Test Step CC22.
• DTC 55	• Missing sensor signal—LH front sensor (long term failure).	• Go to Pinpoint Test Step CC1.
• DTC 56	• Missing sensor signal—RH front sensor (long term failure).	• Go to Pinpoint Test Step CC8.
• DTC 57	• Missing sensor signal—RH rear sensor (long term failure).	• Go to Pinpoint Test Step CC15.

Fig. 11 On-board self-test service code index (Part 2 of 3). 1994 Sable & Taurus

CONDITION	POSSIBLE SOURCE	ACTION
• DTC 58	• Missing sensor signal—LH rear sensor (long term failure).	• Go to Pinpoint Test Step CC22.
• DTC 61	• Short circuit to ground—FLS #2 or wire harness.	• Go to Pinpoint Test Step DD1.
• DTC 62	• Short circuit to ground—anti-lock brake pedal sensor switch or wire harness.	• Go to Pinpoint Test Step DD1.
• DTC 63	• No pump motor speed signal during initial check at 31 km/h (19 mph), wire harness or damaged anti-lock brake control module.	• Go to Pinpoint Test Step DD7.
• DTC 64	• Pump unable to build pressure during an ABS stop.	• Go to Pinpoint Test Step DD29.
• DTC 67	• Pump motor running not triggered by anti-lock brake control module.	• Go to Pinpoint Test Step E1.
• DTC 75	• Intermittent missing LH front sensor signal at speeds below 40 km/h (25 mph).	• Go to Pinpoint Test Step CC1.
• DTC 76	• Intermittent missing RH front sensor signal at speeds below 40 km/h (25 mph).	• Go to Pinpoint Test Step CC8.
• DTC 77	• Intermittent missing RH rear sensor signal at speeds below 40 km/h (25 mph).	• Go to Pinpoint Test Step CC15.
• DTC 78	• Intermittent missing LH rear sensor signal at speeds below 40 km/h (25 mph).	• Go to Pinpoint Test Step CC22.

Fig. 11 On-board self-test service code index (Part 3 of 3). 1994 Sable & Taurus

Refer to wiring diagrams, Figs. 19 through 33, when performing Pinpoint Tests to locate wire circuits indicated in test procedure. Each test is completely independent of the other test and within each test are sequences that can identify a problem without requiring completion of entire diagnostic test procedure.

For 1992 Test diagnostic procedures, refer to **Figs. 34 through 157.** For 1993-94 Test diagnostic procedures, refer to **Figs. 158 through 188.**

NOTE: Before performing tests below, the Pre-Test Checks must be performed as outlined.
NOTE: If fault is intermittent the tests listed below will NOT find the fault. Use controller service code or call Hot-Line if this situation occurs.

Item to be Tested	Ignition Mode	Measure Between Pin Numbers	Tester Scale/Range	Specification	Test Step
Battery Check	ON	60 + 53	VOLTS	10 minimum	A1
Main Relay Coil	OFF	53 + 34	OHMS	45 to 90 ohms	A3a
Jumper pins 60 + 34					
Power from Main Relay	ON	19 + 33	VOLTS	10 minimum	A2
Remove jumper from pins 60 + 34					
Main Relay Circuit	OFF	60 + 33	CONTINUITY	continuity	A4
Sensor Resistance (RR)	OFF	27 + 45	K OHMS	0.8-1.4 Kohms	C3
Sensor Resistance (LF)	OFF	30 + 48	K OHMS	0.8-1.4 Kohms	C1
Sensor Resistance (LR)	OFF	28 + 46	K OHMS	0.8-1.4 Kohms	C1
Sensor Resistance (RF)	OFF	29 + 47	K OHMS	0.8-1.4 Kohms	C2
Valve Resistance (IFL)	OFF	3 + 20	OHMS	5-8 ohms	BB2
Valve Resistance (IFR)	OFF	3 + 38	OHMS	5-8 ohms	BB4
Valve Resistance (IRL)	OFF	3 + 54	OHMS	5-8 ohms	BB8
Valve Resistance (IRR)	OFF	3 + 55	OHMS	5-8 ohms	BB6
Valve Resistance (OFL)	OFF	3 + 2	OHMS	3-6 ohms	BB3
Valve Resistance (OFR)	OFF	3 + 21	OHMS	3-6 ohms	BB5
Valve Resistance (ORR)	OFF	3 + 18	OHMS	3-6 ohms	BB7
Valve Resistance (ORL)	OFF	3 + 36	OHMS	3-6 ohms	BB9
Pump Motor Speed Sensor Resistance	OFF	31 + 94	OHMS	5-100 ohms	EE5
Reservoir Warning (FLS #2)	OFF	8 + 26	OHMS	LESS THAN 5 OHMS	A6
Pedal Travel Switch: Pedal NOT Applied	OFF	5 + 26	CONTINUITY	continuity	D1
With Minimum 3 Inch Apply	OFF	5 + 26	CONTINUITY	no continuity	D2
Sensor Cable Continuity Wiring to Ground (RR)	OFF	27 + 60	CONTINUITY	no continuity	B2
(LF)	OFF	30 + 60	CONTINUITY	no continuity	B4
(LR)	OFF	28 + 60	CONTINUITY	no continuity	B1
(RF)	OFF	29 + 60	CONTINUITY	no continuity	B3
Sensor Voltage: Rotate wheels (RR)	OFF	27 + 45	AC MVOLTS	100-1400 mvolts	C11
@ 1 revolution (LF)	OFF	30 + 48	AC MVOLTS	100-1400 mvolts	C9
per second. (LR)	OFF	28 + 46	AC MVOLTS	100-1400 mvolts	C12
(RF)	OFF	29 + 47	AC MVOLTS	100-1400 mvolts	C10

① If Quick Test does not isolate symptom, refer to Diagnostic Indicator Symptom Chart.

Fig. 12 Quick Check. 1992–93 Continental, Sable & Taurus

NOTE: Before performing tests below, the Pre-Test Checks must be performed as outlined.

Item to be Tested	Ignition Mode	Measure Between Pin Numbers	Tester Scale/Range	Specification	Test Step
Battery Check	ON	60 + 53	VOLTS	10 minimum	A1
Main Relay Coil	OFF	53 + 34	OHMS	45 to 90 ohms	A3a
Jumper pins 60 + 34					
Power from Main Relay	ON	19 + 33	VOLTS	10 minimum	A2
Remove jumper from pins 60 + 34					
Main Relay Circuit	OFF	60 + 33	CONTINUITY	continuity	A4
Sensor Resistance (RR)	OFF	27 + 45	K OHMS	0.8-1.4 Kohms	C3
Sensor Resistance (LF)	OFF	30 + 48	K OHMS	0.8-1.4 Kohms	C1
Sensor Resistance (LR)	OFF	28 + 46	K OHMS	0.8-1.4 Kohms	C4
Sensor Resistance (RF)	OFF	29 + 47	K OHMS	0.8-1.4 Kohms	C2
Valve Resistance (IFL)	OFF	3 + 20	OHMS	5-8 ohms	BB2
Valve Resistance (IFR)	OFF	3 + 38	OHMS	5-8 ohms	BB4
Valve Resistance (IRL)	OFF	3 + 54	OHMS	5-8 ohms	BB8
Valve Resistance (IRR)	OFF	3 + 55	OHMS	5-8 ohms	BB6
Valve Resistance (OFL)	OFF	3 + 2	OHMS	3-6 ohms	BB3
Valve Resistance (OFR)	OFF	3 + 21	OHMS	3-6 ohms	BB5
Valve Resistance (ORR)	OFF	3 + 18	OHMS	3-6 ohms	BB7
Valve Resistance (ORL)	OFF	3 + 36	OHMS	3-6 ohms	BB9
Reservoir Warning (FLS #2)	OFF	8 + 26	OHMS	LESS THAN 5 OHMS	A6
Pedal Travel Switch:					
Pedal NOT Applied:	OFF	5 + 26	CONTINUITY	continuity	D1
With Minimum 3 Inch Apply	OFF	5 + 26	CONTINUITY	no continuity	D2
Sensor Cable Continuity Wiring to Ground (RR)	OFF	27 + 60	CONTINUITY	no continuity	B2
(LF)	OFF	30 + 60	CONTINUITY	no continuity	B4
(LR)	OFF	28 + 60	CONTINUITY	no continuity	B1
(RF)	OFF	29 + 60	CONTINUITY	no continuity	B3
Sensor Voltage: Rotate wheels (RR)	OFF	27 + 45	AC MVOLTS	100-1400 mvolts	C11
@ 1 revolution (LF)	OFF	30 + 48	AC MVOLTS	100-1400 mvolts	C9
per second (LR)	OFF	28 + 46	AC MVOLTS	100-1400 mvolts	C12
(RF)	OFF	29 + 47	AC MVOLTS	100-1400 mvolts	C10
Pump Motor Speed Sensor Resistance	OFF	31 + 49	OHMS	5-100 ohms	EE7
Additional Tests for Traction — Assist Only					
Valve Resistance (SV1)	OFF	3 + 37	OHMS	5-8 ohms	BB11
Valve Resistance (SV2)	OFF	3 + 40	OHMS	5-8 ohms	BB12
Pressure Switch (Brake Pedal Not Applied)	OFF	13 + 26	CONTINUITY	Continuity	K3

FM4029100315000X

Fig. 13 Quick Check. 1992–93 Crown Victoria, Grand Marquis & Town Car

Item to be Tested	Ignition Mode	Measure Between Pin Numbers	Tester Scale/Range	Specification	Test Step
Battery Check	ON	60 + 53	VOLTS	10 minimum	A1
Main Relay Coil	OFF	53 + 34	OHMS	45 to 90 ohms	A6
Jumper pins 60 and 34					
Power from Main Relay	ON	19 + 33	VOLTS	10 minimum	A5
Remove jumper from pins 60 and 34					
Main Relay Circuit	OFF	60 + 33	CONTINUITY	continuity	A12
Sensor Resistance (RR)	OFF	27 + 45	K OHMS	0.8-1.4K ohms	C5
Sensor Resistance (LF)	OFF	30 + 48	K OHMS	0.8-1.4K ohms	C1
Sensor Resistance (LR)	OFF	28 + 46	K OHMS	0.8-1.4K ohms	C7
Sensor Resistance (RF)	OFF	29 + 47	K OHMS	0.8-1.4K ohms	C3
Valve Resistance (FL)	OFF	3 + 20	OHMS	5-8 ohms	BB2
Valve Resistance (IFR)	OFF	3 + 38	OHMS	5-8 ohms	BB8
Valve Resistance (IRL)	OFF	3 + 54	OHMS	5-8 ohms	BB20
Valve Resistance (IRR)	OFF	3 + 55	OHMS	5-8 ohms	BB14
Valve Resistance (OFL)	OFF	3 + 2	OHMS	3-6 ohms	BB5
Valve Resistance (OFR)	OFF	3 + 21	OHMS	3-6 ohms	BB11
Valve Resistance (ORR)	OFF	3 + 18	OHMS	3-6 ohms	BB17
Valve Resistance (ORL)	OFF	3 + 36	OHMS	3-6 ohms	BB23
Reservoir Warning (FLS #2)	OFF	8 + 26	OHMS	Less Than 5 Ohms	A14
Anti-Lock Brake Pedal Sensor Switch					
Pedal NOT Applied:	OFF	5 + 26	CONTINUITY	continuity	D1
With Minimum 3 Inch Apply	OFF	5 + 26	CONTINUITY	no continuity	D3
Sensor Cable Continuity Wiring to Ground (RR)	OFF	27 + 60	CONTINUITY	no continuity	B3
(LF)	OFF	30 + 60	CONTINUITY	no continuity	B7
(LR)	OFF	28 + 60	CONTINUITY	no continuity	B1
(RF)	OFF	29 + 60	CONTINUITY	no continuity	B5
Sensor Voltage: Rotate wheels (RR)	OFF	27 + 45	AC MVOLTS	100-1400 mvolts	C19
@ 1 revolution (LF)	OFF	30 + 48	AC MVOLTS	100-1400 mvolts	C17
per second (LR)	OFF	28 + 46	AC MVOLTS	100-1400 mvolts	C20
(RF)	OFF	29 + 47	AC MVOLTS	100-1400 mvolts	C19
Pump Motor Speed Sensor Resistance	OFF	31 + 49	OHMS	5-100 ohms	DD7
Valve Resistance (SV1)②	OFF	3 + 37	OHMS	5-8 ohms	BB26
Valve Resistance (SV2)②	OFF	3 + 40	OHMS	5-8 ohms	BB29

FM4029400435000X

Fig. 15 Quick Check. 1994 Crown Victoria, Grand Marquis & Town Car

Item to be Tested	Ignition Mode	Measure Between Pin Numbers	Tester Scale/Range	Specification	Pinpoint Test Step
Battery Check	ON	60 + 53	VOLTS	10 Minimum	A1
Main Relay Coil	OFF	53 + 34	OHMS	45 to 90 ohms	A6
Jumper Pins 60 and 34					
Power from Main Relay	ON	19 + 33	VOLTS	10 minimum	A5

FM4029400436010X

Fig. 16 Quick Check (Part 1 of 2). 1994 Sable & Taurus

Item to be Tested	Ignition Mode	Measure Between Pin Numbers	Tester Scale/Range	Specification	Test Step
Battery Check	ON	60 + 53	VOLTS	10 Minimum	A1
Main Relay Coil	OFF	53 + 34	OHMS	45 to 90 ohms	A7
Jumper Pins 60 and 34					
Power from Main Relay	ON	19 + 33	VOLTS	10 minimum	A6
Remove Jumper from Pins 60 and 34					
Main Relay Circuit	OFF	60 + 33	CONTINUITY	Continuity	A13
Sensor Resistance (RR)	OFF	27 + 45	K OHMS	0.8-1.4K ohms	C5
Sensor Resistance (LF)	OFF	30 + 48	K OHMS	0.8-1.4K ohms	C1
Sensor Resistance (LR)	OFF	28 + 46	K OHMS	0.8-1.4K ohms	C7

FM4029400434010X

Fig. 14 Quick Check (Part 1 of 2). 1994 Continental

Item to be Tested	Ignition Mode	Measure Between Pin Numbers	Tester Scale/Range	Specification	Test Step
Sensor Resistance (RF)	OFF	29 + 47	K OHMS	0.8-1.4K ohms	C3
Valve Resistance (IFL)	OFF	3 + 20	OHMS	5-8 ohms	BB2
Valve Resistance (IFR)	OFF	3 + 38	OHMS	5-8 ohms	BB8
Valve Resistance (IRL)	OFF	3 + 54	OHMS	5-8 ohms	BB20
Valve Resistance (IRR)	OFF	3 + 55	OHMS	5-8 ohms	BB14
Valve Resistance (OFL)	OFF	3 + 2	OHMS	3-6 ohms	BB5
Valve Resistance (OFR)	OFF	3 + 21	OHMS	3-6 ohms	BB11
Valve Resistance (ORR)	OFF	3 + 18	OHMS	3-6 ohms	BB17
Valve Resistance (ORL)	OFF	3 + 36	OHMS	3-06 ohms	BB23
Pump Motor Speed Sensor Resistance	OFF	31 + 49	OHMS	5-100 ohms	DD5
Reservoir Warning (FLS #2)	OFF	8 + 26	OHMS	Less Than 5 ohms	A15
Pedal Travel Switch					
Pedal NOT Applied	OFF	5 + 26	CONTINUITY	Continuity	D2
With Minimum 3 Inch Apply	OFF	5 + 26	CONTINUITY	No Continuity	D4
Sensor Cable Continuity Wiring to Ground (RR)	OFF	27 + 60	CONTINUITY	No Continuity	B3
(LF)	OFF	30 + 60	CONTINUITY	No Continuity	B7
(LR)	OFF	28 + 60	CONTINUITY	No Continuity	B1
(RF)	OFF	29 + 60	CONTINUITY	No Continuity	B5
Sensor Voltage (Rotate Wheels at 1 Revolution Per Second) (RR)	OFF	27 + 45	AC MVOLTS	100-1400 mvolts	C19
(LF)	OFF	30 + 48	AC MVOLTS	100-1400 mvolts	C17
(LR)	OFF	28 + 46	AC MVOLTS	100-1400 mvolts	C20
(RF)	OFF	29 + 47	AC MVOLTS	100-1400 mvolts	C18

FM4029400434020X

Fig. 14 Quick Check (Part 2 of 2). 1994 Continental

Item to be Tested	Ignition Mode	Measure Between Pin Numbers	Tester Scale/Range	Specification	Pinpoint Test Step
Remove Jumper from Pins 60 and 34					
Main Relay Circuit	OFF	60 + 33	CONTINUITY	Continuity	A9
Sensor Resistance (RR)	OFF	27 + 45	K OHMS	0.8-1.4K ohms	C5
Sensor Resistance (LF)	OFF	30 + 48	K OHMS	0.8-1.4K ohms	C1
Sensor Resistance (LR)	OFF	28 + 46	K OHMS	0.8-1.4K ohms	C7
Sensor Resistance (RF)	OFF	29 + 47	K OHMS	0.8-1.4K ohms	C3
Valve Resistance (IFL)	OFF	3 + 20	OHMS	5-8 ohms	BB2
Valve Resistance (IFR)	OFF	3 + 38	OHMS	5-8 ohms	BB8
Valve Resistance (IRL)	OFF	3 + 54	OHMS	5-8 ohms	BB20
Valve Resistance (IRR)	OFF	3 + 55	OHMS	5-8 ohms	BB14
Valve Resistance (OFL)	OFF	3 + 2	OHMS	3-6 ohms	BB5
Valve Resistance (OFR)	OFF	3 + 21	OHMS	3-6 ohms	BB11
Valve Resistance (ORR)	OFF	3 + 18	OHMS	3-6 ohms	BB17
Valve Resistance (ORL)	OFF	3 + 36	OHMS	3-6 ohms	BB23
Pump Motor Speed Sensor Resistance	OFF	31 + 49	OHMS	5-100 ohms	DD7
Reservoir Warning (FLS #2)	OFF	8 + 26	OHMS	Less than 5 ohms	A14
Anti-Lock Brake Pedal Sensor Switch					
Pedal NOT Applied	OFF	5 + 26	CONTINUITY	Continuity	D2
With Minimum 3 Inch Apply	OFF	5 + 26	CONTINUITY	No Continuity	D4
Sensor Cable Continuity Wiring to Ground RR	OFF	27 + 60	CONTINUITY	No Continuity	B3
LF	OFF	30 + 60	CONTINUITY	No Continuity	B7
LR	OFF	28 + 60	CONTINUITY	No Continuity	B1
RF	OFF	29 + 60	CONTINUITY	No Continuity	B5
Sensor Voltage Rotate Wheels at 1 Revolution Per Second RR	OFF	27 + 45	AC MVOLTS	100-1400 mvolts	C19
LF	OFF	30 + 48	AC MVOLTS	100-1400 mvolts	C17
LR	OFF	28 + 46	AC MVOLTS	100-1400 mvolts	C20
RF	OFF	29 + 47	AC MVOLTS	100-1400 mvolts	C18

FM4029400436020X

Fig. 16 Quick Check (Part 2 of 2). 1994 Sable & Taurus

Fig. 17 Diagnostic warning lamp symptom chart. Continental, Sable & Taurus

Symptom (With Parking Brake Released)	Warning Lamps	Ignition On	Cranking Engine	Engine Running	Vehicle Moving	Braking with/without Anti-Lock	Vehicle Stopped	Engine Idle	Ignition Off	Diagnostic Test To Be Performed
Normal Light Sequence		←	4 Seconds							
Normal Warning Lamps Sequences. (System OK)	Check Anti-lock (Amber)	▨	▨	▨						
	Brake (Red)		■							
Abnormal Warning Lamps Sequences.										
• "Check Anti-Lock Brakes" Warning Lamp On. Normal "Brake" Warning Lamp Sequence.	Check Anti-lock (Amber)	▨	▨	▨	▨	▨	▨	▨		A
	Brake (Red)		■							
• "Check Anti-Lock Brakes" Warning Lamp On After Starting Engine. Normal "Brake" Warning Lamp Sequence.	Check Anti-lock (Amber)	▨		▨	▨	▨	▨	▨		B
	Brake (Red)		■							
• "Check Anti-Lock Brakes" Warning Lamp Comes On Again After Vehicle Starts Moving. Normal "Brake" Warning Lamp Sequence.	Check Anti-lock (Amber)	▨	▨		▨	▨				C
	Brake (Red)		■							
• False Cycling of Anti-Lock System Normal Warning Lamp Sequence.	Check Anti-lock (Amber)	▨	▨							C
	Brake (Red)		■							
• Normal Warning Lamp Sequence. Brake Pedal Rises or Drops Excessively During ABS Cycling.	Check Anti-lock (Amber)	▨	▨							D
	Brake (Red)		■							
• Normal Warning Lamp Sequence. ABS Pump Motor Runs Continuously.	Check Anti-lock (Amber)	▨	▨							E
	Brake (Red)		■							
• Normal "Check Anti-Lock Brakes" Warning Lamp Sequence. "Brake" Warning Lamp On.	Check Anti-lock (Amber)	▨	▨							F
	Brake (Red)		■	■	■	■	■			
• No "Check Anti-Lock Brakes" Warning Lamp During Test Cycle. Normal "Brake" Warning Lamp Sequence.	Check Anti-lock (Amber)									G
	Brake (Red)		■							
• Spongy Brake Pedal. Normal Warning Lamp Sequence.	Check Anti-lock (Amber)	▨	▨							H
	Brake (Red)		■							
• Rear Vehicle Tracking During Anti-Lock Braking. Normal Warning Lamp Sequence.	Check Anti-lock (Amber)	▨	▨							J
	Brake (Red)		■							
• Anti-Lock Light Out for Approximately 4 Seconds Then On All The Time	Check Anti-lock (Amber)	▨		▨	▨	▨	▨	▨		Check Diode
	Brake (Red)		■							

▨ "Check Anti-Lock Brakes" Warning Lamp On.   ■ "Brake" Warning Lamp On.

FM4029100316000X

Fig. 18 Diagnostic warning lamp symptom chart. Crown Victoria, Grand Marquis & Town Car

Symptom (With Parking Brake Released)	Warning Indicators	Ignition On	Cranking Engine	Engine Running	Vehicle Moving	Braking with/without Anti-Lock	Vehicle Stopped	Engine Idle	Ignition Off	Diagnostic Test To Be Performed
Normal Sequence		←	4 Seconds							
Normal Warning Indicator Sequences. (System OK)	Check Anti-lock (Amber)	▨		▨						
	Brake (Red)		■							
Abnormal Warning Indicator Sequences.										
• "Check Anti-Lock Brakes" Warning Indicator On. Normal "Brake" and "Anti-Lock" Warning Indicator Sequence.	Check Anti-lock (Amber)	▨		▨	▨	▨	▨			A
	Brake (Red)		■							
• "Check Anti-Lock Brakes" Warning Indicator On After Starting Engine. Normal "Brake" and "Anti-Lock" Warning Indicator Sequence.	Check Anti-lock (Amber)	▨		▨	▨	▨	▨			B
	Brake (Red)		■							
• "Check Anti-Lock Brakes" Warning Indicator Comes On Again After Vehicle Starts Moving. Normal "Brake" and "Anti-Lock" Warning Lamp Sequence.	Check Anti-lock (Amber)	▨		▨	▨					C
	Brake (Red)		■							
• False Cycling of Anti-Lock System Normal Warning Indicator Sequence.	Check Anti-lock (Amber)	▨		▨						C
	Brake (Red)		■							
• Normal Warning Indicator Sequence. Brake Pedal Rises or Drops Excessively During ABS Cycling.	Check Anti-lock (Amber)	▨		▨						D
	Brake (Red)		■							
• Normal Warning Indicator Sequence. ABS Pump Motor Runs Continuously.	Check Anti-lock (Amber)	▨		▨						E
	Brake (Red)		■							
• Normal "Check Anti-Lock Brakes" Warning Indicator Sequence. "Brake" and "Anti-Lock" Warning Indicator On.	Check Anti-lock (Amber)	▨		▨						F
	Brake (Red)		■	■	■	■	■			
• No "Check Anti-Lock Brakes" Warning Indicator During Test Cycle. Normal "Brake" and "Anti-Lock" Warning Indicator Sequence.	Check Anti-lock (Amber)									G
	Brake (Red)		■							
• Spongy Brake Pedal. Normal Warning Indicator Sequence.	Check Anti-lock (Amber)	▨		▨						H
	Brake (Red)		■							
• Rear Vehicle Tracking During Anti-Lock Braking. Normal Warning Indicator Sequence.	Check Anti-lock (Amber)	▨		▨						J
	Brake (Red)		■							
• Normal Indicator Sequence. Traction Assist Inoperative.	Check Anti-lock (Amber)	▨		▨						K
	Brake (Red)		■							
• Normal Indicator Sequence. Traction Assist False Cycling.	Check Anti-lock (Amber)	▨		▨						L
	Brake (Red)		■							
• Anti-Lock Indicator Out for Approximately 4 Seconds Then On All The Time.	Check Anti-lock (Amber)	▨		▨	▨	▨	▨			Check Diode
	Brake (Red)		■							

▨ "Check Anti-Lock Brakes" Warning Indicator On   ■ "Brake and Anti-Lock" Warning Indicator On.

FM4029100317000X

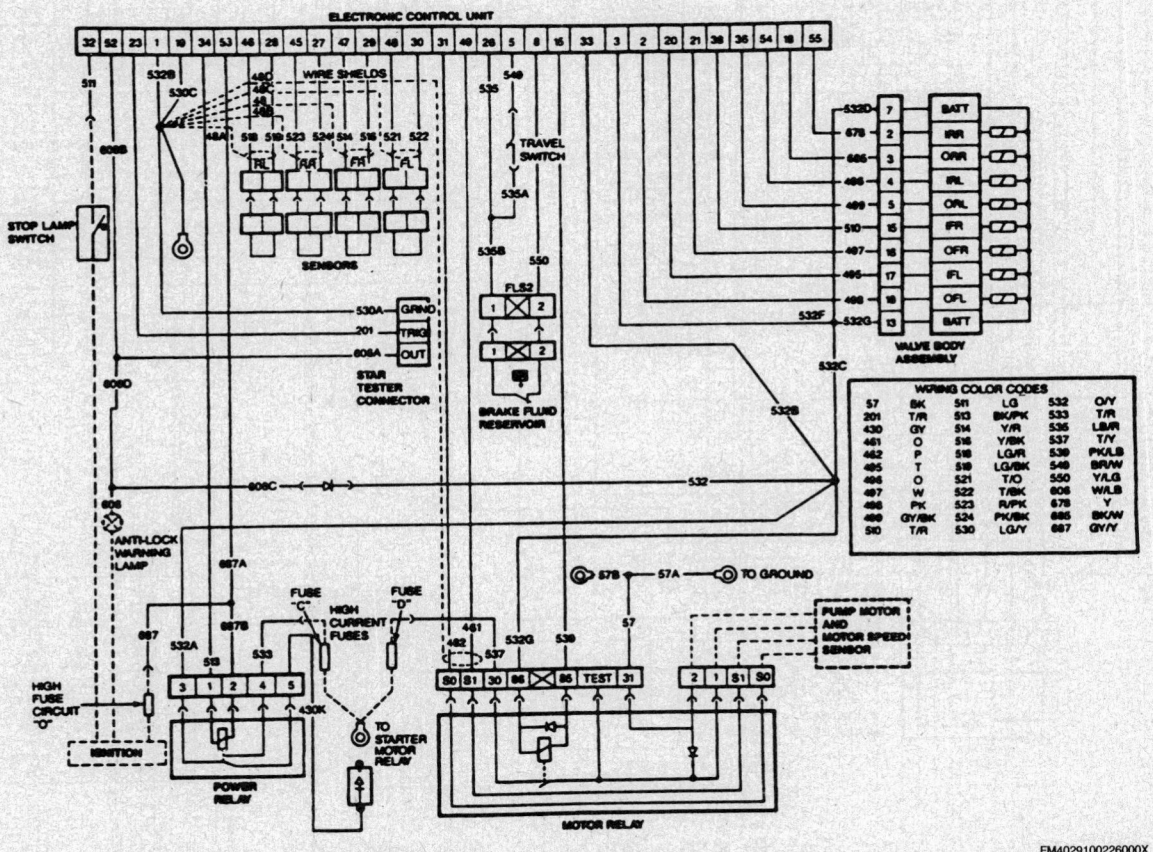

Fig. 19 ABS wiring circuit. 1992 Continental

FM4029100226000X

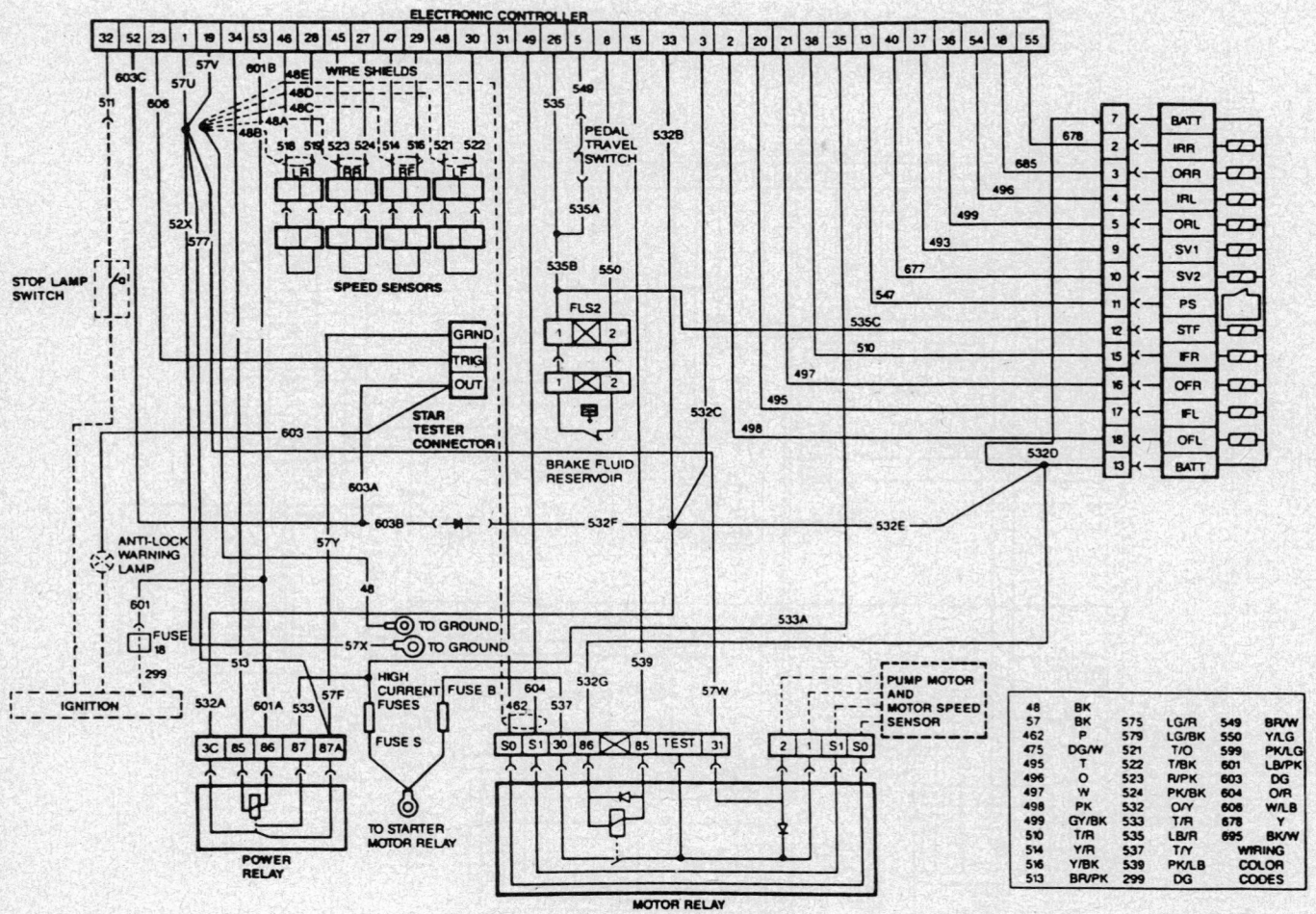

Fig. 20 ABS wiring circuit. 1992 Town Car

FM4029100227000X

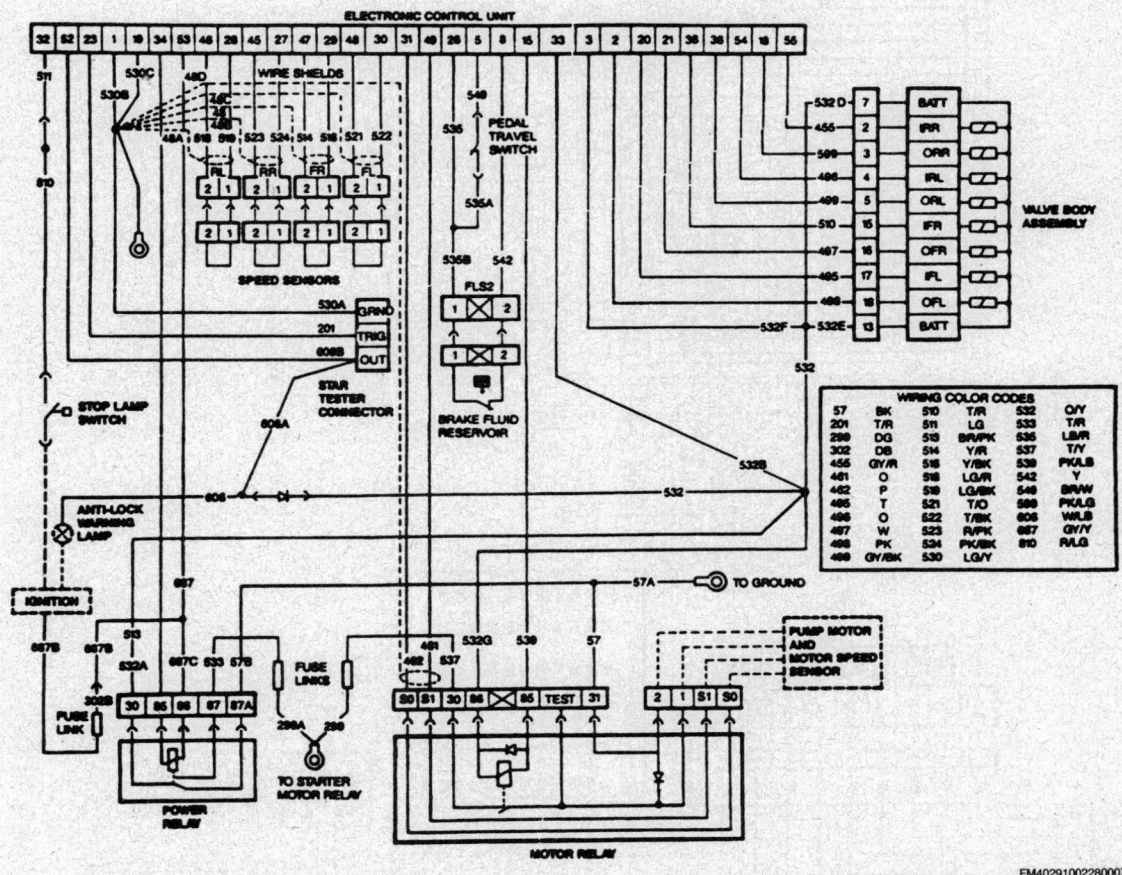

Fig. 21   ABS wiring circuit. 1992 Sable & Taurus except SHO

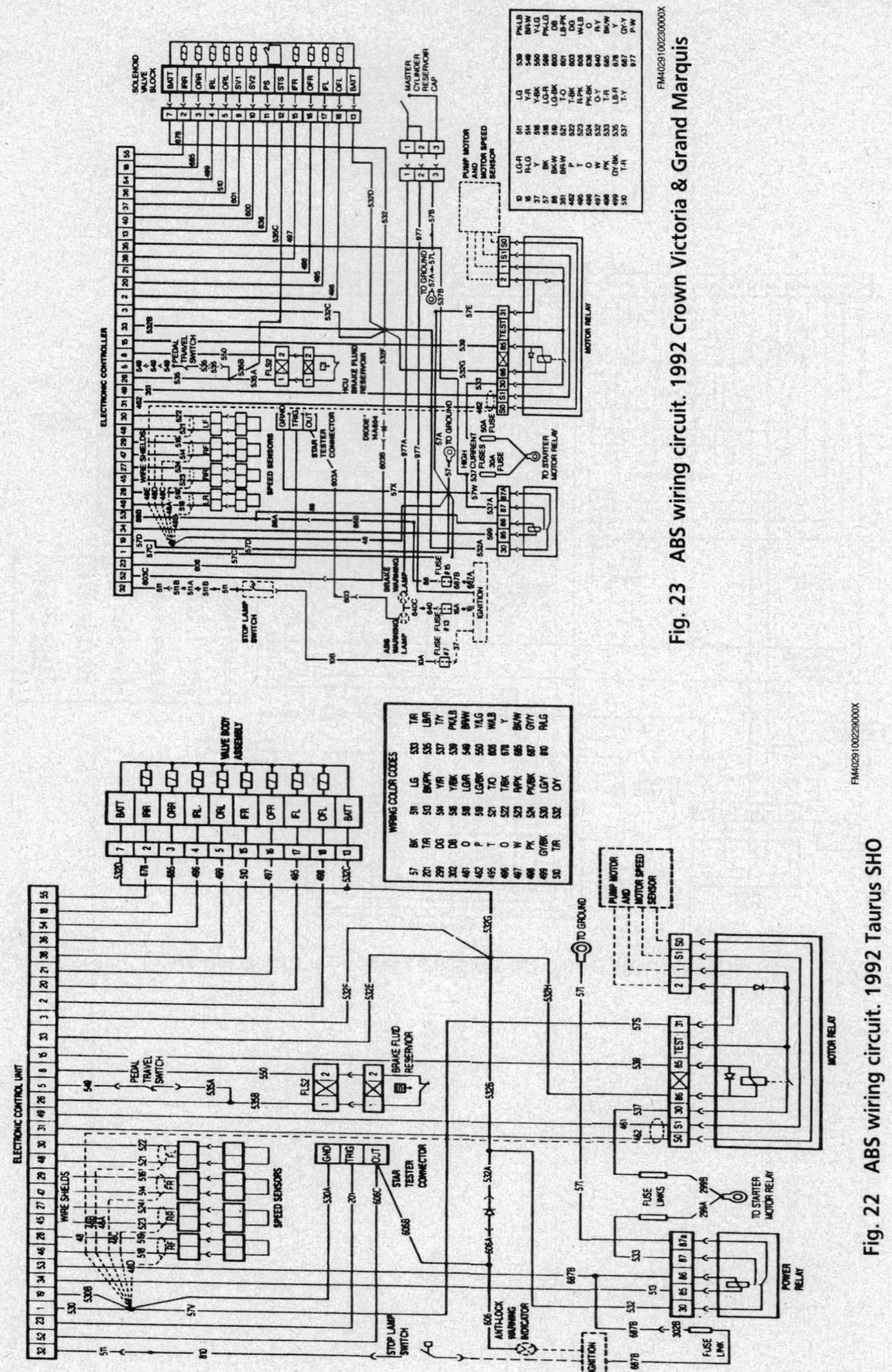

Fig. 23 ABS wiring circuit. 1992 Crown Victoria & Grand Marquis

Fig. 22 ABS wiring circuit. 1992 Taurus SHO

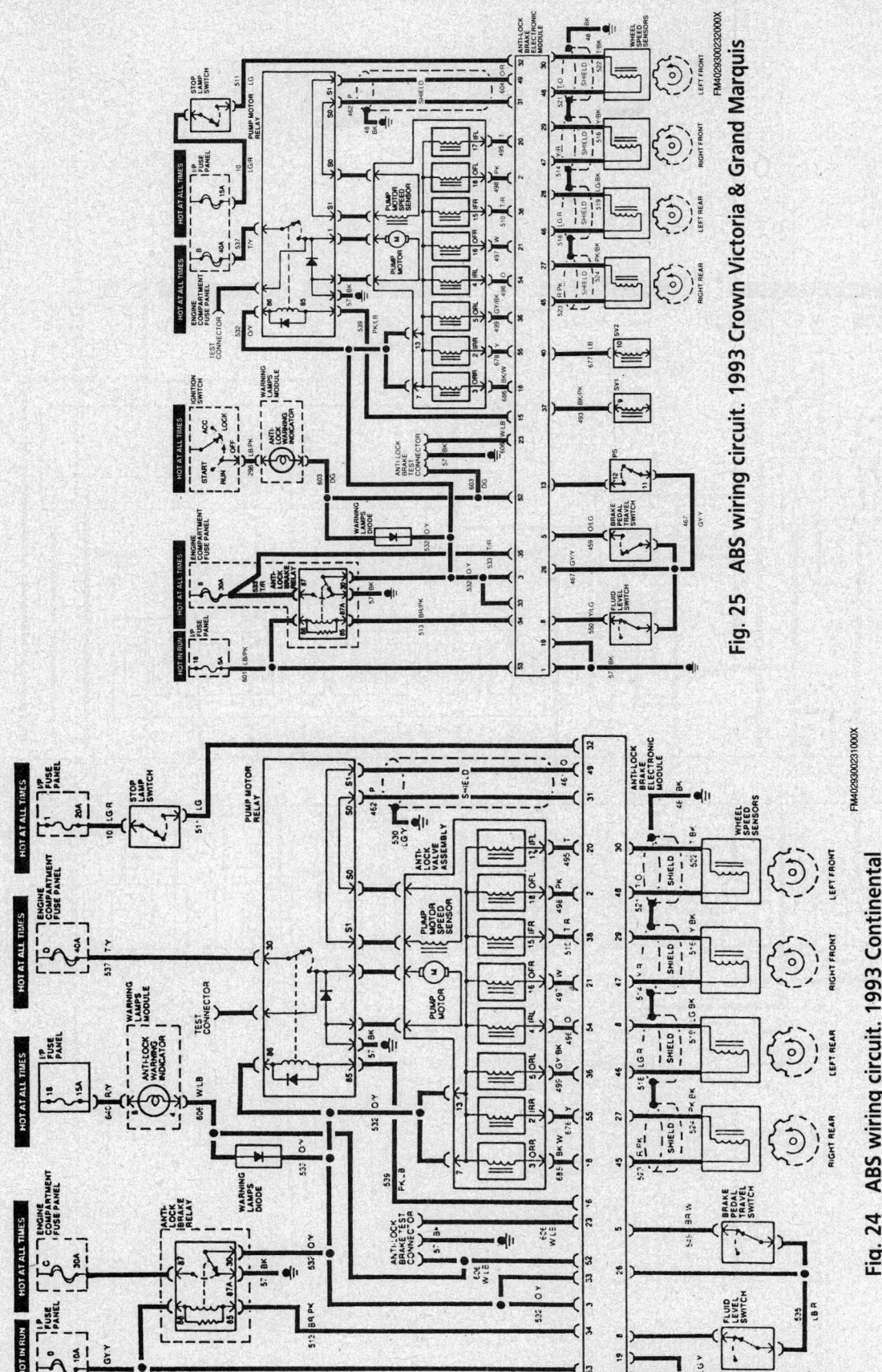

Fig. 25 ABS wiring circuit. 1993 Crown Victoria & Grand Marquis

Fig. 24 ABS wiring circuit. 1993 Continental

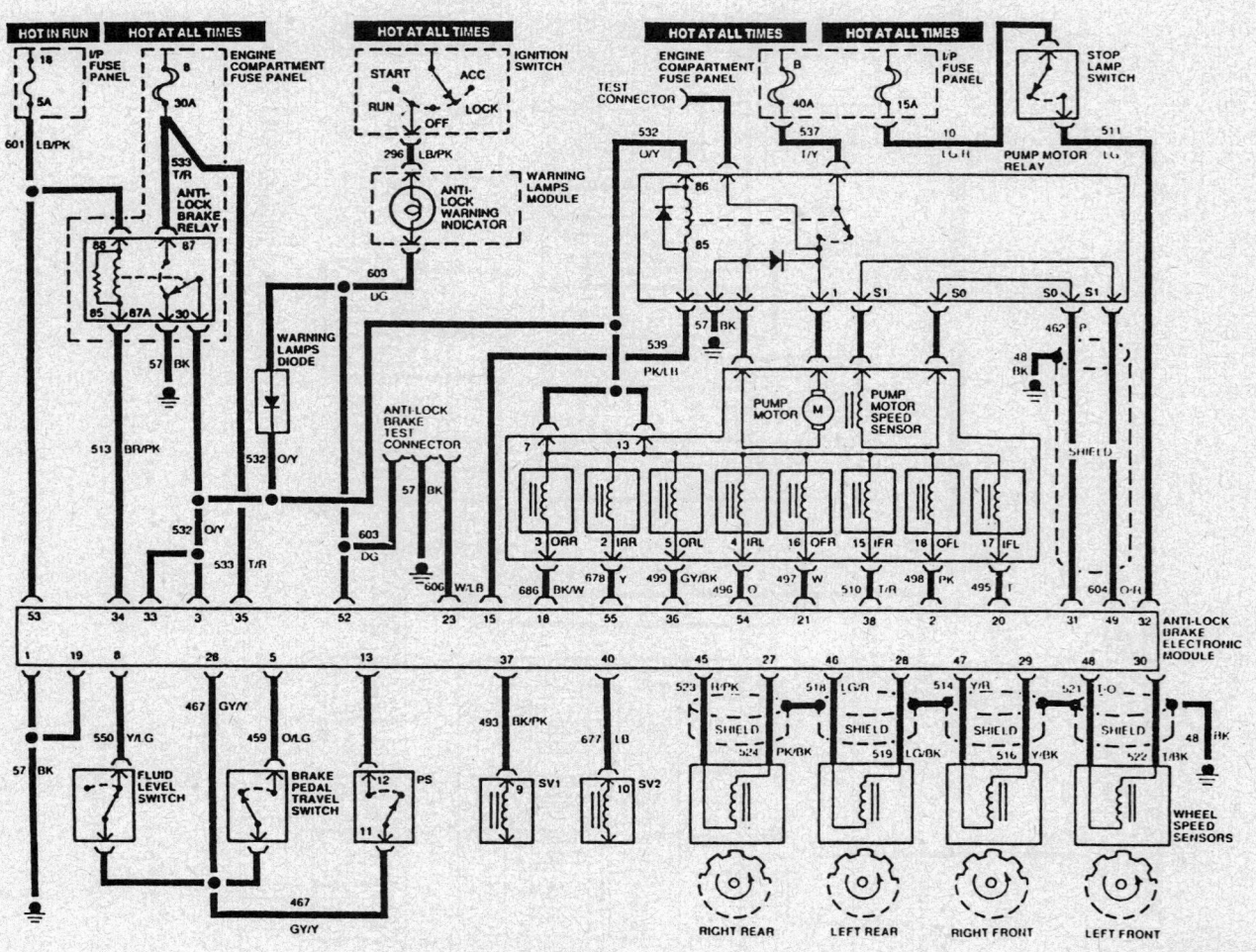

Fig. 26   ABS wiring circuit. 1993 Town Car

FM4029300233000X

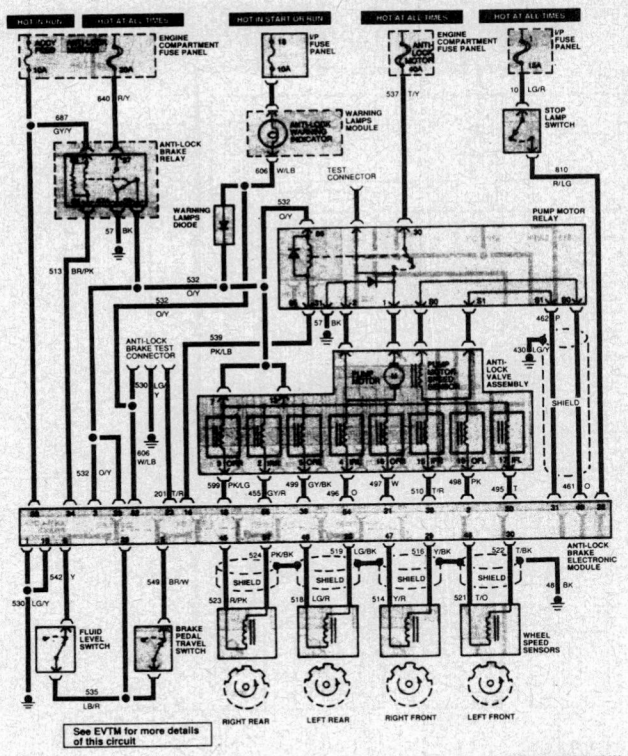

Fig. 27   ABS wiring circuit. 1993 Sable & Taurus except SHO

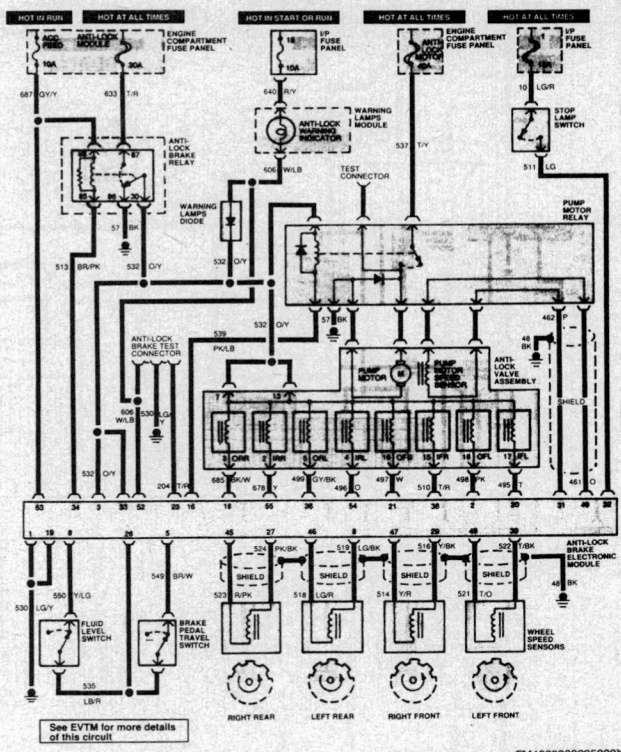

Fig. 28   ABS wiring circuit. 1993 Taurus SHO

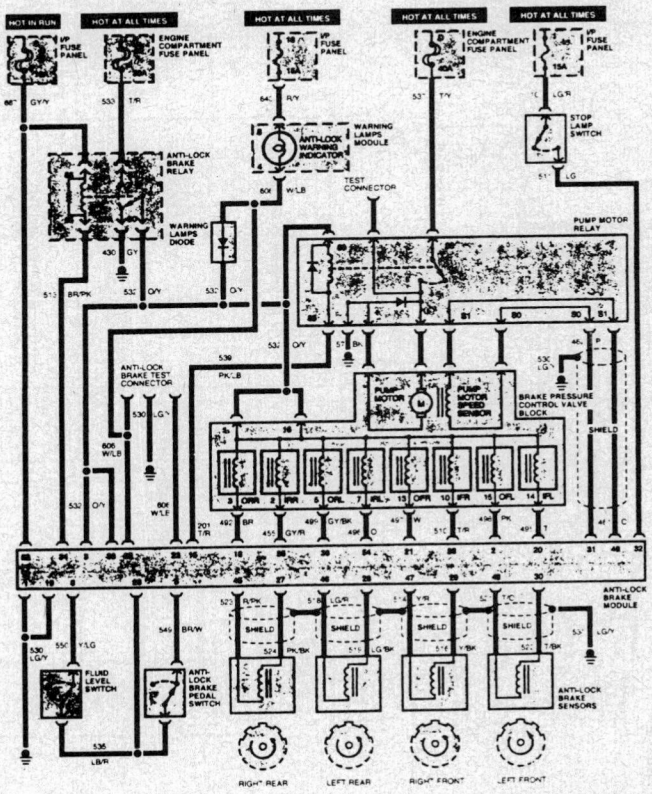

Fig. 29   ABS wiring circuit. 1994 Continental

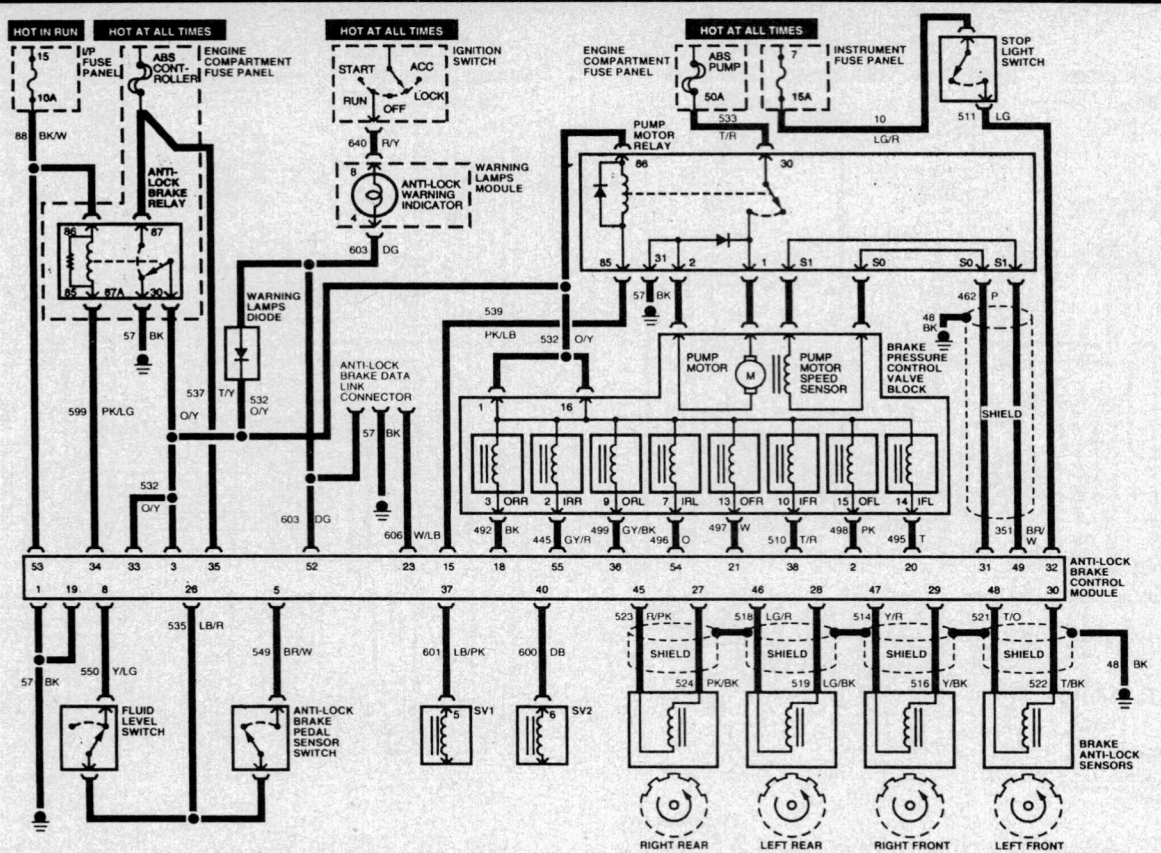

Fig. 30   ABS wiring circuit. 1994 Crown Victoria & Grand Marquis

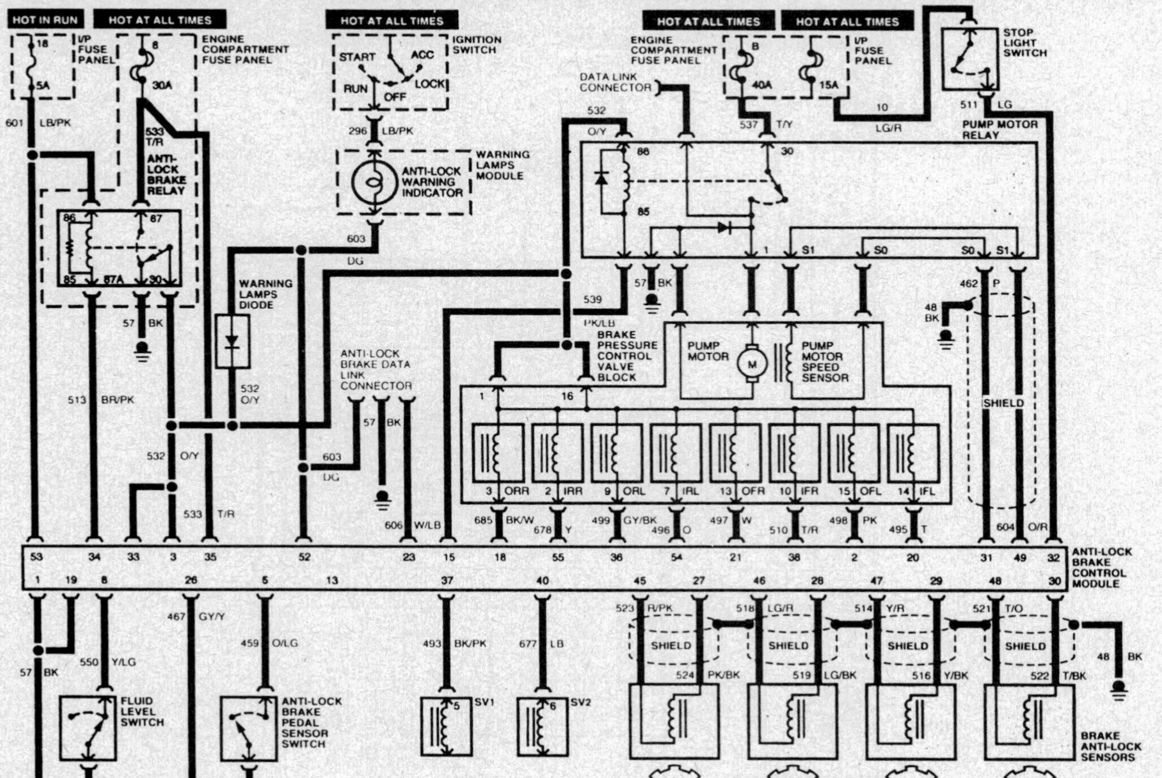

Fig. 31   ABS wiring circuit. 1994 Town Car

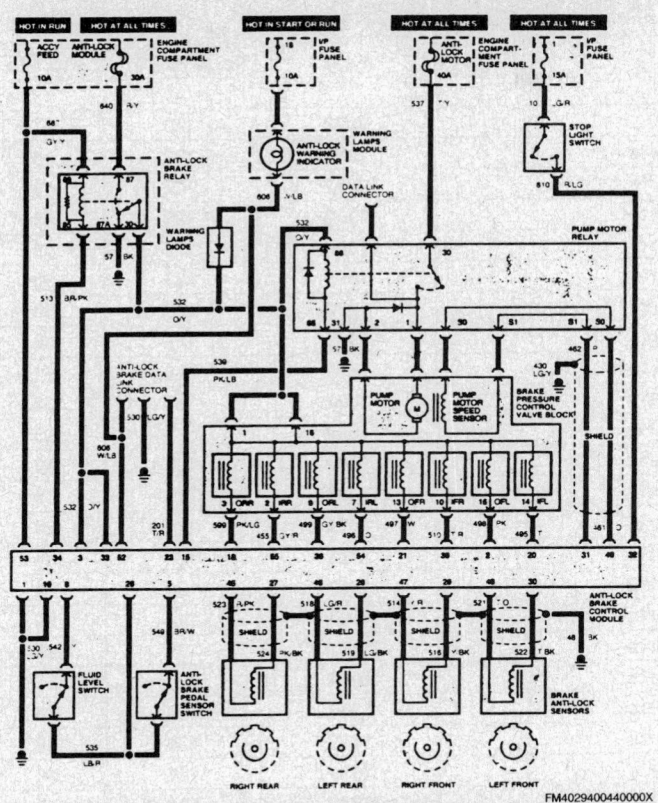

Fig. 32   ABS wiring circuit. 1994 Sable & Taurus except SHO

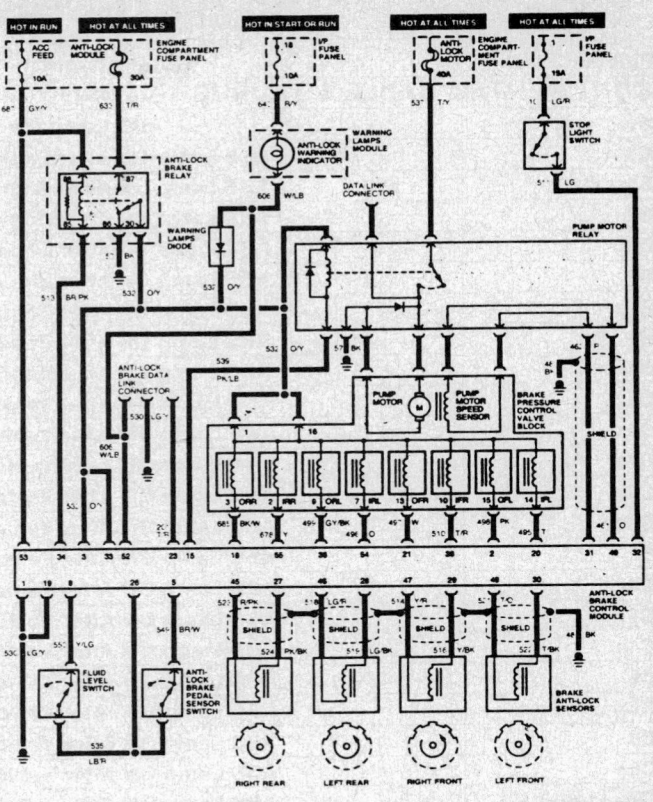

Fig. 33   ABS wiring circuit. 1994 Taurus SHO

DIAGNOSTIC CHART INDEX

Pinpoint Test	Description	Year	Page No. 27-	Fig. No.
CONTINENTAL, SABLE & TAURUS				
A1	ABS Lamp On	1992	119	34
A1a	ABS Lamp On	1992	119	35
A1b	ABS Lamp On	1992	119	35
A2	ABS Lamp On	1992	119	35
A3	ABS Lamp On	1992	119	35
A3a	ABS Lamp On	1992 ①	120	38
A3b	ABS Lamp On	1992 ①	120	38
A3c	ABS Lamp On	1992 ①	120	38
A3a	ABS Lamp On	1992 ②	120	39
A3b	ABS Lamp On	1992 ②	120	39
A3c	ABS Lamp On	1992 ②	120	39
A3d	ABS Lamp On	1992 ①	120	41
A3e	ABS Lamp On	1992 ①	120	41
A3d	ABS Lamp On	1992 ②	121	42
A3e	ABS Lamp On	1992 ②	121	42
A3f	ABS Lamp On	1992 ①	121	44
A4	ABS Lamp On	1992 ①	121	44
A5	ABS Lamp On	1992 ①	121	44
A3f	ABS Lamp On	1992 ②	121	45
A4	ABS Lamp On	1992 ②	121	45
A5	ABS Lamp On	1992 ②	122	45
A6	ABS Lamp On	1992	122	47
6a	ABS Lamp On	1992	122	47

Continued

Pinpoint Test	Description	Year	Page No. 27-	Fig. No.
CONTINENTAL, SABLE & TAURUS-Continued				
A7	ABS Lamp On	1992	122	47
B1	ABS Lamp On After Engine Starts	1992	122	48
B1a	ABS Lamp On After Engine Starts	1992	122	49
B2	ABS Lamp On After Engine Starts	1992	122	49
B2a	ABS Lamp On After Engine Starts	1992	122	49
B3	ABS Lamp On After Engine Starts	1992	123	50
B3a	ABS Lamp On After Engine Starts	1992	123	50
B4	ABS Lamp On After Engine Starts	1992	123	50
B4a	ABS Lamp On After Engine Starts	1992	123	51
C1	ABS Lamp ON After Vehicle Starts	1992	123	52
C1	ABS Lamp ON After Vehicle Starts	1992	123	53
C1a	ABS Lamp ON After Vehicle Starts	1992	123	53
C2	ABS Lamp ON After Vehicle Starts	1992	123	53
C2a	ABS Lamp ON After Vehicle Starts	1992	124	54
C3	ABS Lamp ON After Vehicle Starts	1992	124	54
C3a	ABS Lamp ON After Vehicle Starts	1992	124	54
C4	ABS Lamp ON After Vehicle Starts	1992	124	55
C4a	ABS Lamp ON After Vehicle Starts	1992	124	55
C5	ABS Lamp ON After Vehicle Starts	1992	124	55
C5a	ABS Lamp ON After Vehicle Starts	1992	124	55
C6	ABS Lamp ON After Vehicle Starts	1992	124	56
C6a	ABS Lamp ON After Vehicle Starts	1992	124	56
C7	ABS Lamp ON After Vehicle Starts	1992	124	56
C7a	ABS Lamp ON After Vehicle Starts	1992	124	56
C8	ABS Lamp ON After Vehicle Starts	1992	124	56
C8a	ABS Lamp ON After Vehicle Starts	1992	124	57
C9	ABS Lamp ON After Vehicle Starts	1992	124	57
C10	ABS Lamp ON After Vehicle Starts	1992	124	57
C11	ABS Lamp ON After Vehicle Starts	1992	124	57
C12	ABS Lamp ON After Vehicle Starts	1992	125	58
C13	ABS Lamp ON After Vehicle Starts	1992	125	58
C13a	ABS Lamp ON After Vehicle Starts	1992	125	58
C13b	ABS Lamp ON After Vehicle Starts	1992	125	59
C13c	ABS Lamp ON After Vehicle Starts	1992	125	59
C13d	ABS Lamp ON After Vehicle Starts	1992	125	59
C13e	ABS Lamp ON After Vehicle Starts	1992	125	60
C14	ABS Lamp ON After Vehicle Starts	1992	125	60
C14a	ABS Lamp ON After Vehicle Starts	1992	125	60
C14b	ABS Lamp ON After Vehicle Starts	1992	125	60
C14c	ABS Lamp ON After Vehicle Starts	1992	125	60
C15	ABS Lamp ON After Vehicle Starts	1992	126	62
C15a	ABS Lamp ON After Vehicle Starts	1992	126	62
C15b	ABS Lamp ON After Vehicle Starts	1992	126	62
C15c	ABS Lamp ON After Vehicle Starts	1992	126	62
C16	ABS Lamp ON After Vehicle Starts	1992	126	62
C16a	ABS Lamp ON After Vehicle Starts	1992	126	63
C16b	ABS Lamp ON After Vehicle Starts	1992	126	63
C16c	ABS Lamp ON After Vehicle Starts	1992	126	64
C16d	ABS Lamp ON After Vehicle Starts	1992	126	64
C16e	ABS Lamp ON After Vehicle Starts	1992	126	65
C16f	ABS Lamp ON After Vehicle Starts	1992	126	65
C16g	ABS Lamp ON After Vehicle Starts	1992	126	65
C16h	ABS Lamp ON After Vehicle Starts	1992	126	65

Continued

DIAGNOSTIC CHART INDEX-Continued

Pinpoint Test	Description	Year	Page No. 27-	Fig. No.
CONTINENTAL, SABLE & TAURUS -Continued				
D1	Warning Sequence Normal/Brake Pedal Rises Or Drops Excessively During ABS Cycling	1992	127	67
D1	Warning Sequence Normal/Brake Pedal Rises Or Drops Excessively During ABS Cycling	1992 ②	127	68
D1a	Warning Sequence Normal/Brake Pedal Rises Or Drops Excessively During ABS Cycling	1992 ②	127	68
D2	Warning Sequence Normal/Brake Pedal Rises Or Drops Excessively During ABS Cycling	1992 ②	127	68
D2a	Warning Sequence Normal/Brake Pedal Rises Or Drops Excessively During ABS Cycling	1992 ②	127	68
D3	Warning Sequence Normal/Brake Pedal Rises Or Drops Excessively During ABS Cycling	1992 ②	127	68
E1	Warning Sequence Normal/ABS Pump Motor Run Continuously	1992	128	71
E2	Warning Sequence Normal/ABS Pump Motor Run Continuously	1992	128	71
E3	Warning Sequence Normal/ABS Pump Motor Run Continuously	1992	128	73
E3a	Warning Sequence Normal/ABS Pump Motor Run Continuously	1992	129	74
E4	Warning Sequence Normal/ABS Pump Motor Run Continuously	1992	129	74
F1	Brake Lamp ON w/ABS Lamp OFF, Parking Brake Released & Lining Wear Checked	1992	129	75
F2	Brake Lamp ON w/ABS Lamp OFF, Parking Brake Released & Lining Wear Checked	1992	129	75
F3	Brake Warning Lamp ON w/Anti-Lock Lamp OFF, Parking Brake Released & Lining Wear Checked	1992	129	77
G1	No Warning Lamp ON When Ignition Switch Turned ON	1992	130	79
G2	No Warning Lamp ON When Ignition Switch Turned ON	1992	130	79
G3	No Warning Lamp ON When Ignition Switch Turned ON	1992	130	79
H1	Spongy Pedal With/Without ABS Function, No Warning Lamp	1992	130	80
H2	Spongy Pedal With/Without ABS Function, No Warning Lamp	1992	130	80
J1	Poor Vehicle Tracking During ABS Function	1992	131	82
J2	Poor Vehicle Tracking During ABS Function	1992	131	82
J2	Poor Vehicle Tracking During ABS Function	1992	131	84
J3	Poor Vehicle Tracking During ABS Function	1992	132	86
J4	Poor Vehicle Tracking During ABS Function	1992	132	86
J5	Poor Vehicle Tracking During ABS Function	1992	132	88
AA1	Electronic Controller	1992 ①	133	92
BB1	Solenoid Valve	1992 ①	133	93
BB2	Solenoid Valve	1992 ①	134	94
BB2a	Solenoid Valve	1992 ①	134	94
BB3	Solenoid Valve	1992 ①	134	94
BB3a	Solenoid Valve	1992 ①	134	95
BB4	Solenoid Valve	1992 ①	134	95
BB4a	Solenoid Valve	1992 ①	134	95
BB5	Solenoid Valve	1992 ①	134	95
BB5a	Solenoid Valve	1992 ①	134	96
BB6	Solenoid Valve	1992 ①	134	96
BB6a	Solenoid Valve	1992 ①	134	96
BB7	Solenoid Valve	1992 ①	134	96
BB7a	Solenoid Valve	1992 ①	134	97
BB8	Solenoid Valve	1992 ①	134	97
BdB8a	Solenoid Valve	1992 ①	134	97
BB9	Solenoid Valve	1992 ①	134	97
BB9a	Solenoid Valve	1992 ①	135	98
BB10	Solenoid Valve	1992 ①	135	98
BB10a	Solenoid Valve	1992 ①	135	98

Continued

CONTINENTAL, CROWN VICTORIA, GRAND MARQUIS, SABLE, TAURUS & TOWN CAR

DIAGNOSTIC CHART INDEX-Continued

Pinpoint Test	Description	Year	Page No. 27-	Fig. No.
CONTINENTAL, SABLE & TAURUS-Continued				
BB1	Solenoid Valve	1992②	137	106
BB2	Solenoid Valve	1992②	137	107
BB2a	Solenoid Valve	1992②	137	107
BB3	Solenoid Valve	1992②	137	107
BB3a	Solenoid Valve	1992②	137	108
BB4	Solenoid Valve	1992②	137	108
BB4a	Solenoid Valve	1992②	137	108
BB5	Solenoid Valve	1992②	137	108
BB5a	Solenoid Valve	1992②	137	109
BB6	Solenoid Valve	1992②	137	109
BB6a	Solenoid Valve	1992②	137	109
BB7	Solenoid Valve	1992②	137	109
BB7a	Solenoid Valve	1992②	138	110
BB8	Solenoid Valve	1992②	138	110
BB8a	Solenoid Valve	1992②	138	110
BB9	Solenoid Valve	1992②	138	110
BB9a	Solenoid Valve	1992②	138	111
BB10	Solenoid Valve	1992②	138	111
BB10a	Solenoid Valve	1992②	138	111
CC1	Wheel Sensor	1992	138	112
CC1a	Wheel Sensor	1992	138	113
CC2	Wheel Sensor	1992	138	113
CC3	Wheel Sensor	1992	138	113
CC3a	Wheel Sensor	1992	139	114
CC4	Wheel Sensor	1992	139	114
CC5	Wheel Sensor	1992	139	114
Tests CC6	Wheel Sensor	1992	139	115
CC6a	Wheel Sensor	1992	139	116
CC7	Wheel Sensor	1992	139	116
CC8	Wheel Sensor	1992	139	116
CC8a	Wheel Sensor	1992	139	117
CC9	Wheel Sensor	1992	139	117
CC10	Wheel Sensor	1992	139	117
CC11	Wheel Sensor	1992	140	118
CC11a	Wheel Sensor	1992	140	119
CC12	Wheel Sensor	1992	140	119
CC13	Wheel Sensor	1992	140	119
CC13a	Wheel Sensor	1992	140	120
CC14	Wheel Sensor	1992	140	120
CC15	Wheel Sensor	1992	140	120
CC16	Wheel Sensor	1992	140	121
CC16a	Wheel Sensor	1992	141	122
CC17	Wheel Sensor	1992	141	122
CC18	Wheel Sensor	1992	141	122
CC18a	Wheel Sensor	1992	141	123
CC19	Wheel Sensor	1992	141	123
CC20	Wheel Sensor	1992	141	123
DD1	Wheel Sensor	1992	141	124
DD1a	Wheel Sensor	1992	141	125
DD2	Wheel Sensor	1992	141	125
DD3	Wheel Sensor	1992	141	125
DD4	Wheel Sensor	1992	141	126

Continued

DIAGNOSTIC CHART INDEX-Continued

Pinpoint Test	Description	Year	Page No. 27-	Fig. No.
CONTINENTAL, SABLE & TAURUS-Continued				
DD4a	Wheel Sensor	1992	142	127
DD5	Wheel Sensor	1992	142	127
DD6	Wheel Sensor	1992	142	127
DD7	Wheel Sensor	1992	142	129
DD7a	Wheel Sensor	1992	143	130
DD8	Wheel Sensor	1992	143	130
DD9	Wheel Sensor	1992	143	130
DD10	Wheel Sensor	1992	143	131
DD10a	Wheel Sensor	1992	143	132
DD11	Wheel Sensor	1992	143	132
DD12	Wheel Sensor	1992	143	132
EE1	Fluid Level Indicator, Pedal Travel Switch & Pump Motor	1992	144	134
EE1a	Fluid Level Indicator/Pedal Travel Switch/Pump Motor	1992	144	136
EE2	Fluid Level Indicator/Pedal Travel Switch/Pump Motor	1992	144	136
EE2a	Fluid Level Indicator/Pedal Travel Switch/Pump Motor	1992	144	136
EE3	Fluid Level Indicator/Pedal Travel Switch/Pump Motor	1992	145	138
EE3a	Fluid Level Indicator/Pedal Travel Switch/Pump Motor	1992	145	140
EE4	Fluid Level Indicator/Pedal Travel Switch/Pump Motor	1992	145	140
EE4a	Fluid Level Indicator/Pedal Travel Switch/Pump Motor	1992	145	140
EE5	Fluid Level Indicator/Pedal Travel Switch/Pump Motor	1992	146	142
EE5a	Fluid Level Indicator/Pedal Travel Switch/Pump Motor	1992	146	144
EE5b	Fluid Level Indicator/Pedal Travel Switch/Pump Motor	1992	146	144
EE5c	Fluid Level Indicator/Pedal Travel Switch/Pump Motor	1992	146	144
EE5d	Fluid Level Indicator/Pedal Travel Switch/Pump Motor	1992	146	145
EE5e	Fluid Level Indicator/Pedal Travel Switch/Pump Motor	1992	146	145
EE6	Fluid Level Indicator/Pedal Travel Switch/Pump Motor	1992	146	145
EE6a	Fluid Level Indicator/Pedal Travel Switch/Pump Motor	1992	146	145
EE6b	Fluid Level Indicator/Pedal Travel Switch/Pump Motor	1992	146	145
EE6c	Fluid Level Indicator/Pedal Travel Switch/Pump Motor	1992	147	146
EE7	Fluid Level Indicator/Pedal Travel Switch/Pump Motor	1992	147	146
EE7a	Fluid Level Indicator/Pedal Travel Switch/Pump Motor	1992	147	146
EE7b	Fluid Level Indicator/Pedal Travel Switch/Pump Motor	1992	147	146
EE7c	Fluid Level Indicator/Pedal Travel Switch/Pump Motor	1992	147	146
EE8	Fluid Level Indicator/Pedal Travel Switch/Pump Motor	1992	147	146
EE8a	Fluid Level Indicator/Pedal Travel Switch/Pump Motor	1992	148	150
EE8b	Fluid Level Indicator/Pedal Travel Switch/Pump Motor	1992	148	150
EE8c	Fluid Level Indicator/Pedal Travel Switch/Pump Motor	1992	148	151
EE8d	Fluid Level Indicator/Pedal Travel Switch/Pump Motor	1992	148	151
EE8e	Fluid Level Indicator/Pedal Travel Switch/Pump Motor	1992	148	151
EE8f	Fluid Level Indicator/Pedal Travel Switch/Pump Motor	1992	148	152
EE8g	Fluid Level Indicator/Pedal Travel Switch/Pump Motor	1992	148	152
EE8h	Fluid Level Indicator/Pedal Travel Switch/Pump Motor	1992	148	152
Tests EE9	Fluid Level Indicator/Pedal Travel Switch/Pump Motor	1992	148	153
A	ABS Warning Lamp On w/Brake Warning Lamp Off	1993–94 ①	150	158
A	Anti-Lock Warning Indicator On w/Brake Warning Indicator Off	1993–94 ②	151	160
B	ABS Warning Lamp On After Engine Starts	1993–94	152	161
C	ABS Warning Lamp On After Vehicle Starts To Move Or False Cycling Of ABS System	1993–94	153	162
D	ABS Warning Lamp Sequence Normal/Brake Pedal Rises Or Drops Excessively During ABS Cycling	1993–94	156	163
E	ABS Warning Lamp Sequence Normal/ABS Pump Motor Runs Continuously	1993–94	157	164

Continued

CONTINENTAL, CROWN VICTORIA, GRAND MARQUIS, SABLE, TAURUS & TOWN CAR

DIAGNOSTIC CHART INDEX-Continued

Pinpoint Test	Description	Year	Page No. 27-	Fig. No.
CONTINENTAL, SABLE & TAURUS-Continued				
F	Brake Warning Lamp On w/ABS WarningLamp Off & Parking Brake Released	1993–94 ①	157	165
F	Brake Warning Indicator On w/Anti-Lock Indicator Off, Parking Brake Released & Brake Lining Wear Checked	1993–94 ②	158	166
G	No ABS Warning Lamp When Ignition Turned On	1993–94	158	167
H	Spongy Brake Pedal With/Without ABS Function	1993–94	158	169
J	Poor Vehicle Tracking During ABS Function	1993–94	158	170
AA	ABS Module Diagnosis	1993–94	159	173
BB	Solenoid Valve Diagnosis	1993 & Early Production 1994 ①	160	174
BB	Solenoid Valve Diagnosis	Late Production 1994 ①	161	175
BB	Solenoid Valve Diagnosis	1993–94 ②	167	178
CC	Front Wheel Sensor Diagnosis	1993–94 ①	168	179
CC	Wheel Sensor Diagnosis	1993–94 ②	170	180
DD	Rear Wheel Sensor Diagnosis	1993 ①	173	181
DD	Wheel Sensor Diagnosis	1993 ②	176	183
DD	Brake Fluid Level Switch/Anti-Lock Brake Pedal Sensor Switch/Pump Motor Diagnosis	1994 ①	178	184
DD	Fluid Level Indicator/Anti-Lock Brake Pedal Sensor Switch/Pump Motor & Relay	1994 ②	182	186
EE	Fluid Level Indicator/Pedal Travel Switch/Pump Motor Diagnosis	1993–94	185	187
CROWN VICTORIA, GRAND MARQUIS & TOWN CAR				
Test A1	ABS Lamp On	1992	119	36
Test A1a	ABS Lamp On	1992	119	36
Test A1b	ABS Lamp On	1992	119	36
Test A1c	ABS Lamp On	1992	119	36
Test A2	ABS Lamp On	1992	119	37
Test A3	ABS Lamp On	1992	119	37
Test A3a	ABS Lamp On	1992	119	37
Test A3b	ABS Lamp On	1992	119	37
Test A3c	ABS Lamp On	1992	120	40
Test A3d	ABS Lamp On	1992	120	40
Test A3e	ABS Lamp On	1992	121	43
Test A3f	ABS Lamp On	1992	121	43
Test A4	ABS Lamp On	1992	122	46
Test A5	ABS Lamp On	1992	122	46
Test A6	ABS Lamp On	1992	122	47
Test A6a	ABS Lamp On	1992	122	47
Test A7	ABS Lamp On	1992	122	47
Test B1	ABS Lamp On After Engine Starts	1992	122	48
Test B1a	ABS Lamp On After Engine Starts	1992	122	49
Test B2	ABS Lamp On After Engine Starts	1992	122	49
Test B2a	ABS Lamp On After Engine Starts	1992	122	49
Test B3	ABS Lamp On After Engine Starts	1992	123	50
Test B3a	ABS Lamp On After Engine Starts	1992	123	50
Test B4	ABS Lamp On After Engine Starts	1992	123	50
Test B4a	ABS Lamp On After Engine Starts	1992	123	51
Test C1	ABS Lamp ON After Vehicle Starts	1992	123	52
Test C1	ABS Lamp ON After Vehicle Starts	1992	123	53
Test C1a	ABS Lamp ON After Vehicle Starts	1992	123	53
Test C2	ABS Lamp ON After Vehicle Starts	1992	123	53
Test C2a	ABS Lamp ON After Vehicle Starts	1992	124	54

Continued

DIAGNOSTIC CHART INDEX-Continued

Pinpoint Test	Description	Year	Page No. 27-	Fig. No.
CROWN VICTORIA, GRAND MARQUIS & TOWN CAR-Continued				
Test C3	ABS Lamp ON After Vehicle Starts	1992	124	54
Test C3a	ABS Lamp ON After Vehicle Starts	1992	124	54
Test C4	ABS Lamp ON After Vehicle Starts	1992	124	55
Test C4a	ABS Lamp ON After Vehicle Starts	1992	124	55
Test C5	ABS Lamp ON After Vehicle Starts	1992	124	55
Test C5a	ABS Lamp ON After Vehicle Starts	1992	124	55
Test C6	ABS Lamp ON After Vehicle Starts	1992	124	56
Test C6a	ABS Lamp ON After Vehicle Starts	1992	124	56
Test C7	ABS Lamp ON After Vehicle Starts	1992	124	56
Test C7a	ABS Lamp ON After Vehicle Starts	1992	124	56
Test C8	ABS Lamp ON After Vehicle Starts	1992	124	56
Test C8a	ABS Lamp ON After Vehicle Starts	1992	124	57
Test C9	ABS Lamp ON After Vehicle Starts	1992	124	57
Test C10	ABS Lamp ON After Vehicle Starts	1992	124	57
Test C11	ABS Lamp ON After Vehicle Starts	1992	124	57
Test C12	ABS Lamp ON After Vehicle Starts	1992	125	58
Test C13	ABS Lamp ON After Vehicle Starts	1992	125	58
Test C13a	ABS Lamp ON After Vehicle Starts	1992	125	58
Test C13b	ABS Lamp ON After Vehicle Starts	1992	125	59
Test C13c	ABS Lamp ON After Vehicle Starts	1992	125	59
Test C13d	ABS Lamp ON After Vehicle Starts	1992	125	59
Test C13e	ABS Lamp ON After Vehicle Starts	1992	125	61
Test C14	ABS Lamp ON After Vehicle Starts	1992	125	61
Test C14a	ABS Lamp ON After Vehicle Starts	1992	125	61
Test C14b	ABS Lamp ON After Vehicle Starts	1992	125	61
Test C14c	ABS Lamp ON After Vehicle Starts	1992	125	61
Test C15	ABS Lamp ON After Vehicle Starts	1992	126	62
Test C15a	ABS Lamp ON After Vehicle Starts	1992	126	62
Test C15b	ABS Lamp ON After Vehicle Starts	1992	126	62
Test C15c	ABS Lamp ON After Vehicle Starts	1992	126	62
Test C16	ABS Lamp ON After Vehicle Starts	1992	126	62
Test C16a	ABS Lamp ON After Vehicle Starts	1992	126	63
Test C16b	ABS Lamp ON After Vehicle Starts	1992	126	63
Test C16c	ABS Lamp ON After Vehicle Starts	1992	126	64
Test C16d	ABS Lamp ON After Vehicle Starts	1992	126	64
Test C16e	ABS Lamp ON After Vehicle Starts	1992	127	66
Test C16f	ABS Lamp ON After Vehicle Starts	1992	127	66
Test C16g	ABS Lamp ON After Vehicle Starts	1992	127	66
Test C16h	ABS Lamp ON After Vehicle Starts	1992	127	66
Test D1	Warning Sequence Normal/Brake Pedal Rises Or Drops Excessively During ABS Cycling	1992	127	69
Test D1	Warning Sequence Normal/Brake Pedal Rises Or Drops Excessively During ABS Cycling	1992	128	70
Test D1a	Warning Sequence Normal/Brake Pedal Rises Or Drops Excessively During ABS Cycling	1992	128	70
Test D2	Warning Sequence Normal/Brake Pedal Rises Or Drops Excessively During ABS Cycling	1992	128	70
Test D2a	Warning Sequence Normal/Brake Pedal Rises Or Drops Excessively During ABS Cycling	1992	128	70
Test D3	Warning Sequence Normal/Brake Pedal Rises Or Drops Excessively During ABS Cycling	1992	128	70
Test E1	Warning Sequence Normal/ABS Pump Motor Run Continuously	1992	128	72
Test E2	Warning Sequence Normal/ABS Pump Motor Run Continuously	1992	128	72
Test E3	Warning Sequence Normal/ABS Pump Motor Run Continuously	1992	128	73

Continued

DIAGNOSTIC CHART INDEX-Continued

Pinpoint Test	Description	Year	Page No. 27-	Fig. No.
CROWN VICTORIA, GRAND MARQUIS & TOWN CAR-Continued				
Test E3a	Warning Sequence Normal/ABS Pump Motor Run Continuously	1992	129	74
Test E4	Warning Sequence Normal/ABS Pump Motor Run Continuously	1992	129	74
Test F1	Brake Lamp ON w/ABS Lamp OFF, Parking Brake Released & Lining Wear Checked	1992	129	76
Test F2	Brake Lamp ON w/ABS Lamp OFF, Parking Brake Released & Lining Wear Checked	1992	129	76
Test F3	Brake Warning Lamp ON w/Anti-Lock Lamp OFF, Parking Brake Released & Lining Wear Checked	1992	129	77
Test G1	No Warning Lamp ON When Ignition Switch Turned ON	1992	130	78
Test G2	No Warning Lamp ON When Ignition Switch Turned ON	1992	130	78
Test G3	No Warning Lamp ON When Ignition Switch Turned ON	1992	130	78
Test G4	No Warning Lamp ON When Ignition Switch Turned ON	1992	130	78
Test H1	Spongy Pedal With/Without ABS Function, No Warning Lamp	1992	130	81
Test H2	Spongy Pedal With/Without ABS Function, No Warning Lamp	1992	130	81
Test J1	Poor Vehicle Tracking During ABS Function	1992	131	83
Test J2	Poor Vehicle Tracking During ABS Function	1992	131	83
Test J2	Poor Vehicle Tracking During ABS Function	1992	131	85
Test J3	Poor Vehicle Tracking During ABS Function	1992	132	87
Test J4	Poor Vehicle Tracking During ABS Function	1992	132	87
Test J5	Poor Vehicle Tracking During ABS Function	1992	132	89
Test K1	ABS Indicator Sequence Normal, False Cycling Of Traction Aassist	1992	133	90
Test K2	ABS Indicator Sequence Normal, False Cycling Of Traction Aassist	1992	133	90
Test K3	ABS Indicator Sequence Normal, False Cycling Of Traction Aassist	1992	133	90
Test K3a	ABS Indicator Sequence Normal, False Cycling Of Traction Aassist	1992	133	90
Test K4	ABS Indicator Sequence Normal, False Cycling Of Traction Aassist	1992	133	90
Test AA1	Electronic Controller	1992	133	92
Test L1	ABS Indicator Sequence Normal, False Cycling Of Traction Assist	1992	133	91
Test BB1	Solenoid Valve	1992	135	99
Test BB2	Solenoid Valve	1992	135	100
Test BB2a	Solenoid Valve	1992	135	100
Test BB3	Solenoid Valve	1992	135	100
Test BB3a	Solenoid Valve	1992	135	101
Test BB4	Solenoid Valve	1992	135	101
Test BB4a	Solenoid Valve	1992	135	101
Test BB5	Solenoid Valve	1992	135	101
Test BB5a	Solenoid Valve	1992	136	102
Test BB6	Solenoid Valve	1992	136	102
Test BB6a	Solenoid Valve	1992	136	102
Test BB7	Solenoid Valve	1992	136	102
Test BB7a	Solenoid Valve	1992	136	103
Test BB8	Solenoid Valve	1992	136	103
Test BB8a	Solenoid Valve	1992	136	103
Test BB9	Solenoid Valve	1992	136	103
Test BB9a	Solenoid Valve	1992	136	104
Test BB10	Solenoid Valve	1992	136	104
Test BB10a	Solenoid Valve	1992	136	104
Test BB11	Solenoid Valve	1992	136	105
Test BB11a	Solenoid Valve	1992	136	105
Test BB12	Solenoid Valve	1992	136	105
Test BB12a	Solenoid Valve	1992	136	105
Test CC1	Wheel Sensor	1992	138	112
Test CC1a	Wheel Sensor	1992	138	113

Continued

DIAGNOSTIC CHART INDEX-Continued

Pinpoint Test	Description	Year	Page No. 27-	Fig. No.
CROWN VICTORIA, GRAND MARQUIS & TOWN CAR-Continued				
Test CC2	Wheel Sensor	1992	138	113
Test CC3	Wheel Sensor	1992	138	113
Test CC3a	Wheel Sensor	1992	139	114
Test CC4	Wheel Sensor	1992	139	114
Test CC5	Wheel Sensor	1992	139	114
Tests CC6	Wheel Sensor	1992	139	115
Test CC6a	Wheel Sensor	1992	139	116
Test CC7	Wheel Sensor	1992	139	116
Test CC8	Wheel Sensor	1992	139	116
Test CC8a	Wheel Sensor	1992	139	117
Test CC9	Wheel Sensor	1992	139	117
Test CC10	Wheel Sensor	1992	139	117
Test CC11	Wheel Sensor	1992	140	118
Test CC11a	Wheel Sensor	1992	140	119
Test CC12	Wheel Sensor	1992	140	119
Test CC13	Wheel Sensor	1992	140	119
Test CC13a	Wheel Sensor	1992	140	120
Test CC14	Wheel Sensor	1992	140	120
Test CC15	Wheel Sensor	1992	140	120
Test CC16	Wheel Sensor	1992	140	121
Test CC16a	Wheel Sensor	1992	141	122
Test CC17	Wheel Sensor	1992	141	122
Test CC18	Wheel Sensor	1992	141	122
Test CC18a	Wheel Sensor	1992	141	123
Test CC19	Wheel Sensor	1992	141	123
Test CC20	Wheel Sensor	1992	141	123
Test DD1	Wheel Sensor	1992	141	124
Test DD1a	Wheel Sensor	1992	141	125
Test DD2	Wheel Sensor	1992	141	125
Test DD3	Wheel Sensor	1992	141	125
Test DD4	Wheel Sensor	1992	142	126
Test DD4a	Wheel Sensor	1992	142	128
Test DD5	Wheel Sensor	1992	142	128
Test DD6	Wheel Sensor	1992	142	128
Test DD7	Wheel Sensor	1992	142	129
Test DD7a	Wheel Sensor	1992	143	130
Test DD8	Wheel Sensor	1992	143	130
Test DD9	Wheel Sensor	1992	143	130
Test DD10	Wheel Sensor	1992	143	131
Test DD10a	Wheel Sensor	1992	143	133
Test DD11	Wheel Sensor	1992	143	133
Test DD12	Wheel Sensor	1992	143	133
Test EE1	Fluid Level Indicator/Pedal Travel Switch/Pump Motor	1992	144	135
Test EE1a	Fluid Level Indicator/Pedal Travel Switch/Pump Motor	1992	144	137
Test EE2	Fluid Level Indicator/Pedal Travel Switch/Pump Motor	1992	144	137
Test EE2a	Fluid Level Indicator/Pedal Travel Switch/Pump Motor	1992	144	137
Test EE3	Fluid Level Indicator/Pedal Travel Switch/Pump Motor	1992	145	139
Test EE3a	Fluid Level Indicator/Pedal Travel Switch/Pump Motor	1992	145	139
Test EE4	Fluid Level Indicator/Pedal Travel Switch/Pump Motor	1992	145	139
Test EE4a	Fluid Level Indicator/Pedal Travel Switch/Pump Motor	1992	145	141
Test EE5	Fluid Level Indicator/Pedal Travel Switch/Pump Motor	1992	146	143

Continued

DIAGNOSTIC CHART INDEX-Continued

Pinpoint Test	Description	Year	Page No. 27-	Fig. No.
CROWN VICTORIA, GRAND MARQUIS & TOWN-Continued				
Test EE5a	Fluid Level Indicator/Pedal Travel Switch/Pump Motor	1992	146	143
Test EE6	Fluid Level Indicator/Pedal Travel Switch/Pump Motor	1992	146	143
Test EE6a	Fluid Level Indicator/Pedal Travel Switch/Pump Motor	1992	146	143
Test EE7	Fluid Level Indicator/Pedal Travel Switch/Pump Motor	1992	147	147
Test EE7a	Fluid Level Indicator/Pedal Travel Switch/Pump Motor	1992	147	148
Test EE7b	Fluid Level Indicator/Pedal Travel Switch/Pump Motor	1992	147	148
Test EE7c	Fluid Level Indicator/Pedal Travel Switch/Pump Motor	1992	147	148
Test EE7d	Fluid Level Indicator/Pedal Travel Switch/Pump Motor	1992	147	149
Test EE7e	Fluid Level Indicator/Pedal Travel Switch/Pump Motor	1992	147	149
Test EE8	Fluid Level Indicator/Pedal Travel Switch/Pump Motor	1992	147	149
Test EE8a	Fluid Level Indicator/Pedal Travel Switch/Pump Motor	1992	147	149
Test EE8	Fluid Level Indicator/Pedal Travel Switch/Pump Motor	1992	147	149
Test EE8c	Fluid Level Indicator/Pedal Travel Switch/Pump Motor	1992	149	154
Test EE9	Fluid Level Indicator/Pedal Travel Switch/Pump Motor	1992	149	154
Test EE9a	Fluid Level Indicator/Pedal Travel Switch/Pump Motor	1992	149	154
Test EE9b	Fluid Level Indicator/Pedal Travel Switch/Pump Motor	1992	149	154
Test EE9c	Fluid Level Indicator/Pedal Travel Switch/Pump Motor	1992	149	154
Test EE10	Fluid Level Indicator/Pedal Travel Switch/Pump Motor	1992	149	154
Test EE10a	Fluid Level Indicator/Pedal Travel Switch/Pump Motor	1992	149	155
Test EE10b	Fluid Level Indicator/Pedal Travel Switch/Pump Motor	1992	149	155
Test EE10c	Fluid Level Indicator/Pedal Travel Switch/Pump Motor	1992	149	156
Test EE10d	Fluid Level Indicator/Pedal Travel Switch/Pump Motor	1992	149	156
Test EE10e	Fluid Level Indicator/Pedal Travel Switch/Pump Motor	1992	149	156
Test EE10f	Fluid Level Indicator/Pedal Travel Switch/Pump Motor	1992	149	157
Test EE10g	Fluid Level Indicator/Pedal Travel Switch/Pump Motor	1992	149	157
Test EE10h	Fluid Level Indicator/Pedal Travel Switch/Pump Motor	1992	149	157
A	Anti-Lock Warning Indicator On w/Brake Warning Indicator Off	1993–94	151	159
B	ABS Warning Lamp On After Engine Starts	1993–94	152	161
C	ABS Warning Lamp On After Vehicle Starts To Move Or False Cycling Of ABS System	1993–94	153	162
D	ABS Warning Lamp Sequence Normal/Brake Pedal Rises Or Drops Excessively During ABS Cycling	1993–94	156	163
E	ABS Warning Lamp Sequence Normal/ABS Pump Motor Runs Continuously	1993–94	157	164
F	Brake Warning Lamp On w/ABS Warning Lamp Off & Parking Brake Released	1993–94	157	165
G	No Anti-Lock Warning Indicator On When Ignition Switch Turned On	1993–94	158	168
H	Spongy Brake Pedal With/Without ABS Function	1993–94	158	169
J	Poor Vehicle Tracking During ABS Function	1993–94	158	170
K	ABS Warning Lamp Sequence Normal/Traction Assist Inoperative	1993–94	159	171
L	ABS Warning Lamp Sequence Normal/False Cycling Of Traction Assist	1993–94	159	172
AA	ABS Module Diagnosis	1993–94	159	173
BB	Solenoid Valve Diagnosis	1993	163	176
BB	Solenoid Valve Diagnosis	1994	165	177
CC	Front Wheel Sensor Diagnosis	1993–94	168	179
DD	Wheel Sensor Diagnosis	1993	175	182
DD	Fluid Level Indicator/Anti-Lock Brake Pedal Sensor Switch/Pump Motor Diagnosis	1994	180	185
EE	Fluid Level Indicator/Pedal Travel Switch/Pressure Switch	1993–94	188	188

①—Continental.
②—Sable & Taurus.

Warning Lights Sequence

Warning Lamps	Ignition On	Cranking Engine	Engine Running	Vehicle Moving	Braking with/without Anti-Lock	Vehicle Stopped	Engine Idle	Ignition Off
Check Anti-Lock (Amber)	//////	//////	//////	//////	//////	//////	//////	
Brake (Red)		██						

TEST STEP	RESULT ▶	ACTION TO TAKE
A1 CHECK POWER TO CONTROLLER		
• Disconnect 55-pin plug from electronic controller.	Over 10 volts ▶	GO to Step **A2**.
	Under 10 volts ▶	GO to Step **A1a**.
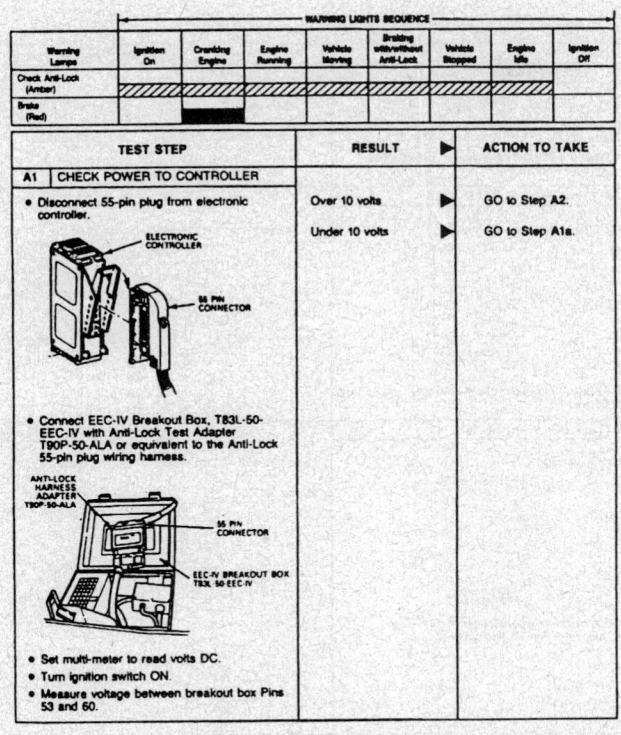		
• Connect EEC-IV Breakout Box, T83L-50-EEC-IV with Anti-Lock Test Adapter T90P-50-ALA or equivalent to the Anti-Lock 55-pin plug wiring harness.		
• Set multi-meter to read volts DC.		
• Turn ignition switch ON.		
• Measure voltage between breakout box Pins 53 and 60.		

Fig. 34   Test A1: ABS Lamp On. 1992 Continental, Sable & Taurus

TEST STEP	RESULT ▶	ACTION TO TAKE
A1a CHECK ELECTRONIC CONTROLLER TO GROUND WIRE		
• Check continuity between breakout box Pin 60 and body ground.	Continuity ▶	GO to Step **A1b**.
	No Continuity ▶	SERVICE or REPLACE cable harness Circuit 530 or 530B (Taurus/Sable). Circuit 530, 57U or 57R (Taurus SHO).
A1b CHECK IGNITION TO ELECTRONIC CONTROLLER WIRE		
• Check for continuity between breakout box Pin 53 and ignition switch wire 687B.	Continuity ▶	CHECK ignition switch.
	No Continuity ▶	SERVICE or REPLACE cable harness circuit 687, 687B, 302B or Fuse Link.
A2 CHECK GROUND		
• Check for continuity between breakout box Pins 19 and 60.	Continuity ▶	GO to Step **A3**.
	No Continuity ▶	SERVICE or REPLACE cable harness circuit 530C (Taurus/Sable). Circuit 530B (Taurus SHO).
A3 CHECK MAIN RELAY OPERATION		
• Jumper pins 34 and 60 at breakout box.	Over 10 volts DC ▶	GO to Step **A4**.
• Turn ignition to ON.	Under 10 volts DC ▶	GO to Step **A3a**.
• Measure voltage between breakout box Pins 33 and 19.		

Fig. 35   Pinpoint Tests A1a, A1b, A2 & A3: ABS Lamp On. 1992 Continental, Sable & Taurus

Warning Indicators Sequence

Warning Indicators	Ignition On	Cranking Engine	Engine Running	Vehicle Moving	Braking with/without Anti-Lock	Vehicle Stopped	Engine Idle	Ignition Off
Check Anti-Lock (Amber)	//////		//////	//////	//////	//////	//////	
Brake (Red)	██		██					

TEST STEP	RESULT ▶	ACTION TO TAKE
A1 CHECK POWER TO CONTROLLER		
• Disconnect 55-pin plug from electronic controller.	Over 10V ▶	GO to Step **A2**.
• Connect EEC-IV Breakout Box, T83L-50-EEC-IV with Anti-Lock Test Adapter T90P-50-ALA or equivalent to the Anti-Lock 55-pin plug wiring harness.	Under 10V ▶	GO to Step **A1a**.
• Set multi-meter to read volts DC.		
• Turn ignition switch ON.		
• Measure voltage between breakout box Pins 53 and 60.		
A1a CHECK ELECTRONIC CONTROLLER TO GROUND WIRE		
• Check continuity between breakout box Pin 60 and body ground.	Continuity ▶	GO to Step **A1b**.
	No Continuity ▶	SERVICE or REPLACE cable harness Circuit 57V, or 57X.
A1b CHECK IGNITION TO ELECTRONIC CONTROLLER WIRE		
• Check for continuity between breakout box Pin 53 and ignition switch wire 299.	Continuity ▶	GO to Step **A1c**.
	No Continuity ▶	SERVICE or REPLACE cable harness Circuit 299, 601 or 601b.
A1c CHECK FUSE 18		
• Check fuse 18.	Fuse good ▶	CHECK ignition switch.
	Fuse bad ▶	REPLACE fuse.

Fig. 36   Pinpoint Tests A1, A1a, A1b & A1c: ABS Lamp On. 1992 Crown Victoria, Grand Marquis & Town Car

TEST STEP	RESULT ▶	ACTION TO TAKE
A2 CHECK GROUND		
• Check for continuity between breakout box Pins 19 and 60.	Continuity ▶	GO TO Step **A3**.
	No Continuity ▶	SERVICE or REPLACE cable harness Circuit 57V.
A3 CHECK MAIN RELAY OPERATION		
• Jumper Pins 34 and 60 at breakout box.	Over 10V DC ▶	GO to Step **A4**.
• Turn ignition to ON.	Under 10V DC ▶	GO to Step **A3a**.
• Measure voltage between breakout box Pins 33 and 19.		
A3a CHECK MAIN RELAY COIL		
• Turn ignition to OFF.	45 to 90 ohms ▶	GO to Step **A3c**.
• Remove jumper from breakout box Pins 34 and 60.	Any other reading ▶	GO to Step **A3b**.
• Measure resistance between breakout box Pins 53 and 34.		
A3b CHECK MAIN RELAY COIL		
• Remove main power relay.	45 to 90 ohms ▶	SERVICE or REPLACE cable harness Circuit 513, 601a or 601b.
	Any other reading ▶	REPLACE main relay.
• Measure resistance between main relay Pins 85 and 86.		

```
      87A ┌──────────┐ 87
          │          │
       86 │  ▯    ▯  │ 85
          │          │
       30 └──────────┘
       MAIN POWER RELAY
          CONNECTOR
```

Fig. 37   Pinpoint Tests A2, A3, A3a & A3b: ABS Lamp On. 1992 Crown Victoria, Grand Marquis & Town Car

TEST STEP	RESULT	▶	ACTION TO TAKE
A3a CHECK MAIN RELAY COIL			
• Turn ignition to OFF. • Remove jumper from breakout box Pins 34 and 60. • Measure resistance between breakout box Pins 53 and 34.	45 to 90 ohms Any other reading	▶ ▶	GO to Step **A3c**. GO to Step **A3b**.
A3b CHECK MAIN RELAY COIL			
• Remove main power relay. MAIN POWER RELAY BASE • Measure resistance between main relay pins 1 and 2.	45 to 90 ohms Any other reading	▶ ▶	SERVICE or REPLACE cable harness circuit 513 or 687a or 687b. REPLACE main relay.
A3c CHECK CIRCUIT 687b			
• Turn ignition ON. MAIN POWER RELAY CONNECTOR • Measure voltage between main relay connector Pin 2 and ground.	Over 10 volts DC Under 10 volts DC	▶ ▶	GO to Step **A3d**. SERVICE cable harness circuit 687b.

Fig. 38 Pinpoint Tests A3a, A3b, A3c: ABS Lamp On. 1992 Continental

TEST STEP	RESULT	▶	ACTION TO TAKE
A3a CHECK MAIN RELAY COIL			
• Turn ignition to OFF position. • Remove jumper from breakout box Pins 34 and 60. • Measure resistance between breakout box Pins 53 and 34.	45 to 90 ohms Any other reading	▶ ▶	GO to Step **A3c**. GO to Step **A3b**.
A3b CHECK MAIN RELAY COIL			
• Remove main power relay. MAIN POWER RELAY • Measure resistance between main relay Pins 85 and 86.	45 to 90 ohms Any other reading	▶ ▶	SERVICE or REPLACE cable harness Circuit 513, 687 or 687C (Taurus/Sable). Circuit 513, 687B or 687C (Taurus SHO). REPLACE main relay.
A3c CHECK CIRCUIT 687c			
• Turn ignition ON. MAIN POWER RELAY CONNECTOR (HARNESS SIDE) • Measure voltage between main relay connector Pin 86 and ground.	Over 10V DC Under 10V DC	▶ ▶	GO to Step **A3d**. SERVICE cable harness Circuit 687C.

Fig. 39 Pinpoint Tests A3a, A3b, A3c: ABS Lamp On. 1992 Sable & Taurus

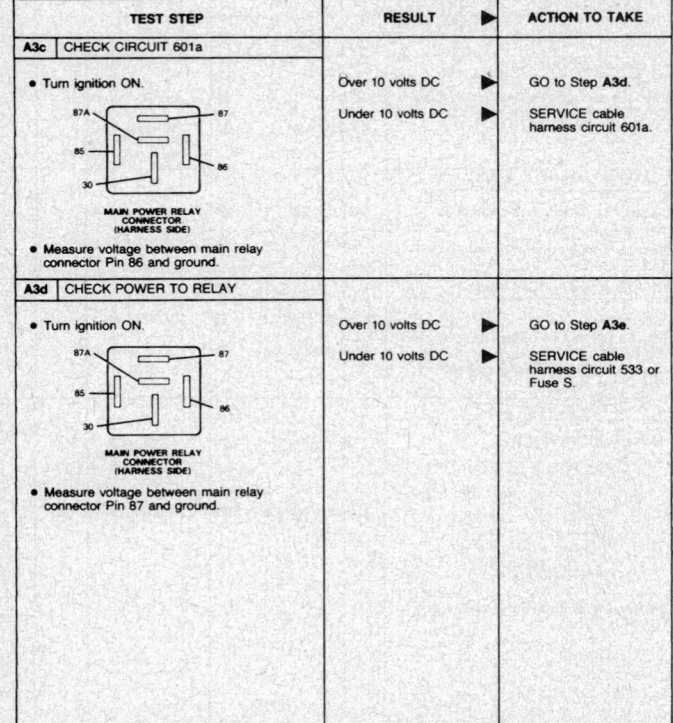

TEST STEP	RESULT	▶	ACTION TO TAKE
A3c CHECK CIRCUIT 601a			
• Turn ignition ON. MAIN POWER RELAY CONNECTOR (HARNESS SIDE) • Measure voltage between main relay connector Pin 86 and ground.	Over 10 volts DC Under 10 volts DC	▶ ▶	GO to Step **A3d**. SERVICE cable harness circuit 601a.
A3d CHECK POWER TO RELAY			
• Turn ignition ON. MAIN POWER RELAY CONNECTOR (HARNESS SIDE) • Measure voltage between main relay connector Pin 87 and ground.	Over 10 volts DC Under 10 volts DC	▶ ▶	GO to Step **A3e**. SERVICE cable harness circuit 533 or Fuse S.

Fig. 40 Pinpoint Tests A3c & A3d: ABS Lamp On. 1992 Crown Victoria, Grand Marquis & Town Car

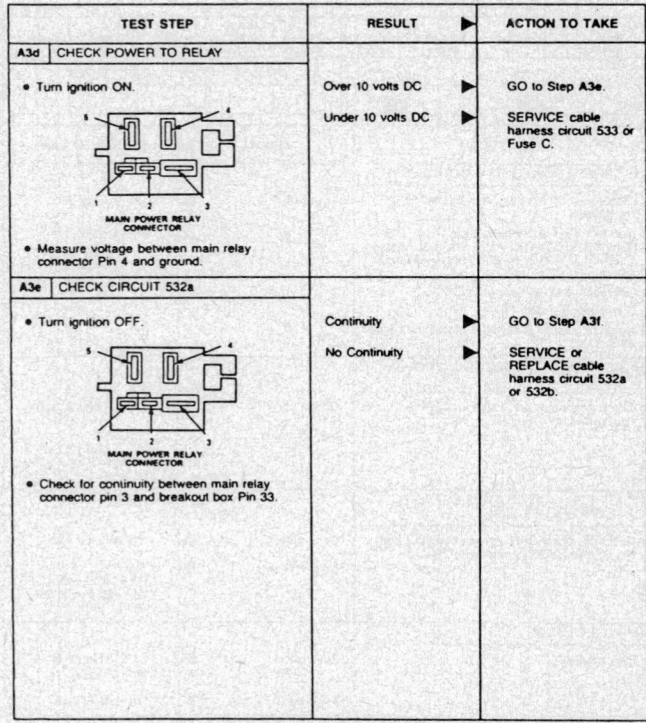

TEST STEP	RESULT	▶	ACTION TO TAKE
A3d CHECK POWER TO RELAY			
• Turn ignition ON. MAIN POWER RELAY CONNECTOR • Measure voltage between main relay connector Pin 4 and ground.	Over 10 volts DC Under 10 volts DC	▶ ▶	GO to Step **A3e**. SERVICE cable harness circuit 533 or Fuse C.
A3e CHECK CIRCUIT 532a			
• Turn ignition OFF. MAIN POWER RELAY CONNECTOR • Check for continuity between main relay connector pin 3 and breakout box Pin 33.	Continuity No Continuity	▶ ▶	GO to Step **A3f**. SERVICE or REPLACE cable harness circuit 532a or 532b.

Fig. 41 Pinpoint Tests A3d & A3e: ABS Lamp On. 1992 Continental

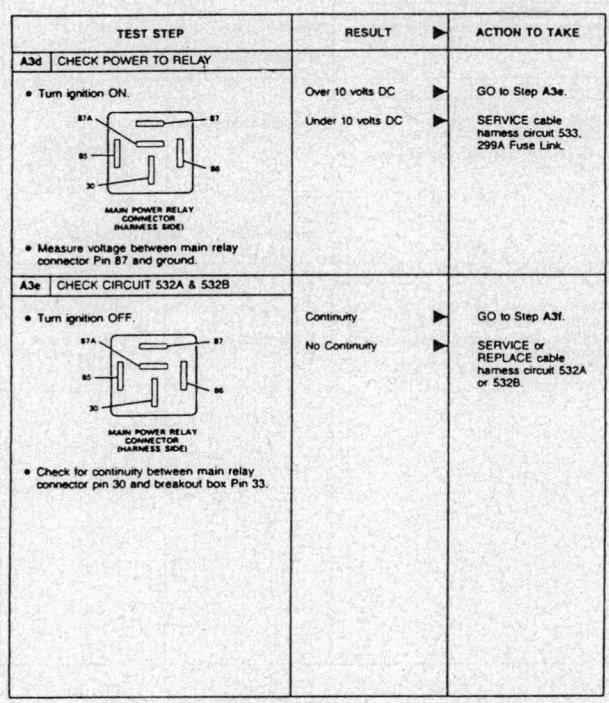

TEST STEP	RESULT ▶	ACTION TO TAKE
A3d CHECK POWER TO RELAY • Turn ignition ON. • Measure voltage between main relay connector Pin 87 and ground.	Over 10 volts DC ▶ Under 10 volts DC ▶	GO to Step **A3e**. SERVICE cable harness circuit 533, 299A Fuse Link.
A3e CHECK CIRCUIT 532A & 532B • Turn ignition OFF. • Check for continuity between main relay connector pin 30 and breakout box Pin 33.	Continuity ▶ No Continuity ▶	GO to Step **A3f**. SERVICE or REPLACE cable harness circuit 532A or 532B.

Fig. 42   Pinpoint Tests A3d & A3e: ABS Lamp On. 1992 Sable & Taurus

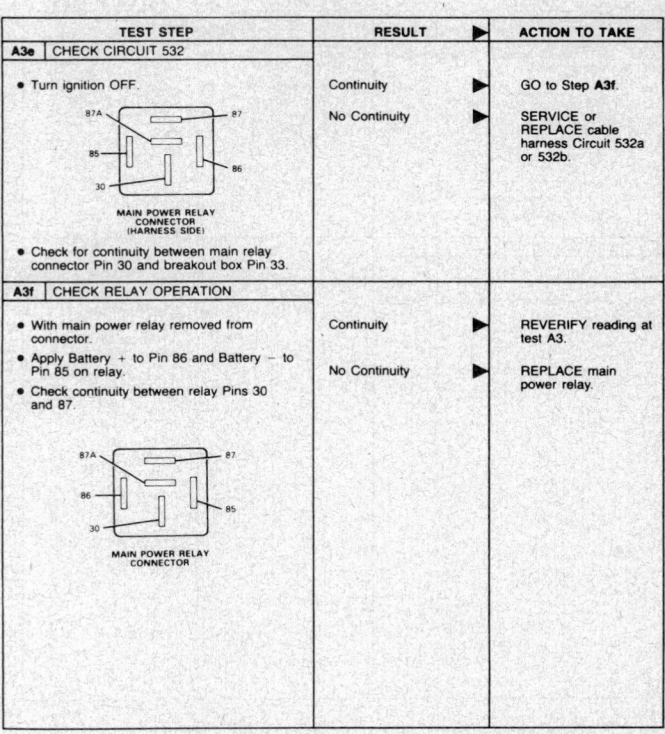

TEST STEP	RESULT ▶	ACTION TO TAKE
A3e CHECK CIRCUIT 532 • Turn ignition OFF. • Check for continuity between main relay connector Pin 30 and breakout box Pin 33.	Continuity ▶ No Continuity ▶	GO to Step **A3f**. SERVICE or REPLACE cable harness Circuit 532a or 532b.
A3f CHECK RELAY OPERATION • With main power relay removed from connector. • Apply Battery + to Pin 86 and Battery − to Pin 85 on relay. • Check continuity between relay Pins 30 and 87.	Continuity ▶ No Continuity ▶	REVERIFY reading at test A3. REPLACE main power relay.

Fig. 43   Pinpoint Tests A3e & A3f: ABS Lamp On. 1992 Crown Victoria, Grand Marquis & Town Car

TEST STEP	RESULT ▶	ACTION TO TAKE
A3f CHECK RELAY OPERATION • With main power relay removed from connector. • Apply Battery voltage to pin 2 and Battery ground to pin 1 on relay. • Check continuity between relay pins 3 and 4.	Continuity ▶ No Continuity ▶	REVERIFY reading at test A3. REPLACE main power relay.
A4 CHECK CIRCUIT 430K • Check for continuity between relay connector Pin 5 and ground.	Continuity ▶ No Continuity ▶	GO to Step A5. SERVICE or REPLACE cable harness circuit 430K.
A5 CHECK CIRCUIT 606 • Turn ignition ON. • Check voltage between breakout box Pins 52 and 60.	Over 10 volts DC ▶ Under 10 volts DC ▶	GO to Step A6. SERVICE or REPLACE cable harness circuits 606, 606b or 606d.

Fig. 44   Pinpoint Tests A3f, A4 & A5: ABS Lamp On. 1992 Continental

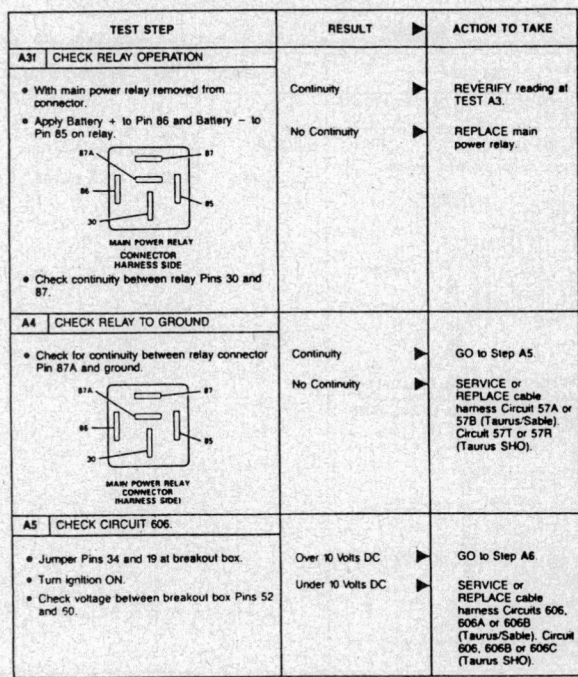

TEST STEP	RESULT ▶	ACTION TO TAKE
A3f CHECK RELAY OPERATION • With main power relay removed from connector. • Apply Battery + to Pin 86 and Battery − to Pin 85 on relay. • Check continuity between relay Pins 30 and 87.	Continuity ▶ No Continuity ▶	REVERIFY reading at TEST A3. REPLACE main power relay.
A4 CHECK RELAY TO GROUND • Check for continuity between relay connector Pin 87A and ground.	Continuity ▶ No Continuity ▶	GO to Step A5. SERVICE or REPLACE cable harness Circuit 57A or 57B (Taurus/Sable). Circuit 57T or 57R (Taurus SHO).
A5 CHECK CIRCUIT 606. • Jumper Pins 34 and 19 at breakout box. • Turn ignition ON. • Check voltage between breakout box Pins 52 and 50.	Over 10 Volts DC ▶ Under 10 Volts DC ▶	GO to Step A6. SERVICE or REPLACE cable harness Circuits 606, 606A or 606B (Taurus/Sable). Circuit 606, 606B or 606C (Taurus SHO).

Fig. 45   Pinpoint Tests A3f, A4 & A5: ABS Lamp On. 1992 Sable & Taurus

TEST STEP	RESULT ▶	ACTION TO TAKE
A4 CHECK CIRCUIT 57T.		
• Check for continuity between relay connector Pin 87a and ground.	Continuity ▶	GO to Step **A5**.
	No Continuity ▶	SERVICE or REPLACE cable harness Circuit 57T.
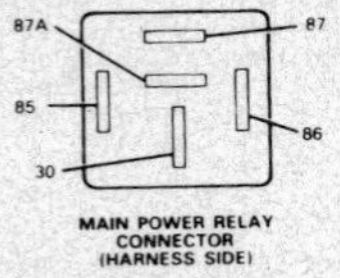 **A5** CHECK CIRCUIT 603		
• Turn ignition ON.	Over 10V DC ▶	GO to Step **A6**.
• Check voltage between breakout box Pins 52 and 60.	Under 10V DC ▶	SERVICE or REPLACE cable harness Circuits 603, 603a or 603c.

MAIN POWER RELAY CONNECTOR (HARNESS SIDE)

87A 87
85 86
30

Fig. 46   Pinpoint Tests A4 & A5: ABS Lamp On. 1992 Crown Victoria, Grand Marquis & Town Car

TEST STEP	RESULT ▶	ACTION TO TAKE
A6 CHECK FLI #2 AND CIRCUITRY		
• Measure resistance between breakout box Pins 8 and 26.	Less than 5 ohms ▶	GO to Step **A7**.
	Any other reading ▶	GO to Step **A6a**.
A6a CHECK FLI #2		
• Disconnect 2-pin plug from FLI #2, located on HCU reservoir.	Less than 5 ohms ▶	SERVICE or REPLACE cable harness Circuit 542, 535 or 535B (Taurus/Sable). Circuit 550, 535 or 535B (Taurus SHO).
• Measure resistance between Pins 1 and 2 on HCU reservoir.	Any other reading ▶	REPLACE HCU reservoir.
A7 ELECTRONIC CONTROLLER CHECK		
• If Self-Diagnostics, ABS Quick Test and Test A did not find problem.	ABS lamp off ▶	REPLACE Controller.
• Replace Electronic Controller with a known good controller.	ABS lamp still on ▶	REVERIFY that all tests have been performed.

Fig. 47   Pinpoint Tests A6, A6a & A7: ABS Lamp On. 1992

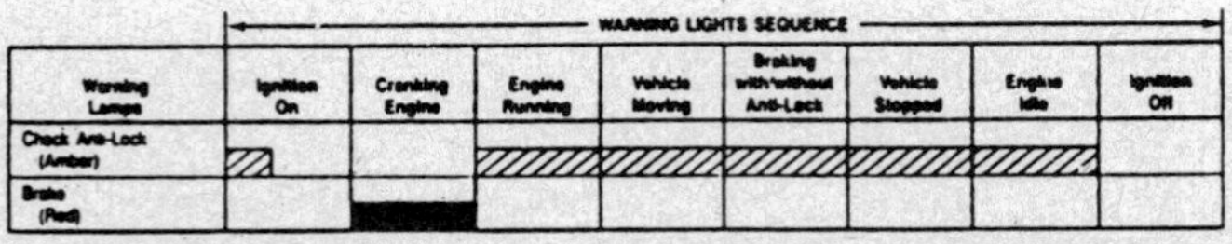

Warning Lamps		Ignition On	Cranking Engine	Engine Running	Vehicle Moving	Braking with/without Anti-Lock	Vehicle Stopped	Engine Idle	Ignition Off
WARNING LIGHTS SEQUENCE									
Check Anti-Lock (Amber)									
Brake (Red)									

TEST STEP	RESULT ▶	ACTION TO TAKE
B1 CHECK CONTINUITY OF CIRCUITS 518 and 519		
• Turn ignition switch Off.	Continuity ▶	GO to Step **B1a**.
• Disconnect 55-pin plug from controller.	No Continuity ▶	GO to Step **B2**.

ELECTRONIC CONTROLLER
55 PIN CONNECTOR

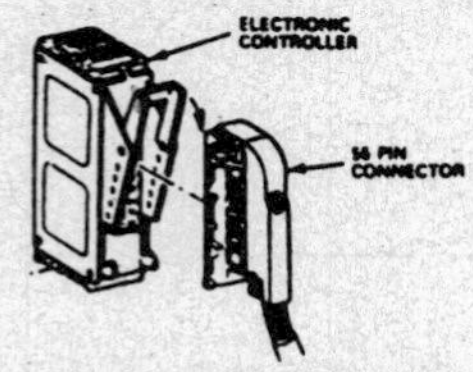

Connect EEC-IV Breakout Box T83L-50-EEC-IV with Anti-Lock Test Adapter T90P-50-ALA or equivalent to the Anti-Lock 55-pin plug on the wiring harness.

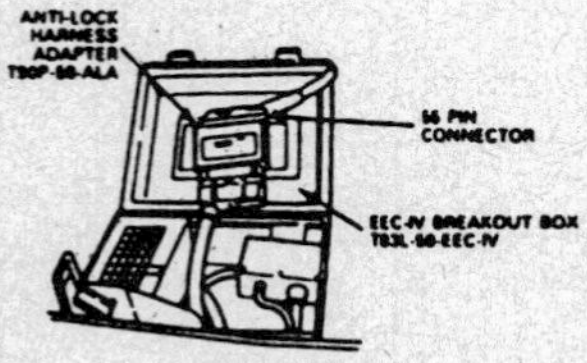

ANTI-LOCK HARNESS ADAPTER T90P-50-ALA
55 PIN CONNECTOR
EEC-IV BREAKOUT BOX T83L-50-EEC-IV

• Check continuity between breakout box Pins 26 and 60.

Fig. 48   Test B1: ABS Lamp On After Engine Starts. 1992

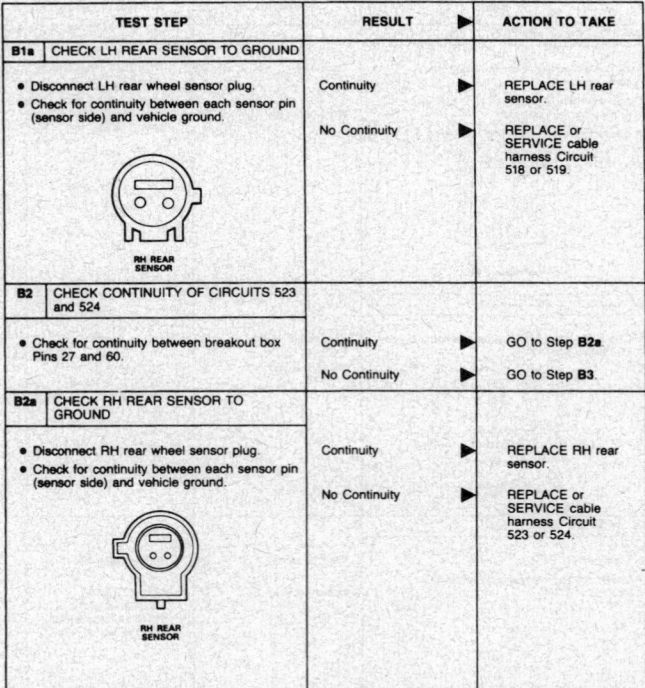

TEST STEP	RESULT ▶	ACTION TO TAKE
B1a CHECK LH REAR SENSOR TO GROUND		
• Disconnect LH rear wheel sensor plug.	Continuity ▶	REPLACE LH rear sensor.
• Check for continuity between each sensor pin (sensor side) and vehicle ground.	No Continuity ▶	REPLACE or SERVICE cable harness Circuit 518 or 519.
B2 CHECK CONTINUITY OF CIRCUITS 523 and 524		
• Check for continuity between breakout box Pins 27 and 60.	Continuity ▶	GO to Step **B2a**.
	No Continuity ▶	GO to Step **B3**.
B2a CHECK RH REAR SENSOR TO GROUND		
• Disconnect RH rear wheel sensor plug.	Continuity ▶	REPLACE RH rear sensor.
• Check for continuity between each sensor pin (sensor side) and vehicle ground.	No Continuity ▶	REPLACE or SERVICE cable harness Circuit 523 or 524.

Fig. 49   Pinpoint Tests B1a, B2 & B2a: ABS Lamp On After Engine Starts. 1992

TEST STEP	RESULT	►	ACTION TO TAKE
B3 CHECK CONTINUITY OF CIRCUITS 514 and 516			
• Check for continuity between breakout box Pins 29 and 60.	Continuity	►	GO to Step **B3a**.
	No Continuity	►	GO to Step **B4**.
B3a CHECK RH FRONT SENSOR TO GROUND			
• Disconnect RH front wheel sensor plug. • Check for continuity between each sensor pin (sensor side) and vehicle ground.	Continuity	►	REPLACE RH front sensor.
	No Continuity	►	REPLACE or SERVICE cable harness circuit (514 or 516).
B4 CHECK CONTINUITY OF CIRCUITS 521 and 522			
• Check for continuity between breakout box Pins 30 and 60.	Continuity	►	GO to Step **B4a**.
	No Continuity	►	Test complete. If Anti-Lock lamp pattern remains, REPEAT Test B.

RH FRONT SENSOR

Fig. 50 Pinpoint Tests B3, B3a & B4: ABS Lamp On After Engine Starts. 1992

TEST STEP	RESULT	►	ACTION TO TAKE
B4a CHECK LH FRONT SENSOR TO GROUND			
• Disconnect LH front wheel sensor plug. • Check for continuity between each sensor pin (sensor side) and vehicle ground.	Continuity	►	REPLACE LH front sensor.
	No Continuity	►	REPLACE or SERVICE cable harness circuit (521 or 522).

LH FRONT SENSOR

Fig. 51 Test B4a: ABS Lamp On After Engine Starts. 1992

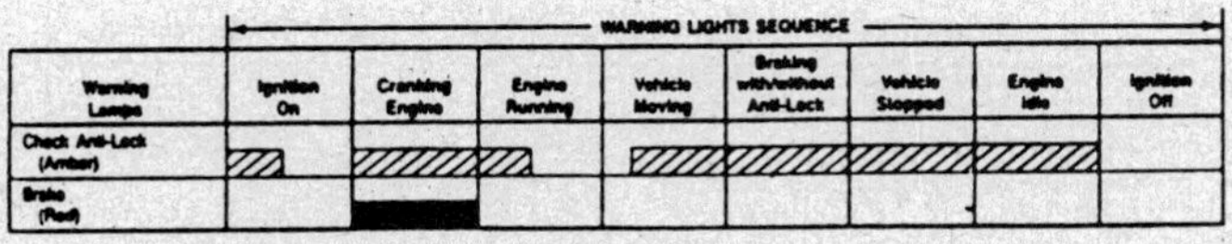

WARNING LIGHTS SEQUENCE

Warning Lamps	Ignition On	Cranking Engine	Engine Running	Vehicle Moving	Braking with/without Anti-Lock	Vehicle Stopped	Engine Idle	Ignition Off
Check Anti-Lock (Amber)								
Brake (Red)								

WARNING LIGHTS SEQUENCE

Warning Lamps	Ignition On	Cranking Engine	Engine Running	Vehicle Moving	Braking with/without Anti-Lock	Vehicle Stopped	Engine Idle	Ignition Off
Check Anti-Lock (Amber)								
Brake (Red)								

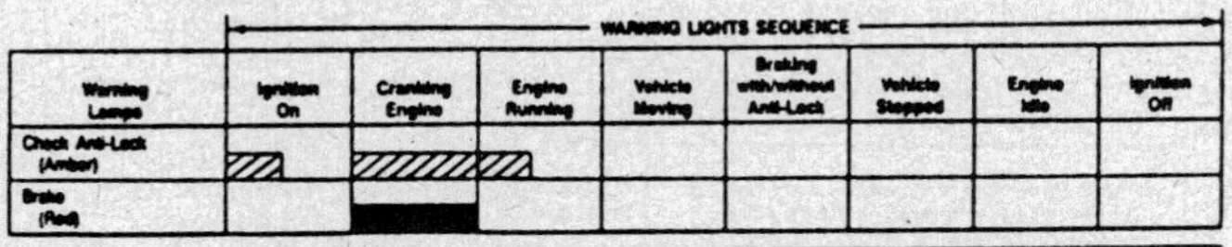

TEST STEP	RESULT	►	ACTION TO TAKE
C1 MEASURE LH FRONT SENSOR CIRCUIT RESISTANCE			
• Turn ignition switch OFF. • Disconnect 55-pin connector from electronic controller.			

ELECTRONIC CONTROLLER

55 PIN CONNECTOR

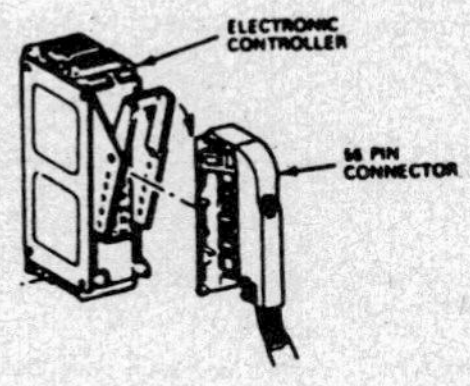

Fig. 52 Test C1: ABS Lamp ON After Vehicle Starts. 1992

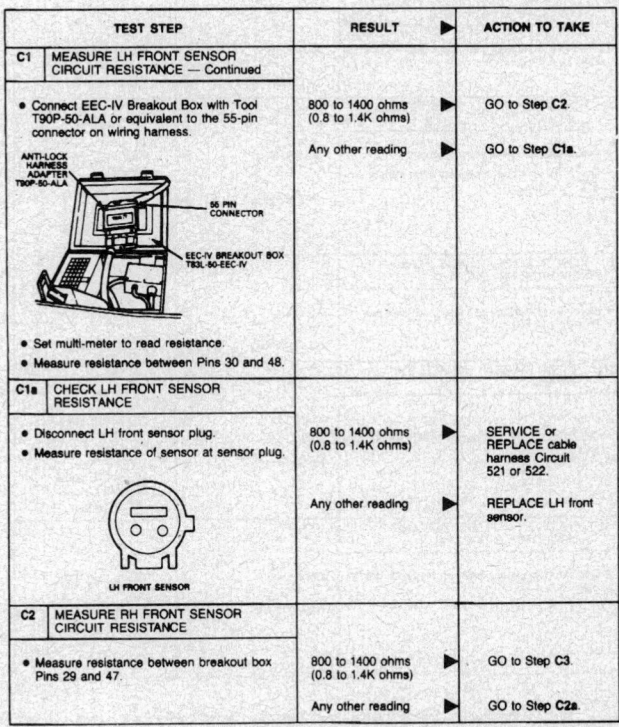

TEST STEP	RESULT	►	ACTION TO TAKE
C1 MEASURE LH FRONT SENSOR CIRCUIT RESISTANCE — Continued			
• Connect EEC-IV Breakout Box with Tool T90P-50-ALA or equivalent to the 55-pin connector on wiring harness.	800 to 1400 ohms (0.8 to 1.4K ohms)	►	GO to Step C2.
	Any other reading	►	GO to Step C1a.
• Set multi-meter to read resistance. • Measure resistance between Pins 30 and 48.			
C1a CHECK LH FRONT SENSOR RESISTANCE			
• Disconnect LH front sensor plug. • Measure resistance of sensor at sensor plug.	800 to 1400 ohms (0.8 to 1.4K ohms)	►	SERVICE or REPLACE cable harness Circuit 521 or 522.
	Any other reading	►	REPLACE LH front sensor.
C2 MEASURE RH FRONT SENSOR CIRCUIT RESISTANCE			
• Measure resistance between breakout box Pins 29 and 47.	800 to 1400 ohms (0.8 to 1.4K ohms)	►	GO to Step C3.
	Any other reading	►	GO to Step C2a.

ANTI-LOCK HARNESS ADAPTER T90P-50-ALA

55 PIN CONNECTOR

EEC-IV BREAKOUT BOX T83L-50-EEC-IV

LH FRONT SENSOR

Fig. 53 Pinpoint Tests C1, C1a & C2: ABS Lamp ON After Vehicle Starts. 1992

Fig. 54 (Tests C2a, C3 & C3a)

TEST STEP	RESULT ▶	ACTION TO TAKE
C2a CHECK RH FRONT SENSOR RESISTANCE		
• Disconnect RH front sensor plug. • Measure resistance of sensor at sensor plug.	800 to 1400 ohms (0.8 to 1.4K ohms) ▶	SERVICE or REPLACE cable harness Circuit 514 or 516.
	Any other reading ▶	REPLACE RH front sensor.
C3 MEASURE RH REAR SENSOR CIRCUIT RESISTANCE		
• Measure resistance between Breakout box Pins 27 and 45.	800 to 1400 ohms (0.8 to 1.4K ohms) ▶	GO to Step **C4**.
	Any other reading ▶	GO to Step **C3a**.
C3a CHECK RH REAR SENSOR RESISTANCE		
• Disconnect RH rear sensor plug. • Measure resistance of sensor at sensor plug.	800 to 1400 ohms (0.8 to 1.4K ohms) ▶	SERVICE or REPLACE cable harness Circuit 523 or 524.
	Any other reading ▶	REPLACE RH rear sensor.

Fig. 54 Pinpoint Tests C2a, C3 & C3a: ABS Lamp ON After Vehicle Starts. 1992

Fig. 55 (Tests C4, C4a, C5 & C5a)

TEST STEP	RESULT ▶	ACTION TO TAKE
C4 MEASURE LH REAR SENSOR CIRCUIT RESISTANCE		
• Measure resistance between breakout box Pins 28 and 46.	800 to 1400 ohms (0.8 to 1.4K ohms) ▶	GO to Step **C5**.
	Any other reading ▶	GO to Step **C4a**.
C4a CHECK LH REAR SENSOR RESISTANCE		
• Disconnect LH rear sensor plug. • Measure resistance of sensor at sensor plug.	800 to 1400 ohms (0.8 to 1.4K ohms) ▶	SERVICE or REPLACE cable harness Circuit 518 or 519.
	Any other reading ▶	REPLACE LH rear sensor.
C5 CHECK LH FRONT SENSOR AND CIRCUITRY TO GROUND		
• Check for continuity between breakout box Pins 30 and 60.	Continuity ▶	GO to Step **C5a**.
	No Continuity ▶	GO to Step **C6**.
C5a CHECK LH FRONT SENSOR TO GROUND		
• Disconnect LH front sensor plug. • Check for continuity between each sensor pin and body ground.	Continuity ▶	REPLACE LH front sensor.
	No Continuity ▶	REPAIR OR REPLACE cable harness Circuit 521 or 522.

Fig. 55 Pinpoint Tests C4, C4a, C5 & C5a: ABS Lamp ON After Vehicle Starts. 1992

Fig. 56 (Tests C6, C6a, C7, C7a & C8)

TEST STEP	RESULT ▶	ACTION TO TAKE
C6 CHECK RH FRONT SENSOR AND CIRCUITRY TO GROUND		
• Check for continuity between breakout box Pins 29 and 60.	Continuity ▶	GO to Step **C6a**.
	No Continuity ▶	GO to Step **C7**.
C6a CHECK RH FRONT SENSOR TO GROUND		
• Disconnect RH front sensor plug. • Check for continuity between each sensor pin and body ground.	Continuity ▶	REPLACE RH front sensor.
	No Continuity ▶	REPAIR OR REPLACE cable harness Circuit 514 or 516.
C7 CHECK RH REAR SENSOR AND CIRCUITRY TO GROUND		
• Check for continuity between breakout box Pins 27 and 60.	Continuity ▶	GO to Step **C7a**.
	No Continuity ▶	GO to Step **C8**.
C7a CHECK RH REAR SENSOR TO GROUND		
• Disconnect RH rear sensor plug. • Check for continuity between each sensor pin and body ground.	Continuity ▶	REPLACE RH rear sensor.
	No Continuity ▶	REPAIR OR REPLACE cable harness Circuit 523 or 524.
C8 CHECK LH REAR SENSOR AND CIRCUITRY TO GROUND		
• Check for continuity between breakout box Pins 28 and 60.	Continuity ▶	GO to Step **C8a**.
	No Continuity ▶	GO to Step **C9**.

Fig. 56 Pinpoint Tests C6, C6a, C7, C7a & C8: ABS Lamp ON After Vehicle Starts. 1992

Fig. 57 (Tests C8a, C9, C10 & C11)

TEST STEP	RESULT ▶	ACTION TO TAKE
C8a CHECK LH REAR SENSOR TO GROUND		
• Disconnect LH rear sensor plug. • Check for continuity between each sensor pin and body ground.	Continuity ▶	REPLACE LH rear sensor.
	No Continuity ▶	REPAIR OR REPLACE cable harness Circuit 518 or 519.
C9 CHECK LH FRONT SENSOR VOLTAGE OUTPUT		
• Measure voltage between breakout box Pins 30 and 48 while spinning LH front wheel at approximately 1 revolution per second.	Between 0.10 and 1.40 volts AC ▶	GO to Step **C10**.
	Less than 0.10 or more than 1.40 volts AC ▶	CHECK wheel sensor mounting, air gap, or toothed wheel. CORRECT as required.
C10 CHECK RH FRONT SENSOR VOLTAGE OUTPUT		
• Measure voltage between breakout box Pins 29 and 47 while spinning RH front wheel at approximately 1 revolution per second.	Between 0.10 and 1.40 volts AC ▶	GO to Step **C11**.
	Less than 0.10 or more than 1.40 volts AC ▶	CHECK wheel sensor mounting, air gap, or toothed wheel. CORRECT as required.
C11 CHECK RH REAR SENSOR VOLTAGE OUTPUT		
• Measure voltage between breakout box Pins 27 and 45 while spinning RH rear wheel at approximately 1 revolution per second.	Between 0.10 and 1.40 volts AC ▶	GO to Step **C12**.
	Less than 0.10 or more than 1.40 volts AC ▶	CHECK wheel sensor mounting, air gap, or toothed wheel. CORRECT as required.

Fig. 57 Pinpoint Tests C8a, C9, C10 & C11: ABS Lamp ON After Vehicle Starts. 1992

TEST STEP	RESULT ▶	ACTION TO TAKE
C12 CHECK LH REAR SENSOR VOLTAGE OUTPUT		
• Measure voltage between breakout box Pins 28 and 45 while spinning LH rear wheel at approximately 1 revolution per second.	Between 0.10V and 1.40V AC ▶	GO to Step C13.
	Less than 0.10V or more than 1.40V AC ▶	CHECK wheel sensor mounting, air gap, or toothed wheel. CORRECT as required.
C13 CHECK MOTOR SPEED SENSOR AND CIRCUITRY		
• Measure resistance between breakout box Pins 31 and 49.	5-100 ohms ▶	GO to Step C14.
	Any other reading ▶	GO to Step C13a.
C13a CHECK PUMP MOTOR SPEED SENSOR		
• Disconnect 4-Pin plug on pump motor. • Measure resistance between Pins S0 and S1 on pump motor.	5-100 ohms ▶	GO to Step C13b.
	Any other reading ▶	REPLACE pump and motor.

Fig. 58 Pinpoint Tests C12, C13 & C13a: ABS Lamp ON After Vehicle Starts. 1992

TEST STEP	RESULT ▶	ACTION TO TAKE
C13b CHECK PUMP MOTOR RELAY		
• Disconnect 7-pin plug on pump motor relay and remove relay. • Check continuity from Pin S0 on 7-pin side to Pin S0 on 4-pin side of relay.	Continuity ▶	GO to Step C13c.
	No Continuity ▶	REPLACE pump motor relay.
C13c CHECK PUMP MOTOR RELAY		
• Check continuity from Pin S1 on 7-pin side to Pin S1 on 4-pin side of relay.	Continuity ▶	GO to Step C13d.
	No Continuity ▶	REPLACE pump motor relay.
C13d CHECK CIRCUIT 462		
• Check continuity between breakout box Pin 31 and Pin S0 on pump motor connector 7-pin plug (harness side).	Continuity ▶	GO to Step C13e.
	No Continuity ▶	SERVICE or REPLACE cable harness Circuit 462.

Fig. 59 Pinpoint Tests C13b, C13c & C13d: ABS Lamp ON After Vehicle Starts. 1992

TEST STEP	RESULT ▶	ACTION TO TAKE
C13e CHECK CIRCUIT 461		
• Check continuity between breakout box Pin 49 and Pin S1 on pump motor connector 7-pin plug (harness side).	Continuity ▶	REVERIFY reading at C13.
	No Continuity ▶	SERVICE or REPLACE cable harness Circuit 461.
C14 CHECK MOTOR SPEED SENSOR SHORT TO BATTERY +		
• Turn ignition switch to ON. • Measure voltage between breakout box Pins 31 and 60.	No voltage ▶	GO to Step C15.
	12 volts ▶	GO to Step C14a.
C14a CHECK PUMP MOTOR		
• Disconnect pump motor to relay 4-pin plug connector. • Turn ignition switch to ON. • Measure voltage between breakout box Pins 31 and 60.	No voltage ▶	REPLACE pump and motor.
	12 volts ▶	GO to Step C14b.
C14b CHECK CIRCUIT 462		
• Disconnect wire harness to relay 7-pin plug. • Turn ignition switch to ON. • Measure voltage between breakout box Pins 31 and 60.	No voltage ▶	GO to Step C14c.
	12 volts ▶	SERVICE or REPLACE cable harness Circuit 462.
C14c CHECK CIRCUIT 461		
• Turn ignition switch to ON. • Measure voltage between breakout box Pins 49 and 60.	No voltage ▶	REPLACE pump motor relay.
	12 volts ▶	SERVICE or REPLACE cable harness Circuit 461.

Fig. 60 Pinpoint Tests C13e, C14, C14a, C14b & C14c: ABS Lamp ON After Vehicle Starts. 1992 Continental, Sable & Taurus

TEST STEP	RESULT ▶	ACTION TO TAKE
C13e CHECK CIRCUIT 604		
• Check continuity between breakout box Pin 49 and Pin S1 on pump motor connector 7-pin plug (harness side).	Continuity ▶	REVERIFY reading at C13.
	No Continuity ▶	SERVICE or REPLACE cable harness Circuit 604.
C14 CHECK MOTOR SPEED SENSOR SHORT TO BATTERY +		
• Turn ignition switch to ON. • Measure voltage between breakout box Pins 31 and 60.	No voltage ▶	GO to Step C15.
	12 volts ▶	GO to Step C14a.
C14a CHECK PUMP MOTOR		
• Disconnect pump motor to relay 4-pin plug connector. • Turn ignition switch to ON. • Measure voltage between breakout box Pins 31 and 60.	No voltage ▶	REPLACE pump and motor.
	12 volts ▶	GO to Step C14b.
C14b CHECK CIRCUIT 462		
• Disconnect wire harness to relay 7-pin plug. • Turn ignition switch to ON. • Measure voltage between breakout box Pins 31 and 60.	No voltage ▶	GO to Step C14c.
	12 volts ▶	SERVICE or REPLACE cable harness Circuit 462.
C14c CHECK CIRCUIT 604		
• Turn ignition switch to ON. • Measure voltage between breakout box Pins 49 and 60.	No voltage ▶	REPLACE pump motor relay.
	12 volts ▶	SERVICE or REPLACE cable harness Circuit 604.

Fig. 61 Pinpoint Tests C13e, C14, C14a, C14b & C14c: ABS Lamp ON After Vehicle Starts). 1992 Crown Victoria, Grand Marquis & Town Car

TEST STEP		RESULT	▶	ACTION TO TAKE
C15	CHECK MOTOR SPEED SENSOR SHORT TO GROUND			
	• Check for continuity between breakout box Pins 31 and 60.	No Continuity	▶	GO to Step **C16**.
		Continuity	▶	GO to Step **C15a**.
C15a	CHECK PUMP MOTOR			
	• Disconnect pump to motor relay 4-pin plug connector.	Continuity	▶	GO to Step **C15b**.
	• Check for continuity between breakout box Pins 31 and 60.	No Continuity	▶	REPLACE pump and motor.
C15b	CHECK CIRCUIT 462			
	• Disconnect wire harness to relay 7-pin plug.	Continuity	▶	SERVICE or REPLACE cable harness Circuit 462.
	• Check for continuity between breakout box Pins 31 and 60.	No Continuity	▶	GO to Step **C15c**.
C15c	CHECK CIRCUIT 461			
	• Check for continuity between breakout box Pins 49 and 60.	Continuity	▶	SERVICE Or REPLACE cable harness Circuit 461.
		No Continuity	▶	REPLACE pump motor relay.
C16	CHECK PUMP MOTOR OPERATION			
	• Reconnect pump motor relay to pump and wire harness. • Jumper Pins 15, 34 and 60 at breakout box. • Turn ignition to ON position.	Pump motor runs	▶	VERIFY Symptom.
		Pump motor does not run	▶	GO to Step **C16a**.

Fig. 62 Pinpoint Tests C15, C15a, C15b, C15c & C16: ABS Lamp ON After Vehicle Starts. 1992

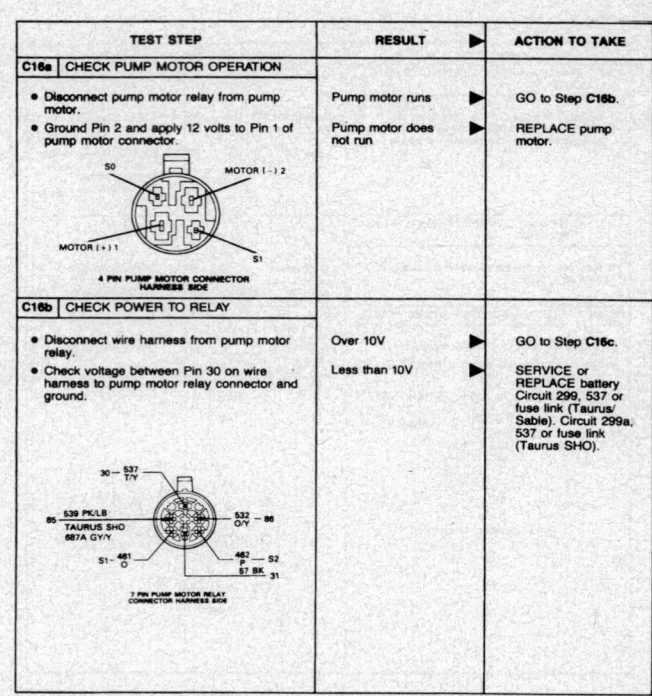

TEST STEP		RESULT	▶	ACTION TO TAKE
C16a	CHECK PUMP MOTOR OPERATION			
	• Disconnect pump motor relay from pump motor.	Pump motor runs	▶	GO to Step **C16b**.
	• Ground Pin 2 and apply 12 volts to Pin 1 of pump motor connector.	Pump motor does not run	▶	REPLACE pump motor.
C16b	CHECK POWER TO RELAY			
	• Disconnect wire harness from pump motor relay.	Over 10V	▶	GO to Step **C16c**.
	• Check voltage between Pin 30 on wire harness to pump motor relay connector and ground.	Less than 10V	▶	SERVICE or REPLACE battery Circuit 299, 537 or fuse link (Taurus/Sable). Circuit 299a, 537 or fuse link (Taurus SHO).

Fig. 63 Pinpoint Tests C16a & C16b: ABS Lamp ON After Vehicle Starts. 1992

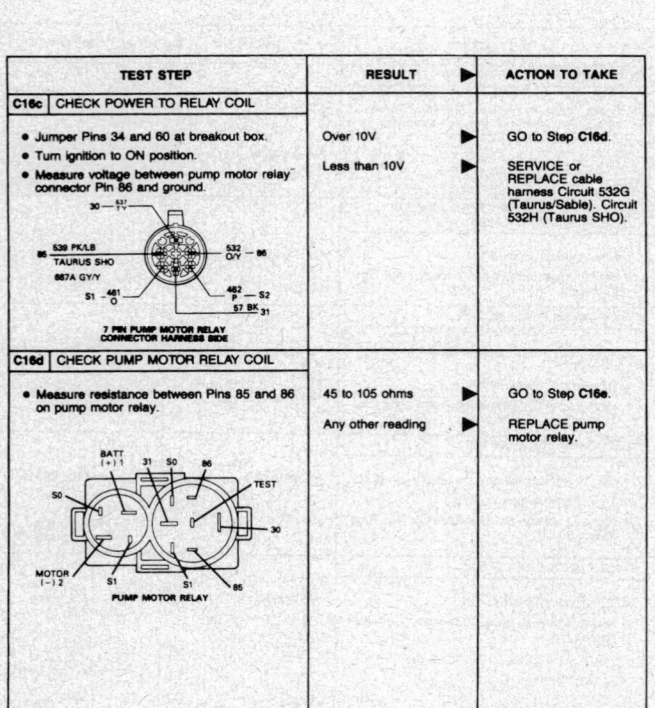

TEST STEP		RESULT	▶	ACTION TO TAKE
C16c	CHECK POWER TO RELAY COIL			
	• Jumper Pins 34 and 60 at breakout box. • Turn ignition to ON position. • Measure voltage between pump motor relay connector Pin 86 and ground.	Over 10V	▶	GO to Step **C16d**.
		Less than 10V	▶	SERVICE or REPLACE cable harness Circuit 532G (Taurus/Sable). Circuit 532H (Taurus SHO).
C16d	CHECK PUMP MOTOR RELAY COIL			
	• Measure resistance between Pins 85 and 86 on pump motor relay.	45 to 105 ohms	▶	GO to Step **C16e**.
		Any other reading	▶	REPLACE pump motor relay.

Fig. 64 Pinpoint Tests C16c & C16d: ABS Lamp ON After Vehicle Starts. 1992

TEST STEP		RESULT	▶	ACTION TO TAKE
C16e	CHECK CIRCUIT 539			
	• Check for continuity between Breakout Box Pin 15 and Pin 85 on wire harness to pump motor relay connector.	Continuity	▶	GO to Step **C16f**.
		No Continuity	▶	SERVICE or REPLACE cable harness Circuit 539.
C16f	CHECK CIRCUIT 57			
	• Check for continuity between wire harness to pump motor relay connector Pin 31 and ground.	Continuity	▶	GO to Step **C16g**.
		No Continuity	▶	SERVICE or REPLACE cable harness Circuit 57 or 57A (Taurus/Sable). Circuit 57S or 57R (Taurus SHO).
C16g	CHECK PUMP MOTOR RELAY			
	• Connect battery + to Pin 86 and battery – to Pin 85 of pump motor relay. • Check for continuity between Pin 30 and Pin 1 on relay.	Continuity	▶	GO to Step **C16h**.
		No Continuity	▶	REPLACE pump motor relay.
C16h	CHECK PUMP MOTOR RELAY			
	• Check continuity between Pins 2 and 31 on pump motor relay.	Continuity	▶	REPLACE computer module.
		No Continuity	▶	REPLACE pump motor relay.

Fig. 65 Pinpoint Tests C16e, C16f, C16g & C16h: ABS Lamp ON After Vehicle Starts. 1992 Continental, Sable & Town Car

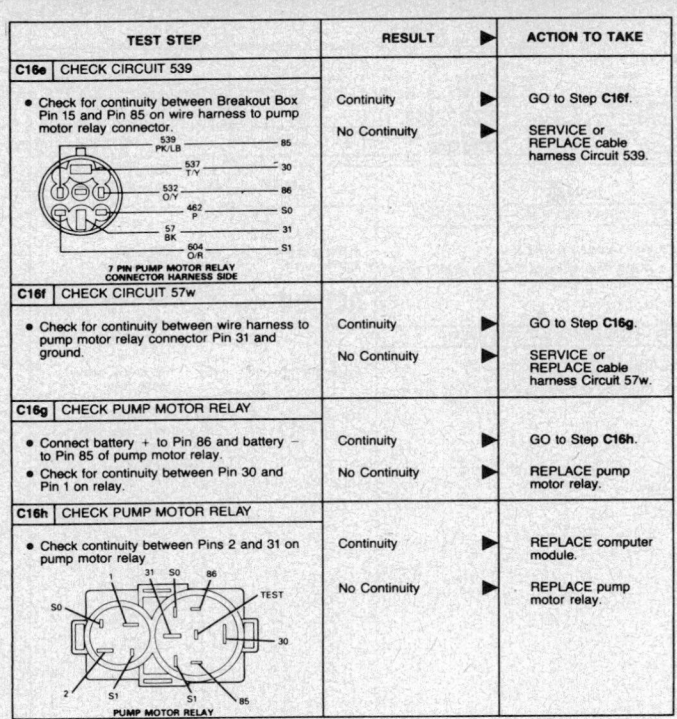

TEST STEP	RESULT	▶	ACTION TO TAKE
C16e CHECK CIRCUIT 539			
• Check for continuity between Breakout Box Pin 15 and Pin 85 on wire harness to pump motor relay connector.	Continuity	▶	GO to Step **C16f**.
	No Continuity	▶	SERVICE or REPLACE cable harness Circuit 539.
C16f CHECK CIRCUIT 57w			
• Check for continuity between wire harness to pump motor relay connector Pin 31 and ground.	Continuity	▶	GO to Step **C16g**.
	No Continuity	▶	SERVICE or REPLACE cable harness Circuit 57w.
C16g CHECK PUMP MOTOR RELAY			
• Connect battery + to Pin 86 and battery – to Pin 85 of pump motor relay.	Continuity	▶	GO to Step **C16h**.
• Check for continuity between Pin 30 and Pin 1 on relay.	No Continuity	▶	REPLACE pump motor relay.
C16h CHECK PUMP MOTOR RELAY			
• Check continuity between Pins 2 and 31 on pump motor relay	Continuity	▶	REPLACE computer module.
	No Continuity	▶	REPLACE pump motor relay.

Fig. 66 Pinpoint Tests C16e, C16f, C16g & C16h: ABS Lamp ON After Vehicle Starts. 1992 Crown Victoria, Grand Marquis & Town Car

	WARNING LIGHTS SEQUENCE							
Warning Lamps	Ignition On	Cranking Engine	Engine Running	Vehicle Moving	Braking with/without Anti-Lock	Vehicle Stopped	Engine Idle	Ignition Off
Check Anti-Lock (Amber)	▨		▨					
Brake (Red)								

TEST STEP	RESULT	▶	ACTION TO TAKE
BEFORE RUNNING TEST STEP D — ADJUST PEDAL POSITION SWITCH	Pedal feel normal during ABS cycling		Condition corrected.
	Pedal feel not normal during ABS		PERFORM Test D.
D1 CHECK PEDAL TRAVEL SWITCH AND CIRCUITRY			
• Turn ignition switch Off.			
• Disconnect 55-pin plug from controller.			

Fig. 67 Test D1: Warning Sequence Normal/Brake Pedal Rises Or Drops Excessively During ABS Cycling. 1992 Continental, Sable & Taurus

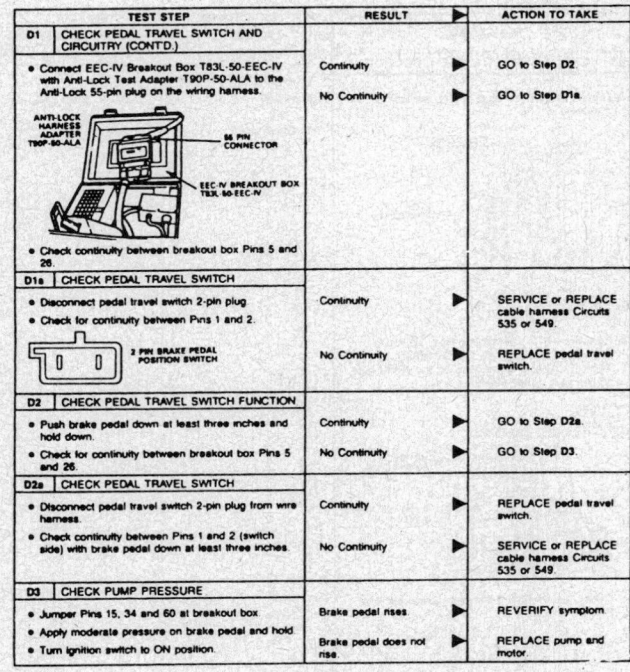

TEST STEP	RESULT	▶	ACTION TO TAKE
D1 CHECK PEDAL TRAVEL SWITCH AND CIRCUITRY (CONT'D.)			
• Connect EEC-IV Breakout Box T83L-50-EEC-IV with Anti-Lock Test Adapter T90P-50-ALA to the Anti-Lock 55-pin plug on the wiring harness.	Continuity	▶	GO to Step **D2**.
	No Continuity	▶	GO to Step **D1a**.
• Check continuity between breakout box Pins 5 and 26.			
D1a CHECK PEDAL TRAVEL SWITCH			
• Disconnect pedal travel switch 2-pin plug.	Continuity	▶	SERVICE or REPLACE cable harness Circuits 535 or 549.
• Check for continuity between Pins 1 and 2.	No Continuity	▶	REPLACE pedal travel switch.
D2 CHECK PEDAL TRAVEL SWITCH FUNCTION			
• Push brake pedal down at least three inches and hold down.	Continuity	▶	GO to Step **D2a**.
• Check for continuity between breakout box Pins 5 and 26.	No Continuity	▶	GO to Step **D3**.
D2a CHECK PEDAL TRAVEL SWITCH			
• Disconnect pedal travel switch 2-pin plug from wire harness.	Continuity	▶	REPLACE pedal travel switch.
• Check continuity between Pins 1 and 2 (switch side) with brake pedal down at least three inches.	No Continuity	▶	SERVICE or REPLACE cable harness Circuits 535 or 549.
D3 CHECK PUMP PRESSURE			
• Jumper Pins 15, 34 and 60 at breakout box	Brake pedal rises	▶	REVERIFY symptom.
• Apply moderate pressure on brake pedal and hold.	Brake pedal does not rise.	▶	REPLACE pump and motor.
• Turn ignition switch to ON position.			

Fig. 68 Pinpoint Tests D1, D1a, D2, D2a & D3: Warning Sequence Normal/Brake Pedal Rises Or Drops Excessively During ABS Cycling. 1992 Sable & Taurus

	WARNING INDICATORS SEQUENCE							
Warning Indicators	Ignition On	Cranking Engine	Engine Running	Vehicle Moving	Braking with/without Anti-Lock	Vehicle Stopped	Engine Idle	Ignition Off
Check Anti-Lock (Amber)	▨		▨					
Brake (Red)	▮		▮					

TEST STEP	RESULT	▶	ACTION TO TAKE
BEFORE RUNNING TEST STEP D — ADJUST PEDAL POSITION SWITCH AS OUTLINED IN THIS SECTION.	Pedal feel normal during ABS cycling		Condition corrected.
	Pedal feel not normal during ABS		PERFORM Test D.
D1 CHECK PEDAL TRAVEL SWITCH AND CIRCUITRY			
• Turn ignition switch to OFF position.			
• Disconnect 55-pin plug from controller.			

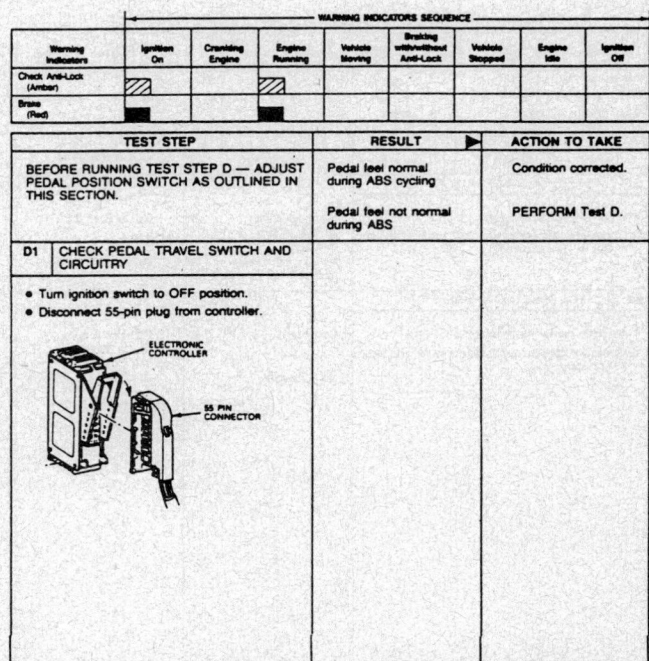

Fig. 69 Test D1: Warning Sequence Normal/Brake Pedal Rises Or Drops Excessively During ABS Cycling. 1992 Crown Victoria, Grand Marquis & Town Car

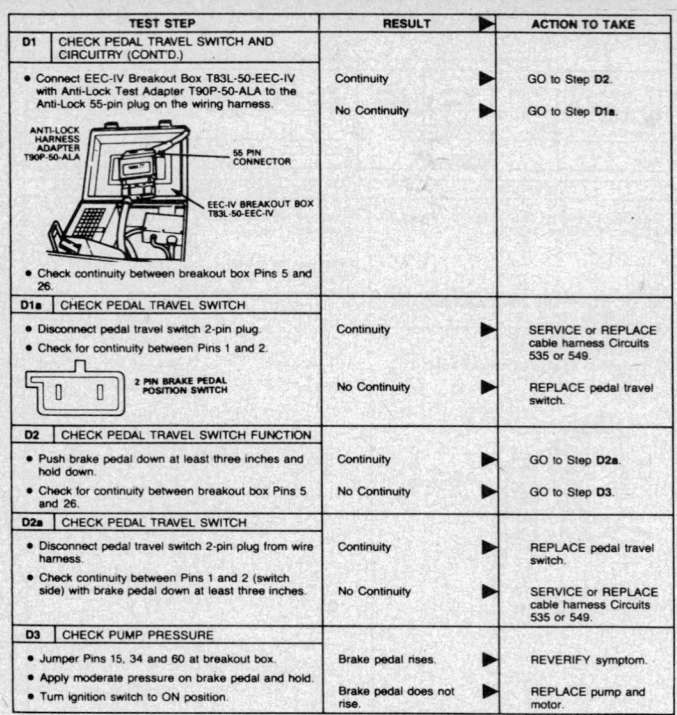

TEST STEP	RESULT	▶	ACTION TO TAKE
D1 CHECK PEDAL TRAVEL SWITCH AND CIRCUITRY (CONT'D.)			
• Connect EEC-IV Breakout Box T83L-50-EEC-IV with Anti-Lock Test Adapter T90P-50-ALA to the Anti-Lock 55-pin plug on the wiring harness.	Continuity	▶	GO to Step D2.
	No Continuity	▶	GO to Step D1a.
• Check continuity between breakout box Pins 5 and 26.			
D1a CHECK PEDAL TRAVEL SWITCH			
• Disconnect pedal travel switch 2-pin plug.	Continuity	▶	SERVICE or REPLACE cable harness Circuits 535 or 549.
• Check for continuity between Pins 1 and 2.	No Continuity	▶	REPLACE pedal travel switch.
D2 CHECK PEDAL TRAVEL SWITCH FUNCTION			
• Push brake pedal down at least three inches and hold down.	Continuity	▶	GO to Step D2a.
• Check for continuity between breakout box Pins 5 and 26.	No Continuity	▶	GO to Step D3.
D2a CHECK PEDAL TRAVEL SWITCH			
• Disconnect pedal travel switch 2-pin plug from wire harness.	Continuity	▶	REPLACE pedal travel switch.
• Check continuity between Pins 1 and 2 (switch side) with brake pedal down at least three inches.	No Continuity	▶	SERVICE or REPLACE cable harness Circuits 535 or 549.
D3 CHECK PUMP PRESSURE			
• Jumper Pins 15, 34 and 60 at breakout box.	Brake pedal rises.	▶	REVERIFY symptom.
• Apply moderate pressure on brake pedal and hold.	Brake pedal does not rise.	▶	REPLACE pump and motor.
• Turn ignition switch to ON position.			

Fig. 70   Pinpoint Tests D1, D1a, D2, D2a & D3: Warning Sequence Normal/Brake Pedal Rises Or Drops Excessively During ABS Cycling. 1992 Crown Victoria, Grand Marquis & Town Car

Warning Lamps	WARNING LIGHTS SEQUENCE							
	Ignition On	Cranking Engine	Engine Running	Vehicle Moving	Braking with/without Anti-Lock	Vehicle Stopped	Engine Idle	Ignition Off
Check Anti-Lock (Amber)	▨		▨▨					
Brake (Red)		▨						

TEST STEP	RESULT	▶	ACTION TO TAKE
E1 VERIFY PUMP MOTOR CONDITION			
• With vehicle standing still:	Pump runs with ignition in OFF.	▶	GO to Step E2.
• Check if pump motor runs with ignition switch in ON or OFF position.	Pump runs with ignition in ON.	▶	GO to Step E3.
E2 CHECK PUMP MOTOR RELAY			
• Remove pump motor relay.	Continuity	▶	REPLACE pump motor relay
• Check for continuity between Pin 30 and test pin on the relay.	No Continuity	▶	REVERIFY that pump motor runs with ignition OFF

Fig. 71   Pinpoint Tests E1 & E2: Warning Sequence Normal/ABS Pump Motor Run Continuously. 1992 Continental, Sable & Taurus

Warning Indicators	WARNING INDICATORS SEQUENCE							
	Ignition On	Cranking Engine	Engine Running	Vehicle Moving	Braking with/without Anti-Lock	Vehicle Stopped	Engine Idle	Ignition Off
Check Anti-Lock (Amber)	▨		▨					
Brake (Red)	■		■					

TEST STEP	RESULT	▶	ACTION TO TAKE
E1 VERIFY PUMP MOTOR CONDITION			
• With vehicle standing still:	Pump runs with ignition in OFF position.	▶	GO to Step E2.
• Check if pump motor runs with ignition switch in ON or OFF position.	Pump runs with ignition in ON position.	▶	GO to Step E3.
E2 CHECK PUMP MOTOR RELAY			
• Remove pump motor relay.	Continuity	▶	REPLACE pump motor relay.
• Check for continuity between Pin 30 and test pin on the relay.	No Continuity	▶	REVERIFY that pump motor runs with ignition in OFF position.

Fig. 72   Pinpoint Tests E1 & E2: Warning Sequence Normal/ABS Pump Motor Run Continuously. 1992 Crown Victoria, Grand Marquis & Town Car

TEST STEP	RESULT	▶	ACTION TO TAKE
E3 CHECK CIRCUIT 539 TO GROUND			
• Disconnect 55-pin plug from electronic controller.	Continuity	▶	GO to Step E3a.
	No Continuity	▶	GO to Step E4.
• Connect EEC-IV Breakout Box, T83L-50-EEC-IV with Anti-Lock Test Adapter T90P-50-ALA or equivalent to the Anti-Lock 55-pin plug wiring harness.			
• Check for continuity between breakout box Pins 15 and 60.			

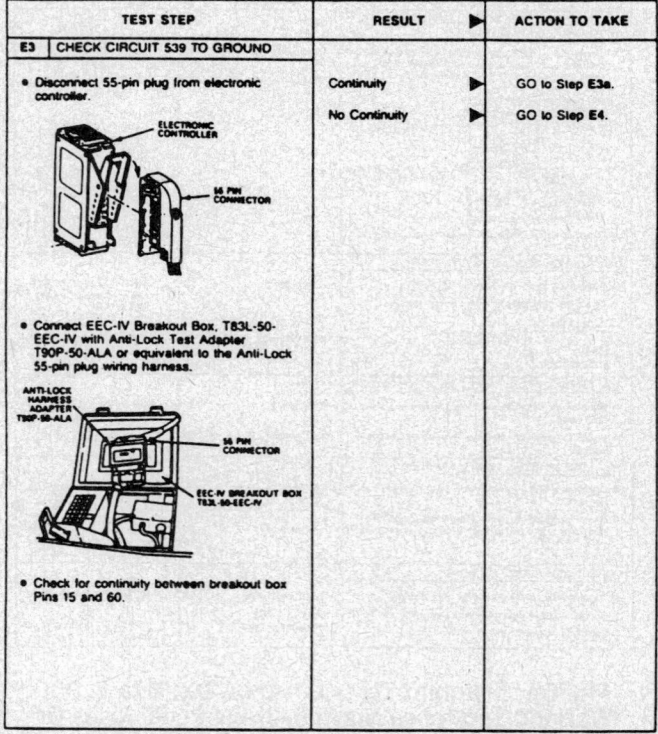

Fig. 73   Test E3: Warning Sequence Normal/ABS Pump Motor Run Continuously. 1992

Fig. 74 (Pinpoint Tests E3a & E4)

TEST STEP	RESULT ▶	ACTION TO TAKE
E3a CHECK CIRCUIT 539		
• Disconnect pump motor relay from wire harness. • Check for continuity between breakout box Pins 15 and 60.	Continuity ▶	SERVICE or REPLACE cable harness circuit
	No Continuity ▶	REPLACE pump motor relay.
E4 CHECK CONTROLLER		
• Reconnect pump motor relay and electronic controller. • Turn ignition to ON.	Pump motor runs ▶	REPLACE electronic controller.
	Pump motor does not run. ▶	REVERIFY symptom.

Fig. 74   Pinpoint Tests E3a & E4: Warning Sequence Normal/ABS Pump Motor Run Continuously. 1992

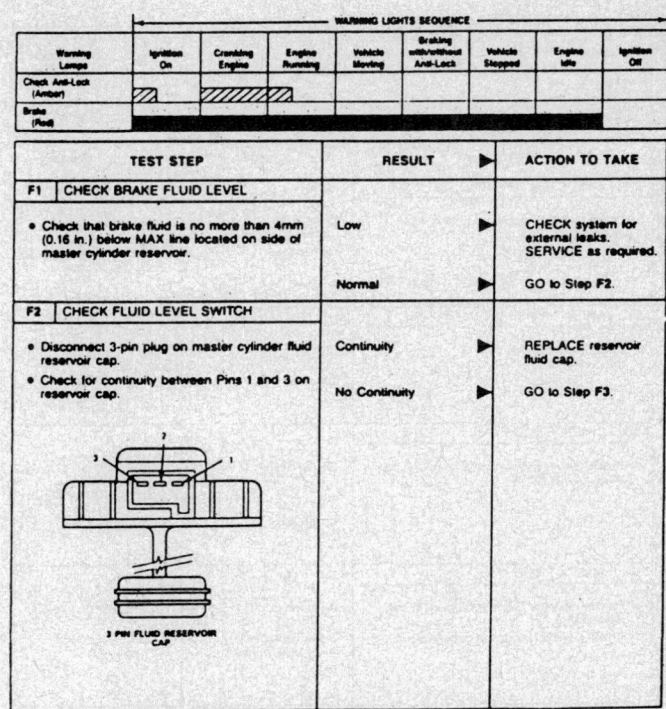

Warning Lamps	Ignition On	Cranking Engine	Engine Running	Vehicle Moving	Braking with/without Anti-Lock	Vehicle Stopped	Engine Idle	Ignition Off
Check Anti-Lock (Amber)	▨		▨▨					
Brake (Red)								

TEST STEP	RESULT ▶	ACTION TO TAKE
F1 CHECK BRAKE FLUID LEVEL		
• Check that brake fluid is no more than 4mm (0.16 in.) below MAX line located on side of master cylinder reservoir.	Low ▶	CHECK system for external leaks. SERVICE as required.
	Normal ▶	GO to Step F2.
F2 CHECK FLUID LEVEL SWITCH		
• Disconnect 3-pin plug on master cylinder fluid reservoir cap. • Check for continuity between Pins 1 and 3 on reservoir cap.	Continuity ▶	REPLACE reservoir fluid cap.
	No Continuity ▶	GO to Step F3.

Fig. 75   Pinpoint Tests F1 & F2: Brake Lamp ON w/ABS Lamp OFF, Parking Brake Released & Lining Wear Checked. 1992 Continental, Sable & Taurus

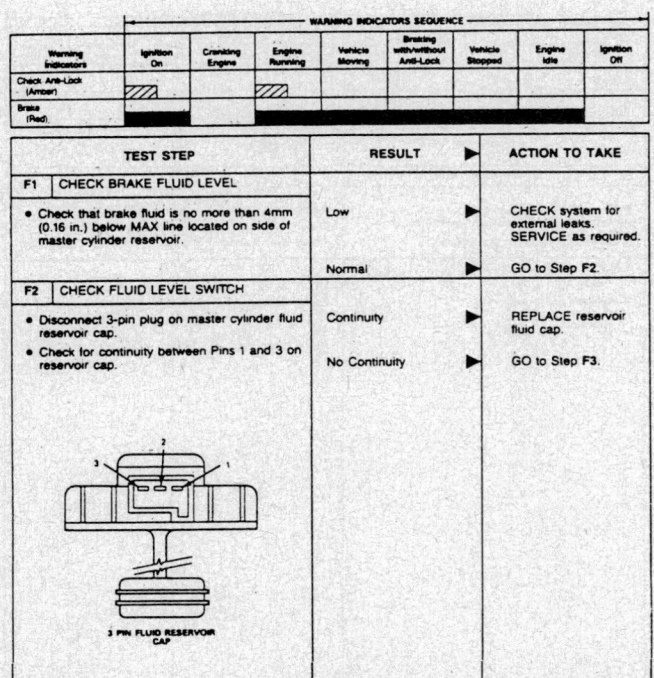

Warning Indicators	Ignition On	Cranking Engine	Engine Running	Vehicle Moving	Braking with/without Anti-Lock	Vehicle Stopped	Engine Idle	Ignition Off
Check Anti-Lock (Amber)	▨		▨▨					
Brake (Red)								

TEST STEP	RESULT ▶	ACTION TO TAKE
F1 CHECK BRAKE FLUID LEVEL		
• Check that brake fluid is no more than 4mm (0.16 in.) below MAX line located on side of master cylinder reservoir.	Low ▶	CHECK system for external leaks. SERVICE as required.
	Normal ▶	GO to Step F2.
F2 CHECK FLUID LEVEL SWITCH		
• Disconnect 3-pin plug on master cylinder fluid reservoir cap. • Check for continuity between Pins 1 and 3 on reservoir cap.	Continuity ▶	REPLACE reservoir fluid cap.
	No Continuity ▶	GO to Step F3.

Fig. 76   Pinpoint Tests F1 & F2: Brake Lamp ON w/ABS Lamp OFF, Parking Brake Released & Lining Wear Checked. 1992 Crown Victoria, Grand Marquis & Town Car

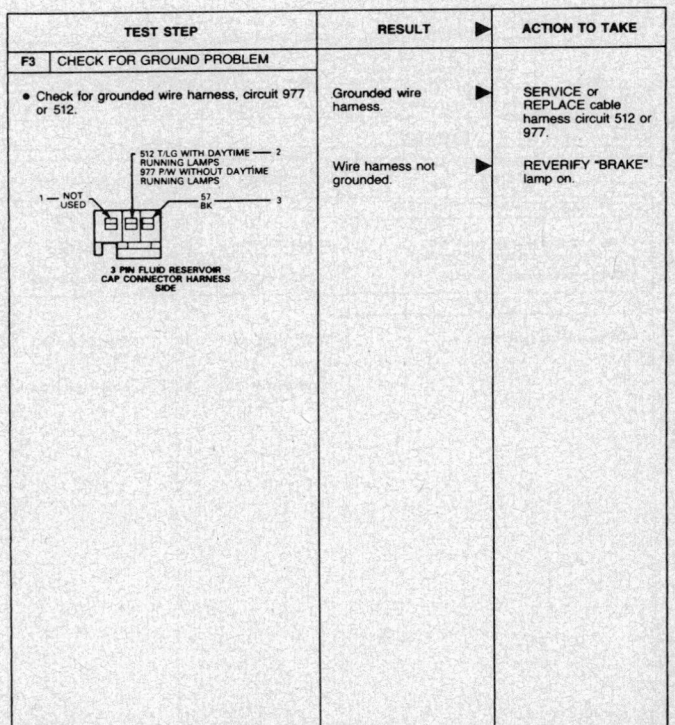

TEST STEP	RESULT ▶	ACTION TO TAKE
F3 CHECK FOR GROUND PROBLEM		
• Check for grounded wire harness, circuit 977 or 512.	Grounded wire harness. ▶	SERVICE or REPLACE cable harness circuit 512 or 977.
	Wire harness not grounded. ▶	REVERIFY "BRAKE" lamp on.

Fig. 77   Test F3: Brake Warning Lamp ON w/Anti-Lock Lamp OFF, Parking Brake Released & Lining Wear Checked. 1992

CONTINENTAL, CROWN VICTORIA, GRAND MARQUIS, SABLE, TAURUS & TOWN CAR

Fig. 78 — Warning Indicators Sequence

Warning Indicators	Ignition On	Cranking Engine	Engine Running	Vehicle Moving	Braking with/without Anti-Lock	Vehicle Stopped	Engine Idle	Ignition Off
Check Anti-Lock (Amber)								
Brake (Red)	■		■					

TEST STEP	RESULT ▶	ACTION TO TAKE
G1 CHECK IGNITION FEED AND FUSE		
• Check for 12 volts to lamp socket with ignition ON.	12V ▶	GO to Step G2.
	No voltage ▶	SERVICE ignition feed or fuse as required.
G2 CHECK WARNING LAMP BULB		
• Check warning lamp bulb	Bulb good ▶	GO to Step G3.
	Bulb bad ▶	REPLACE Bulb.
G3 CHECK CIRCUIT 603		
• Check continuity between lamp socket and breakout box Pin 52	No Continuity ▶	SERVICE or REPLACE cable harness Circuit 603.
	Continuity ▶	GO to Step G4.
G4 CHECK DIODE		
• Inspect diode for damage or loose or bad connection.	Diode good ▶	REVERIFY symptom.
• Check if diode is installed backwards.	Diode damaged or installed backwards. ▶	REPLACE diode.

FM4029100364000X

Fig. 78 Pinpoint Tests G1, G2, G3 & G4: No Warning Lamp ON When Ignition Switch Turned ON. 1992 Crown Victoria, Grand Marquis & Town Car

Fig. 79 — Warning Lights Sequence

Warning Lamp	Ignition On	Cranking Engine	Engine Running	Vehicle Moving	Braking with/without Anti-Lock	Vehicle Stopped	Engine Idle	Ignition Off
Check Anti-Lock (Amber)								
Brake (Red)		■						

TEST STEP	RESULT ▶	ACTION TO TAKE
G1 CHECK IGNITION FEED AND FUSE		
• Check for 12 volts to lamp socket with ignition ON	12 volts ▶	GO to Step G2.
	No voltage ▶	SERVICE ignition feed or fuse as required.
G2 CHECK WARNING LAMP BULB		
• Check warning lamp bulb	Bulb good ▶	GO to Step G3.
	Bulb bad ▶	REPLACE Bulb
G3 CHECK CIRCUIT 606		
• Check continuity between lamp socket and breakout box Pin 52	No Continuity ▶	SERVICE or REPLACE cable harness Circuit 606, 606A or 606B (Taurus/Sable). Circuit 606, 606B or 606D (Taurus SHO)
	Continuity ▶	REVERIFY symptom.

FM4029100365000X

Fig. 79 Pinpoint Tests G1, G2 & G3: No Warning Lamp ON When Ignition Switch Turned ON. 1992 Continental, Sable & Taurus

Fig. 80 — Warning Lights Sequence

Warning Lamps	Ignition On	Cranking Engine	Engine Running	Vehicle Moving	Braking with/without Anti-Lock	Vehicle Stopped	Engine Idle	Ignition Off
Check Anti-Lock (Amber)	▨	▨▨						
Brake (Red)	■	■						

TEST STEP	RESULT ▶	ACTION TO TAKE
H1 CHECK COMPONENT MOUNTING		
• Check for proper brake pedal and booster/master cylinder attachment.	Pedal still spongy ▶	GO to Step H2
• Bleed brake system as outlined.	Pedal feels normal ▶	Condition corrected.
H2 BLEED BRAKE SYSTEM		
• Rebleed brake system.	Pedal still spongy ▶	REPLACE master cylinder
	Pedal feels normal ▶	Condition corrected.

FM4029100366000X

Fig. 80 Pinpoint Tests H1 & H2: Spongy Pedal With/Without ABS Function, No Warning Lamp. 1992 Continental, Sable & Taurus

Fig. 81 — Warning Indicators Sequence

Warning Indicators	Ignition On	Cranking Engine	Engine Running	Vehicle Moving	Braking with/without Anti-Lock	Vehicle Stopped	Engine Idle	Ignition Off
Check Anti-Lock (Amber)	▨		▨					
Brake (Red)	■		■					

TEST STEP	RESULT ▶	ACTION TO TAKE
H1 CHECK COMPONENT MOUNTING		
• Check for proper brake pedal and booster/master cylinder attachment.	Pedal still spongy ▶	GO to Step H2.
• Bleed brake system as outlined.	Pedal feels normal ▶	Condition corrected.
H2 BLEED BRAKE SYSTEM		
• Rebleed brake system.	Pedal still spongy ▶	REPLACE master cylinder.
	Pedal feels normal ▶	Condition corrected.

FM4029100367000X

Fig. 81 Pinpoint Tests H1 & H2: Spongy Pedal With/Without ABS Function, No Warning Lamp. 1992 Crown Victoria, Grand Marquis & Town Car

Warning Lamps	Ignition On	Cranking Engine	Engine Running	Vehicle Moving	Braking with/without Anti-Lock	Vehicle Stopped	Engine Idle	Ignition Off
Check Anti-Lock (Amber)	▨	▨▨▨						
Brake (Red)		███						

— WARNING LIGHTS SEQUENCE —

TEST STEP	RESULT ▶	ACTION TO TAKE
J1 VERIFY CONDITION		
• Verify condition exists as reported. • Turn air suspension OFF if so equipped. • Bleed brake system as outlined. • Turn air suspension back ON when vehicle is off hoist.	Vehicle tracks properly ▶ Vehicle still tracks poorly. ▶	Condition corrected. GO to Step J2.
J2 CHECK ANTI-LOCK VALVE OPERATION		
• Turn air suspension OFF if so equipped. • Turn ignition switch OFF. • Disconnect 55-pin plug from electronic controller.		

ELECTRONIC CONTROLLER

55 PIN CONNECTOR

FM4029100368000X

Fig. 82 Pinpoint Tests J1 & J2: Poor Vehicle Tracking During ABS Function. 1992 Continental, Sable & Taurus

Warning Indicators	Ignition On	Cranking Engine	Engine Running	Vehicle Moving	Braking with/without Anti-Lock	Vehicle Stopped	Engine Idle	Ignition Off
Check Anti-Lock (Amber)	▨		▨					
Brake (Red)		██	██					

— WARNING INDICATORS SEQUENCE —

TEST STEP	RESULT ▶	ACTION TO TAKE
J1 VERIFY CONDITION		
• Verify condition exists as reported. • Turn air suspension OFF if so equipped. • Bleed brake system as outlined. • Turn air suspension back ON when vehicle is off hoist.	Vehicle tracks properly ▶ Vehicle still tracks poorly. ▶	Condition corrected. GO to Step J2.
J2 CHECK ANTI-LOCK VALVE OPERATION		
• Turn air suspension OFF if so equipped. • Turn ignition switch OFF. • Disconnect 55-pin plug from electronic controller.		

ELECTRONIC CONTROLLER

55 PIN CONNECTOR

FM4029100369000X

Fig. 83 Pinpoint Tests J1 & J2: Poor Vehicle Tracking During ABS Function. 1992 Crown Victoria, Grand Marquis & Town Car

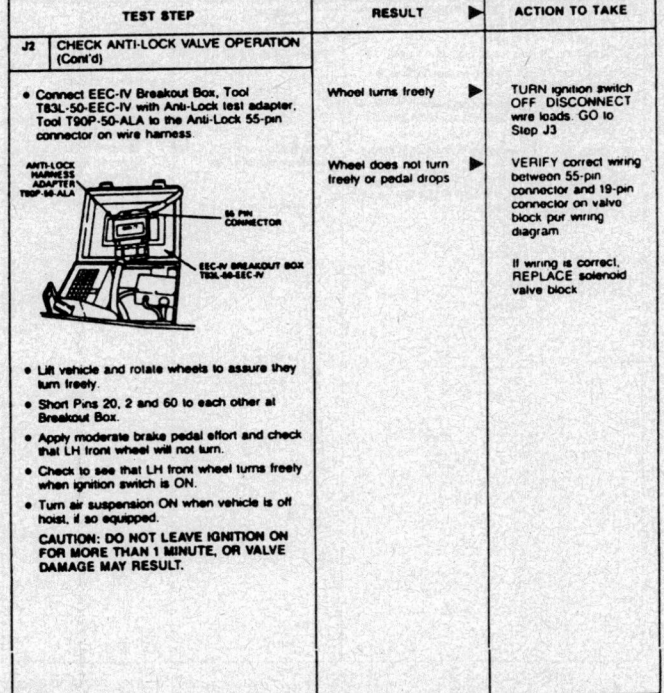

TEST STEP	RESULT ▶	ACTION TO TAKE
J2 CHECK ANTI-LOCK VALVE OPERATION (Cont'd)		
• Connect EEC-IV Breakout Box, Tool T83L-50-EEC-IV with Anti-Lock test adapter, Tool T90P-50-ALA to the Anti-Lock 55-pin connector on wire harness.	Wheel turns freely ▶ Wheel does not turn freely or pedal drops ▶	TURN ignition switch OFF. DISCONNECT wire loads. GO to Step J3 VERIFY correct wiring between 55-pin connector and 19-pin connector on valve block per wiring diagram If wiring is correct, REPLACE solenoid valve block
• Lift vehicle and rotate wheels to assure they turn freely. • Short Pins 20, 2 and 60 to each other at Breakout Box. • Apply moderate brake pedal effort and check that LH front wheel will not turn. • Check to see that LH front wheel turns freely when ignition switch is ON. • Turn air suspension ON when vehicle is off hoist, if so equipped. **CAUTION: DO NOT LEAVE IGNITION ON FOR MORE THAN 1 MINUTE, OR VALVE DAMAGE MAY RESULT.**		

FM4029100370000X

Fig. 84 Test J2: Poor Vehicle Tracking During ABS Function. 1992 Continental, Sable & Taurus

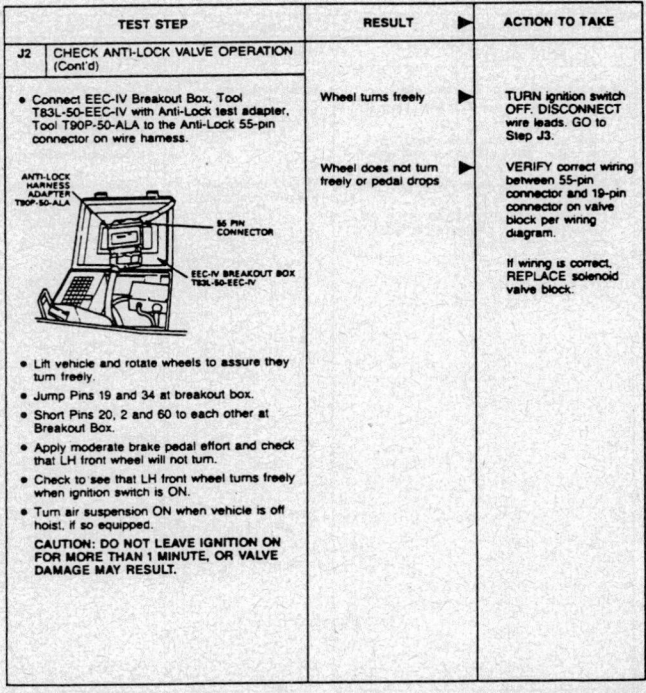

TEST STEP	RESULT ▶	ACTION TO TAKE
J2 CHECK ANTI-LOCK VALVE OPERATION (Cont'd)		
• Connect EEC-IV Breakout Box, Tool T83L-50-EEC-IV with Anti-Lock test adapter, Tool T90P-50-ALA to the Anti-Lock 55-pin connector on wire harness.	Wheel turns freely ▶ Wheel does not turn freely or pedal drops ▶	TURN ignition switch OFF. DISCONNECT wire leads. GO to Step J3. VERIFY correct wiring between 55-pin connector and 19-pin connector on valve block per wiring diagram. If wiring is correct, REPLACE solenoid valve block.
• Lift vehicle and rotate wheels to assure they turn freely. • Jump Pins 19 and 34 at breakout box. • Short Pins 20, 2 and 60 to each other at Breakout Box. • Apply moderate brake pedal effort and check that LH front wheel will not turn. • Check to see that LH front wheel turns freely when ignition switch is ON. • Turn air suspension ON when vehicle is off hoist, if so equipped. **CAUTION: DO NOT LEAVE IGNITION ON FOR MORE THAN 1 MINUTE, OR VALVE DAMAGE MAY RESULT.**		

FM4029100371000X

Fig. 85 Test J2: Poor Vehicle Tracking During ABS Function. 1992 Crown Victoria, Grand Marquis & Town Car

TEST STEP	RESULT ▶	ACTION TO TAKE
J3 CHECK ANTI-LOCK OPERATION RH FRONT WHEEL • Jump Pins 19 and 34 at breakout box. • Short Pins 38, 21 and 60 to each other at breakout box. • Apply moderate brake pedal effort. Check that RH front wheel will not turn with ignition OFF. • Check that RH front wheel turns freely with ignition ON. CAUTION: DO NOT LEAVE IGNITION ON FOR MORE THAN 1 MINUTE OR VALVE DAMAGE MAY RESULT.	Wheel turns freely ▶ Wheel does not turn freely or pedal drops	TURN ignition switch off. DISCONNECT wire leads. GO to Step J4. VERIFY correct wiring between 55-pin connector and 19-pin connector on valve block per wiring diagram. If wiring is correct, REPLACE solenoid valve block.
J4 CHECK ANTI-LOCK OPERATION RH REAR WHEEL • Jump Pins 19 and 34 at breakout box. • Short Pins 55, 18 and 60 to each other at breakout box. • Apply moderate brake pedal effort. Check that RH rear wheel will not turn with ignition OFF. • Check that RH rear wheel turns freely with ignition ON. CAUTION: DO NOT LEAVE IGNITION ON FOR MORE THAN 1 MINUTE OR VALVE DAMAGE MAY RESULT.	Wheel turns freely ▶ Wheel does not turn freely or pedal drops	TURN ignition switch off. DISCONNECT wire leads. GO to Step J5. VERIFY correct wiring between 55-pin connector and 19-pin connector on valve block per wiring diagram. If wiring is correct, REPLACE solenoid valve block.

FM4029100372000X

Fig. 86   Pinpoint Tests J3 & J4: Poor Vehicle Tracking During ABS Function. 1992 Sable & Taurus

TEST STEP	RESULT ▶	ACTION TO TAKE
J3 CHECK ANTI-LOCK OPERATION RH FRONT WHEEL • Jump Pins 19 and 34 at breakout box. • Short Pins 38, 21 and 60 to each other at breakout box. • Apply moderate brake pedal effort. Check that RH front wheel will not turn with ignition OFF. • Check that RH front wheel turns freely with ignition ON. CAUTION: DO NOT LEAVE IGNITION ON FOR MORE THAN 1 MINUTE OR VALVE DAMAGE MAY RESULT.	Wheel turns freely ▶ Wheel does not turn freely or pedal drops ▶	TURN ignition switch off. DISCONNECT wire leads. GO to Step J4. VERIFY correct wiring between 55-pin connector and 19-pin connector on valve block per wiring diagram. If wiring is correct, REPLACE solenoid valve block.
J4 CHECK ANTI-LOCK OPERATION RH REAR WHEEL • Jump Pins 19 and 34 at breakout box. • Short Pins 55, 18 and 60 to each other at breakout box. • Apply moderate brake pedal effort. Check that RH rear wheel will not turn with ignition OFF. • Check that RH rear wheel turns freely with ignition ON. CAUTION: DO NOT LEAVE IGNITION ON FOR MORE THAN 1 MINUTE OR VALVE DAMAGE MAY RESULT.	Wheel turns freely ▶ Wheel does not turn freely or pedal drops ▶	TURN ignition switch off. DISCONNECT wire leads. GO to Step J5. VERIFY correct wiring between 55-pin connector and 19-pin connector on valve block per wiring diagram. If wiring is correct, REPLACE solenoid valve block.

FM4029100373000X

Fig. 87   Pinpoint Tests J3 & J4: Poor Vehicle Tracking During ABS Function. 1992 Crown Victoria, Grand Marquis & Town Car

TEST STEP	RESULT ▶	ACTION TO TAKE
J5 CHECK ANTI-LOCK OPERATION LH REAR WHEEL • Jump Pins 19 and 34 at breakout box. • Short Pins 36, 54 and 60 to each other at breakout box. • Apply moderate brake pedal effort. Check that LH rear wheel will not turn with ignition OFF. • Check that LH rear wheel turns freely with ignition ON. CAUTION: DO NOT LEAVE IGNITION ON FOR MORE THAN 1 MINUTE OR VALVE DAMAGE MAY RESULT.	Wheel turns freely ▶ Wheel does not turn freely or pedal drops ▶	TURN ignition switch off. DISCONNECT wire leads and Breakout Box. LOWER vehicle. REVERIFY symptom. VERIFY correct wiring between 55-pin connector and 19-pin connector on valve block per wiring diagram. If wiring is correct, REPLACE solenoid valve block.

FM4029100374000X

Fig. 88   Test J5: Poor Vehicle Tracking During ABS Function. 1992 Sable & Taurus

TEST STEP	RESULT ▶	ACTION TO TAKE
J5 CHECK ANTI-LOCK OPERATION LH REAR WHEEL • Jump Pins 19 and 34 at breakout box. • Short Pins 36, 54 and 60 to each other at breakout box. • Apply moderate brake pedal effort. Check that LH rear wheel will not turn with ignition OFF. • Check that LH rear wheel turns freely with ignition ON. CAUTION: DO NOT LEAVE IGNITION ON FOR MORE THAN 1 MINUTE OR VALVE DAMAGE MAY RESULT.	Wheel turns freely ▶ Wheel does not turn freely or pedal drops ▶	TURN ignition switch off. DISCONNECT wire leads and Breakout Box. LOWER vehicle. REVERIFY symptom. VERIFY correct wiring between 55-pin connector and 19-pin connector on valve block per wiring diagram. If wiring is correct, REPLACE solenoid valve block.

FM4029100375000X

Fig. 89   Test J5: Poor Vehicle Tracking During ABS Function. 1992 Crown Victoria, Grand Marquis & Town Car

TEST STEP		RESULT	▶	ACTION TO TAKE
K1	**VERIFY CONDITION — ONE SIDE OR BOTH SIDES**			
• Traction assist inoperative:		Both rear wheels	▶	GO to Step **K2**.
		One rear wheel only	▶	GO to Step **K4**.
K2	**CHECK BRAKELAMP SWITCH**			
• Connect EEC-IV Breakout Box T831-50-EEC-IV with Anti-Lock test adapter, Tool T90P-50-ALA to the Anti-Lock 55-pin connector on the wire harness. • Turn ignition switch to ON position. • Measure voltage between breakout box Pins 32 and 60. • NOTE: DO NOT apply brake pedal while performing this test.		No voltage	▶	GO to Step **K3**.
		12V	▶	REPLACE brakelamp switch or SERVICE cable harness Circuit 511.
K3	**CHECK PRESSURE SWITCH AND CIRCUITRY**			
• Check continuity between breakout box Pins 13 and 26.		Continuity	▶	VERIFY Symptom.
		No Continuity	▶	GO to Step **K3a**.
K3a	**CHECK PRESSURE SWITCH**			
• Disconnect 19-pin valve body connector from harness. • Check continuity between valve body Pins 11 and 12.		Continuity	▶	SERVICE or REPLACE cable harness Circuit 535, 535c or 547.
		No Continuity	▶	REPLACE valve body.
K4	**CHECK ABS FUNCTION**			
• Make an Anti-Lock stop on a slippery surface. • Notice if brake pedal rises when pump comes on or if the pedal continues downward when pump comes on.		Brake pedal rises	▶	REPLACE valve body.
		Brake pedal falls	▶	REPLACE pump and motor.

Fig. 90   Pinpoint Tests K1, K2, K3, K3a & K4: ABS Indicator Sequence Normal, False Cycling Of Traction Assist. 1992 Crown Victoria, Grand Marquis & Town Car

	Warning Indicators	Ignition On	Cranking Engine	Engine Running	Vehicle Moving	Braking with/without Anti-Lock	Vehicle Stopped	Engine Idle	Ignition Off
WARNING INDICATOR SEQUENCE									
	Check Anti-Lock (Amber)	▨		▨					
	Brake (Red)	■		■					

TEST STEP		RESULT	▶	ACTION TO TAKE
L1	**RUN SELF-TEST**			
• Refer to On-Board-Self-Test to run Self-Test.		Sensor code received.	▶	REPLACE sensor for code received.
		No codes in E-module	▶	VERIFY that traction assist system is false cycling.

Fig. 91   Test L1: ABS Indicator Sequence Normal, False Cycling Of Traction Assist. 1992 Crown Victoria, Grand Marquis & Town Car

TEST STEP		RESULT	▶	ACTION TO TAKE
AA1	**SERVICE CODE 11: ELECTRICAL DISTURBANCE**			
• Read all service codes and record. • After all service codes are read and written down, drive vehicle above 40 km/h (25 mph) to clear memory. • Read all service codes again		Service code 11 repeated	▶	REPLACE electronic controller.
		Memory erased or other service codes present except code 11	▶	PERFORM test step associated with service code or codes. REFER to On-Board Self-Test service code index, and SERVICE next code.

Fig. 92   Test AA1: Electronic Controller. 1992

TEST STEP		RESULT	▶	ACTION TO TAKE
BB1	**SERVICE CODE 22: NO REFERENCE VOLTAGE OR LH FRONT INLET VALVE**			
• Disconnect 55-pin plug from electronic controller.		10 volts minimum	▶	GO to Step **BB2**.
		Less than 10 volts	▶	REPLACE or SERVICE cable harness Circuit 532, 532C, 532D, 532E, 532F, 606, or 606C.

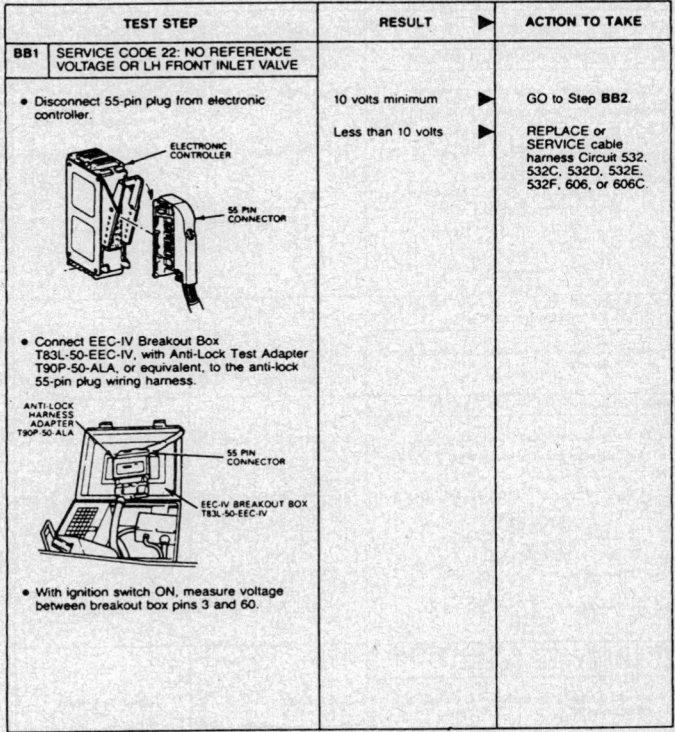

• Connect EEC-IV Breakout Box T83L-50-EEC-IV, with Anti-Lock Test Adapter T90P-50-ALA, or equivalent, to the anti-lock 55-pin plug wiring harness.

• With ignition switch ON, measure voltage between breakout box pins 3 and 60.

Fig. 93   Test BB1: Solenoid Valve. 1992 Continental

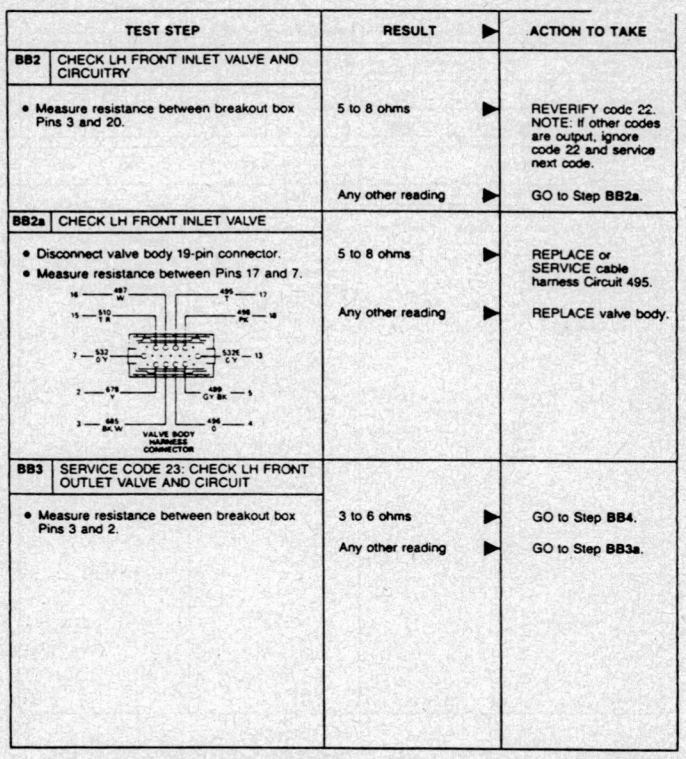

TEST STEP	RESULT ▶	ACTION TO TAKE
BB2 CHECK LH FRONT INLET VALVE AND CIRCUITRY		
• Measure resistance between breakout box Pins 3 and 20.	5 to 8 ohms ▶	REVERIFY code 22. NOTE: If other codes are output, ignore code 22 and service next code.
	Any other reading ▶	GO to Step BB2a.
BB2a CHECK LH FRONT INLET VALVE		
• Disconnect valve body 19-pin connector. • Measure resistance between Pins 17 and 7.	5 to 8 ohms ▶	REPLACE or SERVICE cable harness Circuit 495.
	Any other reading ▶	REPLACE valve body.
BB3 SERVICE CODE 23: CHECK LH FRONT OUTLET VALVE AND CIRCUIT		
• Measure resistance between breakout box Pins 3 and 2.	3 to 6 ohms ▶	GO to Step BB4.
	Any other reading ▶	GO to Step BB3a.

Fig. 94 Pinpoint Tests BB2, BB2a & BB3: Solenoid Valve. 1992 Continental

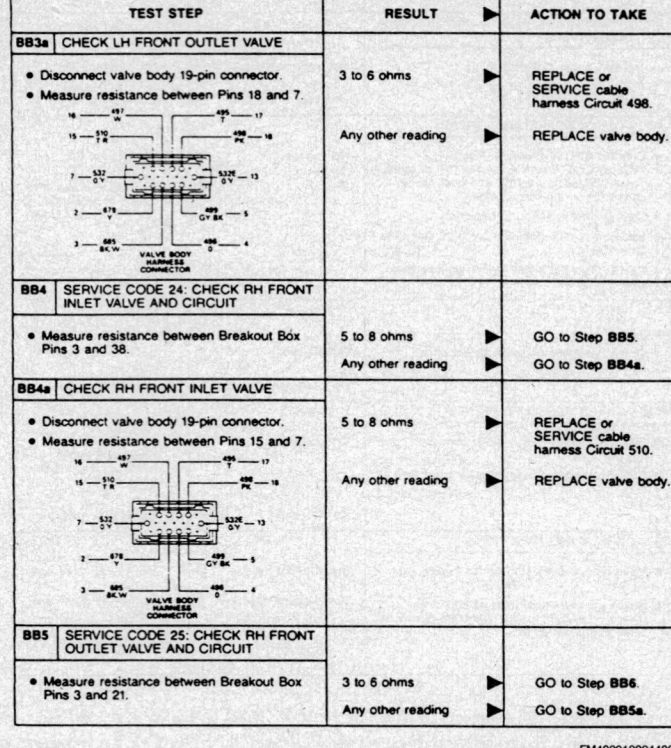

TEST STEP	RESULT ▶	ACTION TO TAKE
BB3a CHECK LH FRONT OUTLET VALVE		
• Disconnect valve body 19-pin connector. • Measure resistance between Pins 18 and 7.	3 to 6 ohms ▶	REPLACE or SERVICE cable harness Circuit 498.
	Any other reading ▶	REPLACE valve body.
BB4 SERVICE CODE 24: CHECK RH FRONT INLET VALVE AND CIRCUIT		
• Measure resistance between Breakout Box Pins 3 and 38.	5 to 8 ohms ▶	GO to Step BB5.
	Any other reading ▶	GO to Step BB4a.
BB4a CHECK RH FRONT INLET VALVE		
• Disconnect valve body 19-pin connector. • Measure resistance between Pins 15 and 7.	5 to 8 ohms ▶	REPLACE or SERVICE cable harness Circuit 510.
	Any other reading ▶	REPLACE valve body.
BB5 SERVICE CODE 25: CHECK RH FRONT OUTLET VALVE AND CIRCUIT		
• Measure resistance between Breakout Box Pins 3 and 21.	3 to 6 ohms ▶	GO to Step BB6.
	Any other reading ▶	GO to Step BB5a.

Fig. 95 Pinpoint Tests BB3a, BB4, BB4a & BB5: Solenoid Valve. 1992 Continental

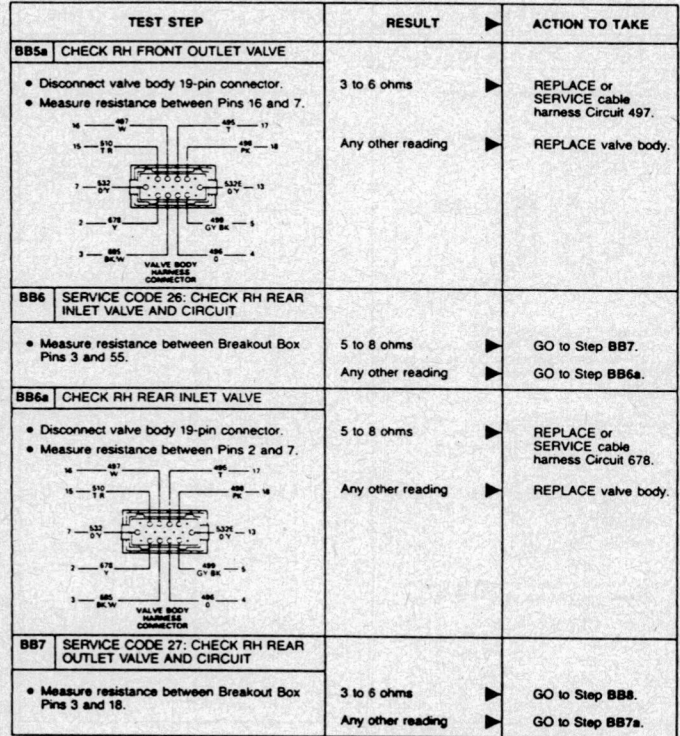

TEST STEP	RESULT ▶	ACTION TO TAKE
BB5a CHECK RH FRONT OUTLET VALVE		
• Disconnect valve body 19-pin connector. • Measure resistance between Pins 16 and 7.	3 to 6 ohms ▶	REPLACE or SERVICE cable harness Circuit 497.
	Any other reading ▶	REPLACE valve body.
BB6 SERVICE CODE 26: CHECK RH REAR INLET VALVE AND CIRCUIT		
• Measure resistance between Breakout Box Pins 3 and 55.	5 to 8 ohms ▶	GO to Step BB7.
	Any other reading ▶	GO to Step BB6a.
BB6a CHECK RH REAR INLET VALVE		
• Disconnect valve body 19-pin connector. • Measure resistance between Pins 2 and 7.	5 to 8 ohms ▶	REPLACE or SERVICE cable harness Circuit 678.
	Any other reading ▶	REPLACE valve body.
BB7 SERVICE CODE 27: CHECK RH REAR OUTLET VALVE AND CIRCUIT		
• Measure resistance between Breakout Box Pins 3 and 18.	3 to 6 ohms ▶	GO to Step BB8.
	Any other reading ▶	GO to Step BB7a.

Fig. 96 Pinpoint Tests BB5a, BB6, BB6a & BB7: Solenoid Valve. 1992 Continental

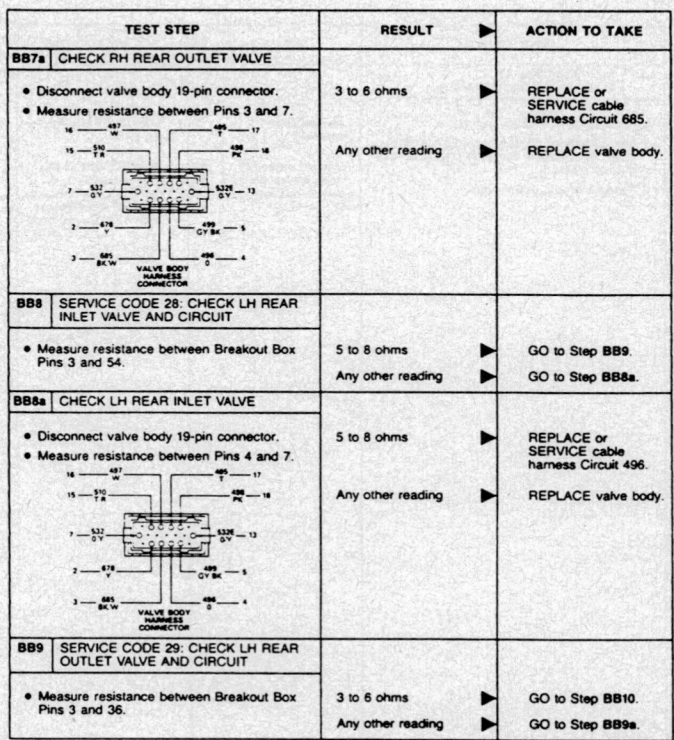

TEST STEP	RESULT ▶	ACTION TO TAKE
BB7a CHECK RH REAR OUTLET VALVE		
• Disconnect valve body 19-pin connector. • Measure resistance between Pins 3 and 7.	3 to 6 ohms ▶	REPLACE or SERVICE cable harness Circuit 685.
	Any other reading ▶	REPLACE valve body.
BB8 SERVICE CODE 28: CHECK LH REAR INLET VALVE AND CIRCUIT		
• Measure resistance between Breakout Box Pins 3 and 54.	5 to 8 ohms ▶	GO to Step BB9.
	Any other reading ▶	GO to Step BB8a.
BB8a CHECK LH REAR INLET VALVE		
• Disconnect valve body 19-pin connector. • Measure resistance between Pins 4 and 7.	5 to 8 ohms ▶	REPLACE or SERVICE cable harness Circuit 496.
	Any other reading ▶	REPLACE valve body.
BB9 SERVICE CODE 29: CHECK LH REAR OUTLET VALVE AND CIRCUIT		
• Measure resistance between Breakout Box Pins 3 and 36.	3 to 6 ohms ▶	GO to Step BB10.
	Any other reading ▶	GO to Step BB9a.

Fig. 97 Pinpoint Tests BB7a, BB8, BdB8a & BB9: Solenoid Valve. 1992 Continental

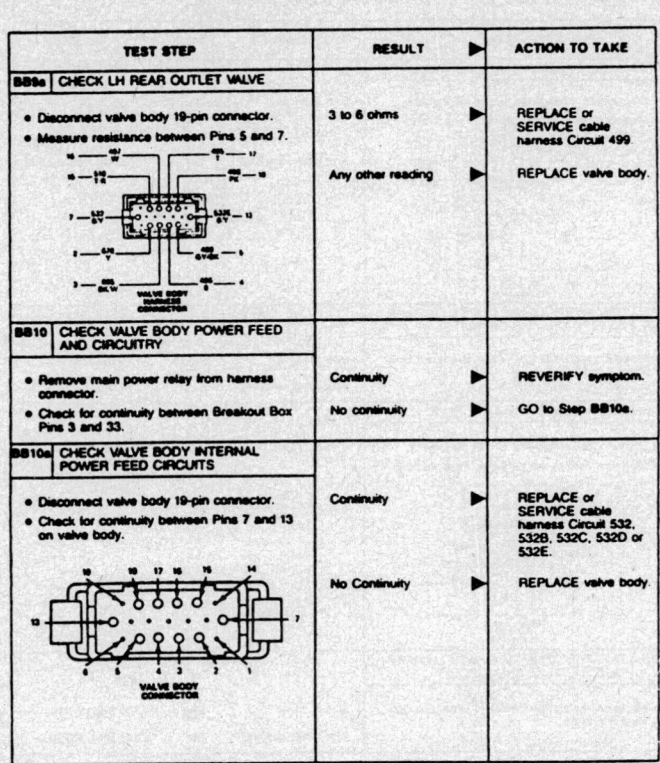

TEST STEP	RESULT ▶	ACTION TO TAKE
BB9a CHECK LH REAR OUTLET VALVE		
• Disconnect valve body 19-pin connector. • Measure resistance between Pins 5 and 7.	3 to 6 ohms ▶	REPLACE or SERVICE cable harness Circuit 499.
	Any other reading ▶	REPLACE valve body.
BB10 CHECK VALVE BODY POWER FEED AND CIRCUITRY		
• Remove main power relay from harness connector. • Check for continuity between Breakout Box Pins 3 and 33.	Continuity ▶	REVERIFY symptom.
	No continuity ▶	GO to Step BB10a.
BB10a CHECK VALVE BODY INTERNAL POWER FEED CIRCUITS		
• Disconnect valve body 19-pin connector. • Check for continuity between Pins 7 and 13 on valve body.	Continuity ▶	REPLACE or SERVICE cable harness Circuit 532, 532B, 532C, 532D or 532E.
	No Continuity ▶	REPLACE valve body.

Fig. 98   Pinpoint Tests BB9a, BB10 & BB10a: Solenoid Valve. 1992 Continental

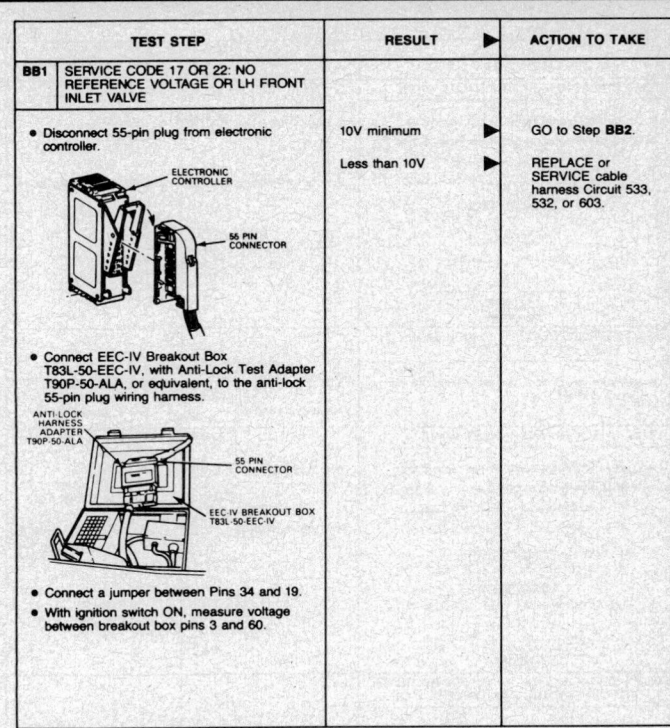

TEST STEP	RESULT ▶	ACTION TO TAKE
BB1 SERVICE CODE 17 OR 22: NO REFERENCE VOLTAGE OR LH FRONT INLET VALVE		
• Disconnect 55-pin plug from electronic controller.	10V minimum ▶	GO to Step BB2.
	Less than 10V ▶	REPLACE or SERVICE cable harness Circuit 533, 532, or 603.
• Connect EEC-IV Breakout Box T83L-50-EEC-IV, with Anti-Lock Test Adapter T90P-50-ALA, or equivalent, to the anti-lock 55-pin plug wiring harness.		
• Connect a jumper between Pins 34 and 19. • With ignition switch ON, measure voltage between breakout box pins 3 and 60.		

Fig. 99   Test BB1: Solenoid Valve. Crown Victoria, Grand Marquis & 1992 Town Car

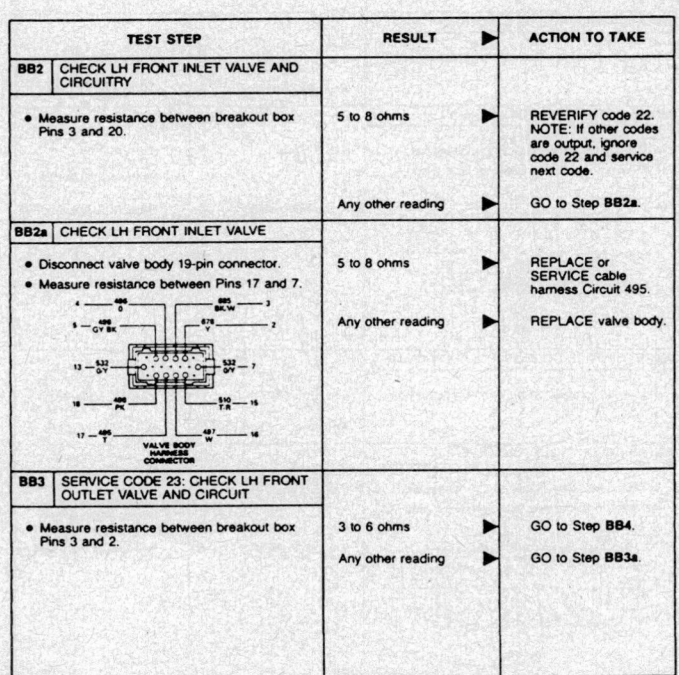

TEST STEP	RESULT ▶	ACTION TO TAKE
BB2 CHECK LH FRONT INLET VALVE AND CIRCUITRY		
• Measure resistance between breakout box Pins 3 and 20.	5 to 8 ohms ▶	REVERIFY code 22. NOTE: If other codes are output, ignore code 22 and service next code.
	Any other reading ▶	GO to Step BB2a.
BB2a CHECK LH FRONT INLET VALVE		
• Disconnect valve body 19-pin connector. • Measure resistance between Pins 17 and 7.	5 to 8 ohms ▶	REPLACE or SERVICE cable harness Circuit 495.
	Any other reading ▶	REPLACE valve body.
BB3 SERVICE CODE 23: CHECK LH FRONT OUTLET VALVE AND CIRCUIT		
• Measure resistance between breakout box Pins 3 and 2.	3 to 6 ohms ▶	GO to Step BB4.
	Any other reading ▶	GO to Step BB3a.

Fig. 100   Pinpoint Tests BB2, BB2a & BB3: Solenoid Valve. 1992 Crown Victoria, Grand Marquis & Town Car

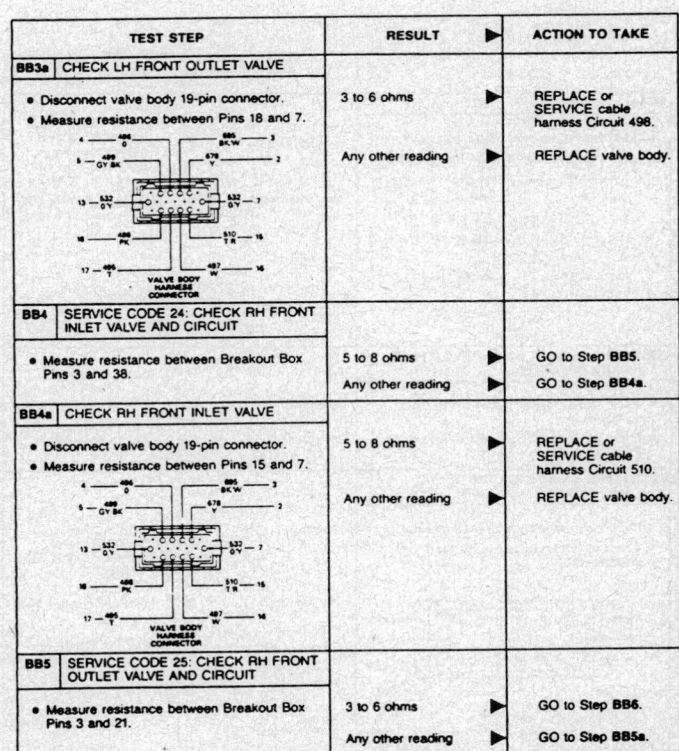

TEST STEP	RESULT ▶	ACTION TO TAKE
BB3a CHECK LH FRONT OUTLET VALVE		
• Disconnect valve body 19-pin connector. • Measure resistance between Pins 18 and 7.	3 to 6 ohms ▶	REPLACE or SERVICE cable harness Circuit 498.
	Any other reading ▶	REPLACE valve body.
BB4 SERVICE CODE 24: CHECK RH FRONT INLET VALVE AND CIRCUIT		
• Measure resistance between Breakout Box Pins 3 and 38.	5 to 8 ohms ▶	GO to Step BB5.
	Any other reading ▶	GO to Step BB4a.
BB4a CHECK RH FRONT INLET VALVE		
• Disconnect valve body 19-pin connector. • Measure resistance between Pins 15 and 7.	5 to 8 ohms ▶	REPLACE or SERVICE cable harness Circuit 510.
	Any other reading ▶	REPLACE valve body.
BB5 SERVICE CODE 25: CHECK RH FRONT OUTLET VALVE AND CIRCUIT		
• Measure resistance between Breakout Box Pins 3 and 21.	3 to 6 ohms ▶	GO to Step BB6.
	Any other reading ▶	GO to Step BB5a.

Fig. 101   Pinpoint Tests BB3a, BB4, BB4a & BB5: Solenoid Valve. 1992 Crown Victoria, Grand Marquis & Town Car

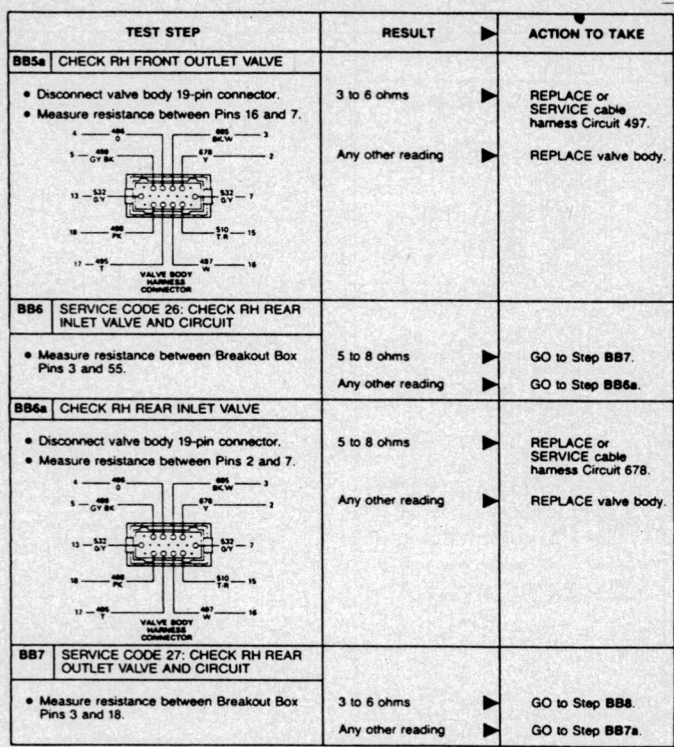

TEST STEP	RESULT ▶	ACTION TO TAKE
BB5a CHECK RH FRONT OUTLET VALVE		
• Disconnect valve body 19-pin connector. • Measure resistance between Pins 16 and 7.	3 to 6 ohms ▶	REPLACE or SERVICE cable harness Circuit 497.
	Any other reading ▶	REPLACE valve body.
BB6 SERVICE CODE 26: CHECK RH REAR INLET VALVE AND CIRCUIT		
• Measure resistance between Breakout Box Pins 3 and 55.	5 to 8 ohms ▶	GO to Step **BB7**.
	Any other reading ▶	GO to Step **BB6a**.
BB6a CHECK RH REAR INLET VALVE		
• Disconnect valve body 19-pin connector. • Measure resistance between Pins 2 and 7.	5 to 8 ohms ▶	REPLACE or SERVICE cable harness Circuit 678.
	Any other reading ▶	REPLACE valve body.
BB7 SERVICE CODE 27: CHECK RH REAR OUTLET VALVE AND CIRCUIT		
• Measure resistance between Breakout Box Pins 3 and 18.	3 to 6 ohms ▶	GO to Step **BB8**.
	Any other reading ▶	GO to Step **BB7a**.

Fig. 102 Pinpoint Tests BB5a, BB6, BB6a & BB7: Solenoid Valve. 1992 Crown Victoria, Grand Marquis & Town Car

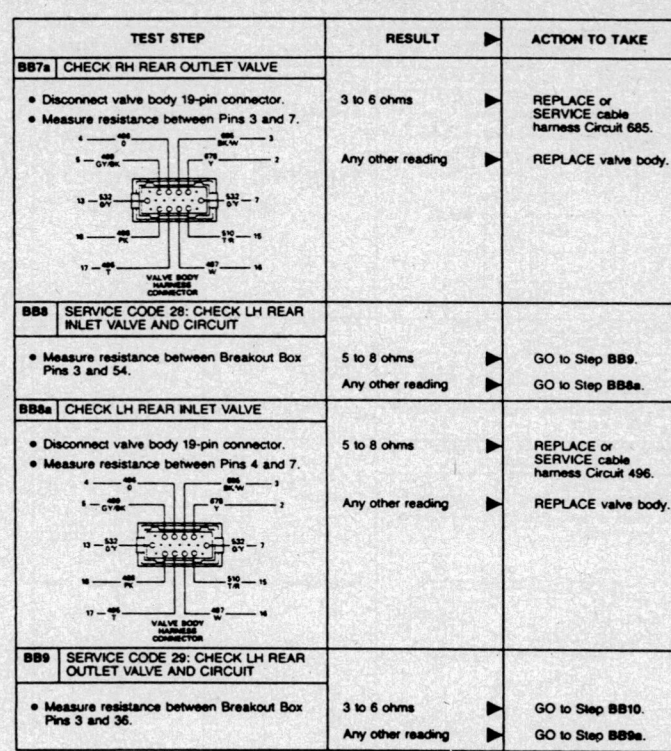

TEST STEP	RESULT ▶	ACTION TO TAKE
BB7a CHECK RH REAR OUTLET VALVE		
• Disconnect valve body 19-pin connector. • Measure resistance between Pins 3 and 7.	3 to 6 ohms ▶	REPLACE or SERVICE cable harness Circuit 685.
	Any other reading ▶	REPLACE valve body.
BB8 SERVICE CODE 28: CHECK LH REAR INLET VALVE AND CIRCUIT		
• Measure resistance between Breakout Box Pins 3 and 54.	5 to 8 ohms ▶	GO to Step **BB9**.
	Any other reading ▶	GO to Step **BB8a**.
BB8a CHECK LH REAR INLET VALVE		
• Disconnect valve body 19-pin connector. • Measure resistance between Pins 4 and 7.	5 to 8 ohms ▶	REPLACE or SERVICE cable harness Circuit 496.
	Any other reading ▶	REPLACE valve body.
BB9 SERVICE CODE 29: CHECK LH REAR OUTLET VALVE AND CIRCUIT		
• Measure resistance between Breakout Box Pins 3 and 36.	3 to 6 ohms ▶	GO to Step **BB10**.
	Any other reading ▶	GO to Step **BB9a**.

Fig. 103 Pinpoint Tests BB7a, BB8, BB8a & BB9: Solenoid Valve. 1992 Crown Victoria, Grand Marquis & Town Car

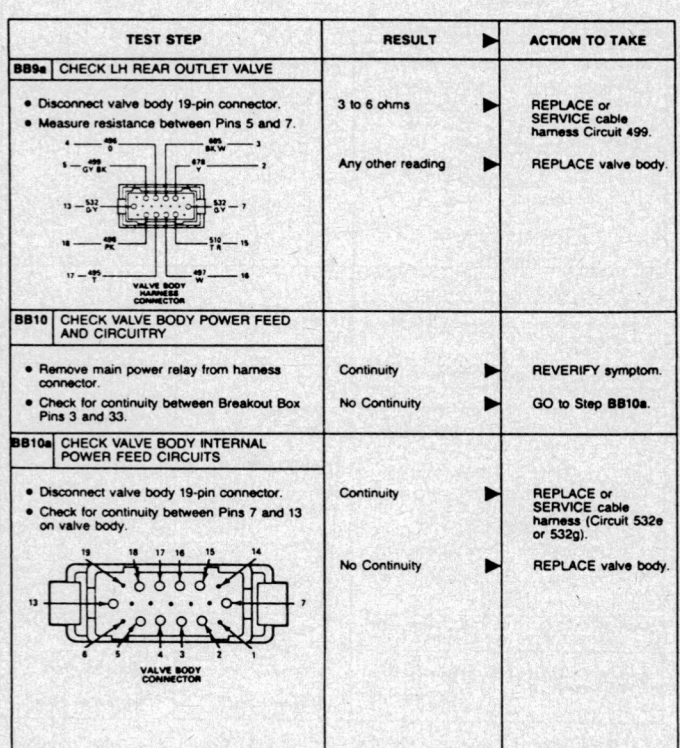

TEST STEP	RESULT ▶	ACTION TO TAKE
BB9a CHECK LH REAR OUTLET VALVE		
• Disconnect valve body 19-pin connector. • Measure resistance between Pins 5 and 7.	3 to 6 ohms ▶	REPLACE or SERVICE cable harness Circuit 499.
	Any other reading ▶	REPLACE valve body.
BB10 CHECK VALVE BODY POWER FEED AND CIRCUITRY		
• Remove main power relay from harness connector. • Check for continuity between Breakout Box Pins 3 and 33.	Continuity ▶	REVERIFY symptom.
	No Continuity ▶	GO to Step **BB10a**.
BB10a CHECK VALVE BODY INTERNAL POWER FEED CIRCUITS		
• Disconnect valve body 19-pin connector. • Check for continuity between Pins 7 and 13 on valve body.	Continuity ▶	REPLACE or SERVICE cable harness (Circuit 532e or 532g).
	No Continuity ▶	REPLACE valve body.

Fig. 104 Pinpoint Tests BB9a, BB10 & BB10a: Solenoid Valve. 1992 Crown Victoria, Grand Marquis & Town Car

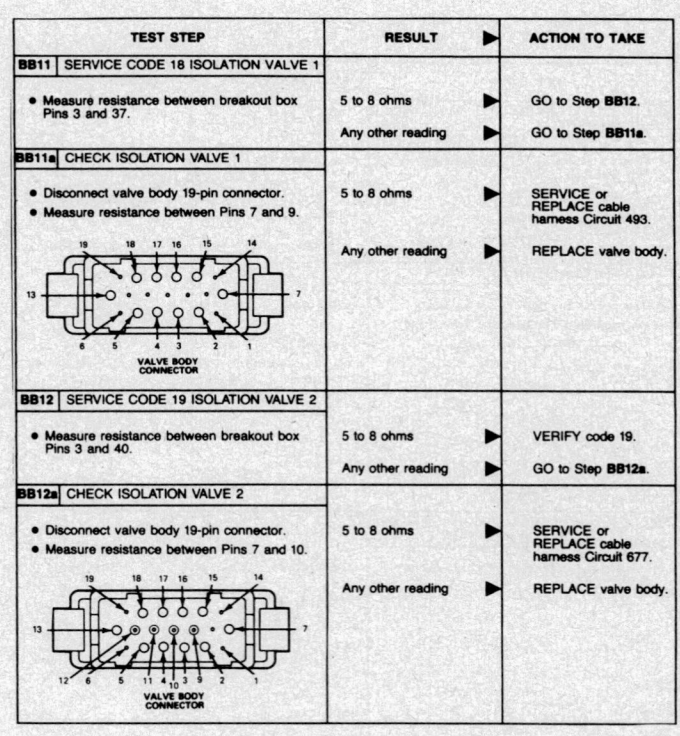

TEST STEP	RESULT ▶	ACTION TO TAKE
BB11 SERVICE CODE 18 ISOLATION VALVE 1		
• Measure resistance between breakout box Pins 3 and 37.	5 to 8 ohms ▶	GO to Step **BB12**.
	Any other reading ▶	GO to Step **BB11a**.
BB11a CHECK ISOLATION VALVE 1		
• Disconnect valve body 19-pin connector. • Measure resistance between Pins 7 and 9.	5 to 8 ohms ▶	SERVICE or REPLACE cable harness Circuit 493.
	Any other reading ▶	REPLACE valve body.
BB12 SERVICE CODE 19 ISOLATION VALVE 2		
• Measure resistance between breakout box Pins 3 and 40.	5 to 8 ohms ▶	VERIFY code 19.
	Any other reading ▶	GO to Step **BB12a**.
BB12a CHECK ISOLATION VALVE 2		
• Disconnect valve body 19-pin connector. • Measure resistance between Pins 7 and 10.	5 to 8 ohms ▶	SERVICE or REPLACE cable harness Circuit 677.
	Any other reading ▶	REPLACE valve body.

Fig. 105 Pinpoint Tests BB11, BB11a, BB12 & BB12a: Solenoid Valve. 1992 Crown Victoria, Grand Marquis & Town Car

TEST STEP	RESULT ▶	ACTION TO TAKE
BB1 SERVICE CODE 22: NO REFERENCE VOLTAGE OR LH FRONT INLET VALVE • Disconnect 55-pin plug from electronic controller.	10V minimum ▶	REMOVE jumper. GO to Step BB2.
	Less than 10V ▶	REPLACE or SERVICE cable harness Circuit 532, 532C, 532F, or 606 (Taurus/Sable). Circuit 532A, 532B, 532F, 606 or 606A (Taurus SHO).
• Connect EEC-IV Breakout Box T83L-50-EEC-IV, with Anti-Lock Test Adapter T90P-50-ALA, or equivalent, to the anti-lock 55-pin plug wiring harness. • Jump Pins 34 and 19. • With ignition switch ON, measure voltage between breakout box pins 3 and 60.		

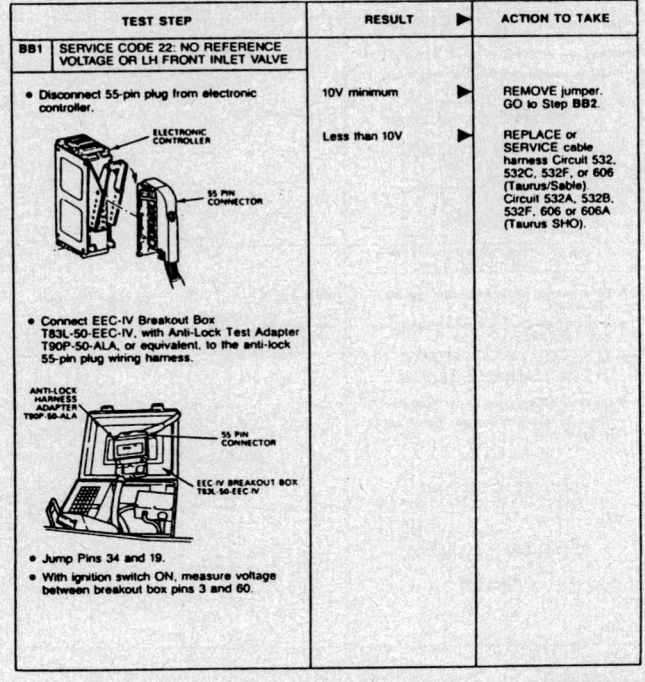

FM4029100255000X

Fig. 106 Test BB1: Solenoid Valve. 1992 Sable & Taurus

TEST STEP	RESULT ▶	ACTION TO TAKE
BB2 CHECK LH FRONT INLET VALVE AND CIRCUITRY • Measure resistance between breakout box Pins 3 and 20.	5 to 8 ohms ▶	REVERIFY code 22. NOTE: If other codes are output, ignore code 22 and service next code.
	Any other reading ▶	GO to Step BB2a.
BB2a CHECK LH FRONT INLET VALVE • Disconnect valve body 19-pin connector. • Measure resistance between Pins 17 and 7.	5 to 8 ohms ▶	REPLACE or SERVICE cable harness Circuit 495, 532C, 532D or 532E (Taurus/Sable). Circuit 495, 532C, 532D or 532G (Taurus SHO).
	Any other reading ▶	REPLACE valve body.
BB3 SERVICE CODE 23: CHECK LH FRONT OUTLET VALVE AND CIRCUIT • Measure resistance between breakout box Pins 3 and 2.	3 to 6 ohms ▶	GO to Step BB4.
	Any other reading ▶	GO to Step BB3a.

FM4029100256000X

Fig. 107 Pinpoint Tests BB2, BB2a & BB3: Solenoid Valve. 1992 Sable & Taurus

TEST STEP	RESULT ▶	ACTION TO TAKE
BB3a CHECK LH FRONT OUTLET VALVE • Disconnect valve body 19-pin connector. • Measure resistance between Pins 18 and 7.	3 to 6 ohms ▶	REPLACE or SERVICE cable harness Circuit 496.
	Any other reading ▶	REPLACE valve body.
BB4 SERVICE CODE 24: CHECK RH FRONT INLET VALVE AND CIRCUIT • Measure resistance between breakout box Pins 3 and 38.	5 to 8 ohms ▶	GO to Step BB5.
	Any other reading ▶	GO to Step BB4a.
BB4a CHECK RH FRONT INLET VALVE • Disconnect valve body 19-pin connector. • Measure resistance between Pins 15 and 7.	5 to 8 ohms ▶	REPLACE or SERVICE cable harness Circuit 510.
	Any other reading ▶	REPLACE valve body.
BB5 SERVICE CODE 25: CHECK RH FRONT OUTLET VALVE AND CIRCUIT • Measure resistance between breakout box Pins 3 and 21.	3 to 6 ohms ▶	GO to Step BB6.
	Any other reading ▶	GO to Step BB5a.

FM4029100257000X

Fig. 108 Pinpoint Tests BB3a, BB4, BB4a & BB5: Solenoid Valve. 1992 Sable & Taurus

TEST STEP	RESULT ▶	ACTION TO TAKE
BB5a CHECK RH FRONT OUTLET VALVE • Disconnect valve body 19-pin connector. • Measure resistance between Pins 16 and 7.	3 to 6 ohms ▶	REPLACE or SERVICE cable harness Circuit 497.
	Any other reading ▶	REPLACE valve body.
BB6 SERVICE CODE 26: CHECK RH REAR INLET VALVE AND CIRCUIT • Measure resistance between breakout box Pins 3 and 55.	5 to 8 ohms ▶	GO to Step BB7.
	Any other reading ▶	GO to Step BB6a.
BB6a CHECK RH REAR INLET VALVE • Disconnect valve body 19-pin connector. • Measure resistance between Pins 2 and 7.	5 to 8 ohms ▶	REPLACE or SERVICE cable harness Circuit 455 (Taurus/Sable). Circuit 678 (Taurus SHO).
	Any other reading ▶	REPLACE valve body.
BB7 SERVICE CODE 27: CHECK RH REAR OUTLET VALVE AND CIRCUIT • Measure resistance between breakout box Pins 3 and 18.	3 to 6 ohms ▶	GO to Step BB8.
	Any other reading ▶	GO to Step BB7a.

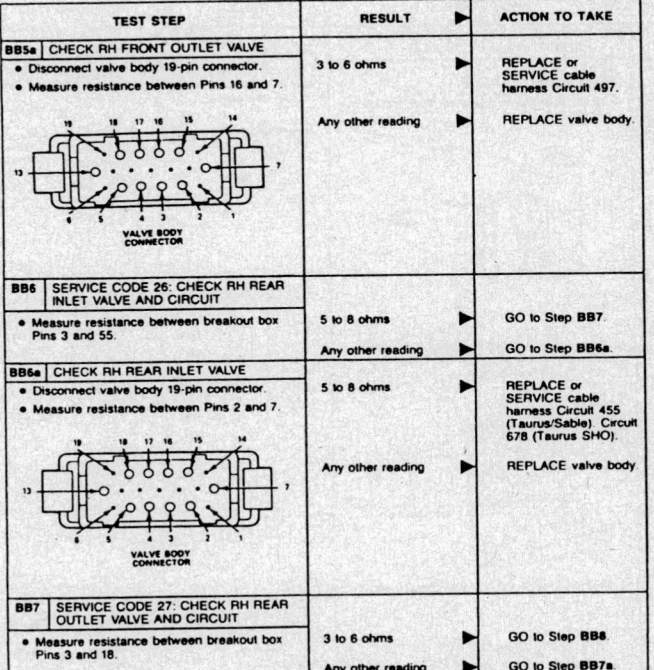

FM4029100258000X

Fig. 109 Pinpoint Tests BB5a, BB6, BB6a & BB7: Solenoid Valve. 1992 Sable & Taurus

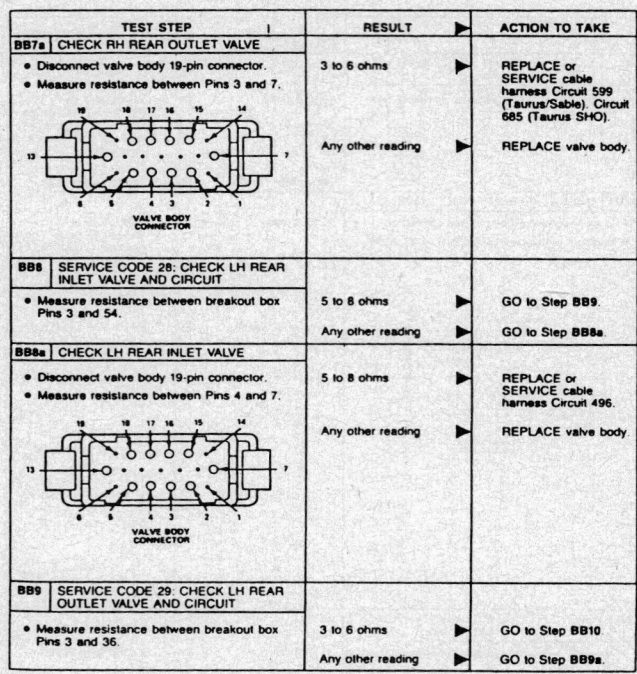

TEST STEP	RESULT	ACTION TO TAKE
BB7a CHECK RH REAR OUTLET VALVE		
• Disconnect valve body 19-pin connector. • Measure resistance between Pins 3 and 7.	3 to 6 ohms	REPLACE or SERVICE cable harness Circuit 599 (Taurus/Sable). Circuit 685 (Taurus SHO).
	Any other reading	REPLACE valve body.
BB8 SERVICE CODE 28: CHECK LH REAR INLET VALVE AND CIRCUIT		
• Measure resistance between breakout box Pins 3 and 54.	5 to 8 ohms	GO to Step BB9.
	Any other reading	GO to Step BB8a.
BB8a CHECK LH REAR INLET VALVE		
• Disconnect valve body 19-pin connector. • Measure resistance between Pins 4 and 7.	5 to 8 ohms	REPLACE or SERVICE cable harness Circuit 496.
	Any other reading	REPLACE valve body.
BB9 SERVICE CODE 29: CHECK LH REAR OUTLET VALVE AND CIRCUIT		
• Measure resistance between breakout box Pins 3 and 36.	3 to 6 ohms	GO to Step BB10.
	Any other reading	GO to Step BB9a.

Fig. 110   Pinpoint Tests BB7a, BB8, BB8a & BB9: Solenoid Valve. 1992 Sable & Taurus

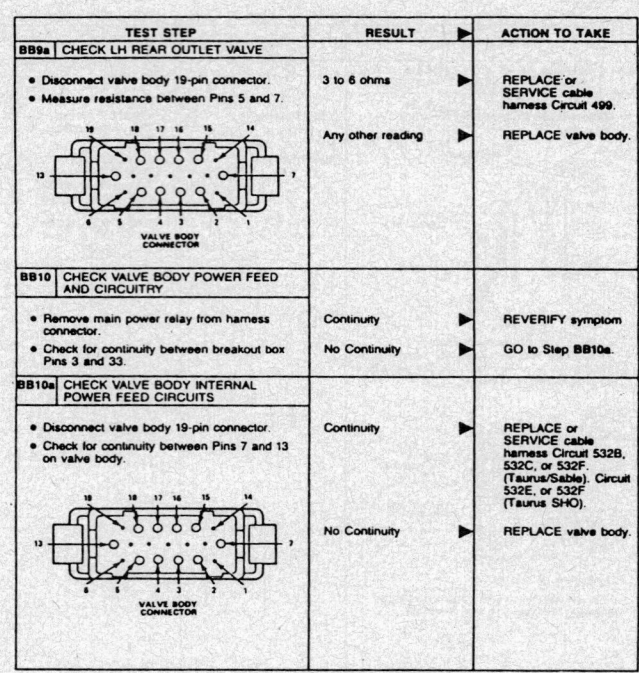

TEST STEP	RESULT	ACTION TO TAKE
BB9a CHECK LH REAR OUTLET VALVE		
• Disconnect valve body 19-pin connector. • Measure resistance between Pins 5 and 7.	3 to 6 ohms	REPLACE or SERVICE cable harness Circuit 499.
	Any other reading	REPLACE valve body.
BB10 CHECK VALVE BODY POWER FEED AND CIRCUITRY		
• Remove main power relay from harness connector.	Continuity	REVERIFY symptom
• Check for continuity between breakout box Pins 3 and 33.	No Continuity	GO to Step BB10a.
BB10a CHECK VALVE BODY INTERNAL POWER FEED CIRCUITS		
• Disconnect valve body 19-pin connector. • Check for continuity between Pins 7 and 13 on valve body.	Continuity	REPLACE or SERVICE cable harness Circuit 532B, 532C, or 532F (Taurus/Sable). Circuit 532E, or 532F (Taurus SHO).
	No Continuity	REPLACE valve body.

Fig. 111   Pinpoint Tests BB9a, BB10 & BB10a: Solenoid Valve. 1992 Sable & Taurus

TEST STEP	RESULT	ACTION TO TAKE
CC1 SERVICE CODES 31/35/41/55/71 OR 75 CHECK LH FRONT SENSOR		
• Turn ignition switch OFF. • Disconnect 55-pin connector from electronic controller.	800 to 1400 ohms (0.8 to 1.4K ohms)	GO to Step CC2.
	Any other reading	GO to Step CC1a.
• Connect EEC-IV Breakout Box with Tool T90P-50-ALA or equivalent to the 55-pin connector or wiring harness. • Measure resistance between Pins 30 and 48.		

Fig. 112   Test CC1: Wheel Sensor. 1992

TEST STEP	RESULT	ACTION TO TAKE
CC1a CHECK LH FRONT SENSOR RESISTANCE		
• Disconnect LH front wheel sensor plug. • Measure resistance of sensor at sensor plug.	800 to 1400 ohms (0.8 to 1.4K ohms)	SERVICE or REPLACE cable harness Circuit 521 or 522.
	Any other reading	REPLACE LH front sensor.
CC2 CHECK LH FRONT SENSOR VOLTAGE		
• Turn ignition switch OFF. • Turn air suspension switch OFF, if so equipped. • Place vehicle on hoist and raise wheels clear of ground. • Set multi-meter to voltage range (2 volt-AC). • Measure voltage between Pins 30 and 48 at Breakout Box while spinning LH front at approximately 1 revolution per second.	Between 0.10 and 1.40 volts AC	GO to Step CC3.
	Less than 0.10 or more than 1.40 volts AC	CHECK sensor mounting, air gap or toothed wheel mounting. CORRECT as required.
CC3 CHECK LH FRONT SENSOR CIRCUIT CONTINUITY TO GROUND		
• Check continuity between Breakout Box Pins 30 and 60.	No Continuity	GO to Step CC4.
	Continuity	GO to Step CC3a.

Fig. 113   Pinpoint Tests CC1a, CC2 & CC3: Wheel Sensor. 1992

TEST STEP	RESULT ▶	ACTION TO TAKE
CC3a CHECK LH FRONT SENSOR TO GROUND		
• Disconnect LH front wheel sensor plug. • Check for continuity between each sensor plug pin (sensor side) and vehicle ground.	Continuity ▶	REPLACE LH front sensor.
	No Continuity ▶	SERVICE or REPLACE cable harness Circuit 521 or 522. RECONNECT sensor plug.
CC4 CHECK ELECTRONIC CONTROLLER TO GROUND WIRE		
• Check continuity between Breakout Box Pin 60 and body ground.	Continuity ▶	GO to Step **CC5.**
	No Continuity ▶	SERVICE or REPLACE cable harness Circuit 530 or 530B (Taurus/Sable). Circuit 530, 57U or 57R (Taurus SHO).
CC5 CHECK LH FRONT WHEEL BEARING		
• Check front wheel bearing end play. • Inspect toothed sensor ring visually for damaged teeth. NOTE: Turn air suspension switch ON when vehicle is off hoist, if so equipped.	Loose or damaged parts ▶	REPLACE faulty parts.
	Not loose or damaged ▶	REVERIFY symptom.

Fig. 114   Pinpoint Tests CC3a, CC4 & CC5: Wheel Sensor. 1992

TEST STEP	RESULT ▶	ACTION TO TAKE
CC6 SERVICE CODES 32/36/42/56/72 OR 76 CHECK RH FRONT SENSOR		
• Turn ignition switch OFF. • Disconnect 55-pin connector from electronic controller.	800 to 1400 ohms (0.8 to 1.4K ohms) ▶	GO to Step **CC7.**
	Any other reading ▶	GO to Step **CC6a.**

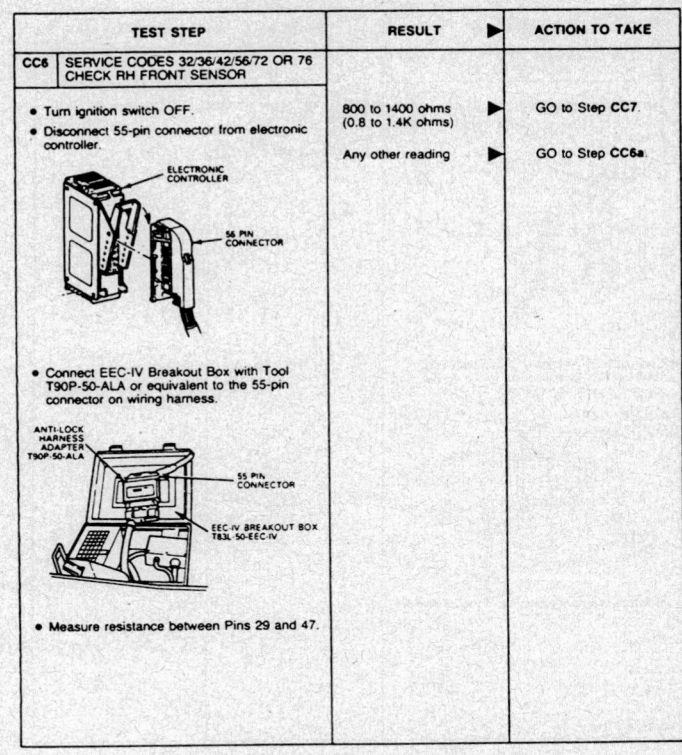

• Connect EEC-IV Breakout Box with Tool T90P-50-ALA or equivalent to the 55-pin connector on wiring harness. • Measure resistance between Pins 29 and 47.		

Fig. 115   Pinpoint Tests CC6: Wheel Sensor. 1992

TEST STEP	RESULT ▶	ACTION TO TAKE
CC6a CHECK RH FRONT SENSOR RESISTANCE		
• Disconnect RH front sensor plug. • Measure resistance of sensor at sensor plug.	800 to 1400 ohms (0.8 to 1.4K ohms) ▶	SERVICE or REPLACE cable harness Circuit 514 or 516.
	Any other reading ▶	REPLACE RH front sensor.
CC7 CHECK RH FRONT SENSOR VOLTAGE		
• Turn ignition switch OFF. • Turn air suspension switch OFF, if so equipped. • Place vehicle on hoist and raise wheels clear of ground. • Set multi-meter to voltage range (2 volt-AC). • Measure voltage between Pins 29 and 47 at Breakout Box while spinning RH front at approximately 1 revolution per second.	Between 0.10 and 1.40 volts AC ▶	GO to Step **CC8.**
	Less than 0.10 or more than 1.40 volts AC ▶	CHECK sensor mounting, air gap or toothed wheel mounting. CORRECT as required.
CC8 CHECK RH FRONT SENSOR CIRCUIT CONTINUITY TO GROUND		
• Check continuity between Breakout Box Pins 29 and 60.	No Continuity ▶	GO to Step **CC9.**
	Continuity ▶	GO to Step **CC8a.**

Fig. 116   Pinpoint Tests CC6a, CC7 & CC8: Wheel Sensor. 1992

TEST STEP	RESULT ▶	ACTION TO TAKE
CC8a CHECK RH FRONT SENSOR TO GROUND		
• Disconnect RH front wheel sensor plug. • Check for continuity between each sensor plug pin (sensor side) and vehicle ground.	Continuity ▶	REPLACE RH front sensor.
	No Continuity ▶	SERVICE or REPLACE cable harness Circuit 514 or 516. RECONNECT sensor plug.
CC9 CHECK ELECTRONIC CONTROLLER TO GROUND WIRE		
• Check continuity between Breakout Box Pin 60 and body ground.	Continuity ▶	GO to Step **CC10.**
	No Continiuty ▶	SERVICE or REPLACE cable harness Circuit 530 or 530B (Taurus/Sable). Circuit 530, 57U or 57R (Taurus SHO).
CC10 CHECK RH FRONT WHEEL BEARING		
• Check front wheel bearing end play. • Inspect toothed sensor ring visually for damaged teeth. NOTE: Turn air suspension switch ON when vehicle is off hoist, if so equipped.	Loose or damaged parts ▶	REPLACE faulty parts.
	Not loose or damaged ▶	REVERIFY symptom.

Fig. 117   Pinpoint Tests CC8a, CC9 & CC10: Wheel Sensor. 1992

TEST STEP	RESULT ▶	ACTION TO TAKE
CC11 SERVICE CODES 33/37/43/57/73 OR 77 CHECK RH REAR SENSOR		
• Turn ignition switch OFF. • Disconnect 55-pin connector from electronic controller.	800 to 1400 ohms (0.8 to 1.4K ohms) ▶	GO to Step **CC12**.
	Any other reading ▶	GO to Step **CC11a**.
• Connect EEC-IV Breakout Box with Tool T90P-50-ALA or equivalent to the 55-pin connector on wiring harness. • Measure resistance between Pins 27 and 45.		

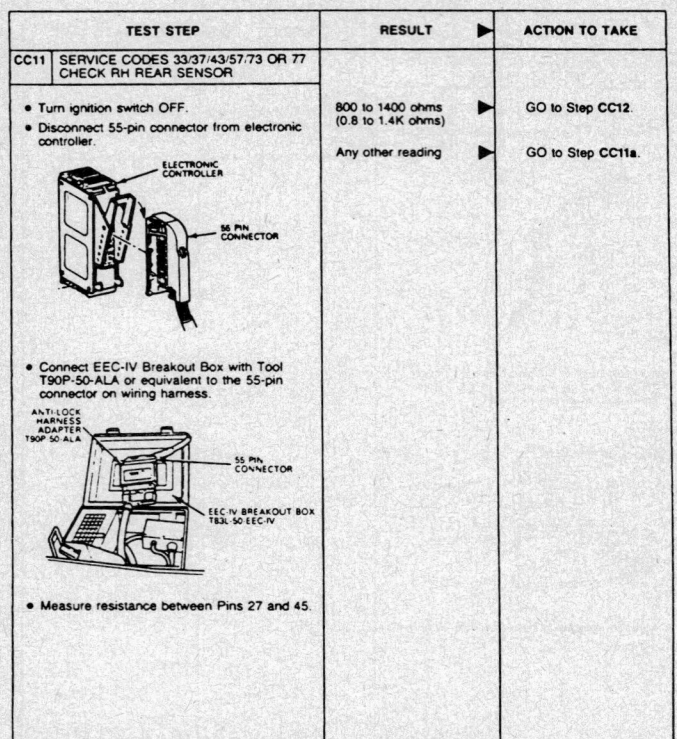

Fig. 118   Test CC11: Wheel Sensor. 1992

TEST STEP	RESULT ▶	ACTION TO TAKE
CC11a CHECK RH REAR SENSOR RESISTANCE		
• Disconnect sensor plug (RH REAR). • Measure resistance of sensor at sensor plug.	800 to 1400 ohms (0.8 to 1.4K ohms) ▶	SERVICE or REPLACE cable harness Circuit 523 or 524.
	Any other reading ▶	REPLACE RH rear sensor.
CC12 CHECK RH REAR SENSOR VOLTAGE		
• Turn ignition switch OFF. • Turn air suspension switch OFF, if so equipped. • Place vehicle on hoist and raise wheels clear of ground. • Set multi-meter to voltage range (2 volt-AC). • Measure voltage between Pins 27 and 45 at Breakout Box while spinning RH rear at approximately 1 revolution per second.	Between 0.10V and 1.40V AC ▶	GO to Step **CC13**.
	Less than 0.10V or more than 1.40V AC ▶	CHECK sensor mounting, air gap or toothed wheel mounting. CORRECT as required.
CC13 CHECK RH REAR SENSOR CIRCUIT CONTINUITY TO GROUND		
• Check continuity between Breakout Box Pins 27 and 60.	No Continuity ▶	GO to Step **CC14**.
	Continuity ▶	GO to Step **CC13a**.

Fig. 119   Pinpoint Tests CC11a, CC12 & CC13: Wheel Sensor. 1992

TEST STEP	RESULT ▶	ACTION TO TAKE
CC13a CHECK RH REAR SENSOR TO GROUND		
• Disconnect RH rear wheel sensor plug. • Check for continuity between each sensor plug pin (sensor side) and vehicle ground.	Continuity ▶	REPLACE RH rear sensor.
	No Continuity ▶	SERVICE or REPLACE cable harness Circuit 523 or 524. RECONNECT sensor plug.
CC14 CHECK ELECTRONIC CONTROLLER TO GROUND WIRE		
• Check continuity between Breakout Box Pin 60 and body ground.	Continuity ▶	GO to Step **CC15**.
	No Continuity ▶	SERVICE or REPLACE cable harness Circuit 530 or 530B (Taurus/Sable). Circuit 530, 57U or 57R (Taurus SHO).
CC15 CHECK FOR EXCESSIVE AXLE VIBRATION		
• Check rear wheel bearings for excessive play. • Inspect toothed sensor ring for damaged teeth. NOTE: Turn air suspension switch ON when vehicle is off hoist, if so equipped.	Loose or damaged parts ▶	SERVICE or REPLACE damaged parts.
	Not loose or damaged ▶	REVERIFY symptom.

Fig. 120   Pinpoint Tests CC13a, CC14 & CC15: Wheel Sensor. 1992

TEST STEP	RESULT ▶	ACTION TO TAKE
CC16 SERVICE CODES 34/38/44/58/74 OR 78 CHECK LH REAR SENSOR		
• Turn ignition switch OFF. • Disconnect 55-pin connector from electronic controller.	800 to 1400 ohms (0.8 to 1.4K ohms) ▶	GO to Step **CC17**.
	Any other reading ▶	GO to Step **CC16a**.
• Connect EEC-IV Breakout Box with Tool T90P-50-ALA or equivalent to the 55-pin connector on wiring harness. • Measure resistance between Pins 28 and 46.		

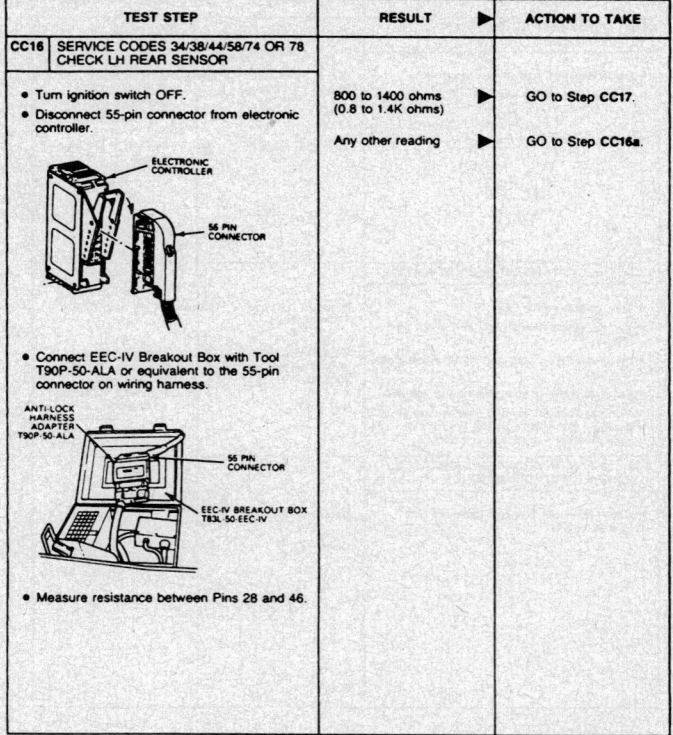

Fig. 121   Test CC16: Wheel Sensor. 1992

TEST STEP	RESULT	▶	ACTION TO TAKE
CC16a CHECK LH REAR SENSOR RESISTANCE			
• Disconnect LH rear sensor plug. • Measure resistance of sensor at sensor plug.	800 to 1400 ohms (0.8 to 1.4K ohms)	▶	SERVICE or REPLACE cable harness Circuit 518 or 519.
	Any other reading	▶	REPLACE LH rear sensor.
CC17 CHECK LH REAR SENSOR VOLTAGE			
• Turn ignition switch OFF. • Turn air suspension switch OFF, if so equipped. • Place vehicle on hoist and raise wheels clear of ground. • Set multi-meter to voltage range (2 volt-AC). • Measure voltage between Pins 28 and 46 at Breakout Box while spinning RH rear at approximately 1 revolution per second.	Between 0.10 and 1.40 volts AC	▶	GO to Step **CC18**.
	Less than 0.10 or more than 1.40 volts AC	▶	CHECK sensor mounting, air gap or toothed wheel mounting. CORRECT as required.
CC18 CHECK LH REAR SENSOR CIRCUIT CONTINUITY TO GROUND			
• Check continuity between Breakout Box Pins 28 and 60.	No Continuity	▶	GO to Step **CC19**.
	Continuity	▶	GO to Step **CC18a**.

Fig. 122   Pinpoint Tests CC16a, CC17 & CC18: Wheel Sensor. 1992

TEST STEP	RESULT	▶	ACTION TO TAKE
CC18a CHECK LH REAR SENSOR TO GROUND			
• Disconnect LH rear wheel sensor plug. • Check for continuity between each sensor plug pin (sensor side) and vehicle ground.	Continuity	▶	REPLACE LH rear sensor.
	No Continuity	▶	SERVICE or REPLACE cable harness Circuit 518 or 519. RECONNECT sensor plug.
CC19 CHECK ELECTRONIC CONTROLLER TO GROUND WIRE			
• Check continuity between Breakout Box Pin 60 and body ground.	Continuity	▶	GO to Step **CC20**.
	No Continuity	▶	SERVICE or REPLACE cable harness Circuit 530 or 530B (Taurus/Sable). Circuit 530, 57U or 57R (Taurus SHO).
CC20 CHECK FOR EXCESSIVE AXLE VIBRATION			
• Check rear wheel bearings for excessive play. • Inspect toothed sensor ring for damaged teeth. NOTE: Turn air suspension switch ON when vehicle is off hoist, if so equipped.	Loose or damaged parts	▶	SERVICE or REPLACE damaged parts.
	Not loose or damaged	▶	REVERIFY symptom.

Fig. 123   Pinpoint Tests CC18a, CC19 & CC20: Wheel Sensor. 1992

TEST STEP	RESULT	▶	ACTION TO TAKE
DD1 SERVICE CODE 51 AND/OR 71 CHECK LH FRONT SENSOR CIRCUIT CONTINUITY			
• Turn ignition switch OFF. • Disconnect 55-pin plug from electronic controller. • Connect EEC-IV Breakout Box, T83L-50-EEC-IV, with Anti-Lock Test Adapter, T90P-50-ALA or equivalent, to the anti-lock 55-pin plug harness. • Check for continuity between Breakout Box Pins 60 and 30.	Continuity	▶	GO to Step **DD1a**.
	No Continuity	▶	GO to Step **DD2**

Fig. 124   Test DD1: Wheel Sensor. 1992

TEST STEP	RESULT	▶	ACTION TO TAKE
DD1a CHECK LH FRONT SENSOR CONTINUITY			
• Disconnect LH front wheel sensor plug. • Check for continuity between each sensor plug pin (sensor side) and vehicle ground.	Continuity	▶	REPLACE LH front sensor.
	No Continuity	▶	SERVICE or REPLACE cable harness Circuit 521 or 522. RECONNECT sensor plug.
DD2 CHECK ELECTRONIC CONTROLLER TO GROUND WIRE			
• Check continuity between Breakout Box Pin 60 and body ground.	Continuity	▶	GO to Step **DD3**.
	No Continuity	▶	SERVICE or REPLACE cable harness Circuit 530 or 530B (Taurus/Sable). Circuit 530, 57U or 57R (Taurus SHO).
DD3 CHECK ANTI-LOCK OPERATION LH FRONT WHEEL			
• Turn air suspension OFF, if so equipped. • Lift vehicle and rotate wheels to ensure they turn freely. • Apply moderate brake pedal effort and check that LH front wheel will not turn. • Jump Pins 34 and 19. • Short Pins 2, 20 and 60 to each other at Breakout Box. • Check that LH front wheel turns freely with ignition switch ON. CAUTION: Do not leave ignition on for more than 1 minute, or valve damage may result. • Turn air suspension ON when vehicle is off hoist, if so equipped.	If wheel turns freely	▶	REVERIFY symptom.
	If wheel does not turn freely or pedal drops	▶	REPLACE solenoid valve body.

Fig. 125   Pinpoint Tests DD1a, DD2 & DD3: Wheel Sensor. 1992

TEST STEP	RESULT ▶	ACTION TO TAKE
DD4 SERVICE CODE 52 AND/OR 72 CHECK RH FRONT SENSOR CIRCUIT CONTINUITY		
• Turn ignition switch OFF. • Disconnect 55-pin plug from electronic controller.	Continuity ▶	GO to Step DD4a.
	No Continuity ▶	GO to Step DD5.
• Connect EEC-IV Breakout Box, T83L-50-EEC-IV, with Anti-Lock Test Adapter, T90P-50-ALA, or equivalent, to the anti-lock 55-pin plug wiring harness.		
• Check for continuity between Breakout Box Pins 60 and 29.		

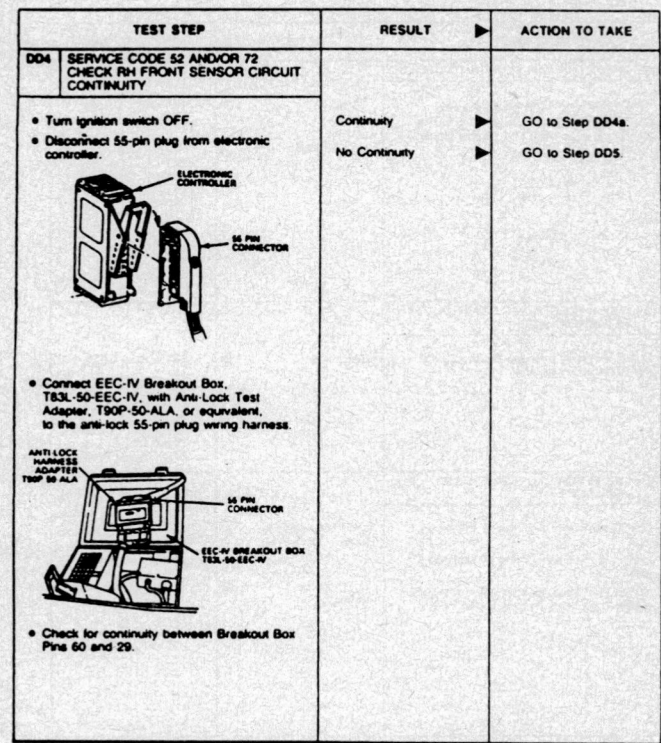

Fig. 126   Test DD4: Wheel Sensor. 1992

TEST STEP	RESULT ▶	ACTION TO TAKE
DD4a CHECK RH FRONT SENSOR CONTINUITY		
• Disconnect RH front wheel sensor. • Check for continuity between each sensor plug pin (sensor side) and vehicle ground.	Continuity ▶	REPLACE RH front sensor.
	No Continuity ▶	SERVICE or REPLACE cable harness Circuit 514 or 516. RECONNECT sensor plug.
DD5 CHECK ELECTRONIC CONTROLLER TO GROUND WIRE		
• Check continuity between Breakout Box Pin 60 and body ground.	Continuity ▶	GO to Step DD6.
	No Continuity ▶	SERVICE or REPLACE cable harness Circuit 530 or 530B (Taurus/Sable). Circuit 530, 57U or 57R (Taurus SHO).
DD6 CHECK ANTI-LOCK OPERATION RH FRONT WHEEL		
• Turn air suspension OFF, if so equipped. • Lift vehicle and rotate wheels to ensure they turn freely. • Apply moderate brake pedal effort and check that RH front wheel will not turn. • Jump Pins 34 and 19. • Short Pins 21, 38 and 60 to each other at Breakout Box. • Check that RH front wheel turns freely with ignition switch ON. • Turn air suspension ON when vehicle is off hoist, if so equipped.	If wheel turns freely ▶	REVERIFY symptom.
	If wheel does not turn freely or pedal drops ▶	REPLACE solenoid valve body.

Fig. 127   Pinpoint Tests DD4a, DD5 & DD6: Wheel Sensor. 1992 Continental, Sable & Taurus

TEST STEP	RESULT ▶	ACTION TO TAKE
DD4a CHECK RH FRONT SENSOR CONTINUITY		
• Disconnect RH front wheel sensor. • Check for continuity between each sensor plug pin (sensor side) and vehicle ground.	Continuity ▶	REPLACE RH front sensor.
	No Continuity ▶	SERVICE or REPLACE cable harness Circuit 514 or 516. RECONNECT sensor plug.
DD5 CHECK ELECTRONIC CONTROLLER TO GROUND WIRE		
• Check continuity between Breakout Box Pin 60 and body ground.	Continuity ▶	GO to Step DD6.
	No Continuity ▶	SERVICE or REPLACE cable harness Circuit 57.
DD6 CHECK ANTI-LOCK OPERATION RH FRONT WHEEL		
• Turn air suspension OFF, if so equipped. • Lift vehicle and rotate wheels to ensure they turn freely. • Apply moderate brake pedal effort and check that RH front wheel will not turn. • Jump Pins 34 and 19. • Short Pins 21, 38 and 60 to each other at Breakout Box. • Check that RH front wheel turns freely with ignition switch ON. • Turn air suspension ON when vehicle is off hoist, if so equipped.	If wheel turns freely ▶	REVERIFY symptom.
	If wheel does not turn freely or pedal drops ▶	REPLACE solenoid valve body.

Fig. 128   Pinpoint Tests DD4a, DD5 & DD6: Wheel Sensor. 1992 Crown Victoria, Grand Marquis & Town Car

TEST STEP	RESULT ▶	ACTION TO TAKE
DD7 SERVICE CODE 53 AND/OR 73 CHECK RH REAR SENSOR CIRCUIT CONTINUITY		
• Turn ignition switch OFF. • Disconnect 55-pin plug from electronic controller.	Continuity ▶	GO to Step DD7a.
	No Continuity ▶	GO to Step DD8.
• Connect EEC-IV Breakout Box, T83L-50-EEC-IV, with Anti-Lock Test Adapter, T90P-50-ALA, or equivalent, to the anti-lock 55-pin plug wiring harness.		
• Check for continuity between Breakout Box Pins 60 and 27.		

Fig. 129   Test DD7: Wheel Sensor. 1992

TEST STEP	RESULT	▶	ACTION TO TAKE
DD7a CHECK RH REAR SENSOR CONTINUITY • Disconnect RH rear wheel sensor plug. • Check for continuity between each sensor plug pin (sensor side) and vehicle ground. RH REAR SENSOR	Continuity No Continuity	▶ ▶	REPLACE RH rear sensor. SERVICE or REPLACE cable harness Circuit 523 or 524. RECONNECT sensor plug.
DD8 CHECK ELECTRONIC CONTROLLER TO GROUND WIRE • Check continuity between Breakout Box Pin 60 and body ground.	Continuity No Continuity	▶ ▶	GO to Step **DD9**. SERVICE or REPLACE cable harness Circuit 530 or 530B (Taurus/Sable). Circuit 530, 57U or 57R (Taurus SHO).
DD9 CHECK ANTI-LOCK OPERATION RH REAR WHEEL • Turn air suspension OFF, if so equipped. • Lift vehicle and rotate wheels to ensure they turn freely. • Apply moderate brake pedal effort and check that RH rear wheel will not turn. • Jump Pins 34 and 19. • Short Pins 18, 55 and 60 to each other at Breakout Box. • Check that RH rear wheel turns freely with ignition switch ON. • Turn air suspension ON when vehicle is off hoist, if so equipped.	If wheel turns freely If wheel does not turn freely or pedal drops	▶ ▶	REVERIFY symptom. REPLACE solenoid valve body.

Fig. 130   Tests DD7a, DD8 & DD9: Wheel Sensor. 1992

TEST STEP	RESULT	▶	ACTION TO TAKE
DD10 SERVICE CODE 54 AND/OR 74 CHECK LH REAR SENSOR CIRCUIT CONTINUITY • Turn ignition switch OFF. • Disconnect 55-pin plug from electronic controller. ELECTRONIC CONTROLLER / 55 PIN CONNECTOR • Connect EEC-IV Breakout Box, T83L-50-EEC-IV, with Anti-Lock Test Adapter, T90P-50-ALA, or equivalent, to the anti-lock 55-pin plug wiring harness. ANTI-LOCK HARNESS ADAPTER T90P-50-ALA / 55 PIN CONNECTOR / EEC-IV BREAKOUT BOX T83L-50-EEC IV • Check for continuity between Breakout Box Pins 60 and 28.	Continuity No Continuity	▶ ▶	GO to Step **DD10a**. GO to Step **DD11**.

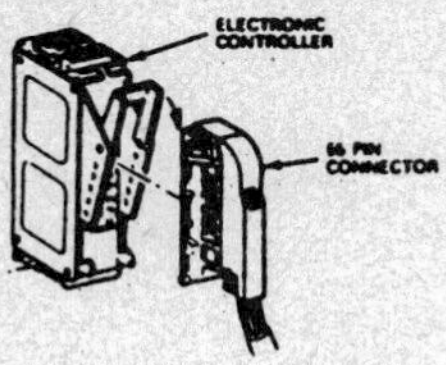

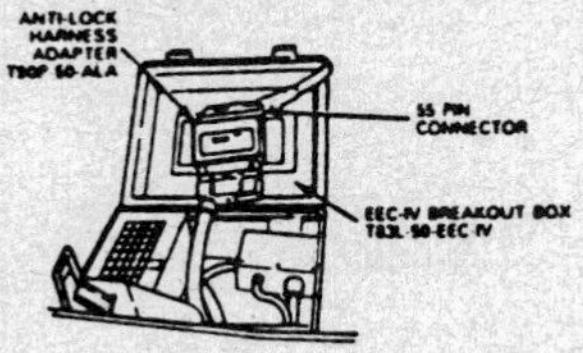

Fig. 131   Test DD10: Wheel Sensor. 1992

TEST STEP	RESULT	▶	ACTION TO TAKE
DD10a CHECK LH REAR SENSOR CONTINUITY • Disconnect LH rear wheel sensor plug. • Check for continuity between each sensor plug pin (sensor side) and vehicle ground. LH REAR SENSOR	Continuity No Continuity	▶ ▶	REPLACE LH rear sensor. SERVICE or REPLACE cable harness Circuit 518 or 519. RECONNECT sensor plug.
DD11 CHECK ELECTRONIC CONTROLLER TO GROUND WIRE • Check continuity between Breakout Box Pin 60 and body ground.	Continuity No Continuity	▶ ▶	GO to Step **DD12**. SERVICE or REPLACE cable harness Circuit 530 or 530B (Taurus/Sable). Circuit 530, 57U or 57R (Taurus SHO).
DD12 CHECK ANTI-LOCK OPERATION LH REAR WHEEL • Turn air suspension OFF, if so equipped. • Lift vehicle and rotate wheels to ensure they turn freely. • Apply moderate brake pedal effort and check that LH rear wheel will not turn. • Jump Pins 34 and 19. • Short Pins 36, 54 and 60 to each other at Breakout Box. • Check that LH rear wheel turns freely with ignition switch ON. CAUTION: Do not leave ignition on for more than 1 minute, or valve damage may result. • Turn air suspension ON when vehicle is off hoist, if so equipped.	If wheel turns freely If wheel does not turn freely or pedal drops	▶ ▶	REVERIFY symptom. REPLACE solenoid valve body.

Fig. 132   Pinpoint Tests DD10a, DD11 & DD12: Wheel Sensor. 1992 Continental, Sable & Taurus

TEST STEP	RESULT	▶	ACTION TO TAKE
DD10a CHECK LH REAR SENSOR CONTINUITY • Disconnect wheel sensor plug (LH Rear). • Check for continuity between each sensor plug pin (sensor side) and vehicle ground. LH REAR SENSOR	Continuity No Continuity	▶ ▶	REPLACE LH rear sensor. SERVICE or REPLACE cable harness Circuit 518 or 519. RECONNECT sensor plug.
DD11 CHECK ELECTRONIC CONTROLLER TO GROUND WIRE • Check continuity between Breakout Box Pin 60 and body ground.	Continuity No Continuity	▶ ▶	GO to Step **DD12**. SERVICE or REPLACE cable harness Circuit 57.
DD12 CHECK ANTI-LOCK OPERATION LH REAR WHEEL • Turn air suspension OFF, if so equipped. • Lift vehicle and rotate wheels to ensure they turn freely. • Apply moderate brake pedal effort and check that LH rear wheel will not turn. • Jump Pins 34 and 19. • Short Pins 36, 54 and 60 to each other at Breakout Box. • Check that LH rear wheel turns freely with ignition switch ON. CAUTION: Do not leave ignition on for more than 1 minute, or valve damage may result. • Turn air suspension ON when vehicle is off hoist, if so equipped.	If wheel turns freely If wheel does not turn freely or pedal drops	▶ ▶	REVERIFY symptom. REPLACE solenoid valve body.

Fig. 133   Pinpoint Tests DD10a, DD11 & DD12: Wheel Sensors. 1992 Crown Victoria, Grand Marquis & Town Car

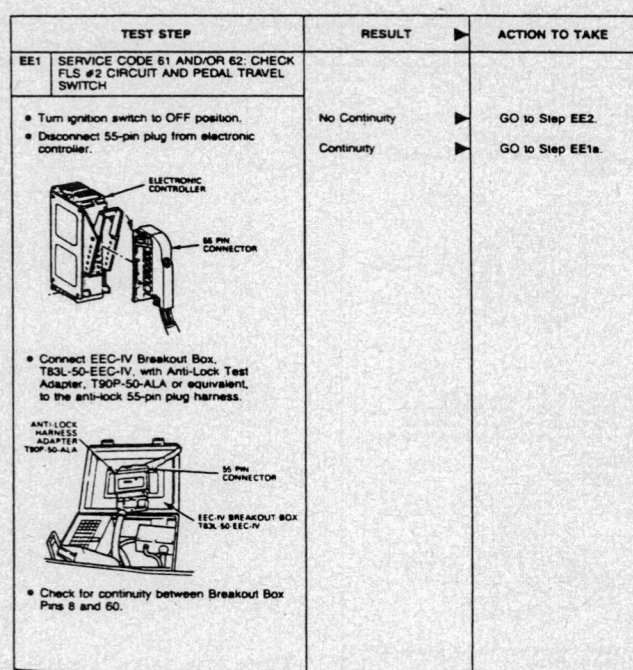

TEST STEP	RESULT ▶	ACTION TO TAKE
EE1 SERVICE CODE 61 AND/OR 62: CHECK FLS #2 CIRCUIT AND PEDAL TRAVEL SWITCH		
• Turn ignition switch to OFF position.	No Continuity ▶	GO to Step EE2.
• Disconnect 55-pin plug from electronic controller.	Continuity ▶	GO to Step EE1a.
• Connect EEC-IV Breakout Box, T83L-50-EEC-IV, with Anti-Lock Test Adapter, T90P-50-ALA or equivalent, to the anti-lock 55-pin plug harness.		
• Check for continuity between Breakout Box Pins 8 and 60.		

Fig. 134   Test EE1: Fluid Level Indicator, Pedal Travel Switch & Pump Motor. 1992 Continental, Sable & Taurus

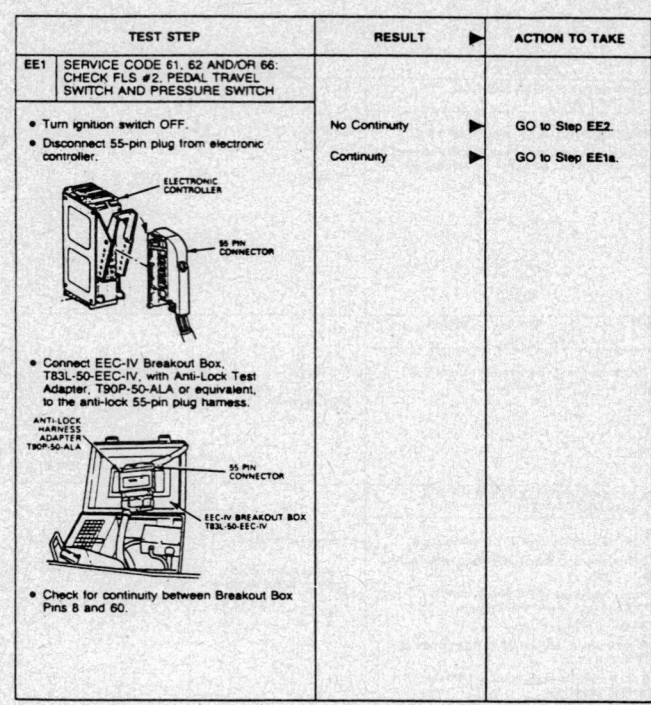

TEST STEP	RESULT ▶	ACTION TO TAKE
EE1 SERVICE CODE 61, 62 AND/OR 66: CHECK FLS #2, PEDAL TRAVEL SWITCH AND PRESSURE SWITCH		
• Turn ignition switch OFF.	No Continuity ▶	GO to Step EE2.
• Disconnect 55-pin plug from electronic controller.	Continuity ▶	GO to Step EE1a.
• Connect EEC-IV Breakout Box, T83L-50-EEC-IV, with Anti-Lock Test Adapter, T90P-50-ALA or equivalent, to the anti-lock 55-pin plug harness.		
• Check for continuity between Breakout Box Pins 8 and 60.		

Fig. 135   Test EE1: Fluid Level Indicator, Pedal Travel Switch & Pump Motor. 1992 Crown Victoria, Grand Marquis & Town Car

TEST STEP	RESULT ▶	ACTION TO TAKE
EE1a CHECK FLI #2 SWITCH		
• Disconnect 2-pin plug on FLI located on small reservoir on Hydraulic Control Unit.	Continuity ▶	REPLACE HCU reservoir.
	No Continuity ▶	SERVICE OR REPLACE cable harness Circuit 542, 535, 535a, 535b or 549 (Taurus/Sable). Circuit 550, 535, 535a, 535b or 549 (Taurus SHO).
• Check for continuity between each pin and body ground.		
EE2 CHECK FOR VOLTAGE ON FLS #2 SWITCH AND CIRCUITRY		
• Turn ignition switch to ON position.	No voltage ▶	GO to Step EE3.
• Measure voltage between Breakout Box Pins 8 and 60.	12V ▶	GO to Step EE2a.
EE2a CHECK FOR VOLTAGE ON FLS #2		
• Disconnect 2-pin plug on FLI located on small reservoir on hydraulic control unit.	12V ▶	REPLACE HCU reservoir.
	No voltage ▶	SERVICE OR REPLACE cable harness Circuit 542, 535, 535a, 535b or 549 (Taurus/Sable). Circuit 550, 535, 535a, 535b or 549 (Taurus SHO).
• Measure voltage between each pin and body ground.		

Fig. 136   Pinpoint Tests EE1a, EE2 & EE2a: Fluid Level Indicator/Pedal Travel Switch/Pump Motor. 1992 Continental, Sable & Taurus

TEST STEP	RESULT ▶	ACTION TO TAKE
EE1a CHECK FLI #2 SWITCH		
• Disconnect 2-pin plug on FLI located on small reservoir on Hydraulic Control Unit.	Continuity ▶	REPLACE HCU reservoir.
	No Continuity ▶	SERVICE OR REPLACE cable harness (Circuit 550, 535, 547 or 549).
• Check for continuity between each pin and body ground.		
EE2 CHECK FOR VOLTAGE ON FLS #2 SWITCH AND CIRCUITRY		
• Turn ignition switch to ON position.	No voltage ▶	GO to Step EE3.
• Measure voltage between Breakout Box Pins 8 and 60.	12V ▶	GO to Step EE2a.
EE2a CHECK FOR VOLTAGE ON FLS #2		
• Disconnect 2-pin plug on FLI located on small reservoir on hydraulic control unit.	12V ▶	REPLACE HCU reservoir.
	No voltage ▶	SERVICE OR REPLACE cable harness (Circuit 550, 535, 547 or 549).
• Measure voltage between each pin and body ground.		

Fig. 137   Pinpoint Tests EE1a, EE2 & EE2a: Fluid Level Indicator/Pedal Travel Switch/Pump Motor. 1992 Crown Victoria, Grand Marquis & Town Car

TEST STEP	RESULT	▶	ACTION TO TAKE
EE3 CHECK PEDAL TRAVEL SWITCH AND CIRCUITRY			
• Turn ignition switch OFF.	No Continuity	▶	GO to Step EE4.
• Disconnect 55-pin plug from electronic controller.	Continuity	▶	GO to Step EE3a.

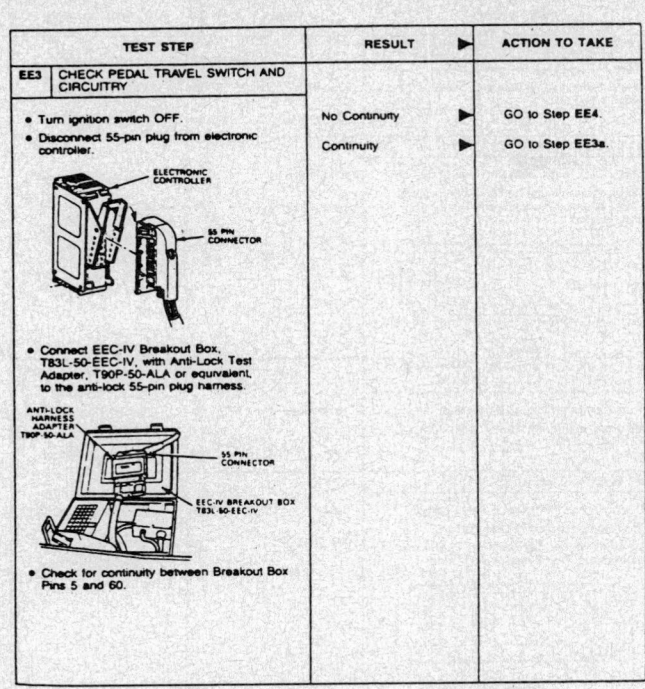

• Connect EEC-IV Breakout Box, T83L-50-EEC-IV, with Anti-Lock Test Adapter, T90P-50-ALA or equivalent, to the anti-lock 55-pin plug harness.			
• Check for continuity between Breakout Box Pins 5 and 60.			

Fig. 138   Test EE3: Fluid Level Indicator/Pedal Travel Switch/Pump Motor. 1992 Continental, Sable & Taurus

TEST STEP	RESULT	▶	ACTION TO TAKE
EE3 SERVICE CODE 62: CHECK PEDAL TRAVEL SWITCH AND CIRCUITRY			
• Check for continuity between Breakout Box Pins 5 and 60.	No Continuity	▶	GO to Step EE4.
	Continuity	▶	GO to Step EE3a.
EE3a CHECK PEDAL TRAVEL SWITCH			
• Disconnect 2-pin plug on pedal travel switch.	Continuity	▶	REPLACE pedal travel switch.
	No Continuity	▶	SERVICE OR REPLACE cable harness (Circuit 535, 547, 549 or 550).
• Check for continuity between each pin and body ground.			
EE4 CHECK FOR VOLTAGE ON PEDAL TRAVEL SWITCH AND CIRCUITRY			
• Turn ignition switch to ON position. • Measure voltage between Breakout Box Pins 5 and 60.	No voltage	▶	If vehicle is equipped with traction assist: Go to EE5. If vehicle is equipped with ABS only: REVERIFY code 61 and/or 62.
	12V	▶	GO to Step EE4a.

Fig. 139   Pinpoint Tests EE3, EE3a & EE4: Fluid Level Indicator/Pedal Travel Switch/Pump Motor. 1992 Crown Victoria, Grand Marquis & Town Car

TEST STEP	RESULT	▶	ACTION TO TAKE
EE3a CHECK PEDAL TRAVEL SWITCH			
• Disconnect 2-pin plug on pedal travel switch.	Continuity	▶	REPLACE pedal travel switch.
	No Continuity	▶	SERVICE OR REPLACE cable harness (Circuit 535, or 549).
• Check for continuity between each pin and body ground.			
EE4 CHECK FOR VOLTAGE ON PEDAL TRAVEL SWITCH AND CIRCUITRY			
• Turn ignition switch to ON position. • Measure voltage between Breakout Box Pins 5 and 60.	No voltage	▶	VERIFY code 61 and/or 62.
	12V	▶	GO to Step EE4a.
EE4a CHECK FOR VOLTAGE ON PEDAL TRAVEL SWITCH			
• Disconnect 2-pin plug on pedal travel switch.	12V	▶	REPLACE pedal travel switch.
	No voltage	▶	SERVICE OR REPLACE cable harness (Circuit 535 or 549).
• Measure voltage between each pin and body ground.			

Fig. 140   Pinpoint Tests EE3a, EE4 & EE4a: Fluid Level Indicator/Pedal Travel Switch/Pump Motor. 1992 Continental, Sable & Taurus

TEST STEP	RESULT	▶	ACTION TO TAKE
EE4a CHECK FOR VOLTAGE ON PEDAL TRAVEL SWITCH			
• Disconnect 2-pin plug on pedal travel switch.	12V	▶	REPLACE pedal travel switch.
	No voltage	▶	SERVICE OR REPLACE cable harness (Circuit 535, 547, 549 or 550).
• Measure voltage between each pin and body ground.			

Fig. 141   Test EE4a: Fluid Level Indicator/Pedal Travel Switch/Pump Motor. 1992 Crown Victoria, Grand Marquis & Town Car

TEST STEP	RESULT ▶	ACTION TO TAKE
EE5 SERVICE CODE 63: CHECK PUMP MOTOR SPEED SENSOR AND CIRCUIT		
NOTE: The computer will check the pump motor, speed sensor and circuitry by running the pump for about 0.5 seconds each time the vehicle reaches 11 km/h (7 mph).	5-100 ohms ▶	GO to Step **EE6**.
	Any other reading ▶	GO to Step **EE5a**.
• Turn ignition switch to OFF position.		
• Disconnect 55-pin plug from electronic.		

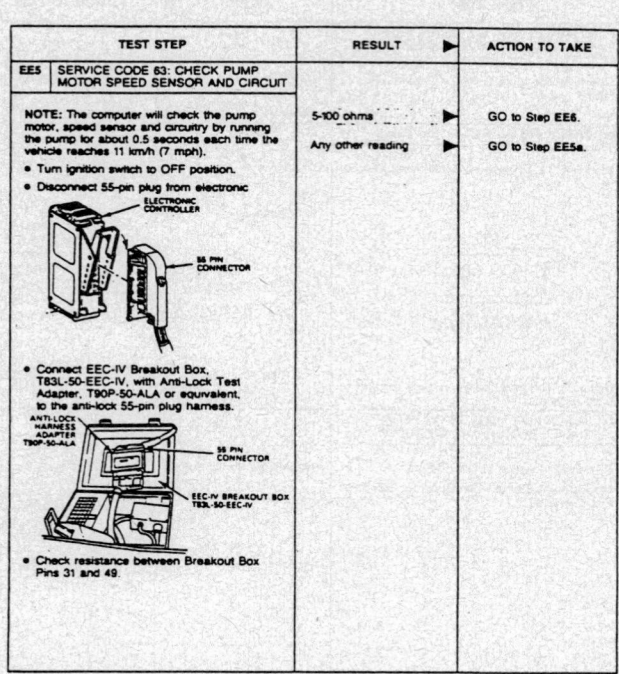

| • Connect EEC-IV Breakout Box, TB3L-50-EEC-IV, with Anti-Lock Test Adapter, T90P-50-ALA or equivalent, to the anti-lock 55-pin plug harness. | | |
| • Check resistance between Breakout Box Pins 31 and 49. | | |

Fig. 142   Test EE5: Fluid Level Indicator/Pedal Travel Switch/Pump Motor. 1992 Continental, Sable & Taurus

TEST STEP	RESULT ▶	ACTION TO TAKE
EE5 CHECK PRESSURE SWITCH AND CIRCUITRY (TRACTION ASSIST)		
• Check for continuity between breakout box Pins 13 and 60.	Continuity ▶	GO to Step **EE5a**.
	No continuity ▶	GO to Step **EE6**.
EE5a CHECK PRESSURE SWITCH		
• Disconnect 19-pin plug on valve body.	Continuity ▶	REPLACE valve body.
• Check for continuity between valve body Pin 11 and body ground, and Pin 12 and body ground.	No continuity ▶	SERVICE or REPLACE cable harness Circuit (547, 535, 549 or 550).
EE6 CHECK FOR VOLTAGE ON PRESSURE SWITCH (TRACTION ASSIST)		
• Turn ignition switch to ON position.	No voltage ▶	VERIFY code 61, 62 or 66.
• Measure voltage between breakout box Pins 13 and 60.	12V ▶	GO to Step **EE6a**.
EE6a CHECK PRESSURE SWITCH		
• Disconnect 19-pin plug on valve body.	12V ▶	REPLACE valve body.
• Turn ignition switch to ON position.	No voltage ▶	SERVICE or REPLACE cable harness Circuit 547 or 535.
• Measure voltage between Pin 11 and body ground and Pin 12 and body ground.		

Fig. 143   Pinpoint Tests EE5, EE5a, EE6 & EE6a: Fluid Level Indicator/Pedal Travel Switch/Pump Motor. 1992 Crown Victoria, Grand Marquis & Town Car

TEST STEP	RESULT ▶	ACTION TO TAKE
EE5a CHECK PUMP MOTOR SPEED SENSOR		
• Disconnect 4-pin plug on pump motor.	5-100 ohms ▶	GO to Step **EE5b**.
• Measure resistance between Pins S0 and S1 on pump motor.	Any other reading ▶	REPLACE pump and motor.
EE5b CHECK PUMP MOTOR RELAY		
• Disconnect 7-pin plug on pump motor relay and remove relay.	Continuity ▶	GO to Step **EE5c**.
• Check continuity from Pin S0 on 7-pin side to Pin S0 on 4-pin side of relay.	No Continuity ▶	REPLACE pump motor relay.
EE5c CHECK PUMP MOTOR RELAY		
• Check continuity from Pin S1 on 7-pin side to Pin S1 on 4-pin side of relay.	Continuity ▶	GO to Step **EE5d**.
	No Continuity ▶	REPLACE pump motor relay.

Fig. 144   Pinpoint Tests EE5a, EE5b & EE5c: Fluid Level Indicator/Pedal Travel Switch/Pump Motor. 1992 Continental, Sable & Taurus

TEST STEP	RESULT ▶	ACTION TO TAKE
EE5d CHECK CIRCUIT 462		
• Check continuity between Breakout Box Pin 31 and Pin S0 on pump motor connector 7-pin plug (harness side).	Continuity ▶	GO to Step **EE5e**.
	No Continuity ▶	SERVICE or REPLACE cable harness Circuit 462.
EE5e CHECK CIRCUIT 461		
• Check continuity between Breakout Box Pin 49 and Pin S1 on pump motor connector 7-pin plug (harness side).	Continuity ▶	REVERIFY reading at EE5.
	No Continuity ▶	SERVICE or REPLACE cable harness Circuit 461.
EE6 CHECK MOTOR SPEED SENSOR SHORT TO BATTERY +		
• Turn ignition switch to ON.	No voltage ▶	GO to Step **EE7**.
• Measure voltage between Breakout Box Pins 31 and 60.	12 volts ▶	GO to Step **EE6a**.
EE6a CHECK PUMP MOTOR		
• Disconnect pump motor to relay 4-pin plug connector.	No voltage ▶	REPLACE pump and motor.
• Turn ignition switch to ON.	12 volts ▶	GO to Step **EE6b**.
• Measure voltage between Breakout Box Pins 31 and 60.		
EE6b CHECK CIRCUIT 462		
• Disconnect wire harness to relay 7-pin plug.	No voltage ▶	GO to Step **EE6c**.
• Turn ignition switch to ON.	12 volts ▶	SERVICE or REPLACE cable harness Circuit 462.
• Measure voltage between Breakout Box Pins 31 and 60.		

Fig. 145   Pinpoint Tests EE5d, EE5e, EE6, EE6a & EE6b: Fluid Level Indicator/Pedal Travel Switch/Pump Motor. 1992 Continental, Sable & Taurus

TEST STEP	RESULT		ACTION TO TAKE
EE6c CHECK CIRCUIT 461			
• Turn ignition switch to ON. • Measure voltage between Breakout Box Pins 49 and 60.	No voltage	▶	REPLACE pump motor relay.
	12V	▶	SERVICE or REPLACE cable harness Circuit 461.
EE7 CHECK MOTOR SPEED SENSOR SHORT TO GROUND			
• Check for continuity between Breakout Box Pins 31 and 60.	No Continuity	▶	GO to Step **EE8**.
	Continuity	▶	GO to Step **EE7a**.
EE7a CHECK PUMP MOTOR			
• Disconnect pump to motor relay 4-pin plug connector. • Check for continuity between Breakout Box Pins 31 and 60.	Continuity	▶	GO to Step **EE7b**.
	No Continuity	▶	REPLACE pump and motor.
EE7b CHECK CIRCUIT 462			
• Disconnect wire harness to relay 7-pin plug. • Check for continuity between Breakout Box Pins 31 and 60.	Continuity	▶	SERVICE or REPLACE cable harness Circuit 462.
	No Continuity	▶	GO to Step **EE7c**.
EE7c CHECK CIRCUIT 461			
• Check for continuity between Breakout Box Pins 49 and 60.	Continuity	▶	SERVICE or REPLACE cable harness Circuit 461.
	No Continuity	▶	REPLACE pump motor relay.
EE8 CHECK PUMP MOTOR OPERATION			
• Reconnect pump motor relay to pump and wire harness. • Jumper Pins 15, 34 and 60 at Breakout Box. • Turn ignition to ON position.	Pump motor runs	▶	VERIFY code 62.
	Pump motor does not run	▶	GO to Step **EE8a**.

Fig. 146   Pinpoint Tests EE6c, EE7, EE7a, EE7b, EE7c & EE8: Fluid Level Indicator/Pedal Travel Switch/Pump Motor. 1992 Continental, Sable & Taurus

TEST STEP	RESULT		ACTION TO TAKE
EE7 SERVICE CODE 63: CHECK PUMP MOTOR SPEED SENSOR AND CIRCUIT	5 to 100 ohms	▶	GO to Step **EE8**.
• Turn ignition switch OFF. • Disconnect 55-pin plug from electronic controller.	Any other reading	▶	GO to Step **EE7a**.
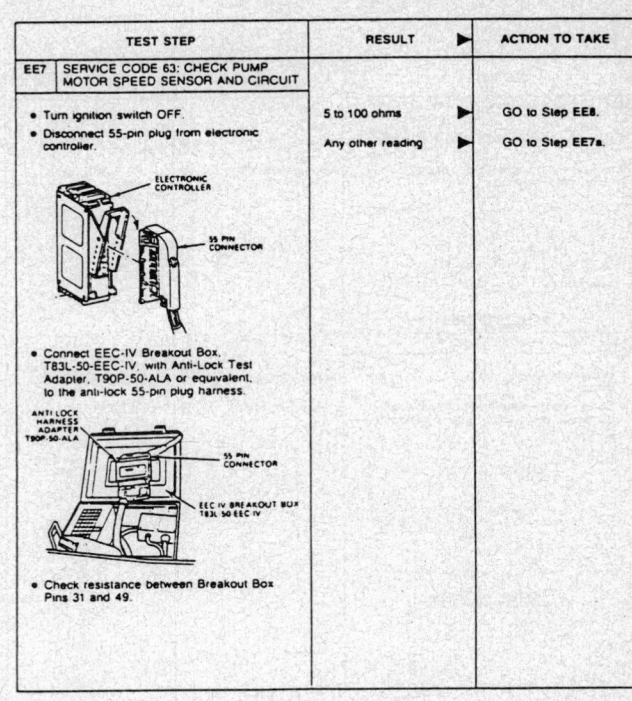			
• Connect EEC-IV Breakout Box, T83L-50-EEC-IV, with Anti-Lock Test Adapter, T90P-50-ALA or equivalent, to the anti-lock 55-pin plug harness.			
• Check resistance between Breakout Box Pins 31 and 49.			

Fig. 147   Test EE7: Fluid Level Indicator/Pedal Travel Switch/Pump Motor. 1992 Crown Victoria, Grand Marquis & Town Car

TEST STEP	RESULT		ACTION TO TAKE
EE7a CHECK PUMP MOTOR SPEED SENSOR			
• Disconnect 4-pin plug on pump motor. • Measure resistance between Pins S0 and S1 on pump motor.	5 to 100 ohms	▶	GO to Step **EE7b**.
	Any other reading	▶	REPLACE pump and motor.
EE7b CHECK PUMP MOTOR RELAY			
• Disconnect 7-pin plug on pump motor relay and remove relay. • Check continuity from Pin S0 on 7-pin side to Pin S0 on 4-pin side of relay.	Continuity	▶	GO to Step **EE7c**.
	No Continuity	▶	REPLACE pump motor relay.
EE7c CHECK PUMP MOTOR RELAY			
• Check continuity from Pin S1 on 7-pin side to Pin S1 on 4-pin side of relay.	Continuity	▶	GO to Step **EE7d**.
	No Continuity	▶	REPLACE pump motor relay.

Fig. 148   Pinpoint Tests EE7a, EE7b & EE7c: Fluid Level Indicator/Pedal Travel Switch/Pump Motor. 1992 Crown Victoria, Grand Marquis & Town Car

TEST STEP	RESULT		ACTION TO TAKE
EE7d CHECK CIRCUIT 462			
• Check continuity between Breakout Box Pin 31 and Pin S0 on pump motor connector 7-pin plug (harness side).	Continuity	▶	GO to Step **EE7e**.
	No Continuity	▶	SERVICE or REPLACE cable harness Circuit 462.
EE7e CHECK CIRCUIT 604			
• Check continuity between Breakout Box Pin 49 and Pin S1 on pump motor connector 7-pin plug (harness side).	Continuity	▶	REVERIFY reading at EE7.
	No Continuity	▶	SERVICE or REPLACE cable harness Circuit 604.
EE8 CHECK MOTOR SPEED SENSOR SHORT TO BATTERY +			
• Turn ignition switch to ON. • Measure voltage between Breakout Box Pins 31 and 60.	No voltage	▶	GO to Step **EE9**.
	12V	▶	GO to Step **EE8a**.
EE8a CHECK PUMP MOTOR			
• Disconnect pump motor to relay 4-pin plug connector. • Turn ignition switch to ON. • Measure voltage between Breakout Box Pins 31 and 60.	No voltage	▶	REPLACE pump and motor.
	12V	▶	GO to Step **EE8b**.
EE8b CHECK CIRCUIT 462			
• Disconnect wire harness to relay 7-pin plug. • Turn ignition switch to ON. • Measure voltage between Breakout Box Pins 31 and 60.	No voltage	▶	GO to Step **EE8c**.
	12V	▶	SERVICE or REPLACE cable harness Circuit 462.

Fig. 149   Pinpoint Tests EE7d, EE7e, EE8, EE8a & EE8: Fluid Level Indicator/Pedal Travel Switch/Pump Motor. 1992 Crown Victoria, Grand Marquis & Town Car

TEST STEP	RESULT ▶	ACTION TO TAKE
EE8a CHECK PUMP MOTOR OPERATION		
• Disconnect pump motor relay from pump motor. • Ground Pin 2 and apply 12 volts to Pin 1 of pump motor connector.	Pump motor runs ▶ Pump motor does not run ▶	GO to Step **EE8b**. REPLACE pump motor.
EE8b CHECK POWER TO RELAY		
• Disconnect wire harness from pump motor relay. • Check voltage between Pin 30 on wire harness to pump motor relay connector and ground.	Over 10V ▶ Less than 10V ▶	GO to Step **EE8c**. SERVICE or REPLACE battery, Circuit 299, 537 or fuse link (Taurus/Sable). Circuit 299B, 537 or fuse link (Taurus SHO).

Fig. 150   Pinpoint Tests EE8a & EE8b: Fluid Level Indicator/Pedal Travel Switch/Pump Motor. 1992 Continental, Sable & Taurus

TEST STEP	RESULT ▶	ACTION TO TAKE
EE8c CHECK POWER TO RELAY COIL		
• Jumper Pins 34 and 60 at Breakout Box. • Turn ignition to ON position. • Measure voltage between Pins 86 and ground.	Over 10V ▶ Less than 10V ▶	GO to Step **EE8d**. SERVICE or REPLACE cable harness Circuit 532A or 532G (Taurus/Sable). Circuit 532, 532B or 532H (Taurus SHO).
EE8d CHECK PUMP MOTOR RELAY COIL		
• Measure resistance between Pins 85 and 86 on pump motor relay.	45 to 105 ohms ▶ Any other reading ▶	GO to Step **EE7e**. REPLACE pump motor relay.
EE8e CHECK CIRCUIT 539		
• Check for continuity between Breakout Box Pin 15 and Pin 85 on wire harness to pump motor relay connector.	Continuity ▶ No Continuity ▶	GO to Step **EE8f**. SERVICE or REPLACE cable harness Circuit 539.

Fig. 151   Pinpoint Tests EE8c, EE8d & EE8e: Fluid Level Indicator/Pedal Travel Switch/Pump Motor. 1992 Continental, Sable & Taurus

TEST STEP	RESULT ▶	ACTION TO TAKE
EE8f CHECK CIRCUIT 57		
• Check for continuity between wire harness to pump motor relay connector Pin 31 and ground.	Continuity ▶ No Continuity ▶	GO to Step **EE8g**. SERVICE or REPLACE cable harness Circuit 57 or 57A (Taurus/Sable). Circuit 57S or 57R (Taurus SHO).
EE8g CHECK PUMP MOTOR RELAY		
• Connect battery positive to Pin 86 and battery negative to Pin 85 of pump motor relay. • Check for continuity between Pin 30 and Pin 1 on relay.	Continuity ▶ No Continuity ▶	GO to Step **EE8h**. REPLACE pump motor relay.
EE8h CHECK PUMP MOTOR RELAY		
• Check continuity between Pins 2 and 31 on pump motor relay.	Continuity ▶ No Continuity ▶	REPLACE computer module. REPLACE pump motor relay.

Fig. 152   Pinpoint Tests EE8f, EE8g & EE8h: Fluid Level Indicator/Pedal Travel Switch/Pump Motor. 1992 Continental, Sable & Taurus

TEST STEP	RESULT ▶	ACTION TO TAKE
EE9 SERVICE CODE 64: CHECK PUMP MOTOR PRESSURE CAPABILITY		
• Turn ignition switch OFF. • Disconnect 55-pin plug from electronic controller. • Connect EEC-IV Breakout Box, T83L-50-EEC-IV, with Anti-Lock Test Adapter, T90P-50-ALA or equivalent, to the anti-lock 55-pin plug harness. • Jumper Pins 15, 34 and 60. • Apply and hold brake pedal. • Turn ignition switch to ON.	Brake pedal rises ▶ Brake pedal does not rise ▶	REVERIFY code 64 REPLACE pump and motor.

Fig. 153   Pinpoint Tests EE9: Fluid Level Indicator/Pedal Travel Switch/Pump Motor. 1992 Continental, Sable & Taurus

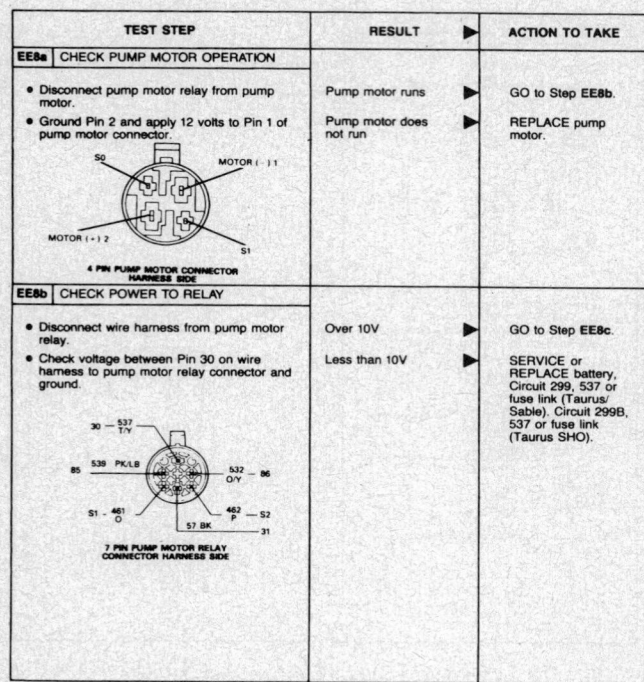

TEST STEP	RESULT	▶	ACTION TO TAKE
EE8c CHECK CIRCUIT 604 • Turn ignition switch to ON. • Measure voltage between Breakout Box Pins 49 and 60.	No voltage	▶	REPLACE pump motor relay.
	12V	▶	SERVICE or REPLACE cable harness Circuit 604.
EE9 CHECK MOTOR SPEED SENSOR SHORT TO GROUND • Check for continuity between Breakout Box Pins 31 and 60.	No Continuity	▶	GO to Step EE10.
	Continuity	▶	GO to Step EE9a.
EE9a CHECK PUMP MOTOR • Disconnect pump to motor relay 4-pin plug connector. • Check for continuity between Breakout Box Pins 31 and 60.	Continuity	▶	GO to Step EE9b.
	No Continuity	▶	REPLACE pump and motor.
EE9b CHECK CIRCUIT 462 • Disconnect wire harness to relay 7-pin plug. • Check for continuity between Breakout Box Pins 31 and 60.	Continuity	▶	SERVICE or REPLACE cable harness Circuit 462.
	No Continuity	▶	GO to Step EE9c.
EE9c CHECK CIRCUIT 604 • Check for continuity between Breakout Box Pins 49 and 60.	Continuity	▶	SERVICE or REPLACE cable harness Circuit 604.
	No Continuity	▶	REPLACE pump motor relay.
EE10 CHECK PUMP MOTOR OPERATION • Reconnect pump motor relay to pump and wire harness. • Jumper Pins 15, 34 and 60 at Breakout Box. • Turn ignition to ON position.	Pump motor runs	▶	GO to Step EE11.
	Pump motor does not run	▶	GO to Step EE10a.

Fig. 154   Pinpoint Tests EE8c, EE9 & EE9a, EE9b, EE9c & EE10: Fluid Level Indicator/Pedal Travel Switch/Pump Motor. 1992 Crown Victoria, Grand Marquis & Town Car

TEST STEP	RESULT	▶	ACTION TO TAKE
EE10a CHECK PUMP MOTOR OPERATION • Disconnect pump motor relay from pump motor. • Ground Pin 2 and apply 12 volts to Pin 1 of pump motor connector.	Pump motor runs	▶	GO to Step EE10b.
	Pump motor does not run	▶	REPLACE pump motor.
EE10b CHECK POWER TO RELAY • Disconnect wire harness from pump motor relay. • Check voltage between Pin 30 on wire harness to pump motor relay connector and ground.	Over 10V	▶	GO to Step EE10c.
	Less than 10V	▶	SERVICE or REPLACE battery, fuse or Circuit 537.

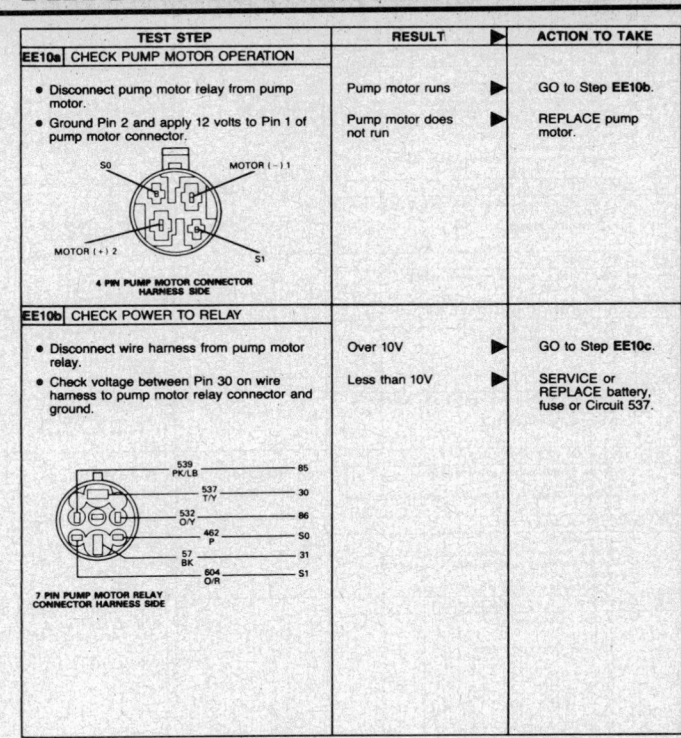

Fig. 155   Pinpoint Tests EE10a & EE10b: Fluid Level Indicator/Pedal Travel Switch/Pump Motor. 1992 Crown Victoria, Grand Marquis & Town Car

TEST STEP	RESULT	▶	ACTION TO TAKE
EE10c CHECK POWER TO RELAY COIL • Jumper Pins 34 and 60 at Breakout Box. • Turn ignition to ON position. • Measure voltage between Pins 86 and ground.	Over 10V	▶	GO to Step EE10d.
	Less than 10V	▶	SERVICE or REPLACE cable harness Circuit 532g.
EE10d CHECK PUMP MOTOR RELAY COIL • Measure resistance between Pins 85 and 86 on pump motor relay.	45 to 105 ohms	▶	GO to Step EE10e.
	Any other reading	▶	REPLACE pump motor relay.
EE10e CHECK CIRCUIT 539 • Check for continuity between Breakout Box Pin 15 and Pin 85 on wire harness to pump motor relay connector.	Continuity	▶	GO to Step EE10f.
	No Continuity	▶	SERVICE or REPLACE cable harness Circuit 539.

Fig. 156   Pinpoint Tests EE10c, EE10d & EE10e: Fluid Level Indicator/Pedal Travel Switch/Pump Motor. 1992 Crown Victoria, Grand Marquis & Town Car

TEST STEP	RESULT	▶	ACTION TO TAKE
EE10f CHECK CIRCUIT 57e • Check for continuity between wire harness to pump motor relay connector Pin 31 and ground.	Continuity	▶	GO to Step EE10g.
	No Continuity	▶	SERVICE or REPLACE cable harness Circuit 57w.
EE10g CHECK PUMP MOTOR RELAY • Connect battery + to Pin 86 and battery − to Pin 85 of pump motor relay. • Check for continuity between Pin 30 and Pin 1 on relay.	Continuity	▶	GO to Step EE10h.
	No Continuity	▶	REPLACE pump motor relay.
EE10h CHECK PUMP MOTOR RELAY • Check continuity between Pins 2 and 31 on pump motor relay.	Continuity	▶	REPLACE computer module.
	No Continuity	▶	REPLACE pump motor relay.

Fig. 157   Pinpoint Tests EE10f, EE10g, EE10h: Fluid Level Indicator/Pedal Travel Switch/Pump Motor. 1992 Crown Victoria, Grand Marquis & Town Car

TEST STEP	RESULT	▶	ACTION TO TAKE
A1 CHECK POWER TO ABS MODULE • Disconnect 55-pin plug from ABS module. • Connect EEC-IV Breakout Box 014-00322 with Anti-Lock Test Adapter T90P-50-ALA or equivalent to the anti-lock 55-pin plug wiring harness. • Set multi-meter to read volts DC. • Turn ignition switch ON. • Measure voltage between breakout box Pins 53 and 60.	Over 10 volts Under 10 volts	▶ ▶	GO to A5. GO to A2.
A2 CHECK ABS MODULE TO GROUND WIRE • Check continuity between breakout box Pin 60 and body ground. • Is continuity present?	Yes No	▶ ▶	GO to A3. SERVICE or REPLACE cable harness Circuit 530.
A3 CHECK FUSE 'O' • Check fuse 'O' in power distribution box. • Is fuse good?	Yes No	▶ ▶	GO to Step A4. REPLACE fuse.
A4 CHECK IGNITION TO ABS MODULE WIRE • Check for continuity between breakout box Pin 53 and ignition switch wire 687. • Is continuity present?	Yes No	▶ ▶	CHECK ignition switch. SERVICE or REPLACE cable harness Circuit 687.
A5 CHECK GROUND • Check for continuity between breakout box Pins 19 and 60. • Is continuity present?	Yes No	▶ ▶	GO to A6. SERVICE or REPLACE cable harness Circuit 530.
A6 CHECK MAIN RELAY OPERATION • Jumper Pins 34 and 60 at breakout box. • Turn ignition to ON. • Measure voltage between breakout box Pins 33 and 19.	Over 10 volts DC Under 10 volts DC	▶ ▶	GO to A13. GO to A7.
A7 CHECK MAIN RELAY COIL • Turn ignition to OFF. • Remove jumper from breakout box Pins 34 and 60. • Measure resistance between Breakout Box Pins 53 and 34. • Is resistance between 45 and 90 ohms?	Yes No	▶ ▶	GO to A9. GO to A8.
A8 CHECK MAIN RELAY COIL (Continued) • Remove main power relay. 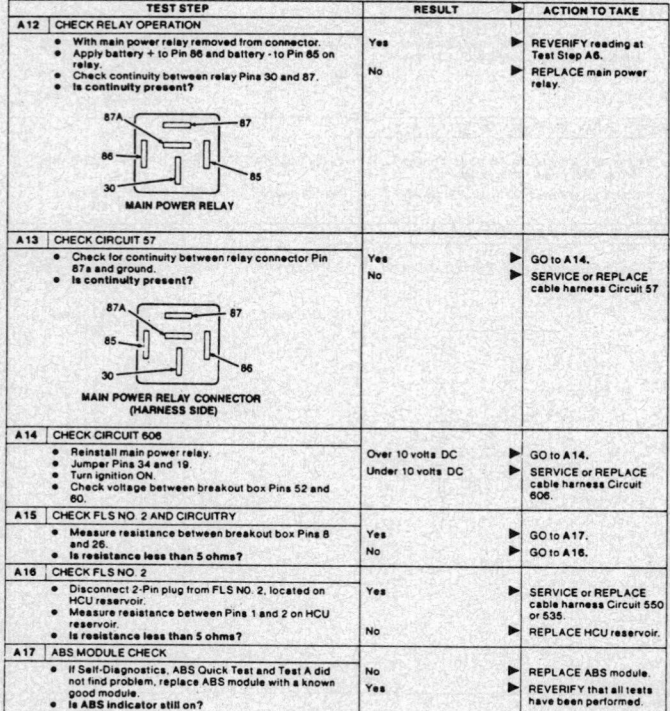 MAIN POWER RELAY • Measure resistance between main relay Pins 85 and 86. • Is resistance between 45 and 90 ohms?	Yes No	▶ ▶	SERVICE or REPLACE cable harness Circuit 687 or 513. REPLACE main relay.

Fig. 158 Test A: ABS Warning Lamp On w/Brake Warning Lamp Off (Part 1 of 3). 1993–94 Continental

TEST STEP	RESULT	▶	ACTION TO TAKE
A9 CHECK CIRCUIT 687 • Turn ignition ON. 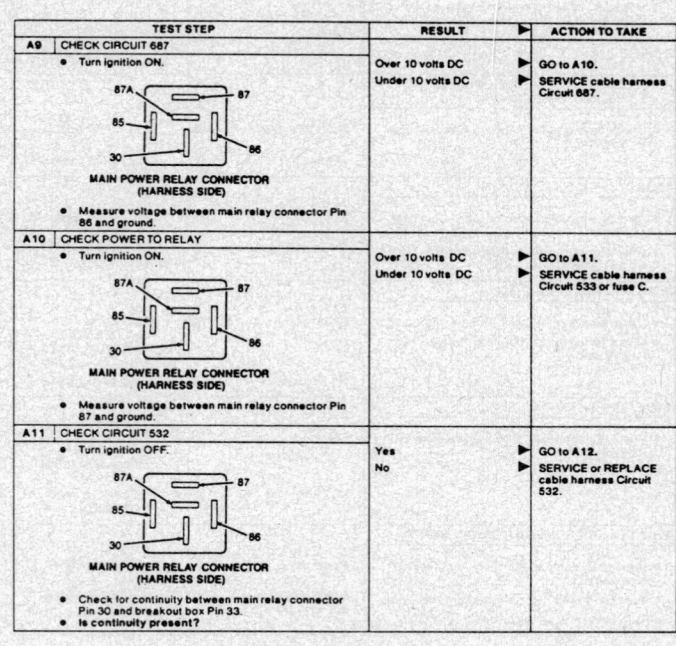 MAIN POWER RELAY CONNECTOR (HARNESS SIDE) • Measure voltage between main relay connector Pin 86 and ground.	Over 10 volts DC Under 10 volts DC	▶ ▶	GO to A10. SERVICE cable harness Circuit 687.
A10 CHECK POWER TO RELAY • Turn ignition ON. MAIN POWER RELAY CONNECTOR (HARNESS SIDE) • Measure voltage between main relay connector Pin 87 and ground.	Over 10 volts DC Under 10 volts DC	▶ ▶	GO to A11. SERVICE cable harness Circuit 533 or fuse C.
A11 CHECK CIRCUIT 532 • Turn ignition OFF. MAIN POWER RELAY CONNECTOR (HARNESS SIDE) • Check for continuity between main relay connector Pin 30 and breakout box Pin 33. • Is continuity present?	Yes No	▶ ▶	GO to A12. SERVICE or REPLACE cable harness Circuit 532.

Fig. 158   Test A: ABS Warning Lamp On w/Brake Warning Lamp Off (Part 2 of 3). 1993–94 Continental

TEST STEP	RESULT	▶	ACTION TO TAKE
A12 CHECK RELAY OPERATION • With main power relay removed from connector. • Apply battery + to Pin 86 and battery - to Pin 85 on relay. • Check continuity between relay Pins 30 and 87. • Is continuity present? MAIN POWER RELAY	Yes No	▶ ▶	REVERIFY reading at Test Step A6. REPLACE main power relay.
A13 CHECK CIRCUIT 57 • Check for continuity between relay connector Pin 87a and ground. • Is continuity present? MAIN POWER RELAY CONNECTOR (HARNESS SIDE)	Yes No	▶ ▶	GO to A14. SERVICE or REPLACE cable harness Circuit 57
A14 CHECK CIRCUIT 606 • Reinstall main power relay. • Jumper Pins 34 and 19. • Turn ignition ON. • Check voltage between breakout box Pins 52 and 60.	Over 10 volts DC Under 10 volts DC	▶ ▶	GO to A14. SERVICE or REPLACE cable harness Circuit 606.
A15 CHECK FLS NO. 2 AND CIRCUITRY • Measure resistance between breakout box Pins 8 and 26. • Is resistance less than 5 ohms?	Yes No	▶ ▶	GO to A17. GO to A16.
A16 CHECK FLS NO. 2 • Disconnect 2-Pin plug from FLS NO. 2, located on HCU reservoir. • Measure resistance between Pins 1 and 2 on HCU reservoir. • Is resistance less than 5 ohms?	Yes No	▶ ▶	SERVICE or REPLACE cable harness Circuit 550 or 535. REPLACE HCU reservoir.
A17 ABS MODULE CHECK • If Self-Diagnostics, ABS Quick Test and Test A did not find problem, replace ABS module with a known good module. • Is ABS indicator still on?	No Yes	▶ ▶	REPLACE ABS module. REVERIFY that all tests have been performed.

Fig. 158   Test A: ABS Warning Lamp On w/Brake Warning Lamp Off (Part 3 of 3). 1993 Continental (1994, step A12 only)

TEST STEP	RESULT	▶	ACTION TO TAKE
A13 CHECK CIRCUIT 57 • Check for continuity between relay connector Pin 87a and ground. • Is continuity present? MAIN POWER RELAY CONNECTOR (HARNESS SIDE)	Yes No	▶ ▶	GO to A14. SERVICE or REPLACE cable harness Circuit 57
A14 CHECK CIRCUIT 606 • Reinstall main power relay. • Jumper Pins 34 and 19. • Turn ignition switch to the ON position. • Check voltage between breakout box Pins 52 and 60. • Is voltage above 10 volts?	Yes No	▶ ▶	GO to A14. SERVICE or REPLACE cable harness Circuit 606 (W/LB).
A15 CHECK FLS NO. 2 AND CIRCUITRY • Measure resistance between breakout box Pins 8 and 26. • Is resistance less than five ohms?	Yes No	▶ ▶	GO to A17. GO to A16.
A16 CHECK FLS NO. 2 • Disconnect 2-Pin plug from FLS NO. 2, located on hydraulic control unit reservoir. • Measure resistance between Pins 1 and 2 on hydraulic control unit reservoir. • Is resistance less than five ohms?	Yes No	▶ ▶	SERVICE or REPLACE cable harness Circuit 550 (Y/LG) or 535 (LB/R). REPLACE hydraulic control unit reservoir.
A17 CHECK DIODE • Check diode between Circuits 606 and 532. • Is diode good?	Yes No	▶ ▶	REPLACE diode. GO to A18.
A18 ABS MODULE CHECK • If On-Board Diagnostics, ABS Quick Test and Test A did not find problem, replace anti-lock brake control module with a known good anti-lock brake control module. • Is ABS indicator still on?	Yes No	▶ ▶	REVERIFY that all tests have been performed. REPLACE anti-lock brake control module.

Fig. 158   Test A: ABS Warning Lamp On w/Brake Warning Lamp Off (Part 3 of 3). 1994 Continental

Fig. 159 Test A: Anti-Lock Warning Indicator On w/Brake Warning Indicator Off (Part 1 of 3). 1993–94 Crown Victoria, Grand Marquis & Town Car

TEST STEP	RESULT	▶	ACTION TO TAKE
A1 CHECK POWER TO ABS MODULE • Disconnect 55-pin plug from ABS Module. • Connect EEC-IV breakout box 014-00322 Anti-Lock Test Adapter T90P-50-ALA or equivalent to the Anti-Lock 55-pin plug wiring harness. • Set multi-meter to read volts DC. • Turn ignition switch ON. • Measure voltage between breakout box Pins 53 and 60. • **Is voltage reading over 10 volts?**	Yes No	▶ ▶	GO to A4. GO to A2.
A2 CHECK ABS MODULE TO GROUND WIRE • Check continuity between breakout box Pin 60 and body ground. • **Is continuity present?**	Yes No	▶ ▶	GO to A3. SERVICE or REPLACE cable harness 57.
A3 CHECK IGNITION TO ABS MODULE WIRE • Check for continuity between breakout box Pin 53 and ignition switch wire 297 for Town Car, Circuit 687 for Crown Victoria/Grand Marquis. • **Is continuity present?**	Yes No	▶ ▶	REVERIFY reading at Test Step A1. SERVICE or REPLACE cable harness Circuit 297, 601, or fuse 18 for Town Car. Circuit 687, 88 or Fuse 15 for Crown Victoria/Grand Marquis.
A4 CHECK GROUND • Check for continuity between breakout box Pins 19 and 60. • **Is continuity present?**	Yes No	▶ ▶	GO to A5. SERVICE or REPLACE cable harness Circuit 57.
A5 CHECK MAIN RELAY OPERATION • Ground breakout box Pin 34. • Jumper Pins 34 and 60 at breakout box. • Turn ignition to ON. • Measure voltage between breakout box Pins 33 and 19. • **Is voltage reading over 10 volts?**	Yes No	▶ ▶	GO to A12. GO to A6.
A6 CHECK MAIN RELAY COIL • Turn ignition to OFF. • Remove jumper from breakout box Pins 34 and 60. • Measure resistance between breakout box Pins 53 and 34. • **Is resistance between 45 and 90 ohms?**	Yes No	▶ ▶	GO to A8. GO to A7.
A7 CHECK MAIN RELAY COIL (Continued) • Remove main power relay. [MAIN POWER RELAY diagram] • Measure resistance between main relay Pins 85 and 86. • **Is resistance between 45 and 90 ohms?**	Yes No	▶ ▶	SERVICE or REPLACE cable harness Circuit 601 or 513 for Town Car. Circuit 599 or 88 for Crown Victoria/Grand Marquis. REPLACE main relay.

Fig. 159 Test A: Anti-Lock Warning Indicator On w/Brake Warning Indicator Off (Part 1 of 3). 1993–94 Crown Victoria, Grand Marquis & Town Car

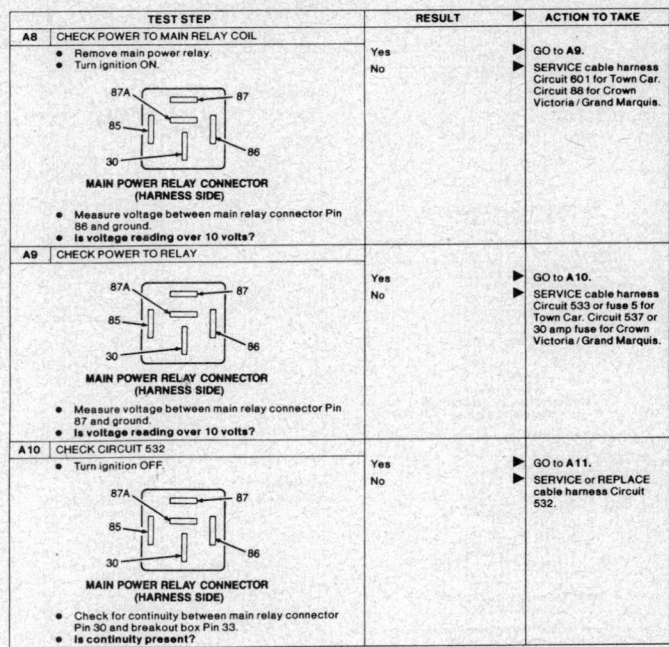

Fig. 159 Test A: Anti-Lock Warning Indicator On w/Brake Warning Indicator Off (Part 2 of 3). 1993–94 Crown Victoria, Grand Marquis & Town Car

TEST STEP	RESULT	▶	ACTION TO TAKE
A8 CHECK POWER TO MAIN RELAY COIL • Remove main power relay. • Turn ignition ON. [MAIN POWER RELAY CONNECTOR (HARNESS SIDE) diagram] • Measure voltage between main relay connector Pin 86 and ground. • **Is voltage reading over 10 volts?**	Yes No	▶ ▶	GO to A9. SERVICE cable harness Circuit 601 for Town Car. Circuit 88 for Crown Victoria/Grand Marquis.
A9 CHECK POWER TO RELAY [MAIN POWER RELAY CONNECTOR (HARNESS SIDE) diagram] • Measure voltage between main relay connector Pin 87 and ground. • **Is voltage reading over 10 volts?**	Yes No	▶ ▶	GO to A10. SERVICE cable harness Circuit 533 or fuse 5 for Town Car. Circuit 537 or 30 amp fuse for Crown Victoria/Grand Marquis.
A10 CHECK CIRCUIT 532 • Turn ignition OFF. [MAIN POWER RELAY CONNECTOR (HARNESS SIDE) diagram] • Check for continuity between main relay connector Pin 30 and breakout box Pin 33. • **Is continuity present?**	Yes No	▶ ▶	GO to A11. SERVICE or REPLACE cable harness Circuit 532.

Fig. 159 Test A: Anti-Lock Warning Indicator On w/Brake Warning Indicator Off (Part 3 of 3). 1993–94 Crown Victoria, Grand Marquis & Town Car

TEST STEP	RESULT	▶	ACTION TO TAKE
A11 CHECK RELAY OPERATION • Apply B+ to Pin 86 and B- to Pin 85 on relay. • Check continuity between relay Pins 30 and 87. • **Is continuity present?** [MAIN POWER RELAY diagram]	Yes No	▶ ▶	REVERIFY reading at Step A5. REPLACE main power relay.
A12 CHECK CIRCUIT 57T OR 57W • Remove main power relay. • Check for continuity between relay connector Pin 87a and ground. • **Is continuity present?** [MAIN POWER RELAY CONNECTOR (HARNESS SIDE) diagram]	Yes No	▶ ▶	GO to A13. SERVICE or REPLACE cable harness Circuit 57.
A13 CHECK CIRCUIT 603 • Jumper Pins 34 and 19. • Reinstall main power relay. • Turn ignition ON. • Check voltage between breakout box Pins 52 and 60. • **Is voltage reading over 10 volts?**	Yes No	▶ ▶	GO to A14. SERVICE or REPLACE cable harness Circuits 295 or 603 for Town Car. Circuits 640 or 603 for Crown Victoria/Grand Marquis.
A14 CHECK FLS NO. 2 AND CIRCUITRY • Measure resistance between breakout box Pins 8 and 26. • **Is resistance less than 5 ohms?**	Yes No	▶ ▶	GO to A16. GO to A15.
A15 CHECK FLS NO. 2 • Disconnect 2-Pin plug from FLS 2, located on HCU reservoir. • Measure resistance between Pins 1 and 2 on HCU reservoir. • **Is resistance less than 5 ohms?**	Yes No	▶ ▶	SERVICE or REPLACE cable harness Circuit 467 or 550 for Town Car. Circuit 550 or 535 for Crown Victoria/Grand Marquis. REPLACE HCU reservoir.
A16 ABS MODULE CHECK • If Self-Diagnostics, ABS Quick Test and Test A did not find concern, replace ABS Module with a known good module. • **Is ABS indicator still on?**	No Yes	▶ ▶	REPLACE ABS Module. REVERIFY that all tests have been performed.

Fig. 160 Test A: Anti-Lock Warning Indicator On w/Brake Warning Indicator Off (Part 1 of 3). 1993–94 Sable & Taurus

TEST STEP	RESULT	▶	ACTION TO TAKE
A1 CHECK POWER TO ABS MODULE • Disconnect 55-pin plug from ABS Module. • Connect EEC-IV Breakout Box 014-00322 with Anti-Lock Test Adapter T90P-50-ALA or equivalent to the Anti-Lock 55-pin plug wiring harness. • Set multi-meter to read volts DC. • Turn ignition switch ON. • Measure voltage between breakout box Pins 53 and 60.	Over 10 volts Under 10 volts	▶ ▶	GO to A4. GO to A2.
A2 CHECK ABS MODULE TO GROUND WIRE • Check continuity between breakout box Pin 60 and body ground.	Continuity No continuity	▶ ▶	GO to A3. SERVICE or REPLACE cable harness Circuit 530 (Taurus/Sable). Circuit 57 or 530 (Taurus SHO).
A3 CHECK IGNITION TO ABS MODULE WIRE • Check for continuity between breakout box Pin 53 and ignition switch wire 687.	Continuity No Continuity	▶ ▶	REVERIFY reading at Test Step A1. SERVICE or REPLACE cable harness Circuit 687, or fuse.
A4 CHECK GROUND • Check for continuity between breakout box Pins 19 and 60.	Continuity No Continuity	▶ ▶	GO to A5. SERVICE or REPLACE cable harness Circuit 530 (Taurus/Sable). Circuit 57 or 530 (Taurus SHO).
A5 CHECK MAIN RELAY OPERATION • Jumper Pins 34 and 60 at breakout box. • Turn ignition to ON. • Measure voltage between breakout box Pins 33 and 19.	Over 10 volts DC Under 10 volts DC	▶ ▶	GO to A12. GO to A6.
A6 CHECK MAIN RELAY COIL • Turn ignition to OFF. • Remove jumper from breakout box Pins 34 and 60. • Measure resistance between breakout box Pins 53 and 34.	45 to 90 ohms Any other reading	▶ ▶	GO to A8. GO to A7.
A7 CHECK MAIN RELAY COIL (Continued) • Remove main power relay. [MAIN POWER RELAY diagram] • Measure resistance between main relay Pins 85 and 86.	45 to 90 ohms Any other reading	▶ ▶	SERVICE or REPLACE cable harness Circuit 513 or 687. REPLACE main relay.

Fig. 160 Test A: Anti-Lock Warning Indicator On w/Brake Warning Indicator Off (Part 1 of 3). 1993–94 Sable & Taurus

Fig. 160 — Test A (Part 2 of 3)

TEST STEP	RESULT	ACTION TO TAKE
A8 CHECK POWER TO MAIN RELAY COIL • Turn ignition ON. MAIN POWER RELAY CONNECTOR (HARNESS SIDE) • Measure voltage between main relay connector Pin 86 and ground.	Over 10 volts DC Under 10 volts DC	▶ GO to A9. ▶ SERVICE cable harness Circuit 687.
A9 CHECK POWER TO RELAY • Turn ignition ON. MAIN POWER RELAY CONNECTOR (HARNESS SIDE) • Measure voltage between main relay connector Pin 87 and ground.	Over 10 volts DC Under 10 volts DC	▶ GO to A10. ▶ SERVICE cable harness Circuit 533 or 30 A fuse.
A10 CHECK CIRCUIT 532 • Turn ignition OFF. MAIN POWER RELAY CONNECTOR (HARNESS SIDE) • Check for continuity between main relay connector Pin 30 and breakout box Pin 33.	Continuity No Continuity	▶ GO to A11. ▶ SERVICE or REPLACE cable harness Circuit 532.
A11 CHECK RELAY OPERATION • With main power relay removed from connector. • Apply battery + to Pin 86 and battery - to Pin 85 on relay. • Check continuity between relay Pins 30 and 87. MAIN POWER RELAY	Continuity No Continuity	▶ REVERIFY reading at Test Step A5. ▶ REPLACE main power relay.

FM4029300443020X

Fig. 160   Test A: Anti-Lock Warning Indicator On w/Brake Warning Indicator Off (Part 2 of 3). 1993–94 Sable & Taurus

Fig. 160 — Test A (Part 3 of 3)

TEST STEP	RESULT	ACTION TO TAKE
A12 CHECK CIRCUIT 57 • Check for continuity between relay connector Pin 87A and ground. MAIN POWER RELAY CONNECTOR (HARNESS SIDE)	Continuity No Continuity	▶ GO to A13. ▶ SERVICE or REPLACE cable harness Circuit 57.
A13 CHECK CIRCUIT 606 • Jumper Pins 34-19. • Turn ignition ON. • Check voltage between breakout box Pins 52 and 60.	Over 10 volts DC Under 10 volts DC	▶ GO to A14. ▶ SERVICE or REPLACE cable harness Circuit 606.
A14 CHECK FLS NO. 2 AND CIRCUITRY • Measure resistance between breakout box Pins 8 and 26.	Less than 5 ohms Any other reading	▶ GO to A16. ▶ GO to A15.
A15 CHECK FLS NO. 2 • Disconnect 2-pin plug from FLS No. 2, located on HCU reservoir. • Measure resistance between Pins 1 and 2 on HCU reservoir.	Less than 5 ohms Any other reading	▶ SERVICE or REPLACE cable harness Circuit 542 or 535 (Taurus / Sable). Circuit 550 or 535 (Taurus SHO). ▶ REPLACE HCU reservoir.
A16 ABS MODULE CHECK • If Self-Diagnostics, ABS Quick Test and Test A did not find problem, replace ABS Module with a known good module. • Is ABS indicator still on?	Yes No	▶ REVERIFY that all tests have been performed. ▶ REPLACE ABS Module.

FM4029300443030X

Fig. 160   Test A: Anti-Lock Warning Indicator On w/Brake Warning Indicator Off (Part 3 of 3). 1993–94 Sable & Taurus

Fig. 161 — Test B (Part 1 of 2)

TEST STEP	RESULT	ACTION TO TAKE
B1 CHECK CONTINUITY OF CIRCUITS 518 AND 519 • Turn ignition switch OFF. • Disconnect 55-pin plug from ABS module. • Check continuity between breakout box Pins 28 and 60.	Yes No	▶ GO to B2. ▶ GO to B3.

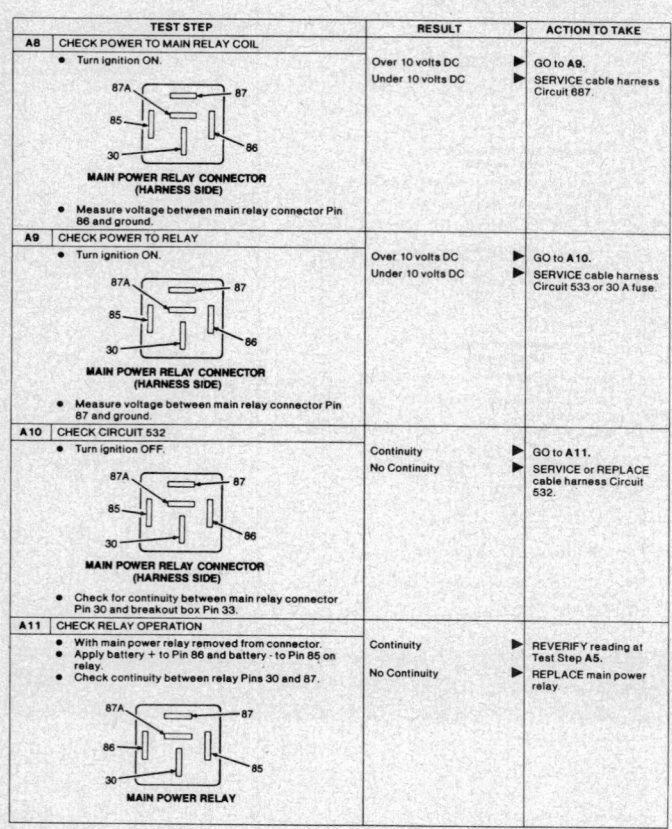

• Connect EEC-IV Breakout Box 014-00322 with Anti-Lock Test Adapter T90P-50-ALA or equivalent to the Anti-Lock 55-pin plug on the wiring harness.

• Is continuity present?

B2 CHECK LH REAR SENSOR TO GROUND • Disconnect LH rear wheel sensor plug. • Check for continuity between each sensor pin (sensor side) and vehicle ground. • Is continuity present? LH REAR SENSOR	Yes No	▶ REPLACE LH rear sensor. ▶ REPLACE or SERVICE cable harness Circuit 518 or 519.
B3 CHECK CONTINUITY OF CIRCUITS 523 AND 524 • Check continuity between breakout box Pins 27 and 60. • Is continuity present?	Yes No	▶ GO to B4. ▶ GO to B5.

FM4029300379010X

Fig. 161   Test B: ABS Warning Lamp On After Engine Starts (Part 1 of 2). 1993–94

Fig. 161 — Test B (Part 2 of 2)

TEST STEP	RESULT	ACTION TO TAKE
B4 CHECK RH REAR SENSOR TO GROUND • Disconnect RH rear wheel sensor plug. • Check for continuity between each sensor pin (sensor side) and vehicle ground. • Is continuity present? RH REAR SENSOR	Yes No	▶ REPLACE RH rear sensor. ▶ REPLACE or SERVICE cable harness Circuit 523 or 524.
B5 CHECK CONTINUITY OF CIRCUITS 514 AND 516 • Check for continuity between breakout box Pins 29 and 60. • Is continuity present?	Yes No	▶ GO to B6. ▶ GO to B7.
B6 CHECK RH FRONT SENSOR TO GROUND • Disconnect RH front wheel sensor plug. • Check for continuity between each sensor pin (sensor side) and vehicle ground. • Is continuity present? RH FRONT SENSOR	Yes No	▶ REPLACE RH front sensor. ▶ REPLACE or SERVICE cable harness Circuit 514 or 516.
B7 CHECK CONTINUITY OF CIRCUITS 521 AND 522 • Check for continuity between breakout box Pins 30 and 60. • Is continuity present?	Yes No	▶ GO to B8. ▶ Test Complete. If Anti-Lock indicator pattern remains, REPEAT Test B.
B8 CHECK LH FRONT SENSOR TO GROUND • Disconnect LH front wheel sensor plug. • Check for continuity between each sensor pin (sensor side) and vehicle ground. • Is continuity present? LH FRONT SENSOR	Yes No	▶ REPLACE LH front sensor. ▶ REPLACE or SERVICE cable harness Circuit 521 or 522.

FM4029300379020X

Fig. 161   Test B: ABS Warning Lamp On After Engine Starts (Part 2 of 2). 1993–94

Part 1

TEST STEP	RESULT	►	ACTION TO TAKE
C1 MEASURE LH FRONT SENSOR CIRCUIT RESISTANCE • Turn ignition switch to OFF position. • Disconnect 55-pin connector from ABS module. *[ABS MODULE, 55 PIN CONNECTOR]* • Connect EEC-IV Breakout Box 014-00322 with Anti-Lock Test Adapter T90P-50-ALA or equivalent to the 55-pin connector on wiring harness. *[ANTI-LOCK TEST ADAPTER T90P-50-ALA, 55 PIN CONNECTOR, EEC-IV BREAKOUT BOX 014-00322]* • Set multi-meter to read resistance. • Measure resistance between Pins 30 and 48. • Is resistance between 800 and 1400 ohms?	Yes No	► ►	GO to C3. GO to C2.
C2 CHECK LH FRONT SENSOR RESISTANCE • Disconnect LH front sensor plug. • Measure resistance of sensor at sensor plug. • Is resistance between 800 and 1400 ohms? *[LH FRONT SENSOR]*	Yes No	► ►	SERVICE or REPLACE cable harness Circuit 521 or 522. REPLACE LH front sensor.
C3 MEASURE RH FRONT SENSOR CIRCUIT RESISTANCE • Measure resistance between breakout box Pins 29 and 47. • Is resistance between 800 and 1400 ohms?	Yes No	► ►	GO to C5. GO to C4.

Fig. 162 Test C: ABS Warning Lamp On After Vehicle Starts To Move Or False Cycling Of ABS System (Part 1 of 8). 1993–94

Part 2

TEST STEP	RESULT	►	ACTION TO TAKE
C4 CHECK RH FRONT SENSOR RESISTANCE • Disconnect RH front sensor plug. • Measure resistance of sensor at sensor plug. • Is resistance between 800 and 1400 ohms? *[RH FRONT SENSOR]*	Yes No	► ►	SERVICE or REPLACE cable harness Circuit 514 or 516. REPLACE RH front sensor.
C5 MEASURE RH REAR SENSOR CIRCUIT RESISTANCE • Measure resistance between breakout box Pins 27 and 45. • Is resistance between 800 and 1400 ohms?	Yes No	► ►	GO to C7. GO to C6.
C6 CHECK RH REAR SENSOR RESISTANCE • Disconnect RH rear sensor plug. • Measure resistance of sensor at sensor plug. • Is resistance between 800 and 1400 ohms? *[RH REAR SENSOR]*	Yes No	► ►	SERVICE or REPLACE cable harness Circuit 523 or 524. REPLACE RH rear sensor.
C7 MEASURE LH REAR SENSOR CIRCUIT RESISTANCE • Measure resistance between breakout box Pins 28 and 46. • Is resistance between 800 and 1400 ohms?	Yes No	► ►	GO to C9. GO to C8.
C8 CHECK LH REAR SENSOR RESISTANCE • Disconnect LH rear sensor plug. • Measure resistance of sensor at sensor plug. • Is resistance between 800 and 1400 ohms? *[LH REAR SENSOR]*	Yes No	► ►	SERVICE or REPLACE cable harness Circuit 518 or 519. REPLACE LH rear sensor.
C9 CHECK LH FRONT SENSOR AND CIRCUITRY TO GROUND • Check for continuity between breakout box Pins 30 and 60. • Is continuity present?	Yes No	► ►	GO to C10. GO to C11.

Fig. 162 Test C: ABS Warning Lamp On After Vehicle Starts To Move Or False Cycling Of ABS System (Part 2 of 8). 1993–94

Part 3

TEST STEP	RESULT	►	ACTION TO TAKE
C10 CHECK LH FRONT SENSOR TO GROUND • Disconnect LH front sensor plug. • Check for continuity between each sensor pin and body ground. • Is continuity present?	Yes No	► ►	REPLACE LH front sensor. SERVICE or REPLACE cable harness Circuit 521 or 522.
C11 CHECK RH FRONT SENSOR AND CIRCUITRY TO GROUND • Check for continuity between breakout box Pins 29 and 60. • Is continuity present?	Yes No	► ►	GO to C12. GO to C13.
C12 CHECK RH FRONT SENSOR TO GROUND • Disconnect RH front sensor plug. • Check for continuity between each sensor pin and body ground. • Is continuity present?	Yes No	► ►	REPLACE RH front sensor. SERVICE or REPLACE cable harness Circuit 514 or 516.
C13 CHECK RH REAR SENSOR AND CIRCUITRY TO GROUND • Check for continuity between breakout box Pins 27 and 60. • Is continuity present?	Yes No	► ►	GO to C14. GO to C15.
C14 CHECK RH REAR SENSOR TO GROUND • Disconnect RH rear sensor plug. • Check for continuity between each sensor pin and body ground. • Is continuity present?	Yes No	► ►	REPLACE RH rear sensor. SERVICE or REPLACE cable harness Circuit 523 or 524.
C15 CHECK LH REAR SENSOR AND CIRCUITRY TO GROUND • Check for continuity between breakout box Pins 28 and 60. • Is continuity present?	Yes No	► ►	GO to C16. GO to C17.
C16 CHECK LH REAR SENSOR TO GROUND • Disconnect LH rear sensor plug. • Check for continuity between each sensor pin and body ground. • Is continuity present?	Yes No	► ►	REPLACE LH rear sensor. SERVICE or REPLACE cable harness Circuit 518 or 519.
C17 CHECK LH FRONT SENSOR VOLTAGE OUTPUT • Measure voltage between breakout box Pins 30 and 48 while spinning LH front wheel at approximately 1 revolution per second.	Between 0.10 and 1.40 volts AC Less than 0.10 or more than 1.40 volts AC	► ►	GO to C18. CHECK wheel sensor mounting, air gap or toothed wheel. CORRECT as required.
C18 CHECK RH FRONT SENSOR VOLTAGE OUTPUT • Measure voltage between breakout box Pins 29 and 47 while spinning RH front wheel at approximately 1 revolution per second.	Between 0.10 and 1.40 volts AC Less than 0.10 or more than 1.40 volts AC	► ►	GO to C19. CHECK wheel sensor mounting, air gap or toothed wheel. CORRECT as required.

Fig. 162 Test C: ABS Warning Lamp On After Vehicle Starts To Move Or False Cycling Of ABS System (Part 3 of 8). 1993–94

Part 4

TEST STEP	RESULT	►	ACTION TO TAKE
C19 CHECK RH REAR SENSOR VOLTAGE OUTPUT • Measure voltage between breakout box Pins 27 and 45 while spinning RH rear wheel at approximately 1 revolution per second.	Between 0.10 and 1.40 volts AC Less than 0.10 or more than 1.40 volts AC	► ►	GO to C20. CHECK wheel sensor mounting, air gap or toothed wheel. CORRECT as required.
C20 CHECK LH REAR SENSOR VOLTAGE OUTPUT • Measure voltage between breakout box Pins 28 and 46 while spinning LH rear wheel at approximately 1 revolution per second.	Between 0.10 and 1.40 volts AC Less than 0.10 or more than 1.40 volts AC	► ►	GO to C21. CHECK wheel sensor mounting, air gap or toothed wheel. CORRECT as required.
C21 CHECK MOTOR SPEED SENSOR AND CIRCUITRY • Measure resistance between breakout box Pins 31 and 49. • Is resistance between 5 and 100 ohms?	Yes No	► ►	GO to C27. GO to C22.
C22 CHECK PUMP MOTOR SPEED SENSOR • Disconnect 4-pin plug on pump motor. • Measure resistance between Pins S0 and S1 on pump motor. • Is resistance between 5 and 100 ohms? *[4 PIN PUMP MOTOR CONNECTOR: S0, MOTOR (-) 2, MOTOR (+) 1, S1]*	Yes No	► ►	GO to C23. REPLACE pump and motor.
C23 CHECK PUMP MOTOR RELAY • Disconnect 7-pin plug on pump motor relay and remove relay. • Check continuity from Pin S0 on 7-pin side to Pin S0 on 4-pin side of relay. • Is continuity present? *[PUMP MOTOR RELAY: BATT (+) 1, 31, S0, 86, S0, TEST, 30, MOTOR (-) 2, S1, S1, 85]*	Yes No	► ►	GO to C24. REPLACE pump motor relay.

Fig. 162 Test C: ABS Warning Lamp On After Vehicle Starts To Move Or False Cycling Of ABS System (Part 4 of 8). 1993–94

TEST STEP		RESULT	▶	ACTION TO TAKE
C24	CHECK PUMP MOTOR RELAY			
	• Check continuity from Pin S1 on 7-pin side to Pin S1 on 4-pin side of relay. • Is continuity present?	Yes	▶	GO TO C25.
		No	▶	REPLACE pump motor relay.
C25	CHECK CIRCUIT 462			
	• Check continuity between breakout box Pin 31 and Pin S0 on pump motor connector 7-pin plug (harness side). • Is continuity present?	Yes	▶	GO to C26.
		No	▶	SERVICE or REPLACE cable harness Circuit 462.

7 PIN PUMP MOTOR RELAY CONNECTOR HARNESS SIDE

C26	CHECK CIRCUIT 461			
	• Check continuity between breakout box Pin 49 and Pin S1 on pump motor connector 7-pin plug (harness side). • Is continuity present?	Yes	▶	REVERIFY reading at C21.
		No	▶	SERVICE or REPLACE cable harness Circuit 461.
C27	CHECK MOTOR SPEED SENSOR SHORT TO BATTERY+			
	• Turn ignition switch to ON. • Measure voltage between breakout box Pins 31 and 60.	No voltage	▶	GO to C31.
		12 volts	▶	GO to C28.
C28	CHECK PUMP MOTOR			
	• Disconnect pump motor relay 4-pin plug connector. • Turn ignition switch to ON. • Measure voltage between breakout box Pins 31 and 60.	No voltage	▶	REPLACE pump and motor.
		12 volts	▶	GO to C29.
C29	CHECK CIRCUIT 462			
	• Disconnect wire harness to relay 7-pin plug. • Turn ignition switch to ON. • Measure voltage between breakout box Pins 31 and 60.	No voltage	▶	GO to C30.
		12 volts	▶	SERVICE or REPLACE cable harness Circuit 462.
C30	CHECK CIRCUIT 461			
	• Turn ignition switch to ON. • Measure voltage between breakout box Pins 49 and 60.	No voltage	▶	REPLACE pump motor relay.
		12 volts	▶	SERVICE or REPLACE cable harness Circuit 461.
C31	CHECK MOTOR SPEED SENSOR SHORT TO GROUND			
	• Turn ignition switch OFF. • Check for continuity between breakout box Pins 31 and 60. • Is continuity present?	No	▶	GO to C35.
		Yes	▶	GO to C32.

Fig. 162   Test C: ABS Warning Lamp On After Vehicle Starts To Move Or False Cycling Of ABS System (Part 5 of 8). 1993–94 Continental

---

TEST STEP		RESULT	▶	ACTION TO TAKE
C25	CHECK CIRCUIT 462			
	• Check continuity between Breakout Box Pin 31 and Pin S0 on pump motor connector 7-pin plug (harness side). • Is continuity present?	Yes	▶	GO to C26.
		No	▶	SERVICE or REPLACE cable harness Circuit 462.

7 PIN PUMP MOTOR RELAY CONNECTOR HARNESS SIDE

C26	CHECK CIRCUIT 351 OR 604			
	• Check continuity between Breakout Box Pin 49 and Pin S1 on pump motor connector 7-pin plug (harness side). • Is continuity present?	Yes	▶	REVERIFY reading at C21.
		No	▶	SERVICE or REPLACE cable harness Circuit 604 for Town Car. Circuit 351 for Crown Victoria / Grand Marquis.
C27	CHECK MOTOR SPEED SENSOR SHORT TO BATTERY +			
	• Turn ignition switch to RUN. • Measure voltage between Breakout Box Pins 31 and 60. • Is B+ present?	Yes	▶	GO to C28.
		No	▶	GO to C30.
C28	CHECK CIRCUIT 462			
	• Disconnect wire harness to relay 7-pin plug. • Disconnect pump motor to relay 4-pin plug. • Turn ignition switch to RUN. • Measure voltage between Breakout Box Pins 31 and 60. • Is B+ present?	Yes	▶	SERVICE or REPLACE cable harness Circuit 462.
		No	▶	GO to C29.
C29	CHECK CIRCUIT 351 OR 604			
	• Turn ignition switch to RUN. • Measure voltage between Breakout Box Pins 49 and 60. • Is B+ present?	Yes	▶	SERVICE or REPLACE cable harness Circuit 604 for Town Car. Circuit 351 for Crown Victoria / Grand Marquis.
		No	▶	REPLACE pump motor relay.
C30	CHECK MOTOR SPEED SENSOR SHORT TO GROUND			
	• Check for continuity between Breakout Box Pins 31 and 60. • Is continuity present?	Yes	▶	GO to C11.
		No	▶	GO to C33.
C31	CHECK CIRCUIT 462			
	• Disconnect wire harness to relay 7-pin plug. • Disconnect pump motor to relay 4-pin plug. • Check for continuity between Breakout Box Pins 31 and 60. • Is continuity present?	Yes	▶	SERVICE or REPLACE cable harness Circuit 462.
		No	▶	GO to C32.

Fig. 162   Test C: ABS Warning Lamp On After Vehicle Starts To Move Or False Cycling Of ABS System (Part 5 of 8). 1993–94 Continental (1993–94 Crown Victoria, Grand Marquis & Town Car, step C24 only)

TEST STEP		RESULT	▶	ACTION TO TAKE
C24	CHECK PUMP MOTOR RELAY			
	• Check continuity from Pin S1 on 7-pin side to Pin S1 on 4-pin side of relay. • Is continuity present?	Yes	▶	GO TO C25.
		No	▶	REPLACE pump motor relay.
C25	CHECK CIRCUIT 462			
	• Check continuity between breakout box Pin 31 and Pin S0 on pump motor connector 7-pin plug (harness side). • Is continuity present?	Yes	▶	GO to C26.
		No	▶	SERVICE or REPLACE cable harness Circuit 462.

7 PIN PUMP MOTOR RELAY CONNECTOR HARNESS SIDE

C26	CHECK CIRCUIT 461			
	• Check continuity between breakout box Pin 49 and Pin S1 on pump motor connector 7-pin plug (harness side). • Is continuity present?	Yes	▶	REVERIFY reading at C21.
		No	▶	SERVICE or REPLACE cable harness Circuit 461.
C27	CHECK MOTOR SPEED SENSOR SHORT TO BATTERY +			
	• Turn ignition switch to ON. • Measure voltage between breakout box Pins 31 and 60.	No voltage	▶	GO to C31.
		12 volts	▶	GO to C28.
C28	CHECK PUMP MOTOR			
	• Disconnect pump motor relay 4-pin plug connector. • Turn ignition switch to ON. • Measure voltage between breakout box Pins 31 and 60.	No voltage	▶	REPLACE pump and motor.
		12 volts	▶	GO to C29.
C29	CHECK CIRCUIT 462			
	• Disconnect wire harness to relay 7-pin plug. • Turn ignition switch to ON. • Measure voltage between breakout box Pins 31 and 60.	No voltage	▶	GO to C30.
		12 volts	▶	SERVICE or REPLACE cable harness Circuit 462.
C30	CHECK CIRCUIT 461			
	• Turn ignition switch to ON. • Measure voltage between breakout box Pins 49 and 60.	No voltage	▶	REPLACE pump motor relay.
		12 volts	▶	SERVICE or REPLACE cable harness Circuit 461.
C31	CHECK MOTOR SPEED SENSOR SHORT TO GROUND			
	• Check for continuity between breakout box Pins 31 and 60. • Is continuity present?	No	▶	GO to C34.
		Yes	▶	GO to C32.

Fig. 162   Test C: ABS Warning Lamp On After Vehicle Starts To Move Or False Cycling Of ABS System (Part 5 of 8). 1993–94 Sable & Taurus

---

TEST STEP		RESULT	▶	ACTION TO TAKE
C32	CHECK CIRCUIT 462			
	• Disconnect wire harness to relay 7-pin plug. • Check for continuity between breakout box Pins 31 and 60. • Is continuity present?	Yes	▶	SERVICE or REPLACE cable harness Circuit 462.
		No	▶	GO to C33.
C33	CHECK CIRCUIT 461			
	• Check for continuity between breakout box Pins 49 and 60. • Is continuity present?	Yes	▶	SERVICE or REPLACE cable harness Circuit 461.
		No	▶	REPLACE pump motor relay.
C34	CHECK PUMP MOTOR OPERATION			
	• Reconnect pump motor relay to pump and wire harness. • Jumper Pins 15, 34 and 60 at breakout box. • Turn ignition to ON position. • Does pump motor run?	Yes	▶	REPLACE ABS module.
		No	▶	GO to C35.
C35	CHECK PUMP MOTOR OPERATION			
	• Disconnect pump motor relay from pump motor. • Ground Pin 2 and apply 12 volts to Pin 1 of pump motor connector. • Does pump motor run?	Yes	▶	GO to C36.
		No	▶	REPLACE pump motor.

4 PIN PUMP MOTOR CONNECTOR

C36	CHECK POWER TO RELAY			
	• Disconnect wire harness from pump motor relay. • Check voltage between Pin 30 on wire harness to pump motor relay connector and ground.	Over 10 volts	▶	GO to C37.
		Less than 10 volts	▶	SERVICE or REPLACE battery, fuse D or Circuit 537.

7 PIN PUMP MOTOR RELAY CONNECTOR HARNESS SIDE

Fig. 162   Test C: ABS Warning Lamp On After Vehicle Starts To Move Or False Cycling Of ABS System (Part 6 of 8). 1993–94 Continental

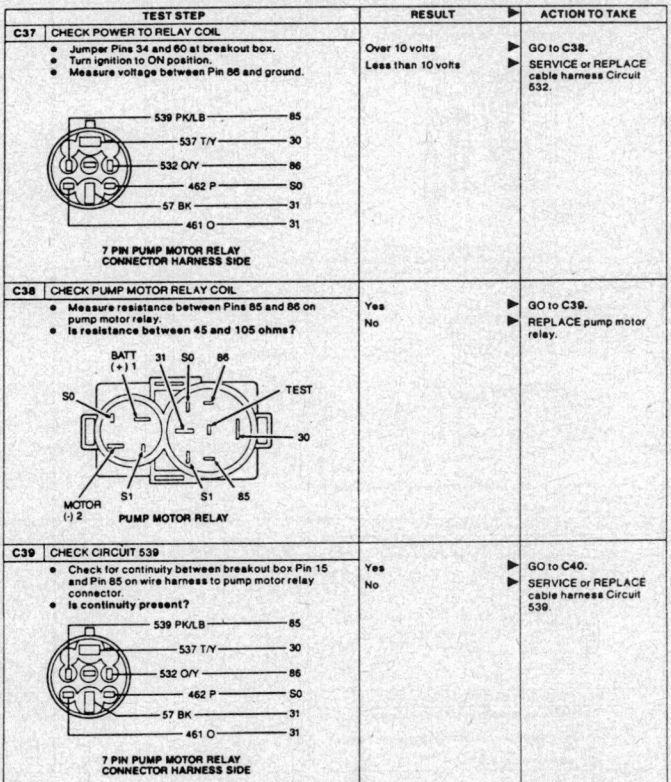

TEST STEP		RESULT	▶	ACTION TO TAKE
C32	**CHECK CIRCUIT 351 OR 604** • Check for continuity between Breakout Box Pins 49 and 60. • **Is continuity present?**	Yes	▶	SERVICE or REPLACE cable harness Circuit 604 for Town Car. Circuit 351 for Crown Victoria/Grand Marquis.
		No	▶	REPLACE pump motor relay.
C33	**CHECK PUMP MOTOR OPERATION** • Reconnect pump motor relay to pump and wire harness. • Jumper Pins 15, 34 and 60 at Breakout Box. • Turn ignition to RUN position. • **Does pump motor run?**	Yes	▶	REPLACE anti-lock brake control module.
		No	▶	GO to **C35**.
C34	**CHECK PUMP MOTOR OPERATION** • Disconnect pump motor relay from pump motor. • Ground Pin 2 and apply 12 volts to Pin 1 of pump motor connector. • **Does pump motor run?**	Yes	▶	GO to **C35**.
		No	▶	REPLACE pump motor.
C35	**CHECK POWER TO RELAY** • Disconnect wire harness from pump motor relay. • Check voltage between Pin 30 on wire harness to pump motor relay connector and ground. • **Is voltage reading over 10 volts?**	Yes	▶	GO to **C36**.
		No	▶	SERVICE or REPLACE battery, fuse B or Circuit 537 for Town Car. Circuit 533 or 50 amp fuse for Crown Victoria/Grand Marquis.

FM402930038006BX

Fig. 162   Test C: ABS Warning Lamp On After Vehicle Starts To Move Or False Cycling Of ABS System (Part 6 of 8). 1993–94 Crown Victoria, Grand Marquis & Town Car

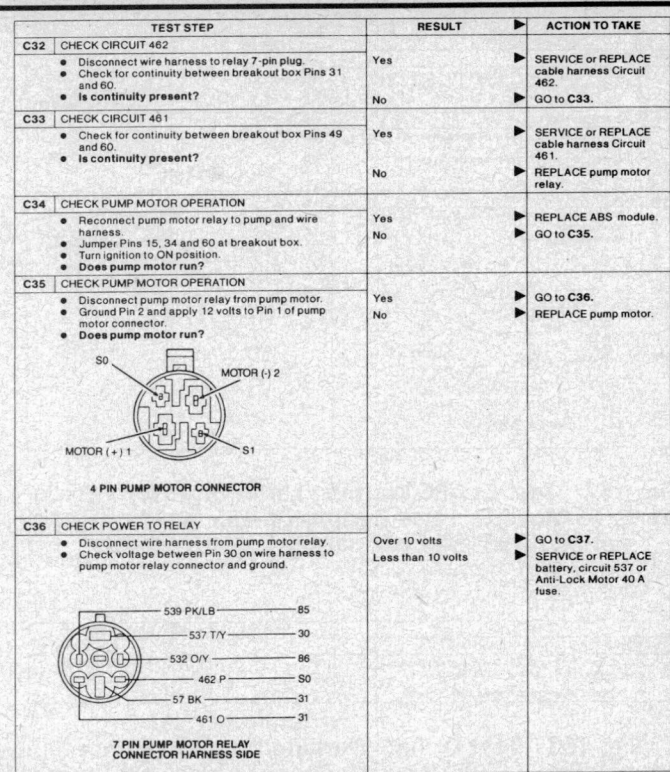

TEST STEP		RESULT	▶	ACTION TO TAKE
C32	**CHECK CIRCUIT 462** • Disconnect wire harness to relay 7-pin plug. • Check for continuity between breakout box Pins 31 and 60. • **Is continuity present?**	Yes	▶	SERVICE or REPLACE cable harness Circuit 462.
		No	▶	GO to **C33**.
C33	**CHECK CIRCUIT 461** • Check for continuity between breakout box Pins 49 and 60. • **Is continuity present?**	Yes	▶	SERVICE or REPLACE cable harness Circuit 461.
		No	▶	REPLACE pump motor relay.
C34	**CHECK PUMP MOTOR OPERATION** • Reconnect pump motor relay to pump and wire harness. • Jumper Pins 15, 34 and 60 at breakout box. • Turn ignition to ON position. • **Does pump motor run?**	Yes	▶	REPLACE ABS module.
		No	▶	GO to **C35**.
C35	**CHECK PUMP MOTOR OPERATION** • Disconnect pump motor relay from pump motor. • Ground Pin 2 and apply 12 volts to Pin 1 of pump motor connector. • **Does pump motor run?**	Yes	▶	GO to **C36**.
		No	▶	REPLACE pump motor.
C36	**CHECK POWER TO RELAY** • Disconnect wire harness from pump motor relay. • Check voltage between Pin 30 on wire harness to pump motor relay connector and ground.	Over 10 volts Less than 10 volts	▶	GO to **C37**. SERVICE or REPLACE battery, circuit 537 or Anti-Lock Motor 40 A fuse.

FM402930038006CX

Fig. 162   Test C: ABS Warning Lamp On After Vehicle Starts To Move Or False Cycling Of ABS System (Part 6 of 8). 1993–94 Sable & Taurus

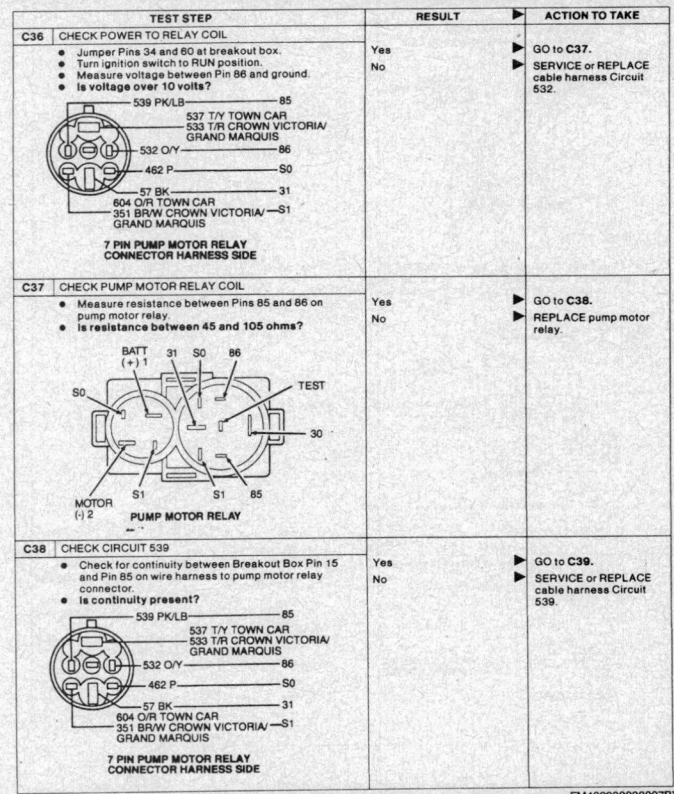

TEST STEP		RESULT	▶	ACTION TO TAKE
C37	**CHECK POWER TO RELAY COIL** • Jumper Pins 34 and 60 at breakout box. • Turn ignition to ON position. • Measure voltage between Pin 86 and ground.	Over 10 volts Less than 10 volts	▶	GO to **C38**. SERVICE or REPLACE cable harness Circuit 532.
C38	**CHECK PUMP MOTOR RELAY COIL** • Measure resistance between Pins 85 and 86 on pump motor relay. • **Is resistance between 45 and 105 ohms?**	Yes	▶	GO to **C39**.
		No	▶	REPLACE pump motor relay.
C39	**CHECK CIRCUIT 539** • Check for continuity between breakout box Pin 15 and Pin 85 on wire harness to pump motor relay connector. • **Is continuity present?**	Yes	▶	GO to **C40**.
		No	▶	SERVICE or REPLACE cable harness Circuit 539.

FM402930038007AX

Fig. 162   Test C: ABS Warning Lamp On After Vehicle Starts To Move Or False Cycling Of ABS System (Part 7 of 8). 1993–94 Continental, Sable & Taurus

TEST STEP		RESULT	▶	ACTION TO TAKE
C36	**CHECK POWER TO RELAY COIL** • Jumper Pins 34 and 60 at breakout box. • Turn ignition switch to RUN position. • Measure voltage between Pin 86 and ground. • **Is voltage over 10 volts?**	Yes	▶	GO to **C37**.
		No	▶	SERVICE or REPLACE cable harness Circuit 532.
C37	**CHECK PUMP MOTOR RELAY COIL** • Measure resistance between Pins 85 and 86 on pump motor relay. • **Is resistance between 45 and 105 ohms?**	Yes	▶	GO to **C38**.
		No	▶	REPLACE pump motor relay.
C38	**CHECK CIRCUIT 539** • Check for continuity between Breakout Box Pin 15 and Pin 85 on wire harness to pump motor relay connector. • **Is continuity present?**	Yes	▶	GO to **C39**.
		No	▶	SERVICE or REPLACE cable harness Circuit 539.

FM402930038007BX

Fig. 162   Test C: ABS Warning Lamp On After Vehicle Starts To Move Or False Cycling Of ABS System (Part 7 of 8). 1993–94 Crown Victoria, Grand Marquis & Town Car

TEST STEP		RESULT	▶	ACTION TO TAKE
C40	CHECK CIRCUIT 57			
	• Check for continuity between wire harness to pump motor relay connector Pin 31 and ground. • Is continuity present?	Yes No	▶ ▶	GO to C41. SERVICE or REPLACE cable harness Circuit 57.
C41	CHECK PUMP MOTOR RELAY			
	• Connect battery + to Pin 86 and battery - to Pin 85 of pump motor relay. • Check for continuity between Pin 30 and Pin 1 on relay. • Is continuity present?	Yes No	▶ ▶	GO to C42. REPLACE pump motor relay.
C42	CHECK PUMP MOTOR RELAY			
	• Check continuity between Pins 2 and 31 on pump motor relay. • Is continuity present?	Yes No	▶ ▶	REVERIFY results at Test Step C34. REPLACE pump motor relay.

BATT (+) 1 · 31 · S0 · 86 · S0 · TEST · 30 · MOTOR (-) 2 · S1 · S1 · 85

PUMP MOTOR RELAY

Fig. 162 Test C: ABS Warning Lamp On After Vehicle Starts To Move Or False Cycling Of ABS System (Part 8 of 8). 1993–94 Continental, Sable & Taurus

TEST STEP		RESULT	▶	ACTION TO TAKE
C39	CHECK CIRCUIT 57			
	• Check for continuity between pump motor relay connector Pin 31 and ground. • Is continuity present?	Yes No	▶ ▶	GO to C40. SERVICE or REPLACE cable harness Circuit 57.
C40	CHECK PUMP MOTOR RELAY			
	• Connect B+ to Pin 86 and B- to Pin 85 of pump motor relay. • Check for continuity between Pin 30 and Pin 1 on relay. • Is continuity present?	Yes No	▶ ▶	GO to C41. REPLACE pump motor relay.
C41	CHECK PUMP MOTOR RELAY			
	• Check continuity between Pins 2 and 31 on pump motor relay. • Is continuity present?	Yes No	▶ ▶	REVERIFY results at Step C33. REPLACE pump motor relay.

BATT (+) 1 · 31 · S0 · 86 · S0 · TEST · 30 · MOTOR (-) 2 · S1 · S1 · 85

PUMP MOTOR RELAY

Fig. 162 Test C: ABS Warning Lamp On After Vehicle Starts To Move Or False Cycling Of ABS System (Part 8 of 8). 1993–94 Crown Victoria, Grand Marquis & Town Car

TEST STEP		RESULT	▶	ACTION TO TAKE
D1	CHECK PEDAL SWITCH ADJUSTMENT			
	NOTE: Before running Test Step D, adjust pedal position switch as outlined in this section. • Is pedal feel normal during ABS cycling?	Yes No	▶ ▶	Condition corrected. GO to D2.

Fig. 163 Test D: ABS Warning Lamp Sequence Normal/Brake Pedal Rises Or Drops Excessively During ABS Cycling (Part 1 of 3). 1993–94

TEST STEP		RESULT	▶	ACTION TO TAKE
D2	CHECK ANTI-LOCK BRAKE PEDAL SENSOR SWITCH AND CIRCUITRY			
	• Turn ignition switch to OFF position. • Disconnect anti-lock brake wiring plug from anti-lock brake control module.	Yes No	▶ ▶	GO to D4. GO to D3.
	• Connect EEC-IV Breakout Box 014-00322 with Anti-Lock Test Adapter T90P-50-ALA or equivalent to the anti-lock 55-pin plug on the wiring harness. • Check continuity between Breakout Box Pins 5 and 26. • Is continuity present?			
D3	CHECK ANTI-LOCK BRAKE PEDAL SENSOR SWITCH			
	• Disconnect anti-lock brake pedal sensor switch 2-pin plug. • Check for continuity between Pins 1 and 2. • Is continuity present?	Yes No	▶ ▶	SERVICE or REPLACE cable harness Circuit 535 or 549 Crown Victoria/Grand Marquis. Circuit 459 or 467 Town Car. REPLACE anti-lock brake pedal sensor switch.

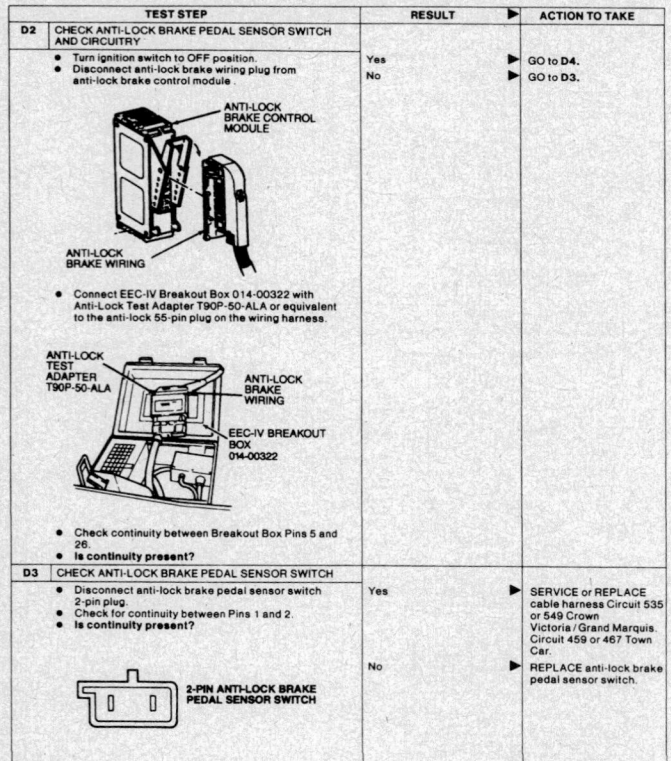

ANTI-LOCK BRAKE CONTROL MODULE

ANTI-LOCK BRAKE WIRING

ANTI-LOCK TEST ADAPTER T90P-50-ALA

ANTI-LOCK BRAKE WIRING

EEC-IV BREAKOUT BOX 014-00322

2-PIN ANTI-LOCK BRAKE PEDAL SENSOR SWITCH

Fig. 163 Test D: ABS Warning Lamp Sequence Normal/Brake Pedal Rises Or Drops Excessively During ABS Cycling (Part 2 of 3). 1993–94 Crown Victoria, Grand Marquis & Town Car

TEST STEP		RESULT	▶	ACTION TO TAKE
D2	CHECK PEDAL TRAVEL SWITCH AND CIRCUITRY			
	• Turn ignition switch to OFF position. • Disconnect 55-pin plug from ABS module.	Yes No	▶ ▶	GO to D4. GO to D3.
	• Connect EEC-IV Breakout Box 014-00322 with Anti-Lock Test Adapter T90P-50-ALA or equivalent to the anti-lock 55-pin plug on the wiring harness. • Check continuity between breakout box Pins 5 and 26. • Is continuity present?			
D3	CHECK PEDAL TRAVEL SWITCH			
	• Disconnect pedal travel switch 2-pin plug. • Check for continuity between Pins 1 and 2. • Is continuity present?	Yes No	▶ ▶	SERVICE or REPLACE cable harness Circuit 535 or 549. REPLACE pedal travel switch.
D4	CHECK PEDAL TRAVEL SWITCH FUNCTION			
	• Push brake pedal down at least 3 inches and hold down. • Check for continuity between breakout box Pins 5 and 26. • Is continuity present?	Yes No	▶ ▶	GO to D5. GO to D6.

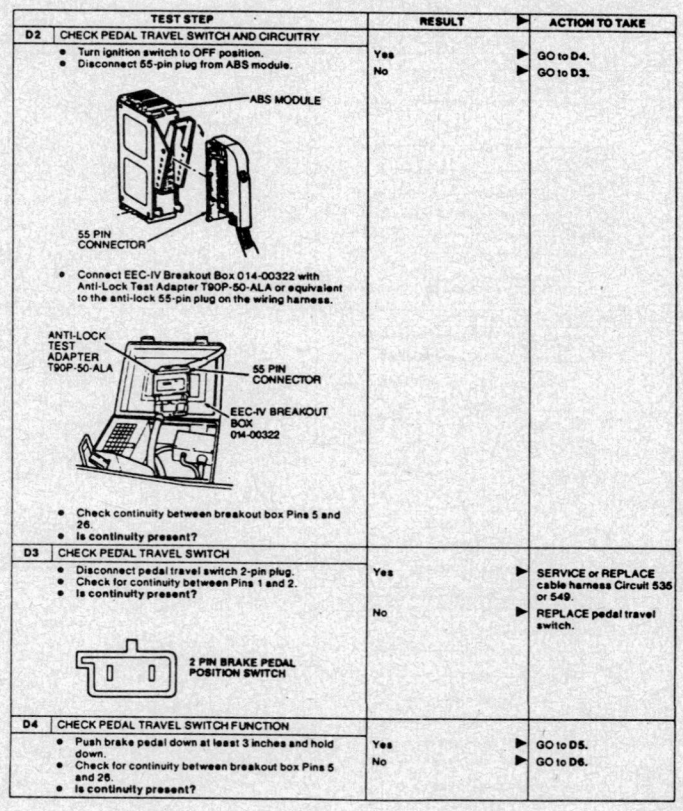

ABS MODULE

55 PIN CONNECTOR

ANTI-LOCK TEST ADAPTER T90P-50-ALA

55 PIN CONNECTOR

EEC-IV BREAKOUT BOX 014-00322

2 PIN BRAKE PEDAL POSITION SWITCH

Fig. 163 Test D: ABS Warning Lamp Sequence Normal/Brake Pedal Rises Or Drops Excessively During ABS Cycling (Part 2 of 3). 1993–94 Continental, Sable & Taurus

TEST STEP		RESULT	▶	ACTION TO TAKE
D5	CHECK PEDAL TRAVEL SWITCH			
	• Disconnect pedal travel switch 2-pin plug from wire harness.	Yes	▶	REPLACE pedal travel switch.
	• Check continuity between Pins 1 and 2 (switch side) with brake pedal down at least 3 inches.	No	▶	SERVICE or REPLACE cable harness Circuit 535 or 549.
	• Is continuity present?			
D6	CHECK PUMP PRESSURE			
	• Jumper Pins 15, 34 and 60 at breakout box.	Yes	▶	REVERIFY symptom.
	• Apply moderate pressure on brake pedal and hold.	No	▶	REPLACE pump and motor.
	• Turn ignition switch to ON position.			
	• Does brake pedal rise?			

Fig. 163   Test D: ABS Warning Lamp Sequence Normal/Brake Pedal Rises Or Drops Excessively During ABS Cycling (Part 3 of 3). 1993–94 Continental, Sable & Taurus

TEST STEP		RESULT	▶	ACTION TO TAKE
D4	CHECK ANTI-LOCK BRAKE PEDAL TRAVEL SWITCH FUNCTION			
	• Push brake pedal down at least 3 inches and hold down.	Yes	▶	GO to D5.
	• Check for continuity between Breakout Box Pins 5 and 26.	No	▶	GO to D6.
	• Is continuity present?			
D5	CHECK ANTI-LOCK BRAKE PEDAL SENSOR SWITCH			
	• Disconnect anti-lock brake pedal sensor switch 2-pin plug from wire harness.	Yes	▶	REPLACE anti-lock brake pedal sensor switch.
	• Check continuity between Pins 1 and 2 (switch side) with brake pedal down at least 3 inches.	No	▶	SERVICE or REPLACE cable harness Circuit 535 or 549 Crown Victoria/Grand Marquis. Circuit 459 or 467 Town Car.
	• Is continuity present?			
D6	CHECK PUMP PRESSURE			
	• Jumper Pins 15, 34 and 60 at Breakout Box.	Yes	▶	REVERIFY symptom.
	• Apply moderate pressure on brake pedal and hold.	No	▶	REPLACE pump motor.
	• Turn ignition switch to RUN.			
	• Does brake pedal rise?			

Fig. 163   Test D: ABS Warning Lamp Sequence Normal/Brake Pedal Rises Or Drops Excessively During ABS Cycling (Part 3 of 3). 1993–94 Crown Victoria, Grand Marquis & Town Car

TEST STEP		RESULT	▶	ACTION TO TAKE
E1	VERIFY PUMP MOTOR CONDITION			
	• With vehicle standing still:	Pump runs with ignition in OFF position	▶	GO to E2
	• Check if pump motor runs with ignition switch in ON or OFF position.	Pump runs with ignition in ON position	▶	GO to E3.
E2	CHECK PUMP MOTOR RELAY			
	• Remove pump motor relay.	Yes	▶	REPLACE pump motor relay.
	• Check for continuity between Pin 30 and test pin on the relay.	No	▶	REVERIFY that pump motor runs with ignition in OFF position.
	• Is continuity present?			

Fig. 164   Test E: ABS Warning Lamp Sequence Normal/ABS Pump Motor Runs Continuously (Part 1 of 2). 1993–94

TEST STEP		RESULT	▶	ACTION TO TAKE
E3	CHECK CIRCUIT 539 TO GROUND			
	• Turn ignition switch OFF.	Yes	▶	GO to E4.
	• Disconnect 55-pin plug from ABS module.	No	▶	GO to E5.

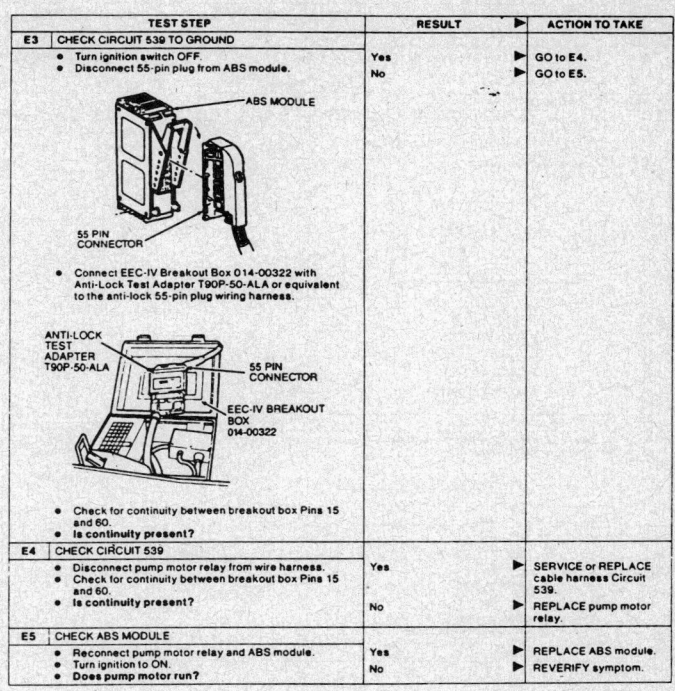

	• Check for continuity between breakout box Pins 15 and 60.
	• Is continuity present?

TEST STEP		RESULT	▶	ACTION TO TAKE
E4	CHECK CIRCUIT 539			
	• Disconnect pump motor relay from wire harness.	Yes	▶	SERVICE or REPLACE cable harness Circuit 539.
	• Check for continuity between breakout box Pins 15 and 60.	No	▶	REPLACE pump motor relay.
	• Is continuity present?			
E5	CHECK ABS MODULE			
	• Reconnect pump motor relay and ABS module.	Yes	▶	REPLACE ABS module.
	• Turn ignition to ON.	No	▶	REVERIFY symptom.
	• Does pump motor run?			

Fig. 164   Test E: ABS Warning Lamp Sequence Normal/ABS Pump Motor Runs Continuously (Part 2 of 2). 1993–94

TEST STEP		RESULT	▶	ACTION TO TAKE
F1	CHECK BRAKE FLUID LEVEL			
	• Check that brake fluid is no more than 4mm (0.16 inch) below MAX line located on side of master cylinder reservoir.	Low	▶	CHECK system for external leaks. SERVICE as required.
		Normal	▶	GO to F2.
F2	CHECK FLUID LEVEL SWITCH			
	• Disconnect 3-pin plug on master cylinder fluid reservoir cap.	Yes	▶	REPLACE reservoir fluid cap.
	• Check for continuity between Pins 1 and 3 on reservoir cap.	No	▶	GO to F3.
	• Is continuity present?			

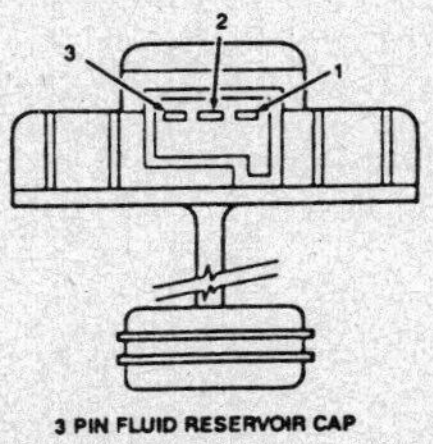

3 PIN FLUID RESERVOIR CAP

F3	CHECK FOR GROUND CONCERN			
	• Check for grounded wire harness Circuit 977.	Yes	▶	SERVICE or REPLACE cable harness Circuit 977.
	• Is wire harness grounded?	No	▶	REVERIFY "BRAKE" indicator on.

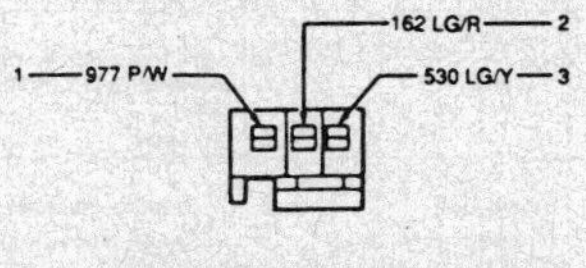

162 LG/R — 2
1 — 977 P/W
530 LG/Y — 3

3 PIN FLUID RESERVOIR CAP CONNECTOR HARNESS SIDE

Fig. 165   Test F: Brake Warning Lamp On w/ABS Warning Lamp Off & Parking Brake Released. 1993–94 Continental, Crown Victoria, Grand Marquis & Town Car

TEST STEP		RESULT	▶	ACTION TO TAKE
F1	CHECK BRAKE FLUID LEVEL			
	• Check that brake fluid is no more than 4mm (0.16 inch) below MAX line located on side of master cylinder reservoir.	Low	▶	CHECK system for external leaks. SERVICE as required.
		Normal	▶	GO to F2.
F2	CHECK FLUID LEVEL SWITCH			
	• Disconnect 3-pin plug on master cylinder fluid reservoir cap.	Yes	▶	REPLACE reservoir fluid cap.
	• Check for continuity between Pins 1 and 3 on reservoir cap.	No	▶	GO to F3.
	• Is continuity present?			
F3	CHECK FOR GROUND CONCERN			
	• Check for grounded wire harness, Circuit 977.	Yes	▶	SERVICE or REPLACE cable harness Circuit 977A.
	• Is wire harness grounded?	No	▶	REVERIFY "BRAKE" indicator on.

3 PIN FLUID RESERVOIR CAP

3 PIN FLUID RESERVOIR CAP CONNECTOR HARNESS SIDE

Fig. 166   Test F: Brake Warning Indicator On w/Anti-Lock Indicator Off, Parking Brake Released & Brake Lining Wear Checked. 1993–94 Sable & Taurus

TEST STEP		RESULT	▶	ACTION TO TAKE
G1	CHECK IGNITION FEED AND FUSE			
	• Check for 12 volts to lamp socket with ignition ON.	12 volts	▶	GO to G2.
		No voltage	▶	SERVICE or REPLACE cable harness Circuit 16, 640 or Fuse 13 Crown Victoria / Grand Marquis, Circuit 262, 295 or fuse 4 Town Car.
G2	CHECK WARNING INDICATOR BULB			
	• Check warning indicator bulb.	Yes	▶	GO to G3.
	• Is bulb good?	No	▶	REPLACE bulb.
G3	CHECK CIRCUIT 603			
	• Check continuity between lamp socket and breakout box Pin 52.	No	▶	SERVICE or REPLACE cable harness Circuit 603.
	• Is continuity present?	Yes	▶	GO to G4.
G4	CHECK DIODE			
	• Inspect diode for damage or loose or bad connection.	Diode good	▶	REVERIFY symptom.
	• Check if diode is installed backwards.	Diode damaged or installed backwards	▶	REPLACE diode.

Fig. 168   Test G: No Anti-Lock Warning Indicator On When Ignition Switch Turned On. 1993–94 Crown Victoria, Grand Marquis & Town Car

TEST STEP		RESULT	▶	ACTION TO TAKE
G1	CHECK IGNITION FEED AND FUSE			
	• Check for 12 volts to lamp socket with ignition ON.	12 volts	▶	GO to G2.
		No voltage	▶	SERVICE ignition feed or fuse as required.

Fig. 167   Test G: No ABS Warning Lamp When Ignition Turned On (Part 1 of 2). 1993–94 Continental, Sable & Taurus

TEST STEP		RESULT	▶	ACTION TO TAKE
H1	CHECK COMPONENT MOUNTING			
	• Check for proper brake pedal and booster / master cylinder attachment.	Yes	▶	GO to H2.
	• Bleed brake system as outlined.	No	▶	Condition corrected.
	• Is pedal spongy?			
H2	BLEED BRAKE SYSTEM			
	• Rebleed brake system.	Yes	▶	REPLACE master cylinder.
	• Is pedal spongy?	No	▶	Condition corrected.

Fig. 169   Test H: Spongy Brake Pedal With/Without ABS Function. 1993–94

TEST STEP		RESULT	▶	ACTION TO TAKE
G2	CHECK WARNING INDICATOR BULB			
	• Check warning indicator bulb.	Yes	▶	GO to G3.
	• Is bulb good?	No	▶	REPLACE bulb.
G3	CHECK CIRCUIT 606			
	• Check continuity between lamp socket and breakout box Pin 52.	No	▶	SERVICE or REPLACE cable harness Circuit 606.
	• Is continuity present?	Yes	▶	GO to G4.
G4	CHECK DIODE			
	• Inspect diode for damage or loose or bad connection.	Diode good	▶	REVERIFY symptom.
	• Check if diode is installed backwards.	Diode damaged or installed backwards	▶	REPLACE diode.

Fig. 167   Test G: No ABS Warning Lamp When Ignition Turned On (Part 2 of 2). 1993–94 Continental, Sable & Taurus

TEST STEP		RESULT	▶	ACTION TO TAKE
J1	VERIFY CONDITION			
	• Verify condition exists as reported.	No	▶	Condition corrected.
	• Turn air suspension OFF if so equipped.	Yes	▶	GO to J2.
	• Bleed brake system as outlined.			
	• Turn air suspension back ON when vehicle is off hoist.			
	• Does vehicle track poorly?			

Fig. 170   Test J: Poor Vehicle Tracking During ABS Function (Part 1 of 3). 1993–94

TEST STEP	RESULT	▶	ACTION TO TAKE
J2 CHECK ANTI-LOCK VALVE OPERATION			
• Turn air suspension OFF if so equipped. • Turn ignition switch OFF. • Disconnect 55-pin plug from ABS module.	Wheel turns freely	▶	TURN ignition switch OFF. DISCONNECT wire leads. GO to J3.
	Wheel does not turn freely or pedal drops	▶	VERIFY correct wiring between 55-pin connector and 19-pin connector on valve block per wiring diagram.
		▶	If wiring is correct, REPLACE solenoid valve block.

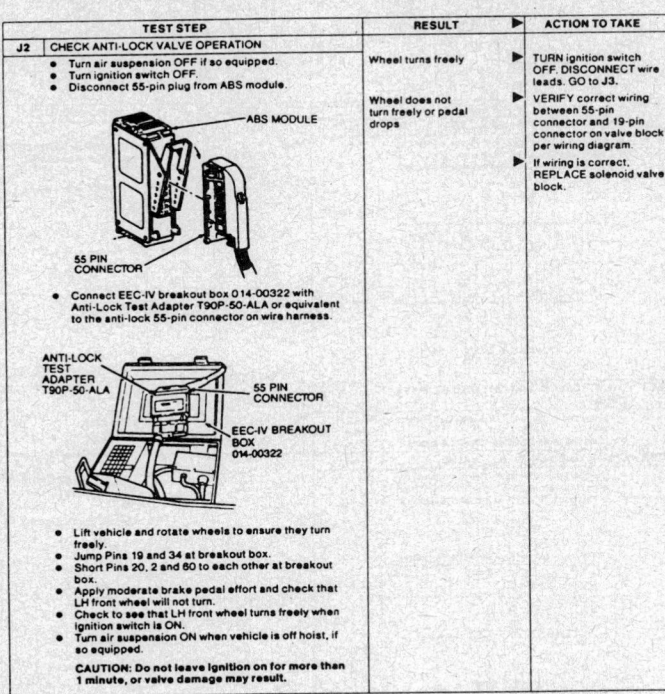

ABS MODULE

55 PIN CONNECTOR

ANTI-LOCK TEST ADAPTER T90P-50-ALA

55 PIN CONNECTOR

EEC-IV BREAKOUT BOX 014-00322

• Connect EEC-IV breakout box 014-00322 with Anti-Lock Test Adapter T90P-50-ALA or equivalent to the anti-lock 55-pin connector on wire harness.

• Lift vehicle and rotate wheels to ensure they turn freely.
• Jump Pins 19 and 34 at breakout box.
• Short Pins 20, 2 and 60 to each other at breakout box.
• Apply moderate brake pedal effort and check that LH front wheel will not turn.
• Check to see that LH front wheel turns freely when ignition switch is ON.
• Turn air suspension ON when vehicle is off hoist, if so equipped.

CAUTION: Do not leave ignition on for more than 1 minute, or valve damage may result.

Fig. 170   Test J: Poor Vehicle Tracking During ABS Function (Part 2 of 3). 1993–94

TEST STEP	RESULT	▶	ACTION TO TAKE
J3 CHECK ANTI-LOCK OPERATION RH FRONT WHEEL			
• Jump Pins 19 and 34 at breakout box. • Short Pins 19, 21 and 60 to each other at breakout box. • Apply moderate brake pedal effort. Check that RH front wheel will not turn with ignition OFF. • Check that RH front wheel turns freely with ignition ON. CAUTION: Do not leave ignition on for more than 1 minute or valve damage may result.	Wheel turns freely	▶	TURN ignition switch OFF. DISCONNECT wire leads. GO to J4.
	Wheel does not turn freely or pedal drops	▶	VERIFY correct wiring between 55-pin connector and 19-pin connector on valve block per wiring diagram.
		▶	If wiring is correct, REPLACE solenoid valve block.
J4 CHECK ANTI-LOCK OPERATION RH REAR WHEEL			
• Jump Pins 19 and 34 at breakout box. • Short Pins 55, 18 and 60 to each other at breakout box. • Apply moderate brake pedal effort. Check that RH rear wheel will not turn with ignition OFF. • Check that RH rear wheel turns freely with ignition ON. CAUTION: Do not leave ignition on for more than 1 minute or valve damage may result.	Wheel turns freely	▶	TURN ignition switch OFF. DISCONNECT wire leads. GO to J5.
	Wheel does not turn freely or pedal drops	▶	VERIFY correct wiring between 55-pin connector and 19-pin connector on valve block per wiring diagram.
		▶	If wiring is correct, REPLACE solenoid valve block.
J5 CHECK ANTI-LOCK OPERATION LH REAR WHEEL			
• Jump Pins 19 and 34 at breakout box. • Short Pins 38, 54 and 60 to each other at breakout box. • Apply moderate brake pedal effort. Check that LH rear wheel will not turn with ignition ON. CAUTION: Do not leave ignition on for more than 1 minute or valve damage may result.	Wheel turns freely	▶	TURN ignition switch OFF. DISCONNECT wire leads and breakout box. LOWER vehicle. REVERIFY symptom.
	Wheel does not turn freely or pedal drops	▶	VERIFY correct wiring between 55-pin connector and 19-pin connector on valve block per wiring diagram.
		▶	If wiring is correct, REPLACE solenoid valve block.

Fig. 170   Test J: Poor Vehicle Tracking During ABS Function (Part 3 of 3). 1993–94

TEST-STEP	RESULT	▶	ACTION TO TAKE
K1 VERIFY CONDITION—ONE SIDE OR BOTH SIDES			
• Traction assist inoperative.	Both rear wheels	▶	GO to K2.
	One rear wheel only	▶	GO to K4.
K2 CHECK STOPLAMP SWITCH			
• Connect EEC-IV Breakout Box 014-00322 with Anti-Lock Test Adapter T90P-50-ALA or equivalent to the Anti-Lock 55-Pin connector on the wire harness. • Turn ignition switch to ON position. • Measure voltage between breakout box Pins 32 and 60. NOTE: DO NOT apply brake pedal while performing this test.	No voltage	▶	GO to K3.
	12 volts	▶	REPLACE stoplamp switch or SERVICE cable harness Circuit 511.

Fig. 171   Test K: ABS Warning Lamp Sequence Normal/Traction Assist Inoperative (Part 1 of 2). 1993–94 Crown Victoria, Grand Marquis & Town Car

TEST STEP	RESULT	▶	ACTION TO TAKE
L1 RUN SELF-TEST			
• Refer to On-Board Diagnostic to run On-Board Diagnostic.	Sensor code received	▶	REPLACE sensor for code received.
	No codes in E-module	▶	VERIFY that traction assist system is false cycling.

Fig. 172   Test L: ABS Warning Lamp Sequence Normal/False Cycling Of Traction Assist. 1993–94 Crown Victoria, Grand Marquis & Town Car

TEST STEP	RESULT	▶	ACTION TO TAKE
K3 CHECK PRESSURE SWITCH AND CIRCUITRY			
• Check continuity between breakout box Pins 13 and 26. • Is continuity present?	Yes	▶	VERIFY Symptom.
	No	▶	GO to K4.
K4 CHECK PRESSURE SWITCH			
• Disconnect 19-pin valve body connector from harness. • Check continuity between valve body Pins 11 and 12. • Is continuity present?	Yes	▶	SERVICE or REPLACE cable harness Circuit 547 or 467 Town Car. Circuit 535 or 536 Crown Victoria/Grand Marquis.
	No	▶	REPLACE valve body.
K5 CHECK ABS FUNCTION			
• Make an Anti-Lock stop on a slippery surface. • Notice if brake pedal rises when pump comes on or if the pedal continues downward when pump comes on.	Brake pedal rises	▶	REPLACE valve body.
	Brake pedal falls	▶	REPLACE pump motor.

Fig. 171   Test K: ABS Warning Lamp Sequence Normal/Traction Assist Inoperative (Part 2 of 2). 1993–94 Crown Victoria, Grand Marquis & Town Car

PINPOINT TEST AA: ABS MODULE DIAGNOSIS			
TEST STEP	RESULT	▶	ACTION TO TAKE
AA1 DTC 11: ELECTRICAL DISTURBANCE			
• Read all DTC's and record. • After all DTC's are read and written down, drive vehicle above 40 km/h (25 mph) to clear memory. • Read all DTC's again.	DTC 11 repeated	▶	REPLACE ABS module.
	Memory erased or other DTC's present except code 11	▶	PERFORM test step associated with DTC's. REFER to On-Board Diagnostic Trouble code index, and SERVICE next code.

Fig. 173   Test AA: ABS Module Diagnosis. 1993–94

Part 1 of 6

TEST STEP	RESULT	▶	ACTION TO TAKE
BB1 DTC 22: NO REFERENCE VOLTAGE OR LH FRONT INLET VALVE • Disconnect 55-pin plug from ABS module. 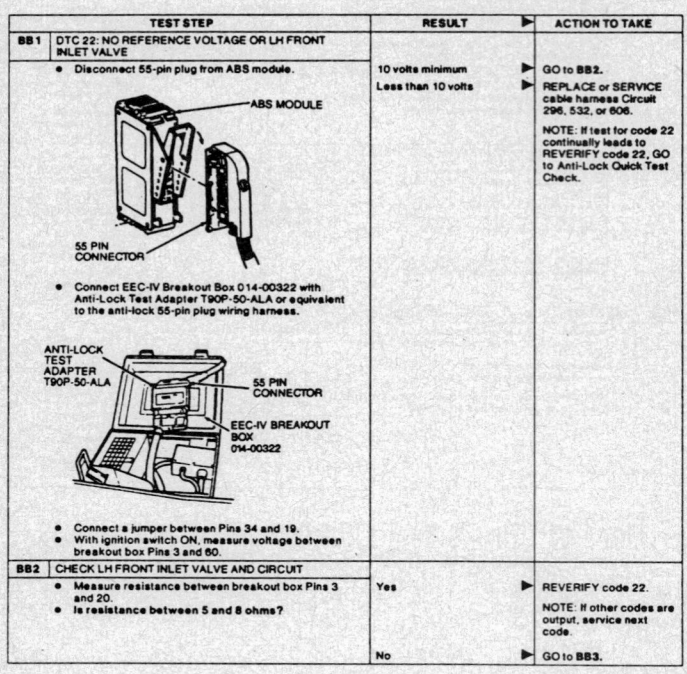 • Connect EEC-IV Breakout Box 014-00322 with Anti-Lock Test Adapter T90P-50-ALA or equivalent to the anti-lock 55-pin plug wiring harness. • Connect a jumper between Pins 34 and 19. • With ignition switch ON, measure voltage between breakout box Pins 3 and 60.	10 volts minimum Less than 10 volts	▶ ▶	GO to BB2. REPLACE or SERVICE cable harness Circuit 296, 532, or 606. NOTE: If test for code 22 continually leads to REVERIFY code 22, GO to Anti-Lock Quick Test Check.
BB2 CHECK LH FRONT INLET VALVE AND CIRCUIT • Measure resistance between breakout box Pins 3 and 20. • Is resistance between 5 and 8 ohms?	Yes No	▶ ▶	REVERIFY code 22. NOTE: If other codes are output, service next code. GO to BB3.

FM4029100308010X

Fig. 174   Test BB: Solenoid Valve Diagnosis (Part 1 of 6). 1993 & Early Production 1994 Continental

Part 2 of 6

TEST STEP	RESULT	▶	ACTION TO TAKE
BB3 CHECK LH FRONT INLET VALVE • Disconnect valve body 19-pin connector. • Measure resistance between Pins 17 and 7. • Is resistance between 5 and 8 ohms? (VALVE BODY CONNECTOR)	Yes No	▶ ▶	REPLACE or SERVICE cable harness Circuit 495. REPLACE valve body.
BB4 DTC 23: CHECK LH FRONT OUTLET VALVE AND CIRCUIT • Measure resistance between breakout box Pins 3 and 2. • Is resistance between 3 and 6 ohms?	Yes No	▶ ▶	GO to BB6. GO to BB5.
BB5 CHECK LH FRONT OUTLET VALVE • Disconnect valve body 19-pin connector. • Measure resistance between Pins 18 and 7. • Is resistance between 3 and 6 ohms? (VALVE BODY CONNECTOR)	Yes No	▶ ▶	REPLACE or SERVICE cable harness Circuit 496. REPLACE valve body.
BB6 DTC 24: CHECK RH FRONT INLET VALVE AND CIRCUIT • Measure resistance between breakout box Pins 3 and 38. • Is resistance between 5 and 8 ohms?	Yes No	▶ ▶	GO to BB8. GO to BB7.

FM4029300308020X

Fig. 174   Test BB: Solenoid Valve Diagnosis (Part 2 of 6). 1993 & Early Production 1994 Continental

Part 3 of 6

TEST STEP	RESULT	▶	ACTION TO TAKE
BB7 CHECK RH FRONT INLET VALVE • Disconnect valve body 19-pin connector. • Measure resistance between Pins 15 and 7. • Is resistance between 5 and 8 ohms? (VALVE BODY CONNECTOR)	Yes No	▶ ▶	REPLACE or SERVICE cable harness Circuit 510. REPLACE valve body.
BB8 DTC 25: CHECK RH FRONT OUTLET VALVE AND CIRCUIT • Measure resistance between breakout box Pins 3 and 21. • Is resistance between 3 and 6 ohms?	Yes No	▶ ▶	GO to BB10. GO to BB9.
BB9 CHECK RH FRONT OUTLET VALVE • Disconnect valve body 19-pin connector. • Measure resistance between Pins 16 and 7. • Is resistance between 3 and 6 ohms? (VALVE BODY CONNECTOR)	Yes No	▶ ▶	REPLACE or SERVICE cable harness Circuit 497. REPLACE valve body.

FM4029300308030X

Fig. 174   Test BB: Solenoid Valve Diagnosis (Part 3 of 6). 1993 & Early Production 1994 Continental

Part 4 of 6

TEST STEP	RESULT	▶	ACTION TO TAKE
BB10 DTC 26: CHECK RH REAR INLET VALVE AND CIRCUIT • Measure resistance between breakout box Pins 3 and 55. • Is resistance between 5 and 8 ohms? 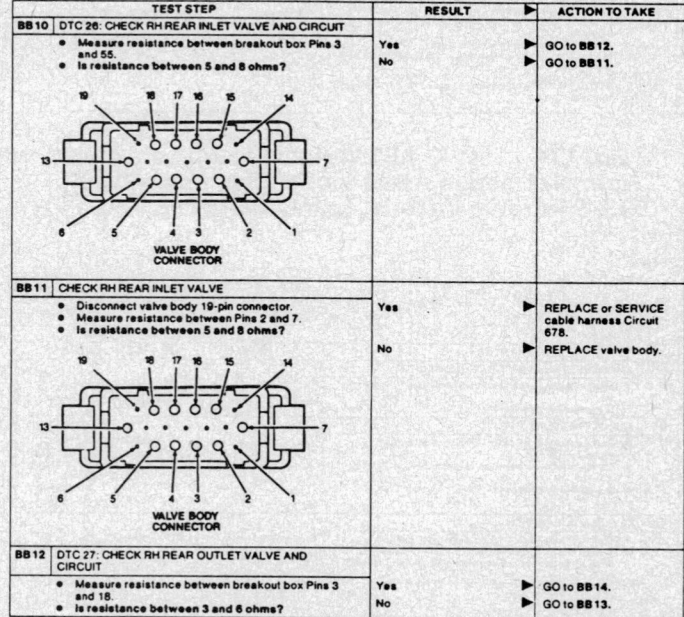 (VALVE BODY CONNECTOR)	Yes No	▶ ▶	GO to BB12. GO to BB11.
BB11 CHECK RH REAR INLET VALVE • Disconnect valve body 19-pin connector. • Measure resistance between Pins 2 and 7. • Is resistance between 5 and 8 ohms? (VALVE BODY CONNECTOR)	Yes No	▶ ▶	REPLACE or SERVICE cable harness Circuit 678. REPLACE valve body.
BB12 DTC 27: CHECK RH REAR OUTLET VALVE AND CIRCUIT • Measure resistance between breakout box Pins 3 and 18. • Is resistance between 3 and 6 ohms?	Yes No	▶ ▶	GO to BB14. GO to BB13.

FM4029300308040X

Fig. 174   Test BB: Solenoid Valve Diagnosis (Part 4 of 6). 1993 & Early Production 1994 Continental

TEST STEP	RESULT		ACTION TO TAKE
BB13 CHECK RH REAR OUTLET VALVE • Disconnect valve body 19-pin connector. • Measure resistance between Pins 3 and 7. • Is resistance between 3 and 6 ohms?	Yes No	▶ ▶	REPLACE or SERVICE cable harness Circuit 685. REPLACE valve body.
BB14 DTC 28: CHECK LH REAR INLET VALVE AND CIRCUIT • Measure resistance between breakout box Pins 3 and 54. • Is resistance between 5 and 8 ohms?	Yes No	▶ ▶	GO to BB16. GO to BB15.
BB15 CHECK LH REAR INLET VALVE • Disconnect valve body 19-pin connector. • Measure resistance between Pins 4 and 7. • Is resistance between 5 and 8 ohms?	Yes No	▶ ▶	REPLACE or SERVICE cable harness Circuit 496. REPLACE valve body.
BB16 DTC 29: CHECK LH REAR OUTLET VALVE AND CIRCUIT • Measure resistance between breakout box Pins 3 and 36. • Is resistance between 3 and 6 ohms?	Yes No	▶ ▶	GO to BB18. GO to BB17.

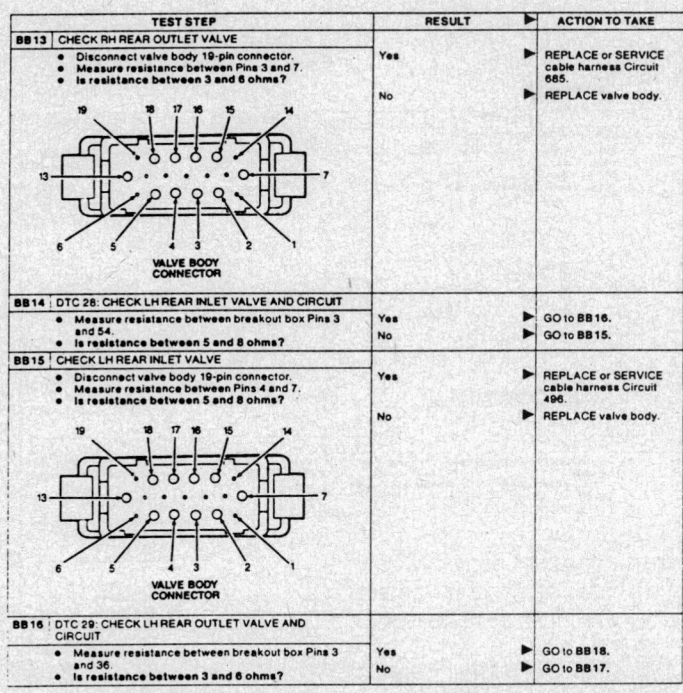

FM4029300308050X

Fig. 174   Test BB: Solenoid Valve Diagnosis (Part 5 of 6). 1993 & Early Production 1994 Continental

TEST STEP	RESULT		ACTION TO TAKE
BB17 CHECK LH REAR OUTLET VALVE • Disconnect valve body 19-pin connector. • Measure resistance between Pins 5 and 7. • Is resistance between 3 and 6 ohms?	Yes No	▶ ▶	REPLACE or SERVICE cable harness Circuit 499. REPLACE valve body.
BB18 CHECK VALVE BODY POWER FEED AND CIRCUITRY • Measure resistance between breakout box Pins 3 and 33. • Is continuity present?	Yes No	▶ ▶	GO to BB19. SERVICE or REPLACE cable harness Circuit 532.
BB19 CHECK VALVE BODY INTERNAL POWER FEED CIRCUITS • Disconnect valve body 19-pin connector. • Check for continuity between Pins 7 and 13. • Is continuity present?	Yes No	▶ ▶	REVERIFY symptom. REPLACE valve body. NOTE: If symptom is reverified and no malfunction is found, go to Anti-Lock Quick Test Check.

FM4029300308060X

Fig. 174   Test BB: Solenoid Valve Diagnosis (Part 6 of 6). 1993 & Early Production 1994 Continental

TEST STEP	RESULT		ACTION TO TAKE
BB1 DTC 17 OR 22: NO REFERENCE VOLTAGE • Disconnect 55-pin plug from anti-lock brake control module.	Yes No	▶ ▶	GO to BB2. REPLACE or SERVICE cable harness Circuit 296 (W/P), 532 (O/Y), or 606 (W/LB). NOTE: If test for code 17 or 22 continually leads to REVERIFY code, GO to Anti-Lock Quick Test Check.
• Connect Rotunda EEC-IV Breakout Box 014-00322 with Anti-Lock Test Adapter T90P-50-ALA or equivalent to the anti-lock 55-pin plug wiring harness. • Connect a jumper between Pins 34 and 19. • With ignition switch ON, measure voltage between breakout box Pins 3 and 60. • Is voltage a minimum of 10 volts?			
BB2 DTC 22: CHECK LH FRONT INLET VALVE AND CIRCUIT • Measure resistance between breakout box Pins 3 and 20. • Is resistance between five and eight ohms?	Yes No	▶ ▶	REVERIFY DTC 22. NOTE: If other DTCs are output, service next code. GO to BB3.

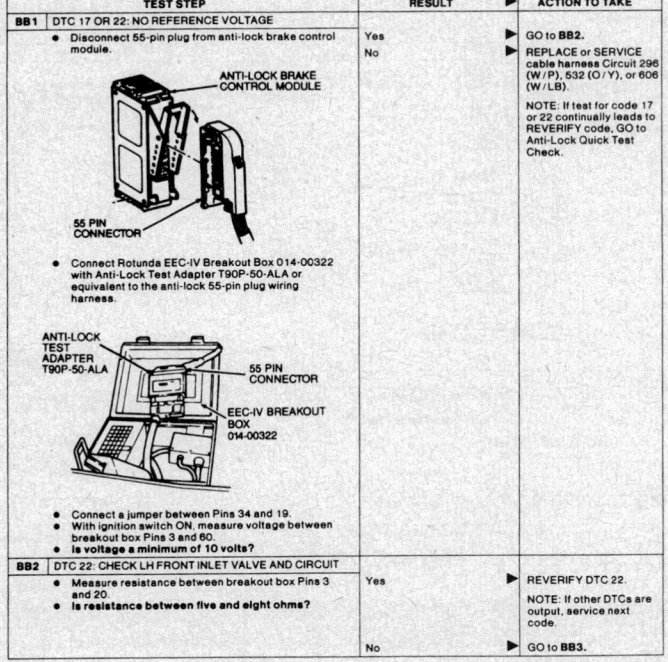

FM4029400448010X

Fig. 175   Test BB: Solenoid Valve Diagnosis (Part 1 of 9). Late Production 1994 Continental

TEST STEP	RESULT		ACTION TO TAKE
BB3 CHECK LH FRONT INLET VALVE • Disconnect brake pressure control valve block 16-pin connector. • Measure resistance between Pins 14 and 1. • Is resistance between five and eight ohms?	Yes No	▶ ▶	REPLACE or SERVICE cable harness Circuit 495 (T). REPLACE brake pressure control valve block.
BB4 CHECK CIRCUIT 495 • Disconnect valve block connector from wire harness. • Check for continuity between breakout box Pins 20 and 60. • Is continuity present?	Yes No	▶ ▶	REPLACE or SERVICE cable harness Circuit 495 (T). REVERIFY DTC 22. NOTE: If other DTCs are output, service next code.
BB5 DTC 23: CHECK LH FRONT OUTLET VALVE AND CIRCUIT • Measure resistance between breakout box Pins 3 and 2. • Is resistance between three and six ohms?	Yes No	▶ ▶	GO to BB7. GO to BB6.

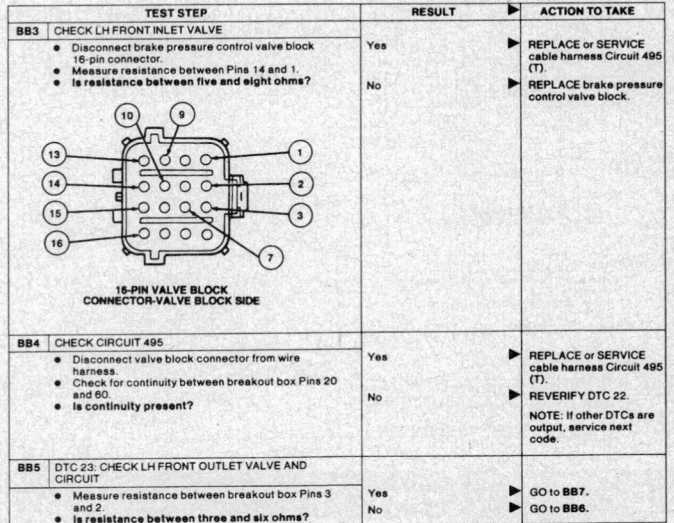

FM4029400448020X

Fig. 175   Test BB: Solenoid Valve Diagnosis (Part 2 of 9). Late Production 1994 Continental

TEST STEP	RESULT	▶	ACTION TO TAKE
BB6 CHECK LH FRONT OUTLET VALVE • Disconnect brake pressure control valve block 16-pin connector. • Measure resistance between Pins 15 and 1. • **Is resistance between three and six ohms?**	Yes No	▶ ▶	REPLACE or SERVICE cable harness Circuit 498 (PK). REPLACE brake pressure control valve block.

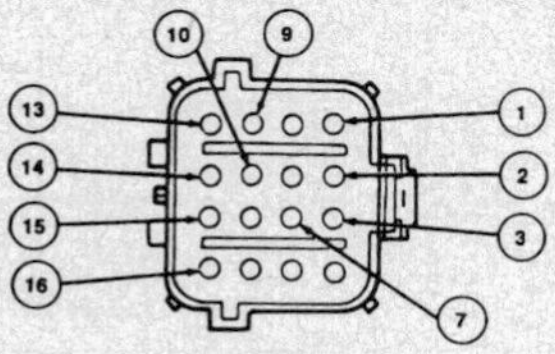

16-PIN VALVE BLOCK
CONNECTOR-VALVE BLOCK SIDE

BB7 CHECK CIRCUIT 498 • Disconnect valve block connector from wire harness. • Check for continuity between breakout box Pins 2 and 60. • **Is continuity present?**	Yes No	▶ ▶	REPLACE or SERVICE cable harness Circuit 498 (PK). REVERIFY DTC 23. NOTE: If other DTCs are output, service next code.
BB8 DTC 24: CHECK RH FRONT INLET VALVE AND CIRCUIT • Measure resistance between breakout box Pins 3 and 38. • **Is resistance between five and eight ohms?**	Yes No	▶ ▶	GO to BB10. GO to BB9.

FM4029400448030X

Fig. 175   Test BB: Solenoid Valve Diagnosis (Part 3 of 9). Late Production 1994 Continental

TEST STEP	RESULT	▶	ACTION TO TAKE
BB9 CHECK RH FRONT INLET VALVE • Disconnect brake pressure control valve block 16-pin connector. • Measure resistance between Pins 10 and 1. • **Is resistance between five and eight ohms?**	Yes No	▶ ▶	REPLACE or SERVICE cable harness Circuit 510 (T/R). REPLACE brake pressure control valve block.

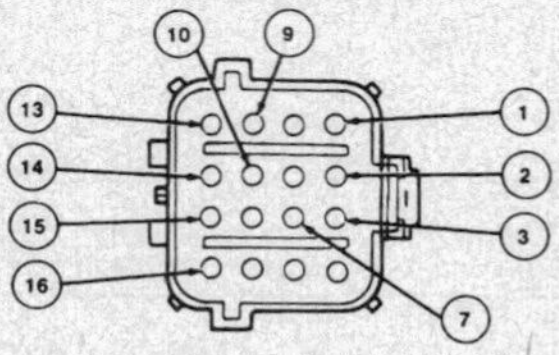

16-PIN VALVE BLOCK
CONNECTOR-VALVE BLOCK SIDE

BB10 CHECK CIRCUIT 510 • Disconnect valve block connector from wire harness. • Check for continuity between breakout box Pins 38 and 60. • **Is continuity present?**	Yes No	▶ ▶	REPLACE or SERVICE cable harness Circuit 510 (T/R). REVERIFY DTC 24. NOTE: If other DTCs are output, service next code.
BB11 DTC 25: CHECK RH FRONT OUTLET VALVE AND CIRCUIT • Measure resistance between breakout box Pins 3 and 21. • **Is resistance between three and six ohms?**	Yes No	▶ ▶	GO to BB13. GO to BB12.

FM4029400448040X

Fig. 175   Test BB: Solenoid Valve Diagnosis (Part 4 of 9). Late Production 1994 Continental

TEST STEP	RESULT	▶	ACTION TO TAKE
BB12 CHECK RH FRONT OUTLET VALVE • Disconnect brake pressure control valve block 16-pin connector. • Measure resistance between Pins 13 and 1. • **Is resistance between three and six ohms?**	Yes No	▶ ▶	REPLACE or SERVICE cable harness Circuit 497 (W). REPLACE brake pressure control valve block.

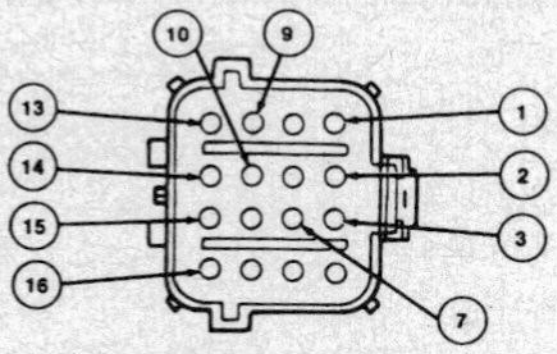

16-PIN VALVE BLOCK
CONNECTOR-VALVE BLOCK SIDE

BB13 CHECK CIRCUIT 497 • Disconnect valve block connection from wire harness. • Check for continuity between breakout box Pins 21 and 60. • **Is continuity present?**	Yes No	▶ ▶	REPLACE or SERVICE cable harness Circuit 497 (W). REVERIFY DTC 25. NOTE: If other DTCs are output, service next code.
BB14 DTC 26: CHECK RH REAR INLET VALVE AND CIRCUIT • Measure resistance between breakout box Pins 3 and 55. • **Is resistance between five and eight ohms?**	Yes No	▶ ▶	GO to BB16. GO to BB15.

FM4029400448050X

Fig. 175   Test BB: Solenoid Valve Diagnosis (Part 5 of 9). Late Production 1994 Continental

TEST STEP	RESULT	▶	ACTION TO TAKE
BB15 CHECK RH REAR INLET VALVE • Disconnect brake pressure control valve block 16-pin connector. • Measure resistance between Pins 2 and 1. • **Is resistance between five and eight ohms?**	Yes No	▶ ▶	REPLACE or SERVICE cable harness Circuit 455 (GY/R). REPLACE brake pressure control valve block.

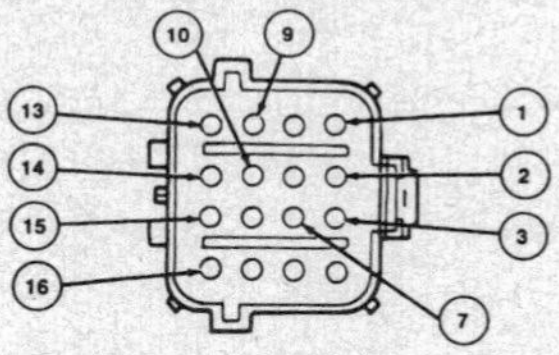

16-PIN VALVE BLOCK
CONNECTOR-VALVE BLOCK SIDE

BB16 CHECK CIRCUIT 455 • Disconnect valve block connector from wire harness. • Check for continuity between breakout box Pins 55 and 60. • **Is continuity present?**	Yes No	▶ ▶	REPLACE or SERVICE cable harness Circuit 455 (GY/R). REVERIFY DTC 26. NOTE: If other DTCs are output, service next code.
BB17 DTC 27: CHECK RH REAR OUTLET VALVE AND CIRCUIT • Measure resistance between breakout box Pins 3 and 18. • **Is resistance between three and six ohms?**	Yes No	▶ ▶	GO to BB19. GO to BB18.

FM4029400448060X

Fig. 175   Test BB: Solenoid Valve Diagnosis (Part 6 of 9). Late Production 1994 Continental

TEST STEP		RESULT	▶	ACTION TO TAKE
BB18	CHECK RH REAR OUTLET VALVE			
• Disconnect brake pressure control valve block 16-pin connector. • Measure resistance between Pins 3 and 1. • **Is resistance between three and six ohms?**		Yes	▶	REPLACE or SERVICE cable harness Circuit 492 (BR).
		No	▶	REPLACE brake pressure control valve block.
BB19	CHECK CIRCUIT 492			
• Disconnect valve block connector from wire harness. • Check for continuity between breakout box Pins 18 and 60. • **Is continuity present?**		Yes	▶	REPLACE or SERVICE cable harness Circuit 492 (BR).
		No	▶	REVERIFY DTC 27. NOTE: If other DTCs are output, service next code.
BB20	DTC 28: CHECK LH REAR INLET VALVE AND CIRCUIT			
• Measure resistance between breakout box Pins 3 and 54. • **Is resistance between five and eight ohms?**		Yes	▶	GO to **BB22**.
		No	▶	GO to **BB21**.

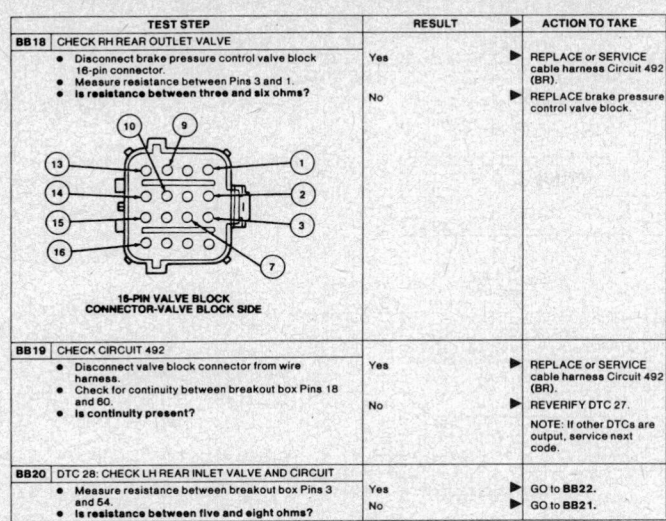

FM4029400448070X

Fig. 175   Test BB: Solenoid Valve Diagnosis (Part 7 of 9). Late Production 1994 Continental

TEST STEP		RESULT	▶	ACTION TO TAKE
BB21	CHECK LH REAR INLET VALVE			
• Disconnect brake pressure control valve block 16-pin connector. • Measure resistance between Pins 7 and 1. • **Is resistance between five and eight ohms?**		Yes	▶	REPLACE or SERVICE cable harness Circuit 496 (O).
		No	▶	REPLACE brake pressure control valve block.
BB22	CHECK CIRCUIT 496			
• Disconnect valve block connector from wire harness. • Check for continuity between breakout box Pins 54 and 60. • **Is continuity present?**		Yes	▶	REPLACE or SERVICE cable harness Circuit 496 (O).
		No	▶	REVERIFY DTC 28. NOTE: If other DTCs are output, service next code.
BB23	DTC 29: CHECK LH REAR OUTLET VALVE AND CIRCUIT			
• Measure resistance between breakout box Pins 3 and 36. • **Is resistance between three and six ohms?**		Yes	▶	GO to **BB25**.
		No	▶	GO to **BB24**.

FM4029400448080X

Fig. 175   Test BB: Solenoid Valve Diagnosis (Part 8 of 9). Late Production 1994 Continental

TEST STEP		RESULT	▶	ACTION TO TAKE
BB24	CHECK LH REAR OUTLET VALVE			
• Disconnect brake pressure control valve block 16-pin connector. • Measure resistance between Pins 9 and 1. • **Is resistance between three and six ohms?**		Yes	▶	REPLACE or SERVICE cable harness Circuit 499 (GY/BK).
		No	▶	REPLACE brake pressure control valve block.
BB25	CHECK CIRCUIT 499			
• Disconnect valve block connector from wire harness. • Check for continuity between breakout box Pins 36 and 60. • **Is continuity present?**		Yes	▶	REPLACE or SERVICE cable harness Circuit 499 (GY/BK).
		No	▶	REVERIFY DTC 29. NOTE: If other DTCs are output, service next code.

FM4029400448090X

Fig. 175   Test BB: Solenoid Valve Diagnosis (Part 9 of 9). Late Production 1994 Continental

TEST STEP		RESULT	▶	ACTION TO TAKE
BB1	DTC 17 OR 22: NO REFERENCE VOLTAGE OR LH FRONT INLET VALVE			
• Disconnect 55-pin plug from ABS Module.		10 volts minimum	▶	GO to **BB2**.
		Less than 10 volts	▶	REPLACE or SERVICE cable harness Circuit 533, 532, 603, fuse S or main power relay for Town Car. Circuit 532, 537, 603, 30 amp fuse or main power relay for Crown Victoria/Grand Marquis. NOTE: If test for code 17 or 22 continually leads to REVERIFY codes 17 or 22, GO to Anti-Lock Quick Check Test.
• Connect EEC-IV breakout box 014-00322 with Anti-Lock Test Adapter T90P-50-ALA or equivalent to the anti-lock 55-pin plug wiring harness.				
• Connect a jumper between Pins 34 and 19. • With ignition switch ON, measure voltage between breakout box Pins 3 and 60.				
BB2	CHECK LH FRONT INLET VALVE AND CIRCUIT			
• Measure resistance between breakout box Pins 3 and 20. • **Is resistance between 5 and 8 ohms?**		Yes	▶	REVERIFY codes 17 or 22. NOTE: If other codes are output, service next code.
		No	▶	GO to **BB3**.

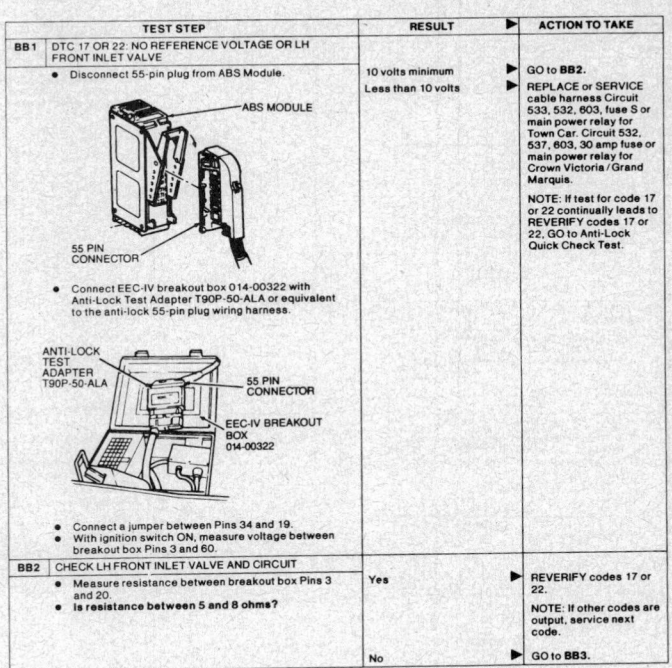

FM4029300309010X

Fig. 176   Test BB: Solenoid Valve Diagnosis (Part 1 of 7). 1993 Crown Victoria, Grand Marquis & Town Car

TEST STEP		RESULT	▶	ACTION TO TAKE
BB3	CHECK LH FRONT INLET VALVE			
• Disconnect valve body 19-pin connector. • Measure resistance between Pins 17 and 7. • **Is resistance between 5 and 8 ohms?**		Yes	▶	REPLACE or SERVICE cable harness Circuit 495.
		No	▶	REPLACE valve body.
BB4	DTC 23: CHECK LH FRONT OUTLET VALVE AND CIRCUIT			
• Measure resistance between breakout box Pins 3 and 2. • **Is resistance between 3 and 6 ohms?**		Yes	▶	REVERIFY code 23. NOTE: If any other codes are output, SERVICE next code.
		No	▶	GO to **BB5**.
BB5	CHECK LH FRONT OUTLET VALVE			
• Disconnect valve body 19-pin connector. • Measure resistance between Pins 18 and 7. • **Is resistance between 3 and 6 ohms?**		Yes	▶	REPLACE or SERVICE cable harness Circuit 498 for Town Car. Circuit 496 for Crown Victoria/Grand Marquis.
		No	▶	REPLACE valve body.
BB6	DTC 24: CHECK RH FRONT INLET VALVE AND CIRCUIT			
• Measure resistance between breakout box Pins 3 and 38. • **Is resistance between 5 and 8 ohms?**		Yes	▶	REVERIFY Code 25. NOTE: If other codes are output, SERVICE next code.
		No	▶	GO to **BB7**.

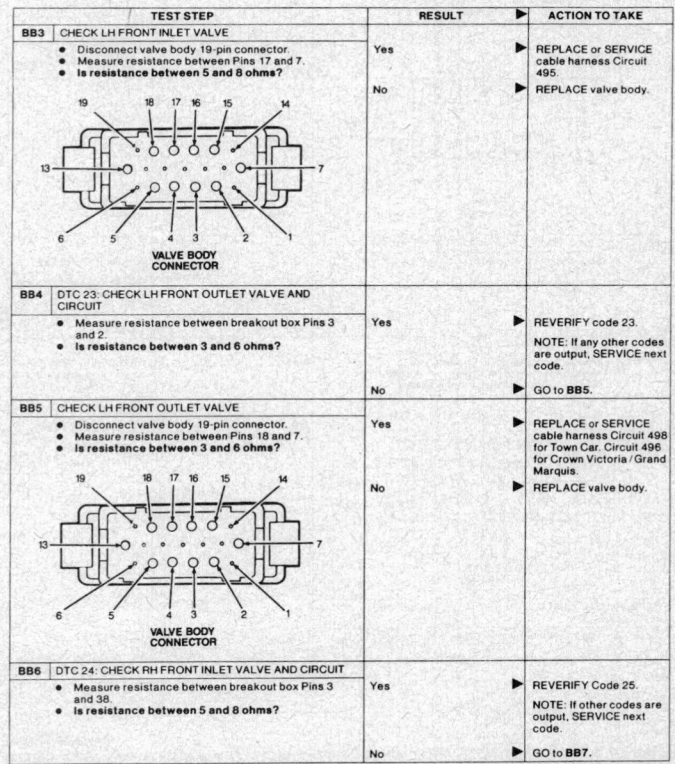

FM4029300309020X

Fig. 176   Test BB: Solenoid Valve Diagnosis (Part 2 of 7). 1993 Crown Victoria, Grand Marquis & Town Car

TEST STEP	RESULT	▶	ACTION TO TAKE
BB7 CHECK RH FRONT INLET VALVE • Disconnect valve body 19-pin connector. • Measure resistance between Pins 15 and 7. • Is resistance between 5 and 8 ohms?	Yes	▶	REPLACE or SERVICE cable harness Circuit 510 for Town Car. Circuit 497 for Crown Victoria / Grand Marquis.
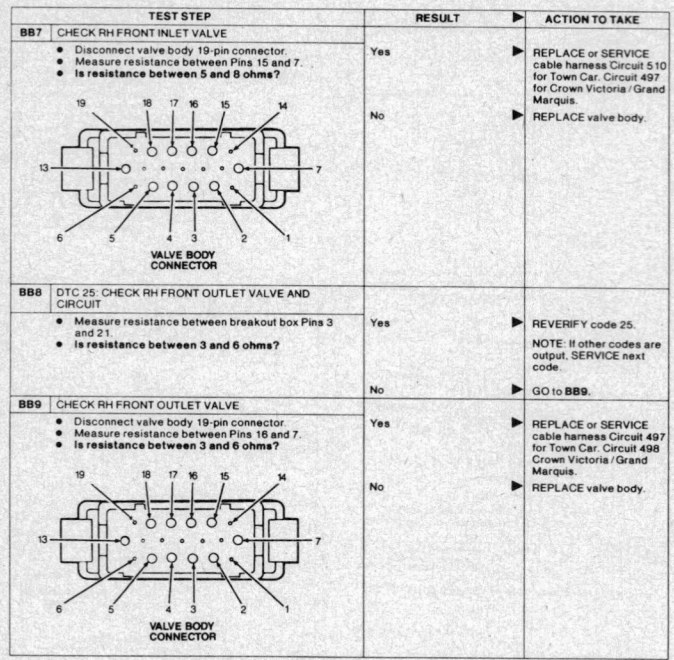	No	▶	REPLACE valve body.
BB8 DTC 25: CHECK RH FRONT OUTLET VALVE AND CIRCUIT • Measure resistance between breakout box Pins 3 and 21. • Is resistance between 3 and 6 ohms?	Yes	▶	REVERIFY code 25. NOTE: If other codes are output, SERVICE next code.
	No	▶	GO to **BB9**.
BB9 CHECK RH FRONT OUTLET VALVE • Disconnect valve body 19-pin connector. • Measure resistance between Pins 16 and 7. • Is resistance between 3 and 6 ohms?	Yes	▶	REPLACE or SERVICE cable harness Circuit 497 for Town Car. Circuit 498 Crown Victoria / Grand Marquis.
	No	▶	REPLACE valve body.

Fig. 176 Test BB: Solenoid Valve Diagnosis (Part 3 of 7). 1993 Crown Victoria, Grand Marquis & Town Car

FM4029300309030X

TEST STEP	RESULT	▶	ACTION TO TAKE
BB10 DTC 26: CHECK RH REAR INLET VALVE AND CIRCUIT • Measure resistance between breakout box Pins 3 and 55. • Is resistance between 5 and 8 ohms?	Yes	▶	REVERIFY code 26. NOTE: If other codes are output, SERVICE next code.
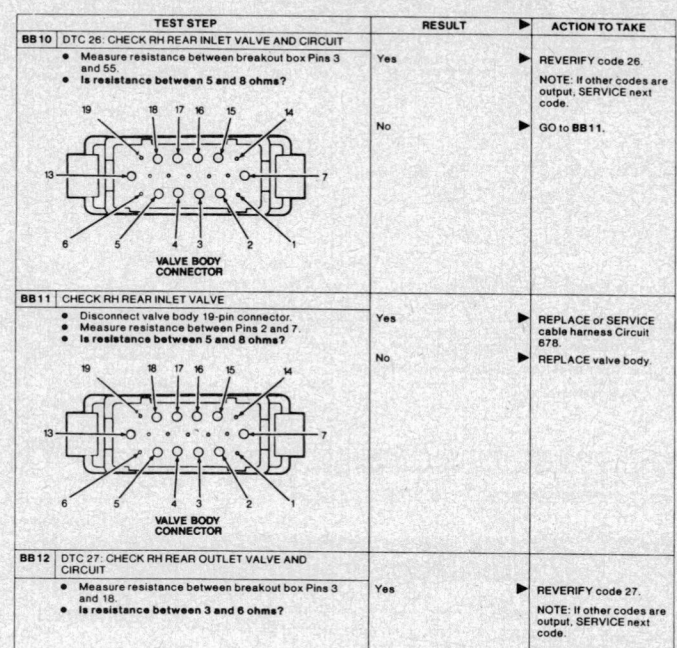	No	▶	GO to **BB11**.
BB11 CHECK RH REAR INLET VALVE • Disconnect valve body 19-pin connector. • Measure resistance between Pins 2 and 7. • Is resistance between 5 and 8 ohms?	Yes	▶	REPLACE or SERVICE cable harness Circuit 678.
	No	▶	REPLACE valve body.
BB12 DTC 27: CHECK RH REAR OUTLET VALVE AND CIRCUIT • Measure resistance between breakout box Pins 3 and 18. • Is resistance between 3 and 6 ohms?	Yes	▶	REVERIFY code 27. NOTE: If other codes are output, SERVICE next code.
	No	▶	GO to **BB13**.

Fig. 176 Test BB: Solenoid Valve Diagnosis (Part 4 of 7). 1993 Crown Victoria, Grand Marquis & Town Car

FM4029300309040X

TEST STEP	RESULT	▶	ACTION TO TAKE
BB13 CHECK RH REAR OUTLET VALVE • Disconnect valve body 19-pin connector. • Measure resistance between Pins 3 and 7. • Is resistance between 3 and 6 ohms?	Yes	▶	REPLACE or SERVICE cable harness Circuit 685.
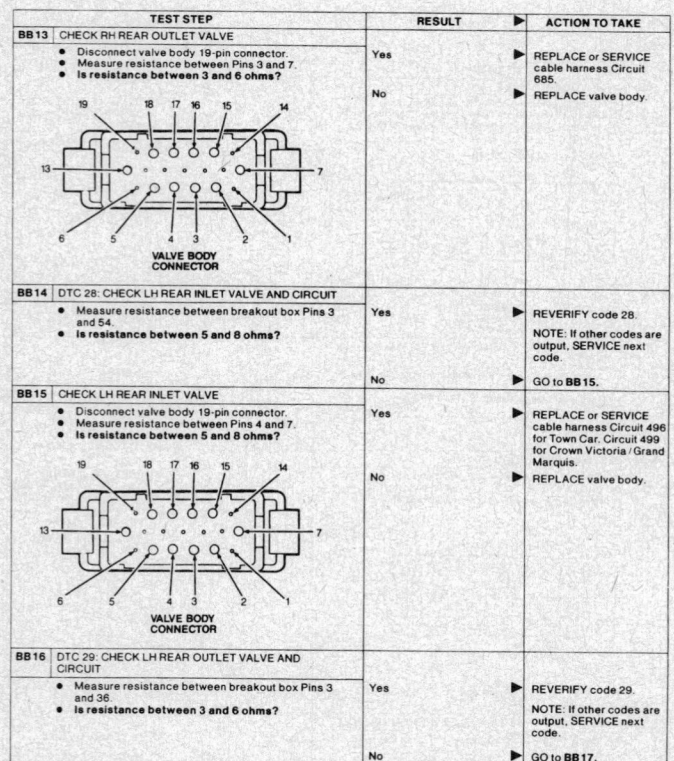	No	▶	REPLACE valve body.
BB14 DTC 28: CHECK LH REAR INLET VALVE AND CIRCUIT • Measure resistance between breakout box Pins 3 and 37. • Is resistance between 5 and 8 ohms?	Yes	▶	REVERIFY code 28. NOTE: If other codes are output, SERVICE next code.
	No	▶	GO to **BB15**.
BB15 CHECK LH REAR INLET VALVE • Disconnect valve body 19-pin connector. • Measure resistance between Pins 4 and 7. • Is resistance between 5 and 8 ohms?	Yes	▶	REPLACE or SERVICE cable harness Circuit 496 for Town Car. Circuit 601 for Crown Victoria / Grand Marquis.
	No	▶	REPLACE valve body.
BB16 DTC 29: CHECK LH REAR OUTLET VALVE AND CIRCUIT • Measure resistance between breakout box Pins 3 and 36. • Is resistance between 3 and 6 ohms?	Yes	▶	REVERIFY code 29. NOTE: If other codes are output, SERVICE next code.
	No	▶	GO to **BB17**.

FM4029300309050X

Fig. 176 Test BB: Solenoid Valve Diagnosis (Part 5 of 7). 1993 Crown Victoria, Grand Marquis & Town Car

TEST STEP	RESULT	▶	ACTION TO TAKE
BB17 CHECK LH REAR OUTLET VALVE • Disconnect valve body 19-pin connector. • Measure resistance between Pins 5 and 7. • Is resistance between 3 and 6 ohms?	Yes	▶	REPLACE or SERVICE cable harness Circuit 499 Town Car. Circuit 510 for Crown Victoria / Grand Marquis.
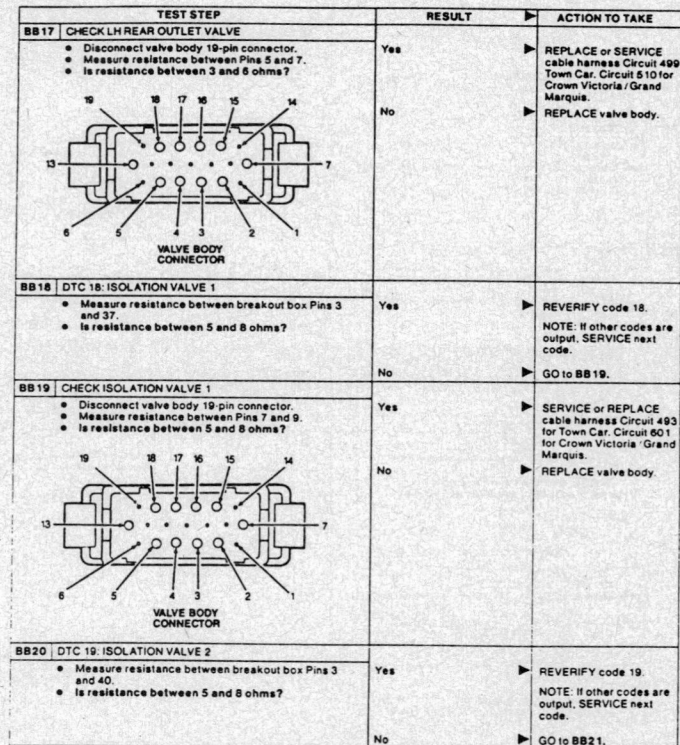	No	▶	REPLACE valve body.
BB18 DTC 18: ISOLATION VALVE 1 • Measure resistance between breakout box Pins 3 and 18. • Is resistance between 5 and 8 ohms?	Yes	▶	REVERIFY code 18. NOTE: If other codes are output, SERVICE next code.
	No	▶	GO to **BB19**.
BB19 CHECK ISOLATION VALVE 1 • Disconnect valve body 19-pin connector. • Measure resistance between Pins 7 and 9. • Is resistance between 5 and 8 ohms?	Yes	▶	SERVICE or REPLACE cable harness Circuit 493 for Town Car. Circuit 601 for Crown Victoria / Grand Marquis.
	No	▶	REPLACE valve body.
BB20 DTC 19: ISOLATION VALVE 2 • Measure resistance between breakout box Pins 3 and 40. • Is resistance between 5 and 8 ohms?	Yes	▶	REVERIFY code 19. NOTE: If other codes are output, SERVICE next code.
	No	▶	GO to **BB21**.

FM4029300309060X

Fig. 176 Test BB: Solenoid Valve Diagnosis (Part 6 of 7). 1993 Crown Victoria, Grand Marquis & Town Car

TEST STEP	RESULT	▶	ACTION TO TAKE
BB21 CHECK ISOLATION VALVE 2			
• Disconnect valve body 19-pin connector. • Measure resistance between Pins 7 and 10. • Is resistance between 5 and 8 ohms?	Yes	▶	SERVICE or REPLACE cable harness Circuit 677 Town Car. Circuit 600 for Crown Victoria / Grand Marquis.
	No	▶	REPLACE valve body.

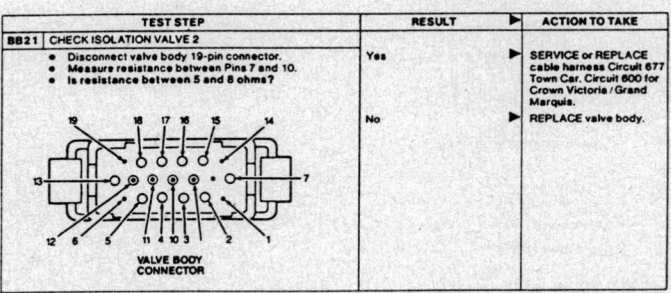

FM4029300309070X

Fig. 176   Test BB: Solenoid Valve Diagnosis (Part 7 of 7). 1993 Crown Victoria, Grand Marquis & Town Car

TEST STEP	RESULT	▶	ACTION TO TAKE
BB1 DTC 17: NO REFERENCE VOLTAGE			
• Disconnect anti-lock brake wiring from anti-lock brake control module.	Yes	▶	REVERIFY DTC 17.
	No	▶	REPLACE or SERVICE cable harness Circuit 533, 532, 603, fuse S or main power relay for Town Car. Circuit 532, 537, 603, 30 amp fuse or main power relay for Crown Victoria / Grand Marquis. NOTE: If test for DTCs 17 or 22 continually leads to REVERIFY DTCs 17 or 22, GO to Anti-Lock Quick Check Test.

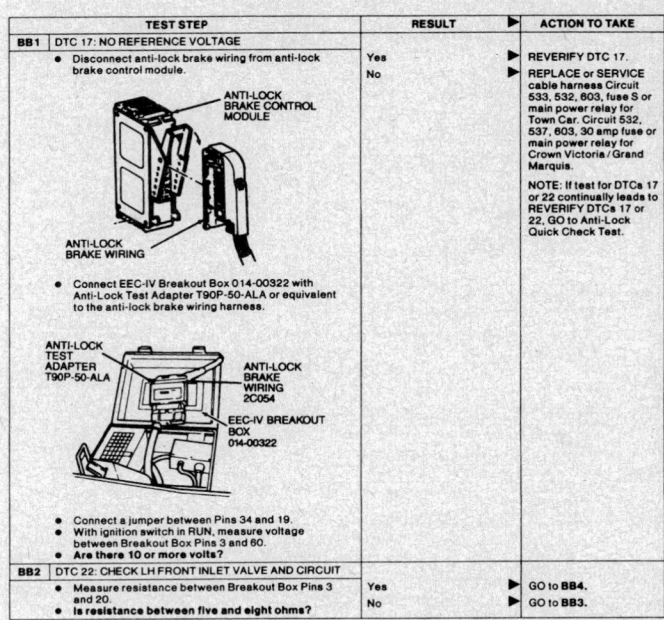

• Connect EEC-IV Breakout Box 014-00322 with Anti-Lock Test Adapter T90P-50-ALA or equivalent to the anti-lock brake wiring harness.

• Connect a jumper between Pins 34 and 19.
• With ignition switch in RUN, measure voltage between Breakout Box Pins 3 and 60.
• Are there 10 or more volts?

TEST STEP	RESULT	▶	ACTION TO TAKE
BB2 DTC 22: CHECK LH FRONT INLET VALVE AND CIRCUIT			
• Measure resistance between Breakout Box Pins 3 and 20. • Is resistance between five and eight ohms?	Yes	▶	GO to BB4.
	No	▶	GO to BB3.

FM4029400449010X

Fig. 177   Test BB: Solenoid Valve Diagnosis (Part 1 of 8). 1994 Crown Victoria, Grand Marquis & Town Car

TEST STEP	RESULT	▶	ACTION TO TAKE
BB3 CHECK LH FRONT INLET VALVE			
• Disconnect brake pressure control valve block 16-pin connector. • Measure resistance between Pins 14 and 1. • Is resistance between five and eight ohms?	Yes	▶	REPLACE or SERVICE cable harness Circuit 495 (T).
	No	▶	REPLACE brake pressure control valve block.

16-PIN VALVE BLOCK CONNECTOR-VALVE BLOCK SIDE

TEST STEP	RESULT	▶	ACTION TO TAKE
BB4 CHECK CIRCUIT 495			
• Disconnect valve block connector from wire harness. • Check for continuity between Breakout Box Pins 20 and 60. • Is continuity present?	Yes	▶	REPLACE or SERVICE cable harness Circuit 495 (T).
	No	▶	REVERIFY DTC 22. NOTE: If other DTCs are output, service next code.
BB5 DTC 23: CHECK LH FRONT OUTLET VALVE AND CIRCUIT			
• Measure resistance between Breakout Box Pins 3 and 2. • Is resistance between three and six ohms?	Yes	▶	GO to BB7.
	No	▶	GO to BB6.
BB6 CHECK LH FRONT OUTLET VALVE			
• Disconnect brake pressure control valve block 16-pin connector. • Measure resistance between Pins 15 and 1. • Is resistance between three and six ohms?	Yes	▶	REPLACE or SERVICE cable harness Circuit 498 (PK).
	No	▶	REPLACE brake pressure control valve block.

16-PIN VALVE BLOCK CONNECTOR-VALVE BLOCK SIDE

FM4029400449020X

Fig. 177   Test BB: Solenoid Valve Diagnosis (Part 2 of 8). 1994 Crown Victoria, Grand Marquis & Town Car

TEST STEP	RESULT	▶	ACTION TO TAKE
BB7 CHECK CIRCUIT 498			
• Disconnect valve block connector from wire harness. • Check for continuity between Breakout Box Pins 2 and 60. • Is continuity present?	Yes	▶	REPLACE or SERVICE cable harness Circuit 498 (PK).
	No	▶	REVERIFY DTC 23. NOTE: If other DTCs are output, service next code.
BB8 DTC 24: CHECK RH FRONT INLET VALVE AND CIRCUIT			
• Measure resistance between Breakout Box Pins 3 and 38. • Is resistance between five and eight ohms?	Yes	▶	GO to BB10.
	No	▶	GO to BB9.
BB9 CHECK RH FRONT INLET VALVE			
• Disconnect brake pressure control valve block 16-pin connector. • Measure resistance between Pins 10 and 1. • Is resistance between five and eight ohms?	Yes	▶	REPLACE or SERVICE cable harness Circuit 510 (T/R).
	No	▶	REPLACE brake pressure control valve block.

16-PIN VALVE BLOCK CONNECTOR-VALVE BLOCK SIDE

TEST STEP	RESULT	▶	ACTION TO TAKE
BB10 CHECK CIRCUIT 510			
• Disconnect valve block connector from wire harness. • Check for continuity between Breakout Box Pins 38 and 60. • Is continuity present?	Yes	▶	REPLACE or SERVICE cable harness Circuit 510 (T/R).
	No	▶	REVERIFY DTC 24. NOTE: If other DTCs are output, service next code.
BB11 DTC 25: CHECK RH FRONT OUTLET VALVE AND CIRCUIT			
• Measure resistance between Breakout Box Pins 3 and 21. • Is resistance between three and six ohms?	Yes	▶	GO to BB13.
	No	▶	GO to BB12.

FM4029400449030X

Fig. 177   Test BB: Solenoid Valve Diagnosis (Part 3 of 8). 1994 Crown Victoria, Grand Marquis & Town Car

TEST STEP	RESULT	►	ACTION TO TAKE
BB12 CHECK RH FRONT OUTLET VALVE • Disconnect brake pressure control valve block 16-pin connector. • Measure resistance between Pins 13 and 1. • **Is resistance between three and six ohms?**	Yes No	► ►	REPLACE or SERVICE cable harness Circuit 497 (W). REPLACE brake pressure control valve block.

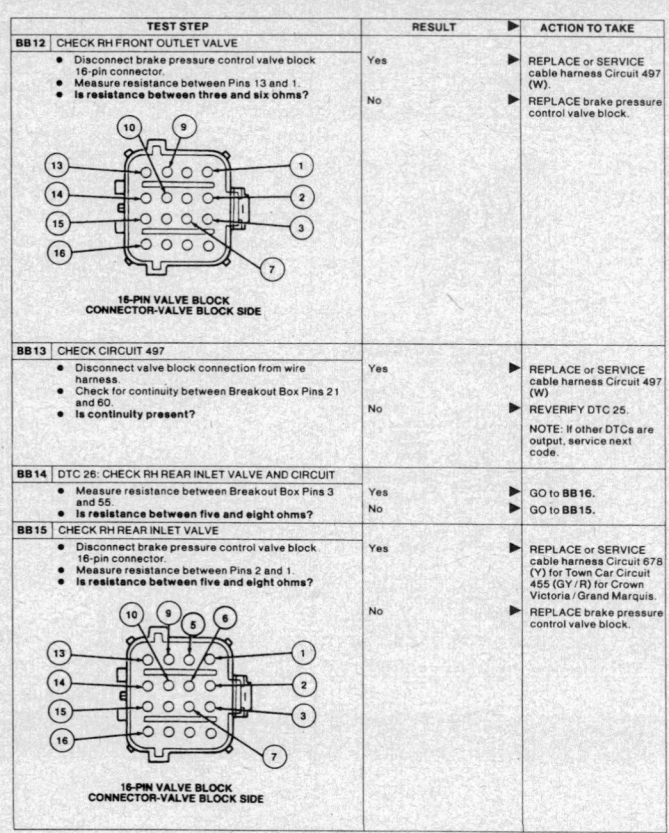

16-PIN VALVE BLOCK CONNECTOR-VALVE BLOCK SIDE

TEST STEP	RESULT	►	ACTION TO TAKE
BB13 CHECK CIRCUIT 497 • Disconnect valve block connection from wire harness. • Check for continuity between Breakout Box Pins 21 and 60. • **Is continuity present?**	Yes No	► ►	REPLACE or SERVICE cable harness Circuit 497 (W). REVERIFY DTC 25. NOTE: If other DTCs are output, service next code.
BB14 DTC 26: CHECK RH REAR INLET VALVE AND CIRCUIT • Measure resistance between Breakout Box Pins 3 and 55. • **Is resistance between five and eight ohms?**	Yes No	► ►	GO to BB16. GO to BB15.
BB15 CHECK RH REAR INLET VALVE • Disconnect brake pressure control valve block 16-pin connector. • Measure resistance between Pins 2 and 1. • **Is resistance between five and eight ohms?**	Yes No	► ►	REPLACE or SERVICE cable harness Circuit 678 (Y) for Town Car Circuit 455 (GY/R) for Crown Victoria/Grand Marquis. REPLACE brake pressure control valve block.

16-PIN VALVE BLOCK CONNECTOR-VALVE BLOCK SIDE

FM4029400449040X

Fig. 177   Test BB: Solenoid Valve Diagnosis (Part 4 of 8). 1994 Crown Victoria, Grand Marquis & Town Car

TEST STEP	RESULT	►	ACTION TO TAKE
BB21 CHECK LH REAR INLET VALVE • Disconnect brake pressure control valve block 16-pin connector. • Measure resistance between Pins 7 and 1. • **Is resistance between five and eight ohms?**	Yes No	► ►	REPLACE or SERVICE cable harness Circuit 496 (O). REPLACE brake pressure control valve block.

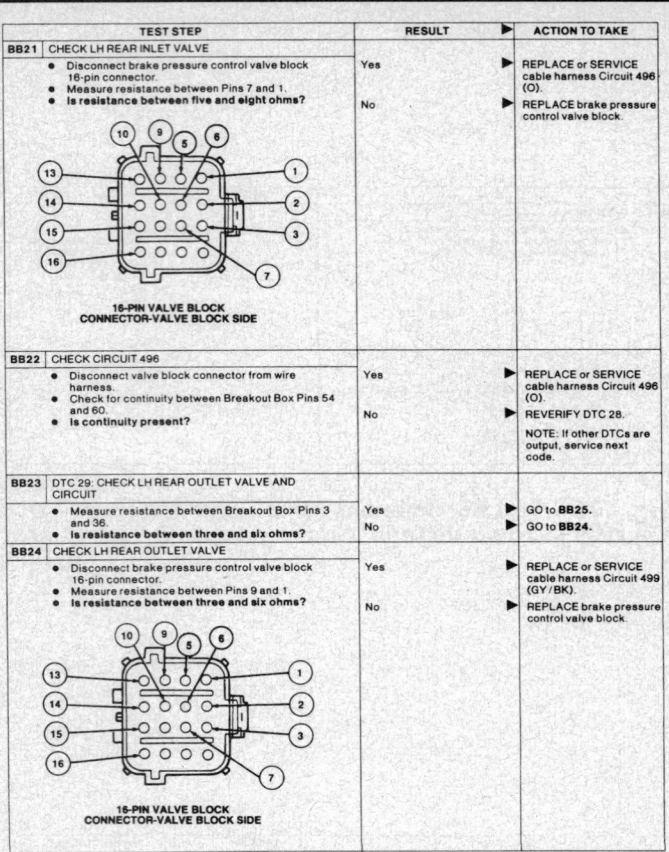

16-PIN VALVE BLOCK CONNECTOR-VALVE BLOCK SIDE

TEST STEP	RESULT	►	ACTION TO TAKE
BB22 CHECK CIRCUIT 496 • Disconnect valve block connector from wire harness. • Check for continuity between Breakout Box Pins 54 and 60. • **Is continuity present?**	Yes No	► ►	REPLACE or SERVICE cable harness Circuit 496 (O). REVERIFY DTC 28. NOTE: If other DTCs are output, service next code.
BB23 DTC 29: CHECK LH REAR OUTLET VALVE AND CIRCUIT • Measure resistance between Breakout Box Pins 3 and 36. • **Is resistance between three and six ohms?**	Yes No	► ►	GO to BB25. GO to BB24.
BB24 CHECK LH REAR OUTLET VALVE • Disconnect brake pressure control valve block 16-pin connector. • Measure resistance between Pins 9 and 1. • **Is resistance between three and six ohms?**	Yes No	► ►	REPLACE or SERVICE cable harness Circuit 499 (GY/BK). REPLACE brake pressure control valve block.

16-PIN VALVE BLOCK CONNECTOR-VALVE BLOCK SIDE

FM4029400449060X

Fig. 177   Test BB: Solenoid Valve Diagnosis (Part 6 of 8). 1994 Crown Victoria, Grand Marquis & Town Car

TEST STEP	RESULT	►	ACTION TO TAKE
BB16 CHECK CIRCUIT 455 • Disconnect valve block connector from wire harness. • Check for continuity between Breakout Box Pins 55 and 60. • **Is continuity present?**	Yes No	► ►	REPLACE or SERVICE cable harness Circuit 678 (Y) for Town Car, Circuit 455 (GY/R) for Crown Victoria/Grand Marquis. REVERIFY DTC 26. NOTE: If other DTCs are output, service next code.
BB17 DTC 27: CHECK RH REAR OUTLET VALVE AND CIRCUIT • Measure resistance between Breakout Box Pins 3 and 18. • **Is resistance between three and six ohms?**	Yes No	► ►	GO to BB19. GO to BB18.
BB18 CHECK RH REAR OUTLET VALVE • Disconnect brake pressure control valve block 16-pin connector. • Measure resistance between Pins 3 and 1. • **Is resistance between three and six ohms?**	Yes No	► ►	REPLACE or SERVICE cable harness Circuit 685 (BK/W) for Town Car, Circuit 492 (BR) for Crown Victoria/Grand Marquis. REPLACE brake pressure control valve block.

16-PIN VALVE BLOCK CONNECTOR-VALVE BLOCK SIDE

TEST STEP	RESULT	►	ACTION TO TAKE
BB19 CHECK CIRCUIT 492 • Disconnect valve block connector from wire harness. • Check for continuity between Breakout Box Pins 18 and 60. • **Is continuity present?**	Yes No	► ►	REPLACE or SERVICE cable harness Circuit 685 (BK/W) for Town Car, Circuit 492 (BR) for Crown Victoria/Grand Marquis. REVERIFY DTC 27. NOTE: If other DTCs are output, service next code.
BB20 DTC 28: CHECK LH REAR INLET VALVE AND CIRCUIT • Measure resistance between breakout box Pins 3 and 54. • **Is resistance between five and eight ohms?**	Yes No	► ►	GO to BB22. GO to BB21.

FM4029400449050X

Fig. 177   Test BB: Solenoid Valve Diagnosis (Part 5 of 8). 1994 Crown Victoria, Grand Marquis & Town Car

TEST STEP	RESULT	►	ACTION TO TAKE
BB25 CHECK CIRCUIT 499 • Disconnect valve block connector from wire harness. • Check for continuity between Breakout Box Pins 36 and 60. • **Is continuity present?**	Yes No	► ►	REPLACE or SERVICE cable harness Circuit 499 (GY/BK). REVERIFY DTC 29. NOTE: If other DTCs are output, service next code.
BB26 DTC 18: CHECK ISOLATION VALVE 1 AND CIRCUIT • Measure resistance between Breakout Box Pins 3 and 37. • **Is resistance between five and eight ohms?**	Yes No	► ►	GO to BB28. GO to BB27.
BB27 CHECK ISOLATION VALVE 1 • Disconnect brake pressure control valve block 16-pin connector. • Measure resistance between Pins 5 and 1. • **Is resistance between five and eight ohms?**	Yes No	► ►	REPLACE or SERVICE cable harness Circuit 498 (PK). REPLACE brake pressure control valve block.

16-PIN VALVE BLOCK CONNECTOR-VALVE BLOCK SIDE

TEST STEP	RESULT	►	ACTION TO TAKE
BB28 CHECK CIRCUIT 601 OR 493 • Disconnect valve block connector from wire harness. • Check for continuity between breakout box Pins 37 and 60. • **Is continuity present?**	Yes No	► ►	REPLACE or SERVICE cable harness Circuit 493 (BK/PK) for Town Car, Circuit 601 (LB/PK) for Crown Victoria/Grand Marquis. REVERIFY DTC 18. NOTE: If other DTCs are output, service next code.
BB29 DTC 19: CHECK ISOLATION VALVE 2 AND CIRCUIT • Measure resistance between Breakout Box Pins 3 and 40. • **Is resistance between five and eight ohms?**	Yes No	► ►	GO to BB31. GO to BB30.

FM4029400449070X

Fig. 177   Test BB: Solenoid Valve Diagnosis (Part 7 of 8). 1994 Crown Victoria, Grand Marquis & Town Car

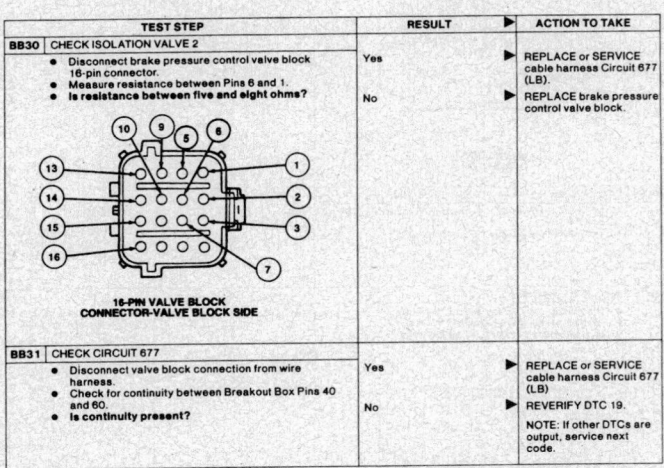

TEST STEP	RESULT	▶	ACTION TO TAKE
BB30 CHECK ISOLATION VALVE 2			
• Disconnect brake pressure control valve block 16-pin connector. • Measure resistance between Pins 6 and 1. • Is resistance between five and eight ohms?	Yes	▶	REPLACE or SERVICE cable harness Circuit 677 (LB).
	No	▶	REPLACE brake pressure control valve block.
BB31 CHECK CIRCUIT 677			
• Disconnect valve block connection from wire harness. • Check for continuity between Breakout Box Pins 40 and 60. • Is continuity present?	Yes	▶	REPLACE or SERVICE cable harness Circuit 677 (LB).
	No	▶	REVERIFY DTC 19. NOTE: If other DTCs are output, service next code.

FM4029400449080X

Fig. 177   Test BB: Solenoid Valve Diagnosis (Part 8 of 8). 1994 Crown Victoria, Grand Marquis & Town Car

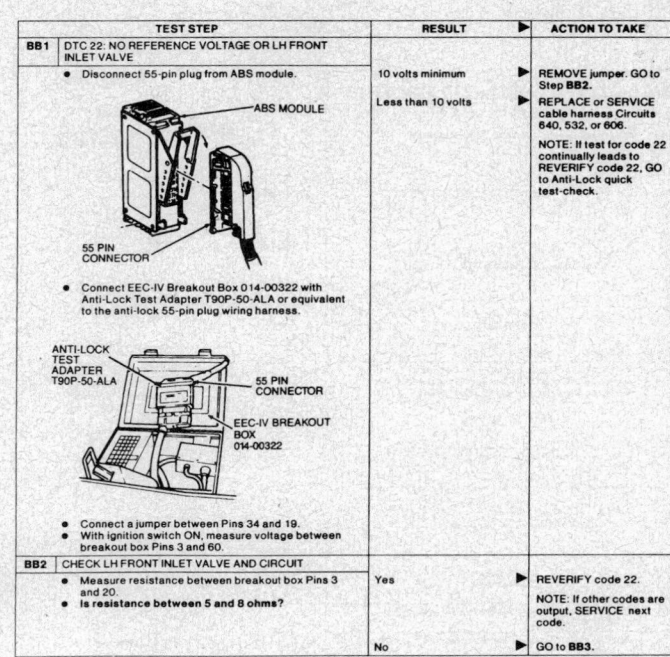

TEST STEP	RESULT	▶	ACTION TO TAKE
BB1 DTC 22: NO REFERENCE VOLTAGE OR LH FRONT INLET VALVE			
• Disconnect 55-pin plug from ABS module.	10 volts minimum	▶	REMOVE jumper. GO to Step BB2.
	Less than 10 volts	▶	REPLACE or SERVICE cable harness Circuits 640, 532, or 606. NOTE: If test for code 22 continually leads to REVERIFY code 22, GO to Anti-Lock quick test-check.
• Connect EEC-IV Breakout Box 014-00322 with Anti-Lock Test Adapter T90P-50-ALA or equivalent to the anti-lock 55-pin plug wiring harness.			
• Connect a jumper between Pins 34 and 19. • With ignition switch ON, measure voltage between breakout box Pins 3 and 60.			
BB2 CHECK LH FRONT INLET VALVE AND CIRCUIT			
• Measure resistance between breakout box Pins 3 and 20. • Is resistance between 5 and 8 ohms?	Yes	▶	REVERIFY code 22. NOTE: If other codes are output, SERVICE next code.
	No	▶	GO to BB3.

FM4029400450010X

Fig. 178   Test BB: Solenoid Valve Diagnosis (Part 1 of 6). 1993–94 Sable & Taurus

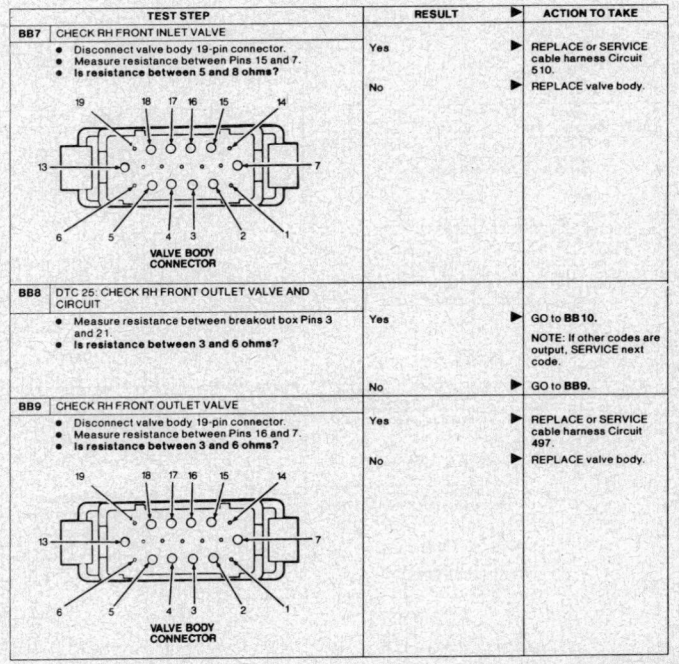

TEST STEP	RESULT	▶	ACTION TO TAKE
BB3 CHECK LH FRONT INLET VALVE			
• Disconnect valve body 19-pin connector. • Measure resistance between Pins 17 and 7. • Is resistance between 5 and 8 ohms?	Yes	▶	REPLACE or SERVICE cable harness Circuits 495.
	No	▶	REPLACE valve body.
BB4 DTC 23: CHECK LH FRONT OUTLET VALVE AND CIRCUIT			
• Measure resistance between breakout box Pins 3 and 2. • Is resistance between 3 and 6 ohms?	Yes	▶	GO to BB.. NOTE: If any other codes are output, SERVICE next code.
	No	▶	GO to BB5.
BB5 CHECK LH FRONT OUTLET VALVE			
• Disconnect valve body 19-pin connector. • Measure resistance between Pins 18 and 7. • Is resistance between 3 and 6 ohms?	Yes	▶	REPLACE or SERVICE cable harness Circuit 498.
	No	▶	REPLACE valve body.
BB6 DTC 24: CHECK RH FRONT INLET VALVE AND CIRCUIT			
• Measure resistance between breakout box Pins 3 and 38. • Is resistance between 5 and 8 ohms?	Yes	▶	GO to BB8. NOTE: If other codes are output, SERVICE next code.
	No	▶	GO to BB7.

FM4029400450020X

Fig. 178   Test BB: Solenoid Valve Diagnosis (Part 2 of 6). 1993–94 Sable & Taurus

TEST STEP	RESULT	▶	ACTION TO TAKE
BB7 CHECK RH FRONT INLET VALVE			
• Disconnect valve body 19-pin connector. • Measure resistance between Pins 15 and 7. • Is resistance between 5 and 8 ohms?	Yes	▶	REPLACE or SERVICE cable harness Circuit 510.
	No	▶	REPLACE valve body.
BB8 DTC 25: CHECK RH FRONT OUTLET VALVE AND CIRCUIT			
• Measure resistance between breakout box Pins 3 and 21. • Is resistance between 3 and 6 ohms?	Yes	▶	GO to BB10. NOTE: If other codes are output, SERVICE next code.
	No	▶	GO to BB9.
BB9 CHECK RH FRONT OUTLET VALVE			
• Disconnect valve body 19-pin connector. • Measure resistance between Pins 16 and 7. • Is resistance between 3 and 6 ohms?	Yes	▶	REPLACE or SERVICE cable harness Circuit 497.
	No	▶	REPLACE valve body.

FM4029400450030X

Fig. 178   Test BB: Solenoid Valve Diagnosis (Part 3 of 6). 1993–94 Sable & Taurus

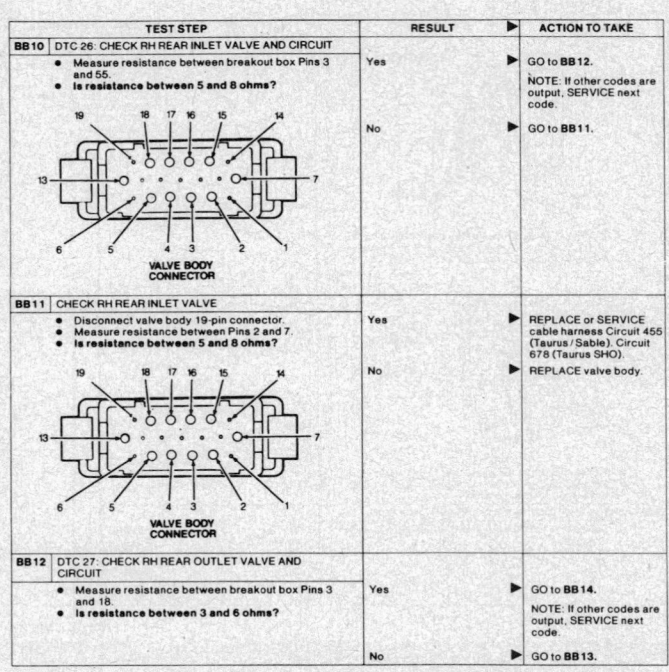

TEST STEP	RESULT	▶	ACTION TO TAKE
BB10 DTC 26: CHECK RH REAR INLET VALVE AND CIRCUIT • Measure resistance between breakout box Pins 3 and 55. • **Is resistance between 5 and 8 ohms?**	Yes	▶	GO to BB12. NOTE: If other codes are output, SERVICE next code.
	No	▶	GO to BB11.
BB11 CHECK RH REAR INLET VALVE • Disconnect valve body 19-pin connector. • Measure resistance between Pins 2 and 7. • **Is resistance between 5 and 8 ohms?**	Yes	▶	REPLACE or SERVICE cable harness Circuit 455 (Taurus / Sable). Circuit 678 (Taurus SHO).
	No	▶	REPLACE valve body.
BB12 DTC 27: CHECK RH REAR OUTLET VALVE AND CIRCUIT • Measure resistance between breakout box Pins 3 and 18. • **Is resistance between 3 and 6 ohms?**	Yes	▶	GO to BB14. NOTE: If other codes are output, SERVICE next code.
	No	▶	GO to BB13.

Fig. 178   Test BB: Solenoid Valve Diagnosis (Part 4 of 6). 1993–94 Sable & Taurus

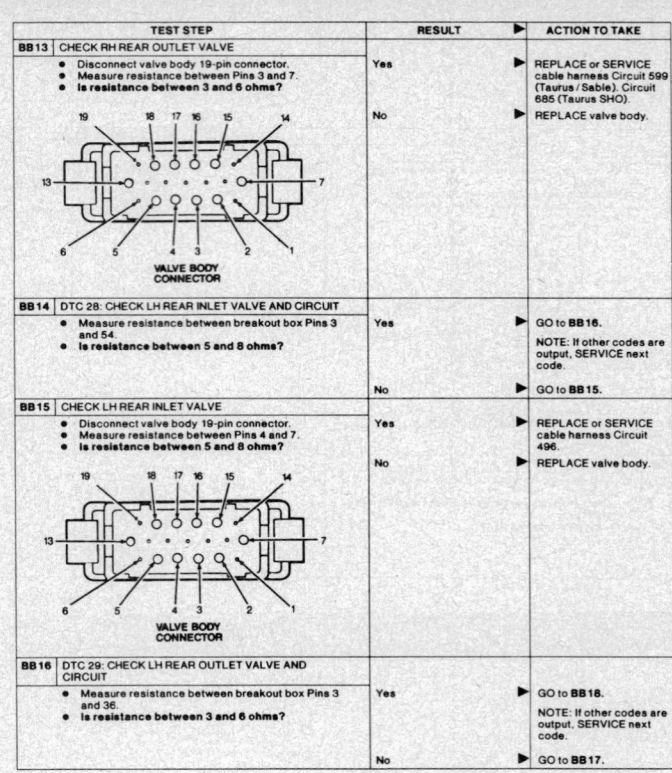

TEST STEP	RESULT	▶	ACTION TO TAKE
BB13 CHECK RH REAR OUTLET VALVE • Disconnect valve body 19-pin connector. • Measure resistance between Pins 3 and 7. • **Is resistance between 3 and 6 ohms?**	Yes	▶	REPLACE or SERVICE cable harness Circuit 599 (Taurus / Sable). Circuit 685 (Taurus SHO).
	No	▶	REPLACE valve body.
BB14 DTC 28: CHECK LH REAR INLET VALVE AND CIRCUIT • Measure resistance between breakout box Pins 3 and 54. • **Is resistance between 5 and 8 ohms?**	Yes	▶	GO to BB16. NOTE: If other codes are output, SERVICE next code.
	No	▶	GO to BB15.
BB15 CHECK LH REAR INLET VALVE • Disconnect valve body 19-pin connector. • Measure resistance between Pins 4 and 7. • **Is resistance between 5 and 8 ohms?**	Yes	▶	REPLACE or SERVICE cable harness Circuit 496.
	No	▶	REPLACE valve body.
BB16 DTC 29: CHECK LH REAR OUTLET VALVE AND CIRCUIT • Measure resistance between breakout box Pins 3 and 36. • **Is resistance between 3 and 6 ohms?**	Yes	▶	GO to BB18. NOTE: If other codes are output, SERVICE next code.
	No	▶	GO to BB17.

Fig. 178   Test BB: Solenoid Valve Diagnosis (Part 5 of 6). 1993–94 Sable & Taurus

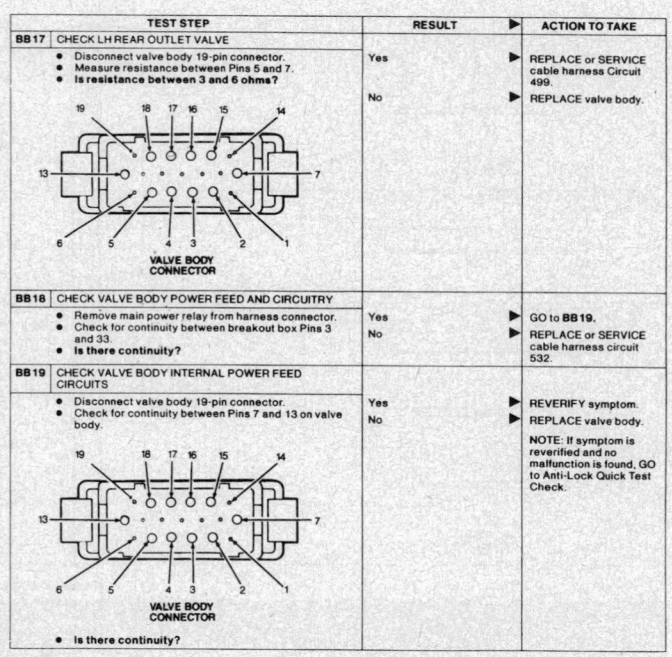

TEST STEP	RESULT	▶	ACTION TO TAKE
BB17 CHECK LH REAR OUTLET VALVE • Disconnect valve body 19-pin connector. • Measure resistance between Pins 5 and 7. • **Is resistance between 3 and 6 ohms?**	Yes	▶	REPLACE or SERVICE cable harness Circuit 499.
	No	▶	REPLACE valve body.
BB18 CHECK VALVE BODY POWER FEED AND CIRCUITRY • Remove main power relay from harness connector. • Check for continuity between breakout box Pins 3 and 33. • **Is there continuity?**	Yes	▶	GO to BB19.
	No	▶	REPLACE or SERVICE cable harness circuit 532.
BB19 CHECK VALVE BODY INTERNAL POWER FEED CIRCUITS • Disconnect valve body 19-pin connector. • Check for continuity between Pins 7 and 13 on valve body. • Is there continuity?	Yes	▶	REVERIFY symptom.
	No	▶	REPLACE valve body. NOTE: If symptom is reverified and no malfunction is found, GO to Anti-Lock Quick Test Check.

Fig. 178   Test BB: Solenoid Valve Diagnosis (Part 6 of 6). 1993–94 Sable & Taurus

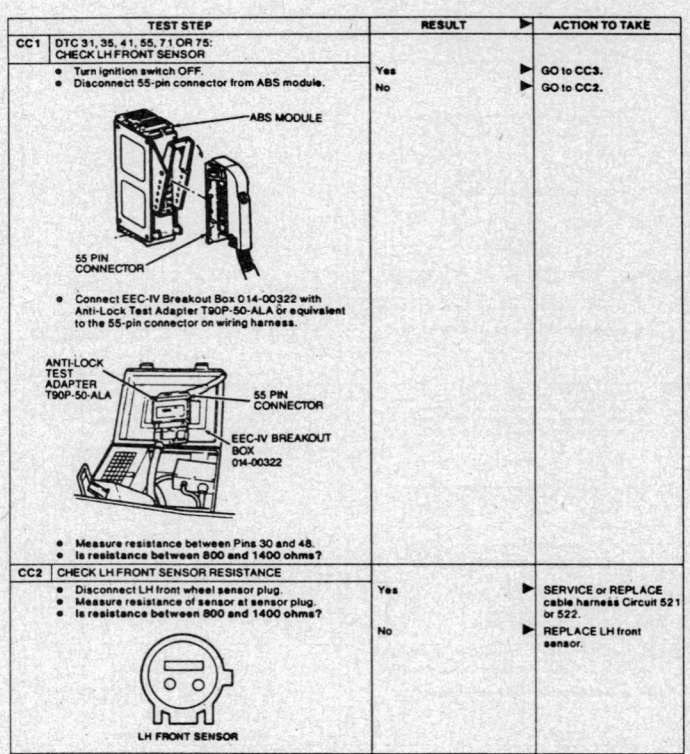

TEST STEP	RESULT	▶	ACTION TO TAKE
CC1 DTC 31, 35, 41, 55, 71 OR 75: CHECK LH FRONT SENSOR • Turn ignition switch OFF. • Disconnect 55-pin connector from ABS module.	Yes	▶	GO to CC3.
	No	▶	GO to CC2.
• Connect EEC-IV Breakout Box 014-00322 with Anti-Lock Test Adapter T90P-50-ALA or equivalent to the 55-pin connector on wiring harness. • Measure resistance between Pins 30 and 48. • **Is resistance between 800 and 1400 ohms?**			
CC2 CHECK LH FRONT SENSOR RESISTANCE • Disconnect LH front wheel sensor plug. • Measure resistance of sensor at sensor plug. • **Is resistance between 800 and 1400 ohms?**	Yes	▶	SERVICE or REPLACE cable harness Circuit 521 or 522.
	No	▶	REPLACE LH front sensor.

Fig. 179   Test CC: Front Wheel Sensor Diagnosis (Part 1 of 8). 1993–94 Continental, Crown Victoria, Grand Marquis & Town Car

TEST STEP		RESULT	▶	ACTION TO TAKE
CC3	CHECK LH FRONT SENSOR VOLTAGE			
	• Turn air suspension switch OFF, if so equipped. • Place vehicle on hoist and raise wheels clear of ground. • Set multi-meter to voltage range (2 volts AC). • Measure voltage between Pins 30 and 48 at breakout box while spinning LH front wheel at approximately 1 revolution per second.	Between 0.10 and 1.40 volts AC	▶	GO to CC4.
		Less than 0.10 or more than 1.40 volts AC	▶	CHECK sensor mounting, air gap or toothed wheel mounting. CORRECT as required.
CC4	CHECK LH FRONT SENSOR CIRCUIT CONTINUITY TO GROUND			
	• Check continuity between breakout box Pins 30 and 60. • Is continuity present?	No	▶	GO to CC6.
		Yes	▶	GO to CC5.
CC5	CHECK LH FRONT SENSOR TO GROUND			
	• Disconnect LH front wheel sensor plug. • Check for continuity between each sensor plug pin (sensor side) and vehicle ground. • Is continuity present?	Yes	▶	REPLACE LH front sensor.
		No	▶	SERVICE or REPLACE cable harness Circuit 521 or 522. RECONNECT sensor plug.

LH FRONT SENSOR

TEST STEP		RESULT	▶	ACTION TO TAKE
CC6	CHECK ABS MODULE TO GROUND WIRE			
	• Check continuity between breakout box Pin 60 and body ground. • Was continuity present?	Yes	▶	GO to CC7.
		No	▶	SERVICE or REPLACE cable harness Circuit 530.
CC7	CHECK FRONT WHEEL BEARING			
	• Check front wheel bearing end play. • Inspect toothed sensor ring visually for damaged teeth. • Were loose or damaged parts found? NOTE: Turn air suspension switch ON when vehicle is off hoist, if so equipped.	Yes	▶	REPLACE damaged parts.
		No	▶	REVERIFY symptom.

Fig. 179   Test CC: Front Wheel Sensor Diagnosis (Part 2 of 8). 1993–94 Continental

TEST STEP		RESULT	▶	ACTION TO TAKE
CC3	CHECK LH FRONT SENSOR VOLTAGE			
	• Turn ignition switch OFF. • Turn air suspension switch OFF, if so equipped. • Place vehicle on hoist and raise wheels clear of ground. Refer to Section 00-02. • Set multi-meter to voltage range (2 volts AC). • Measure voltage between Pins 30 and 48 at breakout box while spinning LH front wheel at approximately 1 revolution per second.	Between 0.10 and 1.40 volts AC	▶	GO to CC4.
		Less than 0.10 or more than 1.40 volts AC	▶	CHECK sensor mounting, air gap or toothed wheel mounting. CORRECT as required.
CC4	CHECK LH FRONT SENSOR CIRCUIT CONTINUITY TO GROUND			
	• Check continuity between breakout box Pins 30 and 60. • Is continuity present?	No	▶	GO to CC6.
		Yes	▶	GO to CC5.
CC5	CHECK LH FRONT SENSOR TO GROUND			
	• Disconnect LH front wheel sensor plug. • Check for continuity between each sensor plug pin (sensor side) and vehicle ground. • Is continuity present?	Yes	▶	REPLACE LH front sensor.
		No	▶	SERVICE or REPLACE cable harness Circuit 521 or 522. RECONNECT sensor plug.

LH FRONT SENSOR

TEST STEP		RESULT	▶	ACTION TO TAKE
CC6	CHECK ELECTRONIC CONTROLLER TO GROUND WIRE			
	• Check continuity between breakout box Pin 60 and body ground. • Is continuity present?	Yes	▶	GO to CC7.
		No	▶	SERVICE or REPLACE cable harness Circuit 57.
CC7	CHECK LH FRONT WHEEL BEARING			
	• Check front wheel bearing end play. • Inspect toothed sensor ring visually for damaged teeth. • Were loose or damaged parts found? NOTE: Turn air suspension switch ON when vehicle is off hoist, if so equipped.	Yes	▶	REPLACE damaged / worn parts.
		No	▶	REVERIFY symptom.

Fig. 179   Test CC: Front Wheel Sensor Diagnosis (Part 2 of 8). 1993–94 Crown Victoria, Grand Marquis & Town Car

TEST STEP		RESULT	▶	ACTION TO TAKE
CC8	DTCs 32, 36, 42, 56, 72 OR 76: CHECK RH FRONT SENSOR			
	• Turn ignition switch OFF. • Disconnect 55-pin connector from ABS module.	Yes	▶	GO to CC10.
		No	▶	GO to CC9.

ABS MODULE

55 PIN CONNECTOR

• Connect EEC-IV Breakout Box 014-00322 with Anti-Lock Test Adapter T90P-50-ALA or equivalent to the 55-Pin connector on wiring harness.

ANTI-LOCK TEST ADAPTER T90P-50-ALA

55 PIN CONNECTOR

EEC-IV BREAKOUT BOX 014-00322

TEST STEP		RESULT	▶	ACTION TO TAKE
	• Measure resistance between Pins 29 and 47. • Is resistance between 800 and 1400 ohms?			
CC9	CHECK RH FRONT SENSOR RESISTANCE			
	• Disconnect RH front sensor plug. • Measure resistance of sensor at sensor plug. • Is resistance between 800 and 1400 ohms?	Yes	▶	SERVICE or REPLACE cable harness Circuit 514 or 516.
		No	▶	REPLACE RH front sensor.

RH FRONT SENSOR

Fig. 179   Test CC: Front Wheel Sensor Diagnosis (Part 3 of 8). 1993–94 Continental, Crown Victoria, Grand Marquis & Town Car

TEST STEP		RESULT	▶	ACTION TO TAKE
CC10	CHECK RH FRONT SENSOR VOLTAGE			
	• Turn air suspension switch OFF, if so equipped. • Place vehicle on hoist and raise wheels clear of ground. • Set multi-meter to voltage range (2 volts AC) • Measure voltage between Pins 29 and 47 at breakout box while spinning RH front wheel at approximately 1 revolution per second.	Between 0.10 and 1.40 volts AC	▶	GO to CC11.
		Less than 0.10 or more than 1.40 volts AC	▶	CHECK sensor mounting, air gap or toothed wheel mounting. CORRECT as required.
CC11	CHECK RH FRONT SENSOR CIRCUIT CONTINUITY TO GROUND			
	• Check continuity between breakout box Pins 29 and 60. • Is continuity present?	No	▶	GO to CC13.
		Yes	▶	GO to CC12.
CC12	CHECK RH FRONT SENSOR TO GROUND			
	• Disconnect RH front wheel sensor plug. • Check for continuity between each sensor plug pin (sensor side) and vehicle ground. • Is continuity present?	Yes	▶	REPLACE RH front sensor.
		No	▶	SERVICE or REPLACE cable harness Circuit 514 or 516. RECONNECT sensor plug.

RH FRONT SENSOR

TEST STEP		RESULT	▶	ACTION TO TAKE
CC13	CHECK ABS MODULE TO GROUND WIRE			
	• Check continuity between breakout box Pin 60 and body ground. • Is continuity present?	Yes	▶	GO to CC14.
		No	▶	SERVICE or REPLACE cable harness Circuit 530.
CC14	CHECK RH FRONT WHEEL BEARING			
	• Check front wheel bearing and play. • Inspect toothed sensor ring visually for damaged teeth. • Were any parts loose or damaged? NOTE: Turn air suspension switch ON when vehicle is off hoist, if so equipped.	Yes	▶	REPLACE damaged parts.
		No	▶	REVERIFY symptom.

Fig. 179   Test CC: Front Wheel Sensor Diagnosis (Part 4 of 8). 1993–94 Continental

TEST STEP	RESULT	► ACTION TO TAKE
CC10 CHECK RH FRONT SENSOR VOLTAGE • Turn ignition switch OFF. • Turn air suspension switch OFF, if so equipped. • Place vehicle on hoist and raise wheels clear of ground. • Set multi-meter to voltage range (2 volts AC) • Measure voltage between Pins 29 and 47 at breakout box while spinning RH front wheel at approximately 1 revolution per second.	Between 0.10 and 1.40 volts AC Less than 0.10 or more than 1.40 volts AC	► GO to CC11. ► CHECK sensor mounting, air gap or toothed wheel mounting. CORRECT as required.
CC11 CHECK RH FRONT SENSOR CIRCUIT CONTINUITY TO GROUND • Check continuity between breakout box Pins 29 and 60. • Is continuity present?	No Yes	► GO to CC13. ► GO to CC12.
CC12 CHECK RH FRONT SENSOR TO GROUND • Disconnect RH front wheel sensor plug. • Check for continuity between each sensor plug pin (sensor side) and vehicle ground. • Is continuity present?	Yes No	► REPLACE RH front sensor. ► SERVICE or REPLACE cable harness Circuit 514 or 516. RECONNECT sensor plug.
CC13 CHECK ABS MODULE TO GROUND WIRE • Check continuity between breakout box Pin 60 and body ground. • Is continuity present?	Yes No Continuity	► GO to CC14. ► SERVICE or REPLACE cable harness Circuit 57.
CC14 CHECK RH FRONT WHEEL BEARING • Check front wheel bearing end play. • Inspect toothed sensor ring visually for damaged teeth. • Were any parts loose or damaged? NOTE: Turn air suspension switch ON when vehicle is off hoist, if so equipped.	Yes No	► REPLACE damaged / worn parts. ► REVERIFY symptom.

Fig. 179   Test CC: Front Wheel Sensor Diagnosis (Part 4 of 8). 1993–94 Crown Victoria, Grand Marquis & Town Car

TEST STEP	RESULT	► ACTION TO TAKE
CC15 DTCs 33, 37, 43, 57, 73 OR 77: CHECK RH REAR SENSOR • Turn ignition switch OFF. • Disconnect 55-pin connector from ABS module.	Yes No	► GO to CC17. ► GO to CC16.

• Connect EEC-IV Breakout Box 014-00322 with Anti-Lock Test Adapter T90P-50-ALA or equivalent to the 55-pin connector on wiring harness.

• Measure resistance between Pins 27 and 45. • Is resistance between 800 and 1400 ohms?		
CC16 CHECK RH REAR SENSOR RESISTANCE • Disconnect RH rear sensor plug. • Measure resistance of sensor at sensor plug. • Is resistance between 800 and 1400 ohms?	Yes No	► SERVICE or REPLACE cable harness Circuit 523 or 524. ► REPLACE RH rear sensor.

Fig. 179   Test CC: Front Wheel Sensor Diagnosis (Part 5 of 8). 1993–94 Continental, Crown Victoria, Grand Marquis & Town Car

TEST STEP	RESULT	► ACTION TO TAKE
CC17 CHECK RH REAR SENSOR VOLTAGE • Turn air suspension switch OFF, if so equipped. • Place vehicle on hoist and raise wheels clear of ground. • Set multi-meter to voltage range (2 volts AC). • Measure voltage between Pins 27 and 45 at Breakout Box while spinning RH rear wheel at approximately 1 revolution per second.	Between 0.10 and 1.40 volts AC Less than 0.10 or more than 1.40 volts AC	► GO to CC18. ► CHECK sensor mounting, air gap or toothed wheel mounting. CORRECT as required.
CC18 CHECK RH REAR SENSOR CIRCUIT CONTINUITY TO GROUND • Check continuity between breakout box Pins 27 and 60. • Is continuity present?	No Yes	► GO to CC20. ► GO to CC19.
CC19 CHECK RH REAR SENSOR TO GROUND • Disconnect RH rear wheel sensor plug. • Check for continuity between each sensor plug pin (sensor side) and vehicle ground. • Is continuity present?	Yes No	► REPLACE RH rear sensor. ► SERVICE or REPLACE cable harness Circuit 523 or 524. RECONNECT sensor plug.
CC20 CHECK ABS MODULE TO GROUND WIRE • Check continuity between breakout box Pin 60 and body ground. • Is continuity present?	Yes No	► GO to CC21. ► SERVICE or REPLACE cable harness Circuit 530.
CC21 CHECK FOR EXCESSIVE AXLE VIBRATION • Check vehicle on hoist for excessive play. • Check rear axle bearings for excessive play. • Inspect toothed sensor ring for damaged teeth. • Were any parts loose or damaged? NOTE: Turn air suspension switch ON when vehicle is off hoist, if so equipped.	Yes No	► SERVICE or REPLACE damaged parts. ► REVERIFY symptom.

FM402930031006AX

Fig. 179   Test CC: Front Wheel Sensor Diagnosis (Part 6 of 8). 1993–94 Continental

TEST STEP	RESULT	► ACTION TO TAKE
CC17 CHECK RH REAR SENSOR VOLTAGE • Turn ignition switch OFF. • Turn air suspension switch OFF, if so equipped. • Place vehicle on hoist and raise wheels clear of ground. • Set multi-meter to voltage range (2 volts AC). • Measure voltage between Pins 27 and 45 at breakout box while spinning RH rear wheel at approximately 1 revolution per second.	Between 0.10 and 1.40 volts AC Less than 0.10 or more than 1.40 volts AC	► GO to CC18. ► CHECK sensor mounting, air gap or toothed wheel mounting. CORRECT as required.
CC18 CHECK RH REAR SENSOR CIRCUIT CONTINUITY TO GROUND • Check continuity between breakout box Pins 27 and 60. • Is continuity present?	No Yes	► GO to CC20. ► GO to CC19.
CC19 CHECK RH REAR SENSOR TO GROUND • Disconnect RH rear wheel sensor plug. • Check for continuity between each sensor plug pin (sensor side) and vehicle ground. • Is continuity present?	Yes No	► REPLACE RH rear sensor. ► SERVICE or REPLACE cable harness Circuit 523 or 524. RECONNECT sensor plug.
CC20 CHECK ABS MODULE TO GROUND WIRE • Check continuity between breakout box Pin 60 and body ground. • Is continuity present?	Yes No	► GO to CC21. ► SERVICE or REPLACE cable harness Circuit 57.
CC21 CHECK FOR EXCESSIVE AXLE VIBRATION • Check differential housing for excessive play. • Check rear axle bearings for excessive play. • Inspect toothed sensor ring for damaged teeth. • Were any parts loose or damaged? NOTE: Turn air suspension switch ON when vehicle is off hoist, if so equipped.	Yes No	► SERVICE or REPLACE damaged parts. ► REVERIFY symptom.

FM402930031006BX

Fig. 179   Test CC: Front Wheel Sensor Diagnosis (Part 6 of 8). 1993–94 Crown Victoria, Grand Marquis & Town Car

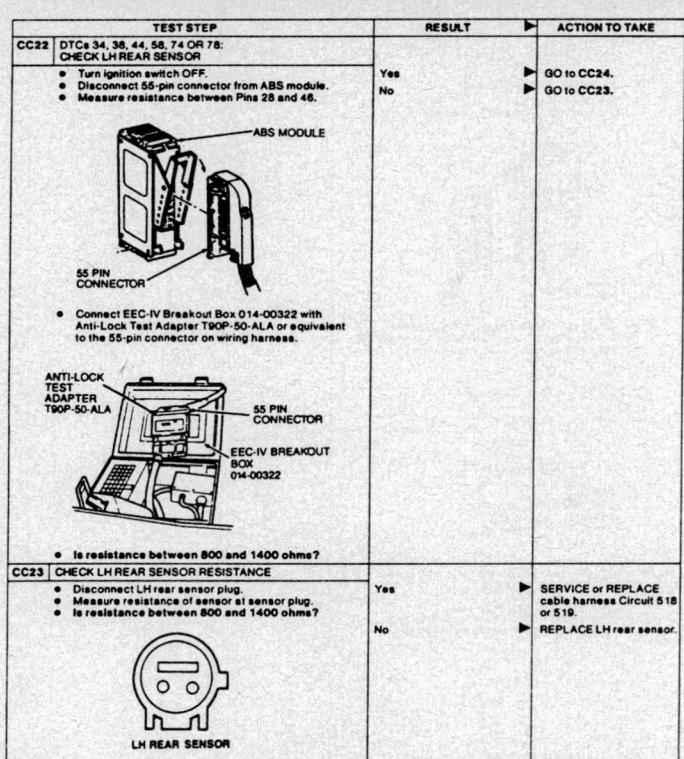

TEST STEP	RESULT	▶	ACTION TO TAKE
CC22 DTCs 34, 38, 44, 58, 74 OR 78: CHECK LH REAR SENSOR • Turn ignition switch OFF. • Disconnect 55-pin connector from ABS module. • Measure resistance between Pins 28 and 46.	Yes No	▶ ▶	GO to CC24. GO to CC23.
• Connect EEC-IV Breakout Box 014-00322 with Anti-Lock Test Adapter T90P-50-ALA or equivalent to the 55-pin connector on wiring harness. • Is resistance between 800 and 1400 ohms?			
CC23 CHECK LH REAR SENSOR RESISTANCE • Disconnect LH rear sensor plug. • Measure resistance of sensor at sensor plug. • Is resistance between 800 and 1400 ohms?	Yes No	▶ ▶	SERVICE or REPLACE cable harness Circuit 518 or 519. REPLACE LH rear sensor.

FM4029300310070X

Fig. 179 Test CC: Front Wheel Sensor Diagnosis (Part 7 of 8). 1993–94 Continental, Crown Victoria, Grand Marquis & Town Car

TEST STEP	RESULT	▶	ACTION TO TAKE
CC24 CHECK LH REAR SENSOR VOLTAGE • Turn air suspension switch OFF, if so equipped. • Place vehicle on hoist and raise wheels clear of ground. • Set multi-meter to voltage range (2 volts AC) • Measure voltage between Pins 28 and 46 at breakout box while spinning LH rear wheel at approximately 1 revolution per second.	Between 0.10 and 1.40 volts AC Less than 0.10 or more than 1.40 volts AC	▶ ▶	GO to CC25. CHECK sensor mounting, air gap or toothed wheel mounting. CORRECT as required.
CC25 CHECK LH REAR SENSOR CIRCUIT CONTINUITY TO GROUND • Check continuity between breakout box Pins 28 and 60. • Is continuity present?	No Yes	▶ ▶	GO to CC27. GO to CC26.
CC26 CHECK LH REAR SENSOR TO GROUND • Disconnect LH rear wheel sensor plug. • Check for continuity between each sensor plug pin (sensor side) and vehicle ground.	Yes No	▶ ▶	REPLACE LH rear sensor. SERVICE or REPLACE cable harness Circuit 518 or 519. RECONNECT sensor plug.
CC27 CHECK ABS MODULE TO GROUND WIRE • Check continuity between breakout box Pin 60 and body ground. • Is continuity present?	Yes No	▶ ▶	GO to CC28. SERVICE or REPLACE cable harness Circuit 530.
CC28 CHECK FOR EXCESSIVE AXLE VIBRATION • Check differential housing for excessive play. • Check rear axle bearings for excessive play. • Inspect toothed sensor ring for damaged teeth. • Were any parts loose or damaged? NOTE: Turn air suspension switch ON when vehicle is off hoist, if so equipped.	Yes No	▶ ▶	SERVICE or REPLACE damaged parts. REVERIFY symptom.

FM402930031008AX

Fig. 179 Test CC: Front Wheel Sensor Diagnosis (Part 8 of 8). 1993–94 Continental

TEST STEP	RESULT	▶	ACTION TO TAKE
CC24 CHECK LH REAR SENSOR VOLTAGE • Turn ignition switch OFF. • Turn air suspension switch OFF, if so equipped. • Place vehicle on hoist and raise wheels clear of ground. • Set multi-meter to voltage range (2 volts AC) • Measure voltage between Pins 28 and 46 at breakout box while spinning LH rear wheel at approximately 1 revolution per second.	Between 0.10 and 1.40 volts AC Less than 0.10 or more than 1.40 volts AC	▶ ▶	GO to CC25. CHECK sensor mounting, air gap or toothed wheel mounting. CORRECT as required.
CC25 CHECK LH REAR SENSOR CIRCUIT CONTINUITY TO GROUND • Check continuity between breakout box Pins 28 and 60. • Is continuity present?	No Yes	▶ ▶	GO to CC27. GO to CC26.
CC26 CHECK LH REAR SENSOR TO GROUND • Disconnect LH rear wheel sensor plug. • Check for continuity between each sensor plug pin (sensor side) and vehicle ground.	Yes No	▶ ▶	REPLACE LH rear sensor. SERVICE or REPLACE cable harness Circuit 518 or 519. RECONNECT sensor plug.
CC27 CHECK ELECTRONIC CONTROLLER TO GROUND WIRE • Check continuity between breakout box Pin 60 and body ground. • Is continuity present?	Yes No	▶ ▶	GO to CC28. SERVICE or REPLACE cable harness Circuit 57.
CC28 CHECK FOR EXCESSIVE AXLE VIBRATION • Check differential housing for excessive play. • Check rear axle bearings for excessive play. • Inspect toothed sensor ring for damaged teeth. • Were any parts loose or damaged? NOTE: Turn air suspension switch ON when vehicle is off hoist, if so equipped.	Yes No	▶ ▶	SERVICE or REPLACE damaged parts. REVERIFY symptom.

FM402930031008BX

Fig. 179 Test CC: Front Wheel Sensor Diagnosis (Part 8 of 8). 1993–94 Crown Victoria, Grand Marquis & Town Car

TEST STEP	RESULT	▶	ACTION TO TAKE
CC1 DTC's 31, 35, 41, 55, 71 OR 75: CHECK LH FRONT SENSOR • Turn ignition switch OFF. • Disconnect 55-pin connector from ABS module.	Yes No	▶ ▶	GO to CC3. GO to CC2.
• Connect EEC-IV Breakout Box 014-00322 with Anti-Lock Test Adapter T90P-50-ALA or equivalent to the 55-pin connector on wiring harness. • Measure resistance between Pins 30 and 48. • Is resistance between 800 and 1400 ohms?			
CC2 CHECK LH FRONT SENSOR RESISTANCE • Disconnect LH front wheel sensor plug. • Measure resistance of sensor at sensor plug. • Is resistance between 800 and 1400 ohms?	Yes No	▶ ▶	SERVICE or REPLACE cable harness Circuit 521 or 522. REPLACE LH front sensor.

Fig. 180 Test CC: Wheel Sensor Diagnosis (Part 1 of 8). 1993–94 Sable & Taurus

TEST STEP	RESULT	▶	ACTION TO TAKE
CC3 CHECK LH FRONT SENSOR VOLTAGE • Turn ignition switch OFF. • Place vehicle on hoist and raise wheels clear of ground. • Set multi-meter to voltage range (2 volts AC). • Measure voltage between Pins 30 and 48 at breakout box while spinning LH front wheel at approximately 1 revolution per second.	Between 0.10 and 1.40 volts AC Less than 0.10 or more than 1.40 volts AC	▶ ▶	GO to **CC4**. CHECK sensor mounting, air gap or toothed wheel mounting. CORRECT as required.
CC4 CHECK LH FRONT SENSOR CIRCUIT CONTINUITY TO GROUND • Check continuity between breakout box Pins 30 and 60. • **Is continuity present?**	No Yes	▶ ▶	GO to **CC6**. GO to **CC5**.
CC5 CHECK LH FRONT SENSOR TO GROUND • Disconnect LH front wheel sensor plug. • Check for continuity between each sensor plug pin (sensor side) and vehicle ground. • **Is continuity present?**	Yes No	▶ ▶	REPLACE LH front sensor. SERVICE or REPLACE cable harness Circuit 521 or 522. RECONNECT sensor plug.
CC6 CHECK ABS MODULE TO GROUND WIRE • Check continuity between breakout box Pin 60 and body ground. • **Was continuity present?**	Yes No	▶ ▶	GO to **CC7**. SERVICE or REPLACE cable harness Circuit 530 (Taurus/Sable). Circuit 57 or 530 (Taurus SHO).
CC7 CHECK LH FRONT WHEEL BEARING • Check front wheel bearing end play. • Inspect toothed sensor ring visually for damaged teeth. • **Were loose or damaged parts found?**	Yes No	▶ ▶	REPLACE damaged parts. REVERIFY symptom.

LH FRONT SENSOR

Fig. 180   Test CC: Wheel Sensor Diagnosis (Part 2 of 8). 1993–94 Sable & Taurus

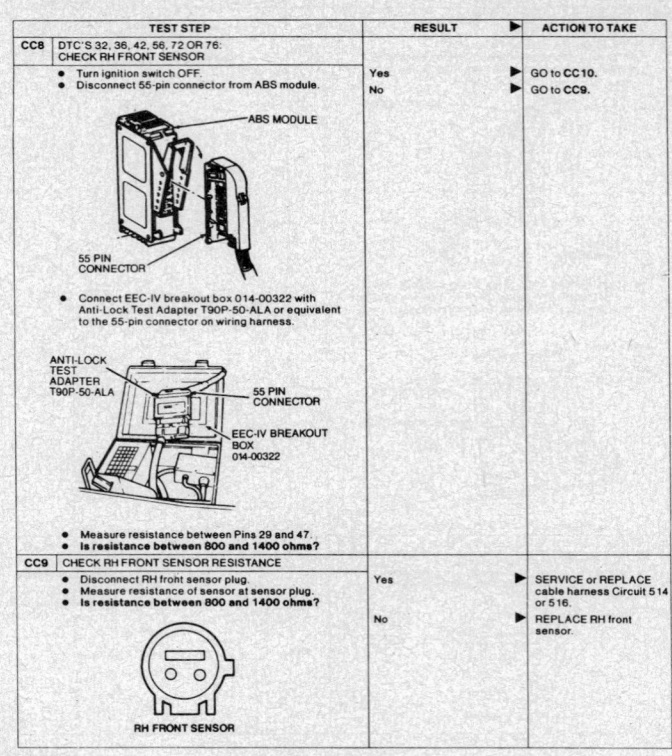

TEST STEP	RESULT	▶	ACTION TO TAKE
CC8 DTC'S 32, 36, 42, 56, 72 OR 76: CHECK RH FRONT SENSOR • Turn ignition switch OFF. • Disconnect 55-pin connector from ABS module.	Yes No	▶ ▶	GO to **CC10**. GO to **CC9**.

• Connect EEC-IV breakout box 014-00322 with Anti-Lock Test Adapter T90P-50-ALA or equivalent to the 55-pin connector on wiring harness.

• Measure resistance between Pins 29 and 47. • **Is resistance between 800 and 1400 ohms?**			
CC9 CHECK RH FRONT SENSOR RESISTANCE • Disconnect RH front sensor plug. • Measure resistance of sensor at sensor plug. • **Is resistance between 800 and 1400 ohms?**	Yes No	▶ ▶	SERVICE or REPLACE cable harness Circuit 514 or 516. REPLACE RH front sensor.

RH FRONT SENSOR

Fig. 180   Test CC: Wheel Sensor Diagnosis (Part 3 of 8). 1993–94 Sable & Taurus

TEST STEP	RESULT	▶	ACTION TO TAKE
CC10 CHECK RH FRONT SENSOR VOLTAGE • Turn ignition switch OFF. • Place vehicle on hoist and raise wheels clear of ground. • Set multi-meter to voltage range (2 volts AC). • Measure voltage between Pins 29 and 47 at breakout box while spinning RH front wheel at approximately 1 revolution per second.	Between 0.10 and 1.40 volts AC Less than 0.10 or more than 1.40 volts AC	▶ ▶	GO to **CC11**. CHECK sensor mounting, air gap or toothed wheel mounting. CORRECT as required.
CC11 CHECK RH FRONT SENSOR CIRCUIT CONTINUITY TO GROUND • Check continuity between breakout box Pins 29 and 60. • **Is continuity present?**	No Yes	▶ ▶	GO to **CC13**. GO to **CC12**.
CC12 CHECK RH FRONT SENSOR TO GROUND • Disconnect RH front wheel sensor plug. • Check for continuity between each sensor plug pin (sensor side) and vehicle ground. • **Is continuity present?**	Yes No	▶ ▶	REPLACE RH front sensor. SERVICE or REPLACE cable harness Circuit 514 or 516. RECONNECT sensor plug.
CC13 CHECK ABS MODULE TO GROUND WIRE • Check continuity between breakout box Pin 60 and body ground. • **Is continuity present?**	Yes No	▶ ▶	GO to **CC14**. SERVICE or REPLACE cable harness Circuit 530 (Taurus/Sable). Circuit 57 or 530 (Taurus SHO).
CC14 CHECK RH FRONT WHEEL BEARING • Check front wheel bearing end play. • Inspect toothed sensor ring visually for damaged teeth. • **Were any parts loose or damaged?**	Yes No	▶ ▶	REPLACE damaged parts. REVERIFY symptom.

RH FRONT SENSOR

Fig. 180   Test CC: Wheel Sensor Diagnosis (Part 4 of 8). 1993–94 Sable & Taurus

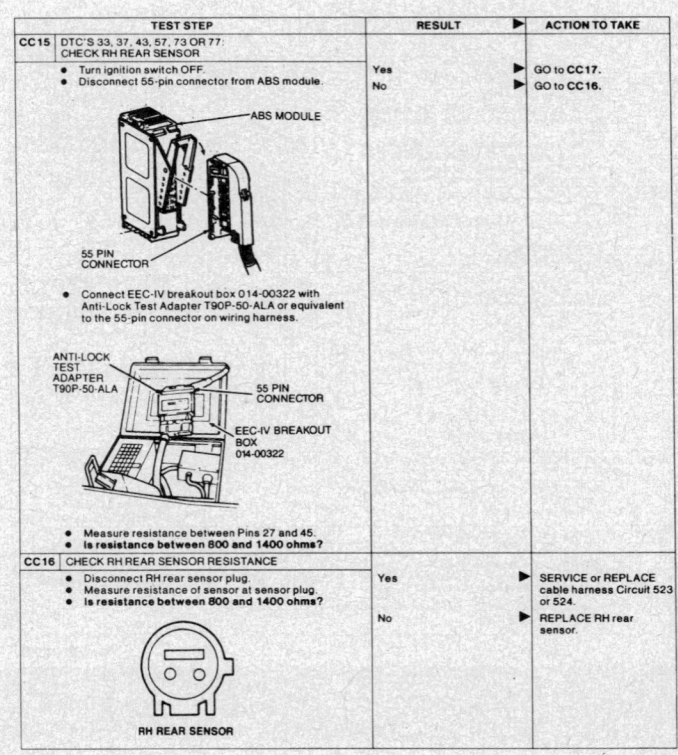

TEST STEP	RESULT	▶	ACTION TO TAKE
CC15 DTC'S 33, 37, 43, 57, 73 OR 77: CHECK RH REAR SENSOR • Turn ignition switch OFF. • Disconnect 55-pin connector from ABS module.	Yes No	▶ ▶	GO to **CC17**. GO to **CC16**.

• Connect EEC-IV breakout box 014-00322 with Anti-Lock Test Adapter T90P-50-ALA or equivalent to the 55-pin connector on wiring harness.

• Measure resistance between Pins 27 and 45. • **Is resistance between 800 and 1400 ohms?**			
CC16 CHECK RH REAR SENSOR RESISTANCE • Disconnect RH rear sensor plug. • Measure resistance of sensor at sensor plug. • **Is resistance between 800 and 1400 ohms?**	Yes No	▶ ▶	SERVICE or REPLACE cable harness Circuit 523 or 524. REPLACE RH rear sensor.

RH REAR SENSOR

Fig. 180   Test CC: Wheel Sensor Diagnosis (Part 5 of 8). 1993–94 Sable & Taurus

TEST STEP	RESULT	▶	ACTION TO TAKE
CC17 CHECK RH REAR SENSOR VOLTAGE • Turn ignition switch OFF. • Place vehicle on hoist and raise wheels clear of ground. • Set multi-meter to voltage range (2 volts AC). • Measure voltage between Pins 27 and 45 at breakout box while spinning RH rear wheel at approximately 1 revolution per second.	Between 0.10 and 1.40 volts AC Less than 0.10 or more than 1.40 volts AC	▶ ▶	GO to CC18. CHECK sensor mounting, air gap or toothed wheel mounting. CORRECT as required.
CC18 CHECK RH REAR SENSOR CIRCUIT CONTINUITY TO GROUND • Check continuity between breakout box Pins 27 and 60. • **Is continuity present?**	No Yes	▶ ▶	GO to CC20. GO to CC19.
CC19 CHECK RH REAR SENSOR TO GROUND • Disconnect RH rear wheel sensor plug. • Check for continuity between each sensor plug pin (sensor side) and vehicle ground. • **Is continuity present?**	Yes No	▶ ▶	REPLACE RH rear sensor. SERVICE or REPLACE cable harness Circuit 523 or 524. RECONNECT sensor plug.
CC20 CHECK ABS MODULE TO GROUND WIRE • Check continuity between breakout box Pin 60 and body ground. • **Is continuity present?**	Yes No	▶ ▶	GO to CC21. SERVICE or REPLACE cable harness Circuit 530 (Taurus/Sable). Circuit 57 or 530 (Taurus SHO).
CC21 CHECK FOR EXCESSIVE AXLE VIBRATION • Check differential housing for excessive play. • Check rear axle bearings for excessive play. • Inspect toothed sensor ring for damaged teeth. • **Were any parts loose or damaged?**	Yes No	▶ ▶	SERVICE or REPLACE damaged parts. REVERIFY symptom.

RH REAR SENSOR

Fig. 180   Test CC: Wheel Sensor Diagnosis (Part 6 of 8). 1993–94 Sable & Taurus

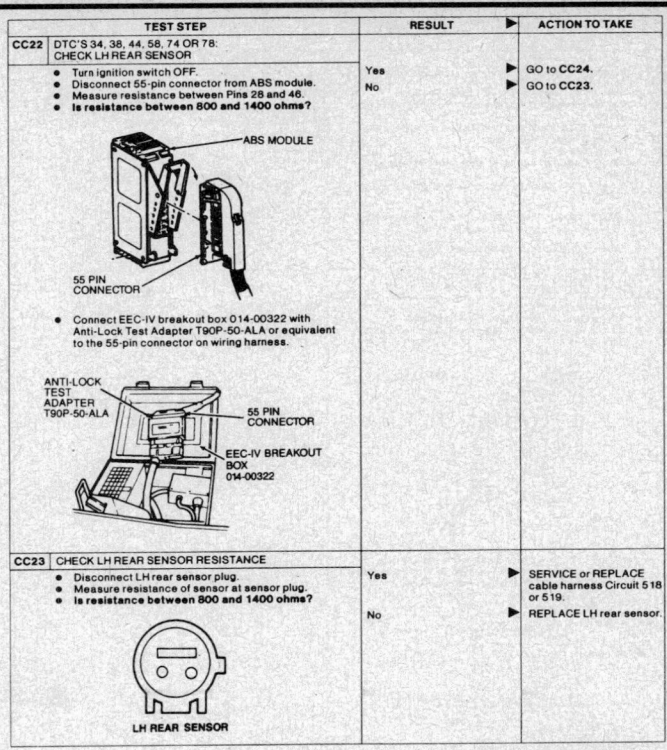

TEST STEP	RESULT	▶	ACTION TO TAKE
CC22 DTC'S 34, 38, 44, 58, 74 OR 78: CHECK LH REAR SENSOR • Turn ignition switch OFF. • Disconnect 55-pin connector from ABS module. • Measure resistance between Pins 28 and 46. • **Is resistance between 800 and 1400 ohms?**	Yes No	▶ ▶	GO to CC24. GO to CC23.
• Connect EEC-IV breakout box 014-00322 with Anti-Lock Test Adapter T90P-50-ALA or equivalent to the 55-pin connector on wiring harness.			
CC23 CHECK LH REAR SENSOR RESISTANCE • Disconnect LH rear sensor plug. • Measure resistance of sensor at sensor plug. • **Is resistance between 800 and 1400 ohms?**	Yes No	▶ ▶	SERVICE or REPLACE cable harness Circuit 518 or 519. REPLACE LH rear sensor.

LH REAR SENSOR

FM4029300451070X

Fig. 180   Test CC: Wheel Sensor Diagnosis (Part 7 of 8). 1993–94 Sable & Taurus

TEST STEP	RESULT	▶	ACTION TO TAKE
CC24 CHECK LH REAR SENSOR VOLTAGE • Turn ignition switch OFF. • Place vehicle on hoist and raise wheels clear of ground. • Set multi-meter to voltage range (2 volts AC). • Measure voltage between Pins 28 and 46 at breakout box while spinning LH rear wheel at approximately 1 revolution per second.	Between 0.10 and 1.40 volts AC Less than 0.10 or more than 1.40 volts AC	▶ ▶	GO to CC25. CHECK sensor mounting, air gap or toothed wheel mounting. CORRECT as required.
CC25 CHECK LH REAR SENSOR CIRCUIT CONTINUITY TO GROUND • Check continuity between breakout box Pins 28 and 60. • **Is continuity present?**	No Yes	▶ ▶	GO to CC27. GO to CC26.
CC26 CHECK LH REAR SENSOR TO GROUND • Disconnect LH rear wheel sensor plug. • Check for continuity between each sensor plug pin (sensor side) and vehicle ground. • **Is continuity present?**	Yes No	▶ ▶	REPLACE LH rear sensor. SERVICE or REPLACE cable harness Circuit 518 or 519. RECONNECT sensor plug.
CC27 CHECK ABS MODULE TO GROUND WIRE • Check continuity between breakout box Pin 60 and body ground. • **Is continuity present?**	Yes No	▶ ▶	GO to CC28. SERVICE or REPLACE cable harness Circuit 530 (Taurus/Sable). Circuit 57 or 530 (Taurus SHO).
CC28 CHECK FOR EXCESSIVE AXLE VIBRATION • Check differential housing for excessive play. • Check rear axle bearings for excessive play. • Inspect toothed sensor ring for damaged teeth. • **Were any parts loose or damaged?**	Yes No	▶ ▶	SERVICE or REPLACE damaged parts. REVERIFY symptom.

LH REAR SENSOR

FM4029300451080X

Fig. 180   Test CC: Wheel Sensor Diagnosis (Part 8 of 8). 1993–94 Sable & Taurus

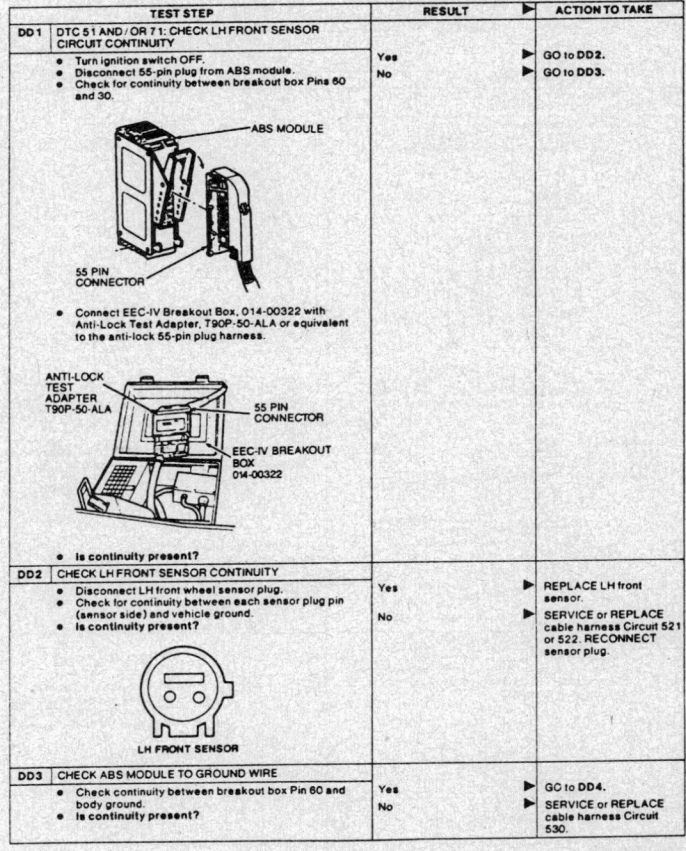

TEST STEP	RESULT	▶	ACTION TO TAKE
DD1 DTC 51 AND/OR 71: CHECK LH FRONT SENSOR CIRCUIT CONTINUITY • Turn ignition switch OFF. • Disconnect 55-pin plug from ABS module. • Check for continuity between breakout box Pins 60 and 30.	Yes No	▶ ▶	GO to DD2. GO to DD3.
• Connect EEC-IV Breakout Box, 014-00322 with Anti-Lock Test Adapter, T90P-50-ALA or equivalent to the anti-lock 55-pin plug harness. • **Is continuity present?**			
DD2 CHECK LH FRONT SENSOR CONTINUITY • Disconnect LH front wheel sensor plug. • Check for continuity between each sensor plug pin (sensor side) and vehicle ground. • **Is continuity present?**	Yes No	▶ ▶	REPLACE LH front sensor. SERVICE or REPLACE cable harness Circuit 521 or 522. RECONNECT sensor plug.
DD3 CHECK ABS MODULE TO GROUND WIRE • Check continuity between breakout box Pin 60 and body ground. • **Is continuity present?**	Yes No	▶ ▶	GO to DD4. SERVICE or REPLACE cable harness Circuit 530.

LH FRONT SENSOR

FM4029300311010X

Fig. 181   Test DD: Rear Wheel Sensor Diagnosis (Part 1 of 6). 1993 Continental

TEST STEP	RESULT	▶	ACTION TO TAKE
DD4 CHECK ANTI-LOCK OPERATION LH FRONT WHEEL • Turn air suspension OFF, if so equipped. • Lift vehicle and rotate wheels to ensure they turn freely. • Apply moderate brake pedal effort and check that LH front wheel will not turn. • Jump Pins 34 and 19. • Short Pins 2, 20 and 60 to each other at breakout box. • Check that LH front wheel turns freely with ignition switch ON. CAUTION: Do not leave ignition on for more than 1 minute, or valve damage may result. • Turn air suspension ON when vehicle is off hoist, if equipped.	Wheel turns freely Wheel does not turn freely or pedal drops	▶ ▶	REVERIFY symptom. REPLACE solenoid valve body.
DD5 DTC 52 AND / OR 72: CHECK RH FRONT SENSOR CIRCUIT CONTINUITY • Turn ignition switch OFF. • Disconnect 55-pin plug from ABS module. • Check for continuity between breakout box Pins 60 and 29.	Yes No	▶ ▶	GO to DD6. GO to DD7.

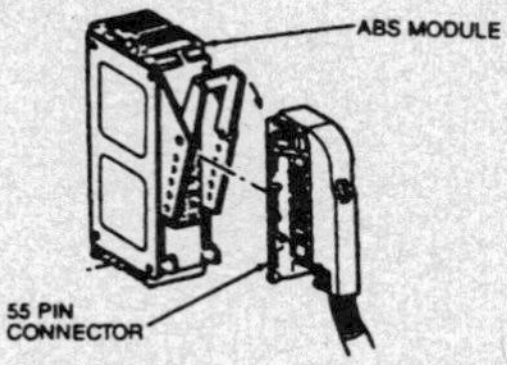

• Connect EEC-IV Breakout Box 014-00322 with Anti-Lock Test Adapter T90P-50-ALA or equivalent to the anti-lock 55-pin plug wiring harness.

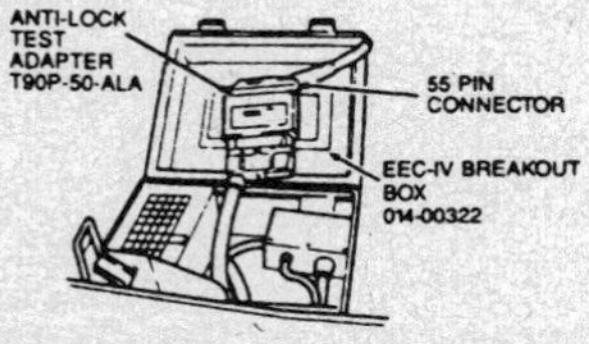

• Is continuity present?

FM4029300311020X

Fig. 181   Test DD: Rear Wheel Sensor Diagnosis (Part 2 of 6). 1993 Continental

TEST STEP	RESULT	▶	ACTION TO TAKE
DD9 DTC 53 AND / OR 73: CHECK RH REAR SENSOR CIRCUIT CONTINUITY • Turn ignition switch OFF. • Disconnect 55-pin plug from ABS module. • Check for continuity between breakout box Pins 60 and 27.	Yes No	▶ ▶	GO to DD10. GO to DD11.

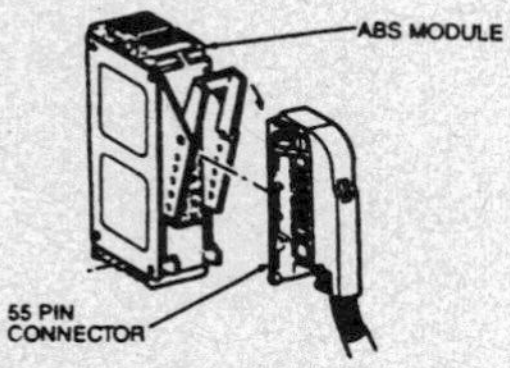

• Connect EEC-IV Breakout Box 014-00322 with Anti-Lock Test Adapter T90P-50-ALA or equivalent to the anti-lock 55-pin plug wiring harness.

• Is continuity present?

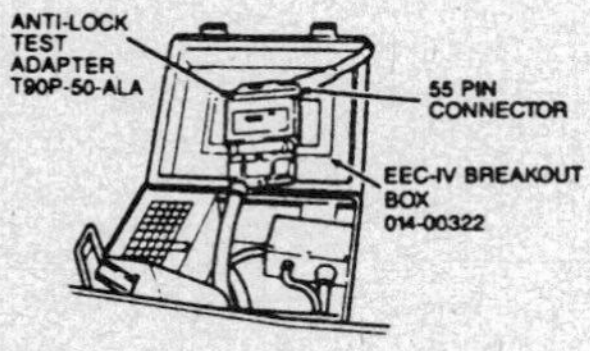

TEST STEP	RESULT	▶	ACTION TO TAKE
DD10 CHECK RH REAR SENSOR CONTINUITY • Disconnect RH rear wheel sensor plug. • Check for continuity between each sensor plug pin (sensor side) and vehicle ground. • Is continuity present?	Yes No	▶ ▶	REPLACE RH rear sensor. SERVICE or REPLACE cable harness Circuit 523 or 524. RECONNECT sensor plug.

RH REAR SENSOR

FM4029300311040X

Fig. 181   Test DD: Rear Wheel Sensor Diagnosis (Part 4 of 6). 1993 Continental

TEST STEP	RESULT	▶	ACTION TO TAKE
DD6 CHECK RH FRONT SENSOR CONTINUITY • Disconnect RH front wheel sensor. • Check for continuity between each sensor plug pin (sensor side) and vehicle ground. • Is continuity present?	Yes No	▶ ▶	REPLACE RH front sensor. SERVICE or REPLACE cable harness Circuit 514 or 516. RECONNECT sensor plug.

RH FRONT SENSOR

TEST STEP	RESULT	▶	ACTION TO TAKE
DD7 CHECK ABS MODULE TO GROUND WIRE • Check continuity between breakout box Pin 60 and body ground. • Is continuity present?	Yes No	▶ ▶	GO to DD8. SERVICE or REPLACE cable harness Circuit 530.
DD8 CHECK ANTI-LOCK OPERATION RH FRONT WHEEL • Turn air suspension OFF, if so equipped. • Lift vehicle and rotate wheels to ensure they turn freely. • Apply moderate brake pedal effort and check that RH front wheel will not turn. • Jump Pins 34 and 19. • Short Pins 21, 38 and 60 to each other at breakout box. • Check that RH front wheel turns freely with ignition switch ON. • Turn air suspension ON when vehicle is off hoist, if so equipped.	Wheel turns freely Wheel does not turn freely or pedal drops	▶ ▶	REVERIFY symptom. REPLACE solenoid valve body.

FM4029300311030X

Fig. 181   Test DD: Rear Wheel Sensor Diagnosis (Part 3 of 6). 1993 Continental

TEST STEP	RESULT	▶	ACTION TO TAKE
DD11 CHECK ABS MODULE TO GROUND WIRE • Check continuity between breakout box Pin 60 and body ground. • Is continuity present?	Yes No	▶ ▶	GO to DD12. SERVICE or REPLACE cable harness Circuit 530.
DD12 CHECK ANTI-LOCK OPERATION RH REAR WHEEL • Turn air suspension OFF, if so equipped. • Lift vehicle and rotate wheels to ensure they turn freely. • Apply moderate brake pedal effort and check that RH rear wheel will not turn. • Jump Pins 34 and 19. • Short Pins 18, 55 and 60 to each other at breakout box. • Check that RH rear wheel turns freely with ignition switch ON. • Turn air suspension ON when vehicle is off hoist, if so equipped.	Wheel turns freely Wheel does not turn freely or pedal drops	▶ ▶	REVERIFY symptom. REPLACE solenoid valve body.
DD13 DTC 54 AND / OR 74: CHECK LH REAR SENSOR CIRCUIT CONTINUITY • Turn ignition switch OFF. • Disconnect 55-pin plug from ABS module. • Check for continuity between breakout box Pins 60 and 28.	Yes No	▶ ▶	GO to DD14. GO to DD15.

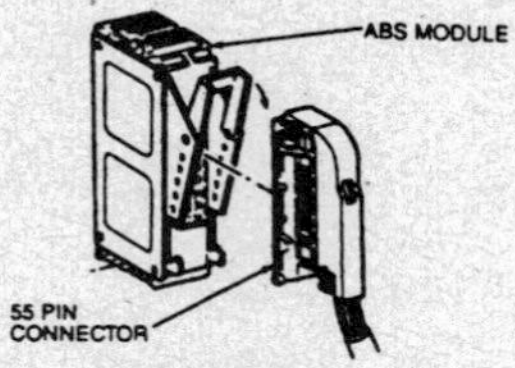

• Connect EEC-IV Breakout Box 014-00322 with Anti-Lock Test Adapter T90P-50-ALA or equivalent to the anti-lock 55-pin plug wiring harness.

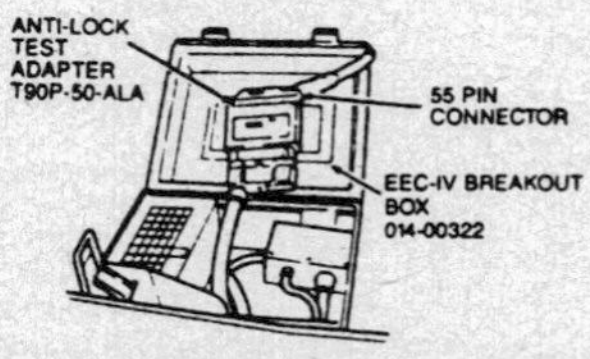

• Is continuity present?

FM4029300311050X

Fig. 181   Test DD: Rear Wheel Sensor Diagnosis (Part 5 of 6). 1993 Continental

TEST STEP	RESULT	►	ACTION TO TAKE
DD14 CHECK LH REAR SENSOR CONTINUITY • Disconnect LH rear wheel sensor plug. • Check for continuity between each sensor plug pin (sensor side) and vehicle ground. • Is continuity present?	Yes No	► ►	REPLACE LH rear sensor. SERVICE or REPLACE cable harness Circuit 518 or 519. RECONNECT sensor plug.
DD15 CHECK ABS MODULE TO GROUND WIRE • Check continuity between breakout box Pin 60 and body ground. • Is continuity present?	Yes No	► ►	GO to DD16. SERVICE or REPLACE cable harness Circuit 530.
DD16 CHECK ANTI-LOCK OPERATION LH REAR WHEEL • Turn air suspension OFF, if so equipped. • Lift vehicle and rotate wheels to ensure they turn freely. • Apply moderate brake pedal effort and check that LH rear wheel will not turn. • Jump Pins 34 and 19. • Short Pins 36, 54 and 60 to each other at breakout box. • Check that LH rear wheel turns freely with ignition switch ON. CAUTION: Do not leave ignition on for more than 1 minute, or valve damage may result. • Turn air suspension ON when vehicle is off hoist, if so equipped.	Wheel turns freely Wheel does not turn freely or pedal drops	► ►	REVERIFY symptom. REPLACE solenoid valve body.

FM4029300311060X

Fig. 181 Test DD: Rear Wheel Sensor Diagnosis (Part 6 of 6). 1993 Continental

TEST STEP	RESULT	►	ACTION TO TAKE
DD3 CHECK ELECTRONIC CONTROLLER TO GROUND WIRE • Check continuity between breakout box Pin 60 and body ground. • Is continuity present?	Yes No	► ►	GO to DD4. SERVICE or REPLACE cable harness Circuit 57.
DD4 CHECK ANTI-LOCK OPERATION LH FRONT WHEEL • Turn air suspension OFF, if so equipped. • Lift vehicle and rotate wheels to ensure they turn freely. • Apply moderate brake pedal effort and check that LH front wheel will not turn. • Jump Pins 34 and 19. • Short Pins 2, 20 and 60 to each other at breakout box. • Check that LH front wheel turns freely with ignition switch ON. CAUTION: Do not leave ignition on for more than 1 minute, or valve damage may result. • Turn air suspension ON when vehicle is off hoist, if equipped.	Wheel turns freely Wheel does not turn freely or pedal drops	► ►	REVERIFY symptom. REPLACE solenoid valve body.
DD5 DTC 52 AND / OR 72: CHECK RH FRONT SENSOR CIRCUIT CONTINUITY • Turn ignition switch OFF. • Disconnect 55-pin plug from ABS Module. • Check for continuity between breakout box Pins 60 and 29. • Connect EEC-IV breakout box 014-00322 with Anti-Lock Test Adapter T90P-50-ALA or equivalent to the anti-lock 55-pin plug wiring harness. • Is continuity present?	Yes No	► ►	GO to DD6. GO to DD7.

FM4029300452020X

Fig. 182 Test DD: Wheel Sensor Diagnosis (Part 2 of 6). 1993 Crown Victoria, Grand Marquis & Town Car

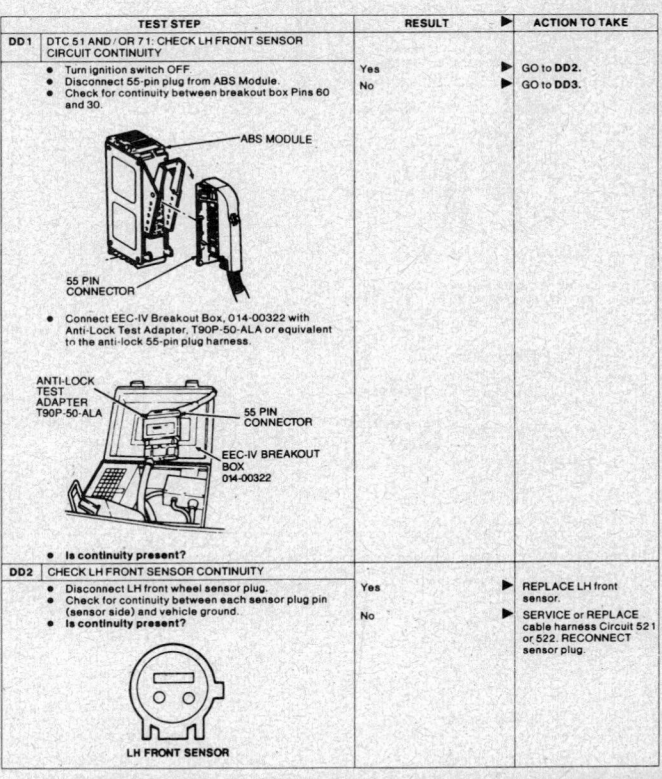

TEST STEP	RESULT	►	ACTION TO TAKE
DD1 DTC 51 AND / OR 71: CHECK LH FRONT SENSOR CIRCUIT CONTINUITY • Turn ignition switch OFF. • Disconnect 55-pin plug from ABS Module. • Check for continuity between breakout box Pins 60 and 30. • Connect EEC-IV Breakout Box, 014-00322 with Anti-Lock Test Adapter, T90P-50-ALA or equivalent to the anti-lock 55-pin plug harness. • Is continuity present?	Yes No	► ►	GO to DD2. GO to DD3.
DD2 CHECK LH FRONT SENSOR CONTINUITY • Disconnect LH front wheel sensor plug. • Check for continuity between each sensor plug pin (sensor side) and vehicle ground. • Is continuity present?	Yes No	► ►	REPLACE LH front sensor. SERVICE or REPLACE cable harness Circuit 521 or 522. RECONNECT sensor plug.

FM4029300452010X

Fig. 182   Test DD: Wheel Sensor Diagnosis (Part 1 of 6). 1993 Crown Victoria, Grand Marquis & Town Car

TEST STEP	RESULT	►	ACTION TO TAKE
DD6 CHECK RH FRONT SENSOR CONTINUITY • Disconnect RH front wheel sensor. • Check for continuity between each sensor plug pin (sensor side) and vehicle ground. • Is continuity present?	Yes No	► ►	REPLACE RH front sensor. SERVICE or REPLACE cable harness Circuit 514 or 516. RECONNECT sensor plug.
DD7 CHECK ELECTRONIC CONTROLLER TO GROUND WIRE • Check continuity between breakout box Pin 60 and body ground. • Is continuity present?	Yes No	► ►	GO to DD8. SERVICE or REPLACE cable harness Circuit 57.
DD8 CHECK ANTI-LOCK OPERATION RH FRONT WHEEL • Turn air suspension OFF, if so equipped. • Lift vehicle and rotate wheels to ensure they turn freely. • Apply moderate brake pedal effort and check that RH front wheel will not turn. • Jump Pins 34 and 19. • Short Pins 21, 38 and 60 to each other at breakout box. • Check that RH front wheel turns freely with ignition switch ON. • Turn air suspension ON when vehicle is off hoist, if so equipped.	Wheel turns freely Wheel does not turn freely or pedal drops	► ►	REVERIFY symptom. REPLACE solenoid valve body.

FM4029300452030X

Fig. 182   Test DD: Wheel Sensor Diagnosis (Part 3 of 6). 1993 Crown Victoria, Grand Marquis & Town Car

TEST STEP	RESULT	▶	ACTION TO TAKE
DD9 DTC 53 AND / OR 73: CHECK RH REAR SENSOR CIRCUIT CONTINUITY • Turn ignition switch OFF. • Disconnect 55-pin plug from ABS Module. • Check for continuity between breakout box Pins 60 and 27.	Yes No	▶ ▶	GO to DD10. GO to DD11.

ABS MODULE

55 PIN CONNECTOR

• Connect EEC-IV Breakout Box 014-00322 with Anti-Lock Test Adapter T90P-50-ALA or equivalent to the anti-lock 55-pin plug wiring harness.

ANTI-LOCK TEST ADAPTER T90P-50-ALA

55 PIN CONNECTOR

EEC-IV BREAKOUT BOX 014-00322

• **Is continuity present?**

DD10 CHECK RH REAR SENSOR CONTINUITY • Disconnect RH rear wheel sensor plug. • Check for continuity between each sensor plug pin (sensor side) and vehicle ground. • **Is continuity present?**	Yes No	▶ ▶	REPLACE RH rear sensor. SERVICE or REPLACE cable harness Circuit 523 or 524. RECONNECT sensor plug.

RH REAR SENSOR

FM4029300452040X

Fig. 182 Test DD: Wheel Sensor Diagnosis (Part 4 of 6). 1993 Crown Victoria, Grand Marquis & Town Car

TEST STEP	RESULT	▶	ACTION TO TAKE
DD14 CHECK LH REAR SENSOR CONTINUITY • Disconnect LH Rear wheel sensor plug. • Check for continuity between each sensor plug pin (sensor side) and vehicle ground. • **Is continuity present?**	Yes No	▶ ▶	REPLACE LH rear sensor. SERVICE or REPLACE cable harness Circuit 518 or 519. RECONNECT sensor plug.

LH REAR SENSOR

DD15 CHECK ELECTRONIC CONTROLLER TO GROUND WIRE • Check continuity between breakout box Pin 60 and body ground. • **Is continuity present?**	Yes No	▶ ▶	GO to DD16. SERVICE or REPLACE cable harness Circuit 57.
DD16 CHECK ANTI-LOCK OPERATION LH REAR WHEEL • Turn air suspension OFF, if so equipped. • Lift vehicle and rotate wheels to ensure they turn freely. • Apply moderate brake pedal effort and check that LH rear wheel will not turn. • Jump Pins 34 and 19. • Short Pins 36, 54 and 60 to each other at breakout box. • Check that LH rear wheel turns freely with ignition switch ON. **CAUTION: Do not leave ignition on for more than 1 minute or valve damage may result.** • Turn air suspension ON when vehicle if off hoist, if so equipped.	Wheel turns freely Wheel does not turn freely or pedal drops	▶ ▶	REVERIFY symptom. REPLACE solenoid valve body.

FM4029300452060X

Fig. 182 Test DD: Wheel Sensor Diagnosis (Part 6 of 6). 1993 Crown Victoria, Grand Marquis & Town Car

TEST STEP	RESULT	▶	ACTION TO TAKE
DD11 CHECK ELECTRONIC CONTROLLER TO GROUND WIRE • Check continuity between breakout box Pin 60 and body ground. • **Is continuity present?**	Yes No	▶ ▶	GO to DD12. SERVICE or REPLACE cable harness Circuit 57.
DD12 CHECK ANTI-LOCK OPERATION RH REAR WHEEL • Turn air suspension OFF, if so equipped. • Lift vehicle and rotate wheels to ensure they turn freely. • Apply moderate brake pedal effort and check that RH rear wheel will not turn. • Jump Pins 34 and 19. • Short Pins 18, 55 and 60 to each other at breakout box. • Check that RH rear wheel turns freely with ignition switch ON. • Turn air suspension ON when vehicle is off hoist, if so equipped.	Wheel turns freely Wheel does not turn freely or pedal drops	▶ ▶	REVERIFY symptom. REPLACE solenoid valve body.
DD13 DTC 54 AND / OR 74: CHECK LH REAR SENSOR CIRCUIT CONTINUITY • Turn ignition switch OFF. • Disconnect 55-pin plug from ABS Module. • Check for continuity between breakout box Pins 60 and 28.	Yes No	▶ ▶	GO to DD14. GO to DD15.

ABS MODULE

55 PIN CONNECTOR

• Connect EEC-IV Breakout Box 014-00322 with Anti-Lock Test Adapter T90P-50-ALA or equivalent to the anti-lock 55-pin plug wiring harness.

ANTI-LOCK TEST ADAPTER T90P-50-ALA

55 PIN CONNECTOR

EEC-IV BREAKOUT BOX 014-00322

• **Is continuity present?**

FM4029300452050X

Fig. 182 Test DD: Wheel Sensor Diagnosis (Part 5 of 6). 1993 Crown Victoria, Grand Marquis & Town Car

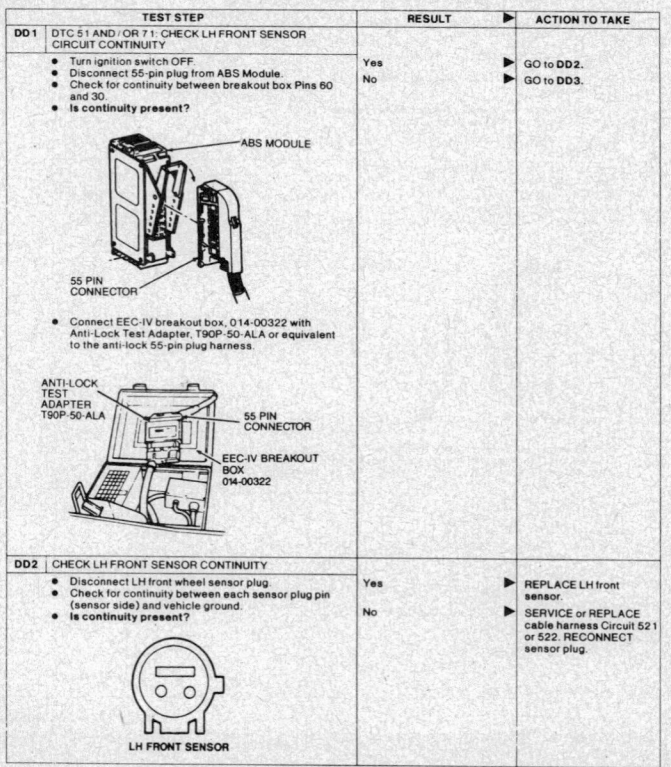

TEST STEP	RESULT	▶	ACTION TO TAKE
DD1 DTC 51 AND / OR 71: CHECK LH FRONT SENSOR CIRCUIT CONTINUITY • Turn ignition switch OFF. • Disconnect 55-pin plug from ABS Module. • Check for continuity between breakout box Pins 60 and 30. • **Is continuity present?**	Yes No	▶ ▶	GO to DD2. GO to DD3.

ABS MODULE

55 PIN CONNECTOR

• Connect EEC-IV breakout box, 014-00322 with Anti-Lock Test Adapter, T90P-50-ALA or equivalent to the anti-lock 55-pin plug harness.

ANTI-LOCK TEST ADAPTER T90P-50-ALA

55 PIN CONNECTOR

EEC-IV BREAKOUT BOX 014-00322

DD2 CHECK LH FRONT SENSOR CONTINUITY • Disconnect LH front wheel sensor plug. • Check for continuity between each sensor plug pin (sensor side) and vehicle ground. • **Is continuity present?**	Yes No	▶ ▶	REPLACE LH front sensor. SERVICE or REPLACE cable harness Circuit 521 or 522. RECONNECT sensor plug.

LH FRONT SENSOR

FM4029300453010X

Fig. 183 Test DD: Wheel Sensor Diagnosis (Part 1 of 6). 1993 Sable & Taurus

TEST STEP	RESULT	▶ ACTION TO TAKE
DD3 CHECK ABS MODULE TO GROUND WIRE • Check continuity between breakout box Pin 60 and body ground. • **Is continuity present?**	Yes No	▶ GO to **DD4**. ▶ SERVICE or REPLACE cable harness Circuit 530 (Taurus/Sable). Circuit 57 or 530 (Taurus SHO).
DD4 CHECK ANTI-LOCK OPERATION LH FRONT WHEEL • Lift vehicle and rotate wheels to ensure they turn freely. • Apply moderate brake pedal effort and check that LH front wheel will not turn. • Jump Pins 34 and 19. • Short Pins 2, 20 and 60 to each other at breakout box. • Check that LH front wheel turns freely with ignition switch ON. **CAUTION: Do not leave ignition on for more than 1 minute, or valve damage may result.**	Wheel turns freely Wheel does not turn freely or pedal drops	▶ REVERIFY symptom. ▶ REPLACE solenoid valve body.
DD5 DTC 52 AND/OR 72: CHECK RH FRONT SENSOR CIRCUIT CONTINUITY • Turn ignition switch OFF. • Disconnect 55-pin plug from ABS Module. • Check for continuity between breakout box Pins 60 and 29. • **Is continuity present?**	Yes No	▶ GO to **DD6**. ▶ GO to **DD7**.

ABS MODULE
55 PIN CONNECTOR
• Connect EEC-IV breakout box 014-00322 with Anti-Lock Test Adapter T90P-50-ALA or equivalent to the anti-lock 55-pin plug wiring harness.
ANTI-LOCK TEST ADAPTER T90P-50-ALA
55 PIN CONNECTOR
EEC-IV BREAKOUT BOX 014-00322

FM4029300453020X

Fig. 183   Test DD: Wheel Sensor Diagnosis (Part 2 of 6). 1993 Sable & Taurus

TEST STEP	RESULT	▶ ACTION TO TAKE
DD6 CHECK RH FRONT SENSOR CONTINUITY • Disconnect RH front sensor. • Check for continuity between each sensor plug pin (sensor side) and vehicle ground. • **Is continuity present?**	Yes No	▶ REPLACE RH front sensor. ▶ SERVICE or REPLACE cable harness Circuit 514 or 516. RECONNECT sensor plug.
DD7 CHECK ABS MODULE TO GROUND WIRE • Check continuity between breakout box Pin 60 and body ground. • **Is continuity present?**	Yes No	▶ GO to **DD8**. ▶ SERVICE or REPLACE cable harness Circuit 530 (Taurus/Sable). Circuit 57 or 530 (Taurus SHO).
DD8 CHECK ANTI-LOCK OPERATION RH FRONT WHEEL • Lift vehicle and rotate wheels to ensure they turn freely. • Apply moderate brake pedal effort and check that RH front wheel will not turn. • Jump Pins 34 and 19. • Short Pins 21, 38 and 60 to each other at breakout box. • Check that RH front wheel turns freely with ignition switch ON.	Wheel turns freely Wheel does not turn freely or pedal drops	▶ REVERIFY symptom. ▶ REPLACE solenoid valve body.

RH FRONT SENSOR

FM4029300453030X

Fig. 183   Test DD: Wheel Sensor Diagnosis (Part 3 of 6). 1993 Sable & Taurus

TEST STEP	RESULT	▶ ACTION TO TAKE
DD9 DTC 53 AND/OR 73: CHECK RH REAR SENSOR CIRCUIT CONTINUITY • Turn ignition switch OFF. • Disconnect 55-pin plug from ABS Module. • Check for continuity between breakout box Pins 60 and 27. • **Is continuity present?**	Yes No	▶ GO to **DD10**. ▶ GO to **DD11**.

ABS MODULE
55 PIN CONNECTOR
• Connect EEC-IV breakout box 014-00322 with Anti-Lock Test Adapter T90P-50-ALA or equivalent to the anti-lock 55-pin plug wiring harness.
ANTI-LOCK TEST ADAPTER T90P-50-ALA
55 PIN CONNECTOR
EEC-IV BREAKOUT BOX 014-00322

TEST STEP	RESULT	▶ ACTION TO TAKE
DD10 CHECK RH REAR SENSOR CONTINUITY • Disconnect RH rear wheel sensor plug. • Check for continuity between each sensor plug pin (sensor side) and vehicle ground. • **Is continuity present?**	Yes No	▶ REPLACE RH rear sensor. ▶ SERVICE or REPLACE cable harness Circuit 523 or 524. RECONNECT sensor plug.

RH REAR SENSOR

FM4029300453040X

Fig. 183   Test DD: Wheel Sensor Diagnosis (Part 4 of 6). 1993 Sable & Taurus

TEST STEP	RESULT	▶ ACTION TO TAKE
DD11 CHECK ABS MODULE TO GROUND WIRE • Check continuity between breakout box Pin 60 and body ground. • **Is continuity present?**	Yes No	▶ GO to **DD12**. ▶ SERVICE or REPLACE cable harness Circuit 530 (Taurus/Sable). Circuit 57 or 530 (Taurus SHO).
DD12 CHECK ANTI-LOCK OPERATION RH REAR WHEEL • Lift vehicle and rotate wheels to ensure they turn freely. • Apply moderate brake pedal effort and check that RH rear wheel will not turn. • Jump Pins 34 and 19. • Short Pins 18, 55 and 60 to each other at breakout box. • Check that RH rear wheel turns freely with ignition switch ON.	Wheel turns freely Wheel does not turn freely or pedal drops	▶ REVERIFY symptom. ▶ REPLACE solenoid valve body.
DD13 DTC 54 AND/OR 74: CHECK LH REAR SENSOR CIRCUIT CONTINUITY • Turn ignition switch OFF. • Disconnect 55-pin plug from ABS Module. • Check for continuity between breakout box Pins 60 and 28. • **Is continuity present?**	Yes No	▶ GO to **DD14**. ▶ GO to **DD15**.

ABS MODULE
55 PIN CONNECTOR
• Connect EEC-IV breakout box 014-00322 with Anti-Lock Test Adapter T90P-50-ALA or equivalent to the anti-lock 55-pin plug wiring harness.
ANTI-LOCK TEST ADAPTER T90P-50-ALA
55 PIN CONNECTOR
EEC-IV BREAKOUT BOX 014-00322

FM4029300453050X

Fig. 183   Test DD: Wheel Sensor Diagnosis (Part 5 of 6). 1993 Sable & Taurus

TEST STEP	RESULT	►	ACTION TO TAKE
DD14 CHECK LH REAR SENSOR CONTINUITY			
• Disconnect LH rear wheel sensor plug. • Check for continuity between each sensor plug pin (sensor side) and vehicle ground. • Is continuity present?	Yes No	► ►	REPLACE LH rear sensor. SERVICE or REPLACE cable harness Circuit 518 or 519. RECONNECT sensor plug.
DD15 CHECK ABS MODULE TO GROUND WIRE			
• Check continuity between breakout box Pin 60 and body ground. • Is continuity present?	Yes No	► ►	GO to **DD16**. SERVICE or REPLACE cable harness Circuit 530 (Taurus / Sable), Circuit 57 or 530 (Taurus SHO).
DD16 CHECK ANTI-LOCK OPERATION LH REAR WHEEL			
• Lift vehicle and rotate wheels to ensure they turn freely. • Apply moderate brake pedal effort and check that LH rear wheel will not turn. • Jump Pins 34 and 19. • Short Pins 36, 54 and 60 to each other at breakout box. • Check that LH rear wheel turns freely with ignition switch ON. CAUTION: Do not leave ignition on for more than 1 minute, or valve damage may result.	Wheel turns freely Wheel does not turn freely or pedal drops	► ►	REVERIFY symptom. REPLACE solenoid valve body.

FM4029300453060X

Fig. 183   Test DD: Wheel Sensor Diagnosis (Part 6 of 6). 1993 Sable & Taurus

TEST STEP	RESULT	►	ACTION TO TAKE
DD1 DTC 61 AND / OR 62: CHECK FLS NO. 2, AND ANTI-LOCK BRAKE PEDAL SENSOR SWITCH			
• Turn ignition switch to the OFF position. • Disconnect 55-pin plug from anti-lock brake control module.	Yes No	► ►	GO to **DD2**. GO to **DD3**.

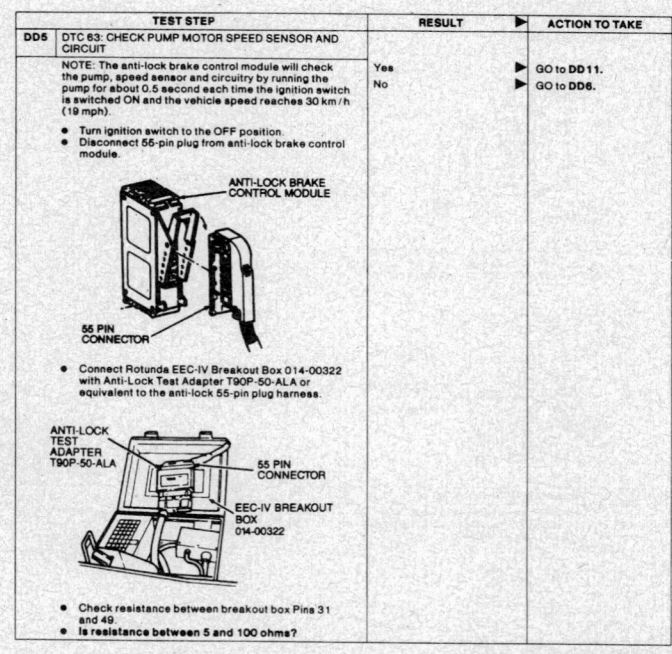

ANTI-LOCK BRAKE CONTROL MODULE

55 PIN CONNECTOR

• Connect Rotunda EEC-IV Breakout Box 014-00322 with Anti-Lock Test Adapter T90P-50-ALA or equivalent to the anti-lock 55-pin plug harness.

ANTI-LOCK TEST ADAPTER T90P-50-ALA

55 PIN CONNECTOR

EEC-IV BREAKOUT BOX 014-00322

• Check for continuity between breakout box Pins 8 and 60. • Is continuity present?			
DD2 CHECK FLS NO. 2 SWITCH			
• Disconnect 2-pin plug on FLS located on hydraulic control unit reservoir on hydraulic control unit.	Yes No	► ►	REPLACE HCU reservoir. SERVICE or REPLACE cable harness (Circuit 550 (Y / LG), 535 (LB / R), or 549 (BR / W)).

2 PIN CONNECTOR ON SMALL RESERVOIR ON HCU

• Check for continuity between each pin and body ground.
• Is continuity present?

FM4029400454010X

Fig. 184   Test DD: Brake Fluid Level Switch/Anti-Lock Brake Pedal Sensor Switch/Pump Motor Diagnosis (Part 1 of 9). 1994 Continental

TEST STEP	RESULT	►	ACTION TO TAKE
DD3 CHECK ANTI-LOCK BRAKE PEDAL SENSOR SWITCH AND CIRCUITRY			
• Check for continuity between breakout box Pins 5 and 60. • Is continuity present?	Yes No	► ►	GO to **DD5**. REVERIFY DTC 61 and / or 62.
DD4 CHECK ANTI-LOCK BRAKE PEDAL SENSOR SWITCH			
• Disconnect 2-pin plug on anti-lock brake pedal sensor switch.	Yes No	► ►	REPLACE anti-lock brake pedal sensor switch. SERVICE or REPLACE cable harness (Circuit 535 (LB / R) or 549 (BR / W)).

2 PIN BRAKE PEDAL POSITION SWITCH

• Check for continuity between each pin and body ground.
• Is continuity present?

FM4029400454020X

Fig. 184   Test DD: Brake Fluid Level Switch/Anti-Lock Brake Pedal Sensor Switch/Pump Motor Diagnosis (Part 2 of 9). 1994 Continental

TEST STEP	RESULT	►	ACTION TO TAKE
DD5 DTC 63: CHECK PUMP MOTOR SPEED SENSOR AND CIRCUIT			
NOTE: The anti-lock brake control module will check the pump, speed sensor and circuitry by running the pump for about 0.5 second each time the ignition switch is switched ON and the vehicle speed reaches 30 km / h (19 mph). • Turn ignition switch to the OFF position. • Disconnect 55-pin plug from anti-lock brake control module.	Yes No	► ►	GO to **DD11**. GO to **DD6**.

ANTI-LOCK BRAKE CONTROL MODULE

55 PIN CONNECTOR

• Connect Rotunda EEC-IV Breakout Box 014-00322 with Anti-Lock Test Adapter T90P-50-ALA or equivalent to the anti-lock 55-pin plug harness.

ANTI-LOCK TEST ADAPTER T90P-50-ALA

55 PIN CONNECTOR

EEC-IV BREAKOUT BOX 014-00322

• Check resistance between breakout box Pins 31 and 49.
• Is resistance between 5 and 100 ohms?

FM4029400454030X

Fig. 184   Test DD: Brake Fluid Level Switch/Anti-Lock Brake Pedal Sensor Switch/Pump Motor Diagnosis (Part 3 of 9). 1994 Continental

TEST STEP	RESULT	▶	ACTION TO TAKE
DD6 CHECK PUMP MOTOR SPEED SENSOR • Disconnect 4-pin plug on pump motor. • Measure resistance between Pins S0 and S1 on pump motor. • **Is resistance between 5 and 100 ohms?**	Yes No	▶ ▶	GO to **DD7**. REPLACE pump and motor.
DD7 CHECK PUMP MOTOR RELAY • Disconnect 7-pin plug on pump motor relay and remove relay. • Check continuity from Pin S0 on 7-pin side to Pin S0 on 4-pin side of relay. • **Is continuity present?**	Yes No	▶ ▶	GO to **DD8**. REPLACE pump motor relay.
DD8 CHECK PUMP MOTOR RELAY • Check continuity from Pin S1 on 7-pin side to Pin S1 on 4-pin side of relay. • **Is continuity present?**	Yes No	▶ ▶	GO to **DD9**. REPLACE pump motor relay.

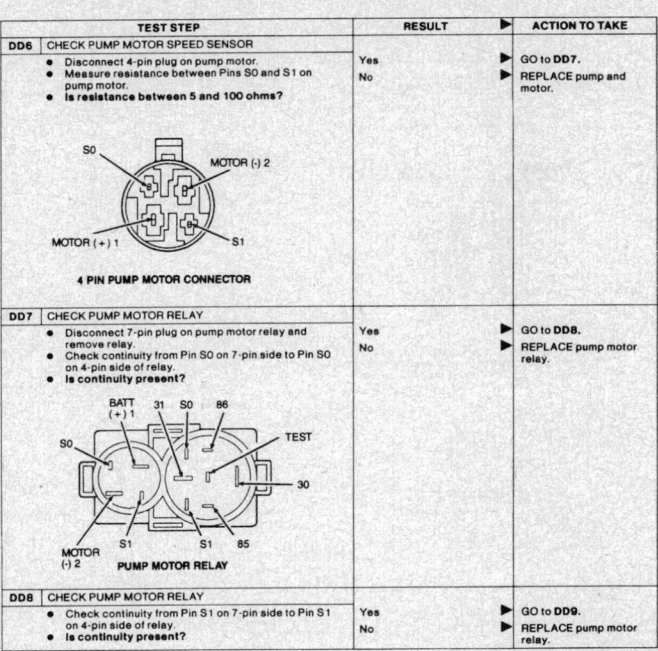

FM4029400454040X

Fig. 184   Test DD: Brake Fluid Level Switch/Anti-Lock Brake Pedal Sensor Switch/Pump Motor Diagnosis (Part 4 of 9). 1994 Continental

TEST STEP	RESULT	▶	ACTION TO TAKE
DD9 CHECK CIRCUIT 462 • Check continuity between breakout box Pin 31 and Pin S0 on pump motor connector 7-pin plug (harness side). • **Is continuity present?**	Yes No	▶ ▶	GO to **DD10**. SERVICE or REPLACE cable harness Circuit 462 (P).
DD10 CHECK CIRCUIT 461 • Check continuity between breakout box Pin 49 and Pin S1 on pump motor connector 7-pin plug (harness side). • **Is continuity present?**	Yes No	▶ ▶	REVERIFY reading at EE9. SERVICE or REPLACE cable harness Circuit 461 (O).
DD11 CHECK MOTOR SPEED SENSOR SHORT TO BATTERY + • Turn ignition switch to the ON position. • Measure voltage between breakout box Pins 31 and 60. • **Is there voltage?**	Yes No	▶ ▶	GO to **DD12**. GO to **DD15**.
DD12 CHECK PUMP MOTOR • Disconnect pump motor to relay 4-pin plug connector. • Turn ignition switch to the ON position. • Measure voltage between breakout box Pins 31 and 60. • **Is there voltage?**	Yes No	▶ ▶	GO to **DD13**. REPLACE pump and motor.
DD13 CHECK CIRCUIT 462 • Disconnect wire harness to relay 7-pin plug. • Turn ignition switch to the ON position. • Measure voltage between breakout box Pins 31 and 60. • **Is there voltage?**	Yes No	▶ ▶	SERVICE or REPLACE cable harness Circuit 462 (P). GO to **DD14**.
DD14 CHECK CIRCUIT 461 • Turn ignition switch to the ON position. • Measure voltage between breakout box Pins 49 and 60. • **Is there voltage?**	Yes No	▶ ▶	SERVICE or REPLACE cable harness Circuit 461 (O). REPLACE pump motor relay.
DD15 CHECK MOTOR SPEED SENSOR SHORT TO GROUND • Turn ignition switch to the OFF position. • Check for continuity between breakout box Pins 31 and 60. • **Is there continuity?**	Yes No	▶ ▶	GO to **DD16**. GO to **DD18**.

FM4029400454050X

Fig. 184   Test DD: Brake Fluid Level Switch/Anti-Lock Brake Pedal Sensor Switch/Pump Motor Diagnosis (Part 5 of 9). 1994 Continental

TEST STEP	RESULT	▶	ACTION TO TAKE
DD16 CHECK CIRCUIT 462 • Disconnect wire harness to relay 7-pin plug. • Check for continuity between breakout box Pins 31 and 60. • **Is continuity present?**	Yes No	▶ ▶	SERVICE or REPLACE cable harness Circuit 462 (P). GO to **DD17**.
DD17 CHECK CIRCUIT 461 • Check for continuity between breakout box Pins 49 and 60. • **Is continuity present?**	Yes No	▶ ▶	SERVICE or REPLACE cable harness Circuit 461 (O). REPLACE pump motor relay.
DD18 CHECK PUMP MOTOR OPERATION • Reconnect pump motor relay to pump and wire harness. • Jumper Pins 15, 34 and 60 at breakout box. • Turn ignition switch to the ON position. • **Does pump motor run?**	Yes No	▶ ▶	REVERIFY code 63. GO to **DD19**.
DD19 CHECK PUMP MOTOR OPERATION • Disconnect pump motor relay from pump motor. • Ground Pin 2 and apply 12 volts to Pin 1 of pump motor connector. • **Does pump motor run?**	Yes No	▶ ▶	GO to **DD20**. REPLACE pump motor.
DD20 CHECK POWER TO RELAY • Disconnect wire harness from pump motor relay. • Check voltage between Pin 30 on wire harness to pump motor relay connector and ground. • **Is voltage above 10 volts?**	Yes No	▶ ▶	GO to **DD21**. SERVICE or REPLACE battery, fuse D or Circuit 537 (T/Y).

FM4029400454060X

Fig. 184   Test DD: Brake Fluid Level Switch/Anti-Lock Brake Pedal Sensor Switch/Pump Motor Diagnosis (Part 6 of 9). 1994 Continental

TEST STEP	RESULT	▶	ACTION TO TAKE
DD21 CHECK POWER TO RELAY COIL • Jumper Pins 34 and 60 at breakout box. • Turn ignition to ON position. • Measure voltage between Pin 86 and ground. • **Is voltage above 10 volts?**	Yes No	▶ ▶	GO to **DD22**. SERVICE or REPLACE cable harness Circuit 532 (O/Y).
DD22 CHECK PUMP MOTOR RELAY COIL • Measure resistance between Pins 85 and 86 on pump motor relay. • **Is resistance between 45 and 105 ohms?**	Yes No	▶ ▶	GO to **DD23**. REPLACE pump motor relay.
DD23 CHECK CIRCUIT 539 • Check for continuity between breakout box Pin 15 and Pin 85 on wire harness to pump motor relay connector. • **Is continuity present?**	Yes No	▶ ▶	GO to **DD24**. SERVICE or REPLACE cable harness Circuit 539 (PK/LB).

FM4029400454070X

Fig. 184   Test DD: Brake Fluid Level Switch/Anti-Lock Brake Pedal Sensor Switch/Pump Motor Diagnosis (Part 7 of 9). 1994 Continental

TEST STEP		RESULT	▶	ACTION TO TAKE
DD24	CHECK CIRCUIT 57			
	• Check for continuity between wire harness to pump motor relay connector Pin 31 and ground. • Is continuity present?	Yes No	▶ ▶	GO to **DD25**. SERVICE or REPLACE cable harness Circuit 57 (BK).
DD25	CHECK PUMP MOTOR RELAY			
	• Connect battery + to Pin 86 and battery – to Pin 85 of pump motor relay. • Check for continuity between Pin 30 and Pin 1 on relay. • Is continuity present?	Yes No	▶ ▶	GO to **DD26**. REPLACE pump motor relay.
DD26	CHECK PUMP MOTOR RELAY			
	• Check continuity between Pins 2 and 31 on pump motor relay. • Is continuity present?	Yes No	▶ ▶	REPLACE anti-lock brake control module. REPLACE pump motor relay.

BATT (+) 1   31   S0   86

S0   TEST

30

MOTOR (–) 2   S1   S1   85

PUMP MOTOR RELAY

FM4029400454080X

Fig. 184 Test DD: Brake Fluid Level Switch/Anti-Lock Brake Pedal Sensor Switch/Pump Motor Diagnosis (Part 8 of 9). 1994 Continental

TEST STEP		RESULT	▶	ACTION TO TAKE
DD27	DTC 64: CHECK PUMP MOTOR PRESSURE CAPABILITY			
	• Turn ignition switch OFF. • Disconnect 55-pin plug from anti-lock brake control module.	Yes No	▶ ▶	REVERIFY DTC 64. REPLACE pump and motor.

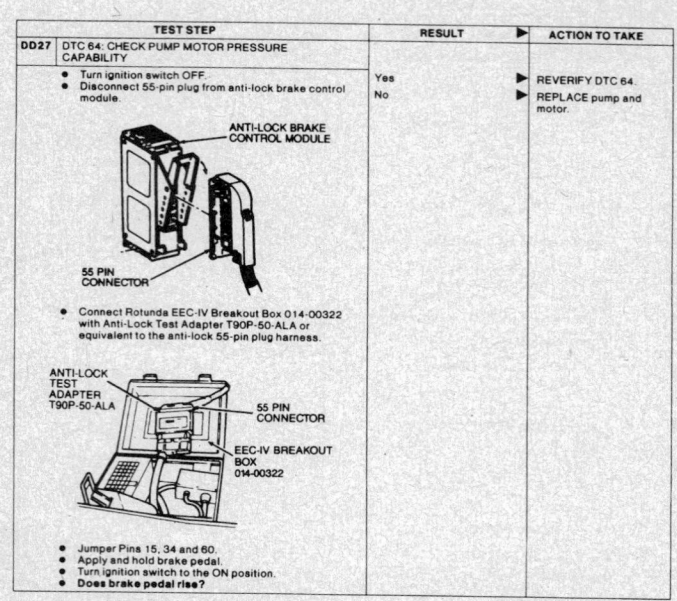

ANTI-LOCK BRAKE CONTROL MODULE

55 PIN CONNECTOR

• Connect Rotunda EEC-IV Breakout Box 014-00322 with Anti-Lock Test Adapter T90P-50-ALA or equivalent to the anti-lock 55-pin plug harness.

ANTI-LOCK TEST ADAPTER T90P-50-ALA

55 PIN CONNECTOR

EEC-IV BREAKOUT BOX 014-00322

• Jumper Pins 15, 34 and 60.
• Apply and hold brake pedal.
• Turn ignition switch to the ON position.
• **Does brake pedal rise?**

FM4029400454090X

Fig. 184 Test DD: Brake Fluid Level Switch/Anti-Lock Brake Pedal Sensor Switch/Pump Motor Diagnosis (Part 9 of 9). 1994 Continental

TEST STEP		RESULT	▶	ACTION TO TAKE
DD1	DTC 61 AND /OR 62: CHECK FLS NO. 2 AND ANTI-LOCK BRAKE PEDAL SENSOR SWITCH			
	• Turn ignition switch OFF. • Disconnect anti-lock brake wiring from anti-lock brake control module.	Yes No	▶ ▶	GO to **DD2**. GO to **DD3**.

ANTI-LOCK BRAKE CONTROL MODULE

ANTI-LOCK BRAKE WIRING

• Connect EEC-IV Breakout Box 014-00322 with Anti-Lock Test Adapter T90P-50-ALA or equivalent to the anti-lock brake wiring harness.

ANTI-LOCK TEST ADAPTER T90P-50-ALA

ANTI-LOCK BRAKE WIRING 2C054

EEC-IV BREAKOUT BOX 014-00322

• Check for continuity between Breakout Box Pins 8 and 60.
• **Is continuity present?**

DD2	CHECK FLS NO. 2 SWITCH			
	• Disconnect 2-pin plug on FLS located on small hydraulic control unit reservoir on brake pressure control valve block.	Yes No	▶ ▶	REPLACE hydraulic control unit reservoir. SERVICE or REPLACE cable harness Circuit 459, 467 or 550 Town Car. Circuit 550, 535, or 549 for Crown Victoria / Grand Marquis.

BRAKE MASTER CYLINDER FILLER CAP SMALL 2-PIN CONNECTOR

• Check for continuity between each pin and body ground.
• **Is continuity present?**

FM4029400455010X

Fig. 185   Test DD: Fluid Level Indicator/Anti-Lock Brake Pedal Sensor Switch/Pump Motor Diagnosis (Part 1 of 9). 1994 Crown Victoria, Grand Marquis & Town Car

TEST STEP		RESULT	▶	ACTION TO TAKE
DD3	CHECK FOR VOLTAGE ON FLS NO. 2 SWITCH AND CIRCUITRY			
	• Turn ignition switch to RUN position. • Measure voltage between breakout box Pins 8 and 60. • Is B+ present?	Yes No	▶ ▶	SERVICE or REPLACE cable harness Circuit 459, 467 or 550 Town Car. Circuit 535, 549, 550 on Crown Victoria / Grand Marquis. GO to **EE4**.
DD4	CHECK ANTI-LOCK BRAKE PEDAL SENSOR SWITCH AND CIRCUITRY			
	• Check for continuity between breakout box Pins 5 and 60. • Is continuity present?	No Yes	▶ ▶	GO to **EE6**. GO to **EE5**.
DD5	CHECK ANTI-LOCK BRAKE PEDAL SENSOR SWITCH			
	• Disconnect 2-pin plug on anti-lock brake pedal sensor switch.	Yes No	▶ ▶	REPLACE anti-lock brake pedal sensor switch. SERVICE or REPLACE cable harness Circuit 550, 467 or 547 Town Car. Circuit 550, 535 or 549 for Crown Victoria / Grand Marquis.

2-PIN ANTI-LOCK BRAKE PEDAL SENSOR SWITCH

• Check for continuity between each pin and body ground.
• **Is continuity present?**

DD6	CHECK FOR VOLTAGE ON ANTI-LOCK BRAKE PEDAL SENSOR SWITCH AND CIRCUITRY			
	• Turn ignition switch to ON position. • Measure voltage between breakout box Pins 5 and 60. • Is B+ present?	Yes No	▶ ▶	SERVICE or REPLACE cable harness circuit 550, 467 or 547 Town Car. Circuit 550, 535 or 549 Crown Victoria / Grand Marquis. REVERIFY DTC 61 and /or 62.

FM4029400455020X

Fig. 185   Test DD: Fluid Level Indicator/Anti-Lock Brake Pedal Sensor Switch/Pump Motor Diagnosis (Part 2 of 9). 1994 Crown Victoria, Grand Marquis & Town Car

TEST STEP	RESULT	▶	ACTION TO TAKE
DD7 DTC 63: CHECK PUMP MOTOR SPEED SENSOR AND CIRCUIT • Turn ignition switch OFF. • Disconnect anti-lock brake wiring from anti-lock brake control module.	Yes No	▶ ▶	GO to DD13. GO to DD8.

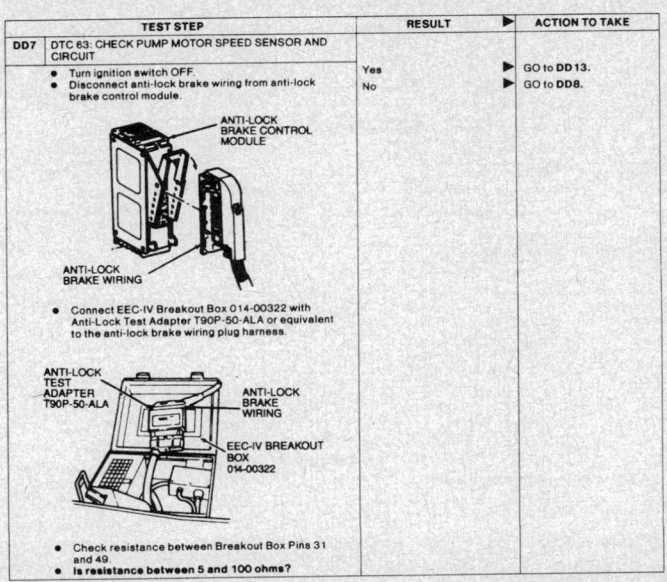

• Connect EEC-IV Breakout Box 014-00322 with Anti-Lock Test Adapter T90P-50-ALA or equivalent to the anti-lock brake wiring plug harness.

• Check resistance between Breakout Box Pins 31 and 49.
• Is resistance between 5 and 100 ohms?

FM4029400455030X

Fig. 185 Test DD: Fluid Level Indicator/Anti-Lock Brake Pedal Sensor Switch/Pump Motor Diagnosis (Part 3 of 9). 1994 Crown Victoria, Grand Marquis & Town Car

TEST STEP	RESULT	▶	ACTION TO TAKE
DD8 CHECK PUMP MOTOR SPEED SENSOR • Disconnect 4-pin plug on pump motor. • Measure resistance between Pins S0 and S1 on pump motor. • Is resistance between 5 and 100 ohms?	Yes No	▶ ▶	GO to DD9. REPLACE pump motor.

S0 — MOTOR (-) 2
MOTOR (+) 1 — S1
4 PIN PUMP MOTOR CONNECTOR

DD9 CHECK PUMP MOTOR RELAY • Disconnect 7-pin plug on pump motor relay and remove relay. • Check continuity from Pin S0 on 7-pin side to Pin S0 on 4-pin side of relay. • Is continuity present?	Yes No	▶ ▶	GO to DD10. REPLACE pump motor relay.

BATT (+) 1 31 S0 86 TEST
S0 30
MOTOR (-) 2 S1 S1 85
PUMP MOTOR RELAY

DD10 CHECK PUMP MOTOR RELAY • Check continuity from Pin S1 on 7-pin side to Pin S1 on 4-pin side of relay. • Is continuity present?	Yes No	▶ ▶	GO to DD11. REPLACE pump motor relay.

FM4029400455040X

Fig. 185 Test DD: Fluid Level Indicator/Anti-Lock Brake Pedal Sensor Switch/Pump Motor Diagnosis (Part 4 of 9). 1994 Crown Victoria, Grand Marquis & Town Car

TEST STEP	RESULT	▶	ACTION TO TAKE
DD11 CHECK CIRCUIT 462 • Check continuity between Breakout Box Pin 31 and Pin S0 on pump motor connector 7-pin plug (harness side). • Is continuity present?	Yes No	▶ ▶	GO to DD12. SERVICE or REPLACE cable harness Circuit 462.

539 PK/LB — 85
537 T/Y TOWN CAR
533 T/R CROWN VICTORIA/GRAND MARQUIS
532 O/Y — 86
462 P — S0
57 BK — 31
604 O/R TOWN CAR
351 BR/W CROWN VICTORIA/GRAND MARQUIS — S1
7 PIN PUMP MOTOR RELAY CONNECTOR HARNESS SIDE

DD12 CHECK CIRCUIT 351 OR 604 • Check continuity between Breakout Box Pin 49 and Pin S1 on pump motor connector 7-pin plug (harness side). • Is continuity present?	Yes No	▶ ▶	REVERIFY reading at DD7. SERVICE or REPLACE cable harness Circuit 604 for Town Car. Circuit 351 for Crown Victoria / Grand Marquis.
DD13 CHECK MOTOR SPEED SENSOR SHORT TO BATTERY + • Turn ignition switch to RUN. • Measure voltage between Breakout Box Pins 31 and 60. • Is B+ present?	Yes No	▶ ▶	GO to DD14. GO to DD16.
DD14 CHECK CIRCUIT 462 • Disconnect wire harness to relay 7-pin plug. • Disconnect pump motor to relay 4-pin plug. • Turn ignition switch to RUN. • Measure voltage between Breakout Box Pins 31 and 60. • Is B+ present?	Yes No	▶ ▶	SERVICE or REPLACE cable harness Circuit 462. GO to DD15.
DD15 CHECK CIRCUIT 351 or 604 • Turn ignition switch to RUN. • Measure voltage between Breakout Box Pins 49 and 60. • Is B+ present?	Yes No	▶ ▶	SERVICE or REPLACE cable harness Circuit 604 for Town Car. Circuit 351 for Crown Victoria / Grand Marquis. REPLACE pump motor relay.
DD16 CHECK MOTOR SPEED SENSOR SHORT TO GROUND • Check for continuity between Breakout Box Pins 31 and 60. • Is continuity present?	No Yes	▶ ▶	GO to DD19. GO to DD17.
DD17 CHECK CIRCUIT 462 • Disconnect wire harness to relay 7-pin plug. • Disconnect pump motor to relay 4-pin plug. • Check for continuity between Breakout Box Pins 31 and 60. • Is continuity present?	Yes No	▶ ▶	SERVICE or REPLACE cable harness Circuit 462. GO to DD18.

FM4029400455050X

Fig. 185 Test DD: Fluid Level Indicator/Anti-Lock Brake Pedal Sensor Switch/Pump Motor Diagnosis (Part 5 of 9). 1994 Crown Victoria, Grand Marquis & Town Car

TEST STEP	RESULT	▶	ACTION TO TAKE
DD18 CHECK CIRCUIT 351 OR 604 • Check for continuity between Breakout Box Pins 49 and 60. • Is continuity present?	Yes No	▶ ▶	SERVICE or REPLACE cable harness Circuit 604 Town Car. Circuit 351 Crown Victoria / Grand Marquis. REPLACE pump motor relay.
DD19 CHECK PUMP MOTOR OPERATION • Reconnect pump motor relay to pump and wire harness. • Jumper Pins 15, 34 and 60 at Breakout Box. • Turn ignition switch to RUN position. • **Does pump motor run?**	Yes No	▶ ▶	REPLACE anti-lock brake control module. GO to DD20.
DD20 CHECK PUMP MOTOR OPERATION • Disconnect pump motor relay from pump motor. • Ground Pin 2 and apply 12 volts to Pin 1 of pump motor connector. • **Does pump motor run?**	Yes No	▶ ▶	GO to DD21. REPLACE pump motor.

S0 — MOTOR (-) 2
MOTOR (+) 1 — S1
4 PIN PUMP MOTOR CONNECTOR

DD21 CHECK POWER TO RELAY • Disconnect wire harness from pump motor relay. • Check voltage between Pin 30 on wire harness to pump motor relay connector and ground. • Is voltage over 10 volts?	Yes No	▶ ▶	GO to DD22. SERVICE or REPLACE battery, 50 amp fuse or Circuit 533 Crown Victoria / Grand Marquis. Battery, 40 amp fuse or circuit 537 Town Car.

539 PK/LB — 85
537 T/Y TOWN CAR
533 T/R CROWN VICTORIA/GRAND MARQUIS
532 O/Y — 86
462 P — S0
57 BK — 31
604 O/R TOWN CAR
351 BR/W CROWN VICTORIA/GRAND MARQUIS — S1
7 PIN PUMP MOTOR RELAY CONNECTOR HARNESS SIDE

FM4029400455060X

Fig. 185 Test DD: Fluid Level Indicator/Anti-Lock Brake Pedal Sensor Switch/Pump Motor Diagnosis (Part 6 of 9). 1994 Crown Victoria, Grand Marquis & Town Car

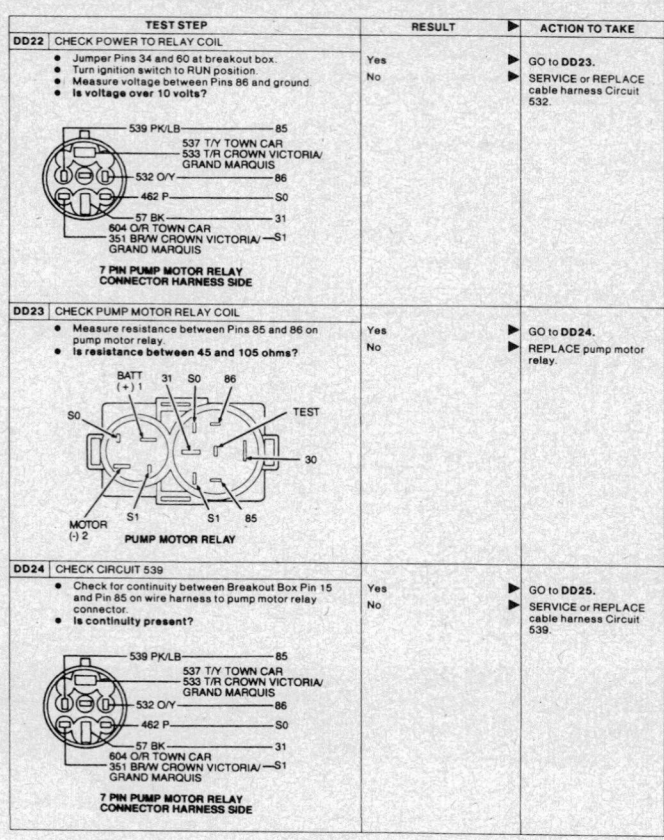

TEST STEP		RESULT	▶	ACTION TO TAKE
DD22	CHECK POWER TO RELAY COIL			
	• Jumper Pins 34 and 60 at breakout box. • Turn ignition switch to RUN position. • Measure voltage between Pins 86 and ground. • **Is voltage over 10 volts?**	Yes No	▶ ▶	GO to **DD23**. SERVICE or REPLACE cable harness Circuit 532.
DD23	CHECK PUMP MOTOR RELAY COIL			
	• Measure resistance between Pins 85 and 86 on pump motor relay. • **Is resistance between 45 and 105 ohms?**	Yes No	▶ ▶	GO to **DD24**. REPLACE pump motor relay.
DD24	CHECK CIRCUIT 539			
	• Check for continuity between Breakout Box Pin 15 and Pin 85 on wire harness to pump motor relay connector. • **Is continuity present?**	Yes No	▶ ▶	GO to **DD25**. SERVICE or REPLACE cable harness Circuit 539.

FM4029400455070X

Fig. 185 Test DD: Fluid Level Indicator/Anti-Lock Brake Pedal Sensor Switch/Pump Motor Diagnosis (Part 7 of 9). 1994 Crown Victoria, Grand Marquis & Town Car

TEST STEP		RESULT	▶	ACTION TO TAKE
DD28	DTC 64: CHECK PUMP MOTOR PRESSURE CAPABILITY			
	• Turn ignition switch OFF. • Disconnect anti-lock brake wiring from anti-lock brake control module.	Yes No	▶ ▶	REVERIFY DTC 64. REPLACE pump motor.
	• Connect EEC-IV Breakout Box 014-00322 with Anti-Lock Test Adapter T90P-50-ALA or equivalent to the anti-lock brake wiring plug harness. • Jumper Pins 15, 34 and 60. • Apply and hold brake pedal. • Turn ignition switch to RUN. • **Does brake pedal rise?**			

FM4029400455090X

Fig. 185 Test DD: Fluid Level Indicator/Anti-Lock Brake Pedal Sensor Switch/Pump Motor Diagnosis (Part 9 of 9). 1994 Crown Victoria, Grand Marquis & Town Car

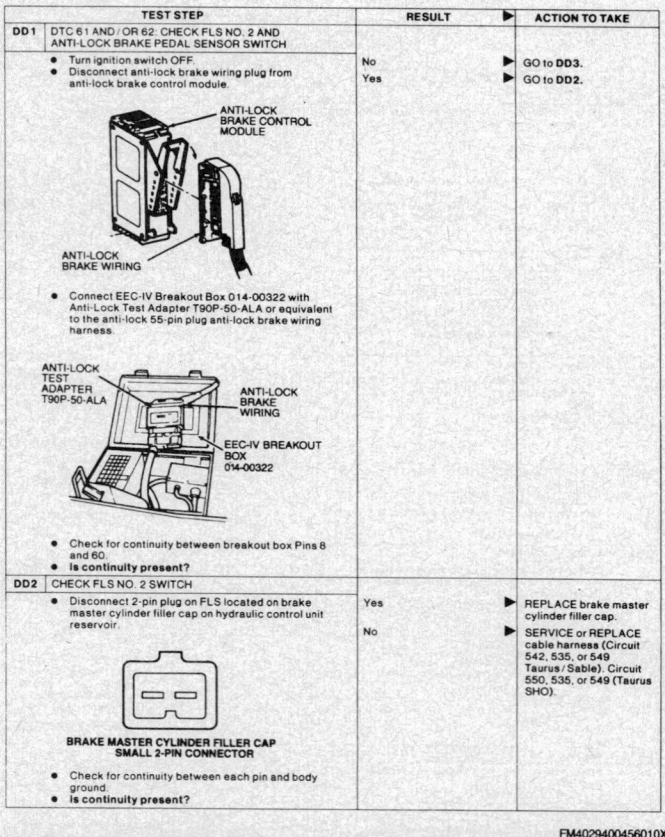

TEST STEP		RESULT	▶	ACTION TO TAKE
DD25	CHECK CIRCUIT 57			
	• Check for continuity between wire harness to pump motor relay connector Pin 31 and ground. • **Is continuity present?**	Yes No	▶ ▶	GO to **DD26**. SERVICE or REPLACE cable harness Circuit 57.
DD26	CHECK PUMP MOTOR RELAY			
	• Connect battery + to Pin 86 and battery - to Pin 85 of pump motor relay. • Check for continuity between Pin 30 and Pin 1 on relay. • **Is continuity present?**	Yes No	▶ ▶	GO to **DD27**. REPLACE pump motor relay.
DD27	CHECK PUMP MOTOR RELAY			
	• Check continuity between Pins 2 and 31 on pump motor relay. • **Is continuity present?**	Yes No	▶ ▶	REPLACE anti-lock brake control module. REPLACE pump motor relay.

FM4029400455080X

Fig. 185 Test DD: Fluid Level Indicator/Anti-Lock Brake Pedal Sensor Switch/Pump Motor Diagnosis (Part 8 of 9). 1994 Crown Victoria, Grand Marquis & Town Car

TEST STEP		RESULT	▶	ACTION TO TAKE
DD1	DTC 61 AND/OR 62: CHECK FLS NO. 2 AND ANTI-LOCK BRAKE PEDAL SENSOR SWITCH			
	• Turn ignition switch OFF. • Disconnect anti-lock brake wiring plug from anti-lock brake control module.	No Yes	▶ ▶	GO to **DD3**. GO to **DD2**.
	• Connect EEC-IV Breakout Box 014-00322 with Anti-Lock Test Adapter T90P-50-ALA or equivalent to the anti-lock 55-pin plug anti-lock brake wiring harness. • Check for continuity between breakout box Pins 8 and 60. • **Is continuity present?**			
DD2	CHECK FLS NO. 2 SWITCH			
	• Disconnect 2-pin plug on FLS located on brake master cylinder filler cap on hydraulic control unit reservoir.	Yes No	▶ ▶	REPLACE brake master cylinder filler cap. SERVICE or REPLACE cable harness (Circuit 542, 535, or 549 Taurus/Sable). Circuit 550, 535, or 549 (Taurus SHO).
	• Check for continuity between each pin and body ground. • **Is continuity present?**			

FM4029400456010X

Fig. 186 Test DD: Fluid Level Indicator/Anti-Lock Brake Pedal Sensor Switch/Pump Motor & Relay (Part 1 of 9). 1994 Sable & Taurus

TEST STEP	RESULT	▶	ACTION TO TAKE
DD3 CHECK FOR VOLTAGE ON FLS NO. 2 SWITCH AND CIRCUITRY • Turn ignition switch to RUN position. • Measure voltage between breakout box Pins 8 and 60. • **Is B+ present?**	Yes	▶	SERVICE or REPLACE cable harness circuit 542, 535, or 549 (Taurus / Sable). Circuit 550, 535, or 549 (Taurus SHO).
	No	▶	GO to **DD4.**
DD4 CHECK ANTI-LOCK BRAKE PEDAL SENSOR SWITCH AND CIRCUITRY • Check for continuity between breakout box Pins 5 and 60. • **Is continuity present?**	No	▶	GO to **DD6.**
	Yes	▶	GO to **DD5.**
DD5 CHECK PEDAL SENSOR SWITCH • Disconnect 2-pin plug on anti-lock brake pedal sensor switch. **2-PIN ANTI-LOCK BRAKE PEDAL SENSOR SWITCH** • Check for continuity between each pin and body ground. • **Is continuity present?**	Yes	▶	REPLACE anti-lock brake pedal sensor switch.
	No	▶	SERVICE or REPLACE cable harness (Circuit 535 or 549).
DD6 CHECK FOR VOLTAGE ON ANTI-LOCK BRAKE PEDAL SENSOR SWITCH AND CIRCUITRY • Turn ignition switch to RUN position. • Measure voltage between breakout box Pins 5 and 60. • **Is B+ present?**	Yes	▶	SERVICE or REPLACE cable harness circuit 542, 535 or 549 (Taurus / Sable). Circuit 550, 535 or 549 (Taurus SHO).
	No	▶	VERIFY DTC 61 and / or 62.

FM4029400456020X

Fig. 186 Test DD: Fluid Level Indicator/Anti-Lock Brake Pedal Sensor Switch/Pump Motor & Relay (Part 2 of 9). 1994 Sable & Taurus

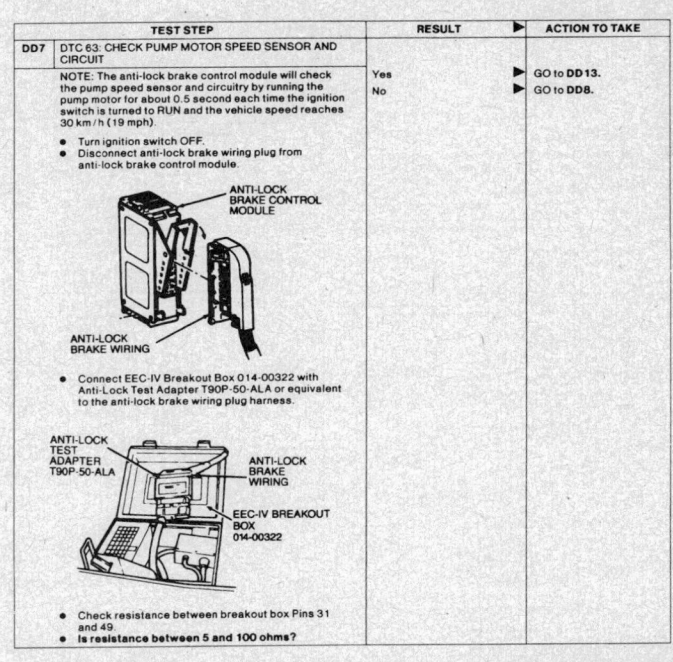

TEST STEP	RESULT	▶	ACTION TO TAKE
DD7 DTC 63: CHECK PUMP MOTOR SPEED SENSOR AND CIRCUIT NOTE: The anti-lock brake control module will check the pump speed sensor and circuitry by running the pump motor for about 0.5 second each time the ignition switch is turned to RUN and the vehicle speed reaches 30 km/h (19 mph). • Turn ignition switch OFF. • Disconnect anti-lock brake wiring plug from anti-lock brake control module. ANTI-LOCK BRAKE CONTROL MODULE ANTI-LOCK BRAKE WIRING • Connect EEC-IV Breakout Box 014-00322 with Anti-Lock Test Adapter T90P-50-ALA or equivalent to the anti-lock brake wiring plug harness. ANTI-LOCK TEST ADAPTER T90P-50-ALA ANTI-LOCK BRAKE WIRING EEC-IV BREAKOUT BOX 014-00322 • Check resistance between breakout box Pins 31 and 49. • **Is resistance between 5 and 100 ohms?**	Yes	▶	GO to **DD13.**
	No	▶	GO to **DD8.**

FM4029400456030X

Fig. 186 Test DD: Fluid Level Indicator/Anti-Lock Brake Pedal Sensor Switch/Pump Motor & Relay (Part 3 of 9). 1994 Sable & Taurus

TEST STEP	RESULT	▶	ACTION TO TAKE
DD8 CHECK PUMP MOTOR SPEED SENSOR • Disconnect 4-pin plug on pump motor. • Measure resistance between Pins S0 and S1 on pump motor. • **Is resistance between 5 and 100 ohms?** S0 ── MOTOR (-) 2 MOTOR (+) 1 ── S1 **4 PIN PUMP MOTOR CONNECTOR**	Yes	▶	GO to **DD9.**
	No	▶	REPLACE pump motor.
DD9 CHECK PUMP MOTOR RELAY • Disconnect 7-pin plug on pump motor relay and remove relay. • Check continuity from Pin S0 on 7-pin side to Pin S0 on 4-pin side of relay. • **Is continuity present?** BATT (+) 1 31 S0 86 S0 ── TEST MOTOR (-) 2 S1 S1 85 30 **PUMP MOTOR RELAY**	Yes	▶	GO to **DD10.**
	No	▶	REPLACE pump motor relay.
DD10 CHECK PUMP MOTOR RELAY • Check continuity from Pin S1 on 7-pin side to Pin S1 on 4-pin side of relay. • **Is continuity present?**	Yes	▶	GO to **DD11.**
	No	▶	REPLACE pump motor relay.

FM4029400456040X

Fig. 186 Test DD: Fluid Level Indicator/Anti-Lock Brake Pedal Sensor Switch/Pump Motor & Relay (Part 4 of 9). 1994 Sable & Taurus

TEST STEP	RESULT	▶	ACTION TO TAKE
DD11 CHECK CIRCUIT 462 • Check continuity between breakout box Pin 31 and Pin S0 on pump motor connector 7-pin plug (harness side). • **Is continuity present?** 539 PK/LB ── 85 537 T/Y ── 30 532 O/Y ── 86 462 P ── S0 57 BK ── 31 461 O ── S1 **7-PIN PUMP MOTOR RELAY CONNECTOR (HARNESS SIDE)**	Yes	▶	GO to **DD12.**
	No	▶	SERVICE or REPLACE cable harness Circuit 462.
DD12 CHECK CIRCUIT 461 • Check continuity between breakout box Pin 49 and Pin S1 on pump motor connector 7-pin plug (harness side). • **Is continuity present?**	Yes	▶	REVERIFY reading in STEP EE7.
	No	▶	SERVICE or REPLACE cable harness Circuit 461.
DD13 CHECK MOTOR SPEED SENSOR SHORT TO BATTERY+ • Turn ignition switch to RUN. • Measure voltage between breakout box Pins 31 and 60. • **Is B+ present?**	Yes	▶	GO to **DD17.**
	No	▶	GO to **DD14.**
DD14 CHECK PUMP MOTOR • Disconnect pump motor to relay 4-pin plug connector. • Turn ignition switch to RUN. • Measure voltage between breakout box Pins 31 and 60. • **Is B+ present?**	Yes	▶	GO to **DD15.**
	No	▶	REPLACE pump and motor.
DD15 CHECK CIRCUIT 462 • Disconnect wire harness to relay 7-pin plug. • Turn ignition switch to RUN. • Measure voltage between breakout box Pins 31 and 60. • **Is B+ present?**	Yes	▶	SERVICE or REPLACE cable harness Circuit 462.
	No	▶	GO to **DD16.**
DD16 CHECK CIRCUIT 461 • Turn ignition switch to RUN. • Measure voltage between breakout box Pins 49 and 60. • **Is B+ present?**	Yes	▶	SERVICE or REPLACE cable harness Circuit 461.
	No	▶	REPLACE pump motor relay.
DD17 CHECK MOTOR SPEED SENSOR SHORT TO GROUND • Turn ignition switch OFF. • Check for continuity between breakout box Pins 31 and 60. • **Is continuity present?**	Yes	▶	GO to **DD18.**
	No	▶	GO to **DD20.**

FM4029400456050X

Fig. 186 Test DD: Fluid Level Indicator/Anti-Lock Brake Pedal Sensor Switch/Pump Motor & Relay (Part 5 of 9). 1994 Sable & Taurus

TEST STEP		RESULT	►	ACTION TO TAKE
DD18	CHECK CIRCUIT 462 • Disconnect wire harness to relay 7-pin plug. • Check for continuity between breakout box Pins 31 and 60. • Is continuity present?	Yes	►	SERVICE or REPLACE cable harness Circuit 462.
		No	►	GO to DD19.
DD19	CHECK CIRCUIT 461 • Check for continuity between breakout box Pins 49 and 60. • Is continuity present?	Yes	►	SERVICE or REPLACE cable harness Circuit 461.
		No	►	REPLACE pump motor relay.
DD20	CHECK PUMP MOTOR OPERATION • Reconnect pump motor relay to pump and wire harness. • Jumper Pins 15, 34 and 60 at breakout box. • Turn ignition switch to RUN position. • Does pump motor run?	Yes	►	REVERIFY DTC 63.
		No	►	GO to DD21.
DD21	CHECK PUMP MOTOR OPERATION • Disconnect pump motor relay from pump motor. • Ground Pin 2 and apply 12 volts to Pin 1 of pump motor connector. • Does pump motor run?	Yes	►	GO to DD22.
		No	►	REPLACE pump motor.

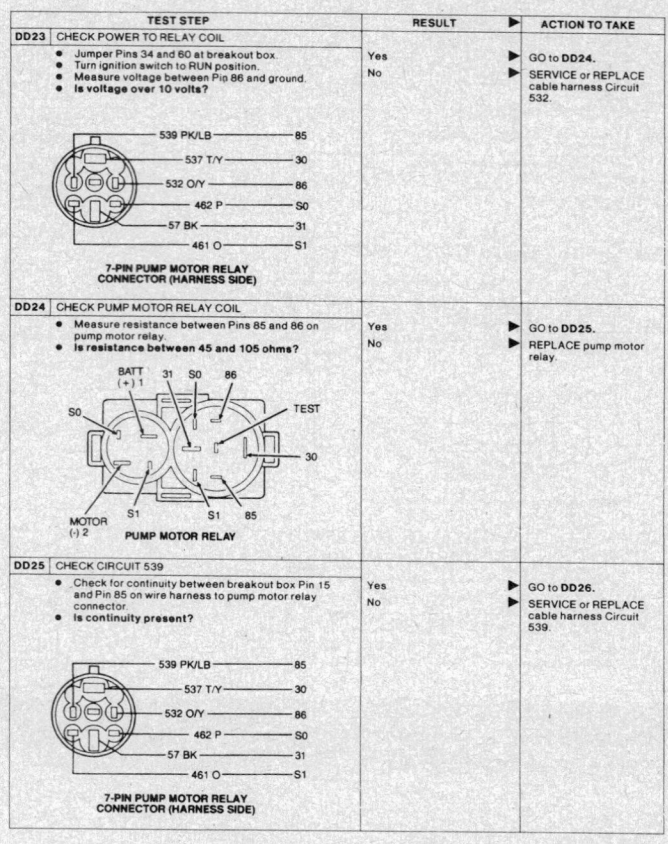

DD22	CHECK POWER TO RELAY • Disconnect wire harness from pump motor relay. • Check voltage between Pin 30 on wire harness to pump motor relay connector and ground. • Is voltage over 10 volts?	Yes	►	GO to DD23.
		No	►	SERVICE or REPLACE battery, Circuit 537 or Anti-Lock Motor 40A Fuse.

Fig. 186   Test DD: Fluid Level Indicator/Anti-Lock Brake Pedal Sensor Switch/Pump Motor & Relay (Part 6 of 9). 1994 Sable & Taurus

TEST STEP		RESULT	►	ACTION TO TAKE
DD23	CHECK POWER TO RELAY COIL • Jumper Pins 34 and 60 at breakout box. • Turn ignition switch to RUN position. • Measure voltage between Pin 86 and ground. • Is voltage over 10 volts?	Yes	►	GO to DD24.
		No	►	SERVICE or REPLACE cable harness Circuit 532.
DD24	CHECK PUMP MOTOR RELAY COIL • Measure resistance between Pins 85 and 86 on pump motor relay. • Is resistance between 45 and 105 ohms?	Yes	►	GO to DD25.
		No	►	REPLACE pump motor relay.
DD25	CHECK CIRCUIT 539 • Check for continuity between breakout box Pin 15 and Pin 85 on wire harness to pump motor relay connector. • Is continuity present?	Yes	►	GO to DD26.
		No	►	SERVICE or REPLACE cable harness Circuit 539.

Fig. 186   Test DD: Fluid Level Indicator/Anti-Lock Brake Pedal Sensor Switch/Pump Motor & Relay (Part 7 of 9). 1994 Sable & Taurus

TEST STEP		RESULT	►	ACTION TO TAKE
DD26	CHECK CIRCUIT 57 • Check for continuity between wire harness to pump motor relay connector Pin 31 and ground. • Is continuity present?	Yes	►	GO to DD27.
		No	►	SERVICE or REPLACE cable harness Circuit 57.
DD27	CHECK PUMP MOTOR RELAY • Connect battery + to Pin 86 and battery - to Pin 85 of pump motor relay. • Check for continuity between Pin 30 and Pin 1 on relay. • Is continuity present?	Yes	►	GO to DD28.
		No	►	REPLACE pump motor relay.
DD28	CHECK PUMP MOTOR RELAY • Check continuity between Pins 2 and 31 on pump motor relay. • Is continuity present?	Yes	►	REPLACE anti-lock brake control module.
		No	►	REPLACE pump motor relay.

Fig. 186   Test DD: Fluid Level Indicator/Anti-Lock Brake Pedal Sensor Switch/Pump Motor & Relay (Part 8 of 9). 1994 Sable & Taurus

TEST STEP		RESULT	►	ACTION TO TAKE
DD29	DTC 64: CHECK PUMP MOTOR PRESSURE CAPABILITY • Turn ignition switch OFF. • Disconnect anti-lock brake wiring plug from anti-lock brake control module.	Yes	►	REVERIFY DTC 64.
		No	►	REPLACE pump motor.

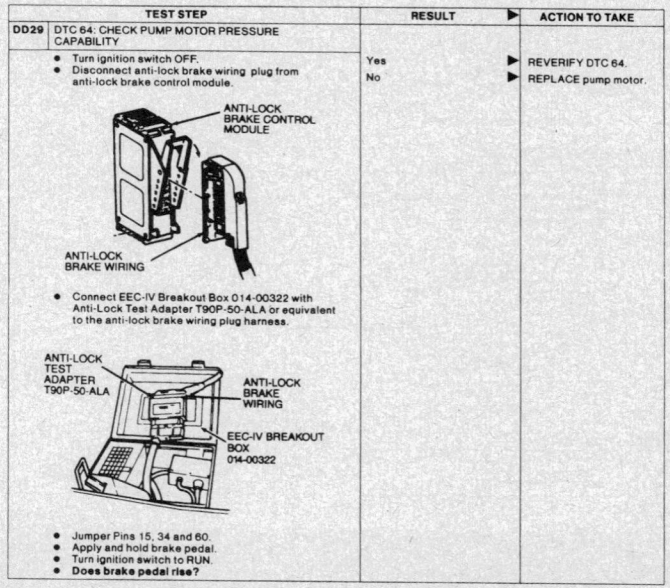

Fig. 186   Test DD: Fluid Level Indicator/Anti-Lock Brake Pedal Sensor Switch/Pump Motor & Relay (Part 9 of 9). 1994 Sable & Taurus

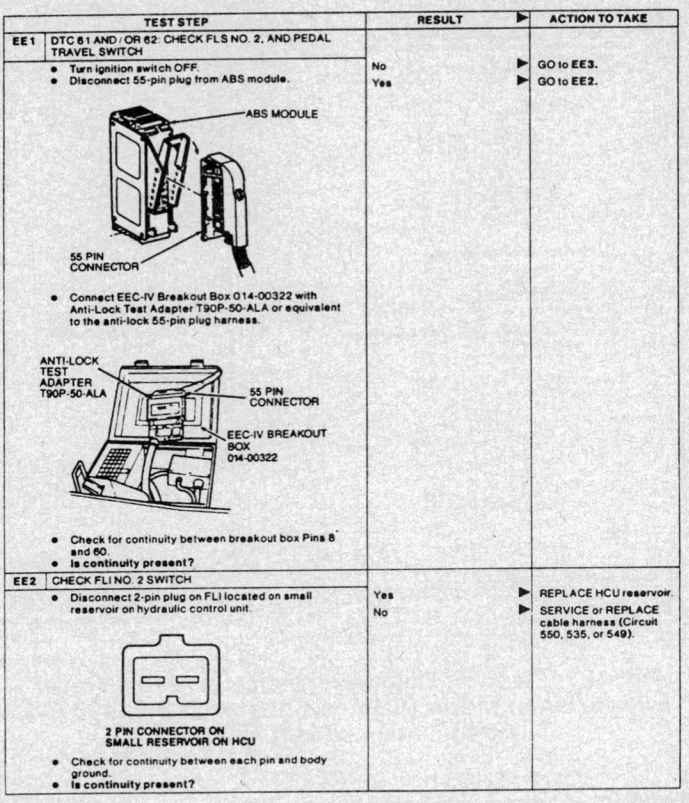

Top-left table (Continental, Part 1 of 9)

TEST STEP	RESULT	▶	ACTION TO TAKE
EE1 DTC 61 AND/OR 62: CHECK FLS NO. 2, AND PEDAL TRAVEL SWITCH			
• Turn ignition switch OFF.	No	▶	GO to EE3.
• Disconnect 55-pin plug from ABS module.	Yes	▶	GO to EE2.
• Connect EEC-IV Breakout Box 014-00322 with Anti-Lock Test Adapter T90P-50-ALA or equivalent to the anti-lock 55-pin plug harness.			
• Check for continuity between breakout box Pins 8 and 60. • Is continuity present?			
EE2 CHECK FLI NO. 2 SWITCH			
• Disconnect 2-pin plug on FLI located on small reservoir on hydraulic control unit.	Yes	▶	REPLACE HCU reservoir.
	No	▶	SERVICE or REPLACE cable harness (Circuit 550, 535, or 549).
• Check for continuity between each pin and body ground. • Is continuity present?			

FM402930031201AX

Fig. 187 Test EE: Fluid Level Indicator/Pedal Travel Switch/Pump Motor Diagnosis (Part 1 of 9). 1993–94 Continental

Top-right table (Sable & Taurus, Part 1 of 9)

TEST STEP	RESULT	▶	ACTION TO TAKE
EE1 DTC 61, AND/OR 62: CHECK FLS NO. 2, PEDAL TRAVEL SWITCH AND PRESSURE SWITCH			
• Turn ignition switch OFF.	No	▶	GO to EE3.
• Disconnect 55-pin plug from ABS module.	Yes	▶	GO to EE2.
• Connect EEC-IV Breakout Box 014-00322 with Anti-Lock Test Adapter T90P-50-ALA or equivalent to the anti-lock 55-pin plug harness.			
• Check for continuity between breakout box Pins 8 and 60. • Is continuity present?			
EE2 CHECK FLS NO. 2 SWITCH			
• Disconnect 2-pin plug on FLS located on small reservoir on hydraulic control unit.	Yes	▶	REPLACE HCU reservoir.
	No	▶	SERVICE or REPLACE cable harness (Circuit 542, 535, or 549 Taurus/Sable). Circuit 550, 535, or 549 (Taurus SHO).
• Check for continuity between each pin and body ground. • Is continuity present?			

FM402930031201BX

Fig. 187 Test EE: Fluid Level Indicator/Pedal Travel Switch/Pump Motor Diagnosis (Part 1 of 9). 1993–94 Sable & Taurus

Bottom-left table (Continental, Part 2 of 9)

TEST STEP	RESULT	▶	ACTION TO TAKE
EE3 CHECK FOR VOLTAGE ON FLS NO. 2 SWITCH AND CIRCUITRY			
• Turn ignition switch to ON position.	No voltage	▶	GO to EE4
• Measure voltage between breakout box Pins 8 and 60.	12 volts	▶	SERVICE or REPLACE cable harness (Circuit 535, 549, or 550).
EE4 CHECK PEDAL TRAVEL SWITCH AND CIRCUITRY			
• Check for continuity between breakout box Pins 5 and 60. • Is continuity present?	No	▶	GO to EE6
	Yes	▶	GO to EE5
EE5 CHECK PEDAL TRAVEL SWITCH			
• Disconnect 2-pin plug on pedal travel switch.	Yes	▶	REPLACE pedal travel switch.
	No	▶	SERVICE or REPLACE cable harness (Circuit 535 or 549).
• Check for continuity between each pin and body ground. • Is continuity present?			
EE6 CHECK FOR VOLTAGE ON PEDAL TRAVEL SWITCH AND CIRCUITRY			
• Measure voltage between breakout box Pins 5 and 60.	No voltage	▶	VERIFY code 61 and/or 62.
	12 volts	▶	SERVICE or REPLACE cable harness (Circuit 535, 549 or 550).

FM402930031202AX

Fig. 187 Test EE: Fluid Level Indicator/Pedal Travel Switch/Pump Motor Diagnosis (Part 2 of 9). 1993–94 Continental

Bottom-right table (Sable & Taurus, Part 2 of 9)

TEST STEP	RESULT	▶	ACTION TO TAKE
EE3 CHECK FOR VOLTAGE ON FLS NO. 2 SWITCH AND CIRCUITRY			
• Turn ignition switch to ON position.	No voltage	▶	GO to EE4.
• Measure voltage between breakout box Pins 8 and 60.	12 volts	▶	SERVICE or REPLACE cable harness circuit 542, 535, or 549 (Taurus/Sable). Circuit 550, 535, or 549 (Taurus SHO).
EE4 CHECK PEDAL TRAVEL SWITCH AND CIRCUITRY			
• Check for continuity between breakout box Pins 5 and 60. • Is continuity present?	No	▶	GO to EE6.
	Yes	▶	GO to EE5.
EE5 CHECK PEDAL TRAVEL SWITCH			
• Disconnect 2-pin plug on pedal travel switch.	Yes	▶	REPLACE pedal travel switch.
	No	▶	SERVICE or REPLACE cable harness (Circuit 535 or 549).
• Check for continuity between each pin and body ground. • Is continuity present?			
EE6 CHECK FOR VOLTAGE ON PEDAL TRAVEL SWITCH AND CIRCUITRY			
• Turn ignition switch to ON position.	No voltage	▶	VERIFY code 61 and/or 62.
• Measure voltage between breakout box Pins 5 and 60.	12 volts	▶	SERVICE or REPLACE cable harness circuit 542, 535 or 549 (Taurus/Sable). Circuit 550, 535 or 549 (Taurus SHO).

FM402930031202BX

Fig. 187 Test EE: Fluid Level Indicator/Pedal Travel Switch/Pump Motor Diagnosis (Part 2 of 9). 1993–94 Sable & Taurus

TEST STEP	RESULT	▶	ACTION TO TAKE
EE7 DTC 63: CHECK PUMP MOTOR SPEED SENSOR AND CIRCUIT NOTE: The ABS module will check the pump, speed sensor and circuitry by running the pump for about 0.5 second each time the ignition is switched ON and the vehicle speed reaches 30 km/h (19 mph). • Turn ignition switch OFF. • Disconnect 55-pin plug from ABS module. 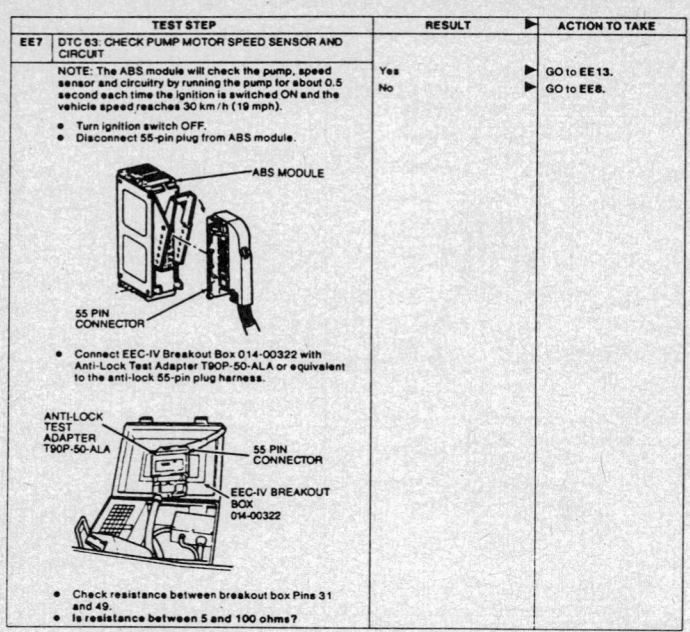 • Connect EEC-IV Breakout Box 014-00322 with Anti-Lock Test Adapter T90P-50-ALA or equivalent to the anti-lock 55-pin plug harness. • Check resistance between breakout box Pins 31 and 49. • Is resistance between 5 and 100 ohms?	Yes No	▶ ▶	GO to EE13. GO to EE8.

FM4029300312030X

Fig. 187   Test EE: Fluid Level Indicator/Pedal Travel Switch/Pump Motor Diagnosis (Part 3 of 9). 1993–94 Continental, Sable & Taurus

TEST STEP	RESULT	▶	ACTION TO TAKE
EE8 CHECK PUMP MOTOR SPEED SENSOR • Disconnect 4-pin plug on pump motor. • Measure resistance between Pins S0 and S1 on pump motor. • Is resistance between 5 and 100 ohms? *(4 PIN PUMP MOTOR CONNECTOR)*	Yes No	▶ ▶	GO to EE9. REPLACE pump and motor.
EE9 CHECK PUMP MOTOR RELAY • Disconnect 7-pin plug on pump motor relay and remove relay. • Check continuity from Pin S0 on 7-pin side to Pin S0 on 4-pin side of relay. • Is continuity present? *(PUMP MOTOR RELAY)*	Yes No	▶ ▶	GO to EE10. REPLACE pump motor relay.
EE10 CHECK PUMP MOTOR RELAY • Check continuity from Pin S1 on 7-pin side to Pin S1 on 4-pin side of relay. • Is continuity present?	Yes No	▶ ▶	GO to EE12. REPLACE pump motor relay.

FM4029300312040X

Fig. 187   Test EE: Fluid Level Indicator/Pedal Travel Switch/Pump Motor Diagnosis (Part 4 of 9). 1993–94 Continental, Sable & Taurus

TEST STEP	RESULT	▶	ACTION TO TAKE
EE11 CHECK CIRCUIT 462 • Check continuity between breakout box Pin 31 and Pin S0 on pump motor connector 7-pin plug (harness side). • Is continuity present? *(7 PIN PUMP MOTOR RELAY CONNECTOR HARNESS SIDE — 539 PK/LB–85, 537 T/Y–30, 532 O/Y–86, 462 P–S0, 57 BK–31, 461 O–31)*	Yes No	▶ ▶	GO to EE12. SERVICE or REPLACE cable harness Circuit 462.
EE12 CHECK CIRCUIT 461 • Check continuity between breakout box Pin 49 and Pin S1 on pump motor connector 7-pin plug (harness side). • Is continuity present?	Yes No	▶ ▶	REVERIFY reading at EE9. SERVICE or REPLACE cable harness Circuit 461.
EE13 CHECK MOTOR SPEED SENSOR SHORT TO BATTERY + • Turn ignition switch to ON. • Measure voltage between breakout box Pins 31 and 60.	No voltage 12 volts	▶ ▶	GO to EE17. GO to EE14.
EE14 CHECK PUMP MOTOR • Disconnect pump motor to relay 4-pin plug connector. • Turn ignition switch to ON. • Measure voltage between breakout box Pins 31 and 60.	No voltage 12 volts	▶ ▶	REPLACE pump and motor. GO to EE15.
EE15 CHECK CIRCUIT 462 • Disconnect wire harness to relay 7-pin plug. • Turn ignition switch to ON. • Measure voltage between breakout box Pins 31 and 60.	No voltage 12 volts	▶ ▶	GO to EE16. SERVICE or REPLACE cable harness Circuit 462.
EE16 CHECK CIRCUIT 461 • Turn ignition switch to ON. • Measure voltage between breakout box Pins 49 and 60.	No voltage 12 volts	▶ ▶	REPLACE pump motor relay. SERVICE or REPLACE cable harness Circuit 461.
EE17 CHECK MOTOR SPEED SENSOR SHORT TO GROUND • Turn ignition switch OFF. • Check for continuity between breakout box Pins 31 and 60. • Is continuity present?	No Yes	▶ ▶	GO to EE20. GO to EE18.
EE18 CHECK CIRCUIT 462 • Disconnect wire harness to relay 7-pin plug. • Check for continuity between breakout box Pins 31 and 60. • Is continuity present?	Yes No	▶ ▶	SERVICE or REPLACE cable harness Circuit 462. GO to EE19.

FM4029300312050X

Fig. 187   Test EE: Fluid Level Indicator/Pedal Travel Switch/Pump Motor Diagnosis (Part 5 of 9). 1993–94 Continental, Sable & Taurus

TEST STEP	RESULT	▶	ACTION TO TAKE
EE19 CHECK CIRCUIT 461 • Check for continuity between breakout box Pins 49 and 60. • Is continuity present?	Yes No	▶ ▶	SERVICE or REPLACE cable harness Circuit 461. REPLACE pump motor relay.
EE20 CHECK PUMP MOTOR OPERATION • Reconnect pump motor relay to pump and wire harness. • Jumper Pins 15, 34 and 60 at breakout box. • Turn ignition to ON position. • Does pump motor run?	Yes No	▶ ▶	REVERIFY code 63. GO to EE21.
EE21 CHECK PUMP MOTOR OPERATION • Disconnect pump motor relay from pump motor. • Ground Pin 2 and apply 12 volts to Pin 1 of pump motor connector. • Does pump motor run? *(4 PIN PUMP MOTOR CONNECTOR)*	Yes No	▶ ▶	GO to EE22. REPLACE pump motor.
EE22 CHECK POWER TO RELAY • Disconnect wire harness from pump motor relay. • Check voltage between Pin 30 on wire harness to pump motor relay connector and ground. *(7 PIN PUMP MOTOR RELAY CONNECTOR HARNESS SIDE — 539 PK/LB–85, 537 T/Y–30, 532 O/Y–86, 462 P–S0, 57 BK–31, 461 O–31)*	Over 10 volts Less than 10 volts	▶ ▶	GO to EE23. SERVICE or REPLACE battery, fuse D or Circuit 537.

FM402930031206AX

Fig. 187   Test EE: Fluid Level Indicator/Pedal Travel Switch/Pump Motor Diagnosis (Part 6 of 9). 1993–94 Continental

TEST STEP	RESULT	▶	ACTION TO TAKE
EE19 CHECK CIRCUIT 461 • Check for continuity between breakout box Pins 49 and 60. • **Is continuity present?**	Yes No	▶ ▶	SERVICE or REPLACE cable harness Circuit 461. REPLACE pump motor relay.
EE20 CHECK PUMP MOTOR OPERATION • Reconnect pump motor relay to pump and wire harness. • Jumper Pins 15, 34 and 60 at breakout box. • Turn ignition to ON position. • **Does pump motor run?**	Yes No	▶ ▶	REVERIFY code 63. GO to EE21.
EE21 CHECK PUMP MOTOR OPERATION • Disconnect pump motor relay from pump motor. • Ground Pin 2 and apply 12 volts to Pin 1 of pump motor connector. • **Does pump motor run?**	Yes No	▶ ▶	GO to EE22. REPLACE pump motor.

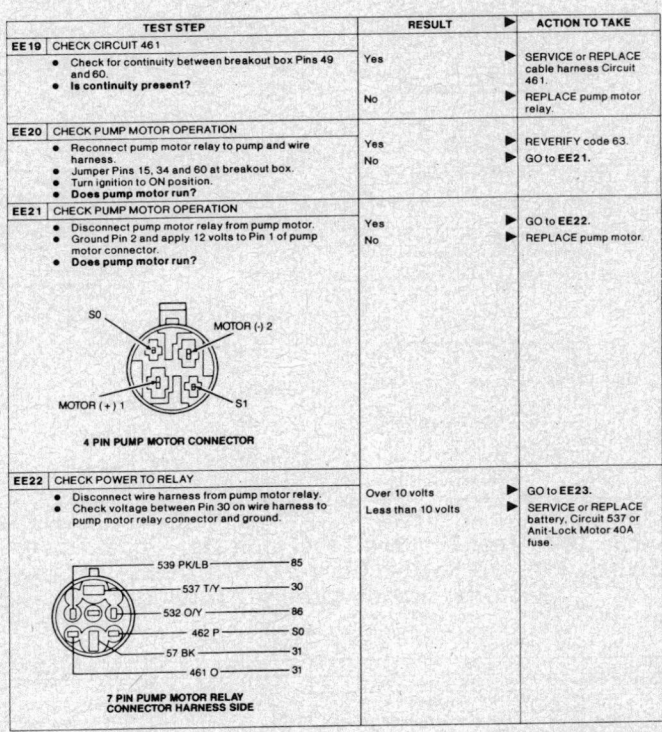

| **EE22** CHECK POWER TO RELAY
 • Disconnect wire harness from pump motor relay.
 • Check voltage between Pin 30 on wire harness to pump motor relay connector and ground. | Over 10 volts
 Less than 10 volts | ▶
 ▶ | GO to EE23.
 SERVICE or REPLACE battery, Circuit 537 or Anit-Lock Motor 40A fuse. |

4 PIN PUMP MOTOR CONNECTOR

7 PIN PUMP MOTOR RELAY CONNECTOR HARNESS SIDE

FM402930031206BX

Fig. 187 Test EE: Fluid Level Indicator/Pedal Travel Switch/Pump Motor Diagnosis (Part 6 of 9). 1993–94 Sable & Taurus

TEST STEP	RESULT	▶	ACTION TO TAKE
EE23 CHECK POWER TO RELAY COIL • Jumper Pins 34 and 60 at breakout box. • Turn ignition to ON position. • Measure voltage between Pin 86 and ground.	Over 10 volts Less than 10 volts	▶ ▶	GO to EE24. SERVICE or REPLACE cable harness Circuit 532.

7 PIN PUMP MOTOR RELAY CONNECTOR HARNESS SIDE

| **EE24** CHECK PUMP MOTOR RELAY COIL
 • Measure resistance between Pins 85 and 86 on pump motor relay.
 • **Is resistance between 45 and 105 ohms?** | Yes
 No | ▶
 ▶ | GO to EE25.
 REPLACE pump motor relay. |

PUMP MOTOR RELAY

| **EE25** CHECK CIRCUIT 539
 • Check for continuity between breakout box Pin 15 and Pin 85 on wire harness to pump motor relay connector.
 • **Is continuity present?** | Yes
 No | ▶
 ▶ | GO to EE26.
 SERVICE or REPLACE cable harness Circuit 539. |

7 PIN PUMP MOTOR RELAY CONNECTOR HARNESS SIDE

FM4029300312070X

Fig. 187 Test EE: Fluid Level Indicator/Pedal Travel Switch/Pump Motor Diagnosis (Part 7 of 9). 1993–94 Continental, Sable & Taurus

TEST STEP	RESULT	▶	ACTION TO TAKE
EE26 CHECK CIRCUIT 57 • Check for continuity between wire harness to pump motor relay connector Pin 31 and ground. • **Is continuity present?**	Yes No	▶ ▶	GO to EE27. SERVICE or REPLACE cable harness Circuit 57.
EE27 CHECK PUMP MOTOR RELAY • Connect battery + to Pin 86 and battery - to Pin 85 of pump motor relay. • Check for continuity between Pin 30 and Pin 1 on relay. • **Is continuity present?**	Yes No	▶ ▶	GO to EE28. REPLACE pump motor relay.
EE28 CHECK PIN MOTOR RELAY • Check continuity between Pins 2 and 31 on pump motor relay. • **Is continuity present?**	Yes No	▶ ▶	REPLACE ABS module. REPLACE pump motor relay.

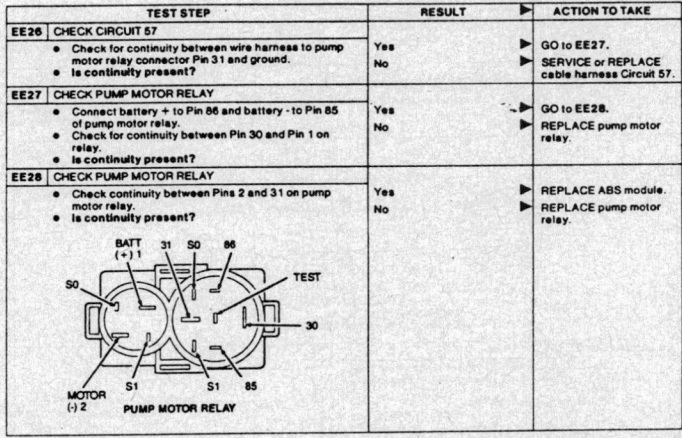

PUMP MOTOR RELAY

FM4029300312080X

Fig. 187 Test EE: Fluid Level Indicator/Pedal Travel Switch/Pump Motor Diagnosis (Part 8 of 9). 1993–94 Continental, Sable & Taurus

TEST STEP	RESULT	▶	ACTION TO TAKE
EE29 DTC 64: CHECK PUMP MOTOR PRESSURE CAPABILITY • Turn ignition switch OFF. • Disconnect 55-pin plug from ABS module.	Yes No	▶ ▶	REVERIFY code 64. REPLACE pump and motor.

ABS MODULE

55 PIN CONNECTOR

• Connect EEC-IV Breakout Box 014-00322 with Anti-Lock Test Adapter T90P-50-ALA or equivalent to the anti-lock 55-pin plug harness.

ANTI-LOCK TEST ADAPTER T90P-50-ALA

55 PIN CONNECTOR

EEC-IV BREAKOUT BOX 014-00322

• Jumper Pins 15, 34 and 60.
• Apply and hold brake pedal.
• Turn ignition switch to ON.
• **Does brake pedal rise?**

FM4029300312090X

Fig. 187 Test EE: Fluid Level Indicator/Pedal Travel Switch/Pump Motor Diagnosis (Part 9 of 9). 1993–94 Continental, Sable & Taurus

TEST STEP	RESULT	►	ACTION TO TAKE
EE3 CHECK FOR VOLTAGE ON FLS NO. 2 SWITCH AND CIRCUITRY • Turn ignition switch to ON position. • Measure voltage between breakout box Pins 8 and 60.	No voltage 12 volts	► ►	GO to EE4. SERVICE or REPLACE cable harness circuit 459, 467, 547 or 550 Town Car. Circuit 535, 550 or 636 on Crown Victoria / Grand Marquis.
EE4 CHECK PEDAL TRAVEL SWITCH AND CIRCUITRY • Check for continuity between breakout box Pins 5 and 60. • Is continuity present?	No Yes	► ►	GO to EE6. GO to EE5.
EE5 CHECK PEDAL TRAVEL SWITCH • Disconnect 2-pin plug on pedal travel switch. [2 PIN BRAKE PEDAL POSITION SWITCH diagram] • Check for continuity between each pin and body ground. • Is continuity present?	Yes No	► ►	REPLACE pedal travel switch. SERVICE or REPLACE cable harness Circuit 550, 467, 459 or 547 Town Car. Circuit 550, 535, 636 or 549 for Crown Victoria / Grand Marquis.
EE6 CHECK FOR VOLTAGE ON PEDAL TRAVEL SWITCH AND CIRCUITRY • Turn ignition switch to ON position. • Measure voltage between breakout box Pins 5 and 60.	No voltage 12 volts	► ►	If vehicle is equipped with Traction Assist option: GO to EE7. If vehicle is equipped with ABS only: Reverify code 61 and / or 62. SERVICE or REPLACE cable harness circuit 550, 467, 459 or 547 Town Car. Circuit 550, 535, 636 or 549 Crown Vic / Grand Marquis.
EE7 CHECK PRESSURE SWITCH AND CIRCUITRY • Check for continuity between breakout box Pins 13 and 60. • Is continuity present?	Yes No	► ►	GO to EE8. GO to EE9.

FM4029300313010X

Fig. 188   Test EE: Fluid Level Indicator/Pedal Travel Switch/Pressure Switch (Part 2 of 10). 1993–94 Crown Victoria, Grand Marquis & Town Car

TEST STEP	RESULT	►	ACTION TO TAKE
EE8 CHECK PRESSURE SWITCH • Disconnect 19-pin plug on valve body. • Check for continuity between valve body Pin 11 and body ground, and Pin 12 and body ground. • Is continuity present?	Yes No	► ►	REPLACE valve body. SERVICE or REPLACE cable harness circuit 550, 467, 459, or 547 Town Car. Circuit 535, 549 or 550 for Crown Victoria / Grand Marquis.
EE9 CHECK FOR VOLTAGE ON PRESSURE SWITCH • Turn ignition switch to ON position. • Measure voltage between breakout box Pins 13 and 60.	No voltage 12 volts	► ►	VERIFY Code 61, 62 or 66. GO to EE10.
EE10 CHECK PRESSURE SWITCH • Disconnect 19-pin plug on valve body. • Turn ignition switch to ON position. • Measure voltage between Pin 11 and body ground and Pin 12 and body ground.	12 volts No voltage	► ►	REPLACE valve body. SERVICE or REPLACE cable harness Circuit 547 or 467 for Town Car. Circuit 636 or 535 for Crown Victoria / Grand Marquis.

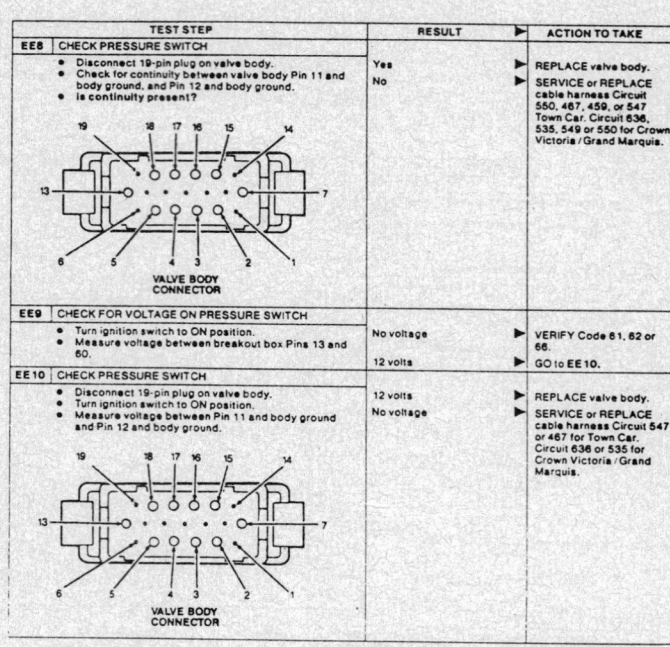

FM4029300313020X

Fig. 188   Test EE: Fluid Level Indicator/Pedal Travel Switch/Pressure Switch (Part 3 of 10). 1993–94 Crown Victoria, Grand Marquis & Town Car

TEST STEP	RESULT	►	ACTION TO TAKE
EE11 DTC 63: CHECK PUMP MOTOR SPEED SENSOR AND CIRCUIT • Turn ignition switch OFF. • Disconnect 55-pin plug from ABS Module.	Yes No	► ►	GO to EE17. GO to EE12.
• Connect EEC-IV Breakout Box 014-00322 with Anti-Lock Test Adapter T90P-50-ALA or equivalent to the anti-lock 55-pin plug harness. • Check resistance between breakout box Pins 31 and 49. • Is resistance between 5 and 100 ohms?			
EE12 CHECK PUMP MOTOR SPEED SENSOR • Disconnect 4-pin plug on pump motor. • Measure resistance between Pins S0 and S1 on pump motor. • Is resistance between 5 and 100 ohms?	Yes No	► ►	GO to EE13. REPLACE pump and motor.

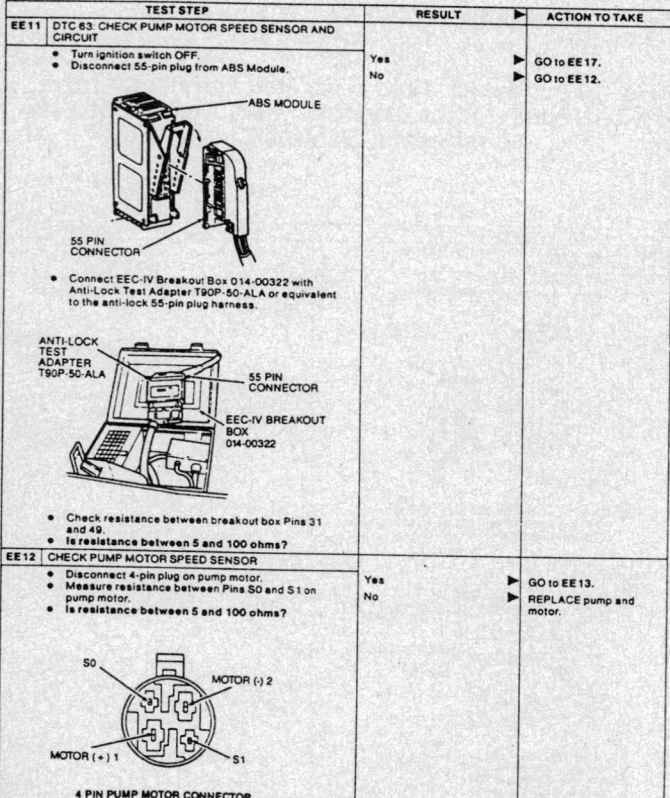

FM4029300313030X

Fig. 188   Test EE: Fluid Level Indicator/Pedal Travel Switch/Pressure Switch (Part 4 of 10). 1993–94 Crown Victoria, Grand Marquis & Town Car

TEST STEP	RESULT	►	ACTION TO TAKE
EE13 CHECK PUMP MOTOR RELAY • Disconnect 7-pin plug on pump motor relay and remove relay. • Check continuity from Pin S0 on 7-pin side to Pin S0 on 4-pin side of relay. • Is continuity present?	Yes No	► ►	GO to EE14. REPLACE pump motor relay.
EE14 CHECK PUMP MOTOR RELAY • Check continuity from Pin S1 on 7-pin side to Pin S1 on 4-pin side of relay. • Is continuity present?	Yes No	► ►	GO to EE15. REPLACE pump motor relay.
EE15 CHECK CIRCUIT 462 • Check continuity between breakout box Pin 31 and Pin S0 on pump motor connector 7-pin plug (harness side). • Is continuity present?	Yes No	► ►	GO to EE16. SERVICE or REPLACE cable harness Circuit 462.
EE16 CHECK CIRCUIT 351 OR 604 • Check continuity between breakout box Pin 49 and Pin S1 on pump motor connector 7-pin plug (harness side). • Is continuity present?	Yes No	► ►	REVERIFY reading at EE11. SERVICE or REPLACE cable harness Circuit 604 for Town Car. Circuit 351 for Crown Victoria / Grand Marquis.
EE17 CHECK MOTOR SPEED SENSOR SHORT TO BATTERY + • Turn ignition switch to ON. • Measure voltage between breakout box Pins 31 and 60.	No voltage 12 volts	► ►	GO to EE20. GO to EE18.

FM4029300313040X

Fig. 188   Test EE: Fluid Level Indicator/Pedal Travel Switch/Pressure Switch (Part 5 of 10). 1993–94 Crown Victoria, Grand Marquis & Town Car

TEST STEP	RESULT	▶	ACTION TO TAKE
EE18 CHECK CIRCUIT 462			
• Disconnect wire harness to relay 7-pin plug. • Disconnect pump motor to relay 4-pin plug. • Turn ignition switch to ON. • Measure voltage between breakout box Pins 31 and 60.	No voltage 12 volts	▶ ▶	GO to EE19. SERVICE or REPLACE cable harness Circuit 462.
EE19 CHECK CIRCUIT 351 or 604			
• Turn ignition switch to ON. • Measure voltage between breakout box Pins 49 and 60.	No voltage 12 volts	▶ ▶	REPLACE pump motor relay. SERVICE or REPLACE cable harness Circuit 604 for Town Car. Circuit 351 for Crown Victoria / Grand Marquis.
EE20 CHECK MOTOR SPEED SENSOR SHORT TO GROUND			
• Check for continuity between breakout box Pins 31 and 60. • Is continuity present?	No Yes	▶ ▶	GO to EE23. GO to EE21.
EE21 CHECK CIRCUIT 462			
• Disconnect wire harness to relay 7-pin plug. • Disconnect pump motor to relay 4 pin plug. • Check for continuity between breakout box Pins 31 and 60. • Is continuity present?	Yes No	▶ ▶	SERVICE or REPLACE cable harness Circuit 462. GO to EE22.
EE22 CHECK CIRCUIT 351 OR 604			
• Check for continuity between breakout box Pins 49 and 60. • Is continuity present?	Yes No	▶ ▶	SERVICE or REPLACE cable harness Circuit 604 Town Car. Circuit 351 Crown Victoria / Grand Marquis. REPLACE pump motor relay.
EE23 CHECK PUMP MOTOR OPERATION			
• Reconnect pump motor relay to pump and wire harness. • Jumper Pins 15, 34 and 60 at breakout box. • Turn ignition to ON position. • Does pump motor run?	Yes No	▶ ▶	REPLACE controller. GO to EE24.
EE24 CHECK PUMP MOTOR OPERATION			
• Disconnect pump motor relay from pump motor. • Ground Pin 2 and apply 12 volts to Pin 1 of pump motor connector. • Does pump motor run?	Yes No	▶ ▶	GO to EE25. REPLACE pump motor.

S0 — MOTOR (-) 2 — MOTOR (+) 1 — S1
4 PIN PUMP MOTOR CONNECTOR

FM4029300313050X

Fig. 188   Test EE: Fluid Level Indicator/Pedal Travel Switch/Pressure Switch (Part 6 of 10). 1993–94 Crown Victoria, Grand Marquis & Town Car

TEST STEP	RESULT	▶	ACTION TO TAKE
EE25 CHECK POWER TO RELAY			
• Disconnect wire harness from pump motor relay. • Check voltage between Pin 30 on wire harness to pump motor relay connector and ground.	Over 10 volts Less than 10 volts	▶ ▶	GO to EE26. SERVICE or REPLACE battery, 50 amp fuse or Circuit 533 Crown Victoria / Grand Marquis. Battery, 40 amp fuse or circuit 537 Town Car.
EE26 CHECK POWER TO RELAY COIL			
• Jumper Pins 34 and 60 at breakout box. • Turn ignition to ON position. • Measure voltage between Pins 86 and ground.	Over 10 volts Less than 10 volts	▶ ▶	GO to EE27. SERVICE or REPLACE cable harness Circuit 532.

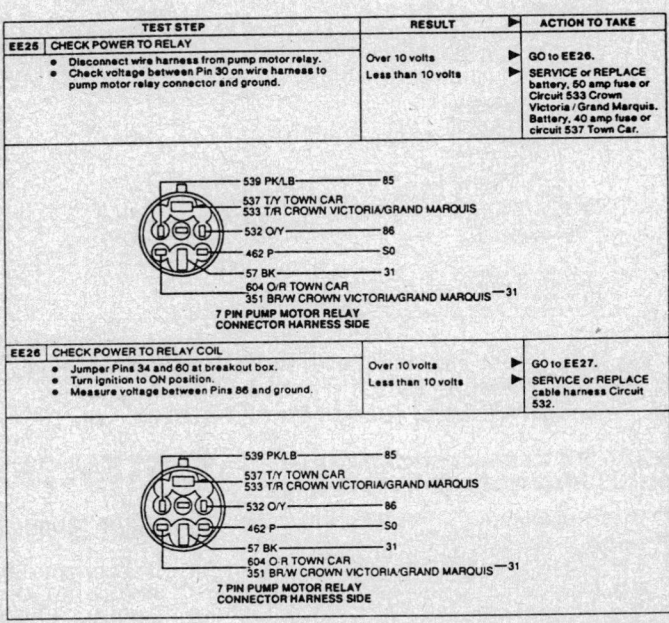

539 PK/LB — 85
537 T/Y TOWN CAR
533 T/R CROWN VICTORIA/GRAND MARQUIS
532 O/Y — 86
462 P — S0
57 BK — 31
604 O/R TOWN CAR
351 BR/W CROWN VICTORIA/GRAND MARQUIS — 31
7 PIN PUMP MOTOR RELAY CONNECTOR HARNESS SIDE

539 PK/LB — 85
537 T/Y TOWN CAR
533 T/R CROWN VICTORIA/GRAND MARQUIS
532 O/Y — 86
462 P — S0
57 BK — 31
604 O/R TOWN CAR
351 BR/W CROWN VICTORIA/GRAND MARQUIS — 31
7 PIN PUMP MOTOR RELAY CONNECTOR HARNESS SIDE

FM4029300313060X

Fig. 188   Test EE: Fluid Level Indicator/Pedal Travel Switch/Pressure Switch (Part 7 of 10). 1993–94 Crown Victoria, Grand Marquis & Town Car

TEST STEP	RESULT	▶	ACTION TO TAKE
EE27 CHECK PUMP MOTOR RELAY COIL			
• Measure resistance between Pins 85 and 86 on pump motor relay. • Is resistance between 45 and 105 ohms?	Yes No	▶ ▶	GO to EE28. REPLACE pump motor relay.
EE28 CHECK CIRCUIT 539			
• Check for continuity between breakout box Pin 15 and Pin 85 on wire harness to pump motor relay connector. • Is continuity present?	Yes No	▶ ▶	GO to EE29. SERVICE or REPLACE cable harness Circuit 539.
EE29 CHECK CIRCUIT 57			
• Check for continuity between wire harness to pump motor relay connector Pin 31 and ground. • Is continuity present?	Yes No	▶ ▶	GO to EE30. SERVICE or REPLACE cable harness Circuit 57.
EE30 CHECK PUMP MOTOR RELAY			
• Connect battery + to Pin 86 and battery - to Pin 85 of pump motor relay. • Check for continuity between Pin 30 and Pin 1 on relay. • Is continuity present?	Yes No	▶ ▶	GO to EE31. REPLACE pump motor relay.

BATT (+) 1 — 31 — S0 — 86
S0 — TEST
MOTOR (-) 2 — S1 — S1 — 85 — 30
PUMP MOTOR RELAY

539 PK/LB — 85
537 T/Y TOWN CAR
533 T/R CROWN VICTORIA/GRAND MARQUIS
532 O/Y — 86
462 P — S0
57 BK — 31
604 O/R TOWN CAR
351 BR/W CROWN VICTORIA/GRAND MARQUIS — 31
7 PIN PUMP MOTOR RELAY CONNECTOR HARNESS SIDE

FM4029300313070X

Fig. 188   Test EE: Fluid Level Indicator/Pedal Travel Switch/Pressure Switch (Part 8 of 10). 1993–94 Crown Victoria, Grand Marquis & Town Car

TEST STEP	RESULT	▶	ACTION TO TAKE
EE31 CHECK PUMP MOTOR RELAY			
• Check continuity between Pins 2 and 31 on pump motor relay. • Is continuity present?	Yes No	▶ ▶	REPLACE ABS module. REPLACE pump motor relay.

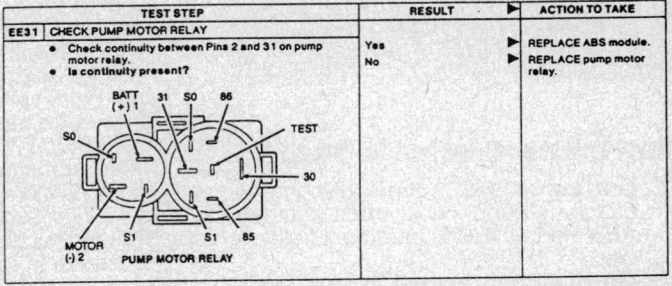

BATT (+) 1 — 31 — S0 — 86
S0 — TEST
MOTOR (-) 2 — S1 — S1 — 85 — 30
PUMP MOTOR RELAY

FM4029300313080X

Fig. 188   Test EE: Fluid Level Indicator/Pedal Travel Switch/Pressure Switch (Part 9 of 10). 1993–94 Crown Victoria, Grand Marquis & Town Car

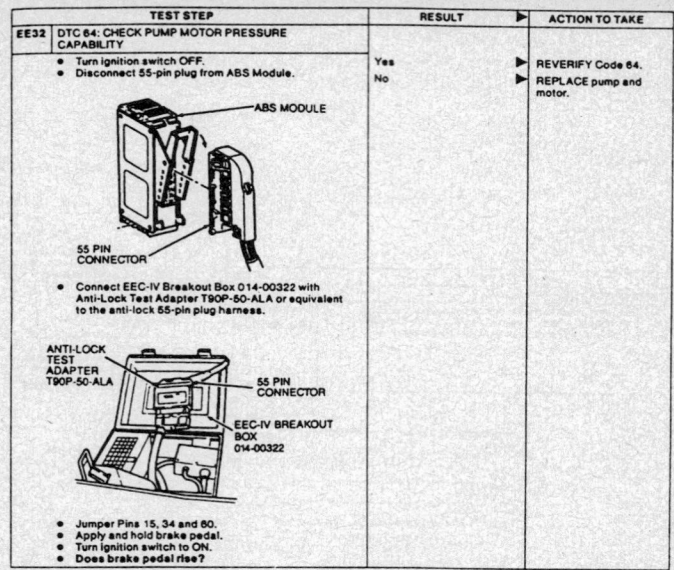

Fig. 188 Test EE: Fluid Level Indicator/Pedal Travel Switch/Pressure Switch (Part 10 of 10). 1993–94 Crown Victoria, Grand Marquis & Town Car

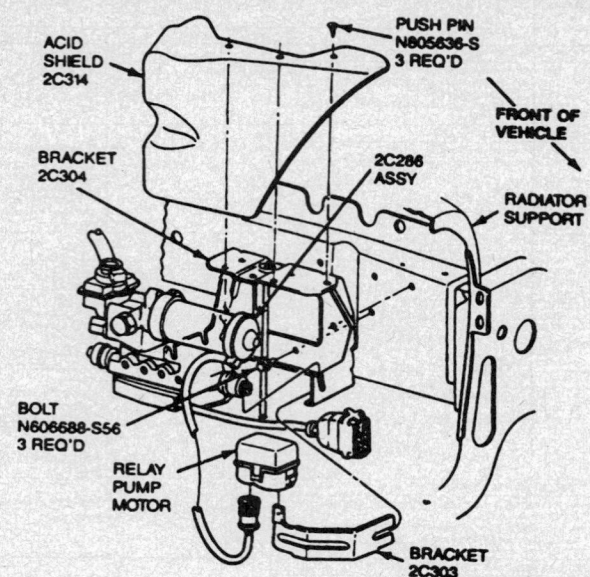

Fig. 189 Hydraulic control unit replacement

1993–94 Crown Victoria, Grand Marquis & Town Car

1. Disconnect battery ground cable, then remove air cleaner and air outlet tube.
2. Disconnect 19-pin connector attaching HCU to wire harness, then the 4-pin connector attaching HCU to pump motor relay.
3. Remove two inlet port tubes, then the four outlet tubes from HCU. Plug each port to prevent brake fluid from spilling on paint and wiring.
4. Remove three HCU to mounting bracket nuts, then the HCU from vehicle. Front nut on bracket also attaches ABS pump motor relay bracket.
5. Reverse procedure to install, noting the following:
   a. **Torque** HCU to mounting bracket nuts to 12–18 ft. lbs.
   b. **Torque** HCU tube fittings to 10–18 ft. lbs.

Continental, Sable & Taurus

1. **On Taurus SHO models,** disconnect battery ground cable, then remove ABS module (ECU) from top of clutch disc.
2. **On all models except Taurus SHO,** disconnect battery cables and remove battery and tray.
3. Remove plastic pushpins holding acid shield to HCU mounting bracket, then the acid shield, **Fig. 189.**
4. **On all models,** disconnect 19-pin connector from HCU wiring harness, then disconnect 4-pin connector from HCU motor pump relay.
5. Remove two inlet and four outlet port tubes from HCU, then plug each port to prevent spilling.
6. Remove relay mounting bracket nut.
7. Remove HCU assembly to mounting bracket nuts, then the assembly.

SYSTEM SERVICE

Brake System Bleed

1. Disconnect 55-pin plug from ABS module (ECU), then attach anti-lock breakout box/bleeding adapter tool No. T90P-50-ALA, or equivalent, to wiring harness 55-pin plug.
2. Place bleed/harness switch in bleed position.
3. Turn ignition to On position. Red Off light should turn on.
4. Push motor button on adapter down to start pump motor. Red Off light will turn off and green On light will turn on. Pump motor will run for 60 seconds once motor button is pushed.
5. If pump motor is turns off before 60 seconds has elapsed, push abort button and pump motor will turn off.
6. After 20 seconds of operation, push and hold valve button down. Hold valve button for 20 seconds, then release.
7. Pump motor will continue to run an additional 20 seconds after valve button is released.
8. Brake lines can be bled in conventional manner in the following sequence:
   a. Right rear.
   b. Left front.
   c. Left rear.
   d. Right front.

Component Replacement

HYDRAULIC CONTROL UNIT

ABS MODULE (ECU)

Continental, Sable & Taurus

1. Disconnect battery ground cable.

2. Remove trim panel in luggage compartment, located behind back seat to expose the electronic control module.
3. Disconnect the 55-pin connector by pulling up lever completely, then move connector away from ABS module (ECU) until all terminals are clear.
4. Remove screws, then the ABS module (ECU).
5. Reverse procedure to install.

Crown Victoria, Grand Marquis & Town Car

1. Disconnect battery ground cable.
2. **On Town Car models,** locate ABS module (ECU) at righthand front side of radiator support.
3. **On Crown Victoria & Grand Marquis models,** locate ABS module (ECU) at lefthand front side of radiator support.
4. **On all models,** disconnect 55-pin electrical connector.
5. Unlock connector by pulling up lever completely, then move top of connector away from ABS module until terminals are clear and pull connector up out of slots in module.
6. Remove three ABS module (ECU) to mounting bracket screws.
7. Reverse procedure to install, noting the following:
   a. Align ABS module (ECU) with bracket so lever is facing up and side with two mounting holes is flat against bracket top.
   b. **Torque** screws to 40–60 inch lbs.
8. Reverse procedure to install.
   a. **On Taurus SHO models, torque** three nuts to 12–18 ft. lbs.
   b. **On all models except Taurus SHO, torque** three screws to 16–4 ft. lbs.

FRONT WHEEL SENSOR

Continental, Sable & Taurus

1. Disconnect wheel sensor electrical

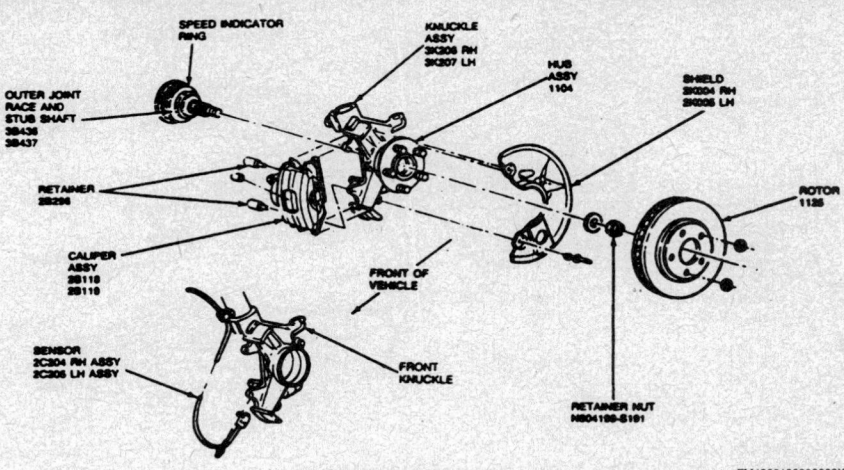

Fig. 190 Front speed sensor removal. Continental

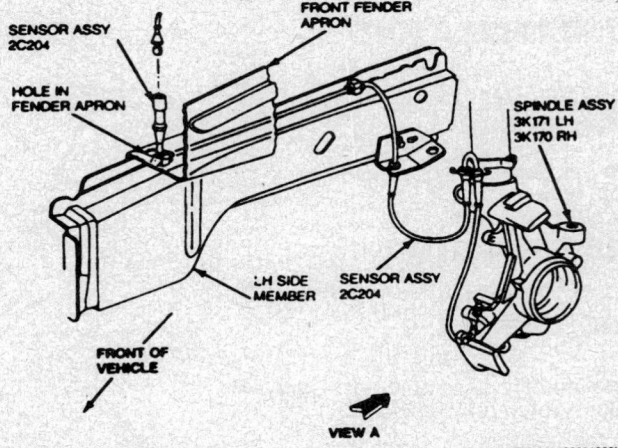

Fig. 191 Front speed sensor removal. Sable & Taurus

connector located in engine compartment.

2. When removing right side sensor, remove plastic push studs and loosen front of splash shield, **Figs. 190 and 191.**

3. When removing left side sensor, remove plastic push studs and loosen rear of splash shield.

4. Thread sensor wire through holes in fender apron. On right front sensor, remove retaining clips behind splash shield.

5. Raise and support vehicle, then remove tire and wheel assembly.

6. Disconnect sensor wire grommets at height sensor bracket, and from retainer clip on shock strut.

7. Loosen screw securing sensor, then remove sensor assembly from front knuckle.

8. Reverse procedure to install. **Torque** sensor attaching screw to 40-60 inch lbs.

Crown Victoria, Grand Marquis & Town Car

1. From inside engine compartment, disconnect sensor assembly two-pin connector from wiring harness.

2. When removing left sensor, remove steel routing clip attaching sensor wire to tube bundle, **Fig. 192.**

3. When removing right sensor, remove plastic routing clip attaching wire to frame and dust shield.

4. Remove rubber coated steel spring clip holding sensor wire to frame.

5. Remove sensor attaching bolt from spindle, then slide sensor out of mounting hole.

6. Reverse procedure to install.

REAR WHEEL SENSOR

CROWN VICTORIA, GRAND MARQUIS & TOWN CAR

1. From inside luggage compartment, disconnect two-pin sensor connector from wiring harness pushing sensor wire through hole in floor.

2. From below vehicle, remove sensor wire from routing bracket located on top of rear axle carrier housing, **Fig. 193.**

3. Remove attaching screw from clip, holding sensor wire and brake tube bracket on axle.

4. Reverse procedure to install, noting the following:

   a. Ensure split ring is located in groove properly. Opening in ring should not line up with notch in tube shaped sensor retainer.

   b. Install sensor into bracket with notch correctly aligned with bracket. Push sensor until split ring locks sensor into place, **Fig. 194.**

5. Remove sensor to rear adapter retaining bolt, then remove sensor.

6. Reverse procedure to install, noting the following:

   a. **Torque** retaining bolt to 40-60 inch lbs.

   b. **Torque** sensor and brake tube to bracket retaining screw to 40-60 inch lbs.

CONTINENTAL

Removal

1. Turn air suspension switch in luggage compartment to off position.

2. Disconnect sensor connector in luggage compartment, then push rubber grommet through sheet metal floorpan.

3. Raise and support vehicle, then remove retaining clips for sensor wire and remove wire from routing position.

4. Loosen sensor retaining screw at caliper anchor plate, then remove sensor.

5. Install spring replacement tool No. T88P-5310-A, or equivalent, on front suspension arm. Then, using 3/4 inch breaker bar, lower arm to provide clearance for sensor connector, **Fig. 195.**

Installation

1. With suspension arm lowered, thread sensor wire connector through opening above arm.

2. Install front suspension arm, then align sensor with mounting holes on caliper anchor plate. **Torque** sensor screw to 40-60 inch lbs.

3. Position sensor wire in routing position, then install retaining clips.

4. Thread sensor connector through hole in floorpan. Push center portion of rubber grommet on sensor wire until properly seated.

5. Connect electrical connector in luggage compartment and turn on air suspension switch.

SABLE & TAURUS SEDAN

Removal

1. Remove rear seat and seat back insulation.

2. Disconnect sensor from harness, then tie one end of string or wire to sensor connector and tie other end to rear seat sheet metal bracket.

3. Push sensor wire grommet and connector through floorpan drawing string or wire with sensor connector, **Fig. 196.**

4. Disconnect string or wire from sensor underneath vehicle.

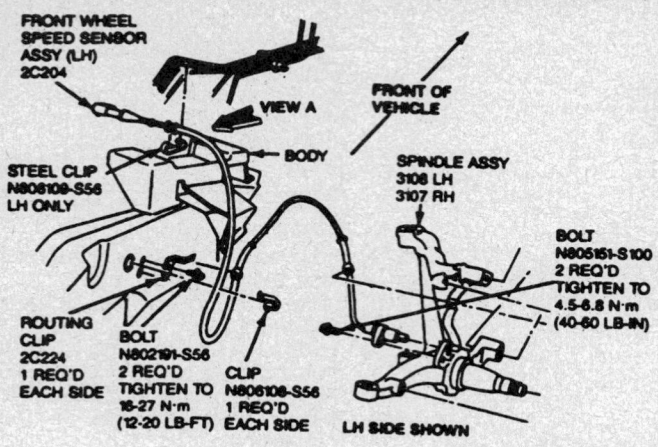

Fig. 192 Front speed sensor removal. Crown Victoria, Grand Marquis & Town Car

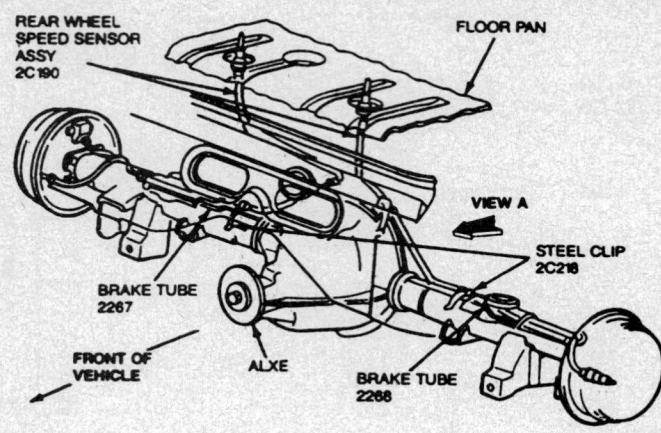

Fig. 193 Rear speed sensor removal. Crown Victoria, Grand Marquis & Town Car

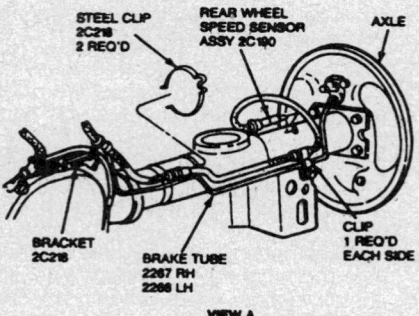

Fig. 194 Rear speed sensor installation. Crown Victoria, Grand Marquis & Town Car

5. Disconnect routing clips from suspension arms, then remove sensor retaining bolts from rear brake adapters.

Installation

1. Attach string or wire to new sensor connector, then pull sensor connector through hole in floorpan using string or wire.
2. Remove string or wire and connect sensor to harness.
3. Insert sensor into hole in adapter, then install retaining bolt. **Torque** bolt to 40-60 inch lbs., **Fig. 197.**
4. Install sensor routing clips to suspension arms, then sensor wire grommet into hole in floorpan.
5. Install rear seat.

SABLE & TAURUS WAGON

1. Raise and support vehicle, then remove sensor wire with attached grommet from hole in floorpan.
2. Disconnect rear brake anti-lock sensor from harness, then remove routing clips.
3. Remove sensor bolt, then the sensor.
4. Reverse procedure to install. **Torque** sensor bolt to 40-60 inch lbs.

FRONT SPEED INDICATOR RING

1. Remove wheel and tire assembly.
2. Remove caliper, rotor and hub assemblies.
3. Using a three jaw puller, remove indicator ring from hub.
4. Reverse procedure to install.

REAR SPEED INDICATOR RING

CONTINENTAL, SABLE & TAURUS

1. Remove wheel and tire assembly.
2. Remove caliper, rotor and rear hub assemblies.
3. Using arbor press, press hub out of speed sensor ring.
4. Reverse procedure to install.

CROWN VICTORIA, GRAND MARQUIS & TOWN CAR

Removal

1. Remove axle shaft and position on workbench.
2. Using a thin blade cold chisel between sensor ring and axle flange, strike evenly around flange, forcing indicator ring off of sensor ring journal. **Do not use a screwdriver or similar tool.** Extreme care must be taken not to scratch or nick wheel bearing and seal journal.

Installation

1. Prior to installation of new ring, remove any burrs or nicks from journal.
2. Position indicator ring installation tool No. T89P-20202-A, or equivalent, on press with pilot ring facing down.
3. Place new indicator ring over installation tool and insert axle shaft through tool.
4. Place spacer tool No. T85T-4616-AH, or equivalent, over hub end of axle shaft.
5. Press axle shaft until it bottoms out on axle flange.
6. Install axle shaft on vehicle.

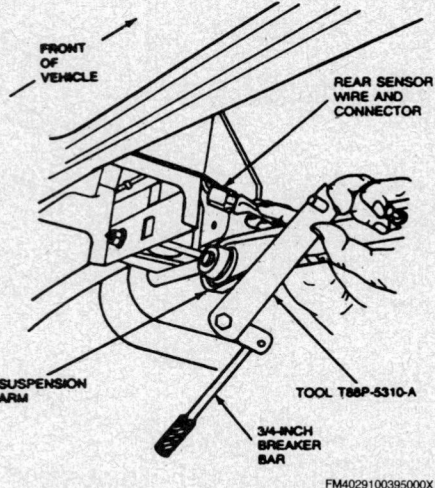

Fig. 195 Rear speed sensor removal. Continental

PEDAL TRAVEL SWITCH

Continental, Sable & Taurus

1. Disconnect battery ground cable, then the wiring harness lead at switch connector.
2. Using screwdriver, pry connector locator from holes in brake pedal support.
3. Unsnap switch hook from pin on dump valve adapter bracket, **Fig. 198.**
4. Using needle nose pliers or equivalent, squeeze ears on switch mounting clip, then push clip through hole in brake pedal support.
5. Remove switch by feeding switch harness through hole of brake pedal support bracket.
6. Reverse procedure to install, noting the following:
   a. Rotate switch and ensure mounting clip ears are completely engaged.
   b. Adjust switch as outlined under "Adjustments."

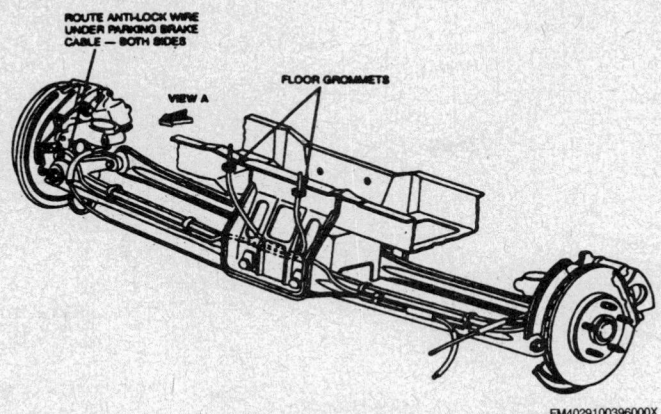

Fig. 196 Rear speed sensor removal. Sable & Taurus

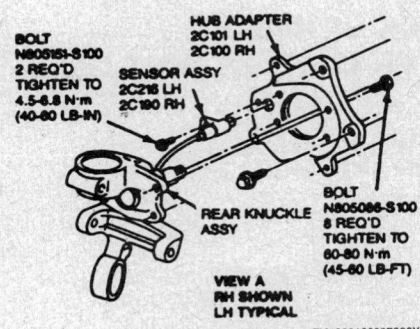

Fig. 197 Rear speed sensor installation. Sable & Taurus

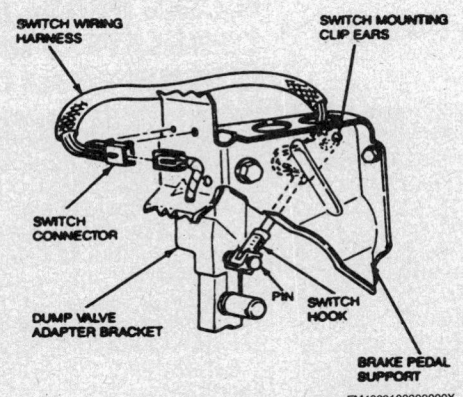

Fig. 198 Pedal travel switch replacement. Except Crown Victoria, Grand Marquis & Town Car

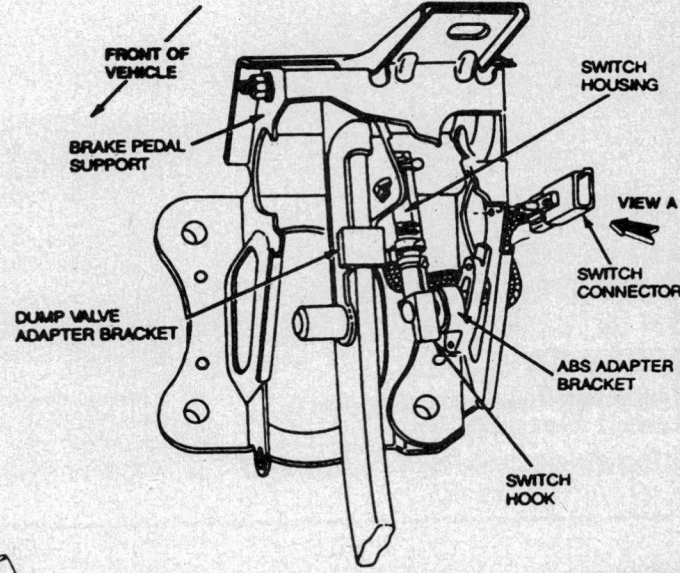

Fig. 199 Pedal travel switch replacement. Crown Victoria, Grand Marquis & Town Car

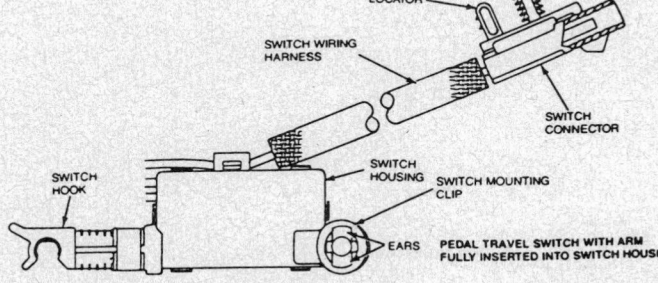

Fig. 200 Pedal travel switch adjustment

Crown Victoria, Grand Marquis & Town Car

1. Disconnect battery ground cable, then the wiring harness lead at switch connector.
2. Using screwdriver, pry connector locator from holes in brake pedal support.
3. Unsnap switch hook from pin on ABS adapter bracket.
4. Hold brake pedal down to gain access, then, using needle nose pliers, squeeze ears on switch mounting clip. Push clip through hole in dump valve adapter bracket, **Fig. 199.**
5. Remove rear attaching screw on ABS adapter bracket, then loosen second screw.
6. Rotate bracket, then remove switch and wire assembly.
7. Reverse procedure to install, noting the following:
   a. Rotate switch and ensure mounting clip ears are completely engaged.
   b. Adjust switch as outlined under in "Pedal Travel Switch, Adjust."

Adjustments
PEDAL TRAVEL SWITCH

1. Push switch plunger completely into switch housing. This zeros out switch adjustment so it can automatically reset to correct dimension, **Fig. 200.**
2. Slowly pull arm back, out of switch housing past detent point. **At this point it should be impossible to reattach arm to pin unless brake pedal is forced down.**
3. Depress brake pedal until switch hook can be snapped onto pin. Snap hook onto pin and pull brake pedal back-up to its normal position. This automatically sets switch to proper adjustment. When switch is unhooked from pin, the above resetting procedure should be performed to ensure correct switch adjustment.

TECHNICAL SERVICE BULLETINS

ANTI-LOCK BRAKE INDICATOR LIGHT STAYS ON

1992 Crown Victoria & Grand Marquis Built Before 2/1/92

The anti-lock brake light may stay on. This occurs because water leaks through the connector into the ABS electronic control unit and corrodes it. The anti-lock feature could stop functioning but the brake system would perform conventionally.

1. Disconnect battery ground cable, then locate ABS electronic control unit at lefthand front side of radiator support.
2. Disconnect 55-pin connector from ECU, then examine connector and ECU for moisture or corrosion.
3. If moisture or corrosion exists, replace ECU and wire assembly as described under "ABS System Service."

ANTI-LOCK BRAKE INDICATOR LIGHT COMES ON INTERMITTENTLY OR STAYS ON

1992–93 Crown Victoria & Grand Marquis

The anti-lock brake light may come on

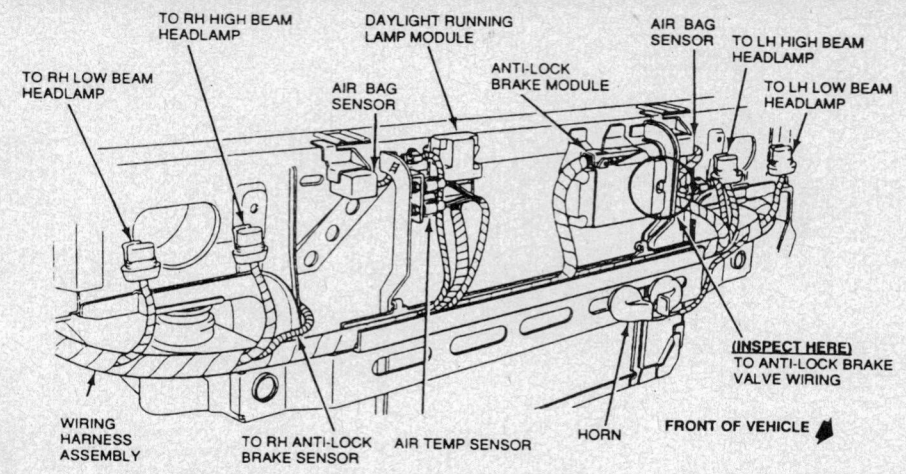

Fig. 201 ABS wiring harness inspection location

intermittently or stay on. This occurs because the wiring harness assembly may rub on the left radiator support and eventually cause an electrical short in the exposed wiring.

1. Inspect wiring harness for damage where takeouts to ABS hydraulic control unit go through the lefthand radiator support, **Fig. 201**.
2. Repair exposed wires and cover repaired area with rubber or thick plastic shielding.
3. If wiring harness appears in good condition and the concern still exists, perform ABS diagnostics as described under "Diagnosis & Testing."

BRAKE PEDAL DOES NOT COMPLETELY RETURN OR IS SLOW TO RETURN

The service brake pedal may be slow to return or it may not completely return after application. This may occur after a high engine vacuum condition, such as a deceleration (brakes off) from above 60 mph. It is caused by the brake booster and only vehicles with the ABS system are affected. Vehicle stopping capacity and distance are not affected.

Replace brake booster as described under "ABS System Service."

If complaint is vibration during brake application and/or excessive lining wear, booster should not be replaced unless the slow or no return brake pedal is confirmed.

Aspire, Escort & Tracer

NOTE: Wire Color Code & Electrical Symbol Identification Located At The Front Of This Manual Can Be Used As An Aid When Using Wiring Circuits Found In This Section.

INDEX

PRECAUTIONS

HYDRAULIC BRAKE FLUID COLOR

Hydraulic brake fluid must conform with the requirements of Federal Motor Vehicle Safety Standard 116. Under this standard, brake fluids are visually different from other automotive fluids such as transmission, power steering and engine.

Fluid color in a normal brake system may vary from its original color for many reasons. A brake master cylinder may show significantly different shades fluid color between the two brake master cylinder reservoirs. Color may also appear to vary between cast steel and die cast aluminum reservoirs. Some reasons for discoloration include the following:

   Heat and/or aging.
   Different operation temperatures or different rates of normal oxidation between two reservoir compartments.
   Different brands and/or shades of fluid are used when topping off during normal service.
   Dissolution of color dye used on master cylinder internal springs during assembly.

Brake fluid contaminated with hydrocarbon/mineral based fluid (power steering or transmission fluid) can be detected by an obvious swelling of the master cylinder cap gasket. If the master cylinder cap gasket is swollen, all brake system rubber parts must be replaced. All brake tubes and hoses must be thoroughly flushed with Ford Heavy Duty Brake Fluid C6Az-19542–AA or –BA or DOT-3 equivalent before the vehicle returns to service.

DESCRIPTION

SYSTEM COMPONENTS

POWER BRAKE BOOSTER

The power brake booster reduces the effort required to push the brake pedal and apply the brakes. Engine vacuum allows for this power assist.

A vacuum booster hose from the engine contains a vacuum booster hose check valve. When the engine is shut off, the valve closes, trapping engine vacuum within the power brake booster. This reserve vacuum allows for several assisted brake applications with the engine off.

BRAKE MASTER CYLINDER

Aspire

The brake master cylinder is a tandem hydraulic servo. When the brake pedal is pressed, the brake master cylinder distributes pressurized brake fluid through steel brake lines to the hydraulic anti-lock actuator assembly ports. The primary circuit of the brake master cylinder supplies brake fluid to the left front and the right rear wheels. The secondary circuit supplies the right front and left rear wheels. The top portion of the brake master cylinder is a brake fluid reservoir.

Escort & Tracer

The brake master cylinder is different than on Escort and Tracer models without anti-lock brakes. The relief port of the brake master cylinder has been eliminated and a center valve with a center port has been included in the secondary piston.

When the brake pedal is not pressed, the secondary piston is pressed toward the stop pin by the return pin, **Fig. 1.** At the same time, the center valve within the secondary piston is pressed open by the stop pin, providing a return path to the brake master cylinder reservoir.

When the brake pedal is pressed, the secondary piston is moved away from the stop pin, **Fig. 2.** The center valve spring presses the center valve against the secondary piston, closing the return path and allowing brake fluid pressure to be generated. Operation of the primary piston is unchanged.

BRAKE PRESSURE CONTROL VALVE

Escort & Tracer

The brake pressure control valve regulates hydraulic pressure in the rear brake circuit. It is located on the firewall. When the brake pedal is applied, full rear circuit pressure passes through the brake pressure control valve until the split point of the valve. Above the split point, the brake pressure control valve begins to reduce hydraulic pressure to the rear brake circuit, creating balanced braking between the front and rear wheels while maintaining balanced hydraulic pressure at each rear wheel.

BRAKE FLUID LEVEL SWITCH

Aspire

If brake fluid is lost from any circuit, a brake fluid level switch in the brake master cylinder reservoir will illuminate a brake system warning indicator in the instrument cluster. Once the circuit is closed, the brake system warning indicator will come on and remain on whenever the ignition switch is in the ON or START position.

HYDRAULIC ANTI-LOCK ACTUATOR ASSEMBLY

The hydraulic anti-lock actuator assembly contains solenoid valves, flow control valves, a pump motor and buffer chambers. The solenoid valves open and close by signals sent by the anti-lock brake control module. The flow control valves move according to the solenoid valve condition and control the hydraulic pressure in the brake calipers (pressure reduction or pressure increase). The hydraulic anti-lock actuator assembly has four solenoid valves which operate the three-channel system.

During normal braking, fluid from the brake master cylinder enters the two inlet ports located on top of the hydraulic anti-lock actuator assembly. The fluid then passes through the normally open solenoid valves to each respective wheel location. If the anti-lock brake control module senses a wheel is about to lock, the anti-lock brake control module sends an electronic signal to close the flow control valve of the affected circuit. This action regulates the brake fluid entering the affected brake circuit, preventing wheel lock up. If the anti-lock brake control module senses the af-

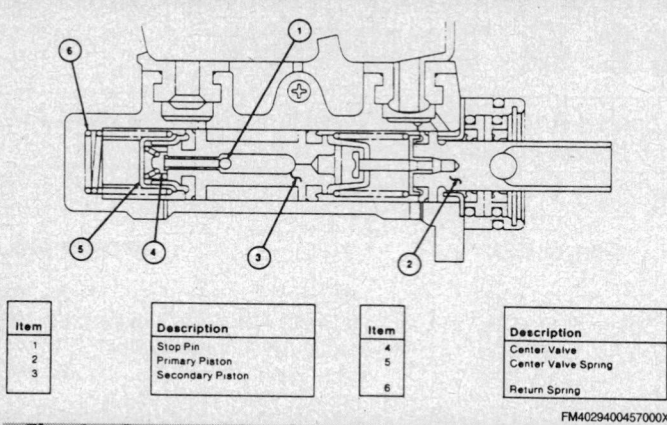

Operating

Fig. 1   Cross-sectional view of non-operating brake master cylinder. Escort & Tracer

Item	Description	Item	Description
1	Stop Pin	4	Center Valve
2	Primary Piston	5	Center Valve Spring
3	Secondary Piston	6	Return Spring

FM4029400457000X

Fig. 2   Cross-sectional view of operating brake master cylinder. Escort & Tracer

Item	Description	Item	Description
1	Stop Pin	4	Center Valve
2	Primary Piston	5	Center Valve Spring
3	Secondary Piston	6	Return Spring

FM4029400458000X

fected wheel is continuing to decelerate, the anti-lock brake control module sends a signal to open the normally closed flow control valve in the affected circuit. This action reduces any pressure trapped between the flow control valve and the affected brake actuator. The brake fluid is returned to the brake master cylinder reservoir.

ANTI-LOCK BRAKE CONTROL MODULE

The anti-lock brake control module controls the entire anti-lock brake system. The module is located behind the lefthand side of the instrument panel, on Aspire models, and under the passenger seat, on Escort and Tracer models.

The anti-lock brake control module continuously calculates wheel speed and vehicle speed based on information it receives from the front and rear brake anti-lock sensors. The module has self-diagnostic capabilities and stores diagnostic trouble codes in its memory. If a diagnostic trouble code is present in module memory, the instrument panel ANTI-LOCK indicator will illuminate when the engine is running.

ANTI-LOCK BRAKE SENSORS

The front anti-lock sensor and brackets are mounted on the front wheel knuckles and the rear brake anti-lock sensors are mounted on the rear wheel spindles. The sensors produce electrical pulses by monitoring the rotation of the sensor indicators which are mounted on the front wheel driveshaft and joints and the rear wheel hubs.

OPERATION

The ABS functions by releasing and applying fluid pressure to the front disc brake calipers and rear wheel cylinders during special braking conditions. The ABS does not function under normal braking conditions, nor does it affect front-to-rear brake proportioning. When one or more wheels approach a slip condition, the ABS automatically senses the slip and activates the pressure control function.

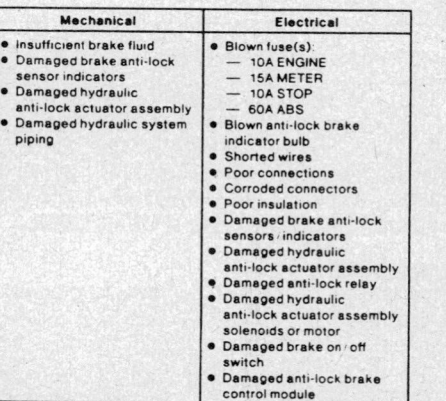

Mechanical	Electrical
• Insufficient brake fluid	• Blown fuse(s):
• Damaged brake anti-lock sensor indicators	— 10A ENGINE
• Damaged hydraulic anti-lock actuator assembly	— 15A METER
• Damaged hydraulic system piping	— 10A STOP
	— 60A ABS
	• Blown anti-lock brake indicator bulb
	• Shorted wires
	• Poor connections
	• Corroded connectors
	• Poor insulation
	• Damaged brake anti-lock sensors / indicators
	• Damaged hydraulic anti-lock actuator assembly
	• Damaged anti-lock relay
	• Damaged hydraulic anti-lock actuator assembly solenoids or motor
	• Damaged brake on / off switch
	• Damaged anti-lock brake control module

FM4029400460000X

Fig. 3   Visual Inspection Chart

Through its preprogramming, the anti-lock brake control module decides which wheel(s)' brake pressure needs modulation. Once determined, the anti-lock brake control module sends appropriate signals to the solenoid valves located in the hydraulic anti-lock actuator assembly. These solenoid valves allow adjoining flow control valves to modulate fluid pressure, resulting in a pressure reduction at the front disc brake calipers and rear wheel cylinders to prevent further lockup.

TROUBLESHOOTING

Inspection & Verification

Verify concern by driving vehicle. Look for problems in other areas which may affect ABS: suspension and steering components, tire integrity and air pressure, wheel bearings and brake components common to all brake systems. **The hydraulic anti-lock actuator assembly is not serviceable nor can it be pressure checked. If any of its components fail, it must be replaced as a complete unit.**

If all systems and components are satisfactory, refer to Visual Inspection Chart, **Fig. 3**, and Symptom Chart, **Fig. 4**. After following Visual Inspection Chart and

Symptom Chart, proceed to "Quick Test" under "Diagnosis & Testing."

DIAGNOSIS & TESTING
QUICK TEST

For Quick Test, refer to **Figs. 5 and 6** on Aspire models and **Figs. 7 and 8** on Escort and Tracer models.

WARNING INDICATOR

The anti-lock brake warning indicator will come on to warn the driver of an ABS failure. Normal brake system operation will still be available. However, the wheels will lock up under hard braking.

ON-BOARD DIAGNOSTICS

On-Board Diagnostics is divided into two specialized tests, the "Key ON-Engine Running (KOER) Test" and the "Continuous Test." Before performing either test, inspect the anti-lock brake warning indicator to verify a fault has been detected by the ABS control module or if the system is operating normally. When the ABS is operating normally, the warning indicator will illuminate during KOEO and go off after the engine has started. **If the ABS warning indicator stays on after the engine starts, this indicates a present failure.** The logic circuit could keep the warning indicator on after the engine starts for up to 60 seconds. Failure codes are stored in the ABS control module until they are erased.

RETRIEVING DIAGNOSTIC TROUBLE CODES

Anti-Lock Brake System (ABS) diagnostic trouble codes may be retrieved using the following methods:
1. Identifying voltage fluctuations with analog voltmeter.
2. Identifying flashes of anti-lock brake warning indicator.
3. Reading digital or audible code from Rotunda Super STAR II Tester tool No. 007-0041B, or equivalent, using Rotunda Super MECS Adapter tool No. 007-00052, or equivalent.

The test connector available for obtaining diagnostic trouble codes is the Data Link Connector (DLC), located near the battery.

CONDITION	POSSIBLE SOURCE	ACTION
• Anti-Lock Brake Warning Indicator Always ON	• Fuse(s). • ABS electrical circuit failure. • Anti-lock brake warning indicator circuit shorted. • Brake anti-lock sensor malfunction. • Anti-lock relay malfunction. • Hydraulic anti-lock actuator assembly malfunction. • Anti-lock brake control module malfunction. • Low generator voltage output.	▶ GO to ABS Quick Test.
• Anti-Lock Brake Warning Indicator Flashes	• Intermittent ABS electrical circuit failure. • Data Link Connector (DLC) shorted to ground. • Anti-lock brake control module malfunction.	▶ GO to ABS Quick Test.
• Noisy Hydraulic Anti-Lock Actuator Assembly	• ABS electrical circuit failure. • Hydraulic anti-lock actuator assembly malfunction.	▶ GO to ABS Quick Test.
• Anti-Lock Brake Warning Indicator On for 1.5 Seconds and Off Before Engine Started	• ABS electrical circuit failure. • Anti-lock brake warning indicator circuit failure. • Low generator voltage output.	▶ GO to ABS Quick Test.
• Anti-Lock Brake Warning Indicator Always Off	• Blown fuse (15A METER). • Blown indicator bulb. • Anti-lock brake warning indicator circuit failure. • Anti-lock brake control module malfunction.	▶ GO to ABS Quick Test.
• ABS Inoperative	• Blown fuse(s). • Insufficient brake fluid. • ABS electrical circuit failure. • Inoperative anti-lock relay. • Hydraulic anti-lock actuator assembly malfunction. • Damaged brake anti-lock sensor(s). • Anti-lock brake control module malfunction.	▶ GO to ABS Quick Test.
• All Other Symptoms	• All other symptoms that are common to all brake systems.	

FM4029400459000X

Fig. 4   Symptom Chart

TEST STEP		RESULT	▶	ACTION TO TAKE
QT2	PERFORM VEHICLE PREPARATION			
• Perform all of the following safety steps required to run ABS Quick Test. • Apply the parking brake. • Place the transaxle firmly into the PARK position (NEUTRAL on MTX). • Block the drive wheels. • Turn off all of the electrical loads. — Radios — Lamps — A/C — Heater blower fans, etc. • Have all of the safety steps been performed and all of the electrical loads turned off?		Yes	▶	PROCEED to Test Step QT3.
		No	▶	Personal safety and correct diagnostic results are dependent on Test Step QT2. Do not PROCEED with Quick Test if vehicle preparation cannot be performed.
QT3	CHECK ANTI-LOCK BRAKE WARNING INDICATOR			
• Turn the ignition key ON without starting the engine. • Does the anti-lock brake warning indicator illuminate continuously?		Yes (Warning indicator illuminated continuously)	▶	Normal operation. PROCEED to Quick Test Step QT4.
		No (Warning indicator not illuminated)	▶	CHECK anti-lock brake warning indicator circuit, 15A METER fuse and bulb. GO to Pinpoint Test G1.
		No (Warning indicator flashing)	▶	VERIFY that the data link connector is not jumped (or shorted to ground) between pins "TBS" and "GND".
		No (Warning indicator illuminates for 1.5 seconds and goes out before engine is started)	▶	Low generator output. GO to Pinpoint Test F1.
QT4	CHECK ANTI-LOCK BRAKE WARNING INDICATOR WITH ENGINE RUNNING			
• Start the engine. • Drive the vehicle if necessary. NOTE: Certain ABS faults require that the vehicle be driven in order for the anti-lock brake warning indicator to come on. Other faults will cause the anti-lock brake warning indicator to turn on each time the engine is started. • Does the anti-lock brake warning indicator illuminate?		Yes (Retrieve codes using Super STAR II Tester)	▶	Indicates a present failure. PROCEED to Quick Test Step QT5.
		Yes (Retrieve codes using VOM)	▶	Indicates a present failure. PROCEED to Quick Test Step QT6.
		No (Warning indicator not illuminated)	▶	Normal operation. If ABS symptom exists, GO to Pinpoint Test H1.
QT5	PERFORM SUPER STAR II HOOKUP			
• Verify that a failure has been detected in the ABS. (An illuminated anti-lock brake warning indicator in the Key ON-Engine Running mode indicates a present failure. If the anti-lock brake warning indicator is not illuminated in Key ON-Engine Running mode but symptom exists, it may indicate a past or intermittent problem.) • Key off. • Access the Data Link Connector (DLC) located in the engine compartment. • Connect a Rotunda Super STAR II Tester 007-0041B or equivalent to the data link connector using Super MECS Adapter 007-00052 or equivalent. • Place the adapter in the "ABS" position. • Place the tester in the "MECS" position. • Latch the Super STAR II tester to the "Test" position. • Is the Super STAR II hooked up properly?		Yes	▶	PROCEED to QT7, ABS Diagnostic Trouble Code Retrieval.
		No	▶	RE-ATTEMPT Step QT5, Super STAR II Hookup. SERVICE any faults if necessary.

FM4029400461020X

Fig. 5   Quick Test (Part 2 of 4). Aspire

TEST STEP		RESULT	▶	ACTION TO TAKE
QT1	PERFORM VISUAL CHECK			
• Check for sufficient brake fluid, damaged brake anti-lock sensors, or leaks, and damaged hydraulic anti-lock actuator assembly. • Check the ABS wiring harness for proper connections, bent or broken pins, corrosion, loose wires, and proper routing. • Check all of the fuses for proper connection or damage. • Check the anti-lock brake control module for physical damage. • Are all of the components OK? NOTE: It may be necessary to disconnect or disassemble harness connector assemblies to do some of the inspections. Note pin locations before disassembly. Disconnect assemblies with key off.		Yes	▶	DRIVE vehicle to verify anti-lock brakes symptom and PROCEED to Test Step QT2.
		No	▶	SERVICE fault(s) in system and then PROCEED to Test Step QT2.

FM4029400461010X

Fig. 5   Quick Test (Part 1 of 4). Aspire

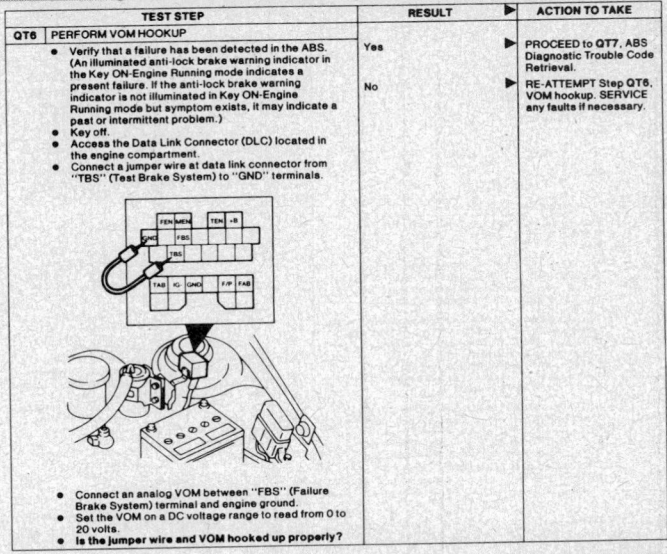

TEST STEP		RESULT	▶	ACTION TO TAKE
QT6	PERFORM VOM HOOKUP			
• Verify that a failure has been detected in the ABS. (An illuminated anti-lock brake warning indicator in the Key ON-Engine Running mode indicates a present failure. If the anti-lock brake warning indicator is not illuminated in Key ON-Engine Running mode but symptom exists, it may indicate a past or intermittent problem.) • Key off. • Access the Data Link Connector (DLC) located in the engine compartment. • Connect a jumper wire at data link connector from "TBS" (Test Brake System) to "GND" terminals. • Connect an analog VOM between "FBS" (Failure Brake System) terminal and engine ground. • Set the VOM on a DC voltage range to read from 0 to 20 volts. • Is the jumper wire and VOM hooked up properly?		Yes	▶	PROCEED to QT7, ABS Diagnostic Trouble Code Retrieval.
		No	▶	RE-ATTEMPT Step QT6, VOM hookup. SERVICE any faults if necessary.

FM4029400461030X

Fig. 5   Quick Test (Part 3 of 4). Aspire

cessing capability. It verifies the various sensors and actuators are connected and operating properly. Code patterns will be indicated through the Data Link Connector (DLC) and the anti-lock brake warning indicator will flash to indicate the type of failure.

CONTINUOUS TEST

This test is intended as an aid in diagnosing intermittent failures in the Anti-Lock Brake System (ABS). It is identical to the KOER Test, but also allows the technician to enter this mode of the test and to attempt to recreate the intermittent failure by tapping, moving and wiggling the harness and/or suspected sensor.

Faults will be indicated by diagnostic trouble codes using a Rotunda 73 Digital Multimeter tool No. 105-00051, Rotunda Super STAR II Tester tool No. 007-0041B, or equivalents. Knowing the affected circuits, a close check of the harness and associated connectors can be made. Remember to keep your eyes on the multimeter, tester and anti-lock brake warning indicator for any change which will indicate where the intermittent fault is located.

When directed to a Pinpoint Test, look carefully at the wiring schematic. Any time a repair is made, erase the anti-lock brake control module memory and repeat the Quick Tests to ensure the repair was effective. If all phases of the Quick Test result in a pass, it is likely the problem is non-electronic related.

The diagnostic trouble codes may indicate different failures so parting from the Quick Test procedure may result in code identification error. Therefore, it is recommended the Quick Test procedure be followed in its entirety. Anti-lock brake warning indicator mode inspection and ABS diagnostic trouble code retrieval are covered in the Quick Test.

Refer to **Fig. 9** for anti-lock brake control module logic specifications for diagnostic trouble codes.

KEY ON-ENGINE RUNNING (KOER) TEST

When activated, this test checks the anti-lock brake control module and system circuitry by testing its integrity and pro-

27-197

TEST STEP		RESULT	▶	ACTION TO TAKE
QT7	PERFORM ABS DIAGNOSTIC TROUBLE CODE RETRIEVAL			
	• Verify that the anti-lock brake warning indicator illuminated (prior to equipment hookup) in the Key ON-Engine Off test before continuing. • Key ON. If using a Super STAR II tester, turn the key ON, wait two seconds, then turn the tester ON. • **Does the anti-lock brake warning indicator flash briefly then go out?** NOTE: When a diagnostic trouble code is reported on the analog VOM, it will represent itself as a pulsing or sweeping movement of the voltmeter's needle across the dial face. Codes will be repeated after all memory codes have been displayed once.	Yes	▶	ABS system OK. GO to Section 06-00 for non-ABS related symptoms.
		No (Warning indicator illuminated constantly)	▶	RECORD VOM or Super STAR II diagnostic trouble codes. ERASE diagnostic trouble codes from memory as explained in Erasing Diagnostic Trouble Codes in this section. RE-ATTEMPT diagnostic trouble code retrieval. RECORD all re-created diagnostic trouble codes and REFER to Code Identification Chart. SERVICE re-created codes as necessary. If the problem still exists or if no codes were re-created, PROCEED to QT8. (Codes that were not re-created indicate past or intermittent faults).
		No (Warning indicator flashes codes)	▶	Indicates past or intermittent fault(s). Be sure to RECORD the diagnostic trouble codes before erasing faults. ERASE diagnostic trouble codes from the memory as explained in Erasing Diagnostic Trouble Codes in this section, then PROCEED to QT8.
QT8	PERFORM CONTINUOUS TEST			
	• Hookup the VOM and jumper wire, or the Super STAR II, as in Test Step QT5 or QT6. • Key ON. NOTE: Use the audible warning function on the Super STAR II tester by turning the "SPKR" switch ON. You will be alerted of a continuous test fault without having to visually check the tester. • Tap, move and wiggle the suspected sensor and/or harness working with short sections from the sensor to dash panel and to anti-lock brake control module. Drive vehicle, if necessary. • **Does the anti-lock brake warning indicator illuminate continuously or audible warning heard from Super STAR II Tester?** NOTE: With key ON, any coded fault re-created during continuous test will illuminate anti-lock brake warning indicator constantly. If key is turned off, then back ON without clearing codes from memory, anti-lock brake warning indicator will flash codes along with VOM or Super STAR II indicating a past or intermittent fault.	Yes	▶	RECORD VOM or Super STAR II Diagnostic Trouble Codes and REFER to Code Identification Chart. SERVICE only the codes re-created in this test step.
		No	▶	Normal operation. If intermittent fault cannot be re-created, turn key off. DISCONNECT suspect sensor and anti-lock brake control module from harness very carefully. Visually INSPECT all terminals for corrosion, bad crimps, improperly seated terminals, etc. RECONNECT harness connectors and RE-ATTEMPT continuous test.

FM4029400461040X

Fig. 5   Quick Test (Part 4 of 4). Aspire

	Diagnosis Indication				
ABS Warning Indicator		VOM	Diagnostic Trouble Code	Possible Failure Location	Action To Take
• Illuminated Constantly for Present Failure • Flashes According to VOM Indication for Past or Intermittent Failure			11	RH Front Brake Anti-Lock Sensor RH Front Brake Anti-Lock Sensor Indicator	GO to Pinpoint Test A1.
			12	LH Front Brake Anti-Lock Sensor LH Front Brake Anti-Lock Sensor Indicator	
			13	RH Rear Brake Anti-Lock Sensor RH Rear Brake Anti-Lock Sensor Indicator	
			14	LH Rear Brake Anti-Lock Sensor LH Rear Brake Anti-Lock Sensor Indicator	
			15	Front and Rear Brake Anti-Lock Sensors	GO to Pinpoint Test B1.
			22	Solenoid Valve	GO to Pinpoint Test C1.
			51	Fail-Safe Relay	GO to Pinpoint Test D1.
			53	Motor Relay Motor	GO to Pinpoint Test E1.
			61	Anti-Lock Brake Control Module	REPLACE Anti-Lock Brake Control Module.
• Illuminated Constantly		No Indication	No Code	Generator Anti-Lock Brake Warning Indicator	GO to Pinpoint Test F1.

FM4029400462000X

Fig. 6   Code identification chart. Aspire

TEST STEP		RESULT	▶	ACTION TO TAKE
QT3	CHECK ANTI-LOCK BRAKE WARNING INDICATOR			
	• Turn the ignition switch ON without starting the engine. • **Does the anti-lock brake warning indicator illuminate continuously?**	Yes (Warning indicator illuminates continuously)	▶	Normal operation. PROCEED to Quick Test Step QT4.
		No (Warning indicator not illuminated)	▶	CHECK anti-lock brake warning indicator circuit, 15A METER fuse and miniature bulb. GO to Pinpoint Test H1.
		No (Warning indicator flashing)	▶	VERIFY that the data link connector is not jumped (or shorted to ground) between pins "TBS" and "GND."
		No (Warning indicator illuminates for 1.5 seconds and goes out before engine is started)	▶	Low generator output. GO to Pinpoint Test G1.
QT4	CHECK ANTI-LOCK BRAKE WARNING INDICATOR WITH ENGINE RUNNING			
	• Start the engine. • Drive the vehicle if necessary (read note). NOTE: Certain ABS faults require that the vehicle be driven in order for the warning indicator to come on. Other faults will cause the warning indicator to turn on each time the engine is started. • **Does the anti-lock brake warning indicator illuminate?**	Yes (Retrieve codes using Super STAR II Tester)	▶	Indicates a present failure. PROCEED to Quick Test Step QT5.
		Yes (Retrieve codes using VOM)	▶	Indicates a present failure. PROCEED to Quick Test Step QT6.
		No (Warning indicator not illuminated)	▶	Normal operation. If ABS symptom exists, GO to Pinpoint Test G1.

FM4029400463010X   FM4029400463020X

Fig. 7   Quick Test (Part 1 of 5). Escort & Tracer   **Fig. 7   Quick Test (Part 2 of 5). Escort & Tracer**

TEST STEP		RESULT	▶	ACTION TO TAKE
QT1	PERFORM VISUAL CHECK			
	• Check for sufficient hydraulic brake fluid, damaged anti-lock sensors, leaks, and damaged hydraulic anti-lock actuator assembly. • Check the ABS wiring harness for proper connections, bent or broken pins, corrosion, loose wires, and proper routing. • Check all of the fuses for proper connection or damage. • Check the anti-lock brake control module for physical damage. • **Are all of the components OK?** NOTE: It may be necessary to disconnect or disassemble harness connector assemblies to do some of the inspections. Note pin locations before disassembly. Disconnect assemblies with key OFF.	Yes	▶	DRIVE vehicle to verify Anti-Lock Brakes symptom and PROCEED to Test Step QT2.
		No	▶	SERVICE fault(s) in system and then PROCEED to Test Step QT2.
QT2	PERFORM VEHICLE PREPARATION			

	• Perform all of the following safety steps required to run ABS Quick Test.
	 • Apply the parking brake.
	 • Place the shift control selector lever firmly into the PARK position (NEUTRAL on MTX).
	 • Block the drive wheels.
	 • Turn off all of the electrical loads.
	   — Radios
	   — Indicators
	   — A/C-heater blower fans, etc.
	 • **Have all of the safety steps been performed and all of the electrical loads turned OFF?**
		Yes	▶	PROCEED to Test Step QT3.

		No	▶	Personal safety and correct diagnostic results are dependent on Test Step QT2. Do not PROCEED with Quick Test if vehicle preparation cannot be performed.

CLEARING DIAGNOSTIC TROUBLE CODES

When erasing the diagnostic trouble codes, note the following:

1. Anti-lock brake warning indicator should illuminate while performing memory cancel. When memory cancel operation is completed, indicator should illuminate for 2-3 seconds, then go off.
2. After memory cancel, ABS module performs self-diagnosis.
3. Memory is not cancelled by disconnecting battery.
4. Memory codes cannot be cancelled if intervals for depressing brake pedal exceed one second or stoplamp miniature bulb or Brake On/Off (BOO) switch has malfunctioned.
5. If using analog VOM, be sure to remove jumper wire from data link connector after all checks and repairs are made.

Using Analog VOM

1. Connect pins "TBS" and "GND" at Data Link Connector (DLC) with jumper wire, then output diagnostic trouble codes using analog VOM.
2. After first code is repeated, press brake pedal 10 times at intervals of less than one second.
3. Turn key to OFF position, then disconnect jumper wire at DLC.

Using Rotunda Super STAR II

1. Connect Rotunda Super STAR II Tester tool No. 007-0041B, or equivalent, to the Data Link Connector (DLC) with Rotunda Super MECS Adapter tool No. 007-00052, or equivalent.
2. Turn key to ON position, then output diagnostic trouble codes using tester.
3. After first code is repeated, depress brake pedal 10 times at intervals of less than one second, then turn key to OFF position.
4. Disconnect tester from DLC.

TEST STEP	RESULT	►	ACTION TO TAKE
QT5 PERFORM SUPER STAR II HOOKUP			
• Verify that a failure has been detected in the ABS. (An illuminated anti-lock brake warning indicator in the KOER mode indicates a present failure. If the anti-lock brake warning indicator is not illuminated in KOER mode, but symptom exists, it may indicate a past or intermittent problem). • Turn the ignition switch OFF. • Access the data link connector located in the engine compartment. • Connect Rotunda Super STAR II Tester 007-0041B to the data link connector using Rotunda Super MECS Adapter 007-00052.	Yes	►	PROCEED to QT7, ABS Diagnostic Trouble Code Retrieval.
	No	►	RE-ATTEMPT Step QT5, Super STAR II Hookup. SERVICE any faults if necessary.

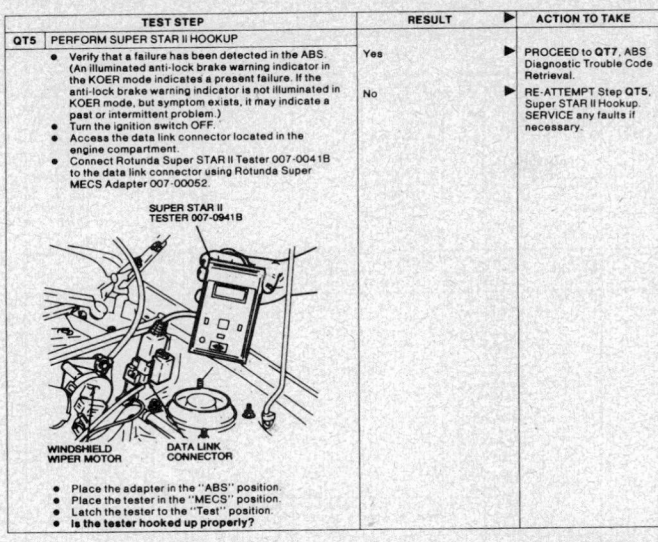

SUPER STAR II
TESTER 007-0941B

WINDSHIELD WIPER MOTOR   DATA LINK CONNECTOR

• Place the adapter in the ''ABS'' position.
• Place the tester in the ''MECS'' position.
• Latch the tester to the ''Test'' position.
• Is the tester hooked up properly?

FM4029400463030X

Fig. 7   Quick Test (Part 3 of 5). Escort & Tracer

TEST STEP	RESULT	►	ACTION TO TAKE
QT6 PERFORM VOM HOOKUP			
• Verify that a failure has been detected in the ABS. (An illuminated anti-lock brake warning indicator in the KOER mode indicates a present failure. If the anti-lock brake warning indicator is not illuminated in KOER mode but symptom exists, it may indicate a past or intermittent failure). • Turn the ignition switch OFF. • Access the data link connector located in the engine compartment. • Connect a jumper wire at data link connector from ''TBS'' (Test Brake System) to ''GND'' terminals (see illustration). • Connect an analog VOM between ''FBS'' (Failure Brake System) terminal and engine ground (see illustration). • Set the VOM on a DC voltage range to read from 0 to 20 volts. • Is the jumper wire and VOM hooked up properly as shown in illustration?	Yes	►	PROCEED to QT7
	No	►	RE-ATTEMPT Step QT6, VOM Hookup. SERVICE any faults if necessary.

JUMPER WIRE

GND   FBS

TBS

FM4029400463040X

Fig. 7   Quick Test (Part 4 of 5). Escort & Tracer

TEST STEP	RESULT	►	ACTION TO TAKE
QT7 PERFORM ABS DIAGNOSTIC TROUBLE CODE RETRIEVAL			
• Verify that the anti-lock brake warning indicator illuminated (prior to equipment hookup) in the KOEO test before continuing. • Key ON. If using Rotunda Super STAR II Tester 007-0041B, turn the key ON, wait two seconds, then turn the tester ON. • **Does the anti-lock brake warning indicator flash briefly then go out?** NOTE: When a diagnostic trouble code is reported on the analog VOM, it will represent itself as a pulsing or sweeping movement of the voltmeter's needle across the dial face. Codes will be repeated after all memory codes have been displayed once.	Yes	►	ABS OK. GO to Section 06-00 for non-ABS related symptoms.
	No (Warning indicator illuminates constantly)	►	RECORD VOM or tester diagnostic trouble codes. ERASE diagnostic trouble codes from memory as explained in Erasing Diagnostic Trouble Codes in this section. RE-ATTEMPT diagnostic trouble code retrieval. RECORD all re-created diagnostic trouble codes and REFER to Code Identification Chart. SERVICE re-created codes as necessary. If the problem still exists or if no codes were re-created, PROCEED to QT8. (Codes that were not re-created indicate past or intermittent faults.)
	No (Warning indicator flashes service codes)	►	Indicates past or intermittent fault(s). Be sure to RECORD the diagnostic trouble codes before erasing faults. ERASE diagnostic trouble codes from the memory as explained in Erasing Diagnostic Trouble Codes in this section, then PROCEED to QT8.
QT8 PERFORM CONTINUOUS TEST			
• Hook up the Rotunda 73 Digital Multimeter 105-00051 or equivalent and jumper wire, or the Rotunda Super STAR II Tester 007-0041B, as in Test Step QT5 or QT6. • Key ON. NOTE: Use the audible warning function on the tester by turning the ''SPKR'' switch ON. You will be alerted of a continuous test fault without having to visually check the tester. • Tap, move, and wiggle the suspected sensor and / or harness working with short sections from the sensor to dash panel and to anti-lock brake control module. Drive vehicle, if necessary. • **Does the indicator illuminate continuously or is an audible warning heard from Super STAR II Tester?** NOTE: With the key ON, any coded fault re-created during continuous test will illuminate the warning indicator constantly. If the key is turned OFF, then back ON without clearing codes from memory, the warning indicator will flash codes along with the VOM or the Super STAR II Tester indicating a past or intermittent fault.	Yes	►	RECORD VOM or tester diagnostic trouble codes and REFER to Code Identification Chart. SERVICE only the codes re-created in this test step.
	No	►	Normal operation. If intermittent fault cannot be re-created, turn key OFF. DISCONNECT suspect sensor and anti-lock brake control module from harness very carefully. Visually INSPECT all terminals for corrosion, bad crimps, improperly seated terminals, etc. RECONNECT harness connectors and RE-ATTEMPT continuous test.

FM4029400463050X

Fig. 7   Quick Test (Part 5 of 5). Escort & Tracer

ABS Warning Indicator	Diagnosis Indication		Diagnostic Trouble Code	Possible Failure Location	Action To Take
		VOM			
• Illuminated Constantly for Present Failure • Flashes According to VOM Indication for Past or Intermittent Failure			11	RH Front Brake Anti-Lock Sensor and Bracket RH Front Brake Anti-Lock Sensor Indicator	
			12	LH Front Brake Anti-Lock Sensor and Bracket LH Front Brake Anti-Lock Sensor Indicator	GO to Pinpoint Test A1.
			13	RH Rear Brake Anti-Lock Sensor RH Rear Brake Anti-Lock Sensor Indicator	
			14	LH Rear Brake Anti-Lock Sensor LH Rear Brake Anti-Lock Sensor Indicator	
			15	Front and Rear Brake Anti-Lock Sensors	GO to Pinpoint Test B1.
			22	Solenoid Valve	GO to Pinpoint Test C1.
			51	Fail-Safe Relay	GO to Pinpoint Test D1.
			53	Motor Relay Motor	GO to Pinpoint Test E1.
			61	Anti-Lock Brake Control Module	REPLACE Anti-Lock Brake Control Module.
• Illuminated Constantly	No Indication	No Code	Generator	GO to Pinpoint Test F1.
	No Indication	No Code	ABS Warning Indicator	GO to Pinpoint Test G1.

FM4029400464000X

Fig. 8   Code identification chart. Escort & Tracer

PINPOINT TESTS

Do not run any of the Pinpoint Tests unless you are instructed to do so by a Quick Test. Each Test assumes a fault has been detected in the system with direction to enter a specific repair routine. Doing any Test without direction from the Quick Test may produce incorrect results and replacement of non-defective components or systems. It may be necessary to correct any defects in the brake system before passing the Quick Test.

Do not replace any parts unless the test results indicate they should be replaced. When more than one diagnostic trouble code is received, always start service with the first code received.

Do not measure voltage or resistance at the ABS control module or connect any test indicators to it unless otherwise specified. Isolate both ends of a circuit and turn key OFF whenever checking for shorts or continuity unless otherwise specified. Disconnect solenoids and switches from the harness before measuring for continuity, resistance or energizing by way of 12-volt source.

When using Pinpoint Tests, follow each step in order, starting from the first step in the appropriate test. Follow each step until the fault is found. After completing any repairs to the ABS, verify all components are properly reconnected and repeat the Quick Test.

When performing Pinpoint Tests, refer to wiring diagrams, **Figs. 10 and 11**, to locate wire circuits indicated in test procedures. Refer to **Figs. 12 through 19** for Aspire

Fig. 9 — Part 1 of 3

Diagnostic Trouble Code	Possible Failure Location	ABS Initialized (KOEO)	Starting Up or Slowing Down	Normal Driving	Driving with ABS Operating	Anti-Lock Brake Indicator	Open	Short	Other
11	RH Front Brake Anti-Lock Sensor and Front Brake Anti-Lock Sensor Indicator	—	No pulse from Anti-Lock Sensor when actual vehicle speed reaches 11 km/h (7 mph)	—	—	ON	X	X	
		—	No pulse from Anti-Lock Sensor but Anti-Lock Brake Control Module receives signal from other Anti-Lock Sensor for 20 sec.	—	—	ON	X	X	
12	LH Front Brake Anti-Lock Sensor and Anti-Lock Sensor Indicator	—	—	Incorrect pulse or no pulse from Anti-Lock Sensor when vehicle speed is above 10 km/h (6.25 mph) without braking	—	ON	X	X	Incorrect voltage from Anti-Lock Sensor (Excessive gap between Anti-Lock Sensor Indicator and Pickup Coil)
		—	—	Incorrect pulse or no pulse from Anti-Lock Sensor when vehicle speed is above 30 km/h (18.75 mph) without braking	—	ON	X	X	
13	RH Rear Brake Anti-Lock Sensor and Rear Brake Anti-Lock Sensor Indicator	—	—	—	No pulse from Anti-Lock Sensor without braking	ON	X	X	
14	LH Rear Brake Anti-Lock Sensor and Rear Brake Anti-Lock Sensor Indicator	—	—	—	No pulse from Anti-Lock Sensor without braking	ON	X	X	
		—	—	—	Incorrect pulse from Anti-Lock Sensor	ON	—	—	Broken Brake Anti-Lock Sensor Indicator Tooth

FM4029400465010X

Fig. 9 Anti-lock brake control module logic specifications for diagnostic trouble codes (Part 1 of 3)

Fig. 9 — Part 2 of 3

Diagnostic Trouble Code	Possible Failure Location	ABS Initialized (KOEO)	Starting Up or Slowing Down	Normal Driving	Driving with ABS Operating	Anti-Lock Brake Indicator	Open	Short	Other
11	RH Front Brake Anti-Lock Sensor	—	Front Brake Anti-Lock Sensor sends anti-lock brake requirement signal to Anti-Lock Brake Control Module before vehicle speed reaches 15 km/h (9.3 mph) without braking	—	—	ON	—	—	Incorrect Anti-Lock Sensor output, Broken Front Brake Anti-Lock Sensor Indicator Tooth
12	LH Front Brake Anti-Lock Sensor	—		—	—				
15	Brake Anti-Lock Control Module	—	—	Current does not flow when output from Anti-Lock Brake Control Module to Anti-Lock Sensor — Anti-Lock Brake detects open circuit in Anti-Lock Sensor	—	ON	X	—	
22	Solenoid	—	—	Power Transistor failure in Anti-Lock Brake Control Module	—	ON	X	X	
		—	—	All solenoids are OFF and Fail-Safe Relay is OFF even though Anti-Lock Brake Control Module sends ON signal to all solenoids	—	ON	X	X	
		—	—	Solenoid is not OFF even though Anti-Lock Brake Control Module sends OFF Signal to solenoid after Fail-Safe Relay is ON	—	ON	X	X	
		—	—	—	Solenoid is not ON even though Anti-Lock Brake Control Module sends ON signal to solenoid	ON	X	X	
	Hydraulic Anti-Lock Actuator Assembly	—	—	—	Vehicle needs more than 2 sec. for pressure reduction periods when slippage is more than 50% and/or coeff. of friction is 4 or more after 2 sec. of pressure reduction control	ON after ABS operation	—	—	Hydraulic Anti-Lock Actuator Assembly cannot reduce pressure

FM4029400465020X

Fig. 9 Anti-lock brake control module logic specifications for diagnostic trouble codes (Part 2 of 3)

Fig. 9 — Part 3 of 3

Diagnostic Trouble Code	Possible Failure Location	ABS Initialized (KOEO)	Starting Up or Slowing Down	Normal Driving	Driving with ABS Operating	Anti-Lock Brake Indicator	Open	Short	Other
51	Fail-Safe Relay	4A terminal voltage does not stay 0 volts for 48 msec. after key ON	—	—	—	ON	—	X	Fail-Safe Relay stays ON
		4A terminal voltage does not stay 12 volts for 48 msec. after Anti-Lock Brake Control Module sends ON signal to Fail-Safe Relay	—	—	—	ON	X	X	Fail-Safe Relay stays OFF
		—	—	4A terminal voltage is 0 volts for 0.2 to 2 seconds	—	ON	X	X	—
53	Motor Relay	—	—	11A terminal voltage is 0 volts even though 12B terminal voltage is 0 volts	—	ON	X	X	—
		—	—	11A terminal voltage is battery voltage even though 12B terminal voltage is battery voltage	—	ON	—	—	Motor Relay stays ON
	Motor	No self-generated voltage from motor after motor turned OFF	—	—	—	ON	—	—	Motor Locked
61	Anti-Lock Brake Control Module	Failure of IC (Integrated Circuit) in Anti-Lock Brake Control Module	—	—	—	ON	—	—	—
—		Failure of ROM, RAM, or timer to Anti-Lock Brake Control Module	—	—	—	ON	—	—	—

FM4029400465030X

Fig. 9 Anti-lock brake control module logic specifications for diagnostic trouble codes (Part 3 of 3)

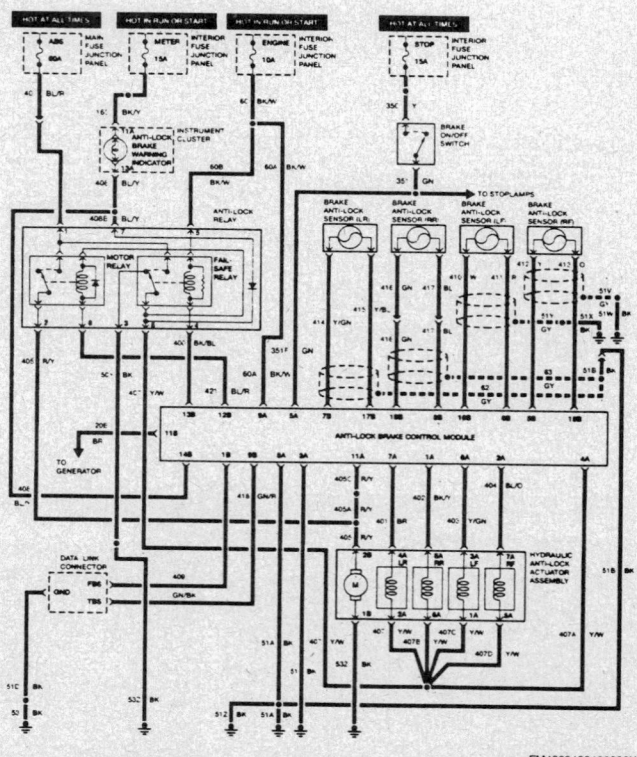

FM4029400466000X

Fig. 10 ABS wiring diagram. Aspire

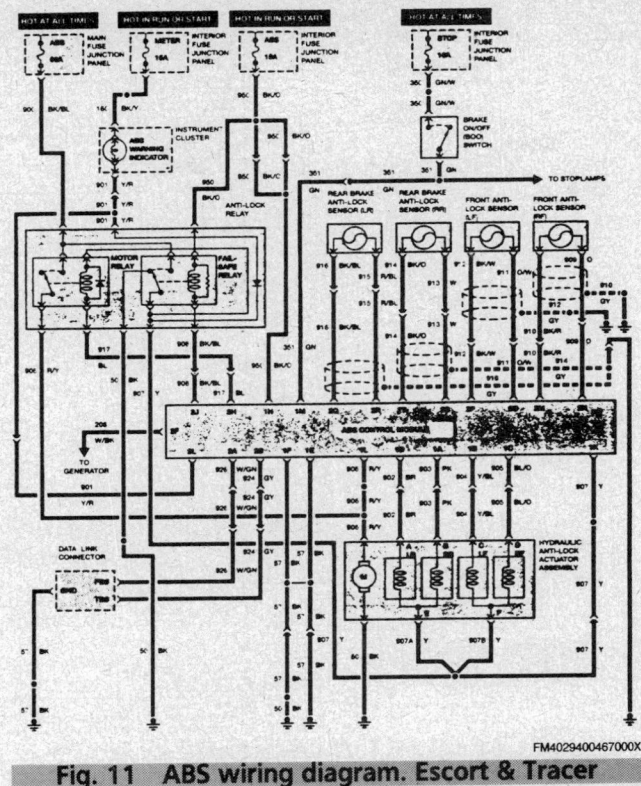

Fig. 11   ABS wiring diagram. Escort & Tracer

DIAGNOSTIC CHART INDEX

Pinpoint Test	Description	Page No. 27-	Fig. No.
ASPIRE			
A	Brake Anti-Lock Sensors & Sensor Indicators	202	12
B	Brake Anti-Lock Sensor Open Circuit	202	13
C	Solenoid Valve	202	14
D	Fail-Safe Relay	203	15
E	Motor & Motor Relay	203	16
F	Generator	203	17
G	Warning Indicator	203	18
H	Hydraulic System	204	19
ESCORT & TRACER			
A	Anti-Lock Sensors & Sensor Indicators	204	20
B	Anti-Lock Sensor Open Circuit	205	21
C	Solenoid Valve	205	22
D	Fail-Safe Relay	205	23
E	Hydraulic Anti-Lock Actuator Motor & Anti-Lock Relay	205	24
F	Generator	206	25
G	Warning Indicator	206	26
H	Hydraulic System	206	27

A1 CHECK SYSTEM INTEGRITY

TEST STEP	RESULT	▶	ACTION TO TAKE
A1 CHECK SYSTEM INTEGRITY • Visually inspect all wiring, wiring harnesses, connectors, brake lines and components for evidence of overheating, insulation damage, looseness, shorting or other damage. • **Is there any cause for concern?**	Yes No	▶ ▶	SERVICE as required. GO to A2.
A2 CHECK FOR SHORT TO GROUND • Key off. • Locate and disconnect the anti-lock brake control module connector. • Measure the resistance between the following anti-lock brake control module connector wire(s) in question and ground:	Yes No	▶ ▶	GO to A3. SERVICE short to ground from sensor(s) to anti-lock brake control module.

Brake Anti-Lock Sensor	Wire Color
Left Rear Brake Anti-Lock Sensor	"Y/GN" and ground
Right Rear Brake Anti-Lock Sensor	"GN" and ground
Left Front Brake Anti-Lock Sensor	"W" and ground
Right Front Brake Anti-Lock Sensor	"Y" and ground

• **Is the resistance greater than 10K ohms?**

TEST STEP	RESULT	▶	ACTION TO TAKE
A3 CHECK RESISTANCE AT ANTI-LOCK BRAKE CONTROL MODULE CONNECTOR • Key off. • Anti-lock brake control module disconnected. • Measure the resistance between the following wire(s) in question at the anti-lock brake control module connector leading to the brake anti-lock sensor(s):	Yes No	▶ ▶	GO to A5. GO to A4.

Brake Anti-Lock Sensor	Wires
Left Front Brake Anti-Lock Sensor	"W" and "R"
Right Front Brake Anti-Lock Sensor	"Y" and "O"
Left Rear Brake Anti-Lock Sensor	"Y/GN" and "Y/BL"
Right Rear Brake Anti-Lock Sensor	"GN" and "BL"

• **Is the resistance reading 1600-2000 ohms?**

FM4029400468010X

Fig. 12   Test A: Brake Anti-Lock Sensors & Sensor Indicators (Part 1 of 4). Aspire

A5 CHECK SIGNAL AT ANTI-LOCK BRAKE CONTROL MODULE CONNECTOR

TEST STEP	RESULT	▶	ACTION TO TAKE
A5 CHECK SIGNAL AT ANTI-LOCK BRAKE CONTROL MODULE CONNECTOR • Key off. • Anti-lock brake control module disconnected. • Multimeter on AC scale. • Measure the voltage between the following wires at the anti-lock brake control module connector leading to the brake anti-lock sensor(s) in question while rotating wheel approximately 60 rpm (approximately one wheel turn per second):	Yes No	▶ ▶	GO to A7. GO to A6.

Brake Anti-Lock Sensor	Wires
Left Front Brake Anti-Lock Sensor	"W" and "R"
Right Front Brake Anti-Lock Sensor	"Y" and "O"
Left Rear Brake Anti-Lock Sensor	"Y/GN" and "Y/BL"
Right Rear Brake Anti-Lock Sensor	"GN" and "BL"

• **Is the voltage reading between 0.25 and 3.0 volts AC?**

TEST STEP	RESULT	▶	ACTION TO TAKE
A6 INSPECT BRAKE ANTI-LOCK SENSOR(S) AND BRAKE ANTI-LOCK SENSOR INDICATOR(S) • Remove the wheel and tire assembly for the brake anti-lock sensor(s) or brake anti-lock sensor indicators in question. • Check for damage to the brake anti-lock sensor(s) or brake anti-lock sensor indicators. • Check for objects sticking to the brake anti-lock sensor(s) or brake anti-lock sensor indicators. • Check the brake anti-lock sensor installation tightening torque: 16-23 N·m (12-17 lb-ft). • Check the clearance between brake anti-lock sensor(s) and brake anti-lock sensor indicators: 0.3-1.1mm (0.012-0.043 inch). • **Are the conditions OK?**	Yes No	▶ ▶	REPLACE the brake anti-lock sensor(s). REPLACE the brake anti-lock sensor(s) or brake anti-lock sensor indicator(s).

FM4029400468030X

Fig. 12   Test A: Brake Anti-Lock Sensors & Sensor Indicators (Part 3 of 4). Aspire

A4 CHECK RESISTANCE AT SENSOR(S)

TEST STEP	RESULT	▶	ACTION TO TAKE
A4 CHECK RESISTANCE AT SENSOR(S) • Locate and disconnect the brake anti-lock sensor(s) in question. • Measure the resistance between the following sensor pins at the connector(s) leading to the brake anti-lock sensor(s) in question:	Yes No	▶ ▶	SERVICE wire(s) from sensor(s) to anti-lock brake control module. REPLACE brake anti-lock sensor(s).

Brake Anti-Lock Sensor	Sensor Pins
Left Front Brake Anti-Lock Sensor	"W" and "R"
Right Front Brake Anti-Lock Sensor	"Y" and "O"
Left Rear Brake Anti-Lock Sensor	"Y/GN" and "Y/BL"
Right Rear Brake Anti-Lock Sensor	"GN" and "BL"

• **Is the resistance reading 1600-2000 ohms?**

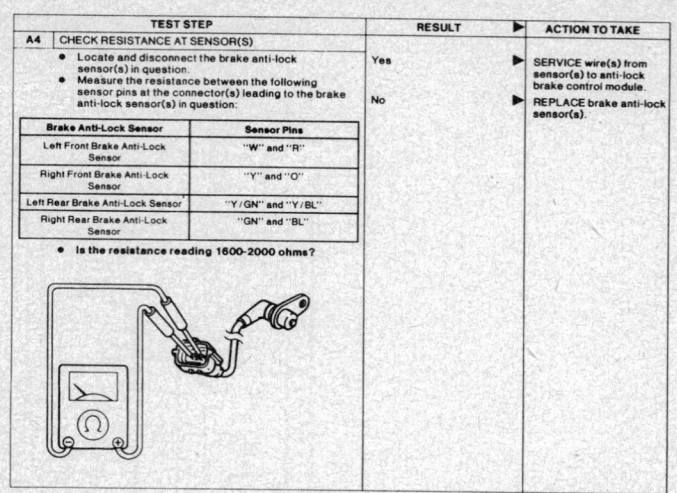

FM4029400468020X

Fig. 12   Test A: Brake Anti-Lock Sensors & Sensor Indicators (Part 2 of 4). Aspire

A7 CHECK STOPLAMP CIRCUIT

TEST STEP	RESULT	▶	ACTION TO TAKE
A7 CHECK STOPLAMP CIRCUIT • Depress the brake pedal. • Check to see that the stoplamps illuminate. • **Do the stoplamps operate properly?**	Yes No	▶ ▶	GO to A8. SERVICE as required.
A8 CHECK BRAKE ON/OFF SWITCH VOLTAGE • Key off. • Disconnect the anti-lock brake control module. • Key ON. • Measure the voltage on the "GN" wire at the anti-lock brake control module connector for the following conditions:	Yes No	▶ ▶	GO to Pinpoint Test H1. SERVICE the "GN" wire between Brake On/Off (BOO) switch and anti-lock brake control module.

Brake Pedal Position	Voltage
Depressed	Above 10 volts
Released	0-2 volts

• **Are the voltage readings OK?**

FM4029400468040X

Fig. 12   Test A: Brake Anti-Lock Sensors & Sensor Indicators (Part 4 of 4). Aspire

B1 CHECK OPEN CIRCUIT

TEST STEP	RESULT	▶	ACTION TO TAKE
B1 CHECK OPEN CIRCUIT • Drive the vehicle at 10 km/h (6 mph). • Recheck the malfunction codes. Refer to the Quick Test in this section. • **Is a Code 11, 12, 13, or 14 obtained?**	Yes No (No codes) No (Code 15 reappears)	▶ ▶ ▶	GO to Pinpoint Test A1. Intermittent fault. REFER to Continuous Test in this section. SUBSTITUTE a known good anti-lock brake control module. PERFORM Test Step B1 again.

FM4029400469000X

Fig. 13   Test B: Brake Anti-Lock Sensor Open Circuit. Aspire

C1 CHECK SYSTEM INTEGRITY

TEST STEP	RESULT	▶	ACTION TO TAKE
C1 CHECK SYSTEM INTEGRITY • Visually inspect all wiring, wiring harness, connectors, brake lines, and components for evidence of overheating, insulation damage, looseness, shorting or other damage. • **Is there any cause for concern?**	Yes No	▶ ▶	SERVICE as required. GO to C2.
C2 CHECK SOLENOID SIGNAL • Key ON. • Measure the voltage at 4A ("Y/W") terminal of the anti-lock brake control module. (Anti-lock brake control module must be connected.) • **Does the voltage reading momentarily read above 10 volts?**	Yes No	▶ ▶	GO to C3. SERVICE "Y/W" wire between anti-lock brake relay and anti-lock brake control module.

FM4029400470010X

Fig. 14   Test C: Solenoid Valve (Part 1 of 2). Aspire

TEST STEP	RESULT	▶	ACTION TO TAKE
C3 CHECK SOLENOID AT ANTI-LOCK BRAKE CONTROL MODULE • Key off. • Locate and disconnect the anti-lock brake control module. • Measure the resistance between the following wires at the anti-lock brake control module connector:	Yes No	▶ ▶	GO to Pinpoint Test H1. GO to C4.

Solenoid	Wires
Left Front	"Y/W" and "Y/GN"
Right Front	"Y/W" and "BL/O"
Left Rear	"Y/W" and "BR"
Right Rear	"Y/W" and "BK/Y"

• Are the resistances about 3 ohms?			
C4 CHECK SOLENOID AT HYDRAULIC ANTI-LOCK ACTUATOR ASSEMBLY • Perform the Hydraulic Anti-Lock Actuator Assembly component test in this section. • Is the hydraulic anti-lock actuator assembly OK?	Yes No	▶ ▶	SERVICE wire(s) between anti-lock brake control module and hydraulic anti-lock actuator assembly. REPLACE anti-lock actuator assembly.

FM4029400470020X

Fig. 14   Test C: Solenoid Valve (Part 2 of 2). Aspire

TEST STEP	RESULT	▶	ACTION TO TAKE
D1 CHECK SYSTEM INTEGRITY • Visually inspect all wiring, wiring harness, connectors, brake lines, and components for evidence of overheating, insulation damage, looseness, shorting, or other damage. • Is there any cause for concern?	Yes No	▶ ▶	SERVICE as required. GO to D2.
D2 CHECK FUSES • Check the 60A ABS fuse in the main fuse junction panel and the 15A METER fuse in the interior fuse junction panel. • Are the fuses OK?	Yes No	▶ ▶	GO to D3. REPLACE the fuse(s).
D3 CHECK ANTI-LOCK RELAY OPERATION • Key off. • Locate and disconnect the anti-lock brake control module. • Key ON. • Connect the "BK/BL" wire at the anti-lock brake control module connector to ground. • Does the anti-lock relay click when wire is grounded?	Yes No	▶ ▶	GO to D4. INSPECT "BK/BL" wire from anti-lock relay to anti-lock brake control module. If OK, GO to D6.
D4 CHECK ANTI-LOCK BRAKE WARNING INDICATOR DIODE • Anti-lock brake control module disconnected. • Key ON. • Connect the "BK/BL" wire at the anti-lock brake control module connector to ground. • Check to see that the anti-lock brake warning indicator does not illuminate when grounded. • Does the anti-lock brake warning indicator illuminate?	Yes No	▶ ▶	GO to D6. GO to D5.

FM4029400471010X

Fig. 15   Test D: Fail-Safe Relay (Part 1 of 2). Aspire

TEST STEP	RESULT	▶	ACTION TO TAKE
D5 CHECK VOLTAGE FROM ANTI-LOCK RELAY • Anti-lock brake control module disconnected. • Key ON. • Connect the "BK/BL" wire at the anti-lock brake control module connector to ground. • Measure the voltage at the "Y/W" wire at the anti-lock brake control module connector. • Is the voltage reading greater than 10 volts?	Yes Yes, if directed to this Pinpoint Test from Step E1 No	▶ ▶ ▶	GO to Pinpoint Test G1. GO to E2. GO to D6.
D6 CHECK ANTI-LOCK RELAY • Perform the Anti-Lock Relay component test in this section. • Is the anti-lock relay OK?	Yes No	▶ ▶	SERVICE the "Y/W" wire between the anti-lock relay and the anti-lock brake control module. REPLACE the anti-lock relay.

FM4029400471020X

Fig. 15   Test D: Fail-Safe Relay (Part 2 of 2). Aspire

TEST STEP	RESULT	▶	ACTION TO TAKE
E1 CHECK FAIL-SAFE RELAY • Go to the Pinpoint Test D1 and check the operation of the fail-safe relay. • Does the fail-safe relay operate properly?	Yes No	▶ ▶	GO to E2. REPLACE the anti-lock relay.
E2 CHECK SYSTEM INTEGRITY • Visually inspect all wiring, wiring harness, connectors, brake lines, and components for evidence of overheating, insulation damage, looseness, shorting, or other damage. • Is there any cause for concern?	Yes No	▶ ▶	SERVICE as required. GO to E3.
E3 CHECK MOTOR RELAY OPERATION **CAUTION: While performing this test step, do not allow motor to operate for more than two seconds.** • Key off. • Locate and disconnect the anti-lock brake control module. • Key ON. • Connect the "BK/BL" wire to ground at the anti-lock brake control module connector. • Connect the "BL/R" wire to ground at the anti-lock brake control module connector for no more than two seconds. • Does the motor relay click and the motor operate when wires are grounded?	Yes No (Motor relay clicks but motor does not operate) No (Motor relay does not click and motor does not operate)	▶ ▶ ▶	GO to E8. GO to E5. GO to E4.
E4 CHECK ANTI-LOCK RELAY • Perform the Anti-Lock Relay component test in this section. • Is the anti-lock relay OK?	Yes No	▶ ▶	GO to E5. REPLACE the anti-lock relay.

FM4029400472010X

Fig. 16   Test E: Motor & Motor Relay (Part 1 of 2). Aspire

TEST STEP	RESULT	▶	ACTION TO TAKE
E5 CHECK MOTOR RESISTANCE • Key off. • Locate and disconnect the hydraulic anti-lock actuator assembly 2-pin motor connector. • Measure the resistance between the "R/Y" and "BK" terminals of the motor.	Yes No	▶ ▶	GO to E6. REPLACE the hydraulic anti-lock actuator assembly.

HYDRAULIC ANTI-LOCK ACTUATOR MOTOR

• Is the resistance less than 1 ohm?			
E6 CHECK MOTOR OPERATION **CAUTION: While performing this test step, do not allow motor to operate for more than two seconds.** • Hydraulic anti-lock actuator assembly 2-pin motor connector disconnected. • Apply battery voltage to the "R/Y" terminal and ground to the "BK" terminal at the hydraulic anti-lock actuator assembly 2-pin motor connector. • Does the motor operate when voltage is applied?	Yes No	▶ ▶	GO to E7. REPLACE the hydraulic anti-lock actuator assembly.
E7 CHECK MOTOR GROUND • Hydraulic anti-lock actuator assembly 2-pin motor connector disconnected. • Measure the resistance between the "BK" wire at the hydraulic anti-lock actuator assembly 2-pin motor connector (harness side) and ground. • Is the resistance less than 5 ohms?	Yes No	▶ ▶	SERVICE the "R/Y" wire between anti-lock relay and hydraulic anti-lock actuator assembly. SERVICE the "BK" wire to ground.
E8 CHECK RESISTANCE AT ANTI-LOCK BRAKE CONTROL MODULE • Key off. • Hydraulic anti-lock actuator assembly connected. • Anti-lock brake control module disconnected. • Measure the resistance between the "R/Y" wire at the anti-lock brake control module and ground. • Is the resistance less than 1 ohm?	Yes No	▶ ▶	GO to Pinpoint Test G1. SERVICE the "R/Y" wire between anti-lock brake control module and hydraulic anti-lock actuator assembly.

FM4029400472020X

Fig. 16   Test E: Motor & Motor Relay (Part 2 of 2). Aspire

TEST STEP	RESULT	▶	ACTION TO TAKE
F1 CHECK BATTERY VOLTAGE • Measure the voltage at the battery. Refer to Section 14-00. • Is the voltage reading as specified?	Yes No	▶ ▶	GO to F2. CHARGE or REPLACE the battery as necessary.

FM4029400473010X

Fig. 17   Test F: Generator (Part 1 of 2). Aspire

TEST STEP	RESULT	▶	ACTION TO TAKE
F2 CHECK BATTERY VOLTAGE AT ANTI-LOCK BRAKE CONTROL MODULE • Measure the voltage at the anti-lock brake control module 9A ("BK/W") terminal under the following conditions:	Yes No	▶ ▶	GO to F3. SERVICE the wiring between anti-lock brake control module and battery.

Ignition Switch	Voltage
Off	0 Volts
ON	Above 10 Volts

• Are the voltage readings as specified?			
F3 CHECK VOLTAGE AT GENERATOR • Measure the voltage at the B ("BK/L"), L ("BR"), and S ("R") terminals at the generator with the engine idling. • Are the voltage readings as specified?	Yes No	▶ ▶	GO to F4. SERVICE or REPLACE the generator.
F4 CHECK GENERATOR VOLTAGE AT ANTI-LOCK BRAKE CONTROL MODULE • Measure the voltage at the 11B ("BR") terminal of the anti-lock brake control module under the following conditions:	Yes No	▶ ▶	GO to Pinpoint Test G1. SERVICE the "BR" wire from anti-lock brake control module to generator.

Condition	Voltage
Key ON Engine Off	0.8 volts to 3 volts
Engine Idling	Above 10 volts

• Are the voltages as specified?			

FM4029400473020X

Fig. 17   Test F: Generator (Part 2 of 2). Aspire

TEST STEP	RESULT	▶	ACTION TO TAKE
G1 CHECK ANTI-LOCK BRAKE WARNING INDICATOR OPERATION • Key off. • Locate and disconnect the anti-lock brake control module. • Key ON. • Does the anti-lock brake warning indicator illuminate?	Yes No	▶ ▶	GO to G2. REPLACE the 15A METER fuse and/or warning indicator bulb if burned out. If OK, SERVICE the "BL/Y" wire from instrument cluster to anti-lock relay.
G2 CHECK FOR SHORT TO GROUND • Key ON. • Anti-lock brake control module disconnected. • Locate and disconnect the anti-lock relay. • Does the anti-lock brake warning indicator go off?	Yes No	▶ ▶	GO to G3. SERVICE the "PK" wire between the instrument cluster and anti-lock relay for short to ground.

FM4029400474010X

Fig. 18   Test G: Warning Indicator (Part 1 of 2). Aspire

TEST STEP	RESULT	►	ACTION TO TAKE
G3 CHECK ANTI-LOCK BRAKE WARNING INDICATOR SIGNAL			
• Anti-lock brake control module disconnected. • Anti-lock relay disconnected. • Key ON. • Connect the "BL/Y" wire at the anti-lock brake control module and the "BL/Y" wire at the anti-lock relay to ground. • **Does the anti-lock brake warning indicator illuminate when both wires are connected to ground?**	Yes	►	GO to **G4**.
	No (Does not illuminate at all)	►	REPLACE the 15A METER fuse and/or warning indicator bulb if burned out. If OK, SERVICE "BL/Y" wire from instrument cluster to anti-lock relay and/or anti-lock brake control module.
	No (Illuminates only when grounded at anti-lock brake control module)	►	SERVICE the "BL/Y" wire to anti-lock relay.
	No (Illuminates only when grounded at anti-lock relay)	►	SERVICE the "BL/Y" wire to anti-lock brake control module.
G4 CHECK GROUNDS AT ANTI-LOCK BRAKE CONTROL MODULE			
• Key off. • Anti-lock brake control module disconnected. • Measure the resistance between the 3A ("BK") terminal and ground and the 8A ("BK") terminal and ground at the anti-lock brake control module. • **Are the resistances less than 5 ohms?**	Yes	►	REPLACE the anti-lock brake control module.
	No	►	SERVICE the "BK" wire(s) to ground.

FM4029400474020X

Fig. 18   Test G: Warning Indicator (Part 2 of 2). Aspire

TEST STEP	RESULT	►	ACTION TO TAKE
A1 CHECK SYSTEM INTEGRITY			
• Visually inspect all wiring, wiring harnesses, connectors, brake tubes, and components for evidence of overheating, insulation damage, looseness, shorting, or other damage. • **Is there any cause for concern?**	Yes	►	SERVICE as required.
	No	►	GO to **A2**.
A2 CHECK FOR SHORT TO GROUND			
• Key OFF. • Locate and disconnect the anti-lock brake control module connector. • Measure the resistance between the following anti-lock brake control module connector wire(s) in question and ground:	Yes	►	GO to **A3**.
	No	►	SERVICE short to ground from sensor(s) to anti-lock brake control module.

Brake Anti-Lock Sensor	Wire Color
LH Front Anti-Lock Sensor	"BK/W" and ground
RH Front Anti-Lock Sensor	"BK/R" and ground
LH Rear Anti-Lock Sensor	"BK/BL" and ground
RH Rear Anti-Lock Sensor	"BK/O" and ground

• **Is the resistance greater than 10,000 ohms?**

TEST STEP	RESULT	►	ACTION TO TAKE
A3 CHECK RESISTANCE AT ANTI-LOCK BRAKE CONTROL MODULE CONNECTOR			
• Key OFF. • Anti-lock brake control module disconnected. • Measure the resistance between the following wire(s) in question at the anti-lock brake control module connector leading to the anti-lock sensor(s):	Yes	►	GO to **A5**.
	No	►	GO to **A4**.

Brake Anti-Lock Sensor	Wires
LH Front Anti-Lock Sensor	"BK/W" and "O/W"
RH Front Anti-Lock Sensor	"BK/R" and "O"
LH Rear Anti-Lock Sensor	"BK/BL" and "R/BL"
RH Rear Anti-Lock Sensor	"BK/O" and "W"

• **Is the resistance reading 1600-2000 ohms?**

FM4029400476010X

Fig. 20   Test A: Anti-Lock Sensors & Sensor Indicators (Part 1 of 4). Escort & Tracer

TEST STEP	RESULT	►	ACTION TO TAKE
A5 CHECK SIGNAL AT ANTI-LOCK BRAKE CONTROL MODULE CONNECTOR			
• Key OFF. • Anti-lock brake control module disconnected. • Multimeter on AC scale. • Measure the voltage between the following wires at the anti-lock brake control module connector leading to the anti-lock sensor(s) in question while rotating wheel approximately 60 rpm (approximately one wheel turn per second):	Yes	►	GO to **A7**.
	No	►	GO to **A6**.

Brake Anti-Lock Sensor	Wires
LH Front Anti-Lock Sensor	"BK/W" and "O/W"
RH Front Anti-Lock Sensor	"BK/R" and "O"
LH Rear Anti-Lock Sensor	"BK/BL" and "R/BL"
RH Rear Anti-Lock Sensor	"BK/O" and "W"

• **Is the voltage reading between 0.25 and 3.0 volts AC?**

FM4029400476030X

Fig. 20   Test A: Anti-Lock Sensors & Sensor Indicators (Part 3 of 4). Escort & Tracer

TEST STEP	RESULT	►	ACTION TO TAKE
H1 CHECK SYSTEM INTEGRITY			
• Visually inspect all wiring, wiring harnesses, connectors, brake lines, and components for evidence of overheating, insulation damage, looseness, shorting, or other damage. • **Is there any cause for concern?**	Yes	►	SERVICE as required.
	No	►	GO to **H2**.

FM4029400475010X

Fig. 19   Test H: Hydraulic System (Part 1 of 2). Aspire

TEST STEP	RESULT	►	ACTION TO TAKE
H2 CHECK HYDRAULIC PRESSURE			
NOTE: This test requires an assistant. The pressure reduction operation occurs within a 2 second period. • Jack up the vehicle so that all the wheels are clear off the ground and the vehicle is properly supported. • Shift the transaxle to NEUTRAL. • Release the parking brake. • Check to see that there is no brake drag while rotating the wheels by hand. • Use a jumper wire to connect the "TBS" and "GND" terminals at the data link connector. • Depress the brake pedal and have an assistant verify that the wheels will not rotate. • With the brake pedal still depressed, turn the key ON and verify that the brake pressure is released momentarily (approximately 0.5 seconds) and that each wheel rotates when pressure reduction operates as shown:	Yes (If directed to this Pinpoint Test from Quick Test Step QT4)	►	ABS functioning properly.
	Yes (If directed to this Pinpoint Test from Step A8)	►	Intermittent Fault. GO to Continuous Test in this section.
	Yes (If directed to this Pinpoint Test from Step C3)	►	GO to Pinpoint Test **G1**.
	No	►	INSPECT the hydraulic system piping and wiring. If OK, REPLACE the hydraulic anti-lock actuator assembly.

• **Does the pressure reduction operate properly?**

FM4029400475020X

Fig. 19   Test H: Hydraulic System (Part 2 of 2). Aspire

TEST STEP	RESULT	►	ACTION TO TAKE
A4 CHECK RESISTANCE AT SENSOR(S)			
• Locate and disconnect the anti-lock sensor(s) in question. • Measure the resistance between the following sensor pins at the connector(s) leading to the anti-lock sensor(s) in question:	Yes	►	SERVICE wire(s) from sensor(s) to anti-lock brake control module.
	No	►	REPLACE anti-lock sensor(s).

Brake Anti-Lock Sensor	Sensor Pins
LH Front Anti-Lock Sensor	"BK/W" and "O/W"
RH Front Anti-Lock Sensor	"BK/R" and "O"
LH Rear Anti-Lock Sensor	"BK/BL" and "R/BL"
RH Rear Anti-Lock Sensor	"BK/O" and "W"

• **Is the resistance reading 1600-2000 ohms?**

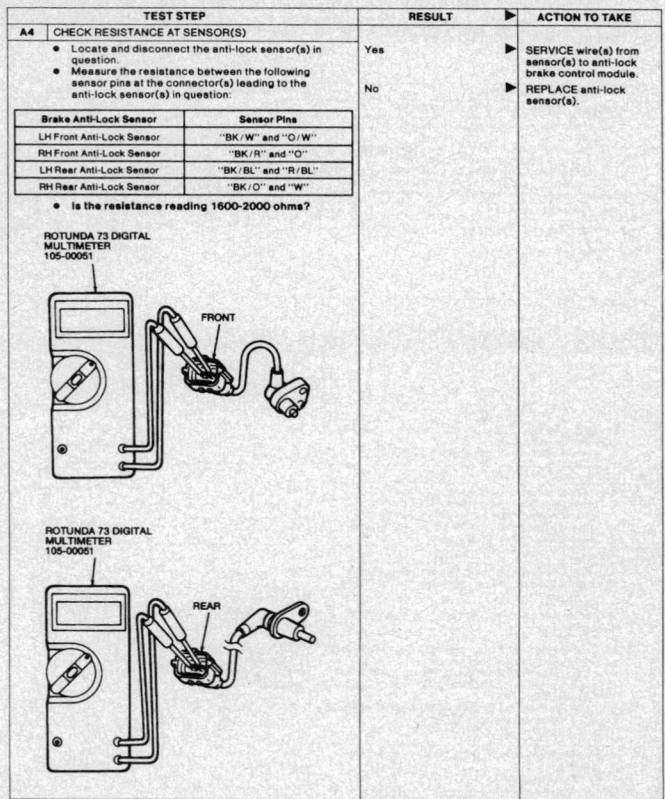

FM4029400476020X

Fig. 20   Test A: Anti-Lock Sensors & Sensor Indicators (Part 2 of 4). Escort & Tracer

TEST STEP	RESULT	▶	ACTION TO TAKE
A6 INSPECT ANTI-LOCK SENSOR(S) AND BRAKE ANTI-LOCK SENSOR INDICATOR(S) • Remove the wheel and tire assembly for the anti-lock sensor(s) or brake anti-lock sensor indicators in question. • Check for damage to the anti-lock sensor(s) or brake anti-lock sensor indicators. • Check for objects sticking to the anti-lock sensor(s) or brake anti-lock sensor indicators. • Check the anti-lock sensor bolt(s) tightening torque: 16-23 N·m (12-17 lb-ft). • Check the clearance between anti-lock sensor(s) and brake anti-lock sensor indicators: 0.3-1.1mm (0.012-0.043 inch). • **Are the conditions OK?**	Yes No	▶ ▶	REPLACE anti-lock sensor(s). REPLACE anti-lock sensor(s) or brake anti-lock sensor indicator(s).

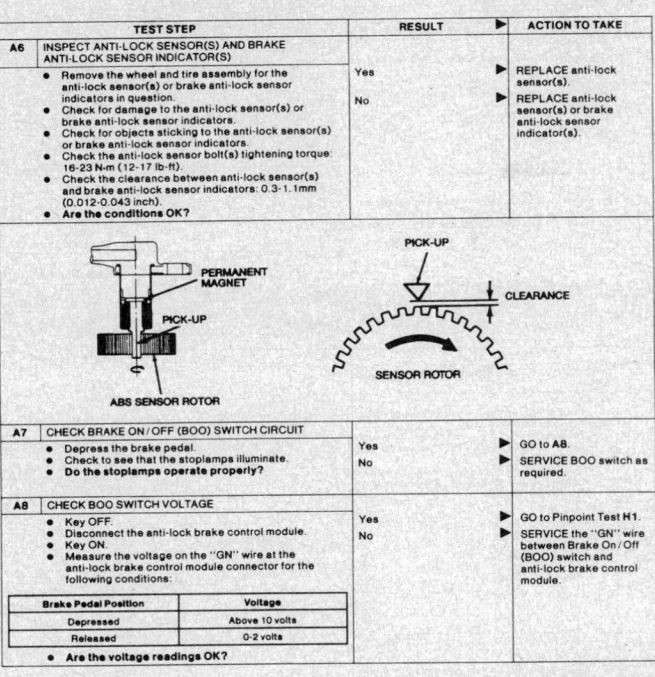

TEST STEP	RESULT	▶	ACTION TO TAKE
A7 CHECK BRAKE ON/OFF (BOO) SWITCH CIRCUIT • Depress the brake pedal. • Check to see that the stoplamps illuminate. • **Do the stoplamps operate properly?**	Yes No	▶ ▶	GO to A8. SERVICE BOO switch as required.
A8 CHECK BOO SWITCH VOLTAGE • Key OFF. • Disconnect the anti-lock brake control module. • Key ON. • Measure the voltage on the "GN" wire at the anti-lock brake control module connector for the following conditions:	Yes No	▶ ▶	GO to Pinpoint Test H1. SERVICE the "GN" wire between Brake On/Off (BOO) switch and anti-lock brake control module.

Brake Pedal Position	Voltage
Depressed	Above 10 volts
Released	0-2 volts

• **Are the voltage readings OK?**

FM4029400476040X

Fig. 20   Test A: Anti-Lock Sensors & Sensor Indicators (Part 4 of 4). Escort & Tracer

TEST STEP	RESULT	▶	ACTION TO TAKE
B1 CHECK OPEN CIRCUIT • Drive the vehicle at 10 km/h (6 mph). • Recheck the malfunction codes. Refer to the Quick Test in this section. • **Is a Code 11, 12, 13, or 14 obtained?**	Yes No (No codes) No (Code 15 reappears)	▶ ▶ ▶	GO to Pinpoint Test A1. Intermittent fault. SUBSTITUTE a known good anti-lock brake control module. PERFORM Test Step B1 again.

FM4029400477000X

Fig. 21   Test B: Anti-Lock Sensor Open Circuit. Escort & Tracer

TEST STEP	RESULT	▶	ACTION TO TAKE
C1 CHECK SYSTEM INTEGRITY • Visually inspect all wiring, wiring harnesses, connectors, brake tubes, and components for evidence of overheating, insulation damage, looseness, shorting, or other damage. • **Is there any cause for concern?**	Yes No	▶ ▶	SERVICE as required. GO to C2.
C2 CHECK SOLENOID SIGNAL • Key ON. • Measure the voltage at 1K ("Y") terminal of the anti-lock brake control module. (Anti-lock brake control module must be connected.) • **Does the voltage reading momentarily read above 10 volts?**	Yes No	▶ ▶	GO to C3. SERVICE "Y" wire between anti-lock brake control module.
C3 CHECK SOLENOID AT ANTI-LOCK BRAKE CONTROL MODULE • Key OFF. • Locate and disconnect the anti-lock brake control module. • Measure the resistance between the following wires at the anti-lock brake control module connector.	Yes No	▶ ▶	GO to Pinpoint Test H1. GO to C4.

Solenoid	Wires
Left Front	"Y" and "Y/BL"
Right Front	"Y" and "BL/O"
Left Rear	"Y" and "BR"
Right Rear	"Y" and "PK"

• **Are the resistances about 3 ohms?**

TEST STEP	RESULT	▶	ACTION TO TAKE
C4 CHECK SOLENOID AT HYDRAULIC ANTI-LOCK ACTUATOR ASSEMBLY • Perform the Hydraulic Anti-Lock Actuator Assembly component test in this section. • **Is the hydraulic anti-lock actuator assembly OK?**	Yes No	▶ ▶	SERVICE wire(s) between anti-lock brake control module and hydraulic anti-lock actuator assembly. REPLACE hydraulic anti-lock actuator assembly.

FM4029400478000X

Fig. 22   Test C: Solenoid Valve. Escort & Tracer

TEST STEP	RESULT	▶	ACTION TO TAKE
D1 CHECK SYSTEM INTEGRITY • Visually inspect all wiring, wiring harnesses, connectors, brake tubes, and components for evidence of overheating, insulation damage, looseness, shorting, or other damage. • **Is there any cause for concern?**	Yes No	▶ ▶	SERVICE as required. GO to D2.
D2 CHECK FUSES • Check the 60A ABS fuse in the main fuse junction panel and the 10A ABS fuse in the interior fuse junction panel. • **Are the fuses OK?**	Yes No	▶ ▶	GO to D3. REPLACE fuse(s).
D3 CHECK ANTI-LOCK RELAY OPERATION • Key OFF. • Locate and disconnect the anti-lock brake control module. • Key ON. • Connect the "BK/BL" wire at the anti-lock brake control module connector to ground. • **Does the anti-lock relay click when wire is grounded?**	Yes No	▶ ▶	GO to D4. INSPECT "BK/BL" wire from anti-lock relay to anti-lock brake control module. If OK, GO to D6.

FM4029400479010X

Fig. 23   Test D: Fail-Safe Relay (Part 1 of 2). Escort & Tracer

TEST STEP	RESULT	▶	ACTION TO TAKE
D4 CHECK ANTI-LOCK BRAKE WARNING INDICATOR DIODE • Anti-lock brake control module disconnected. • Key ON. • Connect the "BK/BL" wire at the anti-lock brake control module connector to ground. • Check to see that the anti-lock brake warning indicator does not illuminate when grounded. • **Does the anti-lock brake warning indicator illuminate?**	Yes No	▶ ▶	GO to D6. GO to D5.
D5 CHECK VOLTAGE FROM ANTI-LOCK RELAY • Anti-lock brake control module disconnected. • Key ON. • Connect the "BK/BL" wire at the anti-lock brake control module connector to ground. • Measure the voltage at the "Y" wire at the anti-lock brake control module connector. • **Is the voltage reading greater than 10 volts?**	Yes Yes, if directed to this Pinpoint Test from Step F1 No	▶ ▶ ▶	GO to Pinpoint Test G1. GO to E2. GO to D6.
D6 CHECK ANTI-LOCK RELAY • Perform the Anti-Lock Relay component test in this section. • **Is the anti-lock relay OK?**	Yes No	▶ ▶	SERVICE the "Y" wire between the anti-lock relay and the anti-lock brake control module. REPLACE the anti-lock relay.

FM4029400479020X

Fig. 23   Test D: Fail-Safe Relay (Part 2 of 2). Escort & Tracer

TEST STEP	RESULT	▶	ACTION TO TAKE
E1 CHECK FAIL-SAFE RELAY • Go to the Pinpoint Test D1 and check the operation of the fail-safe relay. • **Does the fail-safe relay operate properly?**	Yes No	▶ ▶	GO to E2. REPLACE the anti-lock relay.
E2 CHECK SYSTEM INTEGRITY • Visually inspect all wiring, wiring harnesses, connectors, brake tubes, and components for evidence of overheating, insulation damage, looseness, shorting, or other damage. • **Is there any cause for concern?**	Yes No	▶ ▶	SERVICE as required. GO to E3.
E3 CHECK MOTOR RELAY OPERATION **CAUTION: While performing this test step, do not allow motor to operate for more than two seconds.** • Key OFF. • Locate and disconnect the anti-lock brake control module. • Key ON. • Connect the "BK/BL" wire to ground at the anti-lock brake control module harness connector. • Connect the "BL" wire to ground at the anti-lock brake control module harness connector for no more than two seconds. • **Does the motor relay click and the motor operate when wires are grounded?**	Yes No (Motor relay clicks but motor does not operate) No (Motor relay does not click and motor does not operate)	▶ ▶ ▶	GO to E8. GO to E5. GO to E4.
E4 CHECK ANTI-LOCK RELAY • Perform the Anti-Lock Relay component test in this section. • **Is the anti-lock relay OK?**	Yes No	▶ ▶	GO to E5. REPLACE the anti-lock relay.

FM4029400480010X

Fig. 24   Test E: Hydraulic Anti-Lock Actuator Motor & Anti-Lock Relay (Part 1 of 2). Escort & Tracer

FORD—Anti-Lock Brakes

TEST STEP	RESULT	►	ACTION TO TAKE
E5 CHECK MOTOR RESISTANCE • Key OFF. • Locate and disconnect the hydraulic anti-lock actuator assembly 2-pin motor connector. • Measure the resistance between the "R/Y" and "BK" terminals of the motor. **HYDRAULIC ACTUATOR MOTOR** • Is the resistance less than 1 ohm?	Yes No	► ►	GO to E6. REPLACE the hydraulic anti-lock actuator assembly.
E6 CHECK MOTOR OPERATION CAUTION: While performing this test step, do not allow motor to operate for more than two seconds. • Disconnect the hydraulic anti-lock actuator assembly 2-pin motor connector. • Apply battery voltage to the "R/Y" terminal and ground the "BK" terminal at the hydraulic anti-lock actuator assembly 2-pin motor connector. • Does the motor operate when voltage is applied?	Yes No	► ►	GO to E7. REPLACE hydraulic anti-lock actuator assembly.
E7 CHECK MOTOR GROUND • Hydraulic anti-lock actuator assembly 2-pin motor connector disconnected. • Measure the resistance between the "BK" wire at the hydraulic anti-lock actuator assembly 2-pin motor connector (harness side) and ground. • Is the resistance less than 5 ohms?	Yes No	► ►	SERVICE "R/Y" wire between the anti-lock relay and hydraulic anti-lock actuator assembly. SERVICE "BK" wire to ground.
E8 CHECK RESISTANCE AT ANTI-LOCK BRAKE CONTROL MODULE • Key OFF. • Hydraulic anti-lock actuator assembly connected. • ABS control module disconnected. • Measure the resistance between the "R/Y" wire at the anti-lock brake control module and ground. • Is the resistance less than 1 ohm?	Yes No	► ►	GO to Pinpoint Test F1. SERVICE "R/Y" wire between anti-lock brake control module and hydraulic anti-lock actuator assembly.

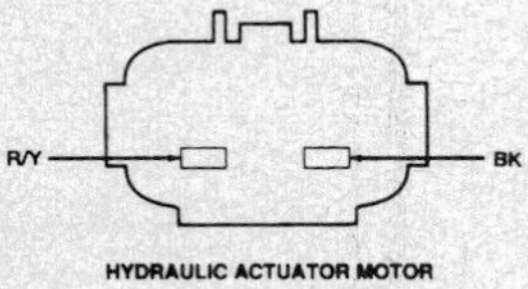

FM4029400480020X

Fig. 24   Test E: Hydraulic Anti-Lock Actuator Motor & Anti-Lock Relay (Part 2 of 2). Escort & Tracer

TEST STEP	RESULT	►	ACTION TO TAKE
F1 CHECK BATTERY VOLTAGE • Measure the voltage at the battery. Refer to Section 14-00. • Is the voltage reading as specified?	Yes No	► ►	GO to F2. CHARGE or REPLACE the battery as necessary.

FM4029400481010X

Fig. 25   Test F: Generator (Part 1 of 2). Escort & Tracer

TEST STEP	RESULT	►	ACTION TO TAKE
F2 CHECK BATTERY VOLTAGE AT ANTI-LOCK BRAKE CONTROL MODULE • Locate and disconnect the ABS control module connectors. • Measure the voltage at the anti-lock brake control module 1H ("BK/O") terminal under the following conditions:	Yes No	► ►	GO to F3. SERVICE the "BK/O" wire.

Ignition Switch	Voltage
OFF	0 Volts
ON	Above 10 Volts

• Are the voltage readings as specified?

TEST STEP	RESULT	►	ACTION TO TAKE
F3 CHECK VOLTAGE AT GENERATOR • Measure the voltage at the B ("BK/W"), L ("W/BK"), and S ("W/R") terminals at the generator with the engine idling. Refer to Section 14-00 for testing procedures and voltage specifications. • Are the voltage readings as specified?	Yes No	► ►	GO to F4. SERVICE or REPLACE generator.
F4 CHECK GENERATOR VOLTAGE AT ANTI-LOCK BRAKE CONTROL MODULE • Measure the voltage at the 2F ("W/BK") terminal of the anti-lock brake control module under the following conditions:	Yes No	► ►	GO to Pinpoint Test G1. SERVICE "W/BK" wire.

Condition	Voltage
Key ON Engine Off	0.8-3 Volts
Engine Idling	Above 10 Volts

• Are the voltages as specified?

FM4029400481020X

Fig. 25   Test F: Generator (Part 2 of 2). Escort & Tracer

Test diagnostic procedures. Refer to **Figs. 20 through 27** for Escort and Tracer Pinpoint Test diagnostic procedures.

SYSTEM SERVICE

BRAKE SYSTEM BLEED

1. Disconnect 55-pin plug from ABS module (ECU), then attach anti-lock breakout box/bleeding adapter tool No. T90P-50-ALA, or equivalent, to wiring harness 55-pin plug.

TEST STEP	RESULT	►	ACTION TO TAKE
G1 CHECK ANTI-LOCK BRAKE WARNING OPERATION • Key OFF. • Locate and disconnect the anti-lock brake control module. • Key ON. • Does the anti-lock brake warning indicator illuminate?	Yes No	► ►	GO to G2. REPLACE the 15A METER fuse and/or warning indicator miniature bulb if burned out. If OK, SERVICE "Y/R" wire from instrument cluster to anti-lock relay.
G2 CHECK FOR SHORT TO GROUND • Key ON. • Anti-lock brake control module disconnected. • Locate and disconnect the anti-lock relay. • Does the anti-lock brake warning indicator go off?	Yes No	► ►	GO to G3. SERVICE the "Y/R" wire between the instrument cluster and anti-lock relay for short to ground.

FM4029400482010X

Fig. 26   Test G: Warning Indicator (Part 1 of 2). Escort & Tracer

TEST STEP	RESULT	►	ACTION TO TAKE
G3 CHECK ANTI-LOCK BRAKE WARNING INDICATOR SIGNAL • Key ON. • Anti-lock brake control module disconnected. • ABS relay disconnected. • Connect the "Y/R" wire at the anti-lock brake control module and the "Y/R" wire at the anti-lock relay to ground. • Does the anti-lock brake warning indicator illuminate when both wires are connected to ground?	Yes No (Does not illuminate at all) No (Illuminates only when grounded at anti-lock brake control module) No (Illuminates only when grounded at anti-lock relay)	► ► ► ►	GO to G4. REPLACE the 15A METER fuse and/or warning indicator bulb if burned out. If OK, SERVICE "Y/R" wire from instrument cluster to anti-lock relay or anti-lock brake control module. SERVICE "Y/R" wire to anti-lock relay. SERVICE "Y/R" wire to anti-lock brake control module.
G4 CHECK GROUNDS AT ABS CONTROL MODULE • Key OFF. • Anti-lock brake control module disconnected. • Measure the resistance between the 1E ("BK") terminal and ground and the 1F ("BK") terminal and ground at the anti-lock brake control module. • Are the resistances less than 5 ohms?	Yes No	► ►	REPLACE anti-lock brake control module. SERVICE the "BK" wire(s) to ground.

FM4029400482020X

Fig. 26   Test G: Warning Indicator (Part 2 of 2). Escort & Tracer

TEST STEP	RESULT	►	ACTION TO TAKE
H1 CHECK SYSTEM INTEGRITY • Visually inspect all wiring, wiring harnesses, connectors, brake tubes, and components for evidence of overheating, insulation damage, looseness, shorting, or other damage. • Is there any cause for concern?	Yes No	► ►	SERVICE as required. GO to H2.

FM4029400483010X

Fig. 27   Test H: Hydraulic System (Part 1 of 2). Escort & Tracer

TEST STEP	RESULT	►	ACTION TO TAKE
H2 CHECK HYDRAULIC PRESSURE NOTE: This test requires an assistant. The pressure reduction operation occurs within a 2 second period. • Jack up the vehicle so that all the wheels are clear off the ground and the vehicle is properly supported. • Shift the transaxle to NEUTRAL. • Release the parking brake. • Check to see that there is no brake drag while rotating the wheels by hand. • Use a jumper wire to connect the "TBS" and "GND" terminals at the data link connector. • Depress the brake pedal and have an assistant verify that the wheels will not rotate. • With the brake pedal still depressed, turn the key ON and verify that the brake pressure is released momentarily (approximately 0.5 seconds) and that each wheel rotates when pressure reduction operates as shown: 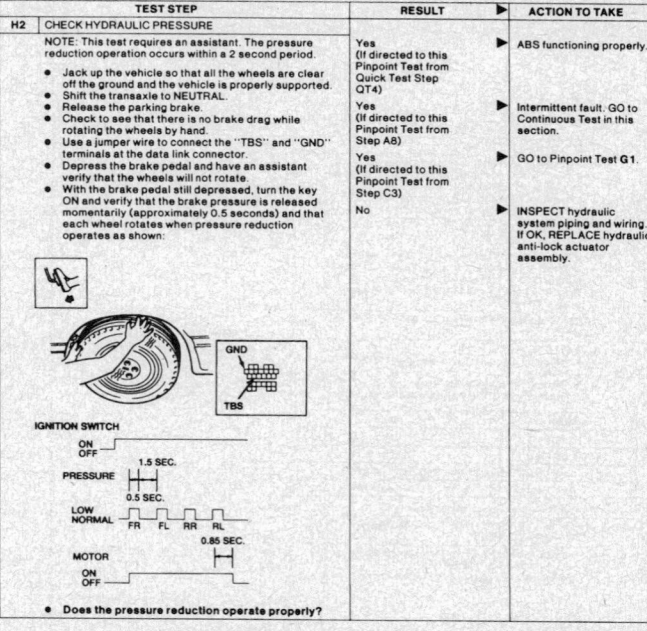 • Does the pressure reduction operate properly?	Yes (If directed to this Pinpoint Test from Quick Test Step QT4) Yes (If directed to this Pinpoint Test from Step A8) Yes (If directed to this Pinpoint Test from Step C3) No	► ► ► ►	ABS functioning properly. Intermittent fault. GO to Continuous Test in this section. GO to Pinpoint Test G1. INSPECT hydraulic system piping and wiring. If OK, REPLACE hydraulic anti-lock actuator assembly.

FM4029400483020X

Fig. 27   Test H: Hydraulic System (Part 2 of 2). Escort & Tracer

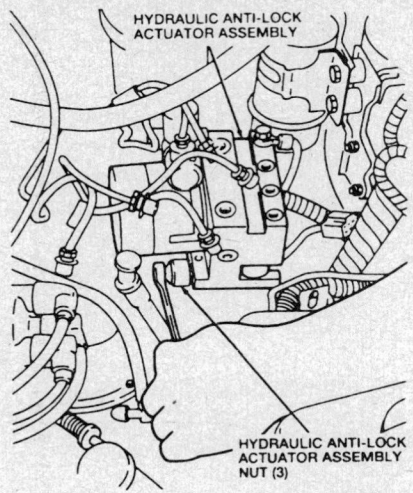

Fig. 28 Hydraulic anti-lock actuator assembly removal. Aspire

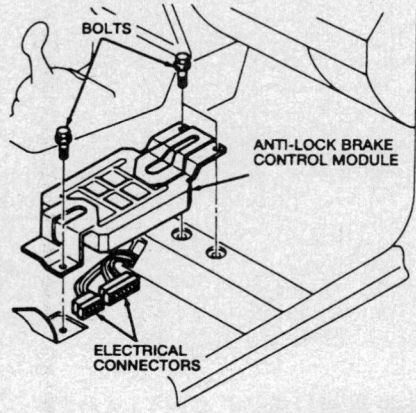

Fig. 31 ABS control module. Escort & Tracer

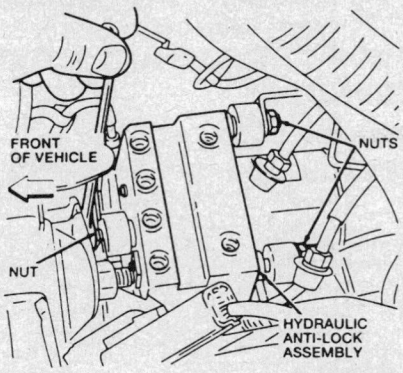

Fig. 29 Hydraulic anti-lock actuator assembly removal. Escort & Tracer

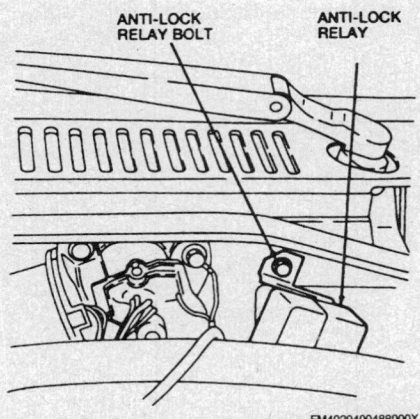

Fig. 32 Anti-lock relay removal. Aspire

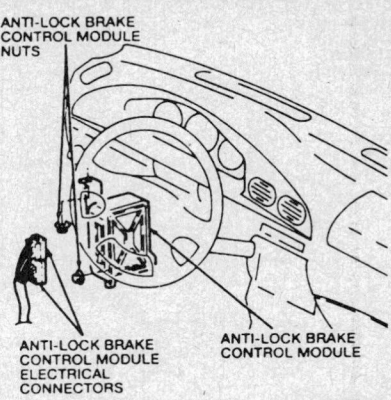

Fig. 30 ABS control module. Aspire

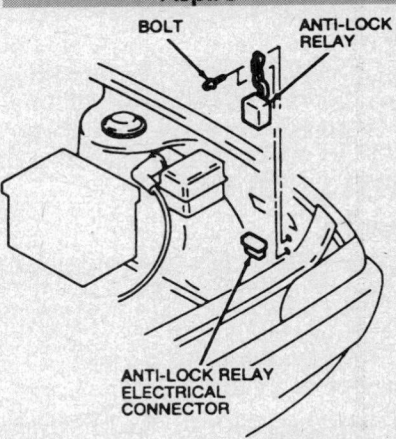

Fig. 33 Anti-lock relay removal. Escort & Tracer

2. Place bleed/harness switch in bleed position.
3. Turn ignition to On position. Red Off light should turn on.
4. Push motor button on adapter down to start pump motor. Red Off light will turn off and green On light will turn on. Pump motor will run for 60 seconds once motor button is pushed.
5. If pump motor is turns off before 60 seconds has elapsed, push abort button and pump motor will turn off.
6. After 20 seconds of operation, push and hold valve button down. Hold valve button for 20 seconds, then release.
7. Pump motor will continue to run an additional 20 seconds after valve button is released.
8. Brake lines can be bled in conventional manner in the following sequence:
   a. Right rear.
   b. Left front.
   c. Left rear.
   d. Right front.

Component Replace

HYDRAULIC ANTI-LOCK ACTUATOR ASSEMBLY

Aspire

1. Remove battery, then the two hydraulic anti-lock actuator assembly electrical connectors from bracket.
2. Disconnect actuator assembly electrical connectors.
3. Note brake line routings to ensure proper installation, then remove brake line fittings from actuator assembly.
4. Loosen three actuator assembly nuts, **Fig. 28,** then remove actuator assembly.
5. Reverse procedure to install, noting the following:
   a. **Torque** hydraulic anti-lock actuator assembly nuts to 14–16 ft. lbs.
   b. **Torque** brake line fittings to 10–15 ft. lbs.
   c. Bleed brake system as described under "Brake System Bleed."

Escort & Tracer

1. Remove battery tray, then the acid shield.
2. Tag and disconnect electrical connectors, then tag brake tubes and

mark corresponding ports.
3. Remove brake tubes from hydraulic anti-lock actuator assembly.
4. Loosen nut on front of actuator assembly, then the two nuts on back of actuator assembly, **Fig. 29.**
5. Remove actuator assembly.
6. Reverse procedure to install, noting the following:
   a. Ensure electrical connectors are properly routed.
   b. **Torque** brake tube fittings to 10–16 inch lbs.
   c. Bleed brake system as described under "Brake System Bleed."

ABS CONTROL MODULE

On Aspire models, the ABS control module is located behind the lefthand side of the instrument panel, **Fig. 30.** On Escort and Tracer models, the ABS control module is located under the passenger seat, **Fig. 31.**
1. Disconnect battery ground cable, then the control module electrical connectors.
2. Remove two module nuts, then the control module.
3. Reverse procedure to install, noting the following:
   a. **On** Aspire models, torque control module nuts to 14–18 ft. lbs.
   b. **On Escort and Tracer models,**

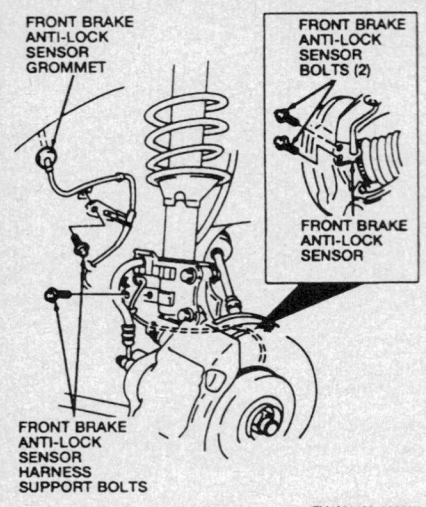

FRONT BRAKE ANTI-LOCK SENSOR GROMMET

FRONT BRAKE ANTI-LOCK SENSOR BOLTS (2)

FRONT BRAKE ANTI-LOCK SENSOR

FRONT BRAKE ANTI-LOCK SENSOR HARNESS SUPPORT BOLTS

FM4029400490000X

Fig. 34   Front brake anti-lock sensor removal. Aspire

torquecontrol module bolts to 61-86 inch lbs.

ANTI-LOCK RELAY

Aspire

1. Disconnect battery ground cable, then remove relay bolt, **Fig. 32.**
2. Disconnect electrical connector, then remove relay.
3. Reverse procedure to install.

Escort & Tracer

1. Remove engine air cleaner, air cleaner intake tube bolt and air cleaner intake tube.
2. Remove anti-lock relay bracket bolt, **Fig. 33**
3. Disconnect relay electrical connector, then remove relay.
4. Reverse procedure to install. **Torque** relay bracket bolts to 61-86 inch lbs.

BRAKE PRESSURE CONTROL VALVE
Escort & Tracer

1. Use suitable tubing wrench to loosen brake pressure control valve brake tubes.
2. Loosen brake tubes at master cylinder with suitable tubing wrench, then remove tubes between valve and master cylinder.
3. Disconnect brake tubes to brake pressure control valve.
4. Remove two control valve bolts, then the valve.
5. Reverse procedure to install, noting the following:
   a. Position control valve on firewall with "R" marks facing driver's side, then loosely install one bolt.
   b. After installing brake tubes into master cylinder and control valve, install other bolt into control valve. **Torque** control valve bolts to 14-17 inch lbs.
   c. **Torque** brake line fittings to 10-16 ft. lbs.

---

d. Bleed brakes as described under "Brake System Bleed."

FRONT BRAKE ANTI-LOCK SENSORS

Aspire

1. Disconnect battery ground cable, then the front brake anti-lock sensor electrical connector and grommet.
2. Raise and support vehicle, then remove front wheel and tire assembly.
3. Remove front brake anti-lock sensor harness support bolts, then the front brake anti-lock sensor bolts, **Fig. 34.**
4. Remove front brake anti-lock sensor from front wheel knuckle.
5. Reverse procedure to install. **Torque** sensor bolts to 12-16 ft. lbs.

Escort & Tracer

1. Disconnect battery ground cable.
2. If necessary, remove battery for access to lefthand front anti-lock sensor electrical connector and grommet.
3. Disconnect electrical connector, then pinch sides of grommet and push grommet through shock tower hole.
4. Raise and support vehicle, then remove wheel and tire assembly.
5. Remove wiring harness clip from bracket on wheel well, then the upper wiring harness bracket from wheel well bracket.
6. Remove wiring harness clip from front shock absorber bracket, then the lower wiring harness bracket from front shock absorber bracket.
7. Remove two anti-lock sensor bolts, then the sensor and bracket, **Fig. 35.**
8. Reverse procedure to install, noting the following:
   a. **Torque** sensor bolts to 12-17 ft. lbs.
   b. **Torque** wheel hub bolt nuts to 65-87 ft. lbs.

REAR BRAKE ANTI-LOCK SENSORS

1. Disconnect battery ground cable, then remove quarter trim panel.
2. Disconnect sensor electrical connector.
3. **On Aspire models,** disconnect sensor grommet.
4. **On Escort and Tracer models,** push grommet through hole in chassis.
5. **On all models,** raise and support vehicle, then remove wheel and tire assembly
6. **On Aspire models,** remove brake drum, then the four sensor harness bolts.
7. **On Escort and Tracer models,** remove upper and lower clips.
8. **On all models,** remove sensor bolt, then the sensor.
9. Reverse procedure to install. **Torque** sensor bolt to 12-16 ft. lbs.

FRONT BRAKE ANTI-LOCK SENSOR INDICATOR

1. Remove front wheel driveshaft and

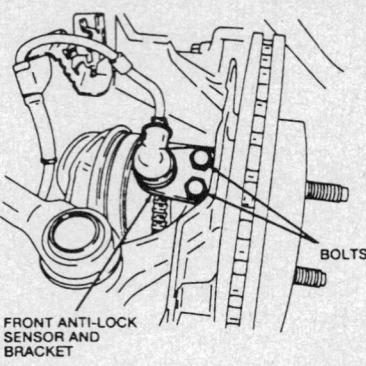

BOLTS

FRONT ANTI-LOCK SENSOR AND BRACKET

FM4029400491000X

Fig. 35   Front brake anti-lock sensor removal. Escort & Tracer

joint as described under "Front Wheel Drive Axles."
2. Use chisel to tap sensor indicator off front wheel driveshaft and joint. Discard sensor.
3. **On Aspire models,** clamp driveshaft and joint in vise equipped with protective jaw cups to prevent damage to parts, then press sensor indicator onto driveshaft and joint using sensor ring replacer tool No. T94C-20202-C, or equivalent.
4. **On Escort and Tracer models,** use dust shield/sensing ring replacer tool No. T93P-20202-A, or equivalent, to install sensor indicator onto driveshaft and joint.
5. **On all models,** install front wheel driveshaft and joint as described under "Front Wheel Drive Axles."

REAR BRAKE ANTI-LOCK SENSOR INDICATOR

Aspire

1. Raise and support vehicle, then remove wheel and tire assembly.
2. Remove brake drum.
3. Using step plate adapter tool No. D80L-630-10, or equivalent, and pulley remover tool No. T71P-19703-B, or equivalent, remove sensor indicator.
4. Using press and sensing ring installer tool No. T89P-20202-A, or equivalent, install sensor indicator.
5. Install brake drum, then the wheel and tire assembly.

Escort & Tracer

1. Raise and support vehicle, then remove wheel and tire assembly.
2. Remove wheel hub.
3. Using chisel, remove sensor indicator. Discard sensor indicator.
4. Using steel plate wider than outside diameter of sensor indicator, press sensor indicator until flush with wheel hub.
5. Install wheel hub, then the wheel and tire assembly.

Mustang

NOTE: Wire Color Code & Electrical Symbol Identification Located At The Front Of This Manual Can Be Used As An Aid When Using Wiring Circuits Found In This Section.

INDEX

PRECAUTIONS
FUEL SYSTEM PRESSURE RELIEF

Fuel supply tubes will remain pressurized for long periods of time after engine shutdown. This pressure must be relieved before performing fuel system service. A valve is provided on the fuel injection supply manifold for this purpose.

1. Remove air cleaner assembly.
2. Connect EFI and CFI fuel pressure gauge tool No. T80L-9974-B, or equivalent, to fuel pressure relief valve cap on fuel injection supply manifold.
3. Open manual valve on gauge tool to relieve fuel system pressure.

HYDRAULIC BRAKE FLUID COLOR

Hydraulic brake fluid must conform with the requirements of Federal Motor Vehicle Safety Standard 116. Under this standard, brake fluids are visually different from other automotive fluids such as transmission, power steering and engine.

Fluid color in a normal brake system may vary from its original color for many reasons. A brake master cylinder may show significantly different shades fluid color between the two brake master cylinder reservoirs. Color may also appear to vary between cast steel and die cast aluminum reservoirs. Some reasons for discoloration include the following:

Heat and/or aging.

Different operation temperatures or different rates of normal oxidation between two reservoir compartments.

Different brands and/or shades of fluid are used when topping off during normal service.

Dissolution of color dye used on master cylinder internal springs during assembly.

Brake fluid contaminated with hydrocarbon/mineral based fluid (power steering or transmission fluid) can be detected by

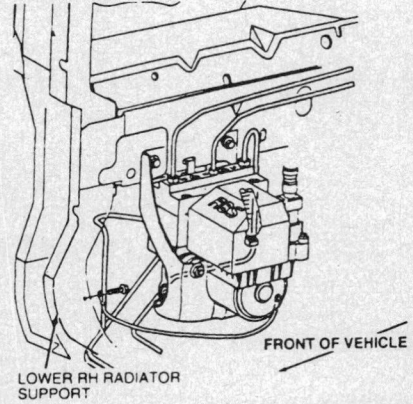

FRONT OF VEHICLE

LOWER RH RADIATOR SUPPORT

FM4029400492000X

Fig. 1   ABS hydraulic control unit & anti-lock brake control module

an obvious swelling of the master cylinder cap gasket. If the master cylinder cap gasket is swollen, all brake system rubber parts must be replaced. All brake tubes and hoses must be thoroughly flushed with Ford Heavy Duty Brake Fluid C6Az-19542-AA or —BA or DOT-3 equivalent before the vehicle returns to service.

DESCRIPTION

SYSTEM COMPONENTS
Power Brake Booster

The diaphragm-type power brake booster is a self-contained unit, mounted on the firewall. The booster uses engine intake manifold vacuum and atmospheric pressure for its power. Other than the power brake booster check valve, the booster is serviced only as an assembly. The booster must be replaced if it becomes damaged or inoperative.

Brake Master Cylinder

The brake master cylinder consists of a fluid reservoir, reservoir control valve and a fluid level indicator. The fluid level indicator is located inside the brake master cylinder reservoir and replaces the previously

used pressure differential valve. The fuel level indicator activates the brake warning indicator whenever the brake fluid level is low.

ABS Hydraulic Control Unit & Anti-Lock Brake Control Module

The ABS hydraulic control unit and anti-lock brake control module are a complete assembly. The assembly is located in the righthand lower front corner of the engine compartment, next to the bottom of the white radiator coolant recovery reservoir, **Fig. 1**. The unit is mounted in a bracket, attached to the righthand frame rail. Both the control unit and control module have on-board diagnostics.

Anti-Lock Brake Sensor

The front brake anti-lock sensor is attached to the front wheel spindle. It is part of the wheel hub assembly and is not adjustable.

The rear brake anti-lock sensor is attached to the rear disc brake caliper anchor plate. It is pressed onto the axle shaft and is not adjustable.

OPERATION

The anti-lock brake control module receives wheel speed readings from each brake anti-lock sensor. The module uses this information to compare wheel speeds. The anti-lock brake sensor electrically senses each tooth of the anti-lock brake sensor indicator as it passes through the anti-lock brake sensor's electrical field. This data is sent on to the ABS control module. The control module monitors the frequency created when the anti-lock brake sensor indicator teeth pass the brake sensor to determine wheel rotational speed.

By continuously monitoring and comparing each wheel's rotational speed, the module activates the ABS only when it senses an impending wheel lock-up under severe braking conditions. During ABS cycling, a brake system pump motor recirculates the brake fluid, **Fig. 2**.

The module then decides which wheels'

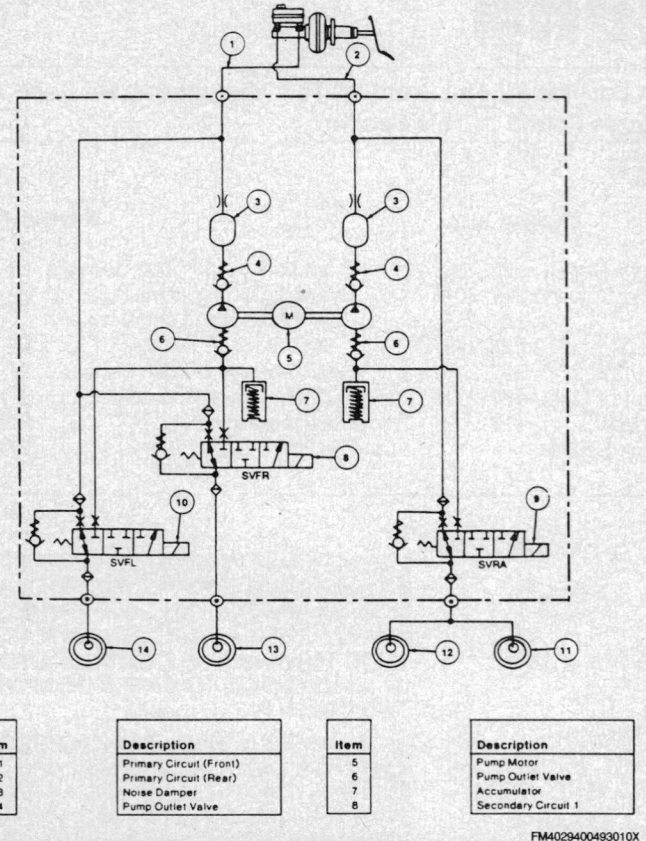

Item	Description	Item	Description
9	Solenoid-operated Valve (Rear)	11	Right Rear Caliper
10	Solenoid-operated Valve (Front)	12	Left Rear Caliper
		13	Right Front Caliper
		14	Left Front Caliper

FM4029400493020X

Fig. 2   ABS hydraulic schematic (Part 2 of 2)

Mechanical	Electrical
• Low brake fluid. • Damaged front brake anti-lock sensor indicator / rear brake anti-lock sensor. • Damaged front brake anti-lock sensor / rear brake anti-lock sensor indicator. • Damaged brake lines. • Damaged wheel bearings.	• Blown fuse(s): — 10A ELECTRON IGN — 15A STOP LAMP — 10A METER • Blown anti-lock indicator lamp bulb. • Damaged wiring harness. • Loose or corroded connection.

FM4029400494000X

Fig. 3   ABS inspection chart

CONDITION	POSSIBLE SOURCE	ACTION
Anti-Lock Warning Lamp Always On	• Fuse(s). • Circuit. • Front brake anti-lock sensor indicator / Rear brake anti-lock sensor. • ABS hydraulic actuator / anti-lock brake control module assembly.	• Go to Pinpoint Test A.
Anti-Lock Warning Lamp Always Off	• Fuse(s). • Circuit. • Anti-lock warning lamp bulb. • ABS control module.	• Go to Pinpoint Test F.

FM4029400495010X

Fig. 4   ABS Symptom Chart (Part 1 of 2)

CONDITION	POSSIBLE SOURCE	ACTION
• ABS Does Not Work	• Fuse(s). • Circuit. • Front brake anti-lock sensor indicator / Rear brake anti-lock sensor. • ABS hydraulic actuator / anti-lock brake control module assembly.	• Go to Pinpoint Test A.

FM4029400495020X

Fig. 4   ABS Symptom Chart (Part 2 of 2)

Item	Description	Item	Description
1	Primary Circuit (Front)	5	Pump Motor
2	Primary Circuit (Rear)	6	Pump Outlet Valve
3	Noise Damper	7	Accumulator
4	Pump Outlet Valve	8	Secondary Circuit 1

FM4029400493010X

Fig. 2   ABS hydraulic schematic (Part 1 of 2)

brakes need to be controlled and sends the appropriate signals to the hydraulic control unit (hydraulic portion of the assembly). Impending wheel lock conditions trigger signals from the hydraulic control unit which opens and closes the appropriate modulator solenoid valves. This may result in moderate pulsations in the brake pedal when applied. During normal braking, the brake pedal feel will be the same as a vehicle with a standard brake system.

TROUBLESHOOTING

INSPECTION & VERIFICATION

1. Verify customer's original concern by operating anti-lock brakes to duplicate concern.
2. Inspect to determine whether problem is mechanical or electrical, **Fig. 3.**
3. If concern remains after inspection, determine symptom and refer to ABS Symptom Chart, **Fig. 4.**

DIAGNOSIS & TESTING
ON-BOARD DIAGNOSTICS

The Quick Test is performed with the key ON and the engine off. Before performing the Quick Test, an inspection of the anti-lock warning lamp is required to verify a fault has been detected by the ABS control module or if the system is operating normally.

When the ABS is operating normally, the anti-lock warning lamp will illuminate for approximately three seconds when the key is turned ON or when the engine starts. If the warning lamp stays on for more than three seconds after the engine starts or illuminates while driving, a malfunction has occurred in the ABS.

Up to three ABS Diagnostic Trouble Codes (DTCs) can be stored in the control module. The DTCs are kept in the module's memory until they are erased. The DTCs can be retrieved with the anti-lock warning lamp. The ABS DTCs may indicate different failures so it is recommended the Quick Test procedure be followed in its entirety.

RETRIEVING DIAGNOSTIC TROUBLE CODES

Using STAR Tester II

1. Turn ignition switch to OFF position.
2. Locate ABS diagnostic terminal on engine compartment power distribution panel.
3. Connect SUPER STAR II Tester connector to ABS diagnostic connector, **Fig. 5.**
4. Turn on SUPER STAR II tester and latch button down in TEST position. Ensure tester is in slow mode.
5. Turn ignition switch to RUN (engine OFF). If any DTCs have been detect-

ed, each code will be flashed out once and only once after entering the diagnostic mode.
6. If no DTCs are stored, a DTC 12 will be output. After all DTCs have been output, ABS warning indicator will remain on until ignition switch is cycled.

Erasing Diagnostic Trouble Codes

After all DTCs have been retrieved, remove SUPER STAR II. Cycle ignition switch on and off, then start vehicle and drive to more than 15 mph. The stored DTCs will be erased. After erasing the DTCs, perform Quick Test.

QUICK TEST

Refer to **Fig. 6** for Quick Test diagnosis. Refer to **Fig. 7** for Diagnostic Trouble Code (DTC) identification.

PINPOINT TESTS

Do not perform any of the following Pinpoint Tests unless you are instructed to do so by the Quick Test. Each Test assumes a fault has been detected in the system with direction to enter a specific repair routine. Doing any Test without direction from the Quick Test may produce incorrect results and replacement of non-defective components. Correct test results for the Quick Test are dependent on the proper

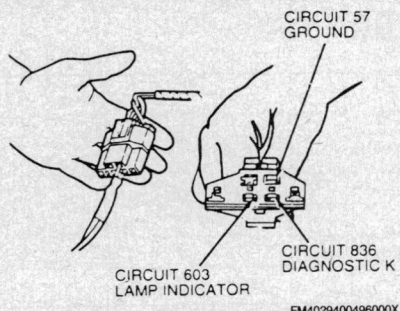

Fig. 5   ABS diagnostic connector

FM4029400496000X

TEST STEP / RESULT / ACTION TO TAKE table (Fig. 6 Part 1)

TEST STEP	RESULT	ACTION TO TAKE
A1 PERFORM VISUAL INSPECTION ● Check for insufficient brake fluid, leaks, damaged wheel speed sensors or rotors, and damaged hydraulic actuator assembly. ● Check the ABS system wiring harness for improper connections, bent or broken pins, corrosion, loose wires, and proper routing. ● Check all of the fuses for proper connection or damage. ● Check the ABS control module for physical damage. ● **Are all of the components OK?**	Yes No	▶ GO to **A2**. ▶ SERVICE the fault(s) in question. GO to **A2**.
A2 PERFORM VEHICLE PREPARATION ● Perform all of the following safety steps required to run ABS Quick Test. — Apply the parking brake. — Place the selector lever firmly into the PARK position. — Block the drive wheels. ● Turn off all of the electrical loads. — Radios — Lamps — A/C — Heater blower fans, etc. ● **Have all of the safety steps been performed and all of the electrical loads been turned off?**	Yes No	▶ GO to **A3**. ▶ Personal safety and correct diagnostic results are dependent on Test Step A2. DO NOT PROCEED with Quick Test if vehicle preparation cannot be performed.
A3 CHECK ANTI-LOCK WARNING LAMP INDICATION ● Key ON. ● Observe the anti-lock warning lamp. ● **Does anti-lock warning lamp illuminate?**	Yes No	▶ GO to **A4**. ▶ GO to Pinpoint Test **F1**.

FM4029400497010X

Fig. 6   Quick Test (Part 1 of 2)

Fig. 7 Diagnostic trouble code identification chart (Part 1 of 2)

DTC	Definition	Action to Take
12	System OK	No faults noted. Go to Pinpoint Test E.
19	Anti-lock control module	Go to Pinpoint Test E.
22	Right front valve	Go to Pinpoint Test B.
24	Left front valve	Go to Pinpoint Test B.
26	Rear ABS valve	Go to Pinpoint Test B.
31	Right front anti-lock brake sensor continuity	Go to Pinpoint Test C.
32	Right rear anti-lock brake sensor continuity fault	Go to Pinpoint Test C.
33	Left front anti-lock brake sensor continuity fault	Go to Pinpoint Test C.
34	Left rear anti-lock brake sensor continuity fault	Go to Pinpoint Test C.
41	Right front anti-lock brake sensor	Go to Pinpoint Test D.
42	Right front anti-lock brake sensor	Go to Pinpoint Test D.

FM4029400498010X

Fig. 7   Diagnostic trouble code identification chart (Part 1 of 2)

DTC	Definition	Action to Take
43	Left front anti-lock brake sensor	Go to Pinpoint Test D.
44	Left front anti-lock brake sensor	Go to Pinpoint Test D.
78	Anti-lock brake sensor frequency fault	Inspect anti-lock brake sensors and anti-lock brake sensor indicators for damage.
69	Vehicle battery voltage less than 10 volts	Go to Pinpoint Test E.
Hard light ABS warning lamp stays on	No DTC	Go to Pinpoint Test F.

FM4029400498020X

Fig. 7   Diagnostic trouble code identification chart (Part 2 of 2)

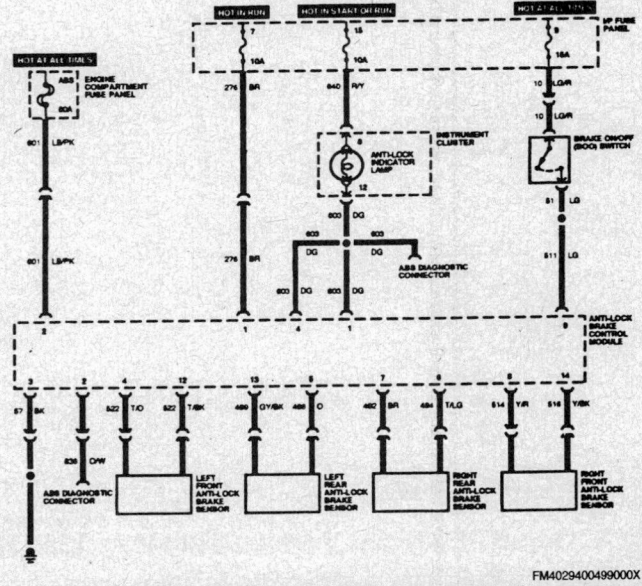

FM4029400499000X

Fig. 8   ABS wiring diagram

TEST STEP / RESULT / ACTION TO TAKE table (Fig. 6 Part 2)

TEST STEP	RESULT	ACTION TO TAKE
A4 CHECK ANTI-LOCK WARNING LAMP WITH ENGINE RUNNING ● Start the engine. NOTE: Certain ABS DTC's require that the vehicle be driven in order for the warning lamp to come on. Other DTC's will cause the lamp to turn on each time the engine is started. ● Drive the vehicle if necessary. (Read note.) ● Observe the anti-lock warning lamp. ● **Does anti-lock warning lamp illuminate?**	Yes No	▶ Indicates a present failure. GO to **A5**. ▶ Normal operation. If ABS symptom exists, there may be an intermittent problem. GO to **A5**. If no ABS symptoms exist, ABS system is operating normally.
A5 PERFORM ABS TROUBLE CODE RETRIEVAL ● Ignition switch OFF. ● Jumper Pin K of the ABS diagnostic connector to ground. CIRCUIT 57 GROUND CIRCUIT 603 LAMP INDICATOR CIRCUIT 836 DIAGNOSTIC K ● Key ON. ● Observe the anti-lock warning lamp. ● **Does anti-lock brake warning lamp flash?** NOTE: The DTC will begin to flash immediately without introduction and flash only once. Ignition switch cycling can repeat DTC's if numbers are missed, as long as vehicle has not been driven.	Yes No	▶ RECORD code(s). GO to the following ABS Trouble Code Identification Chart and PERFORM Pinpoint Test specified for first code retrieved. ▶ GO to Pinpoint Test **F1**.

FM4029400497020X

Fig. 6   Quick Test (Part 2 of 2)

operation of related components and systems. It may be necessary to correct any defects in these areas before passing the Quick Test.

Do not replace any parts unless the test results indicate they should be replaced. When more than one diagnostic trouble code is received, always start with the first code received.

Do not measure voltage or resistance at the processor unless otherwise specified. To ensure correct Test Procedures, follow all steps in order as listed. Follow each step until a fault is found.

After completing any repairs to the ABS, verify all components are properly reconnected and repeat the Quick Test.

When performing Pinpoint Tests, refer to the wiring diagram, **Fig. 8,** to locate wire circuits indicated in test procedures.

Refer to **Figs. 9 through 13** for Test diagnostic procedures.

DIAGNOSTIC CHART INDEX

Pinpoint Test	Description	Page No.	Fig. No.
B	ABS Outlet Valve & Circuit	9	9
C	Anti-Lock Brake Sensor Continuity	10	10
D	Anti-Lock Brake Sensor & Circuit	11	11
E	Voltage Supply	12	12
F	Power Check	13	13

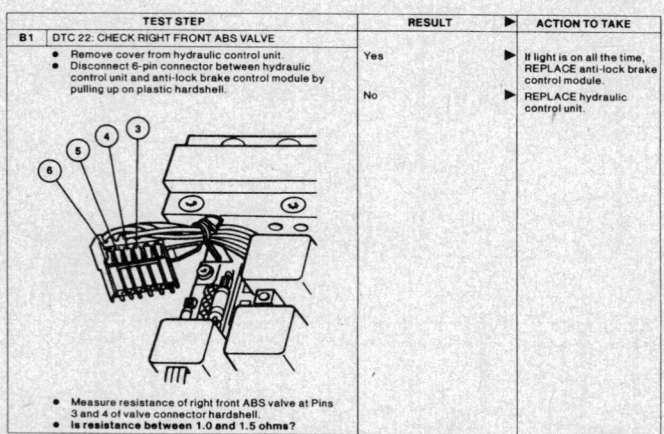

TEST STEP	RESULT	▶	ACTION TO TAKE
B1 DTC 22: CHECK RIGHT FRONT ABS VALVE • Remove cover from hydraulic control unit. • Disconnect 6-pin connector between hydraulic control unit and anti-lock brake control module by pulling up on plastic hardshell.	Yes No	▶ ▶	If light is on all the time, REPLACE anti-lock brake control module. REPLACE hydraulic control unit.

• Measure resistance of right front ABS valve at Pins 3 and 4 of valve connector hardshell.
• Is resistance between 1.0 and 1.5 ohms?

FM4029400500010X

Fig. 9 Test B: ABS Outlet Valve & Circuit (Part 1 of 2)

TEST STEP	RESULT	▶	ACTION TO TAKE
B2 DTC 24: CHECK LEFT FRONT ABS VALVE • Remove cover from hydraulic control unit. • Disconnect 6-pin connector between hydraulic control unit and anti-lock brake control module by pulling up on plastic hardshell. • Measure resistance of right front ABS valve at Pins 1 and 2 of valve connector hardshell. • Is resistance between 1.0 and 1.5 ohms?	Yes No	▶ ▶	If light is on all the time, REPLACE anti-lock brake control module. REPLACE hydraulic control unit.
B3 DTC 26: CHECK REAR AXLE ABS VALVE • Remove cover from hydraulic control unit. • Disconnect 6-pin connector between hydraulic control unit and anti-lock brake control module by pulling up on plastic hardshell. • Measure resistance of right front ABS valve at Pins 5 and 6 of valve connector hardshell.	Yes No	▶ ▶	If light is on all the time, REPLACE anti-lock brake control module. REPLACE hydraulic control unit.

• Is resistance between 1.0 and 1.5 ohms?

FM4029400500020X

Fig. 9 Test B: ABS Outlet Valve & Circuit (Part 2 of 2)

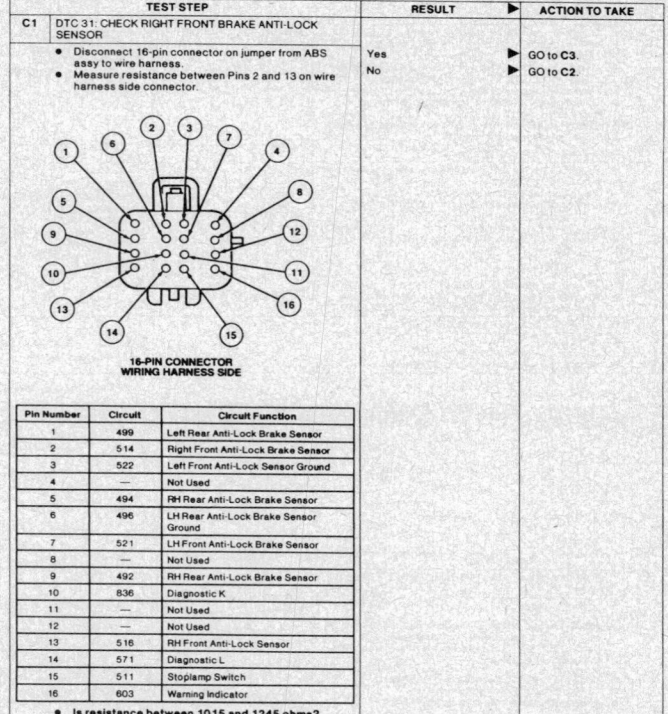

TEST STEP	RESULT	▶	ACTION TO TAKE
C1 DTC 31: CHECK RIGHT FRONT BRAKE ANTI-LOCK SENSOR • Disconnect 16-pin connector on jumper from ABS assy to wire harness. • Measure resistance between Pins 2 and 13 on wire harness side connector.	Yes No	▶ ▶	GO to C3. GO to C2.

16-PIN CONNECTOR WIRING HARNESS SIDE

Pin Number	Circuit	Circuit Function
1	499	Left Rear Anti-Lock Brake Sensor
2	514	Right Front Anti-Lock Brake Sensor
3	522	Left Front Anti-Lock Sensor Ground
4	—	Not Used
5	494	RH Rear Anti-Lock Brake Sensor
6	496	LH Rear Anti-Lock Brake Sensor Ground
7	521	LH Front Anti-Lock Brake Sensor
8	—	Not Used
9	492	RH Rear Anti-Lock Brake Sensor
10	836	Diagnostic K
11	—	Not Used
12	—	Not Used
13	516	RH Front Anti-Lock Sensor
14	571	Diagnostic L
15	511	Stoplamp Switch
16	603	Warning Indicator

• Is resistance between 1015 and 1245 ohms?

FM4029400501010X

Fig. 10 Test C: Anti-Lock Brake Sensor Continuity (Part 1 of 8)

TEST STEP	RESULT	▶	ACTION TO TAKE
C2 CHECK RIGHT FRONT BRAKE ANTI-LOCK SENSOR • Disconnect right front sensor from wire harness. • Measure resistance between Pins 1 and 2 on sensor connector.	Yes No	▶ ▶	SERVICE or REPLACE cable harness Circuit 514 or 516. REPLACE right front brake anti-lock sensor.

RH FRONT BRAKE ANTI-LOCK SENSOR

• Is resistance between 1015 and 1245 ohms?

TEST STEP	RESULT	▶	ACTION TO TAKE
C3 CHECK JUMPER HARNESS • Remove cover from hydraulic control unit. • Disconnect jumper harness from anti-lock brake control module. • Check for broken or damaged wire in jumper between Pin 2 (16-pin side) and Pin 8 (15-pin side) or between Pin 13 (16-pin side) and Pin 14 (15-pin side). • Are both wires OK?	Yes No	▶ ▶	If light is on all the time, REPLACE anti-lock brake control module. SERVICE or REPLACE broken or damaged wire in jumper.

FM4029400501020X

Fig. 10 Test C: Anti-Lock Brake Sensor Continuity (Part 2 of 8)

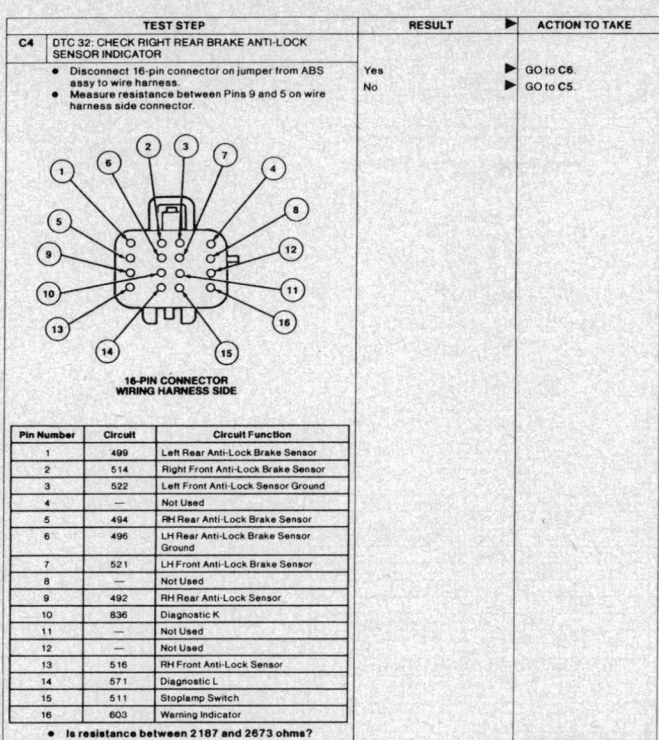

	TEST STEP	RESULT	▶	ACTION TO TAKE
C4	DTC 32: CHECK RIGHT REAR BRAKE ANTI-LOCK SENSOR INDICATOR			
	• Disconnect 16-pin connector on jumper from ABS assy to wire harness. • Measure resistance between Pins 9 and 5 on wire harness side connector.	Yes No	▶ ▶	GO to C6. GO to C5.

16-PIN CONNECTOR WIRING HARNESS SIDE

Pin Number	Circuit	Circuit Function
1	499	Left Rear Anti-Lock Brake Sensor
2	514	Right Front Anti-Lock Brake Sensor
3	522	Left Front Anti-Lock Sensor Ground
4	—	Not Used
5	494	RH Rear Anti-Lock Brake Sensor
6	496	LH Rear Anti-Lock Brake Sensor Ground
7	521	LH Front Anti-Lock Brake Sensor
8	—	Not Used
9	492	RH Rear Anti-Lock Sensor
10	836	Diagnostic K
11	—	Not Used
12	—	Not Used
13	516	RH Front Anti-Lock Sensor
14	571	Diagnostic L
15	511	Stoplamp Switch
16	603	Warning Indicator

• Is resistance between 2187 and 2673 ohms?

FM4029400501030X

Fig. 10   Test C: Anti-Lock Brake Sensor Continuity (Part 3 of 8)

	TEST STEP	RESULT	▶	ACTION TO TAKE
C5	CHECK RIGHT REAR BRAKE ANTI-LOCK SENSOR INDICATOR			
	• Disconnect right rear rear brake anti-lock sensor indicator from wire harness. • Measure resistance between Pins 1 and 2 on sensor connector.	Yes No	▶ ▶	SERVICE or REPLACE cable harness Circuit 492 or 494. REPLACE right rear brake anti-lock sensor indicator.

RH REAR BRAKE ANTI-LOCK SENSOR

• Is resistance between 2187 and 2673 ohms?

C6	CHECK JUMPER HARNESS			
	• Remove cover from hydraulic control unit. • Disconnect jumper harness from anti-lock brake module. • Check for broken or damaged wire in jumper between Pin 9 (16-pin side) and Pin 7 (15-pin side) or between Pin 5 (16-pin side) and Pin 6 (15-pin side). • Are both wires OK?	Yes No	▶ ▶	If light is on all the time, REPLACE electronic control unit. SERVICE or REPLACE broken or damaged wire in jumper.

FM4029400501040X

Fig. 10   Test C: Anti-Lock Brake Sensor Continuity (Part 4 of 8)

	TEST STEP	RESULT	▶	ACTION TO TAKE
C8	CHECK LEFT FRONT BRAKE ANTI-LOCK SENSOR			
	• Disconnect left front brake anti-lock sensor from wire harness. • Measure resistance between Pins 1 and 2 on sensor connector.	Yes No	▶ ▶	SERVICE or REPLACE cable harness Circuit 521 or 522. REPLACE left front brake anti-lock sensor.

LH FRONT BRAKE ANTI-LOCK SENSOR

• Is resistance between 1015 and 1245 ohms?

C9	CHECK LEFT FRONT BRAKE ANTI-LOCK SENSOR			
	• Disconnect jumper harness from anti-lock brake control module. • Check for broken or damaged wire in jumper between Pin 7 (16-pin side) and Pin 4 (15-pin side) or between Pin 3 (16-pin side) and Pin 12 (15-pin side). • Are both wires OK?	Yes No	▶ ▶	If light is on all the time, REPLACE anti-lock brake control module. SERVICE or REPLACE broken or damaged wire in jumper.

FM4029400501060X

Fig. 10   Test C: Anti-Lock Brake Sensor Continuity (Part 6 of 8)

	TEST STEP	RESULT	▶	ACTION TO TAKE
C7	DTC 33: CHECK LEFT FRONT BRAKE ANTI-LOCK SENSOR			
	• Disconnect 16-pin connector on jumper from ABS assy to wire harness. • Measure resistance between Pins 3 and 7 on wire harness side connector.	Yes No	▶ ▶	GO to C9. GO to C8.

16-PIN CONNECTOR WIRING HARNESS SIDE

Pin Number	Circuit	Circuit Function
1	499	Left Rear Anti-Lock Brake Sensor
2	514	Right Front Anti-Lock Brake Sensor
3	522	Left Front Anti-Lock Sensor Ground
4	—	Not Used
5	494	RH Rear Anti-Lock Brake Sensor
6	496	LH Rear Anti-Lock Brake Sensor Ground
7	521	LH Front Anti-Lock Brake Sensor
8	—	Not Used
9	492	RH Rear Anti-Lock Sensor
10	836	Diagnostic K
11	—	Not Used
12	—	Not Used
13	516	RH Front Anti-Lock Sensor
14	571	Diagnostic L
15	511	Stoplamp Switch
16	603	Warning Indicator

• Is resistance between 1015 and 1245 ohms?

FM4029400501050X

Fig. 10   Test C: Anti-Lock Brake Sensor Continuity (Part 5 of 8)

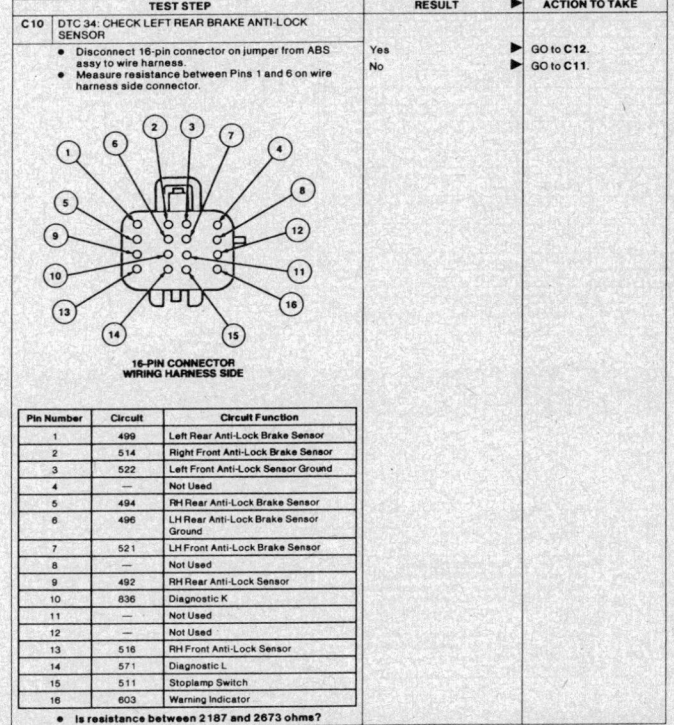

	TEST STEP	RESULT	▶	ACTION TO TAKE
C10	DTC 34: CHECK LEFT REAR BRAKE ANTI-LOCK SENSOR			
	• Disconnect 16-pin connector on jumper from ABS assy to wire harness. • Measure resistance between Pins 1 and 6 on wire harness side connector.	Yes No	▶ ▶	GO to C12. GO to C11.

16-PIN CONNECTOR WIRING HARNESS SIDE

Pin Number	Circuit	Circuit Function
1	499	Left Rear Anti-Lock Brake Sensor
2	514	Right Front Anti-Lock Brake Sensor
3	522	Left Front Anti-Lock Sensor Ground
4	—	Not Used
5	494	RH Rear Anti-Lock Brake Sensor
6	496	LH Rear Anti-Lock Brake Sensor Ground
7	521	LH Front Anti-Lock Brake Sensor
8	—	Not Used
9	492	RH Rear Anti-Lock Sensor
10	836	Diagnostic K
11	—	Not Used
12	—	Not Used
13	516	RH Front Anti-Lock Sensor
14	571	Diagnostic L
15	511	Stoplamp Switch
16	603	Warning Indicator

• Is resistance between 2187 and 2673 ohms?

FM4029400501070X

Fig. 10   Test C: Anti-Lock Brake Sensor Continuity (Part 7 of 8)

TEST STEP	RESULT	►	ACTION TO TAKE
C11 CHECK LEFT REAR BRAKE ANTI-LOCK SENSOR • Disconnect left rear brake anti-lock sensor from wire harness. • Measure resistance between Pins 1 and 2 on sensor connector.	Yes	►	SERVICE or REPLACE cable harness Circuit 496 or 499.
	No	►	REPLACE left rear rear brake anti-lock sensor.
LH REAR BRAKE ANTI-LOCK SENSOR • Is resistance between 2187 and 2673 ohms?			
C12 CHECK JUMPER HARNESS • Remove cover from hydraulic control unit. • Disconnect jumper harness from anti-lock brake control module. • Check for broken or damaged wire in jumper between Pin 1 (16-pin side) and Pin 13 (15-pin side) or between Pin 6 (16-pin side) and Pin 5 (15-pin side). • Are both wires OK?	Yes	►	If light is on all the time, REPLACE anti-lock brake control module.
	No	►	SERVICE or REPLACE broken or damaged wire in jumper.

FM4029400501080X

Fig. 10   Test C: Anti-Lock Brake Sensor Continuity (Part 8 of 8)

TEST STEP	RESULT	►	ACTION TO TAKE
D1 DTC 41: CHECK RIGHT FRONT BRAKE ANTI-LOCK SENSOR • Remove cover from hydraulic control unit. • Disconnect jumper harness from anti-lock brake control module. • Check for a short between Pin 8 or Pin 14 of the 15-pin connector to ground.	Yes	►	SERVICE or REPLACE jumper, Circuit 514 or 516, or right front brake anti-lock sensor.
	No	►	GO to D2.

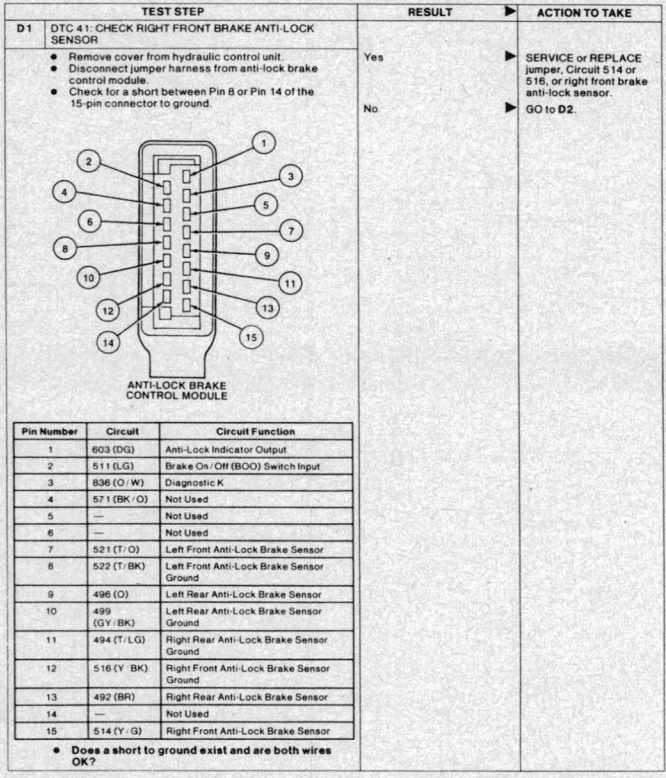

ANTI-LOCK BRAKE CONTROL MODULE

Pin Number	Circuit	Circuit Function
1	603 (DG)	Anti-Lock Indicator Output
2	511 (LG)	Brake On / Off (BOO) Switch Input
3	836 (O / W)	Diagnostic K
4	571 (BK / O)	Not Used
5	—	Not Used
6	—	Not Used
7	521 (T/O)	Left Front Anti-Lock Brake Sensor
8	522 (T/BK)	Left Front Anti-Lock Brake Sensor Ground
9	496 (O)	Left Rear Anti-Lock Brake Sensor
10	499 (GY/BK)	Left Rear Anti-Lock Brake Sensor Ground
11	494 (T/LG)	Right Rear Anti-Lock Brake Sensor Ground
12	516 (Y/BK)	Right Front Anti-Lock Brake Sensor Ground
13	492 (BR)	Right Rear Anti-Lock Brake Sensor
14	—	Not Used
15	514 (Y/G)	Right Front Anti-Lock Brake Sensor

• Does a short to ground exist and are both wires OK?

FM4029400502010X

Fig. 11   Test D: Anti-Lock Brake Sensor & Circuit (Part 1 of 6)

TEST STEP	RESULT	►	ACTION TO TAKE
D2 CHECK RIGHT FRONT BRAKE ANTI-LOCK SENSOR AIR GAP • Remove the right front wheel and tire. • Check for damage to the front brake anti-lock sensor or front brake anti-lock sensor indicator. • Check for objects sticking to the front brake anti-lock sensor or front brake anti-lock sensor indicator. • Check the air gap between the front brake anti-lock sensor indicator and front brake anti-lock sensor (.5mm-.95mm specification). • Are the conditions OK?	Yes	►	If light is coming on all the time, REPLACE anti-lock brake control module.
	No	►	SERVICE condition as required.

FM4029400502020X

Fig. 11   Test D: Anti-Lock Brake Sensor & Circuit (Part 2 of 6)

TEST STEP	RESULT	►	ACTION TO TAKE
D3 DTC 42: CHECK RIGHT REAR BRAKE ANTI-LOCK SENSOR • Remove cover from hydraulic control unit. • Disconnect jumper harness from anti-lock brake control module. • Check for a short between Pin 6 or Pin 7 of the 15-pin connector to ground.	Yes	►	SERVICE or REPLACE jumper, Circuit 191 or 192, or right rear brake anti-lock sensor.
	No	►	GO to D4.

ANTI-LOCK BRAKE CONTROL MODULE

Pin Number	Circuit	Circuit Function
1	603 (DG)	Anti-Lock Indicator Output
2	511 (LG)	Brake On / Off (BOO) Switch Input
3	836 (O / W)	Diagnostic K
4	571 (BK / O)	Not Used
5	—	Not Used
6	—	Not Used
7	521 (T/O)	Left Front Anti-Lock Brake Sensor
8	522 (T/BK)	Left Front Anti-Lock Brake Sensor Ground
9	496 (O)	Left Rear Anti-Lock Brake Sensor
10	499 (GY/BK)	Left Rear Anti-Lock Brake Sensor Ground
11	494 (T/LG)	Right Rear Anti-Lock Brake Sensor Ground
12	516 (Y/BK)	Right Front Anti-Lock Brake Sensor Ground
13	492 (BR)	Right Rear Anti-Lock Brake Sensor
14	—	Not Used
15	514 (Y/G)	Right Front Anti-Lock Brake Sensor

• Does a short to ground exist and are both wires OK?

FM4029400502030X

Fig. 11   Test D: Anti-Lock Brake Sensor & Circuit (Part 3 of 6)

TEST STEP	RESULT	►	ACTION TO TAKE
D4 CHECK RIGHT REAR BRAKE ANTI-LOCK SENSOR AIR GAP • Remove the right rear wheel and tire. • Check for damage to the rear brake anti-lock sensor or rear brake anti-lock sensor indicator. • Check for objects sticking to the rear brake anti-lock sensor or rear brake anti-lock sensor indicator. • Check the air gap between the rear brake anti-lock sensor indicator and rear brake anti-lock sensor (.6mm-1.6mm specification). • Are the conditions OK?	Yes	►	If light is coming on all the time, REPLACE anti-lock brake control module.
	No	►	SERVICE condition as required.
D5 DTC 43: CHECK LEFT FRONT BRAKE ANTI-LOCK SENSOR • Remove cover from hydraulic control unit. • Disconnect jumper harness from anti-lock brake control module. • Check for a short between Pin 4 or Pin 12 of the 15-pin connector to ground. • Does a short to ground exist and are both wires OK?	Yes	►	SERVICE or REPLACE jumper, Circuit 521 or 522, or left front brake anti-lock sensor.
	No	►	GO to D6.
D6 CHECK LEFT FRONT SENSOR AIR GAP • Remove the left front wheel and tire. • Check for damage to the front brake anti-lock sensor or front brake anti-lock sensor indicator. • Check for objects sticking to the sensor or ring. • Check the air gap between the ring and sensor (.5mm-.95mm specification). • Are the conditions OK?	Yes	►	If light is coming on all the time, REPLACE anti-lock brake control module.
	No	►	SERVICE condition as required.

FM4029400502040X

Fig. 11   Test D: Anti-Lock Brake Sensor & Circuit (Part 4 of 6)

TEST STEP	RESULT	▶	ACTION TO TAKE
D7 DTC 44: CHECK LEFT REAR BRAKE ANTI-LOCK SENSOR • Remove cover from hydraulic control unit. • Disconnect jumper harness from anti-lock brake control module. • Check for short between Pin 5 or Pin 13 of the 15-pin connector to ground.	Yes	▶	SERVICE or REPLACE jumper, Circuit 199 or 196, or left rear brake anti-lock sensor.
	No	▶	GO to D8.

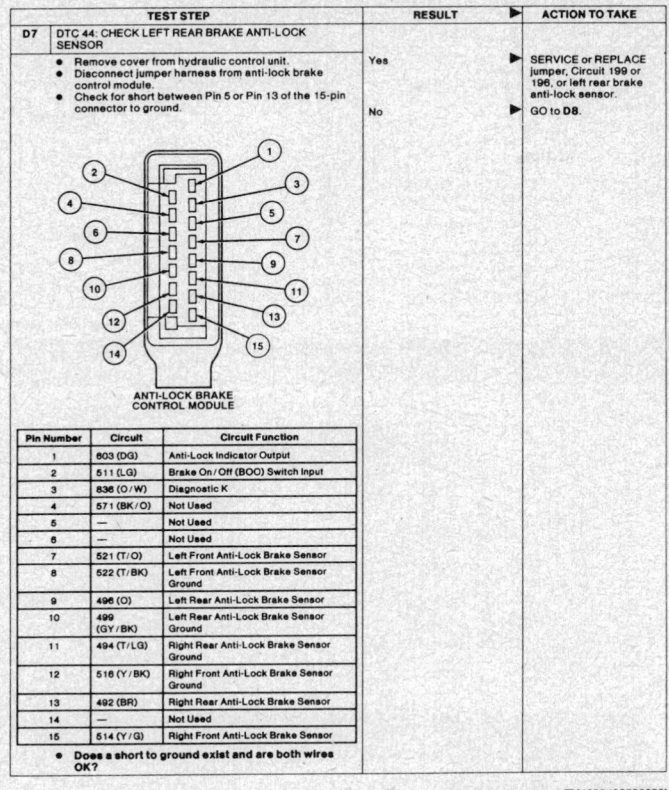

ANTI-LOCK BRAKE CONTROL MODULE

Pin Number	Circuit	Circuit Function
1	603 (DG)	Anti-Lock Indicator Output
2	511 (LG)	Brake On/Off (BOO) Switch Input
3	836 (O/W)	Diagnostic K
4	571 (BK/O)	Not Used
5	—	Not Used
6	—	Not Used
7	521 (T/O)	Left Front Anti-Lock Brake Sensor
8	522 (T/BK)	Left Front Anti-Lock Brake Sensor Ground
9	496 (O)	Left Rear Anti-Lock Brake Sensor
10	499 (GY/BK)	Left Rear Anti-Lock Brake Sensor Ground
11	494 (T/LG)	Right Rear Anti-Lock Brake Sensor Ground
12	516 (Y/BK)	Right Front Anti-Lock Brake Sensor Ground
13	492 (BR)	Right Rear Anti-Lock Brake Sensor
14	—	Not Used
15	514 (Y/G)	Right Front Anti-Lock Brake Sensor

• Does a short to ground exist and are both wires OK?

FM4029400502050X

Fig. 11   Test D: Anti-Lock Brake Sensor & Circuit (Part 5 of 6)

TEST STEP	RESULT	▶	ACTION TO TAKE
D8 CHECK LEFT REAR SENSOR AIR GAP • Remove the left rear wheel and tire. • Check for damage to the rear brake anti-lock sensor or rear brake anti-lock sensor indicator. • Check for objects sticking to the rear brake anti-lock sensor or rear brake anti-lock sensor indicator. • Check the air gap between the rear brake anti-lock sensor indicator and rear brake anti-lock sensor (.6mm-1.6mm specification). • Are the conditions OK?	Yes	▶	If light is coming on all the time, REPLACE anti-lock brake control module.
	No	▶	SERVICE condition as required.

FM4029400502060X

Fig. 11   Test D: Anti-Lock Brake Sensor & Circuit (Part 6 of 6)

TEST STEP	RESULT	▶	ACTION TO TAKE
E1 CHECK 30A ANTI-SKID FUSE • Check the 60A ABS fuse located in the LH engine compartment power distribution panel. • Is the fuse OK?	Yes	▶	GO to E4.
	No	▶	GO to E2.
E2 CHECK HYDRAULIC MOTOR SYSTEM • Ignition switch OFF. • Replace the 60A ABS fuse. • Inspect the fuse. • Does the fuse fail again?	Yes	▶	GO to E3.
	No	▶	GO to E4.
E3 CHECK FOR SHORT TO GROUND IN HYDRAULIC MOTOR POWER CIRCUIT • Ignition switch OFF. • Remove the 60A ABS fuse. • Disconnect the 16-pin connector located at the hydraulic control unit. • Measure the resistance of Circuit 601 (LB/PK) between the 60A ABS fuse terminal and ground. • Is the resistance greater than 10,000 ohms?	Yes	▶	GO to E4.
	No	▶	SERVICE Circuit 601 (LB/PK) between the engine compartment fuse panel and the hydraulic actuator assembly.
E4 CHECK POWER SUPPLY TO HYDRAULIC CONTROL UNIT • Ignition switch OFF. • Disconnect the hydraulic control unit connector. • Measure the voltage on Circuit 601 (LB/PK) at the hydraulic actuator assembly connector. • Is the voltage greater than 10 volts?	Yes	▶	GO to E5.
	No	▶	SERVICE Circuit 601 (LB/PK) between the engine compartment fuse panel and the hydraulic control unit.
E5 CHECK HYDRAULIC ACTUATOR ASSEMBLY GROUND • Ignition switch OFF. • Measure the resistance of the "BK" wire between the screw terminal on the right side of the hydraulic control assembly and ground. • Is the resistance less than 5 ohms?	Yes	▶	GO to E6.
	No	▶	SERVICE the "BK" wire.
E6 CHECK HYDRAULIC PUMP MOTOR • Ignition switch OFF. • Remove anti-lock brake control module. CAUTION: Do not jumper 12 volts to Pin I of the hydraulic actuator assembly for more than 5 seconds. • Apply 12 volts across electric motor. • Is current draw less than 45 amps and motor running?	Yes	▶	REPLACE anti-lock brake control module.
	No	▶	REPLACE the hydraulic control unit.

FM4029400504000X

Fig. 12   Test E: Voltage Supply

TEST STEP	RESULT	▶	ACTION TO TAKE
F1 CHECK METER FUSE • Check fuse 15 (10A) located in the fuse junction panel. • Is the fuse OK?	Yes	▶	GO to F4.
	No	▶	GO to F2.
F2 CHECK SYSTEM • Ignition switch OFF. • Replace fuse 15 (10A) • Ignition switch ON. • Does the fuse fail again?	Yes	▶	GO to F3.
	No	▶	GO to F4.
F3 CHECK POWER SHORT TO GROUND • Ignition switch OFF. • Remove fuse 15 (10A) fuse. • Remove the instrument cluster. Refer to Section 13-01. • Measure the resistance of Circuit 640 (R/Y) wire between the fuse terminal and ground. • Is the resistance greater than 10,000 ohms?	Yes	▶	System OK.
	No	▶	SERVICE Circuit 640 (R/Y) wire between the interior fuse panel and the instrument cluster.

FM4029400505000X

Fig. 13   Test F: Power Check

SYSTEM SERVICE
Brake System Bleed

1. Disconnect 55-pin plug from ABS module (ECU), then attach anti-lock breakout box/bleeding adapter tool No. T90P-50-ALA, or equivalent, to wiring harness 55-pin plug.
2. Place bleed/harness switch in bleed position.
3. Turn ignition to On position. Red Off light should turn on.
4. Push motor button on adapter down to start pump motor. Red Off light will turn off and green On light will turn on. Pump motor will run for 60 seconds once motor button is pushed.
5. If pump motor is turns off before 60 seconds has elapsed, push abort button and pump motor will turn off.
6. After 20 seconds of operation, push and hold valve button down. Hold valve button for 20 seconds, then release.
7. Pump motor will continue to run an additional 20 seconds after valve button is released.
8. Brake lines can be bled in conventional manner in the following sequence:
   a. Right rear.
   b. Left front.
   c. Left rear.
   d. Right front.

Component Replace
VACUUM BRAKE BOOSTER

Refer to **Fig. 14** when replacing the vacuum brake booster.

3.8L/V6-232
Removal

1. **On models equipped with 5.0L/V6-302 engine**, remove engine air cleaner.
2. **On all models**, disconnect battery ground cable.
3. **On models equipped**

3.8L/V6-232 engine, proceed as follows:
a. Disconnect accelerator cable from throttle body.
b. Remove accelerator cable to accelerator shaft bracket screw, then the accelerator cable from bracket.
c. Remove two accelerator shaft bracket to manifold screws and rotate bracket toward engine.
d. Remove horn.
e. Relieve fuel system pressure as described under "Precautions."
f. Disconnect two manifold injector connectors located near oil level indicator bracket, then the two fuel hoses to fuel injection supply manifold assembly.
g. Remove three oil level indicator bracket to upper intake manifold bolts, then the oil level indicator and bracket.
h. Remove windshield wiper motor.
i. Remove vacuum line hoses directly over power brake booster at dash panel vacuum tee.
j. **On models equipped with 3.8L/V6-232 engine and manual transmission**, remove clutch cable stand bolt, then move bracket to side rail at fender inner panel.
k. **On models equipped with**

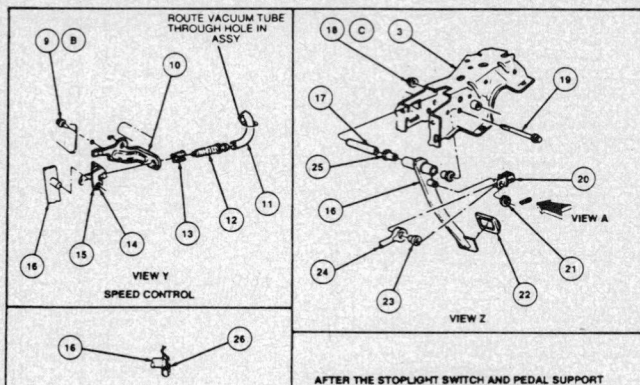

Fig. 14 Vacuum brake booster replacement (Part 1 of 2)

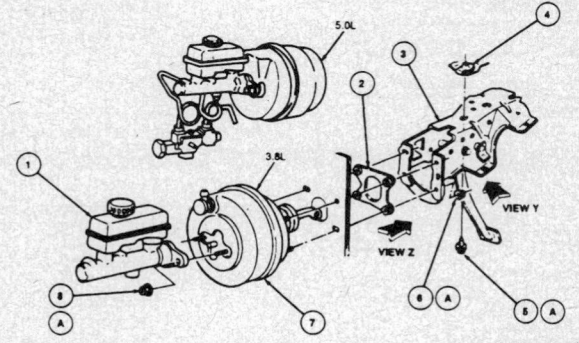

Item	Description	Item	Description
1	Brake Master Cylinder	17	Bushing
2	Spacer	18C	Nut
3	Pedal Support Bracket	19	Bolt
4	J-Nut	20	Stoplight Switch
5A	Screw	21	Brake Master Cylinder Push Rod Spacer (2 Req'd)
6A	Nut (4 Req'd)	22	Brake Pedal Pad
7	Power Brake Booster	23	Brake Master Cylinder Push Rod Bushing
8A	Nut (2 Req'd)		
9B	Screw	24	Push Rod Assy
10	Speed Control Vacuum Dump Valve Mounting Bracket	25	Spacer (2 Req'd)
11	Vacuum Tube	26	Pin
12	Speed Control Dump Valve	A	Tighten to 18-34 N·m (13-24 Lb-Ft)
13	Clip	B	Tighten to 8-13.6 N·m (6-10 Lb-Ft)
14	Mounting Hole	C	Tighten to 14-27 N·m (10-20 Lb-Ft)
15	Speed Control Vacuum Valve Actuator Adapter		
16	Brake Pedal		

Fig. 14 Vacuum brake booster replacement (Part 2 of 2)

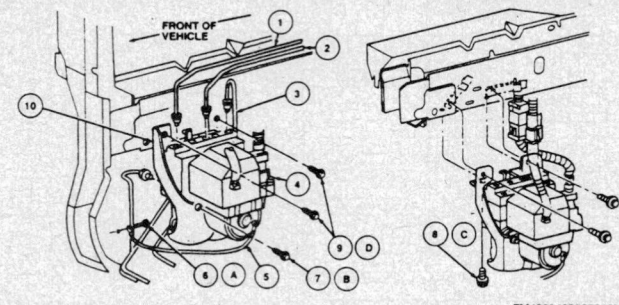

Fig. 15 Hydraulic control unit removal (Part 1 of 2)

Item	Description	Item	Description
1	Brake Tube	9D	Bolt (2 Req'd)
2	Front Brake Tube	1C	Mounting Bracket
3	Front Brake Tube	A	Tighten to 3.4-4.8 N·m (30-42.4 Lb-In)
4	Hydraulic Control Unit	B	Tighten to 10-20 N·m (7.3-14 Lb-Ft)
5	Hydraulic Control Unit Ground Wire	C	Tighten to 10-14 N·m (7.3-10.3 Lb-Ft)
6A	Screw		
7B	Nut (3 Req'd)	D	Tighten to 18-26 N·m (13.2-19 Lb-Ft)
8C	Bolt (2 Req'd)		

Fig. 15 Hydraulic control unit removal (Part 2 of 2)

3.8L/V6-232 engine and speed control, move speed control cable aside to clear power brake booster.

4. **On all models,** disconnect manifold vacuum hose from power brake booster check valve, then remove brake tubes from brake master cylinder primary and secondary outlet ports.

5. Remove two brake master cylinder to power brake booster assembly nuts, then the brake master cylinder.

6. Working inside vehicle below dash panel, proceed as follows:

   a. Remove stoplight switch wiring connector from stoplight switch, then the hairpin retainer and outer brake master cylinder push rod spacer from pedal pin.

   b. Slide stoplight switch off brake pedal pin just far enough for outer arm to clear pin, then remove stoplight switch. Use care not to damage switch during removal.

7. **On models equipped with speed control,** remove and set aside speed control amplifier, mounted to lower outboard booster stud.

8. **On all models,** slide booster push rod, brake master cylinder push rod bushing and inner brake master cylinder push rod bushing off brake pedal pin.

9. Working inside engine compartment, move power brake booster forward until booster studs clear dash panel.

10. Rotate front of booster toward engine and remove booster by raising up until clear.

Installation

1. Position power brake booster in engine compartment.

2. Working inside vehicle, install inner brake master cylinder push rod bushing, booster push rod and brake master cylinder push rod spacers on brake pedal pin.

3. **On models equipped with speed control,** place speed control amplifier bracket over lower outboard booster stud and position bracket locating tab in hole provided in pedal support bracket.

4. Install booster to dash panel nuts. **Torque** nuts to 16-21 ft. lbs.

5. Position stoplight switch so it straddles booster push rod with switch slot toward pedal blade and hole just clearing pin.

6. Slide stoplight switch completely onto pin. Ensure retainer is fully installed and locked over pedal pin, then install stoplight switch wiring connector to switch.

7. Connect manifold vacuum hose to power brake booster check valve, then install master cylinder assembly to booster studs. **Torque** studs to 16-21 ft. lbs.

8. **On models equipped with 3.8L/V6-232 engine,** proceed as follows:

   a. Install brake tube fittings into ports. **Torque** brake tube fittings to 11-17 ft. lbs.

   b. Install accelerator shaft bracket on engine, then route accelerator cable bracket to shaft bracket and connect accelerator cable to throttle body.

   c. Install horn, then connect battery ground cable.

   d. Install oil level indicator tube bracket to upper intake manifold, then connect wiring connectors.

   e. Install windshield wiper motor.

   f. Connect fuel line supply and return hoses to fuel injection supply manifold assembly.

   g. **On models equipped with manual transmission,** connect clutch cable stand off bracket to side rail.

   h. **On all models,** connect vacuum line hoses to vacuum tee over power brake booster.

   i. **On models equipped with speed**

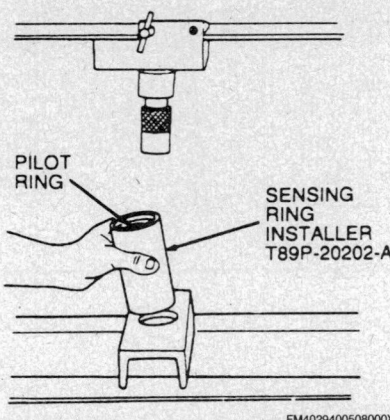

Fig. 16 Sensing ring installer tool positioning

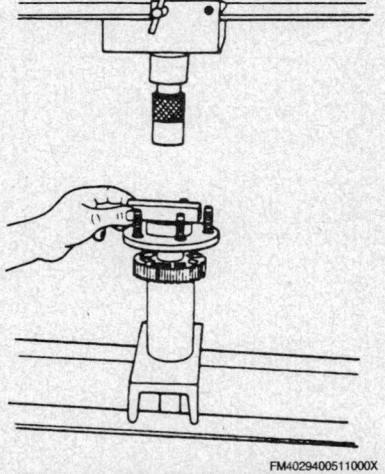

Fig. 19 Steel piece to axle shaft positioning

control, route speed control cable.
9. **On all models,** bleed brake system as described under "System Service."
10. Start engine and check power brake function.

BRAKE MASTER CYLINDER

1. Remove brake tubes from master cylinder primary and secondary outlet ports and brake pressure control valve.
2. Remove master cylinder to power brake booster nuts, then disconnect connector.
3. Slide master cylinder forward and upward from vehicle.
4. Reverse procedure to install, noting the following:
   a. Fill master cylinder, using heavy-duty brake fluid. Fill to MAX line on side of master cylinder reservoir.
   b. Bleed brake system as outlined under "System Service."
   c. Operate brakes several times, then check for external hydraulic leaks.

HYDRAULIC CONTROL UNIT

1. Disconnect battery ground cable, then

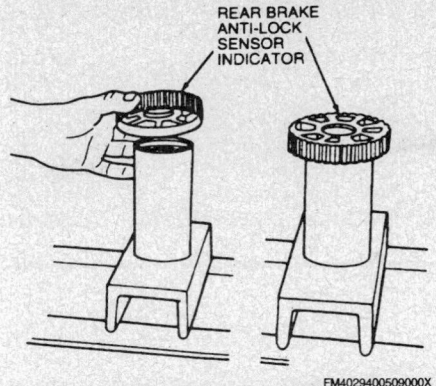

Fig. 17 Anti-lock sensor indicator positioning

clear path to hydraulic control unit, located at bottom of righthand side of radiator.
2. Disconnect two hydraulic control unit wiring harnesses.
3. Disconnect five brake tubes, **Fig. 15,** then remove hydraulic control unit ground wire.
4. Remove four control unit bolts, then the control unit.
5. Remove three nuts and mounting bracket from control unit.
6. Reverse procedure to install, noting the following:
   a. **Torque** mounting bracket to control unit nuts to 7-14 ft. lbs.
   b. **Torque** control unit bottom bolts to 7-10 ft. lbs., then the upper bolts to 13-19 inch lbs.
   c. Bleed brake system as described under "System Service."

ANTI-LOCK BRAKE CONTROL MODULE

1. Remove hydraulic control unit as described under "Hydraulic Control Unit."
2. Remove Torx head screw from black plastic cover, then the cover.
3. Remove 15- and 4-pin connectors.
4. Remove six anti-lock brake control module to hydraulic control unit Torx head bolts.
5. Remove control module by pulling straight up over ground post.
6. Reverse procedure to install.

FRONT BRAKE ANTI-LOCK SENSORS

1. Raise and support vehicle, then remove front wheel and tire assembly.
2. Remove anti-lock brake sensor bolt and pull sensor from front wheel spindle.
3. Remove two anti-lock brake sensor cable bracket bolts and two sensor cable brackets.
4. Push anti-lock brake sensor cable grommet through wheel well.
5. Disconnect anti-lock brake sensor electrical connector in engine compartment and pull harness retainer from vehicle.
6. Remove front brake anti-lock sensor from vehicle.

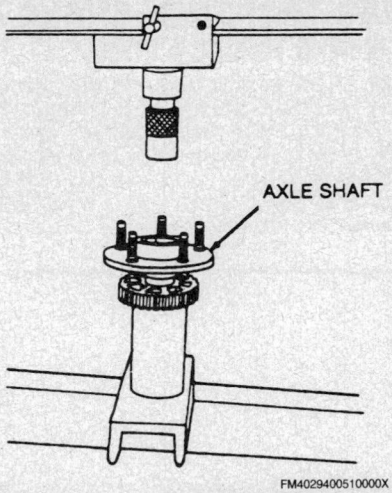

Fig. 18 Axle shaft positioning

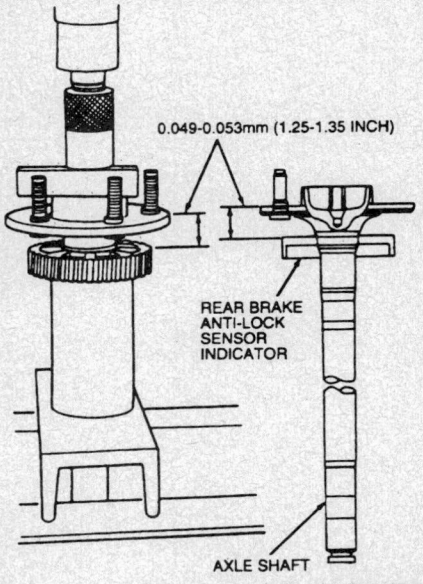

Fig. 20 Rear brake anti-lock sensor indicator installation clearance

7. Reverse procedure to install, noting the following:
   a. **Torque** sensor bolt to 124-133 inch lbs.
   b. **Torque** wheel hub bolt nuts to 78-87 ft. lbs.

REAR BRAKE ANTI-LOCK SENSORS

1. Raise and support vehicle.
2. Remove rear brake anti-lock sensor bolt, then the sensor.
3. Reverse procedure to install. **Torque** anti-lock sensor bolt to 40-60 inch lbs.

FRONT ANTI-LOCK BRAKE SENSOR INDICATOR

The front brake anti-lock sensor indicator is not serviceable. If the sensor indicator is damaged, the wheel hub must be replaced.

REAR ANTI-LOCK BRAKE SENSOR INDICATOR

Do not allow axle shaft flange to contact press bed during rear brake anti-lock sensor indicator removal.

Once a rear brake anti-lock sensor indicator has been removed, it must be replaced with a new rear brake anti-lock sensor indicator.

1. Remove axle shaft as described in "Drive Axles" section.
2. Place axle shaft in press, and remove sensor indicator using bearing pulling attachment tool No. D79L-4621-A, or equivalent.
3. Position sensing ring installer tool No. T89P-20202-A, or equivalent, on press with pilot ring up, **Fig. 16.**
4. Place new sensor indicator on sensor ring installer tool, **Fig. 17.** Ensure sensor indicator is positioned as shown.
5. Position axle shaft, **Fig. 18,** then flat piece of steel on shaft, **Fig. 19.**
6. Press sensor indicator onto shaft to specified dimension, **Fig. 20.**
7. Install axle shaft as described in "Drive Axles" section.

AUTOMATIC TRANSMISSIONS/TRANSAXLES

TABLE OF CONTENTS

Ford A4LD Automatic Overdrive Transmission

INDEX

Continued

INDEX–Continued

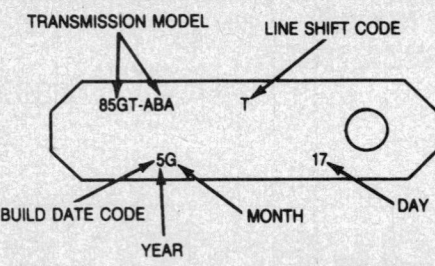

Fig. 1   Transmission identification tag

FM5028800410000X

APPLICATION CHART

Year	Model	Engine
1992-93	Mustang	2.3L/4-140

IDENTIFICATION

Each transmission may be identified by a tag, **Fig. 1**, located at the lower left hand extension attaching bolt. The tag indicates model prefix and suffix, assembly part numbers and the build date code. The service identification number indicates changes to service details which affect interchangeable parts within the same transmission model line. Refer to application chart for transmission identification.

DESCRIPTION

The A4LD transmission, **Fig. 2**, is a fully automatic transmission with four forward and one reverse speed. This transmission consists of a welded lockup torque converter assembly, a three unit planetary gear train and a hydraulic system to control gear selection, automatic shifts and the locking torque converter.

The lockup torque converter is coupled to the engine crankshaft and transmits engine power into the gear train. The output shaft drives the rear wheels through a conventional driveshaft and rear axle. Gear reduction necessary to match engine to axle occurs in the planetary gear train and the locking torque converter.

This 4 speed overdrive transmission is similar to the C3 automatic transmission. On 1992 models electronic controls are integrated in the on-board EEC-IV system. On 1993-94 models, sensors provide inputs to the Powertrain Control Module (PCM). These controls, along with hydrau-

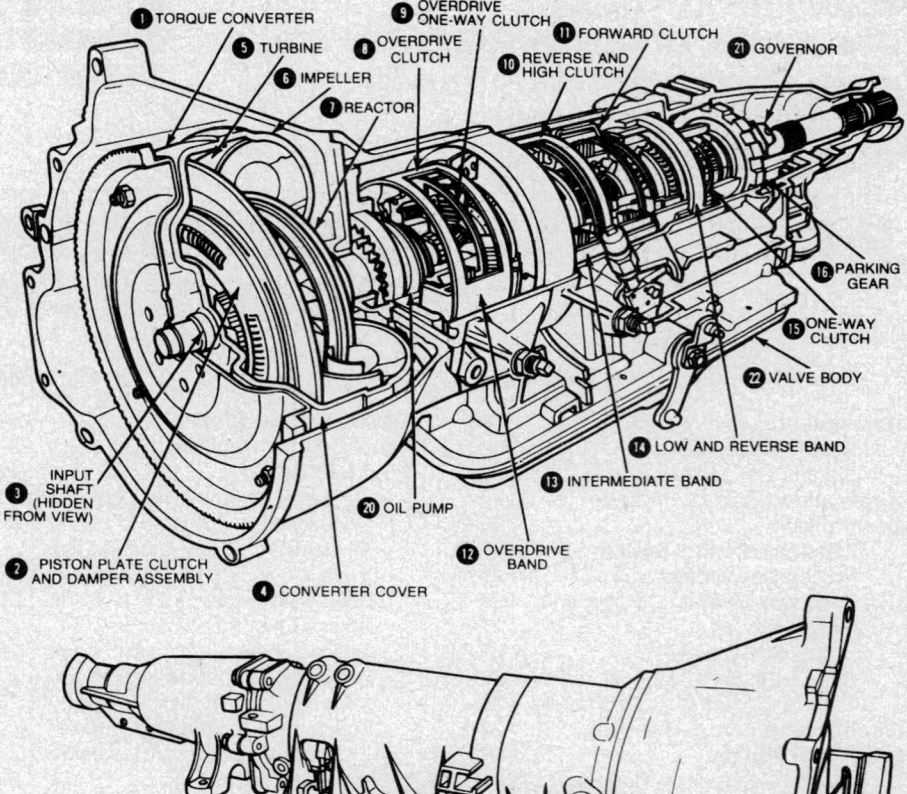

Fig. 2   Cross-sectional view of A4LD transmission

FM5028800411000X

lic controls in the valve body, operate a piston plate clutch in the torque converter that eliminates torque converter slip when applied.

The electronic control of the converter clutch prevents its application in engine modes where noise, vibration and harshness concerns are most evident. These modes are tip-in/tip-out, closed throttle, cold engine, very heavy/wide open throttle and low engine speed to minimize lugging boom.

Components from the intermediate brake drum rearward to the output shaft and extension housing seal are similar to the C3 automatic transmission.

Components forward of the intermediate brake drum are unique to the A4LD transmission. They are the center support assembly, overdrive band and drum, the coast clutch, overdrive sun and planet gear assembly, center support assembly and the converter and clutch/damper assembly.

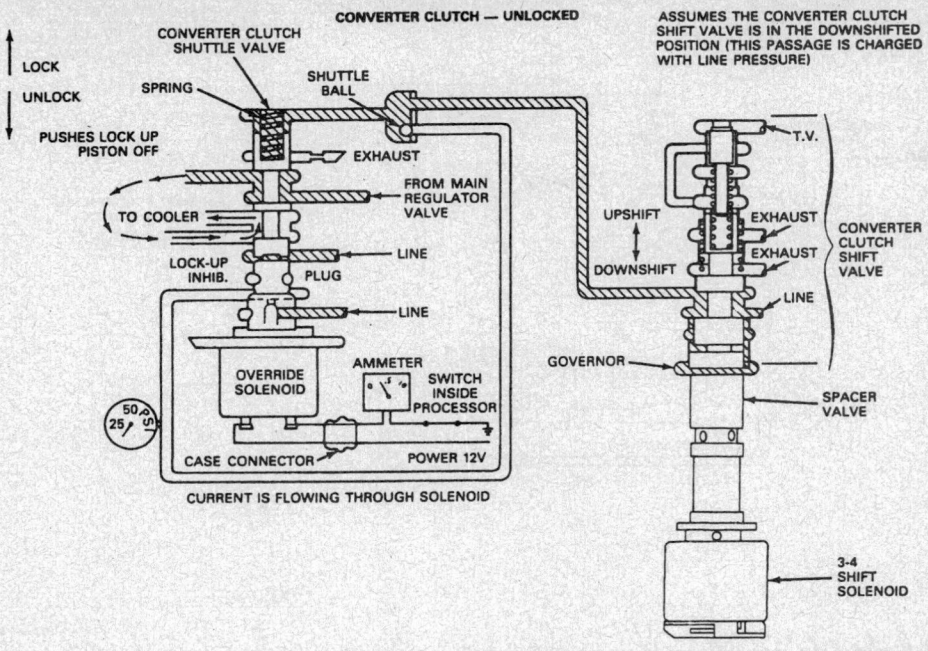

Fig. 3 Hydraulics w/converter clutch unlocked

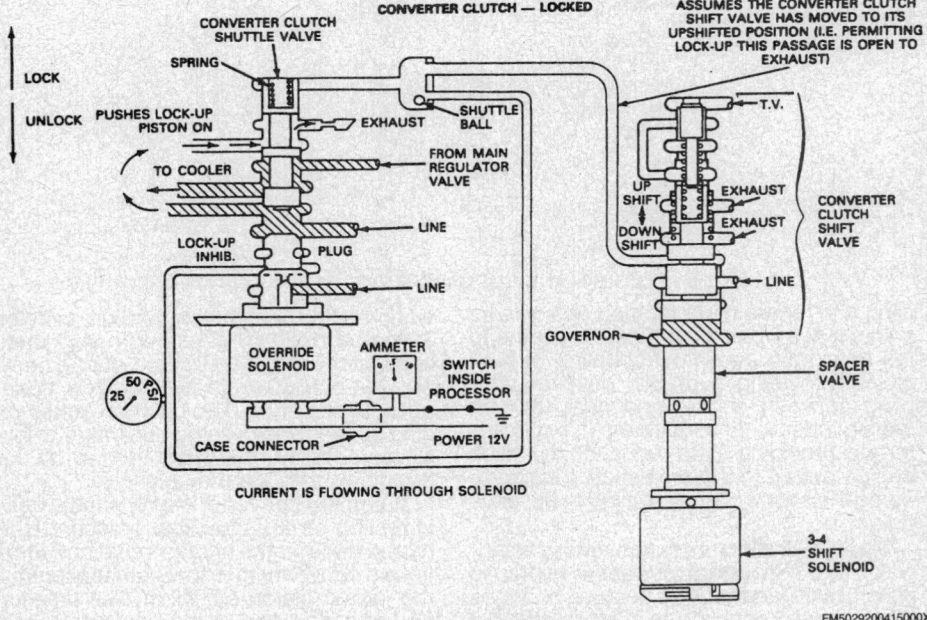

Fig. 4 Hydraulics w/converter clutch locked

The main control (valve body), besides supplying fluid for torque converter operation, piston plate clutch application and pressure for applying bands and clutches, also contains an on-board computer controlled solenoid which electrically overrides the application of the piston plate clutch in the converter.

FUNCTIONS OF MAIN COMPONENTS

The torque converter, **Fig. 2**, (1) couples the engine to the gear train, provides torque multiplication and absorbs shock of gear shifting.

The piston plate clutch and damper assembly (2) transmits engine power to the turbine from the converter cover.

The input shaft (3) transmits power out of the converter into the gear train.

The converter cover (4) transmits power from engine into the converter.

The turbine (5) is splined to the input shaft and driven by fluid from the impeller.

The impeller (6) is driven by the cover and supplies torque multiplication. Its rear hub drives the transmission oil pump.

The reactor (7), also called the stator, contains a one-way clutch to hold it stationary only when reaction is required. It also causes hydraulic reaction during torque multiplication.

The overdrive clutch (8) couples the override sun gear to the override carrier to eliminate the free wheeling effect of the overdrive one-way clutch.

The overdrive one-way clutch (9) transmits power from the input shaft to the center shaft in all gears except 4th gear overdrive.

The reverse and high clutch (10) couples the center shaft to the gear train in reverse, 3rd and 4th gears.

The forward clutch (11) couples the center shaft to the gear train in all forward gears.

The overdrive band (12) holds the overdrive gear train sun gear stationary in overdrive gear.

The intermediate band (13) holds the gear train sun gear stationary in 2nd gear.

The low and reverse band (14) holds the reverse planet carrier stationary in reverse gear and manual low.

The one-way clutch (15) holds the reverse planet carrier stationary in drive low (1st) gear.

The parking gear (16) holds the transmission output shaft to the case in P (Park) position by engagement with a parking pawl.

The reverse servo (17) applies the low reverse band.

The intermediate servo (18) applies the intermediate band for second gear.

The overdrive servo (19) applies the overdrive band.

The oil pump (20) provides a constant supply of oil under pressure to operate, lubricate and cool the transmission.

The governor (21) provides a road speed signal to the hydraulic control system for upshift and downshift control.

The valve body (22) directs fluid under pressure to the converter, band servos, clutches and governor to control transmission operation.

The vacuum diaphragm (23) provides an engine load (manifold vacuum) signal to the hydraulic system to control shifting and capacity for clutches and bands.

SELECTOR & SHIFT PATTERNS

The A4LD uses a seven position, Select Shift control. It is linked to the manual lever on the transmission to select the desired operating position.

In the P (Park) position the transmission is in neutral. The output shaft is locked to the case by engaging a parking pawl within the parking gear. The engine can be started in this selector position. This is the only position in which the ignition key can be removed.

In the R (Reverse) position the transmission is in reverse at a reduced ratio.

In the N (Neutral) position the transmission is in neutral but the output shaft is not locked to the case. The engine can be started, and the parking brake applied, since the rear wheels are free to turn.

The OD (Overdrive) position is the normal driving position. Selection of this position provides all automatic shifts including the application and release of the converter clutch. The transmission may also be shifted manually between all forward ranges.

The D (Drive) position provides all automatic shifts, including the application and release of the converter clutch, except the shift into overdrive. This position can be used when overdrive is not wanted such as hilly/mountainous terrain or trailer towing.

The 2 (Manual Second) position provides only 2nd gear operation regardless of vehicle speed. It is useful for startup on slippery surfaces or to provide engine braking on downgrades.

The 1 (Manual Low) position, when selected at startup, provides only 1st gear operation. Selection of this position at higher speeds results in a downshift to second gear. An automatic downshift to low will occur only after vehicle speed decreases to approximately 30 mph, dependent on axle ratio and tire size. Once in low, the transmission will stay in low until the selector lever is moved to another position.

When operating in the OD position, the transmission will automatically shift gears from 1st to 2nd and from 2nd to 3rd as vehicle speed increases. After the shift into 3rd takes place, the converter clutch may apply. The shift into overdrive decreases engine RPM by 25 percent and occurs when the vehicle approaches the desired cruising speed and the driver eases up on the accelerator pedal. Dependent upon acceleration rate and vehicle speed, the converter clutch may apply before or after the shift into overdrive is accomplished. The converter clutch application is based on both engine speed and vehicle speed by combined transmission hydraulics and on-board computer electronic controls. It can be applied in 3rd gear as well as 4th. Because of this feature, the transmission may be sensed as executing as many shifts as would a 5 speed transmission.

FORCED DOWNSHIFTS

Two functions have been incorporated in the A4LD transmission for times when the driver requires acceleration or more power for negotiating grades or driving into very strong headwinds. These functions are disengagement of the converter clutch to achieve added acceleration from the resultant increase in engine speed and a part throttle 4-3 downshift for further acceleration. These events can also occur during cruise control operation when more power is required to maintain the selected speed.

While driving at highway speeds, four different engine speeds can be obtained by transmission operation in overdrive with the converter clutch engaged, overdrive with the converter clutch disengaged, 3rd gear or full throttle in 2nd gear.

The transmission also provides wide open throttle forced downshifts. When driving in excess of approximately 35 mph and with the accelerator fully depressed to the floor, the transmission will downshift to 2nd gear for maximum acceleration. If the accelerator is depressed fully to the floor at speeds below 30-35 mph, the transmission will downshift to 1st gear.

TORQUE CONVERTER

The torque converter provides fluid cou-

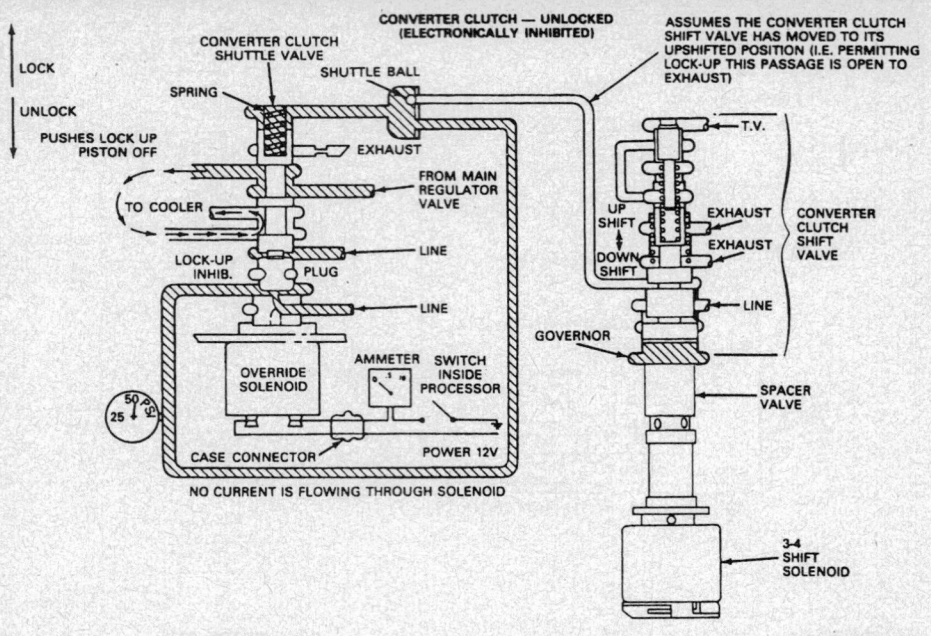

Fig. 5 Hydraulics w/Converter clutch unlocked but electronically inhibited

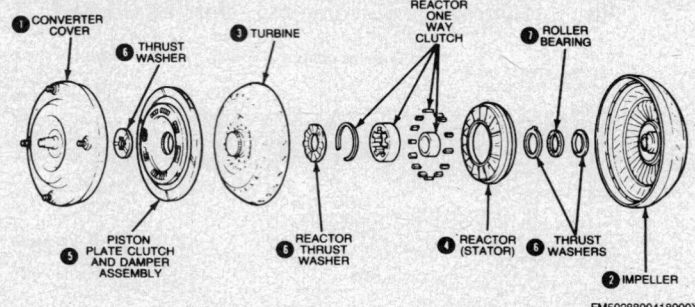

Fig. 6 Exploded view of locking torque converter

pling and torque multiplication and acts as a shock absorber. It couples the engine to the gear train as a fluid coupling or fluid clutch, providing hydraulic drive or coupling between engine and gear train. In certain operating conditions, it multiplies torque, providing extra reduction to match engine output to the driveshaft. It also absorbs the shock of gear shifting in the drive train.

The A4LD 10¼ inch converter resembles other converters, but has a hydraulic piston plate added. This feature changes the hydraulic coupling to a more efficient mechanical coupling.

Converter clutch application is based on both engine speed and vehicle speed by combined transmission hydraulics and on-board computer electronic controls. When this clutch engages there is a mechanical connection between the engine and rear wheels. This feature is provided to improve both driveline efficiency and fuel economy. Whenever the clutch is engaged, the vehicle may respond in ways similar to driving with a manual transmission. This is normal and should not be considered as adverse or indicating need for servicing.

Converter clutch engagements and disengagements are scheduled hydraulically but can be overridden electronically. The converter clutch is inhibited from engaging when engine coolant temperature is below 128 or above 240°F, during heavy brake application, at closed throttle, during heavy or wide open throttle acceleration, during quick tip-ins or tip-outs or when actual engine speed is below a certain value at lower vacuums. During these modes, no current flows through the solenoid.

When the converter clutch shuttle valve is resting on the plug, line pressure is directed through the shuttle valve and to the torque converter in a flow path that pushes the lockup piston off. When line pressure on the spring end of the converter clutch shuttle valve is exhausted, line pressure on the plug end of the valve forces the valve to move and compress the spring. Governor pressure acting on the converter clutch shift valve has not yet moved the valve to the upshifted position. Line pressure is therefore acting on the spring end of the converter clutch shuttle valve. The torque converter is therefore unlocked, **Fig. 3.**

As vehicle speed increases, governor pressure increases and the converter clutch shift valve moves to the upshifted position. Oil on the spring end of the converter clutch shuttle valve now drains to exhaust at the converter clutch shift valve. Line pressure is now directed through the shuttle valve to the converter in a flow path

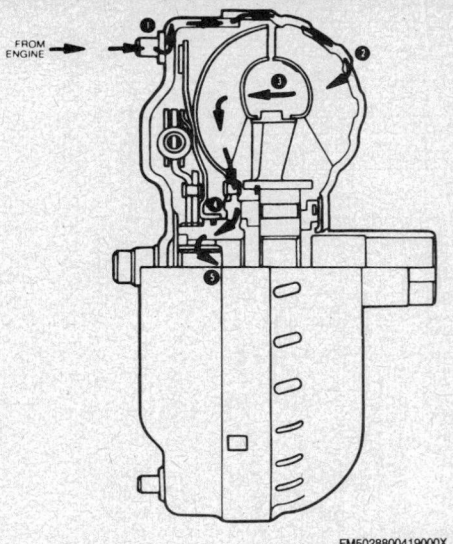

FM5028800419000X

Fig. 7 Torque converter power flow w/hydraulic input

that pushes the piston on, **Fig. 4.**

If the brakes are now applied, or the vehicle is operated in any of the other inhibit modes, current will not flow through the solenoid. With no current to the solenoid, line pressure can flow through the solenoid valve and enter the lockup inhibition passage. Line pressure in the inhibition passage forces the shuttle ball to take its position, **Fig. 5.** The shuttle valve moves against the plug and the converter unlocks. Since this is a hybrid system, it will often be necessary to check both the hydraulic and electronic portions of the system.

Component Functions

The converter cover (1), **Fig. 6,** is bolted to the engine flywheel and is driven at engine speed. It has a hub that pivots in the crankshaft. Thus the cover transmits engine power into the converter.

The impeller (2) is the pumping member for fluid coupling and torque multiplication. It is welded to and driven by the cover. Its rear hub drives the transmission oil pump.

The turbine (3) is the driven member of the converter. It is driven by fluid from the impeller and is splined to the input shaft.

The reactor (4), also called the stator, causes hydraulic reaction during torque multiplication. It includes a one-way clutch to hold it stationary only when reaction is required.

The piston plate clutch and damper assembly (5) has friction material on the outer portion of the plate and a spring cushioned damper assembly. It transmits engine power to the turbine from the converter cover.

Torque Multiplication

Torque multiplication occurs from stall (engine turning but turbine stopped) up to engagement of the converter clutch.

The impeller is driven at engine speed. Fluid is supplied from the valve body to the spaces between the vanes. Centrifugal force causes the fluid to be set in motion and forced out of the openings around the inner ring. The fluid is directed toward the turbine vanes. Striking the turbine vanes, the fluid causes it to turn in the same direction as the impeller. The fluid flows around the turbines' inner ring and is directed to the reactor. The reactor is held stationary by its one-way clutch. Its vanes direct the fluid back to the impeller in a direction that assists the impeller. The impeller again accelerates the fluid and returns it to the turbine with increased energy.

Torque multiplication comes from a reduced turbine speed and reuse of the velocity of the fluid returning from the reactor to the impeller. As turbine speed increases in relation to the impeller, there is less energy in the returning fluid, and therefore less torque multiplication.

Operation & Power Flow

Power flow through the torque converter when the clutch is not active is as shown, **Fig. 7.** The engine drives the converter cover (1). The converter cover drives the impeller (2). The impeller drives the turbine hydraulically (3). The turbine drives the input shaft (4). The input shaft transmits power into the gear train (5).

Power flow through the torque converter when piston plate clutch is engaged is as shown, **Fig. 8.** The clutch is engaged when hydraulic pressure from the valve body is applied to the clutch plate from the turbine side of the plate. The engine drives the converter cover (1). The converter cover drives the piston plate clutch (2). The clutch drives the turbine (3). The turbine drives the input shaft (4). The input shaft transmits power into the gear train (5).

ELECTRONIC CONTROL SYSTEM

The electronic control system consists of several input sensors which provide information to the Powertrain Control Module (PCM). The PCM then controls the actuators which affect the torque converter clutch solenoid during normal transmission operation.

Brake On/Off Switch

The brake on/off switch disengages the torque converter clutch by sending a signal to the PCM when the brakes are applied. The switch is closed when the brakes are applied and open when they are released.

Engine Coolant Temperature (ECT) Sensor

The ECT sensor detects engine coolant temperature and sends the information to the PCM. ECT is used to control torque converter clutch operation. The sensor is threaded into the heater outlet fitting or cooling passage on the engine.

Electronic Ignition (EI) System

The EI system consists of a crankshaft position sensor which sends information to the EI module. The EI module then generates a PIP signal (engine rpm) and sends it to the PCM, which uses rpm signal in the transmission strategy for 3-4 and 4-3 shift scheduling and torque converter clutch engagement.

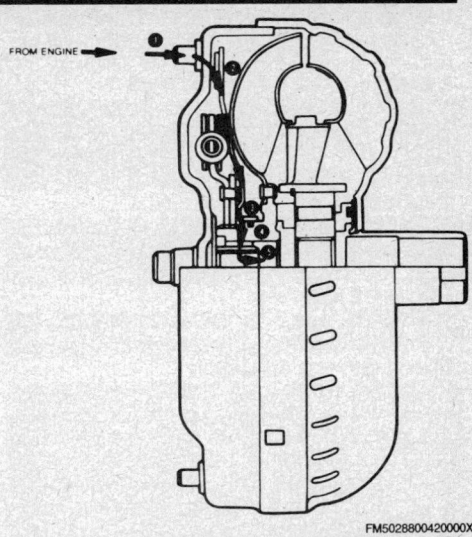

FM5028800420000X

Fig. 8 Torque converter power flow w/mechanical input

Throttle Position (TP) Sensor

The throttle position sensor is mounted on the throttle body. It detects the position of the throttle plate and sends this information to the PCM, which uses rpm signal in determining 3-4 and 4-3 shift scheduling and torque converter clutch engagement.

Vehicle Speed Sensor

The vehicle speed sensor is a magnetic pickup that sends a signal to the PCM. The PCM uses vehicle speed information to determine shift scheduling and torque converter clutch control schedule.

GEAR TRAIN

The transmission case provides a rigid support housing for the gear train. Both shafts are supported individually in the case.

The input shaft is splined at both ends. It has bushing journals next to the splines. The front splines mate with the converter turbine hub, so that the shaft always turns at turbine speed.

The output shaft is supported by two bushings; one at the rear of the case, and the other at the extension slip yoke bushing. The slip yoke fits over the rear and splines of the shaft.

Clutch Drum Assembly

The forward clutch is connected to the intermediate shaft by means of splines. The outer splines of the forward clutch hub mesh with the friction plates of the reverse and high clutch.

Forward Clutch

The forward clutch is engaged in all forward gears. The clutch engages the intermediate shaft with the ring gear of the forward planetary gearset.

Direct Drive

Direct drive is accomplished in the planetary gear set by locking any two members together. Then, regardless of which member is driven, the complete set turns as a unit. If, for example, the pinion carrier is splined to an output shaft, and the ring gear and sun gear are locked together, direct drive through the pinion carrier will occur.

Low & Reverse Band

In reverse and 1st gears, with selector lever in position 1, the reverse band is applied to hold the rear planet carrier by means of the rear clutch drum.

Parking Brake

Allows the output shaft to be mechanically locked by the parking pawl anchored in the case.

Planet Gears

Three gearsets are used to provide the four forward speeds and reverse.

Overdrive Clutch

The overdrive clutch is engaged in 1st and 2nd gear with selector lever in position 1 and 2. It also engages the overdrive sun gear and the input with the intermediate shaft. In this case, the O/D one-way clutch is engaged and on coasting engine braking takes place.

Overdrive Band

In 4th gear, the overdrive band is applied to hold the sun gear of the overdrive planet gearset, by means of the overdrive drum.

Overdrive One-Way Clutch

The overdrive one-way clutch locks in direction of engine rotation and the intermediate shaft. In opposite direction of engine rotation, the clutch free-wheels without the effect of engine braking.

Reduction

One way to obtain reduction in a planetary gear set is to hold the sun gear and drive the ring gear with the planet carrier as the output member.

Rotation of the ring gear makes the planet pinions walk around the sun gear, in the same direction the ring gear is turning, but not as fast. Input torque is increased or multiplied since output speed is less than input.

Reverse

In a simple planetary gear set, a reverse output is obtained by holding the planet pinion carrier and driving another member. The planet pinions just turn on their axes and act as idler gears, reversing the direction of the input.

Thrust Washers

The A4LD gear train uses ten thrust washers and four needle bearing assemblies to provide bearing surfaces where they run together. Washers No. 1 and 4 are selective thickness to control endplay.

The torque converter also has thrust washers and a needle bearing between its components. These are not identified by number because they are not individually serviceable.

Band & Clutch Application

Information on band and clutch application and gear ratios for all possible operating conditions is shown in Fig. 9.

HYDRAULIC SYSTEM

The hydraulic system of the A4LD transmission has several functions: it supplies fluid for torque converter operation, directs fluid under pressure, lubricates the working parts of the transmission, controls upshifts and downshifts as a function of engine load and road speed and removes heat generated by flow in the torque converter and by other parts of the transmission.

Gear	Overdrive Band A	Overdrive Clutch B	Overdrive One Way Clutch C	Intermediate Band D	Reverse and High Clutch E	Forward Clutch F	Low and Reverse Band G	One Way Clutch H	Gear Ratio
1 — Manual First Gear (Low)		Applied	Holding			Applied	Applied	Holding	2.47:1
2 — Manual Second Gear		Applied	Holding	Applied		Applied			1.47:1
D — Drive Auto — 1st Gear		Applied	Holding			Applied		Holding	2.47:1
ⓄD — O/D Auto — 1st Gear		Applied	Holding			Applied		Holding	2.47:1
D — Drive Auto — 2nd Gear		Applied	Holding	Applied		Applied			1.47:1
ⓄD — O/D Auto — 2nd Gear			Holding	Applied		Applied			1.47:1
D — Drive Auto — 3rd Gear		Applied	Holding		Applied	Applied			1.0:1
ⓄD — O/D Auto — 3rd Gear			Holding		Applied	Applied			1.0:1
ⓄD — Overdrive Automatic Fourth Gear	Applied				Applied	Applied			0.75:1
Reverse		Applied	Holding		Applied		Applied		2.1:1

Fig. 9   Band & clutch apply chart

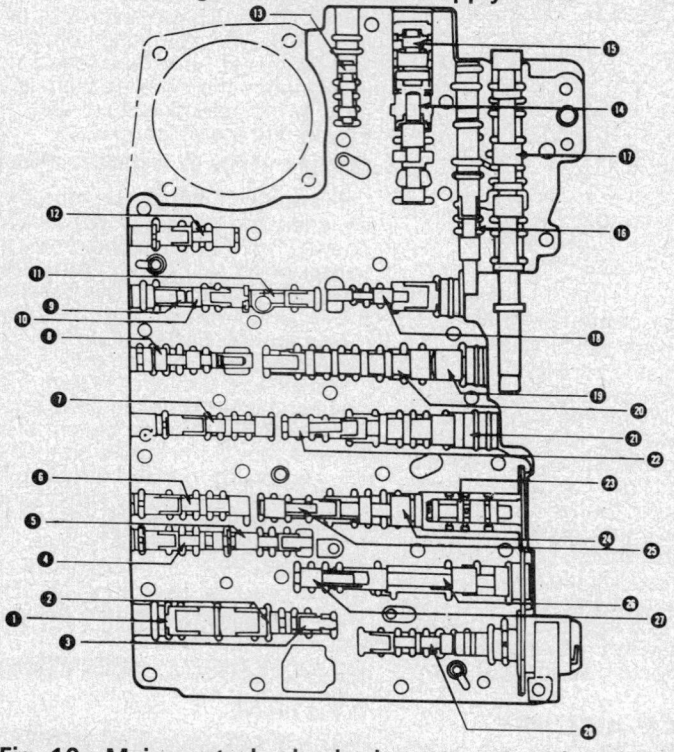

Fig. 10   Main control valve body component identification

The transmission fluid used is composed of mineral oil and additives. In the transmission it is used as a combination power-transmission medium, hydraulic control fluid, heat transfer medium, bearing surface lubricant and gear lubricant. The manufacturer's recommendations should be followed when servicing transmission fluid.

The A4LD has an internal gear pump which is driven by flats on the converter impeller hub. The pump operates whenever the engine is operating, to supply fluid to the rest of the system. As the pump drive gear is driven by the impeller, it causes the internal driven gear to rotate also. Where the gears separate from mesh, a vacuum is created, forming the pump inlet. Atmospheric pressure in the pump forces fluid into the inlet through the pump screen.

At the point of greatest separation, the gears are closely fitted to a crescent in the pump housing. The crescent and the space between the gear teeth form chambers in which the fluid is trapped as the gears rotate past the inlet. Beyond the crescent, the gears begin to come together again. Since the crescent seals the fluid from getting back to the inlet, it now must be squeezed out of the outlet port and into the system.

A pump that has the outlet sealed from the inlet like this is called a positive displacement or positive delivery pump. This means that as long as the pump is turning and fluid is supplied to the inlet, the pump will deliver fluid with its volume being in proportion to the drive speed. The pump is designed to deliver more fluid than the transmission needs, and excess pump delivery is recirculated to pump by the control pressure regulator valve.

Control Valve Functions

The intermediate servo accumulator (1), Fig. 10, controls band capacity on 1-2 shift.

The overdrive servo accumulator (2) controls overdrive band capacity on 3-4 upshifts.

The 3-4 backout valve (3) controls the rate at which overdrive servo release oil exhausts on 3-4 backout shifts.

The 3-2 high clutch release valve (4) controls the rate at which high clutch oil exhausts on higher speed 3-2 downshifts.

The 3-2 intermediate servo release valve (5) controls the rate at which intermediate servo release oil exhausts on higher speed 3-2 downshifts.

The 3-2 kickdown timing valve (6) sends intermediate servo release and high clutch oil to the torque demand valve during 3-2 downshifts at lower speeds. At higher speed, this valve moves down and intermediate servo release and high clutch oil drains through the 3-2 intermediate servo release kickdown control and 3-2 high clutch kickdown control valves.

The 3-2 coast control valve (7) controls the rate at which intermediate servo release and high clutch oil exhaust on 3-2 coasting downshifts.

The throttle pressure booster valve (8) increases throttle pressure output for shift delay at lower engine manifold vacuum levels.

The 1-2 transition valve (9), along with the 2-3 backout valve, will prevent an intermediate to reverse band tie-up on a manual 1-2 shift.

The 2-3 backout valve (10) prevents tie-up if driver backs off accelerator during 2-3 upshift.

The engagement control valve (11) feeds the forward clutch through a small orifice at low T.V. pressures, or through a larger orifice at higher T.V. pressures.

The torque demand control valve (12) controls the rate at which high clutch and intermediate servo release oil exhausts at lower speed 3-2 downshifts.

The cut back valve (13) reduces control pressure as road speed increases.

The oil pressure regulator valve (14) regulates main control pressure.

The main oil pressure booster valve (15) increases or decreases main control pressure in relation to throttle pressure, and provides higher line pressure in reverse.

The throttle downshift valve (16) reroutes line pressure to override the normal automatic upshift schedule and provide forced downshifts.

The manual control valve (17) moves with shift selector and directs control pressure to various passages to provide automatic function.

The 2-Low range coasting boost valve (18) boosts pressure in selector positions 1 and 2 at closed or nearly closed throttle.

The 1-2 shift valve (19) controls upshift from 1st to second and downshift from 2nd to 1st.

The D2 shift valve (20) is used in combination with the 1-2 shift valve to provide a 2nd gear start in 2 range.

The 2-3 shift valve (21) controls upshift from 2nd to high and downshift from high to 2nd.

The 2-3 throttle pressure modulator valve (22) provides a modulated pressure to the 2-3 shift valve at higher T.V. pressures. This modulated pressure helps to delay 2-3 shifts at higher T.V. pressures.

The 4-3 torque demand valve (23) routes high clutch oil to the 3-4 shift valve at lower vacuums. This provides for a higher road speed 4-3 torque demands at lower vacuum.

The converter clutch shift valve (24), along with the converter clutch shuttle valve and solenoid, controls converter clutch engagements and disengagements.

The converter clutch throttle pressure modulator valve (25) sends a modulated pressure to the converter clutch shift valve at higher T.V. pressures. This modulated pressure helps to delay converter clutch upshifts at higher T.V. pressures.

The 3-4 shift valve (26) controls the scheduling for 3-4 upshifts and 4-3 downshifts.

The 3-4 throttle pressure modulator valve (27) provides a modulated pressure on the 3-4 shift valve at high T.V. pressures. This modulated pressure helps to delay 3-4 upshifts at higher T.V. pressures.

The converter clutch shuttle valve (28), when bottomed against the plug, directs flow so the converter clutch will be disengaged. When the valve compresses the spring, flow is directed so the converter clutch engages. The solenoid also controls the position of this valve.

TROUBLESHOOTING

SLOW INITIAL ENGAGEMENT

1. Improper fluid level.
2. Damaged or improperly adjusted manual linkage.
3. Contaminated fluid.
4. Improper clutch and band application or low main control pressure.

ROUGH INITIAL ENGAGEMENT IN FORWARD OR REVERSE

1. Improper fluid level.
2. High engine idle.
3. Propeller shaft, U-joints or engine mounts loose.
4. Improper clutch or band application or low control pressure.
5. Sticking or dirty valve body.
6. Converter clutch not disengaging.

HARSH ENGAGEMENTS, WARM ENGINE

1. Improper fluid level.
2. Curb idle speed too high.
3. Valve body bolts loose or too tight.
4. Sticking or dirty valve body.

NO OR DELAYED FORWARD ENGAGEMENT, REVERSE SATISFACTORY

1. Improper fluid level.
2. Damaged or improperly adjusted manual linkage.
3. Low main control pressure, forward clutch center support seal rings leaking.
4. Forward clutch assembly burnt, damaged or leaking. Check ball in cylinder or leaking piston seal rings.
5. Valve body bolts loose or too tight.
6. Sticking or dirty valve body.
7. Transmission filter plugged.
8. Pump damaged or leaking.

NO OR DELAYED REVERSE ENGAGEMENT, FORWARD SATISFACTORY

1. Improper fluid level.
2. Damaged or improperly adjusted manual linkage.
3. Low main control pressure in reverse.
4. Reverse clutch assembly burnt, worn, leaking check ball in piston or leaking piston seal rings.
5. Valve body bolts loose or too tight.
6. Sticking or dirty valve body.
7. Transmission filter plugged.
8. Pump damaged.
9. Low/reverse servo piston seal cut or leaking.

NO ENGAGEMENT OR DRIVE IN ANY FORWARD OR REVERSE POSITION

1. Improper fluid level.
2. Low main control pressure.
3. Mechanical damage.

NO ENGAGEMENT OR DRIVE IN OVERDRIVE OR DRIVE, MANUAL SECOND & LOW SATISFACTORY

1. Improperly adjusted manual linkage.
2. Rear one-way clutch damaged.
3. Dirty or contaminated fluid.
4. Overdrive one-way clutch damaged.

VEHICLE CREEPING IN NEUTRAL

1. Forward clutch not disengaging.

TORQUE CONVERTER CLUTCH DOES NOT ENGAGE

1. TCC solenoid not being energized electrically (shorted or open circuit).
2. Transmission case connector not seated.
3. Malfunctioning ECT sensor.
4. Malfunctioning MAP sensor.
5. Malfunctioning PCM.
6. Brake switch malfunction.
7. Malfunctioning TP sensor.
8. Vacuum line disconnected from MAP sensor.
9. TCC shuttle valve stuck in unlock position or too high a load spring.
10. TCC shift valve stuck in downshift position.

TCC ALWAYS ENGAGED, EVEN AT ZERO ROAD SPEED

1. TCC shift valve stuck in lock position.
2. TCC shuttle valve stuck in lock position.
3. Lock-up piston in torque converter will not disengage.

NO ENGINE BRAKING IN MANUAL SECOND

1. Intermediate band improperly adjusted.
2. Improper band or clutch application, or oil pressure control system.
3. Intermediate servo leaking.
4. Overdrive clutch or overdrive one-way clutch damaged.
5. Glazed band.

FORWARD ENGAGEMENT SLIPS, SHUDDERS OR CHATTERS

1. Improper fluid level.
2. Damaged or improperly adjusted manual linkage.
3. Low main control pressure.
4. Valve body bolts loose or too tight.
5. Sticking or dirty valve body.
6. Forward clutch piston ball check not seating or leaking.
7. Forward clutch piston seals cut or worn.
8. Overdrive one-way clutch damaged.
9. Rear one-way clutch damaged.

REVERSE SHUDDERS, CHATTERS OR SLIPS

1. Improper fluid level.
2. Low/reverse servo leaking.
3. Low main control pressure in reverse.
4. Overdrive and/or rear one-way clutch damaged.
5. Overdrive and/or rear reverse/high clutch drum bushing damaged.
6. Overdrive and/or rear reverse/high clutch center support seal rings or ring grooves damaged.
7. Overdrive and/or rear reverse/high clutch piston seals cut or worn.
8. Low/reverse servo piston damaged or worn.
9. Low/reverse band improperly adjusted or damaged.
10. Propeller shaft, U-joints or engine mounts loose.
11. Low/reverse servo piston seals or bores damaged.
12. Contamination blockage in cooler lines, in-tank radiator or auxiliary cooler.

NO DRIVE, SLIPS OR CHATTERS IN FIRST GEAR IN OVERDRIVE OR DRIVE RANGE, ALL OTHER GEARS NORMAL

1. Damaged or worn rear one-way clutch.

NO DRIVE, SLIPS OR CHATTERS IN SECOND GEAR

1. Improperly adjusted intermediate band.
2. Improper clutch or band application or control pressure.
3. Damaged or worn intermediate servo piston and/or internal leaks.
4. Sticking or dirty valve body.
5. Polished or glazed intermediate band or drum.

STARTS OUT IN SECOND OR THIRD GEAR

1. Improper clutch or band application or control pressure.
2. Damaged, worn or sticking governor.
3. Valve body loose.
4. Sticking or dirty valve body.
5. Cross leaks between valve body and case mating surface.

INCORRECT SHIFT POINTS

1. Improper fluid level.
2. Vacuum line damaged, clogged or leaking.
3. EGR system operating improperly.
4. Speedometer gear improperly installed.
5. Improper clutch or band application or control pressure.
6. Damaged, worn or sticking governor.
7. Vacuum diaphragm bent, sticking or leaking.
8. Sticking or dirty valve body.

ALL UPSHIFTS HARSH, DELAYED OR NO UPSHIFTS

1. Improper fluid level.
2. Damaged or improperly adjusted manual linkage.
3. Governor sticking.
4. Main control pressure too high.
5. Valve body bolts loose or too tight.
6. Sticking or dirty valve body.
7. Vacuum leak to diaphragm unit.
8. Vacuum diaphragm bent, sticking or leaking.

ALL UPSHIFTS MUSHY, EARLY OR PILE UP

1. Low main control pressure.
2. Valve body bolts loose or too tight.
3. Valve body or throttle control valve sticking.
4. Governor sticking.
5. Kickdown linkage improperly adjusted, sticking or damaged.

NO 1-2 UPSHIFT

1. Improper fluid level.
2. Kickdown system damaged.
3. Improperly adjusted or damaged manual linkage.
4. Governor sticking.
5. Improperly adjusted intermediate band.
6. Vacuum leak to diaphragm unit.
7. Vacuum diaphragm bent, sticking or leaking.
8. Valve body bolts loose or too tight.
9. Sticking or dirty valve body.
10. Intermediate band and/or servo assembly burnt.

ROUGH, HARSH OR DELAYED 1-2 UPSHIFT

1. Improper fluid level.
2. Poor engine performance.
3. Improperly adjusted kickdown linkage.
4. Improperly adjusted intermediate band.
5. Main control pressure too high.
6. Governor sticking.
7. Damaged intermediate servo.
8. Engine vacuum leak.
9. Valve body bolts loose or too tight.
10. Sticking or dirty valve body.
11. Vacuum leak to diaphragm unit.
12. Vacuum diaphragm bent, sticking or leaking.

MUSHY, EARLY, SOFT OR SLIPPING 1-2 UPSHIFT

1. Improper fluid level.
2. Main regulator or throttle valve sticking.

3. Poor engine performance.
4. Improperly adjusted intermediate band.
5. Main control pressure low.
6. Valve body bolts loose or too tight.
7. Sticking or dirty valve body.
8. Governor sticking.
9. Damaged intermediate servo or band.
10. Polished or glazed intermediate band or drum.

NO 2-3 UPSHIFT

1. Improper fluid level.
2. Kickdown system damaged.
3. Low main control pressure to reverse/high clutch.
4. Valve body bolts loose or too tight.
5. Sticking or dirty valve body.
6. Reverse/high clutch assembly burnt or worn.

HARSH OR DELAYED 2-3 UPSHIFT

1. Poor engine performance.
2. Engine vacuum leak.
3. Kickdown system damaged.
4. Damaged or worn intermediate servo release and reverse/high clutch piston check ball.
5. Valve body bolts loose or too tight.
6. Sticking or dirty valve body.
7. Vacuum diaphragm bent, sticking or leaking.
8. Throttle valve sticking.

MUSHY, EARLY OR SOFT 2-3 UPSHIFT

1. Kickdown system damaged.
2. Valve body bolts loose or too tight.
3. Sticking or dirty valve body.
4. Vacuum diaphragm or throttle valve control rod bent, sticking or leaking.
5. Throttle valve sticking.

ERRATIC SHIFTS

1. Poor engine performance.
2. Vacuum line damaged.
3. Valve body bolts loose or too tight.
4. Sticking or dirty valve body.
5. Governor sticking.
6. Output shaft collector body seal rings damaged.

SHIFTS FROM FIRST TO THIRD IN OVERDRIVE OR DRIVE

1. Improperly adjusted intermediate band.
2. Damaged intermediate servo and/or internal leaks.
3. Improper clutch or band application or control pressure.
4. Polished or glazed intermediate band or drum.
5. Sticking or dirty valve body.
6. Governor sticking.
7. Kickdown system improperly adjusted.

ENGINE OVER-SPEEDS ON 2-3 SHIFT

1. Kickdown system damaged.
2. Improper clutch or band application or control pressure.
3. Damaged or worn reverse/high clutch and/or intermediate servo piston.

4. Intermediate servo piston seals cut or leaking.
5. Sticking or dirty valve body.
6. Throttle valve sticking.
7. Vacuum diaphragm damaged.

ROUGH OR SHUDDERING 3-2 SHIFT AT CLOSED THROTTLE IN DRIVE RANGE

1. Incorrect engine idle or performance.
2. Improper kickdown linkage adjustment.
3. Improper clutch or band application or oil pressure control system.
4. Improper governor operation.
5. Sticking or dirty valve body.

NO 3-4 UPSHIFT

1. 3-4 shift solenoid not energizing electrically, wires shorted or an open circuit. Check circuit continuity, 3-4 solenoid wire pin 52 should read approximately 20 ohms resistance.
2. Transmission case electrical connector and harness electrical connector not seated.
3. EEC-IV processor malfunction:
   a. Vacuum line disconnected from MAP sensor.
   b. Map sensor defective.
   c. Throttle position sensor defective.
   d. Vehicle speed sensor defective.
4. Improperly adjusted overdrive band.
5. Overdrive servo damaged or leaking.
6. Polished or glazed overdrive band or drum.
7. Contaminated or sticking 3-4 shift valve.
8. Contaminated or sticking 3-4 solenoid.

SLIPPING FOURTH GEAR

1. Improperly adjusted overdrive band.
2. Overdrive servo damaged or leaking.
3. Polished or glazed overdrive band or drum.

ENGINE STALL SPEED EXCEEDED IN OVERDRIVE, DRIVE OR REVERSE

1. Vacuum system malfunction.
2. Low main control pressure.

ENGINE STALL SPEED EXCEEDED IN REVERSE, SATISFACTORY IN OVERDRIVE, DRIVE, SECOND & FIRST

1. Low/reverse servo/band damaged.
2. Reverse/high clutch damaged.

ENGINE STALL SPEED EXCEEDED IN OVERDRIVE OR DRIVE, SATISFACTORY IN REVERSE

1. Overdrive one-way clutch or rear one-way clutch damaged.

1-2 UPSHIFT IS ABOVE 40 MPH AT MODERATE ACCELERATION

1. Vacuum system malfunction.

2. Main control pressure malfunction.
3. Governor damaged or worn.
4. Sticking or dirty valve body.

KICKDOWN SHIFT SPEEDS TOO EARLY

1. Kickdown system damaged.
2. Main control pressure malfunction.
3. Governor damaged or worn.

NO KICKDOWN INTO SECOND GEAR BETWEEN 40 & 60 MPH IN OVERDRIVE OR DRIVE

1. Kickdown system damaged.
2. Main control pressure malfunction.
3. Sticking or dirty valve body.
4. Improperly adjusted kickdown cable.

NO SHIFT INTO SECOND GEAR w/ACCELERATOR 3/4 DEPRESSED AT 25 MPH IN OVERDRIVE OR DRIVE

1. Main control pressure malfunction.
2. Governor damaged or worn.
3. Sticking or dirty valve body.

WHEN MOVING SELECTOR FROM OVERDRIVE OR DRIVE TO MANUAL 1 AT 55 MPH w/ACCELERATOR RELEASED, NO BRAKING FELT FROM DOWNSHIFT TO SECOND GEAR

1. Main control pressure malfunction.
2. Improperly adjusted intermediate band.
3. Overdrive clutch damaged.

WHEN MOVING SELECTOR FROM OVERDRIVE OR DRIVE TO MANUAL 1 AT 55 MPH w/ACCELERATOR RELEASED, SHIFT INTO FIRST GEAR OCCURS OVER 45 MPH

1. Main control pressure malfunction.
2. Sticking or dirty valve body.
3. Governor damaged or worn.
4. Improperly adjusted or sticking kickdown linkage.

WHEN MOVING SELECTOR FROM OVERDRIVE OR DRIVE TO MANUAL 1 AT 55 MPH w/ACCELERATOR RELEASED, FIRST GEAR SHIFT OCCURS UNDER 15 MPH

1. Main control pressure malfunction.
2. Sticking or dirty valve body.
3. Low/reverse servo damaged.
4. Governor damaged or worn.
5. Overdrive clutch damaged.

NO FORCED DOWNSHIFTS

1. Damaged kickdown cable.
2. Improperly adjusted kickdown cable.
3. Damaged internal kickdown linkage.
4. Improper clutch or band application or oil pressure control system.
5. Sticking or dirty governor.
6. Sticking or dirty valve body.

ENGINE OVER-SPEEDS ON 3-2 DOWNSHIFT

1. Improperly adjusted linkage.
2. Improperly adjusted intermediate band.
3. Improper clutch or band application and one-way clutch or oil pressure control system.
4. Damaged or worn intermediate servo.
5. Polished or glazed band or drum.
6. Sticking or dirty valve body.

SHIFT EFFORTS HIGH

1. Damaged or improperly manual linkage.
2. Inner manual lever nut loose.
3. Manual lever retainer pin damaged.

TRANSMISSION OVERHEATS

1. Improper fluid level.
2. Incorrect engine idle or performance.
3. Improper clutch or band application or oil pressure control system.
4. Restriction in cooler or lines.
5. Seized converter one-way clutch.
6. Sticking or dirty valve body.

TRANSMISSION LEAKS

1. Case breather vent clogged.
2. Faulty gaskets or seals.

POOR VEHICLE ACCELERATION

1. Poor engine performance.
2. Torque converter one-way clutch slipping

TRANSMISSION NOISY, VALVE RESONANCE

1. Improper fluid level.
2. Improperly adjusted linkage.
3. Improper clutch or band application or oil pressure control system.
4. Cooler lines grounding.
5. Sticking or dirty valve body.
6. Internal leakage or pump cavitation.

ENGINE STALLS WHEN SHIFTING INTO FORWARD OR REVERSE

1. Low engine idle.
2. Broken converter clutch shuttle valve spring.

MAINTENANCE

Ford Motor Company recommends the use of Mercon type automatic transmission fluid in this transmission. If Mercon type fluid is not available, Dexron-II Series D automatic transmission fluid may be used. Use of a fluid other than specified may result in transmission malfunction or failure.

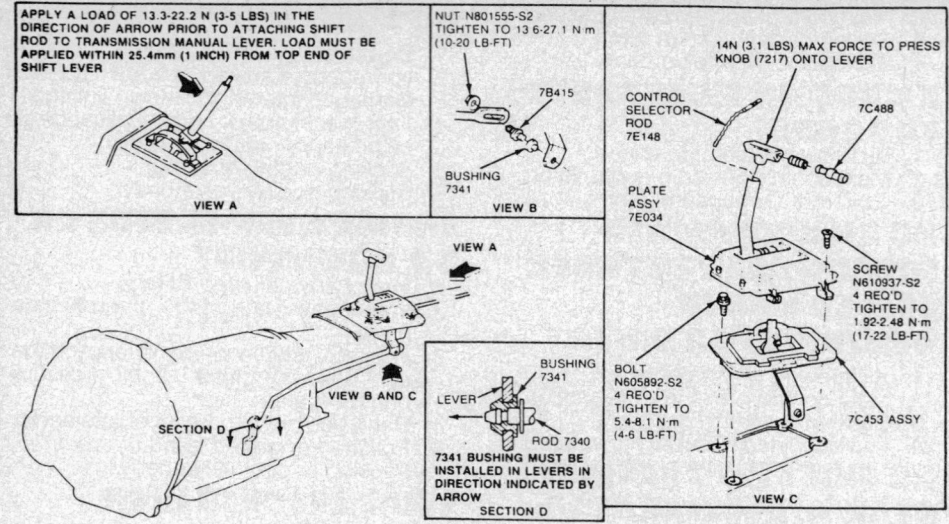

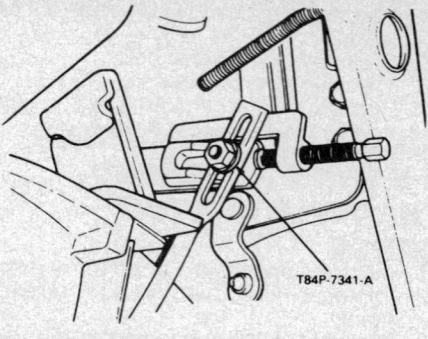

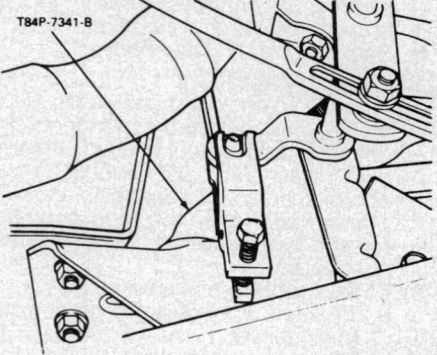

Fig. 11 Manual linkage adjustment

FM5028800446000X

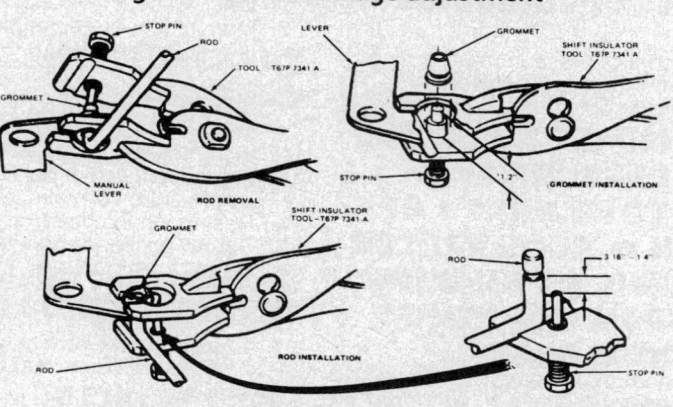

Fig. 12 Shift linkage grommet replacement

FM5028800447000X

FM5028800448000X

Fig. 13 Removing or installing shift linkage grommet in limited space situations

CHECKING FLUID LEVEL

1. With transmission at operating temperature, park vehicle on a level surface.
2. Run engine at idle speed with service and parking brakes applied and move selector lever through each range. Return selector lever to P.
3. With engine idling, remove dipstick and check fluid level. Fluid level should be between the Add and Full marks.
4. Add specified fluid as required to bring the fluid to the proper level.

CHANGING FLUID

Normal maintenance and lubrication requirements do not necessitate periodic fluid changes. If vehicle accumulates 5000 or more miles per month or it is used in continuous stop and go service, change fluid every 30,000 miles.

When filling a dry transmission and converter, install 9.5 quarts of specified fluid. Start engine, shift the selector lever through all ranges and place it at P position. Check fluid level and add enough to raise the level in the transmission to the F (full) mark on the dipstick. When a partial drain and refill is required, proceed as follows:

1. Loosen oil pan retaining bolts and allow pan to drain the oil.
2. Remove and clean pan and replace screen.
3. Place a new gasket on pan and install pan and screen.
4. Add three quarts of specified fluid to transmission.
5. Run engine at a fast idle until it reaches normal operating temperature.
6. Shift selector lever through all ranges and then place it in P position.
7. Add fluid as required to bring the level to the full mark.

ADJUSTMENTS
MANUAL LINKAGE

The shift lever should be held against the rearward Overdrive stop when the linkage is adjusted.

1. Position transmission selector lever in Overdrive position. Ensure that the selector lever is tight against the rearward stop.
2. Position transmission manual lever in Overdrive, third detent position from full counterclockwise position.
3. Loosen the manual lever retaining nut, **Fig. 11**.
4. Ensure the transmission selector lever and manual lever are in Overdrive

position, **torque** attaching nut to 10–20 ft. lbs.
5. Check for operation of the transmission in each selector position.

DOWNSHIFT LINKAGE

1. Ensure cable and transmission bracket are installed at transmission kickdown lever.
2. Rotate throttle body throttle lever to wide open throttle position.
3. While holding throttle at wide open position, push locking cam (white) in place to lock cable adjustment.

IN-VEHICLE REPAIRS
SHIFT LINKAGE
GROMMET, REPLACE
Transmission On Bench

1. Place lower jaw of shift linkage insulator T67P-7341-A or equivalent, between lever and rod, **Fig. 12**, then position stop pin against end of control rod and force rod out of grommet.
2. Remove grommet from lever by cutting off large shoulder with sharp knife, **Fig. 13**.
3. Adjust stop pin to 1/2 inch and coat outside of grommet with suitable multi-purpose lubricant.
4. Place a new grommet on the stop pin and force it into the lever hole, then turn grommet several times to ensure it is properly seated.
5. Squeeze rod into bushing until stopwasher seats against grommet.

Transmission In Vehicle

1. Disconnect linkage from grommet, then position shift linkage grommet

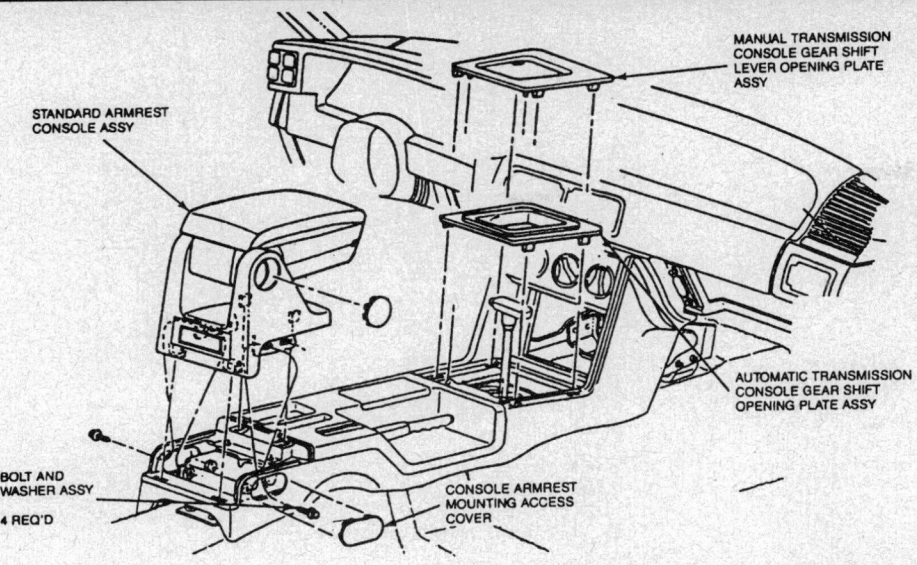

Fig. 14 Console assembly removal. Mustang

remover T84P-7341-A or equivalent, **Fig. 13,** and rotate screw in tool until grommet is forced out of lever.

2. Adjust stop on shift linkage grommet replacer tool No. T84P-7341-B or equivalent, to 1/2 inch, then coat outside of new grommet with suitable multi-purpose lubricant.

3. Position grommet on lever and install grommet replacer on lever, rotate screw to force grommet into position. Turn grommet several times to ensure it is fully seated.

4. Connect linkage and tighten attaching nuts.

INTERLOCK CABLE, REPLACE

1. Remove console assembly as described under "Selector Housing, Replace."

2. Remove lefthand lower instrument panel trim and steering column lower shroud.

3. Remove interlock cable retaining screw, then disconnect cable from shift lever cam.

4. Remove steering column retaining nuts, then lower column to floor.

5. Remove cable retaining clip, then disconnect electrical connector at solenoid.

6. Remove cable retaining screw from steering column, then guide interlock cable out from under console brackets.

7. Reverse procedure to install, **torquing** steering column retaining nuts to 15–24 ft. lbs. and cable retaining screws at steering column and at shifter to 10–13 inch lbs.

8. Test cable for proper operation, ignition key should only be removable with shift lever in Park. Shifter should be locked in Park with ignition key removed, or with key in On position and brake NOT applied. Shifter should release when brakes are applied.

VACUUM DIAPHRAGM, REPLACE

1. **On 1992 models with 2.9L or 4.0L engines,** remove nut from studded bolt, heat shield from studded bolt, then the clips on frame.

2. **On all models,** disconnect hoses from vacuum unit.

3. Remove vacuum unit retaining bracket and bolt, or studded bolt, being careful not to pry or bend bracket.

4. Pull vacuum unit from transmission case, then remove vacuum unit control rod.

5. Reverse procedure to install, noting the following:
   a. **Torque** retaining bolt to 80–106 inch lbs., or studded bolt to 70–98 inch lbs.
   b. **On 1992 models with 2.9L or 4.0L engines,** install heat shield on studded bolt and push retaining clips on pan rail, then **torque** nut on studded bolt to 70–98 inch lbs.

CONTROL VALVE BODY, REPLACE

1. Raise and support vehicle.
2. Loosen pan retaining bolts, then drain fluid from transmission.
3. Remove retaining bolts, pan and gasket.
4. Remove filter screen and O-ring.
5. Remove low/reverse servo cover, piston, spring and gasket.
6. Disconnect electrical connectors from converter clutch solenoid on Mustang models and two additional electrical connectors at 3-4 shift solenoid on Thunderbird models.
7. Remove bolts from control valve body.
8. Reverse procedure to install.

LOW/REVERSE SERVO, REPLACE

1. Raise and support vehicle.
2. Loosen pan retaining bolts and allow transmission fluid to drain.
3. Remove all pan retaining bolts except two bolts at the front to allow fluid to drain further.
4. Remove oil filter screen and gasket.
5. Remove retaining screws, low/reverse servo cover, piston and spring and gasket.
6. Reverse procedure to install.

EXTENSION HOUSING, REPLACE

1. Raise and support vehicle.
2. Install scribe marks on propeller shaft end yoke and rear axle companion flange, then remove propeller shaft.
3. Support transmission with suitable jack.
4. Remove speedometer cable from extension housing.
5. Remove bolts or nuts attaching rear support to crossmember.
6. Raise transmission slightly and remove rear support from extension housing.
7. Loosen extension housing attaching bolts and allow transmission to drain.
8. Remove bolts and the extension housing.
9. Reverse procedure to install, noting the following:
   a. Use new extension housing gasket.
   b. Ensure that parking pawl actuating rod is correctly seated in guide cup bore.
   c. **Torque** attaching bolts to 27–39 ft. lbs.

GOVERNOR, REPLACE

1. Remove extension housing.
2. Remove governor body to coil collector body retaining bolts.
3. Remove governor body, valve, spring and weight from collector body.
4. Reverse procedure to install.

SELECTOR HOUSING, REPLACE

1. Remove console assembly as follows:
   a. Remove two access covers at rear of console, **Fig. 14,** then the armrest retaining bolts.
   b. Remove four armrest to floor bracket retaining bolts, then the armrest assembly.
   c. Remove gearshift lever opening finish panel and shift knob, then slide finish panel up to remove.
   d. Place emergency brake lever in up position, remove four retaining screws and lift top finish panel up, then disconnect electrical connectors and remove top finish panel.
   e. Remove two console to rear floor bracket retaining screws, then insert a small screwdriver into two notches at bottom of front upper finish panel and snap out.
   f. **On models equipped with radio opening cover plate with stowage bin,** use a small screwdriver to pry cover plate out of console.
   g. **On models equipped with radio with stowage bin or radio with graphic equalizer,** disconnect

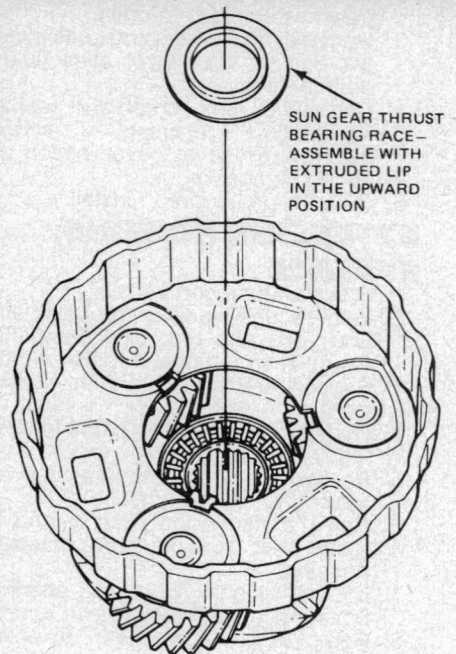

SUN GEAR THRUST BEARING RACE—ASSEMBLE WITH EXTRUDED LIP IN THE UPWARD POSITION

FMA058800012000X

Fig. 15 Bearing race installation

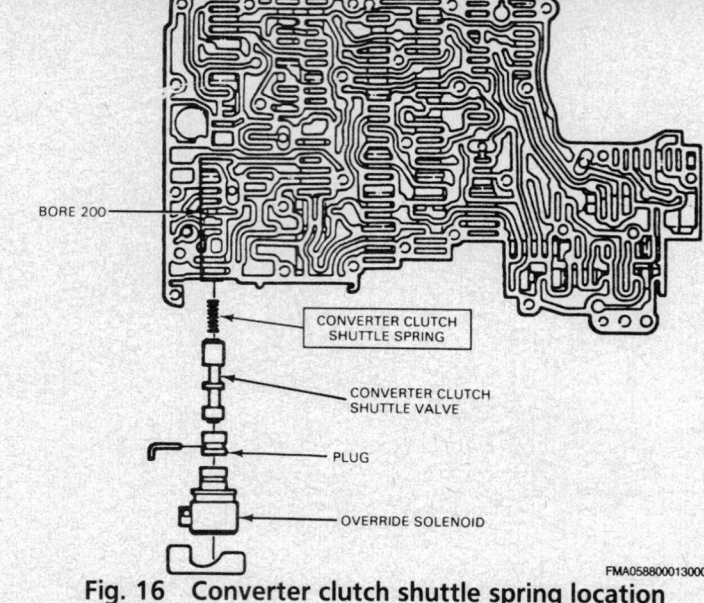

BORE 200

CONVERTER CLUTCH SHUTTLE SPRING

CONVERTER CLUTCH SHUTTLE VALVE

PLUG

OVERRIDE SOLENOID

FMA058800013000X

Fig. 16 Converter clutch shuttle spring location

SPRING -7F263-

FM5029300572000X

Fig. 17 Converter channel spring

battery ground cable, install radio remover tool No. T87P-19061-A or equivalent into radio face plate. Push radio remover in approximately one inch to release clips, apply a light spreading force and pull radio out of dash, then disconnect electrical connectors.

h. **On all models,** open glove compartment door and drop glove compartment assembly down, then remove two console to instrument panel retaining screws.

i. Remove four console to bracket retaining screws, then the console from vehicle.

2. Disconnect shifter interlock cable from shifter housing and interlock cam, then the indicator lamp wire.

3. Place shifter lever in Overdrive, then raise and support vehicle.

4. Remove lower linkage retaining nut, then disconnect shift rod.

5. Lower vehicle, then remove shifter to floor pan retaining screws and shifter assembly.

6. Reverse procedure to install, noting the following:

a. **Torque** shifter retaining bolts to 4-5 ft. lbs., and interlock cable retaining screw to 10-13 inch lbs.

b. Place shifter lever in Overdrive and apply a three pound rearward force to lever, raise and support vehicle, then connect shift rod, replacing plastic grommet as previously described and **torque** to 11-19 ft. lbs.

c. Lower vehicle and check shifter operation. Adjust manual linkage, if necessary.

TRANSMISSION
REPLACE

1. Disconnect battery ground cable, then raise and support vehicle.

2. Loosen oil pan attaching bolts and al-

low fluid to drain.

3. Remove converter access cover and adapter plate attaching bolts from lower end of converter housing.

4. Remove four flywheel to converter attaching nuts. **On belt driven overhead camshaft engines, never turn crankshaft backward.**

5. Install scribe marks on propeller shaft end yoke and rear axle companion flange, then remove propeller shaft and install extension housing oil seal replacer tool No. T74P-77052-A or equivalent.

6. Disconnect speedometer cable from extension housing.

7. Disconnect shift rod or cable from transmission manual lever.

8. Disconnect kickdown cable at transmission kickdown lever.

9. Remove starter to converter housing attaching bolts and position starter out of way.

10. Disconnect all electrical connectors from transmission.

11. Remove vacuum line from transmission vacuum modulator.

12. Position suitable jack under transmission and raise sightly.

13. Remove engine rear support to crossmember attaching bolts.

14. Remove crossmember to frame side support attaching bolts, then the crossmember insulator and support damper.

15. Lower jack and allow transmission to hang.

16. Position suitable jack under engine assembly and raise engine just enough to gain access to two upper converter housing to engine attaching bolts.

17. Disconnect oil cooler lines from transmission, capping all openings.

18. Remove lower converter housing to engine attaching bolts.

19. Remove transmission filler tube.

20. Secure transmission to jack using suitable safety chain.

21. Remove two upper converter housing to engine attaching bolts.

22. Remove transmission from vehicle.

23. Reverse procedure to install, noting the following:

a. **Torque** attaching nuts and bolts to specifications.

b. **All vehicles are equipped with Electronic Engine Control IV (EEC-IV), and when battery has been disconnected and reconnected, some abnormal drive symptoms may occur while the EEC-IV processor relearns its adaptive strategy. It may be necessary to drive vehicle 10 miles or more to allow the processor to relearn its adaptive strategy.**

TECHNICAL SERVICE BULLETINS

FLUID LEAK AT VENT

1. Ensure that transmission fluid leak-

age is originating at left rear of transmission case.

2. Check transmission vent tube connecting hose to the vent fitting for swelling, looseness or any evidence of transmission fluid on hose.

3. If hose exhibits any of the above, discard vent hose and replace with hose No. E3TZ-7A246-F, or equivalent, cut to 5 inch length.

SENSITIVE 4–3 TORQUE DEMAND DOWNSHIFTS AT 45–55 MPH

Before replacing springs, verify sensitivity of 4-3 torque demand shifts, as a torque converter unlock may be mistaken for a 4-3 torque demand shift. This can be accomplished by maintaining the throttle setting that produced the perceived downshift and moving the selector from overdrive to D. If a shift occurs, the previous "shift" was actually a converter unlock.

If a sensitive 4-3 torque demand shift is verified, replace throttle pressure boost spring and 4-3 torque demand control valve spring with those provided in kit No. E5TZ-7E479-A. The new throttle pressure boost spring is green. The new 4-3 torque demand control valve spring is dark green and has a larger diameter than the throttle pressure boost spring.

MISSING BEARING RACE IN SERVICE OVERDRIVE PLANET ASSEMBLIES

Some service overdrive planet assemblies may be missing a sun gear thrust bearing race. Check any service overdrive planet assembly for race and, if necessary, obtain race No. E5TZ-7D235-B or equivalent and install in service overdrive planet assembly, Fig. 15.

ENGINE STALLS WHEN SHIFTING INTO FORWARD OR REVERSE

If engine speeds are set to specification and this problem still occurs, disassemble valve body, removing retainer plate, override solenoid, plug, valve, and spring, Fig. 16. Remove any foreign matter from bore, being careful not to dislodge shuttle balls. Reassemble in reverse order of disassembly, using service spring E5TZ-7L490-A, ensuring shuttle valve moves freely.

LEAKS AT CONVERTER OVERRIDE CLUTCH CONNECTOR

Some vehicles may exhibit a leak at the converter clutch override connector and transmission case.

This condition may be caused by sump fluid migrating up the override connector wires and depositing at the terminals at the top of the connector.

This condition may be corrected by replacing switch (Part No. E5TZ-7E449-A).

SHORT CARRIER HUB

Some E9TZ-7A398-A kits have been packaged with a short carrier hub. If a kit is received with this condition, retain the planet and order the following parts one of each: FOTZ-7D090-A, FOTZ-7D234-A, FOTZ-7D235-A and FOTZ-7D236-A.

ADDITION OF SPRING TO CONVERTER CHANNEL

1992

On A4LD transmissions built after 8/21/91, a spring was installed in the transmission case worm trail to trap large machining chips and reduce engine stall complaints caused by the stuck converter lock-up valve in the main control of the transmission, Fig. 17.

TIGHTENING SPECIFICATIONS

Component	Torque/Ft. Lbs.	Component	Torque/Ft. Lbs.
Center Support (OD) To Case	80–115①	Neutral Start Switch To Case	84–120①
Cooler Line To Case Connector	18–23	Oil Pan To Case	8–10
Cooler Line To Connector Tube Nut	12–18②	Oil Pump To Converter Housing	17–20
Converter Housing & Pump To Case	27–39	Outer Downshift Lever To Inner Lever Shaft Nut	7–11
Converter Housing Lower Cover To Converter Housing	12–16	Overdrive Band Adjusting Screw Locknut To Case	35–45
Converter To Flywheel Attaching Nut	20–34	Pressure Plug To Case	7–11
Detent Spring To Valve Body	80–107①	Push Connect Cooler Line Fitting To Case	18–23
Extension Housing To Case	27–39	Reverse Servo To Case	80–115①
Governor Assembly To Oil Collector Body	84–120①	Separator Plate To Valve Body	54–72①
Intermediate Band Adjusting Screw Locknut To Case	35–45	Transmission To Engine	28–38
Main Control To Case	71–97①	Vacuum Diaphragm Retainer Clip To Case	80–106①
Manual Lever Nut	30–40		

①—Inch lbs.
②—Torque to specification while holding transmission fitting.

Ford AOD Automatic Overdrive Transmission

INDEX

INDEX -Continued

APPLICATION CHART

Year	Vehicle Model	Engine Liter/ CID
1992	Cougar & Thunderbird	3.8L/V6-232
	Cougar & Thunderbird	5.0L/V8-302 HO
	Crown Victoria & Grand Marquis	4.6L/V8-280
	Mark VII	5.0L/V8-302 HO
	Mustang	5.0L/V8-302 HO
	Thunderbird	3.8L/V6-232 SC
	Town Car	4.6L/V8-280
1993	Cougar & Thunderbird	3.8L/V6-232
	Cougar & Thunderbird	5.0L/V8-502 HO
	Mustang	5.0L/V8-302 HO
	Thunderbird	3.8L/V6-232 SC

IDENTIFICATION

This transmission may be identified by the tag attached to the upper righthand extension housing to transmission case bolt. The tag includes model prefix and suffix, a service identification number and a build date code, **Fig. 1.** The service identification number indicates changes to service details which affect interchangeability when the transmission model is not changed. For interpretation of this number the Ford Master Parts Catalog should be consulted.

DESCRIPTION

This unit is a 4 speed automatic transmission incorporating an integral overdrive feature. With selector lever in 1 position, the transmission will start and remain in first gear until the selector lever is moved

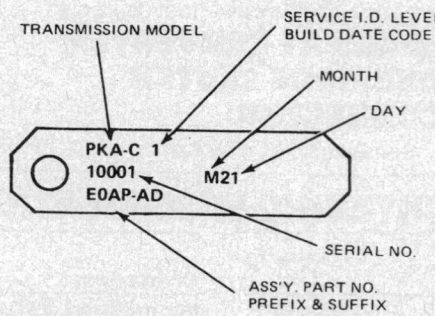

Fig. 1   Identification tag

to another position. In 3 position, the transmission will automatically shift through 1-2-3 range, but will not engage overdrive. In D position, the transmission will automatically select the appropriate time to shift into overdrive (4th gear). The design of the transmission features a split torque path in third gear, where 40% of the engine torque is transmitted hydraulically through the torque converter and 60% is transmitted mechanically through solid connections (direct drive input shaft) to the driveshaft. When transmission is in overdrive (4th gear), 100% of engine torque is transmitted through the direct drive input shaft.

The transmission consists essentially of a torque converter assembly, compound planetary gear train and a hydraulic control system, **Fig. 2.** For gear control the transmission has four friction clutches, two one-way roller clutches and two bands. Overdrive is accomplished by the addition of a band to lock the reverse sun gear while driving the planet carrier. The torque converter operation is similar to other types of automatic transmission, but has an added damper assembly and input shaft for 3rd gear and overdrive. The direct drive input shaft couples the engine directly to the direct clutch. This shaft is driven by the torque converter cover through the damper assembly which cushions engine shock to the transmission.

TROUBLESHOOTING

SLOW INITIAL ENGAGEMENT

1. Improper fluid level.
2. Incorrectly adjusted or damaged linkage.
3. Contaminated fluid.
4. Low main control pressure or improper band and clutch application.

ROUGH INITIAL ENGAGEMENT

1. Improper fluid level.
2. Incorrectly adjusted engine idle.
3. Incorrectly adjusted automatic choke.
4. Looseness in driveshaft, universal joints or engine mounts.
5. Improper oil control pressure or band or clutch application.
6. Sticking or dirty valve body.

HARSH ENGAGEMENTS W/WARM ENGINE

1. Improper fluid level.
2. Incorrectly adjusted, disconnected, sticking or damaged throttle linkage.
3. Throttle linkage return spring disconnected.
4. Incorrectly adjusted engine idle.
5. Valve body bolts improperly torqued.
6. Valve body dirty or valves sticking.

NO OR DELAYED FORWARD ENGAGEMENT

1. Improper fluid level.
2. Incorrectly adjusted or damaged manual linkage.
3. Low main control pressure.
4. Forward clutch stator support seal rings Nos. 3 and/or 4 leaking.
5. Burned and/or damaged forward clutch assembly.
6. Forward clutch cylinder check ball and/or piston seal rings leaking.
7. Valve body bolts improperly torqued.
8. Valve body dirty or valves sticking.

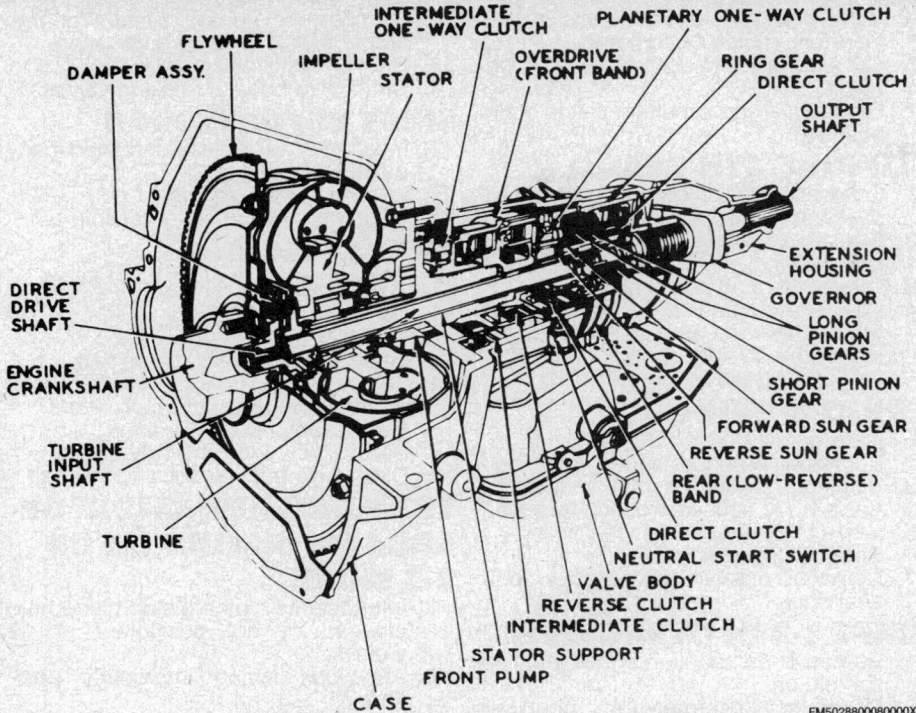

Fig. 2 Cross-sectional view of automatic overdrive transmission

9. Clogged transmission filter.
10. Damaged or leaking pump.

NO OR DELAYED REVERSE ENGAGEMENT

1. Improper fluid level.
2. Incorrectly adjusted or damaged manual linkage.
3. Low main control pressure in reverse.
4. Leaking high reverse clutch or reverse clutch stator support seal rings Nos. 1 and/or 2.
5. Burned or worn reverse clutch assembly.
6. Leaking reverse clutch piston check ball and/or piston seal rings.
7. Valve body bolts improperly torqued.
8. Valve body dirty or valves sticking.
9. Clogged transmission filter.
10. Damaged pump.

NO OR DELAYED REVERSE ENGAGEMENT AND/OR NO ENGINE BRAKING IN MANUAL LOW

1. Improper fluid level.
2. Incorrectly adjusted throttle linkage.
3. Leaking low reverse servo piston seal.
4. Burned or worn low reverse servo piston.
5. Damaged planetary low one-way clutch.
6. Endplay clearance too tight.

NO ENGINE BRAKING IN MANUAL 2ND GEAR

1. Oil pressure control system or improper band or clutch application.
2. Leaking intermediate servo.
3. Damaged intermediate one-way clutch.
4. Polished or glazed band or drum.

FORWARD ENGAGEMENT SLIPS, SHUDDERS AND/OR CHATTERS

1. Improper fluid level.
2. Incorrectly adjusted or damaged linkage.
3. Low main control pressure.
4. Valve body bolts improperly torqued.
5. Valve body dirty or valves sticking.
6. Forward clutch piston check ball leaking and/or not seating.
7. Cut and/or worn forward clutch piston seal.
8. Leaking forward clutch stator support seal rings Nos. 3 and 4.
9. Damaged low one-way clutch (planetary).

REVERSE SHUDDERS, CHATTERS AND/OR SLIPS

1. Improper fluid level.
2. Low main control pressure in reverse.
3. Leaking low reverse servo.
4. Damaged low (planetary) one-way clutch.
5. Damaged reverse clutch drum bushing.
6. Worn or damaged reverse clutch stator support seal rings and/or ring grooves.
7. Cut and/or worn reverse clutch piston seal.
8. Damaged reverse band.
9. Looseness in driveshaft, universal joints and/or engine mounts.

NO DRIVE, SLIPS OR CHATTERS IN 1ST GEAR IN DRIVE OR OVERDRIVE

1. Worn or damaged planetary one-way clutch.

NO DRIVE, SLIPS OR CHATTERS IN 2ND GEAR

1. Worn or damaged friction clutch or one-way clutch.
2. Intermediate clutch piston bleed hole clogged or not positioned at 12 o'clock.
3. Control pressure or improper band or clutch application.
4. Internal leakage.
5. Dirty valve body or sticking valves.

INITIAL DRIVE IN 2ND OR 3RD

1. Oil pressure control system or improper band and/or clutch application.
2. Intermediate clutch pack clearance too tight.
3. Damaged, worn or sticking governor.
4. Valve body bolts too loose.
5. Dirty valve body or sticking valves.
6. Cross leaks between valve body and case mating surface.

SHIFT POINTS INCORRECT

1. Improper fluid level.
2. Incorrectly adjusted throttle linkage.
3. Improper speedometer gear installed.
4. Oil pressure control system or improper band or clutch application.
5. Worn or damaged governor.
6. Dirty valve body or sticking valves.

ALL UPSHIFTS HARSH OR DELAYED OR NO UPSHIFTS

1. Improper fluid level.
2. Incorrectly adjusted, disconnected, damaged or sticking throttle linkage.
3. Throttle return spring disconnected.
4. Damaged or incorrectly adjusted manual linkage.
5. Sticking governor.
6. Main control pressure too high.
7. Valve body bolts improperly torqued.
8. Valve body dirty or valves sticking.

MUSHY AND/OR EARLY UPSHIFTS OR UPSHIFT PILEUP

1. Improper fluid level.
2. Incorrectly adjusted, sticking or damaged throttle linkage.
3. Low main control pressure.
4. Valve body bolts improperly torqued.
5. Valve body valve or throttle control valve sticking.
6. Sticking governor valve.

NO 1-2 UPSHIFT

1. Improper fluid level.
2. Incorrectly adjusted or damaged manual linkage.
3. Low main control pressure to intermediate friction clutch.
4. Bent sticking or leaking vacuum diaphragm.
5. Valve body bolts improperly torqued.
6. Valve body dirty or valves sticking.
7. Burned intermediate servo assembly.

ROUGH, HARSH AND/OR DELAYED 1-2 UPSHIFT

1. Improper fluid level.

2. Poor engine performance.
3. Incorrectly adjusted or damaged throttle linkage.
4. Main control pressure too high.
5. Sticking governor valve.
6. Valve body bolts improperly torqued.
7. Valve body dirty or valves sticking.

MUSHY, EARLY, SOFT AND/OR SLIPPING 1-2 UPSHIFT

1. Improper fluid level.
2. Incorrect engine performance.
3. Incorrectly adjusted, sticking or damaged throttle linkage.
4. Low main control pressure.
5. Valve body bolts improperly torqued.
6. Valve body dirty or valves sticking.
7. Worn or burned intermediate friction clutch.
8. Sticking governor valve.
9. Damaged intermediate servo.

NO 2-3 UPSHIFT

1. Low fluid level.
2. Low main control pressure to direct clutch.
3. Valve body bolts improperly torqued.
4. Valve body dirty or valves sticking.
5. Burned or worn direct or reverse-high clutch assembly.
6. Broken converter damper hub and/or weld.

HARSH AND/OR DELAYED 2-3 UPSHIFT

1. Incorrect engine performance.
2. Incorrectly adjusted, sticking or damaged throttle linkage.
3. Plugged or missing 2-3 accumulator apply passage.
4. Cut or worn 2-3 accumulator piston seals.
5. Damaged 2-3 accumulator.
6. Valve body bolts improperly torqued.
7. Valve body dirty.
8. Sticking 2-3 capacity modulator valve.
9. Bent, sticking or leaking vacuum diaphragm or TV control rod.

SOFT, EARLY AND/OR MUSHY 2-3 UPSHIFT

1. Incorrectly adjusted, bent or sticking throttle linkage.
2. Valve body bolts improperly torqued.
3. Valve body dirty or valves sticking.
4. Burned or worn direct clutch assembly or reverse/high clutch.
5. Bent, sticking or leaking vacuum diaphragm or TV control rod.

NO 3-4 UPSHIFT

1. Incorrectly adjusted, bent or sticking throttle linkage.
2. Direct clutch circuit leakage.
3. Valve body dirty or valves sticking.
4. Distorted main control gasket.
5. Distorted case.
6. Leaking governor.

HARSH AND/OR DELAYED 3-4 UPSHIFT

1. Incorrectly adjusted, bent or sticking throttle linkage.
2. Throttle return spring disconnected.
3. Valve body bolts improperly torqued.

4. Valve body dirty or valves sticking.
5. Incorrect engine performance.
6. Cut or worn 3-4 accumulator piston seals.
7. Clogged 3-4 accumulator piston drain passage.

SLIPPING 4TH GEAR

1. Overdrive circuit leakage or blocked passage.
2. Overdrive servo piston and/or band not applying.
3. Overdrive band mislocated.
4. Converter damper plate and hub fracturing, the weld and/or rivets fatiguing, or the damper springs breaking.
5. Distorted direct driveshaft splines.

ERRATIC SHIFTS

1. Improper fluid level.
2. Poor engine performance.
3. Binding or sticking throttle linkage.
4. Valve body bolts improperly torqued.
5. Valve body dirty or valves sticking.
6. Sticking governor valve.
7. Damaged output shaft collector body seal rings.

SHIFT 1-3 IN OVERDRIVE

1. Burned or damaged intermediate friction clutch.
2. Damaged intermediate one-way clutch.
3. Oil pressure control system or improper band or clutch application.
4. Valve body dirty or valves sticking.
5. Sticking governor valve.

ENGINE OVERSPEEDS ON 2-3 SHIFT

1. Incorrectly adjusted linkage.
2. Oil pressure control system or improper band or clutch application.
3. Damaged or worn high clutch and/or intermediate servo.
4. Cut or leaking intermediate servo piston seals.
5. Dirty valve body or sticking valves.
6. Broken converter damper and/or hub.

SHIFT HUNTING 3-4, 4-3

1. Poor engine performance.
2. Worn or damaged EGR solenoid.
3. Incorrectly adjusted manual linkage.

ROUGH SHUDDER 3-1 SHIFT AT CLOSED THROTTLE IN OVERDRIVE

1. Incorrect engine performance.
2. Incorrectly adjusted engine idle.
3. Incorrectly adjusted manual linkage.
4. Oil pressure control system or improper clutch or band application.
5. Improper governor operation.
6. Dirty valve body or sticking valves.

ROUGH OR MUSHY 4-2 OR 3-1 SHIFT

1. Incorrect engine performance.
2. Incorrectly adjusted linkage.
3. Improper application of intermediate friction and one-way clutch.
4. Dirty valve body or sticking valves.

NO FORCED DOWNSHIFTS

1. Incorrectly adjusted or damaged throttle linkage.

2. Oil pressure control system or improper clutch or band application.
3. Dirty or sticking governor.
4. Dirty valve body or sticking valves.

SHIFT EFFORTS HIGH

1. Incorrectly adjusted or damaged manual shift linkage.
2. Loose inner manual lever nut.
3. Damaged manual lever retainer pin.

TRANSMISSION OVERHEATS

1. Improper fluid level.
2. Incorrect engine performance.
3. Incorrectly adjusted engine idle.
4. Oil pressure control system or improper band or clutch application.
5. Restriction in cooler or lines.
6. Seized converter one-way clutch.
7. Dirty valve body or sticking valves.

TRANSMISSION CLUNK OR SQUAWK DURING 1-2 OR 2-3 SHIFT

1. Intermediate clutch piston bleed hole clogged or not positioned at 12 o'clock.
2. Anti-clunk spring improperly positioned.
3. Converter damper spring brake.

TRANSMISSION LEAKS

1. Case breather vent.
2. Leakage at gaskets or seals.

POOR VEHICLE ACCELERATION

1. Poor engine performance.
2. Torque converter one-way clutch locked up.

TRANSMISSION NOISY
Valve Resonance

1. Improper fluid level.
2. Oil pressure control system or improper band or clutch application.
3. Cooler lines grounding.
4. Dirty valve body or sticking valves.
5. Internal leakage or pump cavitation.

Less Valve Resonance

1. Improper fluid level.
2. Damaged or improperly adjusted linkage.
3. Contaminated fluid.
4. Loose converter to flywheel housing bolts or nuts.
5. Loose or worn speedometer driven gear.
6. Damaged or worn extension housing bushing seal or driveshaft.
7. Damaged or worn front or rear planetary and/or one-way clutch.

HARSH COASTING DOWNSHIFT CLUNK

1. Improperly seated anti-clunk spring.
2. Incorrectly adjusted throttle linkage.
3. Sticking throttle linkage return spring.

INITIAL ENGAGEMENT CLUNK w/ENGINE WARM

1. Engine RPMs above specification.
2. Incorrectly adjusted throttle linkage.
3. Worn, damaged or loose universal

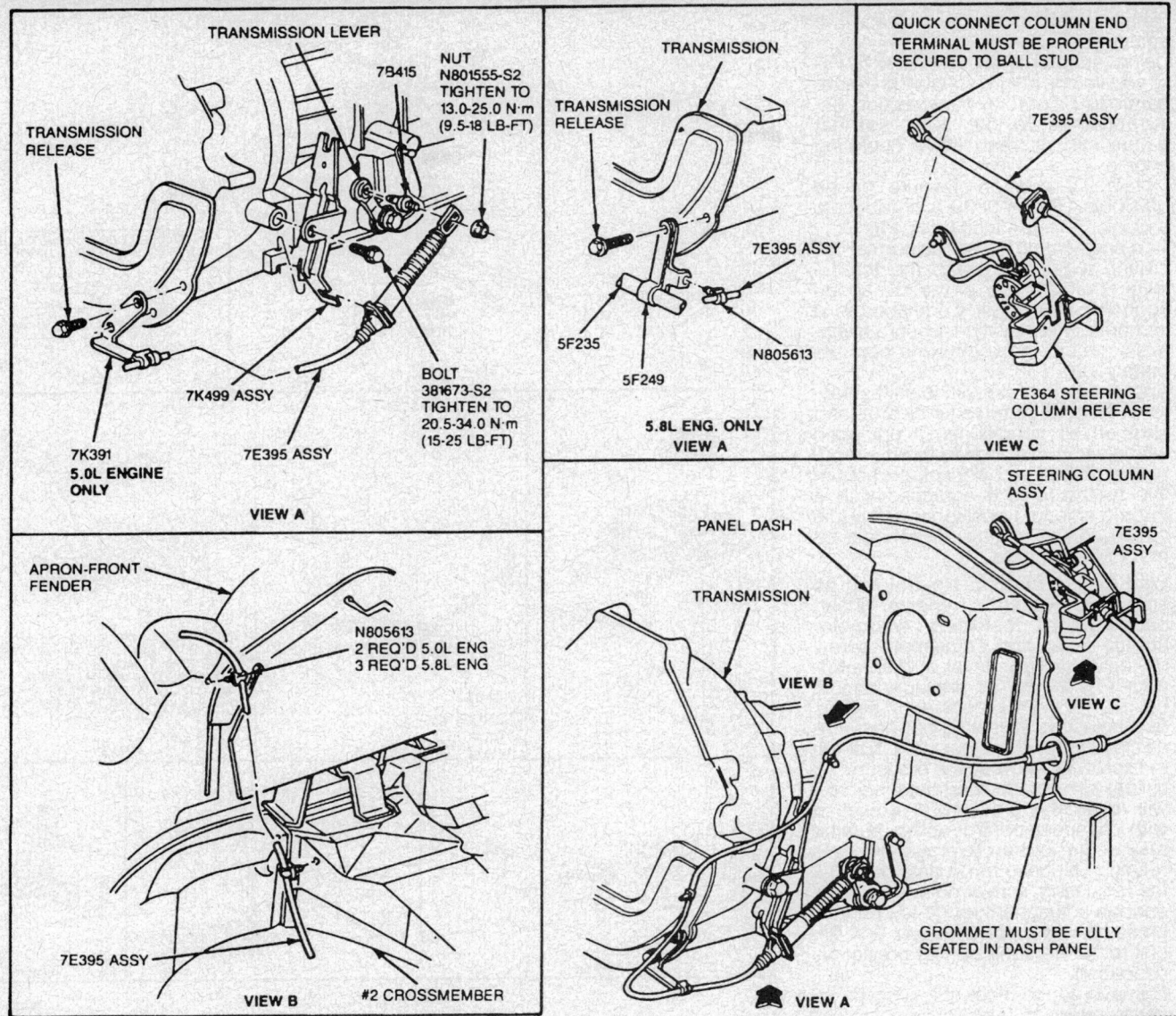

Fig. 3 Manual linkage. 1992

joints, slip yoke, rear axle or rear suspension.
4. Excessive transmission endplay.

VEHICLE WILL NOT START
1. Incorrectly adjusted ignition switch.
2. Defective ignition switch.
3. Defective neutral start switch.

MAINTENANCE
For transmission fluid capacity and type, refer to the "Lubricant Data" chart at the end of this manual.

CHECKING OIL LEVEL
1. With transmission at operating- temperature, park vehicle on level surface.
2. Operate engine at idle speed with parking brake applied and move selector lever through each detent position. Return selector lever to Park.
3. With engine idling, remove dipstick and check fluid level. Fluid level should be between arrows on dipstick.

4. Add fluid as necessary to bring fluid to proper level. Use only fluid meeting Ford Qualification No. M2C-138-CJ, Dexron II or Mercon.

ADJUSTMENTS
SHIFT LINKAGE
COLUMN SHIFT
1992
1. Loosen adjusting nut at transmission shift lever, **Fig. 3.**
2. Place selector lever in overdrive, then hold selector lever in position by placing an 3-5 lb. weight on lever.
3. Rotate transmission manual lever clockwise to low, then return it counterclockwise two detent positions to overdrive position.
4. Align flats of adjusting stud with flats of cable slot, then install cable on stud. **Ensure not to push or pull on rod while assembling rod to stud.**
5. **Torque** attaching nut and washer to 9-18 ft. lbs.

6. Check shift lever for proper operation.

FLOOR SHIFT
1. Place transmission selector lever in overdrive position.
2. Raise and support vehicle and loosen manual lever shift rod retaining nut, **Figs. 4 through 6**
3. Hold selector lever against rearward stop by placing an 3-5 lb. weight on lever.
4. Move transmission manual lever to overdrive position, third detent position from full clockwise position, then **torque** attaching nut to 10-15 ft. lbs.
5. Check transmission operation in all selector lever positions.

THROTTLE VALVE PRESSURE
TV Rod Linkage
1. Check curb idle speed, adjusting as necessary. Ensure curb idle speed is set to specification with and without the throttle solenoid positioner (anti-

diesel solenoid) energized, if equipped.

2. Using adapter fitting D80L-77001-A or equivalent, attach suitable pressure gauge to TV port on transmission, using enough flexible hose so that gauge can be read while operating engine.

3. Obtain TV control pressure gauge block No. D84P-70332-A or fabricate a block .390-.404 inch thick, **Fig. 7.**

4. Run engine until it reaches normal operating temperature and the throttle lever is off fast idle, or the idle speed control (ISC) plunger, if equipped, is at its normal idle position. Ensure transmission fluid temperature is approximately 100-150°F.

5. Apply parking brake, place shift selector in Neutral, remove air cleaner and shut off air conditioner. If equipped with a vacuum operated throttle modulator, disconnect and plug vacuum line to this unit. If equipped with a throttle solenoid positioner or an idle speed control, do not disconnect either of these units.

6. With engine idling in Neutral and no accessory load on engine, insert gauge block between carburetor throttle lever and adjustment screw on the TV linkage lever at the carburetor, **Fig. 7.** The TV pressure should be 28-38 psi. For optimum setting, use adjusting screw to set pressure as close to 33 psi as possible. Turning the screw in will raise the pressure 1.5 psi per turn and backing out the screw will lower the pressure. If equipped with idle speed control, some "hunting may occur and an average pressure reading will have to be determined. If the adjusting screw does not have enough adjustment range to bring TV pressure within specification, first adjust rod at transmission as previously described.

7. Remove gauge block, allowing TV lever to return to idle. With engine still idling in Neutral, TV pressure must be less than 5 psi. If not, back out adjusting screw until TV pressure is less than 5 psi, then reinstall gauge block and ensure TV pressure is still 28-38 psi.

TV Cable Linkage

1. Attach TV pressure gauge with hose, No. T86L-70002-A, or equivalent, to TV port on transmission, using enough hose to make gauge accessible while operating engine.

2. If necessary, remove air cleaner cover and inlet tube from throttle body inlet.

3. Insert tapered end of cable TV gauge tool No. T86L-70332-A or equivalent between crimped slug on end of cable and plastic cable fitting that attaches to throttle lever, **Fig. 8.**

4. Push gauge tool in, forcing the crimped slug away from the plastic fitting, ensuring gauge block is pushed in as far as it will go.

5. Run engine until it reaches normal operating temperature and temperature of transmission fluid is 100-150°F.

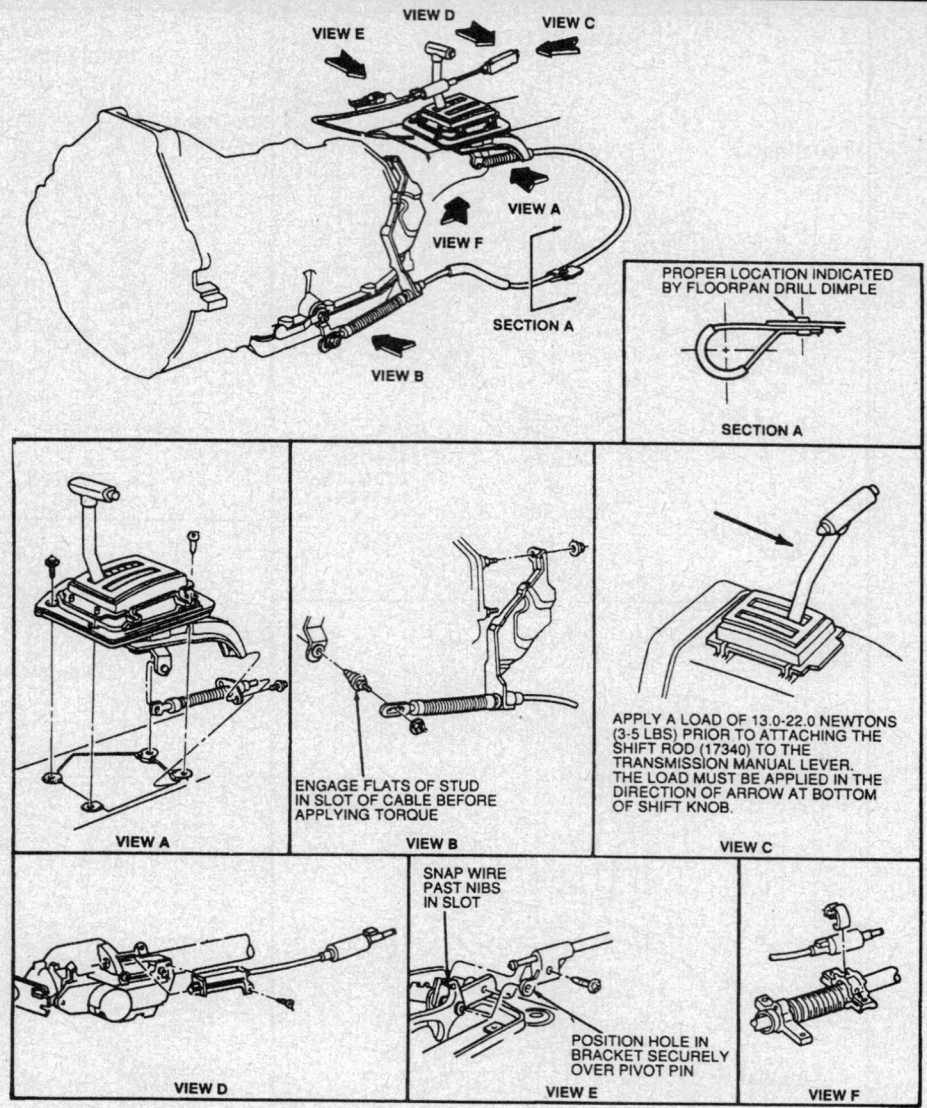

Fig. 4 Manual linkage. 1992-93 Mustang

FM5029100095000X

6. Apply parking brake and place shift selector in Neutral. TV pressure should be 30-40 psi. For best results, set TV pressure as close to 33 psi as possible as follows:

a. Using suitable tool, pry up white toggle lever on cable adjuster located immediately behind throttle body cable mounting bracket. The adjuster preload spring should cause the adjusting slider to move away from the throttle body and TV pressure should increase.

b. Push on slider from behind bracket until TV pressure is 33 psi and, while still holding slider, push down on toggle lever as far as it will go, locking slider in position.

c. Push on slider from behind bracket until TV pressure is 28 psi and, while still holding slider, push down on toggle lever as far as it will go, locking slider in position.

7. Remove gauge tool, allowing cable to return to its normal idle position.

8. If TV pressure is not less than 5 psi,

reinstall gauge block and repeat step 6, setting TV pressure to a pressure of less than 33 psi but not less than 28 psi.

9. Remove gauge block and ensure TV pressure is less than 5 psi.

IN-VEHICLE REPAIRS
VALVE BODY, REPLACE

1. Raise and support vehicle, drain transmission fluid, then remove transmission pan, gasket and filter.

2. Remove detent spring attaching bolt, then the spring.

3. Remove valve body to case attaching bolts, then the valve body.

4. Reverse procedure to install. Use suitable guide pins to align valve body to case.

GOVERNOR, REPLACE

1. Remove extension housing as described above. **If governor body only is being removed, proceed to step 4.**

2. Remove governor to output shaft re-

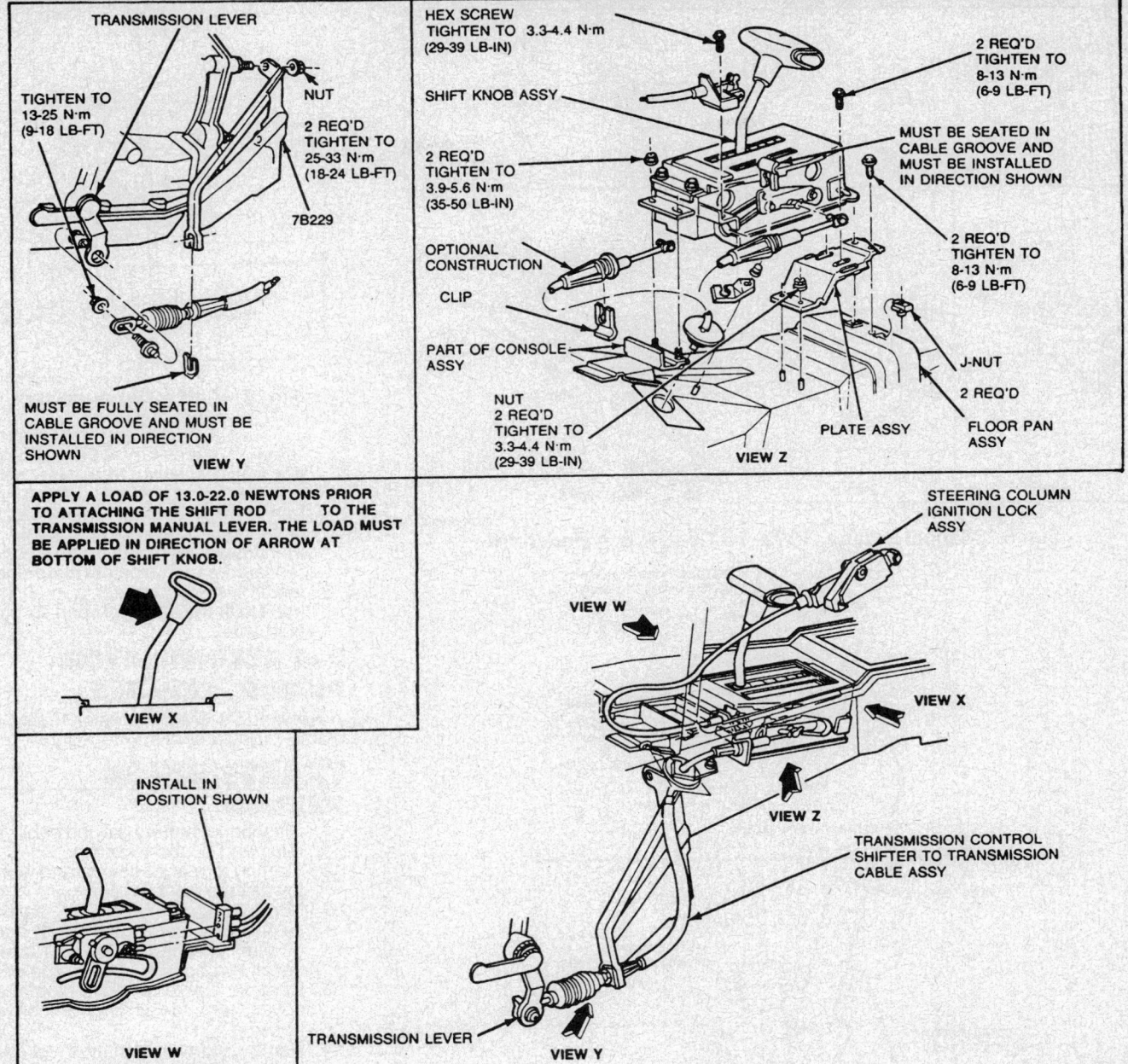

Fig. 5 Manual linkage. Mark VII

taining snap ring.
3. Remove governor assembly from output shaft using suitable tool. Remove governor driveball.
4. Remove governor to counterweight attaching screws. Remove governor from counterweight.
5. Reverse procedure to install.

EXTENSION HOUSING, REPLACE

1. Raise and support vehicle.
2. Disconnect parking brake cable from equalizer, if necessary.
3. Disconnect driveshaft from rear axle flange, then remove driveshaft from transmission.
4. Disconnect speedometer cable from extension housing.

5. Remove engine rear support to extension housing attaching bolts.
6. Support transmission with suitable jack and raise transmission enough to remove weight from rear engine support.
7. Remove engine rear support from crossmember, then lower transmission and remove extension housing attaching bolts. Slide extension housing from output shaft and allow fluid to drain.
8. Reverse procedure to install.

SERVO ASSEMBLY, REPLACE
Overdrive Servo

1. Remove valve body as previously de-

scribed.
2. Compress overdrive servo piston cover with a suitable tool, then remove snap ring retainer.
3. Apply compressed air to servo piston release passage and remove the overdrive servo piston cover and spring. Remove piston from cover, then the rubber seal from piston and cover.
4. Install new servo piston and cover seals on the servo piston and cover.
5. Lubricate all seals, piston and piston bore with transmission fluid.
6. Install servo piston into cover, then the return spring into servo piston.
7. Install overdrive piston assembly into overdrive servo bore.
8. Compress overdrive piston using suit-

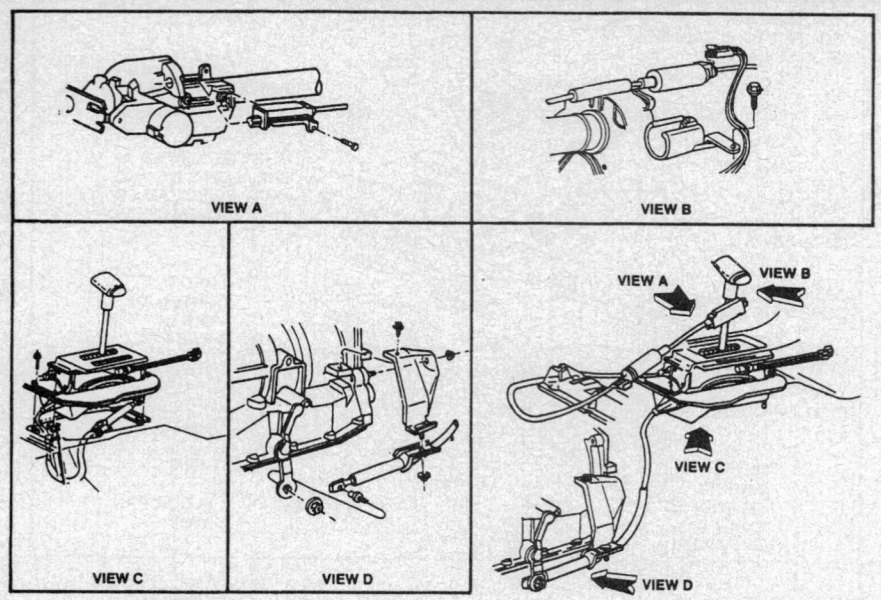

Fig. 6 Manual linkage. 1992–93 Cougar & Thunderbird

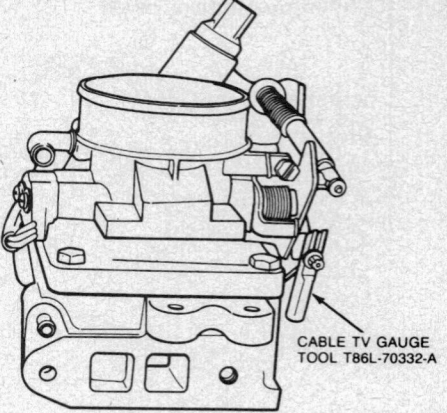

Fig. 8 Cable TV gauge tool installation

cover, if necessary. Lubricate cover pocket of case with transmission fluid.
6. Install 3-4 accumulator piston and return spring into case, then the cover.
7. Compress cover using suitable tool, then install snap ring. Ensure cover is reseated snugly against snap ring.
8. Install valve body, filter, pan and gasket. Refill transmission pan to proper fluid level.

2–3 ACCUMULATOR PISTON, REPLACE

Refer to "3-4 Accumulator Piston, Replace" for replacement procedure.

TRANSMISSION
REPLACE

1. Disconnect battery ground cable, then raise and support vehicle.
2. Starting at rear of oil pan and working toward the front, loosen bolts and allow fluid to drain. Remove remaining oil pan bolts except for two at front of oil pan. After fluid has been drained, install two bolts onto rear side of pan.
3. Remove converter drain plug access cover from lower end of converter housing.
4. Remove converter to flywheel attaching nuts.
5. Turn converter until drain plug is accessible. Remove plug and drain fluid.
6. Install converter drain plug.
7. Remove driveshaft, mark rear driveshaft yoke and companion flange so driveshaft can be installed to its original position.
8. Position a suitable plug into extension housing to prevent fluid leakage.
9. Remove catalytic converter assembly.
10. Remove starter motor and disconnect neutral start switch electrical connector.
11. Remove rear mount to crossmember and two crossmember to frame bolts.
12. Remove engine rear support to extension housing bolts, then disconnect T.V. linkage rod from transmission T.V. lever and manual rod from manual lever at transmission.
13. Remove bolts securing bellcrank bracket to converter housing.

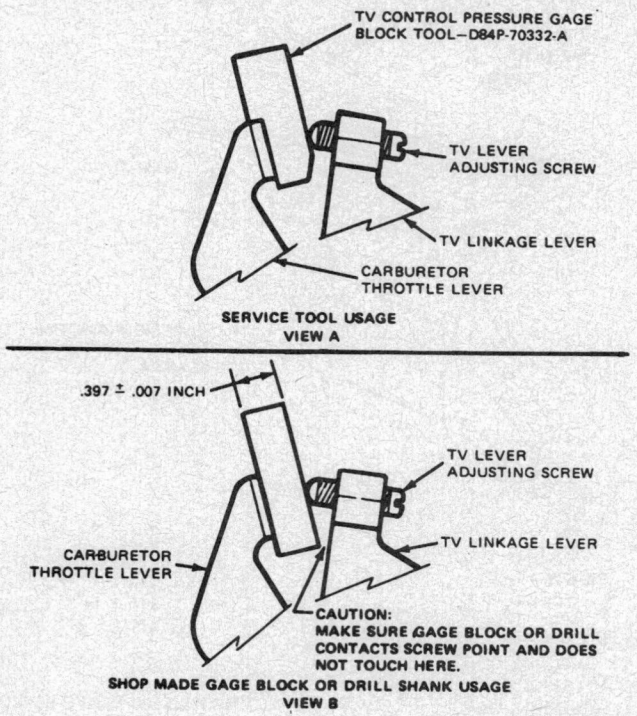

Fig. 7 TV control pressure gauge block tool

able tool, then install snap ring retainer.
9. Install valve body, filter, pan and gasket. Refill transmission to proper fluid level.

Reverse Servo

1. Refer to "Overdrive Servo Assembly" procedure for replacement. Apply compressed air to the servo piston release passage to remove servo piston from case. **Reverse servo piston is under spring pressure. Use caution when removing servo piston cover.**

3–4 ACCUMULATOR PISTON, REPLACE

1. Remove valve body as previously described.
2. Compress 3-4 accumulator piston cover, then remove snap ring retainer.
3. Release cover slowly, then remove piston cover, return spring and piston. Some models do not use a spring.
4. Remove seal from 3-4 accumulator cover and piston and inspect for damage and wear.
5. Install new seals on 3-4 accumulator

14. Using a suitable jack, raise transmission and remove crossmember from side supports. Disconnect and remove any interfering exhaust system components.
15. Remove four bolts retaining driveshaft to companion flange.
16. Position axle stand under front of axle housing and remove forward mounting nuts and bushings. Pull vent tube from hole in sub-frame.
17. Lower front of axle housing with axle stand and slide driveshaft out of transmission above axle housing. Let driveshaft rest on front driveshaft support and axle assembly.
18. Lower transmission and disconnect oil cooler lines from transmission.
19. Disconnect speedometer cable from extension housing.
20. Lower transmission to gain access to oil cooler lines, then disconnect each oil line.
21. Remove bolt and transmission filler tube from transmission.
22. Secure transmission to jack using a suitable chain.
23. Remove converter housing to cylinder block bolts.
24. Carefully move transmission and converter assembly away from engine and at the same time, lower jack to permit the transmission to clear the underside of vehicle.
25. Reverse procedure to install, noting the following:
   a. Lubricate converter pilot with chassis grease prior to installation.
   b. **Torque** converter drain plug to 8-28 ft. lbs.
   c. **Torque** engine to transmission bolts to 40-50 ft. lbs.
   d. **Torque** oil cooler lines to 18-23 ft. lbs.
   e. **Torque** crossmember to side support attaching bolts to 70-100 ft. lbs.
   f. **Torque** converter to flywheel attaching nuts to 20-34 ft. lbs.
   g. **Torque** converter housing access cover attaching bolts to 12-16 ft. lbs.

TIGHTENING SPECIFICATIONS

Component	Torque/Ft. Lbs.	Component	Torque/Ft. Lbs.
Converter Housing Access Cover	12–16	Neutral Start Switch To Case	8–11
Converter Plug To Converter	8–28	Oil Pan To Case	6–10
Converter To Flywheel	20–34	Outer Throttle Lever To Shaft	12–16
Detent Spring Attaching Bolt	80–120 ①	Pressure Plug To Case	6–12
Extension Housing To Case	16–20	Push Connect Fitting To Case	18–23
Filter To Valve Body	80–120 ①	Reinforcing Plate To Valve Body	80–120 ①
Front Pump To Case	10–20	Stator Support To Pump Body	12–16
Governor Body Cover To Governor Body	20–30 ①	Transmission To Engine	40–50
Governor Body To Counterweight	50–60 ①	Valve Body To Case	80–100 ①
Inner Manual Lever To Shaft	19–27	①—Inch lbs.	

Ford AOD-E & 4R70W (AODE-W) Automatic Overdrive Transmissions

INDEX

APPLICATION CHART

Year	Vehicle Model	Engine Liter/CID	Transmission
1992	Ford & Mercury Full Size ②	4.6L/V8-281	AOD-E
	Town Car ②	4.6L/V8-281	AOD-E
	Crown Victoria & Grand Marquis ②	4.6L/V8-281	AOD-E
1993	Crown Victoria & Grand Marquis ②	4.6L/V8-281	AOD-E
	Town Car ②	4.6L/V8-281	AOD-E
	Mark VIII ①	4.6L/V8-281	4R70W (AODE-W)
1994	Town Car ②	4.6L/V8-281	AOD-E
	Crown Victoria & Grand Marquis ②	4.6L/V8-281	AOD-E
	Mustang ②	3.8L/V6-232	AOD-E
	Mustang ②	5.0L/V6-302 HO	AOD-E
	Cougar & Thunderbird ①	3.8L/V6-232	4R70W (AODE-W)
	Cougar & Thunderbird ①	4.6L/V8-281	4R70W (AODE-W)
	Thunderbird SC ①	3.8L/V6-232	4R70W (AODE-W)
	Mark VIII ①	4.6L/V8-281	4R70W (AODE-W)

①—4R70W (AODE-W) Transmission
②—AODE Transmission

IDENTIFICATION

These transmissions may be identified by the tag attached to the upper righthand extension housing to transmission case bolt. The tags include model prefix and suffix, a service identification number and a build date code, **Figs. 1 and 2.** The service identification number indicates changes to service details which affect interchangeability when the transmission model is not changed. For interpretation of this number the Ford Master Parts Catalog should be consulted.

DESCRIPTION

This unit is a 4 speed automatic transmission incorporating an integral overdrive feature. With selector lever in 1 position, the transmission will start and remain in first gear until the selector lever is moved to another position. In 3 position, the transmission will automatically shift through 1-2-3 range, but will not engage overdrive. In D position, the transmission will automatically select the appropriate time to shift into overdrive (4th gear). The design of the transmission features a split torque path in third gear, where 40% of the engine torque is transmitted hydraulically through the torque converter and 60% is transmitted mechanically through solid connections (direct drive input shaft) to the driveshaft.

When transmission is in overdrive (4th gear), 100% of engine torque is transmitted through the direct drive input shaft.

The transmission consists of a torque converter assembly, compound planetary gear train and a hydraulic control system, **Fig. 3.** For gear control the transmission has four friction clutches, two one-way roller clutches and two bands. Overdrive is accomplished by the addition of a band to lock the reverse sun gear while driving the planet carrier. The torque converter operation is similar to other types of automatic transmission, but has an added damper assembly and input shaft for 3rd gear and overdrive. The direct drive input shaft couples the engine directly to the direct clutch. This shaft is driven by the torque converter cover through the damper assembly which cushions engine shock to the transmission.

The 4R70W (AODE-W) transmission is an AOD-E transmission with wide ratio gears and is a four speed rear wheel drive automatic with an electronic shift, torque converter clutch control and line pressure controls. This transmission uses a double pinion compound gearset to produce four forward speeds and reverse. Two bands, two one-way roller clutches and four friction clutches are used to hold or drive various planetary gearset members.

TROUBLESHOOTING
ROUGH INITIAL ENGAGEMENT

1. Improper fluid level.
2. High engine idle.
3. Loose driveshaft, engine mounts or U-joints.
4. Sticking or dirty valve body.
5. Improper clutch or band application, or low oil control pressure.
6. Incorrectly adjusted automatic choke.

SLOW INITIAL ENGAGEMENT

1. Improper fluid level.
2. Damaged or improperly adjusted linkage.
3. Contaminated fluid.
4. Low main control pressure or improper clutch and band application.

HARSH ENGAGEMENTS W/WARM ENGINE

1. Improper fluid level.
2. Damaged or improperly adjusted linkage.
3. High engine idle.
4. Sticking or dirty valve body.
5. Throttle linkage return spring disconnected.

Fig. 1 Identification tag. AOD-E

6. Valve body bolts improperly torqued, loose or too tight.

NO OR DELAYED FORWARD ENGAGEMENT

1. Improper fluid level.
2. Damaged or improperly adjusted linkage.
3. Low main control pressure.
4. Forward clutch stator support seal rings Nos. 3 and/or 4 leaking.
5. Burned and/or damaged forward clutch assembly.
6. Forward clutch cylinder check ball and/or piston seal rings leaking.
7. Valve body bolts improperly torqued.
8. Valve body dirty or valves sticking.
9. Clogged transmission filter.
10. Damaged or leaking pump.

NO OR DELAYED REVERSE ENGAGEMENT

1. Improper fluid level.
2. Damaged or improperly adjusted linkage.
3. Low main control pressure.
4. Leaking high reverse clutch or reverse clutch stator support seal rings Nos. 1 and/or 2.
5. Burned or worn reverse clutch assembly.
6. Leaking reverse clutch piston check ball and/or piston seal rings.
7. Valve body bolts improperly torqued.
8. Valve body dirty or valves sticking.
9. Clogged transmission filter.
10. Damaged pump.

NO OR DELAYED REVERSE ENGAGEMENT AND/OR NO ENGINE BRAKING IN MANUAL LOW

1. Improper fluid level.
2. Damaged or improperly adjusted linkage.
3. Leaking low reverse servo piston seal.
4. Burned or worn low reverse servo piston.
5. Damaged planetary low one-way clutch.
6. Endplay clearance too tight.

NO ENGINE BRAKING IN MANUAL 2ND

1. Improper fluid level.
2. Damaged or improperly adjusted linkage.
3. Improper clutch or band application.
4. Improper control system pressure.
5. Leaking intermediate servo.
6. Damaged intermediate one-way clutch.

FORWARD ENGAGEMENT SLIPS, SHUDDERS AND/OR CHATTERS

1. Improper fluid level.
2. Incorrectly adjusted or damaged linkage.
3. Low main control pressure.
4. Valve body bolts improperly torqued.
5. Valve body dirty or valves sticking.
6. Forward clutch piston check ball leaking and/or not seating.
7. Cut and/or worn forward clutch piston seal.
8. Leaking forward clutch stator support seal rings Nos. 3 and 4.
9. Damaged low one-way clutch (planetary).

REVERSE SHUDDERS, CHATTERS AND/OR SLIPS

1. Improper fluid level.
2. Low main control pressure in reverse.
3. Leaking low reverse servo.
4. Damaged planetary low one-way clutch.
5. Damaged reverse clutch drum bushing.
6. Worn or damaged reverse clutch stator support seal rings or grooves.
7. Cut and/or worn reverse clutch piston.
8. Damaged reverse band.
9. Loosen driveshaft, engine mounts or U-joints.

NO DRIVE, SLIPS OR CHATTERS IN 1ST GEAR IN D OR OVERDRIVE

1. Damaged planetary low one-way clutch.

NO DRIVE, SLIPS OR CHATTERS IN 2ND GEAR

1. Worn or damaged friction clutch or one-way clutch.
2. Intermediate clutch piston belled hole clogged or not positioned at 12 o'clock.
3. Control pressure or improper band or clutch application.
4. Internal leakage.
5. Dirty valve body or sticking valves.

INITIAL DRIVE IN 2ND OR 3RD

1. Improper fluid level.
2. Damaged or improperly adjusted linkage.
3. Oil pressure control system or improper clutch and/or band application.
4. Intermediate clutch pack clearance too tight.
5. Damaged, worn or sticking governor.
6. Sticking or dirty valve body.
7. Valve body bolts too loose.
8. Cross leaks between valve body and case mating surface.

IMPROPER SHIFT POINTS

1. Improper fluid level.
2. Damaged or improperly adjusted linkage.
3. Improper speedometer gear installed.

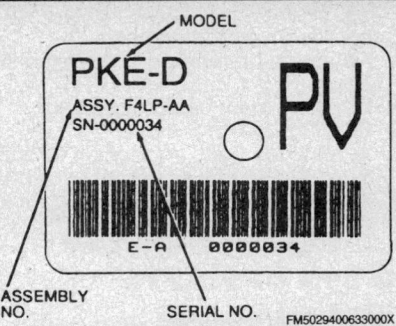

Fig. 2 Identification tag. 4R70W (AODE-W)

4. Improper clutch or band application.
5. Improper control system pressure.
6. Damaged or worn governor.
7. Sticking or dirty valve body.

HARSH, DELAYED OR NO UPSHIFTS

1. Improper fluid level.
2. Damaged or improperly adjusted linkage.
3. Throttle return spring disconnected.
4. Damaged or incorrectly adjusted manual linkage.
5. Governor sticking.
6. High main control pressure.
7. Valve body bolts improperly torqued.
8. Sticking or dirty valve body.

MUSHY AND/OR EARLY UPSHIFTS OR UPSHIFT PILEUP

1. Improper fluid level.
2. Damaged or improperly adjusted linkage.
3. Low main control pressure.
4. Sticking throttle control valve or valve body.
5. Sticking governor valve.
6. Valve body bolts improperly torqued.

NO 1–2 UPSHIFTS

1. Improper fluid level.
2. Damaged or improperly adjusted linkage.
3. Low main control pressure to intermediate friction clutch.
4. Sticking, leaking or bent diaphragm unit.
5. Sticking or dirty valve body.
6. Burned intermediate clutch, band or servo.
7. Valve body bolts improperly torqued.

ROUGH, HARSH AND/OR DELAYED 1–2 UPSHIFT

1. Improper fluid level.
2. Poor engine performance.
3. Incorrectly adjusted or damaged throttle linkage.
4. Main control pressure too high.
5. Sticking governor valve.
6. Valve body bolts improperly torqued.
7. Valve body dirty or valves sticking.

MUSHY, EARLY, SOFT AND/OR SLIPPING 1–2 UPSHIFT

1. Improper fluid level.

2. Improperly tuned engine.
3. Damaged or improperly adjusted linkage.
4. Incorrect main control pressure.
5. Sticking governor valve.
6. Valve body bolts improperly torqued.
7. Valve body dirty or valves sticking.
8. Worn or burned intermediate friction clutch.
9. Damaged intermediate servo.

NO 2–3 UPSHIFTS

1. Improper fluid level.
2. Low main control pressure to direct clutch.
3. Valve body bolts improperly torqued.
4. Sticking or dirty valve body.
5. Burned or worn direct or reverse-high clutch assembly.
6. Broken weld on converter damper hub.

HARSH AND/OR DELAYED 2–3 UPSHIFT

1. Incorrect engine performance.
2. Incorrectly adjusted, sticking or damaged throttle linkage.
3. Plugged or missing 2-3 accumulator apply passage.
4. Cut or worn 2-3 accumulator piston seals.
5. Damaged 2-3 accumulator.
6. Valve body bolts improperly torqued.
7. Valve body dirty.
8. Sticking 2-3 capacity modulator valve.
9. Bent, sticking or leaking vacuum diaphragm or TV control rod.

SOFT, EARLY AND/OR MUSHY 2–3 UPSHIFT

1. Improper fluid level.
2. Improperly tuned engine.
3. Damaged or improperly adjusted linkage.
4. Valve body bolts improperly torqued.
5. Burned or worn direct clutch assembly or reverse/high clutch.
6. Damaged accumulator.
7. Dirty or sticking valve body.
8. Bent, sticking or leaking vacuum diaphragm or TV control rod.

NO 3–4 UPSHIFTS

1. Low fluid level.
2. Damaged or improperly adjusted linkage.
3. Direct clutch circuit leakage.
4. Sticking or dirty valve body.
5. Distorted main control gasket.
6. Distorted case.
7. Leaking governor.

HARSH AND/OR DELAYED 3–4 UPSHIFT

1. Improper fluid level.
2. Damaged or improperly adjusted linkage.
3. Throttle return spring disconnected.
4. Valve body bolts improperly torqued.
5. Valve body dirty or valves sticking.
6. Incorrect engine performance.
7. Cut or worn 3-4 accumulator piston seals.
8. Clogged 3-4 accumulator piston drain passage.

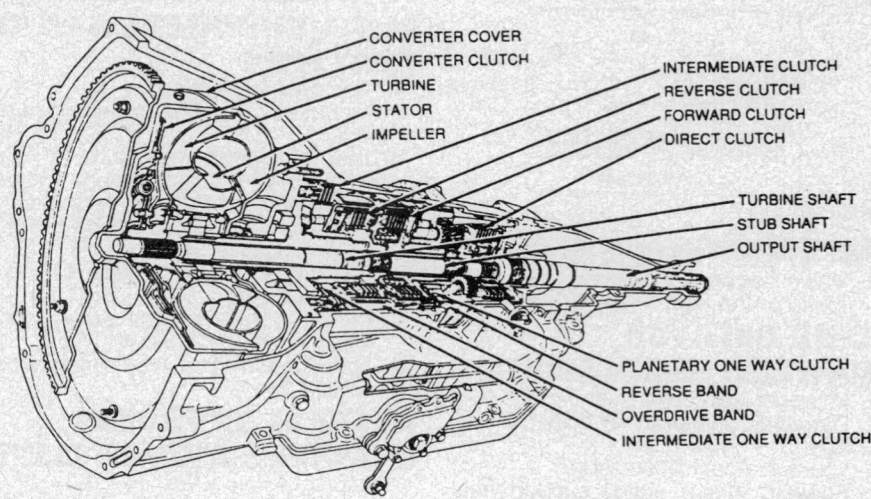

Labels: CONVERTER COVER, CONVERTER CLUTCH, TURBINE, STATOR, IMPELLER, INTERMEDIATE CLUTCH, REVERSE CLUTCH, FORWARD CLUTCH, DIRECT CLUTCH, TURBINE SHAFT, STUB SHAFT, OUTPUT SHAFT, PLANETARY ONE WAY CLUTCH, REVERSE BAND, OVERDRIVE BAND, INTERMEDIATE ONE WAY CLUTCH

FM50292006340000X

Fig. 3   Cross-sectional view of automatic overdrive transmission

SLIPPING 4TH GEAR

1. Overdrive circuit leakage or blocked passage.
2. Overdrive servo piston and/or band not applying.
3. Overdrive band incorrectly located.
4. Converter damper plate and hub damaged.
5. Distorted direct driveshaft splines.

ERRATIC SHIFTS

1. Improper fluid level.
2. Improperly tuned engine.
3. Damaged or improperly adjusted linkage.
4. Dirty or sticking valve body.
5. Sticking governor valve.
6. Damaged output shaft collector body seal rings.
7. Valve body bolts improperly torqued.

SHIFTS 1–3 IN OVERDRIVE

1. Improper fluid level.
2. Damaged or burned intermediate friction clutch.
3. Damaged intermediate one-way clutch.
4. Improper control system pressure or clutch application.
5. Sticking or dirty valve body.
6. Sticking governor valve.

ENGINE OVERSPEEDS ON 2–3 SHIFT

1. Improper fluid level.
2. Damaged or improperly adjusted linkage.
3. Improper control system pressure or clutch application.
4. Damaged or worn high clutch or intermediate servo.
5. Sticking or dirty valve body.
6. Broken converter damper hub.
7. Cut or leaking intermediate servo piston seals.

SHIFT HUNTING 3–4 OR 4–3

1. Improperly tuned engine.

2. Damaged or improperly adjusted linkage.
3. Worn or damaged EGR solenoid.

NO FORCED DOWNSHIFTS

1. Improper fluid level.
2. Damaged or improperly adjusted linkage.
3. Improper control system pressure or clutch application.
4. Sticking or dirty valve body.
5. Sticking or dirty governor.

ROUGH SHUDDER 3–1 SHIFT AT CLOSED THROTTLE IN OVERDRIVE

1. Improper fluid level.
2. Improperly tuned engine.
3. Damaged or improperly adjusted linkage.
4. Improper control system pressure or clutch application.
5. Improper governor operation.
6. Sticking or dirty valve body.

ROUGH OR MUSHY 4–2 OR 3–1 SHIFT

1. Improper fluid level.
2. Improperly tuned engine.
3. Damaged or improperly adjusted linkage.
4. Improper application of intermediate friction and one-way clutch.
5. Sticking or dirty valve body.

HIGH SHIFT EFFORT

1. Damaged or improperly adjusted linkage.
2. Loose manual lever nut.
3. Damaged manual lever retainer pin.

TRANSMISSION OVERHEATS

1. Improper fluid level.
2. Improperly tuned engine.
3. Improper control system pressure or clutch application.

4. Restricted cooler or lines.
5. Seized converter one-way clutch.
6. Sticking or dirty valve body.

CLUNK OR SQUAWK IN 1–2 OR 2–3

1. Blocked intermediate bleed hole or bleed hole not at 12 o'clock position.
2. Incorrectly aligned anti-clunk spring.

HARSH DOWNSHIFT COASTING CLUNK

1. Improperly seated anti-clunk spring.
2. Damaged or improperly adjusted linkage.

TRANSMISSION LEAKS

1. Case breather vent.
2. Leakage at gaskets or seals.

POOR VEHICLE ACCELERATION

1. Improperly tuned engine.
2. Seized torque converter one-way clutch.

SLIPPING SHIFT FOLLOWED BY SUDDEN ENGAGEMENT

1. Throttle valve linkage set too short.

TRANSMISSION NOISY

Valve Resonance

Gauges may aggravate any hydraulic resonance.
1. Improper fluid level.
2. Damaged or improperly adjusted linkage.
3. Improper control system pressure or clutch application.
4. Cooler lines contacting frame, floor pan or other components.
5. Sticking or dirty valve body.
6. Internal leakage or pump cavitation.

Other Than Valve Resonance

1. Improper fluid level.
2. Damaged or improperly adjusted linkage.
3. Contaminated fluid.
4. Loose converter to flywheel housing bolts or nuts.
5. Loose or worn speedometer driven gear.
6. Damaged or worn extension housing bushing seal or driveshaft.
7. Damaged or worn front or rear planetary and/or one-way clutch.

HARSH COASTING DOWNSHIFT CLUNK

1. Improperly seated anti-clunk spring.
2. Incorrectly adjusted throttle linkage.
3. Sticking throttle linkage return spring.

INITIAL ENGAGEMENT CLUNK W/ENGINE WARM

1. Engine idle speed incorrect.
2. Incorrectly adjusted throttle linkage.
3. Worn, damaged or loose universal joints, slip yoke, rear axle or suspension.
4. Excessive transmission endplay.

VEHICLE WILL NOT START

1. Incorrectly adjusted ignition switch.
2. Defective ignition switch.
3. Defective neutral start switch.

MAINTENANCE

Ford Motor Company recommends the use of Mercon type automatic transmission fluid in this transmission. If Mercon type fluid is not available, Dexron-II Series D automatic transmission fluid may be used. Use of a fluid other than specified may result in transmission malfunction of failure.

TRANSMISSION FLUID COOLER FLOW INSPECTION

The linkage, fluid and control pressure must be within specification before performing this flow check.
1. Remove transmission dipstick from filler tube, then place funnel in filler tube.
2. Raise and support vehicle, then remove cooler return line from its fitting in case.
3. Attach hose to cooler return line and fasten free end of hose to funnel installed in filler tube.
4. Start engine and set idle speed at 1000 RPM with transmission in Neutral.
5. Observe fluid flow at funnel. When flow is solid, air bleeding has been completed, flow should be liberal. If there is not a liberal flow at 1000 RPM in Neutral, low pump capacity, main circuit system leakage, or cooler system restriction is indicated.
6. To separate transmission trouble from cooler system trouble, observe flow at transmission case converter out fitting.

FLUID CHECK

1. With transmission at operating temperature, park vehicle on level surface.
2. Operate engine at idle speed with parking brake applied and move selector lever through each detent position. Return selector lever to Park.
3. With engine idling, remove dipstick and check fluid level. Fluid level should be between arrows on dipstick.
4. Add fluid as necessary to bring fluid to proper level. Use only fluid meeting Ford qualification tool No. M2C-138-CJ, Dexron II or Mercon.

FLUID CHANGE

Normal maintenance and lubrication requirements do not necessitate periodic fluid changes. If vehicle accumulates 5,000 or more miles per month or it is used in continuous stop and go service, change fluid every 30,000 miles.

When filling a dry transmission and converter, install approximately 12 quarts of specified fluid. Start engine, shift the selector lever through all ranges and place it at P position. Check fluid level and add enough to raise the level in the transmission to the F (full) mark on the dipstick. When a partial drain and refill is required, proceed as follows:
1. Loosen oil pan bolts and allow pan to drain.
2. Working from rear and both sides of transmission oil pan, remove bolts, allowing pan to drop and drain slowly.
3. Remove and clean pan and replace screen.
4. Place a new gasket on pan and install pan and screen.
5. Add three quarts of specified fluid to transmission.
6. Run engine at a fast idle until it reaches normal operating temperature.
7. Shift selector lever through all ranges and then place it in P position.
8. Add fluid as required to bring the level to the full mark.

ADJUSTMENTS

MANUAL LINKAGE CHECK

Ensure Overdrive detent in the transmission corresponds exactly with the stop in the steering column or console. Hydraulic leakage at the manual valve can cause delay in engagements and/or slipping while operating if the linkage is not correctly adjusted.

Check for improperly adjusted shift linkage. This is done by matching the detents in the shift lever with those in the transmission. If they match, the indicator is improperly adjusted. **Do not adjust the shift linkage.**

MANUAL LINKAGE, ADJUST

COLUMN SHIFT CONTROL CABLE

Except Town Car

1. Loosen adjusting stud nut at transmission shift lever, Fig. 4.
2. Place steering column selector lever in Overdrive and hold selector lever in position by placing a 3 lb. weight on lever.
3. Rotate transmission manual lever to low (clockwise), then return it two detent positions to Overdrive position (counterclockwise).
4. Align flats of adjusting stud with flats of cable slot, then install cable on stud.
5. Tighten adjusting stud nut and washer assembly. **Torque to 10-18 ft. lbs.**
6. Check shift lever for proper operation.

Town Car

1. Place steering column selector lever in Overdrive and hold selector lever in position by placing a 3 lb. weight on lever to ensure lever is located firmly on the Overdrive detent.
2. Insert a small screwdriver in the slot of the slide adjuster to open the adjuster.
3. Move transmission manual shift lever on side of transmission to Overdrive

position, second detent from rearward most position.

4. Push slide adjuster closed.

5. Check operation of transmission in each selector lever position. Ensure park/neutral start switch is functioning correctly.

FLOOR SHIFT

1. Place transmission selector lever in overdrive position. **Shift lever should be held against the rearward overdrive stop while linkage is adjusted.**

2. Raise and support vehicle and loosen manual lever shift rod retaining nut.

3. Move transmission manual lever to Overdrive position and tighten retaining nut.

4. Check transmission operation in all selector lever positions.

THROTTLE VALVE LINKAGE

The 3.8L/V6-232, 3.8L/V6-232 SC & 4.6L/V8-281 SEFI engines use an Air Bypass (ISC) that does not affect throttle position. Therefore, automatic idle setting does not affect TV cable adjustment.

1. Set parking brake, then place shift selector in Neutral position. **Do not check or set TV pressure in Park.**

2. Remove air cleaner cover and inlet tube from throttle body inlet to access throttle lever and cable assembly.

3. Using a wide blade screwdriver, pry cable assembly out of grommet on throttle body lever.

4. Ensure plastic block slides freely on notched rod.

5. While holding throttle lever firmly against its idle stop, push grooved pin into grommet on throttle lever as far as it will go. **While pushing pin into grommet, ensure throttle lever does not move away from idle stop.**

6. Ensure grooved pin is fully installed while holding throttle lever firmly against idle stop.

THROTTLE VALVE PRESSURE ADJUSTMENT

This procedure requires the use of TV Pressure Gauge Set (0-60 psi) tool No. T86L-70002-A or equivalent. The results of the adjustment procedure depends on the accuracy of the pressure gauge.

The pressure gauge should have eight feet of flexible hose to make the gauge accessible while operating the engine.

1. Attach TV Pressure Gauge Set (0-60 psi) tool No. T86L-70002-A or equivalent to the TV port on the transmission.

2. Remove the air cleaner cover and inlet tube from the throttle body inlet to obtain access to the throttle lever.

3. Insert tapered end of the tool between the crimped slug on the end of cable and plastic notched rod. Push in Cable TV Control Pressure Gauge tool No. T86L-70332-A or equivalent forc-

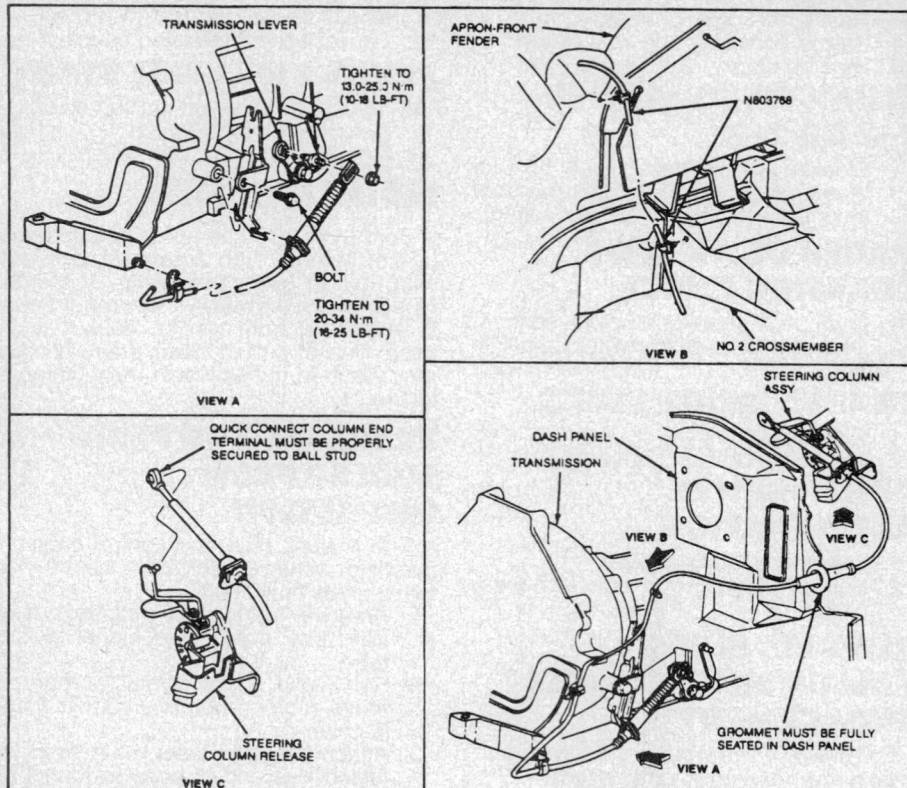

ing the crimped slug away from the plastic rod. Ensure gauge block is pushed in as far as it will go as shown in **Fig. 5.**

4. Operate engine until normal operating temperature is reached. The transmission fluid temperature should be approximately 100-150°F. **Do not perform pressure check if transmission fluid is cold or too hot to touch.**

5. Set parking brake, then place shift selector in Neutral. With gauge tool in place and engine idling in Neutral, TV pressure should be between 30-40 psi. **Do not check or set TV pressure in Park.**

6. If pressure reading is as specified, remove gauge tool No. T86L-70332-A or equivalent, allowing cable to return to its normal idle position. With the engine still idling in Neutral, TV pressure reading must be at or near zero (less than 5 psi).

7. If TV pressure is not as specified in either Steps 5 or 6, remove gauge tool. Check and replace damaged components as necessary. Adjust cable as outlined under "Self-Locking (Core Wire)."

8. Repeat Steps 3 through 6 to recheck TV pressure.

9. If TV pressure is still not as specified, modify adjustment as follows:
   a. Mark or measure location of plastic block on notched rod.
   b. Push out locking tab on plastic block.

c. Using mark or measurement as reference, move plastic block toward throttle body mounting bracket to raise TV pressure or away from bracket to lower TV pressure as shown in **Fig. 6. One notch movement equals 2 psi.**
   d. Push in white locking tab to lock block in position.
   e. Insert grooved pin into grommet as shown in **Fig. 7.**

10. Repeat Steps 3 through 6 to recheck TV pressure.

11. Repeat Step 9, if necessary. TV pressure should be set as close as possible to 33 psi in Neutral with gauge tool installed. Since the TV pressure goes up approximately 2 psi when the shift lever is moved from neutral to a forward gear, this will result in a TV pressure near a desired setting of 35 psi.

IN-VEHICLE REPAIRS

MANUAL SHIFT LINKAGE GROMMET, REPLACE

The automatic transmission linkage system incorporates a polyurethane plastic grommet to connect the various rods, levers and adjusting stud. Whenever a rod is disconnected from a grommet type connector, the old grommet must be removed and a new one installed.

1. Place lower jaw of shift linkage insulator tool No. T67P-7341-A, or equivalent, between lever and rod, **Fig. 8.**

2. Position stop pin against end of con-

Fig. 4 Manual linkage. Crown Victoria, Grand Marquis

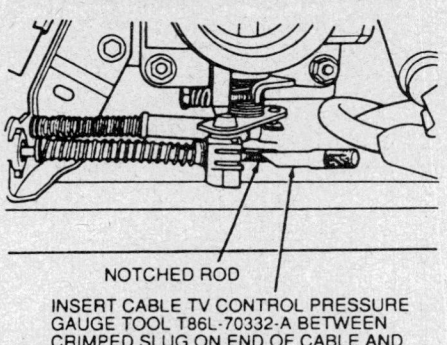

NOTCHED ROD

INSERT CABLE TV CONTROL PRESSURE GAUGE TOOL T86L-70332-A BETWEEN CRIMPED SLUG ON END OF CABLE AND PLASTIC NOTCHED ROD

FM5029200672000X

Fig. 5   Gauge tool installation

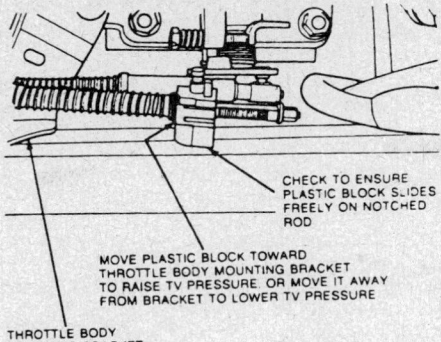

CHECK TO ENSURE PLASTIC BLOCK SLIDES FREELY ON NOTCHED ROD

MOVE PLASTIC BLOCK TOWARD THROTTLE BODY MOUNTING BRACKET TO RAISE TV PRESSURE, OR MOVE IT AWAY FROM BRACKET TO LOWER TV PRESSURE

THROTTLE BODY MOUNTING BRACKET

FM5029200673000X

Fig. 6   Throttle body bracket location

GROMMET   SHIFT LINKAGE INSULATORS

LEVER

STOP PIN

GROMMET INSTALLATION

1/2 INCH

FM5029200675000X

Fig. 8   Shift linkage grommet replacement

IMPORTANT: HOLD THE THROTTLE LEVER FIRMLY AGAINST IDLE STOP WHILE PUSHING GROUND PIN INTO GROMMET.

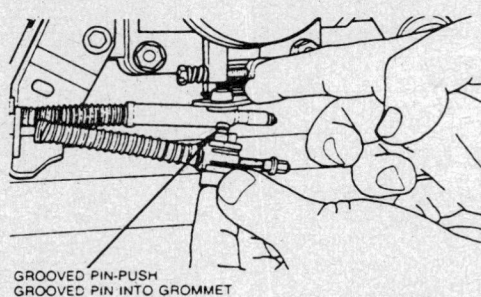

GROOVED PIN-PUSH GROOVED PIN INTO GROMMET

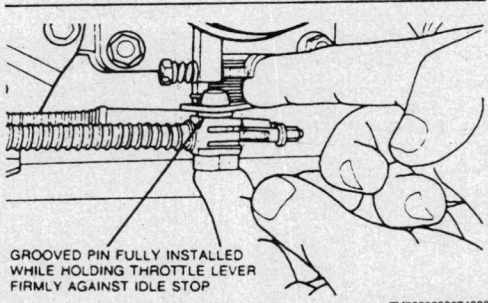

GROOVED PIN FULLY INSTALLED WHILE HOLDING THROTTLE LEVER FIRMLY AGAINST IDLE STOP

FM5029200674000X

Fig. 7   Grooved push pin installation

trol rod and force rod out of grommet.
3. Remove grommet from lever by cutting off large shoulder with sharp knife.
4. Adjust stop pin to ½ inch and coat outside of grommet with suitable lubricant.
5. Place a new grommet on the stop pin and force it into the lever hole, then turn grommet several times to ensure it is properly seated.
6. Readjust stop pin to proper height, **Fig. 8**, coating ends of rods with suitable lubricant.
7. With pin height properly adjusted, position rod on tool and force rod into grommet until groove in rod seats on inner retaining lip of grommet. **Use grommet tool No. T84P-7341-B for limited work space applications.**

VALVE BODY, REPLACE

Some models may require removal of interfering exhaust system components to gain access to control valve body.

1. Raise and support vehicle, drain transmission fluid, then remove transmission pan, gasket and filter.
2. Remove detent spring retaining bolt, then the spring.
3. Remove valve body to case retaining bolts, then the valve body.
4. Reverse procedure to install, noting the following:
   a. Use suitable guide pins to align valve body to case.
   b. **Torque** valve body-to-case retaining bolts to 6.5-8.1 ft. lbs.
   c. **Torque** detent spring retaining bolt to 6.5-8.1 ft. lbs.
   d. **Torque** filter retaining bolts to 6.5-8.1 ft. lbs.
   e. **Torque** oil pan retaining bolts to 6-9 ft. lbs.

OVERDRIVE SERVO ASSEMBLY, REPLACE

1. Remove valve body as previously described.

2. Compress overdrive servo piston cover with a suitable tool, then remove snap ring retainer.
3. Using servo piston removal tool No. T80L-77030-B or equivalent, apply compressed air to servo piston release passage and remove the overdrive servo piston cover and spring. Remove piston from cover, then the rubber seal from piston and cover.
4. Install new servo piston and cover seals on the servo piston and cover.
5. Lubricate all seals, piston and piston bore with transmission fluid.
6. Install servo piston into cover, then the return spring into servo piston.
7. Install overdrive piston assembly into overdrive servo bore.
8. Compress overdrive piston using suitable tool, then install snap ring retainer.
9. Install valve body, filter, pan and gasket. Refill transmission to proper fluid level.

LOW-REVERSE SERVO ASSEMBLY, REPLACE

1. Refer to "Overdrive Servo Assembly, Replace" procedure for replacement. Apply compressed air to the servo piston release passage to remove servo piston from case. **Low-reverse servo piston is under spring pressure. Use caution when removing servo piston cover.**

3-4 ACCUMULATOR PISTON, REPLACE

1. Remove valve body as previously described.
2. Compress 3-4 accumulator piston cover, then remove snap ring retainer.
3. Release cover slowly, then remove piston cover, return spring and piston. Some models do not use a spring.
4. Remove seal from 3-4 accumulator cover and piston and inspect for damage and wear.
5. install new seals on 3-4 accumulator cover, if necessary. Lubricate cover pocket of case with transmission fluid.
6. Install 3-4 accumulator piston and return spring into case, then the cover.
7. Compress cover using suitable tool, then install snap ring. Ensure cover is reseated snugly against snap ring.
8. Install valve body, filter, pan and gas-

ket. Refill transmission pan to proper fluid level.

2–3 ACCUMULATOR PISTON, REPLACE

1. Refer to "3–4 Accumulator Piston, Replace" procedure for replacement.

EXTENSION HOUSING, REPLACE

1. Raise and support vehicle.
2. Disconnect parking brake cable from equalizer, if necessary.
3. Disconnect driveshaft from rear axle flange, then remove driveshaft from transmission.
4. Disconnect speedometer cable from extension housing.
5. Remove engine rear support to extension housing retaining bolts, then the reinforcement plate if equipped.
6. Support transmission with suitable jack and raise transmission enough to remove weight from rear engine support.
7. Remove engine rear support from crossmember, then lower transmission and remove extension housing retaining bolts. Slide extension housing from output shaft and allow fluid to drain.
8. Reverse procedure to install.

GOVERNOR, REPLACE

1. Remove extension housing as outlined above. **If governor body only is being removed, proceed to step 4.**
2. Remove governor to output shaft retaining snap ring.
3. Remove governor assembly from output shaft using suitable tool. Remove governor drive ball.
4. Remove governor to counterweight retaining screws. Remove governor from counterweight.
5. Reverse procedure to install.

SHIFT LINKAGE, REPLACE

It may be necessary to remove fan shroud retaining bolts and position shroud out of way on models that necessitate lowering transmission to gain access to manual lever.
1. Raise and support vehicle.
2. Remove interfering exhaust components and/or lower transmission as necessary.
3. Apply penetrating oil to outer throttle lever retaining nut to prevent breaking inner throttle lever.
4. Grasp outer throttle lever and hold firmly, then remove outer throttle lever retaining nut and lock washer and position lever and TV rod or cable assembly out of way.
5. Carefully disconnect manual rod from transmission manual lever at transmission using shift linkage grommet removal tool No. T84P-7341-A or equivalent.
6. Remove oil pan, gasket and filter.
7. Remove manual lever detent spring and roller assembly.
8. Remove manual lever retaining pin by carefully prying with sharp narrow

screwdriver.
9. Note assembled position of TV lever torsion spring, then remove spring.
10. Slide a 5/8 inch box wrench over inner manual lever close to bottom of lever, not allowing wrench to contact "rooster comb" area, and, using 21 mm wrench, remove manual lever retaining nut. Hold inner manual lever securely with box wrench while applying break torque to manual lever retaining nut.
11. Remove outer manual lever from case.
12. Remove inner throttle lever and shaft assembly.
13. Remove inner manual lever and park pawl actuating rod assembly.
14. Disconnect park pawl actuating rod from inner manual assembly.
15. Remove and discard manual lever oil seal.
16. Reverse procedure to install, then adjust manual and throttle linkages.

TRANSMISSION
REPLACE

EXCEPT MARK VIII

1. Disconnect battery ground cable, then raise and support vehicle.
2. Starting at rear of oil pan and working toward the front, loosen bolts and allow fluid to drain. Remove remaining oil pan bolts except for two at front of oil pan. After fluid has been drained, install two bolts onto rear side of pan.
3. Remove converter drain plug access cover from lower end of converter housing.
4. Remove converter-to-flywheel retaining nuts.
5. Turn converter until drain plug is accessible. Remove plug and drain fluid.
6. Install converter drain plug.
7. **On Cougar and Thunderbird,** remove catalytic converter assembly, then body reinforcement.
8. Remove exhaust pipe and muffler assembly.
9. **On all models,** mark rear driveshaft yoke and companion flange so driveshaft can be installed to its original position. Remove driveshaft assembly.
10. Position a suitable plug into extension housing to prevent fluid leakage.
11. Remove starter motor and disconnect neutral start switch electrical connector.
12. Remove rear mount-to-crossmember and two crossmember-to-frame bolts.
13. Remove engine rear support-to-extension housing bolts, then disconnect TV linkage rod from transmission TV lever and manual rod from manual lever at transmission.
14. Remove bolts securing bellcrank bracket to converter housing.
15. Using a suitable jack, raise transmission and remove crossmember from side supports. Disconnect and remove any interfering exhaust system components.
16. Lower transmission and disconnect

oil cooler lines from transmission.
17. Disconnect speedometer cable from extension housing.
18. Lower transmission to gain access to oil cooler lines, then disconnect each oil line.
19. Remove bolt and transmission filler tube from transmission.
20. Secure transmission to jack using a suitable chain.
21. Remove converter housing-to-cylinder block bolts.
22. Carefully move transmission and converter assembly away from engine and at the same time, lower jack to permit the transmission to clear the underside of vehicle.
23. Reverse procedure to install, noting the following:
   a. Lubricate converter pilot with chassis grease prior to installation.
   b. **Torque** converter drain plug to 8–28 ft. lbs.
   c. **Torque** engine-to-transmission bolts to 40–50 ft. lbs.
   d. **Torque** oil cooler lines to 18–23 ft. lbs.
   e. **Torque** crossmember-to-side support retaining bolts to 70–100 ft. lbs.
   f. **Torque** converter-to-flywheel retaining nuts to 20–34 ft. lbs.
   g. **Torque** converter housing access cover retaining bolts to 12–16 ft. lbs.

MARK VIII

1. Disconnect battery ground cable, then raise and support vehicle.
2. Mark driveshaft and rear axle housing.
3. Remove driveshaft and rear axle housing, then remove four bolts retaining driveshaft assembly to rear axle.
4. Remove catalytic converter inlet pipe, then lower muffler, resonator and tailpipe assembly.
5. Loosen retaining bolts to rear axle housing, then lower housing enough for driveshaft clearance.
6. Slide driveshaft out of transmission and position over rear axle housing.
7. Disconnect transmission shift selector mounting bracket.
8. Disconnect wiring harness electrical connector mounted on crossmember.
9. Remove transmission oil inlet tube.
10. Remove starter motor.
11. Position drain pan under transmission, then drain fluid and converter.
12. Position transmission assembly on suitable jack.
13. Remove crossmember assembly.
14. Remove four converter-to-flywheel retaining nuts, then lower transmission slightly and remove two top housing bolts.
15. Using a suitable jack, raise transmission and remove remaining transmission housing bolts.
16. Loosen EGR tube retaining nut on LH converter and position aside.
17. Remove transmission from vehicle.
18. Remove transmission pad from LH side of converter using a hacksaw.
19. Reverse procedure to install.

TIGHTENING SPECIFICATIONS

Component	Torque/Ft. Lbs.
Converter Housing Access Cover	12–16
Converter Plug To Converter	8–28
Converter To Flywheel	20–34
Detent Spring Attaching Bolt	80–120 ①
Extension Housing To Case	16–20
Filter To Valve Body	80–120 ①
Front Pump To Case	10–20
Governor Body Cover To Governor Body	20–30 ①
Governor Body To Counterweight	50–60 ①
Inner Manual Lever To Shaft	19–27
Neutral Start Switch To Case	8–11
Oil Pan To Case	6–10
Outer Throttle Lever To Shaft	12–16
Pressure Plug To Case	6–12
Push Connect Fitting To Case	18–23
Reinforcing Plate To Valve Body	80–120 ①
Stator Support To Pump Body	12–16
Transmission To Engine	40–50
Valve Body To Case	80–100 ①

① —Inch lbs.

Ford ATX (FLC) Automatic Transaxle

INDEX

APPLICATION CHART

Year	Car Model	Trans. Model
1992	Tempo & Topaz	PMA
1993-94	Tempo & Topaz	PMA

IDENTIFICATION

The transaxle identification tag is located near the valve body (upper) cover, **Fig. 1**.

DESCRIPTION

TRANSAXLE

This transaxle, **Fig. 2**, combines a three-speed automatic transaxle and a differential to form a single powertrain component. Both are housed in a compact, one-piece case. When installed in the vehicle, the engine/transaxle assembly is mounted transversely with the ATX on the lefthand side of the engine compartment.

This transaxle uses a torque converter, a compound planetary gear set, one band, a single one-way clutch, and three friction clutches, **Fig. 3**. These components are applied as necessary to transmit engine torque through a compound planetary gearset. The gearset provides three forward gear ratios and one reverse. The planetary gearset transmits engine torque to the input gear which meshes with the idler gear. Meshing with the idler gear is the final drive (output) gear which is riveted to the differential case. When powerflow reaches the differential, engine torque flows outward to the wheels through the differential gears.

BRAKE SHIFT INTERLOCK

A brake shift interlock system is installed on all Tempo and Topaz models. This device is to prevent shifting the transaxle out of the Park position unless the brake pedal is first depressed.

The system consists of a solenoid assembly attached to the key interlock assembly, a bracket retaining the solenoid, and the necessary wiring. The solenoid is energized when the ignition switch is turned to the On position, locking the shifter in the Park position. When the brake pedal is depressed and the stop lamp switch is activated, the shift lock solenoid is deactivated and the shifter can be moved out of the Park position.

TORQUE CONVERTER

In a standard torque converter, engine torque is transferred to the transaxle through the oil contained in the torque converter. The converter acts as an automatic clutch with the engine mechanically driving the impeller which, in turn, drives the turbine hydraulically. The hydraulically driven turbine is the transaxle drive input member. It is the hydraulic connection between the impeller and the turbine where a certain amount of engine torque is lost to converter slip.

To minimize this converter inefficiency, the ATX converter contains a splitter gear to provide a mechanical connection between the engine and transaxle. The splitter gearset is very similar to a planetary gear set.

Fluid Link Coupling (FLC)

This type of torque converter has a fluid coupling which connects the engine to the

Fig. 1   Transaxle identification tag

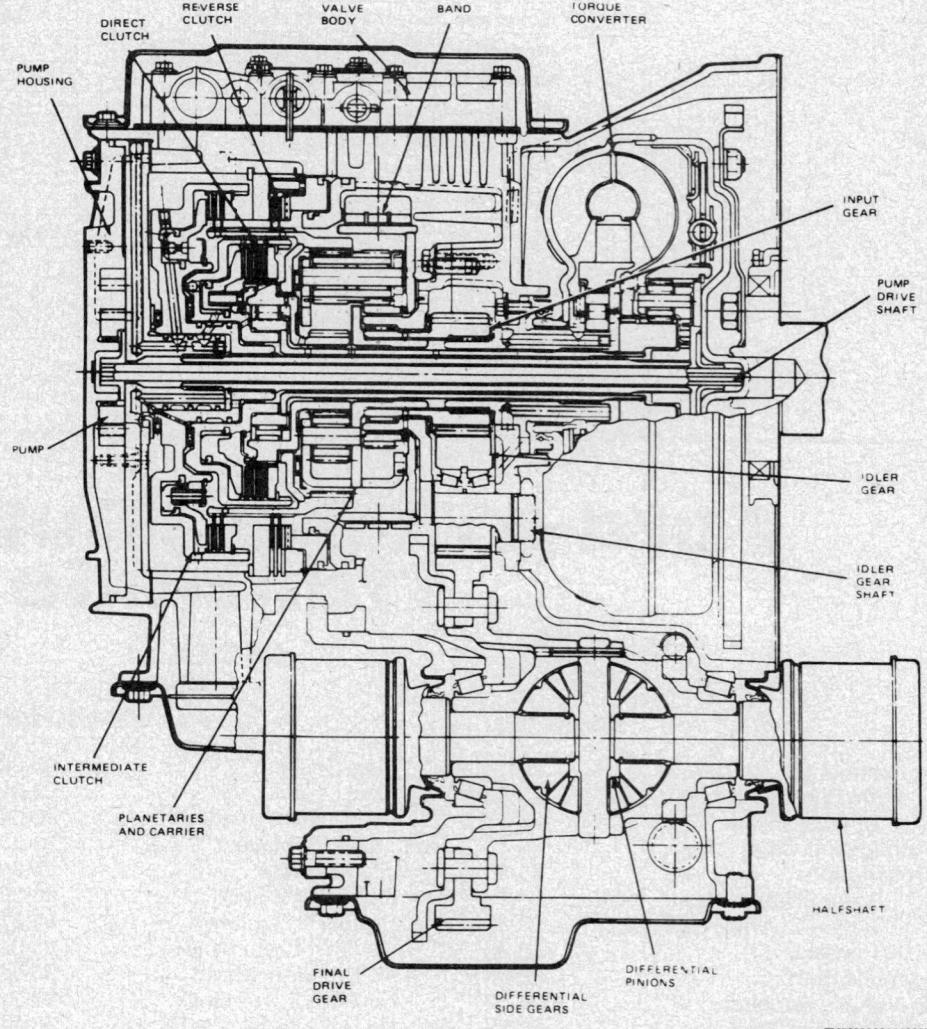

Fig. 2   ATX (FLC) transaxle

geartrain. In certain operating conditions, it multiplies torque by providing an extra reduction to match the engine output to the driveshaft.

All gear ranges with the FLC, engine torque is 100 percent hydraulically transmitted.

TROUBLESHOOTING

SLOW INITIAL ENGAGEMENT

1. Improper fluid level.

2. Damaged or improperly adjusted manual linkage.
3. Incorrect throttle valve linkage adjustment.
4. Contaminated fluid.
5. Improper clutch or band application or oil control pressure.
6. Dirt in valve body.

ROUGH INITIAL ENGAGEMENT IN FORWARD OR REVERSE

1. Improper fluid level.

	Band	Direct Clutch	Interm. Clutch	Reverse Clutch	Interm. One-Way Clutch
1st Gear Manual Low	Applied	Applied			Holding
2nd Gear Manual Low	Applied		Applied		
1st Gear (Drive)	Applied				Holding
2nd Gear (Drive)	Applied		Applied		
3rd Gear (Drive		Applied	Applied		
Reverse (R)		Applied		Applied	Holding
Neutral (N)					Holding
Park (P)					Holding

FM5028800357000X

Fig. 3 Band application chart

2. Engine idle too high.
3. Automatic choke closed on warm engine.
4. Play in halfshafts, constant velocity joints or engine mounts.
5. Improper clutch or band application or oil control pressure.
6. Incorrect throttle valve linkage adjustment.
7. Dirt in valve body.

NO DRIVE, ANY GEAR
1. Improper fluid level.
2. Damaged or improperly adjusted manual linkage.
3. Improper clutch or band application or oil control pressure.
4. Internal leak.
5. Loose valve body.
6. Damaged or worn clutches or bands.
7. Valve body sticking or dirty.

NO DRIVE IN 1, 2 OR D
1. Improper fluid level.
2. Damaged or improperly adjusted manual linkage.
3. Improper one-way clutch or band application.
4. Incorrect oil pressure.
5. Damaged or worn band, servo or clutches.
6. Loose valve body.
7. Valve body sticking or dirty.

NO REVERSE OR SLIPS IN REVERSE
1. Improper fluid level.
2. Damaged or improperly adjusted manual linkage.
3. Play in halfshafts, constant velocity joints or engine mounts.
4. Improper oil pressure control.
5. Damaged or worn reverse clutch.
6. Loose valve body.
7. Valve body sticking or dirty.

ROUGH 1-2 UPSHIFT
1. Improper fluid level.
2. Improper throttle valve linkage adjustment.
3. Incorrect engine idle or performance.
4. Improper intermediate clutch application.
5. Improper oil control pressure.
6. Valve body sticking or dirty.

ROUGH 2-3 UPSHIFT
1. Improper fluid level.
2. Incorrect engine performance.
3. Improper band release or direct clutch application.
4. Improper oil control pressure.
5. Valve body sticking or dirty.
6. Damaged or worn servo release and direct clutch piston check ball.
7. Improper throttle valve linkage adjustment.

ROUGH 3-2 DOWNSHIFT AT CLOSED THROTTLE IN D
1. Improper fluid level.
2. Incorrect engine idle or performance.
3. Improper throttle valve linkage adjustment.
4. Improper band or clutch application.
5. Improper oil control pressure.
6. Improper governor operation.
7. Valve body sticking or dirty.

NO FORCED DOWNSHIFTS
1. Improper fluid level.
2. Improper clutch or band application.
3. Improper oil control pressure.
4. Damaged internal kickdown linkage.
5. Throttle valve linkage improperly adjusted.
6. Valve body sticking or dirty.
7. Dirty or sticking governor.

DOWNSHIFT RUNAWAY
1. Improper fluid level.
2. Throttle valve linkage improperly adjusted.
3. Band improperly adjusted.
4. Improper band or clutch application.
5. Improper oil control pressure.
6. Damaged or worn servo.
7. Glazed band or drum.
8. Valve body sticking or dirty.

NO ENGINE BRAKING IN 1
1. Improper fluid level.
2. Throttle valve linkage improperly adjusted.
3. Damaged or improperly adjusted manual linkage.
4. Improperly adjusted band or clutch.
5. Improper oil control pressure.
6. Glazed band or drum.
7. Valve body sticking or dirty.

NO ENGINE BRAKING IN 2
1. Improper fluid level.
2. Throttle valve linkage improperly adjusted.
3. Manual linkage improperly adjusted.
4. Improper band or clutch application.
5. Improper oil control system.
6. Leaking servo.
7. Glazed band or drum.

NO START IN PARK OR NEUTRAL
1. Neutral start switch improperly adjusted.
2. Neutral start wire damaged.
3. Manual linkage improperly adjusted.

NO DRIVE OR SLIPS IN D
1. Damaged or worn one-way clutch.
2. Improper fluid level.
3. Damaged or worn band.
4. Incorrect throttle valve linkage adjustment.

NO DRIVE OR SLIPS IN 2
1. Improper fluid level.
2. Incorrect throttle valve linkage adjustment.
3. Damaged or worn intermediate friction clutch.
4. Improper clutch application.
5. Internal leakage.
6. Valve body dirty or sticking.
7. Band or drum glazed.

TAKE OFF IN 2ND OR 3RD
1. Improper fluid level.
2. Damaged or improperly adjusted manual linkage.
3. Improper band or clutch application.
4. Damaged or worn governor.
5. Loose valve body.
6. Valve body sticking or dirty.
7. Leaks between valve body and case mating surface.

INCORRECT SHIFT POINTS
1. Improper fluid level.
2. Throttle valve linkage improperly adjusted.
3. Improper clutch or band application.
4. Improper oil control pressure.
5. Damaged or worn governor.
6. Valve body dirty or sticking.

NO UPSHIFT IN D
1. Improper fluid level.
2. Throttle valve linkage improperly adjusted.
3. Improper band or clutch application.
4. Improper oil control pressure.
5. Damaged or worn governor.
6. Valve body sticking or dirty.

SHIFT 1-3 IN D
1. Improper fluid level.
2. Damaged or worn intermediate friction clutch.
3. Improper clutch application.
4. Improper oil control pressure.
5. Valve body sticking or dirty.

RUNAWAY UPSHIFTS
1. Improper fluid level.
2. Improper band or clutch application.

3. Improper oil pressure.
4. Damaged or worn direct clutch or servo.
5. Valve body sticking or dirty.

DELAYED 1-2 SHIFT

1. Improper fluid level.
2. Improper engine performance.
3. Improper throttle valve linkage adjustment.
4. Improper intermediate clutch application.
5. Improper oil control pressure.
6. Damaged intermediate clutch.
7. Valve body sticking or dirty.

MAINTENANCE

FLUID CHECK

To check fluid level, apply parking brake, operate engine at idle speed with vehicle on level surface and transaxle in Park position. Add fluid as necessary to bring mark on dipstick between "Add" and "Full" marks.

FLUID CHANGE

Fluid and filter changes are not required for average passenger car use. Severe usage such as commercial use or prolonged periods of idling require fluid and filter be changed every 30,000 miles. Whenever changing or adding fluid ensure that manufacturer recommended automatic transaxle fluid is used.

1. Raise and support vehicle.
2. Loosen transaxle oil pan attaching bolts and allow fluid to drain.
3. Remove oil pan and clean thoroughly.
4. Install new gasket onto pan, then the pan onto transaxle.
5. Fill transaxle to correct fluid level, then operate engine at idle. With parking brake applied, move selector lever to each position. Place lever in Park position and check fluid level with engine at operating temperature. Add fluid as necessary.

ADJUSTMENTS

SHIFT LINKAGE

1. Position selector lever in Drive position against rearward stop.
2. Raise and support vehicle, then loosen manual lever to control cable retaining nut, or adjusting bolt.
3. Position transaxle manual lever at second detent from most rearward position. This is Drive position.
4. **Torque** attaching nut to 10-15 ft. lbs.
5. Lower vehicle and check for proper operation of transaxle in each selector lever position.

THROTTLE LINKAGE

The TV linkage adjustment is pre-set at the factory. Any time the engine, transaxle or throttle linkage components are removed, it is recommended that the TV linkage adjustment be reset after component installation or replacement.

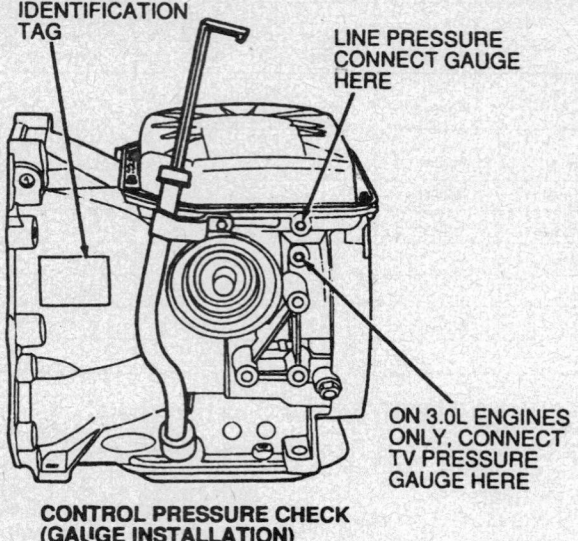

CONTROL PRESSURE CHECK (GAUGE INSTALLATION)

FM5028800365000X

Fig. 4   Control pressure check gauge installation. 3.0L/V6-182

2.3L/4-140

1. Remove splash shield from cable retainer bracket.
2. Loosen trunnion bolt on TV rod.
3. Install plastic clip using TV Linkage Adjustment tool No. T91P-7000-A or equivalent to bottom of TV rod. Ensure clip keeps rod from telescoping.
4. Ensure TV return spring is connected between TV rod and retaining bracket, to hold transaxle TV lever at its idle position.
5. Ensure throttle lever is resting on throttle return control screw, then tighten trunnion bolt on TV rod.
6. Remove TV linkage adjustment tool (plastic clip) from TV rod.
7. Install splash shield. Check for proper operation.

3.0L/V6-182

External Cable

1. Remove throttle body linkage snow shield from cable retainer bracket.
2. Unsnap adjuster locking clip (white) at cable retainer bracket.
3. Hold transaxle lever in the idle position against idle stop.
4. Snap adjuster locking clip (white) into the lock position, then install splash shield.
5. Check linkage for proper operation.

Internal Cable

After external cable has been adjusted, adjust internal cable as follows:

1. Remove throttle body linkage snow shield.
2. Disengage TV adjustment tab. Hold throttle cam pulley on the throttle body and rotate from idle position to Wide Open Throttle (WOT) two times to remove any previously setting in the cable. Do not allow pulley to snap back from WOT position.
3. Using a long screwdriver, insert into

the notch of the transaxle outer TV lever. Hold the TV lever at the transaxle hard set position (towards dash panel) and secure TV adjustment tab by pushing it toward the cable.

4. After TV cable has been adjusted, the TV pressure should be checked as follows:
   a. Remove plug at transaxle TV pressure port shown in **Fig. 4**. TV pressure tap is not visible from above. The tap is located beneath the line pressure tap.
   b. Install a quick disconnect and a 0-100 psi (0-700 kPa) gauge, then start vehicle and place gear selector in drive.
   c. TV pressure should be within 0-5 psi (0-12 kPa) at idle. If zero (0) psi is read, verify gauge is functioning by moving throttle to increase engine RPM.
   d. If TV pressure is not within 0-5 psi, repeat adjustment procedure.
5. If TV pressure is still not 0-5 psi, perform the following procedure:
   a. Disconnect TV cable from transaxle TV lever. Push TV hard to set position. If TV pressure is within 0-5 psi, continue with following procedure. If TV pressure is not 0-5 psi, a line pressure test must be performed. Refer to MOTOR's Domestic Transmission Manual for further information.
   b. Inspect for proper TV cable routing.
   c. Inspect for proper installation of TV cable in TV bracket, ensure cable is secure in bracket and cable tabs are locked into the bracket.
   d. Inspect for proper installation of TV cable at the accelerator bracket.

IN-VEHICLE REPAIRS

VALVE BODY, REPLACE

1. Remove battery and battery tray.

2. Remove ignition coil.
3. Remove transaxle oil dipstick.
4. Disconnect all hoses and lines from air management valve, then remove the valve from transaxle valve body cover. Also, disconnect fuel evaporator hose from frame rail.
5. Disconnect neutral safety switch electrical connector.
6. Disconnect electrical connectors from fan motor and temperature sending unit.
7. Remove valve body cover bolts, then the valve body cover and gasket.
8. Remove valve body bolts, then the valve body and gasket.
9. Reverse procedure to install. Install guide pins to properly align valve body before tightening attaching bolts. One alignment pin may have to be temporarily removed to allow attachment of manual valve. Ensure roller on end of throttle valve plunger engages cam on end of throttle lever shaft. Refer to tightening sequence, **Fig. 5,** and **torque** valve body bolts to 6-8 ft. lbs. and valve body cover bolts to 7-9 ft. lbs.

GOVERNOR, REPLACE

1. Disconnect battery ground cable.
2. Remove air cleaner, then using a long screwdriver, remove governor cover retaining clip.
3. Remove governor cover and governor.
4. Reverse procedure to install, noting the following:
   a. Slide governor into place carefully. **Allow gear teeth to mesh, do not force into place.**

SERVO ASSEMBLY, REPLACE

1. Disconnect battery ground cable.
2. Disconnect electrical connectors from fan motor and temperature sending unit.
3. Disconnect FM capacitor wiring, if equipped.
4. Remove two fan shroud to radiator attaching nuts, then fan and fan shroud.
5. Remove filler tube to case attaching bolt, then rotate the filler tube and dipstick. **Do not remove tube from case.**
6. Remove lower left side front mount to case attaching bolt.
7. Remove servo cap and snap ring with snap ring removal tool No. T81P-70027A or equivalent.
8. Reverse procedure to install.

INTERLOCK CABLE

1. Hold shift knob securely and depress release button, then pull up on shift knob. Ensure that the spring loaded release button does not eject from shift knob rapidly.

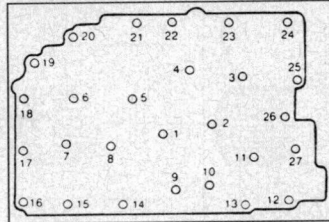

FM5028800409000X

Fig. 5   Valve body bolt tightening sequence

2. Remove console and bezel assembly.
3. Remove screw attaching cable to shifter housing.
4. Disconnect wire from cam plate, then remove retainer pin. Remove bracket from shifter.
5. Remove steering column shrouds, then loosen steering column retaining bolts. Lower the column.
6. Disconnect electrical connector from solenoid.
7. Remove screw retaining cable to steering column.
8. Pull back carpeting under the accelerator pedal, then remove the cable from the retainer clip.
9. Remove solenoid retainer bracket.
10. Remove the cable by pulling from under the carpeting at the shifter.
11. Feed cable forward under the carpet at the shifter until it appears under the accelerator pedal.
12. Pull through and guide up between the steering column support bolts.
13. Install solenoid into retainer bracket.
14. Clip the cable into retainer clip under the accelerator pedal at the cable ferrule.
15. Connect electrical connector to solenoid.
16. With the column on the floor, secure the housing to the column with screw.
17. Attach cable bracket to the shifter pivot pin, then secure with retainer pin.
18. With the shifter in the Park position, attach a wire to the cam plate slot, then secure the bracket to the shifter. **Torque** retaining screw to 25-35 inch. lbs.
19. Check interlock key and shifter operations.
20. Install steering column, shrouds, bezel assembly, console and shift knob.

TRANSAXLE
REPLACE

Due to transaxle case configuration on models equipped with 2.3L/4-140 engines, right hand halfshaft assembly must be removed first using Halfshaft removal tool No. D83P-4026-A or equivalent. The differential rotator tool No. T81P-4026-A or equivalent is then inserted into the transaxle to drive the left hand inboard CV joint assembly from the transaxle case.

1. Disconnect battery ground cable, then isolate cable end with electrical tape or equivalent.
2. Remove air cleaner assembly, then

disconnect electrical connector from neutral safety switch.
3. Disconnect throttle valve linkage (throttle cable on 3.0L/V6-182) and manual lever cable from transaxle levers. **Failure to disconnect linkage during transaxle removal, and allowing the transaxle to hang will fracture the TV cam shaft joint (located under the transaxle cover.**
4. Cover timing window in the converter to prevent contamination.
5. **On 2.3L/4-140 engine,** remove thermactor hose(s) retaining bolts. If equipped. **Position valve and hoses away from brake lines and master cylinder to avoid interference.**
6. Remove ground strap located above upper engine mount, then coil and bracket. If applicable.
7. **On all models,** remove two transaxle to engine upper bolts located below and to either side of distributor.
8. Install Three Bar Engine Support tool No. D88L-6000-A or equivalent, then raise and support vehicle.
9. Remove front wheel and tire assemblies.
10. Remove nut from control arm to steering knuckle bolt, on both sides of vehicle, then drive bolts out using punch and hammer. **The bolts and nuts must be discarded.**
11. Disconnect control arm from steering knuckle on both sides of vehicle using a pry bar, **Fig. 5.** Use care to **avoid damaging ball joint boot. Pry bar must not contact lower arm. Do not use hammer on knuckle to remove ball joints. Plastic splash shield behind rotor has pocket into which lower ball joint fits. When disconnecting lower control arm from knuckle, shield should be bent back to clear ball joint and avoid damaging the shield.**
12. Remove and discard stabilizer bar bracket bolts from both sides of vehicle.
13. Remove and discard stabilizer to control arm nut and washer from both sides of vehicle, then slide stabilizer bar out of control arms.
14. Remove brake hose routing clip attaching bolts from suspension strut bracket on both sides of vehicle.
15. Disconnect tie rod from steering knuckle on both sides of vehicle.
16. Pry halfshaft out of right side of transaxle and position shaft on transaxle housing. **If difficulty is encountered when prying halfshaft, remove transaxle oil pan and discard gasket. Insert a large blade screwdriver between differential pinion shaft and inboard CV joint stub shaft. Tap screwdriver handle to dislodge circlip from side gear and free halfshaft from differential. Prior to installation of the halfshaft, install a new circlip on inboard stub shaft. Also, use a new gasket when installing oil pan.**
17. Disengage left halfshaft from differential side gear using Differential Rotator tool No. T81P-4026-A or equivalent.

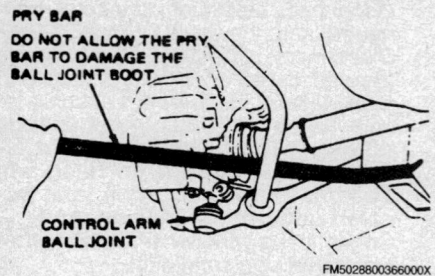

Fig. 6 Disengaging control arm from steering knuckle

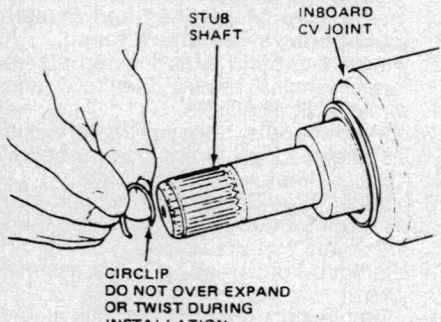

Fig. 7 CV stub shaft circlip replacement

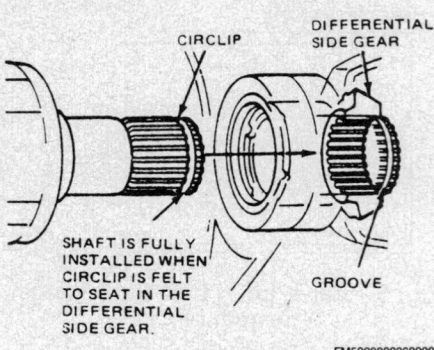

Fig. 8 Halfshaft seating

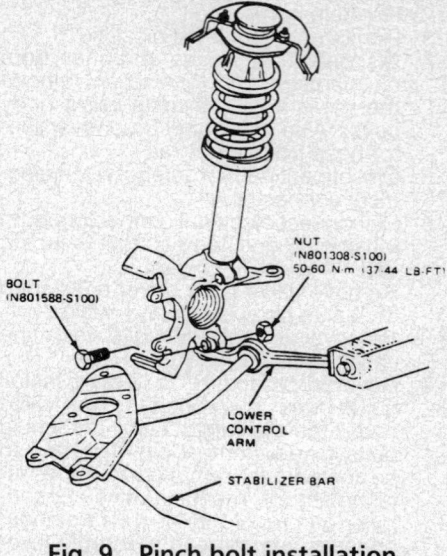

Fig. 9 Pinch bolt installation

18. Slide halfshaft out of transaxle and support end of shaft. **Do not allow end of driveshaft to hang unsupported, as damage to outboard CV joint may result.**
19. Install Transaxle Plugs part No. T81P-1177-B or equivalent into differential seals.
20. **On 2.3L/4-140 engine,** remove starter support bracket.
21. Remove two converter tube bracket retaining bolts, then one exhaust converter retaining bolt from starter.
22. Disconnect exhaust converter Air Injection Reaction (AIR) tubes.
23. **On all models,** disconnect starter motor from wiring harness, then remove starter motor.

24. **On 2.3L/4-140 engine,** remove transaxle support bracket.
25. **On all models,** remove torque converter housing dust cover.
26. Remove torque converter to flywheel attaching nuts. Rotate crankshaft as necessary to provide access to each nut.
27. Position Rotunda Hi-Lift Jack tool No. 014-00210 or equivalent under transaxle, then remove rear support bracket attaching nuts.
28. Remove left front body bracket attaching nuts and bolts and the bracket.
29. Disconnect upper transaxle cooler line using Cooler Line Disconnect tool No. T82L-9500-AH or equivalent. To remove lower cooler line, slide constant tension clamp off tube and remove hose.
30. Remove manual lever bracket attaching bolts from transaxle case.
31. Ensure engine is properly supported, then remove remaining transaxle to engine attaching bolts.
32. Insert a screwdriver between flywheel and torque converter and carefully move transaxle and converter away from engine. When converter studs

clear flywheel, lower transaxle two—three inches and disconnect speedometer cable.
33. **When lowering the transaxle away from the engine, watch the No. 1 insulator. If it contacts the body before the converter studs clear the flywheel, remove the insulator.** Lower transaxle and remove from vehicle.
34. Reverse procedure to install, noting the following:
   a. Replace circlip on CV joint stub shaft, **Fig. 7.** Avoid spreading circlip any more than necessary.
   b. When inserting halfshaft in transaxle, push CV joint into differential until circlip seats in side gear, **Fig. 8.** A rubber mallet may be used to tap the outboard CV joint stub shaft if necessary.
   c. When attaching lower ball joint to steering knuckle, use care to avoid damaging ball joint. Install new pinch bolt and nut, **Fig. 9,** and torque nut to 40-54 ft. lbs. Do not torque bolt.

TIGHTENING SPECIFICATIONS

Component	Torque/Ft. Lbs.
Converter Drain Plug	8–12
Cooler Tube Fitting To Case	18–23
Differential Retainer To Case	15–19
Filler Tube Bracket To Case	7–9
Filter To Case	7–9
Idler Shaft Attaching Nut	110–130
Inner Manual Lever To Shaft Nut	32–48
Neutral Safety Switch To Case	7–9
Oil Pan To Case	15–19

Component	Torque/Ft. Lbs.
Pressure Test Port Plugs To Case	8–11
Pump Assembly To Case	7–9
Pump Support To Pump Body	6–8
Reactor Support To Case	6–8
Separator Plate To Valve Body	6–8
Transfer Housing To Case	18–23
TV Adjuster Locknut	24–36
Valve Body Cover To Case	7–9
Valve Body To Case	7–9

Ford AXOD-E (AX4S) Automatic Overdrive Transaxle

INDEX

APPLICATION CHART

Year	Model	Model
1992–94	Continental, Sable & Taurus	AXOD-E (AX4S)

IDENTIFICATION

The identification tags, **Fig. 1**, located on top of the converter housing, includes transaxle assembly number, serial number and build date.

1992
3.0L/V6-182 .... PNA-AC
3.8L/V6-232 .... PNA-AA
3.8L/V6-232 .... PNA-AB
1993-94
3.0L/V6-182 .... PNA
3.2L/V6-195 .... PNA-EJ
3.8L/V6-232 .... PNA

DESCRIPTION

This automatic overdrive transaxle, **Fig. 2**, is a fully automatic transaxle with four forward speeds and one reverse, in addition to neutral and park.

The AXOD and AXOD-E (AX4S) transaxle has two planetary gear sets and a combination planetary/differential gear set. Four multiple plate clutches, two band assemblies and two one-way clutches.

A lockup torque converter is coupled to the engine crankshaft and transmits engine power to the gear train by means of a drive link assembly (chain) that connects the drive and driven sprockets. Converter clutch application is controlled through an electronic control integrated in the on-

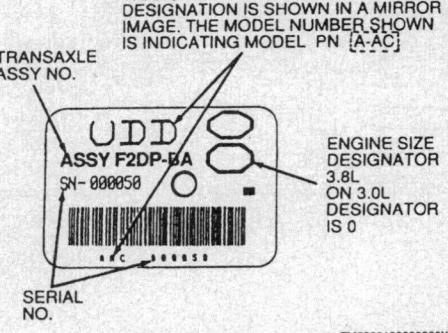

Fig. 1 Identification tag

board EEC-IV system, **Figs. 3 and 4**. These controls, along with the hydraulic controls in the valve body, operate a piston plate clutch in the torque converter to provide improved fuel economy by eliminating converter slip when applied.

TORQUE CONVERTER

Converter

The torque converter couples the engine to the turbine shaft. It also provides torque multiplication and absorbs engine shock of gear shifting.

Piston Plate Clutch & Damper Assembly

The piston plate clutch and damper assembly transmit engine power to the turbine from the converter cover during lockup.

Converter Cover

The converter cover transmits power from the engine into the converter. Also, the oil pump driveshaft is splined to the converter cover.

Turbine

The turbine is splined to the drive sprocket turbine shaft and driven by fluid by the impeller.

Impeller

The impeller is driven by the converter cover, together with the reactor it supplies torque multiplication.

Reactor

The reactor, also called the stator, contains a one-way clutch to hold it stationary only when "reaction" is required. It also causes hydraulic reaction during torque multiplication.

GEAR TRAIN

Forward Clutch

The forward clutch locks the driven sprocket to the low one-way clutch.

Low One-Way Clutch

The low one-way clutch transmits torque from the driven sprocket to the sun gear of the forward planetary gear set in first gear. It also provides engine braking in third gear in connection with the forward clutch.

Overdrive Band

The overdrive band holds the sun gear of the forward planetary gear set stationary in fourth gear (overdrive).

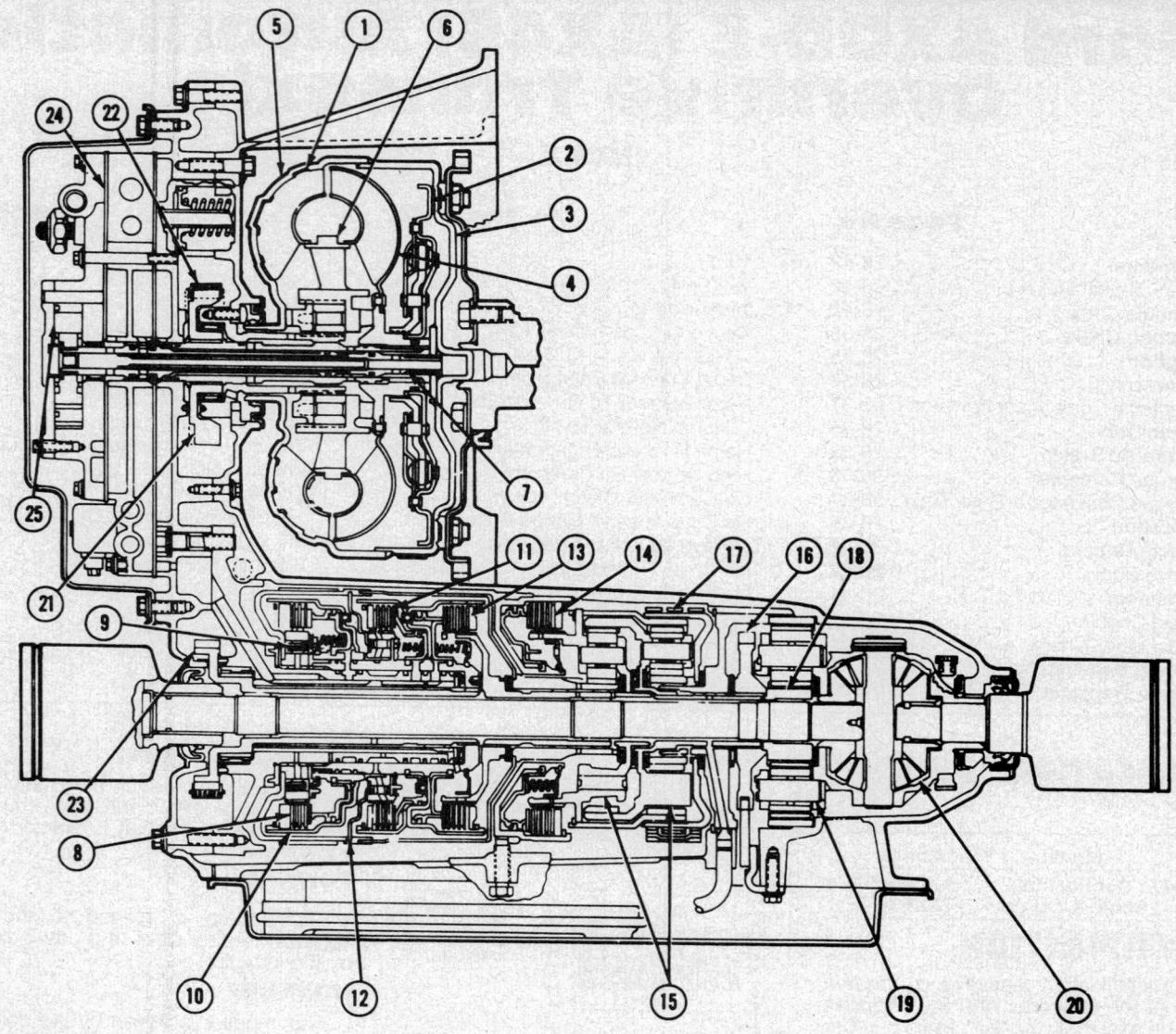

1. TORQUE CONVERTER	13. INTERMEDIATE CLUTCH
2. CONVERTER CLUTCH (PISTON PLATE CLUTCH AND DAMPER ASSEMBLY)	14. REVERSE CLUTCH
	15. PLANETARY GEARS
3. CONVERTER COVER	16. PARKING GEAR
4. TURBINE	17. LOW-INTERMEDIATE BAND
5. IMPELLER	18. FINAL DRIVE SUN GEAR
6. REACTOR	19. FINAL DRIVE PLANET
7. OIL PUMP DRIVESHAFT	20. DIFFERENTIAL ASSEMBLY
8. FORWARD CLUTCH	21. DRIVE SPROCKET
9. LOW ONE-WAY CLUTCH	22. DRIVE LINK ASSEMBLY (CHAIN)
10. OVERDRIVE BAND	23. DRIVEN SPROCKET
11. DIRECT CLUTCH	24. VALVE BODY (MAIN CONTROL ASSEMBLY)
12. DIRECT ONE-WAY CLUTCH	25. OIL PUMP

FM5028800007000X

Fig. 2   Cross-sectional view of Ford AXOD & AXOD-E (AX4S) automatic transaxle

Direct Clutch

The direct clutch locks the sun gear of the planetary assembly of the forward planetary gear set to the direct one-way clutch in third gear.

Direct One-Way Clutch

The direct one-way clutch transmits torque from the driven sprocket to the sun gear of the forward planetary gear set in third gear, and provides engine braking in manual low.

Intermediate Clutch

The intermediate clutch locks the driven sprocket to the planetary assembly of the forward planetary gear set in second and third gear.

Reverse Clutch

The reverse clutch holds the planetary assembly of the forward planetary gear set, and the ring gear of the rear planetary gear set stationary in reverse gear.

Planetary Gears

Two planetary gear sets are used to provide four forward speeds, including reverse, depending upon clutch and/or band applications.

CLUTCH AND BAND APPLICATION CHART

Gear	Lo-Int Band	Overdrive Band	Forward Clutch	Intermediate Clutch	Direct Clutch	Reverse Clutch	Low One-Way Clutch	Direct One-Way Clutch
1st Gear Manual Low	Applied		Applied		Applied		Applied	Applied
1st Gear (Drive)	Applied		Applied				Applied	
2nd Gear (Drive)	Applied		Applied	Applied			Holding	
3rd Gear (Drive)			Applied	Applied	Applied			
4th Gear (Overdrive)		Applied		Applied	Applied			Holding
Reverse (R)			Applied			Applied	Holding	
Neutral (N)								
Park (P)								

FM5028800008000X

Fig. 3   Clutch & band application chart. AXOD

Gear	Lo-Int Band	Overdrive Band	Forward Clutch	Intermediate Clutch	Direct Clutch	Reverse Clutch	Low One-Way Clutch	Direct One-Way Clutch
1st Gear Manual Low	Applied		Applied		Applied		Applied	Applied
1st Gear (Drive)	Applied		Applied				Applied	
2nd Gear (Drive)	Applied		Applied	Applied			Holding	
3rd Gear (Drive)				Applied	Applied			
4th Gear (Overdrive)		Applied		Applied	Applied			Holding
Reverse (R)			Applied			Applied	Applied	
Neutral (N)			Applied					
Park (P)			Applied					

FM5028800009000X

Fig. 4   Clutch & band application chart. AXOD-E (AX4S)

Parking Gear

The parking gear allows the output (axle) shaft to be mechanically locked by the parking pawl anchored in the case.

Low Intermediate Band

The low intermediate band holds the sun gear of the rear planetary gear set stationary in low, first and second gears.

Final Drive Sun Gear

The final drive sun gear transfers torque from the transaxle output to the final drive planetary assembly.

Final Drive Planet

The final drive planet drives the differential assembly.

Differential Assembly

The differential assembly drives the front axle shafts and provides the differential action if driving wheels are turning at different speeds.

TORQUE CONVERTER & GEAR TRAIN

Drive Sprocket

The drive sprocket transmits power from the converter to the drive link assembly (chain).

Drive Link Assembly (Chain)

The drive link assembly transmits converter power to the gear train.

Driven Sprocket

The driven sprocket transmits converter power to the geartrain.

HYDRAULIC SYSTEM

Valve Body

The valve body or main control assem-bly directs fluid (oil) under pressure to the torque converter, band servos, clutches and governor to control transaxle operation.

Oil Pump

The oil pump provides a supply of fluid (oil) under pressure to operate, lubricate and cool the transaxle. The pump is a variable capacity vane and rotor pump with output flow proportional to demand. It is located within the transaxle control valve and pump assembly.

Overdrive Servo

The overdrive servo applies overdrive band in fourth gear.

Low-Intermediate Servo

The low-intermediate servo applies low-intermediate band in manual, low, first and second gears.

Governor

The governor provides a "road speed" signal to the hydraulic control system for shift control, and is driven by a gear on the differential assembly.

Reservoir

Two reservoir areas are used to control oil level, dependent on fluid temperature. Along with the lower sump, a fluid reservoir is located in the lower section of the valve body cover. As fluid temperature in the reservoir increases, a thermostatic element closes, retaining fluid in the upper reservoir.

ELECTRICAL COMPONENT FUNCTION

AXOD

Neutral Pressure Switch (NPS)

The NPS signals the EEC-IV of transax-le engagement shift into "Reverse" or "Drive" for engine control functions.

3/2 Pressure Switch

The 3/2 pressure switch signals the EEC-IV of hydraulic transaxle gear shifts for bypass clutch solenoid control. Detects 3-2 shift.

4/3 Pressure Switch

The 4/3 pressure switch signals the EEC-IV of hydraulic transaxle gear shifts for bypass clutch solenoid control. Detects 4-3 shift.

Bypass Clutch Solenoid

The bypass clutch solenoid applies the torque converter bypass clutch when energized or releases it when deenergized.

Transmission Temperature Switch

The transmission temperature switch signals the EEC-IV of transmission oil temperature and provides additional converter lock-up operation to protect the transaxle when transaxle temperatures exceed 275°F.

AXOD-E (AX4S)

Turbine Speed Sensor

The turbine speed sensor is a variable reluctance sensor used with the vehicle electronic control system. The sensor, along with a rotating exciter wheel on the driven sprocket, sends a signal to the EEC-IV microprocessor. The EEC-IV reads this signal and reacts to the speed information it transmits by controlling the clutch application.

Shift Control Solenoid

The shift control solenoids provide proper operating gear selection and are controlled by the EEC-IV. There are three shift control solenoids in the AXOD-E (AX4S). They are three port, normally open feed to control the flow of oil to a hydraulic spool valve.

Transmission Oil Temperature Sensor

The transmission oil temperature sensor informs the EEC-IV of transaxle oil temperature. It is a thermister whose resistance varies according to temperature.

Variable Force Solenoid

The variable force solenoid is an analog pressure regulator that varies transaxle line pressure as directed by the microprocessor.

Modulated Lock-Up Solenoid Or Modulated Converter Clutch Control

The solenoid receives an electronic signal from the EEC-IV microprocessor and uses this information to vary pressure which sets the slip in the converter clutch.

DOWNSHIFTS

Under certain conditions the transaxle will downshift automatically to a lower gear range without moving the shift selector lever. There are three different types of downshift categories:

Coastdown

The coastdown downshift occurs when vehicle is coasting down to a stop.

Torque Demand

The torque demand downshift occurs during part throttle acceleration when the demand for torque is greater than the engine can provide at that gear ratio. The transaxle will disengage the converter clutch to provide added acceleration, if applied.

Kickdown

The kickdown downshift occurs when the accelerator pedal is depressed fully to the floor. A forced downshift into second gear is possible below 55 mph. Below approximately 25 mph a forced kickdown to first gear will occur. All shift speed specifications will vary due to tire size and engine calibration requirements.

TROUBLESHOOTING

OIL LEAK

1. Side or bottom pan attaching bolts incorrectly torqued.
2. Side or bottom pan gasket or pan rail damaged.
3. Side or bottom pan distorted.
4. TV cable, fill tube or electrical connector loose or damaged.
5. Manual shaft seal damaged.
6. Governor, speedometer and servo cover O-ring seal damaged.
7. Cooler fittings or pressure taps incorrectly torqued or damaged.
8. Converter hub scored or weld seal leaking.
9. Cooler or converter seal damaged or garter spring missing.
10. Halfshaft seals damaged or garter spring missing.
11. Speedometer cable or speed sensor O-ring seal damaged.
12. Turbine speed sensor O-ring seal damaged.

OIL VENTING OR FOAMING

1. Transaxle overfilled.
2. Transaxle fluid contaminated with antifreeze or engine overheating.
3. Bi-metallic element stuck open.
4. Oil filter O-ring damaged.

HIGH OR LOW OIL PRESSURE

AXOD

1. Incorrect oil level.
2. TV cable/linkage stuck or damaged.
3. Pressure regulator spring damaged.
4. Pressure regulator valve or valve bore nicked or scored.
5. Pressure relief valve damaged or relief valve ball and/or spring missing.
6. Oil pump slide stuck.
7. Oil pump seals and/or vanes damaged.
8. Oil pump driveshaft broken or damaged.

AXOD-E (AX4S)

1. Incorrect oil level.
2. EPC solenoid inoperative.
3. Pressure regulator spring damaged.
4. Pressure regulator valve or valve bore nicked or scored.
5. Throttle position sensor (TPS) out of range.
6. Oil pump seals and/or vanes damaged.
7. Oil pump driveshaft broken or damaged.

NO FORWARD ENGAGEMENT

Refer to "No Forward Engagement" in the "Service Bulletins" section.

1. Improper fluid level, low.
2. Worn, damaged and/or improperly assembled driveshafts.
3. Shift linkage damaged or improperly adjusted.
4. Low forward clutch pressure, low line pressure, low intermediate clutch pressure, low EPC pressure.
5. Oil filter or filter seal plugged or damaged.
6. 3-4 shift valve, main regulator valve, forward clutch control valve, manual control valve, 2-3 servo regulator valve-stuck, damaged. These valves are located in the main control valve body.
7. Oil pump assembly loose and/or gasket damaged. Oil pump case porosity/cross leaks.
8. Driven sprocket support assembly loose and/or seal damaged.
9. Forward clutch piston cracked and/or friction elements damaged or worn.
10. Overrunning clutch assembly (planetary) worn, damaged or improperly assembled.
11. Low intermediate servo piston seal worn or damaged.
12. Low intermediate servo apply rod length incorrect.
13. Output shaft splines damaged.

NO 1-2 SHIFT (FIRST GEAR ONLY)

AXOD

1. Governor assembly weights binding.
2. Governor assembly springs and gears damaged.
3. Governor shaft seal missing or damaged.
4. Governor valve (ball) stuck or missing.
5. Governor tube leaking or damaged.
6. Intermediate clutch plates damaged or missing.
7. Intermediate clutch assembly piston or seals damaged.
8. Intermediate clutch check ball assembly stuck or missing.
9. Intermediate clutch cylinder damaged.
10. Direct-intermediate clutch hub seals damaged or missing.
11. Direct-intermediate clutch hub holes blocked.
12. Driven sprocket support seals damaged or missing.

13. Driven sprocket support holes blocked.
14. 1-2 shift valve stuck, nicked or damaged.
15. 1-2 throttle delay valve stuck, nicked or damaged.
16. 1-2 accumulator capacity modulator valve stuck, nicked or damaged.
17. Number 9 check ball missing.
18. Control assembly attaching bolts incorrectly torqued.
19. Carrier damaged.
20. Intermediate clutch tap plug loose or missing.

AXOD-E (AX4S)

1. EEC-IV microprocessor damaged.
2. Shift solenoid No. 1 wiring short or open.
3. Main regulator valve stuck, nicked or damaged.
4. 1-2 shift valve stuck, nicked or damaged.
5. Intermediate clutch shuttle valve stuck, nicked or damaged.
6. 1-2 capacity modulator valve stuck, nicked or damaged.
7. No. 10 check ball missing or damaged.
8. Control assembly bolts improperly torqued.
9. Intermediate clutch tap plug loose or missing.
10. Driven sprocket support seals damaged or missing or holes are blocked.
11. Intermediate clutch assembly clutch plates damaged or missing.
12. Intermediate clutch assembly wave spring damaged or missing.
13. Intermediate clutch assembly piston or seals damaged.
14. Intermediate clutch assembly ball check assembly stuck, damaged or missing.
15. Intermediate clutch assembly clutch cylinder damaged.
16. Direct/intermediate clutch hub seals damaged or missing or holes blocked.
17. Front carrier damaged.

NO MANUAL 2ND GEAR

3.2L/V6—195 SHO

1. Electrical inputs/outputs, vehicle wiring harness, PCM and shift solenoids.
2. Shift linkage/cable, MLP sensor-damaged or improperly adjusted.
3. Main control valve body retaining bolts loose.
4. Main control valve body gaskets improperly positioned.
5. Main control valve body valves stuck or improperly assembled.
6. Shift solenoids stuck or damaged.
7. Clutch assembly stuck, damaged or improperly assembled.
8. Drive sprocket support assembly seals damaged, missing or holes blocked.
9. Low one-way clutch assembly, not overrunning, damaged.
10. Low intermediate band worn, burnt damaged or improperly assembled.

1-2 SHIFT FEELS HARSH OR SOFT

1. Incorrect oil pressure.
2. 1-2 accumulator regulator valve stuck, nicked or damaged.
3. 1-2 accumulator regulator valve spring missing or damaged.
4. 1-2 accumulator capacity modulator valve stuck, nicked or damaged.
5. 1-2 accumulator capacity modulator valve spring missing or damaged.
6. 1-2 accumulator assembly piston stuck or damaged.
7. 1-2 accumulator assembly seal damaged or missing.
8. 1-2 accumulator assembly springs damaged or missing.
9. **On AXOD-E (AX4S) transaxles,** No. 12 check ball missing.
10. **On AXOD-E (AX4S) transaxles,** EPC solenoid inoperative.
11. **On AXOD-E (AX4S) transaxles,** EEC-IV microprocessor inoperative.

1-2 SHIFT SPEED HIGH OR LOW

AXOD

1. Governor weights binding.
2. Governor springs and gear damaged.
3. Governor shaft seal or valve stuck or missing.
4. Governor tube leaking or damaged.
5. TV control valve, TV plunger, TV line modulator valve and 1-2 throttle delay valve stuck, nicked or damaged.
6. TV control valve, TV plunger, TV line modulator valve and 1-2 throttle delay valve springs missing or damaged.

AXOD-E (AX4S)

1. Vehicle speed sensor inoperative.
2. Speedometer gear incorrect or missing gear.
3. 1-2 shift valve and intermediate clutch shuttle valve stuck, nicked or damaged.
4. 1-2 shift valve and intermediate clutch shuttle valve spring missing or damaged.

NO 2-3 SHIFT (1-2 SHIFT OK)

1. Governor weights binding.
2. Governor springs and gear damaged.
3. Governor shaft seal or valve stuck or missing.
4. Governor tube leaking or missing.
5. Low-intermediate servo apply rod too long.
6. Low-intermediate servo bore or piston damaged.
7. Low-intermediate servo piston seals damaged or missing.
8. Low-intermediate servo return spring or retaining clip missing or broken
9. Direct clutch plates damaged or missing.
10. Direct clutch piston or seals damaged.
11. Direct clutch check ball assembly stuck or missing.
12. Direct clutch cylinder damaged.
13. Direct-intermediate clutch hub seals damaged or missing.
14. Direct-intermediate clutch hub holes blocked.
15. Driven sprocket support seals damaged or missing.
16. Driven sprocket support holes blocked.
17. Direct one-way clutch assembly cage, rollers or springs damaged.
18. Direct one-way clutch assembly rollers missing.
19. Direct one-way clutch assembly inner race improperly assembled.
20. Control assembly attaching bolts incorrectly torqued.
21. 2-3 shift valve stuck, nicked or damaged.
22. Number 4 check ball missing.
23. Bypass solenoid not energized during wide open throttle upshift.
24. Case servo release passage blocked.
25. Servo release tube leaking or improperly installed.
26. Direct clutch pressure tap plug loose or missing.
27. **On AXOD-E (AX4S) transaxles, shift solenoid No. 2 inoperative.**
28. **On AXOD-E (AX4S) transaxles,** EEC-IV microprocessor inoperative.
29. **On AXOD-E (AX4S) transaxles,** No. 3 and No. 8 check balls missing.

2-3 SHIFT FEELS HARSH OR SOFT

1. Low oil pressure.
2. Low-intermediate servo apply rod length incorrect.
3. Low-intermediate servo piston, seal, springs or rod damaged.
4. 2-3 servo regulator valve stuck, nicked or damaged.
5. 2-3 servo regulator valve spring damaged.
6. Back-out valve stuck, nicked or damaged.
7. Back-out valve spring damaged.
8. **On AXOD-E (AX4S) transaxles,** EPC solenoid inoperative or damaged.
9. **On AXOD-E (AX4S) transaxles,** EEC-IV microprocessor inoperative.
10. **On AXOD-E (AX4S) transaxles,** No. 9, 10 or 12 check ball missing.

2-3 SHIFT SPEED HIGH OR LOW

AXOD

1. Governor weights binding.
2. Governor springs and gear damaged.
3. Governor shaft seal or valve damaged or missing.
4. Governor tube leaking or damaged.
5. TV cable damaged or disconnected.
6. TV control valve, TV plunger, TV line modulator valve and 2-3 throttle modulator valve stuck, nicked or damaged.
7. TV control valve, TV plunger, TV line modulator valve and 2-3 throttle modulator valve springs missing or damaged.
8. Governor tube leaking.

AXOD-E (AX4S)

1. Vehicle speed sensor inoperative.

2. Speedometer gear incorrect or missing.
3. 1-2 shift valve and 2-3 shift valve VFS erratic pressure.
4. 1-2 shift valve and 2-3 shift valve stuck nicked or damaged.
5. Shift solenoid damaged.

NO 3-4 SHIFT

1. Governor weights binding.
2. Governor springs and gear damaged.
3. Governor shaft seal or valve leaking or missing.
4. Overdrive band assembly not holding.
5. Overdrive servo assembly apply rod too long.
6. Overdrive servo bore or piston damaged.
7. Overdrive servo assembly piston seals damaged or missing.
8. Overdrive servo assembly return spring or retaining clip missing or broken.
9. Forward clutch assembly return springs and piston damaged.
10. Front ring gear damaged.
11. Control assembly attaching bolts incorrectly torqued.
12. **On AXOD transaxles,** 3-4 shift valve stuck, nicked or damaged.
13. **On AXOD transaxles,** 3-4 shift valve spring damaged.
14. **On AXOD transaxles,** 3-4 modulator valve stuck, nicked or damaged.
15. **On AXOD transaxles,** 3-4 modulator valve spring missing.
16. **On AXOD transaxles,** 4-3 scheduling valve stuck, nicked or damaged.
17. **On AXOD transaxles,** 4-3 scheduling valve spring missing.
18. **On AXOD-E (AX4S) transaxles,** shift solenoid No. 3 wiring short or open.
19. **On AXOD-E (AX4S) transaxles,** EEC-IV microprocessor inoperative.
20. **On AXOD-E (AX4S) transaxles,** 1-2 shift valve stuck, nicked or damaged.
21. **On AXOD-E (AX4S) transaxles,** 1-2 shift valve spring missing.
22. **On AXOD-E (AX4S) transaxles,** forward clutch control valve stuck, nicked or damaged.
23. **On AXOD-E (AX4S) transaxles,** forward clutch control valve spring missing.

3-4 SHIFT FEELS HARSH OR SOFT

1. Incorrect oil pressure.
2. 3-4 accumulator piston stuck or damaged.
3. 3-4 accumulator piston seal missing or damaged.
4. 3-4 accumulator springs missing or damaged.
5. **On AXOD transaxles,** No. 14 check ball missing.
6. **On AXOD-E (AX4S) transaxles,** EPC solenoid inoperative.
7. **On AXOD-E (AX4S) transaxles,** EEC-IV microprocessor inoperative.
8. **On AXOD-E (AX4S) transaxles,** No. 4 or 12 check ball missing or damaged.
9. **On AXOD-E (AX4S) transaxles,** ac-

cumulator regulator valve stuck, nicked or damaged.

3-4 SHIFT SPEED HIGH OR LOW

AXOD

1. Governor weights binding.
2. Governor springs and gear damaged.
3. Governor shaft seal or valve missing or damaged.
4. Governor tube leaking.
5. TV cable damaged or disconnected.
6. TV control valve, TV plunger, TV line modulator valve and 3-4 modulator valve stuck, nicked or damaged.
7. TV control valve, TV plunger, TV line modulator valve and 3-4 modulator valve springs missing or damaged.

AXOD-E (AX4S)

1. Vehicle speed sensor damaged.
2. Speedometer gear incorrect or missing gear.
3. 1-2 shift valve and/or 3-4 shift valve stuck nicked or damaged.

NO CONVERTER CLUTCH APPLY

1. No lockup signal to the electronic engine control.
2. Bypass solenoid damaged or inoperative.
3. Transaxle bulkhead electrical connector damaged or electrical system wires pinched.
4. 3-2 or 4-3 pressure switch inoperative.
5. Converter clutch check ball not seating or damaged.
6. Turbine shaft seals damaged.
7. Bypass clutch control valve stuck.
8. Bypass clutch control valve plunger stuck.
9. Pump shaft seals missing or damaged.
10. Valve body pilot sleeve damaged or improperly aligned.

CONVERTER CLUTCH DOES NOT RELEASE

1. No unlock signal to the electronic engine control.
2. Bypass solenoid damaged or inoperative.
3. Bypass clutch control valve or plunger valve stuck, nicked or damaged.
4. Solenoid filter pump, in main control, damaged.

2-1 OR 3-1 DOWNSHIFT HARSH

1. Incorrect oil pressure.
2. Low-intermediate servo piston or seal damaged.
3. Low-intermediate servo assembly springs missing or damaged.
4. Low-intermediate servo apply rod length incorrect.
5. Number 9 check ball missing (3-1 only).

3-2 DOWNSHIFT HARSH

1. Low-intermediate servo assembly

springs missing or damaged.
2. Low-intermediate servo apply rod length incorrect.
3. 3-2 control valve stuck, nicked or damaged.
4. Number 5 check ball missing.
5. **On AXOD-E (AX4S) transaxles,** faulty transaxle electrical system.
6. **On AXOD-E (AX4S) transaxles,** incorrect oil pressure.
7. **On AXOD-E (AX4S) transaxles,** intermediate clutch retaining ring out of position.
8. **On AXOD-E (AX4S) transaxles,** back out valve stuck, nicked or damaged.

NO ENGINE BRAKING IN 3RD GEAR (OD POSITION) W/OD CANCELLED

3.2L/V6—195 SHO

1. Electrical inputs/outputs, vehicle wiring harness, Powertrain Control Module (PCM), shift solenoid No. 3 (SS-3).
2. Shift linkage cable, MLP sensor damaged or misadjusted.
3. Forward clutch pressure, line pressure incorrect.
4. Main control valve body retaining bolts loose.
5. Main control valve body gaskets improperly positioned, missing or damaged.
6. Main control valve body valves stuck, damaged or improperly assembled.
7. Shift solenoid No. 3 (SS-3) damaged or stuck.
8. Forward clutch assembly damaged or improperly assembled.
9. Low one-way clutch assembly not overrunning, damaged.

4-3 DOWNSHIFT HARSH

1. Overdrive servo assembly apply rod length incorrect.
2. Overdrive servo piston or seal damaged.
3. Overdrive servo assembly springs missing or damaged.
4. No converter clutch release.

NO DRIVE IN DRIVE RANGE & NO REVERSE IN REVERSE RANGE

1. Low oil level.
2. Low oil pressure.
3. Linkage improperly adjusted, disconnected, damaged, broken or bent.
4. TV linkage disconnected or missing.
5. Oil pump worn or damaged.
6. Oil pump driveshaft damaged.
7. Drive chain assembly damaged or broken.
8. Drive sprocket shaft to converter turbine spline damaged.
9. Driven sprocket shaft to direct-intermediate clutch hub damaged.
10. Forward clutch plates burned or missing.
11. Forward clutch piston seals or pistons damaged.
12. Forward clutch check ball assembly missing or damaged.

13. Forward clutch driven sprocket support seals damaged or missing.
14. Forward clutch oil holes blocked.
15. Forward clutch direct intermediate hub seals damaged or missing.
16. Low one-way clutch improperly assembled or damaged sprag.
17. Front sun gear/shell damaged.
18. Front and rear carrier pistons/lugs to rear ring gear damaged.
19. Rear ring gear/lugs to forward carrier damaged.
20. Low-intermediate band assembly burned or broken.
21. Low-intermediate servo assembly apply rod too short.
22. Low-intermediate servo assembly piston, seal or rod damaged.
23. Low-intermediate servo oil tubes damaged.
24. Final drive assembly or final drive sun gear shaft pistons or gears damaged.
25. Output shaft misaligned with axles or damaged shaft splines.
26. Halfshaft disengaged from transaxle or damaged shaft splines.
27. Oil filter damaged, missing O-ring or plugged.

NO DRIVE—REVERSE OK

1. 2-3 servo regulator valve stuck.
2. Low/intermediate band assembly incorrect apply rod length.
3. Low/intermediate band assembly piston, seal or rod damaged.
4. Low/intermediate servo oil tubes damaged (leaking).
5. Low/intermediate servo oil tubes damaged case bores.

NO REVERSE—DRIVE OK

AXOD

1. Low oil level or pressure.
2. Linkage improperly adjusted, disconnected, damaged, broken or bent.
3. TV linkage disconnected or missing.
4. Oil pump worn or damaged.
5. Oil pump driveshaft damaged.
6. Drive chain assembly damaged or broken.
7. Drive sprocket shaft to converter turbine spline damaged.
8. Driven sprocket shaft to direct-intermediate clutch hub damaged.
9. Reverse clutch plates missing or burned.
10. Forward clutch plates burned or missing.
11. Forward clutch piston seals or pistons damaged.
12. Forward clutch check ball assembly missing or damaged.
13. Forward clutch driven sprocket support seals damaged or missing.
14. Forward clutch oil holes blocked.
15. Forward clutch direct intermediate hub seals damaged or missing.
16. Low one-way clutch improperly assembled or damaged sprag.
17. Front and rear carrier pistons/lugs to rear ring gear damaged.
18. Reverse apply tube leaking or improperly installed.

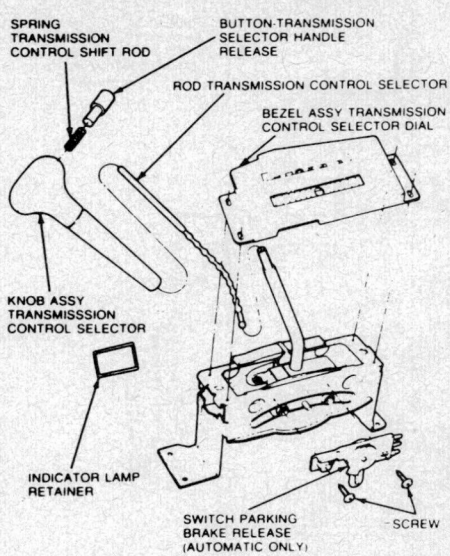

Fig. 5 Manual control linkage adjustment. Except Continental

AXOD-E (AX4S)

1. Reverse clutch burned or missing plates.
2. Reverse apply tube leaking.
3. Reverse apply tube improperly aligned.

NO PARK RANGE

1. Chipped or broken parking pawl or park gear.
2. Broken park pawl return spring.
3. Bent or broken actuating rod.
4. Manual linkage misadjusted.

HARSH NEUTRAL TO REVERSE OR HARSH NEUTRAL TO DRIVE

1. Low-intermediate servo assembly springs damaged or missing.
2. Low-intermediate servo apply rod length incorrect.
3. 3-2 control valve stuck, nicked or damaged.
4. **On AXOD transaxles,** No. 5 ball missing.
5. **On all transaxles,** neutral/drive accumulator piston stuck.
6. Neutral/drive accumulator seal damaged or missing.
7. Neutral/drive accumulator springs damaged or missing.
8. Number 1 check ball missing.
9. Main control separator plate thermal elements do not close when warm.
10. **On AXOD-E (AX4S) transaxles,** No. 3 check ball missing.
11. **On all transaxles,** incorrect oil pressure.

TRANSAXLE OVERHEATS

1. Excessive tow loads.
2. Incorrect fluid level.
3. Incorrect engine idle or performance.
4. Incorrect clutch or band application or oil pressure control system.
5. Restriction in cooler or lines.

6. Seized converter one-way clutch.
7. Dirty or sticking valve body.

TRANSAXLE FLUID LEAKS

1. Incorrect oil level.
2. Defective gaskets, seals, etc.

WHIRRING NOISE

Refer to "Whirring Noise" in the "Service Bulletins" section.

HARSH REVERSE ENGAGEMENT

1. Electrical inputs/outputs, vehicle wiring harnesses, Powertrain Control Module (PCM) EPC solenoid, TOT, TSS, MLP.
2. Incorrect fluid level.
3. Shift linkage damaged or misadjusted.
4. Line pressure high, EPC pressure high.
5. Plugged oil filter, filter and/or seal damaged.
6. Main control valve body retaining bolts loose.
7. Main control valve body gaskets damaged or mispositioned.
8. Main control valve body valves stuck or damaged.
9. Oil pump loose, gasket damaged or mispositioned.
10. Oil pump case leaking or damaged.
11. Reverse clutch assembly friction elements worn or damaged.
12. Reverse clutch apply—oil transfer tube leaking or improperly installed.
13. Reverse clutch return spring piston worn or damaged.

HARSH FORWARD ENGAGEMENT

1. Electrical inputs/outputs, vehicle wiring harnesses, Powertrain Control Module (PCM) EPC solenoid, TOT, TSS, MLP.
2. Incorrect fluid level.
3. Shift linkage damaged or misadjusted.
4. Line pressure high, EPC pressure high.
5. Plugged oil filter, filter and/or seal damaged.
6. Main control valve body retaining bolts loose.
7. Main control valve body gaskets damaged or mispositioned.
8. Main control valve body valves stuck or damaged.
9. Oil pump loose, gasket damaged or mispositioned.
10. Oil pump case leaking or damaged.
11. Low and intermediate servo seals and/or piston damaged or worn.
12. Low and intermediate servo apply rod length incorrect.
13. Low and intermediate servo oil tubes damaged, loose, leaking or improperly assembled.
14. Forward clutch assembly damaged or worn.
15. Low and intermediate band/rear sun gear and drum assembly, damaged or worn.

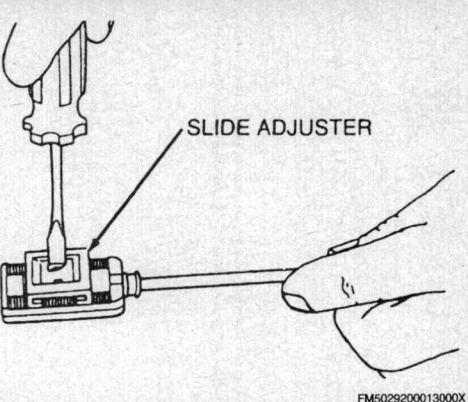

SLIDE ADJUSTER

Fig. 6 Manual control linkage adjustment. Continental

MAINTENANCE

Ford Motor Company recommends the use of Mercon type automatic transmission fluid in this transmission. If Mercon type fluid is not available, Type H automatic transmission fluid maybe used. Use of a fluid other than specified may result in transmission malfunction or failure.

FLUID CHECK

1. Start engine and allow to reach normal operating temperature.
2. Move transaxle selector lever through each range, allowing enough time in each range for transaxle to engage. Return selector lever to the Park position and apply parking brake. **Do not turn off engine during fluid level check.**
3. Clean all dirt from transaxle fluid dipstick cap before removing dipstick from filler tube.
4. Remove dipstick from tube, wipe it clean, then push it all the way back into the tube. Ensure dipstick is fully seated.
5. Pull dipstick out of tube and check fluid level. Fluid should be between the arrows.
6. If vehicle has been operating for an extended period at high speed or in city traffic in hot weather or vehicle is being used to tow a trailer, the transaxle fluid must be allowed to cool for about 30 minutes after the engine has been turned off for an accurate reading to be obtained.

FLUID CHANGE

Normal maintenance and lubrication requirements do not necessitate periodic fluid change. If vehicle is operated under abnormal conditions, fluid should be changed every 30,000 miles. If major failure has occurred in the transaxle, it will have to be removed for service. At this time the converter should be thoroughly flushed to remove any foreign matter.

1. Raise and support vehicle, then position a suitable drain pan under the transaxle.
2. Loosen pump and valve body cover bolts and drain.
3. Loosen lower pan attaching bolts and drain fluid from transaxle.

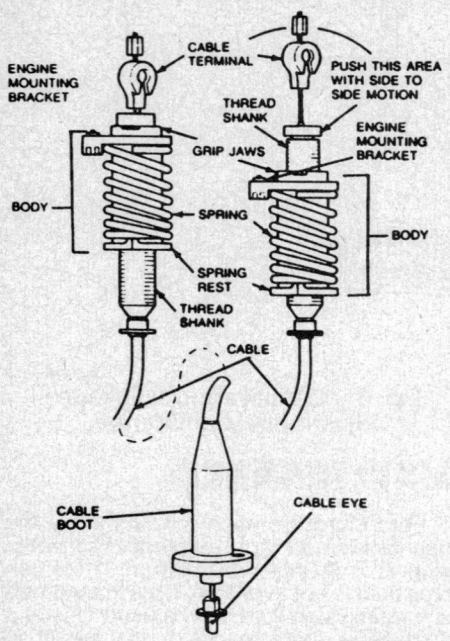

Fig. 7   TV cable adjustment

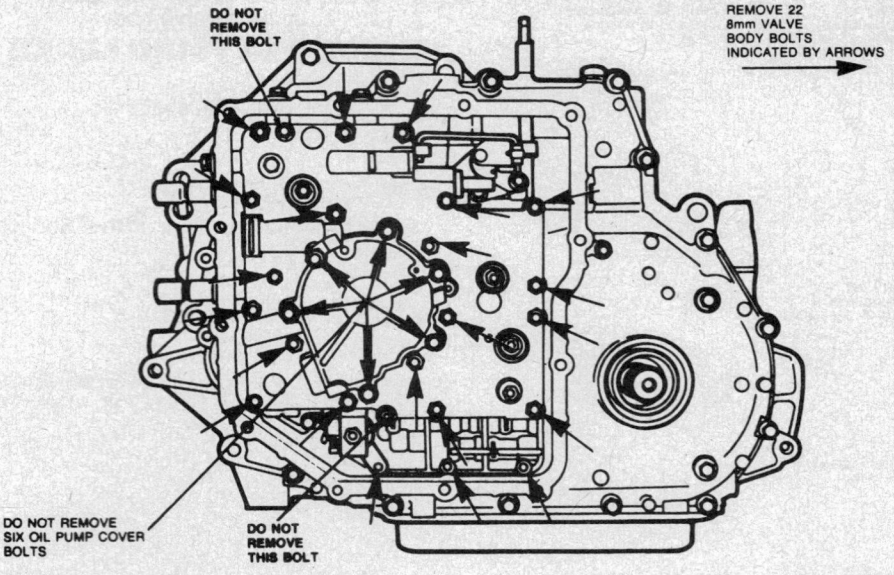

Fig. 8   Oil pump & valve body bolt removal. AXOD

4. When fluid has drained to the level of pan flange, remove pan attaching bolts working from the RH side, allowing pan to drop and drain slowly.
5. When fluid has stopped draining, remove and clean pan and screen. Discard pan gasket.
6. Install pan using a new gasket. **Torque** pan attaching bolts to 10-12 ft. lbs.
7. Tighten pump and valve body cover attaching bolts, then fill transaxle to correct level.

ADJUSTMENTS

MANUAL SHIFT LINKAGE

Except Continental

1. Position selector lever in the Overdrive position against rearward stop, **Fig. 5.** Shift lever should be held in the rearward position while linkage is being adjusted.
2. Loosen manual lever to control cable attaching nut.
3. Place transaxle manual lever in the Overdrive position, second detent from most rearward position, then **torque** cable attaching nut to 10-15 ft. lbs.
4. Check operation of transaxle in each selector lever position. Ensure park and neutral start switch operate satisfactorily.

Continental

1. Place shift lever in OD position, then hang 3 lbs. weight on shift lever ensuring lever is firmly in OD detent.
2. Using suitable screwdriver in slide adjuster slot to open adjuster, **Fig. 6.**
3. Move transaxle manual shift lever to OD position, second detent from most rearward position.

Fig. 9   Manual valve link disengagement. AXOD

4. Push slide adjuster closed.

THROTTLE CABLE

The throttle valve (TV) cable normally does not require adjustment. The only time cable should be adjusted is if one of the following components are replaced: main control assembly, TV cable, TV cable engine mounting bracket, throttle control lever link or lever assembly, engine throttle body or transaxle assembly.

1. Connect TV cable eye to throttle lever link, **Fig. 7,** then attach cable boot to chain cover.
2. With TV cable mounted in engine bracket, ensure threaded shank is fully retracted.
3. **On 3.0L/V6-182 engines,** to retract shank, hold spring rest and wiggle top of thread shank while pressing shank toward spring.
4. **On 3.8L/V6-238 engines,** adjuster spring has two 180° segments, to retract shank span the crack between two segments with suitable large screwdriver or socket extension rod,

compress spring by depressing rod toward throttle body, with spring compressed, push threaded shank toward spring. **Do not pull on cable sheath.**
5. **On all models,** attach end of TV cable to throttle body.
6. Rotate throttle lever to WOT position and release.
7. Threaded shank should show movement or "ratchet" out of grip jaws. If movement is not present, inspect TV cable system for broken or disconnected components and repeat procedure as required.

IN-VEHICLE REPAIRS

VALVE BODY

The oil pump and valve body are removed as an assembly.

AXOD

Removal

1. Disconnect battery ground cable, then remove battery and battery tray.
2. Remove air cleaner assembly, then position all hoses, vacuum lines and wiring away from pump and valve body cover.
3. Raise and support vehicle, then support engine and transaxle using a suitable jack.
4. Remove LH engine mounts and supports.
5. Loosen pump and valve body cover attaching bolts and drain transaxle fluid. After fluid has drained, remove cover and gasket.
6. Remove 22 pump and valve body assembly to chain cover attaching bolts, **Fig. 8.**
7. Pull pump and valve body assembly out enough to clear throttle valve bracket, then rotate valve body clockwise and disconnect manual valve link, **Fig. 9.**

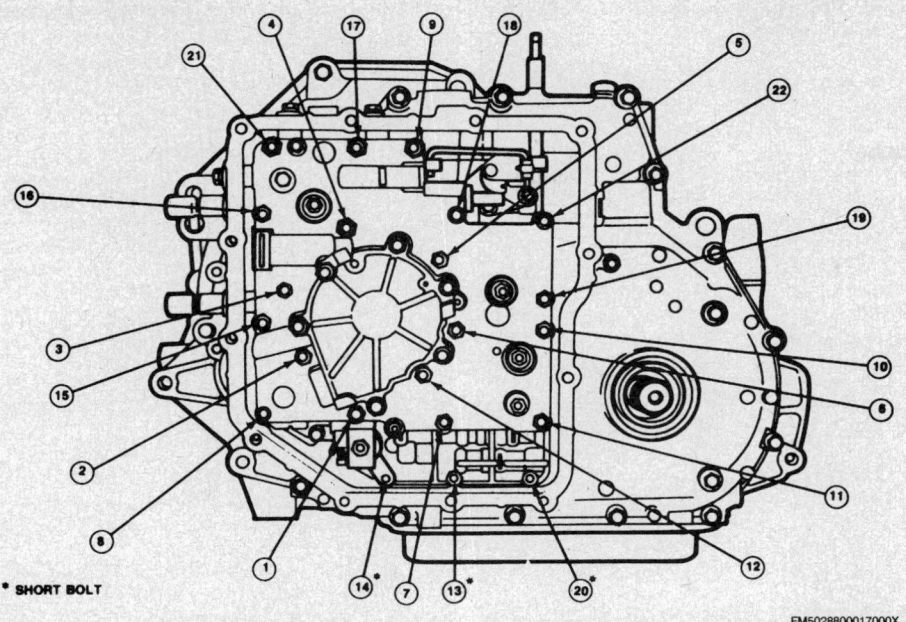

* SHORT BOLT

FM5028800017000X

Fig. 10 Oil pump & valve body bolt tightening sequence. AXOD

8. Remove pump and valve body assembly from vehicle.

Installation

1. Install new pump and valve body to chain cover gasket.
2. Slide pump and valve body assembly into oil pump shaft.
3. Rotate pump and valve body assembly toward dash panel, then engage manual valve link with manual valve.
4. Rotate or jiggle pump and valve body assembly to engage splines on oil pump shaft with splines on oil pump rotor. Valve body should slide flush onto chain cover without force. If full engagement of the pump and valve body assembly is not obtained, perform one of the two following methods:
   a. Rotate engine using 7/8 inch deep well socket on the crankshaft pulley to complete engagement of the pump shaft to pump.
   b. Remove manual valve from valve body, then rotate assembly as necessary to allow full engagement of pump shaft to pump.
5. Using valve body alignment pin tool No. T86P-70100-C or equivalent to position valve body, install pump and valve body attaching bolts. **Torque** attaching bolts to 7-9 ft. lbs. in the sequence shown in **Fig. 10. Use caution not to use attaching bolts to draw pump and valve body into position.**
6. Install pump, valve body cover and new gasket. **Torque** cover attaching bolts to 7-9 ft. lbs.
7. Install LH engine mounts and supports, then remove engine and transaxle supporting jack and lower vehicle.
8. Place hoses and wiring in position, then install air cleaner, battery and tray.

9. Fill transaxle with suitable oil, then start engine and ensure transaxle operates properly.

TRANSAXLE
REPLACE
1992

1. Disconnect battery ground cable, then remove air cleaner, hoses and tubes.
2. Remove battery and battery tray.
3. **On AXOD-E (AX4S) transaxles,** disconnect engine electrical connectors, then remove main wiring harness bracket attaching bolt, position electrical harness aside.
4. **On AXOD transaxles,** remove shift cable and bracket assembly attaching bolt from transaxle.
5. **On AXOD transaxles,** remove two shift cable bracket attaching bolts and bracket from transaxle.
6. **On AXOD transaxles,** disconnect neutral safety switch electrical connector, then the bulkhead electrical connector from rear of transaxle.
7. **On AXOD-E (AX4S) transaxles,** remove shift lever, then remove EGR and throttle body brackets attaching bolts, then install engine lifting eyes.
8. **On all models,** remove dipstick.
9. **On AXOD transaxles with 3.8L/V6-238 engine,** remove throttle cable cover.
10. **On AXOD transaxles,** remove throttle valve cable as follows:
    a. Remove throttle valve cable from throttle body lever.
    b. Remove one throttle valve cable to transaxle case attaching bolt.
    c. Pull up on throttle valve cable, then disconnect throttle valve cable from TV link. **Use caution not to bend internal TV bracket.**
11. **On AXOD-E (AX4S) transaxles,** re-

move radiator sight shield, the turn air suspension switch in luggage compartment to Off position.
12. Disconnect power steering pump pressure and return line bracket.
13. **On all models,** install suitable engine support fixture to three engine lift points, then raise engine slightly to relieve weight from engine mounts.
14. Remove four torque converter housing attaching bolts from top of transaxle.
15. Raise and support vehicle, then remove both front wheels.
16. Proceed as follows:
    a. Disconnect LH outer tie rod end.
    b. Remove front stabilizer bar assembly attaching bolts.
    c. **On AXOD-E (AX4S) transaxles,** remove suspension height sensor, then brake line support brackets.
    d. **On all models,** disconnect RH lower arm assembly.
    e. Disconnect LH lower arm assembly.
    f. Remove steering gear attaching nuts.
17. **On AXOD transaxles with 3.8L/V6-238 engines,** remove front EGO sensor.
18. **On AXOD-E (AX4S) transaxles,** disconnect HEGO sensors.
19. **On AXOD transaxles with 3.0L/V6-182 engine,** remove exhaust Y-pipe from engine and rear portion of exhaust system.
20. **On models except AXOD transaxles with 3.0L/V6-182 engine,** remove front exhaust pipe, converter assembly and bracket.
21. **On all models,** remove two bolts from LH engine support mount.
22. Position suitable subframe removal tool below subframe.
23. Remove power steering gear from sub frame, then secure to rear of engine compartment.
24. Remove sub-frame attaching bolts, then lower sub-frame from vehicle.
25. Remove dust cover attaching bolt.
26. Remove two starter attaching bolts, then position aside.
27. Remove dust cover.
28. Rotate engine with 1/2 inch drive ratchet and a 7/8 inch deep well socket on crankshaft pulley bolt to align torque converter bolts with starter drive hole.
29. Remove four torque converter to flywheel attaching nuts, then using tool No. T86P-77265-AH or equivalent, disconnect transaxle cooler lines.
30. Remove engine to transaxle attaching bolts.
31. Position suitable jack under transaxle oil pan, then remove vehicle speed sensor from transaxle. **Vehicles with electronic instrument clusters do not use a speedometer cable.**
32. Remove halfshafts as follows:
    a. Screw extension tool No. T86P-3514-A2 into CV joint puller tool No. T86P-3514-A1 and install slide hammer tool No. D79P-100-A or equivalent into extension.
    b. Position puller behind CV joint and

remove joint. **Ensure puller does not contact turbine speed sensor or sensor damage may result.**

33. Remove two remaining torque converter housing attaching bolts.
34. Separate transaxle from engine, then lower transaxle out of vehicle.
35. Reverse procedure to install.

1993–94

1. Turn air suspension switch located in luggage compartment to OFF position.
2. Position vehicle on hoist. Do not raise vehicle at this time.
3. Place drain pan under transaxle, then loosen lower pan retaining bolts and drain fluid. When fluid has drained to level of pan flange, remove remaining pan bolts working from the righthand side and allow it to drop and drain slowly.
4. After fluid has drained, reinstall pan and retaining bolts.
5. Remove engine air cleaner assembly, then disconnect and remove battery from vehicle.
6. Remove battery tray, then disconnect electrical connectors from engine assembly.
7. Remove bolt retaining main wiring harness bracket.
8. Remove shift control selector lever.
9. **On models equipped with 3.0L/V6-182 engine,** install Engine Lifting Eye tool No. D81L-6001-D or equivalent to lefthand rear cylinder with M10 x 1.5 x 2.0. The engine plant lifting eye should still be on righthand front cylinder head. If not, install as necessary.
10. **On models equipped with 3.2L/V6-232 engine,** remove bracket on back of engine that retains wiring harness and coolant line, then install Engine Lifting Bracket tool No. D89L-6001-A or equivalent.
11. Install Engine Lifting Eye tool No. D81L-6001-D or equivalent to alternator bracket.
12. **On models equipped with 3.8L/V6-232 engine,** install Engine Lifting Eyes tool No. D81L-6001-D or equivalent, to lefthand front exhaust manifold stud, then righthand rear exhaust manifold stud.
13. **On all models,** position Engine Lifting Bracket tool No. D89L-6000-A or equivalent over engine assembly.
14. Secure engine wiring harness out of way, then remove radiator shield from top of radiator assembly.
15. Remove oil dipstick, then disconnect power steering pump pressure and return line bracket.
16. Remove four 15mm torque converter housing to engine block retaining bolts.
17. Raise and support vehicle, then remove both front tires from vehicle.
18. Disconnect lefthand and righthand outer tie-rod ends from steering knuckle assemblies.
19. Remove air suspension height sensors, then disconnect brake line support brackets.
20. Remove front stabilizer bar links from strut assemblies, then disconnect righthand and lefthand lower control arms from respective steering knuckle.
21. Remove rack and pinion to sub frame retaining bolts.
22. Disconnect oxygen sensor from body harness, then remove front exhaust pipe, catalytic converter and mounting bracket.
23. Remove two 15mm bolts from engine and transaxle support insulator.
24. Remove four 15mm bolts from lefthand engine support, then remove support.
25. Position Rotunda Subframe Removal Kit tool No. 014-00751 or equivalent
26. Remove steering gear from front subframe, and secure to rear of engine compartment.
27. Remove 8mm bolt from dust cover.
28. Remove two starter retaining bolts, then position starter motor out of way.
29. Rotate engine with ½ inch drive rachet and ⅞ inch deep well socket on crankshaft pulley bolt to align torque converter bolts with starter drive hole. Then, remove four 15mm torque converter to flywheel retaining nuts.
30. Remove transaxle cooler line fitting retaining clips.
31. Using Cooler Line Disconnect tool No. T86P-77265-AH, disconnect transaxle cooler lines.
32. Remove engine to transaxle retaining bolts, then speedometer sensor heat shield.
33. Remove vehicle speed sensor from transaxle. Vehicles with electronic instrument cluster do not use a speedometer cable.
34. Using a transaxle jack or equivalent, support transaxle assembly. Due to **weight differences of the front and rear of the vehicle and different types of vehicle hoists, it may be** **necessary to support the rear of the vehicle with jack stands or equivalents, to counterbalance the removal of transaxle assembly.**
35. Remove driveshaft assemblies as follows:
    a. **Ensure puller does not contact transaxle speed sensor or possible damage will result. Do not pry against transaxle case.**
    b. Assemble Impact Slide Hammer tool No. D79P-10-A, Puller Extension tool No. T86P-3514-A2 and CV Joint Puller Adapter or equivalents, then position puller behind front wheel driveshaft joint and remove joint.
    c. Install shipping plugs or equivalent into transaxle case.
36. Remove the two remaining 15mm torque converter housing bolts.
37. Separate transaxle from engine assembly, then carefully lower transaxle out of vehicle.
38. Reverse procedure to install, noting the following:
    a. Place transaxle assembly on jack and raise until aligned with engine.
    b. Position transaxle to engine and align torque converter bolts to flywheel.
    c. Install transaxle housing bolts. **Torque** to 41-50 ft. lbs.
    d. Install four torque converter bolts though starter drive hole by rotating engine at the crankshaft pulley bolt with rachet and socket. **Torque** retaining bolts to 23-39 ft. lbs.
    e. **Torque** speed sensor retaining bolt to 31-39 inch. lbs.
    f. Install transaxle cooler lines. **Torque** lines connecting to transaxle to 18-23 ft. lbs. **Torque** lines at oil cooler to 8-12 ft. lbs.
    g. **Torque** subframe retaining bolts to 55-75 ft. lbs.
    h. **Torque** lefthand engine and transaxle support bolts to 41-55 ft. lbs.
    i. **Torque** engine and transaxle support insulator retaining bolts to 60-85 ft. lbs.
    j. Install front exhaust pipe, then steering gear assembly. **Torque** steering gear retaining bolts to 85-100 ft. lbs.
    k. Install lefthand and righthand lower arm assemblies. **Torque** new pinch bolt to 40-53 ft. lbs.
    l. **Torque** stabilizer retaining bolts to 23-29 ft. lbs.
    m. **Torque** tie-rod retaining nuts to 23-35 ft. lbs.

TIGHTENING SPECIFICATIONS

Component	Torque/Ft. Lbs.	Component	Torque/Ft. Lbs.
Bracket Tubes To Case	7–9	Case To Reverse Clutch Screw	7–9
Brake Hose Routing Clip	8	Case To Stator Support	7–9
Case To Chain Cover (10 mm)	7–9	Chain Cover To Case (10 mm)	7–9
Case To Chain Cover (13 mm)	24–26	Chain Cover To Case (13 mm)	20–22
Case To Reverse Clutch Nut	25–35	Chain Cover To Front Support (7 mm)	25–35

Continued

TIGHTENING SPECIFICATIONS-Continued

Component	Torque/Ft. Lbs.
Chain Cover To Front Support (13 mm)	20–22
Control Arm To Knuckle	36–44
Detent Spring To Chain Cover	7–9
Differential Brace To Case	26–37
Dust Cover To Case	7–9
Dust Cover	15–21
Engine To Case	41–50
Filler Tube To Case	7–9
Governor Cover To Case	7–9
Insulator Bracket To Frame	40–50
Insulator Mount To Transmission	25–33
Insulator To Bracket	55–70
Low/Intermediate Servo Cover To Case	7–9
Main Control Cover To Chain Cover	10–12
Manual Cable Bracket	10–20
Manual Lever To Manual Shaft	12–16
Neutral Start Switch To Case	7–9
Oil Pan To Case	10–12
Oil Pump Assembly To Main Control	7–9
Overdrive Servo Cover To Case	7–9

Component	Torque/Ft. Lbs.
Park Abutment To case	20–22
Pressure Switch To Pump Body	9–13
Pressure Tap plug For Chain Cover & Pump Body	9–13
Pump Body To Chain Cover	7–9
Pump Cover To Pump Body	7–9
Separator Plate To Main Control	7–9
Separator Plate To Pump Body	7–9
Solenoid To Main Control	7–9
Stabilizer To Control Arm	98–125
Stabilizer U-Clamp To Bracket	60–70
Starter	30–40
TV Cable To Case	9–13
Tie Rod To Knuckle	23–35 ①
Torque Converter To Flywheel	23–39
Transaxle To Engine	41–50
TV Control Lever To Chain Cover	7–9
Valve Body/Solenoid To Chain Cover	7–9

①—Tighten to minimum specified torque, then continue tightening to nearest cotter pin slot.

Ford Aspire & Festiva (ATX) Automatic Transaxle

INDEX

DESCRIPTION

This automatic transaxle combines an automatic transmission and differential into a single powertrain unit. This unit is designed specifically for front-wheel drive applications. The transaxle housing is made of a lightweight aluminum alloy and is mounted transversely to the engine.

TROUBLESHOOTING

NO DRIVE IN ANY RANGE

1. Loose valve body.
2. Valve body sticking.
3. Worn or damaged rear clutch.
4. Internal leakage.
5. Damaged pump or turbine shaft.

NO DRIVE IN D

1. Manual linkage adjustment.
2. Improper oil pressure control system operation.
3. Sticking valve body.
4. Worn or damaged one-way clutch.

NO DRIVE IN D, 2 OR 1

1. Valve body sticking.

2. Worn or damaged rear clutch.
3. Improper oil pressure control system operation.

NO DRIVE IN R

1. Improper oil pressure control system operation.
2. Sticking valve body.
3. Worn or damaged rear clutch.

NO SHIFT OUT OF 1ST GEAR IN D

1. Sticking valve body.
2. Worn or damaged governor.
3. Improper oil pressure control system operation.

NO 2–3 SHIFT IN D

1. Sticking valve body.
2. Faulty governor valve.
3. Improper oil pressure control system operation.

SHIFTS FROM 1–3 IN D

1. Improper fluid level.
2. Sticking valve body.
3. Faulty governor valve.
4. Faulty band servo.
5. Worn or damaged band or drum.

SLIPS ON 2–3 SHIFT

1. Improper fluid level.
2. Faulty vacuum diaphragm or vacuum line.
3. Faulty governor valve.
4. Improper front clutch application.
5. Worn or damaged front clutch.
6. Improper oil pressure control system operation.

SLIPS ON 1–2 SHIFT

1. Improper fluid level.
2. Sticking valve body.
3. Improper oil pressure control system operation.
4. Faulty vacuum diaphragm or vacuum line.
5. Faulty band servo.
6. Worn or damaged band or drum.

IMPROPER SHIFT POINTS

1. Defective kickdown switch, solenoid or wiring.
2. Faulty vacuum diaphragm or vacuum line.
3. Worn or damaged governor.
4. Improper band or clutch application.
5. Improper oil pressure control system operation.

NO FORCED DOWNSHIFT IN D

1. Improper oil control system operation.
2. Improper band application.
3. Sticking valve body.
4. Sticking governor valve.
5. Faulty vacuum diaphragm or vacuum line.
6. Defective kickdown switch, solenoid or wiring.

NO 3–2 SHIFT ON MANUAL D TO 2 OR 1 SHIFT

1. Sticking valve body.

2. Improper oil pressure control system operation.
3. Faulty band servo.
4. Worn or damaged band or drum.

DOWNSHIFT AT SPEEDS ABOVE KICKDOWN LIMIT

1. Faulty vacuum diaphragm or vacuum line.
2. Sticking valve body.
3. Improper front clutch application.
4. Improper oil pressure control system operation.

SLIPS ON 3–2 DOWNSHIFT

1. Improper fluid level.
2. Improper band application.
3. Improper oil pressure control system operation.
4. Faulty band servo.
5. Worn or damaged band or drum.

NO ENGINE BRAKING IN 1

1. Improper fluid level.
2. Improperly adjusted manual linkage.
3. Improper oil pressure control system operation.
4. Sticking valve body.
5. Worn or damaged low reverse brake.

SLOW INITIAL ENGAGEMENT

1. Improper fluid level.
2. Contaminated fluid.
3. Sticking valve body.
4. Improper clutch application.
5. Improper oil pressure control system operation.

HARSH INITIAL ENGAGEMENT

1. Improper engine idle speed.
2. Worn halfshaft constant velocity joints.
3. Damaged or loose engine mounts.
4. Faulty vacuum diaphragm or vacuum line.
5. Improper rear clutch application.
6. Improper oil pressure control system operation.
7. Sticking valve body.

HARSH 1–2 SHIFT

1. Sticking valve body.
2. Faulty vacuum diaphragm or vacuum line.
3. Improper band application.
4. Improper oil pressure control system operation.
5. Improper engine performance.

HARSH 2–3 SHIFT

1. Sticking valve body.
2. Improper front clutch application.
3. Improper oil pressure control circuit operation.
4. Faulty band servo.
5. Worn or damaged brake band.

VEHICLE BRAKED WHEN SHIFTED FROM 1 TO 2

1. Sticking valve body.
2. Improper front clutch application.
3. Improper oil control circuit system operation.

4. Worn or damaged low reverse brake.
5. Seized one-way clutch.

VEHICLE BRAKED WHEN SHIFTED FROM 2 TO D

1. Sticking valve body.
2. Improper operation of brake band or servo.

SLIPS OR CHATTERS IN D

1. Improper fluid level.
2. Worn or damaged rear clutch.
3. Improper oil pressure control system operation.

SLIPS OR CHATTERS IN 2ND GEAR IN D

1. Improper fluid level.
2. Internal leakage.
3. Sticking valve body.
4. Improper rear clutch application.
5. Improper oil pressure control system operation.
6. Faulty band servo.
7. Worn or damaged band or drum.

NOISY DURING ACCELERATION OR DECELERATION

1. Improperly routed speedometer cable.
2. Improperly routed shift cable.
3. Defective engine mounts.

NOISY IN P OR N

1. Loose flywheel bolts.
2. Damaged oil pump.
3. Faulty torque converter.

NOISY IN ALL RANGES

1. Worn or damaged drive gear set.
2. Worn or damaged speedometer gears.
3. Worn or damaged bearings.

NOISY IN LOW

1. Worn damaged planetary gear set.

NOISY IN D RANGES OR R

1. Improper fluid level.
2. Improper fluid control pressure.
3. Worn or damaged rear clutch.
4. Worn or damaged oil pump.
5. Worn or damaged one-way clutch.
6. Worn or damaged planetary gears.

TRANSAXLE NOISY

1. Improper fluid level.
2. Improper band or clutch operation.
3. Improper oil pressure control system operation.
4. Improperly routed oil cooler lines.
5. Sticking valve body.
6. Internal leakage.
7. Oil pump cavitation.

TRANSAXLE OVERHEATS

1. Improper fluid level.
2. Improper engine performance.
3. Improper clutch or band application.
4. Improper oil pressure control operation.
5. Restricted oil cooler lines.
6. Sticking valve body.
7. Seized one-way clutch.

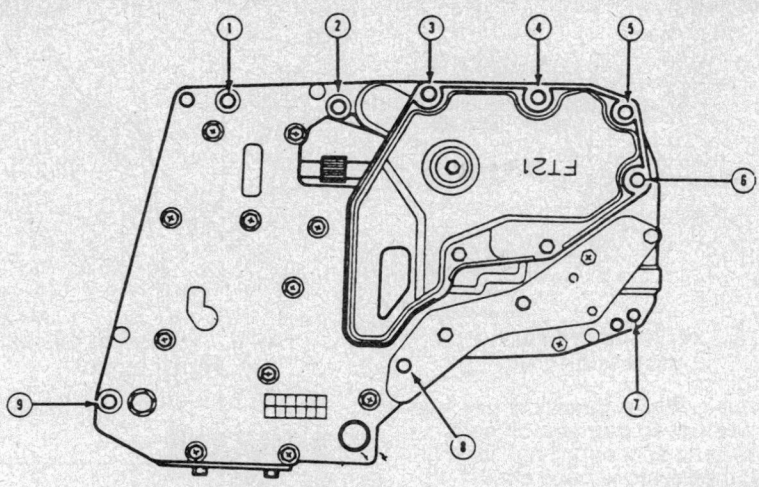

Fig. 1 Valve body retaining bolt removal sequence

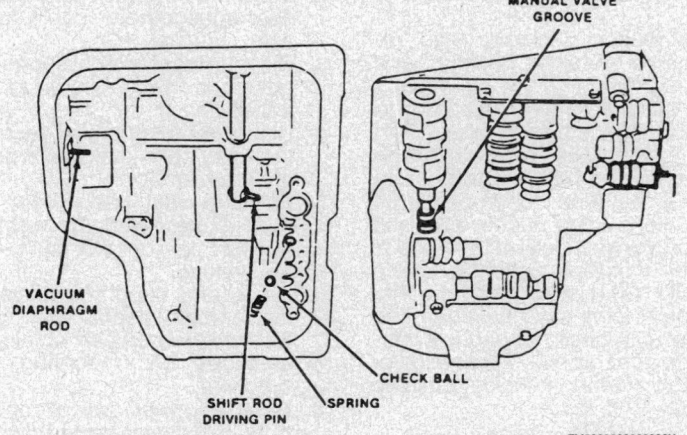

Fig. 2 Vacuum diaphragm rod, check ball & spring installation

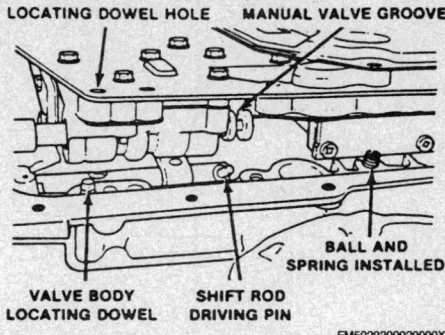

Fig. 3 Valve body installation

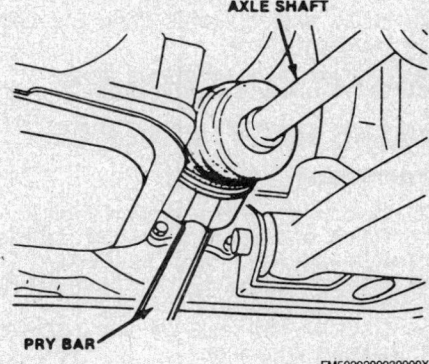

Fig. 4 Separating halfshaft from transaxle

MAINTENANCE

OIL LEVEL CHECK

With vehicle on a level surface, start engine and operate at fast idle for several minutes. With engine at curb idle speed and brakes applied, move selector lever through all gear positions, then return lever to P. With engine still operating at curb idle speed, clean area around transaxle dipstick, then remove dipstick and check fluid level. Fluid level should be between the L and F marks. Add Dexron Type II fluid, as necessary, to bring fluid level between L and F marks. After completing fluid level check, ensure transaxle dipstick is properly seated in dipstick tube.

CHANGING FLUID

Under normal operating circumstances, changing of transaxle fluid is not required. Under severe conditions, such as continuous stop and go driving or accumulation of 5000 miles or more per month, the transaxle fluid should be changed every 30,000 miles.

1. Raise and support front of vehicle, then remove underbody covers to gain access to transaxle drain plug.
2. Position a drain pan under transaxle, then remove drain plug and allow transaxle to drain. The transaxle drain plug is located under the final drive housing.
3. Remove transaxle oil pan retaining bolts and carefully remove oil pan.
4. Clean oil pan and screen. If necessary, replace screen.
5. Install oil pan drain plug and **torque** to 29-40 ft. lbs.
6. Position gasket to transaxle oil pan, then install oil pan on transaxle. **Torque** oil pan-to-transaxle retaining screws to 4-6 ft. lbs. **Do not use any sealer on transaxle oil pan gasket.**
7. Install underbody covers, then lower vehicle.
8. Remove transaxle dipstick and add 3 quarts of Dexron Type II fluid to transaxle through dipstick tube.
9. Start engine and allow to reach operating temperature, then check fluid level as outlined under "Oil Level Check."

ADJUSTMENTS

SHIFT CONTROL CABLE, ADJUST

1. Engage parking brake, then remove the shift quadrant bezel.
2. Remove shift quadrant, then loosen adjuster nuts on shift cable.
3. Shift selector lever to N and ensure detent spring roller is in the N position.
4. Move transaxle shift lever into the N position.
5. Tighten lower adjuster nut by hand until it contacts the T-joint, then loosen nut one-half turn. **Tighten** upper adjuster nut to 69-95 inch lbs.
6. Press selector interlock button, then push selector lever toward R with 4.4 lbs. of force. Measure distance selector lever has moved. This distance should be no more than .31 inch.
7. Repeat step 6 toward the D position.
8. If the distance toward R is greater than toward D, tighten lower adjusting nut until distance is equal. If the distance toward D is greater, loosen lower adjusting nut until distance is equal.
9. Check operation of manual linkage. If shift is not smooth, place selector lever in P. Loosen retaining screws on detent spring and roller assembly, then adjust position of detent spring roller. If this adjustment is made, repeat steps 6 through 9. **Ensure linkage adjustment has not affected operation of neutral safety switch. Engine must crank in P and N positions only.**

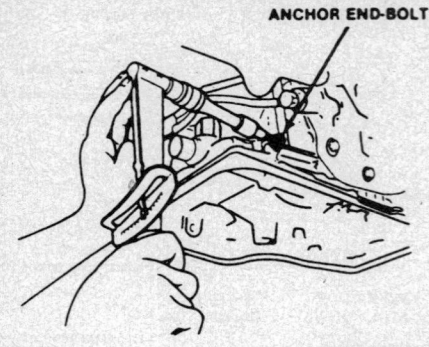

Fig. 5   Band anchor bolt location

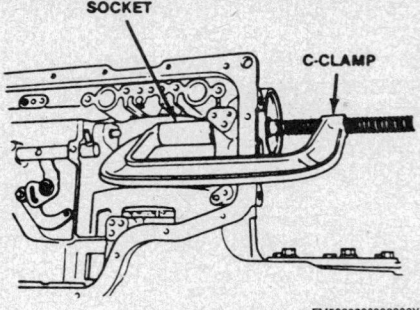

FM5029200932000X

Fig. 6   Servo piston spring compression

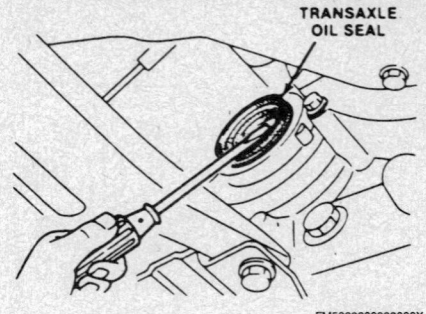

FM5029200933000X

Fig. 7   Transaxle oil seal replacement

10. Install shift quadrant, then the shift quadrant bezel.

IN-VEHICLE REPAIRS

VALVE BODY, REPLACE

Removal

1. Disconnect battery ground cable.
2. Raise and support front of vehicle, then remove body undercovers.
3. Remove transaxle drain plug and allow fluid to drain.
4. Remove transaxle oil pan retaining screws and oil pan.
5. Remove valve body retaining bolts, **Fig. 1,** then carefully remove valve, using care not to loosen vacuum diaphragm rod or ball and spring for converter relief valve.

Installation

1. Position vacuum diaphragm rod to hole in case, **Fig. 2.**
2. Install check ball and spring into case bore, **Fig. 2.** Use petroleum jelly to hold ball and spring in position.
3. Position groove in manual valve with drive pin of shift rod, then index dowel in transaxle case to valve body holes, **Fig. 3.** Install valve body retaining bolts and **torque** to 70-95 inch lbs.
4. Install oil pan and gasket. **Torque** oil pan retaining bolts to 43-69 inch lbs. **Do not use any sealer on oil pan gasket.**
5. Install underbody covers, then lower vehicle.
6. Add three quarts of Dexron Type II fluid to transaxle, then start engine and check fluid level as outlined under "Oil Level Check."

SERVO PISTON, REPLACE

1. Raise and support front of vehicle, then drain transaxle fluid.
2. Remove valve body as outlined under "Valve Body, Replace."
3. Remove left front wheel and tire assembly.
4. Remove stabilizer bar mounting nuts and brackets.
5. Remove lefthand ball joint to steering knuckle retaining bolt, then pull lower control arm downward to separate ball joint from steering knuckle.
6. Using a suitable pry bar, separate halfshaft from differential side gear, **Fig. 4.** Suspend halfshaft from coil spring

using wire. **When inserting pry bar use care not to damage oil seal.**
7. Loosen band anchor bolt and locknut, **Fig. 5,** then remove band strut.
8. Using a C-clamp and socket, compress servo piston, then, using a screwdriver, remove servo snap ring, **Fig. 6.**
9. Carefully loosen C-clamp, then remove servo retainer, piston and spring.
10. Reverse procedure to install. Prior to installation, lubricate servo piston with Dexron Type II fluid. When installing band anchor end bolt, **tighten** bolt to 8.7-10.8 ft. lbs., then loosen bolt three turns. While holding anchor end bolt in position, **torque** locknut to 41-59 ft. lbs. When installing halfshaft, use a new circlip. While supporting at constant velocity joint, slide halfshaft into transaxle until circlip engages differential side gear groove. **Torque** lower ball joint to steering knuckle retaining bolt to 32-40 ft. lbs.

TRANSAXLE OIL SEAL, REPLACE

1. Raise and support front of vehicle, then remove underbody covers.
2. Remove stabilizer bar to lower control arm attachment.
3. Remove wheel and tire assembly.
4. Remove ball joint to steering knuckle retaining bolt, then pull lower control arm downward to separate ball joint from steering knuckle.
5. Remove transaxle drain plug and allow transaxle to drain.
6. Using a suitable pry bar, separate halfshaft from differential side gear, **Fig. 4.** Suspend halfshaft from coil spring using wire. **When inserting pry bar use care not to damage oil seal.**
7. Using a suitable screwdriver, remove oil seal from case, **Fig. 7.**
8. Reverse procedure to install. Use seal installer tool No. T87C-77000-H or equivalent to install oil seal. When installing halfshaft, use a new circlip. While supporting at constant velocity joint, slide halfshaft into transaxle until circlip engages differential side gear groove. **Torque** lower ball joint-to-steering knuckle retaining bolt to 32-40 ft. lbs. When installing stabilizer bar link, **tighten** nut until 7/16 inch of thread extends beyond nut.

TRANSAXLE
REPLACE

1. Disconnect battery ground cable.
2. Drain transmission fluid, then disconnect speedometer cable from transaxle.
3. Disconnect electrical connectors near governor, then the ground wire from transaxle.
4. Disconnect transaxle vacuum hose, then the shift lever nut from manual shaft assembly.
5. Remove shift cable from transaxle, then support engine using engine support bar tool No. D87L-6000-A or equivalent.
6. Raise and support vehicle, then remove front wheels.
7. Remove left splash shield, then the stabilizer bar mounting nuts and brackets.
8. Remove lower arm clamp bolts and nuts. Pull lower arms down, separating lower arms from knuckles.
9. Remove the cotter pin and nut, then disconnect tie rod end from knuckle.
10. Remove halfshafts, then install differential plug tools No. T87C-7025-C or equivalent between the differential side gears.
11. Disconnect oil cooler hoses, then remove the crossmember.
12. Remove gusset plate-to-transaxle bolts, then remove the flywheel cover.
13. Remove the torque converter bolts, then the starter.
14. Remove engine-to-transaxle bolts, then the transaxle from vehicle.
15. Reverse procedure to install, noting the following:
    a. **Torque** engine-to-transaxle bolts to 41-59 ft. lbs.
    b. **Torque** the torque converter bolts to 26-36 ft. lbs.
    c. **Torque** flywheel cover bolts to 61-87 inch lbs.
    d. **Torque** gusset plate-to-transaxle bolts to 27-38 ft. lbs.
    e. **Torque** the crossmember retaining bolts to 47-66 ft. lbs.
    f. **Torque** front engine mount to crossmember bolts to 32-38 ft. lbs.
    g. **Torque** rear engine mount to crossmember bolts to 21-34 ft. lbs.
    h. **Torque** tie rod end to knuckle nut to 26-30 ft. lbs.

i. **Torque** lower arm ball joint to knuckle lower arm clamp nut and bolt to 32-40 ft. lbs.

j. **Torque** left stabilizer body bracket nuts and bolts to 40-45 ft. lbs.

k. **Torque** stabilizer bracket and mounting nuts to 40-50 ft. lbs.

l. **Torque** shift lever nut on manual shaft assembly to 34-57 ft. lbs.

TIGHTENING SPECIFICATIONS

Component	Torque/Ft. Lbs.
Adjuster Locknut	41–59
Anchor End Bolt	104–130 ①
Anchor End Bolt Locknut	41–59
Bearing Housing	14–19
Bearing/Stator Support Bolts	8–10
Crossmember Attaching Bolts	46–66
Differential Ring Gear Bolts	51–62
Engine To Transaxle Bolts	41–59
Flywheel Cover Attaching Bolts	61–87
Front Engine Mount To Crossmember Bolts	32–38
Gasket Plate To Transaxle Bolts	27–38
Governor Cover Attaching Bolts	69–15
Idler Gear Locknut	94–130
Intermediate Band Adjuster Bolt	9–11
Lower Arm Clamp Bolt	32–40
Manual Shaft Nut	22–29
Manual Shaft Support Bolts	43–69 ①
Neutral Safety Switch	14–19

Component	Torque/Ft. Lbs.
Oil Filler Tube Retaining Bolt	61–87 ①
Oil Pan Attaching Bolts	43–69 ①
Oil Pump Cover Bolts	95–122 ①
Oil Pump To Transaxle Bolts	11–16
Parking Paw Actuator Support Bolts	9–12
Rear Engine Mount To Crossmember Nut	21–34
Shift Linkage To Manual Shift Bolt	34–57
Speedometer Drive Gear Bolt	69–95 ①
Stabilizer Body Bracket Nuts	40–45
Stabilizer Mounting Nuts	40–50
Tie Rod End Attaching Nut	26–30
Torque Converter Attaching Bolts	26–36
Transaxle Case To Clutch Housing Bolts	22–34
Transaxle Drain Plug	29–40
Valve Body Mounting Bolts	69–95 ①
Valve Body Side Plate Bolts	22–30 ①
Valve Body Retaining Bolts	69–95 ①

①—Inch lbs.

Ford 4EAT Automatic Transaxle

INDEX

APPLICATION CHART

Year	Model
1992-94	Capri
	Probe
1992-94	Escort
	Tracer

IDENTIFICATION

All vehicles are equipped with a vehicle certification label affixed to the lefthand door jamb below the latch striker, **Fig. 1.** Refer to the code below the space marked "TR" For additional information, such as model, service ID level, or build date, refer to the transaxle service ID tag, **Fig. 2.** The transaxle service ID tag is located on the transaxle case.

DESCRIPTION

The electronically controlled automatic transaxle (4EAT) system **Fig. 3,** features a combination of electronic and mechanical systems to control forward gear shifting and torque converter lockup for quietness and economy, and self-diagnosis capability for simplifying diagnostic procedures. Capri and Probe models are equipped with

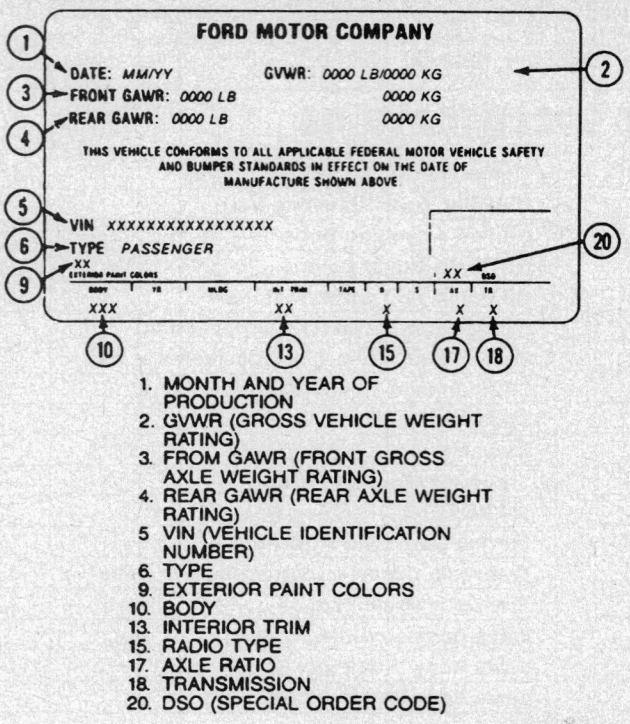

1. MONTH AND YEAR OF PRODUCTION
2. GVWR (GROSS VEHICLE WEIGHT RATING)
3. FROM GAWR (FRONT GROSS AXLE WEIGHT RATING)
4. REAR GAWR (REAR AXLE WEIGHT RATING)
5. VIN (VEHICLE IDENTIFICATION NUMBER)
6. TYPE
9. EXTERIOR PAINT COLORS
10. BODY
13. INTERIOR TRIM
15. RADIO TYPE
17. AXLE RATIO
18. TRANSMISSION
20. DSO (SPECIAL ORDER CODE)

FM5028800297000X

Fig. 1 Vehicle certification label

FM5029000591000X

Fig. 2 Transaxle Identification tag

a manual switch for slow driving on steep or slippery surfaces.

A unique mechanical feature of the 4EAT automatic transaxle is the single compact combination type 4-speed planetary gear instead of the typical two planetary gears used in 3-speed transaxles. This allows for an overall size reduction. Another unique feature is the variable capacity oil pump. This pump provides a constant oil quantity at and above medium speed to reduce power losses caused by pumping more oil than necessary at higher speeds.

The electronic system controls transaxle shifting in forward speeds and controls torque converter lockup through solenoid operated valves. When energized (on), the solenoid valves actuate clutches and bands to control planetary gear shifting. Shift timing and torque converter lockup are regulated by the control unit with programmed logic and in response to input sensors and switches to produce optimum driveability.

TROUBLESHOOTING

VEHICLE DOES NOT MOVE IN OVERDRIVE, D, L OR R RANGE

1. Fluid level too low or fluid contaminated.
2. Incorrectly adjusted selector lever.
3. Malfunctioning control valve(s).
4. Defective oil pump.
5. Problem in hydraulic circuit.
6. Defective torque converter.
7. Defective forward clutch.
8. Defective reverse clutch.
9. Defective one-way clutch No. 1
10. Defective one-way clutch No. 2
11. Defective parking gear.

VEHICLE MOVES IN N RANGE

1. Incorrectly adjusted selector lever.
2. Malfunctioning control valve(s).

EXCESSIVE CREEP

1. Incorrectly adjusted throttle cable.
2. Check idle speed and ignition timing.
3. Defective torque converter.

NO CREEP AT ALL

1. Fluid level too low or fluid contaminated.
2. Incorrectly adjusted selector lever.
3. Incorrectly adjusted throttle cable.
4. Malfunctioning control valve(s).
5. Defective oil pump.
6. Problem in hydraulic circuit.
7. Defective forward clutch.
8. Defective reverse clutch.

NO SHIFT

1. Defective inhibitor switch.
2. Defective hold switch.
3. Defective 1-2 solenoid.
4. Defective 2-3 solenoid.
5. Defective 3-4 solenoid.
6. Fluid level too low or fluid contaminated.
7. Incorrectly adjusted selector cable.
8. Malfunctioning control valve(s).
9. Defective oil pump.

ABNORMAL SHIFT SEQUENCE

1. Defective inhibitor switch.
2. Defective hold switch.
3. Defective throttle sensor.

4. Defective cruise control switch.
5. Defective water temperature switch.
6. Defective pulse generator.
7. Defective 1-2 solenoid.
8. Defective 2-3 solenoid.
9. Defective 3-4 solenoid.
10. Fluid level too low or fluid contaminated.
11. Incorrectly adjusted selector lever.
12. Malfunctioning control valve(s).
13. Defective 2-4 brake band and/or servo.

FREQUENT SHIFTING

1. Defective inhibitor switch.
2. Defective mode switch.
3. Defective throttle sensor.
4. Defective cruise control switch.
5. Defective pulse generator.
6. Defective 1-2 solenoid.
7. Defective 2-3 solenoid.
8. Defective 3-4 solenoid.
9. Defective lockup solenoid.
10. Malfunctioning control valve(s).

EXCESSIVELY HIGH OR LOW SHIFT POINT

1. Defective inhibitor switch.
2. Defective mode switch.
3. Defective hold switch.
4. Defective idle switch.
5. Defective throttle sensor.
6. Defective throttle generator.
7. Defective 1-2 solenoid.
8. Defective 2-3 solenoid.
9. Defective 3-4 solenoid.
10. Incorrectly adjusted selector cable.
11. Malfunctioning control valve(s).

NO LOCKUP

1. Defective brake light switch.
2. Defective throttle sensor.
3. Defective cruise control switch.
4. Defective water temperature switch.
5. Defective pulse generator.
6. Defective 1-2 solenoid.
7. Defective 2-3 solenoid.
8. Defective 3-4 solenoid.
9. Defective lockup solenoid.
10. Incorrectly adjusted selector lever.

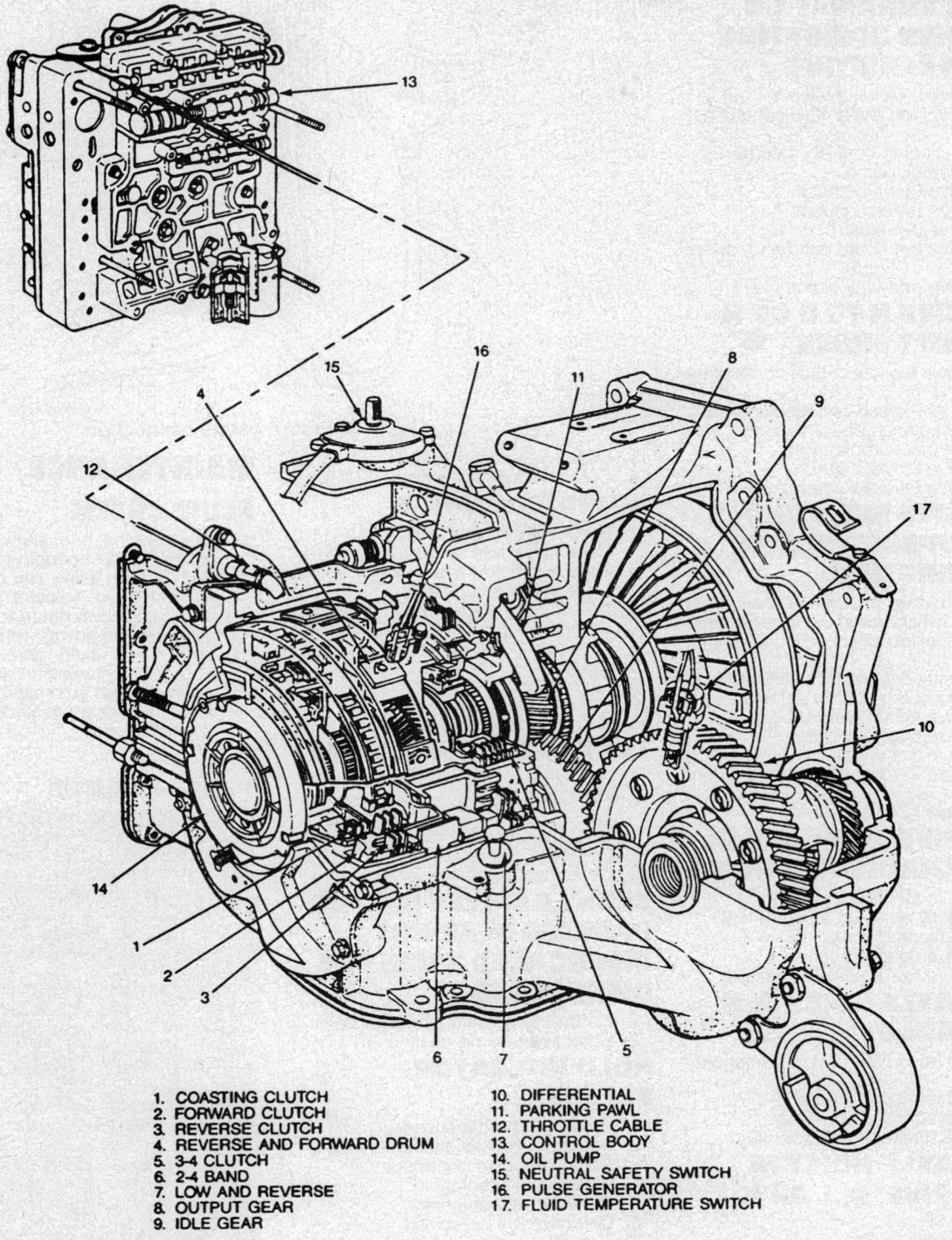

1. COASTING CLUTCH
2. FORWARD CLUTCH
3. REVERSE CLUTCH
4. REVERSE AND FORWARD DRUM
5. 3-4 CLUTCH
6. 2-4 BAND
7. LOW AND REVERSE
8. OUTPUT GEAR
9. IDLE GEAR
10. DIFFERENTIAL
11. PARKING PAWL
12. THROTTLE CABLE
13. CONTROL BODY
14. OIL PUMP
15. NEUTRAL SAFETY SWITCH
16. PULSE GENERATOR
17. FLUID TEMPERATURE SWITCH

FM5028800298000X

Fig. 3   Cross-sectional view of Ford 4EAT automatic transaxle

11. Defective torque converter.

NO KICKDOWN

1. Defective inhibitor switch.
2. Defective hold switch.
3. Defective throttle sensor.
4. Incorrectly adjusted selector lever.

ENGINE RUNAWAY OR SLIP WHEN STARTING VEHICLE

1. Defective inhibitor switch.

2. Fluid level too low or fluid contaminated.
3. Malfunctioning control valve(s).
4. Defective oil pump.
5. Defective forward clutch.
6. Defective one-way clutch No. 1.

FORD 4EAT AUTOMATIC TRANSAXLE

ENGINE RUNAWAY OR SLIP WHEN UPSHIFTING OR DOWNSHIFTING

1. Defective inhibitor switch.
2. Fluid level too low or fluid contaminated.
3. Malfunctioning control valve(s).
4. Defective oil pump.
5. Defective forward clutch.
6. Defective reverse clutch.
7. Defective 3-4 clutch.
8. Defective 2-4 brake band and/or servo.
9. Defective one-way clutch No. 1.

EXCESSIVE N TO D OR N TO R SHIFT SHOCK

1. Fluid level too low or fluid contaminated.
2. Check idle speed and ignition timing.
3. Malfunctioning control valve(s).
4. Defective accumulator(s).
5. Defective forward clutch.
6. Defective reverse clutch.

EXCESSIVE SHIFT SHOCK WHEN UPSHIFTING OR DOWNSHIFTING

The following procedure has been revised by a Technical Service Bulletin.
1. Fluid level too low or fluid contaminated.
2. Incorrectly adjusted throttle cable.
3. Malfunctioning control valve(s).
4. Defective accumulator(s).
5. Defective coasting clutch.
6. Defective 3-4 clutch.
7. Defective 2-4 brake band and/or servo.
8. Weak servo return spring.

EXCESSIVE SHIFT SHOCK WHEN CHANGING RANGES

1. Defective inhibitor switch.
2. Incorrectly adjusted selector lever.
3. Malfunctioning control valve(s).
4. Defective coasting clutch.
5. Defective low and reverse brake.

TRANSAXLE NOISY IN N OR P RANGE

1. Fluid level too low or fluid contaminated.
2. Defective oil pump.
3. Defective torque converter.
4. Defective differential assembly.

TRANSAXLE NOISY IN OVERDRIVE, D, L OR R RANGE

1. Fluid level too low or fluid contaminated.
2. Defective forward clutch.
3. Defective one-way clutch No. 1
4. Defective planetary gear.

NO ENGINE BRAKING

1. Defective 2-3 solenoid.
2. Defective 3-4 solenoid.
3. Malfunctioning control valve(s).
4. Problem in hydraulic circuit.

5. Defective coasting clutch.
6. Defective low and reverse brake.

NO MODE CHANGE

1. Defective inhibitor switch.
2. Defective mode switch.
3. Defective hold switch.
4. Defective throttle sensor.
5. Defective water temperature switch.
6. Defective vehicle speed sensor.
7. Defective pulse generator.
8. Defective 1-2 solenoid.
9. Defective 2-3 solenoid.
10. Defective 3-4 solenoid.
11. Defective lockup solenoid.

TRANSAXLE OVERHEATS

1. Defective lockup solenoid.
2. Fluid level too low or fluid contaminated.
3. Malfunctioning control valve(s).
4. Defective oil pump.
5. Defective torque converter.

VEHICLE MOVES IN P, OR PARKING GEAR NOT DISENGAGED WHEN P IS DISENGAGED

1. Incorrectly adjusted selector lever.
2. Defective parking gear.

HOLD INDICATOR FLASHES

1. Defective throttle sensor.
2. Defective vehicle speed sensor.
3. Defective pulse generator.
4. Defective 1-2 solenoid.
5. Defective 2-3 solenoid.
6. Defective 3-4 solenoid.
7. Defective lockup solenoid.

ENGINE WILL NOT START

1. Defective inhibitor switch.
2. Incorrectly adjusted selector lever.

VEHICLE DRAGS IN FORWARD & REVERSE GEARS

1. Bands improperly adjusted.
2. Improper brake function.

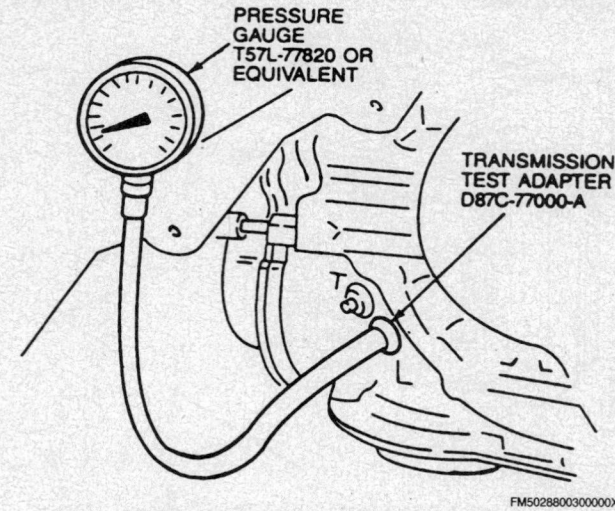

Fig. 4 Pressure gauge connection

MAINTENANCE

FLUID CHECK

1. Start engine and allow transaxle to reach normal operating temperature.
2. With engine idling and parking brake applied, move selector lever through all ranges, then return to P position.
3. With engine idling, remove dipstick and check fluid level. Fluid level should be between full and low marks.
4. Add specified automatic transaxle fluid as necessary to bring level within specifications.

FLUID CHANGE

Normal maintenance and lubrication do not require periodic automatic transaxle fluid changes. If major service, such as a clutch band, bearing, etc. is required, the transaxle will have to be removed for service. At this time the torque converter, cooler and oil cooler tubes must be thoroughly flushed to remove any contamination.

When used after 30,000 miles under continuous or severe conditions, the transaxle and torque converter should be drained and refilled with automatic transaxle fluid. Refer to "Lubricant Data Chart" in this manual.

The following procedure is for partial drain and refill due to in-vehicle service operation.
1. Raise and support vehicle, then remove drain plug and washer. Discard washer. **Avoid spilling hot transaxle fluid.**
2. Loosen oil pan bolts and drain fluid.
3. Slowly loosen oil pan bolts, allowing pan to drop and oil to drain.
4. Remove pan, then thoroughly clean.
5. Remove and discard oil pan to case gasket, oil pan screen and oil pan screen ring. Do not reuse or clean oil pan screen. Filter element material will contaminate transaxle.
6. Reverse procedure to install, noting the following:
   a. Install new oil pan screen, oil pan

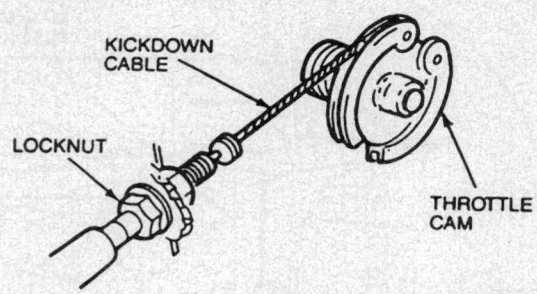

Fig. 5   Kickdown cable adjustment

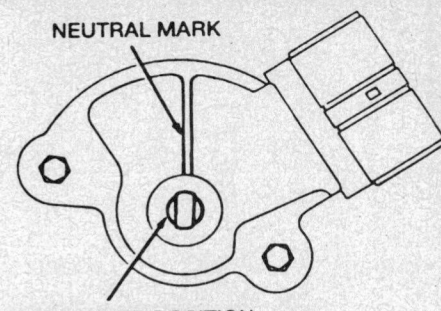

Fig. 6   Rotating manual lever position switch shaft. 1993–94 Probe

Position	Connector terminal								
	A	B	C	D	E	F	G	H	I
P	O			O					
R	O			O		O			
N	O			O			O		
D	O						O		
2	O		O					O	
1	O		O						O

O—O : Continuity

FM5029300593000X

Fig. 7   Manual lever position switch connector terminals. 1993–94 Probe

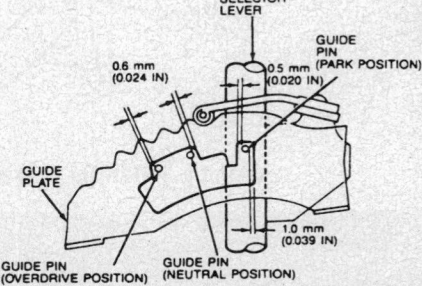

Fig. 8   Guide plate and guide pin clearance check. Escort, Tracer & 1992 Probe

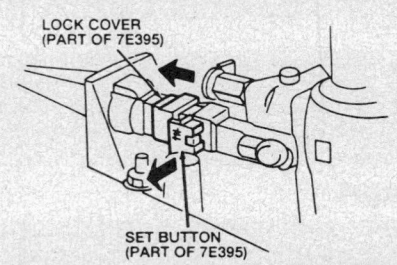

Fig. 9   Sliding back lock cover. 1993–94 Probe

screen ring, oil pan to case gasket and drain plug washer.
b. Tighten oil pan bolts and drain plug to specifications.
c. Add transaxle fluid to specifications. Refer to "Lubricant Data Chart" in this manual.

ADJUSTMENTS

KICKDOWN CABLE

1. Remove splash shield next to left front tire.
2. Remove square head plug (marked L) and install transmission test adapter tool No. D87C-77000-A and pressure gauge tool No. T57L-77820 or equivalents, Fig. 4.
3. Loosen kickdown cable by turning locknuts away from throttle cam, Fig. 5.
4. Shift transaxle into P, then start and run engine until it reaches normal operating temperature. **Ensure engine idle speed is 700-800 RPM.**
5. Turn locknuts toward throttle cam until line pressure indicated on pressure gauge begins to exceed 63-66 psi.
6. Turn locknuts away from throttle cam until a line pressure of 63-66 psi. is reached.
7. Tighten locknuts, then turn engine off.
8. Remove pressure gauge and adapter and install square head plug. **Torque** plug to 43-87 inch lbs.

2-4 BRAKE BAND

1. Raise and support vehicle.
2. Remove oil pan and loosen locknut.
3. **On 1993-94 Probe**, perform the following:
   a. **Torque** piston stem to 105-130 inch lbs.
   b. Loosen piston stem 1½ turns.
4. **On models except 1993—94 Probe**, perform the following:
   a. **Torque** piston stem to 78-95 inch lbs.
   b. Loosen piston stem 2 turns.
5. **On all models, torque** locknut to 18-29 ft. lbs.

NEUTRAL SAFETY SWITCH

Except 1993—94 Probe

1. Disconnect battery ground cable, then remove air cleaner assembly and air inlet tube as necessary.
2. Remove nut securing manual shaft lever to transmission manual shaft.
3. Remove lever from manual shaft.
4. Place selector lever in N range, then loosen switch attaching bolts.
5. Remove switch screw, then move switch so that small hole is aligned with screw hole.
6. Adjust switch by inserting a .079 inch diameter pin through both holes.
7. Tighten neutral safety switch bolts to specifications, then remove alignment pin and install screw.

1993—94 Probe

1. Disconnect battery ground cable, then remove air cleaner assembly.
2. Remove shift cable from manual lever position switch arm by prying with screwdriver or suitable tool.
3. Disconnect manual lever position switch connector, then rotate switch shaft to neutral mark, **Fig. 6.**
4. Loosen switch mounting bolts.
5. Using Rotunda Digital Volt Ohmmeter tool No. 105-00051 or equivalent, ensure there is continuity between ter-

minals, **Fig. 7.**
6. Reverse procedure to install. Tighten manual lever position switch bolts to specifications.

SELECTOR LINKAGE

Escort, Tracer & 1992 Probe

1. Shift gear selector lever to Park position, then disconnect battery ground cable.
2. Remove shift console, then the position indicator mounting screws.
3. Disconnect illumination bulb, shift-lock servo connector and park range switch connector.
4. Remove position indicator, then loosen shift control cable bracket mounting bolts.
5. Push gear selector lever against park range and hold in place.
6. **Torque** shift control cable bracket mounting bolts to 69-95 inch lbs.
7. Lightly press gear selector push rod and ensure guide plate and guide pin clearances are within proper specifications, **Fig. 8.** If clearances are not as specified, readjust shift control cable as outlined above.
8. Reverse procedure to install.

1993—94 Probe

1. Disconnect battery ground cable, then remove floor console.
2. Shift selector lever to P position, then remove position indicator mounting screws and lift position indicator out of the way.
3. Slide lock cover back, then disconnect set button, **Fig. 9.**
4. Slide selector lever to adjust P position, then connect set button.

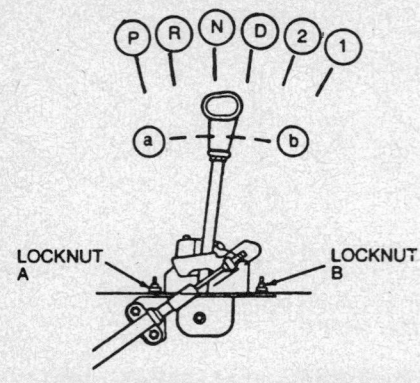

Fig. 10 Shift control cable adjustment. Capri

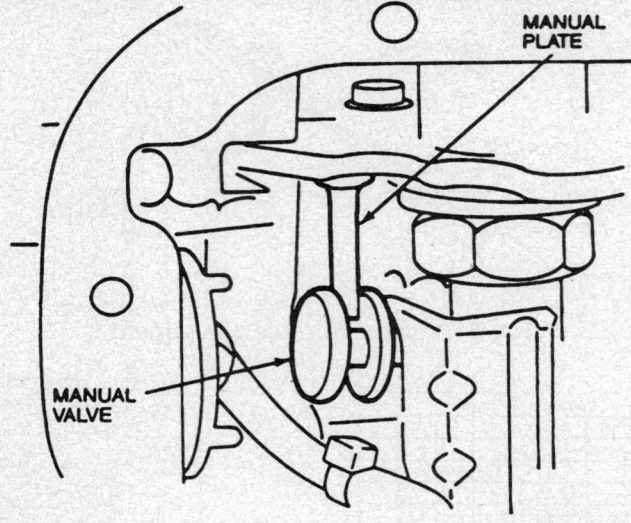

Fig. 11 Manual valve w/manual plate alignment

5. Slide lock cover to lock set button in place.
6. Reverse procedure to install. **Torque** position indicator mounting screws to 17–26 inch lbs.

Capri

1. Position gear selector lever in Neutral position, then remove spring clip and pin attaching shift cable trunnion to transaxle shift lever.
2. Rotate transaxle shift lever counter-clockwise to park position.
3. Position lever between ends of trunnion while rotating lever clockwise two detents to neutral position.
4. If holes in shift lever align with holes in trunnion, cable is properly adjusted. If holes do not align, continue procedure.
5. Remove console shift quadrant, then loosen shift cable adjuster nuts.
6. Position lever in park position and inspect position of detent spring roller.
7. If spring roller is not centered in park detent, proceed as follows:
   a. Loosen retaining screws and center spring in park detent.
   b. Position quadrant and install retaining screws, then position lever in neutral position.
   c. Thread adjuster nuts up or down cable until holes in shift lever and trunnion are aligned.
8. **Torque** adjuster nut to 71–97 inch lbs.
9. Check alignment of cable and install shift lever to shift cable attaching pin and retaining clip.
10. Press in on shift interlock button and carefully push lever forward while an assistant observes. Note shift lever movement, **Fig. 10.**
11. If forward movement of shift lever (A), and rearward movement of gear selector lever (B) are not equal, turn adjuster nuts until they become equal, as follows:
    a. If A is greater, loosen locknut B and tighten locknut A.
    b. If B is greater, loosen locknut A and tighten locknut B.
12. **Torque** adjuster nut to 71–97 inch lbs. **Make sure linkage adjustment has not affected operation of neu-** tral safety switch. With parking brake and service brakes applied, try to start engine in each gearshift position. The engine must crank only in neutral and park positions. If engine cranks in any of the other gear selector lever positions, check linkage adjustment and neutral safety switch operation.
13. Position console and install retaining screws.

IN-VEHICLE REPAIRS

DIFFERENTIAL OIL SEALS, REPLACE

EXCEPT 1993–94 PROBE

Removal

1. **On Escort & Tracer,** install three bar engine support tool No. D88L-6000-A or equivalent.
2. **On all models,** raise and support vehicle, then remove front wheel and tire assemblies.
3. Remove splash shields, then drain transaxle fluid.
4. Remove tie rod nuts and cotter pins, then disconnect both tie rod ends.
5. Remove both stabilizer link assemblies.
6. Remove bolts and nuts from both lower arm ball joints.
7. Pull lower arms down to separate from knuckles.
8. **On Escort & Tracer,** remove lower transaxle crossmember
9. **On all models,** remove righthand joint shaft bracket.
10. Remove halfshafts from transaxle by prying with a bar inserted between shaft and transaxle case. Support halfshafts in vehicle with wire.
11. Remove differential oil seals using a flat-tip screwdriver.

Installation

1. Install new differential oil seals using differential seal replacer tool No. T87C-77000-H or equivalent.
2. Replace circlip on end of each halfshaft, then install halfshafts in transaxle.
3. Attach lower arm ball joints to knuckles.
4. Install tie rod ends and **torque** nuts to 22–33 ft. lbs. Install new cotter pins.
5. Install lower arm ball joint bolts and nuts, **torquing** to 32–40 ft. lbs.
6. **On Escort and Tracer,** install lower transaxle crossmember. **Torque** crossmember to transaxle mount nuts to 27–38 ft. lbs., then the crossmember to vehicle chassis bolts to 47–66 ft. lbs.
7. **On all models,** install stabilizer link assemblies. Tighten nuts on each assembly until one inch (25.4 mm) of bolt thread can be measured from upper nut, then secure upper nut and back off lower nut until a **torque** of 12–17 ft. lbs. is reached.
8. Install splash shields, then the front wheel and tire assemblies. **Torque** lug nuts to 65–87 ft. lbs.
9. **On Escort and Tracer,** remove engine support tool.
10. **On all models,** add specified transaxle fluid, check for leaks and check fluid level.

1993–94 PROBE

Removal

1. Raise and support vehicle, then remove front wheels.
2. Drain transmission fluid, then remove either lefthand or righthand halfshaft and joint.
3. Remove differential oil seals with flat-tip screwdriver.

Installation

1. Use differential seal replacer tool No. T87C-77000-H or equivalent, to install new differential oil seals.
2. Replace halfshaft bearing retainer circlip on end of lefthand halfshaft and joint, then install halfshaft.

3. Install front wheels, then **torque** wheel hub bolt nuts to 66-86 ft. lbs.
4. Lower vehicle, then add specified transaxle fluid.
5. Add specified transaxle fluid, check for leaks and check fluid level.

VALVE BODY, REPLACE

1992 CAPRI & PROBE

Removal

1. Disconnect battery cables, then remove battery and battery carrier.
2. Disconnect main fuse block.
3. Disconnect five transaxle electrical connectors, then separate transaxle wiring harness from transaxle clips.
4. Raise and support vehicle, then drain transaxle fluid.
5. Disconnect oil cooler outlet and inlet hoses. Remove inlet hose.
6. Remove valve body cover and gasket.
7. Disconnect kickdown cable from throttle cam.
8. Disconnect solenoid connector, then pinch tangs of mating connector mounted on transaxle case. Remove by pushing inward.
9. Remove valve body attaching bolts, then the valve body.

Installation

1. Shift transaxle into R to place manual plate in correct position for installation.
2. Install valve body, using a mirror to align groove of manual valve with manual plate, **Fig. 11.**
3. Tighten valve body attaching bolts to specifications.
4. Insert solenoid connector into transaxle case hole, then attach mating connector.
5. Attach kickdown cable to throttle cam.
6. Install valve body cover using a new gasket. Tighten cover attaching bolts to specifications. **Do not use any type of sealer on cover or gasket.**
7. Install oil cooler inlet tube to transaxle. Tighten bolt to specifications.
8. Connect oil cooler hoses.
9. Attach five transaxle electrical connectors, then the transaxle wiring harness to transaxle clips.
10. Connect main fuse block, then install battery carrier and battery. Connect battery cables.
11. Add specified transaxle fluid, check for leaks and check fluid level.

1993–94 CAPRI
Removal

1. Remove air cleaner assembly, then disconnect battery ground cable.
2. Disconnect five transaxle electrical connectors, then separate transaxle harness from clips.
3. Raise and support vehicle, then drain transaxle fluid.
4. Disconnect oil cooler outlet and inlet hoses, then remove inlet tube from transaxle.
5. Remove valve body cover and gasket, then the kickdown cable from throttle cam.

6. Disconnect solenoid connector, then remove from transaxle case by pinching tangs of mating connector and pushing inward.
7. Remove valve body attaching bolts, then the valve body.

Installation

1. Shift transaxle to Reverse position.
2. Install valve body, using mirror to align groove of manual valve with manual plate. Tighten valve body mounting bolts to specifications.
3. Install solenoid connector and attach mating connector.
4. Attach kickdown cable to throttle cam.
5. Install valve body cover and new gasket. **Do not use any type of sealer on valve cover or gasket.**
6. Tighten valve body cover bolts to specifications.
7. Install oil cooler inlet tube, then **torque** bolt to 12-17 ft. lbs.
8. Connect oil cooler hoses.
9. Connect five transaxle electrical connectors and support transaxle harness on clips.
10. Connect battery ground cable.
11. Install air cleaner assembly and add specified transaxle fluid and check for leaks.

1993–94 PROBE

Removal

1. Disconnect battery ground cable, the raise and support vehicle.
2. Remove lefthand splash shield, then drain transaxle fluid.
3. Disconnect and plug transaxle cooler inlet and outlet hoses, then remove transaxle cooler hose mounting bracket from top righthand side of valve body cover.
4. Disconnect vent hose from top lefthand side of valve body cover.
5. Loosen valve body cover mounting bolts and allow any transaxle fluid to drain from cover.
6. Remove valve body cover mounting bolts and cover, then discard gasket.
7. Disconnect transaxle oil temperature sensor connector, then the solenoid connectors. **Note color and position of connectors to ease installation.**
8. Remove valve body mounting bolts, then the valve body.

Installation

1. Position valve body in transaxle case. **Ensure manual valve is aligned with manual plate.**
2. Install valve body mounting bolts and tighten to specifications.
3. Connect vent hose to top lefthand side of valve body cover, then install oil cooler hose mounting bracket on top righthand side of valve body cover.
4. Remove plugs from oil cooler inlet and outlet hoses, then connect hoses.
5. Connect solenoid and TOT sensor connectors.
6. Install new gasket on valve body cover. **Do not use any type of sealer on valve body cover or gasket.**

7. Install valve body cover and tighten mounting bolts to specifications.
8. Install lefthand splash shield. **Torque** screws to 71-88 inch lbs.
9. Lower vehicle, then connect battery ground cable.
10. Fill transaxle with specified transaxle fluid, then check for leaks.

ESCORT & TRACER

Removal

1. Raise and support vehicle, then drain transaxle fluid.
2. Remove transaxle oil pan and oil pan gasket.
3. Remove bolts securing wiring clips to valve body, then disconnect wiring connector.
4. Remove valve body attaching bolts, then the valve body.

Installation

1. Shift transaxle to R position.
2. Install valve body, using a mirror to align groove of manual valve with manual plate.
3. Secure wiring clips to valve body when valve body to transaxle belts are installed. Connect wiring connector.
4. Tighten valve body mounting bolts to specifications.
5. Install transaxle oil pan with new gasket. **Do not use any type of sealer on valve body cover or gasket.**
6. Tighten transaxle oil pan bolts to specifications.
7. Lower vehicle, then add specified transaxle fluid and check for leaks.

TRANSAXLE
REPLACE

1.6L/4-97
Removal

1. Disconnect battery cables, then remove battery.
2. **On 1992-93 models,** remove air cleaner assembly.
3. **On 1994 models,** proceed as follows:
   a. Remove battery tray and battery tray support bracket.
   b. Release wiring harness retaining strap from battery support bracket.
   c. Remove air cleaner/volume air flow sensor assembly and support brackets.
   d. Disconnect ground strap at front of transaxle.
4. **On all models,** disconnect speedometer cable at cable connector.
5. Ensure transaxle is in Park position, then remove shift cable retaining nut from neutral safety switch.
6. Remove shift cable retaining bolts.
7. Disconnect kickdown cable from throttle body housing. Route cable out of straps for removal with transaxle.

8. Disconnect electrical connectors from transaxle, then remove dipstick tube bracket retaining bolt and ground wire.
9. Remove upper starter retaining bolts.
10. Remove two upper intake manifold support retaining bolts.
11. Remove heater bypass tube bracket.
12. Remove transaxle to engine upper retaining bolts.
13. Install three bar engine support tool No. D88L-6000-A or equivalent, then raise and support vehicle.
14. **On 1994 models**, remove splash shields.
15. **On all models**, drain transaxle fluid, then remove three lower intake manifold support retaining bolts.
16. Disconnect starter motor electrical connectors, then remove starter motor lower retaining bolt and starter.
17. Remove front wheels, then the caliper brake hose retaining clips from strut brackets.
18. Remove ball joint pinch bolts, then separate ball joints from control arms.
19. **On 1992-93 models**, remove inner fender splash guards.
20. **On all models**, remove lefthand control arm front retaining bolt.
21. Remove righthand control arm front retaining bolt.
22. Remove frame brace to crossmember retaining bolt.
23. Remove front and rear transaxle mount to crossmember retaining nuts, then the crossmember braces.
24. Remove shift cable retaining nut or screw from crossmember, then the crossmember from vehicle.
25. Remove lefthand axle shaft from vehicle.
26. Disconnect righthand axle shaft from transaxle. Install transaxle plug set tool No. T88C-7025-AH or equivalent, into halfshaft openings on transaxle. **Failure to install transaxle plugs may result in misalignment of differential side gears.**
27. Remove gusset plate center transaxle mount retaining bolts from transaxle, then loosen center transaxle mount retaining bolts on engine.
28. Remove torque converter cover plate, then the exhaust manifold support bracket.
29. Remove front and rear transaxle mounts.
30. **On 1994 models**, remove front mount bracket, then disconnect two oil cooler lines. Save plastic retainers on male tube ends.
31. **On all models**, lower vehicle.
32. Lower, but do not remove, engine transaxle assembly with support bar.
33. Raise vehicle.
34. Remove torque converter to drive plate retaining nuts.
35. Position transmission jack under transaxle and secure with safety chains.
36. Remove lower transaxle to engine retaining bolts, then lower transaxle assembly from vehicle.

Installation
The following procedure has been revised by a Technical Service Bulletin.
A pin is used to hold the throttle valve in a fixed position on new or remanufactured service replacement transaxle assemblies.
The pin is used during the assembling process to make installation of the control valve easier. When installing a new or remanufactured 4EAT transaxle, be sure to remove the pin and install a new retaining bolt. **Failure to remove pin from the throttle cam will hold the transaxle throttle lever in a fixed position resulting in a shift concern.**

1. Slowly raise transaxle assembly into vehicle. **Ensure dipstick tube clears battery tray, then align torque converter studs to drive plate.**
2. Install lower transaxle to engine retaining bolts. **Torque** bolts to 63-89 ft. lbs.
3. Install torque converter to drive plate retaining nuts. **Torque** nuts to 32-44 ft. lbs.
4. Remove transmission jack, then lower vehicle.
5. Raise engine and transaxle assembly into position with support fixture. **Use care in raising engine and transaxle to avoid damage to air conditioning or other engine compartment components.**
6. Raise vehicle.
7. **On 1994 models**, install front mount bracket.
8. **On all models**, install front and rear mounts to transaxle. **Torque** retaining bolts to 27-39 ft. lbs.
9. Install exhaust manifold support. **Torque** exhaust manifold support to transaxle bolt to 50-68 ft. lbs., then the exhaust manifold support to transaxle nut to 23-34 ft. lbs.
10. Install torque converter cover plate. **Torque** retaining bolts to 71-97 inch lbs.
11. Align center transmission mount, then install retaining bolts. **Torque** retaining bolts to 37-52 ft. lbs.
12. Position crossmember to transaxle mounts. Align rear transaxle mount stud first, then loosely install retaining nut.
13. Align front transaxle mount studs, then loosely install retaining nuts.
14. Install crossmember retaining bolts. **Torque** bolts to 27-39 ft. lbs.
15. **Torque** front and rear transaxle mount retaining nuts to 21-33 ft. lbs.
16. Install new circlips to inner CV joint shafts, then the axle shafts into transaxle assembly.
17. Install new hub nut on lefthand axle shaft. **Torque** retaining nut to 116-173 ft. lbs. **Ensure shafts are completely seated.**
18. Position shift cable, then install shift cable lower retaining bolt.
19. Install crossmember braces. **Torque** retaining bolts to 27-39 ft. lbs.
20. Install frame brace. **Torque** crossmember bolt to 27-39 ft. lbs.
21. Install control arm front bolt on both sides. **Torque** bolt to 69-86 ft. lbs.
22. Install ball joint pinch bolts. **Torque** bolts to 32-39 ft. lbs.
23. Install brake hose retaining clips.

24. **On 1992-93 models**, remove splash guards.
25. **On all models**, install starter motor and lower retaining bolts. **Torque** retaining bolts to 18-36 ft. lbs.
26. Connect starter motor electrical connectors.
27. Install intake manifold support bracket, then the retaining bolts loosely.
28. **On 1994 models**, connect oil cooler lines and install splash shields. **Ensure oil cooler fittings are secured to male ends by plastic retainers. Verify by pulling back on connectors.**
29. **On all models**, install tire and wheel assemblies, then lower vehicle.
30. Install transaxle to engine upper retaining bolts. **Torque** bolts to 47-65 ft. lbs.
31. Remove engine support fixture, then install heater bypass tube bracket.
32. Install intake manifold support upper bolts. **Torque** all support retaining bolts to 23-33 ft. lbs.
33. Install starter motor upper retaining bolts. **Torque** to 23-33 ft. lbs.
34. Position ground wire and install dipstick tube retaining bolt.
35. Route shift cable and connect to neutral safety switch, then route and install kickdown cable to throttle housing.
36. Connect transaxle electrical connectors, then the speedometer cable.
37. **On 1994 models**, proceed as follows:
   a. Connect ground strap at front of transaxle.
   b. Install air cleaner/volume air flow sensor assembly support brackets, then the air cleaner/volume air flow sensor assembly.
   c. Install harness retaining strap to battery support bracket, then the battery support bracket, battery and battery tray.
38. **On 1992-93 models**, install air cleaner assembly, then the battery.
39. **On all models**, connect battery terminals, then fill transaxle with fluid according to manufacturer's specifications.
40. Start engine, then check for leaks.

1.8L/4-109 & 1.9L/4-114
Removal

1. Disconnect battery cables from battery, then remove battery and battery tray from vehicle.
2. Disconnect wiring harness retaining clip from battery tray.
3. Remove air cleaner assembly.
4. Disconnect shift control cable from manual lever.
5. Disconnect speedometer cable from transaxle by unsnapping cable at speedometer driven gear.
6. Disconnect transaxle electrical connectors, then separate wiring harness from transaxle clips.
7. Remove neutral safety switch wiring brackets from top of transaxle.
8. Disconnect ground wires from top of transaxle.

9. Remove starter motor, then disconnect neutral safety switch wiring connectors.
10. Install three bar engine support tool No. D88L-6000-A or equivalent.
11. Disconnect kickdown cable at throttle cam.
12. Place drain pan under transaxle, then disconnect cooler lines at transaxle.
13. Remove upper transaxle mount nuts, then the mount.
14. Remove upper transaxle housing to engine retaining bolts.
15. Disconnect oxygen sensor electrical connector, then the transaxle vent hose and vehicle speed sensor.
16. Raise and support vehicle, then remove front wheel and tire assemblies.
17. Using hammer and flat punch, straighten detent in halfshaft nut.
18. Remove halfshaft nuts, then the tie rod to steering knuckle nut.
19. Remove control arm ball joint to steering knuckle nuts and bolts, then separate lower ball joints from steering knuckles.
20. Disconnect halfshaft mid-bearing bracket from back of engine, then remove tie rod ends from both steering knuckles.
21. Remove three lower engine and transaxle splash guards from vehicle.
22. Remove torque converter inspection plate, then torque converter to flexplate retaining nuts.
23. Remove lower transaxle to engine oil pan bolts.
24. Remove lower crossmember from chassis.
25. Remove halfshafts from transaxle, then install transaxle plugs tool No. T88C-7025-AH or equivalent, into differential side gears. **Failure to install plugs may cause differential side gears to become improperly positioned.**
26. Remove transaxle oil pan and drain transaxle fluid.
27. Install transaxle oil pan and drain plug.
28. Position transmission jack under transaxle, then secure transaxle to jack with safety chains or suitable equipment.
29. Remove lower bolts securing transaxle to engine, then carefully lower transaxle from vehicle.

Installation

The following procedure has been revised by a Technical Service Bulletin.

A pin is used to hold the throttle valve in a fixed position on new or remanufactured service replacement transaxle assemblies.

The pin is used during the assembling process to make installation of the control valve easier. When installing a new or remanufactured 4EAT transaxle, ensure to remove the pin and install a new retaining bolt. **Failure to remove pin from the throttle cam will hold the transaxle throttle lever in a fixed position resulting in a shift concern.**

1. Position transaxle to engine, then install lower transaxle bolts. **Torque** bolts to 41-59 ft. lbs.
2. Position torque converter to flex plate, then install torque converter to flexplate nuts. **Torque** nuts to 25-36 ft. lbs.
3. Install torque converter inspection plate.
4. Remove two transaxle plugs from differential side gears, then install halfshaft assemblies.
5. Connect halfshaft mid-bearing bracket to back of engine.
6. Install crossmember to transaxle mounts. **Torque** lower crossmember to transaxle nuts to 27-38 ft. lbs.
7. Install crossmember to chassis bolts. **Torque** bolts to 47-66 ft. lbs.
8. Install lower transaxle to oil pan retaining bolts. **Torque** bolts to 27-38 ft. lbs.
9. Install engine and transaxle splash guards to vehicle.
10. Install starter motor assembly.
11. Position lower ball joints into steering knuckle assemblies. **Torque** lower ball joint to steering knuckle assembly nuts and bolts to 32-43 ft. lbs.
12. Position tie rod ends into steering knuckle assemblies. **Torque** retaining nuts to 31-42 ft. lbs.
13. Install wheel and tire assemblies. **Torque** wheel lug nuts to 65-88 ft. lbs.
14. Lower vehicle.
15. Install upper transaxle to engine retaining bolts. **Torque** to 41-59 ft. lbs.
16. Install upper transaxle mount. **Torque** retaining nuts to 49-69 ft. lbs.
17. Connect transaxle vent hose, then the vehicle speed sensor and oxygen sensor electrical connectors.
18. Connect speedometer cable, cooler lines, then the kickdown cable at throttle body.
19. Remove three bar engine support tool No. T88C-7025-AH, then connect ground wires to transaxle.
20. Connect 4EAT electrical connectors, then the transaxle wiring harness to retaining clips.
21. Connect manual lever position switch bracket and wiring connectors.
22. Connect shift control cable to cable bracket and selector lever. **Torque** selector lever attaching locknut to 33-47 ft. lbs. **Do not use any type of power wrench to tighten locknut. Damage to transaxle may result.**
23. Install battery tray, then the battery.
24. Connect wiring harness clip to battery tray.
25. Install air cleaner assembly, then connect battery cables.
26. Add specified transaxle fluid, then check for proper fluid level and leaks.

2.0L/4-133 & 2.5L/V6-152
Removal

1. Disconnect battery cables from battery, then remove battery hold-down, battery and battery tray from vehicle.
2. Remove air cleaner assembly.

3. Remove shift cable from Manual Lever Position (MLP) switch arm. Use screwdriver to pry cable from switch arm.
4. Remove shift cable from cable bracket as follows:
   a. Remove lock tab retainer.
   b. Press in on lock tabs to release cable, then pull cable through bracket.
5. Disconnect MLP switch electrical connector.
6. **On models with 2.0L/4-121 engine,** disconnect heated oxygen sensor electrical connector.
7. **On models with 2.5L/V6-152 engine,** disconnect two heated oxygen sensor electrical connectors.
8. **On all models,** disconnect 4EAT electrical connector, then remove wiring harness bracket from cable bracket.
9. **On models with 2.5L/V6-152 engine,** remove starter motor.
10. **On all models,** disconnect vehicle speed sensor.
11. Remove ground wire bracket, then the ground wire.
12. **On 1993 models,** remove harness support bracket to engine block located at rear transaxle mount.
13. **On 1994 models,** remove harness support bracket to generator located at rear transaxle mount.
14. **On all models,** disconnect and plug oil cooler outlet and inlet hoses, then remove four transaxle to engine mount bolts.
15. Install Three Bar Engine Support tool No. 014-00750 or equivalent.
16. Remove lefthand transaxle mount nuts and bolts, then the through bolt.
17. Remove fuel filter bracket nuts from lefthand transaxle mount, then position fuel filter and bracket aside.
18. Remove lefthand transaxle mount, then disconnect pulse signal generator electrical connector.
19. Raise and support vehicle, then remove front wheel and tire assemblies and both splash shields.
20. Remove transverse member, then the transaxle cradle.
21. Remove transaxle lower mount bolts, then the lower mount.
22. Remove halfshafts, then install transaxle plug set tool No. T88C-7025-AH or equivalent, into differential side gears. **Failure to install transaxle plugs may allow differential side gears to become improperly positioned.**
23. **On models with 2.0L/4-121 engine,** remove intake manifold support bracket.
24. **On all models,** disconnect transaxle vent hose and dipstick tube.
25. **On models with 2.0L/4-121 engine,** remove starter motor.
26. **On models with 2.5L/V6-152 engine,** remove inspection cover.
27. **On all models,** remove four torque converter to flex plate nuts.
28. Position transmission jack under transaxle, then secure transaxle to jack.

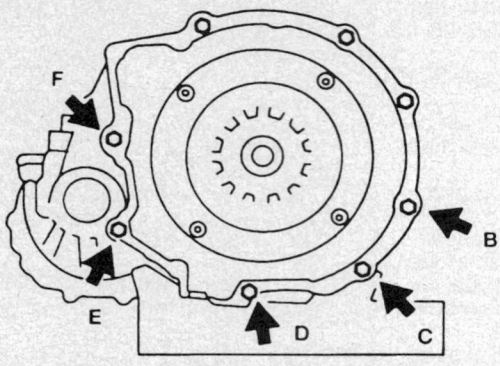

Fig. 12   Transaxle & transaxle to engine bolt tightening sequence. 2.0L/4–121 engine

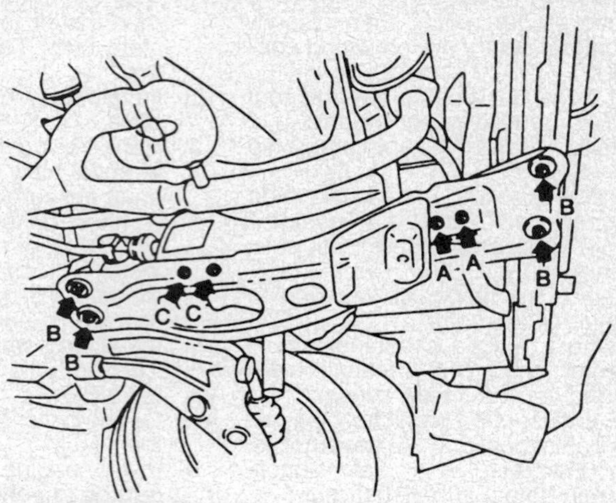

29. Remove engine-to-transaxle and transaxle to engine mounting bolts.
30. Remove three rear transaxle mount bolts.
31. Separate transaxle from engine bock, then slightly tilt transaxle and engine to ease removal.
32. Remove transaxle from engine, then lower transaxle from vehicle.

Installation

1. Place transaxle on transmission jack. **Ensure transaxle is secure.**
2. Raise transaxle to proper height, then align torque converter studs and flexplate holes.
3. **On models with 2.0L/4-121 engine,** install transaxle to engine mounting bolts. **Torque** mounting bolts to (B) 50-73 ft. lbs., (C) to 28-38 ft. lbs. and (F) to 50-73 ft. lbs., **Fig. 12.**
4. Install engine to transaxle mounting bolts. **Torque** mounting bolts to (D) 14-18 ft. lbs., (E) to 28-38 ft. lbs. and (F) to 50-73 ft. lbs., **Fig. 12.**
5. **On models with 2.5L/V6-152 engine,** install engine to transaxle mounting bolts. **Torque** bolts to 50-73 ft. lbs.
6. **On all models,** install rear transaxle mount bolts. **Torque** bolts to 50-68 ft. lbs.
7. **On models with 2.5L/V6-152 engine,** install inspection cover.
8. **On models with 2.0L/4-121 engine,** install intake manifold support bracket and bolts. **Torque** bolts to 27-38 ft. lbs.
9. Install starter motor.
10. **On all models,** connect transaxle vent hose, then install dipstick tube. **Torque** dipstick mounting bolts to 71-88 inch lbs.
11. Remove transaxle plugs, then install halfshafts.
12. Install transaxle lower mount. **Torque** lower mount to 50-68 ft. lbs.
13. Remove jack from under transaxle.
14. Install transaxle cradle. **Torque** cradle bolts to (A) 55-77 ft. lbs., (B) 50-68 ft. lbs. and (C) to 32-44 ft. lbs., **Fig. 13.**
15. Install transverse member. **Torque** bolts to 68-96 ft. lbs.
16. Install splash shields. **Torque** mounting screws to 71-88 inch lbs.

17. Install front wheel and tire assemblies. **Torque** wheel lug nuts to 66-86 ft. lbs.
18. Lower vehicle.
19. Install transaxle to engine mounting bolts. Tighten bolts to specifications.
20. Connect vehicle speed sensor, then install ground wire bracket and ground wire.
21. Connect pulse signal generator electrical connector.
22. **On 1993 models,** install harness support bracket to engine block located at rear transaxle mount.
23. **On 1994 models,** install harness support bracket to generator located at rear transaxle mount.
24. **On all models,** install lefthand transaxle mount, nuts and bolt. **Torque** nuts and bolts to 50-68 ft. lbs.
25. Install lefthand transaxle mount through bolt. **Torque** through bolt to 63-86 ft. lbs.
26. Remove engine support bar.
27. Install fuel filter bracket to lefthand transaxle mount. **Torque** bracket bolts to 71-88 inch lbs.
28. Connect oil cooler outlet and inlet hoses.
29. **On models with 2.5L/V6-152 engine,** install starter motor.
30. **On all models,** connect 4EAT electrical connector.
31. **On models with 2.0L/4-121 engine,** connect heated oxygen sensor electrical connector.
32. **On models with 2.5L/V6-152,** connect two heated oxygen sensor electrical connectors.
33. **On all models,** install shift cable to cable bracket as follows:
    a. Insert shift cable through cable bracket.
    b. Pull cable until lock tabs engage, then install lock tab retainer.
34. Install shift cable on MLP switch arm, then connect MLP switch electrical

Fig. 13

TIGHTENING TORQUE
A: 75 – 104 N·m (55 – 77 LB-FT)
B: 67 – 93 N·m (50 – 68 LB-FT)
C: 44 – 60 N·m (32 – 44 LB-FT)

Fig. 13   Tightening transaxle cradle nuts & bolts. 2.0L/4–133 & 2.5L/V6–152 engines

connector.
35. Snap wiring harness bracket on cable bracket, then install air cleaner assembly.
36. Install battery tray, battery and battery hold-down, then connect battery cables.
37. Add specified transaxle fluid, then check for leaks and check fluid level.

2.2L/4-133

Removal

1. Remove battery and battery carrier.
2. Disconnect main fuse block and distributor lead.
3. Disconnect air flow meter connector, then remove air cleaner assembly.
4. Remove resonance chamber, then the resonance chamber bracket.
5. **On models with electro-mechanical instrument cluster,** disconnect speedometer cable from transaxle.
6. **On models with electronic instrument cluster,** disconnect speed sensor harness connector from transaxle.
7. **On all models,** disconnect five transaxle electrical connectors, then separate transaxle wiring harness from transaxle clips.
8. Disconnect two ground wires, then the range selector cable from transaxle case.
9. Disconnect kickdown cable from throttle cam.
10. Raise and support vehicle, then remove front wheel and tire assemblies.
11. Remove splash shields, then drain transaxle fluid.
12. Disconnect oil cooler inlet and outlet hoses. Plug hoses to prevent fluid leakage.
13. Remove both stabilizer link assemblies.
14. Remove tie rod nuts and cotter pins,

then disconnect both tie rod ends.

15. Remove bolts and nuts from both lower arm ball joints.
16. Pull lower arms down to separate from knuckles.
17. Remove righthand joint shaft bracket.
18. Remove halfshafts from transaxle by prying with a bar inserted between shaft and transaxle case. Support halfshafts in vehicle with wire.
19. Install two transaxle plugs tool No. T88C-7025-AH or equivalent, into differential side gears. **Failure to install transaxle plugs may allow differential side gears to become improperly positioned.**
20. Remove gusset plate to transaxle bolts.
21. Remove torque converter cover, then the torque converter nuts.
22. Remove starter motor and access brackets.
23. Install engine support bar tool No. D79P-6000-A or equivalent, and attach to engine hanger.
24. Remove center transaxle mount and bracket, then the lefthand transaxle mount.
25. Remove nut and bolt attaching righthand transaxle mount to frame.
26. Remove crossmember and the lefthand lower arm as an assembly.
27. Position transmission jack under transaxle, then secure transaxle to jack.
28. Remove six engine to transaxle attaching bolts.
29. Insert screwdriver between flex plate and converter, then carefully disengage studs. **Before transaxle can be lowered out of vehicle, torque converter studs must be clear of flex plate.**
30. Lower transaxle from vehicle.

Installation

The following procedure has been revised by a Technical Service Bulletin.

A pin is used to hold the throttle valve in a fixed position on new or remanufactured service replacement transaxle assemblies.

The pin is used during the assembling process to make installation of the control valve easier. When installing a new or remanufactured 4EAT transaxle, ensure to remove the pin and install a new retaining bolt. **Failure to remove pin from the throttle cam will hold the transaxle throttle lever in a fixed position resulting in a shift concern.**

1. Place transaxle on transmission jack and secure.
2. Raise transaxle to proper height and mount transaxle to engine. **Align torque converter studs and flex plate holes.**
3. Install six engine to transaxle bolts. **Torque** bolts to 66-86 ft. lbs.
4. Install center transaxle mount and bracket. **Torque** bolts to 27-40 ft. lbs. and nuts to 47-66 ft. lbs.
5. Install lefthand transaxle mount. **Torque** transaxle to mount nut to 63-86 ft. lbs., then the mount to bracket nut and bolt to 49-69 ft. lbs.
6. Install crossmember and lefthand lower arm as an assembly. **Torque** bolts to 27-40 ft. lbs., then the nuts to 35-69 ft. lbs.
7. Install righthand transaxle mount bolt and nut. **Torque** bolt and nut to 63-86ft. lbs.
8. Install starter motor and access brackets.
9. Install torque converter to flex plate nuts. **Torque** nuts to 32-45 ft. lbs.
10. Install torque converter cover. **Torque** bolts to 69-95 inch lbs.
11. Install gusset plate to transaxle bolts. **Torque** to 27-38 ft. lbs.
12. Replace circlips on end of each halfshaft, then remove transaxle plugs and install halfshafts to transaxle.
13. Attach lower arm ball joints to knuckles.
14. Install tie rod ends. **Torque** nuts to 22-33 ft. lbs.
15. Install new cotter pins to tie rod ends.
16. Install lower arm ball joint bolts and nuts. **Torque** bolts and nuts to 32-40 ft. lbs.
17. Install stabilizer link assemblies, noting the following:
    a. **Torque** nuts on each assembly until one inch (25.4 mm) of bolt thread can be measured from upper nut.
    b. Secure upper nut and back off lower nut to reach **torque** of 12-17 ft. lbs.
18. Connect oil cooler inlet and outlet hoses, then install splash shields.
19. Install front wheel and tire assemblies. **Torque** lug nuts to 65-87 ft. lbs.
20. Lower vehicle.
21. Connect kickdown cable, then the range selector cable. **Torque** selector cable to transaxle bolt to 22-29 ft. lbs.
22. Connect two ground wires to transaxle case, then **torque** to 69-95 inch lbs.
23. Attach five transaxle electrical connectors to transaxle case, then the transaxle wiring harness to transaxle clips.
24. **On models with electromechanical instrument cluster, connect speedometer cable.**
25. **On models with electronic instrument cluster,** connect speed sensor harness connector.
26. **On all models,** install resonance chamber and bracket. **Torque** to 69-95 inch lbs.
27. Install air cleaner assembly. **Torque** bolt to 23-30 ft. lbs., then the nuts to 69-95 inch lbs.
28. Connect air flow meter electrical connector and distributor lead.
29. Connect main fuse block. **Torque** to 69-95 inch lbs.
30. Install battery carrier and battery, then connect battery cables.
31. Remove engine support bracket.
32. Add specified transaxle fluid, then check for leaks and fluid level.
33. Adjust kickdown cable as outlined under "Adjustments."

3.0L/V6-182
Removal

1. Remove battery and battery carrier,

then disconnect main fuse block.
2. Disconnect air cleaner hose from air cleaner, then remove air cleaner assembly.
3. Remove speed control actuator mounting bolts and nuts, then position speed control actuator aside.
4. Disconnect vehicle speed sensor or speedometer cable from transaxle.
5. Disconnect transaxle fluid cooling lines from radiator assembly, then cap lines.
6. Disconnect electrical connectors from transaxle, then the wiring harness from routing brackets on transaxle.
7. Disconnect shift cable from transaxle by removing 21mm retaining nut.
8. Remove horseshoe clip from shift cable and routing bracket, then disconnect cable from bracket.
9. Remove transaxle wiring harness bracket, then the two ground straps from transaxle assembly.
10. Loosen transaxle kickdown cable adjusting nuts at cable bracket, then disconnect cable from bracket.
11. Disconnect kickdown cable from throttle cam.
12. Install engine support bar tool No. D88L-6000-A with necessary hooks to support engine and transaxle.
13. Remove all accessible transaxle to engine retaining bolts from top of engine compartment.
14. Remove upper transaxle mounting nuts.
15. Raise and support vehicle, then remove front wheels.
16. Remove inner fender splash shields.
17. Drain transaxle fluid.
18. Remove stabilizer link assemblies from lower control arms.
19. Remove lower control arm ball joint to steering knuckle pinch bolts.
20. Separate ball joints from steering knuckle by prying downward on lower control arm while pushing inward on rotor.
21. Remove mounting bolts from righthand halfshaft dynamic damper.
22. Remove halfshaft from transaxle by prying on bar inserted between shaft and transaxle case.
23. Install two transaxle plugs tool No. T88C-7025-AH or equivalent, into differential side gears. **Failure to install transaxle plugs may result in misalignment of differential side gears.**
24. Remove starter motor and bracket, then the transaxle support bracket.
25. Remove inspection plate from transaxle, then the torque converter retaining nuts.
26. Position transmission jack under transaxle for support.
27. Remove transaxle rear lower mount bolts.
28. Remove transaxle front lower mount through bolt.
29. Remove lefthand front crossmember and lower control arm assembly.
30. Remove remaining transaxle to engine bolts.
31. **Before transaxle can be lowered out of vehicle, torque converter studs must be clear of flexplate.** In-

sert screwdriver between flexplate and converter, then carefully disengage studs.

32. Lower transaxle assembly from vehicle.

Installation

The following procedure has been revised by a Technical Service Bulletin.

A pin is used to hold the throttle valve in a fixed position on new or remanufactured service replacement transaxle assemblies.

The pin is used during the assembling process to make installation of the control valve easier. When installing a new or remanufactured 4EAT transaxle, ensure to remove the pin and install a new retaining bolt. **Failure to remove pin from the throttle cam will hold the transaxle throttle lever in a fixed position resulting in a shift concern.**

1. Place transaxle on transmission jack. **Ensure transaxle is secure.**
2. Raise transaxle to proper height, then mount transaxle to engine.
3. Align torque converter studs and flexplate holes, then install transaxle to engine lower bolts. **Torque** bolts to 66-86 ft. lbs
4. Install lefthand front crossmember and lower control arm assembly. **Torque** crossmember bolts to 27-40 ft. lbs, then the crossmember nut to 55-69 ft. lbs.
5. Install transaxle front lower mount through bolt. **Torque** to 66-86 ft. lbs.
6. Install transaxle rear lower mount bolts. **Torque** bolts to 49-69 ft. lbs.
7. Install torque converter nuts. **Torque** nuts to 32-45 ft. lbs.
8. Install inspection plate, then the transaxle support bracket.
9. Install starter motor and bracket.
10. Install new circlips to end of each halfshaft.
11. Remove transaxle plugs, then install halfshafts.
12. Install mounting bolts to righthand halfshaft dynamic damper. **Torque** bolts to 31-46 ft. lbs.
13. Install lower control arm ball joints in steering knuckles.
14. Install ball joint pinch bolts. **Torque** pinch bolts to 27-40 ft. lbs.
15. Install stabilizer link assemblies, noting the following:
    a. **Torque** nuts on each assembly until one inch (25.4 mm) of bolt thread can be measured from upper nut.
    b. Secure upper nut and back off lower nut to reach **torque** of 12-17 ft. lbs.
16. Install right inner fender splash guard. (Installation of the lefthand splash guard will be done after the kickdown cable has been adjusted.)
17. Install front wheels. **Torque** wheel lug nuts to 65-87 ft. lbs.
18. Lower vehicle, then install transaxle upper mount nuts. **Torque** nuts to 47-66 ft. lbs.
19. Install remaining transaxle to engine retaining bolts. **Torque** bolts to 66-86 ft. lbs.
20. Remove engine support bar, then connect transaxle kickdown cable to throttle cam.
21. Connect kickdown cable to cable bracket, then tighten adjusting nuts.
22. Connect two ground straps to transaxle, then Install transaxle wiring harness bracket.
23. Connect shift cable to its routing bracket, then install horseshoe clip.
24. Connect shift cable to transaxle, then install retaining nut. **Torque** nut to 33-47 ft. lbs. **Do not use any type of power wrench to tighten retaining nut. Damage to transaxle may result.**
25. Connect transaxle electrical connectors, then connect wiring harness routing brackets to transaxle.
26. Unplug, then install transaxle cooling lines to radiator assembly.
27. Connect vehicle speed sensor or speedometer cable to transaxle.
28. Install speed control actuator, then the air cleaner assembly.
29. Connect air cleaner hose to air cleaner.
30. Connect main fuse block, then install battery tray and battery.
31. Add specified transaxle fluid, then check for leaks and fluid level.
32. Adjust kickdown cable as outlined under "Adjustments."

TIGHTENING SPECIFICATIONS

Component	Torque/Ft. Lbs.
Actuator Support	8–10
Bearing Housing	14–19
Center Transaxle Mount Bolts	27–40
Center Transaxle Mount Nuts	47–66
Converter Cover	69–95 ①
Crossmember Bolts	27–40
Crossmember Nuts	55–69
Dipstick Tube	61–87 ①
Drain Plug	29–43
Fluid Temperature Switch	22–29
Gusset Plate To Transaxle	27–38
Left Mount To Bracket	49–69
Line Pressure Plug	43–87 ①
Manual Plate	30–41
Neutral Safety Switch	69–95 ①

Component	Torque/Ft. Lbs.
Oil Line Plug	23–35
Oil Pan	69–95
Oil Pump	14–19
Pulse Generator	69–95 ①
Range Selector To Transaxle	22–29
Right Transaxle Mount	63–86
Switch Box	12–17
Throttle Cable Bracket	14–19
Throttle Cam	61–87 ①
Torque Converter	32–45
Transaxle Case To Converter Housing	27–38
Transaxle To Engine	66–86
Transaxle To left Mount	63–86
Valve Body	95–130 ①

① —Inch lbs.

FRONT WHEEL DRIVE AXLES

TABLE OF CONTENTS

Tempo & Topaz

INDEX

TROUBLESHOOTING

NOISE & VIBRATION IN TURNS

Clicking, popping or grinding noises while turning may be caused by the following:

1. Cut or damaged CV joint boots, resulting in contaminated lube in outboard or inboard CV joints.
2. Loose CV joint clamps.
3. Worn, damaged or improperly installed wheel bearings.

VIBRATION AT HIGHWAY SPEEDS

1. Out of balance front wheels or tires.
2. Improperly seated outboard CV joint in front wheel hub.
3. Bent interconnecting shaft.
4. Front tires out of round.

SHUDDER OR VIBRATION DURING ACCELERATION

1. Excessively worn or damaged inboard or outboard CV joint.
2. Excessively high CV joint operating angle caused by improper ride height.

DRIVESHAFT OR CV JOINT PULL-OUT

Engine Or Transaxle Misaligned

1. Check engine mounts for damage.

Front Suspension Components Worn Or Damaged

1. Check for worn bushings or bent front suspension components.

Improperly Installed Or Missing Retainers

1. Check for CV joint circlip missing or not properly seated in transaxle side gear.

DRIVESHAFT

REPLACE

If removing both right and left side driveshafts, plugs, tool No. T81P-1177B or equivalent, must be installed. Failure to do so may result in dislocation of differential side gears, necessitating transaxle disassembly to re-align the gears. Also, driveshaft removal and installation procedures are the same for manual and automatic transaxles except for the following: due to automatic transaxle case configuration the right side driveshaft assembly must be removed first. Removal tool No. T81P-4026A or equivalent is then inserted into transaxle to remove left side inner constant velocity joint assembly from transaxle. If only the left side driveshaft is to be removed from the vehicle, remove right side driveshaft assembly from the transaxle case only and secure to underside of vehicle, then remove left side driveshaft assembly. The hub nut and lower control arm to steering knuckle attaching bolt and nut must be discarded after removal and new nuts and bolts installed.

Driveshaft assembly removal and installation procedures are the same for ATX/FLC (automatic transaxle/fluid lock-up converter) applications as for MTX (manual transaxle) applications except the ATX/FLC case configuration requires that the righthand driveshaft assembly be removed first. Differential rotator, tool No. T81P-4026-A or equivalent, should then be inserted into the transaxle to drive the lefthand inboard constant velocity joint assembly from the transaxle. If only the lefthand driveshaft assembly is to be removed for service, remove the righthand driveshaft assembly from the transaxle only. After removal, support it with a length of wire, then drive the lefthand driveshaft assembly from the transaxle case. **Do not begin this removal procedure unless the following parts are known to be available, a new hub retainer nut, a new longer lower control arm to steering knuckle attaching bolt and nut and a new inboard constant velocity joint stub shaft snap ring. Once removed, these components must not be reused during the assembly procedure. Their torque holding ability or retention capability is greatly diminished during removal.**

1. Loosen hub nut without unstaking. Use of a chisel or similar tool to unstake nut may damage spindle threads.
2. Raise and support vehicle and remove wheel assemblies.
3. Remove hub nut and washer. **Discard hub attaching nut, it is a torque prevailing design and cannot be reused.**
4. Remove bolt attaching brake hose routing clip to suspension strut.
5. Remove nut from ball joint to steering knuckle attaching bolt, then drive bolt from knuckle using a punch and a hammer. **Discard bolt and nut, they are torque prevailing design and cannot be reused.**

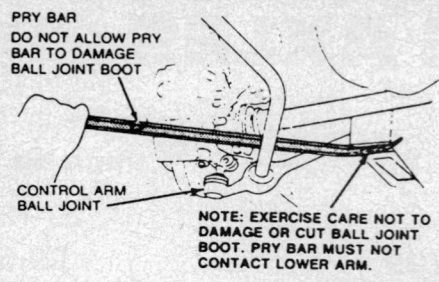

Fig. 1 Ball joint separation from steering knuckle

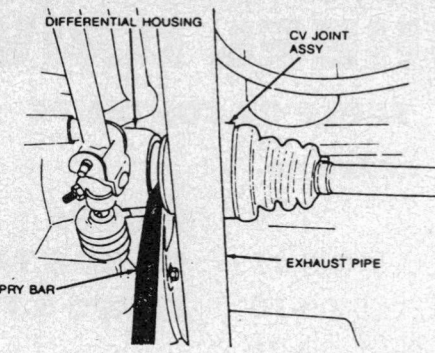

Fig. 2 Driveshaft removal from differential housing

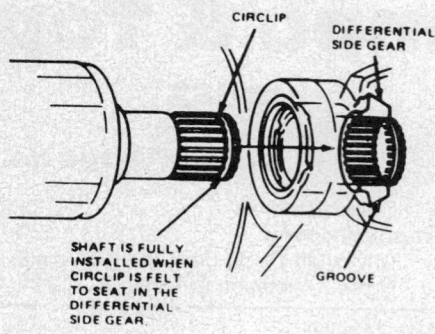

Fig. 4 Inner constant velocity joint installation into differential side gear

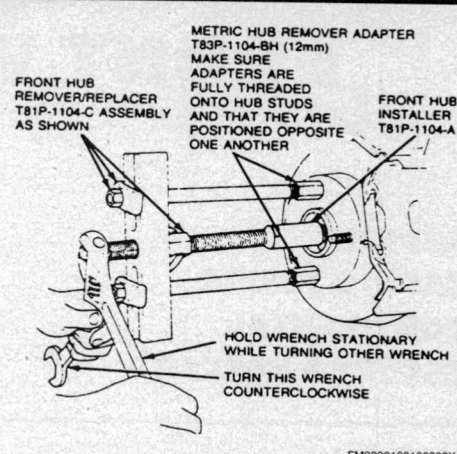

Fig. 3 Outer constant velocity joint separation from hub

6. Separate ball joint from steering knuckle using pry bar, **Fig. 1. Lower ball joints fit into a pocket formed in the plastic disc brake shield. The shield must be positioned away from the ball joint while removing ball joint from steering knuckle.**

7. Remove driveshaft from differential housing using a pry bar. Use caution not to damage dust deflector located between shaft and case, **Fig. 2.** If an automatic transaxle driveshaft assembly cannot be removed from differential by using a pry bar, insert a large bladed screwdriver between differential pinion shaft and inboard constant velocity joint stub shaft. Sharply tap on screwdriver handle, to free driveshaft from differential. **Use caution not to damage differential oil seal, constant velocity joint boot or constant velocity joint dust deflector.**

8. Suspend shaft from a sturdy underbody component. **Do not allow shaft to hang as outboard CV joint damage may result.**

9. Separate outer constant velocity joint from hub using puller, tool No. T81P-1104C or equivalent,**Fig. 3,**and adapters, tools No. T81P-1104B and T81P-1104A or equivalent. **Do not use a hammer to separate outboard constant velocity joint stub shaft from hub as damage to internal components may result.**

10. Reverse procedure to install, noting the following:
   a. Install new circlip on inboard constant velocity joint stub shaft.
   b. Align splines of inboard constant velocity joint stub shaft with splines in differential.
   c. Push joint into differential until circlip seats in side gear, **Fig. 4.**
   d. **Torque** new control arm to steering knuckle nut to 40-54 ft. lbs.
   e. **Torque** brake hose routing clip to strut attaching bolt to 8 ft. lbs.
   f. **Torque** wheel lug nut to 80-105 ft. lbs.
   g. **Torque** new hub nut to 180-200 ft. lbs., during tightening, an audible click will indicate the proper ratcheting function of hub attaching nut, as nut tightens, ensure one of three locking tabs on nut is aligned with CV joint shaft slot, if nut is damaged or more then one locking tab

is missing, replace hub attaching nut.

DRIVESHAFT SERVICE
Constant Velocity Joint
OUTBOARD JOINTS
Removal

Outboard joints are permanently attached to driveshafts during production. Other then dust boot replacement, no attempt to service these assemblies should be made. Boot replacement first requires that the inboard joint be removed from the shaft so the old boot may be withdrawn and the new boot installed from the inboard side. Replace the outboard boot as described under "Outer Joint Service."

Service

Outboard joints are permanently attached to driveshafts during production, **Fig. 5.** Other then dust boot replacement, no attempt to service these assemblies should be made. Boot replacement first requires that the inboard joint be removed from the shaft so that the old boot may be withdrawn and the new boot installed from the inboard side. To replace the outboard boot, refer to "Inner Joint Service" to remove inner joint, then proceed as follows:

1. With inboard joint removed, slide replacement outboard dust boot onto shaft.

2. Prior to positioning the boot over the outer joint, pack joint and boot with about five ounces of High-Temp Constant Velocity Grease part no. E43Z-19590-A or equivalent.

3. Position boot over the joint and install clamps. Install inboard joint as described under "Inboard Joint Service."

Installation

1. Install new stop ring, if removed. Ensure that stop ring is properly seated in groove.

2. Install new circlip in groove nearest end of shaft. To avoid over expansion or twisting of circlip, start one end in groove and work circlip over stub shaft end and into groove. **These non symmetrical interconnecting shafts are different depending on application. The outboard end is approximately ¼ inch longer from end of shaft to end of boot groove than the inboard end. Be sure to install inboard and outboard joints at proper ends of the shaft.**

3. Install constant velocity joint boot, if removed, ensuring that boot is seated in groove. Tighten clamp so that it's secure but not too tight.

4. Before positioning boot over constant velocity joint, pack joint and boot as follows:
   a. **On inboard constant velocity joint,** fill boot with 45 grams of grease and pack joint with 90 grams of grease.
   b. **On outboard constant velocity joint,** fill boot with 45 grams of grease and pack joint with 45 grams of grease. **Use only lubricant E2FZ-19590-A or equivalent.**

5. Position boot upward toward end of shaft, then position constant velocity joint onto shaft and tap to position using plastic mallet. Joint is fully seated when circlip locks in groove cut into joint bearing inner race. Check for proper seating by trying to pull joint from shaft.

6. Remove all excess grease from external surfaces of constant velocity joint,

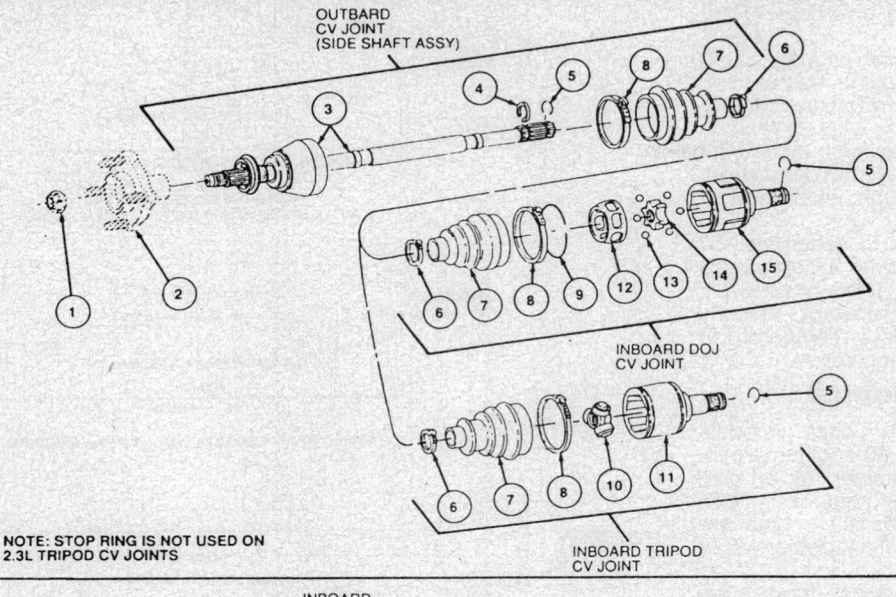

NOTE: STOP RING IS NOT USED ON
2.3L TRIPOD CV JOINTS

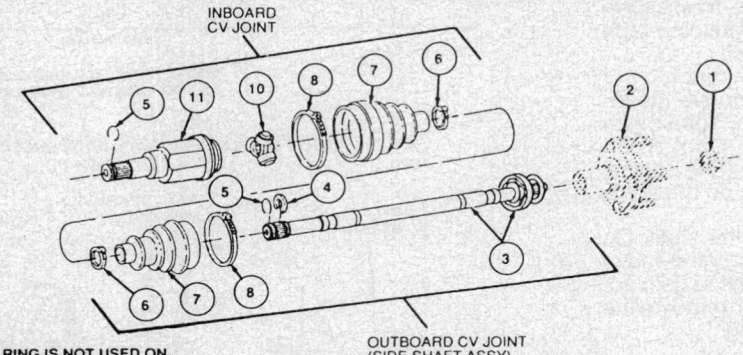

NOTE: STOP RING IS NOT USED ON
2.3L TRIPOD CV JOINTS

Item	Part Number	Description	Item	Part Number	Description
1	—	Hub Nut	10	—	Tripod Assy
2	—	Hub	11	—	Tripod Outer Race
3	—	Side Shaft Assy	12	—	Ball Cage
4	—	Stop Ring	13	—	Balls (Six)
5	—	Circlip	14	—	Inboard Joint Inner Race
6	—	Boot Clamp (Small)	15	—	Inboard Joint Outer Race and Stub Shaft
7	—	Boot	16	—	Circlip
8	—	Boot Clamp (Large)	17	—Dust Seal	
9	—	Wire Ring Ball Retainer			

FM3039200144000X

Fig. 5   Driveshaft assemblies. 1992–93

then position boot over constant velocity joint and move joint in or out to adjust to proper length, Fig. 6.

7. Before installing boot clamp, insert dulled screwdriver blade between boot and outer bearing race to allow trapped air to escape.
8. Ensure that boot is seated in groove, then install clamp securely but not too tight.

INBOARD JOINTS

REMOVAL

Double Offset Inboard Joint

1. Remove large boot clamp, roll boot back, and wipe away excess grease.
2. Remove wire ring bearing retainer

from outer race, then remove outer race.

3. Pull inner race and bearing assembly out until it rests on circlip, then, using pliers, spread stop ring and move it back on shaft.
4. Slide inner race and bearing assembly down shaft to expose circlip, then remove circlip.
5. Remove inner race and bearing assembly and, if necessary, remove boot.

SERVICE

Double Offset Inboard Joint

1. Remove large clamp, then slide boot back and wipe excess grease, **Fig. 7.** Inspect CV joint grease for contam-

ination by rubbing a small amount between two fingers. Any gritty feeling indicates contamination. If grease is contaminated, proceed with disassembly. If grease is not contaminated and joint was operating satisfactorily, add grease and replace boot.

2. Using a suitable tool, remove wire ring ball retainer from race.
3. Remove outer race.
4. Pull inner race and bearing assembly out until race contacts snap ring.
5. Using pliers, spread then slide snap ring back onto shaft.
6. Slide inner race and bearing assembly down the shaft to allow access to the snap ring.
7. Using a screwdriver, remove snap ring.

8. Remove inner race and bearing assembly.
9. Remove bearings from cage by prying with a dulled screwdriver. Use caution not to damage or scratch any components, **Fig. 8.**
10. Rotate inner race to align lands with cage windows, then remove race from bearing cage through wider end of cage, **Fig. 9.**
11. Reverse procedure to assemble. Fill CV joint outer race with 3.2 ounces of grease and spread 1.4 ounces in CV boot. Use Ford Constant Velocity Joint Grease (High Temperature) E43Z-19590-A or equivalent.

Inboard Tripot Joints

1992 Tempo and Topaz models equipped with 2.3L/4-140 engines are fitted with tripot joints retained by an outboard snap-ring. Tripot joints on Tempo/Topaz with 3.0L/V6-182 engine are fixed by an outboard circlip together with a stop ring.

1. Clamp driveshaft in a vise, then slightly bend back the tripot retaining tabs to allow for tripot removal.
2. Separate outer race from tripot.
3. Using snap ring pliers, remove the tripot snap ring on Tempo/Topaz with 2.3L/4-140 engine. On Tempo/Topaz with 3.0L/V6-182 engine, move the snap ring back on the shaft, **Fig. 10.**
4. Remove the tripot from the shaft. On Tempo/Topaz with 3.0L engine, move the tripot back on the shaft to gain access to the circlip, then remove the circlip, tripot and stop ring.
5. Remove joint dust boot.
6. Assemble the inboard joint by first sliding the joint dust boot onto the shaft.
7. **On Tempo/Topaz with 3.0L engine,** install the stop ring.
8. **On all models,** install tripot assembly with chamfered side inboard.
9. Using snap-ring pliers, install tripot snap ring. On Tempo/Topaz with 3.0L engine, install a new circlip. Fit the circlip by starting one end in the circlip groove and working the other over the stub shaft end and into the groove. Do not overexpand or twist the circlip during installation.
10. **On Tempo/Topaz with 3.0L engine,** compress circlip so that tripot assembly may be slid over it to expose stop ring groove, then using snap-ring pliers fully seat the stop ring into its groove.
11. Fill the tripot outer race with High-Temp Constant Velocity Joint Grease part no. E43Z-19590-A or equivalent.
12. Install the race over the tripot assembly and bend the tripot retaining tabs back into their original positions.
13. Remove all excess grease from the joint's external surfaces, then move dust boot into place. Adjust assembled length by manipulating joint axially, **Fig. 7.**
14. When driveshaft assembled length is as specified, use a dull screwdriver to pry up the dust boot so that any

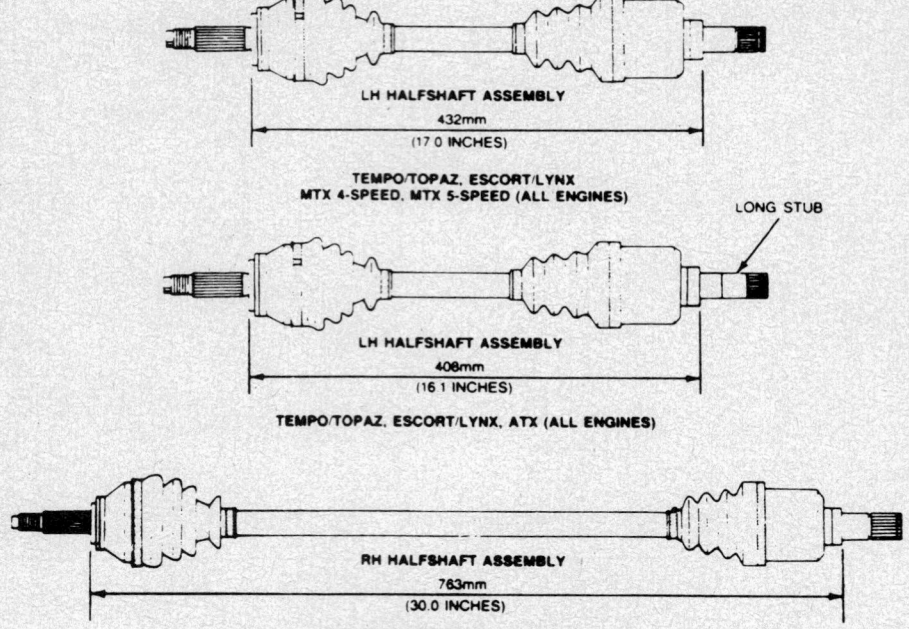

Fig. 6   Driveshaft assembled lengths

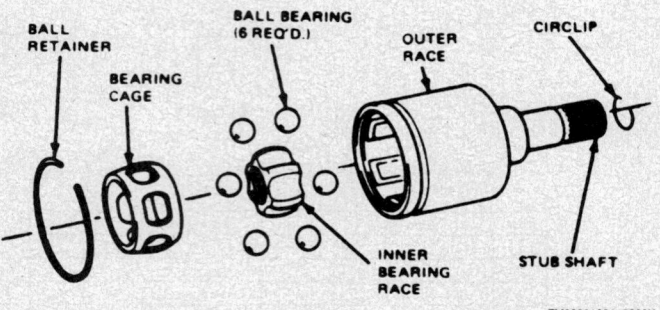

Fig. 7   Inner constant velocity joint assembly. Wire ring ball retainer type

trapped air in the joint assembly's cavity may escape. When the joint has been emptied of air, seat the boot in the race groove and clamp in position with crimping pliers.
15. Install a new circlip in the groove nearest the end of the shaft. **Do not twist or overexpand the circlip during installation.** Work the joint through its full range of travel. The joint should flex, extend and compress smoothly.

INSTALLATION

Double Offset Inboard Joints

1. Move circlip and stop ring back into their respective grooves on shaft. **Left hand interconnecting shaft is symmetrical and inboard and outboard constant velocity joints may be installed on either end. Right hand interconnecting shaft is non symmetrical and care must be taken so** that inboard and outboard constant velocity joints are correctly installed, **Fig. 11.**
2. Install constant velocity joint boot, if removed. Ensure that boot is seated in groove, then install clamp so that it is secure but not too tight.
3. Install new circlip in groove nearest end of shaft. To avoid over-expansion or twisting of circlip, start one end in groove and work circlip over stub shaft end and into groove.
4. Fill boot with 45 grams of grease and fill outer race with 90 grams of grease. Use only lubricant E2FZ-19590-A or equivalent.
5. Push inner race and bearing assembly into outer race by hand.
6. Install ball retainer into groove inside outer race.
7. With boot positioned upward toward end of shaft, install constant velocity joint using a hammer. Ensure that splines are aligned before hammering constant velocity joint onto shaft.

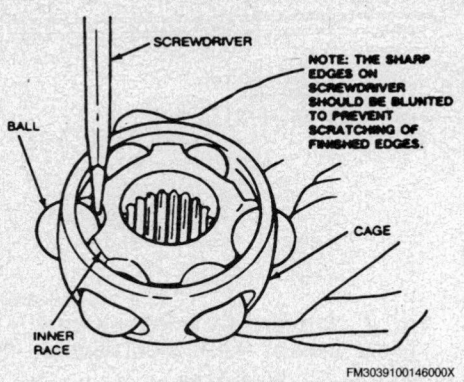

Fig. 8   Bearing removal from cage

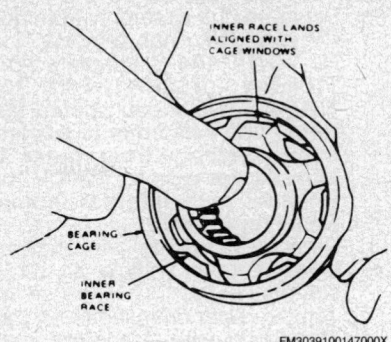

Fig. 9   Inner race removal from bearing cage

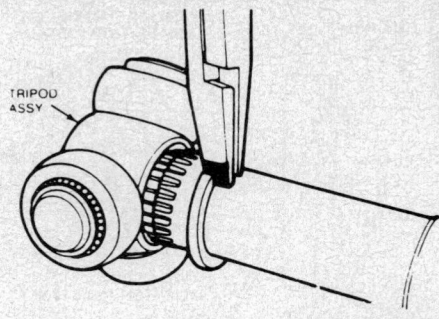

Fig. 10   Snap ring removal from shaft

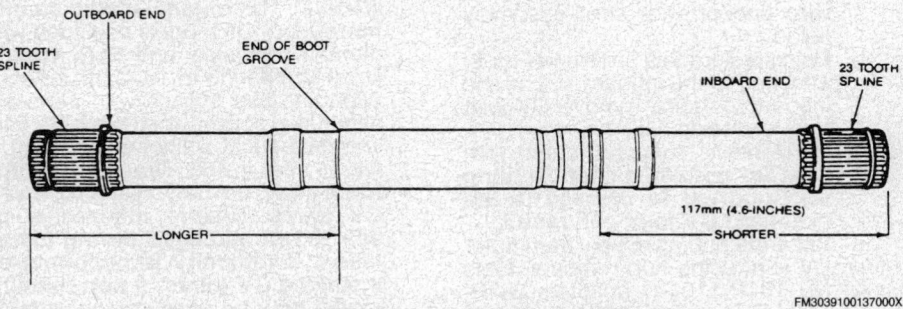

Fig. 11   Interconnecting shaft

8. Remove all excess grease from external surfaces of constant velocity joint, then position boot over constant velocity joint and move joint in or out to adjust to proper length, **Fig. 6.**
9. Before installing boot clamp, insert dulled screwdriver blade between boot and outer bearing race to allow trapped air to escape.
10. Ensure that boot is seated in groove, then install the clamp so that it is secure but not too tight.

Sable & Taurus

INDEX

TROUBLESHOOTING
NOISE & VIBRATION IN TURNS

Clicking, popping or grinding noises while turning may be caused by the following:
1. Cut or damaged CV joint boots, resulting in contaminated lube in outboard or inboard CV joints.
2. Loose CV joint clamps.
3. Worn, damaged or improperly installed wheel bearings.
4. Foreign object contacting driveshaft assembly.

VIBRATION AT HIGHWAY SPEEDS

1. Out of balance front wheels or tires.
2. Improperly seated outboard CV joint in front wheel hub.

3. Bent interconnecting shaft.
4. Front tires out of round.

SHUDDER OR VIBRATION DURING ACCELERATION

1. Excessively worn or damaged inboard or outboard CV joint.
2. Excessively high CV joint operating angles caused by improper ride height.

DRIVESHAFT OR CV JOINT PULL-OUT

1. Inboard CV joint circlip missing or improperly seated in transaxle side gear.
2. Engine or transaxle improperly positioned, check engine mounts.
3. Frame rail or strut tower improperly positioned or damaged.
4. Front suspension components worn or damaged.

DRIVESHAFT
REPLACE

If removing both right and left side driveshafts, plugs, tool No. T81P-1177-B or equivalent must be installed. Failure to do so may result in dislocation of differential side gears, necessitating transaxle disassembly to realign the gears. Also, driveshaft removal and installation procedures are the same for automatic and manual transaxles except for the following: due to the automatic transaxle case configuration, the right side driveshaft and linkshaft must be removed first. Removal tool No. T81P-4026-A or equivalent is then inserted into transaxle to remove left side inner constant velocity (CV) joint assembly from transaxle. If only the left side driveshaft is being removed from the vehicle, remove right side

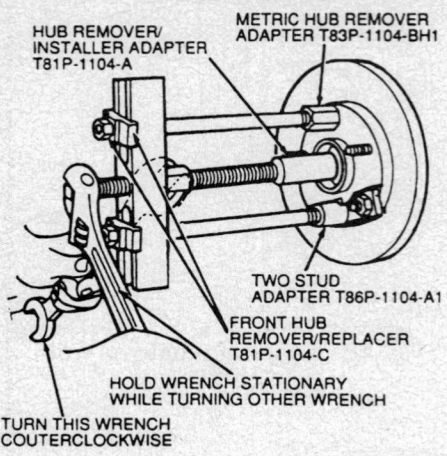

HUB REMOVER/
INSTALLER ADAPTER
T81P-1104-A

METRIC HUB REMOVER
ADAPTER T83P-1104-BH1

TWO STUD
ADAPTER T86P-1104-A1

FRONT HUB
REMOVER/REPLACER
T81P-1104-C

HOLD WRENCH STATIONARY
WHILE TURNING OTHER WRENCH

TURN THIS WRENCH
COUTERCLOCKWISE

FM3039100149000X

Fig. 1   Front hub separation from outer CV joint

driveshaft assembly from the transaxle case and secure it in a horizontal position to the underside of vehicle, then remove left side driveshaft assembly.

Do not begin this removal procedure unless the following parts are known to be available, a new hub retainer nut, a new lower control arm to steering knuckle attaching nut and bolt, a new inboard CV joint stub shaft circlip and a new link shaft snap ring. Once removed these components must not be reused. Their torque holding ability or retention capability is greatly diminished during removal.

Whenever removed, the hub nut, lower control arm-to-steering knuckle attaching nut and bolt and inboard CV joint stub shaft circlip must be replaced as their torque holding ability is destroyed during removal.

1. Loosen hub nut and lug nuts, then raise and support front of vehicle.
2. Remove wheel and tire assemblies, then remove hub nut and washer and discard nut.
3. Remove and discard lower ball joint-to-steering knuckle attaching nut and pinch bolt, then using a pry bar, separate ball joint from steering knuckle. **When separating ball joint from steering knuckle, use caution to avoid cutting or damaging ball joint boot.**
4. **On models equipped with anti-lock brakes,** remove ABS sensor and position aside.
5. **On all models,** remove stabilizer bar link at stabilizer bar.
6. To remove right side driveshaft and linkshaft from all models equipped with manual transaxle and fluid lockup converter (FLC), proceed as follows:
   a. Remove two bearing support-to-bracket attaching bolts, then slide link shaft out of transaxle. With wire, suspend end of shaft in horizontal position. **Do not allow shaft to hang unsupported as damage to the outboard CV joint can result.**

b. Separate hub assembly from outer CV joint using hub remover, tools No. T81P-1104-C, adapters T83P-1104-BH, T86P-1104-A1 and T81P-1104-A or equivalent, **Fig. 1. Never use a hammer to separate hub assembly from outer CV joint as damage to the CV joint threads and internal components may result.**
   c. Remove right side driveshaft and linkshaft from vehicle as an assembly.
7. To remove both driveshafts on models equipped with Automatic Overdrive Transaxles (AXOD) or left side driveshaft on models equipped with manual transaxle, proceed as follows:
   a. Turn steering hub to one side or wire and/or wire strut assembly aside.
   b. Using puller tools shown in **Fig. 2,** attached to the inboard side of the inboard CV joint, remove CV joint from transaxle.
   c. Horizontally suspend shaft with wire. **Do not allow shaft to hang unsupported as damage to the outboard CV joint can result.**
   d. Separate hub assembly from outer CV joint using hub remover, tools No. T81P-1104-C, adapters T83P-1104-BH, T86P-1104-A1 and T81P-1104-A or equivalent, **Fig. 1. Never use a hammer to separate hub assembly from outer CV joint as damage to the CV joint threads and internal components may result.**
   e. Remove driveshaft from vehicle.
8. To remove left side driveshaft from models equipped with fluid lockup converter (FLC), proceed as follows. **If removing both right and left side driveshafts, plugs, tool No. T81P-1177-B or equivalent must be installed. Failure to do so may result in dislocation of differential side gears, necessitating transaxle disassembly to re-align the gears.**
   a. Remove right side driveshaft assembly from the transaxle case and secure it in a horizontal position to the underside of vehicle, then remove left side driveshaft by inserting driver, tool No. T81P-4026-A or equivalent into right side driveshaft opening and driving left side driveshaft and CV joint from transaxle.
   b. Horizontally suspend shaft with wire. **Do not allow shaft to hang unsupported as damage to the outboard CV joint can result.**
   c. Separate hub assembly from outer CV joint using hub remover, tools No. T81P-1104-C, adapters T83P-1104-BH, T86P-1104-A1 and T81P-1104-A or equivalent, **Fig. 1. Never use a hammer to separate hub assembly from outer CV joint as damage to the CV joint threads and internal components may result.**
   d. Remove driveshaft from vehicle.
9. Prior to installation install new circlip

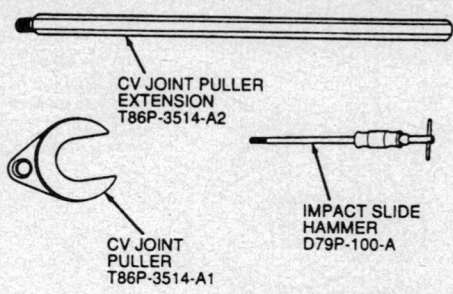

CV JOINT PULLER
EXTENSION
T86P-3514-A2

IMPACT SLIDE
HAMMER
D79P-100-A

CV JOINT
PULLER
T86P-3514-A1

FM3039100150000X

Fig. 2   Inboard CV joint removal tools. Except models equipped w/AXOD

on inboard CV joint stub shaft and/or linkshaft. **The original circlip cannot be reused.** On models equipped with manual transaxle and FLC, **torque** linkshaft bearing to 16-23 ft. lbs.
10. Align CV joint splines with transaxle differential splines, then push CV joint into differential splines until circlip is felt to seat inside side gears. **Some force may be necessary to insert CV joints. Ensure differential oil seal is not damaged during installation. If difficulty is encountered installing CV joints, a non-metallic mallet may be used on the outside joint CV joint stub shaft.**
11. Align CV joint splines with hub splines, then install stub shaft in hub as far as possible.
12. Temporarily fasten rotor to hub with two lug nuts and suitable washers. Install steel rod between lug nuts and use to prevent rotor from turning.
13. Install hub washer and new hub nut, then manually thread nut onto CV joint stub shaft as far as possible.
14. Connect steering knuckle to lower ball joint stud, then install new nut and bolt and **torque** to 40-55 ft. lbs.
15. **On models equipped with anti-lock brakes,** install ABS sensor.
16. **On all models,** connect stabilizer bar to stabilizer bar link, **torque** to 38-48 ft. lbs.
17. Install wheel and tire assembly, then lower vehicle to ground. **Torque** hub nut to 180-200 ft. lbs., **torque** wheel lug nuts to 80-105 ft. lbs.
18. Top off transaxle with lubricant using ESP-M2C185-A Mercon or equivalent.

DRIVESHAFT SERVICE

Constant Velocity Joint

OUTBOARD JOINTS

REMOVAL

C.V. Joint

During manufacture, CV joints components are matched and cannot be interchanged with components of other CV joint. If a CV joint component is defective, the entire CV joint should be replaced.

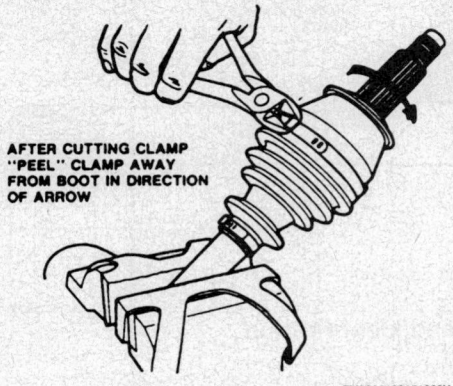

AFTER CUTTING CLAMP "PEEL" CLAMP AWAY FROM BOOT IN DIRECTION OF ARROW

FM3039100151000X

Fig. 3 Boot clamp removal

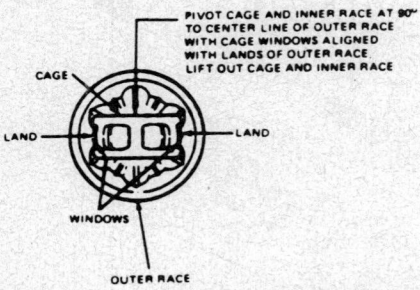

PIVOT CAGE AND INNER RACE AT 90° TO CENTER LINE OF OUTER RACE WITH CAGE WINDOWS ALIGNED WITH LANDS OF OUTER RACE. LIFT OUT CAGE AND INNER RACE

CAGE
LAND
LAND
WINDOWS
OUTER RACE

FM3039100154000X

Fig. 6 Cage & inner race removal

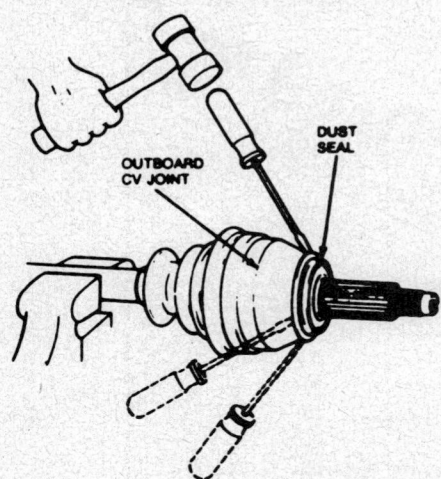

DUST SEAL
OUTBOARD CV JOINT

FM3039100160000X

Fig. 8 Dust seal removal

1. Install soft vise jaw caps in vise to prevent damage to driveshaft, then position driveshaft in vise. Do not allow the vise to contact the CV joint boot or clamps.
2. Using side cutting pliers, cut large boot clamp and peel away from boot. Roll boot back over driveshaft, **Fig. 3**.
3. Turn driveshaft over in vise, then angle CV joint so that inner bearing race is exposed, **Fig. 4**. Using a brass drift and a hammer, give a sharp rap to inner bearing race to dislodge internal snap ring. Separate CV joint from driveshaft. Take care not to drop the CV joint. Remove CV boot from shaft.
4. Inspect CV joint grease for contamination. If grease is contaminated, pro-

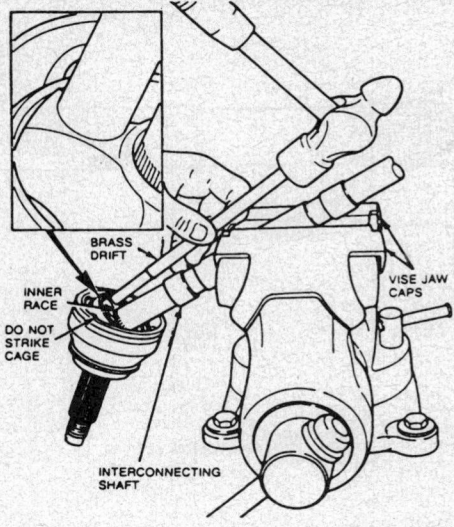

BRASS DRIFT
INNER RACE
DO NOT STRIKE CAGE
VISE JAW CAPS
INTERCONNECTING SHAFT

FM3039100152000X

Fig. 4 Internal snap ring removal

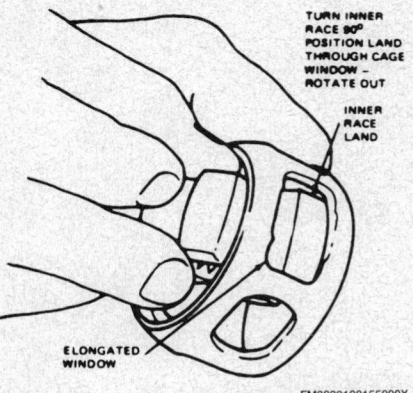

TURN INNER RACE 90° POSITION LAND THROUGH CAGE WINDOW – ROTATE OUT
INNER RACE LAND
ELONGATED WINDOW

FM3039100155000X

Fig. 7 Inner race replacement

ceed with disassembly. If grease is not contaminated and joint was operating satisfactorily, add grease and replace boot.
5. Remove and discard circlip from end of shaft. Inspect stop ring located below circlip, if it is worn or damaged, replace it.
6. Clamp CV joint stub axle in vise with soft vise jaw caps. Be careful not to damage dust seal.
7. Push down on CV joint inner race until it tilts enough to allow ball removal, **Fig. 5. If inner race is tight, it can be tilted by tapping inner race with wooden dowel and hammer. Do not hit cage.**
8. Remove balls from cage. If balls are tight, use blunt screwdriver to pry balls from cage.
9. Pivot cage and inner race assembly until it is straight up, **Fig. 6**. Align cage windows with outer race lands while pivoting bearing cage, then lift out cage and inner race.
10. Rotate inner race up and out of cage, **Fig. 7**.

Dust Seal

1. With driveshaft removed, use a light duty hammer and screwdriver to tap

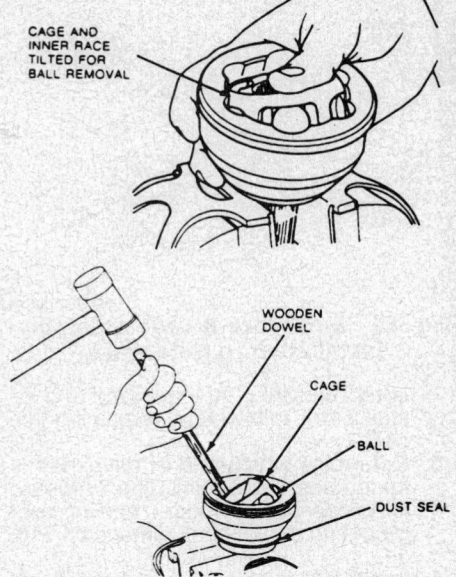

CAGE AND INNER RACE TILTED FOR BALL REMOVAL

WOODEN DOWEL
CAGE
BALL
DUST SEAL

FM3039100153000X

Fig. 5 CV joint ball removal

THE COUNTERBORE MUST FACE UPWARD AFTER THE ASSEMBLY IS INSTALLED IN THE OUTER RACE

BALL GROOVES AND WINDOWS IN ALIGNMENT

FM3039100156000X

Fig. 9 Inner race & cage assembly

evenly around seal until unseated and remove seal, **Fig. 8**.

SERVICE

C.V. Joint

During manufacture, CV joints components are matched and cannot be interchanged with components of other CV joint. If a CV joint component is defective, the entire CV joint should be replaced.

Inspect all parts. If any parts are cracked, broken, severely pitted, worn or otherwise unserviceable, replace CV joint. If any parts appear polished, do not replace CV joint as this is a normal condition.

INSTALLATION

C.V. Joint

1. Apply light coating of Ford constant velocity joint grease No. E2FZ-19590-A or equivalent on inner and outer races, then install inner race in bearing cage, **Fig. 7**.
2. Install inner race and cage assembly in outer race, **Fig. 9**.
3. Install CV joint assembly into outer race and pivot 90° into position, **Fig. 10.**
4. Align bearing cage and inner race with

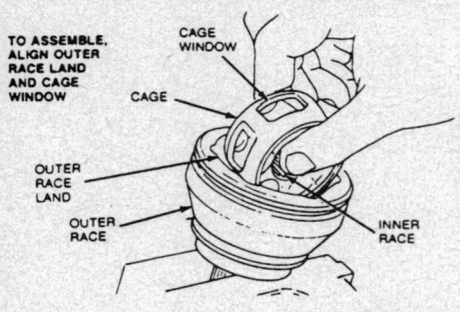

Fig. 10   Inner race & cage assembly installation to outer race

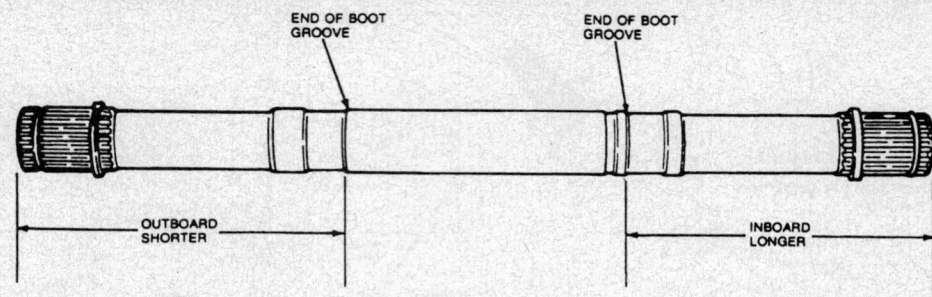

Fig. 11   driveshaft end identification

outer race, then tilt inner race and install a ball, followed by remaining five balls.

5. Determine which end of driveshaft is for outboard CV joint. The outboard joint side has a shorter end of boot groove to end of shaft dimension, **Fig. 11**.

6. Install CV joint boot and small boot clamp. If stop ring was removed, install at this time. If stop ring was not removed, ensure it is seated properly in groove.

7. Install new circlip, **Fig. 12**. **Do not over expand or twist the circlip during installation. To install properly, start one end in the groove and work the circlip over the stub shaft and into the circlip groove.**

8. Pack CV joint with Ford CV joint grease No. E2FZ-19590-A or equivalent. Any remaining grease is to be spread evenly inside CV boot.

9. With boot peeled back, position CV joint on driveshaft and tap into position with a plastic hammer. The CV joint is properly seated when the circlip locks into position. Check for proper retention by attempting to pull off CV joint.

10. Remove all excess grease from CV external surfaces, then position boot over CV joint. Ensure boot is seated in its groove and install clamp.

Dust Seal

Using spindle/axle seal tool T83T-3132-A1 and dust seal installer, tool No. T83P-3425-AH or equivalent, install dust seal, **Fig. 13**. The dust seal flange must face outboard.

INBOARD JOINTS

Removal

These models use two different types of inboard CV joints and boots, **Fig. 14**. The first one is of a conventional boot design that uses a crimped can on the large end. The other is a tri-lobe design CV joint that does not require a crimped can on the large end. Although both designs are similar, they are not interchangeable.

1. Cut and remove both large and small boot clamps from CV joint, then slide boot back on shaft. **All right side inboard CV joints use a reusable low profile large boot clamp. Do not cut this clamp as it will be reused.**

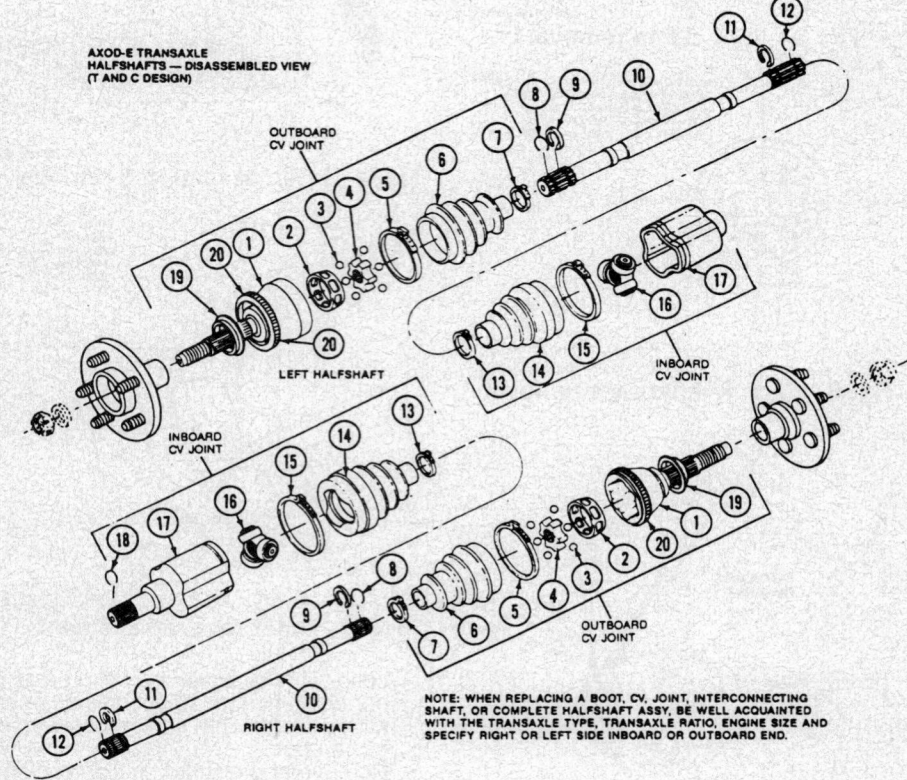

ITEM	DESCRIPTION
1.	OUTBOARD JOINT OUTER RACE AND STUB SHAFT
2.	BALL CAGE
3.	BALLS (SIX)
4.	OUTBOARD JOINT INNER RACE
5.	BOOT CLAMP (LARGE)
6.	BOOT
7.	BOOT CLAMP (SMALL)
8.	CIRCLIP
9.	STOP RING
10.	INTERCONNECTING SHAFT
11.	STOP RING
12.	CIRCLIP
13.	BOOT CLAMP (SMALL)
14.	BOOT
15.	BOOT CLAMP (LARGE)
16.	INBOARD JOINT TRIPOD ASSY
17.	INBOARD JOINT OUTER RACE AND STUB SHAFT
18.	CIRCLIP
19.	DUST SEAL
20.	SPEED INDICATOR RING (ANTI-LOCK BRAKES)

Fig. 12   Exploded view of driveshaft assemblies

2. Slide outer race off tripot assembly. Inspect CV joint grease for contamination by rubbing a small amount between two fingers. Any gritty feeling indicates contamination. If grease is contaminated, proceed with disassembly. If grease is not contaminated and joint was operating satisfactorily, add grease and replace boot.

3. Using snap ring pliers, slide stop ring back on shaft.

4. Slide tripot assembly back on shaft to provide clearance to circlip, then remove circlip, tripot assembly and boot.

Installation

1. Install CV boot on shaft. Ensure boot small end is seated properly in driveshaft groove, then tighten small end clamp.

2. Install tripot assembly on shaft with chamfered side toward stop ring, then

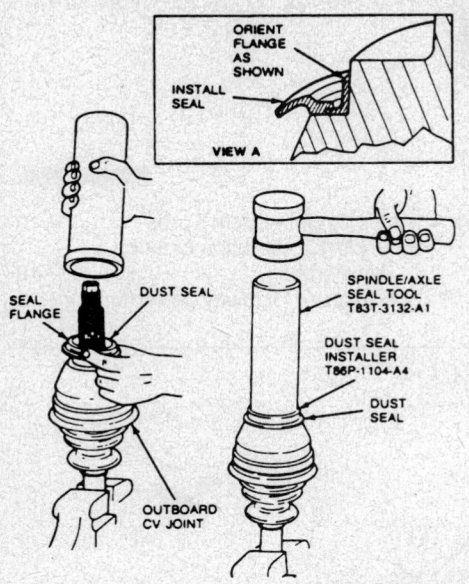

Fig. 13   Dust seal installation

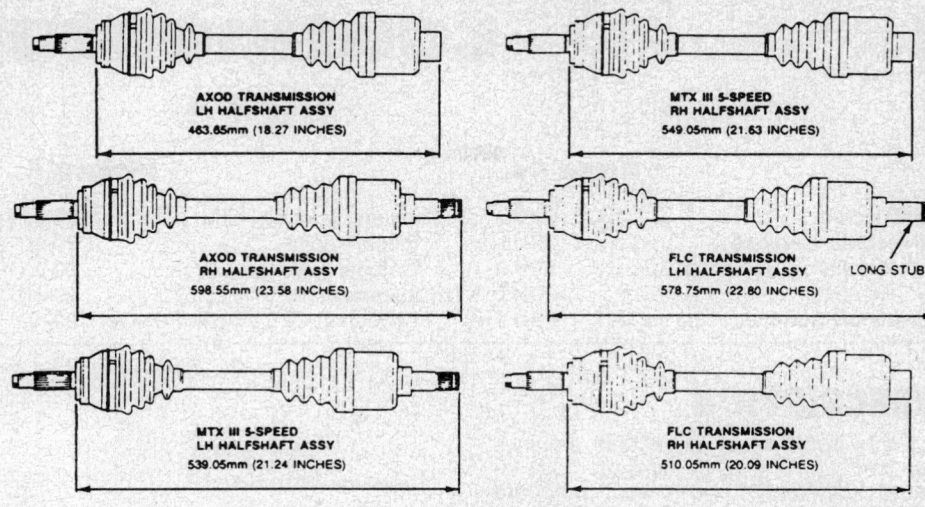

Fig. 15   Driveshaft assembled length

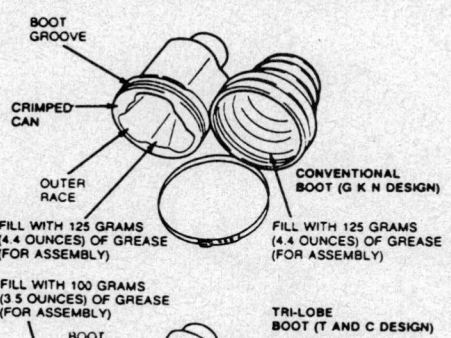

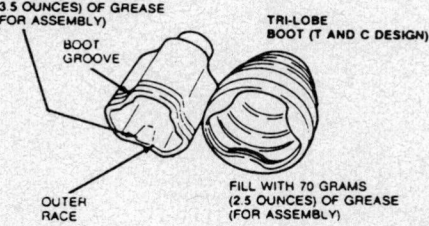

Fig. 14   CV joint identification

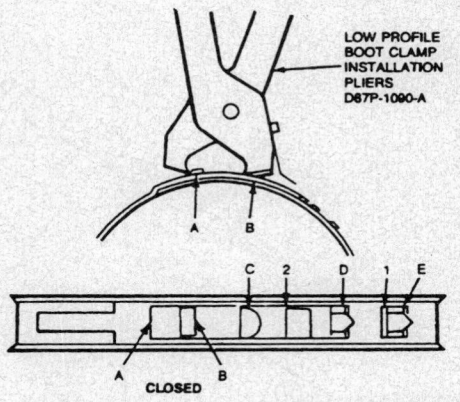

Fig. 16   CV boot clamp installation

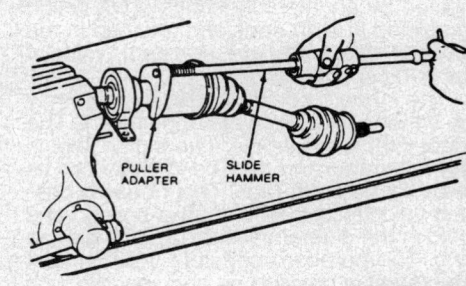

Fig. 17   Linkshaft removal

install new circlip. **Circlips cannot be reused. They must be replaced with new ones.**

3. Slide tripot assembly forward to expose stop ring groove, then slide stop ring into position. Ensure stop ring is fully seated in groove.
4. **On models with conventional design boots, Fig. 14,** fill CV joint outer race with 3.5 ounces and CV boot with 2.5 ounces of Ford CV joint grease-high temperature No. E43Z-19590-A or equivalent. On models with tri-lobe design boots, **Fig. 14,** fill CV joint outer race with 4.4 ounces and CV boot with 4.4 ounces of Ford CV joint grease-high temperature No. E43Z-19590-A or equivalent.
5. Install outer race over tripot assembly, then position boot over outer race. En-sure boot is properly seated in its groove.
6. Remove excess grease from boot exterior. Move CV joint in or out as necessary to adjust driveshaft to length as shown in **Fig. 15.** After driveshaft length has been determined, expel any built up air pressure from boot by inserting a dull screwdriver between boot and outer bearing and allowing air to escape.
7. Install large boot clamp with crimping pliers, tool No. D87P-1098-A or equivalent.
8. **Right side inboard CV joints use a reusable low profile large boot clamp. Do not install clamp with crimping pliers.** To install boot proceed as follows:
   a. With boot seated in groove, install clamp.
   b. Engage hook (C) in window, **Fig. 16.**
   c. Using low profile boot clamp installation pliers, tool No. D87P-1090-A or equivalent, place pincer jaws in closing hooks (A and B).

d. Pull closing hooks together, when 1 and 2 are above locking hooks (D and E) spring tab will press window over locking hooks and engage clamp.
9. Install new circlip. **Do not over expand or twist the circlip during installation. To install properly, start one end in the groove and work the circlip over the stub shaft and into the circlip groove.**

LINKSHAFT/DRIVESHAFT
Service

1. Clamp linkshaft in vise with driveshaft supported on workbench. Using puller adapter, tool No. T86P-3514-A or equivalent and slide hammer, tool No. D79P-100-A or equivalent, separate linkshaft from driveshaft, **Fig. 17.**
2. Pry seal from linkshaft with screwdriver.
3. Position linkshaft in an arbor press, then press off bearing.
4. Press on new bearing and bearing seal with arbor press.
5. Coat shaft splines with Ford CV joint grease No. E2FZ-19590-A or equivalent, then assemble linkshaft to driveshaft.

Continental

INDEX

DESCRIPTION

Each front wheel driveshaft employs constant velocity (CV) joints at both inboard (differential side) and outboard (wheel side) for vehicle operating smoothness. The constant velocity joints are connected by an interconnecting shaft which is splined at both ends and retained in the inboard and outboard constant velocity joints by snap rings, **Fig. 1.**

The inboard constant velocity joint may be either a tripot joint or a triplan joint. The tripot joint is repairable. The triplan joint is not repairable and may be identified by its large round outer race. The inboard constant velocity joint stub shaft is splined and held in the differential side gear by a snap ring. The outboard constant velocity joint stub shaft is pressed on and secured with a prevailing torque nut. The constant velocity joints are lube-for-life with a special constant velocity joint grease and require no periodic lubrication. The constant velocity joint boots, however, should be periodically inspected and replaced immediately when damage or grease leakage is evident. Continued operation may result in constant velocity joint failure due to contamination or loss of the constant velocity joint grease.

Driveshaft removal is accomplished by applying a load to the back face of the inboard constant velocity joint assembly.

TROUBLESHOOTING

NOISE & VIBRATION IN TURNS

Clicking, popping or grinding noises while turning may be caused by the following:
1. Cut or damaged CV joint boots, resulting in contaminated lube in outboard or inboard CV joints.
2. Loose CV joint clamps.
3. Worn, damaged or improperly installed wheel bearings.
4. Foreign object contacting driveshaft assembly.

VIBRATION AT HIGHWAY SPEEDS

1. Out of balance front wheels or tires.
2. Improperly seated outboard CV joint in front wheel hub.
3. Bent interconnecting shaft.
4. Front tires out of round.

SHUDDER OR VIBRATION DURING ACCELERATION

1. Excessively worn or damaged inboard or outboard CV joint.
2. Excessively high CV joint operating angle, caused by improper ride height.

DRIVESHAFT OR CV JOINT PULL-OUT

Engine Or Transaxle Misaligned

1. Check engine mounts for damage.

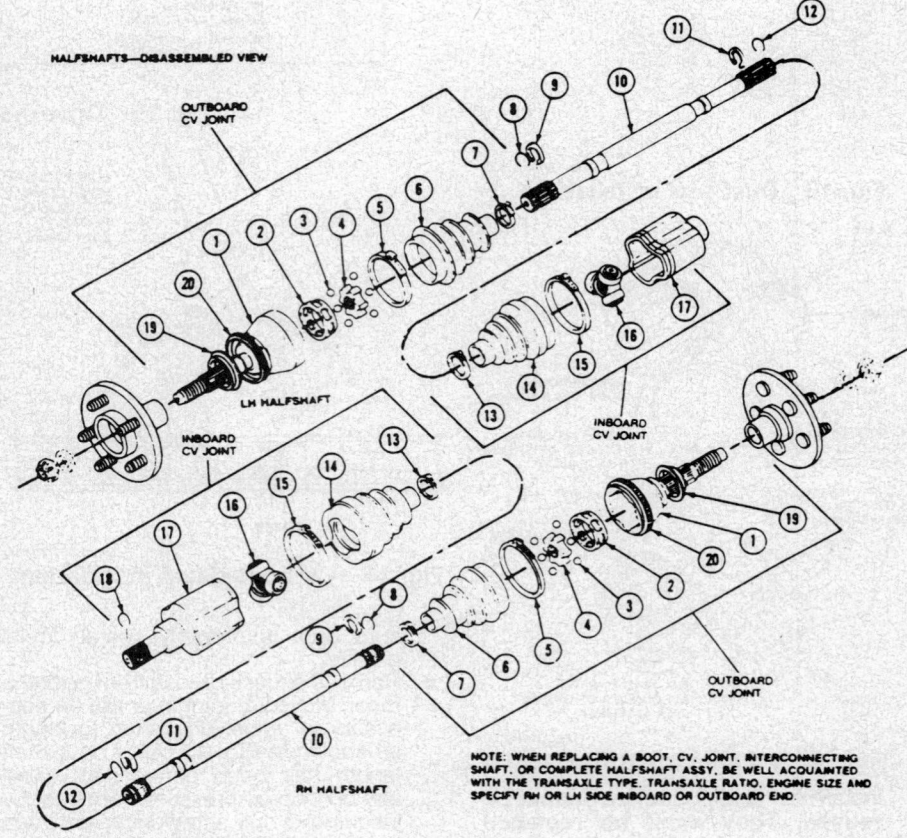

HALFSHAFTS—DISASSEMBLED VIEW

NOTE: WHEN REPLACING A BOOT, CV. JOINT, INTERCONNECTING SHAFT, OR COMPLETE HALFSHAFT ASSY, BE WELL ACQUAINTED WITH THE TRANSAXLE TYPE, TRANSAXLE RATIO, ENGINE SIZE AND SPECIFY RH OR LH SIDE INBOARD OR OUTBOARD END.

ITEM	DESCRIPTION	ITEM	DESCRIPTION
1.	OUTBOARD JOINT OUTER RACE AND STUB SHAFT	11.	STOP RING
2.	BALL CAGE	12.	CIRCLIP
3.	BALLS (SIX)	13.	BOOT CLAMP (SMALL)
4.	OUTBOARD JOINT INNER RACE	14.	BOOT
5.	BOOT CLAMP (LARGE)	15.	BOOT CLAMP (LARGE)
6.	BOOT	16.	INBOARD JOINT TRIPOD ASSY
7.	BOOT CLAMP (SMALL)	17.	INBOARD JOINT OUTER RACE AND STUB SHAFT
8.	CIRCLIP	18.	CIRCLIP
9.	STOP RING	19.	DUST SEAL
10.	INTERCONNECTING SHAFT	20.	SPEED INDICATOR RING (ANTI-LOCK BRAKES)

FM3039100166000X

Fig. 1 Disassembled view of driveshaft assemblies

Front Suspension Components Worn Or Damaged

1. Check for worn bushings or bent front suspension components.

Improperly Installed Or Missing Retainers

1. Check for CV joint circlip missing or not properly seated in transaxle side gear.

DRIVESHAFT
REPLACE
REMOVAL

If removing both right and left side driveshafts, plugs, tool No. T81P-1177B or equivalent must be installed. Failure to do so may result in dislocation of differential side gears, necessitating transaxle disassembly to re-align the gears. Should the gears become misaligned, the differential will have to be removed from the transaxle to re-align the gears.

Do not begin this procedure unless a new hub retainer nut, a new lower control arm to steering knuckle attaching bolt and nut and a new inboard constant velocity joint stub shaft snap ring are available.

Once removed, these components must not be reused during assembly/installation. Their torque holding ability or retention capability is diminished during removal.

1. Remove hub retainer nut and washer. Discard nut after removal.
2. Raise and support vehicle. Remove tire and wheel assemblies.
3. Remove attaching nut from ball joint to steering knuckle attaching bolt.
4. Using a punch and a hammer, drive bolt out of steering knuckle. **Discard bolt and nut.**
5. Remove anti-lock brake sensor from steering knuckle. Remove height sensor link at lower arm ball stud attachment.
6. Remove stabilizer bar link at stabilizer bar.
7. Separate ball joint from steering knuckle using a pry bar. **Position end of pry bar outside of bushing pocket to avoid damage to the bushing.** Tools No. T86P-3514-A2, T86P-3514-A1 and D79P-100-A or equivalents, must be used to perform the following steps.
   1. Install puller, tool No. T86P-3514-A1 or equivalent, between constant velocity joint and transaxle case. Turn steering hub and/or wire strut assembly out of the way.
   2. Screw extension, tool No. T86P-3514-A2 or equivalent, into constant velocity joint puller and hand tighten. Screw impact slide hammer, tool No. D79P-100-A or equivalent onto extension.
   3. Remove constant velocity joint from transaxle.
   4. Support end of shaft by suspending it from a conventional underbody com-

ponent with a length or wire. **Do not allow shaft to hang unsupported, damage to the outboard constant velocity joint may result.**
5. Separate outboard constant velocity joint from hub using front hub remover tools No. T81P-1104-C, T83P-1104-BH, T86P-1104-A1 and T81P-1104-A or equivalents. **Never use a hammer to separate the outboard constant velocity joint stub shaft from the hub. Damage to the constant velocity joint threads and internal components may result.**
6. Remove driveshaft assembly from vehicle.

INSTALLATION

1. Install a new snap ring onto inboard constant velocity joint stub shaft and/or link shaft. **The outboard constant velocity joint stub shaft does not have a snap ring. To install the snap ring correctly, start one end in the groove and work the snap ring over the stub shaft end and into the groove. This will avoid over expanding the snap ring. The old snap ring must not be reused. A new snap ring must be installed each time the inboard constant velocity joint is installed into the transaxle differential.**
2. Carefully align splines of inboard constant velocity joint stub shaft or link shaft with splines in differential. Exerting force, push constant velocity joint into differential until snap ring seats in differential side gear. **Use care to prevent damage to the differential oil seal. A plastic hammer or equivalent, may be used to aid in seating the snap ring into the differential side gear groove.**
3. Carefully align splines of outboard constant velocity joint stub shaft with splines in hub and push the shaft into the hub as far as possible.
4. Temporarily attach rotor to hub with washers and two wheel lug nuts. Insert a steel rod into rotor and rotate clockwise to contact the steering knuckle to prevent rotor from turning during constant velocity joint installation.
5. Install hub nut washer and a new hub retainer nut. Manually thread retainer onto constant velocity joint shaft as far as possible. **A new hub retainer nut must be installed.**
6. Connect control arm to steering knuckle. Install a new nut and bolt. **Torque** nut to 40-55 ft. lbs. **A new nut and bolt must be installed.**
7. Connect stabilizer bar link to stabilizer bar. **Torque** attaching nut to 35-48 ft. lbs.
8. Connect ride height sensor link.
9. Install anti-lock sensor link into control arm and tighten retaining bolt.
10. **Torque** hub retainer nut to 180-200 ft. lbs.
11. Install tire and wheel assembly, then lower vehicle.
12. **Torque** lug nuts to 80-105 ft. lbs.
13. Fill transaxle to proper level with cor-

rect fluid as required.

DRIVESHAFT SERVICE
Constant Velocity Joint
OUTBOARD JOINT
C.V. JOINT
Removal

The constant velocity joint components are matched during manufacture and cannot be interchanged with components from another constant velocity joint. Extreme care should be taken not to intermix or substitute like components between constant velocity joints.

1. Clamp driveshaft into a vise. Do not allow vise jaws to contact boot or clamp.
2. Cut large boot clamp and peel away from boot.
3. Support interconnecting shaft in a soft jaw vise and angle constant velocity joint to expose inner bearing race.
4. Using a brass drift and hammer, give a sharp tap to the inner bearing race to dislodge the internal snap ring and separate the constant velocity joint from the interconnecting shaft. The boot can now be removed from the shaft.
5. inspect constant velocity joint grease for contamination. If constant velocity joints are operating satisfactorily, and grease does not appear to be contaminated, add grease and replace boot. If lubricant appears contaminated, proceed with a complete constant velocity joint disassembly and inspection.
6. Remove snap ring located near end of shaft. Discard snap ring. A new snap ring is supplied with both boot replacement kit and constant velocity joint. **The stop ring, located just below the snap ring, should only be removed if it is damaged.**
7. Clamp the constant velocity joint stub shaft in a vise with outer facing pointing upward. Care should be taken not to damage the dust seal.
8. Press down on inner race until it tilts enough to allow removal of the ball.
9. With cage tilted, remove ball from cage. Repeat until all six balls are removed.
10. Pivot cage and inner race assembly until it is facing straight up and down in outer race. Align cage windows with the outer race lands while pivoting bearing race. With cage pivoted and aligned, lift assembly from outer race.
11. Rotate inner race up and out of cage.

Installation

Because the constant velocity joint components are matched as a set during assembly, individual components are not available for service. If inspection determines a part to be worn or damaged, the constant velocity joint should be replaced as an assembly. Do not replace a joint because the compo-

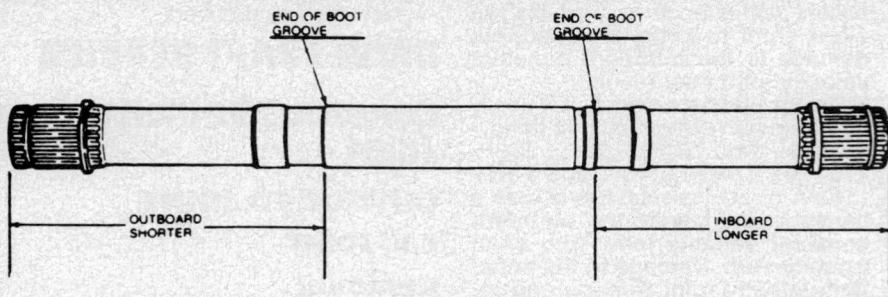

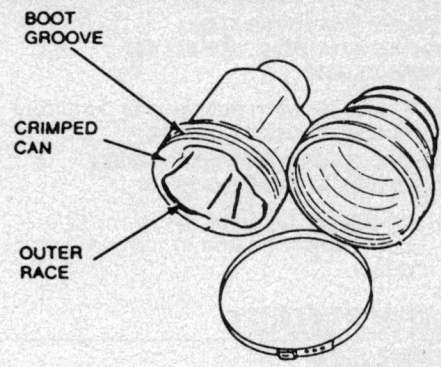

Fig. 2 Interconnecting shaft identification

nents appear polished. Shiny areas in ball races and the cage spheres are normal. **A constant velocity joint should be replaced only if inspection determines a component to be cracked, broken, severely pitted, worn or otherwise unserviceable.**

1. Apply a light coat of grease onto inner and outer ball races. **Use only Ford CV grease E2FZ-19590-A or equivalent.**
2. Install inner race into bearing cage.
3. Install inner race and cage assembly into outer race.
4. Install assembly vertically and pivot 90° into position.
5. Align bearing cage and inner race with outer race.
6. Tilt inner race and cage, then install a ball. Repeat this step until all six balls are installed.
7. The lefthand and righthand interconnecting shafts are not the same end-for-end. The outboard end is shorter from end of shaft to end of boot groove than the inboard end. Take a measurement to ensure correct inboard and outboard constant velocity joint to shaft installation, **Fig. 2.**
8. If removed, install constant velocity joint boot after removing stop ring.
9. Ensure boot is properly seated in its groove and clamp into position.
10. If removed, install stop ring. If not removed, ensure stop ring is properly seated in groove.
11. Install a new snap ring, supplied with service kit, in groove nearest end of shaft.
12. Do not over expand or twist snap ring during installation.
13. Before positioning boot over constant velocity joint, pack constant velocity joint and boot with grease supplied in service kit. Add 3.52 ounces.
14. With boot peeled back, position constant velocity joint on shaft and tap into position. **The constant velocity joint is completely seated when the snap ring locks in groove cut into constant velocity joint inner race. Check for snap ring seating by trying to pull joint from shaft.**
15. Remove all excess grease from the constant velocity joint external surfaces.
16. Position boot over constant velocity joint.
17. Ensure boot is seated in its groove and clamp in position.

DUST SEAL
Removal

Using a hammer, gently and uniformly tap around dust seal until unseated.

Installation

Using tools, No. T83T-3132-A1 and T86P-1104-A4 or equivalents, install dust seal. The dust seal flange must face outboard.

SPEED INDICATOR RING
Removal

1. Remove outboard constant velocity joint as described previously.
2. Position press tool No. T88P-2020-A or equivalent, onto a press.
3. Position constant velocity joint onto tool.
4. With constant velocity joint position on tool, use press ram to apply pressure to the constant velocity joint and remove speed indicator ring.

Installation

1. With tool No. T88P-2020-A or equivalent, positioned on press, place sensor ring on tool.
2. Position constant velocity joint into speed indicator ring tool No.T88P-2020-A or equivalent. Allow constant velocity joint to rest on ring.
3. With constant velocity joint installed on tool, place a steel plate across the constant velocity joint back face. Press constant velocity joint until constant velocity joint bottoms out in tool. The ring will be properly installed when bottomed out in tool.

INBOARD JOINT
Removal

Two different types of inboard constant velocity joints and boots are used. The conventional style uses a crimped can on the large end. The tri-lobe style constant velocity joint does not require a crimped can on the large end. Although the designs are similar, there are no interchangeable components between the two designs, **Fig. 3.** The constant velocity joint tripot, outer race, boot and interconnecting shaft are unique for each style.

1. Cut and remove both boot clamps and slide boot back onto shaft. **The righthand inboard constant velocity joint requires a reusable low**

Fig. 3 Constant velocity joint & boot

profile large boot clamp. A special tool is required to remove and install the clamp.
2. Remove clamp by using tool No. D87P-1090-A or equivalent. Engage jaws of tool in closing hooks and draw hooks on clamp together. Disengage windows and locking hooks, then remove the clamp.
3. Slide outer race off of the tripot.
4. When replacing a damaged constant velocity joint boot, the grease should be checked for contamination. If the constant velocity joints are operating satisfactory and grease does not appear to be contaminated, add grease and replace the boot. If grease appears contaminated, proceed with a complete constant velocity joint disassembly and inspection.
5. Using pliers, move stop ring back on shaft.
6. Move tripot assembly back on shaft to allow access to snap ring.
7. Remove snap ring from shaft.
8. Remove tripot assembly from shaft. Remove boot, if necessary.

Installation

1. Install constant velocity joint boot on shaft, if removed during disassembly. Ensure boot is seated in boot groove on shaft. Tighten clamp using crimping pliers.
2. Install tripot assembly onto shaft with chamfered side toward stop ring.
3. Install a new snap ring.
4. Compress snap ring and slide tripot assembly forward over the snap ring to expose stop ring groove.
5. Move stop ring into groove. Ensure stop ring is completely seated in groove.
6. Fill constant velocity joint outer race and constant velocity boot with suitable grease as shown in **Fig. 3.**
7. Install outer race over tripot assembly and position boot over outer race. Ensure boot is properly seated in groove.
8. Remove all excess grease from constant velocity joint external surfaces. Position boot over constant velocity joint. Move constant velocity joint inward and outward as necessary to length shown in **Fig. 4. Before installing boot clamp, ensure that**

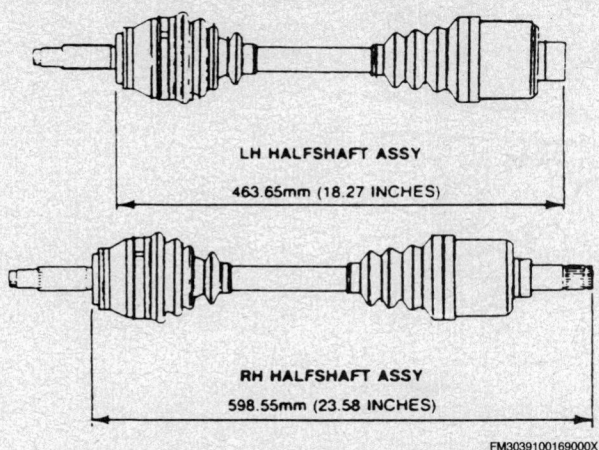

Fig. 4 Driveshaft assembled lengths

LH HALFSHAFT ASSY
463.65mm (18.27 INCHES)

RH HALFSHAFT ASSY
598.55mm (23.58 INCHES)

FM3039100169000X

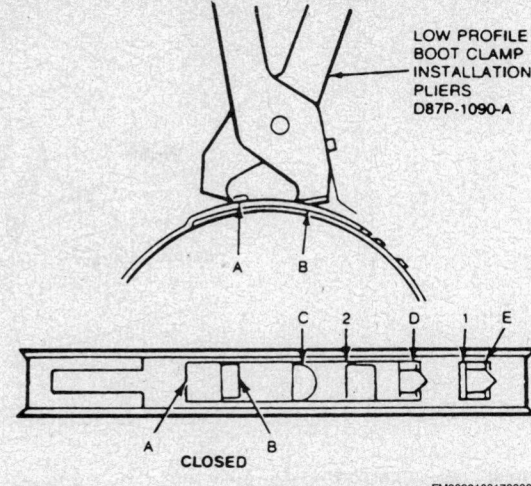

LOW PROFILE
BOOT CLAMP
INSTALLATION
PLIERS
D87P-1090-A

CLOSED

FM3039100170000X

Fig. 5 Boot clamp installation

any air pressure which may have built up in boot is relieved. Insert a dulled tip screwdriver blade between boot and outer bearing race to allow trapped air to escape from boot. The air should be released from the boot only after adjusting to specified dimension.
9. Seat boot into groove and clamp in position. Install clamp as follows:
   a. With boot seated in groove, place clamp over boot.
   b. Engage hook C in window, **Fig. 5.**
   c. Using clamp tool No. D87P-1090-A or equivalent, place tool pincer jaws in closing hooks A and B.
   d. Secure clamp by drawing closing hooks together. When windows 1 and 2 are above locking hooks D and E spring tab will press windows over locking hooks and engage clamp.
10. Install a new snap ring, supplied with service kit, in groove nearest shaft end. Start one end in groove and work snap ring over stub shaft end and into groove.

Festiva

INDEX

TROUBLESHOOTING

NOISE & VIBRATION IN TURNS

Clicking, popping or grinding noises while turning may be caused by the following:
1. Cut or damaged CV joint boots, resulting in contaminated lube in outboard or inboard CV joints.
2. Loose CV joint clamps.
3. Worn, damaged or improperly installed wheel bearings.
4. Foreign object contacting driveshaft assembly.

VIBRATION AT HIGHWAY SPEEDS

1. Out of balance front wheels or tires.
2. Improperly seated outboard CV joint in front wheel hub.
3. Bent interconnecting shaft.

4. Front tires out of round.

SHUDDER OR VIBRATION DURING ACCELERATION

1. Excessively worn or damaged inboard or outboard CV joint.
2. Ensure axle shaft is not twisted or cracked.
3. If equipped with vibration damper, ensure damper is not damaged or loose on shaft.

DRIVESHAFT OR CV JOINT PULL-OUT

Engine Or Transaxle Misaligned

1. Check engine mounts for damage.

Front Suspension Components Worn Or Damaged

1. Check for worn bushings or bent front

suspension components.

Improperly Installed Or Missing Retainers

1. Check for CV joint circlip missing or not properly seated in transaxle side gear.

FAULTY OPERATION OF DRIVESHAFT

1. Check for broken ball joint, tripot joint or worn or seized joint.

DRIVESHAFT

REPLACE

REMOVAL

1. Raise and support front of vehicle, then drain transaxle.
2. Remove front wheel, then the splash shield.
3. Unstake driveshaft attaching nut, apply brakes, then loosen nut. Do not re-

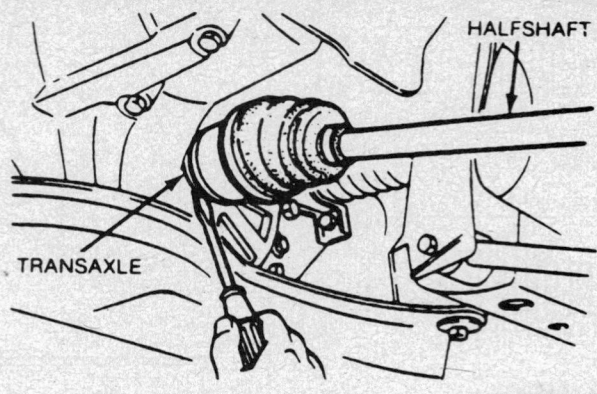

Fig. 1 Driveshaft disengagement from transaxle

move attaching nut at this time.

4. Disconnect stabilizer bar from lower control arm.
5. Remove ball joint to steering knuckle clamp bolt and nut, then pry downward on control arm and disengage ball joint from steering knuckle. **Do not damage ball joint dust boot.**
6. Using a large screwdriver, disengage driveshaft from transaxle, **Fig. 1. Disengage driveshaft gradually to prevent damage to oil seal.**
7. Remove driveshaft attaching nut and lockwasher, then pull outward on steering knuckle and disengage driveshaft from hub. If difficulty is encountered separating hub from driveshaft, tap end of shaft with plastic mallet to facilitate removal.
8. Withdraw driveshaft from vehicle, then install differential plug, tool No. T87C-7025-C or equivalent into transaxle to prevent movement of side gears.

INSTALLATION

1. Install new circlip on inboard end of driveshaft.
2. Lubricate inboard splines of driveshaft with grease, remove differential plug, then carefully install driveshaft into transaxle to avoid damaging oil seal.
3. Lubricate outboard splines of driveshaft with grease, then carefully install driveshaft into hub to avoid damaging oil seal.
4. Install new lockwasher and attaching nut. Do not tighten attaching nut at this time.
5. Push up on control arm, reconnect ball joint to steering knuckle, then install clamp bolt and nut. **Torque** nut to 32–40 ft. lbs.
6. Apply brakes to prevent hub assembly from turning, then **torque** driveshaft attaching nut to 116–174 ft. lbs., then stake crush nut. **Do not stake crush nut with pointed tool, ensure locking tab is bent at least .16 inch into slot in crush nut to assure locking. After staking crush nut, pull rearward strongly on wheel hub ensuring driveshaft is properly installed. Turn wheel hub to ensure smooth operation.**

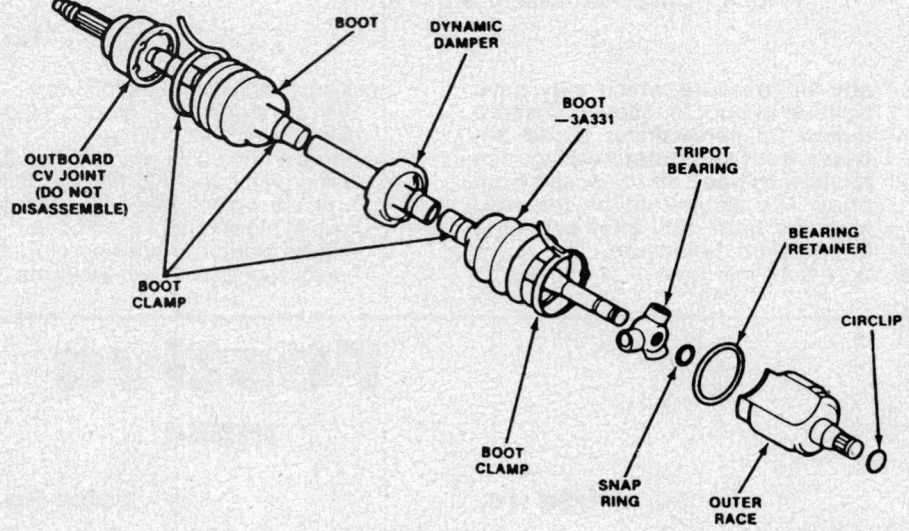

Fig. 2 Driveshaft w/tripot type constant velocity joint

7. Reconnect stabilizer bar to control arm and **torque** attaching nut to 40–50 ft. lbs.
8. Install splash shield and front wheel, then lower vehicle.
9. Fill transaxle with lubricant as required.

DRIVESHAFT SERVICE
CONSTANT VELOCITY JOINT
OUTBOARD JOINT

The outer C.V. joints are of the Birfield type, other than boot replacement no other repairs may be performed.

INBOARD JOINT

These models use a tripot type constant velocity joint at the transaxle end of the driveshaft and a Birfield type constant velocity joint at the hub side of the driveshaft, **Fig. 2.** The tripot type constant velocity type joint can be disassembled and serviced. The Birfield type constant velocity joint should not be disassembled and is serviced only as an assembly with the driveshaft. To service the tripot type constant velocity joint, proceed as follows:

1. Position driveshaft in a soft jawed vise.
2. Remove large boot clamp, the roll boot back over shaft, **Fig. 2.**
3. Check joint grease for contamination, **Fig. 3.** If grease is not contaminated and joint has been operating satisfactorily, add required amount of lubricant and install a replacement bolt. If grease is contaminated, then constant velocity joint must be disassembled and inspected.
4. Remove bearing retaining ring.
5. Place alignment marks on outer race and tripot joint, then remove outer race, **Fig. 4.**
6. Place alignment mark on tripot bearing and driveshaft, then remove snap ring, **Fig. 5.**
7. Using a brass drift, carefully drive tripot joint from driveshaft, **Fig. 6.**
8. If necessary, remove boot small clamp, then wrap tape around driveshaft splines and remove boot.
9. Check tripot joint for wear and damage and replace as necessary.
10. If removed, wrap driveshaft splines with tape and install boot to driveshaft groove.

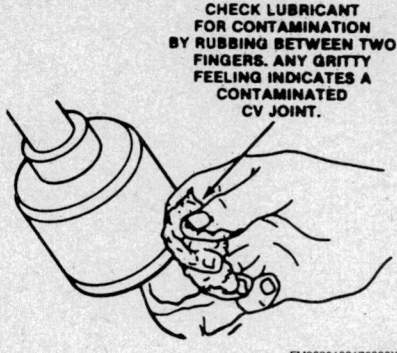

Fig. 3 CV joint lubricant for Checking contamination. Tripot type

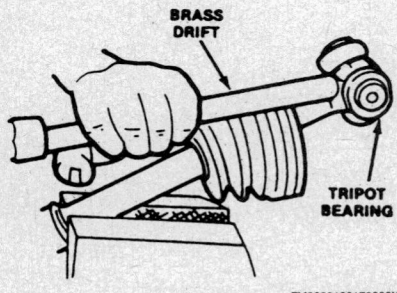

Fig. 6 Tripot joint removal from driveshaft

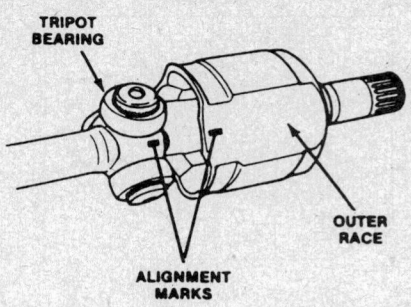

Fig. 4 Outer race & tripot joint, placing alignment marks

11. Align marks on driveshaft and tripot joint made during removal.
12. Using a brass drift, drive tripot joint into position on driveshaft, then install snap ring.
13. Fill outer race with 3.5 ounces of lubricant E43Z-19590-A or equivalent, then position outer race over tripot joint, aligning marks made during removal.
14. Install bearing retaining ring, then position boot in groove on outer race.
15. Position joint so that distance between driveshaft boot groove and outer race groove is 3½ inches, **Fig. 7**.
16. Using a screwdriver with sharp edges filled off, pry up on boot at outer race end to allow trapped air to escape.
17. Install and lock boot clamps, then check joint for smoothness of operation through its full range of travel.

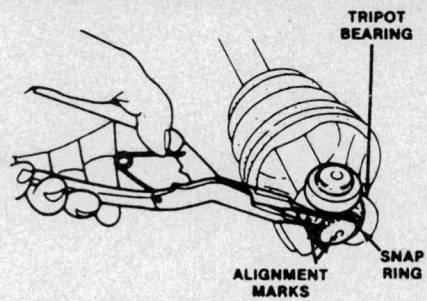

Fig. 5 Tripot joint snap ring removal

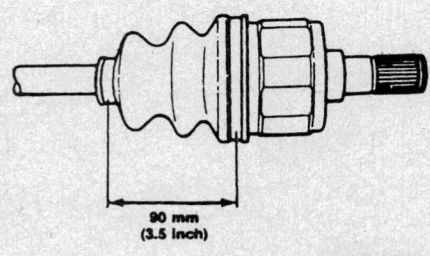

Fig. 7 CV joint on driveshaft, position. Tripot type

Aspire

INDEX

DESCRIPTION

The front wheel driveshaft and joints mechanically link engine torque from the transaxle to the front wheels, **Fig. 1**. At the transaxle end, the front wheel driveshaft joint is splined to the differential side gears. Disengagement of the tri-pot type front wheel driveshaft joint from the differential side gear is prevented by an expanding spring steel driveshaft bearing retainer circlip.

The wheel end of the right and left front driveshaft and joints are splined to the wheel hubs which are supported on opposed tapered front wheel bearing inner and outer cone and rollers. Disengagement of the driveshaft and joint from the wheel hub is prevented by the front axle wheel hub washer and retainer.

Backlash between the wheel hubs and driveshaft joint is eliminated by the splines. The front wheel hub splines are machined straight while the driveshaft joint splined are machined with a slight helical cut. The difference in splines provides a tight, backlash-free coupling without the replacement problems associated with interference fit.

TROUBLESHOOTING

IMPROPER OPERATION OF FRONT WHEEL DRIVESHAFT & JOINT

1. Broken ball joint.
2. Worn or seized front wheel driveshaft joint.

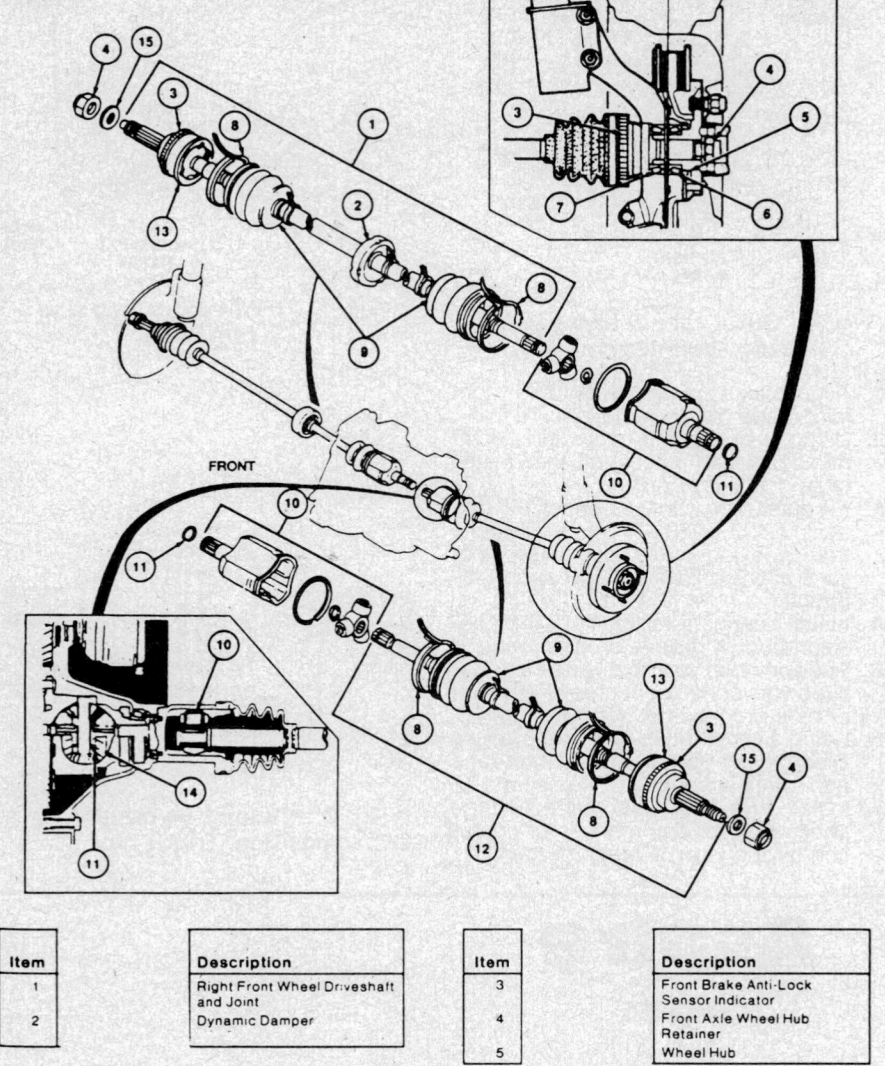

Item	Description
1	Right Front Wheel Driveshaft and Joint
2	Dynamic Damper

Item	Description
3	Front Brake Anti-Lock Sensor Indicator
4	Front Axle Wheel Hub Retainer
5	Wheel Hub

FM3039400237000X

Fig. 1   Disassembled view of front wheel driveshaft & joint

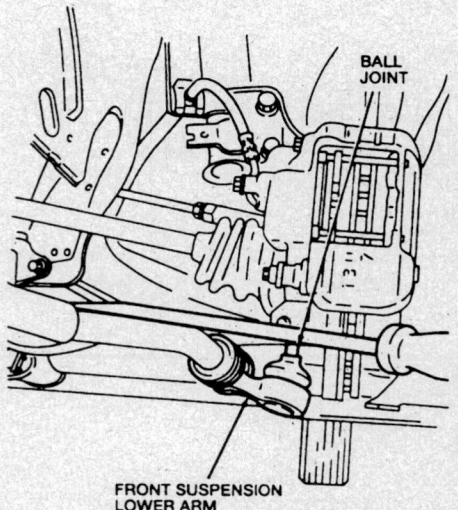

FM3039400238000X

Fig. 2   Clamp bolt & nut removal

FM3039400239000X

Fig. 3   Ball joint separation from wheel knuckle

ABNORMAL NOISE FROM FRONT WHEEL DRIVESHAFT AND JOINT

1. Insufficient grease or front wheel driveshaft joint or spline.
2. Excessive backlash on spline.
3. Worn front wheel driveshaft joint.
4. Loose dynamic damper.

STEERING WHEEL PULLS TOWARD LEFT OR RIGHT SIDE WHILE DRIVING STRAIGHT OR LEVEL

1. Incorrect front wheel bearing inner and outer cone and roller preload adjustment.
2. Bent steering linkage.
3. Fatigued front coil spring.
4. Front suspension lower arm mounting bolt bushing worn or damaged.
5. Bent front wheel knuckle.

6. Bent front suspension lower arm or loose mounting.
7. Incorrect toe adjustment.
8. Improper tire pressure.
9. Unevenly worn tires (difference between LH and RH side tire wear).
10. Brake dragging.

UNSTABLE HANDLING

1. Incorrect front wheel bearing inner and outer cone and roller preload adjustment.
2. Bent steering linkage.
3. Lower steering column shaft worn or damaged.
4. Incorrect steering gear preload adjustment.
5. Fatigued front coil spring.
6. Worn rear spring and shock absorber assemblies.
7. Front suspension lower arm mounting bolt bushing worn or damaged.
8. Incorrect toe adjustment.
9. Improper tire pressure.
10. Wheels bent or out of balance.

EXCESSIVE STEERING WHEEL PLAY

1. Loose front wheel bearing inner and outer cone and roller.
2. Incorrect steering gear preload adjustment.
3. Steering gear worn.
4. Lower steering column shaft worn or damaged.
5. Front suspension lower arm mounting bolt bushing worn or damaged.

TIRES WORN EXCESSIVELY OR UNEVENLY

1. Incorrect front wheel bearing inner and outer cone and roller preload adjustment.
2. Incorrect toe adjustment.
3. Improper tire pressure.
4. Wheels out of balance.

ABNORMAL NOISE FROM WHEEL HUB

1. Faulty front wheel bearing inner and outer cone and roller.

DRIVESHAFT
REPLACE
REMOVAL

1. Raise and support vehicle.
2. Drain transmission fluid from transaxle.
3. Remove front wheel and tire assemblies.
4. Use small cape chisel to carefully raise the staked portion of the front axle wheel hub retainer.
5. While applying brakes, loosen but do not remove front axle wheel hub retainer.
6. Remove clamp bolt and nut, **Fig. 2.**
7. Carefully pry down on front suspension lower arm to separate ball joint from front wheel knuckle, **Fig. 3.**
8. **Separate driveshaft and joint from transaxle gradually. If driveshaft is yanked from transaxle, the differential oil seal may be damaged.**
9. Use pry bar to separate driveshaft and joint from transaxle.
10. Remove front axle wheel hub retainer and washer.
11. If necessary, use suitable drift and hammer to tap driveshaft and joint from front wheel hub.
12. Pry driveshaft bearing retainer circlip off of driveshaft joint.
13. Install differential plugs.

INSTALLATION

1. Before installing driveshaft, inspect and/or replace differential and inner wheel bearing oil seals.
2. Install new driveshaft bearing retainer circlip on driveshaft joint.
3. Lubricate end of driveshaft joint with grease.

Fig. 4 Outer race & tripot bearing alignment marks

FM3039400240000X

4. Remove differential plugs.
5. Install end of driveshaft joint into differential side gear.
6. Lubricate end of driveshaft and joint.
7. Insert end of driveshaft and joint into wheel hub.
8. Install front axle wheel hub retainer and washer onto front wheel driveshaft and joint. Tighten by hand.
9. Install front suspension lower arm by placing ball joint into front wheel knuckle.
10. Install clamp nut and bolt on front suspension lower arm. **Torque** clamp nut to 40-50 ft. lbs.
11. While applying brakes, **torque** front axle wheel hub retainer to 116-174 ft. lbs.
12. Use suitable cape chisel with cutting edge rounded to stake front axle wheel hub retainer.
13. Install front wheel and tire assemblies. **Torque** wheel hub bolts to 65-87 ft. lbs.
14. Fill transaxle to proper level with specified grade of transmission fluid.

DRIVESHAFT SERVICE
DISASSEMBLE

Do not remove the front brake anti-lock sensor indicator if it does not need to be replaced. If it is removed, it must be replaced.

1. Clamp driveshaft and joint in a soft-jaw vise to prevent damage to any parts.
2. Peel driveshaft joint boot clamp away from front wheel driveshaft joint boot.
3. Remove large joint boot clamp and discard.
4. Roll driveshaft joint boot back over driveshaft and joint.
5. Remove wire ring bearing retainer.
6. Paint alignment marks on outer race and tripot bearing, **Fig. 4.**
7. Remove outer race and snap ring.
8. Use suitable drift and hammer to gently tap tripot bearing from driveshaft.

9. If necessary, remove small driveshaft joint boot and clamp.

ASSEMBLE

1. Align marks on tripot bearing and driveshaft.
2. Use suitable soft faced hammer to gently tap tripot bearing onto driveshaft.
3. Use snap ring pliers to remove snap ring.
4. Fill outer race with 3.5 ounces of CV joint grease No. E43Z-19590-A or equivalent.
5. Install outer race over tripot bearing and install wire ring bearing retainer.
6. Position driveshaft joint boot so that it is fully seated in driveshaft grooves and outer race.
7. Extend or compress driveshaft as necessary until distance between joint boot clamp grooves is 4.11 inches.
8. Insert dull screwdriver between driveshaft joint boot and outer race to allow trapped air to escape.
9. Install new driveshaft joint boot clamps

Capri & Probe

INDEX

TROUBLESHOOTING
NOISE & VIBRATION IN TURNS

Clicking, popping or grinding noises while turning may be caused by the following:

1. Cut or damaged CV joint boots, resulting in contaminated lube in outboard or inboard CV joints.
2. Loose CV joint clamps.
3. Worn, damaged or improperly installed wheel bearings.
4. Foreign object contacting driveshaft assembly.

VIBRATION AT HIGHWAY SPEEDS

1. Out of balance front wheels or tires.
2. Improperly seated outboard CV joint in front wheel hub.
3. Bent interconnecting shaft.
4. Front tires out of round.

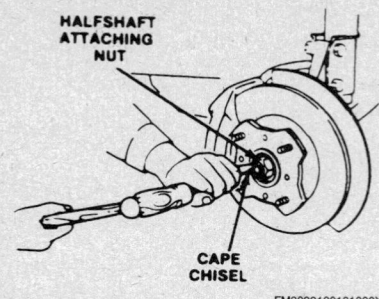

Fig. 1   Axle nut unstaking

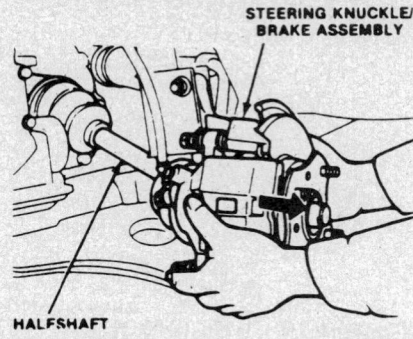

Fig. 2   Driveshaft from differential side gear, separating. Manual transaxle models

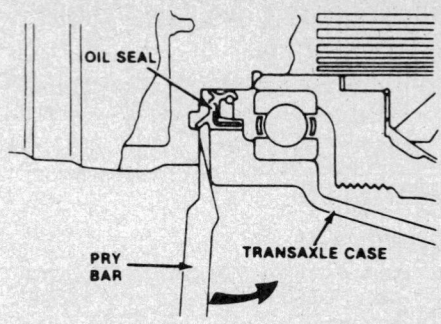

Fig. 3   Driveshaft from differential side gear, inserting pry bar to separate

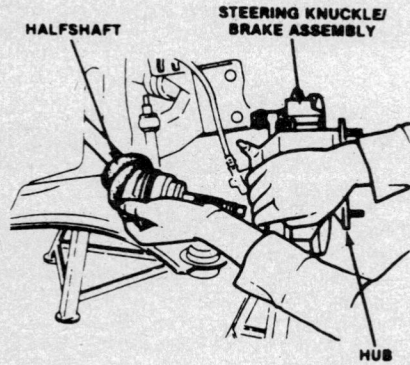

Fig. 4   Driveshaft from hub & steering knuckle, separating

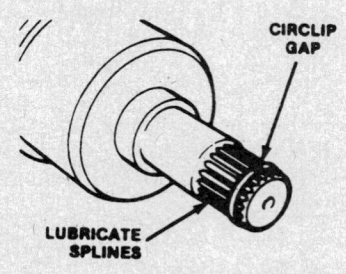

Fig. 5   Circlip on driveshaft spline, position

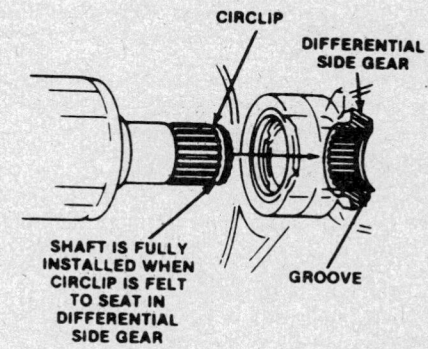

Fig. 6   Driveshaft to differential side gear, installing

SHUDDER OR VIBRATION DURING ACCELERATION

1. Excessively worn or damaged inboard or outboard CV joint.

DRIVESHAFT OR CV JOINT PULL-OUT

Engine Or Transaxle Misaligned

1. Check engine mounts for damage.

Front Suspension Components Worn Or Damaged

1. Check for worn bushings or bent front suspension components.

Improperly Installed Or Missing Retainers

1. Check for CV joint circlip missing or not properly seated in transaxle side gear.

FAULTY OPERATION OF DRIVESHAFT

1. Check for broken ball joint, tripot joint or worn or seized joint.

DRIVESHAFT
REPLACE

When removing driveshafts, differential plugs, tool No. T87C-7025-C or equivalent must be installed to prevent oil leakage.

REMOVAL

1. Raise and support front of vehicle, then remove wheel and tire assembly.
2. Remove underbody covers, then remove stabilizer bar link from control arm.
3. Using a chisel, raise staked portion of axle nut, then with brakes applied, loosen but do not remove nut, **Fig. 1**.
4. **On all models except Probe,** remove clamp bolt attaching lower control arm ball joint to steering knuckle, then pry downward on lower control arm to separate ball joint from steering knuckle.
5. **On Probe models,** remove lower control arm ball joint clamp bolt, then pry lower control arm downward and push inward on rotor to separate ball joint from steering knuckle. **If removing RH driveshaft, remove dynamic damper from cylinder block.**
6. **On models with manual transaxle,** pull outward on steering knuckle and hub assembly to separate driveshaft from differential side gear, **Fig. 2**. Use only enough force to loosen the driveshaft. In some cases, it may be necessary to position a pry bar between driveshaft and transaxle and light tap end of bar to loosen driveshaft from differential side gear, **Fig. 3**. When using a pry bar, use care not to damage transaxle case, oil seal or CV joint or boot. Do not pull driveshaft completely out of transaxle, as damage to oil seal may result.

7. **On models with automatic transaxle,** position pry bar between transaxle case and driveshaft, then lightly tap end of bar to loosen driveshaft from differential side gear, **Fig. 3**. Use care not damage transaxle case, oil seal or CV joint or boot.
8. **On all models,** remove axle nut and washer, then pull driveshaft from hub and steering knuckle assembly, **Fig. 4**. If binding is encountered, use puller D80L-1002-L to separate driveshaft from hub and knuckle assembly.
9. Support driveshaft and carefully slide from transaxle. Use care not to damage transaxle case oil seal when removing driveshaft.
10. Cap transaxle driveshaft openings.

INSTALLATION

1. Position replacement circlip driveshaft groove at transaxle end, **Fig. 5**. To prevent over expanding, position one end of circlip into groove then work other end over shaft and into groove. When installed, gap in circlip should be at top of driveshaft splines.
2. Lightly lubricate driveshaft splines with specified lubricant or its equivalent: C1AZ-1959D on 1992 Probe; C1AZ-19590-BA on Capri models. With proper lubricant applied, position driveshaft splines to differential side splines, **Fig. 6**.
3. Push driveshaft splines into differential until circlip snaps into differential side gear groove, **Fig. 6**.

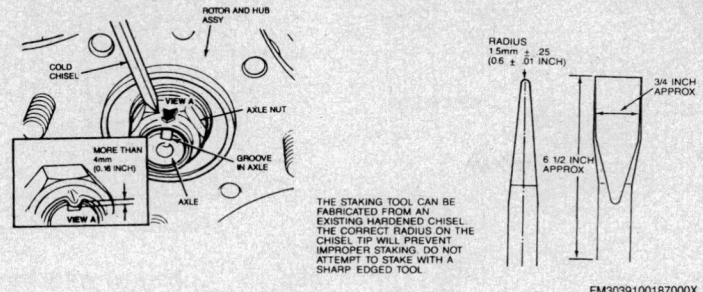

Fig. 7   Axle nut staking

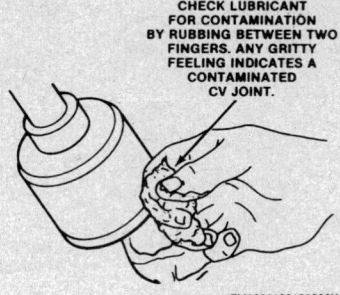

Fig. 9   Constant velocity joint lubricant, checking for contamination

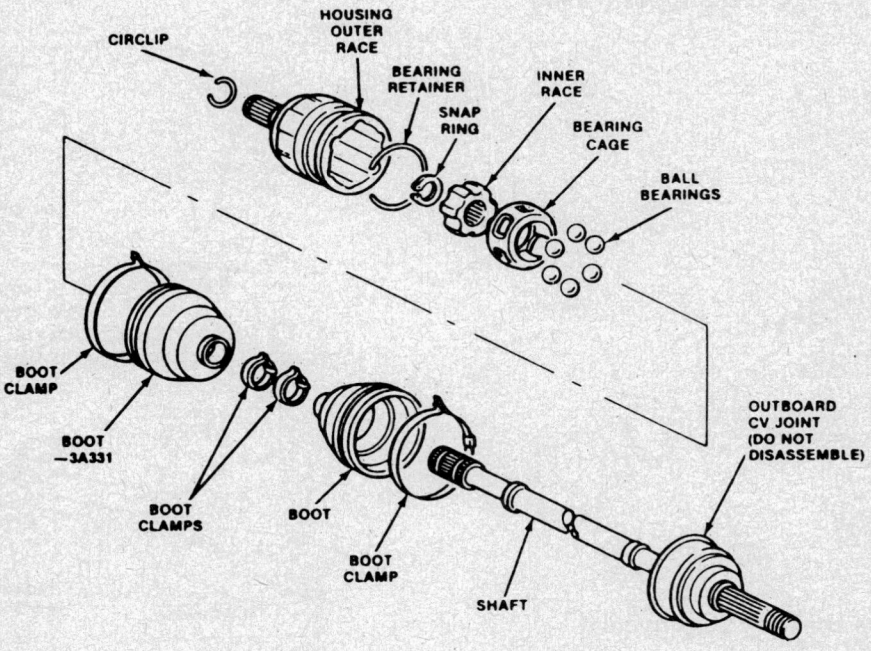

Fig. 8   Driveshaft w/Rzeppa type constant velocity joint

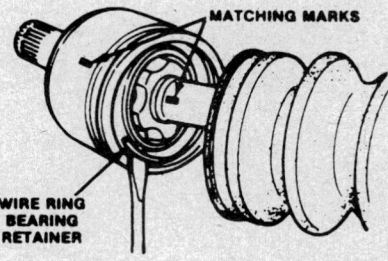

Fig. 10   Bearing retaining ring removal

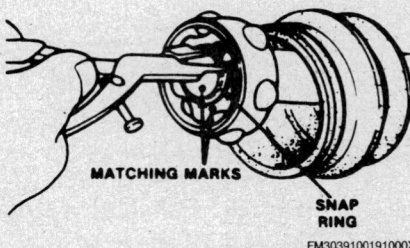

Fig. 11   Inner bearing race snap ring removal

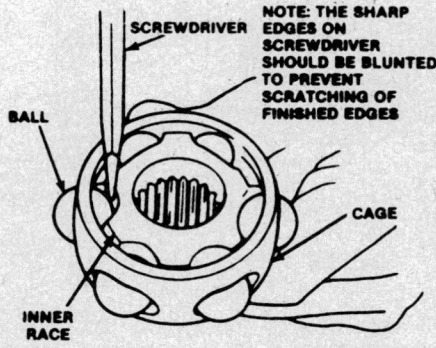

Fig. 12   Ball bearing removal from cage

4. Position driveshaft through hub and steering knuckle and loosely install replacement axle nut and washer, **Fig. 4.**
5. **On Probe models,** install dynamic damper, then **torque** attaching bolts to 31–46 ft. lbs.
6. **On all models,** position lower control arm ball joint to steering knuckle, then install and **torque** clamp bolt to 32–40 ft. lbs.
7. Install stabilizer bar link to lower control arm. Tighten nut until .43 inch of bolt thread extends beyond nut on Capri models or .79 inch on Probe models.
8. Install underbody covers.
9. **Torque** axle nut to 116–174 ft. lbs., then stake nut using a chisel, **Fig. 7.** If nut is damaged during staking, it must be replaced.
10. Install wheel and tire assembly, then lower vehicle.

DRIVESHAFT SERVICE
CONSTANT VELOCITY JOINTS
Rzeppa Type

Models with manual transaxle use a Rzeppa type constant velocity joint at the transaxle end of the driveshaft and a Birfield type constant velocity joint at the hub side of the driveshaft, **Fig. 8.** The Rzeppa type constant velocity type joint can be disassembled and serviced. The Birfield type constant velocity joint should not be disassembled and is serviced only as an assembly with the driveshaft. To service the Rzeppa type constant velocity joint, proceed as follows:

1. Remove driveshaft as described under "Driveshaft, Replace."
2. Position driveshaft in a soft jawed vise.
3. Remove large boot clamp, the roll boot back over shaft, **Fig. 8.**
4. Check joint grease for contamination, **Fig. 9.** If grease is not contaminated and joint has been operating satisfactorily, add required amount of lubricant and install a replacement bolt. If grease is contaminated, then constant velocity joint must be disassembled and inspected.
5. Place alignment marks on bearing outer race and driveshaft, then remove bearing retaining ring, **Fig. 10.**
6. Remove outer race.

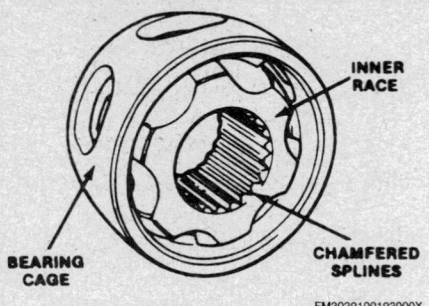

Fig. 13 Inner bearing race to cage positioning

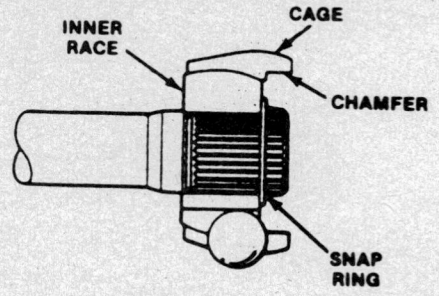

Fig. 14 Bearing cage to driveshaft, positioning

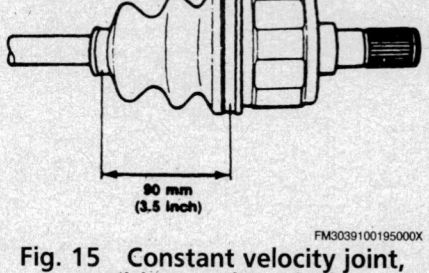

Fig. 15 Constant velocity joint, position on driveshaft

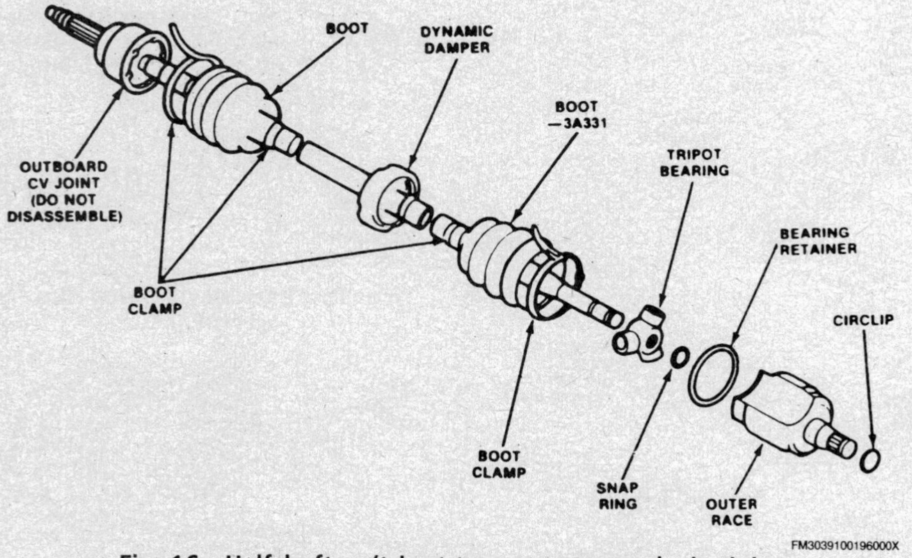

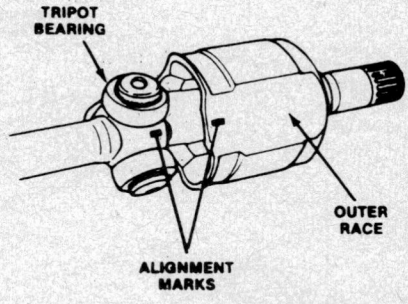

Fig. 17 Outer race & tripot joint, placing alignment marks

Fig. 16 Halfshaft w/tripot type constant velocity joint

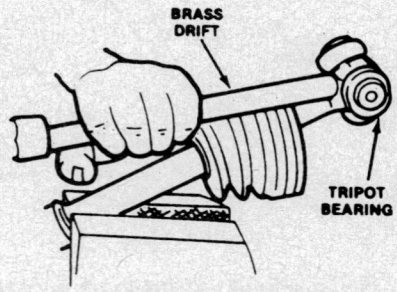

Fig. 19 Tripot joint removal from halfshaft

7. Place alignment marks on bearing inner race and driveshaft, then remove snap ring, **Fig. 11.**
8. Remove inner race, bearing cage and ball bearing assembly.
9. Using a screwdriver with sharp edges filed down, pry ball bearings from cage **Fig. 12.**
10. Place alignment marks on bearing inner race and bearing cage.
11. Rotate bearing cage inner race to align bearing lands, then remove inner race through large end of cage.
12. If necessary, remove small clamp and boot from driveshaft. If boot is to be reused, wrap driveshaft splines with tape before removing.
13. Check all bearing components for wear and damage. Bearing components are matched during the manufacturing process, therefore components from another constant velocity should not be interchanged. If bearing is found to unsatisfactory, replace the constant velocity joint assembly.
14. Cover driveshaft spline with tape and install boot, if removed.
15. Lubricate inner race, bearing cage and ball bearings with lubricant E43Z-19590-A or equivalent.
16. Aligning mark made during disassem-

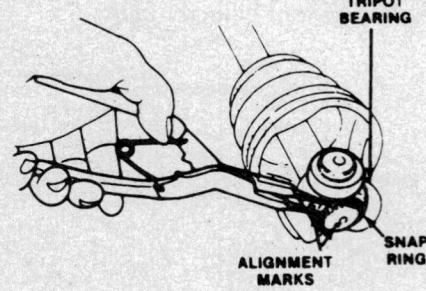

Fig. 18 Tripot joint snap ring removal

bly, position inner race into bearing cage. Inner race chamfered splines should face large end of cage, **Fig. 13.**
17. Using hand pressure, press ball bearings into cage windows.
18. Aligning marks on inner race and driveshaft made during disassembly, position inner race, cage and ball bearing assembly onto driveshaft, then insert snap ring into driveshaft groove. When install bearing assembly on driveshaft, chamfered end of cage should face snap ring, **Fig. 14.**
19. Apply 1.4 to 2.1 ounces of lubricant E43Z-19590-A or equivalent to outer

race, then install outer race over inner race, cage and ball bearing assembly.
20. Add approximately .7 to 1 ounce of lubricant specified in step 19 to outer race, then install outer race bearing retaining ring.
21. Seat boot in grooves on driveshaft and outer race, then extend constant velocity joint until distance between boot grooves is 3½ inches, **Fig. 15.** Keep joint at this distance until after boot clamps have been installed.
22. Using a screwdriver with sharp edges filed off, pry up on boot at outer race to allow trapped air to escape.
23. Install and lock boot clamps.
24. Check constant velocity joint for smoothness of operation through its full range of travel.
25. Install driveshaft on vehicle as described under "Driveshaft, Replace."

Tripot Type

Models with automatic transaxle use a tripot type constant velocity joint at the transaxle end of the halfshaft and a Birfield type constant velocity joint at the hub side of the halfshaft, **Fig. 16.** The tripot type constant velocity type joint can be disassembled and serviced. The Birfield type constant velocity joint should not be disassembled and is serviced only as an assembly with the halfshaft. To service the tripot type constant velocity joint, proceed as follows:

1. Remove halfshaft as described under "Halfshaft, Replace."
2. Position halfshaft in a soft jawed vise.
3. Remove large boot clamp, the roll boot back over shaft, **Fig. 16.**
4. Check joint grease for contamination, **Fig. 9.** If grease is not contaminated and joint has been operating satisfactorily, add required amount of lubricant and install a replacement bolt. If grease is contaminated, then constant velocity joint must be disassembled

and inspected.

5. Remove bearing retaining ring.
6. Place alignment marks on outer race and tripot joint, then remove outer race, **Fig. 17.**
7. Place alignment mark on tripot bearing and halfshaft, then remove snap ring, **Fig. 18.**
8. Using a brass drift, carefully drive tripot joint from halfshaft, **Fig. 19.**
9. If necessary, remove boot small clamp, then wrap tape around halfshaft splines and remove boot.
10. Check tripot joint for wear and damage and replace as necessary.
11. If removed, wrap halfshaft splines with tape and install boot to halfshaft groove.
12. Align marks on halfshaft and tripot joint made during removal.
13. Using a brass drift, drive tripot joint

into position on halfshaft, then install snap ring.

14. Fill outer race with 3.5 ounces of lubricant E43Z-19590-A or equivalent, then position outer race over tripot joint, aligning marks made during removal.
15. Install bearing retaining ring, then position boot in groove on outer race.
16. Position joint so that distance between halfshaft boot groove and outer race groove is 3½ inches, **Fig. 15.**
17. Using a screwdriver with sharp edges filled off, pry up on boot at outer race end to allow trapped air to escape.
18. Install and lock boot clamps, then check joint for smoothness of operation through its full range of travel.
19. Install halfshaft on vehicle as described under "Halfshaft, Replace."

Escort & Tracer

INDEX

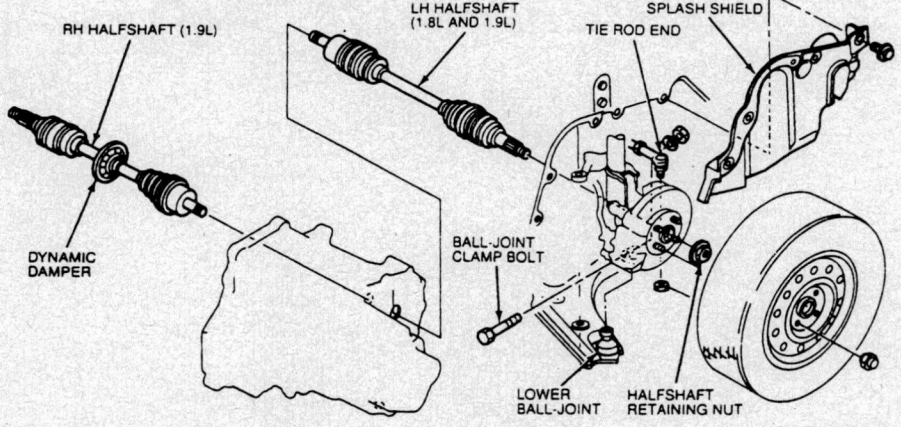

Fig. 1 Halfshaft removal. Except 1.8L RH halfshaft

TROUBLESHOOTING
NOISE & VIBRATION IN TURNS

Clicking, popping or grinding noises while turning may be caused by the following:
1. Cut or damaged CV joint boots, resulting in contaminated lube in outboard or inboard CV joints.
2. Loose CV joint clamps.
3. Worn, damaged or improperly installed wheel bearings.
4. Halfshaft assembly connecting component.

VIBRATION AT HIGHWAY SPEEDS

1. Out of balance front wheels or tires.
2. Front tires out of round.

SHUDDER OR VIBRATION DURING ACCELERATION

1. Excessively worn or damaged inboard or outboard CV joint.
2. Excessively high CV joint operating angles caused by improper ride height.

HALFSHAFT OR CV JOINT PULL-OUT

Engine Or Transaxle Misaligned

1. Check engine mounts for damage.

Front Suspension Components Worn Or Damaged

1. Check for worn bushings or bent front suspension components.

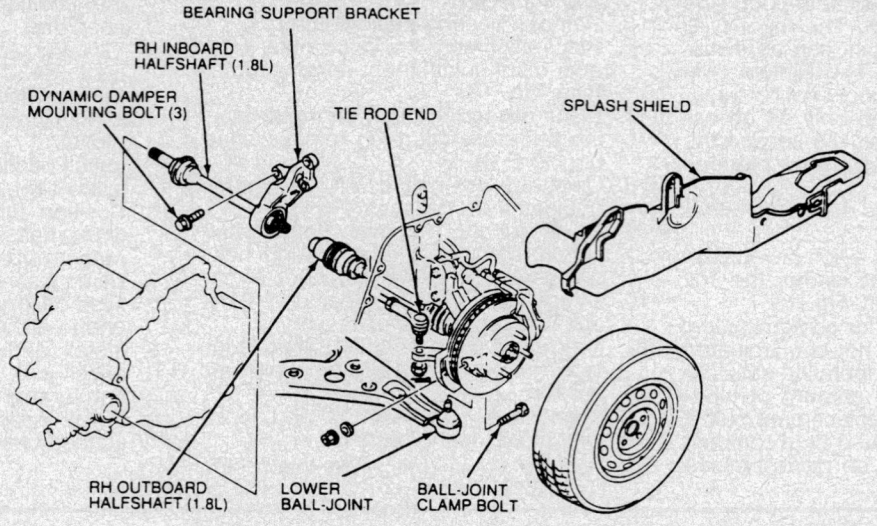

Fig. 2   Halfshaft removal. 1.8L RH halfshaft

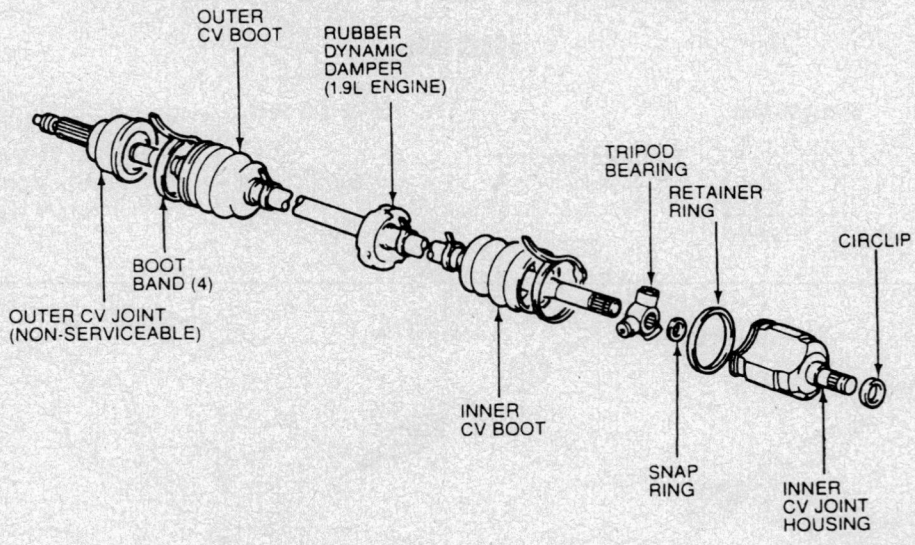

Fig. 3   Halfshaft service

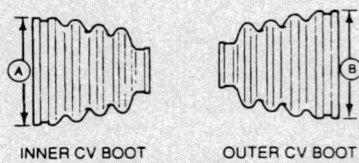

INNER CV BOOT   OUTER CV BOOT

	1.9L Engine		1.8L Engine	
	Right Side	Left Side	Right Side	Left Side
Ⓐ	84.0 mm (3.31 in)	90.0 mm (3.54 in)	89.9 mm (3.54 in)	
Ⓑ	89.0 mm (3.50 in)		85.2 mm (3.35 in)	

Fig. 4   CV joint boots

Item	Model	1.8L Engine	1.9L Engine
Halfshaft			
Length of joint (between center of joint)	Right side	631.2 mm (24.85 in)	918.7 mm (36.16 in)
	Left side	621.7 mm (24.48 in)	640.7 mm (25.22 in)
Shaft diameter	Right side	23.0 mm (0.91 in)	
	Left side	23.0 mm (0.91 in)	

FM3039100206000X

Fig. 5   Halfshaft dimensions

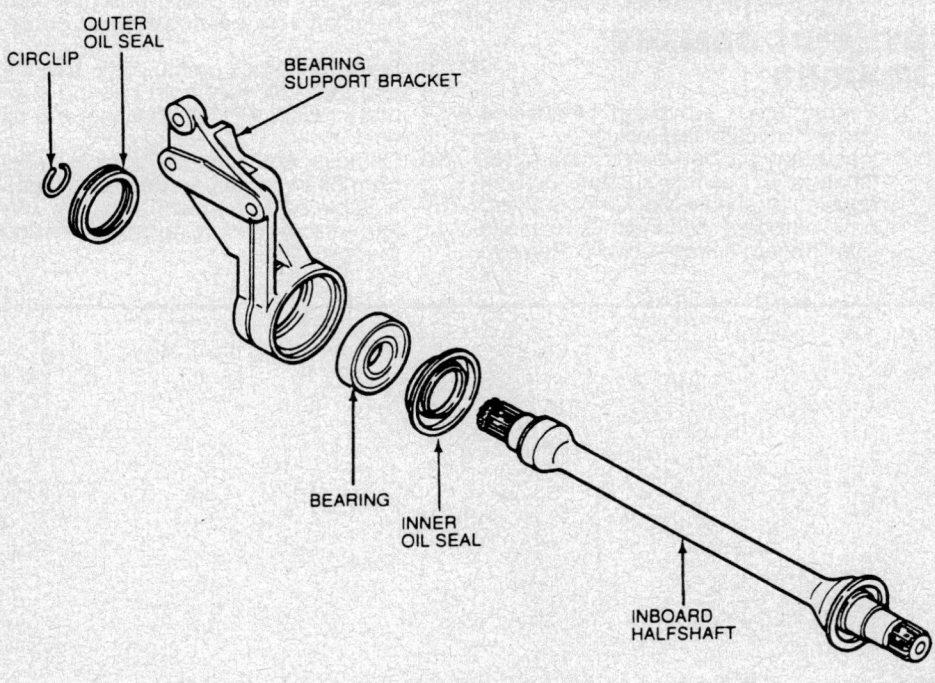

Fig. 6   Dynamic damper bearing. 1.8L/4–112 engine

FM3039100202000X

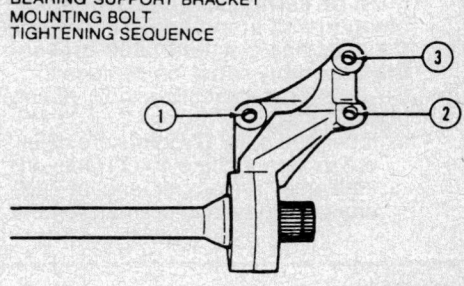

FM3039100203000X

Fig. 7   Bearing support bracket mounting bolt

c. **Torque** crossmember bolts and nuts to 47-66 ft. lbs.
d. **Torque** transaxle to crossmember nuts to 32-43 ft. lbs.
e. **Torque** tie rod end nuts and ball joint clamp bolt to 31-42 ft. lbs.
f. **Torque** halfshaft retaining nut to 174-235 ft. lbs.
g. Stake retaining nut into place. **If nut splits or cracks after staking, replace with a new nut.**

DRIVESHAFT SERVICE

CV JOINT

a. **Torque** bearing support bracket in sequence shown in **Fig. 7** to 31-46 ft. lbs.

The Birfield type CV joint on outboard end of the halfshaft is serviced as a complete CV joint/halfshaft assembly. If only the outer CV joint boot needs to be replaced, follow the applicable disassembly and assembly steps below. The tripot type inner CV joint can be disassembled and serviced.

1. Remove halfshaft as outlined under "Halfshaft, Replace."
2. Secure halfshaft in a soft jawed vise.
3. Using a screwdriver, pry up locking tabs of inner CV joint boot bands, **Fig. 3.**
4. Remove bands with pliers.
5. Slide boot back to expose CV joint.
6. Mark shaft and CV joint housing to ensure correct assembly.
7. Remove retainer ring from CV joint housing.
8. Remove CV joint housing from halfshaft.
9. Mark tripot bearing and shaft to ensure correct assembly.
10. Remove tripot snap ring.
11. Gently tap tripot bearing off shaft using a suitable soft faced hammer.

Improperly Installed Or Missing Retainers

1. Check for CV joint circlip missing or not properly seated in transaxle side gear.

DRIVESHAFT
REPLACE

If removing both right and left side drive shafts, appropriate plugs must be installed. Failure to do so may result in dislocation of differential side gears, necessitating transaxle disassembly to re-align the gears.

1. Raise and support vehicle.
2. Remove wheel and splash shield.
3. Raise staked portion of halfshaft retaining nut.
4. Remove retaining nut and discard.
5. Remove cotter pin from tie rod end and separate tie rod end from steering knuckle using a suitable tie rod remover tool, **Figs. 1 and 2.**
6. Remove lower ball joint clamp bolt and pry down on lower control arm to separate ball joint from steering knuckle.
7. Remove lefthand halfshaft as follows:
   a. Pull outward on steering knuckle/brake assembly.
   b. Carefully pull halfshaft from the steering knuckle and position knuckle aside.
   c. Support transaxle with a suitable jack stand.
   d. Remove four transaxle mount to crossmember nuts.
   e. Remove two rear crossmember attaching nuts.
   f. Support rear of crossmember then remove two front mounting bolts and remove crossmember.
8. **On all models**, position a drain pan under transaxle.
9. **On 1.8L/4-112 engine righthand side halfshaft**, remove three dynamic damper mounting bolts.
10. **On all models**, insert a pry bar between halfshaft and the transaxle case.
11. Remove halfshaft.
12. Reverse procedure to install, noting the following:
    a. Position circlip on inner CV joint spline on circlip gap is at top. Lubricate splines lightly with Motorcraft XG-1-c grease or equivalent.
    b. Position halfshaft so CV joint splines are aligned with differential side gears splines. Push halfshaft into differential.

12. Wrap tape around splines of shaft.
13. Remove inner CV joint boot.
14. If outer CV joint boot is to be replaced proceed as follows:
    a. **On 1.8L engine righthand half-shaft,** pry up rubber damper retaining band locking clip and remove.
    b. **On all models,** pry up on outer CV joint band clamp and remove.
    c. Remove outer CV joint boot.
15. Inspect all CV joint grease for contamination. **A contaminated CV joint must be completely disassembled, cleaned and inspected. If the outer CV joint has contaminated grease, the assembly must be replaced.**
16. Reverse procedure to install, noting the following:
    a. Inner and outer CV joints are different in size. Failure to correctly install boot on proper end of halfshaft could lead to premature boot

and/or CV joint wear, **Fig. 4.**
    b. Wrap CV joint boot clamps in a clockwise direction.
    c. Align marks made during disassembly to ensure correct assembly.
    d. Fill CV joint and boots with specified grease and "burp" air from boot.
    e. Measure assembled halfshaft for correct dimension as shown in **Fig. 5.**

DYNAMIC DAMPER BEARING

1. Perform steps 1 through 14 outlined under "Driveshafts, Replace."
2. Insert a pry bar between outboard halfshaft and bearing support bracket housing at engine block. Pry outward until outboard halfshaft is released from inboard halfshaft circlip. Remove

outboard halfshaft assembly.
3. Remove three bearing support bracket bolts.
4. Insert a pry bar between the bearing support bracket and starter motor brace.
5. Pry outward until inboard halfshaft is released from differential side gear.
6. Remove inboard halfshaft/bearing support bracket assembly, **Fig. 6.**
7. Remove circlip from inboard halfshaft.
8. Using an arbor press, push inboard halfshaft from bearing support bracket.
9. Using an arbor press, push bearing and inner oil seal from bearing support bracket. Discard bearing and oil seal.
10. Remove and discard outer oil seal from bearing support bracket using a suitable seal remover.
11. Reverse procedure to install, noting the following:

DRIVE AXLES

INDEX

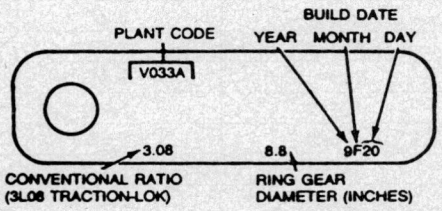

Fig. 1 Rear axle identification tag

IDENTIFICATION

The plant code shown in **Fig. 1** on the axle identification tag is used to identify the axle assembly. The plant code will not change as long as that particular axle assembly does not undergo an external design change. If an internal design change is made to an axle during the production life of the axle and that internal change affects service parts interchangeability, a dash and numerical suffix will be added to the plant code, **Fig. 2**. Refer to **Fig. 3**.

TROUBLESHOOTING

Refer to troubleshooting chart **Fig. 4**, for rear axle symptoms.

NOISE ACCEPTABILITY

As all gear-driven parts do, drive axles produce a certain amount of noise. Some noise is acceptable and may be audible at certain speeds or under various driving conditions such as a newly paved blacktop road. The slight noise is in no way detrimental to operation of the rear axle and may be considered normal.

With Traction-Lok limited slip differential axle, slight chatter noise on slow, tight turns after extended highway driving is considered acceptable and has no detrimental affect on the axle's locking function.

LEAKAGE CONDITIONS

Most rear axle leakage conditions can be corrected without a teardown. However, it is important to clean the leaking area enough to identify the exact source of the leak.

A plugged or seized jiggle cap vent will cause excessive seal lip wear due to internal pressure buildup. When a leak occurs, check cap by pressing down on it with index finger. If the cap moves up and down freely, it is working properly. If it does not move freely, it must be replaced.

Check axle lubricant level. Lubricant should be $9/16$ inch below bottom of filler hole.

Drive Pinion Seal

When the drive pinion seal leaks, it is usually because of improper installation, or because of poor quality of the seal journal surface. Any damage to the seal bore (dings, dents, gouges, etc.) will distort the seal casing and allow leakage past the outer edge of the seal.

Pinion Nut

Some models may experience oil leakage past the threads of the pinion nut. The condition can be corrected by removing the nut and applying pipe sealant with Teflon part No. D8AZ-19554-A or equivalent on the pinion threads and nut face. **Ensure the correct procedure for setting the bearing preload is followed when the nut is installed.**

Porous Casting

The differential carrier may leak through small pockets in the metal. These pockets (casting leakage) are caused by gas bubbles in the casting process.

Because the axle's sound characteristics may be changed if torn down to replace the carrier, servicing the porosity is preferable. Below are two recommended procedures that may be employed to fix a porous axle.

1. Peen a small amount of body lead into the hole, then seal the pocket with Epoxy Sealer Metallic Plastic part No. C6A7-A9554-A or equivalent.
2. In larger pockets, drill a shallow hole and tap it for a small setscrew. Install the setscrew and seal it over with Epoxy Sealer Metallic Plastic part No. C6A7-A9554-A or equivalent.

Axle Vent

There have been some occurrences of

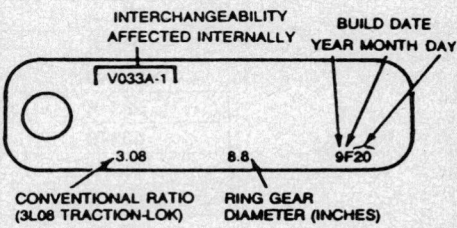

Fig. 2 Rear axle identification tag w/internal modification

lubricant leaking through the axle vent. This may be caused by a clogged or sticking axle vent cap. If this is the case, the vent assembly should be replaced, use Stud and Bearing Mount part No. EOAZ-19554-BA or equivalent on threads of vent to ensure retention.

AXLE NOISE

Gear Noise

Gear noise is the typical "howling" or "whining" of the ring gear and pinion due to an improper gear pattern, gear damage, or improper bearing preload. It can occur at various speeds and driving conditions, or it can be continuous.

Chuckle

Chuckle is a particular "rattling" noise that sounds like a stick against the spokes of a bicycle wheel. It occurs while decelerating from 40 mph and can be heard all the way to a stop. The frequency varies with the speed of the vehicle.

Knock

Knock is very similar to chuckle, though it may be louder and occurs on acceleration or deceleration.

Clunk

Clunk may be a metallic noise heard when the automatic transmission is engaged in reverse or drive, or it may occur when throttle is applied or released. It is caused by backlash somewhere in the driveline, or loose suspension components.

Year	Axle Code	Gear Ratio	Year	Axle Code	Gear Ratio
1992	016-E	3.27	1992-Cont'd	467-A	3.45
	016-H	3.27		467-B	3.45
	016-P	3.27		468-A	3.45
	017-C	3.27		468-B	3.45
	017-D	3.27		477-B	2.73
	017-E	3.27		478-B	2.73
	018-H	3.56		479-B	3.08
	019-E	3.55		480-A	2.73
	020-A	3.08		482-B	3.08
	025-A	3.55		485-B	2.73
	030-A	2.73		486-B	3.27
	030-B	2.73		487-B	2.73
	030-D	2.73		488-B	3.45
	031-A	2.73		491-B	2.73
	031-B	2.73		492-B	3.27
	031-D	2.73		493-B	2.73
	033-A	3.08		493-C	3.45
	033-B	3.08		494-B	3.08
	033-D	3.08		495-B	3.08
	033-E	3.08		496-B	3.27
	033-G	3.08		497-B	3.45
	033-GG	3.08	1993-94	013-B	2.73
	034-A	3.08		012-B	2.73
	034-B	3.08		014-C	3.08
	034-D	3.08		014-B	3.08
	034-E	3.08		015-B	3.08
	034-G	3.08		015-C	3.08
	036-A	3.55		016-B	3.27
	037-C	3.55		017-B	3.27
	037-D	3.55		017-C	3.27
	037-E	3.55		030-B	2.73
	037-G	3.55		031-B	2.73
	037-P	3.55		033-B	3.08
	038-A	3.27		034-B	3.08
	038-B	3.27		037-C	3.55
	038-D	3.27		037-B	3.55
	038-E	3.27		038-B	3.27
	038-G	3.27		039-A	3.27
	039-A	3.27		201-A	2.73
	039-B	3.27		203-F	3.08
	039-D	3.27		205-F	3.27
	039-E	3.27		266-D	3.73
	039-G	3.27		281-D	3.45
	040-A	3.08		404-F	3.08
	266-D	3.73		407-F	3.27
	457-B	2.73		423-F	3.08
	458-A	2.73		424-F	3.27
	458-B	2.73		433-B	3.73
	462-A	3.08		445-C	3.08
	462-B	3.08		447-C	3.08
	463-A	3.08		462-B	3.08
	463-B	3.08		479-B	3.08
	485-B	3.27		502-A	3.27

Fig. 3 Drive axle identification

CONDITION	POSSIBLE SOURCE	
• Noise is the same in all modes	• Road noise • Tire noise • Front wheel bearing noise	• Pinion Bearings • Wheel Bearings • Axle Shaft Surface Finish
• Noise changes with type of road	• Road noise • Tire noise	
• Noise tone lowers as vehicle speed is lowered	• Tire noise	
• Noise most pronounced on turns	• Differential side and pinion gears	
• Similar noise is produced with vehicle standing and driving	• Engine noise • Transmission noise	
• Noise is in one or more modes (Drive, Cruise, Coast, Float)	• Ring and pinion gear	
• Clunk on acceleration or deceleration	• Worn differential cross shaft in case	

REAR AXLE DIAGNOSIS

CONDITION	POSSIBLE SOURCE	ACTION
• Excessive Rear Axle noise.	• Differential carrier	• Road test vehicle to ensure problem is rear axle noise rather than other system noise.
• Loud "Clunk" in the driveshaft when shifting from REVERSE to DRIVE.	• Driveshaft	• Raise vehicle, rotate driveshaft by hand to isolate problem as driveshaft or rear axle problem. Service or replace as required.
	• Rear axle shafts or carrier	• Remove and inspect. Service as necessary.
• Limited-slip or Traction-Lok axle does not work in snow, mud or on ice.	• Differential	• Perform Traction-Lok Differential Operation Check in this Section. Service as required.
• On turns, the rear axle has a high-pitched chattering noise (Limited-slip or Traction-Lok axles only). Slight chatter noise on slow turns after extended highway driving is considered acceptable and has no detrimental effect on the locking axle function.	• Lubricant	• Road test vehicle — Drive vehicle in tight circles — 5 clockwise and 5 counterclockwise. If chatter is still evident, flush and replace with E0AZ-19580-A Limited Slip Lubricant or equivalent — plus 4 ounces of C8AZ-19B546-A Friction Modifier or equivalent.
	• Differential	• Remove differential, service as required.

FM3039100120000X

Fig. 4   Troubleshooting chart

Bearing Whine

Bearing whine is a high pitched sound similar to a whistle. It is usually caused by malfunctioning pinion bearings, which are operating at driveshaft speed. Bearing noise occurs at all driving speeds; this distinguishes it from gear whine, which usually comes and goes as speed changes.

Bearing Rumble

Bearing rumble sounds like marbles being tumbled. This condition is usually caused by a malfunctioning wheel bearing. The lower pitch is because the wheel bearing turns at only about one-third of driveshaft speed. In addition, wheel bearing noise may be high pitched, similar to gear noise but will be evident in all four driving modes.

Chatter On Cornering

Chattering noise when cornering is a condition where the whole rear end vibrates only when the vehicle is moving. The vibration is plainly felt as well as heard. In conventional axles, extra differential thrust washers cause a condition of partial lockup which creates this chatter. Chatter noise on Traction-Lok axles can usually be traced to erratic movement between adjacent clutch plates and can be corrected with a lubricant change.

Click At Engagement

Click at engagement is a condition on axles of a slight noise, distinct from a "clunk" that happens in reverse or drive engagement. It can be corrected by installing a slinger between the companion flange and front pinion bearing.

VIBRATION CONDITIONS

Few vibration conditions are caused by the axle. Most vibration in the rear end is caused by tires or driveline angle.

Vehicles equipped with a traction-lok differential will always have both wheels driving. If, while the vehicle is being serviced, only one wheel is raised off the floor and the rear axle is driven by the engine, the wheel on the floor could drive the vehicle off the safety stand. Ensure both rear wheels are raised off the floor.

Tires

Some vehicles are equipped with directional tires (see tire rotation arrows on tire sidewall). If a directional tire is removed for service, It must be remounted in its original location.

Do not balance the rear wheels and tires while they are mounted on the vehicle. Possible tire disintegration and/or differential failure could result, causing personal injury and/or exten- sive component damage. Use only an off-vehicle wheel and tire balancer.

A vibration can sometimes be corrected by properly rotating or inflating the tires. The best tires should be placed on the rear to minimize vibration, especially on vehicles with rear coil springs.

Driveline Angle

An incorrect driveline (pinion) angle can often be detected by the driving condition when vibration occurs.
1. A vibration during coasting from 35 to 45 mph is often caused by a high pinion angle.
2. A vibration during acceleration from 35 to 45 mph may indicate a lower than specified pinion angle.

TRACTION-LOK DIFFERENTIAL OPERATION CHECK

A Traction-Lok differential can be checked for proper operation without removing it from the axle housing using procedure outlined below:
1. Raise and support one rear wheel, then remove the wheel cover.
2. Install adapter for Traction-Lok differential tool No. T66L-4204-A or equivalent, then connect a torque wrench of at least a 200 foot pound capacity.
3. Rotate the axle shaft. **Ensure the transmission is in neutral, one wheel is on the floor, and the other rear wheel is raised off the floor.**
4. The breakaway torque required to start rotation should be at least 20 ft. lbs. The initial breakaway torque may be higher than the continuous turning torque, this is considered normal.
5. The axle shaft should turn with even pressure throughout the check without slipping or binding. If the torque reading is less than specified, check the differential for improper assembly.

REMOVAL

DIFFERENTIAL CASE ASSEMBLY

1. Raise and support rear of vehicle, then loosen axle housing cover bolts and allow lubricant to drain into suitable container, **Fig. 5.**
2. Remove axle housing cover, then proceed as follows:
   a. Wipe excess lubricant from inside axle housing, then visually inspect parts for wear and/or damage.
   b. Rotate gears and check for roughness, indicating damaged bearings or gears.
   c. Install suitable dial indicator on axle housing cover flange, then check and record ring gear back face runout. Maximum back face runout is .004 inch.
3. Remove rear axles and propeller shaft. Refer to "Rear Axle & Suspension" section for procedures.
4. Scribe reference marks on differential

bearing caps for assembly reference, then loosen bearing cap bolts. **Observe and record direction the arrows are facing on the bearing caps. During installation, the arrows must face in the same direction.**

5. Using suitable tool, pry differential case, bearing cups and shims out of housing until loose in the bearing caps. Remove bearing caps, then the differential assembly. Mark which side cups and shims came from for reference during reassembly.

DRIVE PINION

1. Scribe reference mark between drive pinion and companion flange, then hold flange with suitable tool and remove pinion nut and pinion flange.
2. Using suitable soft faced hammer, drive pinion out of front bearing cone and remove from rear of axle housing.
3. Remove oil seal and front bearing cone and roller from pinion housing.
4. Using suitable arbor press and adapters, remove rear pinion bearing.
5. Using suitable micrometer, measure and record thickness of shim which is found under rear bearing cone.
6. Remove pinion bearing cups from pinion housing with suitable brass drift. Install cups using suitable bearing cup installer. Cups are not properly installed if a .015 feeler gauge can be inserted between cup and bottom of bore at any point around the cup. **If any bearing cups are replaced, the respective bearing cone and roller must be replaced.**

DISASSEMBLE

EXCEPT TRACTION-LOK LIMITED SLIP DIFFERENTIAL

1. If differential bearings are to be replaced, remove and replace with suitable puller.
2. If the ring gear backlash measured during removal exceeded specifications, proceed as follows:
   a. Install differential bearing cups on cones, then install differential case in rear housing with drive pinion removed.
   b. Install a .265 inch shim on left side of case, then install bearing cap and tighten bolts finger tight. Install progressively larger shims on right side of case until the largest shim selected can be installed with a slight drag. Install bearing cap and **torque** bolts to 70–85 ft. lbs.
3. Rotate differential several turns in either direction to ensure free rotation and to seat bearings.
4. Mount suitable dial indicator to axle housing, then check ring gear back face runout. Ring gear back face runout should be within .004 inch. If ring gear back face runout is now within specifications, the original reading was caused by insufficient differential bearing preload. If ring gear back face

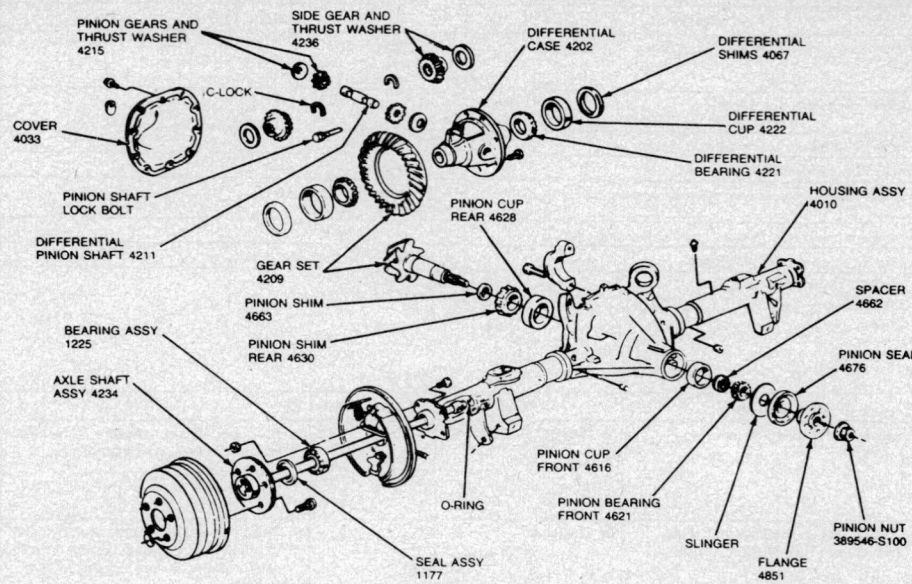

Fig. 5 Exploded view of 7¹/₂ & 8.8 inch ring gear rear axle

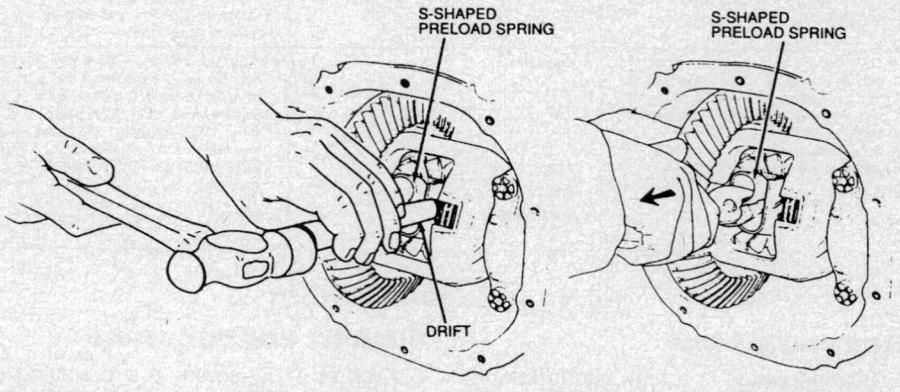

Fig. 6 C-clips and "S" shaped preload spring removal. Ford Traction-Lok

runout is still not within specifications, proceed to step 6.
5. Remove differential case from axle housing, then remove ring gear. Install differential case less ring gear in housing following procedures given above.
6. Check differential case runout. Runout should be within .004 inch. If runout is now within specifications, ring gear is out of specifications and should be replaced. If runout is not within specifications, the differential case is damaged and should be replaced.

TRACTION-LOK LIMITED SLIP DIFFERENTIAL

For differential case and ring gear runout checks and differential bearing replacement, refer to "Except Traction-Lok Limited Slip Differential."

1. Remove and discard ring gear to differential case attaching bolts.
2. Tap on ring gear using a suitable mallet and remove ring gear from case.
3. Remove pinion shaft lock screw and pinion shaft.

4. Remove preloaded "S" shaped spring, **Fig. 6. Use caution when removing "S" shaped spring, since it is under tension.**
5. Rotate pinion gears and thrust washers using 12 inch socket extension inserted into pinion gear rotator tool No. T80P-4205-A or equivalent until they can be removed through access hole.
6. Remove left and right side gears, clutch packs and shims, **Fig. 7.** Note order of removal and side removed from and tag for reference during assembly.

CLEANING & INSPECTION
EXCEPT TRACTION-LOK LIMITED SLIP DIFFERENTIAL

Clean all parts in suitable solvent. Dry all parts except bearings with compressed air or shop towels. Allow bearings to air dry or dry with shop towels. Do not use compressed air to dry bearings, as damage may result.

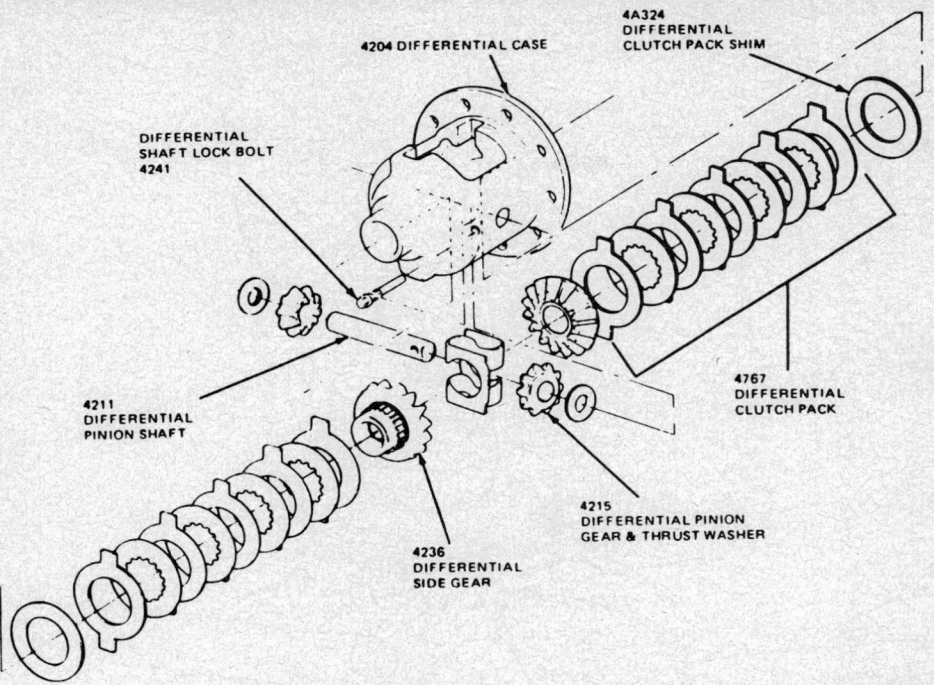

4A324 DIFFERENTIAL CLUTCH PACK SHIM

4204 DIFFERENTIAL CASE

DIFFERENTIAL SHAFT LOCK BOLT 4241

4211 DIFFERENTIAL PINION SHAFT

4236 DIFFERENTIAL SIDE GEAR

4215 DIFFERENTIAL PINION GEAR & THRUST WASHER

4767 DIFFERENTIAL CLUTCH PACK

FM3039100123000X

Fig. 7 Exploded view of Ford Traction-Lok

Inspect differential bearings and cups for wear, pitting, galling, flat spots or cracks. Any bearing or cup showing any signs of wear or damage must be replaced. Bearings and respective cups must be replaced as an assembly only. Do not attempt to interchange bearings and cups as bearing life will be affected.

Inspect non-machined differential case surfaces for nicks and burrs which can be removed with an oil stone or fine tooth file. Inspect pinion shaft bore to ensure it is not elongated or worn. If damage is evident, differential case must be replaced. Inspect machined differential surfaces and counterbores. They must be smooth and free of nicks, gouges, cracks and other visible damage. If damage is evident, differential case must be replaced.

Inspect pinion shaft for excessive wear, scoring or galling. Ensure shaft is smooth and concentric. If any wear or damage is evident, replace shaft. Inspect pinion shaft lockpin for damage and to ensure it has a snug fit in differential case. Replace lockpin or case as necessary.

Inspect pinion and ring gears for worn or chipped teeth, cracks, damaged bearing journals or attaching bolt threads. If any of the above are evident, replace ring gear and pinion as a matched set.

Inspect pinion and side gears. Gears must exhibit a uniform contact pattern without any signs of cracks, wear, scoring or galling. If any of the above are evident, replace all the gears. Inspect thrust washers for wear and replace as necessary.

Inspect pinion and ring gears for worn or chipped teeth, cracks, damaged bearing journals or attaching bolt threads. If any of the above are evident, replace ring gear and pinion as a matched set.

Inspect axle shaft C-locks (if equipped) for signs of cracks or wear and replace as necessary.

TRACTION-LOK LIMITED SLIP DIFFERENTIAL

The cleaning and inspection of these units is the same as for conventional differentials except that cleaning solvent should not be allowed to contact the clutch plates. The clutch plates should be wiped clean only. In addition, the following steps should be performed which apply to the Traction-Lok differential only.

Visually inspect clutch packs, side gears, pinion gears and pinion shaft for damage or wear and replace as necessary.

Place each clutch pack without shims into tool No.T80P-4946-A or equivalent, **Fig. 8.** **Torque** nut to 60 inch lbs. Using feeler gauge, determine thickness of new shims by inserting thickest blade possible between clutch pack and tool, **Fig. 9**, and note size for use during reassembly.

ASSEMBLE
DIFFERENTIAL CASE ASSEMBLY
Except Traction-Lok Limited Slip Differential

1. Install replacement ring gear (if removed). Apply suitable locking compound to new bolts and **torque** to 70-85 ft. lbs.

Traction-Lok Limited Slip Differential

1. Apply suitable lubricant to clutch plates, then install left side gear,

clutch pack and new shim into differential case. Repeat procedure for right hand side.
2. Install pinion gears and thrust washers 180° apart and in contact with side gears.
3. Align gears with pinion shaft bore, **Fig. 10,** using 12 inch socket extension inserted in pinion shaft rotator.
4. Install "S" shaped preload spring into differential using soft faced hammer.

DETERMINING DRIVE PINION DEPTH

Prior to determining drive pinion depth, clean pinion bearing cups and differential bearing pedestals thoroughly to ensure an accurate reading. Apply only a light oil film to bearing assemblies to avoid false readings.

1. Assemble aligning adapter, gauge disc and gauge block to tool No. T79P-4020-A, **Fig. 11.**
2. Place rear pinion bearing over aligning adapter, then insert tool and bearing in rear pinion bearing cup in pinion housing bore. Place front pinion bearing over screw in front pinion bearing cup and assemble tool handle onto screw. **Torque** handle to 20 inch lbs. Ensure tool is mounted securely between front and rear bearings.
3. Rotate gauge block several half turns to ensure bearings are seated properly. Rotational **torque** should be 20 inch lbs. with new bearings. Set gauge block at an angle approximately 45° from horizontal, **Fig. 12.**
4. Install gauge tube in differential bearing mounts, then install bearing caps and bearing cap bolts.
5. Use pinion shims to determine pinion depth by inserting shims between gauge block and gauge tube. The correct shim will fit with a slight drag. Do not attempt to force a shim between block and tube. **Do not use shims that are bent, dirty, nicked or mutilated as a gauge.**
6. Make note of proper shim size and remove tool from axle housing.
7. Using suitable arbor press and adapters, remove rear pinion bearing.
8. Install shim determined in step 5 above on pinion shaft, then reinstall bearing using arbor press. **The rear pinion bearing used to determine drive pinion depth must be used in the final assembly of the axle.**

DRIVE PINION INSTALLATION

1. Lubricate pinion bearings with suitable axle lubricant, then install pinion shaft and rear bearing, collapsible spacer and front bearing.
2. Install slinger (if equipped) and pinion oil seal, then insert pinion flange in seal and hold firmly in place against front bearing. From rear of housing, insert pinion shaft into flange.
3. Install pinion nut. While holding pinion

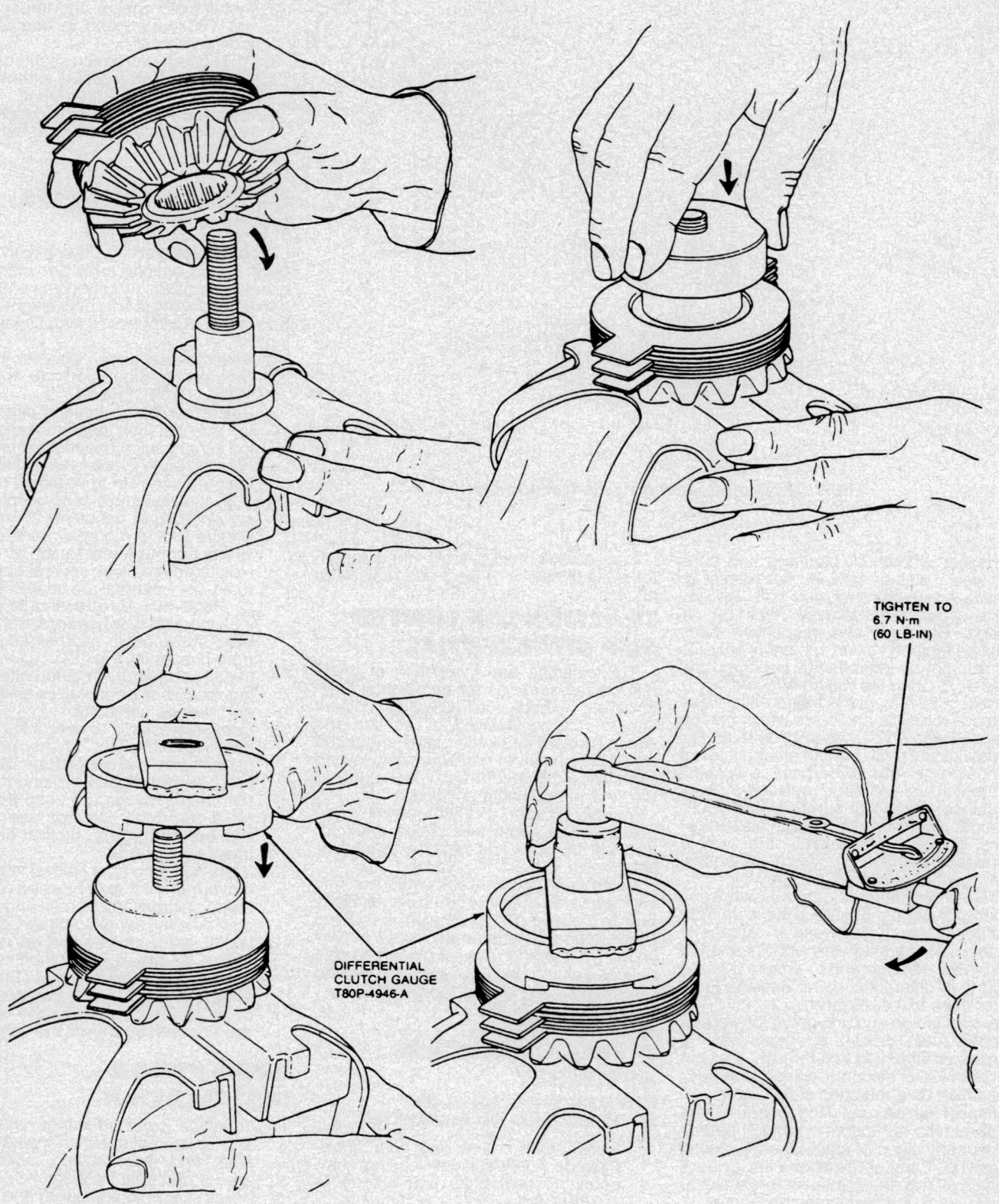

DIFFERENTIAL
CLUTCH GAUGE
T80P-4946-A

TIGHTEN TO
6.7 N·m
(60 LB-IN)

Fig. 8   Shim thickness measuring. Ford Traction-Lok

FM3039100124000X

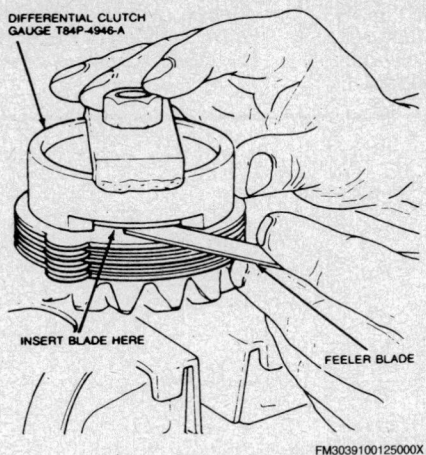

Fig. 9 Shim thickness measurement using tool No. T80P-4946-A or equivalent. Ford Traction-Lok

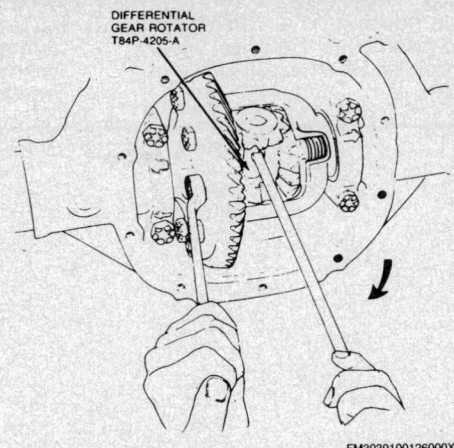

Fig. 10 Pinion gear removal & installation. Ford Traction-Lok

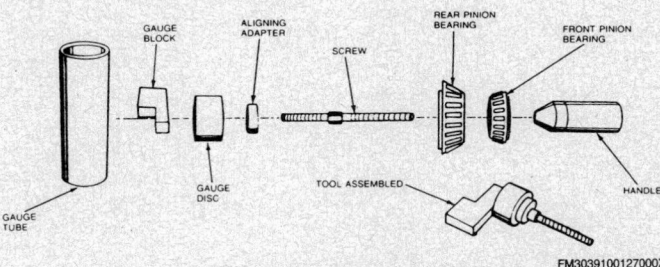

Fig. 11 Rear axle pinion depth gauge

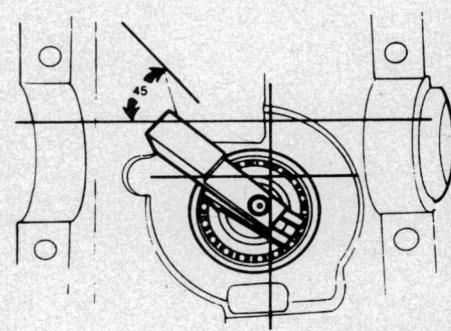

Fig. 12 Pinion depth gauge block installation

flange, tighten nut only enough to remove bearing endplay. When an increase in pinion nut turning effort is noted, stop tightening pinion nut. Rotate pinion several times in both directions to seat bearings.

4. Continue to tighten pinion nut in very small increments, then, every so often, using suitable inch lbs. torque wrench, measure pinion rotational torque. The rotating torque must not exceed specifications. **Do not exceed specified preload torque. Do not loosen pinion nut if preload torque is exceeded. If preload torque is exceeded, remove pinion nut, yoke, oil seal, slinger (if equipped) and collapsible spacer. Replace collapsible spacer and oil seal with new ones and repeat procedure.**

DIFFERENTIAL CASE INSTALLATION

1. Apply suitable axle lubricant to differential bearing bores.
2. Place differential bearing cups on bearings, then set differential assembly in axle housing. **If ring gear and pinion gear have punch marks, assemble ring gear in carrier so that marked tooth on pinion is indexed between the marked teeth of ring gear.**
3. Check and adjust backlash as follows:
   a. Mount suitable dial indicator on axle housing cover flange, then

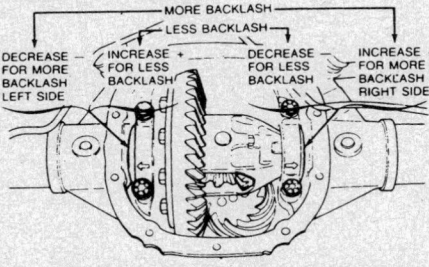

Fig. 13 Rear axle backlash adjustment

BACKLASH CHANGE REQUIRED	THICKNESS CHANGE REQUIRED	BACKLASH CHANGE REQUIRED	THICKNESS CHANGE REQUIRED
.001	.002	.009	.012
.002	.002	.010	.014
.003	.004	.011	.014
.004	.006	.012	.016
.005	.006	.013	.018
.006	.008	.014	.018
.007	.010	.015	.020
.008	.010		

measure ring gear backlash. If backlash is within specifications, proceed to step f. If backlash is not within specifications, proceed to step c. If backlash is zero, proceed to step b.

b. If backlash measured above is zero, add .020 inch (.5 mm) to right side of case and subtract .020 inch (.5 mm) from left side of case, then recheck backlash. If backlash is now within specifications, proceed to step d.

c. If backlash is not within specifications, correct backlash by increas-

ing thickness of one shim and decreasing thickness on the other shim by the same amount. Refer to **Fig. 13,** for approximate shim change.

d. Install shims and bearing caps. **Torque** bearing cap bolts to 70–85 ft. lbs., then rotate differential case assembly several turns in both directions.

e. Check backlash. If backlash is within specifications, proceed to step f. If not within specifications, repeat step c.

f. Increase both left and right side shims by .006 inch to provide proper differential bearing preload. Ensure shims are fully seated and the case assembly turns freely.

g. Using suitable white marking compound applied to ring gear, check tooth mesh contacting pattern. **Tooth mesh contacting pattern can be improved by installing the propeller shaft and axle assemblies and rotating both tires in the drive and coast direction.**

h. Contacting pattern should be within the primary area of the ring gear tooth surface avoiding narrow contact with the outer perimeter of tooth. Inspect pattern on the drive (pull) side of the ring gear. If serious error is determined, recheck pinion shim selection.

4. Install axle housing cover, driveshaft and axle assemblies. Refer to "Rear Axles, Propeller Shaft & Brakes" for procedures.

5. Fill rear axle assembly with axle lubricant recommended by manufacturer. On models equipped with 7½ inch Traction-Lok differentials, subtract 3 ounces of axle lubricant and replace with 3 ounces of Friction Modifier part No. C8AZ-19546-A or equivalent.

ACTIVE SUSPENSION SYSTEMS

TABLE OF CONTENTS

Application Chart

Year	Model	System	Page No.
1992	Mark VII	Air Suspension	31-1
	Probe	Programmed Ride Control	31-151
1992-93	Cougar & Thunderbird	Automatic Ride Control	31-138
1992-94	Continental	Air Suspension	31-1
	Town Car	Air Suspension	31-1
1992-94	Crown Victoria & Grand Marquis	Air Suspension	31-1
1993-94	Mark VIII	Air Suspension	31-1
1994	Thunderbird SC	Automatic Ride Control	31-138

Air Suspension

TABLE OF CONTENTS

MARK VII

INDEX

DESCRIPTION

The compressor relay, compressor vent solenoid and all air spring solenoids incorporate internal diodes for electrical noise suppression and are polarity sensitive. Care must be taken when servicing these components not to switch the battery feed and ground circuits or components damage will result. The electrical power supply to the air suspension system must be shutoff prior to hoisting, jacking or towing vehicle. This can be accomplished by disconnecting the battery or turning off the power switch located in the luggage compartment. Failure to do so may result in unexpected inflation or deflation of the air springs which may result in shifting of the vehicle during service procedures. Do not attempt to install or inflate any air spring that has become unfolded. Any spring which has unfolded must be refolded prior to being installed in a vehicle. The air spring refolding procedure should only be used to service an air spring which has never supported the vehicle's weight while in the improperly folded position. Do not attempt to inflate any spring which has been collapsed while uninflated from the rebound (hanging) position to the jounce stop. When installing a new air spring, care must be taken not to apply a load to the suspension until air springs have been inflated using air spring fill procedure. When front air springs are replaced, the height sensor must be checked and replaced if damaged. After inflating an air spring in hanging position, it must be inspected for proper shape. Failure to follow the above information may result in a sudden failure of the air spring or suspension system.

Used on Mark VII models, the Air Suspension System, **Fig. 1**, is an air operated, microprocessor controlled suspension which replaces conventional coil springs with air springs, providing automatic front and rear load leveling.

The front air springs, **Fig. 2**, are mounted to the upper spring pocket in the crossmember and on the lower suspension arms as in conventional suspension systems. The rear springs, **Fig. 3**, are mounted ahead of the rear axle, outboard of the body side members and on the lower suspension arm.

A piston type electrically operated air compressor, attached to the left fender apron, supplies the air pressure necessary for system operation. All air passing through the system is filtered through a regenerative type dryer, located on the compressor manifold. A vent solenoid, also located on the manifold, controls exhaust air.

Air flow through the entire system is controlled by the interaction of the air compressor, solenoids, height sensors and the control module.

OPERATION

System operation is maintained by the addition or removal of air to or from the air springs, resulting in a predetermined front and rear suspension height. This predetermined height is known as the vehicle trim height. The trim height is controlled by three height sensors, two of which are located at the front wheels and a third at the rear suspension, **Fig. 1**. The height sensors are attached to the body and suspension arms and will lengthen or shorten, depending on the amount of suspension travel. As weight is added to the vehicle, the body settles, shortening the height sensors. The height sensors signal the control module, which then activates the air compressor through a relay, and signals the air spring solenoids to open. As

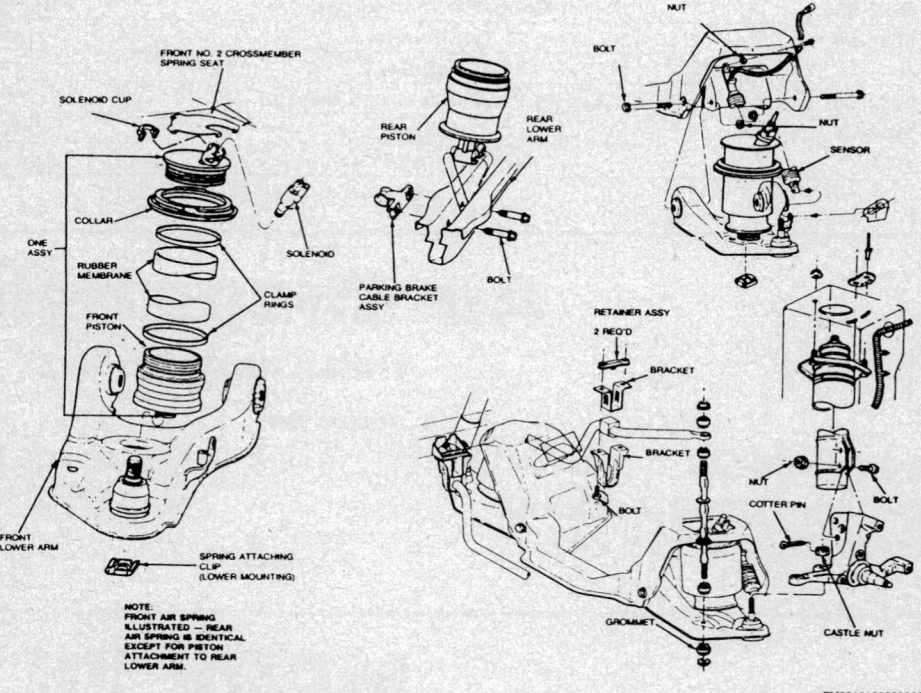

THE SYSTEM CONSISTS OF AN ELECTRIC AIR COMPRESSOR WITH REGENERATIVE AIR DRYER, THREE ELECTRONIC HEIGHT SENSORS, EIGHT QUICK CONNECT AIR FITTINGS, FOUR AIR SPRINGS WITH INTEGRAL SOLENOIDS, FOUR ONE-PIECE AIR LINES CONNECTING EACH SPRING TO THE COMPRESSOR AND A CONTROL MODULE WITH A SINGLE CHIP MICROCOMPUTER.

FM2019100001000X

Fig. 1   Air suspension system

Fig. 2   Exploded view of front suspension

FM2019100002000X

the body rises, the height sensors lengthen. When the predetermined trim height is reached, the air compressor and solenoid valves are deactivated by the control module. As weight is removed, the body rises, lengthening the height sensors, and the height sensors signal the control module. The control module then opens the air compressor vent solenoid and the air spring solenoid valves. As the body lowers, the height sensors shorten. When the predetermined trim height is reached, the air compressor vent valve and air spring solenoid valves are closed by the control module.

The air required for leveling the vehicle is distributed from the air compressor to each spring by four nylon air lines which

start at the dryer and end at the individual springs. Each air line is color coded to identify the spring to which they belong. The dryer is used to dry the air before it is delivered to each spring. The air required for compression and the vent air enter and exit through a common port on the compressor head. Vented air is controlled by a solenoid valve in the compressor head.

Electrical power to operate the system is distributed by the main body harness. The control module controls the air compressor relay, vent solenoid and the four air spring solenoids to provide the air requirements of the springs. The module also provides the power and ground circuits to the height sensors, while monitoring the input from the sensors and the Igni-

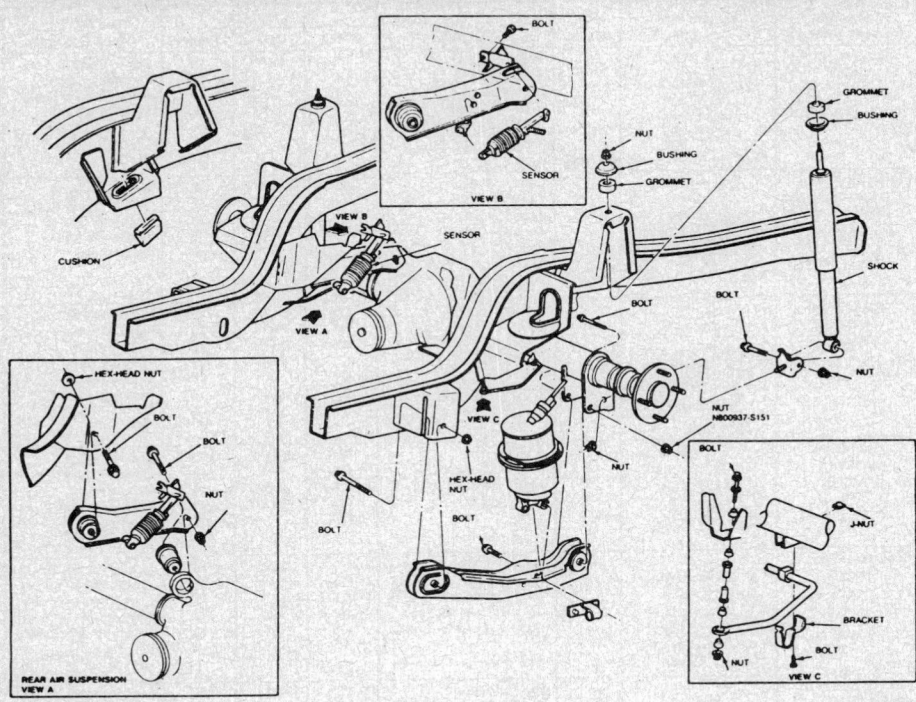

Fig. 3 Exploded view of rear suspension

FM2019100003000X

tion Run/Brake and On/Door Open circuits. These inputs are used by the module in determining vehicle leveling requirements, which are then carried out by the air system components controlled by the module. The control module also provides for system self-diagnosis, a routine for filling the air springs and operation of the system warning lamp.

CONTROL LOGIC

Ignition Off

When the ignition switch is turned off, the system will continue to operate for approximately one hour. During this time, the system will service requests to lower the vehicle as required, provided no sensor was reading high at the time the ignition switch was turned off. Vent time is limited to 10 seconds for the rear springs and 3 seconds for the front. Approximately 1 hour after the ignition switch is turned off, the system will correct for a low vehicle height by activating the air compressor. Compressor run time is limited to 15 seconds for the rear springs and 30 seconds for the front.

Ignition In Run

When the ignition switch is first turned to the RUN position, the system will raise the vehicle as necessary. No down requests will be serviced for approximately 45 seconds. After the 45 second period, up and down requests will be serviced provided no door is open. If any door is open, no down requests will be serviced until the door is closed. However, if the brakes are applied with the doors closed, neither up nor down requests will be serviced except for a rear up request already in progress.

GENERAL OPERATING CONDITIONS

1. Requests are serviced in the following Order: Rear Up, Front Up, Rear Down, Front Down.
2. With ignition in RUN, failure to service any request within 3 minutes will result in warning lamp activation. The lamp will stay on during that complete ignition cycle. However, only the request that was being serviced will be affected. The control module will continue to service all other requests as usual.
3. The rear spring solenoids will always be operated in tandem, while the front solenoids may operate independently.
4. Front and rear requests are never serviced at the same time.
5. Turning the ignition from RUN to OFF will clear all memory in the control module, and the warning lamp may not indicate failure when the ignition is returned to the ON position. **When charging the battery, ensure ignition switch is off, as damage to the compressor or compressor relay may result.**

DIAGNOSIS & TESTING

WARNING LAMP DIAGNOSIS

The "Check Suspension" warning light, located in the overhead console, serves the following diagnostic functions:
1. During normal operation with the ignition switch in the Run position and the "Check Suspension" light glowing, a possible air suspension problem is indicated.

2. During self-diagnosis testing, the "Check Suspension" light blinks 1.8 times per second to indicate the diagnostic routine has been entered, then blinks the test number being run during the test sequence.
3. During "Air Spring Refill" procedure, the "Check Suspension" light blinks once every 2 seconds to indicate the air spring fill routine has been entered.
4. Observing the "Check Suspension" light during normal operation with the ignition switch On can aid in detecting the following Air Suspension System problems:
   a. During normal operation, the "Check Suspension" light will glow for approximately one second and go out when ignition switch is turned from Off to Run position. The lamp does not operate with the ignition in the Off or Start position.
   b. If "Check Suspension" light fails to go out after turning ignition switch from Off to Run position, no battery 12 volt power to the module is indicated.
   c. If after turning ignition switch from Off to Run position, "Check Suspension" light glows for approximately one-half second, goes out and then glows continuously after five to eight seconds, a height sensor or harness problem is indicated.
   d. If after turning ignition switch from Off to Run position, "Check Suspension" light comes on and glows continuously any time after 8 seconds, an Air Suspension System problem is indicated.
   e. Once the "Check Suspension" light comes On during an ignition On cycle, it will continue to glow for the duration of the ignition On cycle.

ACCESSING SELF-DIAGNOSTIC SYSTEM

1. Turn air suspension switch to On position. Diagnostic pigtail must be ungrounded.
2. Install battery charger to reduce battery drain.
3. Cycle ignition from Off to Run position, hold in run position for a minimum of 5 seconds, then return to Off position. Driver's door is open with all other doors shut.
4. Attach a lead from diagnostic pigtail to vehicle ground. The pigtail must remain grounded during the diagnostic sequence.
5. Turn ignition switch to Run position (Do not start vehicle). The warning indicator will blink continuously at a rate of 1.8 blinks per second to indicate diagnostics has been entered and is ready.
6. Close, the open driver's door once to initiate Test 1. The warning indicator will blink one, pause, blink, pause and continue pattern until next test is started.

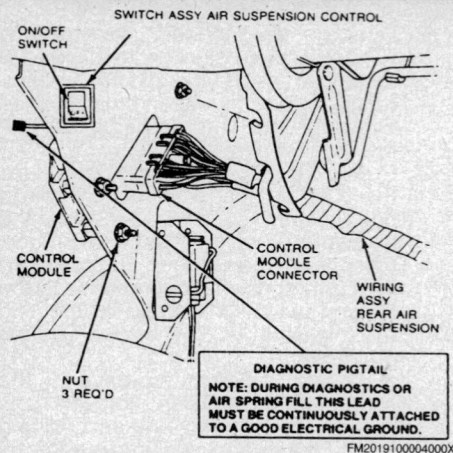

Fig. 4 Air suspension switch & diagnostic pigtail location

7. Each successive transition from door closed to door open will cause module to advance to next step in test sequence. The warning indicator will blink the current test number.

TERMINATING SELF-DIAGNOSTIC SYSTEM

Diagnostics may be terminated and the module returned to normal operational mode at any time by cycling the ignition, actuating the brake or ungrounding the diagnostic pigtail.

DIAGNOSTIC PROCEDURE/SELF TEST
Tests 1, 2 & 3

Perform the each of the following steps during tests 1 through 3:

1. Raise the affected portion of the vehicle for 15 seconds, then continue raising an additional 15 seconds (30 seconds total maximum) or until a "Vehicle High" signal or illegal sensor reading is received from the appropriate height sensor.
2. The affected portion of the vehicle will lower for 30 seconds or until a "Vehicle Low" signal or illegal sensor reading is received from the appropriate height sensor.
3. The affected portion of the vehicle will raise for 30 seconds or until a "Vehicle Trim" signal or illegal sensor reading is received from the appropriate height sensor.

If the expected signal is not received within 30 seconds (total maximum), the test will stop and the warning light will glow continuously. If an improper sensor reading is obtained, the test will stop and the warning light will flash rapidly. The failed test may then be repeated by closing or opening the car door, or the next test may be started by opening and closing the car door twice within 15 seconds.

Test 1 is used for checking the rear suspension.
Test 2 is used for checking the right front suspension.
Test 3 is used for checking the left front suspension.

Test 4

During test 4, the compressor is cycled

Component (Harness Number)	Harness Side Connector	Pin Number	Function	Circuit	Color	Gauge	Circuit End Point
Compressor (1) (14290)		1	Solenoid Feed	175	BK/Y	14	Starter Relay
		2	Motor Feed	417	P/O	14	Compressor Relay
		3	Motor Ground	430	GY	14	Battery Ground Cable
		4	Solenoid Control	578	LB/PK	18	Module Pin No. 23
Spring Solenoid (4) (14290 LF/RF) (12614 LR/RR)		1	Control — LR	429	P/LG	18	Module Pin No. 9
			Control — RR	416	LB/BK	18	Module Pin No. 10
			Control — LF	415	LG/O	18	Module Pin No. 11
			Control — RF	414	O/R	18	Module Pin No. 12
		2	Feed	175	BK/Y	16	Starter Relay
Front Height Sensor (2) (14290)		1	Ground	432	BK/PK	18	Module Pin No. 14
		2	Feed — LF (RF)	431	PK/W	18	Module Pin No. 4
		3	Logic Line B — RF	425	BR/PK	18	Module Pin No. 16
			Logic Line B — LF	423	P/LG	18	Module Pin No. 17
		4	Logic Line A — RF	424	T	18	Module Pin No. 5
			Logic Line A — LF	422	PK/BK	18	Module Pin No. 6
Rear Height Sensor (1) (12614)		1	Ground	432	BK/PK	18	Module Pin No. 14
		2	Feed	426	R/BK	18	Module Pin No. 3
		3	Logic Line B	428	O/BK	18	Module Pin No. 18
		4	Logic Line A	427	PK/BK	18	Module Pin No. 13
Compressor Relay (1) (14290)		1	Control	420	DB/Y	18	Module Pin No. 22
		2	Feed (Coil)	175	BK/Y	18	Starter Relay
		3	Feed (Contacts)	175	BK/Y	12	Starter Relay
		4	Compressor Motor Feed	417	P/O	14	Compressor
		5	Compressor Motor Ground	430	GY	12	Battery Ground Cable
On/Off Switch (1) (12614)		1	Feed to Module	418	DG/Y	14	Module Pin No. 20
		2	Feed to Switch	175	BK/Y	14	Starter Relay
Warning Lamp (1) (14A005)		8	Control	419	DG/LG	20	Module Pin No. 21
		6	Feed	640	R/Y	20	Fuse Panel
Battery Ground Cable (14290)	—	—	System Ground	577	LG/RD	12	Module Pin No. 1 and 24
Diagnostic Pigtail	—	—	Access to System Diagnostics and Air Fill	606	W/LB	18	Module Pin No. 2
Ignition Switch (14401)	Branch of Existing Circuit	—	Ignition Sense	687	GY/Y	12	Module Pin No. 7
Stoplamp Switch (14A005)	Branch of Existing Circuit	—	Brake Sense	511	LG	18	Module Pin No. 15
Courtesy Lamp Door Switch (14488)	Branch of Existing Circuit	—	Door Sense	24	DB/O	20	Module Pin No. 19
Module (1) (12614)							

Fig. 5 Air suspension system circuit identification

On and Off at .25 Hz. The compressor is limited to a maximum of 50 cycles.

Test 5

The compressor vent solenoid is cycled (open and closed) at 1 Hz.

Test 6

Left front solenoid is cycled (open and closed) at 1 Hz and the compressor vent solenoid is opened. As the test progresses, the left front of the vehicle will drop slowly.

Test 7

Right front solenoid is cycled (open and closed) at 1 Hz and the compressor vent solenoid is opened. As the test progresses, the right front of the vehicle will drop slowly.

Test 8

Right rear solenoid is cycled (open and closed) at 1 Hz and the compressor vent solenoid is opened. As the test progresses, the right rear of the vehicle will drop slowly.

Test 9

Left rear solenoid is cycled (open and closed) at 1 Hz and the compressor vent solenoid is opened. As the test progresses, the left rear of the vehicle will drop slowly.

Test 10

Disconnecting the diagnostic lead, depressing the brake pedal or turning ignition Off will return the module from diagnostics to the normal operating mode.

Allow time for vehicle to return to proper height, the turn ignition switch to Off position. Remove diagnostic ground lead in luggage compartment.

SELF-DIAGNOSIS

Refer to **Figs. 4 through 6**, for diagnostic pigtail location, connector terminal identification and wiring diagram. **Refer to Fig. 7, for Quick Test wiring and circuit checks.**

Refer to **Fig. 8**, for troubleshooting chart. Refer to **Figs. 9 through 16**, for self-diagnostic flow charts.

Continued on page 31-16

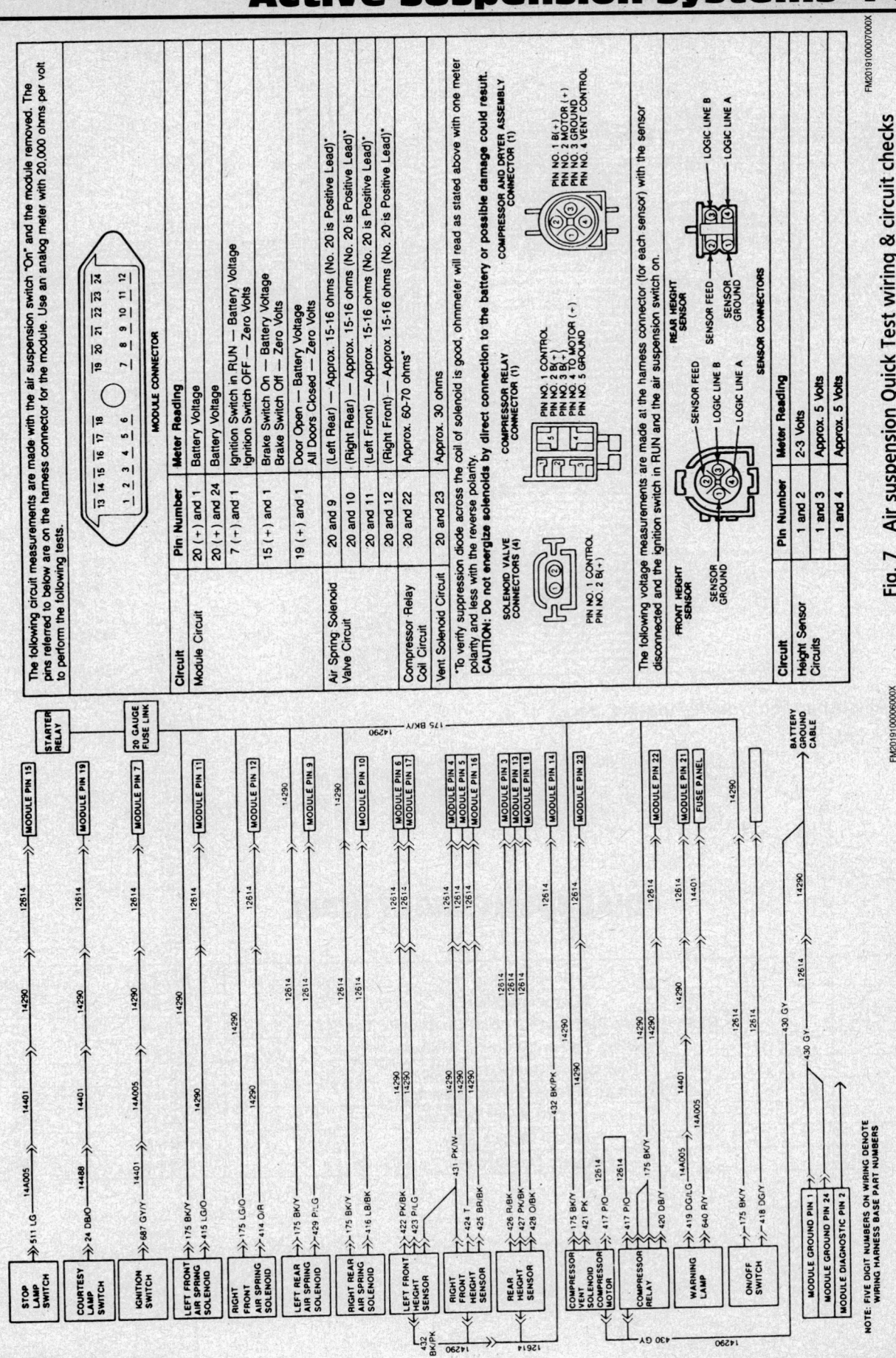

The following circuit measurements are made with the air suspension switch "On" and the module removed. The pins referred to below are on the harness connector for the module. Use an analog meter with 20,000 ohms per volt to perform the following tests.

MODULE CONNECTOR

Circuit	Pin Number	Meter Reading
Module Circuit	20 (+) and 1	Battery Voltage
	20 (+) and 24	Battery Voltage
	7 (+) and 1	Ignition Switch in RUN — Battery Voltage Ignition Switch OFF — Zero Volts
	15 (+) and 1	Brake Switch On — Battery Voltage Brake Switch Off — Zero Volts
	19 (+) and 1	Door Open — Battery Voltage All Doors Closed — Zero Volts
Air Spring Solenoid Valve Circuit	20 and 9	(Left Rear) — Approx. 15-16 ohms (No. 20 is Positive Lead)*
	20 and 10	(Right Rear) — Approx. 15-16 ohms (No. 20 is Positive Lead)*
	20 and 11	(Left Front) — Approx. 15-16 ohms (No. 20 is Positive Lead)*
	20 and 12	(Right Front) — Approx. 15-16 ohms (No. 20 is Positive Lead)*
Compressor Relay Coil Circuit	20 and 22	Approx. 60-70 ohms*
Vent Solenoid Circuit	20 and 23	Approx. 30 ohms

*To verify suppression diode across the coil of solenoid is good, ohmmeter will read as stated above with one meter polarity and less with the reverse polarity.
CAUTION: Do not energize solenoids by direct connection to the battery or possible damage could result.

SOLENOID VALVE CONNECTORS (4)

PIN NO. 1 CONTROL
PIN NO. 2 B(+)

COMPRESSOR RELAY CONNECTOR (1)

PIN NO. 1 CONTROL
PIN NO. 2 B(+)
PIN NO. 3 —
PIN NO. 4 TO MOTOR (+)
PIN NO. 5 GROUND

COMPRESSOR AND DRYER ASSEMBLY CONNECTOR (1)

PIN NO. 1 B(+)
PIN NO. 2 MOTOR (+)
PIN NO. 3 GROUND
PIN NO. 4 VENT CONTROL

The following voltage measurements are made at the harness connector (for each sensor) with the sensor disconnected and the ignition switch in RUN and the air suspension switch on.

SENSOR CONNECTORS

FRONT HEIGHT SENSOR

SENSOR FEED
LOGIC LINE B
LOGIC LINE A
SENSOR GROUND

REAR HEIGHT SENSOR

SENSOR FEED
LOGIC LINE B
LOGIC LINE A
SENSOR GROUND

Circuit	Pin Number	Meter Reading
Height Sensor Circuits	1 and 2	2-3 Volts
	1 and 3	Approx. 5 Volts
	1 and 4	Approx. 5 Volts

Fig. 7 Air suspension Quick Test wiring & circuit checks

FM2019100007000X

FM2019100006000X

Fig. 6 Air suspension wiring circuit

NOTE: FIVE DIGIT NUMBERS ON WIRING DENOTE WIRING HARNESS BASE PART NUMBERS

STARTER RELAY

20 GAUGE FUSE LINK

STOP LAMP SWITCH
COURTESY LAMP SWITCH
IGNITION SWITCH
LEFT FRONT AIR SPRING SOLENOID
RIGHT FRONT AIR SPRING SOLENOID
LEFT REAR AIR SPRING SOLENOID
RIGHT REAR AIR SPRING SOLENOID
LEFT FRONT HEIGHT SENSOR
RIGHT FRONT HEIGHT SENSOR
REAR HEIGHT SENSOR
COMPRESSOR VENT SOLENOID
COMPRESSOR MOTOR
COMPRESSOR RELAY
WARNING LAMP
ON/OFF SWITCH
MODULE GROUND PIN 1
MODULE GROUND PIN 24
MODULE DIAGNOSTIC PIN 2

BATTERY GROUND CABLE

AIR SUSPENSION TROUBLESHOOTING HINTS

Normal Air Suspension Check Light Operation is: When ignition switch is turned ON, light comes on for five seconds, turns OFF and stays off (IP light check).

CONDITION	CAUSAL FACTOR	SUGGESTED ACTION
Suspension check light REMAINS on during normal operation.	No power to module (0 VDC between Pins 20 and 1).	• See if system switch in luggage compartment is on. • Check switch, connector, and wiring in luggage compartment. • Check system ground and lead wires near battery.
Suspension check light COMES BACK ON 10 SECONDS AFTER normal light check.	Module detects improper condition in sensor circuit.	• Run Steps 1, 2 and 3 of Air Suspension Diagnostic Procedure (Self-Test) to find which sensor circuit has fault — check for loose or damaged connectors and harness wiring. • Swap sensor with another sensor.
Suspension check light COMES BACK ON AFTER a minimum of THREE MINUTES and stays on.	Module detects excessive correction time.	• Run Steps 1, 2 and 3 of Diagnostic Procedure and check for compressor and vent solenoid operation for all three — if any or all three fail, check for leaks. • Run Steps 6, 7, 8 and 9 of Diagnostic Procedure to check for restricted air line or non-functioning air spring solenoid valve circuit.
Suspension check light COMES BACK ON while driving and may STAY ON or may TURN OFF.	Module detects sensor system faulty signal or there is an interruption in the module ground, ignition sensing or module B + voltage (24 pin connector, Pins 1 and 24, Pins 7, 20).	• Check for loose connections and damaged wire or faulty wire crimps to terminals. • Rapid blinking suspension check light on Steps 1, 2 or 3 of Diagnostic Procedure means fault in sensor system of wiring harness for that side of the vehicle.
Front down or all corners down and system cannot pump-up.	Compressor does not run.	• Run Step 4 of Diagnostic Procedure if no response, check wiring and connector at compressor. • Check compressor relay, wiring and connector.
	Compressor does not run with voltage at compressor connector.	• Disconnect relay, wait five minutes to reset compressor internal circuit breaker. Install new compressor relay. Run Step 4 of Diagnostic Procedure to verify compressor operation. If compressor fails, check wiring harness and connectors.
Front down and cannot pump up (compressor operates).	Severe air leak at dryer air line fittings.	• Check dryer fittings for severe leaks, replace dryer if needed; look for other air line leaks if fault remains. (Measured air pressure must be 90 psi or greater).
	Air line leak	• Check front air lines by disconnecting rear air lines at dryer, seal both fittings by inserting an 8-inch length of tubing and disconnect electrical connectors at the rear solenoid valves. Verify if the front will raise when air suspension is activated. If so, leak is in rear line.

FM2019100008010X

Fig. 8   Air suspension troubleshooting (Part 1 of 2)

AIR SUSPENSION TROUBLESHOOTING HINTS — Continued

Normal Air Suspension Check Light Operation is: When ignition switch is turned ON, light comes on for five seconds, turns OFF and stays off (IP light check).

CONDITION	CASUAL FACTOR	SUGGESTED ACTION
Rear raises very high and then levels during otherwise normal operation. One or more air springs leaks down overnight, but system will trim itself when system is operated (temperature sensitive).	Front solenoid valves fail to open to service a front corner leveling request.	• Run Steps 6 and 7 of Diagnostic Procedure to check solenoid valve operation. Inspect for loose or damaged connectors and wiring in solenoid circuits and replace solenoid valve if necessary. Check circuit resistance in both directions, as outlined in Air Suspension Quick Wiring and Circuit Checks.
	Compressor relay sticking or welded (can be intermittent).	• Replace relay after checking for damaged wiring.
	Leaking dual nose O-rings on one or more air spring solenoid valves (temperature sensitive).	• Replace leaking nose O-rings or solenoid valve.

NOTE: In Diagnostic Procedure a failed test can be repeated by operating door switch. Operating door switch twice in 15 seconds advances tests to next Step.

FM2019100008020X

Fig. 8   Air suspension troubleshooting (Part 2 of 2)

DIAGNOSTIC CHART INDEX

Test	Description	Page No.	Fig. No.
A	Diagnostic Test	31-7	9
B	Cannot Enter Sequence Or Exit Diagnostic Test	31-8	10
C	Problem Sensing Vehicle Attitude	31-9	11
D	Problem At Rear Of Vehicle	31-12	12
E	Problem At Right Front Of Vehicle	31-13	13
F	Problem At Left Front Of Vehicle	31-14	14
G	Problem During Fill	31-15	15
H	Problem During Vent	31-15	16

Part 1 of 5

DIAGNOSTIC TEST

TEST STEP	RESULT	ACTION TO TAKE
A1 CHECK VEHICLE LOAD		
• Check vehicle passenger compartment and luggage compartment for overloading, and unload as necessary		▶ GO to A2.
• Allow the vehicle to sit with the ignition switch in the RUN position for five minutes minimum (door closed, brake off).		
A2 LEVEL VEHICLE, INITIALIZE SYSTEM		
• Turn the ignition switch to the OFF position.	Warning lamp blinks or turns on	▶ GO to A3.
• Turn the ignition switch to the RUN position and observe the air suspension warning lamp.	Warning lamp does not blink or turn on	▶ GO to B1.
A3 ENTER DIAGNOSTICS		
• Before entering diagnostics, connect a battery charger to the vehicle and leave on, until completion of diagnostics.	Warning lamp blinks continuously	▶ Diagnostics entered. GO to A4.
• After diagnostics are entered do not open the door, depress the brake pedal, or start the engine unless you are specifically asked to do so.	The warning lamp blinks once	▶ Diagnostics not entered. GO to B10.
• Turn the ignition switch to the OFF position.	Warning lamp stays on	▶ Warning lamp not functioning properly. GO to B13.
• Ground the diagnostic pigtail.		
• Turn the ignition switch to the RUN position. Do not start the engine, open the door, or depress the brake.		
A4 RUN TEST NO. 1 — REAR SUSPENSION		
• To start Test No. 1 open and close the door.	Warning lamp flashes rapidly (approx. four blinks per second), or warning lamp on	▶ Rear failed test. GO to A5.
• After Test No. 1 has been entered, a properly operating vehicle will raise the rear evenly for 15 to 30 seconds. When a vehicle high is received from the rear sensor, the rear will be lowered for a maximum of 30 seconds. When a rear low is received at the module, the rear of the vehicle will raise for a maximum of 30 seconds or until a rear trim signal is received at the module. Test 1 is now completed. The warning lamp will flash test No. 1 at a constant rate during the whole test. Maximum test time is 90 seconds.	Warning lamp flashes the test number	▶ Rear passed test. GO to A5.
• After 90 seconds observe the warning lamp.	Warning lamp does not flash the test number, flash rapidly, or turn on	▶ GO to B22.
• Record the test results for future reference.		

FM2019100009010X

Fig. 9   Test A: Diagnostic Test (Part 1 of 5)

Part 2 of 5

DIAGNOSTIC TEST — Continued

TEST STEP	RESULT	ACTION TO TAKE
A5 RUN TEST NO. 2 — RIGHT FRONT SUSPENSION		
• To start Test No. 2 open and close the door. If Test No. 1 failed, open and close the door twice.	Warning lamp flashes rapidly (approx. four blinks per second), or warning lamp is on	▶ Right front failed test. GO to A6.
• After Test No. 2 has been entered, a properly operating vehicle will raise the right front for 15 to 30 seconds. When a vehicle high is received from the right front sensor, the right front will be lowered for a maximum of 30 seconds. When a right front low is received at the module, the right front of the vehicle will raise for a maximum of 30 seconds or until a right front trim signal is received at the module. Test 2 is now completed. The warning lamp will flash test No. 2 at a constant rate during the whole test. Maximum test time is 90 seconds.	Warning lamp flashes the test number	▶ Right front passed test. GO to A6.
• After 90 seconds observe the warning lamp.		
• Record the test results for future reference.		
A6 RUN TEST NO. 3 — LEFT FRONT SUSPENSION		
• To start Test No. 3 open and close the door. If Test No. 2 failed, open and close the door twice.	Warning lamp flashes rapidly (approx. four blinks per second) or warning lamp is on steady	▶ Left front failed test. GO to A7
• After Test No. 3 has been entered, a properly operating vehicle will raise the left front for 15 to 30 seconds. When a vehicle high is received from the left front sensor, the left front of the vehicle will raise for a maximum of 30 seconds or until a left front trim signal is received at the module. Test No. 3 is now completed. The warning lamp will flash Test No. 3 at a constant rate during the test. Maximum test time is 90 seconds.	Warning lamp flashes the test number	▶ Left front passed test. GO to A7.
• After 90 seconds observe the warning lamp.		
• Record the test results for future reference.		
A7 RUN TEST NO. 4 — COMPRESSOR		
• To start Test No. 4 open and close the door. If Test No. 3 failed, open and close the door twice.	Compressor does not cycle, (runs continuously or does not run at all)	▶ Compressor failed test. GO to A8.
• During Test No. 4 the compressor is cycled on and off. The warning lamp will continuously blink Test No. 4. The compressor will only cycle 50 times.	Compressor cycles	▶ Compressor passed test. GO to A8.
• Lift the hood and listen for the compressor to cycle.		
• Record the test results for future reference.		
NOTE: The rear of the vehicle may raise during this test.		
A8 RUN TEST NO. 5 — VENT SOLENOID		
• To start Test No. 5, open and close the door to cycle the vent solenoid (part of compressor assembly).	Vent solenoid does not cycle	▶ Vent solenoid failed test. GO to A9.
• During Test No. 5, vent solenoid is cycled on and off, and the warning lamp will continuously blink Test No. 5.	Vent solenoid cycles	▶ Vent solenoid passed test. GO to A9.
• Lift the hood and listen for the vent solenoid to cycle.		
• Record the test results for future reference		

FM2019100009020X

Fig. 9   Test A: Diagnostic Test (Part 2 of 5)

Part 3 of 5

DIAGNOSTIC TEST — Continued

TEST STEP	RESULT	ACTION TO TAKE
A9 RUN TEST NO. 6 — LEFT FRONT AIR SPRING SOLENOID		
• Open and close the door to cycle the left front air spring solenoid.	Left front air spring solenoid does not cycle, or air is not escaping from the vent solenoid	▶ Left front air spring system failed test. GO to A10.
• Listen for air escaping from the vent solenoid.		
• Listen for the solenoid to cycle at the left front wheel well opening.	Left front air spring solenoid cycles, and air is escaping from the vent solenoid	▶ Left front air spring system passes test. GO to A10.
• Record the test results for future reference.		
NOTE: The left front corner of the vehicle will drop during this test.		
A10 RUN TEST NO. 7 — RIGHT FRONT AIR SPRING SOLENOID		
• Open and close the door to cycle the right front air spring solenoid.	Right front air spring solenoid does not cycle, or air is not escaping from the vent solenoid	▶ Right front air spring system failed test. GO to A11.
• Listen for air escaping from the vent solenoid.		
• Listen for the solenoid to cycle at the right front wheel well opening.	Right front air spring solenoid cycles, and air is escaping from the vent solenoid	▶ Right front air spring system passed test. GO to A11.
• Record the test results for future reference.		
NOTE: The right front corner of the vehicle will drop during this test.		
A11 RUN TEST NO. 8 — RIGHT REAR AIR SPRING SOLENOID		
• Open and close the door to cycle the right rear air spring solenoid.	Right rear air spring solenoid does not cycle, or air is not escaping from the vent solenoid	▶ Right rear air spring system failed test. GO to A12.
• Listen for air escaping from the vent solenoid.		
• Listen for the solenoid to cycle at the right rear wheel well opening.	Right rear air spring solenoid cycles, and air is escaping from the vent solenoid	▶ Right rear air spring system passed test. GO to A12.
• Record the test results for future reference.		
NOTE: The right rear corner of the vehicle will drop during this test.		
A12 RUN TEST NO. 9 — LEFT REAR AIR SPRING SOLENOID		
• Open and close the door to cycle the left rear air spring solenoid.	Left rear air spring solenoid does not cycle, or air is not escaping from the vent solenoid	▶ Left rear air spring system failed test. GO to A13.
• Listen for air escaping from the vent solenoid.		
• Listen for the solenoid to cycle at the left rear wheel well opening.	Left rear air spring solenoid cycles, and air is escaping from the vent solenoid	▶ Left rear air spring system passed test. GO to A13.
• Record the test results for future reference.		
NOTE: The left rear corner of the vehicle will drop during this test.		

FM2019100009030X

Fig. 9   Test A: Diagnostic Test (Part 3 of 5)

Part 4 of 5

TEST STEP	RESULT	ACTION TO TAKE
A13 RUN TEST NO. 10 — BRAKE CIRCUIT		
• Open the door and sit in the driver's seat.	Warning lamp continues to blink	▶ Brake circuit fails test. GO to B30.
• Depress the brake pedal and observe the warning lamp.	Warning lamp stops blinking	▶ Brake circuit passes test. Diagnostic sequence completed. Unground the diagnostic pigtail. GO to A14.
A14 ANY FAILURES?		
• Have any failures occured during diagnostics?	Yes	▶ GO to A15.
	No	▶ Air spring suspension system OK. No further diagnostics required.
• To perform pinpoint tests, the following special equipment will be required: 1) A test lamp using a No. 194 bulb with test pointed probes. 2) A volt/ohm meter (Rotunda DVOM 007-00001 or equivalent). 3) A pressure gauge capable of indicating 1034 kPa (150 psi).		
A15		
• Did the warning lamp flash rapidly for any of the first three tests?	Yes	▶ The module read the sensor incorrectly. GO to C1.
	No	▶ Sensors OK. GO to A16.
A16		
• Did the warning lamp stay on after the completion of Test No. 1?	Yes	▶ CHECK rear of vehicle. GO to D1.
	No	▶ GO to A17.
A17		
• Did the warning lamp stay on after the completion of Test No. 2?	Yes	▶ CHECK right front. GO to E1.
	No	▶ Right front OK. GO to A18.
A18		
• Did the warning lamp stay on after the completion of Test No. 3?	Yes	▶ CHECK left front. GO to F1.
	No	▶ Left front OK. GO to A19.

FM2019100009040X

Fig. 9   Test A: Diagnostic Test (Part 4 of 5)

DIAGNOSTIC TEST — Continued

TEST STEP	RESULT	▶	ACTION TO TAKE
A19			
• Did the left front solenoid cycle during Test No. 6?	Yes	▶	Left front solenoid OK. GO to A20.
	No	▶	GO to F1.
A20			
• Did the right front solenoid cycle during Test No. 7?	Yes	▶	Right front solenoid OK. GO to A21.
	No	▶	GO to E1.
A21			
• Did the right rear solenoid cycle and air escape from the vent solenoid during Test No. 8?	Yes	▶	Right rear solenoid OK. GO to A20.
	No	▶	Check right rear solenoid system. GO to D1.
A22			
• Did the left rear solenoid cycle and air escape from the vent solenoid during Test No. 9?	Yes	▶	Left rear solenoid OK. GO to A1.
	No	▶	Check left rear solenoid system. GO to D1.

FM2019100009050X

Fig. 9 Test A: Diagnostic Test (Part 5 of 5)

CANNOT ENTER, SEQUENCE, OR EXIT DIAGNOSTIC TEST —Continued

TEST STEP	RESULT	▶	ACTION TO TAKE
B7 CHECK MODULE GROUND CIRCUIT			
• Attach one test lamp lead to ignition Circuit No. 687 Pin 7 of the module connector. • Turn the ignition switch to RUN and observe the test lamp. • Attach the other test lamp to ground Circuit No. 430 Pin 1 of the module connector. • Move the test lamp lead attached to Pin 1 of the module connector to Pin 24.	Test lamp on	▶	Ground circuit OK. GO to B8.
	Test lamp off	▶	SERVICE open in Circuit No. 430. REPEAT Diagnostic Test.
B8 CHECK WARNING LAMP CIRCUIT			
• Set up a volt meter to read 12 volts DC. • Attach the negative (black) test lead to a good ground. • Attach the positive (red) test lead to the warning lamp Circuit No. 419 Pin 21 of the module connector. • Turn the ignition switch to the RUN position.	Voltage greater than 5V	▶	Warning lamp circuit OK. GO to B9.
	Voltage less than or equal to 5V	▶	SERVICE open in the warning lamp Circuit No. 419 from the module connector to the warning lamp Circuit No. 419 Pin 21 of the module connector. Turn air suspension on/off switch to the ON position. REPEAT Diagnostic Test.
B9 CHECK BATTERY VOLTAGE			
• Attach the negative (black) test lead to ground Circuit No. 430 Pin 24 of the module connector. • Attach the positive (red) test lead to battery Circuit No. 418 Pin 20 at the module connector. • Measure DC Voltage.	Less than 11V	▶	SERVICE low voltage condition due to a damaged connection, low battery, etc. REPEAT Diagnostic Test.
	Greater than 11V	▶	REPLACE air suspension module. REPEAT Quick Test.
B10			
• Repeat Steps A2 and A3 and ensure the diagnostic pigtail is grounded to a good ground. **NOTE: Steps A2 and A3 must be performed exactly as indicated to enter diagnostics.**	Warning lamp blinks once	▶	GO to B11.
	Warning lamp blinks	▶	REPEAT Diagnostic Test
B11 MAKE A TEST LAMP			
• Attach two test leads, with probes, to a No. 194 lamp for use as a test lamp. Any other lamp will cause damage to the air suspension lamp.		▶	GO to B12.

FM2019100010020X

Fig. 10 Test B: Cannot Enter Sequence Or Exit Diagnostic Test (Part 2 of 6)

CANNOT ENTER, SEQUENCE OR EXIT DIAGNOSTIC TEST

TEST STEP	RESULT	▶	ACTION TO TAKE
Will not initialize or enter diagnostics			
B1 CHECK BULB			
• Is air suspension warning lamp bulb burned out?	Yes	▶	REPLACE bulb. REPEAT Diagnostic Test.
	No	▶	GO to B2.
B2 MAKE A TEST LAMP			
• Attach two test leads, with pointed probes, to a No. 194 lamp for use as a test lamp. Any other lamp will cause damage to the air suspension system.		▶	GO to B3.
B3 CHECK IGNITION CIRCUIT			
• Turn the air suspension on/off switch to the OFF position. • Turn ignition switch to the OFF position.	Warning lamp on	▶	SERVICE short to battery on ignition Circuit No. 687 or the ignition switch. Turn air suspension On/Off switch to the ON position. REPEAT Diagnostic Test.
	Warning lamp off	▶	GO to B4.
B4 CHECK IGNITION CIRCUIT			
• Attach one lead of the test lamp to ignition Circuit No. 640 at the warning lamp. Attach the other lead to ground. • Turn the ignition switch to RUN and observe the test lamp.	Test lamp on	▶	GO to B6.
	Test lamp off	▶	GO to B5.
B5 CHECK FUSE			
• Check fuse in ignition Circuit No. 640.	Fuse OK	▶	SERVICE open in ignition Circuit No. 640. REPEAT Diagnostic Test.
	Fuse blown	▶	REPLACE fuse. SERVICE short in ignition Circuit No. 640, if second fuse fails. REPEAT Diagnostic Test.
B6 CHECK IGNITION CIRCUIT			
• Attach one test lamp lead to ignition Circuit No. 687 Pin 7 of the module connector. • Attach the other test lamp lead to a good ground. • Turn the ignition switch to RUN and observe the test lamp.	Test lamp on	▶	Ignition circuit OK. GO to B7.
	Test lamp off	▶	SERVICE open or short in ignition Circuit No. 687. Turn air suspension On/Off switch to ON position. REPEAT Diagnostic Test.

FM2019100010010X

Fig. 10 Test B: Cannot Enter Sequence Or Exit Diagnostic Test (Part 1 of 6)

TEST STEP	RESULT	▶	ACTION TO TAKE
B12 CHECK PIGTAIL			
• Attach one test lamp lead to diagnostic Circuit No. 606 Pin 2 at the module connector. • Attach the other test lamp lead to ignition Circuit No. 687 Pin 7 at the module connector. • Turn ignition switch to RUN. • Ground and then unground the pigtail.	Test lamp on then off	▶	Pigtail OK. GO to B9.
	Test lamp on or off	▶	SERVICE open or short to ground in the diagnostic pigtail Circuit No. 606. REPEAT Diagnostic Test.
B13 CHECK FOR SYSTEM IN DIAGNOSTIC			
• Open and close the door and observe the compressor.	Compressor starts running	▶	In diagnostics. GO to B20.
	Compressor is already running or does not start running	▶	Not in diagnostics. GO to B14.
B14 MAKE A TEST LAMP			
• Attach two test leads, with pointed probes, to a No. 194 lamp for use as a test lamp. Any other lamp will cause damage to the air suspension system.		▶	GO to B15.
B15 CHECK BATTERY CIRCUIT			
• Attach one test lamp lead to battery Circuit No. 418 Pin 20 at the module connector. • Attach the other test lamp lead to a good ground.	Test lamp on	▶	GO to B21.
	Test lamp off	▶	GO to B16.
B16 CHECK FUSE LINK			
• Check the fuse link in battery Circuit No. 175.	Fuse link OK	▶	GO to B17.
	Fuse link blown	▶	REPLACE fuse link. REPEAT Diagnostic Test.
B17			
• Verify that the air suspension on/off switch is in the ON position.	Switch in ON position	▶	GO to B18.
	Switch in OFF position	▶	PLACE switch in ON position. REPEAT Diagnostic Test.
B18 CHECK BATTERY CIRCUIT			
• Attach one test lamp lead to battery Circuit No. 175 at the air suspension on/off switch Pin 2 (battery side).	Test lamp on	▶	GO to B19.
	Test lamp off	▶	SERVICE the open or short in battery Circuit No. 175 from the air suspension on/off switch Pin 2 to the battery. REPEAT Diagnostic Test.

FM2019100010030X

Fig. 10 Test B: Cannot Enter Sequence Or Exit Diagnostic Test (Part 3 of 6)

Fig. 10 Test B: Cannot Enter Sequence Or Exit Diagnostic Test (Part 4 of 6)

CANNOT ENTER, SEQUENCE, OR EXIT DIAGNOSTIC TEST — Continued

TEST STEP	RESULT	ACTION TO TAKE
B19 CHECK ON/OFF SWITCH • Attach one test lamp lead to battery Circuit No. 418 at the air suspension on/off switch Pin 1 (module side). • Attach the other test lead to a good ground.	Test lamp on	SERVICE the open or short in battery Circuit No. 418 from the air suspension on/off switch Pin 1 to the battery. REPEAT Diagnostic Test.
	Test lamp off	REPLACE the air suspension on/off switch. REPEAT Diagnostic Test.
B20 CHECK WARNING LAMP CIRCUIT • Disconnect the module connector and observe the warning lamp.	Warning lamp on	SERVICE short to ground in the warning lamp Circuit No. 419 from the module connector to the warning lamp. RECONNECT the module connector. REPEAT Diagnostic Test.
	Warning lamp off	Warning lamp circuit OK. GO to B21.
B21 CHECK BATTERY VOLTAGE • Attach the negative (black) test lead to ground Circuit No. 430 Pin 24 of the module connector. • Attach the positive (red) test lead to battery Circuit No. 418 Pin 20 at the module connector. • Measure DC voltage.	Less than 11 V	SERVICE low voltage condition due to a damaged connection, low battery, etc. RECONNECT connectors as required. REPEAT Diagnostic Test.
	Greater than 11 V	REPLACE the air suspension module. RECONNECT connectors as required. REPEAT Diagnostic Test.
B22 MAKE A TEST LAMP • Attach two test leads with pointed probes to a No. 194 lamp for use as a test lamp. Any other lamp will damage the air suspension system.		GO to B23.

FM2019100010040X

Fig. 10 Test B: Cannot Enter Sequence Or Exit Diagnostic Test (Part 5 of 6)

CANNOT ENTER, SEQUENCE, OR EXIT DIAGNOSTIC TEST — Continued

TEST STEP	RESULT	ACTION TO TAKE
B23 CHECK DOOR CIRCUIT • Attach one test lamp lead to door Circuit No. 24 Pin 19 at the module connector. • Attach the other test lamp lead to a good ground. • Close the door.	Test lamp on	SERVICE short to battery or ignition in door Circuit No. 24 or damaged door switch. REPEAT Diagnostic Test.
	Test lamp off	GO to B24.
B24 CHECK DOOR CIRCUIT • Open the door.	Test lamp on	Door circuit OK. GO to B25.
	Test lamp off	SERVICE open or short in door Circuit No. 24 or malfunctioning door switch. REPEAT Diagnostic Test.
B25 CHECK BRAKE CIRCUIT • Depress and release the brake pedal. Observe the rear brake lamps.	Brake lamps operate properly	Brake circuit OK. GO to B26.
	Brake lamps do not operate properly	SERVICE as necessary. REPEAT Diagnostic Test
B26 CHECK COMPRESSOR CIRCUIT • Disconnect the compressor relay electrical connector. • Perform Steps A2-A4. • Observe the warning lamp.	Warning lamp flashes rapidly, flashes the test number or stays on	GO to B27
	Warning lamp does something else	Compressor circuit OK. GO to B21.
B27 CHECK COMPRESSOR CIRCUIT • Do not reconnect the compressor relay connector. • Attach the negative (black) lead of volt-ohm meter to ground. • Attach the positive (red) lead to compressor Circuit No. 417 Pin 2 on the harness side of the compressor connector. • Measure resistance.	Greater than 1000 Ohms	GO to B28
	Less than 1000 Ohms	SERVICE short to ground on compressor Circuit No. 417. REPEAT Diagnostic Test.

FM2019100010050X

Fig. 10 Test B: Cannot Enter Sequence Or Exit Diagnostic Test (Part 6 of 6)

CANNOT ENTER, SEQUENCE, OR EXIT DIAGNOSTIC TEST — Continued

TEST STEP	RESULT	ACTION TO TAKE
B28 CHECK COMPRESSOR CURRENT • Disconnect compressor connector. • Connect a jumper (14 ga. wire minimum) between compressor connector (compressor side) Pin 3 and a good ground. • Attach the negative (black) lead of an ammeter to Pin 3 at the compressor connector (compressor side). The ammeter must be capable of measuring 40 amps minimum. • Attach the positive (red) lead to battery positive (+) terminal. • Measure current after the compressor has run for 10 seconds. Do not allow the compressor to run more than 60 seconds.	Greater than 35 amps	REPLACE and RECONNECT a new compressor assembly. REPEAT Diagnostic Test.
	Less than 35 amps	GO to B29.
B29 CHECK COMPRESSOR VOLTAGE • Perform Step B28 except measure the battery voltage while the compressor is running.	Greater than 11 volts	REPLACE the air suspension module. RECONNECT connectors as required. REPEAT Diagnostic Test.
	Less than 11 volts	CHARGE battery. REPEAT Diagnostic Test.
B30 MAKE A TEST LAMP • Attach two test leads with pointed probes to a No. 194 lamp for use as a test lamp. Any other lamp will damage the air suspension system.		GO to B31.
B31 CHECK BRAKE CIRCUIT • Depress and release the brake pedal and verify the rear brake lamps operate properly.	Brake lamps operate properly	GO to B32.
	Brake lamps do not operate properly	SERVICE as necessary. REPEAT Diagnostic Test.
B32 CHECK BRAKE CIRCUIT • Attach one lead of the test lamp to brake Circuit No. 511 Pin 15 at the module connector. • Attach the other test lead to a good ground. • Depress the brake pedal and observe the test lamp.	Test lamp on	REPLACE the air suspension module. RECONNECT connectors as required. REPEAT Diagnostic Test.
	Test lamp off	SERVICE open or short in the brake Circuit No. 511. REPEAT Diagnostic Test.

FM2019100010060X

Fig. 11 Test C: Problem Sensing Vehicle Attitude (Part 1 of 9)

PROBLEM SENSING VEHICLE ATTITUDE

TEST STEP	RESULT	ACTION TO TAKE
C1 • Did the warning lamp flash for all three tests? (Test No. 1, 2 and 3).	Yes	GO to C2.
	No	GO to C11.
C2 CHECK SENSOR GROUND CIRCUIT • Attach one lead of the test lamp to sensor ground Circuit No. 432 Pin 1 at the left front sensor connector. • Attach the other test lamp lead to the battery positive (+) terminal. • Observe the test lamp.	Test lamp on	Sensor ground circuit OK. GO to C5.
	Test lamp off	GO to C3.
C3 CHECK SENSOR GROUND CIRCUIT • Attach one lead of the test lamp to sensor ground Circuit No. 432 Pin 14 at the module connector (do not disconnect the module connector). • Attach the other test lamp lead to battery Pin No. 20 at the module connector (do not disconnect the module connector).	Test lamp on	SERVICE open in sensor ground Circuit No. 432. REPEAT Quick Test.
	Test lamp off	GO to C4
C4 Disconnect the module connector and inspect sensor ground Pin 14, module ground Pins 1 and 24 for corrosion and or damage.	Corrosion or damage found	SERVICE as necessary. REPEAT Quick Test.
	No corrosion or damage found	REPLACE the air suspension module. REPEAT Quick Test.
C5 • Set up a voltmeter to read 3 volts DC. • Attach the negative (black) test lead to sensor ground Circuit No. 432 Pin 14 of the module connector. • Attach the positive (red) test lead to sensor power Circuit No. 431 Pin 4 of the module connector. • Turn ignition to RUN and observe the voltmeter.	Voltage less than 1V and steady	GO to C6.
	Voltage erratic or greater than 1V but less than 5V	SERVICE open in sensor power Circuit No. 426 or 431 between the module and the sensors. REPEAT Quick Test.
	Voltage greater than 5V and steady	REPLACE air suspension module. REPEAT Quick Test
C6 CHECK LEFT FRONT SENSOR • Electrically disconnect the left front sensor and observe the voltmeter.	Voltage less than 1V and steady	Left front sensor OK. GO to C7.
	Voltage erratic or greater than 1V	REPLACE and connect the left front sensor. REPEAT Quick Test.

FM2019100011010X

PROBLEM SENSING VEHICLE ATTITUDE — Continued

TEST STEP	RESULT	ACTION TO TAKE
C7 CHECK RIGHT FRONT SENSOR • Do not reconnect the left front sensor. • Electrically disconnect the right front sensor and observe the voltmeter.	Voltage less than 1V and steady	Right front sensor OK. GO to C8.
	Voltage erratic or greater than 1V	REPLACE and connect the right front sensor. RECONNECT the left front sensor. REPEAT Quick Test.
C8 CHECK THE REAR SENSOR • Do not reconnect the right front sensor. • Electrically disconnect the rear sensor and observe the voltmeter.	Voltage less than 1V and steady	Rear sensor OK. GO to C9
	Voltage erratic or greater than 1V	REPLACE and connect the rear sensor. RECONNECT the left front and right front sensors. REPEAT Quick Test.
C9 CHECK SENSOR POWER CIRCUIT • Do not reconnect the rear sensor. • Disconnect the air suspension module. • Attach the negative (black) test lead of a volt-ohm meter to module ground Circuit No. 430 Pin 1 of the module connector. • Attach the positive (red) test lead to sensor power Circuit No. 426 Pin 3 at the module connector. • Measure resistance.	Greater than 1000 Ohms	GO to C10.
	Less than 1000 Ohms	SERVICE short to ground in sensor power Circuit No. 426. RECONNECT right front sensor, left front sensor, rear sensor and control module. REPEAT Quick Test.
C10 CHECK SENSOR POWER CIRCUIT • Move the positive (red) test lead to sensor power Circuit No. 431 Pin 4 at module connector. • Measure resistance.	Greater than 1000 Ohms	REPLACE the air suspension control module. REPEAT Quick Test.
	Less than 1000 Ohms	SERVICE short to ground in sensor power Circuit No. 431. RECONNECT right front sensor, left front sensor, rear sensor and control module. REPEAT Quick Test.
C11 • Did the warning lamp flash rapidly for Test No. 1?	Yes	GO to C12.
	No	GO to C23.

FM2019100011020X

Fig. 11   Test C: Problem Sensing Vehicle Attitude (Part 2 of 9)

PROBLEM SENSING VEHICLE ATTITUDE — Continued

TEST STEP	RESULT	ACTION TO TAKE
C12 CHECK SENSOR GROUND CIRCUIT • Turn the air suspension on/off switch to the OFF position. • Attach the positive (red) test lead of a volt-ohm meter to sensor ground Circuit No. 432 Pin 1 at the rear sensor. • Attach the negative (black) test lead to a good ground. • Measure resistance.	Greater than 5 Ohms	SERVICE the open in sensor ground Circuit No. 432 between the module connector and the rear sensor. REPEAT Quick Test.
	Less than 5 Ohms	GO to C13.
C13 CHECK SENSOR POWER CIRCUIT • Place the air suspension ON/OFF switch in the ON position. • Attach the negative (black) test lead to sensor ground Pin 1 Circuit No. 432 at the rear sensor connector. • Attach the positive (red) test lead to sensor power Pin 2 Circuit No. 426 at the rear sensor connector. • Turn ignition to the RUN position. • Measure resistance.	Voltage less than 1V and steady	SERVICE open in sensor power Circuit No. 426 from the rear sensor to the module. REPEAT Quick Test.
	Voltage erratic or greater than 1V	Sensor power circuit OK. GO to C14.
C14 CHECK REAR SENSOR A CIRCUIT • Move the positive (red) test lead to rear sensor A Circuit No. 427 Pin 4 at the rear sensor. • Measure DC voltage.	Greater than 1.5V or erratic	Rear sensor A Circuit OK. GO to C18.
	Less than 1.5V	GO to C15.
C15 CHECK REAR SENSOR • Disconnect the rear sensor connector. • Measure DC voltage.	Greater than 1.5V	REPLACE the rear sensor. REPEAT Quick Test.
	Less than 1.5V	GO to C16.
C16 CHECK REAR SENSOR A CIRCUIT • Do not reconnect the rear sensor. • Attach the negative (black) test lead of a volt-ohm meter to sensor ground Pin 14 Circuit No. 432 at the module connector. • Attach the positive (red) test lead to rear sensor A Circuit No. 427 Pin 13 at the module connector. • Measure DC voltage.	Greater than 1.5V	SERVICE open in rear sensor A Circuit No. 427 between the module and the sensor. RECONNECT the rear sensor connector. REPEAT Quick Test.
	Less than 1.5V	GO to C17.

FM2019100011030X

Fig. 11   Test C: Problem Sensing Vehicle Attitude (Part 3 of 9)

PROBLEM SENSING VEHICLE ATTITUDE — Continued

TEST STEP	RESULT	ACTION TO TAKE
C17 CHECK REAR SENSOR A CIRCUIT • Disconnect the module. • Attach the negative (black) test lead of a volt-ohm meter to module ground Pin 1 Circuit No. 430 at the module connector. • Attach the positive (red) test lead to rear sensor A Circuit No. 427 Pin 13 at the module connector. • Measure resistance.	Greater than 1000 Ohms	REPLACE the air suspension module. RECONNECT the rear sensor. REPEAT Quick Test.
	Less than 1000 Ohms	SERVICE short to ground on rear sensor A Circuit No. 427 between the module and the rear sensor. RECONNECT the rear sensor. REPEAT Quick Test.
C18 CHECK REAR B SENSOR CIRCUIT • Move the positive (red) test lead to rear sensor B Circuit No. 428 Pin 3 at the rear sensor connector. • Measure the DC voltage.	Greater than 1.5V or erratic	Rear Sensor B Circuit OK. GO to C19.
	Less than 1.5V	REPEAT Quick Test. GO to C20.
C19 CHECK FOR MODULE DAMAGE • Rerun diagnostics test No. 1 by performing Steps A2-A4.	Warning lamp flashing rapidly	REPLACE the air suspension control module. REPEAT Quick Test.
	Warning lamp not flashing rapidly	REPEAT Quick Test.
C20 CHECK REAR SENSOR • Disconnect the rear sensor connector. • Measure the DC voltage.	Greater than 1.5V	INSTALL a new rear sensor. REPEAT Quick Test.
	Less than 1.5V	Rear sensor OK. GO to C21.
C21 CHECK REAR SENSOR B CIRCUIT • Do not reconnect the rear sensor. • Attach the negative (black) test lead of a volt-ohm meter to sensor ground Pin 14 Circuit No. 432 at the module connector. • Attach the positive (red) test lead to rear sensor B Circuit No. 428 Pin 18 at the module connector. • Measure DC voltage.	Greater than 1.5V	SERVICE open in rear sensor B Circuit No. 428 between the module and the sensor. RECONNECT the rear sensor connector. REPEAT Quick Test.
	Less than 1.5V	GO to C22.

FM2019100011040X

Fig. 11   Test C: Problem Sensing Vehicle Attitude (Part 4 of 9)

PROBLEM SENSING VEHICLE ATTITUDE — Continued

TEST STEP	RESULT	ACTION TO TAKE
C22 CHECK REAR SENSOR B CIRCUIT • Disconnect the module. • Attach the negative (black) test lead of a volt-ohm meter to module ground Pin 1 Circuit No. 430 at the module connector. • Attach the positive (red) test lead to rear sensor B Circuit No. 428 Pin 18 at the module connector. • Measure resistance.	Greater than 1000 Ohms	REPLACE the air suspension module. RECONNECT the rear sensor. REPEAT Quick Test.
	Less than 1000 ohms	SERVICE short to ground on rear sensor B Circuit No. 428 between the module and the rear sensor. REPEAT Quick Test.
C23 • Did the warning lamp flash rapidly for Test No. 2?	Yes	GO to C24.
	No	GO to C35.
C24 CHECK SENSOR GROUND CIRCUIT • Attach one test lamp lead to sensor ground Circuit No. 432 Pin 1 at the right front sensor. • Attach the other test lamp lead to the battery positive (+) terminal. • Observe the test lamp.	Test lamp on	Sensor ground circuit OK. GO to C25.
	Test lamp off	SERVICE the open in sensor ground Circuit No. 432 between the module connector and the right front sensor. REPEAT Quick Test.
C25 CHECK SENSOR POWER CIRCUIT • Attach the negative (black) test lead of a volt-ohm meter to sensor ground Pin 1 Circuit No. 432 at the right front sensor connector. • Attach the positive (red) test lead to sensor power Pin 2 Circuit No. 431 at the right front sensor connector. • Turn ignition to the RUN position. • Measure DC voltage.	Voltage less than 1V and steady	SERVICE open in sensor power Circuit No. 431 from the right front sensor to the module. REPEAT Quick Test.
	Voltage erratic or greater than 1V	Sensor power OK. GO to C26.
C26 CHECK RIGHT FRONT SENSOR A CIRCUIT • Move the positive (red) test lead to right front sensor A Circuit No. 424 Pin 4 at the right front sensor connector. • Measure DC voltage.	Greater than 1.5V or erratic	Right front sensor A Circuit OK. GO to C30.
	Less than 1.5V	OK. GO to C27.
C27 CHECK RIGHT FRONT SENSOR • Disconnect the right front sensor connector. • Measure DC voltage.	Greater than 1.5V	REPLACE the right front sensor. REPEAT Quick Test.
	Less than 1.5V	Right front sensor OK. GO to C28.

FM2019100011050X

Fig. 11   Test C: Problem Sensing Vehicle Attitude (Part 5 of 9)

PROBLEM SENSING VEHICLE ATTITUDE — Continued

TEST STEP	RESULT	▶	ACTION TO TAKE
C28 CHECK RIGHT FRONT SENSOR A CIRCUIT • Do not reconnect the right front sensor. • Attach the negative (black) test lead of a volt-ohm meter to sensor ground Pin 14 Circuit No. 432 at the module connector. • Attach the positive (red) test lead to right front Sensor A Circuit No. 424 Pin 5 at the module connector. • Measure DC voltage.	Greater than 1.5V	▶	SERVICE open in right front Sensor A Circuit No. 424 between the module and the sensor. RECONNECT the right front sensor connector. REPEAT Quick Test.
	Less than 1.5V	▶	GO to C29.
C29 CHECK RIGHT FRONT SENSOR A CIRCUIT • Disconnect the module. • Attach the negative (black) test lead of a volt-ohm meter to module ground Pin 1 Circuit No. 430 at the module connector. • Attach the positive (red) test lead to right front Sensor A Circuit No. 424 Pin 5 at the module connector. • Measure resistance.	Greater than 1000 Ohms	▶	REPLACE the air suspension module. RECONNECT the right front sensor. REPEAT Quick Test.
	Less than 1000 Ohms	▶	SERVICE short to ground on right front Sensor A Circuit No. 424 between the module and the right front sensor. RECONNECT the right front sensor. REPEAT Quick Test.
C30 CHECK RIGHT FRONT SENSOR B CIRCUIT • Move the positive (red) test lead to right front Sensor B Circuit No. 425 Pin 3 at the right front sensor connector. • Measure DC voltage.	Greater than 1.5V or erratic	▶	REPLACE right front sensor. GO to C31.
	Less than 1.5V	▶	GO to C32.
C31 CHECK MODULE FOR DAMAGE • RERUN diagnostics test No. 2 by performing Steps A2-A5.	Warning light flashing rapidly during test No. 2	▶	REPLACE the air suspension control module. REPEAT Quick Test.
	Warning light not flashing rapidly during test No. 2	▶	REPEAT Quick Test.
C32 CHECK RIGHT FRONT SENSOR • Disconnect the right front sensor connector. • Measure DC voltage.	Greater than 1.5V or erratic	▶	INSTALL a new right front sensor. REPEAT Quick Test.
	Less than 1.5V	▶	GO to C33.

FM2019100011060X

Fig. 11 Test C: Problem Sensing Vehicle Attitude (Part 6 of 9)

PROBLEM SENSING VEHICLE ATTITUDE — Continued

TEST STEP	RESULT	▶	ACTION TO TAKE
C33 CHECK RIGHT FRONT SENSOR B CIRCUIT • Do not reconnect the right front sensor. • Attach the negative (black) test lead of a volt-ohm meter to sensor ground Pin 14 Circuit No. 432 at the module connector. • Attach the positive (red) test lead to right front Sensor B Circuit No. 425 Pin 16. • Measure DC voltage.	Greater than 1.5V	▶	SERVICE open in right front Sensor B Circuit No. 425 between the module and the sensor. RECONNECT the right front sensor connector. REPEAT Quick Test.
	Less than 1.5V	▶	GO to C34.
C34 CHECK RIGHT FRONT SENSOR B CIRCUIT • Disconnect the module. • Attach the negative (black) test lead of a volt-ohm meter to module ground Pin 1 Circuit No. 430 at the module connector. • Attach the positive (red) test lead to right front Sensor B Circuit No. 425 Pin 16 at the module connector. • Measure resistance.	Greater than 1000 ohms	▶	REPLACE the air suspension module. RECONNECT the right front sensor. REPEAT Quick Test.
	Less than 1000 Ohms	▶	SERVICE short to ground on right front Sensor B Circuit No. 425 between the module and the right front sensor. REPEAT Quick Test.
C35 CHECK SENSOR GROUND CIRCUIT • Attach one test lamp lead to sensor ground Circuit No. 432 Pin 1 at the left front sensor circuits. • Attach the other test lamp lead to the battery positive (+) terminal. • Observe the test lamp.	Test lamp on	▶	Sensor ground OK. GO to C36.
	Test lamp off	▶	SERVICE the open in sensor ground Circuit No. 432 between the module connector and the left front sensor. REPEAT Quick Test.
C36 CHECK SENSOR POWER CIRCUIT • Attach the negative (black) test lead of a volt-ohm meter to sensor ground Pin 1 Circuit No. 432 at the left front sensor connector. • Attach the positive (red) test lead to sensor power Pin 2 Circuit No. 431 at the left front sensor connector. • Turn ignition to the RUN position. • Measure DC voltage.	Voltage less than 1V and steady	▶	SERVICE open in sensor power Circuit No. 431 from the left front sensor to the module. REPEAT Quick Test.
	Voltage erratic or greater than 1V	▶	Sensor power circuit OK. GO to C37.
C37 CHECK LEFT FRONT SENSOR A CIRCUIT • Move the positive (red) test lead to left front Sensor A Circuit No. 422 Pin 4 at the left front sensor connector. • Measure DC voltage.	Greater than 1.5V or erratic	▶	Left front sensor A Circuit OK. GO to C41.
	Less than 1.5V	▶	GO to C38.

FM2019100011070X

Fig. 11 Test C: Problem Sensing Vehicle Attitude (Part 7 of 9)

PROBLEM SENSING VEHICLE ATTITUDE — Continued

TEST STEP	RESULT	▶	ACTION TO TAKE
C38 CHECK LEFT FRONT SENSOR • Disconnect the left front sensor connector. • Measure DC voltage.	Greater than 1.5V	▶	REPLACE the front left sensor. REPEAT Quick Test.
	Less than 1.5V	▶	Left front sensor OK. GO to C39.
C39 CHECK LEFT FRONT SENSOR A CIRCUIT • Do not reconnect the left front sensor. • Attach the negative (black) test lead of a volt-ohm meter to sensor ground Pin 14 Circuit No. 432 at the module connector. • Attach the positive (red) test lead to right front Sensor A Circuit No. 422 Pin 6 at the module connector. • Measure DC voltage.	Greater than 1.5V	▶	SERVICE open in left Sensor A Circuit No. 422 between the module and the sensor. RECONNECT the sensor connector. REPEAT Quick Test.
	Less than 1.5V	▶	GO to C40.
C40 CHECK LEFT FRONT SENSOR A CIRCUIT • Disconnect the module. • Attach the negative (black) test lead of a volt-ohm meter to module ground Pin 1 Circuit No. 430 at the module connector. • Attach the positive (red) test lead to left front Sensor A Circuit No. 422 Pin 6 at the module connector. • Measure resistance.	Greater than 1000 Ohms	▶	REPLACE the air suspension module. RECONNECT the left front sensor. REPEAT Quick Test.
	Less than 1000 Ohms	▶	SERVICE short to ground on left front Sensor A Circuit No. 422 between the module and the left front sensor. RECONNECT the left front sensor. REPEAT Quick Test.
C41 CHECK LEFT FRONT SENSOR B CIRCUIT • Move the positive (red) test lead to left front Sensor B Circuit No. 423 Pin 3 at the left front sensor connector. • Measure the DC voltage.	Greater than 1.5V or erratic	▶	REPLACE left front sensor. GO to C42.
	Less than 1.5V	▶	GO to C43.
C42 CHECK MODULE FOR DAMAGE • Rerun diagnostics test No. 3 by performing steps A2-A6.	Warning lamp flashing rapidly during test No. 3	▶	REPLACE the air suspension control module. REPEAT Quick Test.
	Warning lamp not flashing rapidly during test No. 3	▶	REPEAT Quick Test.

FM2019100011080X

Fig. 11 Test C: Problem Sensing Vehicle Attitude (Part 8 of 9)

PROBLEM SENSING VEHICLE ATTITUDE — Continued

TEST STEP	RESULT	▶	ACTION TO TAKE
C43 CHECK THE LEFT FRONT SENSOR • Disconnect the left front sensor connector. • Measure the DC voltage.	Greater than 1.5V or erratic	▶	INSTALL a new left front sensor. REPEAT Quick Test.
	Less than 1.5V	▶	Left front sensor OK. GO to C44.
C44 CHECK LEFT FRONT SENSOR B CIRCUIT • Do not reconnect the left front sensor. • Attach the negative (black) test lead of a volt-ohm meter to sensor ground Pin 14 Circuit No. 432 at the module connector. • Attach the positive (red) test lead to left front Sensor B Circuit No. 423 Pin 17 at the module connector. • Measure DC voltage.	Greater than 1.5V	▶	SERVICE open in left front Sensor B Circuit No. 423 between the module and the sensor. RECONNECT the left front sensor connector. REPEAT Quick Test.
	Less than 1.5V	▶	GO to C45.
C45 CHECK LEFT FRONT SENSOR B CIRCUIT • Disconnect the module. • Attach the negative (black) test lead of a volt-ohm meter to module ground Pin 1 Circuit No. 430 at the module connector. • Attach the positive (red) test lead to left front Sensor B Circuit No. 423 Pin 17 at the module connector. • Measure resistance.	Greater than 1000 Ohms	▶	REPLACE the air suspension module. RECONNECT the left front sensor. REPEAT Quick Test.
	Less than 1000 Ohms	▶	SERVICE short to ground on left front Sensor B Circuit No. 423 between the module and the left front sensor. REPEAT Quick Test.

FM2019100011090X

Fig. 11 Test C: Problem Sensing Vehicle Attitude (Part 9 of 9)

PROBLEM AT REAR OF VEHICLE

TEST STEP	RESULT	ACTION TO TAKE
D1		
• Did the compressor cycle during test No. 4?	Yes	GO to D2.
	No	GO to G1.
D2		
• Did the right rear solenoid cycle during test No. 8?	Yes	GO to D3.
	No	GO to D12.
D3		
• Did the left front rear solenoid cycle during test No. 9?	Yes	GO to D4.
	No	GO to D23.
D4		
• Did the vent solenoid cycle during test No. 5?	Yes	GO to D5.
	No	GO to H1.
D5 CHECK COMPRESSOR		
• Perform Steps A2-A3.	Pressure greater than 827 kPa (120 psi)	Compressor OK. GO to D6.
• Disconnect all the air lines at the compressor.		
• Plug three of the four air line fittings at the compressor.	Pressure less than 827 kPa (120 psi)	INSTALL a new compressor. RECONNECT all the air lines at the compressor. REPEAT Diagnostic Test.
• Attach a pressure gauge capable of reading 1034 kPa (150 psi) to the remaining fitting at the compressor.		
• Open and close the door and observe the pressure gauge.		
D6 CHECK REAR SENSOR CONNECTION		
• Check the rear sensor, ball studs, and bracket for secure mechanical connection.	Securely connected	GO to D7.
	Not securely connected	SECURE rear sensor as necessary. REPEAT Diagnostic Test.
D7 CHECK IN REAR AIR SYSTEM		
• Disconnect the air lines going to the right and left rear air spring at the compressor.	Air escaping from both air lines	GO to D8.
• Perform Steps A2-A3.	Air not escaping from one rear air line	GO to D10.
• Open and close a door and verify that air is escaping from the air lines.	Air not escaping from either air line because of no air in either air spring	GO to D8.

FM2019100012010X

Fig. 12   Test D: Problem At Rear Of Vehicle (Part 1 of 6)

PROBLEM AT REAR OF VEHICLE — Continued

TEST STEP	RESULT	ACTION TO TAKE
D8		
• Did vehicle fail tests 2 and 3?	Yes	GO to D9.
	No	LOCATE and SERVICE leak in left or right spring and solenoid assembly.
D9		
• Is rear of vehicle at rebound (high)?	Yes	REPLACE the compressor assembly. REPEAT Diagnostic Test.
	No	SERVICE leaking air line or fitting. Any of the four air lines or eight fittings may be leaking. RECONNECT all air lines. REPEAT Diagnostic Test.
D10 CHECK FOR RESTRICTION IN REAR SOLENOID		
• Reconnect the air lines to the rear air spring at the compressor.	Air escaping from rear solenoid	SERVICE leak or obstruction in the affected air line or fitting. RECONNECT all air lines. REPEAT Diagnostic Test.
• Perform Steps A2-A3.		
• Disconnect the air line going to the affected rear air spring at the air spring solenoid.	Air is not escaping from the rear solenoid	GO to D11.
• Open and close a door and verify that air is escaping from the affected rear air spring.		
NOTE: The rear of the vehicle may fall during this test.		
D11		
• Check for leaks at affected air spring and solenoid assembly.	No leaks	REPLACE the solenoid at the affected air spring. REPEAT Diagnostic Test.
	Leaks found	SERVICE or REPLACE leaky air spring or solenoid. REPEAT Diagnostic Test.
D12 CYCLE RIGHT REAR SOLENOID		
• Perform Steps A2-A3.		GO to D13.
• Open and close the door until the warning lamp blinks test No. 8.		
D13 CHECK RIGHT REAR SOLENOID CIRCUIT		
• Attach one lead of the test lamp to right rear solenoid Circuit No. 416 at the right rear solenoid connector.	Test lamp blinking	REPLACE right rear solenoid. REPEAT Diagnostic Test.
• Attach the other test lamp lead to battery Circuit No. 175 at the right rear solenoid connector.	Test lamp off	GO to D14.
• Observe the test lamp.	Test lamp on	GO to D21.

FM2019100012020X

Fig. 12   Test D: Problem At Rear Of Vehicle (Part 2 of 6)

PROBLEM AT REAR OF VEHICLE — Continued

TEST STEP	RESULT	ACTION TO TAKE
D14 CHECK FOR CONNECTOR POLARITY		
• Attach one lead of test lamp to the right rear solenoid connector Pin 2.	Test lamp on	GO to D17.
• Attach the other lead of test lamp to a good ground.	Test lamp off	GO to D15.
D15		
• Attach one lead of test lamp to the right rear solenoid connector Pin 1.	Test lamp off	GO to D17.
• Attach the other lead of test lamp to a good ground.	Test lamp on	REPAIR crossed wires in the solenoid connector and repeat D16.
D16 CHECK BATTERY CIRCUIT		
• Move the test lead connected to right rear solenoid Circuit No. 416 to a good ground.	Test lamp on	Battery circuit OK. GO to D17.
• Observe the test lamp.	Test lamp off	SERVICE open in Circuit No. 175 between the right rear solenoid and fuse link. REPEAT Diagnostic Test.
D17 CHECK CONTROL MODULE		
• Attach one test lamp lead to right rear solenoid Circuit No. 416 Pin 10 at the module connector.	Test lamp blinking	SERVICE open in Circuit No. 416 between the module and the right rear solenoid. REPEAT Diagnostic Test.
• Attach the other test lamp lead to battery Circuit No. 418 Pin 20 at the module connector.		
• Observe the test lamp.	Test lamp off	GO to D18.
NOTE: Test must be performed without disconnecting harness connector at module.		
D18		
• Is the warning lamp blinking test No. 8?	Yes	GO to D19.
	No	GO to D12.
D19 CHECK MODULE CONNECTOR PINS		
• Disconnect module connector and inspect pins.	Pins OK	GO to D20.
	Problem found	SERVICE connector at the air suspension module. REPEAT Diagnostic Test.

FM2019100012030X

Fig. 12   Test D: Problem At Rear Of Vehicle (Part 3 of 6)

PROBLEM AT REAR OF VEHICLE — Continued

TEST STEP	RESULT	ACTION TO TAKE
D20 CHECK RIGHT REAR SOLENOID		
• Attach the negative (black) test lead of a volt-ohm meter to connector Pin 1 of the right rear solenoid.	Greater than 13 ohms	REPLACE air suspension control module. REPEAT Diagnostic Test.
• Attach the positive (red) test lead to connector Pin 2 at the right rear solenoid.	Less than 13 Ohms	REPLACE right rear solenoid and air suspension module. REPEAT Diagnostic Test.
• Measure the resistance.		
D21		
• Is the warning lamp blinking test No. 8?	Yes	GO to D22.
	No	GO to D12.
D22 CHECK RIGHT REAR SOLENOID CIRCUIT		
• Disconnect the module connector.	Test lamp on	SERVICE short to ground on right rear solenoid Circuit No. 416 between the module connector and the right rear solenoid. REPEAT Diagnostic Test.
• Observe the test lamp.		
	Test lamp off	REPLACE the air suspension module. REPEAT Diagnostic Test.
D23 CYCLE THE LEFT REAR SOLENOID		
• Perform Steps A2-A3.		GO to D24.
• Open and close the door until the warning lamp blinks test No. 9.		
D24 CHECK LEFT REAR SOLENOID CIRCUIT		
• Attach one lead of the test lamp to left rear solenoid Circuit No. 429 at the left rear solenoid connector.	Test lamp blinking	REPLACE the left rear solenoid. REPEAT Diagnostic Test.
• Attach the other test lamp lead to battery Circuit No. 175 at the left rear solenoid connector.	Test lamp off	GO to D25.
• Observe the test lamp.	Test lamp on	GO to D32.
D25 CHECK FOR CONNECTOR POLARITY		
• Attach one lead of test lamp to the left rear solenoid connector Pin 2.	Test lamp on	GO to D28.
• Attach the other lead of test lamp to a good ground.	Test lamp off	GO to D26.

FM2019100012040X

Fig. 12   Test D: Problem At Rear Of Vehicle (Part 4 of 6)

PROBLEM AT REAR OF VEHICLE — Continued

TEST STEP	RESULT	▶	ACTION TO TAKE
D26 • Attach one lead of test lamp to the left rear solenoid connector Pin 1. • Attach the other lead of test lamp to a good ground.	Test lamp off	▶	GO to D28.
	Test lamp on	▶	SERVICE crossed wires in solenoid connector and REPEAT D27.
D27 CHECK BATTERY CIRCUIT • Move the test lead connected to the left rear solenoid Circuit No. 429 to a good ground. • Observe the test lamp.	Test lamp on	▶	Battery circuit OK. GO to D28.
	Test lamp off	▶	SERVICE open or short to ground in Circuit No. 418 between the air suspension system On/Off switch and the right rear solenoid. REPEAT Diagnostic Test.
D28 CHECK CONTROL MODULE • Attach one test lamp lead to left rear solenoid Circuit No. 429 Pin 9 at the module connector. • Attach the other test lamp lead to battery Circuit No. 418 Pin 20 at the module connector. NOTE: Test must be performed without disconnecting harness connector of module.	Test lamp blinking	▶	SERVICE open in Circuit No. 429 between the module and the left rear solenoid. REPEAT Diagnostic Test.
	Test lamp off	▶	GO to D29.
D29 • Is the warning lamp blinking test No. 9?	Yes	▶	GO to D30.
	No	▶	GO to D23.
D30 CHECK MODULE CONNECTOR PINS • Disconnect module connector and inspect pins.	Pins OK	▶	GO to D31.
	Problem found	▶	SERVICE connector at the air suspension module. REPEAT Diagnostic Test.

FM2019100012050X

Fig. 12   Test D: Problem At Rear Of Vehicle (Part 5 of 6)

PROBLEM AT REAR OF VEHICLE — Continued

TEST STEP	RESULT	▶	ACTION TO TAKE
D31 CHECK LEFT REAR SOLENOID • Attach the negative (black) test lead of a volt-ohm meter to connector Pin 1 of the left rear solenoid. • Attach the positive (red) lead to connector Pin 2 of the left rear solenoid. • Measure the resistance.	Greater than 13 Ohms	▶	REPLACE the air suspension control module. REPEAT Diagnostic Test.
	Less than 13 Ohms	▶	REPLACE the left rear solenoid and air suspension module. REPEAT Diagnostic Test.
D32 • Is the warning lamp blinking test No. 9?	Yes	▶	GO to D33.
	No	▶	GO to D23.
D33 CHECK LEFT REAR SOLENOID CIRCUIT • Disconnect the module connector. • Observe the test lamp.	Test lamp on	▶	SERVICE short to ground on the left rear solenoid Circuit No. 429 between the module connector and the left rear solenoid. REPEAT Diagnostic Test.
	Test lamp off	▶	REPLACE the air suspension module. REPEAT Diagnostic Test.

FM2019100012060X

Fig. 12   Test D: Problem At Rear Of Vehicle (Part 6 of 6)

PROBLEM AT RIGHT FRONT OF VEHICLE

TEST STEP	RESULT	▶	ACTION TO TAKE
E1 • Did vehicle pass test No. 1?	Yes	▶	GO to E2.
	No	▶	GO to D1.
E2 • Did the right front solenoid pass test No. 7?	Yes	▶	GO to E3.
	Does not pass air	▶	GO to E4.
	Passes air but does not click	▶	GO to E16.
E3 CHECK RIGHT FRONT SENSOR • Check the right front sensor and ball studs for a secure mechanical connection.	Securely connected	▶	GO to E6.
	Not securely connected	▶	SECURE the right front sensor. REPEAT Diagnostic Test.
E4 CHECK RIGHT FRONT SOLENOID CIRCUIT • Perform Steps A2-A3. • Open and close the door until the warning lamp blinks test No. 7. • Attach one lead of the test lamp to the right front solenoid Circuit No. 414 at the right front solenoid connector. • Attach other test lamp lead to battery Circuit No. 175 at the right front solenoid connector. • Observe the test lamp.	Test lamp blinking	▶	Electrical system OK. GO to E5.
	Test lamp off	▶	GO to E7.
	Test lamp on	▶	GO to E14.
E5 CHECK FOR RESTRICTION IN RIGHT FRONT AIR LINE • Perform Steps A2-A3. • Disconnect the air lines at the right front air spring solenoid. • Open and close the door twice and verify that air is escaping from the spring solenoid line. NOTE: The right front of the vehicle will drop during this test.	Air escaping from the air spring solenoid	▶	SERVICE kink or obstruction in the right front air line. RECONNECT air lines. REPEAT Diagnostic Test.
	Air is not escaping from the air spring solenoid	▶	GO to E6.
E6 CHECK FOR SOLENOID OR AIR SPRING LEAKS • Reconnect air lines. • Perform Steps A2-A3. • Open and close the door twice and verify that air is not leaking from the right front air spring or solenoid.	Air not leaking from the air spring or solenoid	▶	SERVICE or REPLACE right front air spring solenoid due to an obstruction. REPEAT Diagnostic Test.
	Air leaking from the air spring or solenoid	▶	SERVICE or REPLACE leaky right front air spring or solenoid. REPEAT Diagnostic Test.

FM2019100013010X

Fig. 13   Test E: Problem At Right Front Of Vehicle (Part 1 of 3)

PROBLEM AT RIGHT FRONT OF VEHICLE — Continued

TEST STEP	RESULT	▶	ACTION TO TAKE
E7 CHECK FOR CONNECTOR POLARITY • Attach one lead of test lamp to right front solenoid connector Pin 2. • Attach the other lead of test lamp to a good ground.	Test lamp on	▶	GO to E10.
	Test lamp off	▶	GO to E8.
E8 • Attach one lead of test lamp to the right front solenoid connector Pin 1. • Attach the other lead of test lamp to a good ground.	Test lamp off	▶	GO to E10.
	Test lamp on	▶	SERVICE crossed wires in solenoid connector and REPEAT E9.
E9 CHECK BATTERY CIRCUIT • Move the test lead connected to the right front solenoid Circuit No. 414 to a good ground. • Observe the test lamp.	Test lamp on	▶	Battery circuit OK. GO to E10.
	Test lamp off	▶	SERVICE open or short to ground in battery Circuit No. 175 between the battery and the right front solenoid. REPEAT Diagnostic Test.
E10 CHECK MODULE • Attach one test lamp lead to right front solenoid Circuit No. 414 Pin 12 at the module connector. • Attach the other test lamp lead to battery Circuit No. 418 Pin 20 at the module connector. • Observe the test lamp. NOTE: Test must be performed without disconnecting the harness connector at the module.	Test lamp blinking	▶	SERVICE open in right front solenoid Circuit No. 414 between the module and the right front solenoid. REPEAT Diagnostic Test.
	Test lamp off	▶	GO to E11.
E11 • Is the warning lamp blinking test No. 7?	Yes	▶	GO to E12.
	No	▶	GO to E4.
E12 CHECK MODULE CONNECTOR • Disconnect module connector and inspect pins.	Pins OK	▶	GO to E13.
	Problem found	▶	SERVICE connector at the air suspension module. REPEAT Diagnostic Test.

FM2019100013020X

Fig. 13   Test E: Problem At Right Front Of Vehicle (Part 2 of 3)

PROBLEM AT RIGHT FRONT OF VEHICLE — Continued

TEST STEP		RESULT	▶	ACTION TO TAKE
E13	CHECK RIGHT FRONT SOLENOID			
	• Disconnect the right front solenoid connector. • Attach the negative (black) test lead of a volt-ohm meter to connector Pin 1 of the right front solenoid connector. • Attach the positive (red) test lead to connector Pin 2 of the right front solenoid connector. • Measure resistance.	Greater than 13 Ohms	▶	REPLACE the air suspension control module. REPEAT Diagnostic Test.
		Less than 13 Ohms	▶	REPLACE the right front solenoid and air suspension module. REPEAT Diagnostic Test.
E14				
	• Is the warning lamp blinking test No. 7?	Yes	▶	GO to E15.
		No	▶	GO to E4.
E15				
	• Disconnect the module connector, leaving test lamp connected across Circuits No. 414 and No. 175. • Observe the test lamp.	Test lamp on	▶	SERVICE short to ground or right front solenoid Circuit No. 414 between the module connector and the right front solenoid. REPEAT Diagnostic Test.
		Test lamp off	▶	REPLACE the air suspension module. REPEAT Diagnostic Test.
E16				
	• Disconnect the right front solenoid connector. • Attach one lead of the test lamp to the right front solenoid Circuit No. 414 on the harness side of the connector. • Attach the other lead to battery Circuit No. 175 on the harness side of the connector. • Observe the test lamp.	Test lamp on	▶	SERVICE short to ground in solenoid control Circuit No. 414. REPEAT Diagnostic Test.
		Test lamp off	▶	REPLACE solenoid. REPEAT Diagnostic Test.

FM2019100013030X

Fig. 13　Test E: Problem At Right Front Of Vehicle (Part 3 of 3)

PROBLEM AT LEFT FRONT OF VEHICLE

TEST STEP		RESULT	▶	ACTION TO TAKE
F1				
	• Did vehicle pass test No. 1?	Yes	▶	GO to F2.
		No	▶	GO to D1.
F2				
	• Did the left front solenoid pass test No. 6?	Yes	▶	GO to F3.
		Does not pass air	▶	GO to F4.
		Passes air but does not click	▶	GO to F16.
F3	CHECK LEFT FRONT SENSOR			
	• Check the left front sensor and ball stud for a secure mechanical connection.	Left front sensor securely connected	▶	GO to F6.
		Left front sensor not securely connected	▶	SECURE the left front sensor. REPEAT Diagnostic Test.
F4	CHECK LEFT FRONT SOLENOID CIRCUIT			
	• Perform Steps A2-A3. • Open and close the door until the warning lamp blinks test No. 6. • Attach one lead of the test lamp to the left front solenoid Circuit No. 415 at the left front solenoid connector. • Attach the other test lamp lead to battery Circuit No. 175 at the left front solenoid connector. • Observe the test lamp.	Test lamp blinking	▶	Electrical system OK. GO to F5.
		Test lamp off	▶	GO to F7.
		Test lamp on	▶	GO to F14.
F5	CHECK FOR RESTRICTIONS IN LEFT FRONT AIR LINE			
	• Perform Steps A2-A3. • Disconnect the air lines at the left front air spring solenoid. • Open and close the door three times and verify that air is escaping the spring solenoid. NOTE: The left front of the vehicle will drop during this test.	Air escaping from the air spring solenoid	▶	SERVICE kink or obstruction in the left front air line RECONNECT air lines. REPEAT Diagnostic Test.
		Air is not escaping from the air spring solenoid	▶	GO to F6.

FM2019100014010X

Fig. 14　Test F: Problem At Left Front Of Vehicle (Part 1 of 3)

PROBLEM AT LEFT FRONT OF VEHICLE — Continued

TEST STEP		RESULT	▶	ACTION TO TAKE
F6	CHECK FOR SOLENOID OR AIR SPRING LEAKS			
	• Reconnect air lines. • Perform Steps A2-A3. • Open and close the door three times and verify that air is not leaking from the left front air spring or solenoid.	Air is not leaking from the air spring or solenoid	▶	SERVICE or REPLACE left front air spring solenoid due to obstruction. REPEAT Diagnostic Test.
		Air is leaking from the air spring or solenoid	▶	SERVICE or REPLACE leaky left front air spring or solenoid. REPEAT Diagnostic Test.
F7	CHECK FOR CONNECTOR POLARITY			
	• Attach one lead of test lamp to left front solenoid connector Pin 2. • Attach the other lead of test lamp to a good ground.	Test lamp on	▶	GO to F10.
		Test lamp off	▶	GO to F8.
F8				
	• Attach one lead of test lamp to right front solenoid connector Pin 1. • Attach the other lead of test lamp to a good ground.	Test lamp off	▶	GO to F10.
		Test lamp on	▶	SERVICE crossed wires in solenoid connector and REPEAT F9.
F9	CHECK BATTERY CIRCUIT			
	• Move the test lead connected to the left front solenoid Circuit No. 415 to a good ground. • Observe the test lamp.	Test lamp on	▶	Battery circuit OK. Go to F10.
		Test lamp off	▶	SERVICE open or short to ground in battery Circuit No. 175 between the battery and the left front solenoid. REPEAT Diagnostic Test.
F10	CHECK MODULE			
	• Attach one test lamp lead to left front solenoid Circuit No. 415 Pin 11 at the module connector. • Attach the other test lamp lead to battery Circuit No. 418 Pin 20 at the module connector. • Observe the test lamp. NOTE: Test must be performed without disconnecting connector at module.	Test lamp blinking	▶	SERVICE open in left front solenoid Circuit No. 415 between the module and the left front solenoid. REPEAT Diagnostic Test.
		Test lamp off	▶	GO to F11.
F11				
	• Is the warning lamp blinking test No. 6?	Yes	▶	GO to F12.
		No	▶	GO to F4.

FM2019100014020X

Fig. 14　Test F: Problem At Left Front Of Vehicle (Part 2 of 3)

PROBLEM AT LEFT FRONT OF VEHICLE — Continued

TEST STEP		RESULT	▶	ACTION TO TAKE
F12				
	• Disconnect module connector and inspect pins.	Pins OK	▶	GO to F13.
		Problem found	▶	SERVICE connector at the air suspension module. REPEAT Diagnostic Test.
F13				
	• Disconnect the left front solenoid connector. • Attach the negative (black) test lead of a volt-ohm meter to connector Pin 1 of the left front solenoid connector. • Attach the positive (red) test lead to connector Pin 2 of the left front solenoid connector. • Measure resistance.	Greater than 13 Ohms	▶	REPLACE the air suspension control module. REPEAT Diagnostic Test.
		Less than 13 Ohms	▶	REPLACE the left front solenoid and air suspension module. REPEAT Diagnostic Test.
F14				
	• Is the warning lamp blinking test No. 6?	Yes	▶	GO to F15.
		No	▶	GO to F4.
F15				
	• Disconnect the module connector leaving test lamp connected across Circuits No. 415 and No. 175. • Observe the test lamp.	Test lamp on	▶	SERVICE short to ground on left front solenoid Circuit No. 415 between the module connector and the left front solenoid. REPEAT Diagnostic Test.
		Test lamp off	▶	REPLACE the air suspension module. REPEAT Diagnostic Test.
F16				
	• Disconnect the left front solenoid connector. • Attach one lead of the test lamp to the left front solenoid Circuit No. 415 on the harness side of the connector. • Attach the other lead to battery Circuit No. 175 on the harness side of the connector. • Observe the test lamp.	Test lamp on	▶	SERVICE short to ground in solenoid control Circuit No. 415. REPEAT Diagnostic Test.
		Test lamp off	▶	REPLACE solenoid. REPEAT Diagnostic Test.

FM2019100014030X

Fig. 14　Test F: Problem At Left Front Of Vehicle (Part 3 of 3)

PROBLEM DURING FILL

TEST STEP	RESULT	►	ACTION TO TAKE
G1 CHECK THE COMPRESSOR RELAY			
• Perform Steps A2-A3.	Compressor relay cycling	►	GO to G2.
• Open and close the door until the warning lamp blinks test No. 4.			
• The compressor circuit will only be cycled 50 times during test No. 4 (approximately three minutes). At the end of 50 cycles the compressor will turn off and not cycle until test No. 4 is reentered.	Compressor relay is not cycling	►	GO to G5.
• Verify that the compressor relay is cycling.			
NOTE: The rear of the vehicle may raise during test No. 4.			
G2 CHECK COMPRESSOR CIRCUIT			
• Disconnect the compressor connector.	Test lamp blinking	►	Compressor circuit OK. GO to G3.
• Attach one lead of the test lamp to compressor Circuit No. 417 at the compressor connector (harness side).	Test lamp on	►	REPLACE the compressor relay. RECONNECT the compressor connector. REPEAT Quick Test.
• Attach the other test lamp lead to good ground.			
• Observe the test lamp.	Test lamp off	►	GO to G4
G3 CHECK COMPRESSOR GROUND CIRCUIT			
• Move the test lamp attached to battery ground, to ground Circuit No. 430 at the compressor connector (harness side).	Test lamp blinking	►	INSTALL a new compressor. RECONNECT compressor. REPEAT Quick Test.
• Observe the test lamp.	Test lamp off	►	SERVICE open in ground Circuit No. 430 between the compressor and the battery. RECONNECT compressor connector. REPEAT Quick Test.
G4 CHECK COMPRESSOR CIRCUIT			
• Reconnect the compressor connector.	Test lamp blinking	►	SERVICE open or short to ground on Circuit No. 417 between the compressor and the compressor relay. REPEAT Quick Test.
• Perform Step G1.			
• Attach one lead of the test lamp to compressor Circuit No. 417 at the compressor relay.			
• Attach the other test lamp lead to a good ground.	Test lamp off	►	REPLACE the compressor relay. RECONNECT the compressor connector. REPEAT Quick Test.
• Observe test lamp.			

FM2019100015010X

Fig. 15 Test G: Problem During Fill (Part 1 of 3)

PROBLEM DURING FILL — Continued

TEST STEP	RESULT	►	ACTION TO TAKE
G10 CHECK MODULE			
• Perform Step G1.	Test lamp blinking	►	SERVICE open in compressor relay Circuit No. 420 between the compressor relay and the module. REPEAT Quick Test.
• Attach one test lamp lead to compressor relay Circuit No. 420 Pin 22 at the module connector.			
• Attach the other test lamp lead to battery Circuit No. 418 Pin 20 at the module connector.			
• Observe the test lamp.	Test lamp off	►	REPLACE air suspension control module. REPEAT Quick Test.
NOTE: This test must be performed without disconnecting module harness connector.			

FM2019100015030X

Fig. 15 Test G: Problem During Fill (Part 3 of 3)

PROBLEM DURING FILL — Continued

TEST STEP	RESULT	►	ACTION TO TAKE
G5 CHECK COMPRESSOR RELAY CIRCUIT			
• Attach one lead of the test lamp to compressor relay Circuit No. 420 at the compressor relay.	Test lamp blinks	►	Module relay circuit OK. GO to G6.
• Attach the other test lamp lead to the battery positive (+) terminal.	Test lamp on	►	GO to G8.
• Observe the test lamp.	Test lamp off	►	GO to G9.
G6 CHECK JUMPER CIRCUIT			
• Attach one test lamp lead to jumper Circuit No. 175A at the compressor relay Pin 2	Test lamp on	►	REPLACE compressor relay. RECONNECT compressor connector. REPEAT Quick Test.
• Attach the other lead to a good ground.			
• Observe the test lamp.	Test lamp off	►	GO to G7.
G7 CHECK BATTERY CIRCUIT			
• Attach one test lamp lead to battery Circuit No. 175 at the compressor relay Pin 3	Test lamp on	►	SERVICE open or short to ground in jumper Circuit 175A. REPEAT Quick Test.
• Attach the other test lamp lead to a good ground.			
• Observe the test lamp.	Test lamp off	►	SERVICE open or short to ground on battery Circuit No. 175 between the compressor relay and the battery. REPEAT Quick Test.
G8 CHECK MODULE			
• Disconnect the module connector and observe the test lamp.	Test lamp on	►	SERVICE compressor relay Circuit No. 420 for a short to ground. REPEAT Quick Test.
	Test lamp off	►	REPLACE the air suspension control module. REPEAT Quick Test.
G9 CHECK COMPRESSOR RELAY			
• Disconnect the compressor relay connector.	Greater than 54 Ohms	►	Compressor relay OK. GO to G10.
• Attach the negative (black) test lead of a volt-ohm meter to connect Pin 2 at the compressor relay connector.	Less than 54 Ohms	►	REPLACE the compressor relay. REPEAT Quick Test.
• Attach the positive (red) test lead to connector Pin 1 at the compressor relay connector.			NOTE: This failure may have damaged the air suspension control module.
• Measure resistance.			

FM2019100015020X

Fig. 15 Test G: Problem During Fill (Part 2 of 3)

PROBLEM DURING VENT

TEST STEP	RESULT	►	ACTION TO TAKE
H1 CHECK VENT SOLENOID CIRCUIT			
• Perform Steps A2-A3.	Test lamp blinks	►	REPLACE the compressor assembly. REPEAT Quick Test.
• Open and close the door until the warning lamp blinks test No. 5.			
• Disconnect air compressor connector.	Test lamp off	►	GO to H3.
• Attach one test lamp lead to vent solenoid Circuit No. 421 at Pin 4 on the harness side of the connector.	Test lamp on	►	GO to H2.
• Attach the other test to battery Circuit No. 175 Pin 1 at the harness side of the connector.			
• Observe the test lamp.			
H2 CHECK MODULE			
• Disconnect the air suspension module connector.	Test lamp on	►	SERVICE short in vent solenoid Circuit No. 421 between the compressor assembly and the module. RECONNECT air suspension module connector. REPEAT Quick Test.
• Observe the test lamp.			
	Test lamp off	►	REPLACE the air suspension control module. REPEAT Quick Test.
H3 CHECK BATTERY CIRCUIT			
• Move the test lamp at vent solenoid Circuit No. 421 to a good ground.	Test lamp on	►	Battery circuit OK. GO to H4.
• Observe the test lamp.	Test lamp off	►	SERVICE open or short in battery Circuit No. 175 between the vent solenoid and battery. REPEAT Quick Test.
H4 CHECK MODULE			
• Attach one test lamp lead to vent solenoid Circuit No. 421 Pin 23 at the module connector.	Test lamp blinking	►	SERVICE open in vent solenoid Circuit No. 421 between the module and the compressor relay. REPEAT Quick Test.
• Attach the other test lamp lead to battery Circuit No. 418 Pin 20 at the module connector.			
• Observe the test lamp.	Test lamp off	►	GO to H5.
NOTE: Test must be performed without disconnecting harness connector at module.			
H5 CHECK WARNING LAMP			
• Is the warning lamp blinking test No. 5?	Yes	►	GO to H6.
	No	►	GO to H1.

FM2019100016010X

Fig. 16 Test H: Problem During Vent (Part 1 of 2)

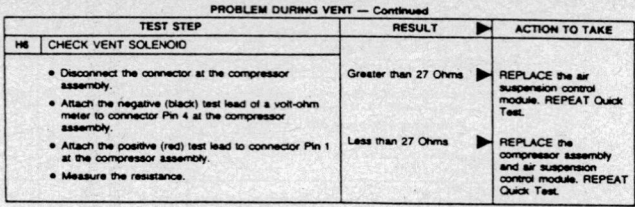

PROBLEM DURING VENT — Continued			
TEST STEP	**RESULT**	▶	**ACTION TO TAKE**
H6 CHECK VENT SOLENOID			
• Disconnect the connector at the compressor assembly.	Greater than 27 Ohms	▶	REPLACE the air suspension control module. REPEAT Quick Test.
• Attach the negative (black) test lead of a volt-ohm meter to connector Pin 4 at the compressor assembly.	Less than 27 Ohms	▶	REPLACE the compressor assembly and air suspension control module. REPEAT Quick Test.
• Attach the positive (red) test lead to connector Pin 1 at the compressor assembly.			
• Measure the resistance.			

FM2019100016020X

Fig. 16   Test H: Problem During Vent (Part 2 of 2)

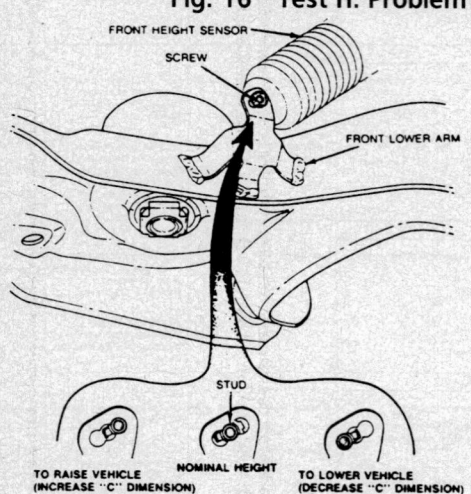

FM2019100018000X

Fig. 18   Front suspension ride height adjustment

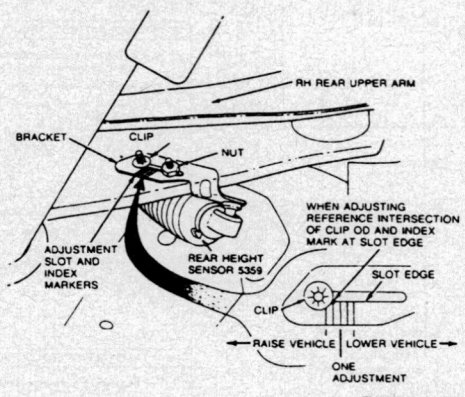

FM2019100019000X

Fig. 19   Rear suspension ride height adjustment

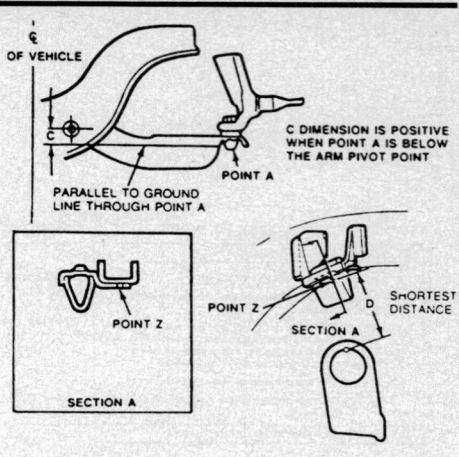

FM2019100017000X

SUSPENSION RIDE HEIGHT

VEHICLE		C	D
MARK VII	INCHES	+ 0.24	5.06
	MM	+ 6.0	128.6

Fig. 17   Ride height "C" & "D" dimensions

SYSTEM SERVICE

ADJUSTMENTS

PRE-ADJUSTMENT

This procedure must be performed before checking ride height and/or wheel alignment.

If vehicle is significantly warmer or colder than test area, allow it to warm or cool to surrounding air temperature before performing the following procedure.

1. Position vehicle on alignment rack, turn ignition off, then exit vehicle.
2. Re-enter vehicle and turn ignition to RUN position. Do not start engine.
3. Allow vehicle to level for approximately one minute, then push trunk release to open trunk area.
4. Turn ignition OFF and exit vehicle.
5. Allow vehicle to vent to trim height (approximately 20 seconds), then close all doors and turn off air suspension switch in trunk, **Fig. 4.**

RIDE HEIGHT

All doors must be closed when adjusting ride height.

Front Suspension

The front suspension ride height or "C" dimension, **Fig. 17**, is adjusted by moving the front left and/or right lower sensor attaching stud to one of the three adjustment positions as shown, **Fig. 18.** Loosen the attaching screw and adjust up or down as required. Changing the sensor attachment point one position will result in a .50 inch change in the "C" dimension. The "C" dimension should be indicated at .24 inches.

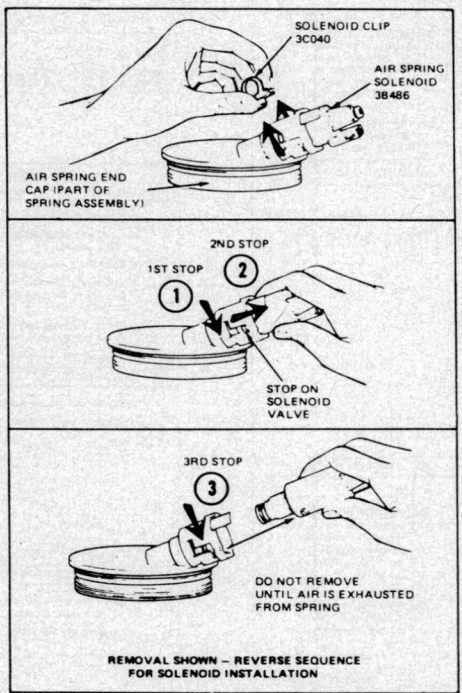

FM2019100020000X

Fig. 20   Air spring solenoid removal

Rear Suspension

The rear suspension ride height or "D" dimension, **Fig. 17**, is adjusted by moving the rear sensor attaching bracket up or down in relation to the right rear upper control arm, **Fig. 19.** Loosen the attaching nut and position up or down as required. A change to the sensor attaching point by one index mark will result in a .250 inch

change to the "D" dimension. The "D" dimension should be indicated at 5.06 inches.

COMPONENT REPLACEMENT

AIR SPRING SOLENOID

1. Turn air suspension switch off, then raise and support vehicle at body.
2. Remove wheel assembly.
3. Disconnect electrical connector and air line from air spring solenoid, then remove solenoid retaining clip.
4. Rotate solenoid counterclockwise to first stop, then pull outward to second stop and allow air to bleed from system as shown, **Fig. 20. Failure to allow air to fully bleed from system may result in personal injury.**
5. Rotate solenoid counterclockwise to third stop and remove from air spring assembly.
6. Reverse procedure to install.

AIR SPRING

Removal

1. Remove air spring solenoid as outlined previously.
2. If replacing front spring, remove spring to lower control arm retaining clip. If replacing rear spring, remove retaining clip and/or bolts.
3. Push down on air spring collar spring clip, then rotate collar counterclockwise until spring releases from body spring seat.
4. Remove spring from vehicle.

Installation

1. Install air spring solenoid. If left side spring is being replaced, position solenoid so notch on spring collar is inline with center line of solenoid. If right side spring is being replaced, position solenoid so flat on collar is inline with

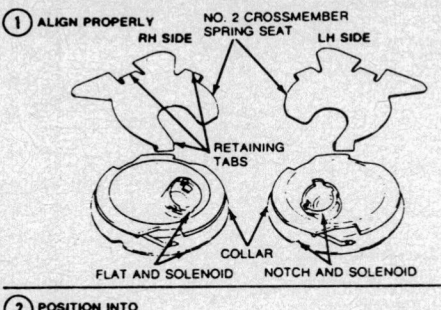

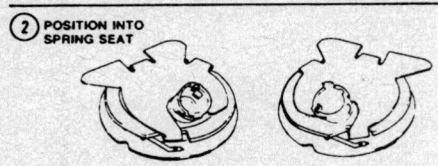

Fig. 21 Positioning solenoid onto spring collar

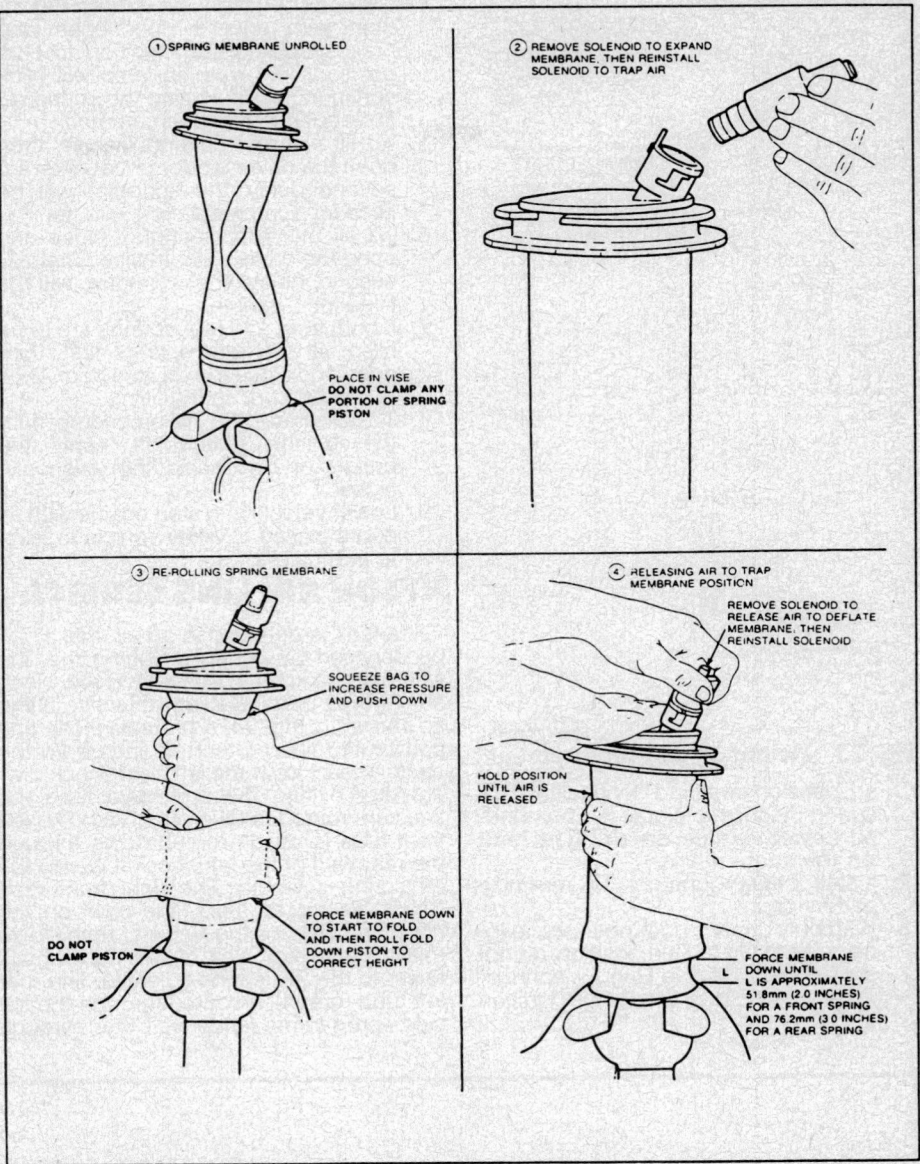

Fig. 22 Refolding air spring

center line of solenoid. Refer to **Fig. 21**, for correct positioning. **Do not attempt to install or inflate any air spring which has become unfolded. If any spring has been unfolded, refold spring as shown in Fig. 22, before installing into vehicle.**

2. Install air spring into body spring seat, then rotate spring collar until spring clip snaps into position, **Fig. 21**.
3. Connect air line and electrical connector to solenoid.
4. Align and secure spring to lower control arm. **The suspension must be at its full travel when replacing the springs, as damage to spring may result.**
5. Replace wheel assembly.
6. Refill air springs as outlined in "Air Spring Refill" procedure.

CONTROL MODULE

1. Turn air suspension switch to OFF position.
2. Remove left side luggage compartment trim panel, then disconnect wiring harness from module.
3. Remove control module retaining nuts, then the control module.
4. Reverse procedure to install.

AIR COMPRESSOR/DRYER ASSEMBLY

1. Turn air suspension switch to OFF position.
2. Disconnect compressor electrical connector.
3. Remove air line protector cap from dryer by releasing the 2 pins located at bottom of cap.
4. Disconnect air lines from dryer.
5. Remove air compressor/dryer as-

sembly to mounting bracket retaining screws, then the assembly.
6. Reverse procedure to install.

HEIGHT SENSOR

Front

1. Turn air suspension switch to OFF position.
2. Working from engine compartment, disconnect sensor electrical connector.
3. Push connector through access hole at rear of shock tower, then raise and support vehicle.
4. Disconnect bottom and top ends of sensor from attaching studs as shown, **Fig. 23.**
5. Disconnect wiring harness from plastic clips on shock tower and remove sensor.
6. Reverse procedure to install.

Rear

Whenever the front air springs have been replaced, always check rear height sensor for damage. Replace, if necessary.
1. Turn air suspension switch to OFF position.
2. Working from luggage compartment, disconnect sensor electrical connector. Pull luggage compartment carpet back to gain access to sensor sealing grommet.
3. Raise and support vehicle, then disconnect bottom and top ends of sensor from the attaching studs, **Fig. 23.**
4. Pushing upwards, unseat sensor from grommet, then push sensor through floor pan into luggage compartment.
5. Reverse procedure to install.

AIR SPRING REFILL

1. With suspension unloaded, turn air

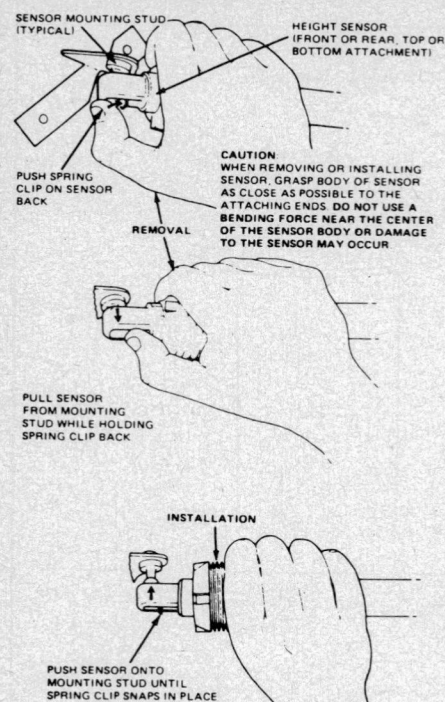

Fig. 23 Height sensor replacement

suspension switch to ON position, ensuring diagnostic pigtail is ungrounded. **Lower vehicle, ensuring no load on the suspension.**

2. Install battery charger to minimize battery drain.

3. With only driver's door open, cycle ignition from Off to Run position, do not start engine. Hold in Run for approximately 5 seconds, then return ignition to Off.

4. Ground the diagnostic pigtail, **Fig. 4**, then with driver's door open and brakes applied, turn ignition to Run position. The warning lamp will blink continuously, indicating the spring refill sequence has been entered.

5. To fill the rear spring(s), close, then open the driver's door once. After a 6 second delay, the spring(s) will be filled for approximately 1 minute.

6. To fill the front spring(s), close and open the driver's door twice. After a 6 second delay, the spring(s) will be filled for 1 minute.

7. If both front and rear springs are to be filled, fill the rear springs first, then open and close the driver's door once to initiate front spring filling.

8. To terminate the fill procedure, turn the ignition switch off, apply the brakes or disconnect the diagnostic pigtail.

9. Lower vehicle and start engine with all doors closed to allow vehicle to level to trim height.

NYLON AIR LINE SERVICE

If a leak is detected in an air line, it can be serviced by carefully cutting the line with a sharp knife to ensure a good, clean straight cut and installing a service fitting as shown in, **Fig. 24**. A protective cap and convoluted line protect air lines from the air dryer back over the left front shock tower. After exiting the protective tube the lines are routed to different areas. The left front tube (gray), is routed down through the rear wall of the left shock tower to the air spring solenoid. The right front tube (black), is routed along the cowl on the righthand side of the vehicle, then down through the rear wall of the right shock tower to the SIR spring solenoid. The rear left tube (green), is routed through the left side apron to the fenderwell, then through

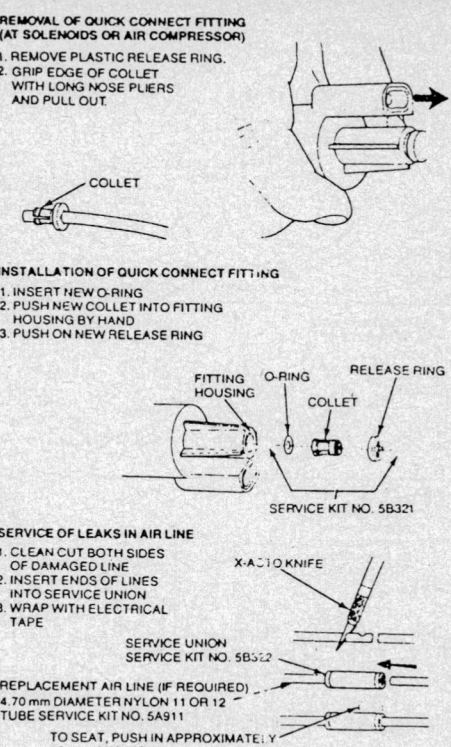

Fig. 24 Nylon air line repair

the lefthand upper dash panel to the passenger compartment, down the dash panel to the lefthand rocker panel, then to the luggage compartment over the rear fenderwell. The left air line routes down through the floorpan in front of the left rear shock tower. The right rear tube (tan), is routed across the rear seat support, then down through the floorpan in front of the right rear shock tower.

INDEX

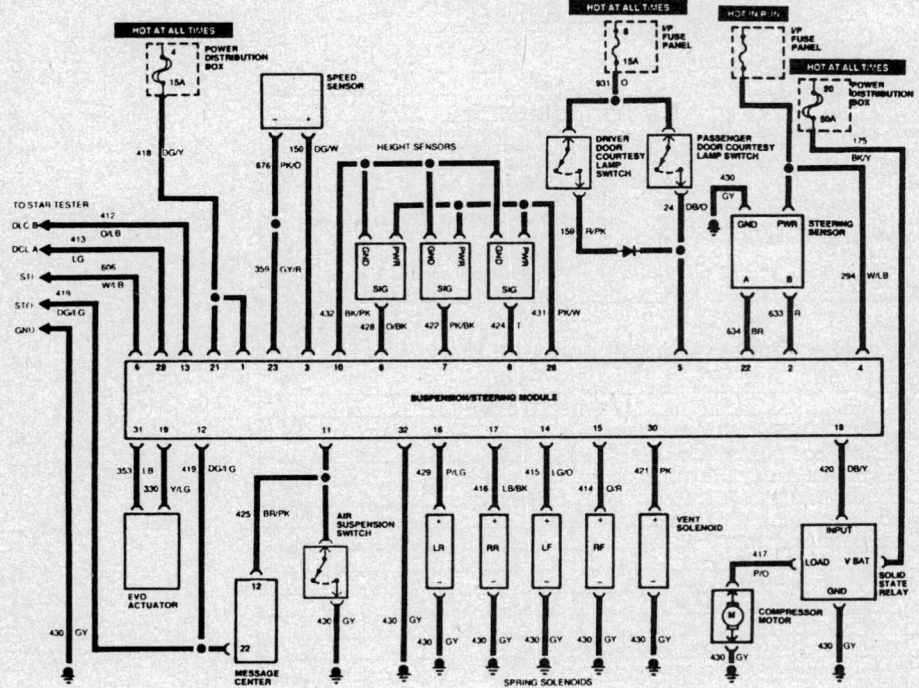

Fig. 1 Air suspension schematics. Mark VIII

DESCRIPTION

SYSTEM OPERATION

The Mark VIII suspension system is a microprocessor controlled active air suspension system, **Fig. 1**. The microprocessor constantly determines the height position of the vehicle body relative to the wheels. System operation is maintained by the addition or removal of air to or from the air springs, resulting in a predetermined front and rear suspension height. This predetermined height is known as the vehicle trim height. The system maintains a predetermined trim height regardless of road conditions or vehicle passenger load.

The microprocessor also uses vehicle speed to determine the proper trim height of the air suspension system. At 65 mph, the suspension system lowers the vehicle trim for a more stable high speed profile.

SYSTEM COMPONENTS

The Mark VIII air suspension system includes the following major units:
1. An EVO control module, located in the

passenger compartment right of the glove compartment, controls both the suspension system and the power steering boost, **Fig. 2.**
2. Height sensors, located parallel to LH and RH front wheels and LH rear wheel, send a continuous voltage signal to the control module relative to the positions of the wheels and body.
3. A speed sensor, located on the transmission housing at the forward end of the extension housing, sends a signal to the control module to lower the vehicle at 65 mph and to determine the amount of power steering boost commanded by the control module.
4. Air spring solenoids are located on the air springs at each wheel. The control module opens these solenoids to let air into or out of the air springs.
5. A vent solenoid, located on the rear of the compressor assembly, opens on command from the control module to remove air from the air springs.
6. The ignition switch is located on the steering column. The signal sent to

the control module when the switch is in RUN position commands the module to control both steering boost and the suspension system. The air suspension system remains active for one hour after ignition switch is turned off. This allows for trim correction after passengers and cargo have been removed.

DIAGNOSIS & TESTING

WARNING LAMP DIAGNOSIS

When the "Check Air Ride" warning message is displayed in the message center, the system error that has been detected by the control module is stored in the module's memory. The diagnostic trouble code will be retained for the next 80 ignition cycles. If there is no repeat of the same error during these 80 ignition cycles, the control module will erase the code.

DIAGNOSTIC TEST PROCEDURES

The diagnosis for the air suspension consists of the Function Test procedure, Auto Test procedure and the Diagnostic Pinpoint Tests. The Function Test and Auto Test procedures require a Rotunda Super Star II Tester, 007-0041A, connected to the diagnostic connector located on the RH front shock absorber tower. During the Auto Test procedure, the Super Star II Tester will display any diagnostic trouble codes stored in the control module. In general, most diagnostic and service actions will contain the following steps:
1. Perform function test 211 to retrieve stored codes.
2. Perform the Auto Test to find current system errors.
3. Service current errors by performing pinpoint tests indicated for the error code.
4. Service codes retrieved by original function test.
5. Perform Auto Test to verify that all concerns have been corrected.

Function Test Procedure

1. Open hood and locate diagnostic connector on front of RH front shock tower. Install battery charger to provide power during testing.

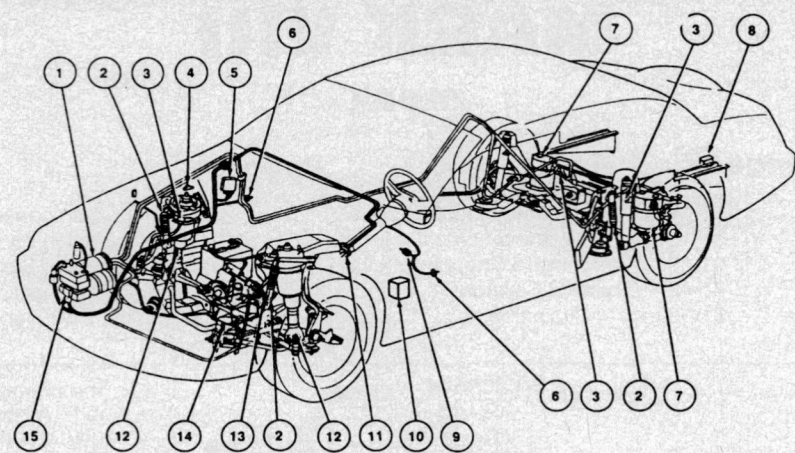

Fig. 2 Air suspension system components. Mark VIII

Item	Description
1	Air Compressor / Vent Solenoid / Drier Assembly
2	Height Sensor
3	Spring Solenoid
4	Air Suspension / EVO Diagnostic Connector
5	Air Suspension / EVO Control (Data Link Connector (DLC)) Module
6	Door Switch
7	Rear Air Spring

Item	Description
8	Air Suspension Service Switch (Inside Luggage Compartment)
9	Vehicle Speed Sensor
10	Fuse Panel
11	Steering Sensor
12	Front Air Spring and Shock Absorber Assembly
13	EVO Actuator
14	Power Distribution Box
15	Air Compressor Solid State Relay

FM2019100026000X

Code	Description
211	Display All Diagnostic Trouble Codes In Memory
212	LF Pump with Audible Sensor Check
213	LF Vent with Audible Sensor Check
214	RF Pump with Audible Sensor Check
215	RF Vent with Audible Sensor Check
216	LR Pump with Audible Sensor Check
217	LR Vent with Audible Sensor Check
218	RR Pump with Audible Sensor Check
219	RR Vent with Audible Sensor Check
221	Compressor Run
222	Actuator Output Test (Cycles All Solenoids and EVO Actuator)
223	LF Height Sensor Trim Detection, Audible Output
224	RF Height Sensor Trim Detection, Audible Output
225	LR Height Sensor Trim Detection, Audible Output
226	Speed Sensor Detection
227	Pulse EVO Actuator through Duty Cycle
228	Erase All Codes Stored in Module Memory

FM2019100027000X

Fig. 3 Function test index

2. Open luggage compartment and ensure air suspension switch is OFF.
3. Set Super Star II Tester mode switch to FAST, set selector switch to EEC/MCU and turn power switch on. Set HOLD/TEST push button in HOLD position, UP.
4. Turn ignition switch to OFF, then ON. Ensure both doors on vehicle are closed.
5. Install Super Star II Tester in diagnostic connector, then press HOLD/TEST button and latch in TEST position, DOWN.
6. Codes for function tests will be displayed one after the other, **Fig. 3**. To select and run a function test, perform the following steps:
   a. When the desired code number appears, release and depress the HOLD/TEST button.
   b. Unlatch HOLD/TEST button to end selected test. Relatch button to re-enter code display function.

Auto Test Procedure

1. Open hood and locate diagnostic connector on front of RH front shock tower. Install battery charger to provide power during testing.
2. Open luggage compartment and ensure air suspension switch is ON.
3. Set Super Star II Tester mode switch to FAST, set selector switch to EEC/MCU and turn power switch on. Set HOLD/TEST push button in HOLD position, UP.
4. Turn ignition switch to OFF, then ON. Ensure both doors on vehicle are closed.
5. Install Super Star II Tester in diagnostic connector, then press HOLD/TEST button and latch in TEST position, DOWN.

6. Code 10 will be displayed while Auto Test is running. Any faults detected will stop the test and be displayed on the Super Star II Tester. **Do not lean on vehicle or open doors while code 10 is displayed, as this will introduce false errors into the test.**
7. When code 12 is displayed, open driver side door, turn steering wheel 1/4 turn in either direction, then close door.
8. Unlatch HOLD/TEST button.
9. Press HOLD/TEST button and read displayed codes, **Fig. 4.**

TROUBLESHOOTING PROCEDURES

Refer to **Fig. 5**, for troubleshooting chart. Refer to **Figs. 6 through 24**, for pinpoint test flowcharts.

Continued on page 31-34

Fig. 5 Troubleshooting flowchart (Part 1 of 3)

CONDITION	POSSIBLE SOURCE	ACTION
• CHECK AIR RIDE is Displayed in Less Than 5 Seconds After Vehicle is Started	• Control Module detects an electrical problem before a leveling correction is attempted.	(1) Retrieve the code that caused CHECK AIR RIDE to actuate from module memory. (Run Functional Test 211.) (2) Run the Auto Test to see what codes are currently seen by the module. (3) Service current codes. Service codes 25, 50 through 95 first. Service codes 98 and 99 second. Service codes 29 and 45 third. Service error codes stored in module memory if different from Auto Test codes. NOTE: If no codes are retrieved and CHECK AIR RIDE is constantly displayed a concern may exist with Circuit 419 or the message center.
• CHECK AIR RIDE Displayed at Differing Times. No Apparent Sequence of Events, Random Order	• Control module detects either an electrical concern or encounters excessive correction time while attempting to level vehicle. Will occur most frequently at: — Start up if vehicle is sitting low — 65 mph when module attempts to lower vehicle 20mm (0.75 inch) — 35 mph when module attempts to raise vehicle 20mm (0.75 inch)	(1) Retrieve codes stored in module memory. (Run Function Test 211). (2) Run Auto Test. (3) Service current codes. (4) Service concerns from module memory not already addressed.
• CHECK AIR RIDE Not Displayed, One or More Corners High or Low	• System inactive and cannot turn on CHECK AIR RIDE display. • System operating correctly, ride heights out of adjustment. • Height sensor popped off ball stud.	• Run Auto Test. If no codes are output, go to Pinpoint Test JA. • If the vehicle passes the Auto Test with a Code 11, or the manual test codes 29 or 45 and one or more corners appear high or low, adjust ride heights. Go to Pinpoint Test NA. WARNING: DO NOT ATTEMPT TO RESET RIDE HEIGHTS UNTIL THE SYSTEM PASSES THE AUTO TEST AND DISPLAYS CODE 11 OR THE MANUAL TEST CODES 29 OR 45.

FM2019100029010X

Fig. 4 Diagnostic trouble codes

Code	P.P.T.	Description	Error Handling	Display	Generated	Validation
10		Auto test in progress			A.T.	
11		Auto test passed			A.T.	
12		Perform manual tests			A.T.	
15		No faults stored in memory			A.T.	
18	PA	Module detects low battery	Disable AS and EVO until module senses more than 13 volts for 1 second continuous		A.T.	Less than 11 volts for 1 second continuous
19	PB	Module detects high battery	Disable AS and EVO until module senses less than 17.5 volts for 1 second continuous		A.T.	More than 19 volts for 1 second continuous
20		Module memory error 2	Disable AS	On after 1 second		Replace module
25	A	Height sensor power not 5 volts	Disable AS	On after 1 second	D.C. / A.T.	Fault after 1 second continuous
29	B	2 Door cycles not sensed			A.T.	
35	C	EVO actuator	AS normal, EVO full assist		D.C. / A.T.	Fault after 1 second continuous
45	D	Steering sensor		On after 1 second	A.T.	Fault after 1 second continuous
50	E	LF height sensor out of range	Disable AS	On after 1 second	D.C. / A.T.	Fault after 1 second continuous
55	E	RF height sensor out of range	Disable AS	On after 1 second	D.C. / A.T.	Fault after 1 second continuous
60	E	LR height sensor out of range	Disable AS	On after 1 second	D.C. / A.T.	Fault after 1 second continuous
70	F	Vent solenoid	Disable AS	On after 1 second	D.C. / A.T.	Fault after 1 second continuous
75	GA	Compressor relay control circuit	Disable AS	On after 1 second	D.C. / A.T.	Fault after 1 second continuous
80	H	LF spring solenoid	Disable AS	On after 1 second	D.C. / A.T.	Fault after 1 second continuous
85	H	RF spring solenoid	Disable AS	On after 1 second	D.C. / A.T.	Fault after 1 second continuous
90	H	LR spring solenoid	Disable AS	On after 1 second	D.C. / A.T.	Fault after 1 second continuous
95	H	RR spring solenoid	Disable AS	On after 1 second	D.C. / A.T.	Fault after 1 second continuous
98	I	Compressor run time exceeded	Disable AS	On after ON-REST-ON cycle. 11.5 minutes	D.C.	Fault after ON-REST-ON cycle. 11.5 minutes
99	J	Unable to detect raising or lowering of one or more corners	Disable AS	On after either maximum vent or maximum pump time-out (45-second vent, 90-second pump)	D.C. / A.T.	Fault after either max. vent or max. pump time-out (45-second vent, 90-second pump)

FM2019100028000X

CONDITION	POSSIBLE SOURCE	ACTION
• One or More Corners Drop Overnight. Vehicle Achieves Trim When Ignition Turned On	• A large drop in temperature overnight causes the air in the air springs to contract. This will cause lowering of vehicle corners, and is normal. • A minor leak in either air springs or spring solenoids. This may trigger a Code 98 if the leak is severe enough to cause excessive compressor run time before trim is reached.	• Retrieve stored error codes. (Run Function Test 211). • If Code 98 is retrieved from memory, go to Pinpoint Test GB.
• One or More Corners Low and CHECK AIR RIDE Displayed 90 Seconds to 2 Minutes After Starting Vehicle	• Module has detected excessive correction time. This is caused by either: — Compressor will not operate — A large air leak in either the compressor, air springs or the air lines	• Retrieve code causing CHECK AIR RIDE to be displayed (Run Function Test 211). This should be Code 99. • Check for compressor and/or air line leaks using Pinpoint Test I7 and Proceed to other tests as required.
• Front Air Springs are Completely High and/or Rear Air Springs are Completely Low. CHECK AIR RIDE Displayed 45 to 90 Seconds After Starting Vehicle • One Front Corner is Completely Low. CHECK AIR RIDE Displayed 45 to 90 Seconds After Starting Vehicle • Rear Air Springs are Completely Low. CHECK AIR RIDE Displayed 45 to 90 Seconds After Starting Vehicle	• Height sensor is off ball stud • Height sensor ground is open on corners that are not trim. Module does not detect this as an electrical error. • Wiring harness has intermittent open circuit.	• Examine height sensors and reinstall on ball stud if required. • Run Function Test 211 to retrieve stored codes. • Run Auto Test. • Service Auto Test error codes. • If Code 99 is received from either memory or Auto Test, go to Pinpoint Test I4 and check for open sensor ground. • Run Function Test 223, 224 or 225 to test for intermittent sensor and/or wiring problem.
• Irregular Air Suspension Operation at Low Temperatures	• Moisture frozen in air lines and/or drier. NOTE: In severe cases, water will build up in air springs and recontaminate the system.	• Warm vehicle to room temperature. • Disconnect both ends of ALL air lines. • Blow out air lines to dry. • Replace drier assembly. • It may be required to remove air springs and drain water.

FM2019100029020X

Fig. 5   Troubleshooting flowchart (Part 2 of 3)

CONDITION	POSSIBLE SOURCE	ACTION
• Air Suspension Does Not Lower at 65 mph and Power Steering Efforts are Constantly Very Light NOTE: Most customers will not be able to detect vehicle lowering at speed but will report very sensitive steering.	• Control module is not receiving vehicle speed signal.	• No error codes will be stored if the module is not receiving the speed signal (1) Install the Star Tester in a manner that will permit driving the vehicle. (2) Turn off the Air Suspension Service switch located in the luggage compartment. (3) Run Function Test 226. (4) Drive the vehicle at speeds over 10 mph. Note speed displayed on SUPER STAR II Tester. (5) If no speed is displayed over 10 mph, go to Pinpoint Test KA1. (6) If speed is displayed, run Auto Test. (7) If Code 45 is not received during Auto Test, replace module.
• Customer Complains of Poor Ride Quality, or Vehicle Leans to One Side and Vehicle Passes Auto Test	• Air cannot flow freely into or out of one of the rear air springs. • A concern with one of the rear air springs may not be detected during the Auto Test. • Tire pressure too high.	• Run Function Test 216, 217, 218 and 219 to make sure both rear air springs can be filled or vented. If a problem is suspected, refer to appropriate Section.
• Cannot Retrieve Stored Codes or Enter Auto Test	• Module is not active due to wiring problem or there is a problem with the Star Tester circuits.	• Go to Pinpoint Test JA.
• Nothing Seems to be Working Correctly. Cannot Identify the Root Condition Do Not Know What to Do Next	• Intermittent problem with wiring harness, sensors, actuators or module. • Several malfunctions existing in a combination that is not covered by normal diagnostics.	• Perform the "Quick Wiring and Circuit Checks". Refer to Pinpoint Test OA. This will help isolate malfunctions.
• Do Not Have a SUPER STAR II Tester to Retrieve Codes or Perform Tests		• Use the "Quick Wiring and Circuit Checks" to isolate malfunctions.

FM2019100029030X

Fig. 5   Troubleshooting flowchart (Part 3 of 3)

DIAGNOSTIC CHART INDEX

Test/Code	Description	Page No.	Fig. No.
A/25	Sensor Supply Not 5 Volts	31-24	6
B/29	Two-Door Cycles Not Detected	31-24	7
C/35	EVO Actuator	31-24	8
D/45	Steering Sensor	31-25	9
E/55, 60	Height Sensor Out Of Range	31-26	10
F/70	Vent Solenoid	31-28	11
GA/75	Compressor Relay Control Circuit	31-28	12
GB	Compressor Electrical Diagnosis	31-29	13
H/85, 90	Spring Solenoids	31-30	14
I/98	Compressor Run Time Exceeded	31-31	15
J/99	Unable To Detect Raising Or Lowering Of Corner(s)	31-31	16
JA	Unable To Detect Raising Or Lowering Of Corner(s)	31-31	17
JB	Unable To Detect Raising Or Lowering Of Corner(s)	31-31	18
JC	Unable To Detect Raising Or Lowering Of Corner(s)	31-32	19
KA	Unable To Enter Auto Test	31-32	20
KB	No Codes Displayed While Auto Test Is Running	31-33	21
L	Speed Greater Than 5 mph Not Detected	31-34	22
PA	Module Detects Low Battery	31-34	23
PB	Module Detects High Battery Voltage	31-34	24

TEST STEP		RESULT	▶	ACTION TO TAKE
A1	CHECK HEIGHT SENSOR CONNECTION FOR DAMAGE			
• Disconnect height sensor connectors and check for damage, corrosion or bent pins. • Make sure height sensor connectors are firmly seated and not damaged. • Are connectors worn or damaged?		Yes	▶	SERVICE or REPLACE as required. REPEAT Auto Test.
		No	▶	GO to A2.

FM2019100030010X

Fig. 6   Test A: Sensor Supply Not 5 Volts (Part 1 of 4)

TEST STEP		RESULT	▶	ACTION TO TAKE
A2	DETERMINE CONCERN			
• Air suspension service switch ON. • Ignition switch ON. • Control module connected. • Backprobe gray connector: — Positive voltmeter lead to Circuit 431 (PK/W) — Negative voltmeter lead to a known good ground • Read meter voltage.		Zero volts	▶	GO to A3.
		7 to 10 volts	▶	GO to A6.
		Battery voltage	▶	GO to A7.
		4.8 to 5.2 volts	▶	REPLACE control module. REPEAT Auto Test.

MODULE GRAY CONNECTOR

A3	ZERO VOLTS OUT SENSOR POWER			
• Disconnect all height sensors. • Turn ignition switch OFF. • Turn ignition switch ON. • Backprobe gray connector: — Connect voltmeter positive lead to Circuit 431 (PK/W) — Connect voltmeter negative lead to a known good ground • Does meter read 4.8 to 5.2 volts?		Yes	▶	GO to A4.
		No	▶	GO to A5.

MODULE GRAY CONNECTOR

FM2019100030020X

Fig. 6   Test A: Sensor Supply Not 5 Volts (Part 2 of 4)

TEST STEP		RESULT	▶	ACTION TO TAKE
A4	INTERNAL SHORT TO GROUND IN HEIGHT SENSOR			
• Backprobe gray connector: — Connect voltmeter positive lead to Circuit 431 (PK/W) — Connect voltmeter negative lead to known good ground • Connect height sensors one at a time. • Read meter after connecting each height sensor. • Does meter read zero volts after connecting height sensor?		Yes	▶	REPLACE suspect sensor. CONTINUE connecting sensors until all are tested. REPEAT Auto Test.
		No	▶	CONTINUE connecting sensors until all are tested. REPEAT Auto Test.

MODULE GRAY CONNECTOR

A5	EXTERNAL SHORT TO GROUND IN HEIGHT SENSORS			
• Air suspension switch ON. • Ignition switch OFF. • Remove gray connector from control module. • Connect ohmmeter between Circuit 431 (PK/W) and known good ground. • Does meter indicate continuity?		Yes	▶	SERVICE short to ground of Circuit 431 (PK/W) in harness. RECONNECT height sensors. REPEAT Auto Test.
		No	▶	REPLACE control module. RECONNECT height sensors. REPEAT Auto Test.

MODULE GRAY CONNECTOR

FM2019100030030X

Fig. 6   Test A: Sensor Supply Not 5 Volts (Part 3 of 4)

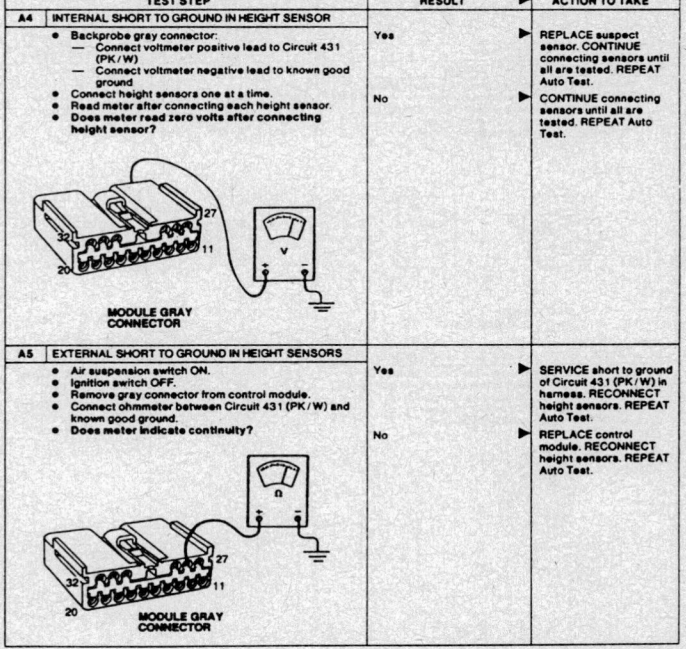

TEST STEP	RESULT	▶	ACTION TO TAKE
A6 SEVEN TO TEN VOLTS ON SENSOR POWER OUTPUT • Air suspension service switch ON. • Ignition switch ON. • Control module connected. • Backprobe gray connector: — Positive voltmeter lead connected to Circuit 431 (PK/W) — Negative voltmeter lead connected to known good ground • Observe meter reading: — Disconnect height sensors one at a time, note meter reading — Leave disconnected • Does meter indicate zero volts?	Yes	▶	SERVICE short to battery positive in suspect sensor signal line. RECONNECT height sensors. REPEAT Auto Test.
A7 BATTERY VOLTAGE ON HEIGHT SENSOR POWER SUPPLY • Air suspension service switch ON. • Ignition switch OFF. • Remove gray connector from control module. • Connect voltmeter positive lead to Circuit 431 (PK/W). • Connect voltmeter negative lead to known good ground. • Does meter indicate zero volts?	Yes No	▶ ▶	REPLACE control module. REPEAT Auto Test. SERVICE short to battery positive of Circuit 431 (PK/W). RECONNECT control module. REPEAT Auto Test.

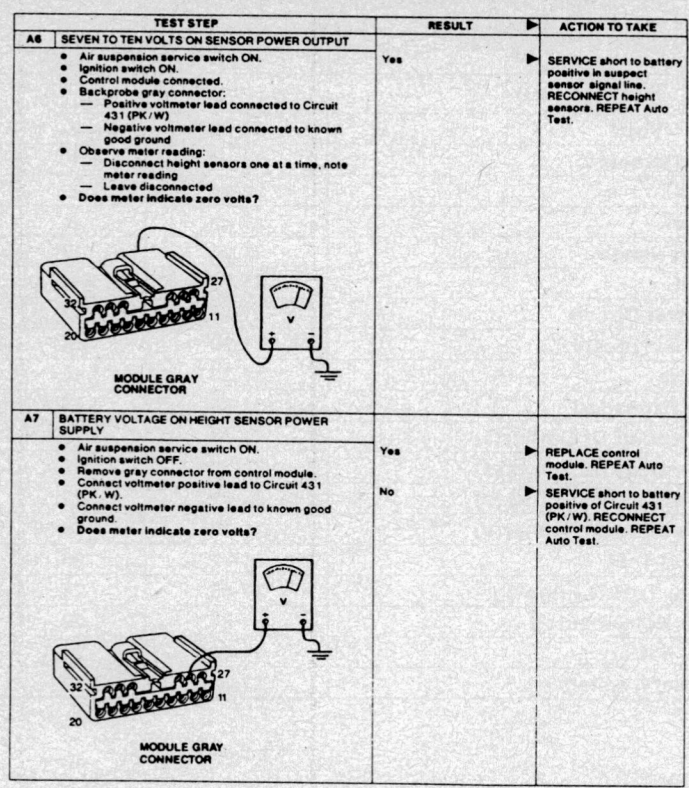

Fig. 6   Test A: Sensor Supply Not 5 Volts (Part 4 of 4)

FM2019100030040X

TEST STEP	RESULT	▶	ACTION TO TAKE
B1 CYCLE DOOR SWITCHES • Disconnect control module gray connector. • Connect voltmeter between Circuit 24 (DB/O) at control module connector and a good ground. • Close both doors. • Open and close each door while observing meter. • Does meter indicate zero volts with door closed and battery voltage with door open? NOTE: Courtesy lamps should light with doors open.	Zero volts with doors closed, battery voltage with doors open Battery voltage with both doors closed Zero volts with one door open, battery voltage with other door open Zero volts with both doors open, courtesy lamps do not light	▶ ▶ ▶ ▶	REPLACE control module. REPEAT Auto Test. LEAVE meter connected. GO to B2. GO to B3. LEAVE meter connected. GO to B5.
B2 CHECK CIRCUIT 24 (DB/O) AND 159 (R/PK) FOR SHORT TO BATTERY • Open doors and remove door switches from door jambs. • Disconnect door switch connectors from switches. • Connect voltmeter between Circuit 24 (DB/O) (RH) and a good ground. • Connect voltmeter between Circuit 159 (R/PK) (LH) and a good ground. • Does meter indicate zero volts at both circuits?	Yes No	▶ ▶	CHECK continuity at switches. REPLACE damaged switch. GO to B4. LOCATE and SERVICE short to battery in Circuit 24 (DB/O) or 159 (R/PK). REPEAT Auto Test.

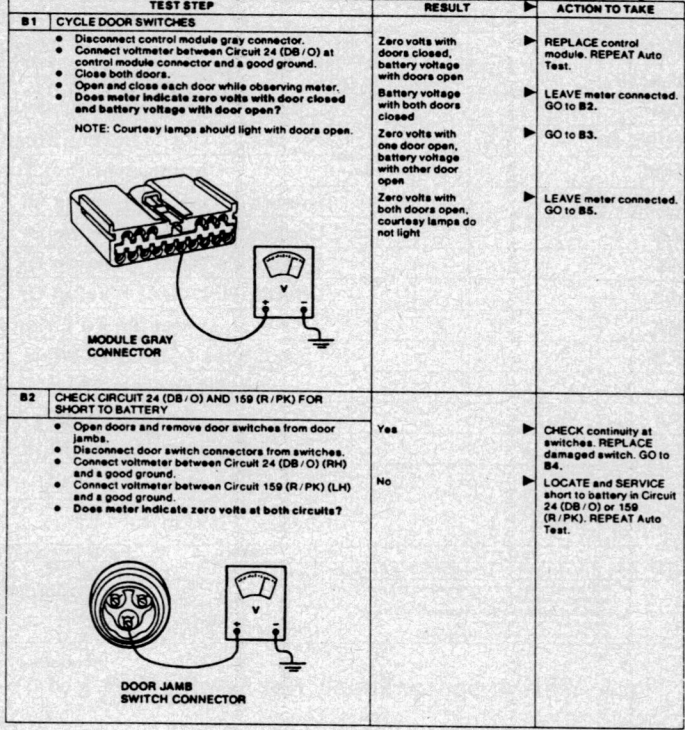

Fig. 7   Test B: Two-Door Cycles Not Detected (Part 1 of 2)

FM2019100031010X

TEST STEP	RESULT	▶	ACTION TO TAKE
B3 CHECK SUSPECT DOOR CIRCUIT • Remove suspect door switch from door jamb. • Disconnect door switch connector. • Connect voltmeter between Circuit 931 (O) at switch connector and a good ground. • Does meter indicate battery voltage?	Yes No	▶ ▶	GO to B4. GO to B5.
B4 CHECK CIRCUIT 24 (DB/O) OR 159 (R/PK) FOR OPEN • Connect ohmmeter between Circuit 24 (DB/O) or 159 (R/PK) at door switch connector and Circuit 24 (DB/O) at control module black connector. (Negative lead to module connector.) • Does meter indicate continuity?	Yes No	▶ ▶	REPLACE door switch. REPEAT Auto Test. SERVICE open in circuit between door switch connector and control module connector. REPEAT Auto Test.
B5 CHECK CIRCUIT 931 (O) FOR OPEN • Operate power outside mirror. • Does mirror operate?	Yes No	▶ ▶	LOCATE and SERVICE open in Circuit 931 (O) between mirror and door switch. LOCATE and SERVICE open in Circuit 931 (O).

Fig. 7   Test B: Two-Door Cycles Not Detected (Part 2 of 2)

FM2019100031020X

TEST STEP	RESULT	▶	ACTION TO TAKE
C1 ELIMINATE EVO ACTUATOR • Disconnect EVO actuator harness connector. • Connect ohmmeter across EVO actuator terminals; note meter reading. • Does meter indicate less than 8 ohms or more than 16 ohms?	Yes No	▶ ▶	REPLACE EVO actuator. REPEAT Auto Test. GO to C2.

FM2019100032010X

Fig. 8   Test C: EVO Actuator Concern (Part 1 of 4)

TEST STEP	RESULT	▶	ACTION TO TAKE
C2 ELIMINATE HARNESS SHORT TO BATTERY • With EVO actuator disconnected. • Disconnect control module gray connector. • Connect voltmeter negative lead to known good ground. • Connect voltmeter positive to Circuit 353 (LB); note meter reading. • Connect voltmeter positive to Circuit 353 (Y/LG); note meter reading. • Does meter indicate voltage in either circuit?	Yes No	▶ ▶	LOCATE and SERVICE short to battery in suspect circuit. GO to C3.

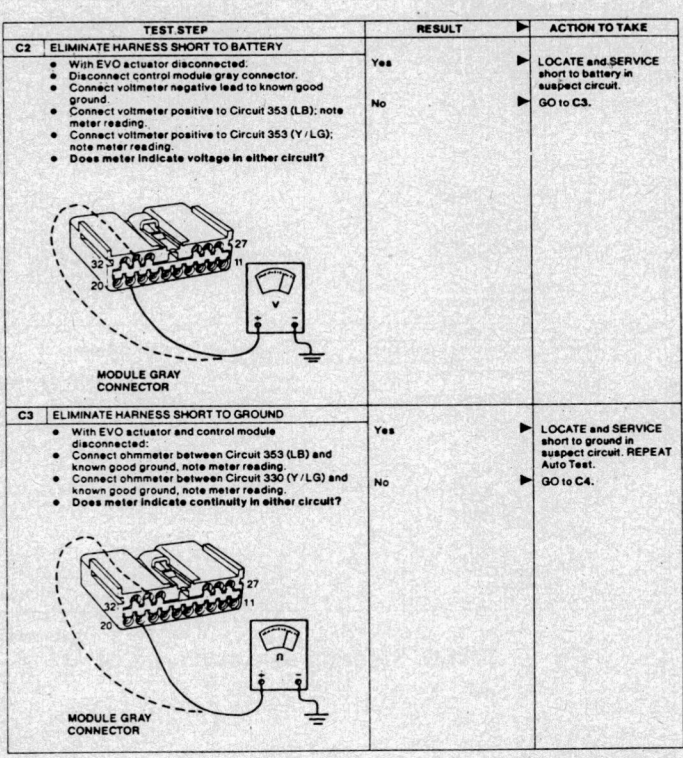

MODULE GRAY CONNECTOR

TEST STEP	RESULT	▶	ACTION TO TAKE
C3 ELIMINATE HARNESS SHORT TO GROUND • With EVO actuator and control module disconnected: • Connect ohmmeter between Circuit 353 (LB) and known good ground, note meter reading. • Connect ohmmeter between Circuit 330 (Y/LG) and known good ground, note meter reading. • Does meter indicate continuity in either circuit?	Yes No	▶ ▶	LOCATE and SERVICE short to ground in suspect circuit. REPEAT Auto Test. GO to C4.

MODULE GRAY CONNECTOR

Fig. 8   Test C: EVO Actuator Concern (Part 2 of 4)

FM2019100032020X

TEST STEP	RESULT	▶	ACTION TO TAKE
C4 ELIMINATE SHORT BETWEEN CIRCUITS 353 (LB) AND 330 (Y/LG) • EVO actuator and control module disconnected. • Connect ohmmeter between Circuit 353 (LB) and Circuit 330 (Y/LG); note meter reading. • Does meter indicate continuity?	Yes No	▶ ▶	LOCATE and SERVICE short between circuits. REPEAT Auto Test. GO to C5.

MODULE GRAY CONNECTOR

Fig. 8   Test C: EVO Actuator Concern (Part 3 of 4)

FM2019100032030X

TEST STEP	RESULT	▶	ACTION TO TAKE
C5 ELIMINATE OPEN IN CIRCUIT 353 (LB) AND CIRCUIT 330 (Y/LG) • EVO actuator and control module disconnected. • Connect ohmmeter between Circuit 353 (LB) at gray control module connector and EVO connector; note meter reading. • Connect ohmmeter between Circuit 330 (Y/LG) at gray control module connector and EVO connector; note meter reading. • Does meter indicate continuity in both circuits?	Yes No	▶ ▶	REPLACE control module. REPEAT Auto Test. LOCATE and SERVICE open in suspect circuit(s). REPEAT Auto Test.

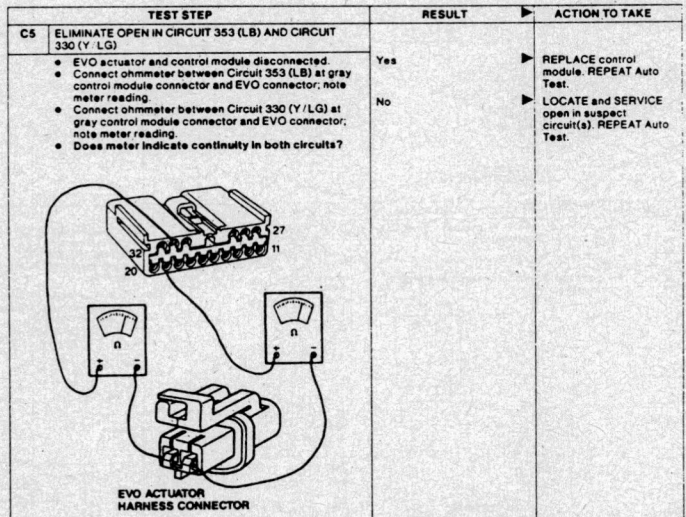

EVO ACTUATOR HARNESS CONNECTOR

Fig. 8   Test C: EVO Actuator Concern (Part 4 of 4)

FM2019100032040X

TEST STEP	RESULT	▶	ACTION TO TAKE
D1 CHECK FOR POWER AND GROUND AT STEERING SENSOR • Disconnect steering sensor connector. • Connect voltmeter between Circuits 294 (W/LB) and 430 (GY) at steering sensor connector. • Does meter indicate battery voltage?	Yes No	▶ ▶	GO to D3. GO to D2.

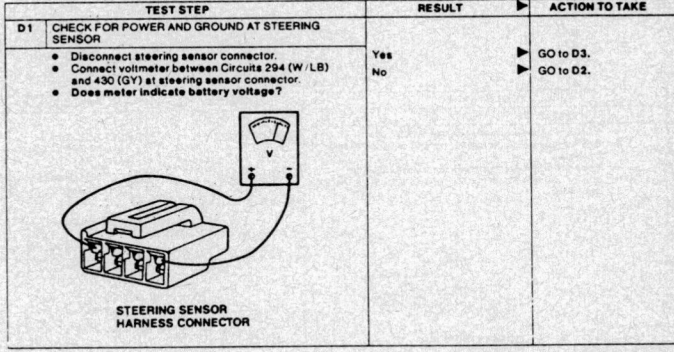

STEERING SENSOR HARNESS CONNECTOR

Fig. 9   Test D: Steering Sensor (Part 1 of 4)

FM2019100033010X

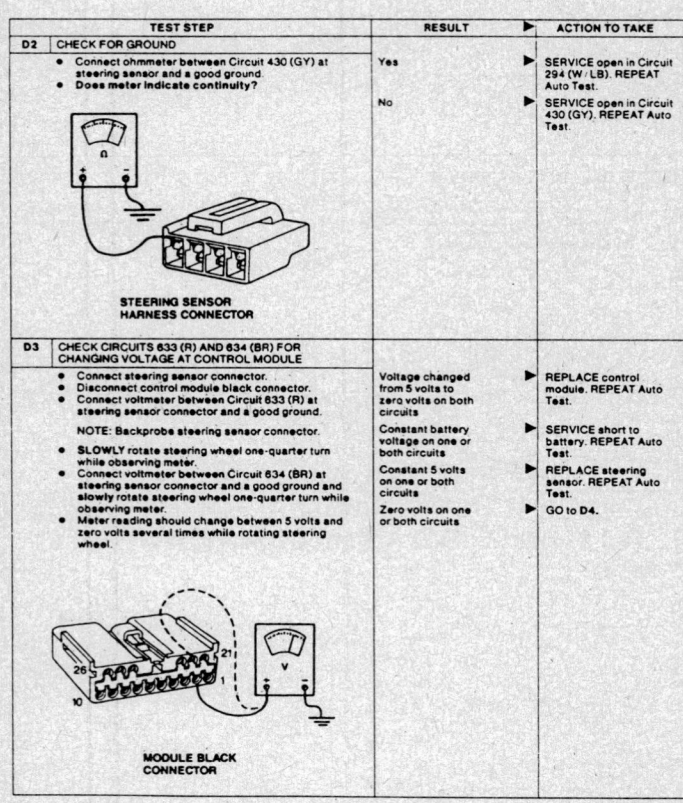

TEST STEP		RESULT	▶	ACTION TO TAKE
D2	CHECK FOR GROUND			
	• Connect ohmmeter between Circuit 430 (GY) at steering sensor and a good ground. • Does meter indicate continuity?	Yes	▶	SERVICE open in Circuit 294 (W/LB). REPEAT Auto Test.
		No	▶	SERVICE open in Circuit 430 (GY). REPEAT Auto Test.
D3	CHECK CIRCUITS 633 (R) AND 634 (BR) FOR CHANGING VOLTAGE AT CONTROL MODULE			
	• Connect steering sensor connector. • Disconnect control module black connector. • Connect voltmeter between Circuit 633 (R) at steering sensor connector and a good ground. NOTE: Backprobe steering sensor connector. • SLOWLY rotate steering wheel one-quarter turn while observing meter. • Connect voltmeter between Circuit 634 (BR) at steering sensor connector and a good ground and slowly rotate steering wheel one-quarter turn while observing meter. • Meter reading should change between 5 volts and zero volts several times while rotating steering wheel.	Voltage changed from 5 volts to zero volts on both circuits	▶	REPLACE control module. REPEAT Auto Test.
		Constant battery voltage on one or both circuits	▶	SERVICE short to battery. REPEAT Auto Test.
		Constant 5 volts on one or both circuits	▶	REPLACE steering sensor. REPEAT Auto Test.
		Zero volts on one or both circuits	▶	GO to D4.

FM2019100033020X

Fig. 9   Test D: Steering Sensor (Part 2 of 4)

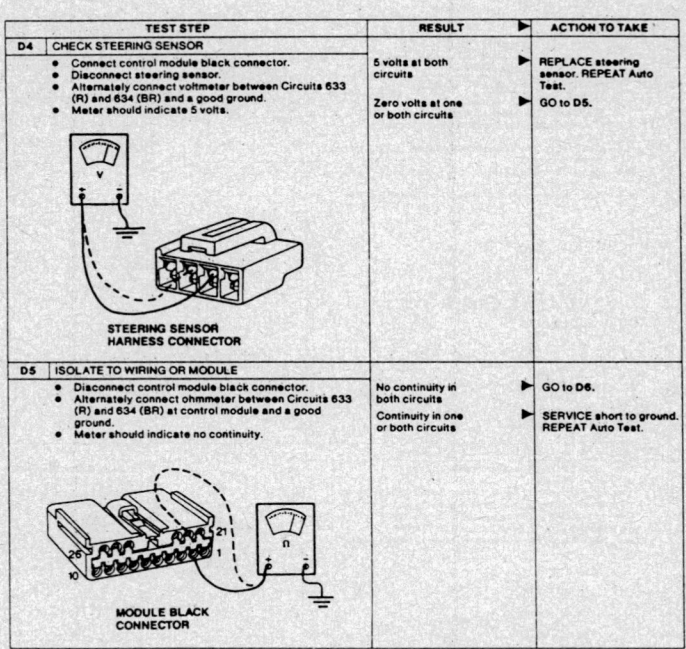

TEST STEP		RESULT	▶	ACTION TO TAKE
D4	CHECK STEERING SENSOR			
	• Connect control module black connector. • Disconnect steering sensor. • Alternately connect voltmeter between Circuits 633 (R) and 634 (BR) and a good ground. • Meter should indicate 5 volts.	5 volts at both circuits	▶	REPLACE steering sensor. REPEAT Auto Test.
		Zero volts at one or both circuits	▶	GO to D5.
D5	ISOLATE TO WIRING OR MODULE			
	• Disconnect control module black connector. • Alternately connect ohmmeter between Circuits 633 (R) and 634 (BR) at control module and a good ground. • Meter should indicate no continuity.	No continuity in both circuits	▶	GO to D6.
		Continuity in one or both circuits	▶	SERVICE short to ground. REPEAT Auto Test.

FM2019100033030X

Fig. 9   Test D: Steering Sensor (Part 3 of 4)

TEST STEP		RESULT	▶	ACTION TO TAKE
D6	CHECK FOR OPEN			
	• Connect ohmmeter between Circuit 633 (R) at control module black connector and steering sensor connector. • Connect ohmmeter between Circuit 634 (BR) at control module black connector and steering sensor connector.	Continuity in both circuits	▶	REPLACE control module. REPEAT Auto Test.
		No continuity in one or both circuits	▶	SERVICE open circuit(s). REPEAT Auto Test.

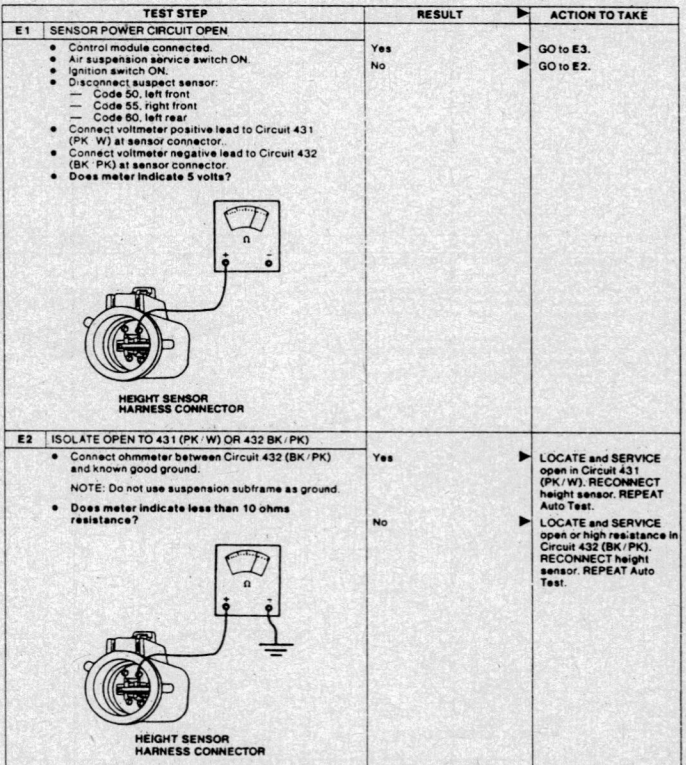

FM2019100033040X

Fig. 9   Test D: Steering Sensor (Part 4 of 4)

TEST STEP		RESULT	▶	ACTION TO TAKE
E1	SENSOR POWER CIRCUIT OPEN			
	• Control module connected. • Air suspension service switch ON. • Ignition switch ON. • Disconnect suspect sensor: — Code 50, left front — Code 55, right front — Code 60, left rear • Connect voltmeter positive lead to Circuit 431 (PK/W) at sensor connector. • Connect voltmeter negative lead to Circuit 432 (BK/PK) at sensor connector. • Does meter indicate 5 volts?	Yes	▶	GO to E3.
		No	▶	GO to E2.
E2	ISOLATE OPEN TO 431 (PK/W) OR 432 BK/PK)			
	• Connect ohmmeter between Circuit 432 (BK/PK) and known good ground. NOTE: Do not use suspension subframe as ground. • Does meter indicate less than 10 ohms resistance?	Yes	▶	LOCATE and SERVICE open in Circuit 431 (PK/W). RECONNECT height sensor. REPEAT Auto Test.
		No	▶	LOCATE and SERVICE open or high resistance in Circuit 432 (BK/PK). RECONNECT height sensor. REPEAT Auto Test.

FM2019100034010X

Fig. 10   Test E: Height Sensor Out Of Range (Part 1 of 5)

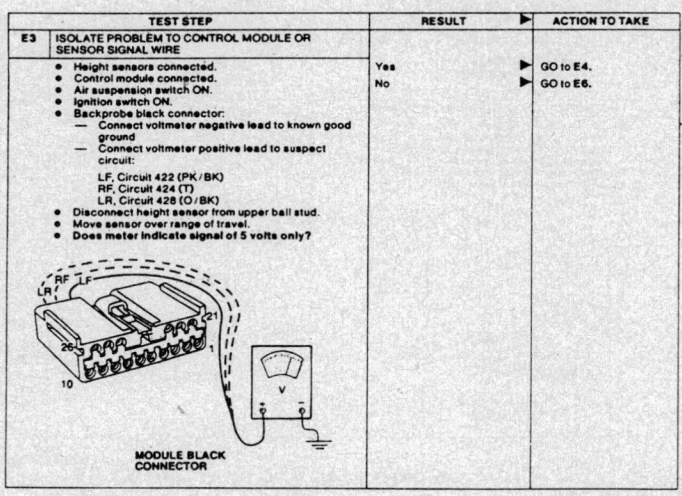

TEST STEP		RESULT	▶	ACTION TO TAKE
E3	**ISOLATE PROBLEM TO CONTROL MODULE OR SENSOR SIGNAL WIRE**			

• Height sensors connected.
 • Control module connected.
 • Air suspension switch ON.
 • Ignition switch ON.
 • Backprobe black connector:
 — Connect voltmeter negative lead to known good ground
 — Connect voltmeter positive lead to suspect circuit:
    LF, Circuit 422 (PK/BK)
    RF, Circuit 424 (T)
    LR, Circuit 428 (O/BK)
 • Disconnect height sensor from upper ball stud.
 • Move sensor over range of travel.
 • Does meter indicate signal of 5 volts only?
		Yes
		
		 No
			▶
			
			 ▶
				GO to E4.
				
				 GO to E6.

FM2019100034020X

Fig. 10 Test E: Height Sensor Out Of Range (Part 2 of 5)

TEST STEP		RESULT	▶	ACTION TO TAKE
E4	**ISOLATE SHORT TO MODULE OR HARNESS**			

• Disconnect black connector.
 • Connect voltmeter negative to known good ground.
 • Connect voltmeter positive to suspect signal circuit:
    LF, Circuit 422 (PK/BK)
    RF, Circuit 424 (T)
    LR, Circuit 428 (O/BK)
 • Does meter indicate zero volts?
		Yes
		
		 No
			▶
			
			 ▶
				REPLACE control module. REPEAT Auto Test.
				
				 GO to E5.

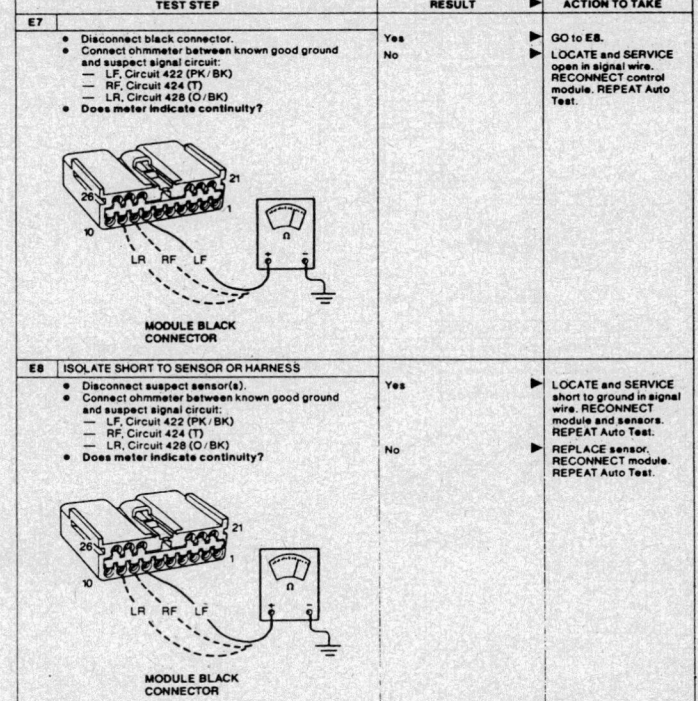

TEST STEP		RESULT	▶	ACTION TO TAKE
E5	**ISOLATE SHORT TO SENSOR POWER**			
• Disconnect black connector. • Connect voltmeter negative to known good ground. • Connect voltmeter positive to suspect signal circuit: — LF, Circuit 422 (PK/BK) — RF, Circuit 424 (T) — LR, Circuit 428 (O/BK) • Disconnect suspect height sensor connector. • Does meter indicate zero volts?		Yes No	▶ ▶	REPLACE suspect sensor. RECONNECT module. REPEAT Auto Test. LOCATE and SERVICE short to Circuit 431 (PK/W) or sensor signal circuit. RECONNECT sensor and module. REPEAT Auto Test.

FM2019100034030X

Fig. 10 Test E: Height Sensor Out Of Range (Part 3 of 5)

TEST STEP		RESULT	▶	ACTION TO TAKE
E6	**ISOLATE CONCERN TO CONTROL MODULE OR SENSOR SIGNAL WIRE**			

• Control module connected.
 • Air suspension switch ON.
 • Ignition switch ON.
 • Backprobe black connector:
 — Connect voltmeter negative lead to known good ground
 — Connect voltmeter positive lead to suspect circuit:
    LF, Circuit 422 (PK/BK)
    RF, Circuit 424 (T)
    LR, Circuit 428 (O/BK)
 • Disconnect height sensor from upper ball stud.
 • Move sensor over range of travel.
 • Does meter indicate signal varying from 0.5 to 4.5 volts?
		Yes
		
		 No
			▶
			
			 ▶
				REPLACE control module. REPEAT Auto Test.
				
				 GO to E7.

FM2019100034040X

Fig. 10 Test E: Height Sensor Out Of Range (Part 4 of 5)

TEST STEP		RESULT	▶	ACTION TO TAKE
E7				
• Disconnect black connector. • Connect ohmmeter between known good ground and suspect signal circuit: — LF, Circuit 422 (PK/BK) — RF, Circuit 424 (T) — LR, Circuit 428 (O/BK) • Does meter indicate continuity?		Yes No	▶ ▶	GO to E8. LOCATE and SERVICE open in signal wire. RECONNECT control module. REPEAT Auto Test.

TEST STEP		RESULT	▶	ACTION TO TAKE
E8	**ISOLATE SHORT TO SENSOR OR HARNESS**			
• Disconnect suspect sensor(s). • Connect ohmmeter between known good ground and suspect signal circuit: — LF, Circuit 422 (PK/BK) — RF, Circuit 424 (T) — LR, Circuit 428 (O/BK) • Does meter indicate continuity?		Yes No	▶ ▶	LOCATE and SERVICE short to ground in signal wire. RECONNECT module and sensors. REPEAT Auto Test. REPLACE sensor. RECONNECT module. REPEAT Auto Test.

FM2019100034050X

Fig. 10 Test E: Height Sensor Out Of Range (Part 5 of 5)

TEST STEP	RESULT	▶	ACTION TO TAKE
F1 CHECK VENT SOLENOID CONNECTOR FOR DISCONNECT OR DAMAGE	No	▶	GO to F2.
• Turn air suspension service switch OFF. • Make sure compressor assembly connector is firmly seated and not damaged. • Disconnect compressor assembly connectors and check terminals for damage, corrosion or push-out. • Are connectors worn or damaged?	Yes	▶	SERVICE or REPLACE as required. REPEAT Auto Test.
F2 CHECK VENT SOLENOID FOR OPEN	Yes	▶	GO to F3.
• Connect ohmmeter across vent solenoid terminals Circuits 421 (BL) and 430 (W). • Is resistance 19-24 ohms?	No	▶	REPLACE compressor assembly. REPEAT Auto Test.

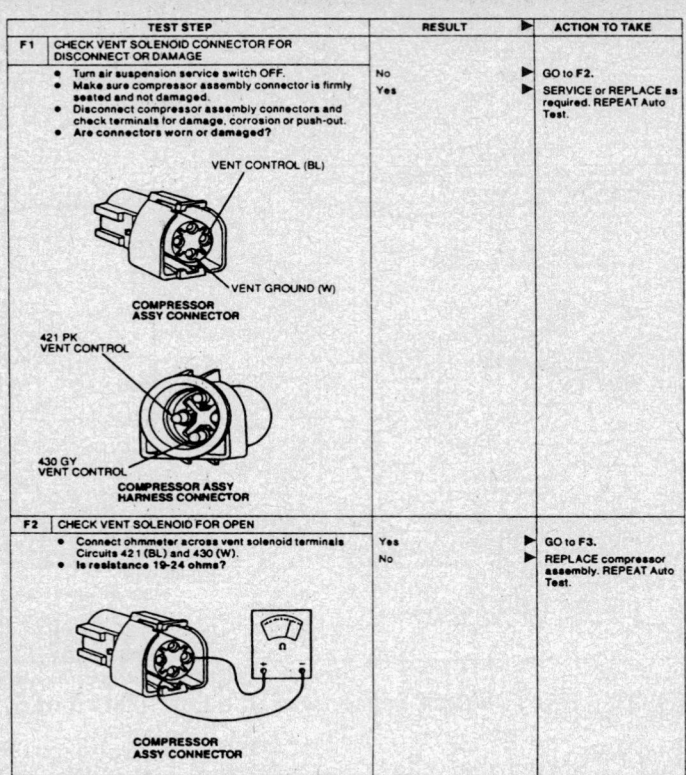

Fig. 11   Test F: Vent Solenoid (Part 1 of 4)

FM2019100035010X

TEST STEP	RESULT	▶	ACTION TO TAKE
F3 CHECK CIRCUIT 430 (GY) FOR OPEN	Yes	▶	GO to F4.
• Connect ohmmeter between vent solenoid Circuit 430 (GY) at compressor harness connector and a good ground. • Does meter indicate continuity?	No	▶	LOCATE and SERVICE open in Circuit 430 (GY). REPEAT Auto Test.
F4 CHECK CIRCUIT 421 (PK) FOR SHORT TO BATTERY	Yes	▶	GO to F5.
• Turn air suspension service switch OFF. • Disconnect air compressor connector. • Disconnect control module gray connector. • Connect voltmeter between Circuit 421 (PK) at module gap connector and a good ground. • Does indicator read zero volts?	No	▶	LOCATE and SERVICE short to battery in Circuit 421 (PK). REPEAT Auto Test.

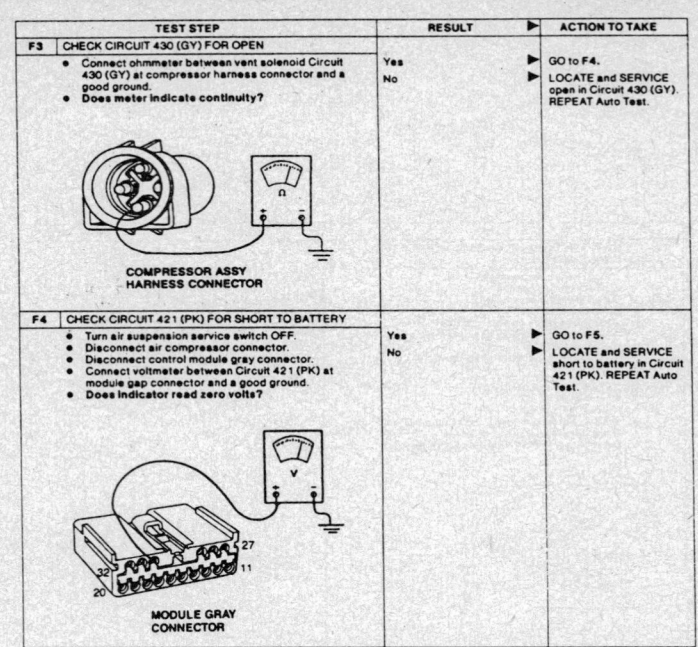

Fig. 11   Test F: Vent Solenoid (Part 2 of 4)

FM2019100035020X

TEST STEP	RESULT	▶	ACTION TO TAKE
F5 ISOLATE FAULT TO HARNESS	Yes	▶	LOCATE and SERVICE short to ground in Circuit 421 (PK). REPEAT Auto Test.
• Disconnect control module gray connector. • Connect an ohmmeter between Circuit 421 (PK) at control module gray connector and a good ground. • Does meter indicate continuity?	No	▶	GO to F6.
F6 CHECK CIRCUIT 421 (PK) FOR OPEN	Yes	▶	GO to F7.
• Disconnect control module gray connector. • Connect ohmmeter between Circuit 421 (PK) at control module gray connector and air compressor connector. • Does meter indicate continuity?	No	▶	LOCATE and SERVICE open in Circuit 421 (PK). REPEAT Auto Test.

Fig. 11   Test F: Vent Solenoid (Part 3 of 4)

FM2019100035030X

TEST STEP	RESULT	▶	ACTION TO TAKE
F7 TEST CONTROL MODULE OUTPUT TO SOLENOID	Yes	▶	REPLACE vent solenoid. REPEAT Auto Test.
• Control module connected. • Air suspension service switch OFF. • Ignition switch ON. • Backprobe gray module connector: — Connect voltmeter positive lead to Circuit 421 (PK) — Connect voltmeter negative lead to known good ground • Run vent function test 213, 215, 217 or 219. • Observe output to solenoid with meter. • Does output pulse to solenoid?	No	▶	REPLACE control module. REPEAT Auto Test.

Fig. 11   Test F: Vent Solenoid (Part 4 of 4)

FM2019100035040X

TEST STEP	RESULT	▶	ACTION TO TAKE
GA1 CHECK CIRCUIT 175 (BK/Y) FOR OPEN	Yes	▶	GO to GA2.
• Turn air suspension service switch OFF. • Ignition switch ON. WARNING: THE AIR COMPRESSOR RELAY CAN GET EXTREMELY HOT DURING OPERATION. USE CARE WHEN HANDLING THE RELAY. • Remove air compressor relay connector. • Connect voltmeter between Circuit 175 (BK/Y) at relay connector and a good ground. • Does meter indicate battery voltage?	No	▶	LOCATE and SERVICE open in Circuit 175 (BK/Y). REPEAT Auto Test. NOTE: Circuit 175 (BK/Y) starts at air compressor fuse in power distribution box.

Fig. 12   Test GA: Compressor Relay Control Circuit (Part 1 of 4)

FM2019100036010X

TEST STEP	RESULT	►	ACTION TO TAKE
GA2 CHECK CIRCUIT 420 (DB/Y) FOR OPEN			
• Turn air suspension service switch OFF. • Ignition switch ON. • Connect voltmeter between Circuit 420 (DB/Y) at relay connector and a good ground. • Note meter reading.	12 volts 0 volts 2-4 volts Note: 2-4 volts is normal feedback voltage from module to open Circuit 420.	► ► ►	LEAVE meter connected. GO to GA5. GO to GA3. GO to GA4.
GA3 SHORT TO GROUND CIRCUIT 420			
• Disconnect module gray connector. • Connect ohmmeter between Circuit 420 (DB/Y) at relay connector and known good ground. • Does meter indicate continuity?	Yes No	►	LOCATE and SERVICE short to ground in Circuit 420 (DB/Y). REPEAT Auto Test. LOCATE and SERVICE open in Circuit 420 (DB/Y).

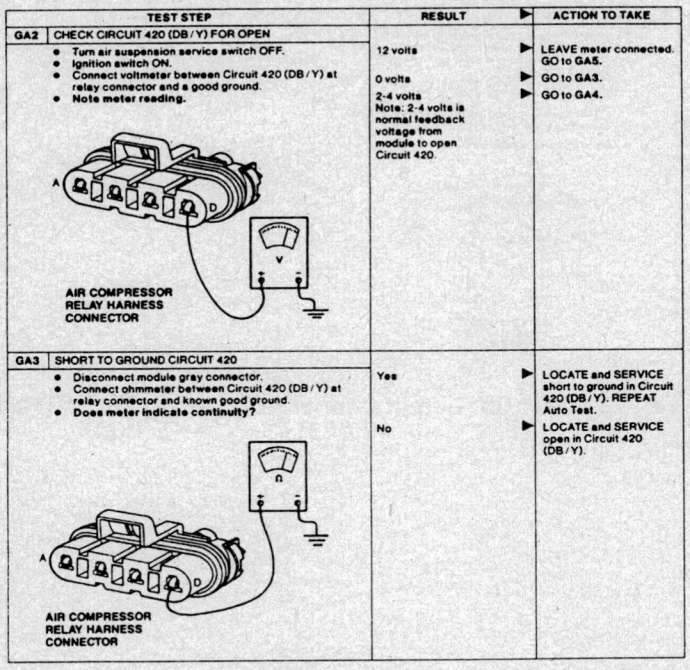

FM2019100036020X

Fig. 12   Test GA: Compressor Relay Control Circuit (Part 2 of 4)

TEST STEP	RESULT	►	ACTION TO TAKE
GA4 CHECK CIRCUIT 430 (GY) FOR CONTINUITY TO GROUND			
• Connect ohmmeter between Circuit 430 (GY) at compressor relay connector and a good ground. • Does meter indicate continuity?	Yes No	►	GO to GA6. LOCATE and SERVICE open to ground in Circuit 430 (GY).
GA5 CIRCUIT 420 (DB/Y) FOR SHORT TO BATTERY			
• Disconnect control module gray connector. • Connect voltmeter between Circuit 420 (DB/Y) at control module gray connector and a good ground. • Does meter indicate zero volts?	Yes No	►	GO to GA6. LOCATE and SERVICE short to battery in Circuit 420 (DB/Y). REPEAT Auto Test.

FM2019100036030X

Fig. 12   Test GA: Compressor Relay Control Circuit (Part 3 of 4)

TEST STEP	RESULT	►	ACTION TO TAKE
GA6 CHECK COMPRESSOR RELAY			
• Reconnect compressor assembly connector. • Using a fused (30 amp) jumper, jumper Circuit 417 to 175. This should apply battery voltage to Circuit 417 (P/O). • The compressor should run when Circuit 417 is jumpered to Circuit 175. NOTE: Compressor assembly connector must be connected to perform this test step. • Does air compressor run?	Yes No	►	REPLACE relay. REPEAT Auto Test. GO to GB1.

FM2019100036040X

Fig. 12   Test GA: Compressor Relay Control Circuit (Part 4 of 4)

TEST STEP	RESULT	►	ACTION TO TAKE
GB1 THERMAL OVERLOAD OPEN CIRCUIT 417 (P/O) SHORT TO BATTERY			
WARNING: THE AIR COMPRESSOR RELAY CAN BECOME EXTREMELY HOT DURING OPERATION. USE CARE WHEN HANDLING THE RELAY. NOTE: Diagnostic Trouble Code 98 may indicate that the air compressor has been running continuously. The compressor has a built-in thermal limiter. If the compressor gets too hot, the thermal limiter will open. Disconnect compressor assembly harness connector. Allow time for the compressor to cool down before performing this pinpoint test. • Reconnect compressor harness assembly connector. • Turn air suspension service switch OFF. • Remove air compressor relay. • Turn air suspension service switch ON. • Does air compressor run?	Yes No	►	LOCATE and SERVICE short to battery in Circuit 417 (P/O). REPEAT Auto Test. GO to GB2.
GB2 CHECK COMPRESSOR CONNECTORS			
• Visually inspect compressor assembly connector. • Disconnect connector and inspect both halves of connector for terminal pushout, corrosion or damage. • Are connectors OK?	Yes No	►	GO to GB3. SERVICE connectors as required. REPEAT Auto Test.

FM2019100037010X

Fig. 13   Test GB: Compressor Electrical Diagnostics (Part 1 of 3)

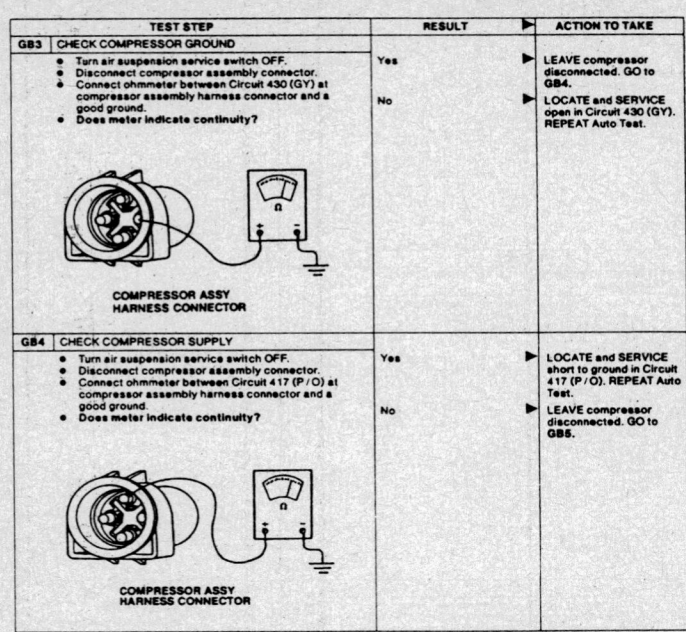

TEST STEP	RESULT	▶	ACTION TO TAKE
GB3 CHECK COMPRESSOR GROUND			
• Turn air suspension service switch OFF. • Disconnect compressor assembly connector. • Connect ohmmeter between Circuit 430 (GY) at compressor assembly harness connector and a good ground. • Does meter indicate continuity?	Yes No	▶ ▶	LEAVE compressor disconnected. GO to GB4. LOCATE and SERVICE open in Circuit 430 (GY). REPEAT Auto Test.
GB4 CHECK COMPRESSOR SUPPLY			
• Turn air suspension service switch OFF. • Disconnect compressor assembly connector. • Connect ohmmeter between Circuit 417 (P/O) at compressor assembly harness connector and a good ground. • Does meter indicate continuity?	Yes No	▶ ▶	LOCATE and SERVICE short to ground in Circuit 417 (P/O). REPEAT Auto Test. LEAVE compressor disconnected. GO to GB5.

FM2019100037020X

Fig. 13   Test GB: Compressor Electrical Diagnostics (Part 2 of 3)

TEST STEP	RESULT	▶	ACTION TO TAKE
GB5 CHECK COMPRESSOR RELAY			
• Reconnect compressor assembly connector. • Using a fused (30 amp) jumper, jumper Circuit 417 to Circuit 175. This should apply battery voltage to Circuit 417 (P/O). • The compressor should run when Circuit 417 is jumpered to Circuit 175. NOTE: Compressor assembly connector must be connected to perform this test step. • Does air compressor run?	Yes No	▶ ▶	Compressor OK. RETURN to original test. REPLACE compressor assembly. RETURN to original test.

FM2019100037030X

Fig. 13   Test GB: Compressor Electrical Diagnostics (Part 3 of 3)

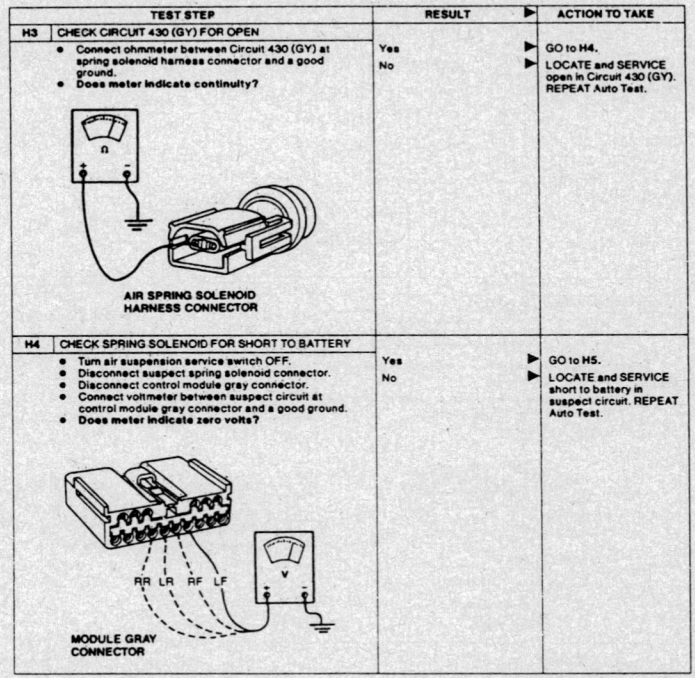

TEST STEP	RESULT	▶	ACTION TO TAKE
H1 CHECK SPRING SOLENOID CONNECTOR FOR DISCONNECT OR DAMAGE			
• Turn air suspension service switch OFF. • Disconnect spring solenoids and connectors and check terminals for damage, corrosion or push-out. • Make sure spring solenoid connectors are firmly seated and not damaged. • Are connectors/solenoids worn or damaged?	No Yes	▶ ▶	GO to H2. SERVICE or REPLACE as required. REPEAT Auto Test.
H2 CHECK SPRING SOLENOID FOR OPEN			
• Connect ohmmeter across spring solenoid terminals. • Is resistance between 14-18 ohms?	Yes No	▶ ▶	GO to H3. REPLACE spring solenoid. REPEAT Auto Test.

FM2019100038010X

Fig. 14   Test H: Spring Solenoids (Part 1 of 4)

TEST STEP	RESULT	▶	ACTION TO TAKE
H3 CHECK CIRCUIT 430 (GY) FOR OPEN			
• Connect ohmmeter between Circuit 430 (GY) at spring solenoid harness connector and a good ground. • Does meter indicate continuity?	Yes No	▶ ▶	GO to H4. LOCATE and SERVICE open in Circuit 430 (GY). REPEAT Auto Test.
H4 CHECK SPRING SOLENOID FOR SHORT TO BATTERY			
• Turn air suspension service switch OFF. • Disconnect suspect spring solenoid connector. • Disconnect control module gray connector. • Connect voltmeter between suspect circuit at control module gray connector and a good ground. • Does meter indicate zero volts?	Yes No	▶ ▶	GO to H5. LOCATE and SERVICE short to battery in suspect circuit. REPEAT Auto Test.

FM2019100038020X

Fig. 14   Test H: Spring Solenoids (Part 2 of 4)

TEST STEP	RESULT	▶	ACTION TO TAKE
H5 CHECK SOLENOID CIRCUITS FOR SHORT TO GROUND			
• Disconnect control module gray connector. • Connect ohmmeter between suspect circuit at control module gray connector and a good ground. • Does meter indicate continuity?	Yes	▶	LOCATE and SERVICE short to ground in suspect circuit. REPEAT Auto Test.
	No	▶	GO to H6.
H6 CHECK SPRING SOLENOID-TO-CONTROL MODULE CIRCUIT FOR OPEN			
• Disconnect control module gray connector. • Connect ohmmeter between suspect circuit at control module gray connector and spring solenoid harness connector. • Does meter indicate continuity?	Yes	▶	GO to H7.
	No	▶	LOCATE and SERVICE open in suspect circuit. REPEAT Auto Test.

FM2019100038030X

Fig. 14   Test H: Spring Solenoids (Part 3 of 4)

TEST STEP	RESULT	▶	ACTION TO TAKE
H7 TEST CONTROL MODULE OUTPUT TO SOLENOID			

• Control module connected.
• Air suspension service switch OFF.
• Ignition switch ON
• Backprobe gray module connector:
— Connect voltmeter positive lead to suspect circuit:
  LF, Circuit 415 (LG/O)
  RF, Circuit 414 (O/R)
  LR, Circuit 429 (P/LG)
  RR, Circuit 416 (LB/BK)
— Connect voltmeter negative lead to known good ground.
• Execute pump or vent function test for suspect solenoid:
— 212: Pump LF
— 213: Vent LF
— 214: Pump RF
— 215: Vent RF
— 216: Pump LR
— 217: Vent LR
— 218: Pump RR
— 219: Vent RR
• Observe output to solenoid with meter.
• Does output pulse to solenoid?
	Yes	▶	REPLACE spring solenoid. REPEAT Auto Test.

	No	▶	REPLACE control module. REPEAT Auto Test.

FM2019100038040X

Fig. 14   Test H: Spring Solenoids (Part 4 of 4)

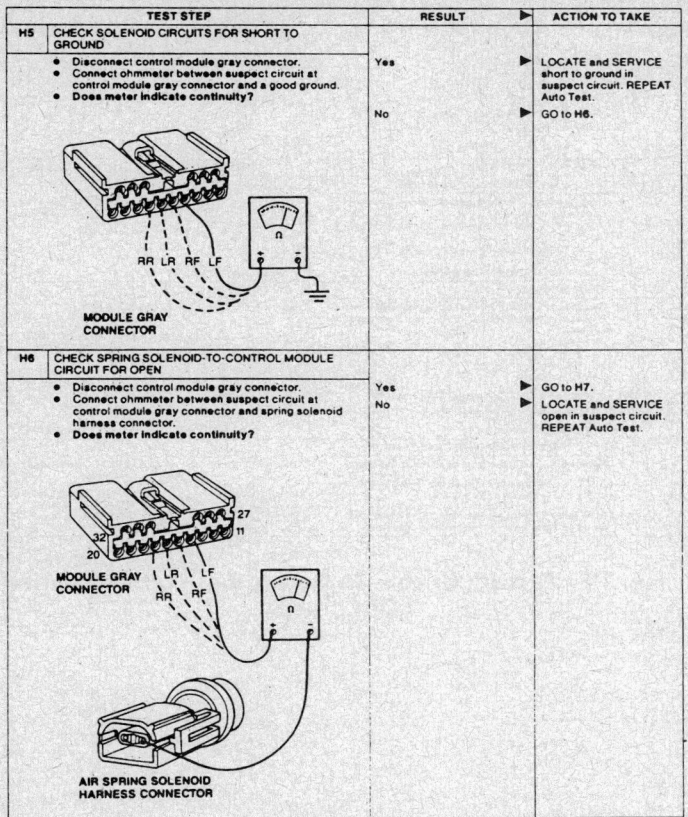

TEST STEP	RESULT	▶	ACTION TO TAKE
I1 ENCOUNTERED DURING FUNCTION TEST			
• Function tests are manual start and manual stop commanded. If the function tests controlling compressor function are used for long periods or in rapid succession of ON/OFF cycles a code 98 may be generated. • Function Tests: — 212-LF Pump — 214-RF Pump — 216-LR Pump — 218-RR Pump — 221-Compressor Run • Has a code 98 been generated during function testing?	Yes	▶	HALT function testing. ALLOW compressor to cool and protective timer to reset.
I2 RETRIEVED FROM MEMORY WHEN FUNCTION TEST 211 WAS RUN			
• Function test 211 is executed as the first step in all service procedures. • Run Auto Test. • Was code 98 retrieved from memory?	Yes	▶	GO to JB1 and execute procedures through JB4 to determine cause.

FM2019100039000X

Fig. 15   Test I: Compressor Run Time Exceeded

TEST STEP	RESULT	▶	ACTION TO TAKE
J1 INSPECT VEHICLE			
• Look for corners sitting obviously lower or higher than trim height.	Low	▶	SERVICE first. GO to J2.
	High	▶	SERVICE second. GO to J3.
	All corners sitting at about trim height	▶	GO to J4.
J2 PUMP LOW CORNER(S)			
• Air suspension service switch OFF. • Run appropriate function test to pump suspect corner: — Test 212-LF — Test 214-RF — Test 216-LR — Test 218-RR NOTE: If air spring is at very low pressure, it may take 1 to 1.5 minutes for spring to raise. • Can you hear compressor run or feel compressor vibration in RH front fender?	Yes	▶	OBSERVE if vehicle corner begins to raise. If no, GO to JB1. If yes, GO to JA1.
	No	▶	GO to GA6 for compressor relay and compressor assembly electrical diagnostics.
J3 VENT HIGH CORNERS			
• Air suspension service switch OFF. • Enter appropriate function test to vent high air spring: — Test 213-LF — Test 215-RF — Test 217-LR — Test 219-RR NOTE: If air spring is at very high pressure it may take up to 1 minute for corner to begin to lower. • Does corner go down?	Yes	▶	GO to JA1. SUSPECT height sensor concern.
	No	▶	GO to JC1.

FM2019100040000X

Fig. 16   Test J: Unable To Detect Raising Or Lowering Of Corners

TEST STEP	RESULT	▶	ACTION TO TAKE
JA1 INSPECT VEHICLE			
• Air suspension service switch OFF. • Vehicle over lubrication pit or on alignment rack. • Inspect height sensors. • Are ball stud brackets damaged or are height sensors off ball studs?	Yes	▶	REPLACE ball stud brackets. TIGHTEN loose brackets. REINSTALL height sensors on ball studs. RETURN to original test.
	No	▶	GO to JA2.
JA2 TEST FOR OPEN HEIGHT SENSOR GROUND			
• Air suspension service switch OFF. • Disconnect accessible end of height sensor from ball stud. • Enter function test for trim detection, audible output for suspect height sensor(s): — Test 223-LF — Test 224-RF — Test 225-LR • Slowly move sensor over full range of travel. (Full stroke in about 5 seconds). • Does frequency of tone pulses remain constant?	Yes	▶	LOCATE and SERVICE open ground Circuit 432 (BK/PK). REPEAT the test.
	No	▶	NOTE change in tone. Steady tone indicates trim length of sensor. REINSTALL sensor to ball stud. RETURN to original test.

FM2019100041000X

Fig. 17   Test JA: Unable To Detect Raising Or Lowering Of Corners

TEST STEP	RESULT	▶	ACTION TO TAKE
JB1 PINCHED, KINKED OR BLOCKED AIR LINES			
• Disconnect air line from drier canister for suspect air spring. • Disconnect air line from spring solenoid at suspect air spring. • Attach hand vacuum pump to air line at drier end. • Draw vacuum. • Can a vacuum be drawn and held?	Yes	▶	LOCATE and SERVICE kink or pinch in air line. NOTE: It may be faster to simply replace air line.
	No	▶	GO to JB2.
JB2 OPEN IN AIR LINE			
• Reinstall suspect air line to air spring. • Remove air line of known good air spring from drier and attach vacuum pump. • Pull vacuum. • Can vacuum be drawn and held?	Yes	▶	GO to JB3.
	No	▶	LOCATE and SERVICE open in air line. REPEAT Auto Test.
JB3 CHECK SPRING SOLENOID			
• Attach shop air supply to drier end of air line to suspect spring assembly. • Enter function test to open suspect spring solenoid: — Test 213-LF — Test 215-RF — Test 217-LR — Test 219-RR • Inflate air spring to full up travel. • Does air flow into suspect air spring and are no leaks detected?	Yes	▶	GO to JB4.
	No	▶	REPLACE air spring solenoid or leaking air spring. RESTORE system. REPEAT Auto Test.

FM2019100042010X

Fig. 18   Test JB: Unable To Detect Raising Or Lowering Of Corners (Part 1 of 2)

TEST STEP		RESULT	▶	ACTION TO TAKE
JB4	CHECK COMPRESSOR FOR OUTPUT AND LEAKS			
• Remove RF air spring line at spring solenoid. • Connect line to pressure gauge having at least a 200 psi range. • Run Function Test 221. • Within 30 seconds, pressure gauge should reach at least 130 psi. • Halt Function Test 221. • Pressure gauge should hold pressure reading until relieved by vent (Function Test 213, 215, 217 or 219) or until gauge is disconnected. • **Does compressor output reach and hold minimum 130 psi?**		Reaches 130 psi, does not hold. Does not reach 130 psi.	▶ ▶	LOCATE and SERVICE leak in drier. REPLACE Compressor Assembly.
JB5	ALL CORNERS EVEN AND AT ABOUT TRIM HEIGHT			

• Air suspension service switch OFF.
• Run function tests to alternately pump and vent each corner in succession:
  — Test 212-LF Pump
  — Test 213-LF Vent
  — Test 214-RF Pump
  — Test 215-RF Vent
  — Test 216-LR Pump
  — Test 217-LR Vent
  — Test 218-RR Pump
  — Test 219-RR Vent
• **Note corner(s) responses.**
		Corner(s) go down but not up.
		
		Corner(s) go up but not down.
			▶
			
			▶
				GO to JA1.
				
				GO to JC1.

FM2019100042020X

Fig. 18   Test JB: Unable To Detect Raising Or Lowering Of Corners (Part 2 of 2)

TEST STEP		RESULT	▶	ACTION TO TAKE
JC1	PINCHED, KINKED OR BLOCKED AIR LINE			
• Disconnect air line of suspect air spring from drier canister. • Disconnect air line of suspect air spring from spring solenoid. • Attach hand vacuum pump to air line at drier end. • Draw vacuum. • **Can vacuum be drawn and held?**		Yes No	▶ ▶	LOCATE and SERVICE kink or pinch in air line. GO to JC2.
JC2	VENT AIR SPRING			

• Disconnect air line from suspect air spring solenoid.
• Enter appropriate function test to vent suspect air spring:
  — Test 213-LF
  — Test 215-RF
  — Test 217-LR
  — Test 219-RR
 	
  NOTE: Expect air spring to vent rapidly, lowering the vehicle rapidly.
 	
• **Does air spring vent?**
		Yes
		
		No
			▶
			
			▶
				GO to JC3.
				
				REPLACE air spring solenoid. RESTORE system. REPEAT Auto Test.

JC3	CHECK DRIER AND COMPRESSOR ASSEMBLY			
• Remove drier canister from compressor assembly. NOTE: Do not lose or damage the O-ring on the nose of the drier canister. • Blow shop air through disconnected air line port. • **Does air flow freely through drier canister?**		Yes No	▶ ▶	REPLACE compressor assembly. REPLACE drier canister. RESTORE system. REPEAT Auto Test.

FM2019100043000X

Fig. 19   Test JC: Unable To Detect Raising Or Lowering Of Corners

TEST STEP		RESULT	▶	ACTION TO TAKE
KA1	RECHECK PROCEDURE			
• Recheck SUPER STAR II switch settings • Check that air suspension service switch is ON. • Repeat Auto Test. • If SUPER STAR II Tester continuously displays Functional Test Codes 211 through 228, control module Pin 4 is not at ground because of a damaged air suspension service switch or a fault in the switch circuits.		No Star codes displayed Diagnostic Trouble Codes 221, 222, 223, 235 and 245 displayed	▶ ▶	GO to KA2. GO to KA7.

FM2019100044010X

Fig. 20   Test KA: Unable To Enter Auto Test (Part 1 of 5)

TEST STEP		RESULT	▶	ACTION TO TAKE
KA4	CHECK CIRCUIT 419 (DG/LG) FOR SHORT TO GROUND			
• Connect voltmeter between Circuit 419 (DG/LG) at control module gray connector and a good ground. • **Does meter indicate 6 volts?**		Yes No	▶ ▶	GO to KB5. GO to KA5.

MODULE GRAY CONNECTOR

KA5	ISOLATE TO HARNESS OR MESSAGE CENTER			
• Disconnect message center 16-pin connector.		Yes No	▶ ▶	Message center is damaged. SERVICE as required. LOCATE and SERVICE short to ground in Circuit 419 (DG/LG).

MESSAGE CENTER 16-PIN CONNECTOR   F7634-A

• Connect ohmmeter between Circuit 419 (DG/LG) at control module gray connector and a good ground.
• **Does meter indicate no continuity?**

NOTE: A short to ground in Circuit 419 (DG/LG) will cause CHECK AIR RIDE to be displayed on message center even if no air suspension damage exists.

MODULE GRAY CONNECTOR

FM2019100044030X

Fig. 20   Test KA: Unable To Enter Auto Test (Part 3 of 5)

TEST STEP		RESULT	▶	ACTION TO TAKE
KA2	CHECK CONTROL MODULE FOR BATTERY VOLTAGE			
• Disconnect control module black connector. • Turn ignition to RUN position. • Connect voltmeter between Circuit 418 (DG/Y) at control module black connector and a good ground. • **Does meter indicate battery voltage at both circuits?**		Yes No	▶ ▶	GO to KA3. LOCATE and SERVICE open in circuit(s). REPEAT Auto Test.

MODULE BLACK CONNECTOR

KA3	CHECK CONTROL MODULE GROUNDS			
• Disconnect control module gray connector. • Connect ohmmeter between each 430 (GY) circuit at control module gray connector and a good ground. • **Does meter indicate continuity?**		Yes No	▶ ▶	GO to KA4. LOCATE and SERVICE open in circuit 430 (GY). REPEAT Auto Test.

MODULE GRAY CONNECTOR

FM2019100044020X

Fig. 20   Test KA: Unable To Enter Auto Test (Part 2 of 5)

	TEST STEP	RESULT	▶	ACTION TO TAKE
KA6	CHECK DIAGNOSTIC CONNECTOR (DATA LINK CONNECTOR (DLC)) CIRCUITS FOR CONTINUITY • Use an ohmmeter to check continuity of Circuit 419 (DG/LG) between control module gray connector and diagnostic connector (data link connector (DLC)) and Circuits 430 (GY) and 806 (W/LB) between control module black connector and diagnostic connector (data link connector (DLC)). • Does meter indicate continuity on all circuits?	Yes No	▶ ▶	GO to KA7. SERVICE open in suspect circuit(s). REPEAT Auto Test.

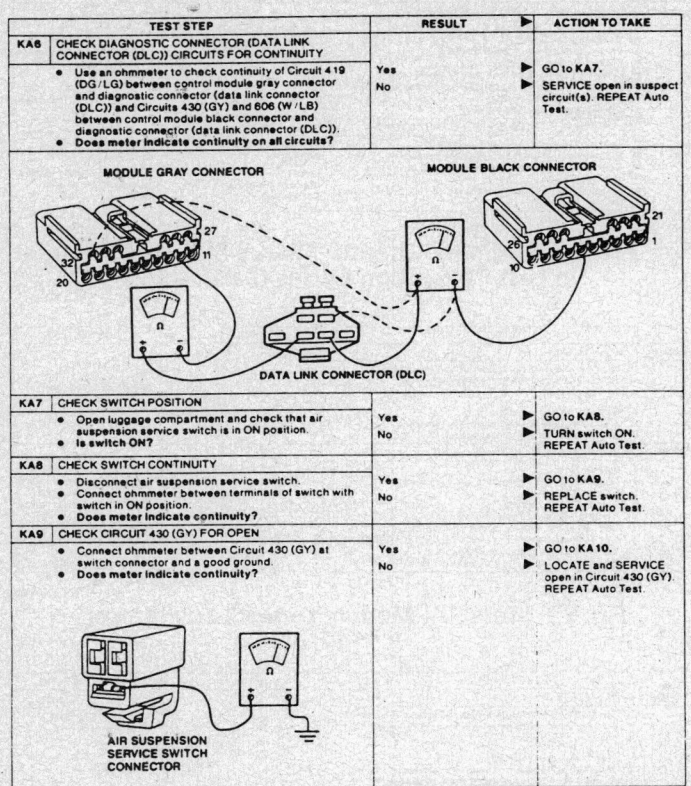

	TEST STEP	RESULT	▶	ACTION TO TAKE
KA7	CHECK SWITCH POSITION • Open luggage compartment and check that air suspension service switch is in ON position. • Is switch ON?	Yes No	▶ ▶	GO to KA8. TURN switch ON. REPEAT Auto Test.
KA8	CHECK SWITCH CONTINUITY • Disconnect air suspension service switch. • Connect ohmmeter between terminals of switch with switch in ON position. • Does meter indicate continuity?	Yes No	▶ ▶	GO to KA9. REPLACE switch. REPEAT Auto Test.
KA9	CHECK CIRCUIT 430 (GY) FOR OPEN • Connect ohmmeter between Circuit 430 (GY) at switch connector and a good ground. • Does meter indicate continuity?	Yes No	▶ ▶	GO to KA10. LOCATE and SERVICE open in Circuit 430 (GY). REPEAT Auto Test.

FM2019100044040X

Fig. 20　Test KA: Unable To Enter Auto Test (Part 4 of 5)

	TEST STEP	RESULT	▶	ACTION TO TAKE
KA10	CHECK CIRCUIT 425 (BR·PK) FOR OPEN • Disconnect control module gray connector. • Connect ohmmeter between Circuit 425 (BR·PK) at control module gray connector and air suspension service switch connector. • Does meter indicate continuity?	Yes No	▶ ▶	GO to KB5. LOCATE and SERVICE open in Circuit 425 (BR/PK). REPEAT Auto Test.

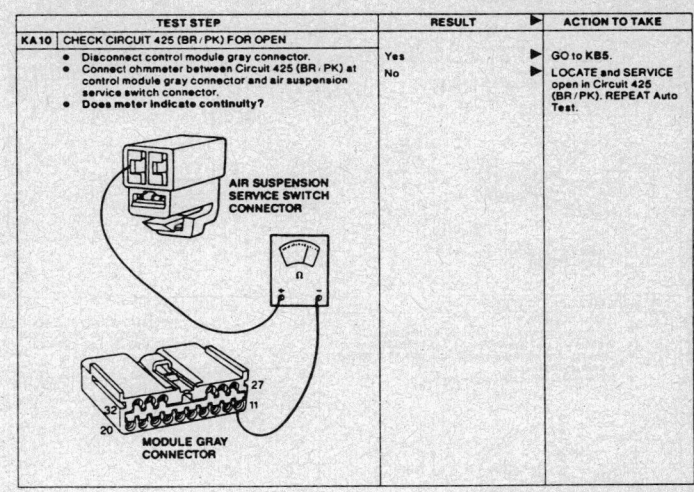

FM2019100044050X

Fig. 20　Test KA: Unable To Enter Auto Test (Part 5 of 5)

	TEST STEP	RESULT	▶	ACTION TO TAKE
KB1	NO CODES DISPLAYED, AUTO TEST IS RUNNING • Auto Test is running: 　— Solenoids can be heard clicking, compressor running and air venting • Does message Center display "Check Air Ride".	Yes No	▶ ▶	GO to KB2. GO to KB4.

FM2019100045010X

Fig. 21　Test KB: No Codes Displayed While Auto Test Is Running (Part 1 of 4)

	TEST STEP	RESULT	▶	ACTION TO TAKE
KB2	STO SHORT TO GROUND • Ignition OFF. • Star Tester in place. • Disconnect control module gray connector. • Connect ohmmeter between Circuit 419 (DG/LG) at Pin 12 and a known good ground. • Does meter indicate continuity?	Yes No	▶ ▶	LOCATE and SERVICE short to ground of Circuit 419. REPEAT Auto Test. GO to KB3.
KB3	STO OPEN • Ignition OFF. • Disconnect Star Tester. • Disconnect control module gray connector. • Connect ohmmeter between gray connector Pin 12 and STO Circuit 419 (DG/LG) at diagnostic connector. • Does meter indicate continuity?	Yes No	▶ ▶	GO to KB4. LOCATE and SERVICE open in Circuit 419 (DG/LG). REPEAT Auto Test.

FM2019100045020X

Fig. 21　Test KB: No Codes Displayed While Auto Test Is Running (Part 2 of 4)

	TEST STEP	RESULT	▶	ACTION TO TAKE
KB4	STO SHORT TO BATTERY POSITIVE • Ignition OFF. • Disconnect SUPER STAR II Tester. • Disconnect control module gray connector. • Connect voltmeter positive lead to Pin 12 socket of gray connector (Circuit 419 (DG/LG)). • Connect voltmeter negative lead to known good ground. • Does meter indicate battery voltage?	Yes No	▶ ▶	LOCATE and SERVICE short to battery positive in Circuit 419 (DG/LG). REPEAT Auto Test. GO to KB5.
KB5	CHECK IGNITION SWITCH SIGNAL • Control module black connector disconnected. • Ignition switch ON. • Connect voltmeter positive lead to Circuit 294 (W/LB) at Pin 4. • Connect voltmeter negative lead to known good ground. • Does meter indicate battery voltage?	Yes No	▶ ▶	REPLACE control module. REPEAT Auto Test. GO to KB6.
KB6	NO VOLTAGE SEEN ON CIRCUIT 298 (P/O) • Ignition switch off. • Inspect fuse 10 in fuse module. • Is fuse open?	Yes No	▶ ▶	GO to KB7. GO to OA1.

FM2019100045030X

Fig. 21　Test KB: No Codes Displayed While Auto Test Is Running (Part 3 of 4)

TEST STEP	RESULT	▶	ACTION TO TAKE
KB7 FUSE 10 OPEN			
• Ignition switch OFF. • Control module black connector disconnected. • Connect ohmmeter between Circuit 294 (W/LB) and known good ground. • Does meter indicate continuity?	Yes No	▶ ▶	GO to KB8. REPLACE control module. REPEAT Auto Test.
KB8 ISOLATE SHORT TO GROUND			
• Ignition switch OFF. • Control module black connector disconnected. • Disconnect steering sensor harness connection. • Connect ohmmeter between Circuit 294 (W/LB) and known good ground. • Does meter indicate continuity?	Yes No	▶ ▶	LOCATE and SERVICE short to ground in Circuit 294 (W/LB). REPEAT Auto Test. GO to Pinpoint Test D to service steering sensor.

FM2019100045040X

Fig. 21 Test KB: No Codes Displayed While Auto Test Is Running (Part 4 of 4)

TEST STEP	RESULT	▶	ACTION TO TAKE
L3 CHECK CONTINUITY BETWEEN VEHICLE SPEED SENSOR AND CONTROL MODULE			
• Disconnect control module black connector. • Disconnect vehicle speed sensor connector. • Check continuity of Circuits 359 (GY/R)/676 (PK/O) and 150 (DG/W) between control module black connector and vehicle speed sensor connector.	Continuity in both circuits No continuity in one or both circuits	▶ ▶	GO to L4. LOCATE and SERVICE suspect circuit(s). REPEAT Auto Test.
L4 CHECK VEHICLE SPEED SENSOR CIRCUIT CONTINUITY			
• Disconnect control module black connector. • Connect vehicle speed sensor connector. • Connect ohmmeter between Circuits 150 (DG/W) and 359 (GY/R) at control module black connector. • Meter should indicate resistance of 180 ohms to 240 ohms.	180 ohms to 240 ohms Less than 180 ohms More than 240 ohms	▶ ▶ ▶	REPLACE control module. REPEAT Auto Test. SERVICE short between Circuits 150 (DG/W) and 359 (GY/R). REPEAT Auto Test. LOCATE and SERVICE in high resistance Circuit 150 (DG/W) or 359 (GY/R). REPEAT Auto Test.

FM2019100046020X

Fig. 22 Test L: Speed Greater Than 5 mph Not Detected In Last 16 Ignition Cycles (Part 2 of 2)

TEST STEP	RESULT	▶	ACTION TO TAKE
L1 CONFIRM CONTROL MODULE SPEED SIGNAL ACCEPTANCE			
• Connect Star Tester. • Air suspension service switch OFF. • Enter Function Test 22b. • Drive vehicle at speed(s) over 10 mph. • Compare speed displayed on Star Tester and speed displayed on speedometer. • Do displayed speeds agree?	Yes No	▶ ▶	GO to Pinpoint Test C for Diagnosis Procedures for EVO Actuator. GO to L2.
L2 CHECK VEHICLE SPEED SENSOR CONTINUITY			
• Turn air suspension service switch OFF. • Disconnect vehicle speed sensor connector. • Connect ohmmeter between terminals of vehicle speed sensor. • Meter should indicate resistance of 180 ohms to 240 ohms.	180 ohms to 240 ohms Less than 180 ohms or more than 240 ohms	▶ ▶	RECONNECT vehicle speed sensor. GO to L3. REPLACE vehicle speed sensor. REPEAT Auto Test.

FM2019100046010X

Fig. 22 Test L: Speed Greater Than 5 mph Not Detected In Last 16 Ignition Cycles (Part 1 of 2)

TEST STEP	RESULT	▶	ACTION TO TAKE
PA1 CHECK VOLTAGE			
NOTE: This code will not be displayed unless the module detects that the battery system is currently below 13 volts. • Key ON, engine running. • Measure voltage across battery terminals. • Does meter indicate more than 13.5 volts?	Yes No	▶ ▶	GO to PA2. SERVICE charging system.
PA2 DETERMINE IF MODULE IS DAMAGED			
• Ignition OFF. • Disconnect control module black and gray connectors. • Engine on and running. • Connect voltmeter positive lead to Circuit 294 (W/LB) at Pin 4 on the black connector. • Connect voltmeter negative lead to Circuit 430 (GY) at Pin 32 on the gray connector. • Does meter indicate less than 13.5 volts?	Yes No	▶ ▶	LOCATE and SERVICE open or high resistance in wiring harness Circuit 294. REPEAT Auto Test. REPLACE control module. REPEAT Auto Test.

FM2019100047000X

Fig. 23 Test PA: Module Detects Low Battery

TEST STEP	RESULT	▶	ACTION TO TAKE
PB1 CHECK VOLTAGE			
NOTE: Code 19 will not be displayed unless the control module detects a voltage level above 17.5 volts for longer than 1 second. • Key ON, engine running. • Measure voltage across battery terminals. • Does meter indicate more than 17.5 volts?	Yes No	▶ ▶	SERVICE charging system. GO to PB2.
PB2 DETERMINE IF CONCERN IS IN MODULE			
• Disconnect control module black connector. • Disconnect control module gray connector. • Key ON and engine running. • Connect oscilloscope input to display input Circuit 294. • Connect second oscilloscope input to display input Circuit 418. • Do either of the displays indicate AC on the line at or above 17.5 volts?	Yes No	▶ ▶	SERVICE charging system. REPLACE control module. REPEAT Auto Test.

FM2019100048000X

Fig. 24 Test PB: Module Detects High Battery Voltage

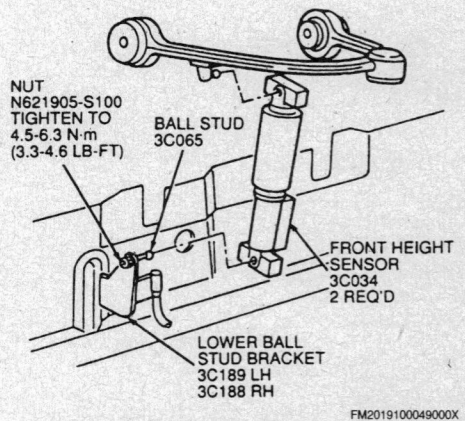

NUT
N621905-S100
TIGHTEN TO
4.5-6.3 N·m
(3.3-4.6 LB-FT)

BALL STUD
3C065

FRONT HEIGHT
SENSOR
3C034
2 REQ'D

LOWER BALL
STUD BRACKET
3C189 LH
3C188 RH

FM2019100049000X

Fig. 25 Ride height adjustment

SYSTEM SERVICE
ADJUSTMENTS
RIDE HEIGHT
Front Suspension

The front suspension ride height or "C" dimension is adjusted by moving the front LH and/or RH lower sensor attaching stud. (An adjustment slot is provided on the bracket.) Loosen the retaining screw and adjust up or down as required, **Fig. 25.** A 1.0 mm change in the height sensor attachment point results in approximately a 3.0 mm change at the "C" dimension.

Rear Suspension

The rear suspension ride height, or "D" dimension, is adjusted by moving the LH rear height sensor upper ball stud bracket on the subframe. An adjustment slot is provided on the bracket. Loosen the retaining screws and adjust bracket up or down as required. A 1.0 mm change in the LH rear height sensor attachment point results in approximately a 3.0 mm change in the "D" dimension.

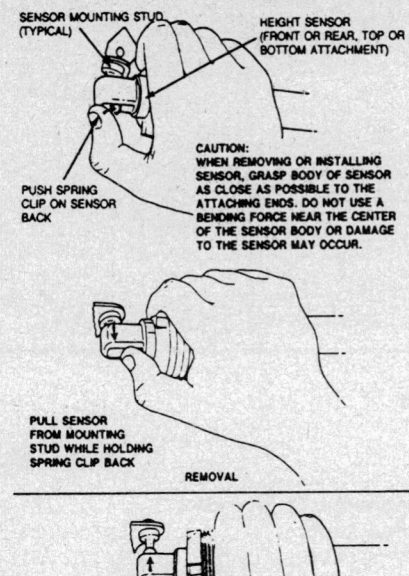

Fig. 26 Height sensor replacement

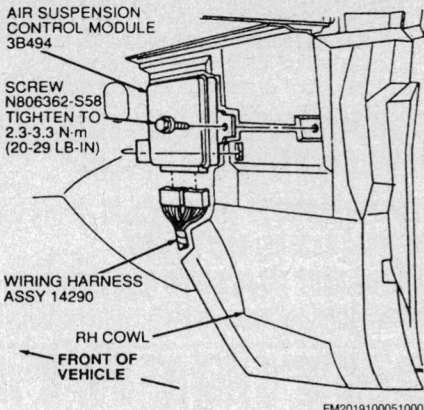

Fig. 27 Control module replacement

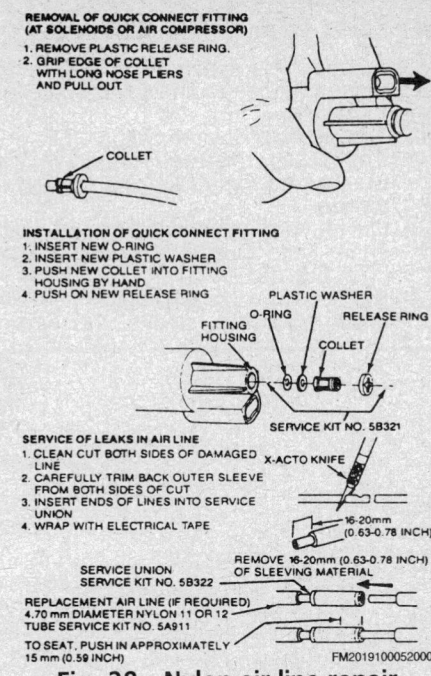

Fig. 28 Nylon air line repair

COMPONENT REPLACEMENT
HEIGHT SENSOR
Front Sensor

1. Turn air suspension switch OFF, then raise and support vehicle at body.
2. Remove forward section of front wheel splash shield to allow access to connector and height sensor clips.
3. Pull out height sensor clips.
4. Disconnect height sensor electrical connector.
5. Remove height sensor from retaining studs by gently pulling back on sensor spring clips, **Fig. 26.**
6. Reverse procedure to install.

Rear Sensor

1. Turn air suspension switch OFF.
2. Disconnect height sensor connector from wire harness.
3. Remove height sensor from retaining studs by gently pulling back on sensor spring clips, **Fig. 26.**
4. Reverse procedure to install.

AIR SPRING SOLENOID

1. Turn air suspension switch OFF, then raise and support vehicle at body.
2. Remove wheel and tire assembly.
3. Disconnect electrical connector and air line.
4. Remove solenoid clip.
5. Rotate solenoid counterclockwise to the first stop.
6. Pull solenoid out slowly to the second stop to bleed air from system.
7. Rotate solenoid counterclockwise to third stop and remove from air spring assembly.
8. Reverse procedure to install.

AIR SPRING
Front Air Spring & Shock Absorber

1. Turn air suspension switch OFF, then raise and support vehicle
2. Remove tire and wheel assembly.
3. Remove height sensor as previously outlined.
4. Remove air spring solenoid as previously outlined.
5. Remove cover from air spring attachments in engine compartment.
6. Remove retaining nuts and collar holding air spring studs to shock tower.
7. Remove lower nut and bolt to detach shock absorber from lower suspension arm. **Do not remove front shock absorber's large center nut, as this may result in a permanent air leak through top of air spring.**
8. Carefully remove air spring/shock absorber.
9. Reverse procedure to install, noting the following:
   a. **Torque** three upper retaining nuts over shock tower to 17.2–23.4 ft. lbs.
   b. Refill air springs as outlined under "Air Spring Refill."
   c. Tighten lower shock absorber nut to 199–243 ft. lbs.

Rear Air Spring

1. Turn air suspension switch OFF, then raise and support vehicle
2. Remove tire and wheel assembly.
3. Remove electrical connector and air line from air spring solenoid valve, then remove air spring solenoid valve as previously outlined.
4. Depress four plastic locking fingers in bottom of air spring piston to detach air spring from lower suspension arm.
5. Depress metal locking tab at top of air spring and rotate to disengage air spring cap from body bracket.
6. Carefully remove rear air spring from vehicle.
7. Reverse procedure to install. **Do not fill or pressurize air spring before it is correctly installed.**

AIR SPRING REFILL

1. Turn air suspension switch OFF.
2. Connect Super Star II Tester to data link connector on front side of RH shock tower.
3. Install battery charger to reduce battery drain.
4. Enter function test to pump appropriate air springs:
   a. 212 LF-Air Spring.
   b. 214 RF-Air Spring.
   c. 216 LR-Air Spring.
   d. 218 RR-Air Spring.
5. After completion of air spring fill, inspect all air springs for proper inflation.

CONTROL MODULE

1. Turn air suspension switch and ignition switch OFF.
2. Remove LH front passenger kick panel.
3. Disconnect wire harness from module.
4. Remove retaining screw and control module, **Fig. 27.**
5. Reverse procedure to install.

AIR COMPRESSOR/DRIER ASSEMBLY

1. Remove front bumper cover.
2. Remove fuel system carbon canister.
3. Disconnect compressor motor electrical connector.
4. Disconnect solid state relay connector.
5. Disconnect four air lines from compressor drier.
6. Disconnect wire harness and front left air line clip from rear face of compressor bracket.
7. Remove two lower screws attaching bracket to body.
8. Remove upper screw attaching top of compressor bracket to body.
9. Remove compressor/drier assembly from vehicle.
10. Reverse procedure to install.

NYLON AIR LINE SERVICE

If a leak is detected in the air line, it can be serviced with an air line splice in the following manner:

1. Turn air suspension switch OFF.
2. If necessary, raise and support vehicle to allow access to leaking section of air line.
3. Cut out leaking section of air line with sharp knife to ensure clean, straight cuts, **Fig. 28.**
4. If leak occurs in section of air line with black protective sleeve, the sleeve should be cut back 22mm from cut ends to allow inner tube to be inserted into splice quick connector fittings.
5. Insert cut ends into air line splice.

TECHNICAL SERVICE BULLETINS

IMPROPER VEHICLE ATTITUDE/HEIGHT SENSOR WATER ENTRY

Improper vehicle attitude with rear suspension low and front high may be caused by water entry into the height sensor. To correct this problem, proceed as follows:

1. Let vehicle sit for ten minutes, then start vehicle.
2. If vehicle comes to level attitude, height sensors are not malfunctioning.
3. Perform normal system diagnosis.
4. If concern still exists, replace all height sensors. The new design sensors have a gray wire protector instead of the black wire protector used on the old design height sensors.

CONTINENTAL
INDEX

PRECAUTIONS

SERVICE

When lifting the vehicle to perform service, position vehicle over hoist and turn ignition switch to OFF position. Turn air suspension switch to OFF position. The switch is located in the luggage compartment on the left side. A body type hoist is the recommended method for lifting the vehicle. When the hoist is used, raise vehicle using standard support procedures. The suspension will be supported in the rebound by the front and rear struts after the vehicle is lifted. As stated previously, ensure to either disconnect battery ground cable or turning the power switch located in the luggage compartment on the left side. Failure to do so may result in unexpected inflation or deflation of the air springs which may result in shifting of the vehicle during these procedures.

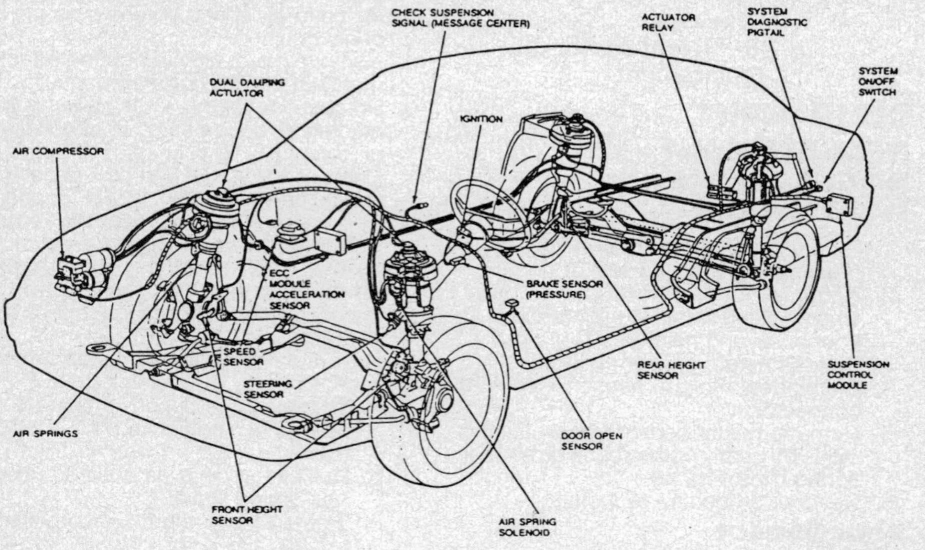

DESCRIPTION
AIR SUSPENSION SYSTEM

The air suspension system, **Fig. 1**, incorporates air leveling and dual ride control into one suspension system. Air leveling maintains the vehicle at the proper level under varying operating conditions. Dual damping ride control switches the shock absorbers between soft and firm.

The air suspension system includes the following major components:

1. An air compressor to supply air to the air springs.
2. Variable rate air springs which are integral with the shock absorber struts at each corner of the vehicle.
3. Three rotary height sensors; one rear and two front height sensors to maintain the vehicle at the proper ride height.

Fig. 1 Air suspension system

4. Dual damping front and rear shock absorber struts with externally mounted actuators/drivers.

AIR SUSPENSION CONTROL MODULE

The control module responds to signals from the various sensors in the vehicle to maintain the desired ride height while the vehicle is either moving or stopped. It accomplishes this by opening and closing the air spring valves. It also turns on the compressor through the compressor relay or opens the vent solenoid in response to signal inputs from the height sensors.

This module receives inputs from several different sources. The information inputs include the following:

1. Vehicle speed.
2. Steering wheel turning rotation.
3. Engine vacuum level.
4. Throttle position angle (which is supplied by the EEC-IV system).
5. Braking applications.
6. Ignition switch position.
7. Shock absorber damping position.
8. Door switch position.
9. Height sensor position.

AIR COMPRESSOR

A single cylinder piston type electrically operated air compressor, mounted on the right fender apron, supplies the required air pressure for system operation.

A regenerative type dryer is attached to the compressor manifold assembly. All airflow during the compression or vent cycles, pass through the dryer. A vent solenoid, located on the compressor manifold, controls air exhaustion.

Air required for leveling the vehicle is distributed from the air compressor to

STEP 1 of 1	DRIVE CYCLE DIAGNOSTICS ENTRANCE PROCEDURE	RESULT	ACTION TO TAKE
	In order to enter/activate DRIVE CYCLE DIAGNOSTICS the following actions are required: • After driving the vehicle for at least four minutes above a speed of 15 mph turn the ignition switch to the "OFF" position. • Turn off headlights to battery voltage. • Open trunk lid and verify that the air suspension "ON/OFF" switch is in the "ON" position. (NOTE: If this switch was turned "OFF" while the ignition was also "OFF" DRIVE CYCLE DIAGNOSTICS can not be entered.) • Release the "STAR" test button so that it remains in the up "HOLD" position and turn the "STAR" tester "ON". • Connect the "STAR" tester to the air suspension diagnostic connector and turn "STAR" tester on. After waiting a minimum of 5 seconds depress the "STAR" test button so that it remains down in the "TEST" position. NOTE: Drive Cycle faults will be saved for up to 55 minutes after the ignition is turned to the "OFF" (NON-RUN) position. Any time the ignition switch is turned to the "ON" position the air suspension control module will erase all fault codes that were detected.	Within twenty seconds the STAR tester will continuously display one of the following code sets: "15" ▶ "40" to "71" ▶ ALL OTHER CODES ▶	 DRIVE CYCLE DIAGNOSTICS is completed and NO faults were detected. Disconnect the "STAR" tester to exit DRIVE CYCLE DIAGNOSTICS. DRIVE CYCLE DIAGNOSTICS is completed and system faults were detected. Write down the complete list of system faults only after they have been displayed at least two times. Then run SERVICE BAY DIAGNOSTICS. GO TO AA1

STEP 1 of 4	SERVICE BAY DIAGNOSTICS ENTRANCE PROCEDURE	RESULT	ACTION TO TAKE
	In order to enter/activate SERVICE BAY DIAGNOSTICS the following actions are required: • Connect a battery charger to the vehicle's battery and leave connected for the duration of the test sequence. • If required release the STAR test button so that it remains in "HOLD" up position. • Open trunk lid and connect the STAR tester to the air suspension diagnostic connector and turn the STAR tester "ON". • Turn the air suspension "ON/OFF" switch to the "OFF" position and then back to the "ON" position. • Check vehicle passenger compartment and trunk for loads. Remove all loads; vehicle must be at curb weight. • Make sure the ignition switch is in the "OFF" position and wait ten seconds. • With the brake pedal NOT depressed turn the ignition switch to the "ON/RUN" position (not necessary to start engine). • Verify that the headlights, heater fan, windshield wipers, ..., etc. are turned off. • Wait a minimum of 5 seconds and then depress the STAR test button so that it remains down in the "TEST" position.	Within twenty seconds the STAR tester will display one of the following codes: "10" ▶ "21" to "28" ▶ "80" ▶ SOMETHING ELSE ▶	 GO TO SERVICE BAY DIAGNOSTICS "STEP 2 of 4". GO TO BB1 GO TO DA1 GO TO BA1

FM2019100054000X   FM2019100055010X

Fig. 2 Drive cycle diagnostic procedure   **Fig. 3 Service bay diagnostic procedure (Part 1 of 4)**

each air spring by four nylon air lines which start at the compressor dryer and terminate at the individual air springs. The dryer is a common pressure manifold for all four air lines. The air lines are color coded to identify to which air spring they are attached. **The compressor relay, compressor vent solenoid and all air spring solenoids incorporate internal diodes for electrical noise suppression and are polarity sensitive. Care must be taken when servicing these components not to switch the battery positive and ground cables or system/component damage will result. When charging the battery, the ignition switch must be in the OFF position if the air suspension switch is in the ON position or damage to the air compressor relay or motor may occur.**

AIR SPRING & SHOCK STRUT ASSEMBLY

The front and rear suspension system incorporate MacPherson type strut assemblies with integral air springs and two stage (dual) dampening mechanisms. The two stage dampening is achieved by varying the piston orifice area with an externally mounted electronic rotary actuator. The front struts are mounted to the body through a precision ball bearing and rubber mount system. The ball bearing provides a smooth and durable pivot point for the strut/wheel assembly.

The rear struts incorporate a dual path mount which separates the strut and air spring mounting surfaces to provide for maximum isolation.

ELECTRONIC HEIGHT SENSOR

The electronic height sensor is a rotary style design that uses an internal hall effect device to determine ride height. These sensors will indicate conditions of above trim, trim and below trim to the control module. The three sensors are located at the left front, right front and right rear of the vehicle. Each one of the sensors measures the actual difference between known reference points so that the control module can respond to variations in ride height. In the parking mode, additional height positions allow the system to accurately determine if an obstruction was encountered during a parking maneuver. In the driving mode, variations in road surfaces are sensed by checking road wheel vertical speed and vertical travel. If the average wheel speed and travel is above a predetermined level, the shock absorbers are switched to the firm position. This reduces the chance of grounding out of the subframe when traveling over bumpy road surfaces.

DUAL DAMPENING SYSTEM

The function of the dual dampening system is to automatically switch the shock strut settings from soft to firm when driving conditions require it. The system monitors vehicle accelerations, decelerations, up and down road wheel travel and also steering wheel position and steering wheel turning rates before responding to individual sensor inputs.

DIAGNOSIS & TESTING

The Rotunda SUPER STAR II tester No. 007-00041-A or equivalent, must be used to properly test and diagnose this system. Follow tool manufacturer's instructions for installation and operation of the tool.

DRIVE CYCLE DIAGNOSTICS

On models built after 12/1/90, the suspension module will not erase system trouble codes stored in memory when the ignition switch is cycled to the Run position within an hour of turning ignition switch Off. To erase trouble codes, turn ignition switch Off and allow vehicle to sit for more than one hour or switch module power Off at trunk mounted suspension system switch.

On all models, the drive cycle diagnostics will illuminate the "Ride Control" warning lamp in the message center when a trouble code is detected while driving the vehicle. Up to 32 trouble codes will remain in memory for one hour after ignition switch is turned Off. The air suspension switch in luggage compartment must remain On. If the vehicle has not been driven in over an hour or the ignition switch has been turned to Run and the air suspension switch has been turned Off, vehicle must be driven to duplicate faults, refer to **Fig. 2.**

STEP 2 of 4	SERVICE BAY DIAGNOSTICS AUTOMATIC MODE TESTING		RESULT	ACTION TO TAKE
	The STAR tester is displaying a code "10". The air suspension control module has completed a self check of itself and is now conducting the automatic portion of diagnostics. Do not touch or lean on the vehicle while automatic testing is being conducted (STAR code "10"). This test will take approximately three to four minutes to complete if there are no air leveling problems. IF THERE ARE AIR LEVELING PROBLEMS THIS TEST MAY TAKE FOURTEEN MINUTES. At the end of the test the STAR tester will display a code "12" or "13".		STAR tester is displaying a code:	
		▶	"12"	No system faults were detected in the automatic mode. Go to SERVICE BAY DIAGNOSTICS "STEP 3 of 4".
		▶	"13"	System faults were detected in the automatic mode. Go to SERVICE BAY DIAGNOSTICS "STEP 3 of 4".

FM2019100055020X

Fig. 3   Service bay diagnostic procedure (Part 2 of 4)

STEP 3 of 4	SERVICE BAY DIAGNOSTICS TESTING COMPLETED		RESULT	ACTION TO TAKE
	The air suspension control module has completed its automatic checks and is now waiting for the service technician to perform the following manual operations: * Open the driver's door and be seated in the vehicle leaving the driver's door open. * Depress the accelerator pedal to the floor and then release it. * Depress the brake pedal hard and then release it. * Turn the steering wheel a minimum of a 1/4 turn in both directions. * Exit the vehicle and shut the driver's door. Then open and shut the other three vehicle doors one at a time. * After completing the above release the STAR test button to the "HOLD" position. After five seconds depress the STAR test button again so that it remains in the down "TEST" position. NOTE: The detected system fault codes will be displayed in a numerical order one at a time. After the last detected system fault code is displayed the list will be repeated. This scrolling manner will continue as long as the STAR test button remains in the up "TEST" position.		The STAR tester is displaying one of the following codes:	
		▶	"11"	Service Bay Diagnostics is completed and NO faults were detected. Go to SERVICE BAY DIAGNOSTICS "STEP 4 of 4".
		▶	"40" to "79"	Service Bay Diagnostics is completed and faults were detected. Write down the complete list of system faults only after they have been displayed at least two times. Go to SERVICE BAY DIAGNOSTICS "STEP 4 of 4".

FM2019100055030X

Fig. 3   Service bay diagnostic procedure (Part 3 of 4)

SERVICE BAY DIAGNOSTICS

Refer to **Fig. 3.** for Service Bay Diagnostics procedures.

Auto/Manual Diagnostic Check

This test allows the air suspension control module to verify itself and to check the operation of various components. After performing these tests, the Star tester will display trouble code 12 or 13. The manual checks should be performed at this time.

Trouble Code Display

Trouble codes can be displayed using the Star Tester. Each code detected will be displayed for approximately 15 seconds. Trouble codes should be recorded at this time. Refer to diagnostic code priorities chart, **Fig. 4**, for order of diagnosis.

Pinpoint Tests

Each trouble code has it own pinpoint test. These tests have priorities assigned with "1" being the highest priority and "7" being the lowest. One malfunction may cause other trouble codes to be displayed. Perform pinpoint tests in order of priority starting with the highest. Refer to **Fig. 4** for diagnostic code priorities chart. Refer to **Figs. 5 and 6** for connector terminal identification. Refer to **Figs. 7 through 44** for diagnosis and testing.

STEP 4 of 4	SERVICE BAY DIAGNOSTICS DETECTED SYSTEM FAULTS		RESULT	ACTION TO TAKE
	If the "DRIVE CYCLE DIAGNOSTICS" fault list included STAR code "55" add it to the "SERVICE BAY DIAGNOSTICS" detected faults list just generated. Those "DRIVE CYCLE DIAGNOSTIC" detected faults that are not repeated in "SERVICE BAY DIAGNOSTICS" are to be handled as an intermittent fault. In order to minimize the time and labor involved in fixing a detected system fault the fault codes have been grouped.		In DRIVE CYCLE or SERVICE BAY DIAGNOSTICS system faults were detected:	
		▶	YES	
		▶	NO	To exit SERVICE BAY DIAGNOSTICS turn the ignition switch to the "OFF" position.
	NOTE: The detected system fault codes will be displayed in a numerical order one at a time. After the last detected system fault code is displayed the list will be repeated. This scrolling manner will continue as long as the STAR test button remains in the "TEST" position.			

FM2019100055040X

Fig. 3   Service bay diagnostic procedure (Part 4 of 4)

STAR CODE	PINPOINT PROCEDURE	DESCRIPTION	SERVICE PRIORITY
10		Service Bay Diagnostics Entered	
11		System Checked out okay	
12		Automatic Test Completed — No Faults Detected	
		Perform Manual Inputs	
13		Automatic Test Completed — Faults Detected	
		Perform Manual Inputs	
15		No Faults Detected	
21		Vent Right Front Air Spring	
22		Vent Left Front Air Spring	
23		Vent Right Rear Air Spring	
24		Inflate Right Front Air Spring	
25		Inflate Left Front Air Spring	
26		Inflate Right Rear Air Spring	
27		Vent Left Rear Air Spring	
28		Inflate Left Rear Air Spring	
31		Air Compressor Toggle	
32		Vent Solenoid Valve Toggle	
33		Air Spring Solenoid Valve Toggle	
34		Shock Actuator Toggle (Firm/Soft)	
35		Door Open & Door Closed Detection	
40	EA	Short — Left Frt. Air Spring Solenoid Valve Circuit	2nd
41	EB	Short — Right Frt. Air Spring Solenoid Valve Circuit	2nd
42	EC	Short — Left Rear Air Spring Solenoid Valve Circuit	2nd
43	ED	Short — Right Rear Air Spring Solenoid Valve Circuit	2nd
44	EE	Short — Vent Solenoid Valve Circuit	2nd
45	EF	Short — Air Compressor Relay Circuit	2nd
46	EG	Short — Height Sensor Power Supply Circuit	2nd
47	EH	Short — Soft Shock Actuator Relay Circuit	2nd
48	EI	Short — Firm Shock Actuator Relay Circuit	2nd
49	HA	Unable to Detect Lowering of Right Front Corner	5th

NOTE: System faults have been prioritized for repair. Start with those codes identified with a service priority of: 1st, then 2nd, then 3rd, ...and finally 7th.

FM2019100056010X

Fig. 4   Air suspension diagnostic code priority chart (Part 1 of 2)

STAR CODE	PINPOINT PROCEDURE	DESCRIPTION	SERVICE PRIORITY
50	HB	Unable to Detect Lowering of Left Front Corner	5th
51 *	HC	Unable to Detect Lowering of Right Rear Corner	5th
51 *		Unable to Detect Lowering of Rear of Vehicle	5th
52	IA	Unable to Detect Raising of Right Front Corner	6th
53	IB	Unable to Detect Raising of Left Front Corner	6th
54 *	IC	Unable to Detect Raising of Right Rear Corner	6th
54 *		Unable to Detect Raising of Rear of Vehicle	6th
55	JA	Speed Greater Than 15 mph Not Detected	7th
56	GA	Soft Not Detected — Left Rear Shock Actuator Circuit	4th
57	GB	Soft Not Detected — Right Frt. Shock Actuator Circuit	4th
58	GC	Soft Not Detected — Left Frt. Shock Actuator Circuit	4th
59	GD	Soft Not Detected — Right Rear Shock Actuator Circuit	4th
60	GA	Firm Not Detected — Left Rear Shock Actuator Circuit	4th
61	GB	Firm Not Detected — Right Frt. Shock Actuator Circuit	4th
62	GC	Firm Not Detected — Left Frt. Shock Actuator Circuit	4th
63	GD	Firm Not Detected — Right Rear Shock Actuator Circuit	4th
64	GE	Soft Not Detected — All Shock Actuator Circuits	4th
65	GE	Firm Not Detected — All Shock Actuator Circuits	4th
66	EJ	Short — Right Front Height Sensor Circuit	2nd
67	EK	Short — Left Front Height Sensor Circuit	2nd
68	EL	Short — Rear Height Sensor Circuit	2nd
69	FA	Open — Right Front Height Sensor Circuit	3rd
70	FB	Open — Left Front Height Sensor Circuit	3rd
71	FC	Open — Rear Height Sensor Circuit	3rd
72	JB	At Least Four Open & Closed Door Signals Not Detected	7th
73	JC	Brake Pressure Switch Activation Not Detected	7th
74	JD	Steering Wheel Rotations Not Detected	7th
75	JE	Acceleration Signal Not Detected	7th
78	HD	Unable to Detect Lowering of Left Rear Corner	5th
79	ID	Unable to Detect Raising of Left Rear Corner	6th
80	DA	Insufficient Battery Voltage to Run Diagnostics	1st

NOTE: System faults have been prioritized for repair. Start with those codes identified with a service priority of: 1st, then 2nd, then 3rd, ...and finally 7th.

FM2019100056020X

Fig. 4   Air suspension diagnostic code priority chart (Part 2 of 2)

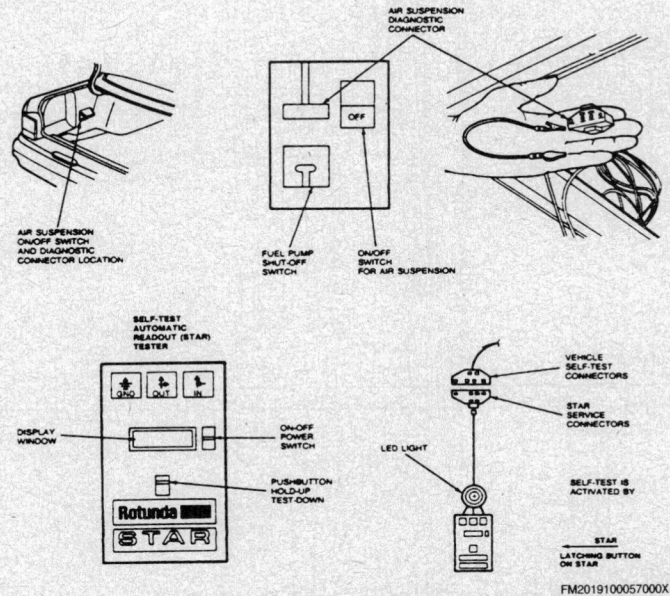

Fig. 5   Air suspension diagnostic connector location

FM2019100057000X

SPRING FILL DIAGNOSTICS

Refer to **Fig. 45** to perform spring fill diagnostic procedure.

ACCESSING TROUBLE CODES

Trouble codes can be displayed using the Star Tester. Each code detected will be displayed for approximately 15 seconds.

CLEARING TROUBLE CODES

To clear trouble codes, turn ignition switch Off and allow vehicle to sit for more than one hour or switch module power Off at trunk mounted suspension system switch.

Continued on page 31-112

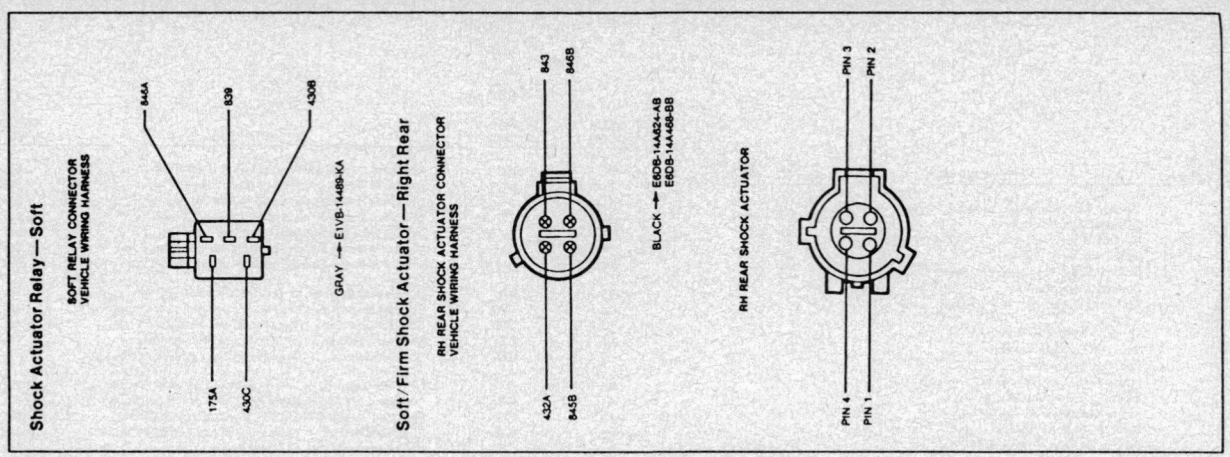

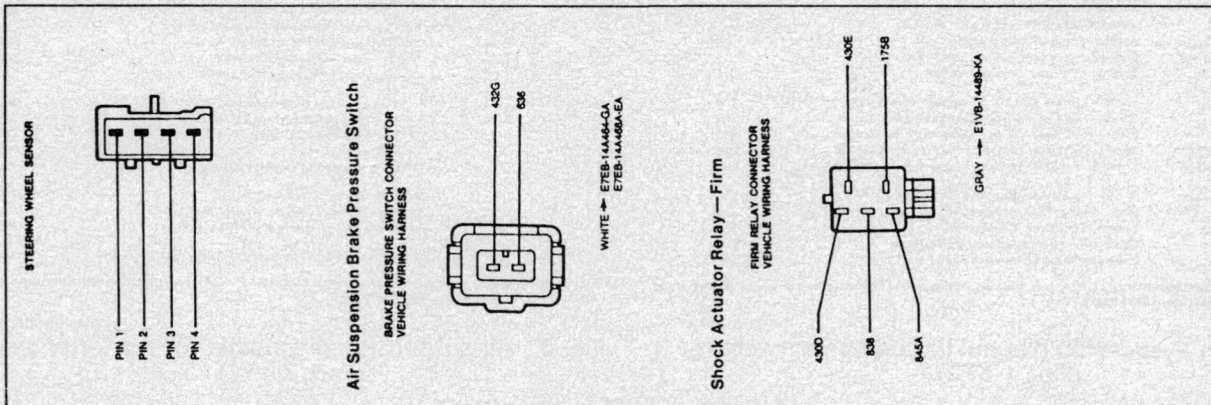

Fig. 6   Air suspension connector identification (Part 2 of 6)

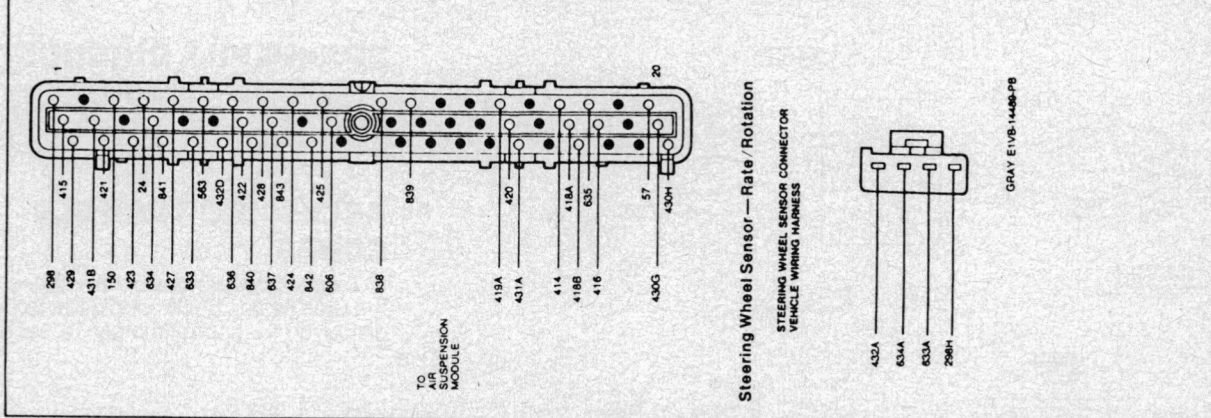

Fig. 6   Air suspension connector identification (Part 1 of 6)

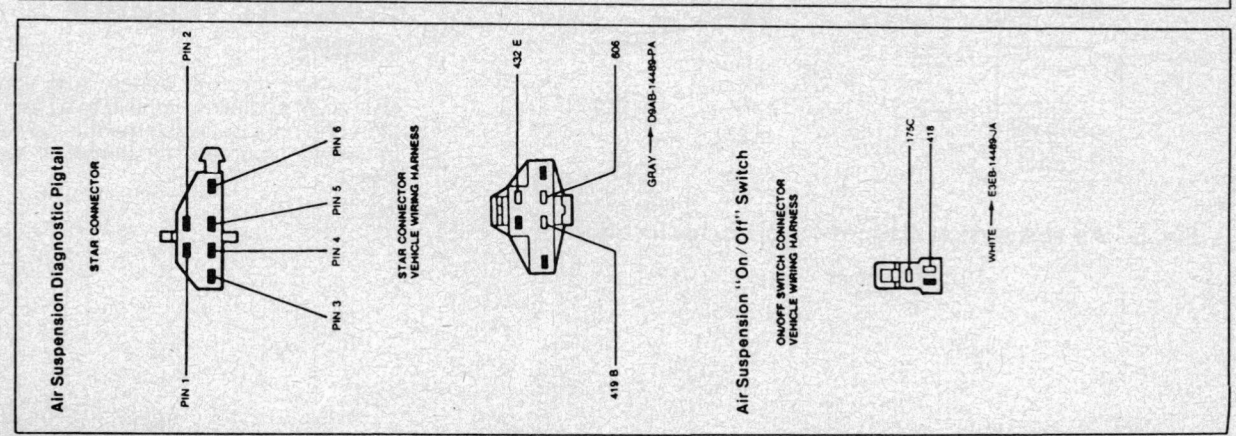

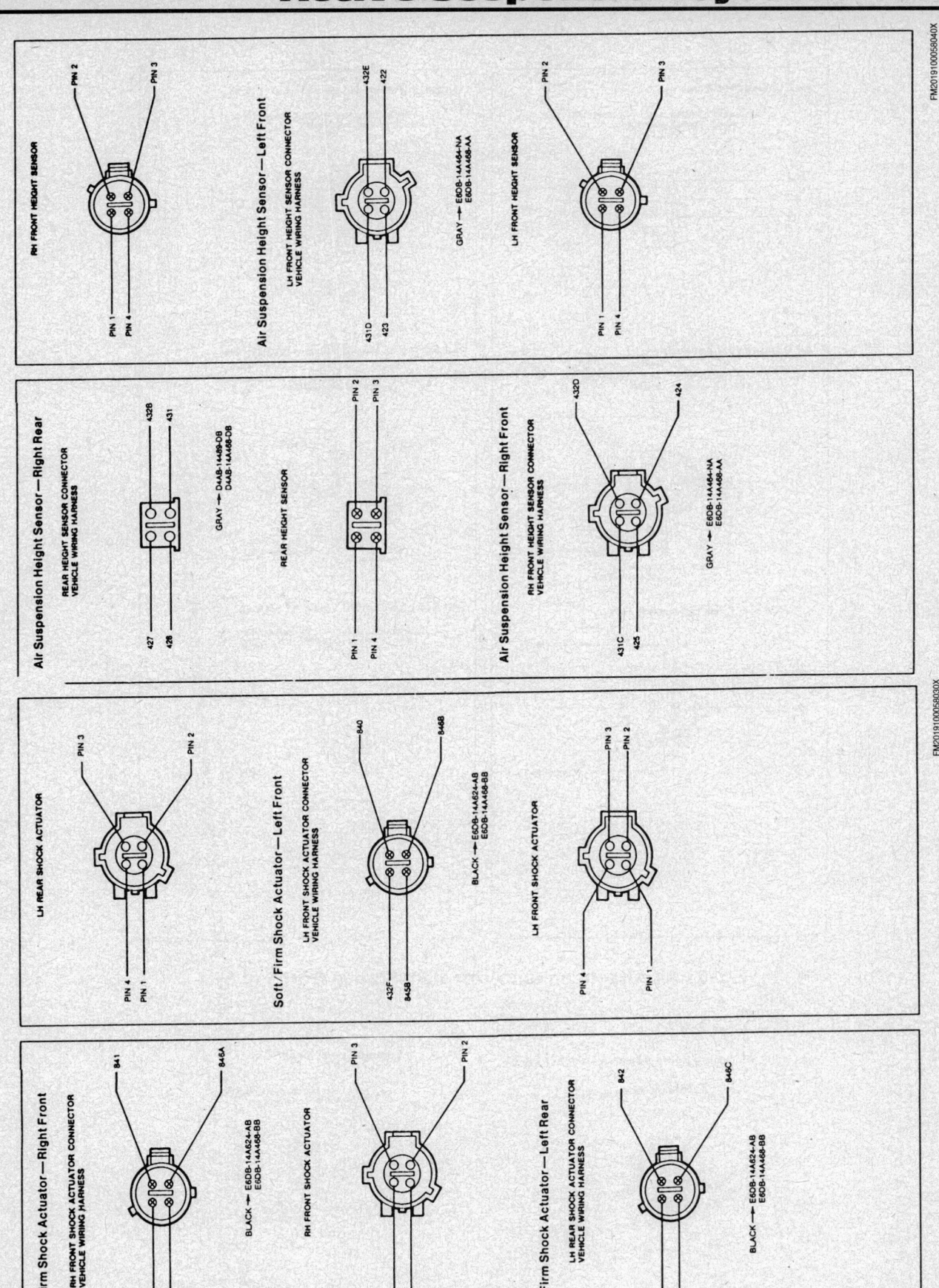

Fig. 6   Air suspension connector identification (Part 4 of 6)

Fig. 6   Air suspension connector identification (Part 3 of 6)

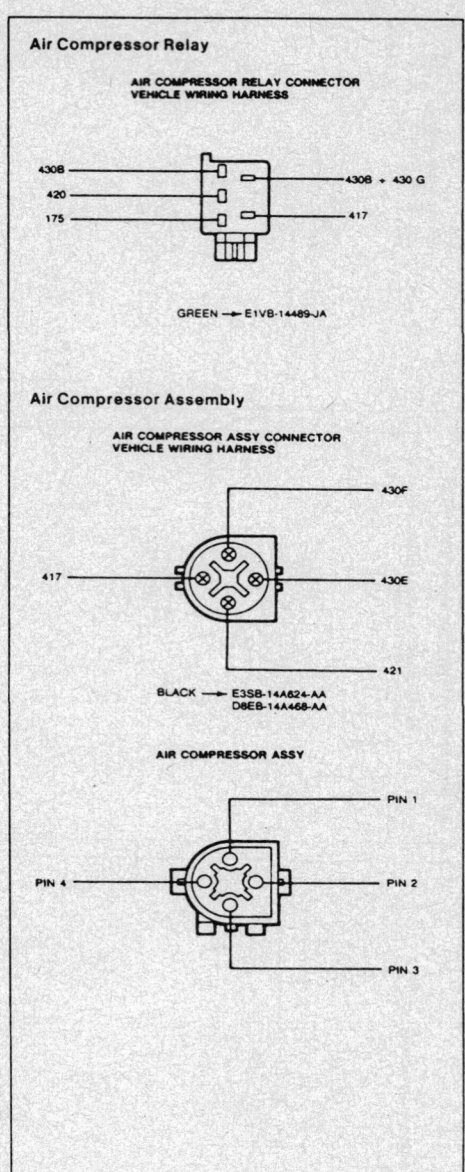

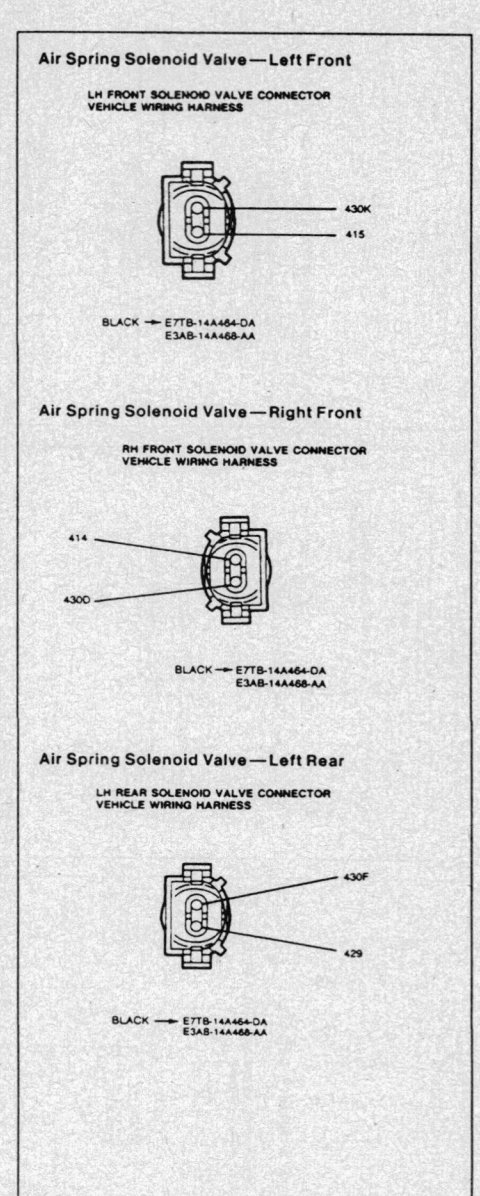

Fig. 6   Air suspension connector identification (Part 5 of 6)

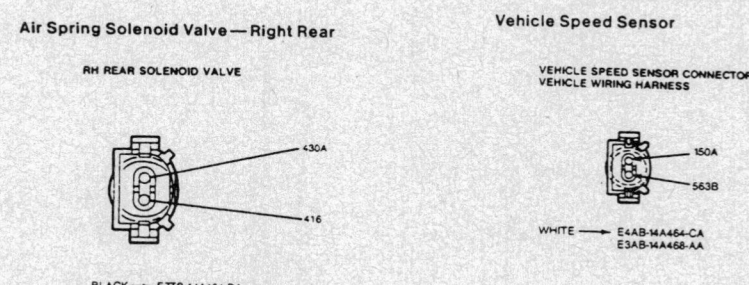

Fig. 6   Air suspension connector identification (Part 6 of 6)

DIAGNOSTIC CHART INDEX

Test/Code	Description	Page No.	Fig. No.
AA	Unable To Enter Drive Cycle Diagnostics	31-44	7
BA	Unable To Enter Service Bay Diagnostics	31-45	8
BB	Brake Pressure Switch Circuit Voltage Check	31-46	9
CA	Unable To Enter Spring Fill Diagnostics	31-47	10
DA/80	Low Power Supply Voltage	31-48	11
EA/40	Short In Left Front Air Spring Solenoid Valve Circuit	31-49	12
EB/41	Short In Right Front Air Spring Solenoid Valve Circuit	31-50	13
EC/42	Short In Left Rear Air Spring Solenoid Valve Circuit	31-51	14
ED/43	Short In Right Rear Air Spring Solenoid Valve Circuit	31-52	15
EE/44	Short In Vent Solenoid Valve Circuit	31-53	16
EF/45	Short In Air Compressor Relay Circuit	31-54	17
EG/46	Short In Height Sensor Power Supply Circuit	31-55	18
EH/47	Short In Soft Shock Actuator Relay Circuit	31-56	19
EI/48	Short In Firm Shock Actuator Relay Circuit	31-57	20
EJ/66	Short In Right Front Height Sensor Circuit	31-59	21
EK67	Short In Left Front Height Sensor Circuit	31-59	22
EL/68	Short In Rear Height Sensor Circuit	31-60	23
FA/69	Open In Right Front Height Sensor Circuit	31-61	24
FB/70	Short In Left Front Height Sensor Circuit	31-62	25
FC/71	Open In Rear Height Sensor Circuit	31-63	26
GA/56, 60	Actuator Desired Position Not Detected	31-65	27
GB/57. 61	Actuator Desired Position Not Detected	31-66	28
GC/58, 62	Actuator Desired Position Not Detected	31-68	29
GD/59, 63	Actuator Desired Position Not Detected	31-69	30
GE/64, 65	All Shock Actuators Not In Desired Position	31-70	31
HA/49	Unable To Detect Lowering Of Right Front Corner	31-73	32
HB/50	Unable To Detect Lowering Of Left Front Corner	31-77	33
HC/51	Unable To Detect Lowering Of Right Rear Corner	31-81	34
HD/78	Unable To Detect Lowering Of Left Rear Corner	31-85	35
IA/52	Unable To Detect Raising Of Right Front Corner	31-90	36
IB/53	Unable To Detect Raising Of Left Front Corner	31-94	37
IC/54	Unable To Detect Raising Of Right Rear Corner	31-98	38
ID/79	Unable To Detect Raising Of Left Rear Corner	31-101	39
JA/55	Speed Greater Than 5 mph Not Detected	31-105	40
JB/72	Did Not Detect At Least Four Open And Close Door Signals	31-105	41
JC/73	Brake Pressure Switch Activation Not Detected	31-109	42
JD/74	Steering Wheel Rotation In Both Directions Not Detected	31-110	43
JE/75	Acceleration Signal Not Detected	31-111	44

AA1	UNABLE TO ENTER DRIVE CYCLE DIAGNOSTICS	RESULT	ACTION TO TAKE
	DRIVE CYCLE DIAGNOSTICS has not entered. There are five possible causes which are listed below: • The STAR tester is defective. • B+ power supply circuit is defective. • The ignition switch circuit is defective. • The STI circuit is defective. • The STO circuit is defective.	▶	GO TO AA2
AA2	STAR TESTER CHECK		
	DRIVE CYCLE DIAGNOSTICS has not been entered possibly due to a defective STAR tester. To determine if this is the case the following actions are required: • Disconnect the STAR tester and get another STAR tester if possible. • On the new STAR tester release the STAR test button if required so that it remains in the up "HOLD" position. • Connect the new STAR tester to the air suspension diagnostic connector and turn it "ON". • After waiting a minimum of 5 seconds depress the STAR test button so that it remains down in the "TEST" position. NOTE: Drive Cycle faults will be saved for up to 55 minutes after the ignition is turned to the "OFF" (NON-RUN) position. Any time the ignition switch is turned to the "ON" position the air suspension control module will erase all fault codes that were detected.	Within twenty seconds the STAR tester will display one of the following codes: "15" ▶ "40" to "71" ▶ ALL OTHER CODES ▶	DRIVE CYCLE DIAGNOSTICS is completed and NO faults were detected. Disconnect the STAR tester to exit DRIVE CYCLE DIAGNOSTICS. DRIVE CYCLE DIAGNOSTICS is completed and system faults were detected. Write down the complete list of system faults only after they have been displayed at least two times. Then run SERVICE BAY DIAGNOSTICS. GO TO AA3

FM2019100059010X

Fig. 7   Test AA: Unable To Enter Drive Cycle Diagnostics (Part 1 of 5)

AA3	WIRING HARNESS/POWER SUPPLY CIRCUIT CHECK	RESULT	ACTION TO TAKE
	DRIVE CYCLE DIAGNOSTICS has not been entered possibly due to low power supply voltage. The following actions are required: • Release the STAR test button so that it remains in the up "HOLD" position and remove STAR tester. • Turn the air suspension "ON/OFF" switch "OFF" and disconnect the air suspension control module from the wiring harness connector. • Using an analog voltmeter place the positive voltage lead in the wiring harness connector pin location #37 (circuit #418A) and the negative lead to pin #40 (circuit #430G).	A positive voltage of 11 volts or greater is present. YES ▶ NO ▶	GO TO AA4 determine why battery voltage is not present.
AA4	WIRING HARNESS / POWER SUPPLY CIRCUIT CHECK		
	• Using an analog voltmeter place the positive voltage lead in the wiring harness connector pin location #57 (circuit #418B) and the negative lead to pin #60 (circuit #430H).	A positive voltage of 11 volts or greater is present: YES ▶ NO ▶	GO TO AA5 determine why battery voltage is not present.

FM2019100059020X

Fig. 7   Test AA: Unable To Enter Drive Cycle Diagnostics (Part 2 of 5)

AA5	WIRING HARNESS / CHECK IGNITION SWITCH CIRCUIT	RESULT	ACTION TO TAKE
	• Turn the ignition switch in the "OFF" position. • Using an analog voltmeter place the positive voltage lead in the wiring harness connector (for the control module) pin location #1 (circuit #298) and the negative lead to pin #40 (circuit #430G).	Zero voltage is present. YES ▶ NO ▶	GO TO AA6 determine why voltage is present.
AA6	WIRING HARNESS / CHECK IGNITION SWITCH CIRCUIT		
	• Turn the ignition switch to the "ON" position. • Using an analog voltmeter place the positive voltage lead in the wiring harness connector (for the control module) pin location #1 (circuit #298) and the negative lead to pin #40 (circuit #430G).	A positive voltage of 11 volts or greater is present: YES ▶ NO ▶	GO TO AA7 determine why a positive 11 volts is not present.
AA7	WIRING HARNESS / STI SHORT TO GROUND CHECK		
	• Using an analog ohmmeter place one lead in the wiring harness connector (for the control module) pin location #30 (circuit #606) and the other to pin location #40 (circuit #430G).	Ohmmeter reading is greater than 10,000 ohms: YES ▶ NO ▶	GO TO AA8 The STI circuit #606 is shorted to ground.

FM2019100059030X

Fig. 7   Test AA: Unable To Enter Drive Cycle Diagnostics (Part 3 of 5)

AA8	WIRING HARNESS STI OPEN CHECK	RESULT	ACTION TO TAKE
	• Using an analog ohmmeter place one lead in the wiring harness connector (for the air control module) pin location #30 (circuit #606) and the other to the wiring harness connector (for the STAR tester) pin location #2 (circuit #432E).	Ohmmeter reading is less than 5.0 ohms. YES ▶ NO ▶	GO TO AA9 The STI circuit #606/432E has an open in it.
AA9	WIRING HARNESS /STO SHORT TO GROUND CHECK		
	• Using an analog ohmmeter place one lead in the wiring harness connector (for the air control module) pin location #15 (circuit #419A) and the other to pin location #40 (circuit #430G).	Ohmmeter reading is greater than 10,000 ohms: YES ▶ NO ▶	GO TO AA10 The STO circuit #419A is shorted to ground.

FM2019100059040X

Fig. 7   Test AA: Unable To Enter Drive Cycle Diagnostics (Part 4 of 5)

AA10	WIRING HARNESS / STO OPEN CIRCUIT CHECK	RESULT	ACTION TO TAKE
	• Using an analog ohmmeter place one lead in the wiring harness connector (for the air control module) pin location #15 (circuit #419A) and the other to the wiring harness connector (for the STAR tester) pin location #4 (circuit #419B).	Ohmmeter reading is less than 5.0 ohms: YES	Turn the air suspension "ON/OFF" switch to the "OFF" position and replace air suspension control module and connect to vehicle wiring harness.
		NO	The STO circuit #419A/419B has an open in it. run SERVICE BAY DIAGNOSTICS after repair is made.

FM2019100059050X

Fig. 7   Test AA: Unable To Enter Drive Cycle Diagnostics (Part 5 of 5)

BA1	UNABLE TO ENTER SERVICE BAY DIAGNOSTICS	RESULT	ACTION TO TAKE
	SERVICE BAY DIAGNOSTICS has not been entered. There are five possible causes which are listed below: • The STAR tester is defective. • B+ power supply circuit is defective. • The ignition switch circuit is defective. • The STI circuit is defective. • The STO circuit is defective.		GO TO BA2
BA2	STAR TESTER CHECK		
	SERVICE BAY DIAGNOSTICS has not been entered possibly due to a defective STAR tester. To determine if this is the case the following actions are required: • Disconnect the STAR tester and get another STAR tester if possible. • On the new STAR tester release the STAR test button if required so that it remains in the up "HOLD" position. • Connect the new STAR tester to the air suspension diagnostic connector and turn it "ON". • Turn the ignition switch to the "OFF" position and wait ten seconds. After that turn the ignition switch back to the "ON/RUN" position and leave there. • After waiting a minimum of 5 seconds depress the STAR test button so that it remains down in the "TEST" position.	Within twenty seconds the STAR tester will display one of the following codes: "10" "21" to "28" ALL OTHER CODES	SERVICE BAY DIAGNOSTICS has been entered. Proceed to "Step 2 of 4" of SERVICE BAY DIAGNOSTICS. GO TO BB1 GO TO BA3

FM2019100060010X

Fig. 8   Test BA: Unable To Enter Service Bay Diagnostics (Part 1 of 5)

BA3	WIRING HARNESS/POWER SUPPLY CIRCUIT CHECK	RESULT	ACTION TO TAKE
	SERVICE BAY DIAGNOSTICS has not been entered possibly due to low power supply voltage. The following actions are required: • Release the STAR test button so that it remains in the up "HOLD" position. • Turn the air suspension "ON/OFF" switch "OFF" and disconnect the air suspension control module from the wiring harness connector. • Now turn the air suspension "ON/OFF" switch back to the "ON" position. • Using an analog voltmeter place the positive voltage lead in the wiring harness connector pin location #37 (circuit #418A) and the negative lead to pin #40 (circuit #430G).	A positive voltage of 11 volts or greater is present: YES NO	GO TO BA4 determine why battery voltage is not present.
BA4	WIRING HARNESS / POWER SUPPLY CIRCUIT CHECK		
	• Using an analog voltmeter place the positive voltage lead in the wiring harness connector pin location #57 (circuit #418B) and the negative lead to pin #60 (circuit #430H).	A positive voltage of 11 volts or greater is present. YES NO	GO TO BA5 determine why battery voltage is not present.

FM2019100060020X

Fig. 8   Test BA: Unable To Enter Service Bay Diagnostics (Part 2 of 5)

BA5	WIRING HARNESS / CHECK IGNITION SWITCH CIRCUIT	RESULT	ACTION TO TAKE
	• Turn the ignition switch in the "OFF" position. • Using an analog voltmeter place the positive voltage lead in the wiring harness connector (for the control module) pin location #1 (circuit #298) and the negative lead to pin #40 (circuit #430G).	Zero voltage is present. YES NO	GO TO BA6 determine why voltage is present.
BA6	WIRING HARNESS / CHECK IGNITION SWITCH CIRCUIT		
	• Turn the ignition switch to the "ON/RUN" position. • Using an analog voltmeter place the positive voltage lead in the wiring harness connector (for the control module) pin location #1 (circuit #298) and the negative lead to pin #40 (circuit #430G).	A positive voltage of 11 volts or greater is present or the test light is lit with no dimming present. YES NO	GO TO BA7 determine why a positive 11 volts is not present.
BA7	WIRING HARNESS / STI SHORT TO GROUND CHECK		
	• Using an ohmmeter place one lead in the wiring harness connector (for the control module) pin location #30 (circuit #606) and the other to pin location #40 (circuit #430G).	Ohmmeter reading is greater than 10,000 ohms: YES NO	GO TO BA8 The STI circuit #606 is shorted to ground.

FM2019100060030X

Fig. 8   Test BA: Unable To Enter Service Bay Diagnostics (Part 3 of 5)

BA8	WIRING HARNESS STI OPEN CHECK	RESULT	ACTION TO TAKE
	* Using an ohmmeter place one lead in the wiring harness connector (for the air control module) pin location #30 (circuit #606) and the other to the STAR tester vehicle wiring harness connector circuit #432E.	Ohmmeter reading is less than 5.0 ohms. YES ▶ NO ▶	GO TO BA9 The STI circuit #606/432E has an open in it.
BA9	WIRING HARNESS / STO SHORT TO GROUND CHECK		
	* Using an ohmmeter place one lead in the wiring harness connector (for the control module) pin location #15 (circuit #419A) and the other to pin location #40 (circuit #430G).	Ohmmeter reading is greater than 10,000 ohms: YES ▶ NO ▶	GO TO BA10 The STO circuit #419A is shorted to ground.

FM2019100060040X

Fig. 8   Test BA: Unable To Enter Service Bay Diagnostics (Part 4 of 5)

BA10	WIRING HARNESS / STO OPEN CIRCUIT CHECK	RESULT	ACTION TO TAKE
	* Using an ohmmeter place one lead in the wiring harness connector (for the air control module) pin location #15 (circuit #419A) and the other to the STAR tester vehicle wiring harness connector circuit #419B.	Ohmmeter reading is less than 5.0 ohms. YES ▶ NO ▶	Turn the air suspension "ON/OFF" switch to the "OFF" position, replace the suspension control module with a new one and connect it to the vehicle wiring harness. The STO circuit #419A/419B has an open in it.

FM2019100060050X

Fig. 8   Test BA: Unable To Enter Service Bay Diagnostics (Part 5 of 5)

BB1	BRAKE PRESSURE SWITCH CIRCUIT VOLTAGE CHECK	RESULT	ACTION TO TAKE
	SERVICE BAY DIAGNOSTICS has not been entered but SPRING FILL was. The following actions are required if SERVICE BAY DIAGNOSTICS is desired: * Release the STAR test button so that it remains in the up "HOLD" position. * Turn the air suspension "ON/OFF" switch to the "OFF" position. Disconnect the air suspension control module from the wiring harness connector. * Using an analog voltmeter place the positive voltage lead in the wiring harness connector pin location #7 (circuit #636) and the negative lead to pin #40 (circuit #430G).	Any voltage present: YES ▶ NO ▶	There should never be voltage on this circuit. GO TO BB2
BB2	BRAKE PRESSURE SWITCH CIRCUIT RESISTANCE CHECK		
	* Using an ohmmeter measure the resistance from pin location #7 (circuit #636) and pin location #40 (circuit #430G).	Ohmmeter reading is greater than 10,000 ohms: YES ▶ NO ▶	Replace air suspension control module with a new one and connect to vehicle wiring harness. Run SERVICE BAY DIAGNOSTICS after repair is made. GO TO BB3

FM2019100061010X

Fig. 9   Test BB: Brake Pressure Switch Circuit Voltage Check (Part 1 of 2)

BB3	BRAKE PRESSURE SWITCH CHECK	RESULT	ACTION TO TAKE
	* Disconnect the brake pressure switch from the vehicle wiring harness. * Using an analog ohmmeter place one lead in the air suspension control module wiring harness connector pin location #7 and (circuit #636) and the other lead to pin #46 (circuit #432D).	Ohmmeter reading is greater than 10,000 ohms: YES ▶ NO ▶	replace the brake pressure switch. Connect the air suspension control module to the vehicle wiring harness and run SERVICE BAY DIAGNOSTICS after repair is made. This circuit #636 has a short After repair is made run SERVICE BAY DIAGNOSTICS.

FM2019100061020X

Fig. 9   Test BB: Brake Pressure Switch Circuit Voltage Check (Part 2 of 2)

CA1	UNABLE TO ENTER SPRING FILL DIAGNOSTICS	RESULT	ACTION TO TAKE
	SPRING FILL DIAGNOSTICS has not been entered. There are six possible causes which are listed below: • The STAR tester is defective. • Brake switch circuit is defective. • B+ power supply circuit is defective. • The ignition switch circuit is defective. • The STI circuit is defective. • The STO circuit is defective.		▶ GO TO CA2

CA2	STAR TESTER CHECK	RESULT	ACTION TO TAKE
	SPRING FILL DIAGNOSTICS has not been entered possibly due to a defective STAR tester. To determine if this is the case the following actions are required: • Disconnect the STAR tester and get another STAR tester if possible. • On the new STAR tester release the STAR test button if required so that it remains in the up "HOLD" position. • Connect the new STAR tester to the air suspension diagnostic connector and turn it "ON". • Turn the ignition switch to the "OFF" position and wait ten seconds. After that turn the ignition switch back to the "ON/RUN" position and leave there. • After waiting a minimum of 5 seconds depress the STAR test button so that it remains down in the "TEST" position.	Within twenty seconds the STAR tester will display one of the following codes: "21" to "28" ALL OTHER CODES	▶ SPRING FILL DIAGNOSTICS has been entered. Refer to SPRING FILL DIAGNOSTIC for instructions. ▶ GO TO CA3

FM2019100062010X

Fig. 10   Test CA: Unable To Enter Spring Fill Diagnostics (Part 1 of 6)

CA3	BRAKE PRESSURE SWITCH CIRCUIT VOLTAGE CHECK	RESULT	ACTION TO TAKE
	• Release the STAR test button so that it remains in the up "HOLD" up position. • Turn the air suspension "ON/OFF" switch to the "OFF" position. Disconnect the air suspension control module from the wiring harness connector. • Now turn the air suspension "ON/OFF" switch back to the "ON" position. • Using an analog voltmeter place the positive voltage lead in the wiring harness connector pin location #7 (circuit #636) and the negative lead to pin #40 (circuit #430G).	Any voltage present: YES NO	▶ There should never be voltage on this circuit. ▶ GO TO CA4

CA4	BRAKE PRESSURE SWITCH CIRCUIT RESISTANCE CHECK	RESULT	ACTION TO TAKE
	• Using an ohmmeter measure the resistance from pin location #7 (circuit #636) and pin location #40 (circuit #430G).	Ohmmeter reading is greater than 10,000 ohms: YES NO	▶ GO TO CA6 ▶ GO TO CA5

FM2019100062020X

Fig. 10   Test CA: Unable To Enter Spring Fill Diagnostics (Part 2 of 6)

CA5	BRAKE PRESSURE SWITCH CHECK	RESULT	ACTION TO TAKE
	• Disconnect the brake pressure switch from the vehicle wiring harness. • Using an analog ohmmeter place one lead in the wiring harness connector pin location #7 (circuit #636) and the other lead to pin #46 (circuit #432D).	Ohmmeter reading is greater than 10,000 ohms: YES NO	▶ replace the brake pressure switch. Connect the air suspension control module to the vehicle wiring harness and run SPRING FILL DIAGNOSTICS after repair is made. ▶ This circuit #636 has a short After repair is made run SPRING FILL DIAGNOSTICS.

CA6	WIRING HARNESS / POWER SUPPLY CIRCUIT CHECK	RESULT	ACTION TO TAKE
	SPRING FILL DIAGNOSTICS has not been entered possibly due to low power supply voltage. The following actions are required: • Release the STAR test button so that it remains in the up "HOLD" up position. • Using an analog voltmeter place the positive voltage lead in the wiring harness connector pin location #37 (circuit #418A) and the negative lead to pin #40 (circuit #430G).	A positive voltage of 11 volts or greater is present: YES NO	▶ GO TO CA7 determine why battery voltage is not present.

FM2019100062030X

Fig. 10   Test CA: Unable To Enter Spring Fill Diagnostics (Part 3 of 6)

CA7	WIRING HARNESS / POWER SUPPLY CIRCUIT CHECK	RESULT	ACTION TO TAKE
	• Using an analog voltmeter place the positive voltage lead in the wiring harness connector pin location #57 (circuit #418B) and the negative lead to pin #60 (circuit #430H).	A positive voltage of 11 volts or greater is present: YES NO	▶ GO TO CA8 determine why battery voltage is not present.

CA8	WIRING HARNESS / CHECK IGNITION SWITCH CIRCUIT	RESULT	ACTION TO TAKE
	• Turn the ignition switch in the "OFF" position. • Using an analog voltmeter place the positive voltage lead in the wiring harness connector (for the control module) pin location #1 (circuit #298) and the negative lead to pin #40 (circuit #430G).	Zero voltage is present. YES NO	▶ GO TO CA9 determine why voltage is present.

CA9	WIRING HARNESS / CHECK IGNITION SWITCH CIRCUIT	RESULT	ACTION TO TAKE
	• Turn the ignition switch to the "ON/RUN" position. • Using an analog voltmeter place the positive voltage lead in the wiring harness connector (for the control module) pin location #1 (circuit #298) negative lead to pin #40 (circuit #430G).	A positive voltage of 11 volts or greater is present. YES NO	▶ GO TO CA10 determine why a positive 11 volts is not present.

FM2019100062040X

Fig. 10   Test CA: Unable To Enter Spring Fill Diagnostics (Part 4 of 6)

CA10	WIRING HARNESS / STI SHORT TO GROUND CHECK	RESULT	ACTION TO TAKE
	• Using an ohmmeter place one lead in the wiring harness connector (for the control module) pin location #30 (circuit #606) and the other to pin location #40 (circuit #430G).	Ohmmeter reading is greater than 10,000 ohms:	
		YES ▶	GO TO CA11
		NO ▶	The STI circuit #606 is shorted to ground.
CA11	WIRING HARNESS STI OPEN CHECK		
	• Using an ohmmeter place one lead in the wiring harness connector (for the air control module) pin location #30 (circuit #606) and the other to the vehicle wiring harness connector (for the STAR tester) pin location #2 (circuit #432E).	Ohmmeter reading is less than 5.0 ohms:	
		YES ▶	GO TO CA12
		NO ▶	The STI circuit #606/432E has an open in it.
CA12	WIRING HARNESS / STO SHORT TO GROUND CHECK		
	• Using an ohmmeter place one lead in the wiring harness connector (for the control module) pin location #15 (circuit #419A) and the other to pin location #40 (circuit #430G).	Ohmmeter reading is greater than 10,000 ohms:	
		YES ▶	GO TO CA13
		NO ▶	The ST0 circuit #419A is shorted to ground.

FM2019100062050X

Fig. 10   Test CA: Unable To Enter Spring Fill Diagnostics (Part 5 of 6)

CA13	WIRING HARNESS / STO OPEN CIRCUIT CHECK	RESULT	ACTION TO TAKE
	• Using an ohmmeter place one lead in the wiring harness connector (for the air control module) pin location #15 (circuit #419A) and the other to the vehicle wiring harness connector for the STAR tester circuit #419B.	Ohmmeter reading is less than 5.0 ohms:	
		YES ▶	Turn the air suspension "ON/OFF" switch to the "OFF" position and replace air suspension control module with a new one and connect to vehicle wiring harness.
		NO ▶	The STO circuit #419A/419B has an open in it.

FM2019100062060X

Fig. 10   Test CA: Unable To Enter Spring Fill Diagnostics (Part 6 of 6)

DA1	STAR CODE: 80 LOW POWER SUPPLY VOLTAGE	RESULT	ACTION TO TAKE
	The air suspension control module has detected a low power supply voltage. The following actions are required:	A positive voltage of 11 volts or greater is present:	
	• Release the "STAR" test button so that it remains in the up "HOLD" position.	YES ▶	GO TO DA2
	• Turn the air suspension "ON/OFF" switch to "OFF" and disconnect the air suspension control module from the wiring harness connector.	NO ▶	
	• Now turn the air suspension "ON/OFF" switch back to the "ON" position.		determine why a positive 11 volts is not present. Run SERVICE BAY DIAGNOSTICS after repair is made.
	• Using an analog voltmeter place the positive voltage lead in the wiring harness connector pin location #37 (circuit #418A) and the negative lead to pin #40 (circuit #430G).		
DA2	WIRING HARNESS / POWER SUPPLY CIRCUIT CHECK		
	• Using an analog voltmeter place the positive voltage lead in the wiring harness connector (for the control module) pin location #57 (circuit #418B) and the negative lead to pin #60 (circuit #430H)	A positive voltage of 11 volts or greater is present:	
		YES ▶	GO TO DA3
		NO ▶	
			determine why a positive 11 volts is not present. Run SERVICE BAY DIAGNOSTICS after repair is made.

FM2019100063010X

Fig. 11   Test DA: Low Power Supply Voltage (Part 1 of 2)

DA3	WIRING HARNESS / POWER SUPPLY CIRCUIT CHECK	RESULT	ACTION TO TAKE
	• Turn the ignition key to the "OFF" position.	A voltage of 1.0 volts or less is present:	
	• Using an analog voltmeter place the positive voltage lead in the wiring harness connector (for the control module) pin location #1 (circuit #298) and the negative lead to pin #60 (circuit #430H).	YES ▶	Turn the air suspension "ON/OFF" switch to the "OFF" position and replace the air suspension control module with a new one and connect to the vehicle wiring harness. Run SERVICE BAY DIAGNOSTICS after repair is made.
		NO ▶	
			reconnect the air suspension control module to the vehicle wiring harness. Then run SERVICE BAY DIAGNOSTICS.

FM2019100063020X

Fig. 11   Test DA: Low Power Supply Voltage (Part 2 of 2)

EA1	STAR CODE: 40 SHORT IN LEFT FRONT AIR SPRING SOLENOID VALVE CIRCUIT	RESULT	ACTION TO TAKE
	The air suspension control module has detected a short in the circuit used to activate the left front air spring solenoid valve. There are four possible causes of this short which are listed below:		▶ GO TO EA2
	• B + power supply circuit is shorted to ground.		
	• The vehicle wiring harness has the B + power supply and ground return circuit to the solenoid valve reversed.		
	• Air spring solenoid valve is defective.		
	• The air suspension control module is defective.		
	The left front air spring solenoid valve has a diode in it. When current is applied in the reverse direction this diode will act like a short. Because all ohmmeters do not have the same positive and negative polarity the following test procedures are being used to locate the cause of the short.		
EA2			
	• Turn the air suspension "ON/OFF" switch to the "OFF" position.		▶ GO TO EA3
	• Disconnect air suspension control module connector.		

FM2019100064010X

Fig. 12 Test EA: Short In Left Front Air Spring Solenoid Valve Circuit (Part 1 of 4)

EA3	CHECKING WIRING HARNESS	RESULT	ACTION TO TAKE
	Using an analog ohmmeter measure and record the following:	At least one of the two ohmmeter readings is greater than 8.0 ohms:	
	• Connect the positive lead of the ohmmeter to the wiring harness connector pin front location #21 (circuit #415) and the negative lead to pin location #40 (circuit #430G).	YES ▶	GO TO EA5
	• Now connect the positive lead of the ohmmeter to the wiring harness connector pin location #40 (circuit #430G) and the negative lead to pin location #21 (circuit #415).	NO ▶	GO TO EA4
EA4	**CHECKING WIRING HARNESS**		
	• Disconnect the left front air spring solenoid valve from the vehicle wiring harness.	Ohmmeter reading is greater than 10,000 ohms:	
	• Using an analog ohmmeter connect one lead to the wiring harness connector pin location #21 (circuit #415) and other to pin location #40 (circuit #430G).	YES ▶	The left front air spring solenoid valve has an internal short circuit. Install a new air spring solenoid valve and rerun SERVICE BAY DIAGNOSTICS.
		NO ▶	A short has been detected in the wiring harness circuit #415/430G. Rerun SERVICE BAY DIAGNOSTICS after repair is made.

FM2019100064020X

Fig. 12 Test EA: Short In Left Front Air Spring Solenoid Valve Circuit (Part 2 of 4)

EA5	CHECKING WIRING HARNESS	RESULT	ACTION TO TAKE
	• Disconnect the left front air spring solenoid valve from the vehicle wiring harness.	Ohmmeter reading is less than 2.0 ohms:	
	• Using an analog ohmmeter connect one lead to the left front air spring solenoid valve vehicle wiring harness connector circuit #430K and other to a known good chassis ground.	YES ▶	GO TO EA7
		NO ▶	GO TO EA6
EA6	**CHECKING WIRING HARNESS**		
	In order to determine if the vehicle wiring harness has the air spring solenoid valve circuits in the proper location the following test is required:	Ohmmeter reading is less than 2.0 ohms:	
	• Using an analog ohmmeter connect one lead to the left front air spring solenoid valve vehicle wiring harness connector circuit #415 and other to a known good chassis ground.	YES ▶	The air spring solenoid power circuit (#415) and ground circuit (#430K) are reversed. Relocate these circuits to the proper location, reconnect the air spring solenoid valve and air suspension control module. Rerun SERVICE BAY DIAGNOSTICS after repairs are made.
		NO ▶	The left front air spring solenoid valve's ground circuit (#430K) has a resistance to chassis ground that is above acceptable limits. The resistance to ground should always be less than 2.0 ohms. Rerun SERVICE BAY DIAGNOSTICS after repairs are made.

FM2019100064030X

Fig. 12 Test EA: Short In Left Front Air Spring Solenoid Valve Circuit (Part 3 of 4)

EA7	COMPONENT CHECK	RESULT	ACTION TO TAKE
	The previous steps have verified that the vehicle wiring harness is not the cause of the short. There are two possible causes that must now be checked (solenoid valve or control module). In order to determine which one is causing the short the following is required:	The STAR tester displayed code "40" again.	
	• Turn the air suspension "ON/OFF" switch to the "OFF" position.	YES ▶	Turn the air suspension "ON/OFF" switch to the "OFF" position. Remove the air suspension control module and install a new one. Rerun SERVICE BAY DIAGNOSTICS afterwards.
	• Reconnect the air suspension control module to the vehicle wiring harness.		
	• Turn the air suspension "ON/OFF" switch to the "ON" position.	NO ▶	Remove the left front air spring solenoid valve
	• Rerun SERVICE BAY DIAGNOSTICS without reconnecting the left front air spring solenoid valve connected to the vehicle wiring harness.		and install a new one. Rerun SERVICE BAY DIAGNOSTICS afterwards.
	NOTE: This test procedure will generate extra error codes because the left front air spring solenoid valve is not connected to the vehicle wiring harness.		

FM2019100064040X

Fig. 12 Test EA: Short In Left Front Air Spring Solenoid Valve Circuit (Part 4 of 4)

EB1	STAR CODE: 41 SHORT IN RIGHT FRONT AIR SPRING SOLENOID VALVE CIRCUIT	RESULT	ACTION TO TAKE
	The air suspension control module has detected a short in the circuit used to activate the right front air spring solenoid valve. There are four possible causes of this short which are listed below:		▶ GO TO EB2
	• B+ power supply circuit is shorted to ground.		
	• The vehicle wiring harness has the B+ power supply and ground return circuit to the solenoid valve are reversed.		
	• Air spring solenoid valve is defective.		
	• The air suspension control module is defective.		
	The right front air spring solenoid valve has a diode in it. When current is applied in the reverse direction this diode will act like a short. Because all ohmmeters do not have the same positive and negative polarity the following test procedures are being used to locate the cause of the short.		
EB2	CHECKING WIRING HARNESS		
	• Turn the air suspension "ON/OFF" switch to the "OFF" position.		▶ GO TO EB3
	• Disconnect air suspension control module connector.		

FM2019100065010X

Fig. 13 Test EB: Short In Right Front Air Spring Solenoid Valve Circuit (Part 1 of 4)

EB3	CHECKING WIRING HARNESS	RESULT	ACTION TO TAKE
	Using an analog ohmmeter measure and record the following:	At least one of the two ohmmeter readings is greater than 8.0 ohms:	
	• Connect the positive lead of the ohmmeter to the wiring harness connector pin location #17 (circuit #414) and the negative lead to pin location #40 (circuit #430G).	YES ▶	GO TO EB5
	• Now connect the positive lead of the ohmmeter to the wiring harness connector pin location #40 (circuit #430G) and the negative lead to pin location #17 (circuit #414).	NO ▶	GO TO EB4
EB4	CHECKING WIRING HARNESS		
	• Disconnect the right front air spring solenoid valve from the vehicle wiring harness.	Ohmmeter reading is greater than 10,000 ohms:	
	• Using an analog ohmmeter connect one lead to the wiring harness connector pin location #17 (circuit #414) and other pin location #40 (circuit #430G).	YES ▶	The right front air spring solenoid valve has an internal short circuit. Install a new air spring solenoid valve and rerun SERVICE BAY DIAGNOSTICS.
		NO ▶	A short has been detected in the wiring harness circuit #414/430G. Rerun SERVICE BAY DIAGNOSTICS after repair is made.

FM2019100065020X

Fig. 13 Test EB: Short In Right Front Air Spring Solenoid Valve Circuit (Part 2 of 4)

EB5	CHECKING WIRING HARNESS	RESULT	ACTION TO TAKE
	• Disconnect the right front air spring solenoid valve from the vehicle wiring harness.	Ohmmeter reading is less than 2.0 ohms:	
	• Using an analog ohmmeter connect one lead to the right front air spring solenoid valve vehicle wiring harness connector circuit #430D and other to a known good chassis ground.	YES ▶	GO TO EB7
		NO ▶	GO TO EB6
EB6	CHECKING WIRING HARNESS		
	In order to determine if the vehicle wiring harness has the air spring solenoid valve circuits in the proper location the following test is required:	Ohmmeter reading is less than 2.0 ohms:	
	• Using an analog ohmmeter connect one lead to the right front air spring solenoid valve vehicle wiring harness connector circuit #414 and other to a known good chassis ground.	YES ▶	The air spring solenoid power circuit (#414) and ground circuit (#430D) are reversed. Relocate these circuits to the proper location, reconnect the air spring solenoid valve and air suspension control module. Rerun SERVICE BAY DIAGNOSTICS after repairs are made.
		NO ▶	The right front air spring solenoid valve's ground circuit (#430D) has a resistance to chassis ground that is above acceptable limits. The resistance to ground should always be less than 2.0 ohms. Rerun SERVICE BAY DIAGNOSTICS after repairs are made.

FM2019100065030X

Fig. 13 Test EB: Short In Right Front Air Spring Solenoid Valve Circuit (Part 3 of 4)

EB7	COMPONENT CHECK	RESULT	ACTION TO TAKE
	The previous steps have verified that the vehicle wiring harness is not the cause of the short. There are two possible causes that must now be checked (solenoid valve or control module). In order to determine which one is causing the short the following is required:	The STAR tester displayed code "41" again.	
	• Turn the air suspension "ON/OFF" switch to the "OFF" position.	YES ▶	Turn the air suspension "ON/OFF" switch to the "OFF" position. Remove the air suspension control module and install a new one. Rerun SERVICE BAY DIAGNOSTICS afterwards.
	• Reconnect the air suspension control module to the vehicle wiring harness.		
	• Turn the air suspension "ON/OFF" switch to the "ON" position.	NO ▶	Remove the right front air spring solenoid valve
	• Rerun SERVICE BAY DIAGNOSTICS without reconnecting the right front air spring solenoid valve connected to the vehicle wiring harness.		and install a new one. Rerun SERVICE BAY DIAGNOSTICS afterwards.
	NOTE: This test procedure will generate extra error codes because the right front air spring solenoid valve is not connected to the vehicle wiring harness.		

FM2019100065040X

Fig. 13 Test EB: Short In Right Front Air Spring Solenoid Valve Circuit (Part 4 of 4)

EC1	STAR CODE: 42 SHORT IN LEFT REAR AIR SPRING SOLENOID VALVE CIRCUIT	RESULT	ACTION TO TAKE
	The air suspension control module has detected a short in the circuit used to activate the left rear air spring solenoid valve. There are four possible causes of this short which are listed below:		▶ GO TO EC2
	• B+ power supply circuit is shorted to ground.		
	• The vehicle wiring harness has the B+ power supply and ground return circuit to the solenoid valve reversed.		
	• Air spring solenoid valve is defective.		
	• The air suspension control module is defective.		
	The left rear air spring solenoid valve has a diode in it. When current is applied in the reverse direction this diode will act like a short. Because all ohmmeters do not have the same positive and negative polarity the following test procedures are being used to locate the cause of the short.		
EC2	• Turn the air suspension "ON/OFF" switch to the "OFF" position. • Disconnect air suspension control module connector.		▶ GO TO EC3

FM2019100066010X

Fig. 14 Test EC: Short In Left Rear Air Spring Solenoid Valve Circuit (Part 1 of 4)

EC3	CHECKING WIRING HARNESS	RESULT	ACTION TO TAKE
	Using an analog ohmmeter measure and record the following: • Connect the positive lead of the ohmmeter to the wiring harness connector pin location #41 (circuit #429) and the negative lead to pin location #40 (circuit #430G). • Now connect the positive lead of the ohmmeter to the wiring harness connector pin location #40 (circuit #430G) and the negative lead to pin location #41 (circuit #429).	At least one of the two ohmmeter readings is greater than 8.0 ohms: YES NO	 ▶ GO TO EC5 ▶ GO TO EC4
EC4	CHECKING WIRING HARNESS		
	• Disconnect the left rear air spring solenoid valve from the vehicle wiring harness. • Using an analog ohmmeter connect one lead to the wiring harness connector pin location #41 (circuit #429) and other to pin location #40 (circuit #430G).	Ohmmeter reading is greater than 10,000 ohms: YES	 ▶ The left rear air spring solenoid valve has an internal short circuit. Install a new air spring solenoid valve and rerun SERVICE BAY DIAGNOSTICS
		NO	▶ A short has been detected in the wiring harness circuit #429/430G. Rerun SERVICE BAY DIAGNOSTICS after repair is made.

FM2019100066020X

Fig. 14 Test EC: Short In Left Rear Air Spring Solenoid Valve Circuit (Part 2 of 4)

EC5	CHECKING WIRING HARNESS	RESULT	ACTION TO TAKE
	• Disconnect the left rear air spring solenoid valve from vehicle wiring harness. • Using an analog ohmmeter connect one lead to the left rear air spring solenoid valve vehicle wiring harness connector circuit #430F and other to a known good chassis ground.	Ohmmeter reading is less than 2.0 ohms: YES NO	 ▶ GO TO EC7 ▶ GO TO EC6
EC6	CHECKING WIRING HARNESS		
	In order to determine if the vehicle wiring harness has the air spring solenoid valve circuits in the proper location the following test is required: • Using an analog ohmmeter connect one lead to the left rear air spring solenoid valve vehicle wiring harness connector circuit #429 and other to a known good chassis ground.	Ohmmeter reading is less than 2.0 ohms: YES	 ▶ The air spring solenoid power circuit (#429) and ground circuit (#430F) are reversed. Relocate these circuits to the proper location, reconnect the air spring solenoid valve and air suspension control module. Rerun SERVICE BAY DIAGNOSTICS after repairs are made.
		NO	▶ The left rear air spring solenoid valve's ground circuit (#430F) has a resistance to chassis ground that is above acceptable limits. The resistance to ground should always be less than 2.0 ohms. Rerun SERVICE BAY DIAGNOSTICS after repairs are made.

FM2019100066030X

Fig. 14 Test EC: Short In Left Rear Air Spring Solenoid Valve Circuit (Part 3 of 4)

EC7	COMPONENT CHECK	RESULT	ACTION TO TAKE
	The previous steps have verified that the vehicle wiring harness is not the cause of the short. There are two possible causes that must now be checked (solenoid valve or control module). In order to determine which one is causing the short the following is required: • Turn the air suspension "ON/OFF" switch to the "OFF" position. • Reconnect the air suspension control module to the vehicle wiring harness. • Turn the air suspension "ON/OFF" switch to the "ON" position. • Rerun SERVICE BAY DIAGNOSTICS without reconnecting the left rear air spring solenoid valve connected to the vehicle wiring harness. NOTE: This test procedure will generate extra error codes because the left rear air spring solenoid valve is not connected to the vehicle wiring harness.	The STAR tester displayed code "42" again. YES NO	 ▶ Turn the air suspension "ON/OFF" switch to the "OFF" position. Remove the air suspension control module and install a new one. Rerun SERVICE BAY DIAGNOSTICS afterwards. ▶ Remove the left rear air spring solenoid valve (refer to shop manual for procedure) and install a new one. Rerun SERVICE BAY DIAGNOSTICS AFTERWARDS.

FM2019100066040X

Fig. 14 Test EC: Short In Left Rear Air Spring Solenoid Valve Circuit (Part 4 of 4).

ED1	STAR CODE: 43 SHORT IN RIGHT REAR AIR SPRING SOLENOID VALVE CIRCUIT	RESULT	ACTION TO TAKE
	The air suspension control module has detected a short in the circuit used to activate the right rear air spring solenoid valve. There are four possible causes of this short which are listed below:		► GO TO ED2
	• B+ power supply circuit is shorted to ground.		
	• The vehicle wiring harness has the B+ power supply and ground return circuit to the solenoid valve are reversed.		
	• Air spring solenoid valve is defective.		
	• The air suspension control module is defective.		
	The right rear air spring solenoid valve has a diode in it. When current is applied in the reverse direction this diode will act like a short. Because all ohmmeters do not have the same positive and negative polarity the following test procedures are being used to locate the cause of the short.		
ED2	• Turn the air suspension "ON/OFF" switch to the "OFF" position. • Disconnect air suspension control module connector.		► GO TO ED3

FM2019100067010X

Fig. 15   Test ED: Short In Right Rear Air Spring Solenoid Valve Circuit (Part 1 of 5)

ED3	CHECKING WIRING HARNESS	RESULT	ACTION TO TAKE
	Using an analog ohmmeter measure and record the following:	At least one of the two ohmmeter readings is greater than 8.0 ohms:	
	• Connect the positive lead of the ohmmeter to the wiring harness connector pin location #38 (circuit #416) and the negative lead to pin location #40 (circuit #430G).	YES	► GO TO ED5
	• Now connect the positive lead of the ohmmeter to the wiring harness connector pin location #40 (circuit #430G) and the negative lead to pin location #38 (circuit #416).	NO	► GO TO ED4
ED4	CHECKING WIRING HARNESS		
	• Disconnect the right rear air spring solenoid valve from the vehicle wiring harness.	Ohmmeter reading is greater than 10,000 ohms:	
	• Using an analog ohmmeter connect one lead to the wiring harness connector pin location #38 (circuit #416) and other to pin location #40 (circuit #430G).	YES	► The right rear air spring solenoid valve has an internal short circuit. Install a new air spring solenoid valve and rerun SERVICE BAY DIAGNOSTICS.
		NO	► A short has been detected in the wiring harness circuit #416/430G. Rerun SERVICE BAY DIAGNOSTICS after repair is made.

FM2019100067020X

Fig. 15   Test ED: Short In Right Rear Air Spring Solenoid Valve Circuit (Part 2 of 5)

ED5	CHECKING WIRING HARNESS	RESULT	ACTION TO TAKE
	• Disconnect the right rear air spring solenoid valve from the vehicle wiring harness.	Ohmmeter reading is less than 2.0 ohms:	
	• Using an analog ohmmeter connect one lead to the right rear air spring solenoid valve vehicle wiring harness connector circuit #430A and other to a known good chassis ground.	YES	GO TO ED7
		NO	GO TO ED6

FM2019100067030X

Fig. 15   Test ED: Short In Right Rear Air Spring Solenoid Valve Circuit (Part 3 of 5)

ED6	CHECKING WIRING HARNESS	RESULT	ACTION TO TAKE
	In order to determine if the vehicle wiring harness has the air spring solenoid valve circuits in the proper location the following test is required:	Ohmmeter reading is less than 2.0 ohms:	
	• Using an analog ohmmeter connect one lead to the right rear air spring solenoid valve vehicle wiring harness connector circuit #416 and other to a known good chassis ground.	YES	► The air spring solenoid power circuit (#416) and ground circuit (#430A) are reversed. Relocate these circuits to the proper location, reconnect the air spring solenoid valve and air suspension control module. Rerun SERVICE BAY DIAGNOSTICS after repairs are made.
		NO	► The right rear air spring solenoid valve's ground circuit (#430A) has a resistance to chassis ground that is above acceptable limits. The resistance to ground should always be less than 2.0 ohms. Rerun SERVICE BAY DIAGNOSTICS after repairs are made.

FM2019100067040X

Fig. 15   Test ED: Short In Right Rear Air Spring Solenoid Valve Circuit (Part 4 of 5)

ED7	COMPONENT CHECK	RESULT	ACTION TO TAKE
	The previous steps have verified that the vehicle wiring harness is not the cause of the short. There are two possible causes that must now be checked (solenoid valve or control module). In order to determine which one is causing the short the the following is required: • Turn the air suspension "ON/OFF" switch to the "OFF" position. • Reconnect the air suspension control module to the vehicle wiring harness. • Turn the air suspension "ON/OFF" switch to the "ON" position. • Rerun SERVICE BAY DIAGNOSTICS without reconnecting the right rear air spring solenoid valve connected to the vehicle wiring harness. NOTE: This test procedure will generate extra error codes because the right rear air spring solenoid valve is not connected to the vehicle wiring harness.	The STAR tester displayed code "43" again: YES NO	► Turn the air suspension "ON/OFF" switch to the "OFF" position. Remove the air suspension control module and install a new one. Rerun SERVICE BAY DIAGNOSTICS afterwards. ► Remove the right rear air spring solenoid valve and install a new one. Rerun SERVICE BAY DIAGNOSTICS afterwards.

FM2019100067050X

Fig. 15   Test ED: Short In Right Rear Air Spring Solenoid Valve Circuit (Part 5 of 5)

EE1	STAR CODE: 44 SHORT IN VENT SOLENOID VALVE CIRCUIT	RESULT	ACTION TO TAKE
	The air suspension control module has detected a short in the circuit used to activate the vent solenoid valve. There are four possible causes of this short which are listed below: • B + power supply circuit is shorted to ground. • The vehicle wiring harness has the B + power supply circuit and ground return circuit in the wrong location. • Vent solenoid valve is defective. • The air suspension control module is defective. The vent solenoid valve has a diode in it. When current is applied in the reverse direction this diode will act like a short. Because all ohmmeters do not have the same positive and negative polarity the following test procedures are being used to locate the cause of the short.		► GO TO EE2
EE2	• Turn the air suspension "ON/OFF" switch to the "OFF" position. • Disconnect air suspension control module connector.		► GO TO EE3

FM2019100068010X

Fig. 16   Test EE: Short In Vent Solenoid Valve Circuit (Part 1 of 4)

EE3	CHECKING WIRING HARNESS	RESULT	ACTION TO TAKE
	Using an analog ohmmeter measure and record the following: • Connect the positive lead of the ohmmeter to the wiring harness connector pin location #42 (circuit #421) and the negative lead to pin location #40 (circuit #430G). • Now connect the positive lead of the ohmmeter to the wiring harness connector pin location #40 (circuit #430G) and the negative lead to pin location #42 (circuit #421).	At least one of the two ohmmeter readings is greater than 20 ohms: YES NO	► GO TO EE5 ► GO TO EE4
EE4	CHECKING WIRING HARNESS		
	• Disconnect the air compressor assembly from the vehicle wiring harness. • Using an analog ohmmeter connect one lead to the wiring harness connector pin location #42 (circuit #421) and other to pin location #40 (circuit #430G).	Ohmmeter reading is greater than 10,000 ohms: YES NO	► The vent solenoid valve has an internal short circuit. Install a new air compressor assembly and rerun SERVICE BAY DIAGNOSTICS. ► A short has been detected in the wiring harness circuit #421/430G. Rerun SERVICE BAY DIAGNOSTICS after repair is made.

FM2019100068020X

Fig. 16   Test EE: Short In Vent Solenoid Valve Circuit (Part 2 of 4)

EE5	CHECKING WIRING HARNESS	RESULT	ACTION TO TAKE
	• Disconnect the air compressor assembly from the vehicle wiring harness. • Using an analog ohmmeter connect one lead to the vent solenoid valve vehicle wiring harness connector circuit #430E and other to a known good chassis ground.	Ohmmeter reading is less than 2.0 ohms: YES NO	► GO TO EE7 ► GO TO EE6
EE6	CHECKING WIRING HARNESS		
	In order to determine if the vehicle wiring harness has the vent solenoid valve circuits in the proper location the following test is required: • Using an analog ohmmeter connect one lead to the vent solenoid valve vehicle wiring harness connector circuit #421 and other to a known good chassis ground.	Ohmmeter reading is less than 2.0 ohms: YES NO	► The vent solenoid power circuit (#421) and ground circuit (#430E) are reversed. Relocate these circuits to the proper location, reconnect the air compressor assembly and air suspension control module. Rerun SERVICE BAY DIAGNOSTICS after repairs are made. ► The vent solenoid valve's ground circuit (#430E) has a resistance to chassis ground that is above acceptable limits. The resistance to ground should always be less than 2.0 ohms. Rerun SERVICE BAY DIAGNOSTICS after repairs are made.

FM2019100068030X

Fig. 16   Test EE: Short In Vent Solenoid Valve Circuit (Part 3 of 4)

EE7	COMPONENT CHECK	RESULT	ACTION TO TAKE
	The previous steps have verified that the vehicle wiring harness is not the cause of the short. There are two possible causes that must now be checked (vent solenoid valve or control module). In order to determine which one is causing the short the following is required: • Turn the air suspension "ON/OFF" switch to the "OFF" position. • Reconnect the air suspension control module to the vehicle wiring harness. • Turn the air suspension "ON/OFF" switch to the "ON" position. • Rerun SERVICE BAY DIAGNOSTICS without the air compressor assembly connected to the vehicle wiring harness. NOTE: This test procedure will generate extra error codes because the air compressor assembly is not connected to the vehicle wiring harness.	The STAR tester displayed code "40" again: YES NO	▶ Turn the air suspension "ON/OFF" switch to the "OFF" position. Remove the air suspension control module and install a new one. Rerun SERVICE BAY DIAGNOSTICS afterwards. ▶ Remove the air compressor assembly and install a new one. Rerun SERVICE BAY DIAGNOSTICS afterwards.

FM2019100068040X

**Fig. 16 Test EE: Short In Vent Solenoid Valve Circuit
(Part 4 of 4)**

EF4	CHECKING WIRING HARNESS	RESULT	ACTION TO TAKE
	• Disconnect the air compressor relay from the vehicle wiring harness. • Using an analog ohmmeter connect one lead to the wiring harness connector pin location #35 (circuit #420) and other to pin location #40 (circuit #430G).	Ohmmeter reading is greater than 10,000 ohms: YES NO	▶ The air compressor relay has an internal short circuit. Install a new air compressor relay and rerun SERVICE BAY DIAGNOSTICS. ▶ A short has been detected in the wiring harness circuit #420/430G. Rerun SERVICE BAY DIAGNOSTICS after repair is made.
EF5	CHECKING WIRING HARNESS		
	• Disconnect the air compressor relay from the vehicle wiring harness. • Using an analog ohmmeter connect one lead to the air compressor relay vehicle wiring harness connector circuit #430B and other to a known good chassis ground.	Ohmmeter reading is less than 2.0 ohms: YES NO	▶ GO TO EF8 ▶ GO TO EF6

FM2019100069020X

**Fig. 17 Test EF: Short In Air Compressor Relay Circuit
(Part 2 of 5)**

EF1	STAR CODE: 45 SHORT IN AIR COMPRESSOR RELAY CIRCUIT	RESULT	ACTION TO TAKE
	The air suspension control module has detected a short in the circuit used to activate the air compressor relay. There are four possible causes of this short which are listed below. • B+ power supply circuit is shorted to ground. • The vehicle wiring harness has the B+ power supply circuit and ground return circuit in the wrong location. • Air compressor relay is defective. • The air suspension control module is defective. The air compressor relay has a diode in it. When current is applied in the reverse direction this diode will act like a short. Because all ohmmeters do not have the same positive and negative polarity the following test procedures are being used to locate the cause of the short.	▶	GO TO EF2
EF2			
	• Turn the air suspension "ON/OFF" switch to the "OFF" position. • Disconnect air suspension control module connector.		▶ GO TO EF3
EF3	CHECKING WIRING HARNESS		
	Using an analog ohmmeter measure and record the following: • Connect the positive lead of the ohmmeter to the wiring harness connector pin location #35 (circuit #420) and the negative lead to pin location #40 (circuit #430G). • Now connect the positive lead of the ohmmeter to the wiring harness connector pin location #40 (circuit #430G) and the negative lead to pin location #35 (circuit #420).	At least one of the two ohmmeter readings is greater than 40 ohms: YES NO	▶ GO TO EF5 ▶ GO TO EF4

FM2019100069010X

**Fig. 17 Test EF: Short In Air Compressor Relay Circuit
(Part 1 of 5)**

EF6	CHECKING WIRING HARNESS	RESULT	ACTION TO TAKE
	In order to determine if the vehicle wiring harness has the air compressor relay circuits in the proper location the following test is required: • Using an analog ohmmeter connect one lead to the air compressor relay vehicle wiring harness connector circuit #420 and other to a known good chassis ground.	Ohmmeter reading is less than 2.0 ohms: YES NO	▶ The air compressor relay power circuit (#420) and ground circuit (#430B) are reversed. Relocate these circuits to the proper location, reconnect the air compressor relay and air suspension control module. Rerun SERVICE BAY DIAGNOSTICS after repairs are made. ▶ GO TO EF7

FM2019100069030X

**Fig. 17 Test EF: Short In Air Compressor Relay Circuit
(Part 3 of 5)**

EF7	CHECKING WIRING HARNESS	RESULT	ACTION TO TAKE
	• Verify that all the wires going to the air compressor relay are in the proper location.	All wires are in the proper location:	
		YES ▶	The air compressor relay ground circuit (#430B) has a resistance to chassis ground that is above acceptable limits. The resistance to ground should always be less than 2.0 ohms. Rerun SERVICE BAY DIAGNOSTICS after repairs are made.
		NO ▶	Relocate wires to the proper location, reconnect the air compressor relay and air suspension control module. Rerun SERVICE BAY DIAGNOSTICS after repairs are made.

FM2019100069040X

Fig. 17   Test EF: Short In Air Compressor Relay Circuit (Part 4 of 5)

EF8	COMPONENT CHECK	RESULT	ACTION TO TAKE
	The previous steps have verified that the vehicle wiring harness is not the cause of the short. There are two possible causes that must now be checked (air compressor relay or control module). In order to determine which one is causing the short the following is required:	The STAR tester displayed code "45" again:	
	• Turn the air suspension "ON/OFF" switch to the "OFF" position.	YES ▶	Turn the air suspension "ON/OFF" switch to the "OFF" position. Remove the air suspension control module and install a new one. Rerun SERVICE BAY DIAGNOSTICS afterwards.
	• Reconnect the air suspension control module to the vehicle wiring harness.		
	• Turn the air suspension "ON/OFF" switch to the "ON" position.	NO ▶	Remove the air compressor relay and install a new one. Rerun SERVICE BAY DIAGNOSTICS afterwards
	• Rerun SERVICE BAY DIAGNOSTICS without reconnecting the air compressor relay connected to the vehicle wiring harness.		
	NOTE: This test procedure will generate extra error codes because the air compressor relay is not connected to the vehicle wiring harness.		

FM2019100069050X

Fig. 17   Test EF: Short In Air Compressor Relay Circuit (Part 5 of 5)

EG1	STAR CODE: 46 SHORT IN HEIGHT SENSOR POWER SUPPLY CIRCUIT	RESULT	ACTION TO TAKE
	The air suspension control module has detected a short in circuit used to provide power to the air suspension height sensors. There are six possible causes of this short which are listed below:		GO TO EG2
	• B+ power supply circuit is shorted to ground.		
	• The vehicle wiring harness has the B+ power supply circuit and ground return circuit in the wrong location.		
	• The left front height sensor is defective.		
	• The right front height sensor is defective.		
	• The rear height sensor is defective.		
	• The air suspension control module is defective.		
	The three height sensors on the vehicle have a common B+ power supply circuit coming out of the air suspension control module. For this reason the following test procedure will be used to locate the cause of the short:		
EG2	ENTERING DRIVE CYCLE DIAGNOSTICS		
	In order to determine where the short is located a modified DRIVE CYCLE DIAGNOSTICS will be utilized. In order to do this the following preliminary actions are required:		GO TO EG3
	• Release the STAR test button to the "HOLD" position.		
	• Disconnect the left front height sensor from the vehicle wiring harness.		
	• With the ignition switch in the "ON/RUN" position turn the air suspension "ON/OFF" switch to the "ON" position and wait 15 seconds.		

FM2019100070010X

Fig. 18   Test EG: Short In Height Sensor Power Supply Circuit (Part 1 of 5)

EG3	COMPONENT CHECK	RESULT	ACTION TO TAKE
	• Turn the ignition switch to the "OFF" position.	The STAR tester is displaying code "46" again:	
	• Depress the STAR test button so that it remains down in the "TEST" position.	YES ▶	GO TO EG4
	NOTE: This type of DRIVE CYCLE DIAGNOSTIC test will cause code "55" to be displayed, since a vehicle speed of 15mph or greater was not detected.	NO ▶	Remove the left front height sensor and replace it with a new one. Rerun SERVICE BAY DIAGNOSTICS after repair is made.
EG4	ENTERING DRIVE CYCLE DIAGNOSTICS		
	Again the modified DRIVE CYCLE DIAGNOSTICS will be used to help locate the cause of the short.		GO TO EG5
	• Release the STAR test button to the "HOLD" position.		
	• Turn the air suspension "ON/OFF" switch to the "OFF" position.		
	• Disconnect the right front height sensor also from the vehicle wiring harness.		
	• With the ignition switch in the "ON/RUN" position turn the air suspension "ON/OFF" switch to the "ON" position and wait 15 seconds.		

FM2019100070020X

Fig. 18   Test EG: Short In Height Sensor Power Supply Circuit (Part 2 of 5)

EG5	COMPONENT CHECK	RESULT	ACTION TO TAKE
	• Turn the ignition switch to the "OFF" position.	The STAR tester is displaying code "46" again:	
	• Depress the STAR test button so that it remains down in the "TEST" position.	YES ▶	GO TO EG6
	NOTE: This type of DRIVE CYCLE DIAGNOSTIC test will cause code "55" to be displayed, since a vehicle speed of 15mph or greater was not detected.	NO ▶	Remove the right front height sensor, replace it with a new one and reconnect the left front height sensor to the vehicle wiring harness. Rerun SERVICE BAY DIAGNOSTICS after repair is made.
EG6	ENTERING DRIVE CYCLE DIAGNOSTICS		
	Again the modified DRIVE CYCLE DIAGNOSTICS will be used to help locate the cause of the short.		
	• Release the STAR test button to the "HOLD" position.	▶	GO TO EG7
	• Turn the air suspension "ON/OFF" switch to the "OFF" position.		
	• Disconnect the rear height sensor also from the vehicle wiring harness.		
	• With the ignition switch in the "ON/RUN" position turn the air suspension "ON/OFF" switch to the "ON" position and wait 15 seconds.		

FM2019100070030X

Fig. 18 Test EG: Short In Height Sensor Power Supply Circuit (Part 3 of 5)

EG7	COMPONENT CHECK	RESULT	ACTION TO TAKE
	• Turn the ignition switch to the "OFF" position.	The STAR tester is displaying code "46" again:	
	• Depress the STAR test button so that it remains down in the "TEST" position.	YES ▶	GO TO EG8
	NOTE: This type of DRIVE CYCLE DIAGNOSTIC test will cause code "55" to be displayed, since a vehicle speed of 15mph or greater was not detected.	NO ▶	Remove the rear height sensor, replace it with a new one and reconnect the left and right front height sensors to the vehicle wiring harness. Rerun SERVICE BAY DIAGNOSTICS after repair is made.
EG8	CHECKING WIRING HARNESS		
	The air suspension control module has detected a short in the circuit which is used to provide power to the air suspension height sensors even with all three height sensors removed from the circuit. This leaves just two possible causes of the short (vehicle wiring harness or air suspension control module). In order to determine which one is the the cause of the short the following actions are required:	Ohmmeter reading is greater than 10,000 ohms:	
		YES ▶	GO TO EG9
	• Disconnect air suspension control module connector.	NO ▶	A short has been detected in the wiring harness circuit #431B.
	• Turn the air suspension "ON/OFF" switch to the "ON" position.		rerun SERVICE BAY DIAGNOSTICS after repair is made.
	• Using an analog ohmmeter connect one lead to the wiring harness connector pin location #22 (circuit #431B) and other to pin location #40 (circuit #430G).		

FM2019100070040X

Fig. 18 Test EG: Short In Height Sensor Power Supply Circuit (Part 4 of 5)

EG9	CHECKING WIRING HARNESS	RESULT	ACTION TO TAKE
	• Using an analog ohmmeter (20,000 ohms is recommended) connect one lead to the wiring harness connector pin location #55 (circuit #431A) and other to pin location #60 (circuit #430H).	Ohmmeter reading is greater than 10,000 ohms:	
		YES ▶	Remove the air suspension control module and install a new one. Reconnect all three height sensors to the vehicle wiring harness and rerun SERVICE BAY DIAGNOSTICS afterwards.
		NO ▶	A short has been detected in the wiring harness circuit #431B.
			rerun SERVICE BAY DIAGNOSTICS after repair is made.

FM2019100070050X

Fig. 18 Test EG: Short In Height Sensor Power Supply Circuit (Part 5 of 5)

EH1	STAR CODE: 47 SHORT IN SOFT SHOCK ACTUATOR RELAY CIRCUIT	RESULT	ACTION TO TAKE
	The air suspension control module has detected a short in the circuit used to activate the soft shock position relay. There are four possible causes of this short which are listed below:	▶	GO TO EH2
	• B+ power supply circuit is shorted to ground.		
	• The vehicle wiring harness has the B+ power supply circuit and ground return circuit in the wrong location.		
	• Soft shock relay is defective.		
	• The air suspension control module is defective.		
	The soft shock position relay has a diode in it. When current is applied in the reverse direction this diode will act like a short. Because all ohmmeters do not have the same positive and negative polarity the following test procedures are being used to locate the cause of the short.		
EH2			
	• Turn the air suspension "ON/OFF" switch to the "OFF" position.	▶	GO TO EH3
	• Disconnect air suspension control module connector.		
EH3	CHECKING WIRING HARNESS		
	Using an analog ohmmeter measure and record the following:	At least one of the two ohmmeter readings is greater than 40 ohms:	
	• Connect the positive lead of the ohmmeter to the wiring harness connector pin location #12 (circuit #839) and the negative lead to pin location #40 (circuit #430G).	YES ▶	GO TO EH5
	• Now connect the positive lead of the ohmmeter to the wiring harness connector pin location #40 (circuit #430G) and the negative lead to pin location #12 (circuit #839).	NO ▶	GO TO EH4

FM2019100071010X

Fig. 19 Test EH: Short In Soft Shock Actuator Relay Circuit (Part 1 of 4)

EH4	CHECKING WIRING HARNESS	RESULT	ACTION TO TAKE
	• Disconnect the soft shock relay from the vehicle wiring harness.	Ohmmeter reading is greater than 10,000 ohms:	
	• Using an analog ohmmeter connect one lead to the wiring harness connector pin location #12 (circuit #839) and other to pin location #40 (circuit #430G).	YES ▶	The soft shock relay has an internal short circuit. Install a new one and rerun SERVICE BAY DIAGNOSTICS.
		NO ▶	A short has been detected in the wiring harness circuit #839/430G. Rerun SERVICE BAY DIAGNOSTICS after repair is made.

EH5	CHECKING WIRING HARNESS		
	• Disconnect the soft shock relay from the vehicle wiring harness.	Ohmmeter reading is less than 2.0 ohms:	
	• Using an analog ohmmeter connect one lead to the soft shock relay vehicle wiring harness connector circuit #430B and other to a known good chassis ground.	YES ▶	GO TO EH8
		NO ▶	GO TO EH6

Fig. 19 Test EH: Short In Soft Shock Actuator Relay Circuit (Part 2 of 4)

FM2019100071020X

EH6	CHECKING WIRING HARNESS	RESULT	ACTION TO TAKE
	In order to determine if the vehicle wiring harness has the soft shock relay circuits in the proper location the following test is required:	Ohmmeter reading is less than 2.0 ohms:	
	• Using an analog ohmmeter connect one lead to the soft shock relay vehicle wiring harness connector circuit #839 and other to a known good chassis ground.	YES ▶	The soft shock relay power circuit (#839) and ground circuit (#430B) are reversed. Relocate these circuits to the proper location, reconnect the soft shock relay and air suspension control module. Rerun SERVICE BAY DIAGNOSTICS after repairs are made.
		NO ▶	GO TO EH7

EH7	CHECKING WIRING HARNESS		
	• Verify that all the wires going to the soft shock relay are in the proper location.	All wires are in the proper location:	
		YES ▶	The soft shock relay ground circuit (#430B) has a resistance to chassis ground that is above acceptable limits. The resistance to ground should always be less than 2.0 ohms. Rerun SERVICE BAY DIAGNOSTICS after repairs are made.
		NO ▶	Relocate wires to the proper location, reconnect the soft shock relay and air suspension control. Rerun SERVICE BAY DIAGNOSTICS after repairs are made.

Fig. 19 Test EH: Short In Soft Shock Actuator Relay Circuit (Part 3 of 4)

FM2019100071030X

EH8	COMPONENT CHECK	RESULT	ACTION TO TAKE
	The previous steps have verified that the vehicle wiring harness is not the cause of the short. There are two possible causes that must now be checked (soft shock relay or control module). In order to determine which one is causing the short the following is required:	The STAR tester displayed code "47" again:	
		YES ▶	Turn the air suspension "ON/OFF" switch to the "OFF" position. Remove the air suspension control module and install a new one. Rerun SERVICE BAY DIAGNOSTICS afterwards.
	• Turn the air suspension "ON/OFF" switch to the "OFF" position.		
	• Reconnect the air suspension control module to the vehicle wiring harness.		
	• Turn the air suspension "ON/OFF" switch to the "ON" position.		
	• Rerun SERVICE BAY DIAGNOSTICS without the soft shock relay connected to the vehicle wiring harness.	NO ▶	Remove the soft shock relay and install a new one. Rerun SERVICE BAY DIAGNOSTICS afterwards.
	NOTE: This test procedure will generate extra error codes because the soft shock relay is not connected to the vehicle wiring harness.		

Fig. 19 Test EH: Short In Soft Shock Actuator Relay Circuit (Part 4 of 4)

FM2019100071040X

EI1	STAR CODE: 48 SHORT IN FIRM SHOCK ACTUATOR RELAY CIRCUIT	RESULT	ACTION TO TAKE
	The air suspension control module has detected a short in the circuit used to activate the firm shock position relay. There are four possible causes of this short which are listed below:		▶ GO TO EI2
	• B+ power supply circuit is shorted to ground.		
	• The vehicle wiring harness has the B+ power supply circuit and ground return circuit in the wrong location.		
	• Firm shock relay is defective.		
	• The air suspension control module is defective.		
	The firm shock position relay has a diode in it. When current is applied in the reverse direction this diode will act like a short. Because all ohmmeters do not have the same positive and negative polarity the following test procedures are being used to locate the cause of the short.		

EI2			
	• Turn the air suspension "ON/OFF" switch to the "OFF" position.		▶ GO TO EI3
	• Disconnect air suspension control module connector.		

EI3	CHECKING WIRING HARNESS		
	Using an analog ohmmeter measure and record the following:	At least one of the two ohmmeter readings is greater than 40 ohms:	
	• Connect the positive lead of the ohmmeter to the wiring harness connector pin location #11 (circuit #838) and the negative lead to pin location #40 (circuit #430G).	YES ▶	GO TO EI5
	• Now connect the positive lead of the ohmmeter to the wiring harness connector pin location #40 (circuit #430G) and the negative lead to pin location #11 (circuit #838).	NO ▶	GO TO EI4

FM2019100072010X

Fig. 20 Test EI: Short In Firm Shock Actuator Relay Circuit (Part 1 of 5)

E14	CHECKING WIRING HARNESS	RESULT		ACTION TO TAKE
	• Disconnect the firm shock relay from the vehicle wiring harness. • Using an analog ohmmeter connect one lead to the wiring harness connector pin location #11 (circuit #838) and other to pin location #40 (circuit #430G).	Ohmmeter reading is greater than 10,000 ohms: YES	▶	The firm shock relay has an internal short circuit. Install a new one and rerun SERVICE BAY DIAGNOSTICS.
		NO	▶	A short has been detected in the wiring harness circuit #838/430G. Rerun SERVICE BAY DIAGNOSTICS after repair is made.

E15	CHECKING WIRING HARNESS	RESULT		ACTION TO TAKE
	• Disconnect the firm shock relay from the vehicle wiring harness. • Using an analog ohmmeter connect one lead to the soft shock relay vehicle wiring harness connector circuit #430D and other to a known good chassis ground.	Ohmmeter reading is less than 2.0 ohms: YES	▶	GO TO E18
		NO	▶	GO TO E16

Fig. 20 Test EI: Short In Firm Shock Actuator Relay Circuit (Part 2 of 5)

FM2019100072020X

E16	CHECKING WIRING HARNESS	RESULT		ACTION TO TAKE
	In order to determine if the vehicle wiring harness has the firm shock relay circuits in the proper location the following test is required: • Using an analog ohmmeter connect one lead to the soft shock relay vehicle wiring harness connector circuit #838 and other to a known good chassis ground.	Ohmmeter reading is less than 2.0 ohms: YES	▶	The firm shock relay power circuit (#838) and ground circuit (#430D) are reversed. Relocate these circuits to the proper location, reconnect the firm shock relay and air suspension control module. Rerun SERVICE BAY DIAGNOSTICS after repairs are made.
		NO	▶	GO TO E17

Fig. 20 Test EI: Short In Firm Shock Actuator Relay Circuit (Part 3 of 5)

FM2019100072030X

E17	CHECKING WIRING HARNESS	RESULT		ACTION TO TAKE
	• Verify that all the wires going to the firm shock relay are in the proper location.	All wires are in the proper location: YES	▶	The firm shock relay ground circuit (#430D) has a resistance to chassis ground that is above acceptable limits. The resistance to ground should always be less than 2.0 ohms. Rerun SERVICE BAY DIAGNOSTICS after repairs are made.
		NO	▶	Relocate wires to the proper location, reconnect the firm shock relay and air suspension control. Rerun SERVICE BAY DIAGNOSTICS after repairs are made.

Fig. 20 Test EI: Short In Firm Shock Actuator Relay Circuit (Part 4 of 5)

FM2019100072040X

E18	COMPONENT CHECK	RESULT		ACTION TO TAKE
	The previous steps have verified that the vehicle wiring harness is not the cause of the short. There are two possible causes that must now be checked (firm shock relay or control module). In order to determine which one is causing the short the following is required: • Turn the air suspension "ON/OFF" switch to the "OFF" position. • Reconnect the air suspension control module to the vehicle wiring harness. • Turn the air suspension "ON/OFF" switch to the "ON" position. • Rerun SERVICE BAY DIAGNOSTICS without the firm shock relay being connected to the vehicle wiring harness. NOTE: This test procedure will generate extra error codes because the firm shock relay is not connected to the vehicle wiring harness.	The STAR tester displayed code "48" again: YES	▶	Turn the air suspension "ON/OFF" switch to the "OFF" position. Remove the air suspension control module and install a new one. Rerun SERVICE BAY DIAGNOSTICS afterwards.
		NO	▶	Remove the firm shock relay and install a new one. Rerun SERVICE BAY DIAGNOSTICS afterwards.

Fig. 20 Test EI: Short In Firm Shock Actuator Relay Circuit (Part 5 of 5)

FM2019100072050X

EJ1	STAR CODE: 66 SHORT IN RIGHT FRONT HEIGHT SENSOR CIRCUIT	RESULT	ACTION TO TAKE
	The air suspension control module has detected a short in the circuit used to to receive signals from the right front height sensor. There are four possible causes of this short which are listed below: • Channel "A" signal return circuit is shorted to ground. • Channel "B" signal return circuit is shorted to ground. • The right front height sensor is defective. • The air suspension control module is defective.		▶ GO TO EJ2
EJ2	In order to determine where the short is located a modified DRIVE CYCLE DIAGNOSTICS will be utilized. In order to do this the following preliminary actions are required: • Turn the air suspension "ON/OFF" switch to the "OFF" position. • Disconnect the right front height sensor from the vehicle wiring harness. • With the ignition switch in the "ON/RUN" position turn the air suspension "ON/OFF" switch to the "ON" position and wait 15 seconds.		▶ GO TO EJ3

FM2019100073010X

Fig. 21   Test EJ: Short In Right Front Height Sensor (Part 1 of 3)

EJ3	COMPONENT CHECK	RESULT	ACTION TO TAKE
	• Turn the ignition switch to the "OFF" position. • Depress the STAR test button so that it remains down in the "TEST" position. NOTE: This type of DRIVE CYCLE DIAGNOSTIC test will cause code "55" to be displayed, since a vehicle speed of 15 mph or greater was not detected.	The STAR tester is displaying code "66" again: YES NO	▶ GO TO EJ4 ▶ Remove the right front height sensor and replace it with a new one. Rerun SERVICE BAY DIAGNOSTICS after repair is made.
EJ4	WIRING HARNESS CHECK		
	• Turn the air suspension "ON/OFF" switch to the "OFF" position. • Disconnect air suspension control module connector. • Using an analog ohmmeter connect one lead to the air suspension control module wiring harness connector pin location #9 (circuit #424) and other to a known good chassis ground.	Ohmmeter reading is greater than 10,000 ohms: YES NO	▶ GO TO EJ5 ▶ A short to ground has been detected in the wiring harness circuit #424. Reconnect the right front height sensor, air suspension control module and rerun SERVICE BAY DIAGNOSTICS after repair is made.

FM2019100073020X

Fig. 21   Test EJ: Short In Right Front Height Sensor (Part 2 of 3)

EJ5	WIRING HARNESS CHECK	RESULT	ACTION TO TAKE
	• Using an analog ohmmeter connect one lead to the air suspension control module wiring harness connector pin location #10 (circuit #425) and other to a known good chassis ground.	Ohmmeter reading is greater than 10,000 ohms: YES NO	▶ Turn the air suspension "ON/OFF" switch to the "OFF" position. Remove the air suspension control module and install a new one. Reconnect the right front height sensor and rerun SERVICE BAY DIAGNOSTICS afterwards. ▶ A short to ground has been detected in the wiring harness circuit #425. Reconnect the right front height sensor, air suspension control module and rerun SERVICE BAY DIAGNOSTICS after repair is made.

FM2019100073030X

Fig. 21   Test EJ: Short In Right Front Height Sensor (Part 3 of 3)

EK1	STAR CODE: 67 SHORT IN LEFT FRONT HEIGHT SENSOR CIRCUIT	RESULT	ACTION TO TAKE
	The air suspension control module has detected a short in the circuit used to receive signals from the left front height sensor. There are four possible causes of this short which are listed below: • Channel "A" signal return circuit is shorted to ground. • Channel "B" signal return circuit is shorted to ground. • The left front height sensor is defective. • The air suspension control module is defective.		▶ GO TO EK2
EK2	In order to determine where the short is located a modified DRIVE CYCLE DIAGNOSTICS will be utilized. In order to do this the following preliminary actions are required: • Turn the air suspension "ON/OFF" switch to the "OFF" position. • Disconnect the left front height sensor from the vehicle wiring harness. • With the ignition switch in the "ON/RUN" position turn the air suspension "ON/OFF" switch to the "ON" position and wait 15 seconds.		▶ GO TO EK3
EK3	COMPONENT CHECK		
	• Turn the ignition switch to the "OFF" position. • Depress the STAR test button so that it remains down in the "TEST" position. NOTE: This type of DRIVE CYCLE DIAGNOSTIC test will cause code "55" to be displayed, since a vehicle speed of 15 mph or greater was not detected.	The STAR tester is displaying code "67" again: YES NO	▶ GO TO EK4 ▶ Remove the left front height sensor and replace it with a new one. Rerun SERVICE BAY DIAGNOSTICS after repair is made.

FM2019100074010X

Fig. 22   Test EK: Short In Left Front Height Sensor Circuit (Part 1 of 3)

EK4	WIRING HARNESS CHECK	RESULT	ACTION TO TAKE
	* Turn the air suspension "ON/OFF" switch to the "OFF" position. * Disconnect air suspension control module connector. * Using an analog ohmmeter connect one lead to the air suspension control module wiring harness connector pin location #27 (circuit #422) and other to a known good chassis ground.	Ohmmeter reading is greater than 10,000 ohms: YES NO	▶ GO TO EK5 ▶ A short to ground has been detected in the wiring harness circuit #422. Reconnect the left front height sensor, air suspension control module and rerun SERVICE BAY DIAGNOSTICS after repair is made.

Fig. 22   Test EK: Short In Left Front Height Sensor Circuit (Part 2 of 3)

FM2019100074020X

EK5	WIRING HARNESS CHECK	RESULT	ACTION TO TAKE
	* Using an analog ohmmeter connect one lead to the air suspension control module wiring harness connector pin location #43 (circuit #423) and other to a known good chassis ground.	Ohmmeter reading is greater than 10,000 ohms: YES NO	▶ Turn the air suspension "ON/OFF" switch to the "OFF" position. Remove the air suspension control module and install a new one. Reconnect the left front height sensor and rerun SERVICE BAY DIAGNOSTICS afterwards. ▶ A short to ground has been detected in the wiring harness circuit #423. Reconnect the left front height sensor, air suspension control module and rerun SERVICE BAY DIAGNOSTICS after repair is made.

FM2019100074030X

Fig. 22   Test EK: Short In Left Front Height Sensor Circuit (Part 3 of 3)

EL1	STAR CODE: 68 SHORT IN REAR HEIGHT SENSOR CIRCUIT	RESULT	ACTION TO TAKE
	The air suspension control module has detected a short in the circuit used to receive signals from the rear height sensor. There are four possible causes of this short which are listed below: * Channel "A" signal return circuit is shorted to ground. * Channel "B" signal return circuit is shorted to ground. * The rear height sensor is defective. * The air suspension control module is defective.		▶ GO TO EL2
EL2	In order to determine where the short is located a modified DRIVE CYCLE DIAGNOSTICS will be utilized. In order to do this the following preliminary actions are required: * Turn the air suspension "ON/OFF" switch to the "OFF" position. * Disconnect the rear height sensor from the vehicle wiring harness. * With the ignition switch in the "ON/RUN" position turn the air suspension "ON/OFF" switch to the "ON" position and wait 15 seconds.		▶ GO TO EL3
EL3	COMPONENT CHECK * Turn the ignition switch to the "OFF" position. * Depress the STAR test button so that it remains down in the "TEST" position. NOTE: This type of DRIVE CYCLE DIAGNOSTIC test will cause code "55" to be displayed, since a vehicle speed of 15 mph or greater was not detected.	The STAR tester is displaying code "68" again: YES NO	▶ GO TO EL4 ▶ Remove the rear height sensor and replace it with a new one. Rerun SERVICE BAY DIAGNOSTICS after repair is made.

FM2019100075010X

Fig. 23   Test EL: Short In Rear Height Sensor Circuit (Part 1 of 3)

EL4	WIRING HARNESS CHECK	RESULT	ACTION TO TAKE
	* Turn the air suspension "ON/OFF" switch to the "OFF" position. * Disconnect air suspension control module connector. * Using an analog ohmmeter connect one lead to the air suspension control module wiring harness connector pin location #5 (circuit #427) and other to a known good chassis ground.	Ohmmeter reading is greater than 10,000 ohms: YES NO	▶ GO TO EL5 ▶ A short to ground has been detected in the wiring harness circuit #427. Reconnect the rear height sensor, air suspension control module and rerun SERVICE BAY DIAGNOSTICS after repair is made.

FM2019100075020X

Fig. 23   Test EL: Short In Rear Height Sensor Circuit (Part 2 of 3)

EL5	WIRING HARNESS CHECK	RESULT		ACTION TO TAKE
	• Using an analog ohmmeter connect one lead to the air suspension control module wiring harness connector pin location #8 (circuit #428) and other to a known good chassis ground.	Ohmmeter reading is greater than 10,000 ohms:		
		YES	▶	Turn the air suspension "ON/OFF" switch to the "OFF" position. Remove the air suspension control module and install a new one. Reconnect the rear height sensor and rerun SERVICE BAY DIAGNOSTICS afterwards.
		NO	▶	A short to ground has been detected in the wiring harness circuit #428. Reconnect the rear height sensor, air suspension control module and rerun SERVICE BAY DIAGNOSTICS after repair is made.

FM2019100075030X

Fig. 23   Test EL: Short In Rear Height Sensor Circuit (Part 3 of 3)

FA1	STAR CODE: 69 OPEN IN RIGHT FRONT HEIGHT SENSOR CIRCUIT	RESULT		ACTION TO TAKE
	The air suspension control module has detected an open in the circuit used to receive signals from the right front height sensor. There are seven possible causes of this open which are listed below: • The B + power supply circuit to the right front height sensor has an open in it. • The ground return circuit from the right front height sensor has an open in it. • Channel "A" signal return circuit has an open in it. • Channel "B" signal return circuit has an open in it. • The right front height sensor linkage arm is not connected to the lower arm. • The right front height sensor is defective. • The air suspension control module is defective.		▶	GO TO FA2
FA2	RIGHT FRONT HEIGHT SENSOR VISUAL CHECK			
	Make a visual check of the right front height sensor to ensure that linkage arm and electrical connector are connected and have no obvious damage.	Visual inspection revealed problems with the linkage or electrical connector:		
		YES	▶	Make required repairs and rerun SERVICE BAY DIAGNOSTICS afterwards.
		NO	▶	GO TO FA3

FM2019100076010X

Fig. 24   Test FA: Open In Right Front Height Sensor Circuit (Part 1 of 5)

FA3	B+ POWER SUPPLY CIRCUIT CHECK	RESULT		ACTION TO TAKE
	Disconnect the right front height sensor from the vehicle wiring harness and make the following check: • Using a voltmeter connect the positive lead to circuit #431C on the right front height sensor vehicle wiring harness connector and the negative lead to a known good chassis ground.	Voltage reading is greater than 4.0 volts:		
		YES	▶	GO TO FA5
		NO	▶	GO TO FA4
FA4	CHECKING WIRING HARNESS			
	• Turn the air suspension "ON/OFF" switch to the "OFF" position. • Disconnect air suspension control module connector. • Using an ohmmeter connect one lead to the air suspension control module wiring harness connector pin location #22 (circuit #431B) and other to circuit #431C of the right front height sensor vehicle wiring harness connector.	Ohmmeter reading is less than 5.0 ohms:		
		YES	▶	Turn the air suspension "ON/OFF" switch to the "OFF" position and remove the air suspension control module. Install a new control module and reconnect the right front height sensor. Then rerun SERVICE BAY DIAGNOSTICS.
		NO	▶	The right front height sensor power supply circuit (#431B/431C) resistance is above acceptable limits. The resistance to ground should always be less than 5.0 ohms. Reconnect the right front height sensor and rerun SERVICE BAY DIAGNOSTICS after repairs are made.

FM2019100076020X

Fig. 24   Test FA: Open In Right Front Height Sensor Circuit (Part 2 of 5)

FA5	B+ POWER RETURN CIRCUIT CHECK	RESULT		ACTION TO TAKE
	• Using an ohmmeter connect one lead to circuit #432D of the right front height sensor vehicle wiring harness connector and the other to a known good chassis ground.	Ohmmeter reading is less than 5.0 ohms:		
		YES	▶	GO TO FA7
		NO	▶	GO TO FA6
FA6	CHECKING WIRING HARNESS			
	• Turn the air suspension "ON/OFF" switch to the "OFF" position. • Disconnect air suspension control module connector. • Using an ohmmeter connect one lead to the air suspension control module wiring harness connector pin location #46 (circuit #432D) and other to circuit #432D of the right front height sensor vehicle wiring harness connector.	Ohmmeter reading is less than 5.0 ohms:		
		YES	▶	Turn the air suspension "ON/OFF" switch to the "OFF" position and remove the air suspension control module. Install a new control module and reconnect the right front height sensor. Then rerun SERVICE BAY DIAGNOSTICS.
		NO	▶	The right front height sensor power return circuit (#432D) resistance is above acceptable limits. The resistance to ground should always be less than 5.0 ohms. Reconnect the right front height sensor and rerun SERVICE BAY DIAGNOSTICS after repairs are made.

FM2019100076030X

Fig. 24   Test FA: Open In Right Front Height Sensor Circuit (Part 3 of 5)

FA7	HEIGHT SENSOR CHANNEL "A" CHECK	RESULT	ACTION TO TAKE
	• Using a voltmeter connect the positive lead to circuit #424 of the right front height sensor vehicle wiring harness connector and the negative lead to a known good chassis ground.	Voltage reading is greater than 4.0 volts:	
		YES ▶	GO TO FA9
		NO ▶	GO TO FA8
FA8	CHECKING WIRING HARNESS		
	• Turn the air suspension "ON/OFF" switch to the "OFF" position. • Disconnect air suspension control module connector. • Using an analog ohmmeter connect one lead to the air suspension control module wiring harness connector pin location #9 (circuit #424) and other to circuit #424 of the right front height sensor vehicle wiring harness connector.	Ohmmeter reading is less than 5 ohms: YES ▶	Turn the air suspension "ON/OFF" switch to the "OFF" position and remove the air suspension control module. Install a new control module and reconnect the right front height sensor. Then rerun SERVICE BAY DIAGNOSTICS afterwards.
		NO ▶	The right front height sensor channel "A" circuit (#424) resistance is above acceptable limits. The resistance to ground should always be less than 5.0 ohms. Reconnect the right front height sensor and rerun SERVICE BAY DIAGNOSTICS after repairs are made.

FM2019100076040X

Fig. 24   Test FA: Open In Right Front Height Sensor Circuit (Part 4 of 5)

FA9	HEIGHT SENSOR CHANNEL "B" CHECK	RESULT	ACTION TO TAKE
	• Using a voltmeter connect the positive lead to circuit #425 of the right front height sensor vehicle wiring harness connector and the negative lead to a known good chassis ground.	Voltage reading is greater than 4.0 volts:	
		YES ▶	Remove the right front height sensor and install a new one. Rerun SERVICE BAY DIAGNOSTICS afterwards.
		NO ▶	GO TO FA10
FA10	CHECKING WIRING HARNESS		
	• Turn the air suspension "ON/OFF" switch to the "OFF" position. • Disconnect air suspension control module connector. • Using an analog ohmmeter connect one lead to the air suspension control module wiring harness connector pin location #10 (circuit #425) and other to circuit #425 of the right front height sensor vehicle wiring harness connector.	Ohmmeter reading is less than 5 ohms: YES ▶	Turn the air suspension "ON/OFF" switch to the "OFF" position and remove the air suspension control module. Install a new control module and reconnect the right front height sensor. Then rerun SERVICE BAY DIAGNOSTICS afterwards.
		NO ▶	The right front height sensor channel "B" circuit (#425) resistance is above acceptable limits. The resistance to ground should always be less than 5.0 ohms. Reconnect the right front height sensor and rerun SERVICE BAY DIAGNOSTICS after repairs are made.

FM2019100076050X

Fig. 24   Test FA: Open In Right Front Height Sensor Circuit (Part 5 of 5)

FB1	STAR CODE: 70 OPEN IN LEFT FRONT HEIGHT SENSOR CIRCUIT	RESULT	ACTION TO TAKE
	The air suspension control module has detected an open in the circuit used to receive signals from the left front height sensor. There are six possible causes of this open which are listed below: • The B+ power supply circuit to the right front height sensor has an open in it. • The ground return circuit from the right front height sensor has an open in it. • Channel "A" signal return circuit is shorted to ground. • Channel "B" signal return circuit is shorted to ground. • The left front height sensor is defective. • The air suspension control module is defective.	▶	GO TO FB2
FB2	LEFT FRONT HEIGHT SENSOR VISUAL CHECK		
	Make a visual check of the left front height sensor to ensure that linkage arm and electrical connector are connected and have no obvious damage.	Visual inspection revealed problems with the linkage or electrical connector:	
		YES ▶	Make required repairs and rerun SERVICE BAY DIAGNOSTICS afterwards.
		NO ▶	GO TO FB3

FM2019100077010X

Fig. 25   Test FB: Short In Left Front Height Sensor Circuit (Part 1 of 5)

FB3	B+ POWER SUPPLY CIRCUIT CHECK	RESULT	ACTION TO TAKE
	Disconnect the left front height sensor from the vehicle wiring harness and make the following check: • Using a voltmeter connect the positive lead to circuit #431C of the left front height sensor vehicle wiring harness connector and the negative lead to a known good chassis ground.	Voltage reading is greater than 4.0 volts: YES ▶ NO ▶	GO TO FB5 GO TO FB4
FB4	CHECKING WIRING HARNESS		
	• Turn the air suspension "ON/OFF" switch to the "OFF" position. • Disconnect air suspension control module connector. • Using an ohmmeter connect one lead to the air suspension control module wiring harness connector pin location #22 (circuit #431B) and other to circuit #431D of the left front height sensor vehicle wiring harness connector.	Ohmmeter reading is less than 5.0 ohms: YES ▶	Turn the air suspension "ON/OFF" switch to the "OFF" position and remove the air suspension control module. Install a new control module and reconnect the left front height sensor. Then rerun SERVICE BAY DIAGNOSTICS.
		NO ▶	The left front height sensor power supply circuit (#431B/431D) resistance is above acceptable limits. The resistance to ground should always be less than 5.0 ohms. Reconnect the left front height sensor and rerun SERVICE BAY DIAGNOSTICS after repairs are made.

FM2019100077020X

Fig. 25   Test FB: Short In Left Front Height Sensor Circuit (Part 2 of 5)

31-62

FB5	B+ POWER RETURN CIRCUIT CHECK	RESULT	ACTION TO TAKE
	* Using an ohmmeter connect one lead to circuit #432E of the left front height sensor vehicle wiring harness connector and the other to a known good chassis ground.	Ohmmeter reading is less than 5.0 ohms:	
		YES ▶	GO TO FB7
		NO ▶	GO TO FB6
FB6	CHECKING WIRING HARNESS		
	* Turn the air suspension "ON/OFF" switch to the "OFF" position	Ohmmeter reading is less than 5.0 ohms:	
	* Disconnect air suspension control module connector.	YES ▶	Turn the air suspension "ON/OFF" switch to the "OFF" position and remove the air suspension control module. Install a new control module and reconnect the left front height sensor. Then rerun SERVICE BAY DIAGNOSTICS.
	* Using an ohmmeter connect one lead to the air suspension control module wiring harness connector pin location #46 (circuit #432D) and other to circuit #432E of the left front circuit height sensor vehicle wiring harness connector.	NO ▶	The left front height sensor power return circuit (#432D/432E) resistance is above acceptable limits. The resistance to ground should always be less than 5.0 ohms. Reconnect the left front height sensor and rerun SERVICE BAY DIAGNOSTICS after repairs are made.

FM2019100077030X

Fig. 25   Test FB: Short In Left Front Height Sensor Circuit (Part 3 of 5)

FB7	HEIGHT SENSOR CHANNEL "A" CHECK	RESULT	ACTION TO TAKE
	* Using a voltmeter connect the positive lead to circuit #422 of the left front height sensor vehicle wiring harness connector and the negative lead to a known good chassis ground.	Voltage reading is greater than 4.0 volts:	
		YES ▶	GO TO FB9
		NO ▶	GO TO FB8
FB8	CHECKING WIRING HARNESS		
	* Turn the air suspension "ON/OFF" switch to the "OFF" position.	Ohmmeter reading is less than 5 ohms:	
	* Disconnect air suspension control module connector.	YES ▶	Turn the air suspension "ON/OFF" switch to the "OFF" position and remove the air suspension control module. Install a new control module and reconnect the left front height sensor. Then rerun SERVICE BAY DIAGNOSTICS afterwards.
	* Using an analog ohmmeter (20,000 ohms per volt is recommended) connect one lead to the air suspension control module wiring harness connector pin location #27 (circuit #422) and other to circuit #422 of the left front height sensor vehicle wiring harness connector.	NO ▶	The left front height sensor channel "A" circuit (#422) resistance is above acceptable limits. The resistance to ground should always be less than 5.0 ohms. Reconnect the left front height sensor and rerun SERVICE BAY DIAGNOSTICS after repairs are made.

FM2019100077040X

Fig. 25   Test FB: Short In Left Front Height Sensor Circuit (Part 4 of 5)

FB9	HEIGHT SENSOR CHANNEL "B" CHECK	RESULT	ACTION TO TAKE
	* Using a voltmeter connect the positive lead to circuit #425 of the left front height sensor vehicle wiring harness connector and the negative lead to a known good chassis ground.	Voltage reading is greater than 4.0 volts:	
		YES ▶	Remove the left front height sensor and install a new one. Rerun SERVICE BAY DIAGNOSTICS afterwards.
		NO ▶	GO TO FB10
FB10	CHECKING WIRING HARNESS		
	* Turn the air suspension "ON/OFF" switch to the "OFF" position.	Ohmmeter reading is less than 5 ohms:	
	* Disconnect air suspension control module connector.	YES ▶	Turn the air suspension "ON/OFF" switch to the "OFF" position and remove the air suspension control module. Install a new control module and reconnect the left front height sensor. Then rerun SERVICE BAY DIAGNOSTICS afterwards.
	* Using an analog ohmmeter (20,000 ohms per volt is recommended) connect one lead to the air suspension control module wiring harness connector pin location #43 (circuit #423) and other to circuit #423 of the left front height sensor vehicle wiring harness connector.	NO ▶	The left front height sensor channel "B" circuit (#423) resistance is above acceptable limits. The resistance to ground should always be less than 5.0 ohms. Reconnect the left front height sensor and rerun SERVICE BAY DIAGNOSTICS after repairs are made.

FM2019100077050X

Fig. 25   Test FB: Short In Left Front Height Sensor Circuit (Part 5 of 5)

FC1	STAR CODE: 71 OPEN IN REAR HEIGHT SENSOR CIRCUIT	RESULT	ACTION TO TAKE
	The air suspension control module has detected an open in the circuit used to receive signals from the rear height sensor. There are six possible causes of this open which are listed below:	▶	GO TO FC2
	* The B+ power supply circuit to the right front height sensor has an open in it.		
	* The ground return circuit from the right front height sensor has an open in it.		
	* Channel "A" signal return circuit is shorted to ground.		
	* Channel "B" signal return circuit is shorted to ground.		
	* The rear front height sensor is defective.		
	* The air suspension control module is defective.		
FC2	REAR HEIGHT SENSOR VISUAL CHECK		
	Make a visual check of the rear height sensor to ensure that linkage arm and electrical connector are connected and have no obvious damage.	Visual inspection revealed problems with the linkage or electrical connector:	
		YES ▶	Make required repairs and rerun SERVICE BAY DIAGNOSTICS afterwards.
		NO ▶	GO TO FC3

FM2019100078010X

Fig. 26   Test FC: Open In Rear Height Sensor Circuit (Part 1 of 5)

FC3	B+ POWER SUPPLY CIRCUIT CHECK	RESULT	ACTION TO TAKE
	Disconnect the rear height sensor from the vehicle wiring harness and make the following check:	Voltage reading is greater than 4.0 volts:	
	• Using a voltmeter connect the positive lead to circuit #431 of the rear height sensor vehicle wiring harness connector and the negative lead to a known good chassis ground.	YES	GO TO FC5
		NO	GO TO FC4
FC4	CHECKING WIRING HARNESS		
	• Turn the air suspension "ON/OFF" switch to the "OFF" position.	Ohmmeter reading is less than 5.0 ohms:	
	• Disconnect air suspension control module connector.	YES	Turn the air suspension "ON/OFF" switch to the "OFF" position and remove the air suspension control module. Install a new control module and reconnect the rear height sensor. Then rerun SERVICE BAY DIAGNOSTICS.
	• Using an ohmmeter connect one lead to the air suspension control module wiring harness connector pin location #22 (circuit #431B) and other to circuit #431 of the rear height sensor vehicle wiring harness connector.	NO	The rear height sensor power supply circuit (#431B/431) resistance is above acceptable limits. The resistance to ground should always be less than 5.0 ohms. Reconnect the rear height sensor and rerun SERVICE BAY DIAGNOSTICS after repairs are made.

FM2019100078020X

Fig. 26   Test FC: Open In Rear Height Sensor Circuit (Part 2 of 5)

FC5	B+ POWER RETURN CIRCUIT CHECK	RESULT	ACTION TO TAKE
	• Using an ohmmeter connect one lead to circuit #432B of the rear height sensor vehicle wiring harness connector and the other to a known good chassis ground.	Ohmmeter reading is less than 5.0 ohms:	
		YES	GO TO FC7
		NO	GO TO FC6
FC6	CHECKING WIRING HARNESS		
	• Turn the air suspension "ON/OFF" switch to the "OFF" position.	Ohmmeter reading is less than 5.0 ohms:	
	• Disconnect air suspension control module connector.	YES	Turn the air suspension "ON/OFF" switch to the "OFF" position and remove the air suspension control module. Install a new module and reconnect the rear height sensor. Then rerun SERVICE BAY DIAGNOSTICS.
	• Using an ohmmeter connect one lead to the air suspension control module wiring harness connector pin location #46 (circuit #432D) and other to circuit #432B of the rear height sensor vehicle wiring harness connector.	NO	The rear height sensor power return circuit (#432B/432D) resistance is above acceptable limits. The resistance to ground should always be less than 5.0 ohms. Reconnect the rear height sensor and rerun SERVICE BAY DIAGNOSTICS after repairs are made.

FM2019100078030X

Fig. 26   Test FC: Open In Rear Height Sensor Circuit (Part 3 of 5)

FC7	HEIGHT SENSOR CHANNEL "A" CHECK	RESULT	ACTION TO TAKE
	• Using a voltmeter connect the positive lead to circuit #427 of the rear height sensor vehicle wiring harness connector and the negative lead to a known good chassis ground.	Voltage reading is greater than 4.0 volts:	
		YES	GO TO FC9
		NO	GO TO FC8
FC8	CHECKING WIRING HARNESS		
	• Turn the air suspension "ON/OFF" switch to the "OFF" position.	Ohmmeter reading is less than 5 ohms:	
	• Disconnect air suspension control module connector.	YES	Turn the air suspension "ON/OFF" switch to the "OFF" position and remove the air suspension control module. Install a new control module and reconnect the rear height sensor. Then rerun SERVICE BAY DIAGNOSTICS afterwards.
	• Using an analog ohmmeter connect one lead to the air suspension control module wiring harness connector pin location #5 (circuit #427) and other to circuit #427 of the rear height sensor vehicle wiring harness connector.	NO	The rear height sensor channel "A" circuit (#427) resistance is above acceptable limits. The resistance to ground should always be less than 5.0 ohms. Reconnect the rear height sensor and rerun SERVICE BAY DIAGNOSTICS after repairs are made.

FM2019100078040X

Fig. 26   Test FC: Open In Rear Height Sensor Circuit (Part 4 of 5)

FC9	HEIGHT SENSOR CHANNEL "B" CHECK	RESULT	ACTION TO TAKE
	• Using a voltmeter connect the positive lead to circuit #428 of the rear height sensor vehicle wiring harness connector and the negative lead to a known good chassis ground.	Voltage reading is greater than 4.0 volts:	
		YES	Remove the rear height sensor and install a new one. Rerun SERVICE BAY DIAGNOSTICS afterwards.
		NO	GO TO FC10
FC10	CHECKING WIRING HARNESS		
	• Turn the air suspension "ON/OFF" switch to the "OFF" position.	Ohmmeter reading is less than 5 ohms:	
	• Disconnect air suspension control module connector.	YES	Turn the air suspension "ON/OFF" switch to the "OFF" position and remove the air suspension control module. Install a new control module and reconnect the rear height sensor. Then rerun SERVICE BAY DIAGNOSTICS afterwards.
	• Using an analog ohmmeter connect one lead to the air suspension control module wiring harness connector pin location #8 (circuit #428) and other to circuit #428 of the rear height sensor vehicle wiring harness connector.	NO	The rear height sensor channel "B" circuit (#428) resistance is above acceptable limits. The resistance to ground should always be less than 5.0 ohms. Reconnect the rear height sensor and rerun SERVICE BAY DIAGNOSTICS after repairs are made.

FM2019100078050X

Fig. 26   Test FC: Open In Rear Height Sensor Circuit (Part 5 of 5)

GA1	STAR CODE: 56 or 60 ACTUATOR DESIRED POSITION NOT DETECTED	RESULT	ACTION TO TAKE
	The air suspension control module did not receive a signal that the left rear shock actuator went to the desired position when activated. There are eight possible causes of the actuator not switching to the desired position. • The "SOFT" and/or "FIRM" relay is defective. • The "SOFT" or "FIRM" shock relay circuit is defective. • The vehicle wiring harness power supply circuit to the left rear shock actuator is shorted to ground or has an open in it. • The left rear shock actuator position circuit is shorted to ground or has an open in it. • The vehicle wiring harness connector for the left rear shock actuator does not have all the wires in the correct location. • The left rear shock actuator is defective. • The left rear shock/strut assembly on the vehicle is binding preventing the actuator from switching to the desired position. • The air suspension control module is defective.	Was STAR code "64" or "65" also displayed: YES NO	▶ GO TO GE1 ▶ GO TO GA2
GA2	LEFT REAR ACTUATOR VISUAL CHECK		
	The air suspension control module did not receive a signal that the left rear shock actuator went to the desired position when activated. In order to determine why this did not happen the following actions are required: • Examine the four wires of the left rear actuator connector and also those wires on the wiring harness side to ensure that there is no obvious damage and that all of the wires are in the proper location.	All wires are in the proper location with no obvious damage. YES NO	▶ GO TO GA3 ▶ Service wires as necessary and rerun SERVICE BAY DIAGNOSTICS after repair is made.

FM2019100079010X

Fig. 27   Test GA: Actuator Desired Position Not Detected (Part 1 of 7)

GA3	COMPONENT CHECK LEFT REAR ACTUATOR	RESULT	ACTION TO TAKE
	In order to determine if the actuator is working properly the following actions are required: • Disconnect the left rear actuator from the vehicle wiring harness connector. • Using an analog ohmmeter measure the resistance across the actuator pin position #1 and pin position #2.	Ohmmeter reading is: 10,000 ohms or greater 5 ohms or less	▶ GO TO GA4 ▶ GO TO GA6
GA4	COMPONENT CHECK ACTUATE TO SOFT POSITION		
	• Use a 12 volt power supply and connect the negative lead to actuator pin position #4 and the positive lead to pin position #3 for 1 to 2 seconds. This procedure should drive the actuator to the "SOFT" position. After this has been done remove power supply leads. • Using an analog ohmmeter measure the resistance across the actuator pin position #1 and pin position #2.	Ohmmeter reading is: 10,000 ohms or greater 5 ohms or less	▶ GO TO GA5 ▶ GO TO GA13
GA5	COMPONENT CHECK ACTUATE TO FIRM POSITION		
	• Again use a 12 volt power supply and connect the negative lead to actuator pin position #3 and the positive lead to pin position #4 for 1 to 2 seconds. This procedure should drive the actuator to the "FIRM" position. After this has been done remove power supply leads. • Using an analog ohmmeter measure the resistance across the actuator pin position #1 and pin position #2.	Ohmmeter reading is: 10,000 ohms or greater 5 ohms or less	▶ GO TO GA8 ▶ The power supply circuits (pin location #3 & #4) are reversed. Replace the left rear actuator with a new one. After repairs are made rerun SERVICE BAY DIAGNOSTICS.

FM2019100079020X

Fig. 27   Test GA: Actuator Desired Position Not Detected (Part 2 of 7)

GA6	COMPONENT CHECK ACTUATE TO FIRM POSITION	RESULT	ACTION TO TAKE
	• Use a 12 volt power supply and connect the negative lead to actuator pin position #3 and the positive lead to pin position #4 for 1 to 2 seconds. This procedure should drive the actuator to the "FIRM" position. After this has been done remove power supply leads. • Using an analog ohmmeter measure the resistance across the actuator pin position #1 and pin position #2.	Ohmmeter reading is: 10,000 ohms or greater 5 ohms or less	▶ GO TO GA13 ▶ GO TO GA7
GA7	COMPONENT CHECK ACTUATE TO SOFT POSITION		
	• Again use a 12 volt power supply and connect the negative lead to actuator pin position #4 and the positive lead to pin position #3 for 1 to 2 seconds. This procedure should drive the actuator to the "SOFT" position. After this has been done remove power supply leads. • Using an analog ohmmeter measure the resistance across the actuator pin position #1 and pin position #2.	Ohmmeter reading is: 10,000 ohms or greater 5 ohms or less	▶ The power supply circuits (pin location #3 & #4) are reversed. Replace the left rear actuator with a new one. After repairs are made rerun SERVICE BAY DIAGNOSTICS. ▶ GO TO GA8
GA8	COMPONENT CHECK POSITION CIRCUIT		
	• Remove the left rear actuator from the top of the left rear shock/strut. • Use a small blade screwdriver to rotate the control tube on the bottom of the actuator to the "S" ("SOFT") position). • Using an analog ohmmeter measure the resistance across pin position #1 and #2.	Ohmmeter reading is: 5.0 ohms or less 10,000 ohms or greater	▶ GO TO GA9 ▶ REPLACE the left rear actuator and rerun SERVICE BAY DIAGNOSTICS after repair is made.

FM2019100079030X

Fig. 27   Test GA: Actuator Desired Position Not Detected (Part 3 of 7)

GA9	COMPONENT CHECK POSITION CIRCUIT	RESULT	ACTION TO TAKE
	• Use a small blade screwdriver to rotate the control tube on the bottom of the actuator to the "H" ("FIRM" position). • Using an analog ohmmeter measure the resistance across pin position #1 and #2.	Ohmmeter reading is: 5.0 ohms or less 10,000 ohms or greater	▶ REPLACE the left rear actuator and rerun SERVICE BAY DIAGNOSTICS after repair is made. ▶ GO TO GA10
GA10	COMPONENT CHECK ACTUATE TO SOFT POSITION		
	• If required use a small blade screwdriver to rotate the control tube on the bottom of the actuator to the "H" ("FIRM" position). • Use a 12 volt power supply and connect the negative lead to actuator pin position #4 and the positive lead to pin position #3 for 1 to 2 seconds. This procedure should rotate the control tube on the bottom of the actuator to the "S" position.	Control tube rotated to the "S" position: YES NO	▶ GO TO GA11 ▶ REPLACE the left rear shock actuator and rerun SERVICE BAY DIAGNOSTICS after repair is made.
GA11	COMPONENT CHECK ACTUATE TO FIRM POSITION		
	• If required use a small blade screwdriver to rotate the control tube on the bottom of the actuator to the "S" ("SOFT") position). • Use a 12 volt power supply and connect the negative lead to actuator pin position #3 and the positive lead to pin position #4 for 1 to 2 seconds. This procedure should rotate the control tube on the bottom of the actuator to the "H" position.	Control tube rotated to the "H" position: YES NO	▶ GO TO GA12 ▶ REPLACE the left rear shock actuator and rerun SERVICE BAY DIAGNOSTICS after repair is made.

FM2019100079040X

Fig. 27   Test GA: Actuator Desired Position Not Detected (Part 4 of 7)

GA12	COMPONENT CHECK STRUT ASSEMBLY CHECK	RESULT	ACTION TO TAKE
	• Remove known good right rear actuator and exchange places with the suspected left rear actuator.	The STAR tester displayed a code 56 and/or 60:	
	• Install and reconnect the two shock actuators to the vehicle shocks and wiring harness.	YES ▶	service the left rear shock/strut assembly for binding (force required to switch from "SOFT" to "FIRM"). Rerun SERVICE BAY DIAGNOSTICS after repairs are made.
	• Rerun SERVICE BAY DIAGNOSTICS	NO ▶	The problem of not switching to the desired position may have been due the actuator not being properly mounted to the strut and is now corrected.
GA13	WIRING HARNESS CHECK		
	• Turn the air suspension "ON/OFF" switch to the "OFF" position.	Ohmmeter reading is greater than 5.0 ohms (OPEN CIRCUIT):	
	• Release the STAR test button so that it remains in the up "HOLD" position and turn the STAR tester "OFF".	NO ▶	GO TO GA14
	• Disconnect the air suspension control module from the vehicle wiring harness.	YES ▶	There is an electrical problem in the circuit. Rerun SERVICE BAY DIAGNOSTICS after repair is made.
	• Using an analog ohmmeter place one lead to the wiring harness control module connector pin location #49 (circuit #842) and the other to the left rear actuator vehicle connector circuit #842.		

FM2019100079050X

Fig. 27 Test GA: Actuator Desired Position Not Detected (Part 5 of 7)

GA16	WIRING HARNESS CHECK	RESULT	ACTION TO TAKE
	• Disconnect the FIRM SHOCK RELAY from the vehicle wiring harness connector.	Ohmmeter reading is greater than 5.0 ohms (OPEN CIRCUIT):	
	• Using an analog ohmmeter (20,000 ohms per volt is recommended) place one lead to the SOFT SHOCK RELAY connector circuit #845A and the other to the left rear actuator's vehicle wiring harness connector circuit #845C.	NO ▶	Rerun SERVICE BAY DIAGNOSTICS and if problem still exists replace the air suspension control module.
	NOTE: Your ohmmeter leads may not be long enough for this test and a jumper wire may be required.	YES ▶	There is an electrical problem in the circuit. Rerun SERVICE BAY DIAGNOSTICS after repair is made.

FM2019100079070X

Fig. 27 Test GA: Actuator Desired Position Not Detected (Part 7 of 7)

GA14	WIRING HARNESS CHECK	RESULT	ACTION TO TAKE
	• Using an analog ohmmeter place one lead to the wiring harness control module connector pin location #46 (circuit #432D) and the other to the left rear actuator vehicle connector circuit #432C.	Ohmmeter reading is greater than 5.0 ohms (OPEN CIRCUIT):	
		NO ▶	GO TO GA15
		YES ▶	There is an electrical problem in the circuit. Rerun SERVICE BAY DIAGNOSTICS after repair is made.
GA15	WIRING HARNESS CHECK		
	• Disconnect the SOFT SHOCK RELAY from the vehicle wiring harness connector.	Ohmmeter reading is greater than 5.0 ohms (OPEN CIRCUIT):	
	• Using an analog ohmmeter place one lead to the SOFT SHOCK RELAY connector circuit #846A and the other to the left rear actuator's vehicle wiring harness connector circuit #846C.	NO ▶	GO TO GA16
		YES ▶	There is an electrical problem in the circuit. Rerun SERVICE BAY DIAGNOSTICS after repair is made.

FM2019100079060X

Fig. 27 Test GA: Actuator Desired Position Not Detected (Part 6 of 7)

GB1	STAR CODE: 57 or 61 ACTUATOR DESIRED POSITION NOT DETECTED	RESULT	ACTION TO TAKE
	The air suspension control module did not receive a signal that the right front shock actuator went to the desired position when activated. There are eight possible causes of the actuator not switching to the desired position.	Was STAR code "64" or "65" also displayed:	
	• The "SOFT" and/or "FIRM" shock relay is defective.	YES ▶	GO TO GE1
	• The "SOFT" or "FIRM" shock relay circuit is defective.	NO ▶	GO TO GB2
	• The vehicle wiring harness power supply circuit to the right front shock actuator is shorted to ground or has an open in it.		
	• The right front shock actuator position circuit is shorted to ground or has an open in it.		
	• The vehicle wiring harness connector for the right front shock actuator does not have all the wires in the correct location.		
	• The right front shock actuator is defective.		
	• The right front shock/strut assembly on the vehicle is binding preventing the actuator from switching to the desired position.		
	• The air suspension control module is defective.		
GB2	RIGHT FRONT ACTUATOR VISUAL CHECK		
	The air suspension control module did not receive a signal that the right front shock actuator went to the desired position when activated. In order to determine why this did not happen the following actions are required:	All wires are in the proper location with no obvious damage.	
	• Examine the four wires of the right front actuator connector and also those wires on the wiring harness side to ensure that there is no obvious damage and that all of the wires are in the proper location.	YES ▶	GO TO GB3
		NO ▶	Service wires as necessary and rerun SERVICE BAY DIAGNOSTICS after repair is made.

FM2019100080010X

Fig. 28 Test GB: Actuator Desired Position Not Detected (Part 1 of 6)

GB3	COMPONENT CHECK RIGHT FRONT ACTUATOR	RESULT	ACTION TO TAKE
	In order to determine if the actuator is working properly the following actions are required: * Disconnect the right front actuator from the vehicle wiring harness connector. * Using an analog ohmmeter measure the resistance across the actuator pin position #1 and pin position #2.	Ohmmeter reading is: 10,000 ohms or greater 5 ohms or less	GO TO GB4 GO TO GB6

GB4	COMPONENT CHECK ACTUATE TO SOFT POSITION	RESULT	ACTION TO TAKE
	* Use a 12 volt power supply and connect the negative lead to actuator pin position #4 and the positive lead to pin position #3 for 1 to 2 seconds. This procedure should drive the actuator to the "SOFT" position. After this has been done remove power supply leads. * Using an analog ohmmeter measure the resistance across the actuator pin position #1 and pin position #2.	Ohmmeter reading is: 10,000 ohms or greater 5 ohms or less	GO TO GB5 GO TO GB13

GB5	COMPONENT CHECK ACTUATE TO FIRM POSITION	RESULT	ACTION TO TAKE
	* Again use a 12 volt power supply and connect the negative lead to actuator pin position #3 and the positive lead to pin position #4 for 1 to 2 seconds. This procedure should drive the actuator to the "FIRM" position. After this has been done remove power supply leads. * Using an analog ohmmeter measure the resistance across the actuator pin position #1 and pin position #2.	Ohmmeter reading is: 10,000 ohms or greater 5 ohms or less	GO TO GB8 The power supply circuits (pin location #3 & #4) are reversed. Replace the right front actuator with a new one. After repairs are made rerun SERVICE BAY DIAGNOSTICS.

FM2019100080020X

Fig. 28   Test GB: Actuator Desired Position Not Detected (Part 2 of 6)

GB6	COMPONENT CHECK ACTUATE TO FIRM POSITION	RESULT	ACTION TO TAKE
	* Use a 12 volt power supply and connect the negative lead to actuator pin position #3 and the positive lead to pin position #4 for 1 to 2 seconds. This procedure should drive the actuator to the "FIRM" position. After this has been done remove power supply leads. * Using an analog ohmmeter measure the resistance across the actuator pin position #1 and pin position #2.	Ohmmeter reading is: 10,000 ohms or greater 5 ohms or less	GO TO GB13 GO TO GB7

GB7	COMPONENT CHECK ACTUATE TO SOFT POSITION	RESULT	ACTION TO TAKE
	* Again use a 12 volt power supply and connect the negative lead to actuator pin position #4 and the positive lead to pin position #3 for 1 to 2 seconds. This procedure should drive the actuator to the "SOFT" position. After this has been done remove power supply leads. * Using an analog ohmmeter measure the resistance across the actuator pin position #1 and pin position #2.	Ohmmeter reading is: 10,000 ohms or greater 5 ohms or less	The power supply circuits (pin locations #3 & #4) are reversed. Replace the right front actuator with a new one. After repairs are made rerun SERVICE BAY DIAGNOSTICS. GO TO GB8

GB8	COMPONENT CHECK POSITION CIRCUIT	RESULT	ACTION TO TAKE
	* Remove the right front actuator from the top of the right front shock/strut. * Use a small blade screwdriver to rotate the control tube on the bottom of the actuator to the "S" ("SOFT" position). * Using an analog ohmmeter measure the resistance across pin position #1 and #2.	Ohmmeter reading is: 5.0 ohms or less 10,000 ohms or greater	GO TO GB9 REPLACE the right front actuator and rerun SERVICE BAY DIAGNOSTICS after repair is made.

FM2019100080030X

Fig. 28   Test GB: Actuator Desired Position Not Detected (Part 3 of 6)

GB9	COMPONENT CHECK POSITION CIRCUIT	RESULT	ACTION TO TAKE
	* Use a small blade screwdriver to rotate the control tube on the bottom of the actuator to the "H" ("FIRM" position). * Using an analog ohmmeter measure the resistance across pin position #1 and #2.	Ohmmeter reading is: 5.0 ohms or less 10,000 ohms or greater	REPLACE the right front actuator and rerun SERVICE BAY DIAGNOSTICS after repair is made. GO TO GB10

GB10	COMPONENT CHECK ACTUATE TO SOFT POSITION	RESULT	ACTION TO TAKE
	* If required use a small blade screwdriver to rotate the control tube on the bottom of the actuator to the "H" ("FIRM" position). * Use a 12 volt power supply and connect the negative lead to actuator pin position #4 and the positive lead to pin position #3 for 1 to 2 seconds. This procedure should rotate the control tube on the bottom of the actuator to the "S" position.	Control tube rotated to the "S" position: YES NO	GO TO GB11 REPLACE the right front shock actuator and rerun SERVICE BAY DIAGNOSTICS after repair is made.

GB11	COMPONENT CHECK ACTUATE TO FIRM POSITION	RESULT	ACTION TO TAKE
	* If required use a small blade screwdriver to rotate the control tube on the bottom of the actuator to the "S" ("SOFT" position). * Use a 12 volt power supply and connect the negative lead to actuator pin position #3 and the positive lead to pin #4 for 1 to 2 seconds. This procedure should rotate the control tube on the bottom of the actuator to the "H" position.	Control tube rotated to the "H" position: YES NO	GO TO GB12 REPLACE the right front shock actuator and rerun SERVICE BAY DIAGNOSTICS after repair is made.

FM2019100080040X

Fig. 28   Test GB: Actuator Desired Position Not Detected (Part 4 of 6)

GB12	COMPONENT CHECK STRUT ASSEMBLY CHECK	RESULT	ACTION TO TAKE
	* Remove known good left front actuator and exchange places with the suspected right front actuator. * Install and reconnect the two shock actuators to the vehicle shocks and wiring harness. * Rerun SERVICE BAY DIAGNOSTICS.	The STAR tester displayed a code 57 and/or 61: YES NO	service the right front shock/strut assembly for binding (force required to switch from "SOFT" to "FIRM"). Rerun SERVICE BAY DIAGNOSTICS after repairs are made. The problem of not switching to the desired position may have been due the actuator not being properly mounted to the strut and is now corrected.

GB13	WIRING HARNESS CHECK	RESULT	ACTION TO TAKE
	* Turn the air suspension "ON/OFF" switch to the "OFF" position. * Release the "STAR" test button so that it remains in the up "HOLD" position and turn the "STAR" tester "OFF". * Disconnect the air suspension control module from the vehicle wiring harness. * Using an analog ohmmeter place one lead to the wiring harness control module connector pin location #44 (circuit #841) and the other to the right front actuator vehicle connector circuit #841.	Ohmmeter reading is greater than 5.0 ohms (OPEN CIRCUIT): NO YES	GO TO GB14 There is an electrical problem in the circuit. Rerun SERVICE BAY DIAGNOSTICS after repair is made.

FM2019100080050X

Fig. 28   Test GB: Actuator Desired Position Not Detected (Part 5 of 6)

GB14	WIRING HARNESS CHECK	RESULT	ACTION TO TAKE
	• Using an analog ohmmeter place one lead to the wiring harness control module connector pin location #46 (circuit #432D) and the other to the right front actuator vehicle connector circuit #432C.	Ohmmeter reading is greater than 5.0 ohms (OPEN CIRCUIT): NO ▶ YES ▶	GO TO GB15 There is an electrical problem in the circuit Rerun SERVICE BAY DIAGNOSTICS after repair is made.
GB15	WIRING HARNESS CHECK		
	• Disconnect the SOFT SHOCK RELAY from the vehicle wiring harness connector. • Using an analog ohmmeter place one lead to the SOFT SHOCK RELAY connector circuit #846A and the other to the right front actuator's vehicle wiring harness connector circuit #846A.	Ohmmeter reading is greater than 5.0 ohms (OPEN CIRCUIT): NO ▶ YES ▶	GO TO GB16 There is an electrical problem in the circuit Rerun SERVICE BAY DIAGNOSTICS after repair is made.
GB16	WIRING HARNESS CHECK		
	• Disconnect the FIRM SHOCK RELAY from the vehicle wiring harness connector. • Using an analog ohmmeter (20,000 ohms per volt is recommended) place one lead to the SOFT SHOCK RELAY connector circuit #845A and the other to the right front actuator's vehicle wiring harness connector circuit #845A. NOTE: Your ohmmeter leads may not be long enough for this test and a jumper wire may be required.	Ohmmeter reading is greater than 5.0 ohms (OPEN CIRCUIT): NO ▶ YES ▶	Rerun SERVICE BAY DIAGNOSTICS and if problem still exists replace the air suspension control module. There is an electrical problem in the circuit. Rerun SERVICE BAY DIAGNOSTICS after repair is made.

FM2019100080060X

Fig. 28   Test GB: Actuator Desired Position Not Detected (Part 6 of 6)

GC1	STAR CODE: 58 or 62 ACTUATOR DESIRED POSITION NOT DETECTED	RESULT	ACTION TO TAKE
	The air suspension control module did not receive a signal that the left front shock actuator went to the desired position when activated. There are eight possible causes of the actuator not switching to the desired position. • The "SOFT" and/or "FIRM" relay is defective. • The "SOFT" or "FIRM" shock relay circuit is defective. • The vehicle wiring harness power supply circuit to the left front shock actuator is shorted to ground or has an open in it. • The left front shock actuator position circuit is shorted to ground or has an open in it. • The vehicle wiring harness connector for the left front shock actuator does not have all the wires in the correct location. • The left front shock actuator is defective. • The left front shock/strut assembly on the vehicle is binding preventing the actuator from switching to the desired position. • The air suspension control module is defective.	Was STAR code "64" or "65" also displayed: YES ▶ NO ▶	GO TO GE1 GO TO GC2
GC2	LEFT FRONT ACTUATOR VISUAL CHECK		
	The air suspension control module did not receive a signal that the left front shock actuator went to the desired position when activated. In order to determine why this did not happen the following actions are required: • Examine the four wires of the left front actuator connector and also those wires on the wiring harness side to ensure that there is no obvious damage and that all of the wires are in the proper location.	All wires are in the proper location with no obvious damage. YES ▶ NO ▶	GO TO GC3 Service wires as necessary and rerun SERVICE BAY DIAGNOSTICS after repair is made.

FM2019100081010X

Fig. 29   Test GC: Actuator Desired Position Not Detected (Part 1 of 6)

GC3	COMPONENT CHECK LEFT FRONT ACTUATOR	RESULT	ACTION TO TAKE
	In order to determine if the actuator is working properly the following actions are required: • Disconnect the left front actuator from the vehicle wiring harness connector. • Using an analog ohmmeter measure the resistance across the actuator pin position #1 and pin position #2.	Ohmmeter reading is: 10,000 ohms or greater ▶ 5 ohms or less ▶	GO TO GC4 GO TO GC6
GC4	COMPONENT CHECK ACTUATE TO SOFT POSITION		
	• Use a 12 volt power supply and connect the negative lead to actuator pin position #4 and the positive lead to pin position #3 for 1 to 2 seconds. This procedure should drive the actuator to the "SOFT" position. After this has been done remove power supply leads. • Using an analog ohmmeter measure the resistance across the actuator pin position #1 and pin position #2.	Ohmmeter reading is: 10,000 ohms or greater ▶ 5 ohms or less ▶	GO TO GC5 GO TO GC13
GC5	COMPONENT CHECK ACTUATE TO FIRM POSITION		
	• Again use a 12 volt power supply and connect the negative lead to actuator pin position #3 and the positive lead to pin position #4 for 1 to 2 seconds. This procedure should drive the actuator to the "FIRM" position. After this has been done remove power supply leads. • Using an analog ohmmeter measure the resistance across the actuator pin position #1 and pin position #2.	Ohmmeter reading is: 10,000 ohms or greater ▶ 5 ohms or less ▶	GO TO GC8 The power supply circuits (pin location #3 & #4) are reversed. Replace the left front actuator with a new one. After repairs are made rerun SERVICE BAY DIAGNOSTICS.

FM2019100081020X

Fig. 29   Test GC: Actuator Desired Position Not Detected (Part 2 of 6)

GC6	COMPONENT CHECK ACTUATE TO FIRM POSITION	RESULT	ACTION TO TAKE
	• Use a 12 volt power supply and connect the negative lead to actuator pin position #3 and the positive lead to pin position #4 for 1 to 2 seconds. This procedure should drive the actuator to the "FIRM" position. After this has been done remove power supply leads. • Using an analog ohmmeter measure the resistance across the actuator pin position #1 and pin position #2.	Ohmmeter reading is: 10,000 ohms or greater ▶ 5 ohms or less ▶	GO TO GC13 GO TO GC7
GC7	COMPONENT CHECK ACTUATE TO SOFT POSITION		
	• Again use a 12 volt power supply and connect the negative lead to actuator pin position #4 and the positive lead to pin position #3 for 1 to 2 seconds. This procedure should drive the actuator to the "SOFT" position. After this has been done remove power supply leads. • Using an analog ohmmeter measure the resistance across the actuator pin position #1 and pin position #2.	Ohmmeter reading is: 10,000 ohms or greater ▶ 5 ohms or less ▶	The power supply circuits (pin location #3 & #4) are reversed. Replace the left front actuator with a new one. After repairs are made rerun SERVICE BAY DIAGNOSTICS. GO TO GC8
GC8	COMPONENT CHECK POSITION CIRCUIT		
	• Remove the left front actuator from the top of the left front shock/strut. • Use a small blade screwdriver to rotate the control tube on the bottom of the actuator to the "S" ("SOFT" position). • Using an analog ohmmeter measure the resistance across pin position #1 and #2.	Ohmmeter reading is: 5.0 ohms or less ▶ 10,000 ohms or greater ▶	GO TO GC9 REPLACE the left front actuator and rerun SERVICE BAY DIAGNOSTICS after repair is made.

FM2019100081030X

Fig. 29   Test GC: Actuator Desired Position Not Detected (Part 3 of 6)

GC9	COMPONENT CHECK POSITION CIRCUIT	RESULT		ACTION TO TAKE
	• Use a small blade screwdriver to rotate the control tube on the bottom of the actuator to the "H" ("FIRM" position). • Using an analog ohmmeter measure the resistance across pin position #1 and #2.	Ohmmeter reading is: 5.0 ohms or less	▶	REPLACE the left front actuator and rerun SERVICE BAY DIAGNOSTICS after repair is made.
		10,000 ohms or greater	▶	GO TO GC10

GC10	COMPONENT CHECK ACTUATE TO SOFT POSITION	RESULT		ACTION TO TAKE
	• If required use a small blade screwdriver to rotate the control tube on the bottom of the actuator to the "H" ("FIRM" position). • Use a 12 volt power supply and connect the negative lead to actuator pin position #4 and the positive lead to pin position #3 for 1 to 2 seconds. This procedure should rotate the control tube on the bottom of the actuator to the "S" position.	Control tube rotated to the "S" position: YES	▶	GO TO GC11
		NO	▶	REPLACE the left front shock actuator and rerun SERVICE BAY DIAGNOSTICS after repair is made.

GC11	COMPONENT CHECK ACTUATE TO FIRM POSITION	RESULT		ACTION TO TAKE
	• If required use a small blade screwdriver to rotate the control tube on the bottom of the actuator to the "S" ("SOFT" position). • Use a 12 volt power supply and connect the negative lead to actuator pin position #3 and the positive lead to pin position #4 for 1 to 2 seconds. This procedure should rotate the control tube on the bottom of the actuator to the "H" position.	Control tube rotated to the "H" position: YES	▶	GO TO GC12
		NO	▶	REPLACE the left front shock actuator and rerun SERVICE BAY DIAGNOSTICS after repair is made.

FM2019100081040X

Fig. 29 Test GC: Actuator Desired Position Not Detected (Part 4 of 6)

GC12	COMPONENT CHECK STRUT ASSEMBLY CHECK	RESULT		ACTION TO TAKE
	• Remove known good actuator from right front corner of the vehicle and exchange places with the suspected left front actuator. • Install and reconnect the two shock actuators to the vehicle shocks and wiring harness. • Rerun SERVICE BAY DIAGNOSTICS.	The STAR tester displayed a code 58 and/or 62: YES	▶	service the left front shock/strut assembly for binding (force required to switch from "SOFT" to "FIRM"). Rerun SERVICE BAY DIAGNOSTICS after repairs are made.
		NO	▶	The problem of not switching to the desired position may have been due the actuator not being properly mounted to the strut and is now corrected.

GC13	WIRING HARNESS CHECK	RESULT		ACTION TO TAKE
	• Turn the air suspension "ON/OFF" switch to the "OFF" position. • Release the "STAR" test button so that it remains in the up "HOLD" position and turn the "STAR" tester "OFF". • Disconnect the air suspension control module from the vehicle wiring harness. • Using an analog ohmmeter place one lead to the wiring harness control module connector pin location #47 (circuit #840) and the other to the left rear actuator vehicle connector circuit #840.	Ohmmeter reading is greater than 5.0 ohms (OPEN CIRCUIT): NO	▶	GO TO GC14
		YES	▶	There is an electrical problem in the circuit. Rerun SERVICE BAY DIAGNOSTICS after repair is made.

FM2019100081050A

Fig. 29 Test GC: Actuator Desired Position Not Detected (Part 5 of 6)

GC14	WIRING HARNESS CHECK	RESULT		ACTION TO TAKE
	• Disconnect the SOFT SHOCK RELAY from the vehicle wiring harness connector. • Using an analog ohmmeter place one lead to the SOFT SHOCK RELAY connector circuit #846A and the other to the left front actuator's vehicle wiring harness connector circuit #846B.	Ohmmeter reading is greater than 5.0 ohms (OPEN CIRCUIT): NO	▶	GO TO GC15
		YES	▶	There is an electrical problem in the circuit. Rerun SERVICE BAY DIAGNOSTICS after repair is made.

GC15	WIRING HARNESS CHECK	RESULT		ACTION TO TAKE
	• Disconnect the FIRM SHOCK RELAY from the vehicle wiring harness connector. • Using an analog ohmmeter place one lead to the SOFT SHOCK RELAY connector circuit #845A and the other to the left front actuator's vehicle wiring harness connector circuit #845B.	Ohmmeter reading is greater than 5.0 ohms (OPEN CIRCUIT): NO	▶	Rerun SERVICE BAY DIAGNOSTICS and if problem still exists replace the air suspension control module.
		YES	▶	There is an electrical problem in the circuit. Rerun SERVICE BAY DIAGNOSTICS after repair is made.

FM2019100081060X

Fig. 29 Test GC: Actuator Desired Position Not Detected (Part 6 of 6)

GD1	STAR CODE: 59 or 63 ACTUATOR DESIRED POSITION NOT DETECTED	RESULT		ACTION TO TAKE
	The air suspension control module did not receive a signal that the right rear shock actuator went to the desired position when activated. There are eight possible causes of the actuator not switching to the desired position. • The "SOFT" and/or "FIRM" relay is defective. • The "SOFT" or "FIRM" shock relay circuit is defective. • The vehicle wiring harness power supply circuit to the right rear shock actuator is shorted to ground or has an open in it. • The right rear shock actuator position circuit is shorted to ground or has an open in it. • The vehicle wiring harness connector for the right rear shock actuator does not have all the wires in the correct location. • The right rear shock actuator is defective. • The right rear shock/strut assembly on the vehicle is binding preventing the actuator from switching to the desired position. • The air suspension control module is defective.	Was STAR code "64" or "65" also displayed: YES	▶	GO TO GE1
		NO	▶	GO TO GD2

GD2	RIGHT REAR ACTUATOR VISUAL CHECK	RESULT		ACTION TO TAKE
	The air suspension control module did not receive a signal that the right rear shock actuator went to the desired position when activated. In order to determine why this did not happen the following actions are required: • Examine the four wires of the right rear actuator connector and also those wires on the wiring harness side to ensure that there is no obvious damage and that all of the wires are in the proper location.	All wires are in the proper location with no obvious damage. YES	▶	GO TO GD3
		NO	▶	Service wires as necessary and rerun SERVICE BAY DIAGNOSTICS after repair is made.

FM2019100082010X

Fig. 30 Test GD: Actuator Desired Position Not Detected (Part 1 of 6)

GD3 — COMPONENT CHECK — RIGHT REAR ACTUATOR

COMPONENT CHECK	RESULT	ACTION TO TAKE
In order to determine if the actuator is working properly the following actions are required: • Disconnect the right rear actuator from the vehicle wiring harness connector. • Using an analog ohmmeter measure the resistance across the actuator pin position #1 and pin position #2.	Ohmmeter reading is: 10,000 ohms or greater 5 ohms or less	GO TO **GD4** GO TO **GD6**

GD4 — COMPONENT CHECK — ACTUATE TO SOFT POSITION

COMPONENT CHECK	RESULT	ACTION TO TAKE
• Use a 12 volt power supply and connect the _negative lead_ to actuator pin position #4 and the _positive lead_ to pin position #3 for _1 to 2 seconds_. This procedure should drive the actuator to the "SOFT" position. After this has been done remove power supply leads. • Using an analog ohmmeter measure the resistance across the actuator pin position #1 and pin position #2.	Ohmmeter reading is: 10,000 ohms or greater 5 ohms or less	GO TO **GD5** GO TO **GD13**

GD5 — COMPONENT CHECK — ACTUATE TO FIRM POSITION

COMPONENT CHECK	RESULT	ACTION TO TAKE
• Again use a 12 volt power supply and connect the _negative lead_ to actuator pin position #3 and the _positive lead_ to pin position #4 for _1 to 2 seconds_. This procedure should greater drive the actuator to the "FIRM" position. After this has been done remove power supply leads. • Using an analog ohmmeter (20,000 ohms per volt is recommended) measure the resistance across the actuator pin position #1 and pin position #2.	Ohmmeter reading is: 10,000 ohms or greater 5 ohms or less	GO TO **GD8** The power supply circuits (pin locations #3 & #4) are reversed. Replace the right rear actuator with a new one. After repairs are made rerun SERVICE BAY DIAGNOSTICS.

FM2019100082020X

Fig. 30   Test GD: Actuator Desired Position Not Detected (Part 2 of 6)

GD6 — COMPONENT CHECK — ACTUATE TO FIRM POSITION

COMPONENT CHECK	RESULT	ACTION TO TAKE
• Use a 12 volt power supply and connect the _negative lead_ to actuator pin position #3 and the _positive lead_ to pin position #4 for _1 to 2 seconds_. This procedure should drive the actuator to the "FIRM" position. After this has been done remove power supply leads. • Using an analog ohmmeter measure the resistance across the actuator pin position #1 and pin position #2.	Ohmmeter reading is: 10,000 ohms or greater 5 ohms or less	GO TO **GD13** GO TO **GD7**

GD7 — COMPONENT CHECK — ACTUATE TO SOFT POSITION

COMPONENT CHECK	RESULT	ACTION TO TAKE
• Again use a 12 volt power supply and connect the _negative lead_ to actuator pin position #4 and the _positive lead_ to pin position #3 for _1 to 2 seconds_. This procedure should drive the actuator to the "SOFT" position. After this has been done remove power supply leads. • Using an analog ohmmeter (20,000 ohms per volt is recommended) measure the resistance across the actuator pin position #1 and pin position #2.	Ohmmeter reading is: 10,000 ohms or greater 5 ohms or less	The power supply circuits (pin locations #3 & #4) are reversed. Replace the right rear actuator with a new one. After repairs are made rerun SERVICE BAY DIAGNOSTICS. GO TO **GD8**

GD8 — COMPONENT CHECK — POSITION CIRCUIT

COMPONENT CHECK	RESULT	ACTION TO TAKE
• Remove the right rear actuator from the top of the right rear shock/strut. • Use a small blade screwdriver to rotate the control tube on the bottom of the actuator to the "S" ("SOFT) position. • Using an analog ohmmeter measure the resistance across pin position #1 and #2.	Ohmmeter reading is: 5.0 ohms or less. 10,000 ohms or greater	GO TO **GD9** REPLACE the right rear actuator and rerun SERVICE BAY DIAGNOSTICS after repair is made.

FM2019100082030X

Fig. 30   Test GD: Actuator Desired Position Not Detected (Part 3 of 6)

GD9 — COMPONENT CHECK — POSITION CIRCUIT

COMPONENT CHECK	RESULT	ACTION TO TAKE
• Use a small blade screwdriver to rotate the control tube on the bottom of the actuator to the "H" ("FIRM) position). • Using an analog ohmmeter measure the resistance across pin position #1 and #2.	Ohmmeter reading is: 5.0 ohms or less 10,000 ohms or greater	REPLACE the right rear actuator and rerun SERVICE BAY DIAGNOSTICS after repair is made. GO TO **GD10**

GD10 — COMPONENT CHECK — ACTUATE TO SOFT POSITION

COMPONENT CHECK	RESULT	ACTION TO TAKE
• If required use a small blade screwdriver to rotate the control tube on the bottom of the actuator to the "H" ("FIRM" position). • Use a 12 volt power supply and connect the _negative lead_ to actuator pin position #4 and the _positive lead_ to pin position #3 for _1 to 2 seconds_. This procedure should rotate the control tube on the bottom of the actuator to the "S" position.	Control tube rotated to the "S" position: YES NO	GO TO **GD11** REPLACE the right rear shock actuator and rerun SERVICE BAY DIAGNOSTICS after repair is made.

GD11 — COMPONENT CHECK — ACTUATE TO FIRM POSITION

COMPONENT CHECK	RESULT	ACTION TO TAKE
• If required use a small blade screwdriver to rotate the control tube on the bottom of the actuator to the "S" ("SOFT" position). • Use a 12 volt power supply and connect the _negative lead_ to actuator pin position #3 and the _positive lead_ to pin position #4 for _1 to 2 seconds_. This procedure should rotate the control tube on the bottom of the actuator to the "H" position.	Control tube rotated to the "H" position: YES NO	GO TO **GD12** REPLACE the right rear shock actuator and rerun SERVICE BAY DIAGNOSTICS after repair is made.

FM2019100082040X

Fig. 30   Test GD: Actuator Desired Position Not Detected (Part 4 of 6)

GD12 — COMPONENT CHECK — STRUT ASSEMBLY CHECK

COMPONENT CHECK	RESULT	ACTION TO TAKE
• Remove known good left rear actuator and exchange places with the suspected right rear actuator. • Install and reconnect the two shock actuators to the vehicle shocks and wiring harness. • Rerun SERVICE BAY DIAGNOSTICS.	The STAR tester displayed a code 59 and/or 63: YES NO	service the right rear shock/strut assembly for binding (force required to switch from "SOFT" to "FIRM"). Rerun SERVICE BAY DIAGNOSTICS after repairs are made. The problem of not switching to the desired position may have been due to the actuator not being properly mounted to the strut and is now corrected.

GD13 — WIRING HARNESS CHECK

COMPONENT CHECK	RESULT	ACTION TO TAKE
• Turn the air suspension "ON/OFF" switch to the "OFF" position. • Release the "STAR" test button so that it remains in the up "HOLD" position and turn the STAR tester "OFF". • Disconnect the air suspension control module from the vehicle wiring harness. • Using an analog ohmmeter place one lead to the wiring harness control module connector pin location #48 (circuit #843) and the other to the left rear actuator vehicle connector circuit #843.	Ohmmeter reading is greater than 5.0 ohms (OPEN CIRCUIT): NO YES	GO TO **GD14** There is an electrical problem in the circuit. Rerun SERVICE BAY DIAGNOSTICS after repair is made.

FM2019100082050X

Fig. 30   Test GD: Actuator Desired Position Not Detected (Part 5 of 6)

GD14	WIRING HARNESS CHECK	RESULT	ACTION TO TAKE
	• Disconnect the SOFT SHOCK RELAY from the vehicle wiring harness connector. • Using an analog ohmmeter place one lead to the SOFT SHOCK RELAY connector circuit #846A and the other to the right rear actuator's vehicle wiring harness connector circuit #84GB.	Ohmmeter reading is greater than 5.0 ohms (OPEN CIRCUIT): NO YES	▶ GO TO GD15 ▶ There is an electrical problem in the circuit. Rerun SERVICE BAY DIAGNOSTICS after repair is made.

GD15	WIRING HARNESS CHECK		
	• Disconnect the FIRM SHOCK RELAY from the vehicle wiring harness connector. • Using an analog ohmmeter place one lead to the SOFT SHOCK RELAY connector circuit #845A and the other to the right rear actuator's vehicle wiring harness connector circuit #845C.	Ohmmeter reading is greater than 5.0 ohms (OPEN CIRCUIT): NO YES	▶ Rerun SERVICE BAY DIAGNOSTICS and if problem still exists replace the air suspension control module. ▶ There is an electrical problem in the circuit. Rerun SERVICE BAY DIAGNOSTICS after repair is made.

FM2019100082060X

Fig. 30   Test GD: Actuator Desired Position Not Detected (Part 6 of 6)

GE1	STAR CODE: 64 or 65 ALL SHOCK ACTUATORS NOT IN THE DESIRED POSITION	RESULT	ACTION TO TAKE
	The air suspension control module has detected that all shock actuators did not go to the desired position when activated. There are six possible causes of the actuator not switching to the desired position. • The "SOFT" and/or "FIRM" shock relay is defective. • The vehicle wiring harness power supply circuit to the shock actuator relays is shorted to ground or has an open in it. • The vehicle wiring harness power supply circuit to the shock actuators is shorted to ground or has an open in it. • The shock actuator position circuit is shorted to ground or has an open in it. • The vehicle wiring harness connector for the "SOFT" and/or "FIRM" relay does not have all the wires in the correct location. • The air suspension control module is defective.		▶ GO TO GE2

GE2	ENTERING FUNCTIONAL TEST MODE OF SERVICE BAY DIAG		
	In order to determine why all the shock actuators did not go to the desired position when activated the following actions are required: • Release the "STAR" test button to the up "HOLD" position. After five seconds depress the "STAR" test button again so that it remains in the down "TEST" position. This will allow the control module to enter the SERVICE BAY DIAGNOSTIC FUNCTIONAL TEST mode.	The "STAR" tester is displaying code: "31", "32", "33", "34", or "35" NO	▶ GO TO GE4 ▶ GO TO GE3

FM2019100083010X

Fig. 31   Test GE: All Shock Actuators Not In Desired Position (Part 1 of 7)

GE3	RETRY ENTERING FUNCTIONAL TEST MODE	RESULT	ACTION TO TAKE
	The air suspension control module has not entered the SERVICE BAY DIAGNOSTIC FUNCTIONAL TEST mode and the following actions are required: • Make sure that the "STAR" tester is still plugged into the air suspension diagnostic pigtail. • Make sure that the "STAR" tester is turned "ON". • Release the "STAR" test button to the up "HOLD" position. After five seconds depress the "STAR" test button again so that it remains in the down "TEST" position. This will allow the control module to enter the functional test mode.	The "STAR" tester is displaying code: "31", "32", "33", "34", or "35" NO	▶ GO TO GE4 ▶ Rerun SERVICE BAY DIAGNOSTICS and if still unable to enter the functional test mode, install a new air suspension control module.

GE4	CHECKING WIRING HARNESS		
	It is desired to activate the "FIRM/SOFT ACTUATOR TOGGLE" test. In order to do this the following action is required: • Remove the left front shock actuator from the top of the left front strut. • Release the "STAR" test button so that it remains in the up "HOLD" position after the code "34" has been displayed for at least 5 seconds. NOTE: As long as the "STAR" test button is in the up "HOLD" position the "FIRM/SOFT ACTUATOR TOGGLE" test will continue.	The control tube switches from "S" to "H" to "S" continuously. YES NO	▶ GO TO GE5 ▶ GO TO GE6

FM2019100083020X

Fig. 31   Test GE: All Shock Actuators Not In Desired Position (Part 2 of 7)

GE5	WIRING HARNESS CHECK	RESULT	ACTION TO TAKE
	• Turn the "STAR" tester "ON/OFF" switch to the "OFF" position. • Turn the air suspension "ON/OFF" switch to the "OFF" position and disconnect the air suspension control module. • Using a small blade screwdriver rotate the control tube on the bottom of the left front actuator to the "S" position. • Using an analog ohmmeter connect one lead to the control module wiring harness connector pin position #47 and the other to pin position #46.	The resistance reading is less than 5.0 ohms: YES NO	▶ Reconnect the air suspension control module and "SOFT" and "FIRM" relays. Then rerun SERVICE BAY DIAGNOSTICS. If code "64" and/or "65" is displayed again install a new air suspension control module. ▶ There is an open in the actuator position signal return circuit. Rerun SERVICE BAY DIAGNOSTICS after repair is made.

GE6	CHECKING WIRING HARNESS		
	• Depress the "STAR" test button down so that it remains in the down "TEST" position. • Remove both the "SOFT" and "FIRM" actuator relays from the vehicle. • Using an analog voltmeter place the positive voltage lead on circuit #175A and the negative lead on circuit #430C (of the "SOFT" actuator relay connector).	Voltage reading is battery voltage: YES NO	▶ GO TO GE7 ▶ There is an electrical problem in the vehicle wiring harness. Rerun SERVICE BAY DIAGNOSTICS after repair is made.

FM2019100083030X

Fig. 31   Test GE: All Shock Actuators Not In Desired Position (Part 3 of 7)

GE7	CHECKING WIRING HARNESS	RESULT	ACTION TO TAKE
	• Using an analog voltmeter place the positive voltage lead on circuit #175B and the negative lead on circuit #430E (of the "FIRM" actuator relay connector).	Voltage reading is battery voltage:	
		YES ▶	GO TO GE8
		NO ▶	There is an electrical problem in the vehicle wiring harness. Rerun SERVICE BAY DIAGNOSTICS after repair is made.

GE8	WIRING HARNESS CHECK		
	The next step is to determine if a problem exists in the actuator activation circuit. In order to do this the following actions are required:	The resistance reading is greater than 10,000 ohms:	
	• Using an analog ohmmeter connect one lead to circuit #846A of the "SOFT" relay connector and the other lead to a known good chassis ground.	YES ▶	GO TO GE9
		NO ▶	The actuator activation circuit has a short to ground in it. Replace both the "SOFT" and "FIRM" relays with new ones and rerun SERVICE BAY DIAGNOSTICS after repair is made.

Fig. 31 Test GE: All Shock Actuators Not In Desired Position (Part 4 of 7)

FM2019100083040X

GE9	WIRING HARNESS CHECK	RESULT	ACTION TO TAKE
	• Using an analog ohmmeter connect one lead to circuit #845A of the "FIRM" relay connector and the other lead to a known good chassis ground.	The resistance reading is greater than 10,000 ohms:	
		YES ▶	GO TO GE10
		NO ▶	The actuator activation circuit has a short to ground in it. Replace both the "SOFT" and "FIRM" relays with new ones and rerun SERVICE BAY DIAGNOSTICS after repair is made.

GE10	WIRING HARNESS CHECK		
	• Using an analog ohmmeter connect one lead to circuit #846A of the "SOFT" relay connector and the other lead to circuit #845A of the "FIRM" relay connector.	The resistance reading is less than 10 ohms:	
		YES ▶	GO TO GE11
		NO ▶	The actuator activation circuit has an open in it. Rerun SERVICE BAY DIAGNOSTICS after repair is made.

Fig. 31 Test GE: All Shock Actuators Not In Desired Position (Part 5 of 7)

FM2019100083050X

GE11	WIRING HARNESS CHECK	RESULT	ACTION TO TAKE
	The next step in determining where this problem is located is to determine if the control module signal to activate the actuator relays is reaching the relays. In order to do this the following actions are required:	The voltage reading pulses (between zero and battery voltage) continuously:	
	• Release the "STAR" test button so that it remains in the up "HOLD" position after the code "34" been displayed for at least 5 seconds.	YES ▶	GO TO GE13
	• Using a VOM place the positive lead on circuit #839 and the negative lead on circuit #430C of the "SOFT" relay connector.	NO ▶	GO TO GE12
	NOTE: As long as the "STAR" test button is in the up "HOLD" position the "FIRM/SOFT ACTUATOR TEST" will continue.		

GE12	WIRING HARNESS CHECK		
	• Turn the "STAR" tester "ON/OFF" switch to the "OFF" position.	The resistance reading is less than 5.0 ohms:	
	• Turn the air suspension "ON/OFF" switch to the "OFF" position and disconnect the air suspension control module.	YES ▶	Replace the air suspension control module with a new one and rerun SERVICE BAY DIAGNOSTICS.
	• Using an analog ohmmeter connect one lead to the control module wiring harness connector pin position #12 and the other lead to the "SOFT" relay connector circuit #839.	NO ▶	There is an open in circuit #839. Rerun SERVICE BAY DIAGNOSTICS after repair is made.

Fig. 31 Test GE: All Shock Actuators Not In Desired Position (Part 6 of 7)

FM2019100083060X

GE13	WIRING HARNESS CHECK	RESULT	ACTION TO TAKE
	• This time place the positive lead of VOM on circuit #838 and the negative lead on circuit #430E of the "SOFT" relay connector.	The voltage reading pulses (between zero and battery voltage) continuously:	
	NOTE: As long as the "STAR" test button is in the up "HOLD" position the "FIRM/SOFT ACTUATOR TEST" will continue.	YES ▶	Replace both the "SOFT" and "FIRM" relays with new ones and rerun SERVICE BAY DIAGNOSTICS after repairs are made.
		NO ▶	GO TO GE14

GE14	WIRING HARNESS CHECK		
	• Turn the "STAR" tester "ON/OFF" switch to the "OFF" position.	The resistance reading is less than 5.0 ohms:	
	• Turn the air suspension "ON/OFF" switch to the "OFF" position and disconnect the air suspension control module.	YES ▶	Replace the air suspension control module with a new one and rerun SERVICE BAY DIAGNOSTICS.
	• Using an analog ohmmeter connect one lead to the control module wiring harness connector pin position #11 and the other lead to the "FIRM" relay connector circuit #838.	NO ▶	There is an open in circuit #838. Rerun SERVICE BAY DIAGNOSTICS after repair is made.

Fig. 31 Test GE: All Shock Actuators Not In Desired Position (Part 7 of 7)

FM2019100083070X

HA1	STAR CODE: 49 UNABLE TO DETECT LOWERING OF RIGHT FRONT CORNER	RESULT	ACTION TO TAKE
	The air suspension control module has not received the signal that the right front corner of the vehicle vented during the SERVICE BAY DIAGNOSTIC check. There are ten possible causes: • The height sensor linkage arm is not connected properly to the vehicle and/or height sensor. • The air line for the right front air spring may be plugged. • The right front air spring solenoid valve may be defective. • The right front air spring B+ power supply circuit may have an open in it. • The right front air spring ground return circuit may have an open in it. • The vent solenoid valve may be defective. • The vent solenoid B+ power supply circuit have an open in it. • The vent solenoid ground return circuit may have an open in it. • The air suspension control module may be defective. • The left front air spring may be unable to vent.	▶	GO TO HA2

FM2019100084010X

Fig. 32   Test HA: Unable To Detect Lowering Of Right Front Corner (Part 1 of 17)

HA2	VISUAL COMPONENT CHECK	RESULT	ACTION TO TAKE
	• Check the right front corner of the vehicle to verify that the height sensor has no obvious damage and that the linkage is connected.	The right front height sensor is installed correctly with no obvious damage: YES NO	 ▶ GO TO HA3 ▶ Make needed repairs as required and rerun SERVICE BAY DIAGNOSTICS.
HA3	ENTERING FUNCTIONAL TEST MODE OF SERVICE BAY DIAG		
	The next step in determining why the the right front corner of the vehicle did not vent is: • Release the "STAR" test button to the up "HOLD" position. After five seconds depress the "STAR" test button again so that it remains in the down "TEST" position. This will allow the control module to enter FUNCTIONAL TEST mode.	The "STAR" tester is displaying code: "31", "32", "33", "34", or "35" SOMETHING ELSE	 ▶ GO TO HA5 ▶ GO TO HA4
HA4	RETRY FUNCTIONAL TEST ENTRANCE PROCEDURE		
	The air suspension control module has not entered the FUNCTIONAL TEST mode and the following actions are required: • Make sure that the "STAR" tester is still plugged into the air suspension diagnostic pigtail. • Make sure that the "STAR" tester is turned "ON". • Release the "STAR" test button to the up "HOLD" position. After five seconds depress "STAR" test button again so that it remains in the down "TEST" position. This will allow the control module to enter FUNCTIONAL TEST mode.	The "STAR" tester is displaying code: "31", "32", "33", "34", or "35" SOMETHING ELSE	 ▶ GO TO HA5 ▶ Rerun SERVICE BAY DIAGNOSTICS and if still unable to enter FUNCTIONAL TEST mode install a new air suspension control module and then rerun SERVICE BAY DIAGNOSTICS

FM2019100084020X

Fig. 32   Test HA: Unable To Detect Lowering Of Right Front Corner (Part 2 of 17)

HA5	VENT SOLENOID VALVE COMPONENT CHECK	RESULT	ACTION TO TAKE
	It is desired to activate the "VENT" SOLENOID VALVE TOGGLE" functional test. In order to do this the following actions are required: • Raise the vehicle's hood up completely. • Release the "STAR" test button so that it remains in the up "HOLD" position after the code "32" has been displayed for at least 5 seconds. NOTE: As long as the "STAR" test button is in the up "HOLD" position the selected functional test will continue. The "VENT SOLENOID VALVE TOGGLE" test is used to verify that the air suspension control module can activate the vent solenoid valve by cycling it "ON" and "OFF" continuously until the "STAR" test button is depressed down again.	The air compressor assembly vent solenoid is: CYCLING "ON/OFF" CONTINUOUSLY VENT SOLENOID REMAINS "OFF"	 ▶ Depress the "STAR" test button so that it remains in the down "TEST" position. This action will stop the "VENT SOLENOID VALVE TOGGLE" functional test since it is no longer required. Then: GO TO HA11 ▶ GO TO HA6
HA6	CHECKING WIRING HARNESS		
	Since the air suspension control module can not activate the vent solenoid valve the following actions are required: • Disconnect the air compressor assembly electrical connector from the vehicle wiring harness connector. • Examine both electrical connectors for damage and proper installation of wires.	Electrical connectors are good: YES NO	 ▶ GO TO HA7 ▶ Make repairs as required and rerun SERVICE BAY DIAGNOSTICS.

FM2019100084030X

Fig. 32   Test HA: Unable To Detect Lowering Of Right Front Corner (Part 3 of 17)

HA7	CHECKING WIRING HARNESS	RESULT	ACTION TO TAKE
	The next steps in determining why the air suspension control module could not activate the vent solenoid valve are: • Turn the air suspension "ON/OFF" switch to the "OFF" position. • Disconnect air suspension control module connector. • Disconnect air compressor assembly electrical connector. • Using an analog ohmmeter connect one lead to the air suspension control module wiring harness connector pin location #42 (circuit #421) and other to pin pin location #40 (circuit #430G).	Ohmmeter reading is greater than 10,000 ohms: YES NO	 ▶ GO TO HA8 ▶ A short to ground has been detected in the wiring harness circuit #421. rerun SERVICE BAY DIAGNOSTICS after repair is made.
HA8	CHECKING WIRING HARNESS		
	• Again using an analog ohmmeter connect one lead to the air suspension control module wiring harness connector pin location #42 (circuit #421) and the other to the air compressor assembly vehicle wiring harness connector circuit #421.	Ohmmeter reading is greater than 10 ohms: YES NO	 ▶ The circuit used to activate the vent solenoid valve (circuit #421) has an open in it. Rerun SERVICE BAY DIAGNOSTICS after repair is made. ▶ GO TO HA9
HA9	CHECKING WIRING HARNESS		
	• Again using an analog ohmmeter connect one lead to the air suspension control module wiring harness connector pin location #40 (circuit #430G) and the other to the air compressor assembly vehicle wiring harness connector circuit #430E.	Ohmmeter reading is greater than 10 ohms: YES NO	 ▶ Circuit #430E has an open in it. Rerun SERVICE BAY DIAGNOSTICS after repair is made. ▶ GO TO HA10

FM2019100084040X

Fig. 32   Test HA: Unable To Detect Lowering Of Right Front Corner (Part 4 of 17)

HA10	COMPONENT CHECK	RESULT		ACTION TO TAKE
	* Using a 12 volt power supply connect the positive lead to the air compressor assembly connector pin location #1 and the negative lead to the air compressor assembly connector pin location #2 for 2 to 3 seconds. Repeat this as required.	The vent solenoid makes an audible click sound when voltage is applied:		
		YES	▶	Install a new air suspension control module and rerun SERVICE BAY DIAGNOSTICS.
		NO	▶	Install a new air compressor assembly and rerun SERVICE BAY DIAGNOSTICS.
HA11	COMPONENT CHECK			
	It is now desired to activate the "AIR SPRING SOLENOID VALVE TOGGLE" functional test. In order to do this the following action is required:	The right front air spring solenoid valve is:		
	* Release the "STAR" test button so that it remains in the up "HOLD" position after the code "33" has been displayed for at least 5 seconds.	CYCLING "ON/OFF" CONTINUOUSLY	▶	GO TO HA15
		REMAINS "OFF"	▶	GO TO HA12
	NOTE: As long as the "STAR" test button is in the up "HOLD" position the selected functional test will continue. The "AIR SPRING SOLENOID TOGGLE" test is used to verify that the air suspension control module can activate each of the air spring solenoid valves by cycling them "ON" and "OFF" continuously until the "STAR" test button is depressed down again.			

FM2019100084050X

Fig. 32 Test HA: Unable To Detect Lowering Of Right Front Corner (Part 5 of 17)

HA12	WIRING HARNESS CHECK	RESULT		ACTION TO TAKE
	The air suspension control module cannot activate the right front air spring solenoid valve. In order to determine the cause of this the following actions are required:	The voltage reading pulses between zero and battery voltage (check is to be made over a one minute time period):		
	* Electrically disconnect the air spring solenoid from the vehicle wiring harness connector.	YES	▶	Install a new right front air spring spring solenoid and then rerun SERVICE BAY DIAGNOSTICS.
	* Using a voltmeter connect the positive lead to the air spring solenoid valve wiring harness connector circuit #414 and the negative lead to circuit #430D of the same connector.	NO	▶	GO TO HA13
	NOTE: The "AIR SPRING SOLENOID VALVE TOGGLE" functional test is still being conducted. During this functional test the front ride height of the vehicle may lower and the rear ride height may raise.			
HA13	CHECKING WIRING HARNESS			
	* Turn the air suspension "ON/OFF" switch to the "OFF" position.	Ohmmeter reading is greater than 10 ohms:		
	* Disconnect the air suspension control module connector.	YES	▶	GO TO HA14
	* Using an analog ohmmeter connect one lead to the air suspension control module wiring harness connector pin location #17 (circuit #414) and other to the right front air spring solenoid valve wiring harness connector circuit #414.	NO	▶	An open in circuit #414 has been detected in the wiring harness.
				rerun SERVICE BAY DIAGNOSTICS after repair is made.

FM2019100084060X

Fig. 32 Test HA: Unable To Detect Lowering Of Right Front Corner (Part 6 of 17)

HA14	WIRING HARNESS CHECK	RESULT		ACTION TO TAKE
	* Again using an analog ohmmeter connect one lead to the air suspension control module wiring harness connector pin location #60 (circuit #430H) and other to the right front air spring solenoid valve vehicle wiring harness connector circuit #430D.	Ohmmeter reading is less than 10 ohms:		
		YES	▶	Install a new air suspension control module and rerun SERVICE BAY DIAGNOSTICS.
		NO	▶	An open in circuit #430H/430D exists. Rerun SERVICE BAY DIAGNOSTICS after repair is made.
HA15	ENTER SPRING FILL DIAGNOSTICS			
	At this time it will be required to exit SERVICE BAY DIAGNOSTICS and enter SPRING FILL (refer to SPRING FILL DIAGNOSTIC section for instructions).	The "STAR" tester is displaying one of the following codes:		
		"21" to "28"	▶	GO TO HA16
		SOMETHING ELSE	▶	Repeat SPRING FILL entrance procedure until entered.

FM2019100084070X

Fig. 32 Test HA: Unable To Detect Lowering Of Right Front Corner (Part 7 of 17)

HA16	INFLATE RIGHT FRONT AIR SPRING	RESULT		ACTION TO TAKE
	In order to perform the right front air spring vent test we must first inflate it above the normal position. In order to do this the following action is required:	The vehicle's right front air spring has been inflated so that the right front corner of the vehicle has approximately a two inch gap between the fender lip opening and the top of the tire:		
	* Release the "STAR" test button so that it remains in the up "HOLD" position after the code "24" has been displayed for at least 5 seconds.	YES	▶	Depress the "STAR" test button down so that it remains in the "TEST" position. Then: GO TO HA17
	NOTE: As long as the "STAR" test button remains in the up "HOLD" position the right front air spring will continue to be inflated. When the desired amount of inflating has occurred depress the "STAR" test button so that it remains in the down "TEST" position.	NO	▶	Continue with step "HA16" until the right front corner of the vehicle is at the desired position. If unable to the raise the vehicle look for an air line and/or air spring leak.

FM2019100084080X

Fig. 32 Test HA: Unable To Detect Lowering Of Right Front Corner (Part 8 of 17)

HA17	VENT RIGHT FRONT SPRING	RESULT	ACTION TO TAKE
	To vent the right air spring the following action is required: * Release the "STAR" test button so that it remains in the up "HOLD" position after the code "21" has been displayed for at least 5 seconds. NOTE: As long as the "STAR" test button remains in the up "HOLD" position the right front air spring will continue to vent. When the desired amount of venting has occurred depress the "STAR" test button so that it remains in the "TEST" position.	The right front corner of the vehicle has vented down to the normal ride height: VERY SLOWLY OR NONE AT ALL ▶ SLOWLY OR AT A NORMAL RATE ▶	Depress the "STAR" test button down so that it remains in the "TEST" position. Then: GO TO HA18 If the left front corner of the vehicle also has leveling problems fix them first. Otherwise rerun SERVICE DIAGNOSTICS and if this problem still occurs install a new air suspension control module and then rerun SERVICE BAY DIAGNOSTICS.

FM2019100084090X

Fig. 32   Test HA: Unable To Detect Lowering Of Right Front Corner (Part 9 of 17)

HA18	INFLATE RIGHT FRONT AIR SPRING	RESULT	ACTION TO TAKE
	Again it is desired to first inflate the right front corner of the vehicle above the normal position. In order to do this the following action is required: * Release the "STAR" test button so that it remains in the up "HOLD" position after the code "24" has been displayed for at least 5 seconds. NOTE: As long as the "STAR" test button remains in the up "HOLD" position the right front air spring will continue to be inflated. When the desired amount of inflating has occurred depress the "STAR" test button so that it remains in the down "TEST" position.	The vehicle's right front air spring has been inflated so that the right front corner of the vehicle has approximately a two inch gap between the fender lip opening and the top of the tire: YES ▶ NO ▶	Depress the "STAR" test button down so that it remains in the "TEST" position. Then: GO TO HA19 Continue with step "HA18" until the right front corner of the vehicle is at the desired position.

FM2019100084100X

Fig. 32   Test HA: Unable To Detect Lowering Of Right Front Corner (Part 10 of 17)

HA19	VENT RIGHT FRONT SPRING	RESULT	ACTION TO TAKE
	In order to determine why the right front corner of the vehicle is venting "VERY SLOWLY OR NONE AT ALL" the following actions are required: * Disconnect the right front air line from the right front air spring solenoid valve. * Release the "STAR" test button so that it remains in the "HOLD" position after the code "21" has been displayed for at least 5 seconds. NOTE: THIS TEST STEP MAY RESULT IN A RAPID DROP IN VEHICLE RIDE HEIGHT	The right front corner of the vehicle has vented down to the normal ride height: VERY SLOWLY OR NONE AT ALL ▶ AT A FAST OR NORMAL RATE ▶	Depress the "STAR" test button down so that it remains in the "TEST" position. Then: GO TO HA24 Depress the "STAR" test button down so that it remains in the "TEST" position. Then: GO TO HA20

FM2019100084110X

Fig. 32   Test HA: Unable To Detect Lowering Of Right Front Corner (Part 11 of 17)

HA20	INFLATE RIGHT FRONT AIR SPRING	RESULT	ACTION TO TAKE
	From the previous tests we have determined that the cause of the venting problem is due to a restriction in the air line or compressor assembly. In order to isolate the cause of this problem the following actions are required: * Reconnect the air line to the right front solenoid valve. * Inflate the right front corner of the vehicle so that the vehicle ride height is above the normal position. Then release the "STAR" test button so that it remains in the up "HOLD" position after the code "24" has been displayed for at least 5 seconds. NOTE: As long as the "STAR" test button remains in the up "HOLD" position the right front air spring will continue to be inflated. When the desired amount of inflating has occurred depress the "STAR" test button so that it remains in the down "TEST" position.	The vehicle's right front air spring has been inflated so that the right front corner of the vehicle has approximately a two inch gap between the fender lip opening and the top of the tire: YES ▶ NO ▶	Depress the "STAR" test button down so that it remains in the "TEST" position. Then: GO TO HA21 Continue with step "HA20" until the right front corner of the vehicle is at the desired position. If unable to depress the STAR test button down to the "TEST" position, wait 10 minutes and repeat step "HA20".

FM2019100084120X

Fig. 32   Test HA: Unable To Detect Lowering Of Right Front Corner (Part 12 of 17)

HA21	VENT RIGHT FRONT SPRING	RESULT	ACTION TO TAKE
	In order to determine if the air line or air compressor assembly is the problem the following actions are required: • Disconnect one of the air lines from the air compressor drier assembly • Release the "STAR" test button so that it remains in the "HOLD" position after the "21" has been displayed for at least 5 seconds. NOTE: THIS TEST STEP MAY RESULT IN A RAPID DROP IN VEHICLE RIDE HEIGHT.	The right front corner of the vehicle has vented down to a normal ride height: VERY SLOWLY OR NONE AT ALL	Depress the "STAR" test button down so that it remains in the "TEST" position. The air line for the right front corner of the vehicle is restricted. Rerun SERVICE BAY DIAGNOSTICS after repairs are made.
		AT A FAST OR NORMAL RATE	Depress the "STAR" test button down so that it remains in the "TEST" position. Then: GO TO HA22

HA22	COMPONENT CHECK		
	• Disconnect all of the air lines to the air compressor assembly drier. • Remove the air compressor assembly from the vehicle. • Remove the air compressor drier cap (air lines are inserted into this part) from the drier assembly (refer to the shop manual for instructions since it is spring loaded).	The white filter material in the air compressor drier cap is oily: YES	GO TO HA23
		NO	Install a new air compressor assembly. Then rerun SERVICE BAY DIAGNOSTICS.

Fig. 32   Test HA: Unable To Detect Lowering Of Right Front Corner (Part 13 of 17)

FM2019100084130X

HA23	COMPONENT CHECK	RESULT	ACTION TO TAKE
	One of the shock/strut assemblies on the vehicle has leaked a large amount of shock fluid into the air spring canister. In addition to replacing the shock/strut the following components must also be replaced: • All air suspension air lines. • Air compressor assembly. • Drier assembly. • Remove all air spring solenoid valves and replace the filter located at the opposite end of where the air line attaches.	All repairs completed.	Rerun SERVICE BAY DIAGNOSTICS.

HA24	COMPONENT CHECK		
	From the previous tests we have determined that the cause of the venting problem is located in the air spring solenoid valve or shock/strut assembly. In order to determine which is the problem the following actions are required: • Using a body hoist raise the vehicle off the floor (tire rotation height) so that no weight is on the tires. • Vent the right front air spring as in step "HA19" and remove the air spring solenoid valve (refer to shop manual if required). • Remove the air spring solenoid valve shock fluid mist filter.	The shock fluid mist filter is: CLEAN OR SLIGHTLY OILY	GO TO HA25
		VERY OILY	GO TO HA26

Fig. 32   Test HA: Unable To Detect Lowering Of Right Front Corner (Part 14 of 17)

FM2019100084140X

HA25	COMPONENT CHECK	RESULT	ACTION TO TAKE
	In order to determine if the right front air spring solenoid valve is operational the following actions are required: • Make sure that the air line and vehicle electrical wiring harness connector are connected to the removed right front air spring solenoid valve. • Release the "STAR" test button so that it remains in the "HOLD" position after the code "24" has been displayed for at least 5 seconds.	The right front air spring solenoid valve is passing air through it: NO	Depress the "STAR" test button down so that it remains in the "TEST" position. Install a new right front air spring solenoid valve, reinflate the air spring before setting weight on the tire and rerun SERVICE BAY DIAGNOSTICS.
		YES	Depress the STAR test button down so that it remains in the "TEST" position binding of the shock/strut and repair procedures. Rerun SERVICE BAY DIAGNOSTICS after repairs are made.

Fig. 32   Test HA: Unable To Detect Lowering Of Right Front Corner (Part 15 of 17)

FM2019100084150X

HA26	COMPONENT CHECK	RESULT	ACTION TO TAKE
	In order to determine if the right front air spring solenoid valve is operational the following actions are required: • Make sure that the air line and vehicle electrical wiring harness connector are connected to the removed right front air spring solenoid valve. • Release the "STAR" test button so that it remains in the "HOLD" position after the code "24" has been displayed for at least 5 seconds.	The right front air spring solenoid valve is passing air through it: NO	Depress the "STAR" test button down so that it remains in the "TEST" position. Install a new right front air spring solenoid valve, reinflate the air spring before setting weight on the tire. Then: GO TO HA27
		YES	Depress the "STAR" test button down so that it remains in the "TEST" position. Then: GO TO HA27

HA27	COMPONENT CHECK		
	• Disconnect all of the air lines to the air compressor assembly drier. • Remove the air compressor assembly from the vehicle. • Remove the air compressor drier cap (air lines are inserted into this part) from the drier assembly (refer to the shop manual for instructions since it is spring loaded).	The white filter material in the air compressor drier cap is oily: YES	GO TO HA28
		NO	Install a new right front air spring shock fluid mist filter and then rerun SERVICE BAY DIAGNOSTICS.

Fig. 32   Test HA: Unable To Detect Lowering Of Right Front Corner (Part 16 of 17)

FM2019100084160X

HA28	COMPONENT CHECK	RESULT	ACTION TO TAKE
	The right front shock/strut assembly on the vehicle has leaked a large amount of shock fluid into the air spring canister. Refer to the shop manual for replacement procedures. In addition to replacing this shock/strut the following components must also be replaced. • All air suspension air lines. • Air compressor assembly. • Drier assembly. • Remove all air spring solenoid valves and replace the filter located at the opposite end of where the air line attaches.	All repairs completed. ▶	Rerun SERVICE BAY DIAGNOSTICS.

Fig. 32   Test HA: Unable To Detect Lowering Of Right Front Corner (Part 17 of 17)

HB1	STAR CODE: 50 / UNABLE TO DETECT LOWERING OF LEFT FRONT CORNER	RESULT	ACTION TO TAKE
	The air suspension control module has not received the signal that the left front corner of the vehicle vented during the SERVICE BAY DIAGNOSTIC check. There are ten possible causes: • The height sensor linkage arm is not connected properly to the vehicle and/or height sensor. • The air line for the left front air spring may be plugged. • The left front air spring solenoid valve may be defective. • The left front air spring B+ power supply circuit may have an open in it. • The left front air spring ground return circuit may have an open in it. • The vent solenoid valve may be defective. • The vent solenoid B+ power supply circuit may have an open in it. • The vent solenoid ground return circuit may have an open in it. • The air suspension control module may be defective. • The right front air spring may be unable to vent.	▶	GO TO HB2

Fig. 33   Test HB: Unable To Detect Lowering Of Left Front Corner (Part 1 of 17)

HB2	VISUAL COMPONENT CHECK	RESULT	ACTION TO TAKE
	• Check the left front corner of the vehicle to verify that the height sensor has no obvious damage and that the linkage is connected.	The left front height sensor is installed correctly with no obvious damage: YES ▶ NO ▶	 GO TO HB3 Make needed repairs as required and rerun SERVICE BAY DIAGNOSTICS.
HB3	ENTERING FUNCTIONAL TEST MODE OF SERVICE BAY DIAG		
	The next step in determining why the left front corner of the vehicle did not vent is: • Release the "STAR" test button to the up "HOLD" position. After five seconds depress the "STAR" test button again so that it remains in the down "TEST" position. This will allow the control module to enter FUNCTIONAL TEST mode.	The "STAR" tester is displaying code: "31", "32", "33", "34", or "35" ▶ SOMETHING ELSE ▶	 GO TO HB5 GO TO HB4
HB4	RETRY FUNCTIONAL TEST ENTRANCE PROCEDURE		
	The air suspension control module has not entered the FUNCTIONAL TEST mode and the following actions are required: • Make sure that the "STAR" tester is still plugged into the air suspension diagnostic pigtail. • Make sure that the "STAR" tester is turned "ON". • Release the "STAR" test button to the up "HOLD" position. After five seconds depress the "STAR" test button again so that it remains in the down "TEST" position. This will allow the control module to enter FUNCTIONAL TEST mode.	The "STAR" tester is displaying code: "31", "32", "33", "34", or "35" ▶ SOMETHING ELSE ▶	 GO TO HB5 Rerun SERVICE BAY DIAGNOSTICS and if still unable to enter FUNCTIONAL TEST mode install a new air suspension control module.

Fig. 33   Test HB: Unable To Detect Lowering Of Left Front Corner (Part 2 of 17)

HB5	VENT SOLENOID VALVE COMPONENT CHECK	RESULT	ACTION TO TAKE
	It is desired to activate the "VENT SOLENOID VALVE TOGGLE" functional test. In order to do this the following action are required: • Raise the vehicle's hood up completely. • Release the "STAR" test button so that it remains in the up "HOLD" position after the code "32" has been displayed for at least 5 seconds. NOTE: As long as the "STAR" test button is in the up "HOLD" position the selected functional test will continue. The "VENT SOLENOID VALVE TOGGLE" test is used to verify that the air suspension control module can activate the vent solenoid valve by cycling it "ON" and "OFF" continuously until the "STAR" test button is depressed down again.	The air compressor assembly vent solenoid is: CYCLING "ON/OFF" CONTINUOUSLY ▶ VENT SOLENOID REMAINS "OFF" ▶	 Depress the "STAR" test button so that it remains in the down "TEST" position. This action will stop the "VENT SOLENOID VALVE TOGGLE" functional test since it is no longer required. Then: GO TO HB11 GO TO HB6
HB6	CHECKING WIRING HARNESS		
	Since the air suspension control module can not activate the vent solenoid valve the following actions are required: • Disconnect the air compressor assembly electrical connector from the vehicle wiring harness connector. • Examine both electrical connectors for damage and proper installation of wires	Electrical connectors are good: YES ▶ NO ▶	 GO TO HB7 Make repairs as required and rerun SERVICE BAY DIAGNOSTICS.

Fig. 33   Test HB: Unable To Detect Lowering Of Left Front Corner (Part 3 of 17)

HB7	CHECKING WIRING HARNESS	RESULT	ACTION TO TAKE
	The next steps in determining why the air suspension control module could not activate the vent solenoid valve are: • Turn the air suspension "ON/OFF" switch to the "OFF" position. • Disconnect air suspension control module connector. • Disconnect the air compressor assembly electrical connector. • Using an analog ohmmeter connect one lead to the air suspension control module wiring harness connector pin location #42 (circuit #421) and other to pin location #40 (circuit #430G).	Ohmmeter reading is greater than 10,000 ohms: YES ▶ NO ▶	GO TO HB8 A short to ground has been detected in the wiring harness circuit #421. rerun SERVICE BAY DIAGNOSTICS after repair is made.
HB8	CHECKING WIRING HARNESS		
	• Again using an analog ohmmeter connect one lead to the air suspension control module wiring harness connector pin location #42 (circuit #421) and the other to the air compressor assembly vehicle wiring harness connector circuit #421.	Ohmmeter reading is greater than 10 ohms: YES ▶ NO ▶	The circuit used to activate the vent solenoid valve (circuit #421) has an open in it. Rerun SERVICE BAY DIAGNOSTICS after repair is made. GO TO HB9
HB9	CHECKING WIRING HARNESS		
	• Again using an analog ohmmeter connect one lead to the air suspension control module wiring harness connector pin location #40 (circuit #430G) and the other to the air compressor assembly vehicle wiring harness connector circuit #430E.	Ohmmeter reading is greater than 10 ohms: YES ▶ NO ▶	Circuit #430E has an open in it. Rerun SERVICE BAY DIAGNOSTICS after repair is made. GO TO HB10

FM2019100085040X

Fig. 33 Test HB: Unable To Detect Lowering Of Left Front Corner (Part 4 of 17)

HB12	CHECKING WIRING HARNESS	RESULT	ACTION TO TAKE
	The air suspension control module can not activate the left front air spring solenoid valve. In order to determine the cause of this the following actions are required: • Electrically disconnect the air spring solenoid from the vehicle wiring harness connector. • Using a voltmeter connect the positive lead to the air spring solenoid valve wiring harness connector circuit #415 and the negative lead to circuit #430K of the same connector. NOTE: The "AIR SPRING SOLENOID VALVE TOGGLE" functional test is still being conducted. During this functional test the front ride height of the vehicle may lower and the rear ride height may raise.	The voltage reading pulses between zero and battery voltage (check is to be made over a one minute time period): YES ▶ NO ▶	Install a new left front air spring solenoid valve and rerun SERVICE BAY DIAGNOSTICS after repair is made. GO TO HB13
HB13	CHECKING WIRING HARNESS		
	• Turn the air suspension "ON/OFF" switch to the "OFF" position • Disconnect air suspension control module connector. • Using an analog ohmmeter connect one lead to the air suspension control module wiring harness connector pin location #21 (circuit #415) and other to the left front air spring solenoid valve wiring harness connector circuit #415.	Ohmmeter reading is greater than 10 ohms: YES ▶ NO ▶	GO TO HB14 An open in circuit #415 has been detected in the wiring harness. rerun SERVICE BAY DIAGNOSTICS after repair is made.

FM2019100085060X

Fig. 33 Test HB: Unable To Detect Lowering Of Left Front Corner (Part 6 of 17)

HB10	COMPONENT CHECK	RESULT	ACTION TO TAKE
	• Using a 12 volt power supply connect the positive lead to the air compressor assembly connector pin location #1 and the negative lead to the air compressor assembly connector pin location #2 for 2 to 3 seconds. Repeat this as required.	The vent solenoid valve makes an audible click sound when voltage is applied: YES ▶ NO ▶	Install a new air suspension control module and rerun SERVICE BAY DIAGNOSTICS. Install a new air compressor assembly and rerun SERVICE BAY DIAGNOSTICS.
HB11	COMPONENT CHECK		
	It is now desired to activate the "AIR SPRING SOLENOID VALVE TOGGLE" functional test. In order to do this the following action is required: • Release the "STAR" test button so that it remains in the up "HOLD" position after the code "33" has been displayed for at least 5 seconds. NOTE: As long as the "STAR" test button is in the up "HOLD" position the selected functional test will continue. The "AIR SPRING SOLENOID TOGGLE" test is used to verify that the air suspension control module can activate each of the air spring solenoid valves by cycling them "ON" and "OFF" continuously until the "STAR" test button is depressed down again.	The left front air spring solenoid valve is: CYCLING "ON/OFF" CONTINUOUSLY ▶ REMAINS "OFF" CONTINUOUSLY ▶	GO TO HB15 GO TO HB12

FM2019100085050X

Fig. 33 Test HB: Unable To Detect Lowering Of Left Front Corner (Part 5 of 17)

HB14	WIRING HARNESS CHECK	RESULT	ACTION TO TAKE
	• Again using an analog ohmmeter connect one lead to the air suspension control module wiring harness connector pin location #60 (circuit #430H) and other to the left front air spring solenoid valve vehicle wiring harness connector circuit #430K.	Ohmmeter reading is less than 10 ohms: YES ▶ NO ▶	Install a new air suspension control module and rerun SERVICE BAY DIAGNOSTICS. An open in circuit #430H/430K exists. Rerun SERVICE BAY DIAGNOSTICS after repair is made.
HB15	ENTER SPRING FILL DIAGNOSTICS		
	At this time it will be required to exit SERVICE BAY DIAGNOSTICS and enter SPRING FILL (refer to SPRING FILL DIAGNOSTIC for instructions).	The STAR tester is displaying one of the following codes: "21" to "28" ▶ SOMETHING ELSE ▶	GO TO HB16 Repeat SPRING FILL entrance procedure until entered.

FM2019100085070X

Fig. 33 Test HB: Unable To Detect Lowering Of Left Front Corner (Part 7 of 17)

HB16	INFLATE LEFT FRONT AIR SPRING	RESULT	ACTION TO TAKE
	In order to perform the left front air spring vent test we must first inflate it above the normal position. In order to do that the following action is required: * Release the "STAR" test button so that it remains in the up "HOLD" position after the code "25" has been displayed for at least 5 seconds. NOTE: As long as the "STAR" test button remains in the up "HOLD" position the left front air spring will continue to be inflated. When the desired amount of inflating has occurred depress the "STAR" test button so that it remains in the down "TEST" position.	The vehicle's left front air spring has been inflated so that the left front corner of the vehicle has approximately a two inch gap between the fender lip opening and the top the tire:	
		YES ▶	Depress the "STAR" test button down so that it remains in the "TEST" position. Then: GO TO HB16
		NO ▶	Continue with step "HB16" until the left front corner of the vehicle is at the desired position. If unable to raise the vehicle look for an air line and/or air spring leak.

FM2019100085080X

Fig. 33 Test HB: Unable To Detect Lowering Of Left Front Corner (Part 8 of 17)

HB17	VENT LEFT FRONT SPRING	RESULT	ACTION TO TAKE
	To vent the left front air spring the following action is required: * Release the "STAR" test button so that it remains in the up "HOLD" position after the code "22" has been displayed for at least 5 seconds. NOTE: As long as the "STAR" test button remains in the up "HOLD" position the left front air spring will continue to vent. When the desired amount of venting has occurred depress the STAR test button so that it remains in the "TEST position.	The left front corner of the vehicle has vented down to the normal ride height: VERY SLOWLY OR NONE AT ALL ▶	Depress the "STAR" test button down so that it remains in the "TEST" position. Then: GO TO HB18
		SLOWLY OR AT A NORMAL RATE ▶	If the right front corner of the vehicle also has leveling problems fix them first. Otherwise rerun SERVICE BAY DIAGNOSTICS and if this problem still occurs install a new air suspension control module and then rerun SERVICE BAY DIAGNOSTICS.

FM2019100085090X

Fig. 33 Test HB: Unable To Detect Lowering Of Left Front Corner (Part 9 of 17)

HB18	INFLATE LEFT FRONT AIR SPRING	RESULT	ACTION TO TAKE
	Again it is desired to first inflate the left front corner of the vehicle above the normal position. In order to do that the following action is required: * Release the "STAR" test button so that it remains in the up "HOLD" position after the code "25" has been displayed for at least 5 seconds. NOTE: As long as the "STAR" test button remains in the up "HOLD" position the left front air spring will continue to be inflated. When the desired amount of inflating has occurred depress the "STAR" test button so that it remains in the down "TEST" position.	The vehicle's left front air spring has been inflated so that the left front corner of the vehicle has approximately a two inch gap between the fender lip opening and the top of the tire:	
		YES ▶	Depress the "STAR" test button down so that it remains in the "TEST" position. Then: GO TO HB19
		NO ▶	Continue with step "HB18" until the left front corner of the vehicle is at the desired position.

FM2019100085100X

Fig. 33 Test HB: Unable To Detect Lowering Of Left Front Corner (Part 10 of 17)

HB19	VENT LEFT FRONT SPRING	RESULT	ACTION TO TAKE
	In order to determine why the left front corner of the vehicle is venting "VERY SLOWLY OR NONE AT ALL" the following actions are required: * Disconnect the left front air line from the left front air spring solenoid valve. * Release the "STAR" test button so that it remains in the "HOLD" position after the the code "22" has been displayed for at least 5 seconds. NOTE: THIS TEST STEP MAY RESULT IN A <u>RAPID DROP IN VEHICLE RIDE HEIGHT</u>	The left front corner of the vehicle has vented down to the normal ride height: VERY SLOWLY OR NONE AT ALL ▶	Depress the "STAR" test button down so that it remains in the "TEST" position. Then: GO TO HB24
		AT A FAST OR NORMAL RATE ▶	Depress the "STAR" test button down so that it remains in the "TEST" position. Then: GO TO HB20

FM2019100085110X

Fig. 33 Test HB: Unable To Detect Lowering Of Left Front Corner (Part 11 of 17)

HB20	INFLATE LEFT FRONT AIR SPRING	RESULT	ACTION TO TAKE
	From the previous tests we have determined that the cause of the venting problem is due to a restriction in the air line or compressor assembly. In order to isolate the cause of this problem the following actions are required: * Reconnect the air line to the left front solenoid valve. * Inflate the left front corner of the vehicle so that the vehicle ride height is above the normal position. Then release the "STAR" test button so that it remains in the up "HOLD" position after the code "25" has been displayed for at least 5 seconds. NOTE: As long as the "STAR" test button remains in the "HOLD" position the left front air spring will continue to be inflated. When the desired amount of inflating has occurred depress the "STAR" test button so that it remains in the down "TEST" position.	The vehicle's left front air spring has been inflated so that the right front corner of the vehicle remains approximately a two inch gap between the fender lip opening and the top of the tire: YES ▶ NO ▶	 Depress the "STAR" test button down so that it remains in the "TEST" position. Then: GO TO HB21. Continue with step "HB20" until the left front corner of the vehicle is at the desired position.

Fig. 33 Test HB: Unable To Detect Lowering Of Left Front Corner (Part 12 of 17)

FM2019100085120X

HB21	VENT LEFT FRONT SPRING	RESULT	ACTION TO TAKE
	In order to determine if the air line or air compressor assembly is the problem the following actions are required: * Disconnect one of the air lines from the air compressor dryer assembly. * Release the "STAR" test button so that it remains in the "HOLD" position after the code "22" has been displayed for at least 5 seconds. NOTE: THIS TEST STEP MAY RESULT IN A RAPID LOSS IN VEHICLE RIDE HEIGHT	The left front corner of the vehicle has vented down to a normal ride height: VERY SLOWLY OR NONE AT ALL ▶ AT A FAST OR NORMAL RATE ▶	 Depress the "STAR" test button down so that it remains in the "TEST" position. The air line for the left front corner of the vehicle is restricted. Rerun SERVICE BAY DIAGNOSTICS after repairs are made. Depress the "STAR" test button down so that it remains in the "TEST" position. Then: GO TO HB22
HB22	COMPONENT CHECK		
	* Disconnect all of the air lines to the air compressor assembly drier. * Remove the air compressor assembly from the vehicle. * Remove the air compressor drier cap (air lines are inserted into this part) from the drier assembly	The white filter material in the air compressor drier cap is oily: YES ▶ NO ▶	 GO TO HB23 Install a new air compressor assembly and then rerun SERVICE BAY DIAGNOSTICS.

Fig. 33 Test HB: Unable To Detect Lowering Of Left Front Corner (Part 13 of 17)

FM2019100085130X

HB23	COMPONENT CHECK	RESULT	ACTION TO TAKE
	One of the shock/strut assemblies on the vehicle has leaked a large amount of shock fluid into the air spring canister. In addition to replacing the shock/strut assembly the following components must also be replaced: * All air suspension air lines. * Air compressor assembly. * Drier assembly. * Remove all air spring solenoid valves and replace the filter located at the opposite end of where the air line attaches.	All repairs completed. ▶	Rerun SERVICE BAY DIAGNOSTICS.
HB24	COMPONENT CHECK		
	From the previous tests we have determined that the cause of the venting problem is located in the air spring solenoid valve or shock/strut assembly. In order to determine which is the problem the following actions are required: * Using a body hoist raise the vehicle off the floor (tire rotation height) so that no weight is on the tires. * Vent the left front air spring as in step "HB19" and remove the air spring solenoid valve (refer to shop manual if required). * Remove the air spring solenoid valve shock fluid mist filter.	The shock fluid mist filter is: CLEAN OR SLIGHTLY OILY ▶ VERY OILY ▶	 GO TO HB25 GO TO HB26

Fig. 33 Test HB: Unable To Detect Lowering Of Left Front Corner (Part 14 of 17)

FM2019100085140X

HB25	COMPONENT CHECK	RESULT	ACTION TO TAKE
	In order to determine if the left front air spring solenoid valve is operational the following actions are required: * Make sure that the air line and vehicle electrical wiring harness connector are connected to the removed left front air spring solenoid valve. * Release the "STAR" test button so that it remains in the "HOLD" position after the code "25" has been displayed for at least 5 seconds.	The left front air spring solenoid valve is passing air through it: NO ▶ YES ▶	 Depress the "STAR" test button down so that it remains in the "TEST" position. Install a new left front air spring solenoid valve, reinflate the air spring before setting weight on the tire and rerun SERVICE BAY DIAGNOSTICS. Depress the "STAR" test button down so that it remains in the "TEST" position. Replace the shock fluid mist filter and refer to the shop manual for detection of binding in the shock/strut and repair procedures. Rerun SERVICE BAY DIAGNOSTICS after repairs are made.

Fig. 33 Test HB: Unable To Detect Lowering Of Left Front Corner (Part 15 of 17)

FM2019100085150X

HB26	COMPONENT CHECK	RESULT	ACTION TO TAKE
	In order to determine if the left front air spring solenoid valve is operational the following actions are required: * Make sure that the air line and vehicle electrical wiring harness connector are connected to the removed left front air spring solenoid valve. * Release the "STAR" test button so that it remains in the "HOLD" position after the code "25" has been displayed for at least 5 seconds.	The left front air spring solenoid valve is passing air through it: NO ▶ YES ▶	Depress the "STAR" test button down so that it remains in the test position. Install a new left front air spring solenoid valve, reinflate the air spring before setting weight on the tire. Then: GO TO HB27 Depress the "STAR" test button down so that it remains in the "TEST" position. Then: GO TO HB27

HB27	COMPONENT CHECK		
	* Disconnect all of the air lines to the air compressor assembly drier. * Remove the air compressor assembly from the vehicle. * Remove the air compressor drier cap (air lines are inserted into this part) from the drier assembly (refer to the shop manual for instructions since it is spring loaded).	The white filter material in the air compressor drier cap is oily: YES ▶ NO ▶	GO TO HB28 Install a new left front air spring shock fluid mist filter and then rerun SERVICE BAY DIAGNOSTICS.

FM2019100085160X

Fig. 33 Test HB: Unable To Detect Lowering Of Left Front Corner (Part 16 of 17)

HB28	COMPONENT CHECK	RESULT	ACTION TO TAKE
	The left front shock/strut assembly on the vehicle has leaked a large amount of shock fluid into the air spring canister. Refer to the shop manual for replacement procedures. In addition to replacing this shock/strut the following components must also be replaced: * All air suspension air lines. * Air compressor assembly. * Drier assembly. * Remove all air spring solenoid valves and replace the filter located at the opposite end of where the air line attaches.	All repairs completed ▶	Rerun SERVICE BAY DIAGNOSTICS.

FM2019100085170X

Fig. 33 Test HB: Unable To Detect Lowering Of Left Front Corner (Part 17 of 17)

HC1	STAR CODE: 51 / UNABLE TO DETECT LOWERING OF RIGHT REAR CORNER	RESULT	ACTION TO TAKE
	The air suspension control module has not received the signal that the right rear corner of the vehicle vented during the SERVICE BAY DIAGNOSTIC check. There are ten possible causes: * The height sensor linkage arm is not connected properly to the vehicle and/or height sensor. * The air line for the right rear air spring may be plugged. * The right rear air spring solenoid valve may be defective. * The right rear air spring B + power supply circuit may have an open in it. * The right rear air spring ground return circuit may have an open in it. * The vent solenoid valve may be defective. * The vent solenoid B + power supply circuit may have an open in it. * The vent solenoid ground return circuit may have an open in it. * The air suspension control module may be defective. * The left rear air spring may be unable to vent.	▶	GO TO HC2

FM2019100086010X

Fig. 34 Test HC: Unable To Detect Lowering Of Right Rear Corner (Part 1 of 17)

HC2	VISUAL COMPONENT CHECK	RESULT	ACTION TO TAKE
	* Check the right rear corner of the vehicle to verify that the height sensor has no obvious damage and that the linkage is connected.	The right rear height sensor is installed correctly with no obvious damage: YES ▶ NO ▶	GO TO HC3 Make needed repairs as required and rerun SERVICE BAY DIAGNOSTICS.
HC3	ENTERING FUNCTIONAL TEST MODE OF SERVICE BAY DIAG		
	The next step in determining why the right rear corner of the vehicle did not vent is: * Release the "STAR" test button to the up "HOLD" position. After five seconds depress the "STAR" test button again so that it remains in the down "TEST" position. This will allow the control module to enter FUNCTIONAL TEST mode.	The "STAR" tester is displaying code: "31", "32", "33", "34", or "35" ▶ SOMETHING ELSE ▶	GO TO HC5 GO TO HC4
HC4	RETRY FUNCTIONAL TEST ENTRANCE PROCEDURE		
	The air suspension control module has not entered the PIN POINT TEST mode and the following actions are required: * Make sure that the "STAR" tester is still plugged into the air suspension diagnostic pigtail. * Make sure that the "STAR" tester is turned "ON". * Release the "STAR" test button to the up "HOLD" position. After five seconds depress the "STAR" test button again so that it remains in the down "TEST" position. This will allow the control module to enter FUNCTIONAL TEST mode.	The "STAR" tester is displaying code: "31", "32", "33", "34", or "35" ▶ SOMETHING ELSE ▶	GO TO HC5 Rerun SERVICE BAY DIAGNOSTICS and if still unable to enter FUNCTIONAL TEST mode install a new air suspension control module and then rerun SERVICE BAY DIAGNOSTICS.

FM2019100086020X

Fig. 34 Test HC: Unable To Detect Lowering Of Right Rear Corner (Part 2 of 17)

HC5	VENT SOLENOID VALVE COMPONENT CHECK	RESULT		ACTION TO TAKE
	It is desired to activate the "VENT SOLENOID VALVE TOGGLE" functional test. In order to do this the following action is required: * Raise the vehicle's hood up completely. * Release the "STAR" test button so that it remains in the up "HOLD" position after the code "32" has been displayed for at least 5 seconds. NOTE: As long as the "STAR" test button is in the up "HOLD" position the selected FUNCTIONAL TEST will continue. The "VENT SOLENOID VALVE TOGGLE" test is used to verify that the air suspension control module can activate the vent solenoid valve by cycling it "ON" and "OFF" continuously until the "STAR" test button is depressed down again.	The air compressor assembly vent solenoid is: CYCLING "ON/OFF" CONTINUOUSLY	►	Depress the "STAR" test button so that it remains in the down "TEST" position. This action will stop the "VENT SOLENOID VALVE TOGGLE" functional test since it is no longer required. Then: GO TO HC11
		VENT SOLENOID REMAINS "OFF"	►	GO TO HC6
HC6	CHECKING WIRING HARNESS			
	Since the air suspension control module can not activate the vent solenoid valve the following actions are required: * Disconnect the air compressor assembly electrical connector from the vehicle wiring harness connector. * Examine both electrical connectors for damage and proper installation of wires.	Electrical connectors are good: YES NO	► ►	GO TO HC7 Make repairs as required and rerun SERVICE BAY DIAGNOSTICS.

FM2019100086030X

Fig. 34   Test HC: Unable To Detect Lowering Of Right Rear Corner (Part 3 of 17)

HC7	CHECKING WIRING HARNESS	RESULT		ACTION TO TAKE
	The next steps in determining why the air suspension control module could not activate the vent solenoid valve are: * Turn the air suspension "ON/OFF" switch to the "OFF" position. * Disconnect air suspension control module connector. * Disconnect the air compressor assembly electrical connector. * Using an analog ohmmeter connect one lead to the air suspension control module wiring harness connector pin location #42 (circuit #421) and other to pin location #40 (circuit #430G).	Ohmmeter reading is greater than 10,000 ohms: YES NO	► ►	GO TO HC8 A short to ground has been detected in the wiring harness circuit #421. and rerun SERVICE BAY DIAGNOSTICS after repair is made.
HC8	CHECKING WIRING HARNESS			
	* Again using an analog ohmmeter connect one lead to the air suspension control module wiring harness connector pin location #42 (circuit #421) and the the other to the air compressor assembly vehicle wiring harness connector #421.	Ohmmeter reading is greater than 10 ohms: YES NO	► ►	The circuit used to activate the vent solenoid valve (circuit #421) has an open in it. Rerun SERVICE BAY DIAGNOSTICS after repair is made. GO TO HC9
HC9	CHECKING WIRING HARNESS			
	* Again using an analog ohmmeter connect one lead to the air suspension control module wiring harness connector pin location #40 (circuit #430G) and the other to the air compressor assembly vehicle wiring harness connector circuit #430E.	Ohmmeter reading is greater than 10 ohms: YES NO	► ►	Circuit #430E has an open in it. Rerun SERVICE BAY DIAGNOSTICS after repair is made. GO TO HC10

FM2019100086040X

Fig. 34   Test HC: Unable To Detect Lowering Of Right Rear Corner (Part 4 of 17)

HC10	COMPONENT CHECK	RESULT		ACTION TO TAKE
	* Using a 12 volt power supply connect the positive lead to the air compressor assembly connector pin location #1 and the negative lead to the air compressor assembly connector pin location #2 for 2 to 3 seconds. Repeat this as required.	The vent solenoid valve is activated when the voltage is applied: YES NO	► ►	Install a new air suspension control module and rerun SERVICE BAY DIAGNOSTICS. Replace the air compressor assembly and rerun SERVICE BAY DIAGNOSTICS.
HC11	COMPONENT CHECK			
	It is now desired to activate the "AIR SPRING SOLENOID VALVE TOGGLE" functional test. In order to do this the following actions are required: * Release the "STAR" test button so that it remains in the up "HOLD" position after the code "33" has been displayed for at least 5 seconds. NOTE: As long as the "STAR" test button is in the up "HOLD" position the selected functional test will continue. The "AIR SPRING SOLENOID TOGGLE" test is used to verify that the air suspension control module can activate each of the air spring solenoid valves by cycling them "ON" and "OFF" continuously until the "STAR" test button is depressed down again.	The right rear air spring solenoid valve is: CYCLING "ON/OFF" CONTINUOUSLY REMAINS "OFF"	► ►	GO TO HC15 GO TO HC12

FM2019100086050X

Fig. 34   Test HC: Unable To Detect Lowering Of Right Rear Corner (Part 5 of 17)

HC12	CHECKING WIRING HARNESS	RESULT		ACTION TO TAKE
	The air suspension control module can not activate the right rear air spring solenoid valve. In order to determine the cause of this the following actions are required: * Electrically disconnect the air spring solenoid from the vehicle wiring harness connector. * Using a voltmeter connect the positive lead to the air spring solenoid valve wiring harness connector circuit #416 and the negative lead to circuit #430A of the same connector. NOTE: The "AIR SPRING SOLENOID VALVE TOGGLE" functional test is still being conducted. During this functional test the front ride height of the vehicle may lower and the rear ride height may raise.	The voltage reading pulses between zero and battery voltage (check is to be made over a one minute time period): YES NO	► ►	Install a new right rear air spring solenoid and then rerun SERVICE BAY DIAGNOSTICS. GO TO HC13
HC13	CHECKING WIRING HARNESS			
	* Turn the air suspension "ON/OFF" switch to the "OFF" position. * Disconnect air suspension control module connector. * Using an analog ohmmeter connect one lead to the air suspension control module wiring harness connector pin location #38 (circuit #416) and other to the right rear air spring solenoid valve wiring harness connector circuit #416.	Ohmmeter reading is greater than 10 ohms: YES NO	► ►	GO TO HC14 An open in circuit #416 has been detected in the wiring harness. rerun SERVICE BAY DIAGNOSTICS after repair is made.

FM2019100086060X

Fig. 34   Test HC: Unable To Detect Lowering Of Right Rear Corner (Part 6 of 17)

HC14 WIRING HARNESS CHECK	RESULT	ACTION TO TAKE
• Again using an analog ohmmeter connect one lead to the air suspension control module wiring harness connector pin location #60 (circuit #430H) and other to the right rear air spring solenoid valve vehicle wiring harness connector circuit #430A.	Ohmmeter readings is less than 10 ohms: YES NO	▶ Install a new air suspension control module and rerun SERVICE BAY DIAGNOSTICS. ▶ An open in circuit #430H/430A exists. Rerun SERVICE BAY DIAGNOSTICS after repair is made.
HC15 ENTER SPRING FILL DIAGNOSTICS		
At this time it will be required to exit SERVICE BAY DIAGNOSTICS and enter SPRING FILL (refer to SPRING FILL DIAGNOSTIC for instructions).	The "STAR" tester is displaying one of the following codes: "21" to "28" SOMETHING ELSE	 ▶ GO TO HC16 ▶ Repeat SPRING FILL entrance procedure until entered.

Fig. 34 Test HC: Unable To Detect Lowering Of Right Rear Corner (Part 7 of 17)

HC16 INFLATE RIGHT REAR AIR SPRING	RESULT	ACTION TO TAKE
In order to perform the right rear air spring vent test we must first inflate above the normal position. In order to do that the following action is required: • Release the "STAR" test button so that it remains in the up "HOLD" position after the code "26" has been displayed for at least 5 seconds. NOTE: As long as the "STAR" test button remains in the up "HOLD" position the right rear air spring will continue to be inflated. When the desired amount of inflating has occurred depress the "STAR" test button so that it remains in the down "TEST" position.	The vehicle's right rear air spring has been inflated so that the right rear corner of the vehicle has approximately a two inch gap between the fender lip opening and the top of the tire: YES NO	 ▶ Depress the "STAR" test button down so that it remains in the "TEST" position. Then: GO TO HC17 ▶ Continue with step "HC16" until the right rear corner of the vehicle is at the desired position. If unable to raise vehicle look for an air line and/or air spring leak.

Fig. 34 Test HC: Unable To Detect Lowering Of Right Rear Corner (Part 8 of 17)

HC17 VENT RIGHT REAR SPRING	RESULT	ACTION TO TAKE
To vent the right rear air spring the following action is required: • Release the "STAR" test button so that it remains in the up "HOLD" position after the code "23" has been displayed for at least 5 seconds. NOTE: As long as the "STAR" test button remains in the up "HOLD" position the right rear air spring will continue to vent. When the desired amount of venting has occurred depress the "STAR" test button so that it remains in the "TEST" position.	The right rear corner of the vehicle has vented down to the normal ride height. VERY SLOWLY OR NONE AT ALL SLOWLY OR AT A NORMAL RATE	 ▶ Depress the "STAR" test button down so that it remains in the "TEST" position. Then: GO TO HC18 ▶ If the left rear corner of the vehicle also has leveling problems fix them first. Otherwise rerun SERVICE DIAGNOSTICS and if this problem still occurs install a new air suspension control module and then rerun SERVICE BAY DIAGNOSTICS.

Fig. 34 Test HC: Unable To Detect Lowering Of Right Rear Corner (Part 9 of 17)

HC18 INFLATE RIGHT REAR AIR SPRING	RESULT	ACTION TO TAKE
Again it is desired to first inflate the right rear corner of the vehicle above the normal position. In order to do this the following action is required: • Release the "STAR" test button so that it remains in the up "HOLD" position after the code "26" has been displayed for at least 5 seconds. NOTE: As long as the "STAR" test button remains in the up "HOLD" position the right rear air spring will continue to be inflated. When the desired amount of inflating has occurred depress the "STAR" test button so that it remains in the down "TEST" position.	The vehicle's right rear air spring has been inflated so that the right rear corner of the vehicle has approximately a two inch gap between the fender lip opening and the top of the tire: YES NO	 ▶ Depress the STAR test button down so that it remains in the "TEST" position. Then: GO TO HC19 ▶ Continue with step "HC18" until the right rear corner of the vehicle is at the desired position.

Fig. 34 Test HC: Unable To Detect Lowering Of Right Rear Corner (Part 10 of 17)

HC19	VENT RIGHT REAR SPRING	RESULT	ACTION TO TAKE
	In order to determine why the right rear corner of the vehicle is venting "VERY SLOWLY OR NONE AT ALL" the following actions are required: * Disconnect the right rear air line from the right rear air spring solenoid valve. * Release the "STAR" test button so that it remains in the "HOLD" position after the code "23" has been displayed for at least 5 seconds. NOTE: THIS TEST STEP MAY RESULT IN A RAPID LOSS OF VEHICLE RIDE HEIGHT	The right rear corner of the vehicle has vented down to the normal ride height:	
		VERY SLOWLY OR NONE AT ALL	Depress the STAR test button down so that it remains in the "TEST" position. Then: GO TO HC24
		AT A FAST OR NORMAL RATE	Depress the "STAR" test button down so that it remains in the "TEST" position. Then: GO TO HC20

Fig. 34 Test HC: Unable To Detect Lowering Of Right Rear Corner (Part 11 of 17)

HC20	INFLATE RIGHT REAR AIR SPRING	RESULT	ACTION TO TAKE
	From the previous tests we have determined that the cause of the venting problem is due to a restriction in the air line or compressor assembly. In order to isolate the cause of this problem the following actions are required: * Reconnect the air line to the right rear solenoid valve. * Inflate the right rear corner of the vehicle so that the vehicle ride height is above the normal position. Then release the "STAR" test button so that it remains in the up "HOLD" position after the code "26" has been displayed for at least 5 seconds. NOTE: As long as the "STAR" test button remains in the up "HOLD" position the right rear air spring will continue to be inflated. When the desired amount of inflating has occurred depress the "STAR" test button so that it remains in the down "TEST" position.	The vehicle's right rear air spring has been inflated so that the right rear corner of the vehicle has approximately a two inch gap between the fender lip opening and the top of the tire:	
		YES	Depress the "STAR" test button down so that it remains in the "TEST" position. Then: GO TO HC21.
		NO	Continue with step "HC20" until the right rear corner of the vehicle is at the desired position.

Fig. 34 Test HC: Unable To Detect Lowering Of Right Rear Corner (Part 12 of 17)

HC21	VENT RIGHT REAR SPRING	RESULT	ACTION TO TAKE
	In order to determine if the air line or air compressor assembly is the problem the following actions are required: * Disconnect one of the air lines from the air compressor dryer assembly. * Release the STAR test button so that it remains in the "HOLD" position after the code "23" has been displayed for at least 5 seconds. NOTE: THIS TEST STEP MAY RESULT IN A RAPID LOSS OF AIR FROM THE AIR SPRING .	The right rear corner of the vehicle has vented down to a normal ride height:	
		VERY SLOWLY OR NONE AT ALL	Depress the "STAR" test button down so that it remains in the "TEST" position. The air line for the right rear corner of the vehicle is restricted. Rerun SERVICE BAY DIAGNOSTICS after repairs are made.
		AT A FAST OR NORMAL RATE	Depress the "STAR" test button down so that it remains in the "TEST" position. Then: GO TO HC22
HC22	COMPONENT CHECK		
	* Disconnect all of the air lines to the air compressor assembly drier. * Remove the air compressor assembly from the vehicle. * Remove the air compressor drier cap (air lines are inserted into this part) from the drier assembly (refer to the shop manual for instructions since it is spring loaded).	The white filter material in the air compressor drier cap is oily:	
		YES	GO TO HC23
		NO	Install a new air compressor assembly and then rerun SERVICE BAY DIAGNOSTICS.

Fig. 34 Test HC: Unable To Detect Lowering Of Right Rear Corner (Part 13 of 17)

HC23	COMPONENT CHECK	RESULT	ACTION TO TAKE
	One of the shock/strut assemblies on the vehicle has leaked a large amount of shock fluid into the air spring canister. Refer to the shop manual for determination and replacement procedures of the bad shock/strut. In addition to replacing the shock/strut the following components must also be replaced: * All air suspension air lines. * Air compressor assembly. * Drier assembly. * Remove all air spring solenoid valves and replace the filter located at the opposite end of where the air line attaches.	All repairs completed	Rerun SERVICE BAY DIAGNOSTICS.
HC24	COMPONENT CHECK		
	From the previous tests we have determined that the cause of the venting problem is located in the air spring solenoid valve or shock/strut assembly. In order to determine which is the problem the the follow actions are required: * Using a body hoist raise the vehicle off the floor (tire rotation height) so that no weight is on the tires. * Vent the right rear air spring as in step "HC19" and remove the air spring solenoid valve (refer to shop manual if required) * Remove the air spring solenoid valve shock fluid mist filter.	The shock fluid mist filter is:	
		CLEAN OR SLIGHTLY OILY	GO TO HC25
		VERY OILY	GO TO HC26

Fig. 34 Test HC: Unable To Detect Lowering Of Right Rear Corner (Part 14 of 17)

HC25	COMPONENT CHECK	RESULT	ACTION TO TAKE
	In order to determine if the right rear air spring solenoid valve is operational the following actions are required: * Make sure that the air line and vehicle electrical wiring harness connector are connected to the removed right rear air spring solenoid valve. * Release the "STAR" test button so that it remains in the "HOLD" position after the code "26" has been displayed for at least 5 seconds.	The right rear air spring solenoid valve is passing air through it: NO YES	▶ Depress the "STAR" test button down so that it remains in the "TEST" position. Install a new right rear air spring solenoid valve, reinflate the air spring before setting weight on the tire and rerun SERVICE BAY DIAGNOSTICS. ▶ Depress the "STAR" test button down so that it remains in the "TEST" position. Install a new shock fluid mist filter and refer to the shop manual for detection of binding of the shock/strut and repair procedures. Rerun SERVICE BAY DIAGNOSTICS after repairs are made.

Fig. 34 Test HC: Unable To Detect Lowering Of Right Rear Corner (Part 15 of 17)

HC26	COMPONENT CHECK	RESULT	ACTION TO TAKE
	In order to determine if the right rear air spring solenoid valve is operational the following actions are required: * Make sure that the air line and vehicle electrical wiring harness connector are connected to the removed right rear air spring solenoid valve. * Release the "STAR" test button so that it remains in the "HOLD" position after the code "26" has been displayed for at least 5 seconds.	The right rear air spring solenoid valve is passing air through it: NO YES	▶ Depress the "STAR" test button down so that it remains in the "TEST" position. Install a new right rear air spring solenoid valve, reinflate the air spring before setting weight on the tire. Then: GO TO HC26 ▶ Depress the "STAR" test button down so that it remains in the "TEST" position. Then: GO TO HC26
HC27	COMPONENT CHECK		
	* Disconnect all of the air lines to the air compressor assembly drier. * Remove the air compressor assembly from the vehicle. * Remove the air compressor drier cap (air lines are inserted into this part) from the drier assembly	The white filter material in the air compressor drier cap is oily: YES NO	▶ GO TO HC28 ▶ Install a new right rear air spring shock fluid mist filter with a new one and then rerun SERVICE BAY DIAGNOSTICS.

Fig. 34 Test HC: Unable To Detect Lowering Of Right Rear Corner (Part 16 of 17)

HC28	COMPONENT CHECK	RESULT	ACTION TO TAKE
	The right rear shock/strut assembly on the vehicle has leaked a large amount of shock fluid into the air spring canister. In addition to replacing this shock/strut the following components must also be replaced: * All air suspension air lines. * Air compressor assembly. * Drier assembly. * Remove all air spring solenoid valves and replace the filter located at the opposite end of where the air line attaches.	All repairs completed.	▶ Rerun SERVICE BAY DIAGNOSTICS.

Fig. 34 Test HC: Unable To Detect Lowering Of Right Rear Corner (Part 17 of 17)

HD1	STAR CODE: 78 UNABLE TO DETECT LOWERING OF LEFT REAR CORNER	RESULT	ACTION TO TAKE
	The air suspension control module has not received the signal that the left rear corner of the vehicle vented during the SERVICE BAY DIAGNOSTIC check. There are ten possible causes: * The height sensor linkage arm is not connected properly to the vehicle and/or height sensor. * The air line for the left rear air spring may be plugged. * The left rear air spring solenoid valve may be defective. * The left rear air spring B+ power supply circuit may have an open in it. * The left rear air spring ground return circuit may have an open in it. * The vent solenoid valve may be defective. * The vent solenoid B+ power supply circuit may have an open in it. * The vent solenoid ground return circuit may have an open in it. * The air suspension control module may be defective. * The right rear air spring may be unable to vent.		▶ GO TO HD2
HD2	VISUAL COMPONENT CHECK		
	* Check the left rear corner of the vehicle to verify that the height sensor has no obvious damage and that the linkage is connected.	The left rear height sensor is installed correctly with no obvious damage. YES NO	▶ GO TO HD3 ▶ Make needed repairs as required and rerun SERVICE BAY DIAGNOSTICS.

Fig. 35 Test HD: Unable To Detect Lowering Of Left Rear Corner (Part 1 of 17)

HD3	ENTERING FUNCTIONAL TEST MODE OF SERVICE BAY DIAG	RESULT	ACTION TO TAKE
	The next steps in determining why the left rear corner of the vehicle did not vent is:	The "STAR" tester is displaying code:	
	* Release the "STAR" test button to the up "HOLD" position. After five seconds depress the "STAR" test button again so that it remains in the down "TEST" position. This will allow the control module to enter FUNCTIONAL TEST mode.	"31", "32", "33", "34", or "35"	GO TO HD5
		SOMETHING ELSE	GO TO HD4
HD4	RETRY FUNCTIONAL TEST ENTRANCE PROCEDURE		
	The air suspension control module has not entered the FUNCTIONAL TEST mode and the following actions are required:	The "STAR" tester is displaying code:	
	* Make sure that the "STAR" tester is still plugged into the air suspension diagnostic pigtail.	"31", "32", "33", "34", or "35"	GO TO HD5
	* Make sure that the "STAR" tester is turned "ON"	SOMETHING ELSE	Rerun SERVICE BAY DIAGNOSTICS and if still unable to enter FUNCTIONAL TEST mode install a new air suspension control module and then rerun SERVICE BAY DIAGNOSTICS.
	* Release the "STAR" test button to the up "HOLD" position. After five seconds depress the "STAR" test button again so that it remains in the down "TEST" position. This will allow the control module to enter FUNCTIONAL TEST mode.		

FM2019100087020X

Fig. 35 Test HD: Unable To Detect Lowering Of Left Rear Corner (Part 2 of 17)

HD5	VENT SOLENOID VALVE COMPONENT CHECK	RESULT	ACTION TO TAKE
	It is desired to activate the "VENT SOLENOID VALVE TOGGLE" functional test. In order to do this the following action is required:	The air compressor assembly vent solenoid is:	
	* Raise the vehicle's hood up completely.	CYCLING "ON" CONTINUOUSLY	Depress the "STAR" test button so that it remains in the down "TEST" position. This action will stop the "VENT SOLENOID VALVE TOGGLE" functional test since it is no longer required. Then: GO TO HD11
	* Release the "STAR" test button so that it remains in the up "HOLD" position after the code "32" has been displayed for at least 5 seconds.		
	NOTE: As long as the "STAR" test button is in the up "HOLD" position the selected functional test will continue. The "VENT SOLENOID VALVE TOGGLE" test is used to verify that the air suspension control module can activate the vent solenoid valve by cycling it "ON" and "OFF" continuously until the "STAR" test button is depressed down again.		
		VENT SOLENOID REMAINS "OFF"	GO TO HD6
HD6	CHECKING WIRING HARNESS		
	Since the air suspension control module can not activate the vent solenoid valve the following actions are required:	Electrical connectors are good:	
	* Disconnect the air compressor assembly electrical connector from the vehicle wiring harness connector.	YES	GO TO HD7
	* Examine both electrical connectors for damage and proper installation of wires.	NO	Make repairs as required and rerun SERVICE BAY DIAGNOSTICS.

FM2019100087030X

Fig. 35 Test HD: Unable To Detect Lowering Of Left Rear Corner (Part 3 of 17)

HD7	CHECKING WIRING HARNESS	RESULT	ACTION TO TAKE
	The next steps in determining why the air suspension control module could not activate the vent solenoid valve are:	Ohmmeter reading is greater than 10,000 ohms:	
	* Turn the air suspension "ON/OFF" switch to the "OFF" position.	YES	GO TO HD8
	* Disconnect air suspension control module connector	NO	A short to ground has been detected in the wiring harness circuit #421.
	* Disconnect the air compressor assembly electrical connector.		
	* Using an analog ohmmeter connect one lead to the air suspension control module wiring harness connector pin location #42 (circuit #421) and other to pin location #40 (circuit #430G).		rerun SERVICE BAY DIAGNOSTICS after repair is made.
HD8	CHECKING WIRING HARNESS		
	* Again using an analog ohmmeter connect one lead to the air suspension control module wiring harness connector pin location #42 (circuit #421) and the other to the air compressor assembly vehicle wiring harness connector circuit	Ohmmeter reading is greater than 10 ohms:	
		YES	The circuit used to activate the #421 vent solenoid valve (circuit #421) has an open in it. Rerun SERVICE BAY DIAGNOSTICS after repair is made.
		NO	GO TO HD9
HD9	CHECKING WIRING HARNESS		
	* Again using an analog ohmmeter connect one lead to the air suspension control module wiring harness connector pin location #40 (circuit #430G) and the other to the air compressor assembly vehicle wiring harness connector circuit #430E.	Ohmmeter reading is greater than 10 ohms:	
		YES	Circuit #430E has an open in it. Rerun SERVICE BAY DIAGNOSTICS after repair is made.
		NO	GO TO HD10

FM2019100087040X

Fig. 35 Test HD: Unable To Detect Lowering Of Left Rear Corner (Part 4 of 17)

HD10	COMPONENT CHECK	RESULT	ACTION TO TAKE
	* Using a 12 volt power supply connect the positive lead to the air compressor assembly connector pin location #1 and the negative lead to the air compressor assembly connector pin location #2 for 2 to 3 seconds. Repeat this as required.	The vent solenoid valve is activated when the voltage is applied:	
		YES	Install a new air suspension control module and rerun SERVICE BAY DIAGNOSTICS.
		NO	Replace the air compressor assembly and rerun SERVICE BAY DIAGNOSTICS.
HD11	COMPONENT CHECK		
	It is now desired to activate the "AIR SPRING SOLENOID VALVE TOGGLE" functional test. In order to do this the following action is required:	The left rear air spring solenoid valve is:	
	* Release the "STAR" test button so that it remains in the up "HOLD" position after the code "33" has been displayed for at least 5 seconds.	CYCLING "ON/OFF" CONTINUOUSLY	GO TO HD15
	NOTE: As long as the "STAR" test button is in the up "HOLD" position the selected functional test will continue. The "AIR SPRING SOLENOID TOGGLE" test is used to verify that the air suspension control module can activate each of the air spring solenoid valves by cycling them "ON" and "OFF" continuously until the "STAR" test button is depressed down again.	REMAINS "OFF"	GO TO HD12

FM2019100087050X

Fig. 35 Test HD: Unable To Detect Lowering Of Left Rear Corner (Part 5 of 17)

HD12 CHECKING WIRING HARNESS	RESULT	ACTION TO TAKE
The air suspension control module can not activate the left rear air spring solenoid valve. In order to determine the cause of this the following actions are required: • Electrically disconnect the air spring solenoid from the vehicle harness connector. • Using a voltmeter connect the position lead to the air spring solenoid valve wiring harness connector circuit #429 and the negative lead to circuit #430F of the same connector. NOTE: The "AIR SPRING SOLENOID VALVE TOGGLE" functional test is still being conducted. During this functional test the front ride height of the vehicle may lower and the rear ride height may raise.	The voltage reading pulses between zero and battery voltage (check is to be made over a one minute time period): YES ▶ NO ▶	Install a new left rear air spring solenoid and then rerun SERVICE BAY DIAGNOSTICS. GO TO HD13
HD13 CHECKING WIRING HARNESS		
• Turn the air suspension "ON/OFF" switch to the "OFF" position. • Disconnect air suspension control module connector. • Using an analog ohmmeter connect one lead to the air suspension control module wiring harness connector pin location #41 (circuit #429) and other to the left rear air spring solenoid valve wiring harness connector circuit #429.	Ohmmeter reading is greater than 10 ohms: YES ▶ NO ▶	GO TO HD14 An open in circuit #429 has been detected in the wiring harness. rerun SERVICE BAY DIAGNOSTICS after repair is made.

FM2019100087060X

Fig. 35 Test HD: Unable To Detect Lowering Of Left Rear Corner (Part 6 of 17)

HD14 WIRING HARNESS CHECK	RESULT	ACTION TO TAKE
• Again using an analog ohmmeter connect one lead to the air suspension control module wiring harness connector pin location #60 (circuit #430H) and other to the left rear air spring solenoid valve vehicle wiring harness connector circuit #430F.	Ohmmeter reading is less than 10 ohms: YES ▶ NO ▶	Install a new air suspension control module and rerun SERVICE BAY DIAGNOSTICS. An open in circuit #430H/430F exists. Rerun SERVICE BAY DIAGNOSTICS after repair is made.
HD15 ENTER SPRING FILL DIAGNOSTICS		
At this time it will be required to exit SERVICE BAY DIAGNOSTICS and enter SPRING FILL (refer to SPRING FILL DIAGNOSTIC for instructions).	The "STAR" tester is displaying one of the following codes: "21" to "26" ▶ SOMETHING ELSE ▶	GO TO HD16 Repeat SPRING FILL entrance procedure until entered.

FM2019100087070X

Fig. 35 Test HD: Unable To Detect Lowering Of Left Rear Corner (Part 7 of 17)

HD16 INFLATE LEFT REAR AIR SPRING	RESULT	ACTION TO TAKE
In order to perform the left rear air spring vent test we must first inflate it above the normal position. In order to do that the following action is required: • Release the "STAR" test button so that it remains in the up "HOLD" position after the code "26" has been displayed for at least 5 seconds NOTE: As long as the "STAR" test button remains in the up "HOLD" position the left rear air spring will continue to be inflated. When the desired amount of inflating has occurred depress the "STAR" test button so that it remains in the down "TEST" position.	The vehicle's left rear air spring has been inflated so that the left rear corner of the vehicle has approximately a two inch gap between the fender lip opening and the top of the tire: YES ▶ NO ▶	Depress the "STAR" test button down so that it remains in the "TEST" position. Then: GO TO HD17 Continue with step "HD16" until the left rear corner of the vehicle is at the desired position. If unable to raise vehicle look for an air line and/or air spring leak.

FM2019100087080X

Fig. 35 Test HD: Unable To Detect Lowering Of Left Rear Corner (Part 8 of 17)

HD17 VENT LEFT REAR SPRING	RESULT	ACTION TO TAKE
To vent the left rear air spring the following action is required: • Release the "STAR" test button so that it remains in the up "HOLD" position after the code "27" has been displayed for at least 5 seconds. NOTE: As long as the "STAR" test button remains in the up "HOLD" position the left rear air spring will continue to vent. When the desired amount of venting has occurred depress the "STAR" test button so that it remains in the "TEST" position.	The left rear corner of the vehicle has vented down to the normal ride height: VERY SLOWLY OR NONE AT ALL ▶ SLOWLY OR AT A NORMAL RATE ▶	Depress the "STAR" test button down so that it remains in the "TEST" position. Then: GO TO HD18 If the left rear corner of the vehicle also has leveling problems fix them first. Otherwise rerun SERVICE DIAGNOSTICS and if this problem still occurs install a new air suspension control module and then rerun SERVICE BAY DIAGNOSTICS.

FM2019100087090X

Fig. 35 Test HD: Unable To Detect Lowering Of Left Rear Corner (Part 9 of 17)

HD18	INFLATE LEFT REAR AIR SPRING	RESULT	ACTION TO TAKE
	Again it is desired to first inflate the left rear corner of the vehicle above the normal position. In order to do this the following action is required: * Release the "STAR" test button so that it remains in the up "HOLD" position after the code "28" has been displayed for at least 5 seconds. NOTE: As long as the "STAR" test button remains in the up "HOLD" position the left rear air spring will continue to be inflated. When the desired amount of inflating has occurred depress the "STAR" test button so that it remains in the down "TEST" position.	The vehicle's left rear air spring has been inflated so that the left rear corner of the vehicle has approximately a two inch gap between the fender lip opening and the top of the tire: YES ▶ NO ▶	 Depress the "STAR" test button down so that it remains in the "TEST" position. Then: GO TO HD19 Continue with step "HD18" until the left rear corner of the vehicle is at the desired position.

Fig. 35   Test HD: Unable To Detect Lowering Of Left Rear Corner (Part 10 of 17)

FM2019100087100X

HD19	VENT LEFT REAR SPRING	RESULT	ACTION TO TAKE
	In order to determine why the left front corner of the vehicle is venting "VERY SLOWLY OR NONE AT ALL" the following actions are required: * Disconnect the left rear air line from the left rear air spring solenoid valve. * Release the "STAR" test button so that it remains in the "HOLD" position after the code "27" has been displayed for at least 5 seconds. NOTE: THIS TEST STEP MAY RESULT IN A RAPID LOSS OF VEHICLE RIDE HEIGHT	The left rear corner of the vehicle has vented down to the normal ride height: VERY SLOWLY OR NONE AT ALL ▶ AT A FAST OR NORMAL RATE ▶	 Depress the "STAR" test button down so that it remains in the "TEST" position. GO TO HD24 Depress the "STAR" test button down so that it remains in the "TEST" position. Then: GO TO HD20

Fig. 35   Test HD: Unable To Detect Lowering Of Left Rear Corner (Part 11 of 17)

FM2019100087110X

HD20	INFLATE LEFT REAR AIR SPRING	RESULT	ACTION TO TAKE
	From the previous tests we have determined that the cause of the venting problem is due to a restriction in the air line or compressor assembly. In order to isolate the cause of this problem the following actions are required: * Reconnect the air line to the left rear solenoid valve. * Inflate the left rear corner of the vehicle so that the vehicle ride height is above the normal position. Then release the "STAR" test button so that it remains in the up "HOLD" position after the code "28" has been displayed for at least 5 seconds. NOTE: As long as the "STAR" test button remains in the up "HOLD" position the left rear air spring will continue to be inflated. When the desired amount of inflating has occurred depress the "STAR" test button so that it remains in the down "TEST" position.	The vehicle's left rear air spring has been inflated so that the left rear corner of the vehicle has approximately a two inch gap between the fender lip opening and the top of the tire: YES ▶ NO ▶	 Depress the "STAR" test button down so that it remains in the "TEST" position. Then: GO TO HD21. Continue with step "HD20" until the left rear corner of the vehicle is at the desired position.

Fig. 35   Test HD: Unable To Detect Lowering Of Left Rear Corner (Part 12 of 17)

FM2019100087120X

HD21	VENT LEFT REAR SPRING	RESULT	ACTION TO TAKE
	In order to determine if the air line or air compressor assembly is the problem the following actions are required: * Disconnect one of the air lines from the air compressor drier assembly. * Release the "STAR" test button so that it remains in the "HOLD" position after the code "27" has been displayed for at least 5 seconds. NOTE: THIS TEST STEP MAY RESULT IN A RAPID LOSS OF VEHICLE RIDE HEIGHT	The left rear corner of the vehicle has vented down to a normal ride height: VERY SLOWLY OR NONE AT ALL ▶ AT A FAST OR NORMAL RATE ▶	 Depress the "STAR" test button down so that it remains in the "TEST" position. The air line for the left rear corner of the vehicle is restricted. Rerun SERVICE BAY DIAGNOSTICS after repairs are made. Depress the "STAR" test button down so that it remains in the "TEST" position. Then: GO TO HD22
HD22	COMPONENT CHECK		
	* Disconnect all of the air lines to the air compressor assembly drier. * Remove the air compressor assembly from the vehicle. * Remove the air compressor drier cap (air lines are inserted into this part) from the drier assembly	The white filter material in the air compressor drier cap is oily: YES ▶ NO ▶	 GO TO HD23 Install a new air compressor assembly and then rerun SERVICE BAY DIAGNOSTICS.

Fig. 35   Test HD: Unable To Detect Lowering Of Left Rear Corner (Part 13 of 17)

FM2019100087130X

HD23	COMPONENT CHECK	RESULT	ACTION TO TAKE
	One of the shock/strut assemblies on the vehicle has leaked a large amount of shock fluid into the air spring canister. Refer to the shop manual for determination and replacement procedures of the bad shock/strut. In addition to replacing the shock/strut the following components must also be replaced: • All air suspension air lines • Air compressor assembly. • Drier assembly. • Remove all air spring solenoid valves and replace the filter located at the opposite end of where the air line attaches.	All repairs completed. ▶	Rerun SERVICE BAY DIAGNOSTICS.

HD24	COMPONENT CHECK	RESULT	ACTION TO TAKE
	From the previous tests we have determined that the cause of the venting problem is located in the air spring solenoid valve or shock/strut assembly. In order to determine which is the problem the following actions are required: • Using a body hoist raise the vehicle off the floor (tire rotation height) so that no weight is on the tires. • Vent the left rear air spring as in step "HD19" and remove the air spring solenoid valve (refer to shop manual if required). • Remove the air spring solenoid valve shock fluid mist filter.	The shock fluid mist filter is: CLEAN OR SLIGHTLY OILY ▶ VERY OILY ▶	GO TO HD25 GO TO HD26

FM2019100087140X

Fig. 35   Test HD: Unable To Detect Lowering Of Left Rear Corner (Part 14 of 17)

HD25	COMPONENT CHECK	RESULT	ACTION TO TAKE
	In order to determine if the left rear air spring solenoid valve is operational the following actions are required: • Make sure that the air line and vehicle electrical wiring harness connector are connected to the removed left rear air spring solenoid valve. • Release the "STAR" test button so that it remains in the "HOLD" position after the code "28" has been displayed for at least 5 seconds.	The left rear air spring solenoid valve is passing air through it: NO ▶ YES ▶	Depress the "STAR" test button down so that it remains in the "TEST" position. Install a new left rear air spring solenoid valve, reinflate the air spring before setting weight on the tire and rerun SERVICE BAY DIAGNOSTICS. Depress the "STAR" test button down so that it remains in the "TEST" position. Replace the shock fluid mist filter and refer to the shop manual for detection of binding of the shock/strut and repair procedures. Rerun SERVICE BAY DIAGNOSTICS after repairs are made.

FM2019100087150X

Fig. 35   Test HD: Unable To Detect Lowering Of Left Rear Corner (Part 15 of 17)

HD26	COMPONENT CHECK	RESULT	ACTION TO TAKE
	In order to determine if the left rear air spring solenoid valve is operational the following actions are required: • Make sure that the air line and vehicle electrical wiring harness connector are connected to the removed left rear air spring solenoid valve. • Release the "STAR" test button so that it remains in the "HOLD" position after the code "28" has been displayed for at least 5 seconds.	The left rear air spring solenoid valve is passing air through it: NO ▶ YES ▶	Depress the "STAR" test button down so that it remains in the "TEST" position. Install a new left rear air spring solenoid valve, reinflate the air spring before setting weight on the tire. Then: GO TO HD27 Depress the "STAR" test button down so that it remains in the "TEST" position. Then: GO TO HD27

HD27	COMPONENT CHECK	RESULT	ACTION TO TAKE
	Disconnect all of the air lines to the air compressor assembly drier. • Remove the air compressor assembly from the vehicle. • Remove the air compressor drier cap (air lines are inserted into this part) from the drier assembly (refer to the shop manual for instructions since it is spring loaded).	The white filter material in the air compressor drier cap is oily: YES ▶ NO ▶	GO TO HD28 Install a new left rear air spring shock fluid mist filter and then rerun SERVICE BAY DIAGNOSTICS.

FM2019100087160X

Fig. 35   Test HD: Unable To Detect Lowering Of Left Rear Corner (Part 16 of 17)

HD28	COMPONENT CHECK	RESULT	ACTION TO TAKE
	The left rear shock/strut assembly on the vehicle has leaked a large amount of shock fluid into the air spring canister. Refer to the shop manual for replacement procedures. In addition to replacing this shock/strut the following components must also be replaced: • All air suspension air lines. • Air compressor assembly. • Drier assembly. • Remove all air spring solenoid valves and replace the filter located at the opposite end of where the air line attaches.	All repairs completed. ▶	Rerun SERVICE BAY DIAGNOSTICS.

FM2019100087170X

Fig. 35   Test HD: Unable To Detect Lowering Of Left Rear Corner (Part 17 of 17)

AIR SUSPENSION, CONTINENTAL

IA1	STAR CODE: 52 UNABLE TO DETECT RAISING OF RIGHT FRONT CORNER	RESULT	ACTION TO TAKE
	The air suspension control module has not received the signal that the right front corner of the vehicle was raised during the SERVICE BAY DIAGNOSTIC check. There are nine possible causes which are listed below: * The height sensor linkage arm is not connected properly to the vehicle and/or height sensor. * An air line may be defective. * The right front air spring solenoid valve may be defective. * The right front air spring B + power supply circuit may have an open in it. * The right front air spring ground return circuit may have an open in it. * The air compressor may be defective. * The air compressor B + power supply circuit may have an open in it. * The air compressor ground return circuit may have an open in it. * The air suspension control module may be defective.		GO TO IB2
IA2	VISUAL COMPONENT CHECK * Check under the vehicle to verify that the vehicle is not hanging up on something. * Check the right front corner of the vehicle to verify that the height sensor has no obvious damage and that the linkage is connected.	The right front height sensor is installed correctly with no obvious damage and under the vehicle is clear of all obstructions: YES NO	 GO TO IA3 Make needed repairs as required and rerun SERVICE BAY DIAGNOSTICS.

FM2019100088010X

Fig. 36 Test IA: Unable To Detect Raising Of Right Front Corner (Part 1 of 16)

IA3	ENTERING FUNCTIONAL TEST MODE OF SERVICE BAY DIAG	RESULT	ACTION TO TAKE
	FUNCTIONAL TEST mode will be used to determine why the right front corner of the vehicle did not raise. * Release the "STAR" test button to the up "HOLD" position. After five seconds depress the "STAR" test button again so that it remains in the down "TEST" position. This will allow the control module to enter FUNCTIONAL TEST mode.	The "STAR" tester is displaying code: "31", "32", "33", "34", or "35" SOMETHING ELSE	 GO TO IA5 GO TO IA4
IA4	RETRY FUNCTIONAL TEST ENTRANCE PROCEDURE		
	The air suspension control module has not entered the FUNCTIONAL TEST mode and the following actions are required: * Make sure that the "STAR" tester is still plugged into the air suspension diagnostic pigtail. * Make sure that the "STAR" tester is turned "ON". * Release the "STAR" test button to the up "HOLD" position. After five seconds depress the "STAR" test button again so that it remains in the down "TEST" position. This will allow the control module to enter FUNCTIONAL TEST mode.	The "STAR" tester is displaying code: "31", "32", "33", "34", or "35" SOMETHING ELSE	 GO TO IA5 Rerun SERVICE BAY DIAGNOSTICS and if still unable to enter FUNCTIONAL TEST mode install a new air suspension control module and then rerun SERVICE BAY DIAGNOSTICS.

FM2019100088020X

Fig. 36 Test IA: Unable To Detect Raising Of Right Front Corner (Part 2 of 16)

IA5	AIR COMPRESSOR COMPONENT CHECK	RESULT	ACTION TO TAKE
	It is desired to activate the "COMPRESSOR TOGGLE" FUNCTIONAL TEST mode. In order to do this the following action is required: * Raise the vehicle's hood up completely. * Release the "STAR" test button so that it remains in the up "HOLD" position after the code "31" has been displayed for at least 5 seconds. NOTE: As long as the "STAR" test button is in the up "HOLD" position the selected functional test will continue. The "COMPRESSOR TOGGLE" test is used to verify that the air suspension control module can activate the air compressor. This is done by cycling it "ON" AND "OFF" continuously until the "STAR" test button is depressed down again.	The air compressor is: CYCLING "ON/OFF" CONTINUOUSLY AIR COMPRESSOR REMAINS "OFF"	 Depress the STAR test button so that it remains in the "TEST" position. This action will stop the "COMPRESSOR TOGGLE" functional test since it is no longer required. Then: GO TO IA17 GO TO IA6
IA6	CHECKING WIRING HARNESS		
	Since the air suspension control module can not activate the air compressor the following actions are required: * Depress the "STAR" test button so that it remains in the down "HOLD" position. This action will stop the "COMPRESSOR TOGGLE" functional test. * Disconnect the air compressor assembly electrical connector from the vehicle wiring harness connector. * Examine both electrical connectors for damage and proper installation of wires.	Electrical connectors are good: YES NO	 GO TO IA7 Make repairs as required and rerun SERVICE BAY DIAGNOSTICS.

FM2019100088030X

Fig. 36 Test IA: Unable To Detect Raising Of Right Front Corner (Part 3 of 16)

IA7	COMPRESSOR COOL DOWN	RESULT	ACTION TO TAKE
	The air compressor has an internal thermal non-cycling circuit breaker in it that opens the B + power supply to the air compressor armature when the internal temperature exceeds a predetermined limit. In order for this thermal circuit breaker to be reset the following two things must happen: 1) the internal temperature must drop below the predetermined limit and 2) the power to the compressor must be off. In this part of the test we will allow the compressor to cool down for 15 minutes. The air compressor thermal circuit breaker may have been tripped by repeatedly running diagnostic checks.	At least 15 minutes has elapsed since the air compressor was disconnected from the vehicle wiring harness: YES NO	 GO TO IA8 Continue with step "IA7" until 15 minutes has elapsed.
IA8	WIRING HARNESS CHECK		
	* Reconnect the air compressor to the vehicle wiring harness.	The air compressor remains off: YES NO	 GO TO IA10 GO TO IA9

FM2019100088040A

Fig. 36 Test IA: Unable To Detect Raising Of Right Front Corner (Part 4 of 16)

IA9	WIRING HARNESS CHECK	RESULT	ACTION TO TAKE
	• Remove the air compressor relay from its vehicle wiring harness connector.	The air compressor stops running and remains off: YES ▶ NO ▶	Install a new air compressor relay and then rerun SERVICE BAY DIAGNOSTICS. Circuit #417 has a short to B+ which is causing the air compressor to run until the air compressor's internal thermal circuit breaker is tripped. Rerun SERVICE BAY DIAGNOSTICS after repair is made and the air compressor relay has been installed again.

FM2019100088050X

Fig. 36   Test IA: Unable To Detect Raising Of Right Front Corner (Part 5 of 16)

IA10	AIR COMPRESSOR COMPONENT CHECK	RESULT	ACTION TO TAKE
	It is desired to activate the "COMPRESSOR TOGGLE/CYCLE" functional test mode again. In order to do this the following action is required: • Release the "STAR" test button so that it remains in the up "HOLD" position after the code "31" has been displayed for at least 5 seconds. NOTE: As long as the "STAR" test button is in the up "HOLD" position the selected functional test will continue. The "COMPRESSOR TOGGLE" test is used to verify that the air suspension control module can activate the air compressor. This is done by cycling it "ON" and "OFF" continuously until the STAR test button is depressed down again.	The air compressor is: CYCLING "ON/OFF" CONTINUOUSLY ▶ AIR COMPRESSOR REMAINS "OFF" ▶	Depress the "STAR" test button so that it remains in the "TEST" position. This action will stop the "COMPRESSOR TOGGLE" functional test since it is no longer required. Rerun SERVICE BAY DIAGNOSTICS after waiting 30 minutes. GO TO IA11
IA11	CHECKING WIRING HARNESS		
	The next step in determining why the air suspension control could not activate the air compressor is: • Disconnect the air compressor assembly electrical connector from the vehicle wiring harness connector. • Using a voltmeter connect the positive lead to circuit #417 of the air compressor vehicle wiring harness connector and the negative lead to circuit #430F.	The voltage reading fluctuates between zero and battery voltage (check is to be made over a one minute time period): YES ▶ NO ▶	Install a new air compressor assembly and then rerun SERVICE BAY DIAGNOSTICS after repair is made. GO TO IA12

FM2019100088060X

Fig. 36   Test IA: Unable To Detect Raising Of Right Front Corner (Part 6 of 16)

IA12	CHECKING WIRING HARNESS	RESULT	ACTION TO TAKE
	• Depress the "STAR" test button so that it remains in the down "TEST" position. • Remove the air compressor relay from its vehicle wiring harness connector. • Using an analog ohmmeter attach one lead to the air compressor relay vehicle harness connector (circuit #417) and the other lead to the air compressor vehicle wiring harness connector (circuit #417).	Ohmmeter reading is greater than 5 ohms: YES ▶ NO ▶	The circuit used to active the air compressor (circuit #417) has an open in it. Rerun SERVICE BAY DIAGNOSTICS after repair is made. GO TO IA13
IA13	CHECKING WIRING HARNESS		
	• Again using an analog ohmmeter connect one lead to the air compressor relay circuit #430B and the other to a known good ground.	Ohmmeter reading is greater than 5 ohms: YES ▶ NO ▶	Circuit #430B has an open in it. Rerun SERVICE BAY DIAGNOSTICS after repair is made. GO TO IA14

FM2019100088070X

Fig. 36   Test IA: Unable To Detect Raising Of Right Front Corner (Part 7 of 16)

IA14	CHECKING WIRING HARNESS	RESULT	ACTION TO TAKE
	• Using a voltmeter connect the positive lead to circuit #175 of the air compressor relay's wiring harness connector and the negative lead to circuit #430B.	The voltage reading is greater than 10 volts: YES ▶ NO ▶	GO TO IA15 This circuit has an open or short in it. There should always be battery voltage on this circuit. Rerun SERVICE BAY DIAGNOSTICS after repairs are made.

FM2019100088080X

Fig. 36   Test IA: Unable To Detect Raising Of Right Front Corner (Part 8 of 16)

IA15	CHECKING WIRING HARNESS		RESULT		ACTION TO TAKE
	It is desired to activate the "COMPRESSOR TOGGLE/CYCLE" functional test again. In order to do this the following action is required:		The voltage reading fluctuates between zero and battery voltage (check is to be made over a one minute time period):		
	• Release the "STAR" test button so that it remains in the up "HOLD" position after the code "31" has been displayed at least 5 seconds.				Install a new compressor relay, reconnect the air compressor assembly to the vehicle wiring harness and then rerun SERVICE BAY DIAGNOSTICS.
	• Using a voltmeter connect the position positive lead to circuit #420 of the air compressor relay's wiring harness connector and the negative lead to circuit #430B.		YES	▶	
	NOTE As long as the "STAR" test button is in the up "HOLD" position the selected functional test will continue. The "COMPRESSOR TOGGLE" test is used to verify that the air suspension control module can activate the air compressor. This is done cycling it "ON" and "OFF" continuously until the "STAR" test button is depressed down again.		NO	▶	GO TO IA16

IA16	CHECKING WIRING HARNESS				
	• Turn the air suspension "ON/OFF" switch to the "OFF" position and disconnect the air suspension control module from the vehicle wiring harness.		The resistance reading is less than 5.0 ohms:		
	• Using an analog ohmmeter connect the positive lead to circuit #420 of the air compressor relay wiring harness connector and the other lead to pin position #35 (circuit #420) of the air suspension control module wiring harness connector.		YES	▶	Install a new air suspension control module, reconnect the air compressor relay and then rerun SERVICE BAY DIAGNOSTICS.
			NO	▶	The circuit (#420) used to provide B+ power to the air compressor relay has an open in it. Rerun SERVICE BAY DIAGNOSTICS after repair is made.

Fig. 36   Test IA: Unable To Detect Raising Of Right Front Corner (Part 9 of 16)

FM2019100088090X

IA17	SPRING SOLENOID VALVE COMPONENT CHECK		RESULT		ACTION TO TAKE
	It is now desired to activate the "AIR SPRING SOLENOID VALVE TOGGLE" functional test. In order to do this the following actions are required:		The right front air spring solenoid valve is making an audible click sound:		
	• Release the "STAR" test button so that it remains in the up "HOLD" position after the code "33" has been displayed for at least 5 seconds.		CYCLING "ON/OFF" CONTINUOUSLY	▶	GO TO IA21
	NOTE: As long as the "STAR" test button is in the up "HOLD" position the selected functional test will continue. The "AIR SPRING SOLENOID TOGGLE" test is used to verify that the air suspension control module can activate each of the air spring solenoid valves by cycling them "ON" and "OFF" continuously until the STAR test button is depressed down again.		REMAINS "OFF"	▶	GO TO IA18

IA18	CHECKING WIRING HARNESS				
	The air suspension control module can not activate the right front air spring solenoid valve. In order to determine the cause of this the following actions are required:		The voltage reading pulses between zero and battery voltage (check is to be made over a one minute time period):		
	• Electrically disconnect the right front air spring solenoid from the vehicle wiring harness connector.				
	• Using a voltmeter connect the positive lead to the air spring solenoid valve wiring harness connector circuit #414 and the negative lead to circuit #430D of the same connector.		YES	▶	Install a new right front air spring solenoid and return SERVICE BAY DIAGNOSTICS.
	NOTE: The "AIR SPRING SOLENOID VALVE TOGGLE" functional test is still being conducted. During this functional test the front ride height of the vehicle may lower and the rear ride height may raise.		NO	▶	GO TO IA19

Fig. 36   Test IA: Unable To Detect Raising Of Right Front Corner (Part 10 of 16)

FM2019100088100X

IA19	CHECKING WIRING HARNESS		RESULT		ACTION TO TAKE
	• Turn the air suspension "ON/OFF" switch to the "OFF" position.		Ohmmeter reading is less than 10 ohms:		
	• Disconnect air suspension control module connector.		YES	▶	GO TO IA20
	• Using an analog ohmmeter connect one lead to the air suspension control module wiring harness connector pin location #17 (circuit #414) and other to the right front air spring solenoid valve wiring harness connector circuit #414.		NO	▶	An open in circuit #414 has been detected in the wiring harness. Refer to the electrical system section and rerun SERVICE BAY DIAGNOSTICS after repair is made.

IA20	WIRING HARNESS CHECK				
	• Again using an analog ohmmeter connect one lead to the air suspension control module wiring harness connector pin location #60 (circuit #430H) and other to the right front air spring solenoid valve vehicle wiring harness connector circuit #430D.		Ohmmeter reading is less than 10 ohms:		
			YES	▶	Install a new air suspension control module and rerun SERVICE BAY DIAGNOSTICS.
			NO	▶	An open in circuit #430H/430D exists. Rerun SERVICE BAY DIAGNOSTICS after repair is made.

IA21	ENTER SPRING FILL DIAGNOSTICS				
	At this time it will be required to exit SERVICE BAY DIAGNOSTICS and enter SPRING FILL (refer to SPRING FILL DIAGNOSTIC section for instructions).		The "STAR" tester is displaying one of the following codes:		
			"21" to "28"	▶	GO TO IA22
			SOMETHING ELSE	▶	Repeat SPRING FILL entrance procedure until entered.

Fig. 36   Test IA: Unable To Detect Raising Of Right Front Corner (Part 11 of 16)

FM2019100088110X

IA22	VISUAL CHECK		RESULT		ACTION TO TAKE
	In order to perform the right front air spring inflation test we must first determine if it is above the normal position.		The vehicle's right front corner has approximately a two inch gap or greater between the fender lip opening and the top of the tire:		
			YES	▶	GO TO IA23
			NO	▶	GO TO IA24

IA23	VENT RIGHT FRONT AIR SPRING				
	In order to perform the right front air spring inflation test we must first vent it below the normal position. In order to do that the following action is required:		The vehicle's right front corner has been lowered:		
	• Release the "STAR" test button so that it remains in the up "HOLD" position after the code "21" has been displayed for at least 5 seconds.		YES	▶	Depress the "STAR" test button down so that it remains in the "TEST" position. Then: GO TO IA24
	• Continue venting the right front corner of the vehicle until the gap between the fender lip opening and the top of the tire is one inch or less.		NO	▶	Continue with step "IA23" until the desired height is reached.
	NOTE: As long as the "STAR" test button remains in the up "HOLD" position the right front air spring will continue to be vented. When the desired amount of of venting has occurred depress the "STAR" test button so that it remains in the down "TEST" position.				

Fig. 36   Test IA: Unable To Detect Raising Of Right Front Corner (Part 12 of 16)

FM2019100088120X

IA24	INFLATE RIGHT FRONT AIR SPRING	RESULT	ACTION TO TAKE
	To inflate the right front air spring the following action is required: • Release the "STAR" test button so that it remains in the "HOLD" position after the code "25" has been displayed for at least 5 seconds. NOTE: As long as the "STAR" test button remains in the up "HOLD" position the right front air spring will continue to be inflated. When the desired amount of inflating has occurred depress the "STAR" test button so that it remains in the "TEST" position.	The right front corner of the vehicle has been raised so that the gap between the fender lip tire opening and the top of the tire is approximately three inches or greater. VERY SLOWLY OR NONE AT ALL SLOWLY OR AT A NORMAL RATE	 Depress the "STAR" test button down so that it remains in the "TEST" position. Then: GO TO IA25 Rerun SERVICE BAY DIAGNOSTICS and if this problem still occurs install a new air suspension control module and then rerun SERVICE BAY DIAGNOSTICS.

FM2019100088130X

Fig. 36 Test IA: Unable To Detect Raising Of Right Front Corner (Part 13 of 16)

IA25	AIR LINE CHECK	RESULT	ACTION TO TAKE
	In order to determine why the left front corner of the vehicle is inflating "VERY SLOWLY OR NONE AT ALL" the following actions are required: • Disconnect the right front air line from the right front air spring solenoid valve. • Disconnect the right front air spring solenoid valve electrical connector so that the solenoid valve is not connected to the vehicle wiring harness. • Release the "STAR" test button so that it remains in the up "HOLD" position after the code "24" has been displayed for at least 5 seconds. NOTE: As long as the "STAR" test button remains in the up "HOLD" position the air compressor assembly will continue to pump air through the air line.	Air is coming out of the air line: VERY SLOWLY OR NONE AT ALL AT A NORMAL RATE	 GO TO IA26 GO TO IA27
IA26	AIR LINE CHECK		
	From the previous tests we have determined that cause of the UNABLE TO INFLATE problem is due to a restriction in the air line or compressor assembly. In order to isolate the cause of this problem the following actions are required: • Disconnect any one of the air lines that are plugged into the air compressor drier assembly. NOTE: As long as the "STAR" test button remains in the up "HOLD" position the air compressor assembly will continue to pump air through the drier assembly.	The rate that the air is coming out of the drier assembly is: SAME AS IN STEP "IA25" OR SLIGHTLY GREATER RATE IS FASTER THAN IN STEP "IA25"	 Install a new air compressor assembly and then rerun SERVICE BAY DIAGNOSTICS. There is a restriction in the left front air line. Rerun SERVICE BAY DIAGNOSTICS after repair is made.

FM2019100088140X

Fig. 36 Test IA: Unable To Detect Raising Of Right Front Corner (Part 14 of 16)

IA27	AIR LEAK TEST	RESULT	ACTION TO TAKE
	• Depress the "STAR" test button so that it remains in the down "TEST" position. • Reconnect the air line to the air compressor drier assembly and right front air spring solenoid valve. • Reconnect the vehicle wiring harness connector to the right front air spring. • Take a piece of masking tape and mark a spot on the wheel lip opening. Measure and record the vertical height between wheel lip opening and the bottom of the wheel rim. • Wait at least 15 minutes, remeasure and record wheel lip opening again.	The second wheel lip opening is: APPROXIMATELY THE SAME AS THE FIRST LESS THAN THE FIRST	 GO TO IA28 GO TO IA29
IA28	AIR LEAK CHECK		

	• Release the "STAR" test button so that it remains in the up "HOLD" position after the code "24" has been displayed for at least 5 seconds.
	
	• Inspect the following for air leakage:
	  • air compressor / dryer assembly connection point
	  • dryer assembly / air line connection point
	  • air line / air spring solenoid valve connection point.
	
	NOTE: As long as the "STAR" test button remains in the up "HOLD" position the right front air spring will continue to be inflated. When the desired amount of inflating has occurred depress the "STAR" test button so that it remains in the "TEST" position.
		A leak path was detected:
		
		YES
		
		NO
			
			Make required repairs and rerun SERVICE BAY DIAGNOSTICS.
			
			Install a new air suspension control module and then rerun SERVICE BAY DIAGNOSTICS.

FM2019100088150X

Fig. 36 Test IA: Unable To Detect Raising Of Right Front Corner (Part 15 of 16)

IA29	AIR LEAK CHECK	RESULT	ACTION TO TAKE

	• Inspect the following for air leakage on the left front air spring/strut assembly:
	  • air spring bag
	  • air spring bag / canister connection
	  • canister / mount connection
	  • air spring solenoid valve / canister connection
			Rerun SERVICE BAY DIAGNOSTICS after repairs are made.

FM2019100088160X

Fig. 36   Test IA: Unable To Detect Raising Of Right Front Corner (Part 16 of 16)

IB1	STAR CODE: 53 UNABLE TO DETECT RAISING OF LEFT FRONT CORNER	RESULT	ACTION TO TAKE
	The air suspension control module has not received the signal that the left front corner of the vehicle was raised during the SERVICE BAY DIAGNOSTIC check. There are nine possible causes of this which are listed below: • The height sensor linkage arm is not connected properly to the vehicle and/or height sensor. • An air line may be defective. • The left front air spring solenoid valve may be defective. • The left front air spring B+ power supply circuit may have an open in it. • The left front air spring ground return circuit may have an open in it. • The air compressor may be defective. • The air compressor B+ power supply circuit may have an open in it. • The air compressor ground return circuit may have an open in it. • The air suspension control module may be defective.		GO TO IB2

FM2019100089010X

Fig. 37   Test IB: Unable To Detect Raising Of Right Front Corner (Part 1 of 16)

IB2	VISUAL COMPONENT CHECK	RESULT	ACTION TO TAKE
	• Check under the vehicle to verify that the vehicle is not hanging up on something. • Check the left front corner of the vehicle to verify that the height sensor has no obvious damage and that the linkage is connected.	The left front height sensor is installed correctly with no obvious damage and under the vehicle is clear of all obstructions: YES NO	GO TO IB3 Make needed repairs as required and rerun SERVICE BAY DIAGNOSTICS.
IB3	ENTERING FUNCTIONAL TEST MODE OF SERVICE BAY DIAG		
	FUNCTIONAL TEST mode will be used to determine why the left front corner of the vehicle did not raise. • Release the "STAR" test button to the up "HOLD" position. After five seconds depress the "STAR" test button again so that it remains in the down "TEST" position. This will allow the control module to enter FUNCTIONAL TEST mode.	The "STAR" tester is displaying code: "31", "32", "33", "34", or "35" SOMETHING ELSE	GO TO IB5 GO TO IB4
IB4	RETRY FUNCTIONAL TEST ENTRANCE PROCEDURE		
	The air suspension control module has not entered the FUNCTIONAL TEST mode and the following actions are required: • Make sure that the "STAR" tester is still plugged into the air suspension diagnostic diagnostic pigtail. • Make sure that the "STAR" tester is turned "ON". • Release the "STAR" test button to the up "HOLD" position. After five seconds depress the "STAR" test button again so that it remains in the down "TEST" position. This will allow the control module to enter FUNCTIONAL TEST mode.	The "STAR" tester is displaying code: "31", "32", "33", "34", or "35" SOMETHING ELSE	GO TO IB5 Rerun SERVICE BAY DIAGNOSTICS and if still unable to enter FUNCTIONAL TEST mode install a new air suspension control module and then rerun SERVICE BAY DIAGNOSTICS.

FM2019100089020X

Fig. 37   Test IB: Unable To Detect Raising Of Right Front Corner (Part 2 of 16)

IB5	AIR COMPRESSOR COMPONENT CHECK	RESULT	ACTION TO TAKE
	It is desired to activate the "COMPRESSOR TOGGLE" FUNCTIONAL TEST mode. In order to do this the following action is required: • Raise the vehicle's hood up completely. • Release the "STAR" test button so that it remains in the up "HOLD" position after the code "31" has been displayed for at least 5 seconds. NOTE: As long as the "STAR" test button is in the up "HOLD" position the selected FUNCTIONAL TEST will continue. The "COMPRESSOR TOGGLE" test is used to verify that the air suspension control module can activate the air compressor. This is done by cycling it "ON" and "OFF" continuously until the "STAR" test button is depressed down again.	The air compressor is: CYCLING "ON/OFF" CONTINUOUSLY AIR COMPRESSOR REMAINS "OFF"	Depress the STAR test button so that it remains in the "TEST" position. This action will stop the "COMPRESSOR TOGGLE" functional test since it is no longer required. Then: GO TO IB17 GO TO IB6
IB6	CHECKING WIRING HARNESS		
	Since the air suspension control module can not activate the air compressor the following actions are required: • Depress the "STAR" test button so that it remains in the down "HOLD" position. This action will stop the PIN POINT "COMPRESSOR TOGGLE" test. • Disconnect the air compressor assembly electrical connector from the vehicle wiring harness connector. • Examine both electrical connectors for damage and proper installation of wires.	Electrical connectors are good: YES NO	GO TO IB7 Make repairs as required and rerun SERVICE BAY DIAGNOSTICS.

FM2019100089030X

Fig. 37   Test IB: Unable To Detect Raising Of Right Front Corner (Part 3 of 16)

IB7	COMPRESSOR COOL DOWN	RESULT	ACTION TO TAKE
	The air compressor has an internal thermal non-cycling circuit breaker in it that opens the B+ power supply to the air compressor armature when the internal temperature exceeds a predetermined limit. In order for this thermal circuit breaker to be reset the following two things must happen: 1) the internal temperature must drop below the predetermined limit and 2) the power to the compressor must be removed. In this part of the test we will allow the compressor to cool down for 15 minutes. The air compressor thermal circuit breaker may have been tripped by repeatedly running diagnostic checks.	At least 15 minutes has elapsed since the air compressor was disconnected from the vehicle wiring harness: YES NO	GO TO IB8 Continue with step "IB7" until 15 minutes has elapsed.
IB8	WIRING HARNESS CHECK		
	• Reconnect the air compressor to the vehicle wiring harness.	The air compressor remains off: YES NO	GO TO IB10 GO TO IB9

FM2019100089040X

Fig. 37   Test IB: Unable To Detect Raising Of Right Front Corner (Part 4 of 16)

IB9	WIRING HARNESS CHECK	RESULT	ACTION TO TAKE
	• Remove the air compressor relay from its vehicle wiring harness connector.	The air compressor stops running and remains off:	
		YES ▶	Install a new air compressor relay and rerun SERVICE BAY DIAGNOSTICS.
		NO ▶	Circuit #417 has a short to B+ which is causing the air compressor to run until the air compressor's internal thermal circuit breaker is tripped. Rerun SERVICE BAY DIAGNOSTICS after repair is made and the air compressor relay has been installed again.

FM2019100089050X

Fig. 37 Test IB: Unable To Detect Raising Of Right Front Corner (Part 5 of 16)

IB10	AIR COMPRESSOR COMPONENT CHECK	RESULT	ACTION TO TAKE
	It is desired to activate the "COMPRESSOR "TOGGLE" functional test mode again. In order to do this the following action is required:	The air compressor is: CYCLING "ON/OFF" CONTINUOUSLY ▶	Depress the STAR test button so that it remains in the "TEST" position. This action will stop the "COMPRESSOR TOGGLE" functional test since it is no longer required. Rerun SERVICE BAY DIAGNOSTICS after waiting 30 minutes.
	• Release the "STAR" test button so that it remains in the up "HOLD" position after the code "31" has been displayed for at least 5 seconds.		
	NOTE: As long as the "STAR" test button is in the up "HOLD" position the selected functional test will continue. The "COMPRESSOR TOGGLE" test is used to verify that the air suspension control module can activate the air compressor. This is done by cycling it "ON" and "OFF" continuously until the STAR test button is depressed down again.	AIR COMPRESSOR REMAINS "OFF" ▶	GO TO IB11

FM2019100089060X

Fig. 37 Test IB: Unable To Detect Raising Of Right Front Corner (Part 6 of 16)

IB11	CHECKING WIRING HARNESS	RESULT	ACTION TO TAKE
	The next step in determining why the air suspension control module could not activate the air compressor is:	The voltage reading fluctuates between zero and battery voltage (check is to be made over a one minute time period):	
	• Disconnect the air compressor assembly electrical connector from the vehicle wiring harness connector.		
	• Using a voltmeter connect the positive lead to circuit #417 of the air compressor vehicle wiring harness connector and the negative lead to circuit #430F.	YES ▶	Install a new air compressor assembly and rerun SERVICE BAY DIAGNOSTICS.
		NO ▶	GO TO IB12

IB12	CHECKING WIRING HARNESS	RESULT	ACTION TO TAKE
	• Depress the "STAR" test button so that it remains in the down "TEST" position.	Ohmmeter reading is greater than 5 ohms:	
	• Remove the air compressor relay from its vehicle wiring harness connector.	YES ▶	The circuit used to activate the air compressor (circuit #417) has an open in it. Rerun SERVICE BAY DIAGNOSTICS after repair is made.
	• Using an analog ohmmeter connect one lead to circuit #417 of the air compressor relay connector and the other lead to circuit #417 of the air compressor vehicle wiring harness connector.	NO ▶	GO TO IB13

IB13	CHECKING WIRING HARNESS	RESULT	ACTION TO TAKE
	• Again using an analog ohmmeter connect one lead to the air compressor relay circuit #430B and the other to a known good ground.	Ohmmeter reading is greater than 5 ohms:	
		YES ▶	Circuit #430B has an open in it. Rerun SERVICE BAY DIAGNOSTICS after repair is made.
		NO ▶	GO TO IB14

FM2019100089070X

Fig. 37 Test IB: Unable To Detect Raising Of Right Front Corner (Part 7 of 16)

IB14	CHECKING WIRING HARNESS	RESULT	ACTION TO TAKE
	• Using a voltmeter connect the positive lead to circuit #175 of the air compressor relay's wiring harness connector and the negative lead to circuit #430B.	The voltage reading is greater than 10 volts:	
		YES ▶	GO TO IB15
		NO ▶	This circuit has an open or short in it. There should always be battery voltage on this circuit. Rerun SERVICE BAY DIAGNOSTICS after repairs are made.

IB15	CHECKING WIRING HARNESS	RESULT	ACTION TO TAKE
	It is desired to activate the "COMPRESSOR TOGGLE" functional test mode again. In order to do this the following action is required:	The voltage reading fluctuates between zero and battery voltage (check is to be over a one minute time period):	
	• Release the "STAR" test button so that it remains in the up "HOLD" position after the code "31" has been displayed for at least 5 seconds.		
	• Using a voltmeter connect the positive lead to circuit #420 of the air compressor relay's wiring harness connector and the negative lead to circuit #430B.	YES ▶	Reconnect the air compressor assembly to the vehicle wiring harness, install a new air compressor relay and then rerun SERVICE BAY DIAGNOSTICS.
	NOTE: As long as the "STAR" test button is in the up "HOLD" position the selected functional test will continue. The "COMPRESSOR TOGGLE" test is used to verify that the air suspension control module can activate the air compressor. This is done by cycling it "ON" and "OFF" continuously until the STAR test button is depressed down again.	NO ▶	GO TO IB16

FM2019100089080X

Fig. 37 Test IB: Unable To Detect Raising Of Right Front Corner (Part 8 of 16)

AIR SUSPENSION, CONTINENTAL

IB16	CHECKING WIRING HARNESS	RESULT	ACTION TO TAKE
	• Turn the air suspension "ON/OFF" switch to the "OFF" switch position and disconnect the air suspension control module from the vehicle wiring harness. • Using an analog ohmmeter connect the positive lead to circuit #420 of the air compressor relay wiring harness connector and the other lead to pin position #35 (circuit #420) of the air suspension control module wiring harness connector.	The resistance reading is less than 5.0 ohms: YES NO	▶ Install a new air suspension control module, reconnect the air compressor relay and rerun SERVICE BAY DIAGNOSTICS. ▶ The circuit (#420) used to provide B+ power to the air compressor relay has an open in it. Rerun SERVICE BAY DIAGNOSTICS after repair is made.

IB17	SPRING SOLENOID VALVE COMPONENT CHECK		
	It is now desired to activate the "AIR SPRING SOLENOID VALVE CYCLE" functional test. In order to do this the following actions are required: • Release the "STAR" test button so that it remains in the up "HOLD" position after the code "33" has been displayed for at least 5 seconds. NOTE: As long as the "STAR" test button is in the up "HOLD" position the selected functional test will continue. The "AIR SPRING SOLENOID CYCLE" test is used to verify that the air suspension control module can activate each of the air spring solenoid valves by cycling them "ON" and "OFF" continuously until the STAR test button is depressed down again.	The right front air spring solenoid makes an audible click sound when voltage is applied: CYCLING "ON/OFF" CONTINUOUSLY REMAINS "OFF"	▶ GO TO IB21 ▶ GO TO IB18

Fig. 37   Test IB: Unable To Detect Raising Of Right Front Corner (Part 9 of 16)

IB18	CHECKING WIRING HARNESS	RESULT	ACTION TO TAKE
	The air suspension control module can not activate the left front air spring solenoid valve. In order to determine the cause of this the following actions are required: • Electrically disconnect the left front air spring solenoid from the vehicle wiring harness connector. • Using a voltmeter connect the positive lead to the air spring solenoid valve wiring harness connector circuit #415 and the negative lead to circuit #430K of the same connector. NOTE: The "AIR SPRING SOLENOID VALVE CYCLE" functional test is still being conducted. During this functional test the front ride height of the vehicle may lower and the rear ride height may raise.	The voltage reading pulses between zero and battery voltage (check is to be made over a one minute time period): YES NO	▶ Install a new left front air spring solenoid and then rerun SERVICE BAY DIAGNOSTICS. ▶ GO IB19

IB19	CHECKING WIRING HARNESS		
	• Turn the air suspension "ON/OFF" switch to the "OFF" position. • Disconnect air suspension control module connector. • Using an analog ohmmeter connect one lead to the air suspension control module wiring harness connector pin location #21 (circuit #415) and other to the left front air spring solenoid valve wiring harness connector circuit #415.	Ohmmeter reading is less than 10 ohms: YES NO	▶ GO TO IB20 ▶ An open in circuit #415 has been detected in the wiring harness. Refer to the electrical system section and rerun SERVICE BAY DIAGNOSTICS after repair is made.

Fig. 37   Test IB: Unable To Detect Raising Of Right Front Corner (Part 10 of 16)

IB20	WIRING HARNESS CHECK	RESULT	ACTION TO TAKE
	• Again using an analog ohmmeter connect one lead to the air suspension control module wiring harness connector pin location #60 (circuit #430H) and other to the left front air spring solenoid valve vehicle wiring harness connector circuit #430K.	Ohmmeter reading is less than 10 ohms: YES NO	▶ Install a new air suspension control module and rerun SERVICE BAY DIAGNOSTICS. ▶ An open in circuit #430H/430K exists. Rerun SERVICE BAY DIAGNOSTICS after repair is made.

IB21	ENTER SPRING FILL DIAGNOSTICS		
	At this time it will be required to exit SERVICE BAY DIAGNOSTICS and enter SPRING FILL (refer to SPRING FILL DIAGNOSTIC section for instructions).	The STAR tester is displaying one of the following codes: "21" to "28" SOMETHING ELSE	▶ GO TO IB22 ▶ Repeat SPRING FILL entrance procedure until entered.

IB22	VISUAL CHECK		
	In order to perform the left front air spring inflation test we must first determine if it is above the normal position.	The vehicle's left front corner has approximately a two inch gap or greater between the fender lip opening and the top of the tire: YES NO	▶ GO TO IB23 ▶ GO TO IB24

Fig. 37   Test IB: Unable To Detect Raising Of Right Front Corner (Part 11 of 16)

IB23	VENT LEFT FRONT AIR SPRING	RESULT	ACTION TO TAKE
	In order to perform the left front air spring inflation test we must first vent it below the normal position. In order to do that the following action is required: • Release the STAR test button so that it remains in the up "HOLD" position after the code "22" has been displayed for at least 5 seconds. • Continue venting the left corner of the vehicle until gap between the fender lip opening and the top of the tire is one inch or less. NOTE: As long as the "STAR" test button remains in the up "HOLD" position the left front air spring will continue to be vented. When the desired amount of venting has occurred depress the "STAR" test button so that it remains in the down "TEST" position.	The vehicle's left front corner has been lowered: YES NO	▶ Depress the STAR test button down so that it remains in in the "TEST" position. Then: GO TO IB24 ▶ Continue with step "IB23" until the desired height is reached.

Fig. 37   Test IB: Unable To Detect Raising Of Right Front Corner (Part 12 of 16)

IB24	INFLATE LEFT FRONT AIR SPRING	RESULT	ACTION TO TAKE
	To inflate the left front air spring the following action is required:	The left front corner of the vehicle has been raised so that the gap between the fender lip opening and the top of the tire is approximately three inches or greater.	
	• Release the STAR test button so that it remains in the "HOLD" position after the code "25" has been displayed for at least 5 seconds		
	NOTE: As long as the STAR test button remains in the up "HOLD" position the left front air spring will continue to be inflated. When the desired amount of inflating has occurred depress STAR test button down so that it remains in the "TEST" position.	VERY SLOWLY OR NONE AT ALL	Depress the STAR test button down so that it remains in the "TEST" position. Then: GO TO IB25
		SLOWLY OR AT A NORMAL RATE	Rerun SERVICE BAY DIAGNOSTICS and if this problem still occurs install a new air suspension control module and then rerun SERVICE BAY DIAGNOSTICS.

FM2019100089130X

Fig. 37   Test IB: Unable To Detect Raising Of Right Front Corner (Part 13 of 16)

IB25	AIR LINE CHECK	RESULT	ACTION TO TAKE
	In order to determine why the left front corner of the vehicle is inflating "VERY SLOWLY OR NONE AT ALL" the following actions are required:	Air is coming out of the air line:	
	• Disconnect the left front air line from the left front air spring solenoid valve.	VERY SLOWLY OR NONE AT ALL	GO TO IB26
	• Disconnect the left front air spring solenoid valve electrical connector so that the solenoid valve is not connected to the vehicle wiring harness.	AT A NORMAL RATE	GO TO IB27
	• Release the "STAR" test button so that it remains in the up "HOLD" position after the code "25" has been displayed for at least 5 seconds.		
	NOTE: As long as the "STAR" test button remains in the up "HOLD" position the air compressor assembly will continue to pump air through the air line.		

IB26	AIR LINE CHECK		
	From the previous tests we have determined that cause of the UNABLE TO INFLATE problem is due to a restriction in the air line or compressor assembly. In order to isolate the cause of this problem the following actions are required:	The rate that the air is coming out of the drier assembly is:	
	• Disconnect any one of the air lines that are plugged into the air compressor drier assembly.	SAME AS IN STEP "IB25" OR SLIGHTLY GREATER	Install a new air compressor assembly and rerun SERVICE BAY DIAGNOSTICS.
	NOTE: As long as the "STAR" test button remains in the up "HOLD" position the air compressor assembly will continue to pump air through the drier assembly.	RATE IS FASTER THAN IN STEP "IB25"	There is a restriction in the left front air line. Rerun SERVICE BAY DIAGNOSTICS after repair is made.

FM2019100089140X

Fig. 37   Test IB: Unable To Detect Raising Of Right Front Corner (Part 14 of 16)

IB27	AIR LEAK TEST	RESULT	ACTION TO TAKE
	• Depress the "STAR" test button so that it remains in the down "TEST" position.	The second wheel lip opening is:	
	• Reconnect the air line to the air compressor drier assembly and left front air spring solenoid valve.	APPROXIMATELY THE SAME AS THE FIRST	GO TO IB28
	• Reconnect the vehicle wiring harness connector to the left front air spring.	LESS THAN THE FIRST	GO TO IB29
	• Take a piece of masking tape and mark a spot on the wheel lip opening. Measure and record the vertical height between wheel lip opening and the bottom of the wheel rim.		
	• Wait at least 15 minutes, remeasure and record wheel lip opening again.		

IB28	AIR LEAK CHECK		
	• Release the STAR test button so that it remains in the up "HOLD" position after the code "25" has been displayed for at least 5 seconds.	A leak path was detected:	
	• Inspect the following for air leakage: • air compressor / dryer assembly connection point • dryer assembly / air line connection point • air line / air spring solenoid valve connection point	YES	Make required repairs and rerun SERVICE BAY DIAGNOSTICS.
	NOTE: As long as the "STAR" test button remains in the up "HOLD" position the left front air spring will continue to be inflated. When the desired amount of inflating has occurred depress the STAR test button so that it remains in the "TEST" position.	NO	Install a new air suspension control and rerun SERVICE BAY DIAGNOSTICS.

FM2019100089150X

Fig. 37   Test IB: Unable To Detect Raising Of Right Front Corner (Part 15 of 16)

IB29	AIR LEAK CHECK	RESULT	ACTION TO TAKE
	• Inspect the following for air leakage on the left front air spring / strut assembly: • air spring bag • air spring bag / canister connection • canister / mount connection • air spring solenoid valve / canister connection		Rerun SERVICE BAY DIAGNOSTICS after repairs are made.

FM2019100089160X

Fig. 37   Test IB: Unable To Detect Raising Of Right Front Corner (Part 16 of 16)

IC1	STAR CODE: 54 UNABLE TO DETECT RAISING OF RIGHT REAR CORNER	RESULT	ACTION TO TAKE
	The air suspension control module has not received the signal that the right rear corner of the vehicle was raised during the SERVICE BAY DIAGNOSTIC check. There are nine possible causes of this listed below:		▶ GO TO IC2
	• The height sensor linkage arm is not connected properly to the vehicle and/or height sensor.		
	• An air line may be defective.		
	• The right rear air spring solenoid valve may be defective.		
	• The right rear air spring B + power supply circuit may have an open in it.		
	• The right rear air spring ground return circuit may have an open in it.		
	• The air compressor may be defective.		
	• The air compressor B + power supply circuit may have an open in it.		
	• The air compressor ground return circuit may have an open in it.		
	• The air suspension control module may be defective.		

FM2019100090010X

Fig. 38 Test IC: Unable To Detect Raising Of Right Rear Corner (Part 1 of 13)

IC2	VISUAL COMPONENT CHECK	RESULT	ACTION TO TAKE
	• Check under the vehicle to verify that the vehicle is not hanging up on something. • Check the right rear corner of the vehicle to verify that the height sensor has no obvious damage and that the linkage is connected.	The right rear height sensor is installed correctly with no obvious damage and under the vehicle is clear of all obstructions:	
		YES	▶ GO TO IC3
		NO	▶ Make needed repairs as required and rerun SERVICE BAY DIAGNOSTICS.
IC3	ENTERING FUNCTIONAL TEST MODE OF SERVICE BAY DIAG		
	FUNCTIONAL TEST mode will be used to determine why the right rear corner of the vehicle did not raise. • Release the "STAR" test button to the up "HOLD" position. After five seconds depress the "STAR" test button again so that it remains in the down "TEST" position. This will allow the control module to enter FUNCTIONAL TEST mode.	The "STAR" tester is displaying code:	
		"31", "32", "33", "34", or "35"	▶ GO TO IC5
		SOMETHING ELSE	▶ GO TO IC4

FM2019100090020X

Fig. 38 Test IC: Unable To Detect Raising Of Right Rear Corner (Part 2 of 13)

IC4	RETRY FUNCTIONAL TEST ENTRANCE PROCEDURE	RESULT	ACTION TO TAKE
	The air suspension control module has not entered the FUNCTIONAL TEST mode and the following actions are required: • Make sure that the "STAR" tester is still plugged into the air suspension diagnostic pigtail. • Make sure that the "STAR" tester is "ON". • Release the "STAR" test button to the up "HOLD" position. After five seconds depress the "STAR" test button again so that it remains in the down "TEST" position. This will allow the control module to enter FUNCTIONAL TEST mode.	The "STAR" tester is displaying code: "31", "32", "33", "34", or "35" SOMETHING ELSE	▶ GO TO IC5 ▶ Rerun SERVICE BAY DIAGNOSTICS and if still unable to enter FUNCTIONAL TEST mode install new air suspension control module and then rerun SERVICE BAY DIAGNOSTICS.
IC5	AIR COMPRESSOR COMPONENT CHECK		
	It is desired to activate the "COMPRESSOR TOGGLE" functional test. In order to do this the following action is required: • Raise the vehicle's hood up completely. • Release the "STAR" test button so that it remains in the up "HOLD" position after the code "31" has been displayed for at least 5 seconds. NOTE: As long as the "STAR" test button is in the up "HOLD" position the selected functional test will continue. The "COMPRESSOR TOGGLE" test is used to verify that the air suspension control module can activate the air compressor. This is done by cycling it "ON" and "OFF" continuously until the "STAR" test button is depressed down again.	The air compressor: CYCLING "ON/OFF" CONTINUOUSLY AIR COMPRESSOR REMAINS "OFF" CONTINUOUSLY	▶ Depress the "STAR" test button so that it remains in the "TEST" position. This action will stop the "COMPRESSOR TOGGLE" functional test since it is no longer required. Then: GO TO IC17 ▶ GO TO IC6

FM2019100090030X

Fig. 38 Test IC: Unable To Detect Raising Of Right Rear Corner (Part 3 of 13)

IC6	CHECKING WIRING HARNESS	RESULT	ACTION TO TAKE
	Since the air suspension control module can not activate the air compressor the following actions are required: • Depress the "STAR" test button so that it remains in the down "HOLD" position. This action will stop the "COMPRESSOR TOGGLE" functional test. • Disconnect the air compressor assembly electrical connector from the vehicle wiring harness connector. • Examine the both electrical connectors for damage and proper installation of wires.	Electrical connectors are good: YES NO	▶ GO TO IC7 ▶ Make repairs as required and rerun SERVICE BAY DIAGNOSTICS.
IC7	COMPRESSOR COOL DOWN		
	The air compressor has an internal thermal non-cycling circuit breaker in it that opens the B + power supply to the air compressor armature when the internal temperature exceeds a predetermined limit. In order for this thermal circuit breaker to be reset the following two things must happen: 1) the internal temperature must drop below the predetermined limit and 2) the power to to the compressor must be off. In this part of the test we will allow the compressor to cool down for 15 minutes. The air compressor thermal circuit breaker may have been tripped by repeatedly running diagnostic checks.	At least 15 minutes has elapsed since the air compressor was disconnected from the vehicle wiring harness: YES NO	▶ GO TO IC8 ▶ Continue with step "IC7" until 15 minutes has elapsed.
IC8	WIRING HARNESS CHECK		
	• Reconnect the air compressor to the the vehicle wiring harness.	The air compressor remains off: YES NO	▶ GO TO IC10 ▶ GO TO IC9

FM2019100090040X

Fig. 38 Test IC: Unable To Detect Raising Of Right Rear Corner (Part 4 of 13)

IC9	WIRING HARNESS CHECK	RESULT	ACTION TO TAKE
	• Remove the air compressor relay from its vehicle wiring harness connector.	The air compressor stops running and remains off:	
		YES ▶	Install a new air compressor relay and rerun SERVICE BAY DIAGNOSTICS.
		NO ▶	Circuit #417 has a short to B+ which is causing the air compressor to run until the air compressor's internal thermal circuit breaker is tripped. Rerun SERVICE BAY DIAGNOSTICS after repair is made and the air compressor relay has been installed again.
IC10	AIR COMPRESSOR COMPONENT CHECK	The air compressor is:	
	It is desired to activate the "COMPRESSOR TOGGLE" functional test again. In order to do this the following action is required:		
	• Release the "STAR" test button so that it remains in the up "HOLD" position after the code "31" has been displayed for at least 5 seconds.	CYCLING "ON/OFF" CONTINUOUSLY ▶	Depress the "STAR" test button so that it remains in the "TEST" position. This action will stop the "COMPRESSOR TOGGLE functional test since it is no longer required. Rerun SERVICE BAY DIAGNOSTICS after waiting 30 minutes.
	NOTE: As long as the "STAR" test button is in the up "HOLD" position the selected functional test will continue. The "COMPRESSOR TOGGLE" test is used to verify that the air suspension control module can activate the air compressor. This is done by cycling it "ON" and "OFF" continuously until the "STAR" test button is depressed down again.		
		AIR COMPRESSOR REMAINS "OFF" ▶	GO TO IC11

FM2019100090050X

Fig. 38 Test IC: Unable To Detect Raising Of Right Rear Corner (Part 5 of 13)

IC11	CHECKING WIRING HARNESS	RESULT	ACTION TO TAKE
	The next step in determining why the air suspension control module could not activate the air compressor is:	The voltage reading fluctuates between zero and battery voltage (check is to be made over a one minute time period):	
	• Disconnect the air compressor assembly electrical connector from the vehicle wiring harness connector.		
	• Using a voltmeter connect the positive lead to circuit #417 of the air compressor vehicle wiring harness connector and the negative lead to circuit #430F.	YES ▶	Install a new air compressor assembly and then rerun SERVICE BAY DIAGNOSTICS.
		NO ▶	GO TO IC12
IC12	CHECKING WIRING HARNESS	Ohmmeter reading is greater than 5 ohms:	
	• Depress the "STAR" test button so that it remains in the down "TEST" position.		
	• Remove the air compressor relay from its vehicle wiring harness connector.	YES ▶	The circuit used to active the air compressor (circuit #417) has an open in it. Rerun SERVICE BAY DIAGNOSTICS after repair is made.
	• Using an analog ohmmeter connect one lead to circuit #417 of the air compressor relay connector and the other lead to #417 of the air compressor vehicle wiring harness connector.		
		NO ▶	GO TO IC13
IC13	CHECKING WIRING HARNESS	Ohmmeter reading is greater than 5 ohms:	
	• Again using an analog ohmmeter connect one lead to the air compressor relay circuit #430B and the other to a known good ground.		
		YES ▶	Circuit #430B has an open in it. Rerun SERVICE BAY DIAGNOSTICS after repair is made.
		NO ▶	GO TO IC14

FM2019100090060X

Fig. 38 Test IC: Unable To Detect Raising Of Right Rear Corner (Part 6 of 13)

IC14	CHECKING WIRING HARNESS	RESULT	ACTION TO TAKE
	• Using a voltmeter connect the positive lead to circuit #175 of the air compressor relay's wiring harness connector and the negative lead to circuit #430B	The voltage reading is greater than 10 volts:	
		YES ▶	GO TO IC15
		NO ▶	This circuit has an open or short in it. There should always be battery voltage on this circuit. Rerun SERVICE BAY DIAGNOSTICS after repairs are made.
IC15	CHECKING WIRING HARNESS	The voltage reading fluctuates between zero and battery voltage (check is to be made over a one time period):	
	It is desired to activate the "COMPRESSOR TOGGLE" functional test again. In order to do this the following action is required:		
	• Release the "STAR" test button so that it remains in the up "HOLD" position after after the code "31" has been displayed at least 5 seconds.		
	• Using a voltmeter connect the positive lead to circuit #420 of the air compressor relay's wiring harness connector the negative lead to circuit #430B.	YES ▶	Install a new air compressor relay, reconnect the air compressor assembly and then rerun SERVICE BAY DIAGNOSTICS.
	NOTE: As long as the "STAR" test button is in the up "HOLD" position the selected functional test will continue. The "COMPRESSOR TOGGLE" test is used to verify that the air suspension control module can activate the air compressor. This is done by cycling it "ON" and "OFF" continuously until the "STAR" test button is depressed down again.	NO ▶	GO TO IC16

FM2019100090070X

Fig. 38 Test IC: Unable To Detect Raising Of Right Rear Corner (Part 7 of 13)

IC16	CHECKING WIRING HARNESS	RESULT	ACTION TO TAKE
	• Turn the air suspension "ON/OFF" switch to the "OFF" position and disconnect the air suspension control module from the vehicle wiring harness.	The resistance reading is less than 5.0 ohms:	
		YES ▶	Install a new air suspension control module, reconnect the air compressor relay and then rerun SERVICE BAY DIAGNOSTICS.
	• Using an analog ohmmeter (20,000 ohms per volt is recommended) connect the the air compressor positive lead to circuit #420 of the air compressor relay wiring harness connector and the other lead to pin position #35 (circuit #420) of the air suspension control module wiring harness connector.	NO ▶	The circuit (#420) used to provide B+ power to the air compressor relay has an open in it. Rerun SERVICE BAY DIAGNOSTICS after repair is made.
IC17	SPRING SOLENOID VALVE COMPONENT CHECK	The right front air spring solenoid valve is making an audible click sound:	
	It is now desired to activate the "AIR SPRING SOLENOID VALVE CYCLE" functional test. In order to do this the following actions are required:		
	• Release the "STAR" test button so that it remains in the up "HOLD" position after the code "33" has been displayed for at least 5 seconds.	CYCLING "ON/OFF" CONTINUOUSLY ▶	GO TO IC21
	NOTE: As long as the "STAR" test button is in the up "HOLD" position the selected functional test will continue. The "AIR SPRING SOLENOID CYCLE" test is used to verify that the air suspension control module can activate each of the air spring solenoid valves by cycling them "ON" and "OFF" continuously until the "STAR" test button is depressed down again.	REMAINS "OFF" ▶	GO TO IC18

FM2019100090080X

Fig. 38 Test IC: Unable To Detect Raising Of Right Rear Corner (Part 8 of 13)

Part 9 of 13

IC18 CHECKING WIRING HARNESS	RESULT	ACTION TO TAKE
The air suspension control module can not activate the right rear air spring solenoid valve. In order to determine the cause of this the following actions are required: * Electrically disconnect right rear air spring solenoid from the vehicle wiring harness connector. * Using a voltmeter connect the positive lead to the air spring solenoid valve wiring harness connector circuit #416 and the negative lead to circuit #430A of the same connector. NOTE: The "AIR SPRING SOLENOID VALVE CYCLE" functional test is still being conducted. During this functional test the front ride height of the vehicle may lower and the rear ride height may raise.	The voltage reading pulses between zero and battery voltage (check is to made over a one time period): YES NO	▶ Install a new right rear air spring solenoid and then rerun SERVICE BAY DIAGNOSTICS. ▶ GO TO IC19
IC19 CHECKING WIRING HARNESS		
* Turn the air suspension "ON/OFF" switch to the "OFF" position. * Disconnect air suspension control module connector. * Using an analog ohmmeter connect one lead to the air suspension control module wiring harness connector pin location #38 (circuit #416) and other to the right rear air spring solenoid valve wiring harness connector circuit #416.	Ohmmeter reading is less than 10 ohms: YES NO	▶ GO TO IC20 ▶ An open in circuit #416 has been detected in the wiring harness. Refer to the electrical system section and rerun SERVICE BAY DIAGNOSTICS after repair is made.

FM2019100090090X

Fig. 38   Test IC: Unable To Detect Raising Of Right Rear Corner (Part 9 of 13)

Part 10 of 13

IC20 WIRING HARNESS CHECK	RESULT	ACTION TO TAKE
* Again using an analog ohmmeter connect one lead to the air suspension control module wiring harness connector pin location #60 (circuit #430H) and other to the right rear air spring solenoid valve vehicle wiring harness connector circuit #430A.	Ohmmeter reading is less than 10 ohms: YES NO	▶ Install a new air suspension control module and then rerun SERVICE BAY DIAGNOSTICS. ▶ An open in circuit #430H/430A exists. Rerun SERVICE BAY DIAGNOSTICS after repair is made.
IC21 ENTER SPRING FILL DIAGNOSTICS		
At this time it will be required to exit SERVICE BAY DIAGNOSTICS and enter SPRING FILL (refer to SPRING FILL DIAGNOSTIC section for instructions).	The STAR tester is displaying one of the following codes: "21" to "28" SOMETHING ELSE	▶ GO TO IC22 ▶ Repeat SPRING FILL entrance procedure until entered.
IC22 VISUAL CHECK		
In order to perform the right rear air spring inflation test we must first determine if it is above the normal position.	The vehicle's right rear corner has approximately a two inch gap or greater between the fender lip opening and the top of the tire: YES NO	▶ GO TO IC23 ▶ GO TO IC24

FM2019100090100X

Fig. 38   Test IC: Unable To Detect Raising Of Right Rear Corner (Part 10 of 13)

Part 11 of 13

IC23 VENT RIGHT REAR AIR SPRING	RESULT	ACTION TO TAKE
In order to perform the right rear air spring inflation test we must first vent it below the normal position. To do that the following action is required: * Release the "STAR" test button down so that it remains in the up "HOLD" position after the code "23" has been displayed for at least 5 seconds. * Continue venting the right rear corner of the vehicle until the gap between the fender lip opening and the top of the tire is one inch or less. NOTE: As long as the "STAR" test button remains in the up "HOLD" position the right rear air spring will continue to be vented. When the desired amount of venting has occurred depress the "STAR" test button so that it remains in the "TEST" position..	The vehicle's right rear corner has been lowered: YES NO	▶ Depress the "STAR" test button down so that it remains in the "TEST" position; then: GO TO IC24 ▶ Continue with step "IA23" until the desired height is reached.
IC24 INFLATE RIGHT REAR AIR SPRING		
To inflate the right rear air spring the following action is required: * Release the "STAR" test button so that it remains in the "HOLD" position after the code "26" has been displayed for at least 5 seconds. NOTE: As long as the STAR test button remains in the up "HOLD" position the right rear air spring will continue to be inflated. When the desired amount of inflating has occurred depress the test button so that it remains in the "TEST" position.	The right rear corner of the vehicle has been raised so that the gap between the fender lip opening and the top of the tire is approximately three inches or greater. VERY SLOWLY OR NONE AT ALL SLOWLY OR AT A NORMAL RATE	▶ Depress the "STAR" test button down in the "TEST" position Then: GO TO IC25 ▶ Rerun SERVICE BAY DIAGNOSTICS. If this problem still occurs install a new suspension control module and rerun SERVICE BAY DIAGNOSTICS.

FM2019100090110X

Fig. 38   Test IC: Unable To Detect Raising Of Right Rear Corner (Part 11 of 13)

Part 12 of 13

IC25 AIR LINE CHECK	RESULT	ACTION TO TAKE
In order to determine why the right rear corner of the vehicle is inflating "VERY SLOWLY OR NONE AT ALL" the following actions are required: * Disconnect the right rear air line from the right rear air spring solenoid valve. * Disconnect the right rear air spring solenoid valve electrical connector so that the solenoid valve is not connected to the vehicle wiring harness. * Release the "STAR" test button so that it remains in the up "HOLD" position after the code "26" has been displayed for at least 5 seconds. NOTE: As long as the "STAR" test button remains in the up "HOLD" position the air compressor assembly will continue to pump air through the air line.	Air is coming out of the air line: VERY SLOWLY OR NONE AT ALL AT A NORMAL RATE	▶ GO TO IC26 ▶ GO TO IC27
IC26 AIR LINE CHECK		
From the previous tests we have determined that the cause of the UNABLE TO INFLATE problem is due to a restriction in the air line or compressor assembly. In order to isolate the cause of this problem the following actions are required: * Disconnect any one of the air lines that are plugged into the air compressor drier assembly. NOTE: As long as the "STAR" test button remains in the up "HOLD" position the air compressor assembly will continue to pump air through the drier assembly.	The rate that the air is coming out of the drier assembly is: SAME AS IN STEP "IC25" OR SLIGHTLY GREATER RATE IS FASTER THEN IN STEP "IC25"	▶ Install a new air compressor assembly and then rerun SERVICE BAY DIAGNOSTICS. ▶ There is a restriction in the right rear air line. Rerun SERVICE BAY DIAGNOSTICS after repair is made.

FM2019100090120X

Fig. 38   Test IC: Unable To Detect Raising Of Right Rear Corner (Part 12 of 13)

IC27	AIR LEAK TEST	RESULT	ACTION TO TAKE
	• Depress the "STAR" test button so that it remains in the down "TEST" position.	The second wheel lip opening is :	
	• Reconnect the air line to the air compressor drier assembly and right rear air spring solenoid valve.	APPROXIMATELY THE SAME AS THE FIRST	GO TO IC28
	• Reconnect the vehicle wiring harness connector to the right rear air spring.	LESS THAN THE FIRST	GO TO IC29
	• Take a piece of masking tape and mark a spot on the wheel lip opening. Measure and record the vertical height between wheel lip opening and the bottom of the wheel rim.		
	• Wait at least 15 minutes, remeasure and record wheel lip opening again.		
IC28	AIR LEAK CHECK		
	• Release the "STAR" test button so that it remains in the up "HOLD" position after the code "26" has been displayed for at least 5 seconds.	A leak path was detected:	
	• Inspect the following for air leakage: • air compressor / dryer assembly connection point • dryer assembly / air line connection point • air line / air spring solenoid valve connection point	YES	Make required repairs and then rerun SERVICE BAY DIAGNOSTICS.
	NOTE: As long as the "STAR" test button remains in the up "HOLD" position the right rear air spring will continue to be inflated. When the desired amount of inflating has occurred depress the "STAR" test button so that it remains in the "TEST" position.	NO	Install a new air suspension control module and then rerun SERVICE BAY DIAGNOSTICS.
IC29	AIR LEAK CHECK		
	• Inspect the following for air leakage on the right rear air spring / strut assembly: • air spring bag • air spring bag / canister connection • canister / mount connection • air spring solenoid valve / canister connection		Rerun SERVICE BAY DIAGNOSTICS after repairs are made.

FM2019100090130X

Fig. 38   Test IC: Unable To Detect Raising Of Right Rear Corner (Part 13 of 13)

ID1	STAR CODE: 79 UNABLE TO DETECT RAISING OF LEFT REAR CORNER	RESULT	ACTION TO TAKE
	The air suspension control module has not received the signal that the left rear corner of the vehicle was raised during the SERVICE BAY DIAGNOSTIC check. There are nine possible causes of this which are listed below:		GO TO ID2
	• The height sensor linkage arm is not connected properly to the vehicle and/or height sensor.		
	• An air line may be defective.		
	• The left rear air spring solenoid valve maybe defective.		
	• The left rear air spring B+ power supply circuit may have an open in it.		
	• The left rear air spring ground return circuit may have an open in it.		
	• The air compressor may be defective.		
	• The air compressor B+ power supply circuit may have an open in it.		
	• The air compressor ground return circuit may have an open in it.		
	• The air suspension control module may be defective.		

FM2019100091010X

Fig. 39   Test ID: Unable To Detect Raising Of Left Rear Corner (Part 1 of 16)

ID2	VISUAL COMPONENT CHECK	RESULT	ACTION TO TAKE
	• Check under the vehicle to verify that the vehicle is not hanging up on something.	The left rear height sensor is installed correctly with no obvious damage and under the vehicle is clear of all obstructions:	
	• Check the left rear corner of the vehicle to verify that the height sensor has no obvious damage and that the linkage is connected.	YES	GO TO ID3
		NO	Make needed repairs as required and rerun SERVICE BAY DIAGNOSTICS.
ID3	ENTERING FUNCTIONAL TEST MODE OF SERVICE BAY DIAG		
	FUNCTIONAL TEST mode will be used to determine why the left rear corner of the vehicle did not raise.	The "STAR" tester is displaying code:	
	• Release the "STAR" test button to the up "HOLD" position. After five seconds depress the "STAR" test button again so that it remains in the down "TEST" position. This will allow the control module to enter FUNCTIONAL TEST mode.	"31", "32", "33", "34", or "35"	GO TO ID5
		SOMETHING ELSE	GO TO ID4

FM2019100091020X

Fig. 39   Test ID: Unable To Detect Raising Of Left Rear Corner (Part 2 of 16)

ID4	RETRY FUNCTIONAL TEST ENTRANCE PROCEDURE	RESULT	ACTION TO TAKE
	The air suspension control module has not entered the FUNCTIONAL TEST mode and the following actions are required:	The "STAR" tester is displaying code:	
	• Make sure that the "STAR" tester is still plugged into the air suspension diagnostic pigtail.	"31", "32", "33", "34", or "35"	GO TO ID5
	• Make sure the "STAR" tester is turned "ON"	SOMETHING ELSE	Rerun SERVICE BAY DIAGNOSTICS and if still unable to enter FUNCTIONAL TEST model install a new air suspension control module and then rerun SERVICE BAY DIAGNOSTICS.
	• Release the "STAR" test button to the up "HOLD" position. After five seconds depress the "STAR" test button again so that it remains in the down "TEST" position. This will allow the control module to enter FUNCTIONAL TEST mode.		
ID5	AIR COMPRESSOR COMPONENT CHECK		
	It is desired to activate the "COMPRESSOR TOGGLE" FUNCTIONAL TEST mode. In order to do this the following action is required:	The air compressor is:	
	• Raise the vehicle's hood up completely.	CYCLING "ON/OFF" CONTINUOUSLY	Depress the "STAR" test button so that it remains in the "TEST" position. This action will stop the "COMPRESSOR TOGGLE" functional test since it is no longer required. Then: GO TO ID17
	• Release the "STAR" test button so that it remains in the up "HOLD" position after the code "31" has been displayed for at least 5 seconds. NOTE: As long as the "STAR" test button is in the up "HOLD" position the selected functional test will continue. The "COMPRESSOR TOGGLE" test is used to verify that the air suspension control module can activate the air compressor. This is done by cycling it "ON" and "OFF" continuously until the "STAR" test button is depressed down again.	AIR COMPRESSOR REMAINS "OFF"	GO TO ID6

FM2019100091030X

Fig. 39   Test ID: Unable To Detect Raising Of Left Rear Corner (Part 3 of 16)

ID6	CHECKING WIRING HARNESS	RESULT	ACTION TO TAKE
	Since the air suspension control module can not activate the air compressor the following actions are required:	Electrical connectors are good:	
	* Depress the "STAR" test button so that it remains in the down "HOLD" position. This action will stop the "COMPRESSOR TOGGLE" functional test.	YES ▶	GO TO ID7
	* Disconnect the air compressor assembly electrical connector from the vehicle wiring harness connector.	NO ▶	Make repairs as required and rerun SERVICE BAY DIAGNOSTICS.
	* Examine the both electrical connectors for damage and proper installation of wires.		

ID7	COMPRESSOR COOL DOWN		
	The air compressor has an internal thermal non-cycling circuit breaker in it that opens the B+ power supply to the air compressor armature when the internal temperature exceeds a predetermined limit. In order for this thermal circuit breaker to be reset the following two things must happen: 1) the internal temperature must drop below the predetermined limit and 2) the power to the compressor must be off. In this part of the test we will allow the compressor to cool down for 15 minutes. The air compressor thermal circuit breaker been tripped by repeatedly running diagnostic checks.	At least 15 minutes has elapsed since the air compressor was disconnected from the vehicle wiring harness	
		YES ▶	GO TO ID8
		NO ▶	Continue with step "ID7" until may have 15 minutes has elapsed.

ID8	WIRING HARNESS CHECK		
	* Reconnect the air compressor to the vehicle wiring harness.	The air compressor remains off:	
		YES ▶	GO TO ID10
		NO ▶	GO TO ID9

FM2019100091040X

Fig. 39 Test ID: Unable To Detect Raising Of Left Rear Corner (Part 4 of 16)

ID10	AIR COMPRESSOR COMPONENT CHECK	RESULT	ACTION TO TAKE
	It is desired to activate the "COMPRESSOR TOGGLE" functional test again. In order to do this the following action is required:	The air compressor is:	
	* Release the "STAR" test button so that it remains in the up "HOLD" position after the code "31" has been displayed for at least 5 seconds.	CYCLING "ON/OFF" CONTINUOUSLY ▶	Depress the "STAR" test button so that it remains in the "TEST" position. This action will stop the "COMPRESSOR TOGGLE" functional test since it is no longer required. Rerun SERVICE BAY DIAGNOSTICS after waiting 30 minutes.
	NOTE: As long as the "STAR" test button is in the up "HOLD" position the selected functional test will continue. The "COMPRESSOR TOGGLE" test is used to verify that the air suspension control module can activate the air compressor. This is done by cycling it "ON" and "OFF" continuously until the "STAR" test button is depressed down again.	AIR COMPRESSOR REMAINS "OFF" ▶	GO TO ID11

ID11	CHECKING WIRING HARNESS		
	The next step in determining why the air suspension control module could not activate the air compressor is:	The voltage reading fluctuates between zero and battery voltage (check is to be made over a one minute time period):	
	* Disconnect the air compressor assembly electrical connector from the vehicle wiring harness connector.		
	* Using a voltmeter connect the positive lead to circuit #417 of the air compressor vehicle wiring harness connector and the negative lead to circuit #430F.	YES ▶	Install a new air compressor assembly and then rerun SERVICE BAY DIAGNOSTICS
		NO ▶	GO TO ID12

FM2019100091060X

Fig. 39 Test ID: Unable To Detect Raising Of Left Rear Corner (Part 6 of 16)

ID9	WIRING HARNESS CHECK	RESULT	ACTION TO TAKE
	* Remove the air compressor relay from its vehicle wiring harness connector.	The air compressor stops running and remains off:	
		YES ▶	Install a new air compressor relay and then rerun SERVICE BAY DIAGNOSTICS.
		NO ▶	Circuit #417 has a short to B+ which is causing the air compressor to run until the air compressor's internal thermal circuit breaker is tripped. Rerun SERVICE BAY DIAGNOSTICS after repair is made and the air compressor relay has been installed again.

FM2019100091050X

Fig. 39 Test ID: Unable To Detect Raising Of Left Rear Corner (Part 5 of 16)

ID12	CHECKING WIRING HARNESS	RESULT	ACTION TO TAKE
	* Depress the "STAR" test button so that it remains in the down "TEST" position.	Ohmmeter reading is greater than 5 ohms:	
	* Remove the air compressor relay from its vehicle wiring harness connector.	YES ▶	The circuit used to activate the air compressor (circuit #417) has an open in it. Rerun SERVICE BAY DIAGNOSTICS after repair is made.
	* Using an analog ohmmeter connect one lead to circuit #417 of the air compressor relay connector and the other lead to circuit #417 of the air compressor vehicle wiring harness connector.	NO ▶	GO TO ID13

ID13	CHECKING WIRING HARNESS		
	* Again using an analog ohmmeter connect one lead to the air compressor relay circuit #430B and the other to a known good ground.	Ohmmeter reading is greater than 5 ohms:	
		YES ▶	Circuit #430B has an open in it. Rerun SERVICE BAY DIAGNOSTICS after repair is made.
		NO ▶	GO TO ID14

ID14	CHECKING WIRING HARNESS		
	* Using a voltmeter connect the positive lead to circuit #175 of the air compressor relay's wiring harness connector and the negative lead to circuit #430B.	The voltage reading is greater than 10 volts:	
		YES ▶	GO TO ID15
		NO ▶	This circuit has an open or short in it. There should always be battery voltage on this circuit. Rerun SERVICE BAY DIAGNOSTICS after repairs are made.

FM2019100091070X

Fig. 39 Test ID: Unable To Detect Raising Of Left Rear Corner (Part 7 of 16)

ID15 — CHECKING WIRING HARNESS

	RESULT	ACTION TO TAKE
It is desired to activate the "COMPRESSOR TOGGLE" functional test again. In order to do this the following action is required: • Release the "STAR" test button so that it remains in the up "HOLD" position after the code "31" has been displayed for at least 5 seconds. • Using a voltmeter connect the positive lead to circuit #420 of the air compressor relay's wiring harness connector and the negative lead to circuit #430B. NOTE: As long as the "STAR" test button is in the up "HOLD" position the selected functional test will continue. The "COMPRESSOR TOGGLE" test is used to verify that the air suspension control module can activate the air compressor. This is done by cycling it "ON" and "OFF" continuously until the "STAR" test button is depressed down again.	The voltage reading fluctuates between zero and battery voltage (check is to be made over a one minute time period): YES NO	Install a new air compressor relay, reconnect the air compressor assembly and then and rerun SERVICE BAY DIAGNOSTICS. GO TO ID16

ID16 — CHECKING WIRING HARNESS

	RESULT	ACTION TO TAKE
• Turn the air suspension "ON/OFF" switch to the "OFF" position and disconnect the air suspension control module from the vehicle wiring harness. • Using an analog ohmmeter connect the positive lead to circuit #420 of the air compressor relay wiring harness connector and the other lead to pin position #35 (circuit #420) of the air suspension control module wiring harness connector.	The resistance reading is less than 5.0 ohms: YES NO	Install a new air suspension control module, reconnect the air compressor relay and then rerun SERVICE BAY DIAGNOSTICS. The circuit (#420) used to provide B+ power to the air compressor relay has an open in it. Rerun SERVICE BAY DIAGNOSTICS after repair is made.

FM2019100091080X

Fig. 39   Test ID: Unable To Detect Raising Of Left Rear Corner (Part 8 of 16)

ID17 — SPRING SOLENOID VALVE COMPONENT CHECK

	RESULT	ACTION TO TAKE
It is now desired to activate the "AIR SPRING SOLENOID VALVE CYCLE" functional test. In order to do this the following actions are required: • Release the "STAR" test button so that it remains in the up "HOLD" position after the code "33" has been displayed for at least 5 seconds. NOTE: As long as the "STAR" test button is in the up "HOLD" position the selected FUNCTIONAL TEST will continue. The "AIR SPRING SOLENOID CYCLE" test is used to verify that the air suspension control module can activate each of the air spring solenoid valves by cycling them "ON" and "OFF" continuously until the "STAR" test button is depressed down again.	The right front air spring solenoid valve is making an audible click sound: CYCLING "ON/OFF" CONTINUOUSLY REMAINS "OFF"	GO TO ID21 GO TO ID18

ID18 — CHECKING WIRING HARNESS

	RESULT	ACTION TO TAKE
The air suspension control module can not activate the left rear air spring solenoid valve. In order to determine the cause of this the following actions are required: • Electrically disconnect the left rear air spring solenoid from the vehicle wiring harness connector. • Using a voltmeter connect the positive lead to the air spring solenoid valve wiring harness connector circuit #429 and the negative lead to circuit #430F of the same connector. NOTE: The "AIR SPRING SOLENOID VALVE CYCLE" functional test is still being conducted. During this functional test the front ride height of the vehicle may lower and the rear ride height may raise.	The voltage reading pulses between zero and battery voltage (check is to made over a one minute time period): YES NO	Install a new left rear air spring solenoid and then rerun SERVICE BAY DIAGNOSTICS. GO TO ID19

FM2019100091090X

Fig. 39   Test ID: Unable To Detect Raising Of Left Rear Corner (Part 9 of 16)

ID19 — CHECKING WIRING HARNESS

	RESULT	ACTION TO TAKE
• Turn the air suspension "ON/OFF" switch to the "OFF" position. • Disconnect air suspension control module connector. • Using an analog ohmmeter (20,000 ohms per volt is recommended) connect one lead to the air suspension control module wiring harness connector pin location #41 (circuit #429) and other to the right rear air spring solenoid valve wiring harness connector circuit #429.	Ohmmeter reading is less than 10 ohms: YES NO	GO TO ID20 An open in circuit #429 has been detected in the wiring harness. rerun SERVICE BAY DIAGNOSTICS after repair is made.

ID20 — WIRING HARNESS CHECK

	RESULT	ACTION TO TAKE
• Again using an analog ohmmeter connect one lead to the air suspension control module wiring harness connector pin location #60 (circuit #430H) and other to the left rear air spring solenoid valve vehicle wiring harness connector circuit #430F.	Ohmmeter reading is less than 10 ohms: YES NO	Install a new air suspension control module and then rerun SERVICE BAY DIAGNOSTICS. An open in circuit #430H/430F exists. Rerun SERVICE BAY DIAGNOSTICS after BAY DIAGNOSTICS.

FM2019100091100X

Fig. 39   Test ID: Unable To Detect Raising Of Left Rear Corner (Part 10 of 16)

ID21 — ENTER SPRING FILL DIAGNOSTICS

	RESULT	ACTION TO TAKE
At this time it will be required to exit SERVICE BAY DIAGNOSTICS and enter SPRING FILL (refer to SPRING FILL DIAGNOSTIC for instructions).	The "STAR" tester is displaying one of the following codes: "21" to "28" SOMETHING ELSE	GO TO ID22 Repeat SPRING FILL entrance procedure until entered.

ID22 — VISUAL CHECK

	RESULT	ACTION TO TAKE
In order to perform the left rear air spring inflation test we must first determine if it is above the normal position.	The vehicle's left rear corner has approximately a two inch gap or greater between the fender lip opening and the top of the tire: YES NO	GO TO ID23 GO TO ID24

FM2019100091110X

Fig. 39   Test ID: Unable To Detect Raising Of Left Rear Corner (Part 11 of 16)

ID23	VENT LEFT REAR AIR SPRING	RESULT	ACTION TO TAKE
	In order to perform the left rear air spring inflation test we must first vent it below the normal position. In order to do that the following action is required: • Release the "STAR" test button so that it remains in the up "HOLD" position after the code "27" has been displayed for at least 5 seconds. • Continue venting the left rear corner of vehicle until the gap between the fender lip opening and the top of the tire is one inch or less. NOTE: As long as the "STAR" test button remains in the up "HOLD" position the left rear air spring will continue to be vented. When the desired amount of venting as occurred depress the "STAR" test button so that it remains in the down "TEST" position.	The vehicle's left rear corner has been lowered: YES NO	▶ Depress the "STAR" test button down so that it remains in the "TEST" position. Then: GO TO ID24 ▶ Continue with step "ID23" until the desired height is reached.

Fig. 39 Test ID: Unable To Detect Raising Of Left Rear Corner (Part 12 of 16)

ID24	INFLATE LEFT REAR AIR SPRING	RESULT	ACTION TO TAKE
	To inflate the left rear air spring the following action is required: • Release the "STAR" test button so that it remains in the "HOLD" position after the code "28" has been displayed for at least 5 seconds. NOTE: As long as the "STAR" test button remains in the up "HOLD" position the left rear air spring will continue to be inflated. When the desired amount of inflating has occurred depress the "STAR" test button so that it remains in the "TEST" position.	The left rear corner of the vehicle has been raised so that the gap between the fender lip opening and the top of the tire is approximately three inches or greater: VERY SLOWLY OR NONE AT ALL SLOWLY OR AT A NORMAL RATE	Depress the "STAR" test button down so that it remains in the "TEST" position. Then: GO TO ID25 Rerun SERVICE BAY DIAGNOSTICS and if this problem still occurs install a new air suspension control module and then rerun SERVICE BAY DIAGNOSTICS.

Fig. 39 Test ID: Unable To Detect Raising Of Left Rear Corner (Part 13 of 16)

ID25	AIR LINE CHECK	RESULT	ACTION TO TAKE
	In order to determine why the left rear corner of the vehicle is inflating "VERY SLOWLY OR NONE AT ALL" the following actions are required: • Disconnect the left rear air line from the left rear air spring solenoid valve. • Disconnect the left rear air spring solenoid valve electrical connector so that the solenoid valve is not connected to the vehicle wiring harness. • Release the "STAR" test button so that it remains in the up "HOLD" position. after the code "28" has been displayed for at least 5 seconds. NOTE: As long as the "STAR" test button remains in the up "HOLD" position the air compressor assembly will continue to pump air through the air line.	Air is coming out of the air line: VERY SLOWLY OR NONE AT ALL AT A NORMAL RATE	 GO TO ID26 GO TO ID27
ID26	AIR LINE CHECK		
	From the previous tests we have determined that cause of the UNABLE TO INFLATE problem is due to a restriction in the air line or compressor assembly. In order to isolate the cause of this problem the following actions are required: • Disconnect any one of the air lines that are plugged into the air compressor drier assembly. NOTE: As long as the "STAR" test button remains in the up "HOLD" position the air compressor assembly will continue to pump air through the drier assembly.	The rate that the air is coming out of the drier assembly is: SAME AS IN STEP "ID25" OR SLIGHTLY GREATER RATE IS FASTER THAN IN STEP "ID25"	 ▶ Install a new air compressor assembly and then rerun SERVICE BAY DIAGNOSTICS. ▶ There is a restriction in the left rear air line. Rerun SERVICE BAY DIAGNOSTICS after repair is made.

Fig. 39 Test ID: Unable To Detect Raising Of Left Rear Corner (Part 14 of 16)

ID27	AIR LEAK TEST	RESULT	ACTION TO TAKE
	• Depress the "STAR" test button so that it remains in the down "TEST" position. • Reconnect the air line to the air compressor drier assembly and left rear air spring solenoid valve. • Reconnect the vehicle wiring harness connector to the left rear air spring. • Take a piece of masking tape and mark a spot on the wheel lip opening. Measure and record the vertical height between wheel lip opening and the bottom of the wheel rim. • Wait at least 15 minutes, remeasure and record wheel lip opening again.	The second wheel lip opening is : APPROXIMATELY THE SAME AS THE FIRST LESS THAN THE FIRST	 ▶ GO TO ID28 ▶ GO TO ID29
ID28	AIR LEAK CHECK		

	• Release the "STAR" test button so that it remains in the up "HOLD" position after the code "28" has been displayed for at least 5 seconds.
	
	• Inspect the following for air leakage:
	  • air compressor / dryer assembly connection point
	  • dryer assembly / air line connection point
	  • air line / air spring solenoid valve connection point
	
	NOTE: As long as the "STAR" test button remains in the up "HOLD" position the left rear air spring will continue to be inflated. When the desired amount of inflating has occurred depress the "STAR" test button so that it remains in the "TEST" position.
		A leak path was detected:
		
		YES
		
		NO
			
			▶ Make required repairs and rerun SERVICE BAY DIAGNOSTICS.
			
			▶ Install a new air suspension control module and then rerun SERVICE BAY DIAGNOSTICS.

Fig. 39 Test ID: Unable To Detect Raising Of Left Rear Corner (Part 15 of 16)

ID29	AIR LEAK CHECK	RESULT	ACTION TO TAKE
	• Inspect the following for air leakage on the left rear air spring / strut assembly: • air spring bag • air spring bag / canister connection • canister / mount connection • air spring solenoid valve / canister connection		▶ Rerun SERVICE BAY DIAGNOSTICS after repairs are made.

FM2019100091160X

Fig. 39   Test ID: Unable To Detect Raising Of Left Rear Corner (Part 16 of 16)

JA1	STAR CODE: 55 SPEED GREATER THAN 15 mph NOT DETECTED	RESULT	ACTION TO TAKE
	The air suspension control module has not received a signal the vehicle speed was above 15 mph during the DRIVE CYCLE DIAGNOSTIC test. There are five possible causes for this which are listed below: • The vehicle was not driven above 15 mph during DRIVE CYCLE DIAGNOSTICS. • The B+ power circuit of the speed sensor circuit has an open or short in it. • The ground return circuit of the speed sensor has an open in it. • The vehicle speed sensor may be defective. • The air suspension control module may be defective.	The vehicle was driven above a speed of 15 mph for at least four minutes, the ignition switch has been turned to the "OFF" position and remained there. The air suspension "ON/OFF" switch has remained in the "ON" position: YES NO	▶ GO TO JA2 ▶ Drive the vehicle above 15 mph for at least four minutes.
JA2	SPEED SENSOR COMPONENT CHECK		
	Refer to the shop manual to reverify that the vehicle speed sensor is operating properly at all speeds.	The speed sensor has been verified to operate at all speeds properly: YES NO	▶ GO TO JA3 ▶ After the required repairs to the vehicle speed sensor are made rerun DRIVE CYCLE DIAGNOSTICS.

FM2019100092010X

Fig. 40   Test JA: Speed Greater Than 5 Mph Not Detected (Part 1 of 2)

JA3	WIRING HARNESS CHECK	RESULT	ACTION TO TAKE
	• Turn the ignition switch to the "OFF" position. • Turn the air suspension "ON/OFF" switch to the "OFF" position and disconnect the air suspension control module from the vehicle wiring harness. • Using an analog ohmmeter connect one lead to the air suspension control module vehicle wiring harness connector pin position #6 (circuit #563) and the other to pin position #40 (circuit #430G).	The ohmmeter reading was less than 5.0 ohms: YES NO	▶ GO TO JA4 ▶ The ground circuit (#563) of the vehicle speed sensor has an open in it. Rerun DRIVE CYCLE DIAGNOSTICS after repair is made.
JA4	WIRING HARNESS CHECK		
	• Using an analog ohmmeter connect one lead to the air suspension control module vehicle wiring harness connector pin #3 (circuit #150) and the other to circuit #150A of the vehicle speed sensor wiring harness connector.	The ohmmeter reading is less than 5.0 ohms: YES NO	▶ Install a new air suspension control module and drive the vehicle again above 15 mph. Afterwards rerun DRIVE CYCLE DIAGNOSTICS to verify repairs. ▶ An open has been detected in the speed sensor circuit (#150). Rerun DRIVE CYCLE DIAGNOSTICS after repair is made.

FM2019100092020X

Fig. 40   Test JA: Speed Greater Than 5 Mph Not Detected (Part 2 of 2)

JB1	STAR CODE: 72 / DID NOT DETECT AT LEAST 4 OPEN AND CLOSE DOOR SIGNALS	RESULT	ACTION TO TAKE
	The air suspension control module has not received all four door "OPEN" and "CLOSE" signals after the STAR tester displayed a code "12" or "13". There are four possible causes of the air suspension control module not detecting that all the doors were "OPEN" and "CLOSED". • The door sense circuit used to detect when a door or doors are open or closed may have an open or short. • The door open/close sense switch may not be installed properly. • The door open/close sense switch may be defective. • The air suspension control module may be defective.	After the STAR tester displayed a code "12" or "13" each of the vehicle's doors were opened and shut once: YES NO	▶ GO TO JB2 ▶ Rerun SERVICE BAY DIAGNOSTICS.
JB2	WIRING HARNESS CHECK		
	The air suspension control module has not received all four door "OPEN" and "CLOSE" signals. In order to determine where the problem is located the following actions are required: • Release the "STAR" test button to the up "HOLD" position. After five seconds depress the "STAR" test button again so that it remains in the down "TEST" position. This will allow the control module to enter FUNCTIONAL TEST mode.	The "STAR" tester is displaying code: "31", "32", "33", "34", or "35" NO	▶ GO TO JB4 ▶ GO TO JB3

FM2019100093010X

Fig. 41   Test JB: Did Not Detect At Least Four Open And Close Door Signals (Part 1 of 14)

JB3	CHECKING WIRING HARNESS	RESULT	ACTION TO TAKE
	The air suspension control module has not entered the SERVICE BAY DIAGNOSTICS FUNCTIONAL TEST mode and the following actions are required: * Make sure that the "STAR" tester is still plugged into the air suspension diagnostic pigtail. * Make sure that the "STAR" tester is turned "ON". * Release the "STAR" test button to the up "HOLD" position. After five seconds depress the "STAR" test button again so that it remains in the down "TEST" position. This will allow the control module to enter FUNCTIONAL TEST mode.	The "STAR" tester is displaying code: "31", "32", "33", "34", or "35" NO	GO TO JB4 Rerun SERVICE BAY DIAGNOSTICS and if still unable to enter its FUNCTIONAL TEST mode replace air suspension control module.

JB4	CHECKING WIRING HARNESS	RESULT	ACTION TO TAKE
	It is desired to activate the "DOOR FUNCTIONAL TEST". In order to do this the following action is required: * Raise the vehicle's hood up completely. * Close all vehicle doors. * Release the "STAR" test button so that it remains in the up "HOLD" position after the code "35" has been displayed for at least 5 seconds. NOTE: As long as the "STAR" test button is in the up "HOLD" position the "DOOR FUNCTIONAL TEST" will continue. The "DOOR FUNCTIONAL TEST" is used to verify that the air suspension control module is receiving the door "OPEN" and "CLOSED" signals. This functional test provides the operator with two different types of audible signals. When all doors are "CLOSED" the vent solenoid located in the air compressor assembly will cycle "ON" and "OFF" continuously. If at least one door is "OPEN" then the air compressor and vent solenoid valve will cycle "ON" and "OFF" continuously.	The air compressor assembly is doing the following: Vent solenoid cycling "ON" & "OFF" Air compressor & vent solenoid cycling "ON" & "OFF" Neither the air compressor or vent solenoid are cycling "ON" & "OFF"	GO TO JB5 GO TO JB23 "DOOR FUNCTIONAL TEST" was not entered. Repeat step "JB4".

FM2019100093020X

Fig. 41   Test JB: Did Not Detect At Least Four Open And Close Door Signals (Part 2 of 14)

JB5	CHECKING WIRING HARNESS	RESULT	ACTION TO TAKE
	Since the air suspension control module has received the signal that all the doors are "CLOSED" the problem becomes simply to determine which door or doors the air suspension control module did not receive an "OPEN" door signal from. In order to do this the following action is required: * Open one of the vehicle doors and leave it open.	The air compressor and vent solenoid valve are cycling together: YES NO	This door circuit is operating properly. Close this door and repeat step "JB5" until all the vehicle doors have been checked. The air suspension control module has not received the signal that the door was "OPEN". Record the location of this door and repeat step "JB5" until all doors have been checked. Then: GO TO JB6

FM2019100093030X

Fig. 41   Test JB: Did Not Detect At Least Four Open And Close Door Signals (Part 3 of 14)

JB6		RESULT	ACTION TO TAKE
		The following door "OPEN" circuits were recorded as having a problem in step "JB5": LEFT REAR RIGHT REAR RIGHT FRONT LEFT FRONT (This door circuit is to be repaired last due to the diode in its circuit.)	GO TO JB7 GO TO JB11 GO TO JB15 GO TO JB19

JB7	VISUAL COMPONENT CHECK	RESULT	ACTION TO TAKE
	In order to determine the reason why the air suspension control module did not receive the left rear door "OPEN" signal the following action is required: * Open the left rear door and examine the door "COURTESY SWITCH" for obvious damage.	The left rear door "COURTESY SWITCH" is damaged: YES NO	Replace the left rear door "COURTESY SWITCH" and repeat step "JB5" to verify that the problem has been corrected. GO TO JB8

FM2019100093040X

Fig. 41   Test JB: Did Not Detect At Least Four Open And Close Door Signals (Part 4 of 14)

JB8	CHECKING WIRING HARNESS	RESULT	ACTION TO TAKE
	* Disconnect the left rear door "COURTESY SWITCH" from the vehicle wiring harness. * Using a voltmeter connect the positive lead to the "COURTESY SWITCH" wiring harness connect circuit #54H and negative lead to battery ground.	The voltage reading is greater than 10 volts: YES NO	GO TO JB9 The battery supply voltage circuit has an open/short. Rerun SERVICE BAY DIAGNOSTICS after repair is made.

JB9	CHECKING WIRING HARNESS	RESULT	ACTION TO TAKE
	* Using a jumper wire connect the "COURTESY SWITCH" wiring harness connector circuit #54H and circuit #24B.	The air compressor and vent solenoid valve are cycling together: YES NO	Replace the left rear door "COURTESY SWITCH" and rerun SERVICE BAY DIAGNOSTICS after repair is made. GO TO JB10

FM2019100093050X

Fig. 41   Test JB: Did Not Detect At Least Four Open And Close Door Signals (Part 5 of 14)

JB10	CHECKING WIRING HARNESS	RESULT	ACTION TO TAKE
	• Turn the air suspension "ON/OFF" switch to the "OFF" position. Disconnect the air suspension control module from the wiring harness connector. • Using an analog ohmmeter connect one lead to the "COURTESY SWITCH" wiring harness connector circuit #24B and the other to the air suspension control module pin location #4 (circuit #24).	The ohmmeter reading is less than 5.0 ohms: YES ▶ NO ▶	Replace the air suspension control module and rerun SERVICE BAY DIAGNOSTICS afterwards. The left rear door circuit has an open in it. Rerun SERVICE BAY DIAGNOSTICS after repair is made.

JB11	CHECKING WIRING HARNESS		
	In order to determine the reason why the air suspension control module did not receive the right rear door "OPEN" signal the following action is required: • Open the right rear door and examine the door "COURTESY SWITCH for obvious damage.	The right rear door "COURTESY SWITCH" is damaged: YES ▶ NO ▶	Replace the right rear door "COURTESY SWITCH" and repeat step "JB5" to verify that the problem has been corrected. GO TO JB12

FM2019100093060X

Fig. 41 Test JB: Did Not Detect At Least Four Open And Close Door Signals (Part 6 of 14)

JB12	CHECKING WIRING HARNESS	RESULT	ACTION TO TAKE
	• Disconnect the right rear door "COURTESY SWITCH" from the vehicle wiring harness. • Using a voltmeter connect the positive lead to the "COURTESY SWITCH" wiring harness connect circuit #54F and negative lead to battery ground.	The voltage reading is greater than 10 volts: YES ▶ NO ▶	GO TO JB13 The battery supply voltage circuit has an open/short. Rerun SERVICE BAY DIAGNOSTICS after repair is made.

JB13	CHECKING WIRING HARNESS		
	• Using a jumper wire connect the "COURTESY SWITCH" wiring harness connector circuit #54F and circuit #24E.	The air compressor and vent solenoid valve are cycling together: YES ▶ NO ▶	Replace the right rear door "COURTESY SWITCH" and rerun SERVICE BAY DIAGNOSTICS after repair is made. GO TO JB14

FM2019100093070X

Fig. 41 Test JB: Did Not Detect At Least Four Open And Close Door Signals (Part 7 of 14)

JB14	CHECKING WIRING HARNESS	RESULT	ACTION TO TAKE
	• Turn the air suspension "ON/OFF" switch to the "OFF" position. Disconnect the air suspension control module from the wiring harness connector. • Using an analog ohmmeter connect one lead to the "COURTESY SWITCH" wiring harness connector circuit #24E and the other to the air suspension control module pin location #4 (circuit #24).	The ohmmeter reading is less than 5.0 ohms: YES ▶ NO ▶	Replace the air suspension control module and rerun SERVICE BAY DIAGNOSTICS afterwards. The right rear door circuit has an open in it. Rerun SERVICE BAY DIAGNOSTICS after repair is made.

JB15	CHECKING WIRING HARNESS		
	In order to determine the reason why the air suspension control module did not receive the right front door "OPEN" signal the following action is required: • Open the right front door and examine the door "COURTESY SWITCH" for obvious damage.	The right front door "COURTESY SWITCH" is damaged: YES ▶ NO ▶	Replace the right front door "COURTESY SWITCH" and repeat step "JB5" to verify that the problem has been corrected. GO TO JB16

FM2019100093080X

Fig. 41 Test JB: Did Not Detect At Least Four Open And Close Door Signals (Part 8 of 14)

JB16	CHECKING WIRING HARNESS	RESULT	ACTION TO TAKE
	• Disconnect the right front door "COURTESY SWITCH" from the vehicle wiring harness. • Using a voltmeter connect the positive lead to the "COURTESY SWITCH" wiring harness connect circuit #54G and negative lead to battery ground.	The voltage reading is greater than 10 volts: YES ▶ NO ▶	GO TO JB17 The battery supply voltage circuit has an open/short. Rerun SERVICE BAY DIAGNOSTICS after repair is made.

JB17	CHECKING WIRING HARNESS		
	• Using a jumper wire connect the "COURTESY SWITCH" wiring harness connector circuit #54G and circuit #24F.	The air compressor and vent solenoid valve are cycling together: YES ▶ NO ▶	Replace the right front door "COURTESY SWITCH" and rerun SERVICE BAY DIAGNOSTICS after repair is made. GO TO JB18

FM2019100093090X

Fig. 41 Test JB: Did Not Detect At Least Four Open And Close Door Signals (Part 9 of 14)

AIR SUSPENSION, CONTINENTAL

JB18	CHECKING WIRING HARNESS	RESULT	ACTION TO TAKE
	• Turn the air suspension "ON/OFF" switch to the "OFF" position. Disconnect the air suspension control module from the wiring harness connector. • Using an analog ohmmeter connect one lead to the "COURTESY SWITCH" wiring harness connector circuit #24F and the other to the air suspension control module pin location #4 (circuit #24).	The ohmmeter reading is less than 5.0 ohms: YES NO	Replace the air suspension control module and rerun SERVICE BAY DIAGNOSTICS afterwards. The right front door circuit has an open in it. Rerun SERVICE BAY DIAGNOSTICS after repair is made.
JB19	CHECKING WIRING HARNESS		
	In order to determine the reason why the air suspension control module did not receive the left front door "OPEN" signal the following action is required: • Open the left front door and examine the door "COURTESY SWITCH" for obvious damage.	The left front door "COURTESY SWITCH" is damaged: YES NO	Replace the left front door "COURTESY SWITCH" and repeat step "JB5" to verify that the problem has been corrected. GO TO JB20

FM2019100093100X

Fig. 41   Test JB: Did Not Detect At Least Four Open And Close Door Signals (Part 10 of 14)

JB20	CHECKING WIRING HARNESS	RESULT	ACTION TO TAKE
	• Disconnect the left front door "COURTESY SWITCH" from the vehicle wiring harness. • Using a voltmeter connect the positive lead to the "COURTESY SWITCH" wiring harness connect circuit #54D and negative lead to battery ground.	The voltage reading is greater than 10 volts: YES NO	GO TO JB21 The battery supply voltage circuit has an open/short. Rerun SERVICE BAY DIAGNOSTICS after repair is made.
JB21	CHECKING WIRING HARNESS		
	• Using a jumper wire connect the "COURTESY SWITCH" wiring harness connector circuit #54D and circuit #159A.	The air compressor and vent solenoid valve are cycling together: YES NO	Replace the left front door "COURTESY SWITCH" and rerun SERVICE BAY DIAGNOSTICS after repair is made. GO TO JB22

FM2019100093110X

Fig. 41   Test JB: Did Not Detect At Least Four Open And Close Door Signals (Part 11 of 14)

JB22	CHECKING WIRING HARNESS	RESULT	ACTION TO TAKE
	• Turn the air suspension "ON/OFF" switch to the "OFF" position. Disconnect the suspension control module from the wiring harness connector. • Using an analog ohmmeter connect one lead to the "COURTESY SWITCH" wiring harness connector circuit #159A and the other to the air suspension control module pin location #4 (circuit #24).	The ohmmeter reading is less than 5.0 ohms: YES NO	Replace the air suspension control module and rerun SERVICE BAY DIAGNOSTICS afterwards. The left front door circuit has an open in it. Rerun SERVICE BAY DIAGNOSTICS after repair is made.
JB23	CHECKING WIRING HARNESS		
	Since the air compressor and vent solenoid valve are cycling continuously the air suspension control module has not received the signal that all doors are closed. In order to minimize the work involved in locating this problem the following action is required: • Select any door and open it. Then manually depress the "COURTESY SWITCH" fully.	Only the vent solenoid valve is cycling continuously: YES NO	This door "COURTESY SWITCH" is not positioned correctly to detect when the door is closed. Rerun the "DOOR FUNCTIONAL TEST" after repair is made to verify that problem has been corrected. Repeat step "JB23" until all doors have been checked. If the air compressor and vent solenoid valve continue to cycle continuously then: GO TO JB24

FM2019100093120X

Fig. 41   Test JB: Did Not Detect At Least Four Open And Close Door Signals (Part 12 of 14)

JB24	CHECKING WIRING HARNESS	RESULT	ACTION TO TAKE
	The next step in finding the problem requires the following action: • Select any door and open it. Then disconnect the door "COURTESY SWITCH" from the vehicle wiring harness.	Only the vent solenoid valve is cycling continuously: YES NO	Replace this door "COURTESY SWITCH", close the door and then rerun the "DOOR FUNCTIONAL TEST" after repair is made to verify that problem has been corrected then: GO TO JB25 Repeat step "JB24" until all door "COURTESY SWITCHES" have been disconnected then: GO TO JB26

FM2019100093130X

Fig. 41   Test JB: Did Not Detect At Least Four Open And Close Door Signals (Part 13 of 14)

JB25 — CHECKING WIRING HARNESS

	RESULT	ACTION TO TAKE
If more then one door "COURTESY SWITCH" was disconnected then the following is required: • Reconnect one of the remaining disconnected door "COURTESY SWITCHES" and shut the door.	Only the vent solenoid valve is cycling continuously: YES NO	▶ Repeat step "JB25" until all door "COURTESY SWITCHES" have been reconnected. ▶ Replace this door "COURTESY SWITCH", close the door and verify that problem was corrected. Repeat step "JB25" until all door "COURTESY SWITCHES" have been reconnected.

JB26 — CHECKING WIRING HARNESS

	RESULT	ACTION TO TAKE
• Turn the air suspension "ON/OFF" switch to the "OFF" position. Disconnect the air suspension control module from the wiring harness connector. • Shut all vehicle doors. • Using analog voltmeter connect the positive lead to the air suspension control module pin location #4 (circuit #24) and the negative lead to battery ground.	The voltage reading is greater than 1.0 volts: YES NO	▶ The door "OPEN/CLOSE" circuit is shorted to a voltage source. Rerun the "DOOR FUNCTIONAL TEST" after repair is made to verify problem has been corrected. ▶ Replace the air suspension control module and rerun SERVICE BAY DIAGNOSTICS.

FM2019100093140X

Fig. 41 Test JB: Did Not Detect At Least Four Open And Close Door Signals (Part 14 of 14)

JC1 — STAR CODE: 73 — BRAKE PRESSURE SWITCH ACTIVATION NOT DETECTED

	RESULT	ACTION TO TAKE
The air suspension control module has not received the signal that the vehicle's brake pedal was depressed hard after the STAR tester displayed a code "12" or "13". There are four possible causes of the air suspension control module not detecting that the brake pressure switch was activated by pressing down hard on the brake pedal. • The brake pedal was not depressed hard at the proper time. • The brake pressure switch circuit may have an open or short. • The brake pressure switch may be defective. • The air suspension control module may be defective.	After the STAR tester displayed a code "12" or "13" the vehicle's brake pedal was depressed hard: YES NO	 ▶ GO TO JC2 ▶ Rerun SERVICE BAY DIAGNOSTICS.

JC2 — VISUAL CHECK

	RESULT	ACTION TO TAKE
The first step in trying to locate the reason why the brake pressure switch was not activated is to make a visual check. Look and make sure that there is no obvious damage and that the brake pressure switch is properly connected to the vehicle wiring harness.	Visual check revealed no obvious damage and switch is connected properly: YES NO	 ▶ GO TO JC3 ▶ Make needed repairs and rerun SERVICE BAY DIAGNOSTICS after repairs are made.

FM2019100094010X

Fig. 42 Test JC: Brake Pressure Switch Activation Not Detected (Part 1 of 3)

JC3 — WIRING HARNESS CHECK

	RESULT	ACTION TO TAKE
• Release the "STAR" test button so that it remains in "HOLD" up position and turn it "OFF". • Turn the air suspension "ON/OFF" switch to the "OFF" position. Disconnect the air suspension control module from the wiring harness connector. • Using an analog ohmmeter (20,000 ohms per volt is recommended) connect one lead to the wiring harness connector pin location #7 (circuit #636) and the other lead to pin #40 (circuit #430G).	Ohmmeter reading is greater than 10,000 ohms: YES NO	 ▶ GO TO JC4 ▶ There is a short to ground in brake pressure switch circuit. Rerun SERVICE BAY DIAGNOSTICS after repair is made.

JC4 — WIRING HARNESS CHECK

	RESULT	ACTION TO TAKE
• Using an analog ohmmeter connect one lead to the wiring harness connector pin location #7 (circuit #636) and the other lead to pin #46 (circuit #432D).	Ohmmeter reading is greater than 10,000 ohms: YES NO	 ▶ GO TO JC6 ▶ GO TO JC5

JC5 — WIRING HARNESS CHECK

	RESULT	ACTION TO TAKE
• Disconnect the vehicle's electrical wiring harness connector from the brake pressure switch. • Using an analog ohmmeter again connect one lead to the wiring harness connector pin location #7 (circuit #636) and the other lead to pin #46 (circuit #432D).	Ohmmeter reading is greater than 10,000 ohms: YES NO	 ▶ Replace the brake pressure switch and rerun SERVICE BAY DIAGNOSTICS after repair is made. ▶ The brake pressure switch circuits (#636/432D) are shorted together. Rerun SERVICE BAY DIAGNOSTICS after repair is made.

FM2019100094020X

Fig. 42 Test JC: Brake Pressure Switch Activation Not Detected (Part 2 of 3)

JC6 — COMPONENT CHECK

	RESULT	ACTION TO TAKE
• Using an analog ohmmeter again connect one lead to the wiring harness connector pin location #7 (circuit #636) and the other lead to pin #46 (circuit #432D). • Depress the vehicle's brake pedal hard and keep it down until ohmmeter reading is completed.	Ohmmeter reading is greater than 10,000 ohms when the brake pedal was depressed: YES NO	 ▶ Replace the brake pressure switch and rerun SERVICE BAY DIAGNOSTICS after repair is made. ▶ Replace the air suspension control module and rerun SERVICE BAY DIAGNOSTICS afterwards.

FM2019100094030X

Fig. 42 Test JC: Brake Pressure Switch Activation Not Detected (Part 3 of 3)

JD1	STAR CODE: 74 / STEERING WHEEL ROTATION IN BOTH DIRECTIONS NOT DETECTED	RESULT	ACTION TO TAKE
	The air suspension control module has not received the signal that the vehicle's steering wheel was rotated in both directions after the STAR tester displayed a code "12" or "13". There are seven possible causes of the air suspension control module not detecting that the steering wheel was rotated at least a 1/4 turn in both directions.	After the STAR tester displayed a code "12" or "13" the vehicle's steering wheel was rotated 1/4 turn in both directions:	
	* The steering wheel was not rotated at least a 1/4 turn in both directions at the proper time.	YES	GO TO JD2
		NO	Rerun SERVICE BAY DIAGNOSTICS.
	* The B+ power supply circuit to the steering wheel sensor may have an open or short in it.		
	* The ground return circuit may have an open in it.		
	* The steering sensor channel "A" circuit may have an open or short in it.		
	* The steering sensor channel "B" circuit may have an open or short in it.		
	* The steering wheel sensor may be defective.		
	* The air suspension control module may be defective.		
JD2	STEERING SENSOR CHECK		
	The steering wheel sensor is made up of two components. One of these is the electrical sensor and the other is a metal shutter wheel. In order to determine where the problem is located the following visual inspections are required:	The steering sensor wiring has no damage and all wires are in the proper location:	
	* Check the wires to the steering wheel sensor located on the lower portion of the steering column to ensure that there is no obvious damage and that they are in proper location and connected to the the vehicle wiring harness.	YES	GO TO JD3
		NO	Repair wiring problems and rerun SERVICE BAY DIAGNOSTICS after repairs are made.

FM2019100095010X

Fig. 43 Test JD: Steering Wheel Rotation In Both Directions Not Detected (Part 1 of 4)

JD3	STEERING SENSOR CHECK	RESULT	ACTION TO TAKE
	* Check the metal shutter wheel for damage and/or dust/grease build up in the slots.	The shutter wheel has no damage and the slots are clean:	
		YES	GO TO JD4
		NO	Repair shutter wheel and rerun SERVICE BAY DIAGNOSTICS.
JD4	COMPONENT CHECK		
	In order to determine were the electrical problem is located the following actions are required:	The ohmmeter needle swings from a low reading to a higher resistance and to low again approximately every nine degrees of steering wheel rotation:	
	* Turn the "STAR" tester "ON/OFF" switch to the "OFF" position.		
	* Turn the air suspension "ON/OFF" switch to the "OFF" position and disconnect the air suspension control module.		
	* Using a jumper wire connect the air suspension control module wiring harness connector pin location #46 to a known good chassis ground.	YES	GO TO JD5
		NO	GO TO JD6
	* Using an analog ohmmeter (set on 1K scale) connect one lead to the control module wiring harness connector pin position #45 (circuit #633) and the other to a known good chassis ground.		
	* Slowly rotate the vehicle's steering wheel.		

FM2019100095020X

Fig. 43 Test JD: Steering Wheel Rotation In Both Directions Not Detected (Part 2 of 4)

JD5	COMPONENT CHECK	RESULT	ACTION TO TAKE
	* Using an analog ohmmeter (set on the 1K scale) connect one lead to the control module wiring harness connector pin position #24 (circuit #634) and the the other to a known good chassis ground.	The ohmmeter needle swings from a low reading to a higher resistance and to low again approximately every nine degrees of steering wheel rotation:	
	* Slowly rotate the vehicle's steering wheel.	YES	Reconnect the air suspension control module and rerun SERVICE BAY DIAGNOSTICS. If the STAR tester still displays code "74" replace the air suspension control module.
		NO	GO TO JD6
JD6	WIRING HARNESS CHECK		
	* Disconnect the steering wheel sensor (located on the lower portion of the steering column) from the vehicle wiring harness.	The voltage reading is battery voltage:	
	* Using a voltmeter connect the positive lead to the steering sensor wiring harness connector circuit #298H and the negative lead to a known good chassis ground.	YES	GO TO JD7
		NO	There is an open in circuit #298H used to supply battery voltage to the steering wheel sensor. Rerun SERVICE BAY DIAGNOSTICS after repair is made.

FM2019100095030X

Fig. 43 Test JD: Steering Wheel Rotation In Both Directions Not Detected (Part 3 of 4)

JD7	WIRING HARNESS CHECK	RESULT	ACTION TO TAKE
	* Using an analog ohmmeter and jumper wire connect one lead to the control module wiring harness connector pin position #46 (circuit #432D) and the other to steering sensor wiring harness connector circuit #432A.	The ohmmeter reading is 5.0 ohms or less:	
		YES	GO TO JD8
		NO	There is an open in circuit #432D/432A. Rerun SERVICE BAY DIAGNOSTICS after repair is made.
JD8	WIRING HARNESS CHECK		
	* Using an analog ohmmeter and jumper wire connect one lead to the control module wiring harness connector pin position #45 (circuit #633) and the other to steering sensor wiring harness connector circuit #633A.	The ohmmeter reading is 5.0 ohms or less:	
		YES	GO TO JD9
		NO	There is an open in circuit #633/#633A. Rerun SERVICE BAY DIAGNOSTICS after repair is made.
JD9	WIRING HARNESS CHECK		
	* Using an analog ohmmeter and jumper wire connect one lead to the control module wiring harness connector pin position #24 (circuit #634) and the other to steering sensor wiring harness connector circuit #634A.	The ohmmeter reading is 5.0 ohms or less:	
		YES	Replace the steering sensor and rerun SERVICE BAY DIAGNOSTICS after repair is made.
		NO	There is an open in circuit #634/#634A. Rerun SERVICE BAY DIAGNOSTICS after repair is made.

FM2019100095040X

Fig. 43 Test JD: Steering Wheel Rotation In Both Directions Not Detected (Part 4 of 4)

JE1	STAR CODE: 75 ACCELERATION SIGNAL NOT DETECTED	RESULT	ACTION TO TAKE
	The air suspension control module has not received the acceleration signal after the "STAR" tester displayed a code "12" or "13". There are four possible causes of the air suspension control module not receiving the acceleration signal:	After the STAR tester displayed a code "12" or "13" the vehicle's accelerator pedal was depressed to the floor:	
	• The accelerator pedal was not fully depressed to the floor at the proper time.	YES ▶	GO TO JE2
	• The accelerator sense circuit may have an open or short in it.	NO ▶	Rerun SERVICE BAY DIAGNOSTICS but this time have the engine running.
	• The EEC-IV module may be defective.		
	• The air suspension control module may be defective.		
JE2	WIRING HARNESS CHECK		
	• Disconnect the 60 pin vehicle wiring harness connector from the engine EEC-IV control module (refer to the shop manual for EEC-IV disconnect instructions).	The voltage reading is:	
	• Using a voltmeter place the positive voltage lead in the EEC-IV wiring harness connector pin location #32 (circuit #637) and the negative lead to battery ground (refer to the shop manual for EEC-IV wiring harness pin location and voltage measuring information).	4.0 to 6.0 volts ▶	GO TO JE3
		0.0 to 0.5 volts ▶	GO TO JE4

FM2019100096010X

Fig. 44 Test JE: Acceleration Signal Not Detected (Part 1 of 2)

JE3	CONTROL MODULE CHECK	RESULT	ACTION TO TAKE
	The acceleration signal detection problem has been narrowed down to either the air suspension control module or the engine EEC-IV control module. In order to determine which one is causing the problem the following actions are required:	The "STAR" tester has displayed the code "72" again:	
	• Rerun the automatic portion of SERVICE BAY DIAGNOSTICS with the engine off and and the engine EEC-IV control module disconnected.	YES ▶	Replace the air suspension control module and rerun SERVICE BAY DIAGNOSTICS.
	• When the STAR tester displays a code "12" or "13" take a jumper wire and connect one end to the EEC-IV wiring harness connector pin location #32 (circuit #637) and the other end to BATTERY GROUND for about three to four seconds. Remove the jumper wire afterwards.	NO ▶	The acceleration signal is not being produced by the engine EEC-IV control module. This may be due to the module itself or the components that generate the signal (vacuum level and throttle position). Refer to the shop manual to determine the corrective action to take. Rerun SERVICE BAY DIAGNOSTICS after repair is made.
	• Perform all the other manual checks and then release the "STAR" test button to the up "HOLD" position. After waiting five seconds depress the "STAR" test button again to the down "TEST" position.		
JE4	WIRING HARNESS CHECK		
	• Release the "STAR" test button so that it remains in the up "HOLD" position and turn the "STAR" tester "OFF".	The ohmmeter reading is less than 5.0 ohms:	
	• Turn the air suspension "ON/OFF" switch to the "OFF" position. Disconnect the suspension control module from the wiring harness connector.	YES ▶	Replace the air suspension control module and rerun SERVICE BAY DIAGNOSTICS.
	• Using an analog ohmmeter connect one lead to the air suspension control module wiring harness connector pin location #28 (circuit #637) and the other lead to the engine EEC-iv control module wiring harness connector pin location #32 (circuit #637).	NO ▶	The acceleration signal circuit #637 has an open in it. Rerun SERVICE BAY DIAGNOSTICS after repair is made.

FM2019100096020X

Fig. 44 Test JE: Acceleration Signal Not Detected (Part 2 of 2)

STEP 1 of 2	SPRING FILL DIAGNOSTICS ENTRANCE PROCEDURE	RESULT	ACTION TO TAKE
	In order to enter/activate SPRING FILL DIAGNOSTICS the following actions are required:	Within twenty seconds the STAR tester will display one of the following codes:	
	• Connect a battery charger to the vehicles battery and leave connected for the duration of the test sequence.		
	• If required release the STAR test button so that it remains in "HOLD" up position.	"21" to "28" ▶	GO TO SPRING FILL DIAGNOSTICS "STEP 2 of 2".
	• Open trunk lid and connect the STAR tester to the air suspension diagnostic connector and turn the STAR tester "ON".	SOMETHING ELSE ▶	GO TO CA1
	• Turn the air suspension "ON/OFF" switch to the "OFF" position and then back to the "ON" position.		
	• Check vehicle passenger compartment and trunk for loads. Remove all loads; vehicle must be at curb weight.		
	• Make sure the ignition switch is in the "OFF" position and wait ten seconds.		
	• With the brake pedal DEPRESSED HARD turn the ignition switch to the "ON/RUN" position (not necessary to start engine) and after 5 seconds release the brake pedal.		
	• Verify that the headlights, heater fan, windshield wipers, ..., etc. are turned off.		
	• Wait a minimum of 5 seconds and then depress the STAR test button so that it remains down in the "TEST" position.		

FM2019100097010X

Fig. 45 Spring fill diagnostic procedure (Part 1 of 2)

STEP 2 of 2	SPRING FILL DIAGNOSTICS ENTERED	RESULT	ACTION TO TAKE
	SPRING FILL DIAGNOSTICS has been entered. In order to select/activate any desired SPRING FILL tests shown release the STAR test button to the up "HOLD" position after the desired code has been displayed for at least 5 seconds. The selected function will continue as long as the STAR test button remains in that position. When the desired amount of venting or inflating has occurred depress the STAR test button down so that it remains in the "TEST" position. This action will stop the test and start the scrolling of test codes again.	STAR tester is displaying the following codes:	
		"21 - Vent Right Front Air Spring"	
		"22 - Vent Left Front Air Spring"	
		"23 - Vent Right Rear Air Spring"	
	NOTE: Each of the spring fill codes to vent or inflate any corner of the vehicle will be displayed in numerical order one at a time. After the largest numerical code is displayed the list will be repeated. This scrolling manner will continue as long as the STAR test button remains in the down "TEST" position.	"24 - Inflate Right Front Air Spring"	
		"25 - Inflate Right Rear Air Spring"	
		"26 - Inflate Right Rear Air Spring"	
		"27 - Vent Left Rear Air Spring"	
		"28 - Inflate Left Rear Air Spring"	
		DESIRED TO EXIT SPRING FILL ▶	Turn the ignition key to the "OFF" position.

FM2019100097020X

Fig. 45 Spring fill diagnostic procedure (Part 2 of 2)

SYSTEM SERVICE

ADJUSTMENT
Ride Height Setup & Measurement

This adjustment must be used prior to front caster and camber alignment or ride height checking.

1. Position vehicle on alignment rack.
2. To ensure ride heights are measured at a consistent point they should be measured only after the service bay diagnostic auto mode has successfully been completed and the Star tester displays a code 12. At this time, place the suspension power switch in the OFF position, remove the Star tester and leave the ignition switch in the RUN position.
3. At this point the vehicle is at the top of the trim band.
4. Measure the front suspension "C" dimension as shown in **Fig. 46**. The front ride height (C) is the vertical difference of the lower arm inner pivot attachment height minus the outer pivot height.
5. Measure the rear suspension "D" dimension as shown in **Fig. 46**. The rear ride height "D" is the vertical difference of the rear lower arm inner pivot attachment height minus the outer pivot height.
6. The suspension heights for the top of the trim band are:
   a. C dimension, 1.72 inch (43.6mm).
   b. D dimension, minus .36 inch (minus 9.3mm).
7. If the suspension heights are not within the listed specifications, ride height adjustment is required.
8. For reference purposes, the ride heights at the center of the trim band are approximately .35 inch (8.8mm) lower than the above suspension heights in the front and approximately .47 inch (12mm) lower in the rear.
9. If adjustment to front ride height is required, it should be performed by replacing the height sensor link according to chart, **Fig. 47**.
10. When removing a link, carefully separate it from the ball stud with a wide blade screwdriver. Do not damage the link or ball stud. When installing a link to the sensor, support the sensor lever from behind to avoid possible damage to the sensor.
11. Rear height sensor adjustment is performed by loosening and repositioning the height sensor lever adjustment screw. For adjustment purposes, each notch on the rear height sensor lever provides approximately .60 inch (15mm) of ride height adjustment.

COMPONENT REPLACEMENT

STEERING SENSOR

The steering sensor is located at the lower end of the steering column. It may be removed with the column in or out of the vehicle. The sensor and sensor ring are separate items.

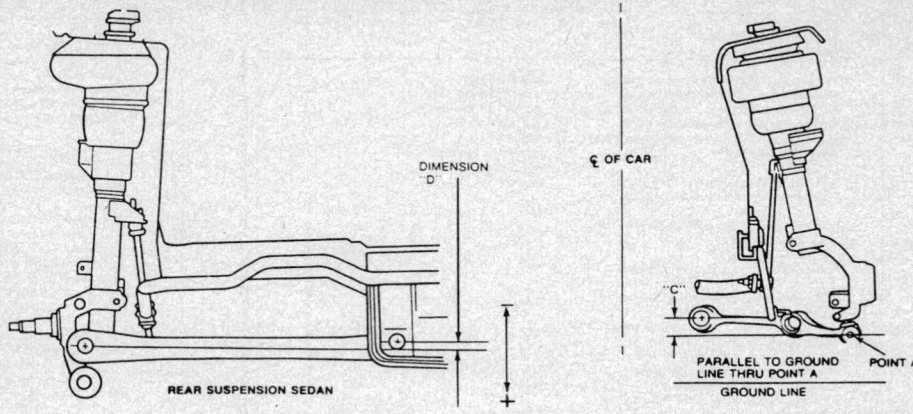

Fig. 46   Ride height setup & measuring

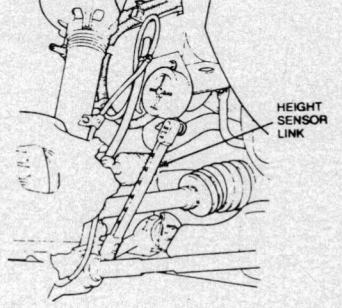

Link Part Number		Height Sensor Link Change	Front Ride Height Affect With Respect To The Nominal Link
LH Front	RH Front		
E80F-3C111-CA	E80F-3C111-GA	Plus One (Green)	+6mm (+0.24 IN)
E80F-3C111-BA	E80F-3C111-FA	Minus One (Red)	-6mm (-0.24 IN)
E80F-3C111-JA	E80F-3C111-KA	Nominal (Blue)	-0-
E80F-3C111-DA	E80F-3C111-HA	Plus Two (Yellow)	+12mm (+0.47 IN)
E80F-3C111-AA	E80F-3C111-EA	Minus Two (White)	-12mm (-0.47 IN)

Fig. 47   Height sensor link specifications chart

1. Disconnect battery ground cable.
2. Disconnect sensor electrical connector from wiring harness.
3. Disconnect sensor electrical connector from shift control cable bracket located under instrument panel.
4. Remove two attaching screws, then the sensor.
5. Reverse procedure to install.

STEERING SENSOR RING

1. Disconnect battery ground cable.
2. Remove steering column.
3. Remove steering shaft from column.
4. Remove sensor ring.
5. Reverse procedure to install.

ACTUATOR

Front

1. Disconnect battery ground cable.
2. Place vehicle on a level surface and apply parking brake.
3. Turn ignition switch to OFF or either LOCK position and raise hood.
4. Remove engine compartment covers.
5. Disconnect actuator electrical connector from wiring harness connector.
6. Remove actuator clips from upper mount attaching studs.
7. Remove two attaching screws retaining actuator to mounting bracket.
8. Remove actuator by lifting off.
9. Reverse procedure to install.

Rear

1. Disconnect battery ground cable.
2. Remove strut assembly from vehicle.
3. Remove actuator.
4. Reverse procedure to install.

AIR SPRING SOLENOID

1. Disconnect battery ground cable.
2. Ensure air suspension service switch is in the ON position.
3. Turn ignition switch to the OFF position.
4. Connect a trickle battery charger to reduce battery drain.
5. Open access door in left side of luggage compartment trim panel to plug Star tester into air suspension diagnostic wiring harness connector.
6. The Star test button should be in the hold (up) position.
7. Press Star test button until it is in the TEST (down) position.
8. At this time the air suspension control module will start sending out spring fill selection codes to be displayed on the Star tester. These codes will be displayed in a scrolling manner. Note the following:
   a. Code 21, describes the right front vent.
   b. Code 22, describes the left front vent.
   c. Code 23, describes the right rear vent.
   d. Code 24, describes the right front compress.
   e. Code 25, describes the left front compress.
   f. Code 26, describes the right rear compress.
   g. Code 27, describes the left rear vent.
   h. Code 28, describes the left rear compress.

9. Select desired spring fill operation by releasing Star button when desired code is displayed. As long as the Star test button is released the desired operation (inflation or deflation) will continue. To stop a selected operation, depress Star button back down to Test position. At this time spring fill codes will again be displayed in a scrolling manner. **When deflating air springs, have vehicle raised off the ground.**
10. Turn the air suspension switch to the OFF position.
11. Remove wheel and tire assembly.
12. Disconnect electrical connector and then the air line.
13. Remove solenoid clip. **The air spring solenoid valve has a two stage solenoid pressure relief fitting similar to a radiator cap. A clip is first removed, and then rotation of the solenoid out of the spring releases air from the assembly before the solenoid can be removed.**
14. Rotate solenoid counterclockwise to the first stop.
15. Pull solenoid straight out slowly to second stop to bleed air from system. **Do not fully release solenoid until all air is completely bled from system.**
16. After air is bled from system, rotate solenoid counterclockwise to the third stop and remove solenoid from air spring assembly.
17. Inspect filter. If very oily, replace filter. **A very oily filter indicates a leaking air strut assembly.**
18. Reverse procedure to install. The following air spring filling procedure must be performed as follows:
   a. Disconnect battery ground cable.
   b. Ensure air suspension service switch is in the ON position.
   c. Turn ignition switch to the OFF position.
   d. Install a battery charger to reduce battery drain.
   e. Open access door in left side of the luggage compartment trim panel to plug Star tester into air suspension diagnostic wiring harness connector.
   f. The Star test button should be in the hold (up) position. With brake pedal depressed hard, turn ignition switch to the RUN position.
   g. Press Star test button until it is in the TEST (down) position.
   h. At this time the air suspension control module will start sending out spring fill selection codes to be displayed on the Star tester. These codes will be displayed in a scrolling manner.
   i. Select the desired spring fill operation by releasing the Star button when the desired code is displayed (as described previously). As long as the Star tester button is re-

leased the desired operation (inflation or deflation) will continue. To stop a selected operation, depress the Star tester button back down to the Test position. At this time the spring fill codes will again be displayed in a scrolling manner. **When installing deflated are springs, lower hoist as required but do not apply a load to the suspension until after the air spring has been inflated at least 60 seconds.**
   j. After completion of operation, exit the spring fill mode by disconnecting the Star tester and turning the ignition switch to the OFF position.

AIR COMPRESSOR & DRYER ASSEMBLY

1. Disconnect battery ground cable.
2. Turn air suspension switch to the OFF position.
3. Disconnect electrical connector located on the compressor.
4. Remove air line protector cap from dryer by releasing two latching pins located on bottom of the cap 180° apart.
5. Disconnect four air lines from dryer.
6. Remove three screws attaching air compressor to mounting bracket.
7. Reverse procedure to install.

AIR COMPRESSOR DRYER

1. Disconnect battery ground cable.
2. Turn air suspension switch to the OFF position.
3. Remove air line protector cap from dryer by releasing two latching pins located on bottom of cap 180° apart.
4. Disconnect four air lines from dryer.
5. Remove dryer from head assembly.
6. Reverse procedure to install.

AIR COMPRESSOR MOUNTING BRACKET

1. Disconnect battery ground cable.
2. Turn air suspension switch OFF.
3. Remove air compressor and dryer assembly.
4. Remove three nuts attaching mounting bracket to body side apron.
5. Reverse procedure to install.

HEIGHT SENSOR

Front

1. Disconnect battery ground cable.
2. Turn air suspension switch OFF.
3. Disconnect sensor electrical connectors. Left front sensor connector is located in the engine compartment behind the shock tower. Right front connector is located in the engine compartment, next to the air compressor.

4. Push front sensor connector through access hole in the rear of the shock tower.
5. Hoist vehicle as described previously.
6. Disconnect bottom and then top end of height sensor link from attaching studs.
7. Disconnect anti-lock wire from bracket.
8. Disconnect brake line from bracket.
9. Remove sensor attaching screws and then the sensor.
10. Reverse procedure to install. **Torque sensor bracket attaching screw to 8-12 ft. lbs.**

Rear

1. Disconnect battery ground cable.
2. Turn air suspension switch OFF.
3. Disconnect sensor electrical connector located in luggage compartment in front of forward trim panel. Also, pull luggage compartment carpet back for access to sensor sealing grommet located on floorpan.
4. Hoist vehicle as described previously.
5. Disconnect bottom and then top end of height sensor link from attaching studs.
6. Remove sensor attaching screws, then the sensor.
7. Reverse procedure to install. **Torque sensor and link assembly attaching screws to 5-6.2 ft. lbs.**

AIR SUSPENSION CONTROL MODULE

1. Disconnect battery ground cable.
2. Turn ignition switch to the OFF position.
3. Turn air suspension switch to the OFF position.
4. Remove left side luggage compartment trim panel.
5. Disconnect wire harness from module. **Use care, harness ground wire is attached to vehicle frame.**
6. Remove upper attaching nuts and loosen two lower nuts.
7. While the module mounting bracket is held to vehicle frame by two lower attaching nuts, slip module from attaching bracket by pulling it toward rear of vehicle.
8. Reverse procedure to install. **Torque wire harness to module attaching screw to 28-35 inch lbs.**

AIR SUSPENSION SWITCH

1. Disconnect battery ground cable.
2. Disconnect electrical connector.
3. Depress retaining clips attaching switch to brace, and remove switch.
4. Reverse procedure to install.

COMPRESSOR RELAY

1. Disconnect battery ground cable.
2. Disconnect electrical connector.
3. Remove screw retaining relay to relay block, then the relay.
4. Reverse procedure to install.

CROWN VICTORIA, GRAND MARQUIS & TOWN CAR

INDEX

PRECAUTIONS

SERVICE

Before servicing an air suspension component, disconnect power to system by turning air suspension switch to Off position or disconnect battery ground cable. Do not remove air spring when there is pressure in air spring. Do not remove air spring supporting components without exhausting air or supporting air spring.

DESCRIPTION

AIR SUSPENSION SYSTEM

The rear air suspension, **Fig. 1**, is an air operated microprocessor controlled, suspension system which replaces the conventional suspension. This system allows low spring rates for improved ride and automatic rear load leveling.

Two air springs replace the conventional steel springs and support the vehicle load at the rear wheels. The air springs are mounted on the axle spring seats and to the frame upper spring seats.

The system is operational when the ignition is in the Run position and is limited for one hour after the ignition has been turned to the Off position. The air suspension switch, located on the right side of the luggage compartment, must in the Off position when the vehicle is on a hoist, being towed or jump started.

The check sir suspension warning lamp is located in the instrument panel message center, to the right of the speedometer. The warning lamp flashes five times and then stays on when the service switch is turned to the Off position or there is a system malfunction.

The rear leveling system operates by adding or removing air in the springs to maintain the level of the vehicle at a predetermined rear suspension "D" ride height dimension and is controlled by a microcomputer module.

The rear air suspension system module also controls the electronic variable orifice (EVO) steering.

The air required for the leveling is distributed from the air compressor to the air springs by a nylon air line which runs from the compressor dryer through a "Y" fitting to each individual air spring.

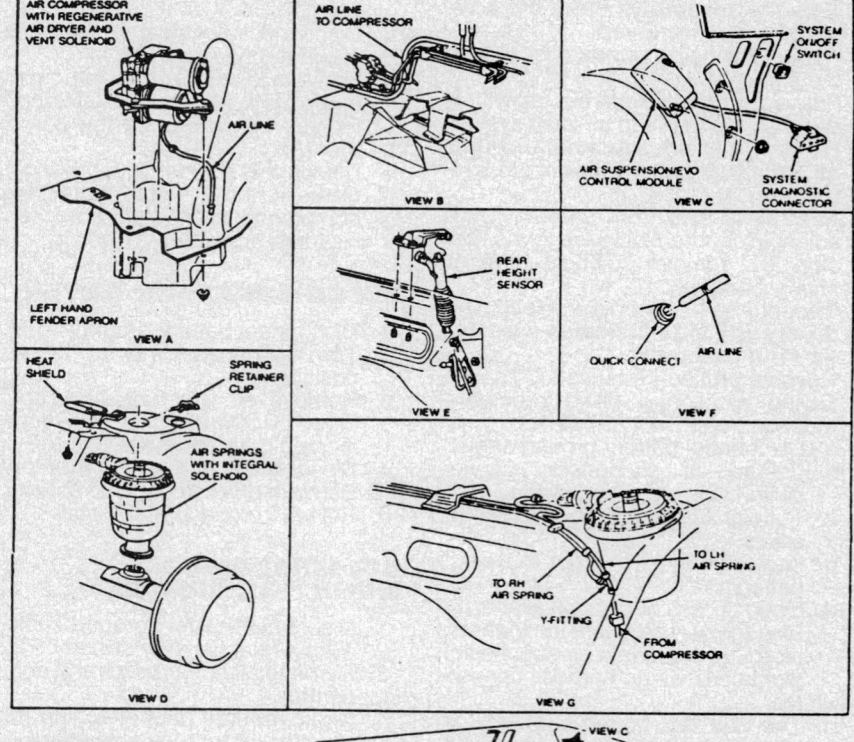

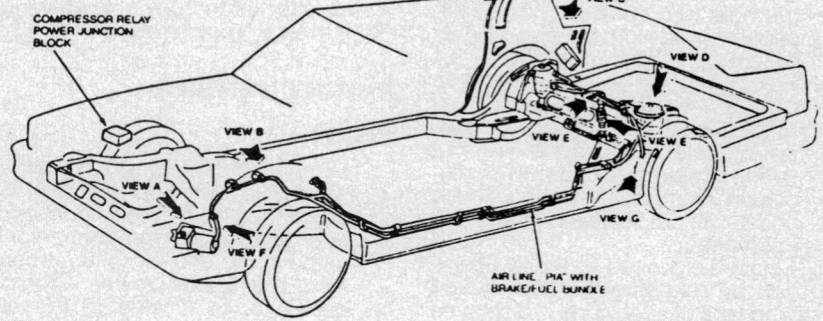

Fig. 1 Air suspension system

FM2019100100000X

AIR COMPRESSOR

The air compressor assembly consists of a compressor and a vent solenoid, both

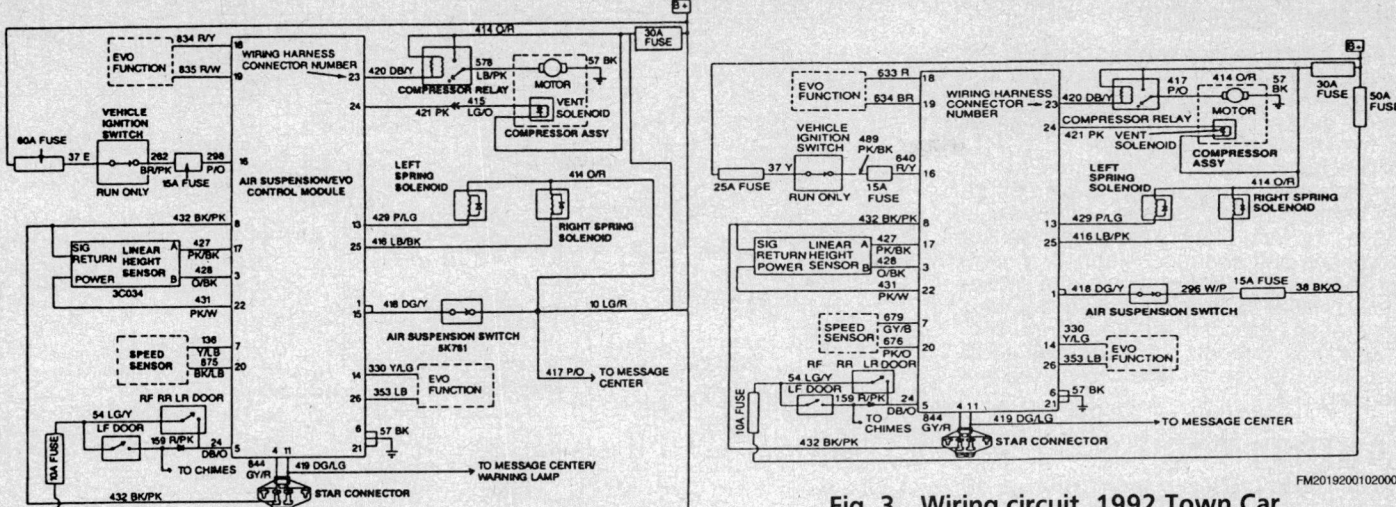

Fig. 2 Wiring circuit. 1992 Crown Victoria & Grand Marquis

Fig. 3 Wiring circuit. 1992 Town Car

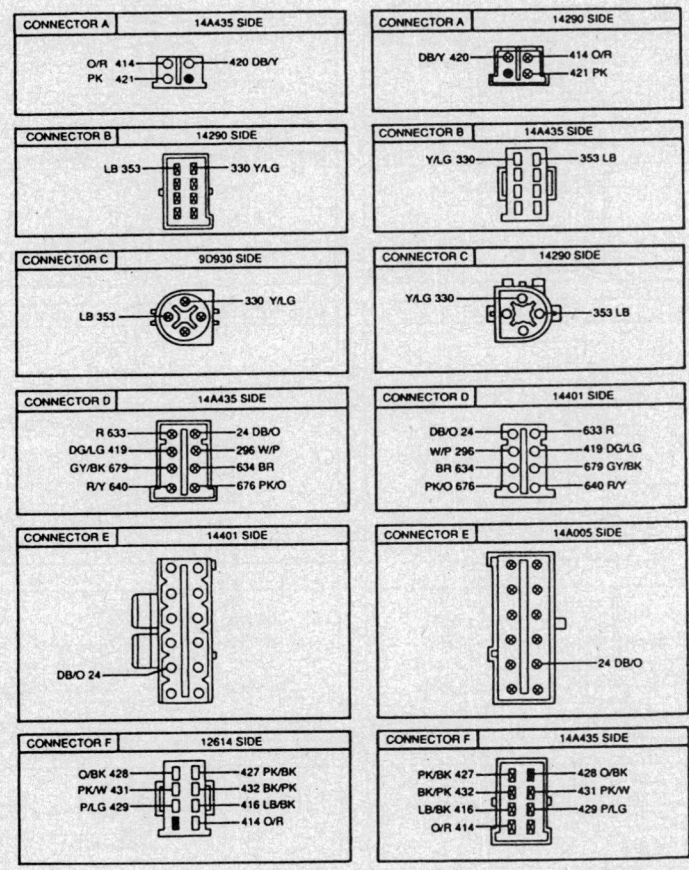

Fig. 4 Connector identification. 1992 Town Car

VENT SOLENOID VALVE

The vent solenoid valve allows air to escape the system during venting corrections. The valve is located in the air compressor head and shares an electrical connector with the motor. The valve is enclosed in the cylinder head casting which forms an integral valve housing which allows the valve tip to enter the pressurized side of the system. Leakage is prevented by an O-ring seal.

The vent valve solenoid opens when, the rear of the vehicle is high and the control module determines lowering is necessary. When the vent solenoid valve is open pressurized air is allowed to escape. However, the vehicle will not lower unless the air spring solenoid valves are also opened to allow air to leave the springs.

The vent solenoid valve has an internal diode for electrical noise suppression and is polarity sensitive. Do not switch battery feed and ground circuits or component damage may result.

AIR SPRING SOLENOID VALVE

The air spring solenoid valve allows air to enter and exit the air spring during leveling. The valve is electrically operated and is controlled by the module. The air spring solenoid valve is completely air tight, therefore the air lines are not required to be air tight. The air lines only contain pressurized air during vent and compress operations.

The valve is a two-stage pressure relief system. A clip is removed and rotation of the solenoid out of the seat will release air from the spring before the solenoid can be removed. **Never rotate an air spring solenoid valve to the release slot in the end fitting until all of the pressurized air has escaped the system.**

COMPRESSOR RELAY

The compressor relay assists the control module in providing the necessary electrical current required to run the compressor motor.

are non-serviceable. The compressor assembly is mounted in the engine compartment on the left fender area below the air cleaner. The air compressor is a single cylinder electric motor which supplies pressurized air as needed. The air compressor is powered by a relay that is controlled by the control module.

The pressurized air from the air compressor passes through the dryer assembly which contains a drying agent (silica gel). The moisture is removed from the air dryer when vented air passes out of the system during vent operation.

HEIGHT SENSOR

The height sensor sends signals to the control module. The three conditions that the control module interprets from the height sensor are that the vehicle is either at, above or below trim height.

The height sensor is attached to the frame crossmember and to the left rear upper control arm. As the rear of the vehicle moves up and down the height sensor lengthens and shortens. Magnets mounted on the lower slide portion of the sensor move relative to the to the sensor housing, generating a signal that is sent to the control module, through two small Hall effect switches that are attached to the sensor housing.

CONTROL MODULE

The module uses approximately a 45 second averaging interval to determine when compress and vent operations are needed. Door inputs can override the 45 second averaging interval, so compress and vent operations can begin immediately. This interval is used to keep the module from making unneeded corrections. The module does not allow any vent operations for the first 45 seconds after the ignition has been turned to the ON position.

DIAGNOSIS & TESTING

The Star Tester model No. 007-0004 or the Super Star II Tester model No. 007-00041 or equivalents, are required to properly diagnose and test this system. **Do not use Super Star Tester model No. 007-00019.** Follow tool manufacturer's instructions for installation and operation of the tool.

Refer to **Figs. 2 through 6** for wiring circuits and connector identification.

SERVICE BAY DIAGNOSTICS

Refer to **Fig. 7,** to perform service bay diagnostic procedures.

AUTO/MANUAL DIAGNOSTIC CHECK

The automatic portion of this test begins with checking the control module for shorts or opens that would create STAR codes 39 through 46, and 68 through 71. If shorts or opens are detected, the automatic portion of the test is over and a STAR code 13, auto test failed, will be displayed. If no shorts or opens are detected, the automatic portion of the test continues. The control module attempts to raise and lower the vehicle to verify that all three height positions can be reached. A normally functioning vehicle will be at trim height by the end of the test. If all three height positions are not reached, the auto test will end and STAR code 13 will be displayed. STAR code 12 will be displayed at the end of the auto test if everything is satisfactory.

After STAR code 12 or 13 is displayed the control module will check for manual inputs. The manual inputs check the steering sensor and the door circuits. To pass

the manual test the control module must detect that all four doors have been opened and closed, and the steering wheel has been turned at least ¼ turn in each direction. After the manual test, the tester must be toggled, or the control module will continue to monitor the manual test inputs indefinitely. Either STAR code 11, air sus-

pension normal, or other STAR codes will be displayed.

STAR CODE DISPLAY

STAR codes will be automatically displayed after the "Auto/Manual Diagnostic Check" is completed. Each code detected will be displayed for about 15 seconds.

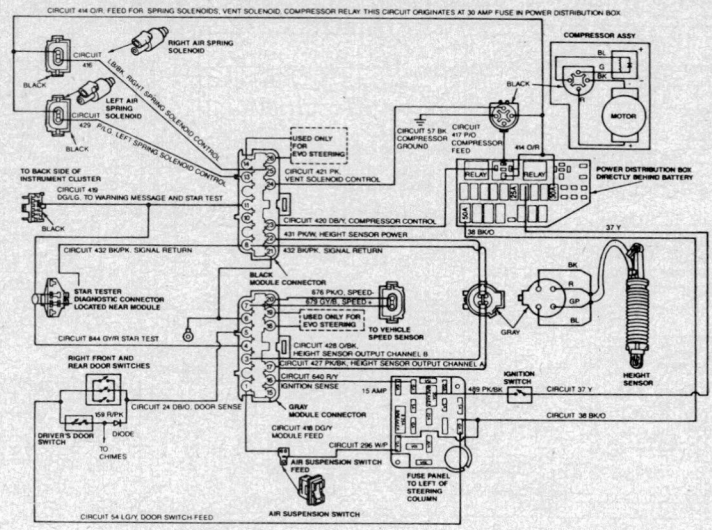

Fig. 5   Wiring circuit. 1993—94 Town Car

FM2019300104000X

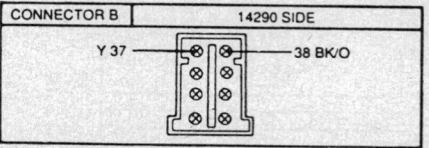
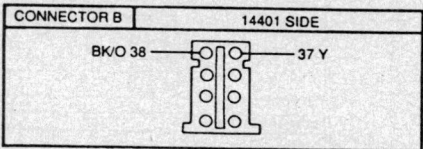
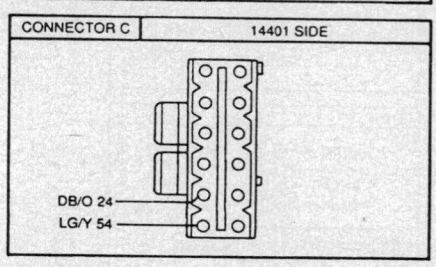
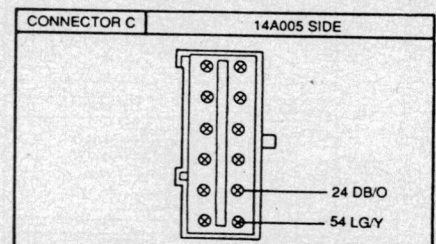
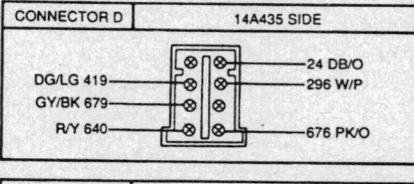
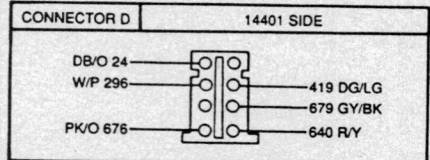
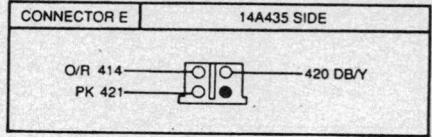
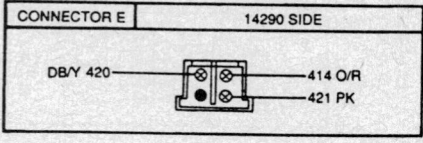

FM2019300105000X

Fig. 6   Connector identification. 1993—94 Town Car

Continued on page 31-135

AIR SUSPENSION, CROWN VICTORIA, GRAND MARQUIS & TOWN CAR

Codes should be recorded at this time, refer to diagnostic code priorities chart, **Fig. 8**.

FUNCTIONAL TESTS

This test is run after the "Auto/Manual Diagnostic Check." Refer to **Fig. 9**, for test procedure.

PINPOINT TESTS

Each trouble code has its own pinpoint test. These tests have priorities assigned with "1" being the highest priority and "4" being the lowest. One malfunction may cause other trouble codes to be displayed. Perform pinpoint tests in order of priority starting with the highest. Refer to **Fig. 8** for Star Diagnostic Codes.

Refer to **Figs. 10 through 28** for Pinpoint Tests.

DIAGNOSTIC CHART INDEX

Test	Description	Page No.	Fig. No.
CROWN VICTORIA & GRAND MARQUIS			
—	Service Bay Diagnostic Procedure	31-118	7
—	Diagnostic Codes & Priority Chart	31-118	8
—	Functional Test	31-119	9
A	Compressor Relay Circuit Shorted To Battery	31-119	10
B	Air Spring Solenoid Shorted To Ground	31-120	12
C	Air Spring Solenoid Shorted To Battery	31-121	14
D	Vent Solenoid Shorted To Battery	31-121	15
E	Compressor Relay Circuit Shorted To Ground Or Vent Solenoid Circuit Shorted To Ground	31-123	17
F	Height Sensor Power Supply Shorted	31-123	19
G	Unable To Detect Lowering Or Rear	31-124	20
H	Unable To Detect Raising Of Rear	31-126	21
J	Sensor Output Circuit Shorted To Ground	31-131	23
K	Height Sensor Circuit Open	31-132	24
L	Four Open And Close Door Signals Not Detected	31-133	25
M	Insufficient Battery Voltage To Run Diagnostics	31-133	26
N	Unable To Enter Service Bay Diagnostics	31-135	28
TOWN CAR			
—	Service Bay Diagnostic Procedure	31-118	7
—	Diagnostic Codes & Priority Chart	31-118	8
—	Functional Test	31-119	9
A	Compressor Relay Circuit Shorted To Battery	31-119	11
B	Air Spring Solenoid Shorted To Ground	31-120	13
C	Air Spring Solenoid Shorted To Battery	31-121	14
D	Vent Solenoid Shorted To Battery	31-122	16
E	Compressor Relay Circuit Shorted To Ground Or Vent Solenoid Circuit Shorted To Ground	31-123	18
F	Height Sensor Power Supply Shorted	31-123	19
G	Unable To Detect Lowering Or Rear	31-124	20
H	Unable To Detect Raising Of Rear	31-129	22
J	Sensor Output Circuit Shorted To Ground	31-131	23
K	Height Sensor Circuit Open	31-132	24
L	Four Open And Close Door Signals Not Detected	31-133	25
M	Insufficient Battery Voltage To Run Diagnostics	31-134	27
N	Unable To Enter Service Bay Diagnostics	31-135	28

SERVICE BAY DIAGNOSTIC PROCEDURE

TEST STEP	RESULT	▶	ACTION TO TAKE
AA1 | **STEP 1** • STAR Tester 007-0004 or SUPER STAR II Tester 007-0041A must be used for this procedure. SUPER STAR Tester 007-00019 may not be used. • Remove all extra loads from luggage and passenger compartments. • Set STAR Tester as follows: STAR: EEC/MCU Setting SUPER STAR II: EEC/MCU Setting, FAST codes • Turn ignition switch OFF. • Turn air suspension switch (RH side of luggage compartment) OFF, then ON. • Remove RH luggage compartment trim panel. • Connect STAR Tester to diagnostic connector. NOTE: Ensure STAR test button is in HOLD (up) position before connecting to vehicle.	STAR CODE 10 displayed STAR CODE 80 displayed No STAR CODES displayed	▶ ▶ ▶	System is in AUTO Test Mode. GO to AA2. GO to Pinpoint Test M. GO to Pinpoint Test N.

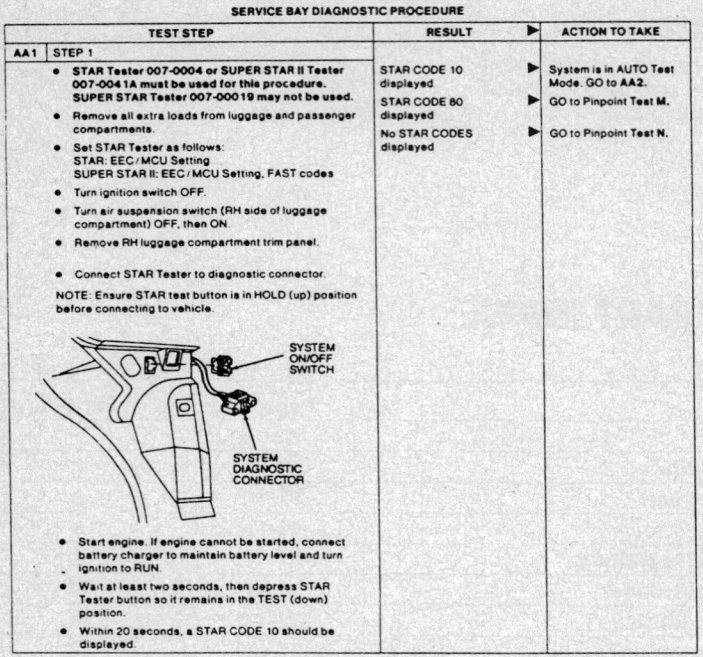

SYSTEM ON/OFF SWITCH

SYSTEM DIAGNOSTIC CONNECTOR

• Start engine. If engine cannot be started, connect battery charger to maintain battery level and turn ignition to RUN.
• Wait at least two seconds, then depress STAR Tester button so it remains in the TEST (down) position.
• Within 20 seconds, a STAR CODE 10 should be displayed.

FM2019200106010X

Fig. 7   Service Bay Diagnostic Procedure, (Part 1 of 2)

SERVICE BAY DIAGNOSTIC PROCEDURE (Continued)

TEST STEP	RESULT	▶	ACTION TO TAKE
AA2 | **STEP 2** • STAR CODE 10 will be displayed for up to two minutes. • DO NOT put any weight on vehicle while STAR CODE 10 is displayed. • When Auto Test is complete a STAR CODE 12 (Auto Test passed) or STAR CODE 13 (Auto Test failed) will be displayed. • With STAR CODE 12 or 13 displayed: —Open and close all four doors sequentially —Turn steering wheel 1/4 turn in both directions. NOTE: The above manual inputs can be done in any sequence. • Release STAR TEST button to HOLD (up) position. • Wait two seconds and depress button to TEST (down) position. • Within 20 seconds STAR CODES will be displayed. NOTE: The STAR CODES will be displayed for about 15 seconds each. After all codes have been displayed, the codes will be repeated. The STAR CODES will continue to repeat as long as the STAR tester button is in the TEST (down) position. • Is STAR CODE 11 displayed?	Yes No	▶ ▶	Vehicle passes. EXIT diagnostics by disconnecting STAR tester and turning ignition off. RECORD STAR CODES. REFER to Air Suspension STAR CODE chart for Pinpoint Tests for STAR CODES displayed. DO NOT disconnect or turn off STAR Tester, ignition switch or air suspension switch. GO to Pinpoint Tests for STAR codes displayed.

FM2019200106020X

Fig. 7   Service Bay Diagnostic Procedure, (Part 2 of 2)

AIR SUSPENSION STAR CODES

Star Code	Pinpoint Test	Description	Service Priority
10		Diagnostics Entered, Auto Test in Progress	
11		Vehicle Passes	
12		Auto Tested Passed	
13		Auto Test Failed	
16		EVO Error Code	
17		EVO Error Code	
18		EVO Error Code	
23		Functional Test, Vent Rear	
26		Functional Test, Compress Rear	
31		Functional Test, Air Compressor Toggle	
32		Functional Test, Vent Solenoid Toggle	
33		Functional Test, Air Spring Solenoid Toggle	
39	A	Compressor Relay Circuit Shorted to Battery	2nd
42	B	Air Spring Solenoid Circuit Shorted to Ground or Blown Fuse	2nd
43	C	Air Spring Solenoid Circuit Shorted to Battery	2nd
44	D	Vent Solenoid Circuit Shorted to Battery	2nd
45	E	Air Compressor Relay Circuit Shorted to Ground or Vent Solenoid Circuit Shorted to Ground	2nd
46	F	Height Sensor Power Supply Circuit Shorted to Ground or Battery	2nd
51	G	Unable to Detect Lowering of Rear	3rd
54	H	Unable to Detect Raising of Rear	3rd
68	J	Height Sensor Output Circuit Shorted to Ground	2nd
70		Replace Air Suspension/EVO Module	
71	K	Open Height Sensor Circuit	3rd
72	L	Four Open and Closed Door Signals Not Detected	4th
74		EVO Error Code	
80	M	Insufficient Battery Voltage to Run Diagnostics	1st
—	N	Unable to Enter Service Bay Diagnostics	

FM2019200107000X

Fig. 8   Diagnostic Codes & Priority Chart

FUNCTIONAL TEST PROCEDURE

TEST STEP	RESULT	▶	ACTION TO TAKE
AB1 STEP 1 • Functional Tests are used in some of the STAR CODE Pinpoint Tests to aid in system diagnosis. • The Functional Test mode can only be entered after Service Bay Diagnostics have been performed. A STAR CODE 11 or any other STAR CODES must be displayed before the Functional Test mode can be entered. • **Are STAR CODES displayed?**	Yes No	▶ ▶	GO to AB2. REPEAT Service Bay Diagnostics. If Service Bay Diagnostics cannot be entered, GO to Pinpoint Test N.
AB2 STEP 2 • Release STAR Tester button to the HOLD (up) position. • Wait at least 20 seconds. • Depress STAR Tester button to the TEST (down) position. • STAR CODE 23 should be displayed, then STAR CODES 26, 31, 32 and 33 will be displayed in order. Each STAR CODE will be displayed for about 15 seconds. After all the STAR CODES are displayed, they will be repeated as long as the STAR Test button is in TEST (down) position. • **Are functional test STAR CODES displayed?**	Yes No	▶ ▶	GO to AB3. RELEASE STAR Tester button to HOLD (up) position. Wait 20 seconds and depress button to TEST (down) position. If Functional Test STAR CODES are still not displayed, REPEAT Service Bay Diagnostics.

FM2019200107010X

Fig. 9   Functional Test (Part 1 of 2)

FUNCTIONAL TEST PROCEDURE (Continued)

TEST STEP	RESULT	▶	ACTION TO TAKE
AB3 STEP 3 • The following chart lists the Functional Test STAR CODES:		▶	RETURN to Pinpoint Test from which you were directed here.

STAR CODE	DESCRIPTION
23	Vent Rear
26	Compress Rear
31	Cycle Compressor on and off repeatedly
32	Cycle vent solenoid valve on and off repeatedly
33	Cycle air spring solenoid valves on and off repeatedly

• Within four seconds after the desired Functional Test STAR CODE is displayed, release the STAR Tester button to the HOLD (up) position.

NOTE: Waiting longer than four seconds will cause the next Function Test to be entered.

• As long as the STAR Tester button is in the HOLD (up) position, the Functional Test will continue.

NOTE: The STAR Tester may or may not display the STAR CODE for the Functional Test selected.

• Example: Functional Test STAR CODE 32 is selected. STAR Tester may display STAR CODE 31, even though Functional Test 32 is being run.
• To exit a Functional Test, depress the STAR Tester button to the TEST (down) position.
• The Functional Test STAR CODES will be displayed. The STAR CODES will be displayed for about 15 seconds each and will be repeated over and over. The Functional Tests may be entered and exited as often as desired.

FM2019200107020X

Fig. 9   Functional Test (Part 2 of 2)

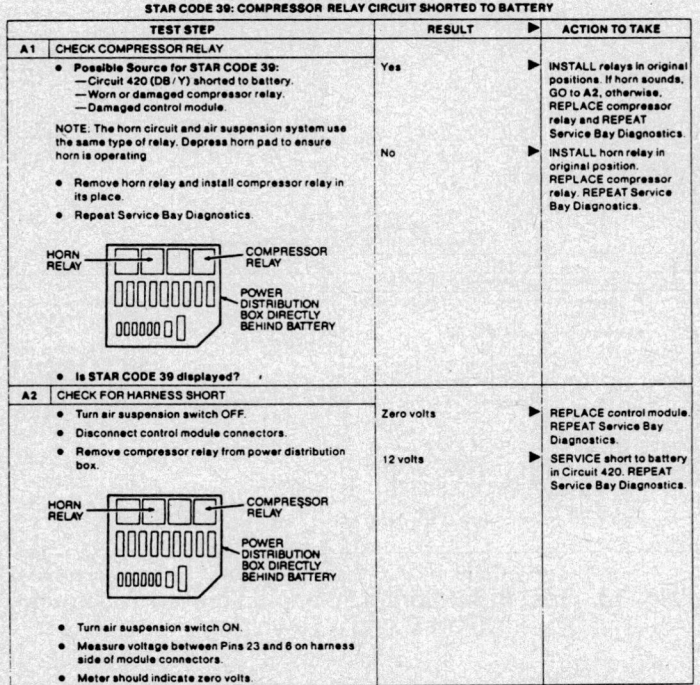

PINPOINT TEST A
STAR CODE 39: COMPRESSOR RELAY CIRCUIT SHORTED TO BATTERY

TEST STEP	RESULT	▶	ACTION TO TAKE
A1 CHECK COMPRESSOR RELAY • Possible Source for STAR CODE 39: —Circuit 420 (DB / Y) shorted to battery. —Worn or damaged compressor relay. —Damaged control module. NOTE: The horn circuit and air suspension system use the same type of relay. Depress horn pad to ensure horn is operating • Remove horn relay and install compressor relay in its place. • Repeat Service Bay Diagnostics. • **Is STAR CODE 39 displayed?**	Yes No	▶ ▶	INSTALL relays in original positions. If horn sounds, GO to A2, otherwise, REPLACE compressor relay and REPEAT Service Bay Diagnostics. INSTALL horn relay in original position. REPLACE compressor relay. REPEAT Service Bay Diagnostics.
A2 CHECK FOR HARNESS SHORT • Turn air suspension switch OFF. • Disconnect control module connectors. • Remove compressor relay from power distribution box. • Turn air suspension switch ON. • Measure voltage between Pins 23 and 6 on harness side of module connectors. • Meter should indicate zero volts.	Zero volts 12 volts	▶ ▶	REPLACE control module. REPEAT Service Bay Diagnostics. SERVICE short to battery in Circuit 420. REPEAT Service Bay Diagnostics.

FM2019200109000X

Fig. 10   Test A: Compressor Relay Circuit Shorted To Battery. Crown Victoria & Grand Marquis

PINPOINT TEST A
STAR CODE 39: COMPRESSOR RELAY CIRCUIT SHORTED TO BATTERY

TEST STEP	RESULT	▶	ACTION TO TAKE
A1 CHECK COMPRESSOR RELAY • Possible Source for STAR CODE 39: —Circuit 420 (DB / Y) shorted to battery —Worn or damaged compressor relay. —Damaged control module. NOTE: The horn circuit and air suspension system use the same type of relay. Depress horn pad to ensure horn is operating • Remove horn relay and install compressor relay in its place. • Repeat Service Bay Diagnostics. • **Is STAR CODE 39 displayed?**	Yes No	▶ ▶	INSTALL relays in original positions. If horn sounds, GO to A2, otherwise, REPLACE compressor relay and REPEAT Service Bay Diagnostics. INSTALL horn relay in original position. REPLACE compressor relay. REPEAT Service Bay Diagnostics.

FM2019200110010X

Fig. 11   Test A: Compressor Relay Circuit Shorted To Battery (Part 1 of 2). Town Car

PINPOINT TEST A
STAR CODE 39: COMPRESSOR
RELAY CIRCUIT SHORTED TO BATTERY (Continued)

TEST STEP	RESULT	▶	ACTION TO TAKE
A2 CHECK FOR HARNESS SHORT			
• Turn air suspension switch OFF.	Zero volts	▶	REPLACE control module. REPEAT Service Bay Diagnostics.
• Disconnect control module connectors.			
• Remove compressor relay from power distribution box.	12 volts	▶	SERVICE short to battery in Circuit 420. REPEAT Service Bay Diagnostics.
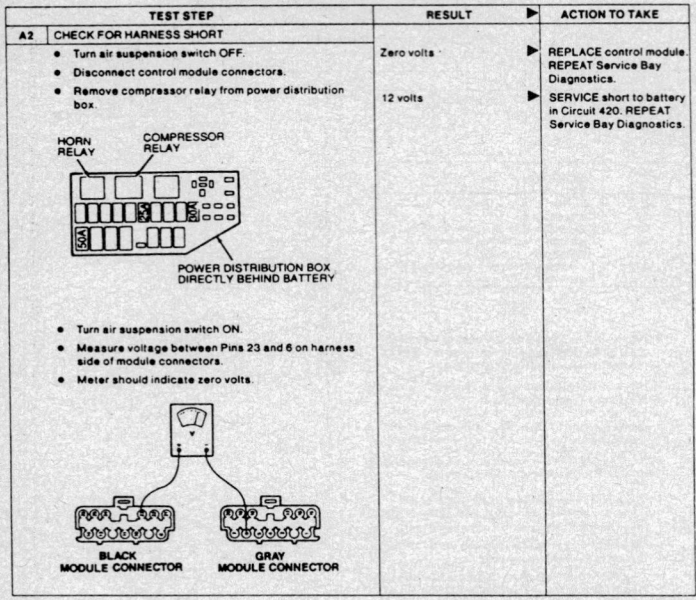			
• Turn air suspension switch ON.			
• Measure voltage between Pins 23 and 6 on harness side of module connectors.			
• Meter should indicate zero volts.			

FM2019200110020X

Fig. 11   Test A: Compressor Relay Circuit Shorted To Battery (Part 2 of 2). Town Car

PINPOINT TEST B
STAR CODE 42: AIR SPRING SOLENOID SHORTED TO GROUND

TEST STEP	RESULT	▶	ACTION TO TAKE
B1 CHECK CIRCUIT 429 (P/LG) FOR SHORT TO GROUND			
• **Possible Source for STAR CODE 42:**	12 volts	▶	GO to B2.
—Circuit 429 (P/LG) shorted to ground.	Zero volts	▶	Circuit 429 (P/LG) has short to ground. GO to B2 before servicing Circuit 429.
—Circuit 416 (LB/BK) shorted to ground.			
—Circuit 414 (O/R) shorted to ground.			
—Damaged control module.			
• Turn air suspension switch OFF.			
• Disconnect module connectors.			
• Turn air suspension switch ON.			
• Measure voltage between Pin 13 and 6 of module connectors.			
• Meter should indicate 12 volts.			
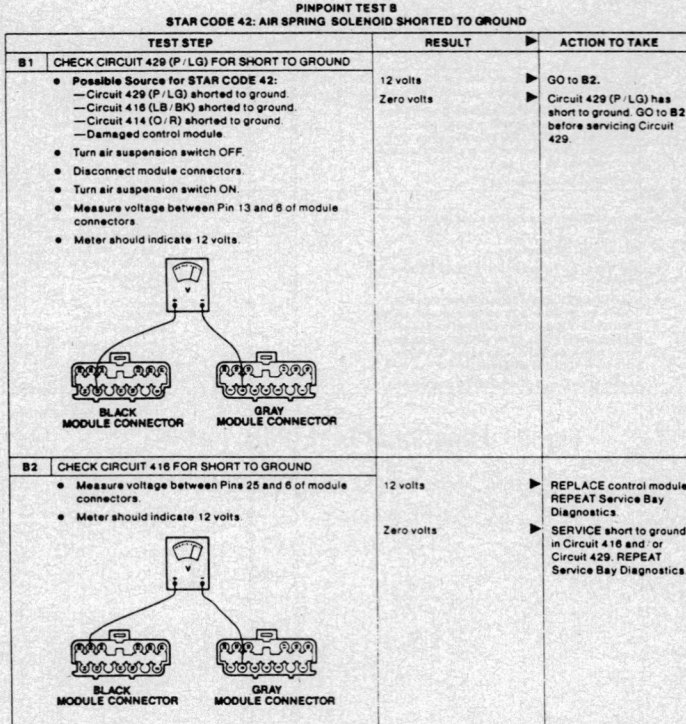			
B2 CHECK CIRCUIT 416 FOR SHORT TO GROUND			
• Measure voltage between Pins 25 and 6 of module connectors.	12 volts	▶	REPLACE control module. REPEAT Service Bay Diagnostics.
• Meter should indicate 12 volts.	Zero volts	▶	SERVICE short to ground in Circuit 416 and/or Circuit 429. REPEAT Service Bay Diagnostics.

FM2019200111000X

Fig. 12   Test B: Air Spring Solenoid Shorted To Ground. Crown Victoria & Grand Marquis

PINPOINT TEST B
STAR CODE 42: AIR SPRING SOLENOID SHORTED TO GROUND

TEST STEP	RESULT	▶	ACTION TO TAKE
B1 CHECK CIRCUIT 429 (P/LG) FOR SHORT TO GROUND			
• **Possible Source for STAR CODE 42:**	12 volts	▶	GO to B2.
—Circuit 429 (P/LG) shorted to ground.	Zero volts	▶	Circuit 429 (P/LG) has short to ground. GO to B2 before servicing Circuit 429.
—Circuit 416 (LB/BK) shorted to ground.			
—Circuit 414 (O/R) shorted to ground.			
—Damaged control module.			
• Turn air suspension switch OFF.			
• Disconnect module connectors.			
• Turn air suspension switch ON.			
• Measure voltage between Pin 13 and 6 of module connectors.			
• Meter should indicate 12 volts.			
NOTE: If Circuit 416 LB/BK or 429 P/LG is shorted to ground, the corresponding spring solenoid valve will always be open, even with the ignition OFF.			
B2 CHECK 30 AMP FUSE			
• Remove and inspect 30 amp fuse for Circuit 414 O/R (located in power distribution box).	Fuse not blown	▶	GO to B3.
	Fuse blown	▶	SERVICE short to ground in Circuit 414 O/R. REPLACE 30 amp fuse.
			NOTE: Circuit 414 (O/R) feeds power to the spring solenoids, vent solenoid and compressor relay. Check for shorts at the compressor assembly.
			REPEAT Service Bay Diagnostics.

FM2019200112010X

Fig. 13   Test B: Air Spring Solenoid Shorted To Ground (Part 1 of 2). Town Car

PINPOINT TEST B
STAR CODE 42: AIR SPRING SOLENOID SHORTED TO GROUND (Continued)

TEST STEP	RESULT	▶	ACTION TO TAKE
B3 CHECK CIRCUIT 416 FOR SHORT TO GROUND			
• Measure voltage between Pins 25 and 6 of module connectors.	12 volts	▶	REPLACE control module. REPEAT Service Bay Diagnostics.
• Meter should indicate 12 volts.	Zero volts	▶	SERVICE short to ground in Circuit 416 and/or Circuit 429. REPEAT Service Bay Diagnostics.

FM2019200112020X

Fig. 13   Test B: Air Spring Solenoid Shorted To Ground (Part 2 of 2). Town Car

PINPOINT TEST C
STAR CODE 43: AIR SPRING
SOLENOID SHORTED TO BATTERY

TEST STEP	RESULT	▶	ACTION TO TAKE
C1 CHECK LH AIR SPRING SOLENOID CIRCUIT			
• **Possible Source for STAR CODE 43:** —Damaged air spring solenoid(s). —Circuit 416 (LB/BK) shorted to battery. —Circuit 429 (P/LG) shorted to battery —Wire terminals for circuits 414 (O/R) and 416 (LB/BK) or 414 (O/R) and 429 (P/LG) reversed at air spring solenoid connectors. —Damaged control module.	Higher reading is 15 to 18 ohms, lower reading is 5 to 10 ohms below higher reading	▶	Solenoid and wiring OK. GO to C2.
	Both readings are the same, zero to 18 ohms	▶	SERVICE LH air spring solenoid or wiring. GO to C2.
NOTE: The resistance measurements in this procedure check the condition of the air spring solenoid valve coil and diode. A digital ohmmeter will not pass enough current through the diode to check its condition. Use Rotunda Inductive Dwell-Tach-Volt-Ohm Tester 059-00010 or equivalent analog (needle-type) meter. • Turn air suspension switch OFF. • Disconnect control module connectors. • Turn air suspension switch ON. NOTE: Air suspension switch must be ON for this test. • Measure resistance between Pins 13 and 1 on module connectors. • Reverse leads and measure resistance again between Pins 13 and 1. • Meter should indicate 15 to 18 ohms one way, and 5 to 10 ohms less the other way.			

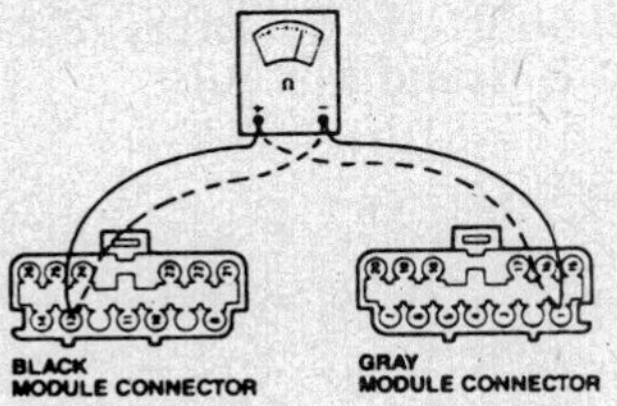

FM2019200113010X

Fig. 14   Test C: Air Spring Solenoid Shorted To Battery (Part 1 of 3)

PINPOINT TEST C
STAR CODE 43: AIR SPRING
SOLENOID SHORTED TO BATTERY (Continued)

TEST STEP	RESULT	▶	ACTION TO TAKE
C2 CHECK RH AIR SPRING SOLENOID VALVE CIRCUIT 416 (LB/BK)			
• Air suspension switch must be ON for this test. • Measure resistance between Pins 25 and 1 on module connectors. • Reverse leads and measure resistance again between Pins 25 and 1. • Meter should indicate 15 to 18 ohms one way, and 5 to 10 ohms less the other way.	Higher reading is 15 to 18 ohms, lower reading is 5 to 10 ohms below higher reading and LH air spring solenoid was OK in Test Step C1	▶	REPLACE control module. REPEAT Service Bay Diagnostics.
	Both readings the same for this step and/or Test Step C1	▶	GO to C3.

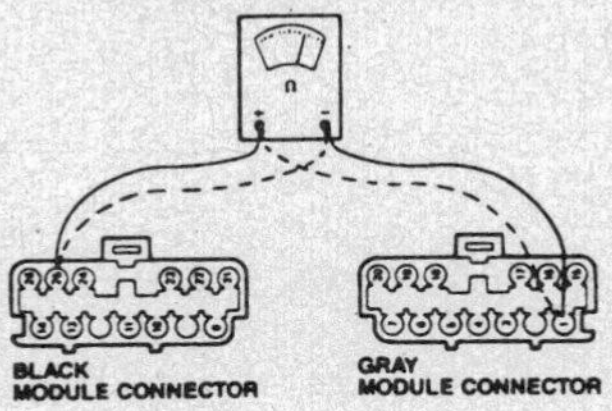

FM2019200113020X

Fig. 14   Test C: Air Spring Solenoid Shorted To Battery (Part 2 of 3)

PINPOINT TEST C
STAR CODE 43: AIR SPRING
SOLENOID SHORTED TO BATTERY (Continued)

TEST STEP	RESULT	▶	ACTION TO TAKE
C3 CHECK FOR SHORT TO BATTERY AND REVERSED CIRCUITS			
• Air suspension switch must be ON and control module connectors disconnected. • Raise vehicle on hoist. • Disconnect air spring solenoid valve connector. • Inspect connector to ensure that Circuit 414 (O/R) and 416 (LB/BK) or 414 (O/R) and 429 (P/LG) are not reversed in the connector.	Circuit 416 (LB/BK) or 429 (P/LG) at zero volts	▶	REPLACE air spring solenoids. REPEAT Service Bay Diagnostics.
	Battery voltage at Circuit 414 (O/R) and Circuit 416 (LB/BK) or 429 (P/LG)	▶	SERVICE short to battery in Circuit 416 (LB/BK) and/or 429 (P/LG). REPEAT Service Bay Diagnostics.
	Circuits reversed in connector	▶	INSTALL circuits in correct terminals. REPEAT Service Bay Diagnostics.

• Measure voltage between Circuit 416 (LB/BK) and ground and/or Circuit 429 (P/LG) and ground.
• Meter should indicate zero volts.
• Measure voltage between Circuit 414 (O/R) and ground.
• Meter should indicate battery voltage.

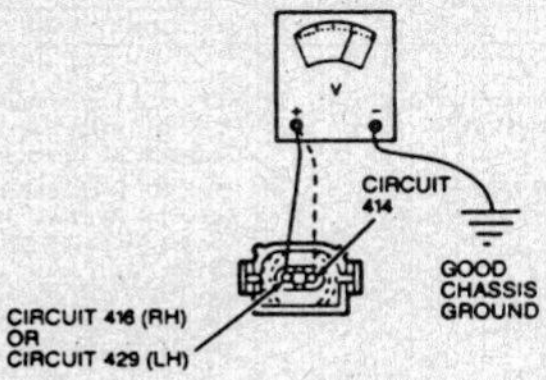

FM2019200113030X

Fig. 14   Test C: Air Spring Solenoid Shorted To Battery (Part 3 of 3)

PINPOINT TEST D
STAR CODE 44: VENT SOLENOID SHORTED TO BATTERY

TEST STEP	RESULT	▶	ACTION TO TAKE
D1 CHECK HARNESS			
• **Possible Source for STAR CODE 44:** —Circuit 421 (PK) shorted to battery. —Damaged vent solenoid. —Circuits 414 (O/R) and 421 (P/K) reversed in connector at air compressor. —Damaged module.	Yes	▶	GO to D2.
	No	▶	REPLACE as required.
NOTE: The resistance measurements in this procedure check the condition of the vent solenoid valve coil and diode. A digital ohmmeter will not pass enough current through the diode to check its condition. Use Rotunda Inductive Dwell-Tach-Volt-Ohm Tester 059-00010 or equivalent analog (needle-type) meter. • Remove air cleaner assembly and plastic shield protecting air compressor assembly as outlined. • Disconnect air compressor connector. • Inspect connector for obvious damage or corrosion. Ensure that wire terminals are located correctly and fully seated in connector.			

• Inspect air compressor assembly connector to ensure it is wired correctly.

• Are harness connectors functional?

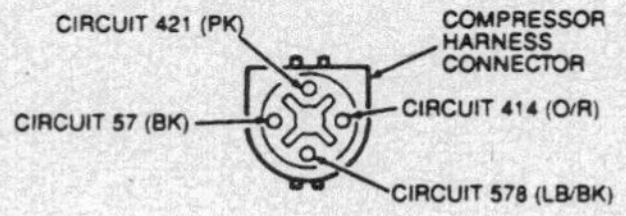

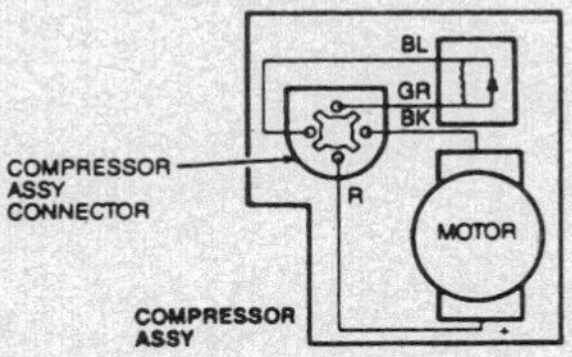

FM2019200114010X

Fig. 15   Test D: Vent Solenoid Shorted To Battery (Part 1 of 3). Crown Victoria & Grand Marquis

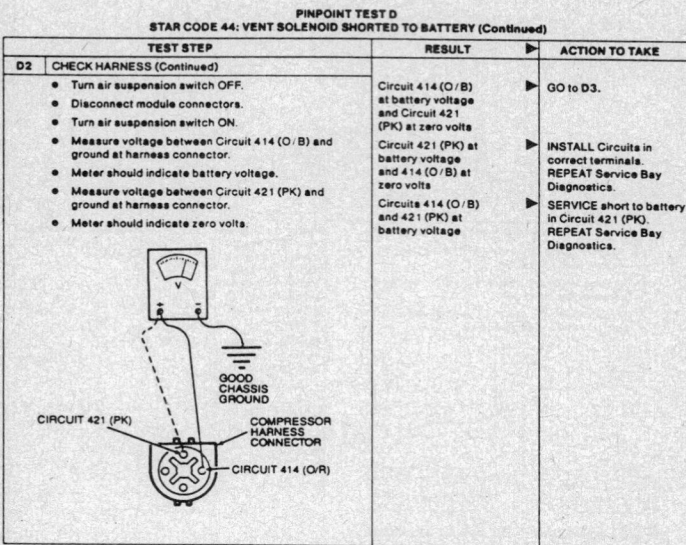

PINPOINT TEST D
STAR CODE 44: VENT SOLENOID SHORTED TO BATTERY (Continued)

TEST STEP	RESULT	▶	ACTION TO TAKE
D2 CHECK HARNESS (Continued) • Turn air suspension switch OFF. • Disconnect module connectors. • Turn air suspension switch ON. • Measure voltage between Circuit 414 (O/B) and ground at harness connector. • Meter should indicate battery voltage. • Measure voltage between Circuit 421 (PK) and ground at harness connector. • Meter should indicate zero volts.	Circuit 414 (O/B) at battery voltage and Circuit 421 (PK) at zero volts	▶	GO to D3.
	Circuit 421 (PK) at battery voltage and 414 (O/B) at zero volts	▶	INSTALL Circuits in correct terminals. REPEAT Service Bay Diagnostics.
	Circuits 414 (O/B) and 421 (PK) at battery voltage	▶	SERVICE short to battery in Circuit 421 (PK). REPEAT Service Bay Diagnostics.

FM2019200114020X

Fig. 15 Test D: Vent Solenoid Shorted To Battery (Part 2 of 3). Crown Victoria & Grand Marquis

PINPOINT TEST D
STAR CODE 44: VENT SOLENOID SHORTED TO BATTERY (Continued)

TEST STEP	RESULT	▶	ACTION TO TAKE
D3 CHECK RESISTANCE OF VENT SOLENOID • Measure resistance between blue wire and green wire on compressor assembly connector. • Reverse leads and measure resistance again between blue and green wires. • Meter should indicate 25 to 35 ohms one way, less than 25 ohms the other way.	Highest reading is 25 to 35 ohms	▶	REPLACE control module. REPEAT Service Bay Diagnostics.
	Both readings are less than 25 ohms	▶	REPLACE compressor assembly. REPEAT Service Bay Diagnostics. If STAR CODE 44 is repeated, REPLACE control module. REPEAT Service Bay Diagnostics.

FM2019200114030X

Fig. 15 Test D: Vent Solenoid Shorted To Battery (Part 3 of 3). Crown Victoria & Grand Marquis

PINPOINT TEST D
STAR CODE 44: VENT SOLENOID SHORTED TO BATTERY

TEST STEP	RESULT	▶	ACTION TO TAKE
D1 CHECK HARNESS • Possible Source for STAR CODE 44: —Circuit 421 (PK) shorted to battery. —Damaged vent solenoid. —Circuits 414 (O/R) and 421 (P/K) reversed in connector at air compressor. —Damaged module.	Yes	▶	GO to D2.
	No	▶	REPLACE as required.

NOTE: The resistance measurements in this procedure check the condition of the vent solenoid valve coil and diode. A digital ohmmeter will not pass enough current through the diode to check its condition. Use Rotunda Inductive Dwell-Tach-Volt-Ohm Tester 059-000 10 or equivalent analog (needle-type) meter.

- Remove air cleaner assembly and plastic shield protecting air compressor assembly as outlined
- Disconnect air compressor connector.
- Inspect connector for obvious damage or corrosion. Ensure that wire terminals are located correctly and fully seated in connector.

- Inspect air compressor assembly connector to ensure it is wired correctly.

- Are harness connectors functional?

FM2019200115010X

Fig. 16 Test D: Vent Solenoid Shorted To Battery (Part 1 of 3). Town Car

PINPOINT TEST D
STAR CODE 44: VENT SOLENOID SHORTED TO BATTERY (Continued)

TEST STEP	RESULT	▶	ACTION TO TAKE
D2 CHECK HARNESS (Continued) • Turn air suspension switch OFF. • Disconnect vent solenoid connector. • Turn air suspension switch ON. • Measure voltage between Circuit 414 (O/B) and ground at harness connector. • Meter should indicate battery voltage. • Measure voltage between Circuit 421 (PK) and ground at harness connector. • Meter should indicate zero volts.	Circuit 414 (O/B) at battery voltage and Circuit 421 (PK) at zero volts	▶	GO to D3.
	Circuit 421 (PK) at battery voltage and 414 (O/B) at zero volts	▶	INSTALL Circuits in correct terminals. REPEAT Service Bay Diagnostics.
	Circuits 414 (O/B) and 421 (PK) at battery voltage	▶	SERVICE short to battery in Circuit 421 (PK). REPEAT Service Bay Diagnostics.

FM2019200115020X

Fig. 16 Test D: Vent Solenoid Shorted To Battery (Part 2 of 3). Town Car

PINPOINT TEST D
STAR CODE 44: VENT SOLENOID SHORTED TO BATTERY (Continued)

TEST STEP	RESULT	▶	ACTION TO TAKE
D3 CHECK RESISTANCE OF VENT SOLENOID • Measure resistance between B wire and G wire on compressor assembly connector. • Reverse leads and measure resistance again between blue and green wires. • Meter should indicate 25 to 35 ohms one way, less than 25 ohms the other way.	Highest reading is 25 to 35 ohms	▶	REPLACE control module. REPEAT Service Bay Diagnostics.
	Both readings are less than 25 ohms	▶	REPLACE compressor assembly. REPEAT Service Bay Diagnostics. If STAR CODE 44 is repeated, REPLACE control module. REPEAT Service Bay Diagnostics.

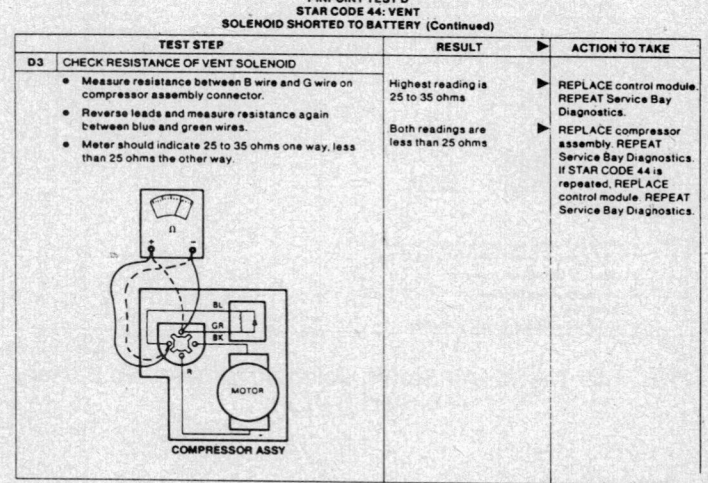

FM2019200115030X

Fig. 16 Test D: Vent Solenoid Shorted To Battery (Part 3 of 3). Town Car

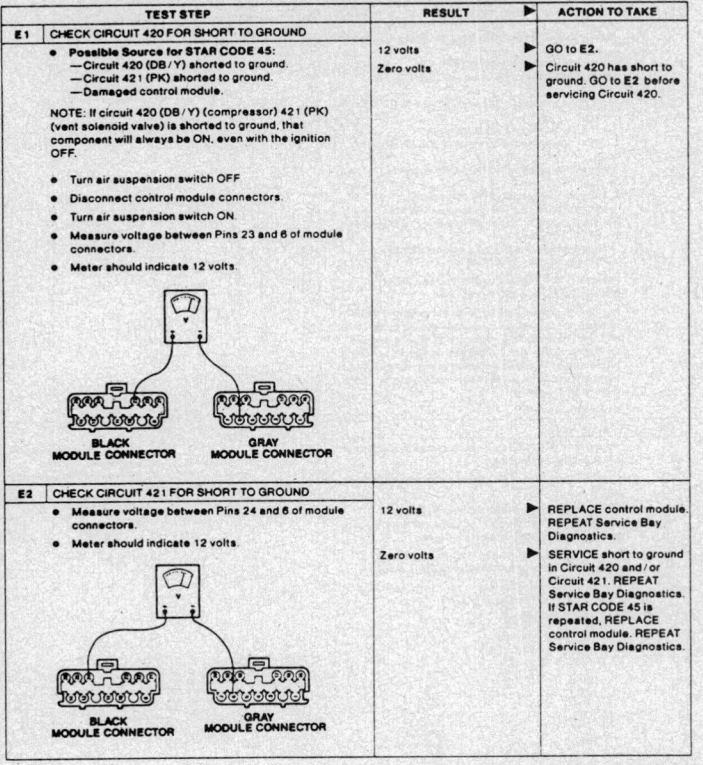

PINPOINT TEST E
STAR CODE 45: COMPRESSOR RELAY CIRCUIT SHORTED TO GROUND OR VENT SOLENOID CIRCUIT SHORTED TO GROUND

TEST STEP	RESULT	▶	ACTION TO TAKE
E1 CHECK CIRCUIT 420 FOR SHORT TO GROUND			
• **Possible Source for STAR CODE 45:** —Circuit 420 (DB / Y) shorted to ground. —Circuit 421 (PK) shorted to ground. —Damaged control module. NOTE: If circuit 420 (DB/Y) (compressor) 421 (PK) (vent solenoid valve) is shorted to ground, that component will always be ON, even with the ignition OFF. • Turn air suspension switch OFF. • Disconnect control module connectors. • Turn air suspension switch ON. • Measure voltage between Pins 23 and 6 of module connectors. • Meter should indicate 12 volts.	12 volts Zero volts	▶ ▶	GO to E2. Circuit 420 has short to ground. GO to E2 before servicing Circuit 420.
E2 CHECK CIRCUIT 421 FOR SHORT TO GROUND			
• Measure voltage between Pins 24 and 6 of module connectors. • Meter should indicate 12 volts.	12 volts Zero volts	▶ ▶	REPLACE control module. REPEAT Service Bay Diagnostics. SERVICE short to ground in Circuit 420 and / or Circuit 421. REPEAT Service Bay Diagnostics. If STAR CODE 45 is repeated, REPLACE control module. REPEAT Service Bay Diagnostics.

FM2019200116000X

Fig. 17   Test E: Compressor Relay Circuit Shorted To Ground Or Vent Solenoid Circuit Shorted To Ground. Crown Victoria & Grand Marquis

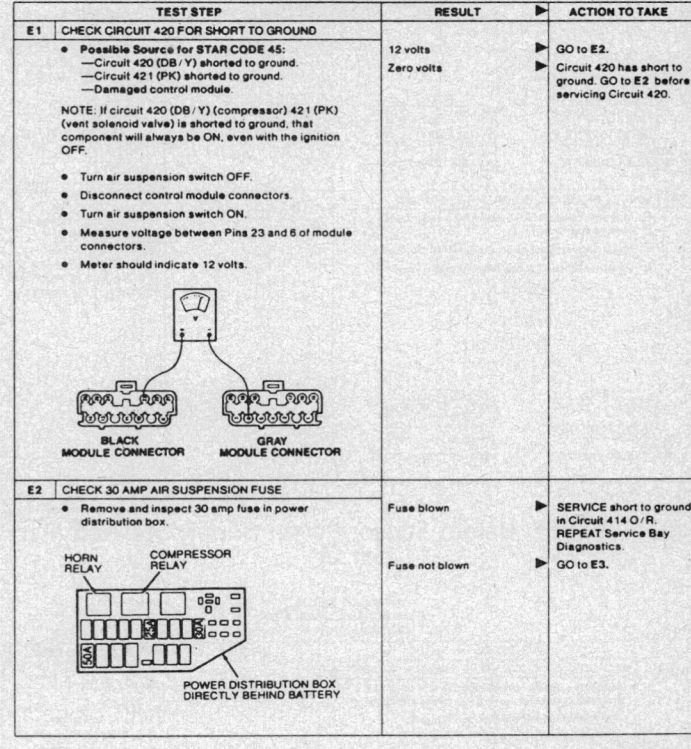

PINPOINT TEST E
STAR CODE 45: COMPRESSOR RELAY CIRCUIT SHORTED TO GROUND OR VENT SOLENOID CIRCUIT SHORTED TO GROUND

TEST STEP	RESULT	▶	ACTION TO TAKE
E1 CHECK CIRCUIT 420 FOR SHORT TO GROUND			
• **Possible Source for STAR CODE 45:** —Circuit 420 (DB / Y) shorted to ground. —Circuit 421 (PK) shorted to ground. —Damaged control module. NOTE: If circuit 420 (DB/Y) (compressor) 421 (PK) (vent solenoid valve) is shorted to ground, that component will always be ON, even with the ignition OFF. • Turn air suspension switch OFF. • Disconnect control module connectors. • Turn air suspension switch ON. • Measure voltage between Pins 23 and 6 of module connectors. • Meter should indicate 12 volts.	12 volts Zero volts	▶ ▶	GO to E2. Circuit 420 has short to ground. GO to E2 before servicing Circuit 420.
E2 CHECK 30 AMP AIR SUSPENSION FUSE			
• Remove and inspect 30 amp fuse in power distribution box.	Fuse blown Fuse not blown	▶ ▶	SERVICE short to ground in Circuit 414 O / R. REPEAT Service Bay Diagnostics. GO to E3.

FM2019200117010X

Fig. 18   Test E: Compressor Relay Circuit Shorted To Ground Or Vent Solenoid Circuit Shorted To Ground (Part 1 of 2). Town Car

PINPOINT TEST E
STAR CODE 45: COMPRESSOR RELAY CIRCUIT SHORTED TO GROUND OR VENT SOLENOID CIRCUIT SHORTED TO GROUND (Continued)

TEST STEP	RESULT	▶	ACTION TO TAKE
E3 CHECK CIRCUIT 421 FOR SHORT TO GROUND			
• Measure voltage between Pins 24 and 6 of module connectors. • Meter should indicate 12 volts.	12 volts Zero volts	▶ ▶	REPLACE control module. REPEAT Service Bay Diagnostics. SERVICE short to ground in Circuit 420 and / or Circuit 421. REPEAT Service Bay Diagnostics. If STAR CODE 45 is repeated, REPLACE control module. REPEAT Service Bay Diagnostics.

FM2019200117020X

Fig. 18   Test E: Compressor Relay Circuit Shorted To Ground Or Vent Solenoid Circuit Shorted To Ground (Part 2 of 2). Town Car

PINPOINT TEST F
STAR CODE 46: HEIGHT SENSOR POWER SUPPLY SHORTED

TEST STEP	RESULT	▶	ACTION TO TAKE
F1 CHECK SENSOR			
• **Possible Source for STAR CODE 46:** —Circuit 431 (PK / W) shorted to ground. —Circuit 431 (PK / W) shorted to battery. —Circuits 431 (PK / W) and 432 (BK / PK) reversed in connector at height sensor. —Damaged control module. • Turn air suspension switch OFF. • Raise vehicle on hoist. • Disconnect height sensor electrical connector. • Lower vehicle. • Turn air suspension switch ON. • Perform Service Bay Diagnostics. • Ignore all STAR CODES except Code 46. • Is error code 46 received?	Yes No	▶ ▶	GO to F2. REPLACE height sensor. REPEAT Service Bay Diagnostics. If STAR CODE 46 is again received, REPLACE control module. REPEAT Service Bay Diagnostics.

FM2019200118010X

Fig. 19   Test F: Height Sensor Power Supply Shorted (Part 1 of 2)

TEST STEP	RESULT	▶	ACTION TO TAKE
F2 CHECK CIRCUIT 431 FOR SHORT TO BATTERY			
• Turn air suspension switch OFF.	Zero volts	▶	GO to F3.
• Disconnect control module connectors.	12 volts	▶	SERVICE short to battery in Circuit 431. REPEAT Service Bay Diagnostics.
• Turn air suspension switch ON.			
• Measure voltage between Pins 22 and 6 of module connectors.			
• Meter should indicate zero volts.			
F3 CHECK CIRCUIT 431 FOR SHORT TO GROUND			
• Measure resistance between Pins 22 and 6 of module connectors.	Yes	▶	REPLACE control module. REPEAT Service Bay Diagnostics.
• Meter should indicate greater than 10,000 ohms.	No	▶	SERVICE short to ground in Circuit 431. REPEAT Service Bay Diagnostics.
• Does meter read more than 10,000 ohms?			

FM2019200118020X

Fig. 19   Test F: Height Sensor Power Supply Shorted (Part 2 of 2)

TEST STEP	RESULT	▶	ACTION TO TAKE
G3 CHECK VENT SOLENOID VALVE CIRCUIT 414 (O/R)			
• Measure voltage between Circuit 414 (O/R) at harness connector and a good chassis ground.	Yes	▶	GO to G4.
• Meter should indicate battery voltage.	No	▶	SERVICE open in Circuit 414 (O/R). REPEAT Service Bay Diagnostics.
• Is there battery voltage?			
G4 CHECK CIRCUIT 421 (PK) FOR OPEN			
• Turn air suspension switch OFF.	Yes	▶	REPLACE control module. REPEAT Service Bay Diagnostics.
• Disconnect module connectors.	No	▶	SERVICE open in Circuit 421 (PK). REPEAT Service Bay Diagnostics.
• Measure resistance between Circuit 421 (PK) at compressor connector and Pin 24 of module connector.			
• Meter should indicate less than 10 ohms.			
• Is resistance less than 10 ohms?			
G5 CHECK AIR SPRING SOLENOID VALVES			
• Enter STAR Tester Functional Test 33. Refer to Service Bay Diagnostics.	Valves cycle	▶	GO to G10.
• Leave air suspension switch ON and raise vehicle on hoist.	One or both valves do not cycle	▶	DO NOT EXIT Functional Test 33. GO to G6.
• Feel each spring solenoid valve to see if they are cycling ON and OFF. A clicking noise will be heard when they cycle, but each valve must be felt to ensure both are operating.			

FM2019200119020X

Fig. 20   Test G: Unable To Detect Lowering Or Rear (Part 2 of 8)

TEST STEP	RESULT	▶	ACTION TO TAKE
G1 PERFORM FUNCTIONAL TEST			
• Possible Source for STAR CODE 51:	Yes	▶	GO to G5.
—Vent solenoid valve control Circuit 421 (PK) has an open.	No	▶	GO to G2.
—Vent solenoid valve battery Circuit 414 (O/R) has an open.			
—Vent solenoid valve damaged.			
—LH spring solenoid Circuit 429 (PK/LG) has an open.			
—LH spring solenoid battery Circuit 414 (O/R) has an open.			
—LH spring solenoid valve damaged.			
—RH spring solenoid Circuit 416 (DB/BK) has an open.			
—RH spring solenoid battery Circuit 414 (O/R) has an open.			
—RH spring solenoid valve damaged.			
—Height sensor may be disconnected from one or both ball studs, or upper attachment bracket is bent.			
—Air lines blocked.			
—Compressor dryer or air passages blocked.			
—Control module damaged.			
• Perform STAR Tester Functional Test. Refer to Service Bay Diagnostic Procedure.			
• During Functional Test 32, the vent solenoid valve located in compressor assembly should cycle ON and OFF repeatedly (one second ON, one second OFF) during the test. As the valve cycles, a clicking noise can be heard by listening at the front of the LH front wheel opening. This test must be performed in a quiet environment.			
• Does valve cycle?			
G2 CHECK HARNESS			
• Remove air cleaner intake tube and air compressor plastic shield as outlined.	Yes	▶	REPLACE compressor assembly. REPEAT Service Bay Diagnostics.
• Inspect compressor for obvious signs of water entry.	No	▶	GO to G3.
• Disconnect compressor connector. Inspect connector for corrosion or obvious damage. Ensure terminals are fully seated in connector.			
• Measure voltage between Circuit 421 (PK) in harness connector and a good chassis ground.			
• Meter should pulse between zero volts and battery voltage (during functional test 32).			
• Does voltage pulse?			

FM2019200119010X

Fig. 20   Test G: Unable To Detect Lowering Or Rear (Part 1 of 8)

TEST STEP	RESULT	▶	ACTION TO TAKE
G6 CHECK AIR SPRING SOLENOID HARNESS AND CONTROL MODULE			
• Disconnect inoperative spring solenoid connector.	Yes	▶	REPLACE inoperative spring solenoid. REPEAT Service Bay Diagnostics.
• Measure voltage between both circuits in connector.	No	▶	EXIT Functional Test 33. GO to G7.
• Meter should pulse between zero volts and battery voltage.			
• Are there voltage pulses?			
G7 CHECK AIR SPRING SOLENOID BATTERY FEED CIRCUIT 414 (O/R)			
• Measure voltage between Circuit 414 (O/R) at spring solenoid connector and a good chassis ground.	Yes	▶	GO to G8.
• Meter should indicate battery voltage.	No	▶	SERVICE open in Circuit 414 (O/R). REPEAT Service Bay Diagnostics.
• Is there voltage?			

FM2019200119030X

Fig. 20   Test G: Unable To Detect Lowering Or Rear (Part 3 of 8)

TEST STEP	RESULT	►	ACTION TO TAKE
G8 CHECK CONTINUITY OF SPRING SOLENOID CONTROL CIRCUITS			
• Turn air suspension switch OFF. • Disconnect control module connectors. • Measure resistance of spring solenoid control circuit between solenoid connector and black control module connector as shown: • Is resistance less than 10 ohms?	Yes No	► ►	GO to G9. SERVICE open in Circuit between control module and solenoid valve connector. REPEAT Service Bay Diagnostics.

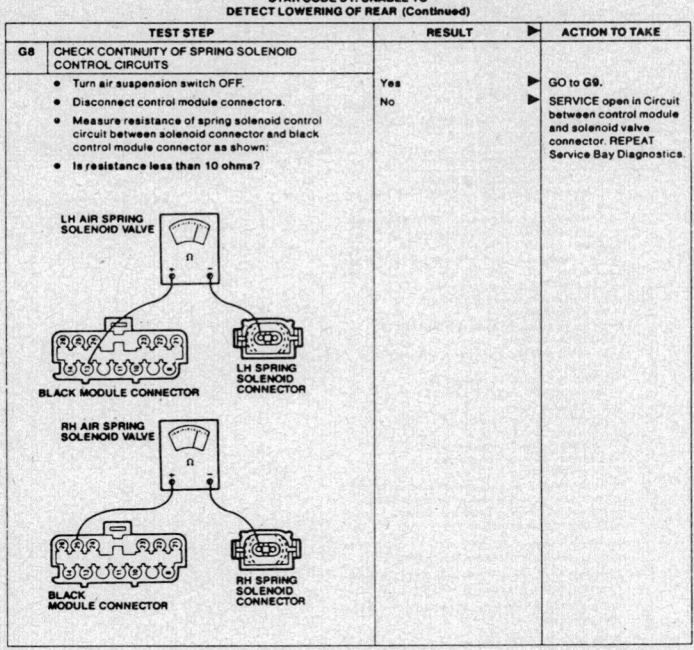

Fig. 20 Test G: Unable To Detect Lowering Or Rear (Part 4 of 8)

TEST STEP	RESULT	►	ACTION TO TAKE
G9 CHECK LH AIR SPRING SOLENOID CIRCUITS			
• The resistance measurements in this procedure check the condition of the air spring solenoid valve coil and diode. A digital ohmmeter will not pass enough current through the diode to check its condition. Use Rotunda Inductive Dwell-Tach-Volt Ohm Tester 059-00010 or equivalent analog (needle-type) meter. • Turn air suspension switch OFF. • Disconnect control modules connectors. • Turn air suspension switch ON. NOTE: Air suspension switch must be ON for this test. Measure resistance between Pins 13 and 1 on module connectors (checking LH). • Reverse leads and measure resistance again between Pins 13 and 1. • Meter should indicate 15 to 18 ohms one way, and 5 to 10 ohms less the other way.	Higher reading is 15 to 18 ohms, lower reading is 5 to 10 ohms below higher reading for both spring solenoids. Both readings are the same, zero to 18 ohms	► ►	GO to G10. REPLACE damaged spring solenoid. REPEAT Service Bay Diagnostics.

Fig. 20 Test G: Unable To Detect Lowering Or Rear (Part 5 of 8)

TEST STEP	RESULT	►	ACTION TO TAKE
G10 CHECK RH AIR SPRING SOLENOID CIRCUITS			
• Measure resistance between Pins 25 and 1 on module connectors. • Reverse leads and measure resistance again between Pins 25 and 1 (RH solenoid). • Meter should indicate 15 to 18 ohms one way, 5 to 10 ohms less the other way.	Higher reading is 15 to 18 ohms, lower reading is 5 to 10 ohms below higher reading for both solenoids. Both readings are the same, zero to 18 ohms	► ►	REPLACE control module. REPEAT Service Bay Diagnostics. If Star Code 51 occurs again, GO to G11. REPLACE damaged spring solenoid. REPEAT Service Bay Diagnostics.
G11 CHECK HEIGHT SENSOR			
• Leave STAR Tester in Functional Test mode, but do not select a Pinpoint Test (STAR Tester button should be depressed — down). • Leave air suspension switch ON. • Making sure that STAR tester is accessible, raise vehicle on hoist. • Check that height sensor is attached to both ball studs. • Check upper and lower height sensor mounting brackets for obvious damage.	Sensor attachments OK One or both ends off ball stud Height sensor attachments bent or damaged	► ► ►	GO to G12. PUSH sensor onto ball studs. ENSURE sensor fits securely on both ball studs. If not, REPLACE sensor. LOWER vehicle. REPEAT Service Bay Diagnostics. SERVICE brackets. LOWER vehicle. REPEAT Service Bay Diagnostics.

Fig. 20 Test G: Unable To Detect Lowering Or Rear (Part 6 of 8)

TEST STEP	RESULT	►	ACTION TO TAKE
G12 CHECK AIR FLOW THROUGH SPRING SOLENOIDS			
• CAUTION: Rear of vehicle must be supported by frame. If rear is supported by axle, rear of vehicle will lower during this test. NOTE: Some air must be in each air spring to perform this test. • Disconnect air lines at both spring solenoid valves. • Remove air spring solenoid heat shields, if so equipped. • Enter STAR Tester Functional Test 33 to cycle air spring solenoid valve. Refer to Service Bay Diagnostics. • Air should flow from each air spring solenoid when it is cycled open.	Air flows from both solenoid valves Air does not flow from one or both solenoid valves	► ►	EXIT Functional Test 33. CONNECT solenoid air lines and heat shields. GO to G13. REPLACE inoperative spring solenoid valve. REPEAT Service Bay Diagnostics.
G13 CHECK FOR ADEQUATE SPRING PRESSURE			
• Lower vehicle. There should be nothing supporting vehicle. • Measure distance between center of lip rear wheel opening and bottom of wheel (not bottom of tire). • Measurement should be a minimum of 610-635mm (24-25 inch). This is vehicle trim height.	Vehicle higher Vehicle low	► ►	GO to G14. GO to G16.
G14 CHECK AIR FLOW THROUGH LINES			
• Remove air cleaner assembly and plastic shield from compressor assembly as outlined. • Disconnect air line at compressor dryer. • Enter STAR Tester Functional Test 23 — vent rear. Refer to Service Bay Diagnostics. Air should flow from disconnected air line and vehicle should drop about one inch in 10-20 seconds. CAUTION: Rear of vehicle may drop rapidly once Functional Test 23 is entered.	Little or no air flow and vehicle does not lower or lowers very slowly Air flow from air line and vehicle drops	► ►	SERVICE air line from compressor to solenoid valves for blockage or kinks. REPEAT Service Bay Diagnostics. EXIT Functional Test 23 before rear of vehicle becomes too low. GO to G15.
G15 CHECK AIR FLOW THROUGH COMPRESSOR DRYER			
• Remove air dryer from compressor as outlined. • Connect air line to air dryer. • Enter Functional Test 23 — vent rear. Refer to Service Bay Diagnostics.	Little or no air flows through air dryer Air flows through air dryer	► ►	REPLACE air dryer. INSTALL compressor assembly. REPEAT Service Bay Diagnostics. REPLACE air compressor assembly. REPEAT Service Bay Diagnostics.
G16 INFLATE REAR SPRINGS			
• Enter Functional Test 26 — compress rear. Refer to Service Bay Diagnostics. • Exit Functional Test 26 when rear of vehicle is raised about 50mm (2 inch) above trim height. • Distance should be about 660-685mm (26-27 inch) from bottom of wheel (not bottom of tire) and center of rear wheel lip opening.	Rear of vehicle raises Rear of vehicle does not raise, but air compressor runs Rear of vehicle does not raise and air compressor does not run	► ► ►	GO to G14. EXIT Functional Test 26. GO to G17. GO to Pinpoint Test H.

Fig. 20 Test G: Unable To Detect Lowering Or Rear (Part 7 of 8)

PINPOINT TEST G
STAR CODE 51: UNABLE TO
DETECT LOWERING OF REAR (Continued)

TEST STEP	RESULT	▶	ACTION TO TAKE
G17 CHECK FOR AIR FLOW FROM AIR COMPRESSOR ● Raise rear of vehicle. **CAUTION: Support rear of vehicle on frame. If rear of vehicle is supported by axle, air springs will be damaged during this test.** ● Disconnect air line from air dryer. ● Enter Functional Test 26—compress rear. Refer to Service Bay Diagnostics. ● Air should flow from air dryer while compressor is running.	Air flows from air dryer. Little or no air flow from air dryer	▶ ▶	SERVICE blocked or kinked air line. REPEAT Service Bay Diagnostics. EXIT Functional Test 26. GO to G18.
G18 CHECK AIR FLOW WITH DRYER REMOVED ● Remove air dryer from air compressor as outlined. ● Enter Functional Test 26—compress rear. Refer to Service Bay Diagnostics. ● Air should flow from air dryer fitting on compressor while compressor is running.	Air flows from compressor Little or no air flow from compressor	▶ ▶	REPLACE air dryer. REPEAT Service Bay Diagnostics. **CAUTION: Enter Functional Test 26 while in Service Bay Diagnostics and fill air springs for about 90 seconds before lowering rear of vehicle.** REPLACE compressor assembly. REPEAT Service Bay Diagnostics. **CAUTION: Enter Functional Test 26 while in Service Bay Diagnostics and fill air springs for about 90 seconds before lowering rear of vehicle.**

FM2019200119080X

Fig. 20   Test G: Unable To Detect Lowering Or Rear (Part 8 of 8)

PINPOINT TEST H
STAR CODE 54: UNABLE TO DETECT RAISING OF REAR

TEST STEP	RESULT	▶	ACTION TO TAKE
H1 PERFORM COMPRESSOR FUNCTIONAL TEST ● Possible Source for STAR CODE 54: —Compressor battery Circuit 578 (LB/PK) has an open or short. —Compressor ground Circuit 57 (BK) has an open. —Compressor relay battery Circuit 414 (O/R) has an open. —Compressor relay control Circuit 420 (DB/Y) has an open. —Compressor relay worn or damaged. —Air lines disconnected or leaking. —Air springs leaking. —LH spring solenoid valve control Circuit 429 (PK/LG) has an open. —LH spring solenoid valve battery Circuit 414 (O/R) has an open. —LH spring solenoid valve damaged. —RH spring solenoid valve control Circuit 416 (LB/BK) has an open. —RH spring solenoid valve battery Circuit 414 (O/R) has an open. —RH spring solenoid valve damaged. —Air compressor worn or damaged. —Air line blocked. —Air compressor air passages or air dryer blocked. —Height sensor may be disconnected at one or both ball studs, or mounting brackets bent. —Control module damaged. ● Enter STAR Tester Functional Test 31—compressor relay toggle. Refer to Service Bay Diagnostics. ● Compressor should cycle ON and OFF repeatedly (one second ON, one second OFF) during this test. ● Cycling of the compressor can be heard from the LH front wheel well. ● Does compressor cycle?	Yes No	▶ ▶	GO to H9. DO NO EXIT Functional Test 31. GO to H2.

FM2019200120010X

Fig. 21   Test H: Unable To Detect Raising Of Rear (Part 1 of 11). Crown Victoria & Grand Marquis

PINPOINT TEST H
STAR CODE 54: UNABLE TO DETECT RAISING OF REAR (Continued)

TEST STEP	RESULT	▶	ACTION TO TAKE
H2 MEASURE VOLTAGE AT COMPRESSOR ● Remove air cleaner assembly and compressor plastic shield as outlined. ● Disconnect compressor electric connector. ● Measure voltage between Circuits 578 (LB/PK) and 57 (BK) of compressor harness connector. ● Meter should pulse between battery voltage and zero volts.	Meter pulses Meter reads zero volts	▶ ▶	CONNECT compressor connector. WAIT 10 minutes for compressor internal circuit breaker to cool down and close. Circuit breaker may have opened due to excessive compressor run-time during diagnostics. If compressor does not start to cycle on and off after 10 minutes, REPLACE compressor. REPEAT Service Bay Diagnostics. DO NOT EXIT Functional Test 31. GO to H3.

CIRCUIT 578 LB/PK
CIRCUIT 57 BK

H3 CHECK COMPRESSOR RELAY ● Compressor relay should cycle ON and OFF (one second ON, one second OFF) during this test. As the relay cycles a clicking noise will be heard. ● Does relay cycle?	Yes No	▶ ▶	EXIT Functional Test 31. GO to H7. EXIT Functional Test 31. GO to H4.

HORN RELAY
COMPRESSOR RELAY
POWER DISTRIBUTION BOX DIRECTLY BEHIND BATTERY

FM2019200120020X

Fig. 21   Test H: Unable To Detect Raising Of Rear (Part 2 of 11). Crown Victoria & Grand Marquis

PINPOINT TEST H
STAR CODE 54: UNABLE TO DETECT RAISING OF REAR (Continued)

TEST STEP	RESULT	▶	ACTION TO TAKE
H4 CHECK COMPRESSOR RELAY (Continued) ● The horn circuit and the air suspension system use the same type of relay. Depress horn pad to ensure horn is operating. ● Remove compressor relay and install horn relay in its place. ● Repeat Service Bay Diagnostics. ● Is Code 54 displayed?	Yes No	▶ ▶	INSTALL relays in original positions. GO to H5. INSTALL horn relay in original position. REPLACE compressor relay. REPEAT Service Bay Diagnostics.

HORN RELAY
COMPRESSOR RELAY
POWER DISTRIBUTION BOX DIRECTLY BEHIND BATTERY

H5 CHECK RELAY BATTERY FEED CIRCUIT 414 (O/R) ● Measure voltage between Circuit 414 (O/R) at relay terminal and a good chassis ground. ● Meter should indicate battery voltage. ● Is there battery voltage?	Yes No	▶ ▶	GO to H6. SERVICE Circuit 414 (O/R) for open. REPEAT Service Bay Diagnostics.

GOOD CHASSIS GROUND
POWER DISTRIBUTION BOX DIRECTLY BEHIND BATTERY

FM2019200120030X

Fig. 21   Test H: Unable To Detect Raising Of Rear (Part 3 of 11). Crown Victoria & Grand Marquis

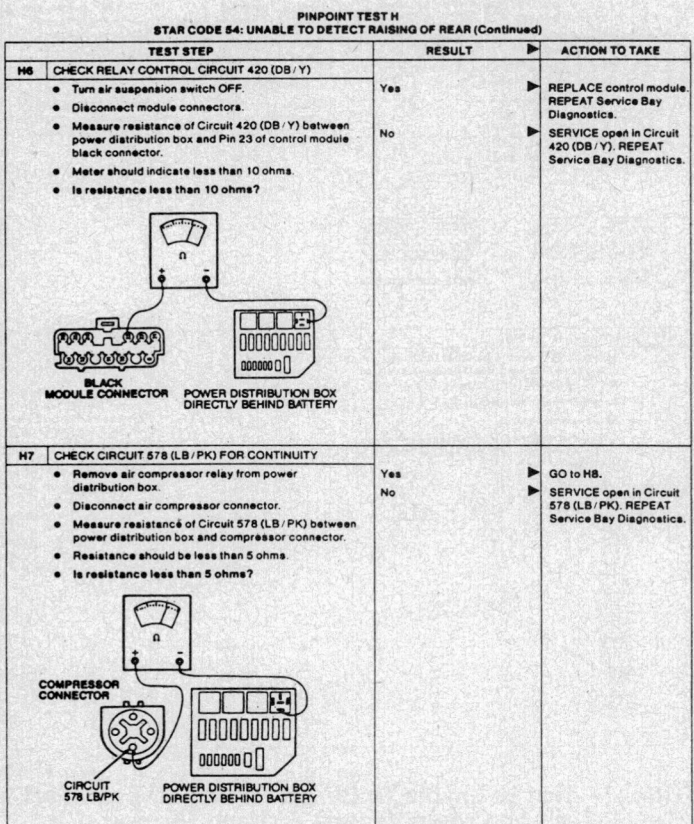

PINPOINT TEST H
STAR CODE 54: UNABLE TO DETECT RAISING OF REAR (Continued)

TEST STEP	RESULT	▶	ACTION TO TAKE
H6 CHECK RELAY CONTROL CIRCUIT 420 (DB / Y) • Turn air suspension switch OFF. • Disconnect module connectors. • Measure resistance of Circuit 420 (DB / Y) between power distribution box and Pin 23 of control module black connector. • Meter should indicate less than 10 ohms. • Is resistance less than 10 ohms?	Yes No	▶ ▶	REPLACE control module. REPEAT Service Bay Diagnostics. SERVICE open in Circuit 420 (DB / Y). REPEAT Service Bay Diagnostics.
H7 CHECK CIRCUIT 578 (LB / PK) FOR CONTINUITY • Remove air compressor relay from power distribution box. • Disconnect air compressor connector. • Measure resistance of Circuit 578 (LB / PK) between power distribution box and compressor connector. • Resistance should be less than 5 ohms. • Is resistance less than 5 ohms?	Yes No	▶ ▶	GO to H8. SERVICE open in Circuit 578 (LB / PK). REPEAT Service Bay Diagnostics.

FM2019200120040X

Fig. 21   Test H: Unable To Detect Raising Of Rear (Part 4 of 11). Crown Victoria & Grand Marquis

PINPOINT TEST H
STAR CODE 54: UNABLE TO DETECT RAISING OF REAR (Continued)

TEST STEP	RESULT	▶	ACTION TO TAKE
H8 CHECK GROUND CIRCUIT 57 (BK) • Measure resistance between Circuit 57 (BK) at compressor connector and a good chassis ground. • Meter should indicate less than 5 ohms. • Is resistance less than 5 ohms?	Yes No	▶ ▶	REPLACE compressor assembly. REPEAT Service Bay Diagnostics. SERVICE open in Circuit 57. REPEAT Service Bay Diagnostics.
H9 CHECK AIR SPRING SOLENOID VALVES • Enter Functional Test 33. Refer to Functional Test procedure. • Leave air suspension switch ON and raise vehicle on hoist. • Feel each spring solenoid valve to see if they are cycling ON and OFF. A clicking noise will be heard when they cycle, but each valve must be felt to ensure that both are operating.	Valve cycle One or both valves do not cycle	▶ ▶	GO to H14. DO NOT EXIT Functional Test 33. GO to H10.
H10 CHECK AIR SPRING SOLENOID HARNESS AND CONTROL MODULE CIRCUITS • Disconnect inoperative spring solenoid connector. • Measure voltage between both circuits in connector. • Meter should pulse between zero volts and battery voltage. • Are there meter pulses?	Yes No	▶ ▶	REPLACE inoperative spring solenoid valve. REPEAT Service Bay Diagnostics. EXIT Functional Test 33. GO to H11.

FM2019200120050X

Fig. 21   Test H: Unable To Detect Raising Of Rear (Part 5 of 11). Crown Victoria & Grand Marquis

PINPOINT TEST H
STAR CODE 54: UNABLE TO DETECT RAISING OF REAR (Continued)

TEST STEP	RESULT	▶	ACTION TO TAKE
H11 CHECK AIR SPRING SOLENOID VALVE BATTERY FEED CIRCUIT 414 (O / R) • Measure voltage between 414 (O / R) circuit at spring solenoid connector and a good chassis ground. • Meter should indicate battery voltage. • Is there battery voltage?	Yes No	▶ ▶	GO to H12. SERVICE open in circuit 414 (O / R). REPEAT Service Bay Diagnostics.

FM2019200120060X

Fig. 21   Test H: Unable To Detect Raising Of Rear (Part 6 of 11).Crown Victoria & Grand Marquis

PINPOINT TEST H
STAR CODE 54: UNABLE TO DETECT RAISING OF REAR (Continued)

TEST STEP	RESULT	▶	ACTION TO TAKE
H12 CHECK CONTINUITY OF SPRING SOLENOID CONTROL CIRCUITS • Turn air suspension switch OFF. • Disconnect control module connectors. • Measure resistance of spring solenoid control circuit between solenoid connector and control module connector as shown: • Is resistance less than 10 ohms?	Yes No	▶ ▶	GO to H13. SERVICE open in circuit between control module and solenoid valve connector. REPEAT Service Bay Diagnostics.

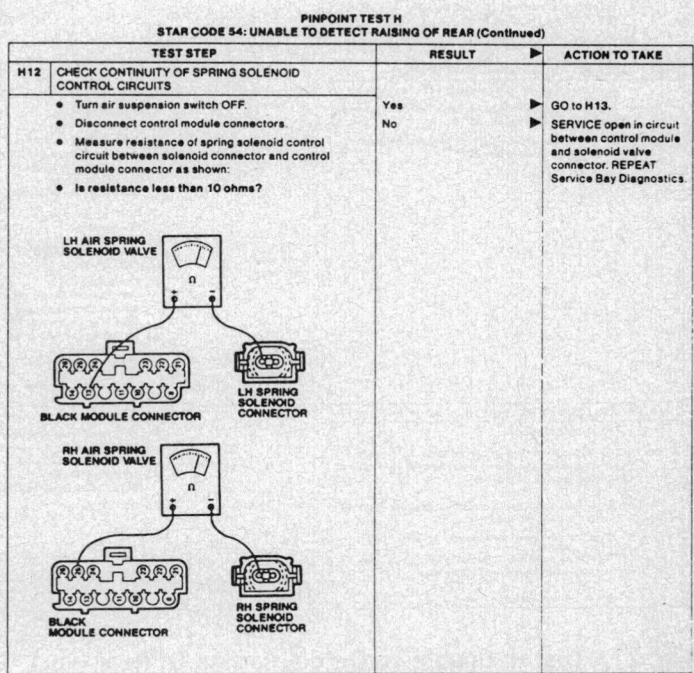

FM2019200120070X

Fig. 21   Test H: Unable To Detect Raising Of Rear (Part 7 of 11). Crown Victoria & Grand Marquis

TEST STEP	RESULT	▶	ACTION TO TAKE
H13 CHECK LH AIR SPRING SOLENOID CIRCUITS			
• The resistance measurements in this procedure check the condition of the air spring solenoid valve coil and diode. A digital ohmmeter will not pass enough current through the diode to check its condition. Use Rotunda Inductive Dwell-Tach-Volt-Ohm Tester 059-00010 or equivalent analog (needle-type) meter.	Higher reading is 15 to 18 ohms, lower reading is 5 to 10 ohms below higher reading	▶	GO to H14.
• Turn air suspension switch OFF.	Both readings are the same, zero to 18 ohms	▶	REPLACE damaged spring solenoid. REPEAT Service Bay Diagnostics.
• Disconnect control modules connectors.			
• Turn air suspension switch ON.			
NOTE: Air suspension switch must be ON for this test.			
• Measure resistance between Pins 13 and 1 on module connectors (checking LH).			
• Reverse leads and measure resistance again between pins 13 and 1.			
• Meter should indicate 15 to 18 ohms one way, and 5 to 10 ohms less the other way.			

BLACK MODULE CONNECTOR   GRAY MODULE CONNECTOR

Fig. 21 Test H: Unable To Detect Raising Of Rear (Part 8 of 11). Crown Victoria & Grand Marquis

TEST STEP	RESULT	▶	ACTION TO TAKE
H14 CHECK RH AIR SPRING SOLENOID CIRCUITS			
• Measure resistance between Pins 25 and 1 on module connectors.	Higher reading is 15 to 18 ohms, lower reading is 5 to 10 ohms below higher reading for both spring solenoids	▶	REPLACE control module. REPEAT Service Bay Diagnostics. If Star Code 54 occurs again, GO to H15.
• Reverse leads and measure resistance again between Pins 25 and 1 (checking RH).			
• Meter should indicate 15 to 18 ohms one way, 5 to 10 ohms less the other way.	Both readings are the same, zero to 18 ohms	▶	REPLACE damaged or spring solenoid. REPEAT Service Bay Diagnostics.

BLACK MODULE CONNECTOR   GRAY MODULE CONNECTOR

TEST STEP	RESULT	▶	ACTION TO TAKE
H15 CHECK HEIGHT SENSOR			
• Leave STAR Tester in Functional Test mode, but do not select a Functional Test (STAR tester button should be depressed—down).	Sensor attachments OK	▶	GO to H16.
• Leave air suspension switch ON.	One or both ends off ball stud	▶	PUSH sensor onto ball studs. ENSURE sensor fits securely on both ball studs. If not, REPLACE sensor. LOWER vehicle. REPEAT Service Bay Diagnostics.
• Raise vehicle on hoist.			
• Check that height sensor is attached to both ball studs and that mounting brackets are not bent or damaged.	Sensor brackets bent or damaged	▶	SERVICE sensor brackets. REPEAT Service Bay Diagnostics.

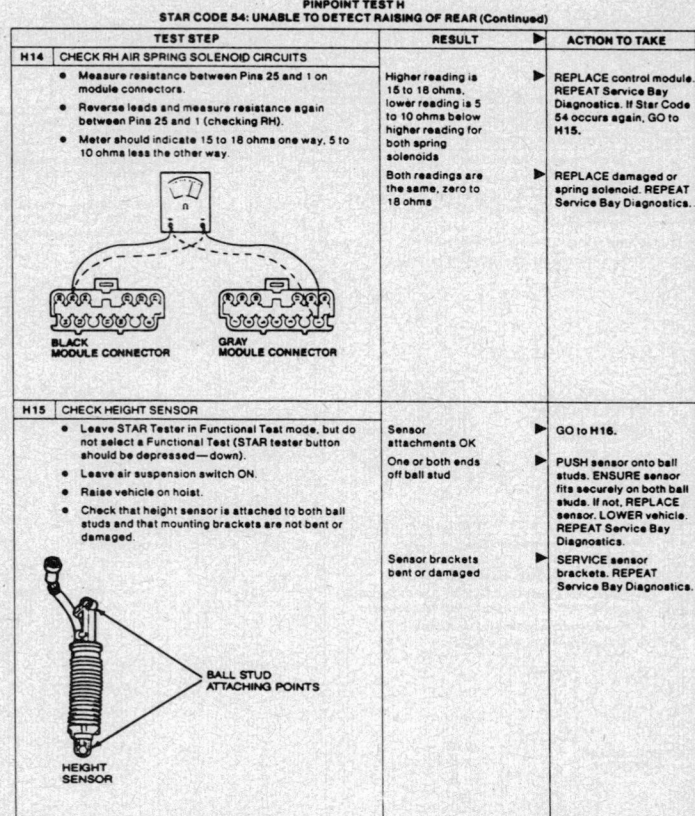

BALL STUD ATTACHING POINTS

HEIGHT SENSOR

Fig. 21 Test H: Unable To Detect Raising Of Rear (Part 9 of 11). Crown Victoria & Grand Marquis

TEST STEP	RESULT	▶	ACTION TO TAKE
H16 CHECK FOR AIR FLOW FROM AIR COMPRESSOR			
• Lower and support rear of vehicle.	Air flows from air dryer	▶	EXIT Functional Test 26. CONNECT air line to air dryer. GO to H18.
CAUTION: Support rear of vehicle on frame. If rear of vehicle is supported by axle, air springs will be damaged during this test.	Little or no air flow from air dryer	▶	EXIT Functional Test 26. GO to H17.
• Disconnect air line from air dryer.			
• Enter Functional Test 26—compressor rear. Refer to Functional Test Procedure.			
• Air should flow from air dryer while compressor is running.			
H17 CHECK AIR FLOW WITH DRYER REMOVED			
• Remove air dryer from air compressor as outlined.	Air flows from compressor	▶	REPLACE air dryer. CAUTION: Enter Functional Test 26 as outlined in Functional Test Procedure and fill air springs for about 90 seconds before lowering rear of vehicle. REPEAT Service Bay Diagnostics.
• Enter Functional Test 26—compress rear. Refer to Functional Test Procedure.			
• Air should flow from air dryer fitting on compressor while compressor is running.	Little or no air flows from compressor	▶	REPLACE compressor assembly. CAUTION: Enter Functional Test 26 as outlined in Functional Test Procedure and fill air springs for about 90 seconds before lowering rear of vehicle. REPEAT Service Bay Diagnostics.
H18 CHECK FOR AIR LEAKS IN LINES AND SPRINGS			
• Raise rear of vehicle.	Yes	▶	EXIT Functional Test 26. SERVICE leaks in air lines and/or REPLACE air spring(s). REPEAT Service Bay Diagnostics.
NOTE: Support rear of vehicle on frame, not on axle. Supporting vehicle by the frame allows full extension of air springs for leak detection.			
• Enter Functional Test 26—compress rear. Refer to Functional Test Procedure.	No	▶	GO to H19.
• Check air lines and air springs for leaks.			
NOTE: The air lines are routed along the LH rocker panel along with the fuel and brake lines.			
• Are leaks detected?			

Fig. 21 Test H: Unable To Detect Raising Of Rear (Part 10 of 11). Crown Victoria & Grand Marquis

TEST STEP	RESULT	▶	ACTION TO TAKE
H19 CHECK FOR BLOCKED AIR LINES			
• Disconnect air lines at bold air spring solenoid valves. Remove air spring solenoid heat shields, if so equipped.	No air flow from air lines	▶	SERVICE blocked air lines. REPEAT Service Bay Diagnostics.
• Support rear of vehicle on frame to prevent vehicle from lowering during functional test.	No air flow from air spring(s)	▶	REPLACE air spring solenoid(s). REPEAT Service Bay Diagnostics.
• Enter Functional Test 26—compress rear. Refer to Functional Test Procedure.			
• Air should flow from both air lines and from both air spring solenoid valves.			

Fig. 21 Test H: Unable To Detect Raising Of Rear (Part 11 of 11). Crown Victoria & Grand Marquis

PINPOINT TEST H
STAR CODE 54: UNABLE TO
DETECT RAISING OF REAR

TEST STEP	RESULT	▶	ACTION TO TAKE
H1 PERFORM COMPRESSOR FUNCTIONAL TEST			
• Possible Source for STAR CODE 54: —Compressor battery Circuit 578 (LB/PK) has an open or short. —Compressor ground Circuit 57 (BK) has an open. —Compressor relay battery Circuit 414 (O/R) has an open. —Compressor relay control Circuit 420 (DB/Y) has an open. —Compressor relay worn or damaged. —Air lines disconnected or leaking. —Air springs leaking. —LH spring solenoid valve control Circuit 429 (PK/LG) has an open. —LH spring solenoid valve battery Circuit 414 (O/R) has an open. —LH spring solenoid valve damaged. —RH spring solenoid valve control Circuit 416 (LB/BK) has an open. —RH spring solenoid valve battery Circuit 414 (O/R) has an open. —RH spring solenoid valve damaged. —Air compressor worn or damaged. —Air line blocked. —Air compressor air passages or air dryer blocked. —Height sensor may be disconnected at one or both ball studs, or mounting brackets bent. —Control module damaged. • Enter STAR tester Functional Test 31—compressor relay toggle. Refer to Service Bay Diagnostics. • Compressor should cycle ON and OFF repeatedly (one second ON, one second OFF) during this test. • Cycling of the compressor can be heard from the LH front wheel well. • Does compressor cycle?	Yes No	▶ ▶	GO to H9. DO NO EXIT Functional Test 31. GO to H2.

FM2019200121010X

Fig. 22   Test H: Unable To Detect Raising Of Rear (Part 1 of 11). Town Car

---

PINPOINT TEST H
STAR CODE 54: UNABLE TO
DETECT RAISING OF REAR (Continued)

TEST STEP	RESULT	▶	ACTION TO TAKE
H2 MEASURE VOLTAGE AT COMPRESSOR			
• Remove air cleaner assembly and compressor plastic shield as outlined. • Disconnect compressor electric connector. • Measure voltage between Circuits 578 (LB/PK) and 57 (BK) of compressor harness connector. • Meter should pulse between battery voltage and zero volts.	Meter pulses Meter reads zero volts	▶ ▶	CONNECT compressor connector. WAIT 10 minutes for compressor internal circuit breaker to cool down and close. Circuit breaker may have opened due to excessive compressor run-time during diagnostics. If compressor does not start to cycle on and off after 10 minutes, REPLACE compressor. REPEAT Service Bay Diagnostics. DO NOT EXIT Functional Test 31. GO to H3.
H3 CHECK COMPRESSOR RELAY			
• Compressor relay should cycle ON and OFF (one second ON, one second OFF) during this test. As the relay cycles a clicking noise will be heard. • Does relay cycle?	Yes No	▶ ▶	EXIT Functional Test 31. GO to H7. EXIT Functional Test 31. GO to H4.

FM2019200121020X

Fig. 22   Test H: Unable To Detect Raising Of Rear (Part 2 of 11). Town Car

---

PINPOINT TEST H
STAR CODE 54: UNABLE TO
DETECT RAISING OF REAR (Continued)

TEST STEP	RESULT	▶	ACTION TO TAKE
H4 CHECK COMPRESSOR RELAY (Continued)			
• The horn circuit and the air suspension system use the same type of relay. Depress horn pad to ensure horn is operating. • Remove compressor relay and install horn relay in its place. • Repeat Service Bay Diagnostics. • Is Code 54 displayed?	Yes No	▶ ▶	INSTALL relays in original positions. GO to H5. INSTALL horn relay in original position. REPLACE compressor relay. REPEAT Service Bay Diagnostics.
H5 CHECK RELAY BATTERY FEED CIRCUIT 414 (O/R)			
• Measure voltage between Circuit 414 (O/R) at relay terminal and a good chassis ground. • Meter should indicate battery voltage. • Is there battery voltage?	Yes No	▶ ▶	GO to H6. SERVICE Circuit 414 (O/R) for open. REPEAT Service Bay Diagnostics.

FM2019200121030X

Fig. 22   Test H: Unable To Detect Raising Of Rear (Part 3 of 11). Town Car

---

PINPOINT TEST H
STAR CODE 54: UNABLE TO
DETECT RAISING OF REAR (Continued)

TEST STEP	RESULT	▶	ACTION TO TAKE
H6 CHECK RELAY CONTROL CIRCUIT 420 (DB/Y)			
• Turn air suspension switch OFF. • Disconnect module connectors. • Measure resistance of Circuit 420 (DB/Y) between power distribution box and Pin 23 of control module black connector. • Meter should indicate less than 10 ohms. • Is resistance less than 10 ohms?	Yes No	▶ ▶	REPLACE control module. REPEAT Service Bay Diagnostics. SERVICE open in Circuit 420 (DB/Y). REPEAT Service Bay Diagnostics.
H7 CHECK CIRCUIT 417 (P/O) FOR CONTINUITY			
• Remove air compressor relay from power distribution box. • Disconnect air compressor connector. • Measure resistance of Circuit 417 (P/O) between power distribution box and compressor connector. • Resistance should be less than 5 ohms. • Is resistance less than 5 ohms?	Yes No	▶ ▶	GO to H8. SERVICE open in Circuit 417 (P/O). REPEAT Service Bay Diagnostics.

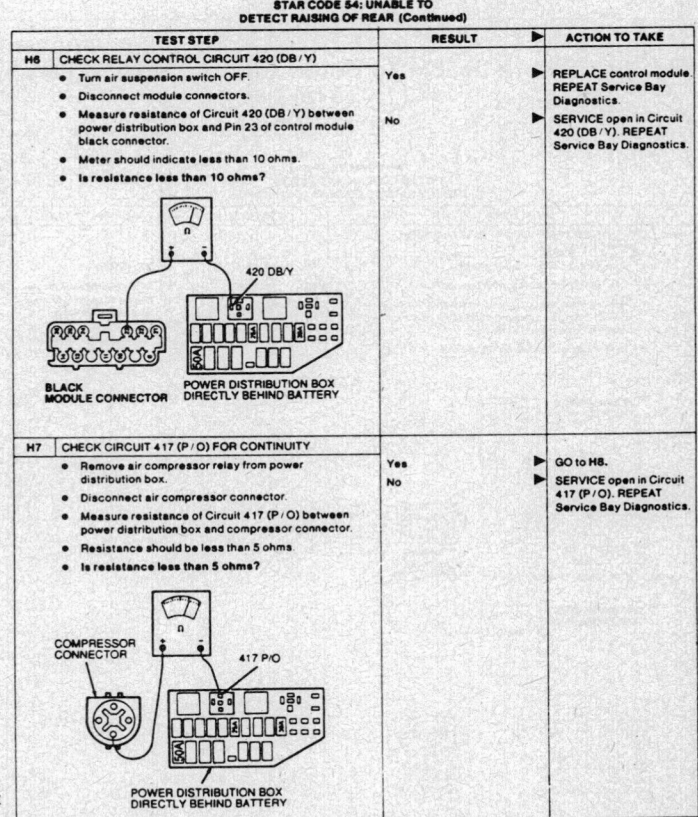

FM2019200121040X

Fig. 22   Test H: Unable To Detect Raising Of Rear (Part 4 of 11). Town Car

PINPOINT TEST H
STAR CODE 54: UNABLE TO
DETECT RAISING OF REAR (Continued)

TEST STEP	RESULT	▶	ACTION TO TAKE
H8 CHECK GROUND CIRCUIT 57 (BK)			
• Measure resistance between Circuit 57 (BK) at compressor connector and a good chassis ground.	Yes	▶	REPLACE compressor assembly. REPEAT Service Bay Diagnostics.
• Meter should indicate less than 5 ohms.	No	▶	SERVICE open in Circuit 57. REPEAT Service Bay Diagnostics.
• Is resistance less than 5 ohms?			
H9 CHECK AIR SPRING SOLENOID VALVES			
• Enter Functional Test 33. Refer to Functional Test procedure.	Valve cycle	▶	GO to H14.
• Leave air suspension switch ON and raise vehicle on hoist.	One or both valves do not cycle	▶	DO NOT EXIT Functional Test 33. GO to H10.
• Feel each spring solenoid valve to see if they are cycling ON and OFF. A clicking noise will be heard when they cycle, but each valve must be felt to ensure that both are operating.			
H10 CHECK AIR SPRING SOLENOID HARNESS AND CONTROL MODULE CIRCUITS			
• Disconnect inoperative spring solenoid connector.	Yes	▶	REPLACE inoperative spring solenoid valve. REPEAT Service Bay Diagnostics.
• Measure voltage between both circuits in connector.	No	▶	EXIT Functional Test 33. GO to H11.
• Meter should pulse between zero volts and battery voltage.			
• Are there meter pulses?			

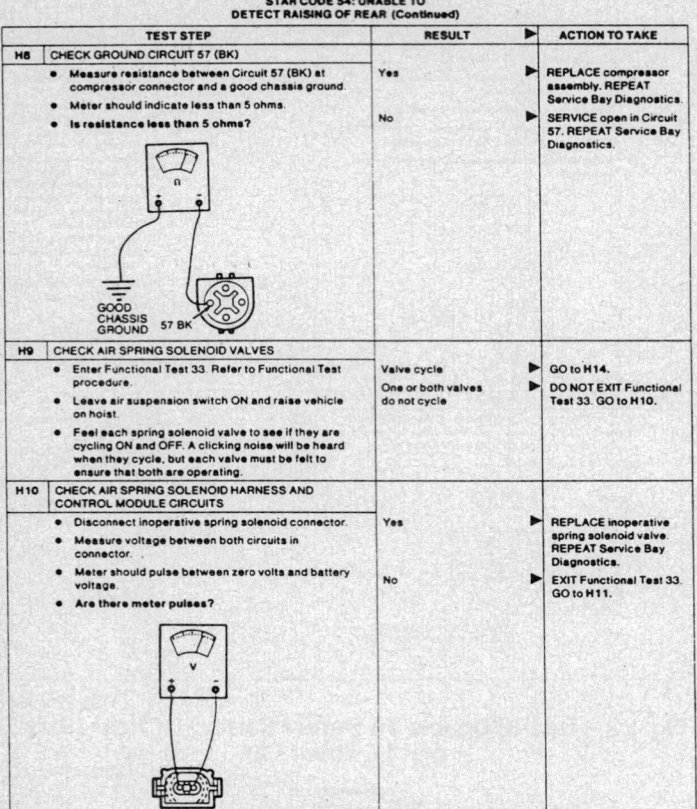

FM2019200121050X

Fig. 22   Test H: Unable To Detect Raising Of Rear (Part 5 of 11). Town Car

PINPOINT TEST H
STAR CODE 54: UNABLE TO
DETECT RAISING OF REAR (Continued)

TEST STEP	RESULT	▶	ACTION TO TAKE
H11 CHECK AIR SPRING SOLENOID VALVE BATTERY FEED CIRCUIT 414 (O/R)			
• Measure voltage between 414 (O/R) circuit at spring solenoid connector and a good chassis ground.	Yes	▶	GO to H12.
• Meter should indicate battery voltage.	No	▶	SERVICE open in circuit 414 (O/R). REPEAT Service Bay Diagnostics.
• Is there battery voltage?			

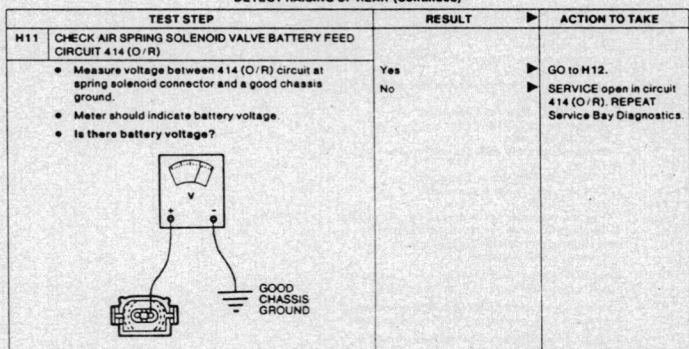

FM2019200121060X

Fig. 22   Test H: Unable To Detect Raising Of Rear (Part 6 of 11). Town Car

PINPOINT TEST H
STAR CODE 54: UNABLE TO
DETECT RAISING OF REAR (Continued)

TEST STEP	RESULT	▶	ACTION TO TAKE
H12 CHECK CONTINUITY OF SPRING SOLENOID CONTROL CIRCUITS			
• Turn air suspension switch OFF.	Yes	▶	GO to H13.
• Disconnect control modules connectors.	No	▶	SERVICE open in circuit between control module and solenoid valve connector. REPEAT Service Bay Diagnostics.
• Measure resistance of spring solenoid control circuit between solenoid connector and control module connector as shown:			
• Is resistance less than 10 ohms?			

LH AIR SPRING
SOLENOID VALVE

BLACK MODULE CONNECTOR   LH SPRING SOLENOID CONNECTOR

RH AIR SPRING
SOLENOID VALVE

BLACK MODULE CONNECTOR   RH SPRING SOLENOID CONNECTOR

FM2019200121070X

Fig. 22   Test H: Unable To Detect Raising Of Rear (Part 7 of 11). Town Car

PINPOINT TEST H
STAR CODE 54: UNABLE TO
DETECT RAISING OF REAR (Continued)

TEST STEP	RESULT	▶	ACTION TO TAKE
H13 CHECK LH AIR SPRING SOLENOID CIRCUITS The resistance measurements in this procedure check the condition of the air spring solenoid valve coil and diode. A digital ohmmeter will not pass enough current through the diode to check its condition. Use Rotunda Inductive-Dwell-Tach-Volt-Ohm Tester 059-00010 or equivalent analog (needle-type) meter.			
• Turn air suspension switch OFF.	Higher reading is 15 to 18 ohms, lower reading is 5 to 10 ohms below higher reading	▶	GO to H14.
• Disconnect control modules connectors.			
• Turn air suspension switch ON.	Both readings are the same, zero to 18 ohms	▶	REPLACE damaged spring solenoid. REPEAT Service Bay Diagnostics.
NOTE: Air suspension switch must be ON for this test.			
• Measure resistance between Pins 13 and 1 on module connectors (checking LH).			
• Reverse leads and measure resistance again between pins 13 and 1.			
• Meter should indicate 15 to 18 ohms one way, and 5 to 10 ohms less the other way.			

BLACK MODULE CONNECTOR   GRAY MODULE CONNECTOR

FM2019200121080X

Fig. 22   Test H: Unable To Detect Raising Of Rear (Part 8 of 11). Town Car

TEST STEP	RESULT	▶	ACTION TO TAKE
H14 CHECK RH AIR SPRING SOLENOID CIRCUITS • Measure resistance between Pins 25 and 1 on module connectors. • Reverse leads and measure resistance again between Pins 25 and 1 (checking RH). • Meter should indicate 15 to 18 ohms one way, 5 to 10 ohms less the other way.	Higher reading is 15 to 18 ohms, lower reading is 5 to 10 ohms below higher reading for both spring solenoids Both readings are the same, zero to 18 ohms	▶ ▶	REPLACE control module. REPEAT Service Bay Diagnostics. If Star Code 54 occurs again, GO to H15. REPLACE damaged or spring solenoid. REPEAT Service Bay Diagnostics.
H15 CHECK HEIGHT SENSOR • Leave STAR Tester in Functional Test mode, but do not select a Functional Test (STAR tester button should be depressed—down). • Leave air suspension switch ON. • Raise vehicle on hoist. • Check that height sensor is attached to both ball studs and that mounting brackets are not bent or damaged.	Sensor attachments OK One or both ends off ball stud Sensor brackets bent or damaged	▶ ▶ ▶	GO to H16. PUSH sensor onto ball studs. ENSURE sensor fits securely on both ball studs. If not, REPLACE sensor. LOWER vehicle. REPEAT Service Bay Diagnostics. SERVICE sensor brackets. REPEAT Service Bay Diagnostics.

FM2019200121090X

Fig. 22   Test H: Unable To Detect Raising Of Rear (Part 9 of 11). Town Car

TEST STEP	RESULT	▶	ACTION TO TAKE
H16 CHECK FOR AIR FLOW FROM AIR COMPRESSOR • Lower and support rear of vehicle. CAUTION: Support rear of vehicle on frame. If rear of vehicle is supported by axle, air springs will be damaged during this test. • Disconnect air line from air dryer. • Enter Functional Test 26—compressor rear. Refer to Functional Test Procedure. • Air should flow from air dryer while compressor is running.	Air flows from air dryer Little or no air flow from air dryer	▶ ▶	EXIT Functional Test 26. CONNECT air line to air dryer. GO to H18. EXIT Functional Test 26. GO to H17.
H17 CHECK AIR FLOW WITH DRYER REMOVED • Remove air dryer from air compressor as outlined. • Enter Functional Test 26—compress rear. Refer to Functional Test Procedure. • Air should flow from air dryer fitting on compressor while compressor is running.	Air flows from compressor Little or no air flows from compressor	▶ ▶	REPLACE air dryer. CAUTION: Enter Functional Test 26 as outlined in Functional Test Procedure and fill air springs for about 90 seconds before lowering rear of vehicle. REPEAT Service Bay Diagnostics REPLACE compressor assembly. CAUTION: Enter Functional Test 26 as outlined in Functional Test Procedure and fill air springs for about 90 seconds before lowering rear of vehicle. REPEAT Service Bay Diagnostics
H18 CHECK FOR AIR LEAKS IN LINES AND SPRINGS • Raise rear of vehicle. NOTE: Support rear of vehicle on frame, not on axle. Supporting vehicle by the frame allows full extension of air springs for leak detection. • Enter Functional Test 26—compress rear. Refer to Functional Test Procedure. • Check air lines and air springs for leaks. NOTE: The air lines are routed along the LH rocker panel along with the fuel and brake lines. • Are leaks detected?	Yes No	▶ ▶	EXIT Functional Test 26. SERVICE leaks in air lines and / or REPLACE air spring(s). REPEAT Service Bay Diagnostics. GO to H19.

FM2019200121100X

Fig. 22   Test H: Unable To Detect Raising Of Rear (Part 10 of 11). Town Car

TEST STEP	RESULT	▶	ACTION TO TAKE
H19 CHECK FOR BLOCKED AIR LINES • Disconnect air lines at bold air spring solenoid valves. Remove air spring solenoid heat shields, if so equipped. • Support rear of vehicle on frame to prevent vehicle from lowering during functional test. • Enter Functional Test 26—compress rear. Refer to Functional Test Procedure. • Air should flow from both air lines and from both air spring solenoid valves.	No air flow from air lines No air flow from air spring(s) Airflow from both air lines	▶ ▶ ▶	SERVICE blocked air lines. REPEAT Service Bay Diagnostics. REPLACE air spring solenoid(s). REPEAT Service Bay Diagnostics. REPLACE control module. REPEAT Service Bay Diagnostics.

FM2019200121110X

Fig. 22   Test H: Unable To Detect Raising Of Rear (Part 11 of 11). Town Car

TEST STEP	RESULT	▶	ACTION TO TAKE
J1 CHECK HEIGHT SENSOR • Possible Source for STAR CODE 68: —Circuit 427 (PK / BK) shorted to ground. —Circuit 428 (O / BK) shorted to ground. —Damaged height sensor. —Damaged control module. • Turn air suspension switch OFF. • Disconnect rear height sensor electrical connector. • Turn air suspension switch ON. • Perform Service Bay Diagnostics.	Code 68 Code 71	▶ ▶	GO to J2. REPLACE height sensor. REPEAT Service Bay Diagnostics.

FM2019200122010X

Fig. 23   Test J: Sensor Output Circuit Shorted To Ground (Part 1 of 2)

TEST STEP	RESULT	▶	ACTION TO TAKE
J2 CHECK CIRCUIT 428 FOR SHORT TO GROUND • Turn air suspension switch OFF. • Disconnect control module connectors. • Measure resistance between Pins 6 and 3 of gray module connector. • Meter should indicate more than 10,000 ohms. • Is resistance more than 10,000 ohms?	Yes No	▶ ▶	GO to J3. Circuit 428 has short to ground. GO to J3 before servicing short in Circuit 428.
J3 CHECK CIRCUIT 427 FOR SHORT TO GROUND • Measure resistance between Pins 6 and 17 of gray module connector. • Meter should indicate more than 10,000 ohms.	More than 10,000 ohms this Test Step and Test Step J2 Less than 10,000 ohms this Test Step and/or Test J2	▶ ▶	REPLACE control module REPEAT Service Bay Diagnostics. SERVICE short to ground in Circuit 427 and / or Circuit 428. REPEAT Service Bay Diagnostics.

FM2019200122020X

Fig. 23   Test J: Sensor Output Circuit Shorted To Ground (Part 2 of 2)

PINPOINT TEST K
STAR CODE 71: HEIGHT
SENSOR CIRCUIT OPEN

TEST STEP	RESULT	▶	ACTION TO TAKE
K1 **VISUAL INSPECTION**			
• Possible Source for STAR CODE 71: —Circuit 431 (PK/W) open. —Circuit 432 (BK/PK) open. —Circuit 427 (PK/BK) open. —Circuit 428 (O/BK) open. —Height sensor connector disconnected. —Damaged height sensor. —Damaged control module. • Turn ignition switch to RUN. • Turn air suspension switch ON. • Enter Functional Test mode. Refer to Functional Test procedure. DO NOT select a Functional Test at this time. STAR tester button should remain in TEST (down) position. NOTE: If the module is not in the functional test mode, the voltages in the following test steps will be incorrect. • Raise vehicle on hoist. • Ensure that height sensor electrical connector is connected and that connector and wiring have no obvious damage. • Are connector and/or wiring worn or damaged?	No Yes	▶ ▶	GO to K2. SERVICE connector and/or wiring as necessary. REPEAT Service Bay Diagnostics.
K2 **CHECK CIRCUITS 427 (PK/BK) AND 428 (O/BK)**			
• Disconnect height sensor. • Measure voltage between Circuits 427 (PK/BK) and 428 (O/BK) and a good chassis ground. • Meter should indicate 4 volts for each circuit. HEIGHT SENSOR HARNESS CONNECTOR · CIRCUIT 427 · CIRCUIT 428 · GOOD CHASSIS GROUND	4 volts Zero volts at either circuit	▶ ▶	GO to K4. GO to K3.

Fig. 24   Test K: Height Sensor Circuit Open (Part 1 of 4)

FM2019200123010X

PINPOINT TEST K
STAR CODE 71: HEIGHT
SENSOR CIRCUIT OPEN (Continued)

TEST STEP	RESULT	▶	ACTION TO TAKE
K3 **ISOLATE OPEN IN CIRCUITS 427 (PK/BK) AND/OR 428 (O/BK) OR MODULE**			
• Turn air suspension switch OFF. • Disconnect control module connectors. • Measure resistance of damaged circuits between height sensor connector and module connector. • Resistance should be less than 10 ohms. • Is resistance less than 10 ohms? HEIGHT SENSOR HARNESS CONNECTOR · CIRCUIT 427 (PK/BK) · CIRCUIT 428 O/BK · CIRCUIT 427 PK/BK · GRAY MODULE CONNECTOR	Yes No	▶ ▶	REPLACE control module. REPEAT Service Bay Diagnostics. LOCATE and SERVICE open in Circuit 427 (PK/BK) and/or 428 (O/BK). REPEAT Service Bay Diagnostics.
K4 **CHECK CIRCUIT 432 (BK/PK)**			
• Measure resistance between Circuit 432 (BK/PK) in height sensor connector and a good ground. • Meter should indicate less than 10 ohms. • Is resistance less than 10 ohms? CIRCUIT 432 HEIGHT SENSOR HARNESS CONNECTOR · GOOD CHASSIS GROUND	Yes No	▶ ▶	GO to K6. GO to K5.

Fig. 24   Test K: Height Sensor Circuit Open (Part 2 of 4)

FM2019200123020X

PINPOINT TEST K
STAR CODE 71: HEIGHT
SENSOR CIRCUIT OPEN (Continued)

TEST STEP	RESULT	▶	ACTION TO TAKE
K5 **ISOLATE OPEN IN CIRCUIT 432 (BK/PK) OR MODULE**			
• Turn air suspension switch OFF. • Disconnect control module connectors. • Measure resistance of Circuit 432 (BK/PK) between the height sensor connector and module connector. • Resistance should be less than 10 ohms. • Is resistance less than 10 ohms? CIRCUIT 432 BK/PK · CIRCUIT 432 BK/PK · HEIGHT SENSOR HARNESS CONNECTOR · BLACK MODULE CONNECTOR	Yes No	▶ ▶	REPLACE control module. REPEAT Service Bay Diagnostics. LOCATE and SERVICE open in Circuit 432 (BK/PK). REPEAT Service Bay Diagnostics.
K6 **CHECK CIRCUIT 431 (PK/W)**			
• Measure voltage between Circuit 431 (PK/W) and a good chassis ground. • Meter should pulse between 4 and 6 volts. CIRCUIT 431 PK/W · GOOD CHASSIS GROUND · HEIGHT SENSOR HARNESS CONNECTOR	Pulsing 4 to 6 volts Zero volts	▶ ▶	Circuit 431 (PK/W) OK, REPEAT Service Bay Diagnostics. GO to K7.

Fig. 24   Test K: Height Sensor Circuit Open (Part 3 of 4)

FM2019200123030X

PINPOINT TEST K
STAR CODE 71: HEIGHT
SENSOR CIRCUIT OPEN (Continued)

TEST STEP	RESULT	▶	ACTION TO TAKE
K7 **ISOLATE OPEN IN CIRCUIT 431 (PK/W) OR MODULE**			
• Turn air suspension switch OFF. • Disconnect control module connectors. • Measure resistance of Circuit 431 (PK/W) between height sensor connector and module connector. • Resistance should be less than 10 ohms. • Is resistance less than 10 ohms? CIRCUIT 431 PK/W · CIRCUIT 431 PK/W · BLACK MODULE CONNECTOR	Yes No	▶ ▶	REPLACE control module. REPEAT Service Bay Diagnostics. LOCATE and SERVICE open in Circuit 431 (PK/W). REPEAT Service Bay Diagnostics.

Fig. 24   Test K: Height Sensor Circuit Open (Part 4 of 4)

FM2019200123040X

PINPOINT TEST L
STAR CODE 72: FOUR OPEN AND CLOSE DOOR SIGNALS NOT DETECTED (Continued)

TEST STEP	RESULT	▶	ACTION TO TAKE
L4 CHECK DOOR HARNESS • Disconnect door switch connector. • Measure voltage at connector between Circuit 54 (LG/Y) and a good chassis ground. • Meter should indicate battery voltage. • Is there battery voltage?	Yes	▶	LEAVE meter connected. GO to L5.
	No	▶	SERVICE open in Circuit 54 (LG/Y) between door switches and fuse panel. REPEAT Service Bay Diagnostics.
L5 JUMPER DOOR HARNESS • Connect a fused jumper between Circuit 54 (LG/Y) and Circuit 159 (R/PK) (driver's door) or 24 (DB/O) (other doors) and observe meter. • Meter should indicate battery voltage. • Is there battery voltage?	Yes	▶	REPLACE door switch. REPEAT Service Bay Diagnostics.
	No	▶	SERVICE open in Circuit 24 (DB/O) between door switch and control module. REPEAT Service Bay Diagnostics.
L6 CHECK FOR SHORT TO BATTERY • Disconnect door switches one at a time and leave disconnected. • Observe meter each time a switch is disconnected.	Meter drops to zero volts when a switch is disconnected	▶	REPLACE door switch. REPEAT Service Bay Diagnostics.
	Meter still reads battery voltage with all four switches disconnected	▶	SERVICE short to battery in Circuit 159 (R/PK) for driver's door Circuit or 24 (DB/O) for other doors. REPEAT Service Bay Diagnostics.

FM2019200124020X

Fig. 25   Test L: Four Open And Close Door Signals Not Detected (Part 2 of 2)

PINPOINT TEST L
STAR CODE 72: FOUR OPEN AND CLOSE DOOR SIGNALS NOT DETECTED

TEST STEP	RESULT	▶	ACTION TO TAKE
L1 CHECK DOOR CIRCUITS • **Possible Source for STAR CODE 72:** —Circuit 159 (R/PK) or 24 (DB/O) has an open circuit. —Worn or damaged door jamb switches. —Circuit 54 (LG/Y) has an open circuit. —Damaged module. • Turn air suspension switch OFF. • Disconnect control module connectors. • Measure voltage between Pins 5 and 6 of gray module connector. NOTE: Leave meter connected during entire pinpoint test. • Open and close each door. • Meter should indicate battery voltage with doors open, zero volts with doors closed.	Battery voltage with doors open, zero volts with door closed	▶	GO to L2.
	No battery voltage	▶	LEAVE meter connected. GO to L3.
	Battery voltage with doors open or closed	▶	LEAVE meter connected. GO to L6.

GRAY MODULE CONNECTOR

TEST STEP	RESULT	▶	ACTION TO TAKE
L2 REPEAT SERVICE BAY DIAGNOSTICS • Repeat Service Bay Diagnostics. • During manual tests, forcefully open and close doors. • Observe error codes. • Does error Code 72 activate?	Yes	▶	REPLACE control module. REPEAT Service Bay Diagnostics.
	No	▶	System OK.
L3 CHECK DOOR SWITCH • Open each door not indicating battery voltage one at a time. • Manually depress door switch several times while observing meter. • Meter should indicate battery voltage with switch released, zero volts with switch depressed.	Meter reading OK	▶	ADJUST door switch. REPEAT Service Bay Diagnostics.
	No battery voltage	▶	LEAVE meter connected. GO to L4.

FM2019200124010X

Fig. 25   Test L: Four Open And Close Door Signals Not Detected (Part 1 of 2)

PINPOINT TEST M
STAR CODE 80: INSUFFICIENT BATTERY VOLTAGE TO RUN DIAGNOSTICS

TEST STEP	RESULT	▶	ACTION TO TAKE
M1 MEASURE SYSTEM VOLTAGE • Turn air suspension switch OFF. • Disconnect control module connectors. • Turn air suspension switch ON. • Measure voltage between Pins 1 and 6 of control module connector, then between Pins 15 and 6.	11 volts or more	▶	GO to M2.
	Less than 11 volts but more than zero volts	▶	CHECK and SERVICE charging system. REPEAT Service Bay Diagnostics.
	Zero volts	▶	LEAVE meter connected. GO to M4.

GRAY MODULE CONNECTOR

FM2019200125010X

Fig. 26   Test M: Insufficient Battery Voltage To Run Diagnostics (Part 1 of 3). Crown Victoria & Grand Marquis

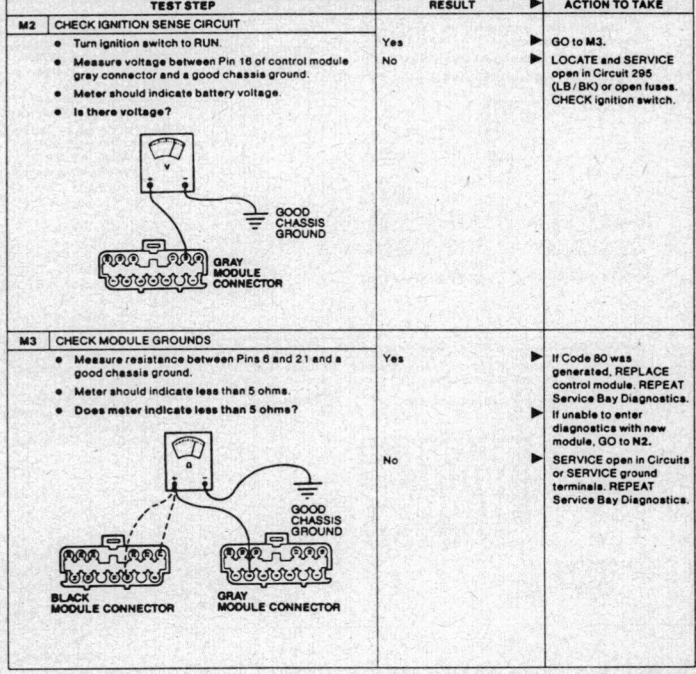

PINPOINT TEST M
STAR CODE 80: INSUFFICIENT BATTERY VOLTAGE TO RUN DIAGNOSTICS (Continued)

TEST STEP	RESULT	▶	ACTION TO TAKE
M2 CHECK IGNITION SENSE CIRCUIT • Turn ignition switch to RUN. • Measure voltage between Pin 16 of control module gray connector and a good chassis ground. • Meter should indicate battery voltage. • Is there voltage?	Yes	▶	GO to M3.
	No	▶	LOCATE and SERVICE open in Circuit 295 (LB/BK) or open fuses. CHECK ignition switch.
M3 CHECK MODULE GROUNDS • Measure resistance between Pins 6 and 21 and a good chassis ground. • Meter should indicate less than 5 ohms. • Does meter indicate less than 5 ohms?	Yes	▶	If Code 80 was generated, REPLACE control module. REPEAT Service Bay Diagnostics. If unable to enter diagnostics with new module, GO to N2.
	No	▶	SERVICE open in Circuits or SERVICE ground terminals. REPEAT Service Bay Diagnostics.

FM2019200125020X

Fig. 26   Test M: Insufficient Battery Voltage To Run Diagnostics (Part 2 of 3). Crown Victoria & Grand Marquis

TEST STEP	RESULT	▶	ACTION TO TAKE
M4 CHECK AIR SUSPENSION SWITCH • Disconnect air suspension switch. • Connect a fused jumper between Circuit 37 (Y) and 418 (DG / Y) at connector. • Read meter. • Is there voltage?	Yes No	▶ ▶	REPLACE air suspension switch. REPEAT Service Bay Diagnostics. REMOVE jumper. GO to M5.
M5 CHECK BATTERY CIRCUIT • Measure voltage between Circuit 414 (O / R) of air suspension switch connector and a good chassis ground. • Read meter. • Is there voltage?	Yes No	▶ ▶	SERVICE open in Circuit 418 (DG / Y) between switch and control module. REPEAT Service Bay Diagnostics. CHECK feed fuses or SERVICE open in Circuit 414 (O / R) between switch and fuse panel.

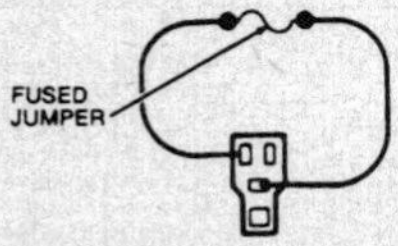

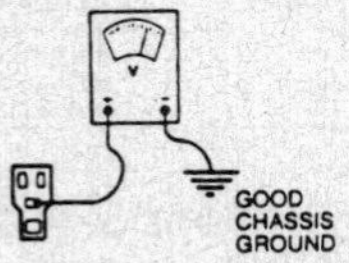

FM2019200125030X

Fig. 26   Test M: Insufficient Battery Voltage To Run Diagnostics (Part 3 of 3). Crown Victoria & Grand Marquis

TEST STEP	RESULT	▶	ACTION TO TAKE
M1 MEASURE SYSTEM VOLTAGE • Turn air suspension switch OFF. • Disconnect control module connectors. • Turn air suspension switch ON. • Measure voltage between Pins 1 and 6 of control module connector.	11 volts or more Less than 11 volts but more than zero volts Zero volts	▶ ▶ ▶	GO to M2. CHECK and SERVICE charging system. REPEAT Service Bay Diagnostics. LEAVE meter connected. GO to M4.
M2 CHECK IGNITION SENSE CIRCUIT • Turn ignition switch to RUN. • Measure voltage between Pin 16 of control module gray connector and a good chassis ground. • Meter should indicate battery voltage. • Is there voltage?	Yes No	▶ ▶	GO to M3. LOCATE and SERVICE open in Circuit 295 (LB / BK) or open fuses. CHECK ignition switch.

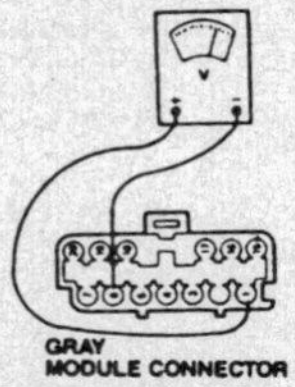

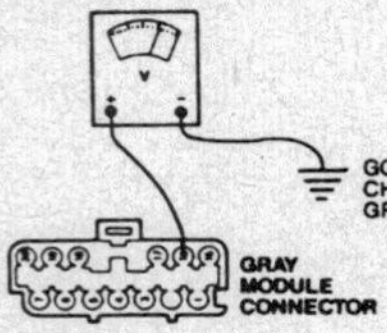

FM2019200126010X

Fig. 27   Test M: Insufficient Battery Voltage To Run Diagnostics (Part 1 of 3). Town Car

TEST STEP	RESULT	▶	ACTION TO TAKE
M3 CHECK MODULE GROUNDS • Measure resistance between Pins 6 and 21 and a good chassis ground. • Meter should indicate less than 5 ohms. • Does meter indicate less than 5 ohms?	Yes No	▶ ▶	If Code 80 was generated, REPLACE control module. REPEAT Service Bay Diagnostics. If unable to enter diagnostics with new module, GO to N2. SERVICE open in Circuits or SERVICE ground terminals. REPEAT Service Bay Diagnostics.
M4 CHECK FUSES • Remove and inspect 15 amp fuse in fuse panel and 50 amp fuse in power distribution box. NOTE: If dome lamp works, 50 amp fuse is OK.	Fuses good Fuses blown	▶ ▶	LEAVE meter connected. GO to M5. LOCATE and SERVICE short to ground in circuits for fuses. REPEAT Service Bay Diagnostics.

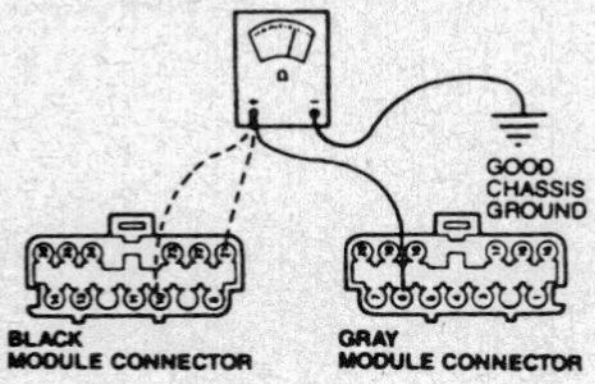

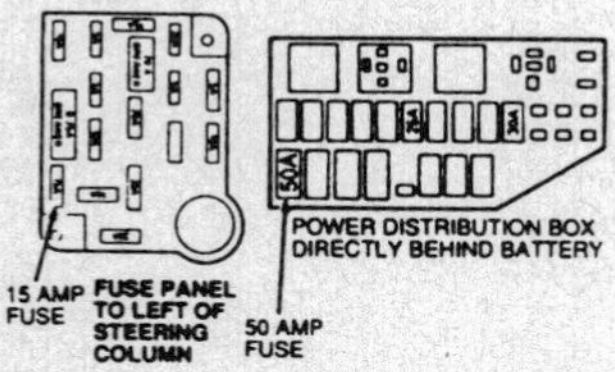

FM2019200126020X

Fig. 27   Test M: Insufficient Battery Voltage To Run Diagnostics (Part 2 of 3). Town Car

TEST STEP	RESULT	▶	ACTION TO TAKE
M5 CHECK AIR SUSPENSION SWITCH • Disconnect air suspension switch. • Connect a fused jumper between Circuit 296 (W / P) and 418 (DG / Y) at connector. • Read meter. • Is there voltage?	Yes No	▶ ▶	REPLACE air suspension switch. REPEAT Service Bay Diagnostics. REMOVE jumper. GO to M6.
M6 CHECK BATTERY CIRCUIT • Measure voltage between Circuit 296 (W / P) of air suspension switch connector and a good chassis ground. • Read meter. • Is there voltage?	Yes No	▶ ▶	SERVICE open in Circuit 418 (DG / Y) between switch and control module. REPEAT Service Bay Diagnostics. CHECK feed fuses or SERVICE open in Circuit 296 (W / P) between switch and fuse panel.

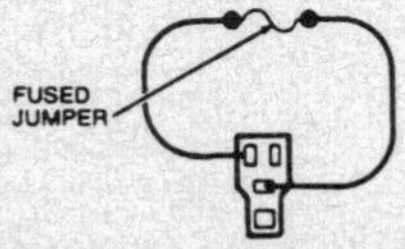

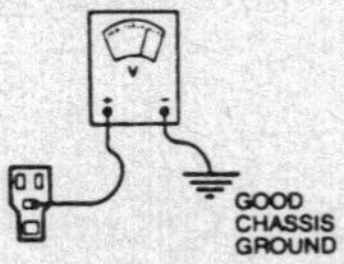

FM2019200126030X

Fig. 27   Test M: Insufficient Battery Voltage To Run Diagnostics (Part 3 of 3). Town Car

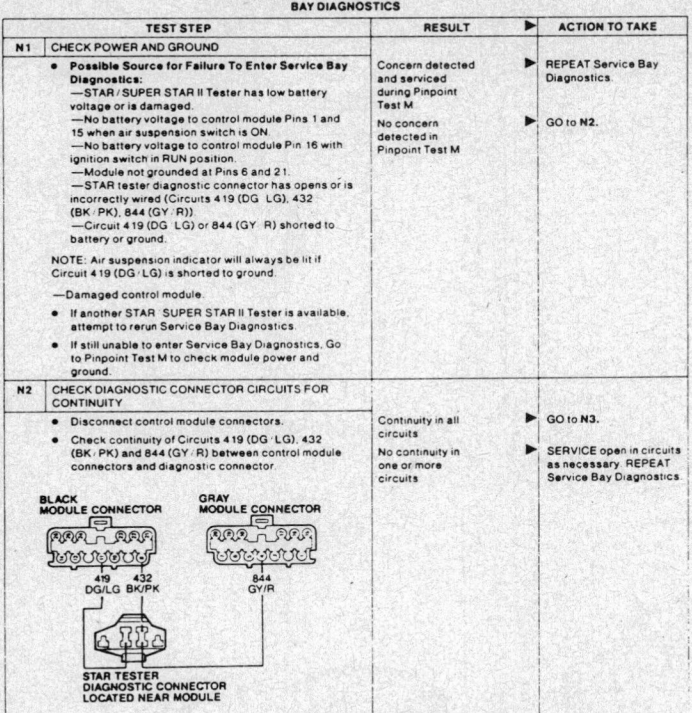

PINPOINT TEST N
UNABLE TO ENTER SERVICE
BAY DIAGNOSTICS

TEST STEP	RESULT	▶	ACTION TO TAKE
N1 CHECK POWER AND GROUND			
• **Possible Source for Failure To Enter Service Bay Diagnostics:** —STAR / SUPER STAR II Tester has low battery voltage or is damaged. —No battery voltage to control module Pins 1 and 15 when air suspension switch is ON. —No battery voltage to control module Pin 16 with ignition switch in RUN position. —Module not grounded at Pins 6 and 21. —STAR tester diagnostic connector has opens or is incorrectly wired (Circuits 419 (DG LG), 432 (BK / PK), 844 (GY / R)). —Circuit 419 (DG LG) or 844 (GY R) shorted to battery or ground. NOTE: Air suspension indicator will always be lit if Circuit 419 (DG·LG) is shorted to ground. —Damaged control module. • If another STAR SUPER STAR II Tester is available, attempt to rerun Service Bay Diagnostics. • If still unable to enter Service Bay Diagnostics, Go to Pinpoint Test M to check module power and ground.	Concern detected and serviced during Pinpoint Test M No concern detected in Pinpoint Test M	▶	REPEAT Service Bay Diagnostics. ▶ GO to N2.
N2 CHECK DIAGNOSTIC CONNECTOR CIRCUITS FOR CONTINUITY			
• Disconnect control module connectors. • Check continuity of Circuits 419 (DG / LG), 432 (BK · PK) and 844 (GY · R) between control module connectors and diagnostic connector.	Continuity in all circuits No continuity in one or more circuits	▶	GO to N3. ▶ SERVICE open in circuits as necessary. REPEAT Service Bay Diagnostics.

FM2019200127010X

Fig. 28 Test N: Unable To Enter Service Bay Diagnostics (Part 1 of 3)

PINPOINT TEST N
UNABLE TO ENTER SERVICE
BAY DIAGNOSTICS (Continued)

TEST STEP	RESULT	▶	ACTION TO TAKE
N3 CHECK FOR SHORT TO BATTERY			
• Measure voltage between diagnostic connector Circuit 419 (DG/LG) and a good ground. • Measure voltage between diagnostic connector Circuit 844 (GY / R) and a good ground. • Meter should indicate zero volts at both circuits.	Zero volts for both measurements Battery voltage on Circuit 419 (DG/LG) and / or 844 (GY/R)	▶	GO to N4. ▶ SERVICE short to battery as necessary. REPEAT Service Bay Diagnostics.
N4 CHECK CIRCUITS FOR SHORT TO GROUND			
• Measure resistance between diagnostic connector Circuit 419 (DG/LG) and a good ground. • Measure resistance between diagnostic connector Circuit 844 (GY / R) and a good ground. • Meter should indicate more than 10,000 ohms.	More than 10,000 ohms for both measurements Less than 10,000 ohms on Circuit 419 (DG / LG) and / or 844 (GY / R)	▶	GO to N5. ▶ SERVICE short to ground as necessary. REPEAT Service Bay Diagnostics.

FM2019200127020X

Fig. 28 Test N: Unable To Enter Service Bay Diagnostics (Part 2 of 3)

PINPOINT TEST N
UNABLE TO ENTER SERVICE
BAY DIAGNOSTICS (Continued)

TEST STEP	RESULT	▶	ACTION TO TAKE
N5 MEASURE RESISTANCE OF POWER FEED			
• Disconnect positive battery cable. • Measure resistance between Pin 1 on module connector and positive battery terminal. • **Is resistance less than 5 ohms?** NOTE: Look for bad connections at harness connectors.	Yes No	▶	REPLACE control module. REPEAT Service Bay Diagnostics. ▶ SERVICE open or bad connection on Circuits 797 and 62. REPEAT Service Bay Diagnostics.

FM2019200127030X

Fig. 28 Test N: Unable To Enter Service Bay Diagnostics (Part 3 of 3)

SYSTEM SERVICE

ADJUSTMENT

RIDE HEIGHT SETUP & MEASUREMENT

1. Position vehicle on level surface.
2. Ensure air suspension switch is in ON position, then turn ignition switch to Run position, waiting about 2 minutes.
3. Rock vehicle sideways to remove effect of suspension friction, then allow to settle.
4. Turn air suspension switch to Off position.
5. Measure vertical dimension from rear axle tube frame inboard reinforcement rail, **Fig. 29.**
6. Position suitable height gauge, **Fig. 30,** then measure rear ride height "D" dimension.
7. If "D" ride height dimension is not within specifications, **Fig. 29,** adjust by moving rear height sensor attaching bracket up or down, **Fig. 31.** Moving bracket one index mark up or down will change vertical "D" dimension about .35 inch.
8. After adjustment is made, repeat steps 4 through 6.

COMPONENT REPLACEMENT

AIR SPRING SOLENOID

1. Disconnect battery ground cable.
2. Turn air suspension switch to Off position.
3. Raise and support vehicle, ensuring suspension is at full rebound.
4. Remove heat shield, if equipped.
5. Disconnect air spring solenoid electrical connector.
6. Push down and hold air line plastic release ring, then disconnect attaching air line.
7. Remove air spring solenoid attaching clip.

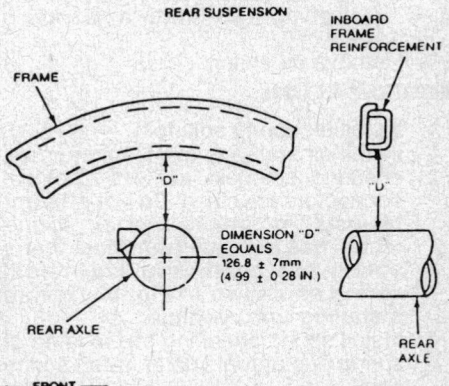

MEASURE "D" DIMENSION VERTICALLY FROM AXLE
TUBE TO FRAME INBOARD REINFORCEMENT RAIL

FM2019100128000X

Fig. 29 Vertical "D" dimension

DIMENSION "D" EQUALS 126.8 ± 7mm (4.99 ± 0.28 IN)

8. Rotate solenoid counterclockwise to first stop.
9. Pull solenoid out to second stop, then bled air from system. **Do not fully release solenoid until air is completely bled from air spring.**
10. Rotate air spring solenoid counterclockwise to third stop, then remove solenoid from housing.
11. Remove O-ring from solenoid housing.
12. Reverse procedure to install.

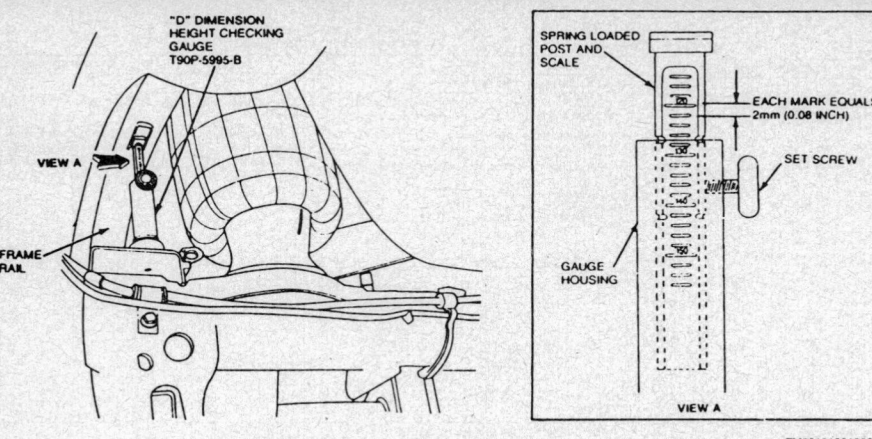

Fig. 30 Ride height "D" dimension

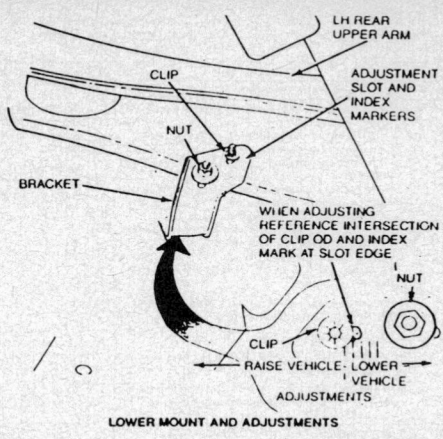

Fig. 31 Height Sensor Adjustment

AIR SPRING

Removal

1. Turn air suspension switch to Off position.
2. Raise and support vehicle.
3. Remove heat shield attaching screws, then remove heat shield.
4. Remove air spring solenoid as outlined under "Air Spring Solenoid."
5. Remove spring piston to axle spring seat as follows:
   a. Insert air spring removal tool No. T90P-5310-A or equivalent, between axle and spring seat on forward side of axle.
   b. Position tool so flat end is on piston knob.
   c. Push downward, forcing piston and attaching clip from axle spring seat.
6. Remove air spring.

Installation

1. Install air spring solenoid.
2. Install air spring to frame spring seat, ensuring solenoid air and electrical connectors are clean. **Do not attempt to install or inflate any air spring which has become unfolded. If any spring has been unfolded, refold spring as shown in Fig. 32, before installing unto vehicle.**
3. Install spring attaching clip to knob of spring cap at top side of frame spring seat.
4. Connect air solenoid air line and electrical connector.
5. Install heat shield.
6. Align air spring piston to axle seats. Squeeze to increase pressure and push downward on piston, then snap piston to axle seat at rebound. **Air spring may be damaged if suspension is allowed to compress before spring is inflated.**
7. Refill air springs as outlined in "Air Spring Refill."

CONTROL MODULE

1. Disconnect battery ground cable.
2. Turn sir suspension switch to the Off position.
3. Remove right luggage compartment trim panel.

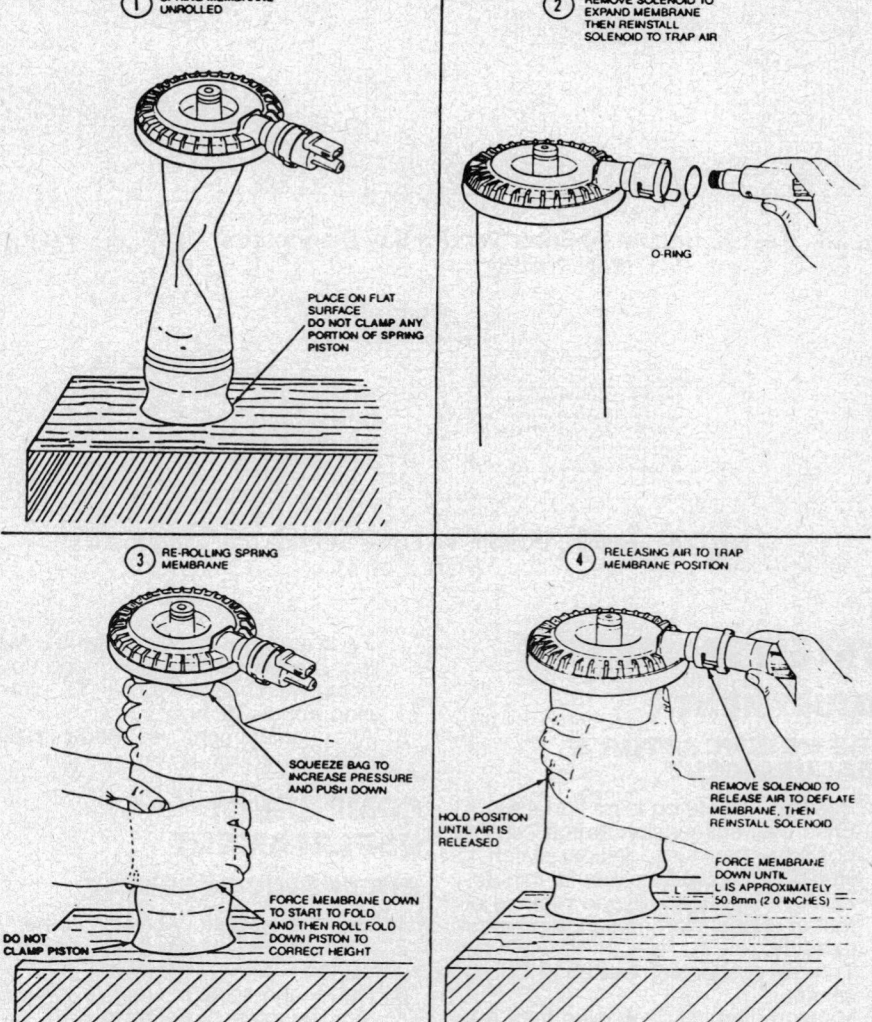

Fig. 32 Refolding air spring

4. Remove control module attaching nuts, **Fig. 1.**
5. Pull module forward to gain access to electrical connectors.
6. Push control module electrical connector release button, then pull connector from module.
7. Reverse to install. **Torque** module attaching nuts to 5-7 ft. lbs.

AIR COMPRESSOR & DRYER ASSEMBLY

1. Disconnect battery ground cable.
2. Turn air suspension switch to Off position.
3. Remove air cleaner housing assembly as follows:
   a. Loosen air tube to throttle body clamp, then remove air tube end.
   b. Unfasten air cleaner lid attaching clips, then remove air cleaner lid.
   c. Remove air filter element.
   d. Remove 2 outer and 1 inner lower air cleaner assembly attaching nuts.
   e. Remove lower air cleaner assembly.
4. Remove air compressor and dryer assembly splash shield and pushpins, **Fig. 1.**
5. Push dryer air line retainer inward, then pull air line outward to remove.
6. Disconnect compressor electrical connectors.
7. Raise and support vehicle.
8. Remove compressor to fender apron attaching nuts.
9. Lower vehicle.
10. Remove compressor and dryer assembly.
11. Reverse to procedure install.

AIR COMPRESSOR DRYER

1. Turn air suspension switch to the Off position.
2. Disconnect battery ground cable.
3. Remove air compressor and dryer assembly as outlined previously.
4. Remove dryer to compressor attaching screw.
5. Rotate dryer clockwise, then remove from compressor.
6. Remove O-ring seal, then discard O-ring.
7. Reverse procedure to install. **Torque** dryer to compressor attaching screw to 15-25 inch lbs.

REAR HEIGHT SENSOR

1. Turn air suspension switch to Off position.
2. Disconnect battery ground cable.
3. Raise and support vehicle, ensuring

Code	Description
23	Vent Rear
26	Compress Rear
31	Cycle Compressor On and Off Repeatedly
32	Cycle Vent Solenoid Valve Open and Closed Repeatedly
33	Cycle Spring Solenoid Valves Open and Closed Repeatedly

FM2019100132000X

Fig. 33   STAR code order

suspension is at full rebound.
4. Disconnect height sensor electrical connector.
5. Depress spring clip at bottom and top of sensor from ball studs, then pull sensor, **Fig. 1.**
6. Reverse procedure to install.

AIR SUSPENSION SWITCH

1. Disconnect battery ground cable.
2. Depress air suspension switch attaching clips, **Fig. 1.**
3. Disconnect switch electrical connector, then remove switch.
4. Reverse procedure to install.

COMPRESSOR RELAY

1. Disconnect battery ground cable.
2. Remove power distribution box cover.
3. Remove compressor relay from distribution box.
4. Reverse procedure to install.

AIR SPRING REFILL

1. Raise and support vehicle, ensuring rear wheels are off ground and no load to rear suspension. **Do not apply any load to suspension until springs have been inflated for at least 90 seconds.**
2. Turn air suspension switch to ON position.
3. Install battery charger to minimize battery drain.
4. Turn ignition switch to ON position, then allow engine to run.
5. Remove right luggage compartment trim panel, then connect STAR/SUPER STAR II tester to air suspension diagnostic connector, **Fig. 1.**
6. Set tester to EEC-IV/MCU mode and fast mode, then release tester button to hold position, then turn tester to ON position.
7. Depress tester button to test position, Code 10 should be indicated.
8. Within 2 minutes Code 13 should be indicated, then release tester to UP position, wait 5 seconds, then depress tester button to DOWN position (ignore codes indicated).
9. Release tester button to UP position, wait 20 seconds, then depress tester

button to DOWN position, within 10 seconds codes will be indicated in order **Fig. 33.**
10. Within 4 seconds after Code 26 is indicated release tester button to UP position, waiting longer than 4 seconds may allow Functional Test 31 to be entered.
11. Compressor will fill air springs until tester button is depressed to DOWN position. **Overheating compressor is possible during this operation. The self resetting circuit breaker in compressor will open and remain open for 15 minutes to allow compressor to cool.**
12. Disconnect tester, then turn ignition switch to Off position.

TECHNICAL SERVICE BULLETINS

REAR AIR SUSPENSION/ELECTRONIC VARIABLE ORIFICE MODULE OVERLY SENSITIVE

1992 Grand Marquis & Town Car

Some power steering systems may be overly sensitive to small variations in the level of assist made by the RAS/EVO module. A light pulsation may be felt through the steering wheel during freeway exit ramp turns at speeds of about 44 mph. These conditions occur because the RAS/EVO module is fine tuning the level of power steering assist. Test drive vehicle and, if necessary, replace RAS/EVO module

1. Turn Off air suspension/variable power steering switch located on right rear quarter panel in trunk compartment.
2. Test drive vehicle to confirm that pulsation is gone.
3. If pulsation is gone, replace RAS/EVO module. On Town Car, RAS/EVO module is located on the righthand side of the luggage compartment. On Crown Victoria and Grand Marquis, the module is located on the left side seat back/package tray and is accessed through the luggage compartment.
4. **Torque** module mounting screws to 45–53 inch lbs.
5. Turn On air suspension/variable power steering switch.

Automatic Ride Control

INDEX

DESCRIPTION

The automatic ride control (ARC) system, used on Thunderbird Super Coupe and Cougar XR7 models, provides the selection of either a firm (sport) suspension tuning or an automatic ride control.

The ARC system is activated using a rocker switch mounted on the instrument panel to the right of the steering column. With the switch in the "FIRM" position, the ride control module adjusts shock absorber damping to provide a firm (sport) suspension tuning.

With the switch in the "AUTO" position, the ride control module adjusts shock absorber damping to provide a soft (plush) ride during normal driving conditions. The module instantly changes suspension tuning to firm during hard braking, acceleration or cornering to provide improved handling at high speed.

A green "FIRM RIDE" indicator lamp is located at the lower righthand corner of the tachometer. The lamp is normally illuminated whenever the suspension is firm. This includes any time the switch is in the "FIRM" position or any time the system switches to the firm tuning in the "AUTO" switch position.

In the event of a system malfunction, the indicator lamp will flash On and Off. Moving the ride control switch between positions will usually clear any false malfunction indication. If the indicator lamp continues to flash, the system should be checked for possible malfunctions.

OPERATION

The ARC system, **Fig. 1**, monitors the following conditions to determine when additional shock absorber damping is required for improved handling:

1. Brake hydraulic pressure.
2. Throttle position.
3. Super charger boost.
4. Steering wheel angle.
5. Vehicle speed.

Any one of the following approximate conditions will cause shock absorber damping to switch to FIRM:

1. Hard braking, brake hydraulic pressure above 400 psi.
2. More than 90 percent of full throttle.
3. Hard cornering, above 0.35g lateral acceleration.
4. Vehicle speed above 90 mph.

The shock damping will return to the softer ride a few seconds after these conditions are no longer present, providing vehicle speed has dropped below 83 mph.

The ARC system will not respond to hard turns during the first 80 seconds of driving. This delay allows the ARC system to calculate the straight ahead steering wheel position. Severe or repeated turns in one direction could lengthen the wheel position calculation time by several minutes. All other features of the system operate normally during this period.

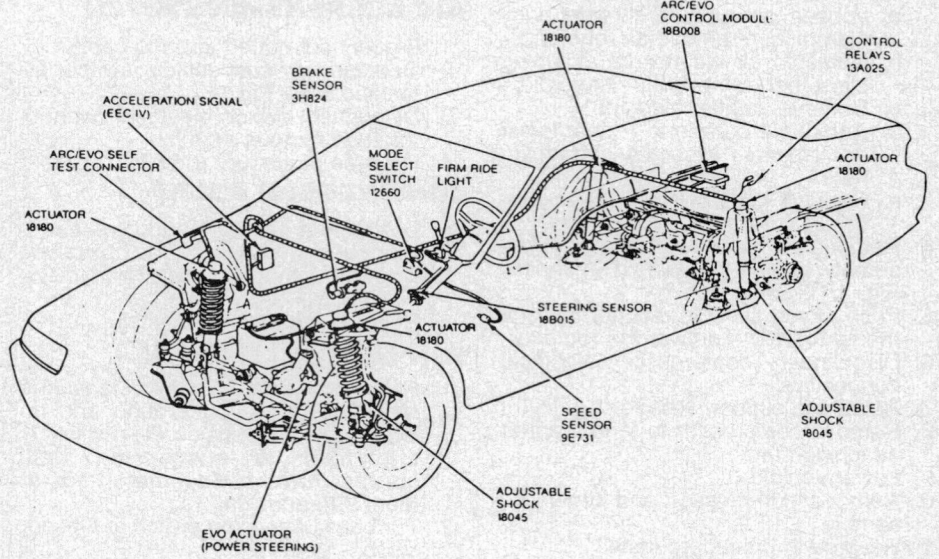

Fig. 1 Automatic ride control system

TROUBLESHOOTING

SHOCK DAMPENING CONTROL INOPERATIVE

1. Open or shorted circuitry.
2. Blown fuses.
3. Damaged relays.
4. Damaged shock absorber electronic system control.
5. Damaged shock absorber electronic steering sensor.
6. Damaged vehicle speed sensor.
7. Damaged brake pressure control valve.
8. Damaged air spring suspension drive switch.

RIDE TOO STIFF/TOO SOFT

1. Open or shorted circuitry.
2. Damaged relays.
3. Damaged air spring suspension drive switch.
4. Damaged shock absorber electronic system control.

RIDE CONTROL INDICATOR LAMP NOT OPERATING CORRECTLY

1. Open or shorted circuitry.
2. Damaged shock absorber electronic system control.

SINGLE SHOCK ABSORBER/ELECTRONIC ACTUATOR INOPERATIVE

1. Open or shorted circuitry.
2. Open or shorted shock absorber actuator.

WIRING CIRCUITS & CONNECTOR PIN IDENTIFICATION

Refer to **Figs. 2 through 5**, for wiring circuits and connector pin identifications.

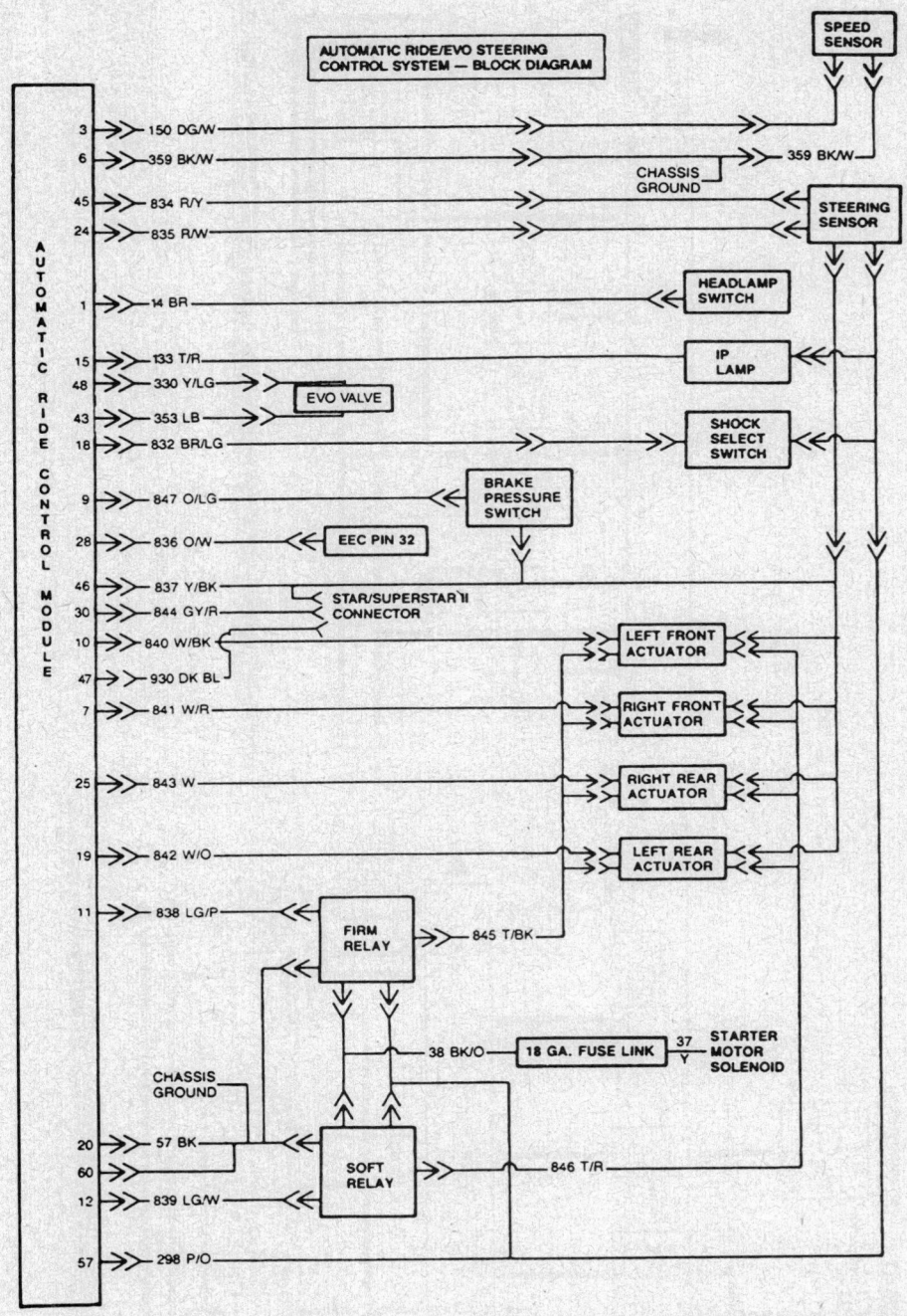

Fig. 2   ARC system wiring circuit. 1992–93

FM2019200139000X

DIAGNOSIS & TESTING

Whenever a diagnostic procedure requires testing circuits at the ARC module connector, the Rotunda EEC-IV 60-pin Breakout Box tool No. 014-00322 or equivalent, should be used to facilitate testing.

Probing directly into the harness connector can damage the terminals and cause intermittent system malfunctions.

Refer to the quick test, **Fig. 6,** and the related pinpoint tests, **Figs. 7 through 14,** as directed from the quick test, to diagnose the ARC system.

Continued on page 31-150

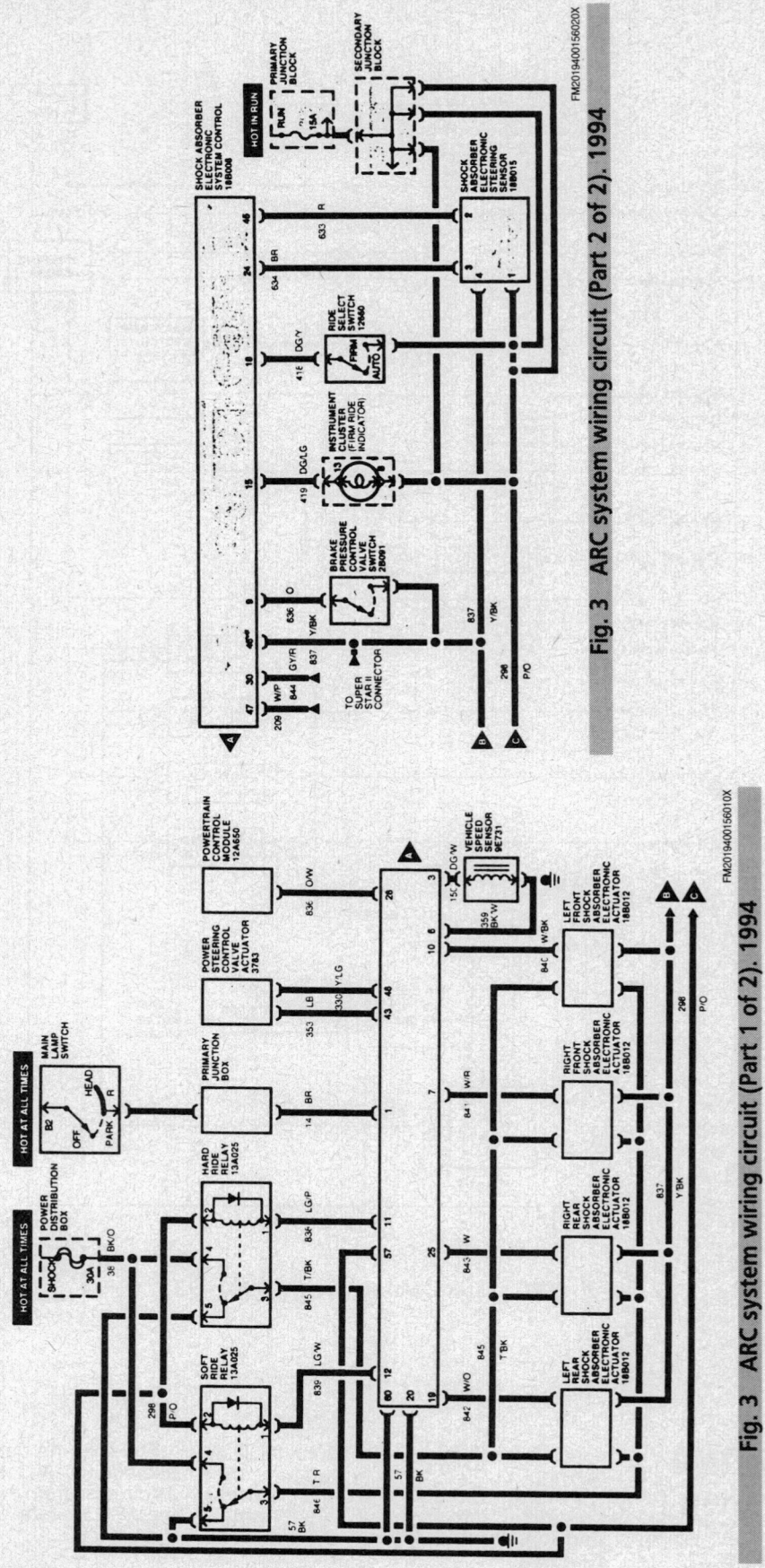

Fig. 3 ARC system wiring circuit (Part 2 of 2). 1994

Fig. 3 ARC system wiring circuit (Part 1 of 2). 1994

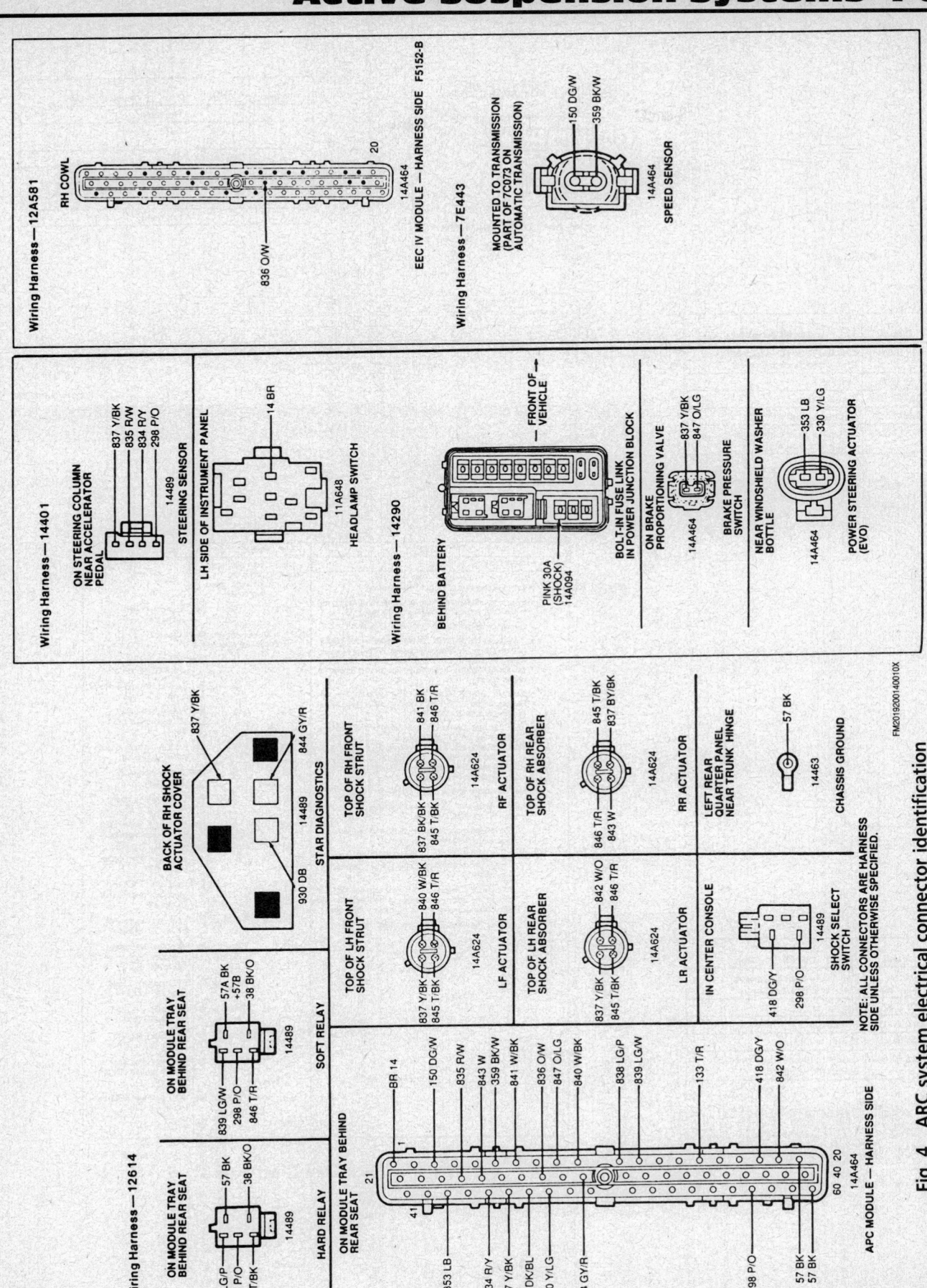

Fig. 4 ARC system electrical connector identification (Part 2 of 2). 1992–93

Fig. 4 ARC system electrical connector identification
(Part 1 of 2). 1992–93

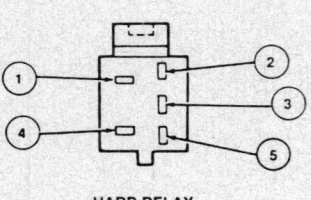

HARD RELAY

Pin Number	Circuit	Circuit Function
1	838 (LG/P)	Coil Out to Shock Absorber Electronic System Control
2	57 (BK)	Ground
3	38 (BK/O)	Switch Supply
4	298 (P/O)	Supply to Coil
5	845 (T/BK)	Output to Shock Absorber Electronic Actuator

FM2019400157010X

Fig. 5 ARC system electrical connector identification (Part 1 of 3). 1994

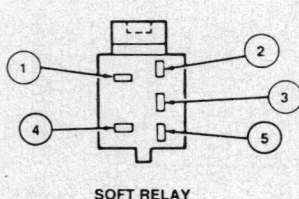

SOFT RELAY

Pin Number	Circuit	Circuit Function
1	839 (LG/W)	Coil Out to Shock Absorber Electronic System Control
2	57 (BK)	Ground
3	38 (BK/O)	Switch Supply
4	298 (P/O)	Supply to Coil
5	846 (T/R)	Output to Shock Absorber Electronic Actuator

FM2019400157020X

Fig. 5 ARC system electrical connector identification (Part 2 of 3). 1994

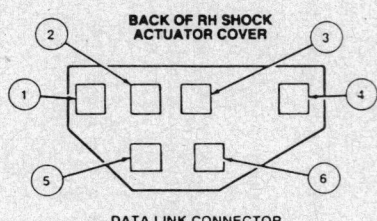

BACK OF RH SHOCK ACTUATOR COVER

DATA LINK CONNECTOR

Pin Number	Circuit	Circuit Function
1	—	Not Used
2	844 (GY/R)	STO
3	209 (W/P)	STI
4	—	Not Used
5	837 (Y/BK)	Reference Voltage
6	—	Not Used

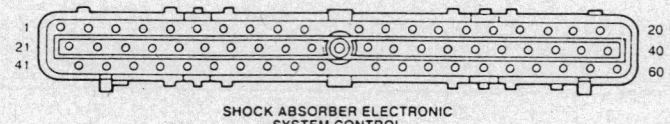

SHOCK ABSORBER ELECTRONIC SYSTEM CONTROL

FM2019400157030X

Fig. 5 ARC system electrical connector identification (Part 3 of 3). 1994

QUICK TEST

TEST STEP		RESULT		ACTION TO TAKE
A1	**ENTER DIAGNOSTICS**	Star codes	Firm ride lamp blinks the following codes two times	
	• Turn ignition switch to the OFF position.	11	1 THEN 1	No problem yet GO to A2.
	• Ensure headlamps, parking lamps and auto lamps are in the OFF position during the entire test.			GO to B1.
	• Set shock select switch to the AUTO position.	NOTE: If all four actuator codes are received.		
	• Take Rotunda SUPER STAR II (Model 007-00019, 007-00028) or Star (Model 007-00017) Tester or equivalent and place in the "HOLD" up position. Format for the SUPER STAR II can be in slow or fast format for status codes.	10	1	Fault in LH rear actuator circuit GO to B8.
		20	2	Fault in RH rear actuator circuit GO to B8.
	• Connect SUPER STAR II or Star tester to STI connecter marked "ARC/EVO", located under hood by the passenger side shock tower.	30	3	Fault in RH front actuator circuit GO to B8.
	• Turn the Star Tester on, and depress the Star test button to the "TEST" down position.	40	4	Fault in LH front actuator circuit GO to B8.
	NOTE: If using a SUPER STAR II tester, make sure the mode switch is in the EEC-IV, MCU mode not the MECS mode. If in MECS mode you will get invalid error codes.	50	5	Short in soft relay GO to B21.
	• Do NOT move shock select switch during test.	60	6	EVO steering open circuit GO to E1.
	• Start engine and perform the following steps while engine is running.	70	7	REPLACE automatic ride control module.
	1. The following procedure must be initiated within 20 seconds after starting the engine.	12	1 then 2	Soft relay short to ground or open circuit GO to B21.
	2. Release Star tester in the "TEST" mode to the "HOLD" mode and back to the "TEST" mode within 5 seconds.	13	1 THEN 3	Hard relay short to ground or open circuit GO to B21.
	3. The ARC/EVO module will run through self-test procedure and record error codes to the Star tester and also pulse out error codes to the firm ride lamp.	14	1 THEN 4	Fault in relay control circuit GO to B25.
	NOTE: The lamp will blink the same code two times.	15	ON ALWAYS	Firm ride lamp short to ground or open circuit GO to C9.
		16	1 THEN 6	EVO steering circuit short GO to E4.
		22	2 THEN 2	Soft relay short to battery GO to B21.
		23	2 THEN 3	Hard relay short to battery GO to B21.
		25		Firm ride lamp short to battery ground GO to C2.
		26	2 THEN 6	EVO steering valve bad GO to E4.
		00		GO to C1.

FM2019200141010X

Fig. 6 Quick Test (Part 1 of 3)

QUICK TEST

TEST STEP	RESULT	▶	ACTION TO TAKE
A2 CHECK STEERING SENSOR			
NOTE: Steps A2 and A3 may be repeated as many times and in any order desired to ensure proper test results. However, once the engine is turned off or the shock select switch is moved, you must proceed to step A4 or start over at step A1. • Wait until lamp has stopped blinking. • With the vehicle at rest and engine running, test the steering sensor by turning the steering wheel from lock in one direction to lock in the other direction (3 full turns) or until firm ride lamp turns on. NOTE: The lamp will usually turn on before the wheel has completed the lock turn. This is normal.	Firm ride lamp turns on for 5 seconds, then turns off	▶	GO to A3.
	Firm ride lamp does not turn on	▶	Fault in steering sensor circuit. GO to D13.
A3 CHECK SPEED SENSOR			
• Wait until lamp has turned off from Step A2. • Drive the vehicle at any desired speed above 29 Km·h (18 mph).	Firm ride lamp turns on and stays on until vehicle speed drops below (18 mph) 29 Km/h	▶	GO to A4.
	Firm ride lamp does not turn on	▶	Fault in speed sensor circuit. PERFORM Test Step D19.
A4 PREPARE FOR REMAINING TESTS			
• Stop vehicle and turn engine off. • Move shock select switch to AUTO if it is not already there. • Move the ignition switch to the RUN position, leaving the engine off. • Wait until the firm ride indicator has turned off (usually after 4 seconds).	Firm ride lamp turns on for 4 seconds, then turns off	▶	GO to A5.
	Firm ride lamp turns on and stays on even though switch is in AUTO position	▶	False firm signal. PERFORM Test Step D6.
	Firm ride lamp turns on for 4 seconds, then flashes a code	▶	RECORD code and REFER to Step A1 for action to take.
A5 CHECK SHOCK SELECT SWITCH			
NOTE: Step A5 through A6 may be performed in any order and as many times as desired to ensure satisfactory results. • Move the shock select switch to AUTO if it is not already there. • After the firm ride lamp has turned off, move the shock select switch to the FIRM position. • After the firm ride lamp has turned on, move the shock select switch back to the AUTO position.	Firm ride lamp turns on in FIRM, off in AUTO	▶	GO to A6.
	Firm ride lamp does not turn on	▶	Fault in shock select switch circuit. PERFORM Pinpoint Test Step D23.
	Firm ride lamp flashes a code	▶	RECORD code and REFER to Step A1 for action to take.

FM2019200141020X

Fig. 6   Quick Test (Part 2 of 3)

TEST STEP	RESULT	▶	ACTION TO TAKE
A6 CHECK BRAKE SENSOR			
• Move the shock select switch to AUTO if it is not already there. • After the firm ride lamp has turned off, depress the brake pedal until the firm ride lamp turns on. • After the firm ride lamp has turned on, release the brake pedal.	Firm ride lamp turns on	▶	GO to A7.
	Firm ride lamp does not turn on	▶	Fault in brake sensor circuit. PERFORM Pinpoint Test Step D27.
	Firm ride lamp flashes a code	▶	RECORD code and REFER to Step A1 for action to take.
A7 CHECK ACCELERATION SIGNAL			
• Move the shock select switch to AUTO if it is not already there. • After the firm ride lamp has turned off, depress the accelerator pedal to the floor. The firm ride lamp should turn on. • After the firm ride lamp has turned on, release the accelerator pedal.	Firm ride lamp turns on when pedal is pressed to the floor, off 4 seconds after the pedal is released	▶	GO to A8.
	Firm ride lamp does not turn on	▶	Fault in acceleration signal circuit. PERFORM Pinpoint Test Step D31.
	Firm ride lamp flashes a code	▶	RECORD code and REFER to Step A1 for action to take.
A8 CHECK DIMMING FUNCTION			
• Move the shock selector switch to the FIRM position to turn on instrument panel indicator. • Cycle headlamps on and off while observing FIRM ride indicator.	Firm ride lamp is bright with headlamps off, dimmer with headlamps on	▶	If test has been completed (Steps A1 through A8) and the vehicle has passed diagnostics.
	Firm ride lamp does not get dimmer with headlamps on	▶	PERFORM Pinpoint Test Step C6.

FM2019200141030X

Fig. 6   Quick Test (Part 3 of 3)

DIAGNOSTIC CHART INDEX

Test	Description	Page No.	Fig. No.
1992-93			
B	**Actuator Control Circuit**	31-144	7
C	**Firm Ride Indicator Lamp Circuit**	31-145	8
D	**Module Input Circuit**	31-146	9
E	**Module Input Circuit**	31-147	10
1994			
A	**Shock Damping Inoperative**	31-148	11
B	**Ride Too Stiff/Soft**	31-149	12
C	**Ride Control Indicator Lamp Not Operating Correctly**	31-149	13
D	**Single Shock Absorber/Electronic Actuator Inoperative**	31-149	14

**PINPOINT TEST B: ACTUATOR CONTROL CIRCUIT
DIAGNOSIS**

	TEST STEP	RESULT	►	ACTION TO TAKE
B1	CHECK CONNECTOR WIRES			
	• Turn ignition to the OFF position.	No	►	GO to B2.
	• Examine the wires on all actuator connectors and on the wiring harness side to ensure that there is no obvious damage and that all of the wires are in the proper location.	Yes	►	SERVICE wires as necessary.
	• **Are wires damaged or in wrong position?**			
B2	SIGNAL RETURN CONTINUITY			
	• Go to luggage compartment and lower the control module packaging tray behind the driver's side back seat.	Greater than 1000 ohms	►	SERVICE open circuit in signal return line (Circuit 837).
	• Disconnect the 60-pin electrical connector from the ARC module. Connect harness to 60-Pin Breakout Box.	Less than 10 ohms	►	GO to B3.
	• Measure resistance between signal return Pin-46 (Circuit 837) in the wiring harness side of the actuator connector, and chassis ground.			

FM2019200142010X

**Fig. 7   Test B: Actuator Control Circuit (Part 1 of 7).
1992–93**

**PINPOINT TEST B: ACTUATOR CONTROL CIRCUIT
DIAGNOSIS (Continued)**

	TEST STEP	RESULT	►	ACTION TO TAKE
B3	DO POSITION SWITCHES OPEN?			
	• Turn the ignition to RUN position.	All four switches are open	►	GO to B4.
	• Use a jumper wire to connect Pin 11 to 60 on the wiring harness side of the 60-pin connector for 1 or 2 seconds.	All four switches are closed	►	Fault in power distribution. GO to B12.
	• Use an ohmmeter to measure the resistance between the following pairs of wiring harness connector Pins:	Pin 19 closed	►	Fault in LH rear actuator. GO to B5.
	— 46 and 19	Pin 25 closed	►	Fault in RH rear actuator. GO to B5.
	— 46 and 25	Pin 7 closed	►	Fault in RH front actuator. GO to B5.
	— 46 and 7	Pin 10 closed	►	Fault in LH front actuator. GO to B5.
	— 46 and 10			
	• If the measured resistance is: — Greater than 1000 ohms, the switch is open. — Less than 10 ohms, the switch is closed.			
B4	DO POSITION SWITCHES CLOSE?			
	• Use a jumper wire to connect Pin 12 to Pin 60 on the wiring harness side of the 60-pin connector for 1 or 2 seconds.	All four switches are closed	►	REPLACE ARC module.
	• Use an ohmmeter to measure the resistance between the following pairs of wiring harness connector Pins:	All four switches are open	►	Fault in power distribution. GO to B12.
	— 46 and 19	Pin 19 open	►	Fault in LH rear actuator. GO to B5.
	— 46 and 25	Pin 25 open	►	Fault in RH rear actuator. GO to B5.
	— 46 and 7	Pin 7 open	►	Fault in RH front actuator. GO to B5.
	— 46 and 10	Pin 10 open	►	REPLACE ARC module.
	• If the measured resistance is: — Greater than 1000 ohms, the switch is open. — Less than 10 ohms, the switch is closed.			
B5	CHECK ACTUATOR CONNECTOR WIRES			
	• Turn ignition to the OFF position.	No	►	GO to B6.
	• Disconnect harness from 60-Pin Breakout Box.	Yes	►	SERVICE wires as necessary.
	• Reconnect the 60-pin electrical connector to the PRC module.			
	NOTE: Do not reattach the module mounting panel at this time.			
	• If the ignition is not already OFF, turn it to the OFF position.			
	• Examine the wires on the inoperative actuator connectors and on the wiring harness side to ensure that there is no obvious damage and that all of the wires are in the proper location.			
	• **Are wires damaged or in wrong position?**			

FM2019200142020X

**Fig. 7   Test B: Actuator Control Circuit (Part 2 of 7).
1992–93**

**PINPOINT TEST B: ACTUATOR CONTROL CIRCUIT
DIAGNOSIS (Continued)**

	TEST STEP	RESULT	►	ACTION TO TAKE
B6	DO ACTUATORS ROTATE TO HARD POSITION?			
	• Disconnect all inoperative actuators from the top of their struts or shock absorbers.	Rotated from S to H	►	GO to B8.
	NOTE: Leave the electrical connectors plugged in.	Did not rotate (stayed in H or S position)	►	GO to B7.
	• Turn ignition to the RUN position and wait 5 seconds.	Rotated from H to S	►	SERVICE crossed power feed Circuits 845 and 846 at inoperative actuator as necessary.
	• Move the ride control switch to the AUTO position.			
	• Record the position (SOFT or HARD) (S or H) of the control tube on the bottom of the inoperative actuators.			
	• Move the ride control switch to the FIRM position and wait 5 seconds.			
	• Observe the position (S or H) of the control tube on the bottom of the inoperative actuators.			
	• **Did all inoperative actuators rotate from the S position after step B9 to the H position now?**			
B7	CAN ACTUATOR ROTATE			
	• Turn ignition to OFF position.	No	►	REPLACE actuator.
	• Unplug the inoperative actuators and plug them into the wiring harness at any position where the current actuator is functioning properly.	Yes	►	SERVICE open in either Circuit 845 or 846 between relays and the original actuator connector as necessary.
	• Turn ignition to RUN position and wait 5 seconds. Move the ride control switch to the AUTO position.			
	• **Are the control tubes on the bottom of the inoperative actuators in the S position?**			
	• Move the ride control switch to the FIRM position. **Do the control tubes on the bottom of the inoperative actuators rotate from the S to the H position?**			
B8	DO ACTUATOR POSITION SWITCHES WORK?			
	• Disconnect the electrical connectors of the inoperative actuators.	Switches closed in S position and open in the H position	►	GO to B9.
	• Use a small-blade screwdriver to rotate the control tube on the bottom of the inoperative actuators to the S position.	Switches always open	►	REPLACE actuator.
	• Use Rotunda Digital Volt Ohmmeter 007-00001 or equivalent to measure the resistance between the position sense and signal return pins of the actuator electrical connector.	Switches always closed	►	REPLACE actuator.
	• Rotate the control tube on the bottom of the inoperative actuators to the H position. Remeasure the resistance between the position sense and signal return pins. If the measured resistance is: — Greater than 1000 ohms, the switch is open — Less than 10 ohms, the switch is closed			
B9	DOES ACTUATOR HAVE INTERNAL SHORT			
	• Use a small-blade screwdriver to rotate the control tube on the bottom of the inoperative actuators to the H position.	Greater than 1000 ohms	►	GO to B10.
	• Measure the resistance between the position sense and soft power pins of the actuator electrical connector.	Less than 10 ohms	►	REPLACE actuator.

FM2019200142030X

**Fig. 7   Test B: Actuator Control Circuit (Part 3 of 7).
1992–93**

**PINPOINT TEST B: ACTUATOR CONTROL CIRCUIT
DIAGNOSIS (Continued)**

	TEST STEP	RESULT	►	ACTION TO TAKE
B10	SIGNAL RETURN CONTINUITY TO GROUND			
	• Measure the resistance between the signal return Pin 46 (Circuit 837) in the wiring harness side of the actuator connector and chassis ground.	Greater than 1000 ohms	►	SERVICE open circuit in signal return line (Circuit 837).
		Less than 10 ohms	►	GO to B11.
B11	TEST POSITION SENSOR WIRING FOR CONTINUITY			
	• Turn ignition to the OFF position.	Yes	►	SERVICE wires as necessary.
	• Go to luggage compartment and lower the control module packaging tray behind driver's side back seat.	No	►	GO to B26.
	• Disconnect the 60-pin electrical connector from the ARC module. Connect harness to 60-Pin Breakout Box.			
	• Examine wire at Pin 46 for damage or mislocation.			
	• Examine the position sensors wires for the inoperative actuators at the 60-pin connector to ensure that there is no obvious damage and that they are in the proper location.			
	• Test the continuity of the position sensor wires for the inoperative actuators, and the wire at Pin 46 of the 60-pin connector to the wiring harness side of the actuator connectors.			
	• **Any wiring concerns found?**			
B12	TEST RELAY POWER FEED			
	• Turn ignition to the OFF position.	No	►	GO to B13.
	• Go to luggage compartment and unplug both ride control relays.	Yes	►	GO to B14.
	• Turn ignition to RUN position.			
	• Use Rotunda Digital Volt Ohmmeter 007-00001 or equivalent to measure the voltage from Circuits 38 to 57 at the wiring harness side of both relay connectors.			
	• **Is voltage reading 12 volts?**			
B13	TEST HARD POWER FEED			
	• Use a voltmeter to measure the voltage from Circuit 38 at the wiring harness side of both relay connectors to chassis ground.	No	►	SERVICE short or open in Circuit 38 or blown fuse link as necessary.
	• **Is voltage reading 12 volts?**	Yes	►	SERVICE open in Circuit 57 as necessary.
B14	TEST CONTINUITY TO ACTUATORS			
	• Unplug the RH rear actuator.	Continuity in both circuits	►	GO to B15.
	• Test the continuity of the wiring harness power feed Circuits 845 and 846 from the relays to the actuator.	Open in one or both circuits	►	SERVICE wires as necessary.
B15	ARE RELAY CONTROL CIRCUITS CROSSED?			
	• Examine the wires on the wiring harness side of both relay electrical connectors to verify that: — Circuits 838 and 845 are in the same connector. — Circuits 839 and 846 are in the same connector.	Yes	►	SERVICE wires as necessary.
	• **Are wires crossed?**	No	►	REPLACE firm relay.

FM2019200142040X

**Fig. 7   Test B: Actuator Control Circuit (Part 4 of 7).
1992–93**

PINPOINT TEST B: ACTUATOR CONTROL CIRCUIT
DIAGNOSIS (Continued)

	TEST STEP	RESULT	►	ACTION TO TAKE
B16	QUICK TEST			
	• Perform Quick Test	All four actuator codes are received again.	►	REPLACE soft relay.
B17	CHECK FOR SHORT IN RELAY CONTROL CIRCUIT			
	• Turn ignition to the OFF position.	Both circuits greater than 1000 ohms	►	REPLACE ARC module.
	• Go to luggage compartment and lower the control module packaging tray behind driver's side back seat.	Pin 11 less than 10 ohms	►	Fault in hard relay circuit. GO to B18.
	• Disconnect the 60-pin electrical connector from the ARC module. Connect harness to 60-Pin Breakout Box.	Pin 12 less than 10 ohms	►	Fault in soft relay circuit. GO to B18.
	• Examine the wiring harness side of the 60-pin connector to verify that there is no obvious damage and that:			
	— Circuit 838 is in Pin 11			
	— Circuit 839 is in Pin 12			
	• Use an ohmmeter to measure the resistance on the harness side of the 60-pin connector from:			
	— Pin 11 to Pin 60			
	— Pin 12 to Pin 60			
B18	DISCONNECT INOPERATIVE RELAY			
	• Disconnect inoperative relay. Examine the harness wires at the relay connector to ensure that there is no obvious damage and that they are in the proper location.	Yes	►	SERVICE wires as necessary.
		No	►	GO to B19.
	• Are wires damaged or crossed?			
B19	RETEST RELAY CONTROL CIRCUITS			
	• Use an ohmmeter to measure the resistance on the harness side of the 60-pin connector from:	Both circuits greater than 1000 ohms	►	REPLACE inoperative relay.
	— Pin 11 to Pin 60	Less than 10 ohms	►	SERVICE short in circuit as necessary.
	— Pin 12 to Pin 60			
B20	DO POSITION SWITCHES OPEN?			
	• Go to luggage compartment and lower the control module mounting panel on the back of the passenger side seat.	All four switches are open	►	GO to B21.
	• Disconnect the 60-pin electrical connector from the ARC module. Connect harness to 60-Pin Breakout Box.	All four switches are closed	►	Fault in hard relay control. GO to B22.
	• Turn the ignition to RUN position.			
	• Use a jumper wire to connect Pin 11 to Pin 60 on the wiring harness side of the 60-pin connector for 1 or 2 seconds.			
	• Use an ohmmeter to measure the resistance between the following pairs of wiring harness connector Pins:			
	— 46 and 19			
	— 46 and 25			
	— 46 and 7			
	— 46 and 10			
	• If the measured resistance is:			
	— Greater than 1000 ohms, the switch is open			
	— Less than 10 ohms, the switch is closed			

FM2019200142050X

Fig. 7   Test B: Actuator Control Circuit (Part 5 of 7). 1992–93

PINPOINT TEST B: ACTUATOR CONTROL CIRCUIT
DIAGNOSIS (Continued)

	TEST STEP	RESULT	►	ACTION TO TAKE
B21	DO POSITION SWITCHES CLOSE?			
	• Use a jumper wire to connect Pin 12 to Pin 60 on the wiring harness side of the 60-pin connector for 1 or 2 seconds.	All four switches ar closed	►	REPLACE ARC module.
	• Use an ohmmeter to measure the resistance between the following pairs of wiring harness connector Pins:	All four switches are open	►	Fault in soft relay control. GO to B22.
	— 46 and 19			
	— 46 and 25			
	— 46 and 7			
	— 46 and 10			
	• If the measured resistance is:			
	— Greater than 1000 ohms, the switch is open			
	— Less than 10 ohms, the switch is closed			
B22	DISCONNECT INOPERATIVE RELAY			
	• Disconnect inoperative relay. Examine the harness wires at the relay connector to ensure that there is no obvious damage and that they are in the proper location.	Yes	►	SERVICE wires as necessary.
		No	►	GO to B23.
	• Are wires damaged or crossed?			
B23	TEST COIL POWER FEED			
	• Use a voltmeter to measure the voltage from Circuit 298 at the wiring harness side of both relay connectors to chassis ground.	No	►	SERVICE short / open in Circuit 298 as necessary.
		Yes	►	GO to B24.
	• Are 12 volts present?			
B24	TEST RELAY CONTROL CIRCUIT			
	• Test the continuity of the inoperative relay control circuit from the relay to the 60-pin connector at the ARC module as follows:	Yes	►	REPLACE relay.
	— Circuit 838 to Pin 11	No	►	SERVICE wire as necessary. GO to B25.
	— Circuit 839 to Pin 12			
	• Is continuity present?			

FM2019200142060X

Fig. 7   Test B: Actuator Control Circuit (Part 6 of 7). 1992–93

PINPOINT TEST C: FIRM RIDE INDICATOR LAMP
CIRCUIT DIAGNOSIS

	TEST STEP	RESULT	►	ACTION TO TAKE
C1	OBSERVE KEY ON SEQUENCE			
	• Turn ignition to the OFF position.	Firm ride lamp does not turn on	►	REPLACE bulb. GO to C2.
	• Set shock select switch to the FIRM position.	Firm ride lamp is dim	►	GO to C5.
	• Shield the firm ride lamp from bright sunlight so that you can see the lamp even if it is dim, and turn the ignition switch to RUN position.	Firm ride lamp turns on	►	Did not enter diagnostics PERFORM Pinpoint Test D1.

FM2019200143010X

Fig. 8   Test C: Firm Ride Indicator Lamp Circuit (Part 1 of 3). 1992–93

PINPOINT TEST B: ACTUATOR CONTROL CIRCUIT
DIAGNOSIS (Continued)

	TEST STEP	RESULT	►	ACTION TO TAKE
B25	DOES POSITION SWITCH OPEN?			
	• Attach inoperative actuator to shock absorber.	Switch of inoperative actuator is open	►	GO to B26.
	• Connect actuator electrical connector to wiring harness connector.	Switch of inoperative actuator is closed	►	REPLACE actuator and shock absorber. (Parts are mechanically binding.)
	• Turn ignition to RUN position.			
	• Use jumper wire to connect Pin 11 to Pin 60 on the wiring harness side of the 60-pin connector for 1 or 2 seconds.			
	• Use an ohmmeter to measure the resistance of the wiring harness pins for the inoperative actuator as follows:			

Inoperative Actuator	Harness Connector Pins
LH rear	46 and 14
RH rear	46 and 25
RH front	46 and 7
LH front	46 and 10

	• If the measured resistance is:			
	— Greater than 1000 ohms, the switch is open.			
	— Less than 10 ohms, the switch is closed.			
B26	DOES POSITION SWITCH CLOSE?			
	• Use a jumper wire to connect Pin 12 to Pin 60 on the wiring harness side of the 60-pin connector for 1 or 2 seconds.	Switch of inoperative actuator is closed	►	REPLACE ARC module.
	• Use an ohmmeter to measure the resistance of the wiring harness pins for the inoperative actuator as follows:	Switch of inoperative actuator is open	►	REPLACE actuator and shock absorber. (Parts are mechanically binding.)

Problem Actuator	Harness Connector Pins
LH rear	46 and 19
RH rear	46 and 25
RH front	46 and 7
LH front	46 and 10

FM2019200142070X

Fig. 7   Test B: Actuator Control Circuit (Part 7 of 7). 1992–93

PINPOINT TEST C: FIRM RIDE INDICATOR LAMP
CIRCUIT DIAGNOSIS (Continued)

	TEST STEP	RESULT	►	ACTION TO TAKE
C2	DOES FIRM RIDE LAMP WORK?			
	• Go to luggage compartment and lower the control module packaging tray behind driver's side back seat.	Yes	►	Fault in module power circuitry. GO to C3.
	• Disconnect the 60-pin electrical connector from the ARC module. Connect harness to 60-Pin Breakout Box.	No	►	Fault in light control circuitry. GO to C4.
	• Turn ignition to RUN position.			
	• Use a jumper wire to connect Pin 15 to Pin 60 on the wiring harness side of the 60-pin connector.			
	• Does firm ride lamp turn on?			
C3	DOES MODULE HAVE POWER?			
	• Use a voltmeter to measure the voltage from Pin 57 to Pin 60 on the wiring harness side of the 60-pin connector.	No	►	SERVICE short to ground or open in Circuit 298 as necessary.
		Yes	►	REPLACE ARC module.
	• Are 2 volts present?			
C4	TEST LAMP CIRCUIT			
	• Locate firm ride lamp wire on instrument cluster connector. Check for continuity.	No	►	SERVICE Circuit 133 as necessary.
	• Is continuity present?	Yes	No ►	CHECK instrument panel power, ground and bulb.
C5	CHECK LAMP DIMMING			
	• Move the shock select switch to the FIRM position to turn on FIRM ride lamp.	Firm ride lamp is bright with headlamps off, dimmer with headlamps on	►	
	• Cycle headlamps on and off while observing FIRM ride lamp.	Firm ride lamp does not get dimmer with headlamps on	►	GO to C6.
C6	CHECK HEADLAMP WIRING			
	• Go to luggage compartment and lower the module packaging tray behind driver's side back seat.	12 volts with headlamps on 0 volts with headlamps off	►	REPLACE ARC module.
	• Disconnect the 60-pin connector from the ARC module. Connect harness to 60-Pin Breakout Box.	12 volts always or 0 volts always	►	SERVICE fault in headlamp switch Circuit 14 as necessary.
	• Use a voltmeter to measure the voltage from Circuit 14 of the harness connector (Pin 1) and (Pin 60) of the harness side connector. Cycle headlamps.			

FM2019200143020X

Fig. 8   Test C: Firm Ride Indicator Lamp Circuit (Part 2 of 3). 1992–93

PINPOINT TEST C: FIRM RIDE INDICATOR LAMP CIRCUIT DIAGNOSIS (Continued)

TEST STEP	RESULT	►	ACTION TO TAKE
C7 CHECK FOR SHORT IN FIRM RIDE LAMP CIRCUIT • Turn ignition to the OFF position. • Go to luggage compartment and lower the control module mounting panel on the back of the passenger side seat. • Disconnect the 60-pin electrical connector from the ARC module. Connect harness to 60-Pin Breakout Box. • Check Circuit 133 at the 60-pin connector to ensure that there is no obvious damage and that it it in Pin 15. • Use an ohmmeter to measure the resistance from Pin 15 to Pin 60 on the harness side of the 60-pin connector.	Greater than 1000 ohms Less than 10 ohms	► ►	REPLACE module. SERVICE short to ground in Circuit 133 as necessary.

FM2019200143030X

Fig. 8   Test C: Firm Ride Indicator Lamp Circuit (Part 3 of 3). 1992–93

PINPOINT TEST D: MODULE INPUT CIRCUIT DIAGNOSIS

TEST STEP	RESULT	►	ACTION TO TAKE
D1 REPEAT ATTEMPT TO ENTER DIAGNOSIS • Verify that diagnostic connector used in Step A1 is clean and free of corrosion. • Repeat attempt to enter diagnostics (Step A1), ensuring all tester switches are in the proper position and the button is depressed at the proper time. • Is second attempt successful?	Yes No	► ►	PERFORM Quick Test GO to D2.
D2 TEST SIGNAL RETURN WIRE CONTINUITY • Check the signal return, diagnostic and STAR wires (Circuits 844, 837 and 930 respectively) at the star connector to ensure that there is no obvious damage. • Test the continuity of Circuit 837 to chassis ground.	Damaged wires No continuity No concerns detected	► ► ►	SERVICE wires as necessary. SERVICE open in Circuit 837 as necessary. GO to D3.
D3 CHECK DIAGNOSTIC CIRCUIT FOR SHORT TO GROUND • Examine Circuit 844 at the 60-pin connector to ensure that there is no obvious damage and that it is in Pin 30. • Use an ohmmeter to measure the resistance from Pin 30 to Pin 60 on the harness side of the 60-pin connector. • Use an ohmmeter to measure the resistance from Pin 47 to Pin 60 on the harness side of the 60-pin connector.	Greater than 1000 ohms Less than 10 ohms	► ► ►	GO to D4. SERVICE short to ground in Circuit 844 as necessary. SERVICE short to ground in Circuit 930 as necessary.

FM2019200144010X

Fig. 9   Test D: Module Input Circuit (Part 1 of 6). 1992–93

PINPOINT TEST D: MODULE INPUT CIRCUIT DIAGNOSIS (Continued)

TEST STEP	RESULT	►	ACTION TO TAKE
D4 CHECK DIAGNOSTIC CIRCUIT • Connect tester into diagnostic connector. • Go to luggage compartment and use an ohmmeter to measure the resistance from Pin 30 to Pin 46 on the harness side of the 60-pin connector. • Measure resistance with tester button depressed and not depressed.	Greater than 1000 ohms always Greater than 1000 ohms undepressed. Less than 10 ohms depressed. Less than 10 ohms always	► ► ►	SERVICE open in Circuit 844 or poor contact between tester and diagnostic connector. Check tester. REPLACE ARC module. CHECK STAR Tester.
D5 CHECK SWITCH POSITIONS • Move switch to FIRM position. • Does lamp stay on?	Yes No	► ►	GO to D6. Switch positions reversed. REPLACE switch.
D6 CHECK BRAKE CIRCUIT FOR SHORT TO GROUND • Turn ignition to the OFF position. • Set shock select switch to the AUTO position. • Go to luggage compartment and lower the module packaging tray behind driver's side seat. • Disconnect the 60-pin electrical connector from the ARC module. Connect harness to 60-Pin Breakout Box. • Check Circuit 847 at the 60-pin connector to ensure that there is no obvious damage and that it is in pin 9. • Use an ohmmeter to measure the resistance from Pin 9 to Pin 60 on the harness side of the 60-pin connector.	Greater than 1000 ohms Less than 10 ohms	► ►	GO to D7. SERVICE short to ground in Circuit 847 as necessary.
D7 IS BRAKE CIRCUIT ALWAYS CLOSED? • Use an ohmmeter to measure the resistance from Pin 9 to Pin 46 on the harness side of the 60-pin connector.	Greater than 1000 ohms Less than 10 ohms	► ►	GO to D8. REPLACE brake pressure switch.
D8 IS SHOCK SELECT CIRCUIT ALWAYS CLOSED? • Verify that the shock select switch is in the AUTO position. • Check Circuit 832 at the 60-pin connector to ensure that there is no obvious damage and that it is in Pin 18. • Use a voltmeter to measure the voltage from Pin 18 to Pin 60 on the harness side of the 60-pin connector. • Are 12 volts present?	No Yes	► ►	GO to D9. REPLACE shock select switch.

FM2019200144020X

Fig. 9   Test D: Module Input Circuit (Part 2 of 6). 1992–93

PINPOINT TEST D: MODULE INPUT CIRCUIT DIAGNOSIS (Continued)

TEST STEP	RESULT	►	ACTION TO TAKE
D9 IS ACCELERATION SIGNAL ALWAYS CLOSED? • Check Circuit 836 at the 60-pin connector to ensure that there is no obvious damage and that it is in Pin 28. • Use an ohmmeter to measure the resistance from Pin 28 to Pin 60 on the harness side of the 60-pin connector.	Greater than 1000 ohms Less than 10 ohms	► ►	REPLACE damaged ARC module. GO to D10.
D10 CHECK FOR SHORTED ACCELERATION CIRCUIT • Turn ignition switch to the OFF position. • Unplug the EEC-IV control module from the wiring harness. • Return to luggage compartment and remeasure the resistance from Pin 28 to Pin 60 on the harness side of the ARC module 60-pin connector.	Greater than 1000 ohms Less than 10 ohms	► 	damaged or worn throttle position signal or EEC-IV. SERVICE short to ground in Circuit 836 as necessary.
D11 CHECK STEERING SENSOR WIRES • Turn ignition to the OFF position. • Go to luggage compartment and lower the control module packaging tray behind the driver's side back seat. • Disconnect the 60-pin electrical connector from the ARC module. Connect harness to 60-Pin Breakout Box. • Examine the wiring harness side of the 60-pin connector to verify that there is no obvious damage and that: — Circuit 834 is in Pin 45 — Circuit 835 is in Pin 24 • Any damage found? NOTE: If these two circuits are reversed it will not affect function. Therefore, treat as no concern.	Yes No	► ►	SERVICE wires as necessary. GO to D12.
D12 TEST STEERING SENSOR SIGNALS • Use a jumper to connect module Pin 46 to Pin 60 for this steering sensor signal test. • Start engine. • Use an analog ohmmeter on the 1k scale to measure the resistance on the harness side of the 60-pin connector from: —Pin 45 to Pin 60 —Pin 24 to Pin 60 while rotating the steering wheel slowly. NOTE: The resistance values will vary with the meter, but the needle on all meters should swing from a low to a higher resistance and back approximately every nine degrees of steering wheel rotation.	Meter needle does not swing for one or both circuits Meter needle swings for both circuits	► ►	GO to D13. SHUT off engine. REPLACE ARC module.

FM2019200144030X

Fig. 9   Test D: Module Input Circuit (Part 3 of 6). 1992–93

PINPOINT TEST D: MODULE INPUT CIRCUIT DIAGNOSIS (Continued)

TEST STEP	RESULT	▶	ACTION TO TAKE
D13 UNPLUG STEERING SENSOR			
• Turn ignition switch to the OFF position.	Damaged or crossed wires	▶	SERVICE wires as necessary.
• Go to the lower portion of the steering column near the brake pedal and unplug steering sensor.	No continuity	▶	SERVICE open in Circuit 834 or 835 as necessary.
• Check the wires at the steering sensor connector to ensure that there is no obvious damage and that they are in the proper location.	No concerns detected	▶	GO to D14.
• Test continuity of Circuits 834 and 835 from steering sensor to 60-pin ARC module connector.			
D14 TEST STEERING SENSOR POWER			
• Turn ignition switch to RUN position.	No	▶	GO to D15.
• Use a voltmeter to measure the voltage from Circuit 298 to 837 at the wiring harness side of the steering sensor connector.	Yes	▶	REPLACE steering sensor.
• Are 12 volts present?			
D15 TEST STEERING SENSOR POWER CIRCUIT			
• Use a voltmeter to measure the voltage from Circuit 298 at the wiring harness side of the steering sensor connector to chassis ground.	No	▶	SERVICE short or open in Circuit 298 as necessary.
• Are 12 volts present?	Yes	▶	SERVICE open in Circuit 837 as necessary.
D16 TEST SPEED SENSOR SIGNAL			
• Turn ignition switch to the OFF position.	Yes	▶	SERVICE wires as necessary.
• Go to luggage compartment and lower the control module packaging tray behind the driver's side back seat.	No	▶	GO to D17.
• Disconnect the 60-pin electrical connector from the ARC module. Connect harness to 60-Pin Breakout Box.			
• Check the wiring harness side of the 60-pin connector to verify that there is no obvious damage and that: — Circuit 150 is in Pin 3 — Circuit 359 is in Pin 6			
• Are wires crossed or damaged?			
D17 TEST SPEED SENSOR GROUND CIRCUIT			
• Test the continuity of the speed sensor ground Circuit 359 from Pin 6 to Pin 60 of the 60-pin connector at the ARC module.	Yes	▶	GO to D18.
• Is continuity present?	No	▶	SERVICE wire or ground eyelet as necessary.
D18 TEST SPEED SENSOR			
• Turn ignition switch to RUN position.	Yes	▶	SERVICE
	No	▶	REPLACE ARC module.
• Are there concerns?			

FM2019200144040X

Fig. 9 Test D: Module Input Circuit (Part 4 of 6).
1992–93

PINPOINT TEST D: MODULE INPUT CIRCUIT DIAGNOSIS (Continued)

TEST STEP	RESULT	▶	ACTION TO TAKE
D23 DISCONNECT BRAKE PRESSURE SWITCH			
• Turn ignition switch to the OFF position.	Yes	▶	SERVICE wires as necessary.
• Go to the brake proportioning valve and disconnect brake pressure switch.	No	▶	GO to D24.
• Check the wires at the brake pressure switch connector to ensure that there is no obvious damage.			
• Are wires damaged?			
NOTE: If these two circuits are reversed it will not affect function. Therefore, treat as no concern.			
D24 TEST BRAKE SWITCH GROUND CIRCUIT			
• Use an ohmmeter to measure the resistance from Circuit 837 at the wiring harness side of the brake pressure switch connector to chassis ground.	Greater than 1000 ohms	▶	SERVICE open or short in Circuit 837 as necessary.
	Less than 10 ohms	▶	REPLACE brake pressure switch.
D25 CHECK MODULE CONNECTOR			
• Turn ignition switch to the OFF position.	Yes	▶	SERVICE wires as necessary.
• Go to luggage compartment and lower the control module packaging tray behind the driver's side rear seat.	No	▶	GO to D26.
• Disconnect the 60-pin electrical connector from the ARC module. Connect harness to 60-Pin Breakout Box.			
• Examine Circuit 836 at the 60-pin connector to ensure that there is no obvious damage and that it is in Pin 28.			
• Is there damage or crossed wires?			
D26 CHECK EEC-IV CONNECTOR			
• Disconnect the 60-pin electrical connector from the EEC-IV module.	Yes	▶	SERVICE wires as necessary.
• Check Circuit 836 at the 60-pin connector to ensure that there is no obvious damage and that it is in Pin 35.	No	▶	GO to D27.
• Are wires crossed or damaged?			
D27 TEST ACCELERATION CIRCUIT CONTINUITY			
• Test for continuity of Circuit 836 from the ARC module to the EEC-IV module.	No	▶	SERVICE open Circuit 836 as necessary.
• Is continuity present?	Yes	▶	REPLACE ARC module.

FM2019200144060X

Fig. 9 Test D: Module Input Circuit (Part 6 of 6).
1992–93

PINPOINT TEST D: MODULE INPUT CIRCUIT DIAGNOSIS (Continued)

TEST STEP	RESULT	▶	ACTION TO TAKE
D19 DOES SWITCH SEND FIRM SIGNAL?			
• Turn ignition switch to the OFF position.	No	No ▶	GO to D2.
• Go to luggage compartment and lower the control module packaging tray behind the driver's side rear seat.	Yes	▶	REPLACE ARC module.
• Disconnect the 60-pin electrical connector from the ARC module. Connect harness to 60-Pin Breakout Box.			
• Check Circuit 832 at the 60-pin connector to ensure that there is no obvious damage and that it is in Pin 18.			
• Turn ignition switch to RUN position.			
• Set shock select switch to FIRM position.			
• Use a voltmeter to measure the voltage from Pin 18 to Pin 60 on the harness side of the 60-pin connector.			
• Are 12 volts present?			
D20 DISCONNECT SHOCK SELECT SWITCH			
• Turn ignition switch to the OFF position.	Yes	▶	SERVICE wires as necessary.
• Go to the instrument panel and disconnect shock select switch.	No	▶	GO to D21.
• Check wires at the shock select switch connector to ensure there is no obvious damage.			
• Was damage found?			
NOTE: If these two circuits are reversed it will not affect function. Therefore, treat as no concern.			
D21 TEST SHOCK SELECT SWITCH POWER FEED			
• Turn ignition switch to RUN position.	No	▶	SERVICE open or short in Circuit 298 as necessary.
• Use a voltmeter to measure the voltage from Circuit 298 at the wiring harness side of the shock select switch connector to chassis ground.	Yes	▶	REPLACE shock select switch.
• Are 12 volts present?			
D22 DOES BRAKE SWITCH CLOSE?			
• Turn ignition switch to the OFF position.	Greater than 1000 ohms	▶	GO to D23.
• Go to luggage compartment and lower the control module packaging tray behind the driver's side rear seat.	Less than 10 ohms	▶	REPLACE ARC module.
• Disconnect the 60-pin electrical connector from the ARC module. Connect harness to 60-Pin Breakout Box.			
• Check Circuit 847 at the 60-pin connector to ensure that there is no obvious damage and that it is in Pin 9.			
• Start engine and press brake pedal firmly to the floor.			
• Use an ohmmeter to measure the resistance from Pin 9 to Pin 60 on the harness side of the 60-pin connector WHILE THE BRAKE PEDAL IS DEPRESSED.			

FM2019200144050X

Fig. 9 Test D: Module Input Circuit (Part 5 of 6).
1992–93

PINPOINT TEST E: MODULE INPUT CIRCUIT DIAGNOSIS

TEST STEP	RESULT	▶	ACTION TO TAKE
E1 CHECK CONNECTOR WIRES			
• Turn ignition switch to the OFF position.	No	▶	RESEAT connector.
• Locate connector on power steering pump for EVO valve.	Yes	▶	GO to E2.
• Is EVO connector seated properly on EVO valve?			

FM2019200145010X

Fig. 10 Test E: Module Input Circuit (Part 1 of 2).
1992–93

Fig. 10 Test E: Module Input Circuit (Part 2 of 2). 1992–93

TEST STEP	RESULT	▶	ACTION TO TAKE
E2 CHECK EVO STEERING • Turn ignition switch to the OFF position. • Go to luggage compartment and lower the control module packaging tray behind driver's side back seat. • Disconnect the 60-pin electrical connector from ARC module. Connect harness to 60-Pin Breakout Box. • Use an ohmmeter to measure the resistance between the following pair of wiring harness connector pins: 43 and 48. If the measured resistance is greater than 1000 ohms, the circuit is open.	Measured resistance is greater than 1000 ohms	▶	CHECK EVO connector. GO to E3.
	Measured resistance is greater than 18 ohms	▶	CHECK EVO connector. GO to E4.
	Measured resistance is less than 18 ohms	▶	CHECK EVO connector. GO to E3.
E3 CHECK CONTINUITY OF WIRING • Disconnect EVO connector from EVO valve located on power steering pump. • Check continuity of module harness connector Pin 48 to EVO valve, connector Circuit 330, and Pin 43 to EVO valve connector Circuit 353. • Is continuity present?	No	▶	SERVICE wiring as necessary.
	Yes	▶	GO to E4.
E4 CHECK EVO VALVE ON POWER STEERING PUMP • Disconnect EVO connector from EVO valve located on power steering pump. • Measure the resistance of the EVO valve across the two valve connector pins.	Measured resistance is greater than 20 ohms	▶	REPLACE EVO valve.
	Measured resistance is less than 5 ohms	▶	REPLACE EVO valve.
	Measured resistance is greater than 5 but less than 20 ohms	▶	GO to E5.
E5 CHECK WIRE HARNESS FOR GROUND SHORT • Turn ignition switch to OFF position. • Go to luggage compartment and lower the control module packaging tray behind the driver's side back seat. • If necessary, disconnect the 60-pin electrical connector from ARC module. Connect harness to 60-Pin Breakout Box. • Use an ohmmeter to measure the resistance between Pin 60 and Pin 43 of 60-pin harness.	Greater than 1000 ohms	▶	GO to E6.
	Less than 10 ohms	▶	INSPECT harness for shorts to ground.
E6 CHECK WIRE HARNESS FOR SHORT • Use an ohmmeter to measure the resistance between Pin 60 of harness with Pin 48 of harness.	Greater than 1000 ohms	▶	EVO harness OK. REPLACE ARC/EVO module.
	Less than 10 ohms	▶	INSPECT harness for shorts to ground.

FM2019200145020X

Fig. 10 Test E: Module Input Circuit (Part 2 of 2). 1992–93

Fig. 11 Test A: Shock Damping Inoperative (Part 2 of 3). 1994

TEST STEP	RESULT	▶	ACTION TO TAKE
A8 CHECK SUPPLY TO SOFT/HARD RELAYS • Gain access to SHOCK fuse (30A) at POWER DISTRIBUTION BOX. • Using a test lamp check for power at SHOCK Fuse (30A). • Did test lamp illuminate?	Yes No	▶	GO to A10. GO to A9.
A9 CHECK CIRCUIT 38 (BK/O) • Remove SHOCK Fuse (30A), using an ohmmeter connected to a known good ground, connect second lead to Circuit 38 (BK/O) at output side of SHOCK (30A) fuse cavity. • Measure resistance. • Is resistance 5 ohms or less?	Yes No	▶	SERVICE Circuit 38 (BK/O) for short. RETEST system. REPLACE SHOCK Fuse (30A). GO to A10.
A10 CHECK CONTROL MODULE GROUND • Using an ohmmeter connected to a known good ground, connect second lead to Circuit 57 (BK) Pin 60 at 60 pin module connector. • Measure resistance. • Is resistance 5 ohms or less?	Yes No	▶	REPLACE SHOCK shock absorber electronic system control. RESTORE vehicle. RETEST system. SERVICE Circuit 57 (BK) for open. GO to A11.
A11 CHECK RIDE SELECT SWITCH INPUT • Verify that the ride select switch is in the AUTO position. • Turn ignition switch to the RUN position. • Using a voltmeter connect one lead to Circuit 418 (DG/Y) Pin 18 at 60 pin connector. Connect second lead to Circuit 57 (BK) Pin 60 at 60 pin connector. • Is battery voltage present?	Yes No	▶	REPLACE ride select switch. RESTORE vehicle. RETEST system. GO to A12.
A12 CHECK ACCELERATION CIRCUIT INPUT • Using an ohmmeter connect one lead to Circuit 836 (O/W) at Pin 28 of 60 pin connector, connect second lead to Circuit 57 (BK) Pin 60 at 60 pin connector. • Measure resistance. • Is resistance 5 ohms or less?	Yes No	▶	GO to A13. LEAVE ohmmeter connected. REPLACE SHOCK shock absorber electronic system control. RESTORE vehicle. RETEST system.
A13 CHECK ACCELERATION CIRCUIT FOR SHORT • Turn ignition switch to the OFF position. • Unplug the powertrain control module from wiring harness. • Return to the luggage compartment and remeasure resistance of Circuit 418 (DG/Y). • Is resistance 5 ohms or less?	Yes No	▶	SERVICE Circuit 418 (DG/Y) for short. RESTORE vehicle. RETEST system. GO to A14.
A14 CHECK ELECTRONIC STEERING SENSOR INPUT • Using a jumper wire connect Circuit 837 (Y/BK) Pin 46 to Circuit 57 (BK) Pin 60 of 60 pin connector. • Start engine. • Using an ohmmeter on the 1K scale measure the resistance of Circuit 633 (R) on the harness side of 60 pin connector, while rotating the steering wheel slowly. NOTE: The resistance values will vary from a low to a higher resistance and back approximately every nine degrees of steering wheel rotation. • Did ohmmeter resistance vary?	Yes No	▶	REPLACE shock absorber electronic system control module. RESTORE vehicle. RETEST system. GO to A15.

FM2019400158020X

Fig. 11 Test A: Shock Damping Inoperative (Part 2 of 3). 1994

Fig. 11 Test A: Shock Damping Inoperative (Part 1 of 3). 1994

TEST STEP	RESULT	▶	ACTION TO TAKE
A1 ATTEMPT TO ENTER DIAGNOSTICS • Gain access to the data link connector as outlined in test set-up. • Attempt to enter diagnostic as outlined in set-up. • Is attempt successful?	Yes No	▶	GO to Quick Test. GO to A2.
A2 TURN SIGNAL WIRE CONTINUITY • Turn ignition switch to the off position. • Using an ohmmeter connected to a known good ground, connect second lead to Circuit 837 (Y/BK) Pin 5 at data link connector. • Check for continuity. • Is there continuity?	Yes No	▶	GO to A3. SERVICE Circuit 837 (Y/BK) for open. RETEST system.
A3 CHECK CIRCUIT 844 (GY/R) • Go to luggage compartment and lower the control module mounting panel at back of the passenger side seat. • Using an ohmmeter check resistance of Circuit 844 (GY/R) Pin 30 to Circuit 57 (BK) Pin 60 at control module 60 pin connector. • Is resistance 5 ohms or less?	Yes No	▶	SERVICE Circuit 844 (GY/R) for short. RETEST system. GO to A4.
A4 CHECK CIRCUIT 209 (W/P) • Using an ohmmeter check resistance of Circuit 209 (W/P) Pin 47 to Circuit 57 (BK) Pin 60 at control module 60 pin connector. • Is resistance 5 ohms or less?	Yes No	▶	SERVICE Circuit 209 (W/P) for short. RETEST system. GO to A5.
A5 CHECK CIRCUIT 298 (P/O) • Turn ignition switch to the RUN position. • Using a voltmeter check Circuit 298 (P/O) Pin 57 at 60 pin connector for voltage. • Is battery voltage present?	Yes No	▶	GO to A8. GO to A6.
A6 CHECK SUPPLY TO CONTROL MODULE • Gain access to the primary junction block. Check RUN Fuse (15A). • Is fuse OK?	Yes No	▶	SERVICE Circuit 298 (P/O) for short. RETEST system. GO to A7.
A7 CHECK CIRCUIT 298 (P/O) FOR SHORT • Turn ignition switch off. Remove RUN Fuse (15A). • Using an ohmmeter connected to a known good ground, connect second lead to Circuit 298 (P/O) Pin 57 at 60 pin connector. • Measure resistance. • Is resistance 5 ohms or less?	Yes No	▶	SERVICE Circuit 298 (P/O) for short. RETEST system. REPLACE RUN Fuse (15A). GO to A8.

FM2019400158010X

Fig. 11 Test A: Shock Damping Inoperative (Part 1 of 3). 1994

Fig. 11 Test A: Shock Damping Inoperative (Part 3 of 3). 1994

TEST STEP	RESULT	▶	ACTION TO TAKE
A15 CHECK STEERING SENSOR RESISTANCE • Using an ohmmeter on the 1K scale measure the resistance of Circuit 634 (BR) on the harness side of 60 pin connector, while rotating the steering wheel slowly. NOTE: The resistance values will vary from a low to a higher resistance and back approximately every nine degrees of steering wheel rotation. • Did ohmmeter resistance vary?	Yes No	▶	REPLACE shock absorber electronic system control. RESTORE vehicle. RETEST system. GO to A16.
A16 CHECK SPEED SENSOR GROUND CIRCUIT • Using an ohmmeter check continuity of Circuit 359 (GY/R) Pin 6 at 60 pin connector to Circuit 57 (BK) Pin 60 at 60 pin connector. • Is continuity present?	Yes No	▶	GO to A17. SERVICE Circuit 359 (GY/R) for open. RESTORE vehicle. RETEST system.
A17 CHECK SPEED SENSOR INPUT CIRCUIT • Turn ignition switch to the RUN position. • Perform "speedometer reads 0 MPH at all speeds" pinpoint test. • Did speedometer test OK?	Yes No	▶	REPLACE shock absorber electronic system control. RESTORE vehicle. RETEST system. GO to A18.
A18 CHECK BRAKE PRESSURE SWITCH INPUT • Using an assistant, have assistant start engine and press brake pedal firmly to the floor and hold. • Using an ohmmeter measure the resistance of Circuit 836 (O) Pin 9 of 60 pin connector to Circuit 57 (BK) Pin 60 while the brake pedal is applied. • Is resistance 5 ohms or less?	Yes No	▶	REPLACE shock absorber electronic system control. RESTORE vehicle. RETEST system. GO to A19.
A19 CHECK BRAKE PRESSURE SWITCH GROUND • Turn ignition switch to OFF position. • Disconnect the brake pressure switch at the brake pressure control valve. • Using an ohmmeter connected to a known good ground, check resistance of Circuit 837 (Y/BK) at switch connector. • Is resistance 5 ohms or less?	Yes No	▶	REPLACE brake pressure control valve switch. GO to A20. SERVICE Circuit 832 (Y/BK) for open. RESTORE vehicle. RETEST system.
A20 CHECK RIDE SELECT SWITCH • Turn ignition switch to RUN position. • Set ride select switch to the FIRM position. • Using a voltmeter check Circuit 418 (DG/Y) from Pin 18 to Circuit 57 (BK) Pin 60 for value. • Is battery voltage present?	Yes No	▶	REPLACE brake pressure control valve switch. RESTORE vehicle. RETEST system. GO to A21.
A21 CHECK SUPPLY AT RIDE SELECT SWITCH • Disconnect ride select switch as outlined. • Using a test lamp check Circuit 298 (P/O) for voltage. • Did test lamp illuminate?	Yes No	▶	REPLACE ride select switch. RESTORE vehicle. RETEST system. SERVICE Circuit 298 (P/O) for open. RESTORE vehicle. RETEST system.

FM2019400158030X

Fig. 11 Test A: Shock Damping Inoperative (Part 3 of 3). 1994

Fig. 12 Test B (Part 1) — left top table

TEST STEP	RESULT	▶	ACTION TO TAKE
B1 CHECK SUPPLY TO RELAYS • Turn ignition switch to OFF position. • Go to luggage compartment and disconnect both ride select relays as outlined. • Turn ignition switch to RUN position. • Using a voltmeter 007-0001 or equivalent, measure voltage at Circuit 38 (BK/O) Pin 4 at each relay. • Is battery voltage present?	Yes No	▶ ▶	GO to B4. GO to B2.
B2 CHECK CIRCUIT 38 (BK/O) • Gain access to "shock" Fuse (30A) at power distribution box and harness. • Using a test lamp check Circuit 38 (BK/O) for voltage, at shock Fuse (30A). • Did test lamp illuminate?	Yes No	▶ ▶	SERVICE Circuit 38 (BK/O) for open. RESTORE vehicle. RETEST system. GO to B3.
B3 CHECK CIRCUIT 38 (BK/O) FOR SHORT • Remove "SHOCK" Fuse (30A). • Turn ignition switch to OFF position. • Using an ohmmeter connected to a known good ground, connect second lead to Circuit 38 (BK/O) at output side of "SHOCK" Fuse (30A) cavity. Measure resistance. • Is resistance 5 ohms or less?	Yes No	▶ ▶	SERVICE Circuit 38 (BK/O) for short. RESTORE vehicle. RETEST system. REPLACE damaged "SHOCK" Fuse (30A). GO to B4.
B4 CHECK SWITCH SUPPLY TO RELAYS • Ignition switch in RUN position. • Using a voltmeter check Circuit 298 (P/O) Pin 2 at both relays for voltage. • Is battery voltage present?	Yes No	▶ ▶	GO to B6. GO to B5.
B5 CHECK CIRCUIT 298 (P/O) SUPPLY • Gain access to "RUN" Fuse (15A) at primary junction block. Remove fuse. • Disconnect both soft/hard relays. • Using a jumper wire connected to a known good ground, connect free end to Circuit 298 (P/O) at Pin 2 of each relay connector. • Using an ohmmeter connected to a known good ground, connect second lead to Circuit 298 (P/O) at output side of "RUN" Fuse (15A) cavity. Measure resistance. • Is resistance 5 ohms or less?	Yes No	▶ ▶	REPLACE damaged "RUN" Fuse (15A). GO to B6. SERVICE Circuit 298 (P/O) for open. RESTORE vehicle. RETEST system.
B6 CHECK SOFT/HARD RELAYS GROUND CIRCUIT • Using an ohmmeter connected to a known good ground, connect second lead to Circuit 57 (BK) at Pin 5 of each relay. • Measure resistance. • Is resistance 5 ohms or less?	Yes No	▶ ▶	GO to B7. SERVICE Circuit 57 (BK) for open. RESTORE vehicle. RETEST system.
B7 CHECK SOFT RIDE RELAY CONTROL CIRCUIT • Turn ignition switch to OFF position. • Disconnect shock absorber electronic system control. • Using an ohmmeter measure resistance of Circuit 839 (LG/W) from soft ride relay Pin 1 to Pin 12 at shock absorber electronic control module 60 pin connector. • Is resistance 5 ohms or less?	Yes No	▶ ▶	GO to B8. SERVICE Circuit 839 (LG/W) for open. RESTORE vehicle. RETEST system.

FM2019400159010X

Fig. 12 Test B: Ride Too Stiff/Soft (Part 1 of 2). 1994

Fig. 12 Test B (Part 2) — right top table

TEST STEP	RESULT	▶	ACTION TO TAKE
B8 CHECK SOFT RIDE RELAY OUTPUT CIRCUIT • Reconnect soft ride relay and shock absorber electronic system control. • Ensure ride select switch is in "AUTO" position. • Turn ignition switch to RUN position. • Using a voltmeter connected to a known good ground, back-probe Circuit 846 (T/R) Pin 3 at relay harness connector. Measure voltage. • Is voltage present?	Yes No	▶ ▶	SERVICE Circuit 846 (T/R) for open. RESTORE vehicle. RETEST system. REPLACE soft ride relay. GO to B9.
B9 CHECK HARD RIDE RELAY CONTROL CIRCUIT • Turn ignition switch to OFF position. • Disconnect shock absorber electronic control module. • Using an ohmmeter measure resistance of Circuit 838 (LG/P) from hard ride relay Pin 1 to Pin 11 at shock absorber electronic control module 60 pin connector. • Is resistance 5 ohms or less?	Yes No	▶ ▶	GO to B10. SERVICE Circuit 838 (LG/P) for open. RESTORE vehicle. RETEST system.
B10 CHECK HARD RIDE RELAY OUTPUT CIRCUIT • Reconnect hard ride relay and shock absorber electronic control module 60 pin connector. • Actuator ride select switch to FIRM position. • Start engine. • Have assistant depress brake pedal firmly to floor, and turn steering wheel completely to one direction and hold. • Using a voltmeter connected to a known good ground, back-probe Circuit 845 (T/BK) Pin 3 at relay harness connector. Measure voltage. • Is voltage present?	Yes No	▶ ▶	SERVICE Circuit 845 (T/BK) for open. RESTORE vehicle. RETEST system. REPLACE hard ride relay. GO to B11.
B11 CHECK RIDE SELECT SWITCH SUPPLY • Remove ride select switch as outlined. • Using a test lamp check Circuit 298 (P/O) for voltage. • Did test lamp illuminate?	Yes No	▶ ▶	GO to B12. SERVICE Circuit 298 (P/O) for open. RESTORE vehicle. RETEST system.
B12 CHECK RIDE SELECT SWITCH • Actuate ride select switch to FIRM position. • Using a test lamp back-probe Circuit 418 (DG/Y) at switch connector. • Did test lamp illuminate?	Yes No	▶ ▶	REPLACE shock shock absorber electronic system control. RESTORE vehicle. RETEST system. REPLACE air spring suspension drive switch. RESTORE vehicle. RETEST system.

FM2019400159020X

Fig. 12 Test B: Ride Too Stiff/Soft (Part 2 of 2). 1994

Fig. 13 Test C (Part 1) — left middle table

TEST STEP	RESULT	▶	ACTION TO TAKE
C1 CHECK FIRM RIDE INDICATOR LAMP OPERATION • Turn ignition switch to OFF position. • Set ride select switch to FIRM position. • Turn ignition switch to RUN position. • Did FIRM ride indicator illuminate?	Yes No	▶ ▶	GO to C3. GO to C2.

FM2019400160010X

Fig. 13 Test C: Ride Control Indicator Lamp Not Operating Correctly (Part 1 of 2). 1994

Fig. 14 Test D (Part 1) — right middle table

TEST STEP	RESULT	▶	ACTION TO TAKE
D1 CHECK AIR SPRING SUSPENSION DRIVE SWITCH • Disconnect the electrical connector at the inoperative shock absorber. • Using a small blade screwdriver, rotate the control tube at the bottom of the inoperative shock absorber to the "S" position. • Using an ohmmeter connect one lead to the position sense circuit, connect second lead to signal return circuit at actuator connector. Measure resistance. • Is resistance less than 10 ohms?	Yes No	▶ ▶	GO to D2. LEAVE odometer connected. REPLACE shock absorber electronic actuator. RESTORE vehicle. RETEST system.

FM2019400161010X

Fig. 14 Test D: Single Shock Absorber/Electronic Actuator Inoperative (Part 1 of 2). 1994

Fig. 13 Test C (Part 2) — left bottom table

TEST STEP	RESULT	▶	ACTION TO TAKE
C2 CHECK FIRM RIDE INDICATOR CIRCUIT • Go to luggage compartment and lower the shock absorber electronic system control. • Turn ignition switch to OFF position. • Using a jumper wire, connect one end to Circuit 419 (DG/LB) Pin 15, connect other to Circuit 57 (BK) Pin 60 at control module 60 pin connector. • Turn ignition switch to RUN position. • Did FIRM ride indicator illuminate?	Yes No	▶ ▶	REPLACE shock absorber electronic system control. RESTORE vehicle. RETEST system.
C3 CHECK LAMP DIMMING • Cycle headlamps on and off while observing FIRM RIDE indicator. • Did FIRM RIDE indicator dim with headlamps on?	Yes No	▶ ▶	SYSTEM OK. RETEST system. GO to C4.
C4 CHECK HEADLAMP INPUT • Go to luggage compartment and lower the shock absorber electronic system control as outlined. • Turn ignition switch to OFF position. Disconnect control module 60 pin connector. • Using a voltmeter, connect one lead to Circuit 14 (BR) Pin 1, connect second lead to Circuit 57 (BK) Pin 60 at 60 pin connector. • Turn headlamps switch to the ON position. Measure voltage. • Is battery voltage present?	Yes No	▶ ▶	GO to C6. SERVICE Circuit 14 (BR) for open. GO to C5.
C5 CHECK FIRM RIDE INDICATOR IN AUTO POSITION • Reconnect control module 60 pin connector. • Set air spring suspension drive switch to AUTO position. • Start engine. • Depress brake pedal firmly to floor. • Turn steering wheel completely to one direction. Observe FIRM RIDE lamp. • Did lamp illuminate?	Yes No	▶ ▶	SYSTEM OK. RESTORE vehicle. GO to Pinpoint Test A.
C6 CHECK FIRM RIDE INDICATOR FOR SHORT TO BATTERY • Using a voltmeter, connect one lead to Circuit 298 (P/O) Pin 57, connect second lead to Circuit 57 (BK) Pin 60 at 60 pin connector. Measure voltage. • Is battery voltage present?	Yes No	▶ ▶	SERVICE Circuit 298 (P/O) for short to voltage. RESTORE vehicle. RETEST system. REPLACE shock absorber electronic system control. RESTORE vehicle. RETEST system.

FM2019400160020X

Fig. 13 Test C: Ride Control Indicator Lamp Not Operating Correctly (Part 2 of 2). 1994

Fig. 14 Test D (Part 2) — right bottom table

TEST STEP	RESULT	▶	ACTION TO TAKE
D2 CHECK SHOCK ABSORBER ACTUATOR FOR INTERNAL SHORT • Using a small blade screwdriver rotate the control tube to the "H" position. • Using an ohmmeter still connected measure resistance. • Is resistance less than 10 ohms?	Yes No	▶ ▶	REPLACE shock absorber electronic actuator. RESTORE vehicle. RETEST system. GO to D3.
D3 CHECK SIGNAL RETURN CIRCUIT • Using an ohmmeter connected to a known good ground, connect second lead to Circuit 837 (Y/BK) at shock absorber actuator harness connector. Measure resistance. • Is resistance 10 ohms or less?	Yes No	▶ ▶	GO to D4. SERVICE Circuit 837 (Y/BK) for open. RESTORE vehicle. RETEST system.
D4 CHECK POSITION SENSE CIRCUIT • Turn ignition switch to OFF position. • Go to luggage compartment and lower shock absorber electronic system control as outlined. • Disconnect control module 60 pin connector. • Using an ohmmeter connect one lead to suspect position sense circuit at shock absorber actuator harness connector. Connect second lead to same circuit at 60 pin connector. Measure resistance. • Is resistance 5 ohms or less?	Yes No	▶ ▶	GO to D5. SERVICE suspect circuit for open. RESTORE vehicle. RETEST system.
D5 CHECK SUSPECT SHOCK ABSORBER ELECTRONIC ACTUATOR • Reconnect control module 60 pin connector, and suspect shock absorber electronic actuator. • Turn ignition switch to RUN position. • Using a jumper wire connect Circuit 839 (LG/W) to Circuit 57 (BK) Pin 60 at 60 pin connector, for one to two seconds. • Using an ohmmeter measure resistance of suspect shock absorber electronic actuator per the following chart.	Yes No	▶ ▶	REPLACE shock absorber electronic system control. RESTORE vehicle. RETEST system. REPLACE shock absorber electronic system control and front shock absorber/rear shock absorber (parts are mechanically binding.)

Suspect Shock Absorber Electronic Actuator	Harness Connector Pins
LH Rear	46 and 19
RH Rear	46 and 25
RH Front	46 and 7
LH Front	46 and 10

• Is resistance 10 ohms or less?

FM2019400161020X

Fig. 14 Test D: Single Shock Absorber/Electronic Actuator Inoperative (Part 2 of 2). 1994

SYSTEM SERVICE
COMPONENT REPLACEMENT
ARC SWITCH

1. Remove console top to console base attaching screws, then disconnect top panel from console base.
2. Disconnect fog lamp switch and ride control switch electrical connectors.
3. Remove switch attaching screws under panel.
4. Reverse procedure to install.

ACTUATOR
Front

1. Position vehicle on level surface, then apply parking brake.
2. Turn ignition switch to Off or LOCK position, then raise hood.
3. Disconnect actuator electrical connectors from wiring harness electrical connectors.
4. Unsnap actuator protective cover.
5. Remove actuator connector from protective cover by inserting small screwdriver tip between connector and white X-mas tree track, **Fig. 15.**
6. Depress actuator attaching tabs, then remove actuator.
7. Grasp shock absorber piston rod end, noting position of piston rod flat on thread and actuator mounting bracket.
8. Remove actuator mounting bracket to shock absorber attaching nut.
9. Reverse procedure to install, noting the following:
   a. Ensure flat on actuator mounting bracket aligns with flat on shock absorber piston end.
   b. **Torque** actuator mounting bracket attaching nut to 27-35 ft. lbs.

Rear

1. Position vehicle on a level surface.

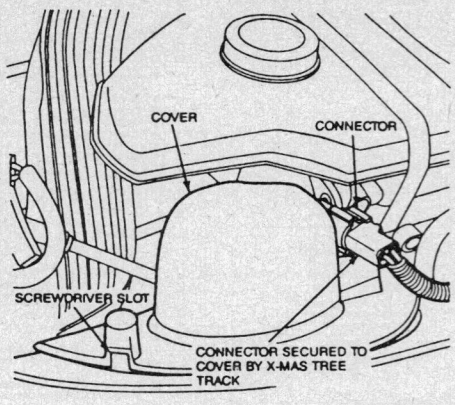

Fig. 15   Front actuator connector removal

2. Turn ignition switch to Off or LOCK position.
3. Remove luggage compartment side trim panel.
4. Disconnect actuator electrical connector from harness connector.
5. Depress actuator attaching tabs, then remove actuator.
6. Grasp mounting bracket using a suitable tool.
7. While holding mounting bracket, loosen bracket attaching nut.
8. Remove mounting bracket. **Do not attempt to raise vehicle after nut is removed. If shock absorber is to be removed, install mounting bracket retaining nut.**
9. Reverse procedure to install, ensuring flat of shock absorber piston rods aligns with mounting bracket. **Torque** mounting bracket nut to 27-35 ft. lbs.

BRAKE SENSOR SWITCH

On models with anti-lock brakes, system hydraulic pressure must be discharged. Refer to "Anti-Lock Brake" section for pressure relief procedure.

1. Disconnect battery ground cable.
2. Disconnect electrical connector from brake sensor switch.
3. Remove sensor switch from brake control valve body.
4. Reverse procedure to install. **Torque** brake sensor switch to 8-10 ft. lbs.

SPEED SENSOR

1. Disconnect battery ground cable.
2. Raise and support vehicle.
3. Remove sensor and driven gear from transmission.
4. Disconnect electrical connector and speedometer cable from speed sensor. **Do not attempt to remove the spring retainer clip with the speedometer cable in the sensor.**
5. Remove driven gear retainer and remove driven gear from sensor.
6. Reverse procedure to install, ensuring internal O-ring is seated in sensor housing.

CONTROL MODULE & RELAYS

1. Turn ignition switch to Off or LOCK position.
2. Working from inside luggage compartment, disconnect push pin at left side of package tray.
3. Swing tray downward.
4. Disconnect control module or relay electrical connectors, then remove control module or relays.
5. Reverse procedure to install.

STEERING SENSOR

The steering sensor is located at the lower end of the steering column. It may be removed with the steering column either in or out of the vehicle.

1. Disconnect sensor electrical connectors from wiring harness.
2. Disconnect sensor electrical connectors at bracket under instrument panel.
3. Remove speed sensor attaching screws, then remove sensor.
4. Reverse procedure to install.

Programmed Ride Control

INDEX

DESCRIPTION

PROGRAMMED RIDE CONTROL

The programmed ride control system (PRC) used on Probe GT models, provides the selection of sport, normal and soft combinations of damping control from the front and rear shock absorbers. The PRC switch, located in the center console, allows selection for either manual or automatic control modes of the PRC suspension.

With the PRC switch in the SOFT position, the ride control computer adjusts the shock absorber damping to provide a soft (plush) ride at all times, under all driving conditions.

With selection of NORMAL or SPORT position this will engage the automatic adjusting suspension feature. This provides combinations of hard or very hard damping upon sensor inputs to the computer during acceleration, braking or cornering and provide improved handling at high speeds.

In the event of a system malfunction, there is no indicator lamp to alert the driver of a malfunction. The driver may or may not notice a change in driveability. The PRC system should be checked at regular service intervals for any malfunction.

The programmed ride control system, **Fig. 1**, monitors the following conditions to determine when additional damping is required when the PRC switch is set in automatic modes of NORMAL or SPORT:
1. Vehicle speed.
2. Steering wheel angle.
3. Abrupt acceleration.
4. Hard braking.

CONTROL UNIT

The control unit is located below the front passenger seat. This processor receives input from various sensors and is used to switch the ride control mode based on driver input and input of the sensors.

VEHICLE SPEED SENSOR

On models with analog instrument cluster, the vehicle speed sensor is located within the speedometer subassembly. **On models with electronic instrument cluster,** the speed sensor is located on the transaxle. This is used by the PRC control unit for vehicle speed.

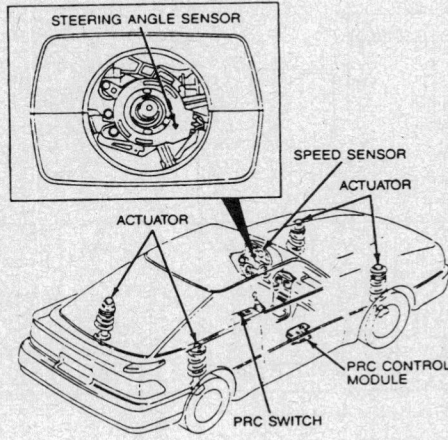

Fig. 1 Programmed ride control system

STEERING ANGLE SENSOR

The steering angle sensor is located within the steering column and used by the PRC control unit for determination of lateral forces acting on the vehicle during normal driving conditions.

PRC ACTUATORS

The PRC actuators are located at the top of each strut assembly. These devices are used to change the dampening of the shock absorber within each assembly.

ADJUSTABLE STRUTS

The struts are located at each wheel of the vehicle, these devices are use for shock absorbing control of the vehicle.

DIAGNOSIS & TESTING

Refer to **Fig. 2** for the PRC system wiring circuit.

PRELIMINARY CHECK

1. Check front and rear struts for damage, leaks, cracks, and proper mounting.
2. Check PRC system wiring harness for proper connections.
3. Check control unit, sensors, and actuators for damage.
4. Check tires for proper pressure.

QUICK TEST

The Quick Test procedure should be used only when diagnosing programmed ride control malfunction symptoms. The test is divided into two specialized functions: Key On/Engine Off Test and Continuous Test.

Refer to **Fig. 3** for Quick Test procedure. Record all codes and proceed to pinpoint tests. Refer to **Fig. 4**, for trouble code pattern identification.

PINPOINT TESTS

Do not proceed with any pinpoint tests, unless instructed by the "Quick Test," Fig. 3.

Each pinpoint test assumes a malfunction has been detected in the system with direction to enter a specific repair routine. Performing any pinpoint test without direction from the Quick Test may produce incorrect results and unnecessary component replacement.

Refer to the pinpoint test index, along with the pinpoint tests, **Figs. 5 through 9,** for pinpoint test procedures.

Test Precautions

Correct test results for the Quick Test are dependent on the proper operation of related components and systems. It may be necessary to correct any defects in these areas before passing the Quick Test.

Do not replace any components unless test results instruct to replace.

When more than one trouble code is received, always begin service with the first code.

Do not measure voltage or resistance at the control unit, or connect any test lights to it, unless specified.

Disconnect solenoids and switches from the harness before measuring for continuity, resistance, or energizing with a 12 volt source.

Follow each pinpoint test in order, starting from the first step in the appropriate test. Completely follow each step until the malfunction is identified.

Following completion of repairs the PRC system, verify all components are properly connected and repeat the Quick Test, **Fig. 3.**

An open is defined as any resistance reading greater than 10,000 ohms.

A short is defined as any resistance reading less than 5 ohms to ground.

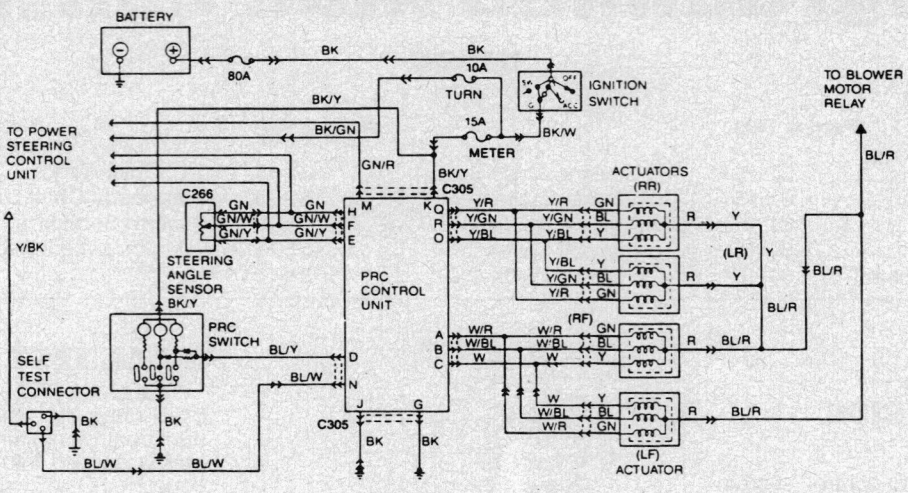

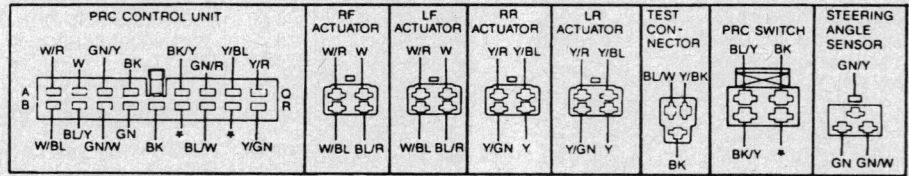

NOTE: Connector pinout is shown looking into harness side of connectors.

FM2019100148000X

Fig. 2   Programmed ride control system wiring circuit

TEST STEP		RESULT	▶	ACTION TO TAKE
QT1	PERFORM VISUAL INSPECTION			
	• Check the front and the rear struts for damage, leaks, cracks, and proper mounting.	Yes	▶	PROCEED to QT2.
	• Check the PRC system wiring harness for proper connections, bent or broken pins, corrosion, loose wires, and proper routing.	No	▶	SERVICE the fault(s) in the system and then PROCEED to QT2.
	• Check the PRC control unit, the sensors, and the actuators for physical damage.			
	• Are all of the PRC system components OK?			
	NOTE: It may be necessary to disconnect or disassemble harness connector assemblies to do some of the inspections. Note pin locations before disassembly.			

Fig. 3   Quick Test (Part 1 of 4)

FM2019100149010X

TEST STEP		RESULT	▶	ACTION TO TAKE
QT2	PERFORM SAFETY STEPS			
	• Perform all the following safety steps required to run the PRC Quick Test.	Yes	▶	PROCEED to QT3.
	— Apply the parking brake.	No	▶	Personal safety and correct diagnostic results are dependent on the test step QT2. Do not PROCEED with the Quick Test if the vehicle preparation cannot be performed.
	— Place the shift lever firmly into the PARK position (neutral on MTX).			
	— Block the drive wheels.			
	• Turn off all electrical loads.			
	— ·Radios			
	— ·Lights			
	— A. C·Heater Blower Fans, etc...			
	• Have all of the safety steps been performed and all electrical loads turned off?			
QT3	PERFORM EQUIPMENT HOOKUP			
	• Turn the ignition key to OFF.	Yes	▶	PROCEED to QT4.
	• Set the VOM on a DC voltage range to read from 0 to 15 volts.	No	▶	RE-ATTEMPT QT3.
	• Connect the VOM positive lead to the "BL/W" and the negative lead to the "BK" terminals of the suspension test connector as shown below.			
	• Is analog VOM hooked up properly?			

NOTE: For correct reading of service codes use only an analog VOM.

FM2019100149020X

Fig. 3   Quick Test (Part 2 of 4)

TEST STEP		RESULT	▶	ACTION TO TAKE
QT4	**PERFORM KEY ON ENGINE OFF TEST**			
	• Turn the ignition key to OFF.	Code 2	▶	Indicates a PASS CODE. PROCEED to [QT5]. If Code 2 is also received with the steering wheel straight, perform the Pinpoint Test [B].
	• Verify that the vehicle has been properly prepared per Quick Test steps QT2 and QT3.			
	• Turn the ignition key to ON.			
	• Set the PRC switch in the NORM position.	No Codes	▶	PERFORM the Pinpoint Test [B].
	• Set the steering wheel in the straight ahead position.	Code Unlisted	▶	PERFORM the Pinpoint Test [Q].
	• Activate the self test by turning the analog VOM to ON.			
	• Turn the steering wheel to full lock right and then to full lock left.			
	• Record any service codes.			
	NOTE: When a service code is reported on the analog VOM, it will represent itself as a pulsing or a sweeping movement of the voltmeter's needle across the dial face. Code 1 will be represented by one pulse and code 2 by two pulses and so on. After two seconds the code will repeat itself. Refer to the code identification chart			
QT5	**PERFORM KEY ON ENGINE OFF TEST**			
	• Turn the ignition key to OFF to reset the processor.	Code 2	▶	INDICATES A PASS CODE. PROCEED to [QT6].
	• Set the steering wheel in the straight ahead position.	Code 4	▶	PERFORM the Pinpoint Test [C].
	• Turn the ignition key to ON.			
	• Turn the VOM to ON.	Code 5	▶	PERFORM the Pinpoint Test [D].
	• Change the PRC switch (located on the center console) position from NORMAL to SPORT and from NORMAL to SOFT position.	No Codes	▶	PERFORM the Pinpoint test [Q].
	• Record any service codes.	Code Unlisted	▶	PERFORM the Pinpoint Test [Q].
QT6	**PERFORM KEY ON ENGINE OFF TEST**			
	• Turn the ignition key to OFF to reset the processor.	Code 1	▶	PASS CODE. PERFORM the Pinpoint Test [B] to verify the Steering Angle Sensor VREF and SIGRTN circuits are OK. For intermittent Symptoms PROCEED to QT7.
	• Set the steering wheel in the straight ahead position.			
	• Turn the ignition key to ON.			
	• Turn the VOM to ON.			
	• Hoist the vehicle and rotate the front wheels (using an on-vehicle wheel balancer or a dynometer, if available) at a speed above 15km/h (9.3 MPH).	Code 2	▶	PERFORM the Pinpoint Test [B]. If no faults are found, proceed to Pinpoint Test A.
	• Record any service codes.	No Codes	▶	PERFORM the Pinpoint Test [A].
		Code Unlisted	▶	PERFORM the Pinpoint Test [Q].

FM2019100149030X

Fig. 3 Quick Test (Part 3 of 4)

TEST STEP		RESULT	▶	ACTION TO TAKE
QT7	**PERFORM CONTINUOUS TEST**			
	• Verify that a pass code was indicated in all steps of the Key ON Engine OFF Test.	Code 2	▶	Indicates a PASS CODE. PROCEED to [QT8].
	• Verify that the vehicle has been properly prepared per Quick Test steps QT2 and QT3.	No Codes	▶	PERFORM the Pinpoint Test [B].
	• Turn the ignition key to ON.	Code Unlisted	▶	PERFORM the Pinpoint Test [Q].
	• Activate the self test by turning the analog VOM to ON.			
	• While turning steering wheel to full lock left and then full lock right, tap, move and wiggle steering angle sensor and/or the PRC harness while observing for any service code indication on the VOM.			
	• Record any service codes.			
QT8	**PERFORM CONTINUOUS TEST**			
	• Turn the ignition key to OFF to reset the processor.	Code 2	▶	Indicates a PASS CODE. PROCEED to [QT9].
	• Set the steering wheel in the straight ahead position.	Code 4	▶	PERFORM the Pinpoint Test [C].
	• Turn the ignition key to ON.	Code 5	▶	PERFORM the Pinpoint Test [D].
	• Turn the VOM to ON.	No Codes	▶	PERFORM the Pinpoint Test [Q].
	• While changing the PRC switch position from NORMAL to SPORT and from NORMAL to SOFT, tap, move and wiggle all the PRC actuators, the PRC switch and/or the PRC harness while observing for any service code indication on the VOM.	Code Unlisted	▶	PERFORM the Pinpoint Test [Q].
	• Record any service codes.			
QT9	**PERFORM CONTINUOUS TEST**			
	• Turn the ignition key to OFF to reset the processor.	Code 1	▶	Indicates a PASS CODE. PERFORM the Pinpoint Test [Q] to verify that the PRC control module and the circuitry are OK.
	• Set the steering wheel in the straight ahead position.			
	• Turn the ignition key to ON.			
	• Turn the VOM to ON.	Code 2	▶	PERFORM the Pinpoint Test [B]. If no faults are found, PROCEED to the Pinpoint Test [A].
	• Hoist the vehicle.			
	• While rotating the front wheels (using an on-vehicle wheel balancer or dynometer, if available) at a speed above 15km/h (9.3MPH), tap, move and wiggle the speed sensor and/or the PRC harness while observing for any service code indication on the VOM.	No Codes	▶	PERFORM the Pinpoint Test [A].
		Code Unlisted	▶	PERFORM the Pinpoint Test [Q].
	• Record any service codes.			

FM2019100149040X

Fig. 3 Quick Test (Part 4 of 4)

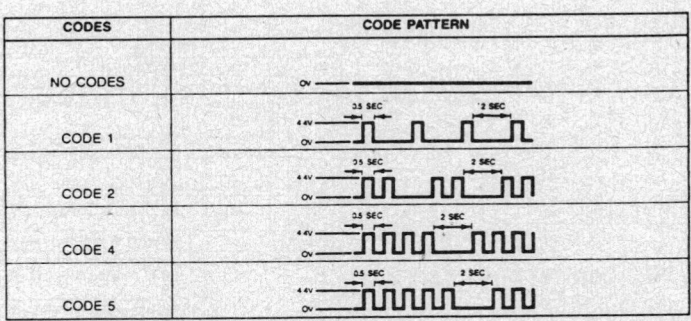

Fig. 4 Trouble code pattern identification

FM2019100150000X

DIAGNOSTIC CHART INDEX

Test	Description	Page No.	Fig. No.
A	**Speed Sensor & PRC Control Unit**	31-154	5
B	**Steering Angle Sensor & PRC Control Unit**	31-154	6
C	**Front Actuators**	31-155	7
D	**Rear Actuators**	31-156	8
Q	**PRC Switch, Control Unit & Test Connector**	31-157	9

TEST STEP		RESULT	▶	ACTION TO TAKE
1	CHECK SYSTEM INTEGRITY			
	• Visually inspect all wiring, wiring harness, connectors and components for evidence of overheating, insulation damage, looseness, shorting or other damage.	Yes	▶	SERVICE as required.
		No	▶	GO to A2.
	• Is there any cause for concern?			
	NOTE: Refer to the index for system component location illustration.			

FM2019100151010X

Fig. 5   Test A: Speed Sensor & PRC Control Unit (Part 1 of 2)

TEST STEP		RESULT	▶	ACTION TO TAKE
A2	CHECK SPEED SENSOR CIRCUIT CONTINUITY			
	• Turn the key to OFF.	Yes	▶	SERVICE the "GN/R" wire between the PRC control unit and the instrument panel for opens.
	• Disconnect the PRC control unit and the instrument panel connectors.			
	• Set the VOM on 200 ohm scale.			
	• Measure the resistance between the PRC control unit connector terminal M ("GN/R") and the instrument panel connector terminal 2C ("GN/R")	No	▶	GO to A3.
	• Is the resistance greater than 5 ohms?			
A3	CHECK SHORT TO GROUND			
	• Disconnect the PRC control unit connector.	Yes (Analog instrument panel)	▶	GO to A4.
	• Disconnect the power steering control unit connector (if equipped).	No	▶	SERVICE the "GN/R" wire between the PRC control unit and the instrument panel for shorts to ground.
	• Set the VOM on 200K ohm scale.			
	• Measure the resistance between the PRC control unit connector terminal M ("GN/R") and ground.			
	• Is the resistance greater than 10,000 ohms?			
A4	CHECK SPEED SENSOR FUNCTION (ANALOG DISPLAY ONLY)			
	• Turn the key to OFF	Yes	▶	GO to A5.
	• Disconnect the speedometer cable from the instrument cluster.	No	▶	REPLACE the speedometer assembly.
	• Connect an ohmmeter between the terminal 2C ("GN/R") and the terminal 2R ("BK") of the cluster connector.			
	• Rotate the speedometer cable connector on the back of the instrument cluster with a screwdriver or a piece of speedometer cable.			
	• Are there 4 continuity interruptions of the speedometer cable connector?			
A5	CHECK SHORT TO VPWR			
	• Turn the key to ON; leave the engine OFF.	Yes	▶	GO to Pinpoint Test Q.
	• Disconnect the power steering control unit connector, the instrument panel connector and the PRC control unit connector.	No	▶	SERVICE the "GN/R" wire for shorts to VPWR.
	• Place the transmission in Park (ATX) or Neutral (MTX).			
	• Set the VOM on the 20 volt scale.			
	• Measure the voltage between the PRC control unit connector "GN/R" wire and ground.			
	• Is the voltage reading below 6 volts?			

FM2019100151020X

Fig. 5   Test A: Speed Sensor & PRC Control Unit (Part 2 of 2)

TEST STEP		RESULT	▶	ACTION TO TAKE
B1	CHECK SYSTEM INTEGRITY			
	• Inspect all wiring, wiring harnesses, connectors and components for evidence of overheating, insulation damage, looseness, shorting or other damage.	Yes	▶	SERVICE as required.
		No	▶	GO to B2.
	• Is there any cause for concern?			
	NOTE: Refer to the index for system component location illustration.			

FM2019100152010X

Fig. 6   Test B: Steering Angle Sensor & PRC Control Unit (Part 1 of 5)

TEST STEP		RESULT	▶	ACTION TO TAKE
B2	CHECK STEERING ANGLE SENSOR RESISTANCE			
	• Turn the key to OFF.	Yes	▶	GO to B3.
	• Remove the steering column cover and disconnect the steering angle sensor connector.	No	▶	REPLACE the steering angle sensor.
	• Set the steering wheel so the wheels are in a straight ahead position.			
	• Measure the resistance between the following steering angle sensor terminals.			

Terminal	Resistance
1. "GN" - "GN/W"	0-15K ohms
2. "GN" - "GN/Y"	40-60K ohms
3. "GN/Y" - "GN/W"	30-50K ohms

• Are all resistances within specification?

FM2019100152020X

Fig. 6   Test B: Steering Angle Sensor & PRC Control Unit (Part 2 of 5)

TEST STEP		RESULT	▶	ACTION TO TAKE
B3	CHECK STEERING ANGLE SENSOR			
	• Disconnect the steering angle sensor connector.	Yes	▶	GO to B4.
	• Set the steering wheel in the straight ahead position.	No	▶	REPLACE the steering angle sensor.
	• Set the VOM on 200K ohm scale.			
	• Measure the resistance as described in the table below.			
	• Are all resistances within specification?			

Terminal	Steering Wheel Position	Resistance Value
GN-GN/W	Turn the wheel a little at a time from the straight ahead position 180 degrees to the right.	Increases approximately 20K ohms from the straight ahead value.
	Straight ahead position	0–15K ohms

FM2019100152030X

Fig. 6   Test B: Steering Angle Sensor & PRC Control Unit (Part 3 of 5)

TEST STEP	RESULT	▶	ACTION TO TAKE
B4 CHECK STEERING ANGLE SENSOR			
• Disconnect the steering angle sensor connector.	Yes	▶	GO to **B5**.
• Set the steering wheel in the straight ahead position.	No	▶	REPLACE the steering angle sensor.
• Set the VOM on 200K ohm scale.			
• Measure the resistance as described in the table below.			
• Observe the ohmmeter reading at the straight ahead position. This is your base reading. As you turn the wheel to your left, the reading will decrease to 0 ohms. The reading will then change to 45K ohms and continue to decrease from that value.			
• Are all resistances within specification?			

Terminal	Steering Wheel Position	Resistance Value
GN-GN/W	Turn the wheel a little at a time from the straight ahead position 180 degrees to the left.	Decreases approximately 20K ohms from the straight ahead value.
GN-GN/W	Straight ahead position.	0–15K ohms.

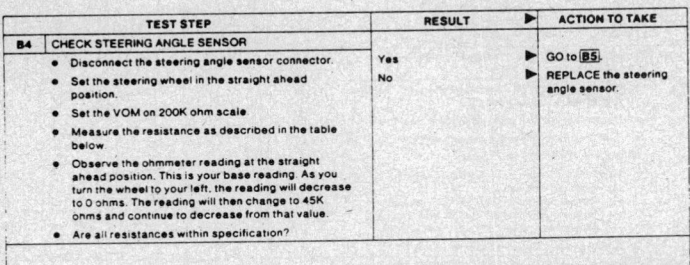

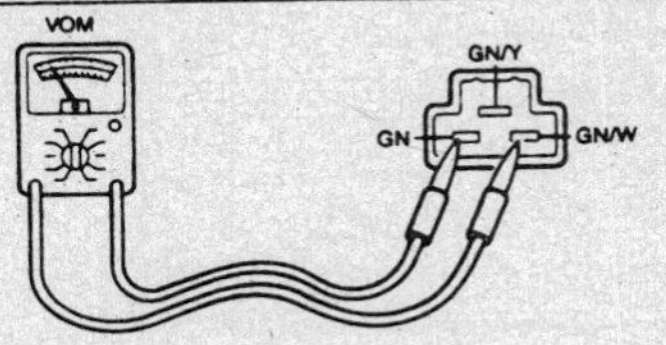

TEST STEP	RESULT	▶	ACTION TO TAKE
B5 CHECK CIRCUIT CONTINUITY			
• Disconnect the steering angle sensor connector.	Yes	▶	GO to **B6**.
• Disconnect the PRC control unit connector.	No	▶	REPAIR the wire in question for opens.
• Set the VOM on 200 ohm scale.			
• Measure the resistance between the connectors as follows:			

PRC CONTROL UNIT	STEERING ANGLE SENSOR
Terminal H "GN" Wire	"GN" Wire
Terminal F "GN/W" Wire	"GN/W" Wire
Terminal E "GN/Y" Wire	"GN/Y" Wire

• Are all resistances readings less than 5 ohms?

FM2019100152040X

Fig. 6   Test B: Steering Angle Sensor & PRC Control Unit (Part 4 of 5)

TEST STEP	RESULT	▶	ACTION TO TAKE
B6 CHECK SHORT TO GROUND			
• Turn the key to OFF.	Yes	▶	GO to **B7**.
• Disconnect the PRC control unit connector.	No	▶	REPAIR the wire in question for shorts to ground.
• Disconnect the power steering control unit connector.			
• Set the VOM on 200K ohms scale.			
• Measure the resistance between the PRC control unit connector and ground as follows:			
— Between terminal H "GN" and ground			
— Between terminal F "GN/W" and ground			
— Between terminal E "GN/Y" and ground			
• Are all resistance readings greater than 10,000 ohms?			
B7 CHECK SHORT TO VPWR			
• Disconnect the PRC control unit connector and steering angle sensor connector.	Yes	▶	GO to the Pinpoint Test **Q**.
• Disconnect the power steering control unit connector (if equipped).	No	▶	REPAIR the wire in question for shorts to VPWR.
• Turn the key to ON; leave the engine OFF.			
• Set the VOM on 20 volt scale.			
• Measure the voltage at the PRC control unit connector as follows:			
— Between terminal H "GN" and ground			
— Between terminal F "GN/W" and ground			
— Between terminal E "GN/Y" and ground			
• Are the voltage readings approximately 0 volts?			
NOTE: If directed here from Quick Test Steps QT6 or QT9 (Code 2), GO to Pinpoint Test A.			

FM2019100152050X

Fig. 6   Test B: Steering Angle Sensor & PRC Control Unit (Part 5 of 5)

TEST STEP	RESULT	▶	ACTION TO TAKE
C1 CHECK SYSTEM INTEGRITY			
• Inspect all wiring, wiring harnesses, connectors and components for evidence of overheating, insulation damage, looseness, shorting or other damage.	Yes	▶	SERVICE as required.
• Is there any cause for concern?	No	▶	GO to **C2**.
NOTE: Refer to the index for system component location illustration.			

FM2019100153010X

Fig. 7   Test C: Front Actuators (Part 1 of 4)

TEST STEP	RESULT	▶	ACTION TO TAKE
C2 CHECK RIGHT FRONT ACTUATOR (RF) VOLTAGE AT CONTROL UNIT			
• Disconnect the PRC control unit connector and (left front) actuator connector.	Yes	▶	GO to **C3**.
• Turn the key to ON; leave the engine OFF.	No	▶	GO to **C6**.
• Set the VOM on 20 volt scale.			
• Measure the voltage at the PRC control unit connector as follows:			
— Between the terminal A "W/R" and ground			
— Between the terminal B "W/BL" and ground			
— Between the terminal C "W" and ground.			
• Are all voltages above 10 volts?			
C3 CHECK LEFT FRONT ACTUATOR (LF) VOLTAGE AT CONTROL UNIT			
• Disconnect the PRC control unit connector and the (right front) actuator connector.	Yes	▶	GO to **C4**.
• Reconnect the (left front) actuator connector.	No	▶	GO to **C8**.
• Turn the key to ON; leave the engine OFF.			
• Set the VOM on 20 volt scale.			
• Measure the voltage at the PRC control unit as follows:			
— Between the terminal A "W/R" and ground			
— Between the terminal B "W/BL" and ground			
— Between the terminal C "W" and ground.			
• Are all voltages above 10 volts?			
C4 CHECK ACTUATOR INTEGRITY (RIGHT FRONT)			
• Turn the key to OFF.	Yes	▶	GO to **C5**.
• Leave the PRC control unit disconnected.	No	▶	REPLACE the (right front) actuator.
• Disconnect the (right front) actuator connector.			
• Jump battery voltage to the terminal D "R" with a jumper wire.			
• Ground the terminal A "GN" with another jumper wire, then the terminal B "BL", then the terminal C "W" and verify that the motor operates as each terminal is grounded.			
• Does the actuator motor operate when each terminal is grounded?			
C5 CHECK ACTUATOR INTEGRITY (LEFT FRONT)			
• Turn the key to OFF.	Yes	▶	GO to the Pinpoint Test **Q**.
• Leave the PRC unit disconnected.	No	▶	REPLACE the (left front) actuator.
• Disconnect the (left front) actuator connector.			
• Jump battery voltage to the terminal D "R" with a jumper wire.			
• Ground terminal A "GN" with another jumper wire, then the terminal B "BL", then the terminal C "Y", and verify that the motor operates as each terminal is grounded.			
• Does the actuator motor operate when each terminal is grounded?			

FM2019100153020X

Fig. 7   Test C: Front Actuators (Part 2 of 4)

TEST STEP	RESULT	▶	ACTION TO TAKE
C6 CHECK VOLTAGE AT ACTUATOR (RIGHT FRONT)			
• Leave the (left front) actuator connector disconnected. • Connect the harness to the PRC control unit. • Turn the key to ON; leave the engine OFF. • Set the VOM on 20 volt scale. • Probe from the rear of (right front) actuator connector to measure the voltage as follows: — Between terminal A ("W / R") and ground — Between terminal B ("W / BL") and ground — Between terminal C ("W") and ground • Are all voltages above 10 volts?	Yes No	▶ ▶	REPAIR the wire(s) in question between the (right front) actuator and the PRC control unit. GO to C7
C7 CHECK POWER TO (RIGHT FRONT) ACTUATOR			
• Disconnect the (right front) actuator connector. • Turn the key to ON; leave the engine OFF. • Set the VOM on 20 volt scale. • Measure the voltage between the terminal D "BL / R" and ground. • Is the voltage above 10 volts?	Yes No	▶ ▶	GO to C10 REPAIR the "BL / R" wire between the (right front) actuator and the blower motor relay.
C8 CHECK VOLTAGE AT ACTUATOR (LEFT FRONT)			
• Leave the (right front) connector disconnected. • Turn the key to ON; leave the engine OFF. • Set the VOM on 20 volt scale. • Probe from the rear of (front left) actuator connector to measure the voltage as follows: — Between terminal A "W / R" and ground. — Between terminal B "W / BL" and ground. — Between terminal C "W" and ground. • Are all of the voltages above 10 volts?	Yes No	▶ ▶	REPAIR the wire(s) in question between the (left front) actuator and the PRC control unit. Go to C9
C9 CHECK POWER TO (FRONT LEFT) ACTUATOR			
• Disconnect the (left front) actuator connector. • Turn the key ON; leave the engine OFF. • Set the VOM on 20 volt scale. • Measure the voltage between the terminal D "BL / R" and the ground. • Is the voltage above 10 volts?	Yes No	▶ ▶	GO to C11 REPAIR the "BL / R" wire between the (left front) actuator and the blower motor relay.

FM2019100153030X

Fig. 7   Test C: Front Actuators (Part 3 of 4)

TEST STEP	RESULT	▶	ACTION TO TAKE
C10 CHECK SHORT TO GROUND AT (RIGHT FRONT) ACTUATOR			
• Leave the PRC control unit connector disconnected. • Turn the key to OFF. • Measure the resistance between the RF actuator terminals and ground as follows: — "W / R" terminal and ground — "W / BL" terminal and ground — "W" terminal and ground • Are all resistance readings greater than 10,000 ohms?	Yes No	▶ ▶	REPLACE the right front actuator. SERVICE the wire(s) in question between the right front actuator and the PRC control unit for short to ground.
C11 CHECK SHORT TO GROUND AT (FRONT LEFT) ACTUATOR			
• Leave the PRC control unit connector disconnected. • Turn the key to OFF. • Measure the resistance between the LF actuator terminals and ground as follows: — "W / R" terminal and ground — "W BL" terminal and ground — "W" terminal and ground • Are all resistance readings greater than 10,000 ohms?	Yes No	▶ ▶	REPLACE the left front actuator. SERVICE the wire(s) in question between the left front actuator and the PRC control unit for short to ground.

FM2019100153040X

Fig. 7   Test C: Front Actuators (Part 4 of 4)

TEST STEP	RESULT	▶	ACTION TO TAKE
D1 CHECK SYSTEM INTEGRITY			
• Inspect all wiring, wiring harnesses, connectors and components for evidence of overheating, insulation damage, looseness, shorting or other damage. • Is there any cause for concern?	Yes No	▶ ▶	SERVICE as required. Go to D2
D2 CHECK RIGHT REAR ACTUATOR (RR) VOLTAGE AT CONTROL UNIT			
• Disconnect the PRC control unit connector and the (left rear) actuator connector. • Turn the key to ON; leave the engine OFF. • Set the VOM on 20 volt scale. • Measure the voltage at the PRC control unit connector as follows: — Between terminal Q "Y / R" and ground — Between terminal R "Y / GN" and ground — Between terminal O "Y / BL" and ground • Are all of the voltages above 10 volts?	Yes No	▶ ▶	GO to D3 GO to D6

FM2019100154010X

Fig. 8   Test D: Rear Actuators (Part 1 of 4)

TEST STEP	RESULT	▶	ACTION TO TAKE
D3 CHECK LEFT REAR ACTUATOR (LR) VOLTAGE AT CONTROL UNIT			
• Disconnect the PRC control unit connector and the (right rear) actuator connector. • Reconnect the (left rear) actuator connector. • Turn the key to ON; leave the engine OFF • Set the VOM on 20 volt scale. • Measure the voltage at the PRC control unit connector as follows: — Between terminal Q "Y / R" and ground — Between terminal R "Y / GN" and ground — Between terminal O "Y / BL" and ground • Are all of the voltages above 10 volts?	Yes No	▶ ▶	GO to D4 GO to D8
D4 CHECK ACTUATOR INTEGRITY (RIGHT REAR)			
• Turn the key to OFF. • Disconnect the (rear right) actuator connector. • Jump battery voltage to the terminal D "R" with a jumper wire. • Ground the terminal Q "G / N" with another jumper wire, then the terminal R "BL", then the terminal O "Y" and verify that the motor operates as each terminal is grounded. • Does the actuator motor operate when each terminal is grounded?	Yes No	▶ ▶	GO to D5 REPLACE the (right rear) actuator.
D5 CHECK ACTUATOR INTEGRITY (LEFT REAR)			
• Turn the key to OFF. • Disconnect the (left rear) actuator connector. • Jump battery voltage to the terminal D "R" with a jumper wire. • Ground the terminal Q "GN" with another jumper wire, then the terminal R "BL", then terminal O "Y" and verify that the motor operates as each terminal is grounded. • Does the actuator motor operate when each terminal is grounded?	Yes No	▶ ▶	GO to the Pinpoint Test Q. REPLACE the (left rear) actuator.

FM2019100154020X

Fig. 8   Test D: Rear Actuators (Part 2 of 4)

TEST STEP	RESULT	▶	ACTION TO TAKE
D6 CHECK VOLTAGE AT ACTUATOR (RIGHT REAR)			
• Leave the (left rear) actuator connector disconnected. • Connect the harness to the PRC control unit. • Turn the key to ON; leave the engine OFF. • Set the VOM on 20 volt scale. • Probe from the rear of (right rear) actuator connector to measure the voltages as follows: — Between terminal Q "Y / R" and ground — Between terminal R "Y / GN" and ground — Between terminal O "Y / BL" and ground • Are all of the voltages above 10 volts?	Yes No	▶ ▶	REPAIR the wire(s) in question between the (right rear) actuator and the PRC control unit. GO to D7
D7 CHECK POWER TO (RIGHT REAR) ACTUATOR			
• Disconnect the (right rear) actuator connector. • Turn the key to ON; leave the engine OFF. • Set the VOM on 20 volt scale. • Measure the voltage between the terminal D ("Y") and ground. • Is the voltage above 10 volts?	Yes No	▶ ▶	GO to D10 REPAIR the "Y" wire between the (right rear) actuator and the blower motor relay.
D8 CHECK VOLTAGE AT ACTUATOR (LEFT REAR)			
• Leave the (right rear) connector disconnected. • Turn the key to ON; leave the engine OFF. • Set the VOM on 20 volt scale. • Probe from the rear of the (left rear) actuator connector to measure the voltages as follows: — Between terminal Q "Y / R" and ground — Between terminal R "Y / GN" and ground — Between terminal O "Y / BL" and ground • Are all of the voltages above 10 volts?	Yes No	▶ ▶	REPAIR the wire(s) in question between the (left rear) actuator and the PRC control unit. GO to D9
D9 CHECK POWER TO (LEFT REAR) ACTUATOR			
• Disconnect the (left rear) actuator connector. • Turn the key to ON; leave the engine OFF. • Set the VOM on 20 volt scale. • Measure the voltage between the terminal D ("Y") and ground. • Is the voltage above 10 volts?	Yes No	▶ ▶	GO to D11 REPAIR the "Y" wire between the (left rear) actuator and the blower motor relay.

CF8221-F

FM2019100154030X

Fig. 8   Test D: Rear Actuators (Part 3 of 4)

TEST STEP		RESULT	▶	ACTION TO TAKE
D10	**CHECK SHORT TO GROUND AT (RIGHT REAR) ACTUATOR**			
	• Leave the PRC control unit connector disconnected.	Yes	▶	REPLACE the right rear actuator.
	• Turn the key to OFF.	No	▶	SERVICE the wire(s) in question between the right rear actuator and the PRC control unit for short to ground.
	• Measure the resistance between the right rear actuator terminals and ground as follows: — "Y/R" terminal and ground — "Y/GN" terminal and ground — "Y/BL" terminal and ground			
	• Are all resistance readings greater than 10,000 ohms?			
D11	**CHECK SHORT TO GROUND AT (LEFT REAR) ACTUATOR**			
	• Leave the PRC control unit connector disconnected.	Yes	▶	REPLACE the left rear actuator.
	• Turn the key to OFF.	No	▶	SERVICE the wire(s) in question between the left rear actuators and the PRC control unit for short to ground.
	• Measure the resistance between the left rear actuator terminals and ground as follows: — "Y/R" terminal and ground — "Y/GN" terminal and ground — "Y/BL" terminal and ground			
	• Are all resistance readings greater than 10,000 ohms?			

FM2019100154040X

Fig. 8   Test D: Rear Actuators (Part 4 of 4)

TEST STEP		RESULT	▶	ACTION TO TAKE
Q1	**CHECK SYSTEM INTEGRITY**			
	• Inspect all wiring, wiring harnesses, connectors and components for evidence of overheating, insulation damage, looseness, shorting or other damage.	Yes	▶	SERVICE as required.
	• Is there any cause for concern?	No	▶	GO to Q2.

FM2019100155010X

Fig. 9   Test Q: RC Switch, Control Unit & Test Connector (Part 1 of 4)

TEST STEP		RESULT	▶	ACTION TO TAKE
Q8	**CHECK POWER TO PRC SWITCH**			
	• Leave the PRC control unit disconnected.	Yes	▶	REPLACE the 15A METER fuse or REPAIR the "BK/Y" wire between the fuse box and the PRC switch.
	• Disconnect the PRC switch connector.	No	▶	GO to Q9.
	• Turn the key to ON; leave the engine OFF.			
	• Set the VOM on 20 volt scale.			
	• Measure the voltage between the PRC switch connector "BK/Y" wire and ground.			
	• Is the voltage reading less than 10 volts?			
Q9	**CHECK PRC SWITCH GROUND**			
	• Leave the PRC switch connector disconnected.	Yes	▶	GO to Q10.
	• Set the VOM on 200 ohm scale.	No	▶	REPAIR the "BK" wire between the PRC switch and the chassis ground for opens.
	• Measure the resistance between the PRC switch connector "BK" wire and ground.			
	• Is the resistance less than 5 ohms?			
Q10	**CHECK CONTINUITY BETWEEN PRC CONTROL UNIT AND SWITCH**			
	• Disconnect the PRC control unit connector and the PRC switch connector.	Yes	▶	GO to Q11.
	• Set the VOM on 200 ohm scale.	No	▶	REPAIR the "BL/Y" wire between the PRC control unit and the PRC switch for opens.
	• Measure the resistance between the PRC control unit connector terminal D "BL/Y" and the PRC switch connector "BL/Y" wire.			
	• Is the resistance less than 5 ohms?			
Q11	**CHECK PRC CIRCUIT FOR SHORT TO GROUND**			
	• Disconnect the PRC control unit connector and the PRC switch connector.	Yes	▶	GO to Q12.
	• Set the VOM on 200K ohm scale.	No	▶	REPAIR the "BL/Y" wire between the PRC control unit and the PRC switch for short to ground.
	• Measure the resistance between the PRC control unit connector terminal D "BL/Y" and ground.			
	• Is the resistance greater than 10,000 ohms?			

FM2019100155030X

Fig. 9   Test Q: RC Switch, Control Unit & Test Connector (Part 3 of 4)

TEST STEP		RESULT	▶	ACTION TO TAKE
Q2	**CHECK POWER TO PRC CONTROL UNIT**			
	• Disconnect the PRC control unit connector.	Yes	▶	GO to Q3.
	• Turn the key to ON; leave the engine OFF.	No	▶	REPLACE 15A METER fuse or REPAIR the "BK/Y" wire between the PRC control unit and the interior fuse box.
	• Set the VOM on 20 volt scale.			
	• Measure the voltage between the terminal K "BK/Y" and ground.			
	• Is the voltage above 10 volts?			
Q3	**CHECK PRC CONTROL UNIT GROUNDS**			
	• Leave the PRC control unit connector disconnected.	Yes	▶	GO to Q4.
	• Set the VOM on 200 ohm scale.	No	▶	REPAIR the "BK" wire in question between the PRC control unit and the chassis ground for opens.
	• Measure the resistance as follows: — Between the terminal J "BK" and ground — Between the terminal G "BK" and ground			
	• Are the resistance readings less than 5 ohms?			
Q4	**CHECK TEST CONNECTOR GROUND**			
	• Disconnect the test connector from the mounting bracket.	Yes	▶	GO to Q5.
	• Set the VOM on 200 ohm scale.	No	▶	REPAIR the "BK" wire between the test connector and the chassis ground.
	• Measure the resistance between the terminal "BK" wire and ground.			
	• Is the resistance reading less than 5 ohms?			
Q5	**CHECK CONTINUITY BETWEEN PRC CONTROL UNIT AND TEST CONNECTOR**			
	• Disconnect the PRC control unit connector.	Yes	▶	GO to Q6.
	• Set the VOM on 200 ohm scale.	No	▶	REPAIR the "BL/W" wire between the PRC control unit and the test connector for opens.
	• Measure the resistance between the PRC control unit connector terminal N "BL/W" and test connector "BL/W" wire.			
	• Is the resistance less than 5 ohms?			
Q6	**CHECK TEST CONNECTOR FOR SHORT TO GROUND**			
	• Leave the PRC control unit connector disconnected.	Yes	▶	GO to Q7.
	• Turn the key to OFF.	No	▶	REPAIR the "BL/W" wire between the PRC control unit and the test connector for short to ground.
	• Set the VOM on 200K ohm scale.			
	• Measure the resistance between the PRC control unit connector terminal N "BL/W" and ground.			
	• Is the resistance greater than 10,000 ohms?			
Q7	**CHECK TEST CONNECTOR CIRCUIT FOR SHORT TO VPWR**			
	• Leave the PRC control unit connector disconnected.	Yes	▶	GO to Q8.
	• Turn the key to ON; leave the engine OFF.	No	▶	REPAIR the "BL/W" wire between the PRC control unit and the test connector for short to VPWR.
	• Set the VOM on 20 volt scale.			
	• Measure the voltage between the PRC control unit connector terminal N "BL/W" and ground.			
	• Is the voltage reading approximately 0 volts?			

FM2019100155020X

Fig. 9   Test Q: RC Switch, Control Unit & Test Connector (Part 2 of 4)

TEST STEP		RESULT	▶	ACTION TO TAKE
Q12	**CHECK PRC SWITCH OPERATION**			
	• Remove the PRC switch from center console.	Yes	▶	REPLACE the PRC control unit.
	• Set the VOM on 200 ohm scale.	No	▶	REPLACE the PRC switch.
	• Measure the continuity between the PRC switch terminals in all positions (SOFT, NORMAL, SPORT).			

NOTE: Reverse VOM polarity and check continuity twice between each terminal indicated in the table below.

• Does the PRC switch function properly?

NOTE: If directed here from Quick Test Step Q9 PASS CODE, "DO NOT REPLACE THE PRC CONTROL UNIT. Re-attempt to recreate the intermittent fault.

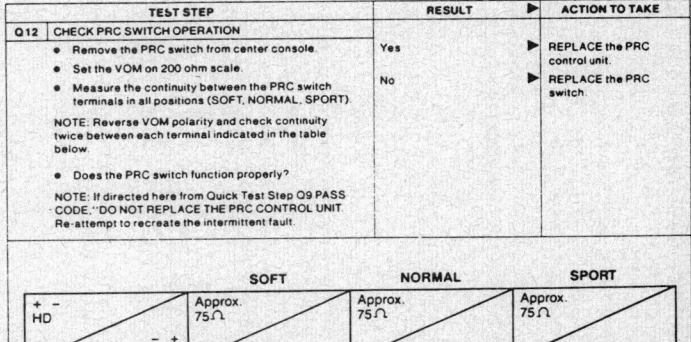

		SOFT	NORMAL	SPORT
+ − HD		Approx. 75 Ω	Approx. 75 Ω	Approx. 75 Ω
	− + HD	Infinity (∞)	Infinity (∞)	Infinity (∞)
+ − HF		Approx. 45 Ω	Approx. 50 Ω	Approx. 55 Ω
	− + HF	Approx. 45 Ω	Approx. 50 Ω	Approx. 55 Ω
+ − DF		Infinity (∞)	Infinity (∞)	Infinity (∞)
	− + DF	Approx. 90 Ω	Approx. 90 Ω	Approx. 20 Ω

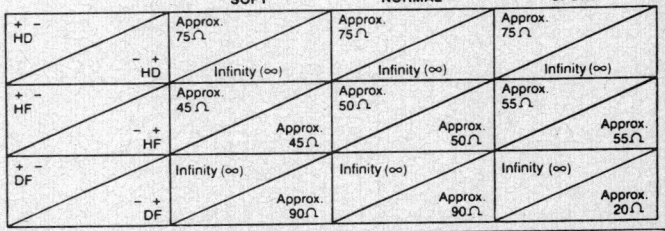

FM2019100155040X

Fig. 9   Test Q: RC Switch, Control Unit & Test Connector (Part 4 of 4)

SYSTEM SERVICE

COMPONENT REPLACEMENT

PRC CONTROL SWITCH

1. Disconnect battery ground cable.
2. Remove center console from vehicle.
3. Press in on release tabs, located on each side of switch, then disconnect electrical connectors and remove switch through front of center console.
4. Reverse procedure to install.

ACTUATOR

Front

1. Place vehicle on a level surface.
2. Apply parking brake, then raise hood.
3. Remove rubber cap from strut mounting block, then disconnect PRC control unit electrical connector, if equipped.
4. Remove PRC control unit.
5. Reverse procedure to install.

Rear

1. Place vehicle on a level surface.
2. Remove upper trunk side molding and lower trim panel.
3. Disconnect PRC electrical connector, if equipped.
4. Remove PRC control unit.
5. Reverse procedure to install.

SPEED SENSOR

1. Disconnect battery ground cable.
2. **On models with electronic instrument cluster,** disconnect electrical connector from sensor.
3. Remove sensor attaching bolt from transaxle housing.
4. Pull sensor from transaxle housing.
5. **On models with analog instrument cluster,** remove cluster and lens assembly.
6. Remove attaching screws, then the speedometer subassembly.
7. Remove speed sensor.
8. **On all models,** reverse procedure to install.

CONTROL UNIT

1. Disconnect battery ground cable.
2. Remove front passenger seat.
3. Remove attaching bolts from control unit.
4. Disconnect PRC electrical connector from the control unit.
5. Remove control unit from vehicle.
6. Reverse procedure to install.

TROUBLESHOOTING SUPPLEMENT

INDEX

HIGH SPEED SHAKE DIAGNOSIS

TEST STEP	RESULT	▶ ACTION TO TAKE
A0 ROAD TEST • Accelerate vehicle to the speed which the customer indicated the shake occurred.	No Shake Shake Felt	▶ Vehicle OK. ▶ GO to **A1**.
A1 INSPECT TIRES • Raise vehicle on hoist. Inspect tires for extreme wear or damage, cupping or flat spots. CUPPED OR DISHED TREADS	Tires are OK Cupped or Dished Tire Treads are present	▶ GO to **A2**. ▶ CHECK suspension components for misalignment, abnormal wear, or damage that may have contributed to the tire wear. CORRECT suspension problems, and REPLACE damaged tires. ROAD TEST vehicle.
A2 INSPECT WHEEL BEARINGS • Spin front tires by hand to check for wheel bearing roughness. Check bearing end play.	Bearing End Play OK Wheel Bearing	▶ GO to **A3**. ▶ ADJUST or REPLACE and lubricate bearings as necessary. ROAD TEST vehicle.
A3 WHEEL/TIRE RUNOUT ON VEHICLE • Measure wheel/tire assembly runouts on vehicle using Radial Run-Out Gauge 007-00014 or equivalent. Assembly runout should be less than 1.14 mm (.045-inch) radial and lateral. Warm up tires prior to taking measurement to eliminate slight flat spotting.	Measurement within specification Measurement not within specification	▶ GO to **A8**. ▶ GO to **A4**.
A4 WHEEL/TIRE RUNOUT OFF VEHICLE • Measure wheel/tire assembly from any position that exceeds 1.14 mm (.045-inch) radial or lateral. Before removing wheel/tire assembly, mark wheel stud and corresponding bolt hole so assembly can be installed in same position. Remove assembly and mount on wheel balancer. Measure runout as in Step A3. Assembly runout should be less than 1.14 mm (0.45-inch) radial and lateral.	Measurement within specification Measurement not within specification	▶ CHECK rotor drum and bolt circle runout. GO to **A7**. ▶ GO to **A5**.

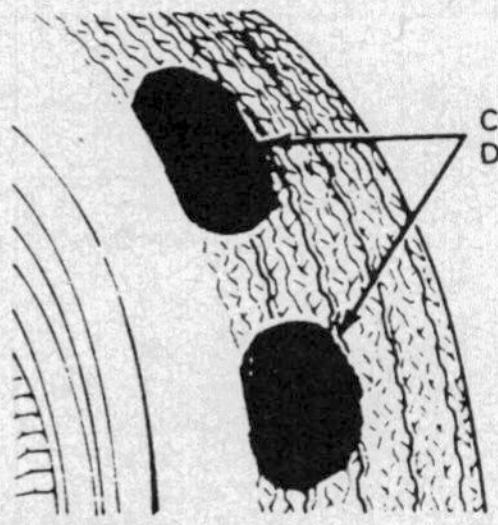

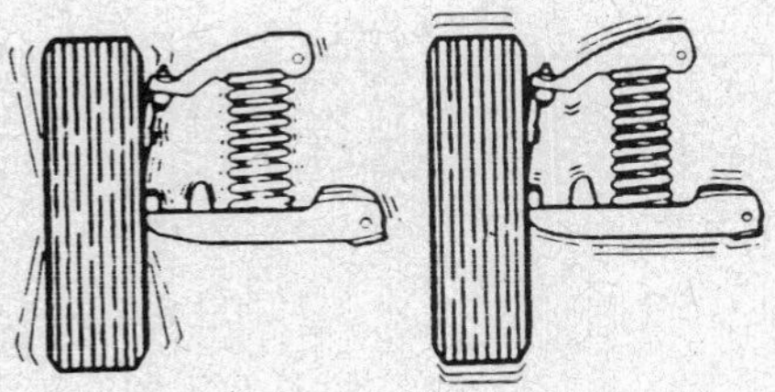

FM2019100001010X

Fig. 1   Noise, Vibration & Harshness (NVH) (Part 1 of 14)

HIGH SPEED SHAKE DIAGNOSIS — Continued

TEST STEP	RESULT	▶	ACTION TO TAKE
A5 MATCH MOUNTING • Mark the high runout location on the tire and also on the wheel. Break the assembly down and rotate the tire 180 degrees (half-way around) on the wheel. Inflate the tire and measure the runouts.	Proper balance achieved	▶	BALANCE assembly and INSTALL on vehicle. ROAD TEST.
	Improper balance	▶	If high spot is within 101.6 mm (4 inches) of first high spot ON THE TIRE, REPLACE tire. BALANCE assembly and INSTALL on vehicle. ROAD TEST.
	Improper balance	▶	If high spot is not within 101.6 mm (4 inches) of first high spot on the tire. GO to **A6**.
A6 WHEEL RUNOUT • Dismount tire and mount wheel on wheel balancer. Measure runouts on both flanges. Runout should be less than 1.14 mm (.045-inch) radial and lateral.	Proper runout	▶	LOCATE and MARK low spot on wheel and INSTALL tire matching high spot on wheel. BALANCE assembly and ROAD TEST.
	Improper runout	▶	REPLACE wheel. CHECK runouts on new wheel. If new wheel is within limits, LOCATE and MARK the low spot. INSTALL tire, matching high spot of tire with low spot of wheel. BALANCE assembly and INSTALL on vehicle. ROAD TEST.

FM2019100001020X

Fig. 1   Noise, Vibration & Harshness (NVH) (Part 2 of 14)

HIGH SPEED SHAKE DIAGNOSIS — Continued

TEST STEP	RESULT		ACTION TO TAKE
A7 AXLE, ROTOR OR DRUM AND BOLT CIRCLE RUNOUTS			
• For rear wheel positions remove rotor or drum and measure axle flange face runout (greater than .254mm (.010-inch)). Bolt circuit runout (greater than .397mm (.015-inch)) and drum/rotor pilot radial runout (greater than .152mm (.006-inch)).	Measurements OK	▶	REPLACE wheel, balance assembly, reinstall on vehicle and ROAD TEST.
• For front wheel positions, measure rotor lateral runout (greater than .127mm (.005-inch)) bolt circle runout (greater than .381mm (.015-inch)) and rotor pilot radial runout (greater than .152mm (.006-inch)). 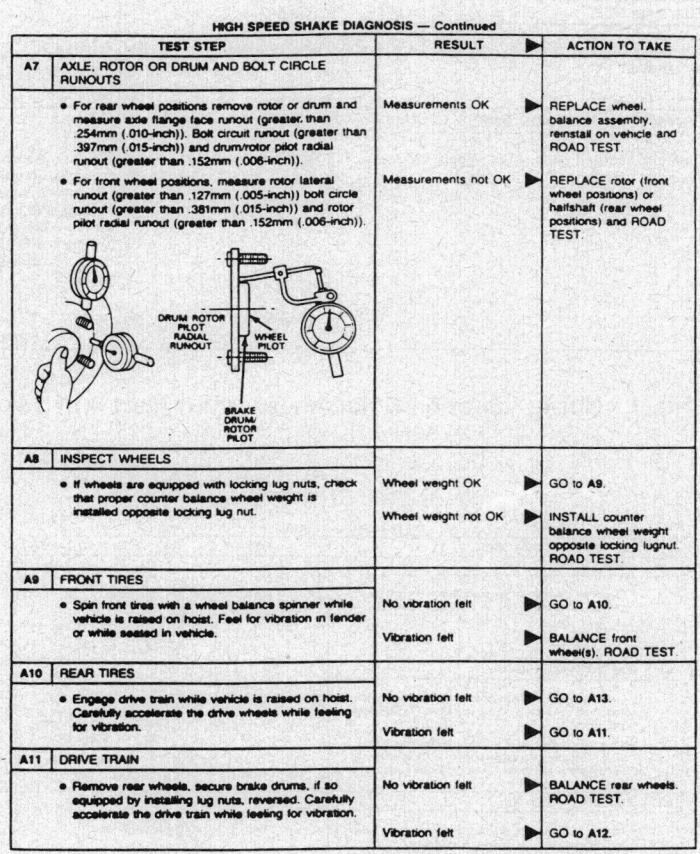	Measurements not OK	▶	REPLACE rotor (front wheel positions) or halfshaft (rear wheel positions) and ROAD TEST.
A8 INSPECT WHEELS			
• If wheels are equipped with locking lug nuts, check that proper counter balance wheel weight is installed opposite locking lug nut.	Wheel weight OK	▶	GO to A9.
	Wheel weight not OK	▶	INSTALL counter balance wheel weight opposite locking lugnut. ROAD TEST.
A9 FRONT TIRES			
• Spin front tires with a wheel balance spinner while vehicle is raised on hoist. Feel for vibration in fender or while seated in vehicle.	No vibration felt	▶	GO to A10.
	Vibration felt	▶	BALANCE front wheel(s). ROAD TEST.
A10 REAR TIRES			
• Engage drive train while vehicle is raised on hoist. Carefully accelerate the drive wheels while feeling for vibration.	No vibration felt	▶	GO to A13.
	Vibration felt	▶	GO to A11.
A11 DRIVE TRAIN			
• Remove rear wheels, secure brake drums, if so equipped by installing lug nuts, reversed. Carefully accelerate the drive train while feeling for vibration.	No vibration felt	▶	BALANCE rear wheels. ROAD TEST.
	Vibration felt	▶	GO to A12.

FM2019100001030X

Fig. 1   Noise, Vibration & Harshness (NVH) (Part 3 of 14)

HIGH SPEED SHAKE DIAGNOSIS — Continued

TEST STEP	RESULT ▶	ACTION TO TAKE
A12 REAR DRUMS OR ROTORS • Remove the brake drums or rotors. Carefully accelerate the drive train while feeling for vibration.	No vibration felt ▶ Vibration felt ▶	REPLACE drums or rotors. ROAD TEST. GO to Driveline Vibration Diagnosis.
A13 WHEEL BALANCE • Balance all wheels not previously balanced. Road test vehicle.	Wheels balanced ▶ Wheels not balanced ▶	Vehicle OK. GO to **A14**.
A14 SUBSTITUTE WHEELS AND TIRES • Substitute a known good set of wheels and tires. Road test vehicle.	No vibration ▶ Vibration felt ▶	INSTALL the original tire/wheel assemblies, one by one, road testing at each step, until the defective tire(s) is identified. REPLACE tire(s) as necessary and RETEST. REFER to Driveline Vibration Diagnosis.

FM2019100001040X

Fig. 1   Noise, Vibration & Harshness (NVH) (Part 4 of 14)

TIP-IN MOAN DIAGNOSIS

TEST STEP	RESULT ▶	ACTION TO TAKE
B0 AIR CLEANER • Check air cleaner for proper installation of base gasket, lid, element and air inlet duct assembly.	(OK) ▶ (OK̸) ▶	GO to B1. CORRECT condition and ROAD TEST. If moan persists, GO to B1.
B1 POWERTRAIN RESONANCE • Loosen all converter or clutch housing-to-engine attaching bolts 3/4 turn and road test. Tighten bolts after test. • Check for presence of an engine-to-transmission brace (usually runs from LH front engine mount to transmission converter housing). Ensure proper installation.	Moan reduced or eliminated ▶ (OK) ▶	CHANGE or INSTALL damper as indicated and RETEST. If moan still persists, GO to B2. GO to B2.
B2 ENGINE MOUNTS • Normalize engine mounts by loosening them and, with engine running, shifting transmission from NEUTRAL to DRIVE and back to NEUTRAL. With manual transmission, load engine by slipping clutch in gear. Tighten mounting bolts and road test.	(OK) ▶ (OK̸) ▶	Vehicle OK. GO to B3.
B3 EXHAUST SYSTEM • Warm up system to normal operating temperature. Loosen all hanger attachments and reposition hangers until they hang free and straight. Then loosen all flange joints and, with engine running, shift transmission from NEUTRAL to DRIVE and back to NEUTRAL (or load engine with clutch). Tighten all hanger clamps and flanges. Road test vehicle.	(OK) ▶ (OK̸) ▶	Vehicle OK. REFER to Engine Accessory Vibration Diagnosis.
B4 AXLE GEAR NOISE • With vehicle on hoist, engine off, visually inspect isolation components for damaged and/or misaligned mounting.	(OK) ▶ (OK̸) ▶	REFER to Gear Noise Analysis. REMOVE and REPLACE damaged components. ROAD TEST.

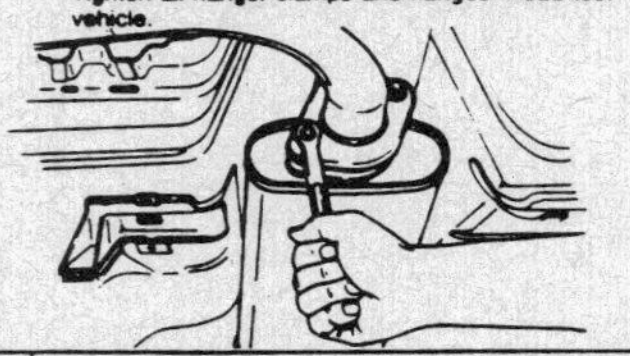

FM2019100001050X

Fig. 1   Noise, Vibration & Harshness (NVH) (Part 5 of 14)

DRIVELINE VIBRATION DIAGNOSIS

	TEST STEP	RESULT ▶	ACTION TO TAKE
C0	**WHEELS AND TIRES**		
	• Verify that the observed condition is not a high speed shake caused by wheels/tires.	(OK)	REFER to High Speed Shake Diagnosis for drive-wheel runout and balance procedures.
		(OK̸) ▶	GO to C1.
C1	**DRIVESHAFT**		
	• Inspect driveshaft for physical damage, undercoating, or improperly seated, worn, or binding universal joints. Check index marks (paint spots) on rear of shaft and pinion yoke or companion flange. If these marks are more than 90 degrees apart, disconnect shaft and re-index to align marks as close as possible.	(OK) ▶	GO to C2.
		(OK̸) ▶	CLEAN shaft and REPLACE universal joints as necessary, or REPLACE shaft if damaged. RECHECK vibration at road test speed. If gone, INSTALL wheels and road test. If vibration persists, GO to C2.
C2	**DRIVESHAFT RUNOUT**		
	• With vehicle on hoist measure runout at front, center, and rear of driveshaft, 0.711 mm (0.028-inch).	(OK) ▶	GO to C5.
		At front or center (OK̸) ▶	REPLACE driveshaft.
		At rear (OK̸) ▶	MARK the rear runout high point. GO to C3.
C3	**DRIVESHAFT RE-INDEXING**		
	• Note or mark indexing of driveshaft to rear axle pinion flange. Disconnect the shaft, re-index 180 degrees, and reconnect. Recheck runout at rear of shaft. Maximum runout is 0.711 mm (0.028-inch).	(OK) ▶	CHECK for vibration at road-test speed. If still present, GO to C5.
	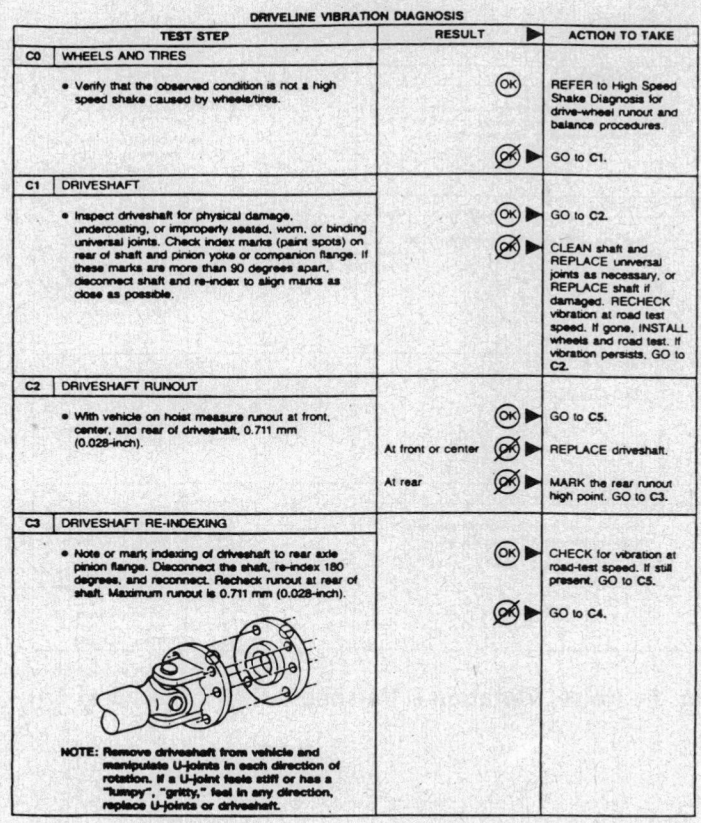	(OK̸) ▶	GO to C4.
	NOTE: Remove driveshaft from vehicle and manipulate U-joints in each direction of rotation. If a U-joint feels stiff or has a "lumpy", "gritty," feel in any direction, replace U-joints or driveshaft.		

FM2019100001060X

Fig. 1   Noise, Vibration & Harshness (NVH) (Part 6 of 14)

DRIVELINE VIBRATION DIAGNOSIS — Continued

	TEST STEP	RESULT ▶	ACTION TO TAKE
C4	PINION YOKE OR FLANGE		
	• Compare the two high points marked in C2 and C3.	Marks within 25mm (1 inch) of each other ▶	REPLACE driveshaft. RECHECK vibration.
		Marks 180 degrees apart ▶	REPLACE pinion yoke on flange. RECHECK driveshaft runout. 0.89 mm (0.035 inch). ROAD TEST for vibration. If vibration persists, GO to C5.
C5	DRIVESHAFT VIBRATION		
	• The driveshaft can be re-indexed to any of eight positions to minimize imbalance. Refer to Driveshaft Indexing.	(OK) ▶	Vehicle OK.
		(OK̸) ▶	REFER to Driveshaft Balance Diagnosis F1. If vibration still persists GO to C6.

FM2019100001070X

Fig. 1   Noise, Vibration & Harshness (NVH) (Part 7 of 14)

DRIVELINE ANGLES DIAGNOSIS

TEST STEP	RESULT	▶	ACTION TO TAKE
D0 UNIVERSAL JOINTS • Raise vehicle on drive-on type hoist, or back onto a front-end alignment rack. Inspect U-joints for proper installation, seizure, or excessive wear.	(OK) ▶		GO to D1.
	(OK̸) ▶		INDEX-MARK driveshaft and flange, REMOVE shaft, and REPLACE the worn U-joints. GO to D1.
D1 RIDE HEIGHT • Check ride height between the axle and rear bumper bracket on frame rail.	(OK) ▶		GO to D2.
	(OK̸) ▶		CHECK to make sure vehicle is not abnormally loaded. CORRECT ride height if necessary. GO to D2.
D2 DRIVELINE ANGLES • Check driveline angles	(OK) ▶		GO to D3.
	(OK̸) ▶		CORRECT driveline angle GO to D3.
D3 AXLE RING AND PINION • If driveline angle corrections do not eliminate vibration, check ring and pinion backlash.	(OK) ▶		GO to Engine Accessory Vibration Diagnosis.
	(OK̸) ▶		ADJUST or REPLACE ring and pinion gearset. If vibration still exists, GO to Engine Accessory Vibration Diagnosis.

FM2019100001080X

Fig. 1   Noise, Vibration & Harshness (NVH) (Part 8 of 14)

ENGINE ACCESSORY VIBRATION DIAGNOSIS

TEST STEP	RESULT	▶	ACTION TO TAKE
E0 ENGINE RUN-UP • Run-up to problem rpm observed in road test, with vehicle stationary.	Vibration occurs	▶	GO to E1.
	Vibration does not occur	▶	PERFORM stall test in Drive with brakes locked (or load engine by slipping clutch in gear with manual transmission). If vibration occurs, GO to Tip-in Moan Diagnosis in this Section.
E1 DRIVE BELTS AND PULLEYS • With engine stopped, inspect all engine accessory drive belts and pulleys for wear or damage, and check belt tension, using Belt Tension Gauge T83L-8620-A.	(OK) ▶		GO to E2.
	(OK̸) ▶		REPLACE worn or damaged belts or pulleys. CORRECT belt tension. GO to E2.
E2 MOUNTING HARDWARE • Inspect mounting brackets and adjusting hardware for proper alignment and tightness.	(OK) ▶		GO to E3.
	(OK̸) ▶		ALIGN and TIGHTEN mounting hardware to specifications. CORRECT belt tension. START UP engine and run-up to problem rpm. If vibration still exists, GO to E3.

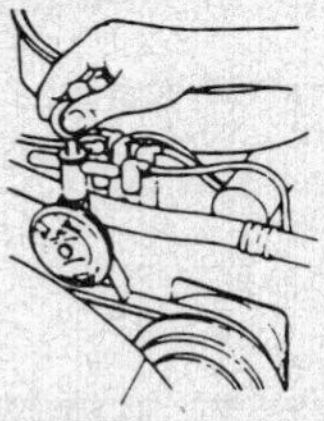

FM2019100001090X

Fig. 1   Noise, Vibration & Harshness (NVH) (Part 9 of 14)

ENGINE ACCESSORY VIBRATION DIAGNOSIS

TEST STEP	RESULT ▶	ACTION TO TAKE
E3 ENGINE IDLING		
• With engine idling, visually check all accessory drive belts and pulleys for misalignment, runout or irregular motion. Maximum runout is 3mm (1/8 inch).	(OK) ▶	GO to **E4**.
	(ØK) ▶	If pulley(s) exceeds maximum runout, REPLACE pulley. If belt rides up and down in pulley, a variable-width condition exists. If it occurs on just one pulley, REPLACE that pulley. Otherwise, REPLACE the belt. RUN engine up to problem RPM. If belt whips, ADJUST belt tension to specifications. If belt still whips, REPLACE belt. If vibration still exists, GO to **E4**.
E4 ACCESSORIES		
• Run-up engine to problem RPM and, with stethoscope-type device, check each component. • If the source cannot be detected by probing, remove each belt, one at a time, until vibration goes away.	Noisy component located ▶	REPLACE belt. If vibration still exists, SERVICE or REPLACE component.
	Unable to locate vibration ▶	Possible engine component imbalance. This situation is possible, but unlikely.

FM2019100001100X

Fig. 1 Noise, Vibration & Harshness (NVH) (Part 10 of 14)

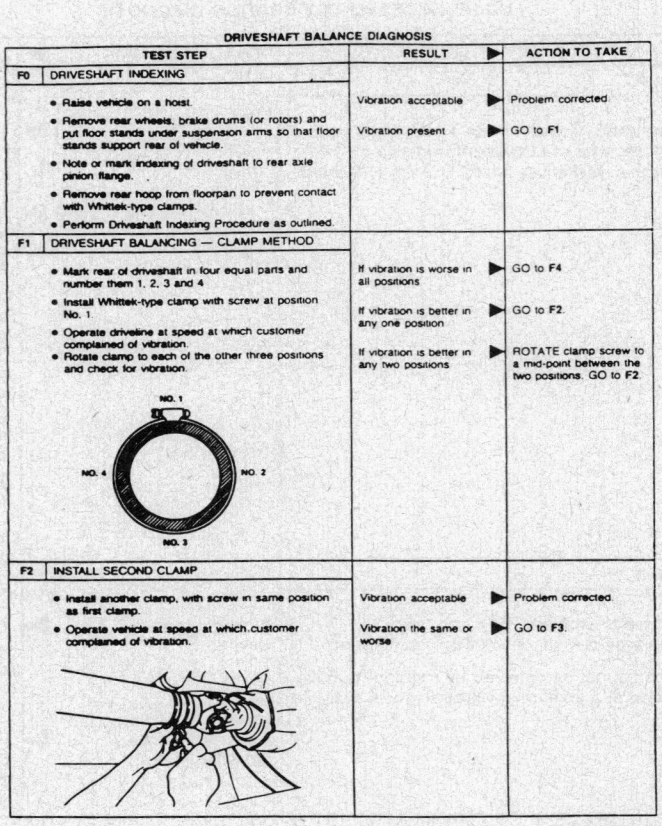

DRIVESHAFT BALANCE DIAGNOSIS

TEST STEP	RESULT	▶	ACTION TO TAKE
F0 DRIVESHAFT INDEXING			
• Raise vehicle on a hoist.	Vibration acceptable	▶	Problem corrected.
• Remove rear wheels, brake drums (or rotors) and put floor stands under suspension arms so that floor stands support rear of vehicle.	Vibration present	▶	GO to F1
• Note or mark indexing of driveshaft to rear axle pinion flange.			
• Remove rear hoop from floorpan to prevent contact with Whittek-type clamps.			
• Perform Driveshaft Indexing Procedure as outlined.			
F1 DRIVESHAFT BALANCING — CLAMP METHOD			
• Mark rear of driveshaft in four equal parts and number them 1, 2, 3 and 4.	If vibration is worse in all positions	▶	GO to F4
• Install Whittek-type clamp with screw at position No. 1.	If vibration is better in any one position	▶	GO to F2.
• Operate driveline at speed at which customer complained of vibration.	If vibration is better in any two positions	▶	ROTATE clamp screw to a mid-point between the two positions. GO to F2.
• Rotate clamp to each of the other three positions and check for vibration.			
F2 INSTALL SECOND CLAMP			
• Install another clamp, with screw in same position as first clamp.	Vibration acceptable	▶	Problem corrected.
• Operate vehicle at speed at which customer complained of vibration.	Vibration the same or worse	▶	GO to F3.

FM2019100001110X

Fig. 1   Noise, Vibration & Harshness (NVH) (Part 11 of 14)

DRIVESHAFT BALANCE DIAGNOSIS — Continued

TEST STEP	RESULT	▶	ACTION TO TAKE
F3 REPOSITION CLAMP			
• Rotate screws of clamps equally away from each other about 12.7mm (1/2 inch).	Vibration acceptable	▶	Problem corrected.
• Operate vehicle at speed at which customer complained of vibration.	Vibration not acceptable	▶	GO to **F4**.

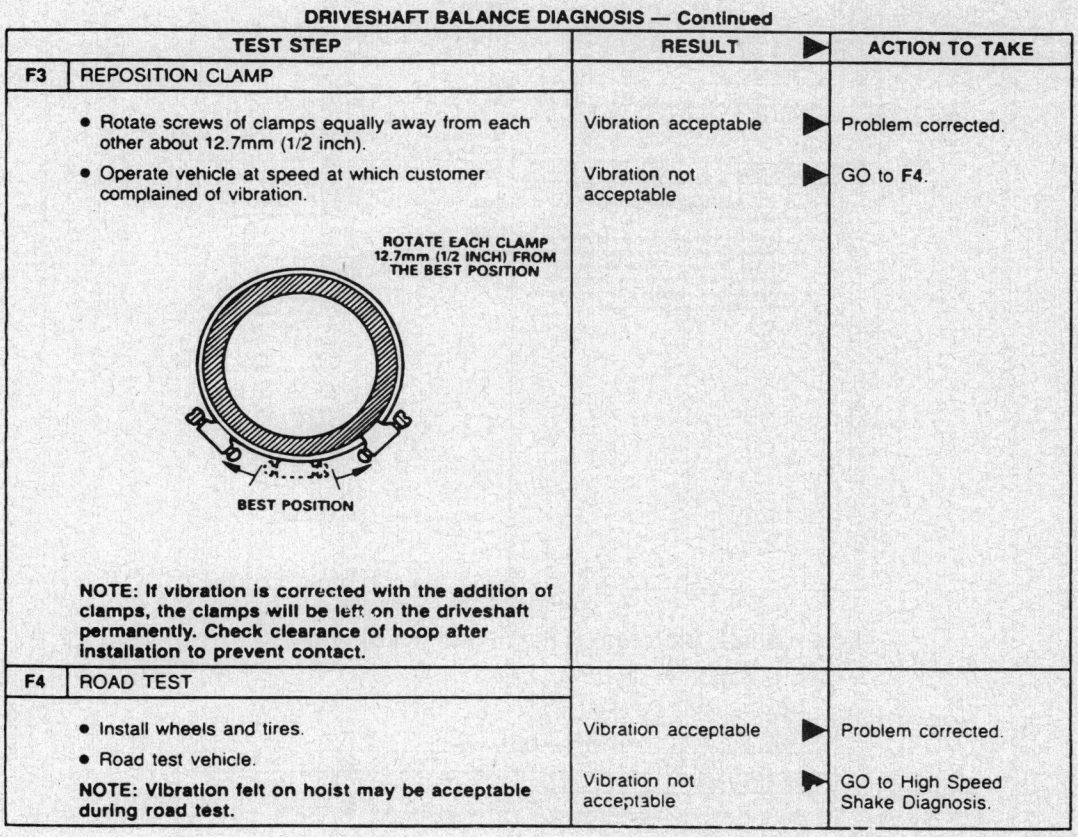

ROTATE EACH CLAMP
12.7mm (1/2 INCH) FROM
THE BEST POSITION

BEST POSITION

NOTE: If vibration is corrected with the addition of clamps, the clamps will be left on the driveshaft permanently. Check clearance of hoop after installation to prevent contact.

TEST STEP	RESULT	▶	ACTION TO TAKE
F4 ROAD TEST			
• Install wheels and tires.	Vibration acceptable	▶	Problem corrected.
• Road test vehicle.	Vibration not acceptable	▶	GO to High Speed Shake Diagnosis.
NOTE: Vibration felt on hoist may be acceptable during road test.			

FM2019100001120X

Fig. 1   Noise, Vibration & Harshness (NVH) (Part 12 of 14)

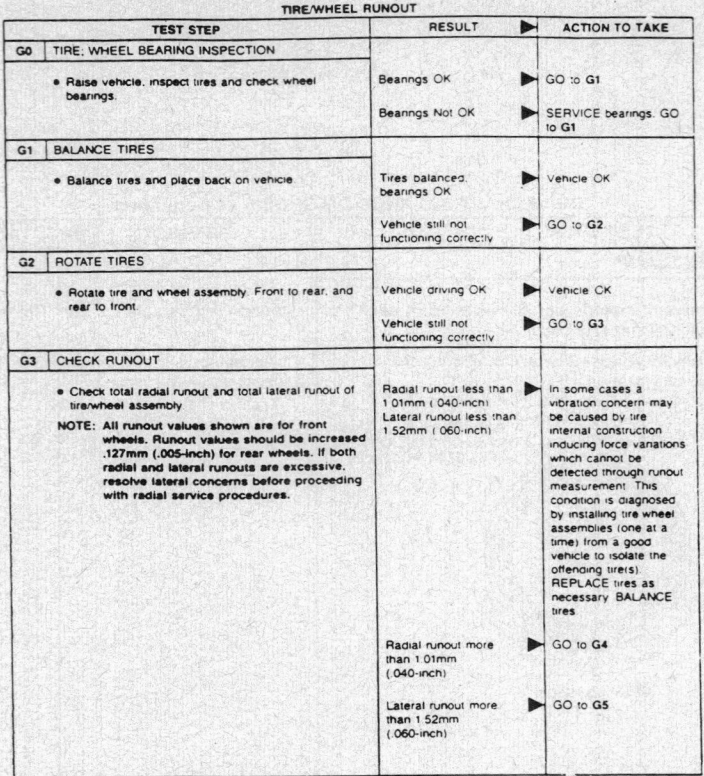

TIRE/WHEEL RUNOUT

TEST STEP	RESULT	▶	ACTION TO TAKE
G0 TIRE: WHEEL BEARING INSPECTION			
• Raise vehicle, inspect tires and check wheel bearings.	Bearings OK	▶	GO to G1
	Bearings Not OK	▶	SERVICE bearings. GO to G1
G1 BALANCE TIRES			
• Balance tires and place back on vehicle	Tires balanced, bearings OK	▶	Vehicle OK
	Vehicle still not functioning correctly	▶	GO to G2
G2 ROTATE TIRES			
• Rotate tire and wheel assembly. Front to rear, and rear to front.	Vehicle driving OK	▶	Vehicle OK
	Vehicle still not functioning correctly	▶	GO to G3
G3 CHECK RUNOUT			
• Check total radial runout and total lateral runout of tire/wheel assembly NOTE: All runout values shown are for front wheels. Runout values should be increased .127mm (.005-inch) for rear wheels. If both radial and lateral runouts are excessive, resolve lateral concerns before proceeding with radial service procedures.	Radial runout less than 1.01mm (.040-inch) Lateral runout less than 1.52mm (.060-inch)	▶	In some cases a vibration concern may be caused by tire internal construction inducing force variations which cannot be detected through runout measurement. This condition is diagnosed by installing tire/wheel assemblies (one at a time) from a good vehicle to isolate the offending tire(s). REPLACE tires as necessary. BALANCE tires.
	Radial runout more than 1.01mm (.040-inch)	▶	GO to G4
	Lateral runout more than 1.52mm (.060-inch)	▶	GO to G5

FM2019100001130X

Fig. 1   Noise, Vibration & Harshness (NVH) (Part 13 of 14)

TIRE/WHEEL RUNOUT — Continued

TEST STEP	RESULT	▶	ACTION TO TAKE
G4 INDEX TIRE ON WHEEL			
• Index tire on wheel. Align highest runout point to wheel low runout point.	Total radial runout less than 1.01mm (.040-inch)	▶	GO to G5.
	Total radial runout more than 1.01mm (.040-inch)	▶	GO to G6.
G5 BALANCE TIRE			
• Check and balance tires. • Road test.	Vehicle OK	▶	No further service required.
	Vehicle still not functioning correctly	▶	In some cases a vibration concern may be caused by tire internal construction inducing force variations which cannot be detected through runout measurement. This condition is diagnosed by installing tire/wheel assemblies (one at a time) from a good vehicle to isolate the offending tire(s). REPLACE tires as necessary. BALANCE tires. ROAD TEST.
G6 CHECK WHEEL RADIAL RUNOUT			
• Check wheel radial runout and ensure it is correct. NOTE: Although maximum wheel runout shown exceeds acceptable total tire/wheel assembly runout. Acceptable assembly runout may be achieved by indexing tire on wheel.	Wheel runout less than 1.14mm (.045-inch)	▶	REPLACE tire. BALANCE tire. ROAD TEST. If still not OK, CHECK radial runout.
	Wheel runout more than 1.14mm (.045-inch)	▶	REPLACE wheel. BALANCE tire. ROAD TEST. If still not OK, CHECK radial runout.

FM2019100001140X

Fig. 1   Noise, Vibration & Harshness (NVH) (Part 14 of 14)

ENGINE REBUILDING SPECIFICATIONS

NOTE: For Engine Tightening Specifications, Refer To The Engine Section In The Appropriate Chassis Chapter Of This Manual.

INDEX

CYLINDER HEAD, VALVE GUIDE & VALVE SEATS

All Measurements Given In Inches, Unless Otherwise Specified.

Engine Liter/CID	Year	Cylinder Head Warpage Limit	Valve Guides			Seat Angle	Valve Seats			Seat Insert Bore Diameter	
			Inside Diameter	Stem to Guide Clearance			Seat Width		Run-Out		
				Intake	Exhaust		Intake	Exhaust		Intake	Exhaust
1.3L/4-80.8	1992-94	.006	.2760-.2768	.0080	.0080	45°	.0430-.0670	.0430-.0670	.0016	—	—
1.6L/4-97.4	1992-94	.006	.2366-.2374	.0010-.0024	.0012-.0026	45°	.0315-.0551	.03150-.05510	—	—	—
1.8L/4-112	1992-94	.004	.2366-.2374	.0010-.0024	.0012-.0026	45°	.0310-.0550	.0310-.0550	—	—	—
1.9L/4-116	1992-94	.003	.3174-.3187	.0008-.0027	.0018-.0037	45°	.0690-.0910	.0690-.0910	.0030	⑤	⑥
2.0L/4-121	1993-94	.002	.2366-.2374	.0010-.0024	.0008-.0026	45°	.0350-.0510	.0350-.0510	—	—	—
2.2L/4-133	1992	.006	—	.0080	.0080	45°	.0470-.0630	.0470-.0630	—	—	—
2.3L/4-140 ①	1992-93	.003	.3433-.3443	.0010-.0027	.0015-.0032	45°	.0600-.0800	.0700-.0900	.0016	—	—
2.3L/4-140 ②	1992-94	.003	.3433	.0018	.0023	44-45°	.0800	.0900	.0018	—	—
2.5L/V6-152	1993-94	.006	—	.0010-.0023	.0012-.0025	45°	.0315-.0551	.0315-.0551	—	—	—
3.0L/V6-182	1992-94	.007	.3140-.3150	.0010-.0028	.0015-.0033	45°	.0600-.0800	.0800-.1000	.0010	—	—
3.0L/V6-182 SHO	1992-94	.008	.2362-.2369	.0010-.0023	.0012-.0025	45°	.0390-.0550	.0390-.0550	—	—	—
3.2L/V6-195 SHO	1993-94	.008	.2362-.2369	.0010-.0023	.0012-.0025	45°	.0390-.0550	.0390-.0550	—	—	—
3.8L/V6-232	1992-94	.007	.3433-.3443	.0010-.0028	.0015-.0033	44.5°	.0600-.0800	.0600-.0800	.003	1.8532-1.8542	1.5645
4.6L/V8-281	1992-94	—	—	.0008-.0027	.0018-.0037	45°	③	③	④	—	—
5.0L/V8-302	1992-94	.006	.3433-.3443	.0010-.0027	.0015-.0032	45°	.0600-.0800	.0600-.0800	.002	—	—

① —Mustang.
② —Tempo & Topaz.
③ —Except 32-valve engine, .075-.083 inch; 32-valve engine, .071-.087 inch.
④ —Except 32-valve engine, .001 inch; 32-valve engine, .002 inch.
⑤ —EFI-HO, .1723-1.724 inches; EFI, 1.572-1.573 inches.
⑥ —EFI-HO, 1.506-1.507 inches; EFI 1.375-1.573 inches.

VALVE SPRINGS
All Measurements Given In Inches Unless Otherwise Specified.

Engine Liter/CID	Year	Free Length	Installed Height	Seated Pressure Pounds @ Inches	Comp. Pressure Pounds @ Inches	Out Of Square Limit
1.3L/4-80.8	1992-94	1.1717	—	—	—	.059
1.6L/4-97.4	1992-94	1.858	—	44 @ 1.54	—	.063
1.8L/4-112	1992-94	1.821	—	—	—	.064
1.9L/4-116	1992-94	1.900	1.44-1.48	95 @ 1.46	200 @ 1.09	.060
2.0L/4-121	1993-94	1.732	—	—	—	.061
2.2L/4-133	1992	②	—	—	—	—
2.3L/4-140③	1992-93	1.877	1.49-1.55	71-79 @ 1.52	—	.078
2.3L/4-140④	1992-94	1.850	1.49	76-84 @ 1.50	178-193 @ 1.09	—
2.5L/V6-152	1993-94	⑤	—	—	—	.064
3.0L/V6-182	1992-94	1.840	1.58	65 @ 1.58	180 @ 1.16	—
3.0L/V6-182 SHO	1992-94	1.760	—	42 @ 1.52	121 @ 1.19	—
3.2L/V6-195 SHO	1992-94	1.760	—	42 @ 1.52	121 @ 1.19	—
3.8L/V6-232①	1992-94	—	1.97	85 @ 1.65	220 @ 1.65	—
3.8L/V6-232③	1994	2.020	—	85 @ 1.65	220 @ 1.18	—
4.6L/V8-281	1992-94	⑦	—	⑧	⑨	.056
5.0L/V8-302	1992-94	⑩	⑪	⑫	⑬	.078

①—Continental, Cougar, Sable, Taurus & Thunderbird.
②—Intake, 1.949 inch; exhaust, 1.984 inch.
③—Mustang.
④—Tempo & Topaz.
⑤—Intake, 1.729 inch; exhaust, 1.847 inch.
⑥—Except Cobra: exhaust, 200-226 lbs. @ 1.15 inch; intake, 211-230 lbs. @ 1.33 inch. Cobra: exhaust, 264 lbs. @ 1.12 inch; intake, 280 lbs. @ 1.30 inch.
⑦—Except 32-valve engine, 1.95 inch; 32-valve engine, 1.66 inch.
⑧—Except 32-valve engine, 54 lbs. @ 1.57 inch; 32-valve engine, 55 lbs. @ 1.42 inch.
⑨—Except 32-valve engine, 132 lbs. @ 1.10 inch; 32-valve engine, 160 lbs. @ 1.03 inch.
⑩—Except Cobra: exhaust, 1.79 inch; intake, 2.02 inch. Cobra: exhaust, 1.39 inch; intake, 2.02 inch.
⑪—Except Cobra: exhaust, 1.57-1.64 inch; intake, 1.75-1.81 inch. Cobra: exhaust, 1.62 inch; intake, 1.80 inch.
⑫—Cobra: exhaust, 85 lbs. @ 1.60 inch; intake, 90 lbs. @ 1.78 inch.

VALVES

All Measurements Given In Inches, Unless Otherwise Specified.

Engine Liter/ CID	Year	Stem Diameter Intake	Stem Diameter Exhaust	Maxi-TipRefinish	Face Angle	Margin① Int.	Margin① Exh.	Clearance Int.	Clearance Exh.
1.3L/4-80.8	1992-94	.2744-.2750	.2742-.2748	—	45.0°	—	—	.012	.012
1.6L/4-97.4	1992-94	.2350-.2356	.2348-.2354	—	45.0°	.020	.020	.001	.001
1.8L/4-112	1992-94	.2350-.2356	.2348-.2354	—	—	.035	.036	—	—
1.9L/4-116	1992-94	.3159-.3167	.3149-.3156	—	45.6°	—	—	—	—
2.0L/4-121	1993-94	.2350-.2356	.2348-.2354	—	45.0°	—	—	0.00	0.00
2.2L/4-133	1992	.2744-.2750	.2742-.2748	—	—	—	—	—	—
2.3L/4-140②	1992-93	.3416-.3423	.3411-.3418	—	44.0°	—	—	—	—
2.3L/4-140③	1992-94	.3415-.3422	.3411-.3418	—	44.0-45.0°	—	—	—	—
2.5L/V6-152	1993-94	.2351-.2356	.2349-.2354	—	45.0°	—	—	—	—
3.0L/V6-182	1992-94	.3126-.3134	.3121-.3129	—	44.0°	—	—	—	—
3.0L/V6-182 SHO	1992-94	.2346-.2352	.2344-.2350	—	45.5°	.020	.020	.006-.010	.010-.014
3.2L/V6-195 SHO	1992-94	.2346-.2352	.2344-.2350	—	45.5°	.020	.020	.006-.010	.010-.014
3.8L/V6-232	1992-94	.3415-.3423	.3410-.3418	—	45.8°	—	—	—	—
4.6L/V8-281	1992-94	.2746-.2750	.2736-.2744	—	45.5°	—	—	—	—
5.0L/V8-302	1992-94	.3416-.3423	.3411-.3418	—	44.0°	—	—	—	—

①—Minimum.
②—Mustang.
③—Tempo & Topaz.

CAMSHAFT

All Measurements Given In Inches Unless Otherwise Specified.

Engine Liter/ CID	Year	Camshaft Journal Diameter	Camshaft Bearing Inside Diameter	Camshaft Bearing Clearance	Camshaft Endplay	Lifter Bore Diameter	Lifter Diameter	Lifter To Bore Clearance
1.3L/4-80.8	1992-94	①	—	—	.0020-.0070	—	—	—
1.6L/4-97.4	1992-94	1.0213-1.0222	—	.0014-.0032	.0028-.0075	—	—	.0010-.0026
1.8L/4-112	1992-94	1.0213-1.0220	—	.0014-.0032	.0028-.0075	.8760	.8740-.8745	.0009-.0026
1.9L/4-116②	1992-94	1.8007-1.8017	1.8030-1.8040	.0013-.0033	.0006-.0018	.8760	.8740-.8745	.0009-.0026
2.0L/4-121	1993-94	1.0213-1.0222	—	.0014-.0032	.0031-.0079	—	—	—
2.2L/4-133	1992	—	—	③	.0030-.0060	—	—	—
2.3L/4-140④	1992-93	1.7713-1.7720	—	.0010-.0030	.0010-.0070	.8449-.9449	.8422-.8427	.0007-.0027
2.3L/4-140⑤	1992-94	—	2.0090-2.0100	.0010-.0030	—	—	.8740-.8744	—
2.5L/V6-152	1993-94	⑥	—	⑦	.0020-.0039	—	—	.0010-.0025
3.0L/V6-182	1992-94	2.0074-2.0084	2.0094-2.0104	.0010-.0030	.0010-.0050	.8752-.8767	.8740	.0007-.0027
3.0L/V6-182 SHO	1992-94	1.2189-1.2195	1.2205-1.2215	.0010-.0026	.0120	—	1.2587-1.2596	.0009-.0014
3.2L/V6-195 SHO	1993-94	1.2189-1.2195	1.2205-1.2215	.0010-.0026	.0120	—	1.2587-1.2596	.0009-.0014
3.8L/V6-232	1992-94	2.0505-2.0515	2.0525-2.0535	.0010-.0030	⑩	.8767-.8752	.8740-.8745	.0007-.0027
4.6L/V8-281	1992-94	1.0604-1.0614	1.0624-1.0635	.0010-.0030	.0010-.0064	—	.6294-.6299	.0007-.0027
5.0L/V8-302	1992-94	⑧	⑨	.0010-.0030	.0005-.0055	.8752-.8767	.8740-.8745	.0007-.0027

① —Nos. 1 & 3, 1.7103-1.7112 inch; No. 2, 1.7091-1.7100 inch.

② —Engines may be encountered with oversize tappets (all eight) and/or oversized camshaft. Oversize tappets will be identified by stamping of .254 OT on machined pad below rocker arm rail and above No. 1 exhaust port. Oversize camshafts will be identified by stamping of .38 O/C on cover rail above No. 4 exhaust port and by stamping of .38 O/S on distributor drive end of camshaft.

③ —Nos. 1 & 5, .0014-.003 inch; Nos. 2, 3, & 4, .0026-.0045 inch.

④ —Mustang.

⑤ —Tempo & Topaz.

⑥ —Righthand cylinder head: No. 1 intake, 1.180-1.1811 inch; No. 1 exhaust, 1.0213-1.0220 inch; Nos. 2, 3, & 4 intake & exhaust, 1.0201-1.0209 inch; No. 5 intake & exhaust, 1.0213-1.0220 inch. Lefthand cylinder head: No. 1 intake, 1.0213-1.0220 inch; No. 1 exhaust, 1.1802-1.1809 inch; Nos. 2, 3, & 4 intake & exhaust, 1.0201-1.0209 inch; No. 5 intake & exhaust, 1.0213-1.0220 inch.

⑦ —Nos. 1 & 5, .0016-.0032 inch; Nos. 2, 3, & 4, .0028-.0044 inch.

⑧ —No. 1, 2.0805-2.0815 inch; No. 2, 2.0655-2.0665 inch; No. 3, 2.0505-2.0515 inch; No. 4, 2.0355-2.0365 inch; No. 5, 2.0205-2.0215 inch.

⑨ —No. 1, 2.0825-2.0835 inch; No. 2, 2.0675-2.0685 inch; No. 3, 2.0525-2.0535 inch; No. 4, 2.0375-2.0385 inch; No. 5, 2.0225-2.0235 inch.

⑩ —No endplay. Camshaft is retained by spring.

CRANKSHAFT, BEARINGS & RODS

All Measurements Given In Inches Unless Otherwise Specified.

| Engine Liter/ CID | Year | Crankshaft | | | | Bearing Clearance | | | Connecting Rods | |
		Main Bearing Journal Diameter	Connecting Rod Journal Diameter	Max. Out of Round All	Max. Taper All	Main Bearings	Connecting Rod Bearings	Crankshaft Endplay	Pin Bore Diameter	Side Clearance
1.3L/4-80.8	1992-94	1.9661-1.9668	1.5724-1.5731	.0020	.0020	—	.0009-.0017	.0031-.0111	.7854-.7859	.0120
1.6L/4-97.4	1992-94	1.9661-1.9668	1.7693-1.7699	.0020	.0020	.0010-.0017	.0011-.0027	.0031-.0110	.7855-.7880	.0043-.0103
1.8L/4-112	1992-94	1.9661-1.9668	1.7692-1.7699	.020	—	.0030	.0120	.0040-.0080	.7875-.7880	.0004-.0011
1.9L/4-116	1992-94	2.2827-2.2835	1.7279-1.7287	.0003	.0003	.0011-.0019	.0008-.0015	.0040-.0080	.8106-.8114	.0040-.0110
2.0L/4-121	1993-94	2.2022-2.2029	1.8874-1.8880	.0001	.0002	①	.0005-.0015	.0031-.0110	.7476-.7480	.0043-.0103
2.2L/4-133	1992	2.3597-2.3604	2.0055-2.0061	.0020		②	.0011-.0026	.0031-.0071	.8640-.8646	.0040-.0100
2.3L/4-140 ③	1992-93	2.2051-2.2059	2.0462-2.0472	.0006	.0006	.0008-.0015	.0008-.0015	.003-.008	.9096-.9112	.0035-.0105
2.3L/4-140 ④	1992-94	2.2489-2.2490	2.1232-2.1240	.0004	.0003	.0008-.0015	.0008-.0015	.0040-.0080	.9096-.9112	.0035-.0105
2.5L/V6-152	1993-94	2.4385-2.4392	—	.0020	.0020	.0015-.0022	.0009-.0017	.0032-.0111	.7864-.7866	.0070-.0130
3.0L/V6-182	1992-94	2.5190-2.5198	2.1253-2.1261	.0003	.0003	.0010-.0014	.0010-.0014	.0040-.0080	.9096-.9112	.0060-.0140
3.0L/V6-182 SHO	1992-94	2.5187-2.5197	2.0463-2.0472	.0008	.0008	.0011-.0022	.0090-.0022	.0008-.0087	.8270-.8274	.0063-.0123
3.2L/V6-195 SHO	1993-94	2.5187-2.5197	2.0463-2.0472	.0008	.0008	.0011-.0022	.0090-.0022	.0008-.0087	.8663-.8668	.0063-.0123
3.8L/V6-232	1992-94	⑤	2.3103-2.3111	.0006	.0003	⑥	.0010-.0014	.0040-.0080	.9096-.9112	.0047-.0114
4.6L/V8-281	1992-94	2.6570	2.0866	.0019	—	⑦	.0011-.0027	.0051-.0119	⑧	.0006-.0177
5.0L/V8-302	1992	2.2482-2.2490	2.1228-2.1236	.0006	.0004	.0004-.0015	.0008-.0015	.0040-.0080	.9096-.9112	.0100-.0200
5.0L/V8-302	1993-94	2.2482-2.2490	2.1228-2.1236	.0006	.0006	.0004-.0015	.0008-.0015	.0040-.0080	.9096-.9112	.0100-.0200

① —Nos. 1, 2, 4 & 5, .0009-.0020 inch; No. 3, .0012-.0022 inch.
② —Nos. 1, 2, 4 & 5, .0010-.0017 inch: No. 3, .0012-.0019 inch.
③ —Mustang.
④ —Tempo & Topaz.
⑤ —EFI & SC Nos. 1, 2, & 3, 2.519-2.5198 inch; SC No. 4, 2.5104-2.5096 inch.
⑥ —EFI, .0010-0014 inch; SC Nos. 1, 2 & 3, .0009-.0026 inch; SC No. 4, .0014-.0032 inch.
⑦ —Except 32-valve engine, .0011-.0026 inch; 32-valve engine, .0010-.0018 inch.
⑧ —Except 32-valve engine, .8645-.8653 inch; 32-valve engine, .8664-.8668 inch.

PISTONS, PINS & RINGS

All Measurements Given In Inches Unless Otherwise Specified.

| Engine Liter/ CID | Year | Piston Diameter (Std.) | Piston Clearance | Piston Pin Diameter | Pin To Piston Clearance | Piston End Ring Gap ① | | Piston Ring Side Clearance | |
						Comp.	Oil	Comp.	Oil
1.3L/4-80.8	1992-94	2.7930-2.7940	.0060	.7864-.7866	.0000-.0010	.006	.008	.0010-.0030	—
1.6L/4-97.4	1992-94	3.0690-3.0698	.0010-.0026	.7869-.7871	.0004-.0012	②	.008	.0012-.0026	.0012-.0026
1.8L/4-112	1992-94	3.2659-3.2667	.0015-.0020	.7869-.7871	.0002-.0005	.006	.008	.0012-.0028	—
1.9L/4-116	1992-94	③	.0016-.0024	.8119-.8124	.0003-.0005	.010	.016	④	—
2.0L/4-121	1993-94	3.2659-3.2667	.0015-.0020	.7470-.7472	—	.006	.008	.0014-.0026	—
2.2L/4-133	1992	3.3836-3.3844	.0014-.0030	.8651-.8654	.0003-.0009	②	⑤	.0010-.0030	—
2.3L/4-140 ⑥	1992-93	⑦	—	.9118-.9124	.0003-.0005	⑧	.010	.0016-.0033	—
2.3L/4-140 ⑨	1992-94	⑩	.0012-.0022	.9119-.9124	.0002-.0005	.008	.015	.0020-.0040	—
2.5L/V6-152	1993-94	3.3250-3.3261	.0012-.0022	.7470-.7472	.0004-.0010	㉗	.008	㉘	—

Continued

PISTONS, PINS & RINGS-Continued

All Measurements Given In Inches Unless Otherwise Specified.

Engine Liter/ CID	Year	Piston Diameter (Std.)	Piston Clearance	Piston Pin Diameter	Pin To Piston Clearance	Piston End Ring Gap ①		Piston Ring Side Clearance	
						Comp.	Oil	Comp.	Oil
3.0L/V6-182	1992-93	⑪	.0014-.0022	.9119-.9124	.0002-.0005	.010	.015	.0012-.0031	—
3.0L/V6-182	1994	⑪	.0014-.0022	.9119-.9124	.0002-.0005	.010	.010	.0012-.0031	—
3.0L/V6-182 SHO	1992-94	3.5023-3.5035	.0012-.0020	.8267-.8271	.0004	.012	.008	⑫	.0024-.0059
3.2L/V6-195 SHO	1993-94	3.6205-3.6217	.0012-.0020	.8660-.8665	.0004	⑬	.008	⑭	.0024-.0059
3.8L/V6-232	1992-94	⑮	⑯	.9119-.9124	⑰	⑱	.015	.0016-.0034	—
4.6L/V8-281	1992-94	⑲	.0008-.0018	⑳	㉑	㉒	㉓	㉔	.0006
5.0L/V8-302	1992-94	㉕	㉖	.9119-.9124	.0002-.0004	.010	.015	.0020-.0040	—

① —Minimum.
② —Top ring, .008 inch; 2nd ring, .006 inch.
③ —Coded red, 3.224-3.225 inch; coded blue, 3.225-3.226 inch.
④ —Top ring, .0015-.0032 inch; 2nd ring, .0015-.0035 inch.
⑤ —Turbo, .008-.028 inch; non-turbo, .012-.035 inch.
⑥ —Mustang.
⑦ —Coded red, 3.7795-3.7810 inch; coded blue, 3.7810-3.7825 inch.
⑧ —Top ring, .010 inch; 2nd ring, .015 inch.
⑨ —Tempo & Topaz.
⑩ —Coded red, 3.6783-3.6789 inch; coded blue, 3.6795-3.6801 inch; coded yellow, 3.6807-3.6811 inch.
⑪ —Coded red, 3.5024-3.5031 inch; coded blue, 3.5035-3.5041 inch; coded yellow, 3.5045-3.5051 inch.

⑫ —Top ring, .0008-.0024 inch; 2nd ring, .0006-.0022 inch.
⑬ —Top ring, .012 inch; 2nd ring, .018 inch.
⑭ —Top ring, .0016-.0031 inch; 2nd ring, .0008-.0024 inch.
⑮ —Coded red, 3.8095-3.8101 inch; coded blue, 3.8107-3.8113 inch; coded yellow, 3.8119-3.8125 inch.
⑯ —EFI, .0014-.0032 inch; SC, .0015-.0025 inch.
⑰ —Continental: EFI, .0002-.0005 inch; SC, .0003-.0006 inch; Mustang: .01 inch.
⑱ —Top ring, .011 inch; 2nd ring, .009 inch.
⑲ —Coded red, 3.5498-3.5503 inch; coded blue, 3.5503-3.5509 inch; coded yellow, 3.5509-3.5514 inch.
⑳ —Except 32-valve engine, .8659-.8661 inch; 32-valve engine, .8662-.8663 inch.

㉑ —Except 32-valve engine, .0002-.0039 inch; 32-valve engine, .0001-.0007 inch.
㉒ —Except 32-valve engine: top & 2nd ring, .009 inch; 32-valve engine: top ring, .010 inch; 2nd ring, .009 inch.
㉓ —Except 32-valve engine, .010 inch; 32-valve engine, .006 inch.
㉔ —Top ring, .002-.004 inch; 2nd ring, .001-.003 inch.
㉕ —1992: coded red, 3.9991-3.9997 inch; coded blue, 4.0003-4.0009 inch; coded yellow, 4.0015-4.0021 inch. 1993-94: coded red, 3.9972-3.9980 inch; coded blue, 3.9984-3.9992 inch; coded yellow, 3.9996-4.0004 inch.
㉖ —1992, .0030 to .0038 inch; 1993, .0012-.0020 inch.
㉗ —Top ring, .006 inch; 2nd ring, .010 inch.
㉘ —Top ring, .0008-.0026 inch; 2nd ring, .0012-.0026 inch.

CYLINDER BLOCK

All Measurements Given In Inches Unless Otherwise Specified.

Engine Liter/CID	Year	Cylinder Bore Diameter (Std.)	Cylinder Bore Taper Max.	Cylinder Bore Out of Round Max.
1.3L/4-80.8	1992-94	2.7953-2.7960	.0007	.0007
1.6L/4-97.4	1992-94	3.0709-3.0717	.0007	.0090
1.8L/4-112	1992-94	3.2679-3.2682	.0007	.0070
1.9L/4-116	1992-94	3.2300	.0010	.0050
2.0L/4-121	1993-94	3.2677-3.2685	.0004	.0004
2.2L/4-133	1992	3.3858-3.3866	.0007	.0007
2.3L/4-140 ①	1992-93	3.7795-3.7825	.0100	.0050
2.3L/4-140 ②	1992-94	3.6790-3.6830	.0100	.0040
2.5L/V6-152	1993-94	3.3268-3.3276	.0008	.0008
3.0L/V6-182	1992-94	3.5040	.0020	.0020
3.0L/V6-182 SHO	1992-94	3.5039-3.5051	.0008	.0008
3.2L/V6-195 SHO	1993-94	3.6220-3.6232	.0008	.0008
3.8L/V6-232	1992-94	3.8100	.0020	.0020
4.6L/V8-281	1992-94	3.5510	.0006	.0020
5.0L/V8-302	1992-94	4.0000-4.0048	.0100	.0050

① —Mustang.
② —Tempo & Topaz.

OIL PUMP

All Measurements Given In Inches Unless Otherwise Specified.

Engine Liter/ CID	Year	Rotor Backlash	Rotor To Body Clearance	Rotor Endplay ①	Maximum Cover Flatness Variation	Driveshaft To Pump Body Clearance	Relief Valve To Body Clearance	Relief Spring Pressure Lbs. @ Inches
1.3L/4-80.8	1992-94	—	.0087	.0050	—	—	—	—
1.6L/4-97.4	1992-94	.0008-.0063 ②	.0035-.0071	.0012-.0043	—	—	—	—
1.8L/4-112	1992-94	.0079 ②	.0087	.0055	—	—	—	—
1.9L/4-116	1992-94	.0020-.0070 ②	.0029-.0063	.0005-.0035	③	—	.0008-.0031	9.3-10.3 @ 1.11
2.0L/4-121	1993-94	—	—	—	—	—	—	—
2.2L/4-133	1992	—	—	—	—	—	—	—
2.3L/4-140 ④	1992-93	—	.0010-.0130	.0040	③	.0015-.0030	.0015-.0030	12.6-14.5 @ 1.20
2.3L/4-140 ⑤	1992-94	—	.0010-.0120	.0040	③	.0014-.0026	.0015-.0029	14.2-16.2 @ 1.20
2.5L/V6-152	1993-94	.0078	.0087	.0051	—	—	—	—
3.0L/V6-182	1992-94	.0080-.0012	.0020-.0055	.0005-.0055	—	⑥	.0017-.0029	9.1-10.1 @ 1.11
3.0L/V6-182 SHO	1992-94	.0024-.0071	.0012-.0035	.0039-.0069	—	.0012-.0035	.0020-.0035	—
3.2L/V6-195 SHO	1993-94	.0024-.0071	.0012-.0035	.0039-.0069	—	.0012-.0035	.0020-.0035	—
3.8L/V6-232	1992-94	.0080-.0012	.0020-.0055	.0005-.0055	—	⑦	.0017-.0029	15.2-17.1 @ 1.20
4.6L/V8-281	1992-94	—	—	—	—	—	—	—
5.0L/V8-302	1992-94	—	.0010-.0130	.0040	③	.0015-.0030	.0015-.0030	10.6-12.2 @ 1.70

①—Measured between pump cover mounting surface & end of gear, using straightedge and feeler gauge.
②—Maximum inner & outer rotor tip clearance.
③—Pump should be replaced if cover is damaged, scored or worn.
④—Mustang.
⑤—Tempo & Topaz.
⑥—Driver shaft to body clearance, .0005-.0019 inch; idler shaft to idler clearance, .0004-.0017 inch.
⑦—Driver shaft to body clearance, .0015-.0030 inch; idler shaft to idler clearance, .0005-.0017 inch.

DECIMAL & MILLIMETER EQUIVALENTS

INCH	INCH	MM		INCH	INCH	MM		INCH	INCH	MM
1/64	.015625	.397		23/64	.359375	9.128		11/16	.6875	17.462
1/32	.03125	.794		3/8	.375	9.525		45/64	.703125	17.859
3/64	.046875	1.191		25/64	.390625	9.922		23/32	.71875	18.265
1/16	.0625	1.587		13/32	.40625	10.319		47/64	.734375	18.653
5/64	.078125	1.984		27/64	.421875	10.716		3/4	.75	19.050
3/32	.09375	2.381		7/16	.4375	11.113		49/64	.765625	19.447
7/64	.109375	2.778		29/64	.453125	11.509		25/32	.78125	19.884
1/8	.125	3.175		15/32	.46875	11.906		51/64	.796875	20.240
9/64	.140625	3.572		31/64	.484375	12.303		13/16	.8125	20.637
5/32	.15625	3.969		1/2	.5	12.700		53/64	.828125	21.034
11/64	.171875	4.366		33/64	.515625	13.097		27/32	.84375	21.431
3/16	.1875	4.762		17/32	.53125	13.494		55/64	.859375	21.828
13/64	.203125	5.159		35/64	.546875	13.890		7/8	.875	22.225
7/32	.21875	5.556		9/16	.5625	14.287		57/64	.890625	22.622
15/64	.234375	5.953		37/64	.578125	14.684		29.32	.90625	23.019
1/4	.25	6.350		19/32	.59375	15.081		59/64	.921875	23.415
17/64	.265625	6.747		39/64	.609375	15.478		15/16	.9375	23.812
9/32	.28125	7.144		5/8	.625	15.875		61/64	.953125	24.209
19/64	.296875	7.541		41/64	.640625	16.272		31/32	.96875	24.606
5/16	.3125	7.937		21/32	.65625	16.669		63/64	.984375	25.003
21/64	.328125	8.334		43/64	.671875	17.065		1		25.400
11/32	.34375	8.731								

Special Service Tools

Throughout this manual references are made to and illustrations may depict the use of special tools required to perform certain jobs. These special tools can generally be ordered through the dealers of the make vehicle being serviced. It is also suggested that you check with local automotive supply firms as they also supply tools manufactured by other firms that will assist in the performance of these jobs. The vehicle manufacturers special tools are supplied by:

Chrysler Corporation . . . .
Miller Special Tools
SPX Corporation
12842 Farmington Rd.
Livonia, Michigan 48150

Ford Motor Company . . . .
Owatonna Tool Company
Owatonna, Minnesota 55060

General Motors . . . .
Kent-Moore
SPX Corporation
29784 Little Mack
Roseville, Michigan 48066

Manual Information Locator

Operation/Subject/Topic	Auto Repair Manual	Auto Engine Tune Up & Electronics (Engine Performance) Manual
Air Bags	X	—
Air Conditioning	X	—
AIR Systems	—	X
All-Wheel Drive Systems	X	—
Alternator Specifications	X	—
Alternator Systems	X	—
Anti-Lock Brake Systems	X	—
Automatic Transaxle In-Vehicle Service	X	—
Automatic Transmission In-Vehicle Service	X	—
Axle Shaft Service	X	—
Back-Up Light Switch, Replace	X	—
Balance Shaft Service	X	—
Ball Joint Service	X	—
Belt Tension Data	X	—
Blower Motor, Replace	X	—
Brake Booster Service	X	—
Brake Service	X	—
Camber Adjustment	X	—
Camshaft Service	X	—
Capacity Data	X	—
Carburetor Adjustments	—	X
Carburetor Overhaul	—	X
Caster Adjustment	X	—
Catalytic Converters	—	X
Clutch Service	X	—
Clutch Start Switch, Replace	X	—
Coil Spring, Replace	X	—
Compression Check	—	X
Compression Pressures	—	X
Computer System Diagnostics	—	X
Computer System Identification	—	X
Computer Terminal Connector Identification	—	X
Computerized Engine Control Systems	—	X
Control Arm Service	X	—
Cooling System Bleed	X	—
Cooling System Data	X	—
Crankshaft Pulley, Replace	X	—
Crankshaft Rear Oil Seal Service	X	—
Cruise Control Systems	X	—
Cylinder Block Specifications	X	—
Cylinder Head Service	X	—
Cylinder Head Specifications	X	—
Cylinder Head, Replace	X	—
Cylinder Liner, Replace	X	—
Dash Panel Service	X	—
Differential Service	X	—
Dimmer Switch, Replace	X	—
Disc Brake Service	X	—
Distributor Service	—	X
Distributor, Replace	X	X
Distributorless Ignition Systems	—	X
Drive Axle Service	X	—

Operation/Subject/Topic	Auto Repair Manual	Auto Engine Tune Up & Electronics (Engine Performance) Manual
Drive Belt Tension Data	X	—
Drum Brake Service	X	—
EGR System	—	X
Electric Engine Cooling Fans	X	—
Electric Fuel Pumps	X	X
Electrical Symbol Identification	X	X
Electronic Fuel Injection	—	X
Electronic Ignition	—	X
Electronic Instrumentation	—	X
Electronic Level Controls	X	—
Emission Control Application Charts	—	X
Emission Controls	—	X
Emission Vacuum Hose Routing	—	X
Engine Compartment Reference Diagrams	—	X
Engine Cooling Fans	X	—
Engine Electronic Control Module, Replace	—	X
Engine Electronic Control Unit, Replace	—	X
Engine Front Cover Service	X	—
Engine Mounts, Replace	X	—
Engine Oil Seal Service	X	—
Engine Rebuilding Specifications	X	—
Engine Repairs	X	—
Engine Sensor Location	—	X
Engine Sensor Replacement	—	X
Engine Sensor Specification Charts	—	X
Engine Specifications	X	—
Engine System Identification Charts	—	X
Engine Tightening Specifications	X	—
Engine, Replace	X	—
Evaporator Core, Replace	X	—
Exhaust Gas Recirculation (EGR) Systems	—	X
Exhaust Manifold, Replace	X	—
Fast Idle Speed Adjustment	—	X
Feedback Carburetors	—	X
Flasher Location	X	—
Front Drive Axle Service	X	—
Front Wheel Alignment	X	—
Fuel Control System Identification	—	X
Fuel Filter, Replace	X	—
Fuel Injection Systems	—	X
Fuel Injector Cleaning Procedures	—	X
Fuel Injector, Replace	—	X
Fuel Pump Pressure Specifications	X	X
Fuel Pump Pressure Test	—	X
Fuel Pump Replacement	X	X
Fuse Panel Location	X	—
General Engine Specifications	X	—
Headlight Switch, Replace	X	—
Heated Air Cleaners	—	X